STATISTICAL SUMMARIES

GEOGRAPHIC SECTION
Companies sorted by city in alphabetical order
In-depth company data listed

STANDARD INDUSTRIAL CLASSIFICATIONS
Alphabetical index of classification descriptions
Numerical index of classification descriptions
Companies sorted by SIC product groupings

ALPHABETIC SECTION
Company listings in alphabetical order

SERVICES INDEX
Service categories are listed in alphabetical order

SERVICES SECTION
Companies sorted by service classifications

2011
Harris
Minnesota
Services Directory

Published annually by

HARRIS INFOSOURCE™

A Division of D&B

103 JFK Parkway
Short Hills, NJ 07078
866.281.6415
www.dnb.com

Published January 2011, next update January 2012

Publisher

Harris InfoSource *A Division of D&B®*
103 JFK Parkway
Short Hills, NJ 07078

©Dun & Bradstreet All Rights Reserved
2011 Harris Minnesota Services Directory
ISSN 1536-5719
ISBN 978-1-60073-288-1

TABLE OF CONTENTS

EXPLANATORY NOTES

How to Cross-Reference in This Directory

Sequential Entry Numbers. Each company in the Geographic Section is numbered sequentially *(G-0000)*. The number assigned to each company is referred to as its "entry number". To make cross-referencing easier, each listing in the Geographic, SIC, Alphabetic and Service Sections includes the company's entry number. To facilitate locating an entry number in the Geographic Section, the entry numbers for the first listing on the left page and the last listing on the right page are printed at the top of the page next to the city name.

Source Suggestions Welcome

Although all known sources were used to compile this directory, it is possible that companies were inadvertently omitted. Your assistance in calling attention to such omissions would be greatly appreciated. A special form on the facing page will help you in the reporting process.

Analysis

Every effort has been made to contact all firms to verify their information. The one exception to this rule is the annual sales figure, which is considered by many companies to be confidential information. Therefore, estimated sales have been calculated by multiplying the nationwide average sales per employee for the firm's major SIC/NAICS code by the firm's number of employees. Nationwide averages for sales per employee by SIC/NAICS codes are provided by the U.S. Department of Commerce and are updated annually. All sales—sales (est)—have been estimated by this method. The exceptions are parent companies (PA), division headquarters (DH) and headquarter locations (HQ) which may include an actual corporate sales figure—sales (corporate-wide) if available.

Types of Companies

Descriptive and statistical data are included for service companies in the entire state with 25 or more employees. These comprise agriculture, contractors, wholesale/distribution, mining, construction, transportation, finance, insurance, real estate, lodging, repair, entertainment, health, legal, social & business services, engineering, communications & utilities. Also identified are corporate offices pertaining to these services.

Employment Data

This directory contains companies with 25 or more employees in the service industry. The actual employment shown in the Geographic Section includes male & female employees and embraces all levels of the company. This figure is for the facility listed and does not include other offices or branches. It should be recognized that these figures represent an approximate year-round average. These employment figures are broken into codes A-E and used in the SIC and Services Sections to further help you in qualifying a company. Be sure to check the footnotes on the bottom of the page for the code breakdowns.

Standard Industrial Classification (SIC)

The Standard Industrial Classification (SIC) system used in this directory was developed by the federal government for use in classifying establishments by the type of activity they are engaged in. The SIC classifications used in this directory are from the 1987 edition published by the *U.S. Government's Office of Management and Budget.* The SIC system separates all activities into broad industrial divisions (e.g., manufacturing, mining, retail trade). It further subdivides each division. The range of manufacturing industry classes extends from two-digit codes (major industry group) to four-digit codes (product).

For example:

Industry Breakdown	Code	Industry, Service, etc.
*Major industry group	50	Wholesale Trade-Durable Goods
Industry group	505	Metals & Minerals Except Petroleum
*Industry	5051	Metals Service Centers & Offices

*Classifications used in this directory

Only two-digit and four-digit codes are used in this directory.

Arrangement

1. The **Statistical Summary** is a summary of contents and company information changes.

2. The **Geographic Section** contains complete in-depth corporate data. This section is sorted by cities listed in alphabetical order and companies listed alphabetically within each city. A County/City Index for referencing cities within counties preceeds this section.

> **IMPORTANT NOTICE:** It is a violation of both federal and state law to transmit an unsolicited advertisement to a facsimile machine. Any user of this product that violates such laws may be subject to civil and criminal penalties, which may exceed $500 for each transmission of an unsolicited facsimile. Harris InfoSource provides fax numbers for lawful purposes only and expressly forbids the use of these numbers in any unlawful manner.

3. The **Standard Industrial Classification (SIC) Section** lists companies under four-digit SIC codes. An alphabetical and a numerical index precedes this section. Codes are listed in numerical order with companies listed alphabetically under each code.

4. The **Alphabetic Section** lists all companies with their full physical or mailing addresses and telephone number.

5. The **Services Section** lists companies under unique Harris categories. An index precedes this section. Companies can be listed under several categories.

Selectory® Online Business Database

Get unlimited online access to the most accurate, up-to-date company profiles for ALL companies in the U.S., Mexico and Canada, as well as 200 countries worldwide. Build targeted lists and find new opportunities for sales in minutes! Register for your free trial at **www.selectory.com**.

USER'S GUIDE TO LISTINGS

GEOGRAPHIC SECTION

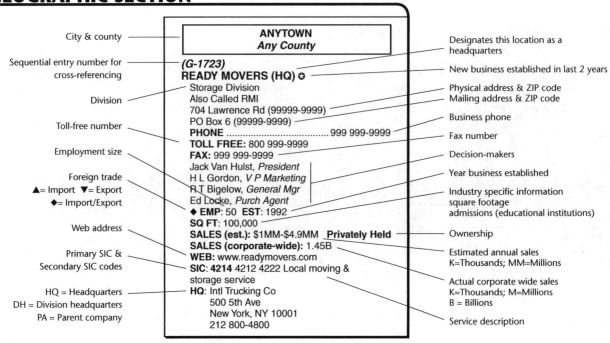

City & county

Sequential entry number for cross-referencing

Division

Toll-free number

Employment size

Foreign trade
▲= Import ▼= Export
◆= Import/Export

Web address

Primary SIC & Secondary SIC codes

HQ = Headquarters
DH = Division headquarters
PA = Parent company

ANYTOWN
Any County

(G-1723)
READY MOVERS (HQ) ✿
Storage Division
Also Called RMI
704 Lawrence Rd (99999-9999)
PO Box 6 (99999-9999)
PHONE 999 999-9999
TOLL FREE: 800 999-9999
FAX: 999 999-9999
Jack Van Hulst, *President*
H L Gordon, *V P Marketing*
R T Bigelow, *General Mgr*
Ed Locke, *Purch Agent*
◆ **EMP:** 50 **EST:** 1992
SQ FT: 100,000
SALES (est.): $1MM-$4.9MM **Privately Held**
SALES (corporate-wide): 1.45B
WEB: www.readymovers.com
SIC: 4214 4212 4222 Local moving & storage service
HQ: Intl Trucking Co
500 5th Ave
New York, NY 10001
212 800-4800

Designates this location as a headquarters

New business established in last 2 years

Physical address & ZIP code
Mailing address & ZIP code

Business phone

Fax number

Decision-makers

Year business established

Industry specific information
square footage
admissions (educational institutions)

Ownership

Estimated annual sales
K=Thousands; MM=Millions

Actual corporate wide sales
K=Thousands; M=Millions
B = Billions

Service description

SIC SECTION

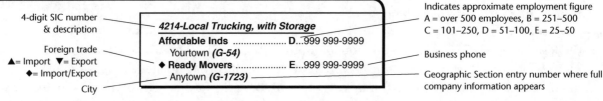

4-digit SIC number & description

Foreign trade
▲= Import ▼= Export
◆= Import/Export

City

4214-Local Trucking, with Storage
Affordable Inds .... D...999 999-9999
Yourtown *(G-54)*
◆ **Ready Movers** .... E...999 999-9999
Anytown *(G-1723)*

Indicates approximate employment figure
A = over 500 employees, B = 251–500
C = 101–250, D = 51–100, E = 25–50

Business phone

Geographic Section entry number where full company information appears

ALPHABETIC SECTION

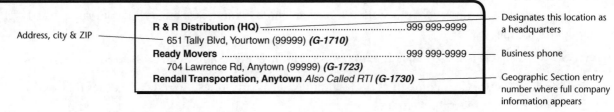

Address, city & ZIP

R & R Distribution (HQ) ──────────────999 999-9999
651 Tally Blvd, Yourtown (99999) *(G-1710)*
Ready Movers 999 999-9999
704 Lawrence Rd, Anytown (99999) *(G-1723)*
Rendall Transportation, Anytown *Also Called RTI (G-1730)*

Designates this location as a headquarters

Business phone

Geographic Section entry number where full company information appears

SERVICES SECTION

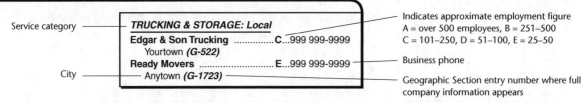

Service category

City

TRUCKING & STORAGE: Local
Edgar & Son Trucking ....C...999 999-9999
Yourtown *(G-522)*
Ready Movers ....E...999 999-9999
Anytown *(G-1723)*

Indicates approximate employment figure
A = over 500 employees, B = 251–500
C = 101–250, D = 51–100, E = 25–50

Business phone

Geographic Section entry number where full company information appears

Several convenient ways to order:

- ◆ **Retail store** Open 8 a.m. - 5 p.m. Monday - Friday, 660 Olive Street, St. Paul
- ◆ **Phone** (credit cards): 8 a.m. - 5 p.m. Monday - Friday, 651.297.3000 (Twin Cities) or 1.800.657.3757 (nationwide toll-free)
- ◆ **On-line orders**: www.minnesotasbookstore.com
- ◆ **Minnesota Relay Service**: 8 a.m. - 5 p.m. Monday - Friday, 1.800.627.3529 (nationwide toll-free)
- ◆ **Fax** (credit cards): 651.215.5733 (fax line available 24 hours)
- ◆ **Mail orders**: Orders can be sent to Minnesota's Bookstore, 660 Olive Street, St. Paul, MN 55155

Minnesota's Bookstore accepts VISA, MasterCard, American Express & Discover for all purchases.

PREPAYMENT REQUIRED. *Prices and availability subject to change.* **Fax and phone orders** require credit card. Please allow 1-2 weeks for delivery. For **mail orders**, complete order blank and send to address above. Enclose check or include credit card information. Please allow 2-3 weeks for delivery. Please make checks payable to "Minnesota's Bookstore." A $20.00 fee will be charged for returned checks.

Stock No.	Title	Quantity	Unit Price	Total

Send my order to:

Company:	
Name:	
Street Address: *(Not deliverable to P.O. boxes)*	
City: **State:** **Zip:**	
Daytime phone: ( ) *(In case we have a question about your order - please include area code)*	

Credit card number:	
Expiration date: **3- or 4- digit security code:** *(found on back of card)*	
Signature:	

Email me about new publications, special offers or related products: _____

Printed on recycled paper with a minimum of 10% post-consumer waste.

Shipping Charges

If Product Subtotal is:	Please Add:
Up to $15.00	$ 5.00
$15.01-$25.00	$ 6.00
$25.01-$50.00	$ 9.00
$50.01-$100.00	$ 14.00
$100.01-$1,000	$ 17.00*

*$17 to an address in MN, WI, SD, ND, IA. If delivered to an address in other states, Canada or internationally, we will contact you if there are additional charges.

More than $1,000 Call

Product Subtotal _____

Shipping _____
(see chart at left)

Subtotal _____

Sales tax _____
(6.875% sales tax if shipped to MN address, 7.625% if shipped to St. Paul address. 7.125% MN transit tax or other local sales tax if applicable)

TOTAL _____

If tax exempt, please provide ES number or completed exemption form.
ES#_____

STATISTICAL SUMMARIES

This data relates only to reporting service establishments with 25 or more employment and may not be comparable to data published by other government agencies due to variations in survey response, timing, and differences in industrial definitions.

	TOTAL	% Change Since Last Edition

SUMMARY OF CONTENTS

Number of Companies. 10,224

Number of Decision-Makers. 31,162

SUMMARY OF CHANGES SINCE LAST EDITION

COMPANY INFORMATION CHANGES

	TOTAL	% Change Since Last Edition
Companies Added	535	5%
Companies Deleted*.	798	8%
Companies with Address Changes.	777	8%
Changes of Company Name	342	3%

* Companies have been deleted because they went out of business or no longer meet criteria for inclusion.

Minnesota
County Map

COUNTY/CITY CROSS-REFERENCE INDEX

County/City Cross-Reference Index

2011 Harris Minnesota
Services Directory

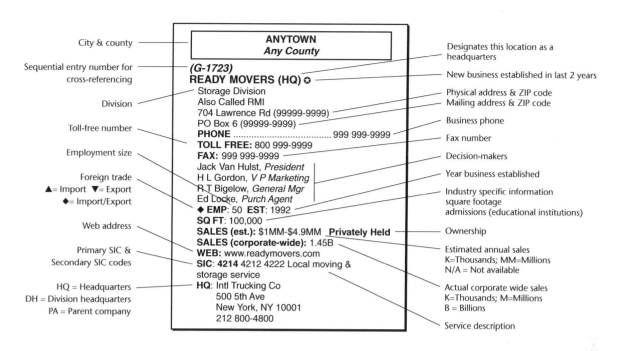

City & county —— ANYTOWN / Any County —— Designates this location as a headquarters

Sequential entry number for cross-referencing —— (G-1723)

READY MOVERS (HQ) ✪ —— New business established in last 2 years

Division —— Storage Division / Also Called RMI

704 Lawrence Rd (99999-9999) —— Physical address & ZIP code

PO Box 6 (99999-9999) —— Mailing address & ZIP code

PHONE .... 999 999-9999 —— Business phone

Toll-free number —— TOLL FREE: 800 999-9999

FAX: 999 999-9999 —— Fax number

Jack Van Hulst, *President*

H L Gordon, *V P Marketing* —— Decision-makers

R T Bigelow, *General Mgr*

Ed Locke, *Purch Agent*

Employment size —— ◆ EMP: 50 EST: 1992 —— Year business established

Foreign trade
▲ = Import ▼ = Export
◆ = Import/Export

SQ FT: 100,000 —— Industry specific information square footage admissions (educational institutions)

Web address —— SALES (est.): $1MM-$4.9MM **Privately Held** —— Ownership

SALES (corporate-wide): 1.45B

WEB: www.readymovers.com —— Estimated annual sales K=Thousands; MM=Millions N/A = Not available

Primary SIC & Secondary SIC codes —— SIC: 4214 4212 4222 Local moving & storage service

HQ = Headquarters —— HQ: Intl Trucking Co —— Actual corporate wide sales K=Thousands; M=Millions B = Billions

DH = Division headquarters
PA = Parent company
500 5th Ave
New York, NY 10001
212 800-4800 —— Service description

See footnotes for symbols and codes identification.

- This section is in alphabetical order by city.
- Companies are sorted alphabetically under their respective cities.
- To locate cities within a county refer to the County–City Cross Reference Index.

IMPORTANT NOTICE: It is a violation of both federal and state law to transmit an unsolicited advertisement to a facsimile machine. Any user of this product that violates such laws may be subject to civil and criminal penalties which may exceed $500 for each transmission of an unsolicited facsimile. Harris InfoSource provides fax numbers for lawful purposes only and expressly forbids the use of these numbers in any unlawful manner.

ADA
Norman County

(G-1)
CITY OF ADA
Also Called: Bridges Medical Services
201 9th St W Ste 1 (56510-1279)
PHONE..............................218 784-5000
FAX: 218 784-5262
Andrea Konoske, *Purchasing*
Ruben Alvarez, *Engineering*
Shayla Henneberg, *Human Res Dir*
David Hall, *Pub Rel Dir*
Kristi Slette, *Office Mgr*
EMP: 130
SALES (est): 10MM-24.9MM **Privately Held**
SIC: 8062 Medical hospital
PA: City of Ada
15 4th Ave E
ADA MN 56510
218 784-2211

(G-2)
NORMAN COUNTY AMBULANCE GARAGE
Also Called: Bridges Medical Services
201 9th St W Ste 1 (56510-1279)
PHONE..............................218 784-5000
Wally Nyland, *Safety Dir*
Jesse Vega, *Facilities Dir*
Ruben Alvarez, *Plant Mgr*
Andrea Konoske, *Purch Agent*
Shayla Henneberg, *Human Res Mgr*
EMP: 200 EST: 1991
SALES (est): 5MM-9.9MM **Privately Held**
WEB: www.bridgesmed.com
SIC: 4119 Ambulance service

ADAMS
Mower County

(G-3)
CITY OF ADAMS
Also Called: Adams Health Care Center
810 W Main St (55909-9764)
810 W Main St (55909-9764)
PHONE..............................507 582-3263
FAX: 507 582-7793
Julie Schmitz, *Vice Pres*
James Thalberg, *Administrator*
EMP: 87
SALES (est): 1MM-4.9MM **Privately Held**
SIC: 8059 8051 Personal care home, with health care; skilled nursing care facility
PA: City of Adams
303 W Main St
Adams MN 55909
507 582-3601

ADRIAN
Nobles County

(G-4)
PAT S ELECTRIC
320 Delaware Ave (56110-1211)
PHONE..............................507 483-2857
Pat Strassberg, *Owner*
EMP: 43 EST: 1997
SALES (est): 1MM-4.9MM **Privately Held**
SIC: 1731 Electrical contractor

(G-5)
SON-D-FARMS INC
25751 State Highway 91 (56110-3059)
PHONE..............................507 483-2245
Douglas Bullerman, *President*
Delbert Bullerman, *Principal*
Vernon Bullerman, *Principal*
EMP: 35 EST: 1989 **Privately Held**
SIC: 0213 0191 Hog & pig farming; crop farming

AFTON
Washington County

(G-6)
AFTON ST CROIX CO
Also Called: Historic Afton House Inn
3291 Saint Croix Trl S (55001)
PO Box 326 (55001-0326)
PHONE..............................651 436-8883
FAX: 651 436-6859
Garold Jarvis, *President*
Dan Jarvis, *Vice Pres*
Kathy Jarvis, *Vice Pres*
Ricky Nichols, *Exec Dir*
EMP: 50 EST: 1977
SQ FT: 89,298
SALES (est): 1MM-4.9MM **Privately Held**
WEB: www.aftonhouseinn.com
SIC: 4489 7011 Eating place; sightseeing boat operator; cocktail lounge; inn

(G-7)
B J TRANSPORT INC
12720 Hudson Rd S (55001-9798)
PHONE..............................651 436-4300
FAX: 651 436-4336
William P Turcotte, *CEO*
Jefferey Turcotte, *Ch of Bd*
Michael Hedstrom, *President*
Joanne Turcotte, *Vice Pres*
Denise Fudally, *CFO*
EMP: 25 EST: 1979
SQ FT: 30,000
SALES (est): 1MM-4.9MM **Privately Held**
WEB: www.bjtransport.com
SIC: 4213 Contract haulers

(G-8)
CHANDLER EXHIBITS INC
13523 Hudson Rd S (55001-9709)
PHONE..............................651 389-5900
John Chandler, *President*
Lee Bartelt, *General Mgr*
Tina Ducharme, *Accountant*
Kayleen Schoeder, *Manager*
Angie Kath, *Director*
EMP: 85 EST: 1982
SQ FT: 125,000
SALES (est): 5MM-9.9MM **Privately Held**
SIC: 8711 Manufactures wood nonrefrigerated show & display cabinets; ship, boat, machine & product design services

(G-9)
LANDSCAPE RENOVATIONS INC
12515 40th St S (55001-9616)
PHONE..............................651 769-0010
Robert Palmer, *CEO*
Scott Frampton, *President*
EMP: 30 EST: 2000 **Privately Held**
SIC: 0782 Landscaping services

(G-10)
ST PAUL PUBLIC SCHOOL
Also Called: Belwin Outdoor Educational Lab
1553 Stagecoach Trl S (55001-9703)
PHONE..............................651 436-5243
FAX: 651 436-5984
Maria Carstarfin, *Superintendent*
Thomas Degree, *Principal*
Lucy Bell, *Manager*

Charlie Hartwell, *Bd of Directors*
Nancy Gibson, *Bd of Directors*
EST: 1971 **Privately Held**
WEB: www.belwin.org
SIC: 8999 Natural resource preservation
services

(G-11)
STIVLAND INC
Also Called: Harbor Shelter
15234 50th St S (55001-9636)
PHONE..............................651 436-1153
Rod Stivland, *President*
Dan Johnson, *General Mgr*
Barb Compton, *Director*
EMP: 30 **EST:** 2000
SALES (est): 1MM-4.9MM **Privately Held**
SIC: 8322 Child & youth services

AITKIN
Aitkin County

(G-12)
AICOTA HEALTHCARE CENTER
850 2nd St NW (56431-1140)
PHONE..............................218 927-2164
FAX: 218 927-6360
Priscilla Blom, *Manager*
Barry Foss, *Administrator*
Allison Foss, *Administration*
EMP: 120 **EST:** 1933
SALES (est): 1MM-4.9MM **Privately Held**
SIC: 8051 Skilled nursing care facility

(G-13)
AITKIN COUNTY
Also Called: Family Services
204 1st St NW (56431-1260)
PHONE..............................218 927-3744
FAX: 218 927-7210
Sue Tange, *Manager*
Chris Sutch, *Comp Spec*
Steve Bennett, *MIS Staff*
Tom Burke, *Director*
EMP: 45
SALES (est): 1MM-4.9MM **Privately Held**
WEB: www.cmncc.org
SIC: 8322 Family services agency; county
supervisors' & executives' office
PA: Aitkin County
      209 2nd St NW
      Aitkin MN 56431
      218 927-7345

(G-14)
AITKIN COUNTY
Also Called: Highway Department
1211 Air Park Dr (56431-5627)
PHONE..............................218 927-3741
FAX: 218 927-2356
John Welle, *Manager*
EMP: 25
SALES (est): 1MM-4.9MM **Privately Held**
WEB: www.cmncc.org
SIC: 1611 Highway & street maintenance
service
PA: Aitkin County
      209 2nd St NW
      Aitkin MN 56431
      218 927-7345

(G-15)
AITKIN HEALTH SERVICES
301 Minnesota Ave S (56431-1626)
PHONE..............................218 927-5545
FAX: 218 927-2385
Mike Hagen, *Administrator*
Michele Halvorson, *Administrator*
EMP: 60 **EST:** 2007
SALES (est): 1MM-4.9MM **Privately Held**
WEB: www.ahs.sfhs.org
SIC: 8059 Nursing home

(G-16)
AMERICAN LEGION CLUB
Also Called: Aitkin Legion Post
20 1st Ave NE (56431-1508)
PHONE..............................218 927-2965
Willard Hagman, *Manager*
Donna Miller, *Manager*
EMP: 40 **EST:** 1919 **Privately Held**
SIC: 8641 Civic & social organization

(G-17)
BLUE VALLEY SOD CO
39095 Osprey Ave (56431-7423)
PHONE..............................218 927-4557
FAX: 218 927-3210
Bob Weerts, *President*
EMP: 25 **EST:** 2002 **Privately Held**
WEB: www.bluevalleysod.com
SIC: 0181 Sod farm

(G-18)
DAM LAKE SPORTMENS CLUB
316 4th St NW (56431-1214)
PHONE..............................218 927-6263
Tony Klee, *President*
EMP: 30 **EST:** 1999
SALES (est): 5MM-9.9MM **Privately Held**
SIC: 7941 Sports support services

(G-19)
GREAT RIVER GARDEN
43507 US Highway 169 (56431-4097)
PHONE..............................218 927-2521
FAX: 218 927-2521
Joe Riehle, *Owner*
EMP: 32
SALES (est): 5MM-9.9MM **Privately Held**
SIC: 0181 5193 Retails nursery stock,
seeds & bulbs; wholesales nursery stock;
nursery stock production

(G-20)
J C TRUX INC
40538 Diamond Lake Rd (56431)
PHONE..............................218 927-4450
John H Carlson, *President*
EST: 1992
SQ FT: 312 **Privately Held**
SIC: 4213 Contract haulers

(G-21)
LAKE STATES LUMBER INC
995 Pacific St NW (56431)
PO Box 310 (56431-0310)
PHONE..............................218 927-2125
FAX: 218 927-3513
Tim Ross, *General Mgr*
Jerry Lipovetz, *Principal*
Todd Brooks, *Info Tech Mgr*
EMP: 50
SALES (est): 25MM-49.9MM **Privately Held**
SIC: 5031 Wholesales rough, dressed &
finished lumber

(G-22)
MILLE LACS ELECTRIC CO-OP
36559 US Highway 169 (56431-4201)
PO Box 230 (56431-0230)
PHONE..............................218 927-2191
FAX: 218 927-6822
Ralph Mykkannen, *President*
Donald Hyytinen, *Corp Secy*
Vern Watters, *Vice Pres*
Deborah Epshulz, *Finance Mgr*
Ralph Moykkan, *Manager*
EMP: 53 **EST:** 1939
SQ FT: 33,000
SALES (est): 25MM-49.9MM **Privately Held**
SIC: 4911 Electric power distribution service

AITKIN
Crow Wing County

(G-23)
AITKIN COMMUNITY HOSPITAL INC
200 Bunker Hill Dr (56431-1865)
PHONE..............................218 927-2121
Michael Hagen, *President*
Jim West, *Vice Pres*
Janet Rinlin, *Marketing Mgr*
Janet Lingren, *Marketing Mgr*
Rebecca Meinecke, *Med Doctor*
EMP: 320 **EST:** 1948
SQ FT: 150,000
SALES (est): 25MM-49.9MM **Privately Held**
WEB: www.riverwoodhealthcare.com
SIC: 8062 Medical hospital

(G-24)
AITKIN IRON WORKS INC
301 Bunker Hill Dr (56431-1844)
PHONE..............................218 927-2400
FAX: 218 927-3451
Jeffrey Chatelle, *President*
John Buisman, *Manager*
EMP: 62 **EST:** 1943
SQ FT: 95,000
SALES (est): 5MM-9.9MM **Privately Held**
WEB: www.aiw.com
SIC: 7692 Machine shop; sheet metal
fabricator; welding service

AKELEY
Hubbard County

(G-25)
BAUDORA STATE FOREST NURSERY
13885 State 64 (56433-8323)
PHONE..............................218 652-2385
Doug Anderson, *Director*
EMP: 70 **EST:** 1933 **Privately Held**
SIC: 0181 Nursery stock production

ALBANY
Stearns County

(G-26)
COMMUNITY HEALTH NETWORK
Also Called: Albany Medical Center
300 3rd Ave (56307-9363)
PHONE..............................320 845-2121
Ben Kopplement, *President*
Larry Schultz, *President*
Tom Jopp, *Opers Staff*
Larry Novakoske, *Treasurer*
Bernie Cekalla, *Human Res Dir*
EMP: 110 **EST:** 1989
SQ FT: 30,000
SALES (est): 5MM-9.9MM **Privately Held**
SIC: 8062 Medical hospital

(G-27)
J T ELECTRIC SERVICE INC
111 County Road 10 (56307-4517)
PO Box 476 (56307-0476)
PHONE..............................320 845-4789
FAX: 320 845-4920
Terry Oehrlein, *President*
Jerry Mergen, *Vice Pres*
Patti Oehrlein, *Manager*
EMP: 25 **EST:** 1976
SQ FT: 7,000
SALES (est): 1MM-4.9MM **Privately Held**
SIC: 1731 General electrical contractor

(G-28)
RAMLER TRUCKING INC
400 13th St (56307-6402)
PHONE..............................320 845-4500
FAX: 320 845-7245
John G Ramler, *President*
Greg Ramler, *Corp Secy*
EMP: 46 **EST:** 1954
SALES (est): 5MM-9.9MM **Privately Held**
WEB: www.ramlertrucking.com
SIC: 4213 Over the road trucking

(G-29)
STEARNS COUNTY NATIONAL ASSN
500 13th St (56307-6401)
PO Box 750 (56307-0750)
PHONE..............................320 845-2149
Scott Powers, *Vice Pres*
Dick Thomas, *Officer*
EMP: 70
SALES (est): 10MM-24.9MM **Privately Held**
WEB: www.stearns-bank.com
SIC: 6022 State commercial bank
HQ: Stearns County National Assn
      4191 2nd St S
      Saint Cloud MN 56301
      320 253-6607

ALBERT LEA
Freeborn County

(G-30)
ALBERT LEA BUS CO INC
1407 Saint John Ave (56007-3156)
PHONE..............................507 373-1467
FAX: 507 373-2714
William Regan, *President*
Sally Regan, *Vice Pres*
Steven P Gannings, *Manager*
EMP: 44 **EST:** 1936
SQ FT: 18,700
SALES (est): 1MM-4.9MM **Privately Held**
SIC: 4151 4141 School bus service; local
bus charter service

(G-31)
ALBERT LEA FAMILY YMCA
Also Called: Y M C A
2021 W Main St (56007-4335)
PHONE..............................507 373-8228
FAX: 507 373-1053
Kevin Miland, *Corp Secy*
Jan Mattson, *Treasurer*
Darleen Dorager, *Manager*
Dennis Deiser, *Director*
EMP: 40 **EST:** 1914 **Privately Held**
WEB: www.ymcaal.org
SIC: 8641 7032 7991 8322 8351 Youth
organizations; youth camps; child day care
service; individual & family social services;
physical fitness center

(G-32)
ALBERT LEA MEDICAL CENTER-MAYO
404 W Fountain St (56007-2437)
PHONE..............................507 373-2384
FAX: 507 377-6248
Mark Ciota, *CEO*
Michael G Moore, *Treasurer*
Sara Lewer, *Finance Dir*
Myrna Montag, *Accountant*
Julian R Waggone MD, *Med Doctor*
EMP: 1238 **EST:** 1905
SQ FT: 190,000
SALES (est): 100MM-499.9MM **Privately
Held**
SIC: 8062 8011 8051 8063 8069 Medical
hospital; substance abuse hospital; clinic
operated by physicians; psychiatric hospital;
skilled nursing care facility
PA: Mayo Clinic
      200 1st St SW
      Rochester MN 55905
      507 284-2511

(G-33)
ALBERT LEA SEED HOUSE INC
1414 W Main St (56007-1816)
PO Box 127 (56007-0127)
PHONE..............................507 373-3161
FAX: 507 373-7031
George M Ehrhardt, *President*
Marget Ehrhardt, *Corp Secy*
Anne Ehrhardt, *Vice Pres*
Rodney Hunt, *Exec Dir*
Oscar Adams, *Director*
EMP: 25 **EST:** 1923
SQ FT: 100,000
SALES (est): 1MM-4.9MM **Privately Held**
WEB: www.alseed.com
SIC: 5191 Retails farm supplies; wholesales
field, garden & flower seeds; wholesales
farm supplies

(G-34)
ALBERT LEE MEDICAL CENTER INC
210 North Ln (56007-1436)
PHONE..............................507 377-6393
Jowell Horman, *Manager*
EMP: 200
SALES (est): 5MM-9.9MM **Privately Held**
SIC: 8082 Home health care services
PA: Albert Lee Medical Center Inc
      404 W Fountain St
      Albert Lea MN 56007
      507 373-2384

G E O G R A P H I C

(G-35)
ALLIANCE BENEFIT GROUP
201 E Clark St (56007-2421)
PO Box 1206 (56007-1206)
PHONE..............................507 377-9344
FAX: 507 377-9103
Bradley K Arends, *President*
Alan Arends, *Chairman*
Tempest A Arends, *Corp Secy*
Grant Arends, *Exec VP*
Steve Pulley, *Vice Pres*
EMP: 77 **EST:** 1984
SQ FT: 14,000
SALES (est): 5MM-9.9MM **Privately Held**
SIC: 8748 6282 6371 8721 Employee
programs administration consultant;
investment advisory service; pension, health
& welfare funds services; payroll services

(G-36)
ALMCO INC
507 W Front St (56007-2751)
PHONE..............................507 377-2102
Dave Squires, *Purchasing*
Richard Rocklin, *Branch Mgr*
Dan Jacobs, *MIS/IT Dir*
EMP: 43
SALES (est): 10MM-24.9MM **Privately Held**
WEB: www.innovanceinc.com
SIC: 5084 Wholesales metalworking
machinery
HQ: Almco Inc
507 W Front St
Albert Lea MN 56007
507 377-2102

(G-37)
ALTERNATIVE CONTINUM OF CARE
Also Called: Oak Park Place Assisted Living
1615 Bridge Ave Apt 261 (56007-2109)
PHONE..............................507 373-5600
FAX: 507 373-1121
Joyce Nixon, *Administrator*
EMP: 60
SALES (est): 1MM-4.9MM **Privately Held**
SIC: 8051 Skilled nursing care facility

(G-38)
AMERICAN BANK OF ST PAUL
217 S Newton Ave (56007-2563)
PHONE..............................507 377-7000
FAX: 507 377-2126
Adrienne Thorson, *Vice Pres*
Rhonda Allison, *Manager*
Jane Swehla, *Manager*
Meta Johnson, *Manager*
Amber Amunds, *Manager*
EMP: 25
SALES (est): 5MM-9.9MM **Privately Held**
SIC: 6022 State commercial bank
HQ: American Bank of St Paul
1578 University Ave W
Saint Paul MN 55104
651 452-1320

(G-39)
AMERICAN BAPTIST HOMES OF THE
Also Called: Crest Services
617 E 10th St (56007-3202)
PHONE..............................507 373-0188
Dave Charron, *General Mgr*
Kay Goodmanson, *Mktg Dir*
Carol Coppiac, *Director*
EMP: 60
SALES (est): 1MM-4.9MM **Privately Held**
WEB: www.abhomes.net
SIC: 8361 8093 Home for the mentally
handicapped; outpatient rehabilitation
treatment center
PA: American Baptist Homes of The
14850 Scenic Heights Rd
Eden Prairie MN 55344
952 941-3175

(G-40)
AMERICAN BAPTIST HOMES OF THE
Also Called: Thorn Crest South
1201 Garfield Ave (56007-3637)
PHONE..............................507 373-9656
Dave Charron, *General Mgr*

Randall Parks, *Administrator*
Carol L Coppiac, *Director*
EMP: 40
SALES (est): 1MM-4.9MM **Privately Held**
WEB: www.abhomes.net
SIC: 8051 Convalescent home
PA: American Baptist Homes of The
14850 Scenic Heights Rd
Eden Prairie MN 55344
952 941-3175

(G-41)
BECKER HI-WAY FRATE
2401 Becker Dr (56007-6301)
PHONE..............................507 373-8513
Joseph A Becker, *Owner*
EMP: 25 **EST:** 1950
SQ FT: 5,400
SALES (est): 1MM-4.9MM **Privately Held**
SIC: 4213 Over the road trucking

(G-42)
CEDAR VALLEY SERVICES INC
1839 SE Broadway Ave (56007-3266)
PHONE..............................507 373-6064
FAX: 507 373-7105
Michele Sorensen, *Manager*
Karen Joavain, *Manager*
EMP: 40
SALES (est): 1MM-4.9MM **Privately Held**
SIC: 8331 Vocational training agency;
vocational rehabilitation agency
PA: Cedar Valley Services Inc
2111 4th St NW
Austin MN 55912
507 433-2303

(G-43)
CEDAR VALLEY SERVICES INC
2205 Myers Rd (56007-3392)
PHONE..............................507 377-2893
FAX: 507 377-1890
Rich Pavek, *Dir Ops-Prd-Mfg*
EMP: 25
SALES (est): 1MM-4.9MM **Privately Held**
SIC: 8331 Sheltered workshop
PA: Cedar Valley Services Inc
2111 4th St NW
Austin MN 55912
507 433-2303

(G-44)
CHILDREN'S CENTER
605 James Ave (56007-2914)
PHONE..............................507 373-7979
FAX: 507 377-8664
Kristen Houg, *Director*
EMP: 45 **EST:** 1969
SALES (est): 1MM-4.9MM **Privately Held**
SIC: 8351 Child day care service

(G-45)
CROSSROADS TRAILER SALES & SVC
Hwy 65 S (56007)
PO Box 490 (56007-0490)
PHONE..............................507 373-4443
FAX: 507 373-0739
Darvin Habben, *CEO*
Stephen Flaa, *Corp Secy*
Todd Wayne, *Vice Pres*
Todd Kriewall, *Vice Pres*
Scott Hanna, *Finance*
EMP: 30 **EST:** 1986
SQ FT: 20,000
SALES (est): 25MM-49.9MM **Privately Held**
WEB: www.crossroadtrailer.com
SIC: 5012 5078 7539 Wholesales new &
used trailers for trucks; wholesales motor
vehicle refrigeration units; trailer repair
service

(G-46)
DAVE SYVERSON INC
Also Called: Syverson, Dave Volkswagen
2310 E Main St (56007-3923)
PO Box 251 (56007-0251)
PHONE..............................507 373-1438
FAX: 507 373-3063
David Syverson, *President*
Robert Syverson, *Corp Secy*
Chuck Koziolek, *Parts Mgr*
Randy Goodnature, *Parts Mgr*
Jay Klemp, *Sales Mgr*
EMP: 80

EST: 1967
SQ FT: 48,000
SALES (est): 25MM-49.9MM **Privately Held**
WEB: www.davesyverson.com
SIC: 7513 Retails new & used automobiles;
truck leasing service, without drivers

(G-47)
DIMA CORP
400 W Front St (56007-2770)
PHONE..............................507 373-6969
FAX: 507 377-9696
Lisa Meaney, *President*
Mel Prinzing, *Corp Secy*
EMP: 30 **EST:** 1978
SALES (est): 10MM-24.9MM **Privately Held**
WEB: www.dimacorp.com
SIC: 5099 Wholesales video cassettes,
accessories & supplies

(G-48)
ENDERES TOOL CO INC
Also Called: Premium Tools
924 E 14th St (56007-3218)
PO Box 691 (56007-0691)
PHONE..............................507 373-2396
FAX: 507 373-2398
Todd Dahl, *Finance*
Mark Palkovich, *Sales Staff*
Dale Elvebba, *Manager*
Dawn Deimer, *Manager*
EMP: 50
SQ FT: 25,000
SALES (est): 5MM-9.9MM **Privately Held**
WEB: www.enderes.com
SIC: 5072 Manufactures hand tools;
wholesales hand tools

(G-49)
EVANGELICAL LUTHERAN GOOD
Also Called: Good Samaritan Center
700 County Road 14 (56007-9549)
PHONE..............................507 379-2707
Blair Jackson, *Branch Mgr*
EMP: 240
SALES (est): 5MM-9.9MM **Privately Held**
WEB: www.good-sam.com
SIC: 8051 Convalescent home
PA: Evangelical Lutheran Good
4800 W 57th St
Sioux Falls SD 57108
605 362-3100

(G-50)
EVANGELICAL LUTHERAN GOOD
Also Called: Albert Lea Good Samaritan Ctr
75507 240th St (56007-7537)
PHONE..............................507 373-0683
FAX: 507 373-3229
Bonnie Ruble, *Purchasing*
Dawn Thompson, *Human Resources*
Sandy Fredrickson, *Manager*
Lois Ball, *Manager*
Lois Bahl, *Manager*
EMP: 300
SALES (est): 10MM-24.9MM **Privately Held**
WEB: www.good-sam.com
SIC: 8051 Skilled nursing care facility
PA: Evangelical Lutheran Good
4800 W 57th St
Sioux Falls SD 57108
605 362-3100

(G-51)
FOUNTAIN CENTERS
408 W Fountain St (56007-2437)
PHONE..............................507 377-6411
FAX: 507 377-6375
Ginny Larson, *Director*
EMP: 40 **EST:** 1975 **Privately Held**
SIC: 0711 8069 Soil chemical treatment
services; specialty hospital

(G-52)
FOUNTAIN LAKE TREATMENT CENTER
408 W Fountain St (56007-2437)
PHONE..............................507 373-2384
Garth Barker, *Director*
EMP: 80 **EST:** 1970
SALES (est): 1MM-4.9MM **Privately Held**
SIC: 8361 Self-help group home

(G-53)
FOUR SEASONS SERVICES INC
636 E 11th St (56007-5201)
PHONE..............................507 373-9666
FAX: 507 373-8266
David Nelson, *President*
Dennis Honsey, *Vice Pres*
Lauris C Nelson, *Director*
EMP: 25 **EST:** 1966
SQ FT: 1,000
SALES (est): 5MM-9.9MM **Privately Held**
SIC: 5087 Wholesales vending machines &
supplies

(G-54)
FREEBORN COUNTRY FAIR ASSN
1031 Bridge Ave (56007-2205)
PO Box 128 (56007-0128)
PHONE..............................507 373-6965
Gordon Toeneges, *President*
EMP: 50 **EST:** 1890
SALES (est): 1MM-4.9MM **Privately Held**
WEB: www.freeborncountyfair.com
SIC: 7999 Fair

(G-55)
INNOVANCE INC
507 W Front St (56007-2751)
PHONE..............................507 373-5152
Steve Tufte, *Finance Mgr*
Mike Larson, *Manager*
EMP: 50
SALES (est): 5MM-9.9MM **Privately Held**
WEB: www.innovanceinc.com
SIC: 5013 Manufactures automotive
maintenance equipment; wholesales
automotive body repair or paint shop
supplies
PA: Innovance Inc
505 W Front St
Albert Lea MN 56007
507 377-8910

(G-56)
INTERSTATE MEAT SERVICE INC
2309 Myers Rd (56007-3395)
PO Box 529 (56007-0529)
PHONE..............................507 377-2228
FAX: 507 377-2229
Donald Falk, *President*
Steve Falk, *Executive*
EMP: 45 **EST:** 1978
SQ FT: 26,164
SALES (est): 25MM-49.9MM **Privately Held**
SIC: 5147 Wholesales fresh meat;
wholesales cured or smoked meat

(G-57)
INTERSTATE MOTOR TRUCKS INC
1900 Sorenson Rd (56007-6300)
PO Box 730 (56007-0730)
PHONE..............................507 373-0653
FAX: 507 373-0234
Terrance Kvenvold, *President*
Thayne Nordland, *Corp Secy*
Michael Jacobs, *Vice Pres*
C T Nordland, *Director*
Phyllis Jacobs, *Shareholder*
EMP: 26 **EST:** 1973
SQ FT: 13,600
SALES (est): 10MM-24.9MM **Privately Held**
WEB: www.imtrucks.com
SIC: 7515 Passenger car leasing

(G-58)
INTERSTATE POWER & LIGHT CO
100 N Broadway Ave (56007-2401)
PHONE..............................507 373-2371
FAX: 507 373-0853
Bill Hareid, *Branch Mgr*
EMP: 60
SALES (est): 25MM-49.9MM **Publicly Held**
WEB: www.alliantenergy.com
SIC: 4911 Electric services; provides
electric power generation services
PA: Alliant Energy Corp
4902 N Biltmore Ln
Madison WI 53718
608 458-3311

GEOGRAPHIC

(G-59)
LARSON CONTRACTING INC
508 W Main St (56007-2601)
PO Box 68, Lake Mills IA (50450-0068)
PHONE...............................507 373-6645
Al Larson, *Branch Mgr*
EMP: 56
SALES (est): 10MM-24.9MM **Privately Held**
WEB: www.larsoncontracting.com
SIC: 1542 Commercial & office building
contractor
PA: Larson Contracting Inc
       508 W Main St
       Lake Mills IA 50450
       641 592-5800

(G-60)
LEA ALBERT ELECTRIC CO
1410 Olsen Dr (56007-6305)
PHONE...............................507 373-6650
FAX: 507 373-4124
Mitchell Delgar, *President*
Callen Johnson, *Corp Secy*
Joshua Quinlivan, *Purch Mgr*
Darla Schnaith, *Manager*
Cathy Odonnell, *Manager*
EMP: 30 **EST:** 1919
SQ FT: 6,000
SALES (est): 1MM-4.9MM **Privately Held**
WEB: www.albertleaelectric.com
SIC: 1731 Electrical contractor; retails
electrical construction materials

(G-61)
MAYO CLINIC ROCHESTER
Also Called: Health Reach
1705 SE Broadway Ave (56007-3265)
PHONE...............................507 377-5900
Tonia Lauer, *Project Mgr*
EMP: 40
SALES (est): 1MM-4.9MM **Privately Held**
SIC: 8011 8093 Physicians' office & clinic;
outpatient rehabilitation treatment center
PA: Mayo Clinic
       200 1st St SW
       Rochester MN 55905
       507 284-2511

(G-62)
MORNING STAR HOME HEALTH
1008 Dunham St (56007-1646)
PHONE...............................507 373-0201
Sylvia Meuser, *Owner*
EMP: 30 **EST:** 1999
SALES (est): 1MM-4.9MM **Privately Held**
SIC: 8082 Home health care services

(G-63)
SAFE AIR REPAIR INC
401 Airport Rd (56007-2080)
PHONE...............................507 373-7129
FAX: 507 373-6673
John Roscoe, *President*
Mike Hansen, *General Mgr*
Arleigh Canny, *Mfg Staff*
Sandra Roscoe, *Treasurer*
Joe Bolinger, *Manager*
EMP: 65 **EST:** 1981
SALES (est): 5MM-9.9MM **Privately Held**
WEB: www.safeairrepair.com
SIC: 4581 5088 Manufactures custom
machinery; manufactures aircraft parts &
equipment; wholesales aircraft equipment &
supplies; sheet metal fabricator; steel
fabricator; airport, flying field & services

(G-64)
SAR INC
401 Airport Rd (56007-2080)
PHONE...............................507 373-7129
John Roscoe, *President*
Al Roscoe, *Engineering*
Jason Larue, *IT/INT Sup*
Joe Bolinger, *Director*
Mike Rysavy, *Technician*
EMP: 35 **EST:** 2004
SALES (est): 500-999K **Privately Held**
SIC: 7363 Industrial help service

(G-65)
SECURITY BANK MINNESOTA
437 Bridge Ave (56007-2954)
PO Box 891 (56007-0891)
PHONE...............................507 373-1481
FAX: 507 373-1723
Phillis Munson, *CEO*
Timothy Lenhart, *President*
Julie Claussen, *Vice Pres*
Thomas J Rotramel, *CFO*
Nick Austin, *Loan Officer*
EMP: 28 **EST:** 1906
SQ FT: 11,000
SALES (est): 5MM-9.9MM **Privately Held**
WEB: www.securitybankmn.com
SIC: 6022 State commercial bank

(G-66)
SOYMOR BIODIESEL LLC
15200 780th Ave (56007-7082)
PHONE...............................507 448-0124
Richard Stadkeim, *Member*
Jennifer Hanna, *Member*
Kelly Pestorious, *Controller*
Gary Pestorious, *Mng Member*
EMP: 30 **EST:** 2004
SQ FT: 5,000
SALES (est): 1MM-4.9MM **Privately Held**
SIC: 8732 Commercial nonphysical
research laboratory

(G-67)
ST JOHNS LUTHERAN HOME
901 Luther Pl (56007-1562)
PHONE...............................507 373-8226
Wanda Wangsenss, *Materials Mgr*
Duane Mallon, *CFO*
Angela Beier, *Human Res Dir*
Scot Spates, *Administrator*
Peggy Qual, *Director*
EMP: 300 **EST:** 1962
SQ FT: 93,000
SALES (est): 10MM-24.9MM **Privately Held**
SIC: 8051 Skilled nursing care facility

(G-68)
ULLAND BROTHERS INC
2400 Myers Rd (56007-5315)
PHONE...............................507 373-1960
FAX: 507 377-9867
Joan Ford, *General Mgr*
Murray Srock, *Corp Secy*
Joan Rouse, *Vice Pres*
Ken Johnson, *Vice Pres*
Ryan Swanson, *Vice Pres*
EMP: 25
SALES (est): 1MM-4.9MM **Privately Held**
WEB: www.ulland.com
SIC: 1611 General highway & street
construction service; manufactures asphalt
paving mixtures & blocks
PA: Ulland Brothers Inc
       1634 Highway 210
       Carlton MN 55718
       218 384-4266

(G-69)
UNITED PARCEL SERVICE INC
Also Called: UPS
707 E 12th St (56007-3257)
PHONE...............................507 373-4392
FAX: 507 373-2721
Merle McDold, *Branch Mgr*
Cory Shea, *Manager*
Ryan Miller, *Manager*
Holton Lais, *Manager*
EMP: 50
SALES (est): 1MM-4.9MM **Publicly Held**
WEB: www.ups.com
SIC: 4215 Parcel delivery services by
vehicle
HQ: United Parcel Service Inc
       55 Glenlake Pkwy NE
       Atlanta GA 30328
       404 828-6000

(G-70)
WASTE MANAGEMENT OF MINNESOTA
Junction County Rd 22 25 (56007)
PHONE...............................507 826-3610
FAX: 507 826-3620
Ginger Kaladas, *Credit Staff*
Good Sell, *Manager*
EMP: 50
SALES (est): 5MM-9.9MM **Privately Held**
SIC: 4953 Refuse systems services
PA: Waste Management Inc
       1001 Fannin St Ste 4000
       Houston TX 77002
       713 512-6200

(G-71)
WELLS FARGO BANK, NATIONAL
122 E Main St (56007-4548)
PHONE...............................507 373-1423
FAX: 507 377-1725
Lori Jongbloedt, *Manager*
David Lundak, *Manager*
EMP: 30
SALES (est): 5MM-9.9MM **Publicly Held**
SIC: 6021 6211 National commercial bank;
security broker & dealer service
HQ: Wfc Holdings, Corp
       420 Montgomery St
       San Francisco CA 94104
       415 396-7392

(G-72)
ZUMBRO RIVER BRAND INC
1215 Hershey St (56007-3413)
PHONE...............................507 377-9776
FAX: 507 379-2525
Jim Fischer, *Exec VP*
Ginny Busch, *Vice Pres*
EMP: 32
SALES (est): 10MM-24.9MM **Privately Held**
WEB: www.zumbroriverbrand.com
SIC: 5046 Wholesales commercial cooking
& food services equipment
PA: Zumbro River Brand Inc
       138 W Front St
       Owatonna MN 55060
       507 446-9097

ALBERTVILLE
Wright County

(G-73)
DENNIS FEHN GRAVEL
5050 Barthel Indus Dr (55301)
PO Box 256 (55301-0256)
PHONE...............................763 497-2428
FAX: 763 497-3893
Dennis Fehn, *President*
Bertha Fehn, *Corp Secy*
Gary Fehn, *Vice Pres*
Mike Fehn, *Vice Pres*
Michele Williamson, *Government Rel*
EMP: 40 **EST:** 1971
SQ FT: 4,000
SALES (est): 5MM-9.9MM **Privately Held**
WEB: www.dennisfehn.com
SIC: 1442 1794 Common sand mining;
gravel mining; excavating contractor

(G-74)
DON'S BUS SERVICE INC
11108 60th St (55301)
PO Box 166 (55301-0166)
PHONE...............................763 497-2585
Albert Barthel, *President*
Betty Barthel, *Vice Pres*
Jason Barthel, *Director*
EMP: 25 **EST:** 1958
SALES (est): 500-999K **Privately Held**
SIC: 4151 School bus service

(G-75)
LONG HAUL TRUCKING INC
6600 Jansen Ave NE (55301-9686)
PO Box 167 (55301-0167)
PHONE...............................763 497-3727
John S Daniels, *President*
Dino Buege, *Exec VP*
Tiffani Steinke, *Controller*
Iris Harris, *Human Res Mgr*
Jason Michels, *Sales Staff*
EMP: 60 **EST:** 1985
SQ FT: 15,000
SALES (est): 5MM-9.9MM **Privately Held**
WEB: www.longhaultrucking.com
SIC: 4213 Over the road trucking

(G-76)
PROMISES + INC
6600 Jansen Ave NE (55301-9686)
PO Box 167 (55301-0167)
PHONE...............................763 497-3727
John Daniel, *President*
EST: 1997 **Privately Held**
SIC: 4731 Truck transportation brokers

(G-77)
TRUDELL TRAILERS OF MINNESOTA
9600 71st St NE (55301-3946)
PHONE...............................763 497-7084
FAX: 763 497-7085
Greg Giergielewicz, *Vice Pres*
EMP: 30
SALES (est): 25MM-49.9MM **Privately Held**
SIC: 5012 5013 Wholesales new & used
trailers for trucks; wholesales automotive
trailer parts & accessories; retails new &
used trucks, tractors & trailers
HQ: Trudell Trailers of Minnesota
       2049 Creamery Rd
       De Pere WI 54115
       920 336-0601

ALDEN
Freeborn County

(G-78)
ALDEN AREA FOOD SHELF
191 Water St (56009-1108)
PHONE...............................507 377-3683
Rosie Rasmussen, *Director*
EMP: 25
SALES (est): 1MM-4.9MM **Privately Held**
SIC: 8999 Miscellaneous services

ALEXANDRIA
Douglas County

(G-79)
AL MINNERATH INC
6325 County Road 87 SW (56308-5361)
PHONE...............................320 762-7289
Joseph Minnerath, *President*
John Minnerath, *Treasurer*
Ella Koehn, *MIS Staff*
EMP: 240 **EST:** 1955
SQ FT: 8,500
SALES (est): 25MM-49.9MM **Privately Held**
SIC: 1611 1771 General highway & street
construction service; concrete contractor

(G-80)
ALEXANDRIA CLINIC PROPERTIES
610 30th Ave W (56308-3426)
PHONE...............................320 763-5123
Tom Storer, *Facilities Mgr*
Lisa Malmgren, *Purchasing*
Andrew Langenfeld, *CFO*
Tina Frigaard, *Human Res Dir*
Gloria Otte, *Nursing Spvr*
EMP: 160 **EST:** 1950
SQ FT: 52,000
SALES (est): 10MM-24.9MM **Privately Held**
WEB: www.alexclinic.com
SIC: 8011 Clinic operated by physicians

(G-81)
ALEXANDRIA GOLF CLUB
2300 N Nokomis Ln (56308)
PO Box 206 (56308-0206)
PHONE...............................320 762-1093
FAX: 320 762-1093
Rick Nelson, *Corp Secy*
Tim Cullen, *Vice Pres*
Kurt Sieve, *Treasurer*
Perry Wahlin, *Treasurer*
Judy Schlosser, *Office Mgr*
EMP: 25 **EST:** 1915
SALES (est): 1MM-4.9MM **Privately Held**
WEB: www.alexandriagolfclub.com
SIC: 7997 Country club

(G-82)
ALEXANDRIA PRO-FAB CO INC
8210 State Highway 29 N (56308-8025)
PHONE 320 852-7918
FAX: 320 852-7513
Donald E Wilkins, *President*
Ed Wilkins, *Corp Secy*
Tom Wilkins, *Vice Pres*
Joe Klimek, *Engineer*
Dee D Neumann, *Manager*
EMP: 65 **EST:** 1976
SQ FT: 42,000
SALES (est): 5MM-9.9MM **Privately Held**
WEB: www.alexprofab.com
SIC: 7692 Machine shop, jobbing & repair services; sheet metal fabricator; welding service

(G-83)
ANDERSON FLORISTS
1610 6th Ave E (56308-2105)
PHONE 320 763-5115
FAX: 320 763-5116
Lori Sehultz, *President*
David Pederson, *President*
Janice Pederson, *Treasurer*
EMP: 25 **EST:** 1950
SQ FT: 25,000
SALES (est): 1MM-4.9MM **Privately Held**
SIC: 0181 Retails fresh flowers; flower farming undercover

(G-84)
BEVERAGE WHOLESALERS
2720 Latoka Ln SW (56308-9176)
PO Box 577 (56308-0577)
PHONE 320 759-9009
FAX: 320 759-7242
Randy Christianson, *Owner*
Greg Huss, *Manager*
EMP: 55 **EST:** 2002
SALES (est): 10MM-24.9MM **Privately Held**
SIC: 5181 Wholesales beer & ale

(G-85)
BREMER BANK
720 Broadway St (56308-1812)
PO Box 309 (56308-0309)
PHONE 320 763-6622
David Kjos, *President*
EMP: 50
SALES (est): 10MM-24.9MM **Privately Held**
SIC: 6029 Commercial bank
DH: Bremer Bank
　　2100 Bremer Tower 445
　　Saint Paul MN 55101
　　800 908-2265

(G-86)
BREMMER BANK
720 Broadway St (56308-1812)
PO Box 309 (56308-0309)
PHONE 320 763-6622
David Kjos, *President*
John Rolf, *Senior VP*
Du W Johnson, *Senior VP*
EMP: 60
SQ FT: 4,000
SALES (est): 10MM-24.9MM **Privately Held**
SIC: 6022 State commercial bank
HQ: Bremer Financial Corp
　　445 Minnesota St Ste 2000
　　Saint Paul MN 55101
　　651 227-7621

(G-87)
BROADWAY MEDICAL CENTER LTD
1527 Broadway St (56308-2537)
PHONE 320 762-0399
FAX: 320 762-6830
Connie Schnitzler, *Corp Secy*
Ashley Bradley, *Persnl Dir*
Bruce A Evink MD, *Med Doctor*
Jerry M Crery MD, *Med Doctor*
Sara Englund, *Supervisor*
EMP: 130 **EST:** 1996
SALES (est): 10MM-24.9MM **Privately Held**
WEB: www.broadwaymedicalcenter.com
SIC: 8011 Physicians' office & clinic

(G-88)
CENTRAL SPECIALTIES INC
6325 County Road 87 SW (56308-5361)
PHONE 320 762-7289
Joe Minnerath, *President*
Kevin Minnerath, *Vice Pres*
John Minnerath, *Treasurer*
EMP: 55 **EST:** 1976
SALES (est): 5MM-9.9MM **Privately Held**
WEB: www.centralspecialties.com
SIC: 1611 General highway & street construction service

(G-89)
CONTINENTAL BRIDGE INC
8301 State Highway 29 N (56308-8025)
PHONE 320 852-7500
FAX: 320 852-7735
Randy Eggen, *General Mgr*
Tom Bishop, *General Mgr*
Tony Schneider, *Corp Secy*
Gregory Peterson, *Purch Mgr*
EMP: 65 **EST:** 2000
SQ FT: 59,000
SALES (est): 10MM-24.9MM **Privately Held**
WEB: www.contech-cpi.com
SIC: 1541 Steel building construction
HQ: Contech Construction Products
　　9025 Centre Pointe Dr # 400
　　West Chester OH 45069
　　513 645-7000

(G-90)
COUNTY OF DOUGLAS
Also Called: Douglas County Hospital
700 Cedar St Ste 154 (56308-1695)
PHONE 320 762-2400
Catie Lee, *Branch Mgr*
Dave Pederson, *Manager*
Maryann Rollie, *Exec Dir*
EMP: 25
SALES (est): 1MM-4.9MM **Privately Held**
SIC: 8063 Mental hospital
PA: County of Douglas
　　305 8th Ave W
　　Alexandria MN 56308
　　320 762-3077

(G-91)
COUNTY OF DOUGLAS
Also Called: Douglas County Hospital
111 17th Ave E (56308-3703)
PHONE 320 762-1511
FAX: 320 762-6034
Linda Vickstrom, *Corp Secy*
D P Weigel, *Ch of Surgery*
Gary Boesen, *Opers Mgr*
Gary Boeser, *Facilities Mgr*
David Pedersen, *Engineer*
EMP: 600
SALES (est): 50MM-99.9MM **Privately Held**
SIC: 8062 8049 8093 Medical hospital; speech specialist office; outpatient rehabilitation treatment center
PA: County of Douglas
　　305 8th Ave W
　　Alexandria MN 56308
　　320 762-3077

(G-92)
COUNTY OF DOUGLAS
Also Called: Douglas County Public Health
725 Elm St Ste 1200 (56308-1760)
PHONE 320 763-6018
FAX: 320 763-4127
Melissa Howe, *Manager*
Mark Lundin, *Exec Dir*
Sandy Tubbs, *Director*
EMP: 70
SALES (est): 5MM-9.9MM **Privately Held**
SIC: 1711 8011 Heating & air conditioning contractor; county general government administration office; medical center
PA: County of Douglas
　　305 8th Ave W
　　Alexandria MN 56308
　　320 762-3077

(G-93)
CULLEN'S HOME CENTER OF
1620 N Nokomis St NE (56308-5069)
PHONE 320 762-1249
FAX: 320 762-5105
Timothy P Cullen, *President*

Kathie Cullen, *Vice Pres*
Lee Olmschenk, *Project Mgr*
Janice Grandt, *Manager*
Mike Pray, *Executive*
EMP: 51 **EST:** 1980
SQ FT: 5,000
SALES (est): 5MM-9.9MM **Privately Held**
WEB: www.cullenshomecenter.com
SIC: 1742 1761 Retails household appliances; building insulation installation service; siding contractor; retails television sets

(G-94)
DENTISTRY AT THE CENTER INC
2306 S Broadway St Ste 4 (56308-3461)
PHONE 320 762-5216
FAX: 320 762-8222
David A Golke DDS, *President*
Paul M Odland DDS, *Vice Pres*
Rick Theiry, *Treasurer*
Thomas C Dewitt DDS, *Treasurer*
Deanna McCabe, *Office Mgr*
EMP: 25 **EST:** 1985
SALES (est): 1MM-4.9MM **Privately Held**
SIC: 8021 Dentists' office & clinic

(G-95)
DONNELLY CUSTOM MANUFACTURING
105 Donovan Dr (56308-8531)
PHONE 320 762-2396
FAX: 320 762-1770
Stan Donnelly, *CEO*
Ron Kirscht, *President*
Gerald Bienias, *Vice Pres*
Jerry Bienias, *Vice Pres*
Jim McCarthy, *Vice Pres*
▲ **EMP:** 200 **EST:** 1984
SQ FT: 110,000
SALES (est): 25MM-49.9MM **Privately Held**
WEB: www.donnmfg.com
SIC: 8711 Manufactures injection molded plastic products; engineering services; plastic product coloring & finishing; manufactures molded plastic products

(G-96)
DVCM SERVICEMASTER OF THE
Also Called: ServiceMaster of Lakes Area
203 Lake St (56308-1509)
PO Box 714 (56308-0714)
PHONE 320 763-5551
Dennis Strong, *President*
Vicki Strong, *Corp Secy*
Matt Strong, *Vice Pres*
Nicki Strong, *Manager*
EMP: 40 **EST:** 1993
SQ FT: 5,500
SALES (est): 1MM-4.9MM **Privately Held**
SIC: 7349 1799 Building cleaning & maintenance services; post disaster renovations service

(G-97)
E & H ENTERPRISES OF
Also Called: Ellingson Plumbing & Heating
2510 S Broadway St (56308-3417)
PHONE 320 762-8645
Phillip Ellingson, *President*
Tom J Hills, *Vice Pres*
EMP: 78 **EST:** 1981
SQ FT: 20,000
SALES (est): 5MM-9.9MM **Privately Held**
SIC: 1711 Plumbing service; retails fireworks; warm air heating & air conditioning contractor

(G-98)
ECUMEN
Also Called: Bethany Home
1020 Lark St (56308-2219)
PHONE 320 762-1567
FAX: 320 762-5316
Darold Thorson, *Maint Spvr*
Gary Brink, *Branch Mgr*
Kathleen Otte, *Manager*
Carol Kvidt, *Administrator*
Grady Third, *Director*
EMP: 200
SALES (est): 5MM-9.9MM **Privately Held**
WEB: www.augustanahomes.org

SIC: 8051 Skilled nursing care facility
PA: Ecumen
　　3530 Lexington Ave N
　　Saint Paul MN 55126
　　651 766-4300

(G-99)
EDINA REALTY HOME SERVICES
815 Broadway St (56308-1856)
PHONE 320 762-8181
FAX: 320 763-2628
Eldon Matz, *Treasurer*
Gaylam Leror, *Manager*
Gerard T Lynch, *Manager*
EMP: 27
SALES (est): 5MM-9.9MM **Publicly Held**
WEB: www.ilovetennis.net
SIC: 6531 Real estate agency & broker
HQ: Edina Realty Home Services
　　6800 France Ave S Ste 600
　　Minneapolis MN 55435
　　952 928-5900

(G-100)
FARMERS UNION OIL CO OF
Also Called: Cenex
1705 Broadway St (56308-2705)
PHONE 320 763-6557
Lane Colina, *Manager*
Lane Kalina, *Manager*
EMP: 45 **EST:** 1955
SQ FT: 8,400
SALES (est): 10MM-24.9MM **Privately Held**
SIC: 5191 Gas station; wholesales farm supplies

(G-101)
FERGUSON BROTHERS EXCAVATING
2050 County Road 82 NW (56308-8107)
PHONE 320 762-0622
FAX: 320 762-0682
Tim Ferguson, *President*
Anita Ferguson, *Corp Secy*
Jean Ferguson, *Corp Secy*
Terry Ferguson, *Vice Pres*
Ronald T Ferguson, *Director*
EMP: 25 **EST:** 1978
SQ FT: 20,000
SALES (est): 1MM-4.9MM **Privately Held**
SIC: 1794 4959 Excavating contractor; snow plowing services

(G-102)
GENEVA CAPITAL LLC
522 Broadway St Ste 4 (56308-1498)
PHONE 320 762-8400
Brian Strater, *Member*
Mark Watkins, *Member*
Carey Kroll, *Vice Pres*
Janel Mounsdon, *Vice Pres*
Paul Wilmesmeier, *CFO*
EMP: 25 **EST:** 2000
SQ FT: 3,500
SALES (est): Under 500K **Privately Held**
WEB: www.gogenevacapital.com
SIC: 7359 6159 Equipment rental & leasing services; machinery & equipment finance leasing service

(G-103)
HEARTLAND ORTHOPEDIC
1500 Irving St (56308-2515)
PHONE 320 762-1144
FAX: 320 762-1935
Dennis Weigle, *President*
Dianne Doyle, *Phys Therapist*
Gary Webskowski, *Phys Therapist*
Terence J Kennedy MD, *Med Doctor*
Mike Doyle, *Administrator*
EMP: 40 **EST:** 1974
SQ FT: 11,000
SALES (est): 1MM-4.9MM **Privately Held**
WEB: www.alexortho.com
SIC: 8011 Physicians' office & clinic

(G-104)
HENRY'S FOODS INC
104 McKay Ave N (56308-8596)
PO Box 1057 (56308-1057)
PHONE 320 763-3194
FAX: 320 763-6250
Tom Eidsvold, *President*
Jim Eidsvold, *Vice Pres*

Terry Loeffler, *Vice Pres*
Bev Clausen-Kieffer, *Controller*
Karren Janachovsky, *Office Mgr*
EMP: 150 **EST:** 1929
SQ FT: 150,000
SALES (est): 100MM-499.9MM **Privately Held**
WEB: www.henrysfoods.com
SIC: 5194 5111 5113 5141 5145
Wholesales tobacco & tobacco products; wholesales confectionery products; wholesales general line groceries; wholesales industrial & personal service paper; wholesales printing & writing paper

(G-105)
INDEPENDENT SCHOOL DISTRICT
Also Called: Alexandria Public Schl Bus Off
617 18th Ave E (56308-3706)
PHONE 320 762-2148
Kevin McMenimen, *Director*
EMP: 100
SALES (est): 1MM-4.9MM **Privately Held**
WEB: www.alexandria.k12.mn.us
SIC: 4151 School bus service
PA: Independent School District
   715 Elm St
   Alexandria MN 56308
   320 762-2141

(G-106)
INFINITY MOTEL HOLDINGS LLC
Also Called: Country Suites By Carlson
5304 Highway 29 S (56308-6079)
PHONE 320 763-9900
FAX: 320 763-7564
Kent Oliver, *Member*
Carl Svendsen, *Vice Pres*
Mark Johnson, *Accountant*
Meena McCollar, *Manager*
EMP: 29 **EST:** 1995
SALES (est): 1MM-4.9MM **Privately Held**
SIC: 7011 Traveler accommodations

(G-107)
KNUTE NELSON (PA)
420 12th Ave E (56308-2612)
PHONE 320 763-6653
FAX: 320 763-7548
Katie Perry, *Vice Pres*
Angie Urman, *Vice Pres*
Marnie Gugisberg, *CFO*
Stewart Henrickson, *Treasurer*
Rachel Jahner, *Human Res Mgr*
EMP: 330 **EST:** 1969
SQ FT: 180,000
SALES (corp-wide): 14.75M **Privately Held**
WEB: www.knutenelson.org
SIC: 8051 Skilled nursing care facility

(G-108)
LAKE CARLOS VILLAS
3954 County Road 42 NE (56308-6621)
PHONE 320 846-1784
FAX: 320 846-0258
Rosemary Schneiderhan, *President*
Al Olsen, *Manager*
EMP: 25 **EST:** 1980
SALES (est): 1MM-4.9MM **Privately Held**
WEB: www.lakecarlosvillas.com
SIC: 7389 Condominium time share exchange services

(G-109)
LAKELAND DISTRIBUTION SERVICES
225 7th Ave E (56308-1831)
PO Box 549 (56308-0549)
PHONE 320 762-8385
Jody Hanson, *Publisher*
Diann Drew, *Manager*
Lynn Mounson, *Director*
EMP: 45 **EST:** 2000
SALES (est): 1MM-4.9MM **Privately Held**
SIC: 7319 5192 Advertising material distribution services; wholesales newspapers

(G-110)
LAKELAND LODGING LP
Also Called: Holiday Inn
5637 Hwy 9 S (56308)
PHONE 218 829-8730
Steve Madison, *Partner*

Tracy Berninghaus, *Program Dir*
EMP: 100 **EST:** 1999
SALES (est): 5MM-9.9MM **Privately Held**
SIC: 7011 Traveler accommodations

(G-111)
LEE'S CONSTRUCTION INC
615 Nokomis St Ste 200 (56308-2374)
PHONE 320 762-0325
Henry L Saeugling, *President*
Janet Saeugling, *Corp Secy*
Marlene Clark, *Attorney*
EMP: 55 **EST:** 1985
SQ FT: 4,000
SALES (est): 10MM-24.9MM **Privately Held**
SIC: 1542 New commercial & office building construction; commercial & office building renovation & repair services

(G-112)
MADISON PROPERTIES INC
Also Called: Holiday Inn Alexandria
5637 Highway 29 S (56308-6034)
PHONE 320 763-2498
Steve Madison, *Vice Pres*
Karen Behn, *Opers Mgr*
William Shoultz, *Opers Staff*
EMP: 74
SALES (est): 5MM-9.9MM **Privately Held**
SIC: 7011 Casino hotel

(G-113)
MINNESOTA RURAL EDUCATION ASSN
700 Cedar St Ste 208 (56308-1764)
PO Box 155, Brandon (56315-0155)
PHONE 320 762-6574
FAX: 320 762-2854
Cindy Gerber, *Office Mgr*
Dennis Rettke, *Exec Dir*
Vernae Hasbargen, *Director*
EMP: 150 **EST:** 1985
SALES (est): 10MM-24.9MM **Privately Held**
SIC: 8732 Educational research services

(G-114)
NODLAND CONSTRUCTION CO
322 Fairgrounds Rd (56308-1330)
PO Box 338 (56308-0338)
PHONE 320 763-5159
FAX: 320 763-5197
Rich Nodland, *President*
Jim Rentz, *Manager*
Henry Nodland Jr, *Director*
EMP: 60 **EST:** 1945
SQ FT: 1,000
SALES (est): 5MM-9.9MM **Privately Held**
SIC: 1623 Sewer line construction; water main construction

(G-115)
NORTH MEMORIAL HEALTH CARE
708 Nokomis St (56308-1927)
PHONE 320 763-6160
Jerry Moen, *Vice Pres*
Rick Wagnor, *Manager*
EMP: 26
SALES (est): 1MM-4.9MM **Privately Held**
WEB: www.northmemorial.com
SIC: 4119 Ambulance service
PA: North Memorial Health Care
   3300 Oakdale Ave N
   Minneapolis MN 55422
   763 520-5200

(G-116)
NORTHLAND POWER WASHING
2401 Basswood Ln (56308-8502)
PHONE 320 763-6593
Lynard Engal, *Owner*
EMP: 31 **EST:** 2001
SALES (est): 1MM-4.9MM **Privately Held**
SIC: 7542 Car wash

(G-117)
POPE DOUGLAS SOLID WASTE MGT
Also Called: R Pope Douglas Solid Waste MGT
2115 Jefferson St (56308-2701)
PHONE 320 763-9340
FAX: 320 763-9342
Marvin Cook, *Sales Staff*

Dennis Nagle, *Director*
EMP: 34 **EST:** 1982
SALES (est): 10MM-24.9MM **Privately Held**
SIC: 4953 Incinerator operation; hazardous waste collection & disposal services; waste material recycling services

(G-118)
PRIME WEST CENTRAL COUNTY
2209 Jefferson St Ste 101 (56308-2847)
PHONE 320 763-4135
Jim Przybilla, *CEO*
Kathy Hungness, *Director*
EMP: 114 **EST:** 1998
SALES (est): 10MM-24.9MM **Privately Held**
WEB: www.primewest.org
SIC: 6411 Insurance agent

(G-119)
REGENCY MIDWEST VENTURES LP
Also Called: Arrowwood Rsort Conference Ctr
2100 Arrowwood Ln NW (56308-9063)
PHONE 320 762-1124
FAX: 320 762-0133
Amy Parod, *Vice Pres*
Tracey Hugley, *Purch Dir*
Dave Benson, *Engrg Mgr*
Norma Kloehn, *Accounting Mgr*
Vicky Sullivan, *Sales Mgr*
EMP: 225
SALES (est): 10MM-24.9MM **Privately Held**
WEB: www.regency-mgmt.com
SIC: 7011 Traveler accommodations
HQ: US Hotel & Resort Management
   3211 W Sencore Dr
   Sioux Falls SD 57107
   605 334-2371

(G-120)
RICK L SCHOENROCK
Also Called: Pro-Maintenance Service
1208 Lakeside Dr (56308-2304)
PO Box 535 (56308-0535)
PHONE 320 763-7144
Rick L Schoenrock, *Owner*
EMP: 30
SALES (est): 1MM-4.9MM **Privately Held**
SIC: 7217 7349 Carpet & upholstery cleaning services; building cleaning & maintenance services

(G-121)
RUNESTONE ELECTRIC ASSOCIATION
Lake Mary Township (56308)
PO Box 9 (56308-0009)
PHONE 320 763-6641
William Boogaard, *Exec VP*
EMP: 45
SALES (est): 10MM-24.9MM **Privately Held**
WEB: www.runestoneelectric.com
SIC: 4911 Electric power distribution service
PA: Runestone Electric Association
   124 7th Ave W
   Alexandria MN 56308
   320 762-1121

(G-122)
RURAL CELLULAR CORP (DH)
3905 Dakota St (56308-3391)
PHONE 320 762-2000
FAX: 320 808-2102
Jack D Plating, *President*
Thomas Mahr, *Corp Secy*
Anthony J Melone, *Senior VP*
Margaret P Feldman, *Vice Pres*
Robert Moore, *Vice Pres*
EMP: 165 **EST:** 1990
SQ FT: 50,000
SALES (corp-wide): 107.80B **Publicly Held**
WEB: www.verizon.com
SIC: 4812 Cellular telephone services; retails mobile telephones & equipment; paging services
HQ: Cellco Partnership
   1 Verizon Way
   Basking Ridge NJ 07920
   908 559-5490

(G-123)
STARRY CONSTRUCTION CO INC
Also Called: Central Specialties
6325 County Road 87 SW (56308-5361)
PHONE 320 762-7289
FAX: 320 762-7290
Joe Minnerath, *President*
Jim Minnerath, *Corp Secy*
Kevin Minnerath, *Vice Pres*
John Minnerath, *Treasurer*
Stephen Minnerath, *Director*
EMP: 50 **EST:** 1945
SQ FT: 8,500
SALES (est): 5MM-9.9MM **Privately Held**
SIC: 1611 Highway & street paving contractor

(G-124)
SUNOPTA ASEPTIC INC
3915 Minnesota St (56308-3332)
PHONE 320 763-9822
FAX: 320 762-7916
Mark Tagatz, *President*
Jim Albrecht, *Controller*
Carol Engretson, *Human Res Dir*
Vick Ford, *Manager*
Tom Ludwig, *Manager*
EMP: 100 **EST:** 1999
SQ FT: 70,000 **Privately Held**
SIC: 4783 Packing goods for shipping
PA: Sunopta Food Group LLC
   3915 Minnesota St
   Alexandria MN 56308
   320 763-5977

(G-125)
SUNOPTA FOOD GROUP LLC (PA)
3915 Minnesota St (56308-3332)
PHONE 320 763-5977
Allan Routh, *Member*
Paul V Weelie, *Member*
Mark Taggets, *Vice Pres*
EST: 2004
SALES (corp-wide): 989.13M **Privately Held**
SIC: 8731 5149 Commercial food research services; manufactures flour & other grain mill products; manufactures flavoring extracts & syrups; wholesales flavorings & fragrances; soybean processing

(G-126)
SWEDBERG WOOD PRODUCTS INC
1420 County Road 82 NW (56308-8106)
PHONE 320 762-0738
FAX: 320 762-1237
Jim Swedberg, *President*
Rod Skramstead, *Corp Secy*
Jerry Swedberg, *Vice Pres*
Tim Erickson, *Mfg Staff*
Jim Sater, *Data Proc Dir*
EMP: 30 **EST:** 1982
SQ FT: 12,000
SALES (est): 1MM-4.9MM **Privately Held**
WEB: www.swedbergwood.com
SIC: 1751 Cabinet building & installation service; manufactures wooden kitchen cabinets; manufactures office furniture; manufactures wood office furniture; retails furniture; manufactures wood household furniture

(G-127)
UNITED PARCEL SERVICE INC
Also Called: UPS
Hwy 27 E (56308)
PHONE 320 762-2746
Ken Link, *Manager*
EMP: 30
SALES (est): 1MM-4.9MM **Publicly Held**
WEB: www.ups.com
SIC: 4215 Parcel delivery services by vehicle
HQ: United Parcel Service Inc
   55 Glenlake Pkwy NE
   Atlanta GA 30328
   404 828-6000

(G-128)
VIKING SAVINGS ASSOCIATION
1311 Broadway St Ste 1 (56308-2646)
PO Box 966 (56308-0966)
PHONE 320 762-0236
Stuart Henrickson, *President*
Susan Skoglund, *Exec VP*
Sherry Lavine, *Vice Pres*
Pamela A Langseth, *Auditor*
EMP: 30 **EST:** 1981
SQ FT: 10,000
SALES (est): 5MM-9.9MM **Privately Held**
WEB: www.vikingsavings.com
SIC: 6035 Federal savings & loan association
PA: Viking Financial Corp of
    1311 Broadway St
    Alexandria MN 56308
    320 762-0236

(G-129)
WELLS FARGO BANK
304 Maple St (56308-1558)
PHONE 320 762-2181
Michael Lillenhaugen, *Treasurer*
Judy Welsh, *Manager*
Adelle V Overbeke, *Manager*
EMP: 30
SALES (est): 5MM-9.9MM **Publicly Held**
SIC: 6021 National commercial bank
HQ: Wfc Holdings, Corp
    420 Montgomery St
    San Francisco CA 94104
    415 396-7392

(G-130)
WIDSETH, SMITH, NOLTING
610 Fillmore St (56308-2006)
PO Box 1028 (56308-1028)
PHONE 320 762-8149
FAX: 320 762-0263
Tim Moe, *Manager*
EMP: 30
SALES (est): 1MM-4.9MM **Privately Held**
WEB: www.wsn-mn.com
SIC: 8711 Engineering services; mayors' office
PA: Widseth, Smith, Nolting
    216 S Main St Ste 1
    Crookston MN 56716
    218 281-6522

ALTURA
Winona County

(G-131)
DIAMOND K DAIRY INC
19622 County Road 28 (55910-4083)
PHONE 507 689-2058
Alan Kreidermacher, *President*
Dan Kreidermacher, *Vice Pres*
EMP: 25 **EST:** 2000 **Privately Held**
SIC: 0241 Dairy farming

AMBOY
Blue Earth County

(G-132)
SYNGENTA SEEDS INC
11307 US Highway 169 (56010-4011)
PO Box 38 (56010-0038)
PHONE 507 674-3320
FAX: 507 674-3354
Barry R Kuhlmann, *Opers-Prdtn-Mfg*
EMP: 35 **Publicly Held**
WEB: www.syngenta.com
SIC: 0181 0723 Ornamental nursery products; post harvest crop activities
HQ: Syngenta Seeds Inc
    11055 Wayzata Blvd
    Minnetonka MN 55305
    612 656-8600

ANGORA
Saint Louis County

(G-133)
K G M CONTRACTORS INC
9211 Hwy 53 N (55703)
PO Box 7 (55703-0007)
PHONE 218 666-5698
FAX: 218 666-5708
Karla Abramson, *President*
Mark Abramson, *Corp Secy*
Gary Abramson, *Vice Pres*
Tom Kvas, *Engineer*
Pauline Rutchasky, *Accountant*
EMP: 30 **EST:** 1979
SALES (est): 1MM-4.9MM **Privately Held**
WEB: www.kgmcontractors.com
SIC: 1611 Grading services

ANNANDALE
Wright County

(G-134)
ANNANDALE CARE CENTER
500 Park St E (55302-3060)
PHONE 320 274-3737
FAX: 320 270-3641
John A Nelson, *President*
Debbie Flygore, *Business Mgr*
Angie Derosier, *Persnl Dir*
EMP: 150 **EST:** 1982
SALES (est): 5MM-9.9MM **Privately Held**
WEB: www.ahcsmn.org
SIC: 8051 Skilled nursing care facility

(G-135)
ANNANDALE CONGREGATE HOUSING
500 Park St E (55302-3060)
PHONE 320 274-3737
John Nelson, *President*
Kevin Geisinger, *Corp Secy*
Roger Milner, *Vice Pres*
Roger Millner, *Vice Pres*
EMP: 100 **EST:** 1986
SALES (est): 10MM-24.9MM **Privately Held**
SIC: 6513 Apartment building operator

(G-136)
ANNANDALE STATE BANK INC
40 Chestnut St W (55302-1133)
PO Box 310 (55302-0310)
PHONE 320 274-8216
FAX: 320 274-3581
Dwayne Bruns, *CEO*
Bryan Bruns, *President*
Paul Gandrud, *Vice Pres*
Jim Peterson, *Vice Pres*
Keith Jerpseth, *Loan Officer*
EMP: 31 **EST:** 1893
SQ FT: 10,000
SALES (est): 5MM-9.9MM **Privately Held**
WEB: www.annabank.com
SIC: 6022 State commercial bank

(G-137)
ARCHITECTURAL ENHANCEMENTS, LL
475 Annandale Blvd (55302-3141)
PO Box 1124 (55302-1324)
PHONE 320 274-6909
EMP: 25
SALES (est): 1MM-4.9MM **Privately Held**
SIC: 8712 Architectural service

(G-138)
BISHOP COMMUNICATIONS CORP (DH)
9938 State Highway 55 NW (55302-3031)
PO Box 340 (55302-0340)
PHONE 320 274-8201
John Bishop, *President*
Gene South, *Vice Pres*
Jeff Gardner, *Vice Pres*
EMP: 60 **EST:** 1983
SQ FT: 16,000
SALES (corp-wide): 2.99B **Publicly Held**
WEB: www.iowatelecom.com

SIC: 4813 Local telephone communications services
HQ: Iowa Telecommunications Svcs
    403 W 4th St N Ste 1
    Newton IA 50208
    641 787-2000

(G-139)
CENTENNIAL VILLA APARTMENTS
660 Park St E (55302-3057)
PHONE 320 274-3737
John Nelson, *Director*
EMP: 25 **EST:** 2000
SALES (est): 1MM-4.9MM **Privately Held**
SIC: 6513 Apartment building operator

(G-140)
LAKEDALE TELEPHONE CO
9938 State Highway 55 NW (55302-3031)
PO Box 340 (55302-0340)
PHONE 320 274-8201
John M Bishop, *President*
Jill Bishop, *Corp Secy*
Gene R South Sr, *Vice Pres*
Kurt Olson, *Plant Engr*
Curt Olsen, *Engineering*
EMP: 85 **EST:** 1946
SQ FT: 11,000 **Publicly Held**
WEB: www.lakedalelink.net
SIC: 4813 Local & long distance telephone communications services
DH: Bishop Communications Corp
    9938 State Highway 55 NW
    Annandale MN 55302
    320 274-8201

(G-141)
LINK LAKEDALE INC
9938 State Highway 55 NW (55302-3031)
PO Box 340 (55302-0340)
PHONE 320 274-7777
Alan L Wells, *President*
Bob Thompson, *Asst Treas*
Barbara Bouley, *Manager*
EMP: 40 **Publicly Held**
WEB: www.iowatelecom.com
SIC: 4813 Wired telecommunications carrier & service; local telephone communications services; long distance telephone communications services; internet connectivity services
HQ: Iowa Telecommunications Svcs
    403 W 4th St N Ste 1
    Newton IA 50208
    641 787-2000

(G-142)
M & M BUS SERVICE INC
10606 Hemlock St NW (55302)
PHONE 320 274-8313
FAX: 320 274-8027
Roger Millner, *President*
Karen Millner, *Vice Pres*
Shelley Jonas, *Controller*
EMP: 45 **EST:** 1973
SQ FT: 12,000
SALES (est): 1MM-4.9MM **Privately Held**
SIC: 4151 School bus service

(G-143)
MALCO PRODUCTS INC
14080 State Highway 55 NW (55302-3457)
PO Box 400 (55302-0400)
PHONE 320 274-8246
FAX: 320 274-2269
Paul Keymer, *CEO*
Paul Hansen, *President*
Donald Schmidt, *Exec VP*
Kevin Keymer, *Vice Pres*
David Keymer, *Vice Pres*
▲ **EMP:** 180 **EST:** 1950
SQ FT: 100,000
SALES (est): 10MM-24.9MM **Privately Held**
SIC: 5072 Manufactures hand tools; wholesales hardware; manufactures garden & farm tools, including shovels; manufactures tools & accessories for machine tools; manufactures metal stampings

(G-144)
WEE CARE WE SHARE
8222 132nd St NW (55302-2800)
PHONE 320 274-8881
Daryl Turner, *President*
Vernon Turner, *Manager*
EMP: 30 **EST:** 1989
SALES (est): 1MM-4.9MM **Privately Held**
SIC: 8322 Individual & family social services

ANOKA
Anoka County

(G-145)
AAA ALL AMERICAN LAWN
21202 Saint Francis Blvd (55303-9668)
PHONE 763 537-5733
John Rohach, *President*
Mary J Rohach, *Vice Pres*
EMP: 30 **EST:** 1993 **Privately Held**
SIC: 0781 4959 Landscape services; snow plowing services

(G-146)
ACE SOLID WASTE INC
6601 McKinley St NW (55303-9150)
PHONE 763 427-3110
FAX: 763 427-1691
Andy Schweizer, *President*
Mike Berkopec, *Business Mgr*
Dawn Rodriguez, *Office Mgr*
Steve Perra, *Manager*
Charles Connors, *Director*
EMP: 75 **EST:** 1968
SQ FT: 3,000
SALES (est): 10MM-24.9MM **Privately Held**
WEB: www.acesolidwaste.com
SIC: 4212 Garbage collection & transportation services without disposal

(G-147)
AIR MECHANICAL INC (PA)
16411 Aberdeen St NE (55304-5427)
PHONE 763 434-7747
FAX: 763 434-1599
Ross Erickson, *President*
Kurt Wolbeck, *Controller*
Nancy Mulberge, *Controller*
Jim Johanneck, *Manager*
Leeanne Rybachek, *Manager*
EMP: 118 **EST:** 1985 **Privately Held**
WEB: www.airmechanicalinc.com
SIC: 1711 Warm air heating & air conditioning contractor; ventilation & duct work contractor

(G-148)
AIRGAS - NORTH CENTRAL INC
6191 McKinley St NW (55303-9120)
PHONE 763 712-5100
Tony Litwinchuk, *Vice Pres*
Buzz Larson, *Sales Staff*
Ron Hintz, *Manager*
Mark Jensen, *Manager*
Cindy Doerr, *Manager*
EMP: 48
SALES (est): 10MM-24.9MM **Publicly Held**
WEB: www.airtecinc.net
SIC: 5084 5169 Wholesales welding equipment & supplies; wholesales compressed gas
HQ: Airgas - North Central Inc
    10 W 4th St Fl 2
    Waterloo IA 50701
    319 233-3540

(G-149)
ALL AGAPE CONSTRUCTION CO LLC
14453 Hummingbird Ct NW (55304-7741)
PHONE 763 205-1313
Vertrice Griffin, *Member*
EMP: 40 **EST:** 2005
SALES (est): 10MM-24.9MM **Privately Held**
SIC: 1542 Commercial & institutional building construction

G E O G R A P H I C

(G-150)
ALLINA HEALTH SYSTEM
5300 153rd Ave NW (55303-4250)
PHONE.................763 427-7180
FAX: 763 427-6936
Rebecca Forsell, *Office Mgr*
Shanna Johnson, *Phys Therapist*
Amy Borg, *Phys Therapist*
Laurel Nygaard-Bluhn, *Phys Therapist*
Linda Ernst, *Manager*
EMP: 40
SQ FT: 10,446
SALES (est): 1MM-4.9MM **Privately Held**
WEB: www.allina.com
SIC: 8011 8049 Clinic operated by
physicians; physical therapist office
PA: Allina Health System
　　2925 Chicago Ave
　　Minneapolis MN 55407
　　612 775-5000

(G-151)
AMERIC INN OF HAM LAKE
Also Called: Americinn
13440 Highway 65 NE (55304-6918)
PHONE.................763 755-2100
FAX: 763 755-2100
Bhahta Sam, *Sales Executive*
Gloria Lien, *Manager*
EMP: 30 **EST:** 1999
SALES (est): 1MM-4.9MM **Privately Held**
SIC: 7011 Traveler accommodations

(G-152)
AMERICAN LEGION CLUB
Also Called: Edward B Cutter Post 102
400 W Main St (55303-2018)
PHONE.................763 421-0883
Richard Oelschlager, *Principal*
Daryl Redepenning, *Principal*
Clifford E Nwman, *Manager*
EMP: 27 **EST:** 1919 **Privately Held**
SIC: 8641 7299 7389 Civic & social
organization; banquet hall facility;
accommodation locating service

(G-153)
ANDOVER CINEMA
1836 Bunker Lake Blvd NW (55304-4004)
PHONE.................763 767-8401
Mary Felix, *General Mgr*
EMP: 40 **EST:** 1999
SALES (est): 1MM-4.9MM **Privately Held**
WEB: www.andovercinema.com
SIC: 7832 Indoor movie theater

(G-154)
ANOKA BRASS BAND ASSOC INC
Also Called: Lake Wobegon Brass Band
16021 Sodium St NW (55304-4106)
PHONE.................763 427-2790
Eric Anderson, *President*
EMP: 30 **EST:** 1993
SALES (est): 1MM-4.9MM **Privately Held**
WEB: www.lwbb.com
SIC: 7929 Orchestra & bands

(G-155)
ANOKA CHILD CARE CENTER
3738 7th Ave 4273983 (55303-1465)
PHONE.................763 427-1897
FAX: 763 712-8482
Mary J Sentyrz, *Director*
EMP: 27
SALES (est): 500-999K **Privately Held**
SIC: 8351 Child day care service

(G-156)
ASSOCIATES PLUS INC
Also Called: Re Max Associates Plus
3351 Round Lake Blvd NW Ste 1
(55303-5019)
PHONE.................763 323-8080
Robin Lee, *Finance*
Julie Larsen, *Manager*
Dennis Anderson, *Manager*
Lyle Petersen, *Info Tech Mgr*
EMP: 140
SALES (est): 25MM-49.9MM **Privately Held**
WEB: www.stenvig.com

SIC: 6531 Real estate services
PA: Associates Plus Inc
　　480 Highway 96 W Ste 200
　　Saint Paul MN 55126
　　651 484-8800

(G-157)
ATLAS PET SUPPLY INC
Also Called: APS
3347 167th Ln NW (55304-1967)
PHONE.................763 753-4818
Douglas Szurek, *President*
Joann M Szurek, *Vice Pres*
EMP: 32 **EST:** 1989
SALES (est): 10MM-24.9MM **Privately Held**
SIC: 5199 6531 Wholesales pet supplies;
real estate leasing & rental agency

(G-158)
BALLANTINE INC
840 McKinley St (55303-1162)
PHONE.................763 427-3959
FAX: 763 427-2277
Myron Timmer, *President*
Joe Newfield, *President*
Jeff Heaser, *Purch Mgr*
David Beck, *Controller*
Al Chandler, *Marketing Staff*
EMP: 30 **EST:** 1966
SQ FT: 30,000
SALES (est): 10MM-24.9MM **Privately Held**
WEB: www.ballantineinc.com
SIC: 5082 Wholesales construction &
mining machinery; manufactures bucket or
scarifier teeth
PA: US Tsubaki Inc
　　301 E Marquardt Dr
　　Wheeling IL 60090
　　847 459-9500

(G-159)
BORDER FOODS INC
Also Called: Taco Bell
13057 Round Lake Blvd (55304)
PHONE.................763 323-4731
Deb Prese, *Branch Mgr*
EMP: 30
SALES (est): 1MM-4.9MM **Privately Held**
SIC: 8742 Limited service fast-food chain
restaurant; management consulting services
PA: Border Foods Inc
　　965 Decatur Ave N
　　Golden Valley MN 55427
　　763 559-7338

(G-160)
BUG CO OF MINNESOTA
15941 Tippecanoe St NE (55304-5924)
PHONE.................763 434-0550
FAX: 763 434-0549
Gordy Vados, *President*
Sandra Davis, *Owner*
Hong Ji, *Vice Pres*
EMP: 39 **EST:** 2001
SALES (est): 1MM-4.9MM **Privately Held**
WEB: www.ebugco.com
SIC: 8999 Personal services

(G-161)
CARBIDE TOOL SERVICES INC
1020 Lund Blvd (55303-1089)
PHONE.................763 421-2210
FAX: 763 421-2686
Julie Reiling, *President*
Tonya McLafferty, *Manager*
Brad Barker, *Manager*
EMP: 50 **EST:** 1988
SQ FT: 20,000
SALES (est): 5MM-9.9MM **Privately Held**
WEB: www.carbidetool.com
SIC: 5085 7389 Manufactures metal cutting
type machine tool replacement & repair
parts; wholesales industrial tools;
commercial or industrial precision grinding
service

(G-162)
CECO CONCRETE CONSTRUCTION DE
15924 Lincoln St NE (55304-5535)
PHONE.................763 434-4637
Shirley Beilke, *Corp Secy*
Brian Anderson, *Engineer*
James Paquin, *Branch Mgr*
EMP: 100

SALES (est): 5MM-9.9MM **Privately Held**
WEB: www.cecoconcrete.com
SIC: 1799 Erection & dismantling of forms
for poured concrete contractor;
manufactures sheet metal concrete forms
HQ: Ceco Concrete Construction DE
　　10100 NW Ambassador Dr
　　Kansas City MO 64153
　　816 459-7000

(G-163)
CEDA INC
Also Called: Chemical Engineering Dev Assn
15830 Lincoln St NE (55304-5535)
PO Box 490069, Minneapolis
(55449-0069)
PHONE.................763 434-4403
Cindy Voss, *Human Res Mgr*
EMP: 40
SALES (est): 1MM-4.9MM **Privately Held**
SIC: 7349 Building cleaning & maintenance
services; building cleaning service; chemical
cleaning service; janitorial & custodial
services
HQ: Ceda Inc
　　802 Seaco Ct
　　Deer Park TX 77536
　　281 842-9960

(G-164)
CENTRAL POWER DISTRIBUTORS INC (PA)
3801 Thurston Ave NW (55303-1064)
PHONE.................763 576-0901
FAX: 763 576-0920
John Schaller, *President*
Rick Lau, *General Mgr*
John Hedges, *Sales Mgr*
Paul Siemieniak, *Manager*
▲ **EMP:** 50 **EST:** 1985
SQ FT: 51,000
SALES (corp-wide): 26M **Privately Held**
WEB: www.cpdonline.com
SIC: 5084 Wholesales industrial air-cooled
engines & parts

(G-165)
CHALICH TRUCKING INC
8049 146th Ave NW (55303-7069)
PHONE.................763 421-1095
FAX: 763 427-0922
Peter Chalich, *President*
Cheri Cook, *Corp Secy*
EMP: 45 **EST:** 1965
SQ FT: 3,800
SALES (est): 5MM-9.9MM **Privately Held**
WEB: www.chalichtrucking.com
SIC: 4213 Over the road trucking

(G-166)
CITY HEIGHTS INC
2804 5th Ave (55303-1165)
PHONE.................763 421-3345
Richard Spartz, *President*
EMP: 35 **EST:** 1987
SQ FT: 10,000
SALES (est): 500-999K **Privately Held**
SIC: 7349 Window cleaning services

(G-167)
CITY OF ANOKA
Also Called: Utility Bill Inquiries
2015 1st Ave (55303-2245)
PHONE.................763 576-2750
FAX: 763 421-9194
Chuck Kramaker, *Manager*
Shelly Peterson, *Manager*
EMP: 50
SALES (est): 1MM-4.9MM **Privately Held**
WEB: www.bettervaluesliquor.com
SIC: 8721 Billing & bookkeeping services
PA: City of Anoka
　　2015 1st Ave
　　Anoka MN 55303
　　763 576-2700

(G-168)
CITYWIDE WINDOW SERVICES INC
2804 5th Ave (55303-1165)
PHONE.................763 421-3345
FAX: 763 421-3394
Richard Spartz, *President*
EMP: 25 **EST:** 1987
SALES (est): 500-999K **Privately Held**

SIC: 7349 Window cleaning services

(G-169)
CONNEXUS ENERGY
14601 Ramsey Blvd NW (55303-6024)
PHONE.................763 323-2600
FAX: 763 323-2603
Mike Rajala, *CEO*
Peter Wojciechowski, *Chairman*
Larry Peterson, *Vice Pres*
John Gasal, *Vice Pres*
Don Haller, *Vice Pres*
EMP: 250 **EST:** 1937
SQ FT: 250,000
SALES (est): 100MM-499.9MM **Privately Held**
WEB: www.connexusenergy.com
SIC: 4911 Electric power distribution service

(G-170)
COUNTY OF ANOKA
Also Called: Bunker Beach
550 Bunker Lake Blvd NW (55304-4122)
PHONE.................763 767-2871
Kevin Simmons, *Branch Mgr*
EMP: 70
SALES (est): 1MM-4.9MM **Privately Held**
SIC: 7996 Theme park

(G-171)
CROSSTOWN MASONRY INC
1322 159th Ave NE (55304-5566)
PHONE.................763 434-6371
FAX: 763 434-7693
Tammy Braastad, *President*
Jason Landborg, *Corp Secy*
Jeff Landborg, *Vice Pres*
Bruce Braastad, *Vice Pres*
EMP: 40 **EST:** 1981
SQ FT: 9,000
SALES (est): 1MM-4.9MM **Privately Held**
SIC: 1771 1741 Concrete contractor;
masonry & stonework contractor

(G-172)
DAN DAHLIN INC
Also Called: Ham Lake Lanes
16465 Highway 65 NE (55304-5348)
PHONE.................763 434-6010
FAX: 763 434-3146
Dan T Dahlin, *President*
EMP: 50 **EST:** 1999
SQ FT: 25,536
SALES (est): 1MM-4.9MM **Privately Held**
WEB: www.hamlakelanes.com
SIC: 7933 Bowling center

(G-173)
DEHN'S GARDENS INC
16485 Tulip St NW (55304-2429)
PHONE.................763 753-2806
Robert Dehn Jr, *President*
Bonnie L Dehn, *VP Systems*
EMP: 30 **EST:** 1979 **Privately Held**
WEB: www.dehnsgardenherbs.com
SIC: 0139 0723 Open field herb farm;
vegetable packing services

(G-174)
DEPOTSTAR INC
6180 140th Ave NW (55303-4501)
PHONE.................763 506-9990
FAX: 763 506-9988
Mark Korin, *President*
James Korin, *CFO*
Doug Franzen, *Accounts Exec*
Tom Korin, *Manager*
Chuck Milne, *Manager*
▲ **EMP:** 40 **EST:** 1989
SQ FT: 21,000
SALES (est): 5MM-9.9MM **Privately Held**
WEB: www.depotstar.com
SIC: 8711 Electrical or electronic engineers

(G-175)
DIVERSIFIED CONTRACTING INC
13950 Radium St NW # 300 (55303-9415)
PHONE.................763 712-8087
FAX: 763 712-1473
Charlie Wilcox, *President*
Lee Saeugling, *Corp Secy*
Dave Johnson, *Finance*
EMP: 30 **EST:** 1999
SQ FT: 5,000
SALES (est): 1MM-4.9MM **Privately Held**

WEB: www.calldci.net
SIC: 1799 1711 Epoxy application service; heating systems repair & maintenance service; heating & air conditioning contractor

(G-176)
EGAN OIL CO LLC
500 Bunker Lake Blvd NW (55303-5012)
PHONE 763 421-0410
FAX: 763 421-2658
William A Egan, *Member*
EMP: 30 EST: 1962
SQ FT: 14,000
SALES (est): 50MM-99.9MM **Privately Held**
WEB: www.eganoil.com
SIC: 5171 5172 Wholesales petroleum bulk stations; wholesales gasoline; wholesales lubricating oils & greases; wholesales fuel oil

(G-177)
ENIVA CORP
1 Eniva Way (55303-4945)
PHONE 763 795-8870
FAX: 763 795-8890
Andrew Baechler, *President*
Benjamin Baechler, *Vice Chairman*
Dan Conley, *Opers Staff*
Mark Veloske, *Sales Staff*
Ann Bertsch, *Mktg Dir*
EMP: 45 EST: 1998
SALES (est): 50MM-99.9MM **Privately Held**
WEB: www.eniva.com
SIC: 5122 Wholesales animal medicines

(G-178)
EVANGELICAL LUTHERAN GOOD
Also Called: Anoka Care Center
1040 Madison St (55303-2657)
PHONE 763 421-2311
FAX: 763 421-2683
Merile Sampson, *Human Res Dir*
Dean McDevitt, *Manager*
Nancy Brainerd, *Admin Dir*
EMP: 154
SALES (est): 5MM-9.9MM **Privately Held**
WEB: www.good-sam.com
SIC: 8051 Skilled nursing care facility
PA: Evangelical Lutheran Good
    4800 W 57th St
    Sioux Falls SD 57108
    605 362-3100

(G-179)
EVERYDAY MIRACLES INC
936 Monroe St (55303-2651)
PHONE 763 323-0012
Debra L Prudhomme, *Exec Dir*
EMP: 34 **Privately Held**
SIC: 8399 Community development groups

(G-180)
FAMILY INNOVATIONS INC
1833 3rd Ave (55303-2424)
PHONE 763 421-5535
FAX: 763 430-0226
Steve Gray, *President*
Jeffrey Doheny, *Vice Pres*
EMP: 65 EST: 2001
SALES (est): 1MM-4.9MM **Privately Held**
SIC: 8322 General counseling services

(G-181)
FIRESTONE METAL PRODUCTS LLC (DH)
1001 Lund Blvd (55303-1089)
PHONE 763 576-9595
FAX: 763 576-9596
John Bernardi, *Member*
Jeff Peterson, *Member*
Michael Wallace, *Member*
Sheila Mason, *Purch Mgr*
Steve Gravelle, *Controller*
▲ EMP: 250 EST: 1972
SQ FT: 300,000 **Privately Held**
WEB: www.unaclad.com
SIC: 5051 Metal service center; steel fabricator
HQ: Firestone Diversified Products
    250 W 96th St Fl 2
    Indianapolis IN 46260
    317 575-7000

(G-182)
FIRST STUDENT INC
Also Called: Hunts Bus
650 South St (55303-5207)
PHONE 763 421-3199
FAX: 763 421-8430
Daniel Mulbauer, *Opers Staff*
Troy Sheppard, *Manager*
EMP: 130
SALES (est): 1MM-4.9MM **Privately Held**
WEB: www.firststudentinc.com
SIC: 4151 School bus service
HQ: First Student Inc
    600 Vine St Ste 1400
    Cincinnati OH 45202
    513 241-2200

(G-183)
GLOBAL MEDICAL INSTRUMENTATION
6511 Bunker Lake Blvd NW (55303-5409)
PHONE 763 712-8717
Richard Powell, *CEO*
Tom Fagrelius, *VP Sls/Mktg*
Paula Moon, *Director*
EMP: 27 EST: 1996
SQ FT: 23,000
SALES (est): 10MM-24.9MM **Privately Held**
WEB: www.gmi-inc.com
SIC: 5047 Wholesales medical & hospital equipment

(G-184)
GREEN VALLEY GREENHOUSE INC
6530 Green Valley Rd (55303-6301)
PHONE 763 753-1621
FAX: 763 753-5943
John Rowe, *President*
Sharon Rowe, *Vice Pres*
Phil Johnson, *CFO*
▲ EMP: 75 EST: 1977
SALES (est): 1MM-4.9MM **Privately Held**
WEB: www.greenvalleygreenhouse.com
SIC: 5193 Retails potted plants; wholesales potted plants

(G-185)
GREYSTONE MASONRY INC
1548 164th Ln NE (55304-5428)
PHONE 763 413-9633
FAX: 763 413-9636
Kurt Merkle, *President*
Amy Merkle, *Vice Pres*
EMP: 40 EST: 1986
SQ FT: 6,110
SALES (est): 1MM-4.9MM **Privately Held**
WEB: www.greystonemasonry.com
SIC: 1741 1521 Masonry & stonework contractor; single-family housing construction

(G-186)
HALVERSON CONCRETE INC
1345 157th Ave NE Ste C (55304-5525)
PHONE 763 434-0318
FAX: 763 434-0317
Joe Janowiak, *President*
David L Halverson, *Vice Pres*
EMP: 30 EST: 1973
SALES (est): 1MM-4.9MM **Privately Held**
WEB: www.halversonconcrete.com
SIC: 1771 Driveway contractor; curb construction; sidewalk contractor

(G-187)
HAM LAKE AMERICAN LEGION
14750 Palm St NW (55304-3532)
PHONE 763 434-7762
Nordeen Baron, *Principal*
EMP: 30 EST: 1998 **Privately Held**
SIC: 8641 Veterans' organization

(G-188)
HANSON MCFARLAND INC
2501 4th Ave (55303-2222)
PHONE 763 421-9554
Tony McFarland, *President*
Mark Haglie, *General Mgr*
Jamille Pearson, *General Mgr*
Todd Dorn, *Corp Secy*
Wayne Hanson, *Treasurer*
EMP: 97

EST: 1970
SQ FT: 1,800
SALES (est): 10MM-24.9MM **Privately Held**
SIC: 8742 7349 Industry specialist consultant; janitorial & custodial services

(G-189)
HEELSIDE INC
305 Oakwood Dr (55303-2755)
PHONE 612 508-0887
Derek Freeburg, *President*
EMP: 28 EST: 1993
SQ FT: 9,300
SALES (est): 10MM-24.9MM **Privately Held**
SIC: 5091 Wholesales sporting & recreational goods & supplies

(G-190)
HERITAGE MILLWORK INC
6190 McKinley St NW (55303-9120)
PHONE 763 323-7501
FAX: 763 323-7655
Pat Menth, *President*
Jack Lee, *Vice Pres*
Tom Keller, *Purch Mgr*
EMP: 27 EST: 1997
SQ FT: 62,000
SALES (est): 10MM-24.9MM **Privately Held**
WEB: www.heritagemillworkinc.com
SIC: 5031 Wholesales lumber, plywood & millwork

(G-191)
HOME SMART REALTY & LOGO DSGN
4401 158th Ave NW (55304-2259)
PHONE 763 421-0481
Larry Stenquist, *Principal*
EMP: 36 EST: 2004
SALES (est): 5MM-9.9MM **Privately Held**
SIC: 6531 Real estate services

(G-192)
INDUSTRIAL AUTOMATION ENGG
14022 Lincoln St NE (55304-4205)
PHONE 763 450-3800
FAX: 763 450-3850
Brian Beaufeaux, *President*
Jason Grahek, *Vice Pres*
Abdou Balde, *Project Engr*
Nathan Wirkkula, *Project Engr*
Evann Beaufeaux, *CFO*
EMP: 50 EST: 1995
SQ FT: 18,000
SALES (est): 5MM-9.9MM **Privately Held**
SIC: 8711 Engineering services

(G-193)
JADE CATERING INC
13545 Martin St NW (55304-4568)
PHONE 763 767-3336
Anne D Luca, *Owner*
Joel W Schauer, *Principal*
Anne Deluca, *Manager*
EMP: 30 EST: 2000
SALES (est): 1MM-4.9MM **Privately Held**
SIC: 7299 Caterer; banquet hall facility

(G-194)
JAM HOPS GYMNASTICS FACTORY
14216 Lincoln St NE (55304-4626)
PHONE 763 413-0647
FAX: 763 413-0647
Diane Assimacopoulos, *President*
Chris Assimacrapoulls, *Technician*
EMP: 25 EST: 1997
SALES (est): 1MM-4.9MM **Privately Held**
WEB: www.jamhops.com
SIC: 7999 Gymnastics instruction

(G-195)
KALWAY CONSTRUCTION CO INC
14160 Basalt St NW (55303-4567)
PHONE 651 746-0179
Lenny Kalway, *President*
Don Krystek, *Manager*
EMP: 25 EST: 1992
SALES (est): 5MM-9.9MM **Privately Held**
WEB: www.kalwayco.com
SIC: 1542 Commercial & office building contractor

(G-196)
L H BOLDUC CO INC
649 Garfield St W (55303-6208)
PO Box 815 (55303-0815)
PHONE 763 427-4330
FAX: 763 427-4012
Robert G Werness, *President*
Lance Werness, *Vice Pres*
EMP: 100 EST: 1879
SQ FT: 2,000
SALES (est): 10MM-24.9MM **Privately Held**
SIC: 1629 Pile driving service

(G-197)
LANDMARK COMMUNITY BANK
14150 Saint Francis Blvd # 1 (55303-6111)
PHONE 763 444-7787
FAX: 763 444-7779
Kevin Johnson, *President*
John Satrom, *Area Mgr*
Lon Helgemo, *Finance*
Joan Wood, *Manager*
EMP: 27 EST: 1998
SQ FT: 3,821
SALES (est): 5MM-9.9MM **Privately Held**
SIC: 6029 6163 Commercial bank; loan broker

(G-198)
LARSON PLUMBING INC
3095 162nd Ln NW Ste 100 (55304-2470)
PHONE 763 427-7680
FAX: 763 427-9448
James Larson, *President*
Kari Larson, *Vice Pres*
EMP: 43 EST: 1980
SQ FT: 7,000
SALES (est): 5MM-9.9MM **Privately Held**
SIC: 1711 Plumbing service

(G-199)
LEONE ENTERPRISES INC
Also Called: Leone's Building Services
2040 N Ferry St (55303-6753)
PHONE 763 427-9657
Dione L Leone, *President*
Gerald Leone, *Vice Pres*
Greg Berry, *Manager*
Harry Krieger, *Manager*
Brad Cochran, *Manager*
EMP: 220 EST: 1974
SQ FT: 12,000
SALES (est): 5MM-9.9MM **Privately Held**
WEB: www.leonesent.com
SIC: 7349 Janitorial & custodial services

(G-200)
LINKS AT NORTHFORK LLP
9333 Alpine Dr NW (55303-4705)
PHONE 763 241-0506
FAX: 763 241-1236
Mike Tozier, *Manager/Ptnr*
EMP: 40 EST: 2002
SALES (est): 1MM-4.9MM **Privately Held**
WEB: www.golfthelinks.com
SIC: 7992 Public golf course

(G-201)
LORD OF LIFE LUTHERAN CHURCH
14501 Nowthen Blvd NW (55303-6151)
PHONE 763 427-1100
FAX: 763 427-1058
Blair Anderson, *Pastor*
EMP: 40 EST: 1973
SQ FT: 1,936 **Privately Held**
SIC: 8351 Provides Lutheran church services; bible school; child day care service

(G-202)
MACHINE & PROCESS DESIGN INC
820 McKinley St (55303-1162)
PHONE 763 427-9991
FAX: 763 427-8777
Stanley L Davis, *President*
Gary Stolhanske, *Vice Pres*
Clark Kreider, *Engineer*
Valerie Jolley, *Sales Staff*
EMP: 25 EST: 1985
SALES (est): 1MM-4.9MM **Privately Held**

GEOGRAPHIC

WEB: www.mpd-inc.com
SIC: 8711 Mechanical engineering services

(G-203)
MATE PRECISION TOOLING INC
1295 Lund Blvd (55303-1092)
PHONE...........................763 421-0230
Dean Sundquist, *CEO*
Jack Schneider, *President*
Frank Baeumler, *Vice Pres*
Chet Ferger, *Vice Pres*
Kevin Nicholson, *Vice Pres*
▲ EMP: 350 EST: 1962
SQ FT: 300,000
SALES (est): 50MM-99.9MM Privately Held
WEB: www.mate.com
SIC: 5084 Manufactures punching & shearing machines; machine tools & accessories; wholesales industrial machinery & equipment; manufactures tools, dies, jigs & fixtures

(G-204)
MIDWEST FIXTURE GROUP INC
900 McKinley St (55303-1100)
PHONE...........................763 712-9637
FAX: 763 712-9677
Wylt Chipman, *CEO*
Milton Chipman, *President*
Darren Remore, *Corp Secy*
Bunny Benson, *Controller*
Bev Chipman, *Manager*
▲ EMP: 40 EST: 1994
SQ FT: 53,000
SALES (est): 1MM-4.9MM Privately Held
WEB: www.ffr.com
SIC: 5046 Manufactures nonwood store fixtures; wholesales store fixtures

(G-205)
MINNESOTA CLERICAL INC
17230 Uplander St NW (55304-1461)
PHONE...........................763 753-7243
FAX: 763 753-7246
Roxanne Olsen, *President*
EMP: 130 EST: 1981
SALES (est): 5MM-9.9MM Privately Held
SIC: 7338 8721 Secretarial services; payroll services

(G-206)
NATIONAL COMMUNICATIONS SVCS
1100 Lund Blvd (55303-1091)
PHONE...........................763 576-9977
FAX: 763 576-9985
Doug M Leod, *President*
Gary Hegarty, *CFO*
Brant McLeod, *Manager*
EMP: 28 EST: 1991
SQ FT: 11,500
SALES (est): 1MM-4.9MM Privately Held
WEB: www.natcomm.com
SIC: 7378 Computer & office machine maintenance & repair services

(G-207)
NATIONAL RECOVERIES INC
14735 Highway 65 NE # 100 (55304-6120)
PHONE...........................763 754-1931
Steve Cundiff, *President*
Jim Kunza, *Vice Pres*
James Kunts, *Vice Pres*
Don Weber, *Treasurer*
Joel Kunza, *Natl Sales Mgr*
EMP: 45 EST: 1991
SQ FT: 8,000
SALES (est): 1MM-4.9MM Privately Held
SIC: 7322 Collection agency

(G-208)
NORTH ANOKA CONTROL SYSTEMS
13828 Lincoln St NE (55304-6949)
PHONE...........................763 444-4747
William Doty, *President*
Tisha Pynes, *General Mgr*
Tricia Brassard, *Corp Secy*
Mae Guay, *Corp Secy*
Robert Doty, *Vice Pres*
EMP: 45 EST: 1991
SQ FT: 28,000
SALES (est): 5MM-9.9MM Privately Held
WEB: www.nacsinc.com

SIC: 8711 Manufactures relays & industrial controls; engineering services

(G-209)
NORTH COUNTRY CONCRETE INC
7040 143rd Ave NW (55303-6014)
PHONE...........................763 576-8602
FAX: 763 576-8636
Karl Virkus, *President*
Beth Virkus, *Vice Pres*
Mary Babcock, *Controller*
Amy Gangle, *Manager*
EMP: 70 EST: 1996
SQ FT: 5,500
SALES (est): 5MM-9.9MM Privately Held
WEB: www.northcountryconcrete.com
SIC: 1771 Curb & sidewalk contractor

(G-210)
NORTHERN COUNTIES SECRETARIAL
6139 157th Ln NW (55303-4139)
PHONE...........................763 427-0166
FAX: 763 427-9259
Carol Lublin, *President*
Lynette Pelletier, *Office Mgr*
EMP: 85 EST: 1984
SQ FT: 5,000
SALES (est): 1MM-4.9MM Privately Held
WEB: www.ncssinc.com
SIC: 7338 7363 Secretarial services; temporary help service

(G-211)
NORTHWEST DAIRY FORWARDING CO
1305 159th Ave NE (55304-5567)
PHONE...........................763 434-6654
Shawn Nelson, *President*
Willard Nelson, *Vice Pres*
EMP: 62 EST: 1926
SQ FT: 6,000
SALES (est): 5MM-9.9MM Privately Held
WEB: www.nwdfc.com
SIC: 4213 Over the road trucking; long-distance refrigerated trucking services

(G-212)
ONLY FOR KIDS INC
13654 Thrush St NW (55304-3782)
PHONE...........................763 754-2594
FAX: 763 755-8713
Lauri Pfeiffer, *CEO*
Judy Gieske, *President*
EMP: 35 EST: 1990
SQ FT: 3,600
SALES (est): 500-999K Privately Held
SIC: 8351 Child day care service

(G-213)
PATRIOT BUILDERS INC
17162 Lincoln St NE 100 (55304-4721)
PHONE...........................763 434-1702
FAX: 763 434-0903
Tim Bruner, *President*
EMP: 30 EST: 1996
SALES (est): 5MM-9.9MM Privately Held
SIC: 1522 Residential construction

(G-214)
PECK CONSTRUCTION INC
13900 Sunfish Lake Blvd NW (55303-4542)
PHONE...........................763 421-2201
Mark Peck, *President*
Tracy Peck, *Vice Pres*
EMP: 70 EST: 1991
SQ FT: 24,000
SALES (est): 5MM-9.9MM Privately Held
WEB: www.peckconstruction.com
SIC: 1771 1741 Concrete contractor; masonry & stonework contractor

(G-215)
PRESBYTERIAN HOME FARM STEAD
13733 Quay St NW Ofc (55304-3620)
PHONE...........................763 712-7000
FAX: 763 712-7001
Debra Lawrence, *Director*
EMP: 50 EST: 1998
SALES (est): 1MM-4.9MM Privately Held
SIC: 8051 Skilled nursing care facility

(G-216)
PRESTIGE DRYWALL INC
800 Industry Ave (55303-1037)
PHONE...........................763 506-0030
FAX: 763 506-0040
David Johnson, *President*
Marcy Johnson, *Corp Secy*
EMP: 50 EST: 1979
SQ FT: 3,200
SALES (est): 10MM-24.9MM Privately Held
WEB: www.prestigedrywall.com
SIC: 1542 1742 New commercial & office building construction; drywall, plastering & insulation contractor

(G-217)
PRIME RIDGE PET CARE
7245 Highway 10 NW (55303-6004)
PHONE...........................763 427-2220
Daryl Hartman, *Partner*
Amy Bear, *Partner*
Michael Cook, *Partner*
EMP: 40 Privately Held
SIC: 0742 Animal hospital services

(G-218)
R J M ENTERPRISES OF MINNESOTA
6650 143rd Ave NW (55303-4613)
PHONE...........................763 323-8389
Jim Lundeen, *President*
Shannon Minster, *Administrator*
EMP: 200 EST: 1992
SQ FT: 14,000
SALES (est): 10MM-24.9MM Privately Held
WEB: www.rjmgpp.com
SIC: 7389 Packaging & labeling services

(G-219)
REGISTERED ABSTRACTORS INC
2115 3rd Ave (55303-2236)
PHONE...........................763 427-3012
FAX: 763 427-6948
Jan Thomas, *President*
Rick Thomas, *Vice Pres*
EMP: 25 EST: 1985
SQ FT: 5,000
SALES (est): 1MM-4.9MM Privately Held
WEB: www.registered-abstracters.com
SIC: 6361 6541 Title insurance carrier; title abstract service

(G-220)
RESHETAR SYSTEMS INC
730 Bunker Lake Blvd NW (55303-5014)
PHONE...........................763 421-1152
Brett M Reshetar, *President*
EMP: 50
SQ FT: 4,000
SALES (est): 10MM-24.9MM Privately Held
SIC: 1542 New commercial & office building construction

(G-221)
RETAILER SERVICES CORP
3750 Thurston Ave (55303-1117)
PHONE...........................763 421-6868
FAX: 763 421-7695
Jim Sullivan, *CEO*
John Froehling, *President*
Scott Schwab, *CFO*
Windy Schwab, *Manager*
EMP: 40 EST: 1991
SQ FT: 55,000
SALES (est): 1MM-4.9MM Privately Held
WEB: www.rscor.com
SIC: 5046 Manufactures wood store fixtures; wholesales store fixtures; manufactures wood nonrefrigerated show & display cabinets; manufactures partitions & fixtures

(G-222)
RIVERWAY CLINIC
1833 2nd Ave (55303-2432)
PHONE...........................763 712-6000
FAX: 763 421-2942
Donald Collins MD, *President*
Charles Erickson MD, *Corp Secy*
Steve Bentz MD, *Vice Pres*
Tina Goskey, *Project Mgr*
Sandy Dinsmore, *Human Resources*

EMP: 200 EST: 1931
SQ FT: 19,000
SALES (est): 10MM-24.9MM Privately Held
SIC: 8011 Clinic operated by physicians

(G-223)
RURAL COMMUNITY INSURANCE AGCY (DH)
3501 Thurston Ave (55303-1062)
PHONE...........................763 427-0290
Mike Connealy, *President*
Timothy A Verbrugge, *Corp Secy*
Allison Janney, *Corp Secy*
Marlene C Merten, *Corp Secy*
Jerilyn Jeri, *Corp Secy*
EMP: 240 EST: 1991
SQ FT: 40,000
SALES (corp-wide): 98.63B Publicly Held
SIC: 6411 Insurance services
HQ: Wells Fargo Insurance Inc
　　600 Highway 169 S Fl 12
　　Minneapolis MN 55426
　　612 667-5600

(G-224)
SCHWARTZMAN CO INC
2905 N Ferry St (55303-1149)
PHONE...........................763 421-1187
FAX: 763 421-4704
John Schwartzman, *President*
David Schwartzman, *Vice Pres*
David Chilefone, *Manager*
Tim Rosengren, *Manager*
Warren Wingness, *Exec Dir*
EMP: 30 EST: 1935
SQ FT: 3,200
SALES (est): 10MM-24.9MM Privately Held
SIC: 5093 4953 Wholesales metal scrap & waste materials; waste material recycling services

(G-225)
SHAW TRUCKING INC
15850 Lincoln St NE (55304-5535)
PHONE...........................763 434-3300
FAX: 763 434-3100
Don Shaw, *President*
EMP: 32 EST: 1983
SQ FT: 5,000
SALES (est): 1MM-4.9MM Privately Held
WEB: www.shawtruckinginc.com
SIC: 4213 Over the road trucking

(G-226)
SIERRA CORP OF SHOREVIEW
17149 Lincoln St NE # 100 (55304-4748)
PHONE...........................763 783-9616
John Leukam, *President*
EMP: 30
SQ FT: 2,000
SALES (est): 1MM-4.9MM Privately Held
WEB: www.sierrateam.com
SIC: 1751 Framing contractor

(G-227)
SIGN-ZONE INC
6400 Bunker Lake Blvd NW (55303-5849)
PHONE...........................763 746-1350
FAX: 763 746-1311
Edward F Flaherty, *President*
George Frost, *CFO*
Bill Kilrain, *CFO*
Halek Tom, *Sales Executive*
Roger Moritz, *Manager*
▲ EMP: 130 EST: 1992
SQ FT: 44,000
SALES (est): 10MM-24.9MM Privately Held
WEB: www.edgeexhibits.com
SIC: 7389 Manufactures signs & advertising specialties; laminating service

(G-228)
SIMONSON VENTURE INC (PA)
Also Called: Simonson's Salon & Day Spa
3507 Round Lake Blvd NW S (55303-5001)
PHONE...........................763 416-7823
FAX: 763 427-0358
Kyle Simonson, *President*
Katie Troye, *General Mgr*
EMP: 50 EST: 1984
SALES (corp-wide): 4.20M Privately Held
SIC: 7231 Cosmetology & personal hygiene salon

(G-229)

SUNFISH EXPRESS INC
6401 Highway 10 NW (55303-4551)
PHONE...................................763 433-8383
FAX: 763 433-8891
Frank Yomoutpor, *President*
EMP: 25 EST: 2003
SALES (est): 1MM-4.9MM **Privately Held**
SIC: 7389 Personal service agents

(G-230)

SUPERIOR MASONRY & CONCRETE
19960 Saint Francis Blvd (55303-9543)
PHONE...................................651 786-0884
Beverly Ulferts, *President*
Mandy Hendrickson, *Manager*
EMP: 40 EST: 1989
SQ FT: 15,000
SALES (est): 1MM-4.9MM **Privately Held**
SIC: 1771 1741 Concrete contractor; masonry & stonework contractor

(G-231)

T RAY CONSTRUCTION CO INC
13535 Johnson St NE (55304-6930)
PHONE...................................763 757-6859
Steven Sunderland, *President*
Warren O Sunderland, *Corp Secy*
James T Sunderland, *Vice Pres*
EMP: 100 EST: 1981
SALES (est): 10MM-24.9MM **Privately Held**
SIC: 1623 Cable laying service

(G-232)

TAMARISK RESOURCES INC
1657 161st Ave NW (55304-2531)
PHONE...................................763 572-1950
FAX: 763 572-1956
Karen Vougel, *Director*
EMP: 40 EST: 1992
SALES (est): 1MM-4.9MM **Privately Held**
WEB: www.tamarisk.org
SIC: 8322 Individual & family social services

(G-233)

TES CONSTRUCTION INC
17149 Lincoln St NE # 600 (55304-4748)
PHONE...................................763 783-2496
Tony Schwieters, *President*
Angie Nyberg, *Administrator*
EMP: 30 EST: 1992
SQ FT: 3,500
SALES (est): 5MM-9.9MM **Privately Held**
SIC: 1521 Single-family housing construction

(G-234)

THERMO LEASING CORP
8390 Highway 10 NW (55303-7242)
PHONE...................................763 421-2505
FAX: 763 506-0415
Daniel Santarsiero, *President*
Anthony Santarsiero, *General Mgr*
Bonnie Santarsiero, *Treasurer*
Kristine Paulson, *Manager*
EMP: 50 EST: 1995
SQ FT: 10,000
SALES (est): 10MM-24.9MM **Privately Held**
WEB: www.shorewoodrv.com
SIC: 7519 7538 Recreational vehicle dealer; recreational vehicle rental service; recreational vehicle repair services

(G-235)

THOMAS KOLL
6230 McKinley St NW Ste C2
(55303-8621)
PHONE...................................763 323-9797
Thomas Koll, *Owner*
EMP: 25 EST: 1994 **Privately Held**
SIC: 4899 Data communication services

(G-236)

TRANSFORMATION HOUSE INC
1410 S Ferry St (55303-2152)
PHONE...................................763 427-7155
Betty Mathews, *President*
EMP: 25 EST: 1992
SQ FT: 1,920
SALES (est): 500-999K **Privately Held**
SIC: 8082 Home health care services

(G-237)

VOLUNTEERS OF AMERICA INC
22426 Saint Francis Blvd (55303-9670)
PHONE...................................763 753-2500
FAX: 763 753-2500
Terry Malecha, *Maint Spvr*
Tom Gajeski, *Finance*
Bonnie Nelson, *Office Mgr*
Chris Harnack, *Manager*
David Watercott, *Manager*
EMP: 100
SALES (est): 5MM-9.9MM **Privately Held**
WEB: www.voa.org
SIC: 8322 8361 Individual & family social services; residential care facility
PA: Volunteers of America Inc
    1660 Duke St Ste 100
    Alexandria VA 22314
    703 341-5000

(G-238)

WALGREEN CO
Also Called: Walgreens
1911 S Ferry St (55303-2143)
PHONE...................................763 576-0388
FAX: 763 576-0732
D E Bjorlin, *Manager*
EMP: 30
SALES (est): 1MM-4.9MM **Publicly Held**
WEB: www.walgreens.com
SIC: 7384 Non-prescription medicine proprietary store; photofinishing laboratory
PA: Walgreen Co
    200 Wilmot Rd
    Deerfield IL 60015
    847 914-2500

(G-239)

WALKER PLAZA
131 Monroe St Ofc (55303-2484)
PHONE...................................763 422-1226
FAX: 763 422-8115
Mark Anderson, *Manager*
Betty Schweppe, *Officer*
EMP: 35 EST: 1988
SALES (est): 5MM-9.9MM **Privately Held**
WEB: www.walkermeth.org
SIC: 6513 Apartment building operator
PA: Walker Methodist Senior Svcs
    3737 Bryant Ave S
    Minneapolis MN 55409
    612 827-5931

(G-240)

WELLE CONSTRUCTION INC
6361 Sunfish Lake Ct NW Ste 40
(55303-2945)
PHONE...................................763 427-5830
Jeff Welle, *President*
Jean M Welle, *Corp Secy*
EMP: 40 EST: 1991
SQ FT: 2,500
SALES (est): 1MM-4.9MM **Privately Held**
SIC: 1751 Framing contractor

(G-241)

YALE MATERIALS HANDLING - MN
15735 Central Ave NE (55304-5614)
PHONE...................................763 434-3832
FAX: 763 434-8328
Gary Fairchild, *President*
Joe Mayck, *General Mgr*
Tom Larose, *CIO*
▲ EMP: 55 EST: 1970
SQ FT: 36,000
SALES (est): 10MM-24.9MM **Privately Held**
WEB: www.yalegb.com
SIC: 5084 5063 7699 Wholesales industrial lift trucks & parts; wholesales electrical apparatus & equipment; wholesales batteries; industrial machinery repair & maintenance services
PA: Yale Materials Handling-Green
    2140 Hutson Rd
    Green Bay WI 54303
    920 494-8726

APPLE VALLEY
Dakota County

(G-242)

A BRIGHTER CHRISTMAS
14157 Flagstone Trl (55124-5016)
PHONE...................................651 808-7495
Joshua Moe, *President*
EMP: 25
SALES (est): 1MM-4.9MM **Privately Held**
SIC: 8999 Miscellaneous services

(G-243)

DICK'S VALLEY SERVICE INC
6781 146th St W (55124-7285)
PHONE...................................952 891-4431
Richard Tuthill, *President*
Marilyn Tuthill, *Corp Secy*
Jeff Tuthill, *Vice Pres*
EMP: 30 EST: 1965
SALES (est): 1MM-4.9MM **Privately Held**
SIC: 7538 General automotive repair services

APPLETON
Swift County

(G-244)

APPLETON AREA HEALTH SERVICES
30 S Behl St (56208-1616)
PHONE...................................320 289-2422
FAX: 320 289-1797
Jason Carlson, *CEO*
Dennis Mahlen, *Engineering*
Mike Defoe, *CFO*
Judy Carruth, *Office Mgr*
Judith Caruth, *Manager*
EMP: 159 EST: 1952
SQ FT: 50,000
SALES (est): 10MM-24.9MM **Privately Held**
SIC: 8062 8011 8051 Medical hospital; skilled nursing care facility; medical center

(G-245)

CORRECTIONS CORP OF AMERICA
445 S Munsterman St (56208-2608)
PHONE...................................320 289-2052
FAX: 320 289-2059
Jim Genteel, *Manager*
Deanne Munsterman, *Manager*
Tim Wengler, *Warden*
EMP: 350
SALES (est): 25MM-49.9MM **Publicly Held**
WEB: www.correctionscorp.com
SIC: 8744 Correctional facility operations
PA: Corrections Corp of America
    10 Burton Hills Blvd
    Nashville TN 37215
    615 263-3000

ARDEN HILLS
Ramsey County

(G-246)

GALIL MEDICAL USA
4364 Round Lake Rd W (55112-3923)
PHONE...................................877 639-2796
Martin Emerson, *CEO*
EMP: 52 EST: 2005
SALES (est): 1MM-4.9MM **Privately Held**
SIC: 8082 Home health care services

ARGYLE
Marshall County

(G-247)

MARSHALL COUNTY GROUP HOMES
603 Cedar Ave (56713-4200)
PHONE...................................218 437-6695
FAX: 218 437-6695
Sue Holter, *President*
Sara Kuznia, *Corp Secy*

EMP: 53 EST: 1975
SALES (est): 1MM-4.9MM **Privately Held**
SIC: 8361 8052 Home for the mentally retarded; intermediate care facility

---

ARLINGTON
Sibley County

(G-248)

ARLINGTON STATE BANK INC
230 W Main St (55307-9700)
PO Box 650 (55307-0650)
PHONE...................................507 964-2256
FAX: 507 964-5550
David K Hennies, *President*
David J Welch, *Exec VP*
Sheila Arneson, *Senior VP*
Mary Hennies, *Vice Pres*
Sheila Amerson, *Marketing Staff*
EMP: 25 EST: 1895
SQ FT: 7,500
SALES (est): 5MM-9.9MM **Privately Held**
SIC: 6022 State commercial bank

(G-249)

EVANGELICAL LUTHERAN GOOD
Also Called: Arlington Good Samaritan Ctr
411 7th Ave NW (55307-2156)
PO Box 645 (55307-0645)
PHONE...................................507 964-2251
FAX: 507 964-2255
Norma Schauer, *Purch Mgr*
Heidi Weiman, *Human Resources*
Barb Easland, *Manager*
Todd Howell, *Director*
EMP: 100
SALES (est): 1MM-4.9MM **Privately Held**
WEB: www.good-sam.com
SIC: 8059 8051 Nursing home; skilled nursing care facility
PA: Evangelical Lutheran Good
    4800 W 57th St
    Sioux Falls SD 57108
    605 362-3100

(G-250)

SIBLEY MEDICAL CENTER
601 W Chandler St (55307-2127)
PHONE...................................507 964-2271
FAX: 507 964-2941
Benita Jones, *Corp Secy*
Dennis Gremel, *Ch Pathology*
Bev Moorman, *Ch Radiology*
John Zaske, *Engineering*
Darla Anderson, *CFO*
EMP: 120 EST: 1947
SQ FT: 12,500
SALES (est): 10MM-24.9MM **Privately Held**
SIC: 8062 Medical hospital

ASHBY
Grant County

(G-251)

FIRST STATE BANK OF ASHBY
110 Main St (56309-4687)
PO Box 10 (56309-0010)
PHONE...................................218 747-2235
James R Jorstad, *Principal*
Twila Stierlen, *Vice Pres*
EST: 2007 **Privately Held**
SIC: 6022 State commercial bank

ATWATER
Kandiyohi County

(G-252)

JENNIE-O TURKEY STORE INC
501 Pleasant Ave W (56209-1076)
PHONE...................................320 974-8891
Elbert Mahn, *Superintendent*
Steve Black, *Manager*
EMP: 35 **Publicly Held**
WEB: www.hormel.com

G E O G R A P H I C

SIC: **0253** Turkey farm
HQ: Jennie-O Turkey Store Inc
2505 Willmar Ave SW
Willmar MN 56201
320 235-2622

(G-253)
KANDI-WORKS DEVELOPMENTAL (PA)
111 5th St (56209)
PO Box 119 (56209-0119)
PHONE 320 974-8840
FAX: 320 974-8035
Deb Terwischa, *Director*
EMP: 36 EST: 1976
SQ FT: 4,000
SALES (corp-wide): 1.76M Privately Held
SIC: **8331** Job training & vocational rehabilitation services

AUDUBON
Becker County

(G-254)
COOP AUDUBON ELEVATOR ASSN
445 Front St (56511)
PO Box 159 (56511-0159)
PHONE 218 439-6111
FAX: 218 439-6111
Brian Klumbd, *President*
Charles Morrison, *Manager*
EST: 1914
SQ FT: 800 Privately Held
SIC: **5153** 5191 Wholesales grain & field beans; wholesales field, garden & flower seeds

(G-255)
R & R TRANSPORTATION INC
500 N Main St (56511)
PO Box 216 (56511-0216)
PHONE 218 439-6144
EMP: 85 EST: 1974
SALES (est): 10MM-24.9MM Privately Held
SIC: **7513** 4213 Truck rental service, without drivers; over the road trucking

AURORA
Saint Louis County

(G-256)
CLYDE JOHNSON
327 S 2nd St W (55705-1402)
PHONE 218 229-2847
Clyde Johnson, *Owner*
EMP: 40 EST: 1994
SALES (est): 1MM-4.9MM Privately Held
WEB: www.clydejohnson.com
SIC: **8322** Adult daycare center

(G-257)
WHITE COMMUNITY HOSPITAL CORP
5211 Highway 110 (55705-1522)
PHONE 218 229-2211
FAX: 218 229-2042
Laura Ackman, *CEO*
Chris Devney, *CFO*
Gordy Forbeit, *CFO*
Gordy Forbert, *CFO*
Paula Schafbauer, *CFO*
EMP: 140 EST: 1960
SALES (est): 5MM-9.9MM Privately Held
WEB: www.whitech.org
SIC: **8051** 8062 Skilled nursing care facility; medical hospital

AUSTIN
Mower County

(G-258)
ACCENTRA CREDIT UNION
400 4th Ave NE (55912-3372)
PO Box 657 (55912-0657)
PHONE 507 433-1829
FAX: 507 433-7233

Mahlon Krueger, *President*
David Raffelson, *Vice Chairman*
Bruce Huffer, *Corp Secy*
Michel Case, *Vice Pres*
Aaron Dejong, *Vice Pres*
EMP: 36 EST: 1930
SQ FT: 16,000
SALES (est): 5MM-9.9MM Privately Held
SIC: **6062** State chartered credit union

(G-259)
AUSTIN COACHES INC
103 10th St SE (55912-3802)
PO Box 581 (55912-0581)
PHONE 507 433-5358
Elizabeth Crumb, *President*
Mark Crumb, *President*
EMP: 50 EST: 1986
SQ FT: 5,000
SALES (est): 1MM-4.9MM Privately Held
SIC: **4141** Local bus charter service

(G-260)
AUSTIN COUNTRY CLUB INC
1202 28th St NE (55912-6405)
PO Box 474 (55912-0474)
PHONE 507 437-7631
FAX: 507 433-9690
Jeffery Follett, *President*
Brad Bure, *Accountant*
EMP: 70 EST: 1920
SQ FT: 22,000
SALES (est): 1MM-4.9MM Privately Held
SIC: **7997** Country club; eating place; beer garden drinking establishment

(G-261)
AUSTIN MEDICAL CENTER-MAYO
1000 1st Dr NW (55912-2941)
PHONE 507 433-7351
FAX: 507 434-1477
Pierre Rioux, *Corp Secy*
Nancy Hoverstein, *Senior VP*
Monica Hennessy, *Assistant VP*
Candace Clark-Brown, *Technical Mgr*
Sheri Dankert, *CFO*
EMP: 650 EST: 1896
SQ FT: 150,000 Privately Held
SIC: **8399** Health systems agency
PA: Mayo Clinic
200 1st St SW
Rochester MN 55905
507 284-2511

(G-262)
AUSTIN UTILITIES
400 4th St NE (55912-3495)
PHONE 507 433-8886
Jerome McCarthy, *Corp Secy*
Randy Judd, *Store Mgr*
Alex Bumgardner, *Production*
Ann Christianson, *Finance*
Thomas Tylutki, *Manager*
EMP: 98 EST: 1900
SQ FT: 400,000
SALES (est): 50MM-99.9MM Privately Held
WEB: www.austinutilities.com
SIC: **4931** Electric & related services

(G-263)
BIRTHRIGHT OF AUSTIN INC
215 4th Ave NE Ste 2 (55912-3308)
PHONE 507 437-2373
Joanne Hansen, *President*
EMP: 28 EST: 1971
SALES (est): 1MM-4.9MM Privately Held
SIC: **8322** Individual & family social services

(G-264)
CEDAR VALLEY CONSERVATION CLUB
Hwy 218 N (55912)
PO Box 502 (55912-0502)
PHONE 507 433-4937
Arlen Schamber, *President*
Donald Hanson, *Treasurer*
EMP: 400 EST: 1940
SQ FT: 1,800
SALES (est): 25MM-49.9MM Privately Held
SIC: **6411** Insurance agency & broker

(G-265)
CEDAR VALLEY SERVICES INC (PA)
2111 4th St NW (55912-1810)
PHONE 507 433-2303
FAX: 507 433-8880
Karen Baier, *Manager*
Ken Kraft, *Manager*
James R Mueller, *Exec Dir*
Cindy Lefebre, *Director*
Christine Jensen, *Director*
EMP: 200 EST: 1963
SQ FT: 30,000
SALES (corp-wide): 12.09M Privately Held
SIC: **8331** Vocational rehabilitation agency; vocational training agency

(G-266)
CEDARS OF AUSTIN
700 1st Dr NW (55912-3095)
PHONE 507 437-3246
FAX: 507 437-3248
Sandy Archer, *Director*
EMP: 40 EST: 1986
SALES (est): 1MM-4.9MM Privately Held
SIC: **8361** Home for the elderly

(G-267)
COOPERATIVE RESPONSE CENTER (PA)
Also Called: C R C
2000 8th St NW (55912-2474)
PHONE 507 437-2400
Todd Penske, *President*
Bob Trombley, *General Mgr*
Cosy Trytten, *General Mgr*
Darlene Thompson, *General Mgr*
Kerry Weinmann, *General Mgr*
EMP: 80 EST: 1992
SQ FT: 12,000
SALES (corp-wide): 8.19M Privately Held
SIC: **7389** Telephone service

(G-268)
COUNTY OF MOWER (PA)
Also Called: MOWER COUNTY HISTORICAL SOCIET
201 1st St NE (55912-3475)
PHONE 507 437-9440
Denise Barthelf, *Assistant*
EMP: 250 EST: 1858 Privately Held
SIC: **8412** Government office; county government executive offices; museum

(G-269)
CRYPTIC MASONS OF MINNESO
303A N Main St (55912-3407)
PHONE 507 437-2851
Anthony W Lecakis, *Principal*
EMP: 40 EST: 2001 Privately Held
SIC: **8641** Fraternal association

(G-270)
EVANGELICAL LUTHERAN GOOD
Also Called: Comfort Care Good Smaritan Ctr
205 14th St NW (55912-4644)
PHONE 507 437-4526
FAX: 507 437-9024
Paul Cerny, *Maint Spvr*
Susan Amick, *Office Mgr*
Cynthia Neumann, *Manager*
Jo Jack, *Manager*
Georgett Hinkle, *Administrator*
EMP: 65
SALES (est): 1MM-4.9MM Privately Held
WEB: www.good-sam.com
SIC: **8051** Convalescent home
PA: Evangelical Lutheran Good
4800 W 57th St
Sioux Falls SD 57108
605 362-3100

(G-271)
FOX ELECTRICAL CO
500 10th St NE (55912-3756)
PHONE 507 433-7184
FAX: 507 433-5111
Terry Fox, *President*
Jan Fox, *Corp Secy*
Scott Fox, *Vice Pres*
EMP: 25

EST: 1954
SQ FT: 4,000
SALES (est): 1MM-4.9MM Privately Held
WEB: www.foxelectricinc.com
SIC: **1731** General electrical contractor

(G-272)
GAMES PEOPLE PLAY INC
701 18th Ave NW (55912-1850)
PHONE 507 433-7593
FAX: 507 433-9791
Lance R Pogones, *President*
Corey Anderson, *Manager*
John Garry, *Consultant*
Ronald J Pogones, *Director*
Jon G Olson, *Director*
EMP: 40 EST: 1983
SQ FT: 11,000
SALES (est): 1MM-4.9MM Privately Held
WEB: www.gppaustin.com
SIC: **7389** Embroidery advertising service; retails athletic footwear; retails sports apparel; manufactures trimming fabrics; pleating & stitching service

(G-273)
HARTY MECHANICAL INC
1600 1st Ave NE (55912-4502)
PO Box 277 (55912-0277)
PHONE 507 437-8201
FAX: 507 437-8378
Maurice P Harty, *President*
Renee M Harty, *Corp Secy*
EMP: 32 EST: 1979
SQ FT: 3,750
SALES (est): 1MM-4.9MM Privately Held
WEB: www.hartymechanical.com
SIC: **1711** Plumbing service; retails building products & materials; warm air heating & air conditioning contractor

(G-274)
HORMEL FINANCIAL SERVICES
1 Hormel Pl (55912-3673)
PHONE 507 437-5611
James Sheehan, *President*
Jody Feragen, *CFO*
Roland Gentzler, *Treasurer*
EMP: 39 EST: 1997
SALES (est): 1MM-4.9MM Publicly Held
WEB: www.hormel.com
SIC: **8741** Financial management services for business
PA: Hormel Foods Corp
1 Hormel Pl
Austin MN 55912
507 437-5611

(G-275)
HORMEL FOODS CORP (PA)
1 Hormel Pl (55912-3673)
PHONE 507 437-5611
Jeffrey M Ettinger, *President*
Greg N Longstreet, *President*
Susan Craven, *Managing Dir*
Goldner Johnson, *Managing Dir*
Brian D Johnson, *Corp Secy*
◆ EMP: 650 EST: 1891
SQ FT: 231,000
SALES (corp-wide): 6.53B Publicly Held
WEB: www.hormel.com
SIC: **0253** Meat packing plant; turkey farm; manufactures hams & picnics from slaughtered meat; manufactures frankfurters from slaughtered meat; manufactures sausages from slaughtered meat; manufactures beef stew from purchased meat

(G-276)
HORMEL FOODS CORPORATE SVCS (HQ)
1 Hormel Pl (55912-3673)
PHONE 507 437-5611
Jeffrey Ettinger, *President*
Harriet Ulland, *Manager*
EMP: 75 EST: 2004
SALES (corp-wide): 6.53B Publicly Held
WEB: www.hormel.com
SIC: **5147** Wholesales meat & meat products
PA: Hormel Foods Corp
1 Hormel Pl
Austin MN 55912
507 437-5611

(G-277)

HORMEL FOODS INTERNATIONAL

1 Hormel Pl (55912-3673)
PO Box 367 (55912-0367)
PHONE..............................507 437-5611
FAX: 507 437-9815
Richard Broff, *President*
Tom Leake, *Corp Secy*
EMP: 80 **EST:** 1967
SALES (est): 50MM-99.9MM **Publicly Held**
WEB: www.hormel.com
SIC: 5147 8742 Wholesales meat & meat products; food & beverage consultant
PA: Hormel Foods Corp
1 Hormel Pl
Austin MN 55912
507 437-5611

(G-278)

INTERNATIONAL PAPER CO

1900 8th St NE (55912-4932)
PHONE..............................507 433-3467
FAX: 507 437-0803
Jeffrey Linkous, *Site Mgr*
Andy Schippers, *Mfg Staff*
Tom Hughes, *Purchasing*
Ivan Winship, *Accounting Dir*
Robbin Knudtson, *Human Res Mgr*
EMP: 150
SALES (est): 25MM-49.9MM **Publicly Held**
WEB: www.internationalpaper.com
SIC: 5113 7336 Manufactures corrugated boxes; wholesales corrugated & solid fiber boxes; package design service; manufactures metal containers
PA: International Paper Co
6400 Poplar Ave
Memphis TN 38197
901 419-7000

(G-279)

JOSEPH CO INC

2003 14th St NE Ste 106 (55912-4939)
PO Box 427 (55912-0427)
PHONE..............................507 437-3284
FAX: 507 437-7093
Carter Wagner, *President*
Joseph Pedott, *Vice Pres*
Susan Simitz, *Buyer*
Melinda Anderson, *Natl Sales Mgr*
EMP: 45 **EST:** 1965
SQ FT: 2,500
SALES (est): 10MM-24.9MM **Privately Held**
WEB: www.joseph-company.com
SIC: 1542 1541 Commercial & institutional building construction; industrial building & warehouse construction

(G-280)

L L HAGE SEAMLESS GUTTERS INC

1700 8th St SE (55912-3976)
PHONE..............................507 433-1158
Eric Anderson, *President*
EMP: 35 **EST:** 1958
SALES (est): 1MM-4.9MM **Privately Held**
SIC: 1761 1751 Gutter & downspout contractor; carpentry contractor

(G-281)

LARON ALLEN WEISHAIR & CO LLP

Also Called: Larson Allen
109 N Main St (55912-3484)
PO Box 217 (55912-0217)
PHONE..............................507 437-4518
FAX: 507 437-8997
David Crandall, *Partner*
Angela Ross, *Office Admin*
Andrew King, *Technology*
EMP: 57 **EST:** 1950
SQ FT: 2,800
SALES (est): 1MM-4.9MM **Privately Held**
SIC: 8721 Accounting service; certified public accountant services

(G-282)

MCK OF AUSTIN LTD

Also Called: Citgo
1509 10th Pl NE (55912-4007)
PHONE..............................507 437-6702
FAX: 507 437-0089
Kermit Watts, *Owner*

EMP: 80 **EST:** 1990
SQ FT: 12,000
SALES (est): 10MM-24.9MM **Privately Held**
SIC: 7538 Retail gasoline filling station; general automotive repair services; eating place

(G-283)

MIDWEST KAAL CORP

Also Called: Kaal TV
1701 10th Pl NE (55912-4003)
PO Box 577 (55912-0577)
PHONE..............................507 437-6666
FAX: 507 433-9560
Clark Cipra, *General Mgr*
David Harbert, *General Mgr*
Deb Nerud, *Business Mgr*
Laura L Bauer, *Corp Secy*
Gerald Jones, *Vice Pres*
EMP: 45
SQ FT: 1,200
SALES (est): 10MM-24.9MM **Privately Held**
SIC: 4833 Television broadcasting station

(G-284)

RAM WOODVALE

301 N Main St (55912-3498)
PO Box 1047 (55912-1047)
PHONE..............................507 433-4924
FAX: 507 433-4597
Janet Baldus, *Corp Secy*
Connie Charnecki, *Office Mgr*
Sue Martin, *Director*
Pat Maysaga, *Director*
EMP: 50 **EST:** 1990
SQ FT: 1,700
SALES (est): 1MM-4.9MM **Privately Held**
SIC: 8322 Child & youth services

(G-285)

S KB ENVIRONMENTAL

251 Starkey St (55912)
PHONE..............................507 433-8131
EMP: 25 **EST:** 2007
SALES (est): 5MM-9.9MM **Privately Held**
SIC: 4953 7389 Sanitary landfill operation; crane & aerial lift service

(G-286)

SACRED HEART CARE CENTER

1200 12th St SW (55912-2619)
PHONE..............................507 433-1808
FAX: 507 433-8012
Robert Kolb, *Maint Spvr*
Becky Mathews-Halvers, *Director*
EMP: 150 **EST:** 1964
SALES (est): 5MM-9.9MM **Privately Held**
SIC: 8051 8082 Skilled nursing care facility; home health care services

(G-287)

SHOPKO STORES OPERATING CO LLC

1209 18th Ave NW (55912-1881)
PHONE..............................507 437-7785
Rodney Middlebrook, *Manager*
Mary Daly, *Manager*
Gary Vosko, *Manager*
EMP: 142
SALES (est): 10MM-24.9MM **Privately Held**
WEB: www.shopko.com
SIC: 8042 Discount department store; drug store; optometrists' office; retails optical goods
HQ: Shopko Stores Operating Co LLC
700 Pilgrim Way
Green Bay WI 54304
920 429-2211

(G-288)

ST MARK'S LUTHERAN HOME INC

400 15th Ave SW (55912-3232)
PHONE..............................507 437-4594
FAX: 507 434-7201
Barbara Rollie, *Purch Dir*
Pam Wolter, *Human Res Dir*
Kari Wilson, *Office Mgr*
Dimothy Samuelson, *Administrator*
Christine Harris, *Administrator*
EMP: 210 **EST:** 1958
SQ FT: 75,600
SALES (est): 5MM-9.9MM **Privately Held**
SIC: 8051 Skilled nursing care facility

(G-289)

STERLING BANCORPORATION INC (PA)

1419 1st Ave SW (55912-1603)
PO Box 128 (55912-0128)
PHONE..............................507 433-7325
FAX: 507 433-0074
Barry Irish, *President*
Jay Nelson, *Corp Secy*
Tom Winkels, *Vice Pres*
Cindy Wiste, *Manager*
Julie Mulloy, *Officer*
EMP: 40 **EST:** 1970
SQ FT: 10,000
SALES (corp-wide): 16.96M **Privately Held**
SIC: 6712 Bank holding company

(G-290)

TORGERSON PROPERTIES LP

Also Called: Perkins Family Restaurant
701 17th Ave NW (55912-1839)
PHONE..............................507 433-6720
FAX: 507 433-1276
Larry Eisenberg, *General Mgr*
Sheryl Walton, *Senior VP*
EMP: 55
SALES (est): 1MM-4.9MM **Privately Held**
WEB: www.torgersonproperties.com
SIC: 7011 Traveler accommodations
PA: Torgerson Properties Inc
103 15th Ave NW Ste 200
Willmar MN 56201
320 235-7207

(G-291)

TPI CORE INC

Also Called: Holiday Inn
1701 4th St NW (55912-1803)
PHONE..............................507 433-1000
Thomas R Torgerson, *CEO*
Dwayne Osterhout, *General Mgr*
Sheryl D Walton, *Senior VP*
Daryl Engelking, *Vice Pres*
EMP: 99 **EST:** 2004
SALES (est): 5MM-9.9MM **Privately Held**
WEB: www.torgersonproperties.com
SIC: 7011 Traveler accommodations
PA: Torgerson Properties Inc
103 15th Ave NW Ste 200
Willmar MN 56201
320 235-7207

(G-292)

UNITED SUPPORT GROUP

1013 4th Ave NE (55912-3737)
PHONE..............................507 437-4110
EMP: 50 **EST:** 2002
SALES (est): 1MM-4.9MM **Privately Held**
SIC: 8322 Individual & family social services

AVON

Stearns County

(G-293)

ADIUM OIL CO INC

310 Blattner Dr (56310-8674)
PO Box 67 (56310-0067)
PHONE..............................320 356-7350
Dean Mielke, *President*
EMP: 45 **EST:** 1994
SALES (est): 100MM-499.9MM **Privately Held**
WEB: www.adiumoilcompany.com
SIC: 5172 Wholesales petroleum products; convenience store; retails bottled propane gas

(G-294)

DH BLATTNER & SONS INC (PA)

392 County Road 50 (56310-8684)
PHONE..............................320 356-7351
Scott W Blattner, *CEO*
Christopher Blattner, *Exec VP*
C J Blatner, *Vice Pres*
Roland I Wek, *Vice Pres*
James Potter, *Vice Pres*
EMP: 60 **EST:** 1907
SQ FT: 10,000 **Privately Held**
WEB: www.dhblattner.com

SIC: 1081 1429 1611 1622 1629 Mining exploration & development services; bridge construction; crushed & broken boulder quarrying; general highway & street construction service; dam construction; waterway construction; waste water & sewage treatment plant construction

(G-295)

HAVCO INC

Also Called: SEITZ STAINLESS
17578 400th St (56310-9735)
PO Box 100 (56310-0100)
PHONE..............................320 746-2781
FAX: 320 746-2782
Jeff Haviland, *President*
Janet Haviland, *Corp Secy*
EMP: 25 **EST:** 1985
SQ FT: 10,000
SALES (est): 1MM-4.9MM **Privately Held**
WEB: www.seitzstainless.com
SIC: 7699 Manufactures industrial vessels, tanks & containers; tank repair service

(G-296)

LUMBER ONE, AVON INC

101 2nd St NW (56310-9507)
PO Box 7 (56310-0007)
PHONE..............................320 356-7342
FAX: 320 356-7631
Barbara Brandes, *CEO*
Cindi Grunloh, *Corp Secy*
Ted Schmid, *COO*
Charles Brandes, *Vice Pres*
Judith C Schmid, *CFO*
EMP: 55 **EST:** 1940
SQ FT: 8,000
SALES (est): 10MM-24.9MM **Privately Held**
SIC: 1521 1522 Retails building products & materials; new single-family home construction service; multi-family housing construction

(G-297)

PREFINISHING SPECIALISTS INC

314 Blattner Dr (56310-8674)
PO Box 186 (56310-0186)
PHONE..............................320 356-2217
Robert Heurung, *President*
Jane Heurung, *Vice Pres*
Cathy Brix, *Exec Dir*
▲ **EMP:** 30 **EST:** 1977
SQ FT: 10,800
SALES (est): 1MM-4.9MM **Privately Held**
WEB: www.psi.clearwire.net
SIC: 1721 Residential painting contractor; commercial painting contractor

---

BABBITT

Saint Louis County

(G-298)

RURAL LIVING ENVIRONMENTS INC

20 Balsam Cir (55706-1224)
PHONE..............................218 827-3495
Donald Negley, *CEO*
EMP: 25 **EST:** 2006
SALES (est): 500-999K **Privately Held**
SIC: 8361 Home for the elderly

BADGER

Roseau County

(G-299)

NORTHWEST COMMUNITY ACTION INC

312 N Main St (56714-4004)
PO Box 67 (56714-0067)
PHONE..............................218 528-3258
FAX: 218 528-3259
Cari Dostal, *Corp Secy*
Randy Nordin, *Exec Dir*
John Wynne, *Director*
Carl Frigaard, *Director*
EMP: 70 **EST:** 1965
SALES (est): 1MM-4.9MM **Privately Held**
WEB: www.nwcaa.org
SIC: 8322 8351 Social services center; child day care service

BAGLEY
Clearwater County

(G-300)
CLEARWATER COUNTY MEMORIAL (PA)
203 4th St NW (56621-8305)
PHONE..............................218 694-6501
FAX: 218 694-3528
Jon Brovold, *CEO*
Patty Traaseth, *Purch Agent*
Nora Jennings, *Envir Svcs Dir*
Bryan Johnson, *Engineering*
Gladys Luecken, *CFO*
EMP: 105 **EST:** 1950
SQ FT: 29,000 **Privately Held**
WEB: www.clearwaterhs.com
SIC: 8062 8051 Medical hospital; skilled nursing care facility

(G-301)
CLEARWATER HOSPICE
212 Main Ave N (56621-8313)
PHONE..............................218 694-6581
John Nelson, *Commissioner*
Duane Hayes, *Commissioner*
Bonnie Engine, *Exec Dir*
EMP: 50 **EST:** 1996
SALES (est): 1MM-4.9MM **Privately Held**
SIC: 8082 Home health care services

(G-302)
TEAM INDUSTRIES INC (PA)
105 Park Ave NW (56621)
PHONE..............................218 694-3550
David Ricke, *President*
Dave Osterman, *General Mgr*
Michael Matthews, *Exec VP*
Robert Skawski, *Senior VP*
Micah Ricke, *Design Engr*
EMP: 147 **EST:** 1993
SQ FT: 140,000
SALES (corp-wide): 165M **Privately Held**
SIC: 8711 Machine shop, jobbing & repair services; engineering services

(G-303)
TGP INC
421 6th St NE Ofc (56621-8138)
PHONE..............................218 694-2378
Lai Johnson, *Owner*
EMP: 30 **EST:** 2003
SALES (est): 1MM-4.9MM **Privately Held**
SIC: 8082 Home health care services

BALATON
Lyon County

(G-304)
COLONIAL MANOR OF BALATON
551 US Highway 14 (56115-3231)
PO Box 219 (56115-0219)
PHONE..............................507 734-3511
FAX: 507 734-2337
Elaine Fischer, *Finance Mgr*
Paul Luitjens, *Administrator*
EMP: 85 **EST:** 1992
SALES (est): 1MM-4.9MM **Privately Held**
SIC: 8051 Skilled nursing care facility

BARNESVILLE
Clay County

(G-305)
EVANGELICAL LUTHERAN GOOD
Also Called: Barnesville Good Samaritan Ctr
600 5th Ave SE (56514-3908)
PHONE..............................218 354-2254
FAX: 218 354-2153
Nathan Johnson, *Manager*
EMP: 80
SALES (est): 1MM-4.9MM **Privately Held**
WEB: www.good-sam.com

SIC: **8059** Nursing home
PA: Evangelical Lutheran Good
　　4800 W 57th St
　　Sioux Falls SD 57108
　　605 362-3100

BARNUM
Carlton County

(G-306)
CARLTON COUNTY FAIR ASSN
Front St (55707)
PO Box 216 (55707-0216)
PHONE..............................218 389-6737
Allysha Sample, *Owner*
EMP: 40 **EST:** 1892
SALES (est): 1MM-4.9MM **Privately Held**
SIC: 7999 Fair

BARRETT
Grant County

(G-307)
BARRETT AUTOMATIC PRODUCTS CO
418 2nd St (56311-0156)
PHONE..............................320 528-2512
FAX: 320 528-2511
David Lien, *President*
Judy Lien, *Corp Secy*
EMP: 30 **EST:** 1983
SQ FT: 5,600
SALES (est): 1MM-4.9MM **Privately Held**
SIC: 5084 Manufactures screw machine products; machine shop, jobbing & repair services; wholesales industrial machinery & equipment

(G-308)
BARRETT CARE CENTER INC
800 Spruce Ave (56311-4505)
PHONE..............................320 528-2527
Vernon Junker, *President*
Joan Junker, *Corp Secy*
EMP: 70 **EST:** 1966
SALES (est): 1MM-4.9MM **Privately Held**
SIC: 8051 8052 Skilled nursing care facility; intermediate care facility

(G-309)
PALMER BUS SERVICE
302 Hawkins Ave (56311-4506)
PHONE..............................320 528-2670
Floyd Palmer, *Owner*
Robin Lloyd, *Manager*
EMP: 40 **EST:** 2003
SALES (est): 1MM-4.9MM **Privately Held**
SIC: 4151 School bus service

BATTLE LAKE
Otter Tail County

(G-310)
EVANGELICAL LUTHERAN GOOD
Also Called: Battle Lake Good Samaritan Ctr
105 Glen Haven Dr (56515-4010)
PHONE..............................218 864-5231
FAX: 218 864-5498
Diana Haber, *Bookkeeper*
Jim Wolf, *Administrator*
Jim Wols, *Administrator*
Traill Vosberg, *Exec Dir*
EMP: 70
SALES (est): 1MM-4.9MM **Privately Held**
WEB: www.good-sam.com
SIC: 8051 Convalescent home
PA: Evangelical Lutheran Good
　　4800 W 57th St
　　Sioux Falls SD 57108
　　605 362-3100

(G-311)
KALK-YOUNG INC
Also Called: Shoreline Restaurant & Lanes
505 N Lake Ave (56515-4056)
PHONE..............................218 864-5265
FAX: 218 864-5265
Pat Kalk, *CEO*
Steven Young, *President*
EMP: 26 **EST:** 1971
SQ FT: 11,000
SALES (est): 500-999K **Privately Held**
SIC: 7933 Eating place; bowling center

(G-312)
OTTER TAIL NURSING HOME
28930 County Highway 145 (56515-9350)
PHONE..............................218 495-2993
FAX: 218 495-2979
Denise Hjelmstad, *Manager*
Glenn Pearl, *Administrator*
Lisa Augustus, *Director*
Tim Bush, *Director*
EMP: 63 **EST:** 2003
SALES (est): 1MM-4.9MM **Privately Held**
SIC: 8051 Skilled nursing care facility

BAUDETTE
Lake Of The Woods County

(G-313)
ADRIAN'S RESORT INC
3362 Red Oak Rd NW (56623-8851)
PHONE..............................218 634-1985
Marlene Adrian, *President*
Cory Ney, *Principal*
Bryan Ney, *Principal*
Darlene Adrian, *Corp Secy*
EMP: 64 **EST:** 1952
SALES (est): 1MM-4.9MM **Privately Held**
SIC: 7011 Resort hotel

(G-314)
BRIGGS HENNUM INC
Also Called: Wigwam Resort
3502 Four Mile Bay Dr NW (56623-8870)
PHONE..............................218 634-2168
FAX: 218 634-1616
Tom Braggs, *President*
Jerry Hennum, *Vice Pres*
EMP: 35 **EST:** 1919
SALES (est): 1MM-4.9MM **Privately Held**
WEB: www.wigwamresortlow.com
SIC: 7011 7999 Tourist lodgings; cocktail lounge; eating place; pleasure boat rental services

(G-315)
J & L HENNUM INC
Also Called: Sportsman's Lodge
3244 Bur Oak Rd NW (56623-8849)
PHONE..............................218 634-1342
FAX: 218 634-9497
Gregg Hennum, *President*
Diana Hennum, *Vice Pres*
Jerry Hennum, *Vice Pres*
Patty Beckel, *Accounting Staf*
EMP: 75 **EST:** 1993
SQ FT: 33,000
SALES (est): 1MM-4.9MM **Privately Held**
WEB: www.sportsmanslodgelow.com
SIC: 7011 Motel; bar; full service independent family restaurant

(G-316)
LAKE OF WOODS AMBULANCE
111 1st St SW (56623-2879)
PHONE..............................218 634-2100
Nancy Swenson, *Director*
Gwenn Johnson, *Director*
EMP: 34 **EST:** 1980
SALES (est): 1MM-4.9MM **Privately Held**
SIC: 4119 Ambulance service

(G-317)
LAKEWOOD HEALTH CENTER
600 Main Ave S (56623-2855)
PHONE..............................218 634-2120
FAX: 218 634-1307
Sha R Palm, *President*
Gloria Lund, *Opers Mgr*
Lois Slick, *Purchasing*

Gary E Davis, *Engineering*
Lynn Ellis, *CFO*
EMP: 167 **EST:** 1956
SQ FT: 36,000
SALES (est): 10MM-24.9MM **Privately Held**
SIC: 8062 8051 Medical hospital; skilled nursing care facility
PA: Catholic Health Initiatives
　　98 Inverness Dr W Ste 800
　　Englewood CO 80112
　　303 298-9100

BAXTER
Crow Wing County

(G-318)
A & R LEASING INC
Also Called: Dondelinger Chevrolet Cadillac
7915 State Highway 210 (56425-8468)
PO Box 323, Brainerd (56401-0323)
PHONE..............................218 829-4787
Roger H Dondelinger, *President*
EMP: 60 **EST:** 1970
SALES (est): 25MM-49.9MM **Privately Held**
WEB: www.arleasing.com
SIC: 7515 7532 7538 Passenger car leasing; automotive body, paint & interior repair & maintenance services; general automotive repair services; retails new & used automobiles; used car dealer

(G-319)
AMERICAN CELLULAR CORP
Also Called: Cellular One
14039 Edgewood Dr Ste 106 (56425-8653)
PO Box 2690 (56425-2690)
PHONE..............................218 828-8000
FAX: 218 828-9661
Steve Tanner, *General Mgr*
EMP: 25 **Publicly Held**
WEB: www.sbc.com
SIC: 4812 Cellular telephone services
HQ: American Cellular Corp
　　14201 Wireless Way
　　Oklahoma City OK 73134
　　405 529-8500

(G-320)
AMERICAN NATIONAL BANK OF MN
7638 Woida Rd (56425-8730)
PO Box 2600 (56425-2600)
PHONE..............................218 829-1484
Terry Baltes, *Manager*
Robert Sefkow, *Officer*
EMP: 80
SALES (est): 25MM-49.9MM **Privately Held**
SIC: 6036 State savings bank
PA: American National Bank of MN
　　1920 S 6th St
　　Brainerd MN 56401
　　218 824-7900

(G-321)
BRAINERD BUS LINES INC
Also Called: Reichert Bus Lines
8342 Industrial Park Rd (56425-8272)
PHONE..............................218 829-6955
FAX: 218 829-6671
Mark Moran, *President*
Joyce Moran, *Corp Secy*
Mike Moran, *Vice Pres*
Gae Wicklund, *Treasurer*
EMP: 100 **EST:** 1986
SQ FT: 5,000
SALES (est): 5MM-9.9MM **Privately Held**
WEB: www.reichertbus.com
SIC: 4142 Long-distance bus charter service
PA: Reichert Enterprises Inc
　　8342 Industrial Park Rd
　　Brainerd MN 56425
　　218 829-6955

(G-322)
CARLSON & LYTER DISTRIBUTING
13394 Dogwood Dr (56425-8623)
PHONE..............................218 829-2978
Tom Dick, *Manager*
EMP: 30
SALES (est): 10MM-24.9MM **Privately Held**

▲=Import ▼=Export
◆=Import/Export

WEB: www.budtime.com
SIC: 5181 Wholesales beer & ale
PA: Carlson & Lyter Distributing
1020 Industrial Dr S
Sauk Rapids MN 56379
320 251-7375

(G-323)
CENTRAL LAKES LODGING LLC
7818 Excelsior Rd (56425-8427)
PHONE................................218 828-0629
Bob Sullivian, *Member*
EMP: 25 EST: 2004
SALES (est): 1MM-4.9MM Privately Held
SIC: 7011 Vacation lodge

(G-324)
CITI INVESTOR SERVICES INC
Also Called: Baxter Service Center
7651 Universal Dr (56425-8438)
PO Box 979, Brainerd (56401-0979)
PHONE................................218 825-5000
FAX: 218 825-5010
Keith Crussie, *Accounts Exec*
Naomi Galema, *Marketing Mgr*
Steve Christensen, *Manager*
EMP: 500
SALES (est): 50MM-99.9MM Publicly Held
WEB: www.citibank.com
SIC: 6411 Pension & retirement plan consulting service
DH: Citi Investor Services Inc
105 Eisenhower Pkwy Ste 2
Roseland NJ 07068
973 461-2500

(G-325)
CITI INVESTOR SERVICES INC
14221 Golf Course Rd (56425-8432)
PHONE................................218 829-4781
J Potts, *Vice Pres*
Chuck Klepperich, *Facilities Mgr*
Jeremy Klomp, *Engineer*
Mickey Hendrickson, *Accountant*
Steven Christenson, *Manager*
EMP: 400
SALES (est): 25MM-49.9MM Publicly Held
WEB: www.citibank.com
SIC: 6411 Pension & retirement plan consulting service
DH: Citi Investor Services Inc
105 Eisenhower Pkwy Ste 2
Roseland NJ 07068
973 461-2500

(G-326)
COMPLETE TITLE SERVICES LLC
14275 Golf Course Rd (56425-8670)
PHONE................................218 828-9611
David Lauer, *President*
James M Gammello, *Vice Pres*
EMP: 43 EST: 2002
SALES (est): 5MM-9.9MM Privately Held
WEB: www.fatc.com
SIC: 6361 Title insurance carrier
PA: First American Title Insurance
1 First American Way
Santa Ana CA 92707
714 800-3000

(G-327)
DONDELINGER CHEVROLET
7915 State Highway 210 (56425-8468)
PO Box 323, Brainerd (56401-0323)
PHONE................................218 829-4787
FAX: 218 829-0511
Roger H Dondelinger, *President*
D J Dondelinger, *Corp Secy*
Debb Mitzel, *Controller*
EMP: 56 EST: 1968
SQ FT: 20,000
SALES (est): 25MM-49.9MM Privately Held
SIC: 7538 Retails new & used automobiles; general automotive repair services; retails new & used pickups; retails new & used vans

(G-328)
GOOD NEIGHBOR HOME HEALTH CARE
14387 Edgewood Dr (56425-8460)
PO Box 481, Brainerd (56401-0481)
PHONE................................218 829-9238
FAX: 218 829-2144
Sherrie Christensen, *President*
Donna Bzdok, *CFO*
Dale Christensen, *VP Persnl*
Shannon Ramsbell, *Nursing Dir*
Barbara J Smude, *Nurse*
EMP: 160 EST: 1984
SALES (est): 5MM-9.9MM Privately Held
WEB: www.gnhomecare.com
SIC: 8082 Home health care services

(G-329)
HOME DEPOT USA INC
7207 Foley Rd (56425-2203)
PHONE................................218 829-0341
FAX: 218 855-8496
Todd Peterson, *Manager*
EMP: 110
SALES (est): 10MM-24.9MM Publicly Held
SIC: 7359 Home center store; tool rental
HQ: Home Depot International Inc
2455 Paces Ferry Rd SE
Atlanta GA 30339
770 319-1669

(G-330)
IN FISHERMAN INC
7819 Highland Scenic Rd (56425)
PHONE................................218 829-1648
FAX: 218 829-3091
Steve Hoffman, *President*
Rob Newmann, *General Mgr*
Mike Curry, *Manager*
Kris Dieter, *Manager*
Jim McConville, *Manager*
EMP: 48 EST: 1975
SALES (est): 10MM-24.9MM Privately Held
WEB: www.in-fisherman.com
SIC: 7812 7221 Television film production service; publishes magazines without printing; educational television motion picture production service; portrait studio; video tape production services
HQ: PRIMEDIA Inc
3585 Engrg Dr Ste 100
Norcross GA 30092
678 421-3000

(G-331)
J THOMAS & ASSOCIATES
Also Called: Spectrum Electronics & Distrg
5244 Ashdale Ln (56425-8303)
PHONE................................218 829-6622
John Thomas, *Owner*
EST: 1975 Privately Held
SIC: 8742 Business management consultant; fast food restaurant; retails electronic parts & equipment

(G-332)
KLIZ FM POWERLOON 107 5
13225 Dogwood Dr (56425-8669)
PHONE................................218 822-4440
Bob Koomerstad, *Principal*
Dan Wild, *Mfg Staff*
EMP: 30 EST: 2007
SALES (est): 1MM-4.9MM Privately Held
SIC: 4832 Radio broadcasting station

(G-333)
KNIFE RIVER CORP - NORTH
7925 Industrial Park Rd (56425-8268)
PHONE................................218 829-4726
Joel Lindahl, *Manager*
EMP: 40
SALES (est): 5MM-9.9MM Publicly Held
WEB: www.mdu.com
SIC: 1611 Highway & street paving contractor
DH: Knife River Corp - North
4787 Shadowwood Dr NE
Sauk Rapids MN 56379
320 251-9472

(G-334)
KUEPERS CONSTRUCTION INC
14643 Edgewood Dr Ste 115 (56425-9770)
PHONE................................888 829-0707
Douglas Kuepers, *President*
Steven Kuepers, *Exec VP*
Jeremy Adams, *Prdtn Mgr*
Mike Patrick, *Controller*
Stan Weiser, *Manager*
EMP: 40 EST: 1974
SQ FT: 14,564
SALES (est): 10MM-24.9MM Privately Held
WEB: www.kuepers.com
SIC: 1542 1521 1522 New commercial & office building construction; new single-family home construction service; apartment building construction service

(G-335)
LARSONALLEN LLP
581 Edgewood Dr N (56425-9603)
PO Box 648, Brainerd (56401-0648)
PHONE................................218 825-2919
Bill Potbin, *Mng Member*
EMP: 40
SALES (est): 1MM-4.9MM Privately Held
SIC: 8721 Accounting, auditing & bookkeeping services
PA: Larsonallen LLP
220 S 6th St Ste 300
Minneapolis MN 55402
612 376-4500

(G-336)
MINI KIX INC
Also Called: JUST FOR KIX PRECISION DANCE
7842 College Rd (56425-8620)
PO Box 724, Brainerd (56401-0724)
PHONE................................218 829-7107
FAX: 218 829-7618
Stephen J Clough, *President*
EMP: 150 EST: 1982
SQ FT: 8,000
SALES (est): 10MM-24.9MM Privately Held
WEB: www.justforkix.com
SIC: 7922 7929 Theatrical production service; drum & bugle corps

(G-337)
MINNESOTA DEPARTMENT OF TRANS
Also Called: Mindot
7694 Industrial Park Rd (56425-8266)
PHONE................................218 828-2678
Robert Bush, *Manager*
EMP: 165
SALES (est): 5MM-9.9MM Privately Held
WEB: www.me.umn.edu
SIC: 4173 Bus maintenance facilities; transportation program regulation & administration services; state government transportation program regulation or administration
DH: Minnesota Department of Trans
395 John Ireland Blvd
Saint Paul MN 55155
651 296-3000

(G-338)
MORGAN TIRE & AUTO INC
14370 Dellwood Dr 100 (56425-9742)
PHONE................................218 828-8552
Clay Parkin, *Manager*
EMP: 30
SALES (est): 1MM-4.9MM Privately Held
WEB: www.bfsusa.com
SIC: 7534 Tire recapping & retreading services
HQ: Bfs Retail Operations LLC
333 E Lake St Ste 300
Bloomingdale IL 60108
630 259-9000

(G-339)
NOR-SON INC
7900 Hastings Rd (56425-8465)
PHONE................................218 828-1722
FAX: 218 828-0487
Brooke Silvernail, *President*
Robert Sweeney, *Vice Pres*
Kevin Stangel, *Vice Pres*
Cathy Collett, *Human Res Mgr*
Sandy Olson, *Marketing Staff*
EMP: 185 EST: 1978
SQ FT: 6,000
SALES (est): 50MM-99.9MM Privately Held
WEB: www.nor-son.com
SIC: 1521 1541 1542 New single-family home construction service; new industrial building construction; industrial building renovating, remodeling & repair service; new commercial & office building construction; commercial & office building renovation & repair services

(G-340)
RETKA ENTERPRISES INC
7611 College Rd Ste 105 (56425-8625)
PO Box 2805 (56425-2805)
PHONE................................218 829-4076
Jerry Retka, *President*
Jeannette Retka, *Corp Secy*
Ken Retka, *Vice Pres*
Jackie Retka, *Accounting Mgr*
Deb Retka, *Office Mgr*
EMP: 30 EST: 1972
SQ FT: 8,000
SALES (est): 500-999K Privately Held
SIC: 7349 Industrial or commercial cleaning services

(G-341)
TEAM INDUSTRIES BAXTER INC
13143 Cypress Dr (56425-8466)
PO Box 2510 (56425-2510)
PHONE................................218 829-1901
David Ricke, *President*
Steven Kast, *Corp Secy*
Michael Matthews, *Exec VP*
Robert Skawski, *Vice Pres*
◆ EMP: 48 EST: 2000
SQ FT: 25,000
SALES (est): 1MM-4.9MM Privately Held
SIC: 8711 Machine shop, jobbing & repair services; engineering services
PA: Team Industries Inc
105 Park Ave NW
Bagley MN 56621
218 694-3550

(G-342)
THOMAS P KOOP CPA
14275 Golf Course Rd # 300 (56425-8674)
PO Box 648, Brainerd (56401-0648)
PHONE................................218 825-2903
Thomas Koop, *Partner*
EMP: 35
SALES (est): 1MM-4.9MM Privately Held
SIC: 8721 Certified public accountant services

(G-343)
TIMOTHY V BERGIN
581 Edgewood Dr N (56425-9603)
PHONE................................218 825-2902
Timothy V Bergin V, *Partner*
EMP: 45 EST: 2001
SALES (est): 1MM-4.9MM Privately Held
SIC: 8721 Accounting, auditing & bookkeeping services

(G-344)
VIKING COCA COLA BOTTLING CO
Also Called: Coca-Cola
7842 Industrial Park Rd (56425-8267)
PHONE................................218 829-2204
FAX: 218 829-9331
Mark Jeffers, *Manager*
EMP: 30
SALES (est): 10MM-24.9MM Privately Held
WEB: www.vikingcocacola.com
SIC: 5149 Manufactures nonalcoholic carbonated beverages; wholesales beverages

(G-345)
WIDSETH, SMITH, NOLTING
7804 Industrial Park Rd (56425-8267)
PO Box 2720 (56425-2720)
PHONE................................218 829-5117
FAX: 218 829-2517
Donald Anderson, *Sales Staff*
Bruce Buckson, *Manager*
Kevin Donnay, *Manager*
EMP: 55
SALES (est): 5MM-9.9MM Privately Held

GEOGRAPHIC

WEB: www.wsn-mn.com
SIC: 8711 Engineering services
PA: Widseth, Smith, Nolting
216 S Main St Ste 1
Crookston MN 56716
218 281-6522

BAYPORT
Washington County

(G-346)
BAYPORT SENIOR CENTER
Also Called: Community Volunteer Services
263 3rd St N (55003-1028)
PHONE..............................651 275-8907
Richard Peterson, *Manager*
Valerie Jones, *Director*
EMP: 36 EST: 2000
SALES (est): 500-999K **Privately Held**
SIC: 8322 Senior citizen center

(G-347)
CROIXDALE APTS
750 Highway 95 N (55003-1085)
PHONE..............................651 275-4800
Mark Camball, *Chairman*
Rene Roeser, *Manager*
EMP: 60 EST: 1980
SALES (est): 5MM-9.9MM **Privately Held**
SIC: 6513 Apartment building operator

(G-348)
FIRST AID & TRUST (PA)
950 Highway 95 N (55003-1014)
PHONE..............................651 439-5195
Greg Benson, *President*
Peter J Clements, *Corp Secy*
EMP: 35 EST: 1995 **Privately Held**
WEB: www.bayportbank.com
SIC: 6022 State commercial bank

(G-349)
FIRST STATE BANK & TRUST
950 Highway 95 N (55003-1014)
PHONE..............................651 439-5195
FAX: 651 439-4027
Gregory L Benson, *President*
Dewayne Stafne, *Senior VP*
Peter J Clements, *Senior VP*
EMP: 55 EST: 1914
SQ FT: 19,000
SALES (est): 10MM-24.9MM **Privately Held**
WEB: www.bayportbank.com
SIC: 6022 State commercial bank
PA: First State & Trust
950 Highway 95 N
Bayport MN 55003
651 439-5195

(G-350)
NORTHERN STATES POWER CO
Also Called: XCEL Energy
1103 King Plant Rd (55003-1000)
PHONE..............................651 731-5701
Tom Smith, *Plant Mgr*
Mark Fritsth, *Manager*
Dan Peikert, *Manager*
Mike Miser, *Manager*
Darrell Knutson, *Manager*
EMP: 100
SALES (est): 25MM-49.9MM **Publicly Held**
WEB: www.middletownpower.com
SIC: 4911 Provides electric power
transmission services
HQ: Northern States Power Co
414 Nicollet Mall
Minneapolis MN 55401
612 330-5500

(G-351)
WASHINGTON COUNTY ASSOCIATION
Also Called: Croixdale Residents
334 7th Ave N (55003-1217)
PHONE..............................651 439-4946
FAX: 651 439-0245
Alis Delisle, *Bookkeeper*
Rene Roeser, *Administrator*
EMP: 55 EST: 1961
SALES (est): 1MM-4.9MM **Privately Held**
WEB: www.wcasc.snowclubs.com
SIC: 8059 8052 Personal care home, with
health care; intermediate care facility

BEAVER BAY
Lake County

(G-352)
COVE POINT LODGE
Hwy 61 (55601)
PHONE..............................218 226-3221
FAX: 218 226-4445
Marcia Hillestad, *Owner*
Steve Hillestad, *General Ptnr*
Todd Krynski, *Manager*
EMP: 40 EST: 1995
SALES (est): 1MM-4.9MM **Privately Held**
SIC: 7011 Motel; eating place

BEAVER CREEK
Rock County

(G-353)
CITY OF BEAVER CREEK ✪
311 E 1st Ave (56116-1114)
PHONE..............................507 673-2266
Carolyn Deboer, *Mayor*
Jane Blank, *Corp Secy*
EMP: 25 EST: 2009
SALES (est): 1MM-4.9MM **Privately Held**
SIC: 7389 Business services at a
non-commercial site

BECKER
Sherburne County

(G-354)
ANDERSON-GILYARD (PA)
12431 Pine St (55308)
PO Box 307 (55308-0307)
PHONE..............................763 261-5161
FAX: 763 261-2238
Virgil E Gilyard, *Owner*
EMP: 40 EST: 1940
SQ FT: 22,000 **Privately Held**
SIC: 5171 Wholesales petroleum bulk
stations; retail chain grocery store; retail
gasoline filling station; fuel oil dealer

(G-355)
CITY OF BECKER
Also Called: Pebble Creek Country Club
14220 Clubhouse Ln (55308)
PO Box 250 (55308-0250)
PHONE..............................763 261-4656
FAX: 763 261-2909
David Simeon, *Superintendent*
EMP: 25
SALES (est): 1MM-4.9MM **Privately Held**
SIC: 7992 Public golf course; retails golf
goods & equipment; fast food restaurant
PA: City of Becker
12060 Sherburne Ave
Becker MN 55308
763 261-4302

(G-356)
LIBERTY PAPER INC
13500 Liberty Ln (55308)
PO Box 429 (55308-0429)
PHONE..............................763 261-6100
Benjamin Fiterman, *Chairman*
David Lenzen, *Corp Secy*
Steve Richardson, *CFO*
Dean Flicker, *VP Sales*
Lora Aure, *Manager*
EMP: 91 EST: 1993
SALES (est): 10MM-24.9MM **Privately Held**
WEB: www.libertypaper.com
SIC: 4953 Manufactures corrugated paper;
waste material recycling services;
paperboard mill
PA: Liberty Diversified Industries
5600 Highway 169 N
Minneapolis MN 55428
763 536-6600

(G-357)
NORTHERN STATES POWER CO
Also Called: XCEL Energy
13999 Industrial Blvd (55308-8800)
PHONE..............................763 261-4100
FAX: 763 261-3154
Ron Sundeen, *Purchasing*
Donna Reinarts, *Manager*
Chris Olson, *Manager*
Duane Wold, *Manager*
Thomas Krych, *Consultant*
EMP: 400
SALES (est): 100MM-499.9MM **Publicly Held**
WEB: www.middletownpower.com
SIC: 4911 Electric services
HQ: Northern States Power Co
414 Nicollet Mall
Minneapolis MN 55401
612 330-5500

(G-358)
SHERBURNE STATE BANK
12500 Sherburne Ave (55308)
PO Box 428 (55308-0428)
PHONE..............................763 261-4200
FAX: 763 261-4737
Roger W Haugen, *President*
Janice L Burggraff, *Assistant VP*
Peter Haugen, *Vice Pres*
Tanya Danielson, *Vice Pres*
Brian Johnson, *Vice Pres*
EMP: 30 EST: 1920
SALES (est): 5MM-9.9MM **Privately Held**
SIC: 6022 State commercial bank

(G-359)
TELIN TRANSPORTATION GROUP LLC ✪
14990 Industry Ave SE (55308-8813)
PHONE..............................763 262-3328
Tod Telin, *Member*
Lori Kohorst, *Accountant*
EMP: 32 EST: 2008
SQ FT: 42,000
SALES (est): 1MM-4.9MM **Privately Held**
SIC: 4731 Transportation agents & brokers

BELGRADE
Stearns County

(G-360)
BAYER BUILT WOODWORKS INC
24614 Highway 71 (56312-8819)
PHONE..............................320 254-3651
FAX: 320 254-3601
Joseph Bayer, *CEO*
Michael Bayer, *CFO*
Philip Terry, *Finance*
Laurie Bayer, *Human Res Mgr*
Jeff Stuewe, *Manager*
EMP: 241 EST: 1983
SQ FT: 265,636
SALES (est): 100MM-499.9MM **Privately Held**
WEB: www.bayerbuilt.com
SIC: 5031 Wholesales millwork

(G-361)
BAYER TRUCKING LLC
24614 Highway 71 (56312-8819)
PHONE..............................320 254-3651
Mike Bayer, *Member*
Joseph Bayer, *Member*
EMP: 50 EST: 1994
SALES (est): 1MM-4.9MM **Privately Held**
SIC: 4212 Local trucking without storage
services

(G-362)
BELGRADE COMMERICAL CLUB
321 Washburn Ave (56312-4626)
PO Box 189 (56312-0189)
PHONE..............................320 254-8271
George Borgerdin, *Principal*
EMP: 40
SALES (est): 5MM-9.9MM **Privately Held**
SIC: 6531 Real estate services

(G-363)
BELGRADE COOPERATIVE ASSN
218 Wells St (56312)
PO Box 369 (56312-0369)
PHONE..............................320 254-8231
Jeff Koehler, *CEO*
EMP: 25 EST: 1928
SALES (est): 25MM-49.9MM **Privately Held**
SIC: 5171 5141 5191 Wholesales
petroleum bulk stations; wholesales
agricultural fertilizer; wholesales agricultural
chemicals; retails bottled propane gas; food
broker; fuel oil dealer

(G-364)
BELGRADE NURSING HOME INC
103 School St (56312)
PO Box 340 (56312-0340)
PHONE..............................320 254-8215
FAX: 320 254-8238
Char Wold, *Director*
Philip Lord, *Director*
EMP: 75 EST: 1968
SALES (est): 1MM-4.9MM **Privately Held**
SIC: 8052 8051 Intermediate care facility;
skilled nursing care facility

(G-365)
NORTH AMERICAN STATE BANK (PA)
321 Washburn Ave (56312)
PO Box 189 (56312-0189)
PHONE..............................320 254-8271
George Borgerding, *Ch of Bd*
Brian Borgerding, *President*
Deb Vanburen, *Vice Pres*
Paul Borgerding, *Vice Pres*
David Bauer, *Vice Pres*
EMP: 38 EST: 1889
SQ FT: 11,000
SALES (corp-wide): 6.94M **Privately Held**
SIC: 6022 State commercial bank

BELLE PLAINE
Scott County

(G-366)
BELLE PLAINE BANCORPORATION
201 W Main St (56011-1615)
PO Box 87 (56011-0087)
PHONE..............................952 873-2296
Paul D Gatz, *President*
EMP: 25 EST: 1985 **Privately Held**
SIC: 6712 Bank holding company

(G-367)
BELLE PLAINE COOPERATIVE
820 E Main St (56011-2204)
PHONE..............................952 873-4244
John Nagel, *President*
Einard Karnitz, *Corp Secy*
Robert Raleigh, *Vice Pres*
Katie Brigan, *Prdtn Mgr*
Chad Swanepoel, *Prdtn Mgr*
EMP: 25 EST: 1917
SQ FT: 22,000
SALES (est): 10MM-24.9MM **Privately Held**
SIC: 5191 5172 Wholesales farm supplies;
wholesales agricultural fertilizer; wholesales
feed; wholesales field, garden & flower
seeds; retails bottled propane gas;
manufactures fertilizers; wholesales
petroleum products

(G-368)
MORRIS-WALKER LTD
Also Called: Jennifer's Restaurant
351 Enterprise Dr E (56011-2338)
PHONE..............................952 873-4334
FAX: 952 873-6993
Philip A Morris, *President*
Shirley Meger, *General Mgr*
Tom Floris, *Office Mgr*
EMP: 200 EST: 1969
SQ FT: 15,000
SALES (est): 5MM-9.9MM **Privately Held**
WEB: www.emmakrumbee.com
SIC: 0175 Full service independent family
restaurant; commercial bakery; retail
bakery; retail gift shop; apple orchard

(G-369)
ORCHARD PARK LLC
Also Called: American Lodge & Suite
510 S Elm St (56011-2100)
PHONE..............................952 873-6017
FAX: 952 873-6018
Phillip Morris, *Owner*
EMP: 30 EST: 1997
SALES (est): 1MM-4.9MM Privately Held
SIC: 7011 Motel

(G-370)
STATE BANK OF BELLE PLAINE
201 W Main St (56011-1615)
PO Box 87 (56011-0087)
PHONE..............................952 873-2296
FAX: 952 873-2877
Paul Gatz, *President*
Kevin G Gaffney, *Principal*
Dave Vandlein, *Senior VP*
Janel Schmidt, *Mfg Staff*
Wendy Kepp, *Manager*
EMP: 27 EST: 1882
SQ FT: 5,000
SALES (est): 1MM-4.9MM Privately Held
SIC: 6162 6022 Mortgage & loan lending;
state commercial bank

(G-371)
STIER TRANSPORT SERVICES INC
406 S Meridian St (56011-1922)
PHONE..............................952 873-2362
FAX: 952 873-6499
Jim Koonst, *President*
John Steer, *Vice Pres*
EMP: 25 EST: 1933
SQ FT: 10,500
SALES (est): 500-999K Privately Held
SIC: 4151 School bus service

BELLE PLAINE
Sibley County

(G-372)
CHARD TILING & EXCAVATING INC
Also Called: Sibley Aggregates, Div
26239 State Highway 25 (56011-5050)
PHONE..............................952 873-6152
Le R Chard, *President*
Connie Chard, *Vice Pres*
EMP: 55
SQ FT: 9,000
SALES (est): 5MM-9.9MM Privately Held
SIC: 1629 1794 Drainage system
construction; excavating contractor

(G-373)
JMDL INC
Also Called: Tidy Disposal
20652 255th Ave (56011-5037)
PHONE..............................952 873-2636
Mark Johnson, *President*
EMP: 40 EST: 1997
SALES (est): 5MM-9.9MM Privately Held
WEB: www.jmdl.com
SIC: 4953 Waste material recycling services

BEMIDJI
Beltrami County

(G-374)
AMERIPRIDE SERVICES INC
300 Paul Bunyan Dr SE (56601-3249)
PHONE..............................218 751-3260
FAX: 218 751-5150
Rick Siebels, *Manager*
EMP: 50
SALES (est): 1MM-4.9MM Privately Held
WEB: www.ameripride.com
SIC: 7213 Linen supply service
PA: Ameripride Services Inc
     10801 Wayzata Blvd # 100
     Hopkins MN 55305
     952 738-4200

(G-375)
BELTRAMI ELECTRIC CO-OP INC
4111 Technology Dr NW (56601-5128)
PO Box 488 (56619-0488)
PHONE..............................218 444-2540
FAX: 218 444-3676
Lynette Nieuwsma, *General Mgr*
Paul Wrolstad, *Systems Mgr*
Jared Eschternech, *Director*
EMP: 59 EST: 1940
SQ FT: 62,000
SALES (est): 25MM-49.9MM Privately Held
WEB: www.beltramielectric.com
SIC: 4911 Electric services

(G-376)
BELTRAMI'S TALLY INC
Also Called: Buena Vista Ski Area
19276 Lake Julia Dr NW (56601-7792)
PHONE..............................218 243-2231
FAX: 218 243-2544
Suzanne Thomas, *President*
EMP: 50 EST: 1949
SALES (est): 1MM-4.9MM Privately Held
WEB: www.bvskiarea.com
SIC: 7011 Ski lodge; retails skiing
equipment

(G-377)
BEMIDJI AVIATION SERVICES INC (PA)
4125 Hangar Dr NW (56601-6243)
PO Box 624 (56619-0624)
PHONE..............................218 751-1880
FAX: 218 759-3552
Larry Diffley, *President*
Mark Shough, *Vice Pres*
Arlen Rinkenberger, *Program Dir*
EMP: 45 EST: 1946
SQ FT: 15,000 Privately Held
WEB: www.bemidjiaviation.com
SIC: 4581 5088 Fixed base operator;
aircraft maintenance & repair services;
wholesales transportation equipment &
supplies

(G-378)
BEMIDJI CLINIC MERIT CARE INC
1233 34th St NW (56601-5112)
PHONE..............................218 333-5000
Bonnie Anderson, *Business Mgr*
Bruce Pitts, *Exec VP*
Brent Teiken, *Treasurer*
Randy Beck, *Administrator*
Gail Conway, *Supervisor*
EMP: 100
SALES (est): 10MM-24.9MM Privately Held
WEB: www.meritcare.com
SIC: 8011 Ambulatory surgical center
PA: MeritCare Health System
     801 Broadway N
     Fargo ND 58102
     701 234-6000

(G-379)
BEMIDJI COOPERATIVE ASSN
Also Called: Cenex
320 3rd St NW (56601-3113)
PO Box 980 (56619-0980)
PHONE..............................218 751-4260
FAX: 218 751-1976
Richard Speck, *Vice Pres*
Raeburn Gladen, *Vice Pres*
Robert Edwards, *Treasurer*
Susan Nyberg, *Controller*
Justin Brooks, *Manager*
EMP: 40 EST: 1933
SQ FT: 16,000
SALES (est): 100MM-499.9MM Privately
Held
WEB: www.bemidjicoop.com
SIC: 5172 5191 Wholesales petroleum
products; wholesales agricultural fertilizer;
wholesales agricultural chemicals;
wholesales feed; wholesales field, garden &
flower seeds; retail gasoline filling station;
hardware store

(G-380)
BEMIDJI TOWN & COUNTRY CLUB
2425 Birchmont Beach Rd NE
(56601-9879)
PHONE..............................218 751-9215
Steve Hagenah, *President*
Brent Knutson, *Manager*
Paul Grovem, *Manager*
Gretchen Fjerstad, *Manager*
EMP: 80 EST: 1913
SQ FT: 5,000
SALES (est): 1MM-4.9MM Privately Held
WEB: www.bemidjigolf.com
SIC: 7997 7991 7992 7999 Country club;
cocktail lounge; golf driving range; eating
place; public golf course; physical fitness
center

(G-381)
BEMIDJI TOWN & COUNTRY CLUB
2425 Birchmont Dr NE (56601-2327)
PHONE..............................218 751-4535
Russ Moen, *President*
EMP: 50
SALES (est): 1MM-4.9MM Privately Held
SIC: 7997 Membership recreation club

(G-382)
BI-COUNTY COMMUNITY ACTION
2529 15th St NW (56601-8772)
PO Box 579 (56619-0579)
PHONE..............................218 751-4631
FAX: 218 751-8452
Anita Spangler, *Manager*
Deborah Allison, *Exec Dir*
EMP: 30 EST: 1966
SQ FT: 3,400
SALES (est): 1MM-4.9MM Privately Held
SIC: 8322 Social services center

(G-383)
C D HAUGEN INC
Also Called: Haugen Trucking
5049 Scribner Rd NW (56601-7255)
PHONE..............................218 751-2738
FAX: 218 751-0426
Douglas C Haugen, *President*
EMP: 50 EST: 1955
SQ FT: 7,500
SALES (est): 1MM-4.9MM Privately Held
SIC: 4212 4213 4214 Local trucking without
storage services; local trucking with storage;
over the road trucking

(G-384)
CHRISTIANSEN INDUSTRIAL
2805 Washington Ave SE (56601-8847)
PO Box 456 (56619-0456)
PHONE..............................218 751-4663
FAX: 218 444-4807
Michael Christiansen, *President*
Jason Christiansen, *Manager*
EMP: 40 EST: 1979
SQ FT: 600
SALES (est): 5MM-9.9MM Privately Held
WEB: www.cidcraneservice.com
SIC: 1611 1794 Heavy highway & street
construction; grading services; excavating
contractor

(G-385)
COOPERATIVE DEVELOPMENT LLC
1831 Anne St NW Ste 100 (56601-5660)
PHONE..............................218 444-1143
Bonnie Wichern, *Office Mgr*
Paul Freude, *Mng Member*
EMP: 53 EST: 1996
SQ FT: 1,865
SALES (est): 5MM-9.9MM Privately Held
SIC: 1623 Underground utilities contractor

(G-386)
COUNTY OF BELTRAMI
Also Called: Beltrami County Health Svcs
616 America Ave NW (56601-3818)
PHONE..............................218 333-8206
FAX: 218 333-4150
Kay Mack, *Manager*
Mary Marschel, *Director*
EMP: 75 Privately Held
WEB: www.beltrami.org
SIC: 7361 Nurses' registry service
PA: County of Beltrami
     701 Minnesota Ave NW # 235
     Bemidji MN 56601
     218 333-4109

(G-387)
DAVIS DRYWALL INC
1100 Industrial Park Dr SE (56601-6198)
PHONE..............................218 444-2532
FAX: 218 444-2583
Brad Davis, *President*
EMP: 40 EST: 2004
SALES (est): 1MM-4.9MM Privately Held
SIC: 1742 Drywall contractor

(G-388)
DICKSON ENTERPRISES INC
Also Called: Team Tires Plus
2525 Middle School Rd NW (56601-4016)
PHONE..............................218 759-2000
FAX: 218 759-0047
Bob Dickson, *Principal*
EMP: 30
SALES (est): 1MM-4.9MM Privately Held
SIC: 7534 Tire recapping & retreading
services
PA: Dickson Enterprises Inc
     1295 Wolf Lake Dr SE
     Bemidji MN 56601
     218 444-8444

(G-389)
EDGEWATER MANAGEMENT LLC
Also Called: Hampton Inn
1019 Paul Bunyan Dr S (56601-3223)
PHONE..............................218 751-3603
FAX: 218 751-3600
Richard Siegert, *President*
Mindy Siegert, *Corp Secy*
Joyce Siegert, *Vice Pres*
Christopher Siegert, *Treasurer*
Eric Nelson, *Manager*
EMP: 45 EST: 2003
SQ FT: 85,000
SALES (est): 1MM-4.9MM Privately Held
SIC: 7011 Traveler accommodations

(G-390)
ELDER CARE OF BEMIDJI INC
Also Called: Havenwood Care Center
1633 Delton Ave NW (56601-2537)
PHONE..............................218 444-1745
FAX: 218 444-1744
Jim Birchem, *President*
Barbara Caspers, *Business Mgr*
Kathleen Birchem, *Corp Secy*
Jerry Kapsner, *Vice Pres*
Julie Beauchne, *Human Res Mgr*
EMP: 170 EST: 1968
SALES (est): 5MM-9.9MM Privately Held
SIC: 8051 8059 Skilled nursing care facility;
nursing home

(G-391)
EXECU SYSTEMS INC
1499 Anne St NW (56601-5113)
PHONE..............................218 444-1021
Matt Sparby, *Manager*
EMP: 30
SALES (est): 5MM-9.9MM Privately Held
WEB: www.dougjones.net
SIC: 6531 Real estate agency & broker
PA: Execu Systems Inc
     4427 N 36th St
     Phoenix AZ 85018
     602 957-0444

(G-392)
FAST LANE CAR WASH
1702 Paul Bunyan Dr NW (56601-4106)
PHONE..............................218 444-9130
FAX: 218 444-3106
Allen Korpi, *Owner*
EMP: 25 EST: 2000
SALES (est): 500-999K Privately Held
SIC: 7542 Car wash

GEOGRAPHIC

(G-393)
FEDEX FREIGHT INC
3400 Butterfly Dr NW (56601-4040)
PHONE..................................218 751-9122
Ken Ellis, *Manager*
EMP: 25
SALES (est): 1MM-4.9MM **Publicly Held**
WEB: www.fedexfreight.fedex.com
SIC: 4213 Long-distance less than
truckload freight trucking services
DH: Fedex Freight Inc
    2200 Forward Dr
    Harrison AR 72601
    870 741-9000

(G-394)
FIRST NATIONAL BANK OF BEMIDJI
502 Minnesota Ave NW (56601-3060)
PO Box 670 (56619-0670)
PHONE..................................218 751-2430
Thomas E Welle, *President*
Barbara Mountain, *Human Res Mgr*
EMP: 65 EST: 1897
SQ FT: 20,000
SALES (est): 10MM-24.9MM **Privately Held**
WEB: www.fnbbemidji.com
SIC: 6021 National commercial bank
PA: First Bemidji Holding Co Inc
    1600 Paul Bunyan Dr NW
    Bemidji MN 56601
    218 751-2430

(G-395)
FIRST REALTY GMAC
1425 Paul Bunyan Dr NW (56601-4164)
PHONE..................................218 751-2511
FAX: 218 751-0405
Douglas Fuller, *Owner*
Ruby Christopher, *Administrator*
EMP: 28 EST: 1989
SALES (est): 5MM-9.9MM **Privately Held**
SIC: 6531 Real estate agency & broker

(G-396)
GLEN LINDSETH
513 Beltrami Ave NW (56601-3009)
PHONE..................................218 751-6300
Kenneth A Mc Donald, *Principal*
EMP: 38
SALES (est): 1MM-4.9MM **Privately Held**
SIC: 8721 Certified public accountant
services

(G-397)
HANSON ELECTRIC OF BEMIDJI INC
3125 Bemidji Ave N (56601-4326)
PHONE..................................218 751-5833
Richard Hanson, *President*
Steve Hanson, *Corp Secy*
Tom Runningun, *Accountant*
Jennifer Wilford, *Receptionist*
EMP: 30 EST: 1981
SQ FT: 3,200
SALES (est): 1MM-4.9MM **Privately Held**
WEB: www.hansonelec.com
SIC: 1731 General electrical contractor

(G-398)
JC CUSTOM WELDING INC
489 Amos Way NW (56601-4370)
PHONE..................................218 444-9353
Joshua Copiskey, *President*
Jean Ron, *Manager*
EMP: 30 EST: 1996
SALES (est): 5MM-9.9MM **Privately Held**
SIC: 1731 Steel fabricator; general electrical
contractor

(G-399)
K L L Z F M
502 Beltrami Ave NW (56601-3010)
PHONE..................................218 444-1500
Lou Buron, *President*
EMP: 35 EST: 2001
SALES (est): 1MM-4.9MM **Privately Held**
SIC: 4832 Radio broadcasting station

(G-400)
KRAUS-ANDERSON CONSTRUCTION CO
206 Beltrami Ave NW (56601-4008)
PHONE..................................218 759-0596
FAX: 218 759-0995
Jeff Iisakka, *Vice Pres*
John Davies, *Vice Pres*
EMP: 40
SALES (est): 10MM-24.9MM **Privately Held**
WEB: www.krausanderson.com
SIC: 1542 7389 7997 Commercial &
institutional building construction; crane &
aerial lift service; membership recreation
club
PA: Kraus-Anderson Inc
    523 S 8th St
    Minneapolis MN 55404
    612 332-7281

(G-401)
L & M SUPPLY INC
2740 Paul Bunyan Dr NW (56601-8796)
PHONE..................................218 751-3237
FAX: 218 751-7418
Daryl Potter, *General Mgr*
EMP: 62
SQ FT: 21,000
SALES (est): 5MM-9.9MM **Privately Held**
SIC: 5013 Hardware store; wholesales
automotive supplies & parts; retails
automotive parts
PA: L & M Supply Inc
    1200 E US Highway 169
    Grand Rapids MN 55744
    218 326-9451

(G-402)
MINNESOTA DEPARTMENT OF
Also Called: Northwestern Minn Juvenile Ctr
1231 5th St NE (56601-3316)
PO Box 247 (56619-0247)
PHONE..................................218 751-3196
FAX: 218 751-3229
William C Frey, *Superintendent*
EMP: 100
SALES (est): 5MM-9.9MM **Privately Held**
WEB: www.minncor.com
SIC: 8744 Correctional facility operations
DH: Department of Corrections MN
    1450 Energy Park Dr # 200
    Saint Paul MN 55108
    651 361-7200

(G-403)
MINNESOTA STATE COMMUNITY
Also Called: Custom Tring Svcs Economic
Dev
905 Grant Ave SE (56601-4907)
PHONE..................................218 755-4270
Mary Eaton, *Vice Pres*
EMP: 100
ADMISSIONS: 1200 **Privately Held**
WEB: www.msus.edu
SIC: 8742 Junior college; management
consulting services
HQ: Minnesota State Community
    150 2nd St SW Ste B
    Perham MN 56573
    218 347-6202

(G-404)
MURRAY WILLIAMSON
Also Called: Super 8 Motel
1815 Paul Bunyan Dr NW (56601-5602)
PHONE..................................218 751-8481
FAX: 218 751-8870
Murray Williamson, *Owner*
Kevin Williamson, *Manager*
EMP: 35 EST: 1980
SALES (est): 1MM-4.9MM **Privately Held**
WEB: www.murraywilliamson.org
SIC: 7011 Traveler accommodations

(G-405)
NAYLOR ELECTRICAL CONSTRUCTION
Also Called: Naylor's
1430 Paul Bunyan Dr NW (56601-4103)
PO Box 100 (56619-0100)
PHONE..................................218 751-2620
FAX: 218 751-8931

James D Naylor, *President*
Robb H Naylor, *Treasurer*
Deb Larue, *Manager*
EMP: 40 EST: 1923
SQ FT: 20,000
SALES (est): 1MM-4.9MM **Privately Held**
WEB: www.naylorelectric.com
SIC: 1731 Electrical contractor; retails
electric household appliances

(G-406)
NAYLOR HEATING & REFRIGERATION
1430 Paul Bunyan Dr NW (56601-4103)
PO Box 100 (56619-0100)
PHONE..................................218 444-4328
Deb Larue, *Member*
Robb Naylor, *Sales Executive*
EMP: 25 EST: 1999
SQ FT: 20,000
SALES (est): 1MM-4.9MM **Privately Held**
SIC: 7623 Refrigeration repair service &
repair; retails complete kitchens, including
sinks & cabinets; retails plumbing & heating
supplies

(G-407)
NEI BOTTLING INC
Also Called: Pepsico
730 Industrial Park Dr SE (56601-5421)
PO Box 516 (56619-0516)
PHONE..................................218 751-3847
FAX: 218 751-1462
Jeff Nei, *President*
Mike Nei, *Purch Agent*
EMP: 40 EST: 1935
SQ FT: 46,750
SALES (est): 25MM-49.9MM **Privately Held**
SIC: 5149 Wholesales soft drinks;
wholesales juices; wholesales bottled
mineral or spring water

(G-408)
NORTH COUNTRY BUSINESS PRDTS (PA)
1112 Railroad St SE (56601-4871)
PO Box 910 (56619-0910)
PHONE..................................218 751-4140
FAX: 218 751-1722
Dean Crotty, *President*
Darlene Geller, *Exec VP*
Curt Crotty, *Vice Pres*
Lin Anderson, *Purch Agent*
Dave Johnson, *Supervisor*
EMP: 65 EST: 1948
SQ FT: 25,000
SALES (corp-wide): 30M **Privately Held**
WEB: www.ncbpinc.com
SIC: 5021 5044 5112 7629 Wholesales
office furniture; electric business machine
repair service; wholesales office equipment;
wholesales stationery & office supplies

(G-409)
NORTH COUNTRY HOSPITAL
1000 Anne St NW (56601)
PHONE..................................218 751-0220
FAX: 218 751-7249
Vic Hagstrom, *Vice Pres*
Tom Conzemius, *Purch Dir*
Robert Verchota, *VP Human Res*
Penny Echpermach, *Marketing Mgr*
Sandy Runningen-Bense, *Manager*
EMP: 120
SALES (est): 1MM-4.9MM **Privately Held**
SIC: 8059 8051 Nursing home; skilled
nursing care facility
PA: North Country Hospital
    1300 Anne St NW
    Bemidji MN 56601
    218 751-5430

(G-410)
NORTH COUNTRY HOSPITAL (PA)
1300 Anne St NW (56601-5103)
PHONE..................................218 751-5430
Paul Hanson, *President*
Thomas Yuo, *Ch of Anesth*
Joseph Corser, *Ch of ER*
Sandra L Bensen, *Vice Pres*
Joseph J Dahlby, *Vice Pres*
EMP: 650 EST: 1930
SQ FT: 127,655 **Privately Held**
SIC: 8062 8051 Medical hospital; extended
care facility

(G-411)
NORTH COUNTRY HOSPITAL
3525 Pine Ridge Ave NW (56601-5115)
PHONE..................................218 333-5665
FAX: 218 333-5642
Susan Dobbelstein, *Manager*
Susan Dobelstein, *Exec Dir*
Marsha Kaehne, *Admin Asst*
EMP: 42
SALES (est): 1MM-4.9MM **Privately Held**
SIC: 8082 Home health care services
PA: North Country Hospital
    1300 Anne St NW
    Bemidji MN 56601
    218 751-5430

(G-412)
NORTH COUNTRY REGIONAL HOSP
1300 Anne St NW (56601-5103)
PHONE..................................218 751-5430
James Hanko, *President*
Hans Serleth, *Ch of Surgery*
Beth Solheim, *Manager*
John C Cota, *Lab Dir*
EMP: 400 EST: 1898
SQ FT: 225,000
SALES (est): 25MM-49.9MM **Privately Held**
SIC: 8062 Medical hospital
PA: North Country Hospital
    1300 Anne St NW
    Bemidji MN 56601
    218 751-5430

(G-413)
NORTHERN MINNESOTA PUBLIC
Also Called: KAWE TV, CHANNEL 9
1500 Birchmont Dr NE (56601-2600)
PHONE..................................218 751-3407
FAX: 218 759-0460
William Sanford, *President*
Jess Skala, *Opers Mgr*
Deb McGregor, *Sales Mgr*
Dennis Weimann, *Manager*
Jeff Hanks, *Manager*
EMP: 26 EST: 1970
SQ FT: 2,000
SALES (est): 5MM-9.9MM **Privately Held**
SIC: 4833 Television broadcasting station

(G-414)
NORTHLAND HARDWOOD LUMBER CO
4445 Cardinal Rd (56601)
PO Box 1411 (56619)
PHONE..................................218 751-0550
FAX: 218 751-5924
B S Curb, *President*
Davey Mills, *Vice Pres*
Deb Prestby, *Vice Pres*
Richard Curb, *Vice Pres*
Alan Curb, *Vice Pres*
EMP: 25 EST: 1969
SQ FT: 5,000
SALES (est): 10MM-24.9MM **Privately Held**
SIC: 5031 Wholesales lumber, plywood &
millwork; produces resawn small dimension
lumber

(G-415)
NORTRAX EQUIPMENT CO SE
3419 Washington Ave SE (56601-8803)
PHONE..................................218 759-1996
FAX: 218 759-1790
Dana Gellately, *Manager*
EMP: 28
SALES (est): 10MM-24.9MM **Publicly Held**
WEB: www.deere.com
SIC: 5082 Wholesales contractor's
materials
HQ: Nortrax Equipment Co SE
    3802 Corporex Park Dr # 100
    Tampa FL 33619
    813 635-2300

(G-416)
NOTHERN CASS BEMIDJI INC
Also Called: Dac Bemidji
735 Mahnomen Dr SE (56601-5408)
PHONE..................................218 759-0052
FAX: 218 444-6446
David Terdan, *Exec Dir*
EMP: 32 EST: 1992
SALES (est): 1MM-4.9MM **Privately Held**

SIC: 8322 Rehabilitation services

(G-417)
OCCUPATIONAL DEVELOPMENT CTR
Also Called: O D C
1260 Industrial Park Dr SE (56601-5419)
PHONE 218 751-6001
FAX: 218 751-9189
Emily Helgeson, *Corp Secy*
Joanne Olson, *Director*
EMP: 30
SALES (est): 1MM-4.9MM **Privately Held**
WEB: www.odcmn.com
SIC: 8331 Vocational rehabilitation agency; manufactures silverware & plated ware
PA: Occupational Development Ctr
1520 Highway 32 S
Thief River Falls MN 56701
218 681-4949

(G-418)
PAUL BUNYAN BROADCASTING CO
Also Called: Kbhp-Fm
502 Beltrami Ave NW (56601-3080)
PO Box 1656 (56619-1656)
PHONE 218 444-1011
Lou Buron, *President*
Susan Buron, *Corp Secy*
Mary Campbell, *Vice Pres*
Harry Hastings, *Advt Staff*
EMP: 28 **EST:** 1956
SQ FT: 4,000
SALES (est): 1MM-4.9MM **Privately Held**
WEB: www.omnibroadcasting.com
SIC: 4832 Radio broadcasting station

(G-419)
PAUL BUNYAN COMMUNITY THEATER
314 Beltrami Ave NW (56601-3105)
PHONE 218 751-7270
FAX: 218 751-2838
Karen M Moe, *President*
Jack Balnchard, *Admin Asst*
EMP: 30 **EST:** 1951
SALES (est): 1MM-4.9MM **Privately Held**
SIC: 7922 Community theater production service

(G-420)
PAUL BUNYAN RURAL TELEPHONE
1831 Anne St NW Ste 100 (56601-5660)
PHONE 218 444-1234
FAX: 218 586-3121
Kathy Peterson, *President*
Jack High, *Pastor*
Bruce Blanchard, *Vice Pres*
Rob S Clair, *Plant Mgr*
Paul Fruede, *Project Mgr*
EMP: 75 **EST:** 1954 **Privately Held**
SIC: 4813 Local telephone communications services

(G-421)
POLICE RANGE
Also Called: Bemidji Police Training Center
329 Rako St SW (56601-3455)
PHONE 218 751-7641
Jay B Preece, *Manager*
EMP: 30
SALES (est): 1MM-4.9MM **Privately Held**
SIC: 8742 Training & development consultant

(G-422)
RICHARD SIGERT
Also Called: Green Mill Restaurant
1025 Paul Bunyan Dr S (56601-3223)
PHONE 218 444-1875
FAX: 218 444-1880
EMP: 73
SALES (est): 1MM-4.9MM **Privately Held**
SIC: 7011 6513 Motel; full service American restaurant; apartment building operator
PA: Richard Sigert
1015 Paul Bunyan Dr S
Bemidji MN 56601
218 751-3603

(G-423)
RIVERWOOD BANK
214 5th St NW (56601-3005)
PO Box 458 (56619-0458)
PHONE 218 751-5120
Dave Lamdgrede, *President*
Dave Landgrebe, *President*
Karen Jacobson, *Corp Secy*
Denise Andree, *Assistant VP*
Sue Kringen, *Vice Pres*
EMP: 25 **EST:** 1910
SQ FT: 10,000
SALES (est): 5MM-9.9MM **Privately Held**
SIC: 6021 6712 National commercial bank; bank holding company
PA: First Federal Bank Corp
214 5th St NW
Bemidji MN 56601
218 751-5120

(G-424)
RURAL MINNESOTA CEP INC
Also Called: Workforce Center
616 America Ave NW # 220 (56601-3848)
PHONE 218 755-4458
FAX: 218 755-4458
Tom Allen, *Manager*
EMP: 37 **Privately Held**
SIC: 7361 Employment agency services; human resource, social work & welfare administration services; state government administration of social & manpower programs
PA: Rural Minnesota Cep Inc
803 Roosevelt Ave Ste 203
Detroit Lakes MN 56501
218 846-7400

(G-425)
RUTTGER'S BIRCHMONT LODGE INC
530 Birchmont Beach Rd NE (56601-8507)
PHONE 218 751-4131
FAX: 218 444-7245
Randy Ruttger, *President*
EMP: 25 **EST:** 1937
SQ FT: 12,000
SALES (est): 1MM-4.9MM **Privately Held**
WEB: www.ruttger.com
SIC: 7011 Tourist lodgings; eating place

(G-426)
SECURITY BANK USA
1025 Paul Bunyan Dr NW (56601-2133)
PO Box 1630 (56619-1630)
PHONE 218 751-1510
FAX: 218 751-0007
John Baer, *President*
William C Mawe, *Senior VP*
Linda Vettel, *Mfg Staff*
Paula Meyer, *Manager*
Karen Fullmer, *Info Tech Mgr*
EMP: 30 **EST:** 1909
SALES (est): 5MM-9.9MM **Privately Held**
WEB: www.securitybankusa.com
SIC: 6022 6163 State commercial bank; loan broker

(G-427)
SHANNON-PETERSON INC
Also Called: Peterson Sheet Metal
3728 Bemidji Ave N (56601-4335)
PHONE 218 751-4502
FAX: 218 751-5320
Orville Peterson, *President*
Alton Shannon, *Principal*
Jaime Quello, *Controller*
Donna Anderson, *Manager*
EMP: 33 **EST:** 1982
SQ FT: 6,000
SALES (est): 1MM-4.9MM **Privately Held**
WEB: www.petersonsm.com
SIC: 1711 Warm air heating & air conditioning contractor; ventilation & duct work contractor

(G-428)
STELLHER HUMAN SERVICES INC
514 Beltrami Ave NW (56601-3010)
PO Box 430 (56619-0430)
PHONE 218 751-5919
FAX: 218 444-2847

Steve Jackelen, *President*
EMP: 40 **EST:** 1994
SALES (est): 1MM-4.9MM **Privately Held**
SIC: 8322 Child & youth services

(G-429)
TRUSTCORP MORTGAGE CO
Also Called: Trust Mortgage
1499 Anne St NW (56601-5113)
PHONE 218 444-5626
Matt Sparby, *Owner*
EMP: 35
SALES (est): 1MM-4.9MM **Publicly Held**
SIC: 6162 Mortgage & loan lending
HQ: Trustcorp Mortgage Co
100 N Michigan St Ste 800
South Bend IN 46601
574 237-5265

(G-430)
UNITED PARCEL SERVICE OF NEW
Also Called: UPS
945 Industrial Park Dr SE (56601-5425)
PHONE 218 751-9109
Barry Sarbanka, *Manager*
EMP: 30
SALES (est): 1MM-4.9MM **Publicly Held**
WEB: www.martrac.com
SIC: 4215 Package delivery services by vehicle
HQ: United Parcel Service of New
55 Glenlake Pkwy NE
Atlanta GA 30328
404 828-6000

(G-431)
UPPER MISSISSIPPI MENTAL
722 15th St NW (56601-2528)
PO Box 640 (56619-0640)
PHONE 218 751-3280
FAX: 218 751-3298
Kristie Miller, *Office Mgr*
Jean Christensen, *Director*
Robert C Cole, *Director*
James R Jarmuskewicz, *Psychiatry*
Cindy Berget, *Receptionist Se*
EMP: 53 **EST:** 1960
SALES (est): 1MM-4.9MM **Privately Held**
SIC: 8093 Outpatient mental health clinic

(G-432)
WELLS TECHNOLOGY INC (PA)
4885 Windsor Ct NW (56601-7659)
PHONE 218 751-5117
FAX: 218 751-0493
Andrew Wells III, *President*
Carol Y Wells, *Treasurer*
Wendy Wells, *VP Mktg*
James W Hyden, *Incorporator*
EMP: 28 **EST:** 1989
SQ FT: 31,664
SALES (corp-wide): 58.65M **Privately Held**
SIC: 5085 Manufactures metal screws; manufactures butcher's, hunting or pocket knives; manufactures hand scissors; manufactures automobile garage frame straighteners; wholesales industrial fasteners including nuts, bolts, screws, etc; manufactures wood screws

(G-433)
WELLS TECHNOLOGY INC
5015 Windsor Ct NW (56601-8061)
PHONE 218 751-1412
Wendy Wells, *Manager*
EMP: 31
SALES (est): 1MM-4.9MM **Privately Held**
SIC: 5085 Manufactures metal screws; manufactures butcher's, hunting or pocket knives; manufactures hand scissors; manufactures automobile garage frame straighteners; wholesales industrial fasteners including nuts, bolts, screws, etc; manufactures wood screws
PA: Wells Technology Inc
4885 Windsor Ct NW
Bemidji MN 56601
218 751-5117

(G-434)
YOUNG & DAVIS DRYWALL INC
170 Anne St NW (56601-4200)
PO Box 605 (56619-0605)
PHONE 218 751-6048
FAX: 218 751-0336
Robert D Young, *President*
Janna Smith, *Treasurer*
EMP: 40 **EST:** 1990
SALES (est): 1MM-4.9MM **Privately Held**
SIC: 1742 1771 Drywall contractor; interior stucco contractor; exterior concrete stucco contractor

---

BEMIDJI
Hubbard County

(G-435)
POTLATCH CORP
50518 County 45 (56601-6587)
PHONE 218 751-6144
FAX: 218 751-6517
Peter Auve, *Manager*
EMP: 90
SALES (est): 50MM-99.9MM **Publicly Held**
WEB: www.potlatchcorp.com
SIC: 5099 Wholesales wood chips
PA: Potlatch Corp
601 W 1st Ave Ste 1600
Spokane WA 99201
509 835-1500

BENSON
Swift County

(G-436)
AFFILIATED MEDICAL CENTER
1805 Wisconsin Ave (56215-1653)
PHONE 320 843-2030
FAX: 320 843-4806
Julie Coleshaw, *Marketing Staff*
Caryn McGeary, *Office Mgr*
Mary Felt, *Nurse Practr*
Stacy Kurkosky, *Receptionist Se*
Stasia Kent, *Receptionist Se*
EMP: 35 **EST:** 1982
SALES (est): 1MM-4.9MM **Privately Held**
SIC: 8011 General & family practice physician or surgeon office

(G-437)
AGRALITE ELECTRIC COOPERATIVE
320 Highway 12 SE (56215-1398)
PO Box 228 (56215-0228)
PHONE 320 843-4150
FAX: 320 843-3738
Ramon Millett, *President*
Kory Johnson, *General Mgr*
Dilley Lidia, *Safety Mgr*
Denise Runge, *Office Mgr*
EMP: 29 **EST:** 1938
SQ FT: 30,000
SALES (est): 10MM-24.9MM **Privately Held**
WEB: www.agralite.com
SIC: 4911 Electric power distribution service

(G-438)
BEVERLY ENTERPRISES - MN
Also Called: Meadow Lane Health Care Center
2209 Utah Ave (56215-1000)
PHONE 320 843-2225
FAX: 320 843-2496
Eric Everson, *Exec Dir*
Phyllis Saunders, *Director*
EMP: 65
SALES (est): 1MM-4.9MM **Privately Held**
WEB: www.beverlynet.com
SIC: 8051 Skilled nursing care facility; convalescent home
HQ: Beverly Enterprises - MN
650 Ramer Ave S
Rush City MN 55069
320 358-4765

(G-439)
GLACIAL PLAINS COOPERATIVE
195 30th Ave NE (56215-1088)
PHONE..................................320 843-4820
FAX: 320 843-4002
Tom Trean, *General Mgr*
Steve Stassen, *Branch Mgr*
Carol Sachs, *Manager*
Al Goldenstein, *Manager*
Julie Jaeger, *Director*
EMP: 64 **EST:** 2001
SALES (est): 25MM-49.9MM **Privately Held**
SIC: 5191 Wholesales agricultural fertilizer

(G-440)
GLACIEL PLANS COOP
260 20th St NW (56215-1039)
PHONE..................................320 843-2563
FAX: 320 842-4577
Tom Train, *General Mgr*
EMP: 40 **EST:** 1996
SALES (est): 50MM-99.9MM **Privately Held**
SIC: 5153 Wholesale grain elevator

(G-441)
HEARTLAND RANCH
185 Highway 9 NE (56215-1160)
PHONE..................................320 843-4815
Catie Lee, *Sales Staff*
Deyna Lethem, *Director*
EMP: 32 **EST:** 1999
SALES (est): 1MM-4.9MM **Privately Held**
WEB: www.heartlandranch.net
SIC: 8361 Group foster home

(G-442)
SWIFT COUNTY HOMES INC
1650 Stone Ave (56215-1751)
PHONE..................................320 843-3509
Margaret D Marce, *Principal*
EMP: 39 **EST:** 1977
SQ FT: 2,100
SALES (est): 1MM-4.9MM **Privately Held**
SIC: 8361 8052 Home for the mentally
retarded; intermediate care facility

(G-443)
SWIFT COUNTY-BENSON HOSPITAL
1815 Wisconsin Ave (56215-1653)
PHONE..................................320 843-4232
FAX: 320 843-4172
Frank Lawatsch, *CEO*
Sara Fernholz, *Vice Pres*
Greg Roraff, *Vice Pres*
Pam Lawatsch, *Facilities Mgr*
Jayne Thielke, *CFO*
EMP: 87 **EST:** 1912
SQ FT: 12,000
SALES (est): 5MM-9.9MM **Privately Held**
SIC: 8062 Medical hospital

BIG LAKE
Sherburne County

(G-444)
ADVANCE WALL SYSTEMS INC
16927 231st Ave NW (55309-8986)
PHONE..................................763 263-8512
Chad Hess, *President*
Al Mobley, *Vice Pres*
EMP: 28 **EST:** 1999
SALES (est): 5MM-9.9MM **Privately Held**
WEB: www.advancewallsystems.com
SIC: 1522 1711 Residential construction;
plumbing, heating & air conditioning
contractor

(G-445)
CARGILL INC
20021 176th St NW (55309-8017)
PHONE..................................763 262-1900
Julie Stevens, *Controller*
EMP: 45
SALES (est): 25MM-49.9MM **Privately Held**
SIC: 5147 Wholesales meat & meat
products

(G-446)
H & G MARKETING INC
17217 198th Ave NW (55309-4684)
PO Box 408 (55309-0408)
PHONE..................................763 263-8998
Robert Giarusso, *President*
Mary Giarusso, *Treasurer*
EMP: 27 **EST:** 1978
SALES (est): 10MM-24.9MM **Privately Held**
SIC: 5091 Wholesales sporting &
recreational goods & supplies

(G-447)
HULL CO
19672 172nd St NW (55309-9201)
PHONE..................................763 262-4855
FAX: 763 262-4859
Steve Finlayson, *President*
Kevin Danielzuk, *General Mgr*
John Alstrup, *Vice Pres*
EMP: 25 **EST:** 1969
SQ FT: 20,000 **Privately Held**
SIC: 0723 5148 Potato curing services;
vegetable packing services; wholesales
fresh potatoes; wholesales fresh vegetables

(G-448)
J & J PACKING INC
19292 County Rd 43 S (55309)
PHONE..................................763 263-2296
FAX: 763 263-6482
James Sanford, *CEO*
Jeffery Sanford, *Treasurer*
EMP: 30 **EST:** 1985
SQ FT: 12,000 **Privately Held**
SIC: 0723 Vegetable crop market
preparation services

(G-449)
JOSUDA INC
Also Called: Shade Tree
575 Humboldt Dr (55309-9466)
PO Box 650 (55309-0650)
PHONE..................................763 263-0313
FAX: 763 263-0350
Bob Green, *Manager*
EMP: 30 **EST:** 1983
SQ FT: 14,810
SALES (est): 5MM-9.9MM **Privately Held**
SIC: 5091 Snowmobile dealer; wholesales
boat accessories & parts; retails all-terrain
vehicle parts & accessories

(G-450)
K&G ENTERPRISES INC
Also Called: Wacker Stucco
20033 176th St NW (55309-8017)
PO Box 117 (55309-0117)
PHONE..................................763 263-7997
FAX: 763 263-5102
Karl Efenzler, *President*
EMP: 40 **EST:** 2004
SALES (est): 10MM-24.9MM **Privately Held**
SIC: 5032 Wholesales stucco

(G-451)
MINNESOTA LIMITED INC
18640 200th St (55309)
PO Box 410 (55309-0410)
PHONE..................................763 428-4444
FAX: 763 428-8219
Reuben Leines, *President*
Joyce Leines, *Corp Secy*
Paulette Britzius, *Corp Secy*
Chris Leines, *Vice Pres*
Daniel Ruza, *Treasurer*
EMP: 71 **EST:** 1966
SQ FT: 10,000
SALES (est): 5MM-9.9MM **Privately Held**
WEB: www.mnlimited.com
SIC: 1623 Oil & gas pipeline construction

(G-452)
OPTIONS INC
16820 197th Ave NW (55309-4828)
PHONE..................................763 263-3684
FAX: 763 263-8110
Richard Simonson, *Exec Dir*
EMP: 60 **EST:** 1979
SQ FT: 17,000
SALES (est): 1MM-4.9MM **Privately Held**
SIC: 8331 Vocational rehabilitation agency;
vocational training agency

(G-453)
PARAGON STORE FIXTURES INC
20020 176th St NW (55309-8017)
PO Box 364 (55309-0364)
PHONE..................................763 263-0660
FAX: 763 263-0661
Jim Johnson, *President*
Jaci Miskowic, *Manager*
EMP: 44 **EST:** 1995
SALES (est): 1MM-4.9MM **Privately Held**
WEB: www.paragonstorefixtures.com
SIC: 5046 Manufactures wood
nonrefrigerated show & display cabinets;
wholesales store fixtures & display
equipment

(G-454)
REMMELE ENGINEERING INC
17465 198th Ave NW (55309-4685)
PHONE..................................763 263-3650
George Ronning, *Plant Mgr*
Jim Frazier, *Plant Mgr*
Steve Elleraaf, *QC Mgr*
Lee Tingelstad, *Manager*
Leo A Huht, *Manager*
EMP: 92
SALES (est): 10MM-24.9MM **Privately Held**
WEB: www.remmeleautomation.com
SIC: 7692 Manufactures custom machinery;
welding service
HQ: Remmele Engineering Inc
10 Old Highway 8 SW
Saint Paul MN 55112
651 635-4100

(G-455)
SHERBURNE COUNTY RURAL
440 Eagle Lake Rd N (55309-9027)
PO Box 310 (55309-0310)
PHONE..................................763 262-4100
FAX: 763 263-7711
Robert K Eddy, *President*
Donna Eddy, *Corp Secy*
Karlen Fowler, *Corp Secy*
Paavo Pyykkonen, *Senior VP*
William Glaeser, *Vice Pres*
EMP: 50 **EST:** 1905
SQ FT: 21,950 **Publicly Held**
WEB: www.scripophily.net
SIC: 4813 Local telephone communications
services
DH: Sherburne Tele Systems Inc
440 Eagle Lake Rd N
Big Lake MN 55309
763 262-4100

(G-456)
SHERBURNE TELE SYSTEMS INC (DH)
440 Eagle Lake Rd N (55309-9027)
PHONE..................................763 262-4100
FAX: 763 262-7711
Robert K Eddy, *President*
Elaine Bergquis, *Mktg Dir*
Elaine Bergquist, *Marketing Mgr*
Chuck Balk, *Manager*
Jerry Keeton, *Supervisor*
EMP: 45 **EST:** 1902
SQ FT: 21,950
SALES (corp-wide): 2.99B **Publicly Held**
WEB: www.connections-etc.com
SIC: 4813 Local telephone communications
services
HQ: Iowa Telecommunications Svcs
403 W 4th St N Ste 1
Newton IA 50208
641 787-2000

(G-457)
ST COTTER TURBINE SERVICES INC
16804 170th St SE (55309-4606)
PHONE..................................763 263-5611
Nichole Cotter, *President*
Shawn Cotter, *Vice Pres*
Jenifer Anderson, *CFO*
EMP: 150 **EST:** 2007
SALES (est): 10MM-24.9MM **Privately Held**
SIC: 7629 High voltage electrical equipment
repair service

(G-458)
SUPERIOR FIRE PROTECTION INC
11560 185th Ave SE (55309-8931)
PHONE..................................763 263-1929
Greg Miller, *President*
EMP: 35
SQ FT: 5,000
SALES (est): 1MM-4.9MM **Privately Held**
SIC: 1711 1731 Fire sprinkler system
installation service; fire detection & burglar
alarm systems specialization contractor

(G-459)
WHIRL-AIR-FLOW CORP
20055 177th St NW (55309-8015)
PHONE..................................763 262-1200
FAX: 763 262-1212
Edward Mueller, *President*
Gregg Hedtke, *Vice Pres*
Patricia Hedtke, *Vice Pres*
Ken Hanley, *Mfg Staff*
Richard Fucault, *Sales Mgr*
EMP: 35 **EST:** 1946
SQ FT: 50,000
SALES (est): 5MM-9.9MM **Privately Held**
WEB: www.whirlair.com
SIC: 7692 Manufactures pneumatic tube
conveyor systems; manufactures general
industrial use belt conveyor systems;
machine shop, jobbing & repair services;
metal heat treating services; welding service

BIGFORK
Itasca County

(G-460)
COOK AREA HEALTH SERVICES INC
Also Called: Scenic Rivers Health Services
135 Pine Tree Dr (56628)
PO Box 135 (56628-0135)
PHONE..................................218 743-3232
FAX: 218 743-4223
Carmen Magnus, *Office Mgr*
Jeff E Scrivner, *Director*
George E Rounds, *Director*
Denyse Trebs, *Nurse Practr*
Linda Jacobson, *Receptionist Se*
EMP: 25
SALES (est): 1MM-4.9MM **Privately Held**
SIC: 8011 General & family practice
physician or surgeon office
PA: Cook Area Health Services Inc
20 5th St SE
Cook MN 55723
218 666-5941

(G-461)
NORTHERN ITASCA HOSPITAL DIST (PA)
258 Pinetree Dr (56628)
PO Box 258 (56628-0258)
PHONE..................................218 743-3177
FAX: 218 743-4161
H D Odegaard, *CEO*
Meryl Ostendorf, *QA Dir*
Bill Loosbrock, *Engineer*
Barb Rahier, *Finance Mgr*
Sandra L Blanc-Boland, *Human Res Dir*
EMP: 180 **EST:** 1938
SQ FT: 46,000
SALES (corp-wide): 16.18M **Privately Held**
SIC: 8062 6513 8051 Medical hospital;
apartment building operator; skilled nursing
care facility

(G-462)
NORTHERN ITASCA HOSPITAL DIST
Also Called: Bigfork Valley Communities
258 Pine Tree Dr (56628)
PHONE..................................218 743-3177
Laurence Swanlund, *Chf Purch Ofc*
Sandra L Blanc, *Human Res Dir*
EMP: 80
SALES (est): 1MM-4.9MM **Privately Held**
SIC: 8059 Nursing home
PA: Northern Itasca Hospital Dist
258 Pinetree Dr
Bigfork MN 56628
218 743-3177

(G-463)
REGENTS OF THE UNIVERSITY OF
Also Called: Research Lab
1 Gayley Ave (56628)
PO Box 188, Coleraine (55722-0188)
PHONE...................................218 245-2200
Rodney L Bleifuss, *Branch Mgr*
EMP: 25 **Privately Held**
WEB: www.umn.edu
SIC: 8731 Commercial physical research services; university
PA: Regents of The University of
106 Pleasant St SE # 210
Minneapolis MN 55455
612 625-5000

(G-464)
SWAMPSIDERS SNOWMOBILE CLUB
29730 County Road 52 (56628-4624)
PHONE...................................218 245-3222
Myrta Venkner, *President*
Jim Cox, *Vice Pres*
EMP: 130 **EST:** 1978
SALES (est): 1MM-4.9MM **Privately Held**
SIC: 7997 Membership recreation club

(G-465)
TENSON CONSTRUCTION INC
39036 County Road 225 (56628-4648)
PHONE...................................218 743-3874
FAX: 218 743-6048
Mike Gilbertson, *President*
Steve Tendrop, *Corp Secy*
Albert Tendrup, *Director*
EMP: 30 **EST:** 1990
SALES (est): 1MM-4.9MM **Privately Held**
SIC: 1611 Heavy highway & street construction; highway & street maintenance service

BINGHAM LAKE
Cottonwood County

(G-466)
COUNTRY PRIDE SERVICES CO-OP (PA)
144 9th St (56118-9601)
PHONE...................................507 831-2580
FAX: 507 831-3651
Ray Elston, *President*
Kevin Jackson, *General Mgr*
Curt Wall, *General Mgr*
Sue Horn, *Manager*
Tammy Fast, *Director*
EMP: 25 **EST:** 1937
SQ FT: 7,500
SALES (corp-wide): 30.61M **Privately Held**
SIC: 5191 5171 Wholesales agricultural chemicals; wholesales agricultural fertilizer; wholesales petroleum bulk stations; manufactures fertilizers; gas station

(G-467)
MILLER SELLNER EQUIPMENT INC
495 2nd Ave (56118-9640)
PHONE...................................507 831-1106
FAX: 507 831-1044
Doug Miller, *President*
Mark Miller, *President*
Gerald Sellner, *Vice Pres*
EMP: 45 **EST:** 1997
SQ FT: 4,500
SALES (est): 10MM-24.9MM **Privately Held**
WEB: www.millersellner.com
SIC: 5083 Wholesales farm implements; snowmobile dealer; retails lawnmowers & tractors
PA: Miller Sellner Implement Inc
22024 State Highway 4
Sleepy Eye MN 56085
507 794-2131

BIRD ISLAND
Renville County

(G-468)
RURAL COMPUTER CONSULTANTS INC
104 Main St (55310-1233)
PO Box 197 (55310-0197)
PHONE...................................320 365-4027
FAX: 320 365-4435
Brian Sheehan, *President*
Susan Peterson, *Corp Secy*
Kevin Sheehan, *Vice Pres*
EMP: 35 **EST:** 1979
SQ FT: 6,000
SALES (est): 25MM-49.9MM **Privately Held**
WEB: www.rccbi.com
SIC: 5045 7371 7372 Wholesales computers; computer programming service; software publisher

(G-469)
TIM ORTH MEMORIAL FOUNDATION
80850 400th St (55310-2090)
PHONE...................................320 365-4419
Bill Neubauer, *President*
Nancy Rosol, *Corp Secy*
Jeanelle Neubauer, *Vice Pres*
EMP: 30 **EST:** 1995
SALES (est): 1MM-4.9MM **Privately Held**
WEB: www.timorthfoundation.org
SIC: 8099 Medical services organization

BIWABIK
Saint Louis County

(G-470)
LODGE AT GIANTS RIDGE
6373 Wynne Creek Dr (55708)
PO Box 590 (55708-0590)
PHONE...................................218 865-7170
FAX: 218 865-7135
Jim Loch, *President*
Zac Swarthout, *General Mgr*
Jonanthan Plese, *Accountant*
Gregg Klohn, *Manager*
EMP: 83 **EST:** 1999
SQ FT: 80,000
SALES (est): 1MM-4.9MM **Privately Held**
WEB: www.lodgeatgiantsridge.com
SIC: 7011 Motel

(G-471)
QUARRY AT GIANTS RIDGE
5832 Giants Ridge Rd (55708)
PO Box 190 (55708-0190)
PHONE...................................218 865-3092
FAX: 218 865-4733
Jared Finch, *Superintendent*
EMP: 40 **EST:** 2005
SALES (est): 1MM-4.9MM **Privately Held**
SIC: 7992 Public golf course

(G-472)
VILLA
Also Called: Villsaat The Giants Ridge
6266 Giants Ridge Rd (55708)
PO Box 350 (55708-0350)
PHONE...................................218 865-4155
Michelle Cramer, *General Mgr*
EMP: 35 **EST:** 2002
SALES (est): 1MM-4.9MM **Privately Held**
WEB: www.thevilla.com
SIC: 7011 Resort hotel

BLACKDUCK
Beltrami County

(G-473)
CITY OF BLACKDUCK
8 Summit Ave E (56630)
PHONE...................................218 835-4803
Scott Palmer, *Mayor*
EMP: 35 **EST:** 1901 **Privately Held**
WEB: www.blackduckmn.com
SIC: 8611 City & town managers' office; local government executive offices; business association

(G-474)
EVANGELICAL LUTHERAN GOOD
Also Called: Northern Pnes Good Smritan Ctr
172 Summit Ave W (56630-2140)
PHONE...................................218 835-4218
FAX: 218 836-6737
Becky Nestberg, *Bookkeeper*
Maryann Hanson, *Administrator*
EMP: 63
SALES (est): 1MM-4.9MM **Privately Held**
WEB: www.good-sam.com
SIC: 8051 Skilled nursing care facility
PA: Evangelical Lutheran Good
4800 W 57th St
Sioux Falls SD 57108
605 362-3100

BLOMKEST
Kandiyohi County

(G-475)
GORANS BROTHERS INC
14277 15th St SE (56216-9620)
PHONE...................................320 995-6564
FAX: 320 995-6565
Kim Gorans, *President*
Peter Swenson, *Corp Secy*
Douglas Gorans, *Vice Pres*
EMP: 45 **EST:** 1944
SQ FT: 150,000 **Privately Held**
WEB: www.goransbrothers.com
SIC: 0253 0115 0116 Turkey farm; corn farm; soybean farm

BLOOMING PRAIRIE
Steele County

(G-476)
ARKEMA INC
157 Hwy Ave N (55917)
PO Box 188 (55917-0188)
PHONE...................................507 583-6641
FAX: 507 854-0669
Anthony D Cristofaro, *Plant Engr*
Rodney Earlywine, *Branch Mgr*
Ricky Soto, *Manager*
EMP: 50
SALES (est): 25MM-49.9MM **Privately Held**
WEB: www.arkema-inc.com
SIC: 5169 Wholesales food additives & preservatives
HQ: Arkema Inc
2000 Market St Ste 2200
Philadelphia PA 19103
215 419-7000

(G-477)
PRAIRIE MANOR NURSING HOME
220 3rd St NW (55917-1121)
PHONE...................................507 583-4434
FAX: 507 583-2401
Deb Brown, *Manager*
Mark Robinson, *Administrator*
EMP: 115 **EST:** 1966
SQ FT: 21,523
SALES (est): 1MM-4.9MM **Privately Held**
WEB: www.prairiemanorinc.com
SIC: 8051 Skilled nursing care facility

(G-478)
SPRAY CONTROL SYSTEMS INC
500 Minimizer Way (55917-1436)
PHONE...................................507 583-2112
FAX: 507 583-7540
Craig Kruckeberg, *President*
Lorraine Kruckeberg, *Corp Secy*
Dick L Kruckeberg, *CFO*
EMP: 32 **EST:** 1986
SQ FT: 45,000
SALES (est): 25MM-49.9MM **Privately Held**
WEB: www.minimizer.com
SIC: 5162 Wholesales plastics products

(G-479)
TANDEM PRODUCTS INC
520 Industrial Dr (55917)
PO Box 157 (55917-0157)
PHONE...................................507 583-7222
FAX: 507 583-2231
Nash Helmy, *Vice Pres*
Jim Foster, *Purchasing*
Nagy Helmy, *Manager*
EMP: 60
SALES (est): 10MM-24.9MM **Privately Held**
SIC: 5083 Manufactures farm fertilizing machinery; manufactures cattle feeding, handling & watering equipment; manufactures hog feeding, handling & watering equipment; wholesales livestock equipment
PA: Tandem Products Inc
3444 Dight Ave
Minneapolis MN 55406
612 721-2911

BLOOMINGTON
Hennepin County

(G-480)
A G EDWARDS & SONS INC
8500 Normandale Lake Blvd (55437-3813)
PHONE...................................952 832-1600
FAX: 952 832-5088
Denise Olson, *Manager*
EMP: 62
SALES (est): 10MM-24.9MM **Publicly Held**
WEB: www.agedwards.com
SIC: 6211 7389 Stock broker & dealer service; brokers' service
HQ: A G Edwards & Sons Inc
1 N Jefferson Ave
Saint Louis MO 63103
314 955-3000

(G-481)
ACUO TECHNOLOGIES LLC
8009 34th Ave S Ste 900 (55425-1789)
PHONE...................................952 905-3440
Gerald M Fitterer, *Member*
James Jundt, *Member*
Michael Simon, *Vice Pres*
Mike Dolan, *VP Sales*
Jeff Timbrook, *Mng Member*
EMP: 50 **EST:** 2000
SQ FT: 7,800
SALES (est): 5MM-9.9MM **Privately Held**
WEB: www.acuotech.com
SIC: 7371 Computer software development

(G-482)
ADVANCED COMMUNICATION DESIGN
Also Called: A C D
7901 12th Ave S (55425-1017)
PHONE...................................952 854-4000
FAX: 952 854-5774
Marco Scibora, *President*
Fran Scibora, *COO*
Don Steinis, *COO*
Jay Stone, *IT/INT Sup*
Richard Grossman, *Director*
EMP: 30 **EST:** 1986
SQ FT: 13,000
SALES (est): 1MM-4.9MM **Privately Held**
WEB: www.acdstar.com
SIC: 7373 Computer integrated systems design services; manufactures test equipment for electronic & electric measurement; retails telephone equipment & systems; manufactures telecommunication systems & equipment

(G-483)
AMERICAN HEARING SYSTEMS INC
8001 E Bloomington Fwy (55420-1036)
PHONE...................................763 404-1122
Carsten Buhl, *President*
Jim Hammerstedt, *VP Opers-Prdtn-*
Rich Grose, *Controller*
Deneen Flanary, *Finance Mgr*
Lisa Rose, *Human Res Mgr*
EMP: 130 **EST:** 2001
SALES (est): 50MM-99.9MM **Privately Held**
WEB: www.interton-usa.com

GEOGRAPHIC

SIC: **5047** Wholesales hearing aids; manufactures surgical appliances & supplies

(G-484)
AMERICAN MULTI-CINEMA INC
Also Called: AMC
402 S Avenue (55425-5528)
PHONE....................................952 851-0073
FAX: 952 851-0840
Jeff Wittig, *General Mgr*
EMP: 50
SALES (est): 1MM-4.9MM **Privately Held**
WEB: www.amctheatres.com
SIC: **7832** Indoor movie theater
DH: American Multi-Cinema Inc
    920 Main St Fl 14
    Kansas City MO 64105
    816 221-4000

(G-485)
AMI IMAGING SYSTEMS INC
7815 Telegraph Rd (55438-1133)
PHONE....................................952 828-0080
FAX: 952 828-1976
Susan K Olson, *President*
Ronald J Olson, *Vice Pres*
Jane Carlson, *Controller*
Gregory Runyan, *Technology Dir*
Urvish Trivedi, *IT/INT Sup*
EMP: 45 EST: 1982
SQ FT: 17,000
SALES (est): 10MM-24.9MM **Privately Held**
WEB: www.ami-imaging.com
SIC: **5044** 7374 Wholesales office equipment; wholesales microfilm equipment; optical scanning services

(G-486)
ANIXTER INC
8111 Lyndale Ave S (55420-1136)
PHONE....................................952 887-8191
EMP: 25
SALES (est): 10MM-24.9MM **Publicly Held**
WEB: www.anixter.com
SIC: **5063** Wholesales electrical apparatus & equipment; wholesales wire & cable; wholesales control & signal wire & cable, including coaxial
HQ: Anixter Inc
    2301 Patriot Blvd
    Glenview IL 60026
    224 521-8000

(G-487)
ASHFORD TRS NICKEL, LP
Also Called: Hilton Minneapolis St Paul
3800 American Blvd E (55425-1658)
PHONE....................................952 854-2100
FAX: 952 854-8002
Charles Goldberg, *General Mgr*
Dean Olveson, *Controller*
Vishwa Ural, *Credit Mgr*
Nancy Montgomery, *Human Res Dir*
Shawn Anderson, *Sales Staff*
EMP: 99
SALES (est): 5MM-9.9MM **Privately Held**
SIC: **7011** Hotel

(G-488)
ASML US INC
8054 26th Ave S (55425-1302)
PHONE....................................952 876-0713
FAX: 952 876-0728
Rob Whiteford, *Manager*
EMP: 34
SALES (est): 25MM-49.9MM **Publicly Held**
WEB: www.asml.com
SIC: **5065** Wholesales electronic parts & equipment
PA: ASML US Inc
    8555 S River Pkwy
    Tempe AZ 85284
    480 383-4422

(G-489)
AVNET INC
2740 Amercn Blvd W Ste 150
(55431-1267)
PHONE....................................952 346-3000
John Hunter, *District Mgr*
Kevin Gorham, *Human Resources*
Heywood Jublome, *Sales Mgr*
Jeff Varela, *Manager*
EMP: 26

SALES (est): 10MM-24.9MM **Publicly Held**
WEB: www.avnet.com
SIC: **5065** Wholesales electronic parts & equipment
PA: Avnet Inc
    2211 S 47th St
    Phoenix AZ 85034
    480 643-2000

(G-490)
BLUE GREEN VACATION CORP
Also Called: Bluegreen Preview Center
1701 E 79th St Ste 19 (55425-1401)
PHONE....................................888 456-0412
Mike Webb, *Manager*
Steven Kimbrough, *Manager*
Katricia Pacal, *Telecom Exec*
EMP: 50 EST: 2005
SALES (est): 1MM-4.9MM **Privately Held**
SIC: **4724** Tourist agency arranging transport, lodging & car rental

(G-491)
CANAM THEATRES MOA LLC ✪
Also Called: Theatres At Mall of America
60 E Broadway (55425-5510)
PHONE....................................952 883-8810
Robert Larson, *Member*
Russell Jonas, *Member*
Maureen Bausch, *Member*
Althea Jenkins, *Accounts Mgr*
David Haselman, *Mng Member*
EMP: 30 EST: 2008
SALES (est): 1MM-4.9MM **Privately Held**
SIC: **7832** Indoor movie theater

(G-492)
CP SADDLE BROOK LLC
Also Called: Marriott
2020 American Blvd E (55425-1239)
PHONE....................................952 854-7441
FAX: 952 854-7671
Tod Oswold, *General Mgr*
William Hoffman, *General Mgr*
Steve Frean, *Engineering*
Shirley Gunstrom, *Controller*
Bethann Wiberg, *Marketing Staff*
EMP: 150
SALES (est): 5MM-9.9MM **Privately Held**
SIC: **7011** Traveler accommodations; cocktail lounge; full service chain family restaurant; retail gift shop
PA: CP Saddle Brook LLC
    138 Pehle Ave
    Saddle Brook NJ 07663
    201 843-9500

(G-493)
CROSS TELECOM CORP
10900 Nesbitt Ave S (55437-3124)
PHONE....................................952 983-3500
FAX: 952 831-4421
Robert Coughlin, *President*
Jennifer Coughlin, *Corp Secy*
Doug Johnson, *Regional VP*
Doug Lang, *Vice Pres*
Brian Curtis, *Project Mgr*
EMP: 68 EST: 1996
SQ FT: 85,000
SALES (est): 50MM-99.9MM **Privately Held**
SIC: **5065** Wholesales electrical telephone & telegraphic equipment; wholesales communications equipment

(G-494)
DUN & BRADSTREET INC
3600 Amercn Blvd W Fl 6 (55431-1069)
PHONE....................................952 841-9961
Dan Millis, *Branch Mgr*
EMP: 26
SALES (est): 1MM-4.9MM **Publicly Held**
WEB: www.dnb.com
SIC: **7323** Commercial credit reporting bureau
HQ: Dun & Bradstreet Inc
    103 J F K Pkwy
    Short Hills NJ 07078
    973 921-5500

(G-495)
ECOLOGIC ANALYTICS LLC
8011 34th Ave S Ste 205 (55425-1631)
PHONE....................................952 843-6000
Gary Lutz, *Member*
Ani Gupta, *Member*

Craig Mataczynski, *Member*
Darren Varney, *Member*
Kristine Beck, *COO*
EMP: 47 EST: 2000
SQ FT: 5,900
SALES (est): 10MM-24.9MM **Privately Held**
SIC: **7372** Application software publishing; business & professional software publishers

(G-496)
ECUMEN HOME CARE INC
Also Called: Martin Luther Manor
1401 E 100th St (55425-2615)
PHONE....................................952 888-7751
Dave Shaw, *Manager*
EMP: 280
SALES (est): 10MM-24.9MM **Privately Held**
WEB: www.augustanahomes.org
SIC: **8051** Skilled nursing care facility
PA: Ecumen
    3530 Lexington Ave N
    Saint Paul MN 55126
    651 766-4300

(G-497)
FIDELITY BUILDING SERVICES INC
951 American Blvd E (55420-1331)
PHONE....................................952 854-1447
FAX: 952 854-3635
David A Kramer, *President*
Matt Piioia, *Director*
Lisa Gleason, *Director*
EMP: 270 EST: 1983
SQ FT: 6,500
SALES (est): 5MM-9.9MM **Privately Held**
WEB: www.fidelityservices.com
SIC: **7349** Building & office cleaning service

(G-498)
FOUR51 INC
8300 Norman Center Dr (55437-1027)
PHONE....................................952 294-0451
Mark Johnson, *CEO*
Jon D Wylie, *Vice Pres*
EMP: 35 EST: 1999
SQ FT: 16,000
SALES (est): 5MM-9.9MM **Privately Held**
SIC: **7372** Business & professional software publishers

(G-499)
HEALTH FITNESS CORP   (HQ)
1650 W 82nd St Ste 1100 (55431-1475)
PHONE....................................952 831-6830
FAX: 952 897-5173
Gregg O Lehman PhD, *President*
John E Griffin, *COO*
Brian Gagne, *Senior VP*
J M McConnell, *Senior VP*
David T Hurt, *Vice Pres*
EMP: 40 EST: 1981
SQ FT: 28,000 **Privately Held**
WEB: www.hfitcenter.com
SIC: **7991** 8099 Physical fitness center; health screening services
PA: Trustmark Mutual Holding Co
    400 N Field Dr
    Lake Forest IL 60045
    847 615-1300

(G-500)
HEALTHPARTNERS INC   (PA)
8170 33rd Ave S (55425-4516)
PO Box 1309, Minneapolis (55440-1309)
PHONE....................................952 883-6000
FAX: 952 883-5380
Mary Brainerd, *President*
Ann Gjelten, *President*
Bradley E Cooper, *Managing Prtnr*
Margaret A Lund, *Vice Chairman*
Craig Amundson DDS, *COO*
EMP: 1000 EST: 1984
SQ FT: 280,000
SALES (corp-wide): 3.38B **Privately Held**
WEB: www.healthpartners.com
SIC: **6324** 8011 Health insurance maintenance organization; physicians' office & clinic

(G-501)
HGIB LLC
5140 American Blvd W (55437-1235)
PHONE....................................952 831-1012
FAX: 952 831-0738
Dave Brott, *General Mgr*

Sheryl D Walton, *Senior VP*
Thomas R Torgerson, *Mng Member*
EMP: 35
SALES (est): 1MM-4.9MM **Privately Held**
WEB: www.torgersonproperties.com
SIC: **7011** Traveler accommodations
PA: Torgerson Properties Inc
    103 15th Ave NW Ste 200
    Willmar MN 56201
    320 235-7207

(G-502)
KNIGHTS OF COLUMBUS
1114 79th St W (55420-1023)
PHONE....................................952 888-1492
FAX: 952 888-8974
Jim Rasmussen, *General Mgr*
Patrick Monahan, *General Mgr*
Cynthia Lambert, *Manager*
Darcy Lacquay, *Manager*
EMP: 35 **Privately Held**
WEB: www.kofc.org
SIC: **8641** Civic & social organization
PA: Knights of Columbus
    1 Columbus Plz Ste 1700
    New Haven CT 06510
    203 752-4000

(G-503)
LEINVESTORS INC
7800 Metro Pkwy Ste 300 (55425-1509)
PHONE....................................952 854-1114
Jim Halverson, *President*
Judy Magy, *Executive Asst*
EMP: 45
SQ FT: 4,500
SALES (est): 5MM-9.9MM **Privately Held**
SIC: **6531** Real estate services

(G-504)
MARCUS BLOOMINGTON LLC
Also Called: Hilton Minneapolis Bloomington
3900 American Blvd W (55437-1117)
PHONE....................................952 893-9500
Douglas A Neis, *Member*
Thomas F Kissinger, *Member*
Jim Waldvogel, *Manager*
EMP: 180 EST: 2006
SALES (est): 10MM-24.9MM **Privately Held**
WEB: www.marcushotels.com
SIC: **8741** Hotel or motel management services

(G-505)
MIDWEST HERITAGE INN OF
2401 American Blvd E (55425-1317)
PHONE....................................952 858-8475
FAX: 952 858-8475
Gary D Tharaldson, *President*
Duane Palmer, *General Mgr*
EMP: 220 EST: 1995
SALES (est): 10MM-24.9MM **Privately Held**
SIC: **7011** Traveler accommodations

(G-506)
MINNESOTA VALLEY COUNTRY CLUB
6300 Auto Club Rd (55438-2406)
PHONE....................................612 884-2409
Linda Modlinski, *President*
Craig Rollingson, *Manager*
Craig Rollianson, *Manager*
Ron Mehrman, *Manager*
Steve Gillis, *Manager*
EMP: 60 EST: 1924
SQ FT: 33,000
SALES (est): 1MM-4.9MM **Privately Held**
WEB: www.mvccgolf.com
SIC: **7997** Country club

(G-507)
MOAC MALL HOLDINGS LLC
Also Called: Mall of America
60 E Broadway (55425-5510)
PHONE....................................952 883-8810
Bob Larson, *Member*
Russell Jonas, *Member*
Maureen Bausch, *Member*
David Haselman, *Member*
Althea Jenkins, *Accounting Mgr*
EMP: 600 EST: 1992
SQ FT: 2,790,300
SALES (est): 100MM-499.9MM **Privately Held**
SIC: **6512** Shopping center & mall operator

(G-508)

OSBORNE PROPERTIES LP
4210 W Old Shakopee Rd (55437-2951)
PHONE............................952 881-8166
Rosemary A Manthe, *Corp Secy*
EMP: 30
SALES (est): 5MM-9.9MM **Privately Held**
SIC: 6512 Nonresidential building operator
PA: Osborne Properties LP
420 Gateway Blvd
Burnsville MN 55337
952 707-8200

(G-509)

OWENS CO'S INC
930 E 80th St (55420-1322)
PHONE............................952 854-3800
John J Owens, *President*
EMP: 80 **EST:** 1957
SQ FT: 20,000
SALES (est): 5MM-9.9MM **Privately Held**
WEB: www.owensco.com
SIC: 1711 8711 Heating & air conditioning
contractor; heating & ventilation engineers
PA: Owens Technology Co's Inc
930 E 80th St
Bloomington MN 55420
952 854-3800

(G-510)

PLATO LEARNING INC
10801 Nesbitt Ave S (55437-3109)
PHONE............................952 832-1000
Vincent Riera, *President*
Tom Colling, *General Mgr*
Gloria Karels, *Business Mgr*
Mark Allen, *Vice Pres*
Michael Silverglate, *Project Mgr*
EMP: 170 **EST:** 1989
SALES (est): 25MM-49.9MM **Privately Held**
SIC: 7372 Educational software publishers

(G-511)

PRAGMATEK CONSULTING GROUP LTD
8500 Normandale Lake Blvd (55437-3813)
PHONE............................612 333-3164
Steven B Bloom, *Ch of Bd*
Jeff Larson, *Senior VP*
Jay Nelson, *Senior VP*
Myron Goeser, *Vice Pres*
Jeff Etten, *CFO*
EMP: 77 **EST:** 1989
SQ FT: 10,000
SALES (est): 10MM-24.9MM **Privately Held**
WEB: www.pragmatek.com
SIC: 8742 Management consulting services

(G-512)

SANFORD HOSPITALITY LLC
Also Called: Ramada Mall of America
2300 American Blvd E (55425-1220)
PHONE............................952 854-3411
Jim Soccman, *General Mgr*
Vit Kotrapu, *Member*
Kevin Sawatsky, *Member*
EST: 2001
SQ FT: 150,000 **Privately Held**
SIC: 7011 Hotel

(G-513)

SCHWAN'S CONSUMER BRANDS NORTH (HQ)
8500 Normandale Lake Blvd (55437-3813)
PHONE............................952 832-4300
Mark Dalrymple, *President*
Mark Simonett, *Corp Secy*
Mark Jansen, *Vice Pres*
John Maness, *Vice Pres*
Thomas M Neizke, *CFO*
EMP: 120 **EST:** 2002 **Privately Held**
WEB: www.theschwanfoodcompany.com
SIC: 5142 Wholesales packaged frozen
foods
PA: Schwan Food Co
115 W College Dr
Marshall MN 56258
507 532-3274

(G-514)

SFM MUTUAL INSURANCE CO (PA)
3500 Amercn Blvd W # 700 (55431-4439)
PO Box 582992, Minneapolis
(55458-2992)
PHONE............................952 838-4200
Robert T Lund, *President*
Scott Brener, *Vice Pres*
David Kaiser, *Vice Pres*
Michael Happe, *Vice Pres*
Diana Friede, *Vice Pres*
EMP: 170 **EST:** 1983
SQ FT: 50,000
SALES (corp-wide): 94.55M **Privately Held**
WEB: www.sfmic.com
SIC: 6331 Worker's compensation
insurance carrier

(G-515)

SHOPJIMMYCOM LLC
9701 Penn Ave S Ste 105 (55431-2544)
PHONE............................952 881-6492
FAX: 952 888-6039
Jim Vosika, *Member*
Adam Nyenhuis, *Sales Mgr*
EMP: 46 **EST:** 2007
SALES (est): 25MM-49.9MM **Privately Held**
SIC: 5065 Wholesales electronic parts

(G-516)

SIERRA BRAVO CORP
9555 James Ave S Ste 245 (55431-2547)
PHONE............................952 948-1211
FAX: 952 948-1611
Luke Bucklin, *President*
Mike Schmidt, *Vice Pres*
Mike Derheim, *Vice Pres*
Jeff Meyers, *VP Eng R&D*
Bill Brakeman, *Bus Dvlpt Dir*
EMP: 105 **EST:** 2003
SQ FT: 16,800
SALES (est): 10MM-24.9MM **Privately Held**
WEB: www.sierra-bravo.com
SIC: 7371 Computer software development

(G-517)

SOUTH SIDE ELECTRIC INC
9201 E Bloomington Fwy Ste X
(55420-3413)
PHONE............................952 888-5500
FAX: 952 888-1415
David Wintheiser, *President*
Mike Pfiffner, *Principal*
Patricia V Kuiken, *Corp Secy*
Allen Johnson, *Vice Pres*
Harlan Madsen, *Treasurer*
EMP: 70 **EST:** 1968
SQ FT: 4,000
SALES (est): 5MM-9.9MM **Privately Held**
SIC: 1731 General electrical contractor

(G-518)

SSB LLC
Also Called: Staybridge Suites
5150 American Blvd W (55437-1235)
PHONE............................952 831-7900
FAX: 952 831-7999
Jason Hall, *General Mgr*
Sheryl D Walton, *Senior VP*
EMP: 35
SALES (est): 1MM-4.9MM **Privately Held**
WEB: www.torgersonproperties.com
SIC: 7011 Hotel
PA: Torgerson Properties Inc
103 15th Ave NW Ste 200
Willmar MN 56201
320 235-7207

(G-519)

TORO CO (PA)
8111 Lyndale Ave S (55420-1136)
PHONE............................952 888-8801
FAX: 952 887-8258
Michael J Hoffman, *President*
Mark Stinson, *General Mgr*
Richard W Rodier, *General Mgr*
John Caron, *General Mgr*
Tom Evans, *General Mgr*
◆ **EMP:** 625 **EST:** 1914
SQ FT: 300,000
SALES (corp-wide): 1.52B **Publicly Held**
WEB: www.toro.com

SIC: 6153 Manufactures fertilizing,
spraying, dusting & irrigation machinery;
manufactures field sprinkler systems;
manufactures greens mowing equipment;
manufactures grounds mowing equipment;
manufactures commercial turf equipment

(G-520)

TRAVELSMART LLC
7800 Metro Pkwy Ste 300 (55425-1509)
PHONE............................952 854-1114
Jim Halverson, *Member*
EMP: 45
SALES (est): 5MM-9.9MM **Privately Held**
SIC: 8748 Business consulting services

(G-521)

TRI-CITY IV INC
Also Called: Woolleys Restaurant
8030 Cedar Ave S Ste 120 (55425-1214)
PHONE............................952 854-7405
Robert B Kinsella, *CEO*
EMP: 85
SALES (est): 5MM-9.9MM **Privately Held**
SIC: 8741 Restaurant management
services; hotel or motel management
services

(G-522)

U S BANK HOME MORTGAGE (HQ)
Also Called: US Bank
1550 Amrcn Blvd E Ste 880 (55425)
PHONE............................952 851-5494
John F Grundhofer, *Ch of Bd*
Robert Peifer, *Exec VP*
Janet Hanks, *Exec VP*
Rick Aneshansel, *CFO*
Tom Lyngholm, *Branch Mgr*
EST: 2000
SALES (corp-wide): 19.49B **Publicly Held**
WEB: www.usbank.com
SIC: 6162 Mortgage banking service
PA: U S Bancorp
800 Nicollet Mall Ste 800
Minneapolis MN 55402
651 466-3000

(G-523)

UNITED PROPERTIES INVESTMENT
1650 W 82nd St Ste 1500 (55431-1467)
PHONE............................952 893-8272
Frank Dutke, *Member*
Kim Wolff, *Corp Secy*
EMP: 45
SALES (est): 5MM-9.9MM **Privately Held**
SIC: 6513 Apartment building operator

(G-524)

VCA ANIMAL HOSPITALS INC
8830 Lyndale Ave S (55420-2740)
PHONE............................952 884-3228
Tomas W Fuller, *Vice Pres*
EMP: 40 **Privately Held**
SIC: 0742 Veterinary services

(G-525)

W2005 FARGO HOTELS REALTY, LP
1601 American Blvd E (55425-1145)
PHONE............................952 854-1687
FAX: 952 854-9604
Jamie Seaberg, *General Mgr*
Lawler Tony, *Manager*
EMP: 35
SALES (est): 1MM-4.9MM **Privately Held**
SIC: 7011 Traveler accommodations

(G-526)

WINGS FINANCIAL CREDIT UNION
8101 34th Ave S Ste 100 (55425-1606)
PHONE............................612 726-2073
Matthew Nelson, *Vice Pres*
Marilyn Kaschner, *VP Human Res*
Paul Parrish, *Branch Mgr*
David Toll, *Manager*
Steve Ness, *Manager*
EMP: 26
SALES (est): 1MM-4.9MM **Privately Held**

SIC: 6061 Federally chartered credit union
PA: Wings Financial Credit Union
14985 Glazier Ave Ste 100
Saint Paul MN 55124
952 997-8000

(G-527)

WSI - RWP LLC ✪
Also Called: Radisson Hotel Bloomington
1700 American Blvd E (55425-1216)
PHONE............................901 821-4117
Larry Mills, *Member*
EMP: 99 **EST:** 2010
SALES (est): 5MM-9.9MM **Privately Held**
SIC: 7011 Traveler accommodations

BLUE EARTH
Faribault County

(G-528)

AGSTAR FINANCIAL SERVICES, ACA
1700 Giant Dr (56013)
PHONE............................507 526-7366
FAX: 507 526-2928
Mary Irvine, *Manager*
EMP: 28
SALES (est): 10MM-24.9MM **Privately Held**
WEB: www.agstar.com
SIC: 6111 6159 Federal land credit bank;
agricultural credit institution
PA: Agstar Financial Services, Aca
1921 Premier Dr
Mankato MN 56001
507 387-4174

(G-529)

BEVCOMM INC
123 W 7th St (56013-1309)
PHONE............................507 526-3252
William Eckles, *President*
Neil Eckles, *Chairman*
Rob Hammond, *COO*
Amy Steckelberg, *Office Mgr*
Shane Becker, *Sr Ntwrk Engine*
EMP: 30 **EST:** 2000
SQ FT: 21,000 **Privately Held**
WEB: www.bevcomm.net
SIC: 4813 Wired telecommunications carrier
& service

(G-530)

BLUE EARTH AREA MENTORS
216 E 11th St (56013-2146)
PO Box 213 (56013-0213)
PHONE............................507 526-5219
FAX: 507 526-5219
Joel Deneui, *President*
Mary Lucas, *Manager*
EMP: 42 **EST:** 2001 **Privately Held**
SIC: 8699 Charitable organization

(G-531)

CENTRAL MINNESOTA MUNICIPAL (PA)
Also Called: C M M
459 S Grove St (56013-2629)
PHONE............................507 526-2193
Tessa Anderson, *Manager*
Donald Kom, *Exec Dir*
Steve Thomson, *Director*
Colleen Knudtson, *Admin Asst*
EST: 1987
SALES (corp-wide): 4.28M **Privately Held**
SIC: 8611 4911 Public utility association;
provides electric power broker services

(G-532)

CITY OF BLUE EARTH
Also Called: Swimming Pool
114 W 14th St Apt 111 (56013-1618)
PHONE............................507 526-2715
Michelle Hall, *Manager*
EMP: 28
SALES (est): 500-999K **Privately Held**
WEB: www.belw.org
SIC: 7997 Membership recreation club;
mayors' office
PA: City of Blue Earth
125 W 6th St
Blue Earth MN 56013
507 526-7336

GEOGRAPHIC (side tab)

(G-533)
DARLING INTERNATIONAL INC
9000 382nd Ave (56013-5805)
PHONE....................507 526-3296
Mark Zojonc, *General Mgr*
Mark Zojo, *General Mgr*
Bob Benjamin, *Manager*
EMP: 53
SALES (est): 10MM-24.9MM **Publicly Held**
WEB: www.darlingii.com
SIC: 5159 Manufactures rendered inedible grease; manufactures animal feed; manufactures inedible feather meal; manufactures inedible meat meal & tankage; wholesales hides
PA: Darling International Inc
251 Oconnor Ridge Blvd S
Irving TX 75038
972 717-0300

(G-534)
ECKLES TELEPHONE CO INC
123 W 7th St (56013-1309)
PHONE....................507 526-3252
FAX: 507 526-4963
Neil Eckles, *Ch of Bd*
Bill Eckles, *President*
Jake Anderson, *Business Mgr*
Gail Eckles, *Corp Secy*
Susan Eckles, *Vice Pres*
EMP: 50 **EST:** 1940
SQ FT: 15,000 **Privately Held**
WEB: www.bevcomm.com
SIC: 4813 Local telephone communications services

(G-535)
FNB BANK OF BLUE EARTH
306 S Main St (56013-2016)
PO Box 40 (56013-0040)
PHONE....................507 526-3241
FAX: 507 526-4614
Bruce Hanson, *CEO*
Mike Verdoorn, *Principal*
Dan Mensing, *Vice Pres*
Paul Carr, *Vice Pres*
Bruce Hanke, *CFO*
EMP: 25 **EST:** 1987
SALES (est): 5MM-9.9MM **Privately Held**
SIC: 6022 State commercial bank

(G-536)
HUMAN SERVICES OF FARIBAULT
Also Called: Fmw Human Svcs Faribault
412 N Nicollet St (56013-1247)
PO Box 217 (56013-0217)
PHONE....................507 526-3265
FAX: 507 526-2039
Juanita Krull, *Finance Mgr*
Vickie Savick, *Office Mgr*
Warren Knudsen, *Manager*
EMP: 30 **EST:** 1996 **Privately Held**
SIC: 8399 Health & welfare council

(G-537)
ST LUKE'S LUTHERAN CARE CENTER
1219 S Ramsey St (56013-2227)
PHONE....................507 526-2184
FAX: 507 526-7427
Erin Farland, *CFO*
Sheryl Eckhardt, *Human Res Dir*
Mark Robinson, *Administrator*
Gene Nelson, *Exec Dir*
Bob Lake, *Administration*
EMP: 220 **EST:** 1956
SQ FT: 84,000
SALES (est): 5MM-9.9MM **Privately Held**
SIC: 8051 Skilled nursing care facility

(G-538)
UNITED CLINIC OF FARIBAULT
435 S Grove St Ste 1 (56013-2629)
PHONE....................507 526-7388
FAX: 507 526-2467
Terence Cahill, *Owner*
Sue Hassing, *Office Mgr*
William Lee, *Surgeon*
Stephen Razi, *Surgeon*
Ladonna Dutton, *Nursing Dir*
EMP: 25 **EST:** 1993
SALES (est): 1MM-4.9MM **Privately Held**
SIC: 8011 Physicians' office

(G-539)
UNITED HOSPITAL DISTRICT (PA)
515 S Moore St (56013-2158)
PO Box 160 (56013-0160)
PHONE....................507 526-3273
FAX: 507 526-3285
Sandy Hill, *COO*
Tim Pytleski, *Purchasing*
Steve Rozenboom, *CFO*
Daniel Rabideaux, *CFO*
Karen Gossen, *Accountant*
EMP: 170 **EST:** 1967
SQ FT: 76,000
SALES (corp-wide): 22.81M **Privately Held**
SIC: 8062 Medical hospital

BOVEY
Itasca County

(G-540)
CONE CORP
25929 County Road 59 (55709-7106)
PHONE....................218 245-2313
Shelly Brandstrom, *President*
Elmer W Cone, *Corp Secy*
Margaret Cone, *Vice Pres*
Michelle Cone, *Treasurer*
EMP: 25 **EST:** 1963
SALES (est): 1MM-4.9MM **Privately Held**
SIC: 1771 1611 5085 Curb construction; concrete road, highway & sidewalk construction; sidewalk contractor; wholesales industrial bottler supplies

BRAHAM
Isanti County

(G-541)
EAST CENTRAL ENERGY (PA)
412 Main Ave N (55006-4707)
PO Box 39 (55006-0039)
PHONE....................320 396-3351
FAX: 320 396-4114
Garry Bye, *CEO*
Gwen Thomas, *Senior VP*
Cheryl Hagfors, *Finance Mgr*
Deb Eck, *Finance Spvr*
John Heino, *Manager*
EMP: 126 **EST:** 1936
SQ FT: 30,000
SALES (corp-wide): 95.51M **Privately Held**
SIC: 4911 Electric power distribution service

(G-542)
FIVE COUNTY MENTAL HEALTH CTR
521 Broadway Ave N (55006-4711)
PHONE....................320 396-3333
FAX: 320 396-0144
James Hermanson, *President*
Gina Mullen, *Accounting Staf*
Marie Grunberg, *Manager*
EMP: 30 **EST:** 1964
SQ FT: 5,000
SALES (est): 1MM-4.9MM **Privately Held**
SIC: 8093 Outpatient mental health clinic

(G-543)
MILLE LACS OIL CO
Also Called: Kline Oil Co
209 N Main St (55006)
PHONE....................320 396-2693
Bonnie McKinn, *Sales/Mktg Mgr*
EMP: 25
SALES (est): 1MM-4.9MM **Privately Held**
SIC: 5171 Convenience store; wholesales petroleum bulk stations
PA: Mille Lacs Oil Co
102 Main St N
Cambridge MN 55008
763 689-2220

BRAINERD
Cass County

(G-544)
CRAGUN ENTERPRISES INC
Also Called: Legacy Courses At Cragun
11000 Craguns Dr (56401-2020)
PHONE....................218 825-2800
Merrill Cragun, *President*
Rebecca Mies, *Manager*
Jenelle Hewitt, *Director*
EMP: 25 **EST:** 1996
SALES (est): 1MM-4.9MM **Privately Held**
SIC: 7992 Public golf course

(G-545)
KAVCO INC
Also Called: Kavanaugh's
1685 Kavanaugh Dr (56401-2063)
PHONE....................218 829-5226
John Kavanaugh, *President*
Vicki Kavanaugh, *Corp Secy*
David Kavanaugh, *Vice Pres*
Thomas Kavanaugh, *Vice Pres*
Mark Kavanaugh, *Vice Pres*
EST: 1969
SQ FT: 6,800 **Privately Held**
WEB: www.kavanaughs.com
SIC: 7011 Resort hotel

(G-546)
MADDEN BROTHERS INC
Also Called: Madden's On Gull Lake
11266 Pine Beach Peninsula Rd (56401-2080)
PHONE....................218 829-2811
FAX: 218 829-2811
C B Thuringer, *CEO*
Emily Swarthout, *Human Resources*
Bill Crumley, *Marketing Staff*
Cara Norquist, *Manager*
Maureen Kehborn, *Manager*
EMP: 45 **EST:** 1929
SALES (est): 1MM-4.9MM **Privately Held**
WEB: www.maddens.com
SIC: 7011 7992 7997 7999 Resort hotel; eating place; membership recreation club; indoor or outdoor non-membership tennis courts; golf professionals; public golf course; retails sporting goods

BRAINERD
Crow Wing County

(G-547)
ALMOND HOUSE
Also Called: Linda Kay Properties
802 28th St SE (56401-6308)
PHONE....................218 825-9255
FAX: 218 855-0748
Sue Johnson, *Owner*
EMP: 25
SALES (est): 1MM-4.9MM **Privately Held**
WEB: www.almondhouse.com
SIC: 8052 Intermediate care facility

(G-548)
AMERICAN NATIONAL BANK OF MN (PA)
1920 S 6th St (56401-4527)
PO Box 303 (56401-0303)
PHONE....................218 824-7900
FAX: 218 829-1265
Thomas J Johnson, *CEO*
Robert J Sefkow, *COO*
David W Jones, *Vice Pres*
Robert A Slagter, *CFO*
EMP: 28 **EST:** 1983
SALES (corp-wide): 19.38M **Privately Held**
SIC: 6036 State savings bank

(G-549)
ANDERSON BROTHERS CONSTRUCTION
11325 E Hwy 210 (56401)
PO Box 668 (56401-0668)
PHONE....................218 829-1768
FAX: 218 829-7607
James Anderson, *CEO*
David R Johnson, *President*
Linnea Anderson, *Corp Secy*
John Bendson, *Vice Pres*
EMP: 220 **EST:** 1940
SQ FT: 2,800
SALES (est): 10MM-24.9MM **Privately Held**
WEB: www.andersonbrothers.com
SIC: 1771 1611 Concrete contractor; general highway & street construction service

(G-550)
ATEK MANUFACTURING LLC
210 10th Ave NE (56401-2802)
PHONE....................218 829-4719
Christine B Orris, *CEO*
William F Bieber, *Ch of Bd*
S K Phillips, *President*
Alan Howard, *Plant Mgr*
Bob Imgrund, *Maint Mgr*
EMP: 70 **EST:** 1984
SQ FT: 65,000
SALES (est): 5MM-9.9MM **Privately Held**
SIC: 8748 Telecommunications consulting services; manufactures electrical equipment & supplies; manufactures telecommunication systems & equipment

(G-551)
BARNABAS HEALTH CARE SERVICES
223 Washington St (56401-3336)
PHONE....................218 829-0901
FAX: 218 825-0170
Bobbi L Debros, *President*
EMP: 200 **EST:** 1993
SALES (est): 5MM-9.9MM **Privately Held**
WEB: www.barnabashealth.com
SIC: 8082 8322 Home health care services; visiting nurse services; oxygen tent services; individual & family social services

(G-552)
BRAINERD MEDICAL CENTER
2024 S 6th St (56401-4529)
PHONE....................218 828-7100
FAX: 218 828-7107
John Agre, *CFO*
Susan Bremer, *Insur/Bill Sup*
Celeste Gardner, *Human Res Dir*
Colleen Pitt, *Personnel*
Kim Deiss, *Marketing Staff*
EMP: 240 **EST:** 1974
SQ FT: 55,000
SALES (est): 25MM-49.9MM **Privately Held**
WEB: www.brainerdclinic.com
SIC: 8011 Clinic operated by physicians; retails hearing aids

(G-553)
BRAINERD SCHOOL DISTRICT 181
Also Called: Prep Preschool Program
311 10th Ave NE (56401-2859)
PHONE....................218 829-0412
FAX: 218 829-7697
Connie Nelson, *Director*
EMP: 25 **EST:** 1980
SALES (est): 500-999K **Privately Held**
SIC: 8351 Preschool center

(G-554)
BRAINERD SPORTS & MARINE LLC
13377 State Highway 25 (56401-4662)
PO Box 732 (56401-0732)
PHONE....................218 828-4728
FAX: 218 829-1488
Carol M Halverson, *Member*
James Halverson, *Member*
Jim Helveson, *Manager*
EST: 1997 **Privately Held**
WEB: www.brainerdsportsandmarine.com
SIC: 7699 Boat dealer; boat repair service

(G-555)
BREMER BANK (DH)
321 S 7th St (56401-3614)
PHONE....................218 829-8781
Mike Reilly, *President*
Bob Verkennes, *Vice Pres*
Diane Runberg, *Vice Pres*
John Ohlin, *Vice Pres*
Mike Riley, *Vice Pres*
EMP: 51 **EST:** 1889 **Privately Held**

SIC: **6036** State savings bank
HQ: Bremer Financial Corp
445 Minnesota St Ste 2000
Saint Paul MN 55101
651 227-7621

(G-556)

CAREFREE LIVING OF AMERICA

Also Called: Brainerd Manor
2723 Oak St (56401-3818)
PHONE 952 988-0011
Kathleen Zeller, *Owner*
EMP: 30 EST: 1984
SALES (est): 1MM-4.9MM **Privately Held**
SIC: **6513** Operators of retirement hotels

(G-557)

CITI INVESTOR SERVICES INC

Also Called: Brainerd Service Center
823 Maple St (56401-3770)
PO Box 979 (56401-0979)
PHONE 218 825-0552
FAX: 218 825-0454
Steve Christenson, *Manager*
EMP: 50
SALES (est): 5MM-9.9MM **Publicly Held**
WEB: www.citibank.com
SIC: **6411 7371** Pension & retirement plan
consulting service; computer programming
service
DH: Citi Investor Services Inc
105 Eisenhower Pkwy Ste 2
Roseland NJ 07068
973 461-2500

(G-558)

CLARK LAKE HOMES INC

10471 State Highway 25 (56401-1401)
PHONE 218 829-1699
Shelley Peterson, *Administrator*
Lynn Peterson, *Administrator*
EMP: 40 EST: 1999
SALES (est): 1MM-4.9MM **Privately Held**
SIC: **8361** Home for the mentally
handicapped

(G-559)

CLARK LAKE HOMES INC

2700 Oak St (56401-3867)
PHONE 218 833-1322
FAX: 218 833-1327
Lynn Peterson, *Owner*
EMP: 48 EST: 2001 **Privately Held**
SIC: **8399** Social change association

(G-560)

CORE PROFESSIONAL SERVICES

617 Oak St (56401-3610)
PHONE 218 829-7140
FAX: 218 829-7124
Brenda Weber, *Owner*
Joni Meyer, *Manager*
EMP: 25 EST: 1995
SALES (est): 1MM-4.9MM **Privately Held**
SIC: **8093** Outpatient mental health clinic

(G-561)

CRANNYS 4 CARE LLC

Also Called: Home Instead Senior Care
108 S 6th St Ste 3 (56401-3594)
PHONE 218 824-0077
Deb Cranny, *Managing Prtnr*
EMP: 37 EST: 2005
SALES (est): 1MM-4.9MM **Privately Held**
SIC: **8082** Home health care services

(G-562)

CROW WING COOPERATIVE POWER (PA)

17330 State Highway 371 (56401-6832)
PO Box 507 (56401-0507)
PHONE 218 829-2827
FAX: 218 822-2678
Bruce Kraemer, *CEO*
Rob Mouser, *Safety Mgr*
Steve Smolke, *Accountant*
Anne Hof, *Accounts Mgr*
Mike Marlatt, *Manager*
EMP: 75 EST: 1936
SQ FT: 60,000
SALES (corp-wide): 55.84M **Privately Held**
WEB: www.cwpower.com
SIC: **4911** Electric power distribution service

(G-563)

CROW WING COUNTY HWY DEPT

16589 County Road 142 (56401-5946)
PHONE 218 824-1110
FAX: 218 828-2972
Dwayne Blake, *Administrator*
EMP: 35 EST: 2006
SALES (est): 1MM-4.9MM **Privately Held**
SIC: **8711** Engineering services

(G-564)

DR PETER SCHMITZ INC

Also Called: Northern Orthopedics
2014 S 6th St (56401-4529)
PHONE 218 829-7812
FAX: 218 829-9751
Peter Schmitz, *President*
Karen Johnson, *Office Mgr*
Amy E Lelwica, *Surgeon*
Esme Kummet, *Nursing Dir*
Bob Brown, *Executive*
EMP: 25 EST: 1975
SALES (est): 1MM-4.9MM **Privately Held**
SIC: **8011** Physicians' office

(G-565)

EVANGELICAL LUTHERAN GOOD

Also Called: Bethany Good Samaritan Village
804 Wright St (56401-4441)
PHONE 218 829-1407
Rich Nelson, *Maintenance Dir*
Monica Andrew, *Human Resources*
Laura Dilley, *Office Mgr*
Craig Ammermann, *Manager*
Genelle Harmon, *Manager*
EMP: 300
SALES (est): 10MM-24.9MM **Privately Held**
WEB: www.good-sam.com
SIC: **8059 8051** Nursing home; skilled
nursing care facility
PA: Evangelical Lutheran Good
4800 W 57th St
Sioux Falls SD 57108
605 362-3100

(G-566)

EVANGELICAL LUTHERAN GOOD

Also Called: Woodland Good Samaritan Vlg
100 Buffalo Hills Ln (56401-5519)
PHONE 218 829-1429
FAX: 218 829-4729
Mike Deuth, *Director*
EMP: 130
SALES (est): 5MM-9.9MM **Privately Held**
WEB: www.good-sam.com
SIC: **8051 8082** Convalescent home; home
health care services
PA: Evangelical Lutheran Good
4800 W 57th St
Sioux Falls SD 57108
605 362-3100

(G-567)

GEO'S PAINT & FINISH LLC

26392 State Highway 18 (56401-4825)
PHONE 320 692-2027
George Erickson, *President*
Cathy Evai, *Assistant*
EMP: 50 EST: 1990
SALES (est): 1MM-4.9MM **Privately Held**
SIC: **1721** Interior residential painting
contractor; interior commercial painting
contractor

(G-568)

GOLDLEAF PARTNERS

605 Laurel St Ste 17 (56401-3671)
PO Box 806 (56401-0806)
PHONE 218 824-6119
Heather N Hess, *Partner*
Michael E King, *Partner*
EMP: 25 EST: 2005
SALES (est): 1MM-4.9MM **Privately Held**
SIC: **8742** Financial management
consulting services

(G-569)

HORIZON HEALTH INC

Also Called: Harmony House West
218 SW 9th St (56401-3239)
PHONE 218 828-4142
FAX: 218 828-4132
Shiela Johnson, *Manager*
Shelley Bartella, *Manager*
EMP: 35
SALES (est): 1MM-4.9MM **Privately Held**
WEB: www.horizonhealth.net
SIC: **8361** Residential care facility
PA: Horizon Health Inc
26814 143rd St
Pierz MN 56364
320 468-6451

(G-570)

HY-TEC CONSTRUCTION OF

11360 Business 371 (56401-1779)
PO Box 621 (56401-0621)
PHONE 218 829-8529
FAX: 218 829-5383
Craig Feierabend, *President*
Brad Arnold, *Corp Secy*
Stanley Weiser, *Vice Pres*
Brenda K Bray, *Treasurer*
Bill Spar, *Human Res Mgr*
EMP: 40 EST: 1989
SALES (est): 10MM-24.9MM **Privately Held**
WEB: www.hytecconst.com
SIC: **1542 1541** New commercial & office
building construction; commercial & office
building renovation & repair services;
industrial building & warehouse construction

(G-571)

JACK'S HOUSE

300 Highway 25 S (56401-7405)
PHONE 218 824-5225
FAX: 218 824-5227
Virginia Lorentz, *Partner*
Kevin Lorentz, *Partner*
Mike Almer, *Partner*
Shirley Almer, *Partner*
EMP: 25 EST: 2003
SALES (est): 500-999K **Privately Held**
WEB: www.jackshousebowl.com
SIC: **7933** Bowling center

(G-572)

LAKESIDE HOSPITALITY LLP

Also Called: Holiday Inn
2215 S 6th St (56401-5549)
PHONE 218 847-2121
Tracy Berninghaus, *Principal*
EMP: 75 EST: 1999
SALES (est): 1MM-4.9MM **Privately Held**
SIC: **7011** Traveler accommodations

(G-573)

LODGE AT BRAINERD LAKE

6967 Lake Forest Rd (56401-6963)
PHONE 218 822-5634
FAX: 218 822-4044
Joel Carey, *President*
Jill Ferrie, *VP Sales*
Jim Benson, *Manager*
EMP: 70 EST: 2005
SALES (est): 1MM-4.9MM **Privately Held**
SIC: **7011** Vacation lodge

(G-574)

MID MINNESOTA FEDERAL CREDIT

200 S 6th St (56401-3536)
PO Box 2907, Baxter (56425-6607)
PHONE 218 829-0371
FAX: 218 829-4947
Charles Albrecht, *President*
Laurie Line, *General Mgr*
Mary Pedersen, *Vice Pres*
Martin J Kelly, *Vice Pres*
Missy Borg, *Mfg Staff*
EMP: 49 EST: 1956
SQ FT: 13,000
SALES (est): 5MM-9.9MM **Privately Held**
SIC: **6061** Federally chartered credit union

(G-575)

MINNESOTA DEPARTMENT OF HUMAN

Also Called: Brainerd Rgional Humn Svcs Ctr
1777 Highway 18 E (56401-7388)
PHONE 218 828-2379
FAX: 218 828-2595
David Bauer, *Vice Pres*
Gary Binsfeld, *CFO*
Mary Skarda, *Human Resources*
Becky Melby, *Manager*
Shirley Jacobson, *Manager*
EMP: 650
SALES (est): 25MM-49.9MM **Privately Held**
WEB: www.state.mn.us
SIC: **8322** Individual & family social
services; human resource, social work &
welfare administration services; state
government administration of social &
manpower programs
DH: Minnesota Department of Human
540 Cedar St
Saint Paul MN 55101
651 431-2000

(G-576)

MORRIS COMMUNICATIONS CORP

Also Called: Brainerd Daily Dispatch
506 James St (56401-2942)
PO Box 974 (56401-0974)
PHONE 218 829-4705
FAX: 218 829-7735
Ben Carter, *Publisher*
Deann Barry, *Vice Pres*
Brandon Dobson, *Vice Pres*
Robert Oswaldson, *Vice Pres*
Jim Voiss, *Vice Pres*
EMP: 85
SALES (est): 10MM-24.9MM **Privately Held**
WEB: www.morris.com
SIC: **8742** Periodical publisher;
management consulting services;
commercial lithographic printing; newspaper
publisher
HQ: Morris Communications Co LLC
725 Broad St
Augusta GA 30901
706 724-0851

(G-577)

NORTH MEMORIAL HEALTH CARE

210 NW 5th St (56401-3214)
PHONE 218 829-8767
Kevin Lee, *Manager*
Mark Stemsberry, *Supervisor*
EMP: 60
SALES (est): 1MM-4.9MM **Privately Held**
WEB: www.northmemorial.com
SIC: **4119** Ambulance service
PA: North Memorial Health Care
3300 Oakdale Ave N
Minneapolis MN 55422
763 520-5200

(G-578)

NORTH STAR CAMP

1214 Eagleview Dr NE (56401-9705)
PHONE 218 829-6631
David Vandenveer, *Treasurer*
David Dandevere, *Treasurer*
Derral Reeve, *Director*
Erick Hanson, *Director*
EMP: 33 EST: 1952
SALES (est): 1MM-4.9MM **Privately Held**
SIC: **7032** Recreational & sporting camp

(G-579)

OAK RIDGE HOMES OF WADENA INC (PA)

Also Called: Oakridge Homes
1021 Industrial Pk Rd SW (56401-8338)
PHONE 218 829-7599
FAX: 218 631-4134
David Felske, *President*
EMP: 27 EST: 1983 **Privately Held**
SIC: **8361** Residential care facility

GEOGRAPHIC

(G-580)
PEPSI-COLA METROPOLITAN BTLNG
2024 SE 13th St (56401-4714)
PHONE..................................218 829-4196
FAX: 218 829-4506
Rick Sweet, *Manager*
Tom Perpich, *Manager*
Peter Paszkiewiz, *Technical Staff*
Judy Sturm, *Admin Asst*
EMP: 34
SQ FT: 20,000
SALES (est): 10MM-24.9MM **Publicly Held**
WEB: www.joy-of-cola.com
SIC: 5149 Manufactures bottled & canned soft drinks; manufactures soft drinks; wholesales soft drinks
HQ: Pepsi-Cola Metropolitan Btlng
    1 Pepsi Way Ste 1
    Somers NY 10589
    914 767-6000

(G-581)
PORT GROUP HOME OFFICE
115 N 1st St (56401-3338)
PO Box 488 (56401-0488)
PHONE..................................218 828-6274
John Forest, *Chairman*
Joe Rubado, *Manager*
Karen Johnston, *Director*
EMP: 45 EST: 2006
SALES (est): 1MM-4.9MM **Privately Held**
SIC: 8361 Group foster home

(G-582)
POSITIVE REALTY & INVESTMENT
514 S 6th St (56401-3542)
PHONE..................................218 829-1777
FAX: 218 828-1130
Jack Antolak, *President*
Joe Zak, *Corp Secy*
Dale Johnson, *Manager*
EMP: 25 EST: 1979
SQ FT: 4,000
SALES (est): 1MM-4.9MM **Privately Held**
WEB: www.positiverealty.com
SIC: 6531 Real estate agency & broker

(G-583)
PRODUCTIVE ALTERNATIVES INC
213 NW 4th St (56401-3219)
PHONE..................................218 825-8148
FAX: 218 825-8362
Kevin Larson, *Branch Mgr*
EMP: 28 **Privately Held**
WEB: www.paiff.org
SIC: 8399 Community development groups
PA: Productive Alternatives Inc
    1205 N Tower Rd
    Fergus Falls MN 56537
    218 998-5630

(G-584)
REICHERT ENTERPRISES INC (PA)
8342 Industrial Park Rd (56425-8272)
PHONE..................................218 829-6955
Mike Moran, *President*
Mark Moran, *Vice Pres*
Gae Wicklund, *Treasurer*
EMP: 105 EST: 1947
SQ FT: 5,000 **Privately Held**
WEB: www.reichertbus.com
SIC: 4151 4141 School bus service; local bus charter service

(G-585)
ROHLFING OF BRAINERD INC
923 Wright St (56401-4404)
PHONE..................................218 829-0303
FAX: 218 829-4229
Robert Rohlfing, *President*
Elizabeth Rohlfing, *Vice Pres*
Dave Weiss, *Branch Mgr*
▲ EMP: 30 EST: 1967
SQ FT: 22,000
SALES (est): 10MM-24.9MM **Privately Held**
SIC: 5181 5113 5149 Wholesales beer & ale; wholesales industrial & personal service paper; wholesales soft drinks

(G-586)
SKY BLUE LEASING INC
26392 State Highway 18 (56401-4825)
PHONE..................................320 692-2027
FAX: 320 692-2031
George Erickson, *President*
EMP: 30 EST: 2006
SALES (est): Under 500K **Privately Held**
WEB: www.skybluebeach.com
SIC: 7359 Equipment rental & leasing services

(G-587)
ST JOSEPH'S MEDICAL CENTER
523 N 3rd St (56401-3054)
PHONE..................................218 829-2861
Thomas K Prusak, *President*
Ross B Bengtson, *Ch of Surgery*
Hal Leland, *Ch OB/GYN*
Dianne M Kendall, *Ch Pathology*
James J O' Hearne, *Ch Radiology*
EMP: 990 EST: 1983
SQ FT: 210,000
SALES (est): 50MM-99.9MM **Privately Held**
SIC: 8062 Medical hospital
HQ: Essentia Health
    502 E 2nd St
    Duluth MN 55805
    218 786-8376

(G-588)
UNITED PARCEL SERVICE INC
Also Called: UPS
1009 Madison St (56401-4478)
PHONE..................................218 829-6240
Barrett Cervemka, *Manager*
Craig Zelmer, *Exec Dir*
EMP: 55
SALES (est): 1MM-4.9MM **Publicly Held**
WEB: www.ups.com
SIC: 4215 Parcel delivery services by vehicle
HQ: United Parcel Service Inc
    55 Glenlake Pkwy NE
    Atlanta GA 30328
    404 828-6000

(G-589)
WOOD PRODUCTS UNLIMITED INC
15909 Inglewood Dr (56401-6913)
PHONE..................................218 829-4353
FAX: 218 829-0067
Alan Andres, *CEO*
Donald Andres, *President*
Joanna Buresh, *Sales Staff*
Dave Moore, *Agent*
EMP: 30 EST: 1992
SQ FT: 2,148
SALES (est): 1MM-4.9MM **Privately Held**
SIC: 1751 Millwork; manufactures wooden kitchen cabinets; cabinet building & installation service; manufactures wood office furniture; manufactures wood partitions & fixtures

(G-590)
YOUNG MEN'S CHRITN ASSOC OF
Also Called: Y'S World of Learning
602 Oak St (56401-3611)
PO Box 381 (56401-0381)
PHONE..................................218 829-4767
FAX: 218 829-4768
Don Ryan, *Corp Secy*
Ann Silgen, *Vice Pres*
Randy Klinger, *Exec Dir*
EMP: 100 **Privately Held**
SIC: 8641 Youth organizations; recreation association

BRANDON
Douglas County

(G-591)
VOYAGER ALUMINUM INC
803 Central Ave N (56315)
PO Box 566 (56315-0566)
PHONE..................................320 834-4940
FAX: 320 834-4439
Gary Suckow, *President*

Jon Boutain, *Corp Secy*
Bill Ruppert, *Exec Dir*
EMP: 45 EST: 1997
SQ FT: 40,000
SALES (est): 10MM-24.9MM **Privately Held**
WEB: www.voyageraluminum.com
SIC: 5051 Manufactures welded aluminum tubes; wholesales aluminum bars, rods, ingots, sheets, pipes, plates, etc

(G-592)
WAGNER TRUCKING INC
15380 Long Lake Rd NW (56315)
PHONE..................................320 524-2250
Kenneth Wagner, *President*
Scott Wagner, *Manager*
EST: 1969
SQ FT: 800 **Privately Held**
SIC: 5153 4212 4213 Wholesales grains; local trucking without storage services; over the road trucking

---

BRECKENRIDGE
Wilkin County

(G-593)
CITY OF BRECKENRIDGE
Also Called: Breckenridge Public Utilities
420 Nebraska Ave (56520-1444)
PO Box 410 (56520-0410)
PHONE..................................218 643-1431
Jeff Muehler, *Principal*
Clifford Barth, *Mayor*
Nancy Froemke, *Vice Pres*
Blaine Hill, *Treasurer*
Stan Thurlow, *Manager*
EMP: 33 EST: 1898 **Privately Held**
SIC: 8611 Mayors' office; business association

(G-594)
HEALTHCARE & WELLNESS FNDTN
2400 St Francis Dr (56520-1025)
PHONE..................................218 643-0410
Becky Ruthenbeck, *Exec Dir*
Merlin W Granfor, *Director*
Nancy E Torson, *Psychiatry*
Lawrence H Licht, *Radiology*
EMP: 99
SALES (est): 5MM-9.9MM **Privately Held**
SIC: 8062 Medical hospital

(G-595)
MINN-KOTA AG PRODUCTS INC (PA)
90 8th St N (56520-1556)
PHONE..................................218 643-8464
FAX: 218 643-4555
George Schuler III, *President*
Brian Arnhalt, *General Mgr*
Hal Fisher, *Branch Mgr*
Don Holmstrom, *Branch Mgr*
Rory McCann, *Info Tech Mgr*
EMP: 36 EST: 1985
SQ FT: 4,000
SALES (corp-wide): 178.55M **Privately Held**
WEB: www.mkap.com
SIC: 5191 5153 Wholesales agricultural fertilizer; wholesales agricultural chemicals; wholesale grain elevator; wholesales feed

(G-596)
RAPE & ABUSE CRISIS CENTER
317 8th St S (56520-2013)
PHONE..................................218 643-6110
FAX: 218 643-3227
Jennifer Malley, *Manager*
Beth Hazetin, *Director*
EMP: 25 EST: 1977
SALES (est): 1MM-4.9MM **Privately Held**
SIC: 8322 Crisis center

(G-597)
RDO AGRICULTURE EQUIPMENT CO
905 Buffalo Ave (56520-2538)
PHONE..................................218 643-2601
Jeff Lemna, *Manager*
EMP: 40
SALES (est): 10MM-24.9MM **Privately Held**

SIC: 5083 Wholesales agricultural machinery & equipment; retails lawnmowers & tractors
HQ: Rdo Agriculture Equipment Co
    700 7th St S
    Fargo ND 58103
    701 239-8730

(G-598)
RED RIVER IMPLEMENT CO INC
905 Buffalo Ave (56520-2538)
PHONE..................................218 643-2601
Ronald Offutt, *President*
Louie Weber, *Manager*
Jeff Lemna, *Manager*
EMP: 40 EST: 1957
SQ FT: 20,000
SALES (est): 10MM-24.9MM **Privately Held**
SIC: 5083 Wholesales agricultural machinery & equipment

(G-599)
RED RIVER VALLEY & WESTERN
501 Minnesota Ave (56520-2032)
PHONE..................................218 643-4994
FAX: 218 643-4980
Sharon Trudell, *Manager*
Dan Keogh, *Manager*
EMP: 30 **Privately Held**
SIC: 4011 Long haul railroad
PA: Red River Valley & Western
    116 4th St S Frnt
    Wahpeton ND 58075
    701 642-8257

(G-600)
SEEDS 2000 INC
115 3rd St N (56520-1406)
PO Box 200 (56520-0200)
PHONE..................................218 643-2410
Steve Kent, *President*
Leland Falck, *Corp Secy*
Monica Onchuck, *Controller*
Don Rezac, *Manager*
Jay Schuller, *Exec Dir*
▲ EMP: 45 EST: 1992
SQ FT: 6,000
SALES (est): 1MM-4.9MM **Privately Held**
WEB: www.seeds2000.net
SIC: 5191 Retails farm equipment & supplies; wholesales field, garden & flower seeds

(G-601)
ST FRANCIS MEDICAL CENTER
2400 St Francis Dr (56520-1025)
PHONE..................................218 643-3000
FAX: 218 643-7502
Vertan Malkasian, *Ch Pathology*
Mary Helland, *Vice Pres*
Ann Trebesch, *Vice Pres*
Steve Mann, *Engineering*
Nancy Whitney, *CFO*
EMP: 300 EST: 1891
SQ FT: 117,000
SALES (est): 25MM-49.9MM **Privately Held**
SIC: 8062 8051 Medical hospital; skilled nursing care facility
PA: Catholic Health Initiatives
    98 Inverness Dr W Ste 800
    Englewood CO 80112
    303 298-9100

(G-602)
SUNRICH LLC
Also Called: Sunopta Sunflower
227 6th St N (56520-1503)
PO Box 331 (56520-0331)
PHONE..................................218 643-8467
FAX: 218 643-8702
Paul Schaubert, *Plant Mgr*
Cathy Kutter, *Controller*
Steve Arnhalt, *Finance Mgr*
Young Kim, *Sales Mgr*
Peter Reinecke, *VP Mktg*
EMP: 100
SALES (est): 50MM-99.9MM **Privately Held**
SIC: 5191 0723 Wholesales field, garden & flower seeds; manufactures food preparations; post harvest crop activities
HQ: Sunrich LLC
    3824 SW 93rd St
    Hope MN 56046
    507 451-4724

(G-603)
WEST CENTRAL COMMUNITY SERVICE
732 5th St S (56520-2326)
PO Box 71 (56520-0071)
PHONE..............................218 643-5952
FAX: 218 643-5721
Fay Beighley, *Manager*
Bruce Miller, *Administrator*
EMP: 75 EST: 1975
SALES (est): 1MM-4.9MM **Privately Held**
SIC: 8361 Residential care facility

BREWSTER
Nobles County

(G-604)
CASPAR INC
36694 190th St (56119-1967)
PHONE..............................507 842-5978
Rodney Casper, *President*
EMP:
SALES (est): 1MM-4.9MM **Privately Held**
SIC: 8999 Miscellaneous services

(G-605)
MINNESOTA SOYBEAN PROCESSORS ✪
121 Zeh Ave (56119)
PO Box 100 (56119-0100)
PHONE..............................507 842-6677
Richard Galloway, *CEO*
Jim Sallstrom, *Ch of Bd*
Darrell Petersen, *CFO*
Taryl P Enderson, *Controller*
Kim Collin, *Executive Asst*
EMP: 90 EST: 2008
SALES (est): 100MM-499.9MM **Privately Held**
WEB: www.mnsoy.com
SIC: 5153 Wholesales soybeans; manufactures soybean oil, cake or meal

BROOKLYN PARK
Hennepin County

(G-606)
BORDER STATES INDUSTRIES INC
9100 Wyoming Ave N Ste 550 (55445-1862)
PHONE..............................763 425-5500
FAX: 763 315-9550
Steve Kuntz, *Manager*
Bjorn Zimba, *Manager*
EMP: 63
SALES (est): 25MM-49.9MM **Privately Held**
WEB: www.bseweb.com
SIC: 5063 Wholesales electrical apparatus & equipment

(G-607)
COGENT TECHNOLOGIES INC (HQ)
7041 Boone Ave N (55428-1504)
PHONE..............................952 941-3300
Claude C Johnson, *Ch of Bd*
Brad Yopp, *President*
John G Colwell Jr, *Principal*
Edward L Lundstrom, *Principal*
Gerald E Magnuson, *Principal*
EMP: 129 EST: 1952
SQ FT: 90,000 **Privately Held**
WEB: www.researchinc.com
SIC: 8711 Manufactures industrial process radiant heating systems; manufactures industrial process control instruments; manufactures relays & industrial controls; engineering services; manufactures heating equipment & supplies
PA: Squid Ink Manufacturing Inc
7041 Boone Ave N
Minneapolis MN 55428
763 795-8856

(G-608)
DEPENDABLE CARE INC
6001 78th Ave N Ste 201 (55443-2978)
PHONE..............................763 438-2811
Abimbola Bakare, *President*
EMP: 30
SALES (est): 1MM-4.9MM **Privately Held**
SIC: 7299 Escort services

(G-609)
EGAN CO (PA)
7625 Boone Ave N (55428-1011)
PHONE..............................763 544-4131
FAX: 763 595-4380
James J Malecha, *CEO*
William Marshall, *Exec VP*
Duane Hendricks, *Exec VP*
Jack Galvin, *Exec VP*
Bruce G Richey, *Vice Pres*
EMP: 150 EST: 1948
SQ FT: 127,000
SALES (corp-wide): 124.46M **Privately Held**
SIC: 1711 1731 7623 Plumbing service; refrigeration repair service & repair; warm air heating & air conditioning contractor; safety & security specialization contractor; general electrical contractor; manufactures metal ventilating equipment

(G-610)
GENESIS GROUP HOMES INC
4650 Oak Grove Pkwy N (55443-4062)
PHONE..............................763 390-0773
Jay Freshour, *CEO*
EMP: 53
SALES (est): 1MM-4.9MM **Privately Held**
SIC: 8322 Adult daycare center

(G-611)
INTEGRA GROUP INC
7100 Northland Cir N # 205 (55428-1500)
PHONE..............................763 951-7400
Chris Pulling, *President*
EMP: 33 EST: 2002 **Privately Held**
WEB: www.integracts.com
SIC: 8731 Commercial physical research laboratory

(G-612)
K N R COMMUNICATION SERVICES
7180 Northland Cir N Ste 138 (55428-1541)
PHONE..............................763 478-2058
Brian Schnappauf, *President*
EMP: 25 EST: 1992
SQ FT: 9,000 **Privately Held**
SIC: 4813 Wired telecommunications carrier & service

(G-613)
LAKE STATES LUMBER INC
9110 83rd Ave N Ste 100 (55445-2123)
PHONE..............................763 425-0204
Donn Priebe, *Principal*
John Gerlech, *Manager*
Alan Vanderhoeven, *MIS Mgr*
Alan V Hoeven V, *MIS Mgr*
Marjorie Arnold, *Information Mgr*
EMP: 30
SALES (est): 10MM-24.9MM **Privately Held**
SIC: 5031 Wholesales lumber, plywood & millwork

(G-614)
MAAX US CORP ✪
9224 73rd Ave N (55428-1111)
PHONE..............................763 424-3335
Paul Golden, *President*
Mark Bandrauk, *Corp Secy*
David Lipkin, *Vice Pres*
Denis Aubin, *CFO*
Mark Weinberg, *Director*
EMP: 60 EST: 2008
SALES (est): 1MM-4.9MM **Privately Held**
SIC: 7991 Spas

(G-615)
MAINS'L SERVICES INC
7000 78th Ave N (55445-2744)
PHONE..............................763 494-4553
Teresa Williams, *CEO*

Jody Smith, *Vice Pres*
Donna Olson, *Vice Pres*
EMP: 40 EST: 1989 **Privately Held**
SIC: 8399 Health systems agency

(G-616)
MALARK LOGISTICS INC
9100 85th Ave N Ste 200 (55445-2169)
PO Box 438, Maple Grove (55369-0438)
PHONE..............................763 428-3564
Sheryl Malark, *President*
Mark Wills, *Vice Pres*
Douglas Malark, *Vice Pres*
EMP: 66 EST: 1998
SQ FT: 110,000
SALES (est): 1MM-4.9MM **Privately Held**
SIC: 4231 1541 Freight trucking terminal; warehouse construction

(G-617)
PREMIER ELECTRICAL CORP
4401 85th Ave N (55443-1937)
PHONE..............................763 424-6551
FAX: 763 424-5225
Fred Jahnke, *CEO*
Doug Olson, *President*
Lonnie Bellin, *Corp Secy*
Stephanie Mattock, *Corp Secy*
Howard Eknes, *Manager*
EMP: 115 EST: 1902
SQ FT: 16,000
SALES (est): 5MM-9.9MM **Privately Held**
WEB: www.premiercorp.net
SIC: 1799 1731 8748 Athletic & recreation facility construction; general electrical contractor; lighting consultant

(G-618)
RELIABLE MEDICAL SUPPLY INC
9401 Winnetka Ave N (55445-1618)
PHONE..............................763 255-3800
FAX: 763 566-4026
Jeffrey Hall, *President*
Debbie Kalk, *General Mgr*
John Hall, *Corp Secy*
EMP: 75 EST: 1989
SQ FT: 40,000
SALES (est): 5MM-9.9MM **Privately Held**
WEB: www.reliamed.com
SIC: 5047 Retails medical apparatus & supplies; wholesales medical equipment & supplies

(G-619)
TOYOTA-LIFT OF MINNESOTA INC
8601 Xylon Ct (55445-1840)
PHONE..............................763 425-9066
FAX: 763 425-4926
Lester Nielsen, *President*
Mark Juelich, *Vice Pres*
John Scheunemann, *Vice Pres*
Greg Sanders, *Vice Pres*
Kyle Thill, *Treasurer*
EMP: 66 EST: 1978
SQ FT: 63,000
SALES (est): 25MM-49.9MM **Privately Held**
WEB: www.mltonline.com
SIC: 5084 Wholesales industrial machinery & equipment

(G-620)
UNISOURCE WORLDWIDE INC
9001 Wyoming Ave N (55445-1835)
PO Box 1401, Minneapolis (55440-1401)
PHONE..............................763 488-7200
FAX: 763 331-0892
Keith Labla, *Vice Pres*
Mike Mathisen, *Vice Pres*
Keith Lablanc, *VP Sls/Mktg*
Lamar Lundell, *VP Mktg*
Peter Abell, *Business Anlyst*
EMP: 480
SQ FT: 500,000
SALES (est): 500MM-999.9MM **Privately Held**
WEB: www.unisourcelink.com
SIC: 5111 5112 5113 Wholesales printing & writing paper; wholesales industrial & personal service paper; wholesales stationery & office supplies
HQ: Unisource Worldwide Inc
6600 Governors Lake Pkwy
Norcross GA 30071
770 447-9000

(G-621)
VISIONS INC
8801 Wyoming Ave N (55445-1833)
PHONE..............................763 425-4251
Jon Otto, *CEO*
Rick Hanson, *President*
Stacy Swierenga, *Manager*
EMP: 100 EST: 1985
SQ FT: 35,000
SALES (est): 10MM-24.9MM **Privately Held**
WEB: www.visionsfirst.com
SIC: 7371 7336 7373 8742 Computer software development & applications; marketing consulting service; computer systems analysis & design; commercial art & graphic design services; commercial gravure printing; commercial lithographic printing

BROOKS
Red Lake County

(G-622)
PARADIS MAIL SERVICE INC
Hwy 92 (56715)
PO Box 97 (56715-0097)
PHONE..............................218 698-4613
Roger Paradis, *President*
Arnie Paradis, *Corp Secy*
Pam Paradis, *Office Mgr*
EMP: 50 EST: 1978
SALES (est): 1MM-4.9MM **Privately Held**
SIC: 4212 Local trucking without storage services

(G-623)
PARADIS MAIL SERVICE INC
812 Highway 92 W (56715-1505)
PO Box 97 (56715-0097)
PHONE..............................218 698-4613
Arnold Paradis, *President*
Roger Paradis, *Vice Pres*
Lonnie Paradis, *Treasurer*
Bryan Paradis, *Director*
Reza Roohi, *Bd of Directors*
EMP: 50 EST: 1960
SALES (est): 5MM-9.9MM **Privately Held**
WEB: www.paradisinc.com
SIC: 4212 4213 Contract mail carriers; long-distance refrigerated trucking services

BROOKSTON
Saint Louis County

(G-624)
ARROWHEAD TOWN HALL
9798 Highway 2 (55711-8027)
PHONE..............................218 879-6916
Troy Casper, *Superintendent*
Randy Willeck, *Superintendent*
Steve Emerson, *Superintendent*
Judy Ario, *Treasurer*
EMP: 30 EST: 1994
SALES (est): 5MM-9.9MM **Privately Held**
SIC: 6512 Operators of auditoriums & halls

BROWERVILLE
Todd County

(G-625)
LITTLE ELK YOUTH RANCH INC
31500 291st Ave (56438-4901)
PHONE..............................320 594-2750
Sheila M Johnston, *President*
Ronald B Johnston, *Corp Secy*
EMP: 28
SALES (est): 1MM-4.9MM **Privately Held**
WEB: www.littleelkranch.com
SIC: 7032 Boys' camp; girls' camp; religious organization

BROWNS VALLEY
Traverse County

(G-626)
BORDER STATES COOPERATIVE (PA)
23 4th St N (56219-0353)
PO Box 353 (56219-0353)
PHONE.................320 695-2575
FAX: 320 695-2441
Mike Toelle, *President*
Dale Rinas, *Vice Pres*
EMP: 30 EST: 1999
SALES (corp-wide): 13.50M Privately Held
WEB: www.bscoop.com
SIC: 5172 5191 Wholesales petroleum products; liquefied petroleum gas dealer; manufactures fertilizers; wholesales farm supplies; gas station

(G-627)
BROWNS VALLEY HEALTH CENTER
114 Jefferson St S (56219-9637)
PHONE.................320 695-2165
FAX: 320 695-2166
Carol Row, *CFO*
Jean Karst, *Human Res Mgr*
Claudia Ward, *Administrator*
EMP: 72 EST: 1990
SQ FT: 30,412
SALES (est): 1MM-4.9MM Privately Held
WEB: bvhc.sfhs.org
SIC: 8051 Skilled nursing care facility

(G-628)
SYNERGY ADVANTAGE GROUP INC
201 W Broadway (56219)
PHONE.................320 695-2000
Wendy Henning, *President*
April Meyer, *CFO*
EMP: 70 EST: 2002
SQ FT: 4,500
SALES (est): 1MM-4.9MM Privately Held
SIC: 7389 Telemarketing services

BROWNSDALE
Mower County

(G-629)
FIRST FARMERS & MERCHANTS
106 W Main St (55918-8818)
PO Box 157 (55918-0157)
PHONE.................507 567-2219
FAX: 507 498-3588
Dale Larson, *President*
Steve Drennan, *President*
Don N Peterson, *Exec VP*
Colleen Tebay, *Vice Pres*
Robert Gaulke, *Vice Pres*
EST: 1908 Privately Held
SIC: 6022 State commercial bank

(G-630)
I B INDUSTRIES INC
27199 State Highway 56 (55918-8018)
PHONE.................507 567-2701
FAX: 507 567-2152
Katherine Harte, *President*
Sue Anderson-Beyer, *Executive*
EMP: 55 EST: 1986
SQ FT: 110,000
SALES (est): 10MM-24.9MM Privately Held
WEB: www.ibidata.com
SIC: 7376 Computer facilities management service

BRUNO
Pine County

(G-631)
NEMADJI RESEARCH CORP
100 Birch St (55712)
PO Box 100 (55712-0100)
PHONE.................320 838-3838
FAX: 320 838-1414
Kim Bohnsack, *CEO*

Heidi Lourey, *Corp Secy*
Rebbeca J Lourey, *COO*
Aaron Oetterer, *Opers Staff*
Kevin Bostroum, *Manager*
EMP: 45 EST: 1991
SQ FT: 2,500
SALES (est): 5MM-9.9MM Privately Held
SIC: 7379 Data processing consulting service

BUCKMAN
Morrison County

(G-632)
SUNRISE AG COOPERATIVE (PA)
9361 Creamery Dr (56317)
PO Box 458 (56317-0458)
PHONE.................320 468-6433
FAX: 320 468-2807
Jack Hales, *Manager*
EMP: 36 EST: 1911
SQ FT: 3,200
SALES (corp-wide): 40M Privately Held
SIC: 5143 5191 Wholesales fluid milk & cream; wholesales agricultural chemicals; wholesales feed

BUFFALO
Wright County

(G-633)
ALLINA HEALTH SYSTEM
Also Called: Buffalo Hospital
303 Catlin St (55313-1947)
PHONE.................763 682-1212
FAX: 763 684-3884
Susan E Hunt, *Ch of Surgery*
Michael Murphy, *Ch of Surgery*
Jennifer B Emery, *Ch OB/GYN*
Kevin T Stieglbauer, *Ch Pathology*
Kurt K Scheurer, *Ch Radiology*
EMP: 425
SALES (est): 25MM-49.9MM Privately Held
WEB: www.allina.com
SIC: 8062 Medical hospital
PA: Allina Health System
    2925 Chicago Ave
    Minneapolis MN 55407
    612 775-5000

(G-634)
AUDITOR WRIGHT COUNTY
10 2nd St NW Rm 230 (55313-2159)
PHONE.................763 682-7578
FAX: 763 241-2869
Robert Hiivala, *Treasurer*
Douglas Gruber, *Manager*
Patrick Melvin, *Coordinator*
EMP: 26 EST: 1998
SALES (est): 1MM-4.9MM Privately Held
SIC: 8721 Auditing services

(G-635)
B & B SHEET METAL & ROOFING
210 Centennial Dr (55313-9000)
PHONE.................763 682-4233
FAX: 763 682-5620
Brad Burns, *President*
John Rosseau, *Vice Pres*
Richard Brown, *CFO*
Wes Jung, *Accounting Staf*
Dan Weber, *Info Tech Mgr*
EMP: 25 EST: 1982
SQ FT: 10,000
SALES (est): 1MM-4.9MM Privately Held
WEB: www.bbsheetmetalroofing.com
SIC: 1761 Roofing, siding & sheet metal work

(G-636)
BRUNSKILL ENTERPRISES
Also Called: Classic Cleaning Co
2992 Gabler Ave SE (55313-5202)
PHONE.................763 477-4546
Rick Brunskill, *Owner*
EMP: 30 EST: 1980
SALES (est): 500-999K Privately Held
SIC: 7349 Building cleaning service

(G-637)
BUFFALO CLINIC
1700 Highway 25 N (55313-1930)
PHONE.................763 682-1313
Thomas Ahrens MD, *President*
Tim J Cady MD, *Corp Secy*
Tracy Raiche, *Human Res Mgr*
Mary Huisman, *Office Mgr*
Brett G Oden MD, *Med Doctor*
EMP: 88 EST: 1973
SQ FT: 30,000
SALES (est): 10MM-24.9MM Privately Held
WEB: www.buffaloclinic.com
SIC: 8011 General & family practice physician or surgeon office

(G-638)
BUFFALO DRYCLEANERS
213 1st St S (55313-1403)
PHONE.................763 682-1061
FAX: 763 682-1666
Cheryl Ernesti, *President*
Ron Ernesti, *Vice Pres*
Crystal Boike, *Manager*
EMP: 49 EST: 1951
SALES (est): 1MM-4.9MM Privately Held
SIC: 7216 7213 Drycleaning collecting & distributing agency; linen supply service

(G-639)
BUFFALO LODGING
Also Called: Ruhr Development
1002 Highway 55 E (55313-8923)
PHONE.................763 682-5660
Kevin Homland, *Manager*
EMP: 25 EST: 1994
SALES (est): 1MM-4.9MM Privately Held
SIC: 7011 Hotel

(G-640)
CAMP GREENWOOD GIRL SCOUT
100 Garrison Ave NE (55313-9510)
PHONE.................763 684-4243
Shelley Jacobson, *CEO*
EMP: 30 EST: 1925
SALES (est): 1MM-4.9MM Privately Held
SIC: 7032 Girls' camp

(G-641)
CENTRAL MINNESOTA MENTAL
308 12th Ave S Ste 1 (55313-2322)
PHONE.................763 682-4400
FAX: 763 682-1353
Mickie Levine, *Office Mgr*
Bill Tregaskin, *Manager*
Fortunata G Milano, *Psychiatry*
Roger P Handrich, *Psychiatry*
EMP: 30
SALES (est): 1MM-4.9MM Privately Held
SIC: 8322 8093 Individual & family social services; outpatient mental health clinic
PA: Central Minnesota Mental
    1321 13th St N
    Saint Cloud MN 56303
    320 252-5010

(G-642)
CLASS ACT ESTATES SENIOR
801 Griffing Park Rd (55313-2018)
PHONE.................612 229-3881
Renee Robinson, *Owner*
EMP: 99
SALES (est): 1MM-4.9MM Privately Held
SIC: 8059 Nursing & personal care facility

(G-643)
COLDWELL BANKER BURNET REALTY
700 Highway 55 E (55313-1706)
PHONE.................763 682-2882
FAX: 763 684-5050
Todd Urvanski, *President*
Becky Schauft, *President*
Backy Chaust, *Vice Pres*
Tracie Bebeau, *Office Admin*
Donald Oudekerk, *Info Tech Dir*
EMP: 40 EST: 2003
SALES (est): 5MM-9.9MM Privately Held
SIC: 6531 Real estate services

(G-644)
FIRST STUDENT INC
1111 Bison Blvd (55313-4246)
PHONE.................763 682-5530
Patricia Gulden, *Manager*
EMP: 75
SALES (est): 1MM-4.9MM Privately Held
WEB: www.firststudentinc.com
SIC: 4151 School bus service
HQ: First Student Inc
    600 Vine St Ste 1400
    Cincinnati OH 45202
    513 241-2200

(G-645)
FUNCTIONAL INDUSTRIES INC
1801 N State Hwy 25 (55313)
PO Box 336 (55313-0336)
PHONE.................763 682-4336
FAX: 763 682-4336
Rodney N Pederson, *President*
Gary Schiro, *Production*
Laurie Cameron, *Director*
EMP: 72 EST: 1970
SQ FT: 16,500
SALES (est): 1MM-4.9MM Privately Held
WEB: www.functionalindustries.org
SIC: 8331 Work experience center

(G-646)
KID'S HAVEN OF BUFFALO INC
302 12th Ave S (55313-2305)
PHONE.................763 682-3072
FAX: 763 682-9552
Terry Peterson, *President*
Shawna Fadden, *Corp Secy*
Shawna Kenmir, *Sales/Mktg Mgr*
EMP: 55 EST: 1982
SQ FT: 17,000
SALES (est): 1MM-4.9MM Privately Held
WEB: www.kidshaven.net
SIC: 8351 Child day care service; preschool center

(G-647)
KLEINBANK
910 Commercial Dr (55313-1725)
PO Box 40 (55313-0040)
PHONE.................763 682-1142
Mary Reed, *Purch Agent*
EMP: 40
SALES (est): 10MM-24.9MM Privately Held
SIC: 6021 Commercial national trust companies with deposits

(G-648)
LAKE REGION CO-OP OIL ASSN
512 7th St NE (55313-1711)
PHONE.................763 682-1431
FAX: 763 682-1447
Jeff Johnson, *General Mgr*
Doug Triplett, *Vice Chairman*
Foley R Domjahn, *Member*
Bill Holthaus, *Treasurer*
Dan Malinski, *Office Mgr*
EMP: 25
SALES (est): 25MM-49.9MM Privately Held
SIC: 5171 Wholesales petroleum bulk stations; retail gasoline filling station
PA: Lake Region Co-Op Oil Assn
    4825 State Highway 55 NW
    Maple Lake MN 55358
    320 963-3137

(G-649)
LAKE RIDGE CARE CENTER OF
310 Lake Blvd S (55313-1456)
PHONE.................763 682-1434
Lesley Estoddard, *Office Mgr*
Chloe Luebbers, *Manager*
Krista Lindberg, *Manager*
Joel Nyquist, *Administrator*
Cindy Wandersee, *Coordinator*
EMP: 120 EST: 1918
SQ FT: 40,000
SALES (est): 1MM-4.9MM Privately Held
SIC: 8051 8059 Extended care facility; personal care home, with health care

(G-650)
MENARD INC
1415 County Road 134 (55313-9200)
PHONE 763 684-0830
Kevin Bahl, *Branch Mgr*
EMP: 250
SALES (est): 50MM-99.9MM **Privately Held**
WEB: www.menards.com
SIC: 5039 Wholesales prefabricated structures
PA: Menard Inc
5101 Menard Dr
Eau Claire WI 54703
715 876-5911

(G-651)
MIDLAND NURSERY INC
3536 State Highway 55 SE (55313-5241)
PHONE 763 478-6122
FAX: 763 478-9542
Harvey Foss, *President*
Terence D Marais, *Vice Pres*
EMP: 26 **EST:** 1965
SQ FT: 7,300 **Privately Held**
WEB: www.midlandnursery.com
SIC: 0782 5193 Landscaping services; wholesales nursery stock; retails nursery stock, seeds & bulbs

(G-652)
MINNESOTA DAIRY HERD
307 Brighton Ave S (55313-2303)
PHONE 763 682-1091
FAX: 763 682-1117
Larry Eggler, *President*
Bruce Dokebakken, *General Mgr*
Paul Fritsche, *Corp Secy*
Lisette Wright, *Controller*
Brian Munsterteiger, *Manager*
EMP: 63 **EST:** 1906
SQ FT: 5,000
SALES (est): 5MM-9.9MM **Privately Held**
WEB: www.mndhia.org
SIC: 8741 Management services

(G-653)
MORGAN TIRE & AUTO LLC
Also Called: Team Tires Plus
1002 3rd St S (55313-2309)
PHONE 763 682-4979
Russ Peterson, *Manager*
EMP: 30
SALES (est): 1MM-4.9MM **Privately Held**
WEB: www.bfsusa.com
SIC: 7534 Tire recapping & retreading services
HQ: Bfs Retail Operations LLC
333 E Lake St Ste 300
Bloomingdale IL 60108
630 259-9000

(G-654)
MORRIES NEW BUFFALO CHRYSLER
705 Highway 55 E (55313-1705)
PO Box 577 (55313-0577)
PHONE 763 682-1800
FAX: 763 765-1883
Maurice Wagner, *President*
Roy Quady, *General Mgr*
Michelle Mosbek, *Manager*
EMP: 48 **EST:** 1975
SQ FT: 10,300
SALES (est): 25MM-49.9MM **Privately Held**
SIC: 7538 New & used car dealer; general automotive repair services

(G-655)
OTTO ASSOCIATES ENGINEERS
9 Division St W (55313-1158)
PHONE 763 682-4727
FAX: 763 682-3522
Edward Otto, *President*
Paul Otto, *Vice Pres*
Cara Otto, *Vice Pres*
Martin P Campion, *Vice Pres*
Cara Schwahn, *Engineer*
EMP: 25 **EST:** 1980
SQ FT: 2,700
SALES (est): 1MM-4.9MM **Privately Held**
WEB: www.ottoassociates.com
SIC: 8713 8711 Surveying service; civil engineering services

(G-656)
PARK VIEW CARE CENTER INC
200 Park Ln (55313-1336)
PHONE 763 682-1131
FAX: 763 684-1044
Robert Dahl, *President*
Ronald Sanford, *CFO*
Christine Eilertson, *Finance Dir*
Chris Berg, *Office Mgr*
Angela Brown, *Manager*
EMP: 200 **EST:** 1962
SQ FT: 68,000
SALES (est): 5MM-9.9MM **Privately Held**
SIC: 8051 Skilled nursing care facility

(G-657)
SUNRISE SENIOR LIVING INC
201 1st St NE Ofc OFC (55313-1547)
PHONE 763 682-5489
FAX: 763 682-6511
Cheryl Klinkhammer, *Manager*
EMP: 35
SALES (est): 1MM-4.9MM **Publicly Held**
WEB: www.sunrise.com
SIC: 8051 Skilled nursing care facility
PA: Sunrise Senior Living Inc
7900 Westpark Dr Ste T900
Mc Lean VA 22102
703 273-7500

(G-658)
TOWER HILL ASSOCIATION
110 1st Ave NE (55313-1537)
PHONE 763 682-2321
Doc Evans, *Principal*
Wallace Peterson, *Chairman*
EMP: 39 **EST:** 1984 **Privately Held**
SIC: 8641 6531 Homeowners association; condominium managers

(G-659)
VON RUDEN MANUFACTURING INC
1008 1st St NE (55313-1755)
PO Box 699 (55313-0699)
PHONE 763 682-3122
FAX: 763 682-3954
Al Anderson, *President*
Mike Gutridge, *Sales Mgr*
Brandon Anderson, *Sales Staff*
Glen Stanberry, *Info Tech Mgr*
Larry Baldwin, *Maintence Staff*
EMP: 71 **EST:** 1989
SQ FT: 50,000
SALES (est): 10MM-24.9MM **Privately Held**
WEB: www.vonruden.com
SIC: 5013 Manufactures motor vehicle transmissions; manufactures speed changers, drives & gears; wholesales automotive supplies & parts; gray & ductile iron foundry

(G-660)
WILD MARSH GOLF CLUB LLC
1710 Montrose Blvd (55313-4477)
PHONE 763 682-4476
FAX: 763 682-0545
Dave Deem, *Member*
Joe Malone, *Mng Member*
Travis Nelson, *Manager*
EMP: 30 **EST:** 1999
SALES (est): 1MM-4.9MM **Privately Held**
WEB: www.wildmarsh.com
SIC: 7992 7997 Public golf course; membership recreation club

(G-661)
WRIGHT CONNECTION DTNH INC
Also Called: Functional Industries
1803 Hwy 25 N (55313)
PO Box 336 (55313-0336)
PHONE 763 682-2910
FAX: 763 682-9692
Rod Pederson, *President*
EMP: 25 **EST:** 1991
SALES (est): 1MM-4.9MM **Privately Held**
SIC: 8093 Outpatient rehabilitation treatment center

BUFFALO LAKE
Renville County

(G-662)
C J'S HOME HEALTH CARE INC
114 Church Ave W (55314)
PO Box 111 (55314-0111)
PHONE 320 833-2253
Julie Ufkes, *President*
Connie Augustine, *Vice Pres*
EMP: 45 **EST:** 2000
SALES (est): 1MM-4.9MM **Privately Held**
SIC: 8082 Home health care services

(G-663)
DUANE KOTTKE TRUCKING CORP
211 Hwy 212 E (55314)
PO Box 206 (55314-0206)
PHONE 320 833-5385
FAX: 320 833-5856
Kory Kottke, *President*
Kyle Kottke, *Corp Secy*
EMP: 30 **EST:** 1971
SQ FT: 2,000
SALES (est): 1MM-4.9MM **Privately Held**
WEB: www.kottke-trucking.com
SIC: 4212 Truck rental services with drivers

(G-664)
JULIE'S HELPING HANDS
114 Church Ave W (55314)
PO Box 111 (55314-0111)
PHONE 320 833-6082
Julie Ufkes, *Principal*
EMP: 140
SALES (est): 1MM-4.9MM **Privately Held**
SIC: 8082 Home health care services

(G-665)
K & S MILLWRIGHTS INC
217 E Hall Ave (55314)
PO Box 126 (55314-0126)
PHONE 320 833-2228
FAX: 320 833-2204
Bradley Krumrey, *President*
Susan Krumrey, *Corp Secy*
EMP: 32 **EST:** 1994
SALES (est): 1MM-4.9MM **Privately Held**
WEB: www.ksmillwrights.com
SIC: 1796 7699 Millwright; agricultural machinery & equipment repair services

(G-666)
KOTTKE TRUCKING INC
211 Hwy 212 E (55314)
PO Box 206 (55314-0206)
PHONE 320 833-5385
Kurt Kottke, *President*
Kyle Kottke, *Corp Secy*
Pam Kottke, *Manager*
EMP: 25 **EST:** 1940
SQ FT: 2,000
SALES (est): 1MM-4.9MM **Privately Held**
SIC: 4213 Long-distance refrigerated trucking services

(G-667)
OAKDALE COUNTRY CLUB INC
55106 County Road 38 (55314-2070)
PHONE 320 833-5518
FAX: 320 587-0526
Fred Glaeser, *President*
Tim A Franzeen, *President*
Mike Knodel, *General Mgr*
Oliver Schaeffer, *Corp Secy*
Chuck Brown, *Treasurer*
EMP: 30 **EST:** 1964
SALES (est): 1MM-4.9MM **Privately Held**
WEB: www.oakdalegolfclub.com
SIC: 7992 Public golf course

BUFFALO LAKE
Renville County

BUHL
Saint Louis County

(G-668)
OCCUPATIONAL DEVELOPMENT CTR
100 S Industrial Park Rd (55713)
PO Box B (55713)
PHONE 218 258-8926
Mike White, *Opers Staff*
EMP: 75
SALES (est): 1MM-4.9MM **Privately Held**
WEB: www.odcmn.com
SIC: 8331 Vocational rehabilitation agency
PA: Occupational Development Ctr
1520 Highway 32 S
Thief River Falls MN 56701
218 681-4949

(G-669)
ZIEGLER INC
10081 Hwy 169 (55713-0730)
PO Box 730 (55713-0730)
PHONE 218 258-3232
FAX: 218 258-3224
Pat Donnelly, *Manager*
EMP: 60
SALES (est): 25MM-49.9MM **Privately Held**
SIC: 5082 Wholesales construction & mining machinery
PA: Ziegler Inc
901 W 94th St
Minneapolis MN 55420
952 888-4121

BURNSVILLE
Dakota County

(G-670)
AAA MINNESOTA IOWA (PA)
600 W Travelers Trl (55337-2518)
PHONE 952 707-4222
FAX: 952 707-4978
Duane Crandall, *President*
Ron Siegmund, *Corp Secy*
Jeffrey Ogden, *CFO*
Megan Alessi, *Human Res Dir*
Megan Williams, *Human Res Dir*
EMP: 230 **EST:** 1907
SQ FT: 35,000 **Privately Held**
SIC: 8699 6331 Automobile owners' association; property & casualty insurance carrier

(G-671)
ABDALLAH INC
3501 County Road 42 W (55306-3805)
PHONE 952 890-4770
Steven R Hegedus Sr, *President*
Carrie Woolery, *CFO*
Stacy Schmidt, *Director*
EMP: 100 **EST:** 1937
SQ FT: 30,000
SALES (est): 25MM-49.9MM **Privately Held**
WEB: www.abdallahcandies.com
SIC: 5145 Wholesales confectionery products; manufactures chocolate candy; retail candy store

(G-672)
ACTION MOVING SERVICES INC
12400 Washburn Ave S (55337-1773)
PHONE 952 894-8888
FAX: 952 894-0020
Willard Everson, *CEO*
Paul Quehl, *Controller*
EMP: 60 **EST:** 1981
SQ FT: 30,000
SALES (est): 5MM-9.9MM **Privately Held**
WEB: www.actionmoving.com
SIC: 4213 4214 Long-distance moving services; contract haulers; local furniture moving & storage; local moving service & storage

(G-673)
ADVENTURE ZONE
13700 Nicollet Ave (55337-4003)
PHONE 952 890-7961
FAX: 952 686-9713
Jim Nodberg, *Owner*

EMP: 25 EST: 1988
SALES (est): 1MM-4.9MM **Privately Held**
WEB: www.adventurezone.com
SIC: 7999 Recreation services

(G-674)
AL'S CABINETS INC
14255 W Burnsville Pkwy (55306)
PHONE..................952 890-3500
FAX: 952 890-0355
Al Ellingson, *President*
Kevin L Croix, *Engineering*
Ray Olsen, *CFO*
Kevin Lac, *Manager*
EMP: 75 EST: 1978
SQ FT: 41,000
SALES (est): 5MM-9.9MM **Privately Held**
SIC: 1751 Manufactures wooden kitchen cabinets; cabinet & finish work carpentry service

(G-675)
ALTOBELLA HAIR PRODUCTS INC
14301 W Burnsville Pkwy (55306-4844)
PHONE..................952 707-1900
Rocco Altobelli, *President*
Diane Altobelli, *President*
Carmine Pontecorvo, *Vice Pres*
Tad Wells, *Vice Pres*
Mary Johns, *Controller*
EMP: 25 EST: 1984
SALES (est): 5MM-9.9MM **Privately Held**
SIC: 5087 Manufactures hair care products; wholesales beauty parlor equipment & supplies

(G-676)
AMES CONSTRUCTION INC (PA)
14420 County Road 5 (55306-4869)
PHONE..................952 435-7106
FAX: 952 435-7142
Raymond G Ames, *President*
Richard J Ames, *Chairman*
John A Ames, *Senior VP*
A A John Sr, *Senior VP*
Mark R Brennan, *Senior VP*
EMP: 400 EST: 1960
SQ FT: 30,000
SALES (corp-wide): 707.70M **Privately Held**
WEB: www.amesconstruction.com
SIC: 1611 1021 1041 1794 Airport runway construction; open pit copper ore mining; open pit gold mining; highway & street paving contractor; excavating contractor

(G-677)
ANALOG TECHNOLOGIES, CORP
11441 Rupp Dr (55337-1276)
PHONE..................952 894-9228
FAX: 952 894-2966
William Berg, *President*
Joshua Muonio, *Engineer*
Dave Lucas, *Manager*
Lee Lindberg, *Manager*
Kristen Chock, *Systems Mgr*
EMP: 35 EST: 1988
SQ FT: 3,000
SALES (est): 1MM-4.9MM **Privately Held**
WEB: www.analog-tech.com
SIC: 8711 8742 Electrical or electronic engineers; industrial consultant

(G-678)
ANDERSON DIESEL TRUCK SERVICE
12308 Dupont Ave S (55337-1603)
PHONE..................952 890-1580
Lois Anderson, *General Mgr*
EMP: 50
SALES (est): 1MM-4.9MM **Privately Held**
SIC: 7538 General truck repair services
PA: Anderson Diesel Truck Service
3686 140th St E
Rosemount MN 55068
651 480-7991

(G-679)
APOTHECARY PRODUCTS INC (PA)
11750 12th Ave S (55337-1297)
PHONE..................952 890-1940
FAX: 952 890-0418

Terrance Noble, *CEO*
Ron Barg, *President*
John A Creel, *COO*
James R Koeppl, *Senior VP*
Jacque Mathiason, *Purch Agent*
▲ **EMP: 130 EST:** 1975
SQ FT: 180,000 **Privately Held**
SIC: 5122 Manufactures druggists' pharmaceutical preparations; manufactures druggist's rubber sundries; manufactures rubber baby pacifiers; manufactures rubber teething rings; wholesales pharmaceuticals

(G-680)
ARBORS AT RIDGES
13810 Community Dr Ste A (55337-5502)
PHONE..................952 898-4005
FAX: 952 435-6686
Kim Worrel, *Manager*
EMP: 30 EST: 2004
SALES (est): 1MM-4.9MM **Privately Held**
SIC: 8361 8052 Residential care facility; intermediate care facility

(G-681)
ASTLEFORD EQUIPMENT CO INC
12541 Dupont Ave S (55337-1686)
PHONE..................952 894-9200
FAX: 952 890-5801
H S Dawson, *President*
Leon Astleford, *Corp Secy*
Layne Waters, *Controller*
Bill Wright, *Manager*
Mark Hagner, *Manager*
EMP: 45 EST: 1945
SQ FT: 35,000
SALES (est): 50MM-99.9MM **Privately Held**
WEB: www.astleford.com
SIC: 5012 5013 7538 Wholesales truck tractors; wholesales commercial trucks; truck engine repair service; wholesales truck parts & accessories

(G-682)
AUGUSTANA REGENT AT BURNSVILLE
14500 Regent Ln Apt 333 (55306-5571)
PHONE..................952 898-1910
FAX: 952 898-7257
Craig Kittelson, *Member*
April Barnhart, *Accounting Mgr*
EMP: 88 EST: 2004
SALES (est): 10MM-24.9MM **Privately Held**
SIC: 6513 Operators of retirement hotels

(G-683)
BECKHOFF AUTOMATION LLC
12150 Nicollet Ave (55337-1647)
PHONE..................952 890-0000
Hans Beckhoff, *Member*
Graham Harris, *Member*
Shane Novacek, *Marketing Staff*
Gerd Hoppe, *CTO*
EMP: 25 EST: 1998
SQ FT: 15,000
SALES (est): 10MM-24.9MM **Privately Held**
WEB: www.beckhoff.com
SIC: 5045 Wholesales computers, peripherals & software

(G-684)
BELCOURT CORP
3100 W Park Dr (55306-6971)
PHONE..................952 894-0406
Don N Belcourt, *President*
Wayne Fillbrandt, *General Mgr*
Linda Lucas, *Corp Secy*
Joy Wicklund, *Safety Mgr*
Jessica Hill, *Purchasing*
EMP: 48 EST: 1988
SQ FT: 30,000
SALES (est): 5MM-9.9MM **Privately Held**
WEB: www.belcourt.com
SIC: 5085 5199 Manufactures gaskets & sealing devices; manufactures die-cut paper & board; manufactures medical & laboratory rubber sundries & related products; manufactures rubber automotive products; manufactures rubber hardware; wholesales industrial gaskets

(G-685)
BEN FRANKLIN ELECTRIC INC
12401 Washburn Ave S (55337-1773)
PHONE..................952 888-2210
George Bruestle, *CEO*
Laura Bruestle, *Corp Secy*
Richard Lundberg, *Vice Pres*
Dave Lee, *Director*
Terry Bruestle, *Director*
EMP: 57 EST: 1979
SQ FT: 6,000
SALES (est): 5MM-9.9MM **Privately Held**
WEB: www.benfranklinelectric.com
SIC: 1731 General electrical contractor

(G-686)
BEREAN BAPTIST CHURCH
309 County Road 42 E (55306-4522)
PHONE..................952 432-7168
FAX: 952 431-0914
Art Morrow, *Managing Dir*
Roger Thompson, *Pastor*
Gary Anderson, *Manager*
Holly Calvillo, *Administrator*
EST: 1963
SQ FT: 48,500 **Privately Held**
WEB: www.bereanbaptist.com
SIC: 8351 Provides Baptist church services; child day care service

(G-687)
BUCA INC
14300 Burnhaven Dr (55306-4928)
PHONE..................952 892-7272
FAX: 952 892-5452
Jason Lyons, *Manager*
EMP: 60
SALES (est): 1MM-4.9MM **Privately Held**
WEB: www.bucainc.com
SIC: 7299 Full service Italian restaurant; banquet hall facility
PA: Buca Inc
1300 Nicollet Ave # 5003
Minneapolis MN 55403
612 225-2382

(G-688)
BUCK HILL INC (PA)
15400 Buck Hill Rd (55306-5418)
PHONE..................952 435-7174
Nancy Stone, *President*
Colby Lund, *Corp Secy*
Donald McClure, *Vice Pres*
Thomas Warner, *Vice Pres*
Doug Nordmeyer, *Administrator*
EST: 1954
SQ FT: 6,000 **Privately Held**
WEB: www.skibuck.com
SIC: 7011 7999 Ski lodge; eating place; retails skiing equipment; provides ski instruction; ski rental concession services

(G-689)
BURNSVILLE DEVELOPMENT LTD
Also Called: Holiday Inn Burnsville
14201 Nicollet Ave (55337-5773)
PO Box 5128, Mankato (56002-5128)
PHONE..................952 435-2100
William Schiebler, *Partner*
Richard Bienapfl, *Partner*
Arthur Petrie, *General Ptnr*
EMP: 95 EST: 1985
SALES (est): 5MM-9.9MM **Privately Held**
WEB: www.hiburnsville.com
SIC: 7011 Traveler accommodations; eating place; drinking establishment

(G-690)
BURNSVILLE FAMILY PHYSICIANS
625 E Nicollet Blvd # 100 (55337-6734)
PHONE..................952 435-0303
FAX: 952 892-5166
Barry A Bershow MD, *President*
Michelle Turner, *Administrator*
Barbara Sterner, *Officer*
Laura Schers, *Officer*
John D Rhoades MD, *Officer*
EMP: 30 EST: 1982
SALES (est): 1MM-4.9MM **Privately Held**
SIC: 8011 Clinic operated by physicians

(G-691)
BURNSVILLE HOCKEY CLUB
75 Civic Center Pkwy (55337-3807)
PHONE..................952 890-2333
Gerald Morris, *President*
EMP: 50 EST: 2001
SALES (est): 1MM-4.9MM **Privately Held**
WEB: www.blazehockey.com
SIC: 7997 Membership recreation club

(G-692)
BURNSVILLE VOLKSWAGEN INC
14700 Buck Hill Rd (55306-4984)
PHONE..................952 892-9400
C D Luther, *President*
Jay Radue, *General Mgr*
Barbara Hilbert, *Corp Secy*
Erich Wunderlich, *Parts Mgr*
Jon Eidness, *Parts Mgr*
EMP: 95 EST: 1978
SQ FT: 14,000
SALES (est): 25MM-49.9MM **Privately Held**
WEB: www.burnsvillevolkswagen.com
SIC: 7538 Retails new & used automobiles; general automotive repair services; retails auto & home supplies; used car dealer

(G-693)
C & C BUSINESS SOLUTIONS
2409 W 140th St (55337-4267)
PHONE..................612 875-9488
Brian Courrier, *Managing Prtnr*
EMP: 52 EST: 2004 **Privately Held**
SIC: 7375 Information retrieval services

(G-694)
C E C ENTERTAINMENT INC
Also Called: Chuck E Cheese's
1025 Burnsville Ctr (55306-4447)
PHONE..................952 892-7786
Dave Moss, *Manager*
EMP: 30
SALES (est): 1MM-4.9MM **Publicly Held**
WEB: www.chuckecheese.com
SIC: 7299 Limited service chain pizzeria restaurant; party & special event planning services
PA: C E C Entertainment Inc
4441 W Airport Fwy
Irving TX 75062
972 258-8507

(G-695)
CASH PASS NETWORK
181 S River Ridge Cir (55337-1627)
PHONE..................952 358-7080
Brad Rixminn, *Owner*
Jason Martin, *Co-Owner*
EMP: 40 EST: 2004
SALES (est): 1MM-4.9MM **Privately Held**
SIC: 7389 Financial service

(G-696)
CHARTHOUSE INTERNATIONAL
221 S River Ridge Cir (55337-1610)
PHONE..................952 890-1800
FAX: 952 890-0505
John Christensen, *President*
Vee Kanda, *Corp Secy*
Michael Schechter, *Corp Secy*
Charles Bragg, *COO*
Ray J Christensen, *Vice Pres*
EMP: 33 EST: 1959
SQ FT: 7,300
SALES (est): 5MM-9.9MM **Privately Held**
SIC: 7812 Educational motion picture production service; training motion picture production service

(G-697)
CHIN LEEANN INC
1132 Highway 13 E (55337-2901)
PHONE..................952 890-9012
FAX: 952 890-1056
Pat Perkins, *Manager*
Brandee Frank, *Manager*
Tom Webber, *Manager*
EMP: 50
SALES (est): 25MM-49.9MM **Privately Held**
WEB: www.leeannchin.com

SIC: **5146** Wholesales fish & seafood
HQ: Chin Leeann Inc
3600 Amercn Blvd W Ste 52
Bloomington MN 55431
952 896-3606

(G-698)
CITYSCAPE CONTRACTORS INC
12362 River Ridge Blvd (55337-1665)
PHONE...............................952 882-0020
FAX: 952 885-9173
Jeff Reiland, *President*
EMP: 80 EST: 1989
SQ FT: 7,000
SALES (est): 5MM-9.9MM **Privately Held**
WEB: www.cityscapepainting.com
SIC: **1721** Exterior residential painting
contractor; interior residential painting
contractor

(G-699)
CM CONSTRUCTION CO INC
12215 Nicollet Ave (55337-1650)
PHONE...............................952 895-8223
FAX: 952 895-8183
Mary L Peterson, *President*
Charles M Peterson, *Vice Pres*
Chuck Often, *Manager*
Jim Oliver, *Manager*
Jeff Sandnas, *Manager*
EMP: 40 EST: 1992
SQ FT: 4,500
SALES (est): 10MM-24.9MM **Privately Held**
SIC: **1541** Industrial building & warehouse
construction

(G-700)
COLDWELL BANKER BURNET INC (PA)
190 Cobblestone Ln (55337-4578)
PHONE...............................952 898-5100
Catherine Fucile, *Manager*
Tammy McWain, *Office Admin*
Lucy Petermeier, *Administrator*
Pete Kubiczki, *Administrator*
EMP: 84 EST: 1980
SQ FT: 6,900 **Privately Held**
WEB: www.ginnyandtim.com
SIC: **6531** Residential real estate agency

(G-701)
COMMUNITY ACTION COUNCIL INC
501 Highway 13 E Ste 102 (55337-2877)
PHONE...............................952 985-5300
Mary Ajax, *President*
Sharon Diedrich, *Manager*
Connie Mealman, *Manager*
Margarette Rindel, *Executive Asst*
EMP: 25 EST: 1970
SQ FT: 5,000
SALES (est): 1MM-4.9MM **Privately Held**
WEB: www.communityactioncouncil.org
SIC: **8322** Community center; multi-services
center; social services center

(G-702)
COMMUNITY DRUG & ALCOHOL SVCS
Also Called: Options Family & Behavior Svcs
501 Highway 13 E Ste 108 (55337-2877)
PHONE...............................952 564-3000
Brian P Sammon, *President*
Patricia M Patche, *Corp Secy*
Lisa Miller, *Manager*
EMP: 40 EST: 1998 **Privately Held**
SIC: **8399** Advocacy group

(G-703)
COORDINATED BUSINESS SYSTEMS
851 W 128th St (55337-2482)
PHONE...............................952 894-9460
FAX: 952 894-9238
James Oricchio, *President*
Donna Oricchio, *Treasurer*
Rebecca Noyes, *Manager*
Rick Silverston, *Manager*
Randy Olejnicak, *IT/INT Sup*
EMP: 58 EST: 1983
SQ FT: 26,000
SALES (est): 10MM-24.9MM **Privately Held**
WEB: www.coordinated.com
SIC: **5044** Wholesales office equipment

(G-704)
CSI INTERNATIONAL
615 E 132nd St (55337-3815)
PHONE...............................952 882-9115
John Rankin, *CEO*
EMP: 40
SALES (est): 5MM-9.9MM **Privately Held**
WEB: www.cuestasys.com
SIC: **7371** Computer software development

(G-705)
CYGNUS EXPOSITIONS
801 Cliff Rd E Ste 201 (55337-1534)
PHONE...............................952 894-8007
Julie Thompson, *Senior VP*
Robert Brice, *Vice Pres*
Steve Schneiderman, *Vice Pres*
Dave Holcomb, *Vice Pres*
Dave Iannone, *Vice Pres*
EMP: 60 EST: 1981
SALES (est): 5MM-9.9MM **Privately Held**
WEB: www.cygnusb2b.com
SIC: **7389** Trade show arrangement service
PA: Cygnus Business Media Inc
1233 Janesville Ave
Fort Atkinson WI 53538
920 563-6388

(G-706)
D & G PACKAGING CO
12039 Riverwood Dr (55337-1506)
PHONE...............................952 890-7525
FAX: 952 890-1697
Keith Reierson, *President*
Barb Nelson, *Corp Secy*
Curt Reierson, *Vice Pres*
Sandy Harme, *Manager*
Debbie Bolton, *Executive*
EMP: 40 EST: 1963
SQ FT: 30,000
SALES (est): 1MM-4.9MM **Privately Held**
WEB: www.dgpackaging.com
SIC: **7389** Packaging & labeling services

(G-707)
D D P MARKETING INC
13965 W Preserve Blvd (55337-7733)
PHONE...............................952 808-7615
Darin Pavlish, *CEO*
Dawn Otterblad, *Administrator*
EMP: 70 EST: 2000
SALES (est): 5MM-9.9MM **Privately Held**
SIC: **6411** Insurance agent

(G-708)
DAKOTA SUPPLY GROUP
12205 Nicollet Ave (55337-1650)
PHONE...............................952 890-3811
Todd Kumm, *Principal*
Ross Westby, *Controller*
EMP: 99
SALES (est): 50MM-99.9MM **Privately Held**
SIC: **5063** Wholesales electrical apparatus
& equipment

(G-709)
DATA LISTING SERVICES LLC (PA)
Also Called: Connection
11351 Rupp Dr Ste G (55337-1200)
PHONE...............................952 948-5488
FAX: 952 948-5498
Karen Soupir, *Vice Pres*
Corey Kotlarz, *Vice Pres*
Carol Cafferty, *Vice Pres*
Harvey Johnson, *VP Opers-Prdtn-*
Tim Austrums, *VP Sls/Mktg*
EMP: 80 EST: 1981
SQ FT: 12,000 **Privately Held**
WEB: www.the-connection.com
SIC: **7389** Telemarketing services

(G-710)
DATA SALES CO INC (PA)
3450 W Burnsville Pkwy (55337-4203)
PHONE...............................952 890-8838
FAX: 952 890-8917
Ronald C Breckner, *Ch of Bd*
Paul Breckner, *President*
Judith Breckner, *Corp Secy*
Robert Breckner, *Vice Pres*
William Breckner, *Vice Pres*
EMP: 90 EST: 1973
SQ FT: 177,000 **Privately Held**
WEB: www.datasales.com
SIC: **5045** **7377** Wholesales computers,
peripherals & software; computer hardware
rental or leasing; computer peripheral
equipment rental & leasing

(G-711)
DKG MANAGEMENT
12213 17th Ave S Apt B (55337-6836)
PHONE...............................214 776-1155
David Grubbs, *Partner*
EMP: 31 EST: 2002
SALES (est): 5MM-9.9MM **Privately Held**
WEB: www.dkgmanagementinc.com
SIC: **7999** Lifeguard services

(G-712)
DODGE OF BURNSVILLE INC
12101 Highway 35W S (55337-1642)
PHONE...............................952 894-9000
FAX: 952 894-9006
John J Adamich, *President*
Jenny Tidrick, *Parts Mgr*
Chuck Carlson, *CFO*
Keith Kirk, *Finance Mgr*
Greg Adamich, *Sales Mgr*
EMP: 50 EST: 1983
SQ FT: 15,000
SALES (est): 25MM-49.9MM **Privately Held**
WEB: www.dodgeofburnsville.com
SIC: **7538** Retails new & used automobiles;
automotive engine repair service

(G-713)
DUKE & KING ACQUISITION CORP (PA)
12252 Nicollet Ave (55337-1649)
PHONE...............................952 288-2300
Rodger Head, *President*
Becky M Hauer, *Vice Pres*
Babette Kittel, *Accounts Mgr*
EMP: 2800 EST: 2006 **Privately Held**
SIC: **6794** Selling or licensing of franchises

(G-714)
EAC DESIGN INC
14501 Judicial Rd Ste 10 (55306-5577)
PHONE...............................952 435-5533
FAX: 952 435-2440
Thane Hathaway, *President*
Bill Lough, *Vice Pres*
Robert Miller, *Vice Pres*
Edie Siemens, *Bookkeeper*
EMP: 49 EST: 1996
SQ FT: 1,600
SALES (est): 5MM-9.9MM **Privately Held**
WEB: www.eacdesign.com
SIC: **8711** Mechanical engineering services

(G-715)
EBENEZER RIDGES INC
13820 Community Dr (55337-4519)
PHONE...............................952 898-8400
Mark Thomas, *President*
Sharon Klessaas, *Vice Pres*
Kim Worrel, *Manager*
Lynn Lloyd, *Manager*
Julie Brewers, *Manager*
EMP: 180 EST: 1976
SQ FT: 15,000
SALES (est): 5MM-9.9MM **Privately Held**
WEB: www.mail.state.mn.us
SIC: **8051** Skilled nursing care facility

(G-716)
EBENEZER SOCIETY
13820 Community Dr (55337-4519)
PHONE...............................952 435-8116
Erin Hilligan, *Administrator*
EMP: 75
SALES (est): 1MM-4.9MM **Privately Held**
WEB: www.fairview.org
SIC: **8051** **8741** Skilled nursing care facility;
management services
HQ: Ebenezer Society
2722 Park Ave
Minneapolis MN 55407
612 874-3460

(G-717)
ELDERLY CARE SERVICES LLC
Also Called: Home Instead Senior Care
1600 Cliff Rd E (55337-1300)
PHONE...............................952 882-9300
FAX: 952 882-9301
Irina Salo, *Member*
Vitaly Salo, *Member*
EMP: 85 EST: 2003
SALES (est): 1MM-4.9MM **Privately Held**
SIC: **8082** Home health care services

(G-718)
EMERALD CREST OF BURNSVILLE
455 E Travelers Trl (55337-2891)
PHONE...............................952 736-0766
Sara Wilhelm, *Director*
EMP: 40 EST: 1998
SALES (est): 1MM-4.9MM **Privately Held**
WEB: www.emeraldcrest.com
SIC: **8052** Intermediate care facility

(G-719)
ERMC II LP
Also Called: Burnsville Center
1178 Burnsville Ctr (55306-6218)
PHONE...............................952 435-8182
Wendy Thompson, *Principal*
Pete Hurd, *Manager*
EMP: 30
SALES (est): 500-999K **Privately Held**
SIC: **7349** Lighting maintenance service
PA: Ermc II, LP
1 Park Pl 6148
Chattanooga TN 37421
423 899-2753

(G-720)
FAIRVIEW HEALTH SERVICES
201 E Nicollet Blvd (55337-5714)
PHONE...............................952 892-2910
FAX: 952 892-2041
Sara Criger, *CEO*
Steven Bernstein, *Ch of Surgery*
Raina Young, *Ch OB/GYN*
Laura D Neui, *Vice Pres*
Alan Lem, *Vice Pres*
EMP: 310
SALES (est): 25MM-49.9MM **Privately Held**
WEB: www.fairview.org
SIC: **8062** Medical hospital
PA: Fairview Health Services
2450 Riverside Ave
Minneapolis MN 55454
612 672-6300

(G-721)
FEDEX OFFICE & PRINT SERVICES
700 County Road 42 W (55337-4425)
PHONE...............................952 892-0200
FAX: 952 892-0241
Emily Isaac, *Manager*
John Heyer, *Manager*
Kevin Becker, *Manager*
EMP: 30
SALES (est): 1MM-4.9MM **Publicly Held**
WEB: www.kinkos.com
SIC: **7334** **4822** **7389** Photocopying &
duplicating services; book binding service;
manufactures coated & laminated paper;
facsimile transmission services; laminating
service; typesetting service
HQ: Fedex Office & Print Services
13155 Noel Rd Ste 1600
Dallas TX 75240
214 550-7000

(G-722)
FORCE AMERICA INC (PA)
501 Cliff Rd E Ste 100 (55337-1674)
PHONE...............................952 707-1300
FAX: 952 895-5312
Gerard Budzien, *Ch of Bd*
Steve Loeffler, *President*
Michael Lynch, *Senior VP*
John Stenz, *Senior VP*
Vincent Ahlers, *Vice Pres*
▲ EMP: 50 EST: 1969
SQ FT: 15,000 **Privately Held**
WEB: www.forceamerica.com

SIC: 5084 Wholesales industrial hydraulic systems equipment & supplies; manufactures drives, chains & sprockets

(G-723)
FRED MEYER JEWELERS INC
1043 Burnsville Ctr (55306-4447)
PHONE.............................952 892-6374
Damon Sanders, *Manager*
Brandon Meyer, *Manager*
EMP: 25
SALES (est): 10MM-24.9MM **Publicly Held**
WEB: www.kroger.com
SIC: 5094 Wholesales jewelry & precious stones
HQ: Fred Meyer Jewelers Inc
       3800 SE 22nd Ave
       Portland OR 97202
       503 232-8844

(G-724)
FREEDOM SERVICES INC
425 W Travelers Trl (55337-2554)
PO Box 3110 (55337-8110)
PHONE.............................952 890-6524
FAX: 952 890-7344
Ray Haugland, *President*
Yvonne Haugland, *Vice Pres*
EMP: 38 **EST:** 1978
SALES (est): 1MM-4.9MM **Privately Held**
SIC: 6411 Contract or fee basis medical insurance claim processing

(G-725)
FRONTIER COMMUNICATIONS OF MN
1405 W 150th St (55306-4949)
PHONE.............................952 898-6422
Beckie Blumenstein, *Branch Mgr*
EMP: 200 **Publicly Held**
WEB: www.czn.net
SIC: 4813 Wired telecommunications carrier & service
PA: Frontier Communications Corp
       3 High Ridge Park
       Stamford CT 06905
       203 614-5600

(G-726)
G C M INC
1211 Cliff Rd E (55337-1401)
PHONE.............................952 882-8500
Henry Meuwissen, *President*
Dave Baumgartner, *Vice Pres*
Jaysen Ruhoff, *Manager*
▲ **EMP:** 39 **EST:** 2001
SALES (est): 25MM-49.9MM **Privately Held**
SIC: 5045 Wholesales computers, peripherals & software

(G-727)
GENERAL PET SUPPLY INC
12155 Nicollet Ave (55337-1648)
PHONE.............................952 890-2300
FAX: 952 890-5800
Dan Eliott, *Manager*
EMP: 50
SALES (est): 25MM-49.9MM **Privately Held**
WEB: www.generalpet.com
SIC: 5199 5047 Wholesales pet supplies; wholesales veterinarians' equipment & supplies
HQ: General Pet Supply Inc
       7711 N 81st St
       Milwaukee WI 53223
       414 365-2600

(G-728)
GENZ-RYAN PLUMBING & HEATING
2200 Highway 13 W (55337-6024)
PHONE.............................952 882-1144
Daniel Ryan, *President*
John Ryan, *Corp Secy*
Michael Ryan, *Vice Pres*
Bob Ryan, *Treasurer*
EMP: 175 **EST:** 1950
SQ FT: 16,000
SALES (est): 10MM-24.9MM **Privately Held**
WEB: www.genzryan.com
SIC: 1711 Plumbing service; warm air heating & air conditioning contractor; retails plumbing & heating supplies

(G-729)
GLOBAL COMMUNICATION SERVICES
2224 E 117th St (55337-1265)
PHONE.............................952 890-3911
FAX: 952 890-4002
Allen Novine, *President*
Neal Neao, *Vice Pres*
Mario A Tristain, *Consultant*
EMP: 37 **EST:** 1988
SQ FT: 3,200
SALES (est): 1MM-4.9MM **Privately Held**
SIC: 7371 Computer programming service

(G-730)
GROSSMAN CHEVROLET CO INC
1200 W 141st St (55337-4437)
PHONE.............................952 435-8501
FAX: 952 435-9370
Harold Grossman, *Ch of Bd*
Michael Grossman, *President*
Ron Robinson, *Controller*
James Thomas, *Finance*
Bill Bent, *Human Res Mgr*
EMP: 120 **EST:** 1919
SQ FT: 43,000
SALES (est): 50MM-99.9MM **Privately Held**
SIC: 5013 Retails new & used automobiles; wholesales automotive supplies & parts; retails new & used pickups; retails new & used vans

(G-731)
HI-TECH FLOORS INC
12701 Sheridan Ave # 101 (55337-1993)
PHONE.............................952 895-1602
FAX: 952 894-2616
David L Phillips Jr, *President*
Andrea Dessler, *Corp Secy*
Albert Snow, *Vice Pres*
Andrea Pears, *Manager*
EMP: 30 **EST:** 1981
SQ FT: 28,000
SALES (est): 1MM-4.9MM **Privately Held**
WEB: www.hi-techfloors.com
SIC: 1771 Flooring contractor

(G-732)
HOLLSTADT & ASSOCIATES INC
200 E Travelers Trl # 210 (55337-4191)
PHONE.............................952 892-3660
FAX: 952 892-5044
James J Jungbauer, *President*
Nancy Quinnellsenior, *Vice Pres*
Suann Shelleny, *CFO*
Amy Jensen, *CFO*
Steve Ask, *Controller*
EMP: 100 **EST:** 1990
SALES (est): 10MM-24.9MM **Privately Held**
WEB: www.hollstadt.com
SIC: 8742 Management consulting services

(G-733)
HUBER BROS BUILDING MAINTENCE
12040 Riverwood Cir (55337-1527)
PHONE.............................952 224-7000
FAX: 952 224-7006
Dan Huber, *President*
Jacob Beebe, *Vice Pres*
Bob Hawkins, *Manager*
EMP: 31 **EST:** 1990
SALES (est): 500-999K **Privately Held**
SIC: 7349 Building cleaning service

(G-734)
ICENTERA INC
14551 Judicial Rd Ste 121 (55306-5188)
PHONE.............................952 898-0888
Craig A Nelson, *President*
Richard J Pleczko, *Member*
Steve Odom, *Member*
David Hsieh, *Member*
Craig Dembeck, *Senior VP*
EMP: 40 **EST:** 2003
SQ FT: 4,500
SALES (est): 5MM-9.9MM **Privately Held**
SIC: 7371 Computer software development

(G-735)
IMAGE SEA CO'S INC
11900 Portland Ave (55337-1516)
PHONE.............................952 882-0884
Pete Mattson, *President*
Bob Conzemius, *Assistant VP*
Marty Dudenhoffer, *Vice Pres*
Roger Campbell, *Buyer*
Nicole Rosga, *Accounts Mgr*
EMP: 80 **EST:** 1980
SALES (est): 5MM-9.9MM **Privately Held**
WEB: www.mhccom.com
SIC: 7389 Printing broker

(G-736)
INNOVATIVE OFFICE SOLUTIONS
151 Cliff Rd E Ste 40 (55337-1586)
PO Box 270107, Minneapolis (55427-6107)
PHONE.............................952 808-9900
Jason Player, *Member*
Brooks Smith, *CFO*
Jennifer Smith, *Mng Member*
Jennifer Rosenzweig, *Manager*
EMP: 57 **EST:** 2001
SQ FT: 15,000
SALES (est): 10MM-24.9MM **Privately Held**
WEB: www.innovativeos.com
SIC: 5112 5021 Wholesales office supplies; wholesales office furniture

(G-737)
IRONWOOD ELECTRONICS INC
11351 Rupp Dr Ste 400 (55337-1200)
PHONE.............................952 229-8200
Mickiel P Fedde, *President*
Kenneth Krawza, *Opers Staff*
Ranjit Patil, *Rsch/Dvlpt Dir*
Prem Borse, *QC Mgr*
Sultan Faiz, *Electrical Engi*
EMP: 33 **EST:** 1986
SQ FT: 9,600
SALES (est): 1MM-4.9MM **Privately Held**
WEB: www.ironwoodelectronics.com
SIC: 5065 Manufactures electronic circuits; manufactures electronic connectors; wholesales electronic parts & equipment

(G-738)
JAMES R HILL INC
Also Called: Jim Hill & Associates
2500 County Road 42 W # 120 (55337-6945)
PHONE.............................952 890-6044
FAX: 952 890-6244
Joel Cooper, *President*
Harold Peterson, *Vice Pres*
Kurt Quaintance, *Vice Pres*
James Hill, *Treasurer*
EMP: 50 **EST:** 1976
SALES (est): 1MM-4.9MM **Privately Held**
WEB: www.jrhinc.com
SIC: 8713 8711 Surveying service; engineering services

(G-739)
KEEP IN TOUCH OF BURNSVILLE
1100 County Road 42 E # 104 (55337-6730)
PHONE.............................952 953-3313
Phillis Schwartz, *President*
EMP: 30 **EST:** 1980
SALES (est): 1MM-4.9MM **Privately Held**
SIC: 7299 Massage parlor

(G-740)
KELLEHER CONSTRUCTION CORP
11531 Rupp Dr (55337-1248)
PHONE.............................952 890-6772
Thomas Kelleher, *President*
Jim Carey, *Controller*
Chad Bagne, *Manager*
EMP: 30 **EST:** 1983
SQ FT: 4,300
SALES (est): 1MM-4.9MM **Privately Held**
WEB: www.kelleherconstruction.com
SIC: 1771 Concrete contractor

(G-741)
KENSINGTON EQUITY PARTNERS INC
11974 Portland Ave (55337-1516)
PHONE.............................952 808-1800
William Schluter, *CEO*
Gary Gangstee, *President*
Richard Palmer, *Manager*
Jason Nyberg, *Manager*
EST: 2003
SQ FT: 3,800 **Privately Held**
SIC: 8748 Business consulting services

(G-742)
KIT FUCILE
190 Cobblestone Ln (55337-4578)
PHONE.............................952 435-3030
Kit Fucile, *Principal*
Donna Kenny, *Finance*
EMP: 80 **EST:** 2003
SALES (est): 10MM-24.9MM **Privately Held**
SIC: 6531 Real estate agency & broker

(G-743)
KRL EXTERIOR INC
15501 Kings Ct (55306-5375)
PHONE.............................612 296-0222
Ken Lang, *Principal*
Joy Lang, *CFO*
EMP: 69 **EST:** 1990
SALES (est): 10MM-24.9MM **Privately Held**
SIC: 1521 Residential remodeling

(G-744)
L A FITNESS INTERNATIONAL LLC
1801 County Road 42 W (55306-6220)
PHONE.............................952 392-4400
Nate Hainline, *Manager*
EMP: 35
SALES (est): 1MM-4.9MM **Privately Held**
WEB: www.proresultsfit.com
SIC: 7991 Exercise facilities
PA: L A Fitness International LLC
       2600 Michelson Dr Ste 300
       Irvine CA 92612
       949 255-7200

(G-745)
L&W SUPPLY CORP
Also Called: M & S Drywall Supply
12450 Beard Ave S (55337-1704)
PHONE.............................952 890-0828
FAX: 952 890-2320
Scott Holt, *Manager*
Jeff Hessa, *Manager*
Michael J Brings, *Manager*
EMP: 25
SQ FT: 16,380
SALES (est): 5MM-9.9MM **Publicly Held**
WEB: www.lwsupply.com
SIC: 5032 Wholesales brick, stone & related products
HQ: L & W Supply Corp
       125 S Franklin St Fl 7
       Chicago IL 60606
       312 436-4000

(G-746)
LAMETTRY COLLISION INC
Also Called: Lamettry's Collision
14601 Burnhaven Dr (55306-6127)
PHONE.............................952 898-1636
Denise Koukal, *Manager*
Steve Daniels, *Manager*
EMP: 30
SALES (est): 1MM-4.9MM **Privately Held**
WEB: www.lamettrys.com
SIC: 7532 Automotive body, paint & interior repair & maintenance services

(G-747)
LANCET SOFTWARE DEVELOPMENT
11980 Portland Ave (55337-1516)
PHONE.............................952 230-7360
Thomas M Niccum, *President*
Jaime Plante Vice Pre, *Vice Pres*
Chris Holtan, *Vice Pres*
Ken Tarr, *Controller*
Kathie Doty, *Accounting Dir*
EMP: 36 **EST:** 1997

SALES (est): 1MM-4.9MM Privately Held
SIC: 7371 Computer software development

(G-748)
LEMASTER RESTORATION INC
14261 W Burnsville Pkwy (55306-6975)
PHONE...........................952 707-1256
FAX: 952 707-8125
Verdean Lemaster, President
Glaeser Marcia, Sales Executive
EMP: 50 EST: 1988
SALES (est): 10MM-24.9MM Privately Held
SIC: 1522 1521 1799 Multi-family home remodeling service; post disaster renovations service; single-family housing construction

(G-749)
LINDHAUS USA INC
2500 County Road 42 W # 12 (55337-6945)
PO Box 159, Savage (55378-0159)
PHONE...........................952 707-1131
Michele Massaro, President
Enrico Massaro, Vice Pres
Sam Theis, Accounting Mgr
▲ EMP: 35 EST: 1992
SQ FT: 2,000
SALES (est): 25MM-49.9MM Privately Held
WEB: www.lindhaususa.com
SIC: 5064 Wholesales household vacuum cleaners

(G-750)
MACKIN BOOK CO
3505 County Road 42 W (55306-3803)
PHONE...........................952 895-9540
FAX: 952 894-8806
Randal Heise, President
Pat Kempton, General Mgr
Kay M Heise, Vice Pres
Bob Dearen, Sales Staff
Joanne Richards, Sales Staff
EMP: 350 EST: 1985
SQ FT: 57,000
SALES (est): 100MM-499.9MM Privately Held
WEB: www.mackin.com
SIC: 5192 Wholesales books

(G-751)
MARTIN CALIBRATION INC
11965 12th Ave S Ste 100 (55337-1421)
PHONE...........................952 882-1528
FAX: 952 882-4086
Richard L Brion, President
Kim McDonald, Accountant
Monte Martin, Info Tech Dir
Bill Martin, Info Tech Dir
EMP: 25 EST: 1980
SQ FT: 6,000
SALES (est): 1MM-4.9MM Privately Held
WEB: www.martincalibration.com
SIC: 8734 Calibrating & certification services

(G-752)
MEDIA RELATIONS INC
350 W Burnsville Pkwy # 350 (55337-8804)
PHONE...........................612 798-7200
Lonny Kocina, President
Michelle Roddie, VP Purch
Robin Kocina, CFO
Cynthia Bock, CTO
EMP: 44 EST: 1988
SQ FT: 8,100
SALES (est): 5MM-9.9MM Privately Held
SIC: 7336 7371 8743 Art design service; public relations & publicity services; computer programming service

(G-753)
METRO DENTAL CARE
14344 Burnhaven Dr (55306-4928)
PHONE...........................952 435-8525
FAX: 952 435-6229
Shelly Ryan, Owner
Deanna Alevizos DDS, Dentist
EMP: 40 EST: 1979
SALES (est): 1MM-4.9MM Privately Held
WEB: www.metrodentalcare.com
SIC: 8021 Dental office

(G-754)
METROPOLITAN PEDIATRIC
303 E Nicollet Blvd Ste 260 (55337-4592)
PHONE...........................952 435-2450
FAX: 952 892-0217
Sally Vissers, Administrator
Thomas R Sealey, Director
Laurie Harris, Lab Dir
Mari B Daniels, Pediatrics
Melissa A Clark, Pediatrics
EMP: 35
SALES (est): 1MM-4.9MM Privately Held
SIC: 8011 Pediatrician office

(G-755)
MG KRAUS CONSTRUCTION LLC
1504 E 122nd St (55337-6804)
PHONE...........................952 895-5300
Geris Kraus, Member
EMP: 25
SALES (est): 1MM-4.9MM Privately Held
SIC: 1742 Drywall, plastering & insulation contractor

(G-756)
MHC SOFTWARE INC ✪
11900 Portland Ave (55337-1516)
PO Box 1749 (55337-0749)
PHONE...........................952 882-0884
FAX: 952 882-0484
John Shields, President
Robert Convemius, Vice Pres
Pete Mattson, Treasurer
Sherry Diedrich, Advt Staff
EMP: 80 EST: 2008
SALES (est): 10MM-24.9MM Privately Held
SIC: 7371 Retails computer software & accessories; computer software development & applications

(G-757)
MICHAEL C MAGNUSON
625 E Nicollet Blvd # 100 (55337-6734)
PHONE...........................952 435-0303
Michael C Magnuson, Partner
EMP: 25 EST: 2001
SALES (est): 1MM-4.9MM Privately Held
SIC: 8011 Physicians' office & clinic

(G-758)
MIDWEST SPINE INSTITUTE LLC
675 E Nicollet Blvd # 245 (55337-6741)
PHONE...........................651 430-3800
Thomas Rieser, President
Craig S Wilson, Administrator
Tad Swanson, Administrator
Greg Maurer, Administrator
EMP: 50 EST: 1987
SQ FT: 5,054
SALES (est): 5MM-9.9MM Privately Held
SIC: 8011 Orthopedic physician office

(G-759)
MIDWEST VETERINARY SUPPLY INC (PA)
11965 Larc Ind Blvd (55337-1416)
PO Box 946 (55337-0946)
PHONE...........................952 894-4350
Guy G Flickinger, President
Cheryl Peterson, Exec VP
Thomas Wheeler, Vice Pres
Scott Davis, Treasurer
Jay Kottke, Controller
EMP: 50 EST: 1959
SQ FT: 25,000 Privately Held
SIC: 5122 5047 Wholesales animal medicines; wholesales veterinarians' equipment & supplies

(G-760)
MOTOROLA INC
2900 County Road 42 W # 120 (55337-4855)
PHONE...........................952 895-7800
Greg Kester, Opers Staff
Al Uecker, Senior Engr
Guy Kelnhoser, Branch Mgr
Greg Pfaff, Manager
Tam Huynh, IT/INT Sup
EMP: 150 Publicly Held
WEB: www.motorola.com

SIC: 4812 Cellular telephone services
PA: Motorola Inc
1303 E Algonquin Rd
Schaumburg IL 60196
847 576-5000

(G-761)
MUNTERS CORP
Also Called: Moisture Control Services
1800 Cliff Rd E Ste 8 (55337-1375)
PHONE...........................952 831-9418
FAX: 952 736-0115
Tom Harrhala, Manager
EMP: 300
SALES (est): 100MM-499.9MM Privately Held
WEB: www.muntersamerica.com
SIC: 5075 Wholesales dehumidifiers
HQ: Munters Corp
210 6th St
Fort Myers FL 33907
239 936-1555

(G-762)
NATIONAL CAMERA EXCHANGE INC
14380 Burnhaven Dr (55306-4928)
PHONE...........................952 898-4888
FAX: 952 898-3396
Steve Carroll, Manager
EMP: 26
SALES (est): 1MM-4.9MM Privately Held
SIC: 7384 7622 Retails cameras; retails video cameras, recorders & accessories; retails photographic supplies; retails binoculars; photofinishing laboratory; video repair service

(G-763)
NORTHERN COMPUTER TECHNOLOGIES (PA)
Also Called: Nor-Tech
901 Cliff Rd E (55337-1512)
PHONE...........................952 808-1000
FAX: 952 808-1001
David Bollig, President
Bob Dreis, General Mgr
Lina MA, Corp Secy
David Chang, Treasurer
EMP: 30 EST: 1998
SQ FT: 26,000 Privately Held
WEB: www.nor-tech.com
SIC: 5045 Wholesales computers, peripherals & software

(G-764)
NORTHERN TOOL & EQUIPMENT CO
12205 River Ridge Blvd (55337-1607)
PHONE...........................952 894-0326
Charles Albrecht, Exec VP
Brad Beckman, Controller
Barry Johnson, Manager
Jean Krogen, CTO
EMP: 40
SALES (est): 1MM-4.9MM Privately Held
WEB: www.northerntool.com
SIC: 7389 Personal service agents
PA: Northern Tool & Equipment Co
2800 Southcross Dr W
Burnsville MN 55306
952 894-9510

(G-765)
NORTHLAND CONCRETE & MASONRY
12026 Riverwood Dr (55337-1507)
PHONE...........................952 890-1650
FAX: 952 890-1699
Doug Schieffer, President
Allan Skogquist, Vice Pres
Mary Feldt, Controller
EMP: 89 EST: 1976
SQ FT: 18,000
SALES (est): 5MM-9.9MM Privately Held
WEB:
www.northlandconcreteandmasonry.com
SIC: 1741 1771 Masonry & stonework contractor; concrete contractor

(G-766)
NORTHLAND TRANSPORTATION INC
11990 Riverwood Dr (55337-1505)
PHONE...........................952 922-6876
Sherri L Howard, President
EMP: 50 EST: 1992
SALES (est): 1MM-4.9MM Privately Held
SIC: 4119 Local passenger transportation service

(G-767)
NORTHWEST BITUMINOUS INC
12400 Beard Ave S (55337-1704)
PHONE...........................952 890-3005
Clayton Larson, President
Mark Larson, Vice Pres
EMP: 50 EST: 1989
SQ FT: 7,000
SALES (est): 5MM-9.9MM Privately Held
WEB: www.northwestbit.com
SIC: 1611 Highway & street resurfacing contractor

(G-768)
NORTHWEST INVESTORS INC
Also Called: Lakeview Care Center
1905 E 123rd St (55337-2907)
PHONE...........................952 894-7795
Antonio Cruz, President
Milagros Cruz, Vice Pres
EMP: 30
SALES (est): 1MM-4.9MM Privately Held
SIC: 8051 Skilled nursing care facility

(G-769)
NU-LOOK EXTERIORS INC
3801 W 145th St (55306-5098)
PHONE...........................952 882-8787
FAX: 952 882-7860
Harley Williams, President
Michael Seaton, Vice Pres
Juli Strot, Manager
Brett Looney, Manager
EMP: 30 EST: 1977
SQ FT: 13,000
SALES (est): 1MM-4.9MM Privately Held
WEB: www.nulook.net
SIC: 1761 Architectural sheet metal work contractor

(G-770)
OPTIONS RESIDENTIAL INC
2709 Highland Dr (55337-2117)
PHONE...........................952 564-3030
Brian P Sammon, President
Patricia M Patche, Corp Secy
EMP: 127 EST: 2005
SALES (est): 1MM-4.9MM Privately Held
SIC: 8322 Adult daycare center

(G-771)
OSBORNE PROPERTIES LP
Also Called: Kraus-Anderson Insurance Agcy
420 Gateway Blvd (55337-2790)
PHONE...........................952 890-0414
Dennis Diessner, General Mgr
EMP: 60
SQ FT: 5,074
SALES (est): 5MM-9.9MM Privately Held
SIC: 6411 Insurance agent
PA: Osborne Properties LP
420 Gateway Blvd
Burnsville MN 55337
952 707-8200

(G-772)
OSBORNE PROPERTIES LP (PA)
Also Called: Kraus Anderson Insurance
420 Gateway Blvd (55337-2790)
PHONE...........................952 707-8200
FAX: 952 890-0535
Daniel Engelsma, Partner
Barbara Diessner, Ltd Ptnr
Bruce Engelsma, Ltd Ptnr
Sharon Korsh, Ltd Ptnr
Susan Wilcox, Ltd Ptnr
EMP: 60 EST: 1972
SQ FT: 25,000 Privately Held
SIC: 6411 6512 Insurance agent; nonresidential building operator

GEOGRAPHIC

(G-773)
OSLAND JANITORIAL SUPPLY INC
1401 Cliff Rd E (55337-1413)
PHONE 952 894-4815
FAX: 952 895-1539
Charlie Osland, *President*
Paul Osland, *Office Mgr*
EMP: 45 EST: 1985
SQ FT: 3,000
SALES (est): 10MM-24.9MM **Privately Held**
SIC: 5087 7349 Wholesales cleaning & maintenance equipment & supplies; wholesales janitorial equipment & supplies; janitorial & custodial services

(G-774)
PAL MANAGEMENT INC
181 S River Ridge Cir (55337-1627)
PHONE 952 646-1792
Brad Hixmann, *President*
Brad Rixmann, *President*
EMP: 99 EST: 2001
SALES (est): 5MM-9.9MM **Privately Held**
WEB: www.pawnamerica.com
SIC: 8741 Management services

(G-775)
PARK NICOLLET CLINIC
14000 Fairview Dr (55337-5713)
PHONE 952 993-8700
FAX: 952 993-8516
Ann Symington, *Office Mgr*
Edward Szklarczuk, *Chiropractor*
Thuy Husmann, *Manager*
Barbra Hedding, *Administrator*
Dale N Akkerman, *Obstetrician*
EMP: 300
SALES (est): 25MM-49.9MM **Privately Held**
WEB: www.ccopnet.com
SIC: 8011 Physicians' office & clinic
HQ: Park Nicollet Clinic
    3800 Park Nicollet Blvd
    Minneapolis MN 55416
    952 993-3123

(G-776)
PARTNERS IN EXCELLENCE INC
14301 Ewing Ave S (55306-5515)
PHONE 952 746-5350
FAX: 952 746-6131
Debbie Thomas, *Principal*
EMP: 60 EST: 2000
SALES (est): 1MM-4.9MM **Privately Held**
SIC: 8093 Outpatient mental health clinic

(G-777)
PAYDAY AMERICA LLC
181 S River Ridge Cir (55337-1627)
PHONE 952 646-1793
Brad Rixmann, *President*
Bradley Rickman, *Member*
Allisa Pemple, *Manager*
EMP: 34 EST: 2000
SALES (est): 5MM-9.9MM **Privately Held**
WEB: www.paydayamerica.net
SIC: 6141 Personal consumer finance company

(G-778)
PCL CONSTRUCTION SERVICES INC
12200 Nicollet Ave (55337-1652)
PHONE 952 882-9600
Bruce K Lowell, *Corp Secy*
G M Hannaway, *Treasurer*
Collin Terras, *Human Res Mgr*
Fred Auch, *Branch Mgr*
Don Fromme, *Manager*
EMP: 25
SALES (est): 5MM-9.9MM **Privately Held**
WEB: www.pcl.com
SIC: 1542 Commercial & institutional building construction
DH: PCL Construction Services Inc
    2000 S Colorado Blvd 2-500
    Denver CO 80222
    303 365-6500

(G-779)
PCL CONSTRUCTION SERVICES INC
12200 Nicollet Ave (55337-1652)
PHONE 952 882-9600
EMP: 60
SALES (est): 10MM-24.9MM **Privately Held**
WEB: www.pcl.com
SIC: 1542 New commercial & office building construction; hospital construction; school building construction; specialized public building contractors
DH: PCL Construction Services Inc
    2000 S Colorado Blvd 2-500
    Denver CO 80222
    303 365-6500

(G-780)
PEOPLE INC
904 McAndrews Rd W (55337-4460)
PHONE 952 736-7802
Tim Bricketts, *President*
EMP: 29 EST: 2005 **Privately Held**
SIC: 8699 Charitable organization

(G-781)
PHOENIX DISTRIBUTING INC
Also Called: Comm Center
451 Cliff Rd E Ste 108 (55337-1675)
PHONE 952 882-9949
Carl Hartell, *President*
Pat Hartell, *Corp Secy*
Jamie Liebrecht, *Manager*
Rob O'Neill, *Bd of Directors*
John Young, *Assistant*
EMP: 25 EST: 1976
SQ FT: 8,000
SALES (est): 1MM-4.9MM **Privately Held**
SIC: 7622 7629 Retails two-way, citizens band, weather & short-wave radios; radio repair & installation service; automotive radio repair service; telecommunication equipment repair service

(G-782)
PRIMERICA FINANCIAL SERVICES
900 W 128th St Ste 110A (55337-2456)
PHONE 952 895-1091
FAX: 952 440-6578
Melanie Eldeen, *Assistant VP*
Dallas Eldeen, *Manager*
EMP: 60
SALES (est): 5MM-9.9MM **Publicly Held**
WEB: www.primerica.com
SIC: 6411 6282 Insurance services; financial investment advice service
HQ: Primerica Financial Services
    3120 Breckinridge Blvd
    Duluth GA 30099
    800 544-5445

(G-783)
R & D BATTERIES INC
3300 Corporate Center Dr (55306)
PO Box 5007 (55337-0697)
PHONE 952 890-0629
FAX: 952 890-7912
Randall C Noddings, *President*
Barbara Noddings, *Vice Pres*
Gloria Kowalke, *Manager*
◆ EMP: 44 EST: 1989
SQ FT: 15,000
SALES (est): 5MM-9.9MM **Privately Held**
WEB: www.rdbatteries.net
SIC: 5063 Manufactures storage batteries; manufactures dry & wet batteries; wholesales industrial storage batteries; manufactures rechargeable batteries

(G-784)
RDO CONSTRUCTION EQUIPMENT CO
12500 Dupont Ave S (55337-1604)
PHONE 952 890-8880
FAX: 952 890-3886
Christi Offutt, *President*
Steve Tufto, *Finance*
EMP: 64
SALES (est): 25MM-49.9MM **Privately Held**
SIC: 5082 5083 Wholesales road construction equipment; wholesales general construction machinery & equipment; wholesales farm equipment parts & supplies
HQ: Rdo Construction Equipment Co
    2829 University Dr S
    Fargo ND 58103
    701 223-5798

(G-785)
RE MAX ADVISORS
1500 McAndrews Rd W Ste 200 (55337-4445)
PHONE 952 898-1112
FAX: 952 892-8464
Ray Droede, *President*
Mike Safi, *Vice Pres*
EMP: 30 EST: 1996
SALES (est): 5MM-9.9MM **Privately Held**
SIC: 6531 Residential real estate agency

(G-786)
RECOVERY ONE INC
14420 County Road 5 (55306-4869)
PHONE 952 435-7106
Richard J Ames, *President*
EMP: 250 EST: 1963
SALES (est): 10MM-24.9MM **Privately Held**
SIC: 8741 Construction management services

(G-787)
RED ROOF INNS INC
12920 Aldrich Ave S (55337-2388)
PHONE 952 890-1420
FAX: 952 890-1586
Tim Cramer, *General Mgr*
Dean Hoyt, *General Mgr*
Eric Homstad, *General Mgr*
Merissa Crowell, *Asst Mgr*
EMP: 25
SALES (est): 1MM-4.9MM **Privately Held**
WEB: www.redroof.com
SIC: 7011 Traveler accommodations
HQ: Red Roof Inns Inc
    605 S Front St Ste 150
    Columbus OH 43215
    614 744-2600

(G-788)
REGAL CINEMAS INC
Also Called: Movies At Burnsville II
14300 Buck Hill Rd (55306-4504)
PHONE 952 435-8080
Kelly Smith, *Branch Mgr*
EMP: 30
SALES (est): 1MM-4.9MM **Privately Held**
WEB: www.regalcinemas.com
SIC: 7832 Indoor movie theater
HQ: Regal Cinemas Inc
    7132 Regal Ln
    Knoxville TN 37918
    865 922-1123

(G-789)
REGIS CORP
915 County Road 42 W (55306-4427)
PHONE 952 435-5545
Babara Boudewyn, *Sales Executive*
Mike Shaughnessy, *Manager*
Barbara Boudewyns, *Manager*
EMP: 25
SALES (est): 500-999K **Publicly Held**
WEB: www.regiscorp.com
SIC: 7231 Beauty salon
PA: Regis Corp
    7201 Metro Blvd
    Minneapolis MN 55439
    952 947-7777

(G-790)
RELIABILITY MANAGEMENT GROUP
151 W Burnsville Pkwy # 224 (55337-7300)
PHONE 952 882-8122
Pam Wensmann, *Business Mgr*
Greg Fisher, *Vice Pres*
Donald Deutsch, *VP Sales*
Chuck Morgan, *Mng Member*
Nimisha Trivedi, *CIO*
EMP: 46 EST: 1986
SALES (est): 5MM-9.9MM **Privately Held**
WEB: www.reliabilitymanagement.com
SIC: 8742 Management consulting services

(G-791)
RIVER HILLS EARLY CHILDHOOD
11100 River Hills Dr (55337-3281)
PHONE 952 895-0413
Janet Sammersel, *Owner*
Janet Latham, *Manager*
EMP: 25 EST: 1991
SALES (est): 500-999K **Privately Held**
SIC: 8351 Child day care service

(G-792)
RJS SOFTWARE SYSTEMS INC
2970 Judicial Rd Ste 100 (55337-7822)
PO Box 1408 (55337-0408)
PHONE 952 736-5800
Dennis R Johnson, *Chairman*
Marsha Dahl, *Manager*
EMP: 32 EST: 1990
SALES (est): 1MM-4.9MM **Privately Held**
SIC: 7371 Computer software development & applications

(G-793)
ROCCO ALTOBELLI INC (PA)
14301 W Burnsville Pkwy (55306-4844)
PHONE 952 707-1900
Rocco Altobelli, *CEO*
Diane Altobelli, *President*
Michelle Krynski, *Vice Pres*
Mary Johns, *Controller*
Terry Osperdyk, *Accountant*
EMP: 175 EST: 1972 **Privately Held**
WEB: www.roccoaltobelli.com
SIC: 7231 Beauty salon

(G-794)
SAFE HAVEN
13212 Irving Ave S (55337-2413)
PHONE 952 846-0608
Cherry Funk, *Principal*
Dan Saan, *Exec Dir*
Warren Regan, *Exec Dir*
EMP: 25 EST: 2004
SALES (est): 1MM-4.9MM **Privately Held**
SIC: 8322 Child & youth services

(G-795)
SEARS, ROEBUCK & CO
14250 Buck Hill Rd (55306-4925)
PHONE 952 435-2380
Scott Erickson, *Manager*
Dennis Lockwood, *Manager*
EMP: 350
SQ FT: 169,725
SALES (est): 25MM-49.9MM **Publicly Held**
SIC: 7629 Department store; retails appliance parts; vacuum cleaner repair service; tire dealer
HQ: Sears, Roebuck & Co
    3333 Beverly Rd
    Hoffman Estates IL 60179
    847 286-2500

(G-796)
SHOOTERS BILLIARD CLUB & PRO
1934 Highway 13 E (55337-1303)
PHONE 952 894-1100
FAX: 952 894-1896
Craig Zoschke, *Owner*
Duane Marquardt, *Co-Owner*
Phil Lefever, *Manager*
EMP: 50 EST: 1989
SALES (est): 1MM-4.9MM **Privately Held**
SIC: 7999 Billiard parlor

(G-797)
SIGNSEARCH INC
1548 Cliff Rd E (55337-1415)
PHONE 952 960-4470
Rick Stewart, *President*
EMP: 30 EST: 1999
SALES (est): 1MM-4.9MM **Privately Held**
SIC: 7336 Commercial art & graphic design services

(G-798)

SKYLINE DISPLAYS MIDWEST INC
11901 Portland Ave Ste A   (55337-1500)
PHONE 952 895-6000
FAX: 952 890-2364
Michael W Boyce, *President*
Dan Poff, *Vice Pres*
Wayne Last, *Mktg Dir*
Mark Balster, *Manager*
Jeff Johnson, *Director*
EMP: 48 **EST:** 1991
SQ FT: 40,000
SALES (est): 25MM-49.9MM **Privately Held**
SIC: 5099 5046 7389 Wholesales signs;
advertising, promotional & trade show
service; wholesales commercial equipment

(G-799)

SOCCER BLAST MINNESOTA
3601 W 145th St   (55306-5091)
PHONE 952 895-1962
FAX: 952 895-7203
Tanis Carter, *Owner*
Ron Carter, *General Mgr*
EMP: 50 **EST:** 1998
SQ FT: 49,409
SALES (est): 10MM-24.9MM **Privately Held**
WEB: www.soccerblastmn.com
SIC: 7941 Soccer club

(G-800)

SOUTHDALE OB GYN CONSULTANTS
305 E Ncltte Blvd Ste 393   (55337-8328)
PHONE 952 435-9505
FAX: 952 435-6205
Silvia Wilson, *CFO*
Kitty Warden, *Office Mgr*
Heather A McKay, *Med Doctor*
Dottie Yung, *Administrator*
Liz A Crandall, *Obstetrician*
EMP: 35 **EST:** 1990
SALES (est): 1MM-4.9MM **Privately Held**
SIC: 8011 Obstetrician office

(G-801)

SOUTHDALE PEDIATRICS ASSOCS
14050 Nicollet Ave Ste 204   (55337-5738)
PHONE 952 898-5900
FAX: 952 898-5914
Barb Wann, *Manager*
Bev Kruger, *Administrator*
Barbara J Hansen, *Pediatrics*
Carol Carlson, *Pediatrics*
Thomas Bodine, *Pediatrics*
EMP: 25
SALES (est): 1MM-4.9MM **Privately Held**
WEB: www.southdalepeds.com
SIC: 8011 Pediatrician office
PA: Southdale Pediatrics Assocs
     3955 Parklawn Ave Ste 120
     Minneapolis MN 55435
     952 831-4454

(G-802)

SOUTHERN LIGHTING INC
12550 W Frontage Rd   (55337-2473)
PHONE 952 890-8977
FAX: 952 890-4822
Craig Motz, *President*
EMP: 40 **EST:** 1986
SALES (est): 25MM-49.9MM **Privately Held**
WEB: www.southernlightsinc.com
SIC: 5063 Wholesales lighting fixtures;
retails lighting fixtures

(G-803)

STATE FARM MUTUAL AUTOMOBILE
12281 Nicollet Ave   (55337-1622)
PHONE 952 895-3900
FAX: 952 895-3916
Anne Viltoft, *Manager*
Roy Erowen, *Manager*
EMP: 40
SALES (est): 1MM-4.9MM **Privately Held**
WEB: www.statefarm.com

SIC: 6411 Insurance agency & broker
PA: State Farm Mutual Automobile
     1 State Farm Plz
     Bloomington IL 61701
     309 766-2311

(G-804)

SUPERIOR CONCEPTS INC
Also Called: Ciattis Italian Restaurant
14296 Plymouth Ave   (55337-5785)
PHONE 952 892-7555
FAX: 952 435-3187
John London, *General Mgr*
EMP: 75
SALES (est): 1MM-4.9MM **Privately Held**
SIC: 7299 Full service Italian restaurant;
banquet hall facility

(G-805)

SWEENEY BROTHERS TRACTOR CO
12540 Dupont Ave S   (55337-1604)
PHONE 952 894-9595
FAX: 952 894-1619
Michael Sweeney, *Manager*
EMP: 26
SQ FT: 12,432
SALES (est): 10MM-24.9MM **Privately Held**
SIC: 5082 7699 Wholesales general
construction machinery & equipment;
industrial machinery repair & maintenance
services
PA: Sweeney Brothers Tractor Co
     4001 38th St S
     Fargo ND 58104
     701 492-7300

(G-806)

TCI BUSINESS CAPITAL INC
12270 Nicollet Ave   (55337-1649)
PO Box 202061, Minneapolis
(55420-7061)
PHONE 952 656-3400
Daniel Robbins, *President*
Mary Vasilis, *Controller*
Eric Schoch, *Executive*
EMP: 65 **EST:** 1994
SQ FT: 24,000
SALES (est): 10MM-24.9MM **Privately Held**
WEB: www.tcibizcap.com
SIC: 6153 Short-term business credit
services

(G-807)

TEMP-AIR INC (PA)
3700 W Preserve Blvd   (55337-7746)
PHONE 952 707-5203
Jim Korn, *CEO*
Rebecca Pilgrim, *General Mgr*
Linda Brubaker, *Corp Secy*
Tom Danley, *Vice Pres*
Ed Armit, *Vice Pres*
EMP: 70 **EST:** 1963
SQ FT: 142,000 **Privately Held**
WEB: www.temp-air.com
SIC: 7359 Manufactures refrigeration &
heating equipment; manufactures small
electric household appliances; equipment
rental & leasing services; manufactures
heating equipment & supplies

(G-808)

THRIVENT FINANCIAL FOR
350 W Burnsville Pkwy   (55337-2585)
PHONE 952 894-6772
FAX: 952 277-2591
Scott Wardell, *Partner*
Michael Conlon, *Manager*
EMP: 25
SALES (est): 1MM-4.9MM **Privately Held**
WEB: www.thrivent.com
SIC: 6411 6211 Insurance services;
securities broker & dealer
PA: Thrivent Financial For
     625 4th Ave S Ste 100
     Minneapolis MN 55415
     920 734-5721

(G-809)

TPC LANDSCAPE INC
Also Called: Ticen's Pro Care
14284 Newton Ave S   (55306-4899)
PO Box 1718   (55337-0718)
PHONE 952 898-7600
Thomas Ticen, *President*

EMP: 40 **EST:** 1986
SQ FT: 9,000 **Privately Held**
WEB: www.tpclandscape.com
SIC: 0782 Landscaping services

(G-810)

TRANS-ALARM INC (PA)
500 E Travelers Trl # 600   (55337-7503)
PHONE 952 894-1700
FAX: 952 894-1850
J C Kiser, *Ch of Bd*
Terrance Mullett, *President*
Todd Sellner, *Opers Mgr*
Carol Lunberg, *VP Finance*
Brian Torney, *Sales Mgr*
EMP: 85 **EST:** 1966
SQ FT: 17,000 **Privately Held**
WEB: www.transalarm.com
SIC: 1731 7382 Safety & security
specialization contractor; access control
systems specialization contractor; closed
circuit television installation; fire detection &
burglar alarm systems specialization
contractor; burglar alarm maintenance &
monitoring service

(G-811)

TRANSPORT DESIGNS INC
3451 W Burnsville Pkwy   (55337-4257)
PO Box 43, Savage   (55378-0043)
PHONE 952 894-8242
FAX: 952 894-9371
Leonard Korbel, *President*
Jerry Johnson, *Vice Pres*
Mike Hogan, *CFO*
Joanne Cerand, *Accounting Dir*
Cliff Bannon, *Sales Staff*
EMP: 30 **EST:** 1985
SQ FT: 8,000
SALES (est): 1MM-4.9MM **Privately Held**
WEB: www.transportdesigninc.com
SIC: 4213 Over the road trucking

(G-812)

TRI STATE MACHINERY CO
13400 Bryant Ave S   (55337-4307)
PHONE 952 224-1500
Don Shilling, *President*
EMP: 25 **EST:** 1962
SQ FT: 1,000
SALES (est): 10MM-24.9MM **Privately Held**
WEB: www.tri-statemachinery.com
SIC: 5082 7353 Wholesales general
construction machinery & equipment;
construction & mining equipment leasing &
rental

(G-813)

TRUDEAU HOLDINGS LLC (PA)
25 Cliff Rd W Ste 115   (55337-1680)
PHONE 952 882-8295
FAX: 952 882-8397
Stuart Bell, *Member*
Mike Reineck, *Member*
Jason Dugan, *Member*
Tina Manor, *Accountant*
EMP: 110 **EST:** 1980
SQ FT: 26,000
SALES (corp-wide): 62.03M **Privately Held**
WEB: www.trudeaudistributing.com
SIC: 5142 5147 Wholesales packaged
frozen foods; wholesales packaged frozen
meats; wholesales packaged frozen poultry;
wholesales meat & meat products

(G-814)

TRUGREEN LTD PTN
Also Called: Tru Green-Chemlawn
14360 Ewing Ave S   (55306-4884)
PO Box 1109   (55337-0109)
PHONE 952 895-3400
Ben Zaffke, *Office Mgr*
Carol Tuszynski, *Office Mgr*
Rick Troy, *Manager*
EMP: 35 **Privately Held**
WEB: www.trugreen.com
SIC: 0782 Lawn services
DH: Trugreen LP
     860 Ridge Lake Blvd Ste G02
     Memphis TN 38120
     901 681-1800

(G-815)

UNITED HOMECARE INC
15001 Willa Ct   (55306-4301)
PHONE 952 898-9780
Shane Lovestran, *President*
Marilyn Lovestrand, *Vice Pres*
EMP: 30 **EST:** 1996
SALES (est): 1MM-4.9MM **Privately Held**
SIC: 8082 Home health care services

(G-816)

VAC SYSTEM INDUSTRIES OF MN
Also Called: V S I
1800 Cliff Rd E Ste 11   (55337-1375)
PHONE 952 808-1616
FAX: 952 808-1584
Doug Groen, *President*
Ken Witte, *Vice Pres*
Tom Simbeck, *Project Mgr*
Pete Haugen, *Director*
EMP: 30 **EST:** 1987
SQ FT: 3,463
SALES (est): 500-999K **Privately Held**
WEB: www.vacsystem.com
SIC: 7349 5084 Air duct cleaning service;
manufactures purification & dust collection
equipment; wholesales industrial processing
& packaging equipment

(G-817)

VANTRO SYSTEMS LLC
Also Called: Infopet Identification Systems
11401 Rupp Dr   (55337-1276)
PHONE 952 890-2080
FAX: 952 890-2054
Keith Myhre, *Member*
Wayne Culberth, *Member*
Paul Kenworthy, *Member*
Jan Nelson, *Accountant*
Bonnie Hagen, *Marketing Staff*
EMP: 25 **EST:** 1991
SQ FT: 9,000 **Privately Held**
SIC: 7361 Registry service

(G-818)

VIDEOTRONIX INC
Also Called: Vti Security Integrators
401 W Travelers Trl   (55337-2554)
PHONE 952 894-5343
Thomas G Asp, *President*
Bryan W Viau, *Exec VP*
John M Nowak, *Vice Pres*
Mark Besser, *Project Mgr*
Kathy Hammer, *Purchasing*
EMP: 67 **EST:** 1980
SQ FT: 21,700
SALES (est): 1MM-4.9MM **Privately Held**
SIC: 7382 Security systems services

(G-819)

WALGREEN CO
Also Called: Walgreens
2200 Highway 13 E   (55337-3030)
PHONE 952 882-7998
FAX: 952 882-6561
Eric Harthan, *Manager*
EMP: 25
SALES (est): 1MM-4.9MM **Publicly Held**
WEB: www.walgreens.com
SIC: 7384 Drug store; photofinishing
laboratory
PA: Walgreen Co
     200 Wilmot Rd
     Deerfield IL 60015
     847 914-2500

(G-820)

WASTE MANAGEMENT OF MINNESOTA
1601 Highway 13 E Ste 100   (55337-6847)
PHONE 952 736-2428
FAX: 952 641-3020
Troy Hanson, *Branch Mgr*
EMP: 30
SALES (est): 1MM-4.9MM **Privately Held**
SIC: 4953 Refuse systems services
PA: Waste Management Inc
     1001 Fannin St Ste 4000
     Houston TX 77002
     713 512-6200

GEOGRAPHIC

(G-821)
WELLS FARGO BANK, NATIONAL
350 W Burnsville Pkwy Ste 100
(55337-5769)
PHONE 952 890-1424
Craig Krenz, *Area Mgr*
Rebecca Demos, *Branch Mgr*
Alvin Stafford, *Manager*
Teresa Raner, *Manager*
Chad Krueger, *Manager*
EMP: 30
SALES (est): 1MM-4.9MM **Publicly Held**
SIC: 6162 Mortgage & loan lending
HQ: Wfc Holdings, Corp
　　420 Montgomery St
　　San Francisco CA 94104
　　415 396-7392

BYRON
Olmsted County

(G-822)
BIGELOW-LENNON CONSTRUCTION
211 1st St SW (55920-1565)
PHONE 507 775-7068
FAX: 507 775-6083
Randy Lennon, *Partner*
Jerome Bigelow, *Partner*
EMP: 30 **EST:** 1975
SALES (est): 5MM-9.9MM **Privately Held**
WEB: www.bigelowlennon.com
SIC: 1521 Single-family housing construction

(G-823)
GREENWAY CO-OPERATIVE SERVICE
302 Byron Ave N (55920-1480)
PO Box 127 (55920-0127)
PHONE 507 287-6676
Larry Mulert, *Mfg Staff*
Mike Kuhlmann, *Manager*
EMP: 27
SALES (est): 50MM-99.9MM **Privately Held**
SIC: 5153 Wholesale grain elevator
PA: Greenway Co-Operative Service
　　3520 E River Rd NE
　　Rochester MN 55906
　　507 289-4086

(G-824)
GREENWAY CO-OPERATIVE SERVICE
312 Byron Ave N (55920-1480)
PO Box 127 (55920-0127)
PHONE 507 775-2900
FAX: 507 775-2905
Tim Clemens, *General Mgr*
Keith Allen, *Sales Mgr*
EMP: 30
SALES (est): 10MM-24.9MM **Privately Held**
SIC: 5153 5171 5191 Manufactures flour & other grain mill products; wholesales agricultural fertilizer; wholesale grain elevator; petroleum bulk station
PA: Greenway Co-Operative Service
　　3520 E River Rd NE
　　Rochester MN 55906
　　507 289-4086

(G-825)
OSHKOSH, MCNEILUS FINANCIA
1067 4th St NE (55920-5002)
PHONE 507 775-3310
McNeilus F Oshkosh, *Principal*
EMP: 32 **EST:** 2006
SALES (est): 5MM-9.9MM **Privately Held**
SIC: 6282 Financial investment advice service

CALEDONIA
Houston County

(G-826)
CALEDONIA HAULERS LLC
420 W Lincoln St (55921-1042)
PO Box 31 (55921-0031)
PHONE 507 725-9000
FAX: 507 725-9015
William Koch, *Member*
Mark Conniff, *Treasurer*
Sherree Cavanaugh, *Accounting Staf*
Vicki Breeser, *Accounting Staf*
Dennis Gavin, *Mng Member*
EMP: 135 **EST:** 1958
SQ FT: 5,000
SALES (est): 10MM-24.9MM **Privately Held**
WEB: www.caledoniahaulers.com
SIC: 4213 7538 Over the road trucking; general truck repair services

(G-827)
EDUCATIONAL BIOMETRIC TECH
21002 Engen Rd (55921-5711)
PHONE 507 724-5773
Bob Engen, *Owner*
EMP: 46 **EST:** 2004
SALES (est): 10MM-24.9MM **Privately Held**
SIC: 7372 Business & professional software publishers

(G-828)
SENIOR MANAGEMENT INC
425 N Badger St (55921-1567)
PHONE 507 725-3351
Lloyd Swalve, *President*
EMP: 95 **EST:** 2004
SALES (est): 1MM-4.9MM **Privately Held**
SIC: 8059 Nursing & personal care facility

(G-829)
SKEMP WALK IN CLINIC
Also Called: Franciscus Skemp Health Care
701 N Sprague St (55921-1066)
PHONE 507 724-3353
FAX: 507 724-5650
Connie Meiners, *Office Mgr*
Michelle Johnson, *Office Mgr*
Dean A Wetzel, *Optometrist*
Patti Newsome, *Manager*
Debbie Peterson, *Manager*
EMP: 25 **EST:** 1990
SALES (est): 1MM-4.9MM **Privately Held**
SIC: 8011 8069 8093 Clinic operated by physicians; alcoholism rehabilitation hospital; outpatient alcohol treatment clinic

CAMBRIDGE
Isanti County

(G-830)
A R I INC
Also Called: Lake Haven Manor
1995 E Rum River Dr S (55008-2656)
PHONE 763 689-1162
Barry Halm, *CEO*
EMP: 45
SALES (est): 1MM-4.9MM **Privately Held**
WEB: www.ari.com
SIC: 8051 Skilled nursing care facility

(G-831)
ALLINA HEALTH SYSTEM
Also Called: Cambridge Medical Center
701 Dellwood St S (55008-1920)
PHONE 763 689-7700
Duncan P Gallagher, *CFO*
Randall J Rouse MD, *Med Doctor*
B Rohr, *Manager*
Dennis Doran, *Administrator*
Becky Baker, *Obstetrician*
EMP: 900
SQ FT: 1,368
SALES (est): 100MM-499.9MM **Privately Held**
WEB: www.allina.com

SIC: 8011 Clinic operated by physicians
PA: Allina Health System
　　2925 Chicago Ave
　　Minneapolis MN 55407
　　612 775-5000

(G-832)
B'S HOMECARE INC ✪
546 21st Ct SE (55008-2567)
PHONE 763 689-8984
Brandy Herbst, *President*
EMP: 36 **EST:** 2008
SALES (est): 1MM-4.9MM **Privately Held**
SIC: 8082 Home health care services

(G-833)
BEHAVIORAL HEALTH SERVICES INC
Also Called: Behaviorl Hlth Svcs Allina CAM
701 Dellwood St S (55008-1920)
PHONE 763 689-7887
FAX: 763 689-7981
Donna Krzmarzick, *General Mgr*
EMP: 50
SALES (est): 1MM-4.9MM **Privately Held**
SIC: 8093 Outpatient mental health clinic
PA: Behavioral Health Services Inc
　　15519 Crenshaw Blvd
　　Gardena CA 90249
　　310 679-9031

(G-834)
BENEDICTINE TEAM HEALTH SYSTS
1995 E Rum River Dr S (55008-2656)
PHONE 763 689-1162
Dale Thompson, *President*
Bert Norman, *VP Finance*
Kathy M Rostberg, *Admin Asst*
EMP: 30 **Privately Held**
SIC: 8621 Health association

(G-835)
CAMBRIDGE NURSING HOME INC
548 1st Ave W (55008-1020)
PHONE 763 689-2323
FAX: 763 689-9450
Robert Sundberg, *President*
Dale Thompson, *Vice Pres*
Kari Woodworth, *Office Mgr*
Deb Prahl, *Manager*
Jackie Peterson, *Manager*
EMP: 170 **EST:** 1947
SQ FT: 64,000
SALES (est): 5MM-9.9MM **Privately Held**
SIC: 8051 Skilled nursing care facility

(G-836)
CHRISTIAN GRANDVIEW HOME
135 Fern St N (55008-1033)
PHONE 763 689-1474
FAX: 763 691-2200
Greg Carlson, *President*
Suzan Minar, *Vice Pres*
Julie Tooker, *CFO*
Sonya Towle, *Human Res Dir*
Deanna Dunbar, *Manager*
EMP: 240 **EST:** 1959
SQ FT: 120,000
SALES (est): 5MM-9.9MM **Privately Held**
SIC: 8051 8052 Extended care facility; intermediate care facility

(G-837)
ECM PUBLISHERS INC
Also Called: County News Scottsman
234 Main St S (55008-1643)
PHONE 763 689-1981
FAX: 763 689-4862
Alexis Todd, *Sales/Mktg Dir*
Marge Winkelman, *Manager*
Sharon Scholl, *Info Tech Dir*
EMP: 30
SALES (est): 1MM-4.9MM **Privately Held**
WEB: www.ecm-inc.com
SIC: 5021 5044 Home delivery newspaper routes; retails art supplies; wholesales photocopy machines; wholesales office furniture
PA: ECM Publishers Inc
　　4095 Coon Rapids Blvd NW
　　Minneapolis MN 55433
　　763 712-2400

(G-838)
INDUSTRIES INC
601 Cleveland St S (55008-1752)
PHONE 763 689-5434
FAX: 763 689-5434
Denise Johnson, *Director*
EMP: 26
SALES (est): 1MM-4.9MM **Privately Held**
WEB: www.industriesinc.org
SIC: 8361 Halfway group home for persons with social or personal problems
PA: Industries Inc
　　500 Walnut St S
　　Mora MN 55051
　　320 679-2354

(G-839)
INTERNATIONAL ASSOCIATION OF
31122 Polk St NE (55008-6828)
PHONE 763 689-3898
Mary Mack, *President*
EMP: 35 **Privately Held**
WEB: www.iaopc.com
SIC: 8641 Civic associations
PA: International Association of
　　300 W 22nd St
　　Oak Brook IL 60523
　　630 571-5466

(G-840)
LOWE'S HOME CENTERS INC
2324 3rd Ave NE (55008-4159)
PHONE 763 691-6040
EMP: 158
SALES (est): 25MM-49.9MM **Publicly Held**
WEB: www.lowes.com
SIC: 5031 5064 Retails building products & materials; wholesales exterior building materials; wholesales interior building materials; wholesales electrical appliances; retails household appliances
HQ: Lowe's Home Centers Inc
　　1605 Curtis Bridge Rd
　　Wilkesboro NC 28697
　　336 658-4000

(G-841)
M & M SANITATION INC
Also Called: East Central Sanitation
33368 Xylite St NE (55008-7806)
PO Box 671 (55008-0671)
PHONE 320 358-4078
FAX: 320 689-5818
Loren Jennings, *President*
Bradley Cook, *Corp Secy*
Gerald M Moses, *CFO*
EMP: 25 **EST:** 1972
SQ FT: 32,000
SALES (est): 5MM-9.9MM **Privately Held**
WEB: www.eastcentralsanitation.com
SIC: 4953 Rubbish collection & disposal services; waste material recycling services

(G-842)
MEMORIAL HOSPITAL ASSOCIATION
Also Called: Cambridge Medical Center
701 Dellwood St S (55008-1920)
PHONE 763 689-7700
FAX: 763 689-7739
Dennis Doran, *President*
Shawn Shrawny, *Ch Radiology*
Michelle E Haroldson MD, *Med Doctor*
Paul S Ander MD, *Med Doctor*
Christophe A Wnner MD, *Med Doctor*
EMP: 770 **EST:** 1954
SALES (est): 50MM-99.9MM **Privately Held**
SIC: 8062 Medical hospital

(G-843)
MINNCO CREDIT UNION
235 1st Ave W (55008-1528)
PHONE 763 689-1071
FAX: 763 689-9659
Steve Oien, *President*
Lila Renstrom, *Corp Secy*
Doug Hallstrom, *Vice Pres*
Jason Knutson, *Loan Officer*
EMP: 80 **EST:** 1996
SALES (est): 10MM-24.9MM **Privately Held**
SIC: 6062 State chartered credit union

(G-844)
NORTHSTAR ACCESS
210 Main St S (55008-1611)
PHONE...........................763 691-0885
FAX: 763 552-9992
Marine Oneal, *Managing Prtnr*
Julie Olson, *Manager*
EMP: 40 **EST:** 2000 **Privately Held**
SIC: 4813 Wired telecommunications carrier
& service

(G-845)
PEOPLES BANK OF COMMERCE
234 1st Ave E (55008-1210)
PO Box 592 (55008-0592)
PHONE...........................763 689-1212
FAX: 763 689-9628
David Hyduke, *CEO*
Clyde Bloyer, *Senior VP*
Dana Anderson, *Vice Pres*
Rick Pankow, *Vice Pres*
Tommy Woo, *CFO*
EMP: 40 **EST:** 1916
SALES (est): 10MM-24.9MM **Privately Held**
SIC: 6022 6029 State commercial bank;
commercial bank
PA: Duke Financial Group Inc
80 S 8th St Ste 2900
Minneapolis MN 55402
612 204-0255

(G-846)
WATSON CO INC
1555 320th Ln NE (55008)
PO Box 111 (55008-0111)
PHONE...........................763 689-3722
FAX: 763 689-5108
James R Watson Sr, *President*
Jeanne Watson, *Corp Secy*
Steven P Watson, *Vice Pres*
Terry Engberg, *Manager*
Jeff Holmen, *Manager*
EMP: 30 **EST:** 1930
SQ FT: 10,000
SALES (est): 10MM-24.9MM **Privately Held**
WEB: www.watsonmn.com
SIC: 5145 5113 5141 5194 Wholesales
confectionery products; wholesales general
line groceries; wholesales industrial &
personal service paper; wholesales tobacco
& tobacco products

(G-847)
WOLCYN TREE FARMS
4542 Highway 95 NW (55008-7526)
PHONE...........................763 689-3346
FAX: 763 689-0837
Tom A Wolcyn, *Owner*
Adrienne M Wolcyn, *Owner*
Marvel Regehr, *Corp Secy*
EMP: 25 **EST:** 1969
SQ FT: 9,000 **Privately Held**
WEB: www.wolcyntreefarms.com
SIC: 0811 0181 Tree farm; nursery stock
production

CANBY
Yellow Medicine County

(G-848)
CANBY COMMUNITY HOSPITAL DIST
112 Saint Olaf Ave S (56220-1433)
PHONE...........................507 223-7277
Ralph Hentges, *Ch of Bd*
Benjamin Madsen, *Corp Secy*
Eugene Berckes, *Treasurer*
Robert Salmon, *Administrator*
EMP: 170 **EST:** 1963
SALES (est): 10MM-24.9MM **Privately Held**
SIC: 8062 Medical hospital

(G-849)
CANBY CONERNED CITIZENS
409 1st St E (56220-1514)
PHONE...........................507 223-7061
Jennie Seidel, *Principal*
EMP: 30
SALES (est): 1MM-4.9MM **Privately Held**
SIC: 7389 Business services at a
non-commercial site

(G-850)
MULTI-COUNTY AG LLC
1204 Saint Olaf Ave N (56220-1139)
PO Box 149 (56220-0149)
PHONE...........................507 223-5634
FAX: 507 223-5823
Alan Saltee, *Mng Member*
EMP: 28
SALES (est): 50MM-99.9MM **Privately Held**
SIC: 5171 5191 Wholesales petroleum bulk
stations; wholesales agricultural fertilizer;
wholesales agricultural chemicals;
wholesales field, garden & flower seeds;
gas station; hardware store

(G-851)
R E M SOUTHWEST SERVICES C
110 Saint Olaf Ave N (56220-1372)
PHONE...........................507 223-5633
Laurie Drissen, *CEO*
EMP: 100 **EST:** 1974
SALES (est): 5MM-9.9MM **Privately Held**
SIC: 8322 Individual & family social services

(G-852)
SANFORD HEALTH NETWORK
112 Saint Olaf Ave S (56220-1433)
PHONE...........................507 223-7272
Bob Salmon, *Principal*
EMP: 275
SALES (est): 10MM-24.9MM **Privately Held**
SIC: 8741 8011 Hospital management
services; physicians' office & clinic
PA: Sanford Health Network
1305 W 18th St
Sioux Falls SD 57105
605 328-2929

(G-853)
SIOUX VALLEY CANBY CAMPUS
112 Saint Olaf Ave S (56220-1433)
PHONE...........................507 223-7221
FAX: 507 223-7305
Robert Salmon, *Owner*
Sue Schanning, *Ch Radiology*
Sally Vogt, *Administrator*
Efthimios A Bakalakos, *Surgeon*
Charley Anderson, *Director*
EMP: 120 **EST:** 1956
SQ FT: 100,000
SALES (est): 10MM-24.9MM **Privately Held**
SIC: 8011 8051 8062 Clinic operated by
physicians; medical hospital; skilled nursing
care facility; physicians' office

CANNON FALLS
Dakota County

(G-854)
GOPHER HILLS INC
26155 Nicolai Ave (55009-9153)
PHONE...........................507 263-2507
William Holst III, *CEO*
Ryan Timm, *General Mgr*
Jim Orlando, *Manager*
EMP: 25 **EST:** 2003
SALES (est): 1MM-4.9MM **Privately Held**
WEB: www.gopherhills.com
SIC: 7992 Public golf course; eating place

CANNON FALLS
Goodhue County

(G-855)
CANNON FALLS MEDICAL CENTER
1116 Mill St W (55009-1824)
PHONE...........................507 263-4221
FAX: 507 263-0221
Gregory Angstman, *President*
Charlotte Nordrum, *CFO*
Ed Tusa, *CFO*
Ginger Bauer, *Corp Comm Staff*
Ginger Bower, *Corp Comm Staff*
EMP: 130 **EST:** 1958
SQ FT: 28,000
SALES (est): 10MM-24.9MM **Privately Held**
WEB: www.cannonfallshospital.com

SIC: 8062 Medical hospital
PA: Mayo Clinic
200 1st St SW
Rochester MN 55905
507 284-2511

(G-856)
FILMOR EXPRESS INC
32453 64th Avenue Way (55009-4270)
PHONE...........................507 263-2608
FAX: 507 263-2715
Richard Olson, *President*
Stephen Pelner, *Vice Pres*
Patrick Haney, *Vice Pres*
Mark Schmidt, *Vice Pres*
Darold McKinley, *Maint Spvr*
EMP: 200 **EST:** 1983
SQ FT: 22,000
SALES (est): 25MM-49.9MM **Privately Held**
SIC: 4213 Over the road trucking

(G-857)
LORENTZ ETC INC
705 Cannon Ind Blvd W (55009-1249)
PHONE...........................507 263-3618
FAX: 507 263-2510
Robert Lorentz, *President*
Michael Lorentz, *Vice Pres*
Laura Lutjen, *Controller*
Larry Hoffman, *Director*
EMP: 64 **EST:** 1968
SQ FT: 13,800
SALES (est): 10MM-24.9MM **Privately Held**
WEB: www.lorentzmeats.com
SIC: 0751 Meat processing; custom
livestock slaughtering services

(G-858)
MIDWEST - CBK INC
32057 64th Ave (55009-4340)
PHONE...........................507 263-4261
FAX: 507 263-7751
Bill Althoff, *Vice Pres*
Greg Mikel, *Programmer Anys*
EMP: 100
SALES (est): 50MM-99.9MM **Publicly Held**
WEB: www.cbkhome.com
SIC: 5199 Wholesales gifts & novelties
HQ: Midwest - Cbk Inc
600 Sherwood Dr
Union City TN 38261
731 885-7836

(G-859)
MIDWEST RECREATIONAL
6352 320th Street Way # 200
(55009-4074)
PHONE...........................507 263-9234
FAX: 507 263-5350
Brian Livingston, *Member*
Gregg Bryski, *Sales Mgr*
EMP: 70 **EST:** 2001
SQ FT: 60,000
SALES (est): 5MM-9.9MM **Privately Held**
SIC: 7389 Arbitration & conciliation services

(G-860)
MMK INTERNATIONAL MARINE SVCS
101 State St W Ste 2 (55009-2033)
PHONE...........................507 263-0975
Robert Volante, *CEO*
EMP: 35 **EST:** 2007
SALES (est): 1MM-4.9MM **Privately Held**
SIC: 6411 Insurance services

(G-861)
NASH-FINCH CO
Also Called: Econofoods
425 Main St W (55009-2044)
PHONE...........................507 263-3643
Tom Schnellman, *Manager*
EMP: 93
SALES (est): 50MM-99.9MM **Publicly Held**
WEB: www.nashfinch.com
SIC: 5141 Wholesales general line
groceries
PA: Nash-Finch Co
7600 France Ave S Ste 200
Edina MN 55435
952 832-0534

(G-862)
PETERSON TURKEY HATCHERY INC
31659 County 24 Blvd (55009-7100)
PHONE...........................507 263-2352
FAX: 507 263-0495
Dick Peterson, *President*
EMP: 35 **EST:** 1939 **Privately Held**
SIC: 0254 Poultry hatchery

(G-863)
VOANS HEALTH SERVICES CORP
Also Called: Angels Care Center
300 Dow St N (55009-1810)
PHONE...........................507 263-4658
FAX: 507 263-4127
Charles Gould, *President*
Michael Spilane, *Corp Secy*
Ron Patterson, *Senior VP*
Carol Moore, *Treasurer*
Mark Faas, *Manager*
EMP: 98 **EST:** 1996
SALES (est): 1MM-4.9MM **Privately Held**
SIC: 8051 Skilled nursing care facility

(G-864)
WHITE ROCK BANK (HQ)
31377 County 24 Blvd (55009-4282)
PO Box 548 (55009-0551)
PHONE...........................507 263-3030
FAX: 507 263-3033
Joseph Tapp, *President*
Debra Norstad, *Vice Pres*
Kenneth Mara, *Loan Officer*
Timothy Anderson, *Loan Officer*
Vanessa Samuelson, *Marketing Staff*
EMP: 106 **EST:** 1906 **Privately Held**
SIC: 6022 State commercial bank
PA: Bancmidwest Services Corp
360 Robert St N Ste 700
Saint Paul MN 55101
651 222-3081

CANYON
Saint Louis County

(G-865)
MILLERS ROOFING
7283 Highway 53 (55717-8720)
PHONE...........................218 263-4406
FAX: 218 345-6753
Jeff Carlson, *Partner*
Dennis Miller, *Partner*
EMP: 25 **EST:** 1989
SALES (est): 1MM-4.9MM **Privately Held**
SIC: 1761 Roofing contractor

CARLOS
Douglas County

(G-866)
ALEX IRRIGATION INC
2750 E Lake Carlos Ln NE (56319-8122)
PHONE...........................320 852-7595
Dan O'Brien, *President*
EMP: 36 **EST:** 1988
SQ FT: 5,000 **Privately Held**
SIC: 0782 5083 Landscaping services; lawn
seeding services; wholesales irrigation
equipment

CARLTON
Carlton County

(G-867)
FOND DU LAC RESERVATION
Also Called: Black Bear Casino
1785 Highway 210 (55718-8161)
PO Box 777 (55718-0777)
PHONE...........................218 878-2327
FAX: 218 878-2414
Jack Bassett, *General Mgr*
Dale Maiers, *Accounting Mgr*
Leanne Marteau, *Human Res Mgr*
Eleanore Laflave, *Security Mgr*
Leyla Aktekin, *Manager*

GEOGRAPHIC

EMP: 600
SALES (est): 25MM-49.9MM **Privately Held**
WEB: www.fdlrez.com
SIC: 7011 7992 Casino hotel; eating place;
public golf course; drinking establishment
PA: Fond Du Lac Reservation
1720 Big Lake Rd
Cloquet MN 55720
218 879-4593

(G-868)
FOND DULAC DEVELOPMENT CORP
Also Called: Black Bear Casino Resort
1789 Highway 210 (55718-8161)
PHONE 218 722-8633
Kathy Whelan, *Principal*
Corey Vanguilber, *Manager*
EMP: 80 EST: 2005
SALES (est): 1MM-4.9MM **Privately Held**
SIC: 7011 Resort hotel

(G-869)
INTERFAITH CARE CENTER INC
811 3rd St (55718-9228)
PHONE 218 384-4258
Ginger Henschel, *Facilities Dir*
George Verkovich, *Maint Spvr*
Cindy Washenesky, *Manager*
Larry C Penk, *Director*
EMP: 140 EST: 1962
SALES (est): 5MM-9.9MM **Privately Held**
SIC: 8051 Skilled nursing care facility

CASS LAKE
Cass County

(G-870)
BOYS & GIRLS CLUBS OF THE
208 Central Ave NW (56633-3373)
PO Box 817 (56633-0817)
PHONE 218 335-8144
Chief Oakes, *Sales Staff*
Palmer Tuleah, *Exec Dir*
Julia Palmer, *Exec Dir*
Ronda Conn, *Director*
EMP: 25 EST: 1997
SALES (est): 1MM-4.9MM **Privately Held**
WEB: www.bgcleechlake.com
SIC: 8322 Youth center

(G-871)
DEPARTMENT OF HEALTH MINNESOTA
Also Called: Public Indian Hospital
425 7th St NW (56633-3360)
PHONE 218 335-3200
FAX: 218 335-3408
Cindy Anda, *Office Mgr*
Luela Brown, *Manager*
Jenny Jinkins, *Manager*
Donald Sherman, *Director*
Joseph Rubash, *Physician Asst*
EMP: 99
SALES (est): 50MM-99.9MM **Privately Held**
WEB: www.health.state.mn.us
SIC: 6324 Hospital & medical insurance
carrier; public health program services;
state government administration of public
health programs
DH: Department of Health Minnesota
625 Robert St N
Saint Paul MN 55155
651 201-5000

(G-872)
LEECH LAKE PALACE & CASINO
Also Called: Palace Bingo & Casino
6280 Upper Cass Frontage Rd
(56633-3058)
PHONE 218 335-7000
FAX: 218 335-6899
Dawn Fairbanks, *General Mgr*
Leann Swan, *Human Res Mgr*
Connie Headbird, *Office Mgr*
Guy Beaulieu, *Info Tech Dir*
Mark Tsugi, *Info Tech Mgr*
EMP: 900 EST: 1983
SQ FT: 15,750
SALES (est): 50MM-99.9MM **Privately Held**
SIC: 7011 Casino hotel

CEDAR
Anoka County

(G-873)
ADVISORS MORTGAGE LLC
20720 Yellowpine St NW (55011-9187)
PHONE 763 753-8133
Mark Svihel, *Mng Member*
EMP: 30 EST: 2001
SALES (est): 1MM-4.9MM **Privately Held**
SIC: 6162 Mortgage & loan lending

(G-874)
CARL HANSON DRYWALL INC
19580 Camarack St (55011)
PHONE 763 753-4112
FAX: 763 753-1664
Carl Hanson, *President*
Mike Hughes, *General Mgr*
EMP: 34 EST: 1998
SALES (est): 1MM-4.9MM **Privately Held**
WEB: www.chdrywall.com
SIC: 1742 Drywall contractor

(G-875)
CEDAR EAST BETHEL LIONS
18440 Jackson St NE (55011-9583)
PHONE 763 434-8323
Jill Hoffman, *President*
EMP: 52 EST: 2001 **Privately Held**
SIC: 8699 Charitable organization

(G-876)
CENTRAL WOOD PRODUCTS
19801 Highway 65 NE (55011-9403)
PHONE 763 753-7374
Mike Rivard, *President*
EMP: 30 EST: 2005
SALES (est): 10MM-24.9MM **Privately Held**
SIC: 5099 Wholesales wood & wood
by-products

(G-877)
CLASSIC CONSTRUCTION OF CEDAR
18542 NE Ulysses St (55011-9526)
PHONE 763 434-8870
FAX: 763 434-7120
Curtis Strandlund, *President*
Linda Koch, *Corp Secy*
Diane Strandlund, *Vice Pres*
Skeeter Breitzmann, *Manager*
Kristin Erickson, *Administrator*
EMP: 39 EST: 1984
SALES (est): 1MM-4.9MM **Privately Held**
SIC: 1741 Masonry & stonework contractor

(G-878)
FRONTIER ENTERPRISES CORP
Also Called: Loger Builders
18533 Buchanan St NE (55011-9538)
PO Box 460 (55011-0460)
PHONE 763 434-6913
FAX: 763 434-6938
Corey S Loger, *President*
EMP: 30 EST: 1997
SALES (est): 5MM-9.9MM **Privately Held**
WEB: www.logerbuilders.com
SIC: 1521 Single-family housing
construction

(G-879)
HIDDEN HAVEN GOLF COURSE INC
20520 Polk St NE (55011-9413)
PHONE 763 434-6867
Mike Krogftad, *Treasurer*
Mark Hetland, *Manager*
Deanna Lee, *Executive*
EMP: 30 EST: 1988
SALES (est): 1MM-4.9MM **Privately Held**
SIC: 7992 7299 7997 Public golf course;
banquet hall facility; membership recreation
club

(G-880)
JALA CONTRACTING CO
Also Called: Hidden Haven Country Club
20520 Polk St NE (55011-9413)
PHONE 763 434-4626
FAX: 763 434-6648

Deanna Lee, *President*
Mike Krogftad, *Treasurer*
EMP: 50 EST: 1986
SQ FT: 13,000
SALES (est): 1MM-4.9MM **Privately Held**
SIC: 7299 7992 Bar; full service American
restaurant; banquet hall facility; public golf
course

(G-881)
JORDAN RAY SONS
1901 Klondike Dr NE (55011-4652)
PHONE 763 434-1644
FAX: 763 434-1637
Richard Jordan, *President*
EMP: 32 EST: 1958 **Privately Held**
SIC: 0781 Landscape services

(G-882)
METRO HOME SERVICES NETWORK
Also Called: Pleasant Lake Landscaping
19925 Butternut St NW (55011-9437)
PHONE 612 827-0643
Rodger Amundson, *Partner*
Brad Amundson, *Partner*
Debbie Nutter, *Manager*
EMP: 30 EST: 1985 **Privately Held**
SIC: 0781 0782 1741 Landscape services;
retaining wall construction; landscaping
services

(G-883)
OUR SAVIOR'S LUTHERAN CHURCH
19001 Jackson St NE (55011-9544)
PHONE 763 434-6117
FAX: 763 434-3093
Cindy Harvey, *Principal*
Brian D Fragodt, *Pastor*
Kay Carlson, *Bookkeeper*
Cynthia Delmonico, *Manager*
Terry Fischer, *Exec Dir*
EMP: 25 EST: 1873 **Privately Held**
WEB: www.oursaviourslc.org
SIC: 8351 Provides Lutheran church
services; preschool center

(G-884)
RIVARD CONTRACTING INC
19801 Highway 65 NE (55011-9403)
PHONE 763 753-7888
Lisa Rivard, *President*
Micheal J Rivard, *Vice Pres*
EMP: 45 EST: 1989
SALES (est): 5MM-9.9MM **Privately Held**
SIC: 1629 Construction site preparation
services

(G-885)
VIKING MEADOWS INC
1788 Viking Blvd NE (55011-9484)
PHONE 763 434-4205
FAX: 763 413-2881
Ronald N Olson, *President*
EMP: 30 EST: 1986
SALES (est): 1MM-4.9MM **Privately Held**
SIC: 7992 Public golf course

CENTER CITY
Chisago County

(G-886)
SYSTEMS MANAGEMENT & BALANCING
332 Summit Ave (55012-9704)
PHONE 651 257-7380
Walt Kalen, *Principal*
Doris Kalen, *Corp Secy*
Sally A Reavely, *Incorporator*
EMP: 25 EST: 2004
SALES (est): 1MM-4.9MM **Privately Held**
WEB: www.smbmn.com
SIC: 8741 Management services

CHAMPLIN
Hennepin County

(G-887)
ADVANCED SPINE ASSOCIATES
12225 Champlin Dr Ste 2 (55316-1930)
PHONE 763 577-1877
David Kraker, *Partner*
Peter Herard, *Neurology*
EMP: 50
SALES (est): 1MM-4.9MM **Privately Held**
SIC: 8049 Health practitioners' office

(G-888)
ALLINA HEALTH SYSTEM
11269 Jefferson Hwy N # 1 (55316-3165)
PHONE 763 427-9620
FAX: 763 427-9626
Georgeann Thompson, *Principal*
Donna H Olson, *Office Mgr*
Jennifer Meister, *Optometrist*
Sarah Theisen, *Phys Therapist*
Randolph T Jackson, *Med Doctor*
EMP: 33
SALES (est): 1MM-4.9MM **Privately Held**
WEB: www.allina.com
SIC: 8011 Medical center
PA: Allina Health System
2925 Chicago Ave
Minneapolis MN 55407
612 775-5000

(G-889)
AMERICAN RESIDENTIAL MORTGAGE
11132 Zealand Ave N (55316-3594)
PHONE 763 784-2022
Larry Shedd, *Managing Prtnr*
Joe Brill, *Manager*
EMP: 30
SALES (est): 1MM-4.9MM **Privately Held**
WEB: www.amresonline.com
SIC: 6162 Mortgage & loan lending

(G-890)
CARDINAL HEALTH 200 INC
9000 109th Ave N (55316-3138)
PHONE 763 323-9666
FAX: 763 323-0644
Alana Kaminski, *Corp Secy*
Jerome Beck, *Senior VP*
Dean Kurtti, *Manager*
Dave Bremmer, *Manager*
EMP: 68
SALES (est): 25MM-49.9MM **Publicly Held**
WEB: www.allegiancehealth.com
SIC: 5047 Wholesales medical & hospital
equipment
HQ: Cardinal Health 200 LLC
1430 S Waukegan Rd
Waukegan IL 60085
847 689-8410

(G-891)
CATERPILLAR PAVING PRODUCTS
8700 109th Ave N Ste 410 (55316-3865)
PHONE 763 712-3000
FAX: 763 712-3030
Denice Wojack, *Sales Staff*
Ty Huls, *Branch Mgr*
Terry Sharp, *Manager*
EMP: 25
SALES (est): 1MM-4.9MM **Publicly Held**
WEB: www.cat.com
SIC: 1611 Street surfacing & paving
construction
HQ: Caterpillar Paving Products
9401 85th Ave N
Minneapolis MN 55445
763 425-4100

(G-892)
DECO INC (PA)
11140 Zealand Ave N (55316-3594)
PHONE 763 576-9572
Robert A Dorr, *President*
Derek J Dorr, *President*
Tom Buckingham, *CFO*
EMP: 554 EST: 1986
SQ FT: 2,200
SALES (corp-wide): 62.49M **Privately Held**
WEB: www.deco-inc.com

SIC: **7381** Security guard service; guard protective service

(G-893)
FIRST STUDENT INC
11911 Champlin Dr (55316-2379)
PHONE..................763 421-5785
FAX: 763 421-5915
Troy Sheppard, *Manager*
Troy Schreifelf, *Manager*
EMP: 80
SALES (est): 1MM-4.9MM **Privately Held**
WEB: www.firststudentinc.com
SIC: **4151** School bus service
HQ: First Student Inc
    600 Vine St Ste 1400
    Cincinnati OH 45202
    513 241-2200

(G-894)
FOAM INDUSTRIES INC
8700 109th Ave N Ste 500 (55316-3864)
PHONE..................763 503-9265
FAX: 763 503-9270
Christine Nelson, *CEO*
Scott Nelson, *President*
Clyde Harrison, *Manager*
EMP: 35 **EST:** 2001
SALES (est): 10MM-24.9MM **Privately Held**
WEB: www.foam-industries.com
SIC: **5199** Wholesales foams & rubber; steel fabricator

(G-895)
LIFE TIME FITNESS INC
11989 Champlin Dr (55316-2379)
PHONE..................763 576-3000
FAX: 763 421-3400
Justin Stoltman, *Manager*
David Dotlich, *Manager*
Justin Saltman, *Manager*
EMP: 200
SALES (est): 5MM-9.9MM **Publicly Held**
SIC: **7991** 7299 Health club; retails health & dietetic foods; personal appearance service
PA: Life Time Fitness Inc
    2902 Corporate Pl
    Chanhassen MN 55317
    952 947-0000

(G-896)
MLS ONLINE
11144 Commerce Ln N (55316-3112)
PHONE..................763 427-0539
FAX: 763 576-8276
Keith Castonguay, *Owner*
EMP: 70 **EST:** 2005
SALES (est): 10MM-24.9MM **Privately Held**
SIC: **6531** Residential real estate agency

(G-897)
PDHC LTD
Also Called: Champlin Dental Center
11269 Jefferson Hwy N (55316-3123)
PHONE..................763 421-5206
FAX: 763 421-8320
Sandy Spencer, *Manager*
EMP: 30
SALES (est): 1MM-4.9MM **Publicly Held**
WEB: www.parkdental.com
SIC: **8021** Dentists' office & clinic
HQ: PDHC Ltd
    6415 Brooklyn Blvd
    Minneapolis MN 55429
    612 338-4546

(G-898)
PRIMA LASERDYNE INC
8600 109th Ave N Ste 400 (55316-3862)
PHONE..................763 433-3700
FAX: 763 433-3701
Howard Ray, *Engineer*
Evert Lehtola, *Engineering*
Gianfranco Carbonato, *CEO*
Paolo Cigna, *President*
Barb Wenner, *General Mgr*
EMP: 35 **EST:** 1992
SQ FT: 33,000
SALES (est): 10MM-24.9MM **Privately Held**
SIC: **5084** Wholesales metalworking machinery; wholesales welding equipment & supplies

(G-899)
RAPID PACKAGING INC
8700 109th Ave N Ste 300 (55316-3867)
PHONE..................763 404-8900
Michael R Sime, *President*
Mike Sage, *General Mgr*
Julie Fischer, *Accounts Mgr*
Tom Hughes, *Director*
▲ **EMP:** 35 **EST:** 1976
SQ FT: 105,000
SALES (est): 10MM-24.9MM **Privately Held**
SIC: **5084** 5113 Wholesales industrial packaging machinery & equipment; wholesales shipping supplies

(G-900)
SECOA INC
8650 109th Ave N (55316-3743)
PHONE..................763 506-8800
FAX: 763 506-8844
Jeff Jones, *President*
Steve Hagan, *COO*
Don Christiansan, *Opers Mgr*
Laurie Zuidmulder, *Opers Mgr*
Zia McNeal, *CFO*
EMP: 61 **EST:** 1972
SQ FT: 82,000
SALES (est): 1MM-4.9MM **Privately Held**
WEB: www.secoa.com
SIC: **1799** 5063 Theatrical prop, set & scenery construction; theatrical rigging contractor; drapery track installation service; wholesales electrical commercial & industrial lighting fixtures

(G-901)
SNYDER'S DRUG STORES INC
12455 Champlin Dr (55316-1907)
PHONE..................763 427-8111
FAX: 763 427-2384
Ron Barstow, *Manager*
EMP: 28
SALES (est): 1MM-4.9MM **Privately Held**
WEB: www.snyderdrug.com
SIC: **7384** Drug store; photofinishing laboratory
PA: Snyder's Drug Stores Inc
    7111 Cedar Lake Rd S
    Saint Louis Park MN 55426
    952 935-5441

(G-902)
SUNSHINE READERS INC
11156 Zealand Ave N (55316-3594)
PO Box 178 (55316-0178)
PHONE..................763 433-2534
Patrick V Mus V, *President*
EMP: 30 **EST:** 1999
SALES (est): 1MM-4.9MM **Privately Held**
WEB: www.sunshinereaders.com
SIC: **7389** Telemarketing services

(G-903)
TWIN CITY TWISTERS INC
9001 123rd Ave N (55316-1917)
PHONE..................763 421-3046
FAX: 763 421-1448
Michael Hunger, *President*
EMP: 30 **EST:** 1987
SQ FT: 8,400
SALES (est): 1MM-4.9MM **Privately Held**
SIC: **7999** Gymnastics instruction

(G-904)
TWIN COURIER CORP
11029 Woodhaven Ct N (55316-3031)
PHONE..................763 576-1133
Peter Farrell, *President*
EMP: 175 **EST:** 2005
SALES (est): 10MM-24.9MM **Privately Held**
SIC: **4215** Ground courier services

(G-905)
WALGREEN CO
Also Called: Walgreens
11401 Marketplace Dr N (55316-3794)
PHONE..................763 427-6389
FAX: 763 427-2520
Brian Nelson, *Manager*
EMP: 30
SALES (est): 1MM-4.9MM **Publicly Held**
WEB: www.walgreens.com

SIC: **7384** Non-prescription medicine proprietary store; photofinishing laboratory
PA: Walgreen Co
    200 Wilmot Rd
    Deerfield IL 60015
    847 914-2500

(G-906)
WILCOX PAPER LLC
111000 Jefferson Hwy N (55316)
PHONE..................763 404-8400
Terry Hudy, *President*
Craig Pearson, *Vice Pres*
Geoffrey Miller, *CFO*
Patrice Swan, *Manager*
▲ **EMP:** 40 **EST:** 1923
SQ FT: 135,000
SALES (est): 25MM-49.9MM **Privately Held**
WEB: www.wilcoxpaper.com
SIC: **5111** Wholesales printing paper; wholesales writing paper

CHANHASSEN
Carver County

(G-907)
ALLIANCENET INC
2230 Timberwood Dr (55317-9668)
PHONE..................952 934-4104
Peter Neva, *President*
EMP: 25 **Privately Held**
SIC: **7361** Employment agency services

(G-908)
ANALYTICS INC
18750 Lake Dr E (55317-9384)
PHONE..................952 404-5700
Patricia Bauser, *CEO*
Richard Simmons, *President*
Ingrid Hoyt, *Treasurer*
EMP: 25 **EST:** 1970
SALES (est): 1MM-4.9MM **Privately Held**
WEB: www.classadmin.com
SIC: **8748** Business consulting services

(G-909)
BERGQUIST CO (PA)
18930 W 78th St (55317-9347)
PHONE..................952 835-2322
Carl R Bergquist, *President*
Monica Gordon, *Vice Pres*
Skip Cantrel, *Engrg Mgr*
Justin Kolbe, *Engineer*
Jeff Olson, *Engineer*
▲ **EMP:** 110 **EST:** 1964
SQ FT: 130,000
SALES (corp-wide): 113.39M **Privately Held**
SIC: **5065** Manufactures electronic switches; manufactures pressed & blown glass; manufactures electrical insulators & insulation materials; wholesales electronic parts; manufactures synthetic rubber; wholesales electronic parts & equipment

(G-910)
BOEDECKER CO
Also Called: Nu-Con Equipment
1600 Lake Dr W (55317-8583)
PHONE..................952 279-5205
FAX: 952 279-5206
Marvin Deam, *CEO*
Michael Salvador, *President*
EMP: 40 **EST:** 1972
SQ FT: 35,000
SALES (est): 10MM-24.9MM **Privately Held**
WEB: www.boedecker.com
SIC: **5084** Wholesales industrial environmental air pollution control equipment; wholesales industrial environmental water pollution control equipment; wholesales industrial conveyor systems

(G-911)
BUSINESS IMPACT GROUP LLC
2411 Galpin Ct Ste 120 (55317-4634)
PHONE..................952 278-7800
Peter Vos, *Member*
Carol Overman, *Accounts Mgr*
Paul Taunton, *Mng Member*
▲ **EMP:** 60 **EST:** 2003
SQ FT: 40,000 **Privately Held**

WEB: www.impactgroup.us
SIC: **4783** 8742 Packing & crating service; marketing consulting service

(G-912)
C H SUITES OF CHANHASSEN MN
Also Called: Country Suites By Carlson
591 W 78th St (55317-9677)
PO Box 1010 (55317-1010)
PHONE..................952 937-2424
FAX: 952 937-2424
Angela Wisely, *Vice Pres*
EMP: 45 **EST:** 1990
SQ FT: 57,000
SALES (est): 1MM-4.9MM **Privately Held**
SIC: **7011** 7991 Traveler accommodations; physical fitness center

(G-913)
CHANHASSEN THEATRE LLC ✿
501 W 78th St (55317-9677)
PO Box 100 (55317-0100)
PHONE..................952 934-1500
Steven L Peters, *Member*
Doug Lennick, *Member*
Sandi Jensen, *Member*
Jim Jensen, *Member*
Tamara K Erickson, *Member*
EMP: 250 **EST:** 2010
SALES (est): 10MM-24.9MM **Privately Held**
SIC: **7299** 7922 Dinner theater; banquet hall facility; legitimate live theater producers

(G-914)
CHECKPOINT SECURITY SYSTEMS
8180 Upland Cir (55317-9625)
PHONE..................952 942-9431
George Off, *CEO*
Nick Khalil, *Senior VP*
Steve Champeau, *Vice Pres*
Angie Larson, *Project Mgr*
Scott Salazar, *Opers Staff*
EMP: 125 **EST:** 1966
SQ FT: 12,000
SALES (est): 10MM-24.9MM **Publicly Held**
WEB: www.checkpointsystems.com
SIC: **1731** 7382 Fire detection & burglar alarm systems specialization contractor; closed circuit television installation; burglar alarm maintenance & monitoring service; fire alarm maintenance & monitoring service
PA: Checkpoint Systems Inc
    101 Wolf Dr
    Thorofare NJ 08086
    856 848-1800

(G-915)
CHECKPOINT SYSTEMS INC
8180 Upland Cir (55317-9625)
PHONE..................952 943-3853
Nick Khalil, *President*
Steve Champeau, *Vice Pres*
Ed Knutson, *Purch Mgr*
Tom Griep, *Administrator*
Tom Beynon, *Director*
EMP: 125
SALES (est): 10MM-24.9MM **Publicly Held**
WEB: www.checkpointsystems.com
SIC: **1731** 7382 Fire detection & burglar alarm systems specialization contractor; closed circuit television installation; burglar alarm maintenance & monitoring service; fire alarm maintenance & monitoring service
PA: Checkpoint Systems Inc
    101 Wolf Dr
    Thorofare NJ 08086
    856 848-1800

(G-916)
CHRISTIANS INC
1480 Park Rd (55317-9591)
PHONE..................952 470-2001
FAX: 952 470-2024
Robert Christians, *President*
Carmen Christians, *Corp Secy*
Chuck Kellington, *Manager*
Dale Henderson, *Manager*
Christa Johnson, *Director*
EMP: 34 **EST:** 1988
SQ FT: 17,000
SALES (est): 1MM-4.9MM **Privately Held**
WEB: www.christiansinc.com

SIC: 7217 1521 1542 7349 Carpet & furniture cleaning service on location; commercial & office building renovation & repair services; residential remodeling; building cleaning service; industrial or commercial cleaning services

(G-917)
DATALINK CORP (PA)
8170 Upland Cir (55317-9625)
PHONE..................................952 944-3462
Paul F Lidsky, *President*
Curt Dahn, *General Mgr*
Greg Gacroch, *General Mgr*
Tom Obrien, *Superintendent*
Jeffrey C Robbins, *Corp Secy*
EMP: 55 **EST:** 1963
SQ FT: 49,000
SALES (corp-wide): 178.08M **Publicly Held**
WEB: www.datalink.com
SIC: 7373 Computer integrated systems design services

(G-918)
DAYCO CONCRETE CO INC
1850 Lake Dr W (55317-8585)
PHONE..................................952 556-0278
David W Brockpahler, *President*
John Douglas, *Controller*
EMP: 75 **EST:** 1974
SQ FT: 3,394
SALES (est): 5MM-9.9MM **Privately Held**
SIC: 1771 1741 Concrete contractor; masonry & stonework contractor

(G-919)
DIRECT RESPONSE INSURANCE
7930 Century Blvd (55317-8000)
PHONE..................................952 556-5600
FAX: 952 556-8168
Richard Votel, *President*
Ulrike D Iverson, *Corp Secy*
Debra Robetcek, *Corp Secy*
Scott Allison, *Vice Pres*
Cynthia E Lapadula, *Vice Pres*
EMP: 100 **EST:** 1982
SQ FT: 51,000
SALES (est): 10MM-24.9MM **Privately Held**
WEB: www.directinsurancexchange.com
SIC: 6411 Insurance information & consulting service

(G-920)
DIRECT SOURCE INC
8176 Mallory Ct (55317-8586)
PHONE..................................952 934-8000
FAX: 952 934-8030
John Hillen, *CEO*
Brad Fick, *President*
Stacey Delp, *Corp Secy*
Brad Moore, *Controller*
Kristy Brass, *Manager*
EMP: 80 **EST:** 1992
SQ FT: 37,000
SALES (est): 25MM-49.9MM **Privately Held**
SIC: 5046 5045 Wholesales commercial equipment; wholesales computer software

(G-921)
EDINA REALTY HOME SERVICES
2655 W 78th St (55317-4502)
PHONE..................................952 442-1700
FAX: 952 442-1738
Chris Kellogg, *Manager*
Barb Edeskuty, *Director*
EMP: 70
SALES (est): 10MM-24.9MM **Publicly Held**
WEB: www.ilovetennis.net
SIC: 6531 Real estate agency & broker
HQ: Edina Realty Home Services
6800 France Ave S Ste 600
Minneapolis MN 55435
952 928-5900

(G-922)
ELIZABETH CHARLES CORP
Also Called: Spalon Montage Chanhassen
7828 Market Blvd (55317-9440)
PHONE..................................952 915-2900
Gail M Kellip, *General Mgr*
EMP: 59
SALES (est): 1MM-4.9MM **Privately Held**

SIC: 7991 7231 Spas; unisex hair salon; cosmetologist; facial salon
PA: Elizabeth Charles Corp
3909 W 49 1/2 St
Minneapolis MN 55424
952 915-2900

(G-923)
FCA CONSTRUCTION CO LLC
2902 Corporate Pl (55317-4560)
PHONE..................................952 229-7521
Steve Rowland, *Member*
Eric Buss, *Member*
Chris Lacher, *Finance*
EMP: 215 **EST:** 1998
SALES (est): 50MM-99.9MM **Publicly Held**
SIC: 1521 Single-family housing construction
PA: Life Time Fitness Inc
2902 Corporate Pl
Chanhassen MN 55317
952 947-0000

(G-924)
GEODIGM CORP (PA)
1630 Lake Dr W (55317-8583)
PHONE..................................952 556-5657
FAX: 952 556-5677
Andrew Hofmeister, *President*
Martin Freshwater, *Vice Pres*
Mike Marshall, *Vice Pres*
Travis Murphy, *CFO*
Dave Wohlberg, *CFO*
EMP: 35 **EST:** 1996
SQ FT: 10,000 **Privately Held**
WEB: www.geodigmcorp.com
SIC: 8731 Computer hardware development services

(G-925)
IDW LLC
Also Called: ID Wholesaler
18640 Lake Dr E (55317-9383)
PHONE..................................952 949-6690
Jacob Brafman, *Member*
EMP: 30 **EST:** 2003 **Privately Held**
WEB: www.idwholesaler.com
SIC: 8611 Business association

(G-926)
INFINITY PRECISION SYSTEMS LLC
7850 Park Dr (55317-9500)
PHONE..................................952 401-4600
FAX: 952 380-9796
Peter Davis, *CEO*
Matthew Bartell, *General Mgr*
Robert Musselman, *Vice Pres*
David J Raffel, *Director*
EMP: 25 **EST:** 2002
SALES (est): 1MM-4.9MM **Privately Held**
WEB: www.infinityprecision.com
SIC: 8711 Engineering services

(G-927)
INSULATION DISTRIBUTORS INC (PA)
Also Called: IDI Distributors
8303 Audubon Rd (55317-9494)
PHONE..................................952 937-2000
Joe Novogratz, *President*
Thomas Bird, *General Mgr*
Chris Novogratz, *Vice Pres*
Don Hedquist, *CFO*
EMP: 25 **EST:** 1979
SQ FT: 6,000 **Privately Held**
WEB: www.idimn.com
SIC: 5033 Wholesales insulation materials

(G-928)
INTERNATIONAL ASSOCIATION OF
7406 Frontier Trl (55317-9737)
PHONE..................................952 975-2985
Glenn Mattson, *Branch Mgr*
EMP: 40 **Privately Held**
WEB: www.iaopc.com
SIC: 8641 Civic associations
PA: International Association of
300 W 22nd St
Oak Brook IL 60523
630 571-5466

(G-929)
LIFE TIME FITNESS INC (PA)
Also Called: Lifetime Fitness
2902 Corporate Pl (55317-4560)
PHONE..................................952 947-0000
FAX: 952 947-0077
Bahram Akradi, *CEO*
Steve Waryan, *Chief*
Shari Schumacher, *Member*
Rachel Kroon, *Member*
Eric J Buss, *Corp Secy*
▲ **EMP:** 700 **EST:** 1990
SQ FT: 105,000
SALES (corp-wide): 837M **Publicly Held**
SIC: 7991 Health club

(G-930)
LTF CLUB OPERATIONS CO INC
2902 Corporate Pl (55317-4560)
PHONE..................................952 229-7427
Bahram Akradi, *CEO*
Michael R Robinson, *CFO*
Steven P Kerzman, *Treasurer*
Eric J Buss, *Incorporator*
EMP: 60 **EST:** 2005
SQ FT: 203,301
SALES (est): 1MM-4.9MM **Privately Held**
SIC: 7991 Physical fitness center

(G-931)
LYMAN LUMBER CO
18900 W 78th St (55317-9343)
PO Box 130 (55317-0130)
PHONE..................................952 470-4800
FAX: 952 470-4810
Tim Liester, *Branch Mgr*
EMP: 66
SALES (est): 25MM-49.9MM **Privately Held**
WEB: www.abc-kitchens.com
SIC: 5031 Wholesales rough, dressed & finished lumber
PA: Lyman Lumber Co
300 Morse Ave
Excelsior MN 55331
952 470-3600

(G-932)
MINNESOTA PIPESTONE
250 Lake Dr E (55317-9364)
PHONE..................................952 294-5100
Arnold Angeloni, *CEO*
EMP: 60 **EST:** 2005
SALES (est): 1MM-4.9MM **Privately Held**
WEB: www.pipestoneminnesota.com
SIC: 7021 Lodging house not for organizations

(G-933)
NORTHCOTT HOSPITALITY INTL
Also Called: AmericInn
570 Pond Promenade (55317-8311)
PHONE..................................952 934-3888
FAX: 952 974-9394
Angela Lalim, *Manager*
Susan Jespersen, *Manager*
EMP: 25
SQ FT: 75,728
SALES (est): 1MM-4.9MM **Privately Held**
WEB: www.trhospitality.com
SIC: 7011 Traveler accommodations
PA: Northcott Hospitality Intl
250 Lake Dr E
Chanhassen MN 55317
952 294-5000

(G-934)
NORTHCOTT HOSPITALITY INTL (PA)
Also Called: Perkins Family Restaurant
250 Lake Dr E (55317-9364)
PHONE..................................952 294-5000
Robert Rippe, *General Mgr*
Clark E Cummings, *Vice Pres*
Brian J Schwen, *CFO*
Joe Martin, *CFO*
Arnold Angeloni, *Mng Member*
EMP: 60 **EST:** 1994
SQ FT: 40,000 **Privately Held**
WEB: www.trhospitality.com
SIC: 7011 Traveler accommodations; full service chain family restaurant

(G-935)
POWER SYSTEMS LLC
8325 Commerce Dr (55317-8427)
PHONE..................................952 361-6800
FAX: 952 361-6801
Allan Bergren, *Opers Mgr*
Pam Gutzke, *Purch Mgr*
Duane Eischens, *Engrg Mgr*
Julie Gibson, *Controller*
Tom Steinkamp, *VP Sales*
EMP: 44
SALES (est): 10MM-24.9MM **Publicly Held**
WEB: www.powersystems-mn.com
SIC: 5083 Wholesales farm & garden machinery
HQ: Power Systems LLC
330 Grant St Ste 1212
Pittsburgh PA 15219
412 770-9922

(G-936)
PRC CONSULTING INC
600 W 78th St Ste 230 (55317-9585)
PO Box 969 (55317-0969)
PHONE..................................952 906-0801
Mark Tibbles, *President*
Julie Tibbles, *Vice Pres*
EMP: 42 **EST:** 1998
SQ FT: 1,500
SALES (est): 5MM-9.9MM **Privately Held**
WEB: www.prcconsulting.com
SIC: 8742 Management consulting services

(G-937)
RESOURCE GROUP INC
Also Called: Technical Resources
7935 Stone Creek Dr # 110 (55317-4611)
PHONE..................................952 974-9225
Robert Schoewe, *President*
Tavis Hudson, *Partner*
EMP: 40 **EST:** 1992 **Privately Held**
SIC: 7361 Employment agency services

(G-938)
ROISUM ELITE ROSIUM FOODS
1400 Lake Dr W (55317-8518)
PHONE..................................952 227-3199
John Rosium, *President*
Jill Casey, *Marketing Staff*
Diane Syhre, *Director*
EMP: 25 **EST:** 1981
SALES (est): 10MM-24.9MM **Privately Held**
SIC: 5141 Food broker

(G-939)
ROSEMOUNT INC (DH)
8200 Market Blvd (55317-9685)
PHONE..................................952 949-7000
FAX: 952 949-7001
Edward L Monser, *President*
Steven A Chelesnik, *Corp Secy*
Richard Ballintine, *Vice Pres*
Kathleen P Iverson, *Vice Pres*
Jeffrey W Schmitt, *Vice Pres*
▲ **EMP:** 1659 **EST:** 1956
SQ FT: 278,000
SALES (corp-wide): 20.91B **Publicly Held**
WEB: www.gotoemerson.com
SIC: 5084 Manufactures process control instruments; manufactures industrial process type temperature instruments; manufactures industrial process type analyzers; manufactures measuring & controlling devices; machine tools & accessories
HQ: Emerson Electric Holding Corp
8100 W Florissant Ave
Saint Louis MO 63136
314 553-2000

(G-940)
SIRIUS COMPUTER SOLUTIONS INC
856 Kimberly Ln (55317-9705)
PHONE..................................952 470-6144
Deby Dove, *Branch Mgr*
EMP: 70
SALES (est): 50MM-99.9MM **Privately Held**
WEB: www.siriuscom.com

SIC: **5045** Wholesales computer peripheral equipment
PA: Sirius Computer Solutions Inc
613 NW Loop 410 Ste 1000
San Antonio TX 78216
210 369-8000

(G-941)
SUPERVALU INC
19011 Lake Dr E (55317-9322)
PO Box 479, Minneapolis (55440-0479)
PHONE..............................952 906-6260
Dan Eisenger, *Engineer*
Jean Binfet, *Human Resources*
Ron Schrodpfer, *Manager*
EMP: 113
SALES (est): 100MM-499.9MM **Publicly Held**
WEB: www.supervalu.com
SIC: **5141** 5142 5143 5147 5148 Wholesales general line groceries; convenience store; wholesales fresh fruits; wholesales vegetables; retail supermarkets; retail independent grocery store; wholesales fresh dairy products; wholesales meat & meat products
PA: SUPERVALU Inc
11840 Valley View Rd
Eden Prairie MN 55344
952 828-4000

(G-942)
SUPERVALU INC
18791 Lake Dr E (55317-9384)
PO Box 9340, Minneapolis (55440-9340)
PHONE..............................952 906-6600
Joill Tolkenin, *Manager*
EMP: 113
SALES (est): 100MM-499.9MM **Publicly Held**
WEB: www.supervalu.com
SIC: **5141** Wholesales general line groceries
PA: SUPERVALU Inc
11840 Valley View Rd
Eden Prairie MN 55344
952 828-4000

(G-943)
TESTQUEST INC
18976 Lake Dr E (55317-9348)
PHONE..............................952 936-7887
Martin Hahn, *President*
Prabha Gopintha, *Exec VP*
Fred Ketcho, *Vice Pres*
David Haggerty, *Vice Pres*
Ken Heckmann, *QA Mgr*
EMP: 40 EST: 1983
SQ FT: 20,000
SALES (est): 5MM-9.9MM **Privately Held**
WEB: www.testquest.com
SIC: **7371** 7372 Custom computer software systems analysis & design service; software publisher

(G-944)
TOTAL AUTOMOTIVE INC
Also Called: National Parts & Abrasive's
2431 Galpin Ct Ste 110 (55317-4724)
PHONE..............................952 448-7750
FAX: 952 448-5794
Ronald Lehner, *President*
◆ EMP: 25 EST: 1993
SQ FT: 20,000
SALES (est): 5MM-9.9MM **Privately Held**
WEB: www.totalauto.com
SIC: **5013** Wholesales automotive supplies & parts

(G-945)
WAYTEK INC
2440 Galpin Ct (55317-4621)
PO Box 690 (55317-0690)
PHONE..............................952 949-0765
Bob Lamoreaux, *President*
Norman Larson, *Chairman*
Wayne J Larson, *Chairman*
Pete Larson, *Corp Secy*
Mark Larson, *Vice Pres*
EMP: 38 EST: 1970
SQ FT: 113,000
SALES (est): 25MM-49.9MM **Privately Held**
SIC: **5065** Wholesales electronic parts

(G-946)
WILSON'S NURSERY INC
9150 Great Plains Blvd (55317-8606)
PO Box 160, New Germany (55367-0160)
PHONE..............................952 445-3630
FAX: 952 445-6219
James D Wilson, *President*
Jennifer J Wilson, *Vice Pres*
Bill Boyle, *Executive*
EMP: 30 EST: 1983
SQ FT: 1,400 **Privately Held**
SIC: **0181** Plant, foliage & shrubbery farming; shrubbery field nursery; nursery stock production

CHASKA
Carver County

(G-947)
AERATION INDUSTRIES INTL
4100 Peavey Rd (55318-2386)
PO Box 59144, Minneapolis (55459-0144)
PHONE..............................952 448-6789
Daniel J Durda, *CEO*
Bryan Cohen, *Vice Pres*
EMP: 30 EST: 1986
SALES (est): 10MM-24.9MM **Privately Held**
WEB: www.aireo2.com
SIC: **5084** Wholesales industrial machinery & equipment
PA: Aeration Industries Intl
4100 Peavey Rd
Chaska MN 55318
952 448-6789

(G-948)
AMERIPRISE FINANCIAL SERVICES
1 Oakridge Dr (55318-1030)
PHONE..............................952 368-3100
Patricia McCarthy, *Manager*
John Quam, *Info Tech Mgr*
EMP: 29
SQ FT: 118,356
SALES (est): 5MM-9.9MM **Publicly Held**
SIC: **6282** 7011 Investment advisory service; hotel
HQ: Ameriprise Financial Inc
1099 Ameriprise Financial Ctr
Minneapolis MN 55474
612 671-3131

(G-949)
APEX INTERNATIONAL MFG INC
134 Columbia Ct (55318-2304)
PHONE..............................952 227-3000
FAX: 952 227-3080
David Goldberg, *President*
Rod Prochaska, *COO*
James Grill, *Vice Pres*
Rick Vos, *Maint Mgr*
Greg Poirier, *VP Opers-Prdtn-*
▲ EMP: 250 EST: 2001
SQ FT: 240,000
SALES (est): 10MM-24.9MM **Privately Held**
SIC: **7299** Personal item care & storage services

(G-950)
BAILIWICK DATA SYSTEMS INC
4260 Norex Dr (55318-3047)
PHONE..............................952 556-5502
Bill Travis, *President*
Tim Andersen, *Chairman*
Eldon Bott, *Vice Pres*
Tom Gervais, *Vice Pres*
Bob Marko, *Vice Pres*
EMP: 75 EST: 1995
SQ FT: 57,250
SALES (est): 10MM-24.9MM **Privately Held**
WEB: www.bailiwick.com
SIC: **7379** Computer system consulting services

(G-951)
BASE EIGHT INC
615 Lakota Ln (55318-9455)
PHONE..............................952 941-5888
Bill Swansen, *President*
EST: 1995 **Privately Held**
WEB: www.base8.com

SIC: **5049** Wholesales scientific & engineering equipment & supplies

(G-952)
BENTLEY INSTRUMENTS INC
4004 Peavey Rd (55318-2344)
PHONE..............................952 448-7600
FAX: 952 368-3355
Bent Lyder, *President*
Joy Lyder, *Vice Pres*
Kristine Johnson, *Purchasing*
Todd Schilling, *Marketing Mgr*
Pierre Broutin, *Manager*
EMP: 40 EST: 1983
SQ FT: 19,500
SALES (est): 5MM-9.9MM **Privately Held**
WEB: www.bentleyinstruments.com
SIC: **7699** Manufactures dairy equipment; industrial machinery repair & maintenance services

(G-953)
BERG DRYWALL LLC
118 Peavey Cir (55318-2347)
PHONE..............................952 448-3130
FAX: 952 448-3008
Kristi Mittelstaedt, *Member*
Randy Schneewind, *Member*
Kathy Berg, *Vice Pres*
Mark Rislund, *Bd of Directors*
EMP: 150 EST: 1967
SALES (est): 10MM-24.9MM **Privately Held**
WEB: www.bergdrywall.com
SIC: **1742** Drywall contractor

(G-954)
BERNARD GROUP INC
102 N Jonathan Blvd (55318-2341)
PHONE..............................952 934-1900
Phil Hazel, *President*
Liesl Beck, *Manager*
▲ EMP: 55 EST: 1998
SQ FT: 77,000
SALES (est): 1MM-4.9MM **Privately Held**
SIC: **7334** Photocopying & duplicating services; manufactures planning, display & notice

(G-955)
BEST WESTERN CHASKA RIVER INN
1 River Bend Pl (55318-3302)
PHONE..............................952 448-7877
FAX: 952 448-5060
Dean Johnson, *Partner*
Paul Skaiem, *General Mgr*
EMP: 30 EST: 1997
SALES (est): 1MM-4.9MM **Privately Held**
SIC: **7011** Traveler accommodations

(G-956)
BIXBY INC
Also Called: Great Clips
10455 Jersey Ave (55318-9368)
PHONE..............................952 448-6520
Gene Nimitz, *President*
Tina Nimitz, *Vice Pres*
EST: 1990 **Privately Held**
SIC: **7231** Unisex hair salon

(G-957)
CHASKA MEDICAL CENTER (PA)
Also Called: Crossroads Medical Centers
3000 N Chestnut St Ste 120 (55318-3061)
PHONE..............................952 448-2050
FAX: 952 448-5952
Gene Ek, *Administrator*
John Rekow, *Administrator*
Peter Grofkerautz, *Director*
Victoria Broun, *Receptionist Se*
Anne Paulson, *Physician Asst*
EMP: 25 EST: 1969 **Privately Held**
SIC: **8011** Clinic operated by physicians

(G-958)
CHECKPOINT SYSTEMS INC
4250 Norex Dr (55318-3047)
PHONE..............................952 227-5350
Robin Ryan, *Senior VP*
Larry Jacobson, *Purchasing*
Nick Khalil, *Finance*
Kim McHudh, *Personnel*
Steve Eameeau, *Marketing Staff*

EMP: 30
SALES (est): 1MM-4.9MM **Publicly Held**
WEB: www.checkpointsystems.com
SIC: **1731** 5063 7382 Fire detection & burglar alarm systems specialization contractor; wholesales electrical apparatus & equipment; closed circuit television installation; burglar alarm maintenance & monitoring service; fire alarm maintenance & monitoring service
PA: Checkpoint Systems Inc
101 Wolf Dr
Thorofare NJ 08086
856 848-1800

(G-959)
CITY OF CHASKA
Also Called: Chaska Town Course
3000 Town Course Dr (55318-3406)
PHONE..............................952 443-3748
FAX: 952 443-3172
John Kellin, *Manager*
Noel Graczyk, *Director*
EMP: 30
SQ FT: 8,178
SALES (est): 1MM-4.9MM **Privately Held**
SIC: **7992** 7999 Public golf course; golf services & professionals

(G-960)
COMMUNITY BANK CHASKA
706 N Walnut St Ste 100 (55318-2267)
PO Box 114 (55318-0114)
PHONE..............................952 361-2265
FAX: 952 361-2200
Jeff Burzinski, *CEO*
Paul Maahs, *Vice Pres*
Barb Hanson, *VP Opers*
EMP: 25 EST: 1999
SQ FT: 5,000
SALES (est): 5MM-9.9MM **Privately Held**
WEB: www.cbchaska.com
SIC: **6029** Commercial bank

(G-961)
DOLCE INTERNATIONAL
Also Called: Oak Ridge Conference Center
1 Oakridge Dr (55318-1030)
PHONE..............................952 368-3100
FAX: 952 368-1494
Carl Blanz, *General Mgr*
William Niemer, *Opers Staff*
Larry Meltzer, *Controller*
Diane Reardon, *Sales Staff*
Mary Vogel, *Marketing Mgr*
EMP: 40 EST: 2001
SALES (est): 1MM-4.9MM **Privately Held**
SIC: **7389** Advertising, promotional & trade show service

(G-962)
DUPLICATION FACTORY LLC
4275 Norex Dr (55318-3046)
PHONE..............................952 448-9912
FAX: 952 856-7509
Bill Gibb, *Editor*
Peter M Carthy, *Member*
Jane Johnson, *Vice Pres*
Phil Smith, *Engineering*
Kathryn Johnson, *Treasurer*
EMP: 75 EST: 1986
SQ FT: 52,000
SALES (est): 10MM-24.9MM **Privately Held**
WEB: www.duplicationfactory.com
SIC: **7819** Motion picture production allied services

(G-963)
EARLY CHILDHOOD CENTER
110600 Village Rd (55318-1354)
PHONE..............................952 556-6400
FAX: 952 368-7251
Jim Miller, *Principal*
Sue Asthenbeck, *Librarian*
EMP: 85 EST: 1989
SALES (est): 1MM-4.9MM **Privately Held**
SIC: **8351** Preschool center

(G-964)
EMBARQ MINNESOTA INC
164 Pioneer Trl (55318-1167)
PHONE..............................952 556-5679
Gail Trustman, *Branch Mgr*
EMP: 100 **Publicly Held**
WEB: www.centurytel.com

GEOGRAPHIC

SIC: **4813** 4812 Wired telecommunications carrier & service; wireless telecommunications carrier & service
HQ: Embarq Minnesota Inc
　　5454 W 110th St
　　Overland Park KS 66211
　　913 323-4637

(G-965)
ENTEGRIS INC
117 N Jonathan Blvd　(55318-2342)
PHONE..............................952 556-3131
Gregory Graves, *Vice Pres*
Ross Hanson, *Branch Mgr*
Smelter Elizabeth, *Web Proj Mgr*
EMP: 200
SALES (est): 10MM-24.9MM **Publicly Held**
WEB: www.entegris.com
SIC: 8741 Management services; manufactures semiconductors & related devices
PA: Entegris Inc
　　129 Concord Rd
　　Billerica MA 01821
　　978 436-6500

(G-966)
EXACTEC INC
1200 Lakeview Dr　(55318-9506)
PHONE..............................952 448-7722
FAX: 952 448-7876
Kenneth Carney, *President*
Allan Paschke, *Finance*
Ken Herr, *Manager*
Paul Borgmann, *Manager*
Brett Benecke, *Manager*
EMP: 35 **EST:** 1976
SALES (est): 1MM-4.9MM **Privately Held**
WEB: www.exactec.net
SIC: 5046 Manufactures processed plastics; wholesales store fixtures; manufactures nonwood store fixtures

(G-967)
FINANCIAL AFFAIRS CONSULTING
1212 Adrian Dr　(55318-1582)
PHONE..............................952 443-4188
Chris Hause, *President*
Daniel Hause, *Principal*
EMP: 54 **EST:** 2006
SALES (est): 5MM-9.9MM **Privately Held**
SIC: 8748 Business consulting services

(G-968)
HOMETIME VIDEO PUBLISHING INC
4355 Peavey Rd Ste 300　(55318-2331)
PHONE..............................952 448-3812
FAX: 952 556-1106
Dean Johnson, *President*
Jane Johnson, *Vice Pres*
Kathryn Johnson, *Treasurer*
Mary Johnson, *Human Resources*
Bradley Gossell, *Info Tech Mgr*
EMP: 30 **EST:** 1984
SQ FT: 52,000
SALES (est): 5MM-9.9MM **Privately Held**
SIC: 7812 Video tape production services; audio-visual program production service

(G-969)
IMPORT SPECIALTIES INC
Also Called: Heartland America
8085 Century Blvd　(55318-3056)
PHONE..............................952 361-3640
FAX: 952 361-5780
Bruce Brekke, *CEO*
Mark Platt, *President*
Thomas Bulver, *Vice Pres*
Darcy Jerome, *Vice Pres*
Dave Laviolette, *Vice Pres*
▲ **EMP:** 250 **EST:** 1985
SQ FT: 80,000
SALES (est): 50MM-99.9MM **Privately Held**
WEB: www.rockbottomauctions.com
SIC: 5072 Retail mail-order general merchandise; wholesales hardware; wholesales power hand tools; wholesales bolts, nuts & screws; wholesales power tools & accessories

(G-970)
JAVAOLOGY ENTERPRISES LLC
114215 Hundertmark Rd　(55318-1154)
PHONE..............................952 943-3990
Stephen F Holderman, *Mng Member*
EMP: 100 **EST:** 2004
SALES (est): 50MM-99.9MM **Privately Held**
SIC: 5149 Manufactures coffee; wholesales green or roasted coffee

(G-971)
JOSHCO CONSTRUCTION INC
Also Called: Royal Palms Senior Residence
1107 Hazeltine Blvd # 200　(55318-1070)
PHONE..............................952 361-8000
Dan Peterka, *President*
EMP: 80 **EST:** 1988
SALES (est): 10MM-24.9MM **Privately Held**
SIC: 6513 1542 8051 Operators of retirement hotels; specialized public building contractors; skilled nursing care facility

(G-972)
KLEIN FINANCIAL INC
Also Called: K B I
1550 Audubon Rd　(55318-9508)
PHONE..............................952 448-2924
George Ruth, *Senior VP*
James Renekekens, *Senior VP*
James Renckens, *Senior VP*
Jay Hansen, *Senior VP*
Karie Sorknes, *Assistant VP*
EMP: 100
SALES (est): 10MM-24.9MM **Privately Held**
SIC: 7374 Data processing & preparation services

(G-973)
KLINGELHUTZ CO'S INC
2970 Chaska Blvd　(55318-2285)
PO Box 89　(55318-0089)
PHONE..............................952 448-6776
John Klinglehutz, *President*
Sue Kerber, *Vice Pres*
Reiny Grasmick, *VP Finance*
Doug V Orden, *Manager*
James Robertson, *Director*
EMP: 55 **EST:** 1999
SALES (est): 10MM-24.9MM **Privately Held**
SIC: 1522 Residential construction; hotel, motel & multi-family housing construction service; hardware store

(G-974)
LAKEVIEW INDUSTRIES INC
1225 Lakeview Dr　(55318-9506)
PHONE..............................952 368-3500
FAX: 952 368-3599
Lorretta C Magnuson, *President*
Bruce Dreblow, *General Mgr*
Bruce Deblow, *Managing Dir*
Gregory Magnuson, *Vice Pres*
Jon Heimerl, *Opers Mgr*
▲ **EMP:** 45 **EST:** 1982
SQ FT: 40,000
SALES (est): 5MM-9.9MM **Privately Held**
WEB: www.lakeviewindustries.com
SIC: 5013 Manufactures hard rubber molded rubber products; wholesales new motor vehicle parts & supplies; manufactures rubber products for mechanical use

(G-975)
LENZEN CHEVROLET BUICK INC
2860 Chaska Blvd　(55318-2294)
PO Box 149　(55318-0149)
PHONE..............................952 448-2850
FAX: 952 448-5350
John Lenzen, *President*
Sandra Spaude, *Corp Secy*
Jeff Lenzen, *Vice Pres*
Donna Laabs, *Accountant*
EMP: 44 **EST:** 1978
SQ FT: 16,000
SALES (est): 10MM-24.9MM **Privately Held**
WEB: www.lenzenchevbuick.com
SIC: 7532 Retails new & used automobiles; automotive body shop

(G-976)
MORAVIAN CARE MINISTRIES
Also Called: Auburn Manor
501 Oak St N　(55318-2072)
PHONE..............................952 448-9303
FAX: 952 361-3005
Warren Decker, *CEO*
Mike Senden, *CEO*
Kim Schriener, *Accounting Mgr*
Joan Wiese, *Accountant*
Lou Robb, *Human Res Dir*
EMP: 160 **EST:** 1928
SALES (est): 5MM-9.9MM **Privately Held**
WEB: www.moraviancare.org
SIC: 8051 Skilled nursing care facility

(G-977)
NOVA CONSULTING GROUP INC
1107 Hazeltine Blvd # 400　(55318-1049)
PHONE..............................952 448-9393
FAX: 952 448-9572
Steven B Cummings, *President*
Kari Wescott, *Med Doctor*
Bruce Carbon, *Manager*
Brenda Johnson, *IT/INT Sup*
EMP: 50 **EST:** 1987
SQ FT: 15,000
SALES (est): 5MM-9.9MM **Privately Held**
SIC: 8748 8734 Business consulting services; hazardous waste testing laboratory

(G-978)
RBM SERVICES INC
1107 Hazeltine Blvd Ste 120　(55318-1064)
PHONE..............................952 361-0897
Chuck Greenberg, *President*
Mark Kunzor, *VP Persnl*
EMP: 80 **EST:** 1982
SQ FT: 2,500
SALES (est): 1MM-4.9MM **Privately Held**
SIC: 7349 Janitorial & custodial services

(G-979)
SAFEWAY HYDRAULICS INC
4040 Norex Dr　(55318-3000)
PHONE..............................952 466-6220
Steven J Berkey, *President*
Cindy Sons, *Purch Agent*
Paul Bennyhoff, *QC Mgr*
Mike Savage, *Manager*
Curt Michaelson, *Manager*
EMP: 50 **EST:** 1969
SQ FT: 20,000
SALES (est): 5MM-9.9MM **Privately Held**
WEB: www.safewayhyd.com
SIC: 5085 Manufactures hydraulic or pneumatic hose & tube couplings; wholesales industrial supplies; manufactures hardware

(G-980)
SOURCE FLUID POWER INC
331 Lake Hazeltine Dr　(55318-1033)
PHONE..............................952 448-4440
FAX: 952 448-3392
Charles B Holmes, *Ch of Bd*
Gary Miller, *President*
Joan Holmes, *Corp Secy*
Dan Erdmann, *Vice Pres*
Lee Ernst, *Vice Pres*
EMP: 46 **EST:** 1990
SQ FT: 26,000
SALES (est): 1MM-4.9MM **Privately Held**
SIC: 5084 Machine shop, jobbing & repair services; wholesales industrial machinery & equipment

(G-981)
STEINKRAUS PLUMBING INC
112 E 5th St Ste 101　(55318-2253)
PHONE..............................952 361-0128
FAX: 952 361-5908
Merle Steinkraus, *President*
EMP: 25 **EST:** 1993
SALES (est): 1MM-4.9MM **Privately Held**
SIC: 1711 Plumbing service

(G-982)
STEP BY STEP MONTESSORI SCHOOL
1485 White Oak Dr　(55318-2525)
PHONE..............................952 368-4456
Rose Minor, *Owner*

Jean Steele, *Director*
EMP: 30 **EST:** 2001
SQ FT: 13,074
SALES (est): 500-999K **Privately Held**
SIC: 8351 Child development center providing Montessori based instruction

(G-983)
VILLAGE HEALTH CARE INC
1107 Hazeltine Blvd # 200　(55318-1070)
PHONE..............................952 361-8000
John B Goodman, *President*
EST: 1996 **Privately Held**
SIC: 8082 Home health care services

(G-984)
WALGREEN CO
Also Called: Walgreens
3110 Chaska Blvd　(55318-2275)
PHONE..............................952 448-1180
FAX: 952 448-1176
Wayne Johnson, *Manager*
EMP: 30
SALES (est): 1MM-4.9MM **Publicly Held**
WEB: www.walgreens.com
SIC: 7384 Drug store; photofinishing laboratory
PA: Walgreen Co
　　200 Wilmot Rd
　　Deerfield IL 60015
　　847 914-2500

(G-985)
WESTERN EASTERN OB GYN LIMITED
3000 Hundertmark Rd Ste 9　(55318-1152)
PHONE..............................952 556-0071
FAX: 952 556-0081
Nancy Cooley, *Partner*
Shari Ohland, *Manager*
Robert A Nordland, *Obstetrician*
Dennis R Mohling, *Obstetrician*
Matthew A Weinrich, *Obstetrician*
EMP: 40 **EST:** 2000
SALES (est): 1MM-4.9MM **Privately Held**
WEB: www.westernobgyn.com
SIC: 8011 Gynecologist office

CHATFIELD
Fillmore County

(G-986)
CHOSEN VALLEY CARE CENTER INC
1102 Liberty St SE　(55923-1448)
PHONE..............................507 867-4220
FAX: 507 867-4812
Karen Tuohy, *Corp Secy*
Charles Johnson, *Treasurer*
Ellen Strandy, *VP Finance*
Antony J Newman, *Administrator*
Craig Bakken, *Director*
EMP: 120 **EST:** 1976
SQ FT: 40,000
SALES (est): 1MM-4.9MM **Privately Held**
WEB: www.cvcccares.com
SIC: 8051 6513 Skilled nursing care facility; operators of retirement hotels

---

CHATFIELD
Olmsted County

(G-987)
BERNARD BUS SERVICE INC (PA)
103 Division St NW　(55923-1106)
PHONE..............................507 867-3410
Clifford Bernard, *President*
EMP: 35 **EST:** 1943
SQ FT: 8,000 **Privately Held**
WEB: www.bernardbusservice.com
SIC: 4151 School bus service

CHISAGO CITY
Chisago County

(G-988)
CB & L INC
Also Called: Chisago Lakes Lanes
11580 Lake Ln (55013-9592)
PO Box 444 (55013-0444)
PHONE 651 257-8047
FAX: 651 257-9687
Tom Demorett, *President*
Holly Cruse, *General Mgr*
Carol Demorett, *Corp Secy*
Pat Roth, *Corp Secy*
EMP: 30 **EST:** 1996
SQ FT: 14,000
SALES (est): 500-999K **Privately Held**
SIC: 7933 Full service American restaurant;
bar; bowling center

(G-989)
CHISAGO LAKES ACHIEVEMENT CTR
11685 Lake Blvd (55013-7327)
PO Box 410 (55013-0410)
PHONE 651 257-6709
FAX: 651 257-8495
Alan Olson, *Exec Dir*
Dan Brown, *Director*
EMP: 40 **EST:** 1972
SALES (est): 1MM-4.9MM **Privately Held**
SIC: 8331 Community services employment
training program; vocational counseling

(G-990)
DRESEL CONTRACTING INC
24044 July Ave (55013-5018)
PHONE 651 257-9469
Bruce Dresel, *President*
Robert Dresel, *Corp Secy*
Pat Dresel, *Treasurer*
EMP: 45 **EST:** 1960
SQ FT: 2,500
SALES (est): 5MM-9.9MM **Privately Held**
SIC: 1611 Heavy highway & street
construction

(G-991)
ECUMEN
Also Called: Parmly Senior Housing & Svcs
28210 Old Towne Rd (55013-9556)
PHONE 651 257-0575
FAX: 651 257-0579
Mary Cordts, *Branch Mgr*
Lorri Rice, *Coordinator*
Brian Whitson, *Maintence Staff*
EMP: 150
SALES (est): 5MM-9.9MM **Privately Held**
WEB: www.augustanahomes.org
SIC: 8051 Skilled nursing care facility
PA: Ecumen
3530 Lexington Ave N
Saint Paul MN 55126
651 766-4300

(G-992)
LINNEA RESIDENTIAL HOME INC
28770 Old Towne Rd (55013-9598)
PO Box 450 (55013-0450)
PHONE 651 257-2211
FAX: 651 257-9430
Scott Foss, *CEO*
Jone Chauonard, *Chairman*
Sue Whernend, *Corp Secy*
Jone Johnson, *Treasurer*
Scott Foff, *Administrator*
EMP: 40 **EST:** 1979
SQ FT: 4,660
SALES (est): 1MM-4.9MM **Privately Held**
SIC: 8361 8052 Home for the mentally
handicapped; intermediate care facility

(G-993)
PETERSON CO'S INC
8326 Wyoming Trl (55013-9382)
PHONE 651 257-6864
FAX: 651 257-3393
Jonathan Peterson, *President*
Karen Peterson, *Corp Secy*
Michael Peterson, *Vice Pres*
EMP: 60 **EST:** 1999
SALES (est): 5MM-9.9MM **Privately Held**
SIC: 8748 Business consulting services

(G-994)
ROOM FOR GROWING
11125 Lake Blvd (55013-9667)
PHONE 651 257-2441
FAX: 651 257-2441
Jennifer Nellis, *President*
EMP: 28 **EST:** 1995
SALES (est): 500-999K **Privately Held**
SIC: 8351 Child day care service

CHISHOLM
Saint Louis County

(G-995)
CHISHOLM HEALTH CENTER
321 6th St NE Ste 1 (55719-1263)
PHONE 218 254-5765
FAX: 218 254-5767
Lori Kne, *Manager*
Geoffrey Ryan, *Administrator*
EMP: 105 **EST:** 1989
SALES (est): 1MM-4.9MM **Privately Held**
SIC: 8051 Convalescent home

(G-996)
E H LAWRENCE CO
6 1st St SE (55719-1808)
PHONE 218 254-5705
FAX: 218 254-2088
Eric L Howard, *President*
EMP: 40 **EST:** 1996
SALES (est): 1MM-4.9MM **Privately Held**
WEB: www.ehlawrence.com
SIC: 1761 1799 Roof repair contractor;
waterproofing service

(G-997)
FIRST NATIONAL BANK
101 W Lake St (55719-1818)
PO Box 547 (55719-0547)
PHONE 218 254-3371
Charles Wangensteen, *CEO*
Debbie Rajkovich, *COO*
Dan Scinto, *Vice Pres*
EMP: 30 **EST:** 1905
SALES (est): 5MM-9.9MM **Privately Held**
WEB: www.fnbchisholm.com
SIC: 6021 National commercial bank

(G-998)
IRONWORLD DEVELOPMENT CORP
1005 Discovery Dr (55719-1980)
PHONE 218 254-7959
Brian Kolner, *President*
Crystal Powers, *Corp Secy*
EMP: 65 **EST:** 2005
SALES (est): 5MM-9.9MM **Privately Held**
WEB: www.ironworld.com
SIC: 8412 Museum

(G-999)
NORTHWEST AIRLINES INC
601 Iron Dr (55719-1983)
PHONE 218 254-7575
Jason Hendrickson, *Engineer*
Sue Ball, *Manager*
Pat Blacker, *Manager*
Michael Cooper, *Regional*
EMP: 600
SALES (est): 100MM-499.9MM **Publicly Held**
WEB: www.nwairlines.com
SIC: 4512 Passenger airline services
HQ: Northwest Airlines Inc
7500 Airline Dr
Minneapolis MN 55450
612 726-2111

(G-1000)
RANGE CENTER INC (PA)
1001 8th Ave NW (55719-1148)
PHONE 218 254-3347
FAX: 218 254-4813
Debby Hanson, *Vice Pres*
Jim Zahorsky, *CFO*
Brenda Fagan, *Human Resources*
Shelley Robinson, *Exec Dir*
Nancy Tepovich, *Director*
EMP: 170

EST: 1963
SQ FT: 15,000
SALES (corp-wide): 6.56M **Privately Held**
WEB: www.rangecenter.com
SIC: 8361 Home for the mentally retarded

CHOKIO
Stevens County

(G-1001)
ONVOY INC
Also Called: Means Telcom
206 Main St (56221)
PO Box 8 (56221-0008)
PHONE 320 324-7530
Melody Varnum, *Branch Mgr*
EMP: 36 **Privately Held**
WEB: www.onvoy.com
SIC: 4813 Wired telecommunications carrier
& service
HQ: Onvoy Inc
300 Highway 169 S Ste 700
Minneapolis MN 55426
952 230-4100

CIRCLE PINES
Anoka County

(G-1002)
ASPLUNDH TREE EXPERT CO
4501 103rd Ct Ste 180 (55014-3534)
PHONE 763 785-2300
Keith Erickson, *Regional Mgr*
Keith Ericson, *Manager*
Heather Koonce, *Office Admin*
EMP: 250 **Privately Held**
WEB: www.asplundh.com
SIC: 0783 Ornamental shrub & tree service
PA: Asplundh Tree Expert Co
708 Blair Mill Rd
Willow Grove PA 19090
215 784-4200

(G-1003)
BFI WASTE SYSTEMS OF NORTH
Also Called: Site U71
8661 Rendova St NE (55014-4102)
PHONE 763 259-5570
Tom Chovan, *Manager*
EMP: 103
SALES (est): 10MM-24.9MM **Publicly Held**
WEB: www.republicservices.com
SIC: 4953 Refuse collection & disposal
services
HQ: Allied Waste Industries Inc
18500 N Allied Way # 100
Phoenix AZ 85054
480 627-2700

(G-1004)
CENTENNIAL INDEPENDENT SCHOOL
Also Called: Early Childhood Development
4707 North Rd (55014-1545)
PHONE 763 792-6120
Pat Gulden, *Administrator*
EMP: 30
SALES (est): 500-999K **Privately Held**
WEB: www.centennial.k12.mn.us
SIC: 8351 Preschool center
PA: Centennial Independent School
4707 North Rd
Circle Pines MN 55014
763 792-6000

(G-1005)
CENTENNIAL INDEPENDENT SCHOOL (PA)
4707 North Rd (55014-1545)
PHONE 763 792-6000
FAX: 763 792-6050
Roger Worner, *Superintendent*
Paul Stremick, *Superintendent*
Laura Lund, *Accounts Mgr*
Becky D Ibble, *Info Tech Mgr*
Carol Kluznik, *Info Tech Mgr*
EMP: 25 **EST:** 1958
ADMISSIONS: 6938
SALES (corp-wide): 81.14M **Privately Held**

WEB: www.centennial.k12.mn.us
SIC: 8351 Public school; preschool center

(G-1006)
CONSTRUCTION LABOR FORCE INC
Also Called: Rite-Way Waterproofing
448 Lilac St (55014-1054)
PHONE 651 786-0550
FAX: 651 786-0555
Charlene Messerich, *CEO*
EMP: 45
SQ FT: 5,000
SALES (est): 1MM-4.9MM **Privately Held**
SIC: 1799 Waterproofing service

(G-1007)
CONTRACT HARDWARE CO INC
374 Apollo Dr (55014-3018)
PHONE 651 780-0010
FAX: 651 780-0020
Jeffrey L Mc Gowan, *CEO*
Michael R Mc Cann, *President*
Edward J Ladwig, *CFO*
Connie Ladwig, *Treasurer*
EMP: 26 **EST:** 1992
SQ FT: 18,000
SALES (est): 25MM-49.9MM **Privately Held**
SIC: 5122 5031 5072 Wholesales toilet
preparations; bath shop; wholesales door
frames constructed of all materials;
wholesales metal doors, sash & trim;
wholesales window frames constructed of
all materials; wholesales builders' hardware

(G-1008)
COUNTY OF ANOKA
Also Called: Chomonix Golf Course
646 Sandpiper Dr (55014-1327)
PHONE 651 482-8484
Kevin Symens, *Manager*
John Delinde, *Manager*
Bill Hauck, *Manager*
EMP: 35
SALES (est): 1MM-4.9MM **Privately Held**
SIC: 7992 Public golf course; county
supervisors' & executives' office

(G-1009)
CUSTOM REMODELERS INC
474 Apollo Dr Ste 60A (55014-3042)
PHONE 651 784-2646
FAX: 651 783-9050
Craig Carpenter, *President*
Chad Carpenter, *Corp Secy*
Kevin Carpenter, *Vice Pres*
Gene Heath, *Manager*
EMP: 125 **EST:** 1990
SQ FT: 32,000
SALES (est): 25MM-49.9MM **Privately Held**
WEB: www.customremodelersinc.com
SIC: 1521 Single-family home general
remodeling service

(G-1010)
DELKOR SYSTEMS INC
8700 Rendova St NE (55014-4103)
PHONE 763 783-0855
Dale Andersen, *President*
Bill Jameson, *Electrical Engi*
Terry Cook, *CFO*
Dan Altman, *Accounting Dir*
Patricia Andersen, *Human Res Mgr*
EMP: 100 **EST:** 1990
SQ FT: 65,000
SALES (est): 50MM-99.9MM **Privately Held**
WEB: www.delkorsystems.com
SIC: 5199 5084 Wholesales packaging
materials; wholesales industrial packaging
machinery & equipment; manufactures
packaging machinery

(G-1011)
E J M PIPE SERVICES INC
7807 Lake Dr (55014-1135)
PHONE 651 786-8041
Allen Montgomery, *President*
Beth Petersen, *Corp Secy*
Mark Montgomery, *Vice Pres*
Vicki Lundgren, *Vice Pres*
Melissa Bailey, *Accountant*
EMP: 50 **EST:** 1976
SQ FT: 13,440
SALES (est): 5MM-9.9MM **Privately Held**
WEB: www.ejmpipe.com
SIC: 1623 Underground utilities contractor

(G-1012)
INTERPOLL LABORATORIES INC
4500 Ball Rd NE (55014-1819)
PHONE 763 786-6020
Gregg W Holman, *Vice Pres*
Sherry Gust, *Administration*
EMP: 33 **EST:** 1973
SQ FT: 16,000
SALES (est): 1MM-4.9MM Privately Held
WEB: www.interpoll-labs.com
SIC: 8734 7389 8711 8748 Pollution testing laboratory; engineering consulting services; inspection & testing service; air pollution measuring service; soil analysis laboratory; water testing laboratory; environmental consultant

(G-1013)
KRAUS-ANDERSON CONSTRUCTION CO
8625 Rendova St NE (55014-4102)
PO Box 158 (55014-0158)
PHONE 763 786-7711
FAX: 763 786-2650
Rich Jacobson, *Senior VP*
Dave Kummer, *Opers Mgr*
Gary Grahek, *Accounting Staf*
Diane Duguay, *Human Resources*
Gary Hook, *Manager*
EMP: 80
SQ FT: 34,661
SALES (est): 10MM-24.9MM Privately Held
WEB: www.krausanderson.com
SIC: 1542 Commercial & institutional building construction
PA: Kraus-Anderson Inc
523 S 8th St
Minneapolis MN 55404
612 332-7281

(G-1014)
LANG BUILDERS INC
620 Civic Heights Dr Ste 100
(55014-4709)
PHONE 763 780-9090
Timothy S Lang, *President*
Paula Lang, *Principal*
EMP: 25 **EST:** 1980
SQ FT: 4,500
SALES (est): 5MM-9.9MM Privately Held
WEB: www.langbuilders.com
SIC: 1521 Single-family home general remodeling service; new single-family home construction service; townhouse construction service

(G-1015)
MAGNUM LTL INC
3686 Flowerfield Rd (55014-3939)
PHONE 763 795-9534
Jim Tolson, *Manager*
EMP: 35
SALES (est): 1MM-4.9MM Privately Held
WEB: www.magnumlog.com
SIC: 4214 Local trucking with storage
PA: Magnum Ltl Inc
3000 7th Ave N Ste 1
Fargo ND 58102
701 293-8082

(G-1016)
MARCO INVESTMENTS LLC
Also Called: Team Tires Plus
9280 Lake Dr (55014-3766)
PHONE 763 795-8145
FAX: 763 792-8986
Nate Matchey, *Manager*
EMP: 26
SALES (est): 1MM-4.9MM Privately Held
SIC: 7534 Tire recapping & retreading services
PA: Marco Investments LLC
1315 Larpenteur Ave W Ste B
Saint Paul MN 55113
651 642-1523

(G-1017)
MATTHEW'S FAMILY RESTAURANT
2 Pine Dr (55014-1619)
PHONE 763 784-1499
Matthew Salo, *President*
EMP: 45 **EST:** 1996
SALES (est): 5MM-9.9MM Privately Held

SIC: 8748 Business consulting services; eating place

(G-1018)
NOL-TEC SYSTEMS INC
425 Apollo Dr (55014-1093)
PHONE 651 780-8600
Vern Hudalla, *President*
Wayne E Johnson, *Corp Secy*
Roger Schmitz, *Vice Pres*
Lynn Joachim, *Accounts Mgr*
EMP: 63 **EST:** 1983
SQ FT: 32,000
SALES (est): 10MM-24.9MM Privately Held
WEB: www.nol-tec.com
SIC: 8711 Manufactures conveyors & conveying equipment; ship, boat, machine & product design services

(G-1019)
NORTH AMERICAN COMPOSITES CO (HQ)
300 Apollo Dr (55014-3018)
PHONE 651 481-6860
James D Wallenfelsz, *President*
Leonard Jackson, *District Mgr*
Morris Brandt, *District Mgr*
Thomas Bush, *District Mgr*
James Keeffe, *District Mgr*
▲ **EMP:** 150 **EST:** 1962
SALES (corp-wide): 400M Privately Held
WEB: www.interplastic.com
SIC: 5162 Wholesales plastics materials
PA: Interplastic Corp
1225 Willow Lake Blvd
Saint Paul MN 55110
651 481-6860

(G-1020)
PTA MINNESOTA CONGRESS 28
Also Called: Golden Lake Pta
1 School Rd (55014-1783)
PHONE 763 792-5900
Jane Whitney, *President*
EMP: 70 Privately Held
SIC: 8641 Parent teacher association

(G-1021)
REHBEIN TRANSIT INC
6298 Hodgson Rd (55014-1430)
PHONE 651 484-1809
FAX: 651 484-8816
Richard Rehbein, *President*
Russell Rehbein, *Vice Pres*
Reid Rehbein, *Treasurer*
Roger Rehbein, *Director*
EMP: 130
SQ FT: 8,400
SALES (est): 1MM-4.9MM Privately Held
SIC: 4151 School bus service

(G-1022)
UNITED STATES MECHANICAL INC
3527 88th Ave NE (55014-4108)
PHONE 763 780-9030
FAX: 763 780-9036
Steven Brown, *President*
Paul Goski, *Vice Pres*
George Fredericks, *Project Mgr*
Candy Sartell, *Manager*
EMP: 30 **EST:** 1995
SQ FT: 2,000
SALES (est): 1MM-4.9MM Privately Held
WEB: www.usmech.us
SIC: 1711 Plumbing, heating & air conditioning contractor

(G-1023)
UPS GROUND FREIGHT INC
8600 Rendova St NE (55014-4101)
PHONE 763 780-9800
FAX: 763 780-4009
Mark Pierro, *Manager*
EMP: 75
SQ FT: 78,831
SALES (est): 5MM-9.9MM Publicly Held
WEB: www.overnite.com
SIC: 4213 Over the road trucking
HQ: UPS Ground Freight Inc
1000 Semmes Ave
Richmond VA 23224
804 231-8000

(G-1024)
WALGREEN CO
Also Called: Walgreens
9273 Lake Dr (55014-3764)
PHONE 763 783-7005
FAX: 763 780-8205
Danny Walace, *Manager*
EMP: 40
SALES (est): 5MM-9.9MM Publicly Held
WEB: www.walgreens.com
SIC: 7384 Drug store; photofinishing laboratory
PA: Walgreen Co
200 Wilmot Rd
Deerfield IL 60015
847 914-2500

(G-1025)
WATERPROOFING BY EXPERTS INC
448 Lilac St (55014-1054)
PHONE 651 786-5042
Steve Messerich, *President*
Charlene Messerich, *Corp Secy*
EMP: 30 **EST:** 1978
SQ FT: 5,000
SALES (est): 1MM-4.9MM Privately Held
SIC: 1799 Waterproofing service

CLARA CITY
Chippewa County

(G-1026)
CLARA CITY COMMUNITY NURSING
1012 Division St N (56222-1141)
PO Box 797 (56222-0797)
PHONE 320 847-2221
FAX: 320 847-3553
Alice Mohn, *Manager*
Marge Swenson, *Administrator*
John Davidson, *Administrator*
EMP: 100 **EST:** 1962
SALES (est): 1MM-4.9MM Privately Held
SIC: 8051 Skilled nursing care facility

(G-1027)
FARMERS CO-OP OIL CO OF CLARA (PA)
200 Hwy 7 W (56222)
PO Box 717 (56222-0717)
PHONE 320 847-2318
Ralph Thissen, *President*
Erv Ahrenhold, *Manager*
EST: 1955
SQ FT: 8,000 Privately Held
SIC: 5171 5191 Petroleum bulk station; wholesales agricultural fertilizer; retail gasoline filling station; retails bottled propane gas

(G-1028)
IMPACT INNOVATIONS INC (PA)
223 1st Ave SE (56222)
PHONE 320 847-1210
FAX: 320 367-1055
John Dammermann, *CEO*
Ron Noyes, *CFO*
Laurie Liebl, *Finance*
Jane Hagert, *Training Dir*
▲ **EMP:** 80 **EST:** 2001 Privately Held
SIC: 5023 7299 Manufactures narrow lace & decorative trim fabric; gift wrapping service; wholesales home furnishings

(G-1029)
MIDWEST - CBK INC
Also Called: Jmc Impact
223 1st Ave SE (56222)
PO Box 550 (56222-0550)
PHONE 320 847-1210
Monica Orwick, *Payroll Mgr*
EMP: 50
SALES (est): 25MM-49.9MM Publicly Held
WEB: www.cbkhome.com
SIC: 5199 Wholesales gifts & novelties
HQ: Midwest - Cbk Inc
600 Sherwood Dr
Union City TN 38261
731 885-7836

(G-1030)
MONTEVIDEO HOSPITAL HOME CARE
1100 Warrings Ave Apt 129 (56222-1001)
PHONE 320 367-2877
Rita Luchen, *Manager*
EMP: 28 **EST:** 1982
SALES (est): 500-999K Privately Held
SIC: 8082 Home health care services

(G-1031)
NORTHERN GRAIN DESIGN & CONSTR
8015 Highway 7 SE (56222-1017)
PHONE 320 367-2881
Kelly Pauling, *President*
EMP: 25 **EST:** 1997
SALES (est): 1MM-4.9MM Privately Held
SIC: 4221 Grain elevator with storage only

(G-1032)
PALMER BUS SERVICE
22 Division St S (56222-1038)
PHONE 320 847-3109
FAX: 320 847-3157
Floyd Palmer, *Owner*
Lowell Knapper, *Manager*
EMP: 25 **EST:** 2000
SALES (est): 500-999K Privately Held
SIC: 4151 School bus service

CLARISSA
Todd County

(G-1033)
CENTRAL TODD COUNTY CARE CTR
406 Highway 71 E (56440-2000)
PO Box 38 (56440-0038)
PHONE 218 756-3636
FAX: 218 756-3639
Margaret Taggart, *Principal*
EMP: 120 **EST:** 1977
SALES (est): 1MM-4.9MM Privately Held
SIC: 8051 Skilled nursing care facility

CLARKFIELD
Yellow Medicine County

(G-1034)
CITY OF CLARKFIELD
Also Called: Clarkfield Care Center
805 5th St (56223-1229)
PO Box 458 (56223-0458)
PHONE 320 669-7561
FAX: 320 669-7409
Julie Londgren, *Manager*
Paul Litjens, *Administrator*
EMP: 115
SALES (est): 1MM-4.9MM Privately Held
WEB: www.clarkfieldminnesota.com
SIC: 8059 8051 Nursing home; skilled nursing care facility
PA: City of Clarkfield
904 10th Ave
Clarkfield MN 56223
320 669-4435

CLEAR LAKE
Sherburne County

(G-1035)
KWIK KARGO INC TRUCKING
230 State St (55319-9646)
PO Box 304 (55319-0304)
PHONE 320 743-2021
FAX: 320 743-3542
Kenny Kotzer, *President*
Kathleen Kotzer, *Corp Secy*
Chris Kotzer, *Manager*
EMP: 50 **EST:** 1977
SALES (est): 5MM-9.9MM Privately Held
SIC: 4213 Over the road trucking

CLEARBROOK
Clearwater County

(G-1036)
C & G CONSTRUCTION INC OF
Hwy 5 Lot 4INDUSTRIAL Par (56634)
PHONE..............................218 776-3080
Kenneth Charpentier, *President*
Sandy Charpentier, *CFO*
EMP: 100 **EST:** 2005
SALES (est): 10MM-24.9MM **Privately Held**
SIC: 1623 Pipeline construction

(G-1037)
C & G HOLDING CO OF CLEARBROOK
Hwy 5 N Lot 4 Indus Park (56634)
PHONE..............................218 776-3080
Kenneth Charpentier, *President*
Kristopher Munter, *Controller*
Sandy Charpentier, *Controller*
EMP: 65 **EST:** 2005 **Privately Held**
SIC: 6719 Investment holding company

(G-1038)
EVANGELICAL LUTHERAN GOOD
Also Called: Good Samaritan Ctr Nursing HM
305 3rd Ave SW (56634)
PO Box 47 (56634-0047)
PHONE..............................218 776-3157
FAX: 218 776-3836
Jennifer Faldet, *Bookkeeper*
Linda Schmidt, *Human Res Mgr*
Becky Moe, *Office Mgr*
EMP: 95
SALES (est): 1MM-4.9MM **Privately Held**
WEB: www.good-sam.com
SIC: 8051 8069 Convalescent home;
specialty hospital
PA: Evangelical Lutheran Good
4800 W 57th St
Sioux Falls SD 57108
605 362-3100

(G-1039)
NORTH CENTRAL SERVICE INC
227 1st Ave SW (56634)
PO Box 213 (56634-0213)
PHONE..............................218 776-3855
Troy Torgerson, *President*
Sheryll Torgerson, *Vice Pres*
EMP: 140 **EST:** 1978
SALES (est): 10MM-24.9MM **Privately Held**
WEB: www.ncsmn.com
SIC: 1731 Fiber optic cable installation
contractor

(G-1040)
RIVIANA INTERNATIONAL INC
Also Called: Gourmet House
301 Tower St NW (56634-4236)
PO Box 290 (56634-0290)
PHONE..............................218 776-3118
FAX: 218 776-3119
Jenell Strandberg, *Accountant*
Steve Wraa, *Branch Mgr*
Julie Wraa, *Manager*
Bob Mowitt, *Supervisor*
EMP: 60 **Privately Held**
SIC: 0112 Rice farm
PA: Riviana Foods Inc
2777 Allen Pkwy Fl 15
Houston TX 77019
713 529-3251

CLEARWATER
Stearns County

(G-1041)
TELCOM CONSTRUCTION INC
2218 200th St E (55320-1636)
PO Box 189 (55320-0189)
PHONE..............................320 558-9485
Mark Muller, *President*
Steve Drings, *Vice Pres*
Steve Brings, *Manager*
EMP: 100 **EST:** 2000
SALES (est): 10MM-24.9MM **Privately Held**
WEB: www.telcomconstruction.com

SIC: 1623 Utility line construction

CLEARWATER
Wright County

(G-1042)
CLEARWATER TRUCK CENTER INC
925 Shorty St (55320)
PO Box 277 (55320-0277)
PHONE..............................320 558-6565
FAX: 320 558-2186
Greg Beuning, *President*
Todd Beuning, *Vice Pres*
Wendy Johnson, *Manager*
▲ **EMP:** 25 **EST:** 1986
SALES (est): 1MM-4.9MM **Privately Held**
SIC: 7538 General automotive repair
services

(G-1043)
D & E TRANSPORT INC
4141 150th St NW (55320-6110)
PHONE..............................763 878-2880
Daniel J Grundman, *President*
Tony Grundman, *Safety Dir*
Douglas R Foth, *Manager*
EMP: 85 **EST:** 1994
SQ FT: 9,000
SALES (est): 10MM-24.9MM **Privately Held**
SIC: 4213 Over the road trucking

CLINTON
Big Stone County

(G-1044)
LISMORE HUTTERIAN BRETHERN
80391 330th St (56225-2025)
PHONE..............................320 325-5485
FAX: 320 325-5256
Clarence Hoefer, *President*
Herbert Hoefer, *President*
Melvin Domine, *Branch Mgr*
Tom Hoser, *Manager*
EMP: 59 **EST:** 1999 **Privately Held**
SIC: 0191 0212 Crop farming; beef cattle
ranch

CLONTARF
Swift County

(G-1045)
CHAMBERLAIN OIL CO INC
112 Grace Ave (56226)
PO Box 278 (56226-0278)
PHONE..............................320 843-3434
FAX: 320 843-3372
William Chamberlain, *President*
Mary Chamberlain, *Corp Secy*
Laura Rentz, *Corp Secy*
John Chamberlain, *Vice Pres*
Anthony Chamberlain, *Vice Pres*
EMP: 26 **EST:** 1949
SQ FT: 15,300
SALES (est): 50MM-99.9MM **Privately Held**
WEB: www.chamberlainoil.com
SIC: 5172 Wholesales petroleum products

CLOQUET
Carlton County

(G-1046)
BEST OIL CO (PA)
Also Called: Little Store
30 8th St N (55720-1601)
PHONE..............................218 879-4666
FAX: 218 879-4680
John M Kinney, *President*
Mike M Kinney, *Corp Secy*
Christopher M Kinney, *Vice Pres*
Bruce Larson, *Treasurer*
Lori Bloomer, *Manager*
EMP: 50 **EST:** 1938
SQ FT: 3,500 **Privately Held**
WEB: www.bestoilcompany.com

SIC: 5171 5013 5172 Petroleum bulk
station; wholesales lubricating oils &
greases; retail chain convenience stores;
gas station; fuel oil dealer; wholesales new
motor vehicle parts & supplies

(G-1047)
BOLDT CO
1001 Tall Pine Ln (55720-3152)
PO Box 287 (55720-0287)
PHONE..............................218 879-1293
FAX: 218 879-5290
Mark Walch, *Project Dir*
Greg Wegler, *Sales Staff*
Ron Hanson, *Systems Mgr*
Shelly Peterson, *Officer*
EMP: 150
SALES (est): 25MM-49.9MM **Privately Held**
SIC: 1541 1542 8741 Industrial building &
warehouse construction; food product
manufacturing or packing plant construction;
paper & pulp mill construction; specialized
public building contractors; construction
management services

(G-1048)
CLOQUET COUNTRY CLUB
400 Country Club Dr (55720-3202)
PHONE..............................218 879-8858
John Turoni, *President*
Dick Brenner, *President*
EMP: 30 **EST:** 1917
SQ FT: 5,000
SALES (est): 1MM-4.9MM **Privately Held**
SIC: 7997 Membership golf club

(G-1049)
CLOQUET TRANSIT CO INC
1203 Avenue B (55720-1608)
PHONE..............................218 879-3391
Jeff Lane, *President*
Jack Lane, *Vice Pres*
EMP: 50 **EST:** 1930
SALES (est): 1MM-4.9MM **Privately Held**
WEB: www.lcscoaches.com
SIC: 4151 School bus service

(G-1050)
COMMUNITY MEMORIAL HOSPITAL
512 Skyline Blvd Ste 1 (55720-1139)
PHONE..............................218 879-4641
FAX: 218 879-9167
Rick Breuer, *CEO*
Bev Phkonen, *Corp Secy*
Steve B Vopat, *Ch of Surgery*
Brance Modin, *Ch of Surgery*
Steven J Eastep, *Ch Pathology*
EMP: 360 **EST:** 1958
SQ FT: 155,000
SALES (est): 25MM-49.9MM **Privately Held**
WEB: www.cloquethospital.com
SIC: 8062 Medical hospital

(G-1051)
EIKILL & SCHILLING LTD CPA
807 Cloquet Ave Ste 1 (55720-1675)
PHONE..............................218 879-1503
Dean Agear, *President*
Debra Benoit, *Principal*
Tom Eling, *Principal*
Debra Medlin, *Principal*
Thomas Sykes, *Principal*
EMP: 30
SALES (est): 1MM-4.9MM **Privately Held**
SIC: 8721 Certified public accountant
services

(G-1052)
FOND DU LAC MANAGEMENT INC
1720 Big Lake Rd (55720-9702)
PHONE..............................218 879-4593
Peter Defoe, *Chairman*
EMP: 100 **EST:** 1994
SQ FT: 80,000
SALES (est): 5MM-9.9MM **Privately Held**
WEB: www.fdlrez.com
SIC: 7999 Gambling establishment
PA: Fond Du Lac Reservation
1720 Big Lake Rd
Cloquet MN 55720
218 879-4593

(G-1053)
FOND DU LAC RESERVATION
Also Called: Min-No-Aya-win Clinic Pharmacy
927 Trettel Ln (55720-1345)
PHONE..............................218 879-1227
FAX: 218 879-8378
Rollin Smith, *Project Mgr*
Gregory Ash, *Chiropractor*
Nicol Campbell, *Med Doctor*
Julia R Jaakola, *Manager*
Phillip Norrgard, *Manager*
EMP: 250
SALES (est): 25MM-49.9MM **Privately Held**
WEB: www.fdlrez.com
SIC: 8011 Clinic operated by physicians;
pharmacy & drug store
PA: Fond Du Lac Reservation
1720 Big Lake Rd
Cloquet MN 55720
218 879-4593

(G-1054)
GODBOUT'S VIKING INTALLATION
516 Adams St (55720-1104)
PHONE..............................218 879-2199
FAX: 218 879-1105
Craig Godbout, *President*
EMP: 25 **EST:** 1999
SQ FT: 2,400
SALES (est): 1MM-4.9MM **Privately Held**
SIC: 1796 Machinery installation service

(G-1055)
L C S COACHES INC
1203 Avenue B (55720-1608)
PHONE..............................218 879-3391
FAX: 218 879-2020
Jeffery Lane, *President*
Jack Lane, *Vice Pres*
EMP: 25 **EST:** 1985
SQ FT: 6,500
SALES (est): 1MM-4.9MM **Privately Held**
SIC: 4142 Long-distance bus charter
service

(G-1056)
MCDONALD RENTALS INC
1208 Highway 33 S (55720-2625)
PHONE..............................218 879-9060
FAX: 218 879-2455
Robert McDonald, *President*
Betty McDonald, *Corp Secy*
Pat McDonald, *Vice Pres*
EMP: 29 **EST:** 1980
SQ FT: 14,000
SALES (est): 1MM-4.9MM **Privately Held**
SIC: 7841 7359 7549 Video tape & disc
rental; home appliance, furniture &
entertainment rental service; work zone
traffic flags, cones, barrels & other
equipment; automotive lubrication service

(G-1057)
MEMBERS COOPERATIVE CREDIT
101 14th St (55720-1903)
PHONE..............................218 879-3304
Del Prevost, *President*
Larry Champeaux, *Vice Pres*
Tammy Heilkkinen, *Vice Pres*
Teri Tanjen, *Vice Pres*
Ross Peterson, *Vice Pres*
EMP: 70 **EST:** 1936
SALES (est): 10MM-24.9MM **Privately Held**
SIC: 6062 State credit unions

(G-1058)
NELS NELSON & SONS INC
1000 Tall Pine Ln (55720-3151)
PHONE..............................218 879-4561
David Nelson, *President*
Mark R Deutsch, *Corp Secy*
Karen Nelson-Deutsch, *Vice Pres*
Lindsey Downing, *Human Res Dir*
Lindsay Foss, *Manager*
EMP: 110 **EST:** 1919
SALES (est): 10MM-24.9MM **Privately Held**
SIC: 1629 1611 1623 Dam, waterway, dock
& other marine structure construction;
grading services; sewer line construction;
water main construction

(G-1059)
PINE RIDGE HOMES INC
1509 14th St (55720-3133)
PHONE.....................218 879-1257
FAX: 218 879-6856
Michelle Matuzak, *Manager*
Ross Milberger, *Administrator*
Kim Bryant, *Director*
EMP: 85 **EST:** 1975
SALES (est): 1MM-4.9MM **Privately Held**
SIC: 8361 6531 8052 8741 Home for the
mentally retarded; intermediate care facility;
real estate services; management services

(G-1060)
PINEWOOD CLOQUET
915 18th St (55720-2437)
PHONE.....................218 879-4566
FAX: 218 878-1221
Roberta Stolarzyk, *Manager*
Toni Rothmeier, *Exec Dir*
Toni Nelson, *Exec Dir*
EMP: 42 **EST:** 1964
SQ FT: 13,000
SALES (est): 1MM-4.9MM **Privately Held**
SIC: 8331 8351 Skill training center; child
day care service

(G-1061)
PREMIERE THEATRES
904 Highway 33 S (55720-2624)
PHONE.....................218 879-7985
Rick Stowell, *President*
EMP: 28 **EST:** 1994
SALES (est): 1MM-4.9MM **Privately Held**
SIC: 7832 Indoor movie theater

(G-1062)
RAIPER CLINIC
417 Skyline Blvd (55720-1164)
PHONE.....................218 879-1271
Leslie Reiss, *Partner*
EMP: 60
SALES (est): 5MM-9.9MM **Privately Held**
SIC: 8011 General & family practice
physician or surgeon office

(G-1063)
RAITER CLINIC LTD
417 Skyline Blvd (55720-1164)
PHONE.....................218 879-1271
Steven B Vopat, *Principal*
Jessica Larson, *Corp Secy*
Deb Langley, *Office Mgr*
Shelley A Breyen, *Manager*
Kathy Jezeirski, *Supervisor*
EMP: 45 **EST:** 1930
SQ FT: 15,000
SALES (est): 5MM-9.9MM **Privately Held**
WEB: www.raiterclinic.com
SIC: 8011 Physicians' office

(G-1064)
RAY RIIHILUOMA INC
1415 Highway 33 S (55720-2626)
PHONE.....................218 879-3317
FAX: 218 879-3319
John Riihiluoma, *President*
John Franzen, *Vice Pres*
Joan Pedersen, *Manager*
EMP: 45 **EST:** 1956
SQ FT: 12,000
SALES (est): 10MM-24.9MM **Privately Held**
WEB: www.riihiluoma.com
SIC: 1541 1542 Industrial building &
warehouse construction; new industrial
building construction; commercial & office
building contractor; commercial & office
building renovation & repair services

(G-1065)
SENIOR FRIEND
116 Avenue C (55720-1546)
PHONE.....................218 878-0990
FAX: 218 878-0974
Karen Stocke, *Partner*
Theresa Wappes, *Branch Mgr*
Dawn Eller, *Manager*
EMP: 44 **EST:** 1982
SALES (est): 1MM-4.9MM **Privately Held**
WEB: www.seniorfriendinc.com
SIC: 8082 Home health care services

(G-1066)
UPPER LAKES FOODS INC (PA)
801 Industry Ave (55720-1635)
PHONE.....................218 879-1265
FAX: 218 879-1940
Scott Sorensen, *Ch of Bd*
Sue Ryan, *President*
Patricia Sorensen, *Corp Secy*
John Worth, *Purchasing*
Jeff Laabs, *CFO*
EMP: 185 **EST:** 1964
SQ FT: 120,000
SALES (corp-wide): 1.75M **Privately Held**
SIC: 5141 5046 5142 5147 Wholesales
general line groceries; wholesales fresh
meat; wholesales commercial equipment;
wholesales packaged frozen foods

(G-1067)
**US BANK NATIONAL
ASSOCIATION**
715 Cloquet Ave (55720-1629)
PHONE.....................218 878-7878
FAX: 218 879-5923
Joseph Sirba, *Manager*
EMP: 25
SALES (est): 5MM-9.9MM **Publicly Held**
WEB: www.firstar.com
SIC: 6021 National commercial bank
HQ: U S Bank National Association
425 Walnut St Fl 1
Cincinnati OH 45202
513 632-4234

(G-1068)
USG INTERIORS INC
35 Arch St (55720-1570)
PHONE.....................218 878-4000
FAX: 218 879-3673
Joe Jameson, *Maint Mgr*
Sue Welna, *Safety Mgr*
John Bleskacek, *Engineering*
Michael Shea, *Controller*
Holly Seidl, *Human Res Dir*
EMP: 450
SALES (est): 100MM-499.9MM **Publicly
Held**
WEB: www.gypsumsolutions.com
SIC: 5031 Wholesales lumber, plywood &
millwork; manufactures reconstituted wood
products; manufactures mineral wool
PA: USG Corp
550 W Adams St
Chicago IL 60661
312 436-4000

(G-1069)
**WISCONSIN PUBLIC SERVICE
CORP**
910 Cloquet Ave (55720-1616)
PHONE.....................218 879-1571
Ken Bergstedt, *Branch Mgr*
EMP: 44
SALES (est): 25MM-49.9MM **Publicly Held**
WEB: www.integrysgroup.com
SIC: 4911 Electric services
PA: Integrys Energy Group Inc
130 E Randolph St
Chicago IL 60601
312 228-5400

COHASSET
Itasca County

(G-1070)
ALLETE INC
1210 NW 3rd St (55721-8706)
PO Box 128 (55721-0128)
PHONE.....................218 328-5711
Bill Poulter, *Engineering*
Tom Lagergrem, *CFO*
Brenda Flayton, *Human Res Dir*
Al Hodnik, *Manager*
Warren L Candy, *Manager*
EMP: 258
SALES (est): 100MM-499.9MM **Publicly
Held**

SIC: 4911 Provides electric power
generation services
PA: Allete Inc
30 W Superior St
Duluth MN 55802
218 279-5000

(G-1071)
**LAKEHEAD CONSTRUCTORS
INC**
856 NW 3rd St (55721)
PO Box 228 (55721-0228)
PHONE.....................218 328-5429
FAX: 218 328-6532
Mark Hubburd, *Manager*
EMP: 40
SALES (est): 10MM-24.9MM **Privately Held**
SIC: 1521 Single-family housing
construction
HQ: Lakehead Constructors Inc
2916 Hill Ave
Superior WI 54880
715 392-5181

(G-1072)
LODGE AT SUGAR LAKE INC
Also Called: Ruttger's Sugar Lake Lodge
37584 Otis Ln (55721-8940)
PO Box 847, Grand Rapids (55744-0847)
PHONE.....................218 327-1462
FAX: 218 327-0454
Fred Bobich, *President*
Gwynne Bobich, *Corp Secy*
Chad Simons, *Sales Staff*
Shannon Mann, *Manager*
EMP: 50 **EST:** 1992
SQ FT: 28,000
SALES (est): 1MM-4.9MM **Privately Held**
WEB: www.sugarlakelodge.com
SIC: 7011 Resort hotel

(G-1073)
WILLE TRANSPORT INC
521 W Highway 2 (55721-2300)
PHONE.....................218 999-0900
Randy Cook, *President*
EMP: 60 **EST:** 2006
SALES (est): 5MM-9.9MM **Privately Held**
WEB: www.willetransport.com
SIC: 4213 Over the road trucking

COKATO
Wright County

(G-1074)
**ADVANCED PROCESS
TECHNOLOGIES**
Also Called: A P T
150 Swendra Blvd NE (55321-4740)
PO Box 939 (55321-0939)
PHONE.....................320 286-5060
FAX: 320 286-3055
Craig Campbell, *President*
Daniel Lechelt, *Corp Secy*
Melvin Briggs, *Vice Pres*
Russell Scherping, *Director*
EMP: 52 **EST:** 2000
SQ FT: 40,000
SALES (est): 5MM-9.9MM **Privately Held**
WEB: www.apt-inc.com
SIC: 1791 Structural steel erection
contractor

(G-1075)
AME COMMUNITY SERVICE INC
615 Mooers Ave SE (55321-4231)
PO Box 728 (55321-0728)
PHONE.....................320 286-6421
Martin McGraw, *President*
Corinne McGraw, *Vice Pres*
Cindy Newstrom, *Consultant*
EST: 1992 **Privately Held**
WEB: www.amecommunity.com
SIC: 8052 Residential mentally
handicapped facility

(G-1076)
COKATO CHARITABLE TRUST
182 Sunset Ave NW (55321-9620)
PHONE.....................320 286-2158
FAX: 320 286-2031
Michelle Haefner, *Principal*

Deb Loe, *Manager*
Nancy Stratman, *Administrator*
Jon Riewer, *Administrator*
Scott Smith, *Maintence Staff*
EMP: 130 **EST:** 1975
SQ FT: 21,379
SALES (est): 10MM-24.9MM **Privately Held**
SIC: 8093 8051 8082 8322 Outpatient
rehabilitation treatment center; geriatric
social services; home health care services;
skilled nursing care facility

(G-1077)
PAISLEY CONSULTING INC
400 Cokato St E (55321-4244)
PO Box 578 (55321-0578)
PHONE.....................320 286-5870
FAX: 320 286-6196
Timothy Welu, *CEO*
Stacey Welu, *President*
Kinne Caryne, *Vice Pres*
Brian Koehler, *QA Mgr*
Stacey Billy, *Mktg Dir*
EMP: 125 **EST:** 1995
SALES (est): 25MM-49.9MM **Publicly Held**
WEB: www.thomsonreuters.com
SIC: 7372 8748 Business & professional
software publishers; business consulting
services
HQ: Thomson Reuters tax
195 Broadway
New York NY 10007
212 367-6300

(G-1078)
PENGO CORP
13369 60th St SW (55321-4210)
PHONE.....................320 286-5581
FAX: 320 845-2497
Miron Dahlke, *President*
Brent McDonald, *Vice Pres*
Brian Rickards, *Vice Pres*
Dale Hofmaster, *Purch Agent*
Rich Gehrig, *Controller*
EMP: 30 **EST:** 2002
SALES (est): 10MM-24.9MM **Privately Held**
SIC: 1221 Bituminous coal auger mining

(G-1079)
SAUNATEC INC (PA)
575 Cokato St E (55321-4247)
PHONE.....................320 286-5584
FAX: 320 286-6100
Keith Raisanen, *President*
Pentti Piisku, *Chairman*
D Hawkinson, *Mfg Staff*
Diane Coles, *Controller*
Joe Harmale, *Cust Svc Dir*
▲ **EMP:** 60 **EST:** 1984
SQ FT: 50,000 **Privately Held**
WEB: www.saunatec.com
SIC: 5091 Wholesales spa equipment &
supplies; manufactures small electric
household appliances; manufactures
prefabricated wood buildings; manufactures
heating equipment & supplies

(G-1080)
STATE BANK OF COKATO
101 3rd St SE (55321-9600)
PO Box 220 (55321-0220)
PHONE.....................320 286-2146
FAX: 320 286-6207
Don M Peroutka, *Exec VP*
Beverly Irvin, *Vice Pres*
Connie Isaacson, *Vice Pres*
Kristina Nelson, *Mfg Staff*
Carol Entinger, *Mfg Staff*
EMP: 26 **EST:** 1892
SALES (est): 5MM-9.9MM **Privately Held**
WEB: www.statbank.com
SIC: 6022 State commercial bank

(G-1081)
SYNGENTA SEEDS INC
4915 Reardon Ave SW (55321-4532)
PHONE.....................320 286-5511
Lonnie Carrigan, *Manager*
EMP: 25
SALES (est): 10MM-24.9MM **Publicly Held**
WEB: www.syngenta.com
SIC: 5191 Wholesales farm supplies
HQ: Syngenta Seeds Inc
11055 Wayzata Blvd
Minnetonka MN 55305
612 656-8600

COLD SPRING
Stearns County

(G-1082)
ASSUMPTION HOME INC
715 1st St N (56320-1401)
PHONE 320 685-3693
FAX: 320 685-7044
Jan Luthens, *President*
Erik Burr, *Manager*
Clara Schueller, *Manager*
Keith Stanhill, *Manager*
Christa Benning, *Administrator*
EMP: 145 **EST:** 1962
SQ FT: 33,000
SALES (est): 5MM-9.9MM **Privately Held**
SIC: 8051 Skilled nursing care facility

(G-1083)
COLD SPRING GRANITE CO INC (PA)
17482 Granite West Rd (56320-4578)
PHONE 320 685-3621
FAX: 320 685-4638
Patrick D Alexander, *CEO*
John Mattke, *President*
Stephanie Barthel, *General Mgr*
Rosemary Alexander, *Corp Secy*
Dan REA, *Senior VP*
▲ **EMP:** 800 **EST:** 1898
SQ FT: 40,000 **Privately Held**
WEB:
www.granitemountainstonedesign.com
SIC: 1741 Manufactures dimension stone
for buildings; manufactures cut stone
monuments; manufactures cut stone
tombstones; quarries & processes stone;
manufactures bronze foundry; masonry &
stonework contractor

(G-1084)
COLD SPRING ST JOSEPH
111 Red River Ave S (56320-2538)
PHONE 320 685-3237
FAX: 320 685-7682
Fred Mehr DVM, *President*
Rick Bohlman, *Vice Pres*
Tom Carlson, *Treasurer*
EMP: 35 **EST:** 1960
SQ FT: 2,000
SALES (est): 10MM-24.9MM **Privately Held**
WEB: www.cssjpvets.com
SIC: 5047 Wholesales veterinarians'
equipment & supplies; retails pet supplies

(G-1085)
FIRST NATIONAL BANK OF COLD
301 Main St (56320-2534)
PO Box 416 (56320-0416)
PHONE 320 685-8611
FAX: 320 685-5260
Glenn D Heitzman, *President*
Daniel G Steil, *Exec VP*
Brenda Holthauf, *Assistant VP*
Brenda Widmer, *Assistant VP*
Jim Eiynck, *Vice Pres*
EMP: 26 **EST:** 1902
SALES (est): 5MM-9.9MM **Privately Held**
WEB: www.fnbcs.com
SIC: 6021 Commercial national trust
companies with deposits
PA: First Bancshares Inc of Cold
301 Main St
Cold Spring MN 56320
320 685-8611

(G-1086)
FOUR TS INC
27023 Hidden Cove Rd (56320-1051)
PHONE 320 685-7407
Roger Negard, *President*
Gail Negard, *Vice Pres*
EMP: 30 **EST:** 1997
SALES (est): 500-999K **Privately Held**
SIC: 7349 Industrial or commercial cleaning
services

(G-1087)
LUMBER ONE, COLD SPRING INC
700 3rd St S (56320-2117)
PO Box 395 (56320-0395)
PHONE 320 685-3631
FAX: 320 685-3619
Ted R Schmid, *CEO*
Barbara Barandes, *Corp Secy*
David Ruegemer, *Vice Pres*
James Green, *Vice Pres*
EMP: 30 **EST:** 1967
SQ FT: 19,000
SALES (est): 5MM-9.9MM **Privately Held**
SIC: 1521 1522 Retails building products &
materials; new single-family home
construction service; apartment building
construction service

(G-1088)
MINNERATH CONSTRUCTION INC
500 3rd Ave S (56320-2542)
PHONE 320 685-3162
FAX: 320 685-8137
Loren Minnerath, *President*
EST: 1955
SQ FT: 900 **Privately Held**
SIC: 1611 General highway & street
construction service

(G-1089)
RICH-SPRING GOLF CLUB INC
17467 Fairway Cir (56320-9708)
PHONE 320 685-8810
Matt Miller, *President*
Chuck Schneider, *Superintendent*
Jim Johnson, *Superintendent*
Pat Gardanier, *Corp Secy*
Jerry Muggli, *Treasurer*
EMP: 30 **EST:** 1960
SALES (est): 1MM-4.9MM **Privately Held**
WEB: www.richspringgolf.com
SIC: 7997 Membership golf club

(G-1090)
ROGER ILLIES REALTOR
15637 241st St (56320-9632)
PHONE 320 685-8119
Roger Illies, *Agent*
EMP: 30
SALES (est): 5MM-9.9MM **Privately Held**
SIC: 6531 Real estate agency & broker

COLOGNE
Carver County

(G-1091)
COUNTY OF CARVER
Also Called: Public Works Department
11360 Highway 212 Ste 2 (55322-8017)
PHONE 952 466-5200
Mary Schuler, *General Mgr*
Roger Gustason, *Director*
EMP: 60
SALES (est): 5MM-9.9MM **Privately Held**
SIC: 1611 Concrete road, highway &
sidewalk construction
PA: County of Carver
600 E 4th St
Chaska MN 55318
952 361-1510

(G-1092)
JA-CEE CONSULTANTS INC
8570 Maple View Dr (55322-9625)
PHONE 952 466-4785
Joel Ciaccio, *President*
Elke Ciaccio, *Vice Pres*
EMP: 25 **EST:** 1996
SALES (est): 1MM-4.9MM **Privately Held**
SIC: 8748 Business consulting services

(G-1093)
VERIZON BUSINESS NETWORK SVCS
7383 County Road 140 (55322-9161)
PHONE 612 607-1116
Baron Zumach, *Manager*
EMP: 50 **Publicly Held**

WEB: www.mccmt.com
SIC: 4813 4812 Wired telecommunications
carrier & service; wireless
telecommunications carrier & service
HQ: Verizon Business Global LLC
22001 Loudoun County Pkwy
Ashburn VA 20147
703 886-5600

COOK
Saint Louis County

(G-1094)
COOK AREA HEALTH SERVICES INC (PA)
20 5th St SE (55723-9702)
PHONE 218 666-5941
FAX: 218 666-5099
Michael Holmes, *CEO*
Lawrence Gustafson, *President*
Gail Blackmer, *Corp Secy*
Myrna Malm, *CFO*
EMP: 30 **EST:** 1979
SQ FT: 3,000
SALES (corp-wide): 6.99M **Privately Held**
SIC: 8011 8021 8049 Physicians' office &
clinic; dental hygienists' office; dental office

COSMOS
Meeker County

(G-1095)
RASKE BUILDING SYSTEMS INC
240 Milkyway St N (56228-9749)
PO Box 98 (56228-0098)
PHONE 320 877-7221
Earl Raske, *President*
Shelia Tews, *Branch Mgr*
Chuck Raske, *Officer*
EMP: 25 **EST:** 1959
SQ FT: 2,100
SALES (est): 5MM-9.9MM **Privately Held**
WEB: www.raskebuilding.com
SIC: 1542 Commercial & institutional
building construction; commercial & office
building contractor

COTTAGE GROVE
Washington County

(G-1096)
ALLIED SYSTEMS LTD
9450 Ideal Ave S (55016-3845)
PHONE 651 458-3005
FAX: 651 458-1805
Howard Gibson, *Terminal Mgr*
Don Strachota, *Manager*
EMP: 200
SALES (est): 25MM-49.9MM **Publicly Held**
SIC: 4213 Automobile carrier services
HQ: Allied Automotive Group Inc
2302 Parklake Dr NE Ste 600
Atlanta GA 30345
404 373-4285

(G-1097)
ALLINA HEALTH SYSTEM
8611 W Point Douglas Rd S (55016-4005)
PHONE 651 458-1884
FAX: 651 241-0460
Cece Xiong, *Optometrist*
Bruce D Babcock, *Optometrist*
Ronald Otremba MD, *Med Doctor*
Mary Rahman, *Manager*
Jennifer R Smith-Kistensen, *Manager*
EMP: 60
SALES (est): 5MM-9.9MM **Privately Held**
WEB: www.allina.com
SIC: 8011 Clinic operated by physicians
PA: Allina Health System
2925 Chicago Ave
Minneapolis MN 55407
612 775-5000

(G-1098)
AMERICAN AGCO INC (PA)
7900 97th St S (55016-4343)
PHONE 651 451-1349
Gary Duclos, *President*

Prestegord Gary, *COO*
Brian Becker, *Purch Mgr*
Anthony Duclos Jr, *Treasurer*
Corrine Baker, *Human Res Dir*
▲ **EMP:** 80 **EST:** 1936
SQ FT: 70,000 **Privately Held**
WEB: www.americanagco.com
SIC: 5191 5149 Wholesales farm supplies;
wholesales pet food; wholesales feed;
wholesales garden supplies

(G-1099)
AMERICAN LOGISTICS SERVICES
7900 97th St S (55016-4343)
PHONE 651 451-1349
Greg Jenson, *Member*
Jon Duclos, *Member*
Anthony Duclos, *Member*
Gary Duclos, *Member*
EMP: 65 **EST:** 1999
SQ FT: 85,000
SALES (est): 25MM-49.9MM **Privately Held**
SIC: 5149 4214 Wholesales pet food; local
trucking with storage

(G-1100)
AUTO WAREHOUSING CO INC
9250 Ideal Ave S (55016-4018)
PHONE 651 769-8383
FAX: 651 769-8388
Jeff Phetteplace, *Manager*
Rayleen Baker, *Manager*
EMP: 28
SALES (est): 1MM-4.9MM **Privately Held**
SIC: 4226 Automobile dead storage
PA: Auto Warehousing Co Inc
2810 Marshall Ave Ste B
Tacoma WA 98421
253 922-0540

(G-1101)
COTTAGE GROVE, CITY OF INC
8635 W Point Douglas Rd S (55016-3318)
PHONE 651 458-2808
FAX: 651 458-6080
Ryan Schroeder, *Administrator*
Les Burshten, *Director*
EMP: 40 **Privately Held**
SIC: 4931 City & town managers' office;
electric & related services
PA: Cottage Grove, City of Inc
7516 80th St S Ste 2
Cottage Grove MN 55016
651 458-2800

(G-1102)
GROVE COTTAGE ATHLETIC ASSN
Also Called: Cottage Grove Bingo
7240 E Point Douglas Rd S (55016-3032)
PO Box 337 (55016-0337)
PHONE 651 459-9278
Al Boche, *President*
Brad Bacon, *President*
Mary Terren, *Manager*
Jacjlyn Perren, *Manager*
EMP: 35 **EST:** 1999 **Privately Held**
SIC: 8641 Civic & social organization

(G-1103)
GROVE COTTAGE EMERGENCY MED
Also Called: Cottage Grove Ems
7516 80th St S Ste 2 (55016-3328)
PHONE 651 458-2865
John Mickelson, *Director*
EMP: 85
SALES (est): 1MM-4.9MM **Privately Held**
SIC: 4119 Local passenger transportation
service

(G-1104)
LINKS ON THE MISSISSIPPI INC
Also Called: Mississippi Dunes Golf Links
10351 Grey Cloud Trl S (55016-4324)
PHONE 651 768-7611
William C Doebler, *President*
Greg W Doebler, *Vice Pres*
Dennis Neitz, *Finance*
Lisabeth E Mackall, *Director*
EMP: 25 **EST:** 1992
SQ FT: 5,600
SALES (est): 1MM-4.9MM **Privately Held**
WEB: www.mississippidunes.com

GEOGRAPHIC

SIC: 7992 7299 Public golf course; banquet hall facility

(G-1105)
MORGAN TIRE & AUTO LLC
7199 E Point Douglas Rd S (55016-3026)
PHONE...............................651 458-1812
Jim Cker, *Manager*
EMP: 30
SALES (est): 1MM-4.9MM **Privately Held**
WEB: www.bfsusa.com
SIC: 7534 Tire recapping & retreading services
HQ: Bfs Retail Operations LLC
    333 E Lake St Ste 300
    Bloomingdale IL 60108
    630 259-9000

(G-1106)
NORRIS SQUARE ✪
8200 Hadley Ave S Ofc OFC (55016-2694)
PHONE...............................651 769-2447
EMP: 25 EST: 2008
SALES (est): 500-999K **Privately Held**
SIC: 8361 Geriatric residential care

(G-1107)
SCHMID & SON PACKAGING INC
7699 95th St S (55016-3945)
PHONE...............................651 452-0588
Mary Schmid, *CEO*
Steve Schmid, *President*
Jeff Schmid, *Vice Pres*
Seinphy Vu, *Administration*
EMP: 100 EST: 1980
SALES (est): 5MM-9.9MM **Privately Held**
WEB: www.schmidpackaging.com
SIC: 7389 Packaging & labeling services

(G-1108)
TRAVELNET SOLUTIONS INC
9900 Hemingway Ave S (55016-4344)
PHONE...............................651 757-4905
Charles Bailey, *President*
Ryan Bailey, *Vice Pres*
Patty Schweiger, *Assistant*
EMP: 29 EST: 2003
SQ FT: 25,000
SALES (est): 1MM-4.9MM **Privately Held**
WEB: www.travelnetsolutions.com
SIC: 4724 Travel agency

(G-1109)
WERNER ELECTRIC VENTURES LLC (PA)
7450 95th St S (55016)
PHONE...............................651 769-6841
Kevin Powell, *Member*
Steve Hesser, *Opers Mgr*
Bob Matthew, *Opers Mgr*
Craig Amerson, *Purchasing*
EMP: 125 EST: 2001 **Privately Held**
WEB: www.wernermn.com
SIC: 5063 Wholesales electrical apparatus & equipment

COTTON
Saint Louis County

(G-1110)
MILLERS ROOFING & SIDING CO
7393 Randall Rd (55724-8025)
PO Box 1323, Bemidji (56619-1323)
PHONE...............................218 751-4337
Doug Miller, *Partner*
EMP: 50 EST: 1991
SALES (est): 5MM-9.9MM **Privately Held**
SIC: 1761 Roofing contractor

COTTONWOOD
Lyon County

(G-1111)
CENTROL INC COTTONWOOD, MN
90 W Main (56229)
PO Box 198 (56229-0198)
PHONE...............................507 423-5423
FAX: 507 423-6219
Conrad Bostron, *President*
Curt Fettig, *General Mgr*
Leo Langer, *Manager*
Brad Manderson, *Manager*
Paula Muller, *Manager*
EMP: 25 EST: 1980 **Publicly Held**
WEB: www.centrol.com
SIC: 0762 Farm management services
PA: CHS Inc
    5500 Cenex Dr
    Inver Grove Heights MN 55077
    651 355-6000

(G-1112)
EXTREME PANEL TECHNOLOGIES INC
475 E 4th St (56229-2256)
PO Box 435 (56229-0435)
PHONE...............................507 423-5530
FAX: 507 423-5531
Terry Dieken, *CEO*
Linda Dieken, *CFO*
Jodi Bofferding, *Office Mgr*
EMP: 29 EST: 1991
SQ FT: 40,000
SALES (est): 10MM-24.9MM **Privately Held**
WEB: www.extremepanel.com
SIC: 5031 Wholesales prefabricated wood structural assemblies

(G-1113)
MINNESOTA RURAL HEALTH CO-OP
190 E 4th St (56229-2263)
PO Box 155 (56229-0155)
PHONE...............................507 423-5300
Paula Soine, *QC Mgr*
Heather Gniffke, *Manager*
Charles Ness, *Exec Dir*
EMP: 99 EST: 1999
SALES (est): 10MM-24.9MM **Privately Held**
WEB: www.mrhc.net
SIC: 8011 Health maintenance organization or HMO

(G-1114)
NORTH STAR GENERAL INSURANCE
269 Barstad Rd S (56229)
PHONE...............................507 423-6262
Jeff Mauland, *President*
Joe Hoff, *Vice Pres*
Melinda Smith, *VP Persnl*
EMP: 55 EST: 1920
SQ FT: 48,000
SALES (est): 5MM-9.9MM **Privately Held**
SIC: 6411 Insurance services
PA: North Star Mutual Insurance Co
    269 Barstad Rd S
    Cottonwood MN 56229
    507 423-6262

COURTLAND
Nicollet County

(G-1115)
AMERICA MIDWEST TRANSPORTATION
148 Zieske Rd (56021-4327)
PO Box 997, New Ulm (56073-0997)
PHONE...............................507 359-4450
Barry Bloedel, *Mng Member*
Roxann Sabo, *Manager*
EMP: 30 EST: 2003
SALES (est): 1MM-4.9MM **Privately Held**
SIC: 4789 Railroad cargo loading & unloading services

CRANE LAKE
Saint Louis County

(G-1116)
CAMPBELLS CABINS & TRADING
7540 Gold Coast Rd (55725-8010)
PHONE...............................218 993-2361
Jay Handberg, *Branch Mgr*
EMP: 50
SALES (est): 1MM-4.9MM **Privately Held**
SIC: 7011 Resort hotel

CROMWELL
Carlton County

(G-1117)
VISTA VILLA INC
1197 N Hwy 73 (55726)
PHONE...............................218 644-3331
FAX: 218 644-3331
Stacy Hedin, *President*
EMP: 50 EST: 1973
SQ FT: 13,000
SALES (est): 1MM-4.9MM **Privately Held**
SIC: 8052 Intermediate care facility

CROOKSTON
Polk County

(G-1118)
ALL TRUE CLINIC CROOKSTON INC
400 S Minnesota St (56716-1808)
PHONE...............................218 281-9100
FAX: 218 281-9116
Greg Gerloss, *CEO*
Casey Ryan, *President*
Aliya A Shamsi MD, *Med Doctor*
Mirzabasit Baig MD, *Med Doctor*
Rose B Brandt MD, *Med Doctor*
EMP: 70 EST: 1987
SALES (est): 5MM-9.9MM **Privately Held**
SIC: 8011 Clinic operated by physicians

(G-1119)
CROOKSTON FAMILY SERVICE CTR
1407 Erskine St (56716-2535)
PHONE...............................218 281-1343
FAX: 218 281-2147
Phil Wold, *Principal*
Greg Dufuot, *Info Tech Mgr*
Patty Deery, *Director*
Jeannine Windels, *Bd of Directors*
EMP: 45 EST: 2000
SALES (est): 1MM-4.9MM **Privately Held**
SIC: 8351 Child day care service; head Start center

(G-1120)
CROOKSTON FIREFIGHTER RELIEF
620 S Main St (56716-2433)
PHONE...............................218 281-4584
FAX: 218 281-4594
Mike Swenson, *Corp Secy*
Tom Seiro, *Treasurer*
Chris Cournia, *Director*
EMP: 25 EST: 2001 **Privately Held**
SIC: 8641 Civic & social organization

(G-1121)
CROOKSTON FUEL CO
Also Called: Ampride Convenience Mart
1020 Highway 75 S (56716-2129)
PO Box 702 (56716-0702)
PHONE...............................218 281-2157
FAX: 218 281-2728
Eugene Hanson, *President*
Wayne Melbye, *General Mgr*
Duane Hanson, *Corp Secy*
Gary Hoerner, *Vice Pres*
EMP: 28 EST: 1945
SQ FT: 1,400
SALES (est): 50MM-99.9MM **Privately Held**
SIC: 5172 Wholesales petroleum products

(G-1122)
CROOKSTON WELDING MACHINE CO
Also Called: NAPA CROOKSTON WELDING
Hwy 75S (56716)
PO Box 377 (56716-0377)
PHONE...............................218 281-6911
FAX: 218 281-7255
Larry Altringer, *President*
Orrin Halvorson, *Vice Pres*
Gary Reitmeier, *Mfg Staff*
Diane Altringer, *Treasurer*
EMP: 35 EST: 1965
SQ FT: 23,200
SALES (est): 1MM-4.9MM **Privately Held**
SIC: 5013 Retails automotive parts; machine shop, jobbing & repair services; wholesales automotive supplies & parts

(G-1123)
DAHLGREN & CO INC (PA)
1220 Sunflower St (56716-2480)
PO Box 609 (56716-0609)
PHONE...............................218 281-2985
FAX: 218 281-6218
Charles Considine, *President*
Tom Miller, *Chairman*
Tim Egeland, *CFO*
Kurt Heldsta, *Controller*
Julie Oertwich, *Human Res Dir*
▼ EMP: 130 EST: 1961
SQ FT: 12,000 **Privately Held**
WEB: www.sunflowerseed.com
SIC: 0723 Manufactures dried, dehydrated, salted or roasted seeds; manufactures animal feed; manufactures food preparations; post harvest crop activities

(G-1124)
FIRST AMERICAN BANK VALLEY
201 N Broadway Ste 1 (56716-1727)
PHONE...............................218 281-4182
FAX: 218 281-5206
Gerry Henneberg, *Assistant VP*
Doreen Mickelson, *QC Dir*
Bamson Fadipe, *Branch Mgr*
John Rolf, *Branch Mgr*
Pam Kramer, *Branch Mgr*
EMP: 30
SALES (est): 5MM-9.9MM **Privately Held**
SIC: 6021 National commercial bank
DH: First American Bank Valley
    3100 S Columbia Rd
    Grand Forks ND 58201
    701 795-4580

(G-1125)
GLENMORE FOUNDATION
323 S Minnesota St (56716-1601)
PO Box 497 (56716-0497)
PHONE...............................218 281-3123
William H Doran, *CEO*
Tom Fuch, *Director*
EMP: 40 EST: 1973
SQ FT: 150
SALES (est): 1MM-4.9MM **Privately Held**
SIC: 7389 Fundraising services

(G-1126)
INDEPENDENCE PLUS INC
27885 170th Ave SW (56716-9444)
PHONE...............................218 281-3506
Ruby Baranski, *President*
Michelle Kyler, *Corp Secy*
Patrick Barnski, *Vice Pres*
EMP: 200 EST: 2000
SALES (est): 5MM-9.9MM **Privately Held**
WEB: www.independenceplus.com
SIC: 8082 Home health care services

(G-1127)
LUTHERAN SOCIAL SERVICE OF MN
Also Called: Home & Community Service
1601 Summerfield Dr (56716-2670)
PHONE...............................218 281-6418
FAX: 218 281-6137
Amy Jalan, *Manager*
EMP: 25
SALES (est): 500-999K **Privately Held**
WEB: www.lssmn.org

SIC: **8351** Child day care service
PA: Lutheran Social Service Of MN
2485 Como Ave
Saint Paul MN 55108
651 642-5990

(G-1128)
MINNESOTA NORTHERN RAILROAD
28997 255th Ave SW (56716)
PO Box 705 (56716-0705)
PHONE 218 281-4704
FAX: 218 281-4705
Thomas G Kotnour, *President*
George Lapray, *General Mgr*
George L Pray, *Manager*
EMP: 25 EST: 1996 **Privately Held**
SIC: **4011** Long haul railroad

(G-1129)
NORTHLAND INN OF CROOKSTON
2200 University Ave (56716-2816)
PHONE 218 281-5210
FAX: 218 281-1019
Linda Stenger, *General Mgr*
Bhupen Ray, *Mng Member*
Linda Lende, *Manager*
Megan Fitzpatrick, *Director*
EMP: 70 EST: 1978
SQ FT: 17,000
SALES (est): 1MM-4.9MM **Privately Held**
SIC: **7011** Motel; cocktail lounge; eating place

(G-1130)
NORTHWESTERN MENTAL HEALTH CTR (PA)
603 Bruce St (56716-2914)
PO Box 603 (56716-0603)
PHONE 218 281-3940
Curtis Carlson, *President*
Jim Sheaer, *Manager*
Martha Wissmann, *Manager*
Daniel Wilson, *Director*
EMP: 79 EST: 1962
SQ FT: 8,600
SALES (corp-wide): 6.70M **Privately Held**
SIC: **8093** Outpatient alcohol treatment clinic; outpatient drug clinic; outpatient mental health clinic

(G-1131)
NORTHWESTERN MENTAL HEALTH CTR
Also Called: Community Support Program
603 Bruce St (56716-2914)
PO Box 603 (56716-0603)
PHONE 218 281-3940
Dan Wilson, *Director*
EMP: 80
SALES (est): 5MM-9.9MM **Privately Held**
SIC: **8063** Mental hospital
PA: Northwestern Mental Health Ctr
603 Bruce St
Crookston MN 56716
218 281-3940

(G-1132)
OTTER TAIL POWER CO
410 College Ave (56716-2922)
PHONE 218 281-3632
FAX: 218 281-2522
Peter Wasberg, *Manager*
Richard Johnson, *Manager*
EMP: 28
SALES (est): 10MM-24.9MM **Privately Held**
WEB: www.otpco.com
SIC: **4911** Provides electric power generation services
HQ: Otter Tail Power Co
215 S Cascade St
Fergus Falls MN 56537
866 410-8780

(G-1133)
PETERSON BIDDICK CO
63585 W Hwy 10 (56716)
PO Box B, Wadena (56482)
PHONE 218 631-2954
Jeff Wensman, *General Mgr*
EMP: 40
SALES (est): 25MM-49.9MM **Privately Held**
SIC: **5191** Wholesales feed

(G-1134)
POLK COUNTY DEVELOPMENTAL
515 5th Ave S (56716-2525)
PHONE 218 281-4181
FAX: 218 281-2678
Doria Knaack, *Manager*
Joan Bittner, *Director*
EMP: 30 EST: 1964
SALES (est): 1MM-4.9MM **Privately Held**
SIC: **8361** 8331 Residential rehabilitation center with health care incidental; job training & vocational rehabilitation services

(G-1135)
REGENTS OF THE UNIVERSITY OF
131 Kiehle Bldg (56716)
PHONE 218 281-8376
Mark G Yudof, *President*
Peggy Sherven, *Manager*
EMP: 25
SALES (est): 10MM-24.9MM **Privately Held**
WEB: www.umn.edu
SIC: **5045** Wholesales computers; university
PA: Regents of The University of
106 Pleasant St SE # 210
Minneapolis MN 55455
612 625-5000

(G-1136)
RIVERVIEW HEALTHCARE ASSN
Also Called: Home Care & Hospice
323 S Minnesota St (56716-1601)
PHONE 218 281-9478
FAX: 218 281-9248
Carol Janousek, *Manager*
Vicky Korynta, *Director*
EMP: 35
SALES (est): 1MM-4.9MM **Privately Held**
SIC: **8082** Home health care services

(G-1137)
TITAN MACHINERY INC
500 Ingersoll Ave (56716-2112)
PO Box 435 (56716-0435)
PHONE 218 281-4668
FAX: 218 281-4748
Craig Morgan, *Branch Mgr*
EMP: 45
SALES (est): 10MM-24.9MM **Publicly Held**
SIC: **5083** 5012 Wholesales farm implements; wholesales truck tractors

(G-1138)
TRANSYSTEMS LLC
Hwy 25 S B (56716)
PHONE 218 281-7514
Virgil Purrington, *Manager*
EMP: 40
SALES (est): 5MM-9.9MM **Privately Held**
SIC: **4213** Over the road trucking
PA: Transystems LLC
1901 Benefis Ct
Great Falls MT 59405
406 727-7500

(G-1139)
TRI-VALLEY OPPORTUNITY COUNCIL (PA)
102 N Broadway (56716-1731)
PHONE 218 281-5832
Dennis Demers, *CEO*
Nikki Aaker, *Accounts Mgr*
Nate Ellingson, *Manager*
Joan J Perez, *Director*
Herb Mauritson, *Bd of Directors*
EMP: 155 EST: 1965
SQ FT: 15,496
SALES (corp-wide): 18.74M **Privately Held**
SIC: **8399** Community action agency

(G-1140)
TRI-VALLEY OPPORTUNITY COUNCIL
Also Called: Headstart
102 N Broadway (56716-1731)
PO Box 607 (56716-0607)
PHONE 218 281-5832
FAX: 218 281-6681
Julie Aanenson, *Opers Mgr*

Nikki Aaker, *Accounting Mgr*
Greg Dufault, *Info Tech Mgr*
Brenda Floan, *Database Admin*
Dennis Demers, *Exec Dir*
EMP: 65 **Privately Held**
SIC: **8399** Community action agency
PA: Tri-Valley Opportunity Council
102 N Broadway
Crookston MN 56716
218 281-5832

(G-1141)
TRI-VALLEY OPPORTUNITY COUNCIL
102 N Broadway (56716-1731)
PHONE 218 281-5832
Dennis Demers, *Exec Dir*
EMP: 40 **Privately Held**
SIC: **8399** Community action agency
PA: Tri-Valley Opportunity Council
102 N Broadway
Crookston MN 56716
218 281-5832

(G-1142)
VFW POST 1902
Also Called: Veterans of Foreign Wars
121 N Main St (56716-1740)
PO Box 333 (56716-0333)
PHONE 218 281-1902
FAX: 218 281-2303
Dave Abenroth, *Principal*
Dan Morlan, *Human Res Mgr*
Phyllis Sanders, *Manager*
Lisa Larsen, *Manager*
EMP: 30 EST: 1936
SQ FT: 5,000 **Privately Held**
SIC: **8641** Veterans' organization

(G-1143)
VILLA ST VINCENT INC
516 Walsh St Ofc (56716-2750)
PHONE 218 281-3424
FAX: 218 281-4755
Rebecca Langlois, *Human Res Mgr*
Cynthia Hulst, *Marketing Staff*
Julie Hendrickson, *Office Mgr*
Michael Siekas, *Administrator*
Judy Hulst, *Administrator*
EMP: 165 EST: 1951
SQ FT: 155,000
SALES (est): 5MM-9.9MM **Privately Held**
SIC: **8051** 8052 Skilled nursing care facility; intermediate care facility

(G-1144)
WIDSETH, SMITH, NOLTING (PA)
216 S Main St Ste 1 (56716-1939)
PO Box 458 (56716-0458)
PHONE 218 281-6522
FAX: 218 281-6545
Bruce R Buxton, *Ch of Bd*
Timothy Moe, *President*
David Kildahl, *Corp Secy*
Don Anderson, *Exec VP*
Duane Trostad, *Project Engr*
EMP: 25 EST: 1975
SQ FT: 10,000
SALES (corp-wide): 16.47M **Privately Held**
WEB: www.wsn-mn.com
SIC: **8712** 8711 8713 8748 Architectural engineers; environmental consultant; building construction engineering services; surveying service

CROSBY
Crow Wing County

(G-1145)
CENTRAL LAKES MEDICAL CLINIC
318 E Main St (56441-1645)
PHONE 218 546-8375
FAX: 218 546-8320
Debbie Nygard, *General Mgr*
Shannon Senogles, *Corp Secy*
Aj Karpinsky, *CFO*
Debbie Nygard-Norwood, *Office Mgr*
Randall J Cousins MD, *Med Doctor*
EMP: 90 EST: 1914
SQ FT: 23,000
SALES (est): 10MM-24.9MM **Privately Held**

WEB: www.cuyunamed.org
SIC: **8011** Clinic operated by physicians; retails hearing aids

(G-1146)
CROSBY IRONTON TRANSPORTATION
829 8th St NE (56441-1558)
PO Box 116 (56441-0116)
PHONE 218 546-6156
Al Shifler, *Owner*
EMP: 26 EST: 1989
SALES (est): 1MM-4.9MM **Privately Held**
SIC: **4119** Local passenger transportation service

(G-1147)
CUYUNA RANGE HOSPITAL INC (PA)
320 E Main St (56441-1645)
PHONE 218 546-7000
FAX: 218 546-6091
Terri T Ellis, *Corp Secy*
Julie Holmquist, *Corp Secy*
Theresa Sullivan, *COO*
Howard McCollister, *Ch of Surgery*
Michael S Cady, *Ch OB/GYN*
EMP: 480 EST: 1957
SQ FT: 130,000 **Privately Held**
WEB: www.crmc.sisunet.org
SIC: **8062** 8051 Medical hospital; hospital with medical school affiliation; skilled nursing care facility

(G-1148)
CUYUNA RANGE HOSPITAL INC
NE 4th St (56441)
PHONE 218 546-7000
Kathy Bjerke, *Manager*
EMP: 150
SALES (est): 5MM-9.9MM **Privately Held**
WEB: www.crmc.sisunet.org
SIC: **8059** Nursing home
PA: Cuyuna Range Hospital Inc
320 E Main St
Crosby MN 56441
218 546-7000

(G-1149)
HALLETT COTTAGES
350 4th St NE (56441-1557)
PHONE 218 546-6265
FAX: 218 562-6265
Tom Reek, *Owner*
Lea Carlson, *Exec Dir*
EMP: 30 EST: 1996
SALES (est): 1MM-4.9MM **Privately Held**
SIC: **8052** Intermediate care facility

CROSSLAKE
Crow Wing County

(G-1150)
BUILD ALL INSTALLED INC
33106 Industrial Rd (56442-4096)
PHONE 218 692-5115
Matthew Gallaway, *CEO*
Scott Galaway, *Principal*
EMP: 30 EST: 2005
SALES (est): 5MM-9.9MM **Privately Held**
WEB: www.buildalllumber.com
SIC: **1522** 1742 Residential construction; acoustical & insulation work contractor

(G-1151)
LARSONALLEN LLP
35258 County Road 3 (56442-2804)
PHONE 218 692-5750
William Potvin, *Owner*
EMP: 40
SALES (est): 500-999K **Privately Held**
SIC: **7291** Tax return preparation services
PA: Larsonallen LLP
220 S 6th St Ste 300
Minneapolis MN 55402
612 376-4500

GEOGRAPHIC

(G-1152)
LITTLE YUKON GREENHOUSE INC
36318 County Road 66   (56442-2507)
PHONE...........................218 692-3536
FAX: 218 692-5538
Deloren E Anderson, *President*
EMP: 65 EST: 1984
SALES (est): 10MM-24.9MM **Privately Held**
SIC: 5193 0782 Wholesales nursery stock; landscaping services

(G-1153)
PEDERSON TEAM
35548 County Rd 66   (56442)
PO Box 399   (56442-0399)
PHONE...........................218 692-5253
FAX: 218 692-4662
Ted Pederson, *President*
Terry Pederson, *Vice Pres*
EMP: 30 EST: 1984
SALES (est): 5MM-9.9MM **Privately Held**
SIC: 6531 Real estate services

CYRUS
Pope County

(G-1154)
HOMETOWN COMMUNITY BANK
101 W Main St   (56323-4644)
PO Box 99   (56323-0099)
PHONE...........................320 795-2533
John Stellner, *President*
Keith Gades, *Vice Pres*
EST: 1901 **Privately Held**
SIC: 6022 State commercial bank

DALTON
Otter Tail County

(G-1155)
FERGUS FALLS FISH & GAME CLUB
13645 Obrien Ln   (56324-4597)
PO Box 5, Fergus Falls   (56538-0005)
PHONE...........................320 630-0607
Ilga Pollitis, *President*
EMP: 99 **Privately Held**
SIC: 0971 Wildlife management services

(G-1156)
H & R CONST CO
13349 County Highway 35   (56324-4611)
PO Box 756   (56324-0756)
PHONE...........................218 589-8707
FAX: 218 589-8708
Mark Hanson, *President*
John Risbrudt, *Vice Pres*
Robert Ronning, *Vice Pres*
Wayne Ronning, *Treasurer*
EMP: 50
SALES (est): 5MM-9.9MM **Privately Held**
WEB: www.hrconst.com
SIC: 1611 1799 Highway guardrail construction; street sign installation & maintenance; fence construction contractor

DARWIN
Meeker County

(G-1157)
LAKEVIEW RANCH INC
69531 213th St   (55324-6602)
PHONE...........................320 275-4027
EMP: 40 EST: 1999
SALES (est): 1MM-4.9MM **Privately Held**
WEB: www.lakeviewranch.com
SIC: 8059 Personal care home, with health care

(G-1158)
P & D KLITZKE ENTERPRISES INC
Also Called: Curves For Women
68306 215th St   (55324-6525)
PHONE...........................320 275-3555
Penny Klitzke, *President*
EMP: 34
SALES (est): 1MM-4.9MM **Privately Held**
SIC: 7991 Exercise salon

DASSEL
Meeker County

(G-1159)
AUGUSTANA DASSEL LAKESIDE COM
439 William Ave E   (55325-1102)
PO Box 383   (55325-0383)
PHONE...........................320 275-3308
FAX: 320 275-3433
William Ward, *Member*
Juli Miller, *Director*
EMP: 85 EST: 1963
SQ FT: 20,000
SALES (est): 1MM-4.9MM **Privately Held**
SIC: 8051 6513 Skilled nursing care facility; operators of retirement hotels

(G-1160)
CREST ELECTRONICS INC
195 3rd St   (55325)
PO Box 727   (55325-0727)
PHONE...........................320 275-3382
FAX: 320 275-2306
Corey Tisthammer, *President*
Larry Lautt, *Director*
Robert Keith Jr, *Director*
Andrew M Hunter III, *Director*
▲ EMP: 80 EST: 1968
SQ FT: 30,000
SALES (est): 50MM-99.9MM **Privately Held**
WEB: www.cresthealthcare.com
SIC: 5065 Wholesales communications equipment; manufactures radio & television communications equipment; manufactures electric intercommunication systems; manufactures bolts, nuts, rivets & washers; manufactures current carrying wiring devices

(G-1161)
GORDON LUND
Also Called: Lund Poured Walls
23682 727th Ave   (55325-3468)
PHONE...........................320 275-2006
Gordon Lund, *Owner*
EMP: 40 EST: 1984
SALES (est): 1MM-4.9MM **Privately Held**
WEB: www.gordonlund.com
SIC: 1771 Concrete contractor

(G-1162)
MARYNOLE GENETICS & ENERGY
580 Simon Ave W   (55325-1025)
PO Box 212   (55325-0212)
PHONE...........................612 275-2518
Orland Nelson, *Owner*
EMP: 99 EST: 1985
SALES (est): 10MM-24.9MM **Privately Held**
SIC: 8071 Biological laboratory

DAWSON
Lac Qui Parle County

(G-1163)
ASSOCIATED MILK PRODUCERS INC
E Hwy 212   (56232)
PO Box 1013   (56232-1013)
PHONE...........................320 769-2994
FAX: 320 769-4692
Mark Tastad, *Division Mgr*
Richard Johnson, *Prdtn Mgr*
Joe Vaske, *Plt & Fclts Mgr*
Dawn Hoffman, *Human Res Mgr*
Paulette Jelen, *Human Resources*
EMP: 100

SALES (est): 50MM-99.9MM **Privately Held**
WEB: www.ampi.com
SIC: 5143 Wholesales fluid milk & cream; manufactures cheese; manufactures fluid milk
PA: Associated Milk Producers Inc
315 N Broadway St
New Ulm MN 56073
507 354-8295

(G-1164)
DAWSON AREA HOSPITAL DISTRICT
Also Called: Johnson Memorial Health Svcs
1282 Walnut St   (56232-2333)
PHONE...........................320 769-4323
Mary L Daline, *Ch Radiology*
Stacey Lee, *CFO*
Lori Zook, *CFO*
Cori Ochsendorf, *CFO*
Melissa Struxness, *Office Mgr*
EMP: 180 EST: 1914
SALES (est): 10MM-24.9MM **Privately Held**
SIC: 8062 8011 8051 Medical hospital; skilled nursing care facility; physicians' office & clinic

DAYTON
Hennepin County

(G-1165)
ELECTRICAL VISIONS INC
13501 Balsam Ln N Ste 1   (55327-9451)
PHONE...........................763 425-1153
FAX: 763 425-1688
Kim Zimmer, *President*
EMP: 25 EST: 2004
SQ FT: 5,500
SALES (est): 1MM-4.9MM **Privately Held**
WEB: www.electricalvisions.net
SIC: 1731 Electrical contractor

DEER CREEK
Otter Tail County

(G-1166)
STRONGFORM INC
208 Baker St N   (56527)
PO Box 315   (56527-0315)
PHONE...........................218 462-2607
Pennie Astle, *President*
Sheryl Thomes, *Corp Secy*
Duane Thomes, *Vice Pres*
William Rosselot, *Vice Pres*
EMP: 50 EST: 2002
SQ FT: 12,000
SALES (est): 5MM-9.9MM **Privately Held**
WEB: www.astlecorp.com
SIC: 1771 1791 Foundation & footing contractor; structural steel erection contractor

DEER RIVER
Itasca County

(G-1167)
COOP NORTHERN STAR
111 Main Ave W   (56636-8757)
PO Box 458   (56636-0458)
PHONE...........................218 246-8660
FAX: 218 246-8248
Dave Delawyer, *President*
Patti Oelkers, *Manager*
Jim Daigle, *Manager*
Glenn Bullock, *Manager*
Brad Box, *Manager*
EMP: 59 EST: 1934
SQ FT: 3,528
SALES (est): 100MM-499.9MM **Privately Held**
WEB: www.northernstarcoop.com
SIC: 5171 Petroleum bulk station; retail independent convenience store; gas station; grocery store

(G-1168)
DEER RIVER HEALTHCARE CENTER
1002 Comstock Dr   (56636-9700)
PHONE...........................218 246-2900
FAX: 218 246-2454
Jeffry Stampohar, *CEO*
Andrea Yerger, *Corp Secy*
Abe Latava, *Ch Radiology*
Steve Larson, *CFO*
Sandy Tharaldson, *Bookkeeper*
EMP: 200 EST: 1961
SQ FT: 30,000
SALES (est): 10MM-24.9MM **Privately Held**
WEB: www.drhc.org
SIC: 8062 8051 Medical hospital; skilled nursing care facility

(G-1169)
DEER RIVER HIRED HANDS INC
309 3rd Ave SE   (56636-8617)
PO Box 652   (56636-0652)
PHONE...........................218 246-8182
FAX: 218 246-8733
Cheryl Lasalle, *Exec Dir*
Cheryl Gullickson, *Director*
EMP: 43 EST: 1987
SQ FT: 5,280
SALES (est): 1MM-4.9MM **Privately Held**
SIC: 7349 4953 Building cleaning & maintenance services; waste material recycling services

(G-1170)
DEER RIVER WILD RICE
E Hwy 2   (56636)
PO Box 296   (56636-0296)
PHONE...........................218 246-2713
FAX: 218 246-8722
Judy Myers, *President*
Rex Myers, *Vice Pres*
Mary L Carlson, *Office Mgr*
EMP: 55 EST: 1972
SQ FT: 8,700   **Privately Held**
SIC: 0723 5149 Post harvest crop activities; wholesales groceries

(G-1171)
FIRST NATIONAL BANK OF DEER
9 1st St NE   (56636)
PO Box 518   (56636-0518)
PHONE...........................218 246-8221
FAX: 218 246-2866
Lee D Cameron, *President*
Mary Millard, *Bookkeeper*
Rick Hutchinson, *Manager*
EST: 1908
SQ FT: 7,500   **Privately Held**
SIC: 6021 National commercial bank

(G-1172)
FRONTIER CONSTRUCTION CO INC (PA)
48243 Frontier Ln   (56636-2051)
PHONE...........................218 246-9512
FAX: 218 246-9514
Irving L Seelye, *President*
Peter G Bernier, *Corp Secy*
Jeff Tillden, *Vice Pres*
EMP: 40 EST: 1995
SQ FT: 2,400   **Privately Held**
WEB: www.frontierconstruction.net
SIC: 1794 Excavation & grading, building construction contractor

(G-1173)
SMDC HEALTH SYSTEM
Also Called: Duluth Clinic- Deer River
1025 10th Ave NE   (56636-8703)
PHONE...........................218 246-8275
Marsha Weilend, *Manager*
EMP: 28
SALES (est): 1MM-4.9MM **Privately Held**
SIC: 8011 General & family practice physician or surgeon office
PA: Smdc Health System
400 E 3rd St
Duluth MN 55805
218 786-8364

(G-1174)
TROUT ENTERPRISES INC OF NTHN
Hwy 2 E (56636)
PO Box 236 (56636-0236)
PHONE..............................218 246-8165
FAX: 218 246-2086
Douglas Trout, *President*
Carol Trout, *Treasurer*
EMP: 30 EST: 1968
SQ FT: 800
SALES (est): 1MM-4.9MM **Privately Held**
SIC: 1794 1542 4212 4213 Excavation & grading, building construction contractor; local trucking without storage services; over the road trucking; commercial & institutional building construction

DEERWOOD
Crow Wing County

(G-1175)
DEERWOOD BANCSHARES INC (PA)
21236 Archibald Rd (56444-8764)
PO Box 520 (56444-0520)
PHONE..............................218 534-3111
FAX: 218 534-3454
Bradley Houge, *President*
Verne Smith, *President*
David Johnson, *President*
Jennifer Harting, *Exec VP*
Roger Sorben, *VP Opers*
EMP: 62 EST: 1999 **Privately Held**
SIC: 6712 Bank holding company

(G-1176)
DEERWOOD BUILDERS INC
Also Called: Economy Garages of Deerwood
21279 Archibald Rd (56444)
PO Box 487 (56444-0487)
PHONE..............................218 534-5408
FAX: 218 534-9229
Gary Roth, *President*
EMP: 30 EST: 1995
SQ FT: 18,600
SALES (est): 5MM-9.9MM **Privately Held**
WEB: www.economygarages.net
SIC: 1521 1751 New single-family home construction service; garage door contractor

(G-1177)
1ST NATIONAL BANK INC
21236 Archibald Rd (56444)
PO Box 520 (56444-0520)
PHONE..............................218 534-3111
John Oline, *President*
Verne Smith, *President*
Bradley Houge, *Vice Pres*
Roger Sorbec, *Vice Pres*
Roger Sorben, *VP Opers*
EMP: 35 EST: 1910
SALES (est): 5MM-9.9MM **Privately Held**
SIC: 6021 National commercial bank
PA: Deerwood Bancshares Inc
21236 Archibald Rd
Deerwood MN 56444
218 534-3111

(G-1178)
LONESOME PINE RESTAURANT
13726 Katrine Dr (56444-8682)
PHONE..............................218 678-2874
FAX: 218 678-9938
John Metsa, *Owner*
Fran Wilson, *Manager*
Josh Goolsbee, *Manager*
EMP: 30 EST: 1984
SALES (est): 1MM-4.9MM **Privately Held**
SIC: 7011 Resort hotel; eating place

(G-1179)
RANGERLAND DENTAL GROUP INC
Also Called: Smile Center
21343 Archival Rd (56444)
PO Box 385 (56444-0385)
PHONE..............................218 534-3141
FAX: 218 534-3949
Edward Silker DDS, *President*

EMP: 40
SQ FT: 1,600
SALES (est): 1MM-4.9MM **Privately Held**
SIC: 8021 Dental office

(G-1180)
WEYERHAEUSER CO
Also Called: Deerwood Plant
County Rd 102 (56444)
PO Box 460 (56444-0460)
PHONE..............................218 546-8114
Steve Wentworth, *Engrg Mgr*
Gerard Sinner, *Accountant*
Thomas Denig, *Manager*
Grant Kistler, *Manager*
Randy Holmvig, *Manager*
EMP: 202
SALES (est): 100MM-499.9MM **Publicly Held**
WEB: www.weyerhaeuser.com
SIC: 5031 Wholesales lumber, plywood & millwork
PA: Weyerhaeuser Co
33663 Weyerhaeuser Way S
Federal Way WA 98001
253 924-2345

DELANO
Wright County

(G-1181)
APPLE JACK INC
4875 37th St SE (55328-5207)
PHONE..............................763 972-6673
Michael Dekarski, *President*
Kathleen Dekarski, *Partner*
EMP: 42 EST: 1992 **Privately Held**
WEB: www.applejackorchards.com
SIC: 0175 Noncitrus fruit orchard

(G-1182)
CROW RIVER STATE BANK (PA)
710 Babcock Blvd E (55328-8602)
PHONE..............................763 972-3385
FAX: 763 479-2690
Lloyd Jerpbak, *Ch of Bd*
Jaqui Krueger, *Exec VP*
EMP: 28 EST: 1982
SALES (corp-wide): 4.18M **Privately Held**
WEB: www.crowriverbank.com
SIC: 6022 State commercial bank

(G-1183)
STAHLKE BUS SERVICE INC
5280 County Line Rd SE (55328-8800)
PO Box 166 (55328-0166)
PHONE..............................763 972-3991
FAX: 763 972-3757
Julie Bernick, *President*
Mel Bernick, *Vice Pres*
EMP: 30 EST: 1948
SQ FT: 12,000
SALES (est): 500-999K **Privately Held**
WEB: www.stahlkebus.com
SIC: 4151 School bus service

(G-1184)
STATE BANK OF DELANO
1300 Babcock Blvd E (55328-2809)
PO Box 530 (55328-0530)
PHONE..............................763 972-2935
FAX: 763 972-4211
Steven R Gilmer, *President*
Scott Fritz, *Senior VP*
Grady Anderson, *Vice Pres*
Carol J Traen, *Vice Pres*
Dawn Schultz, *Marketing Staff*
EMP: 25 EST: 1908
SALES (est): 5MM-9.9MM **Privately Held**
WEB: www.statebankofdelano.com
SIC: 6022 State commercial bank

(G-1185)
SUPREME BUILDING MAINTENANCE
4735 37th St SE (55328-5207)
PHONE..............................763 972-8425
Don Larson, *President*
EMP: 33 EST: 1982
SALES (est): 500-999K **Privately Held**
SIC: 7349 Building cleaning & maintenance services

DENT
Otter Tail County

(G-1186)
CONCORDIA LANGUAGE VILLAGES
40225 Purlieu Rd (56528-9108)
PHONE..............................218 758-3068
Hana Coen, *Director*
EMP: 27
SALES (est): 1MM-4.9MM **Privately Held**
SIC: 7032 Recreational & sporting camp

DETROIT LAKES
Becker County

(G-1187)
BECKER COUNTY HUMAN SERVICES
Also Called: Childrens Home Society Minn
712 Minnesota Ave (56501-3035)
PHONE..............................218 847-5628
Sue Erickson, *Accountant*
Matt Casey, *Director*
EMP: 70 EST: 2001
SALES (est): 1MM-4.9MM **Privately Held**
SIC: 8322 Adoption services

(G-1188)
BERGEN'S GREENHOUSES INC
801 Willow St W (56501-3808)
PHONE..............................218 847-2138
FAX: 218 847-3515
Robert Bergen, *President*
Kathy Johnson, *Corp Secy*
Kim Green, *Human Res Mgr*
EMP: 50 EST: 1921
SQ FT: 25,000
SALES (est): 5MM-9.9MM **Privately Held**
WEB: www.bergensgreenhouses.com
SIC: 5193 Wholesales flowers & nursery stock; florist

(G-1189)
BREMER BANK
115 Holmes St E (56501-3119)
PO Box 827 (56502-0827)
PHONE..............................218 847-9292
Jeffrey Grabow, *President*
Deborah Pratt, *Marketing Staff*
Doreen Mickelson, *Supervisor*
Judy Gifford, *Admin Asst*
EMP: 40
SALES (est): 10MM-24.9MM **Privately Held**
SIC: 6022 6035 State commercial bank; federally chartered savings institution
DH: Bremer Bank
3131 S Frontage Rd
Moorhead MN 56560
218 299-7603

(G-1190)
COUNTY OF BECKER
Also Called: Becker County Sheriff Dept
925 Lake Ave (56501-3403)
PO Box 702 (56502-0702)
PHONE..............................218 847-2661
Tim Gordon, *Sheriff*
EMP: 50 **Privately Held**
WEB: www.co.becker.mn.us
SIC: 8621 Professional organization; county supervisors' & executives' office
PA: County of Becker
915 Lake Ave
Detroit Lakes MN 56501
218 846-7201

(G-1191)
DIVINE HOUSE INC
26881 County Highway 32 (56501-7705)
PHONE..............................218 847-0574
Karen McDonald, *Director*
EMP: 70
SALES (est): 1MM-4.9MM **Privately Held**
WEB: www.divinehouse.com
SIC: 8361 Group foster home

(G-1192)
EAGLES HALL
112 Holmes St W (56501-3004)
PHONE..............................218 847-5267
Jerry Wageondors, *Corp Secy*
EMP: 50 EST: 1996
SALES (est): 1MM-4.9MM **Privately Held**
SIC: 7997 Membership recreation club

(G-1193)
ECUMEN HOME CARE INC
Also Called: Emmanuel Nursing Home
1415 Madison Ave (56501-4542)
PHONE..............................218 847-4486
FAX: 218 847-4488
Janet Green, *Manager*
Cherie Willette, *Manager*
Jennifer Klabunde, *Director*
Sue Sorensen, *Hlthcr Dir*
EMP: 200
SALES (est): 5MM-9.9MM **Privately Held**
WEB: www.augustanahomes.org
SIC: 8051 Skilled nursing care facility
PA: Ecumen
3530 Lexington Ave N
Saint Paul MN 55126
651 766-4300

(G-1194)
GOLDBERG BAIL BONDS
316 S 4 St Mpls (56501)
PHONE..............................218 847-8122
FAX: 218 339-5155
Patti Goldberg, *Owner*
EMP: 80 EST: 1904
SALES (est): 5MM-9.9MM **Privately Held**
SIC: 7389 Bail bonding services

(G-1195)
HERZOG ROOFING INC
30183 State Highway 34 (56501-7530)
PO Box 245 (56502-0245)
PHONE..............................218 847-1121
FAX: 218 847-3553
Steven Herzog, *President*
Michael Herzog, *Corp Secy*
EMP: 46 EST: 1975
SQ FT: 1,600
SALES (est): 1MM-4.9MM **Privately Held**
WEB: www.herzogroofing.com
SIC: 1761 Roofing contractor

(G-1196)
HOLLAND LODGING INC
935 N Shore Dr (56501-4206)
PHONE..............................218 847-6997
Scott Mehalff, *President*
EMP: 60 EST: 1953
SALES (est): 1MM-4.9MM **Privately Held**
SIC: 7011 Vacation lodge

(G-1197)
HOLMES CENTER INC
826 Summit Ave (56501-2905)
PO Box 1863 (56502-1863)
PHONE..............................218 844-4221
FAX: 218 844-4211
Stuart Omberg, *CEO*
Vickie Singer, *Manager*
EMP: 72 EST: 2000
SQ FT: 160,000
SALES (est): 1MM-4.9MM **Privately Held**
SIC: 7991 7922 Physical fitness center; performing arts center production service

(G-1198)
HOUGH INC
18262 Old Pit Rd (56501-7902)
PO Box 2 (56502-0002)
PHONE..............................218 847-7391
Cindy Hough, *Corp Secy*
Eileen Groth, *Manager*
EMP: 35 EST: 1963 **Privately Held**
SIC: 0782 Landscaping services

(G-1199)
HOUGH INC OF DETROIT LAKES
18262 Old Pit Rd (56501-7902)
PO Box 2 (56502-0002)
PHONE..............................218 847-7391
Michael Hough, *President*
EMP: 35 EST: 1963
SQ FT: 1,000 **Privately Held**

WEB: www.houghinternational.com
SIC: 0781 Landscape consulting & planning services

(G-1200)
INNOVIS HEALTH LLC
125 Frazee St E (56501-3501)
PHONE.............................218 844-2300
Linda L Walz, *Engr R&D*
Julie Smith, *Representative*
EMP: 120
SQ FT: 22,000
SALES (est): 10MM-24.9MM **Privately Held**
SIC: 8011 Clinic operated by physicians
PA: Innovis Health LLC
3000 32nd Ave SW
Fargo ND 58103
701 364-8989

(G-1201)
J & K MARINA
121 W Lake Dr (56501-3900)
PHONE.............................218 847-7291
FAX: 218 844-7292
Jason Macpherson, *President*
Bernadine Rodseth, *Member*
David Rodseth, *Member*
EMP: 40 EST: 1876
SQ FT: 7,200
SALES (est): 1MM-4.9MM **Privately Held**
WEB: www.jkmarine.com
SIC: 4493 Marina

(G-1202)
L&M FLEET SUPPLY TRUE VALUE
1100 Highway 59 S (56501-2238)
PHONE.............................218 847-1171
FAX: 218 847-4070
Dan Purkat, *General Mgr*
EMP: 50 EST: 2004
SALES (est): 10MM-24.9MM **Privately Held**
SIC: 5072 Wholesales hardware

(G-1203)
LAKES HOMES & PROGRAM DEVPT (PA)
847 Highway 10 E (56501-4218)
PO Box 1355 (56502-1355)
PHONE.............................218 847-5642
FAX: 218 847-7176
Thomas Reiffenberger, *Principal*
Lisa Ferrari, *Manager*
EMP: 100 EST: 1980
SALES (corp-wide): 4.48M **Privately Held**
SIC: 8361 Home for the mentally handicapped

(G-1204)
LAKES MEDI-VAN INC
16777 Longview Dr (56501-7968)
PO Box 1053 (56502-1053)
PHONE.............................218 847-1729
FAX: 218 847-9570
Jeff Nustad, *President*
Lori Nustad, *Vice Pres*
EMP: 110 EST: 1985
SQ FT: 12,040
SALES (est): 5MM-9.9MM **Privately Held**
SIC: 4119 Local passenger transportation service

(G-1205)
LAKESHIRTS INC
750 Randolph Rd (56501-3701)
PO Box 52 (56502-0052)
PHONE.............................218 847-2171
FAX: 218 847-2226
Mark Fritz, *President*
Mike Hutchinson, *Vice Pres*
Tom Shoemacker, *Purch Mgr*
Mitch Buboldtz, *Controller*
Terilynne Nelson, *Manager*
▼ EMP: 450 EST: 1984
SQ FT: 120,000
SALES (est): 25MM-49.9MM **Privately Held**
WEB: www.lakeshirts.com
SIC: 7336 Manufactures embroidered emblems; retails custom made clothing & apparel; retails custom printed t-shirts; silk screen design service

(G-1206)
LAND O'LAKES PURINA FEED LLC
1110 13th Ave SE (56501-3737)
PHONE.............................218 847-3176
Ken Schwarzrock, *Manager*
Bruce Moe, *Manager*
EMP: 35
SALES (est): 25MM-49.9MM **Privately Held**
WEB: www.landolakes.com
SIC: 5191 Wholesales feed
HQ: Land O'Lakes Purina Feed LLC
1080 County Rd Fw Fw
Saint Paul MN 55126
800 851-8810

(G-1207)
LANEY'S MECHANICAL INC
1034 Highway 59 S Unit 3 (56501-2234)
PHONE.............................218 847-1309
Scott Nelson, *President*
Kathy Gravelle, *Manager*
Mike Wendt, *Manager*
EMP: 25 EST: 1958
SQ FT: 3,000
SALES (est): 1MM-4.9MM **Privately Held**
SIC: 1711 Plumbing service; heating & air conditioning contractor; refrigeration contractor

(G-1208)
MADISON PROPERTIES INC
Also Called: Holiday Inn
1155 Highway 10 E (56501-4215)
PHONE.............................218 847-2121
FAX: 218 847-2121
Jeff Jasperson, *General Mgr*
Phyllis Weets, *Office Mgr*
Dan Biermier, *Manager*
Kelly Olson, *Manager*
Brenda Lawrence, *Manager*
EMP: 73
SALES (est): 1MM-4.9MM **Privately Held**
SIC: 7011 7299 Traveler accommodations; eating place; banquet hall facility

(G-1209)
MAHUBE COMMUNITY COUNCIL INC
1125 W River Rd (56501-2722)
PO Box 747 (56502-0747)
PHONE.............................218 847-1385
FAX: 218 847-1388
Larry Hanson, *Controller*
Janice Haverkemp, *MIS Staff*
Leah Pigatti, *Exec Dir*
EMP: 75 EST: 1965 **Privately Held**
SIC: 8399 Community action agency

(G-1210)
MERITCARE HEALTH SYSTEM
1245 Washington Ave (56501-3905)
PHONE.............................218 846-2000
FAX: 218 846-2114
Deb Hagenson, *Office Mgr*
Armand Radke, *Optometrist*
Brenda Hurtt MD, *Med Doctor*
Dale Kana MD, *Med Doctor*
Larry D Kobriger MD, *Med Doctor*
EMP: 50
SALES (est): 5MM-9.9MM **Privately Held**
WEB: www.meritcare.com
SIC: 8011 Clinic operated by physicians
PA: MeritCare Health System
801 Broadway N
Fargo ND 58102
701 234-6000

(G-1211)
MIDWEST BANK (PA)
613 Highway 10 E (56501-4127)
PO Box 703 (56502-0703)
PHONE.............................218 847-4771
FAX: 218 847-4812
Steven Daggett, *President*
Merlin Christensen, *Vice Pres*
Carol Zum, *Loan Officer*
Pat Cascaes, *Office Mgr*
Shelly Kohler, *Manager*
EMP: 29 EST: 1980
SALES (corp-wide): 13.87M **Privately Held**
SIC: 6022 State commercial bank

(G-1212)
NORSEMAN MOTORS INC
425 E Hwy 10 (56501)
PHONE.............................218 847-4415
FAX: 218 847-9572
Dan Sauvageau, *President*
John Sauvageau, *Vice Pres*
Paul Hunnel, *Parts Mgr*
John King, *CIO*
EMP: 30 EST: 1962
SALES (est): 1MM-4.9MM **Privately Held**
WEB: www.norsemans.com
SIC: 7537 7538 7542 Automotive transmission repair service; general automotive repair service; automotive washing & polishing service; new & used car dealer

(G-1213)
NORSEMAN MOTORS INC
425 Frazee St E (56501-3605)
PO Box 47 (56502-0047)
PHONE.............................218 847-1639
Dan Sauvageau, *President*
John Sauvageau, *Treasurer*
EMP: 28 EST: 1963
SQ FT: 14,000
SALES (est): 10MM-24.9MM **Privately Held**
SIC: 7538 New & used car dealer; general automotive repair services; retails automotive parts

(G-1214)
PRO SYSTEMS CORP (PA)
1271 Highway 10 W (56501-2231)
PO Box 1807 (56502-1807)
PHONE.............................218 847-9277
Mike Brodsho, *President*
Robert Poolman, *Vice Pres*
Jim Piche, *Treasurer*
Wendy Cole, *Office Mgr*
Harry Maletsky, *Manager*
EMP: 25 EST: 1987
SQ FT: 5,700
SALES (corp-wide): 42.20M **Privately Held**
WEB: www.psys.com
SIC: 8721 8741 Retails computer peripheral equipment; retails business & non-game software; accounting, auditing & bookkeeping services; office management services; retails radios, televisions & consumer electronics

(G-1215)
ROCK 'N WATER
22931 185th St (56501-7910)
PHONE.............................218 439-6400
Bob Spizzo, *President*
EMP: 40 EST: 1999
SALES (est): 1MM-4.9MM **Privately Held**
SIC: 7999 Miniature golf course

(G-1216)
SPEAK EASY RESTAURANT
1100 N Shore Dr (56501-4212)
PHONE.............................218 844-1326
Darrell Marcel, *Owner*
Susan Marcel, *Co-Owner*
EMP: 40 EST: 2003
SALES (est): 1MM-4.9MM **Privately Held**
SIC: 7299 Banquet hall facility; caterer

(G-1217)
ST MARY'S REGIONAL HEALTH CTR (DH)
1027 Washington Ave (56501-3409)
PHONE.............................218 847-5611
FAX: 218 847-0876
Tom Thompson, *CEO*
Christy Brinkman, *Corp Secy*
John Hodgson, *Purch Mgr*
Marilyn Peterson, *Purchasing*
Char Fladmark, *Envir Svcs Dir*
EMP: 205 EST: 1939
SQ FT: 69,000
SALES (corp-wide): 351.82M **Privately Held**
SIC: 8062 8051 Medical hospital; skilled nursing care facility
HQ: Essentia Health
502 E 2nd St
Duluth MN 55805
218 786-8376

(G-1218)
ST MARY'S REGIONAL HEALTH CTR
1040 Lincoln Ave (56501-3508)
PHONE.............................218 847-5611
FAX: 218 847-6978
Patti Boller, *Manager*
EMP: 125
SALES (est): 5MM-9.9MM **Privately Held**
SIC: 8051 Skilled nursing care facility
DH: St Mary's Regional Health Ctr
1027 Washington Ave
Detroit Lakes MN 56501
218 847-5611

(G-1219)
SWANSON'S REPAIR RENTAL CENTER
1145 13th Ave SE (56501-3736)
PO Box 188 (56502-0188)
PHONE.............................218 847-7487
FAX: 218 844-2157
Steve Swanson, *Owner*
EMP: 35 EST: 2000
SALES (est): 5MM-9.9MM **Privately Held**
SIC: 1521 Retails lawnmowers & tractors; single-family housing construction

(G-1220)
ULTEIG ENGINEERS INC
1041 Hawk St (56501)
PHONE.............................218 847-5607
Deb Ness, *Admin Asst*
EMP: 44
SALES (est): 5MM-9.9MM **Privately Held**
WEB: www.ulteig.com
SIC: 8711 Engineering consulting services
PA: Ulteig Engineers Inc
4776 28th Ave S Ste 202
Fargo ND 58104
701 451-8300

(G-1221)
UNITED PARCEL SERVICE INC
Also Called: UPS
1045 13th Ave SE (56501-3706)
PHONE.............................218 847-4439
Curtis Johnson, *Manager*
EMP: 30
SALES (est): 1MM-4.9MM **Publicly Held**
WEB: www.ups.com
SIC: 4215 Parcel delivery services by vehicle
HQ: United Parcel Service Inc
55 Glenlake Pkwy NE
Atlanta GA 30328
404 828-6000

(G-1222)
WELLS FARGO BANK, NATIONAL
211 Holmes St W (56501-3023)
PO Box 786 (56502-0786)
PHONE.............................218 847-1361
FAX: 218 847-0987
Robert Harris, *President*
EMP: 28
SALES (est): 5MM-9.9MM **Publicly Held**
SIC: 6021 National commercial bank
HQ: Wfc Holdings, Corp
420 Montgomery St
San Francisco CA 94104
415 396-7392

┌─────────────────────────┐
│ **DILWORTH** │
│ *Clay County* │
└─────────────────────────┘

(G-1223)
NORTHWESTERN BANK
4 Main St N (56529-1205)
PO Box 10 (56529-0010)
PHONE.............................218 287-2311
FAX: 218 287-2264
Jim Anderson, *President*
Kathy Scheffler, *Assistant VP*
Elizabrth Kirch, *Marketing Staff*
EMP: 52 EST: 1988
SALES (est): 10MM-24.9MM **Privately Held**
SIC: 6022 6163 State commercial bank; loan broker

GEOGRAPHIC (vertical side tab)

(G-1224)

OFFICEMAX NORTH AMERICA INC
1411 Center Ave W (56529-1375)
PHONE..............................218 287-3755
FAX: 218 287-3773
Paul Green, *General Mgr*
Mike Footitt, *Manager*
EMP: 25
SALES (est): 5MM-9.9MM **Publicly Held**
WEB: www.officemax.com
SIC: 5112 Wholesales office supplies
HQ: OfficeMax North America Inc
3462 Mayfield Rd
Cleveland OH 44118
216 297-9789

DODGE CENTER
Dodge County

(G-1225)

COUNTY OF DODGE
Also Called: Fairview Nursing Home
RR 1 (55927)
PO Box 10 (55927-0010)
PHONE..............................507 374-2578
FAX: 507 374-2907
Peggy Barrett, *Office Mgr*
Jane Sheeran, *Administrator*
Dave Deschene, *Info Tech Mgr*
EMP: 90
SALES (est): 1MM-4.9MM **Privately Held**
SIC: 8051 Skilled nursing care facility;
county supervisors' & executives' office
PA: County of Dodge
22 6th St E Dept 31
Mantorville MN 55955
507 635-6212

(G-1226)

DODGE CENTER AMBULANCE SVCS
305 1st St NW (55927-9186)
PO Box 430 (55927-0430)
PHONE..............................507 374-2600
Danielle Deneui, *Principal*
Daniel Stensrud, *Director*
EMP: 25 EST: 1974
SALES (est): 1MM-4.9MM **Privately Held**
SIC: 4119 Ambulance service

(G-1227)

ENERGY ECONOMICS INC
109 South St SE (55927-9679)
PO Box 220 (55927-0220)
PHONE..............................507 374-2557
Ruth Donaldson, *CEO*
Mark Donaldson, *President*
Dan Marquardt, *Division Mgr*
Rhonda Rhodes, *General Mgr*
Jim Hulsebus, *Vice Pres*
EMP: 80 EST: 1975
SQ FT: 26,000
SALES (est): 10MM-24.9MM **Privately Held**
WEB: www.eei.com
SIC: 1623 Utility line construction;
manufactures power related transformers

(G-1228)

FREERKSEN TRUCKING INC
67259 210th Ave (55927-7755)
PHONE..............................507 374-6708
FAX: 507 374-2704
Sheila Freerksen, *President*
Roger Freerksen, *Treasurer*
Mark Freerksen, *Manager*
EMP: 35 EST: 1989
SQ FT: 4,000
SALES (est): 1MM-4.9MM **Privately Held**
WEB: www.freerksentrucking.com
SIC: 4213 Over the road trucking

(G-1229)

MCNEILUS STEEL INC (PA)
702 2nd Ave S (55927)
PO Box 249 (55927-0249)
PHONE..............................507 374-6336
FAX: 507 374-2362
Leland Patrick Mc Neil, *President*
Steve Klomps, *Opers Mgr*
Mike McNeilus, *Traffic Mgr*
Gaylord Gossard, *QC Mgr*

Daniel Blaisdell, *CFO*
▼ EMP: 170 EST: 1948
SQ FT: 440,000
SALES (corp-wide): 323.68M **Privately Held**
WEB: www.mcneilus.com
SIC: 5051 Wholesales iron or steel
structural shapes; wholesales wire
reinforcement mesh; wholesales concrete
reinforcing bars

DOVRAY
Murray County

(G-1230)

DOVRAY COMMUNITY CENTER
Main St (56125)
PHONE..............................507 274-5602
Robert Smith, *Director*
EMP: 50 EST: 1998
SALES (est): 1MM-4.9MM **Privately Held**
SIC: 8322 Community center

DULUTH
Saint Louis County

(G-1231)

A W KUETTEL & SONS INC
1225 Port Terminal Rd (55802-2626)
PHONE..............................218 722-3901
FAX: 218 722-6113
Charles Kuettel, *President*
William Kuettel, *Corp Secy*
Thomas Kuettel, *Corp Secy*
Margaret Geowey, *CIO*
EMP: 80 EST: 1925
SQ FT: 50,000
SALES (est): 5MM-9.9MM **Privately Held**
WEB: www.awkuettel.com
SIC: 1711 1623 1761 Plumbing service;
pipeline construction; heating & air
conditioning contractor; roofing, siding &
sheet metal work; roofing contractor

(G-1232)

ADVANSTAR HOLDINGS CORP
131 W 1st St (55802-2005)
PHONE..............................218 740-7200
Joseph Loggia, *President*
Theodore S Alpert, *CFO*
EST: 2000 **Privately Held**
SIC: 7389 7331 Trade show arrangement
service; publishes magazines without
printing; direct mail advertising service
PA: Vss-Ahc Consolidated Holdings
350 Park Ave
New York NY 10022
212 935-4990

(G-1233)

AFTENRO SOCIETY
510 W College St (55811-4902)
PHONE..............................218 728-6600
Jennifer Bergstorm, *Principal*
Debra Knudsen, *Office Mgr*
Guy Matson, *Administrator*
Mark Govze, *Director*
EMP: 44 EST: 1915
SQ FT: 15,154
SALES (est): 1MM-4.9MM **Privately Held**
SIC: 8361 Home for the elderly

(G-1234)

AIR PARK DT & H
4619 Airpark Blvd (55811-5750)
PHONE..............................218 723-4631
Nadine Cavanaugh, *Principal*
EMP: 42 EST: 1993
SALES (est): 1MM-4.9MM **Privately Held**
SIC: 7331 Mailing services

(G-1235)

ALLETE INC (PA)
30 W Superior St (55802-2030)
PHONE..............................218 279-5000
FAX: 218 279-5050
Donald J Shippar, *CEO*
Alan R Hodnik, *President*
Cheryl Munce, *President*
Deborah A Amberg, *Corp Secy*
Robert D Edwards, *COO*

EMP: 200 EST: 1906
SALES (corp-wide): 759.10M **Publicly Held**
SIC: 4911 1231 4924 4941 6552 Electric
services; anthracite mining; water supply
services; commercial land subdividers &
developers; residential land subdividers &
developers; electric power distribution
service; land subdivision & development
services

(G-1236)

ALLETE INC
4913 W Main St (55807)
PHONE..............................218 628-3627
Bonny Carlson, *Manager*
EMP: 31
SALES (est): 10MM-24.9MM **Publicly Held**
SIC: 4911 Electric services
PA: Allete Inc
30 W Superior St
Duluth MN 55802
218 279-5000

(G-1237)

ALLETE INC
3217 Persons St (55811-4204)
PHONE..............................218 722-2641
Donald J Shippar, *Manager*
Don Shiper, *Manager*
Walter A Prahl, *Manager*
EMP: 50
SALES (est): 25MM-49.9MM **Publicly Held**
SIC: 4911 Electric services
PA: Allete Inc
30 W Superior St
Duluth MN 55802
218 279-5000

(G-1238)

AMERICAN CELLULAR CORP
Also Called: Cellular One
224 E Central Entrance # 1 (55811-5519)
PHONE..............................218 727-4700
FAX: 218 727-5936
Brian Shult, *General Mgr*
EMP: 100 **Publicly Held**
WEB: www.sbc.com
SIC: 4812 Cellular telephone services
HQ: American Cellular Corp
14201 Wireless Way
Oklahoma City OK 73134
405 529-8500

(G-1239)

API ELECTRIC CO (HQ)
Also Called: Lakehead Electric Co
4330 W 1st St Ste B (55807-2756)
PHONE..............................218 628-3323
FAX: 218 624-6534
Brad Boos, *President*
William Beadie, *Corp Secy*
Dennis Gustafson, *Vice Pres*
Gregory Keup, *Treasurer*
Loren Rachey, *Treasurer*
EMP: 60 **Privately Held**
WEB: www.apielectric.com
SIC: 1731 General electrical contractor
PA: API Group Inc
1100 Old Highway 8 NW
Saint Paul MN 55112
651 636-4320

(G-1240)

ARROWHEAD CONCRETE WORKS INC
5572 Miller Trunk Hwy (55811-1204)
PHONE..............................218 729-8274
Douglas Carlson, *President*
Gerald Carlson, *Corp Secy*
Jim Tuhkanen, *Asst Sec*
EMP: 30 EST: 1937
SALES (est): 1MM-4.9MM **Privately Held**
SIC: 5031 Manufactures concrete block &
brick; retails building products & materials;
manufactures ready-mixed concrete;
wholesales exterior building materials;
wholesales interior building materials

(G-1241)

ARROWHEAD HOUSE FOSTER CARE ✪
218 N 1st Ave W (55806-2740)
PHONE..............................218 727-8040
John Kolar, *Principal*

Duge J Bralind, *Manager*
EMP: 40 EST: 2008
SALES (est): 1MM-4.9MM **Privately Held**
SIC: 8361 Residential care facility

(G-1242)

ARROWHEAD REGIONAL DEVELOPMENT
221 W 1st St (55802-1909)
PHONE..............................218 722-5545
FAX: 218 529-7592
Nancy Morselo, *Finance Dir*
Mary Matthew, *Finance*
Pat Henderson, *Exec Dir*
John Chell, *Exec Dir*
Liz Sarabia, *Bd of Directors*
EMP: 35 EST: 1967
SQ FT: 14,000
SALES (est): 1MM-4.9MM **Privately Held**
SIC: 8748 Economic consultant

(G-1243)

ARROWHEAD SECURITY SYSTEMS INC
Also Called: Answer Arrowhead
4901 Woodlawn St (55804-1181)
PHONE..............................218 722-1234
FAX: 218 722-1176
Mike Duffy, *President*
Jean Stenberg, *Personnel*
Robert Stenberg, *Sales Mgr*
Kathryn Grubb, *Manager*
EMP: 28 EST: 1971
SQ FT: 3,300
SALES (est): 1MM-4.9MM **Privately Held**
SIC: 7382 5063 Burglar alarm maintenance
& monitoring service; wholesales electrical
burglar alarm systems; wholesales electrical
fire alarm systems; fire alarm maintenance
& monitoring service

(G-1244)

ARROWHEAD TENNIS INC
4402 Rice Lake Rd (55811-4051)
PHONE..............................218 722-0810
FAX: 218 723-1914
Scott Vesterstein, *President*
Gretchen Patten, *Accountant*
Tracy Broin, *Manager*
Scott Pink, *Manager*
EMP: 30 EST: 1970
SQ FT: 33,212
SALES (est): 500-999K **Privately Held**
SIC: 7997 Membership tennis club

(G-1245)

ARROWHEAD TREE SERVICE INC
4268 W Calvary Rd (55803-1259)
PHONE..............................218 729-9203
Rick Hanson, *CEO*
EMP: 25 EST: 1953
SQ FT: 5,000 **Privately Held**
SIC: 0783 0782 Utility line tree trimming
services; ornamental tree pruning services;
bush & tree removal services; ornamental
tree spraying services; landscaping services

(G-1246)

BARNES HEAD START
2102 N Blackman Ave (55811-4803)
PHONE..............................218 733-2084
FAX: 218 733-2088
Carrie Copperud, *Manager*
Marilyn Larson, *Exec Dir*
Sue Herbach, *Director*
EMP: 35 EST: 1966
SALES (est): 500-999K **Privately Held**
SIC: 8351 Head Start center

(G-1247)

BAY SHORE HEALTH CENTER
1601 Saint Louis Ave (55802-2442)
PHONE..............................218 727-8651
FAX: 218 727-1761
Jackie Koivisto, *Office Mgr*
Paul Libbon, *Administrator*
Shana Jokinen, *Administrator*
Gordon Weller, *Info Tech Dir*
EMP: 240 EST: 1972
SALES (est): 5MM-9.9MM **Privately Held**

SIC: **8051** Convalescent home
PA: Park Associates Inc
300 Gleed Ave
East Aurora NY 14052
716 652-2820

(G-1248)

BCBSM INC

Also Called: Blue Cross
21 W Superior St Ste 110 (55802-2016)
PHONE.........................218 722-3371
FAX: 218 722-0251
Kristin Rognerud, *Opers Mgr*
Brad Christiansen, *Branch Mgr*
Katie Lancaster, *Manager*
EMP: 35
SALES (est): 10MM-24.9MM **Privately Held**
SIC: **6321** Health insurance carrier service
PA: Bcbsm Inc
3535 Blue Cross Rd
Saint Paul MN 55122
651 662-8000

(G-1249)

BENEDICTINE HEALTH CENTER

935 Kenwood Ave (55811-4951)
PHONE.........................218 723-6408
FAX: 218 723-6449
Mark Broman, *President*
Jenny Jackson, *Accounting Mgr*
Julie Erickson, *Office Mgr*
Mark Browman, *Exec Dir*
EMP: 240 EST: 1980
SQ FT: 166,000
SALES (est): 5MM-9.9MM **Privately Held**
SIC: **8051** Skilled nursing care facility
PA: Benedictine Health System
503 E 3rd St Ste 400
Duluth MN 55805
218 786-2370

(G-1250)

BENEDICTINE HEALTH SYSTEM (PA)

503 E 3rd St Ste 400 (55805-1907)
PHONE.........................218 786-2370
FAX: 218 720-2373
Mary F Scala, *Ch of Bd*
Dale Thompson, *President*
Dennis A Acrea, *Senior VP*
Steven E Chies, *Senior VP*
Lowell W Larson, *Senior VP*
EMP: 80 EST: 1985
SQ FT: 8,740
SALES (est): 351.82M **Privately Held**
SIC: **8059** Personal care home, with health care

(G-1251)

BETHEL DULUTH SOCIETY

Also Called: PORT REHABILITATION CENTER
23 Mesaba Ave (55806-2416)
PHONE.........................218 722-1724
FAX: 218 740-3788
John Evans, *CFO*
Lisa Lemmark, *Manager*
Thomas M Dawson, *Exec Dir*
Dennis Cummings, *Director*
Lisa Lenmark, *Director*
EMP: 57 EST: 1873
SQ FT: 33,316
SALES (est): 1MM-4.9MM **Privately Held**
WEB: www.duluthbethel.org
SIC: **8361 8399** Residential rehabilitation center with health care incidental; community action agency

(G-1252)

BILLINGTON CONTRACTING INC

2121 W 3rd St (55806-2005)
PO Box 16125 (55816-0125)
PHONE.........................218 722-1213
FAX: 218 722-8584
Robert O Billington, *President*
EMP: 30 EST: 1971
SALES (est): 1MM-4.9MM **Privately Held**
SIC: **4212 1794** Local trucking without storage services; excavation & grading, building construction contractor

(G-1253)

BILLMAN CONSTRUCTION INC

5010 Miller Trunk Hwy (55811-1490)
PHONE.........................218 729-7570
FAX: 218 729-5007
Mike Billman, *President*
Gregg Billman, *Corp Secy*
Patrick Billman, *VP Finance*
EMP: 40 EST: 1960
SQ FT: 51,796
SALES (est): 10MM-24.9MM **Privately Held**
SIC: **1521 1542** New single-family home construction service; new commercial & office building construction

(G-1254)

BIO-MEDICAL APPLICATIONS OF MN

Also Called: FMC Dialysis Svcs Spirit Vly
4700 Mike Colalillo Dr (55807-2723)
PHONE.........................218 624-7787
FAX: 218 624-7752
Jim Barsanti, *Manager*
EMP: 27
SALES (est): 1MM-4.9MM **Privately Held**
WEB: www.fmcna.com
SIC: **8092** Kidney dialysis center
PA: Fresenius Medical Care
920 Winter St Ste A
Waltham MA 02451
781 699-9000

(G-1255)

BNSF RAILWAY CO

201 S 19th Ave W (55806-2110)
PHONE.........................218 727-8194
Peter Hamell, *Opers Staff*
Fred Rutt, *Manager*
Greg Boutin, *Master*
EMP: 50
SALES (est): 5MM-9.9MM **Publicly Held**
WEB: www.bnsf.com
SIC: **4013** Railroad switching
HQ: Burlington Northern Santa Fe
2650 Lou Menk Dr
Fort Worth TX 76131
800 795-2673

(G-1256)

BRIDGE HOUSE

221 N 1st Ave W (55806-2704)
PHONE.........................218 725-7785
FAX: 218 725-7748
Marie Skalko, *Director*
EMP: 30 EST: 1996
SALES (est): 1MM-4.9MM **Privately Held**
WEB: www.bridgehouse.com
SIC: **8361** Residential care facility

(G-1257)

BRUTGER EQUITIES INC

Also Called: Days Inn
909 Cottonwood Ave (55811-5609)
PHONE.........................218 727-3110
FAX: 218 727-3110
Darrin Wampler, *Manager*
EMP: 25
SQ FT: 14,924
SALES (est): 1MM-4.9MM **Privately Held**
SIC: **7011** Traveler accommodations
PA: Brutger Equities Inc
100 4th Ave S
Saint Cloud MN 56301
320 252-6262

(G-1258)

BUENA VISTA

320 Pinewood Ln (55804-1846)
PHONE.........................218 728-3533
FAX: 218 722-7796
Gerald Strum, *Partner*
Robert Magie, *Partner*
Bob Nylen, *Partner*
EMP: 50 EST: 1963
SQ FT: 20,000
SALES (est): 1MM-4.9MM **Privately Held**
SIC: **7011** Motel; cocktail lounge; full service independent family restaurant

(G-1259)

BUFFALO JUNCTION

2500 Guss Rd (55810-2123)
PHONE.........................218 624-9901
FAX: 218 624-9901
George Stoyanoff, *President*
EMP: 25 EST: 1971
SQ FT: 2,000
SALES (est): 500-999K **Privately Held**
WEB: www.buffalojunction.com
SIC: **7033** Full service independent family restaurant; campground; bar

(G-1260)

CANAL PARK LODGE ✪

250 Canal Park Dr (55802-2314)
PHONE.........................218 279-6000
Regina Frase, *Manager*
Jim Paquette, *Manager*
EMP: 55 EST: 2008
SALES (est): 1MM-4.9MM **Privately Held**
WEB: www.canalparklodge.com
SIC: **7011** Traveler accommodations

(G-1261)

CANAL PROPERTIES INC

Also Called: Hampton Inn
310 Canal Park Dr (55802-2316)
PHONE.........................218 720-3000
FAX: 218 722-3969
Terry Lundberg, *President*
Ronald Anderson, *Treasurer*
Lorri Brake, *Manager*
Jay Scollard, *Shareholder*
Andy Borg, *Shareholder*
EMP: 30 EST: 1996
SALES (est): 1MM-4.9MM **Privately Held**
SIC: **7011** Traveler accommodations

(G-1262)

CARGILL INC

250 Garfield Ave (55802-2627)
PHONE.........................218 727-1594
FAX: 218 727-5919
George Foutch Jr, *Project Mgr*
EMP: 80
SALES (est): 5MM-9.9MM **Privately Held**
SIC: **4491** Stevedoring services

(G-1263)

CASTLE DANGER LP

Also Called: Grand Superior Lodge
2230 London Rd Ste 100 (55812-2129)
PHONE.........................218 728-8060
Robert Ryan, *General Ptnr*
Katie Schmidt, *Asst Controller*
EMP: 65
SALES (est): 1MM-4.9MM **Privately Held**
SIC: **7389** Business support services

(G-1264)

CENTER CITY HOUSING CORP

105 1/2 W 1st St (55802-2180)
PHONE.........................218 722-7161
FAX: 218 720-3483
Kristen Meyer, *Principal*
Gregory Kvam, *CFO*
Richard Klun, *Exec Dir*
EMP: 28 EST: 1986
SALES (est): 1MM-4.9MM **Privately Held**
SIC: **6531** Housing authority operator

(G-1265)

CENTER FOR ALCOHOL & DRUG

Also Called: Duluth Detoxification Center
1402 E Superior St (55805-2430)
PHONE.........................218 723-8444
FAX: 218 723-8446
Laurie Hull, *Manager*
EMP: 25
SALES (est): 1MM-4.9MM **Privately Held**
SIC: **8093** Specialty outpatient clinic
PA: Center for Alcohol & Drug
314 W Superior St Ste 400
Duluth MN 55802
218 723-8444

(G-1266)

CENTER FOR ALCOHOL & DRUG

1025 London Rd Ste 1 (55802-3146)
PHONE.........................218 723-8444
FAX: 218 724-2559
Michelle Immerfall, *CFO*

Julie Seitz, *Manager*
EMP: 99
SALES (est): 5MM-9.9MM **Privately Held**
SIC: **8093** Outpatient drug clinic

(G-1267)

CENTER FOR PERSONAL FITNESS

402 E 2nd St (55805-1906)
PHONE.........................218 725-5400
FAX: 218 725-7217
Scott Hughes, *Sales Mgr*
John W Haugrud, *Exec Dir*
EMP: 29 EST: 1990
SALES (est): 500-999K **Privately Held**
WEB: www.smdc.org
SIC: **7991** Physical fitness center
DH: St Mary's Duluth Clinic Health
400 E 3rd St
Duluth MN 55805
218 786-4000

(G-1268)

CENTRAL TERRITORIAL OF THE

215 S 27th Ave W (55806-1802)
PHONE.........................218 722-7934
FAX: 218 722-9532
Kathy Wilson, *Accountant*
Mark Welsh, *Director*
Jill Buchholz, *Admin Asst*
EMP: 40 **Privately Held**
WEB: www.salarmychicago.org
SIC: **8699** Religious organization; charitable organization
HQ: Central Territorial of The
10 W Algonquin Rd
Des Plaines IL 60016
847 294-2000

(G-1269)

CHARLES R BABST

Also Called: Northern Oral & Faxillofacial
3617 W Arrowhead Rd (55811-4046)
PHONE.........................218 722-8377
Charles R Babst, *Owner*
EMP: 25 EST: 1985
SQ FT: 4,720
SALES (est): 1MM-4.9MM **Privately Held**
SIC: **8021** Dentists' office & clinic

(G-1270)

CHOICE UNLIMITED INC

1829 E Superior St (55812-2044)
PHONE.........................218 724-5869
FAX: 218 724-0359
Saimeona Nygren, *Exec Dir*
Kristie Buchmas, *Director*
Kristie Buchman, *Director*
EMP: 85 EST: 1986 **Privately Held**
WEB: www.choiceunlimited.org
SIC: **7361** Employment agency services

(G-1271)

CHURCHES UNITED IN MINISTRY

Also Called: Chum
102 W 2nd St (55802-2017)
PHONE.........................218 720-6521
FAX: 218 722-6042
Gregory Kvam, *CFO*
Greg CAM, *Manager*
James Soderberg, *Exec Dir*
EMP: 28 EST: 1974 **Privately Held**
WEB: www.chum.org
SIC: **8399** Social services information exchange

(G-1272)

CINEMA ENTERTAINMENT CORP

Also Called: Lakes 10
4351 Stebner Rd (55811-1415)
PHONE.........................218 729-0334
FAX: 218 729-0334
Gene Bondeson, *Manager*
EMP: 30
SALES (est): 1MM-4.9MM **Privately Held**
SIC: **7832** Indoor movie theater
PA: Cinema Entertainment Corp
1621 Division St
Waite Park MN 56387
320 251-9131

(G-1273)
CINEMA ENTERTAINMENT CORP
4191 Haines Rd (55811-3932)
PHONE..............................218 529-1636
Gene Bondeson, *Manager*
EMP: 30
SALES (est): 1MM-4.9MM Privately Held
SIC: 7832 Indoor movie theater
PA: Cinema Entertainment Corp
1621 Division St
Waite Park MN 56387
320 251-9131

(G-1274)
CITON COMPUTER CORP
11 E Superior St Ste 240 (55802-2019)
PHONE..............................218 720-4435
Steven Dastoor, *CEO*
Sean M Dean, *CFO*
Jenna Dahl, *Manager*
Sara Fitzgerald, *Administrator*
Scott Markee, *Info Tech Mgr*
EMP: 32 **EST:** 1994
SQ FT: 1,600
SALES (est): 5MM-9.9MM Privately Held
SIC: 7373 7378 Retails computers &
computer software; computer integrated
systems design services; computer & office
machine maintenance & repair services

(G-1275)
CITY OF DULUTH
9500 Spirit Mountain Pl (55810-2029)
PHONE..............................218 628-2891
FAX: 218 324-0213
Jennifer Carlson, *Finance*
Rick Certano, *Sales Mgr*
Briana Johnson, *Marketing Staff*
Mike Carlson, *Manager*
Leann Jaksha, *CTO*
EMP: 300
SALES (est): 5MM-9.9MM Privately Held
SIC: 7011 7999 Ski lodge; indoor or outdoor
non-membership tennis courts; mayors'
office
PA: City of Duluth
411 W 1st St Rm 105
Duluth MN 55802
218 730-5055

(G-1276)
CITY OF DULUTH
600 Garfield Ave (55802-2632)
PHONE..............................218 730-5230
Don Ness, *Mayor*
Brian Hansen, *Treasurer*
EMP: 878
SALES (est): 100MM-499.9MM Privately
Held
SIC: 4941 Water supply services
PA: City of Duluth
411 W 1st St Rm 105
Duluth MN 55802
218 730-5055

(G-1277)
CLEAR CHANNEL COMMUNICATIONS
Also Called: Kldj-FM
14 E Central Entrance (55811-5508)
PHONE..............................218 727-4500
FAX: 218 727-9356
Ron Stone, *General Mgr*
David Drew, *Opers Mgr*
Randy Wabik, *Engineer*
Howard Leathers, *Sales Executive*
Merry Wallin, *Branch Mgr*
EMP: 40
SALES (est): 1MM-4.9MM Privately Held
SIC: 4832 Radio broadcasting station
HQ: Clear Channel Communications
200 E Basse Rd
San Antonio TX 78209
210 822-2828

(G-1278)
COCA-COLA ENTERPRISES INC
300 S Central Ave (55807-2368)
PHONE..............................218 628-2311
FAX: 218 628-3327
Pat Corcoran, *Branch Mgr*
EMP: 40
SQ FT: 48,000
SALES (est): 25MM-49.9MM Publicly Held

WEB: www.cokecce.com
SIC: 5149 Wholesales soft drinks
PA: Coca-Cola Enterprises Inc
2500 Windy Ridge Pkwy SE
Atlanta GA 30339
770 989-3000

(G-1279)
COMMUNITY CONNECTION OF MN
2701 W Superior St # 101 (55806-1857)
PHONE..............................218 525-4126
FAX: 218 525-5862
John Mack, *Member*
Sharon Mack, *Member*
EMP: 27 **EST:** 2000
SALES (est): 1MM-4.9MM Privately Held
SIC: 8322 General counseling services

(G-1280)
COMO LUBE & SUPPLIES INC
1108 Port Terminal Rd (55802-2619)
PO Box 16987 (55816-0987)
PHONE..............................218 722-2920
FAX: 218 726-0779
Ronald Swanson, *Ch of Bd*
Zane Swanson, *President*
Kristine Swanson, *Corp Secy*
Chad Swanson, *Vice Pres*
Steve Wakefield, *Info Tech Mgr*
▲ **EMP:** 25 **EST:** 1980
SALES (est): 50MM-99.9MM Privately Held
WEB: www.comolube.com
SIC: 5172 5013 Wholesales engine fuels &
oils; wholesales automotive supplies & parts

(G-1281)
CONSOLIDATED TITLE & ABSTRACT
332 W Superior St Ste 100 (55802-1888)
PHONE..............................218 722-1495
FAX: 218 720-6810
Rudy E Wahlsten, *President*
Sara Brown, *Sales Staff*
Bill Oswald, *Manager*
EMP: 30 **EST:** 1900
SALES (est): 1MM-4.9MM Privately Held
SIC: 6541 6361 Title abstract service;
provides real estate title insurance

(G-1282)
COUNTRY INN & SUITES DULUTH
4257 Haines Rd (55811-3955)
PHONE..............................218 740-4500
Cheryl Goldberg, *Principal*
EMP: 80 **EST:** 2005
SALES (est): 1MM-4.9MM Privately Held
SIC: 7011 Traveler accommodations

(G-1283)
COUNTRY LANES-NORTH INC
2327 Mountain Shadow Dr (55811-3803)
PHONE..............................218 722-1741
FAX: 218 722-1742
Robert A Carlson, *President*
Dale Carlson, *Vice Pres*
Barbara Carlson, *Treasurer*
EMP: 32 **EST:** 1976
SQ FT: 22,000
SALES (est): 1MM-4.9MM Privately Held
SIC: 7933 Bowling center; tavern drinking
establishment

(G-1284)
COUNTY ATTORNEY OFFICE
100 N 5th Ave W Ste 501 (55802-1296)
PHONE..............................218 726-2323
FAX: 218 726-2332
Allan Mitchell, *Exec Dir*
Melanie Ford, *Director*
EMP: 32 **EST:** 1979
SALES (est): 1MM-4.9MM Privately Held
SIC: 8111 General practice attorney's or
lawyer's office

(G-1285)
COUNTY OF ST LOUIS
Also Called: Human Service Conference Fund
320 W 2nd St Ste 605 (55802-1410)
PHONE..............................218 726-2140
Mary B Lawson, *Ch of Bd*
Steve Moeller, *Manager*
Vicki Maher, *Manager*

Mary Almly, *Director*
EMP: 99 Privately Held
SIC: 8699 Organization

(G-1286)
CRAIG L GILBERTSON MD
324 W Superior St Ste 302 (55802-1708)
PHONE..............................218 722-6613
Craig L Gilbertson MD, *Principal*
EMP: 50 **EST:** 2001
SALES (est): 5MM-9.9MM Privately Held
SIC: 8011 Physicians' office & clinic

(G-1287)
CSL PLASMA INC
106 W Superior St (55802-3000)
PHONE..............................218 727-8139
Dennis Losald, *Manager*
EMP: 60
SALES (est): 5MM-9.9MM Privately Held
WEB: www.zlbplasma.com
SIC: 8099 Blood bank
PA: Csl Plasma Inc
5201 Congress Ave Ste 220
Boca Raton FL 33487
561 981-3700

(G-1288)
CURTIS OIL & TIRE
4995 Miller Trunk Hwy (55811-1491)
PHONE..............................218 729-8241
FAX: 218 729-8308
Frederick J Curtis, *President*
Tim Gross, *CFO*
Jack A Curtis, *Treasurer*
Jim Curtis, *Sales Mgr*
Sophie Cragin, *Manager*
EMP: 45 **EST:** 1960
SQ FT: 5,000
SALES (est): 100MM-499.9MM Privately
Held
WEB: www.curtisoil.com
SIC: 5172 Wholesales gasoline; fuel oil
dealer; tire dealer

(G-1289)
CUSTOMERLINK LLC
1 E 1st St Ste 300 (55802-3060)
PHONE..............................218 722-2800
FAX: 218 722-3287
Mike Josephson, *President*
Ron Mattila, *COO*
William G Meierhoff, *VP Finance*
Jennifer Malarski, *Marketing Mgr*
Anna Allen, *Manager*
EMP: 160 **EST:** 1999
SQ FT: 15,000
SALES (est): 5MM-9.9MM Privately Held
WEB: www.customerlinkone.com
SIC: 7389 Telemarketing services

(G-1290)
DAMBERG SCOTT GERZINA WAGNER
2 W 1st St Ste 201 (55802-2026)
PO Box 79 (55801-0079)
PHONE..............................218 727-2626
FAX: 218 722-7467
John Scott, *President*
John Geissler, *Principal*
Rebecca Lewis, *Principal*
Jim Mitchell, *Corp Secy*
Randy Wagner, *Corp Secy*
EMP: 25 **EST:** 1938
SQ FT: 2,600
SALES (est): 1MM-4.9MM Privately Held
WEB: www.dsgw.com
SIC: 8712 Architectural service

(G-1291)
DARRELL B JOHNSON DISPOSAL CO
930 Highway 2 (55810-1654)
PHONE..............................218 729-5446
Darrell B Johnson, *Owner*
EMP: 25 **EST:** 1978
SALES (est): 5MM-9.9MM Privately Held
SIC: 4953 Garbage collecting, destroying &
processing services

(G-1292)
DEBBIE BOLEN
1600 Miller Trunk Hwy (55811-5640)
PHONE..............................218 722-0912
Debbie Bolen, *Owner*
EMP: 40 **EST:** 2004
SALES (est): 10MM-24.9MM Privately Held
SIC: 5145 Wholesales candy

(G-1293)
DIAMOND DRILLING & SUPPLY INC
2916 W 1st St (55806-1716)
PO Box 16032 (55816-0032)
PHONE..............................218 628-3671
FAX: 218 628-3302
Robert Elstad, *President*
Seth Peterson, *Info Tech Mgr*
EST: 1972
SQ FT: 8,400 Privately Held
SIC: 5085 Wholesales industrial electric
tools

(G-1294)
DIVERSIFIED MOTEL PROPERTIES
Also Called: Best Western
2400 London Rd (55812-2221)
PHONE..............................218 728-3601
FAX: 218 728-3727
Kristine Howard, *Vice Pres*
Dan Macky, *Manager*
EMP: 150
SALES (est): 5MM-9.9MM Privately Held
SIC: 7011 6512 Traveler accommodations;
nonresidential building operator

(G-1295)
DONALD HOLM CONSTRUCTION CO
3211 W 3rd St (55806-1706)
PHONE..............................218 628-2257
FAX: 218 628-1858
Dean D Holm, *President*
Daniel A Holm, *Treasurer*
EMP: 25 **EST:** 1961
SQ FT: 20,000
SALES (est): 5MM-9.9MM Privately Held
SIC: 1542 New commercial & office building
construction; commercial & office building
renovation & repair services

(G-1296)
DULUTH 10 THEATER
300 Harbor Dr (55802-2600)
PHONE..............................218 722-1573
Jean Bondeson, *Owner*
EMP: 29 **EST:** 2005
SALES (est): 5MM-9.9MM Privately Held
SIC: 6512 Owners & operators of theater
buildings

(G-1297)
DULUTH AREA FAMILY YMCA (PA)
302 W 1st St (55802-1606)
PHONE..............................218 722-4745
FAX: 218 722-4746
Angel Hohenstein, *Member*
Mike Fellbaum, *Maint Mgr*
Paul Snider, *Controller*
Nelle Rhicard, *Human Resources*
Jack Settleland, *Sales Staff*
EMP: 50 **EST:** 1889
SQ FT: 90,000
SALES (corp-wide): 5.59M Privately Held
WEB: www.duluthymca.org
SIC: 8641 7032 7991 8322 8351 Youth
organizations; youth camps; child day care
service; individual & family social services;
physical fitness center

(G-1298)
DULUTH ENTERTAINMENT CONV
Also Called: Decc
350 Harbor Dr (55802-2600)
PHONE..............................218 722-5573
FAX: 218 722-4247
Jim Evans, *CFO*
Kim Asperheim, *Marketing Mgr*
Daniel J Russell, *Manager*

GEOGRAPHIC

Henry Guthard, *Exec Dir*
Craig Samborski, *Director*
EMP: 586 **EST:** 1963
SQ FT: 156,000
SALES (est): 50MM-99.9MM **Privately Held**
WEB: www.decc.org
SIC: 7389 6512 Convention & trade show services; nonresidential building operator; eating place; tourist information bureau

(G-1299)
DULUTH GRADUATE MEDICAL EDUCN
330 N 8th Ave E   (55805-2024)
PHONE..............................218 529-9105
FAX: 218 725-2620
Thomas W Day, *President*
Karen Jensen, *Vice Pres*
Kathy Thielen, *Nursing Spvr*
Paul Remark, *Psychologist*
Heather P Taylor, *Med Doctor*
EMP: 50 **EST:** 1974
SQ FT: 8,206
SALES (est): 5MM-9.9MM **Privately Held**
WEB: www.dfprp.org
SIC: 8011 General & family practice physician or surgeon office

(G-1300)
DULUTH LODGING INC
Also Called: Comfort Inn
3900 W Superior St   (55807-2834)
PHONE..............................218 628-1464
Amanda Kasie, *Manager*
EMP: 25
SALES (est): 1MM-4.9MM **Privately Held**
SIC: 7011 Traveler accommodations
PA: Duluth Lodging Inc
    3900 W Superior St
    Duluth MN 55807
    218 628-1464

(G-1301)
DULUTH LODGING INC (PA)
Also Called: Comfort Inn
3900 W Superior St   (55807-2834)
PHONE..............................218 628-1464
Terry Lundberg, *President*
Robert Lundberg, *Corp Secy*
James Lundberg, *Vice Pres*
Amanda Kasie, *Manager*
EMP: 35 **EST:** 1990
SQ FT: 40,000 **Privately Held**
SIC: 7011 Traveler accommodations

(G-1302)
DULUTH MISSABE & IRON RANGE
227 W 1st St   (55802-1913)
PHONE..............................218 723-2016
FAX: 218 723-2127
Peter D Stephenson, *Principal*
EMP: 550
SALES (est): 50MM-99.9MM **Privately Held**
WEB: www.cn.ca
SIC: 4789 Freight car loading & unloading services
PA: Canadian National Railway Co
    935 rue De La GauchetiSre O 16
    Montr,al Canada
    514 3995430

(G-1303)
DULUTH SOFTBALL PLAYERS ASSN
2132 W 3rd St   (55806-2006)
PHONE..............................218 722-5569
John Vaydach, *Manager*
Maureen Heights, *Exec Dir*
EMP: 35 **EST:** 1982 **Privately Held**
SIC: 8699 Athletic organization

(G-1304)
DULUTH SUPERIOR AREA
Also Called: Wdse Channel 8
632 Niagara Ct   (55811-3098)
PHONE..............................218 724-8567
FAX: 218 724-4269
Allen Harmon, *President*
Jonathan Conant, *Chairman*
Rex Greenwell, *Engineer*
Cheryl Leeper, *Director*
Ron Anderson, *Program Dir*
EMP: 30

EST: 1954
SQ FT: 16,000
SALES (est): 5MM-9.9MM **Privately Held**
SIC: 4833 Television broadcasting station

(G-1305)
DULUTH SUPERIOR ERECTION INC
2385 Becks Rd   (55810-2114)
PO Box 1076   (55810-0076)
PHONE..............................218 626-1112
Gary D Frye, *President*
James R Frye, *Vice Pres*
EMP: 40 **EST:** 1969
SALES (est): 5MM-9.9MM **Privately Held**
SIC: 1611 1623 1771 General highway & street construction service; water & sewer line construction; concrete contractor

(G-1306)
DULUTH TRANSIT AUTHORITY ☉
2402 W Michigan St   (55806-1928)
PHONE..............................218 722-7283
Bob Troolan, *Manager*
Aaron Bransky, *Exec Dir*
Carla J Montgomery, *Director*
EMP: 99 **EST:** 2008
SQ FT: 213,760
SALES (est): 5MM-9.9MM **Privately Held**
SIC: 4111 Passenger transit system

(G-1307)
E B I INC
3921 W 4th St   (55807-1605)
PHONE..............................218 624-3508
Sarah Dickson, *President*
EMP: 25 **EST:** 1986
SALES (est): 500-999K **Privately Held**
SIC: 8351 Child day care service

(G-1308)
EBI INC
625 N 56th Ave W   (55807-1324)
PHONE..............................218 624-3122
Jim L Evans, *Exec Dir*
EMP: 29 **EST:** 1986
SALES (est): 1MM-4.9MM **Privately Held**
WEB: www.ebi.org
SIC: 8361 Home for the mentally retarded

(G-1309)
ECUMEN HOME CARE INC
Also Called: Lakeshore Lutheran Home
4002 London Rd   (55804-2243)
PHONE..............................218 525-1951
FAX: 218 525-7808
Sue Kovisto, *Finance*
Nancy Saralampi, *Human Resources*
Carolyn Fisher, *Mktg Dir*
Colleen Aldridge, *Office Mgr*
John Korzendorfer, *Manager*
EMP: 230
SALES (est): 5MM-9.9MM **Privately Held**
WEB: www.augustanahomes.org
SIC: 8051 Skilled nursing care facility
PA: Ecumen
    3530 Lexington Ave N
    Saint Paul MN 55126
    651 766-4300

(G-1310)
EDGAR SALDANA DR
Also Called: Saint Luke's Plastic Surgery
920 E 1st St Ste 201   (55805-2215)
PHONE..............................218 249-7910
Edgar Saldana, *Principal*
EMP: 35 **EST:** 2002
SALES (est): 1MM-4.9MM **Privately Held**
SIC: 8011 Surgeon's office

(G-1311)
EIKILL & SCHILLING LTD
230 W Superior St Ste 600   (55802-4002)
PHONE..............................218 722-4705
FAX: 218 722-8589
William J Gravelle, *President*
Deborah Medlin, *Principal*
Dean R Ager, *Corp Secy*
Thomas Sykes, *Senior VP*
Darla Benoit, *Vice Pres*
EMP: 35 **EST:** 1898
SALES (est): 1MM-4.9MM **Privately Held**
SIC: 8721 Accounting service; certified public accountant services

(G-1312)
EMPOWERMENT SERVICES OF MN (PA)
Also Called: Esi of Minnesota
2305 E 3rd St   (55812-1852)
PHONE..............................218 724-4014
Clyde Johnson, *President*
EMP: 40 **EST:** 1993
SALES (corp-wide): 1.10M **Privately Held**
SIC: 8322 Social services for the handicapped

(G-1313)
ENVENTIS TELECOM INC
21 W Superior St Ste 200   (55802-2189)
PHONE..............................218 720-2686
Walt Prahl, *COO*
Kenji Ogura, *Manager*
Troy Johnson, *Director*
EMP: 40
SALES (est): 1MM-4.9MM **Publicly Held**
WEB: www.enventis.com
SIC: 7389 Telephone service
HQ: Enventis Telecom Inc
    2950 Xenium Ln N Ste 138
    Minneapolis MN 55441
    763 577-3900

(G-1314)
ESSENTIA HEALTH
502 E 2nd St   (55805-1913)
PHONE..............................218 786-8376
Privately Held
SIC: 8062 Medical hospital

(G-1315)
EVANGELICAL LUTHERAN GOOD
Also Called: Afternro Home
510 W College St   (55811-4902)
PHONE..............................218 728-6600
Jenniffer Bergstrom, *Systems Staff*
EMP: 44
SALES (est): 1MM-4.9MM **Privately Held**
WEB: www.good-sam.com
SIC: 8051 Convalescent home
PA: Evangelical Lutheran Good
    4800 W 57th St
    Sioux Falls SD 57108
    605 362-3100

(G-1316)
EXTENDED FAMILY HEALTH CARE
1700 Mall Dr   (55811-3849)
PHONE..............................218 727-0446
Jill Kaske, *Manager*
EMP: 40 **EST:** 1996
SALES (est): 1MM-4.9MM **Privately Held**
SIC: 8082 Home health care services

(G-1317)
FAIRFIELD INN
901 Joshua Ave   (55811-4508)
PHONE..............................218 723-8607
FAX: 218 722-9465
Jim Brendel, *Manager*
EMP: 80 **EST:** 1998
SALES (est): 1MM-4.9MM **Privately Held**
WEB: www.marriot.com
SIC: 7011 Traveler accommodations

(G-1318)
FALK'S WOODLAND PHARMACY INC (PA)
1 E Calvary Rd   (55803-1514)
PHONE..............................218 728-4242
FAX: 218 728-4247
Steve Preston, *President*
Laurie Edgerton, *Human Resources*
Steve Buboltz, *Branch Mgr*
EMP: 25 **EST:** 1940
SQ FT: 10,000 **Privately Held**
WEB: www.falksrx.com
SIC: 7384 Pharmacy & drug store; film processing & finishing laboratory

(G-1319)
FALK'S WOODLAND PHARMACY INC
221 E 14th St   (55811-2704)
PHONE..............................218 740-2650
Jackie Erickson, *Branch Mgr*
EMP: 30
SALES (est): 1MM-4.9MM **Privately Held**
WEB: www.falksrx.com
SIC: 7384 Pharmacy & drug store; film processing & finishing laboratory
PA: Falk's Woodland Pharmacy Inc
    1 E Calvary Rd
    Duluth MN 55803
    218 728-4242

(G-1320)
FAMILY FOCUS INC
15 Buchanan St   (55802-2328)
PHONE..............................218 740-3146
Deb Langer, *President*
EMP: 30 **EST:** 2004
SALES (est): 1MM-4.9MM **Privately Held**
SIC: 8049 Psychiatric social worker office

(G-1321)
FERGUSON ENTERPRISES INC
4209 Airpark Blvd   (55811-5714)
PHONE..............................218 628-2844
Joseph J Sitek, *Branch Mgr*
Tim Wing, *Manager*
EMP: 35
SALES (est): 10MM-24.9MM **Privately Held**
WEB: www.ferguson.com
SIC: 5074 Wholesales plumbing & heating equipment & supplies
HQ: Ferguson Enterprises Inc
    12500 Jefferson Ave
    Newport News VA 23602
    757 874-7795

(G-1322)
FIFTY BELOW SALES & MARKETING
5 W 1st St Ste 302   (55802-2070)
PO Box 16827   (55816-0827)
PHONE..............................218 720-4828
FAX: 218 722-7546
Mike Rollo, *President*
David Hogge, *Vice Pres*
Aaron Smith, *Marketing Mgr*
Drew Anderson, *IT/INT Sup*
EMP: 130 **EST:** 1997
SQ FT: 6,000
SALES (est): 10MM-24.9MM **Privately Held**
WEB: www.50below.com
SIC: 7374 Data processing & preparation services

(G-1323)
FIRST SOLUTIONS (PA)
525 S Lake Ave Ste 222   (55802-2300)
PHONE..............................218 740-2330
FAX: 218 727-7247
Terry Jacobson, *President*
Diane Holliday-Welsh, *Vice Pres*
Joyce Mireault, *Vice Pres*
Sarah Crom, *Treasurer*
Timothy A Miller, *Controller*
EMP: 60 **EST:** 1944
SQ FT: 7,000 **Privately Held**
SIC: 6321 Provides indemnity health insurance service plans

(G-1324)
FIRST STRIKE OF DULUTH INC
Also Called: Aegis Fire
4921 W Pioneer Rd   (55803-9434)
PHONE..............................218 721-5081
Jay M Sparks, *President*
Dawn M Norlander-Sp, *Vice Pres*
EMP: 35 **EST:** 1995 **Privately Held**
SIC: 0851 Forest fire fighting services

(G-1325)
FITGERS ON THE LAKE LLC
Also Called: Bookstore At Fitgers
600 E Superior St Ste 203   (55802-2237)
PHONE..............................218 727-9077
FAX: 218 722-8826
Paul Vesterstein, *Member*
Scott Vesterstein, *Mng Member*
James Makitalo, *Manager*

Sally Anderson, *Manager*
EMP: 160 **EST:** 1989
SQ FT: 135,000
SALES (est): 5MM-9.9MM **Privately Held**
WEB: www.fitgerswinecellars.com
SIC: 7011 6512 Hotel; shopping center & mall operator

(G-1326)
FRANCISCAN HEALTH CENTER INC

3910 Minnesota Ave (55802-2553)
PHONE...................................218 727-8933
FAX: 218 727-6610
Richard Ludwig, *Administrator*
EMP: 52 **EST:** 1959
SALES (est): 1MM-4.9MM **Privately Held**
SIC: 8051 8052 Skilled nursing care facility; intermediate care facility
PA: Franciscan Health Community
1925 Norfolk Ave
Saint Paul MN 55116
651 696-8400

(G-1327)
FRANKLIN FOODS

1925 W 1st St (55806-2126)
PO Box 16930 (55816-0930)
PHONE...............................218 727-6651
FAX: 218 727-4427
David Holcombe, *General Mgr*
Tom Miller, *General Ptnr*
Gerald Skull, *Mfg Staff*
Jason Loukes, *QC Dir*
James Mueller, *QC Dir*
EMP: 72 **EST:** 1982
SQ FT: 3,300
SALES (est): 25MM-49.9MM **Privately Held**
SIC: 5143 Manufactures fluid milk; wholesales butter; wholesales fresh dairy products

(G-1328)
FREIGHT OFFICE FOR NORTH WEST

Also Called: Regional Elite
4701 Airport Rd (55811)
PHONE...............................218 727-8747
EMP: 25 **EST:** 2002
SALES (est): 1MM-4.9MM **Privately Held**
SIC: 4581 Air freight handling services

(G-1329)
FRYBERGER, BUCHANAN, SMITH (PA)

302 W Superior St Ste 700 (55802-5150)
PHONE...............................218 725-6807
David Overstar, *President*
Robert Taftey, *Principal*
Mary F Skala, *Principal*
EMP: 56 **EST:** 1972 **Privately Held**
SIC: 8111 Legal services

(G-1330)
G G TUCSON INC

Also Called: Rodeway Inn
525 S Lake Ave Ste 405 (55802-2362)
PHONE...............................218 723-8433
Manley Goldfine, *President*
John Goldfine, *President*
EMP: 100 **EST:** 1992
SALES (est): 5MM-9.9MM **Privately Held**
SIC: 7011 Traveler accommodations

(G-1331)
GARDEN HOUSE ESTATES LTD

1 Riverside Dr (55808-1137)
PHONE...............................218 628-0271
Dale Breiland, *President*
EMP: 25 **EST:** 1995
SALES (est): 500-999K **Privately Held**
WEB: www.gardenhouseestates.com
SIC: 8361 Residential care facility

(G-1332)
GARTNER REFRIGERATION CO

2331 W Superior St (55806-1931)
PHONE...............................218 722-4439
FAX: 218 722-3422
Jack W Gartner, *President*
Chuck Palokangas, *Corp Secy*
Jim McCumber, *Vice Pres*
Richard Luck, *Vice Pres*
Jay Koning, *Treasurer*

EMP: 30 **EST:** 1923
SQ FT: 7,800
SALES (est): 1MM-4.9MM **Privately Held**
SIC: 1711 Heating & air conditioning contractor; manufactures automatic temperature controls

(G-1333)
GENERAL CLEANING CORP (PA)

301 W 1st St Ste 511 (55802-1634)
PHONE...............................218 727-4513
FAX: 218 727-4043
Roger Bowman, *Ch of Bd*
Steven Beck, *President*
Cala Schneider, *Vice Chairman*
Dennis D Harvey, *Project Mgr*
EMP: 84 **EST:** 1959
SQ FT: 3,200
SALES (corp-wide): 750K **Privately Held**
SIC: 7349 Building cleaning service; building maintenance service; office cleaning or charring service; janitorial & custodial services

(G-1334)
GENERAL CLEANING SPECIALISTS

301 W 1st St Ste 511 (55802-1634)
PHONE...............................218 727-4513
Steven Beck, *President*
EMP: 78 **EST:** 1959
SALES (est): 5MM-9.9MM **Privately Held**
SIC: 7699 Cleaning service
PA: General Cleaning Corp
301 W 1st St Ste 511
Duluth MN 55802
218 727-4513

(G-1335)
GENERAL MILLS OPERATIONS LLC

200 Garfield Ave (55802-2627)
PHONE...............................218 722-7759
FAX: 218 727-7956
Doug Christianson, *Branch Mgr*
EMP: 30
SQ FT: 5,616
SALES (est): 1MM-4.9MM **Publicly Held**
WEB: www.generalmills.com
SIC: 4221 Grain elevator with storage only
PA: General Mills Inc
1 General Mills Blvd
Minneapolis MN 55426
763 764-7600

(G-1336)
GOLD CROSS AMBULANCE SERVICE

4505 W Michigan St (55807-2706)
PHONE...............................218 628-2885
Dave Johnson, *Manager*
EMP: 80
SALES (est): 1MM-4.9MM **Privately Held**
WEB: www.gcas-duluth.org
SIC: 4119 Ambulance service
PA: Gold Cross Ambulance Service
501 6th Ave NW
Rochester MN 55901
507 255-2230

(G-1337)
GOLDEN OAKS INC

4067 Reinke Rd (55811-3611)
PHONE...............................218 729-5014
Laura B Lokken, *CEO*
Terry Anderson, *Manager*
EMP: 25 **EST:** 2007
SALES (est): 500-999K **Privately Held**
SIC: 8361 Home for the elderly

(G-1338)
GOODWILL INDUSTRIES VOCATIONAL

700 Garfield Ave Ste 1 (55802-2634)
PHONE...............................218 722-6351
FAX: 218 722-6351
Greg Conkins, *Mfg Staff*
Fred Nelson, *Mfg Staff*
Marg Bray, *Exec Dir*
EMP: 75 **EST:** 1967
SQ FT: 176,000
SALES (est): 1MM-4.9MM **Privately Held**
SIC: 8331 Vocational rehabilitation agency

(G-1339)
GPM INC

4432 Venture Ave (55811-5706)
PHONE...............................218 722-9904
FAX: 218 722-2826
Peter L Gemuenden, *CEO*
Phillip Gemuenden, *Corp Secy*
Gary Davidson, *Vice Pres*
Wade Christensen, *Vice Pres*
John Valla, *CFO*
EMP: 29 **EST:** 1978
SQ FT: 24,000
SALES (est): 10MM-24.9MM **Privately Held**
SIC: 5049 Wholesales engineers' equipment & supplies; machine shop, jobbing & repair services

(G-1340)
GRANDVIEW MANOR HRA OFFICE

222 E 2nd St (55805-1843)
PHONE...............................218 529-6300
Rick Ball, *President*
EMP: 60 **EST:** 2001
SALES (est): 5MM-9.9MM **Privately Held**
SIC: 6513 Apartment building operator

(G-1341)
GRANITE BROADCASTING CORP

Also Called: News Dept
246 S Lake Ave (55802-2304)
PHONE...............................218 720-9666
Bob Wilmers, *Manager*
EMP: 60
SALES (est): 10MM-24.9MM **Publicly Held**
WEB: www.granitetv.com
SIC: 4833 Television broadcasting station
PA: Granite Broadcasting Corp
767 3rd Ave Fl 34
New York NY 10017
212 826-2530

(G-1342)
GRANITE BROADCASTING CORP

Also Called: Kbjr Television
246 S Lake Ave (55802-2304)
PHONE...............................218 720-9642
Robert Wilmers, *Manager*
Jayson Saumer, *MIS Mgr*
EMP: 94
SQ FT: 256
SALES (est): 10MM-24.9MM **Publicly Held**
WEB: www.granitetv.com
SIC: 4833 Television broadcasting station
PA: Granite Broadcasting Corp
767 3rd Ave Fl 34
New York NY 10017
212 826-2530

(G-1343)
GRAYBAR ELECTRIC CO INC

2601 W Superior St (55806-1836)
PO Box 16027 (55816-0027)
PHONE...............................218 722-6685
FAX: 218 722-0235
Chris Lammi, *Persnl Mgr*
Steve Holubar, *Sales Executive*
Wallace Gould, *Branch Mgr*
EMP: 28
SQ FT: 24,000
SALES (est): 10MM-24.9MM **Privately Held**
SIC: 5063 5065 Wholesales electrical supplies; wholesales electronic parts & equipment

(G-1344)
GREG HAUG

Also Called: Northern Plains Railroad
414 Aspen Ln (55804-1706)
PHONE...............................218 727-8578
Greg Haug, *Owner*
EMP: 30 **Privately Held**
SIC: 4011 Long haul railroad

(G-1345)
H T KLATZKY & ASSOCIATES INC

1511 E Superior St (55812-1635)
PHONE...............................218 728-3651
FAX: 218 728-6202

Howard T Klatzky, *President*
Laurie Omelia, *Vice Pres*
Lynn Svercl, *Manager*
Kristin Hinirchs, *Supervisor*
Kim M Spelierbery, *Creative Dir*
EMP: 25 **EST:** 1975
SQ FT: 7,000
SALES (est): 1MM-4.9MM **Privately Held**
SIC: 7311 Advertising agency

(G-1346)
HANFT, FRIDE, O'BRIEN

Also Called: Hanft Fride A Prof Assn
130 W Superior St Ste 1000 (55802-2082)
PHONE...............................218 722-4766
FAX: 218 529-2401
Gilbert W Harries, *Ch of Bd*
John D Kelly, *President*
Prince Chyrel, *Corp Secy*
William M Burns, *Treasurer*
Richard Burns, *Corp Counsel*
EMP: 40 **EST:** 1899
SQ FT: 10,000
SALES (est): 5MM-9.9MM **Privately Held**
WEB: www.hanftlaw.com
SIC: 8111 General practice attorney's or lawyer's office

(G-1347)
HARBOR CITY MASONRY INC

310 S Central Ave (55807-2365)
PO Box 7125 (55807-7125)
PHONE...............................218 628-3686
FAX: 218 628-3706
Roger Anderson, *President*
Dianne Anderson, *Vice Pres*
Lee Lorenz, *Manager*
EMP: 70 **EST:** 1983
SQ FT: 15,000
SALES (est): 5MM-9.9MM **Privately Held**
WEB: www.harborcity318.com
SIC: 1741 1771 Masonry & stonework contractor; concrete contractor

(G-1348)
HARBOR CITY OIL CO

3020 W Superior St (55806-1750)
PHONE...............................218 624-3633
FAX: 218 624-3621
Timothy Kolquist, *President*
Jay Kolquist, *Vice Pres*
Mark Kolquist, *Treasurer*
Reed Kolquist, *Manager*
Brad Kolquist, *Manager*
EMP: 25 **EST:** 1926
SQ FT: 2,000
SALES (est): 5MM-9.9MM **Privately Held**
SIC: 1711 5075 Fuel oil dealer; convenience store; heating systems repair & maintenance service; wholesales warm air furnaces; retail gasoline filling station

(G-1349)
HARRISON COMMUNITY CLUB

3002 W 3rd St (55806-1704)
PHONE...............................218 624-1510
Joel Pafetti, *Owner*
EMP: 25 **EST:** 1969 **Privately Held**
SIC: 8641 Community membership club

(G-1350)
HEAT & FROST INSULATORS ASBES

2002 London Rd Ste 210 (55812-2151)
PHONE...............................218 724-3223
Don Holte, *Manager*
Darrell Godbout, *Manager*
EMP: 70 **EST:** 2001
SALES (est): 10MM-24.9MM **Privately Held**
SIC: 1799 Asbestos removal & encapsulation contractor

(G-1351)
HERMANTOWN CLINIC

Also Called: Smdc
4855 W Arrowhead Rd (55811-3936)
PHONE...............................218 786-3540
FAX: 218 725-3691
Chris Russ, *Principal*
Nancy Dettle, *Office Mgr*
Susan Benson, *Phys Therapist*
Joseph Cremers, *Phys Therapist*
Malcolm Macaulay, *Phys Therapist*
EMP: 40 **EST:** 2004
SALES (est): 1MM-4.9MM **Privately Held**
SIC: 8011 Physicians' office

GEOGRAPHIC

(G-1352)
HILLSIDE HOMES
408 N 8th Ave E (55805-2031)
PHONE..............................218 720-5890
FAX: 218 720-6022
Diane Lindsey, *Principal*
EMP: 28 EST: 2003
SALES (est): 1MM-4.9MM **Privately Held**
SIC: 8361 Self-help group home

(G-1353)
HOSPITALITY INVESTORS LLC
4257 Haines Rd (55811-3955)
PHONE..............................218 729-5616
Rick Hayman, *Principal*
EMP: 300 EST: 1997
SALES (est): 25MM-49.9MM **Privately Held**
SIC: 6798 Real estate investment trust service

(G-1354)
HUMAN DEVELOPMENT CENTER (PA)
1401 E 1st St (55805-2407)
PHONE..............................218 728-4491
FAX: 218 728-4404
Tom Wondolkowski, *President*
Gordon Fon, *Corp Secy*
Gary Vogt, *Facilities Mgr*
Paul Almirall, *Finance Dir*
Scott Frisby, *Info Tech Dir*
EMP: 48 EST: 1938
SQ FT: 40,000
SALES (corp-wide): 13.77M **Privately Held**
WEB: www.hdchrc.org
SIC: 8099 Medical services organization

(G-1355)
HUMAN DEVELOPMENT CENTER
1401 E 1st St (55805-2407)
PHONE..............................218 728-5192
FAX: 218 728-5102
Jim Gruba, *Manager*
EMP: 60
SALES (est): 1MM-4.9MM **Privately Held**
WEB: www.hdchrc.org
SIC: 8093 Outpatient mental health clinic
PA: Human Development Center
    1401 E 1st St
    Duluth MN 55805
    218 728-4491

(G-1356)
INDEPENDENT SCHOOL DISTRICT
Also Called: Maintenance Dept
916 E 3rd St (55805-2168)
PHONE..............................218 723-4119
Kerri Leider, *Manager*
EMP: 35
SALES (est): 500-999K **Privately Held**
WEB: www.duluth.k12.mn.us
SIC: 7349 Building cleaning & maintenance services
PA: Independent School District
    215 N 1st Ave E
    Duluth MN 55802
    218 336-8700

(G-1357)
INDUSTRIAL WELDERS
3902 Oneota St (55807-2829)
PO Box 16720 (55816-0720)
PHONE..............................218 628-1011
FAX: 218 624-3319
Ronald Abernethy, *President*
Donald Abernethy, *Vice Pres*
Scott Abernethy, *Vice Pres*
Doug Gandrud, *Finance Dir*
Curt Nelson, *Manager*
EMP: 30 EST: 1952
SQ FT: 20,000
SALES (est): 1MM-4.9MM **Privately Held**
SIC: 7692 Machine shop, jobbing & repair services; welding service

(G-1358)
INTER CITY OIL CO INC
Also Called: I C O
1923 South St (55812-2042)
PO Box 3048 (55803-3048)
PHONE..............................218 728-3641
FAX: 218 728-5140
Judy L Weber, *President*
Randi J Huseby, *Corp Secy*
Donna K Flesher, *Corp Secy*
EMP: 30 EST: 1953
SQ FT: 10,000
SALES (est): 5MM-9.9MM **Privately Held**
SIC: 5172 Retail gasoline filling station; wholesales gasoline; retail chain convenience stores; fuel oil dealer

(G-1359)
INTERIM HEALTHCARE OF LAKE
227 W 1st St Ste 400 (55802-5056)
PHONE..............................218 722-0053
Gary Halgren, *President*
Dale Halgren, *Vice Pres*
Kari Jarvi, *Purch Agent*
Darlene Dower, *Manager*
Sarah Fitzgerald, *Systems Staff*
EMP: 275 EST: 1993
SQ FT: 5,000
SALES (est): 5MM-9.9MM **Privately Held**
SIC: 7363 Temporary help service

(G-1360)
JC PENNEY CORP INC
1600 Miller Trunk Hwy # 3 (55811-5607)
PHONE..............................218 727-8111
FAX: 218 727-8319
Theresa Wojtkowiak, *Manager*
Suzette Goyette, *Manager*
EMP: 230
SALES (est): 50MM-99.9MM **Publicly Held**
WEB: www.jcpenney.com
SIC: 7221 7231 Retail catalog sales; department store; retails optical goods; portrait studio; beauty salon
HQ: JC Penney Corp Inc
    6501 Legacy Dr
    Plano TX 75024
    972 431-1000

(G-1361)
JOHNSON CONTROLS INTERIORS LLC
4627 Airpark Blvd (55811-5750)
PHONE..............................218 727-8996
FAX: 218 727-7945
Mark Dulong, *Manager*
EMP: 27
SALES (est): 10MM-24.9MM **Publicly Held**
WEB: www.jci.com
SIC: 5075 Wholesales heating & air conditioning equipment & supplies
HQ: Johnson Controls Interiors LLC
    915 E 32nd St
    Holland MI 49423
    616 392-5151

(G-1362)
JOHNSON'S CARPET TILE
5611 Grand Ave (55807-2539)
PHONE..............................218 628-2249
FAX: 218 628-2132
Terry Fulda, *President*
Dave Fulda, *Vice Pres*
EMP: 40 EST: 1947
SQ FT: 18,000
SALES (est): 5MM-9.9MM **Privately Held**
SIC: 1752 Retails floor coverings; flooring contractor

(G-1363)
JOHNSON-WILSON CONSTRUCTORS
4431 W Michigan St (55807-2711)
PO Box 16006 (55816-0006)
PHONE..............................218 628-0202
FAX: 218 628-0205
A R Johnson, *Ch of Bd*
Fred G Strom, *President*
Shane Johnson, *Vice Pres*
Laura Varner, *Manager*
Sondra Strom, *Info Tech Mgr*
EMP: 75 EST: 1970
SQ FT: 5,000
SALES (est): 10MM-24.9MM **Privately Held**

WEB: www.johnsonwilson.com
SIC: 1522 1542 New multi-family dwelling construction service; new commercial & office building construction

(G-1364)
JOINT APPRENTICESHIP
4402 Airpark Blvd (55811-5712)
PHONE..............................218 733-9443
John Pezze, *Principal*
EMP: 29 EST: 1999
SALES (est): 1MM-4.9MM **Privately Held**
WEB: www.local11.clearwire.net
SIC: 8331 Community services employment training program

(G-1365)
JUSTIN PAUL INC
26 E Superior St Ste 203 (55802-2196)
PHONE..............................218 727-0034
Justin Paul, *President*
EMP: 25
SALES (est): 500-999K **Privately Held**
SIC: 7231 Beauty salon

(G-1366)
KBJR INC
Also Called: Kbjr-TV
246 S Lake Ave (55802-2304)
PHONE..............................218 727-8484
W D Cornwell, *Ch of Bd*
Robert Wilmers, *President*
Dan Hoffman, *Vice Pres*
Lawrence Wills, *Vice Pres*
Peter Neumann, *Mfg Staff*
EMP: 65 EST: 1974
SQ FT: 20,000
SALES (est): 10MM-24.9MM **Publicly Held**
WEB: www.granitetv.com
SIC: 4833 Television broadcasting station
PA: Granite Broadcasting Corp
    767 3rd Ave Fl 34
    New York NY 10017
    212 826-2530

(G-1367)
KBMX MIX 108 STUDIO
14 E Central Entrance (55811-5508)
PHONE..............................218 740-2649
Lowery Mays, *President*
EMP: 28 EST: 2002
SALES (est): 1MM-4.9MM **Privately Held**
SIC: 7313 Radio advertising representative

(G-1368)
KDLH NEWS CHANNEL
246 S Lake Ave (55802-2304)
PHONE..............................218 733-0303
James Yeager, *President*
EMP: 65 EST: 1954
SALES (est): 10MM-24.9MM **Privately Held**
WEB: www.kdlh.com
SIC: 4833 Television broadcasting station

(G-1369)
KEGLER'S INC
Also Called: Incline Station Bowling Center
601 W Superior St (55802-1501)
PHONE..............................218 722-0671
FAX: 218 722-8556
Tim Sorensen, *President*
Tom Holt, *Treasurer*
EMP: 31 EST: 1986
SQ FT: 27,456
SALES (est): 1MM-4.9MM **Privately Held**
WEB: www.inclinestationbowling.com
SIC: 7933 Bowling center; bar

(G-1370)
KEYSTONE BLUFFS
2528 Trinity Rd (55811-3315)
PHONE..............................218 727-2800
Josh Johnson, *Manager*
EMP: 40 EST: 2000
SALES (est): 10MM-24.9MM **Privately Held**
WEB: www.keystonebluffs.com
SIC: 1522 6552 New multi-family dwelling construction service; residential land subdividers & developers
PA: Keystone Senior LLC
    3965 Airport Dr
    Indianapolis IN 46254
    317 280-8455

(G-1371)
KITCHI GAMMI CLUB
831 E Superior St (55802-2211)
PHONE..............................218 724-8589
FAX: 218 724-9470
Todd Johnson, *President*
Mark Tuttle, *General Mgr*
Josh Johnson, *General Mgr*
Cheryl Meese, *Corp Secy*
Nicholas Ostapenko, *Vice Pres*
EMP: 60 EST: 1883
SQ FT: 40,000 **Privately Held**
WEB: www.kitchigammiclub.com
SIC: 8641 Social club

(G-1372)
KJ & E PROPERTIES
Also Called: Wherley Moving
4845 Miller Trunk Hwy (55811-3948)
PHONE..............................218 727-8811
FAX: 218 727-8086
Edward Meyer Jr, *Partner*
EMP: 50 EST: 1995
SALES (est): 1MM-4.9MM **Privately Held**
SIC: 4214 Local trucking with storage

(G-1373)
KRECH, OJARD & ASSOCIATES
227 W 1st St Ste 200 (55802-5059)
PHONE..............................218 727-3282
Rich Ojard, *President*
Michael J Metso, *COO*
David Krech, *Vice Pres*
Jeffery W Heller, *Vice Pres*
Scott Stevens, *Accountant*
EMP: 31 EST: 1984
SQ FT: 6,500
SALES (est): 1MM-4.9MM **Privately Held**
SIC: 8711 Engineering consulting services; structural engineering services; building construction engineering services; civil engineering services

(G-1374)
KTM PAVING INC
5513 Highway 2 (55810-9570)
PHONE..............................218 628-7025
Penny Michaud, *Principal*
EMP: 30 EST: 2004
SALES (est): 1MM-4.9MM **Privately Held**
WEB: www.ktmpaving.com
SIC: 1611 Street surfacing & paving construction

(G-1375)
LAKE SUPERIOR CENTER
Also Called: Great Lakes Aquarium
353 Harbor Dr (55802-2639)
PHONE..............................218 740-3474
FAX: 218 740-2020
Shawn Berseth, *CEO*
Terry Mattson, *Corp Secy*
Wayne Hibbard, *Treasurer*
Lindsey M Peterson, *Sales Staff*
Kay Nierengarten, *Data Proc Dir*
EMP: 30 EST: 1989
SQ FT: 62,382
SALES (est): 500-999K **Privately Held**
WEB: www.glaquarium.org
SIC: 7999 Recreation center

(G-1376)
LAKE SUPERIOR DENTAL
1225 E 1st St (55805-2402)
PHONE..............................218 728-6445
FAX: 218 724-7003
Melanie Meyer, *Partner*
B D Hustad DDS, *Partner*
Bruce Houston, *Partner*
Rodney Heller, *Partner*
Jeffrey Foster, *Partner*
EMP: 32 EST: 1980
SALES (est): 1MM-4.9MM **Privately Held**
SIC: 8021 Dental office; orthodontist

(G-1377)
LAKE SUPERIOR MEDICAL SOCIETY
324 W Superior St Ste 910 (55802-1705)
PHONE..............................218 727-3325
Sandy Poplam, *President*
Fred Belay, *Med Doctor*
Heather Opsahl, *Director*
EMP: 30 EST: 2001 **Privately Held**

SIC: **8621** Health association

(G-1378)
LAKE SUPERIOR RAILROAD MUSEUM
506 W Michigan St Ste 19 (55802-1533)
PHONE 218 733-7590
FAX: 218 727-1197
William Gravelle, *Treasurer*
Tom Gannon, *Sales Staff*
Alissa Acker, *Software Dev*
Ken Buehler, *Director*
EMP: 60 EST: 1975
SALES (est): 5MM-9.9MM **Privately Held**
WEB: www.lsrm.org
SIC: **8412** Museum

(G-1379)
LAKEHEAD TRUCKING INC
6035 Lavaque Rd (55803-9427)
PHONE 218 721-3521
FAX: 218 721-3247
Gregory J Kaneski, *President*
Paul D Kaneski, *Treasurer*
EMP: 30 EST: 1949
SQ FT: 1,064
SALES (est): 1MM-4.9MM **Privately Held**
SIC: **4212** 1794 4213 Local trucking without storage services; over the road trucking; excavating contractor

(G-1380)
LAKEWALK SURGERY CENTER INC
1420 London Rd Ste 100 (55805-2437)
PHONE 218 728-0650
FAX: 218 728-0657
Andrew Baertsch, *President*
Lynette Greenlee, *Exec Officer*
Hal Heyer, *Med Doctor*
Joe Majerus, *Administrator*
EMP: 50 EST: 1998
SQ FT: 40,000
SALES (est): 5MM-9.9MM **Privately Held**
WEB: www.lakewalk.com
SIC: **8011** Ambulatory surgical center

(G-1381)
LHB INC (PA)
21 W Superior St Ste 500 (55802-2085)
PHONE 218 727-8446
FAX: 218 727-8456
William Bennett, *CEO*
David M Sheedy, *Corp Secy*
Joseph Litman, *Vice Pres*
Michael Fischer, *Vice Pres*
Steve McNeill, *Vice Pres*
EMP: 120 EST: 1964
SQ FT: 35,000
SALES (corp-wide): 19.98M **Privately Held**
WEB: www.lhbcorp.com
SIC: **8711** 8712 Engineering consulting services; architectural service

(G-1382)
LIFEWAY SERVICES
4897 Miller Trunk Hwy # 200 (55811-1584)
PHONE 218 722-1184
Daniel Renfroe, *Principal*
EMP: 25 EST: 2003
SALES (est): 500-999K **Privately Held**
SIC: **8361** Residential care facility

(G-1383)
LIGHTHOUSE ON HOMESTEAD INC ✪
5730 Homestead Rd (55804-9661)
PHONE 218 525-4525
Lynne Compton, *Vice Pres*
EMP: 25 EST: 2008
SALES (est): 1MM-4.9MM **Privately Held**
SIC: **7389** Business services at a non-commercial site

(G-1384)
LIPE BROTHERS CONSTRUCTION INC
5116 Jean Duluth Rd (55803-9752)
PHONE 218 525-3364
FAX: 218 525-8348
Jerry Lipe, *President*
Roger Lipe, *Vice Pres*
Jam Lite, *Manager*
EMP: 25

EST: 1975
SQ FT: 10,000
SALES (est): 5MM-9.9MM **Privately Held**
WEB: www.lipebrothers.com
SIC: **1522** 1521 1751 New multi-family dwelling construction service; garage door contractor; residential remodeling

(G-1385)
LONDON ROAD CAR WASH INC
1530 London Rd (55812-1687)
PHONE 218 728-4201
FAX: 218 728-0859
Scott Pichetti, *President*
Lou Pichetti, *President*
Tim Pichetti, *Corp Secy*
EMP: 30 EST: 1961
SQ FT: 8,000
SALES (est): 1MM-4.9MM **Privately Held**
SIC: **7542** Car wash; retail independent convenience store; retail gasoline filling station

(G-1386)
LYRIC BLOCK DEVELOPMENT CORP
Also Called: Holiday Inn
200 W 1st St (55802-1921)
PHONE 218 722-1202
FAX: 218 722-0233
Lisa Chase, *Manager*
James Bell, *Manager*
EMP: 194
SALES (est): 10MM-24.9MM **Privately Held**
WEB: www.hiduluth.com
SIC: **7011** Traveler accommodations; eating place; drinking establishment
PA: Lyric Block Development Corp
202 W Superior St Ste 800
Duluth MN 55802
218 727-7765

(G-1387)
MCGLADREY & PULLEN, LLP
227 W 1st St Ste 700 (55802-1926)
PHONE 218 727-5025
Jim Spreitzer, *Managing Dir*
Lisa Pomroy, *Accounting Dir*
Joan Jago, *Manager*
Peggy Champion, *Manager*
Bob Gerardi, *Info Tech Dir*
EMP: 55
SALES (est): 5MM-9.9MM **Privately Held**
SIC: **8721** Certified public accountant services
PA: McGladrey & Pullen, LLP
3600 Amercn Blvd W # 300
Minneapolis MN 55431
952 921-7700

(G-1388)
MCGLADREY & PULLEN, LLP
700 Missabe Building (55802)
PHONE 218 727-6857
FAX: 218 727-1438
James Denney, *Manager*
EMP: 75
SALES (est): 5MM-9.9MM **Privately Held**
SIC: **8721** Certified public accountant services
PA: McGladrey & Pullen, LLP
3600 Amercn Blvd W # 300
Minneapolis MN 55431
952 921-7700

(G-1389)
MEMORIAL BLOOD CENTER
Also Called: Arrowhead Regional Blood Ctr
5115 Burning Tree Rd # 300 (55811-1876)
PHONE 218 723-8080
FAX: 218 723-8001
Carol Jacobson, *Manager*
Thomas Becker, *Bd of Directors*
EMP: 39
SALES (est): 1MM-4.9MM **Privately Held**
WEB: www.mbcm.org
SIC: **8099** Blood bank
PA: Memorial Blood Center
737 Pelham Blvd
Saint Paul MN 55114
651 332-7000

(G-1390)
MENARD INC
4809 Miller Trunk Hwy (55811-3948)
PHONE 218 722-0078
FAX: 218 722-0638
Jim Harrison, *President*
Brad Carey, *General Mgr*
EMP: 200
SALES (est): 25MM-49.9MM **Privately Held**
WEB: www.menards.com
SIC: **5031** Retails building products & materials; wholesales lumber, plywood & millwork
PA: Menard Inc
5101 Menard Dr
Eau Claire WI 54703
715 876-5911

(G-1391)
MERRILL LYNCH, PIERCE, FENNER
130 W Superior St Ste 800 (55802-4045)
PHONE 218 726-3140
FAX: 218 726-3179
Paul Nelson, *Manager*
Kristin Gallian, *Manager*
Jess Panichi, *Manager*
EMP: 31
SALES (est): 5MM-9.9MM **Publicly Held**
WEB: www.ml.com
SIC: **6211** Securities broker & dealer
HQ: Merrill Lynch & Co Inc
4 World Financial Ctr # 4
New York NY 10080
212 449-1000

(G-1392)
METROPOLITAN SCHOOL & CHARTER
Also Called: Voyageur Bus Co
3941 E Calvary Rd (55803-1318)
PHONE 218 724-1707
FAX: 218 724-2432
Michael J Krois, *Principal*
Roger Joppa, *Accountant*
EMP: 120
SALES (est): 1MM-4.9MM **Privately Held**
SIC: **4151** 4142 School bus service; long-distance bus charter service
PA: Metropolitan School & Charter
425 31st St E
Hastings MN 55033
651 437-9648

(G-1393)
MIDWEST MEDICAL EQUIPMENT
4418 Haines Rd Ste 1200 (55811-1525)
PHONE 218 722-3420
FAX: 218 720-6158
Pat Winkleman, *General Mgr*
Wendy Purdiak, *Vice Pres*
Peg Vanhouse, *Finance*
Greg Nyquist, *Director*
EMP: 43 EST: 1990
SQ FT: 30,000
SALES (est): 5MM-9.9MM **Privately Held**
SIC: **5047** Retails medical apparatus & supplies; wholesales medical equipment & supplies
DH: St Mary's Medical Center
407 E 3rd St
Duluth MN 55805
218 786-4000

(G-1394)
MIELKE ELECTRIC WORKS INC
2606 W Michigan St (55806-1832)
PO Box 16090 (55816-0090)
PHONE 218 727-7411
FAX: 218 727-7155
Warren F Mielke, *President*
Betty Eklund, *Controller*
Thomas Moilanen, *Manager*
Robert Poulter, *Manager*
Joel Hanson, *Data Proc Dir*
EMP: 45 EST: 1912
SQ FT: 28,000
SALES (est): 5MM-9.9MM **Privately Held**
WEB: www.mielkeelectric.com
SIC: **7694** 5063 Electric motor repair service; wholesales electric motors; manufactures process control instruments; manufactures motors or generators

(G-1395)
MINNESOTA PROGRAM DEVELOPMENT
Also Called: DOMESTIC ABUSE INTERVENTION PR
202 E Superior St (55802-2118)
PHONE 218 722-2781
Jerald Ostensoe, *Ch of Bd*
Cecelia Smith, *Corp Secy*
Beryl Rock, *Vice Pres*
Richard Diver, *Vice Pres*
Susan Olsen, *Treasurer*
EMP: 80 EST: 1980
SQ FT: 20,000 **Privately Held**
WEB: www.duluth-model.org
SIC: **8399** Community action agency

(G-1396)
MONACO AIR DULUTH LLC
4535 Airport Approach Rd (55811-1555)
PHONE 218 727-2911
Michael Magni, *Member*
Donald P Monaco, *Member*
Scott Poulin, *Office Mgr*
Courtney Missinne, *Manager*
Rob Missinne, *Director*
EMP: 40 EST: 2005
SQ FT: 50,000
SALES (est): 25MM-49.9MM **Privately Held**
WEB: www.monacoairduluth.com
SIC: **7359** 5172 7699 Aircraft rental service; aircraft fueling services; aircraft & heavy equipment repair service

(G-1397)
MORGAN BUSINESS TRUST
Also Called: Extended Family Home Care
6016 N Pike Lake Rd (55811-9636)
PHONE 218 348-1359
William Buchanon, *President*
Jill Caske, *Manager*
EMP: 50 EST: 1995
SALES (est): 1MM-4.9MM **Privately Held**
SIC: **8082** Home health care services

(G-1398)
N P D INC
1202 Maple Grove Rd (55811-4523)
PHONE 218 720-3324
FAX: 218 720-3502
John Koralia, *President*
EMP: 25 EST: 1995
SQ FT: 10,000
SALES (est): 1MM-4.9MM **Privately Held**
SIC: **1742** Drywall contractor

(G-1399)
NORTH SHORE BANK OF COMMERCE
131 W Superior St (55802-2031)
PO Box 16450 (55816-0450)
PHONE 218 722-4784
FAX: 218 722-8133
Larry D Johnson, *President*
Douglas H Lewis, *Chairman*
Carol Bubb, *Opers Mgr*
Patricia Tomaino, *Opers Mgr*
Bruce Smith, *Loan Officer*
EMP: 55 EST: 1915
SQ FT: 23,382
SALES (est): 10MM-24.9MM **Privately Held**
WEB: www.banknorthshore.com
SIC: **6022** State commercial bank
PA: North Shore Financial Corp
131 W Superior St
Duluth MN 55802
218 722-4784

(G-1400)
NORTH SHORE FINANCIAL CORP (PA)
131 W Superior St (55802-2031)
PHONE 218 722-4784
Larry D Johnson, *President*
Douglas H Lewis, *Chairman*
Ken Johnson, *Vice Pres*
Casey Russell, *VP Persnl*
Derek Rowan, *IT/INT Sup*
EMP: 63 EST: 1985
SQ FT: 23,382 **Privately Held**
SIC: **6022** State commercial bank

GEOGRAPHIC

(G-1401)

NORTHERN ACCESS TRANSPORTATION

3133 Truck Center Dr (55806-1730)
PHONE 218 728-5464
FAX: 218 727-6871
Brian D Brown, *President*
Julian S Brown, *Vice Pres*
EMP: 30 EST: 1992
SQ FT: 3,000
SALES (est): 1MM-4.9MM Privately Held
WEB: www.northern-access.com
SIC: 8099 Medical rescue squad

(G-1402)

NORTHERN BUSINESS PRODUCTS INC

2326 W Superior St (55806-1932)
PO Box 16127 (55816-0127)
PHONE 218 726-0167
FAX: 218 726-1023
Jim Farrell, *President*
Michael Farrell, *Vice Pres*
Ann Honer, *Office Mgr*
Michael Sundberg, *Manager*
▲ EMP: 40 EST: 1981
SQ FT: 25,000
SALES (est): 5MM-9.9MM Privately Held
WEB: www.nbpoffice.com
SIC: 5021 5112 Retails office forms &
supplies; wholesales stationery & office
supplies; wholesales office furniture

(G-1403)

NORTHERN COMMUNITIES CREDIT

3311 W Arrowhead Rd (55811-4065)
PHONE 218 279-3200
John Thomas, *Principal*
Grant Forsyth, *Vice Chairman*
Robert Troolin, *Vice Chairman*
Richard Ledoux, *Corp Secy*
Kenneth Dahlberg, *Vice Pres*
EST: 2007
SQ FT: 8,214 Privately Held
SIC: 6062 State chartered credit union

(G-1404)

NORTHERN INDUSTRIAL INSULATION

3757 Midway Rd (55810-9572)
PHONE 218 624-0574
FAX: 218 624-0763
John Patton, *CEO*
Steven Johnson, *President*
EMP: 25 EST: 1983
SQ FT: 6,000
SALES (est): 1MM-4.9MM Privately Held
SIC: 1742 Building insulation installation
service

(G-1405)

NORTHLAND CHAPTER AMERICAN RED

2524 Maple Grove Rd (55811-1864)
PHONE 218 722-0071
FAX: 218 740-4406
Jim Paulson, *Treasurer*
Bill Beasley, *Director*
EMP: 110 EST: 1919
SALES (est): 5MM-9.9MM Privately Held
SIC: 8322 Individual & family social services

(G-1406)

NORTHLAND CONSTRUCTORS OF

4843 Rice Lake Rd (55803-1229)
PHONE 218 722-8170
FAX: 218 722-4560
James Holmgren, *Member*
Jim Oswald, *Engineering*
Pat Fredericks, *Office Mgr*
EMP: 25 EST: 1971
SQ FT: 7,000
SALES (est): 1MM-4.9MM Privately Held
SIC: 1611 1422 1623 1771 Heavy highway
& street construction; asphalt contractor;
sewer line construction; crushed & broken
limestone mining
PA: Northland Group of Comapanies
1420 London Rd Ste 204
Duluth MN 55805
218 722-8170

(G-1407)

NORTHLAND COUNTRY CLUB INC

3901 E Superior St (55804-2050)
PHONE 218 525-1941
FAX: 218 525-6245
Gary Schneider, *Manager*
EMP: 35 EST: 1904
SALES (est): 1MM-4.9MM Privately Held
WEB: www.northlandcountryclub.com
SIC: 7997 Country club

(G-1408)

NORTHLAND OB GYN ASSOCIATES

1000 E 1st St Ste LL (55805-2297)
PHONE 218 722-5629
James Sebastian, *Partner*
Stefan Guttormsson, *Partner*
Jamie Heim, *Office Mgr*
Stephen Guttormessom, *Med Doctor*
Kathy Conly, *Manager*
EMP: 26 EST: 1971
SALES (est): 1MM-4.9MM Privately Held
SIC: 8011 Gynecologist office; physicians'
office

(G-1409)

NORTHWEST AIRLINES INC

4701 Grinden Dr Ste 2 (55811-1518)
PHONE 218 727-8791
Darren Eide, *Manager*
Jay Chappel, *Manager*
Doug Wood, *Manager*
Mike Huppert, *Supervisor*
EMP: 26
SALES (est): 1MM-4.9MM Publicly Held
WEB: www.nwairlines.com
SIC: 4513 Air courier services
HQ: Northwest Airlines Inc
7500 Airline Dr
Minneapolis MN 55450
612 726-2111

(G-1410)

NORTHWOOD CHILDRENS HOME SOC

714 W College St (55811-4906)
PHONE 218 724-8815
FAX: 218 724-0251
Richard Wolleat, *COO*
Arnie Hughley, *CFO*
Mary Kosazerk, *CFO*
Sherry Babic, *Human Res Mgr*
Sherry Bavick, *Manager*
EMP: 80 EST: 1883
SQ FT: 81,797
SALES (est): 1MM-4.9MM Privately Held
SIC: 8361 8322 Residential care for
children; juvenile correctional facilities;
individual & family social services

(G-1411)

NURSES THAT CARE

1901 South St Ste 3 (55812-2117)
PHONE 218 724-2800
FAX: 218 724-8200
Deborah Kolpes, *Owner*
EMP: 35 EST: 2001
SALES (est): 1MM-4.9MM Privately Held
SIC: 8082 Home health care services

(G-1412)

ODYSSEY DEVELOPMENT INC

2230 London Rd 100 (55812-2129)
PHONE 218 728-8060
Robert L Ryan, *Principal*
Jason Lind, *Manager*
Tom Marinac, *Manager*
EMP: 40 EST: 2003
SALES (est): 10MM-24.9MM Privately Held
WEB: www.odysseydev.com
SIC: 6552 Commercial land subdividers &
developers

(G-1413)

ONEIDA REALTY CO INC

306 W Superior St Ste 1605 (55802-1816)
PHONE 218 722-0816
FAX: 218 720-6879
Robert K Prescott, *Ch of Bd*
Steven L Flamme, *President*
Thea Littler, *Corp Secy*

Roger D Wedin, *Exec VP*
Jamie Glitsos, *Opers Staff*
EMP: 100 EST: 1902
SQ FT: 90,582
SALES (est): 25MM-49.9MM Privately Held
WEB: www.oneidarealty.com
SIC: 6512 6531 7521 Operators of
commercial & industrial buildings; real
estate services; parking garage

(G-1414)

ORTHOPEDIC ASSOCIATES OF

1000 E 1st St Ste 404 (55805-2297)
PHONE 218 722-5513
FAX: 218 722-6515
Joel Zamzow, *President*
Graham D Ritts, *Corp Secy*
Mark Carlson, *Vice Pres*
Peter Goldschmidt, *Vice Pres*
William Schnell, *Vice Pres*
EMP: 35 EST: 1969
SQ FT: 12,000
SALES (est): 1MM-4.9MM Privately Held
SIC: 8011 Orthopedic physician office;
surgeon's office

(G-1415)

OTIS-MAGIE INSURANCE AGENCY

Also Called: Insurance Service Agency
227 W 1st St Ste 900 (55802-1927)
PO Box 137 (55801-0137)
PHONE 218 722-7753
FAX: 218 722-7756
Larry Haugen, *CEO*
Mike Vanverg, *President*
Brenda Hall, *Principal*
Stephen M Brett, *Corp Secy*
Gary K Bracken, *Vice Pres*
EMP: 29 EST: 1886
SQ FT: 5,200
SALES (est): 1MM-4.9MM Privately Held
SIC: 6411 Insurance services

(G-1416)

OUR PLACE COVENANT ENABLING

322 N 60th Ave W (55807-1904)
PHONE 218 624-3097
FAX: 218 624-3440
Dana Norton, *CEO*
Alana Paplior, *Director*
EMP: 40 EST: 1999
SALES (est): 1MM-4.9MM Privately Held
SIC: 8322 Individual & family social services

(G-1417)

P S RUDIE & ASSOCIATES LTD

324 W Superior St Ste 302 (55802-1708)
PHONE 218 722-6613
FAX: 218 720-0350
Nancy I English, *CEO*
Robert McDonald, *President*
Roger K Waage, *Med Doctor*
Mary Rapps, *Exec Dir*
EMP: 45 EST: 1969
SALES (est): 5MM-9.9MM Privately Held
SIC: 8011 General & family practice
physician or surgeon office

(G-1418)

PARAGON ASSOCIATES INC

4629 Airpark Blvd (55811-5750)
PHONE 218 722-5009
James Annis, *President*
Wendy Annis, *Vice Pres*
EMP: 85 EST: 1992
SALES (est): 1MM-4.9MM Privately Held
SIC: 8361 8322 Residential care for the
handicapped; individual & family social
services

(G-1419)

PAUL SCHINTZ INC

Also Called: Lester Park Golf Course
1860 Lester River Rd (55804-3030)
PHONE 218 525-0828
FAX: 218 525-0806
Paul Schintz, *President*
EMP: 25 EST: 2000
SALES (est): 1MM-4.9MM Privately Held
SIC: 7999 Concession operator

(G-1420)

PAVILION SURGERY CENTER LLC

920 E 1st St Ste 101 (55805-2203)
PHONE 218 279-6200
FAX: 218 279-6205
Debra L Parks, *Member*
Mark Monte, *Treasurer*
Cory Olson, *Manager*
EMP: 50 EST: 2000
SALES (est): 5MM-9.9MM Privately Held
SIC: 8011 Surgeon's office

(G-1421)

PEPSI COLA BOTTLING CO OF

Also Called: Pepsico
4301 W Michigan St (55807-2770)
PO Box 16419 (55816-0419)
PHONE 218 628-0276
FAX: 218 628-0279
David Peterson, *General Mgr*
Pete Hill, *Vice Pres*
Jason Hinnenkamp, *Finance*
David Pederson, *Sales Mgr*
Mark Bernick, *Security Mgr*
EMP: 33
SALES (est): 10MM-24.9MM Privately Held
SIC: 5149 Manufactures nonalcoholic
carbonated beverages; wholesales
groceries

(G-1422)

PEQUAYWAN AREA TRAIL BLAZERS

8926 W Branch Rd (55803-9728)
PHONE 218 848-2510
Mark Jezdzewski, *President*
EMP: 50 EST: 1982
SALES (est): 1MM-4.9MM Privately Held
SIC: 7997 Outdoor field clubs

(G-1423)

PIEDMONT HEIGHTS DENTAL ASSOCS

2860 Piedmont Ave (55811-2938)
PHONE 218 722-0823
FAX: 218 722-7635
Brian Mart MD, *President*
Ken Larson, *Corp Secy*
Clyde Finch MD, *Treasurer*
Mary Johnson, *Manager*
EMP: 40 EST: 1962
SALES (est): 1MM-4.9MM Privately Held
SIC: 8021 Dentists' office & clinic

(G-1424)

PIONEER NATIONAL BANK (PA)

331 N Central Ave (55807-2501)
PHONE 218 624-3676
FAX: 218 723-5101
Wayne E Hibbard, *President*
John Connly, *Vice Pres*
Laurie Smith, *Vice Pres*
Bud Baker, *Vice Pres*
Missy Bakke, *Administrator*
EMP: 33 EST: 1927
SALES (corp-wide): 4.97M Privately Held
SIC: 6021 National commercial bank

(G-1425)

PIONEER NATIONAL BANK

120 Mount Royal Shopping Cir
(55803-3708)
PHONE 218 728-1172
FAX: 218 728-1220
Laurie Smith, *Vice Pres*
EMP: 35
SALES (est): 5MM-9.9MM Privately Held
SIC: 6021 National commercial bank
PA: Pioneer National Bank
331 N Central Ave
Duluth MN 55807
218 624-3676

(G-1426)

POLINSKY REHABILITATION CENTER

530 E 2nd St (55805-1913)
PHONE 218 786-5360
FAX: 218 727-1167
James Seitz, *Treasurer*
Val Caple, *Manager*
Marcia H Courtney, *Manager*

Mari Wagner, *Supervisor*
Ann Bussey, *Director*
EMP: 250 **EST:** 1950
SQ FT: 50,000
SALES (est): 10MM-24.9MM **Privately Held**
SIC: 8093 Outpatient rehabilitation treatment center
HQ: Essentia Health
  502 E 2nd St
  Duluth MN 55805
  218 786-8376

(G-1427)
POLLUTION CONTROL AGENCY, MN
525 S Lake Ave Ste 400A (55802-2302)
PHONE............................218 723-4660
FAX: 218 723-4727
Jeannete Sandstrom, *Owner*
Pat Carey, *Manager*
Suzanne Hanson, *Manager*
Tom Winkler, *IT/INT Sup*
EMP: 52
SALES (est): 5MM-9.9MM **Privately Held**
WEB: www.state.mn.us
SIC: 4953 Refuse systems services; air, water & solid waste programs administration services; state government air, water & solid waste management program administration
DH: Pollution Control Agency, MN
  520 Lafayette Rd N
  Saint Paul MN 55155
  651 296-6300

(G-1428)
POLYPHASE ELECTRIC CO (PA)
2515 W Superior St (55806-1834)
PO Box 16151 (55816-0151)
PHONE............................218 723-1413
FAX: 218 723-0073
Frances Harkonen, *Ch of Bd*
Tim Harkonen, *President*
Peter Clark, *Vice Pres*
Mary Harkonen, *Vice Pres*
Tom McKay, *Vice Pres*
EMP: 65 **EST:** 1975
SQ FT: 11,000
SALES (corp-wide): 12.53M **Privately Held**
SIC: 1731 Electrical contractor

(G-1429)
PREMIER CO'S INC
7511 Grand Ave (55807-2152)
PHONE............................218 348-1991
Joe Kovich, *President*
EMP: 26 **EST:** 1991
SALES (est): 1MM-4.9MM **Privately Held**
WEB: www.premiercompanies.com
SIC: 4959 Snow plowing services

(G-1430)
PRUDENTIAL TRUSCOTT REALTORS
1820 Maple Grove Rd (55811-1811)
PHONE............................218 726-1255
Kenneth A Truscott, *President*
EMP: 28 **EST:** 1991
SQ FT: 6,288
SALES (est): 5MM-9.9MM **Privately Held**
WEB: www.prudentialtruscott.com
SIC: 6531 Real estate services

(G-1431)
RBC WEALTH MANAGMENT
1420 London Rd Ste 201 (55805-2422)
PHONE............................218 724-2100
FAX: 218 728-8410
Cheryl Meese, *Manager*
James Proctor, *Manager*
Wendy Homstad, *Manager*
EMP: 25
SALES (est): 5MM-9.9MM **Privately Held**
WEB: www.hough.com
SIC: 6211 Security broker service
PA: Rbc Wealth Management
  60 S 6th Ste 700
  Minneapolis MN 55402
  612 371-7750

(G-1432)
REAL SERVICES INC
Also Called: Coldwell Banker
1732 London Rd (55812-2033)
PHONE............................218 728-5161
FAX: 218 728-1114
Greg Kamp, *President*
Zeke Fields, *Manager*
Richard Wenaas, *Exec Dir*
EMP: 45 **EST:** 1981
SQ FT: 5,000
SALES (est): 5MM-9.9MM **Privately Held**
WEB: www.carolhesch.com
SIC: 6531 Residential real estate agency

(G-1433)
REGENTS OF THE UNIVERSITY OF
Also Called: Natural Resources RES Inst
5013 Miller Trunk Hwy (55811-1442)
PHONE............................218 720-4294
FAX: 218 720-9412
Denise Endicott, *Accounting Staf*
Patricia Sodahl, *Human Resources*
Nora Kubazewski, *Pub Rel Dir*
Joann Hanowski, *Manager*
Christopher Heim, *IT/INT Sup*
EMP: 150
SALES (est): 10MM-24.9MM **Privately Held**
WEB: www.umn.edu
SIC: 8733 Noncommercial research organization; university
PA: Regents of The University of
  106 Pleasant St SE # 210
  Minneapolis MN 55455
  612 625-5000

(G-1434)
REM INC
1831 E Superior St (55812-2044)
PHONE............................218 724-1872
FAX: 218 724-0230
Joe Modec, *President*
Modeca Joe, *Exec Dir*
EMP: 40
SALES (est): 1MM-4.9MM **Privately Held**
SIC: 8322 Individual & family social services
PA: REM Inc
  2266 2nd St N
  Saint Paul MN 55109
  651 647-9243

(G-1435)
REPUBLIC BANCSHARES INC (PA)
306 W Superior St Ste 100 (55802-5025)
PHONE............................218 722-3445
Luigino Paulucci, *Ch of Bd*
David Gaddie, *President*
Deanna Benson, *Vice Pres*
EMP: 40 **EST:** 1992
SALES (corp-wide): 13.57M **Privately Held**
SIC: 6022 State commercial bank

(G-1436)
RESIDENTIAL SERVICES OF
Also Called: RSI Hartley
707 W Arrowhead Rd (55811-2205)
PO Box 3008 (55803-3008)
PHONE............................218 728-6823
FAX: 218 728-6823
Jon Nelson, *Director*
EMP: 30
SQ FT: 6,027
SALES (est): 1MM-4.9MM **Privately Held**
SIC: 8361 Residential care for the handicapped
PA: Residential Services of
  1309 Rice Lake Rd
  Duluth MN 55811
  218 727-2696

(G-1437)
RICE LAKE LUMBER INC
Also Called: Skip's Home Center
4728 Rice Lake Rd (55803-1613)
PHONE............................218 727-3213
FAX: 218 727-6511
Rich Lepak, *CEO*
Skip Lepak, *President*
John Lepak, *CFO*
Skip Wrede, *Manager*
▲ **EMP:** 35

EST: 1952
SQ FT: 91,000
SALES (est): 10MM-24.9MM **Privately Held**
WEB: www.skipshomecenter.com
SIC: 5031 Wholesales lumber, plywood & millwork; retails building products & materials; manufactures wooden kitchen cabinets; manufactures wooden doors; manufactures wooden pallets

(G-1438)
RIDGEVIEW COUNTRY CLUB INC
700 W Redwing St (55803-1753)
PHONE............................218 728-5128
FAX: 218 728-0586
Mark Fredrickson, *President*
Jean Wade, *Corp Secy*
William Seitz, *Treasurer*
EMP: 30 **EST:** 1920
SALES (est): 1MM-4.9MM **Privately Held**
WEB: www.ridgeviewcountryclub.com
SIC: 7997 Country club; membership tennis club; membership golf club

(G-1439)
ROYAL MEDICAL CENTER
1400 Woodland Ave (55803-2624)
PHONE............................218 249-8800
Steven Long MD, *President*
EMP: 25 **EST:** 2001
SALES (est): 1MM-4.9MM **Privately Held**
SIC: 8011 Physicians' office & clinic

(G-1440)
RSM MCGLADREY INC
227 W 1st St Ste 700 (55802-1926)
PHONE............................218 727-5025
James Denney, *CEO*
Leanne Smith, *Vice Pres*
Peggy Champion, *Manager*
Ken Buck, *CTO*
Drew Sandquist, *Director*
EMP: 60
SALES (est): 5MM-9.9MM **Publicly Held**
WEB: www.hrblock.com
SIC: 8742 8721 Management consulting services; accounting, auditing & bookkeeping services
DH: RSM McGladrey Inc
  3600 American Blvd W Fl 3
  Minneapolis MN 55431
  952 921-7700

(G-1441)
S M D C ST MARY'S DULUTH CLIN
407 E 3rd St (55805-1950)
PHONE............................218 786-4020
FAX: 218 727-7202
Peter Person, *President*
Margaret Wolters, *Owner*
Lynn Jensen, *Corp Secy*
Michael Bronson, *Vice Pres*
Stanley Swedberg, *Purch Dir*
EMP: 6000 **EST:** 2001
SALES (est): 500MM-999.9MM **Privately Held**
SIC: 8062 Medical hospital

(G-1442)
SAINT LUKE'S OUTPATIENT MENTAL
220 N 6th Ave E (55805-1952)
PHONE............................218 249-7000
John Strange, *CEO*
Gayle Potter, *Opers Staff*
Fred Erickson, *Treasurer*
Mary Greene, *Marketing Staff*
Jean Elton, *Branch Mgr*
EMP: 28
SALES (est): 1MM-4.9MM **Privately Held**
SIC: 8011 Physicians' office & clinic

(G-1443)
SAINT LUKES CARDIOLOGY ASSOCS
1001 E Superior St # 201 (55802-2228)
PHONE............................218 249-3057
Laszlo Tekler DO, *President*
Kim Terhaar, *Director*
EMP: 30
SALES (est): 1MM-4.9MM **Privately Held**
SIC: 8011 Cardiologist & cardio-vascular specialist

(G-1444)
SBSB LP
Also Called: Days Inn, Eveleth MN
5713 Grand Ave Ste B (55807-2564)
PHONE............................218 628-2700
Seth Oliver, *Partner*
Debra Oliver, *Partner*
Brent Oliver, *Partner*
Kent Oliver, *Partner*
Suzanne Oliver, *Partner*
EMP: 72 **EST:** 2000
SALES (est): 5MM-9.9MM **Privately Held**
SIC: 8741 Hotel or motel management services

(G-1445)
SCOTT A POLZIN DDS
1225 E 1st St (55805-2402)
PHONE............................218 728-6445
Scott A Polzin, *Owner*
EMP: 32 **EST:** 1980
SALES (est): 1MM-4.9MM **Privately Held**
SIC: 8021 Dentists' office & clinic

(G-1446)
SECURITAS SECURITY SERVICES
394 S Lake Ave Ste 300 (55802-2325)
PHONE............................218 727-7870
Gerald Weeks, *Branch Mgr*
Harold Weeks, *Manager*
EMP: 130
SALES (est): 1MM-4.9MM **Privately Held**
WEB: www.securitasinc.com
SIC: 7381 Security guard service
HQ: Securitas Security Services
  2 Campus Dr Ste 1
  Parsippany NJ 07054
  973 267-5300

(G-1447)
SENIOR FRIEND ASSOCIATES INC
301 W 1st St Ste 309 (55802-1636)
PHONE............................218 727-1111
FAX: 218 720-6819
Karen Stocke, *President*
Randy Leja, *Exec Dir*
EMP: 157 **EST:** 1981
SQ FT: 1,000
SALES (est): 5MM-9.9MM **Privately Held**
WEB: www.seniorfriendhomecare.com
SIC: 8082 8322 Home health care services; geriatric social services

(G-1448)
SHEL DON GROUP INC
124 E Superior St (55802-2116)
PHONE............................218 727-2817
FAX: 218 727-2806
Allan Bradshaw, *President*
Valerie Ouellette, *Sales Mgr*
EMP: 25 **EST:** 1990
SQ FT: 1,200
SALES (est): 1MM-4.9MM **Privately Held**
WEB: www.sheldonreproduction.com
SIC: 7334 Blueprinting services

(G-1449)
SHERATON DULUTH
301 E Superior St (55802-2119)
PHONE............................218 733-5660
EMP: 80 **EST:** 2007
SALES (est): 1MM-4.9MM **Privately Held**
SIC: 7011 Resort hotel

(G-1450)
SHORT-ELLIOTT-HENDRICKSON INC
Also Called: Seh
418 W Superior St Ste 200 (55802-1512)
PHONE............................888 722-0547
Scott Scrotters, *Manager*
Scott Sannes, *Manager*
EMP: 31
SALES (est): 1MM-4.9MM **Privately Held**
WEB: www.sehinc.com
SIC: 8711 Sanitary engineers
PA: Short-Elliott-Hendrickson Inc
  3535 Vadnais Center Dr # 200
  Saint Paul MN 55110
  651 490-2000

(G-1451)
SISU MEDICAL SOLUTIONS LLC
5 W 1st St Ste 200 (55802-2070)
PHONE.............................218 529-7900
Dianne Mandernach, *Member*
Dan McArthy, *Member*
Jodi Nelson, *Member*
Mark Schmidt, *Member*
Christopher Maddy, *Corp Secy*
EMP: 75 **EST:** 2001
SQ FT: 19,400
SALES (est): 10MM-24.9MM **Privately Held**
SIC: 7372 Operating systems software publishing

(G-1452)
SKYLINE BOWLING LANES INC
4894 Miller Trunk Hwy (55811-1504)
PHONE.............................218 727-8555
Dave Kolquist, *President*
EMP: 40 **EST:** 1956
SQ FT: 12,000
SALES (est): 1MM-4.9MM **Privately Held**
SIC: 7933 Bowling center; cocktail lounge

(G-1453)
SMDC HEALTH SYSTEM
Also Called: Duluth Clinic West
4212 Grand Ave (55807-2737)
PHONE.............................218 786-3500
FAX: 218 786-3546
Nancy Dettle, *Office Mgr*
Penny Bennett, *Phys Therapist*
Sue Bussa, *Phys Therapist*
April Bissonet, *Phys Therapist*
Kristine Kerr, *Phys Therapist*
EMP: 45
SALES (est): 5MM-9.9MM **Privately Held**
SIC: 8011 Clinic operated by physicians
PA: Smdc Health System
        400 E 3rd St
        Duluth MN 55805
        218 786-8364

(G-1454)
SMDC HEALTH SYSTEM (PA)
400 E 3rd St (55805-1951)
PHONE.............................218 786-8364
FAX: 218 720-2369
Peter Person MD, *CEO*
Mary Johnson, *COO*
Susan McClemon, *COO*
Dennis Gunderson, *Engineering*
Lashelle Keel, *Finance Mgr*
EMP: 900 **EST:** 1916
SQ FT: 132,000 **Privately Held**
SIC: 8011 Clinic operated by physicians; pharmacy & drug store

(G-1455)
SMDC MEDICAL CENTER
502 E 2nd St (55805-1913)
PHONE.............................218 727-8762
John Smylie, *CEO*
Peter Person, *CEO*
Mathew J Eckman, *Treasurer*
Grant Bellefeuille, *Controller*
Kevin Raihala, *Manager*
EMP: 750 **EST:** 1937
SQ FT: 181,000
SALES (est): 50MM-99.9MM **Privately Held**
SIC: 8062 Medical hospital
DH: St Mary's Medical Center
        407 E 3rd St
        Duluth MN 55805
        218 786-4000

(G-1456)
SOLSTICE CORP
5072 Jennifer Cir (55811-1482)
PHONE.............................218 729-5014
FAX: 218 729-0319
Laura Bromme, *President*
Charles D Miller, *Administrator*
EMP: 35 **EST:** 1992
SALES (est): 1MM-4.9MM **Privately Held**
SIC: 8361 Geriatric residential care

(G-1457)
SPIRIT MOUNTAIN TRAVEL LODGE
5910 Fremont St (55807-2113)
PHONE.............................218 628-3691
FAX: 218 628-2076
Shari Anderson, *Partner*
EMP: 28 **EST:** 1999
SALES (est): 1MM-4.9MM **Privately Held**
SIC: 7011 Motel

(G-1458)
ST ANN'S HOME
330 E 3rd St Apt 532 (55805-1867)
PHONE.............................218 727-8831
FAX: 218 727-8833
Stephanie Maki, *Manager*
Jan Lappy, *Director*
David Kern, *Director*
EMP: 80 **EST:** 1963
SALES (est): 1MM-4.9MM **Privately Held**
SIC: 8059 Retirement community with nursing

(G-1459)
ST FRANCIS HEALTH SERVICES OF
Also Called: Viewcrest Health Center
3111 Church Pl (55811-2925)
PHONE.............................218 727-8801
FAX: 218 727-6460
Donna Viskoe, *Vice Pres*
Carol Raw, *Finance Dir*
Bonnie Ratajek, *Human Resources*
Richard Ludwig, *Administrator*
Robert Dahl, *Administrator*
EMP: 180
SALES (est): 5MM-9.9MM **Privately Held**
SIC: 8051 Skilled nursing care facility
PA: St Francis Health Services of
        801 Nevada Ave Ste 100
        Morris MN 56267
        320 589-2004

(G-1460)
ST GERMAIN'S CABINET INC
5741 Old Highway 61 (55810-2189)
PHONE.............................218 624-1234
FAX: 218 624-0599
Doug Nelson, *President*
Gary Johnson, *Finance*
Vivian Rosandich, *Manager*
Tom Ochocki, *Info Tech Mgr*
Jam Szypkowski, *Admin Asst*
EMP: 28 **EST:** 1986
SALES (est): 1MM-4.9MM **Privately Held**
WEB: www.stgermaincabinets.com
SIC: 1799 Countertop installation service

(G-1461)
ST GERMAIN'S GLASS INC
212 N 40th Ave W (55807-2835)
PHONE.............................218 628-0221
FAX: 218 628-0227
Douglas M Nelson, *President*
Rob Cabe, *Vice Pres*
Michelle Marshall, *Purch Agent*
Beth Gade, *Engineering*
Gary Johnson, *Treasurer*
EMP: 30 **EST:** 1891
SQ FT: 23,000
SALES (est): 5MM-9.9MM **Privately Held**
SIC: 5039 1793 Wholesales glass construction materials; glass & glazing contractor
PA: Brin Glass Co
        2300 N 2nd St
        Minneapolis MN 55411
        612 529-9671

(G-1462)
ST JAMES HOME OF DULUTH
Also Called: Woodland Hills
4321 Allendale Ave (55803-1562)
PHONE.............................218 728-7500
FAX: 218 724-7403
Richard Quigley, *CEO*
Ray Hatinen, *Facilities Mgr*
Terry Leonidas, *CFO*
Susan Sage, *Human Res Dir*
Greg Panula, *Info Tech Mgr*
EMP: 125 **EST:** 1910
SQ FT: 5,500
SALES (est): 1MM-4.9MM **Privately Held**
SIC: 8361 8322 Home for the elderly; boys' towns; children's home; home for the emotionally disturbed; individual & family social services

(G-1463)
ST LOUIS, COUNTY OF INC
Also Called: Chris Jensen Nursing Home
2501 Rice Lake Rd (55811-4819)
PHONE.............................218 720-1500
FAX: 218 720-1567
Mike Smith, *Maintenance Dir*
Simon Clark, *Purch Agent*
Dana Protzien, *Sales Staff*
Leann Nichols, *Manager*
Marvin Bodie, *Manager*
EMP: 278
SALES (est): 10MM-24.9MM **Privately Held**
SIC: 8051 Skilled nursing care facility
PA: St Louis, County of Inc
        100 N 5th Ave W Rm 320
        Duluth MN 55802
        218 726-2340

(G-1464)
ST LOUIS, COUNTY OF INC
320 W 2nd St Ste 505 (55802-1409)
PHONE.............................218 726-2000
FAX: 218 726-2253
Mike Forsman, *Ch of Bd*
Linda L Anderson, *Principal*
Peg Sweeney, *Vice Chairman*
Chuck Hardtke, *Accounting Staf*
Joseph Mertel, *Benefits Mgr*
EMP: 300
SALES (est): 10MM-24.9MM **Privately Held**
SIC: 8322 Social services center
PA: St Louis, County of Inc
        100 N 5th Ave W Rm 320
        Duluth MN 55802
        218 726-2340

(G-1465)
ST LOUIS, COUNTY OF INC
4848 Lackland St (55811-1551)
PHONE.............................218 726-2920
Dan Bergerson, *Manager*
William Beck, *Analyst*
Marvin Bodie, *Analyst*
EMP: 36 **Privately Held**
SIC: 8999 Local general government administration office; communication services
PA: St Louis, County of Inc
        100 N 5th Ave W Rm 320
        Duluth MN 55802
        218 726-2340

(G-1466)
ST LOUIS, COUNTY OF INC
5735 Old Miller Trunk Hwy (55811-1221)
PHONE.............................218 349-8970
Tom Crossman, *Branch Mgr*
Jeff Nowak, *Manager*
EMP: 40
SALES (est): 1MM-4.9MM **Privately Held**
SIC: 8999 Search & rescue services
PA: St Louis, County of Inc
        100 N 5th Ave W Rm 320
        Duluth MN 55802
        218 726-2340

(G-1467)
ST LUKE'S CLINICS
915 E 1st St (55805-2107)
PHONE.............................218 249-5555
FAX: 218 249-3090
Bernadette Katich, *Principal*
Mike Myrterono, *Safety Mgr*
Marla Halvorson, *Human Res Dir*
Barb Crow, *Manager*
John Strange, *Manager*
EMP: 60 **EST:** 2007
SALES (est): 5MM-9.9MM **Privately Held**
SIC: 8011 Physicians' office & clinic

(G-1468)
ST LUKE'S HOSPITAL OF DULUTH
Also Called: Mt Royal Medical Center
1400 Woodland Ave (55803-2624)
PHONE.............................218 249-8800
Julie Nichols, *Branch Mgr*
EMP: 25
SALES (est): 1MM-4.9MM **Privately Held**

WEB: www.slhduluth.com
SIC: 8011 Physicians' office & clinic
PA: St Luke's Hospital of Duluth
        915 E 1st St
        Duluth MN 55805
        218 726-5555

(G-1469)
ST LUKE'S HOSPITAL OF DULUTH (PA)
915 E 1st St (55805-2107)
PHONE.............................218 726-5555
FAX: 218 726-3090
John Strange, *President*
Mark R Dagostino, *Ch Cardiology*
Sarah J Lundeen, *Ch Pathology*
Quinn H Carmichael, *Ch Radiology*
Vickie Owens, *Materials Mgr*
EMP: 1500 **EST:** 1883
SQ FT: 300,000
SALES (corp-wide): 276.15M **Privately Held**
WEB: www.slhduluth.com
SIC: 8062 8011 Hospital with AMA approved residency; physicians' office & clinic

(G-1470)
ST LUKE'S HOSPITAL OF DULUTH
4884 Miller Trunk Hwy (55811-1504)
PHONE.............................218 249-4600
FAX: 218 726-0284
Paul Raj, *Office Mgr*
Donovan James MD, *Med Doctor*
Kim Perhaar, *Manager*
EMP: 30
SQ FT: 11,591
SALES (est): 1MM-4.9MM **Privately Held**
WEB: www.slhduluth.com
SIC: 8011 Clinic operated by physicians
PA: St Luke's Hospital of Duluth
        915 E 1st St
        Duluth MN 55805
        218 726-5555

(G-1471)
ST LUKE'S HOSPITAL OF DULUTH
Also Called: Saint Lukes Microlab
915 E 1st St Fl 2 (55805-2107)
PHONE.............................218 249-5564
Jean Elton, *Branch Mgr*
EMP: 40
SALES (est): 1MM-4.9MM **Privately Held**
WEB: www.slhduluth.com
SIC: 8071 Medical laboratory
PA: St Luke's Hospital of Duluth
        915 E 1st St
        Duluth MN 55805
        218 726-5555

(G-1472)
ST LUKE'S INTERNAL MEDICINE
1001 E Superior St # 101 (55802-2227)
PHONE.............................218 249-7960
John Strange, *Principal*
Char McConnell, *Office Mgr*
Timothy C Kleinshmidt MD, *Med Doctor*
Sharma M Connell, *Manager*
Judith G Arvold, *Internal Med*
EMP: 43
SALES (est): 1MM-4.9MM **Privately Held**
SIC: 8011 Physicians' office & clinic

(G-1473)
ST MARY'S DULUTH CLINIC HEALTH (DH)
Also Called: Smdc
400 E 3rd St (55805-1951)
PHONE.............................218 786-4000
FAX: 218 722-0782
Peter E Person, *CEO*
Jim Stien, *General Mgr*
Ruth Martin, *Controller*
Faye Constantini, *Accountant*
Michael J De Bevec MD, *Med Doctor*
EMP: 3500 **EST:** 1997
SALES (corp-wide): 351.82M **Privately Held**
WEB: www.smdc.com

▲=Import ▼=Export
◆=Import/Export

SIC: **8093** 8011 8062 Outpatient mental health clinic; medical hospital; physicians' office & clinic
HQ: Essentia Health
502 E 2nd St
Duluth MN 55805
218 786-8376

(G-1474)
ST MARY'S MEDICAL CENTER (DH)
407 E 3rd St　(55805-1950)
PHONE..............................218 786-4000
SIS K Hofer, *Ch of Bd*
Jeff Truax, *Project Mgr*
Ernest Peaslee, *Engineering*
Ruth Martin, *Finance Dir*
Joanne Cirrillo, *Marketing Staff*
EMP: 1544 EST: 1985
SQ FT: 720,000
SALES (corp-wide): 351.82M **Privately Held**
SIC: **8062** 8082 8351 Medical hospital; group day care center; home health care services
HQ: Essentia Health
502 E 2nd St
Duluth MN 55805
218 786-8376

(G-1475)
STEPPING STONES FOR LIVING LLC
5270 Miller Trunk Hwy　(55811-1202)
PHONE..............................218 727-7450
FAX: 218 727-7452
Stephanie Ericksen, *Member*
Ronda B Davis, *Member*
Curtis C Davis Sr, *Member*
Cynthia Alexander, *Manager*
EMP: 70 EST: 2002
SQ FT: 4,000
SALES (est): 1MM-4.9MM **Privately Held**
WEB: www.steppingstonesforliving.com
SIC: **8322** Individual & family social services

(G-1476)
STRETAR MASONRY & CONCRETE INC
5719 Roosevelt St　(55807-2454)
PHONE..............................218 624-4824
FAX: 218 624-4825
Terry Radtke, *CEO*
Bill Kero, *Vice Pres*
EMP: 40 EST: 1966
SQ FT: 15,000
SALES (est): 1MM-4.9MM **Privately Held**
SIC: **1741** Masonry & stonework contractor

(G-1477)
STUDENT EXPERIENCE INC
120 Mount Royal Shopping Cir　(55803-3708)
PHONE..............................218 728-8009
FAX: 218 728-8011
Don Pellett, *Manager*
Angela Mattson, *Manager*
Jaime Spry, *Manager*
EMP: 35
SALES (est): 1MM-4.9MM **Privately Held**
SIC: **8082** Home health care services

(G-1478)
SUPERIOR GLASS DULUTH
4911 Matterhorn Dr　(55811-3848)
PHONE..............................218 722-7400
Knute Peterson, *President*
Joan Reindl, *Manager*
EMP: 35 EST: 2006
SALES (est): 1MM-4.9MM **Privately Held**
SIC: **1793** Glass & glazing contractor

(G-1479)
TB DULUTH LLC
Also Called: Radisson Ht Duluth Harborview
505 W Superior St　(55802-1513)
PHONE..............................218 727-8981
FAX: 218 727-0162
Paul Leisner, *General Mgr*
Tammy Harris, *Manager*
Darrin Mass, *Manager*
Jay Rosen, *Manager*
EMP: 126 EST: 1970
SQ FT: 42,805
SALES (est): 5MM-9.9MM **Privately Held**

SIC: **7011** Traveler accommodations

(G-1480)
TBI RESIDENTIAL & COMMUNITY
1615 Piedmont Ave　(55811-5327)
PHONE..............................218 721-3231
Shawn Neumann, *President*
Lori Huffman, *Vice Pres*
EMP: 60 EST: 1996
SALES (est): 1MM-4.9MM **Privately Held**
SIC: **8322** Individual & family social services

(G-1481)
TECH INVESTMENTS INC
Also Called: Twig Bakery & Cafe
4502 Airpark Blvd　(55811-5738)
PHONE..............................218 733-0214
FAX: 218 733-0261
Robert Hargraves, *President*
Martin Hinz, *Treasurer*
EMP: 27 EST: 2007
SQ FT: 8,000
SALES (est): 10MM-24.9MM **Privately Held**
SIC: **5149** Wholesales bakery products; retail bakery; manufactures dry bakery products

(G-1482)
TELE RESOURCES INC
1203 London Rd　(55802-2203)
PHONE..............................218 724-2026
Angela Fetters, *Branch Mgr*
EMP: 70
SALES (est): 1MM-4.9MM **Privately Held**
WEB: www.teleresources.net
SIC: **7389** Telemarketing services
PA: Tele Resources Inc
1203 London Rd
Duluth MN 55802
218 724-2026

(G-1483)
TELE RESOURCES INC　(PA)
1203 London Rd　(55802-2203)
PHONE..............................218 724-2026
Jack Keenan, *CEO*
R P Maxwell, *CFO*
EMP: 110 EST: 1996 **Privately Held**
WEB: www.teleresources.net
SIC: **7389** Telemarketing services

(G-1484)
THOMAS ELING CPA
Also Called: Aekill & Schilling Accounting
230 W Superior St Ste 600　(55802-4002)
PHONE..............................218 722-4705
Thomas Eling, *Owner*
EMP: 35
SALES (est): 1MM-4.9MM **Privately Held**
SIC: **8721** Certified public accountant services

(G-1485)
TIRES TO FUEL LLC
226 N Central Ave　(55807-2463)
PHONE..............................218 624-5009
David Listiak, *Member*
EST: 2007
SQ FT: 3,000　**Privately Held**
SIC: **4953** Waste material recycling services

(G-1486)
TRAUMATIC BRAIN INJURY
1731 W Superior St　(55806-2136)
PHONE..............................218 733-1331
FAX: 218 733-0499
Shawn Newman, *President*
Emily Masterson, *Corp Secy*
Lori Hoffman, *Vice Pres*
Leann Jaksha, *Controller*
Angela Mattensen, *Human Res Dir*
EMP: 60 EST: 1996
SALES (est): 1MM-4.9MM **Privately Held**
WEB: www.tbiduluthmn.com
SIC: **8322** Individual & family social services

(G-1487)
TRUEBLUE INC
4402 Grand Ave　(55807-2739)
PHONE..............................218 624-6222
FAX: 218 624-6003
Darren Haglund, *Manager*

EMP: 120
SALES (est): 1MM-4.9MM **Publicly Held**
WEB: www.laborready.com
SIC: **7363** Help supply services
PA: Trueblue Inc
1015 A St Unit A
Tacoma WA 98402
253 383-9101

(G-1488)
U M D FACILITIES MANAGEMENT
1049 University Dr Rm 241　(55812-3011)
PHONE..............................218 726-8262
John King, *Director*
EMP: 40
SALES (est): 1MM-4.9MM **Privately Held**
SIC: **7349** Building cleaning & maintenance services

(G-1489)
UDAC INC
500 E 10th St　(55805-1326)
PHONE..............................218 722-5867
FAX: 218 722-0209
Todd Sieger, *Treasurer*
Amy Skluzacek, *Controller*
Roberta Lenz, *Exec Dir*
Bill Kleczka, *Director*
Fern Penick, *Receptionist*
EMP: 52 EST: 1963
SQ FT: 18,000
SALES (est): 1MM-4.9MM **Privately Held**
SIC: **8322** Social services for the handicapped

(G-1490)
UNITED HEALTHCARE OF WYOMING
4316 Rice Lake Rd　(55811-4012)
PHONE..............................218 279-5642
FAX: 218 279-6761
Mary Sanstrom, *Office Mgr*
Kelly Vavra, *Manager*
Ellen Rhakowski, *Manager*
Ed Montgomery, *Administrator*
Steven Green, *Administrator*
EMP: 950
SALES (est): 100MM-499.9MM **Publicly Held**
WEB: www.unitedhealthgroup.com
SIC: **8011** Health maintenance organization or HMO
PA: Unitedhealth Group Inc
9900 Bren Rd E
Minnetonka MN 55343
952 936-1300

(G-1491)
UNITED PARCEL SERVICE INC
Also Called: UPS
111 Port Terminal Rd　(55802-2641)
PHONE..............................218 722-0150
FAX: 218 727-8435
Mike Harden, *Manager*
EMP: 150
SQ FT: 28,256
SALES (est): 5MM-9.9MM **Publicly Held**
WEB: www.ups.com
SIC: **4215** 4513 Parcel delivery services by vehicle; air courier services
HQ: United Parcel Service Inc
55 Glenlake Pkwy NE
Atlanta GA 30328
404 828-6000

(G-1492)
UNITED PIPING INC
4510 Airport Rd　(55811-1523)
PHONE..............................218 727-7676
Robert Schoneberger, *President*
Pat Kolb, *Asst Controller*
EMP: 50 EST: 1964
SQ FT: 10,000
SALES (est): 5MM-9.9MM **Privately Held**
WEB: www.unitedpiping.us
SIC: **1623** Utility line construction
PA: API Group Inc
1100 Old Highway 8 NW
Saint Paul MN 55112
651 636-4320

(G-1493)
UNIVERSAL MARKETING
1917 W Superior St　(55806-2140)
PHONE..............................218 722-1698
Rob Olson, *Owner*
EMP: 30 EST: 2007
SALES (est): 1MM-4.9MM **Privately Held**
SIC: **7389** Telemarketing services

(G-1494)
UPPER MINNESOTA PROPERTIES INC
Also Called: Minnesota Power Co
30 W Superior St　(55802-2030)
PHONE..............................218 722-2641
Robert J Adams, *CEO*
Stephen D Sherner, *Senior VP*
Pamela J Krall, *Vice Pres*
William A Carlson, *CFO*
Marilyn Weber, *Adv Mgr*
EMP: 30 EST: 1992
SALES (est): 1MM-4.9MM **Publicly Held**
SIC: **6519** Real estate property leasing & rental
PA: Allete Inc
30 W Superior St
Duluth MN 55802
218 279-5000

(G-1495)
VIKING AUTOMATIC SPRINKLER CO
4425 Venture Ave　(55811-5705)
PHONE..............................218 628-2150
Chris Nelson, *Branch Mgr*
EMP: 50
SALES (est): 5MM-9.9MM **Privately Held**
WEB: www.vikingsprinkler.com
SIC: **1711** Fire sprinkler system installation service
HQ: Viking Automatic Sprinkler Co
301 York Ave
Saint Paul MN 55130
651 558-3300

(G-1496)
VIKING AUTOMATIC SPRINKLER CO
4425 Venture Ave　(55811-5705)
PHONE..............................218 733-0962
FAX: 218 733-0249
EMP: 35
SALES (est): 1MM-4.9MM **Privately Held**
WEB: www.vikingsprinkler.com
SIC: **1711** Sprinkler system contractor
HQ: Viking Automatic Sprinkler Co
301 York Ave
Saint Paul MN 55130
651 558-3300

(G-1497)
VIKING ELECTRIC SUPPLY INC
4531 W 1st St　(55807-2769)
PO Box 7023　(55807-7023)
PHONE..............................952 890-8420
Jolie Goebel, *Purchasing*
Greg Irvine, *Manager*
EMP: 42
SALES (est): 25MM-49.9MM **Privately Held**
WEB: www.vikingelectric.com
SIC: **5063** Wholesales electric motors; wholesales wire & cable
HQ: Viking Electric Supply Inc
451 Industrial Blvd NE # 2
Minneapolis MN 55413
612 627-1300

(G-1498)
WASTE MANAGEMENT OF NORTH MN　(PA)
3101 W Superior St　(55806-1751)
PHONE..............................218 624-7838
Maury Meyers, *CEO*
Rodney Proto, *CEO*
Steve Batchelor, *Vice Pres*
Lee M Corkmick, *Treasurer*
Charles Blascoe, *Manager*
EMP: 75 EST: 1961
SQ FT: 60,000
SALES (corp-wide): 18M **Privately Held**
SIC: **4953** Refuse collection & disposal services; waste material recycling services

GEOGRAPHIC

GEOGRAPHIC *(side tab)*

(G-1499)
WATERFRONT PLAZA HOTEL CO LLC
325 S Lake Ave (55802-2323)
PHONE 218 727-4663
William Meierhoff, *Member*
Kent Oliver, *Member*
Heather Lofstuen, *Human Res Mgr*
George Hovland, *Manager*
EMP: 50 **EST:** 1998
SALES (est): 1MM-4.9MM **Privately Held**
WEB: www.hawthornsuitesduluth.com
SIC: 7011 Traveler accommodations; eating place

(G-1500)
WELLS FARGO BANK, NATIONAL
1339 W Arrowhead Rd (55811-2270)
PHONE 218 726-9325
FAX: 218 726-9329
Diane Takkunen, *Vice Pres*
Becca Cooper, *Store Mgr*
Rebecca Cooper, *Manager*
Cindy Pohl, *Manager*
EMP: 25
SALES (est): 5MM-9.9MM **Publicly Held**
SIC: 6029 Commercial bank
HQ: Wfc Holdings, Corp
420 Montgomery St
San Francisco CA 94104
415 396-7392

(G-1501)
WESLEY RESIDENCE INC
5601 Grand Ave (55807-2545)
PHONE 218 628-2307
FAX: 218 628-6923
Irene Hofstad, *President*
Ann Butler, *Vice Pres*
Arnold Hofstad, *Treasurer*
EMP: 25 **EST:** 1972
SQ FT: 16,000
SALES (est): 500-999K **Privately Held**
SIC: 8361 Residential care facility

(G-1502)
WESTERN LAKE SUPERIOR SANITARY
2626 Courtland St (55806-1813)
PHONE 218 722-3336
FAX: 218 879-7326
Cathy Remington, *Finance Dir*
Jack Ezell, *Technical Staff*
Marianne Bohren, *Exec Dir*
Kurt Soderberg, *Exec Dir*
Molly Haugen, *Director*
EMP: 91 **EST:** 1969
SQ FT: 50,000
SALES (est): 10MM-24.9MM **Privately Held**
WEB: www.wlssd.duluth.mn.us
SIC: 4952 Sewage facility

(G-1503)
WESTERN NATIONAL BANK
Also Called: Mortgage Centers
201 N Central (55807)
PO Box 16050 (55816-0050)
PHONE 218 723-5152
Phil Chapman, *Manager*
Kelly Sager, *Manager*
EMP: 34
SALES (est): 1MM-4.9MM **Privately Held**
SIC: 6162 Mortgage & loan lending
PA: Western National Bank
202 W Superior St Ste 100
Duluth MN 55802
218 723-1000

(G-1504)
WESTNER NATIONAL BANK INC
202 W Superior St Ste 100 (55802-1915)
PO Box 16050 (55816-0050)
PHONE 218 723-5100
Timothy Smith, *President*
Dennis Ramberg, *Exec VP*
EMP: 40 **EST:** 1994
SALES (est): 1MM-4.9MM **Privately Held**
SIC: 6162 Mortgage & loan lending

(G-1505)
YOUNG WOMEN'S CHRISTIAN ASSN
32 E 1st St Ste 202 (55802-3032)
PHONE 218 722-7425
FAX: 218 722-2765
Wendy Ruhnke, *Development*
Faye Reynolds, *Bookkeeper*
Ellen Oneill, *Exec Dir*
Lori Reilly, *Director*
Nancy Marschke, *Associate Dir*
EMP: 52 **EST:** 1908
SQ FT: 80,000
SALES (est): 1MM-4.9MM **Privately Held**
SIC: 8641 7032 7991 8322 8351 Youth organizations; youth camps; child day care service; individual & family social services; physical fitness center

(G-1506)
Z M C HOTELS INC
Also Called: Inn On Lake Superior
350 Canal Park Dr (55802-2316)
PHONE 218 726-1111
FAX: 218 727-3976
John Goldfine, *Vice Pres*
Nikki Anderson, *Manager*
EMP: 30
SALES (est): 1MM-4.9MM **Privately Held**
WEB: www.zmchotels.com
SIC: 7011 Hotel
PA: Z M C Hotels Inc
525 S Lake Ave Ste 405
Duluth MN 55802
218 723-8433

(G-1507)
Z M C HOTELS INC (PA)
525 S Lake Ave Ste 405 (55802-2300)
PHONE 218 723-8433
Kenneth Goldfine, *CEO*
Todd Torvinen, *President*
John Goldfine, *Vice Chairman*
Bill Desanto, *COO*
Jon Driscoll, *Vice Pres*
EMP: 50 **EST:** 1982
SQ FT: 4,000
SALES (corp-wide): 9.20M **Privately Held**
WEB: www.zmchotels.com
SIC: 8741 Hotel or motel management services

(G-1508)
Z M C HOTELS INC
Also Called: Erwin Associates
525 S Lake Ave Ste 405 (55802-2300)
PHONE 218 727-0461
John Goldfine, *President*
Jim Wantaja, *Coordinator*
EMP: 50
SALES (est): 1MM-4.9MM **Privately Held**
WEB: www.zmchotels.com
SIC: 8741 Hotel or motel management services
PA: Z M C Hotels Inc
525 S Lake Ave Ste 405
Duluth MN 55802
218 723-8433

(G-1509)
ZIEGLER INC
210 Garfield Ave (55802-2627)
PHONE 218 722-6628
FAX: 218 722-0307
Rudy Koski, *Manager*
EMP: 25
SALES (est): 10MM-24.9MM **Privately Held**
SIC: 5082 Wholesales construction & mining machinery
PA: Ziegler Inc
901 W 94th St
Minneapolis MN 55420
952 888-4121

DUNDAS
Rice County

(G-1510)
COLLEGE CITY BEVERAGE INC
700 Railway St S (55019-4071)
PHONE 507 645-4106
FAX: 507 645-8785
James Sawyer, *President*
EMP: 85 **EST:** 1953
SQ FT: 48,000
SALES (est): 25MM-49.9MM **Privately Held**
SIC: 5181 Wholesales beer & other fermented malt liquors

(G-1511)
EPIC ENTERPRISE INC
410 Stafford Rd N (55019-3954)
PO Box 186 (55019-0186)
PHONE 507 645-6800
FAX: 507 645-9306
Linda Hibbard, *Director*
EMP: 28 **EST:** 1996
SALES (est): 1MM-4.9MM **Privately Held**
SIC: 8331 7349 Job training & vocational rehabilitation services; building cleaning & maintenance services

(G-1512)
MECHANICAL SYSTEMS INC
800 Weaver Ln Ste A (55019-4127)
PHONE 507 645-5675
Joel T Pumper, *President*
EMP: 30 **EST:** 2000
SALES (est): 10MM-24.9MM **Privately Held**
SIC: 5084 Wholesales industrial machinery & equipment

DUNNELL
Martin County

(G-1513)
ELDON POTTHOFF
60771 740th St (56127-2000)
PHONE 507 695-2784
Eldon Potthoff, *Owner*
EMP: 30 **EST:** 1997 **Privately Held**
SIC: 0115 0116 0213 Corn farm; hog & pig farming; soybean farm

---
EAGAN
Dakota County

(G-1514)
A D G INC
Also Called: Probe Technical Services
3140 Neil Armstrong Blvd (55121-2272)
PHONE 651 287-5858
Gregg Dourgarian, *President*
Jessie Ultgren, *Vice Pres*
EMP: 60 **EST:** 1982
SALES (est): 5MM-9.9MM **Privately Held**
SIC: 8748 Business consulting services

(G-1515)
API OUTSOURCING INC (PA)
2975 Lone Oak Rd (55121)
PHONE 651 675-2600
Gary Halleen, *President*
Peter Donlon, *Principal*
Richard Yee, *Exec VP*
Howard Latham, *Exec VP*
James Hammes, *Opers Mgr*
EMP: 32 **EST:** 1998
SQ FT: 9,000 **Privately Held**
SIC: 7371 Computer software writers

(G-1516)
AVIONTE LLC
1270 Eagan Industrial Rd (55121-1369)
PHONE 651 556-2121
John Long, *Member*
PHI Ngo, *Member*
Samar Basnet, *Member*
Sandeep Acharya, *Member*
Briana Morgan, *Manager*
EMP: 25 **EST:** 2006
SQ FT: 4,500
SALES (est): 10MM-24.9MM **Privately Held**
SIC: 5045 7371 Wholesales computer software; computer software development

(G-1517)
BELL INDUSTRIES INC
580 Yankee Doodle Rd # 1200 (55121-2600)
PHONE 651 203-2300
Doug Larson, *VP Opers*
Charles Troy, *VP Engrg*
Val Felske, *Controller*
Joyce Wonsmos, *Human Res Dir*
Ross Carlson, *VP Sales*
EMP: 150
SALES (est): 50MM-99.9MM **Publicly Held**
WEB: www.bellind.com
SIC: 5013 5091 Wholesales new motor vehicle parts & supplies; wholesales sporting & recreational goods & supplies
PA: Bell Industries Inc
8888 Keystone Xing
Indianapolis IN 46240
317 704-6000

(G-1518)
C W LOGISTICS LLC
2985 Commerce Dr (55121)
PHONE 651 209-6814
FAX: 651 209-6812
Chris Walhof, *Owner*
Lisa Gustafson, *CFO*
Cheri Donovan, *Finance*
Rick Washek, *Manager*
EST: 2003
SQ FT: 35,000 **Privately Held**
WEB: www.cwlogistics.net
SIC: 4214 Local trucking with storage

(G-1519)
C-1 HOLDINGS LLC
3344 Highway 149 (55121-2316)
PHONE 651 994-6800
John McKenna, *Member*
Mike Schenck, *Accountant*
EMP: 99
SALES (est): 50MM-99.9MM **Privately Held**
SIC: 5065 Wholesales communications equipment

(G-1520)
CEVA FREIGHT LLC
3169 Dodd Rd (55121-2308)
PHONE 651 675-4000
FAX: 651 675-4007
Jeff Shear, *Plant Mgr*
EMP: 75
SALES (est): 5MM-9.9MM **Privately Held**
WEB: www.eagleusa.com
SIC: 4731 Freight forwarding services
DH: Ceva Freight LLC
15350 Vickery Dr
Houston TX 77032
281 618-3100

(G-1521)
CON-WAY FREIGHT INC
3450 Dodd Rd (55123-1301)
PHONE 651 686-2868
Mike Monfte, *Branch Mgr*
Mike Clark, *Manager*
EMP: 25
SALES (est): 1MM-4.9MM **Publicly Held**
WEB: www.con-way.com
SIC: 4212 Local trucking without storage services
HQ: Con-way Freight Inc
2211 Old Earhart Rd # 100
Ann Arbor MI 48105
734 994-6600

(G-1522)
CONVERGEONE HOLDINGS CORP (HQ)
3344 Highway 149 (55121-2316)
PO Box 1450, Minneapolis (55485-1450)
PHONE 651 796-6411
John McKenna, *CEO*
Louie Berezovsky, *CFO*
Lisa Tonn, *VP Finance*
EMP: 150 **EST:** 2006 **Privately Held**
SIC: 4813 1731 Wired telecommunications carrier & service; telephone equipment installation; retails telephone equipment & systems
PA: Genstar Capital LLC
4 Embarcadero Ctr Ste 1900
San Francisco CA 94111
415 834-2350

(G-1523)
CS SOLUTIONS INC
4660 Slater Rd Ste 200 (55122-4047)
PHONE 651 603-8288
FAX: 651 603-8289
Paul Kuttikadan, *President*

Rohit Tunj, *COO*
Tod Mitchinson, *Vice Pres*
Priya Srinivasan, *Finance*
Gangadharan Manari, *Director*
EMP: 25 **EST:** 1996
SQ FT: 3,000
SALES (est): 1MM-4.9MM **Privately Held**
WEB: www.cssolutionsinc.com
SIC: 7379 Computer system consulting services

(G-1524)
DAKOTA WOODLANDS INC
3430 Wescott Woodlands   (55123-1229)
PHONE..............................651 456-9110
FAX: 651 456-9244
Jacqueline Miller, *Corp Secy*
Mike Newman, *Vice Pres*
Reyne Branchaud-Linf, *Exec Dir*
R B Linsk, *Director*
EMP: 28 **EST:** 1983
SALES (est): 1MM-4.9MM **Privately Held**
WEB: www.dakotawoodlands.org
SIC: 8322 Emergency shelters

(G-1525)
DON STEVENS INC
980 Discovery Rd   (55121-2093)
PHONE..............................651 452-0872
FAX: 651 452-4189
Jim Zechmann, *President*
David D Sutter, *Vice Pres*
Karen Levra, *Controller*
David F Desutter, *Director*
EMP: 27 **EST:** 1962
SQ FT: 38,000
SALES (est): 10MM-24.9MM **Privately Held**
WEB: www.donstevens.com
SIC: 5078 5046 5075 5149 Wholesales refrigeration equipment & supplies; wholesales air conditioning & ventilation equipment & supplies; wholesales commercial cooking & food services equipment; wholesales warm air heating equipment & supplies; wholesales breading mixes

(G-1526)
EDINA REALTY
1519 Central Pkwy Ste 100   (55121-2507)
PHONE..............................651 450-6876
Keven Finnenginp, *Manager*
EMP: 70
SALES (est): 10MM-24.9MM **Publicly Held**
WEB: www.crosslakeedinarealty.com
SIC: 6531 Real estate services
HQ: Edina Realty
        15354 Danielson Rd
        Brainerd MN 56401
        218 829-7500

(G-1527)
FINAL COAT PAINTING INC
3185 Terminal Dr   (55121-1629)
PHONE..............................651 789-0790
Dawn Campion, *President*
Charles Campion, *Vice Pres*
Nicholas Campion, *Office Mgr*
Linda Taylor, *Manager*
Robert Loukusa, *Manager*
EMP: 80 **EST:** 1990
SALES (est): 5MM-9.9MM **Privately Held**
SIC: 1721 Exterior commercial painting contractor

(G-1528)
HIE LLC
1950 Rahncliff Ct   (55122-3370)
PHONE..............................651 681-9266
FAX: 651 688-6306
Emmett Lincoln, *General Mgr*
Sheryl D Walton, *Senior VP*
Brent Henry, *Engineer*
Thomas R Torgerson, *Mng Member*
EMP: 45
SALES (est): 1MM-4.9MM **Privately Held**
WEB: www.torgersonproperties.com
SIC: 7011 Traveler accommodations
PA: Torgerson Properties Inc
        103 15th Ave NW Ste 200
        Willmar MN 56201
        320 235-7207

(G-1529)
HILTON GARDEN INN
1975 Rahncliff Ct   (55122-3371)
PHONE..............................651 686-4605
FAX: 651 686-4662
Sheryl D Walton, *Senior VP*
Jean Murlatt, *Vice Pres*
Cadee Winnie, *Human Res Mgr*
Thomas R Torgerson, *Mng Member*
EMP: 30
SALES (est): 1MM-4.9MM **Privately Held**
WEB: www.torgersonproperties.com
SIC: 7011 Traveler accommodations
PA: Torgerson Properties Inc
        103 15th Ave NW Ste 200
        Willmar MN 56201
        320 235-7207

(G-1530)
HOME DEPOT USA INC
3220 Denmark Ave   (55121-1366)
PHONE..............................651 452-2323
Ellen Numberg, *Manager*
Joseph Warhol, *Manager*
Anton Lammers, *Manager*
Paul Fortney, *Associate*
EMP: 200
SQ FT: 117,106
SALES (est): 25MM-49.9MM **Publicly Held**
SIC: 7359 Home center store; tool rental
HQ: Home Depot International Inc
        2455 Paces Ferry Rd SE
        Atlanta GA 30339
        770 319-1300

(G-1531)
INSIDE EDGE COMMERCIAL
2700 Blue Waters Rd   (55121-1403)
PHONE..............................651 389-3900
FAX: 651 389-3901
David Moeller, *CEO*
William J Marketon, *Member*
Joseph T Hamand, *Manager*
See File, *Incorporator*
EMP: 35 **EST:** 2004
SALES (est): 1MM-4.9MM **Privately Held**
WEB: www.insideedgecis.com
SIC: 1771 Flooring contractor
PA: Mendota Holdings Inc
        2915 Commers Dr Ste 500
        Saint Paul MN 55121
        651 389-3964

(G-1532)
INTERCIM LLC
1915 Plaza Dr Ste 100   (55122-2960)
PHONE..............................651 289-5700
Brian Hinchley, *Member*
John Todd, *Member*
Mike Dunham, *Corp Secy*
Mary Dasile, *Human Res Mgr*
Barb Balcom, *Personnel*
EMP: 42 **EST:** 2001
SQ FT: 29,000
SALES (est): 5MM-9.9MM **Privately Held**
WEB: www.intercim.com
SIC: 7373 Computer integrated systems design services

(G-1533)
KONE INC
815 Northwest Pkwy # 120   (55121-1581)
PHONE..............................952 688-6827
FAX: 952 688-6401
Randy Strong, *Branch Mgr*
Brian Jones, *Manager*
EMP: 60
SALES (est): 1MM-4.9MM **Privately Held**
WEB: www.us.kone.com
SIC: 7699 Elevators inspection, services & repair
HQ: KONE Inc
        1 Kone Ct
        Moline IL 61265
        309 764-6771

(G-1534)
LIFESPAN OF MINNESOTA INC
3920 Sibley Memorial Hwy   (55122-1414)
PHONE..............................651 681-0616
FAX: 651 681-0747
Traci Hackmann, *CEO*
EMP: 68 **EST:** 2003
SALES (est): 1MM-4.9MM **Privately Held**

SIC: 8093 Outpatient mental health clinic

(G-1535)
MATS INC   (PA)
940 Aldrin Dr Ste 100   (55121-2285)
PHONE..............................651 406-8300
FAX: 651 406-8500
John Dawson, *President*
John Bukavatz, *Opers Mgr*
Daniel Mann, *Accounting Mgr*
Linda Horn, *Sales Staff*
EMP: 40 **EST:** 1975
SQ FT: 40,000
SALES (corp-wide): 3.81M **Privately Held**
SIC: 4212 4213 Local trucking without storage services; long-distance less than truckload freight trucking services

(G-1536)
MENDOTA INSURANCE CO   (HQ)
2805 Dodd Rd Ste 300   (55121-2161)
PO Box 64586, Saint Paul   (55164-0586)
PHONE..............................800 422-0792
Robert Zieper, *President*
Laurie Stanek, *Corp Secy*
John Kottke, *Webmaster*
Stephen Marsden, *Director*
EST: 1989
SQ FT: 85,000 **Privately Held**
WEB: www.kingswayamerica.com
SIC: 6331 Provides property damage insurance
PA: Kingsway America Inc
        150 Northwest Point Blvd Fl 5
        Elk Grove Village IL 60007
        847 871-6400

(G-1537)
MESABA AIRLINES
E Gentian Rd   (55121)
PHONE..............................651 367-5000
John Spanjers, *COO*
Steve Holm, *Vice Pres*
Jeffrey W Wehrenberg, *Vice Pres*
Bill Pal-Freeman, *Vice Pres*
William Donohue, *Vice Pres*
EMP: 25 **EST:** 2007
SALES (est): 5MM-9.9MM **Privately Held**
SIC: 4512 Provides scheduled helicopter carrier services

(G-1538)
MESABA AVIATION INC   (HQ)
1000 Blue Gentian Rd # 200   (55121-1789)
PHONE..............................651 367-5000
FAX: 651 367-5392
John G Spanjers, *President*
Hein Cao, *Managing Dir*
Michael L Bush, *Corp Secy*
Bill P Freeman, *Corp Secy*
Alan T Rooselet, *Corp Secy*
EMP: 1500 **EST:** 1944
SALES (corp-wide): 845.50M **Publicly Held**
WEB: www.mesaba.com
SIC: 4512 Provides scheduled helicopter carrier services
PA: Pinnacle Airlines Corp
        1689 Nonconnah Blvd Ste 111
        Memphis TN 38132
        901 348-4100

(G-1539)
MORTGAGE RESOURCE CENTER INC
Also Called: Allregs
2975 Lone Oak Dr Ste 140   (55121-1784)
PHONE..............................651 683-9705
Jeff Hoerster, *President*
Brook Ostrander, *General Mgr*
Dan Thoms, *Senior VP*
Michelle York, *Finance*
Lisa Springborn, *Human Res Dir*
EMP: 40 **EST:** 1988
SQ FT: 5,000
SALES (est): 5MM-9.9MM **Privately Held**
WEB: www.allregs.com
SIC: 7371 7374 Computer software development; computer service bureau

(G-1540)
NATIONAL BUSINESS SYSTEMS INC   (PA)
2919 W Service Rd   (55121-1224)
PHONE..............................651 688-0202
David Ihle, *CEO*

Joe Tafs, *President*
Joseph D Ryan, *Corp Secy*
Nancy Jonis, *Div Sub Head*
Debb Morgen, *Facilities Mgr*
EMP: 75 **EST:** 1972
SQ FT: 40,000 **Privately Held**
WEB: www.nbsusa.com
SIC: 7374 5044 7334 7389 Data entry service; wholesales microfilm equipment; micropublishing service; data processing service; photocopying & duplicating services; manifold business form printing; microfilm service

(G-1541)
NATIONAL RETIREMENT PLAN INC
2600 Eagan Woods Dr # 450   (55121-1168)
PHONE..............................651 789-1037
Mark A Sletto, *CEO*
EMP: 75
SALES (est): 5MM-9.9MM **Privately Held**
SIC: 7389 Business support services

(G-1542)
NORTH AMERICAN COMMUNICATIONS   (DH)
3344 Highway 149   (55121-2316)
PO Box 1450, Minneapolis   (55485-1450)
PHONE..............................651 994-6800
Tom Roles, *President*
Frank Gustafson, *Exec VP*
Michael Haus, *Exec VP*
Lisa Tonn, *Vice Pres*
David Garlich, *Vice Pres*
EMP: 80 **EST:** 1993 **Privately Held**
WEB: www.nacr.com
SIC: 4813 1731 Wired telecommunications carrier & service; telephone equipment installation; retails telephone equipment & systems
HQ: Convergeone Holdings Corp
        3344 Highway 149
        Eagan MN 55121
        651 796-6411

(G-1543)
NORTHWEST AIRLINES CORP   (HQ)
2700 Lone Oak Pkwy   (55121-1546)
PHONE..............................612 726-2111
Edward H Bastian, *Pres*
Todd Anderson, *Managing Dir*
Kristi Carlson, *Managing Dir*
Bob Gleason, *Managing Dir*
Sally Veith, *Managing Dir*
EMP: 2000 **EST:** 1989
SALES (corp-wide): 28.06B **Publicly Held**
WEB: www.nwa.com
SIC: 4512 Passenger airline services; air freight service
PA: Delta Air Lines Inc
        1030 Delta Blvd
        Atlanta GA 30354
        404 715-2600

(G-1544)
OFFICEMAX NORTH AMERICA INC
1271 Promenade Pl   (55121-2293)
PHONE..............................651 686-6606
FAX: 651 686-9644
Jason L Mott, *Manager*
Dan Bjoraker, *Manager*
Bobby House, *Manager*
EMP: 28
SALES (est): 5MM-9.9MM **Publicly Held**
WEB: www.officemax.com
SIC: 5112 Wholesales office supplies
HQ: OfficeMax North America Inc
        3462 Mayfield Rd
        Cleveland OH 44118
        216 297-9789

(G-1545)
PATTERSON CO'S INC
2930 Waters Rd Ste 160   (55121-1668)
PHONE..............................651 688-9265
EMP: 55
SALES (est): 25MM-49.9MM **Publicly Held**
WEB: www.pattersondental.com

SIC: 5047 Wholesales medical & hospital equipment
PA: Patterson Co's Inc
1031 Mendota Heights Rd
Saint Paul MN 55120
651 686-1600

(G-1546)
PULTE HOMES OF MINNESOTA LLC
815 Northwest Pkwy # 140 (55121-1580)
PHONE 651 452-5200
Keith Tomlinson, *President*
Marty Gergen, *Vice Pres*
Chuck Schultz, *Finance*
EMP: 100 **EST:** 1989
SALES (est): 25MM-49.9MM **Publicly Held**
WEB: www.pulte.com
SIC: 1521 Single-family housing construction
DH: Pulte Homes Corp
100 Bloomfield Hills Pkwy
Bloomfield Hills MI 48304
248 644-7300

(G-1547)
REHDER & ASSOCIATES INC
3440 Federal Dr Ste 110 (55122-3500)
PHONE 651 452-5051
Alvin Rehder, *General Mgr*
EMP: 100 **EST:** 1990
SALES (est): 10MM-24.9MM **Privately Held**
SIC: 8711 8713 Civil engineering services; surveying service

(G-1548)
ROSEMOUNT AEROSPACE INC
1256 Trapp Rd (55121-1217)
PHONE 651 681-8900
FAX: 651 681-8909
Gerry Schloegel, *Manager*
Steve Lenertz, *Director*
EMP: 180
SQ FT: 64,123
SALES (est): 10MM-24.9MM **Privately Held**
SIC: 7699 Aircraft & heavy equipment repair service

(G-1549)
SBSE LLC
Also Called: Staybridge Suites
4675 Rahncliff Rd (55122-3397)
PHONE 651 994-7810
Holly Crompton, *General Mgr*
Sheryl D Walton, *Senior VP*
Thomas R Torgerson, *Mng Member*
EMP: 25
SALES (est): 1MM-4.9MM **Privately Held**
WEB: www.torgersonproperties.com
SIC: 7011 Franchised motel
PA: Torgerson Properties Inc
103 15th Ave NW Ste 200
Willmar MN 56201
320 235-7207

(G-1550)
SCANTRON CORP (HQ)
1313 Lone Oak Rd (55121-1334)
PHONE 651 683-6000
William D Hansen, *President*
Becky Johnson, *Principal*
David Porter, *COO*
Gary Eaton, *Senior VP*
Bruce Kraft, *Senior VP*
◆ **EMP:** 200 **EST:** 1972
SQ FT: 100,010
SALES (corp-wide): 1.81B **Publicly Held**
WEB: www.scantron.com
SIC: 7372 Manufactures optical scanning devices; educational software publishers; manufactures computer terminals; manufactures magnetic ink readers, sorters, inscribers; manifold business form printing; commercial lithographic printing; software publisher
PA: M & F Worldwide Corp
35 E 62nd St
New York NY 10065
212 572-8600

(G-1551)
SCHENKER INC
3191 Mike Collins Dr (55121-2220)
PHONE 651 367-2500
FAX: 651 406-8706

Mark Zeidler, *District Mgr*
Donna Lawrence, *Manager*
EMP: 60
SALES (est): 5MM-9.9MM **Privately Held**
WEB: www.dbschenkerusa.com
SIC: 4731 Freight forwarding services
HQ: Schenker Inc
150 Albany Ave
Freeport NY 11520
516 377-3000

(G-1552)
SOVRAN INC
2915 Commers Dr Ste 100 (55121-2361)
PHONE 651 686-0515
Lisa Loken, *President*
Sue Roes, *Vice Pres*
Kati Fahring, *Engineer*
Michael Taney, *Engineer*
Michael Lomker, *Senior Engr*
EMP: 35 **EST:** 1987
SQ FT: 15,000
SALES (est): 5MM-9.9MM **Privately Held**
WEB: www.sovran.com
SIC: 7373 7378 Computer integrated systems design services; systems integration service; computer & data processing equipment repair & maintenance

(G-1553)
ST PAUL LINOLEUM & CARPET CO
2956 Center Ct (55121-1257)
PHONE 651 686-7770
FAX: 651 926-3143
Clement Commers, *CEO*
Michael J Commers, *President*
Robert L Good, *Corp Secy*
Mark Schmidt, *Vice Pres*
Lynn Hansch, *Vice Pres*
EMP: 76 **EST:** 1939
SQ FT: 45,000
SALES (est): 5MM-9.9MM **Privately Held**
WEB: www.armcom.com
SIC: 1752 5039 Flooring contractor; wholesales ceiling systems & products

(G-1554)
SUPERCLEAN BRANDS LLC ✪
1380 Corporate Center Curv (55121-1200)
PHONE 651 365-7500
Bryan Badzin, *Member*
EMP: 30 **EST:** 2009
SALES (est): 1MM-4.9MM **Privately Held**
SIC: 8742 Management consulting services; marketing consulting service

(G-1555)
SUSHI AVENUE INC
895 Blue Gentian Rd Ste 6 (55121-1570)
PHONE 651 294-7000
Nay HLA, *President*
Nay Lin, *Senior VP*
Doug Dagenais, *Vice Pres*
Steven Awng, *Assistant*
EMP: 75 **EST:** 2004
SQ FT: 12,000
SALES (est): 25MM-49.9MM **Privately Held**
SIC: 5146 Wholesales seafood

(G-1556)
TANDEM PRINTING INC
2970 Lexington Ave S (55121-1420)
PHONE 651 289-2970
FAX: 651 289-4399
John P Kostka, *President*
Steve Kane, *Vice Pres*
Steve Borowiak, *Manager*
EMP: 31 **EST:** 1954
SQ FT: 20,500
SALES (est): 1MM-4.9MM **Privately Held**
WEB: www.tandemprinting.com
SIC: 5199 Offset printing; wholesales advertising specialties

(G-1557)
TRANSPORT CORP OF AMERICA INC (HQ)
1715 Yankee Doodle Rd (55121-1697)
PHONE 651 686-2500
FAX: 651 686-2566
Scott C Arves, *President*
William Stattery, *Member*
Keith R Klein, *COO*
Craig A Coyan, *Senior VP*

Larry Johnson, *Vice Pres*
EMP: 333 **EST:** 1980
SQ FT: 70,707 **Privately Held**
WEB: www.transportamerica.com
SIC: 4213 Contract haulers; long-distance refrigerated trucking services
PA: Patriot Holding Corp
90 S 7th St Ste 3700
Minneapolis MN 55402
612 338-5912

(G-1558)
TRUSEAL AMERICA LLC
4980 Dodd Rd (55123-2115)
PO Box 3230, Burnsville (55337-8230)
PHONE 952 895-9197
Steve Tjornhom, *CEO*
Pete Tjornhom, *President*
Paula Tjornhom, *Partner*
Kevin Komorouski, *Vice Pres*
EMP: 30 **EST:** 2000
SQ FT: 6,000
SALES (est): 1MM-4.9MM **Privately Held**
SIC: 1771 Asphalt contractor

(G-1559)
US FOODSERVICE INC
2864 Eagandale Blvd (55121-1211)
PHONE 651 454-6580
FAX: 651 456-9840
Mike V Hove, *Purch Agent*
Michael Hove, *Purchasing*
Michael Potter, *Branch Mgr*
EMP: 350
SALES (est): 100MM-499.9MM **Privately Held**
WEB: www.usfoodservice.com
SIC: 5141 Food broker
HQ: US Foodservice Inc
9399 W Higgins Rd Ste 500
Rosemont IL 60018
847 720-8000

(G-1560)
WHITE HOUSE CUSTOM COLOUR INC
2840 Lone Oak Pkwy (55121-1550)
PHONE 651 646-8263
FAX: 651 646-9416
Webb White, *President*
Mike Hanline, *Vice Pres*
Thomas Hogan, *Treasurer*
Michele Nelson, *Manager*
EMP: 115 **EST:** 1982
SALES (est): 5MM-9.9MM **Privately Held**
WEB: www.whcc.com
SIC: 7384 Photofinishing laboratory

(G-1561)
WWTC
2110 Cliff Rd (55122-3522)
PHONE 651 289-4404
Lois Cordes, *Principal*
Patrick Campian, *Program Dir*
EMP: 25
SALES (est): 1MM-4.9MM **Privately Held**
SIC: 4832 Radio broadcasting station

(G-1562)
WYDE CORP
4660 Slater Rd Ste 222 (55122-4048)
PHONE 651 882-2400
FAX: 651 882-5018
Didier Lamour, *CEO*
Gail Callahan, *Corp Secy*
Steve Franklin, *Vice Pres*
Dave Shivlay, *Vice Pres*
Keith Flanagan, *Manager*
EMP: 60 **EST:** 2001
SQ FT: 3,000
SALES (est): 5MM-9.9MM **Privately Held**
WEB: www.wyde.com
SIC: 7373 Systems software development service

EAGLE LAKE
Blue Earth County

(G-1563)
PEOPLES STATE BANK OF MADISON (PA)
405 Parkway Ave (56024-7711)
PO Box 66 (56024-0066)
PHONE 507 257-3544
FAX: 507 257-3517
John Ries, *Manager*
EST: 1992
SALES (corp-wide): 1.37M **Privately Held**
SIC: 6022 State commercial bank

EAST GRAND FORKS
Polk County

(G-1564)
A & L POTATO CO
605 4th St NE (56721-3108)
PO Box 193 (56721-0193)
PHONE 218 773-0123
FAX: 218 773-1850
Randy Boushey, *President*
Charles Boushey, *Vice Pres*
Nicole Boushey, *Administration*
EMP: 25
SQ FT: 20,000
SALES (est): 10MM-24.9MM **Privately Held**
WEB: www.aandlpotato.net
SIC: 5148 Wholesales fresh potatoes

(G-1565)
AMERICAN LEGION
1009 Central Ave NW (56721-1610)
PHONE 218 773-1129
FAX: 218 773-2555
Terry Buraas, *Principal*
Ronald Miller, *Commander*
Jim McMillan, *Bookkeeper*
Henry Fiedler, *Manager*
Walter Folendorf, *Manager*
EMP: 35 **EST:** 2001 **Privately Held**
SIC: 8641 8699 Veterans' organization; charitable organization

(G-1566)
AREA SPECIAL EDUCATION CO-OP
1505 Central Ave NW (56721-1301)
PHONE 218 773-0315
FAX: 218 773-0924
Julie Aumock, *Asst Supt*
Colleen Goltz, *Asst Supt*
Shawn Egeland, *Bus/Fin/Pur Dir*
Peggy Gilbertson, *CTO*
Gary O Jones, *Director*
EMP: 33 **EST:** 1969
SQ FT: 2,200
SALES (est): 5MM-9.9MM **Privately Held**
WEB: www.asec.net
SIC: 8748 Educational services; business consulting services

(G-1567)
COMMUNITY OF RED RIVER VALLEY
1413 Central Ave NW (56721-1613)
PHONE 218 773-2451
Keith Sutherland, *President*
Karen Brekke, *VP Opers*
EMP: 83 **EST:** 1964
SQ FT: 3,500
SALES (est): 10MM-24.9MM **Privately Held**
SIC: 6022 State commercial bank

(G-1568)
HARRISTON-MAYO LLC
Business Hwy 2 (56721)
PHONE 218 773-1234
Michael D Delisle, *Principal*
EMP: 27
SALES (est): 10MM-24.9MM **Privately Held**
WEB: www.harriston-mayo.com

SIC: **5084** Wholesales industrial machine parts; manufactures conveyors & conveying equipment
PA: Harriston-Mayo LLC
500 Ordway Ave
Minto ND 58261
701 248-3286

(G-1569)

INDEPENDENT SCHOOL DISTRICT
Also Called: Bus Garage
1319 6th Ave NW (56721-1400)
PHONE..........................218 773-0476
Jeff Hahn, *Manager*
EMP: 32
SALES (est): 1MM-4.9MM **Privately Held**
SIC: **7538** General automotive repair services
PA: Independent School District
1420 4th Ave NW
East Grand Forks MN 56721
218 773-3494

(G-1570)

LIBERTY LANES INC
1500 5th Ave NE (56721-1601)
PO Box 356 (56721-0356)
PHONE..........................218 773-3477
FAX: 218 773-3478
Scott Gaddie, *President*
Patrick Gaddie, *Corp Secy*
Blane Gaddie, *Vice Pres*
Harry J Hanson Jr, *Dentist*
EMP: 25 EST: 1976
SQ FT: 16,600
SALES (est): 500-999K **Privately Held**
WEB: www.waycool3d.com
SIC: **7933** Ten pin center; tavern drinking establishment

(G-1571)

LUMBER MART INC (PA)
1910 Business Hwy 2 (56721)
PO Box 232 (56721-0232)
PHONE..........................218 773-1151
FAX: 218 773-7046
Robert E Peabody, *President*
Jeanine Peabody, *Corp Secy*
Trent Peabody, *Vice Pres*
R T Peabody, *Vice Pres*
Kathy Wolftram, *Manager*
EMP: 25 EST: 1949
SQ FT: 20,000
SALES (corp-wide): 6.81M **Privately Held**
SIC: **5031** Retail lumber sales; wholesales composite board products & woodboard; hardware store

(G-1572)

MINI-DREDGE INC
Also Called: Envi Waste Management
1006 6th Ave SE (56721-2315)
PO Box 341 (56721-0341)
PHONE..........................218 773-3331
Ron Novak, *President*
Paul Schmidt, *Corp Secy*
Harvey Anderson, *Treasurer*
Ron Novack, *Manager*
EST: 1976
SQ FT: 1,000 **Privately Held**
SIC: **1629** Dredging contractor

(G-1573)

PIONEER PEAT INC
Hwy 2 E (56721)
PO Box 14088, Grand Forks ND (58208-4088)
PHONE..........................701 746-4300
Michael Pierce, *President*
Randy Dufault, *Vice Pres*
EST: 1993
SQ FT: 50,000 **Privately Held**
SIC: **1499** Peat mining service; peat grinding service

(G-1574)

R J ZAVORAL & SONS INC
18297 County Highway 72 SW (56721-9258)
PO Box 435 (56721-0435)
PHONE..........................218 773-0586
FAX: 218 773-6423
Peter M Zavoral, *President*
John Zavoral, *Corp Secy*

Robert Zavoral, *Vice Pres*
Lori Friezen, *Manager*
Tom Bye, *Manager*
EMP: 30 EST: 1950
SQ FT: 4,000
SALES (est): 1MM-4.9MM **Privately Held**
WEB: www.rjzavoral.com
SIC: **1611** Heavy highway & street construction

(G-1575)

R J ZAVORAL ED'S CONSTRUCTION
18297 County Highway 72 SW (56721-9258)
PO Box 435 (56721-0435)
PHONE..........................218 773-0586
Edward W Morgan, *Partner*
EMP: 70 EST: 2004
SALES (est): 5MM-9.9MM **Privately Held**
SIC: **1794** Excavating contractor

(G-1576)

TRANSYSTEMS LLC
43994 Business Highway 2 (56721-9228)
PHONE..........................218 773-8813
FAX: 218 773-8813
Jeff Stola, *Branch Mgr*
Troy Carl, *Manager*
EMP: 150
SALES (est): 10MM-24.9MM **Privately Held**
SIC: **4212** 4214 Local trucking without storage services; local trucking with storage
PA: Transystems LLC
1901 Benefis Ct
Great Falls MT 59405
406 727-7500

(G-1577)

VALLEY GOLF ASSOCIATION
1800 21st St NW (56721)
PO Box 461 (56721-0461)
PHONE..........................218 773-1207
Larry Gaddie, *President*
Scott Eggers, *Manager*
EMP: 25 EST: 1971
SQ FT: 3,600
SALES (est): 1MM-4.9MM **Privately Held**
SIC: **7997** Membership golf club

(G-1578)

VALLEY TRUCK PARTS & SERVICE
1717 Central Ave NW (56721-1310)
PHONE..........................218 773-3486
FAX: 218 773-9581
Steven K Corcoran, *President*
Douglas A Runyan, *Vice Pres*
Pam Halvorson, *Assistant*
EMP: 25 EST: 1946
SQ FT: 42,000
SALES (est): 5MM-9.9MM **Privately Held**
WEB: www.valley-truck.com
SIC: **5013** 7538 Wholesales truck parts & accessories; retails new & used trucks, tractors & trailers; retails truck equipment & parts; truck engine repair service

(G-1579)

VFW RED RIVER VALLEY POST 3817
312 Demers Ave (56721-1816)
PHONE..........................218 773-2481
FAX: 218 773-3991
Benjamin Smith, *President*
Mary Crawford, *Bookkeeper*
Ardell Buchholtz, *Master*
EMP: 40 EST: 1987 **Privately Held**
SIC: **8641** Veterans' organization

(G-1580)

VIGEN CONSTRUCTION INC
42247 180th St SW (56721-9267)
PO Box 6109, Grand Forks ND (58206-6109)
PHONE..........................218 773-1159
Alfred Vigen, *President*
Jeffrey T Vigen, *Corp Secy*
Malcolm Stennes, *Manager*
EMP: 25 EST: 1938
SQ FT: 5,000
SALES (est): 5MM-9.9MM **Privately Held**
WEB: www.vigenconstruction.com
SIC: **1541** Grain elevator construction

ECHO
Yellow Medicine County

(G-1581)

FARMERS CO-OPERATIVE OIL CO OF
461 Second Ave W (56237)
PO Box 157 (56237-0157)
PHONE..........................507 925-4114
FAX: 507 925-4159
David Forkrud, *General Mgr*
EMP: 35 EST: 1952
SQ FT: 6,900
SALES (est): 25MM-49.9MM **Privately Held**
SIC: **5191** 5171 Wholesales farm supplies; wholesales agricultural fertilizer; wholesales agricultural chemicals; wholesales petroleum bulk stations; gas station; hardware store

---

EDEN PRAIRIE
Hennepin County

(G-1582)

A S T INC
Also Called: Stanley Steamer Carpet Clg
15900 W 79th St (55344-1810)
PHONE..........................952 888-7340
Audri Schwarz, *Ch of Bd*
Theodore Schwarz, *President*
EMP: 35 EST: 1985
SQ FT: 7,500
SALES (est): 1MM-4.9MM **Privately Held**
SIC: **7217** Carpet & furniture cleaning service on location

(G-1583)

AD EFX OF AMERICA INC
6409 City West Pkwy # 206 (55344-7846)
PHONE..........................952 941-3500
Lessy Jhonson, *President*
EST: 2002 **Privately Held**
SIC: **8611** Business association

(G-1584)

ADC TELECOMMUNICATIONS INC (PA)
13625 Technology Dr (55344-2252)
PO Box 1101, Minneapolis (55440-1101)
PHONE..........................952 938-8080
Richard B Parran, *President*
Jo M Anne Anderson, *President*
Robert E Switz, *President*
Jo A Anderson, *President*
Hilton Nicholson, *President*
▲ EMP: 1300 EST: 1953
SQ FT: 500,000 **Publicly Held**
WEB: www.adc.com
SIC: **8999** Manufactures telephone equipment; manufactures communication wire; manufactures connectors & terminals for electrical devices; manufactures telephone cords, jacks & adapters; communication services; manufactures fiber optic communication equipment

(G-1585)

AFFILIATED EMERGENCY
7717 Flying Cloud Dr (55344-3708)
PHONE..........................952 942-8272
FAX: 952 829-4089
Paul Jenson, *Exec Dir*
Erick Hone, *Technician*
EMP: 50 EST: 1983 **Privately Held**
SIC: **0742** Animal hospital services

(G-1586)

AGING JOYFULLY INC
13050 Pioneer Trl (55347-4110)
PHONE..........................952 941-2510
Joy Hansen, *President*
Joy Folie, *Vice Pres*
EMP: 25 EST: 2006
SALES (est): 500-999K **Privately Held**
SIC: **8361** Residential care facility

(G-1587)

ALLAN MECHANICAL INC
7875 Fuller Rd (55344-2139)
PHONE..........................952 934-3999
FAX: 952 934-3757
Elmer Wedel, *President*
Paul Worwa, *Vice Pres*
EMP: 25 EST: 1969
SQ FT: 25,000
SALES (est): 1MM-4.9MM **Privately Held**
SIC: **1711** Warm air heating & air conditioning contractor; ventilation & duct work contractor

(G-1588)

ALLIED WASTE INDUSTRIES INC
9813 Flying Cloud Dr (55347-4005)
PHONE..........................952 941-5174
Rich Hirstein, *Sales Executive*
Erik Schuck, *Manager*
Paul Roslend, *Manager*
Rick Doering, *Manager*
EMP: 100
SALES (est): 10MM-24.9MM **Publicly Held**
WEB: www.republicservices.com
SIC: **4953** Rubbish collection & disposal services
HQ: Allied Waste Industries Inc
18500 N Allied Way # 100
Phoenix AZ 85054
480 627-2700

(G-1589)

ALTERNATIVE BUSINESS FURNITURE
6533 Flying Cloud Dr # 800 (55344-3323)
PHONE..........................952 937-7688
FAX: 952 937-7691
Mark Frommelt, *CEO*
Ron Beckman, *General Mgr*
Ken Theisen, *Vice Pres*
Tim Koehn, *Manager*
Laron Jackson, *Manager*
EMP: 56 EST: 1993
SQ FT: 35,000
SALES (est): 10MM-24.9MM **Privately Held**
WEB: www.altbusfurn.com
SIC: **5021** Wholesales office furniture

(G-1590)

AMERICAN BAPTIST HOMES OF THE (PA)
14850 Scenic Heights Rd (55344-2243)
PHONE..........................952 941-3175
FAX: 952 941-8567
Robert B Inhoff, *President*
Tim O'Brien, *Corp Secy*
Jim Selvy, *COO*
Polly Schrom, *Vice Pres*
Jeff Hongslo, *Treasurer*
EMP: 27 EST: 1930
SQ FT: 5,100
SALES (corp-wide): 4.81M **Privately Held**
WEB: www.abhomes.net
SIC: **8051** 8052 8361 Convalescent home; residential mentally handicapped facility; mental retardation hospital; rest home with health care incidental

(G-1591)

AMERICAN TELECARE INC
15159 Technology Dr (55344-2273)
PHONE..........................952 897-0000
Randall Moore, *CEO*
Mike Chappuis, *President*
Chad Shaw, *Senior VP*
Lawrence L Akin, *Vice Pres*
Alan Haggerty, *Vice Pres*
▼ EMP: 45 EST: 1993
SQ FT: 7,700
SALES (est): 1MM-4.9MM **Privately Held**
WEB: www.americantelecare.com
SIC: **7363** Medical help service

(G-1592)

AMERISOURCEBERGEN CORP
6810 Shady Oak Rd (55344-3417)
PHONE..........................952 903-7600
Cliff Blotsky, *Manager*
EMP: 300
SALES (est): 100MM-499.9MM **Publicly Held**
WEB: www.amerisourcebergen.net

GEOGRAPHIC

SIC: 5122 Wholesales pharmaceuticals, drug proprietaries & sundries
PA: AmerisourceBergen Corp
　　1300 Morris Dr Ste 100
　　Wayne PA 19087
　　610 727-7000

(G-1593)
APEX ANALYTIX INC
Also Called: Bottomline of NC
6520 Edenvale Blvd Ste 110　(55346-2564)
PHONE....................................952 400-2272
James Cosgrove, *Branch Mgr*
EMP: 40
SALES (est): 1MM-4.9MM **Privately Held**
SIC: 8721 Auditing services
PA: Apex Analytix Inc
　　1501 Highwoods Blvd
　　Greensboro NC 27410
　　336 272-4669

(G-1594)
AQUA ENGINEERING INC
6561 City West Pkwy　(55344-3248)
PHONE....................................952 941-1138
FAX: 952 941-1268
Dean A Holasek, *President*
Mary Holasek, *Corp Secy*
Brice Holsek, *Manager*
EMP: 30 **EST:** 1966
SQ FT: 2,000
SALES (est): 1MM-4.9MM **Privately Held**
SIC: 1629 Irrigation system construction

(G-1595)
ARCHITECTURE TECHNOLOGY CORP (PA)
9977 Valley View Rd # 300　(55344-3586)
PO Box 24859, Minneapolis　(55424-0859)
PHONE....................................952 829-5864
Kenneth Thurber, *President*
M A Thurber, *Vice Pres*
Jane Anderson, *Office Mgr*
EMP: 35 **EST:** 1981
SQ FT: 12,000
SALES (corp-wide): 8M **Privately Held**
WEB: www.atcorp.com
SIC: 7371 7372 7373 8711 Computer programming service; computer integrated systems design services; engineering services; software publisher

(G-1596)
ARIZANT HEALTHCARE INC
10393 W 70th St　(55344-3446)
PHONE....................................952 947-1200
Gary R Maharaj, *President*
Hamid Ziaimehr, *Principal*
Robert G Buehler, *Vice Pres*
Terl L Woodwick Sides, *Vice Pres*
Robert J McCall, *Vice Pres*
▲ **EMP:** 181 **EST:** 2003
SALES (est): 50MM-99.9MM **Privately Held**
SIC: 5047 Wholesales medical & hospital equipment; manufactures surgical appliances & supplies
PA: Arizant Holdings Inc
　　10393 W 70th St
　　Eden Prairie MN 55344
　　952 947-1200

(G-1597)
ARROW ELECTRONICS INC
7629 Anagram Dr　(55344-7310)
PHONE....................................952 949-0053
Davie Johnson, *General Mgr*
Mike Aaron, *Branch Mgr*
John Lietzke, *Manager*
David Ecker, *Manager*
EMP: 30
SALES (est): 10MM-24.9MM **Publicly Held**
WEB: www.arrow.com
SIC: 5065 Wholesales electronic parts
PA: Arrow Electronics Inc
　　50 Marcus Dr
　　Melville NY 11747
　　631 847-2000

(G-1598)
ARTESYN NORTH AMERICA INC
7575 Market Place Dr　(55344-3637)
PHONE....................................952 941-1100
Joseph M O'Donnell, *President*
T G Westman, *Corp Secy*
Pat Bincelli, *Vice Pres*

Kevin Ericson, *Vice Pres*
Don Kline, *Vice Pres*
▲ **EMP:** 102 **EST:** 1983
SQ FT: 28,000
SALES (est): 10MM-24.9MM **Publicly Held**
WEB: www.artesyn.com
SIC: 7629 Manufactures all types of static power supplies; electronic equipment repair service
HQ: Artesyn Technologies Inc
　　5810 Van Allen Way
　　Carlsbad CA 92008
　　760 930-4600

(G-1599)
AUGUSTINE MEDICAL INC
10393 W 70th St　(55344-3446)
PHONE....................................952 947-1288
FAX: 952 947-1400
John E Thomas, *President*
M P Luman, *Corp Secy*
Douglas Hall, *Vice Pres*
Manfred Koch, *Vice Pres*
Marie B Humbert, *Treasurer*
EMP: 100 **EST:** 1987
SQ FT: 70,000
SALES (est): 50MM-99.9MM **Privately Held**
SIC: 5047 Wholesales medical & hospital equipment
PA: Arizant Holdings Inc
　　10393 W 70th St
　　Eden Prairie MN 55344
　　952 947-1200

(G-1600)
AVIATION CHARTER INC
9960 Flying Cloud Dr　(55347-4011)
PHONE....................................952 943-1519
Shirley Wikner, *President*
Roger Wikner, *Corp Secy*
Kirk Otteson, *Sales Mgr*
EMP: 100 **EST:** 1988
SQ FT: 65,000
SALES (est): 10MM-24.9MM **Privately Held**
WEB: www.executive-aviation.com
SIC: 4522 4581 5172 Charter flying services; aircraft servicing & repairing; aircraft fueling services

(G-1601)
BAKEMARK USA LLC
14675 Martin Dr　(55344-2007)
PHONE....................................952 937-9495
FAX: 952 937-9153
Kim Marant, *General Mgr*
Mary L Bounty, *Purch Agent*
EMP: 50
SALES (est): 25MM-49.9MM **Privately Held**
WEB: www.bakemark.com
SIC: 5149 5046 Wholesales bakery products; wholesales bakery equipment & supplies
PA: Bakemark USA LLC
　　7351 Crider Ave
　　Pico Rivera CA 90660
　　562 949-1054

(G-1602)
BARRETT MOVING & STORAGE CO
7100 Washington Ave S　(55344-3512)
PHONE....................................952 944-6550
Mike Collins, *General Mgr*
George Follensbee, *General Mgr*
Kris Siemens, *Opers Staff*
Michael Oliveria, *CFO*
Annette Anger, *Controller*
EMP: 99
SALES (est): 10MM-24.9MM **Privately Held**
WEB: www.barrettmoving.com
SIC: 4213 Long-distance moving services

(G-1603)
BEARPATH GOLF & COUNTRY CLUB
18100 Bearpath Trl　(55347-3452)
PHONE....................................952 975-0123
FAX: 952 975-9710
John Downey, *President*
Judy Jorden, *Manager*
EMP: 100 **EST:** 1994
SQ FT: 42,000
SALES (est): 5MM-9.9MM **Privately Held**
SIC: 7997 Country club; membership golf club

(G-1604)
BERRY COFFEE CO
14825 Martin Dr　(55344-2011)
PHONE....................................952 937-8697
FAX: 952 937-1425
Steve Brehm, *President*
Robert Dilly, *Vice Pres*
Olsen Thielen, *Accountant*
Janet Houdeshell, *Manager*
EMP: 32 **EST:** 1979
SQ FT: 12,000
SALES (est): 10MM-24.9MM **Privately Held**
WEB: www.berrycoffee.com
SIC: 5149 5113 5199 Wholesales green or roasted coffee; manufactures coffee brewing equipment; wholesales disposable plates, cups, napkins & eating utensils; wholesales beverages; wholesales paper novelties

(G-1605)
BHI ADVANCED INTERNET INC
7599 Corporate Way　(55344-2022)
PHONE....................................952 361-5557
Dave Perrill, *President*
John Perrill, *Vice Pres*
David Price, *Manager*
EMP: 50 **EST:** 1982 **Privately Held**
WEB: www.bhi.com
SIC: 4813 Wired telecommunications carrier & service

(G-1606)
BIOSCRIP PHARMACY INC
10050 Crosstown Cir　(55344-3348)
PHONE....................................952 979-3600
Richard Freedman, *President*
Kenneth S Guenthner, *Corp Secy*
Tom Ordeman, *COO*
Alfred Carfora, *COO*
Anthony J Zappa, *Vice Pres*
EMP: 150 **EST:** 1992
SALES (est): 10MM-24.9MM **Publicly Held**
WEB: www.bioscrip.com
SIC: 8741 Management services
HQ: Chronimed Inc
　　10050 Crosstown Cir
　　Eden Prairie MN 55344
　　952 979-3600

(G-1607)
BIRCHWOOD LAB ASSOCIATES LLP
7900 Fuller Rd　(55344-2138)
PHONE....................................952 937-7900
Dan Brooks, *Principal*
EMP: 80 **EST:** 1995
SALES (est): 10MM-24.9MM **Privately Held**
SIC: 6512 Nonresidential building operator

(G-1608)
BIRCHWOOD LABORATORIES INC
7900 Fuller Rd　(55344-2138)
PHONE....................................952 937-7900
FAX: 952 937-7979
Dan Brooks, *President*
Mike Shelton, *President*
Richard Flint, *Corp Secy*
Mark Ruhland, *Vice Pres*
William Shannon, *Vice Pres*
▼ **EMP:** 80 **EST:** 1979
SQ FT: 57,000
SALES (est): 25MM-49.9MM **Privately Held**
WEB: www.birchwoodcasey.com
SIC: 7389 Manufactures gun slushing compounds; manufactures metal treating compounds; manufactures surgical dressings; manufactures surgical appliances & supplies; packaging & labeling services

(G-1609)
BOTTOM LINE ENHANCEMENT SVCS
6520 Edenvale Blvd # 110　(55346-2564)
PHONE....................................952 974-9920
Kent C Buttelmann, *CEO*
James Cosgrove, *President*
Marty Brakel, *Opers Mgr*
Kim Superfin, *Controller*
Leigh Alexander, *Finance Dir*
EMP: 150

EST: 1977
SQ FT: 15,000
SALES (est): 10MM-24.9MM **Privately Held**
SIC: 8721 Auditing services

(G-1610)
BOULAY HEUTMAKER ZIBELL & CO
7500 Flying Cloud Dr　(55344-3748)
PHONE....................................952 893-9320
Nick Basil, *Member*
Bernie Beaver, *Member*
David Bremer, *Member*
James Daleiden, *Member*
Mark Denucci, *Member*
EMP: 120 **EST:** 1934
SQ FT: 24,000
SALES (est): 10MM-24.9MM **Privately Held**
WEB: www.bhz.com
SIC: 8721 Certified public accountant services

(G-1611)
BRAAS CO
7970 Wallace Rd　(55344-2232)
PHONE....................................952 937-8902
FAX: 952 937-8944
Bradley G Morris, *Exec VP*
Tim Bloudek, *Facilities Mgr*
Raymond C Robbel III, *CFO*
Janis Negratti-Samuel, *Human Res Dir*
Jim Hennen, *VP Sales*
EMP: 77 **EST:** 1961
SQ FT: 30,000
SALES (est): 25MM-49.9MM **Privately Held**
WEB: www.braasco.com
SIC: 5084 Wholesales industrial machinery & equipment

(G-1612)
BRUNSWICK BOWLING & BILLIARDS
12200 Singletree Ln　(55344-7902)
PHONE....................................952 941-0445
Mike Walters, *General Mgr*
Mark Larsen, *General Mgr*
Bill Weber, *Pastor*
Christopher Vantine, *Maint Spvr*
Arnold D Fogel, *Manager*
EMP: 35
SALES (est): 1MM-4.9MM **Publicly Held**
WEB: www.bowlbrunswick.com
SIC: 7933 Bowling center
HQ: Brunswick Bowling & Billiards
　　1 N Field Ct
　　Lake Forest IL 60045
　　847 735-4700

(G-1613)
BUREAU OF COLLECTION RECOVERY (HQ)
7575 Corporate Way　(55344-2022)
PHONE....................................952 934-7777
FAX: 952 931-0949
Marty Sarim, *CEO*
Mark Neill, *President*
Ron Roonzani, *Vice Pres*
Leanne Kopischke, *Vice Pres*
Shauna Gerber, *Vice Pres*
EMP: 25 **EST:** 1985 **Privately Held**
WEB: www.nvars.com
SIC: 7322 Collection agency
PA: Minacs Group USA Inc
　　34115 W 12 Mile Rd
　　Farmington Hills MI 48331
　　248 553-8355

(G-1614)
BUSINESS FUNDING GROUP LLC ⊕
6400 Flying Cloud Dr　(55344-3329)
PHONE....................................952 697-0202
Greg Lasica, *Member*
EMP: 25 **EST:** 2008
SQ FT: 5,000
SALES (est): 5MM-9.9MM **Privately Held**
SIC: 6153 Short-term business credit for working capital financing

(G-1615)
C H ROBINSON WORLDWIDE INC (PA)
14701 Charlson Rd (55347-5076)
PHONE 952 937-8500
FAX: 952 937-6714
John P Wiehoff, *CEO*
Marie Stolte, *Editor*
Ben G Campbell, *Corp Secy*
James E Butts, *Senior VP*
Scott A Satterlee, *Senior VP*
◆ EMP: 591 EST: 1905
SQ FT: 105,000
SALES (corp-wide): 7.57B Publicly Held
WEB: www.chrobinson.com
SIC: 4731 Freight forwarding services

(G-1616)
CAC RETAIL INC ✪
6436 City West Pkwy (55344-3245)
PHONE 952 944-5600
Susan Engel, *President*
Timothy Schugel, *Treasurer*
EMP: 80 EST: 2009
SQ FT: 67,000
SALES (est): 50MM-99.9MM Privately Held
SIC: 5199 Wholesales gifts & novelties

(G-1617)
CEILING PRO INTERIOR INC
7456 Washington Ave S Ste A
(55344-4542)
PHONE 952 947-0007
FAX: 952 947-0004
Ken Norman, *CEO*
Brad Matushak, *President*
Angie Pickett, *Exec Sec*
EMP: 25 EST: 1989
SQ FT: 8,000
SALES (est): 1MM-4.9MM Privately Held
WEB: www.cpihq.com
SIC: 1742 1799 5087 7349 Acoustical & ceiling work contractor; asbestos removal & encapsulation contractor; wholesales cleaning & maintenance equipment & supplies; acoustical tile cleaning service

(G-1618)
CELLERATION INC
10250 Valley View Rd # 137 (55344-3577)
PHONE 952 224-8700
Mark Wagner, *President*
Chris Ernster, *Vice Pres*
Joe Bell, *Vice Pres*
Christopher R Geyen, *Vice Pres*
Michael Peterson, *Vice Pres*
EMP: 49 EST: 2000
SQ FT: 3,300
SALES (est): 1MM-4.9MM Privately Held
WEB: www.celleration.com
SIC: 8733 Medical research organization

(G-1619)
CENTRAIRE HEATING & AIR CONDG
7402 Washington Ave S (55344-3704)
PHONE 952 941-1044
FAX: 952 941-1967
Leroy Seurer, *President*
Paul Koepcke, *Vice Pres*
Carol Evanson, *Manager*
Bonnie Andrusick, *Executive*
EMP: 40 EST: 1967
SQ FT: 5,000
SALES (est): 1MM-4.9MM Privately Held
SIC: 1711 Warm air heating & air conditioning contractor; manufactures refrigeration & heating equipment; manufactures heating equipment & supplies

(G-1620)
CENTRAL PORTFOLIO CONTROL INC
6640 Shady Oak Rd Ste 300 (55344-7710)
PHONE 952 944-5440
Robert P Reiter, *CEO*
Mark A Hedge, *Manager*
EMP: 46 EST: 1998
SALES (est): 1MM-4.9MM Privately Held
SIC: 7322 Collection agency

(G-1621)
CH ROBINSON INTERNATIONAL INC (HQ)
8100 Mitchell Rd Ste 200 (55344-2178)
PHONE 952 937-8500
Joseph Mulvehill, *President*
Clark Hange, *Chairman*
Mark Bowers, *Corp Secy*
Chris Gerst, *Counsel*
Gregory Coven, *Senior VP*
EMP: 50 EST: 1989
SQ FT: 60,000
SALES (corp-wide): 7.57B Publicly Held
WEB: www.chrobinson.com
SIC: 4731 Foreign freight forwarding services
PA: C H Robinson Worldwide Inc
14701 Charlson Rd
Eden Prairie MN 55347
952 937-8500

(G-1622)
CH ROBINSON INTERNATIONAL INC
14800 Charlson Rd Ste 400 (55347-5048)
PHONE 952 937-2914
Brian Johnson, *Branch Mgr*
Jennifer Graves, *Manager*
EMP: 70
SALES (est): 5MM-9.9MM Publicly Held
WEB: www.chrobinson.com
SIC: 4731 Freight forwarding services
HQ: CH Robinson International Inc
8100 Mitchell Rd Ste 200
Eden Prairie MN 55344
952 937-8500

(G-1623)
CHERNE CO INC (PA)
9855 W 78th St Ste 400 (55344-8019)
PO Box 975, Minneapolis (55440-0975)
PHONE 952 944-4300
FAX: 952 944-4399
A W Cherne Jr, *President*
David Johnson, *Vice Pres*
Dominque Najjar, *CFO*
Steve Cherne, *Info Tech Mgr*
EMP: 100 EST: 1997
SQ FT: 20,000
SALES (corp-wide): 200.82M Privately Held
SIC: 1629 Waste disposal plant construction; chemical facility construction; power plant construction

(G-1624)
CHRESTOMATHY INC
7465 Eden Prairie Rd (55346-4312)
PHONE 952 974-0339
FAX: 952 906-3844
Linda Moore, *President*
Robyn Noyed, *Vice Pres*
EMP: 80 EST: 1985
SALES (est): 1MM-4.9MM Privately Held
SIC: 8351 8093 Child development center providing Montessori based instruction; outpatient rehabilitation treatment center

(G-1625)
CHRONIMED INC (HQ)
10050 Crosstown Cir (55344-3348)
PHONE 952 979-3600
FAX: 952 979-3969
Henry F Blissenbach, *CEO*
Kenneth S Guenthner, *Corp Secy*
Barry A Posner, *Corp Secy*
Alfred Carfora, *COO*
Colleen Haberman, *Vice Pres*
EMP: 423 EST: 1985
SQ FT: 62,000
SALES (corp-wide): 1.32B Publicly Held
SIC: 8099 Pharmacy & drug store; medical services organization
PA: Bioscrip Inc
100 Clearbrook Rd
Elmsford NY 10523
914 460-1600

(G-1626)
CIGNA BEHAVIORAL HEALTH INC
11095 Viking Dr Ste 350 (55344-7234)
PHONE 952 996-2000
Keith Dixon, *President*

Jodi Aronson, *COO*
Ann McClanathan, *Exec VP*
Rhonda R Beale, *Senior VP*
Zachary Meyer, *Senior VP*
EMP: 400 EST: 1974
SQ FT: 97,000
SALES (est): 100MM-499.9MM Publicly Held
WEB: www.cigna.com
SIC: 6324 Hospital & medical insurance carrier
DH: Connecticut General Corp
900 Cottage Grove Rd
Bloomfield CT 06002
860 226-6000

(G-1627)
CIMA LABS INC (HQ)
10000 Valley View Rd (55344-3510)
PHONE 952 947-8700
FAX: 952 947-8770
Frank Baldino Jr, *CEO*
Peter Barfoot, *Managing Dir*
Amy Oberg, *Corp Secy*
Peter Grebow, *Exec VP*
Sarma P Duddu, *Vice Pres*
EMP: 60 EST: 1986
SQ FT: 75,000
SALES (corp-wide): 2.19B Publicly Held
WEB: www.cimalabs.com
SIC: 8734 Testing laboratory; manufactures pharmaceutical preparations
PA: Cephalon Inc
41 Moores Rd
Malvern PA 19355
610 344-0200

(G-1628)
CITIREACH INTERNATIONAL
Also Called: Goodcities
7340 Hunters Run (55346-4221)
PHONE 952 975-0516
Glenn A Barth Jr, *President*
EMP: 35 Privately Held
SIC: 8399 Social services

(G-1629)
CITY OF EDEN PRAIRIE
Also Called: Eden Prairie Community Center
16700 Valley View Rd (55346-4243)
PHONE 952 949-8470
FAX: 952 949-8492
Mark Lindner, *Vice Pres*
Mike Dent, *Vice Pres*
Nick Rogge, *Treasurer*
Paul Thaden, *Treasurer*
Ed Lippert, *Finance*
EMP: 75
SALES (est): 1MM-4.9MM Privately Held
SIC: 8322 Community center
PA: City of Eden Prairie
8080 Mitchell Rd Ste 2
Eden Prairie MN 55344
952 949-8300

(G-1630)
COLDWELL BANKER BURNET INC
7820 Terrey Pine Ct (55347-1126)
PHONE 952 920-1224
FAX: 952 934-5400
Roland Smaagaard, *Vice Pres*
Anatoliy Katane, *Info Tech Mgr*
EMP: 100
SALES (est): 10MM-24.9MM Privately Held
WEB: www.ginnyandtim.com
SIC: 6531 8111 8742 Real estate services; real estate consultant; legal services
PA: Coldwell Banker Burnet Inc
190 Cobblestone Ln
Burnsville MN 55337
952 898-5100

(G-1631)
COLLOPY & SAUNDERS REAL ESTATE
Also Called: Re Max
11200 W 78th St (55344-3814)
PHONE 952 829-2900
John Collopy, *President*
Marshall Saunders, *Principal*
EST: 1986
SQ FT: 19,500 Privately Held
SIC: 6531 6541 Real estate agency & broker; title & trust company

(G-1632)
COMBINED INSURANCE CO OF AMER
11095 Viking Dr Ste 125 (55344-7204)
PHONE 952 933-2133
Scott Lilya, *Manager*
EMP: 53
SALES (est): 5MM-9.9MM Publicly Held
SIC: 6411 Insurance agent
HQ: Combined Insurance Co of Amer
200 E Randolph St Lbby 10
Chicago IL 60601
800 225-4500

(G-1633)
COMMONSENSE MORTGAGE INC
8110 Eden Rd (55344-5000)
PHONE 952 942-8502
FAX: 952 842-8388
Sophan Pheng, *Manager*
John Daiena, *Manager*
Onesimus Werd, *Manager*
EMP: 25
SALES (est): 1MM-4.9MM Privately Held
SIC: 6163 Mortgage brokers service arranging for loans, using money of others

(G-1634)
CONNEXIONS LOYALTY TRAVEL SOLN ✪
6442 City West Pkwy (55344-3245)
PHONE 952 914-6533
Eric Burdon, *President*
Michael Barr, *Principal*
John D Hara, *Corp Secy*
William Lynchh, *Treasurer*
Matt Robinson, *Controller*
EMP: 70 EST: 2008
SALES (est): 5MM-9.9MM Privately Held
SIC: 8748 Business consulting services
PA: Travel Leaders Group LLC
6442 City West Pkwy
Eden Prairie MN 55344
952 914-6500

(G-1635)
CONSAN INC
7699 Anagram Dr (55344-7310)
PHONE 952 949-0053
FAX: 952 949-0453
Mike Arends, *Vice Pres*
Gregory J Larson, *Manager*
EMP: 58 EST: 1988
SQ FT: 42,000
SALES (est): 25MM-49.9MM Publicly Held
WEB: www.arrow.com
SIC: 5045 Wholesales computer peripheral equipment
PA: Arrow Electronics Inc
50 Marcus Dr
Melville NY 11747
631 847-2000

(G-1636)
COURTYARD BY MARRIOTT
11391 Viking Dr (55344-7239)
PHONE 952 942-9100
FAX: 952 942-8030
Teri Butler, *General Mgr*
EMP: 80 EST: 2007
SALES (est): 1MM-4.9MM Publicly Held
WEB: www.marriott.com
SIC: 7011 Traveler accommodations
HQ: Courtyard By Marriott II L P
6903 Rockledge Dr Ste 1500
Bethesda MD 20817
240 744-1000

(G-1637)
CREATIVE TRAINING TECHNIQUES
14530 Martin Dr (55344-2015)
PHONE 952 829-1954
FAX: 952 829-0260
Robert W Pike, *CEO*
Mark Smith, *COO*
Becky Pluth, *Vice Pres*
Michelle Delarosby, *Mktg Dir*
Pat Shauer, *Manager*
EMP: 25 EST: 1990
SQ FT: 12,000
SALES (est): 1MM-4.9MM Privately Held

GEOGRAPHIC

SIC: **8742** Training & development consultant

(G-1638)
CSM CORP OF MINNESOTA
Also Called: Residence Inn By Marriott
7780 Flying Cloud Dr (55344-3713)
PHONE...............................952 829-0033
Kennedy Shannon, *Sales Executive*
Ronell Raney, *Manager*
EMP: 30
SALES (est): 1MM-4.9MM **Privately Held**
WEB: www.csmcorp.net
SIC: **7011** Traveler accommodations

(G-1639)
CUSHMAN & WAKEFIELD INC
11095 Viking Dr Ste 240 (55344-0025)
PHONE...............................763 450-3600
Scott Kummel, *Broker*
Jeff Minea, *Broker*
EMP: 35
SALES (est): 5MM-9.9MM **Privately Held**
WEB: www.cushwake.com
SIC: **6531** Real estate services
HQ: Cushman & Wakefield Inc
     1290 Avenue Of The Americas
     New York NY 10104
     212 841-7500

(G-1640)
DAKT ENTERPRISES INC
Also Called: Local Motion
7472 Washington Ave S (55344-3704)
PHONE...............................952 474-6683
FAX: 952 941-1255
David Seeley, *President*
John Thorpe, *Vice Pres*
EMP: 120 EST: 1992
SQ FT: 15,000
SALES (est): 10MM-24.9MM **Privately Held**
WEB: www.localmotion.com
SIC: **4214** Local trucking with storage; local furniture moving & storage; local moving service & storage

(G-1641)
DANCE ART CENTRE
7605 Corporate Way (55344-2021)
PHONE...............................952 937-2618
FAX: 952 937-0062
Jill Finn, *Owner*
EMP: 25 EST: 1980
SALES (est): 500-999K **Privately Held**
SIC: **7911** Dance studio, school & hall; retails dancewear

(G-1642)
DATA SYSTEMS INC
Also Called: Retail Data Systems of NM
6566 Edenvale Blvd (55346-2502)
PHONE...............................952 934-4001
FAX: 952 934-4830
George Brady, *CEO*
Dale Schutt, *Opers Mgr*
Sharon Hauser, *Bookkeeper*
Paul Andersen, *Service Mgr*
Andy McDonald, *Manager*
EMP: 45
SALES (est): 10MM-24.9MM **Privately Held**
SIC: **5044** 5046 Wholesales cash registers; wholesales commercial scales
PA: Data Systems Inc
     6515 S 118th St Ste 100
     Omaha NE 68137
     402 553-6220

(G-1643)
DAVISCO FOODS INTERNATIONAL
11000 W 78th St Ste 210 (55344-8012)
PHONE...............................952 914-0400
FAX: 952 914-0887
Anna Bredl, *General Mgr*
John Velgersdyk, *Vice Pres*
Kim Almstedt, *Manager*
Polly Olson, *Manager*
Kim Graumann, *Manager*
EMP: 30
SALES (est): 10MM-24.9MM **Privately Held**

SIC: **5143** Manufactures natural cheese; wholesales fresh dairy products
PA: Davisco Foods International
     704 N Main St
     Le Sueur MN 56058
     507 665-8811

(G-1644)
DEVICIX LLC
7680 Executive Dr (55344-3677)
PHONE...............................952 368-0073
Peter D Lange, *Member*
Darla Delange, *Exec Dir*
EMP: 30 EST: 2004
SALES (est): 1MM-4.9MM **Privately Held**
WEB: www.devicix.com
SIC: **7389** Design services

(G-1645)
DIGITAL RIVER INC (PA)
9625 W 76th St Ste 150 (55344-3775)
PHONE...............................952 253-1234
FAX: 952 253-8497
Joel A Ronning, *CEO*
Mike Ciccolella, *General Mgr*
Kevin L Crudden, *Corp Secy*
Peterson Don, *Senior VP*
Steve West, *Vice Pres*
EMP: 269 EST: 1994
SQ FT: 162,500
SALES (corp-wide): 403.76M **Publicly Held**
SIC: **7373** 7372 7379 Computer integrated systems design services; computer system consulting services; software publisher

(G-1646)
DL-DW HOLDINGS LLC
11905 Technology Dr (55344-3622)
PHONE...............................952 942-6818
Dee Mewer, *Manager*
Amber Moske, *Manager*
EMP: 40
SALES (est): 1MM-4.9MM **Privately Held**
SIC: **7011** Franchised hotel
PA: Esh Hv Properties LLC
     100 Dunbar St
     Spartanburg SC 29306
     864 573-1600

(G-1647)
E A SWEEN DELI EXPRESS (PA)
Also Called: Deli Express
16101 W 78th St (55344-5709)
PHONE...............................952 937-9440
FAX: 952 937-5883
Thomas E Sween, *CEO*
Robert Linner, *President*
William Lewis, *Vice Pres*
Randy Clark, *VP Opers*
Monica Green, *VP Opers*
▲ EMP: 200 EST: 1956
SQ FT: 16,000
SALES (corp-wide): 132M **Privately Held**
WEB: www.easween.com
SIC: **5142** Manufactures sandwiches; wholesales packaged frozen foods

(G-1648)
EATON CORP
14900 Technology Dr (55344-2208)
PHONE...............................952 937-9800
Craig Arnold, *Senior VP*
Ulf Henrikson, *Vice Pres*
Dan Kimmet, *Vice Pres*
James Mason, *Vice Pres*
Billie Rawot, *Vice Pres*
EMP: 500
SALES (est): 100MM-499.9MM **Publicly Held**
WEB: www.eaton.com
SIC: **5084** Manufactures motor vehicle auto steering mechanism hydraulic fluid power pumps; wholesales industrial hydraulic systems equipment & supplies
PA: Eaton Corp
     1111 Superior Ave E Fl 19
     Cleveland OH 44114
     216 523-5000

(G-1649)
EDEN FCH PRAIRIE LLC
6330 Point Chase (55344-7726)
PHONE...............................952 952-9000
Nina Sand, *Principal*
EMP: 40

SALES (est): 1MM-4.9MM **Privately Held**
SIC: **7011** Traveler accommodations

(G-1650)
EDEN PRAIRIE HHP-II LLC
7740 Flying Cloud Dr (55344-3713)
PHONE...............................952 942-9000
Rebecca Reilly, *Member*
EMP: 28 EST: 2007
SALES (est): 1MM-4.9MM **Privately Held**
SIC: **7011** Hotel

(G-1651)
EDINA REALTY HOME SERVICES
11800 Singletree Ln # 401 (55344-7900)
PHONE...............................952 944-7107
FAX: 952 828-9531
Brian Duoos, *Manager*
Leah Woolsey, *Office Admin*
Julie Streator, *Supervisor*
EMP: 70
SALES (est): 10MM-24.9MM **Publicly Held**
WEB: www.ilovetennis.net
SIC: **6531** Real estate agency & broker
HQ: Edina Realty Home Services
     6800 France Ave S Ste 600
     Minneapolis MN 55435
     952 928-5900

(G-1652)
ELIM CARE FOUNDATION
7485 Office Ridge Cir (55344-3690)
PHONE...............................952 259-4500
Robert Dahl, *President*
EMP: 28 EST: 1986
SQ FT: 4,000
SALES (est): 10MM-24.9MM **Privately Held**
SIC: **6799** Investor services

(G-1653)
ELIM CARE INC (PA)
7485 Office Ridge Cir (55344-3690)
PHONE...............................952 259-4500
Robert Dahl, *CEO*
Pat Nuss, *Corp Secy*
Ronald Sanford, *COO*
Kathy Youngquist, *CFO*
Chloe Luebbers, *Manager*
EMP: 30 EST: 1927
SQ FT: 10,000
SALES (corp-wide): 103.72M **Privately Held**
SIC: **8051** Skilled nursing care facility

(G-1654)
ELLIOTT AVIATION INC
13801 Pioneer Trl Ste B (55347-2604)
PHONE...............................952 944-1200
FAX: 952 944-8614
Christa Restad, *General Mgr*
Teresa Jacobson, *Facilities Mgr*
Clyde Hazelton, *Purch Mgr*
Linda Banks, *Accounting Mgr*
Robin Abraham, *Human Res Dir*
EMP: 70
SALES (est): 10MM-24.9MM **Privately Held**
WEB: www.elliottaviation.com
SIC: **4581** 7359 Retails self-propelled aircrafts; aircraft servicing & repairing; aircraft rental service
PA: Elliott Aviation Inc
     6601 74th Ave
     Milan IL 61264
     309 799-3183

(G-1655)
ELVIN SAFETY LLC
Also Called: Fisco
7300 Washington Ave S (55344-3514)
PHONE...............................952 829-2950
FAX: 952 829-2992
Robert Cass, *CEO*
Paul Elvin, *Vice Pres*
Jeff Bourbonais, *Opers Mgr*
Pat Brennan, *CFO*
Linda Wasilewski, *Controller*
EMP: 32 EST: 2006
SALES (est): 10MM-24.9MM **Privately Held**
WEB: www.elvin.com

SIC: **5099** Wholesales safety equipment & supplies
HQ: Conney Safety Products LLC
     3202 Latham Dr
     Madison WI 53713
     608 271-3300

(G-1656)
EMC CORP
10400 Viking Dr Ste 400 (55344-7263)
PHONE...............................952 828-9005
FAX: 952 828-9509
Craig Pratt, *Branch Mgr*
Jim Reding, *Manager*
Michael Gallo, *Manager*
John Miller, *Manager*
Doug Haralson, *Consultant*
EMP: 120
SALES (est): 25MM-49.9MM **Publicly Held**
WEB: www.emc.com
SIC: **7372** Manufactures computer storage devices; software publisher
PA: EMC Corp
     176 South St
     Hopkinton MA 01748
     508 435-1000

(G-1657)
ENHANCED HOME SYSTEMS INC
9940 Hamilton Rd Ste B (55344-4524)
PHONE...............................952 941-5289
FAX: 952 941-5436
David L Wogsland, *President*
Greg Nelson, *Principal*
Lorretta Hasan, *Accountant*
EMP: 30 EST: 1988
SALES (est): 1MM-4.9MM **Privately Held**
WEB: www.esitheater.com
SIC: **1731** Sound equipment installation service; retails high fidelity stereo equipment

(G-1658)
ESPECIALLY FOR CHILDREN INC
6223 Dell Rd (55346-1122)
PHONE...............................952 934-1119
Lynn Seltz, *Branch Mgr*
EMP: 30
SALES (est): 500-999K **Privately Held**
SIC: **8351** Group day care center
PA: Especially For Children Inc
     5223 W 73rd St
     Minneapolis MN 55439
     952 835-6055

(G-1659)
EXPERT SOFTWARE INC
7800 Equitable Dr Ste 200 (55344-7350)
PHONE...............................952 918-9400
Ronald Doornink, *CEO*
Kurt Niederloh, *Controller*
EMP: 31 EST: 1992
SALES (est): 5MM-9.9MM **Privately Held**
WEB: www.activisionvalue.com
SIC: **7372** Publisher's software publishing
PA: Activision Blizzard Inc
     3100 Ocean Park Blvd
     Santa Monica CA 90405
     310 255-2000

(G-1660)
FACET TECHNOLOGY CORP
6517 City West Pkwy (55344-3248)
PHONE...............................952 944-1839
James Retterath, *President*
Robert Laumayer, *Chairman*
Daniel Sullivan, *Exec Dir*
EMP: 40 EST: 1998
SQ FT: 6,500
SALES (est): 5MM-9.9MM **Privately Held**
WEB: www.facet-tech.com
SIC: **7379** 5045 Computer system consulting services; wholesales computer software

(G-1661)
FAFINSKI MARK & JOHNSON
775 Paririe Ctr Dr # 400 (55344-7322)
PHONE...............................952 995-9500
FAX: 952 995-9577
Robert Fafinski, *CEO*
Sean D'Albertis, *Manager*

Kevin Johnson, *Info Tech Mgr*
Donald C Mark, *Shareholder*
EMP: 38 **EST:** 1999
SALES (est): 5MM-9.9MM **Privately Held**
SIC: 8111 General practice attorney's or lawyer's office

(G-1662)
FAIRVIEW HEALTH SERVICES
Also Called: Edencenter Family Physicians
830 Prairie Center Dr (55344-7301)
PHONE 952 826-6500
FAX: 952 826-6584
Julie Grams, *Project Mgr*
Julie Graham, *Office Mgr*
Gina Morgan, *Manager*
Kaye Baum, *Nurse Practr*
EMP: 45
SALES (est): 5MM-9.9MM **Privately Held**
WEB: www.fairview.org
SIC: 8011 Clinic operated by physicians
PA: Fairview Health Services
2450 Riverside Ave
Minneapolis MN 55454
612 672-6300

(G-1663)
FARGO ELECTRONICS INC
6533 Flying Cloud Dr # 1000 (55344-3311)
PHONE 952 941-9470
FAX: 952 941-7836
Denis Herbert, *President*
Thomas C Platner, *Vice Pres*
Robert Cummins, *VP Sls/Mktg*
Leslie Richman, *Human Res Mgr*
Jane Smith, *Human Res Mgr*
▲ **EMP:** 203 **EST:** 1999
SQ FT: 90,000
SALES (est): 25MM-49.9MM **Privately Held**
WEB: www.assaabloy.com
SIC: 7371 Manufactures printing machinery; applications software programming
HQ: Hid Global Corp
15370 Barranca Pkwy
Irvine CA 92618
800 237-7769

(G-1664)
FEDEX OFFICE & PRINT SERVICES
7900 Eden Rd (55344-5302)
PHONE 952 943-4000
Dano Gallagher, *Plant Mgr*
Jason Radford, *Sales Executive*
Curt Damon, *Manager*
EMP: 40
SALES (est): 1MM-4.9MM **Publicly Held**
WEB: www.kinkos.com
SIC: 7334 Photocopying & duplicating services; commercial lithographic printing
HQ: Fedex Office & Print Services
13155 Noel Rd Ste 1600
Dallas TX 75240
214 550-7000

(G-1665)
FLAGSHIP ATHLETIC CLUB INC
755 Prairie Center Dr (55344-5363)
PHONE 952 941-2000
FAX: 952 829-2603
Thomas Lyneis, *President*
Jeremy Benson, *Vice Pres*
Jennifer Anderson, *Exec Dir*
EMP: 300 **EST:** 1985
SQ FT: 180,000
SALES (est): 5MM-9.9MM **Privately Held**
SIC: 7997 7231 7991 Membership recreation club; bar; full service American restaurant; membership tennis club; physical fitness center; beauty salon
HQ: Wellbridge Club Management LLC
8400 E Crescent Pkwy # 200
Englewood CO 80111
303 866-0800

(G-1666)
FOCALPOINT INC
10050 Crosstown Cir # 200 (55344-3343)
PHONE 952 944-0932
Thomas A Doering, *CEO*
Kelly L Doering, *President*
Cindy Scheer, *Vice Pres*
EMP: 65 **EST:** 1997 **Privately Held**
WEB: www.etravelexperts.com
SIC: 4813 Wired telecommunications carrier & service

(G-1667)
FOSS NORTH AMERICA INC
8091 Wallace Rd (55344-2224)
PHONE 952 974-9892
Christian Svensgaard, *President*
Paul Slupecki, *Managing Dir*
Torben Ladegaard, *COO*
Tue Botkjaer, *Vice Pres*
Poul Bundgaard, *Vice Pres*
▲ **EMP:** 35 **EST:** 1985
SALES (est): 10MM-24.9MM **Privately Held**
WEB: www.foss-as.com
SIC: 5049 Wholesales analytical instruments
PA: Foss A S
Slangerupgade 69
HILLEROD Denmark

(G-1668)
FOUR51 INC
7905 Golden Triangle Dr (55344-7220)
PHONE 952 294-0451
Mark D Johnson, *CEO*
Gary Nemcek, *President*
Rich Landa, *President*
Robert Morin, *Exec VP*
John Wangaard, *Vice Pres*
EMP: 45 **EST:** 1999
SQ FT: 10,000
SALES (est): 10MM-24.9MM **Privately Held**
WEB: www.four51.com
SIC: 4813 Online services providers

(G-1669)
FOX TELEVISION STATIONS INC
Also Called: K M S P Fox 9
11358 Viking Dr (55344-7238)
PHONE 952 946-1234
Debbie Sinay, *Vice Pres*
John Feeser, *Vice Pres*
Jeff Grayson, *Finance Mgr*
Carol Rueppel, *Manager*
Andrew Zimmern, *Assoc Editor*
EMP: 125
SALES (est): 25MM-49.9MM **Publicly Held**
WEB: www.foxtv.com
SIC: 4833 Television broadcasting station
DH: Fox Television Stations Inc
1999 S Bundy Dr
Los Angeles CA 90025
310 584-2000

(G-1670)
FRESH START ENTERPRISES INC
Also Called: Richtone Painting
7242 Washington Ave S (55344-3513)
PHONE 952 903-0262
Greg Allen, *President*
Luke Panek, *General Mgr*
EMP: 40 **EST:** 1995
SQ FT: 6,000
SALES (est): 1MM-4.9MM **Privately Held**
WEB: www.richtonepainting.com
SIC: 1721 Exterior commercial painting contractor

(G-1671)
GASSEN CO INC
6438 City West Pkwy (55344-3245)
PHONE 952 922-5575
Catherine Gassen, *President*
Reginald Gassen, *Vice Pres*
Terry Redshaw, *Property Mgr*
Nancy Lewin, *Property Mgr*
Cherise Foslien, *Property Mgr*
EMP: 30 **EST:** 1986
SQ FT: 17,000
SALES (est): 1MM-4.9MM **Privately Held**
WEB: www.gassen.com
SIC: 6531 Condominium managers; commercial real estate agency; cooperative apartment managers

(G-1672)
GELCO INFORMATION NETWORK INC (DH)
10700 Prairie Lakes Dr (55344-3858)
PHONE 952 947-1500
Karen Beckwith, *President*
John Paula, *Managing Dir*
Mark S Coronna, *COO*
Brian Provost, *COO*

Jeffrey Cronin, *Production*
EMP: 250 **EST:** 1894
SQ FT: 40,000
SALES (corp-wide): 247.59M **Publicly Held**
WEB: www.gelco.com
SIC: 7389 Financial service
HQ: H-G Holdings Inc
10700 Prairie Lakes Dr
Eden Prairie MN 55344
952 947-1500

(G-1673)
GENERAL CASUALTY CO OF WI
10400 Viking Dr Ste 300 (55344-7268)
PHONE 952 941-0980
FAX: 952 947-6099
Robert Clarke, *Manager*
EMP: 100
SALES (est): 25MM-49.9MM **Privately Held**
WEB: www.generalcasualty.com
SIC: 6331 6311 Property & casualty insurance carrier; life insurance carrier
DH: General Casualty Co of WI
1 General Dr
Sun Prairie WI 53596
608 837-4440

(G-1674)
GENERAL ELECTRIC FLEET SVCS
Also Called: GE Capital Fleet Services
3 Capital Dr (55344-3890)
PHONE 952 828-1000
FAX: 952 828-1213
J H Ozanne, *Ch of Bd*
M J Donohue, *Vice Ch Bd*
Theresa L Grande, *President*
Rich Green, *Managing Dir*
Rich Chenitz, *Senior VP*
EMP: 500 **EST:** 1967
SQ FT: 1,500
SALES (est): 50MM-99.9MM **Publicly Held**
WEB: www.gecapital.com
SIC: 7514 Rent-a-car service
DH: General Electric Capital Corp
901 Main Ave
Norwalk CT 06851
203 840-6300

(G-1675)
GNAZZO TECHNICAL SERVICES INC
16438 S Manor Rd Ste 4 (55346-2302)
PHONE 952 949-1026
John Gnazzo, *President*
Michelle Gnazzo, *Vice Pres*
EMP: 44 **EST:** 1992
SALES (est): 5MM-9.9MM **Privately Held**
SIC: 7379 Computer system consulting services

(G-1676)
HANSEN, THORP & PELLINEN INC
7510 Market Place Dr # 101 (55344-3679)
PHONE 952 829-0700
FAX: 952 944-4086
Barb Turbett, *Accounting Mgr*
Duncan Schwensohn, *Manager*
Lance Smith, *Director*
Paul Thorp, *Director*
EMP: 32 **EST:** 1980
SQ FT: 9,500
SALES (est): 1MM-4.9MM **Privately Held**
WEB: www.htpo.com
SIC: 8711 8713 Engineering consulting services; surveying service

(G-1677)
HARMON INC (HQ)
11095 Viking Dr Ste 450 (55344-9505)
PHONE 952 944-5700
FAX: 952 944-5727
Michael McComas, *Vice Pres*
Dennis Pilkinton, *Vice Pres*
Brad Sparish, *Vice Pres*
Jim Theisen, *Opers Mgr*
Gary Jacobson, *CFO*
▲ **EMP:** 30 **EST:** 1995
SQ FT: 15,811
SALES (corp-wide): 696.70M **Publicly Held**
WEB: www.harmoninc.com

SIC: 5039 Wholesales glass construction materials
PA: Apogee Enterprises Inc
7900 Xerxes Ave S # 1800
Minneapolis MN 55431
952 835-1874

(G-1678)
HARRIS COMMUNICATIONS INC
15155 Technology Dr (55344-2273)
PHONE 952 906-1180
FAX: 952 906-1099
Robert Harris PhD, *President*
Tricia Meger, *Human Res Mgr*
Michelle Schaben, *Manager*
▲ **EMP:** 27 **EST:** 1982
SQ FT: 13,000
SALES (est): 10MM-24.9MM **Privately Held**
WEB: www.harriscomm.com
SIC: 5047 Wholesales technical aids for the handicapped; retails technical aids for the handicapped

(G-1679)
HARTFIEL CO (PA)
8117 Wallace Rd (55344-2114)
PHONE 952 974-2500
FAX: 952 974-2600
Myron Moser, *President*
Richard N Flint, *Corp Secy*
Theodore Kraft, *Exec VP*
Craig Ohlson, *Vice Pres*
Charlene Brouwer, *Opers Mgr*
EMP: 63 **EST:** 1958
SQ FT: 35,150 **Privately Held**
WEB: www.hartfiel.com
SIC: 5084 Wholesales industrial machinery & equipment; wholesales industrial hydraulic systems equipment & supplies; wholesales industrial power plant machinery

(G-1680)
HD SUPPLY WATERWORKS LTD
15800 W 79th St (55344-1807)
PHONE 952 937-9666
Mark Smith, *Principal*
Tom Orfei, *Opers Mgr*
John Selsdold, *Purch Mgr*
Paul Nelsen, *Sales Mgr*
EMP: 30
SALES (est): 25MM-49.9MM **Privately Held**
WEB: www.waterworks.hdsupply.com
SIC: 5051 Wholesales steel pipe & tubing
HQ: Hd Supply Waterworks Ltd
1820 Metcalf Ave
Thomasville GA 31792
407 841-4755

(G-1681)
HEALTHPARTNERS INC
9700 W 76th St Ste A (55344-4200)
PHONE 952 944-0432
John Curry, *Manager*
Michael Beugen, *Director*
EMP: 75
SALES (est): 25MM-49.9MM **Privately Held**
WEB: www.healthpartners.com
SIC: 6324 Hospital & medical insurance carrier
PA: HealthPartners Inc
8170 33rd Ave S
Bloomington MN 55425
952 883-6000

(G-1682)
HELLMUTH & JOHNSON PLLC
10400 Viking Dr Ste 500 (55344-7264)
PHONE 952 941-4005
J R Keena, *Partner*
Joseph D O'Brien, *Partner*
Maury D Beaulier, *Partner*
Nancy T Polomis, *Partner*
Barton C Gernander, *Partner*
EMP: 65 **EST:** 1995
SALES (est): 5MM-9.9MM **Privately Held**
WEB: www.hjlawfirm.com
SIC: 8111 General practice attorney's or lawyer's office

(G-1683)
HELP SYSTEMS LLC
6533 Flying Cloud Dr # 200 (55344-3335)
PHONE 952 933-0609
Janet Dryer, *President*
Thomas Mueller, *Vice Pres*

Jim Hortsmann, *CFO*
John Lewis, *CFO*
Lori Koppelman, *Human Res Mgr*
EMP: 90 **EST:** 1985
SQ FT: 14,000
SALES (est): 25MM-49.9MM **Privately Held**
WEB: www.helpsystems.com
SIC: 5112 Wholesales stationery & office
supplies
PA: Audax Group, LP
　　101 Huntington Ave # 2450
　　Boston MA 02199
　　617 859-1500

(G-1684)
HICKEY THORSTENSON GROVER LTD
Also Called: Htg Architects
9300 Hennepin Town Rd　(55347-3072)
PHONE..............................952 278-8880
FAX: 952 278-8822
James R Grover, *President*
Jeffery J Pflipsen, *Exec VP*
EMP: 40 **EST:** 1959
SQ FT: 8,000
SALES (est): 1MM-4.9MM **Privately Held**
SIC: 8712 7389 Architectural service;
commercial & industrial design service

(G-1685)
HIGH WIRE NETWORKS INC
7162 Shady Oak Rd　(55344-3517)
PO Box 240098, Saint Paul　(55124-0098)
PHONE..............................952 934-9080
Mark Porter, *Ch of Bd*
John Nonbello, *President*
Nicholas Garifalis, *Business Mgr*
Paul Shirey, *Business Mgr*
Gary Lien, *COO*
EST: 2002
SQ FT: 7,500　**Privately Held**
WEB: www.highwirenetworks.com
SIC: 7373 Computer integrated systems
design services

(G-1686)
HIGHJUMP SOFTWARE INC (PA)
6455 City West Pkwy　(55344-3246)
PHONE..............................952 947-4088
Russell Fleischer, *CEO*
Carol L Bors, *Corp Secy*
Elizabeth Fortier, *Corp Secy*
Liz Fortier, *Corp Secy*
Gregory Twedt, *Exec VP*
EMP: 100 **EST:** 1983
SQ FT: 20,000　**Privately Held**
SIC: 7373 Computer integrated systems
design services; computer systems
value-added resellers

(G-1687)
HORIZON AGENCY INC
6500 City West Pkwy # 100　(55344-7704)
PHONE..............................952 944-2929
FAX: 952 944-3091
Daniel Scattarella, *President*
James Hoeschler, *Exec VP*
Lawrence Kitts, *Treasurer*
Helen Arm, *Sales Staff*
EMP: 42 **EST:** 1974
SQ FT: 11,000
SALES (est): 1MM-4.9MM **Privately Held**
SIC: 6411 Insurance services

(G-1688)
HORMEL FOODS CORPORATE SVCS
6500 City West Pkwy Ste 102
(55344-7735)
PHONE..............................952 931-9030
FAX: 952 931-9372
Brent Payne, *Manager*
Karen Foster, *Manager*
EMP: 40
SALES (est): 25MM-49.9MM **Publicly Held**
WEB: www.hormel.com
SIC: 5147 Wholesales meat & meat
products
HQ: Hormel Foods Corporate Svcs
　　1 Hormel Pl
　　Austin MN 55912
　　507 437-5611

(G-1689)
HYSITRON INC
10025 Valley View Rd # 190　(55344-3563)
PHONE..............................952 835-6366
Jerzy Wyrobek, *Ch of Bd*
Thomas Wyrobek, *President*
Mike Eggers, *Finance*
Teri Keegan, *Office Mgr*
Lance Kuhn, *Manager*
EMP: 57 **EST:** 1993
SALES (est): 10MM-24.9MM **Privately Held**
WEB: www.hysitron.com
SIC: 5049 8731 Manufactures
semiconductors & related devices;
wholesales scientific instruments;
manufactures measuring & controlling
devices; commercial physical research
laboratory

(G-1690)
IMAGE SHOPPE INC
Also Called: Sanctuary Salonspa
995 Prairie Center Dr　(55344-3671)
PHONE..............................952 949-1313
FAX: 952 949-3400
Sheri Oeltjenbruns, *President*
Kelsie Johnson, *Corp Secy*
EMP: 50 **EST:** 1991
SALES (est): 1MM-4.9MM **Privately Held**
WEB: www.imageshoppe.com
SIC: 7231 Unisex hair salon; nail salon

(G-1691)
INFORMATION SPECIALISTS GROUP
9905 Hamilton Rd Frnt　(55344-3477)
PHONE..............................952 941-1600
Robert T McGarry Jr, *President*
EMP: 58 **EST:** 1996
SALES (est): 1MM-4.9MM **Privately Held**
WEB: www.isgmn.com
SIC: 8732 Market analysis, business &
economic research services

(G-1692)
INGENIX INC (HQ)
12125 Technology Dr　(55344-7302)
PHONE..............................952 833-7100
Kevin Pearson, *CEO*
Kevin Roche, *President*
Augustus Crocker, *Managing Dir*
Lawrence B Leisure, *Managing Dir*
Karin Keitel, *Corp Secy*
EMP: 400 **EST:** 1996
SQ FT: 80,000
SALES (corp-wide): 87.13B **Publicly Held**
WEB: www.unitedhealthgroup.com
SIC: 7371 7375 8741 8742 Computer
software development; management
consulting services; database information
retrieval service; business management
services
PA: Unitedhealth Group Inc
　　9900 Bren Rd E
　　Minnetonka MN 55343
　　952 936-1300

(G-1693)
INGRAM EXCAVATING INC
18900 Pioneer Trl　(55347-3210)
PHONE..............................952 934-0917
FAX: 952 934-0901
Richard Ingram, *President*
Todd Ingram, *Vice Pres*
EMP: 65 **EST:** 1948
SQ FT: 50,000
SALES (est): 5MM-9.9MM **Privately Held**
SIC: 1794 Excavating contractor

(G-1694)
INNOVATIVE COMPUTER SYSTEMS
6321 Bury Dr Ste 1　(55346-1739)
PHONE..............................952 934-5665
FAX: 952 937-5815
Peter Kaiser, *President*
Justin Cotton, *Accountant*
Tina Gschlecht, *Accountant*
Dean Blomquist, *Manager*
Jim Salter, *MIS Dir*
EMP: 30 **EST:** 1985
SQ FT: 1,600
SALES (est): 5MM-9.9MM **Privately Held**
WEB: www.icsusa.com

SIC: 7372 7371 Software publisher;
application software publishing; computer
programming service

(G-1695)
INSTRUMENT & VALVE SERVICES CO
12001 Technology Dr　(55344-3620)
PHONE..............................800 654-7768
Dennis Dahill, *President*
EMP: 50
SALES (est): 5MM-9.9MM **Publicly Held**
WEB: www.emersonprocess.com/fisher
SIC: 7699 Industrial equipment service
HQ: Fisher Controls International
　　205 S Center St
　　Marshalltown IA 50158
　　641 754-3011

(G-1696)
INSTYMEDS CORP (PA)
6501 City West Pkwy　(55344-3248)
PHONE..............................952 653-2525
Brad Schraut, *CEO*
Ed Zeman, *CFO*
EMP: 41 **EST:** 1999
SQ FT: 7,800
SALES (corp-wide): 4.20M **Privately Held**
SIC: 5122 Wholesales pharmaceuticals

(G-1697)
INTERSCOPE RECORDS INC
7500 Office Ridge Cir Ste 325
(55344-3786)
PHONE..............................952 828-6060
Kathy Packard, *Manager*
EMP: 30
SALES (est): 1MM-4.9MM **Privately Held**
WEB: www.vivendiuniversal.com
SIC: 7389 Music recording producer
DH: Interscope Records Inc
　　2220 Colorado Ave
　　Santa Monica CA 90404
　　310 865-1000

(G-1698)
ION CORP
7500 Equitable Dr　(55344-3673)
PHONE..............................952 936-9490
FAX: 952 936-7527
Wendell Maddox, *President*
Thomas Jones, *General Mgr*
Michael Davidson, *Business Mgr*
William Meuwissen, *Manager*
Michelle Miller, *CTO*
EMP: 50 **EST:** 1984
SQ FT: 20,000
SALES (est): 5MM-9.9MM **Privately Held**
WEB: www.ioncorp.com
SIC: 8711 8731 8734 Manufactures
electrical equipment & supplies;
manufactures space vehicle equipment;
manufactures aircraft parts & equipment;
engineering services; commercial physical
research laboratory; testing laboratory

(G-1699)
J B DISTRIBUTING CO INC
Also Called: Justice Brothers
14760 Martin Dr　(55344-2010)
PHONE..............................952 934-7354
FAX: 952 934-7675
Glenn D Gillund, *President*
Paul Gillund, *General Mgr*
Lois S Gillund, *Corp Secy*
Leslie Gillund, *Finance*
Jim Gillund, *Marketing Staff*
EMP: 35 **EST:** 1971
SQ FT: 6,500
SALES (est): 10MM-24.9MM **Privately Held**
WEB: www.jb-distributing.com
SIC: 5013 Wholesales automotive supplies
& parts

(G-1700)
J E DUNN CONSTRUCTION CO
9855 W 78th St Ste 270　(55344-8005)
PHONE..............................952 830-9000
EMP: 130
SALES (est): 25MM-49.9MM **Privately Held**
WEB: www.jedunn.com

SIC: 1542 New commercial & office building
construction; commercial & office building
renovation & repair services
HQ: J E Dunn Construction Co
　　1001 Locust St
　　Kansas City MO 64106
　　816 474-8600

(G-1701)
JERRY'S ENTERPRISES INC
Also Called: Cub Food Store 5193
8015 Den Rd Ste 2　(55344-4538)
PHONE..............................952 941-9050
Mike Summers, *Manager*
EMP: 200
SALES (est): 100MM-499.9MM **Privately
Held**
SIC: 5141 Wholesales general line
groceries; pharmacy & drug store; grocery
store
PA: Jerry's Enterprises Inc
　　5101 Vernon Ave S Ste 2A
　　Minneapolis MN 55436
　　952 922-8335

(G-1702)
KINDERCARE LEARNING CENTERS
12760 Anderson Lakes Pkwy
(55344-6606)
PHONE..............................952 941-5054
FAX: 952 943-9872
Missy Schmaltz, *Principal*
April Roth, *Manager*
Brenda Baumann, *Manager*
Angie Conover, *Asst Director*
EMP: 30
SALES (est): 500-999K **Privately Held**
WEB: www.kindercare.com
SIC: 8351 Child day care service
HQ: KinderCare Learning Centers
　　650 NE Holladay St Ste 1400
　　Portland OR 97232
　　503 872-1300

(G-1703)
KNOWLEDGE LEARNING CORP
8825 Aztec Dr　(55347-1901)
PHONE..............................952 944-3801
FAX: 952 944-8272
Bonita Brandel, *Sales Staff*
Susan Hanneson, *Manager*
Tiffany Stapleton, *Director*
EMP: 25
SALES (est): 500-999K **Privately Held**
WEB: www.knowledgelearning.com
SIC: 8351 Preschool center
PA: Knowledge Learning Corp
　　650 NE Holladay St # 1400
　　Portland OR 97232
　　503 872-1300

(G-1704)
KROLL ONTRACK INC (HQ)
9023 Columbine Rd　(55347-4182)
PHONE..............................952 937-1107
Kris Nimsger, *CEO*
Adrian Briscoe, *General Mgr*
Martin Carey, *Managing Dir*
Ben Pasco, *Managing Dir*
Christopher Deresz, *Business Mgr*
EMP: 210 **EST:** 1985
SQ FT: 41,000　**Privately Held**
WEB: www.krollontrack.com
SIC: 7374 7372 Data processing &
preparation services; application software
publishing
PA: Altegrity Inc
　　7799 Leesburg Pike
　　Falls Church VA 22043
　　703 448-0178

(G-1705)
LAKE SUPERIOR SOFTWARE INC
Also Called: LSS Data Systems
6423 City West Pkwy　(55344-3246)
PHONE..............................952 941-1000
FAX: 952 829-4309
Kenneth G Carlson, *CEO*
Stephanie V Petersen V, *President*
Timothy Johnson, *Manager*
Brian Schoenwald, *Manager*
EMP: 200 **EST:** 1982
SALES (est): 25MM-49.9MM **Privately Held**
WEB: www.lssdata.com

SIC: 7371 Computer programming service

(G-1706)
LAWN RANGER INC
6368 Carlson Dr (55346-1727)
PO Box 39451, Minneapolis (55439-0451)
PHONE 952 937-6076
Joseph E Unger, *President*
Gerrie Mattison, *Office Mgr*
EMP: 90 EST: 1981
SQ FT: 3,200 **Privately Held**
SIC: 0781 Landscape services

(G-1707)
LEISURE INC
6811 Flying Cloud Dr (55344-3418)
PHONE 952 401-8440
FAX: 952 983-3400
Rick Polk, *CEO*
Anne Quinn, *Business Mgr*
David Sussman, *Vice Pres*
Leonid Melamud, *Manager*
Jennifer Boyce, *Assistant*
EMP: 40 EST: 1985
SQ FT: 18,000 **Privately Held**
WEB: www.leisure.com
SIC: 8731 7389 8732 Commercial physical
research laboratory; commercial & industrial
design service; market analysis or research
services

(G-1708)
LENOX GROUP INC
6436 City West Pkwy (55344-7712)
PHONE 952 943-4100
Marc L Pfefferle, *CEO*
Stewart M Kasen, *Ch of Bd*
Reatha King, *Managing Dir*
Louis A Fantin, *Corp Secy*
Fred Spivak, *COO*
EMP: 120 EST: 1992
SQ FT: 66,400
SALES (est): 25MM-49.9MM **Privately Held**
WEB: www.department56.com
SIC: 5023 5199 Wholesales kitchenware;
retails kitchenware; wholesales gifts &
novelties; retails gifts & novelties

(G-1709)
LIBERTY PROPERTY TRUST
10400 Viking Dr Ste 130 (55344-7298)
PHONE 952 947-1100
FAX: 952 947-0800
David M Jellison, *Vice Pres*
Tom Shaver, *Vice Pres*
Patty Hogan, *Manager*
EMP: 25
SALES (est): 5MM-9.9MM **Publicly Held**
WEB: www.libertyproperty.com
SIC: 6552 Land subdivision & development
services
PA: Liberty Property Trust
500 Chesterfield Pkwy
Malvern PA 19355
610 648-1700

(G-1710)
LIFETOUCH NATIONAL SCHOOL
(HQ)
11000 Viking Dr Ste 300 (55344-7291)
PHONE 952 826-4000
FAX: 952 826-5730
Paul Harmel, *President*
H Williams, *District Mgr*
Richard A Hassel, *Corp Secy*
Wayne Horntvedt, *COO*
Jim Haeg, *Vice Pres*
EMP: 400 EST: 1946 **Privately Held**
WEB: www.lifetouch.com
SIC: 7221 School photography services
PA: Lifetouch Inc
11000 Viking Dr 400
Eden Prairie MN 55344
952 826-4000

(G-1711)
LIFETOUCH PORTRAIT STUDIOS
INC (HQ)
11000 Viking Dr Ste 200 (55344-7292)
PHONE 952 826-5000
FAX: 952 826-4563
Richard P Erickson, *Ch of Bd*
Paul O Harmel, *President*
Richard H Hassell, *Corp Secy*
Robert H Treuchel, *Corp Secy*

Richard A Hassel, *Senior VP*
EMP: 100 EST: 1930 **Privately Held**
WEB: www.jcpportraits.com
SIC: 7221 Still or video photographer
PA: Lifetouch Inc
11000 Viking Dr 400
Eden Prairie MN 55344
952 826-4000

(G-1712)
LONG TERM CARE GROUP INC
(PA)
11000 Prairie Lakes Dr (55344-3885)
PHONE 952 516-6829
Hugh Lytle, *President*
Peter Levine, *President*
Bruce Baude, *COO*
Patrick Yount, *Exec VP*
Peter Goldstein, *Exec VP*
EMP: 400 EST: 1996
SQ FT: 51,000 **Privately Held**
SIC: 6411 Insurance agency & broker

(G-1713)
LUND FOOD HOLDINGS INC
Also Called: Central Bakery
7752 Mitchell Rd (55344-2014)
PHONE 952 915-4888
FAX: 952 934-5009
Keith Kersten, *Vice Pres*
Dave Huth, *Mfg Staff*
John Johansen, *Opers-Prdtn-Mfg*
Rob Rogstad, *Manager*
Gary Vinter, *MIS Mgr*
EMP: 100
SALES (est): 50MM-99.9MM **Privately Held**
SIC: 5149 Wholesales bakery products;
commercial bakery
PA: Lund Food Holdings Inc
4100 W 50th St Ste 2100
Minneapolis MN 55424
952 927-3663

(G-1714)
MAIL HANDLING INC
7550 Corporate Way (55344-2045)
PHONE 952 975-5000
FAX: 952 975-5020
Brian Ostenso, *President*
Todd Tuma, *MIS Mgr*
EMP: 120 EST: 1968
SQ FT: 150,000
SALES (est): 10MM-24.9MM **Privately Held**
WEB: www.mailhandling.com
SIC: 7331 7374 Offset printing; mailing
services; data processing service

(G-1715)
MAINTENANCE TEAM
10250 Valley View Rd # 133 (55344-3534)
PHONE 952 942-5000
FAX: 952 942-5791
Jeffrey M Chanen, *President*
Beth Hambel, *COO*
EMP: 50 EST: 1989
SQ FT: 7,000
SALES (est): 5MM-9.9MM **Privately Held**
SIC: 1711 7349 Ventilation & duct work
contractor; warm air heating & air
conditioning contractor; building
maintenance service

(G-1716)
MAKEMUSIC INC
7615 Golden Triangle Dr (55344-3733)
PHONE 952 937-9611
Ronald B Raup, *CEO*
Michael Williamson, *Business Mgr*
Mark Maronde, *Project Mgr*
Karen L Vanderbosch, *CFO*
Alan Shuler, *CFO*
EMP: 54 EST: 1990
SQ FT: 22,000
SALES (est): 10MM-24.9MM **Publicly Held**
WEB: www.makemusic.com
SIC: 7372 Software publisher

(G-1717)
MAMMOTH-WEBCO INC
13200 Pioneer Trl Ste 150 (55347-4125)
PHONE 952 361-2711
FAX: 952 361-2700
Eric Roberts, *President*
Bill Haugh, *General Mgr*
A Buchholz, *Managing Dir*

Bill Horsch, *Purchasing*
Owen Golke, *CFO*
◆ EMP: 375 EST: 1930
SQ FT: 230,000
SALES (est): 50MM-99.9MM **Privately Held**
WEB: www.mammoth-inc.com
SIC: 5075 Manufactures refrigeration &
heating equipment; wholesales warm air
heating equipment & supplies;
manufactures heating equipment & supplies
HQ: Ces Group Inc
13200 Pioneer Trl Ste 150
Eden Prairie MN 55347
952 361-2711

(G-1718)
MCC GROUP INC
Also Called: Multihousing Credit Control
10125 Crosstown Cir # 100 (55344-3316)
PHONE 952 941-0552
Richard W Mac Donald, *President*
EMP: 31 EST: 1976
SQ FT: 7,000
SALES (est): 1MM-4.9MM **Privately Held**
WEB: www.mccgrp.com
SIC: 7323 7322 Credit investigation
services; collection agency

(G-1719)
MENARD INC
12600 Plaza Dr (55344-3630)
PHONE 952 941-4400
FAX: 952 941-4504
Steven Gossen, *Branch Mgr*
Casey Steiner, *Manager*
Bill Bush, *Manager*
EMP: 130
SALES (est): 25MM-49.9MM **Privately Held**
WEB: www.menards.com
SIC: 5031 Retails building products &
materials; wholesales lumber, plywood &
millwork
PA: Menard Inc
5101 Menard Dr
Eau Claire WI 54703
715 876-5911

(G-1720)
METROPOLITAN CORP
12475 Plaza Dr (55344-3647)
PHONE 952 944-2438
FAX: 952 947-5427
Mark Stelflug, *Vice Pres*
Bill Preisinger, *Sales Mgr*
Bill Manson, *Manager*
John D Peifer, *Manager*
Dina Boecher, *Data Proc Exec*
EMP: 110
SALES (est): 50MM-99.9MM **Privately Held**
WEB: www.metropolitanford.com
SIC: 7532 7538 Retails new & used
automobiles; automotive body, paint &
interior repair & maintenance services;
general automotive repair services; retails
auto & home supplies; used car dealer
PA: Metropolitan Corp
7625 Metro Blvd Ste 100
Minneapolis MN 55439
952 893-1277

(G-1721)
METROPOLITAN CORP
12790 Plaza Dr (55344-3632)
PHONE 952 943-9000
FAX: 952 946-8633
Roger Maltzen, *Parts Mgr*
Debra Letcher, *Controller*
Eric Bjguard, *Sales Mgr*
Denny Goodman, *Manager*
John D Peifer, *Manager*
EMP: 100
SALES (est): 50MM-99.9MM **Privately Held**
WEB: www.metropolitanford.com
SIC: 7514 7538 Retails new & used
automobiles; general automotive repair
services; retails automotive parts; rent-a-car
service; used car dealer
PA: Metropolitan Corp
7625 Metro Blvd Ste 100
Minneapolis MN 55439
952 893-1277

(G-1722)
METROPOLITAN MECHANICAL
CONTR
7450 Flying Cloud Dr (55344-3723)
PHONE 952 941-7010
FAX: 952 941-9118
Mark Anderson, *President*
Robert Kaczke, *Vice Pres*
Joe S Martin, *Vice Pres*
James E Walker, *Vice Pres*
Todd Hansen, *Safety Dir*
EMP: 350 EST: 1963
SALES (est): 25MM-49.9MM **Privately Held**
WEB: www.metromech.com
SIC: 1711 8711 Mechanical contractor;
plumbing service; warm air heating & air
conditioning contractor; engineering
services

(G-1723)
MIDWAVE CORP
10050 Crosstown Cir Ste 500
(55344-3346)
PHONE 952 279-5600
FAX: 952 279-5601
James Leslie, *CEO*
Bob Krocak, *Exec VP*
Maureen Beyer, *Vice Pres*
Darren Olsen, *Vice Pres*
Wendy Blossom, *Project Mgr*
EMP: 110 EST: 1999
SQ FT: 30,000
SALES (est): 50MM-99.9MM **Privately Held**
WEB: www.midwave.com
SIC: 5045 7379 Wholesales computer
peripheral equipment; computer system
consulting services

(G-1724)
MILLIAN AIR EXECUTIVE
AVIATION
Also Called: Aviation Charter
9960 Flying Cloud Dr (55347-4011)
PHONE 952 943-1519
Sherry Aasen, *Controller*
Roger Wikner, *Manager*
EMP: 50
SALES (est): 1MM-4.9MM **Privately Held**
SIC: 4581 Airport

(G-1725)
MINNESOTA BANKERS
ASSOCIATION
9521 W 78th St (55344-3853)
PHONE 952 835-3900
FAX: 952 941-7965
Joseph Witt, *President*
Albert Alexander, *President*
Eric Guler, *President*
Jefferson Wells, *Managing Dir*
Don Fox, *Vice Chairman*
EMP: 30 EST: 1889
SQ FT: 10,000 **Privately Held**
WEB: www.minnbankers.com
SIC: 8621 Professional organization

(G-1726)
MINNESOTA SUPPLY CO
6470 Flying Cloud Dr (55344-3308)
PHONE 952 828-7300
John E Stromsness, *President*
Steven J Stromsness, *Vice Pres*
Ron Morris, *Maint Mgr*
Peter Carlson, *CFO*
Mark K Olsen, *Treasurer*
▲ EMP: 100 EST: 1919
SALES (est): 25MM-49.9MM **Privately Held**
WEB: www.mnsupply.com
SIC: 5084 7359 7699 Wholesales industrial
machinery & equipment; equipment rental &
leasing services; wholesales materials
handling equipment; industrial machinery
repair & maintenance services

(G-1727)
MINNESOTA VIKINGS
FOOTBALL (PA)
9520 Viking Dr (55344-3825)
PHONE 952 828-6500
Leonard Wilf, *Vice Chairman*
Lester Bagley, *Vice Pres*
Kevin Winston, *Vice Pres*
Nick Tique, *Facilities Dir*
Dale Wysocki, *Facilities Mgr*

EMP: 130 **EST:** 1961 **Privately Held**
WEB: www.vikings.nfl.com
SIC: 6799 7941 Investor services; football club

(G-1728)
MINNESOTA VIKINGS FOOTBALL LLC
9520 Viking Dr (55344-3825)
PHONE.....................952 828-6500
Mark Wilf, *President*
Lenny Wilf, *Member*
Zygmunt Wilf, *Member*
Steve Poppen, *CFO*
EST: 1961
SQ FT: 150,000 **Privately Held**
WEB: www.vikings.nfl.com
SIC: 7941 Football club
PA: Minnesota Vikings Football
9520 Viking Dr
Eden Prairie MN 55344
952 828-6500

(G-1729)
MODERN AERO INC
Also Called: ASI-Aero Services
14801 Pioneer Trl (55347-2643)
PHONE.....................952 941-2595
FAX: 952 941-0307
Timothy Ashenfelter, *President*
Nicole Nelson, *Office Mgr*
Keidei Nelson, *Manager*
Jim Mitchell, *CIO*
EMP: 55 **EST:** 1963
SQ FT: 60,000
SALES (est): 10MM-24.9MM **Privately Held**
SIC: 4581 5088 7359 Retails self-propelled aircrafts; aircraft servicing & repairing; wholesales aircraft & parts; flight training school; aircraft rental service

(G-1730)
MORGAN TIRE & AUTO LLC
Also Called: Team Tires Plus
8453 Joiner Way (55344-7636)
PHONE.....................952 944-0458
FAX: 952 944-5450
Jimmy Browns, *Manager*
EMP: 30
SALES (est): 1MM-4.9MM **Privately Held**
WEB: www.bfsusa.com
SIC: 7534 Tire recapping & retreading services; tire dealer
HQ: Bfs Retail Operations LLC
333 E Lake St Ste 300
Bloomingdale IL 60108
630 259-9000

(G-1731)
MTS SYSTEMS CORP (PA)
14000 Technology Dr (55344-2247)
PHONE.....................952 937-4000
Laura B Hamilton, *President*
John Christiansen, *General Mgr*
Merlin Dewin, *Vice Chairman*
Michael J Hoff, *Corp Secy*
John Houston, *Corp Secy*
◆ **EMP:** 1340 **EST:** 1966
SQ FT: 420,000
SALES (corp-wide): 408.88M **Publicly Held**
WEB: www.mts.com
SIC: 8711 Manufactures measuring & controlling devices; manufactures stress, strain & flow detecting or measuring equipment; manufactures abrasion, shearing & strength testing equipment; engineering services; manufactures vibration instruments

(G-1732)
MULTI-SERVICES INC
7595 Anagram Dr (55344-7399)
PHONE.....................952 944-4000
FAX: 952 937-0811
Bruce Obermann, *CEO*
David Ciaccio, *President*
EMP: 75 **EST:** 1971
SQ FT: 1,800
SALES (est): 1MM-4.9MM **Privately Held**
SIC: 7349 Janitorial & custodial services

(G-1733)
NOVASPECT INC
7565 Corporate Way (55344-2022)
PHONE.....................952 934-5100
FAX: 952 934-1279
Timothy Holzer, *President*
Jim Johnson, *VP Eng R&D*
Becky Flusemann, *Cust Mgr*
George Siemens, *Manager*
Nick Martell, *Administrator*
EMP: 45
SALES (est): 10MM-24.9MM **Privately Held**
WEB: www.novaspect.com
SIC: 5084 Wholesales industrial controlling instruments & accessories
PA: Novaspect Inc
1124 Tower Rd
Schaumburg IL 60173
847 956-8020

(G-1734)
NOVOLOGIX
10400 Viking Dr Ste 200 (55344-7271)
PHONE.....................952 826-2500
FAX: 952 826-2599
David Willcutts, *President*
Glen Udine, *General Mgr*
Gary Loeber, *General Mgr*
Michael Harris, *COO*
Michael Kasner, *CFO*
EMP: 50 **EST:** 2002
SALES (est): 5MM-9.9MM **Privately Held**
SIC: 6411 Contract or fee basis medical insurance claim processing

(G-1735)
OAKWOOD BUILDERS INC
12901 Pioneer Trl (55347-4112)
PHONE.....................952 941-9730
FAX: 952 941-7715
Bruce Haverly, *President*
Sue Haverly, *Corp Secy*
Andy Borna, *Manager*
EMP: 29 **EST:** 1972
SQ FT: 5,000
SALES (est): 5MM-9.9MM **Privately Held**
SIC: 1542 1541 Commercial & office building renovation & repair services; industrial building renovating, remodeling & repair service

(G-1736)
OLYMPIC HILLS CORP
10625 Mount Curve Rd (55347-2905)
PHONE.....................952 941-6262
Kevin Valento, *General Mgr*
Bob Theriault, *Member*
EMP: 50 **EST:** 1969
SQ FT: 27,000
SALES (est): 1MM-4.9MM **Privately Held**
WEB: www.olympichills.com
SIC: 7997 Membership golf club; retails golf goods & equipment; eating place; retails tennis goods & equipment; membership tennis club; drinking establishment
PA: Olympic Hills Land Corp
10625 Mount Curve Rd
Eden Prairie MN 55347
952 941-6262

(G-1737)
OMICRON ASSOCIATES
14850 Scenic Heights Rd (55344-2243)
PHONE.....................952 345-5240
Norbert Nold, *Partner*
Annamarie Lang, *Partner*
Eric Peterson, *General Ptnr*
Lisa Peterson, *Manager*
▲ **EMP:** 180 **EST:** 1989
SQ FT: 3,028
SALES (est): 50MM-99.9MM **Privately Held**
SIC: 5049 Wholesales scientific instruments

(G-1738)
1 MICRO LLC
15153 Technology Dr Ste A (55344-2221)
PHONE.....................952 767-1010
Kris Terp, *Member*
Connie Solomon, *Administration*
EMP: 25 **EST:** 2001
SQ FT: 17,000
SALES (est): 1MM-4.9MM **Privately Held**
SIC: 8742 7389 Marketing consulting service; inventory computing service

(G-1739)
ONTRACK DATA RECOVERY INC
9023 Columbine Rd (55347-4182)
PHONE.....................952 937-1107
FAX: 952 937-5750
Ben Allen, *President*
Nancy Riley, *Director*
EMP: 700 **Privately Held**
SIC: 7375 Remote database information retrieval service

(G-1740)
OVP INC ⊕
Also Called: Lenox
6436 City West Pkwy (55344-3245)
PHONE.....................952 944-5600
Susan Engel, *CEO*
Ed Arion, *Managing Dir*
David W Dewey, *Exec VP*
David J Enright, *Senior VP*
David Weiser, *Senior VP*
▲ **EMP:** 185 **EST:** 2009
SALES (est): 100MM-499.9MM **Privately Held**
SIC: 5199 Wholesales gifts & novelties

(G-1741)
PARK DENTAL EDEN PRAIRIE
18315 Cascade Dr Ste 120 (55347-1190)
PHONE.....................952 949-2536
FAX: 952 949-3942
Linda Calevin, *Principal*
Gregory Swenson, *Manager*
Linda Jepson, *Manager*
Linda Cee, *Director*
EMP: 25 **EST:** 2001
SALES (est): 1MM-4.9MM **Privately Held**
WEB: www.willowportraits.com
SIC: 8021 Dentists' office & clinic

(G-1742)
PARK NICOLLET CLINIC
8455 Flying Cloud Dr Ste 205
(55344-3974)
PHONE.....................952 993-7400
FAX: 952 993-4320
Amber Larson, *Office Mgr*
Jerry Miller, *Manager*
Frank Walters, *Administrator*
Jennifer L Lessin, *Pediatrics*
Anna M Kostanecka, *Pediatrics*
EMP: 30
SALES (est): 1MM-4.9MM **Privately Held**
WEB: www.ccopnet.com
SIC: 8011 Physicians' office & clinic
HQ: Park Nicollet Clinic
3800 Park Nicollet Blvd
Minneapolis MN 55416
952 993-3123

(G-1743)
PARKWAY DENTAL
Also Called: Osberg Psola Scamp Kivo Larson
16518 W 78th St (55346-4302)
PHONE.....................952 937-2137
FAX: 952 937-5820
Dennis Kavio, *Partner*
Warren Scamp, *Partner*
Anthony Pesola, *Partner*
James C Osberg, *Partner*
Dennis Kalvo DDS, *Dentist*
EMP: 45 **EST:** 1984
SALES (est): 1MM-4.9MM **Privately Held**
SIC: 8021 Dental office

(G-1744)
PARTY MUSIC INC
9825 Valley View Rd (55344-3527)
PO Box 11233, Saint Paul (55111-0233)
PHONE.....................952 941-3830
Paul Yeo, *President*
EMP: 40
SALES (est): 1MM-4.9MM **Privately Held**
WEB: www.partymusic.com
SIC: 7929 7629 8742 Disc jockey services; marketing consulting service; electrical equipment repair service; entertainment services

(G-1745)
PDHC LTD
18315 Cascade Dr (55347-1180)
PHONE.....................952 949-2536
Gregory Swenson, *Manager*
EMP: 27
SALES (est): 1MM-4.9MM **Publicly Held**
WEB: www.parkdental.com
SIC: 8021 Dentists' office & clinic
HQ: PDHC Ltd
6415 Brooklyn Blvd
Minneapolis MN 55429
612 338-4546

(G-1746)
PETSMART INC
11200 Prairie Lakes Dr Ste A
(55344-4411)
PHONE.....................952 941-4660
Cara Iverson, *Branch Mgr*
Angie Marlette, *Manager*
EMP: 70
SALES (est): 5MM-9.9MM **Publicly Held**
WEB: www.petsmart.com
SIC: 0752 Retails pet supplies; animal grooming services
PA: Petsmart Inc
19601 N 27th Ave
Phoenix AZ 85027
623 580-6100

(G-1747)
PILGRIM CLEANERS & LAUNDERERS
Also Called: Nokomis Cleaners & Launderers
16382 Wagner Way (55344-5753)
PHONE.....................952 937-9391
Becky Taran, *Manager*
EMP: 40 **EST:** 1993
SALES (est): 1MM-4.9MM **Privately Held**
SIC: 7216 Dry cleaning plant

(G-1748)
PILLSBURY CO LLC
7500 Flying Cloud Dr Ste 670
(55344-3751)
PHONE.....................952 903-5262
Michael Rudy, *Vice Pres*
David Batt, *Vice Pres*
Jeff Stromberg, *Vice Pres*
John Swofford, *Vice Pres*
Dar Swedberg, *Engineering*
EMP: 50
SALES (est): 25MM-49.9MM **Privately Held**
SIC: 5149 Wholesales bakery products; manufactures canned fruits

(G-1749)
PITNEY BOWES INC
7905 Golden Triangle Dr (55344-7220)
PHONE.....................952 983-1600
Tom Stapleton, *Manager*
EMP: 45
SALES (est): 5MM-9.9MM **Publicly Held**
WEB: www.pb.com
SIC: 7359 Manufactures postage meters; business machine & electronic equipment rental service
PA: Pitney Bowes Inc
1 Elmcroft Rd
Stamford CT 06926
203 356-5000

(G-1750)
PLASTICS INTERNATIONAL INC
7600 Anagram Dr (55344-7309)
PHONE.....................952 934-2303
David Carter, *President*
Paul P Carter, *Treasurer*
Lyle Zehnder, *Manager*
Julie Pashina, *Manager*
James Kulhanek, *Director*
EMP: 25 **EST:** 1985
SQ FT: 30,000
SALES (est): 10MM-24.9MM **Privately Held**
WEB: www.plasticsintl.com
SIC: 5162 Wholesales plastics sheets & rods

(G-1751)
PPT VISION INC
12988 Valley View Rd (55344-3657)
PHONE..............................952 942-5747
FAX: 952 942-5752
Joesph Christen, *President*
David Friske, *Vice Pres*
Kevin Byrne, *Engineer*
Michael Pudas, *Engineer*
Timothy Clayton, *CFO*
EMP: 120 EST: 1981
SALES (est): 50MM-99.9MM **Privately Held**
SIC: 5084 Wholesales industrial machinery & equipment

(G-1752)
PRAIRIE ELECTRIC CO INC
6595 Edenvale Blvd # 120 (55346-2567)
PHONE..............................952 949-0074
Ronald G Oswald, *President*
Scot Oswald, *CFO*
EMP: 50 EST: 1974
SQ FT: 4,500
SALES (est): 5MM-9.9MM **Privately Held**
SIC: 1731 General electrical contractor

(G-1753)
PRIDE INSTITUTE INC
14400 Martin Dr (55344-2031)
PHONE..............................952 934-7554
FAX: 952 934-8764
Jim Stoltz, *CEO*
John Grant, *Director*
EMP: 40 EST: 1992
SALES (est): 1MM-4.9MM **Privately Held**
SIC: 8011 7363 Medical center; medical help service

(G-1754)
PROCTER & GAMBLE DISTRIBUTING
7500 Flying Cloud Dr (55344-3748)
PHONE..............................952 942-1857
FAX: 952 941-5332
J R Brunn, *Branch Mgr*
EMP: 160
SALES (est): 10MM-24.9MM **Publicly Held**
WEB: www.pg.com
SIC: 8741 5113 5122 5149 Management services; wholesales green or roasted coffee; wholesales pharmaceuticals, drug proprietaries & sundries; wholesales industrial & personal service paper
HQ: Procter & Gamble Distributing
1 Procter And Gamble Plz
Cincinnati OH 45202
513 983-1100

(G-1755)
PROEX PHOTO SYSTEMS INC
574 Paririe Ctr Dr # 100 (55344-7927)
PHONE..............................952 941-5232
Jeff Curtis, *Manager*
EMP: 40
SALES (est): 1MM-4.9MM **Privately Held**
SIC: 7384 Photofinishing laboratory
PA: Proex Photo Systems Inc
12680 Riverdale Blvd NW
Minneapolis MN 55448
952 893-1915

(G-1756)
QUEST SOFTWARE INC
10340 Viking Dr Ste 100 (55344-7270)
PHONE..............................952 229-3500
Greg Crow, *President*
EMP: 25
SALES (est): 5MM-9.9MM **Publicly Held**
WEB: www.quest.com
SIC: 7372 7371 Software publisher; computer programming service
PA: Quest Software Inc
5 Polaris Way
Aliso Viejo CA 92656
949 754-8000

(G-1757)
R J AHMANN CO
7555 Market Place Dr (55344-3637)
PHONE..............................952 947-9761
Richard Ahmann III, *President*
Richard A III, *President*
Gary McBride, *Vice Pres*

Dean Hildebrandt, *CFO*
Tom Breen, *Controller*
EMP: 55 EST: 1988
SQ FT: 16,500
SALES (est): 5MM-9.9MM **Privately Held**
SIC: 6411 Insurance services

(G-1758)
REBS SUPPLY INC
9911 Valley View Rd (55344-3526)
PHONE..............................952 942-5457
FAX: 952 942-8274
Bud Baker, *President*
Susan Baker, *Vice Pres*
Brian Baker, *Vice Pres*
EMP: 38 EST: 1982
SQ FT: 10,000
SALES (est): 1MM-4.9MM **Privately Held**
WEB: www.rebsmarketing.com
SIC: 7331 Mailing services

(G-1759)
REDEN & ANDERS
12125 Technology Dr (55344-7302)
PHONE..............................800 643-7933
Dewayne Ullsperger, *President*
Brad Anderson, *Principal*
John Berkto, *Principal*
Jon Brunsberg, *Principal*
Tim Feeser, *Principal*
EMP: 50 EST: 1990
SQ FT: 6,000
SALES (est): 5MM-9.9MM **Privately Held**
SIC: 8999 Actuarial consulting services

(G-1760)
REDPHARM DRUG
6501 City West Pkwy (55344-3248)
PHONE..............................952 653-2525
Brad Schraut, *CEO*
EMP: 50
SALES (est): 50MM-99.9MM **Privately Held**
SIC: 5122 Wholesales pharmaceuticals, drug proprietaries & sundries
PA: Instymeds Corp
6501 City West Pkwy
Eden Prairie MN 55344
952 653-2525

(G-1761)
REDPRAIRIE CORP
Also Called: Gagnon & Associates
6385 Old Shady Oak Rd # 180
(55344-7727)
PHONE..............................952 656-5400
FAX: 952 656-5401
Patrick Neville, *Branch Mgr*
Tom Kozenski, *Manager*
EMP: 35
SALES (est): 1MM-4.9MM **Privately Held**
WEB: www.redprairie.com
SIC: 8711 Engineering consulting services
DH: RedPrairie Corp
20700 Swenson Dr Ste 400
Waukesha WI 53186
262 317-2000

(G-1762)
REPLENEX
9815 W 74th St (55344-3522)
PHONE..............................952 941-9150
FAX: 952 941-9159
Richard W Cohen, *CEO*
Mort Harris, *President*
Douglas Cohen, *Vice Pres*
Ron Zeith, *VP Opers*
Augie Klein, *Warehouse Mgr*
EMP: 55 EST: 1946
SQ FT: 33,000
SALES (est): 25MM-49.9MM **Privately Held**
WEB: www.replenex.com
SIC: 5085 Wholesales industrial supplies

(G-1763)
RETAIL SUPPORT INC
6459 Pinnacle Dr (55346-1904)
PHONE..............................952 934-1317
Gary Everett, *President*
Lon K Brush, *Corp Secy*
EMP: 47 EST: 1986
SALES (est): 5MM-9.9MM **Privately Held**
SIC: 8742 8732 Business planning & organizing services; market analysis or research services; survey services, including marketing & location

(G-1764)
REV SOLUTIONS INC ✿
10400 Viking Dr (55344-7232)
PHONE..............................952 746-6005
Steven Stephan, *President*
Mitchell Johnson, *Office Mgr*
EMP: 35 EST: 2009
SALES (est): 1MM-4.9MM **Privately Held**
SIC: 7374 Computer graphics service

(G-1765)
RICOH AMERICAS CORP
10905 Valley View Rd (55344-3730)
PHONE..............................866 856-3000
Gerald Hacker, *Branch Mgr*
EMP: 32
SALES (est): 5MM-9.9MM **Privately Held**
WEB: www.ricoh-usa.com
SIC: 5044 Wholesales dictating machines
PA: Ricoh Americas Corp
5 Dedrick Pl
West Caldwell NJ 07006
973 882-2000

(G-1766)
ROGERS FREELS & ASSOCIATES INC
11495 Valley View Rd (55344-3617)
PHONE..............................952 843-2700
FAX: 952 941-2995
Jon Ness, *President*
Aaron Stritesky, *Corp Secy*
Jay Tschetter, *Vice Pres*
Bruce Birr, *Vice Pres*
David Thoma, *Vice Pres*
EMP: 60 EST: 1943
SQ FT: 16,200
SALES (est): 5MM-9.9MM **Privately Held**
WEB: www.rfamec.com
SIC: 8711 Mechanical engineering services

(G-1767)
RORKE DATA INC
7626 Golden Triangle Dr (55344-3732)
PHONE..............................952 829-0300
FAX: 952 829-1493
Joe Swanson, *President*
J Justice, *General Mgr*
Lori Thrune, *General Mgr*
Fred Snyder, *Corp Secy*
Tim Hanscom, *Vice Pres*
EMP: 63 EST: 1985
SQ FT: 44,000
SALES (est): 25MM-49.9MM **Publicly Held**
WEB: www.rorke.com
SIC: 5045 Wholesales computer peripheral equipment
HQ: Bell Microproducts Inc
1941 Ringwood Ave
San Jose CA 95131
408 451-9400

(G-1768)
ROSS NESBIT AGENCIES INC
7500 Flying Cloud Dr (55344-3748)
PHONE..............................952 941-9418
Ross Nesbit, *President*
Fredrick E Whisenand III, *Corp Secy*
Kathleen Nesbit, *Vice Pres*
Robert Hutter, *Controller*
Bryce Craig, *Marketing Staff*
EMP: 40 EST: 1974
SQ FT: 12,000
SALES (est): 1MM-4.9MM **Privately Held**
WEB: www.nesbitinsurance.com
SIC: 6411 Insurance agency & broker

(G-1769)
RYLAND GROUP INC
7600 Executive Dr (55344-3677)
PHONE..............................952 949-0013
Wayne Sugen, *President*
EMP: 120
SALES (est): 25MM-49.9MM **Publicly Held**
WEB: www.ryland.com
SIC: 1521 New single-family home construction service
PA: Ryland Group Inc
24025 Park Sorrento Ste 100
Calabasas CA 91302
818 223-7500

(G-1770)
SALON 2000 & DAY SPA
574 Paririe Ctr Dr Ste 155 (55344-7941)
PHONE..............................952 942-8444
FAX: 952 833-1417
Carmen Perrizo, *Owner*
Sarah Husnik, *Director*
EMP: 30 EST: 1994
SALES (est): 500-999K **Privately Held**
SIC: 7231 Beauty salon

(G-1771)
SE ROLLING HILLS LLC
Also Called: Colony At Eden Prairie
431 Paririe Ctr Dr # 114 (55344-5376)
PHONE..............................952 828-9500
Daly Geblirsch, *Member*
EMP: 75 EST: 2001
SQ FT: 350,000
SALES (est): 1MM-4.9MM **Privately Held**
WEB: www.the-colony.org
SIC: 8322 Senior citizen center

(G-1772)
SEARS, ROEBUCK & CO
8301 Flying Cloud Dr (55344-5381)
PHONE..............................952 944-4911
FAX: 952 944-4885
Dave Mallory, *Branch Mgr*
Dennis Russler, *Manager*
May Loo, *Manager*
EMP: 64
SALES (est): 5MM-9.9MM **Publicly Held**
SIC: 7629 Department store; electrical household appliance repair; retails appliance parts; hardware store; tire dealer
HQ: Sears, Roebuck & Co
3333 Beverly Rd
Hoffman Estates IL 60179
847 286-2500

(G-1773)
SEASONAL SPECIALTIES LLC
11455 Valley View Rd (55344-3617)
PHONE..............................952 942-6555
David Fagerlee Jr, *Member*
Sean Rage, *Manager*
John Feriancek, *Manager*
▲ EMP: 49 EST: 1996
SQ FT: 34,000
SALES (est): 25MM-49.9MM **Privately Held**
WEB: www.seasonalspecialties.com
SIC: 5199 Wholesales gifts & novelties; wholesales Christmas novelties

(G-1774)
SELECT HOTELS GROUP LLC
Also Called: Hyatt Pl Mnnpolis Eden Prairie
11369 Viking Dr (55344-7239)
PHONE..............................952 944-9700
FAX: 952 944-9799
Barbara Kodluboy, *General Mgr*
Barb Hartman, *Branch Mgr*
EMP: 30
SALES (est): 1MM-4.9MM **Privately Held**
WEB: www.amerisuites.com
SIC: 7011 Hotel
DH: Select Hotels Group LLC
200 W Monroe St Ste 800
Chicago IL 60606
312 706-7400

(G-1775)
7 WEST SECRETARIAL ANSWERING
7525 Mitchell Rd Ste 315 (55344-1958)
PHONE..............................952 936-4000
Karen Podany, *President*
Ned Podany, *VP Opers-Prdtn-*
Jake Phillips, *Finance*
Mike Sampson, *Info Tech Mgr*
Susan Brokaw, *Exec Dir*
EMP: 47 EST: 1979
SQ FT: 3,500
SALES (est): 1MM-4.9MM **Privately Held**
SIC: 7389 7338 Telephone answering service; secretarial services

GEOGRAPHIC

G E O G R A P H I C

(G-1776)
SHADY OAK HOSPITALITY LP
Also Called: Hillton Grdn Inn Eden Prairie
6330 Point Chase (55344-7726)
PHONE..................952 995-9000
FAX: 952 995-9009
Steve Hanson, *Partner*
Colin Klipsel, *General Mgr*
Janet McCutcheon, *Director*
EMP: 40 **EST:** 2000
SALES (est): 1MM-4.9MM **Publicly Held**
WEB: www.hilton.com
SIC: 7011 Traveler accommodations
DH: Hilton Worldwide Inc
7930 Jones Branch Dr
Mc Lean VA 22102
703 883-1057

(G-1777)
SHELARD GROUP INC
Also Called: SCI Services of Minneapolis
6385 Old Shady Oak Rd # 230
(55344-7705)
PHONE..................952 941-7493
Kim A Culp, *President*
EMP: 45 **EST:** 1965
SALES (est): 10MM-24.9MM **Privately Held**
SIC: 6512 6531 Operators of commercial &
industrial buildings; real estate management
services

(G-1778)
SIGNATURE TITLE CO
11010 Prairie Lakes Dr (55344-3884)
PHONE..................952 942-5155
Ryan Yardley, *CEO*
EMP: 28 **EST:** 1999
SALES (est): 1MM-4.9MM **Privately Held**
WEB: www.signaturetitleonline.com
SIC: 6411 Title insurance agent

(G-1779)
SKAMP CORP
17270 Tilia Rdg (55347-0001)
PHONE..................952 937-8990
Steven L Sandness, *President*
Winnifred M Bianconi, *Finance*
EMP: 50 **EST:** 1977
SQ FT: 7,300
SALES (est): 5MM-9.9MM **Privately Held**
SIC: 7379 Computer system consulting
services

(G-1780)
SOLID LOGIC COMPUTER SOLUTIONS
14867 Boulder Pointe Rd (55347-2408)
PHONE..................952 949-0140
Robert Barker, *President*
EMP: 25 **EST:** 1992
SALES (est): 1MM-4.9MM **Privately Held**
WEB: www.slogic.com
SIC: 7379 7371 Computer system
consulting services; computer programming
service

(G-1781)
ST ANDREW LUTHERAN CHURCH
13600 Technology Dr (55344-2251)
PHONE..................952 937-2776
FAX: 952 937-2777
Rod Anderson, *Principal*
EMP: 50 **EST:** 1977 **Privately Held**
WEB: www.standrewlu.org
SIC: 8351 Religious organization; child day
care service

(G-1782)
STERLING COMMERCE INC
7800 Equitable Dr Ste 200 (55344-7350)
PHONE..................952 294-1800
Michael A Meyer, *Corp Secy*
Mary Parker, *Corp Secy*
Donna M Angiulo, *Treasurer*
Kevin Lynch, *Branch Mgr*
John J Stephens, *Director*
EMP: 60
SALES (est): 5MM-9.9MM **Publicly Held**
WEB: www.ibm.com

SIC: 7371 8742 Computer programming
service; management consulting services
PA: International Business
New Orchard Rd
Armonk NY 10504
914 499-1900

(G-1783)
STONE FABRICS INC (PA)
Also Called: Mill End Textiles
6900 Shady Oak Rd (55344-3403)
PHONE..................952 941-2303
FAX: 952 941-2304
James T Greenfield, *President*
Lawrence E Voehl, *Vice Pres*
Linda Weymann, *Manager*
Pat Truesdell, *Manager*
▲ **EMP:** 50 **EST:** 1973
SQ FT: 50,000
SALES (corp-wide): 7.41M **Privately Held**
WEB: www.millendtextiles.com
SIC: 5131 Wholesales woven textiles; fabric
store; wholesales knit fabrics

(G-1784)
SULCO CLEANING SERVICE
6408 Kurtz Ln (55346-1608)
PO Box 1378, Minnetonka (55345-0378)
PHONE..................952 937-8777
FAX: 952 937-8011
Ben Sullivan Jr, *President*
David Smith, *Vice Pres*
EMP: 27 **EST:** 1978
SALES (est): 500-999K **Privately Held**
SIC: 7349 Building cleaning & maintenance
services

(G-1785)
SUPERVALU EQUIPMENT SERVICES ✪
11840 Valley View Rd (55344-3643)
PO Box 1377, Minneapolis (55440-1377)
PHONE..................952 828-4000
Jeff Noddle, *CEO*
Michael Jackson, *President*
David Boehnen, *Vice Pres*
EMP: 40 **EST:** 2008
SALES (est): 10MM-24.9MM **Privately Held**
SIC: 5046 Wholesales commercial
equipment

(G-1786)
SUPERVALU INC
300 2nd Ave S (55343-8375)
PHONE..................952 238-3400
Roger Ohlhauser, *General Mgr*
Greg Doeden, *Traffic Mgr*
EMP: 1000
SALES (est): 50MM-99.9MM **Publicly Held**
WEB: www.supervalu.com
SIC: 4225 Warehousing & storage services
PA: SUPERVALU Inc
11840 Valley View Rd
Eden Prairie MN 55344
952 828-4000

(G-1787)
SUPERVALU INC (PA)
11840 Valley View Rd (55344-3643)
PO Box 990, Minneapolis (55440-0990)
PHONE..................952 828-4000
FAX: 952 828-4171
Jeffrey Noddle, *Ch of Bd*
Michael L Jackson, *President*
Kevin Kemp, *President*
Sue Klug, *President*
Keith Nielsen, *President*
▲ **EMP:** 1000 **EST:** 1925
SALES (corp-wide): 40.59B **Publicly Held**
WEB: www.supervalu.com
SIC: 5141 5142 5143 5147 5148 Retail
supermarkets; wholesales fresh fruits;
wholesales vegetables; wholesales fresh
dairy products; wholesales general line
groceries; wholesales meat & meat
products; wholesales packaged frozen
foods

(G-1788)
SUPERVALU INC
7075 Flying Cloud Dr (55344-3532)
PHONE..................952 947-3700
FAX: 952 947-2693
Allen U Lenzmeier, *Data Proc Staff*
EMP: 113

SALES (est): 100MM-499.9MM **Publicly
Held**
WEB: www.supervalu.com
SIC: 5141 Wholesales general line
groceries; grocery store
PA: SUPERVALU Inc
11840 Valley View Rd
Eden Prairie MN 55344
952 828-4000

(G-1789)
SUPERVALU TRANSPORTATION INC
11840 Valley View Rd (55344-3643)
PHONE..................952 828-4000
Jeff Noddle, *CEO*
Michael W Wright, *Ch of Bd*
R Nilles, *General Mgr*
Haley Meyer, *General Mgr*
Robert Shebeck, *Managing Dir*
EMP: 700 **EST:** 1991
SALES (est): 50MM-99.9MM **Publicly Held**
WEB: www.supervalu.com
SIC: 4213 Contract haulers
PA: SUPERVALU Inc
11840 Valley View Rd
Eden Prairie MN 55344
952 828-4000

(G-1790)
T-CHEK SYSTEMS INC
14800 Charlson Rd Ste 100 (55347-5046)
PHONE..................952 934-3413
FAX: 952 934-3411
Bryan Foe, *President*
Bruce Larson, *Senior VP*
Matt Crumpton, *Vice Pres*
Nancee Ronning, *Vice Pres*
Troy Renner, *Treasurer*
EMP: 80 **EST:** 1969
SALES (est): 25MM-49.9MM **Publicly Held**
WEB: www.tchek.com
SIC: 6099 8742 Electronic funds transfer
network, including switching; management
consulting services
PA: C H Robinson Worldwide Inc
14701 Charlson Rd
Eden Prairie MN 55347
952 937-8500

(G-1791)
TELVENT DTN INC
Also Called: Financial Information MGT
11000 W 78th St Ste 250 (55344-8015)
PHONE..................952 941-6628
FAX: 952 941-7017
Cynthia Bergdorf, *Manager*
EMP: 36
SALES (est): 25MM-49.9MM **Privately Held**
WEB: www.telvent.com
SIC: 5045 Wholesales computer software
PA: Telvent Dtn Inc
9110 W Dodge Rd Ste 200
Omaha NE 68114
402 390-2328

(G-1792)
THREEWIRE INC
Also Called: Dash-Two Advertising
10250 Valley View Rd # 145 (55344-3536)
PHONE..................952 852-5556
Mark A Summers, *CEO*
Mark Stultz, *Senior VP*
Jim Suddendorf, *Senior VP*
Paula J Norbom, *Vice Pres*
Janine Katz, *Director*
EST: 1999
SQ FT: 16,000 **Privately Held**
WEB: www.threewire.com
SIC: 8742 Marketing consulting service

(G-1793)
THUNDERBIRD AVIATION INC
14091 Pioneer Trl (55347-2623)
PHONE..................952 941-1212
FAX: 952 941-6601
EMP: 46
SALES (est): 1MM-4.9MM **Privately Held**
WEB: www.thunderbirdaviation.com
SIC: 4581 5088 7359 Aviation school;
aircraft servicing & repairing; wholesales
aircraft & parts; retails self-propelled
aircraft; aircraft rental service; airline
training

(G-1794)
TMC ENTERPRISES INC
9979 Valley View Rd Ste 200
(55344-3596)
PHONE..................952 943-9077
Barrs Lewis, *President*
Debra Glassman, *Controller*
Terry Wander, *Cust Svc Mgr*
Callie Blomgren, *Info Tech Mgr*
Mike Eastey, *Info Tech Mgr*
EMP: 40 **EST:** 1985
SALES (est): 5MM-9.9MM **Privately Held**
WEB: www.timemgmt.com
SIC: 7372 Software publisher

(G-1795)
TRANSCRIPTIONS INC
6500 City West Pkwy # 310 (55344-7732)
PHONE..................952 831-4480
FAX: 952 944-5739
Clarence Ramsey, *CEO*
Myles Spicer, *President*
Pat Rounds, *Vice Pres*
Denise Flemmer, *Manager*
Christine Fiske, *Manager*
EMP: 90 **EST:** 2002
SQ FT: 2,000
SALES (est): 5MM-9.9MM **Privately Held**
WEB: www.alphatranscription.com
SIC: 8099 Medical services organization

(G-1796)
TRAVEL LEADERS
6409 City West Pkwy # 104 (55344-7845)
PHONE..................952 941-8900
David Lovick, *President*

SQ FT: 2,500 **Privately Held**
WEB: www.twincitieshoneymoon.com
SIC: 4724 Travel agency

(G-1797)
TRAVEL LEADERS GROUP LLC (PA) ✪
6442 City West Pkwy (55344-3245)
PHONE..................952 914-6500
Michael Batt, *President*
Karen Blauw, *Senior VP*
John Brehm, *Senior VP*
Stephen Thomas-Schelere, *Senior VP*
Nicholas Bluhm, *CFO*
EMP: 650 **EST:** 2008 **Privately Held**
SIC: 4725 4724 Tour operator; travel
agency

(G-1798)
TUESDAY NETWORKING INC
9196 Neill Lake Rd (55347-2057)
PHONE..................952 942-7378
William Pauling, *Principal*
EMP: 25 **EST:** 2006
SALES (est): 1MM-4.9MM **Privately Held**
SIC: 7379 Computer system consulting
services

(G-1799)
TWIN CITY CHRISTIAN HOMES INC
Also Called: Castle Ridge Care Center
625 Prairie Center Dr (55344-5326)
PHONE..................952 944-8982
Scott Walter, *Manager*
Eunice Ulshafer, *Administrator*
Donald Flack III, *Administrator*
Marianne Jacovetty RN, *Nursing Dir*
EMP: 100
SALES (est): 1MM-4.9MM **Privately Held**
WEB: www.tcchomes.com
SIC: 8361 8051 8052 Residential care
facility; intermediate care facility; skilled
nursing care facility
PA: Twin City Christian Homes Inc
7645 Lyndale Ave S
Minneapolis MN 55423
612 861-2799

(G-1800)
UNI-SELECT USA INC
7900 Excelsior Blvd (55343-3445)
PHONE..................952 352-8603
EMP: 28
SALES (est): 10MM-24.9MM **Privately Held**

SIC: **5013** Wholesales automotive supplies & parts
PA: UNI-Select USA Inc
20 Hazelwood Dr Ste 100
Amherst NY 14228
716 531-9266

(G-1801)
USA MOBILITY WIRELESS INC
11437 Valley View Rd (55344-3617)
PHONE...............................952 996-0400
FAX: 952 944-0881
Trent Gifford, *President*
EMP: 40 **Publicly Held**
WEB: www.arch.com
SIC: 4812 Wireless telecommunications carrier & service
HQ: USA Mobility Wireless Inc
6850 Versar Ctr Ste 420
Springfield VA 22151
703 269-6850

(G-1802)
V D A ASSOCIATES
17406 ADA Ct (55347-4277)
PHONE...............................952 937-8833
William Gooding, *Manager*
EMP: 50 **EST:** 2000
SALES (est): 5MM-9.9MM **Privately Held**
SIC: 8748 Business consulting services
PA: John A Van Deusen & Associates
5 Regent St Ste 524
Livingston NJ 07039
973 994-9220

(G-1803)
VANCO SERVICES LLC
6499 City West Pkwy (55344-3246)
PHONE...............................952 983-8660
Scott Anderson, *Partner*
Kent R Daley, *Member*
EMP: 30 **EST:** 2001
SALES (est): 10MM-24.9MM **Privately Held**
SIC: 6099 Electronic funds transfer network, including switching

(G-1804)
VIKING COLLECTION SERVICE INC
7500 Office Ridge Cir # 100 (55344-3783)
PO Box 59207, Minneapolis (55459-0207)
PHONE...............................952 944-7575
Gene Kloeckner, *CEO*
Cory Kloeckner, *President*
Eugene F Kloeckner, *Corp Secy*
John C Barrott, *Corp Secy*
Tom Johnson, *Vice Pres*
EMP: 325 **EST:** 1970
SQ FT: 31,000
SALES (est): 10MM-24.9MM **Privately Held**
WEB: www.vikingservice.com
SIC: 7322 Collection agency

(G-1805)
VIKING FOREST PRODUCTS LLC
7615 Smetana Ln Ste 140 (55344-4703)
PHONE...............................952 941-6512
Bruce W Johnson, *Branch Mgr*
◆ **EMP:** 40
SALES (est): 1MM-4.9MM **Privately Held**
WEB: www.vikingforest.com
SIC: 8721 5031 8748 Billing & bookkeeping services; business consulting services; wholesales rough, dressed & finished lumber
DH: Viking Forest Products LLC
7615 Smetana Ln Ste 140
Eden Prairie MN 55344
952 941-6512

(G-1806)
VIRTELLIGENCE INC
6216 Baker Rd Ste 100 (55346-1953)
PHONE...............................952 746-9220
Akhtar Chaudhri, *President*
Catherine Hering, *Senior VP*
Yasmin Akhtar, *CFO*
EMP: 107 **EST:** 1998
SQ FT: 17,000
SALES (est): 10MM-24.9MM **Privately Held**
WEB: www.virtelligence.com

SIC: **7379** 7371 7372 7373 Computer system consulting services; computer integrated systems design services; computer programming service; software publisher

(G-1807)
VIRTUAL RADIOLOGIC CORP
11995 Singletree Ln # 500 (55344-5349)
PHONE...............................952 595-1100
Rob Kill, *President*
Mike Kolar, *Corp Secy*
Betty L Schwall, *Corp Secy*
Phillip M Mapp, *Vice Pres*
Kerri Leopold, *Project Mgr*
EMP: 234 **EST:** 2003
SQ FT: 41,000
SALES (est): 25MM-49.9MM **Privately Held**
WEB: www.virtualrad.com
SIC: 8011 Radiologist office

(G-1808)
VOA ANOKA CARE CENTER INC
7530 Market Place Dr (55344-3636)
PHONE...............................952 941-0305
Charles Gould, *President*
EMP: 99 **EST:** 2006
SALES (est): 1MM-4.9MM **Privately Held**
SIC: 8051 Skilled nursing care facility

(G-1809)
VOLUNTEERS OF AMERICA INC
Also Called: National Service
7530 Market Place Dr (55344-3636)
PHONE...............................952 941-0305
Ron Nolte, *Finance*
Ron Patterson, *Manager*
EMP: 25
SALES (est): 1MM-4.9MM **Privately Held**
WEB: www.voa.org
SIC: 8322 Multi-services center
PA: Volunteers of America Inc
1660 Duke St Ste 100
Alexandria VA 22314
703 341-5000

(G-1810)
VOLUNTEERS OF AMERICA NATIONAL (PA)
7530 Market Place Dr (55344-3636)
PHONE...............................952 941-0305
Nancy Feldman, *Ch of Bd*
Charles Gould, *President*
Ron Patterson, *Treasurer*
Carol Moore, *Director*
EMP: 30 **EST:** 1982
SQ FT: 9,600
SALES (corp-wide): 141.38M **Privately Held**
SIC: 8051 8052 Extended care facility; intermediate care facility

(G-1811)
VOYAGER BANK (PA)
775 Prairie Center Dr Ste 100 (55344-7319)
PHONE...............................952 345-7600
FAX: 952 345-7601
Timothy P Owens, *President*
Timothy Viery, *Exec VP*
Brenda Sonnek, *Vice Pres*
Steve Berg, *Vice Pres*
April Diethelm, *Assoc VP*
EMP: 40 **EST:** 1983
SALES (corp-wide): 28.04M **Privately Held**
SIC: 6035 Federal savings bank

(G-1812)
WALGREEN CO
Also Called: Walgreens
10180 Hennepin Town Rd (55347-3175)
PHONE...............................952 941-8666
Gary Cizadlo, *Manager*
Patricia Adams, *Manager*
EMP: 30
SALES (est): 1MM-4.9MM **Publicly Held**
WEB: www.walgreens.com
SIC: 7384 Drug store; photofinishing laboratory
PA: Walgreen Co
200 Wilmot Rd
Deerfield IL 60015
847 914-2500

(G-1813)
WAND CORP
7593 Corporate Way (55344-2022)
PHONE...............................952 361-6200
John P Perrill, *CEO*
Gregory Perrill, *Vice Pres*
David Perrill, *Vice Pres*
Greg Sicheneder, *Purchasing*
Irene Perrill, *CFO*
▲ **EMP:** 109 **EST:** 1982
SALES (est): 10MM-24.9MM **Privately Held**
WEB: www.wandcorp.com
SIC: 5044 7371 Manufactures electrical equipment & supplies; wholesales cash registers; computer programming service; manufactures calculating & accounting equipment

(G-1814)
WESTLUND DENTAL STUDIO INC
7535 Office Ridge Cir (55344-3644)
PHONE...............................952 942-9464
FAX: 952 942-9531
Robert A Hancock, *President*
David Hancock, *Vice Pres*
EMP: 27 **EST:** 1941
SALES (est): 1MM-4.9MM **Privately Held**
SIC: 8072 8021 Dental laboratory; dentists' office & clinic

(G-1815)
WESTWOOD PROFESSIONAL SERVICES
7699 Anagram Dr (55344-7310)
PHONE...............................952 937-5150
Dennis Marhula, *President*
Troy Owens, *Corp Secy*
Marty Weber, *Corp Secy*
Paul V Greenhagen V, *Vice Pres*
Dale N Beckman, *Vice Pres*
EMP: 110 **EST:** 1972
SQ FT: 2,500
SALES (est): 10MM-24.9MM **Privately Held**
SIC: 8742 Management consulting services

(G-1816)
WINCOM SYSTEMS INC
11840 Valley View Rd (55344-3643)
PHONE...............................952 828-4000
Jeff Noddle, *President*
EMP: 500 **EST:** 1992
SALES (est): 100MM-499.9MM **Publicly Held**
WEB: www.supervalu.com
SIC: 5141 Wholesales general line groceries
DH: Supervalu Holdings Inc
11840 Valley View Rd
Eden Prairie MN 55344
952 828-4000

(G-1817)
WORLD CLASS WINES INC
7666 Washington Ave S (55344-3706)
PO Box 1867, Minnetonka (55345-0867)
PHONE...............................952 941-8795
FAX: 952 941-6156
Martin W Ullman, *President*
Lee Codding, *Vice Pres*
Diana Ullman, *CFO*
Gini Sisson, *Human Resources*
Christopher Griese, *VP Sales*
▲ **EMP:** 25 **EST:** 1982
SQ FT: 6,000
SALES (est): 10MM-24.9MM **Privately Held**
SIC: 5182 Wholesales wine

(G-1818)
XATA CORP (PA)
965 Prairie Center Dr (55344-3671)
PHONE...............................952 707-5600
John J Coughlan, *President*
Wesley C Fredenburg, *Corp Secy*
Thomas L Schlick, *COO*
David A Gagne, *Exec VP*
Thomas N Flies, *Senior VP*
EMP: 115 **EST:** 1985
SQ FT: 26,800
SALES (corp-wide): 65.32M **Publicly Held**
WEB: www.xata.com
SIC: 7372 8741 Business & professional software publishers; management services

(G-1819)
XIOTECH CORP
6455 Flying Cloud Dr (55344-3305)
PHONE...............................952 983-3000
Ken Hendrickson, *Ch of Bd*
Alan Atkinson, *President*
Kenneth F Krutsch, *Senior VP*
George Symons, *Senior VP*
Scott Winkler, *Senior VP*
EMP: 175 **EST:** 1995
SQ FT: 83,000
SALES (est): 10MM-24.9MM **Privately Held**
WEB: www.xiotech.com
SIC: 4226 Document & office records storage services; manufactures computer storage devices
PA: Oak Management Corp
1 Gorham Is Ste 1
Westport CT 06880
203 226-8346

(G-1820)
ZINPRO ANIMAL NUTRITION INC
10400 Viking Dr Ste 240 (55344-7265)
PHONE...............................952 944-2736
Michael D Anderson, *President*
Joseph Carrica, *VP Sls/Mktg*
Mary Kurth, *CFO*
▼ **EMP:** 35 **EST:** 1994
SALES (est): 25MM-49.9MM **Privately Held**
SIC: 5191 Wholesales animal feeds

EDEN VALLEY
Meeker County

(G-1821)
H ENTERPRISES INTERNATIONAL
480 Park Ave E (55329-1644)
PO Box 329 (55329-0329)
PHONE...............................320 453-2626
Phil Radtke, *Manager*
EMP: 25
SALES (est): 10MM-24.9MM **Privately Held**
SIC: 5092 Wholesales toys
PA: H Enterprises International
120 S 6th St Ste 2300
Minneapolis MN 55402
612 340-8849

(G-1822)
SCHOENECKERS INC
479 Meeker Ave E (55329-1629)
PO Box 500 (55329-0500)
PHONE...............................320 453-2600
FAX: 320 453-2610
Guy Schoenecker, *President*
Connie Vadner, *Manager*
EMP: 100
SALES (est): 10MM-24.9MM **Privately Held**
WEB: www.schoeneckers.com
SIC: 8742 8748 Management consulting services; business consulting services
PA: Schoeneckers Inc
7630 Bush Lake Rd
Edina MN 55439
952 835-4800

EDGERTON
Pipestone County

(G-1823)
EDGEBROOK CARE CENTER
505 Trosky Rd W (56128-2748)
PHONE...............................507 442-7121
FAX: 507 442-3952
Bruce Kooiman, *President*
John Doughty, *Administrator*
Barb Obbink, *Nursing Dir*
EMP: 100 **EST:** 1968
SQ FT: 30,000
SALES (est): 1MM-4.9MM **Privately Held**
SIC: 8051 6513 Skilled nursing care facility; operators of retirement hotels

GEOGRAPHIC

(G-1824)
MATHY TRUCKING INC
1585 State Highway 30   (56128-1209)
PHONE..............................507 777-4395
Kathy Bootsma, *President*
Marilyn Bootsma, *Vice Pres*
Bratt Bootsma, *Manager*
EMP: 59 **EST:** 2003
SALES (est): 5MM-9.9MM **Privately Held**
SIC: 4213 Over the road trucking

EDINA
Hennepin County

(G-1825)
AUBURN WOODS CLUBHOMES ASSN
7275 Bush Lake Rd   (55439-2023)
PHONE..............................952 922-5575
Terri Redshaw, *Manager*
EMP: 88 **EST:** 1994
SALES (est): 10MM-24.9MM **Privately Held**
SIC: 1531 7997 Townhouse developer;
membership recreation club

(G-1826)
BJORKLUND REALTY INC
5780 Lincoln Dr Ste 300   (55436-1761)
PHONE..............................952 934-0500
FAX: 952 934-0422
Bruce Bjorklund, *President*
Raeann Mysliwiec, *Manager*
EMP: 94 **EST:** 2004
SALES (est): 10MM-24.9MM **Privately Held**
WEB: www.bjorklundrealty.com
SIC: 8742 Real estate consultant

(G-1827)
BURNET TITLE LLC
5151 Edina Industrial Blvd   (55439-3013)
PHONE..............................952 844-6200
FAX: 952 886-6800
Ronnie Semlak, *President*
Jinnelle Weis, *Senior VP*
Jim Helfman, *Production*
James E Claseman, *CFO*
Lori Hall, *CFO*
EMP: 75 **EST:** 1981
SALES (est): 10MM-24.9MM **Privately Held**
WEB: www.burnettitle.com
SIC: 6361 6541 Provides real estate title
insurance; title & trust company
HQ: Burnet Realty LLC
    7550 France Ave S Ste 300
    Minneapolis MN 55435
    952 844-6400

(G-1828)
CAPERNAUM PEDIATRIC THERAPY
7250 France Ave S Ste 305   (55435-4313)
PHONE..............................612 922-2009
Marcia Mattson, *President*
Allison Bicek, *Manager*
Faye House, *Manager*
EMP: 45 **EST:** 2000
SALES (est): 1MM-4.9MM **Privately Held**
WEB: www.capernaumpeds.com
SIC: 8093 Outpatient rehabilitation
treatment center

(G-1829)
DOHERTY STAFFING SOLUTIONS
7645 Metro Blvd Ste 1   (55439-3071)
PHONE..............................952 832-8300
FAX: 952 356-1961
Valerie K Doherty, *CEO*
Jim Haubrich, *CFO*
Joe Willy, *CIO*
Natalie Rhoden, *Info Tech Mgr*
Tim Doherty, *Shareholder*
EMP: 85 **EST:** 2007
SALES (est): 1MM-4.9MM **Privately Held**
WEB: www.dohertytech.com
SIC: 7363 Temporary help service

(G-1830)
ELOYALTY CORP
7700 France Ave S Ste 325   (55435-5874)
PHONE..............................952 908-8000
Todd Weigand, *Manager*
Jessica Wojtowisz, *Office Admin*
Evan Francen, *Consultant*
Rusty Hanson, *Info Tech Mgr*
Eric Johnson, *Director*
EMP: 50
SALES (est): 5MM-9.9MM **Publicly Held**
WEB: www.eloyaltyco.com
SIC: 8742 Management consulting services
PA: Eloyalty Corp
    150 N Field Dr Ste 250
    Lake Forest IL 60045
    847 582-7000

(G-1831)
GILBERT MECHANICAL CONTRACTORS
4451 W 76th St   (55435-5111)
PHONE..............................952 835-3810
FAX: 952 893-2156
P D Gilbert, *President*
John Gorman, *Vice Pres*
Ed Dahlgren, *Vice Pres*
Dave Deshler, *Project Mgr*
Marylee Skrinner, *Purch Agent*
EMP: 135 **EST:** 2002
SQ FT: 30,000
SALES (est): 10MM-24.9MM **Privately Held**
WEB: www.gilbertmech.com
SIC: 1711 1731 Warm air heating & air
conditioning contractor; plumbing service;
fire sprinkler system installation service;
general electrical contractor; mechanical
contractor

(G-1832)
ILM PROFESSIONAL SERVICES INC
4445 W 77th St Ste 140   (55435-5141)
PHONE..............................952 960-2220
Farhan Muhammad, *President*
Farhana Ahmed, *Vice Pres*
EMP: 30 **EST:** 2001
SALES (est): 1MM-4.9MM **Privately Held**
SIC: 7379 Computer system consulting
services

(G-1833)
INFOSOFT GROUP
7760 France Ave S   (55435-5800)
PHONE..............................952 806-0631
Scott Molitor, *President*
EMP: 80 **EST:** 2007 **Privately Held**
SIC: 7361 Employment agency services

(G-1834)
INTER SAVINGS BANK FSB
Also Called: Interbank Fsb
3400 W 66th St Ste 100   (55435-2179)
PHONE..............................952 920-6700
FAX: 952 920-7308
Fred B Stelter, *President*
Ronald R Fletcher, *Chairman*
Elizabeth Anderson, *Vice Pres*
John Fletcher, *Opers Mgr*
Jeffrey J Willett, *CFO*
EMP: 25 **EST:** 1965
SQ FT: 6,000
SALES (est): 5MM-9.9MM **Privately Held**
WEB: www.interbankfsb.com
SIC: 6035 Federal savings bank

(G-1835)
LPL LLC
Also Called: Lyndale Plant Service
5207 W 73rd St   (55439-2206)
PHONE..............................952 345-8240
Dallas Schwandt, *Member*
Kathy Schwandt, *Member*
EMP: 30 **EST:** 2007
SALES (est): Under 500K **Privately Held**
SIC: 7359 Equipment rental & leasing
services

(G-1836)
MARCUS SOLUTIONS LLC
6101 Zenith Ave S   (55410-2839)
PHONE..............................952 373-4038
EMP: 25 **EST:** 2004

SALES (est): 1MM-4.9MM **Privately Held**
SIC: 8742 Business management
consultant

(G-1837)
MINNESOTA HEART CLINIC INC
6405 France Ave S Ste 200   (55435-2164)
PHONE..............................952 836-3700
William Hession, *President*
EMP: 100 **EST:** 1988
SQ FT: 14,000
SALES (est): 10MM-24.9MM **Privately Held**
WEB: www.minnesotaheart.com
SIC: 8011 Cardiologist & cardio-vascular
specialist; surgeon's office

(G-1838)
NASH-FINCH CO   **(PA)**
7600 France Ave S Ste 200   (55435-5935)
PO Box 355, Minneapolis   (55440-0355)
PHONE..............................952 832-0534
FAX: 952 844-1239
Alec C Covington, *President*
Harry Morford, *President*
Anne Brown, *General Mgr*
Elizabeth Frandle, *General Mgr*
David Herbers, *General Mgr*
▲ **EMP:** 326 **EST:** 1885
SQ FT: 126,000
SALES (corp-wide): 5.21B **Publicly Held**
WEB: www.nashfinch.com
SIC: 5141 5142 5147 5148 Wholesales
general line groceries; wholesales cured or
smoked meat; wholesales fresh meat;
wholesales fresh fruits; wholesales fresh
vegetables; retail supermarket chain;
wholesales packaged frozen foods

(G-1839)
NEW LIFE MULTI-FAMILY MGT
7455 France Ave S 381   (55435-4702)
PHONE..............................952 831-0866
Kevin W Howat, *Member*
Dennis Doyle, *Member*
Marykay Conway, *Corp Secy*
EMP: 150 **EST:** 2005
SQ FT: 65,164
SALES (est): 25MM-49.9MM **Privately Held**
SIC: 6531 Real estate rental agency

(G-1840)
NORTHERN LIGHTS BROADCASTING
5300 Edina Ind Blvd   (55439-2922)
PHONE..............................952 842-7200
Steve Woodbury, *Member*
Terry Hennen, *Controller*
Tracey Waldschmidt, *Manager*
EMP: 25 **EST:** 2007
SQ FT: 5,000
SALES (est): 1MM-4.9MM **Privately Held**
SIC: 4832 Radio broadcasting station
PA: Pohlad Co's
    60 S 6th St Ste 3700
    Minneapolis MN 55402
    612 661-3700

(G-1841)
PROFESSIONAL REPRODUCTIONS INC
Also Called: Data Print Distribution
7415 Cahill Rd   (55439-2726)
PHONE..............................952 946-1200
FAX: 952 946-1253
Patrick Maloney, *President*
Mitch Abbett, *Vice Pres*
Brad Davis, *Vice Pres*
Chris Maloney, *CFO*
EMP: 25 **EST:** 1980
SQ FT: 22,000
SALES (est): 1MM-4.9MM **Privately Held**
WEB: www.dpd-info.com
SIC: 7334 7331 Photocopying & duplicating
services; book binding service; commercial
printing; direct mail advertising service;
offset printing; typesetting service

(G-1842)
ROGHARD FINANCIAL LLC ✪
7505 Metro Blvd Ste 300   (55439-3020)
PHONE..............................952 351-8300
Charlie Hardcastle, *Member*
EMP: 103 **EST:** 2008
SALES (est): 5MM-9.9MM **Privately Held**
SIC: 7389 Financial service

(G-1843)
RYLAND GROUP INC
7599 Anagram Dr   (55439)
PHONE..............................952 229-6000
EMP: 100
SALES (est): 25MM-49.9MM **Publicly Held**
WEB: www.ryland.com
SIC: 1531 6162 New housing operative
builder; mortgage banking service
PA: Ryland Group Inc
    24025 Park Sorrento Ste 100
    Calabasas CA 91302
    818 223-7500

(G-1844)
SCHOENECKERS INC   **(PA)**
7630 Bush Lake Rd   (55439-2805)
PHONE..............................952 835-4800
FAX: 952 844-4034
Guy Schoenecker, *Ch of Bd*
Larry Schoenecker, *President*
Gary Hanson, *Managing Dir*
L M Johnson, *Corp Secy*
Marietta Coursolle, *Senior VP*
▲ **EMP:** 900 **EST:** 1950
SQ FT: 400,000 **Privately Held**
WEB: www.schoeneckers.com
SIC: 8742 Incentive or award program
consultant; training & development
consultant

(G-1845)
SECOND DATA ENTERPRISES INC
3601 Minnesota Dr Ste 800   (55435-5250)
PHONE..............................612 326-6833
Bernie Lemieux, *Director*
EMP: 62
SALES (est): 5MM-9.9MM **Privately Held**
SIC: 7374 Data processing & preparation
services

(G-1846)
THOMSEN & NYBECK
3300 Edinbrgh Way Ste 600   (55435-5962)
PHONE..............................952 835-7000
FAX: 952 835-9450
Donald Smith, *Principal*
William Sjholm, *Principal*
Thomas Kelley, *CFO*
Lucas Robert Jr, *Attorney*
Tom Kelly, *Manager*
EMP: 38 **EST:** 1972
SALES (est): 5MM-9.9MM **Privately Held**
WEB: www.tn-law.com
SIC: 8111 General practice law office

(G-1847)
TRADITION CAPITAL BANK
7601 France Ave S Ste 140   (55435-5997)
PHONE..............................952 806-6600
Reid Evenson-Exec, *Principal*
Dan Fagan, *Exec VP*
Marcia Malzahn, *Senior VP*
EST: 2005 **Privately Held**
SIC: 6022 State commercial bank

(G-1848)
UNITED HEALTHCARE OF WYOMING
5901 Lincoln Dr   (55436-1611)
PHONE..............................952 992-5450
Shelly Tracey, *Publisher*
Melani Longueville, *Principal*
Joan Moe, *Corp Secy*
Sean Gregory, *Vice Pres*
Juan Serrano, *Vice Pres*
EMP: 1200
SALES (est): 500MM-999.9MM **Publicly Held**
WEB: www.unitedhealthgroup.com
SIC: 6324 Health insurance maintenance
organization
PA: Unitedhealth Group Inc
    9900 Bren Rd E
    Minnetonka MN 55343
    952 936-1300

(G-1849)
UNITY BANK NORTH
7101 Washington Ave S   (55439-1517)
PHONE..............................952 465-3000
Job Palesh, *Branch Mgr*

EMP: 65
SALES (est): 10MM-24.9MM **Privately Held**
SIC: 6021 National commercial bank
PA: Unity Bank North
210 Main St
Red Lake Falls MN 56750
218 253-2143

(G-1850)
ZURICH NORTH AMERICAN INSCE
3600 Minnesota Dr Ste 200 (55435-7905)
PHONE 952 229-3600
FAX: 952 229-3610
Terry Gray, *Vice Pres*
Jamie S Hutchins, *Vice Pres*
Kim Guentzel, *Vice Pres*
Marion Olsten, *Branch Mgr*
John Arther, *Manager*
EMP: 55
SALES (est): 5MM-9.9MM **Privately Held**
WEB: www.zurichna.com
SIC: 6411 Insurance services
HQ: Zurich North American Insce
1400 American Ln
Schaumburg IL 60196
847 605-6000

ELBOW LAKE
Grant County

(G-1851)
ELEAH MEDICAL CENTER
930 1st St NE (56531-4611)
PHONE 218 685-4406
Larry Rapp MD, *CEO*
Barb Amundson, *Manager*
Nancy Shaw, *Admin Sec*
EMP: 50 **EST:** 1971
SQ FT: 28,000
SALES (est): 5MM-9.9MM **Privately Held**
SIC: 8031 Osteopathic physicians' office & clinic

(G-1852)
ELEAH MEDICAL CENTRE
930 1st St NE (56531-4611)
PHONE 218 685-4461
Nancy Shah, *Corp Secy*
Nancy Shaw, *Corp Secy*
Jodi McGaffey, *Office Mgr*
Lary Rapp, *Administrator*
Barb Moore, *Phys Thrpy Dir*
EMP: 65 **EST:** 1994
SALES (est): 1MM-4.9MM **Privately Held**
WEB: www.eleahmed.org
SIC: 8322 Individual & family social services

(G-1853)
GATEWAY BUILDING SYSTEMS INC
33424 US Highway 59 (56531-9434)
PHONE 218 685-4420
FAX: 218 685-9975
Ann Moellman, *VP Finance*
Brian Shuck, *Branch Mgr*
EMP: 25
SALES (est): 5MM-9.9MM **Privately Held**
SIC: 1542 5083 Commercial & institutional building construction; wholesales agricultural machinery & equipment; farm building construction; agricultural silo construction
PA: Gateway Building Systems Inc
3451 University Dr S
Fargo ND 58104
701 293-7202

(G-1854)
NORTH DAKOTA PIGS CO-OP
26955 Oak Point Rd (56531-9500)
PHONE 218 685-6888
Jim Merritt, *CEO*
EMP: 26 **EST:** 2004 **Privately Held**
SIC: 0213 Hog & pig farming

(G-1855)
WEST CENTRAL MINNESOTA
411 Industrial Park Blvd (56531)
PO Box 956 (56531-0956)
PHONE 218 685-4486
FAX: 218 685-6741

Stephen Nagel, *Director*
EMP: 75 **EST:** 1965 **Privately Held**
SIC: 8399 Community action agency

ELGIN
Wabasha County

(G-1856)
MISSISSIPPI VALLEY FRUIT LLC
28085 County Road 25 (55932-5320)
PHONE 507 876-2891
Fred Wescott, *Member*
Sam Hecter, *Member*
EMP: 25 **EST:** 2000 **Privately Held**
SIC: 0723 Farm-dried fruit packing services

(G-1857)
WESCOTT AGRI-PRODUCTS INC
28085 County Road 25 (55932-5320)
PHONE 507 876-2891
FAX: 507 876-2820
Fred Wescott, *President*
Susan Wescott, *Corp Secy*
Lenore Wescott, *Vice Pres*
Keith Davis, *Controller*
Jodi Ritzinger, *Bookkeeper*
▲ **EMP:** 45 **EST:** 1974
SALES (est): 10MM-24.9MM **Privately Held**
WEB: www.wescottorchard.com
SIC: 5148 0175 Wholesales fresh fruits; wholesales vegetables; apple orchard

---

ELK RIVER
Anoka County

(G-1858)
NOVON CONSULTING CORP
21453 Nowthen Blvd NW (55330-8447)
PHONE 612 868-7057
Susan Leistico, *President*
Kirsten Cecil, *COO*
EMP: 25 **EST:** 1996
SQ FT: 800
SALES (est): 1MM-4.9MM **Privately Held**
SIC: 8748 Systems engineering consultant

ELK RIVER
Sherburne County

(G-1859)
ABFALTER BROTHERS CONCRETE LLC (PA)
15546 Cleveland St NW (55330-6219)
PHONE 763 635-8088
FAX: 763 263-8108
Gary Klersy, *Partner*
Gilbert Abfalter, *Partner*
Lyn Hendrickson, *Controller*
EMP: 38 **EST:** 1982
SQ FT: 20,000 **Privately Held**
WEB: www.abfalterconcrete.com
SIC: 1741 Masonry & stonework contractor

(G-1860)
AITKIN AGRI-PEAT INC
11555 205th Ave NW (55330-8857)
PO Box 332 (55330-0332)
PHONE 763 441-8387
Todd Plaisted, *President*
Steven A Spigrelli, *Exec Dir*
EMP: 50 **EST:** 1994
SALES (est): 25MM-49.9MM **Privately Held**
SIC: 5191 Wholesales potting & planting soil

(G-1861)
ALLINA HEALTH SYSTEM
14181 Business Ctr Dr NW (55330-4654)
PHONE 763 236-0414
Becky Forsell, *Office Mgr*
Laura Peterson, *Manager*
Evan D Friese, *Obstetrician*
Paul E Havel, *Surgeon*
Martin Zadnik, *Surgeon*
EMP: 50
SALES (est): 5MM-9.9MM **Privately Held**
WEB: www.allina.com

SIC: 8011 Clinic operated by physicians
PA: Allina Health System
2925 Chicago Ave
Minneapolis MN 55407
612 775-5000

(G-1862)
AVALON HOME CARE
20132 Ulysses St NW (55330-2254)
PHONE 763 753-8658
FAX: 763 753-4314
Becky Judich, *Owner*
EMP: 100 **EST:** 2000
SALES (est): 1MM-4.9MM **Privately Held**
SIC: 8082 Home health care services

(G-1863)
BANK OF ELK RIVER (PA)
630 Main St NW (55330-1503)
PHONE 763 441-1000
FAX: 763 441-0847
E P Babcock, *Ch of Bd*
James M Simpson, *President*
Kim Carter, *Vice Pres*
Patrick Dwyer, *Vice Pres*
Mark Faydo, *Vice Pres*
EMP: 47 **EST:** 1885
SQ FT: 9,000
SALES (corp-wide): 31.11M **Privately Held**
SIC: 6022 Commercial state trust companies accepting deposits

(G-1864)
BROTHERS FIRE PROTECTION CO
9950 Highway 10 (55330-6227)
PHONE 763 441-2290
FAX: 763 441-5010
Steve Chieslukowski, *President*
Gary Steinke, *Vice Pres*
Damian Kovatovich, *Vice Pres*
Stephen Cuslelcoski, *Director*
Robert E Cuslelcoski, *Director*
EMP: 60 **EST:** 1994
SQ FT: 4,000
SALES (est): 5MM-9.9MM **Privately Held**
SIC: 1711 Fire sprinkler system installation service

(G-1865)
CARGILL INC
10383 165th Ave NW (55330-6304)
PHONE 763 441-3330
FAX: 763 241-3399
Mike Craig, *Manager*
Julie Racz, *Manager*
Kate Plaisance, *Manager*
Stacy Dillon, *Manager*
Jackie Sadowski, *Administrator*
EMP: 60 **Privately Held**
SIC: 8731 Commercial agricultural research services

(G-1866)
CARGILL INC
10383 165th Ave NW (55330-6304)
PHONE 763 441-6508
Mike Craig, *Branch Mgr*
EMP: 60 **Privately Held**
SIC: 8731 5191 8732 Commercial agricultural research services; wholesales agricultural fertilizer; commercial nonphysical research laboratory

(G-1867)
CITY OF ELK RIVER
Also Called: Elk River Municipal Utilities
13069 Orono Pkwy NW (55330-5600)
PHONE 763 441-2020
FAX: 763 441-8099
Michael Thiry, *Manager*
Bryan Adams, *Manager*
Glenn Sundeen, *Manager*
Theresa Slominski, *Exec Dir*
EMP: 27
SALES (est): 10MM-24.9MM **Privately Held**
SIC: 4911 Electric services; mayors' office
PA: City of Elk River
13065 Orono Pkwy NW
Elk River MN 55330
763 635-1000

(G-1868)
COLDWELL BANKER VISION
231 Main St NW Ste A (55330-1542)
PHONE 763 241-0155
Mark Urista, *Owner*
Debra Urista, *Co-Owner*
Lona Demars, *Finance*
Diane Schaefbauer, *Administrator*
Stephanie Danielson, *Administrator*
EMP: 55 **EST:** 1995
SQ FT: 4,600
SALES (est): 10MM-24.9MM **Privately Held**
WEB: www.coldwellbankervision.com
SIC: 6531 Real estate services

(G-1869)
COUNTRY INN & SUITES BY
18894 Dodge St NW (55330-5708)
PHONE 763 241-6990
FAX: 763 241-7301
Gene Hugh, *Owner*
EMP: 25 **EST:** 1999
SALES (est): 1MM-4.9MM **Privately Held**
SIC: 7011 Traveler accommodations

(G-1870)
CRYSTAL DISTRIBUTION INC
17560 Tyler St NW (55330-4752)
PHONE 763 391-7790
Pat O'Brien, *President*
Amanda Sherman, *Administrator*
EMP: 60 **EST:** 1994
SQ FT: 11,000
SALES (est): 5MM-9.9MM **Privately Held**
WEB: www.cdicurbs.com
SIC: 5075 Sheet metal fabricator; wholesales ventilating equipment & supplies

(G-1871)
D J'S HEATING & AIR CONDG
9940 Highway 10 (55330-6227)
PHONE 763 421-5313
Donald Savitski, *President*
EMP: 30 **EST:** 1976
SALES (est): 1MM-4.9MM **Privately Held**
SIC: 1711 5074 Retails fireplaces; heating & air conditioning contractor; wholesales plumbing & heating equipment & supplies

(G-1872)
ELK RIVER COUNTRY CLUB INC
20015 Elk Lake Rd NW (55330-8529)
PHONE 763 441-4111
FAX: 763 441-7997
Scott Schwab, *President*
Chris Singer, *General Mgr*
Kevin Carter, *Executive*
EMP: 50 **EST:** 1960
SQ FT: 1,500
SALES (est): 1MM-4.9MM **Privately Held**
WEB: www.elkrivercc.com
SIC: 7997 Membership golf club

(G-1873)
ELK RIVER INDEPENDENT SCHOOL
Also Called: Lincoln Elementary School
600 School St NW (55330-1343)
PHONE 763 241-3480
FAX: 763 241-3481
Donna Williams, *Principal*
Cheryl Lany, *Librarian*
Sheilia Deiotte, *Tech/Comp Coord*
EMP: 80
ADMISSIONS: 509 **Privately Held**
SIC: 8351 Public school; child day care service
PA: Elk River Independent School
815 Highway 10
Elk River MN 55330
763 241-3400

(G-1874)
1ST NATIONAL REPOSSESSIONCOM
950 Highway 10 Ste 4 (55330-2525)
PO Box 231, Albertville (55301-0231)
PHONE 763 241-5212
Don Mashak, *President*
EMP: 49 **EST:** 1988
SQ FT: 47,000
SALES (est): 1MM-4.9MM **Privately Held**
WEB: www.repo.net

SIC: 7389 Repossession service; merchandise liquidator

(G-1875)
FULL PRESENT INC
19320 Highway 169 (55330-4645)
PHONE 763 441-5999
Kyle Simonson, *CEO*
Carrie Johnson, *Principal*
Melissa Brookings, *Manager*
Susie Kadlec, *Manager*
Michael Fasching, *Exec Dir*
EMP: 45 EST: 1985
SALES (est): 1MM-4.9MM **Privately Held**
WEB: www.simonsons.com
SIC: 7991 Spas

(G-1876)
GREAT NORTHERN LANDSCAPES INC
Also Called: Nowthen Nursery
19720 Iguana St NW (55330-7049)
PHONE 763 274-2678
John Huninghake, *President*
Timothy Beckman, *Sales Staff*
EMP: 25 EST: 1990
SQ FT: 2,000 **Privately Held**
WEB: www.gnlandscapes.com
SIC: 0782 Landscaping services

(G-1877)
GREAT RIVER ENERGY
17845 Highway 10 (55330-1500)
PHONE 763 441-3121
Louy Theeuwen, *General Mgr*
Wayne Hanson, *General Mgr*
Tom Malone, *General Mgr*
Gordon Pietsch, *General Mgr*
Don Holl, *Vice Chairman*
EMP: 250
SALES (est): 100MM-499.9MM **Privately Held**
WEB: www.greatriverenergy.com
SIC: 4911 Provides electric power generation services; provides electric power transmission services
PA: Great River Energy
12300 Elm Creek Blvd N
Maple Grove MN 55369
763 445-5000

(G-1878)
GUARDIAN ANGELS BY THE LAKE
13439 185th Ln NW Ofc (55330-1767)
PHONE 763 241-7682
FAX: 763 274-1349
Sherry Emerson, *Principal*
Annette Greely, *Director*
EMP: 50 EST: 1999
SALES (est): 1MM-4.9MM **Privately Held**
SIC: 8052 Intermediate care facility

(G-1879)
GUARDIAN ANGELS EVAN HOME CARE
400 Evans Ave NW (55330-2604)
PHONE 763 441-1213
Mary Wells, *Bookkeeper*
Mark Pederson, *Administrator*
Karen Forsberg, *Exec Dir*
Lynn Gerard, *Director*
EMP: 200 EST: 1996
SALES (est): 5MM-9.9MM **Privately Held**
SIC: 8082 Home health care services

(G-1880)
GUARDIAN ANGELS HEALTH SVCS
Also Called: Elk River Nursing Home
280 Evans Ave NW Ofc (55330-3613)
PHONE 763 441-1213
FAX: 763 241-4444
Daniel Dixon, *President*
John Bailey, *Corp Secy*
Jim Bartz, *VP Finance*
EMP: 199 EST: 1963
SALES (est): 5MM-9.9MM **Privately Held**
SIC: 8051 6513 8082 Convalescent home; home health care services; apartment building operator

(G-1881)
GUARDIAN ANGELS OF ELK RIVER
280 Evans Ave NW (55330-3612)
PHONE 763 241-4428
Dan Dixon, *President*
Judy Reistad, *Manager*
EMP: 99
SALES (est): 5MM-9.9MM **Privately Held**
SIC: 8744 Facilities support services

(G-1882)
KOWSARY TURF INC
22968 142nd St NW (55330-3201)
PHONE 763 862-4646
FAX: 763 862-8282
Abdul G Kowsary, *President*
Susan Kowsary, *Vice Pres*
EMP: 30 EST: 1995
SQ FT: 30,000 **Privately Held**
SIC: 0782 0181 Landscaping services; sod farm

(G-1883)
MARCUS THEATRES CORP
Also Called: Elk River Theatres
570 Frport Elk River Mall (55330)
PHONE 763 441-1234
Ben Reiners, *Manager*
EMP: 50
SALES (est): 1MM-4.9MM **Publicly Held**
WEB: www.marcustheatres.com
SIC: 7832 Indoor movie theater
HQ: Marcus Theatres Corp
100 E Wisconsin Ave # 1
Milwaukee WI 53202
414 905-1500

(G-1884)
MIKE WINGARD
19671 Hudson Cir NW (55330-1805)
PHONE 763 441-8247
Mike Wingard, *Owner*
EMP: 40 **Privately Held**
SIC: 0722 Potatoes machine harvesting services

(G-1885)
MORRELL TRANSFER INC
10752 171st Ave NW (55330-6323)
PHONE 763 441-2011
FAX: 763 441-4527
Larry V Morrell V, *President*
Arlyce Morrell, *Treasurer*
Donna Evens, *Human Res Mgr*
Brian Lyons, *Manager*
EMP: 37 EST: 1958
SQ FT: 33,000
SALES (est): 1MM-4.9MM **Privately Held**
WEB: www.morrellco.com
SIC: 4213 4731 Long-distance less than truckload freight trucking services; freight transportation arrangement services

(G-1886)
MORTGAGES UNLIMITED
13737 210th Ave NW (55330-8915)
PHONE 763 633-0576
Alan Sakry, *President*
EMP: 50 EST: 2004
SALES (est): 10MM-24.9MM **Privately Held**
SIC: 6141 6162 Personal credit institution; mortgage & loan lending

(G-1887)
NORTHERN STATES POWER CO
Also Called: XCEL Energy
10700 165th Ave NW (55330-6305)
PHONE 763 441-3800
William Helliwell, *Mfg Staff*
Bill Helliwell, *Manager*
Laurian Reiners, *Manager*
EMP: 66
SALES (est): 25MM-49.9MM **Publicly Held**
WEB: www.middletownpower.com
SIC: 4911 Provides electric power transmission services
HQ: Northern States Power Co
414 Nicollet Mall
Minneapolis MN 55401
612 330-5500

(G-1888)
NYBERG & ASSOC PA INC
303 Main St NW (55330-1531)
PHONE 763 441-9181
Gerome Nyberg, *President*
EMP: 30 EST: 1987
SALES (est): 1MM-4.9MM **Privately Held**
SIC: 8021 Dental office

(G-1889)
OPPORTUNITY PARTNERS INC
Also Called: Lavine Place
11754191 One Half Ave NW (55330)
PHONE 763 441-0960
FAX: 763 441-3205
Tim Hamson, *Manager*
EMP: 30
SALES (est): 1MM-4.9MM **Privately Held**
SIC: 8361 Residential care facility
PA: Opportunity Partners Inc
5500 Opportunity Ct
Hopkins MN 55343
952 938-5511

(G-1890)
PLAISTED CO'S INC
11555 205th Ave NW (55330-8857)
PO Box 332 (55330-0332)
PHONE 763 441-1100
Todd Plaisted, *President*
John Plaisted, *Vice Pres*
Mark Duitsman, *Director*
EMP: 35 EST: 1990
SQ FT: 20,000
SALES (est): 1MM-4.9MM **Privately Held**
WEB: www.plaistedcompanies.com
SIC: 4213 0711 Building materials transportation; heavy hauling transportation services; soil preparation services

(G-1891)
PULTE HOMES
7020 Quaday Ave (55330)
PHONE 763 241-9001
Mike Devoe, *Branch Mgr*
EMP: 100
SALES (est): 25MM-49.9MM **Publicly Held**
WEB: www.pulte.com
SIC: 1531 Single-family home speculative builder
DH: Pulte Homes Corp
100 Bloomfield Hills Pkwy
Bloomfield Hills MI 48304
248 644-7300

(G-1892)
SELECT TRANSCRIPTION INC
11040 183rd Cir NW Ste C (55330-2857)
PHONE 763 441-3021
FAX: 763 241-1924
Jan Olson, *CEO*
EMP: 60 EST: 1995
SALES (est): 1MM-4.9MM **Privately Held**
SIC: 8099 Medical services organization

(G-1893)
SIGNATURE STUCCO CONCEPTS INC
17258 Ulysses St NW (55330-1570)
PHONE 763 241-4110
FAX: 763 241-1442
Steve Caouette, *President*
Scott Swanson, *Vice Pres*
EMP: 25 EST: 1997
SALES (est): 1MM-4.9MM **Privately Held**
WEB: www.signaturestucco.com
SIC: 1742 Interior stucco contractor

(G-1894)
STEVE'S ELK RIVER NURSERY INC
15101 Highway 10 (55330-7609)
PO Box 750 (55330-0750)
PHONE 763 441-3090
FAX: 763 441-5992
Debra A Eid, *President*
EMP: 35 EST: 1978
SQ FT: 18,000 **Privately Held**
WEB: www.steveselkrivernursery.com
SIC: 0782 Landscaping services; retails nursery stock, seeds & bulbs

(G-1895)
VISION OF ELK RIVER INC
12508 Elk Lake Rd NW (55330-2448)
PHONE 763 441-4420
Bill Dickenson, *President*
Mark Ostwald, *Manager*
Arlene Cunningham, *Manager*
EMP: 150 EST: 1967
SALES (est): 1MM-4.9MM **Privately Held**
WEB: www.visionofelkriver.com
SIC: 4151 School bus service

(G-1896)
WINGARD FARMS
457 196th Dr NW (55330-7914)
PHONE 763 263-2635
Mike Wingard, *Partner*
Art Wingard, *Partner*
James McHugh, *Partner*
Tom Wingard, *Partner*
EMP: 27 EST: 1996
SALES (est): 10MM-24.9MM **Privately Held**
SIC: 5148 Wholesales fresh potatoes

(G-1897)
ZYLSTRA HARLEY DAVIDSON INC
19600 Evans St NW (55330-1046)
PHONE 763 241-2000
Thomas C Zylstra, *President*
Robert Zylstra, *Corp Secy*
EMP: 35 EST: 2000
SALES (est): 5MM-9.9MM **Privately Held**
SIC: 7699 Motorcycle dealer; motorcycle repair shop

ELK RIVER
Wright County

(G-1898)
ANOKA EQUINE VETERINARY SVCS
16445 70th St NE (55330-6521)
PHONE 763 441-3797
FAX: 763 441-3683
Thomas Juergens, *President*
John C Thieke, *Principal*
Kim Voller, *Vice Pres*
Kathleen A Schmit, *Manager*
Lisa A Borzynski, *Manager*
EMP: 30 EST: 1981 **Privately Held**
WEB: www.anokaequine.com
SIC: 0742 Veterinarian services

(G-1899)
FUNCITY
9100 Park Ave NE (55330-7261)
PHONE 763 441-8365
FAX: 763 441-5664
Rudy J Thibodeau, *Owner*
EMP: 35 EST: 1988
SALES (est): 1MM-4.9MM **Privately Held**
SIC: 7999 Miniature golf course

(G-1900)
INSTALLED BUILDING PRODUCTS
5861 Queens Ave NE (55330-6472)
PHONE 763 441-2313
Kevin Henry, *Branch Mgr*
EMP: 80
SALES (est): 5MM-9.9MM **Privately Held**
SIC: 1742 1761 Drywall, plastering & insulation contractor; roofing & gutter work contractor

(G-1901)
METRO HOME INSULATION INC
5861 Queens Ave NE (55330-6472)
PHONE 763 441-2313
FAX: 763 441-6618
Kevin Henry, *President*
Pam Kubat, *Office Mgr*
Pam Kuburt, *Manager*
EMP: 36 EST: 1982
SQ FT: 9,000
SALES (est): 1MM-4.9MM **Privately Held**
SIC: 1742 Building insulation installation service

(G-1902)

MIDWEST LANDSCAPES INC
6221 Oakwood Ave NE (55330-0078)
PHONE.............................763 241-1320
FAX: 763 241-1340
Adam Zopfi, *President*
Janell Brumm, *Manager*
EMP: 50 **EST:** 1971 **Privately Held**
WEB: www.midwestlandscapes.com
SIC: 0782 Landscaping services

(G-1903)

OTSEGO HOSPITALITY LLC
9200 Quaday Ave NE (55330-6661)
PHONE.............................763 656-4400
Doug Karle, *Member*
April Erstad, *Office Mgr*
EMP: 100 **EST:** 2003
SALES (est): 5MM-9.9MM **Privately Held**
SIC: 8741 Hotel or motel management
services

(G-1904)

PRAIRIE TECHNOLOGIES INC OF MN
5600 Queens Ave NE # 400 (55330-6411)
PHONE.............................763 255-3200
Michael Day, *President*
Lisa Shykes, *Manager*
EMP: 28 **EST:** 1976
SQ FT: 7,715
SALES (est): 1MM-4.9MM **Privately Held**
WEB: www.directdigital.com
SIC: 1731 Energy management control
service

ELKO
Scott County

(G-1905)

J & D DRYWALL INC
11111 Deuce Rd (55020-9572)
PHONE.............................952 461-4078
FAX: 952 461-5078
Joe Friedges, *President*
Deanna Friedges, *Corp Secy*
John Stanton, *Manager*
EMP: 27 **EST:** 1980
SQ FT: 700
SALES (est): 1MM-4.9MM **Privately Held**
SIC: 1742 Drywall contractor

ELKTON
Mower County

(G-1906)

FARMERS STATE BANK OF ELKTON
105 Main St (55933-8809)
PHONE.............................507 584-6441
Michael Schneider, *Principal*
Eric Lee, *Officer*
EST: 2007 **Privately Held**
SIC: 6022 State commercial bank

(G-1907)

INFORMATION SYSTEMS SCIENCES
100 N School St (55933-8804)
PHONE.............................507 754-4405
Randall Sprau, *President*
EMP: 25 **EST:** 1998
SALES (est): Under 500K **Privately Held**
SIC: 7359 Equipment rental & leasing
services

ELLSWORTH
Nobles County

(G-1908)

PARKVIEW MANOR INC
308 W Sherman Ave (56129-1016)
PHONE.............................507 967-2482
Michael Werner, *Administrator*
EMP: 67 **EST:** 1970

SALES (est): 1MM-4.9MM **Privately Held**
SIC: 8051 Skilled nursing care facility

ELROSA
Stearns County

(G-1909)

BREITBACH CONSTRUCTION CO
802 1st Ave (56325)
PO Box 78 (56325-0078)
PHONE.............................320 697-5525
FAX: 320 697-5559
Mark Breitbach, *President*
Ryan Breitbach, *Vice Pres*
EMP: 55 **EST:** 1938
SQ FT: 25,000
SALES (est): 10MM-24.9MM **Privately Held**
WEB: www.breitbachconstruction.com
SIC: 1542 1541 Commercial & institutional
building construction; school building
construction; religious building construction;
industrial building & warehouse construction

(G-1910)

NORTH AMERICAN STATE BANK
201 Main St (56325)
PO Box 94 (56325-0094)
PHONE.............................320 697-5533
FAX: 320 697-5535
Mary Bauer, *Manager*
EMP: 31
SALES (est): 5MM-9.9MM **Privately Held**
SIC: 6022 State commercial bank
PA: North American State Bank
   321 Washburn Ave
   Belgrade MN 56312
   320 254-8271

ELY
Lake County

(G-1911)

CANADIAN BORDER OUTFITTERS INC
14635 Canadian Border Rd (55731-8298)
PHONE.............................218 365-5847
FAX: 218 365-5847
Mark Beaumont, *President*
Lynn Beaumont, *Corp Secy*
Sheryl Swenson, *CFO*
EMP: 30 **EST:** 1964
SQ FT: 3,500
SALES (est): 1MM-4.9MM **Privately Held**
WEB: www.canoetrip.com
SIC: 7999 7011 Recreation outfitter
services; eating place; motel

ELY
Saint Louis County

(G-1912)

CAMP WIDJI WAGAN
Also Called: YMCA
3788 N Arm Rd (55731-8441)
PHONE.............................218 365-2117
FAX: 218 365-2018
Tom Cran, *Exec Dir*
Karen Pick, *Director*
EMP: 50 **EST:** 1928 **Privately Held**
WEB: www.widji.org
SIC: 8641 7032 7991 8322 8351 Youth
organizations; youth camps; child day care
service; individual & family social services;
physical fitness center

(G-1913)

DULUTH CLINC- ELY INC
300 W Conan St (55731-1145)
PHONE.............................218 365-7900
Phil Eckman, *President*
Frankk Romano, *Business Mgr*
Norma Cersine, *Corp Secy*
Frank Udovich, *Vice Pres*
Manfred Dobler, *Vice Pres*
EMP: 26 **EST:** 1974
SALES (est): 1MM-4.9MM **Privately Held**
WEB: www.stephen-park.com
SIC: 8011 Physicians' office & clinic

(G-1914)

HOLIDAY INN SUNSPREE RESORT
400 N Pioneer Rd (55731-1057)
PHONE.............................218 365-6565
FAX: 218 365-2840
Bill Schultz, *CEO*
Dawn Manning, *Vice Pres*
EMP: 36 **EST:** 1995
SQ FT: 54,000
SALES (est): 1MM-4.9MM **Privately Held**
WEB: www.grandelylodge.com
SIC: 7011 Traveler accommodations; eating
place; drinking establishment

(G-1915)

SMDC HEALTH SYSTEM
Also Called: Duluth Clinic of Ely
300 W Conan St (55731-1145)
PHONE.............................218 365-3151
FAX: 218 365-7975
Charlene Raskovich, *Insur/Bill Sup*
Mary C Biano MD, *Med Doctor*
Joseph Schwinghamer MD, *Med Doctor*
Michael D Vannorstran, *Med Doctor*
Laurie Hall, *Administrator*
EMP: 25
SALES (est): 1MM-4.9MM **Privately Held**
SIC: 8011 Medical center
PA: Smdc Health System
   400 E 3rd St
   Duluth MN 55805
   218 786-8364

(G-1916)

VERMILLION COMMUNITY COLLEGE
1900 E Camp St (55731-1918)
PHONE.............................218 365-7200
FAX: 218 365-7207
Joe Sertich, *President*
Nicole Squires, *Business Mgr*
Cindy Loushin, *Corp Secy*
Patti Delich, *Human Res Dir*
Mary Lee, *Manager*
EMP: 100 **EST:** 1922 **Privately Held**
WEB: www.msus.edu
SIC: 8399 Non-fee basis fund raising
organization
DH: Minnesota State Colleges
   30 7th St E Ste 350
   Saint Paul MN 55101
   651 296-8012

(G-1917)

WINTERGREEN DOGSLED LODGE INC
205 E Sheridan St (55731-1451)
PHONE.............................218 365-6602
FAX: 218 365-6451
Todd Wing, *General Mgr*
Paul Schurke, *Research*
Hollie Cashman, *Branch Mgr*
Tracy Rivers, *MIS/IT Dir*
EMP: 36
SALES (est): 1MM-4.9MM **Privately Held**
WEB: www.wintergreendesign.com
SIC: 7999 Manufactures men's, youths' &
boys' snow & ski clothing; manufactures
women's & misses' outerwear; recreation
outfitter services
PA: Wintergreen Dogsled Lodge Inc
   1101 Ringrock Rd
   Ely MN 55731
   218 365-6022

(G-1918)

YMC CAMP DUNORD
Also Called: Camp Du Nord
3606 N Arm Rd (55731-8440)
PHONE.............................218 365-3681
FAX: 218 365-5677
Nancy Onkka, *President*
Dave Palmer, *Exec Dir*
Brian Rupe, *Exec Dir*
EMP: 27 **EST:** 1960
SALES (est): 1MM-4.9MM **Privately Held**
SIC: 7032 Recreational & sporting camp

(G-1919)

YMCA OF GREATER ST PAUL
Also Called: Environmental Learning Center
3788 N Arm Rd (55731-8441)
PHONE.............................218 365-2117
Karen Peck, *Exec Dir*
EMP: 100 **Privately Held**
WEB: www.ymcastpaul.org
SIC: 8641 7032 7991 8322 8351 Youth
organizations; youth camps; day care
service; individual & family social services;
physical fitness center
PA: YMCA of Greater Saint Paul
   2125 E Hennepin Ave Ste 100
   Minneapolis MN 55413
   612 465-0450

ERSKINE
Polk County

(G-1920)

GARDEN VALLEY TELEPHONE CO
201 Ross Ave (56535)
PO Box 259 (56535-0259)
PHONE.............................218 687-2400
FAX: 218 687-2454
Warren C Larson, *President*
George Fish, *General Mgr*
Ronald Engelstad, *Principal*
Cheryl Sistad, *District Mgr*
Harry Sjulson, *Corp Secy*
EMP: 100 **EST:** 1906
SQ FT: 10,000 **Privately Held**
WEB: www.gvtel.com
SIC: 4813 Local telephone communications
services

(G-1921)

PIONEER MEMORIAL CARE CENTER
23028 347th St SE (56535-9466)
PHONE.............................218 687-2365
FAX: 218 687-2047
Dwayne Arness, *President*
Joanne Hertwig, *Corp Secy*
Devra Carlson, *Treasurer*
Karen Langseth, *Office Mgr*
Clellie Kiecker, *Nursing Dir*
EMP: 100 **EST:** 1949
SQ FT: 38,285
SALES (est): 1MM-4.9MM **Privately Held**
SIC: 8051 Skilled nursing care facility

ESKO
Carlton County

(G-1922)

RAM MUTUAL INSURANCE CO INC
16 E Highway 61 (55733)
PHONE.............................218 879-3321
Steve Knutson, *President*
Lee Bondhus, *President*
Angie Salmi, *COO*
James Faber, *Vice Pres*
Wayne Johnston, *Controller*
EMP: 59 **EST:** 1931
SQ FT: 13,500
SALES (est): 25MM-49.9MM **Privately Held**
WEB: www.rammutual.com
SIC: 6331 6411 Provides mutual fire,
marine & casualty insurance; worker's
compensation insurance carrier; provides
property damage insurance; fire, marine &
casualty reciprocal interinsurance exchange
service; insurance services

(G-1923)

SCHWAN'S HOME SERVICE INC
5 Jay Cooke Rd (55733-9604)
PHONE.............................218 879-5470
FAX: 218 879-9253
Marv Cramer, *Manager*
Scott McNair, *Manager*
EMP: 25
SALES (est): 10MM-24.9MM **Privately Held**
WEB: www.theschwanfoodcompany.com

SIC: 5142 Wholesales packaged frozen foods; retail meat food & freezer plan
HQ: Schwan's Home Service Inc
115 W College Dr
Marshall MN 56258
507 532-3274

EVANSVILLE
Douglas County

(G-1924)
CRESTVIEW MANOR INC
649 State St NW (56326-8124)
PHONE.............................218 948-2219
FAX: 218 948-2004
Robert F O'Dell, *President*
Frances O'Dell, *Vice Pres*
Carol Kvidt, *Administrator*
Judy Stielen, *Exec Dir*
Carrey Bottema, *Exec Dir*
EMP: 100 EST: 1968
SALES (est): 1MM-4.9MM **Privately Held**
WEB: www.crestviewmanor.com
SIC: 8051 Convalescent home

(G-1925)
EVANSVILLE ARTS COALITION
Also Called: Eca
111 Main St NW (56326-4548)
PO Box 68 (56326-0068)
PHONE.............................218 948-2787
Karen Howell, *Principal*
EMP: 99 EST: 2007
SALES (est): 5MM-9.9MM **Privately Held**
SIC: 8412 8699 Arts or science center; reading rooms & other cultural organizations; art council

(G-1926)
EVANSVILLE CARE CAMPUS LLC
649 State St NW (56326-8124)
PHONE.............................218 948-2219
Arlynn Johnson, *Member*
EMP: 49
SALES (est): 1MM-4.9MM **Privately Held**
SIC: 8051 Skilled nursing care facility

(G-1927)
FIRST SECURITY BANK
303 Kron St (56326)
PO Box 100 (56326-0100)
PHONE.............................218 948-2259
Robert Henrichs, *Principal*
Penny Ostendorf, *Loan Officer*
Sharon Griep, *Cashier*
EST: 2007 **Privately Held**
SIC: 6022 State commercial bank

EVELETH
Saint Louis County

(G-1928)
BENEDICTINE HEALTH SYSTEM
Also Called: St Raphels Hlth Rhbltation Ctr
601 Grant Ave (55734-1314)
PHONE.............................218 744-9800
FAX: 218 744-9829
Dawn Chiabotti, *CEO*
Mary Gregorich, *Human Res Mgr*
Helen Spelts, *Human Res Mgr*
Diane Grahek, *Director*
EMP: 125
SALES (est): 10MM-24.9MM **Privately Held**
SIC: 8093 Outpatient rehabilitation treatment center
PA: Benedictine Health System
503 E 3rd St Ste 400
Duluth MN 55805
218 786-2370

(G-1929)
BROWN TRANSPORTATION INC
7799 N Airport Dr (55734-4055)
PHONE.............................218 744-2888
FAX: 218 744-7923
Ward G Brown Jr, *CEO*
Linda Brown, *Vice Pres*
EMP: 26 EST: 1977
SALES (est): 500-999K **Privately Held**

SIC: 4151 School bus service

(G-1930)
EAST RANGE DEVELOPMENTAL
Also Called: ERDAC
800 A Ave (55734-1405)
PHONE.............................218 744-5130
FAX: 218 744-0107
Rodger Presthang, *Business Mgr*
Dale Gilbertson, *Director*
EMP: 33 EST: 1966
SQ FT: 7,000
SALES (est): 1MM-4.9MM **Privately Held**
SIC: 8331 Job training & vocational rehabilitation services

(G-1931)
EVELETH HOSPITAL CORP
227 McKinley Ave (55734-1606)
PHONE.............................218 744-1950
FAX: 218 744-3868
Joseph Begich, *President*
Sue Cuffe, *QC Dir*
Linda Brown, *Treasurer*
Jeff Pajonk, *Nurse*
EMP: 45 EST: 1959
SQ FT: 33,000
SALES (est): 1MM-4.9MM **Privately Held**
SIC: 8051 Skilled nursing care facility

(G-1932)
NORTHERN BELT & CONVEYOR INC
2700 Elliots Lake Rd (55734-8517)
PHONE.............................218 744-9950
FAX: 218 744-9952
Gregg Hill, *President*
Brenda Hill, *Vice Pres*
EMP: 30 EST: 1996
SALES (est): 1MM-4.9MM **Privately Held**
SIC: 7699 Industrial equipment service

(G-1933)
UNITED TACONITE LLC
1200 County Hwy 16 (55734)
PO Box 180 (55734-0180)
PHONE.............................218 744-7800
FAX: 218 744-7866
Todd Roth, *Principal*
Gordy Popovich, *Purch Agent*
Bob Verville, *Treasurer*
Jim Hecimovich, *Controller*
John Baxter, *Human Res Mgr*
EMP: 430
SALES (est): 100MM-499.9MM **Publicly Held**
WEB: www.cliffsnaturalresources.com
SIC: 1011 Open pit taconite mining
HQ: United Taconite LLC
1100 Superior Ave E Fl 15
Cleveland OH 44114
216 694-5700

(G-1934)
WOODLINE MANUFACTURING INC (PA)
4097 Highway 53 (55734-4143)
PHONE.............................218 744-5966
FAX: 218 744-5969
Charles A Baxter, *Ch of Bd*
John Baxter, *President*
Robert Verville, *Vice Pres*
Gary Winkler, *Controller*
Tiffany Schamberger, *Accounting Dir*
EMP: 88 EST: 1982
SQ FT: 17,000 **Privately Held**
WEB: www.woodlinemfg.com
SIC: 5031 Manufactures hardwood furniture stock & parts; manufactures hardwood dimension lumber; wholesales rough, dressed & finished lumber; manufactures hardwood flooring; manufactures hardwood veneer & plywood; millwork

---

EXCELSIOR
Carver County

(G-1935)
FITNESS 19
23730 Highway 7 (55331-2950)
PHONE.............................952 380-9919
Mike Doucette, *Project Mgr*
Howard Humbyrd, *Manager*

EMP: 30 EST: 2004
SALES (est): 500-999K **Privately Held**
SIC: 7991 Physical fitness center

(G-1936)
ML ENTERPRISES LLC
Also Called: College Nannies & Tutors
23570 Highway 7 (55331-2902)
PHONE.............................952 401-9051
Mike Lutz, *Member*
EMP: 39 EST: 2007
SALES (est): 500-999K **Privately Held**
SIC: 8351 Child day care service; academic tutoring services

(G-1937)
SUPERVALU INC
23800 Highway 7 (55331-3152)
PHONE.............................952 380-9900
FAX: 952 380-3609
Robin Gault, *Manager*
EMP: 113
SALES (est): 100MM-499.9MM **Publicly Held**
WEB: www.supervalu.com
SIC: 5141 Wholesales general line groceries
PA: SUPERVALU Inc
11840 Valley View Rd
Eden Prairie MN 55344
952 828-4000

EXCELSIOR
Hennepin County

(G-1938)
AUTOMATED BUILDING COMPONENTS (PA)
Also Called: ABC
300 Morse Ave (55331-3016)
PO Box 418 (55331-0418)
PHONE.............................952 474-4374
Tom Lowe, *CEO*
James Hurd, *President*
John Gilpin, *Corp Secy*
Brian C Balcer, *Treasurer*
Melody Kloida, *Manager*
EMP: 50 EST: 1973
SQ FT: 25,000
SALES (corp-wide): 36.14M **Privately Held**
SIC: 5031 Millwork; manufactures building & structural wood members; wholesales kitchen cabinets; manufactures wooden floor trusses; manufactures wooden roof trusses

(G-1939)
BEACON BANK
19765 Highway 7 (55331-7513)
PHONE.............................952 474-7309
Robert Weiss, *President*
David Peterka, *Exec VP*
Valerie Sjoblom, *Senior VP*
Terry Keller, *Vice Pres*
Jill Christopulos, *Assoc VP*
EMP: 30 EST: 1906
SQ FT: 20,000
SALES (est): 5MM-9.9MM **Privately Held**
WEB: www.beaconbank.com
SIC: 6022 State commercial bank

(G-1940)
BEVERLY ENTERPRISES - MN
Also Called: Excelsior Nursing Home
515 Division St (55331-3233)
PHONE.............................952 474-5488
FAX: 952 474-3864
Nicole Kummala, *Exec Dir*
Linne L Wise, *Nursing Dir*
Joni Redepenning, *Social Worker*
EMP: 150
SALES (est): 5MM-9.9MM **Privately Held**
WEB: www.beverlynet.com
SIC: 8051 Skilled nursing care facility
HQ: Beverly Enterprises - MN
650 Ramer Ave S
Rush City MN 55069
320 358-4765

(G-1941)
CARGILL FRESHWATER
2500 Shadywood Rd (55331-6201)
PO Box 9300, Minneapolis (55440-9300)
PHONE.............................952 742-3050
Warren Staley, *CEO*
EMP: 50 EST: 2002 **Privately Held**
SIC: 0723 Cash grain crop market preparation services

(G-1942)
COLDWELL BANKER BURNET INC
19400 Highway 7 (55331-9133)
PHONE.............................952 474-2525
Dick Hollerud, *General Mgr*
Neil Henney, *Vice Pres*
Jamie Cook, *Administrator*
EMP: 80
SALES (est): 10MM-24.9MM **Privately Held**
WEB: www.ginnyandtim.com
SIC: 6531 8742 Real estate services; real estate consultant
PA: Coldwell Banker Burnet Inc
190 Cobblestone Ln
Burnsville MN 55337
952 898-5100

(G-1943)
FLOOR STORE INC
Also Called: Jerry's Floor Store
2401 Highway 7 (55331-9700)
PHONE.............................952 401-0955
Dawn Iversen, *Owner*
Mike Keenan, *Manager*
EMP: 45
SALES (est): 5MM-9.9MM **Privately Held**
WEB: www.jerrysfloorstore.com
SIC: 5023 Retails floor coverings; wholesales floor coverings
PA: Floor Store Inc
1550 County Highway 10
Minneapolis MN 55432
763 786-7570

(G-1944)
LAKE COUNTRY BUILDERS LTD
339 2nd St (55331-1805)
PHONE.............................952 474-7121
FAX: 952 474-7957
Sue Jacobson, *Partner*
Peter Jacobson, *Partner*
Renee Koenecke, *Marketing Mgr*
Jason Martin, *CIO*
EMP: 35 EST: 1982
SQ FT: 2,500
SALES (est): 5MM-9.9MM **Privately Held**
SIC: 1521 Single-family home general remodeling service

(G-1945)
LYMAN LUMBER CO (PA)
300 Morse Ave (55331-3016)
PO Box 40 (55331-0040)
PHONE.............................952 470-3600
FAX: 952 474-0910
Thomas P Lowe, *Ch of Bd*
James E Hurd, *President*
John Gilpin, *Corp Secy*
Jeanne Scholle, *Vice Pres*
John Waldrown, *Vice Pres*
EMP: 270 EST: 1897
SQ FT: 437,900
SALES (corp-wide): 93.42M **Privately Held**
WEB: www.abc-kitchens.com
SIC: 5031 6162 Wholesales rough, dressed & finished lumber; mortgage & loan lending; retails building products & materials

(G-1946)
MICHAEL NELSON MASONRY INC
4620 Manitou Rd (55331-9449)
PHONE.............................952 496-0217
Michael Nelson, *President*
EMP: 40
SALES (est): 1MM-4.9MM **Privately Held**
SIC: 1741 Masonry & stonework contractor

(G-1947)
MIDWEST CRAFT DISTRIBUTORS INC
2745 Kelly Ave (55331-9537)
PHONE......................952 252-7043
Jay K Wood, *President*
Barbara Woods, *Corp Secy*
Cindy Rome, *Bookkeeper*
EMP: 41 **EST:** 1967
SQ FT: 36,000
SALES (est): 10MM-24.9MM **Privately Held**
SIC: 5092 Wholesales arts & crafts equipment & supplies

(G-1948)
MINNESOTA STRUCTURES INC
21930 Minnetonka Blvd (55331-8615)
PHONE......................952 401-3820
David Erotas, *President*
EMP: 30 **EST:** 2001
SALES (est): 5MM-9.9MM **Privately Held**
SIC: 1521 New single-family home construction service

(G-1949)
MINNETONKA COUNTRY CLUB
24575 Smithtown Rd (55331-8587)
PHONE......................952 474-5222
FAX: 952 474-3514
Bohdan Witrik, *Manager*
EMP: 25 **EST:** 1916
SALES (est): 1MM-4.9MM **Privately Held**
WEB: www.minnetonkacc.com
SIC: 7997 Country club; eating place; membership tennis club; membership golf club

(G-1950)
MINNETONKA HEALTH CARE CENTER
Also Called: Lake Minnetonka Care Center
20395 Summerville Rd (55331-9226)
PHONE......................952 474-4474
Gene Sprinkel, *President*
Jeff Sprinkel, *Corp Secy*
Karen Sprinkel, *Vice Pres*
Jeff Frankle, *Facilities Dir*
EMP: 25 **EST:** 1970
SQ FT: 25,000
SALES (est): 1MM-4.9MM **Privately Held**
SIC: 8052 Intermediate care facility

(G-1951)
OLD LOG THEATER LTD
Also Called: Don Stolz Productions
5175 Meadville St (55331-8791)
PO Box 250 (55331-0250)
PHONE......................952 474-5951
FAX: 952 474-1290
Donald D Stolz, *President*
Dan Kuzlik, *Vice Pres*
Glenn Keller, *Treasurer*
EMP: 40 **EST:** 1940
SQ FT: 20,000
SALES (est): 1MM-4.9MM **Privately Held**
WEB: www.oldlog.com
SIC: 7922 Plays, road & stock companies; eating place; theatrical repertory, road or stock company

(G-1952)
OUR SAVIOR LUTHERAN CHURCH
23290 Highway 7 (55331-3139)
PHONE......................952 474-5181
John Zahrte, *Pastor*
Mickey Doolm, *Librarian*
Jeff Machemehl, *Manager*
Connie Beck, *Manager*
Randy Schallhorn, *Administrator*
EMP: 36 **EST:** 1963
ADMISSIONS: 160 **Privately Held**
WEB: www.oslcs.org
SIC: 8351 Private school; private elementary school; provides Lutheran church services; child day care service

(G-1953)
SEACO INC
20540 Summerville Rd (55331-9215)
PHONE......................952 470-7400
John Marcotte, *President*
EMP: 225 **EST:** 1993

SALES (est): 5MM-9.9MM **Privately Held**
SIC: 7231 Unisex hair salon

(G-1954)
TALUS GROUP INC
19675 Near Mountain Blvd (55331-8146)
PHONE......................952 544-2526
FAX: 952 544-5056
Georgia L Andria, *President*
Solveig Myott, *Consultant*
EMP: 35 **EST:** 1990
SQ FT: 2,500
SALES (est): 5MM-9.9MM **Privately Held**
WEB: www.talusgroup.com
SIC: 7379 7361 Data processing consulting service; employment placement services

FAIRFAX
Renville County

(G-1955)
SOUTH CENTRAL GRAIN & ENERGY
64908 State Hwy 4 (55332)
PO Box E (55332-0905)
PHONE......................507 426-8263
Bruce Beussman, *Safety Dir*
Eugene Lutteke, *Manager*
EMP: 75
SALES (est): 100MM-499.9MM **Privately Held**
SIC: 5153 Wholesales grain & field beans

(G-1956)
WILLOW HOME
1001 1st St SE (55332-9794)
PHONE......................507 426-8277
FAX: 507 426-7710
Joyce Evenson, *Administrator*
EMP: 60 **EST:** 1991
SALES (est): 1MM-4.9MM **Privately Held**
SIC: 8361 Self-help group home

FAIRMONT
Martin County

(G-1957)
AVERY WEIGH-TRONIX LLC (HQ)
1000 Armstrong Dr (56031-1439)
PHONE......................507 238-4461
FAX: 507 238-2373
Gerald Bowe, *Member*
David Castle, *Member*
Carl Cramer, *Member*
Gene Tonne, *Member*
Jerry Bowe, *Member*
◆ **EMP:** 5288 **EST:** 1971
SQ FT: 330,000
SALES (corp-wide): 13.87B **Publicly Held**
WEB: www.agscales.com
SIC: 5083 Manufactures weighing machines & apparatus; wholesales agricultural machinery & equipment
PA: Illinois Tool Works Inc
3600 W Lake Ave
Glenview IL 60026
847 724-7500

(G-1958)
BANK MIDWEST (PA)
118 Downtown Plz (56031-1709)
PO Box 611 (56031-0611)
PHONE......................507 235-3327
FAX: 507 235-6594
Stephan Goodenau, *CEO*
Jean Pike, *Exec VP*
Allen Core, *Senior VP*
Curt Johnson, *Senior VP*
Tom Lytle, *Vice Pres*
EMP: 25 **EST:** 1907
SQ FT: 5,000
SALES (corp-wide): 26.54M **Privately Held**
SIC: 6021 National commercial bank

(G-1959)
CARPE DIEM MEDICAL INC
2492 Albion Ave (56031-3301)
PHONE......................507 399-0262
EMP: 42 **EST:** 2003

SALES (est): 10MM-24.9MM **Privately Held**
WEB: www.carpediemmedical.com
SIC: 5047 Wholesales medical & hospital equipment

(G-1960)
CHS INC
1833 130th St (56031-1329)
PHONE......................507 238-8900
Eric Colvin, *Manager*
Kent Meyers, *Manager*
EMP: 45
SALES (est): 5MM-9.9MM **Publicly Held**
WEB: www.cenexharveststates.com
SIC: 1389 Oil field services
PA: CHS Inc
5500 Cenex Dr
Inver Grove Heights MN 55077
651 355-6000

(G-1961)
CLOVERLEAF COLD STORAGE CO
1400 E 8th St (56031-3845)
PHONE......................507 238-4211
FAX: 507 388-2915
Paul Remsky, *General Mgr*
Tony Wiltgin, *Manager*
EMP: 50
SALES (est): 5MM-9.9MM **Privately Held**
WEB: www.cloverleafco.com
SIC: 4222 Cold storage or refrigerated warehousing
PA: Cloverleaf Cold Storage Co
2800 Cloverleaf Ct
Sioux City IA 51111
712 279-8000

(G-1962)
DEWAR ELECTRIC INC
724 E Blue Earth Ave (56031-4032)
PHONE......................507 235-6677
FAX: 507 235-6427
Kathleen Shane, *CEO*
Jeffery Dewar, *President*
Darrell Dewar, *Vice Pres*
EMP: 25 **EST:** 1952
SQ FT: 4,000
SALES (est): 1MM-4.9MM **Privately Held**
SIC: 1731 General electrical contractor

(G-1963)
FAIRMONT COMMUNITY HOSPITAL
800 Medical Center Dr (56031-4575)
PO Box 800 (56031-0800)
PHONE......................507 238-8100
Philip Vuocolo, *CEO*
Amy Gerken, *Accountant*
Kristin Kusewarren, *Mktg Dir*
David E Suthrland, *Manager*
Anita Dunlayey, *Manager*
EMP: 708 **EST:** 1940
SQ FT: 160,000
SALES (est): 50MM-99.9MM **Privately Held**
SIC: 8062 8051 Medical hospital; skilled nursing care facility

(G-1964)
FAIRMONT MEDICAL CENTER MAYO
800 Clinic Cir (56031-4428)
PO Box 800 (56031-0800)
PHONE......................507 238-4263
FAX: 507 238-5197
Dewayne Hanson, *CEO*
Ruth Morris, *Project Mgr*
Marti Wolter, *Opers Mgr*
Gaylen Darnell, *Maint Mgr*
Ennis Arntson, *VP Mktg*
EMP: 700 **EST:** 1940
SQ FT: 26,000
SALES (est): 50MM-99.9MM **Privately Held**
SIC: 8011 Physicians' office & clinic; internal medicine physician or surgeon; general & family practice physician or surgeon office; surgeon's office
PA: Mayo Clinic
200 1st St SW
Rochester MN 55905
507 284-2511

(G-1965)
FAIRMONT ORTHOPEDICS & SPORTS
Also Called: Center For Specialty Care
717 S State St Ste 900 (56031-4478)
PHONE......................507 238-4949
FAX: 507 238-1997
Corey T Welchlin DO, *President*
Sue Diekmann, *COO*
Karen Jepsen, *VP Finance*
Jared Johnson, *Finance*
Dawn Siegling, *Office Mgr*
EMP: 81 **EST:** 1990
SQ FT: 8,000
SALES (est): 5MM-9.9MM **Privately Held**
SIC: 8011 Physicians' office; orthopedic physician office; thoracic physician office

(G-1966)
FAIRMONT REFRIGERATED SERVICE
Also Called: Cloverleaf Cold Stor Fairmont
1400 E 8th St (56031-3845)
PHONE......................507 238-4211
Morton J Kaplan, *President*
Tony Wiltgen, *Superintendent*
David Feiges, *VP Eng R&D*
William Feiges, *Asst Sec*
EMP: 25 **EST:** 1968
SQ FT: 100,000
SALES (est): 1MM-4.9MM **Privately Held**
SIC: 4222 Cold storage or refrigerated warehousing

(G-1967)
GEORGIE'S FITNESS INC
Also Called: Curves For Women
210 Cottonwood Rd (56031-5076)
PO Box 765 (56031-0765)
PHONE......................507 238-9422
Georgie Pfaffinger, *President*
Douglas Storbeck, *Vice Pres*
EMP: 30 **EST:** 2002
SQ FT: 1,500
SALES (est): 500-999K **Privately Held**
SIC: 7991 Exercise salon

(G-1968)
GOLDFINCH ESTATES
850 Goldfinch St Apt 313 (56031-3045)
PHONE......................507 235-9405
FAX: 507 238-4163
Dean Blomke, *President*
EMP: 34 **EST:** 2002
SALES (est): 1MM-4.9MM **Privately Held**
SIC: 8052 8051 Intermediate care facility; skilled nursing care facility

(G-1969)
GREENLEE TEXTRON INC
507 Downtown Plz (56031-1730)
PHONE......................507 238-4357
Wayne Treaudea, *Manager*
EMP: 75
SALES (est): 10MM-24.9MM **Publicly Held**
WEB: www.textron.com
SIC: 5084 Manufactures power hand tools; wholesales industrial hydraulic systems equipment & supplies; manufactures fluid power pumps & motors; manufactures hand tools
HQ: Greenlee Textron Inc
4455 Boeing Dr
Rockford IL 61109
815 397-7070

(G-1970)
HANCOR INC
1001 Timberlake Rd (56031-1447)
PHONE......................507 238-4791
Jeffrey Lueth, *Plant Mgr*
Rick Rodabaugh, *Research*
Sommer Goerndt, *Human Res Mgr*
Mike Hagen, *Sales Staff*
Paul Iwerks, *Manager*
EMP: 40
SALES (est): 5MM-9.9MM **Privately Held**
WEB: www.ads-pipe.com
SIC: 5032 Manufactures plastic pipe; wholesales clay sewer pipe
DH: Hancor Inc
401 Olive St
Findlay OH 45840
419 422-6521

(G-1971)
HARSCO CORP
415 N Main St (56031-1837)
PHONE.....................507 235-7127
FAX: 507 235-7370
G R Newman, *President*
Norma Seibert, *Purchasing*
Ken Brummond, *Engineer*
David Bates, *Human Res Dir*
Robert Kramer, *VP Sales*
EMP: 40 **Publicly Held**
WEB: www.harsco.com
SIC: **5088** Manufactures railroad related
equipment; wholesales railroad equipment
& supplies; manufactures metal cutting
machine tools; manufactures railroad
equipment
PA: Harsco Corp
350 Poplar Church Rd
Camp Hill PA 17011
717 763-7064

(G-1972)
HAWKEYE FOODSERVICE DISTBN
1500 Winnebago Ave (56031-3641)
PHONE.....................507 238-4721
Akers Scott, *Manager*
Mike Brooks, *Manager*
EMP: 50
SQ FT: 40,000
SALES (est): 25MM-49.9MM **Privately Held**
WEB: www.hawkeyefoodservice.com
SIC: **5141** 5142 Wholesales general line
groceries; wholesales packaged frozen
foods
PA: Hawkeye Foodservice Distbn
3550 2nd St
Coralville IA 52241
319 645-2193

(G-1973)
HAWKINS CHEVROLET-CADILLAC INC
1304 E Blue Earth Ave (56031-4254)
PHONE.....................507 238-4786
FAX: 507 238-2084
Thomas A Hawkins Jr, *President*
Evie Anderson, *General Mgr*
Mark Hawkins, *Corp Secy*
Sadie Mosloski, *Human Res Mgr*
Steve Hawkins, *Manager*
EMP: 25 EST: 1967
SQ FT: 9,600
SALES (est): 10MM-24.9MM **Privately Held**
WEB: www.hawkinsprice.com
SIC: **7538** Retails new & used automobiles;
general automotive repair services

(G-1974)
HEALTHWORKS HOME MEDICAL
820 Winnebago Ave Ste 2 (56031-3646)
PHONE.....................507 238-9200
Daniel Kline, *Principal*
EMP: 80 EST: 2004
SALES (est): 25MM-49.9MM **Privately Held**
SIC: **5047** 8082 Wholesales medical &
hospital equipment; home health care
services

(G-1975)
HUMAN SERVICES OF FAIRBAULT
115 W 1st St (56031-1815)
PHONE.....................507 238-4757
FAX: 507 238-1574
Linda Mohwinkel, *Human Resources*
Kathy Werner, *Director*
Warren Knudson, *Director*
Carmen Reckard, *Nursing Dir*
EMP: 95 EST: 1978 **Privately Held**
WEB: www.fmchs.com
SIC: **8399** 8322 Health & welfare council;
individual & family social services

(G-1976)
LAKEVIEW METHODIST HEALTH CARE
610 Summit Dr Ofc OFC (56031-2254)
PHONE.....................507 235-6606
FAX: 507 235-8363
Darcy Bentc, *Treasurer*

Kara Quam, *Human Res Dir*
Glenda Cliffords, *Manager*
Tammy Fritz, *Manager*
Cindy Neunfeldt, *Manager*
EMP: 200 EST: 1958
SQ FT: 90,000
WEB: www.lakeviewhealthservices.org
SIC: **8051** Religious organization; skilled
nursing care facility

(G-1977)
MINNESOTA MOTOR BUS INC
820 Winnebago Ave Ste 3 (56031-3646)
PHONE.....................507 238-4454
FAX: 507 238-1582
James Schoener, *President*
EMP: 25 EST: 1979
SALES (est): 500-999K **Privately Held**
SIC: **4151** School bus service

(G-1978)
PROFINIUM FINANCIAL INC
105 Lake Ave (56031-1812)
PHONE.....................507 235-5538
Michael Bissen, *CFO*
Linda Bontjes, *Controller*
Gary Hanes, *Manager*
Allen Aukes, *IT/INT Sup*
Gary Hoehn, *Officer*
EMP: 72
SALES (est): 10MM-24.9MM **Privately Held**
SIC: **6021** National commercial bank
HQ: Profinium Financial Inc
414 N 5th Ave E
Truman MN 56088
507 776-2311

(G-1979)
REM CENTRAL LAKES INC
Also Called: Rem-Fairmont
107 Dorothy St (56031-3508)
PHONE.....................507 238-4751
FAX: 507 238-4753
Peggy Kunkel, *Regional Mgr*
EMP: 25
SALES (est): 500-999K **Privately Held**
SIC: **8052** Residential mentally
handicapped facility

(G-1980)
ROSEN'S DIVERSIFIED INC (HQ)
1120 Lake Ave (56031-1939)
PO Box 933 (56031-0933)
PHONE.....................507 238-4201
Ivan Wells, *President*
Steve Guetter, *Finance Dir*
Elmer Rosen, *Director*
EMP: 160 EST: 1946
SQ FT: 3,600 **Privately Held**
SIC: **5191** Wholesales agricultural
chemicals
PA: Rosen's Diversified Inc
1120 Lake Ave
Fairmont MN 56031
507 238-4201

(G-1981)
SOUTH CENTRAL SURGICAL CENTER
717 S State St Ste 1000 (56031-4479)
PHONE.....................507 235-3939
FAX: 507 238-3375
Corey Welchlin, *Member*
Dawn Siegling, *Member*
Kerry Briant, *Manager*
Joseph Klick, *Anesthesiology*
EMP: 50 EST: 1999
SALES (est): 5MM-9.9MM **Privately Held**
SIC: **8011** Orthopedic physician office

(G-1982)
STEP INC
411 S State St (56031-4153)
PO Box 110 (56031-0110)
PHONE.....................507 238-4341
Susan Eisemenger, *Manager*
Sue Eisenmenger, *Director*
EMP: 40 EST: 1970
SALES (est): 1MM-4.9MM **Privately Held**
WEB: www.stepinc.org
SIC: **8331** Skill training center

(G-1983)
TORGERSON PROPERTIES LP
Also Called: Holiday Inn
1200 Torgerson Dr (56031-3600)
PO Box 922 (56031-0922)
PHONE.....................507 238-4771
FAX: 507 238-9371
Thomas R Torgerson, *Managing Prtnr*
Stacy Hanning, *Vice Pres*
Dave Zellmer, *Facilities Mgr*
EMP: 100
SALES (est): 5MM-9.9MM **Privately Held**
WEB: www.torgersonproperties.com
SIC: **7011** Traveler accommodations; eating
place; drinking establishment
PA: Torgerson Properties Inc
103 15th Ave NW Ste 200
Willmar MN 56201
320 235-7207

(G-1984)
WOODWARD BROADCASTING INC
Also Called: K S U M-AM
1371 W Lair Rd (56031-2320)
PO Box 491 (56031-0491)
PHONE.....................507 235-5595
FAX: 507 235-5973
Charles Woodward, *President*
Woody Woodward, *General Mgr*
Ann Brown, *Corp Secy*
Lee Bramer, *Engineering*
Don Kliewer, *Sales Executive*
EMP: 33 EST: 1948
SQ FT: 6,500
SALES (est): 1MM-4.9MM **Privately Held**
WEB: www.kfmc.com
SIC: **4832** Radio broadcasting station;
newspaper publisher

FARIBAULT
Rice County

(G-1985)
ABC BUS CO'S INC (PA)
1506 30th St NW (55021-1800)
PHONE.....................507 334-1871
Dane Cornell, *President*
Robert F Foley, *COO*
Brenda Borwege, *Vice Pres*
Duane Geiger, *Vice Pres*
Jeff Jirik, *Vice Pres*
▲ EMP: 70 EST: 1986
SQ FT: 60,000 **Privately Held**
SIC: **5012** 6159 Bus wholesaler; vehicle
finance leasing service

(G-1986)
ABC BUS INC (HQ)
1506 30th St NW (55021-1800)
PHONE.....................507 334-1871
Dane Cornell, *President*
Thomas D Dematteo, *Corp Secy*
Timothy Wayland, *CFO*
Kara Peterson, *Manager*
▲ EMP: 90 EST: 1979
SQ FT: 60,000 **Privately Held**
WEB: www.abc-companies.com
SIC: **5012** Wholesales motor vehicles
PA: ABC Bus Co's Inc
1506 30th St NW
Faribault MN 55021
507 334-1871

(G-1987)
ABC CO'S
1506 30th St NW (55021-1800)
PHONE.....................877 737-2221
Tom Sullivan, *Principal*
Dane Cornell, *Principal*
Denis Gray, *Vice Pres*
Jim Bernacchi, *Manager*
EMP: 98
SALES (est): 5MM-9.9MM **Privately Held**
SIC: **8999** Miscellaneous services

(G-1988)
ALLINA HEALTH SYSTEM
100 State Ave (55021-6337)
PHONE.....................507 334-3921
Chris Johnson, *Manager*
Nancy Swenson, *Manager*

Nancy Mullinbaugh, *Manager*
Samira B Anderson, *Otolaryngology*
EMP: 60
SALES (est): 5MM-9.9MM **Privately Held**
WEB: www.allina.com
SIC: **8011** Clinic operated by physicians
PA: Allina Health System
2925 Chicago Ave
Minneapolis MN 55407
612 775-5000

(G-1989)
AMERICAN COMMUNICATIONS SUPPLY (PA)
3305 Highway 60 W (55021-4869)
PHONE.....................507 334-2268
Robert Chipley, *President*
Kathleen G Potrah, *Corp Secy*
EST: 1996
SQ FT: 20,000
SALES (corp-wide): 3M **Privately Held**
SIC: **5065** Wholesales electronic parts &
equipment

(G-1990)
B H HESELTON CO
Also Called: Heselton Construction
680 24th St NW (55021-2307)
PO Box 246 (55021-0246)
PHONE.....................507 334-3901
FAX: 507 344-0114
John B Heselton, *Member*
Tom Guth, *Corp Secy*
Patrick Heselton, *Manager*
EMP: 65 EST: 1941
SQ FT: 1,600
SALES (est): 5MM-9.9MM **Privately Held**
WEB: www.heseltonconstruction.com
SIC: **1611** 1623 Heavy highway & street
construction; grading services; sewer line
construction; water main construction

(G-1991)
BCM CONSTRUCTION INC
15760 Acorn Trl (55021-7610)
PO Box 37 (55021-0037)
PHONE.....................507 333-1155
Thomas G Mc Donough, *CEO*
EMP: 30 EST: 1994
SALES (est): 1MM-4.9MM **Privately Held**
WEB: www.bcmgrading.com
SIC: **1623** 1794 Water & sewer line
construction; excavation & grading, building
construction contractor

(G-1992)
BEVERLY ENTERPRISES - MN
Also Called: Faribault Manor Health Care
1738 Hulett Ave (55021-2918)
PHONE.....................507 334-3918
FAX: 507 332-2748
Paula O'Malley, *Human Res Mgr*
Barb Walter, *Office Mgr*
Michelle Mangan, *Administrator*
Sherry Larson, *Asst Admin*
EMP: 100
SALES (est): 1MM-4.9MM **Privately Held**
WEB: www.beverlynet.com
SIC: **8051** Skilled nursing care facility
HQ: Beverly Enterprises - MN
650 Ramer Ave S
Rush City MN 55069
320 358-4765

(G-1993)
BITUMINOUS MATERIALS LLC
680 24th St NW (55021-2307)
PHONE.....................507 334-3901
FAX: 507 334-0114
John B Heselton, *Member*
EMP: 55 EST: 1962
SQ FT: 1,600
SALES (est): 5MM-9.9MM **Privately Held**
SIC: **1611** Highway & street paving
contractor

(G-1994)
C & S VENDING CO INC
1919 2nd St NW (55021-4839)
PO Box 876 (55021-0876)
PHONE.....................507 334-8414
FAX: 507 332-8036
Scott Amundson, *President*
Tammy Malecha, *Manager*
EMP: 90

EST: 1962
SQ FT: 23,000
SALES (est): 5MM-9.9MM **Privately Held**
SIC: 5046 Merchandising machine operator; contract food services; wholesales commercial equipment

(G-1995)

CABLE CONNECTION & SUPPLY CO

1505 30th St NW   (55021-1801)
PHONE..............................507 334-6417
FAX: 507 334-8926
Barbara Vinar, *President*
Shari Lacarre, *Manager*
EMP: 25 **EST:** 1987
SQ FT: 80,000
SALES (est): 10MM-24.9MM **Privately Held**
WEB: www.cableconnectionsupply.com
SIC: 5063 5072 5084 Wholesales wire & cable; wholesales electrical construction materials; wholesales hand tools; wholesales electrical lugs & connectors; wholesales industrial electrical measuring & testing equipment; manufactures current carrying wiring devices

(G-1996)

CANNON VALLEY CLINIC

924 1st St NE   (55021-5441)
PHONE..............................507 266-2620
Kathy Stepka, *Business Mgr*
John T Smith, *Obstetrician*
Brant R Barr, *Obstetrician*
Thomas Howell, *Obstetrician*
Rod Byron, *Surgeon*
EMP: 30
SALES (est): 1MM-4.9MM **Privately Held**
SIC: 8099 Health & allied services

(G-1997)

CANNON VALLEY CLINIC MAYO

924 St NE   (55021)
PHONE..............................507 333-3300
FAX: 507 333-3258
David Beckmann, *President*
Khan Ali MD, *Med Doctor*
Brenda J Hurtt MD, *Med Doctor*
David Helstern, *Administrator*
EMP: 60 **EST:** 1995
SALES (est): 5MM-9.9MM **Privately Held**
SIC: 8011 Clinic operated by physicians
PA: Mayo Clinic
200 1st St SW
Rochester MN 55905
507 284-2511

(G-1998)

CEDAR LAKE ELECTRIC INC

20700 Bagley Ave   (55021-7836)
PHONE..............................507 334-9546
FAX: 507 334-5402
Jay Valentyn, *President*
Jerry Valentyn, *Vice Pres*
Connie Caron, *Accountant*
Karen Krenske, *Manager*
Don Graunke, *Manager*
EMP: 42 **EST:** 1975
SQ FT: 5,600
SALES (est): 1MM-4.9MM **Privately Held**
SIC: 1731 Electrical contractor

(G-1999)

CENNEIDIGH INC

402 Heritage Pl   (55021-5248)
PHONE..............................507 334-4347
Russ Cenneidigh, *President*
Mary Kay, *Corp Secy*
EMP: 250 **EST:** 1977
SALES (est): 10MM-24.9MM **Privately Held**
SIC: 8361 8052 Home for the mentally retarded; intermediate care facility

(G-2000)

CUMULUS MEDIA INC

Also Called: Kdhl Radio
601 Central Ave N   (55021-4307)
PHONE..............................507 334-0061
Gary Frost, *Manager*
Jim Lowe, *Manager*
EMP: 30
SALES (est): 1MM-4.9MM **Publicly Held**
WEB: www.cumulusmedia.com

SIC: 4832 Radio broadcasting station
PA: Cumulus Media Inc
3280 Peachtree Rd NE # 2300
Atlanta GA 30305
404 949-0700

(G-2001)

DONAHUES' GREENHOUSES INC

420 10th St SW   (55021-6816)
PO Box 366   (55021-0366)
PHONE..............................507 334-8404
FAX: 507 334-0485
Lois D Cleary, *President*
Tim Donahue, *Vice Pres*
Mark Donahue, *Vice Pres*
Mary M Intyer, *Vice Pres*
Julie Zweber, *Vice Pres*
EMP: 27 **EST:** 1931
SQ FT: 200,000 **Privately Held**
WEB: www.donahuesclematis.com
SIC: 0181 5193 Ornamental nursery products; potted plant farming; wholesales fresh flowers; wholesales potted plants; retails fresh flowers; retails potted plants

(G-2002)

EMPOWERMENT SERVICES OF RICE

1003 7th St NW   (55021-4724)
PHONE..............................507 333-2583
Linda Olson, *President*
EMP: 100 **EST:** 2003
SALES (est): 1MM-4.9MM **Privately Held**
SIC: 8361 Residential care facility

(G-2003)

FARIBAULT BANCSHARES INC

428 Central Ave N   (55021-5217)
PO Box 429   (55021-0429)
PHONE..............................507 332-7401
Richard Carlander, *President*
Patricia M Langevin, *Corp Secy*
John Carlander, *Vice Pres*
Lorraine H Carlander, *Treasurer*
EMP: 54 **EST:** 1981
SQ FT: 6,000
SALES (est): 10MM-24.9MM **Privately Held**
SIC: 6022 State commercial bank

(G-2004)

FARIBAULT HARLEY DAVIDSON INC

2704 Airport Dr   (55021-7766)
PHONE..............................507 334-5130
FAX: 507 334-6967
Ann Hofmeister, *President*
Ann Hosmeister, *General Mgr*
Janice Vidmar, *Administrator*
EMP: 28 **EST:** 1973
SQ FT: 13,000
SALES (est): 5MM-9.9MM **Privately Held**
WEB: www.faribaulthd.com
SIC: 7699 Motorcycle dealer; motorcycle repair shop

(G-2005)

FARIBAULT TRANSPORTATION CO

2615 1st Ave NW   (55021-1914)
PO Box 163   (55021-0163)
PHONE..............................507 334-5121
FAX: 507 334-2039
Thomas E Merrill, *President*
George E Voracek, *Treasurer*
EMP: 50 **EST:** 1950
SQ FT: 15,000
SALES (est): 1MM-4.9MM **Privately Held**
SIC: 4151 4142 School bus service; long-distance bus charter service

(G-2006)

FARIBO FARM & HOME SUPPLY INC

Also Called: True Value Hardware
80 Western Ave NW   (55021-4517)
PHONE..............................507 334-3232
FAX: 507 334-8605
Mike Ford, *President*
EMP: 25 **EST:** 1969
SQ FT: 18,470
SALES (est): 1MM-4.9MM **Privately Held**
SIC: 5191 Hardware store; retail gasoline filling station; wholesales farm supplies

(G-2007)

FARIBO PLUMBING & HEATING INC

513 Central Ave N   (55021-4322)
PHONE..............................507 334-6409
FAX: 507 334-8681
Dale Schwartz, *President*
Peggy Keylen, *Vice Pres*
EMP: 28 **EST:** 1984
SQ FT: 7,200
SALES (est): 1MM-4.9MM **Privately Held**
SIC: 1711 Plumbing service; heating & air conditioning contractor

(G-2008)

1ST UNITED BANK

430 4th St NW   (55021-5031)
PHONE..............................507 334-2201
FAX: 507 332-0046
Kenneth R Betsinger, *President*
Allen Dowhanivk, *Vice Pres*
Paul Richardson, *Vice Pres*
Jean Larson, *Opers Mgr*
Renee Gergen, *Opers Staff*
EMP: 35 **EST:** 1920
SALES (est): 10MM-24.9MM **Privately Held**
WEB: www.1stunited.com
SIC: 6035 6036 Federal savings & loan association; savings & loan association

(G-2009)

GEMINI 26 INC

Also Called: Bauernfeind & Goedtel
15760 Acorn Trl   (55021-7610)
PO Box 278   (55021-0278)
PHONE..............................507 334-7951
FAX: 507 334-8790
Randy McDonough, *President*
Denny Louis, *Manager*
Cooper Hager, *Manager*
Tim Hager, *Manager*
EMP: 25 **EST:** 1963
SQ FT: 6,500
SALES (est): 1MM-4.9MM **Privately Held**
WEB: www.bgcompanies.com
SIC: 1761 1711 Roofing contractor; manufactures asphalt coatings & sealers; warm air heating & air conditioning contractor; sheet metal work contractor; sheet metal fabricator

(G-2010)

GLENDALOUGH OF AUSTIN INC

402 Heritage Pl   (55021-5248)
PHONE..............................507 334-4347
Rus Kennedy, *CEO*
EMP: 25 **EST:** 2001 **Privately Held**
SIC: 8699 Charitable organization

(G-2011)

I & S GROUP INC

1415 Town Square Ln   (55021-6088)
PHONE..............................507 331-1500
Mark Cipos, *Principal*
Lisa Kottke, *Manager*
EMP: 80 **EST:** 2005
SALES (est): 5MM-9.9MM **Privately Held**
SIC: 8712 Architectural engineers

(G-2012)

I D D D INC

Also Called: Truckers Inn Truck Stop
2519 Lyndale Ave N   (55021-2612)
PHONE..............................507 334-3333
Carol Sierk, *Manager*
EMP: 35
SALES (est): 25MM-49.9MM **Privately Held**
SIC: 1311 Crude petroleum & natural gas production
PA: I D D D Inc
6162 US Highway 51
De Forest WI 53532
608 246-3040

(G-2013)

IFP INC

2125 Airport Dr   (55021-7798)
PHONE..............................507 334-2730
Feephi Eyal, *President*
Tushar Desai, *VP Opers*
Stacy Fiscus, *Maint Mgr*
Carin Draper, *VP Finance*
Renee Spencer, *Accountant*

EMP: 100 **EST:** 1985
SQ FT: 40,000
SALES (est): 25MM-49.9MM **Privately Held**
SIC: 6512 7359 Operators of commercial & industrial buildings; tool rental
PA: Esi Holding Corp
8009 34th Ave S Ste 1492
Minneapolis MN 55425
952 853-0924

(G-2014)

JANINE SAHAGIAN

Also Called: Wipple Hieghts School
310 11th Ave NE   (55021-5405)
PHONE..............................507 332-9894
FAX: 507 333-3918
Janine Sahagian, *Principal*
EMP: 40 **EST:** 1990
SALES (est): 1MM-4.9MM **Privately Held**
SIC: 8322 Aid to Families with Dependent Children or AFDC

(G-2015)

JENNIE-O TURKEY STORE INC

25475 Cabot Ave   (55021-8265)
PHONE..............................507 334-0087
FAX: 507 333-2434
Dave Utzinger, *Manager*
Paul Mertes, *Manager*
Buzz Kornmann, *Manager*
EMP: 25 **Publicly Held**
WEB: www.hormel.com
SIC: 0253 Turkey farm
HQ: Jennie-O Turkey Store Inc
2505 Willmar Ave SW
Willmar MN 56201
320 235-2622

(G-2016)

KCQ INC

402 Heritage Pl   (55021-5248)
PHONE..............................507 334-4393
Ross Kennedy, *President*
Jackie Gretz, *Vice Pres*
EMP: 35 **EST:** 1970
SALES (est): 1MM-4.9MM **Privately Held**
SIC: 8322 Rehabilitation services

(G-2017)

KGP LOGISTICS INC   (HQ)

3305 Highway 60 W   (55021-4869)
PHONE..............................507 334-2268
James Mayfield, *President*
Tana Johnson, *President*
Desi O'Grady, *Vice Pres*
Richard K Summers, *Vice Pres*
Don Shaffer, *CFO*
▲ **EMP:** 800 **EST:** 1884
SQ FT: 472,000 **Privately Held**
WEB: www.kgptel.com
SIC: 5065 Wholesales electrical telephone & telegraphic equipment
PA: Kgp Telecommunications Inc
3305 Highway 60 W
Faribault MN 55021
507 334-2268

(G-2018)

KGP TELECOMMUNICATIONS INC   (PA)

3305 Highway 60 W   (55021-4869)
PHONE..............................507 334-2268
FAX: 507 334-2177
Kathleen G Putrah, *CEO*
Trevor Putrah, *COO*
Ken Marcotte, *Opers Staff*
Don Shaffer, *CFO*
Dawn Beyer, *Human Res Mgr*
EMP: 75 **EST:** 1975
SQ FT: 55,000 **Privately Held**
WEB: www.kgptel.com
SIC: 5065 Wholesales telephone equipment

(G-2019)

LEGACY GOLF CORP

1515 Shumway Ave   (55021-3124)
PHONE..............................507 332-0777
FAX: 507 334-2712
Terry Mead, *President*
Michael Frankenfield, *Corp Secy*
Marsha Culhane, *Manager*
Greg Paine, *Executive*
EMP: 30 **EST:** 1996
SALES (est): 1MM-4.9MM **Privately Held**
WEB: www.legacygolfandhomes.com

SIC: 7992 Public golf course
PA: Shattuck-St Mary's School
1000 Shumway Ave
Faribault MN 55021
507 333-1500

(G-2020)
MC DONOUGH TRUCK LINE INC
3115 Industrial Dr   (55021-1700)
PHONE.............................507 334-9374
FAX: 507 334-8102
David McDonough, *President*
Dave Bossmann, *Opers Mgr*
Kathy Kastner, *Office Mgr*
EMP: 72 **EST:** 1961
SALES (est): 5MM-9.9MM **Privately Held**
WEB: www.mcdonoughtruckline.com
SIC: 4212 Local trucking without storage
services

(G-2021)
MET CON KATO INC
15760 Acorn Trl   (55021-7610)
PO Box 427   (55021-0427)
PHONE.............................507 332-2266
Thomas M Donough, *President*
Julie Peske, *Vice Pres*
EMP: 200 **EST:** 1987
SQ FT: 12,800
SALES (est): 50MM-99.9MM **Privately Held**
SIC: 1542 Commercial & office building
contractor

(G-2022)
MET-CON CONSTRUCTION INC
(PA)
15760 Acorn Trl   (55021-7610)
PHONE.............................507 332-2266
Thomas M Donough, *President*
Scott Brown, *Vice Pres*
Julie Teske, *Vice Pres*
Scott McDonna, *Facilities Mgr*
Sandra M Donough, *Treasurer*
EST: 1978
SQ FT: 12,800 **Privately Held**
SIC: 1541 1542 Industrial building &
warehouse construction; commercial &
office building contractor

(G-2023)
NORTH AMBULANCE
FARIBAULT
1226 Willow St   (55021-8160)
PHONE.............................507 334-6031
David Cress, *President*
EMP: 25 **EST:** 1988
SALES (est): 1MM-4.9MM **Privately Held**
SIC: 4119 Ambulance service

(G-2024)
OUR CIRCLE OF FRIENDS
211 Minnesota Pl   (55021-5346)
PO Box 594   (55021-0594)
PHONE.............................507 334-4346
Cheryle Glende, *Owner*
EMP: 28 **EST:** 1996
SALES (est): 500-999K **Privately Held**
WEB: www.ourcircleoffriends.com
SIC: 8082 Home health care services

(G-2025)
P H SELLY & CO INC
805 3rd Ave SW   (55021-6109)
PO Box 784   (55021-0784)
PHONE.............................507 334-3251
Barbara J Selly, *President*
John Selly, *Corp Secy*
Mark Selly, *Treasurer*
EMP: 49 **EST:** 1960
SALES (est): 1MM-4.9MM **Privately Held**
SIC: 4212 4214 8041 Local star route
transportation services; local trucking with
storage; chiropractors' office; manufactures
hospital gowns; manufactures men's &
boys' work clothing

(G-2026)
PLEASANT MANOR INC
27 Brand Ave   (55021-6411)
PHONE.............................507 334-3558
FAX: 507 334-2038
David E Meillier, *President*
Michael Meillier-, *Manager*
Tim Byrne, *Administrator*

Emily Rinaldi, *Exec Dir*
Cheryl Bartosch, *Management*
EMP: 80 **EST:** 1964
SQ FT: 42,131
SALES (est): 1MM-4.9MM **Privately Held**
SIC: 8051 Skilled nursing care facility

(G-2027)
RICE COUNTY DISTRICT ONE
HOSP
200 State Ave   (55021-6339)
PHONE.............................507 334-6451
FAX: 507 332-4848
James Wolf, *CEO*
Jeanne Campbell, *Corp Secy*
Mark A Arnesen, *Ch Pathology*
Susan Cassidy, *Purch Agent*
Patrick Justin, *CFO*
EMP: 360 **EST:** 1960
SQ FT: 150,000
SALES (est): 25MM-49.9MM **Privately Held**
WEB: www.districtonehospital.com
SIC: 8062 Medical hospital

(G-2028)
RICHIE EYE CLINIC
1575 20th St NW Ste 101   (55021-2931)
PHONE.............................507 332-9900
FAX: 507 332-6800
Michael Richie MD, *Owner*
Karen Deluca, *Business Mgr*
Murray H Hanson, *Optometrist*
Bruce V Gustafson, *Optometrist*
EMP: 30 **EST:** 1981
SALES (est): 1MM-4.9MM **Privately Held**
WEB: www.richieeyeclinic.com
SIC: 8042 Optometrists' office

(G-2029)
RISON HOMES ADMINISTRATIVE
16 5th St NE Ste 1   (55021-4324)
PO Box 774   (55021-0774)
PHONE.............................507 332-0547
FAX: 507 332-2335
Debbie Sonic, *Owner*
EMP: 45 **EST:** 1989
SALES (est): 1MM-4.9MM **Privately Held**
SIC: 8052 Intermediate care facility

(G-2030)
SODEXO MANAGEMENT INC
925 Parshall St   (55021-3921)
PHONE.............................507 333-6772
Terry Ronayne, *Principal*
EMP: 35
SALES (est): 1MM-4.9MM **Privately Held**
WEB: www.compass-mgmt.com
SIC: 8741 Management services
HQ: Sodexo Management Inc
9801 Washingtonian Blvd
Gaithersburg MD 20878
301 987-4000

(G-2031)
SPECTRUM COMMUNITY
HEALTH
211 1st Ave NW Ste 4   (55021-6149)
PO Box 842   (55021-0842)
PHONE.............................507 332-7471
FAX: 507 332-7288
Linda Wilbur, *Office Mgr*
Linda Smith, *Manager*
EMP: 50
SALES (est): 1MM-4.9MM **Privately Held**
SIC: 8082 Home health care services

(G-2032)
ST LUCAS CARE CENTER
500 1st St SE   (55021-6346)
PHONE.............................507 332-5100
FAX: 507 332-5188
Jan Ssheady, *Purchasing*
Karen Ruda, *Administrator*
Brad Molgard, *Administrator*
Tina Swaner, *Exec Dir*
Sharon Gillen, *Officer*
EMP: 150 **EST:** 2003
SALES (est): 5MM-9.9MM **Privately Held**
SIC: 8051 Convalescent home

(G-2033)
STATE BANK OF FARIBAULT
428 Central Ave N   (55021-5217)
PHONE.............................507 332-7401
FAX: 507 332-4600
John R Carlander, *President*
Richard J Carlander, *Chairman*
Darlene Meillier, *Vice Pres*
Julie Finnesgard, *CPA*
Lynden Dirksen, *MIS Mgr*
EMP: 50 **EST:** 1919
SQ FT: 6,000
SALES (est): 10MM-24.9MM **Privately Held**
WEB: www.tsbf.com
SIC: 6022 8721 State commercial bank;
accounting, auditing & bookkeeping
services

(G-2034)
TELEPAK INDUSTRIES INC
1505 30th St NW   (55021-1801)
PHONE.............................507 332-0012
Barbara Vinar, *President*
EMP: 35 **EST:** 2004
SALES (est): 10MM-24.9MM **Privately Held**
WEB: www.telepakindustries.com
SIC: 4911 Electric power distribution service

(G-2035)
THREE RIVERS HEAD START
201 Lyndale Ave S Ste 201   (55021-5799)
PHONE.............................507 333-6450
FAX: 507 333-6462
Mike Thorsteinson, *President*
EMP: 70 **EST:** 2004
SALES (est): 1MM-4.9MM **Privately Held**
SIC: 8322 Individual & family social services

(G-2036)
UNITED PARCEL SERVICE OF
NEW
Also Called: UPS
1820 6th St NW   (55021-4610)
PHONE.............................507 334-7924
Ryan Miller, *Manager*
EMP: 30
SALES (est): 1MM-4.9MM **Publicly Held**
WEB: www.martrac.com
SIC: 4215 Package delivery services by
vehicle
HQ: United Parcel Service of New
55 Glenlake Pkwy NE
Atlanta GA 30328
404 828-6000

(G-2037)
WF NATIONAL BANK SOUTH
CENTRAL
Also Called: Wells Fargo
104 5th St NW   (55021-4205)
PHONE.............................507 334-5546
Mike Dietsch, *President*
Arlie Freiborg, *President*
Amanda Altwegg, *Store Mgr*
Lawrence Denny, *Manager*
EMP: 36 **EST:** 1894
SQ FT: 21,000
SALES (est): 10MM-24.9MM **Publicly Held**
SIC: 6021 National commercial bank
PA: Wells Fargo & Co
420 Montgomery St
San Francisco CA 94104
866 878-5865

FARMINGTON
Dakota County

(G-2038)
ALLINA HEALTH SYSTEM
21260 Chippendale Ave W   (55024-1427)
PHONE.............................952 463-7181
Jan Barbo, *Office Mgr*
Timothy E Savageau, *Optometrist*
Gerald Cunniff, *OB/GYN*
Martin J Gadek, *Gastroenterlgy*
EMP: 40
SALES (est): 1MM-4.9MM **Privately Held**
WEB: www.allina.com

SIC: 8011 Clinic operated by physicians
PA: Allina Health System
2925 Chicago Ave
Minneapolis MN 55407
612 775-5000

(G-2039)
AMERICAN LEGION CLUB
10 8th St   (55024-1162)
PO Box 186   (55024-0186)
PHONE.............................651 460-9909
Leonard Weisbrich, *CEO*
Dawn Paget, *Manager*
Klem Becker, *Director*
EMP: 45 **EST:** 1989
SQ FT: 10,000
SALES (est): 1MM-4.9MM **Privately Held**
SIC: 7299 Banquet hall facility

(G-2040)
BACHMAN'S INC
23000 Cedar Ave   (55024-9551)
PHONE.............................952 469-2102
Mark Grommesch, *Manager*
John Geyem, *Manager*
EMP: 33 **Privately Held**
SIC: 0181 Ornamental nursery products
PA: Bachman's Inc
6010 Lyndale Ave S
Minneapolis MN 55419
612 861-7600

(G-2041)
BACHMAN'S INC
Also Called: Bachmans Nursery Wholesale
Ctr
6877 235th St W   (55024-9638)
PHONE.............................651 463-3288
FAX: 651 463-4747
John Daniels, *Manager*
Scott Lindberg, *Director*
EMP: 50
SALES (est): 5MM-9.9MM **Privately Held**
SIC: 5193 Wholesales nursery stock
PA: Bachman's Inc
6010 Lyndale Ave S
Minneapolis MN 55419
612 861-7600

(G-2042)
C R FISCHER & SONS INC
3240 220th St W   (55024-8800)
PO Box 448   (55024-0448)
PHONE.............................651 463-7300
FAX: 651 463-7033
Curtis Fischer, *President*
Angela Fischer, *Treasurer*
EMP: 30 **EST:** 1992
SQ FT: 2,700
SALES (est): 1MM-4.9MM **Privately Held**
WEB: www.crfischerandsons.com
SIC: 1611 1771 Concrete road, highway &
sidewalk construction; sidewalk
construction; curb construction; street
surfacing & paving construction

(G-2043)
CHRISTIAN LIFE CHURCH
6300 212th St W   (55024-8903)
PHONE.............................651 463-4545
Cheryl Johnson, *Corp Secy*
Jenise Johnson, *Corp Secy*
Darren Kiendle, *Pastor*
Kent Boyum, *Pastor*
Debbie Otterblad, *Manager*
EMP: 35 **EST:** 1940
ADMISSIONS: 208 **Privately Held**
SIC: 8351 Religious organization;
elementary & secondary school; child day
care service

(G-2044)
CITIES ELECTRIC INC
3100 225th St W   (55024-9749)
PHONE.............................651 463-3810
FAX: 651 463-4347
Steve Sowieja, *President*
EMP: 58 **EST:** 1987
SQ FT: 20,000
SALES (est): 5MM-9.9MM **Privately Held**
SIC: 1731 Electrical contractor

(G-2045)
COLLIN GARVEY
22098 Canton Ct (55024-8505)
PHONE 651 463-4825
Collin Garvey, *Owner*
EMP: 25 **EST:** 1990
SALES (est): 1MM-4.9MM **Privately Held**
WEB: www.collingarvey.com
SIC: 1771 Concrete contractor

(G-2046)
CONSULTING ENGINEERS GROUP INC
21210 Eaton Ave Ste C (55024-7949)
PHONE 651 463-6263
Dale Gundberg, *President*
Max Bartholomy, *Vice Pres*
Jim Hanson, *Vice Pres*
Greg Miller, *Director*
Janet Lekson, *Director*
EST: 1996
SQ FT: 4,000 **Privately Held**
SIC: 8711 Engineering consulting services
PA: Dakota Electric Association
4300 220th St W
Farmington MN 55024
651 463-6212

(G-2047)
DAKOTA ELECTRIC ASSOCIATION (PA)
4300 220th St W (55024-9003)
PHONE 651 463-6212
Greg Miller, *President*
Rolin Sampson, *Superintendent*
Bill Holton, *Corp Secy*
Dirk Rotty, *Vice Pres*
William Travis, *Vice Pres*
EMP: 210 **EST:** 1937
SQ FT: 101,000
SALES (corp-wide): 178.81M **Privately Held**
SIC: 4911 Electric power distribution service

(G-2048)
DAKOTA TURF INC
1016 220th St W (55024-9734)
PO Box 67 (55024-0067)
PHONE 651 460-8873
Jason Bakke, *CEO*
John Bakke, *President*
EMP: 40 **EST:** 1989 **Privately Held**
SIC: 0782 0783 Landscaping services; ornamental shrub & tree service

(G-2049)
DEXTERITY DENTAL ARTS INC
310 Division St (55024-1233)
PHONE 651 463-4444
Larry Ihle, *President*
Rosanne Ihle, *Vice Pres*
Tony D Reid, *Opers Mgr*
Lisa Reid, *Sales Executive*
EMP: 47 **EST:** 1976
SQ FT: 3,744
SALES (est): 1MM-4.9MM **Privately Held**
WEB: www.dexteritydental.com
SIC: 8072 Dental laboratory

(G-2050)
FARMINGTON EAGLES CLUB
200 3rd St (55024-1032)
PHONE 651 460-8376
FAX: 651 460-8376
John Quamme, *President*
Kim Cumming, *Sales Staff*
Kimberly Cummings, *Manager*
EMP: 25 **EST:** 1983 **Privately Held**
SIC: 8641 Civic & social organization

(G-2051)
FARMINGTON HEALTH SERVICE
3410 213th St W (55024-1167)
PHONE 651 463-7818
FAX: 651 463-1165
Robin Schmitz, *Principal*
Matt Pomroy, *Human Res Dir*
Jill Kollasch, *Manager*
Christine Schreiner, *Administrator*
Rich Ludwig, *Administrator*
EMP: 50 **EST:** 2001
SALES (est): 1MM-4.9MM **Privately Held**
SIC: 8051 Skilled nursing care facility

(G-2052)
JIRIK SOD FARM INC
20245 Blaine Ave (55024-9306)
PHONE 651 460-6555
FAX: 651 460-8347
Pete Jirik, *CEO*
Lori Jirik, *President*
Troy Nuebel, *Manager*
EMP: 40 **EST:** 1996
SQ FT: 12,800 **Privately Held**
WEB: www.jiriksod.com
SIC: 0782 5191 Sodding contractor; retails sod; wholesales farm supplies

(G-2053)
LA PETITE ACADEMY INC
90 Locust St (55024-1280)
PHONE 651 463-2022
FAX: 651 463-1215
Beth Swan, *Exec Dir*
EMP: 40
SALES (est): 500-999K **Privately Held**
WEB: www.lapetite.com
SIC: 8351 Child day care service
PA: La Petite Academy Inc
130 S Jefferson St # 300
Chicago IL 60661
312 798-1200

(G-2054)
MARSCHALL BUS SERVICE INC
21044 Chippendale Ct (55024-1157)
PO Box 131 (55024-0131)
PHONE 952 463-8689
FAX: 952 463-3504
Tom Severson, *Manager*
EMP: 70
SALES (est): 1MM-4.9MM **Privately Held**
SIC: 4142 Long-distance bus charter service

(G-2055)
NASH-FINCH CO
Also Called: Econo Foods
115 Elm St Ste A (55024-1031)
PHONE 651 463-3404
Herman Raboin, *Manager*
EMP: 70
SALES (est): 50MM-99.9MM **Publicly Held**
WEB: www.nashfinch.com
SIC: 5141 Wholesales general line groceries
PA: Nash-Finch Co
7600 France Ave S Ste 200
Edina MN 55435
952 832-0534

(G-2056)
PICTURE PERFECT CLEANING
18990 Embry Ave (55024-7007)
PO Box 71, Elko (55020-0071)
PHONE 612 865-4522
John M Donald, *Owner*
EMP: 31 **EST:** 2000
SALES (est): 500-999K **Privately Held**
SIC: 7349 Janitorial & custodial services

(G-2057)
PINEHURST DEVELOPMENT INC
Also Called: South Cedar Greenhouses
23111 Cedar Ave (55024-8017)
PHONE 952 469-3202
FAX: 952 469-5335
Alan W Leipnitz, *President*
Judy M Leipnitz, *Corp Secy*
EMP: 25 **EST:** 1984
SQ FT: 135,000 **Privately Held**
WEB: www.southcedar.com
SIC: 0181 5083 5193 Ornamental nursery products; wholesales landscaping equipment; wholesales potted plants

(G-2058)
PRO-TEMP INC
Also Called: Controlled Air
21210 Eaton Ave Ste A (55024-7949)
PHONE 651 460-6022
FAX: 651 460-6717
Randall Cunningham, *CEO*
Cindy Lilienthel, *Sales Staff*
Jeff Pettif, *Marketing Mgr*
Caye Kosir, *Manager*
EMP: 50 **EST:** 1977

SALES (est): 5MM-9.9MM **Privately Held**
WEB: www.controlledairinc.com
SIC: 1711 Warm air heating & air conditioning contractor
PA: Dakota Electric Association
4300 220th St W
Farmington MN 55024
651 463-6212

(G-2059)
RIVER VALLEY HOME CARE
916 8th St (55024-1438)
PHONE 651 460-4201
FAX: 651 460-4208
Rachelle Periseau, *President*
EMP: 120 **EST:** 1998
SALES (est): 1MM-4.9MM **Privately Held**
WEB: www.rivervalleyhomecare.com
SIC: 8082 Home health care services

(G-2060)
STATE MECHANICAL INC
5050 220th St W (55024-8001)
PHONE 651 463-8220
FAX: 651 463-8244
Judith Heintz, *President*
W H Marbert, *Vice Pres*
Marbert W Heintz, *Vice Pres*
EMP: 30 **EST:** 1974
SQ FT: 8,000
SALES (est): 1MM-4.9MM **Privately Held**
SIC: 1711 1623 Plumbing service; underground utilities contractor

(G-2061)
SYPAL LUNDGREN POST NO 7662
421 3rd St (55024-1354)
PHONE 952 460-6888
FAX: 952 460-6946
Linda McLin, *Manager*
Karen Filler, *Manager*
Betty McCarthy, *Director*
EMP: 30 **EST:** 1946
SQ FT: 7,200 **Privately Held**
SIC: 8641 Veterans' organization; bar

(G-2062)
VINGE TILE
Also Called: D & R Vinge
21205 Eaton Ave Ste 1 (55024-8914)
PHONE 952 431-1000
Douglas Vinge, *Owner*
EMP: 35
SALES (est): 1MM-4.9MM **Privately Held**
WEB: www.vingetile.com
SIC: 1743 Ceramic tile installation service

FELTON
Clay County

(G-2063)
SENIOR CITIZENS CENTER OF
Main St (56536)
PO Box 533 (56536-0533)
PHONE 218 494-3750
Kenneth Severtson, *President*
EMP: 30 **EST:** 1970
SALES (est): 500-999K **Privately Held**
SIC: 8322 Senior citizen center

FERGUS FALLS
Otter Tail County

(G-2064)
CARE 2000 HOME HEALTHCARE SVCS
119 E Lincoln Ave Ste 103 (56537-2270)
PHONE 218 736-0246
FAX: 218 736-0265
Jane Fronning, *Administrator*
EMP: 50 **EST:** 1999
SALES (est): 1MM-4.9MM **Privately Held**
SIC: 8082 Home health care services

(G-2065)
CARLSON HIGHLAND CO LLP
403 S Union Ave (56537-2532)
PHONE 218 739-3267
FAX: 218 739-2258
Randall Highland, *Managing Prtnr*
EMP: 60 **EST:** 1986
SALES (est): 1MM-4.9MM **Privately Held**
SIC: 8721 Accounting, auditing & bookkeeping services

(G-2066)
CATHOLIC CHARITIES OF THE
Also Called: St Cloud Children's Home
4D East Dr
PO Box 1006 (56538-1006)
PHONE 218 739-9325
FAX: 218 739-2242
Brian Grandpre, *Manager*
Roger Belisle, *Manager*
EMP: 35
SALES (est): 1MM-4.9MM **Privately Held**
SIC: 8322 Individual & family social services
PA: Catholic Charities of The
911 18th St N
Saint Cloud MN 56303
320 650-1550

(G-2067)
COCA-COLA BOTTLING
832 Industrial Park Blvd (56537-1250)
PHONE 218 736-5661
George Zender, *President*
Phyllis Zender, *Vice Pres*
Judy Johnson, *Office Mgr*
EMP: 200 **EST:** 1962
SQ FT: 45,000
SALES (est): 50MM-99.9MM **Privately Held**
SIC: 5149 Manufactures nonalcoholic carbonated beverages; manufactures soft drinks; wholesales groceries

(G-2068)
COLONIAL VILLAGE APARTMENTS
Also Called: Broadway Apartments
1234 N Broadway (56537-1334)
PHONE 218 739-3795
Chris Levesque, *Manager*
Janice Timrock, *Manager*
EMP: 36
SALES (est): 5MM-9.9MM **Privately Held**
SIC: 6513 Apartment building operator

(G-2069)
COMMUNICATING FOR AGRICULTURE
112 E Lincoln Ave (56537-2217)
PHONE 218 739-3241
Milt Smedsrud, *CEO*
Angie Nelson, *Accounting Staf*
Craig Schmuck, *Manager*
Tom Phormodson, *Data Proc Dir*
EMP: 25 **Privately Held**
SIC: 8611 Business association

(G-2070)
COMMUNICATING FOR AMERICA INC
112 E Lincoln Ave (56537-2217)
PO Box 677 (56538-0677)
PHONE 218 739-3241
FAX: 218 739-3832
Milton Smedsrud, *CEO*
Wayne Nelson, *President*
Luke Propst, *Principal*
Roger Gussias, *Vice Pres*
Peter Risbrudt, *CFO*
EMP: 25 **EST:** 1972
SQ FT: 6,500 **Privately Held**
SIC: 8611 Growers' associations

(G-2071)
COMSTOCK CONSTRUCTION INC, OF
1003 Progress Dr (56537-1054)
PHONE 218 739-5365
Robert Comstock, *President*
Kristi Falk, *Principal*
Jeremy Dufault, *Vice Pres*
Jennifer Beauchamp, *Vice Pres*
Rich Truesdell, *Vice Pres*

GEOGRAPHIC

GEOGRAPHIC (vertical side tab)

EMP: 50 EST: 1998
SALES (est): 5MM-9.9MM **Privately Held**
SIC: 1541 1521 New industrial building
construction; single-family housing
construction

(G-2072)
CONNER ENTERPRISES INC
Also Called: Zero Variance
117 S Mill St Fl 2 (56537-2537)
PHONE 218 998-9376
Patrick K Conner, *President*
Janine A Conner, *Shareholder*
Linda Meade, *Admin Asst*
EMP: 40 EST: 2002
SQ FT: 6,000
SALES (est): 1MM-4.9MM **Privately Held**
SIC: 8721 Auditing services

(G-2073)
DAIRY FARMERS OF AMERICA INC
301 S Buse St (56537-3272)
PHONE 218 736-5691
Darren Wilson, *General Mgr*
Jim Lewis, *Plant Supt*
Jerry Bos, *CFO*
EMP: 100
SALES (est): 25MM-49.9MM **Privately Held**
WEB: www.dfamilk.com
SIC: 5143 8699 Manufactures fluid milk;
food co-operative; manufactures cheese;
wholesales fresh dairy products
PA: Dairy Farmers of America Inc
10220 N Ambassador Dr
Kansas City MO 64153
816 801-6455

(G-2074)
DOUG THORSON SALES CO INC
105 E Lincoln Ave (56537-2216)
PHONE 218 736-2249
Douglas Thorson, *President*
Sherry Thorson, *Vice Pres*
EMP: 25 EST: 1974
SQ FT: 2,000
SALES (est): 10MM-24.9MM **Privately Held**
SIC: 5199 Wholesales gifts & novelties

(G-2075)
FERGUS FALLS AREA FAMILY YOUNG
Also Called: YMCA
1164 Friberg Ave (56537-1580)
PHONE 218 739-4489
FAX: 218 739-5403
Paul Lundeen, *Corp Secy*
Jennifer Godzinski, *Office Mgr*
Ron Raasch, *Director*
Tate Goeden, *Program Dir*
EMP: 70 EST: 1966 **Privately Held**
SIC: 8641 7997 Youth organizations;
membership swimming club; membership
racquetball club

(G-2076)
FERGUS FALLS MEDICAL GROUP
615 S Mill St Ste 4 (56537-2756)
PHONE 218 739-2221
FAX: 218 739-5501
James Wilkus, *CEO*
Bruce E Money, *President*
Kathleen Otte, *Business Mgr*
Alan Williams, *Vice Pres*
E A Williams, *Vice Pres*
EMP: 208 EST: 1967
SQ FT: 30,000
SALES (est): 10MM-24.9MM **Privately Held**
WEB: www.fergusfallsmedicalgrouppa.net
SIC: 8011 Clinic operated by physicians

(G-2077)
INTERSTATE SERVICE OF FERGUS
I94 County Rd 1 (56537)
PHONE 218 739-3284
FAX: 218 739-4742
Leland Rogness, *President*
Lawayne Rogness, *Corp Secy*
Leslie Rogness, *Vice Pres*
Loran Rogness, *Treasurer*
EMP: 27

EST: 1971
SQ FT: 25,000
SALES (est): 10MM-24.9MM **Privately Held**
SIC: 5083 Wholesales farm & garden
machinery; retails garden supplies & tools

(G-2078)
J&M CO
1220 N Tower Rd (56537-4813)
PHONE 218 998-4062
Harrison McCleary, *Owner*
EMP: 30 EST: 2005
SALES (est): 1MM-4.9MM **Privately Held**
SIC: 7389 Folding & collating service for
printers

(G-2079)
JENNIE-O TURKEY STORE INC
428 E Wash Ave (56537-2816)
PO Box 457 (56538-0457)
PHONE 218 736-6931
Gary N Leabo, *Mill Mgr*
EMP: 25 **Publicly Held**
WEB: www.hormel.com
SIC: 0253 Turkey & turkey egg farming
HQ: Jennie-O Turkey Store Inc
2505 Willmar Ave SW
Willmar MN 56201
320 235-2622

(G-2080)
K J COUNTRY 965
Also Called: Lakes Radio
728 Western Ave (56537-1095)
PHONE 218 736-7596
Jerry Papenfuss, *Owner*
Doug Grey, *General Mgr*
EMP: 30 EST: 1926
SALES (est): 1MM-4.9MM **Privately Held**
SIC: 7313 Radio advertising representative

(G-2081)
LAKE REGION HEALTHCARE CORP
712 S Cascade St (56537-2913)
PO Box 728 (56538-0728)
PHONE 218 736-8000
FAX: 218 736-8773
Edward J Mehl, *CEO*
Larry Schulz, *CEO*
Tammy Defiel, *Corp Secy*
Jeff Horak, *Ch of Surgery*
Michael Norgard, *Ch OB/GYN*
EMP: 625 EST: 1904
SQ FT: 201,242
SALES (est): 50MM-99.9MM **Privately Held**
SIC: 8062 Medical hospital

(G-2082)
LAKELAND HOSPICE & HOME CARE
1505 Pebble Lake Rd # 400 (56537-3800)
PO Box 824 (56538-0824)
PHONE 218 998-1400
FAX: 218 736-2231
Ed Strand, *CFO*
Dawn Stavaas, *Treasurer*
Wilma Bothwell, *Manager*
Cheryl Pelaccio, *Manager*
Esther Zosel, *Manager*
EMP: 104 EST: 1984
SALES (est): 1MM-4.9MM **Privately Held**
WEB: www.lakelandhospice.org
SIC: 8361 8051 8082 Residential care
facility; home health care services; skilled
nursing care facility

(G-2083)
LAKELAND MENTAL HEALTH CENTER (PA)
21081 County Highway 1 (56537-7603)
PHONE 218 736-6987
Lynn Wolters, *Finance Dir*
Carol Lejcher, *Office Mgr*
Karyl Lejcher, *Supervisor*
Randy Kennedy, *Technology*
Clair Prody, *Exec Dir*
EMP: 65 EST: 1946
SQ FT: 15,000
SALES (corp-wide): 9M **Privately Held**
SIC: 8093 Outpatient mental health clinic

(G-2084)
LAKES COUNTRY SERVICE CO-OP
1001 E Mount Faith Ave (56537-2375)
PHONE 218 739-3273
FAX: 218 739-2459
Kristen Werner, *Bus/Fin/Pur Dir*
Jill Barlett, *Human Res Mgr*
Jeanette Meyer, *Human Resources*
Ken Busak, *Manager*
Melissa Mattson, *Admin Mgr*
EMP: 58 EST: 1976
SQ FT: 12,500 **Privately Held**
WEB: www.cyberknowledge.org
SIC: 8621 Professional organization

(G-2085)
LAKES HOMES & PROGRAM DEVPT
1381 Lenore Way (56537-1792)
PHONE 218 739-4322
Thomas Reiffenberger, *Principal*
EMP: 27
SALES (est): 500-999K **Privately Held**
SIC: 8322 Social services for the
handicapped
PA: Lakes Homes & Program Devpt
847 Highway 10 E
Detroit Lakes MN 56501
218 847-5642

(G-2086)
LAW CENTER INC
110 N Mill St (56537-2135)
PO Box 866 (56538-0866)
PHONE 218 736-5493
Kent Mattson, *CEO*
Matt McGovern, *Administrator*
EMP: 26 EST: 1964
SQ FT: 9,100
SALES (est): 1MM-4.9MM **Privately Held**
SIC: 8111 General practice attorney's or
lawyer's office

(G-2087)
LUTHERAN BRETHREN HOMES INC
824 S Sheridan St (56537-3022)
PHONE 218 736-5441
John Zwers, *President*
Rebecca Odden, *CIO*
EMP: 200 EST: 1957
SQ FT: 15,000
SALES (est): 25MM-49.9MM **Privately Held**
SIC: 8742 Hospital & health services
consultant

(G-2088)
LUTHERAN BRETHREN RETIREMENT
Also Called: Northwestern Manor
824 S Sheridan St (56537-3022)
PHONE 218 736-5441
John Zwers, *President*
Jean Anderson, *Marketing Staff*
EMP: 225 EST: 1992
SALES (est): 5MM-9.9MM **Privately Held**
WEB: www.lbhomes.org
SIC: 8051 8059 Skilled nursing care facility;
nursing home

(G-2089)
LUTHERAN SOCIAL SERVICE OF MN
731 Western Ave (56537-4804)
PHONE 218 736-5431
FAX: 218 739-4807
Gene Benson, *Manager*
Patty Kline, *Manager*
Jo Kantrud, *Director*
EMP: 110
SALES (est): 5MM-9.9MM **Privately Held**
WEB: www.lssmn.org
SIC: 8322 Individual & family social services
PA: Lutheran Social Service Of MN
2485 Como Ave
Saint Paul MN 55108
651 642-5990

(G-2090)
LUTHERAN TRUST
1421 Terrace Dr (56537-1741)
PHONE 218 998-4058
Kermit Starnes, *President*
EMP: 30 EST: 2005
SALES (est): 1MM-4.9MM **Privately Held**
WEB: www.lutherantrust.com
SIC: 6541 Title & trust company

(G-2091)
LUTHERN BROTHERN SCHOOL INC
Also Called: Sletta-Strom Memorial Hall
815 W Vernon Ave (56537-2676)
PHONE 218 739-3375
FAX: 218 739-3372
Steve Brew, *Principal*
Brad Hoganson, *Manager*
EMP: 70 EST: 1998
SALES (est): 10MM-24.9MM **Privately Held**
SIC: 6512 Operators of auditoriums & halls

(G-2092)
MARK SAND & GRAVEL CO
525 Kennedy Park Rd (56537-2423)
PO Box 458 (56538-0458)
PHONE 218 736-7523
FAX: 218 736-2647
Mark Thorson, *President*
Gregory Marcus, *Corp Secy*
EMP: 85 EST: 1933
SQ FT: 8,000
SALES (est): 10MM-24.9MM **Privately Held**
WEB: www.marksandgravel.com
SIC: 1611 Heavy highway & street
construction

(G-2093)
MDU RESOURCES GROUP INC
105 W Lincoln Ave (56537-2133)
PO Box 176 (56538-0176)
PHONE 218 736-6935
EMP: 25
SALES (est): 25MM-49.9MM **Publicly Held**
WEB: www.mdu.com
SIC: 4924 Natural gas distribution to
consumers
PA: MDU Resources Group Inc
1200 W Century Ave
Bismarck ND 58503
701 530-1000

(G-2094)
MILL STREET RESIDENCE INC
802 S Mill St Ofc (56537-2754)
PHONE 218 739-2900
Edward Mehl, *President*
Sean Larson, *Exec Dir*
Mick Siems, *Director*
EMP: 40 EST: 1998
SQ FT: 50,000
SALES (est): 5MM-9.9MM **Privately Held**
WEB: www.millstreet.org
SIC: 6513 Apartment building operator

(G-2095)
MINN-DAKOTA COACHES INC
1116 N Tower Rd (56537-4800)
PO Box 402 (56538-0402)
PHONE 218 739-3393
Patrick Regan, *President*
Michael Clark, *Vice Pres*
EMP: 50 EST: 1986
SQ FT: 30,000
SALES (est): 1MM-4.9MM **Privately Held**
WEB: www.ottertailcoaches.com
SIC: 4142 Long-distance bus charter
service
PA: Ottertail Coaches Inc
1116 N Tower Rd
Fergus Falls MN 56537
218 739-3393

(G-2096)
MINNESOTA DAKOTA GENERATING CO
215 S Cascade St (56537-2801)
PHONE 218 739-8200
FAX: 218 998-3165
Chuck Macfarland, *President*
Chuck M Farland, *President*
Maynard D Helgaas, *General Mgr*

www.HarrisInfo.com
100

2011 Harris Minnesota
Services Directory

▲=Import ▼=Export
◆=Import/Export

George A Koeck, *Corp Secy*
Jay D Myster, *Corp Secy*
EST: 1949
SQ FT: 100,000 **Privately Held**
SIC: 4953 6531 Manufactures electrical welding equipment; incinerator operation; residential real estate agency
PA: Otter Tail Corp
215 S Cascade St
Fergus Falls MN 56537
866 410-8780

(G-2097)
MINNESOTA DEPARTMENT OF
Also Called: Fergus Falls Veterans Home
1821 N Park St (56537-1247)
PHONE...........................218 736-0400
FAX: 218 739-7686
Kimberly Floyd, *Vice Pres*
Jon Skillingstad, *Manager*
EMP: 50
SALES (est): 1MM-4.9MM **Privately Held**
WEB: www.sbay.mvh.state.mn.us
SIC: 8051 Skilled nursing care facility; veterans' affairs administration services; state government administration of veterans' affairs
DH: Minnesota Department of
20 12th St W Fl 2
Saint Paul MN 55155
651 296-2562

(G-2098)
MINNESOTA DEPARTMENT OF
1509 N 1st Ave (56537-1271)
PHONE...........................218 739-7576
FAX: 218 739-7601
Don Schultz, *Manager*
Alin Schalecamp, *Manager*
EMP: 25
SALES (est): 1MM-4.9MM **Privately Held**
WEB: www.guessmail.com
SIC: 8999 Natural resource preservation services; conservation programs administration services; state government land, mineral & wildlife conservation administration
DH: Minnesota Department of
500 Lafayette Rd N
Saint Paul MN 55155
651 296-6157

(G-2099)
MINNESOTA DEPARTMENT OF HUMAN
Also Called: Fergus FLS Regional Trtmnt Ctr
1400 N Union Ave (56537-1248)
PHONE...........................218 739-7200
FAX: 218 739-7243
Rose Reiman, *Buyer*
Paula Skaalurd, *Human Res Dir*
Tom Geifer, *Program Mgr*
Shirley Jacobson, *Manager*
Bill Dorholt, *Administrator*
EMP: 475
SALES (est): 25MM-49.9MM **Privately Held**
WEB: www.state.mn.us
SIC: 8062 8069 8093 Medical hospital; public health program services; alcoholism rehabilitation hospital; outpatient mental health clinic; state government administration of public health programs
DH: Minnesota Department of Human
540 Cedar St
Saint Paul MN 55101
651 431-2000

(G-2100)
NASH-FINCH CO
1205 W Lincoln Ave (56537-1003)
PHONE...........................218 739-5272
FAX: 218 739-0266
Joe Monahan, *Manager*
Mary Holtz, *Director*
EMP: 154
SALES (est): 100MM-499.9MM **Publicly Held**
WEB: www.nashfinch.com
SIC: 5141 Wholesales general line groceries
PA: Nash-Finch Co
7600 France Ave S Ste 200
Edina MN 55435
952 832-0534

(G-2101)
NATURES GARDEN WORLD INC
1335 Highway 210 E (56537-3814)
PHONE...........................218 739-9641
FAX: 218 998-4769
Thomas Sullivan, *President*
EMP: 25 **EST:** 1979 **Privately Held**
WEB: www.naturesgardenworld.com
SIC: 0782 Landscaping services; lawn care services; retails fresh flowers; retails potted plants

(G-2102)
NELSON CHRYSLER DODGE GMC INC
2228 College Way (56537-1062)
PHONE...........................218 739-2283
FAX: 218 736-7432
Brent Nelson, *President*
Vergil Martinson, *Controller*
Gerry Worner, *Manager*
Denise Hanna, *Manager*
EMP: 30 **EST:** 2001
SALES (est): 10MM-24.9MM **Privately Held**
SIC: 7532 7538 Retails new & used automobiles; general automotive repair services; snowmobile dealer; retails all-terrain vehicle parts & accessories; automotive body shop

(G-2103)
OLSON OIL CO INC
1425 W Lincoln Ave (56537-1005)
PHONE...........................218 736-2786
FAX: 218 736-3120
Steven Olson, *President*
Ginger Rapp, *Controller*
EMP: 45 **EST:** 1974
SQ FT: 59,625
SALES (est): 100MM-499.9MM **Privately Held**
SIC: 5172 Wholesales petroleum products; retail independent convenience store; retail gasoline filling station; fuel oil dealer

(G-2104)
OTTER TAIL CORP
1012 Water Plant Rd (56537-3971)
PO Box 496 (56538-0496)
PHONE...........................218 739-8100
Jeff Olson, *Manager*
EMP: 46
SALES (est): 25MM-49.9MM **Privately Held**
WEB: www.otpco.com
SIC: 4911 Electric services
HQ: Otter Tail Power Co
215 S Cascade St
Fergus Falls MN 56537
866 410-8780

(G-2105)
OTTER TAIL CORP (PA)
215 S Cascade St (56537-2801)
PO Box 496 (56538-0496)
PHONE...........................866 410-8780
John D Erickson, *President*
Becky Wentler, *Corp Secy*
George A Koeck, *Corp Secy*
Lauris N Molbert, *COO*
Todd R Wahlund, *Vice Pres*
EST: 1907
SALES (corp-wide): 1.03B **Privately Held**
SIC: 4911 1731 5047 Electric services; wholesales medical & hospital equipment; general electrical contractor; manufactures dried potatoes packaged with other ingredients; manufactures plastic pipe

(G-2106)
OTTER TAIL COUNTY HUMAN SVCS
530 W Fir Ave (56537-1364)
PHONE...........................218 998-8150
John Dinsmore, *Principal*
EMP: 99 **EST:** 2007 **Privately Held**
SIC: 8399 Social services

(G-2107)
OTTER TAIL ENERGY SERVICES CO
224 E Washington Ave (56537-2812)
PHONE...........................218 739-8888
FAX: 218 739-8817

Charles Macfarlane, *President*
George A Koeck, *Corp Secy*
Lauris N Molbert, *Corp Secy*
Kevin G Mong, *Treasurer*
John D Erickson, *Director*
EMP: 900 **EST:** 1997
SALES (est): 1B-9.9B **Privately Held**
WEB: www.otesco.com
SIC: 4932 Gas & other combined services
PA: Otter Tail Corp
215 S Cascade St
Fergus Falls MN 56537
866 410-8780

(G-2108)
OTTER TAIL POWER CO
216 S Cascade St (56537-2802)
PO Box 747 (56538-0747)
PHONE...........................218 736-6947
FAX: 218 739-8731
Brad Hoeland, *Manager*
EMP: 300
SALES (est): 100MM-499.9MM **Privately Held**
WEB: www.otpco.com
SIC: 4911 Provides electric power generation services
HQ: Otter Tail Power Co
215 S Cascade St
Fergus Falls MN 56537
866 410-8780

(G-2109)
OTTER TAIL POWER CO (HQ)
215 S Cascade St (56537-2801)
PO Box 496 (56538-0496)
PHONE...........................866 410-8780
Chuck Macfarlane, *President*
Cris Kling, *Managing Dir*
Ward L Uggerud, *Senior VP*
Thomas R Brause, *VP Admin*
Todd R Wahlund, *Vice Pres*
◆ **EMP:** 250 **EST:** 1907
SALES (corp-wide): 1.03B **Privately Held**
WEB: www.otpco.com
SIC: 4911 Electric services; manufactures plastic planters; machine shop, jobbing & repair services; provides electric power generation services; provides electric power transmission services; electric power distribution service; machine shop
PA: Otter Tail Corp
215 S Cascade St
Fergus Falls MN 56537
866 410-8780

(G-2110)
OTTER TAIL POWER CO
Also Called: Otpt
215 S Cascade St (56537-2801)
PO Box 496 (56538-0496)
PHONE...........................218 739-8200
John Erickson, *CEO*
Talafous Lori, *Vice Pres*
Richard Muehlhausen, *Vice Pres*
Melissa Barry, *Purch Mgr*
Nancy Salgat, *MIS Mgr*
EMP: 400
SALES (est): 100MM-499.9MM **Privately Held**
WEB: www.otpco.com
SIC: 4911 Electric services; manufactures plastic planters; machine shop, jobbing & repair services; provides electric power generation services; provides electric power transmission services; electric power distribution service; machine shop
HQ: Otter Tail Power Co
215 S Cascade St
Fergus Falls MN 56537
866 410-8780

(G-2111)
OTTER TAIL TELCOM LLC
230 W Lincoln Ave (56537-2101)
PHONE...........................218 998-2000
FAX: 218 998-2050
Mary J Biegler, *Member*
Rob Fiedler, *Corp Secy*
Jeff Wilde, *Engineer*
Karen Thompson, *Human Res Mgr*
Scott Toso, *Sales Mgr*
EMP: 25 **EST:** 1997 **Privately Held**
SIC: 4813 Wired telecommunications carrier & service

(G-2112)
OTTERTAIL COACHES INC (PA)
Also Called: Minn-Dakota Coaches
1116 N Tower Rd (56537-4800)
PO Box 402 (56538-0402)
PHONE...........................218 739-3393
Pat Regan, *President*
Mike Clark, *Vice Pres*
EMP: 60 **EST:** 1973
SQ FT: 30,000
SALES (corp-wide): 1.70M **Privately Held**
WEB: www.ottertailcoaches.com
SIC: 4151 4142 4724 School bus service; long-distance bus charter service; travel agency

(G-2113)
PIONEER HOME INC
1006 S Sheridan St (56537-3518)
PHONE...........................218 739-7701
FAX: 218 739-7770
John Richards, *CEO*
David Schneeberger, *Vice Chairman*
Sharon Wilde, *Treasurer*
Sandi Stromberg, *Accounting Staf*
Joel Rustad, *Sales Staff*
EMP: 240 **EST:** 1928
SQ FT: 16,000
SALES (est): 5MM-9.9MM **Privately Held**
SIC: 8051 6513 Skilled nursing care facility; operators of retirement hotels

(G-2114)
PIONEER SENIOR COTTAGES
1307 S Mabelle Ave (56537-3758)
PHONE...........................218 998-9678
John Richard, *CEO*
Heather Nelson, *Director*
EMP: 50 **EST:** 2005
SALES (est): 1MM-4.9MM **Privately Held**
SIC: 8059 Nursing home

(G-2115)
PRAIRIE COMMUNITY SERVICES
Also Called: Arlington Home
1505 S Arlington St (56537-3744)
PHONE...........................218 739-2045
FAX: 218 736-0089
Nicolle Braatten-Toso, *Manager*
Nicolle Toso, *Manager*
Kris Olson, *Director*
EMP: 28
SALES (est): 1MM-4.9MM **Privately Held**
SIC: 8361 Residential care facility
HQ: Prairie Community Services
801 Nevada Ave Ste 100
Morris MN 56267
320 589-3077

(G-2116)
PRECISION PARTNERS INC
421 N Broadway (56537-2020)
PHONE...........................218 737-0507
Jeffrey Nesbitt, *President*
EST: 1997 **Privately Held**
SIC: 8748 Agricultural consultant

(G-2117)
PRODUCTIVE ALTERNATIVES INC (PA)
1205 N Tower Rd (56537-1077)
PHONE...........................218 998-5630
FAX: 218 736-2541
Steve Skauge, *President*
Steve Lorshbough, *Prdtn Mgr*
Denise Demartelaere, *CFO*
EMP: 90 **EST:** 1959
SQ FT: 41,250
SALES (corp-wide): 7.19M **Privately Held**
WEB: www.paiff.org
SIC: 8331 Vocational rehabilitation agency; manufactures signs; manufactures wood household furniture; manufactures novelties

(G-2118)
RESULT RADIO INC
Also Called: K B R F Radio
728 Western Ave (56537-1095)
PHONE...........................218 736-7596
Gerald Pappenfus, *President*
Patricia Pappenfus, *Corp Secy*
EMP: 30 **EST:** 1977
SALES (est): 1MM-4.9MM **Privately Held**

(PA)=Parent Co (HQ)=Headquarters (DH)=Div Headquarters
✿ = New business established in last 2 years

2011 Harris Minnesota
Services Directory

© Harris InfoSource 1-866-281-6415
101

SIC: 4832 7313 Radio broadcasting station; radio advertising representative

(G-2119)
SKYVISION INC
1010 Frontier Dr (56537-1023)
PHONE...............218 739-5231
FAX: 218 739-4879
Richard D Field, *CEO*
Del Jose, *President*
Bruce Fuhrman, *Purchasing*
Melvin Frank, *Manager*
Gary Birch, *Manager*
▲ **EMP:** 25 **EST:** 1983
SQ FT: 25,000
SALES (est): 1MM-4.9MM **Privately Held**
WEB: www.skyvision.com
SIC: 4813 Retails satellite dish antennas; internet host services; retails video recorders, players, disc players & accessories; retails high fidelity stereo equipment

(G-2120)
SOMEPLACE SAFE
1005 Pebble Lake Rd # 108 (56537-3109)
PO Box 815 (56538-0815)
PHONE...............320 589-3208
Jeanne Jacobs, *Director*
EMP: 59 **EST:** 1980
SALES (est): 1MM-4.9MM **Privately Held**
SIC: 8322 Emergency & relief services

(G-2121)
SVINGEN HAGSTRON CLINE KARKELA
Also Called: Law Office
309 S Mill St Ste 105 (56537-2534)
PO Box 697 (56538-0697)
PHONE...............218 739-4696
Allen Haugrud, *Principal*
EMP: 25 **EST:** 1988
SALES (est): 1MM-4.9MM **Privately Held**
SIC: 8111 Legal services

(G-2122)
UNITED PARCEL SERVICE OF NEW
Also Called: UPS
1515 N 1st Ave (56537-1271)
PHONE...............218 739-4910
Ken Link, *Manager*
EMP: 32
SALES (est): 1MM-4.9MM **Publicly Held**
WEB: www.martrac.com
SIC: 4215 Package delivery services by vehicle
HQ: United Parcel Service of New
   55 Glenlake Pkwy NE
   Atlanta GA 30328
   404 828-6000

(G-2123)
VICTOR LUNDEEN CO (PA)
126 W Lincoln Ave (56537-2123)
PO Box 486 (56538-0486)
PHONE...............218 736-5433
Victor G Lundeen Jr, *President*
David F Lundeen, *Vice Pres*
Chuck Lundeen, *Executive*
EMP: 34 **EST:** 1914
SQ FT: 24,000 **Privately Held**
WEB: www.victorlundeens.com
SIC: 5112 Offset printing; wholesales office supplies; retail gift shop

(G-2124)
WELLS FARGO MINNESOTA WEST
216 S Court St (56537-2524)
PHONE...............218 736-7391
Ron Trehm, *Manager*
EMP: 28
SALES (est): 5MM-9.9MM **Publicly Held**
SIC: 6021 National commercial bank
HQ: Wells Fargo Minnesota West
   730 Center Ave Lbby LBBY
   Moorhead MN 56560
   218 233-6183

FERTILE
Polk County

(G-2125)
CITY OF FERTILE
Also Called: Fair Meadow Nursing Home
300 Garfield Ave SE (56540)
PO Box 8 (56540-0008)
PHONE...............218 945-6194
FAX: 218 945-6459
Emil Belen, *Opers Mgr*
Cheryl Hegg, *Manager*
Barry Robertson, *Administrator*
EMP: 120
SALES (est): 1MM-4.9MM **Privately Held**
SIC: 8361 8051 8059 Home for the elderly; personal care home, with health care; skilled nursing care facility
PA: City of Fertile
   101 S Mill St
   Fertile MN 56540
   218 945-3136

(G-2126)
LEE HYDRA-MAC SALES
11880 360th St SW (56540-9562)
PHONE...............218 574-2237
Gary Lee, *Owner*
Edith Lee, *Corp Secy*
Jody Jensrud, *Corp Secy*
EMP: 30 **EST:** 1970
SALES (est): 10MM-24.9MM **Privately Held**
SIC: 5083 Wholesales farm & garden machinery

(G-2127)
POLK COUNTY HIGHWAY SHOP
355 Garfield Ave SE (56540)
PHONE...............218 945-6952
Rich Sanders, *Director*
EMP: 40 **EST:** 2006
SALES (est): 5MM-9.9MM **Privately Held**
SIC: 1611 Highway & street maintenance service

FINLAND
Lake County

(G-2128)
WOLF RIDGE ENVIRONMENTAL
6282 Cranberry Rd (55603-9727)
PHONE...............218 353-7414
FAX: 218 353-7762
Doug Nakari, *Business Mgr*
Judy Larson, *Manager*
Carrie Anderson, *Technology*
Kimberley Skyelander, *Exec Dir*
Kim Fkyelander, *Director*
EMP: 40 **EST:** 1971
SQ FT: 50,000
SALES (est): 5MM-9.9MM **Privately Held**
WEB: www.wolf-ridge.org
SIC: 8641 Educational services; civic & social organization

FINLAYSON
Pine County

(G-2129)
DEPARTMENT OF CORRECTIONS MN
Also Called: Saint Croix Girl's Camp
61085 State Highway 23 (55735-4514)
PHONE...............320 384-7411
Mike Wolf, *President*
EMP: 80
SALES (est): 1MM-4.9MM **Privately Held**
WEB: www.minncor.com
SIC: 8322 Youth center; correctional institution; state government correctional institution
DH: Department of Corrections MN
   1450 Energy Park Dr # 200
   Saint Paul MN 55108
   651 361-7200

(G-2130)
LUOMA EGG RANCH INC
35705 State Highway 18 (55735-4277)
PHONE...............320 233-6122
FAX: 320 233-6003
Judy Luoma, *President*
Sheri Cabak, *Corp Secy*
Nancy Wilkening, *Vice Pres*
Sandy White, *Treasurer*
EMP: 42 **EST:** 1955
SQ FT: 200,000 **Privately Held**
SIC: 0252 Chicken egg farming

(G-2131)
NORTHVIEW BANK (HQ)
2203 Finland Ave (55735)
PO Box 257 (55735-0257)
PHONE...............320 233-7575
Bruce Pogatchnik, *CEO*
Tom Koerber, *Vice Pres*
EMP: 25 **EST:** 1908
SQ FT: 9,600
SALES (corp-wide): 11.73M **Privately Held**
WEB: www.northviewbank.com
SIC: 6022 State commercial bank
PA: Northview Bank
   2203 Finland Ave
   Finlayson MN 55735
   320 233-7575

(G-2132)
NORTHVIEW BANK (PA)
2203 Finland Ave (55735)
PO Box 257 (55735-0257)
PHONE...............320 233-7575
Bruce Pogatchnik, *President*
Ron Carson, *Exec VP*
Tom Koerber, *Vice Pres*
EST: 1980
SALES (corp-wide): 11.73M **Privately Held**
SIC: 6022 State commercial bank

FISHER
Polk County

(G-2133)
AGRIMAX LLC
21161 330th Ave SW (56723-9421)
PO Box 7 (56723-0007)
PHONE...............218 281-1441
Tom Rongen, *Member*
David Garret, *Member*
EST: 1996 **Privately Held**
WEB: www.agrimaxfuels.com
SIC: 0721 Crop dusting services

(G-2134)
FISHER EDUCATION ASSOCIATION
313 Park Ave (56723-4009)
PHONE...............218 891-4905
Randy Bruer, *Superintendent*
Tim Bird, *Member*
Lien Patricia, *Treasurer*
Patti Lien, *Manager*
EMP: 60 **EST:** 2001 **Privately Held**
WEB: www.fisher.k12.mn.us
SIC: 8699 Personal interest organization; educational services

---

FLOODWOOD
Saint Louis County

(G-2135)
FAFARD INC
10108 Hwy 8 (55736)
PO Box 63 (55736-0063)
PHONE...............218 476-3022
FAX: 218 476-3029
Keelan Pulliam, *President*
Tim Davern, *Manager*
EMP: 25 **EST:** 1986
SQ FT: 7,500 **Privately Held**
SIC: 0831 Moss gathering

FOLEY
Benton County

(G-2136)
CUSTOMER ELATION INC
161st Ave S (56329)
PHONE...............320 968-4438
Amanda Corhonnon, *Manager*
EMP: 40
SALES (est): 5MM-9.9MM **Privately Held**
WEB: www.customerelation.com
SIC: 8742 Marketing consulting service
PA: Customer Elation Inc
   9065 Lyndale Ave S Ste 2
   Minneapolis MN 55420
   952 884-8106

(G-2137)
FOLEY HEALTH CARE INC
253 Pine St (56329-9000)
PHONE...............320 968-6201
FAX: 320 968-7051
Steven Oelrich, *President*
Sandy Ewert, *Safety Dir*
Michelle Spizvka, *Manager*
Annette Brenny, *Director*
Nicole Ruhoff, *Registrd Nurse*
EMP: 99 **EST:** 1971
SQ FT: 40,000
SALES (est): 1MM-4.9MM **Privately Held**
SIC: 8051 Skilled nursing care facility

(G-2138)
FRANDSEN BANK & TRUST
341 4th Ave N (56329-8443)
PO Box 367 (56329-0367)
PHONE...............320 968-6293
FAX: 320 968-6298
Mary E Domeier, *Principal*
Steve Bartness, *Senior VP*
Heather Juetten, *Assistant VP*
Rita Herbrand, *Mfg Spvr*
EMP: 30
SALES (est): 5MM-9.9MM **Privately Held**
SIC: 6022 6029 State commercial bank; commercial bank
PA: Frandsen Bank & Trust
   116 Central St W
   Lonsdale MN 55046
   507 744-2361

(G-2139)
GILMAN PARK & REC ASSOCIATION
11765 Highway 25 NE (56329-9302)
PHONE...............320 387-2941
Randy Spiczka, *President*
Terry Templin, *Member*
EMP: 30 **EST:** 1997 **Privately Held**
SIC: 8699 Charitable organization

(G-2140)
JERRY'S FARM MARKET
991 115th Ave NE (56329-9520)
PHONE...............320 968-7001
Shirley Chmielewski, *Owner*
EMP: 525 **EST:** 1966
SQ FT: 2,500
SALES (est): 50MM-99.9MM **Privately Held**
SIC: 5148 Fruit & vegetable market; wholesales fresh fruits & vegetables

(G-2141)
POUCHTEC INDUSTRIES LLC
347 Sheridan Rd SE (56329-8523)
PHONE...............320 968-4868
FAX: 320 968-4870
Scott Lafortune, *Persnl Mgr*
Denise Caron, *Accounts Mgr*
Robert C Jones, *Mng Member*
Karmen O'Beando, *Director*
Pam Cardinal, *Director*
EMP: 70 **EST:** 1992
SQ FT: 25,000
SALES (est): 5MM-9.9MM **Privately Held**
SIC: 7389 Packaging & labeling services

(G-2142)
WILLMAR POULTRY FARMS INC
411 Pine St (56329-9001)
PHONE...............320 968-6211
FAX: 320 968-6763

www.HarrisInfo.com
102

2011 Harris Minnesota
Services Directory

▲=Import ▼=Export
◆=Import/Export

W Carter, *Manager*
Gregory W Carter, *Manager*
EMP: 48 **Privately Held**
SIC: 0254 Poultry hatchery

FORBES
Saint Louis County

(G-2143)
HARDRIVES INC
2372 N Yoki Rd (55738-8146)
PHONE..............................218 744-2913
FAX: 218 744-0810
Dave Clement, *Manager*
EMP: 30
SALES (est): 1MM-4.9MM **Privately Held**
WEB: www.hardrives.com
SIC: 1611 Highway & street paving
contractor
PA: Hardrives Inc
14475 Quiram Dr Ste 1
Rogers MN 55374
763 428-8886

FOREST LAKE
Anoka County

(G-2144)
CENTRAL TURF FARMS
13655 Lake Dr NE (55025-9444)
PHONE..............................651 464-2130
FAX: 651 464-8288
Deanna Halley, *Partner*
Earl Halley Jr, *Partner*
EMP: 40 **EST:** 1989
SQ FT: 2,400 **Privately Held**
SIC: 0181 Sod farm

(G-2145)
GARY THALER
Also Called: Coldwell Banker
15252 W Freeway Dr NE (55025-8120)
PHONE..............................651 464-5555
Gary Thaler, *Principal*
EMP: 50 **EST:** 2003
SALES (est): 5MM-9.9MM **Privately Held**
SIC: 6531 Residential real estate agency

(G-2146)
GRAFFCO INC
13957 Lake Dr NE (55025-8609)
PO Box 247 (55025-0247)
PHONE..............................651 464-1079
FAX: 651 464-8614
Daniel Graff, *President*
James Elmquist, *CFO*
Ross Grems, *Manager*
EMP: 30 **EST:** 1986
SQ FT: 25,000
SALES (est): 10MM-24.9MM **Privately Held**
WEB: www.graffco.com
SIC: 5013 5172 Wholesales automobile
service station equipment; wholesales
service station petroleum

(G-2147)
JAY BROS INC
9218 Lake Dr NE (55025-9443)
PO Box 865 (55025-0865)
PHONE..............................651 464-6400
FAX: 651 464-1704
Michael J Jay, *President*
Mark Jay, *Corp Secy*
Kelly Brooks, *Bookkeeper*
Josey Jay, *Office Mgr*
EMP: 45 **EST:** 1971
SQ FT: 9,000
SALES (est): 5MM-9.9MM **Privately Held**
WEB: www.jaybros.com
SIC: 1794 Excavating contractor

(G-2148)
NORTH METRO HARNESS INITIATIVE
Also Called: Running Aces Harness Park
15201 Zurich St NE (55025-7908)
PHONE..............................651 925-4600
Robert A Farinella, *Member*
Tracie Wilson, *Member*
Carolyn Morstad, *Executive Asst*

EMP: 450 **EST:** 2003
SQ FT: 166,319
SALES (est): 25MM-49.9MM **Privately Held**
WEB: www.northmetroharness.com
SIC: 7948 Horse racetrack

(G-2149)
NORTH PINE AGGREGATE INC
14551 Lake Dr NE (55025-8606)
PHONE..............................651 464-6802
FAX: 651 464-8456
Dennis Jensen, *President*
Sharilyn Jensen, *Corp Secy*
Brent Jensen, *Vice Pres*
EMP: 85 **EST:** 1984
SQ FT: 20,000
SALES (est): 10MM-24.9MM **Privately Held**
WEB: www.npainc.net
SIC: 1794 Excavation & grading, building
construction contractor

FOREST LAKE
Chisago County

(G-2150)
BEVER & SONS INC
23950 Lake Blvd N (55025-8210)
PHONE..............................651 426-7733
FAX: 651 784-4397
Jim Bever Sr, *President*
Dan Draine, *General Mgr*
Tom Bever, *Vice Pres*
EMP: 25 **EST:** 1983
SQ FT: 2,000 **Privately Held**
WEB: www.beverandsons.com
SIC: 0782 Landscaping services

(G-2151)
COMMERCIAL PLUMBING & HEATING
24428 Greenway Ave (55025-8784)
PHONE..............................651 464-2988
FAX: 651 464-2425
Robert Skeie, *President*
John Marzitelli, *Vice Pres*
EMP: 70 **EST:** 1989
SQ FT: 12,000
SALES (est): 5MM-9.9MM **Privately Held**
WEB: www.cpandh.com
SIC: 1711 Plumbing service; heating & air
conditioning contractor

(G-2152)
INTERSTATE REMOVAL CO
6671 Lake Blvd (55025-8297)
PO Box 1028 (55025-5028)
PHONE..............................651 765-0765
FAX: 651 407-0609
Orville J Rinehart, *President*
Gregory Dumke, *Exec VP*
Jeff Miller, *Vice Pres*
EMP: 50 **EST:** 1997
SQ FT: 40,000
SALES (est): 5MM-9.9MM **Privately Held**
SIC: 1611 Highway & street paving
contractor

(G-2153)
PERFECT PICKLE
Also Called: Perfered Pickle
22520 Elston Ct (55025-6503)
PHONE..............................651 779-6129
David Finger, *President*
EMP: 25 **EST:** 1998
SALES (est): 10MM-24.9MM **Privately Held**
SIC: 5149 Wholesales specialty food items

(G-2154)
RED ROCK FIRE INC
6671 Lake Blvd (55025-8297)
PO Box 1028 (55025-5028)
PHONE..............................651 765-0765
Oj Rinehart, *President*
Gregory Dumke, *Vice Pres*
EMP: 25
SALES (est): 1MM-4.9MM **Privately Held**
WEB: www.redrockfire.com
SIC: 7389 Fire protection services

FOREST LAKE
Washington County

(G-2155)
ALLINA HEALTH SYSTEM
1540 Lake St S (55025-2628)
PHONE..............................651 464-7100
FAX: 651 982-5515
Kathy Dill, *Office Mgr*
Steven Voss MD, *Med Doctor*
Marlys R Winandy MD, *Med Doctor*
Paul Sandager MD, *Med Doctor*
Jeffry Penwarden, *Manager*
EMP: 150
SALES (est): 10MM-24.9MM **Privately Held**
WEB: www.allina.com
SIC: 8011 8093 Clinic operated by
physicians; specialty outpatient clinic
PA: Allina Health System
2925 Chicago Ave
Minneapolis MN 55407
612 775-5000

(G-2156)
AMERICAN LEGION 225 INC
355 W Broadway Ave (55025-1505)
PHONE..............................651 464-2600
FAX: 651 464-4538
Marion Houle, *Vice Pres*
Dwight Dupey, *Finance Mgr*
Ceil Purvif, *Manager*
Ron Weiss, *Director*
EMP: 40 **EST:** 1917 **Privately Held**
WEB: www.post225.com
SIC: 8641 Fraternal association

(G-2157)
ANOKA HENNEPIN SCHOOL DISTRICT
1500 Lake St S Ste 100 (55025-2607)
PHONE..............................651 255-7000
Jeff Clausspn, *President*
EMP: 50
SALES (est): 5MM-9.9MM **Privately Held**
SIC: 6061 Federally chartered credit union
PA: Anoka Hennepin School District
3505 Northdale Blvd NW
Minneapolis MN 55448
763 422-0290

(G-2158)
BIRCHWOOD HEALTH CARE CENTER
604 1st St NE (55025-1202)
PHONE..............................651 464-5600
FAX: 651 464-0992
Steve Daniels, *Maint Spvr*
Sue Larson, *Human Resources*
Jules Benson, *Mktg Dir*
Deb Witt, *Manager*
Dian Willette, *Administrator*
EMP: 200 **EST:** 1964
SQ FT: 8,000
SALES (est): 5MM-9.9MM **Privately Held**
SIC: 8051 Skilled nursing care facility

(G-2159)
COUNTRY INN & SUITES BY
1954 W Broadway Ave (55025-1335)
PHONE..............................651 982-9799
FAX: 651 982-6173
George Sheets, *Owner*
Cindy Meyer, *General Mgr*
EMP: 30 **EST:** 1998
SALES (est): 1MM-4.9MM **Privately Held**
SIC: 7011 Traveler accommodations

(G-2160)
FOREST HILLS GOLF CLUB INC
7530 210th St N (55025-9742)
PO Box 505 (55025-0505)
PHONE..............................651 464-3097
Jerry Anderson, *President*
Karen Hoekstra, *Corp Secy*
EMP: 60 **EST:** 1958
SQ FT: 3,000
SALES (est): 1MM-4.9MM **Privately Held**
SIC: 7997 Membership golf club

(G-2161)
FOREST LAKE FLYAWAYS
255 7th Ave NW (55025-1157)
PHONE..............................651 464-8648
FAX: 651 982-6776
Judy Huntosh, *President*
Bud Huntosh, *Vice Pres*
EMP: 30 **EST:** 1981
SALES (est): 1MM-4.9MM **Privately Held**
WEB: www.flyawaysgymnastics.com
SIC: 7999 Gymnastics instruction

(G-2162)
FOREST LAKE VFW POST 4210 INC
Also Called: Veterans of Foreign Wars
556 12th St SW (55025-1753)
PHONE..............................651 464-6827
FAX: 651 464-2106
Keith Heghstrum, *General Mgr*
Opal Peterson, *Corp Secy*
Jim Bourque, *Bd of Directors*
Louise Dumire, *Bd of Directors*
EMP: 32 **EST:** 1945
SQ FT: 8,400 **Privately Held**
WEB: www.vfwpost4210.com
SIC: 8641 Veterans' organization; bar

(G-2163)
LA GRANDE' SALON LTD
56 E Broadway Ave Ste 106 (55025-1659)
PHONE..............................651 464-4371
FAX: 651 464-6069
Cindy Winnick, *Owner*
EMP: 28 **EST:** 1996
SQ FT: 3,600
SALES (est): 500-999K **Privately Held**
WEB: www.lagrandesalon.com
SIC: 7231 Beauty salon

(G-2164)
MOONDANCE ENTERPRISES
356 2nd Ave NW (55025-1108)
PHONE..............................651 464-1875
Debra Bean, *President*
Leighann Lange, *Vice Pres*
Rolf Peterson, *Treasurer*
EMP: 30 **EST:** 2000
SQ FT: 1,400
SALES (est): 500-999K **Privately Held**
SIC: 7991 Health club

(G-2165)
NATIONAL TACK NORTH INC
7995 200th St N (55025-9724)
PHONE..............................651 464-7733
David L Juelfs, *President*
EMP: 28 **EST:** 1978
SQ FT: 25,000
SALES (est): 10MM-24.9MM **Privately Held**
SIC: 5191 Wholesales equestrian
equipment

(G-2166)
NORTH MEMORIAL AMBULANCE
246 11th Ave SE Ste B (55025-1884)
PHONE..............................651 464-6738
FAX: 651 464-7669
Chuck Lindstrom, *Manager*
EMP: 30 **EST:** 2006
SALES (est): 1MM-4.9MM **Privately Held**
SIC: 4119 Ambulance service

(G-2167)
ROOM FOR GROWING
268 12th St SW (55025-1482)
PHONE..............................651 464-1601
FAX: 651 982-1560
Jennifer Nellis, *President*
EMP: 42 **EST:** 1983
SQ FT: 4,300
SALES (est): 500-999K **Privately Held**
SIC: 8351 Group day care center

(G-2168)
S & S SPA SALON INC
Also Called: Adevia Spasalon
280 12th St SW Ste 1 (55025-3780)
PHONE..............................651 464-6612
FAX: 651 982-0374
Shari Sell, *President*

G
E
O
G
R
A
P
H
I
C

(PA)=Parent Co (HQ)=Headquarters (DH)=Div Headquarters
✪ = New business established in last 2 years
2011 Harris Minnesota
Services Directory
© Harris InfoSource 1-866-281-6415
103

Hope Freeman, *Manager*
EMP: 25 **EST:** 1978
SQ FT: 2,300
SALES (est): 500-999K **Privately Held**
SIC: 7991 7299 Spas; tanning salon

(G-2169)
TANNERS BROOK GOLF CLUB LLP
5810 190th St N (55025-8233)
PHONE..................651 464-2300
FAX: 651 464-2461
Jamie M Govern, *Managing Prtnr*
John Dunlap, *Partner*
Craig Brischke, *Manager*
EMP: 70 **EST:** 1999
SALES (est): 1MM-4.9MM **Privately Held**
SIC: 7992 Public golf course; retails sporting goods

(G-2170)
THEMESCAPES INC
794 15th St SW (55025-1311)
PHONE..................651 778-1784
Peter Nasvik, *CEO*
Michael Carlson, *Project Mgr*
Craig Zehnder, *Project Mgr*
Hai Tieu, *Controller*
Margaret Nasvic, *Manager*
EMP: 50 **EST:** 1997
SQ FT: 5,000
SALES (est): 5MM-9.9MM **Privately Held**
WEB: www.themescapesinc.com
SIC: 1771 Concrete contractor

(G-2171)
VINCO INC
18995 Forest Blvd N (55025-3606)
PO Box 907 (55025-0907)
PHONE..................651 982-4642
FAX: 651 982-4621
Colleen Kotrba, *President*
Steve Anderson, *Corp Secy*
Mark Anderson, *Vice Pres*
Mike Bultmasa, *Engineer*
Steve Huseby, *Manager*
EMP: 94 **EST:** 1997
SQ FT: 6,000
SALES (est): 10MM-24.9MM **Privately Held**
WEB: www.vinco-inc.com
SIC: 1542 1541 Commercial & institutional building construction; industrial building & warehouse construction

(G-2172)
WELLS FARGO BANK
208 Lake St S (55025-2605)
PHONE..................651 464-3334
FAX: 651 464-9410
Steve Flage, *CEO*
EMP: 41 **EST:** 1903
SALES (est): 10MM-24.9MM **Publicly Held**
SIC: 6022 State commercial bank
PA: Wells Fargo & Co
   420 Montgomery St
   San Francisco CA 94104
   866 878-5865

FORT RIPLEY
Crow Wing County

(G-2173)
EAGLE'S LANDING GOLF CLUB INC
14825 263rd St (56449-2015)
PHONE..................320 632-5721
FAX: 320 632-0471
Jim Dahl, *President*
Roger Peterson, *Corp Secy*
EMP: 75 **EST:** 2001
SALES (est): 1MM-4.9MM **Privately Held**
WEB: www.eagleslanding-golf.com
SIC: 7992 Public golf course

(G-2174)
J B WAIVERED SERVICES
867 Lawson Rd (56449-1343)
PHONE..................218 828-4962
Joni Bender, *Owner*
EMP: 31 **EST:** 1990
SALES (est): 1MM-4.9MM **Privately Held**
SIC: 8361 Group foster home

FOSSTON
Polk County

(G-2175)
CUSTOMER TRAAC INC
102 Kaiser Ave S (56542)
PHONE..................218 435-2600
FAX: 218 435-2590
Greg Sturtz, *Manager*
EMP: 30
SALES (est): 1MM-4.9MM **Privately Held**
WEB: www.customertraac.com
SIC: 7389 Telemarketing services
PA: Customer Traac Inc
   3030 Harbor Ln N Ste 132
   Minneapolis MN 55447
   763 553-2989

(G-2176)
FIRST CARE MEDICAL SERVICES
900 Hilligoss Blvd SE (56542-1542)
PHONE..................218 435-1133
FAX: 218 435-1134
Patricia Wangler, *President*
Gemma Scott, *Ch Radiology*
Tammy Carlson, *Purch Mgr*
Scott Kolling, *Engineer*
Mike Manecke, *Engineering*
EMP: 170 **EST:** 1947
SQ FT: 70,000
SALES (est): 10MM-24.9MM **Privately Held**
SIC: 8062 8051 8082 Medical hospital; convalescent home; home health care services
HQ: Essentia Health
   502 E 2nd St
   Duluth MN 55805
   218 786-8376

(G-2177)
MIDWAY CARE CENTER INC
114 2nd St NE (56542-1302)
PHONE..................218 435-1272
FAX: 218 435-6336
Allen Potvin, *President*
Judy Potvin, *Corp Secy*
Cari Swanson, *Administrator*
Kari Swanson, *Administrator*
Tami Lindell, *Director*
EMP: 35 **EST:** 1973
SQ FT: 20,000
SALES (est): 1MM-4.9MM **Privately Held**
SIC: 8051 Skilled nursing care facility

(G-2178)
MINNESOTA DEHYDRATED
915 Omland Ave N (56542)
PO Box 245 (56542-0245)
PHONE..................218 435-1997
James Stewart, *President*
Larry Altringer, *Corp Secy*
John Goehke, *QC Dir*
Keith Stolen, *CFO*
Jodi Brevik, *Controller*
EMP: 82 **EST:** 1991
SQ FT: 28,000
SALES (est): 10MM-24.9MM **Privately Held**
WEB: www.mdvcorp.com
SIC: 5149 Manufactures dried & dehydrated fruits & vegetables & soup mixes; wholesales dried or canned foods

(G-2179)
R E M NORTH STAR INC
323 Mark Ave N (56542-1031)
PHONE..................218 435-6088
FAX: 218 435-6124
Heather Paulson, *Director*
EMP: 33 **EST:** 2003
SALES (est): 1MM-4.9MM **Privately Held**
SIC: 8361 8059 Self-help group home; convalescent home

FRANKLIN
Renville County

(G-2180)
BEVERLY ENTERPRISES - MN
Also Called: Franklin Healthcare Center
900 3rd St (55333-9799)
PHONE..................507 557-2211
FAX: 507 557-2213
Shiela Honel, *Manager*
Drew Fischgrabe, *Manager*
EMP: 50
SALES (est): 1MM-4.9MM **Privately Held**
WEB: www.beverlynet.com
SIC: 8051 Skilled nursing care facility; convalescent home
HQ: Beverly Enterprises - MN
   650 Ramer Ave S
   Rush City MN 55069
   320 358-4765

(G-2181)
LARSON UTILITIES INC (PA)
318 2nd Ave E (55333-1191)
PO Box 310 (55333-0310)
PHONE..................507 557-2275
Katherine Larson, *President*
Paul Larson, *Manager*
Danny Busche, *Manager*
EST: 1976 **Privately Held**
SIC: 4813 Wired telecommunications carrier & service

FRAZEE
Becker County

(G-2182)
ANDERSON BUS & COACH INC
101 W Juniper Ave (56544-4300)
PO Box 98 (56544-0098)
PHONE..................218 334-3171
FAX: 218 334-3172
Ted Anderson, *President*
EMP: 52 **EST:** 1947
SALES (est): 1MM-4.9MM **Privately Held**
SIC: 4151 School bus service

(G-2183)
BURKEL TURKEY FARMS INC
32913 State Highway 87 (56544-9102)
PHONE..................218 334-2833
David Burkel Jr, *President*
Robin Burkel, *Corp Secy*
Angie Ewanika, *Administrator*
EMP: 30 **EST:** 1986 **Privately Held**
SIC: 0253 Turkey farm

(G-2184)
DAGGETT TRUCK LINE INC
32717 County Road 10 (56544)
PO Box 158 (56544)
PHONE..................218 334-3711
FAX: 218 334-2566
Frederic Daggett, *President*
Terry Beilke, *Corp Secy*
Charles Daggett, *Vice Pres*
Christopher Daggett, *Vice Pres*
Laverne Maxwell, *Office Mgr*
EMP: 92 **EST:** 1930
SQ FT: 24,000
SALES (est): 10MM-24.9MM **Privately Held**
WEB: www.daggetttruck.com
SIC: 4213 Long-distance refrigerated trucking services

(G-2185)
MICKELSON FARMS
14870 County Highway 43 (56544-8587)
PHONE..................218 346-3876
Kevin Mickelson, *President*
Thomas Mickelson, *Assistant VP*
EMP: 35 **EST:** 1945 **Privately Held**
SIC: 0253 Turkey & turkey egg farming

(G-2186)
NEW LIFE FARMS LLP
47947 140th St (56544-8588)
PHONE..................218 346-7587
John Anderson, *Principal*
Doug Heubsch, *Member*

Ed Mickolsen, *Member*
EMP: 75 **EST:** 2000 **Privately Held**
SIC: 0253 Turkey farm

FREEPORT
Stearns County

(G-2187)
ARNZEN CONSTRUCTION INC
29033 County Road 17 (56331-9637)
PHONE..................320 836-2284
John Arnzen, *President*
Robert Arnzen, *Corp Secy*
Alvin Leinen, *Vice Pres*
Lillian Arnzen, *Office Mgr*
EMP: 35 **EST:** 1987
SALES (est): 10MM-24.9MM **Privately Held**
WEB: www.arnzenconstruction.net
SIC: 5083 1521 1542 Wholesales agricultural machinery & equipment; commercial & office building contractor; single-family housing construction

(G-2188)
M & B ENTERPRISE OF FREEPORT (PA)
Also Called: Belgrade Milling Co
446 Industrial Dr (56331)
PO Box 7 (56331-0007)
PHONE..................320 836-2145
Al Beste, *President*
Tom Beste, *Corp Secy*
John Beste, *Vice Pres*
EST: 1989
SQ FT: 3,200 **Privately Held**
SIC: 5153 Manufactures livestock feeds; wholesales grains

FRIDLEY
Anoka County

(G-2189)
ALLINA HEALTH SYSTEM
Also Called: Unity Hospital
550 Osborne Rd NE (55432-2718)
PHONE..................763 236-5000
FAX: 763 780-7873
Rickie Ressler, *President*
Rolf F Ulvestad, *Ch of Surgery*
Tracy Steeper, *Ch Pathology*
Patrick Juenemann, *Ch Radiology*
Julie Lapensky, *Vice Pres*
EMP: 1800
SALES (est): 100MM-499.9MM **Privately Held**
WEB: www.allina.com
SIC: 8062 Medical hospital
PA: Allina Health System
   2925 Chicago Ave
   Minneapolis MN 55407
   612 775-5000

(G-2190)
APPLIED STAFFING INC
7687 Main St NE (55432-3119)
PHONE..................763 502-1388
David Linkert, *President*
EMP: 50 **EST:** 1997
SQ FT: 680 **Privately Held**
SIC: 7361 Employment agency services

(G-2191)
BEST SOURCE ELECTRONICS CORP
5301 E River Rd Ste 113 (55421-3778)
PHONE..................763 502-7847
FAX: 763 571-6824
Bradley J Storch, *President*
Angie Matthews, *Exec Dir*
EMP: 30 **EST:** 1997
SQ FT: 25,000
SALES (est): 1MM-4.9MM **Privately Held**
WEB: www.bsec.net
SIC: 5065 Manufactures electronic component making machinery; wholesales electronic parts & equipment

www.HarrisInfo.com
104

2011 Harris Minnesota
Services Directory

▲=Import ▼=Export
◆=Import/Export

(G-2192)
CON-WAY FREIGHT INC
51 81st Ave NE (55432-1760)
PHONE............................763 783-7123
FAX: 763 783-8831
Todd Mellem, *Personnel*
John Johnson, *Manager*
Bob Doder, *Maintence Staff*
EMP: 190
SALES (est): 10MM-24.9MM **Publicly Held**
WEB: www.con-way.com
SIC: 4213 Over the road trucking
HQ: Con-way Freight Inc
2211 Old Earhart Rd # 100
Ann Arbor MI 48105
734 994-6600

(G-2193)
LEE CARLSON CENTER FOR MENTAL
Also Called: Central Ctr For Fmly Resources
7954 University Ave NE (55432-1860)
PHONE............................763 780-3036
Kathleen Samilo, *CEO*
Prem Suppogu, *Finance*
Adam L Fox, *Child Psycholgy*
Suzanne L Aoun, *Child Psycholgy*
EMP: 34 **EST:** 1979
SALES (est): 1MM-4.9MM **Privately Held**
WEB: www.ccffr.org
SIC: 8322 Individual & family social services

FULDA
Murray County

(G-2194)
FIRST NATIONAL BANK
109 N St Paul Ave (56131)
PO Box P (56131-0500)
PHONE............................507 425-2575
FAX: 507 425-2579
J E Grandgeorge, *President*
Darwin Kruse, *Loan Officer*
Michael Brignac, *Finance*
Vicki Sandherst, *Cashier*
EST: 1985 **Privately Held**
SIC: 6022 State commercial bank

(G-2195)
MAPLE LAWN NURSING HOME
400 Th St NE (56131)
PHONE............................507 425-2571
FAX: 507 425-2573
George Brockway, *Principal*
Arlan Swanson, *Principal*
Betty Norton, *Corp Secy*
EMP: 120 **EST:** 1964
SQ FT: 10,000
SALES (est): 1MM-4.9MM **Privately Held**
WEB: www.maplelawn.org
SIC: 8051 Convalescent home

(G-2196)
NEW DAWN INC
101 S Baltimore Ave (56131-1157)
PO Box 324 (56131-0324)
PHONE............................507 425-3278
FAX: 507 425-3278
Terry Morrison, *Dir Lvl Other*
EMP: 110 **EST:** 1973
SQ FT: 1,200
SALES (est): 1MM-4.9MM **Privately Held**
SIC: 8361 8741 Home for the mentally
retarded; management services

GARRISON
Mille Lacs County

(G-2197)
HARDWOOD GOLF RESORT
18517 Captive Lake Rd (56450-9639)
PHONE............................320 692-4325
FAX: 320 692-4915
Tod Christianson, *Owner*
EMP: 45 **EST:** 1964
SQ FT: 1,000
SALES (est): 5MM-9.9MM **Privately Held**
WEB: www.millelacsgolf.com
SIC: 7999 Golf services & professionals

GARY
Norman County

(G-2198)
NORMAN COUNTY EDUCATION ASSOC
Also Called: Education Minnesota Norma
3536 260th Ave (56545-9455)
PO Box 420, Twin Valley (56584-0420)
PHONE............................218 356-8773
Angela Doll, *President*
Mary Swenson, *President*
Randy Knutson, *Vice Pres*
James Bateson, *Treasurer*
EMP: 43 **EST:** 1992 **Privately Held**
SIC: 7361 Teachers' registry service

GAYLORD
Sibley County

(G-2199)
COUNTY OF SIBLEY
Also Called: Health & Human Services
112 5th St S (55334-4463)
PO Box 237 (55334-0237)
PHONE............................507 237-4000
Bonnie Pautsch, *Corp Secy*
Deb Schumacher, *Case Mgr*
Linda Messerli, *Supervisor*
Vicki Stock, *Director*
April Schmidt, *Assistant*
EMP: 40
SALES (est): 1MM-4.9MM **Privately Held**
WEB: www.sibleycounty.net
SIC: 8322 Public welfare center
PA: Sibley County
400 Court Ave
Gaylord MN 55334
507 237-4078

(G-2200)
MICHAEL FOODS INC
3400 Tower St (55334)
PHONE............................507 237-2429
Greg Ostrander, *CEO*
Brent Meyer, *Controller*
Dallas Grack, *Manager*
Patty Uecker, *Manager*
Jeff Erickson, *Manager*
EMP: 40 **EST:** 1996
SALES (est): 25MM-49.9MM **Privately Held**
SIC: 5144 Wholesales poultry & poultry
products

(G-2201)
UNITED FARMERS CO OP
120 High Ave (55334-4418)
PHONE............................507 237-2281
Jeff Polizka, *General Mgr*
Lowell Tangen, *Div Sub Head*
Arlen Anderson, *Marketing Mgr*
Gary Wentzloffr, *Manager*
EMP: 31 **EST:** 1955
SQ FT: 5,000
SALES (est): 50MM-99.9MM **Privately Held**
SIC: 5171 5191 Petroleum bulk station;
wholesales agricultural fertilizer; wholesales
agricultural chemicals; wholesales feed;
wholesales field, garden & flower seeds;
retail gasoline filling station

(G-2202)
WAKEFIELD PORK INC
410 Main Ave E (55334)
PO Box 327 (55334-0327)
PHONE............................507 237-5581
FAX: 507 237-5584
Charles J Peters, *President*
Marylyn Lanlaghorst, *President*
Steven Langhorst, *Vice Pres*
Nick Peters, *Representative*
Shari Webster, *Assistant*
EMP: 100 **EST:** 1991 **Privately Held**
WEB: www.wakefieldpork.com
SIC: 0213 Hog & pig farming

GILBERT
Saint Louis County

(G-2203)
E S I HERITAGE
5024 Heritage Trl (55741-8326)
PHONE............................218 865-4135
Clyde Johnson, *President*
EMP: 65 **EST:** 2006
SALES (est): 1MM-4.9MM **Privately Held**
SIC: 8361 Group foster home

GLENCOE
Mcleod County

(G-2204)
ASSOCIATED MILK PRODUCERS INC
Also Called: A M P I
330 10th St E (55336-2027)
PO Box 100 (55336-0100)
PHONE............................320 864-5561
Russ Pierson, *Branch Mgr*
Dale Hegland, *Manager*
Gown Breene, *Manager*
John Breen, *Director*
EMP: 27
SALES (est): 10MM-24.9MM **Privately Held**
WEB: www.ampi.com
SIC: 5143 Wholesales fresh dairy products
PA: Associated Milk Producers Inc
315 N Broadway St
New Ulm MN 56073
507 354-8295

(G-2205)
FIRST MCLEOD AGENCY INC
Also Called: Professional Insur Providers
613 10th St E (55336-2105)
PHONE............................320 864-5581
FAX: 320 864-5589
Lowell G Wakefield, *President*
Terry Jones, *Manager*
EST: 1984 **Privately Held**
WEB: www.profinsproviders.com
SIC: 6411 Insurance agency & broker

(G-2206)
FIRST MINNESOTA BANK NATIONAL (PA)
606 11th St E Ste E (55336-2110)
PO Box 39 (55336-0039)
PHONE............................320 864-3161
FAX: 320 864-6000
Jeffrey Grant, *President*
Ronald Molstad, *Vice Pres*
EST: 1881
SQ FT: 30,000 **Privately Held**
SIC: 6021 National commercial bank

(G-2207)
GLENCOE REGIONAL HEALTH SVCS
1805 Hennepin Ave N (55336-1416)
PHONE............................320 864-3121
FAX: 320 864-4876
Jon D Braband, *President*
John Uecker, *Ch Pathology*
Bev F Hults, *Vice Pres*
Lowe Thessner, *Safety Mgr*
Brenda Latourelle, *Envir Svcs Dir*
EMP: 400 **EST:** 1999
SQ FT: 218,099
SALES (est): 25MM-49.9MM **Privately Held**
SIC: 8011 Physicians' office & clinic;
medical center

(G-2208)
MCLEOD COOPERATIVE POWER ASSN
1231 Ford Ave N (55336-2127)
PO Box 70 (55336-0070)
PHONE............................320 864-3148
FAX: 320 864-4850
Kris Ingenthron, *General Mgr*
Darrel Beste, *Engineering*
Doug Kashmark, *Manager*
Accouting Supervisor, *Supervisor*
EMP: 35

EST: 1935
SQ FT: 20,000
SALES (est): 10MM-24.9MM **Privately Held**
WEB: www.mcleodcoop.com
SIC: 4911 Electric power distribution service

(G-2209)
MILLER MANUFACTURING CO INC
1400 13th St W (55336-1555)
PHONE............................320 864-4039
Blair Munson, *Manager*
EMP: 60
SALES (est): 10MM-24.9MM **Privately Held**
WEB: www.miller-littlegiant.com
SIC: 5083 Manufactures cattle feeding,
handling & watering equipment;
manufactures hog feeding, handling &
watering equipment; manufactures water
troughs; wholesales poultry equipment;
manufactures pet supplies
HQ: Miller Manufacturing Co Inc
2600 Eagan Woods Dr # 460
Saint Paul MN 55121
651 982-5100

(G-2210)
MILLER MANUFACTURING CO INC
1450 13th St W (55336-1555)
PHONE............................320 864-4189
Robert Brof, *Branch Mgr*
EMP: 100
SALES (est): 50MM-99.9MM **Privately Held**
WEB: www.miller-littlegiant.com
SIC: 5199 Wholesales pet supplies;
manufactures pet supplies
HQ: Miller Manufacturing Co Inc
2600 Eagan Woods Dr # 460
Saint Paul MN 55121
651 982-5100

(G-2211)
MINNESOTA PRAIRIE LINE INC
2925 12th St E (55336-3368)
PHONE............................320 864-7200
Bill Drusch, *CEO*
EMP: 30 **EST:** 2002
SALES (est): 1MM-4.9MM **Privately Held**
WEB: www.tcwr.net
SIC: 4013 Railroad switching & terminal
services
PA: Twin Cities & Western Railroad
2925 12th St E
Glencoe MN 55336
320 864-7200

(G-2212)
RESOURCES FOR YOU INC
1218 Greeley Ave N (55336-2103)
PHONE............................320 864-5871
Rhonda Vandesteeg, *President*
EMP: 61 **EST:** 2003 **Privately Held**
WEB: www.resourcesforyou.com
SIC: 7361 Employment agency services

(G-2213)
SECURITY BANK & TRUST CO INC
735 11th St E (55336-2231)
PHONE............................320 864-3171
Gale Hoese, *CEO*
Larry Herrmann, *President*
Marilee Vacek, *Corp Secy*
Karen Healey, *Manager*
Crystal Dahlke, *Officer*
EMP: 25 **EST:** 1935
SALES (est): 5MM-9.9MM **Privately Held**
SIC: 6022 6021 State commercial bank;
national commercial bank

(G-2214)
SECURITY BANKSHARES CO INC (PA)
735 11th St E (55336-2220)
PO Box 218 (55336-0218)
PHONE............................320 864-3171
Gale Hoese, *President*
Carolyn Lange, *Mfg Staff*
EMP: 30 **EST:** 1935 **Privately Held**
SIC: 6022 State commercial bank

(PA)=Parent Co (HQ)=Headquarters (DH)=Div Headquarters
✿ = New business established in last 2 years

2011 Harris Minnesota
Services Directory

© Harris InfoSource 1-866-281-6415
105

GEOGRAPHIC (vertical side tab)

(G-2215)
STOCKMAN TRANSFER INC
10636 Cameo Cir (55336-5312)
PHONE..........................320 864-2381
Brad Stockman, *President*
Rick Stockman, *Treasurer*
EMP: 50 EST: 1993
SALES (est): 1MM-4.9MM Privately Held
SIC: 4214 Local trucking with storage

(G-2216)
TWIN CITIES & WESTERN RAILROAD (PA)
2925 12th St E (55336-3368)
PHONE..........................320 864-7200
FAX: 320 864-7220
William F Drusch, *CEO*
Mark Wegner, *Ch of Bd*
Douglas Head, *Principal*
Robert Henry, *Vice Pres*
Shauna Gruber, *Accountant*
EMP: 30 EST: 1991
SQ FT: 3,000 Privately Held
WEB: www.tcwr.net
SIC: 4013 4011 Railroad switching & terminal services; long haul railroad

(G-2217)
YOUNG AMERICA HOLDINGS INC
Also Called: Glencoe Warehouse
1207 Cardinal Ave N (55336-3365)
PHONE..........................320 864-6125
Debbi Fisher, *Manager*
EMP: 36
SALES (est): 1MM-4.9MM Privately Held
WEB: www.young-america.com
SIC: 4225 Warehousing & storage services
PA: Young America Corp
    717 Faxon Rd
    Young America MN 55397
    800 533-4529

GLENCOE
Sibley County

(G-2218)
CMI EQUIPMENT & ENGINEERING CO
41663 170th St (55336-5236)
PHONE..........................320 864-5894
FAX: 320 864-6491
Carl M Iliff, *President*
Althea Mathwig, *President*
Joann Iliff, *Corp Secy*
EMP: 25 EST: 1983
SQ FT: 34,000
SALES (est): 1MM-4.9MM Privately Held
WEB: www.cmiequip-eng.com
SIC: 8742 Manufactures food products machinery; industry specialist consultant

GLENWOOD
Pope County

(G-2219)
AMERICAN BUSINESS FORMS INC (PA)
31 E Minnesota Ave (56334-1625)
PO Box 218 (56334-0218)
PHONE..........................320 634-5471
FAX: 320 634-5265
Larry Zavadil, *CEO*
Craig McLain, *Corp Secy*
Steve Hagstrom, *Vice Pres*
Harry I Oconnor, *Vice Pres*
Tim Froemming, *CFO*
EMP: 190 EST: 1981
SQ FT: 100,000 Privately Held
WEB: www.americanbus.com
SIC: 5112 5199 Wholesales business forms; wholesales advertising specialties

(G-2220)
CANADIAN PACIFIC RAILROAD
20 15th St NE (56334-1942)
PHONE..........................320 634-3307
FAX: 320 347-8233
Anthony Fletcher, *Manager*

EMP: 25 Publicly Held
WEB: www.cpr.ca
SIC: 4011 Long haul railroad
PA: Canadian Pacific Railway Co
    855 2nd St Sw
    Calgary Canada T2P 4
    403 2188000

(G-2221)
CP RAIL SYSTEM SOO LINE
20 15th St NE (56334-1942)
PHONE..........................320 634-3307
Anthony Fletcher, *Manager*
Pat Siverlink, *Manager*
EMP: 50 EST: 2007 Privately Held
SIC: 4011 Long haul railroad

(G-2222)
EVANGELICAL LUTHERAN GOOD
Also Called: Lakeview Good Samaritan Center
515 Franklin St S (56334-1545)
PHONE..........................320 634-4552
FAX: 320 634-5109
Kari Kasowski, *Manager*
Randy Wanke, *Administrator*
Sonia Gandrud, *Administrator*
William Brewer, *Administrator*
EMP: 60
SALES (est): 1MM-4.9MM Privately Held
WEB: www.good-sam.com
SIC: 8051 8049 Skilled nursing care facility; physical therapist office
PA: Evangelical Lutheran Good
    4800 W 57th St
    Sioux Falls SD 57108
    605 362-3100

(G-2223)
GLACIAL RIDGE HOSPITAL FNDTN (PA)
10 4th Ave SE (56334-1820)
PHONE..........................320 634-4521
Kirk Stensrud, *President*
Daryl Klous, *Envir Svcs Dir*
Josh V Luik, *Engineering*
Kail Chase, *CFO*
Kyle Chase, *CFO*
EMP: 120 EST: 1940
SQ FT: 30,000
SALES (corp-wide): 16.68M Privately Held
SIC: 8062 8011 Medical hospital; medical center

(G-2224)
GLENWOOD LIONS CLUB
449 2nd Ave SE (56334-1703)
PHONE..........................320 634-3263
Glenn Gunderson, *President*
Charles Bullock, *Corp Secy*
Jim Weires, *Assistant VP*
Russ Amacker, *Treasurer*
EMP: 32 Privately Held
SIC: 8641 Civic associations

(G-2225)
GLENWOOD VILLAGE CARE CENTER
719 2nd St SE (56334-1810)
PHONE..........................320 634-5131
FAX: 320 634-5777
Mary Kruger, *CEO*
Pat Shasto, *Manager*
Debbie Moore, *Manager*
EMP: 150 EST: 1961
SQ FT: 40,000
SALES (est): 5MM-9.9MM Privately Held
SIC: 8051 8059 Skilled nursing care facility; personal care home, with health care

(G-2226)
HEALTHLAND INC (PA)
625 S Lake Shore Dr (56334-1549)
PHONE..........................320 634-5331
James F Burgess, *President*
Margaret Klick, *Corp Secy*
BEI W Aufgaben, *Senior VP*
Wanda Fischer, *Senior VP*
Angela Franks, *Senior VP*
EMP: 120 EST: 1980
SQ FT: 26,000
SALES (corp-wide): 55M Privately Held
SIC: 7373 5045 Computer systems turnkey vendor; wholesales computers

(G-2227)
HUMAN SERVICES
211 Minnesota Ave E Ste 200 (56334-1668)
PHONE..........................320 634-5750
Robert Cornelius, *Director*
EMP: 25
SALES (est): 1MM-4.9MM Privately Held
SIC: 8322 Family services agency

(G-2228)
MHC MATERIAL HANDLING
17835 211th Ave (56334-5063)
PHONE..........................320 634-4593
FAX: 320 634-3306
Jerry Legue, *CEO*
Jim Cornish, *Plant Mgr*
Dave Marthaler, *Purch Mgr*
Bill Bowen, *Engineering*
Dawn Miles, *Personnel*
EMP: 30 EST: 1984
SALES (est): 10MM-24.9MM Privately Held
SIC: 5084 Wholesales materials handling equipment

(G-2229)
PALMER BUS SERVICE INC
17631 210th Ave (56334-4164)
PHONE..........................320 634-3272
FAX: 320 634-3514
Beau Twaddle, *Sales Staff*
Gary Gerdes, *Manager*
EMP: 30 EST: 1978
SALES (est): 1MM-4.9MM Privately Held
SIC: 4142 Long-distance bus charter service

(G-2230)
PETERS SUNSET BEACH INC
20000 S Lake Shore Dr (56334-5005)
PHONE..........................320 634-4501
FAX: 320 634-5606
William Peters, *President*
Mary Peters, *Corp Secy*
EMP: 40 EST: 1947
SALES (est): 1MM-4.9MM Privately Held
WEB: www.petersresort.com
SIC: 7032 Fishing camp

(G-2231)
PEZHEKEE LOUNGE INC
20000 S Lake Shore Dr (56334-5005)
PHONE..........................320 634-4502
William Peters, *President*
EMP: 30 EST: 1977
SQ FT: 2,000
SALES (est): 500-999K Privately Held
SIC: 7997 Membership recreation club

(G-2232)
SCHWIETERS CHEVROLET OF
110 Franklin St N (56334-1123)
PO Box 158 (56334-0158)
PHONE..........................320 634-4507
FAX: 320 634-4500
Robert Schwieters, *President*
EMP: 34 EST: 1946
SALES (est): 10MM-24.9MM Privately Held
WEB: www.schwieters.com
SIC: 7539 Retails new & used automobiles; automotive repair services

(G-2233)
SOO LINE RAILROAD CO INC
Also Called: Glenwood Yard
20 15th St NE (56334-1942)
PHONE..........................320 634-3012
FAX: 320 634-4496
John Ramback, *Manager*
Tony Fletcher, *Manager*
EMP: 35 Privately Held
WEB: www.cpa.ca
SIC: 4011 Long haul railroad
HQ: SOO Line Railroad Co Inc
    501 Marquette Ave # 1500
    Minneapolis MN 55402
    800 766-4357

(G-2234)
TC AMERICAN MONORAIL INC
Also Called: Mhc Machining & Fabricating
17835 211th Ave (56334-5063)
PHONE..........................320 634-4531
Kevin Dermer, *Division Mgr*
Kevin Dermer, *Finance Mgr*
Dawn Miles, *Personnel*
Jim Tornish, *Branch Mgr*
EMP: 30
SALES (est): 5MM-9.9MM Privately Held
WEB: www.tcamerican.com
SIC: 5084 Manufactures overhead cranes; manufactures mineral cleaning machinery; wholesales industrial machinery & equipment; manufactures monorail systems
PA: TC American Monorail Inc
    12070 43rd St NE
    Saint Michael MN 55376
    763 497-7000

GLYNDON
Clay County

(G-2235)
VALLEY MASONRY LLC
Also Called: Green Masonry
205 Foundation Ave (56547-4010)
PHONE..........................218 498-2244
FAX: 218 498-2266
Cody Mitchell, *Member*
Mary Larson, *Corp Secy*
Les Scilley, *Office Spvr*
EMP: 85 EST: 1970
SQ FT: 8,600
SALES (est): 5MM-9.9MM Privately Held
SIC: 1741 Masonry & stonework contractor

GOLDEN VALLEY
Hennepin County

(G-2236)
ACE LABEL SYSTEMS INC
7101 Madison Ave W (55427-3601)
PHONE..........................763 450-3202
Barbara Wilk, *CEO*
Darrell Wilk, *President*
Sam Bakshian, *Vice Pres*
Traci Dougherty, *Accountant*
David Wilk, *Sales Mgr*
EMP: 25 EST: 1980
SQ FT: 14,000
SALES (est): 1MM-4.9MM Privately Held
WEB: www.acelabel.com
SIC: 5084 Label & seal printing service; manufactures coated & laminated paper; wholesales industrial machinery & equipment

(G-2237)
BUILDING MATERIAL SUPPLY INC
2300 Louisiana Ave N (55427-3631)
PHONE..........................763 252-5555
Jeffrey D Lehman, *President*
EMP: 40 EST: 1997
SALES (est): 1MM-4.9MM Privately Held
SIC: 7349 Building cleaning & maintenance services

(G-2238)
CERTES FINANCIAL PROFESSIONALS
5500 Wayzata Blvd Ste 910 (55416-3553)
PHONE..........................952 345-4140
Sally Mainquist, *CEO*
Kris Larson, *Vice Pres*
Mark Schaul, *CFO*
Jim Oman, *Treasurer*
Rebecca Baumgarten, *Director*
EMP: 30 EST: 2007
SALES (est): 1MM-4.9MM Privately Held
WEB: www.certespros.com
SIC: 8721 Accounting, auditing & bookkeeping services
HQ: Staffing Now Inc
    4600 Westown Pkwy Ste 113
    West Des Moines IA 50266
    515 222-6350

(G-2239)
COLONIAL ACRES HOME INC (PA)
5800 Saint Croix Ave N (55422-4446)
PHONE................................763 544-1555
Janet Carlyle, *Manager*
Gary Gardeen, *Exec Dir*
EMP: 226 **EST:** 1959
SQ FT: 461,282
SALES (corp-wide): 15.54M **Privately Held**
SIC: 8051 8361 Skilled nursing care facility; geriatric residential care

(G-2240)
EXPRESSPOINT TECHNOLOGY SVCS
1109 Zane Ave N (55422-4605)
PHONE................................763 543-6000
FAX: 763 949-0750
David Anderson, *CEO*
Mark Duffy, *Vice Pres*
Lyndia Ardoyno, *Vice Pres*
Julie Steen, *Vice Pres*
Daniel Rodich, *Vice Pres*
▲ **EMP:** 160 **EST:** 1997
SALES (est): 100MM-499.9MM **Privately Held**
WEB: www.expresspoint.com
SIC: 5045 7378 7379 7389 7699 8741 Wholesales computers, peripherals & software; wholesales computer peripheral equipment; computer related maintenance service; purchasing service; automated teller machine or ATM repair service; management services

(G-2241)
GRAYBOW COMMUNICATIONS GROUP
1000 Boone Ave N Ste 700 (55427-4474)
PHONE................................952 544-5555
Tom Lutsey, *Member*
Bruce Graybow, *Member*
Jeff Jacobsen, *Member*
Lisa Renee, *Finance Mgr*
Amy Sammler, *Accountant*
EMP: 30 **EST:** 1996
SQ FT: 12,000
SALES (est): 10MM-24.9MM **Privately Held**
WEB: www.graybow.com
SIC: 5065 Wholesales electronic sound equipment; wholesales electronic video equipment

(G-2242)
INTEGRA TELECOM OF MINNESOTA
6160 Golden Hills Dr (55416-1020)
PHONE................................952 746-7100
FAX: 952 746-7001
Dudley Slater, *CEO*
James Huesgen, *President*
Trent Anderson, *Vice Pres*
Bob Digangi, *Vice Pres*
Heidi Soderberg, *Sales Executive*
EMP: 100 **EST:** 1997
SQ FT: 3,000
SALES (est): 25MM-49.9MM **Privately Held**
SIC: 4813 Online services providers
PA: Integra Telecom Inc
1201 NE Lloyd Blvd # 500
Portland OR 97232
503 453-8000

(G-2243)
MEDICAL NETWORK INC
Also Called: Healthztoz
6300 Olson Memorial Hwy (55427-4946)
PHONE................................763 595-3208
FAX: 763 595-3333
Thomas Murray, *CFO*
Deniss Pulemjotov, *Accountant*
Anita Messal, *Marketing Staff*
Scott Heimes, *Manager*
Greg Pederson, *CIO*
EMP: 50 **EST:** 2006
SALES (est): 25MM-49.9MM **Publicly Held**
WEB: www.unitedhealthgroup.com
SIC: 6321 Direct accident & health insurance carrier
PA: Unitedhealth Group Inc
9900 Bren Rd E
Minnetonka MN 55343
952 936-1300

(G-2244)
RUBENSTEIN LOGISTICS SERVICES
Also Called: S-R-F-t-c Brokers
6960 Madison Ave W Ste 7 (55427-3627)
PO Box 5, Minneapolis (55440-0005)
PHONE................................763 542-1121
Bruce Hocum, *President*
Scott Hokum, *Manager*
EMP: 30 **EST:** 1961
SQ FT: 4,000
SALES (est): 1MM-4.9MM **Privately Held**
WEB: www.rubensteinlogistics.com
SIC: 8742 4731 Transportation consultant; shipping broker

(G-2245)
SEGETIS INC
680 Mendelssohn Ave N (55427-4306)
PHONE................................763 795-7200
Snehal Desai, *President*
James Stoppert, *President*
Dan Brecht, *Controller*
Tony Carrillo, *Info Tech Mgr*
EMP: 25 **EST:** 2006 **Privately Held**
WEB: www.segetis.com
SIC: 8731 Commercial agricultural research services; chemical laboratory

(G-2246)
SOLBREKK INC
1000 Boone Ave N Ste 650 (55427-4474)
PHONE................................763 404-4712
Steve Solbrack, *President*
Larry Phelps, *Vice Pres*
William Hafdal, *Vice Pres*
Paul Evans, *Vice Pres*
Bill Hafdal, *Vice Pres*
EMP: 30 **EST:** 2003
SQ FT: 6,000
SALES (est): 1MM-4.9MM **Privately Held**
SIC: 7378 Computer & data processing equipment repair & maintenance

GONVICK
Clearwater County

(G-2247)
GONVICK AMERICAN LEGION
184 Elm St (56644-4175)
PHONE................................218 487-5214
Leroy Sundquist, *Principal*
EMP: 160 **EST:** 1928
SALES (est): 5MM-9.9MM **Privately Held**
SIC: 7997 Membership recreation club

GOODHUE
Goodhue County

(G-2248)
AG PARTNERS COOP (PA)
1st And Broadway (55027)
PO Box 218 (55027-0218)
PHONE................................651 923-4496
FAX: 651 923-4064
Dale Kackman, *President*
Greg Schwanbeck, *General Mgr*
Erling Halverson, *Manager*
Joel Eichelberger, *IT/INT Sup*
EMP: 25 **EST:** 1996
SQ FT: 4,000 **Privately Held**
SIC: 5153 5191 Wholesale grain elevator; wholesales agricultural fertilizer

(G-2249)
KEITH CARLSON TRUCKING INC
19179 385th St (55027-8209)
PHONE................................651 923-4822
Keith Carlson, *President*
Lee A Carlson, *Treasurer*
EMP: 40 **EST:** 1978
SALES (est): 1MM-4.9MM **Privately Held**
SIC: 4212 Animal & farm product transportation services

(G-2250)
LODERMEIERS
103 N 3rd St (55027-9136)
PO Box 8 (55027-0008)
PHONE................................651 923-4441
FAX: 651 923-4070
Richard Lodermeier, *President*
Roxanne Lodermeier, *Corp Secy*
Gary Hinsch, *Parts Mgr*
Todd Dicke, *Sales Mgr*
Vicky Ryan, *Adm Mgr*
EMP: 65 **EST:** 1941
SQ FT: 30,000
SALES (est): 10MM-24.9MM **Privately Held**
SIC: 1542 5083 Farm building construction; new commercial & office building construction; wholesales farm implements

(G-2251)
WEST PLAINS DAIRY LLC
11755 County 1 Blvd (55027-4817)
PHONE................................651 258-4666
Chris Sjoquist, *Office Mgr*
Neal Shoquist, *Mng Member*
EMP: 30 **EST:** 2001
SALES (est): 10MM-24.9MM **Privately Held**
SIC: 5143 Wholesales milk

GRACEVILLE
Big Stone County

(G-2252)
BIGSTONE HUTTERIAN BRETHREN
75217 Big Stone Colony Rd W (56240-4715)
PHONE................................320 748-7916
Clarence Hofer, *Owner*
Jonathan Hofer, *Manager*
EMP: 25 **EST:** 1973 **Privately Held**
SIC: 0115 0119 Corn farm; grain farm

(G-2253)
COOP TRICOUNTY
922 Highway 75 (56240-4795)
PHONE................................320 748-7187
Doug Olsen, *General Mgr*
Karen Ebnet, *Manager*
EMP: 32 **EST:** 1982
SALES (est): 5MM-9.9MM **Privately Held**
SIC: 7513 6519 Truck leasing service, without drivers; convenience store; real estate property leasing & rental

(G-2254)
GRACEVILLE HEALTH CENTER INC
115 W 2 Nd St (56240)
PO Box 157 (56240-0157)
PHONE................................320 748-7223
FAX: 320 748-8238
Helen Jarvey, *CEO*
Tom Montonye, *Engineering*
Diane Sullivan, *CFO*
Mary Bauer, *Human Res Dir*
Carla Gilsdorf, *Pub Rel Dir*
EMP: 120 **EST:** 1976
SALES (est): 1MM-4.9MM **Privately Held**
SIC: 8052 8062 Personal care facility; medical hospital
PA: Benedictine Missionary Sisters
300 N 18th St
Norfolk NE 68701
402 371-3438

(G-2255)
GRACEVILLE MISSIONARY
115 W 2nd St (56240-4845)
PO Box 157 (56240-0157)
PHONE................................320 748-7223
Todd Howell, *CEO*
A T Howell, *CEO*
EMP: 99 **EST:** 1945
SALES (est): 5MM-9.9MM **Privately Held**
SIC: 8062 Medical hospital

GRANADA
Martin County

(G-2256)
DAHL TRUCKING INC
2535 50th St (56039-3125)
PO Box 218, Swea City IA (50590-0218)
PHONE................................507 773-4226
Marlin Dahl, *Branch Mgr*
EMP: 54
SALES (est): 5MM-9.9MM **Privately Held**
WEB: www.dahltrucking.com
SIC: 7538 Retails automotive parts; general truck repair services
PA: Dahl Trucking Inc
305 S Highway 169
Elmore MN 56027
507 943-3410

GRAND MARAIS
Cook County

(G-2257)
COOK COUNTY NORTH SHORE HOSP
Also Called: North Shore Hosp & Care Ctr
515 5th Ave W (55604-3017)
PHONE................................218 387-3040
FAX: 218 387-3016
Darrell Smith, *Purchasing*
Yvonne Gennrich, *Controller*
Teresa Hanson, *Manager*
Diane L Pearson, *Administrator*
Bernadine Precord, *Director*
EMP: 110 **EST:** 1959
SQ FT: 26,000
SALES (est): 1MM-4.9MM **Privately Held**
SIC: 8051 8062 Convalescent home; medical hospital

(G-2258)
COUNTY OF COOK
Also Called: North Shore Hospital
515 5th Ave W (55604-3017)
PHONE................................218 387-3265
FAX: 218 387-1487
Ron Benrud, *Med Doctor*
Shelly Starkey, *Administrator*
Tom Gaylord, *Director*
Christine Buetow, *Director*
Helena Blake, *Director*
EMP: 120
SALES (est): 1MM-4.9MM **Privately Held**
SIC: 8082 Home health care services; public health program services; county government administration of public health programs

(G-2259)
EAST BAY HOTEL CORP
1 Wisconsin St (55604)
PO Box 220 (55604-0220)
PHONE................................218 387-2800
FAX: 218 387-2801
Lois Pedersen, *President*
Mark Pedersen, *Exec Dir*
EMP: 50 **EST:** 1910
SQ FT: 10,000
SALES (est): 1MM-4.9MM **Privately Held**
WEB: www.eastbayhotel.com
SIC: 7011 Eating place; hotel

(G-2260)
GRAND MARAIS HOTEL CO INC
Also Called: Super 8 Motel
1711 E Highway 61 (55604-2116)
PHONE................................218 387-2448
FAX: 218 387-9859
Barney Peet, *Owner*
EMP: 35
SALES (est): 1MM-4.9MM **Privately Held**
WEB: www.grandmarais.com
SIC: 7011 Traveler accommodations
PA: Grand Marais Hotel Co Inc
20 S Broadway Ave
Grand Marais MN 55604
218 387-2178

(PA)=Parent Co (HQ)=Headquarters (DH)=Div Headquarters
✿ = New business established in last 2 years

2011 Harris Minnesota
Services Directory

© Harris InfoSource 1-866-281-6415
107

GEOGRAPHIC

GEOGRAPHIC (vertical side tab)

(G-2261)
GUNFLINT LODGE INC
143 S Gunflint Lk (55604-2087)
PHONE.....................218 388-2294
Bruce Kerfoot, *President*
Susan Kerfoot, *Corp Secy*
Sheryl Hinderman, *Sales Executive*
EMP: 35 **EST:** 1927
SALES (est): 1MM-4.9MM **Privately Held**
WEB: www.gunflint.com
SIC: 7011 4493 6513 Resort hotel; eating place; retail gift shop; apartment building operator; marina

(G-2262)
L JIREH INC
Also Called: Naniboujou Lodge & Rest
20 Naniboujou Trl (55604-2141)
PHONE.....................218 387-2688
FAX: 218 387-2688
Tim Ramey, *President*
Nancy Ramey, *Vice Pres*
EMP: 30 **EST:** 1929
SQ FT: 15,000
SALES (est): 1MM-4.9MM **Privately Held**
WEB: www.naniboujou.com
SIC: 7011 Seasonal hotel; full service American restaurant

GRAND MEADOW
Mower County

(G-2263)
ANDY'S ELECTRICAL SERVICE INC
200 1st St SW (55936-1104)
PO Box 36, Racine (55967-0036)
PHONE.....................507 378-2101
Alva D Andrew, *President*
EMP: 26 **EST:** 1977
SALES (est): 1MM-4.9MM **Privately Held**
SIC: 7629 Manufactures electric motor starters; electrical equipment repair & maintenance services

(G-2264)
GRAND MEADOW HEALTH CARE CTR
210 E Ave (55936)
PO Box 365 (55936-0365)
PHONE.....................507 754-5212
FAX: 507 754-5227
Paula Lewis, *Administrator*
EMP: 60 **EST:** 1964
SALES (est): 1MM-4.9MM **Privately Held**
SIC: 8361 Residential rehabilitation center with health care incidental

(G-2265)
VALLEY TRANSPORTATION
73137 State Highway 16 (55936-8276)
PO Box 414 (55936-0414)
PHONE.....................507 754-5558
FAX: 507 754-5578
Brad Grafe, *President*
Kristi Jack, *Human Resources*
Eric Manahan, *Exec Dir*
Julie Back, *Director*
Rusty Elliott, *Coordinator*
EMP: 53 **EST:** 1989
SQ FT: 2,700
SALES (est): 5MM-9.9MM **Privately Held**
SIC: 4213 Over the road trucking

GRAND PORTAGE
Cook County

(G-2266)
GRAND PORTAGE NATIONAL
211 Mile Creek Rd (55605)
PO Box 426 (55605-0426)
PHONE.....................218 475-2202
Tim Cochrane, *Superintendent*
EMP: 27 **EST:** 2001
SALES (est): 1MM-4.9MM **Privately Held**
SIC: 7996 Amusement park

GRAND RAPIDS
Itasca County

(G-2267)
ACCESS HEALTH CARE INC
400B Wittman Dr (55744-3301)
PHONE.....................218 326-0004
FAX: 218 326-4770
Darlene Collins, *President*
Sean Janecek, *President*
Jeff Janecek, *Vice Pres*
EMP: 70 **EST:** 1998
SQ FT: 800
SALES (est): 1MM-4.9MM **Privately Held**
WEB: www.accesshc.com
SIC: 8082 Home health care services

(G-2268)
ANHEUSER-BUSCH CO'S INC
9 Willow Ln (55744-3938)
PO Box 5151 (55744-5151)
PHONE.....................218 326-0571
Peter Iverson, *Manager*
EMP: 25
SALES (est): 50MM-99.9MM **Privately Held**
SIC: 5153 Wholesales unpolished rice
PA: Anheuser-Busch Co's Inc
        1 Busch Pl
        Saint Louis MO 63118
        314 577-2000

(G-2269)
ARROWHEAD PROMOTION
1105 SE 8th St (55744-4082)
PO Box 808 (55744-0808)
PHONE.....................218 327-1165
FAX: 218 327-2576
Tim Flood, *President*
Gary Prokop, *Exec VP*
Margaret Arnold-Naugle, *Vice Pres*
Nancy Saxhaug, *Vice Pres*
Kati Prokop, *Vice Pres*
▲ **EMP:** 280 **EST:** 1983
SQ FT: 180,000
SALES (est): 25MM-49.9MM **Privately Held**
WEB: www.apfco.com
SIC: 7331 7374 7389 Direct mail advertising service; telemarketing services; computer graphics service

(G-2270)
BLOOMERS GARDEN CENTER
1037 Golf Course Rd (55744-3479)
PHONE.....................218 326-0668
FAX: 218 326-5099
David Clark, *President*
Debbie Clark, *Vice Pres*
EMP: 25 **EST:** 1994
SALES (est): 5MM-9.9MM **Privately Held**
SIC: 0782 Retail nursery & garden center; landscaping services

(G-2271)
CHILDREN'S MENTAL HEALTH SVCS
35382 US Highway 2 (55744-4754)
PHONE.....................218 327-4886
FAX: 218 327-4848
C T Cook, *Director*
EMP: 34 **EST:** 1993
SQ FT: 12,000
SALES (est): 1MM-4.9MM **Privately Held**
SIC: 8093 Outpatient mental health clinic

(G-2272)
CITY OF GRAND RAPIDS
Also Called: Pokegama Golf Course
3910 Golf Course Rd (55744-9680)
PHONE.....................218 326-3444
FAX: 218 327-9542
Bob Cahill, *Branch Mgr*
EMP: 63
SALES (est): 1MM-4.9MM **Privately Held**
WEB: www.pokegamagolf.com
SIC: 7992 Public golf course; retails golf goods & equipment; bar; mayors' office
PA: City of Grand Rapids
        420 N Pokegama Ave
        Grand Rapids MN 55744
        218 326-7600

(G-2273)
CITY OF GRAND RAPIDS
Also Called: Public Utilities
420 N Pokegama Ave (55744-2662)
PHONE.....................218 326-7604
Tony Ward, *Manager*
EMP: 63
SALES (est): 25MM-49.9MM **Privately Held**
WEB: www.pokegamagolf.com
SIC: 4911 Electric services
PA: City of Grand Rapids
        420 N Pokegama Ave
        Grand Rapids MN 55744
        218 326-7600

(G-2274)
CITY OF GRAND RAPIDS
500 SE 4th St (55744-3666)
PO Box 658 (55744-0658)
PHONE.....................218 326-7024
FAX: 218 326-7499
Anthony Ward, *General Mgr*
Jeff Davies, *Manager*
EMP: 50 **Privately Held**
WEB: www.pokegamagolf.com
SIC: 8742 Local government utility program regulation & administration; public utilities consultant; commercial lithographic printing
PA: City of Grand Rapids
        420 N Pokegama Ave
        Grand Rapids MN 55744
        218 326-7600

(G-2275)
CLUSIAU SALES & RENTAL INC
815 NW 4th St (55744-2304)
PHONE.....................218 326-9421
FAX: 218 326-8186
Thomas A Clusiau, *President*
Patricia Clusiau, *Corp Secy*
Theresa Shers, *Accounts Mgr*
EMP: 36 **EST:** 1957
SQ FT: 9,100
SALES (est): 10MM-24.9MM **Privately Held**
WEB: www.tomclusiaus.com
SIC: 7514 Retails new & used automobiles; retails new & used pickups; passenger car rental

(G-2276)
EVERGREEN TERRACE
Also Called: Leisure Hills Health
2801 S Highway 169 (55744-9552)
PHONE.....................218 326-3431
William Hargis, *Managing Prtnr*
Jennifer Edwards, *Human Res Dir*
Julie Casey, *Office Mgr*
William Eckblad, *Administrator*
Lori Sykes, *Administrator*
EMP: 122 **EST:** 1995
SQ FT: 42,000
SALES (est): 1MM-4.9MM **Privately Held**
SIC: 8051 Skilled nursing care facility

(G-2277)
FIGGINS TRANSPORT LTD
1407 E Highway 2 (55744-3245)
PO Box 938 (55744-0938)
PHONE.....................218 326-9477
FAX: 218 326-4311
Marvin Figgins, *President*
Jackie Figgins, *Vice Pres*
Sonia Olson, *Accountant*
Scott Figgins, *Manager*
Cheri Wright, *Manager*
EMP: 60 **EST:** 1957
SQ FT: 9,210
SALES (est): 5MM-9.9MM **Privately Held**
WEB: www.figginstransport.com
SIC: 4213 Over the road trucking

(G-2278)
FTB INC
1407 E Highway 2 (55744-3245)
PO Box 938 (55744-0938)
PHONE.....................218 326-5960
Marvin Figgins, *President*
Darlene Figgins, *Vice Pres*
Jeff Wartchow, *Exec Dir*
EMP: 30 **EST:** 1990
SQ FT: 900
SALES (est): 1MM-4.9MM **Privately Held**
WEB: www.ftb.net
SIC: 8721 Payroll services

(G-2279)
GRAND ITASCA CLINIC & HOSPITAL
111 SE 3rd St (55744-3663)
PHONE.....................218 326-5000
FAX: 218 326-7399
Jack Carlisle MD, *President*
Tina Karges, *Vice Chairman*
Theresa Pavich, *Business Mgr*
Ron Johnson, *Corp Secy*
Richard Helvig, *Vice Pres*
EMP: 210 **EST:** 1991
SQ FT: 42,000
SALES (est): 10MM-24.9MM **Privately Held**
SIC: 8011 Clinic operated by physicians

(G-2280)
GRAND ITASCA CLINIC & HOSPITAL
500 SE 4th St (55744-3666)
PO Box 658 (55744-0658)
PHONE.....................218 326-7024
Steve Feldman, *CEO*
Charlie Muus, *Materials Mgr*
EMP: 380 **EST:** 1918
SQ FT: 171,846
SALES (est): 25MM-49.9MM **Privately Held**
SIC: 8062 8011 Medical hospital; physicians' office & clinic

(G-2281)
GRAND RAPIDS DEVELOPMENT CORP
Also Called: Sawmill Inn
2301 S Highway 169 (55744-9501)
PHONE.....................218 326-8501
FAX: 218 326-1039
Dennis W Jacobson Sr, *President*
Judi Braunworth, *General Mgr*
George Jacobson, *Corp Secy*
Edie McTameney, *Vice Pres*
EMP: 100 **EST:** 1972
SQ FT: 50,000
SALES (est): 5MM-9.9MM **Privately Held**
WEB: www.sawmillinn.com
SIC: 7011 Motel; bar; full service independent family restaurant

(G-2282)
GRAND VILLAGE
923 Hale Lake Pointe (55744-9615)
PHONE.....................218 326-0543
FAX: 218 327-2405
Scott Lane, *Maint Mgr*
Bonnie McBride, *Human Resources*
Cheryl Lemler, *Office Mgr*
Jacob Goering, *Administrator*
EMP: 191 **EST:** 1982
SALES (est): 5MM-9.9MM **Privately Held**
WEB: www.itascanursinghome.org
SIC: 8059 8051 Nursing home; skilled nursing care facility

(G-2283)
HAMMERLUND CONSTRUCTION INC
3201 W US Highway 2 (55744-4742)
PHONE.....................218 326-1881
FAX: 218 326-9296
Thomas Hammerlund Sr, *President*
Todd Hammerlund, *Vice Pres*
EMP: 50 **EST:** 1989
SQ FT: 5,000
SALES (est): 5MM-9.9MM **Privately Held**
SIC: 1794 1623 Excavation & grading; building construction contractor; water & sewer line construction

(G-2284)
HAWK CONSTRUCTION INC
1833 W US Highway 2 A (55744-5660)
PHONE.....................218 327-0069
FAX: 218 327-1642
Douglas G Hanson, *President*
Jeff Worcester, *Corp Secy*
Ray Axley, *Treasurer*
Lisa Horton, *Manager*
EMP: 45 **EST:** 1998
SALES (est): 10MM-24.9MM **Privately Held**
WEB: www.hawkconstruction.com
SIC: 1541 Industrial building & warehouse construction

www.HarrisInfo.com
108

2011 Harris Minnesota
Services Directory

▲=Import ▼=Export
◆=Import/Export

SIC: **0783** Utility line tree trimming services

(G-2285)

HAZTRAN INC
18884 Sherrys Arm Rd (55744-5186)
PHONE..........................218 327-1116
Rankin C Ahlm, *President*
Jeanne A Ahlm, *Vice Pres*
EMP: 35 **EST:** 1985
SQ FT: 1,100
SALES (est): 5MM-9.9MM **Privately Held**
SIC: 1542 Commercial & office building
renovation & repair services

(G-2286)

HISTORICAL SOCIETY OF MN
Also Called: Forest History Center Minn
2609 County Road 76 (55744-8646)
PHONE..........................218 327-4482
FAX: 218 327-4483
Terry Vidal, *Manager*
Perry Vidal, *Manager*
EMP: 25
SALES (est): 1MM-4.9MM **Privately Held**
WEB: www.historictheatres.org
SIC: 8412 Museum; state general
government administration office
PA: Historical Society of MN
345 Kellogg Blvd W
Saint Paul MN 55102
651 259-3160

(G-2287)

ITASCA COUNTY FAMILY YOUNG
Also Called: Y M C A
400 River Rd (55744-3784)
PHONE..........................218 327-1161
FAX: 218 327-8813
Cathy Carrel, *Exec Dir*
Betsy McBride, *Director*
Jenelle Quinn, *Director*
Abbey Bergstrom, *Director*
Sue Beer, *Director*
EMP: 75 **EST:** 1979
SQ FT: 22,500 **Privately Held**
SIC: 8641 7032 7991 8322 8351 Youth
organizations; youth camps; child day care
service; individual & family social services;
physical fitness center

(G-2288)

JOHN L BONNER EYE CLINIC LTD
Also Called: Bonner Eye Clinic
1542 Golf Course Rd Ste 201
(55744-3537)
PHONE..........................218 326-3433
FAX: 218 326-3435
Timothy C Bonner, *Partner*
M J Mariano, *Partner*
Jeff Adrie, *Facilities Dir*
Steven Feltman, *CFO*
Lana Hess, *Office Mgr*
EMP: 31 **EST:** 1962
SQ FT: 11,000
SALES (est): 1MM-4.9MM **Privately Held**
SIC: 8011 Ophthalmologist office

(G-2289)

L & M SUPPLY INC (PA)
1200 E US Highway 169 (55744-3235)
PO Box 280 (55744-0280)
PHONE..........................218 326-9451
Terry W Matteson, *President*
Donald Ley, *Corp Secy*
Josh Villebro, *Administrator*
EMP: 185 **EST:** 1959
SQ FT: 27,000 **Privately Held**
SIC: 5013 Hardware store; variety store;
wholesales new motor vehicle parts &
supplies

(G-2290)

LAKE STATES TREE SERVICE INC
25172 Commercial Dr (55744-2134)
PHONE..........................218 326-5872
FAX: 218 326-3470
Scott Larson, *General Mgr*
Joshua Larson, *Human Res Mgr*
Renee Patrow, *Manager*
Dan Fink, *Manager*
EMP: 100 **EST:** 1958
SQ FT: 9,000 **Privately Held**
WEB: www.lstree.com

(G-2291)

LIFE'S COMPANION PCA INC
Also Called: Hyland Care
111 NW 11th St (55744-2440)
PO Box 128 (55744-0128)
PHONE..........................218 326-1179
Marlyb Lom, *Principal*
Donna Wilson, *Principal*
Trisha Rohde, *Director*
EMP: 90 **EST:** 1999
SALES (est): 1MM-4.9MM **Privately Held**
SIC: 8082 Home health care services

(G-2292)

M D I GOVERNMENT SERVICES
825 Lily Ln (55744-4088)
PHONE..........................218 326-9544
Rod Wood, *Branch Mgr*
EMP: 50
SALES (est): 1MM-4.9MM **Privately Held**
SIC: 7389 Manufactures wooden boxes;
packaging & labeling services
PA: M D I Government Services
1700 Wynne Ave
Saint Paul MN 55108
651 999-8200

(G-2293)

MEDS 1 AMBULANCE SERVICE INC
1328 NW 5th St (55744-2245)
PHONE..........................218 326-0020
William K McNichols, *President*
EMP: 32 **EST:** 1978
SQ FT: 2,500
SALES (est): 1MM-4.9MM **Privately Held**
WEB: www.meds-1.com
SIC: 4119 Ambulance service

(G-2294)

MENSTAR TECHNOLOGIES INC
4201 E US Highway 169 (55744-4414)
PO Box 806 (55744-0806)
PHONE..........................218 326-5566
FAX: 218 326-5511
Mike Rhodes, *President*
Norma Rhodes, *General Mgr*
Jason Larsem, *General Mgr*
EMP: 85 **EST:** 1993
SQ FT: 10,000
SALES (est): 5MM-9.9MM **Privately Held**
WEB: www.mnstar.com
SIC: 5063 Manufactures electronic cable &
wire harness assemblies; manufactures
electric control equipment; manufactures
electric switch boxes; wholesales wire &
cable; manufactures printed circuit boards

(G-2295)

MINNESOTA DIVERSIFIED INDS
825 Lily Ln (55744-4088)
PHONE..........................218 326-9544
FAX: 218 326-1016
Dale Majerus, *Branch Mgr*
EMP: 50
SALES (est): 5MM-9.9MM **Privately Held**
WEB: www.mdi.org
SIC: 8748 Business consulting services
PA: Minnesota Diversified Inds
1700 Wynne Ave
Saint Paul MN 55108
651 999-8200

(G-2296)

MISSION HEALTHCARE LLC
Also Called: Leisure Hills Care Center
2801 Pokegama Ave S (55744)
PHONE..........................218 326-3431
FAX: 218 327-3217
Thomas E Borboom, *Facilities Mgr*
Lori Sykes, *Manager*
EMP: 164
SALES (est): 5MM-9.9MM **Privately Held**
SIC: 8059 8051 Domiciliary care facility;
skilled nursing care facility
PA: Mission Healthcare LLC
7921 S Stephanie Ln
Tempe AZ 85284
480 730-1573

(G-2297)

MONTAVON MOTORS INC
1510 S Pokegama Ave (55744-4238)
PO Box 719 (55744-0719)
PHONE..........................218 326-0551
FAX: 218 326-8562
Jody Montavon, *President*
Mark Greeley, *Parts Mgr*
Jason Charlton, *Parts Mgr*
Michelle Broberg, *Sales Staff*
Tom Downing, *Sales Executive*
EMP: 40 **EST:** 1950
SQ FT: 20,000
SALES (est): 10MM-24.9MM **Privately Held**
WEB: www.montavonmotors.com
SIC: 7514 7515 Retails new & used
automobiles; passenger car rental;
passenger car leasing

(G-2298)

NORTH HOMES INC
Also Called: Knollwood Boys Group Home
1880 River Rd (55744-4085)
PHONE..........................218 327-3055
FAX: 218 327-1871
James Christmas, *Director*
EMP: 100 **EST:** 1990
SALES (est): 1MM-4.9MM **Privately Held**
SIC: 8361 Boys' towns; group foster home

(G-2299)

NORTH WESTERN RESEARCH
1861 E US Highway 169 (55744-3361)
PHONE..........................218 327-4615
Dave Rabas, *Principal*
EMP: 30
SALES (est): 1MM-4.9MM **Privately Held**
SIC: 6411 Insurance research service

(G-2300)

NORTHERN INDUSTRIAL ERECTORS
2500 Glenwood Dr (55744-3347)
PO Box 308 (55744-0308)
PHONE..........................218 326-8466
FAX: 218 328-6163
Stan Bostyancic, *President*
Robin Albrecht, *Administration*
EMP: 100 **EST:** 1985
SALES (est): 10MM-24.9MM **Privately Held**
WEB: www.nie-grmn.com
SIC: 1791 1796 Structural steel erection
contractor; machinery installation service

(G-2301)

NORTHLAND COUNSELING CENTER (PA)
215 SE 2nd Ave (55744-3615)
PHONE..........................218 326-1274
FAX: 218 326-9787
Greg Walker, *President*
Debbie Smith, *Persnl Dir*
Bernie Walker, *Office Mgr*
Debbie Bruns, *Bd of Directors*
David Chesness, *Bd of Directors*
EMP: 30 **EST:** 1959
SQ FT: 12,000 **Privately Held**
WEB: www.northlandcounseling.org
SIC: 8093 8069 Outpatient mental health
clinic; substance abuse hospital; outpatient
substance abuse clinic

(G-2302)

NORTHLAND COUNSELING CENTER
1215 SE 7th Ave (55744-4201)
PHONE..........................218 327-1105
FAX: 218 327-1932
Colleen Mackay, *Exec Dir*
Colleen Maclain, *Director*
EMP: 30
SALES (est): 1MM-4.9MM **Privately Held**
WEB: www.northlandcounseling.org
SIC: 8093 8069 8361 Outpatient drug clinic;
residential care facility; alcoholism
rehabilitation hospital
PA: Northland Counseling Center
215 SE 2nd Ave
Grand Rapids MN 55744
218 326-1274

(G-2303)

NPL CONSTRUCTION CO
Also Called: N P L
21880 US Highway 169 (55744-4945)
PHONE..........................218 327-9467
FAX: 218 327-9509
Kurt Helverson, *Manager*
EMP: 35
SALES (est): 1MM-4.9MM **Publicly Held**
WEB: www.swgas.com
SIC: 1623 Oil & gas pipeline construction
HQ: Npl Construction Co
2355 W Utopia Rd
Phoenix AZ 85027
623 582-1235

(G-2304)

OAK RIDGE HOMES OF WADENA INC
706 Allen Dr (55744-3000)
PHONE..........................218 327-1877
FAX: 218 327-0186
Judy Rasley, *Manager*
Judy Alleman, *Administrator*
EMP: 27
SALES (est): 500-999K **Privately Held**
SIC: 8322 Social services for the
handicapped
PA: Oak Ridge Homes of Wadena Inc
1021 Industrial Pk Rd SW
Brainerd MN 56401
218 829-7599

(G-2305)

OCCUPATIONAL DEVELOPMENT CTR
401 SE 11th St (55744-3954)
PHONE..........................218 326-8574
Tammy Haugen, *Marketing Staff*
Pam Cowan, *Manager*
Pete Lavalier, *Exec Dir*
Patrice Wilson, *Administration*
EMP: 101
SALES (est): 1MM-4.9MM **Privately Held**
WEB: www.odcmn.com
SIC: 8331 8093 Vocational rehabilitation
agency; outpatient rehabilitation treatment
center
PA: Occupational Development Ctr
1520 Highway 32 S
Thief River Falls MN 56701
218 681-4949

(G-2306)

PEPSI-COLA METROPOLITAN BTLNG
1154 E US Highway 169 (55744-3233)
PHONE..........................218 326-1271
FAX: 218 326-8419
Mark Medford, *Manager*
Wendy Brown, *Manager*
Chris Blaine, *Manager*
Steve Seyma, *Manager*
EMP: 50
SALES (est): 10MM-24.9MM **Publicly Held**
WEB: www.joy-of-cola.com
SIC: 5149 Manufactures bottled & canned
soft drinks; wholesales groceries
HQ: Pepsi-Cola Metropolitan Btlng
1 Pepsi Way Ste 1
Somers NY 10589
914 767-6000

(G-2307)

SANDSTROM'S INC
2057 E Highway 2 (55744-3295)
PO Box 200 (55744-0200)
PHONE..........................218 326-0567
FAX: 218 326-0567
David D Sandstrom, *President*
Julie Sandstrom, *Vice Pres*
Dave How, *Controller*
Corey Peck, *Supervisor*
▲ **EMP:** 60 **EST:** 1960
SQ FT: 44,000
SALES (est): 5MM-9.9MM **Privately Held**
WEB: www.sandstroms.com
SIC: 5145 5194 Grocery store; wholesales
candy; wholesales tobacco & tobacco
products

(PA)=Parent Co (HQ)=Headquarters (DH)=Div Headquarters
✿ = New business established in last 2 years

2011 Harris Minnesota
Services Directory

© Harris InfoSource 1-866-281-6415
109

GEOGRAPHIC

(G-2308)
SPECTRUM COMMUNITY HEALTH INC
412 N Pokegama Ave Ste 1 (55744-2684)
PHONE 218 326-4202
FAX: 218 327-2431
Lisa Olsen, *Manager*
EMP: 45 **Privately Held**
SIC: 7361 8082 Nurses' registry service;
home health care services
PA: Spectrum Community Health Inc
6205 Crossman Ln
Inver Grove Heights MN 55076
612 617-1190

(G-2309)
TLC HOME HEALTH CARE INC
32809 S Shoal Lake Rd (55744-4657)
PHONE 218 326-3555
Teresa Linn, *Principal*
EMP: 45
SALES (est): 1MM-4.9MM **Privately Held**
SIC: 8082 Home health care services

(G-2310)
UNITED PARCEL SERVICE OF NEW
Also Called: UPS
425 SE 11th St (55744-3954)
PHONE 218 326-8520
Kevin Geislinger, *Manager*
EMP: 28
SALES (est): 1MM-4.9MM **Publicly Held**
WEB: www.martrac.com
SIC: 4215 Package delivery services by
vehicle
HQ: United Parcel Service of New
55 Glenlake Pkwy NE
Atlanta GA 30328
404 828-6000

(G-2311)
WELLS FARGO BANK, NATIONAL
220 NW 1st Ave Ste 210 (55744-2740)
PHONE 218 326-8521
FAX: 218 326-2002
Stephen Arbour, *Branch Mgr*
Amy Trast, *Info Tech Mgr*
EMP: 38
SALES (est): 10MM-24.9MM **Publicly Held**
SIC: 6021 National commercial bank
HQ: Wfc Holdings, Corp
420 Montgomery St
San Francisco CA 94104
415 396-7392

(G-2312)
WENDIGO PINES ASSISTED LI
20371 Wendigo Park Rd (55744-4675)
PHONE 218 326-6900
FAX: 218 326-6570
Raisa Kotula, *Principal*
EMP: 25 **EST:** 2005
SALES (est): 500-999K **Privately Held**
SIC: 8361 Residential care facility

GRANITE FALLS
Yellow Medicine County

(G-2313)
AFFILIATED COMMUNITY MEDICAL
295 10th Ave (56241-1456)
PHONE 320 564-2511
Ginny Norsten, *Office Mgr*
Kenneth R Carter, *Med Doctor*
Terry Tone, *Administrator*
Eleazar P Briones, *Surgeon*
Bill Jagow, *CIO*
EMP: 30
SALES (est): 1MM-4.9MM **Privately Held**
WEB: www.acmc.com
SIC: 8011 Physicians' office & clinic
PA: Affiliated Community Medical
101 Willmar Ave SW
Willmar MN 56201
320 231-5000

(G-2314)
FAGEN INC (PA)
501 Highway 212 W (56241-1308)
PO Box 159 (56241-0159)
PHONE 320 564-3324
FAX: 320 564-3278
Roland Fagen, *President*
Don Rye, *Finance Dir*
Diane Fagen, *Human Res Dir*
Kevin Russen, *Administrator*
Les Schreiber, *Technology Dir*
EMP: 100 **EST:** 1988
SQ FT: 19,200 **Privately Held**
SIC: 1541 1711 1731 Industrial building &
warehouse construction; food product
manufacturing or packing plant construction;
paper & pulp mill construction; mechanical
contractor; electrical contractor

(G-2315)
FAMILY SERVICE CENTER INC
930 4th St Ste 4 (56241-1463)
PHONE 320 564-2211
Sherilyn A Hubert, *Attorney*
Peggy Heglund, *Director*
EMP: 28 **EST:** 2002
SALES (est): 1MM-4.9MM **Privately Held**
SIC: 8322 Individual & family social services

(G-2316)
GRANITE MEDICAL CENTER
Also Called: Wilmer Medical Center
295 10th Ave (56241-1456)
PHONE 320 564-2511
Ronald Holgren, *President*
Denise Davis, *Admin Sec*
EMP: 33 **EST:** 1955
SQ FT: 2,000 **Privately Held**
SIC: 8621 Medical field association

(G-2317)
PAR PIPING & FABRICATION LLC
114 Winter Dr (56241-1854)
PO Box 57 (56241-0057)
PHONE 320 564-2173
FAX: 320 564-3215
Sheri Parliament, *Member*
Lee Parliament, *Member*
Vonnie Cole, *Corp Secy*
Loren Swenson, *Mfg Staff*
EMP: 40 **EST:** 1992
SQ FT: 30,000
SALES (est): 1MM-4.9MM **Privately Held**
SIC: 7692 Machine shop; steel fabricator;
welding service

(G-2318)
PRAIRIE'S EDGE CASINO RESORT
5616 Prairies Edge Ln (56241-3679)
PO Box 96 (56241-0096)
PHONE 320 564-2121
FAX: 320 564-2547
Pete Lusich, *General Mgr*
Jennifer Beftland, *Principal*
Kevin Jemsbold, *Chairman*
Teresa Peterson, *Vice Chairman*
Elitta Gouge, *Corp Secy*
EMP: 350 **EST:** 1990
SQ FT: 27,000
SALES (est): 10MM-24.9MM **Privately Held**
WEB: www.prairiesedgecasino.com
SIC: 7993 Amusement arcade

(G-2319)
REVERENCE FOR LIFE & CONCERN
Also Called: PROJECT TURNABOUT
660 18th St (56241-1044)
PO Box 116 (56241-0116)
PHONE 320 564-4911
FAX: 320 564-3122
Carie Gordon, *Manager*
Mike Schiks, *Administrator*
Jackie Thielen, *Info Tech Mgr*
EMP: 78 **EST:** 1970
SQ FT: 13,000
SALES (est): 1MM-4.9MM **Privately Held**
SIC: 8361 8052 Residential rehabilitation
center with health care incidental;
intermediate care facility

(G-2320)
STS OPERATING INC
Also Called: Sunsource Fauver
113 Winter Dr (56241-1845)
PHONE 320 564-3057
Tim Opdahl, *District Mgr*
EMP: 30
SALES (est): 10MM-24.9MM **Privately Held**
WEB: www.sun-source.com
SIC: 5084 Wholesales industrial hydraulic
systems equipment & supplies
HQ: STS Operating Inc
2301 W Windsor Ct
Addison IL 60101
630 317-2700

(G-2321)
THORCO INC
Also Called: Valvoline Instant Oil Change
1801 County Rd 38 (56241)
PO Box 182 (56241-0182)
PHONE 320 564-3086
Roger Thorstad, *President*
Delores Thorsad, *CFO*
EMP: 30 **EST:** 1996
SALES (est): 1MM-4.9MM **Privately Held**
SIC: 7549 Automotive maintenance service

(G-2322)
UPPER SIOUX COMMUNITY
2511 565th St (56241-3613)
PHONE 320 564-3853
Kevin Jensvold, *Ch of Bd*
EMP: 50 **EST:** 2005 **Privately Held**
SIC: 8699 Charitable organization

GREEN ISLE
Sibley County

(G-2323)
LOCHER BROS INC (PA)
18098 365th Ave (55338-2137)
PO Box 35 (55338-0035)
PHONE 507 326-5471
FAX: 507 496-3481
Alfred W Locher, *Ch of Bd*
Robert Utendorfer, *President*
Gwen Utendorfer, *Corp Secy*
Tim Hukreide, *VP Persnl*
EMP: 30 **EST:** 1939
SQ FT: 26,000 **Privately Held**
SIC: 5181 Wholesales beer & other
fermented malt liquors

GREENBUSH
Roseau County

(G-2324)
BORDER STATE BANK
133 Main St N (56726-4018)
PO Box 280 (56726-0280)
PHONE 218 782-2151
Patrick Lorenson, *CEO*
Tony McClain, *President*
Lynette Gustafson, *Exec Sec*
EMP: 25 **EST:** 1935
SQ FT: 8,000
SALES (est): 5MM-9.9MM **Privately Held**
WEB: www.borderstars.com
SIC: 6022 State commercial bank
PA: Border Bankshares Inc
133 Main St N
Greenbush MN 56726
218 782-2151

(G-2325)
CENTRAL BOILER INC
20502 160th St (56726-9251)
PHONE 218 782-2575
FAX: 218 782-2580
Dennis Brazier, *CEO*
Terri Brazier, *Corp Secy*
Rodney Tollefson, *Vice Pres*
Mike Hugg, *Purchasing*
Mark Reese, *Engineer*
▲ **EMP:** 200 **EST:** 1984
SQ FT: 140,000
SALES (est): 25MM-49.9MM **Privately Held**
WEB: www.centralboiler.com

SIC: 5074 Manufactures low-pressure
heating steam or hot water boilers;
manufactures boilers & boiler shop work;
wholesales plumbing & heating equipment
& supplies

(G-2326)
LIFECARE MEDICAL CENTER
Also Called: Greenbush Community Nursing
Hm
152 5th St S (56726-4406)
PO Box 250 (56726-0250)
PHONE 218 782-2131
Shannon Carson, *Manager*
Shannon Carlson, *Manager*
William Wogner, *Manager*
EMP: 75
SALES (est): 1MM-4.9MM **Privately Held**
SIC: 8051 8052 8069 Extended care facility;
intermediate care facility; specialty hospital
PA: Lifecare Medical Center
715 Delmore Dr
Roseau MN 56751
218 463-4305

GREENWALD
Stearns County

(G-2327)
THULL CONSTRUCTION
120 2nd Ave S (56335)
PO Box 51 (56335-0051)
PHONE 320 987-3432
Linus Thull, *Manager*
EMP: 48
SALES (est): 5MM-9.9MM **Privately Held**
SIC: 1442 Sand mining
PA: Thull Construction
33814 Overton Rd
Melrose MN 56352
320 987-3432

GROVE CITY
Meeker County

(G-2328)
GROVE CITY LAH BNP
200 South Ave W (56243)
PO Box 192 (56243-0192)
PHONE 320 857-2274
Rhonda Johnson, *Director*
Donna Witcomb, *Director*
EMP: 54 **EST:** 2001
SALES (est): 1MM-4.9MM **Privately Held**
SIC: 8082 Home health care services

(G-2329)
HOLMQUIST LUMBER CO
201 Pacific Ave (56243)
PO Box 128 (56243-0128)
PHONE 320 857-2031
Charles Holmquist, *President*
Lanette Holmquist, *Vice Pres*
EST: 1942
SQ FT: 11,000 **Privately Held**
SIC: 1521 5072 Retails millwork & lumber;
single-family home general remodeling
service; new single-family home
construction service; wholesales builders'
hardware

GRYGLA
Marshall County

(G-2330)
MACHINEWELL INC
115 W State St (56727-0157)
PO Box 157 (56727-0157)
PHONE 218 294-6101
FAX: 218 294-6587
Wayne H Kehler, *President*
Ron Palm, *Vice Pres*
Dave Ederg, *Engineer*
David Edberg, *Engineering*
Tania Haack, *Finance Dir*
▲ **EMP:** 90 **EST:** 1976
SQ FT: 11,000
SALES (est): 5MM-9.9MM **Privately Held**
WEB: www.machinewell.com

www.HarrisInfo.com
110

2011 Harris Minnesota
Services Directory

▲=Import ▼=Export
◆=Import/Export

SIC: 7692 Machine shop, jobbing & repair services; manufactures unsupported plastics profile shapes; steel mill; welding service

HACKENSACK
Cass County

(G-2331)
AFFORDABLE PROFESSIONALS INC
1048 County 11 NW (56452-2559)
PHONE.............................218 682-3351
Joan McGuire, *President*
EMP: 250 **EST:** 1986
SALES (est): 5MM-9.9MM **Privately Held**
SIC: 8082 Home health care services

(G-2332)
COUNTRYSIDE CO-OP
Hwy 371 (56452)
PO Box 62 (56452-0062)
PHONE.............................218 675-6865
Frank Nye, *President*
John McMus, *Director*
EMP: 80 **EST:** 1975 **Privately Held**
SIC: 8699 Food co-operative

HALLOCK
Kittson County

(G-2333)
KITTSON MEMORIAL HOSPITAL ASSN
1010 S Birch Ave (56728-4208)
PO Box 700 (56728-0700)
PHONE.............................218 843-3612
FAX: 218 843-2311
Jim Turson, *Safety Mgr*
Christi Knudson, *Manager*
Richard Faliling, *Manager*
Richard Failling, *Administrator*
EMP: 150 **EST:** 1919
SQ FT: 56,360
SALES (est): 10MM-24.9MM **Privately Held**
SIC: 8062 4119 8059 8082 Medical hospital; nursing home; home health care services; ambulance service

(G-2334)
KITTSON MEMORIAL HOSPITAL ASSN
1010 S Birch Ave (56728-4215)
PO Box 700 (56728-0700)
PHONE.............................218 843-3612
Cedric Gustafson, *President*
Kim Anderson, *Corp Secy*
David Anderson, *Engineering*
Jeni Schwenzfeier, *CFO*
Carlene Cole, *Human Resources*
EMP: 210 **EST:** 1993
SALES (est): 10MM-24.9MM **Privately Held**
SIC: 8062 Medical hospital

HALSTAD
Norman County

(G-2335)
LUTHERAN MEMORIAL HOME
133 4th Ave E (56548-4114)
PHONE.............................218 456-2105
FAX: 218 456-2290
Dwight Fuglie, *Manager*
Wayne Erickson, *Director*
Lori Merkle, *Asst Admin*
EMP: 100
SALES (est): 1MM-4.9MM **Privately Held**
WEB: www.lutheranlivingcenter.com
SIC: 8059 8051 8052 Nursing home; intermediate care facility; skilled nursing care facility
PA: Lutheran Memorial Home
208 Oppegard Ave NW
Twin Valley MN 56584
218 584-5181

HAMEL
Hennepin County

(G-2336)
ADAM'S PEST CONTROL INC
922 Highway 55 Ste 100 (55340-9545)
PHONE.............................763 478-9810
FAX: 763 478-6715
Harold Leyse, *President*
Chuck Macdonald, *General Mgr*
Denison Steve, *COO*
Todd Leyse, *Vice Pres*
EMP: 40 **EST:** 1971
SQ FT: 2,400
SALES (est): 1MM-4.9MM **Privately Held**
SIC: 7342 Pest control in structures service; exterminating & fumigating service

(G-2337)
ADVANCED SERVICE MANAGEMENT
817 Meander Ct (55340-9452)
PHONE.............................763 201-1451
Mark Johnson, *President*
Katie Matson, *Director*
EMP: 27 **EST:** 2003
SQ FT: 7,000
SALES (est): 1MM-4.9MM **Privately Held**
SIC: 4731 Shipping broker; retails computers & computer software

(G-2338)
CORCORAN LIONS CLUB
20121 County Road 10 (55340-9504)
PHONE.............................763 420-2555
Tim Holmquist, *President*
Joseph Andres, *Treasurer*
EMP: 30 **EST:** 1973
SQ FT: 3,000 **Privately Held**
SIC: 8641 Civic & social organization

(G-2339)
DUAL TEMP INC
7550 Commerce St (55340-9462)
PHONE.............................763 494-9358
Coleman Black, *President*
Barbara Black, *Vice Pres*
EMP: 37 **EST:** 1994
SQ FT: 3,000
SALES (est): 1MM-4.9MM **Privately Held**
SIC: 1742 Building insulation installation service

(G-2340)
EVOLVING SOLUTIONS INC
3989 County Road 116 (55340-9358)
PHONE.............................763 516-6500
Jaime Gmach, *President*
Rebecca Olson, *Vice Pres*
Hunt Russell, *Bus Dvlpt Dir*
Joel Wyttenhove, *Controller*
Chris Chu, *Sales Staff*
EMP: 50 **EST:** 1996
SQ FT: 15,000
SALES (est): 25MM-49.9MM **Privately Held**
WEB: www.evolvingsol.com
SIC: 5045 7373 Wholesales computers; systems integration service

(G-2341)
FARMERS STATE BANK OF HAMEL
145 Hamel Rd (55340-9535)
PO Box 236 (55340-0236)
PHONE.............................763 478-6611
FAX: 763 478-6471
D J Dorweiler, *CEO*
Kamara Hopkins, *Vice Pres*
Tracy Nelson, *VP Info Sys*
Travis Wasmoen, *Exec Dir*
EMP: 25
SALES (est): 5MM-9.9MM **Privately Held**
WEB: www.fsboh.com
SIC: 6022 State commercial bank

(G-2342)
FIRST FINANCIAL USA LTD
Also Called: Ffusa
805 Meander Ct (55340-4549)
PHONE.............................763 231-8120
John G Eliason, *President*
EMP: 99

EST: 1996
SQ FT: 13,000
SALES (est): 50MM-99.9MM **Privately Held**
WEB: www.ffusa.net
SIC: 7389 Credit card service

(G-2343)
GWS INC
550 Clydesdale Trl (55340-8602)
PHONE.............................763 551-1700
Mike Fink, *President*
Irving Fink, *Vice Pres*
Harriet Fink, *Treasurer*
Michael McGlinsky, *Marketing Mgr*
Julia Fink, *Manager*
EMP: 25 **EST:** 1931
SQ FT: 15,000
SALES (est): 1MM-4.9MM **Privately Held**
WEB: www.gwspromote.com
SIC: 5199 Wholesales advertising specialties; manufactures signs & advertising specialties

(G-2344)
HICKS CONCRETE CONSTRUCTION
7545 Commerce St (55340-9462)
PO Box 259 (55340-0259)
PHONE.............................763 420-7755
FAX: 763 420-6628
Kerry D Hicks, *President*
EMP: 25 **EST:** 1973
SALES (est): 1MM-4.9MM **Privately Held**
WEB: www.hicksconcrete.com
SIC: 1771 1741 Concrete contractor; masonry & stonework contractor

(G-2345)
HYDRAULIC HEADQUARTERS INC
295 Highway 55 (55340-9542)
PO Box 129 (55340-0129)
PHONE.............................763 478-6220
Bob Pierce, *CEO*
Roger Schwerin, *Partner*
EMP: 50 **EST:** 1996
SALES (est): 10MM-24.9MM **Privately Held**
SIC: 5084 Wholesales industrial machinery & equipment

(G-2346)
LAWN KING INC
7555 County Road 116 (55340-9415)
PHONE.............................763 420-2909
FAX: 763 420-2917
David Remer, *President*
Wayne Remer, *Vice Pres*
EMP: 30 **EST:** 1974
SQ FT: 16,000 **Privately Held**
SIC: 0782 Landscaping services; retails nursery stock, seeds & bulbs

(G-2347)
LORAM ADMIN LLC
3900 Arrowhead Dr (55340-9529)
PHONE.............................763 478-6014
Paul V Wilson V, *President*
Terri Kimball, *Project Mgr*
Kim Berg, *Financial Analy*
Peter Hauer, *Database Admin*
Wayne Iskra, *IT/INT Sup*
EMP: 100 **EST:** 2004
SALES (est): 5MM-9.9MM **Privately Held**
WEB: www.loram.com
SIC: 8741 Office management services
PA: Loram Maintenance Of Way Inc
3900 Arrowhead Dr
Hamel MN 55340
763 478-6014

(G-2348)
LORAM RAIL SERVICES LLC
3900 Arrowhead Dr (55340-9529)
PHONE.............................763 478-6014
Paul V Wilson V, *President*
EMP: 400 **EST:** 2004
SALES (est): 25MM-49.9MM **Privately Held**
WEB: www.loram.com
SIC: 4789 Railroad maintenance & repair services
PA: Loram Maintenance Of Way Inc
3900 Arrowhead Dr
Hamel MN 55340
763 478-6014

(G-2349)
M M MILLER BROTHERS EXCAVATING
Also Called: Miller Bros Excavating
20150 75th Ave N Ste A (55340-8606)
PHONE.............................763 420-9170
FAX: 763 420-9171
Michael Miller, *President*
Mark Miller, *Corp Secy*
EMP: 28 **EST:** 1984
SQ FT: 2,500
SALES (est): 1MM-4.9MM **Privately Held**
WEB: www.mmmillerbros.com
SIC: 1794 Excavating contractor

(G-2350)
MAXXON CORP
Also Called: Infloor Heating System
920 Hamel Rd (55340-9539)
PO Box 253 (55340-0253)
PHONE.............................763 478-6000
FAX: 763 478-9669
Clyde R Jorgenson, *President*
Ronald M Jorgenson, *Treasurer*
Barb Saxton, *Marketing Staff*
Deb Vanantwerp, *Marketing Staff*
Benjamin Rousu, *Manager*
▲ **EMP:** 26 **EST:** 1977
SQ FT: 18,000
SALES (est): 5MM-9.9MM **Privately Held**
WEB: www.infloor.com
SIC: 5032 5074 Wholesales concrete building products; manufactures industrial furnaces & ovens; manufactures heating equipment & supplies; wholesales plumbing & heating equipment & supplies

(G-2351)
MEDINA ELECTRIC INC
22510 Highway 55 (55340-9357)
PHONE.............................763 478-6828
Roger Georges, *President*
Wally Cisewski, *Vice Pres*
Julie Nielson, *CFO*
Julie Benson, *Accountant*
Don Tomann, *Info Tech Mgr*
EMP: 102 **EST:** 1973
SQ FT: 35,000
SALES (est): 10MM-24.9MM **Privately Held**
WEB: www.medinaelectric.net
SIC: 1731 General electrical contractor

(G-2352)
MEDINA INN
500 Highway 55 (55340-9602)
PHONE.............................763 478-6661
FAX: 763 478-2410
Mark Raskob, *Partner*
Paul Raskob, *Partner*
Robert Raskob, *Partner*
Brian Raskob, *Partner*
EMP: 70 **EST:** 1984
SQ FT: 16,000
SALES (est): 1MM-4.9MM **Privately Held**
SIC: 7011 Inn

(G-2353)
OIL-AIR PRODUCTS LLC
295 Highway 55 (55340-9542)
PO Box 129 (55340-0129)
PHONE.............................763 478-8744
FAX: 763 478-8747
Roger Schwerin, *President*
Kyle Britton, *Vice Pres*
Dave Lund, *Purchasing*
Trig Mattson, *Human Res Mgr*
Lynn Schultz, *Accounts Mgr*
▲ **EMP:** 40 **EST:** 1983
SQ FT: 38,000
SALES (est): 10MM-24.9MM **Privately Held**
WEB: www.oilair.com
SIC: 5084 Wholesales industrial hydraulic systems equipment & supplies; manufactures rubber & plastic hoses & beltings; manufactures fluid power pumps & motors; manufactures hardware

(G-2354)
PRISM COMMERCIAL & INDUSTRIAL
7523 Commerce St (55340-9462)
PHONE.............................763 420-4080
FAX: 763 420-7425
Les Kiffe, *President*

GEOGRAPHIC

GEOGRAPHIC (vertical tab)

Lloyd Scotting, *Vice Pres*
EMP: 50 **EST:** 1990
SQ FT: 2,800
SALES (est): 1MM-4.9MM **Privately Held**
WEB: www.prism-paint.com
SIC: 1721 Commercial painting contractor;
industrial painting contractor

(G-2355)
REGIONAL HOME SERVICES OF MINN
Also Called: Everdry of Minneapolis
20170 75th Ave N (55340-8603)
PHONE..............................763 416-5607
Tony R Ciancaglini, *President*
EMP: 30 **EST:** 2007
SALES (est): 1MM-4.9MM **Privately Held**
SIC: 1799 Waterproofing service

(G-2356)
RUSSNICK CONTRACTORS INC
20170 75th Ave N (55340-8603)
PO Box 315 (55340-0315)
PHONE..............................763 420-3737
Todd M Russ, *President*
Douglas D Russ, *Vice Pres*
Brad Smoldt, *Controller*
EMP: 35 **EST:** 1977
SQ FT: 6,850
SALES (est): 1MM-4.9MM **Privately Held**
SIC: 1742 1751 Drywall contractor; finish &
trim carpentry service

(G-2357)
THREE RIVERS PARK DISTRICT
Also Called: Baker National Park Golf Crse
2935 Parkview Dr (55340-9791)
PHONE..............................763 694-7670
Michael Turnbull, *Manager*
EMP: 57
SALES (est): 1MM-4.9MM **Privately Held**
WEB: www.hennepinparks.com
SIC: 7992 7999 Public golf course; golf
driving range
PA: Three Rivers Park District
      3000 Xenium Ln N
      Plymouth MN 55441
      763 559-9000

(G-2358)
TWINCO ROMAX LLC (PA)
4635 Willow Dr (55340-9557)
PO Box 12 (55340-0012)
PHONE..............................763 478-2360
FAX: 763 478-3411
Marc Hasko, *President*
Tami Pautzke, *Corp Secy*
Michael A Schoenberger, *Corp Secy*
Dave Shumaker, *CFO*
Daniel Ribnick, *Treasurer*
EMP: 46 **EST:** 1928
SQ FT: 75,000 **Privately Held**
WEB: www.twincoromax.com
SIC: 5013 Wholesales automotive supplies
& parts

(G-2359)
UNICON INC
Also Called: Acoustical Innovations
7610 Commerce St (55340-9461)
PHONE..............................763 424-7892
Matthew Pitel, *President*
Vera Pitel, *Corp Secy*
▲ **EMP:** 57
SALES (est): 25MM-49.9MM **Privately Held**
SIC: 5065 Wholesales telephone equipment

(G-2360)
WESTSIDE EQUIPMENT INSTALLERS
902 Highway 55 (55340-9545)
PHONE..............................763 478-9572
FAX: 763 478-2026
Dianne Murphy, *President*
Megan Jay, *Manager*
EMP: 25 **EST:** 1977
SQ FT: 8,000
SALES (est): 1MM-4.9MM **Privately Held**
WEB: www.westsideequipment.com
SIC: 1799 5084 Service station equipment
installation, maintenance & repair
contractor; hydraulic equipment installation
& service; wholesales industrial machinery
& equipment

(G-2361)
WESTSIDE WHOLESALE TIRE INC
19925 75th Ave N (55340-9400)
PHONE..............................763 420-2100
FAX: 763 420-2002
Loren Leuer, *President*
Doris Leuer, *Corp Secy*
Shawn Leuer, *Vice Pres*
Herb Schneider, *Accountant*
◆ **EMP:** 26 **EST:** 1984
SQ FT: 30,000
SALES (est): 5MM-9.9MM **Privately Held**
SIC: 5014 Wholesales automotive tires &
tubes; tire dealer

(G-2362)
WW CONSTRUCTORS INC
20095 75th Ave N (55340-9457)
PO Box 231 (55340-0231)
PHONE..............................763 420-4177
FAX: 763 420-4350
Mark Whims, *President*
Anita Whims, *Corp Secy*
Jason Whims, *Manager*
EMP: 25 **EST:** 1990
SQ FT: 6,300
SALES (est): 5MM-9.9MM **Privately Held**
WEB: www.wwconstructors.com
SIC: 1541 1711 1791 Industrial building &
warehouse construction; mechanical
contractor; structural steel erection
contractor

HAMPTON
Dakota County

(G-2363)
BNR EXCAVATING INC
12175 240th St E (55031-9661)
PHONE..............................651 438-8692
Shaonna Nadeau, *President*
EMP: 25 **EST:** 1997
SQ FT: 500
SALES (est): 1MM-4.9MM **Privately Held**
SIC: 1794 1611 1623 Excavating
contractor; grading services; water & sewer
line construction

(G-2364)
BOB FISCHER TRUCKING (PA)
25445 Northfield Blvd (55031-9621)
PHONE..............................507 263-0384
Cheryl Fischer, *President*
Bob Fischer, *Treasurer*
EMP: 30 **EST:** 1994 **Privately Held**
SIC: 4212 4213 Local trucking without
storage services; over the road trucking

(G-2365)
CRAIG G BRAUN TURF FARMS
2950 232nd St E (55031-9726)
PHONE..............................651 463-2302
Craig G Braun, *Owner*
EMP: 75 **EST:** 1972
SQ FT: 4,000 **Privately Held**
SIC: 0782 Sodding contractor

(G-2366)
NADEAU EXCAVATING INC
12175 240th St E (55031-9661)
PHONE..............................651 438-8628
FAX: 651 438-2963
Shonna Nadeau, *CEO*
EMP: 25 **EST:** 2005
SALES (est): 1MM-4.9MM **Privately Held**
SIC: 1794 Excavating contractor

(G-2367)
NEDEAU INC
12175 240th St E (55031-9661)
PHONE..............................651 438-8628
Shauna Nedeau, *President*
Mike Nedeau, *Vice Pres*
EMP: 35
SALES (est): 1MM-4.9MM **Privately Held**
SIC: 1794 Excavating contractor

HANLEY FALLS
Yellow Medicine County

(G-2368)
FARMERS CO-OPERATIVE ELEVATOR
1972 510th St (56245-3082)
PO Box 59 (56245-0059)
PHONE..............................507 768-3448
Scott Dubbelde, *General Mgr*
Dave Leithing, *General Mgr*
Wesley Cole, *Corp Secy*
Steve Doom, *Director*
EMP: 56 **EST:** 1912
SQ FT: 3,200 **Privately Held**
SIC: 0723 Cash grain crop market
preparation services

HANOVER
Wright County

(G-2369)
NORTH METRO LANDSCAPING INC
11050 Lamont Ave NE (55341-4063)
PHONE..............................763 497-4898
Kevin Terhaar, *President*
Bill Swanson, *Vice Pres*
EMP: 50 **EST:** 1984
SQ FT: 1,800 **Privately Held**
WEB: www.northmetrolandscaping.com
SIC: 0782 Landscaping services

HANSKA
Brown County

(G-2370)
FARMERS CO-OPERATIVE OF HANSKA
103 E 1st St (56041)
PO Box 6 (56041-0006)
PHONE..............................507 439-6244
Gearald Gratahwotho, *President*
Randy Rieke, *General Mgr*
Gerald Grathwohl, *Vice Pres*
Scott Schmeising, *Treasurer*
Charles Felton, *Controller*
EMP: 42 **EST:** 1929
SQ FT: 2,500
SALES (est): 50MM-99.9MM **Privately Held**
WEB: www.hanskaco.com
SIC: 5153 5171 5191 Wholesales grains;
wholesales agricultural fertilizer; wholesales
agricultural chemicals; wholesales
petroleum bulk stations; wholesales feed;
wholesales field, garden & flower seeds

HARMONY
Fillmore County

(G-2371)
HARMONY COMMUNITY HEALTHCARE
815 Main Ave S (55939-6625)
PHONE..............................507 886-6544
FAX: 507 886-6584
Timothy Samuelson, *CEO*
Dennis Hansen, *Engineering*
Tim Rieck, *CFO*
Nancy Hagen, *Marketing Staff*
Bonnie Hill, *Manager*
EMP: 96 **EST:** 1948
SQ FT: 30,000
SALES (est): 1MM-4.9MM **Privately Held**
SIC: 8051 8062 Skilled nursing care facility;
medical hospital

(G-2372)
MINNOWA CONSTRUCTION INC
850 Wickett Dr NW (55939)
PO Box 188 (55939-0188)
PHONE..............................507 886-6162
FAX: 507 886-2470
Alan H Thorson, *President*
Steve Thorson, *Vice Pres*
EMP: 65

EST: 1984
SQ FT: 1,500
SALES (est): 5MM-9.9MM **Privately Held**
SIC: 1622 Bridge construction

HARRIS
Chisago County

(G-2373)
GLENN R REHBEIN EXCAVATING INC
42285 Iris Ave (55032-2115)
PHONE..............................651 674-7937
FAX: 651 674-7044
Pete Felland, *Manager*
EMP: 25 **Privately Held**
WEB: www.rehbein.com
SIC: 0181 Sod farm
PA: Glenn Rehbein Excavating Inc
      8651 Naples St NE
      Minneapolis MN 55449
      763 784-0657

HARTLAND
Freeborn County

(G-2374)
FARMERS STATE B OF HARTLAND
601 Broadway St (56042-9782)
PHONE..............................507 845-2233
Privately Held
SIC: 6021 National commercial bank

HASTINGS
Dakota County

(G-2375)
ALLINA HEALTH SYSTEM
1210 1st St W (55033-1147)
PHONE..............................651 438-1800
FAX: 651 438-1969
Terri Kruse, *Business Mgr*
Shirley Turvold, *Insur/Bill Sup*
F J Kouchich, *Optometrist*
Sheryl Notaro, *Phys Therapist*
Steven Biehl, *Med Doctor*
EMP: 150
SALES (est): 10MM-24.9MM **Privately Held**
WEB: www.allina.com
SIC: 8011 Clinic operated by physicians
PA: Allina Health System
      2925 Chicago Ave
      Minneapolis MN 55407
      612 775-5000

(G-2376)
AUGUSTANA HEALTH CARE CENTER
930 16th St W (55033-3335)
PHONE..............................651 437-6176
Kristine Rasmussen, *Human Res Dir*
Jenny Bannett, *Manager*
Larry Danderpole, *Administrator*
Audrey Roche, *Nursing Dir*
EMP: 130 **EST:** 1965
SQ FT: 44,000
SALES (est): 5MM-9.9MM **Privately Held**
SIC: 8059 8051 Nursing home; skilled
nursing care facility
PA: Augustana Care Corp
      1007 E 14th St
      Minneapolis MN 55404
      612 238-5201

(G-2377)
BESKAU TRUCKING INC
19500 Goodwin Ave (55033-8507)
PHONE..............................651 437-9737
Gary Beskau, *President*
Jean Beskau, *Corp Secy*
David Beskau, *Vice Pres*
Mark Beskau, *Treasurer*
EMP: 25 **EST:** 1984
SALES (est): 1MM-4.9MM **Privately Held**
SIC: 4213 4212 Contract haulers; local
liquid hauling services

www.HarrisInfo.com
112

2011 Harris Minnesota
Services Directory

▲=Import ▼=Export
◆=Import/Export

(G-2378)
COCHRAN PROGRAMS
1294 18th St E Bldg 2 (55033-3680)
PHONE..............................651 437-4585
FAX: 651 437-6161
Louise Skogstage, *Director*
EMP: 80 **EST:** 1974
SALES (est): 1MM-4.9MM **Privately Held**
SIC: 8361 Halfway home for delinquents & offenders; halfway group home for persons with social or personal problems

(G-2379)
CONZEMIUS FAMILY LP
13335 Lock Blvd (55033-9595)
PHONE..............................651 437-2107
FAX: 651 437-9715
Leo Conzemius, *Principal*
EMP: 30 **EST:** 1991
SQ FT: 10,000
SALES (est): 1MM-4.9MM **Privately Held**
SIC: 4213 Over the road trucking

(G-2380)
D L R EXCAVATING INC
11545 190th St E (55033-9351)
PHONE..............................651 437-3128
Patrick J Murphy, *President*
EMP: 75 **EST:** 1969
SQ FT: 6,000
SALES (est): 10MM-24.9MM **Privately Held**
SIC: 1611 1794 Grading services; excavating contractor

(G-2381)
DAKOTA COUNTY ABSTRACT & TITLE
1250 N Frontage Rd Ste 105 (55033-1519)
PO Box 456 (55033-0456)
PHONE..............................651 437-5600
FAX: 651 437-8876
Richard Welshons, *President*
Jodie Welshons, *Corp Secy*
David Welshons, *Vice Pres*
Donna Wagner, *Exec Dir*
EMP: 40 **EST:** 1957
SQ FT: 11,000
SALES (est): 1MM-4.9MM **Privately Held**
SIC: 6541 6531 Title abstract service; real estate services

(G-2382)
DAKOTA COUNTY RECEIVING CENTER
1294 18th St E Bldg 1 (55033-3680)
PHONE..............................651 437-4209
Al Kline, *Manager*
Dennis Guerin, *Info Tech Mgr*
Robert Melson, *Exec Dir*
Louise Skogstad, *Director*
EMP: 80 **EST:** 1973
SALES (est): 1MM-4.9MM **Privately Held**
WEB: www.detoxone.org
SIC: 8322 8093 Nontreatment alcoholism counseling; outpatient drug clinic

(G-2383)
DAKOTA RHOADS MASONRY INC
18575 Donnelly Ave (55033-9552)
PHONE..............................651 437-2100
FAX: 651 437-9575
Arlo Rhoads, *President*
Renee Rhoads, *Corp Secy*
Molly Rhoads, *Project Mgr*
EMP: 40 **EST:** 1976
SQ FT: 80,000
SALES (est): 1MM-4.9MM **Privately Held**
WEB: www.swconsulting.com
SIC: 1741 Masonry & stonework contractor

(G-2384)
DOUG SPEEDLING BUILDERS INC
1303 Eddy St (55033-2700)
PHONE..............................651 437-3658
FAX: 651 437-8775
Doug Speedling, *President*
EMP: 60 **EST:** 1979
SALES (est): 5MM-9.9MM **Privately Held**
SIC: 1751 1521 Finish & trim carpentry service; single-family housing construction

(G-2385)
EMILY'S BAKERY & DELI INC
1212 Vermillion St (55033-2847)
PHONE..............................651 437-3338
FAX: 651 437-5634
Steve Fox, *President*
Renee Kasel, *Managing Dir*
Norine Bishop, *Vice Pres*
EMP: 50 **EST:** 1964
SQ FT: 5,000
SALES (est): 1MM-4.9MM **Privately Held**
WEB: www.emilysbakerydeli.com
SIC: 5149 Retail bakery; commercial bakery; delicatessen; manufactures cookies & crackers; wholesales bakery products

(G-2386)
ENGSTROM EXCAVATING INC
17162 Red Wing Blvd (55033-9678)
PHONE..............................651 437-2782
Steven J Engstrom, *President*
EMP: 25 **EST:** 1992
SQ FT: 800
SALES (est): 1MM-4.9MM **Privately Held**
SIC: 1794 Excavating contractor

(G-2387)
FURLONG GOLF INC
Also Called: Emerald Greens Golf Course
14425 Goodwin Ave (55033-9567)
PHONE..............................651 480-8558
Thomas Furlong, *President*
Carrie Furlong, *Vice Pres*
EMP: 25 **EST:** 2000
SQ FT: 3,000
SALES (est): 1MM-4.9MM **Privately Held**
SIC: 7992 Public golf course

(G-2388)
GLOBAL LENDING CORP
1405 Honeysuckle Ln (55033-2415)
PHONE..............................651 438-7976
Brett McIntyre, *CEO*
Rod McIntyre, *President*
Cynthia McIntyre, *Corp Secy*
James Mitchner, *Vice Pres*
Judy Perry, *Treasurer*
EMP: 36 **EST:** 2000
SQ FT: 1,161
SALES (est): 1MM-4.9MM **Privately Held**
SIC: 6163 Mortgage brokers service arranging for loans, using money of others

(G-2389)
HASTINGS COUNTRY CLUB INC
2015 Westview Dr (55033-3202)
PHONE..............................651 437-4612
Jay Johnson, *President*
Julie Lee, *Controller*
Judy Capeti, *Officer*
EMP: 100 **EST:** 1947
SQ FT: 14,000
SALES (est): 5MM-9.9MM **Privately Held**
SIC: 7997 Country club; membership golf club

(G-2390)
HASTINGS YMCA
1175 Nininger Rd (55033-1056)
PHONE..............................651 480-8887
Tim Staley, *Vice Pres*
Terri Blattenbauer, *Exec Dir*
EMP: 26 **EST:** 2001 **Privately Held**
WEB: www.hastingsymca.com
SIC: 8641 7032 7991 8322 8351 Youth organizations; youth camps; child day care service; individual & family social services; physical fitness center

(G-2391)
HEIKES ENTERPRISES INC
19595 Lillehei Ave (55033-9246)
PHONE..............................651 437-3847
Matt Heikes, *President*
Laura Heikes, *VP Finance*
EMP: 25 **EST:** 1990
SALES (est): 1MM-4.9MM **Privately Held**
WEB: www.heikes.net
SIC: 4959 Snow plowing services

(G-2392)
HIDDEN GREENS INC
14176 210th St E (55033-8618)
PHONE..............................651 437-3085
Leonard Swanson, *President*
Brenda Swanson, *Corp Secy*
Allan Swanson, *Vice Pres*
Dorothy Swanson, *Treasurer*
EMP: 30 **EST:** 1976
SALES (est): 1MM-4.9MM **Privately Held**
WEB: www.hiddengreensgolf.com
SIC: 7992 Public golf course

(G-2393)
INNOVATIVE SURFACES INC
515 Spiral Blvd (55033-3650)
PO Box 216 (55033-0216)
PHONE..............................651 437-1004
FAX: 651 480-8191
Bruce Akins, *President*
Todd Akins, *General Mgr*
Kathy Reamer, *Finance*
Korie Babcock, *Manager*
EMP: 50 **EST:** 1984
SQ FT: 35,000
SALES (est): 5MM-9.9MM **Privately Held**
WEB: www.innovativesurfaces.com
SIC: 1799 Manufactures processed plastics; home & office interiors finishing, furnishing & remodeling service; manufactures plastics materials & resins; manufactures wood partitions & fixtures

(G-2394)
KUSSKE MECHANICAL INC
2651 Industrial Ct (55033-3900)
PHONE..............................651 437-8404
FAX: 651 437-8523
Donna Kusske-Thorkels, *President*
Roger L Thorkelson, *Vice Pres*
EMP: 25 **EST:** 1981
SQ FT: 5,000
SALES (est): 1MM-4.9MM **Privately Held**
WEB: www.kusske.com
SIC: 1711 1799 Process piping contractor; on-site welding contractor; pipe & boiler insulating contractor

(G-2395)
LEE'S CERAMIC CONTRACTING INC
10980 180th St E (55033-9304)
PHONE..............................612 720-1653
EMP: 58 **EST:** 1968
SALES (est): 5MM-9.9MM **Privately Held**
SIC: 1752 Carpet laying contractor

(G-2396)
LOYALTON GROUP INC
1620 S Frontage Rd # 200 (55033-2680)
PHONE..............................651 480-3126
Michael R Vaughan, *President*
Martin B Sieh, *COO*
EMP: 35 **EST:** 1995
SALES (est): 1MM-4.9MM **Privately Held**
SIC: 8748 Energy conservation consultant

(G-2397)
OUTDOOR IMAGES INC
2551 Glendale Rd (55033-8301)
PHONE..............................651 480-2000
FAX: 651 480-2008
Trever Sire, *President*
Randy Toth, *Vice Pres*
Cole Ruhie, *Manager*
EMP: 50 **EST:** 1990
SQ FT: 35,000 **Privately Held**
SIC: 0782 Landscaping services

(G-2398)
PINE BEND PAVING INC
16500 Fischer Ave (55033-9056)
PO Box 72, Vermillion (55085-0072)
PHONE..............................651 437-2333
Joel Jacoby, *President*
Edward Jacoby, *Vice Pres*
Richard Jacoby, *Vice Pres*
Edward Oie, *Treasurer*
EMP: 37 **EST:** 1973
SQ FT: 5,000
SALES (est): 5MM-9.9MM **Privately Held**
WEB: www.pinebendpaving.com

SIC: 1611 1771 Highway & street paving contractor; driveway, parking lot & blacktop contractor

(G-2399)
PLEASANT VALLEY TOWNSHIP ASSN
1357 Jefferson St (55033-1080)
PHONE..............................651 437-5660
Roger Shuneson, *President*
EMP: 30 **EST:** 2002 **Privately Held**
SIC: 8611 Business association

(G-2400)
POLKA DOT DAIRY INC
110 17th St E (55033-3101)
PHONE..............................651 438-2793
Wallace Pettit, *President*
Brenda Fahey, *Corp Secy*
Patrick Pettit, *Vice Pres*
Marlene Pettit, *Vice Pres*
Wayne Schuft, *VP Finance*
EMP: 40 **EST:** 1956
SQ FT: 25,000
SALES (est): 25MM-49.9MM **Privately Held**
SIC: 5143 Wholesales fresh dairy products

(G-2401)
PREMIER IRRIGATION INC
1031 Zweber Ln (55033-3333)
PO Box 564 (55033-0564)
PHONE..............................651 480-8857
FAX: 651 480-8854
Patrick Lynch, *President*
EMP: 35 **EST:** 1998
SQ FT: 8,000
SALES (est): 5MM-9.9MM **Privately Held**
SIC: 1629 Irrigation system construction

(G-2402)
REGINA MEDICAL CENTER (PA)
1175 Nininger Rd (55033-1056)
PHONE..............................651 480-4100
FAX: 651 480-4124
Lynn W Olson, *CEO*
Pauline Belkey, *Vice Pres*
Chloe Carlson, *Vice Pres*
Byron Epland, *Vice Pres*
V I Leff V, *Vice Pres*
EMP: 520 **EST:** 1947
SQ FT: 232,000
SALES (corp-wide): 81.91M **Privately Held**
SIC: 8062 8011 8051 8059 Medical hospital; nursing home; skilled nursing care facility; physicians' office & clinic

(G-2403)
REGINA MEDICAL CENTER
1285 Nininger Rd Ste 1 (55033-1086)
PHONE..............................651 480-4200
Mark Wilson, *CEO*
Pat Rother, *Office Mgr*
John Tonsager, *Manager*
David Blackie, *Manager*
Tracy Pfiefer, *Manager*
EMP: 25
SALES (est): 1MM-4.9MM **Privately Held**
SIC: 8011 General & family practice physician or surgeon office
PA: Regina Medical Center
    1175 Nininger Rd
    Hastings MN 55033
    651 480-4100

(G-2404)
REM RIVER BLUFFS INC
919 Vermillion St Ste 110 (55033-2150)
PHONE..............................651 480-4710
Lee Randal, *Director*
EMP: 36 **EST:** 2003
SALES (est): 1MM-4.9MM **Privately Held**
SIC: 8322 Individual & family social services

(G-2405)
SIEWERT CONSTRUCTION CO INC
925 Highway 55 Ste 203 (55033-3736)
PHONE..............................651 437-1728
Todd Siewert, *CEO*
Paul L Siewert, *President*
EST: 1958
SQ FT: 2,400 **Privately Held**

(PA)=Parent Co (HQ)=Headquarters (DH)=Div Headquarters
✿ = New business established in last 2 years

2011 Harris Minnesota
Services Directory

© Harris InfoSource 1-866-281-6415
113

SIC: **1521** 1522 6512 6513 New single-family home construction service; townhouse construction service; apartment building construction service; condominium construction service; operators of commercial & industrial buildings; apartment building operator

(G-2406)
SMEAD MANUFACTURING CO INC (PA)
600 Smead Blvd (55033-2200)
PHONE..............................651 437-4111
FAX: 651 437-9134
Sharon L Avent, *President*
Don Slusarski, *General Mgr*
David Fasbender, *Corp Secy*
Millett O'Connell, *Corp Secy*
Michael Dolan, *COO*
▲ **EMP: 500 EST:** 1906
SQ FT: 310,000 **Privately Held**
SIC: **7372** Manufactures die-cut cards, folders & mats; business & professional software publishers; book binding service; manufactures partitions & fixtures; manufactures index cards, die-cut made from purchased materials; manufactures manila folders

(G-2407)
STAGECOACH EXPRESS INC
7965 190th St E (55033-9538)
PHONE..............................651 437-8138
FAX: 651 437-6127
Gary Ries, *President*
EMP: 25 EST: 1971
SQ FT: 10,000
SALES (est): 1MM-4.9MM **Privately Held**
WEB: www.stagecoachexpress.com
SIC: **4213** Over the road trucking

(G-2408)
THOMAS FURLONG
14690 Furlong Cir (55033-8649)
PHONE..............................651 437-2518
Thomas Furlong, *Owner*
EMP: 30 EST: 1931
SALES (est): 1MM-4.9MM **Privately Held**
WEB: www.thoroughbredinfo.com
SIC: **6519** Real estate property leasing & rental

(G-2409)
TWIN CITY CONTAINER INC (PA)
990 Spiral Blvd (55033-3694)
PHONE..............................651 480-3786
FAX: 651 480-2542
Brad Malecha, *President*
Gary G Fuchs, *CFO*
Phil Amelse, *Finance Mgr*
Joe Slattery, *Manager*
Joe Wirth, *Director*
EMP: 37 EST: 1996
SQ FT: 30,000 **Privately Held**
SIC: **7699** Industrial machinery repair & maintenance services; manufactures metal forming machine tools

(G-2410)
TWIN CITY ORAL & MAXILLOFACIAL
925 Highway 55 Ste 202 (55033-3736)
PHONE..............................651 437-3262
David Broude, *President*
Shirley Harding, *Office Mgr*
Jason E Jenny, *Surgeon*
Michael J Downie, *Surgeon*
Kathy Chaney, *Assistant*
EMP: 28 EST: 2005
SALES (est): 1MM-4.9MM **Privately Held**
WEB: www.tcoralsurgery.com
SIC: **8021** Dental surgeon office

HASTINGS
Washington County

(G-2411)
AFTON ALPS GOLF COURSE
6600 Peller Ave S (55033-9474)
PHONE..............................651 436-1320
Paul Augustine, *Owner*
Amy Augustine, *CIO*

Matthew Koss, *Info Tech Mgr*
EMP: 40 **EST:** 1989
SALES (est): 1MM-4.9MM **Privately Held**
SIC: **7992** Public golf course

(G-2412)
AFTON ALPS INC
6600 Peller Ave S (55033-9474)
PHONE..............................651 436-5245
FAX: 651 436-8584
Paul H Augustine, *President*
Robert L Augustine, *Vice Pres*
Dick Lempke, *CFO*
Amy Augustine, *Controller*
Joe Yasis, *Pub Rel Dir*
EMP: 600 EST: 1963
SALES (est): 10MM-24.9MM **Privately Held**
WEB: www.aftonalps.com
SIC: **7011** 7999 Ski lodge; resort hotel; provides ski instruction

(G-2413)
ANYTIME FITNESS LLC
12181 Margo Ave S Ste 100 (55033-8421)
PHONE..............................651 438-5000
Chuck Ruynon, *President*
Jeffrey Thames, *COO*
Dave Mortensem, *Vice Pres*
Gerry Thomas, *CFO*
Thames Jeff, *Sales Executive*
EMP: 75 EST: 2002
SQ FT: 46,000
SALES (est): 1MM-4.9MM **Privately Held**
SIC: **7997** 7991 Membership recreation club; physical fitness center

(G-2414)
DLO EXCAVATING & POURED WALLS
12151 120th St S (55033-9428)
PHONE..............................651 480-8457
Donald L Oreskovich, *President*
Cindy Oreskovich, *CFO*
EMP: 35 EST: 1991
SQ FT: 6,000
SALES (est): 1MM-4.9MM **Privately Held**
WEB: www.dloexcavating.com
SIC: **1794** Excavating contractor

(G-2415)
FEATHER, LARSON & SYNHORST
12181 Margo Ave S Ste 220 (55033-8421)
PHONE..............................651 480-0123
FAX: 651 480-0111
Scott Miller, *Manager*
EMP: 98 EST: 2000
SQ FT: 1,500
SALES (est): 1MM-4.9MM **Privately Held**
SIC: **7389** Telemarketing services

(G-2416)
GORDY'S GLASS INC
12590 127th St S Ste 1 (55033-8417)
PHONE..............................651 437-5356
Edward Peterson, *President*
Marie Peterson, *Vice Pres*
Gary Bradford, *Controller*
Melissa Christensen, *Assistant*
EMP: 34 EST: 1969
SQ FT: 23,000
SALES (est): 10MM-24.9MM **Privately Held**
SIC: **5023** 5031 Wholesales framed & unframed mirrors & pictures; retails mirrors; wholesales doors & windows

(G-2417)
LIFETIME SIDING & REMODELING
Also Called: ABC Seamless
11825 Point Douglas Dr S (55033-9146)
PHONE..............................651 458-0844
FAX: 651 458-1865
Dave D Bois, *CEO*
Mary Smith, *Human Res Mgr*
Allison Friedley, *Marketing Mgr*
EMP: 40 EST: 1975
SQ FT: 12,000
SALES (est): 1MM-4.9MM **Privately Held**
SIC: **1761** Siding contractor

(G-2418)
STYLEPOINTE LLC
Also Called: Deck Images
12590 127th St S Ste 4 (55033-8417)
PHONE..............................651 437-5356
Marie Peterson, *Member*
Edward L Peterson, *Member*
EMP: 40 EST: 2000
SQ FT: 18,000
SALES (est): 10MM-24.9MM **Privately Held**
SIC: **5039** Wholesales architectural metalwork

HAWLEY
Clay County

(G-2419)
HAWLEY GOLF & COUNTRY CLUB INC
Hwy 10 (56549)
PO Box 734 (56549-0734)
PHONE..............................218 483-4808
FAX: 218 483-0277
Craig Teck, *President*
James Cresap, *Principal*
John Elton, *Corp Secy*
Roger Blakeway, *Vice Pres*
Terri Amman, *Manager*
EMP: 30 EST: 1967
SQ FT: 2,500
SALES (est): 1MM-4.9MM **Privately Held**
SIC: **7992** Public golf course

(G-2420)
HAWLEY RETIREMENT INC
923 5th St (56549-4900)
PHONE..............................218 483-3337
FAX: 218 483-3386
Jim Birchem, *President*
Todd Spies, *Director*
EMP: 36 EST: 1967
SQ FT: 14,422
SALES (est): 1MM-4.9MM **Privately Held**
SIC: **8361** 8052 Residential care facility; intermediate care facility

(G-2421)
RDO EQUIPMENT CO
920 Odonnel St (56549-4309)
PHONE..............................218 483-3353
FAX: 218 483-3355
Marshall Anderson, *Manager*
Troy Kind, *Manager*
EMP: 33
SALES (est): 10MM-24.9MM **Privately Held**
SIC: **5083** 5082 5084 Wholesales farm & garden machinery; wholesales construction & mining machinery; wholesales industrial machinery & equipment
PA: Rdo Holdings Co
　　2829 University Dr S
　　Fargo ND 58103
　　701 237-6062

(G-2422)
SELLIN BROTHERS INC
1204 Hobart St (56549-4042)
PO Box 159 (56549-0159)
PHONE..............................218 483-3522
FAX: 218 483-4678
Mark Sellin, *President*
Joel Sellin, *Vice Pres*
Scott Sellin, *Vice Pres*
Judy Berceau, *Manager*
EMP: 50 EST: 1947
SQ FT: 3,600
SALES (est): 5MM-9.9MM **Privately Held**
WEB: www.sellinbrothers.com
SIC: **1611** 1623 Heavy highway & street construction; water & sewer line construction

(G-2423)
SPRING PRAIRIE HUTTERIAN
6189 170th St N (56549-9094)
PHONE..............................218 498-0222
John Waldner, *President*
Joe Wipf, *Treasurer*
EMP: 120 EST: 1976 **Privately Held**

SIC: **0291** 0191 7539 7694 Livestock farm; crop farming; automotive repair services; electric motor repair service; retails family clothing; commercial lithographic printing

HAYFIELD
Dodge County

(G-2424)
OAKS COUNTRY CLUB INC
Country Club Rd (55940)
PO Box 86 (55940-0086)
PHONE..............................507 477-3233
Tim Schultz, *President*
EMP: 25 EST: 1976
SALES (est): 1MM-4.9MM **Privately Held**
SIC: **7997** Country club; membership golf club

(G-2425)
PALMER BUS SERVICE INC
35 E Main St (55940-2102)
PHONE..............................507 477-3014
Sloyd Palmer, *President*
Louise Palmer, *Vice Pres*
EMP: 30 EST: 2007
SALES (est): 500-999K **Privately Held**
SIC: **4151** School bus service

(G-2426)
SPARE TIMES LANES & LOUNGE
Also Called: Hayfield Lanes
18 2nd St NE (55940)
PO Box 31 (55940-0031)
PHONE..............................507 477-3492
Steve Monahan, *President*
Thomas Monahan, *President*
Ron Monahan, *Vice Pres*
Nancy Monahan, *Manager*
EMP: 25 EST: 1992
SALES (est): 500-999K **Privately Held**
SIC: **7933** Bowling center; full service American restaurant

HAYFIELD
Olmsted County

(G-2427)
FIELD CREST CARE CENTER
318 2nd St NE (55940-8857)
PHONE..............................507 477-3266
Dan E Will, *Principal*
Judy Bowman, *Office Mgr*
EMP: 106 EST: 1969
SALES (est): 1MM-4.9MM **Privately Held**
WEB: www.fieldcrestcare.com
SIC: **8051** Skilled nursing care facility

HENDERSON
Sibley County

(G-2428)
ALTONA HUTTERIAN BRETHREN INC
35227 290th St (56044-3447)
PHONE..............................507 248-3191
Zack Wollman Jr, *President*
EMP: 25 Privately Held
SIC: **0191** 0213 Crop farming; hog & pig farming

HENDRICKS
Lincoln County

(G-2429)
HENDRICKS COMMUNITY HOSPITAL
503 E Lincoln St (56136-9598)
PO Box 106 (56136-0106)
PHONE..............................507 275-3134
FAX: 507 275-3104
Jeff Gollaher, *President*
Julie Hogie, *Business Mgr*
Tabb McCluskey, *Ch of Surgery*

Kristi Christianson, *Human Res Mgr*
Janice Englestead, *Branch Mgr*
EMP: 160 **EST:** 1941
SALES (est): 5MM-9.9MM **Privately Held**
WEB: www.hendrickshosp.org
SIC: 8051 8062 8351 Skilled nursing care facility; child day care service; medical hospital

(G-2430)
KIWANIS INTERNATIONAL INC
306 S Oak St (56136-9530)
PHONE 507 275-3748
Leroy Muller, *President*
EMP: 40 **Privately Held**
SIC: 8641 Civic associations
PA: Kiwanis International Inc
3636 Woodview Trce
Indianapolis IN 46268
317 875-8755

HENNING
Otter Tail County

(G-2431)
BEVERLY ENTERPRISES - MN
Also Called: Henning Health Care Center
907 Marshall Ave (56551-4011)
PO Box 57 (56551-0057)
PHONE 218 583-2965
FAX: 218 583-2719
Joan Johnson, *Dir Ops-Prd-Mfg*
Laurie Nelson, *Office Mgr*
EMP: 65
SALES (est): 1MM-4.9MM **Privately Held**
WEB: www.beverlynet.com
SIC: 8051 Skilled nursing care facility; convalescent home
HQ: Beverly Enterprises - MN
650 Ramer Ave S
Rush City MN 55069
320 358-4765

(G-2432)
JENNIE-O TURKEY STORE INC
375 Fredrick Ln (56551)
PO Box 377 (56551-0377)
PHONE 218 583-2204
Craig Nine, *Manager*
Terri Summers, *Manager*
EMP: 34 **Publicly Held**
WEB: www.hormel.com
SIC: 0253 Turkey farm
HQ: Jennie-O Turkey Store Inc
2505 Willmar Ave SW
Willmar MN 56201
320 235-2622

HERMANTOWN
Saint Louis County

(G-2433)
A G O'BRIEN PLUMBING & HEATING
4907 Lightning Dr (55811-1411)
PHONE 218 729-9662
FAX: 218 729-9774
Derrill J Adatte, *CEO*
Paul Kucza, *Vice Pres*
John Schumann, *Vice Pres*
Gordonna Cain, *Asst Sec*
EMP: 50 **EST:** 1927
SQ FT: 20,000
SALES (est): 5MM-9.9MM **Privately Held**
SIC: 1711 7389 Plumbing service; warm air heating & air conditioning contractor; fire protection services

HERON LAKE
Jackson County

(G-2434)
HERON LAKE BIOENERGY LLC
91246 390th Ave (56137-3175)
PHONE 507 793-0077
FAX: 507 793-0078
Robert J Ferguson, *Ch of Bd*
David J Woestehoff, *Corp Secy*

Brett L Frevert, *CFO*
Michael S Kunerth, *Treasurer*
Catherine Henstein, *Accountant*
EMP: 45 **EST:** 2001
SQ FT: 7,320
SALES (est): 100MM-499.9MM **Privately Held**
SIC: 1321 Natural ethane production

HERON LAKE
Nobles County

(G-2435)
CITY OF HERON LAKE
Also Called: Lakeview Nursing Home
941 County Road 9 (56137-1408)
PHONE 507 793-2349
FAX: 507 793-2348
Paula Roucheleau, *Manager*
EMP: 60
SALES (est): 1MM-4.9MM **Privately Held**
SIC: 8051 Skilled nursing care facility
PA: City of Heron Lake
312 10th St
Heron Lake MN 56137
507 793-2826

HIBBING
Saint Louis County

(G-2436)
AMERIPRIDE SERVICES INC
519 E 19th St (55746-1666)
PHONE 218 263-3611
FAX: 218 263-3822
Reggie Lacarry, *General Mgr*
Reggie Licari, *Manager*
EMP: 60
SALES (est): 1MM-4.9MM **Privately Held**
WEB: www.ameripride.com
SIC: 7218 Industrial laundry service
PA: Ameripride Services Inc
10801 Wayzata Blvd # 100
Hopkins MN 55305
952 738-4200

(G-2437)
API ELECTRIC CO
Also Called: Lakehead Electric
1711 E 13th St Ste 2 (55746-1356)
PHONE 218 741-7313
FAX: 218 741-6838
Cal Turner, *Branch Mgr*
EMP: 25
SALES (est): 1MM-4.9MM **Privately Held**
WEB: www.apielectric.com
SIC: 8711 Electrical or electronic engineers
HQ: API Electric Co
4330 W 1st St Ste B
Duluth MN 55807
218 628-3323

(G-2438)
BARR ENGINEERING CO
3128 14th Ave E (55746-3513)
PHONE 218 262-2262
Duane Kokkinen, *Project Mgr*
Cliff Rasch, *Manager*
Jerry Koschak, *Coordinator*
EMP: 40
SALES (est): 5MM-9.9MM **Privately Held**
SIC: 8711 Engineering services

(G-2439)
CENTER FOR INDEPENDENT LIVING
2104 6th Ave E (55746-1821)
PHONE 218 262-6675
FAX: 218 262-6677
Diane Krier, *Ch of Bd*
Kim Tyler, *Exec Dir*
Kim Haxton, *Exec Dir*
EMP: 400 **EST:** 1981
SALES (est): 10MM-24.9MM **Privately Held**
SIC: 8322 8049 8093 Association for the handicapped; clinical psychologist office; outpatient mental health clinic

(G-2440)
CHISHOLM-HIBBING AIRPORT
11038 Highway 37 Ste 12 (55746-8204)
PHONE 218 262-3451
FAX: 218 262-6245
David Danielson, *Manager*
EMP: 44
SALES (est): 10MM-24.9MM **Privately Held**
WEB: www.hibbingairport.com
SIC: 4512 7514 Scheduled air transportation services; rent-a-car service

(G-2441)
CLIFFS NATURAL RESOURCES INC
Also Called: Hibtac Mining
Highway 5 N (55746)
PHONE 218 262-5917
Ed Latendresse, *Manager*
EMP: 700
SALES (est): 100MM-499.9MM **Publicly Held**
WEB: www.cliffsnaturalresources.com
SIC: 1011 Iron ore mining
PA: Cliffs Natural Resources Inc
200 Public Sq
Cleveland OH 44114
216 694-5700

(G-2442)
DOM-EX LLC
109 Grant St (55746-1540)
PO Box 877 (55746-0877)
PHONE 218 262-6116
FAX: 218 263-8611
Dana Ellefson, *Member*
John Kokotovich, *Member*
Chris Elleson, *Manager*
Mark Troumbly, *Manager*
Mat Senich, *Manager*
◆ **EMP:** 45 **EST:** 2007
SQ FT: 9,800
SALES (est): 10MM-24.9MM **Privately Held**
WEB: www.dom-ex.com
SIC: 5082 Wholesales construction & mining machinery

(G-2443)
FAIRVIEW HEALTH LINE HOME CARE
1101 E 37th St Ste 18 (55746-2973)
PHONE 218 262-6982
FAX: 218 262-5756
David Hall, *Administrator*
Penny Calger, *Director*
EMP: 100 **EST:** 2001
SALES (est): 1MM-4.9MM **Privately Held**
SIC: 8082 7361 Home health care services; nurses' registry service

(G-2444)
FAIRVIEW HEALTH SERVICES
750 E 34th St (55746-2341)
PHONE 218 262-4881
Daniel Courneya, *Ch Radiology*
Carol Bode, *QA Dir*
John Kritz, *CFO*
Mitch Vincent, *VP Human Res*
Jennifer Preston, *Human Res Dir*
EMP: 230
SALES (est): 10MM-24.9MM **Privately Held**
WEB: www.fairview.org
SIC: 8741 8062 Hospital management services; medical hospital
PA: Fairview Health Services
2450 Riverside Ave
Minneapolis MN 55454
612 672-6300

(G-2445)
FRABONI'S WHOLESALE DISTRS
315 E 13th St (55746-1400)
PHONE 218 263-8991
Mark Thune, *President*
Wayne Thune, *Vice Pres*
Don Johnson, *Plant Mgr*
Tom Moberg, *Bookkeeper*
EMP: 27 **EST:** 1994
SQ FT: 1,500
SALES (est): 10MM-24.9MM **Privately Held**
WEB: www.frabonis.com
SIC: 5141 Food broker

(G-2446)
FURIN & SHEA WELDING & FABCTG
1432 E 34th St (55746-3524)
PHONE 218 262-5271
FAX: 218 262-3434
Dan M Shea, *President*
David P Furin, *Corp Secy*
Glen Newman, *Mfg Staff*
Jeff Krauth, *Rsch/Dvlpt Dir*
EMP: 28 **EST:** 1979
SQ FT: 12,000
SALES (est): 1MM-4.9MM **Privately Held**
SIC: 7692 Plate metal fabricator; welding service

(G-2447)
GREENVIEW ALZHEIMER'S
3520 7th Ave E (55746-2609)
PHONE 218 263-3935
FAX: 218 262-6984
Rhonda Wiiliainen, *Manager*
Janet Kiesel, *Manager*
David Hohl, *Administrator*
EMP: 31 **EST:** 1994
SALES (est): 500-999K **Privately Held**
SIC: 8351 8361 Child day care service; residential care facility

(G-2448)
GUARDIAN ANGELS HEALTH & REHAB
1500 3rd Ave E (55746-1462)
PHONE 218 263-7583
FAX: 218 263-3422
Luverne Hoffman, *President*
June Shelde, *Administrator*
Craig Doughty, *Admin Mgr*
Chris Winkler, *Director*
Brad Olson, *Director*
EMP: 200 **EST:** 1966
SQ FT: 71,000
SALES (est): 5MM-9.9MM **Privately Held**
WEB: www.guardianangels.sfhs.org
SIC: 8051 8093 Skilled nursing care facility; outpatient rehabilitation treatment center

(G-2449)
HEALTHLINE INC (HQ)
750 E 34th St (55746-2341)
PHONE 218 362-6760
FAX: 218 362-6684
Jill Johnson, *Accountant*
Stacy French, *Manager*
David H Oi, *Manager*
David J Hohl, *Exec Dir*
EMP: 50 **EST:** 1983
SQ FT: 2,125
SALES (corp-wide): 84.07M **Privately Held**
WEB: www.healthline.com
SIC: 8082 8721 Home health care services; billing & bookkeeping services; retails hospital equipment & supplies
PA: Range Regional Health Services
750 E 34th St
Hibbing MN 55746
218 262-4881

(G-2450)
HEALTHLINE INC
1101 E 37th St Ste 18 (55746-2973)
PHONE 218 262-6981
FAX: 218 262-1723
Jo Bronfeld, *Manager*
Pat Trask, *Exec Dir*
EMP: 25
SALES (est): 500-999K **Privately Held**
WEB: www.healthline.com
SIC: 8082 5047 5169 Home health care services; wholesales medical equipment & supplies; wholesales oxygen; retails telephone & communication equipment
HQ: Healthline Inc
750 E 34th St
Hibbing MN 55746
218 362-6760

(G-2451)
HIBBING PUBLIC UTILITIES COMMN
1902 6th Ave E (55746-1663)
PO Box 249 (55746-0249)
PHONE 218 262-7700
FAX: 218 262-7702

(PA)=Parent Co (HQ)=Headquarters (DH)=Div Headquarters
✿ = New business established in last 2 years

2011 Harris Minnesota
Services Directory

© Harris InfoSource 1-866-281-6415
115

John Berklich, *Chairman*
Kevin Gargano, *Finance*
Joseph Ascoli, *Manager*
Larry McGuire, *Commissioner*
Gary Kleffman, *Commissioner*
EMP: 92 **EST:** 1919
SQ FT: 10,000
SALES (est): 50MM-99.9MM **Privately Held**
WEB: www.hpuc.com
SIC: 4931 Electric & related services

(G-2452)
HIBBING TACONITE CO
County Hwy 5 N (55746)
PO Box 589 (55746-0589)
PHONE..............................218 262-5950
FAX: 218 262-6877
Edward M Latendresse, *Principal*
Jack Croswell, *Area Mgr*
J Christianson, *Div Sub Head*
Tim Tomsich, *Finance Mgr*
John Kannas, *Manager*
EMP: 871
SALES (est): 100MM-499.9MM **Privately Held**
SIC: 1011 Open pit taconite mining
PA: Hibbing Taconite Co
    200 Public Sq Ste 3300
    Cleveland OH 44114
    216 694-5700

(G-2453)
HIBBING, CITY OF INC
1425 E 23rd St Ste 2 (55746-3356)
PHONE..............................218 263-5264
EMP: 27
SALES (est): 1MM-4.9MM **Privately Held**
SIC: 1623 Sewer line construction; mayors' office
PA: Hibbing, City of Inc
    401 E 21st St
    Hibbing MN 55746
    218 262-3486

(G-2454)
HILLIGOSS CHEVROLET INC
Also Called: Ranger-Chevrolet-Cadillac
1502 E Howard St (55746-1263)
PO Box 745 (55746-0745)
PHONE..............................218 263-7578
FAX: 218 263-7576
Donald O Hilligoss II, *President*
Alaena C Hoover, *Finance*
EMP: 27 **EST:** 1949
SQ FT: 19,000
SALES (est): 10MM-24.9MM **Privately Held**
SIC: 7538 Retails new & used automobiles; general automotive repair services; retails new & used pickups; used car dealer

(G-2455)
HOME HEALTH INC
Also Called: Homecare Specialists
101 E Howard St (55746-1733)
PHONE..............................218 262-5887
FAX: 218 262-6228
Rodney Baudeck, *President*
Cathy Baudeck, *Vice Pres*
EMP: 200 **EST:** 1976
SQ FT: 50,000
SALES (est): 5MM-9.9MM **Privately Held**
WEB: www.homehealth.com
SIC: 8082 Home health care services; retails hospital equipment & supplies

(G-2456)
IMPROVEMENT LP
Also Called: Hibbing Park Hotel
1402 E Howard St (55746-1337)
PHONE..............................218 262-3481
Keith Saralamp, *General Mgr*
Jeanette Wennen, *Vice Pres*
Becky Pierret, *Human Res Dir*
Diane Sandvig, *Manager*
Sandy Mettle, *Manager*
EMP: 100
SALES (est): 5MM-9.9MM **Privately Held**
WEB: www.hibbingparkhotel.com
SIC: 7011 7991 Traveler accommodations; eating place; physical fitness center; drinking establishment

(G-2457)
INAC OF VA INC
1114 E 23rd St (55746-1968)
PHONE..............................218 263-3398
FAX: 218 263-6251
Tanya Cunningham, *Manager*
EMP: 35
SALES (est): 1MM-4.9MM **Privately Held**
SIC: 8741 Restaurant management services

(G-2458)
KIDDIE KAROUSEL DAY CARE CTR
3920 13th Ave E Ste 5 (55746-3675)
PHONE..............................218 263-7450
FAX: 218 263-7000
Pat Ives, *President*
EMP: 25
SALES (est): 500-999K **Privately Held**
SIC: 8351 Child day care service; elementary & secondary school

(G-2459)
LOWE'S HOME CENTERS INC
12025 Highway 169 W (55746-3022)
PHONE..............................218 262-7460
EMP: 150
SALES (est): 25MM-49.9MM **Publicly Held**
WEB: www.lowes.com
SIC: 5031 5064 Retails building products & materials; wholesales exterior building materials; wholesales interior building materials; wholesales electrical appliances; retails household appliances
HQ: Lowe's Home Centers Inc
    1605 Curtis Bridge Rd
    Wilkesboro NC 28697
    336 658-4000

(G-2460)
M D I GOVERNMENT SERVICES
1937 4th Ave E (55746-1654)
PHONE..............................218 263-3663
Gary Flesland, *Manager*
EMP: 162
SALES (est): 10MM-24.9MM **Privately Held**
SIC: 7389 Packaging & labeling services; manufactures wooden boxes
PA: M D I Government Services
    1700 Wynne Ave
    Saint Paul MN 55108
    651 999-8200

(G-2461)
MAX GRAY CONSTRUCTION INC
2501 5th Ave W (55746-2040)
PO Box 689 (55746-0689)
PHONE..............................218 262-6622
FAX: 218 262-2109
James M Erickson, *President*
William E Lowry, *Project Dir*
EMP: 50 **EST:** 1947
SQ FT: 3,000
SALES (est): 10MM-24.9MM **Privately Held**
WEB: www.maxgrayconst.com
SIC: 1542 1541 Commercial & office building contractor; new industrial building construction

(G-2462)
MEMORIAL BLOOD CENTER
750 E 34th St (55746-2341)
PHONE..............................218 263-1338
Jerry Haarmann, *CEO*
EMP: 39
SALES (est): 1MM-4.9MM **Privately Held**
WEB: www.mbcm.org
SIC: 8099 Blood bank
PA: Memorial Blood Center
    737 Pelham Blvd
    Saint Paul MN 55114
    651 332-7000

(G-2463)
MESABA CLINIC
3605 Mayfair Ave Ste 2 (55746-2936)
PHONE..............................218 263-9426
Kevin Krause, *President*
Michael Heck MD, *Partner*
John Shenk MD, *Partner*
John Kritz, *CFO*
Mitch Vincent, *Human Resources*

EMP: 110 **EST:** 1956
SQ FT: 28,000
SALES (est): 10MM-24.9MM **Privately Held**
SIC: 8011 Clinic operated by physicians

(G-2464)
MESABA COUNTRY CLUB
Also Called: Gary Yeager Pro Shop
First Ave At 51st St T S (55746)
PHONE..............................218 262-2851
Paul Jenssen, *President*
EMP: 50 **EST:** 1921
SQ FT: 625
SALES (est): 5MM-9.9MM **Privately Held**
SIC: 7999 Golf professionals; retails golf goods & equipment

(G-2465)
MESABA COUNTRY CLUB
415 E 51st St (55746-4005)
PO Box 157 (55746-0157)
PHONE..............................218 262-2851
John Kokotodich, *President*
Todd Scaia, *Corp Secy*
Scott Sosalla, *Vice Pres*
Tony Caucci, *Vice Pres*
Bob Kimmef, *Treasurer*
EMP: 30 **EST:** 1921
SQ FT: 3,500
SALES (est): 1MM-4.9MM **Privately Held**
SIC: 7997 Membership golf club; bar; eating place

(G-2466)
MIDWEST COMMUNICATION INC
807 W 37th St (55746-2839)
PHONE..............................218 749-3000
Duke Wright, *CEO*
Melisa Schinderle, *Business Mgr*
Dan Klaysmat, *Chief Engr*
Kristi Garrity, *Sales Mgr*
EMP: 28 **EST:** 2000
SALES (est): 1MM-4.9MM **Privately Held**
SIC: 4832 Radio broadcasting station

(G-2467)
MINNESOTA DIVERSIFIED INDS
1937 4th Ave E (55746-1654)
PHONE..............................218 263-3663
Lyn Collyard, *Human Res Mgr*
Ted Giosol, *Branch Mgr*
EMP: 50
SALES (est): 5MM-9.9MM **Privately Held**
WEB: www.mdi.org
SIC: 8748 Employee programs administration consultant
PA: Minnesota Diversified Inds
    1700 Wynne Ave
    Saint Paul MN 55108
    651 999-8200

(G-2468)
MINNESOTA DIVERSIFIED INDS
1937 4th Ave E (55746-1654)
PHONE..............................218 263-3663
Gary Flesland, *Branch Mgr*
EMP: 46
SALES (est): 5MM-9.9MM **Privately Held**
WEB: www.mdi.org
SIC: 7389 Manufactures plastic corrugated panels; packaging & labeling services
PA: Minnesota Diversified Inds
    1700 Wynne Ave
    Saint Paul MN 55108
    651 999-8200

(G-2469)
NORAMCO ENGINEERING CORP
2729 13th Ave E (55746-2305)
PHONE..............................218 262-1093
FAX: 218 262-1092
Frank Pengal, *President*
Bruce Kettunen, *Project Engr*
Bernadeth Smith, *Human Res Dir*
Dale Ekmark, *Manager*
Rod Prusi, *Manager*
EMP: 26 **EST:** 1986
SQ FT: 17,000
SALES (est): 1MM-4.9MM **Privately Held**
WEB: www.noramcoeng.com
SIC: 8711 Engineering services

(G-2470)
RANGE CORNICE & ROOFING CO
510 W 41st St (55746-3063)
PHONE..............................218 263-8812
FAX: 218 263-8185
Tim Lee, *President*
Shelley Marty, *Corp Secy*
Terry Marty, *Vice Pres*
EMP: 30 **EST:** 2005
SALES (est): 1MM-4.9MM **Privately Held**
SIC: 1761 Roofing contractor

(G-2471)
RANGE CORNICE & ROOFING CO INC
510 W 41st St (55746-3063)
PHONE..............................218 262-4581
FAX: 218 262-1145
Tim K Lee, *President*
Christopher Lee, *Vice Pres*
Dennis Marchetti, *CFO*
Shelly Marty, *Manager*
EMP: 30 **EST:** 1919
SALES (est): 1MM-4.9MM **Privately Held**
SIC: 1711 1761 Warm air heating & air conditioning contractor; sheet metal fabricator; roofing contractor; steel fabricator

(G-2472)
RANGE MENTAL HEALTH CENTER INC
3203 3rd Ave W (55746-2406)
PHONE..............................218 263-9237
FAX: 218 262-1883
Gina Grahek, *Office Mgr*
Sally Ribarczek, *Branch Mgr*
Craig Stevens, *Director*
Matthew Zak, *Psychiatry*
Emery Ulrich, *Psychiatry*
EMP: 32
SALES (est): 1MM-4.9MM **Privately Held**
WEB: www.rangementalhealth.org
SIC: 8011 8049 Physicians' office & clinic; clinical psychologist office
PA: Range Mental Health Center Inc
    624 13th St S
    Virginia MN 55792
    218 749-2881

(G-2473)
RANGE REGIONAL HEALTH SERVICES (PA)
Also Called: Central Mesabi Medical Center
750 E 34th St (55746-2341)
PHONE..............................218 262-4881
FAX: 218 362-6647
Frances Gardeski, *Ch of Bd*
Richard Jenter, *President*
Carol Bodie, *Safety Mgr*
Andrea Stish, *Buyer*
Pauline Hanson, *Human Res Dir*
EMP: 540 **EST:** 1976
SQ FT: 158,704
SALES (corp-wide): 84.07M **Privately Held**
SIC: 8062 Medical hospital

(G-2474)
REMAX NORTHERN PROPERTIES
4325 9th Ave W (55746-3032)
PHONE..............................218 263-8877
FAX: 218 362-7216
Todd Toman, *Owner*
Tanaya Rites, *Assistant*
EMP: 25 **EST:** 2005
SALES (est): 1MM-4.9MM **Privately Held**
SIC: 6531 Real estate services

(G-2475)
SHUBAT TRANSPORTATION CO
618 W 41st St (55746-3019)
PHONE..............................218 262-1042
FAX: 218 263-7182
Edward L Pajunen, *President*
Nancy Pajunen, *Vice Pres*
Lisa Vondehaar, *Manager*
EMP: 50 **EST:** 1919
SQ FT: 9,100
SALES (est): 1MM-4.9MM **Privately Held**
WEB: www.shubat.com

www.HarrisInfo.com
116
2011 Harris Minnesota
Services Directory
▲=Import ▼=Export
◆=Import/Export

SIC: **4151** 4119 4142 School bus service; long-distance bus charter service; sightseeing bus service

(G-2476)
ST LUKE'S HOSPITAL OF DULUTH
1120 E 34th St (55746-2909)
PHONE...............................218 362-7100
FAX: 218 362-7100
Todd Scaia, *Manager*
Cheryl Smith, *Manager*
Karen Foust, *Nurse*
EMP: 45
SALES (est): 5MM-9.9MM **Privately Held**
WEB: www.slhduluth.com
SIC: **8011** Physicians' office & clinic
PA: St Luke's Hospital of Duluth
915 E 1st St
Duluth MN 55805
218 726-5555

(G-2477)
TLC CLEANING SPECIALISTS
2512 1st Ave (55746-2243)
PHONE...............................218 263-4778
Carrie Kangaf, *Owner*
EMP: 30 EST: 1992
SALES (est): 500-999K **Privately Held**
WEB: www.tlcindoorair.com
SIC: **7349** Building cleaning & maintenance services

(G-2478)
ULLAND BROTHERS INC
505 W 37th St (55746-2827)
PHONE...............................218 262-3406
FAX: 218 262-2101
Orlin Ofstad, *Superintendent*
Roger Sandstrom, *Manager*
Andy Wagner, *Manager*
Cully Hall, *Manager*
David Debevec, *Director*
EMP: 30
SALES (est): 1MM-4.9MM **Privately Held**
WEB: www.ulland.com
SIC: **1611** 7699 General highway & street construction service; construction equipment repair service
PA: Ulland Brothers Inc
1634 Highway 210
Carlton MN 55718
218 384-4266

(G-2479)
VIKING EXPLOSIVES & SUPPLY INC
4469 Highway 5 (55746-8293)
PHONE...............................218 263-8845
FAX: 218 262-4574
Robert Prittinen, *General Mgr*
Mike Lownds, *Vice Pres*
Joel Staeth, *Technical Mgr*
Bob Prittinen, *Manager*
EMP: 28
SALES (est): 10MM-24.9MM **Privately Held**
SIC: **5169** Wholesales explosives; manufactures explosives

HILL CITY
Aitkin County

(G-2480)
HILL CITY LIONS CLUB
66641 345th Pl (55748-4611)
PO Box 57 (55748-0057)
PHONE...............................218 697-8427
Michael Dolan, *President*
EMP: 25 EST: 1976 **Privately Held**
SIC: **8641** Civic associations

(G-2481)
MIKE BISHOFF
Also Called: Trailers Plus
65742 U S Hwy 169 (55748)
PO Box 300 (55748-0300)
PHONE...............................218 697-2800
Mike Bishoff, *President*
EMP: 30 EST: 2001 **Privately Held**
SIC: **8611** Manufacturers' association

HILLS
Rock County

(G-2482)
TUFF MEMORIAL HOMES INC
505 E 4th St (56138-1017)
PHONE...............................507 962-3275
FAX: 507 962-3277
Dana Dahlquist, *Administrator*
EMP: 100 EST: 1960
SALES (est): 1MM-4.9MM **Privately Held**
SIC: **8051** 6513 Skilled nursing care facility; operators of retirement hotels

HINCKLEY
Pine County

(G-2483)
CORPORATE COMMISSION OF THE
Also Called: Grand Casino Hinckley
777 Lady Luck Dr (55037-6400)
PO Box 15 (55037-0015)
PHONE...............................320 384-7101
FAX: 320 384-4849
Mel Towle, *General Mgr*
Jim Lincoln, *Vice Pres*
Steven Perrault, *Opers Staff*
Michael Sam, *Purch Mgr*
Roxanne Hemming, *CFO*
EMP: 1600
SALES (est): 100MM-499.9MM **Privately Held**
WEB: www.grcasinos.com
SIC: **7993** 7011 7033 Gambling establishments operating coin-operated machines; traveler accommodations; recreational vehicle park & campground; full service American restaurant; retail gift shop; drinking establishment
HQ: Corporate Commission of The
777 Grand Ave
Onamia MN 56359
320 532-8800

(G-2484)
FORBY CONTRACTING INC
34363 Swede Aly (55037-6325)
PHONE...............................320 384-6061
FAX: 320 384-7612
Richard Brant, *President*
Vicki E Cathey, *Corp Secy*
Ronald Brant, *Corp Secy*
Stephen R Cathey, *Treasurer*
Lucy Lehman, *Office Mgr*
EMP: 45 EST: 1978
SQ FT: 900
SALES (est): 5MM-9.9MM **Privately Held**
SIC: **1611** Highway & street maintenance service

(G-2485)
LAND & CABINS LLC
24226 Lone Pine Rd (55037-6365)
PHONE...............................320 384-6488
FAX: 320 384-6472
Brian Weidendorf, *Principal*
EMP: 80 EST: 2006
SALES (est): 1MM-4.9MM **Privately Held**
WEB: www.landcabins.com
SIC: **7011** Traveler accommodations

(G-2486)
MAINTENANCE BUILDING
300 Lady Luck Dr (55037-6401)
PHONE...............................320 384-7084
Roger Parkin, *Partner*
EMP: 25
SALES (est): 1MM-4.9MM **Privately Held**
WEB: www.grandnational.com
SIC: **7999** Miniature golf course; nonferrous foundry

(G-2487)
MINNESOTA DEPARTMENT OF
Also Called: St Croix State Park
30065 Saint Croix Park Rd (55037-7410)
PHONE...............................320 384-6591
FAX: 320 384-7070
Jack Nelson, *Manager*
EMP: 30

SALES (est): 1MM-4.9MM **Privately Held**
WEB: www.guessmail.com
SIC: **1799** Parking facility equipment maintenance service
DH: Minnesota Department of
500 Lafayette Rd N
Saint Paul MN 55155
651 296-6157

(G-2488)
PATHFINDER VILLAGE ST CROIX
200 Pathfinder Vlg (55037-9485)
PHONE...............................320 384-7726
Ted Kemma, *President*
James L Seward, *Bd of Directors*
EMP: 25 EST: 1975
SALES (est): 1MM-4.9MM **Privately Held**
WEB: www.pathfindervillage.net
SIC: **7033** Recreational vehicle park

HOFFMAN
Grant County

(G-2489)
EVANGELICAL LUTHERAN GOOD
Also Called: Hoffman Care Center
104 6th St S (56339)
PO Box 337 (56339-0337)
PHONE...............................320 986-2048
FAX: 320 986-2564
Randy Wanke, *Pastor*
Tobi Stein, *Human Resources*
William Brewer, *Administrator*
EMP: 60
SALES (est): 1MM-4.9MM **Privately Held**
WEB: www.good-sam.com
SIC: **8051** Skilled nursing care facility
PA: Evangelical Lutheran Good
4800 W 57th St
Sioux Falls SD 57108
605 362-3100

HOKAH
Houston County

(G-2490)
AAA-AMERICAN CO
205 James St (55941)
PHONE...............................507 894-4156
Terry L Padrnos, *Owner*
EMP: 28 EST: 1984
SALES (est): 1MM-4.9MM **Privately Held**
SIC: **7389** 5074 5099 6531 Building inspection service; wholesales fire extinguishers; wholesales plumbing & heating equipment & supplies; real estate appraiser

HOLDINGFORD
Stearns County

(G-2491)
TWO RIVERS ENTERPRISES INC
490 River St W (56340-4519)
PO Box 70 (56340-0070)
PHONE...............................320 746-3156
FAX: 320 746-3158
Robert Warzecha, *President*
Ron Denning, *General Mgr*
Danny Warzecha, *Vice Pres*
Chad Thompson, *Opers Mgr*
Linus Ebnet, *Purchasing*
EMP: 48 EST: 2001
SQ FT: 27,000
SALES (est): 25MM-49.9MM **Privately Held**
SIC: **5051** Wholesales steel

HOLLANDALE
Freeborn County

(G-2492)
HOLLANDALE MARKETING ASSN
26722 825th Ave (56045-4043)
PHONE...............................507 889-3181
FAX: 507 889-3351
Gerald Edwards, *President*
Larry R Reynen, *Corp Secy*
Robert Muilenburg, *Vice Pres*
Berry Hoffman, *Treasurer*
Peter V Verkel V, *Director*
EMP: 25 EST: 1925
SQ FT: 70,000
SALES (est): 10MM-24.9MM **Privately Held**
SIC: **5148** 5191 Wholesales vegetables; wholesales agricultural fertilizer; wholesales agricultural chemicals

HOLLOWAY
Swift County

(G-2493)
WESTERN CONSOLIDATED CO-OP (PA)
101 Rand St (56249-1107)
PO Box 78 (56249-0078)
PHONE...............................320 394-2171
FAX: 320 289-1576
Dean Isaacson, *CEO*
Dean Isaccson, *General Mgr*
Al Connel, *Controller*
Jeff Schmising, *Sales Executive*
Greg Gades, *Manager*
EMP: 50 EST: 1922
SQ FT: 13,000
SALES (corp-wide): 323.68M **Privately Held**
WEB: www.west-con.com
SIC: **5191** 4221 5153 Wholesales feed; manufactures animal feed; wholesales agricultural fertilizer; wholesales agricultural chemicals; wholesale grain elevator; wholesales field, garden & flower seeds; manufactures fertilizers; farm product warehousing & storage service

HOLT
Marshall County

(G-2494)
DAVIDSON CONSTRUCTION INC
65 State St (56738-3000)
PHONE...............................218 449-4865
FAX: 218 449-4866
Ron Davidson, *President*
Patty Davidson, *Corp Secy*
EMP: 40 EST: 1966
SQ FT: 10,000
SALES (est): 1MM-4.9MM **Privately Held**
SIC: **1794** Excavation & grading, building construction contractor

(G-2495)
DAVIDSON READY MIX INC
65 State St (56738-3000)
PHONE...............................218 449-4865
Ronald Davidson, *President*
Kennidy Davidson, *Vice Pres*
Gerald Larson, *Manager*
EMP: 45 EST: 1991
SQ FT: 6,000
SALES (est): 5MM-9.9MM **Privately Held**
SIC: **1611** Concrete road, highway & sidewalk construction

HOPE
Steele County

(G-2496)
SUNRICH INC
3824 SW 93rd St (56046-2010)
PHONE...............................507 451-3316
Kim Jenkins, *Vice Pres*
Rick W Johnson, *Controller*

(PA)=Parent Co (HQ)=Headquarters (DH)=Div Headquarters
✿ = New business established in last 2 years

2011 Harris Minnesota
Services Directory

© Harris InfoSource 1-866-281-6415
117

Kate Leavitt, *Sales Staff*
Laverne Klecker, *Manager*
EMP: 85 **EST:** 1978
SALES (est): 100MM-499.9MM Privately Held
SIC: 5153 5191 Wholesales grains; wholesales agricultural fertilizer; wholesales agricultural chemicals; wholesales feed; wholesales field, garden & flower seeds

(G-2497)
SUNRICH LLC (HQ)
3824 SW 93rd St (56046-2010)
PO Box 128 (56046-0128)
PHONE..............................507 451-4724
Rick Johnson, *Member*
Jeremy Kendall, *Member*
Ken Damerow, *Plant Mgr*
Edd Ihns, *CFO*
Kate Leavitt, *Sales Mgr*
▲ **EMP:** 60 **EST:** 1978
SQ FT: 2,000
SALES (corp-wide): 989.13M Privately Held
SIC: 5153 Manufactures flour & other grain mill products; wholesales grains; soybean processing
PA: Sunopta Food Group LLC
    3915 Minnesota St
    Alexandria MN 56308
    320 763-5977

HOPKINS
Hennepin County

(G-2498)
ABM EQUIPMENT & SUPPLY INC (PA)
333 2nd St NE (55343-8379)
PHONE..............................952 938-5451
Ron Martens, *President*
Jason Herrmann, *Purch Mgr*
Pete Koop, *Purch Agent*
EST: 2006 Privately Held
WEB: www.abm-highway.com
SIC: 5013 5012 5082 Wholesales new motor vehicle parts & supplies; manufactures backhoes, tractors, cranes, plows & similar equipment; wholesales new & used trailers for trucks; wholesales construction & mining machinery; wholesales truck parts & accessories

(G-2499)
ABM EQUIPMENT & SUPPLY LLC
333 2nd St NE (55343-8379)
PHONE..............................952 938-5451
FAX: 952 938-0159
David Gorres, *Member*
Charles Prescott, *Member*
Tom Weber, *Accountant*
Ron Martens, *Mng Member*
Sam Fahey, *Coordinator*
EMP: 48 **EST:** 2005
SQ FT: 50,000
SALES (est): 10MM-24.9MM Privately Held
WEB: www.abm-highway.com
SIC: 5013 5012 5082 Wholesales new motor vehicle parts & supplies; manufactures backhoes, tractors, cranes, plows & similar equipment; wholesales new & used trailers for trucks; wholesales construction & mining machinery; wholesales truck parts & accessories
PA: ABM Equipment & Supply Inc
    333 2nd St NE
    Hopkins MN 55343
    952 938-5451

(G-2500)
ADAPT INC
5610 Rowland Rd Ste 160 (55343-8982)
PHONE..............................952 939-0538
FAX: 952 939-0361
Karen Koch, *President*
Charity Donovan, *Human Res Mgr*
EMP: 50 **EST:** 1983
SQ FT: 11,000
SALES (est): 5MM-9.9MM Privately Held
WEB: www.adaptdata.com
SIC: 8748 7374 Business consulting services; data processing service

(G-2501)
ADVANCED IMAGING SOLUTIONS INC
6121 Baker Rd Ste 110 (55345-5961)
PHONE..............................952 930-1882
FAX: 952 930-1921
Michael Keating, *CEO*
Tim Keating, *Corp Secy*
Mitch Hatch, *Vice Pres*
Joy Keating, *VP Finance*
Darel Gustafson, *Manager*
EMP: 40 **EST:** 1998
SQ FT: 5,200
SALES (est): 10MM-24.9MM Privately Held
SIC: 5044 5065 Wholesales photocopy machines; wholesales facsimile or fax equipment

(G-2502)
ADVANCEMENTS IN ALLERGY
12450 Wayzata Blvd # 215 (55305-1978)
PHONE..............................952 546-6866
Michael Wexler MD, *President*
Dan Tredwell, *Exec VP*
Clay Bergren, *Vice Pres*
Wendy Markgraf, *Office Mgr*
Pamela M Nallan, *Physician Asst*
EMP: 26 **EST:** 1989
SALES (est): 1MM-4.9MM Privately Held
WEB: www.advancementsinallergy.com
SIC: 8011 Clinic operated by physicians

(G-2503)
AFFIANCE FINANCIAL LLC
10275 Wayzata Blvd # 300 (55305-1661)
PHONE..............................952 253-2564
Steven C Finkelstein, *Member*
EMP: 25 **EST:** 1911
SALES (est): 1MM-4.9MM Privately Held
SIC: 8742 Management consulting services

(G-2504)
AHLES & ASSOCIATES LLC
Also Called: Red Light Rescue
1 Hawthorne Rd (55343-8507)
PHONE..............................952 935-8554
Paul Ahles, *CEO*
EMP: 40 **EST:** 1984
SALES (est): 5MM-9.9MM Privately Held
SIC: 7371 Custom computer programming service

(G-2505)
ALL SYSTEMS GO
6031 Culligan Way (55345-5918)
PHONE..............................651 628-0000
Ronald Esau, *Owner*
Dan Sundin, *Manager*
EMP: 50 **EST:** 1993
SALES (est): 5MM-9.9MM Privately Held
WEB: www.allsystemsgo.com
SIC: 7378 Computer & data processing equipment repair & maintenance

(G-2506)
ALLINA HEALTH SYSTEM
715 2nd Ave S (55343-7782)
PHONE..............................952 936-5600
Kristy Vo, *Corp Secy*
Sue Karoff, *Corp Secy*
Mark Wanderman, *Branch Mgr*
Marilee A Hanson MD, *Med Doctor*
Ward J Godsall, *Med Doctor*
EMP: 30
SALES (est): 1MM-4.9MM Privately Held
WEB: www.allina.com
SIC: 8011 Physicians' office & clinic
PA: Allina Health System
    2925 Chicago Ave
    Minneapolis MN 55407
    612 775-5000

(G-2507)
ALLINA SELF-INSURED
5601 Smetana Dr Ste LL (55343-5000)
PHONE..............................952 992-2500
David Strand, *CEO*
Marcia Ehorn, *Publisher*
Barbara Johnson, *Vice Pres*
Jan Liedle, *Administrator*
Stanley W Hamilton, *Officer*
EMP: 87 **EST:** 1983
SALES (est): 10MM-24.9MM Privately Held

WEB: www.allina.com
SIC: 8011 6321 Group health association; direct accident & health insurance carrier
PA: Allina Health System
    2925 Chicago Ave
    Minneapolis MN 55407
    612 775-5000

(G-2508)
AMCOM SOFTWARE INC (PA)
10400 Yellow Circle Dr # 100 (55343-9248)
PHONE..............................952 230-5200
Chris Heim, *President*
Mike Mehr, *Exec VP*
Dave Green, *Vice Pres*
Greg Stinson, *Vice Pres*
Lavonne Engel, *Vice Pres*
EMP: 97 **EST:** 1984
SQ FT: 29,605
SALES (corp-wide): 20M Privately Held
SIC: 7372 Application software publishing

(G-2509)
AMERICAN FISH & SEAFOOD INC
5501 Opportunity Ct (55343-9019)
PHONE..............................952 935-3474
FAX: 952 935-7861
Lowell P Bialick, *President*
Larry Braufman, *Vice Pres*
Robert Fredrickson, *Director*
EMP: 60 **EST:** 1929
SQ FT: 38,000
SALES (est): 50MM-99.9MM Privately Held
SIC: 5142 5144 5146 Wholesales packaged frozen fish; wholesales packaged frozen poultry; wholesales fish & seafood; fresh or frozen fish & seafood processing; wholesales poultry & poultry products

(G-2510)
AMERIPRIDE SERVICES INC (PA)
10801 Wayzata Blvd # 100 (55305-1531)
PHONE..............................952 738-4200
FAX: 952 738-4252
Lawrence G Steiner, *Ch of Bd*
Bruce M Steiner, *President*
Lisa Chopping, *Corp Secy*
Rojean E Rada, *Corp Secy*
Gerald E Johnson, *COO*
▲ **EMP:** 63 **EST:** 1889 Privately Held
WEB: www.ameripride.com
SIC: 7213 7218 Linen supply service; industrial laundry service

(G-2511)
ANDERSON FROEHLING LTD
5720 Green Circle Dr # 101 (55343-9069)
PHONE..............................952 979-3100
FAX: 952 931-0710
Dave Wasmuth, *President*
Daniel Sjoquist, *Partner*
Mark Kammer, *Partner*
Doug Galka, *Partner*
EMP: 38 **EST:** 1946
SALES (est): 1MM-4.9MM Privately Held
SIC: 8721 Certified public accountant services

(G-2512)
AUGUSTANA CHAPEL VIEW HOMES
Also Called: Chapel View Care Ctr Aprtments
615 Minnetonka Mills Rd (55343-7203)
PHONE..............................952 938-2761
FAX: 952 938-4092
Teri Berndt, *Human Res Mgr*
Steve Fritzke, *Administrator*
Mary Roy, *Administrator*
Sean Johnson, *Director*
Lindsey Hart, *Director*
EMP: 180
SALES (est): 5MM-9.9MM Privately Held
WEB: www.augustanacare.org
SIC: 8051 6513 Skilled nursing care facility; operators of retirement hotels
HQ: Augustana Chapel View Homes
    1007 E 14th St
    Minneapolis MN 55404
    612 333-1551

(G-2513)
AVADA AUDIOLOGY & HEARING CARE
1730 Plymouth Rd Ste 301 (55305-1962)
PHONE..............................952 541-1799
James Neve, *President*
EMP: 35 **EST:** 1988
SALES (est): 1MM-4.9MM Privately Held
SIC: 8099 Hearing testing services

(G-2514)
AVANTGARD
601 2nd Ave S (55343-7779)
PHONE..............................952 935-3300
Herb Hesch, *President*
EMP: 30
SALES (est): 1MM-4.9MM Privately Held
WEB: www.sungard.com
SIC: 7371 Computer software development
DH: Avantgard
    23975 Park Sorrento Fl 4
    Calabasas CA 91302
    818 223-2200

(G-2515)
BEAUTY CRAFT SUPPLY & EQPT
11110 Bren Rd W (55343-9016)
PHONE..............................952 935-4420
Maximillion Wexler Jr, *President*
Marianne Wexler, *Corp Secy*
EMP: 50 **EST:** 1946
SQ FT: 17,000
SALES (est): 10MM-24.9MM Privately Held
SIC: 5087 Wholesales barber shop equipment & supplies; wholesales beauty parlor equipment & supplies

(G-2516)
BEHAVIORAL DIMENSIONS INC
415 Blake Rd N Ste 240 (55343-8192)
PHONE..............................952 814-0207
FAX: 952 938-8838
Nancy Schussler, *President*
Nancy Rueckl, *Vice Pres*
EMP: 30 **EST:** 1997
SALES (est): 1MM-4.9MM Privately Held
WEB: www.behavioraldimensions.com
SIC: 8093 Outpatient mental health clinic

(G-2517)
BENNETT MATERIAL HANDLING INC
1009 Hill St (55343-2057)
PHONE..............................952 933-5544
FAX: 952 933-5913
Gregg Bennett, *President*
Cindy Bennett, *Corp Secy*
Bo Bennett, *Vice Pres*
Ron Lee, *Manager*
EMP: 40 **EST:** 1965
SQ FT: 24,000
SALES (est): 10MM-24.9MM Privately Held
SIC: 5084 Wholesales industrial lift trucks & parts; wholesales materials handling equipment

(G-2518)
BEVERLY ENTERPRISES - MN
Also Called: Golden Livingcenter - Hopkins
725 2nd Ave S (55343-7782)
PHONE..............................952 935-3338
FAX: 952 935-0032
John Arena, *Corp Secy*
Mary Hein, *Corp Secy*
Dwight Kouri, *Vice Pres*
David Merrell, *Vice Pres*
Craig Baca, *Accounting Dir*
EMP: 200
SQ FT: 24,000
SALES (est): 5MM-9.9MM Privately Held
WEB: www.beverlynet.com
SIC: 8051 Skilled nursing care facility
HQ: Beverly Enterprises - MN
    650 Ramer Ave S
    Rush City MN 55069
    320 358-4765

(G-2519)
BLUE RIDGE DENTAL
Also Called: Farish, Robert W DDS
11601 Minnetonka Mls D (55305-5161)
PHONE............................952 938-4767
FAX: 952 938-1992
James Strampe, *Partner*
Gregory Kemmitt, *Dentist*
Janis K Lecer DDS, *Dentist*
Janis K Klecker, *Dentist*
EMP: 30 **EST:** 1985
SALES (est): 1MM-4.9MM **Privately Held**
SIC: 8021 Dentists' office & clinic

(G-2520)
BREHMER CONTRACTING INC
10921 Excelsior Blvd (55343-3442)
PHONE............................952 938-1171
Randy Brehmer, *Principal*
EMP: 25 **EST:** 2003
SALES (est): 5MM-9.9MM **Privately Held**
SIC: 1542 Commercial & office building
renovation & repair services

(G-2521)
BUSINESS BANK
11100 Wayzata Blvd # 150 (55305-5530)
PHONE............................952 847-1100
FAX: 952 847-9016
Bradley C Krohn, *Ch of Bd*
Teresa A Tembreull, *President*
Mark Luukkonen, *COO*
Dee Zajicek, *Assistant VP*
Tor Gloppen, *Vice Pres*
EMP: 30 **EST:** 2000
SQ FT: 30,000
SALES (est): 5MM-9.9MM **Privately Held**
WEB: www.thebusinessbankmn.com
SIC: 6022 State commercial bank

(G-2522)
CAPERNAUM PEDIATRIC THERAPY
13924 Lake Street Ext (55345-3017)
PHONE............................952 938-5348
Marciea Mattson, *President*
Bonna Olson, *Vice Pres*
EMP: 40
SALES (est): 1MM-4.9MM **Privately Held**
SIC: 8049 8093 Physical therapist office;
outpatient rehabilitation treatment center

(G-2523)
CAREGIVERS'S NETWORK INC
10709 Wayzata Blvd Ste 300
(55305-1501)
PHONE............................952 935-5581
FAX: 952 935-5920
Kevin O'Malley, *President*
Lorraine O Malley, *Vice Pres*
Rick Ogren, *Administrator*
EMP: 200 **EST:** 1988
SQ FT: 2,000
SALES (est): 5MM-9.9MM **Privately Held**
WEB: www.cgnhomecare.com
SIC: 8082 Home health care services

(G-2524)
CARGILL FINANCIAL SERVICES (PA)
12700 Whitewater Dr (55343-9438)
PHONE............................952 742-7575
Gregory R Page, *President*
David W Macleunan, *Exec VP*
Wendell Spence, *Exec VP*
Christopher Motley, *Manager*
Paul Collings, *Manager*
EMP: 170 **EST:** 1984
SALES (corp-wide): 107.88B **Privately Held**
SIC: 6211 Securities broker & dealer

(G-2525)
CARGILL INC
12800 Whitewater Dr # 300 (55343-9406)
PO Box 5621, Minneapolis (55440-5621)
PHONE............................952 984-8280
FAX: 952 984-8715
Greg Wold, *Vice Pres*
Clarence Niman, *Manager*
Deb D Huss, *Manager*
Emily Blados, *Info Tech Mgr*
Pamela Foerster, *Info Tech Mgr*

EMP: 80
SALES (est): 25MM-49.9MM **Privately Held**
SIC: 5149 Manufactures salt; wholesales
edible salt

(G-2526)
CARGILL INC
9350 Excelsior Blvd (55343-3444)
PHONE............................952 984-3377
Paul Johnson, *Controller*
Lawrence Prine, *Network Analyst*
EMP: 28
SALES (est): 10MM-24.9MM **Privately Held**
SIC: 5051 Wholesales steel

(G-2527)
CHILDREN'S HEALTH CARE INC
6050 Clearwater Dr (55343-9467)
PHONE............................952 930-8600
FAX: 952 930-8650
Shelley Stern, *Office Mgr*
Brook Wheeler, *Manager*
Sara Kaus, *Director*
Jane Price, *Director*
EMP: 42
SALES (est): 5MM-9.9MM **Privately Held**
SIC: 8011 Ambulatory surgical center
PA: Children's Health Care Inc
2525 Chicago Ave
Minneapolis MN 55404
612 813-6100

(G-2528)
CHILDREN'S HEALTH CARE INC
Also Called: Childrens Hsptals Clinics Minn
5950 Clearwater Dr # 500 (55343-8987)
PHONE............................952 930-8630
FAX: 952 930-8640
John Bricklemeyer, *General Mgr*
Brook Wheeler, *Manager*
EMP: 30
SALES (est): 1MM-4.9MM **Privately Held**
SIC: 8093 Outpatient rehabilitation
treatment center
PA: Children's Health Care Inc
2525 Chicago Ave
Minneapolis MN 55404
612 813-6100

(G-2529)
CHOICES FOR CHILDREN INC
1011 1st St S Ste 315 (55343-9478)
PHONE............................952 935-3515
Kathy Hendrickson, *President*
EMP: 70 **EST:** 1992
SALES (est): 1MM-4.9MM **Privately Held**
WEB: www.cfcaccra.org
SIC: 8082 Home health care services

(G-2530)
CHRISTENSEN GROUP INC
11100 Bren Rd W Ste A (55343-6002)
PHONE............................952 653-1000
FAX: 952 653-1000
Bruce A Christensen, *CEO*
Randy Morgan, *Vice Pres*
William Finley, *Vice Pres*
Cal Simmons, *Vice Pres*
Carol Broback, *Bookkeeper*
EMP: 57 **EST:** 1952
SQ FT: 4,200
SALES (est): 5MM-9.9MM **Privately Held**
WEB: www.cg-iri.com
SIC: 6411 Insurance agent

(G-2531)
CITIGROUP DERIVATIVES MARKETS
130 Cheshire Ln Ste 202 (55305-1027)
PHONE............................952 475-5500
FAX: 952 475-5700
Peter Santoro, *President*
Charles Mogilevsky, *CFO*
EMP: 65 **EST:** 2000
SALES (est): 10MM-24.9MM **Publicly Held**
WEB: www.citigroup.com
SIC: 6211 Securities broker & dealer
PA: Citigroup Inc
399 Park Ave
New York NY 10022
212 559-1000

(G-2532)
CLEAN-IT GROUP INC
10225 Yellow Circle Dr (55343-9101)
PHONE............................952 943-1911
Tom Rentoul, *President*
EMP: 103 **EST:** 1988
SALES (est): 1MM-4.9MM **Privately Held**
WEB: www.cleanitgroup.com
SIC: 7349 Building cleaning & maintenance
services

(G-2533)
CONCORD INC
509 2nd Ave S (55343-7780)
PHONE............................952 697-5500
Jeff Northrup, *CEO*
Christopher Davis, *President*
Stuart Nutting, *Vice Pres*
EMP: 100 **EST:** 2003
SALES (est): 10MM-24.9MM **Privately Held**
SIC: 7379 Computer system consulting
services

(G-2534)
CURRY SALES INC
5700 Smetana Dr Ste 200 (55343-9686)
PHONE............................952 351-4200
Stephen A Curry, *President*
Roberta Rand, *Vice Pres*
Robin Krebs, *Vice Pres*
EMP: 28 **EST:** 1981
SALES (est): 25MM-49.9MM **Privately Held**
SIC: 5122 5064 5072 5112 5141 5199
Wholesales pharmaceuticals, drug
proprietaries & sundries; wholesales
hardware; wholesales gifts & novelties;
wholesales electrical appliances;
wholesales general line groceries;
wholesales stationery & office supplies

(G-2535)
D J BAUNE & J A DOSEN PTR
301 Carlson Pkwy Ste 350 (55305-5394)
PHONE............................952 473-2002
FAX: 952 473-2766
J A Dosen, *Partner*
D J Baune, *Partner*
Steve Wagner, *Principal*
Max Hoffman, *CFO*
Diane McDonell, *Marketing Mgr*
EMP: 25 **EST:** 1974
SALES (est): 1MM-4.9MM **Privately Held**
SIC: 8721 Certified public accountant
services

(G-2536)
EAST VIEW INFORMATION SERVICES
10601 Wayzata Blvd (55305-1515)
PHONE............................952 252-1201
Kent Lee, *President*
Vladimir Frangulov, *Vice Pres*
Kelly Benner, *CFO*
Kimberly Bachand, *CFO*
EMP: 25 **EST:** 1989
SALES (est): 5MM-9.9MM **Privately Held**
WEB: www.eastview.com
SIC: 5192 Book publisher; wholesales
books, periodicals & newspapers;
wholesales books

(G-2537)
EBF & ASSOCIATES LP
601 Carlson Pkwy Ste 200 (55305-5207)
PHONE............................952 476-7200
FAX: 952 476-7201
Michael Frey, *Partner*
John Brandenborg, *Partner*
Dave Eisenlord, *Info Tech Mgr*
Laura Oberg, *Executive Asst*
EMP: 50 **EST:** 1988
SQ FT: 25,000
SALES (est): 10MM-24.9MM **Privately Held**
SIC: 6282 Financial investment advice
service

(G-2538)
EMERALD CREST OF MINNETONKA
13401 Lake Street Ext (55305-4905)
PHONE............................952 933-9903
Shelly Nevels, *Exec Dir*
Stacy Jorgenson, *Exec Dir*

Judy Cline, *Director*
Dee Chesser, *Director*
EMP: 175 **EST:** 2002
SALES (est): 5MM-9.9MM **Privately Held**
SIC: 8052 Intermediate care facility

(G-2539)
EMPLOYERS MUTUAL CASUALTY CO
6120 Blue Circle Dr (55343-9109)
PO Box 1252, Minneapolis (55440-1252)
PHONE............................952 938-4646
Jerry K Harlow, *Branch Mgr*
EMP: 40
SALES (est): 10MM-24.9MM **Privately Held**
WEB: www.emcins.com
SIC: 6331 6311 6321 6519 Provides stock
fire, marine & casualty insurance; accident
& health reinsurance carriers; life insurance
carriers; real estate property leasing &
rental
PA: Employers Mutual Casualty Co
717 Mulberry St
Des Moines IA 50309
515 280-2511

(G-2540)
ENVIRONMENTS INC
13600 County Road 62 (55345-5915)
PHONE............................952 933-9981
FAX: 952 933-8691
Roger W Wothe, *CEO*
Mark G Christopher, *President*
Radford Renstrom, *Purch Agent*
Mike Landro, *Engineering*
Jim Goeman, *Marketing Mgr*
EMP: 30 **EST:** 1969
SQ FT: 66,000
SALES (est): 1MM-4.9MM **Privately Held**
WEB: www.environmentsinc.com
SIC: 7389 Manufactures wood store
fixtures; manufactures wooden kitchen
cabinets; interior designing service;
manufactures wood office furniture; millwork

(G-2541)
FARNAM STREET FINANCIAL INC
5850 Opus Pkwy Ste 240 (55343-9687)
PHONE............................952 908-0850
FAX: 952 908-0796
Steven C Morgan, *President*
Diane K Dolinar, *Corp Secy*
Leif E Stoa, *Corp Secy*
Wesley A Olsen, *Vice Pres*
Dale A Olsen, *Vice Pres*
EMP: 25 **EST:** 2000
SQ FT: 150,000
SALES (est): Under 500K **Privately Held**
SIC: 7359 Equipment rental & leasing
services

(G-2542)
FEDEX OFFICE & PRINT SERVICES
13601 Ridgedale Dr (55305-1766)
PHONE............................952 593-1143
FAX: 952 593-1378
Chris Bakeman, *Branch Mgr*
Christoff Eakeman, *Manager*
EMP: 150
SALES (est): 10MM-24.9MM **Publicly Held**
WEB: www.kinkos.com
SIC: 7334 7338 Photocopying & duplicating
services; book binding service; commercial
printing; secretarial & court reporting
services; commercial lithographic printing;
typesetting service
HQ: Fedex Office & Print Services
13155 Noel Rd Ste 1600
Dallas TX 75240
214 550-7000

(G-2543)
FISHEL INFORMATION SYSTEMS INC
Also Called: Creative Business Solutions
10590 Wayzata Blvd (55305-5512)
PHONE............................952 544-1108
Allan Fishel, *President*
Pat Pannek, *Manager*
Emily Grave, *Manager*
John Johnston, *Consultant*
James Green, *Administrator*
EMP: 25

(PA)=Parent Co (HQ)=Headquarters (DH)=Div Headquarters
✿ = New business established in last 2 years

2011 Harris Minnesota
Services Directory

© Harris InfoSource 1-866-281-6415
119

EST: 1986
SQ FT: 6,500
SALES (est): 1MM-4.9MM **Privately Held**
WEB: www.cbsol.com
SIC: 7379 1731 7372 Computer system consulting services; computer installation service; software publisher

(G-2544)
GILLETTE CHILDREN'S SPECIALTY
6060 Clearwater Dr # 100 (55343-9460)
PHONE.............................952 936-0977
FAX: 952 936-0944
Diane Newman, *Office Mgr*
Deborah Quanbeck, *Surgeon*
Kevin R Walker, *Surgeon*
Stephen B Sundberg, *Surgeon*
Robert J Wood, *Surgeon*
EMP: 30
SALES (est): 1MM-4.9MM **Privately Held**
SIC: 8093 Outpatient rehabilitation treatment center
PA: Gillette Children's Specialty
200 University Ave E
Saint Paul MN 55101
651 291-2848

(G-2545)
GLOBAL CAPITAL MANAGEMENT INC
601 Carlson Pkwy Ste 200 (55305-5207)
PHONE.............................952 476-7222
Mike Frye, *CEO*
EMP: 70 **EST:** 1988
SALES (est): 5MM-9.9MM **Privately Held**
SIC: 8741 Management services

(G-2546)
GOLD COUNTRY INC
4777 Shady Oak Rd S (55343-8815)
PHONE.............................952 935-9887
FAX: 952 935-9515
Ronald S Leafblad, *President*
Troy Amundson, *Rsch/Dvlpt Dir*
Lu Schaefer, *Bookkeeper*
Andy Leafbald, *Sales Mgr*
Cody Singsaas, *Info Tech Mgr*
EMP: 42 **EST:** 1979
SQ FT: 20,000
SALES (est): 1MM-4.9MM **Privately Held**
SIC: 7389 Retails sports apparel; promoters of shows & exhibitions

(G-2547)
H C C LIFE INSURANCE CO
11100 Wayzata Blvd # 350 (55305-5556)
PHONE.............................877 843-5743
Kevin Wilson, *Vice Pres*
Tim Kraskey, *VP Mktg*
EMP: 26
SALES (est): 1MM-4.9MM **Publicly Held**
WEB: www.hcclife.com
SIC: 6411 Insurance broker
HQ: H C C Life Insurance Co
225 Townpark Dr NW # 145
Kennesaw GA 30144
770 973-9851

(G-2548)
HANCE DISTRIBUTING INC
1 Loring Rd (55305-4430)
PHONE.............................952 935-6429
Thomas R Hance, *President*
EMP: 50 **EST:** 1974
SQ FT: 20,000
SALES (est): 10MM-24.9MM **Privately Held**
WEB: www.hanceco.com
SIC: 5083 5013 7699 Wholesales lawn machinery & equipment; wholesales automotive supplies & parts; wholesales garden machinery & equipment; lawn mower repair shop

(G-2549)
HAYWORTH PARTNERS LP
601 Carlson Pkwy Ste 200 (55305-5207)
PHONE.............................952 476-7200
John Bradenborg, *Partner*
Michael Frey, *Partner*
Julie Braun, *Controller*
EMP: 48 **EST:** 1989 **Privately Held**
SIC: 6719 Investment holding company

(G-2550)
HEALTH ACTIVATION MANAGEMENT ✪
2000 Plymouth Rd Ste 245 (55305-2373)
PHONE.............................763 398-8888
Patrick Dunleavy, *President*
John Catouch, *Member*
Dave Lindgren, *Member*
EMP: 55 **EST:** 2009
SALES (est): 5MM-9.9MM **Privately Held**
SIC: 8011 Occupational & industrial specialist, physician or surgeon office

(G-2551)
HEALTHPARTNERS INC
14001 Ridgedale Dr Ste 32 (55305-1753)
PHONE.............................952 546-2500
Colette Maurice, *Branch Mgr*
Coleen Johnston, *Manager*
Lynn Parish, *Manager*
EMP: 50
SALES (est): 5MM-9.9MM **Privately Held**
WEB: www.healthpartners.com
SIC: 8011 Medical center
PA: HealthPartners Inc
8170 33rd Ave S
Bloomington MN 55425
952 883-6000

(G-2552)
HOMELINK MORTGAGE CORP
Also Called: Home Link Mortgage
14550 Excelsior Blvd # 205 (55345-5870)
PHONE.............................952 935-1986
Chirs Guetzkow, *President*
Rick Guetzkow, *President*
EMP: 25 **EST:** 1999
SALES (est): 1MM-4.9MM **Privately Held**
SIC: 7389 Financial service

(G-2553)
HOPKINS AMERICAN LEGION POST
Also Called: American Legion Post 320
10 12th Ave S (55343-7510)
PHONE.............................952 933-1881
FAX: 952 345-0497
Carol Maier, *Corp Secy*
Judy Johnson, *Manager*
EMP: 25 **EST:** 1925 **Privately Held**
SIC: 8641 Fraternal association

(G-2554)
HOPKINS EARLY LEARNING CENTER
125 Monroe Ave S (55343-8405)
PHONE.............................952 988-5050
Mitchell White, *Exec Dir*
Ruth Dolan, *Director*
EMP: 35 **EST:** 1981
SQ FT: 6,576
SALES (est): 500-999K **Privately Held**
SIC: 8351 Child day care service

(G-2555)
IBBERSON INC (PA)
828 5th St S (55343-7752)
PHONE.............................952 938-7007
Steve Kimes, *President*
Robert Hullinger, *Accounts Mgr*
Tara Nienaber, *Manager*
EST: 1978
SQ FT: 20,000 **Privately Held**
SIC: 8711 1541 8741 Engineering services; food product manufacturing or packing plant construction; construction management services; industrial building & warehouse construction; building construction engineering services

(G-2556)
INDEPENDENT SCHOOL DISTRICT
Also Called: Glenn Lake Elementary School
4801 Woodridge Rd (55345-3944)
PHONE.............................952 988-5200
FAX: 952 988-5199
Donald White, *Principal*
George Rota, *Technology*
Christie Boeder, *Technology*
EMP: 95
ADMISSIONS: 500 **Privately Held**
WEB: www.ldinfo.com

SIC: 8641 Public elementary school; civic & social organization
PA: Independent School District
1001 Highway 7
Hopkins MN 55305
952 988-4000

(G-2557)
INTERNATIONAL ASSOCIATION OF
16209 Minnetonka Blvd (55345-1306)
PHONE.............................952 933-5972
Ellie Reimeyer, *President*
EMP: 49 **Privately Held**
WEB: www.iaopc.com
SIC: 8641 Civic associations
PA: International Association of
300 W 22nd St
Oak Brook IL 60523
630 571-5466

(G-2558)
INTERSTATE BRANDS CORP
Also Called: Wonderbread Hostess Cake Bky
8090 Excelsior Blvd 103 (55343-3415)
PHONE.............................952 935-3034
David Erno, *Manager*
EMP: 100
SALES (est): 50MM-99.9MM **Privately Held**
SIC: 5149 Wholesales bakery products
PA: Hostess Brands Inc
6031 Connection Dr
Irving TX 75039
972 532-4500

(G-2559)
J D L TECHNOLOGIES INC (HQ)
10900 Red Circle Dr (55343-9106)
PHONE.............................952 946-1810
Thomas J Lapping, *President*
Mollisa Johnson, *Accountant*
Rodger Harbaugh, *Manager*
▲ **EMP:** 28 **EST:** 1990
SQ FT: 11,000
SALES (corp-wide): 109.79M **Publicly Held**
WEB: www.jdltech.com
SIC: 5045 7379 Wholesales computers, peripherals & software; computer system consulting services
PA: Communications Systems Inc
10900 Red Circle Dr
Minnetonka MN 55343
952 996-1674

(G-2560)
J-I-T SERVICES INC
10550 Wayzata Blvd (55305-1523)
PHONE.............................763 545-6991
Jamie Aragon, *President*
EMP: 50 **EST:** 1991
SALES (est): 1MM-4.9MM **Privately Held**
SIC: 7363 Temporary help service

(G-2561)
JACOBS TRADING LLC
8090 Excelsior Blvd (55343-3415)
PHONE.............................763 843-2066
David Engel, *Member*
Irwin L Jacobs, *Member*
Howard Grodnick, *Member*
David A Mahler, *Member*
Scott Armstrong, *Vice Pres*
EMP: 50 **EST:** 1989
SQ FT: 300,000
SALES (est): 10MM-24.9MM **Privately Held**
SIC: 5021 5023 7389 Wholesales furniture; inventory stocking service; wholesales home furnishings

(G-2562)
JEWISH FAMILY & CHILDREN'S SVC (PA)
13100 Wayzata Blvd # 300 (55305-1811)
PHONE.............................952 546-0616
Judy Halper, *Exec Dir*
EMP: 100 **EST:** 1910
SQ FT: 20,000
SALES (corp-wide): 13.33M **Privately Held**
WEB: www.jfcsmpls.org
SIC: 8322 Individual & family social services; family counseling services

(G-2563)
KEOMED INC
11515 K Tel Dr (55343-8845)
PHONE.............................952 933-3940
FAX: 952 933-3375
Gavin Keogh, *President*
Patricia Keogh, *CFO*
▲ **EMP:** 25 **EST:** 1975
SQ FT: 8,500
SALES (est): 10MM-24.9MM **Privately Held**
WEB: www.keomed.com
SIC: 5047 Wholesales medical equipment & supplies

(G-2564)
KEY SALES GROUP INC
11011 Smetana Rd (55343-3925)
PHONE.............................952 979-1531
Ray J Fowler, *President*
Steven Mueller, *Corp Secy*
Michael Myhre, *Vice Pres*
Linda Garbowicz, *Controller*
David E Tucci, *Director*
EMP: 25 **EST:** 1993
SALES (est): 10MM-24.9MM **Privately Held**
WEB: www.key-sales.com
SIC: 5141 Food broker

(G-2565)
KNIGHT FINANCIAL PRODUCTS LLC
130 Cheshire Ln Ste 102 (55305-1052)
PHONE.............................952 249-5500
Colin Smith, *CEO*
Peter A Santoro, *President*
Rob Vanagteren, *Managing Prtnr*
Jeff Applebaum, *Vice Pres*
Justin Muller, *Manager*
EMP: 80 **EST:** 1995
SALES (est): 10MM-24.9MM **Privately Held**
WEB: www.deephavencapital.com
SIC: 6211 6282 6722 Securities broker & dealer; open-ended investment funds management services; financial investment advice service

(G-2566)
KNW GROUP LLC
4350 Baker Rd Ste 250 (55343-8609)
PHONE.............................952 593-0265
Marty L Nanne, *Member*
Peter A Knoll, *Member*
Patrick Williams, *Member*
EMP: 45 **EST:** 1986
SQ FT: 3,500
SALES (est): 5MM-9.9MM **Privately Held**
WEB: www.knwgroup.com
SIC: 6411 Insurance agency & broker

(G-2567)
KUNZ OIL CO
7900 Excelsior Blvd (55343-3423)
PHONE.............................952 352-8600
FAX: 952 352-8699
David C Kunz, *Vice Pres*
Walter M Kunz III, *Vice Pres*
EMP: 90 **EST:** 1888
SQ FT: 135,000
SALES (est): 25MM-49.9MM **Privately Held**
SIC: 5013 5172 Wholesales new motor vehicle parts & supplies; wholesales petroleum products

(G-2568)
LAKE MINNETONKA ORTHODONTICS
11601 Minnetonka Mills Rd (55305-5161)
PHONE.............................952 938-1443
Douglas Jolstad, *Owner*
Stephen R Nelson, *Executive*
EMP: 30 **EST:** 1966
SALES (est): 1MM-4.9MM **Privately Held**
SIC: 8021 Orthodontist

(G-2569)
LECY CONSTRUCTION
15012 Highway 7 (55345-3634)
PHONE.............................952 944-9499
Mark Lecy, *President*
Roy Lecy, *Corp Secy*
Tari Haunty, *Office Mgr*
EMP: 50

www.HarrisInfo.com
120

2011 Harris Minnesota
Services Directory

▲=Import ▼=Export
◆=Import/Export

EST: 1976
SQ FT: 2,500
SALES (est): 10MM-24.9MM **Privately Held**
WEB: www.lecybros.com
SIC: 1521 1531 New single-family home construction service; single-family home speculative builder

(G-2570)
LENEAVE FINANCIAL GROUP
Also Called: New England Financial
301 Carlson Pkwy Ste 300 (55305-5383)
PHONE 952 542-0777
FAX: 952 542-0720
Patrick Thuecks, *Partner*
Frank J Fasano, *Manager*
EMP: 30 **EST:** 1967
SALES (est): 1MM-4.9MM **Privately Held**
SIC: 6411 Insurance agency & broker

(G-2571)
LINCOLN FINANCIAL ADVISORS
5850 Opus Pkwy Ste 200 (55343-9604)
PHONE 952 933-8000
FAX: 952 933-7589
Ryan Haag, *Manager*
Patrick Thuecks, *Manager*
EMP: 25
SALES (est): 1MM-4.9MM **Publicly Held**
WEB: www.lincolnlife.com
SIC: 6411 8742 Life insurance agent; financial management consulting services
HQ: Lincoln National Life Insce
1300 S Clinton St
Fort Wayne IN 46802
260 455-2000

(G-2572)
LMN CONSULTING INC
1600 Hopkins Xrd (55305-2026)
PHONE 612 805-7288
Eric Larson, *President*
Stuart Noun, *Corp Secy*
John Marshall, *Vice Pres*
EMP: 40 **EST:** 2005
SALES (est): 1MM-4.9MM **Privately Held**
SIC: 8748 Business consulting services

(G-2573)
MACDERMID COLORSPAN INC
11311 K Tel Dr (55343-8869)
PHONE 952 944-9457
FAX: 952 936-8277
Greg Bolingbroke, *Senior VP*
Rinnie Dicenzo, *Vice Pres*
Rick Bigauette, *Vice Pres*
Tracy Hirzel, *Engineer*
Gopal Bhargava, *Manager*
▲ **EMP:** 230 **EST:** 1985
SQ FT: 170,000
SALES (est): 25MM-49.9MM **Privately Held**
WEB: www.macdermid.com
SIC: 5045 5085 Manufactures typesetting machines including linotype, monotype & intertype; wholesales industrial supplies; wholesales computers, peripherals & software; manufactures computer peripheral equipment
DH: MacDermid Printing Solutions
5210 Phillip Lee Dr SW
Atlanta GA 30336
404 696-4565

(G-2574)
MANN THEATERS INC
Also Called: Hopkins Cinema Six
1118 Mainstreet (55343-7519)
PHONE 952 931-3191
Eric Maclean, *Manager*
Steve Saurer, *Manager*
EMP: 30
SALES (est): 1MM-4.9MM **Privately Held**
SIC: 7832 Indoor movie theater

(G-2575)
MARIX TECHNOLOGIES INC
12450 Wayzata Blvd # 121 (55305-1926)
PHONE 952 582-9100
Dennis Johnson, *CEO*
Joseph Caldwell, *Chairman*
Glenn Taylor, *COO*
Brian Niebur, *CFO*
Nancy Lee, *Marketing Staff*
EMP: 25

EST: 1999
SQ FT: 10,000
SALES (est): 1MM-4.9MM **Privately Held**
WEB: www.marix.com
SIC: 7371 Computer software development

(G-2576)
MARKETING FOCUS INC
10601 Red Circle Dr (55343-9107)
PHONE 952 939-9880
FAX: 952 939-9855
Wayne Volland, *President*
Noel Daentl, *Manager*
EMP: 30 **EST:** 1978
SQ FT: 5,000
SALES (est): 10MM-24.9MM **Privately Held**
SIC: 5074 5084 Wholesales plumbing & heating equipment & supplies; wholesales industrial machinery & equipment

(G-2577)
MARSHALL-TEICHERT GROUP LTD
10901 Red Circle Dr # 315 (55343-9302)
PHONE 952 942-0564
James Trice, *CEO*
M T Beckman, *President*
James A Miller, *Vice Chairman*
Jim D Nichols, *Vice Chairman*
Frank Davit, *CFO*
EMP: 75 **EST:** 1983
SQ FT: 2,000
SALES (est): 10MM-24.9MM **Privately Held**
WEB: www.mtgl.com
SIC: 8742 Administrative services consultant; productivity improvement consulting services; quality assurance consultant; corporate objectives & policies consultant

(G-2578)
MATRIX ADHESIVES INC
6035 Baker Rd (55345-5908)
PHONE 952 912-2452
Dan Hourner, *President*
EMP: 30
SALES (est): 10MM-24.9MM **Privately Held**
SIC: 5085 Wholesales industrial tape & plasters adhesives

(G-2579)
MCKINLEY GROUP INC
601 Carlson Pkwy Ste 630 (55305-5215)
PHONE 952 476-2107
Tony Sorensen, *President*
Julie Yedoni, *Sales Associate*
Chris Ohlendorf, *Director*
Paul Beard, *Director*
EMP: 50 **EST:** 2003 **Privately Held**
WEB: www.mckinleygroupinc.com
SIC: 7361 Executive placement & search consulting services

(G-2580)
METRIS CO'S INC
10900 Wayzata Blvd Fl 5 (55305-5602)
PHONE 952 358-4000
David D Wesselink, *CEO*
Bill Livingston, *General Mgr*
Chuck Bies, *Corp Secy*
Richard G Evans, *Corp Secy*
David Gibbons, *Sr Exec VP*
▲ **EMP:** 900 **EST:** 1994
SQ FT: 300,000
SALES (est): 100MM-499.9MM **Privately Held**
WEB: www.metriscompanies.com
SIC: 6141 Personal credit institution
DH: Hsbc Finance Corp
26525 N Riverwoods Blvd
Mettawa IL 60045
224 544-2000

(G-2581)
MID COUTRY BANK
14617 Highway 7 (55345-3706)
PHONE 952 931-2200
FAX: 952 931-2206
Larry Flowers, *President*
EMP: 120 **EST:** 1997
SALES (est): 25MM-49.9MM **Privately Held**
SIC: 6211 Securities broker & dealer

(G-2582)
MIDWEST ASPHALT CORP (HQ)
5929 Baker Rd Ste 420 (55345-5940)
PO Box 5477 (55345-2477)
PHONE 952 937-8033
Blair B Bury, *President*
Blair Berry, *Vice Pres*
Dave Blanski, *Plant Mgr*
Tim Douglas, *CFO*
Sharon Bury, *Manager*
EMP: 25 **EST:** 1968
SQ FT: 7,500 **Privately Held**
WEB: www.midwestasphalt.net
SIC: 1611 5032 Highway & street paving contractor; manufactures asphalt & asphalt products; highway & street resurfacing contractor; wholesales limestone; wholesales gravel; wholesales construction sand
PA: Mac Management Inc
5929 Baker Rd Ste 420
Minnetonka MN 55345
952 938-8048

(G-2583)
MIDWEST FAMILY MUTUAL INSCE
10601 Wayzata Blvd (55305-1515)
PO Box 9425, Minneapolis (55440-9425)
PHONE 952 545-6000
FAX: 952 545-7789
Ronald G Boyd, *President*
Richard Habstritt, *Corp Secy*
William A Laidlaw, *Treasurer*
Sabrina M Nelsen, *Accounts Mgr*
Richard S Habtritt, *Manager*
EMP: 63 **EST:** 1891
SQ FT: 24,000
SALES (est): 25MM-49.9MM **Privately Held**
SIC: 6331 Fire, marine & casualty insurance & carriers

(G-2584)
MINNEAPOLIS JEWISH FEDERATION
13100 Wayzata Blvd Ste 200 (55305-1810)
PHONE 952 593-2600
FAX: 952 593-2544
Don Srink, *Finance Dir*
Karen Hoppe, *Finance*
Tammy Cohen, *Human Res Dir*
Bob Tomasik, *IT Specialist*
Josshua Fogelson, *Exec Dir*
EMP: 35 **EST:** 1930
SQ FT: 10,000
SALES (est): 1MM-4.9MM **Privately Held**
WEB: www.mplsfed.org
SIC: 7389 Fundraising services

(G-2585)
N BRUCE CHRISTENSE
11100 Bren Rd W (55343-6001)
PHONE 952 653-1000
Bruce Christensen, *President*
EMP: 60 **EST:** 2004
SALES (est): 5MM-9.9MM **Privately Held**
SIC: 6411 Insurance services

(G-2586)
N C HOLDINGS (PA)
10395 Yellow Circle Dr (55343-9101)
PHONE 952 933-7060
Tom Mackin, *Director*
Nancy Adelmann, *Director*
Jorma Kasslin, *Director*
▲ **EMP:** 26 **EST:** 1995 **Privately Held**
SIC: 5091 Wholesales sporting & recreational goods & supplies; manufactures artificial fishing bait; wholesales fishing tackle; wholesales hunting equipment & supplies

(G-2587)
NAPCO INTERNATIONAL LLC (PA)
11055 Excelsior Blvd (55343)
PHONE 952 931-2400
FAX: 952 931-2402
Joann L Gren, *Member*
Jo A Lind Gren, *Member*
Vince J Battistelli, *Vice Pres*
Reinhild Hinze, *Vice Pres*
Trish Pham, *Opers Mgr*

▲ **EMP:** 33 **EST:** 1917
SQ FT: 67,500 **Privately Held**
WEB: www.napcointl.com
SIC: 5065 5013 Wholesales security control equipment & systems; wholesales communications equipment; wholesales radio parts & accessories; wholesales truck parts & accessories

(G-2588)
NEW UNBANK CO LLC
10550 Wayzata Blvd Ste C (55305-1582)
PHONE 952 544-5155
Stuart Tapper, *Member*
EMP: 80 **EST:** 2004
SALES (est): 25MM-49.9MM **Privately Held**
WEB: www.unbankcompany.com
SIC: 6099 Foreign currency exchange

(G-2589)
NORMARK CORP (HQ)
10395 Yellow Circle Dr (55343-9101)
PHONE 952 933-7060
FAX: 952 933-0046
Tom Mackin, *President*
Gregg Wolmer, *COO*
Jerry Calengor, *Exec VP*
Nancy Adelmann, *Vice Pres*
Robert Brown, *Vice Pres*
▲ **EMP:** 60 **EST:** 1962
SQ FT: 40,000 **Privately Held**
SIC: 5091 Wholesales sporting & recreational goods & supplies; manufactures artificial fishing bait; wholesales fishing tackle; wholesales hunting equipment & supplies
PA: N C Holdings
10395 Yellow Circle Dr
Hopkins MN 55343
952 933-7060

(G-2590)
NORSTAN INC (HQ)
5101 Shady Oak Rd S (55343-4100)
PHONE 952 352-4000
Scott G Christian, *President*
Jeffery Lusenhop, *President*
Neil Sell, *Corp Secy*
Scott McDonald, *Exec VP*
Kevin Paulsen, *Exec VP*
EMP: 195 **EST:** 1960
SQ FT: 165,000
SALES (corp-wide): 961.39M **Publicly Held**
WEB: www.blackbox.com
SIC: 7389 7379 8748 Telephone service; teleconferencing services; telecommunications consulting services; manufactures electronic secretaries; manufactures message concentrators; computer system consulting services; telephone answering service
PA: Black Box Corp
1000 Park Dr
Lawrence PA 15055
724 746-5500

(G-2591)
NORTH AMERICAN MEMBERSHIP GRP (HQ)
12301 Whitewater Dr (55343-9447)
PHONE 952 936-9333
FAX: 952 936-9169
Robert Pittman, *Ch of Bd*
Nancy Evensen, *President*
Dave Maas, *Publisher*
Kelly Gohman, *Publisher*
Del Austin, *Publisher*
▲ **EMP:** 300 **EST:** 1978
SQ FT: 56,000 **Privately Held**
WEB: www.northamericanmediagroup.com
SIC: 7997 Membership recreation club; publishes & prints magazines; retail mail-order fishing, hunting & camping equipment & supplies; membership hunting club
PA: Pilot Group, LP
75 Rockefeller Plz Fl 23
New York NY 10019
212 486-4446

(G-2592)
NUVO NETWORK MANAGEMENT
5400 Opportunity Ct Ste 140 (55343-7399)
PHONE 952 933-4600
FAX: 952 933-9642
Carl Smith, *CFO*

(PA)=Parent Co (HQ)=Headquarters (DH)=Div Headquarters
✪ = New business established in last 2 years

2011 Harris Minnesota
Services Directory

© Harris InfoSource 1-866-281-6415

121

EMP: 100 **EST:** 1996
SQ FT: 5,000
SALES (est): 10MM-24.9MM **Privately Held**
SIC: 7373 6531 Computer system selling service; real estate services; computer systems value-added resellers

(G-2593)
OAK RIDGE COUNTRY CLUB
700 Oak Ridge Rd (55305-4815)
PHONE............................952 935-7721
FAX: 952 935-1717
Wade Miller, *CEO*
David Schwartzman, *Treasurer*
Emily Sparks, *Human Res Mgr*
Adria Herrmann, *Exec Dir*
EMP: 250 **EST:** 1921
SQ FT: 50,000
SALES (est): 10MM-24.9MM **Privately Held**
SIC: 7997 Country club; membership golf club

(G-2594)
OMEGON INC
2000 Hopkins Xrd (55305-2500)
PHONE............................952 541-4738
Barbara Danielson, *Director*
EMP: 40 **EST:** 1975
SALES (est): 1MM-4.9MM **Privately Held**
WEB: www.usinternet.org
SIC: 8093 8322 8361 Outpatient substance abuse clinic; residential care facility; outpatient mental health clinic; individual & family social services

(G-2595)
OPPORTUNITY PARTNERS INC (PA)
5500 Opportunity Ct (55343-9020)
PHONE............................952 938-5511
FAX: 952 930-4279
Jon Thompson, *President*
George Klauser, *Senior VP*
Bruce K Bester, *Vice Pres*
Cathy Kukielka, *Vice Pres*
Tim Vicchiollo, *Vice Pres*
▲ **EMP:** 175 **EST:** 1953
SQ FT: 97,422
SALES (corp-wide): 28.71MM **Privately Held**
SIC: 8331 8361 Job training & vocational rehabilitation services; residential care facility; job training services; vocational training agency; sheltered workshop

(G-2596)
OPUS ARCHITECTS & ENGINEERS
10350 Bren Rd W (55343-9014)
PO Box 59110, Minneapolis (55459-0110)
PHONE............................952 656-4444
John Albers, *President*
Dennis Neu, *COO*
EMP: 120 **EST:** 1990
SQ FT: 20,000
SALES (est): 10MM-24.9MM **Privately Held**
SIC: 8712 Architectural engineers
PA: Opus Corp
      10350 Bren Rd W
      Hopkins MN 55343
      952 656-4444

(G-2597)
OPUS CORP (PA)
10350 Bren Rd W (55343-9014)
PHONE............................952 656-4444
Keith P Bednarowski, *Ch of Bd*
Mark Rauenhorst, *President*
Tom Kennedy, *General Mgr*
Marshall Burton, *Member*
Tammy Karth, *Member*
EMP: 250 **EST:** 1984
SQ FT: 33,000 **Privately Held**
SIC: 1542 6531 6552 Nonresidential building design & construction service; real estate management services; commercial land subdividers & developers

(G-2598)
OPUS NORTHWEST CONSTRUCTION
10350 Bren Rd W (55343-9014)
PHONE............................952 656-4444
Mark Rauenhorst, *CEO*
John Solberg, *President*
Gerald Rauenhorst, *Founder*

John McKenzie, *Senior VP*
Beth Schorle, *Controller*
EMP: 145 **EST:** 1953
SQ FT: 50,000
SALES (est): 25MM-49.9MM **Privately Held**
SIC: 1542 1541 6552 New commercial & office building construction; new industrial building construction; commercial land subdividers & developers
PA: OPUS Northwest LLC
      13920 SE Eastgate Way 25
      Bellevue WA 98005
      425 467-2700

(G-2599)
OPUS PROPERTIES INC
9900 Bren Rd E (55343-9664)
PHONE............................952 656-4444
Gerald Rauenhorst, *Principal*
EMP: 70 **EST:** 1992
SALES (est): 10MM-24.9MM **Privately Held**
SIC: 6798 Real estate investment trust service
PA: Opus Corp
      10350 Bren Rd W
      Hopkins MN 55343
      952 656-4444

(G-2600)
OVATIONS INC (HQ)
9900 Bren Rd E Ste 300W (55343-9693)
PHONE............................952 936-1300
Larry C Renfro, *CEO*
Martha Jones, *Vice Pres*
Lisa Johnson, *Vice Pres*
Mary Kennedy, *Vice Pres*
Jerry Knutson, *CFO*
EMP: 1305 **EST:** 1998
SALES (corp-wide): 87.13B **Publicly Held**
WEB: www.unitedhealthgroup.com
SIC: 6324 Hospital & medical insurance carrier
PA: Unitedhealth Group Inc
      9900 Bren Rd E
      Minnetonka MN 55343
      952 936-1300

(G-2601)
PARAGON MOVING & STORAGE INC
401 11th Ave N (55343-7207)
PHONE............................952 936-9122
FAX: 952 936-9307
Gerald Blair, *President*
Roy Wirth, *Treasurer*
◆ **EMP:** 25 **EST:** 1989
SALES (est): 1MM-4.9MM **Privately Held**
WEB: www.paragonmoving.com
SIC: 4214 4213 Local moving service & storage; long-distance moving services

(G-2602)
PDHC LTD
Also Called: Park Dental
13911 Ridgedale Dr Ste 395 (55305-1770)
PHONE............................952 545-8603
Brent Rundquist, *Manager*
Connie Townsend, *Manager*
EMP: 25
SALES (est): 1MM-4.9MM **Publicly Held**
WEB: www.parkdental.com
SIC: 8021 Dentists' office & clinic
HQ: PDHC Ltd
      6415 Brooklyn Blvd
      Minneapolis MN 55429
      612 338-4546

(G-2603)
PIPELINE SUPPLY INC
620 16th Ave S (55343-7833)
PHONE............................952 935-0445
FAX: 952 935-7666
Steve Singer, *Co-President*
Doug Canter, *Co-President*
Ken Scholl, *Controller*
EMP: 70 **EST:** 1977
SQ FT: 40,000
SALES (est): 25MM-49.9MM **Privately Held**
WEB: www.pipeline-supply.com
SIC: 5074 Wholesales plumbing fittings & supplies; wholesales hydronic heating equipment

(G-2604)
PRECISION DESIGN INC
10501 Wayzata Blvd # 101 (55305-1519)
PHONE............................952 933-6550
FAX: 952 933-0344
Larry Helgerson, *President*
EMP: 25 **EST:** 1972
SQ FT: 350
SALES (est): 1MM-4.9MM **Privately Held**
WEB: www.precisionjobs.com
SIC: 8711 7361 Engineering consulting services; employment agency services

(G-2605)
PRINCIPAL LIFE INSURANCE CO
11100 Wayzata Blvd # 211 (55305-5537)
PHONE............................952 277-4300
FAX: 952 277-4301
Gary Voggesser, *Branch Mgr*
Steve Schroeder, *Manager*
EMP: 30
SALES (est): 25MM-49.9MM **Privately Held**
WEB: www.ccmaui.net
SIC: 6311 Life insurance carrier
HQ: Principal Life Insurance Co
      711 High St
      Des Moines IA 50392
      515 247-5111

(G-2606)
PROTIVITI INC
601 Carlson Pkwy Ste 1120 (55305-5220)
PHONE............................952 249-2200
Miron Marcotte, *Director*
EMP: 25
SALES (est): 1MM-4.9MM **Publicly Held**
WEB: www.rhii.com
SIC: 8742 Management consulting services
HQ: Protiviti Inc
      2884 Sand Hill Rd Ste 200
      Menlo Park CA 94025
      650 234-6000

(G-2607)
PROVIDERS CHOICE INC
10901 Red Circle Dr Ste 100 (55343-9300)
PHONE............................952 944-7010
Gail Birch, *CEO*
Don Deters, *Systems Admin*
EMP: 56 **EST:** 1984
SQ FT: 10,000
SALES (est): 1MM-4.9MM **Privately Held**
WEB: www.providerschoice.com
SIC: 8322 Individual & family social services

(G-2608)
PUMP & METER SERVICE INC
11303 Excelsior Blvd (55343-7463)
PHONE............................952 933-4800
FAX: 952 939-0418
Joe Radermacher, *President*
Carol Youmans, *Corp Secy*
Ron Komif, *Vice Pres*
Mike Eicher, *Vice Pres*
Tom Radermacher, *Treasurer*
EMP: 46 **EST:** 1930
SQ FT: 23,000
SALES (est): 1MM-4.9MM **Privately Held**
WEB: www.pump-meter.com
SIC: 1799 1542 1796 5087 Service station equipment installation, maintenance & repair contractor; commercial & institutional building construction; building equipment & machinery installation contractor; wholesales service establishment equipment & supplies

(G-2609)
RADCLIFFE SYSTEMS
11900 Wayzata Blvd # 209 (55305-2053)
PHONE............................952 545-2409
FAX: 952 545-2412
Fred Radcliffe, *Administrator*
EMP: 35 **EST:** 1994
SQ FT: 950
SALES (est): 1MM-4.9MM **Privately Held**
SIC: 8748 Systems analysis & engineering consultant

(G-2610)
RBC WEALTH MANAGMENT
601 Carlson Pkwy Ste 500 (55305-5214)
PHONE............................763 476-3700
Kathryn J Hoy, *Opers Mgr*
Kevin Ketelsinger, *Manager*
Eric Thompson, *Manager*
EMP: 32
SALES (est): 5MM-9.9MM **Privately Held**
WEB: www.hough.com
SIC: 6211 Security broker & dealer service; investment banking service
PA: Rbc Wealth Management
      60 S 6th St Ste 700
      Minneapolis MN 55402
      612 371-7750

(G-2611)
RCC LIQUIDATING CORP
13185 Ridgedale Dr (55305-1853)
PHONE............................763 546-3771
FAX: 763 591-9969
Suzanne Hudek, *Manager*
EMP: 30
SALES (est): 1MM-4.9MM **Privately Held**
SIC: 7384 Retails cameras; retails video cameras & accessories; retails photographic supplies; film processing & finishing laboratory

(G-2612)
RCM TECHNOLOGIES INC
Also Called: Programming Alternative of NM
11100 Wayzata Blvd Ste 530 (55305-5519)
PHONE............................952 841-1188
FAX: 952 229-9400
Roxane M Gowen, *Branch Mgr*
EMP: 30
SALES (est): 1MM-4.9MM **Publicly Held**
WEB: www.rcmt.com
SIC: 8742 7379 Management consulting services; computer system consulting services
PA: RCM Technologies Inc
      2500 McClellan Ave # 350
      Pennsauken NJ 08109
      856 356-4500

(G-2613)
RELS LLC
5700 Smetana Dr Ste 400 (55343-9686)
PHONE............................952 933-8804
FAX: 952 933-3944
Joel Robertson, *Finance Mgr*
EMP: 950 **EST:** 1998
SALES (est): 50MM-99.9MM **Privately Held**
WEB: www.rels.com
SIC: 6531 7323 Real estate appraiser; commercial credit reporting bureau

(G-2614)
RELS TITLE SERVICES LLC (PA)
Also Called: ATI Title Co
5700 Smetana Dr Ste 400 (55343-9686)
PHONE............................952 933-8804
Wells Fargo Home Mort, *Member*
Curt Watson, *Vice Pres*
Jason Antes, *IT/INT Sup*
Joel Robertson, *Planning*
EMP: 67 **EST:** 1999 **Privately Held**
SIC: 6361 6411 6541 Title insurance carrier; title insurance agent; title search company

(G-2615)
RENTAL RESEARCH SERVICES INC
11300 Minnetonka Mills Rd C (55305-5108)
PHONE............................952 935-5700
FAX: 952 935-9212
Lee Mikkelson, *President*
Lee P Mikkelson Cls, *President*
Rick Hughley, *General Mgr*
Laura Larson, *Vice Pres*
Nancy Hollis, *VP Sls/Mktg*
EMP: 30 **EST:** 1970
SALES (est): 1MM-4.9MM **Privately Held**
WEB: www.rentalresearch.com
SIC: 7323 Consumer credit reporting bureau

www.HarrisInfo.com
122

2011 Harris Minnesota
Services Directory

▲=Import ▼=Export
◆=Import/Export

(G-2616)
RESIDENTIAL MORTGAGE GROUP INC
Also Called: R M G
11100 Wayzata Blvd # 570 (55305-5534)
PHONE 952 593-1169
Steven M Sherwood, *President*
Kimberly L Onnen, *Corp Secy*
Sunny Nelson, *Vice Pres*
Mike Willis, *Controller*
Daniel Lieberthal, *Manager*
EMP: 34 **EST:** 1995
SQ FT: 6,000
SALES (est): 1MM-4.9MM **Privately Held**
WEB: www.rmgmn.com
SIC: 6163 Mortgage brokers service arranging for loans, using money of others

(G-2617)
RIGHT STAFF INC
12450 Wayzata Blvd (55305-1978)
PO Box 27190, Minneapolis (55427-0190)
PHONE 952 546-1100
Ted Chalupsky, *President*
EMP: 25 **EST:** 2002
SALES (est): 500-999K **Privately Held**
SIC: 7363 Help supply services

(G-2618)
RIVER'S END HOLDINGS LLC (PA)
Also Called: Trimark Sportswear Group
415 11th Ave S (55343-7843)
PHONE 952 912-2543
Richard Ward, *Member*
Micheal Frey, *Member*
John Black, *CFO*
Gigi Trende, *CFO*
▲ **EST:** 2004 **Privately Held**
SIC: 5137 5136 Wholesales women's & children's clothing; wholesales men's & boys' sportswear; wholesales women's & girls' sportswear; wholesales men's & boys' hats, scarves & gloves; wholesales men's & boys' shirts; wholesales women's & children's outerwear

(G-2619)
RIVERS END TRADING CO
415 11th Ave S (55343-7843)
PHONE 952 912-2500
Derrick Mline, *President*
John Black, *CFO*
Susan Lola, *Manager*
Heidi Forsythe, *Exec Dir*
▲ **EMP:** 100 **EST:** 1977
SQ FT: 75,000
SALES (est): 50MM-99.9MM **Privately Held**
WEB: www.trimarksportswear.com
SIC: 5136 5137 Wholesales men's & boys' shirts; wholesales men's & boys' sportswear; wholesales women's & girls' sportswear; wholesales men's & boys' caps; wholesales men's & boys' outerwear; wholesales women's & children's outerwear; wholesales caps & gowns

(G-2620)
RLK INC
6110 Blue Circle Dr Ste 100 (55343-9123)
PHONE 952 933-0972
FAX: 952 434-8007
John Dietriech, *Ch of Bd*
Charles R Poppler, *President*
John P Jamnick, *COO*
Brian Mitch, *CFO*
Brian Muench, *CFO*
EMP: 50 **EST:** 1991
SQ FT: 7,000
SALES (est): 5MM-9.9MM **Privately Held**
WEB: www.rlkinc.com
SIC: 8711 Civil engineering services

(G-2621)
ROBERT A SCHNEIDER AGENCY INC
5620 Smetana Dr Ste 225 (55343-8500)
PHONE 952 938-0655
FAX: 952 938-5187
Robert A Schneider, *President*
Sue Benson, *Vice Pres*
Sally Schneider, *Treasurer*
EMP: 25

EST: 1974
SQ FT: 4,000
SALES (est): 1MM-4.9MM **Publicly Held**
WEB: www.rasinc.com
SIC: 6411 Insurance broker
HQ: Risk Placement Services Inc
2 Pierce Pl Ste 100
Itasca IL 60143
630 773-3800

(G-2622)
ROYAL FOODS INC
8098 Excelsior Blvd (55343-3415)
PHONE 952 936-0336
William Ferrell, *President*
Mary Ferrell, *Vice Pres*
David Beyenhof, *CIO*
EMP: 45 **EST:** 1985
SQ FT: 20,000
SALES (est): 25MM-49.9MM **Privately Held**
SIC: 5142 5147 5149 Wholesales frozen fish, meat & poultry; wholesales fresh meat; wholesales specialty food items

(G-2623)
RUBBLE STONE CO INC
6001 Culligan Way (55345-5918)
PHONE 952 938-2599
FAX: 952 938-8045
Lila Tully, *CEO*
Skip Mathews, *Vice Pres*
Sue Clapsaddle, *Accountant*
▲ **EMP:** 49 **EST:** 1928
SQ FT: 35,000
SALES (est): 10MM-24.9MM **Privately Held**
WEB: www.rubbletile.com
SIC: 5032 Wholesale ceramic floor & wall tiles; wholesales granite building stone; wholesales marble building stone

(G-2624)
RUDY HOPKINS LUTHER'S MOTORS
250 5th Ave S (55343-7766)
PHONE 952 938-1717
FAX: 952 938-3320
David Luther, *President*
Kyle Allison, *General Mgr*
EMP: 104 **EST:** 1977
SALES (est): 5MM-9.9MM **Privately Held**
WEB: www.hopkinshonda.com
SIC: 7532 7538 Automotive body shop; general automotive repair services; retails new & used automobiles

(G-2625)
SAKADA
15306 Highway 7 Ste 100 (55345-3564)
PHONE 952 938-9400
Sandy Ross, *Principal*
EMP: 30 **EST:** 2003
SALES (est): 500-999K **Privately Held**
WEB: www.sakada.com
SIC: 7231 Beauty salon

(G-2626)
SANDMAN MOTELS LLC
Also Called: Comfort Inn
6110 Blue Circle Dr Ste 237 (55343-9132)
PHONE 952 932-9987
Greg Timm, *Mng Member*
EMP: 25 **EST:** 1998
SQ FT: 50,000
SALES (est): 1MM-4.9MM **Privately Held**
WEB: www.sandmanmotels.com
SIC: 7011 Traveler accommodations

(G-2627)
SCENIC HEIGHTS PTA
5650 Scenic Heights Dr (55345-5235)
PHONE 952 401-5400
Linda Crisman, *Principal*
EMP: 85 **EST:** 2001 **Privately Held**
SIC: 8641 Parent teacher association

(G-2628)
SECURITY AMERICAN FINANCIAL (PA)
Also Called: SAFE
10901 Red Circle Dr Fl 4 (55343-9304)
PHONE 952 544-2121
Gil C Rohde Jr, *President*
Bryan Anderson, *Corp Secy*
Kevin Stangler, *CFO*

William Neal, *Treasurer*
Ted Williams, *Manager*
EMP: 30 **EST:** 1972
SQ FT: 22,000 **Privately Held**
WEB: www.securitylifeinsurance.com
SIC: 6311 6321 Life insurance carrier; health insurance carrier service

(G-2629)
SECURITY LIFE INSURANCE CO OF
10901 Red Circle Dr # 400 (55343-9305)
PHONE 952 544-2121
Gil C Rohde Jr, *President*
Orem O Robbins, *Co-COB*
J S Beckman, *Co-COB*
Stuart L Sorensen, *Corp Secy*
Charles Carlson, *Vice Pres*
EMP: 65 **EST:** 1956
SQ FT: 70,000
SALES (est): 50MM-99.9MM **Privately Held**
WEB: www.securitylife.com
SIC: 6311 6321 Life insurance carrier; health insurance carrier service
PA: Security American Financial
10901 Red Circle Dr Fl 4
Hopkins MN 55343
952 544-2121

(G-2630)
SENIOR EPOCH LIVING INC
500 Carlson Pkwy (55305-5304)
PHONE 952 473-3330
FAX: 952 473-7555
Donna Flaata, *Exec Dir*
EMP: 50
SALES (est): 1MM-4.9MM **Privately Held**
SIC: 8059 8051 Nursing home; skilled nursing care facility
PA: Epoch SL III Inc
51 Sawyer Rd Ste 500
Waltham MA 02453
781 891-0777

(G-2631)
SENIOR HOME LIVING MN LLC
Also Called: Visiting Angels
175 Jackson Ave N Ste 429 (55343-8599)
PHONE 952 935-0789
Rochelle Landy, *Member*
Paul Zaslasky, *Member*
EMP: 60 **EST:** 2003
SALES (est): 1MM-4.9MM **Privately Held**
SIC: 8082 Home health care services

(G-2632)
SHORT-ELLIOTT-HENDRICKSON INC
Also Called: S E H
10901 Red Circle Dr # 200 (55343-9301)
PHONE 952 912-2600
FAX: 952 931-1188
Dave Halter, *Manager*
EMP: 43
SALES (est): 5MM-9.9MM **Privately Held**
WEB: www.sehinc.com
SIC: 8711 Engineering consulting services
PA: Short-Elliott-Hendrickson Inc
3535 Vadnais Center Dr # 200
Saint Paul MN 55110
651 490-2000

(G-2633)
SIGNATURE BANK
9800 Bren Rd E Ste 200 (55343-6400)
PHONE 952 936-7800
Ken Brooks, *Principal*
Privately Held
SIC: 6022 State commercial bank

(G-2634)
SILLIKER INC
11585 K Tel Dr (55343-8845)
PHONE 952 932-2800
FAX: 952 932-0764
Bob Colvin, *Vice Pres*
Keith Ainsworth, *Manager*
Keuth Ainswoch, *Director*
EMP: 35
SALES (est): 1MM-4.9MM **Privately Held**

SIC: 8071 Biological laboratory
PA: Silliker Inc
111 E Wacker Dr Ste 2300
Chicago IL 60601
312 938-5151

(G-2635)
SOUTH LAKE PEDIATRICS (PA)
17705 Hutchins Dr Ste 101 (55345-4102)
PHONE 952 401-8300
Dale F Dobrin MD, *President*
David L Estrin MD, *Vice Pres*
Barbara J Richie, *Manager*
Heidi Northrup, *Administrator*
John R Paulson, *Pediatrics*
EMP: 40 **EST:** 1970 **Privately Held**
SIC: 8011 Pediatrician office

(G-2636)
ST DAVID'S CENTER CHILD
3395 Plymouth Rd (55305-3765)
PHONE 952 939-0396
Debbie King, *CFO*
Julie Sjordal, *Exec Dir*
Kathy Riley, *Admin Asst*
EMP: 300 **EST:** 1961
SALES (est): 5MM-9.9MM **Privately Held**
WEB: www.stdavids.net
SIC: 8351 8322 Preschool center; group day care center; individual & family social services

(G-2637)
ST THERESE SOUTH WEST INC
1011 Feltl Ct Apt 905 (55343-3912)
PHONE 952 933-3333
FAX: 952 933-8776
Jill Knokleby, *Administrator*
EMP: 25 **EST:** 1985
SQ FT: 300,000
SALES (est): 1MM-4.9MM **Privately Held**
WEB: www.stthreresesouthwest.com
SIC: 6513 Apartment building operator

(G-2638)
SUDHKO INC
13911 Ridgedale Dr Ste 300 (55305-1743)
PHONE 952 595-8500
FAX: 952 595-0050
Suseela Kodali, *President*
Dharma Kodali, *Vice Pres*
Julie Brunzo, *Manager*
EMP: 40 **EST:** 1993
SALES (est): 5MM-9.9MM **Privately Held**
WEB: www.sdksoft.com
SIC: 7371 Custom computer programming service

(G-2639)
SUNGARD FINANCIAL SYSTEMS LLC
601 2nd Ave S (55343-7779)
PHONE 952 935-3300
FAX: 952 936-8888
Herb Hesch, *President*
Gerard Murphy, *Member*
Lawrence Gross, *Corp Secy*
Jason Snyder, *Engineering*
Rich Warfield, *Treasurer*
EMP: 290 **EST:** 1968
SQ FT: 45,000
SALES (est): 25MM-49.9MM **Privately Held**
WEB: www.sungard.com
SIC: 7374 7372 Data processing service; business & professional software publishers
DH: Sungard Eprocess Intelligence
680 E Swedesford Rd
Wayne PA 19087
484 582-2000

(G-2640)
SUPERVALU INC
101 Jefferson Ave S (55343-8412)
PO Box 1451, Minneapolis (55440-1451)
PHONE 952 932-4300
John B Ferris, *Treasurer*
Len Slade, *Marketing Staff*
Janelle Haugarth, *Manager*
Michael W Wright, *Director*
EMP: 113
SALES (est): 100MM-499.9MM **Publicly Held**
WEB: www.supervalu.com

SIC: 5141 5149 Wholesales general line
groceries; wholesales groceries
PA: SUPERVALU Inc
　　11840 Valley View Rd
　　Eden Prairie MN 55344
　　952 828-4000

(G-2641)
T S P ONE INC
18707 Excelsior Blvd (55345-3122)
PHONE.................................952 474-3291
FAX: 952 474-3928
Richard Gustaf, *President*
Bert Haglund, *Vice Pres*
Rick Wessling, *Vice Pres*
Sarah Suker, *Administrator*
Karen Bufton, *Management*
EMP: 25 EST: 1971
SQ FT: 8,700
SALES (est): 1MM-4.9MM Privately Held
SIC: 8712 Architectural service

(G-2642)
TCF EQUIPMENT FINANCE INC
11100 Wayzata Blvd # 801 (55305-5525)
PHONE.................................952 934-4404
FAX: 952 656-3274
Bill Henak, *General Mgr*
Wladimir Dmitrenko, *Corp Secy*
Joseph T Green, *Corp Secy*
Bradley C Gunstad, *Corp Secy*
Walter Dzielsky, *Senior VP*
EMP: 30
SALES (est): 5MM-9.9MM Publicly Held
WEB: www.merrilliron.com
SIC: 6035 Federally chartered savings
institution
DH: TCF Equipment Finance Inc
　　801 Marquette Ave
　　Minneapolis MN 55402
　　952 656-5080

(G-2643)
TCF NATIONAL BANK
1801 Plymouth Rd (55305-1963)
PHONE.................................763 546-5637
Jeremy Lee, *Manager*
EMP: 25
SALES (est): 5MM-9.9MM Publicly Held
WEB: www.merrilliron.com
SIC: 6035 Federal savings bank
HQ: TCF National Bank
　　801 Marquette Ave
　　Minneapolis MN 55402
　　612 661-6500

(G-2644)
TEN DOLLAR TROPHY LLC ✪
810 1st St S 115 (55343-7676)
PHONE.................................952 912-9972
EMP: 50 EST: 2009
SALES (est): 10MM-24.9MM Privately Held
SIC: 7812 Television film production service

(G-2645)
THOMPSON PLUMBING CO INC
15001 Minnetonka Industrial Rd
(55345-2110)
PHONE.................................952 933-7717
FAX: 952 933-8949
Keith Gause, *President*
EMP: 35 EST: 1964
SQ FT: 10,000
SALES (est): 1MM-4.9MM Privately Held
SIC: 1711 Plumbing service

(G-2646)
TIDY SERVICE OF MINNESOTA INC
4301 Blenheim Cir (55345-2704)
PHONE.................................612 332-5461
Son H Choi, *President*
Susan Yoo, *Manager*
EMP: 50 EST: 1990
SQ FT: 800
SALES (est): 1MM-4.9MM Privately Held
SIC: 7349 Building maintenance service;
janitorial & custodial services

(G-2647)
TRISSENTIAL
301 Carlson Pkwy Ste 303 (55305-5383)
PHONE.................................952 595-7970
Michael Vinje, *Owner*

David Williams, *Principal*
Keith Korsi, *Co-Owner*
EMP: 80 EST: 1
SALES (est): 10MM-24.9MM Privately Held
SIC: 8742 Business management
consultant

(G-2648)
TRUGREEN LP
Also Called: Tru Green-Chemlawn
6010 Culligan Way (55345-5917)
PO Box 1440, Minnetonka (55345-0440)
PHONE.................................952 933-7360
FAX: 952 933-3910
Scott Gross, *Sales Mgr*
Vanessa Gilbertson, *Office Mgr*
Kent Smith, *Manager*
EMP: 75 Privately Held
WEB: www.trugreen.com
SIC: 0782 Lawn care services
DH: Trugreen LP
　　860 Ridge Lake Blvd Ste G02
　　Memphis TN 38120
　　901 681-1800

(G-2649)
TUTTLE'S BOWLING BAR & GRILL
107 Shady Oak Rd S (55343-3202)
PHONE.................................952 938-4090
Tim Tuttle, *President*
Mike Tuttle, *Vice Pres*
Steven Meads, *CIO*
EMP: 45 EST: 2001
SALES (est): 1MM-4.9MM Privately Held
WEB: www.tuttlesbowling.com
SIC: 7933 Bowling center

(G-2650)
TW TELECOM INC
5480 Feltl Rd (55343-7982)
PHONE.................................952 351-2300
FAX: 952 351-2317
Gary Doty, *Vice Pres*
Daren Kalum, *Accounts Mgr*
Steve Hatcher, *Manager*
Tony O'Brien, *Director*
Anthony Capers, *Representative*
EMP: 32 Publicly Held
WEB: www.twtelecom.com
SIC: 4813 Wired telecommunications carrier
& service
PA: TW Telecom Inc
　　10475 Park Meadows Dr Ste 300
　　Littleton CO 80124
　　303 566-1000

(G-2651)
UNITEDHEALTH GROUP INC
Also Called: Specialized Care Services
9900 Bren Rd E Ste 300W (55343-9693)
PHONE.................................952 936-1300
Juanita B Luis, *Corp Secy*
Timothy F Ryan, *Corp Secy*
Thomas Sullivan, *COO*
Mike Mikan, *Exec VP*
William Munsell, *Exec VP*
EMP: 600
SALES (est): 25MM-49.9MM Publicly Held
WEB: www.unitedhealthgroup.com
SIC: 8069 Specialty hospital
PA: Unitedhealth Group Inc
　　9900 Bren Rd E
　　Minnetonka MN 55343
　　952 936-1300

(G-2652)
VISION FINANCIAL & HOME MTGE
509 2nd Ave S (55343-7780)
PHONE.................................952 224-3370
Zack Dyab, *President*
Julia Rozhansky, *CFO*
Ric Carpenter, *Sales Mgr*
Shelly Pates, *Manager*
EMP: 25 EST: 2004
SQ FT: 25,000
SALES (est): 1MM-4.9MM Privately Held
SIC: 6162 Mortgage banking service

(G-2653)
VISUAL PACKAGING CORP
11121 Excelsior Blvd (55343-3434)
PHONE.................................952 938-1575
Dale Thornby, *Principal*

EMP: 25 EST: 2003 Privately Held
WEB: www.visualpkg.com
SIC: 4783 Packing & crating service

(G-2654)
VOSON PLUMBING INC
1515 5th St S Ste A (55343-7816)
PHONE.................................952 938-3143
FAX: 952 938-8910
Don Voss, *President*
Carl Voss, *VP Purch*
Steve Voss, *Treasurer*
EMP: 30 EST: 1991
SALES (est): 1MM-4.9MM Privately Held
WEB: www.vosonplumbing.com
SIC: 1711 1623 Plumbing service; water &
sewer line construction

(G-2655)
W L HALL CO
530 15th Ave S (55343-7834)
PHONE.................................952 937-8400
FAX: 952 937-9126
W L Hall Jr, *President*
Pete Weum, *Vice Pres*
Ronald Weber, *Vice Pres*
Mark Maddox, *Vice Pres*
Dave Brellenthin, *Vice Pres*
EMP: 45 EST: 1948
SQ FT: 9,000
SALES (est): 25MM-49.9MM Privately Held
WEB: www.wlhall.com
SIC: 5031 Wholesales doors & windows;
wholesales Doors, sliding; wholesales
windows

(G-2656)
W2005 NEW CENTURY HOTEL
Also Called: Hampton Inn
10420 Wayzata Blvd (55305-1509)
PHONE.................................763 541-1094
FAX: 763 541-1905
Brian Fannemel, *General Mgr*
Lisa Boushele, *General Mgr*
Paula Verhunce, *Sales Staff*
Ingrid Tverberg, *Office Mgr*
Howard Anderson, *Manager*
EMP: 30
SALES (est): 1MM-4.9MM Privately Held
SIC: 7011 Traveler accommodations

(G-2657)
WALGREEN CO
Also Called: Walgreens
540 Blake Rd N (55343-8123)
PHONE.................................952 938-1168
Steve Oak, *Manager*
Steve Roudabush, *Manager*
EMP: 30
SALES (est): 1MM-4.9MM Publicly Held
WEB: www.walgreens.com
SIC: 5122 7384 Drug store; wholesales
druggists' sundries; photofinishing
laboratory
PA: Walgreen Co
　　200 Wilmot Rd
　　Deerfield IL 60015
　　847 914-2500

(G-2658)
WARECORP
3611 Farmington Rd (55305-4128)
PHONE.................................952 938-5448
Michael Milkovich, *Partner*
EMP: 70 EST: 2005
SALES (est): 5MM-9.9MM Privately Held
WEB: www.warecorp.com
SIC: 7371 Computer programming service

(G-2659)
WEIDT GROUP INC
5800 Baker Rd Ste 100 (55345-5965)
PHONE.................................952 938-1588
FAX: 952 938-1480
Tom M Dougall, *President*
Leo Steidel, *Vice Pres*
Jay Johnson, *Vice Pres*
Dawn Womack, *Accountant*
Joseph Jolton, *Manager*
EMP: 50 EST: 1977
SQ FT: 8,000
SALES (est): 5MM-9.9MM Privately Held
WEB: www.twgi.com
SIC: 7371 8712 8748 Computer software
development; architectural service; energy
conservation consultant

(G-2660)
**WUNDERLICH-MALEC
ENGINEERING (PA)**
5501 Feltl Rd (55343-3944)
PHONE.................................952 933-3222
FAX: 952 933-0608
Neal K Wunderlich, *President*
Walter Malec, *Vice Pres*
Ryan Skara, *Purchasing*
Deborah A Wunderlich, *Treasurer*
Terri Foss, *Human Res Mgr*
EMP: 61 EST: 1981
SQ FT: 21,320
SALES (corp-wide): 34.19M Privately Held
SIC: 8711 Engineering consulting services

HOUSTON
Houston County

(G-2661)
ACE COMMUNICATIONS GROUP
207 E Cedar St (55943-8713)
PO Box 360 (55943-0360)
PHONE.................................507 896-3111
FAX: 507 896-4695
David Freeman, *CEO*
Robert Bulman, *Corp Secy*
Keith Vonderohe, *Purch Agent*
Terry Oesterle, *Treasurer*
Cynthia Sweet, *Controller*
EMP: 80 EST: 1993
SQ FT: 50,880 Privately Held
WEB: www.messiah-lutheran.com
SIC: 4813 Wired telecommunications carrier
& service

(G-2662)
B L E A INC
Also Called: Houston County Group Home
105 W Elm St (55943)
PO Box 245 (55943-0245)
PHONE.................................507 896-3040
FAX: 507 724-2495
Dorothy Duellman, *Director*
EMP: 25
SALES (est): 500-999K Privately Held
SIC: 8059 8361 Home for the mentally
retarded; residential care facility
PA: B L E A Inc
　　216 E South St
　　Caledonia MN 55921
　　507 725-2486

(G-2663)
VALLEY HIGH GOLF CLUB
9203 Mound Prairie Dr (55943-7214)
PHONE.................................507 896-3239
FAX: 507 896-0009
Jack Edwards, *Owner*
Suzzanne Schiebel, *Manager*
Bob Isbell, *Manager*
Dave Bruha, *Manager*
EMP: 40 EST: 1999
SALES (est): 1MM-4.9MM Privately Held
SIC: 7997 Membership golf club

(G-2664)
VALLEY VIEW NURSING HOME OF
510 E Cedar St (55943-8618)
PHONE.................................507 896-3125
FAX: 507 896-3289
Chris Schulz, *Exec Dir*
Tom Lindh, *Director*
EMP: 80 EST: 1967
SQ FT: 26,000
SALES (est): 1MM-4.9MM Privately Held
WEB: www.valleyviewhoustonmn.org
SIC: 8051 Skilled nursing care facility

HOWARD LAKE
Wright County

(G-2665)
ARGENBRIGHT INC
401 13th Ave (55349-9409)
PO Box 707 (55349-0707)
PHONE.................................320 543-3737
FAX: 320 543-3228

Dennis Duval, *General Mgr*
Michael Barga, *Vice Pres*
Arlene Asfeld, *Human Resources*
Ann Vaniest, *MIS Mgr*
EMP: 150
SALES (est): 10MM-24.9MM **Privately Held**
SIC: 7389 7331 Sign lettering & painting services; direct mail advertising service
PA: Argenbright Inc
7600 69th Ave
Rockford MN 55373
763 477-7600

(G-2666)
DURA-SUPREME INC
300 Dura Dr (55349-3000)
PHONE 320 543-3872
Keith P Stotts, *President*
Ken Sterner, *Purchasing*
Gene Schweiss, *Treasurer*
Glen Peterson, *Sales Mgr*
Deb Wilking, *Manager*
EMP: 610 **EST:** 1949
SQ FT: 215,000
SALES (est): 50MM-99.9MM **Privately Held**
WEB: www.durasupreme.com
SIC: 1751 Manufactures wooden kitchen cabinets; cabinet & finish work carpentry service; manufactures wooden bathroom vanities; manufactures cabinets, lockers & shelving

(G-2667)
EVANGELICAL LUTHERAN GOOD
Also Called: Howard Lake Care Center
413 13th Ave (55349)
PHONE 320 543-3800
Marylou Sherwin, *Bookkeeper*
Rebecca Rockwell, *Manager*
Christi Vater, *Administrator*
Kristi Vater, *Administrator*
EMP: 90
SALES (est): 1MM-4.9MM **Privately Held**
WEB: www.good-sam.com
SIC: 8059 8051 Nursing home; skilled nursing care facility
PA: Evangelical Lutheran Good
4800 W 57th St
Sioux Falls SD 57108
605 362-3100

(G-2668)
LAND O'LAKES INC
917 6th St (55349-5647)
PO Box 549 (55349-0549)
PHONE 320 543-2566
Kevin Dahlen, *Vice Pres*
Mark Dahlman, *Branch Mgr*
John Zander, *Manager*
Ray Munson, *Manager*
EMP: 28
SALES (est): 10MM-24.9MM **Privately Held**
WEB: www.landolakes.com
SIC: 5191 Wholesales animal feeds

HOYT LAKES
Saint Louis County

(G-2669)
ERIE L CLIFFS L C
847 County Road NO 666 (55750)
PHONE 218 225-3127
Donald G Gallagher, *President*
George W Hawk, *Corp Secy*
Robert J Leroux, *Controller*
EMP: 50 **EST:** 2001
SALES (est): 10MM-24.9MM **Publicly Held**
WEB: www.cliffsnaturalresources.com
SIC: 1011 Iron ore mining
PA: Cliffs Natural Resources Inc
200 Public Sq
Cleveland OH 44114
216 694-5700

HUGO
Anoka County

(G-2670)
BAROLE TRUCKING INC
6805 20th Ave Ste 300 (55038-8816)
PHONE 651 209-1104
Ray Olson, *President*
Sharen Ramsey, *Manager*
EMP: 25 **EST:** 1984
SQ FT: 60,000
SALES (est): 1MM-4.9MM **Privately Held**
WEB: www.baroletrucking.com
SIC: 4213 Over the road trucking

(G-2671)
NOBEL WELDING & MANUFACTURING
Also Called: Noble Welding
7075 21st Ave (55038-9760)
PHONE 651 426-1511
FAX: 651 426-8063
Bob Sorg Jr, *Vice Pres*
EMP: 25 **EST:** 1979
SQ FT: 13,000
SALES (est): 1MM-4.9MM **Privately Held**
SIC: 7692 Welding service; manufactures metal cutting machine tools; sheet metal fabricator; plating & polishing service

(G-2672)
NORTHERN WHOLESALE SUPPLY INC
6800 Otter Lake Rd Ste 2 (55038-9466)
PHONE 651 429-1515
FAX: 651 429-5757
Nick Gargaro, *President*
Lee N Johnson, *Corp Secy*
Deborah Gargaro, *Vice Pres*
Bill Karas, *Manager*
John Perron, *Executive*
▲ **EMP:** 63 **EST:** 1968
SQ FT: 60,000
SALES (est): 25MM-49.9MM **Privately Held**
WEB: www.northernwholesale.com
SIC: 5091 5012 5013 5074 Wholesales boats, canoes, watercrafts & equipment; wholesales snowmobiles; wholesales hydronic heating equipment; wholesales new motor vehicle parts & supplies

(G-2673)
SCHWIETERS' CO'S INC
13925 Fenway Blvd N (55038-9265)
PHONE 651 407-1618
FAX: 651 407-1437
Joel Schwieters, *President*
Tracey Flack, *Human Res Mgr*
Bill Hosch, *Manager*
EMP: 65 **EST:** 1984
SALES (est): 10MM-24.9MM **Privately Held**
WEB: www.finishcarpenters.com
SIC: 1522 7389 Multi-family housing construction; business services at a non-commercial site

HUGO
Washington County

(G-2674)
COATES RV CENTER INC
14025 Freeway Dr W (55038-9705)
PHONE 651 488-0234
Gerald Coates, *CEO*
Dan Mouch, *General Mgr*
Travis Boyce, *Manager*
Brett Hodroff, *Manager*
EMP: 26 **EST:** 1964
SALES (est): 1MM-4.9MM **Privately Held**
SIC: 7538 General automotive repair services

(G-2675)
COMFORTS OF HOME HUGO
5607 150th St N (55038-8391)
PHONE 651 653-3282
FAX: 651 407-5173
Brain Winges, *Principal*
EMP: 50 **EST:** 2005
SQ FT: 50,094
SALES (est): 1MM-4.9MM **Privately Held**

SIC: 8361 Residential care facility

(G-2676)
DONNER INDUSTRIES INC (PA)
5561 152nd St N (55038-8379)
PO Box 46 (55038-0046)
PHONE 651 429-0890
Joseph Glamos, *CEO*
Mark Burglum, *Controller*
Vickie Pierce, *Accountant*
Steve Thomas, *Marketing Mgr*
Jennifer Mullenbach, *Administrator*
EMP: 45 **EST:** 1899 **Privately Held**
SIC: 5051 Manufactures wire & wire products; wholesales metal wires, ties, cables & screening

(G-2677)
J & L SCHWIETERS CONSTRUCTION
13925 Fenway Blvd N (55038-9265)
PHONE 651 762-1110
John Schwieters, *President*
Peter Kulzer, *General Mgr*
EMP: 150 **EST:** 1979
SQ FT: 2,400
SALES (est): 10MM-24.9MM **Privately Held**
SIC: 1751 Carpentry contractor

(G-2678)
LAMETTI & SONS INC
16028 Forest Blvd N (55038-8396)
PO Box 477 (55038-0477)
PHONE 651 426-1380
FAX: 651 426-0044
Victor G Lametti, *President*
Kyle Lametti, *Corp Secy*
Fred Chase, *Vice Pres*
Todd Novteny, *Controller*
James Vanhoven, *Manager*
EMP: 25 **EST:** 1929
SQ FT: 4,000
SALES (est): 1MM-4.9MM **Privately Held**
WEB: www.lametti.com
SIC: 1623 Sewer line construction; water main construction

(G-2679)
MACIEJ PAINT CORP
Also Called: Industrial Pntg Specialists
5858 152nd St N (55038-8384)
PHONE 651 407-8000
FAX: 651 407-5923
Richard Maciej, *President*
Gary Papermaster, *Vice Pres*
Nancy Andert, *Finance Mgr*
EMP: 25 **EST:** 1992
SQ FT: 180,000
SALES (est): 1MM-4.9MM **Privately Held**
SIC: 1721 1799 Commercial painting contractor; building exterior sandblasting service; window treatment installation service; plating & polishing service

(G-2680)
NORTHSIDE CONSTRUCTION INC
15627 Forest Blvd N (55038-8397)
PO Box 326 (55038-0326)
PHONE 651 426-2632
FAX: 651 653-8823
Richard L Mireault, *President*
Richard D Ophus, *Corp Secy*
Gloria Ophus, *Manager*
EMP: 40 **EST:** 1984
SQ FT: 3,200
SALES (est): 1MM-4.9MM **Privately Held**
SIC: 1751 Carpentry contractor

(G-2681)
PEARSON MECHANICAL SERVICES
13497 Fenway Blvd Cir N 1 (55038-7447)
PHONE 651 275-1100
Troy A Pearson, *President*
Brian Pearson, *Vice Pres*
Eric Pearson, *Vice Pres*
Craig Pearson, *Vice Pres*
Doug Beutel, *Controller*
EMP: 50 **EST:** 2001
SQ FT: 45,000
SALES (est): 5MM-9.9MM **Privately Held**
WEB: www.pearsonms.com
SIC: 1711 Mechanical contractor

(G-2682)
RICA COSTA VENTURES INC
Also Called: Condor Lodge & Beach Resort
13845 Forest Blvd N (55038-8430)
PHONE 651 426-9262
Ozzie Berntson, *President*
Gabe Berntson, *Vice Pres*
EMP: 34 **EST:** 1998
SQ FT: 1,500
SALES (est): 1MM-4.9MM **Privately Held**
SIC: 7011 4724 Resort hotel; travel agency

(G-2683)
STOCKNESS CONSTRUCTION INC
13427 Fenway Blvd Cir N 1 (55038-7451)
PHONE 651 484-1286
Daniel Stockness, *President*
Tim Stockness, *Vice Pres*
Ann Stockness, *Executive*
Guy Peterson, *Contractor*
EMP: 30 **EST:** 1968
SALES (est): 1MM-4.9MM **Privately Held**
WEB: www.stockness.com
SIC: 1771 Concrete contractor

HUTCHINSON
Mcleod County

(G-2684)
AG SYSTEMS INC
1180 Highway 7 E (55350-5637)
PHONE 320 587-4030
FAX: 320 587-8791
Craig Lenz, *President*
Lori Haffley, *Corp Secy*
Paul Lenz, *Vice Pres*
Rod Saar, *Purchasing*
Berta Tiehl, *Accounting Dir*
▲ **EMP:** 45 **EST:** 1963
SQ FT: 40,000
SALES (est): 10MM-24.9MM **Privately Held**
SIC: 5083 Wholesales agricultural machinery; manufactures farm fertilizing machinery
PA: Lenz Inc
1180 Highway 7 E
Hutchinson MN 55350
320 587-4030

(G-2685)
ALLINA HEALTH SYSTEM
Also Called: Hutchinson Community Hospital
1095 Highway 15 S (55350-5000)
PHONE 320 234-4664
Marilyn Buboltz, *Director*
EMP: 50
SALES (est): 1MM-4.9MM **Privately Held**
WEB: www.allina.com
SIC: 8093 Outpatient mental health clinic
PA: Allina Health System
2925 Chicago Ave
Minneapolis MN 55407
612 775-5000

(G-2686)
AMERICA'S RACQUET & FITNESS
1065 Highway 15 S (55350-3153)
PHONE 320 234-7148
Jan Burley, *Manager*
EMP: 30
SALES (est): 500-999K **Privately Held**
SIC: 7991 Health club

(G-2687)
AMERICA'S RACQUET & FITNESS
Also Called: Americas Racquet & Fitness Ctr
Hwy 15 S (55350)
PO Box 712 (55350-0712)
PHONE 320 234-7148
FAX: 320 587-8033
Larry Johnson, *Manager*
EMP: 31
SALES (est): 1MM-4.9MM **Privately Held**
SIC: 7991 Physical fitness center

(PA)=Parent Co (HQ)=Headquarters (DH)=Div Headquarters
✿ = New business established in last 2 years

2011 Harris Minnesota
Services Directory

© Harris InfoSource 1-866-281-6415
125

GEOGRAPHIC

(G-2688)
AVEYRON HOMES INC
360 Lake St SW (55350-2347)
PHONE.................................320 234-6063
FAX: 320 587-3023
Kathy King, *Corp Secy*
David Sebeste, *Treasurer*
Rondy Freund, *Finance*
Jan Stockmann, *Manager*
Kathy Kalenburg, *Exec Dir*
EMP: 120 Privately Held
SIC: 8399 8361 Non-fee basis fund raising organization; home for the mentally handicapped; home for the mentally retarded; antipoverty board
PA: Aveyron Homes Inc
222 5th Ave NW
Hutchinson MN 55350
320 587-6277

(G-2689)
AVEYRON HOMES INC
9 Northwoods Ave NE (55350-1272)
PHONE.................................320 587-6277
K Kalenburg, *Principal*
Debbie Gruenhagen, *Manager*
EMP: 140 Privately Held
SIC: 8399 8361 Non-fee basis fund raising organization; home for the mentally handicapped; home for the mentally retarded; antipoverty board
PA: Aveyron Homes Inc
222 5th Ave NW
Hutchinson MN 55350
320 587-6277

(G-2690)
C-ME MARKETING INC
150 Michigan St SE (55350-1913)
PHONE.................................320 587-6565
Duane M Haefner, *CEO*
EMP: 32
SALES (est): 1MM-4.9MM Privately Held
SIC: 8742 Marketing consulting service

(G-2691)
CEDAR CREST ESTATE
225 Shady Ridge Rd NW (55350-1407)
PHONE.................................320 587-4299
FAX: 320 587-4299
Rosalind Ewald, *President*
EMP: 40 EST: 1984
SQ FT: 5,500
SALES (est): 1MM-4.9MM Privately Held
SIC: 8052 Intermediate care facility

(G-2692)
CITIZENS BANCSHARES OF
102 Main St S (55350-2575)
PO Box 339 (55350-0339)
PHONE.................................320 587-2233
Thomas Burich, *President*
EMP: 40 EST: 1967
SQ FT: 2,500
SALES (est): 1MM-4.9MM Privately Held
SIC: 6411 Insurance services

(G-2693)
CITIZENS BANK & TRUST CO
102 Main St S (55350-2575)
PO Box 339 (55350-0339)
PHONE.................................320 587-2233
FAX: 320 587-5738
Irwin Burich, *Ch of Bd*
Thomas Burich, *President*
Joel Kraft, *Senior VP*
Tim Ulrich, *Senior VP*
Michael Cannon, *Vice Pres*
EMP: 50 EST: 1886
SALES (est): 10MM-24.9MM Privately Held
SIC: 6036 6022 State savings bank; state commercial bank

(G-2694)
CONNECTCARE
710 Park Island Dr SW (55350-2046)
PHONE.................................320 234-5031
Deeann Dicke, *Director*
EMP: 25 EST: 1996
SALES (est): 500-999K Privately Held
WEB: www.connectcare.com
SIC: 8082 Home health care services

(G-2695)
CROW RIVER COUNTRY CLUB
915 Colorado St NW (55350-1924)
PHONE.................................320 587-3070
FAX: 320 234-6728
Jeff Pascal, *President*
Jack Yates, *Principal*
Kevin Frogmming, *Principal*
Pat Docken, *Corp Secy*
Lee Lundstrom, *Vice Pres*
EMP: 35 EST: 1938
SQ FT: 5,000
SALES (est): 1MM-4.9MM Privately Held
WEB: www.crowrivercc.com
SIC: 7997 Country club; membership racquetball club; membership golf club

(G-2696)
DURACOAT INC
10 Michigan St NE (55350-1902)
PO Box 575 (55350-0575)
PHONE.................................320 587-3135
FAX: 320 234-7126
Brian Kaping, *President*
Jerry Holtz, *Vice Pres*
EMP: 30 EST: 2001
SALES (est): 10MM-24.9MM Privately Held
SIC: 1771 Manufactures epoxy coatings; concrete contractor

(G-2697)
GREENCASTLE CONDOMINIUM ASSN
250 Freemont Ave SE # 135 (55350-3162)
PHONE.................................320 587-4040
Roy Fredrickson, *President*
Adrian Schwartz, *Principal*
Marian Pate, *Corp Secy*
Reba Radtke, *Corp Secy*
Audrey Vachow, *Vice Pres*
EMP: 40 EST: 1986 Privately Held
WEB: www.greencastlehome.com
SIC: 8641 6531 Condominium association; condominium managers

(G-2698)
HUTCHINSON AREA HEALTH CARE
1095 Highway 15 S (55350-5000)
PHONE.................................320 234-5000
FAX: 320 234-4652
Phil Graves, *President*
Marilyn Buboltz, *Corp Secy*
Jean Nies, *Corp Secy*
H C Remucal, *Ch of Surgery*
Melanie Newcomb, *Materials Dir*
EMP: 630 EST: 1921 Privately Held
SIC: 8399 8062 Social change association; medical hospital

(G-2699)
HUTCHINSON AUTO CENTER
Also Called: Hutchinsonk Auto Center
1165 Highway 22 S (55350-2921)
PO Box 669 (55350-0669)
PHONE.................................320 587-4748
FAX: 320 587-4281
Bernie Wagnild, *President*
Jim Paul, *Vice Pres*
Dean Wagnild, *Manager*
EMP: 28 EST: 1953
SQ FT: 20,000
SALES (est): 10MM-24.9MM Privately Held
WEB: www.jaymalonemotors.com
SIC: 7532 7538 Retails new & used automobiles; exterior repair service; automotive engine repair service

(G-2700)
HUTCHINSON HEALTH CARE
1095 Highway 15 S (55350-5000)
PHONE.................................320 234-5000
Kay Borgstahl, *Corp Secy*
Pamela Larson, *CFO*
Mary Inglis, *Treasurer*
Lynette M Wendlandt, *Accounts Mgr*
Michael Boo, *Officer*
EMP: 99
SALES (est): 5MM-9.9MM Privately Held
SIC: 8099 Health & allied services

(G-2701)
HUTCHINSON HEALTH CARE
Also Called: Burns Manor Nursing Home
135 N High Dr NE (55350-1248)
PHONE.................................320 234-4906
Steve Mulder, *President*
Pamela Larson, *CFO*
EMP: 99
SALES (est): 1MM-4.9MM Privately Held
SIC: 8051 Skilled nursing care facility

(G-2702)
HUTCHINSON TELEPHONE CO
235 Franklin St SW (55350-2469)
PO Box 279 (55350-0279)
PHONE.................................320 587-2323
FAX: 320 587-6211
Walter S Clay, *CEO*
Thomas M Dahl, *General Mgr*
Lynne M Clay, *Corp Secy*
R McGraw, *Div Sub Head*
Steven N Senart, *CFO*
EMP: 57 EST: 1897 Publicly Held
WEB: www.hutchtel.net
SIC: 4813 4812 4822 Local telephone communications services; cellular telephone services; facsimile transmission services; paging services
PA: New Ulm Telecom Inc
27 N Minnesota St
New Ulm MN 56073
507 354-4111

(G-2703)
HUTCHINSON, CITY OF INC
Also Called: Hutchinson Police Dept
10 Franklin St SW (55350-2419)
PHONE.................................320 587-2242
FAX: 320 587-6427
Steve Madson, *Branch Mgr*
EMP: 30 Privately Held
WEB: www.hutchinsonhra.com
SIC: 8111 Local government police protection; legal services
PA: Hutchinson, City of Inc
111 Hassan St SE
Hutchinson MN 55350
320 587-5151

(G-2704)
JAY MALONE MOTORS
Also Called: Ford Lincoln Mercury
1165 Highway 7 W (55350-1511)
PHONE.................................320 587-4748
Jay Malone, *Principal*
EMP: 35 EST: 2007
SALES (est): 10MM-24.9MM Privately Held
SIC: 7532 7539 Retails new & used automobiles; automotive body shop; automotive wheel alignment service

(G-2705)
KIWANIS INTERNATIONAL INC
645 Waller Dr NE (55350-1300)
PHONE.................................320 587-6874
Bill Arndt, *President*
EMP: 40 Privately Held
SIC: 8641 Civic associations
PA: Kiwanis International Inc
3636 Woodview Trce
Indianapolis IN 46268
317 875-8755

(G-2706)
MC KIMM MILK TRANSIT INC
1145 Adams St SE (55350-2921)
PO Box 51 (55350-0051)
PHONE.................................320 587-3167
FAX: 320 587-0746
Larry M Kimm, *President*
EMP: 35 EST: 1952
SQ FT: 10,000
SALES (est): 1MM-4.9MM Privately Held
SIC: 4213 Long-distance refrigerated trucking services

(G-2707)
MIDCOUNTRY BANK INC
201 Main St S (55350-2570)
PHONE.................................320 234-4500
Craig Almquist, *Facilities Mgr*
Richard Burgart, *CFO*
Stephanie Olson, *Asst Controller*
Marnie Miklulay, *Human Resources*
Megan Kart, *Branch Mgr*
EMP: 50
SALES (est): 100MM-24.9MM Privately Held
WEB: www.midcountrybank.com
SIC: 6021 National commercial bank
PA: Midcountry Bank Inc
14617 Highway 7
Minnetonka MN 55345
952 997-5608

(G-2708)
NASH-FINCH CO
Also Called: Econo Foods
205 Washington Ave E (55350-2612)
PHONE.................................320 587-8233
Mike Kierchhoff, *Manager*
EMP: 50
SALES (est): 25MM-49.9MM Publicly Held
WEB: www.nashfinch.com
SIC: 5141 Wholesales general line groceries
PA: Nash-Finch Co
7600 France Ave S Ste 200
Edina MN 55435
952 832-0534

(G-2709)
NEW DISCOVERIES MONTESSORI
1000 5th Ave SE (55350-7028)
PO Box 305 (55350-0305)
PHONE.................................320 234-6362
Dave Conrad, *Director*
EMP: 35 EST: 2006
SALES (est): 500-999K Privately Held
SIC: 8351 Child development center providing Montessori based instruction

(G-2710)
REINER CONTRACTING INC
21541 Highway 7 W (55350-4340)
PHONE.................................320 587-9886
FAX: 320 587-4847
Craig Reiner, *President*
Dee D Reiner, *Vice Pres*
EMP: 25 EST: 1984
SALES (est): 5MM-9.9MM Privately Held
SIC: 1542 New commercial & office building construction

(G-2711)
RICHARD LARSON BUILDERS INC
Also Called: Larson Custom Cabinets
640 Adams St SE (55350-2926)
PHONE.................................320 587-5555
Richard Larson, *President*
Brad Bonniwell, *Sales Mgr*
EMP: 45 EST: 1968
SQ FT: 9,000
SALES (est): 10MM-24.9MM Privately Held
WEB: www.larsonbuilders.com
SIC: 1521 1751 New single-family home construction service; cabinet & finish work carpentry service

(G-2712)
SENIOR HUTCHINSON CARE SVCS
1555 Sherwood St SE (55350-3285)
PHONE.................................320 234-4751
Pamela Larson, *Principal*
Steven Mulder, *Exec Dir*
EMP: 99
SALES (est): 1MM-4.9MM Privately Held
SIC: 8051 Skilled nursing care facility

(G-2713)
3-D CNC INC
1055 5th Ave SE (55350-7028)
PHONE.................................320 587-5923
FAX: 320 587-7166
Randy Dague, *CEO*
Robert Malone, *CFO*
Linda Duesterhoeft, *Accountant*
Brad Quaft, *Manager*
Kevin Remus, *Manager*
EMP: 34 EST: 1989
SQ FT: 14,500
SALES (est): 1MM-4.9MM Privately Held
WEB: www.3dcnc.com
SIC: 7371 Machine shop, jobbing & repair services; computer programming service; manufactures tools, dies, jigs & fixtures

(G-2714)
VALLEY SALES OF HUTCHINSON INC
525 Highway 7 E   (55350-1921)
PO Box 697   (55350-0697)
PHONE...............................320 587-2240
FAX: 320 587-5926
Bernie E Wagnild, *President*
Jim Paul, *Vice Pres*
Bob Vine, *Controller*
Mike Silvernale, *Manager*
EMP: 25 EST: 1997
SALES (est): 10MM-24.9MM **Privately Held**
SIC: 7538 Retails new & used automobiles; general automotive repair services; used car dealer

(G-2715)
VETERANS OF FOREIGN WARS
Also Called: Post 906
247 1st Ave SE   (55350-2613)
PHONE...............................320 587-9929
Vince Herbert, *Principal*
Dave Blake, *Principal*
Don Merkins, *Principal*
Sue Neubarth, *Manager*
Martin Barnes, *Quartermaster*
EMP: 30 EST: 1960
SQ FT: 5,000 **Privately Held**
SIC: 8641 Veterans' organization; limited service sandwich & submarine shop; tavern drinking establishment

(G-2716)
VICTORIA INN
Also Called: Best Western Victorian Inn
1000 Highway 7 W   (55350-1514)
PHONE...............................320 587-6030
FAX: 320 587-6030
Gary Schwarzrock, *CEO*
Marilyn Wagman, *Exec Dir*
EMP: 60 EST: 1986
SQ FT: 46,000
SALES (est): 1MM-4.9MM **Privately Held**
SIC: 7011 7299 Traveler accommodations; eating place; night club drinking establishment; banquet hall facility

(G-2717)
WAL-MART STORES INC
1300 Trunk Ave Hwy 15 S   (55350)
PHONE...............................320 587-1020
FAX: 320 587-1024
Cathleen Miller, *Manager*
Scott Hilgemann, *Manager*
EMP: 300
SALES (est): 25MM-49.9MM **Publicly Held**
WEB: www.walmartstores.com
SIC: 8011 Discount department store; retail supermarkets or hypermarket, greater than 100,000 square feet; retails optical goods; pharmacy & drug store; physicians' office & clinic
PA: Wal-Mart Stores Inc
    702 SW 8th St
    Bentonville AR 72716
    479 273-4000

(G-2718)
WELLS FARGO BANK, NATIONAL
135 Main St N   (55350-1807)
PHONE...............................320 587-2122
FAX: 320 587-2170
Chris Mallak, *Manager*
EMP: 30
SALES (est): 1MM-4.9MM **Publicly Held**
SIC: 6162 Mortgage & loan lending
HQ: Wfc Holdings, Corp
    420 Montgomery St
    San Francisco CA 94104
    415 396-7392

INTERNATIONAL FALLS
Koochiching County

(G-2719)
DULUTH CLINIC INTERNATIONAL
2501 Keenan Dr   (56649-2181)
PHONE...............................218 283-9431
FAX: 218 285-6278
Douglas Johnson, *President*
Robyn Pelowski, *Office Mgr*
Constante S Avecilla, *Surgeon*
Kathy Hughes, *Nursing Dir*
Kathy Henrickson, *Nurse Practr*
EMP: 60 EST: 1975
SALES (est): 5MM-9.9MM **Privately Held**
SIC: 8011 General & family practice physician or surgeon office

(G-2720)
EVANGELICAL LUTHERAN GOOD
1402 Highway 71   (56649-2154)
PHONE...............................218 283-4768
FAX: 218 283-9497
Daren Bucklin, *Manager*
Mark Williams, *Manager*
EMP: 100
SALES (est): 1MM-4.9MM **Privately Held**
WEB: www.good-sam.com
SIC: 8051 Skilled nursing care facility
PA: Evangelical Lutheran Good
    4800 W 57th St
    Sioux Falls SD 57108
    605 362-3100

(G-2721)
IBT CONSOLIDATED INC
101 2nd St   (56649-2318)
PHONE...............................218 285-5290
William Roufs, *General Mgr*
Art Cassibo, *Superintendent*
Kristen Wold, *Controller*
EMP: 33 EST: 1995
SALES (est): 10MM-24.9MM **Privately Held**
SIC: 4013 4785 Paper mill; railroad switching & terminal services; inspection facility

(G-2722)
INDUSTRIAL COMMERCIAL FARM
4161 County Road 97   (56649-8938)
PHONE...............................218 377-4485
Dan Benedicts, *Owner*
Gary Templeton, *Manager*
EST: 1989
SQ FT: 7,200 **Privately Held**
SIC: 1731 Electrical contractor; steel fabricator

(G-2723)
INTERNATIONAL FALLS, CITY OF
600 4th St   (56649-2442)
PHONE...............................218 283-3500
Jerry Jensen, *Chief*
EMP: 49
SALES (est): 1MM-4.9MM **Privately Held**
WEB: www.gotorainylake.com
SIC: 4119 Ambulance service
PA: International Falls, City of
    600 4th St
    International Falls MN 56649
    218 283-9484

(G-2724)
INTERNATIONAL MANAGEMENT CO
Also Called: Holiday Inn
1500 Highway 71   (56649-2131)
PO Box 81   (56649-0081)
PHONE...............................218 283-4451
FAX: 218 283-3774
Kathleen N Riley, *CEO*
Vern Jones, *President*
Richard Thompson, *Corp Secy*
Freida Hopkins, *Sales Executive*
Kristie Fritz, *Manager*
EMP: 75 EST: 1970
SQ FT: 46,250
SALES (est): 1MM-4.9MM **Privately Held**

SIC: 7011 Traveler accommodations; cocktail lounge; eating place

(G-2725)
K R WAGNER INC
300 Van Lynn Rd   (56649-8912)
PO Box B, S Intl Falls   (56679-0850)
PHONE...............................218 283-3700
Kalan R Wagner, *President*
Wendy Wagner, *Treasurer*
Ann King, *Manager*
EMP: 25 EST: 2007
SALES (est): 1MM-4.9MM **Privately Held**
SIC: 7353 Construction & mining equipment leasing & rental

(G-2726)
LAKE RAINY MEDICAL CENTER
Also Called: Falls Memorial Hospital
1400 Highway 71   (56649-2154)
PHONE...............................218 283-4481
FAX: 218 283-3433
Brian Long, *CEO*
Jeffrey Hardwig, *Member*
Nancy Treacy, *CFO*
Jeri Vergeldt, *Treasurer*
Grace Hauglid, *Manager*
EMP: 140 EST: 1945
SQ FT: 52,884
SALES (est): 10MM-24.9MM **Privately Held**
WEB: www.fmh-mn.com
SIC: 8062 Medical hospital

(G-2727)
MINNESOTA DAKOTA & WESTERN
Also Called: M D & W Railway
101 2nd St   (56649-2318)
PHONE...............................218 285-5690
FAX: 218 283-3000
Bill Roufs, *CEO*
Kristen Wold, *Controller*
Pat Lindvall, *Finance Mgr*
Jill Christie, *Manager*
Lori Lyman, *Executive Asst*
EMP: 39 EST: 1902
SQ FT: 15,000
SALES (est): 1MM-4.9MM **Publicly Held**
SIC: 4785 4011 4013 Toll bridge operation services; railroad switching & terminal services; long haul railroad
PA: Boise Inc
    1111 W Jefferson St # 200
    Boise ID 83702
    208 384-7000

(G-2728)
NATIONAL CAR RENTAL SYSTEM INC
County Rd 108   (56649)
PHONE...............................218 283-8486
James Wherley, *President*
Gerald Wherley, *Vice Pres*
Julie Mercer, *Manager*
Tom Wherley, *Manager*
EMP: 30 EST: 1975
SALES (est): 1MM-4.9MM **Privately Held**
SIC: 7514 Rent-a-car service

(G-2729)
RAINY LAKE HOUSEBOATS INC
2031 Town Road 488   (56649-8744)
PHONE...............................218 286-5391
FAX: 218 286-4010
William Dougherty Sr, *President*
June Dougherty, *Corp Secy*
Tom Dougherty, *Vice Pres*
EMP: 33 EST: 1976
SQ FT: 1,536
SALES (est): 1MM-4.9MM **Privately Held**
WEB: www.raineylake.com
SIC: 7999 4493 Houseboat rental services; marina

(G-2730)
SMDC HEALTH SYSTEM
Also Called: D C International Falls Phrm
2501 Keenan Dr   (56649-2181)
PHONE...............................218 285-6222
Douglas Johnson, *Branch Mgr*
EMP: 53
SALES (est): 5MM-9.9MM **Privately Held**

SIC: 8011 Clinic operated by physicians; pharmacy & drug store
PA: Smdc Health System
    400 E 3rd St
    Duluth MN 55805
    218 786-8364

(G-2731)
SPI GROUP INC
1919 Main Ave   (56649-3331)
PHONE...............................218 283-9397
Alton Shannon, *President*
Joyce Hell, *Corp Secy*
Ron Ruelle, *Vice Pres*
EMP: 65 EST: 1966
SQ FT: 7,000
SALES (est): 5MM-9.9MM **Privately Held**
WEB: www.shannonsinc.us
SIC: 1711 Plumbing service; heating & air conditioning contractor

(G-2732)
THUNDERBIRD LODGE INC
2170 County Road 139   (56649-8833)
PHONE...............................218 286-3151
FAX: 218 286-3004
Richard Dougherty, *President*
Judy Dougherty, *Principal*
Mary J Haanan, *Corp Secy*
EMP: 52 EST: 1981
SALES (est): 1MM-4.9MM **Privately Held**
SIC: 7011 Resort hotel

(G-2733)
TRUSTAR FEDERAL CREDIT UNION
601 4th St   (56649-2436)
PHONE...............................218 283-2000
Dale Johnson, *President*
Tim Fulton, *Exec VP*
Debra Jackson, *VP Human Res*
Keith Boelk, *VP Info Sys*
Sharleen Mitchell, *Admin Asst*
EMP: 37 EST: 1960
SALES (est): 5MM-9.9MM **Privately Held**
WEB: www.trustarfcu.com
SIC: 6061 Federally chartered credit union

(G-2734)
WOODFAM INC
Also Called: Servicemaster
611 11th St   (56649-2723)
PO Box 186   (56649-0186)
PHONE...............................218 283-4775
FAX: 218 283-4775
James Wood, *President*
Jean Wood, *Corp Secy*
EMP: 25 EST: 1988
SALES (est): 500-999K **Privately Held**
WEB: www.woodfam.com
SIC: 7349 Building cleaning & maintenance services

INVER GROVE HEIGHTS
Dakota County

(G-2735)
AG STATES AGENCY LLC   (HQ)
5500 Cenex Dr Ste 1   (55077-1733)
PO Box 64089, Saint Paul   (55164-0089)
PHONE...............................651 355-6000
FAX: 651 355-6359
Corwin Tufte, *President*
Barbara Brannum, *Corp Secy*
Tom Larson, *Exec VP*
Wayne Davis, *Vice Pres*
Scott Sinclair, *Manager*
EMP: 33 EST: 1994
SQ FT: 1,000
SALES (corp-wide): 25.72B **Publicly Held**
WEB: www.cenexharveststates.com
SIC: 6411 Insurance agency & broker
PA: CHS Inc
    5500 Cenex Dr
    Inver Grove Heights MN 55077
    651 355-6000

(G-2736)
AGRILIANCE LLC   (PA)
5500 Cenex Dr   (55077-1733)
PHONE...............................651 451-5000
George Thornton, *President*
Bob Herzfeld, *General Mgr*

GEOGRAPHIC

Gene Hurt, *District Mgr*
Brent Renfrow, *District Mgr*
Paula Jones, *Corp Secy*
▲ **EMP:** 200 **EST:** 2000
SQ FT: 30,000 **Privately Held**
WEB: www.agriliance.com
SIC: 5083 Wholesales agricultural machinery & equipment

(G-2737)
ALLINA HEALTH SYSTEM
5565 Blaine Ave (55076-1207)
PHONE 651 450-8000
Jerry Barnes, *Sr Corp Ofcr*
Sharon Adams, *Med Doctor*
Marilyn Jungbluth, *Manager*
EMP: 35
SALES (est): 1MM-4.9MM **Privately Held**
WEB: www.allina.com
SIC: 8011 Physicians' office & clinic
PA: Allina Health System
2925 Chicago Ave
Minneapolis MN 55407
612 775-5000

(G-2738)
BAHAMA CONSULTING CORP
8950 Almquist Way Ste 415 (55077-3565)
PHONE 651 994-7900
Alison Hill, *President*
Bert Hill, *Vice Pres*
EMP: 25 **EST:** 2002
SQ FT: 3,000
SALES (est): 1MM-4.9MM **Privately Held**
WEB: www.bahama-consulting.com
SIC: 8748 Business consulting services

(G-2739)
BUTLER BROTHERS ENTERPRISES
10730 Briggs Dr Ste C (55077-5358)
PHONE 651 554-9888
Joel Butler, *President*
Jeremy Butler, *Vice Pres*
Kathy Anderson, *Manager*
EMP: 45 **EST:** 2000
SQ FT: 4,500 **Privately Held**
SIC: 0781 Landscape services

(G-2740)
C L T FLOOR COVERINGS INC
8731 Alverno Ave (55077-3531)
PHONE 651 451-0069
Robert Burris, *President*
Dave Dinger, *Vice Pres*
Bob Burris, *Sales Staff*
EMP: 40 **EST:** 1971
SQ FT: 30,000
SALES (est): 1MM-4.9MM **Privately Held**
WEB: www.cltfloorcoverings.com
SIC: 1752 5023 Flooring contractor; wholesales floor coverings; carpet laying contractor; vinyl floor tile & sheet installation contractor; wood floor installation & refinishing contractor; retails floor coverings

(G-2741)
CERNICK ENTERPRISES
Also Called: Direct Pub
6710 Cahill Ave (55076-2027)
PHONE 651 552-9005
Tim Tacula, *Owner*
EMP: 56 **EST:** 2001
SALES (est): 1MM-4.9MM **Privately Held**
WEB: www.directpub.com
SIC: 7933 Bowling center

(G-2742)
CHS INC (PA)
5500 Cenex Dr (55077-1733)
PO Box 64089, Saint Paul (55164-0089)
PHONE 651 355-6000
John D Johnson, *President*
Michael Considine, *General Mgr*
Robert Bass, *Vice Chairman*
David Bielenberg, *Member*
Bruce Anderson, *Corp Secy*
◆ **EMP:** 800 **EST:** 1936
SQ FT: 320,000
SALES (corp-wide): 25.72B **Publicly Held**
WEB: www.cenexharveststates.com

SIC: 5153 1311 Wholesales grain & field beans; crude petroleum production; natural gas production; manufactures durum flour; manufactures semolina flour; manufactures soybean flour & grits; manufactures soybean oil, cake or meal; wholesales corn; wholesales wheat

(G-2743)
CLIMB THEATER INC
6415 Carmen Ave (55076-4428)
PHONE 651 453-9275
Peggy Wetli, *CEO*
Mitchell Johnson, *Business Mgr*
Bonnie Matson, *CFO*
Jim Gambone, *Treasurer*
Marlene Mosher, *Finance Mgr*
EMP: 100 **EST:** 1975
SQ FT: 10,000
SALES (est): 5MM-9.9MM **Privately Held**
WEB: www.climb.org
SIC: 7832 7922 7999 Indoor movie theater; gambling establishment; theatrical producers & services

(G-2744)
CLIMB THEATRE INC
6415 Carmen Ave (55076-4428)
PHONE 651 453-9275
Peg Wetli, *CEO*
Pam Mikacevich, *Executive*
EMP: 100 **EST:** 1985
SALES (est): 10MM-24.9MM **Privately Held**
SIC: 7922 Theatrical producers & services

(G-2745)
CONTRACT SOD SERVICES INC
8140 Courthouse Blvd (55077-3900)
PHONE 651 457-6037
Willard Wagner, *President*
Paul Wagner, *Vice Pres*
Norbert Wagner, *Vice Pres*
EMP: 40 **EST:** 2001 **Privately Held**
SIC: 0181 Sod farm

(G-2746)
COUNTRY HEDGING INC
5500 Cenex Dr Ste 290 (55077-1733)
PO Box 64089, Saint Paul (55164-0089)
PHONE 651 355-6500
Scott A Cordes, *President*
Tom Larson, *Chairman*
Rick Dusek, *Corp Secy*
EMP: 29 **EST:** 1986
SQ FT: 5,100
SALES (est): 10MM-24.9MM **Publicly Held**
WEB: www.cenexharveststates.com
SIC: 6221 Commodity futures broker
PA: CHS Inc
5500 Cenex Dr
Inver Grove Heights MN 55077
651 355-6000

(G-2747)
CUT FRUIT EXPRESS INC
11585 Courthouse Blvd (55077-5911)
PO Box 2532 (55076-8532)
PHONE 651 438-8834
Lawford Baxter, *President*
EMP: 65 **EST:** 1997
SQ FT: 46,000
SALES (est): 25MM-49.9MM **Privately Held**
WEB: www.cutfruitexpress.com
SIC: 5148 Wholesales fresh fruits & vegetables

(G-2748)
EAGAN LODGING GROUP LLC
5653 Bishop Ave (55076-1405)
PHONE 651 450-1100
Don Heikkila, *General Mgr*
Tom Seaberg, *General Mgr*
Mike Wendel, *Principal*
Jordan Dols, *Principal*
Josh Davidson, *Manager*
EMP: 28 **EST:** 1997
SALES (est): 1MM-4.9MM **Privately Held**
WEB: www.countryinnigh.com
SIC: 7011 Traveler accommodations

(G-2749)
EAST METRO FAMILY PRACTICE
2980 Buckley Way (55076-2017)
PHONE 651 457-2748
John J Vukelich MD, *Principal*

Rayann Haried, *Office Mgr*
Anthony B Ferrara, *Med Doctor*
EMP: 30 **EST:** 2001
SALES (est): 1MM-4.9MM **Privately Held**
SIC: 8011 Physicians' office & clinic

(G-2750)
FAMILY HEALTH SERVICES OF MN
2980 Buckley Way (55076-2017)
PHONE 651 457-2748
Raeann Hareid, *Office Mgr*
Sue Mishler, *Supervisor*
Jennifer Wiberg, *Physician Asst*
EMP: 25
SALES (est): 1MM-4.9MM **Privately Held**
SIC: 8031 8011 Osteopathic physicians' office & clinic; general & family practice physician or surgeon office

(G-2751)
GERTEN GREENHOUSES & GARDEN
5500 Blaine Ave (55076-1206)
PHONE 651 450-1501
FAX: 651 450-9380
Louis Gerten, *President*
Glen Gerten, *Vice Pres*
Gino Pitera, *Treasurer*
Roxy Muler, *Accounting Mgr*
Julie Humann, *Manager*
▲ **EMP:** 450 **EST:** 1920
SQ FT: 39,000
SALES (est): 50MM-99.9MM **Privately Held**
WEB: www.gertenswholesale.com
SIC: 5193 Retail nursery & garden center; wholesales nursery stock; retail nurseries; retails nursery stock, seeds & bulbs

(G-2752)
GROVE AQUATIC FITNESS CENTER
8055 Barbara Ave (55077-3430)
PHONE 651 450-2480
Jennelle Teppen, *Manager*
Anne Wilkins, *Manager*
EMP: 400 **EST:** 1996
SALES (est): 10MM-24.9MM **Privately Held**
SIC: 7991 Physical fitness center

(G-2753)
HEALTHPARTNERS INC
Also Called: Inver Grove Heights Clinic
5625 Cenex Dr (55077-1724)
PHONE 651 552-2600
FAX: 651 552-2614
Sudha M Chadalawada, *Med Doctor*
Heidi Lovro, *Manager*
Edith Sandahl, *Administrator*
Charles W Salmen, *Surgeon*
Scott A Oakman, *Psychiatry*
EMP: 88
SALES (est): 5MM-9.9MM **Privately Held**
WEB: www.healthpartners.com
SIC: 8093 Specialty outpatient clinic
PA: HealthPartners Inc
8170 33rd Ave S
Bloomington MN 55425
952 883-6000

(G-2754)
I-STATE TRUCK CENTER
11152 Courthouse Blvd (55077-5902)
PHONE 651 455-9775
FAX: 651 455-9671
Roger Watral, *Manager*
Dawn Manges, *Manager*
Jim Williams, *Manager*
John Tenney, *Manager*
EMP: 28
SALES (est): 10MM-24.9MM **Privately Held**
WEB: www.istatetruck.com
SIC: 5084 Wholesales industrial machinery & equipment
HQ: I-State Truck Center
2601 American Blvd E
Minneapolis MN 55425
952 854-5511

(G-2755)
ISTATE TRUCK CENTER
11152 Courthouse Blvd (55077-5902)
PHONE 651 455-9775
Dawn Manges, *Principal*
Roger Watral, *Manager*

EMP: 75
SALES (est): 5MM-9.9MM **Privately Held**
SIC: 4212 Local trucking without storage services

(G-2756)
J EIDEN CONSTRUCTION INC
1696 63rd St E (55077-2160)
PHONE 651 450-5978
James Eiden, *President*
Sarah Martinez, *Manager*
EMP: 40 **EST:** 1988
SALES (est): 1MM-4.9MM **Privately Held**
SIC: 1751 Carpentry contractor

(G-2757)
LAND O'LAKES PURINA FEED LLC
11620 Courthouse Blvd A (55077-5912)
PHONE 651 681-5917
EMP: 35
SALES (est): 25MM-49.9MM **Privately Held**
WEB: www.landolakes.com
SIC: 5191 Wholesales farm supplies
HQ: Land O'Lakes Purina Feed LLC
1080 County Rd Fw Fw
Saint Paul MN 55126
800 851-8810

(G-2758)
LAND O'LAKES PURINA FEED LLC
3763 117th St E (55077-5847)
PHONE 651 437-7762
Mike Jorgensen, *Plant Supt*
EMP: 35
SALES (est): 25MM-49.9MM **Privately Held**
WEB: www.landolakes.com
SIC: 5191 Wholesales feed
HQ: Land O'Lakes Purina Feed LLC
1080 County Rd Fw Fw
Saint Paul MN 55126
800 851-8810

(G-2759)
LOFTON LABEL INC
6290 Claude Way (55076-4435)
PHONE 651 457-8118
FAX: 651 457-3709
Richard Gajewski, *President*
William Garens, *Vice Pres*
Robin Rightberger, *Safety Dir*
Patricia Danl, *Materials Mgr*
Steven Gaughn, *Manager*
EMP: 100 **EST:** 1981
SQ FT: 40,000
SALES (est): 25MM-49.9MM **Privately Held**
WEB: www.loftonlabel.com
SIC: 5084 Manufactures unprinted, gummed labels made from purchased materials; wholesales printing machinery, equipment & supplies

(G-2760)
LOGOS PRODUCTIONS INC
6160 Carmen Ave (55076-4420)
PHONE 651 451-9945
Paul Truran, *CEO*
Peter Velander, *President*
Sharilyn Figueroa, *General Mgr*
Sharilyn Firle, *General Mgr*
Deborah Madsen, *VP Persnl*
EMP: 36 **EST:** 1965
SQ FT: 12,000
SALES (est): 5MM-9.9MM **Privately Held**
WEB: www.logosproductions.com
SIC: 7336 Periodical publisher; graphic arts & related design service

(G-2761)
MCDONALD HOMES INC
6015 Cahill Ave Ste 100 (55076-1614)
PHONE 651 455-5142
FAX: 651 455-2292
James M Donald, *President*
Margaret M Donald, *Corp Secy*
Margaret McDonald, *Corp Secy*
Jody Byington, *Manager*
Corina Kimmes, *IT/INT Sup*
EMP: 25 **EST:** 1983
SQ FT: 2,000
SALES (est): 5MM-9.9MM **Privately Held**
WEB: www.mcdonaldremodeling.com

SIC: **1521** 1542 New single-family home construction service; new commercial & office building construction

(G-2762)
MGMT FIVE INC
Also Called: Saxon, Mike Inver Grove Ford
4725 S Robert Trl   (55077-1108)
PHONE 651 451-2201
FAX: 651 457-4773
Michael W Saxon, *CEO*
Jerry Bauer, *General Mgr*
Jack W Saxon, *Corp Secy*
Jeff Siegfried, *Parts Mgr*
Teresa Kline, *Controller*
EMP: 82 **EST:** 1990
SQ FT: 40,000
SALES (est): 5MM-9.9MM **Privately Held**
WEB: www.invergroveford.com
SIC: 7532 Automotive body shop; retails new & used automobiles

(G-2763)
MIDWEST MOTORS LLC ✪
Also Called: Inver Grove Toyota
1037 Highway 110   (55077-1111)
PHONE 651 455-6000
Steve McDaniels, *Mng Member*
EMP: 75 **EST:** 2009
SALES (est): 50MM-99.9MM **Privately Held**
SIC: 5012 Automobile wholesaler

(G-2764)
NYCO INC
10730 Briggs Dr Ste B   (55077-5358)
PHONE 651 457-4069
Curt Mages, *President*
Rick Hansen, *Vice Pres*
Pat Kolb, *Asst Controller*
Lynda Weldon, *Office Mgr*
EMP: 60 **EST:** 1988
SQ FT: 11,000
SALES (est): 5MM-9.9MM **Privately Held**
WEB: www.nycoinc.com
SIC: 1742 Building insulation installation service
PA: API Group Inc
     1100 Old Highway 8 NW
     Saint Paul MN 55112
     651 636-4320

(G-2765)
PRESBYTERIAN HOMES OF INVER
6307 Burnham Cir Ofc   (55076-1666)
PHONE 651 451-5959
FAX: 651 552-2801
EMP: 25 **EST:** 2004
SALES (est): 500-999K **Privately Held**
SIC: 8361 8052 Residential care facility; intermediate care facility

(G-2766)
RIVERHEIGHTS CHAMBER OF
5782 Blackshire Path   (55076-1623)
PHONE 651 451-2266
Jennifer Gale, *President*
Jody Hencier, *Vice Pres*
Carol Swenson, *Vice Pres*
Velita Frandrup, *Treasurer*
Kevin Kraus, *Treasurer*
EMP: 26 **EST:** 1903
SQ FT: 795 **Privately Held**
WEB: www.riverheights.com
SIC: 8611 Chamber of commerce

(G-2767)
SAFE-WAY BUS CO (PA)
6030 Carmen Ave   (55076-4418)
PHONE 651 451-1375
FAX: 651 451-3525
Worth Stiles, *President*
Jane Stiles, *General Mgr*
Mary P Stiles, *Corp Secy*
Wurst Stilesretired, *Manager*
EMP: 95 **EST:** 1970
SQ FT: 12,000 **Privately Held**
WEB: www.safewaybus.com
SIC: 4151 School bus service

(G-2768)
SANDRA HAMER
1870 50th St E Ste 9   (55077-1270)
PHONE 651 254-0116
Sandra Hamer, *Manager*

EMP: 30
SALES (est): 1MM-4.9MM **Privately Held**
SIC: 6411 Insurance agency & broker

(G-2769)
SIGMA TAU OMEGA INC
8345 Delaney Cir   (55076-3421)
PO Box 18024, Saint Paul   (55118-0024)
PHONE 651 644-7200
Shawn Murphy, *President*
EMP: 25 **EST:** 2006 **Privately Held**
SIC: 8399 Community development groups

(G-2770)
STEENBERG WATRUD CONSTRUCTION
10967 Clark Rd   (55077-5359)
PHONE 651 457-2291
FAX: 651 457-8535
Steven R Watrud, *President*
Barb Watrud, *Corp Secy*
EMP: 25 **EST:** 1984
SQ FT: 8,000
SALES (est): 1MM-4.9MM **Privately Held**
WEB: www.steenbergwatrud.com
SIC: 1741 Foundation building contractor; bricklaying contractor; concrete block masonry laying contractor

(G-2771)
SWIFT TRANSPORTATION CORP
11380 Courthouse Blvd   (55077-5906)
PHONE 651 480-7850
FAX: 651 480-7857
Gray Croin, *Manager*
EMP: 40
SALES (est): 5MM-9.9MM **Privately Held**
WEB: www.swifttrans.com
SIC: 4213 Over the road trucking
HQ: Swift Transportation Co Inc
     2200 S 75th Ave
     Phoenix AZ 85043
     602 269-9700

(G-2772)
TRAIL DODGE INC
4665 S Robert Trl   (55077-1104)
PO Box 25980, Saint Paul   (55125-0980)
PHONE 651 455-2201
Len O Berg, *President*
Brian Berg, *Corp Secy*
Jacqueline Berg, *Vice Pres*
Scott Berg, *Treasurer*
Justin Erber, *Info Tech Mgr*
EMP: 72 **EST:** 1971
SQ FT: 98,500
SALES (est): 25MM-49.9MM **Privately Held**
WEB: www.traildodge.com
SIC: 7515 Retails new & used automobiles; retails new & used trucks, tractors & trailers; retails new & used vans; passenger car leasing

(G-2773)
WAGNER SOD CO INC
8150 Courthouse Blvd   (55077-3900)
PHONE 651 457-6037
FAX: 651 457-4430
Willard Wagner, *President*
Norbert Wagner, *President*
Mary A Wagner, *President*
Mary K Spychalla, *Executive*
EMP: 30 **EST:** 1962 **Privately Held**
WEB: www.wagnersod.com
SIC: 0181 0782 4959 Sod farm; snow plowing services; landscaping services

(G-2774)
WINCO LANDSCAPE INC
1848 50th St E Ste 102   (55077-1286)
PHONE 651 455-3070
FAX: 651 455-2998
Tim Winters, *President*
David Johnson, *Corp Secy*
Ken Owl, *Vice Pres*
Brenda Porter, *Manager*
EMP: 30 **EST:** 1985
SQ FT: 971 **Privately Held**
WEB: www.wincolandscape.com
SIC: 0782 1731 1741 1771 Landscaping services; lighting system contractor; bricklaying contractor; concrete contractor

(G-2775)
WOODLAND HEIGHTS HEALTH CARE
2060 Upper 55th St E   (55077-1725)
PHONE 651 451-1881
FAX: 651 451-3378
Howard Groff, *President*
Bonnie Campau, *Administrator*
EMP: 110 **EST:** 1966
SQ FT: 55,712
SALES (est): 1MM-4.9MM **Privately Held**
SIC: 8051 Skilled nursing care facility
PA: Tealwood Care Centers Inc
     9031 Penn Ave S
     Minneapolis MN 55431
     952 888-2923

ISABELLA
Lake County

(G-2776)
CAMP BUCKSKIN
9830 Fredrickson Rd   (55607-3312)
PO Box 389, Ely   (55731-0389)
PHONE 218 365-2121
Tom Bauer, *Owner*
EMP: 55 **EST:** 1988
SALES (est): 1MM-4.9MM **Privately Held**
WEB: www.campbuckskin.com
SIC: 7032 Recreational & sporting camp

ISANTI
Isanti County

(G-2777)
AMERICAN MANUFACTURING INC
1 Enterprise Ave NE   (55040-6809)
PHONE 763 444-9225
Curtis Hough, *President*
EMP: 45 **EST:** 1966
SQ FT: 45,000
SALES (est): 5MM-9.9MM **Privately Held**
SIC: 7692 Manufactures motor vehicle parts & accessories; manufactures punching, shearing & bending machines; manufactures lasers welding, drilling & cutting equipment; welding service

(G-2778)
BOB PANKAN & SONS CONCRETE
27594 Youngston St NE   (55040-3607)
PO Box 40   (55040-0040)
PHONE 763 444-5720
FAX: 763 444-6006
Robert Pankan Jr, *President*
Shelly Pankan, *Office Mgr*
EMP: 25 **EST:** 1974
SALES (est): 1MM-4.9MM **Privately Held**
SIC: 1741 1771 Masonry & stonework contractor; concrete contractor

(G-2779)
FIRST STATE TIRE DISPOSAL INC
1500 278th Ln NE   (55040-6314)
PHONE 763 434-0578
FAX: 763 434-3072
Monte K Niemi, *CEO*
Bill Mueller, *Manager*
Francisco Curbs, *Exec Dir*
EMP: 30 **EST:** 1987
SALES (est): 1MM-4.9MM **Privately Held**
SIC: 7534 Automotive tire rebuilding & retreading service

(G-2780)
SAHARA SANDS
465 265th Ave NE   (55040-5259)
PHONE 763 444-6491
Steve Gilbraith, *Treasurer*
EMP: 25 **Privately Held**
WEB: www.saharasands.com
SIC: 8699 Personal interest organization

(G-2781)
SENIOR ISANTI CITIZEN COM
Also Called: Isanti Snior Citizen Cmnty Ctr
121 Norelius St   (55040-5354)
PHONE 763 444-6100
Jim Brodman, *Director*
EMP: 28 **EST:** 1990
SALES (est): 500-999K **Privately Held**
SIC: 8322 Geriatric social services

(G-2782)
YERIGAN CONSTRUCTION CO
27741 University Ave NE   (55040-5270)
PHONE 763 444-5353
FAX: 763 444-6448
Bruce Yerigan, *President*
Kristine Yerigan, *Corp Secy*
EMP: 28 **EST:** 1986
SALES (est): 5MM-9.9MM **Privately Held**
WEB: www.yeriganconstruction.com
SIC: 1521 1741 New single-family home construction service; single-family home general remodeling service; masonry & stonework contractor

---

ISLE
Mille Lacs County

(G-2783)
ISLE VIEW APARTMENTS
205 N 1st St Fl 1   (56342)
PO Box 675   (56342-0675)
PHONE 320 676-8624
William Taufam, *Owner*
EMP: 41 **EST:** 1979
SALES (est): 5MM-9.9MM **Privately Held**
SIC: 6513 Apartment building operator

IVANHOE
Lincoln County

(G-2784)
DIVINE PROVIDENCE HEALTH CTR
312 E George St   (56142-9707)
PO Box 136   (56142-0136)
PHONE 507 694-1414
FAX: 507 694-1191
Pat Hoseck, *Corp Secy*
David Skorczewski, *Facilities Mgr*
Sherry Brown, *Engineering*
Carol Johnson, *CFO*
Andrea Rost, *Manager*
EMP: 130 **EST:** 1963
SQ FT: 56,400
SALES (est): 10MM-24.9MM **Privately Held**
WEB: www.dphc.net
SIC: 8062 8051 Medical hospital; skilled nursing care facility

---

JACKSON
Jackson County

(G-2785)
AG FORTE LLC
76645 US Highway 71   (56143-3287)
PHONE 507 847-5110
Clayton Sexton, *General Mgr*
Roger Bultman, *Sales Executive*
Janis Wrege, *Admin Asst*
EMP: 30 **Privately Held**
WEB: www.agforte.com
SIC: 0253 Turkey farm
PA: AG Forte LLC
     N Highway 39
     Aurora MO 65605
     417 678-5021

(G-2786)
BANK MIDWEST
509 3rd St   (56143-1610)
PO Box 49   (56143-0049)
PHONE 507 847-3010
FAX: 507 847-4645
Roger Lind, *Manager*
EMP: 30
SALES (est): 5MM-9.9MM **Privately Held**

SIC: 6021 National commercial bank
PA: Bank Midwest
118 Downtown Plz
Fairmont MN 56031
507 235-3327

(G-2787)
CITY OF JACKSON
Also Called: Stanford Medical Ctr Jackson
1430 North Hwy (56143-1093)
PHONE..............................507 847-2420
Hans Carlson, *Counsel*
Twilla Vanhal, *Ch Radiology*
Suzanne Prine, *Accountant*
Eva Fransen, *MIS Staff*
Lisa Hartke, *Phys Thrpy Dir*
EMP: 63
SALES (est): 5MM-9.9MM **Privately Held**
SIC: 8062 Medical hospital
PA: City of Jackson
80 W Ashley St
Jackson MN 56143
507 847-4410

(G-2788)
CITY OF JACKSON
Also Called: County Library
80 W Ashley St (56143-1669)
PHONE..............................507 847-4410
Dean Albrecht, *Administrator*
EMP: 40
SALES (est): 5MM-9.9MM **Privately Held**
SIC: 6111 Government national mortgage
association credit agency
PA: City of Jackson
80 W Ashley St
Jackson MN 56143
507 847-4410

(G-2789)
COOP FCA (PA)
105 Jackson St (56143-1118)
PHONE..............................507 847-4160
FAX: 507 847-2521
Mark Eggimann, *President*
Don Stenzel, *Corp Secy*
Gene Michelson, *Treasurer*
Randy Schmidt, *Accounting Dir*
Larry Olson, *Administration*
EMP: 36 **EST:** 1909
SQ FT: 3,000
SALES (corp-wide): 130M **Privately Held**
SIC: 5153 5171 5191 Wholesale grain
elevator; wholesales agricultural chemicals;
wholesales corn; wholesales oats;
wholesales soybeans; wholesales
petroleum bulk stations; wholesales feed;
wholesales field, garden & flower seeds;
wholesales farm supplies

(G-2790)
EARTHLINK INC
924 Highway 71 N (56143-1084)
PO Box 119 (56143-0119)
PHONE..............................507 847-2700
Sandy Phillips, *Branch Mgr*
EMP: 50
SALES (est): 10MM-24.9MM **Publicly Held**
WEB: www.earthlink.com
SIC: 4813 Online services providers
PA: EarthLink Inc
1375 Peachtree St NE Ste A9
Atlanta GA 30309
404 815-0770

(G-2791)
ERICKSON TRUCK SALES & SALVAGE
75196 Petersburg Rd (56143-3274)
PO Box 351 (56143-0351)
PHONE..............................507 847-3664
Jack Erickson, *President*
Angie Hample, *Manager*
EMP: 48 **EST:** 1996
SQ FT: 5,400
SALES (est): 10MM-24.9MM **Privately Held**
WEB: www.ericksontrucks.com
SIC: 5015 Retails used trucks, tractors &
trailers; wholesales & retails used
automotive supplies

(G-2792)
EVANGELICAL LUTHERAN GOOD
Also Called: Jackson Good Samaritan Center
601 West St (56143-1200)
PHONE..............................507 847-3100
FAX: 507 847-2119
Gordy Hormann, *Administrator*
Angel Normandin, *Director*
EMP: 132
SQ FT: 30,000
SALES (est): 5MM-9.9MM **Privately Held**
WEB: www.good-sam.com
SIC: 8059 8051 Nursing home; skilled
nursing care facility
PA: Evangelical Lutheran Good
4800 W 57th St
Sioux Falls SD 57108
605 362-3100

(G-2793)
GORDY'S INC
Also Called: Gordys Food
916 Highway 71 N (56143-1084)
PO Box 266 (56143-0266)
PHONE..............................507 847-2074
Aaron Anderson, *Manager*
EMP: 40
SALES (est): 5MM-9.9MM **Privately Held**
SIC: 5149 Retail chain grocery store;
wholesales groceries

(G-2794)
JACKSON CITY AMBULANCE
309 Sheridan St (56143-1579)
PO Box 242 (56143-0242)
PHONE..............................507 847-5306
FAX: 507 847-3264
Mike Emuchlinski, *Administrator*
EMP: 30 **EST:** 1968
SALES (est): 1MM-4.9MM **Privately Held**
SIC: 4119 Ambulance service

(G-2795)
JACKSON COTTONWOOD COMMUNITY
407 5th St Rm 209 (56143-1586)
PHONE..............................507 847-2366
Patricia A Stewart, *Principal*
Mary Bezdicek, *Principal*
EMP: 33
SALES (est): 1MM-4.9MM **Privately Held**
SIC: 8051 Skilled nursing care facility

(G-2796)
JACKSON MUNICIPAL CLINIC
1430 North Hwy (56143-1093)
PHONE..............................507 847-2200
FAX: 507 847-3808
Mary Ruyter, *CEO*
Jennifer Tewes, *Office Mgr*
Dean Albrecht, *Manager*
Laura Potthoff, *Nursing Dir*
Martha Johnson, *Physician Asst*
EMP: 50 **EST:** 1979
SALES (est): 5MM-9.9MM **Privately Held**
SIC: 8011 Clinic operated by physicians

(G-2797)
NEW FASHION PORK INC
164 Industrial Park (56143-9588)
PO Box 244 (56143-0244)
PHONE..............................507 847-4610
Brad Freking, *President*
Mike Wilson, *Corp Secy*
Conrad Schmit, *Corp Secy*
John M Walsh, *Vice Pres*
Gary Dial, *Treasurer*
EMP: 180 **EST:** 1994
SQ FT: 7,000 **Privately Held**
SIC: 0213 Hog & pig farming

(G-2798)
SANFORD HEALTH
1430 North Hwy (56143-1093)
PHONE..............................507 847-2420
Thomas R Loff, *Branch Mgr*
EMP: 45
SALES (est): 1MM-4.9MM **Privately Held**
WEB: www.sanfordluverne.org

SIC: 8062 Medical hospital
PA: Sanford Health
1305 W 18th St
Sioux Falls SD 57105
605 333-1000

(G-2799)
SANFORD HEALTH NETWORK
Also Called: Jackson Medical Center
1430 North Hwy (56143-1093)
PHONE..............................507 847-2420
Jim Hunt, *Engineering*
Gail Eike, *CFO*
Mary J Ruyter, *Administrator*
Jennifer Tewes, *CIO*
Brenda Anderson, *Director*
EMP: 78
SALES (est): 5MM-9.9MM **Privately Held**
SIC: 8741 8011 Hospital management
services; physicians' office & clinic
PA: Sanford Health Network
1305 W 18th St
Sioux Falls SD 57105
605 328-2929

(G-2800)
USF HOLLAND INC
Also Called: USFreightways
172 Industrial Park (56143-9588)
PHONE..............................507 847-2625
FAX: 507 847-2686
Chris Larson, *Manager*
EMP: 30
SALES (est): 1MM-4.9MM **Publicly Held**
WEB: www.usfc.com
SIC: 4213 Long-distance less than
truckload freight trucking services
HQ: USF Holland Inc
750 E 40th St
Holland MI 49423
616 395-5000

(G-2801)
ZIEGLER AG EQUIPMENT
191 Industrial Park (56143-9589)
PHONE..............................507 847-7600
Robert Hoffman, *Corp Secy*
Rollie Ogren, *Vice Pres*
Larry Hansen, *Mfg Staff*
Gary Robinson, *Mfg Staff*
Dean Trask, *Design Engr*
EMP: 30 **EST:** 2006
SALES (est): 10MM-24.9MM **Privately Held**
SIC: 5083 Wholesales farm & garden
machinery

JANESVILLE
Waseca County

(G-2802)
JANESVILLE NURSING HOME INC
102 E North St (56048-9793)
PHONE..............................507 231-5113
FAX: 507 234-6310
Antony Newman, *Principal*
Pete Madel, *Administrator*
EMP: 70 **EST:** 1965
SALES (est): 1MM-4.9MM **Privately Held**
SIC: 8059 8051 Home for the mentally
retarded; skilled nursing care facility

(G-2803)
SMITH'S MILL IMPLEMENT INC
63065 206th St (56048-4195)
PHONE..............................507 234-5191
FAX: 507 234-5703
Roger Joyce, *President*
Mike Wolf, *President*
Ron Joyce, *Corp Secy*
Patrick Rigdon, *Vice Pres*
EMP: 26
SQ FT: 1,620
SALES (est): 10MM-24.9MM **Privately Held**
SIC: 5083 Wholesales farm equipment
parts & supplies

JASPER
Pipestone County

(G-2804)
LIONS CLUB OF JASPER
221 Wall St E (56144-1101)
PHONE..............................507 348-8605
Donald Plahn, *Manager*
EMP: 36 **EST:** 1975 **Privately Held**
SIC: 8641 Civic associations

JORDAN
Scott County

(G-2805)
JORDAN TRANSFORMER LLC
1000 Syndicate St (55352-1110)
PO Box 98 (55352-0098)
PHONE..............................952 492-2720
FAX: 952 492-2796
Earl Cummings, *General Mgr*
Richard J Ames, *Mng Member*
Cinda Smith, *Manager*
Cathy Fullerton, *Manager*
Ken Kampshoss, *CTO*
EMP: 67 **EST:** 2004
SQ FT: 54,000
SALES (est): 5MM-9.9MM **Privately Held**
WEB: www.jordantransformer.com
SIC: 7629 High voltage electrical equipment
repair service

(G-2806)
MALONE GOLF INC
Also Called: Ridges At Sand Creek
21775 Ridges Dr (55352-9713)
PHONE..............................952 492-2644
Mike Malone, *President*
Joe Gingerelli, *Manager*
EMP: 80 **EST:** 1999
SQ FT: 14,000
SALES (est): 1MM-4.9MM **Privately Held**
WEB: www.ridgesatsandcreek.com
SIC: 7992 Public golf course; retails
sporting goods

(G-2807)
MINNESOTA VALLEY ELECTRIC
125 Minnesota Valley Dr (55352-9369)
PHONE..............................952 492-2313
FAX: 952 492-8274
Roger Geckler, *President*
Tom Kovalak, *General Mgr*
Dan Schoenecker, *Vice Pres*
Dave Beckius, *Opers Mgr*
Gerry Mareck, *CFO*
EMP: 94 **EST:** 1937
SQ FT: 70,000
SALES (est): 25MM-49.9MM **Privately Held**
WEB: www.mvec.net
SIC: 4911 Electric power distribution service

(G-2808)
O K CORRAL INC
20201 Johnson Memorial Dr (55352-9638)
PHONE..............................952 492-6700
FAX: 952 492-5841
Dick Ames, *President*
Kris Lennartson, *Vice Pres*
Shawn Dahl, *Treasurer*
Darwin Goetz, *Manager*
Laurie Malchow, *Director*
EMP: 55 **EST:** 1994
SQ FT: 3,600
SALES (est): 1MM-4.9MM **Privately Held**
SIC: 7299 Full service independent family
restaurant; banquet hall facility

(G-2809)
SCOTT COUNTY HIGHWAY ENGINEER
600 Country Trl E (55352-9339)
PHONE..............................952 496-8346
Brad Larson, *Principal*
Tom Helmrich, *Administrator*
EMP: 50 **EST:** 1991
SALES (est): 5MM-9.9MM **Privately Held**
SIC: 8711 Engineering services

www.HarrisInfo.com
130
2011 Harris Minnesota
Services Directory
▲=Import ▼=Export
◆=Import/Export

(G-2810)
SIWEK LUMBER & MILLWORK INC
350 Valley View Dr (55352-1025)
PHONE..............................952 492-6666
FAX: 952 492-6676
Dave Siwek, *Owner*
Mary Siwek, *Vice Pres*
EMP: 25
SQ FT: 58,140
SALES (est): 1MM-4.9MM **Privately Held**
SIC: 1542 Retails building products & materials; agricultural building construction; manufactures wooden containers; sawing & planing mill
PA: Siwek Lumber & Millwork Inc
2536 Marshall St NE
Minneapolis MN 55418
612 781-3333

(G-2811)
TRENTROY CORP
18440 Langford Ave (55352-9338)
PHONE..............................952 445-3820
Troy Wangerin, *President*
EMP: 58 EST: 1991
SALES (est): 5MM-9.9MM **Privately Held**
SIC: 1794 Excavating contractor

(G-2812)
VALLEY PLUMBING CO INC
860 Quaker Ave (55352-1060)
PHONE..............................952 492-2121
FAX: 952 492-2617
Daniel D Morris, *CEO*
Christopher Morris, *Vice Pres*
Morris Kallene, *Treasurer*
EMP: 125 EST: 1976
SQ FT: 5,000
SALES (est): 10MM-24.9MM **Privately Held**
WEB: www.valleyplumbingco.com
SIC: 1711 Plumbing service

(G-2813)
WOLF MOTORS CO INC
600 2nd St W (55352-1213)
PHONE..............................952 492-2340
David Wolf, *Owner*
EMP: 35 EST: 1982
SALES (est): 1MM-4.9MM **Privately Held**
SIC: 7532 7538 Automotive body shop; automotive engine repair service

KANDIYOHI
Kandiyohi County

(G-2814)
KANDI-WORKS DEVELOPMENTAL
537 Pacific Ave (56251)
PO Box 254 (56251-0254)
PHONE..............................320 382-6156
FAX: 320 382-6157
Deb Terwischa, *Exec Dir*
EMP: 45
SALES (est): 1MM-4.9MM **Privately Held**
SIC: 8331 7331 Vocational rehabilitation agency; direct mail advertising service
PA: Kandi-Works Developmental
111 5th St
Atwater MN 56209
320 974-8840

KARLSTAD
Kittson County

(G-2815)
TEALWOOD CARE CENTERS INC
Also Called: Karlstad Heathcare Center
304 Washington Ave W (56732-4018)
PHONE..............................218 436-2161
FAX: 218 436-4161
Curt Jenson, *Principal*
Diane Morris, *Administrator*
EMP: 100
SALES (est): 1MM-4.9MM **Privately Held**

SIC: 8051 Convalescent home
PA: Tealwood Care Centers Inc
9031 Penn Ave S
Minneapolis MN 55431
952 888-2923

(G-2816)
TRI COUNTY AMBULANCE SERVICE
Karlstad Memorial Hosp (56732)
PHONE..............................218 436-2230
Earl Hougard, *President*
John Wetterlund, *Principal*
Erling Nesteby, *Vice Pres*
James Pederson, *Treasurer*
EMP: 31 EST: 1975
SALES (est): 1MM-4.9MM **Privately Held**
SIC: 4119 Ambulance service

(G-2817)
WIKSTROM TELEPHONE CO INC
212 Main St S (56732-4002)
PO Box 217 (56732-0217)
PHONE..............................218 436-2121
FAX: 218 436-3100
Curtis Wikstrom, *President*
Kathleen Glines, *Corp Secy*
Leslie Wikstrom, *Vice Pres*
George Wikstrom Jr, *Vice Pres*
Neil Wikstrom, *Treasurer*
EMP: 54 EST: 1947
SQ FT: 20,000 **Privately Held**
WEB: www.wiktel.com
SIC: 4813 Local telephone communications services

KASSON
Dodge County

(G-2818)
A & A ELECTRIC & UNDERGROUND
100 9th St SE (55944-3808)
PHONE..............................507 634-7453
Joel Alberts, *President*
Hillary Alberts, *Corp Secy*
Troy Knutson, *Office Mgr*
EMP: 29 EST: 1994
SQ FT: 17,000
SALES (est): 1MM-4.9MM **Privately Held**
SIC: 1731 1623 Electrical contractor; cable laying service

(G-2819)
DIGGERS BAR & GRILL INC
401 8th St SE (55944-1813)
PO Box 5 (55944-0005)
PHONE..............................507 634-7400
FAX: 507 634-3190
Ron Grannick, *President*
Wes Engbrecht, *Principal*
EMP: 60 EST: 1998
SALES (est): 1MM-4.9MM **Privately Held**
SIC: 7299 Limited service grill restaurant; banquet hall facility

(G-2820)
DODGE COUNTY BATTERED WOMEN'S
Also Called: Womens Shelter
402 S Mantorville Ave (55944-1261)
PO Box 457, Rochester (55903-0457)
PHONE..............................507 634-6070
Suzie Christensen, *Principal*
Dennis Nugent, *CIO*
Judy Miller, *Director*
Vicki Duncan, *Asst Director*
Bunny Calahan, *Asst Director*
EMP: 30 EST: 1982
SALES (est): 1MM-4.9MM **Privately Held**
SIC: 8322 Crisis intervention center; self-help organization

(G-2821)
KASSON & MANTORVILLE TELEPHONE
Also Called: Km Telecom
18 2nd Ave NW (55944-1448)
PHONE..............................507 634-2511
FAX: 507 634-2500
Jon R Tollefson, *President*
Beth Tollefson, *Corp Secy*

Mary Emhke, *Vice Pres*
Bruce Ludwig, *Plant Supt*
Glenda Tollefson, *Treasurer*
EMP: 25 EST: 1901
SQ FT: 18,000 **Privately Held**
WEB: www.kmtel.com
SIC: 4813 4841 Local & long distance telephone communications services; cable television services

(G-2822)
MAYO CLINIC ROCHESTER
Also Called: Kasson-Mayo Fmly Prctice Clnic
411 W Main St (55944-1141)
PHONE..............................507 634-4744
FAX: 507 284-8155
Ruth Herman, *Office Mgr*
Halina Woroncow MD, *Med Doctor*
Jane Myers, *Nurse Practr*
Emily Cheid, *Physician Asst*
EMP: 25
SALES (est): 1MM-4.9MM **Privately Held**
SIC: 8011 Clinic operated by physicians
PA: Mayo Clinic
200 1st St SW
Rochester MN 55905
507 284-2511

(G-2823)
REMWOODVALE INC
1406 5th St NW (55944-1630)
PHONE..............................507 634-6073
Tracy Jeno, *Principal*
EMP: 50 EST: 2003
SALES (est): 1MM-4.9MM **Privately Held**
SIC: 8361 Home for the mentally handicapped

(G-2824)
SWENKE CO INC
103 1/2 W Main St (55944-1456)
PO Box 5 (55944-0005)
PHONE..............................507 634-7778
FAX: 507 634-7771
Richard Swenke, *President*
Shelly Coleman, *Admin Asst*
EMP: 46 EST: 1984
SALES (est): 5MM-9.9MM **Privately Held**
SIC: 1623 1622 Sewer line construction; bridge construction

(G-2825)
SWENKE PROPERTIES INC
101 W Main St (55944-1456)
PO Box 5 (55944-0005)
PHONE..............................507 634-7778
Richard Swenke, *President*
Shelly Coleman, *Officer*
EMP: 50 EST: 1993
SQ FT: 3,080
SALES (est): 5MM-9.9MM **Privately Held**
SIC: 1622 Elevated highway construction

KEEWATIN
Itasca County

(G-2826)
UNITED STATES STEEL CORP
Also Called: US Steel Kwtino Taconite Plant
1 Old Mine Rd (55753)
PO Box 217 (55753-0217)
PHONE..............................218 778-8700
FAX: 218 778-6112
Emil Draskovich, *Division Mgr*
Scott Coleman, *COO*
Jeremy Smolich, *Plant Mgr*
Karla McKenzie, *Safety Mgr*
Larry Schmelzer, *Engineer*
EMP: 60
SALES (est): 10MM-24.9MM **Publicly Held**
WEB: www.uss.com
SIC: 1011 Iron ore mining
PA: United States Steel Corp
600 Grant St
Pittsburgh PA 15219
412 433-1121

KELLIHER
Beltrami County

(G-2827)
CORNERSTONE RESIDENCE
280 Main St (56650)
PO Box 189 (56650-0189)
PHONE..............................218 647-8258
Allen Potvin, *Owner*
Britney Hack, *Office Mgr*
EMP: 46 EST: 1990
SALES (est): 1MM-4.9MM **Privately Held**
SIC: 8361 Geriatric residential care

KENYON
Goodhue County

(G-2828)
KENYON SUNSET HOME
127 Gunderson Blvd (55946-1014)
PHONE..............................507 789-6134
FAX: 507 789-6586
David V Dergon, *Administrator*
David Vandergon, *Administrator*
Marie Spidahl, *Coordinator*
EMP: 90
SALES (est): 1MM-4.9MM **Privately Held**
WEB: www.kenyonsunsethome.com
SIC: 8051 8052 Extended care facility; personal care facility

(G-2829)
SECURITY STATE BANK OF KENYON
602 2nd St (55946-1334)
PHONE..............................507 789-6123
FAX: 507 789-6127
Jeffry T Ellingson, *President*
Dawn Simon, *Vice Pres*
Harvey Fossum, *Vice Pres*
EMP: 26 EST: 1934
SALES (est): 5MM-9.9MM **Privately Held**
WEB: www.ssbkenyon.com
SIC: 6036 6022 State savings bank; state commercial bank

KIMBALL
Stearns County

(G-2830)
ARNOLD'S OF MANKATO INC (PA)
701 E Hwy 55 (55353)
PO Box 388 (55353-0388)
PHONE..............................320 398-3800
FAX: 320 398-3814
John Arnold, *President*
Paul Arnold, *Corp Secy*
Peter Arnold, *Vice Pres*
Kathy Miles, *Assistant*
EMP: 25 EST: 1935
SQ FT: 25,000 **Privately Held**
WEB: www.arnoldsinc.com
SIC: 5083 Wholesales agricultural machinery & equipment; retails lawn & garden equipment

(G-2831)
AUGUSTA ELECTRIC INC
19383 E Shore Dr (55353-9779)
PHONE..............................320 398-2189
Bernard Gregory, *President*
Mike Leonard, *Manager*
EMP: 40 EST: 1979
SQ FT: 15,000
SALES (est): 1MM-4.9MM **Privately Held**
WEB: www.augustaelectric.com
SIC: 1731 General electrical contractor

(G-2832)
JOHNSON CO INC, R M
Also Called: Kimball Railcar Repair
211 Willow Creek Rd (55353-9646)
PHONE..............................320 398-6080
FAX: 320 398-6262
Jamie Miller, *Vice Pres*
Pete Vossen, *Manager*

GEOGRAPHIC

(PA)=Parent Co (HQ)=Headquarters (DH)=Div Headquarters
✿ = New business established in last 2 years

2011 Harris Minnesota
Services Directory

© Harris InfoSource 1-866-281-6415
131

EMP: 30
SALES (est): 1MM-4.9MM **Privately Held**
WEB: www.ezcrusher.com
SIC: 4789 Provides railroad car repair services

(G-2833)
KIMBALL GOLF CLUB INC
11823 County Rd 150 (55353)
PO Box 188 (55353-0188)
PHONE..............................320 398-2285
FAX: 320 398-2288
Leo Wirth, *President*
Judd Bonham, *General Mgr*
Diana Hemfling, *Vice Pres*
EMP: 25 **EST:** 1968
SALES (est): 1MM-4.9MM **Privately Held**
WEB: www.kimballgolf.com
SIC: 7992 Public golf course

(G-2834)
KUECHLE UNDERGROUND INC
10998 State Hwy 55 (55353)
PO Box 509 (55353-0509)
PHONE..............................320 398-8888
FAX: 320 398-8889
Jerome Kuechle, *President*
Trudy Kuechle, *Corp Secy*
EMP: 50 **EST:** 1995
SQ FT: 2,000
SALES (est): 5MM-9.9MM **Privately Held**
SIC: 1623 Water & sewer line construction

(G-2835)
WILLOW CREEK CONCRETE PRODUCTS
12626 County Road 150 (55353-2746)
PHONE..............................320 398-5415
FAX: 320 398-5416
Sharon Blomquist, *CEO*
Todd Strand, *President*
Rick Johnson, *Manager*
EMP: 27 **EST:** 1993
SQ FT: 12,000
SALES (est): 1MM-4.9MM **Privately Held**
WEB: www.willowcreekconcrete.com
SIC: 0782 1741 Manufactures concrete block & brick; retaining wall construction; retails masonry materials & supplies; manufactures concrete products; landscaping services

LA CRESCENT
Houston County

(G-2836)
ABILITY BUILDING CENTER
62 N 3rd St (55947-1117)
PHONE..............................507 895-7161
EMP: 25
SALES (est): 500-999K **Privately Held**
WEB: www.abcinc.org
SIC: 8361 Home for the physically handicapped
PA: Ability Building Center
      1911 14th St NW
      Rochester MN 55901
      507 281-6262

(G-2837)
AMERICAN LEGION POST 595
509 N Chestnut St (55947-1189)
PO Box 162 (55947-0162)
PHONE..............................507 895-4595
FAX: 507 895-5595
Jane Groth, *Principal*
EMP: 25 **EST:** 1954 **Privately Held**
SIC: 8641 Veterans' organization

(G-2838)
B L E A INC
Also Called: Lancer House
1700 Lancer Blvd (55947-1624)
PHONE..............................507 895-8111
FAX: 507 895-4505
Darren Winkers, *Director*
EMP: 45
SALES (est): 1MM-4.9MM **Privately Held**

SIC: 8361 Home for the physically handicapped
PA: B L E A Inc
      216 E South St
      Caledonia MN 55921
      507 725-2486

(G-2839)
BAUER'S MARKET & NURSERY INC
221 N 2nd St (55947-1112)
PHONE..............................507 895-4583
FAX: 507 895-4620
Bruce Bauer, *President*
EMP: 40 **EST:** 1957
SQ FT: 10,000
SALES (est): 5MM-9.9MM **Privately Held**
SIC: 0782 Fruit & vegetable market; retail nursery & garden center; landscaping services

(G-2840)
BAUMGARTNER TRUCKING INC
90 N 1st St (55947-1199)
PHONE..............................507 895-8490
FAX: 507 895-4061
Dennis Baumgartner, *President*
Fred Baumgartner, *Vice Pres*
EMP: 35 **EST:** 1955
SALES (est): 1MM-4.9MM **Privately Held**
SIC: 4212 Contract mail carriers; local lumber & log hauling services

(G-2841)
BEVERLY ENTERPRISES - MN
Also Called: La Crescent Healthcare Center
101 S Hill St (55947-1389)
PHONE..............................507 895-4445
Bill Ross, *Manager*
Larry Pupp, *Administrator*
Lynn Meysenbourg, *Director*
EMP: 80
SALES (est): 1MM-4.9MM **Privately Held**
WEB: www.beverlynet.com
SIC: 8051 Skilled nursing care facility
HQ: Beverly Enterprises - MN
      650 Ramer Ave S
      Rush City MN 55069
      320 358-4765

(G-2842)
QUINCY NEWSPAPERS INC
Also Called: Wxow-TV
3705 County Road 25 (55947-9779)
PHONE..............................507 895-9969
FAX: 507 895-8124
Daniel Rasmussen, *Chief Engr*
Jarrett Liddicoat, *Engineering*
Charles F Roth, *Branch Mgr*
Brian Schumacher, *Manager*
David Booth, *Manager*
EMP: 58
SALES (est): 10MM-24.9MM **Privately Held**
WEB: www.whig.com
SIC: 4833 Television broadcasting station; mayors' office
PA: Quincy Newspapers Inc
      130 S 5th St
      Quincy IL 62301
      217 223-5100

(G-2843)
READY BUS LINE CO INC
1369 County Road 6 (55947-9669)
PO Box 256 (55947-0256)
PHONE..............................507 895-2349
FAX: 507 895-2380
Thomas Ready, *President*
Kathryn Ready, *Corp Secy*
EMP: 85 **EST:** 1950
SQ FT: 18,000
SALES (est): 1MM-4.9MM **Privately Held**
WEB: www.readybusline.com
SIC: 4151 4119 4141 4142 School bus service; local passenger transportation service; local bus charter service; long-distance bus charter service

(G-2844)
SMALL CHANGE DIAPER SERVICE
62 N 3rd St (55947-1117)
PHONE..............................507 895-8625
FAX: 507 895-3969
Carman Barthel, *Manager*

Judy Wandring, *Director*
EMP: 25 **EST:** 1990
SALES (est): 1MM-4.9MM **Privately Held**
SIC: 7219 Diaper service

(G-2845)
WIESER BROTHERS GENERAL CONTR ◆
200 Twilite St (55947-1356)
PHONE..............................507 895-8903
FAX: 507 895-8438
Jeff Wieser, *President*
EMP: 80 **EST:** 2008
SALES (est): 10MM-24.9MM **Privately Held**
SIC: 1611 General highway & street construction service

LA SALLE
Watonwan County

(G-2846)
CRYSTAL VALLEY COOP
111 S Broadway (56056-4400)
PO Box 8 (56056-0008)
PHONE..............................507 642-8837
Bryon Chrestenson, *President*
Dave Peters, *General Mgr*
Todd Wilhm, *Manager*
EMP: 35 **EST:** 1908
SQ FT: 2,400
SALES (est): 25MM-49.9MM **Privately Held**
SIC: 5191 5153 5171 Wholesales agricultural fertilizer; manufactures animal feed; manufactures flour & other grain mill products; wholesales agricultural chemicals; wholesales grains; wholesales petroleum bulk stations; wholesales feed

LAFAYETTE
Nicollet County

(G-2847)
UNITED FARMERS COOPERATIVE
840 Pioneer Ave (56054-7727)
PO Box 4 (56054-0004)
PHONE..............................507 228-8224
FAX: 507 228-8766
Shelley Quast, *General Mgr*
Ryan Aultman, *Safety Mgr*
Lorie Reinarts, *CFO*
Kelly Powell, *Sales Executive*
Andy Breeggemann, *Branch Mgr*
EMP: 40
SALES (est): 1MM-4.9MM **Privately Held**
SIC: 5153 Retails farm supplies; wholesales grains
PA: United Farmers Cooperative
      705 E 4th St
      Winthrop MN 55396
      507 647-6600

LAKE BENTON
Lincoln County

(G-2848)
GENERAL ELECTRIC CO
Hwy 14 W (56149)
PO Box 323 (56149-0323)
PHONE..............................507 368-9222
FAX: 507 368-9634
Kurt Eliason, *Manager*
Melissa Carmichael, *Manager*
Richard Soles, *Director*
EMP: 40
SALES (est): 25MM-49.9MM **Publicly Held**
WEB: www.ge.com
SIC: 4911 Electric services; retails insulation & energy conservation products
PA: General Electric Co
      3135 Easton Tpke
      Fairfield CT 06828
      203 373-2211

LAKE CITY
Goodhue County

(G-2849)
LAKE CITY MEDICAL CENTER-MAYO
500 W Grant St (55041-1143)
PHONE..............................651 345-3321
Tom Witt, *CEO*
Douglas Pflaum, *Corp Secy*
Mark Brown, *COO*
Dennis Stano, *Vice Pres*
Steven Kraft, *Med Doctor*
EMP: 300 **EST:** 1918
SQ FT: 30,000
SALES (est): 25MM-49.9MM **Privately Held**
SIC: 8011 Physicians' office & clinic
PA: Mayo Clinic
      200 1st St SW
      Rochester MN 55905
      507 284-2511

LAKE CITY
Wabasha County

(G-2850)
ALLIANCE BANK
105 E Lyon Ave (55041-1013)
PO Box 455 (55041-0455)
PHONE..............................651 345-3311
FAX: 651 345-4489
EMP: 25
SALES (est): 5MM-9.9MM **Privately Held**
SIC: 6022 State commercial bank
PA: Alliance Bank
      322 N Minnesota St
      New Ulm MN 56073
      507 354-3133

(G-2851)
BOILERMAKERS LOCAL LODGE 650
100 W Lyon Ave (55041-1600)
PO Box 460 (55041-0460)
PHONE..............................651 345-5472
Newton High, *President*
Tom Bremer, *Corp Secy*
EMP: 30 **EST:** 1976 **Privately Held**
SIC: 8631 Labor organization

(G-2852)
FOODLINER INC
415 S 10th St (55041)
PHONE..............................651 345-2860
Steve Eason, *Manager*
EMP: 65
SALES (est): 5MM-9.9MM **Privately Held**
SIC: 4213 4212 Over the road trucking; local trucking without storage services
HQ: Foodliner Inc
      2099 Southpark Ct Ste 2
      Dubuque IA 52003
      563 584-2670

(G-2853)
FORESTRY FIELD STATION
1801 S Oak St (55041-1937)
PHONE..............................651 345-3216
Terry Helbig, *Manager*
EMP: 25 **EST:** 2002 **Privately Held**
SIC: 0851 Forestry services

(G-2854)
ROTHGARN ENTERPRISE INC
Also Called: Port of Call
104 N Washington St (55041-1024)
PHONE..............................651 345-2324
Don Rothgarn, *President*
Blake Rothgarn, *Corp Secy*
Marie Rothgarn, *Vice Pres*
Brent Rothgarn, *Treasurer*
EMP: 30 **EST:** 1950
SQ FT: 1,200
SALES (est): 500-999K **Privately Held**
SIC: 7933 Eating place; bar; ten pin center

www.HarrisInfo.com
132
2011 Harris Minnesota
Services Directory
▲=Import ▼=Export
◆=Import/Export

(G-2855)
VALLEY CRAFT INC
2001 S Highway 61 (55041-9555)
PHONE...............................651 345-3386
FAX: 651 345-3606
Julie Schlueter, *General Mgr*
Roger Hollman, *Opers Mgr*
Tom Balow, *Prdtn Mgr*
Dan Seaward, *Maint Mgr*
Wayne Morris, *Mfg Staff*
EMP: 146
SALES (est): 25MM-49.9MM **Privately Held**
WEB: www.valleycraft.com
SIC: 5084 Manufactures fork, platform or
straddle industrial lift trucks; wholesales
industrial machinery & equipment
HQ: Valley Craft Inc
5600 Highway 169 N
Minneapolis MN 55428
763 536-6600

(G-2856)
WILD WINGS LLC (HQ)
2101 S Highway 61 (55041-3327)
PO Box 451 (55041-0451)
PHONE...............................651 345-5355
FAX: 651 345-2981
Sara Koller, *Vice Pres*
Lowell Stray, *CFO*
Tammy Glander, *Accountant*
Deb Pederson, *Human Res Mgr*
Kirk Lineweaver, *Manager*
▲ **EMP:** 70 **EST:** 1964
SQ FT: 35,700
SALES (corp-wide): 2.63B **Publicly Held**
WEB: www.cabelas.com
SIC: 5023 Retail mail-order house; art copy
publishing; retails artcraft & carvings; retail
gift shop; retail mail-order gift items;
wholesales home furnishings; art dealer
PA: Cabela's Inc
1 Cabela Dr
Sidney NE 69160
308 254-5505

LAKE CRYSTAL
Blue Earth County

(G-2857)
CRYSTEEL TRUCK EQUIPMENT INC (PA)
52248 Ember Rd (56055-2389)
PO Box 733 (56055-0733)
PHONE...............................507 726-6041
FAX: 507 726-6695
Glen L Wiens, *President*
Larry Brandenburg, *Vice Pres*
Terry Chesney, *VP Opers*
Chuck Abbott, *Plant Mgr*
Rande Bowman, *Purchasing*
EMP: 40 **EST:** 1974
SQ FT: 16,000
SALES (corp-wide): 17.47M **Privately Held**
WEB: www.crysteeltruckequipment.com
SIC: 4213 5084 Over the road trucking;
wholesales industrial hoists

(G-2858)
LAKE CRYSTAL AREA RECREATION
621 W Nathan St (56055-2116)
PHONE...............................507 726-6730
FAX: 507 726-6876
Matt Lentz, *President*
Don Johnson, *Vice Pres*
Kerry Maas, *Manager*
Susan Gengler, *Manager*
EMP: 35 **EST:** 1997
SQ FT: 50,000
SALES (est): 1MM-4.9MM **Privately Held**
SIC: 7999 Recreation center

(G-2859)
LAKE CRYSTAL FIRE DEPARTMENT
181 S Hunt St (56055-2075)
PO Box 528 (56055-0528)
PHONE...............................507 726-2440
Ed Betz, *Chief*
EMP: 25 **EST:** 2003
SALES (est): 1MM-4.9MM **Privately Held**
SIC: 7389 Business support services

(G-2860)
MINN STAR BANK (PA)
202 N Main St (56055-2112)
PHONE...............................507 726-2137
Fred Lantz, *President*
EMP: 35 **EST:** 1981 **Privately Held**
WEB: www.minnstarbank.com
SIC: 6712 Bank holding company

(G-2861)
MINNSTAR BANK
202 N Main St (56055)
PO Box 270 (56055-0270)
PHONE...............................507 726-2137
Steve Olson, *President*
Betty Ouren, *Assistant VP*
Mary Landkamer, *CFO*
Jason Bufkin, *Info Tech Mgr*
EMP: 25 **EST:** 1902
SALES (est): 5MM-9.9MM **Privately Held**
WEB: www.minnstarbank.com
SIC: 6021 National commercial bank
PA: Minn Star Bank
202 N Main St
Lake Crystal MN 56055
507 726-2137

(G-2862)
NORTHSTAR ARABIAN BREEDERS INC
20827 489th Ave (56055-4415)
PHONE...............................507 947-3541
Warren Jackson, *President*
John Tanner, *President*
EMP: 25 **EST:** 2005 **Privately Held**
SIC: 0272 Horse & equine breeding &
production

(G-2863)
NORTHSTAR ETHANOL LLC
19200 499th Ave (56055)
PHONE...............................507 726-2645
Scott Austin, *General Mgr*
EMP: 42 **EST:** 2003
SALES (est): 25MM-49.9MM **Privately Held**
SIC: 5154 Manufactures industrial organic
chemicals; wholesales livestock

LAKE ELMO
Washington County

(G-2864)
ADVANCED PRACTICE SOLUTIONS
8645 Eagle Point Blvd (55042-8628)
PHONE...............................651 439-8484
FAX: 651 439-9256
Lynn Schiff, *CEO*
Jodi Vance, *Director*
EMP: 47 **EST:** 1998
SQ FT: 2,700 **Privately Held**
WEB: www.advancedpracticesolutions.com
SIC: 7361 Employment agency services

(G-2865)
ASSURED DECONTAMINATION SVCS
Also Called: Biocleaning Specialists
860 Mendel Ave N (55042-7607)
PO Box 18622, Minneapolis (55418-0622)
PHONE...............................651 998-0922
Danny Haman, *Member*
Perry Ebner, *Member*
EMP: 65 **EST:** 2004
SQ FT: 3,000
SALES (est): 1MM-4.9MM **Privately Held**
SIC: 7349 Building cleaning & maintenance
services

(G-2866)
BREMER FINANCIAL SERVICES INC
8555 Eagle Point Blvd # 110 (55042-8627)
PO Box 1000 (55042-1000)
PHONE...............................651 734-4040
Steve Downhour, *Vice Pres*
Connie Weinman, *Vice Pres*
Ron Hansen, *CFO*
Stephanie Ihbe, *VP Finance*
Korwin Lockie, *Branch Mgr*

EMP: 200
SALES (est): 10MM-24.9MM **Privately Held**
SIC: 8741 7374 Management services; data
processing service
DH: Bremer Financial Services Inc
445 Minnesota St Ste 2000
Saint Paul MN 55101
651 227-7621

(G-2867)
BROOKMAN MOTOR SALES INC
Also Called: Lake Elmo Chrysler
11144 Stillwater Blvd N (55042-9501)
PHONE...............................651 777-1316
Mark Schafer, *President*
Burleigh Randolph, *Sales Mgr*
EMP: 39 **EST:** 1932
SQ FT: 22,000
SALES (est): 10MM-24.9MM **Privately Held**
SIC: 7514 7519 7538 Retails new & used
automobiles; general automotive repair
services; utility trailer & RV leasing & rental;
passenger car rental; used car dealer

(G-2868)
DENTAL SPECIALISTS
8650 Hudson Blvd N # 105 (55042-8416)
PHONE...............................952 926-2763
Greg Swenson DDS, *President*
Douglas G Peterson DDS, *Principal*
EMP: 40 **EST:** 2003
SALES (est): 1MM-4.9MM **Privately Held**
SIC: 8021 Periodontist office

(G-2869)
EAST METRO ASC LLC
Also Called: High Pointe Surgery Center
8650 Hudson Blvd N # 235 (55042-9747)
PHONE...............................651 702-7400
FAX: 651 702-7414
Lon Lutz, *Member*
Curt Geissler, *Member*
Jeff Robertson, *Member*
Ryan Karlftad, *Member*
Robert Nuffort, *Member*
EMP: 56 **EST:** 1999
SQ FT: 15,000
SALES (est): 5MM-9.9MM **Privately Held**
WEB: www.hpsurgery.com
SIC: 8011 Ambulatory surgical center

(G-2870)
ELMO LAKE BANK
11465 39th St N (55042-9586)
PO Box 857 (55042-0457)
PHONE...............................651 777-8365
FAX: 651 773-4725
Daniel Raleigh, *President*
Elizabeth Landherr, *Vice Pres*
Ken Soller, *Purch Mgr*
Patricia Wright, *Human Res Mgr*
Brent Saari, *Manager*
EMP: 50 **EST:** 1911
SQ FT: 20,000
SALES (est): 10MM-24.9MM **Privately Held**
SIC: 6022 8721 State commercial bank;
accounting, auditing & bookkeeping
services
PA: Lake Elmo Bancshares
11465 39th St N
Lake Elmo MN 55042
651 773-4758

(G-2871)
FIDELITY NATIONAL INFORMATION
8555 Eagle Point Blvd # 100 (55042-8627)
PHONE...............................651 855-6500
FAX: 651 855-6797
Todd Voge, *Engineer*
Joe Edwards, *Manager*
Diane Fesler, *Manager*
EMP: 60
SALES (est): 5MM-9.9MM **Publicly Held**
WEB: www.goldleaf-tech.com
SIC: 7374 Data processing & preparation
services
PA: Fidelity National Information
601 Riverside Ave
Jacksonville FL 32204
904 854-5000

(G-2872)
FOTH PRODUCTION SOLUTIONS LLC
8550 Hudson Blvd N (55042-5500)
PHONE...............................651 288-8550
Howard Bornstein, *Branch Mgr*
EMP: 53
SALES (est): 5MM-9.9MM **Privately Held**
SIC: 8748 Manufactures custom machinery;
business consulting services
PA: Foth Production Solutions LLC
2737 S Ridge Rd Ste 500
Green Bay WI 54304
920 497-2500

(G-2873)
HOMETOWN AMERICA LLC
Also Called: Cimarron Park
901 Lake Elmo Ave N (55042-9466)
PHONE...............................651 436-2790
FAX: 651 436-2986
Jim Anderson, *Manager*
EMP: 35
SALES (est): 5MM-9.9MM **Privately Held**
WEB: www.hometownamerica.com
SIC: 6531 6515 Real estate services;
mobile home site leasing & rental
PA: Hometown America LLC
150 N Wacker Dr Ste 2800
Chicago IL 60606
312 604-7500

(G-2874)
JARDINE LOGAN & O'BRIEN
8519 Eagle Point Blvd # 100 (55042-8630)
PHONE...............................651 290-6500
John M Kennedy Jr, *Managing Prtnr*
James Golembeck, *Managing Prtnr*
Charles E Gillen, *Partner*
Catherine Koran, *Accounting Mgr*
Timothy S Crom, *Attorney*
EMP: 30 **EST:** 1955
SQ FT: 23,954
SALES (est): 1MM-4.9MM **Privately Held**
WEB: www.jlolaw.com
SIC: 8111 Legal aid services

(G-2875)
JPG & ASSOCIATES INC
8991 Highway 5 (55042-8900)
PHONE...............................651 779-1072
Naomi M Grohovsky, *CEO*
Jerome P Grohovsky, *President*
EMP: 35
SQ FT: 1,500 **Privately Held**
WEB: www.jpgassoc.com
SIC: 7361 7338 7363 Employment agency
services; formal writing service; temporary
help service

(G-2876)
RETAIL CONSTRUCTION SERVICES
11343 39th St N (55042-9586)
PHONE...............................651 704-9000
FAX: 651 704-9100
Stephen M Bachman, *President*
George I Middleton, *Corp Secy*
Joni L Fletty, *COO*
Garth C Wills, *Vice Pres*
Curt Kiesow, *Project Mgr*
EMP: 110 **EST:** 1978
SQ FT: 8,200
SALES (est): 25MM-49.9MM **Privately Held**
WEB: www.retailconstruction.com
SIC: 1542 New commercial & office building
construction; restaurant construction;
shopping center & mall construction;
commercial & office building renovation &
repair services

(G-2877)
3 M CLUB OF ST PAUL INC
Also Called: Tartan Park Recreation Center
11455 20th St N (55042-8458)
PHONE...............................651 733-3466
FAX: 651 736-0534
Deron Adamavich, *Manager*
Craig Hampson, *Manager*
EMP: 75 **EST:** 1959
SALES (est): 1MM-4.9MM **Privately Held**
SIC: 7997 Membership recreation club

(PA)=Parent Co (HQ)=Headquarters (DH)=Div Headquarters
✿ = New business established in last 2 years

2011 Harris Minnesota
Services Directory

© Harris InfoSource 1-866-281-6415
133

LAKE GEORGE
Hubbard County

(G-2878)
COURAGE CENTER
37569 N Courage Dr (56458)
PO Box 1626 (56458-1626)
PHONE..................218 266-3658
FAX: 218 266-3458
Thomas Fogarty, *Branch Mgr*
EMP: 63
SALES (est): 1MM-4.9MM **Privately Held**
WEB: www.courage.org
SIC: 7032 Recreational camp
PA: Courage Center
3915 Golden Valley Rd
Minneapolis MN 55422
763 588-0811

LAKE HUBERT
Cass County

(G-2879)
CAUSEWAY & GULL ASSOCIATES
8087 Lost Lake Rd (56468-2523)
PHONE..................218 963-3675
Dena Kohlgraf, *General Mgr*
Sandi Growney, *Manager*
Jeanette Ayo, *Manager*
EMP: 30 EST: 1984
SALES (est): 1MM-4.9MM **Privately Held**
WEB: www.causewaygull.com
SIC: 7011 Resort hotel

LAKE PARK
Becker County

(G-2880)
SUNNYSIDE CARE CENTER
16561 US Highway 10 (56554-9302)
PHONE..................218 238-5944
Brad Grant, *Chairman*
Jen Manning, *Manager*
Michelle Weber, *Manager*
Katie Lundmard, *Director*
Jac M Taggart, *Director*
EMP: 76 EST: 1951
SALES (est): 1MM-4.9MM **Privately Held**
SIC: 8051 Skilled nursing care facility

LAKEFIELD
Jackson County

(G-2881)
CITY OF LAKEFIELD
Also Called: Colonial Manor Nursing Home
403 Colonial Ave (56150-9573)
PHONE..................507 662-6646
Patrice Goette, *Administrator*
Bill Lindberg, *Administrator*
EMP: 72
SALES (est): 1MM-4.9MM **Privately Held**
WEB: www.lakefieldmn.com
SIC: 8051 8052 Skilled nursing care facility; intermediate care facility
PA: City of Lakefield
301 Main St
Lakefield MN 56150
507 662-5457

(G-2882)
JACKSON COUNTY DEVELOPMENTAL
304 2nd Ave N (56150-1291)
PO Box 805 (56150-0805)
PHONE..................507 662-6156
Nicole Freeman, *Director*
EMP: 27 EST: 1968 **Privately Held**
WEB: www.datashoppe.com
SIC: 8399 Social change association

(G-2883)
RESIDENTIAL ADVANTAGES INC
220 Milwaukee St Ste 2 (56150-9495)
PHONE..................507 831-3804
Bill Olson, *President*
Rachel Frisen, *Manager*
Douglas A Teigen, *Director*
EMP: 70 EST: 1981
SALES (est): 1MM-4.9MM **Privately Held**
SIC: 8361 8052 Home for the mentally retarded; intermediate care facility

LAKELAND
Washington County

(G-2884)
DYNIXA CORP ✪
16440 7th Street Ln S (55043-8402)
PO Box 2143, Stillwater (55082-3143)
PHONE..................651 436-8800
James Staricha, *CEO*
EMP: 290 EST: 2010
SQ FT: 4,500
SALES (est): 25MM-49.9MM **Privately Held**
SIC: 7373 Computer integrated systems design services

(G-2885)
HARDRIVES INC
Also Called: Tower Asphalt
15001 Hudson Blvd (55043-9456)
PHONE..................651 436-8444
EMP: 85
SALES (est): 10MM-24.9MM **Privately Held**
WEB: www.hardrives.com
SIC: 1611 Highway & street paving contractor; manufactures asphalt & asphalt products
PA: Hardrives Inc
14475 Quiram Dr Ste 1
Rogers MN 55374
763 428-8886

(G-2886)
LOWER SAINT CROIX VALLEY FIRE
1520 Saint Croix Trl S (55043-9311)
PO Box 234 (55043-0234)
PHONE..................651 436-7033
FAX: 651 436-1682
Kris Peterson, *CEO*
EMP: 30 EST: 1972
SALES (est): 1MM-4.9MM **Privately Held**
SIC: 7389 Fire protection services

(G-2887)
T D & I CABLE MAINTENANCE INC
1378 Quinlan Ave S (55043-8708)
PO Box 266 (55043-0266)
PHONE..................651 436-3383
FAX: 651 436-1294
Timothy G Stanke, *President*
Debbie Stanke, *Vice Pres*
EMP: 40 EST: 1987
SALES (est): 1MM-4.9MM **Privately Held**
SIC: 1623 Cable television line construction

LAKEVILLE
Dakota County

(G-2888)
A-1 MAINTENANCE SERVICE CORP
7776 Upper 167th St W (55044-9159)
PHONE..................952 891-3711
Richard Patton, *President*
Melrese Patton, *Corp Secy*
Mary J Patton, *VP Engrg*
EMP: 50 EST: 1965
SALES (est): 1MM-4.9MM **Privately Held**
SIC: 7349 5087 Janitorial & custodial services; wholesales janitorial equipment & supplies

(G-2889)
ADVANCED CELLULAR LLC
20809 Kensington Blvd (55044-8353)
PHONE..................952 469-4200
Ken Coons, *Member*
Janet Coons, *Office Mgr*
EMP: 70 EST: 2004
SALES (est): 1MM-4.9MM **Privately Held**
SIC: 7389 Telephone service

(G-2890)
ANDERSON MCDONALD LTD
Also Called: McDonald, A Mod
20094 Kenwood Trl (55044-5404)
PO Box 847 (55044-0847)
PHONE..................952 469-3937
Anthony McDonald, *Owner*
EMP: 30 EST: 2000
SQ FT: 1,504
SALES (est): 1MM-4.9MM **Privately Held**
SIC: 8011 Physicians' office & clinic

(G-2891)
APPLIED POWER PRODUCTS INC
21005 Heron Way (55044-8068)
PHONE..................952 985-5100
Jeff Olson, *Branch Mgr*
EMP: 40
SALES (est): 10MM-24.9MM **Privately Held**
WEB: www.appliedpowerproducts.com
SIC: 5085 Wholesales industrial supplies; manufactures die-cut paper & board
PA: Applied Power Products Inc
1240 Trapp Rd
Saint Paul MN 55121
651 452-2250

(G-2892)
APPLIED POWER PRODUCTS INC
21005 Heron Way (55044-8068)
PHONE..................952 985-5100
Jeff Olson, *Manager*
EMP: 60
SALES (est): 25MM-49.9MM **Privately Held**
WEB: www.appliedpowerproducts.com
SIC: 5085 Wholesales industrial supplies; wholesales industrial hose, belting & packing; wholesales industrial power transmission equipment & apparatus
PA: Applied Power Products Inc
1240 Trapp Rd
Saint Paul MN 55121
651 452-2250

(G-2893)
BURNSVILLE COMMERCIAL CLEANING
12330 210th St W (55044-9516)
PHONE..................952 469-5423
Mia Merickel, *Owner*
EMP: 39 EST: 1989
SALES (est): 500-999K **Privately Held**
SIC: 7349 Building & office cleaning service

(G-2894)
CHEM VESTMENTS INC
8287 214th St W (55044-9009)
PHONE..................952 469-4965
Lynn Buri, *Partner*
Gary Glenna, *Partner*
EMP: 25 EST: 1980
SQ FT: 10,000
SALES (est): 5MM-9.9MM **Privately Held**
SIC: 6512 Operators of commercial & industrial buildings

(G-2895)
CIU
Also Called: Commercial Insur Underwriters
19107 Inca Ave (55044-2506)
PHONE..................952 469-5520
David Hinrichs, *President*
EMP: 30
SALES (est): 1MM-4.9MM **Privately Held**
SIC: 6411 Insurance broker

(G-2896)
CLOVERLEAF COLD STORAGE CO
21755 Cedar Ave (55044-9095)
PHONE..................952 469-1221
Roy Pepper, *Manager*
EMP: 40
SALES (est): 1MM-4.9MM **Privately Held**
WEB: www.cloverleafco.com
SIC: 4222 Cold storage or refrigerated warehousing
PA: Cloverleaf Cold Storage Co
2800 Cloverleaf Ct
Sioux City IA 51111
712 279-8000

(G-2897)
CRYSTAL LAKE AUTOMOTIVE INC
16055 Buck Hill Rd (55044-6438)
PHONE..................952 892-3377
FAX: 952 435-9810
Karl Drotning, *President*
James Siegfried, *Vice Pres*
EMP: 27 EST: 1986
SQ FT: 26,000
SALES (est): 1MM-4.9MM **Privately Held**
WEB: www.crystallakeauto.com
SIC: 7532 7538 Automotive body shop; automotive engine repair service

(G-2898)
CRYSTAL LAKE COUNTRY CLUB INC
16725 Innsbrook Dr (55044-5665)
PHONE..................952 432-6566
FAX: 952 953-6462
Bruce Finzen, *President*
Patty Weisbrich, *Manager*
EMP: 30 EST: 1995
SALES (est): 1MM-4.9MM **Privately Held**
WEB: www.crystallakegolfcourse.com
SIC: 7992 Public golf course

(G-2899)
CRYSTEEL TRUCK EQUIPMENT INC
21470 Grenada Ave (55044-9080)
PO Box 733, Lake Crystal (56055-0733)
PHONE..................952 469-5678
EMP: 38
SALES (est): 10MM-24.9MM **Privately Held**
WEB: www.crysteeltruckequipment.com
SIC: 5013 7699 Wholesales truck parts & accessories; industrial truck repair service
PA: Crysteel Truck Equipment Inc
52248 Ember Rd
Lake Crystal MN 56055
507 726-6041

(G-2900)
D H I MORTGAGE
20860 Kenbridge Ct Ste 140 (55044-8098)
PHONE..................952 985-7850
FAX: 952 985-7851
Jeff Higgins, *Vice Pres*
John Falk, *Vice Pres*
John Ethridge, *Manager*
Alison Diffley, *Manager*
Christopher Arnoldy, *Manager*
EMP: 40 EST: 1998
SALES (est): 1MM-4.9MM **Privately Held**
WEB: www.ch-mortgage.com
SIC: 6162 Mortgage & loan lending

(G-2901)
DAKOTA PEDIATRIC CLINIC
17504 Dodd Blvd (55044-5268)
PHONE..................952 997-2572
Robert Dieb, *Owner*
EMP: 25
SALES (est): 1MM-4.9MM **Privately Held**
WEB: www.dakotapeds.com
SIC: 8011 Pediatrician office
PA: Dakota Pediatric Clinic
5975 Carmen Ave
South Saint Paul MN 55076
651 455-9697

www.HarrisInfo.com
134

2011 Harris Minnesota
Services Directory

▲=Import ▼=Export
◆=Import/Export

(G-2902)
DESIGNED CABINETS INC
7965 215th St W (55044-9016)
PHONE..............................952 469-2700
Jeff Barum, *President*
Lori Barum, *Treasurer*
Patty Anderson, *Manager*
EMP: 60 **EST:** 1991
SQ FT: 52,000
SALES (est): 5MM-9.9MM **Privately Held**
SIC: 1751 Manufactures wooden kitchen cabinets; cabinet & finish work carpentry service

(G-2903)
DICK'S SANITATION SERVICE INC
Also Called: LAKEVILLE SANITARY
8984 215th St W (55044-8338)
PO Box 769 (55044-0769)
PHONE..............................952 469-2239
FAX: 952 469-1146
Richard Clemmer, *President*
Brett Anderson, *Vice Pres*
Debbie Nielson, *Vice Pres*
Mary A Clemmer, *Vice Pres*
David Domack, *Executive*
EMP: 100 **EST:** 1966
SQ FT: 1,100
SALES (est): 10MM-24.9MM **Privately Held**
WEB: www.dickssanitation.com
SIC: 4953 Garbage collecting, destroying & processing services; waste material recycling services

(G-2904)
EDINA REALTY HOME SERVICES
17271 Kenyon Ave Ste 102 (55044-6907)
PHONE..............................952 892-7000
FAX: 952 892-7163
Janelle Blaser, *Manager*
Kim Lindqist, *Manager*
EMP: 85
SALES (est): 10MM-24.9MM **Publicly Held**
WEB: www.ilovetennis.net
SIC: 6531 Real estate agency & broker
HQ: Edina Realty Home Services
    6800 France Ave S Ste 600
    Minneapolis MN 55435
    952 928-5900

(G-2905)
EXECUTIVE SERVICES MIDWEST LLC
19740 Kenrick Ave (55044-7636)
PHONE..............................952 469-4755
Bruce Heikes, *Principal*
Terresa Roller, *Office Mgr*
EMP: 25 **EST:** 2004
SALES (est): 500-999K **Privately Held**
SIC: 7363 Employee leasing service

(G-2906)
FAMILY SWIM SCHOOL
10491 165th St W (55044-5638)
PHONE..............................952 435-1898
Peter Schrock, *Owner*
EMP: 38 **EST:** 1990
SQ FT: 9,815
SALES (est): 1MM-4.9MM **Privately Held**
SIC: 7999 Swimming instruction

(G-2907)
FRIEDGES CONTRACTING CO LLC
21980 Kenrick Ave (55044-9517)
PHONE..............................952 469-2121
John Freidges, *Member*
EMP: 25 **EST:** 2001
SQ FT: 6,500
SALES (est): 1MM-4.9MM **Privately Held**
SIC: 1799 Underground sewage protective lining installation service

(G-2908)
FRIEDGES LANDSCAPING INC
9380 202nd St W (55044-7862)
PHONE..............................952 469-2996
FAX: 952 469-1755
John Freidges, *President*
Rick Lopez, *Technician*
EMP: 40 **EST:** 1973
SQ FT: 2,500 **Privately Held**
WEB: www.friedgeslandscaping.com
SIC: 0782 1623 1794 Landscaping services; sewer line construction; water main construction; excavating contractor

(G-2909)
HEARTH & HOME TECHNOLOGIES INC (HQ)
Also Called: Heatilator
7571 215th St W (55044-9822)
PHONE..............................952 985-6000
Brad Determan, *President*
Jimmy Honeycutt, *Division Mgr*
Kevin Long, *General Mgr*
Steven M Bradford, *Corp Secy*
Dan Shimek, *Corp Secy*
▲ **EMP:** 110 **EST:** 1996
SQ FT: 75,000
SALES (corp-wide): 1.65B **Publicly Held**
WEB: www.heatnglo.com
SIC: 4925 Manufactures fireplace equipment & accessories; gas production & distribution
PA: Hni Corp
    408 E 2nd St
    Muscatine IA 52761
    563 272-7400

(G-2910)
IMAGETREND INC
20855 Kensington Blvd (55044-7486)
PHONE..............................952 469-1589
FAX: 952 985-5671
Michael J McBrady, *President*
Ibrahim Hafidh, *Manager*
Guy Kwon, *Manager*
Melissa Jordan, *Manager*
Collin McBrady, *Info Tech Mgr*
EMP: 126 **EST:** 1998
SQ FT: 33,000
SALES (est): 10MM-24.9MM **Privately Held**
WEB: www.imagetrend.com
SIC: 7371 Computer software development

(G-2911)
INTEGRA HEALTH CARE INC
20726 Ibex Ave (55044-5867)
PHONE..............................952 985-7290
Dimitry Pavkov, *President*
EMP: 30 **EST:** 2003
SALES (est): 1MM-4.9MM **Privately Held**
SIC: 8082 8099 Home health care services; health & allied services

(G-2912)
J A SWENSON & ASSOC INC
20141 Icenic Trl (55044-7708)
PHONE..............................952 469-3585
James A Swenson, *President*
Betty Swenson, *Vice Pres*
EMP: 25 **EST:** 1984
SQ FT: 4,340
SALES (est): 10MM-24.9MM **Privately Held**
SIC: 5084 Wholesales industrial packaging machinery & equipment

(G-2913)
JACKSON LANDSCAPE SUPPLY INC
7870 218th St W (55044-9109)
PHONE..............................952 435-6927
FAX: 952 435-8718
William D Jackson, *President*
Mark Slaikeu, *Controller*
Joy Johnson, *Manager*
EMP: 40 **EST:** 1979 **Privately Held**
SIC: 0781 Landscape services

(G-2914)
KELLER WILLIAMS REALTY INC
10515 165th St W Ste A (55044-5720)
PHONE..............................952 746-9696
John Walsh, *Vice Pres*
Janet Jakobitz, *Vice Pres*
David Christensen, *Branch Mgr*
Karen Tobler, *Bd of Directors*
Greg Paffel, *Bd of Directors*
EMP: 50
SALES (est): 5MM-9.9MM **Privately Held**
WEB: www.devineproperties.com
SIC: 6531 Residential real estate agency
PA: Keller Williams Realty Inc
    807 Las Cimas Pkwy Ste 200
    Austin TX 78746
    512 327-3070

(G-2915)
MANDERS DIESEL REPAIR INC
11250 215th St W (55044-8654)
PHONE..............................952 469-1800
FAX: 952 469-2383
Sidney V Manders Sr, *President*
Dolores Manders, *Vice Pres*
EMP: 25 **EST:** 1958
SQ FT: 50,000
SALES (est): 25MM-49.9MM **Privately Held**
WEB: www.mandersdiesel.com
SIC: 5012 7538 Wholesales commercial trucks; truck engine repair service

(G-2916)
MC GUIRE MECHANICAL SERVICES
20830 Holt Ave (55044-8574)
PO Box 219 (55044-0219)
PHONE..............................952 469-4988
FAX: 952 469-4990
Timothy M Guire, *President*
Chris Lundgren, *Vice Pres*
Mary Leibfried, *Manager*
EMP: 40 **EST:** 1978
SQ FT: 5,000
SALES (est): 1MM-4.9MM **Privately Held**
SIC: 1711 Plumbing service; warm air heating & air conditioning contractor

(G-2917)
MCI PAINT & DRYWALL INC (PA)
21400 Hamburg Ave (55044-8993)
PHONE..............................952 985-7778
Mark Mathiowetz, *President*
Lori Mathiowetz, *Corp Secy*
Dan Turbes, *Manager*
Joe Daleiden, *Manager*
Mark Thelen, *Manager*
EMP: 34 **EST:** 1988
SQ FT: 4,200
SALES (corp-wide): 6.54M **Privately Held**
WEB: www.mcidrywall.com
SIC: 1742 1721 Drywall contractor; painting & wall covering contractor

(G-2918)
MENASHA PACKAGING CO LLC
8085 220th St W (55044-7245)
PHONE..............................952 469-4451
Greg Hauber, *General Mgr*
Michael Waite, *Vice Pres*
Richard Radman, *Plant Mgr*
Ray Donajkowski, *Controller*
Gary Tholkes, *Human Resources*
EMP: 180
SQ FT: 239,596
SALES (est): 50MM-99.9MM **Privately Held**
WEB: www.menashapackaging.com
SIC: 5113 Paperboard mill; manufactures folding paperboard boxes; wholesales corrugated & solid fiber boxes; manufactures corrugated & solid fiber containers
HQ: Menasha Packaging Co LLC
    1645 Bergstrom Rd
    Neenah WI 54956
    920 751-1000

(G-2919)
MID-STATE RECLAMATION INC
21955 Grenada Ave (55044-8055)
PHONE..............................952 985-5555
FAX: 952 985-5656
Tom Johnson, *President*
EMP: 50 **EST:** 1991
SALES (est): 5MM-9.9MM **Privately Held**
SIC: 4953 Refuse systems services

(G-2920)
MINNESOTA PROPHY POWER INC
Also Called: Prophy Power
17799 Kenwood Trl (55044-9493)
PHONE..............................952 898-1594
Roselyn R Wilson, *President*
Joyce D Olafson, *Vice Pres*
EMP: 51 **EST:** 1988
SALES (est): 5MM-9.9MM **Privately Held**
WEB: www.prophypower.com
SIC: 7363 7699 Manufactures dental equipment; help supply services; dental instrument repair service

(G-2921)
NEW HOMES REALTY INC
20638 Hartford Way (55044-4440)
PHONE..............................952 469-6003
Kurt Folstad, *President*
EMP: 40 **EST:** 2000
SALES (est): 5MM-9.9MM **Privately Held**
SIC: 6531 Real estate services

(G-2922)
NEW HORIZON CHILD CARE INC
9085 203rd St W (55044-5979)
PHONE..............................952 469-6659
FAX: 952 431-5959
Lori Heidelberger, *Director*
Kay Beckman, *Director*
Liz Heger, *Asst Director*
EMP: 26
SALES (est): 500-999K **Privately Held**
WEB: www.kidsquest.com
SIC: 8351 Preschool center
HQ: New Horizon Child Care Inc
    16355 36th Ave N Ste 700
    Plymouth MN 55446
    763 557-1111

(G-2923)
NORTHERN GOPHER ENTERPRISES
Also Called: Bracketts Crossing Country CLB
17976 Judicial Rd (55044-9329)
PHONE..............................952 435-7600
FAX: 952 435-7616
Thomas H Smith, *President*
Peggy Smith, *Vice Pres*
Bill Tummett, *Facilities Mgr*
Dawn Henriksen, *Sales Mgr*
Leslie Novak, *Manager*
EMP: 110 **EST:** 1982
SQ FT: 30,000
SALES (est): 5MM-9.9MM **Privately Held**
SIC: 7997 Membership golf club; bar; eating place

(G-2924)
PARKER-HANNIFIN CORP
21337 Hemlock Ave (55044-9068)
PHONE..............................952 469-5000
Fran Caulfield, *Facilities Mgr*
EMP: 30
SALES (est): 10MM-24.9MM **Publicly Held**
WEB: www.parker.com
SIC: 5084 Wholesales industrial machinery & equipment
PA: Parker-Hannifin Corp
    6035 Parkland Blvd
    Cleveland OH 44124
    216 896-3000

(G-2925)
PROBUILD CO LLC
Also Called: United Building Centers
9130 202nd St W (55044-6635)
PHONE..............................952 469-2116
FAX: 952 469-4721
Ken Oetjen, *Chairman*
EMP: 35
SALES (est): 10MM-24.9MM **Privately Held**
WEB: www.probuild.com
SIC: 5031 Wholesales lumber, plywood & millwork
HQ: Probuild Co LLC
    7595 Tech Way Ste 500
    Denver CO 80237
    303 262-8500

(G-2926)
PROBUILD CO LLC
11356 215th St W (55044-8513)
PHONE..............................952 469-3466
Ron Miller, *Purch Mgr*
Bob Benson, *Manager*
EMP: 85
SALES (est): 50MM-99.9MM **Privately Held**
WEB: www.probuild.com

(PA)=Parent Co (HQ)=Headquarters (DH)=Div Headquarters
✿ = New business established in last 2 years
2011 Harris Minnesota
Services Directory
© Harris InfoSource 1-866-281-6415
135

GEOGRAPHIC

SIC: **5031** Wholesales windows; wholesales
Doors, sliding
HQ: Probuild Co LLC
7595 Tech Way Ste 500
Denver CO 80237
303 262-8500

(G-2927)
PROGRESSIVE RAIL INC
21778 Highview Ave   (55044-7541)
PHONE..............................952 985-7245
Lon V Gemert, *CEO*
Dave Fellon, *President*
Doug Whiteley, *CFO*
Karen Wiens, *Manager*
Eric Heieren, *Director*
EMP: 28 **EST:** 1996
SQ FT: 100,000
SALES (est): 1MM-4.9MM **Privately Held**
WEB: www.progressiverail.com
SIC: **4789** Railroad cargo loading &
unloading services

(G-2928)
RAILWORKS TRACK SYSTEMS INC
8485 210th St W   (55044-8502)
PO Box 959   (55044-0959)
PHONE..............................952 469-4907
Keith Kortenbusch, *Corp Secy*
Gene Cellini, *Vice Pres*
David Landreth, *Vice Pres*
John Lapp, *Vice Pres*
Scott Brice, *Manager*
EMP: 70
SQ FT: 6,640
SALES (est): 10MM-24.9MM **Privately Held**
WEB: www.railworks.com
SIC: **1629** Railroad & subway construction
PA: RailWorks Corp
5 Penn Plz Fl 12
New York NY 10001
212 502-7900

(G-2929)
RYT-WAY INDUSTRIES LLC
21850 Grenada Ave   (55044-9076)
PHONE..............................952 469-1417
David Finch, *CEO*
Larry Muma, *COO*
Diane Bornhauser, *CFO*
Mary B Fong, *CFO*
Edward Bolton, *Human Res Dir*
EMP: 640 **EST:** 1965
SQ FT: 633,000
SALES (est): 25MM-49.9MM **Privately Held**
WEB: www.rytway.com
SIC: **7389** Packaging & labeling services;
manufactures dried milk; bottles, cans &
cartons labeling service

(G-2930)
SAFETY SIGNS INC
19784 Kenrick Ave Ste C   (55044-7913)
PHONE..............................952 469-6700
FAX: 952 469-1969
Sue Blanchard, *President*
Jay Blanchard, *Vice Pres*
Annette Grey, *Manager*
Julie Sable, *Manager*
Julie Bain, *Bd of Directors*
▲ **EMP:** 35 **EST:** 1993
SQ FT: 4,000
SALES (est): 1MM-4.9MM **Privately Held**
WEB: www.safetysigns-mn.com
SIC: **7359** 1721 1799 5084 Work zone
traffic flags, cones, barrels & other
equipment; sign installation & maintenance
contractor; pavement marking contractor;
wholesales industrial safety equipment

(G-2931)
SAFETY-KLEEN SYSTEMS INC
21750 Cedar Ave   (55044-9094)
PHONE..............................952 469-8356
Brian Brosnan, *Branch Mgr*
EMP: 27
SALES (est): 1MM-4.9MM **Privately Held**
WEB: www.safety-kleen.com
SIC: **4953** Refuse systems services
HQ: Safety-Kleen Systems Inc
5360 Legacy Dr Bldg 2
Plano TX 75024
972 265-2000

(G-2932)
SCHNEIDERMAN FURNITURE INC
17630 Juniper Path   (55044-9452)
PHONE..............................952 435-3399
FAX: 952 435-8832
Fran Fields, *Finance*
Larry Roony, *Manager*
Mikki Morin, *Manager*
EMP: 40
SALES (est): 5MM-9.9MM **Privately Held**
SIC: **7389** Retails furniture; interior design
service

(G-2933)
SFN GROUP INC
21340 Hamburg Ave   (55044-8342)
PHONE..............................952 469-7583
Ed Jopling, *Manager*
EMP: 150
SALES (est): 1MM-4.9MM **Publicly Held**
SIC: **7363** Temporary help service
PA: Sfn Group Inc
2050 Spectrum Blvd
Fort Lauderdale FL 33309
954 308-7600

(G-2934)
SGO ROOFING & CONSTRUCTION LLC
21017 Heron Way Ste 101   (55044-8091)
PHONE..............................952 469-8560
Steve Olson, *Principal*
Judy Olson, *Member*
EMP: 30 **EST:** 2000
SALES (est): 1MM-4.9MM **Privately Held**
WEB: www.sgoroofing.com
SIC: **1761** Roofing contractor

(G-2935)
STELLAR CONTRACTORS INC
21900 Kenrick Ave   (55044-9517)
PHONE..............................952 469-0900
Daniel J Stanley, *President*
Jim Mahon, *Corp Secy*
Karen J Stanley, *Controller*
Shane Longtin, *Administrator*
Kathy Maxfield, *Supervisor*
EMP: 175 **EST:** 1997
SQ FT: 1,200
SALES (est): 25MM-49.9MM **Privately Held**
WEB: www.stellarcontractors.com
SIC: **1542** Commercial & institutional
building construction

(G-2936)
STYER TRANSPORTATION CO
7870 215th St W   (55044-6046)
PO Box 592   (55044-0592)
PHONE..............................952 469-4491
Melvin Simon Jr, *President*
Russ Simon, *Vice Pres*
Owen Ivey, *Coordinator*
EMP: 42 **EST:** 1965
SQ FT: 2,500
SALES (est): 5MM-9.9MM **Privately Held**
WEB: www.styertrans.com
SIC: **4213** Over the road trucking

(G-2937)
TEMBUA INC
17870 Irons Ct   (55044-8732)
PHONE..............................952 435-8178
FAX: 952 435-3626
Patricia May, *President*
Tom Omalley, *Project Mgr*
Teena Risley, *Executive*
EMP: 34 **EST:** 1993
SALES (est): 1MM-4.9MM **Privately Held**
WEB: www.precisionlanguage.com
SIC: **7389** Translation & interpretation
services

(G-2938)
UNIMED-MIDWEST INC
Also Called: INFECTION CONTROL &
SAFETY SYS
21875 Grenada Ave   (55044-9077)
PHONE..............................952 469-9400
Joan W Knipe, *President*
Chris Robbins, *COO*
Suzanne Coursolle, *CFO*
EMP: 27

EST: 1992
SQ FT: 9,200
SALES (est): 10MM-24.9MM **Privately Held**
WEB: www.unimed-midwest.com
SIC: **5047** Wholesales medical equipment &
supplies; wholesales dental equipment &
supplies

(G-2939)
UPONOR INC
21900 Dodd Blvd   (55044-8553)
PHONE..............................952 891-2000
Tom Bisck, *Branch Mgr*
EMP: 50
SALES (est): 1MM-4.9MM **Privately Held**
WEB: www.wirsbo.com
SIC: **4225** Warehousing & storage services
HQ: Uponor Inc
5925 148th St W
Saint Paul MN 55124
952 891-2000

(G-2940)
VERIFIED CREDENTIALS INC
20890 Kenbridge Ct Ste 2   (55044-8063)
PHONE..............................952 985-2335
Steve Spang, *CEO*
Kevin Spang, *President*
Tom Terry, *CFO*
Chris Holthe, *Accounts Exec*
EMP: 90 **EST:** 1984
SQ FT: 20,000
SALES (est): 10MM-24.9MM **Privately Held**
WEB: www.v-c-i.com
SIC: **7311** Advertising agency

(G-2941)
WAUSAU SUPPLY CO
21700 Highview Ave   (55044-7541)
PHONE..............................952 469-2500
Tom Sherman, *Manager*
EMP: 80
SQ FT: 282,455
SALES (est): 25MM-49.9MM **Privately Held**
WEB: www.wausausupply.com
SIC: **5033** Wholesales thermal insulation
materials; wholesales siding
PA: Wausau Supply Co
4704 Bayberry St
Schofield WI 54476
715 359-2524

LAKEVILLE
Scott County

(G-2942)
GROVE COTTAGE AUTO PARTS INC
Also Called: Champion Auto Store
10186 222nd St E   (55044-9752)
PHONE..............................952 469-2801
Dan Hopkins, *President*
EST: 1985
SQ FT: 5,000 **Privately Held**
SIC: **5013** Retails automotive parts;
wholesales automotive supplies & parts;
retails automotive accessories

(G-2943)
P D MANAGEMENT, LLP
7551 240th St E   (55044-6429)
PHONE..............................612 281-1464
Tom V Sickle, *Partner*
David Jacobsen, *Partner*
EMP: 50 **EST:** 2003
SALES (est): 5MM-9.9MM **Privately Held**
SIC: **6531** Real estate services

(G-2944)
ZWEBER LLC
Also Called: Heritage Links
8075 Lucerne Blvd   (55044-8189)
PHONE..............................952 440-4653
Ann Z Werner, *Member*
Mark R Zweber, *Member*
EMP: 40 **EST:** 1984
SQ FT: 900
SALES (est): 5MM-9.9MM **Privately Held**
SIC: **6531** Real estate agency & broker

LAMBERTON
Redwood County

(G-2945)
CITY OF LAMBERTON
Also Called: Valleyview Manor Nursing Home
200 9th Ave E   (56152-1024)
PHONE..............................507 752-7346
FAX: 507 752-7348
Mavis Pfarr, *Corp Secy*
Bernie Lendt, *Systems Staff*
Jason Swanson, *Exec Dir*
Millie Trost, *Food Svc Dir*
EMP: 46
SALES (est): 1MM-4.9MM **Privately Held**
SIC: **8051** Skilled nursing care facility
PA: City of Lamberton
112 2nd Ave W
Lamberton MN 56152
507 752-7601

LANESBORO
Fillmore County

(G-2946)
COMMONWEAL THEATRE CO
208 Parkway Ave N   (55949-9795)
PO Box 15   (55949-0015)
PHONE..............................507 467-2905
Hal Cropp, *Exec Dir*
Scott Dixon, *Officer*
EMP: 35 **EST:** 2007
SALES (est): 5MM-9.9MM **Privately Held**
SIC: **7922** Theatrical producers & services

(G-2947)
LANESBORO SALES COMMISSION INC
402 Coffee St   (55949-9016)
PO Box 363   (55949-0363)
PHONE..............................507 467-2192
FAX: 507 467-3517
Joe Nelson, *President*
Virgil Bothun, *Treasurer*
Darlys Storhoff, *Office Mgr*
EMP: 40 **EST:** 1950
SQ FT: 8,000
SALES (est): 25MM-49.9MM **Privately Held**
WEB:
www.lanesborosalescommission.com
SIC: **5154** Livestock auction services

LAPORTE
Hubbard County

(G-2948)
GLADEN CONSTRUCTION INC
40739 US 71   (56461-4278)
PHONE..............................218 224-2237
FAX: 218 224-2939
Clayton Gladen, *President*
Wanda Gladen, *Corp Secy*
Tim Gladen, *Vice Pres*
Robert Wiebesick, *Vice Pres*
Connie Gladen, *Treasurer*
EMP: 65 **EST:** 1974
SQ FT: 23,900
SALES (est): 5MM-9.9MM **Privately Held**
SIC: **1611** Grading services

LE CENTER
Le Sueur County

(G-2949)
CAMAS INC
260 W Derrynane St Ste 103
(56057-1343)
PHONE..............................507 357-4929
Bradley Mitteness, *CEO*
EMP: 25 **EST:** 1987 **Privately Held**
SIC: **8731** Commercial physical research
laboratory; manufactures flour & other grain
mill products

www.HarrisInfo.com
136

2011 Harris Minnesota
Services Directory

▲=Import ▼=Export
◆=Import/Export

(G-2950)

CENTRAL HEALTH CARE OF LE CTR

444 N Cordova Ave (56057-1704)
PHONE.............................507 357-2275
FAX: 507 357-4346
Karl Pelovsky, *President*
Gladyce Pelovsky, *Corp Secy*
Debbie Holicky, *Office Mgr*
EMP: 90 EST: 1966
SQ FT: 28,000
SALES (est): 1MM-4.9MM **Privately Held**
SIC: 8051 Skilled nursing care facility

(G-2951)

LE CENTER VOLUNTEER AMBULANCE

175 S Cordova Ave (56057-1803)
PO Box 152 (56057-0152)
PHONE.............................507 357-4844
Tammy Stewig, *President*
Stan Tocker, *President*
EMP: 39 EST: 2001
SALES (est): 1MM-4.9MM **Privately Held**
SIC: 4119 Ambulance service

(G-2952)

MAX JOHNSON TRUCKING INC

240 W Derrynane St (56057-1302)
PO Box 212 (56057-0212)
PHONE.............................507 357-6313
FAX: 507 357-2231
Jeff Johnson, *President*
Max Johnson, *Vice Pres*
Gary Johnson, *Treasurer*
EMP: 25 EST: 1962
SQ FT: 12,000
SALES (est): 1MM-4.9MM **Privately Held**
SIC: 4212 Dump truck hauling services

(G-2953)

O'MALLEY CONSTRUCTION INC

35799 241st Ave (56057-4378)
PHONE.............................507 357-6330
Lori A O'Malley, *President*
Brian O'Malley, *Vice Pres*
EMP: 28 EST: 2001
SALES (est): 1MM-4.9MM **Privately Held**
SIC: 1771 Curb & sidewalk contractor

(G-2954)

TRAXLER CONSTRUCTION INC

625 Commerce Dr (56057-2300)
PHONE.............................507 357-2235
FAX: 507 357-6626
Pat Traxler, *President*
Ramona Zihlke, *Bookkeeper*
Coleen Robinson, *Bookkeeper*
EMP: 25 EST: 1985
SQ FT: 9,000
SALES (est): 1MM-4.9MM **Privately Held**
SIC: 1629 Drainage system construction

LE ROY
Mower County

(G-2955)

WB ENTERPRISES OF AMERICA INC

11384 790th Ave (55951-6715)
PHONE.............................507 324-5050
Daniel Weness, *President*
Micheal Boe, *Corp Secy*
Clark Sipra, *Accountant*
EMP: 50 EST: 1995
SALES (est): 10MM-24.9MM **Privately Held**
SIC: 1521 Single-family housing construction

LE SUEUR
Le Sueur County

(G-2956)

LE SUEUR COUNTRY CLUB

36195 311th Ave (56058-4530)
PO Box 163 (56058-0163)
PHONE.............................507 665-8839
FAX: 507 665-6293

John Miller, *President*
Lois Roemhildt, *Corp Secy*
Leann Haigler, *Vice Pres*
Joe Foley, *Treasurer*
EMP: 50 EST: 1927
SQ FT: 4,500
SALES (est): 1MM-4.9MM **Privately Held**
WEB: www.lesuercountryclub.com
SIC: 7997 Country club; retails golf goods &
equipment; eating place; retails tennis
goods & equipment; membership swimming
club; membership tennis club; membership
golf club; drinking establishment; retails
sporting goods

(G-2957)

LE SUEUR, CITY OF INC

821 Ferry St (56058-1722)
PO Box 176 (56058-0176)
PHONE.............................507 665-3325
FAX: 507 665-2367
Richard Almich, *Manager*
David Johnson, *Director*
EMP: 28
SALES (est): 500-999K **Privately Held**
WEB: www.cityoflesueur.com
SIC: 7999 Recreation center; mayors' office
PA: Le Sueur, City of Inc
203 S 2nd St
Le Sueur MN 56058
507 665-6401

(G-2958)

MINNESOTA VALLEY MEMORIAL HOSP

Also Called: Gardenview Nursing Home
621 S 4th St (56058-2203)
PHONE.............................507 665-3375
FAX: 507 665-2191
Deanna Olson-Eddy, *QA Dir*
Russ Lawrence, *Engineering*
Bonnie Barnhart, *Human Res Dir*
Mary P Sueker, *Human Resources*
Kim Hammes, *Marketing Staff*
EMP: 160 EST: 1959
SALES (est): 10MM-24.9MM **Privately Held**
WEB: www.mvhc.org
SIC: 8062 8011 8051 Medical hospital;
clinic operated by physicians; skilled nursing
care facility
HQ: Essentia Health
502 E 2nd St
Duluth MN 55805
218 786-8376

(G-2959)

SEAVER CO

Also Called: Sunglass Display
200 Minnesota Ave (56058-9787)
PO Box 123 (56058-0123)
PHONE.............................507 665-3321
FAX: 507 665-3775
Dean A Seaver, *President*
Alison R Stevenson, *Vice Pres*
Larry R Seaver, *Vice Pres*
Curtis J Seaver, *Vice Pres*
▲ EMP: 100 EST: 1982
SQ FT: 25,000
SALES (est): 50MM-99.9MM **Privately Held**
WEB: www.sunglassdisplay.com
SIC: 5099 Wholesales sunglasses

(G-2960)

UNIMIN CORP

39770 Ottawa Rd (56058-4292)
PHONE.............................507 665-3386
Grey Lusty, *Superintendent*
Dean G Fletcher, *Vice Pres*
Chuck Collins, *Manager*
EMP: 75
SALES (est): 10MM-24.9MM **Privately Held**
WEB: www.unimin.com
SIC: 1446 Silica sand
PA: Unimin Corp
258 Elm St
New Canaan CT 06840
203 966-8880

(G-2961)

WASTE MANAGEMENT OF WISCONSIN

739 Beaver Ave (56058)
PO Box 336, Mankato (56002-0336)
PHONE.............................507 665-3096
FAX: 507 665-4141
Rick Roemer, *District Mgr*

Angie Vlieger, *Accountant*
Ginger Kaladas, *Credit Staff*
Linda Trydahl, *Hum Res Coord*
Cindy Sowers, *Office Mgr*
EMP: 50
SALES (est): 5MM-9.9MM **Privately Held**
SIC: 4212 Garbage collection &
transportation services without disposal
HQ: Waste Management of Wisconsin
W124N8925 Boundary Rd
Menomonee Falls WI 53051
262 251-4000

LE SUEUR
Nicollet County

(G-2962)

MICHAEL FOODS INC

34187 County Road 20 (56058-3444)
PHONE.............................507 665-8851
Tim Bebee, *Vice Pres*
Greg Ostrander, *Manager*
Jim Beckman, *Manager*
EMP: 200
SALES (est): 100MM-499.9MM **Privately Held**
SIC: 5191 0252 Wholesales animal feeds;
chicken egg farming
DH: Michael Foods Group Inc
301 Carlson Pkwy Ste 400
Minnetonka MN 55305
952 258-4000

LESTER PRAIRIE
Mcleod County

(G-2963)

LESTER BUILDINGS LLC

1111 2nd Ave S (55354-1007)
PHONE.............................320 395-2531
Marcia Langseth, *Member*
John Hill, *Member*
Cathy Telecky, *Opers Staff*
Gary Moen, *Attorney*
EMP: 120 EST: 2004
SALES (est): 25MM-49.9MM **Privately Held**
WEB: www.lesterbuildings.com
SIC: 1542 Commercial & institutional
building construction
PA: Lester Building Systems LLC
1111 2nd Ave S
Lester Prairie MN 55354
320 395-2531

(G-2964)

SHADOWBROOKE GOLF COURSE INC

3192 Highway 7 (55354-6327)
PO Box 575 (55354-0575)
PHONE.............................320 395-4251
Thomas Schmidt, *President*
Elmer Schmidt, *Vice Pres*
EMP: 35
SQ FT: 1,800
SALES (est): 1MM-4.9MM **Privately Held**
SIC: 7992 Public golf course

LEWISTON
Winona County

(G-2965)

DALEY FARM OF LEWISTON LLP

18762 Highway 14 (55952-4223)
PHONE.............................507 523-3687
FAX: 507 523-2273
Steven Daley, *Partner*
EMP: 49 EST: 1998 **Privately Held**
SIC: 0241 Dairy farming

(G-2966)

DELOUGHERY HOME LP

Also Called: Lewiston Villa Nursing Home
505 E Main St (55952-1204)
PHONE.............................507 523-2123
FAX: 507 523-3699
Grace Deloughery, *Partner*
Frank Rekuski, *Partner*
Bonnie Kiese, *Office Mgr*

Linda Krall, *Manager*
Jodi Barton, *Administrator*
EMP: 60 EST: 1981
SALES (est): 1MM-4.9MM **Privately Held**
SIC: 8051 Convalescent home

(G-2967)

LEWISTON AUTO CO INC

US Hwy 14 At Rice St (55952)
PO Box 40 (55952-0040)
PHONE.............................507 523-2164
FAX: 507 523-3323
Lyle J Nienow, *President*
Jon C Nienow, *Corp Secy*
Ralf Nienow, *Manager*
EMP: 25 EST: 1920
SQ FT: 18,500
SALES (est): 10MM-24.9MM **Privately Held**
WEB: www.lewistonauto.com
SIC: 7532 7538 Retails new & used
automobiles; general automotive repair
services; automotive bumper repair shop

LINDSTROM
Chisago County

(G-2968)

CHISAGO LAKES GOLF ESTATES INC

12975 292nd St (55045)
PHONE.............................651 257-1484
FAX: 651 257-1484
Carl Erikson, *President*
Nick Fisk, *Asst Supt*
Todd Kuepters, *Manager*
EMP: 30 EST: 1972
SQ FT: 5,000
SALES (est): 1MM-4.9MM **Privately Held**
WEB: www.chisagolakesgolf.com
SIC: 7997 Membership golf club

(G-2969)

LAKE AREA BANK (HQ)

12790 N 1st Ave (55045-9585)
PO Box 743 (55045-0743)
PHONE.............................651 257-1117
Randy Diers, *President*
Eric Johansen, *Senior VP*
Sean Cole, *Vice Pres*
EST: 1915 **Privately Held**
WEB: www.lakeareabank.com
SIC: 6022 State commercial bank
PA: Freedom Bancorporation Inc
12790 N 1st Ave
Lindstrom MN 55045
651 257-1117

(G-2970)

PLASTIC PRODUCTS CO INC

Also Called: Smith Metal Products
30625 Olinda Trl (55045-9487)
PHONE.............................651 257-3143
FAX: 651 257-2767
Mike Brown, *Manager*
Lori Johnson, *Manager*
Deborah Beto, *Asst Mgr*
EMP: 30
SQ FT: 28,871
SALES (est): 10MM-24.9MM **Privately Held**
WEB: www.plasticproductsco.com
SIC: 5031 Wholesales molding constructed
of all materials
PA: Plastic Products Co Inc
30355 Akerson St
Lindstrom MN 55045
651 257-5980

(G-2971)

TILTON EQUIPMENT CO (PA)

30405 Neal Ave Apt 1 (55045-9520)
PO Box 68, Rye NH (03870-0068)
PHONE.............................763 783-7030
David B Tilton, *President*
Carol A Tilton, *Corp Secy*
Stephen W Tilton, *Vice Pres*
Glen Karnes, *Manager*
▲ EMP: 71 EST: 1969
SQ FT: 16,000 **Privately Held**
SIC: 5084 5083 Wholesales industrial
chainsaws; wholesales farm & garden
machinery

(PA)=Parent Co (HQ)=Headquarters (DH)=Div Headquarters
✿ = New business established in last 2 years

2011 Harris Minnesota
Services Directory

© Harris InfoSource 1-866-281-6415

137

GEOGRAPHIC

LINO LAKES
Anoka County

(G-2972)

INN HAMPTON & SUITES ✪
563 Apollo Dr (55014-3005)
PHONE......................763 746-7999
EMP: 80 **EST:** 2008
SALES (est): 1MM-4.9MM **Privately Held**
SIC: 7011 Inn

(G-2973)

LINO LAKE LODGING LLC ✪
Also Called: Country Suites By Carlson
725 Town Center Pkwy (55014-1180)
PHONE......................763 746-9500
Joseph Shemon, *General Mgr*
April Timp, *Principal*
Greg Holeman, *Principal*
EMP: 30 **EST:** 2008
SALES (est): 1MM-4.9MM **Privately Held**
SIC: 7011 Traveler accommodations

(G-2974)

METRO FIRE PROTECTION INC
8145 Lake Dr (55014-2134)
PHONE......................651 784-0417
FAX: 651 784-8419
Michael Kramer, *President*
Josh Schmitt, *Business Mgr*
Jerry Kramer, *Manager*
EMP: 34 **EST:** 1987
SQ FT: 7,500
SALES (est): 1MM-4.9MM **Privately Held**
WEB: www.metrofireprotection.com
SIC: 1711 Fire sprinkler system installation
service

(G-2975)

NORTHERN SALES & CONSULTING ✪
6800 Otter Lake Rd (55038-9466)
PHONE......................651 429-5757
Steve Anderson, *CFO*
Pat Kennedy, *Administrator*
EMP: 55 **EST:** 2009
SALES (est): 25MM-49.9MM **Privately Held**
SIC: 5074 Wholesales water heaters &
purification equipment

(G-2976)

SUPERL INC
7301 Apollo Ct (55014-3034)
PHONE......................763 571-7464
Mark Dietz, *President*
Maggie Usher, *Principal*
Brita Nau, *Manager*
EMP: 45 **EST:** 1984
SQ FT: 4,000
SALES (est): 1MM-4.9MM **Privately Held**
WEB: www.superl.net
SIC: 1742 Building insulation installation
service

LITCHFIELD
Meeker County

(G-2977)

AFFILIATED COMMUNITY MEDICAL
520 S Sibley Ave (55355-3030)
PHONE......................320 693-3233
FAX: 320 693-3290
David Detert MD, *Principal*
Dawn Gauer, *Business Mgr*
Julie Culshaw, *Purch Mgr*
Tom Rozendaae, *CFO*
Teresa Behm, *Marketing Staff*
EMP: 252
SALES (est): 25MM-49.9MM **Privately Held**
WEB: www.acmc.com
SIC: 8011 General & family practice
physician or surgeon office
PA: Affiliated Community Medical
101 Willmar Ave SW
Willmar MN 56201
320 231-5000

(G-2978)

ARGENBRIGHT INC
Also Called: Archway Marketing Services
225 S Gorman Ave (55355-2438)
PHONE......................320 693-7314
FAX: 320 693-6300
Mark Holmgren, *Branch Mgr*
EMP: 25
SALES (est): 1MM-4.9MM **Privately Held**
SIC: 8742 Management consulting services
PA: Argenbright Inc
7600 69th Ave
Rockford MN 55373
763 477-7600

(G-2979)

AUGUSTANA LUTHERAN HOMES INC
Also Called: Gloria Dei Manor
203 N Armstrong Ave (55355-2272)
PHONE......................320 693-2430
Brandon Pietsch, *Branch Mgr*
Leia Klinghagen, *Social Worker*
EMP: 42
SALES (est): 1MM-4.9MM **Privately Held**
SIC: 8051 Convalescent home
PA: Augustana Lutheran Homes Inc
218 N Holcombe Ave
Litchfield MN 55355
320 693-2430

(G-2980)

CENTER NATIONAL BANK
301 N Ramsey Ave (55355-2125)
PHONE......................320 693-3255
FAX: 320 693-7429
David Daeges, *President*
Mike Boyle, *Member*
Wayne Carlson, *Member*
Clinton Fall, *Member*
Karen Zimmer, *Vice Pres*
EMP: 30 **EST:** 1891
SQ FT: 25,000
SALES (est): 5MM-9.9MM **Privately Held**
SIC: 6021 National commercial bank

(G-2981)

CONSUMERS COOPERATIVE ASSN
1025 E Frontage Rd (55355-2602)
PHONE......................320 693-2821
FAX: 320 693-2362
Terry McNamara, *General Mgr*
Dale Ackman, *Corp Secy*
Gary Cervin, *Vice Pres*
EMP: 28 **EST:** 1936
SQ FT: 8,800
SALES (est): 10MM-24.9MM **Privately Held**
SIC: 5171 Manufactures fertilizers;
wholesales petroleum bulk stations; retail
gasoline filling station; retails bottled
propane gas

(G-2982)

COUNTY OF MEEKER
Also Called: Meeker County Memorial Hosp
612 S Sibley Ave (55355-3340)
PHONE......................320 693-3242
FAX: 320 693-8283
Michael Schrimm, *CEO*
Gary Bridge, *Purchasing*
Jim Guza, *Engineering*
Gary Sogge, *CFO*
Cindi Twardy, *Human Res Dir*
EMP: 125
SALES (est): 10MM-24.9MM **Privately Held**
WEB: www.meekercodevcorp.com
SIC: 8062 Medical hospital
PA: County of Meeker
325 N Sibley Ave
Litchfield MN 55355
320 693-5220

(G-2983)

COUNTY OF MEEKER
Also Called: Meeker Social Services
114 N Holcombe Ave Ste 180
(55355-2349)
PHONE......................320 693-5300
Julie Schrum, *Corp Secy*
Michael Hirman, *Sales Staff*
Clark Gustafson, *Manager*
EMP: 35
SALES (est): 1MM-4.9MM **Privately Held**

WEB: www.meekercodevcorp.com
SIC: 8322 Emergency & relief services;
county government administration of social
& manpower programs
PA: County of Meeker
325 N Sibley Ave
Litchfield MN 55355
320 693-5220

(G-2984)

FORBES, JOHN
60819 US Highway 12 (55355-5227)
PHONE......................320 693-3287
FAX: 320 693-8964
John J Forbes, *Owner*
EMP: 25 **EST:** 1975
SQ FT: 79,000
SALES (est): 5MM-9.9MM **Privately Held**
WEB: www.heartthrobexhaust.com
SIC: 5013 7538 Wholesales automotive
exhaust systems including mufflers & tail
pipes; general automotive repair services;
manufactures motor vehicle exhaust
mufflers; retails automotive accessories

(G-2985)

HICKS TRUCKING CO OF
104 N Gorman Ave (55355-2426)
PHONE......................320 693-3292
Lyle Hicks, *President*
Lee Kathiu, *General Mgr*
Linnea Weida, *Manager*
EMP: 35 **EST:** 1968
SQ FT: 12,000
SALES (est): 1MM-4.9MM **Privately Held**
SIC: 4731 4213 Truck transportation
brokers; contract haulers

(G-2986)

HICKS TRUCKING INC
102 N Gorman Ave (55355-2426)
PHONE......................320 693-3292
FAX: 320 693-8180
Lyle Hicks, *President*
Joann Hicks, *Vice Pres*
Lyynea Weida, *Manager*
EMP: 50 **EST:** 1949
SQ FT: 12,000
SALES (est): 1MM-4.9MM **Privately Held**
SIC: 7363 Truck driver service

(G-2987)

LITCHFIELD GOLF CLUB
405 W Pleasure Dr (55355)
PHONE......................320 693-6059
John Street, *Manager*
EMP: 40 **EST:** 1941
SALES (est): 1MM-4.9MM **Privately Held**
SIC: 7997 Membership golf club; retails golf
goods & equipment; bar; eating place

(G-2988)

MANNANAH SNOW BLAZERS
62384 310th St (55355-4605)
PHONE......................320 693-6658
Ched Holmberg, *President*
EMP: 50 **EST:** 1974
SALES (est): 1MM-4.9MM **Privately Held**
SIC: 7997 Membership recreation club

(G-2989)

RANDT RECYCLING TECHNOLOGIES
60571 US Highway 12 (55355-5227)
PHONE......................763 417-1370
Christian Bame, *President*
EMP: 30 **EST:** 2005
SALES (est): 1MM-4.9MM **Privately Held**
SIC: 4953 Refuse systems services

(G-2990)

RCK INC
27744 Csah 34 (55355-5225)
PHONE......................320 693-7422
Bob Kopplin, *President*
EMP: 26 **EST:** 1997 **Privately Held**
SIC: 0241 Dairy farming

(G-2991)

TRICO TCWIND INC
111 E 10th St (55355-1327)
PO Box 176 (55355-0176)
PHONE......................320 693-6200
Jamie McDonald, *President*
Jason McDonald, *Corp Secy*
Milton Floch, *Manager*
Dallas Drietz, *Manager*
Brice McDonald, *Manager*
EMP: 45 **EST:** 1995
SQ FT: 75,000
SALES (est): 5MM-9.9MM **Privately Held**
WEB: www.tricotcwind.com
SIC: 7694 5063 Electric motor repair
service; wholesales electrical apparatus &
equipment
PA: Integrated Power Services LLC
3 Independence Pt Ste 100
Greenville SC 29615
864 451-5600

(G-2992)

VISION PROCESSING TECHNOLOGIES
125 E Commercial St (55355-2805)
PHONE......................320 593-1796
Pete Balbo, *CEO*
Todd Ringhouse, *Vice Pres*
Donna Bengtson, *Accountant*
EMP: 49 **EST:** 2003
SQ FT: 2,600 **Privately Held**
WEB: www.vision-pharma.com
SIC: 8731 Commercial physical research
services

(G-2993)

WOODLAND CENTERS
114 N Holcombe Ave # 230 (55355-2210)
PHONE......................320 693-7221
FAX: 320 693-7222
Eugene Bonynge, *CEO*
Karin Johnson, *Exec Dir*
Sue Kristofferson, *Receptionist Se*
Kristel Hart, *Registrd Nurse*
William Meller, *Psychiatry*
EMP: 110
SALES (est): 5MM-9.9MM **Privately Held**
WEB: www.woodlandcenters.com
SIC: 8093 Outpatient mental health clinic
PA: Woodland Centers
1125 6th St SE
Willmar MN 56201
320 235-4613

(G-2994)

WORK CONNECTION INC
201 S Sibley Ave Ste 1 (55355-2169)
PHONE......................320 693-8871
Nancy Vedder, *Manager*
EMP: 70 **Privately Held**
SIC: 7361 Employment agency services
PA: Work Connection Inc
979 Arcade St
Saint Paul MN 55106
651 774-9675

LITTLE CANADA
Ramsey County

(G-2995)

CONTINGENT WORK FORCE SOLN
Also Called: C W F Solutions
2860 Middle St (55117-1411)
PHONE......................651 636-5624
FAX: 651 636-5706
Aaron Pouncy, *CEO*
Carmen Colombo, *President*
Willie Pouncy, *Member*
Brian Colombo, *COO*
Sue Vang, *Office Mgr*
EMP: 180 **EST:** 2003 **Privately Held**
WEB: www.cwfsolutions.com
SIC: 7361 Employment agency for labor
contractors

(G-2996)

MCKESSON CORP
3230 Spruce St (55117-1063)
PHONE 651 484-4811
FAX: 651 484-6228
Tracy Morrison, *Opers Mgr*
Tim Bredahl, *Credit Mgr*
Terry Simcox, *Human Resources*
Kim Diemand, *Sales Mgr*
Niel Rafferty, *Manager*
EMP: 75
SALES (est): 50MM-99.9MM **Publicly Held**
WEB: www.imckesson.com
SIC: 5122 Wholesales pharmaceuticals,
drug proprietaries & sundries
  PA: McKesson Corp
    1 Post St Fl 18
    San Francisco CA 94104
    415 983-8300

(G-2997)

RAM CONSTRUCTION SERVICES OF
3065 Spruce St Ste 104 (55117-1062)
PHONE 651 765-1950
FAX: 651 484-0851
Robert Mazur, *Member*
Kevin Houle, *CFO*
EMP: 30 EST: 2004
SALES (est): 1MM-4.9MM **Privately Held**
SIC: 1799 Waterproofing service
  PA: Ram Construction Services of
    13800 Eckles Rd
    Livonia MI 48150
    734 464-3800

(G-2998)

RUSSEL METALS WILLIAMS BAHCALL
3250 Spruce St (55117-1063)
PHONE 651 688-8138
Tim Martin, *Branch Mgr*
Will Hickey, *Manager*
Clay Scherer, *Manager*
Pat Domier, *Manager*
EMP: 25
SALES (est): 10MM-24.9MM **Privately Held**
WEB: www.russelmetals.com
SIC: 5051 Metal service center
  PA: Russel Metals Williams Bahcall
    999 W Armour Ave
    Milwaukee WI 53221
    920 734-9271

LITTLE FALLS
Morrison County

(G-2999)

ALLETE INC
1201 11th St NE (56345-2259)
PO Box 60 (56345-0060)
PHONE 320 632-2311
FAX: 320 632-2310
Lynn Orth, *Manager*
EMP: 83
SALES (est): 50MM-99.9MM **Publicly Held**
SIC: 4911 Electric services
  PA: Allete Inc
    30 W Superior St
    Duluth MN 55802
    218 279-5000

(G-3000)

BRANDL MOTOR SPORTS
14873 113th St (56345-6378)
PHONE 320 632-2908
Joseph Sexton, *President*
Gary Posch, *Vice Pres*
EMP: 42 EST: 2007
SALES (est): 1MM-4.9MM **Privately Held**
SIC: 7549 Automotive services

(G-3001)

EAGLE CONSTRUCTION CO INC
515 9th Ave NW (56345-1010)
PHONE 320 632-5429
FAX: 320 632-5420
Randall Radziej, *President*
EMP: 25 EST: 1973
SQ FT: 1,200
SALES (est): 5MM-9.9MM **Privately Held**

SIC: 1542 New commercial & office building
construction

(G-3002)

EMPLOYMENT ENTERPRISES INC
307 9th Ave NW (56345-1006)
PO Box 303 (56345-0303)
PHONE 320 632-9251
FAX: 320 632-9252
Byron Quinn, *Director*
EMP: 70 EST: 1970
SQ FT: 9,600
SALES (est): 1MM-4.9MM **Privately Held**
SIC: 8331 4953 Sheltered workshop; refuse
systems services; manufactures glass
products; manufactures secondary
nonferrous metals; pulp mill

(G-3003)

FALLS COURT DENTISTS
119 1st St NE Ste 4 (56345-2635)
PHONE 320 632-6621
FAX: 320 632-1829
James N Peters, *President*
Jan Erwin, *Manager*
EMP: 35 EST: 1969
SALES (est): 1MM-4.9MM **Privately Held**
SIC: 8021 Dental office

(G-3004)

FALLS DISTRIBUTION INC
16731 Haven Rd (56345-6490)
PHONE 320 632-3999
FAX: 320 632-5115
Nicholas Lamp, *President*
Heather Morris, *Managing Dir*
Laura Firkus, *Manager*
▲ EMP: 30 EST: 1998
SQ FT: 50,000
SALES (est): 5MM-9.9MM **Privately Held**
WEB: www.fallsco.com
SIC: 4225 Manufactures plastic foam
products; general warehousing

(G-3005)

FALLS FABRICATING
600 9th Ave NW (56345-1013)
PHONE 320 632-2322
FAX: 320 632-2919
Al Williams, *Vice Pres*
Ken Kolb, *Mfg Staff*
John Sorenson, *Mfg Staff*
Ed Shelleny, *CFO*
Dennis Gangestad, *Manager*
EMP: 113
SALES (est): 10MM-24.9MM **Privately Held**
SIC: 7692 Welding service; metal products
painting service; sheet metal fabricator;
metal finishing services
  PA: Falls Fabricating
    5091 Hilltop Ave N
    Lake Elmo MN 55042
    651 777-0777

(G-3006)

HOME SAVINGS OF AMERICA
35 E Broadway (56345-3046)
PHONE 320 632-5461
FAX: 320 632-5463
Dirk Adams, *CEO*
Kathy Jacobs, *Exec VP*
Mary Karnowski, *Senior VP*
Larry Hartwig, *CFO*
Marge Kardell-Smith, *Human Res Mgr*
EMP: 42 EST: 1934
SQ FT: 2,800
SALES (est): 5MM-9.9MM **Privately Held**
WEB: www.commfed.com
SIC: 6162 6035 Mortgage & loan lending;
federal savings & loan association
  PA: Mississippi View Holding Co
    35 E Broadway
    Little Falls MN 56345
    320 632-5461

(G-3007)

INITIATIVE FOUNDATION
405 1st St SE (56345-3007)
PHONE 320 632-9255
FAX: 320 632-9258
Kathy Gaalswyk, *President*
Linda Desjardins, *Member*
Paulette Huddle, *CFO*
Mary Bauer, *Marketing Mgr*

Leah Posterick, *Marketing Mgr*
EMP: 25 EST: 1986
SQ FT: 3,500 **Privately Held**
SIC: 8399 Community development groups

(G-3008)

INSTANT WEB INC
1910 Haven Rd (56345-2287)
PHONE 320 616-5100
Pete Karle, *CFO*
Paul Overn, *Branch Mgr*
Anne Skroch, *Telecom Exec*
EMP: 600
SALES (est): 50MM-99.9MM **Privately Held**
SIC: 7331 Direct mail advertising service

(G-3009)

KASKA INC
920 4th St SE (56345-3540)
PHONE 320 632-9281
Jim Birchem, *President*
EMP: 99 EST: 2007
SALES (est): 1MM-4.9MM **Privately Held**
SIC: 8059 Nursing home

(G-3010)

LINCOLN ELEMENTRY SCHOOL P T A
Also Called: Pta Minnesota Congress
300 6th St SW (56345-1543)
PHONE 320 616-6200
FAX: 320 616-2144
Randy Smith, *Principal*
Vickie Kersten, *Corp Secy*
Ronda Chapman, *Treasurer*
Mark Diehl, *Technology Dir*
Nancy Anderson, *Technician*
EMP: 35 EST: 1967 **Privately Held**
SIC: 8641 Parent teacher association

(G-3011)

LITTLE FALLS GOLF ASSOCIATION
1 Edgewater Dr (56345-3430)
PHONE 320 616-5520
FAX: 320 616-5521
Randy Pankonen, *General Mgr*
Bill Doroff, *Manager*
EMP: 27 EST: 1930
SQ FT: 2,800
SALES (est): 1MM-4.9MM **Privately Held**
SIC: 7992 Public golf course

(G-3012)

LUTHERAN CARE CENTER INC
1200 1st Ave NE (56345-3309)
PHONE 320 632-9211
FAX: 320 632-4360
Kathy Meyers, *Personnel*
Joan Jackson, *Administrator*
Joanne Betker, *Administrator*
Arthur R Upright, *Bd of Directors*
EMP: 95 EST: 1964
SQ FT: 43,800
SALES (est): 1MM-4.9MM **Privately Held**
WEB: www.lutherancarecenter.com
SIC: 8051 Skilled nursing care facility

(G-3013)

MEDICAL CENTER
811 2nd St SE Ste A (56345-3505)
PHONE 320 632-6611
Sharon R Mathiowetz, *Business Mgr*
Irina G Ohanian, *Med Doctor*
Jackie R Och, *Manager*
Dennis D Dvorak, *Administrator*
Steven Brown, *Administrator*
EMP: 80 EST: 1991
SALES (est): 5MM-9.9MM **Privately Held**
SIC: 8011 Physicians' office & clinic

(G-3014)

MINNESOTA WINGS MOTORCYCLE
205 3rd Ave NW (56345-1211)
PHONE 320 632-8427
Dwayne Matthews, *President*
EMP: 35 EST: 1984 **Privately Held**
SIC: 8699 Personal interest organization

(G-3015)

NORTHERN PINES MENTAL HEALTH
1906 5th Ave SE (56345-3317)
PO Box 367 (56345-0367)
PHONE 320 632-6647
Jim Youngman, *Principal*
Mark Bublitz, *Exec Dir*
EST: 1961 **Privately Held**
SIC: 8011 8322 Psychiatric clinic; general
counseling services

(G-3016)

PALMER BUS SERVICE OF N
17043 Haven Rd (56345-2204)
PO Box 757 (56345-0757)
PHONE 320 632-1555
FAX: 320 632-1551
Floyd D Palmer, *President*
Andy Galfton, *Manager*
EMP: 25 EST: 2000
SALES (est): 1MM-4.9MM **Privately Held**
SIC: 4142 Long-distance bus charter
service

(G-3017)

PALMER CHARTER SERVICE INC
17043 Haven Rd (56345)
PO Box 757 (56345-0757)
PHONE 320 632-1555
Floyd Palmer, *President*
EMP: 30
SQ FT: 7,500
SALES (est): 1MM-4.9MM **Privately Held**
SIC: 4141 4142 4151 Local bus charter
service; school bus service; long-distance
bus charter service

(G-3018)

ROBERT LEMIEUR & SONS INC
Also Called: Bob Lemieur Sons Chrtr Bus Svc
14827 Pine Ave (56345-6404)
PHONE 320 632-9141
FAX: 320 632-9141
Robert Lemieur, *President*
Linda Lemieur, *Vice Pres*
EMP: 25 EST: 1980
SALES (est): 1MM-4.9MM **Privately Held**
SIC: 4111 Bus transit system

(G-3019)

SCHUELLER WENNER & CO
109 E Broadway (56345-3038)
PO Box 365 (56345-0365)
PHONE 320 632-6311
FAX: 320 632-0704
Steven Schueller, *Partner*
EMP: 60 EST: 1998
SALES (est): 5MM-9.9MM **Privately Held**
WEB: www.swcocpas.com
SIC: 8721 Certified public accountant
services

(G-3020)

TRI-COUNTY COMMUNITY ACTION (PA)
501 Lemieur St (56345-3367)
PHONE 320 632-3691
FAX: 320 632-3695
Rosanne Erickson, *Technical Staff*
Joseph D Ayers, *Exec Dir*
Larry Katchum, *Director*
Don Meyer, *Bd of Directors*
Dave Hardie, *Bd of Directors*
EMP: 30 EST: 1965
SALES (corp-wide): 5.22M **Privately Held**
SIC: 8322 8351 Individual & family social
services; child & youth services; head Start
center

(G-3021)

UNITY FAMILY HEALTH CARE
Also Called: St Gabriel's Hospital
815 2nd St SE (56345-3505)
PHONE 320 632-5441
FAX: 320 632-2290
Carl Vaagenes, *President*
Ann Bertoch, *Corp Secy*
Deb Herbaugh, *Vice Pres*
Jan Korzeniowski, *Vice Pres*
Mary Bauer, *Opers Mgr*
EMP: 600

GEOGRAPHIC

EST: 1891
SQ FT: 140,000
SALES (est): 50MM-99.9MM **Privately Held**
WEB: www.stgabriels.com
SIC: 8062 Medical hospital
PA: Catholic Health Initiatives
98 Inverness Dr W Ste 800
Englewood CO 80112
303 298-9100

LITTLEFORK
Koochiching County

(G-3022)
CITY OF LITTLEFORK
Also Called: Littlefork Medical Center
912 Main St (56653-9357)
PHONE..........................218 278-6634
FAX: 218 278-6637
Ron Manka, *Engineering*
Kathy Boutin, *Office Mgr*
Kalvin Olsen, *Manager*
Beverly E Houglum, *Manager*
Calvin Olsen, *Administrator*
EMP: 85
SALES (est): 5MM-9.9MM **Privately Held**
SIC: 8011 Medical center

LONG LAKE
Hennepin County

(G-3023)
DALBEC ROOFING INC
2285 Daniels St (55356-9276)
PHONE..........................952 473-8080
Kevin Krolczyk, *President*
Michele Krolcyk, *Exec VP*
Lisa Robison, *Manager*
EMP: 30 **EST:** 1947
SQ FT: 6,000
SALES (est): 1MM-4.9MM **Privately Held**
WEB: www.dalbecroofing.com
SIC: 1761 Roofing contractor; sheet metal work contractor

(G-3024)
FIRST STUDENT INC
505 Tamarack Ave (55356-9417)
PHONE..........................952 475-0038
FAX: 952 475-0312
Gary Schillinger, *Manager*
EMP: 30
SALES (est): 500-999K **Privately Held**
WEB: www.firststudentinc.com
SIC: 4151 School bus service
HQ: First Student Inc
600 Vine St Ste 1400
Cincinnati OH 45202
513 241-2200

(G-3025)
JEM TECHNICAL MARKETING CO INC
2250 Daniels St (55356-9275)
PHONE..........................952 473-5012
FAX: 952 473-6930
John E Menge, *President*
Sheryl Menge, *Vice Pres*
Andrea Tysdal, *Vice Pres*
Mike Barto, *Manager*
Tom T Seinkamp, *Manager*
EMP: 69 **EST:** 1984
SQ FT: 13,000
SALES (est): 25MM-49.9MM **Privately Held**
WEB: www.jemtechnical.com
SIC: 5085 5084 Wholesales industrial valves & fittings; manufactures fluid power valves & hose fittings; wholesales industrial machinery & equipment; manufactures valves & pipe fittings

(G-3026)
KNOWLEDGE COMPUTERS INC
2360 Daniels St (55356-9277)
PHONE..........................952 249-9940
Dave Potter, *President*
MEI Leng, *Managing Prtnr*
Alan Ler, *Managing Prtnr*
Margaret Cramer, *Vice Pres*
Jim Parmar, *Controller*
EMP: 27 **EST:** 2004

SALES (est): 10MM-24.9MM **Privately Held**
WEB: www.knowledgecomputers.net
SIC: 5045 Wholesales computers, peripherals & software

(G-3027)
LAKE COMMUNITY BANK
1964 W Wayzata Blvd (55356-9494)
PHONE..........................952 473-7347
Michael Byrne, *President*
Michael Brown, *General Mgr*
Jerry Taffe, *Senior VP*
Marshall Plontik, *Assistant VP*
Lynn James, *Vice Pres*
EMP: 30 **EST:** 1904
SQ FT: 3,000
SALES (est): 5MM-9.9MM **Privately Held**
WEB: www.sblonglake.com
SIC: 6022 6163 State commercial bank; loan broker

(G-3028)
LITTLE ACORNS CHILD CARE INC
1865 W Wayzata Blvd # 110 (55356-9322)
PHONE..........................952 475-0828
James Smale, *CEO*
Mary Smale, *CFO*
EMP: 35 **EST:** 1998
SALES (est): 500-999K **Privately Held**
WEB: www.littleacornschildcare.com
SIC: 8351 Child day care service

(G-3029)
ORONO HEALTHY YOUTH
705 N Old Crystal Bay Rd (55356-9594)
PHONE..........................952 449-8351
Melanie Deluca, *Director*
EMP: 30
SALES (est): 1MM-4.9MM **Privately Held**
SIC: 8322 Outreach program

(G-3030)
PREMIER TECHNOLOGIES INC
1 Premier Dr (55356-9691)
PO Box 159 (55356-0159)
PHONE..........................952 475-2317
FAX: 952 475-3579
Richard Stark, *President*
Reginald McNutt, *Corp Secy*
Craig Robbins, *Vice Pres*
Brian Schroeder, *Opers-Prdtn-Mfg*
Mike La La Chance, *Purch Agent*
EMP: 70 **EST:** 1990
SQ FT: 28,000
SALES (est): 10MM-24.9MM **Privately Held**
WEB: www.premtech.com
SIC: 5084 Manufactures emergency alarms; wholesales elevators; manufactures telecommunication systems & equipment

(G-3031)
RIDGEDALE ELECTRIC INC
500 Brimhall Ave (55356-9485)
PO Box 410 (55356-0410)
PHONE..........................952 473-2714
Gerald W Wagoner, *President*
Kay Wagoner, *Vice Pres*
Kathy Cleveland, *Controller*
EMP: 35 **EST:** 1977
SQ FT: 4,800
SALES (est): 1MM-4.9MM **Privately Held**
WEB: www.ridgedaleelectric.com
SIC: 1731 Electrical contractor

(G-3032)
SERVICE 800 INC
2190 W Wayzata Blvd (55356-9587)
PO Box 800 (55356-0800)
PHONE..........................952 475-3747
FAX: 952 475-3773
Roger Allen, *President*
Jean M Bredeson, *Treasurer*
Glen Robertson, *International*
Mary Marshik, *Manager*
Dave Welsh, *Info Tech Dir*
EMP: 342 **EST:** 1989
SQ FT: 11,000
SALES (est): 25MM-49.9MM **Privately Held**
WEB: www.service800.com
SIC: 8732 Market analysis or research services

(G-3033)
STERLING SYSTEMS INC
2265 W Wayzata Blvd (55356-4706)
PHONE..........................952 697-1060
Jason Jones, *CEO*
Jill Jones, *President*
Robyn Doty, *Office Mgr*
EMP: 30 **EST:** 1998
SALES (est): 1MM-4.9MM **Privately Held**
SIC: 1799 Asbestos removal & encapsulation contractor

(G-3034)
TREB, DAN PAINTING
Also Called: Dan Treb Painting & Decorating
488 Tamarack Ave (55356-9601)
PO Box 844 (55356-0844)
PHONE..........................952 476-8163
FAX: 952 476-8269
Dan Treb, *President*
Lois Treb, *President*
Bruce Gessell, *Manager*
EMP: 46 **EST:** 1989
SQ FT: 1,500
SALES (est): 1MM-4.9MM **Privately Held**
SIC: 1721 Painting & wall covering contractor

(G-3035)
WESTERN STEEL ERECTION INC
485 Stubbs Bay Rd (55356-9736)
PO Box 575 (55356-0575)
PHONE..........................952 473-4344
FAX: 952 473-9332
Stephanie Jochims, *President*
EMP: 25
SQ FT: 1,000
SALES (est): 1MM-4.9MM **Privately Held**
SIC: 1791 7389 Structural iron work contractor; concrete reinforcement placing contractor; crane & aerial lift service

LONG PRAIRIE
Todd County

(G-3036)
AMERICAN HERITAGE NATIONAL (PA)
24 2nd St S (56347-1327)
PO Box 509 (56347-0509)
PHONE..........................320 732-6131
FAX: 320 732-6136
Roger Johnston, *President*
Denis Irsseld, *Senior VP*
Timothy Gallagher, *Vice Pres*
Raymond Muges, *Vice Pres*
Denise Rosin, *Manager*
EMP: 30 **EST:** 1881
SQ FT: 8,100
SALES (corp-wide): 10.67M **Privately Held**
SIC: 6021 National commercial bank

(G-3037)
CENTRACARE CLINIC
24 9th St SE (56347-1404)
PHONE..........................320 732-2131
Toni Tebben, *Manager*
EMP: 50
SALES (est): 5MM-9.9MM **Privately Held**
WEB: www.centracareclinic.com
SIC: 8011 General & family practice physician or surgeon office
PA: Centracare Clinic
1200 6th Ave N
Saint Cloud MN 56303
320 252-5131

(G-3038)
CENTRACARE HEALTH SERVICES OF
20 9th St SE (56347-1404)
PHONE..........................320 732-2131
Daniel Swenson, *CEO*
Ron Anderson, *Purchasing*
Larry Knutson, *Finance Dir*
Joyce Chan, *Human Resources*
Anita Rademacher, *Mktg Coord*
EST: 1998
SQ FT: 97,000 **Privately Held**
SIC: 8062 Medical hospital

(G-3039)
CIRCLE R RANCH INC
9 Miles East On Hwy 27 (56347)
RR 1 Box 32549 (56347)
PHONE..........................320 547-2176
FAX: 320 732-2176
Jack McCoy, *President*
Shelia McCoy, *Corp Secy*
EMP: 25 **EST:** 1969
SALES (est): 1MM-4.9MM **Privately Held**
SIC: 7032 0752 Boys' camp; animal specialty services; girls' camp; summer camp

(G-3040)
COUNTY OF TODD
Also Called: Todd County Social Services
212 2nd Ave SW (56347-1827)
PHONE..........................320 732-4500
Frank Sandelin, *Manager*
EMP: 56 **Privately Held**
SIC: 8399 Human resource, social work & welfare administration services; social services information exchange; county government administration of social & manpower programs

(G-3041)
CUSTOM TRANSFER INC
23512 230th St (56347-5007)
PO Box 157 (56347-0157)
PHONE..........................320 732-3013
FAX: 320 732-3016
Dave Kamphenkel, *President*
Audrey Kamphenkel, *Corp Secy*
Melissa Terwe, *Manager*
EMP: 48 **EST:** 1983
SQ FT: 20,000
SALES (est): 5MM-9.9MM **Privately Held**
WEB: www.custom-transfer.com
SIC: 4213 Over the road trucking

(G-3042)
DAYBREAK FOODS INC
609 6th St NE (56347-1003)
PHONE..........................320 732-2966
FAX: 320 732-3690
Robert Rehm, *President*
Steven Masia, *Mfg Staff*
Bill Rehm, *Treasurer*
Tony Rehm, *Sales Staff*
Pat Stronger, *Director*
EMP: 75 **EST:** 1989
SALES (est): 50MM-99.9MM **Privately Held**
WEB: www.daybreakfoods.com
SIC: 5144 Wholesale egg cleaning, oil treating, packing & grading; poultry slaughtering & processing

(G-3043)
ISENSEE BUS SERVICE
24496 US 71 (56347-5410)
PHONE..........................320 732-2795
Delores Isensee, *President*
Butch Lambrechd, *Manager*
EMP: 28 **EST:** 1967
SQ FT: 8,400
SALES (est): 500-999K **Privately Held**
SIC: 4151 School bus service

LONSDALE
Rice County

(G-3044)
FRANDSEN BANK & TRUST (PA)
116 Central St W (55046-9626)
PO Box 200 (55046-0200)
PHONE..........................507 744-2361
Chariotte Kodada, *Vice Pres*
Ruth Schaefer, *Mfg Spvr*
Cindy Kuehn-Gleason, *Manager*
James Bowers, *Manager*
Michael Schwartz, *Manager*
EMP: 43 **EST:** 1901 **Privately Held**
SIC: 6022 State commercial bank

www.HarrisInfo.com
140

2011 Harris Minnesota
Services Directory

▲=Import ▼=Export
◆=Import/Export

(G-3045)
LONSDALE PACKAGING
629 Industrial Dr SE (55046-4013)
PHONE.....................507 744-2376
FAX: 507 744-4911
Rod Bush, *Principal*
Allen Malecha, *Vice Pres*
Joe Kellen, *Marketing Mgr*
Barb Malecha, *Executive*
▲ **EMP:** 100 **EST:** 1998
SQ FT: 50,000
SALES (est): 5MM-9.9MM **Privately Held**
WEB: www.lonsdalepackaging.com
SIC: 7389 Packaging & labeling services

LORETTO
Hennepin County

(G-3046)
DOBOSZENSKI & SONS INC
9520 County Road 19 (55357-4611)
PHONE.....................763 478-6945
FAX: 763 478-3186
Kenneth Doboszenski, *CEO*
Doug Doboszenski, *President*
Teresa Doboszenski, *Corp Secy*
Phyllis Doboszenski, *Treasurer*
Timothy Doboszenski, *Director*
EMP: 30 **EST:** 1979
SQ FT: 8,000
SALES (est): 1MM-4.9MM **Privately Held**
WEB: www.doboszenskiandsons.com
SIC: 1629 1794 Earthmoving service;
construction site preparation services;
excavation & grading, building construction
contractor

(G-3047)
EBERT INC
23350 County Road 10 (55357-9775)
PO Box 97 (55357-0097)
PHONE.....................763 498-7844
FAX: 763 498-5591
Gregory Ebert, *President*
Jake Ullery, *Vice Pres*
James O Rasmussen, *CFO*
Aimee Roehl, *Manager*
Josh Nichols, *Manager*
EMP: 45 **EST:** 1968
SQ FT: 7,500
SALES (est): 10MM-24.9MM **Privately Held**
WEB: www.ebertconst.com
SIC: 1542 1522 Commercial & office
building contractor; residential construction;
agricultural building construction

(G-3048)
GREENWORKS INC
8940 Greenfield Rd (55357-9724)
PHONE.....................763 498-7696
FAX: 763 498-7524
Thomas Grygelko, *President*
Heggy Johnson, *Office Mgr*
EMP: 25 **EST:** 1975 **Privately Held**
WEB: www.greenworks.com
SIC: 0782 Landscaping services

(G-3049)
HONDA ELECTRIC INC
5075 Nielsen Cir (55357-9700)
PO Box 236 (55357-0236)
PHONE.....................763 498-8433
FAX: 763 498-8770
Jeff Plzak, *CEO*
Laurie Plzak, *President*
EMP: 30 **EST:** 1994
SALES (est): 1MM-4.9MM **Privately Held**
WEB: www.honda-electric.com
SIC: 1731 Electrical contractor

(G-3050)
LANDSTYLE DESIGN & CONSTR
110 Railway St W (55357)
PO Box 361 (55357-0361)
PHONE.....................763 479-1200
Bruce Wohlrabe, *President*
Sharon Camaron, *Office Mgr*
EMP: 25 **EST:** 1989
SQ FT: 1,000 **Privately Held**
WEB: www.landstyledesign.com
SIC: 0782 Landscaping services

(G-3051)
OPS AMERICA INC
Also Called: Orient Products Services
689 N Medina St Ste 150 (55357-4609)
PHONE.....................763 479-1409
Daniel Cook, *President*
Jeff Anderson, *Vice Pres*
Joel Buckley, *Vice Pres*
Brenda Dupoint, *Accountant*
EMP: 45 **EST:** 2002
SQ FT: 1,500
SALES (est): 5MM-9.9MM **Privately Held**
WEB: www.opsamerica.com
SIC: 8711 Engineering services

(G-3052)
STEP BY STEP MONTESSORI SCHOOL
23610 County Road 10 (55357-9799)
PHONE.....................763 498-5437
FAX: 763 498-6503
Rose Miner, *President*
Kimberly Dornfeld, *Director*
EMP: 26
SALES (est): 500-999K **Privately Held**
SIC: 8351 Child development center
providing Montessori based instruction;
school & educational services

(G-3053)
21ST CENTURY BANK
699 N Medina St (55357)
PHONE.....................763 479-1901
Sarah Nelson, *Vice Pres*
Becky Lapointe, *Vice Pres*
EMP: 30
SALES (est): 5MM-9.9MM **Privately Held**
WEB: www.21stcenturybank.com
SIC: 6022 State commercial bank
HQ: 21st Century Bank
9380 Central Ave NE # 120
Minneapolis MN 55434
763 767-2178

(G-3054)
VINLAND NATIONAL CENTER
3675 Ihduhapi Rd (55357-2120)
PHONE.....................763 479-3555
FAX: 763 479-2605
Nicole Deter-Stader, *Principal*
Larry Winkler, *Exec Dir*
Carol Jackson, *Exec Dir*
Nicole D Spader, *Exec Dir*
Mary Roehl, *Director*
EMP: 45 **EST:** 1977
SQ FT: 3,000
SALES (est): 1MM-4.9MM **Privately Held**
WEB: www.vinlandcenter.org
SIC: 8361 8322 Residential rehabilitation
center with health care incidental; individual
& family social services

LOWRY
Pope County

(G-3055)
LOWRY MANUFACTURING CO
317 Cherry St (56349-0121)
PO Box 121 (56349-0121)
PHONE.....................320 283-5450
FAX: 320 283-5246
John A Dahlseng, *President*
Judi Dahlseng, *Corp Secy*
Karen Johnson, *Corp Secy*
EMP: 25 **EST:** 1972
SQ FT: 15,000
SALES (est): 5MM-9.9MM **Privately Held**
SIC: 7692 Manufactures crop storage bins;
welding service

LUTSEN
Cook County

(G-3056)
LUTSEN RESORT CO
5700 W Hwy 61 (55612)
PO Box 9 (55612-0009)
PHONE.....................218 663-7212
FAX: 218 663-0145
Scott Harrison, *President*
Diane Loh, *General Mgr*
Frederick A Dudderar Jr, *Corp Secy*
William M Burns, *Vice Pres*
Annette Cruser, *Purch Agent*
EMP: 50 **EST:** 1885
SQ FT: 35,000
SALES (est): 1MM-4.9MM **Privately Held**
WEB: www.lutsenresort.com
SIC: 7011 Vacation lodge; eating place;
motel

(G-3057)
SUPERIOR NATIONAL AT LUTSEN
5731 W Hwy 61 (55612)
PO Box 177 (55612-0177)
PHONE.....................218 663-7865
Greg Leland, *General Mgr*
Mike Davies, *Manager*
EMP: 40 **EST:** 1991
SALES (est): 1MM-4.9MM **Privately Held**
SIC: 7992 Public golf course

(G-3058)
TOWNHOMES AT LUTSEN MOUNTAINS
Also Called: Caribou Highlands
371 Ski Hill Rd (55612)
PO Box 99 (55612-0099)
PHONE.....................218 663-7241
Robert L Ryan, *President*
Tom Ryan, *Vice Pres*
Stephanie Slanga, *Sales Staff*
EMP: 50 **EST:** 1981
SALES (est): 1MM-4.9MM **Privately Held**
WEB: www.caribouhighlands.com
SIC: 7011 Resort hotel

LUVERNE
Rock County

(G-3059)
EVANGELICAL LUTHERAN GOOD
Also Called: Mary Jane Brown Good
Samaritan
110 S Walnut Ave (56156-1781)
PHONE.....................507 283-2375
FAX: 507 283-8393
Tony Leverett, *Manager*
Tony Linn, *Administrator*
Juliana Jacobson, *Director*
EMP: 80
SALES (est): 1MM-4.9MM **Privately Held**
WEB: www.good-sam.com
SIC: 8051 Convalescent home
PA: Evangelical Lutheran Good
4800 W 57th St
Sioux Falls SD 57108
605 362-3100

(G-3060)
INTERNATIONAL ASSOCIATION OF
419 W Brown St (56156-1403)
PHONE.....................507 283-9127
Gaylord Keck, *President*
EMP: 150 **Privately Held**
WEB: www.iaopc.com
SIC: 8641 Civic associations
PA: International Association of
300 W 22nd St
Oak Brook IL 60523
630 571-5466

(G-3061)
LUVERNE IND SCHOOL DIST 2184
Also Called: Bus Garage
428 W Dodge St (56156-1220)
PHONE.....................507 283-8197
Lon Reme, *Principal*
EMP: 25
SALES (est): 500-999K **Privately Held**
WEB: www.isd2184.net
SIC: 4151 School bus service
PA: Luverne Ind School Dist 2184
709 N Kniss Ave
Luverne MN 56156
507 283-8088

(G-3062)
LUVERNE RESIDENTIAL ADVANTAGE
107 S Blue Mound Ave (56156-1924)
PHONE.....................507 283-4088
FAX: 507 283-9448
Bill Olson, *President*
Courtny Buzz, *Corp Secy*
Lisa Arndt, *Exec Officer*
EMP: 80 **EST:** 2000
SALES (est): 1MM-4.9MM **Privately Held**
WEB: www.habsvinc.com
SIC: 8059 8052 Nursing & personal care
facility; intermediate care facility

(G-3063)
LUVERNE, CITY OF INC
Also Called: Rock Cnty Cmnty Swimming
Pool
802 N Blue Mound Ave (56156-1354)
PO Box 659 (56156-0659)
PHONE.....................507 449-5036
FAX: 507 449-5038
Sam Honerman, *Manager*
EMP: 30
SALES (est): 500-999K **Privately Held**
SIC: 7999 Non-membership swimming pool;
mayors' office
PA: Luverne, City of Inc
305 E Luverne St
Luverne MN 56156
507 449-2388

(G-3064)
MEULEBROECK TAUBERT & CO PLLP
109 S Freeman Ave (56156-1824)
PO Box 685 (56156-0685)
PHONE.....................507 283-4055
FAX: 507 283-4076
Dave Meulebroeck, *Partner*
Daryl Kanthak, *Executive*
EMP: 25 **EST:** 2003
SALES (est): 1MM-4.9MM **Privately Held**
SIC: 8721 Certified public accountant
services

(G-3065)
MINNESOTA DEPARTMENT OF
Also Called: Luverne Veterans Home
1300 N Kniss Ave (56156-1006)
PO Box 539 (56156-0539)
PHONE.....................507 283-1100
FAX: 507 283-1127
Pamela Borrows, *Manager*
EMP: 150
SALES (est): 5MM-9.9MM **Privately Held**
WEB: www.sbay.mvh.state.mn.us
SIC: 8051 8052 Skilled nursing care facility;
veterans' affairs administration services;
intermediate care facility; state government
administration of veterans' affairs
DH: Minnesota Department of
20 12th St W Fl 2
Saint Paul MN 55155
651 296-2562

(G-3066)
MINNWEST BANK LUVERNE
116 E Main St (56156-1831)
PO Box 899 (56156-0899)
PHONE.....................507 283-2366
Greg S Burger, *President*
James A Boeve, *Exec VP*
Nancy Scheidt, *Vice Pres*
Anna V Batavia, *Vice Pres*
Isaac Deboer, *Loan Officer*
EMP: 30 **EST:** 1882
SALES (est): 5MM-9.9MM **Privately Held**
WEB: www.minnwestbank.com
SIC: 6021 6022 National commercial bank;
state commercial bank
PA: Minnwest Corp
14820 Highway 7 Ste 100
Minnetonka MN 55345
952 545-8815

(G-3067)
SANFORD HEALTH
1600 N Kniss Ave (56156-1067)
PHONE.....................507 283-2321
Gerald Carl, *Manager*
Jill Wolf, *Director*
EMP: 200

(PA)=Parent Co (HQ)=Headquarters (DH)=Div Headquarters
♻ = New business established in last 2 years

2011 Harris Minnesota
Services Directory

© Harris InfoSource 1-866-281-6415
141

SALES (est): 10MM-24.9MM Privately Held
WEB: www.sanfordluverne.org
SIC: 8062 Medical hospital
PA: Sanford Health
1305 W 18th St
Sioux Falls SD 57105
605 333-1000

(G-3068)
SANFORD HEALTH NETWORK
1600 N Kniss Ave (56156-1067)
PHONE 507 283-2321
FAX: 507 283-2091
Wayne Panning, *Ch Radiology*
Stan Knobloch, *CFO*
Brett Christiansen, *Branch Mgr*
Julia Silvrants, *Manager*
Carol Wessels, *Manager*
EMP: 200
SALES (est): 10MM-24.9MM Privately Held
SIC: 8062 Medical hospital
PA: Sanford Health Network
1305 W 18th St
Sioux Falls SD 57105
605 328-2929

(G-3069)
SIOUX VALLEY PHYSICIAN
Also Called: Luverne Medical Center
300 E Brown St (56156-1510)
PHONE 507 283-4476
FAX: 507 283-9086
Larry Lyon, *President*
G J Kuiper, *Partner*
T Ceynowa, *Partner*
R J Morgan, *Partner*
P D Rud, *Partner*
EMP: 30 **EST:** 1968
SQ FT: 7,000
SALES (est): 1MM-4.9MM Privately Held
SIC: 8011 Clinic operated by physicians

(G-3070)
SOUTHWESTERN MENTAL HEALTH CTR (PA)
216 E Luverne St (56156-1610)
PO Box 686 (56156-0686)
PHONE 507 283-9511
Dennis Gyberg, *CFO*
Scott Johnson, *Exec Dir*
Darold Borman, *Director*
William C Fuller, *Psychiatry*
Sarah A Flynn, *Psychiatry*
EST: 1967
SQ FT: 4,000 Privately Held
SIC: 8093 8063 Outpatient alcohol treatment clinic; mental hospital; outpatient drug clinic; outpatient mental health clinic

(G-3071)
TOTAL CARD INC
1 Roundwind Rd (56156-1361)
PHONE 507 449-6401
FAX: 507 449-6503
Jeff Strauss, *Manager*
EMP: 125
SALES (est): 50MM-99.9MM Privately Held
SIC: 6153 Credit card processing services
PA: Total Card Inc
5109 S Broadband Ln
Sioux Falls SD 57108
605 977-5800

MADELIA
Watonwan County

(G-3072)
EIDE BAILLY LLP
8 W Main St (56062-1438)
PHONE 507 387-6031
Joe Willaert, *Branch Mgr*
EMP: 30
SALES (est): 1MM-4.9MM Privately Held
WEB: www.eide.com
SIC: 8721 Certified public accountant services
PA: Eide Bailly LLP
4310 17th Ave S
Fargo ND 58103
701 239-8593

(G-3073)
MADELIA COMMUNITY HOSPITAL INC
121 Drew Ave SE (56062-1841)
PHONE 507 642-3255
FAX: 507 642-8516
Candace Fenske, *CEO*
Bruce Maakstad, *Ch Radiology*
Charlene Saari, *QA Dir*
Mike Storlien, *Engineering*
Donna Klinkner, *CFO*
EMP: 90 **EST:** 1950
SQ FT: 54,677
SALES (est): 5MM-9.9MM Privately Held
SIC: 8062 Medical hospital

(G-3074)
RICHARD KOBERSKI
Also Called: Kober & Sons Nursery
80505 Elm Creek Rd (56062-6025)
PHONE 507 642-8380
Richard Koberski, *Owner*
EST: 1962 Privately Held
SIC: 0181 Nursery stock production; logging camps & contractors

(G-3075)
WOLF ETTER & CO
8 W Main St (56062-1438)
PO Box 130 (56062-0130)
PHONE 507 642-8882
FAX: 507 387-6436
John Wolf, *Partner*
Robert L Etter, *Partner*
EMP: 90 **EST:** 1972
SALES (est): 5MM-9.9MM Privately Held
WEB: www.wolfetter.com
SIC: 8721 Accounting, auditing & bookkeeping services

MADISON
Lac Qui Parle County

(G-3076)
MADISON LUTHERAN HOME
Also Called: Lac Qui Parle Clinic
900 2nd Ave (56256-1006)
PHONE 320 598-7536
FAX: 320 598-3923
Scott C Larson, *CEO*
Monica Rudnick, *Chf Purch Ofc*
Sally Fernholz, *Persnl Dir*
Sally Fernolz, *Persnl Dir*
Cindy Marxen, *Office Mgr*
EMP: 270 **EST:** 1943
SQ FT: 87,000
SALES (est): 10MM-24.9MM Privately Held
SIC: 8051 Skilled nursing care facility

(G-3077)
PRAIRIE FIVE COMMUNITY ACTION
422 5th Ave Ste 307 (56256-1214)
PHONE 320 598-3118
FAX: 320 598-3025
Mavis Ochsendorf, *Manager*
EMP: 45
SALES (est): 1MM-4.9MM Privately Held
WEB: www.prairiefive.com
SIC: 8322 Individual & family social services
PA: Prairie Five Community Action
7th St & Washington Ave S
Montevideo MN 56265
320 269-6578

MADISON LAKE
Blue Earth County

(G-3078)
CRYSTAL LAKE BUS SERVICE INC
Also Called: Lake Crystal Coaches
59780 235th St (56063-4268)
PHONE 507 243-3282
Dennis Heinze, *President*
Tim Heinze, *Vice Pres*
EMP: 33 **EST:** 1965
SQ FT: 19,500
SALES (est): 1MM-4.9MM Privately Held

WEB: www.lakecrystalcoaches.com
SIC: 4142 Long-distance bus charter service

(G-3079)
EVENSON CONCRETE SYSTEMS
23371 610th Ave (56063-4272)
PHONE 507 243-3660
Ryan Evenson, *Principal*
EMP: 26 **EST:** 2004
SALES (est): 1MM-4.9MM Privately Held
SIC: 1771 1521 Concrete contractor; single-family housing construction

(G-3080)
MANSKE BUS SERVICE INC
59780 235th St (56063-4268)
PHONE 507 243-3282
FAX: 507 243-3421
Dennis Heinze, *President*
EMP: 30 **EST:** 1951
SALES (est): 500-999K Privately Held
SIC: 4151 4141 School bus service; local bus charter service

(G-3081)
RON BOELTER WINDOW & SIDING
48636 Orchard Rd (56063-4113)
PHONE 507 243-4354
FAX: 507 243-3818
Ron Boelter, *President*
John Larsen, *Vice Pres*
EMP: 27 **EST:** 1990
SQ FT: 7,000
SALES (est): 1MM-4.9MM Privately Held
WEB: www.boelterwindowandsiding.com
SIC: 1761 1521 1751 1799 Siding contractor; retails spas & hot tubs; patio & deck construction & repair service; spa & hot tub construction & installation; window & door contractor; retails door & window products

MADISON LAKE
Waseca County

(G-3082)
GROEBNER INSURANCE AGENCY
513 Main St (56063-2027)
PO Box 128 (56063-0128)
PHONE 507 243-3102
Jerry Groebner, *Owner*
EST: 1981 Privately Held
SIC: 6411 Insurance services

MAGNOLIA
Rock County

(G-3083)
PINNACLE PROGRAMS INC
401 W Luverne St (56158-2004)
PO Box 40 (56158-0040)
PHONE 507 283-4425
FAX: 507 283-4284
Amanda Hubbling, *Office Mgr*
Don Johnson, *Director*
Rebecca Dreesen, *Director*
EMP: 40 **EST:** 1995
SQ FT: 30,000
SALES (est): 1MM-4.9MM Privately Held
WEB: www.southwestyouth.org
SIC: 8361 Juvenile correctional facilities

MAHNOMEN
Mahnomen County

(G-3084)
COUNTY OF MAHNOMEN
414 W Jefferson Ave (56557-4912)
PO Box 396 (56557-0396)
PHONE 218 935-2511
FAX: 218 935-2370
Karl Kraft, *Purchasing*
Duane Liebl, *Engineering*
Mary Pazdenik, *CFO*
Mary Pazdernick, *CFO*

Kristi Agnew, *Human Res Dir*
EMP: 97
SALES (est): 5MM-9.9MM Privately Held
WEB: www.co.mahnomen.mn.us
SIC: 8062 8051 8069 8093 Medical hospital; specialty hospital; skilled nursing care facility; specialty outpatient clinic
PA: County of Mahnomen
311 N Main St
Mahnomen MN 56557
218 935-5669

(G-3085)
FIRST NATIONAL BANK IN
103 N Main St (56557-4003)
PO Box 378 (56557-0378)
PHONE 218 935-5251
Peter Haddeland, *President*
Harley A Hanson, *Exec VP*
EMP: 25 **EST:** 1926
SALES (est): 5MM-9.9MM Privately Held
WEB: www.mahnomenbank.com
SIC: 6021 National commercial bank
PA: Mahnomen Bancshares Inc
103 N Main St
Mahnomen MN 56557
218 935-5251

(G-3086)
GORDON CONSTRUCTION INC
2222 270th Ave (56557-9374)
PHONE 218 935-2191
Harold Gordon, *President*
Rob Spry, *Manager*
Gladys Gordon, *Manager*
EMP: 50 **EST:** 1983
SQ FT: 5,600
SALES (est): 10MM-24.9MM Privately Held
SIC: 1542 1794 Commercial & office building contractor; excavating contractor

(G-3087)
HUMAN SERVICES
311 S Main St (56557-4711)
PHONE 218 935-2568
FAX: 218 935-5459
Cindy Marihart, *Director*
EMP: 25 **EST:** 2001 Privately Held
SIC: 8399 Social services information exchange

(G-3088)
MAHNOMEN COUNTY HEARTLAND
Also Called: Heartland Express
311 S Main St Fl 6 (56557-4711)
PO Box 460 (56557-0460)
PHONE 218 935-2560
Sharon Grosman, *Branch Mgr*
Shirley Olson, *Manager*
Tammy Foss, *Manager*
Leslie Finseth, *Manager*
Cindy Marihart, *Director*
EMP: 25 **EST:** 1990
SALES (est): 1MM-4.9MM Privately Held
SIC: 4119 Local passenger transportation service

(G-3089)
MAHNOMEN COUNTY SHERIFF'S
311 N Main St (56557-4015)
PHONE 218 935-2255
Douglas A Krier, *Principal*
EMP: 30
SALES (est): 1MM-4.9MM Privately Held
SIC: 7389 Business services at a non-commercial site

(G-3090)
RICE WILD ELECTRIC COOPERATIVE
502 N Main St (56557-4302)
PO Box 438 (56557-0438)
PHONE 218 935-2517
FAX: 218 935-2519
Steven Haaven, *Manager*
Duane Gunderson, *IT/INT Sup*
EMP: 43 **EST:** 1939
SQ FT: 17,000
SALES (est): 10MM-24.9MM Privately Held
WEB: www.wildriceelectric.com
SIC: 4911 Electric power distribution service

www.HarrisInfo.com
142
2011 Harris Minnesota
Services Directory
▲=Import ▼=Export
◆=Import/Export

(G-3091)

WHITE EARTH BAND OF CHIPPEWA

Also Called: Shooting Star Casino
777 SE Casino Rd (56557-5014)
PO Box 418 (56557-0418)
PHONE..............................218 935-2711
FAX: 218 935-9230
Larry Kindseth, *CFO*
Jay Jurina, *Manager*
Elizabeth Anderson, *Manager*
Erick Reitan, *Manager*
Paul Schul, *Manager*
EMP: 1200
SALES (est): 100MM-499.9MM **Privately Held**
SIC: 7999 7011 Gambling establishment; traveler accommodations
PA: White Earth Band of Chippewa
Main Street Hwy 24
White Earth MN 56591
218 983-3285

(G-3092)

WINTER TRUCK LINE INC

1485 230th St (56557-9002)
PHONE..............................218 935-2236
FAX: 218 935-2269
Delores Winter, *President*
Richard Winter, *Vice Pres*
David Winter, *Treasurer*
Barb Peterson, *Accountant*
EMP: 25 EST: 1960
SALES (est): 1MM-4.9MM **Privately Held**
SIC: 7699 Tractor repair service

MAHTOMEDI
Washington County

(G-3093)

CITY OF MAHTOMEDI

600 Stillwater Rd (55115-2007)
PHONE..............................651 426-1080
EMP: 35 **Privately Held**
SIC: 8748 Fire department, not including volunteer; business consulting services

(G-3094)

FEDEX GROUND PACKAGE SYSTEM

7 Long Lake Rd (55115-6889)
PHONE..............................651 748-8636
FAX: 651 704-9649
Greg Lewis, *Human Res Mgr*
Cathy Kerese, *Manager*
Mike Tancig, *Manager*
Christene Kreyer, *Manager*
Katherine Kerekes, *Manager*
EMP: 300
SALES (est): 25MM-49.9MM **Publicly Held**
WEB: www.fedex.com
SIC: 4213 4215 Contract haulers; ground courier services
HQ: Fedex Ground Package System
1000 Fed Ex Dr
Coraopolis PA 15108
412 269-1000

(G-3095)

MULCAHY INC

3050 Echo Lake Ave Ste 300
(55115-4000)
PHONE..............................651 770-5250
Gary Mulcahy, *President*
Tony Rand, *Superintendent*
Shelley Augustine, *Accountant*
Rick Dewhirst, *Manager*
EMP: 200 EST: 1971
SQ FT: 3,500
SALES (est): 10MM-24.9MM **Privately Held**
WEB: www.mulcahy-inc.com
SIC: 1742 1793 1799 Drywall contractor; plain or ornamental plastering contractor; glass & glazing contractor; building fireproofing contractor

(G-3096)

NDN MULCAHY LLC

3050 Echo Lake Ave (55115-1980)
PHONE..............................651 747-4201
Vivian Guerra, *President*

Mark Scally, *Vice Pres*
EMP: 50 EST: 2004
SALES (est): 1MM-4.9MM **Privately Held**
SIC: 7389 Business support services

(G-3097)

NEW PERSPECTIVE OF MINNESOTA

113 East Ave (55115-2225)
PHONE..............................651 407-9076
FAX: 651 407-9084
Karen Binsfeld, *General Mgr*
Karen Einsseld, *Administrator*
EMP: 30 EST: 1995
SQ FT: 10,000
SALES (est): 1MM-4.9MM **Privately Held**
SIC: 8361 Rest home with health care incidental

MANKATO
Blue Earth County

(G-3098)

A H HERMEL CANDY & TOBACCO CO (PA)

23099 Riverfront Dr N (56001-5993)
PO Box 447 (56002-0447)
PHONE..............................507 387-5634
David Hermel, *Ch of Bd*
Jerry Underwood, *President*
Bob Sutch, *Manager*
EMP: 80 EST: 1935
SQ FT: 29,300 **Privately Held**
WEB: www.ahhermel.com
SIC: 7359 5142 5145 5194 Vending machine rental service; wholesales candy; wholesales packaged frozen foods; wholesales tobacco & tobacco products

(G-3099)

ADULT CHILD & FAMILY SERVICES

103 N Broad St (56001-3519)
PHONE..............................507 344-1721
FAX: 507 344-1726
Paul Gronneberg, *Principal*
Jeanne Burhart, *Principal*
Jay Zabel, *Principal*
EMP: 35 EST: 1998
SALES (est): 1MM-4.9MM **Privately Held**
SIC: 8322 General counseling services

(G-3100)

AEP INDUSTRIES INC

2111 3rd Ave (56001-2806)
PHONE..............................507 625-3011
FAX: 507 388-2087
Kevin Monroe, *General Mgr*
Carolyn Steinhaus, *Accounting Staf*
Jodi Ostedahl, *Human Res Mgr*
Steven Gilworth, *Branch Mgr*
Lawrence Reynoso, *Manager*
EMP: 100
SALES (est): 25MM-49.9MM **Publicly Held**
WEB: www.aepinc.com
SIC: 5162 Manufactures unsupported plastics film & sheet; wholesales plastics products; manufactures laminated plastics; manufactures paper packaging materials
PA: AEP Industries Inc
125 Phillips Ave
South Hackensack NJ 07606
201 641-6600

(G-3101)

AEP INDUSTRIES INC

1970 Excel Dr (56001-5903)
PO Box 4309 (56002-4309)
PHONE..............................507 386-4420
Mike Ellis, *Purchasing*
Germaine Nowacki, *QC Dir*
Mik Bryan, *Branch Mgr*
EMP: 100
SALES (est): 25MM-49.9MM **Publicly Held**
WEB: www.aepinc.com
SIC: 5162 Manufactures polyethylene film; manufactures household furnishings; manufactures men's & boys' work clothing; wholesales plastics products
PA: AEP Industries Inc
125 Phillips Ave
South Hackensack NJ 07606
201 641-6600

(G-3102)

AGSTAR FINANCIAL SERVICES, ACA (PA)

1921 Premier Dr (56001-5901)
PO Box 4249 (56002-4249)
PHONE..............................507 387-4174
Paul Debryin, *President*
Lowell Schafer, *Vice Chairman*
Joseph Deufel, *COO*
Dave Hoelmer, *Senior VP*
Manley Wick, *Senior VP*
EMP: 170 EST: 1918
SQ FT: 2,650 **Privately Held**
WEB: www.agstar.com
SIC: 6111 Federal credit agency

(G-3103)

ALTER TRADING CORP

Also Called: Gopher State Scrap & Metal
804 N Industrial Rd (56001-3009)
PHONE..............................507 387-6504
FAX: 507 387-4498
Steve Jacobsen, *Sales Staff*
Tim Bernstein, *Manager*
EMP: 30
SALES (est): 10MM-24.9MM **Privately Held**
WEB: www.altertrading.com
SIC: 5093 Wholesales metal scrap & waste materials
HQ: Alter Trading Corp
700 Office Pkwy
Saint Louis MO 63141
314 872-2400

(G-3104)

AMERICA'S RAQUETTE & FITNESS

Also Called: Americas Racquet & Fitness Ctr
103 Homestead Rd (56001-5735)
PHONE..............................507 345-8833
FAX: 507 345-7321
Paul Pihl, *Owner*
Erica Freesen, *Manager*
EMP: 30 EST: 1978
SQ FT: 50,000
SALES (est): 500-999K **Privately Held**
SIC: 7997 Membership recreation club; membership racquetball club; membership tennis club

(G-3105)

AMERIPRIDE SERVICES INC

1290 S Victory Dr (56001-5308)
PHONE..............................507 345-1039
FAX: 507 345-6767
Milo Hines, *Plant Mgr*
Andy Anderson, *Chief Engr*
Scott Borg, *Sales Mgr*
Dennis Begalle, *Manager*
Cindy Proehl, *Manager*
EMP: 100
SALES (est): 5MM-9.9MM **Privately Held**
WEB: www.ameripride.com
SIC: 7213 7218 Linen supply service; industrial laundry service
PA: Ameripride Services Inc
10801 Wayzata Blvd # 100
Hopkins MN 55305
952 738-4200

(G-3106)

ARCHER DANIELS MIDLAND CO

Also Called: ADM
2019 3rd Ave (56001-2804)
PO Box 728 (56002-0728)
PHONE..............................507 625-7949
FAX: 507 625-6018
Bob Pothast, *Plant Mgr*
Todd Good, *Engineering*
Bill Bangston, *Comms Dir*
Craig Willis, *Manager*
Mike Vandermuss, *Manager*
EMP: 89
SALES (est): 100MM-499.9MM **Publicly Held**
WEB: www.admworld.com
SIC: 5191 Soybean processing; wholesales animal feeds
PA: Archer Daniels Midland Co
4666 E Faries Pkwy Ste 1
Decatur IL 62526
217 424-5200

(G-3107)

ATWOOD LAND CO INC

209 S 2nd St Ste 200 (56001-3639)
PO Box 248 (56002-0248)
PHONE..............................507 388-9375
Charles G Atwood, *President*
Tom Atwood, *Vice Pres*
Gary Dingler, *Engineer*
Atwood Land, *Engineer*
Reid Jensen, *Engineer*
EST: 1934 **Privately Held**
SIC: 6531 Real estate management services

(G-3108)

AUTUMN GRACE SENIOR SERVICES

118 Raven Ct (56001-8431)
PHONE..............................507 388-3660
Brad Bath, *President*
Brad Bass, *Manager*
Nancy Anderson, *Director*
Lana Steuck, *Director*
Julie Bohnert, *Director*
EMP: 50 EST: 2004
SALES (est): 1MM-4.9MM **Privately Held**
SIC: 8322 Geriatric social services

(G-3109)

BECKER MEGGY RL EST

505 Long St (56001-4305)
PHONE..............................507 388-8469
Jim Norland, *Owner*
EMP: 30 EST: 2007
SALES (est): 5MM-9.9MM **Privately Held**
SIC: 6531 Real estate agency & broker

(G-3110)

BEN CO ELECTRIC

Also Called: Benco Electric Cooperative
20946 549th Ave (56001-5935)
PO Box 8 (56002-0008)
PHONE..............................507 387-7963
FAX: 507 387-1269
Wade Hensel, *General Mgr*
David Sunderman, *Sales Staff*
Steve Flo, *Office Mgr*
EMP: 33 EST: 1937
SQ FT: 5,000
SALES (est): 10MM-24.9MM **Privately Held**
SIC: 4911 Electric services

(G-3111)

BIOLIFE PLASMA SERVICES LP

35 Teton Ln (56001-4814)
PHONE..............................507 344-0300
FAX: 507 344-0315
Heidi Valle, *Branch Mgr*
Chad Stevens, *Manager*
Chad Steven, *Manager*
EMP: 40
SALES (est): 1MM-4.9MM **Publicly Held**
WEB: www.biolifeplasma.com
SIC: 8099 Plasmapherous center
HQ: Biolife Plasma Services LP
1435 Lake Cook Rd
Philadelphia PA 19182
847 940-5559

(G-3112)

BOLTON & MENK INC (PA)

1960 Premier Dr (56001-5900)
PHONE..............................507 625-4171
FAX: 507 625-4177
Jon Rippke, *President*
Robert Brown, *Vice Pres*
Ron Roetzel, *Engineer*
Bill Sayre, *Engineer*
Kirk Yahnke, *Engineer*
EMP: 90 EST: 1949
SQ FT: 23,000 **Privately Held**
WEB: www.bolton-menk.com
SIC: 8711 8713 Civil engineering services; engineering consulting services; surveying service

(G-3113)

CARE CORNER

265 Saint Andrews Dr (56001-8584)
PHONE..............................507 386-7444
Carolyn Adrianse, *Owner*
EMP: 25 EST: 1994
SALES (est): 500-999K **Privately Held**

(PA)=Parent Co (HQ)=Headquarters (DH)=Div Headquarters
✪ = New business established in last 2 years

2011 Harris Minnesota
Services Directory

© Harris InfoSource 1-866-281-6415

143

SIC: **8351** Child day care service

(G-3114)
CAROLYN A ADRIANSE
501 Holly Ln Ste 150 (56001-6829)
PHONE............................507 386-7444
Carolyn A Adrianse, *Owner*
EMP: 30 **EST:** 1993
SALES (est): 500-999K **Privately Held**
SIC: 8351 Child day care service

(G-3115)
CHEVYS INC
Also Called: Chevy's
119 S Front St (56001-3622)
PHONE............................507 345-1446
Mike Maes, *Branch Mgr*
EMP: 35
SALES (est): 1MM-4.9MM **Privately Held**
WEB: www.chevys.com
SIC: 7299 Cocktail lounge; limited service
pizza restaurant; banquet hall facility
HQ: Chevys Inc
33508 Central Ave
Union City CA 94587
510 675-9620

(G-3116)
CHS INC
2020 S Riverfront Dr (56001-1613)
PO Box 3247 (56002-3247)
PHONE............................507 345-2253
James Amlie, *Vice Pres*
Stanley Eichten, *Vice Pres*
Gaylen Ferley, *Vice Pres*
Gary Koerbitz, *Vice Pres*
Pam Schubbe, *Vice Pres*
EMP: 200
SALES (est): 100MM-499.9MM **Publicly Held**
WEB: www.cenexharveststates.com
SIC: 5153 Wholesales grain & field beans
PA: CHS Inc
5500 Cenex Dr
Inver Grove Heights MN 55077
651 355-6000

(G-3117)
CINEMARK U S A INC
1850 Adams St Ste 15 (56001-4846)
PHONE............................507 625-1929
EMP: 30
SALES (est): 1MM-4.9MM **Privately Held**
SIC: 7832 Indoor movie theater
HQ: Cinemark USA Inc
3900 Dallas Pkwy Ste 500
Plano TX 75093
972 665-1000

(G-3118)
COMMUNITY BANK VERNON CENTER
951 E Madison Ave (56001-6141)
PHONE............................507 625-1551
FAX: 507 625-1269
Quinton Baedell, *Manager*
Kathleen Goettl, *Manager*
Dick Clarksean, *Manager*
Janet L Rossow, *Cashier*
EMP: 25
SALES (est): 5MM-9.9MM **Privately Held**
SIC: 6022 State commercial bank
PA: Community Bank Vernon Center
201 E Main St
Vernon Center MN 56090
507 549-3679

(G-3119)
COMMUNITY CHARITIES OF MN
114 S Riverfront Dr (56001-3619)
PO Box 819 (56002-0819)
PHONE............................507 386-1934
FAX: 507 386-7134
Gene Glorvigen, *CEO*
Chuck Leon, *Principal*
EMP: 30 **EST:** 1982
SALES (est): 1MM-4.9MM **Privately Held**
SIC: 7999 Provides gambling & lottery
services

(G-3120)
COUGHLAN CO'S INC (PA)
151 Good Counsel Dr # 120 (56001-3143)
PO Box 669 (56002-0669)
PHONE............................507 385-8295
Robert Coughlan, *CEO*
James P Coughlan, *President*
Thomas Ahern, *Owner*
Gail Beer, *Pub Rel Mgr*
Joseph Hilger, *CFO*
▲ **EMP:** 150 **EST:** 1992
SQ FT: 15,000 **Privately Held**
WEB: www.coughlan-companies.com
SIC: 1741 Book publisher; masonry &
stonework contractor

(G-3121)
D D D MOTEL CORP
Also Called: Holiday Inn
101 E Main St (56001-3502)
PHONE............................507 345-1234
FAX: 507 345-1248
Vickie Thorison, *Controller*
Kelly Beelow, *Controller*
Jen Bronwell, *Human Res Dir*
Joe Leonard, *Manager*
EMP: 120
SALES (est): 5MM-9.9MM **Privately Held**
SIC: 7011 Traveler accommodations
PA: D D D Motel Corp
709 S Front St
Mankato MN 56001
507 625-9343

(G-3122)
DAYPORT INC
209 S 2nd St Ste 408 (56001-3639)
PHONE............................507 344-3000
Cory Factor, *CEO*
Glenn Miller, *President*
Andrew Ioannou, *Vice Pres*
Ben Davis, *VP Opers-Prdtn-*
Clayton Stoering, *Engineering*
EMP: 28 **EST:** 1995
SQ FT: 5,000
SALES (est): 1MM-4.9MM **Privately Held**
SIC: 7371 Computer programming service

(G-3123)
EARLY CHILD FAMILY EDUCATION
110 Fulton St (56001-2520)
PHONE............................507 625-4620
Corin Wesley, *Director*
EMP: 31 **EST:** 2005
SALES (est): 500-999K **Privately Held**
SIC: 8351 Preschool center

(G-3124)
ECUMEN
718 Mound Ave Ste A (56001-1651)
PHONE............................507 345-4576
FAX: 507 385-4212
Jan Rolmer, *Manager*
Dustin Lee, *Manager*
Jennifer Pfeffer, *Administrator*
James Gatchel, *Director*
EMP: 140
SALES (est): 5MM-9.9MM **Privately Held**
WEB: www.augustanahomes.org
SIC: 8051 8052 Skilled nursing care facility;
intermediate care facility
PA: Ecumen
3530 Lexington Ave N
Saint Paul MN 55126
651 766-4300

(G-3125)
EIDE BAILLY LLP
1911 Excel Dr (56001-6281)
PHONE............................507 387-6031
Patrick Rogers, *Accounting Dir*
Joe Willaert, *Branch Mgr*
Carla Hedding, *Manager*
Paula Brooks, *Administration*
EMP: 48
SALES (est): 5MM-9.9MM **Privately Held**
WEB: www.eide.com
SIC: 8721 Certified public accountant
services
PA: Eide Bailly LLP
4310 17th Ave S
Fargo ND 58103
701 239-8593

(G-3126)
EMERALD TRAVEL MANAGEMENT CO
500 S Broad St (56001-3706)
PHONE............................507 345-8797
FAX: 507 345-6186
Carolyn Stienhaus, *President*
EST: 1993
SQ FT: 2,250 **Privately Held**
WEB: www.emtravel.com
SIC: 4724 Tourist agency arranging
transport, lodging & car rental

(G-3127)
5 K ENTERPRISES INC
124 E Welcome Ave (56001-4932)
PHONE............................612 216-6292
EMP: 39 **EST:** 1991
SALES (est): 25MM-49.9MM **Privately Held**
SIC: 5199 5046 5084 5142 5149
Wholesales paper novelties; wholesales
commercial cooking & food services
equipment; wholesales industrial food
industry machinery; wholesales dried or
canned foods; wholesales packaged frozen
foods

(G-3128)
FPX LLC
11 Civic Center Plz # 310 (56001-7711)
PHONE............................507 388-5000
FAX: 507 388-0401
Audrey Spangenberg, *CEO*
Craig Christiansen, *President*
Alessandro Campioli, *General Mgr*
Paul Lavalallee, *Exec VP*
Chris Erickson, *Senior VP*
EMP: 58 **EST:** 1983
SQ FT: 12,100
SALES (est): 10MM-24.9MM **Privately Held**
WEB: www.firepond.com
SIC: 7372 Business & professional software
publishers

(G-3129)
FPX LLC ✪
11 Civic Center Plz # 310 (56001-7711)
PHONE............................866 826-6344
Audrey Spangenberg, *CEO*
Craig Christiansen, *President*
James Scheper, *Vice Pres*
Tom Uehling, *Technical Staff*
Danette Rodellmiller, *Analyst*
EMP: 48 **EST:** 2009
SALES (est): 5MM-9.9MM **Privately Held**
SIC: 7371 7372 Applications software
programming; software publisher

(G-3130)
GOLD CROSS AMBULANCE SERVICE
1308 Marsh St (56001-5215)
PHONE............................507 345-7540
Jill Norman, *Manager*
EMP: 30
SALES (est): 1MM-4.9MM **Privately Held**
WEB: www.gcas-duluth.org
SIC: 4119 Ambulance service
PA: Gold Cross Ambulance Service
501 6th Ave NW
Rochester MN 55901
507 255-2230

(G-3131)
GRIFFIN HOUSING SERVICES INC
117 Capri Dr (56001-4118)
PHONE............................507 388-6434
Barrie Evans, *President*
EMP: 30 **EST:** 2001
SALES (est): 500-999K **Privately Held**
SIC: 8059 Home for the mentally retarded

(G-3132)
H&R BLOCK INC
111 Star St Ste 105 (56001-4889)
PHONE............................507 345-1040
FAX: 507 345-4792
Del Smith, *Manager*
EMP: 28
SALES (est): Under 500K **Publicly Held**
WEB: www.hrblock.com
SIC: 7291 Tax return preparation services
PA: H&R Block Inc
1 H And R Block Way
Kansas City MO 64105
816 854-3000

(G-3133)
HABILITATIVE SERVICES INC
1400 E Madison Ave # 206 (56001-5477)
PHONE............................507 625-6047
FAX: 507 625-8867
Betty Padilla, *Manager*
Curt Boffert, *Regional*
EMP: 200
SALES (est): 10MM-24.9MM **Privately Held**
SIC: 8093 Outpatient rehabilitation
treatment center
PA: Habilitative Services Inc
220 Milwaukee St Ste 2
Lakefield MN 56150
507 662-5236

(G-3134)
HAPPY CHEF SYSTEMS INC (PA)
500 S Front St Ste 103 (56001-3717)
PO Box 3328 (56002-3328)
PHONE............................507 345-4571
Thomas Frederick, *President*
Mark Frederick, *Director*
EMP: 25 **EST:** 1953
SQ FT: 2,500 **Privately Held**
WEB: www.happychef.com
SIC: 6512 8742 Full service American
restaurant; operators of commercial &
industrial buildings; food & beverage
consultant

(G-3135)
HARRY MEYERING CENTER INC
109 Homestead Rd Ste OFC
(56001-5741)
PHONE............................507 388-3551
FAX: 507 387-8237
Judi Leibbrand, *Manager*
James Kline, *Info Tech Mgr*
Carol Lee, *Exec Dir*
EMP: 285 **EST:** 1974
SALES (est): 5MM-9.9MM **Privately Held**
WEB: www.harrymeyeringcenter.org
SIC: 8052 8082 8361 Residential mentally
handicapped facility; residential care facility;
home health care services

(G-3136)
HAUNTED LLC
156 Country Club Dr (56001-9338)
PHONE............................507 388-7966
Beverly Smith, *Mng Member*
EMP: 44 **EST:** 2002
SALES (est): 1MM-4.9MM **Privately Held**
WEB: www.haunted.com
SIC: 7999 Tour & guide services; retail
specialty store

(G-3137)
HEALTHWORKS HOME MEDICAL INC
606 N Riverfront Dr (56001-3451)
PHONE............................507 344-8500
Chad Gellum, *President*
EMP: 50
SALES (est): 1MM-4.9MM **Privately Held**
SIC: 8082 Home health care services
PA: Healthworks Home Medical Inc
114 5th St SE
Minneapolis MN 55414
612 617-9562

(G-3138)
HERMEL COFFEE SERVICE
Also Called: Hermal Wholesale & Vending
23099 Riverfront Dr N (56001-5993)
PHONE............................507 387-5634
FAX: 507 345-3496
Dave Hermel, *President*
Thomas Christenson, *General Mgr*
Jerry Underwood, *General Mgr*
John Hermal, *Manager*
Ronald Riley, *Info Tech Mgr*
EMP: 50 **EST:** 1935
SALES (est): 25MM-49.9MM **Privately Held**
SIC: 5194 Wholesales tobacco & tobacco
products

www.HarrisInfo.com
144

2011 Harris Minnesota
Services Directory

▲=Import ▼=Export
◆=Import/Export

(G-3139)

HICKORY TECH INFORMATION SOLN (HQ)
Also Called: Nibi
221 E Hickory St (56001-3610)
PO Box 3248 (56002-3248)
PHONE..............................507 625-1691
Lane Nordquist, *President*
Linda Koepp, *Opers Staff*
Danny Anderson, *Development*
Scott Grill, *Marketing Staff*
Ken Anderson, *Director*
EMP: 100 EST: 1964
SALES (corp-wide): 139.10M **Publicly Held**
SIC: 7374 4812 4813 5045 7375 Computer calculating service; wired telecommunications carrier & service; wireless telecommunications carrier & service; wholesales computers; data processing service; information retrieval services
PA: HickoryTech Corp
221 E Hickory St
Mankato MN 56001
507 386-3636

(G-3140)

HICKORY TECH INFORMATION SOLN
215 E Hickory St (56001-3610)
PHONE..............................507 625-1691
Lane Nordquist, *President*
Myrtta Craig, *Managing Dir*
Tom Benson, *Purch Mgr*
David Christensen, *CFO*
Mary Jacobs, *VP Human Res*
EMP: 80
SALES (est): 5MM-9.9MM **Publicly Held**
SIC: 7374 4812 4813 5045 7375 Computer calculating service; wired telecommunications carrier & service; wireless telecommunications carrier & service; wholesales computers; data processing service; information retrieval services
HQ: Hickory Tech Information Soln
221 E Hickory St
Mankato MN 56001
507 625-1691

(G-3141)

HICKORYTECH CORP (PA)
221 E Hickory St (56001-3610)
PO Box 3248 (56002-3248)
PHONE..............................507 386-3636
John W Finke, *President*
Bruce H Malmgren, *President*
Dale Parker, *Vice Chairman*
Lane C Nordquist, *Vice Pres*
John P Morton, *Vice Pres*
EMP: 290 EST: 1985
SQ FT: 60,000
SALES (corp-wide): 139.10M **Publicly Held**
SIC: 4813 Local telephone communications services; internet connectivity services

(G-3142)

HOLLY PROPERTIES
309 Holly Ln (56001-5422)
PHONE..............................507 388-6265
Paul H Gislason MD, *Partner*
E L Markey MD, *Partner*
Elmer W Lippmann MD, *Partner*
R W Kearney MD, *Partner*
Michael M Kearney MD, *Partner*
EMP: 60 EST: 1964
SALES (est): 10MM-24.9MM **Privately Held**
WEB: www.hollyproperties.com
SIC: 6512 Nonresidential building operator

(G-3143)

HOMEWATCH HOME CARE
209 S 2nd St Ste 307 (56001-3639)
PHONE..............................507 388-5589
Dorothy Muffet, *Branch Mgr*
EMP: 50
SALES (est): 1MM-4.9MM **Privately Held**
SIC: 8082 Home health care services
PA: Homewatch Home Care
4825 Highway 55 Ste 101
Minneapolis MN 55422
763 546-8899

(G-3144)

HORIZON HOME INC
306 Byron St (56001-3846)
PO Box 3032 (56002-3032)
PHONE..............................507 344-3360
FAX: 507 344-3372
Jack Norman, *Ch of Bd*
Michael Pribyl, *Exec Dir*
Mike Prybyl, *Director*
EMP: 53 EST: 1972
SALES (est): 1MM-4.9MM **Privately Held**
SIC: 8361 Home for the mentally handicapped; eating place

(G-3145)

HORIZON MILLING LLC
200 N Riverfront Dr (56001-3570)
PHONE..............................507 388-1680
FAX: 507 388-9949
David Raisbeck, *Vice Chairman*
Darin Elliott, *Facilities Mgr*
Robert Lumpkins, *CFO*
Dale Walton, *Human Res Dir*
Pat Demarce, *Manager*
EMP: 35
SALES (est): 10MM-24.9MM **Privately Held**
WEB: www.horizonmilling.com
SIC: 5149 Manufactures flour & other grain mill products; wholesales flour
PA: Horizon Milling LLC
15407 McGinty Rd W
Wayzata MN 55391
952 742-5031

(G-3146)

I & S GROUP INC
1409 N Riverfront Dr (56001-3254)
PO Box 1026 (56002-1026)
PHONE..............................507 387-6651
FAX: 507 387-3583
Chad Surprenant, *President*
Mary J Surprenant, *Corp Secy*
Kenneth Surprenant, *Vice Pres*
Lynn Bruns, *Manager*
Chuck Vermeersch, *Manager*
EMP: 65 EST: 1973
SALES (est): 5MM-9.9MM **Privately Held**
SIC: 8711 Engineering consulting services

(G-3147)

IMMANUEL ST JOSEPH MAYO HEALTH
1025 Marsh St (56001-4752)
PO Box 8673 (56002-8673)
PHONE..............................507 625-4031
FAX: 507 389-4884
Greg Kutcher, *President*
Norman Nitzkowski, *Ch Radiology*
Jerome Crest, *Vice Pres*
Richard Grace, *Vice Pres*
Sharon Schneller, *Vice Pres*
EMP: 1300 EST: 1984
SALES (est): 25MM-49.9MM **Privately Held**
SIC: 8082 Home health care services
PA: Mayo Clinic
200 1st St SW
Rochester MN 55905
507 284-2511

(G-3148)

IMMANUEL-ST JOSEPH'S HOSPITAL (HQ)
1025 Marsh St (56001-4752)
PO Box 8673 (56002-8673)
PHONE..............................507 625-4031
Jerome Crest, *Vice Pres*
Richard Grace, *Vice Pres*
Dennis Miller, *Vice Pres*
Marcia Hanson, *Purchasing*
Ryan Ashlando, *CFO*
EMP: 1900 EST: 1969
SQ FT: 325,000 **Privately Held**
WEB: www.isj-mhs.net
SIC: 8062 Medical hospital
PA: Mayo Clinic
200 1st St SW
Rochester MN 55905
507 284-2511

(G-3149)

IMMANUEL-ST JOSEPH'S HOSPITAL
1015 Marsh St (56001-4752)
PO Box 8673 (56002-8673)
PHONE..............................507 385-4700
Dick Kakeldey, *Vice Chairman*
Tammie Hudspith, *Benefits Mgr*
Rich Grace, *Office Mgr*
Anton E Colman MD, *Med Doctor*
Jorge M De Leon MD, *Med Doctor*
EMP: 75
SALES (est): 5MM-9.9MM **Privately Held**
WEB: www.isj-mhs.net
SIC: 8093 Specialty outpatient clinic
HQ: Immanuel-St Joseph's Hospital
1025 Marsh St
Mankato MN 56001
507 625-4031

(G-3150)

ISJ REGIONAL WOMEN'S IMAGING
101 Martin Luther King Dr (56001-6460)
PHONE..............................507 304-7770
Anne Chapman, *Owner*
EMP: 80
SALES (est): 10MM-24.9MM **Privately Held**
SIC: 8071 Manufactures medical ultrasonic scanning devices; dental & medical X-ray laboratory

(G-3151)

J C PENNY BEAUTY SALON
Also Called: Kaliski, Cathy Cmt
1850 Adams St Ste 2 (56001-4868)
PHONE..............................507 625-5630
Vicki Young, *General Mgr*
EMP: 30 EST: 1985
SALES (est): 1MM-4.9MM **Privately Held**
SIC: 8049 Health practitioners' office

(G-3152)

JC PENNEY CORP INC
1850 Adams St Ste 2 (56001-4868)
PHONE..............................507 625-1606
FAX: 507 625-1723
Tom Boening, *Manager*
EMP: 90
SALES (est): 25MM-49.9MM **Publicly Held**
WEB: www.jcpenney.com
SIC: 7231 Retail catalog sales; department store; beauty salon
HQ: JC Penney Corp Inc
6501 Legacy Dr
Plano TX 75024
972 431-1000

(G-3153)

JERKY SNACK BRANDS INC
1829 1st Ave (56001-3023)
PHONE..............................507 388-1661
Rob Andrews, *Branch Mgr*
EMP: 90
SALES (est): 25MM-49.9MM **Privately Held**
SIC: 5145 Wholesales snack foods
PA: Jerky Snack Brands Inc
1829 1st Ave
Mankato MN 56001
507 388-1661

(G-3154)

JOHNSON OUTDOORS INC
Also Called: Jwa Mankato
1531 E Madison Ave (56001-5443)
PO Box 8129 (56002-8129)
PHONE..............................507 345-4623
FAX: 507 345-4936
Darrell Wolf, *Managing Dir*
Rodney Kobs, *Purch Mgr*
Ken Tasler, *Engineer*
Paul Mueller, *Controller*
Nancy Manser, *Human Res Dir*
EMP: 200
SQ FT: 220,000
SALES (est): 50MM-99.9MM **Publicly Held**
WEB: www.johnsonoutdoors.com
SIC: 5091 Wholesales sporting & recreational goods & supplies
PA: Johnson Outdoors Inc
555 Main St Ste 500
Racine WI 53403
262 631-6600

(G-3155)

KRISTICO INC
3801 3rd Ave (56001-2735)
PHONE..............................507 625-2900
FAX: 507 625-7085
Kenneth W Christenson, *President*
Susan K Christenson, *VP Finance*
EMP: 30 EST: 1961
SQ FT: 30,000
SALES (est): 10MM-24.9MM **Privately Held**
SIC: 5191 5046 Wholesales animal feeds; wholesales bakery equipment & supplies

(G-3156)

KRUSE FAMILY ENTERPRISES LLC
Also Called: Wynco
125 Kingswood Rd (56001-3015)
PO Box 1002 (56002-1002)
PHONE..............................507 345-5926
Thomas Dougan, *Principal*
EMP: 50
SALES (est): 25MM-49.9MM **Privately Held**
WEB: www.ivesco.com
SIC: 5191 5047 5122 Wholesales insecticides; wholesales pesticides; wholesales veterinarians' equipment & supplies; wholesales animal medicines; wholesales biologicals & allied products; wholesales pharmaceuticals; wholesales feed
HQ: Kruse Family Enterprises LLC
324 Main St
Iowa Falls IA 50126
641 648-2529

(G-3157)

LLOYD MANAGEMENT INC
135 W Lind St (56001-0426)
PO Box 1000 (56002-1000)
PHONE..............................507 625-5573
Steve Weisbecker, *Manager*
Anita Hall, *Manager*
EMP: 75 EST: 1989
SALES (est): 10MM-24.9MM **Privately Held**
SIC: 6513 Apartment building operator

(G-3158)

LOWE'S HOME CENTERS INC
2015 Bassett Dr (56001-6571)
PHONE..............................507 385-3560
EMP: 150
SALES (est): 25MM-49.9MM **Publicly Held**
WEB: www.lowes.com
SIC: 5031 5064 Retails building products & materials; wholesales exterior building materials; wholesales interior building materials; wholesales electrical appliances; retails household appliances
HQ: Lowe's Home Centers Inc
1605 Curtis Bridge Rd
Wilkesboro NC 28697
336 658-4000

(G-3159)

MANKATO AIRPORT
3030 Airport Rd N (56001-7561)
PHONE..............................507 625-2511
FAX: 507 625-5250
Mark Smith, *CEO*
Cheri Anderson, *General Mgr*
Vivian Smith, *Corp Secy*
Scott Ostermann, *CFO*
Alex Haak, *Manager*
EMP: 35 EST: 1991
SALES (est): 1MM-4.9MM **Privately Held**
SIC: 4581 Airport

(G-3160)

MANKATO CLINIC LTD (PA)
1230 E Main St (56001-5066)
PO Box 8674 (56002-8674)
PHONE..............................507 625-1811
FAX: 507 388-3401
Randy Farrow, *CEO*
Bryan Nermoe, *COO*
Laurie Dahl, *Opers Staff*
Robyn Naumann, *Purch Mgr*
Jane Chatleain, *Purchasing*
EMP: 425 EST: 1921 **Privately Held**
SIC: 8011 Clinic operated by physicians

(PA)=Parent Co (HQ)=Headquarters (DH)=Div Headquarters
✪ = New business established in last 2 years

2011 Harris Minnesota
Services Directory

© Harris InfoSource 1-866-281-6415
145

(G-3161)

MANKATO FAIRFIELD INN
141 Apache Pl (56001-6201)
PHONE..................507 386-1220
Paul Schroer, *Principal*
EMP: 25
SALES (est): 1MM-4.9MM **Privately Held**
SIC: 7011 Traveler accommodations

(G-3162)

MANKATO GOLF CLUB INC
Hwy 22 N (56001)
PO Box 3122 (56002-3122)
PHONE..................507 387-5676
Pam Miller, *Controller*
EMP: 50 **EST:** 1919
SQ FT: 8,000
SALES (est): 1MM-4.9MM **Privately Held**
WEB: www.mankatogolfclub.com
SIC: 7997 Membership golf club; bar; full service American restaurant

(G-3163)

MANKATO LODGING LLC
1900 Premier Dr (56001-5900)
PHONE..................507 388-8555
Jason Mortland, *General Mgr*
Leo M Sand, *Member*
EMP: 55 **EST:** 1997
SALES (est): 1MM-4.9MM **Privately Held**
SIC: 7011 Vacation lodge

(G-3164)

MANKATO REHABILITATION CENTER
1611 Monks Ave (56001-5103)
PHONE..................507 386-5799
Cathy Groemer, *Branch Mgr*
EMP: 60
SALES (est): 1MM-4.9MM **Privately Held**
SIC: 8331 Job training & vocational rehabilitation services
PA: Mankato Rehabilitation Center
15 Map Dr
Mankato MN 56001
507 386-5600

(G-3165)

MANKATO REHABILITATION CENTER (PA)
Also Called: Mrci Worksource
15 Map Dr (56001-8944)
PO Box 328 (56002-0328)
PHONE..................507 386-5600
FAX: 507 386-5696
Brian Benshoof, *COO*
Chuck Juntunen, *CFO*
Cathy Groemer, *Manager*
Jerry Schafer, *Info Tech Mgr*
Pamela J Year, *Exec Dir*
EMP: 130 **EST:** 1953
SQ FT: 63,000
SALES (corp-wide): 42.24M **Privately Held**
SIC: 8331 Job training & vocational rehabilitation services; manufactures paper packaging materials

(G-3166)

MANKATO SURGICAL CENTER LLC
1411 Premier Dr (56001-6076)
PHONE..................507 388-6000
FAX: 507 388-6913
Gayle Redig, *Manager*
Joleen Stelter, *Director*
EMP: 34 **EST:** 1998
SQ FT: 18,000
SALES (est): 1MM-4.9MM **Privately Held**
WEB: www.mankatosurgeryctr.com
SIC: 8062 Medical hospital

(G-3167)

MANKATO SYMPHONY ORCHESTRA
223 S St 2 (56001)
PO Box 645 (56002-0645)
PHONE..................507 625-8880
Sonja Jacobsen, *President*
Jane Sletta, *General Mgr*
Charles Christiansen, *Treasurer*
Martin Mitchell, *Exec Dir*
EMP: 80

EST: 1950
SQ FT: 1,100
SALES (est): 10MM-24.9MM **Privately Held**
SIC: 7929 Entertainment services

(G-3168)

MASCHKA RIEDY & RIES
201 N Broad St Ste 200 (56001-3569)
PO Box 7 (56002-0007)
PHONE..................507 625-6600
FAX: 507 625-4002
Chuck Reis, *Partner*
Jack Riedy, *Partner*
John Peterson, *Partner*
Gerald Maschka, *Partner*
Marc Christianson, *Partner*
EMP: 27 **EST:** 1999
SALES (est): 1MM-4.9MM **Privately Held**
WEB: www.mrr-law.com
SIC: 8111 General practice attorney's or lawyer's office

(G-3169)

MIDWEST WIRELESS COMMS
2000 Technology Dr (56001-6074)
PHONE..................507 385-2396
FAX: 507 345-2480
Dennis Miller, *President*
Dennis Findley, *Partner*
Tom Riley, *Partner*
Mark Allen, *Partner*
Brian Fingerson, *Partner*
EMP: 320 **EST:** 1995
SQ FT: 130,000 **Publicly Held**
WEB: www.alltel.com
SIC: 4812 Cellular telephone services
DH: Alltel Corp
1 Allied Dr
Little Rock AR 72202
501 905-8967

(G-3170)

MINNESOTA DEPARTMENT OF TRANS
Also Called: District 7e
501 S Victory Dr (56001-5302)
PHONE..................507 389-6351
FAX: 507 389-6281
James Swanson, *Principal*
Robin Jordan, *Human Resources*
Janet Bergerson, *Office Mgr*
Anthony Bergemann, *Manager*
Marshall Stromberg, *IT/INT Sup*
EMP: 100
SALES (est): 10MM-24.9MM **Privately Held**
WEB: www.me.umn.edu
SIC: 1611 Heavy highway & street construction; transportation program regulation & administration services; state government transportation program regulation or administration
DH: Minnesota Department of Trans
395 John Ireland Blvd
Saint Paul MN 55155
651 296-3000

(G-3171)

MINNESOTA ELEVATOR INC
19336 607th Ave (56001-8560)
PHONE..................507 245-3060
Rick Golish, *CEO*
John W Romnes, *President*
Rick Lowembry, *President*
Ronald Sperb, *Vice Pres*
Bruce Steffen, *Vice Pres*
◆ **EMP:** 200 **EST:** 1971
SQ FT: 50,000
SALES (est): 25MM-49.9MM **Privately Held**
WEB: www.minnesotaelevator.com
SIC: 1796 7699 Manufactures elevators & equipment; elevator installation & conversion; elevators inspection, services & repair

(G-3172)

MINNESOTA VALLEY ACTION
464 Raintree Rd (56001-4804)
PHONE..................507 345-6822
FAX: 507 345-2414
Keith Hamm, *Human Res Dir*
Kathy Leiferman, *IT/INT Sup*
John Woodwick, *Exec Dir*
Judd Schultz, *Director*
Lynn Ruiz, *Director*
EMP: 65

EST: 1966
SQ FT: 11,000
SALES (est): 1MM-4.9MM **Privately Held**
SIC: 8322 Individual & family social services

(G-3173)

MORGAN TIRE & AUTO INC
Also Called: Team Tires Plus
1661 E Madison Ave (56001-5445)
PHONE..................507 388-6461
FAX: 507 388-9974
Paul Schmitt, *Manager*
Paul Schmidt, *Manager*
EMP: 30
SALES (est): 1MM-4.9MM **Privately Held**
WEB: www.bfsusa.com
SIC: 7534 Tire recapping & retreading services
HQ: Bfs Retail Operations LLC
333 E Lake St Ste 300
Bloomingdale IL 60108
630 259-9000

(G-3174)

MORTGAGE ASSURANCE
220 E Main St Ste 4 (56001-3574)
PHONE..................507 388-8140
Mike Abbott, *President*
EMP: 30 **EST:** 2004
SALES (est): 1MM-4.9MM **Privately Held**
SIC: 6162 Mortgage & loan lending

(G-3175)

NATIONAL DENTEX CORP
Also Called: Wornson-Polzin Dental Labs
121 E Main St Ste 308 (56001-3576)
PHONE..................507 625-5079
FAX: 507 625-5080
Fred Polzin, *Branch Mgr*
EMP: 35
SALES (est): 1MM-4.9MM **Privately Held**
WEB: www.nationaldentex.com
SIC: 8072 Dental laboratory
HQ: National Dentex Corp
2 Vision Dr Ste 2
Natick MA 01760
508 907-7800

(G-3176)

NORTHERN STATES POWER CO
210 E Lime St (56001-3348)
PO Box 1090 (56002-1090)
PHONE..................507 387-9629
FAX: 507 387-9604
EMP: 173
SALES (est): 100MM-499.9MM **Publicly Held**
WEB: www.middletownpower.com
SIC: 4911 Electric services
HQ: Northern States Power Co
414 Nicollet Mall
Minneapolis MN 55401
612 330-5500

(G-3177)

NORTHLAND MORTGAGE CORP
79 Navaho Ave Ste 14 (56001-4831)
PHONE..................507 388-8600
FAX: 507 388-5284
Bill Brown, *General Mgr*
EMP: 30
SALES (est): 1MM-4.9MM **Privately Held**
SIC: 6162 Mortgage & loan lending

(G-3178)

NUSS TRUCK GROUP INC
Also Called: Mankato Mack Sales
53976 Two O Eight Ln (56001)
PO Box 969 (56002-0969)
PHONE..................507 345-6225
FAX: 507 387-5886
Greg Nuss, *Vice Pres*
Brad Nuss, *Vice Pres*
Randy Dahms, *Manager*
Justin Vanlaere, *Technology*
EMP: 25
SALES (est): 25MM-49.9MM **Privately Held**
WEB: www.nussgrp.com
SIC: 5012 7538 Wholesales commercial trucks; general automotive repair services; retails new & used pickups
PA: Nuss Truck Group Inc
6500 Highway 63 S
Rochester MN 55904
507 288-9488

(G-3179)

OPEN DOOR HEALTH CENTER
309 Holly Ln (56001-6274)
PHONE..................507 388-2120
FAX: 507 388-3924
Sarah Kruse, *Exec Dir*
Ava Adams-Morris, *Director*
Diane E Witt, *Registrd Nurse*
Ann Vogel, *OB/GYN*
EMP: 34 **EST:** 1992
SQ FT: 2,600
SALES (est): 1MM-4.9MM **Privately Held**
SIC: 8011 8699 Physicians' office & clinic; charitable organization

(G-3180)

ORTHOPEDIC & FRACTURE CLINIC
Also Called: Orthopaedic Fracture Clinic
1431 Premier Dr (56001-6076)
PO Box 4369 (56002-4369)
PHONE..................507 386-6600
John Springer, *President*
Gene Swanson MD, *Corp Secy*
Dar Brandt, *Purch Mgr*
Michael Kearney MD, *Treasurer*
Dennis Baker, *Finance*
EMP: 60 **EST:** 1958
SQ FT: 17,000
SALES (est): 5MM-9.9MM **Privately Held**
WEB: www.ofc-clinic.com
SIC: 8011 Clinic operated by physicians; orthopedic physician office

(G-3181)

PAAPE DISTRIBUTING CO
307 McKinzie St S (56001-1800)
PO Box 3640 (56002-3640)
PHONE..................507 345-8057
FAX: 507 387-3585
Douglas Paape, *President*
Al Vossen, *Sales Executive*
EMP: 40 **EST:** 1979
SQ FT: 8,000
SALES (est): 1MM-4.9MM **Privately Held**
SIC: 1711 5075 Heating & air conditioning contractor; warm air heating & air conditioning contractor; wholesales heating & air conditioning equipment & supplies

(G-3182)

PRAIRIE RIVER HOME CARE INC
227 E Main St Ste 200 (56001-3573)
PHONE..................507 345-8591
FAX: 507 345-1914
Philip Harter, *Business Mgr*
Lynne Smith, *Business Mgr*
Meghan Busch, *Branch Mgr*
EMP: 100
SALES (est): 1MM-4.9MM **Privately Held**
WEB: www.prhomecare.com
SIC: 8082 Home health care services
PA: Prairie River Home Care Inc
4432 Highway 25 SE
Buffalo MN 55313
507 252-9844

(G-3183)

PSYCHIATRIC CLINIC OF MANKATO
1400 E Madison Ave Ste 352
(56001-4458)
PHONE..................507 387-3195
FAX: 507 625-2224
Michael Gozela, *Principal*
Bryan Nermoe, *COO*
Peg Julian, *Controller*
Susie McConville, *Office Mgr*
Keith Bauer, *Manager*
EMP: 26 **EST:** 1968
SALES (est): 1MM-4.9MM **Privately Held**
SIC: 8011 Psychiatric clinic

(G-3184)

R & E ENTERPRISES OF MANKATO
55173 State Highway 68 (56001-4102)
PHONE..................507 388-3364
Bruce S Goodrich, *President*
EMP: 35 **EST:** 1989
SQ FT: 5,600
SALES (est): 1MM-4.9MM **Privately Held**
WEB: www.randeofmn.com

www.HarrisInfo.com
146

2011 Harris Minnesota
Services Directory

▲=Import ▼=Export
◆=Import/Export

SIC: **4212** 4213 Local trucking without storage services; contract haulers

(G-3185)
REM INC
210 Thomas Dr (56001-5679)
PHONE..............................507 387-3181
FAX: 507 387-3182
Mark Turbes, *Director*
EMP: 75
SALES (est): 1MM-4.9MM **Privately Held**
SIC: **8361** 8052 Home for the mentally retarded; intermediate care facility

(G-3186)
RIVER BOAT BINGO
145 Good Counsel Dr (56001-3146)
PHONE..............................507 388-6086
FAX: 507 388-5618
Karen Frericks, *General Mgr*
EMP: 30 **EST:** 1988
SALES (est): 1MM-4.9MM **Privately Held**
WEB: www.riverboatbingo.com
SIC: **7999** Bingo hall

(G-3187)
RIVER VALLEY TRUCK CENTERS INC (PA)
2120 3rd Ave (56001-2805)
PO Box 759 (56002)
PHONE..............................507 345-1129
FAX: 507 345-8334
Gerald Westman, *President*
Joe Arnoldy, *Administrator*
EMP: 100 **EST:** 1970
SQ FT: 21,000 **Privately Held**
WEB: www.rvtc.com
SIC: **7538** 5012 5013 Truck engine repair service; wholesales noncommercial vehicles; wholesales new & used trailers for trucks; wholesales commercial trucks; wholesales truck parts & accessories; new & used car dealer

(G-3188)
RIVERBEND AUTO SALES INC
222 E Madison Ave (56001-3307)
PHONE..............................507 345-8967
Frank A Reichel, *President*
EMP: 25 **EST:** 1984
SALES (est): 5MM-9.9MM **Privately Held**
SIC: **5012** Retails used automobiles; wholesales motor vehicles

(G-3189)
RUG & CARPET CARETAKERS
101 Country Club Dr (56001-9339)
PHONE..............................507 388-5384
FAX: 507 388-0714
Gary Peterson, *Owner*
EMP: 38 **EST:** 1995
SALES (est): 1MM-4.9MM **Privately Held**
WEB: www.rugandcarpetcaretakers.com
SIC: **7217** Carpet & upholstery cleaning services; retails floor coverings

(G-3190)
S P S CO'S INC
1201 N Riverfront Dr (56001-3250)
PHONE..............................507 387-5691
FAX: 507 387-5695
Rick Andreen, *Opers Mgr*
Rick Anderson, *Manager*
Bill Stewart, *Manager*
Clark Diel, *Manager*
Jay Schwitzer, *Info Tech Mgr*
EMP: 26
SALES (est): 10MM-24.9MM **Privately Held**
WEB: www.spscompanies.com
SIC: **5074** Wholesales plumbing & heating equipment & supplies
PA: S P S Co's Inc
6363 Highway 7
Minneapolis MN 55416
952 929-1377

(G-3191)
SAND CO INC
Also Called: Country Suites By Carlson
1900 Premier Dr (56001-5900)
PHONE..............................507 388-8555
FAX: 507 388-0780
Steve Leth, *General Mgr*
Linda Osborne, *Sales Staff*

Jason Mortland, *Manager*
Beth A Beckel, *Manager*
EMP: 45 **EST:** 1998
SALES (est): 1MM-4.9MM **Privately Held**
SIC: **7011** Traveler accommodations; eating place

(G-3192)
SCHEID ELECTRIC INC
53936 208th Ln (56001-5918)
PHONE..............................507 388-9305
Marty R Walgebach, *President*
Mitch Kranz, *Vice Pres*
Marietta Sheefer, *Manager*
EMP: 26 **EST:** 1977
SQ FT: 720
SALES (est): 1MM-4.9MM **Privately Held**
SIC: **1731** General electrical contractor

(G-3193)
SCHWICKERT CO
Also Called: Schwickert's
330 Poplar St (56001-2312)
PO Box 1179 (56002-1179)
PHONE..............................507 387-3101
FAX: 507 387-5327
Kim Schwickert, *President*
Leon Prange, *Vice Pres*
M Prange, *Plant Mgr*
Michele Wheeler, *Treasurer*
Steven Hanson, *Controller*
EMP: 60 **EST:** 1948
SQ FT: 5,000
SALES (est): 5MM-9.9MM **Privately Held**
WEB: www.schwickerts.com
SIC: **1761** 1711 Roofing contractor; warm air heating & air conditioning contractor; sheet metal fabricator
PA: Tecta America Corp
5215 Old Orchard Rd Ste 8
Skokie IL 60077
847 581-3888

(G-3194)
SCHWICKERT INC
221 Minnesota St (56001-2332)
PO Box 487 (56002-0487)
PHONE..............................507 387-3106
Kent Schwickert, *President*
Jill Johnson, *Corp Secy*
Virgil Benesh, *Vice Pres*
Michele Wheeler, *CFO*
Mark Kauffmann, *Asst Controller*
EMP: 75 **EST:** 1924
SQ FT: 5,000
SALES (est): 5MM-9.9MM **Privately Held**
WEB: www.tectaamerica.com
SIC: **1711** 1761 Mechanical contractor; roofing contractor
PA: Tecta America Corp
5215 Old Orchard Rd Ste 8
Skokie IL 60077
847 581-3888

(G-3195)
SCHWICKERT'S OF ROCHESTER INC (HQ)
221 Minnesota St (56001-2332)
PO Box 487 (56002-0487)
PHONE..............................507 387-3106
Jill S Johnson, *Corp Secy*
Virgil Benesh, *Vice Pres*
EMP: 25 **EST:** 1985
SQ FT: 5,000 **Privately Held**
WEB: www.tectaamerica.com
SIC: **1761** Roofing contractor
PA: Tecta America Corp
5215 Old Orchard Rd Ste 8
Skokie IL 60077
847 581-3888

(G-3196)
SENIOR GRACE SERVICES
Also Called: Assisted & Foster Care Svcs
118 Raven Ct (56001-8431)
PHONE..............................507 388-3660
Brad Bass, *CEO*
Heather Bass, *Vice Pres*
EMP: 49 **EST:** 2003
SQ FT: 230,000
SALES (est): 1MM-4.9MM **Privately Held**
SIC: **8361** Group foster home

(G-3197)
SHINE-WAY JANITORIAL SERVICE
22800 Lime Valley Rd (56001-6227)
PHONE..............................507 388-7439
Bruce Johnson, *President*
EMP: 60 **EST:** 1974
SQ FT: 4,000
SALES (est): 1MM-4.9MM **Privately Held**
SIC: **7349** 7217 Janitorial & custodial services; carpet & upholstery cleaning services

(G-3198)
SNYDER'S DRUG STORES INC
602 S Front St (56001-3801)
PHONE..............................507 345-1002
Mike Ostendorf, *Manager*
Kenneth Bohlman, *Systems Staff*
EMP: 25
SALES (est): 1MM-4.9MM **Privately Held**
WEB: www.snyderdrug.com
SIC: **7384** Drug store; photofinishing laboratory
PA: Snyder's Drug Stores Inc
7111 Cedar Lake Rd S
Saint Louis Park MN 55426
952 935-5441

(G-3199)
SOUTH BEND TOWNSHIP FIRE DEPT
306 McKinzie St S (56001-1813)
PHONE..............................507 345-4863
Roger Veldhuisen, *President*
Robert Sutch, *Chief*
EMP: 28 **EST:** 1958
SALES (est): 1MM-4.9MM **Privately Held**
SIC: **7389** Fire protection services

(G-3200)
SOUTHERN MINNESOTA INDEPENDENT
709 S Front St Ste 7 (56001-3887)
PHONE..............................507 345-7139
FAX: 507 345-8429
Dan Robinson, *President*
Doug Miller, *Opers Mgr*
Alan Augustine, *Director*
EMP: 25 **EST:** 1988
SALES (est): 1MM-4.9MM **Privately Held**
WEB: www.smilescil.org
SIC: **8322** Rehabilitation services

(G-3201)
SOUTHERN MINNESOTA ORAL
1990 Premier Dr (56001-5900)
PHONE..............................507 625-9330
Richard Marlow, *President*
Kim Dack, *Office Mgr*
EMP: 30 **EST:** 1998
SALES (est): 1MM-4.9MM **Privately Held**
SIC: **8021** Dental office

(G-3202)
SUNRISE COTTAGE OF MANKATO
300 Bunting Ln (56001-7020)
PHONE..............................507 345-8787
Kim Alinder, *Director*
EMP: 30 **EST:** 1996
SALES (est): 1MM-4.9MM **Publicly Held**
WEB: www.sunrise.com
SIC: **8051** Skilled nursing care facility
PA: Sunrise Senior Living Inc
7900 Westpark Dr Ste T900
Mc Lean VA 22102
703 273-7500

(G-3203)
THRO CO
Also Called: Hillcrest Health Care Center
714 Southbend Ave (56001-5954)
PHONE..............................507 387-3491
FAX: 507 387-6611
Jan Kolb, *Bookkeeper*
Skiann Christiansen, *Human Res Mgr*
Lisa Molden, *Nursing Spvr*
Doug Williams, *Manager*
Dawn Chiabotti, *Administrator*
EMP: 175
SALES (est): 5MM-9.9MM **Privately Held**

WEB: www.throcompany.com
SIC: **8051** Skilled nursing care facility
PA: Thro Co
638 Southbend Ave
Mankato MN 56001
507 625-8741

(G-3204)
THRO CO
Also Called: Mankato House Health
700 James Ave (56001-4090)
PHONE..............................507 345-4631
FAX: 507 345-8509
Melissa Bixler, *Manager*
Travis Gregg, *Administrator*
Andrea Lundstrom, *CTO*
Connie Brady, *Nursing Dir*
EMP: 150
SALES (est): 5MM-9.9MM **Privately Held**
WEB: www.throcompany.com
SIC: **8059** 8051 Personal care home, with health care; skilled nursing care facility
PA: Thro Co
638 Southbend Ave
Mankato MN 56001
507 625-8741

(G-3205)
THRO CO
Also Called: Oaklawn Health Care Ctr
201 Oaklawn Ave (56001-4729)
PHONE..............................507 388-2913
FAX: 507 388-1235
Norman Carlberg, *Maintenance Dir*
Jeanette Hale, *Human Res Dir*
Rick Krant, *Administrator*
Amy Porter, *Administrator*
EMP: 100
SALES (est): 1MM-4.9MM **Privately Held**
WEB: www.throcompany.com
SIC: **8059** 8051 Nursing home; skilled nursing care facility
PA: Thro Co
638 Southbend Ave
Mankato MN 56001
507 625-8741

(G-3206)
TIDY CLEAN LLC
500 Patterson Ave Ste 200 (56001-2319)
PHONE..............................507 344-1742
Kashif Khan, *Member*
Philippe Hamze, *Member*
Jessica Khan, *Manager*
EMP: 55 **EST:** 1996
SALES (est): 1MM-4.9MM **Privately Held**
WEB: www.tidycleanpros.com
SIC: **7349** Industrial or commercial cleaning services

(G-3207)
TIRE ASSOCIATES WAREHOUSE INC
305 Lundin Blvd (56001-2719)
PO Box 787 (56002-0787)
PHONE..............................507 625-2975
FAX: 507 625-2960
Thomas Warrant, *President*
Robert O Warrant, *Co-President*
John Lundegren, *Purch Agent*
Art Willaert, *Treasurer*
EMP: 41 **EST:** 1955
SQ FT: 35,000
SALES (est): 10MM-24.9MM **Privately Held**
WEB: www.tireassociates.com
SIC: **5014** 7534 Wholesales automotive tires & tubes; wholesales truck tires & tubes; automotive tire recapping service; tire dealer

(G-3208)
TOW DISTRIBUTING CORP
3100 3rd Ave (56001-2728)
PO Box 3527 (56002-3527)
PHONE..............................507 388-2931
FAX: 507 388-9997
Keith M Tow, *President*
John Kocina, *General Mgr*
Mike Borneke, *Manager*
EMP: 36 **EST:** 1951
SQ FT: 52,000
SALES (est): 10MM-24.9MM **Privately Held**
WEB: www.towdistributing.com
SIC: **5181** Wholesales beer & other fermented malt liquors

(PA)=Parent Co (HQ)=Headquarters (DH)=Div Headquarters
✿ = New business established in last 2 years

2011 Harris Minnesota
Services Directory

© Harris InfoSource 1-866-281-6415
147

GEOGRAPHIC

(G-3209)
TRUE VALUE CO
2415 3rd Ave (56001-2715)
PHONE 507 625-6021
Beverly McCulloch, *Opers Mgr*
Rick Frenzel, *Maint Mgr*
Cathy Heiminover, *Human Res Mgr*
Leonard Hoffman, *Business Anlyst*
Gerald Gainer, *Manager*
EMP: 124
SALES (est): 50MM-99.9MM **Privately Held**
WEB: www.truevalue.com
SIC: 5072 Wholesales hardware
PA: True Value Co
        8600 W Bryn Mawr Ave 100S
        Chicago IL 60631
        773 695-5000

(G-3210)
TWIN TOWN BOWL INC
Also Called: Jerry Dutler's Bowl
1247 Range St (56001-0436)
PHONE 507 387-3439
FAX: 507 387-4766
Ruth Dutler, *President*
EMP: 25 **EST:** 1950
SQ FT: 30,000
SALES (est): 1MM-4.9MM **Privately Held**
WEB: www.jerrydutlersbowl.com
SIC: 7933 Cocktail lounge; ten pin center

(G-3211)
V-TEK INC (PA)
751 Summit Ave (56001-2717)
PO Box 3104 (56002-3104)
PHONE 507 387-2039
FAX: 507 387-2257
Dennis K Siemer, *President*
Peggy Anderson, *General Mgr*
Jan Sorgatz, *Div Sub Head*
Scott Melham, *Engineer*
Jason Voss, *Engineering*
EMP: 60 **EST:** 1985
SQ FT: 28,000 **Privately Held**
WEB: www.vtekusa.com
SIC: 5113 7389 Manufactures electrical
equipment & supplies; wholesales pressure
sensitive tape; tape slitting service

(G-3212)
VALLEY NEWS CO
1305 Stadium Rd (56001-5355)
PHONE 507 345-4819
FAX: 507 345-6793
Troy Leiferman, *President*
Nancy Nickels, *Corp Secy*
Dave Goettl, *Sales Staff*
EMP: 65 **EST:** 1940
SQ FT: 20,000
SALES (est): 25MM-49.9MM **Privately Held**
WEB: www.valleynewscompany.com
SIC: 5192 Wholesales magazines; retails
books; wholesales books; wholesales
periodicals

(G-3213)
VOLK TRANSFER INC
104 Lundin Blvd (56001-2704)
PHONE 507 388-1683
FAX: 507 388-7859
Troy Volk, *President*
Sandra Blanchard, *Vice Pres*
Marin Christen, *Accountant*
Jenny Kuster, *CTO*
EMP: 40 **EST:** 1948
SQ FT: 20,000
SALES (est): 1MM-4.9MM **Privately Held**
WEB: www.volktransfer.com
SIC: 4212 4731 Local trucking without
storage services; shipping broker

(G-3214)
WEB CONSTRUCTION CO INC
200 Saint Andrews Dr # 300 (56001-8584)
PHONE 507 387-1667
FAX: 507 388-1600
Jerry Williams, *President*
EMP: 25 **EST:** 1968
SQ FT: 6,400
SALES (est): 5MM-9.9MM **Privately Held**
WEB: www.webconmankato.com
SIC: 1542 1771 1791 New commercial &
office building construction; concrete
contractor; structural steel erection
contractor

(G-3215)
**WELLS FARGO BANK,
NATIONAL**
1600 E Madison Ave # 100 (56001-1003)
PO Box 168 (56002-0168)
PHONE 507 387-9254
FAX: 507 387-9223
Debra Ideker, *Manager*
Lynn Sprague, *Manager*
EMP: 32
SALES (est): 5MM-9.9MM **Publicly Held**
SIC: 6021 National commercial bank
HQ: Wfc Holdings, Corp
        420 Montgomery St
        San Francisco CA 94104
        415 396-7392

(G-3216)
**WELLS FARGO BANK,
NATIONAL**
206 E Hickory St (56001-3629)
PO Box 168 (56002-0168)
PHONE 507 625-1872
FAX: 507 387-9217
Chuck Kind, *Manager*
Harlee Olafson, *Manager*
Lynn Sprague, *Manager*
Elaine Cornish, *Assistant*
EMP: 100
SALES (est): 25MM-49.9MM **Publicly Held**
SIC: 6021 National commercial bank
HQ: Wfc Holdings, Corp
        420 Montgomery St
        San Francisco CA 94104
        415 396-7392

(G-3217)
**WESTMAN FREIGHTLINER INC
(PA)**
Also Called: Kato Radiator
2200 4th Ave (56001-2815)
PO Box 699 (56002-0699)
PHONE 507 625-4118
Randy Westman, *President*
Diane Zimmerman, *CFO*
Dale Kanack, *CFO*
Paula O Conner, *Accountant*
EMP: 50 **EST:** 1910
SQ FT: 30,000 **Privately Held**
WEB: www.westmanfreightliner.com
SIC: 7538 5012 5013 Truck engine repair
service; wholesales new & used trailers for
trucks; wholesales commercial trucks;
wholesales truck parts & accessories

(G-3218)
WILCON CONSTRUCTION INC
232 Quail Path (56001-7208)
PHONE 507 345-6653
FAX: 507 345-6653
William Freitag, *CEO*
EMP: 40 **EST:** 2006
SALES (est): 10MM-24.9MM **Privately Held**
SIC: 1521 Single-family housing
construction

(G-3219)
WILLOWBROOK CO-OP
700 Agency Trl (56001-6548)
PHONE 507 388-2886
Delane Renfroe, *Principal*
EMP: 25
SALES (est): 500-999K **Privately Held**
SIC: 8361 Residential care facility

(G-3220)
WRIGHT TREE SERVICE INC
230 Lundin Blvd (56001-2705)
PHONE 507 625-6950
FAX: 507 625-6880
Wade Myers, *General Mgr*
John Church, *Manager*
EMP: 250 **Privately Held**
WEB: www.wrighttree.com
SIC: 0783 0181 Ornamental shrub & tree
service; ornamental nursery products
HQ: Wright Tree Service Inc
        139 6th St
        West Des Moines IA 50265
        515 277-6291

(G-3221)
YAEGER BUS SERVICE INC
56548 Doc Jones Rd (56001-6662)
PHONE 507 345-5470
Dwight Yaeger, *President*
Karem Yaeger, *Treasurer*
EMP: 25 **EST:** 1955
SQ FT: 5,292
SALES (est): 500-999K **Privately Held**
SIC: 4151 School bus service

(G-3222)
YOUNG MEN'S CHRISTIAN ASSN
1401 S Riverfront Dr (56001-2413)
PHONE 507 387-8255
FAX: 507 387-2522
Gohn Kind, *CEO*
Liz Hageman, *Member*
Susan Lyons, *Office Mgr*
Jenni Dillemuth, *Manager*
Joe Tougas, *Manager*
EMP: 120 **EST:** 1876
SQ FT: 30,000
SALES (est): 1MM-4.9MM **Privately Held**
SIC: 7999 8322 8641 Recreation center;
civic & social organization; individual &
family social services

MANKATO
Nicollet County

(G-3223)
CLIFF VIESSMAN INC
1930 Lor Ray Dr (56003-1229)
PHONE 507 625-1435
FAX: 507 388-7045
Doug Viesmann, *Branch Mgr*
EMP: 50
SALES (est): 5MM-9.9MM **Privately Held**
WEB: www.viessmantrucking.com
SIC: 4213 Over the road trucking
PA: Cliff Viessman Inc
        215 1st Ave
        Gary SD 57237
        605 272-5241

(G-3224)
D D D MOTEL CORP
Also Called: Best Western
1111 Range St (56003-2214)
PHONE 507 625-9333
FAX: 507 386-4592
Doug Anderson, *Owner*
Jen Brovald, *Human Res Dir*
Arlene Herzberg, *Manager*
EMP: 100
SALES (est): 5MM-9.9MM **Privately Held**
SIC: 7011 7991 Traveler accommodations;
eating place; physical fitness center;
drinking establishment
PA: D D D Motel Corp
        709 S Front St
        Mankato MN 56001
        507 625-9343

(G-3225)
**GOLDEN HEART CHILD CARE
CENTER**
1825 Commerce Dr (56003-1801)
PHONE 507 625-1454
CAM Willard, *Director*
Pam Willard, *Director*
EMP: 35 **EST:** 2003
SALES (est): 500-999K **Privately Held**
SIC: 8351 Child day care service

(G-3226)
**INDULGE SALON & TANNING
LLP**
1713 Commerce Dr (56003-1802)
PHONE 507 345-3400
Pam Ticketson, *Partner*
EMP: 25 **EST:** 2005
SALES (est): 500-999K **Privately Held**
SIC: 7231 Beauty salon

(G-3227)
LOCHER BROS INC
Also Called: Miller Brands of Mankato
1119 Center St (56003-2108)
PHONE 507 625-4198
FAX: 507 625-6040
Thad Simpson, *Sales Mgr*
Tom Richards, *Manager*
EMP: 30
SALES (est): 10MM-24.9MM **Privately Held**
SIC: 5181 Wholesales beer & other
fermented malt liquors
PA: Locher Bros Inc
        18098 365th Ave
        Green Isle MN 55338
        507 326-5471

(G-3228)
**MANKATO AUTO MALL
OWNERS INC**
2009 Roe Crest Dr (56003-3430)
PHONE 507 387-7877
Peter Etzell, *Manager*
EMP: 25 **EST:** 1986
SALES (est): 500-999K **Privately Held**
SIC: 7542 7537 Automatic carwash service;
automotive transmission repair service;
manufactures motor vehicle parts &
accessories; manufactures internal
combustion engine oil filters; tire dealer

(G-3229)
MANKATO CLINIC LTD
Also Called: North Mankato Med Fmly Clinic
1575 Lookout Dr (56003-2503)
PHONE 507 625-5027
FAX: 507 625-6282
Jodi Weston, *Office Mgr*
Daniel P Anderson, *Med Doctor*
Roger Greenwald, *Manager*
Dan Hart, *Manager*
Pam Shilling, *Physician Asst*
EMP: 30
SALES (est): 1MM-4.9MM **Privately Held**
SIC: 8011 Primary care medical clinic
PA: Mankato Clinic Ltd
        1230 E Main St
        Mankato MN 56001
        507 625-1811

(G-3230)
**PALMER BUS SERVICE OF
MANKATO**
1770 Howard Dr (56003-1516)
PO Box 2026 (56002-2026)
PHONE 507 386-0210
FAX: 507 386-0211
Floyd Palmer, *President*
EMP: 30 **EST:** 1996
SALES (est): 1MM-4.9MM **Privately Held**
SIC: 4142 Long-distance bus charter
service

(G-3231)
**ROOT RIVER VALLEY
TRANSFER INC**
1120 Center St (56003-2110)
PHONE 507 388-7670
FAX: 507 388-7780
Perry Benson, *President*
Mark Reistad, *General Mgr*
Gerry Hakle, *Vice Pres*
Jerry Brelje, *Manager*
EMP: 54 **EST:** 2004
SALES (est): 5MM-9.9MM **Privately Held**
SIC: 4213 Over the road trucking

(G-3232)
**UNITED COMMUNICATIONS
CORP**
Also Called: Keyc TV Channel 12
1570 Lookout Dr (56003-2502)
PHONE 507 625-7905
FAX: 507 625-5745
Denny Wahlstrom, *General Mgr*
John Ginther, *Advt Staff*
Jan Ellanson, *Manager*
EMP: 45
SALES (est): 10MM-24.9MM **Privately Held**
SIC: 4833 Television broadcasting station

www.HarrisInfo.com
148

2011 Harris Minnesota
Services Directory

▲=Import ▼=Export
◆=Import/Export

MANTORVILLE
Dodge County

(G-3233)
DURST BROTHERS
56541 245th Ave (55955-6068)
PHONE..............................507 635-5588
Kenneth Durst, *Partner*
Allen Durst, *Partner*
Ron Durst, *Partner*
EMP: 30 **EST:** 1977 **Privately Held**
SIC: 0241 0191 Dairy farming; crop farming

MAPLE GROVE
Hennepin County

(G-3234)
ALLIED BLACKTOP CO
10503 89th Ave N (55369-4084)
PHONE..............................763 425-0575
Eugene J Capistrant, *President*
Peter Capistrant, *Vice Pres*
Dan Smith, *Vice Pres*
Pam Olson, *Controller*
EMP: 93 **EST:** 1956
SQ FT: 15,000
SALES (est): 10MM-24.9MM **Privately Held**
WEB: www.alliedblacktopmn.com
SIC: 1611 Street surfacing & paving
construction; highway & street paving
contractor; highway & street resurfacing
contractor

(G-3235)
ALLINA HEALTH SYSTEM
7840 Vinewood Ln N (55369-7185)
PHONE..............................763 236-0200
Tami Edwards, *Office Mgr*
Lori Kirschenmann, *Optometrist*
Dianne Mansfield, *Phys Therapist*
Mary K Heruth, *Phys Therapist*
Wendy S Juhlin MD, *Med Doctor*
EMP: 25
SALES (est): 1MM-4.9MM **Privately Held**
WEB: www.allina.com
SIC: 8011 Clinic operated by physicians
PA: Allina Health System
2925 Chicago Ave
Minneapolis MN 55407
612 775-5000

(G-3236)
AMC ENTERTAINMENT INC
12575 Elm Creek Blvd N (55369-7047)
PHONE..............................763 494-0379
Aaron Konigsmark, *Manager*
EMP: 50
SALES (est): 1MM-4.9MM **Privately Held**
WEB: www.amctheatres.com
SIC: 7832 Indoor movie theater
HQ: AMC Entertainment Inc
920 Main St
Kansas City MO 64105
816 221-4000

(G-3237)
AUSTIN MUTUAL INSURANCE CO
15490 101st Ave N (55369-9725)
PO Box 1420 (55311-6420)
PHONE..............................800 328-4628
Jeffrey B Kusch, *President*
Bruce Lonnes, *Chairman*
Harry J Dell, *Exec VP*
Terrell Madsen, *Vice Pres*
Maura Beain, *Treasurer*
EMP: 100 **EST:** 1896
SQ FT: 22,000
SALES (est): 25MM-49.9MM **Privately Held**
SIC: 6331 Property & casualty insurance
carrier

(G-3238)
CYNW LLC
Also Called: Courtyard By Marriott
11871 Fountains Way (55369-7203)
PHONE..............................763 425-5355
Thomas R Torgerson, *Managing Prtnr*
Sheryl D Walton, *Senior VP*
EMP: 35 **EST:** 2007

SALES (est): 1MM-4.9MM **Privately Held**
WEB: www.torgersonproperties.com
SIC: 7011 Traveler accommodations
PA: Torgerson Properties Inc
103 15th Ave NW Ste 200
Willmar MN 56201
320 235-7207

(G-3239)
DATA RECOGNITION CORP (PA)
13490 Bass Lake Rd (55311-3634)
PHONE..............................763 268-2000
FAX: 763 268-3000
Susan Engeleiter, *CEO*
Russell Hagen, *Chairman*
John Adams, *Vice Pres*
Pat Davis, *Vice Pres*
Michelle Edenborg, *Vice Pres*
EMP: 390 **EST:** 1976
SQ FT: 125,000
SALES (corp-wide): 152.66M **Privately Held**
SIC: 8732 Educational research services;
offset printing

(G-3240)
ERICKSON-LARSEN INC (PA)
Also Called: Bjornson SENTINEL-E&L
6425 Sycamore Ct N (55369-6028)
PHONE..............................763 535-0055
Merwyn R Larsen, *President*
EMP: 29 **EST:** 1980
SQ FT: 6,000
SALES (corp-wide): 9.44M **Privately Held**
WEB: www.ericksonlarseninc.com
SIC: 6411 Insurance agency & broker

(G-3241)
FORSTROM & TORGERSON HNW LLC
Also Called: Hampton Inn
7745 Elm Creek Blvd N (55369-7001)
PHONE..............................763 494-4498
FAX: 763 494-4698
Sheryl D Walton, *Senior VP*
Thomas R Torgerson, *Mng Member*
EMP: 30
SALES (est): 1MM-4.9MM **Privately Held**
WEB: www.torgersonproperties.com
SIC: 7011 Traveler accommodations
PA: Torgerson Properties Inc
103 15th Ave NW Ste 200
Willmar MN 56201
320 235-7207

(G-3242)
FORSTROM & TORGERSON SSNW LLC
Also Called: Staybridge Suites
7821 Elm Creek Blvd N (55369-7023)
PHONE..............................763 494-8856
FAX: 763 494-8863
Todd Roy, *General Mgr*
Sheryl D Walton, *Senior VP*
Tracy Kiffmeyer, *Sales Staff*
Thomas R Torgerson, *Mng Member*
EMP: 30
SALES (est): 1MM-4.9MM **Privately Held**
WEB: www.torgersonproperties.com
SIC: 7011 Traveler accommodations
PA: Torgerson Properties Inc
103 15th Ave NW Ste 200
Willmar MN 56201
320 235-7207

(G-3243)
GREAT RIVER ENERGY (PA)
12300 Elm Creek Blvd N (55369-4718)
PHONE..............................763 445-5000
David Saggau, *President*
Don Holl, *Chairman*
Dennis Lamke, *Vice Chairman*
Bruce Leino, *Vice Chairman*
Jim Haasis, *Corp Secy*
▲ **EMP:** 300 **EST:** 1998
SQ FT: 166,000
SALES (corp-wide): 787.78M **Privately Held**
WEB: www.greatriverenergy.com
SIC: 4911 Provides electric power
generation services; provides electric power
transmission services

(G-3244)
GYRUS ACMI, LP
6655 Wedgwood Rd N # 160 (55311-3613)
PHONE..............................763 416-3000
Roy Davis, *General Ptnr*
Todd Frese, *Vice Pres*
EMP: 99 **EST:** 2006
SQ FT: 75,000
SALES (est): 50MM-99.9MM **Privately Held**
WEB: www.circoncorp.com
SIC: 5047 Wholesales medical & hospital
equipment
DH: Gyrus Acmi LP
6655 Wedgwood Rd N # 160
Maple Grove MN 55311
888 524-7266

(G-3245)
HINW LLC
Also Called: Holiday Inn
11801 Fountains Way (55369-7203)
PHONE..............................763 425-3800
Patrick Bissen, *General Mgr*
Sheryl D Walton, *Senior VP*
Thomas R Torgerson, *Mng Member*
EMP: 115
SALES (est): 5MM-9.9MM **Privately Held**
WEB: www.torgersonproperties.com
SIC: 7011 Traveler accommodations
PA: Torgerson Properties Inc
103 15th Ave NW Ste 200
Willmar MN 56201
320 235-7207

(G-3246)
INNOVATIVE PACKAGING
11010 93rd Ave N Ste B (55369-4125)
PHONE..............................763 488-9708
Janelle Iskierka, *President*
EMP: 25 **EST:** 2006
SQ FT: 3,000 **Privately Held**
SIC: 4783 Packing & crating service

(G-3247)
KING SHIPPING INC
11011 Holly Ln N (55369-9203)
PO Box 460, Rogers (55374-0460)
PHONE..............................763 428-5464
Michael Patterson, *President*
Karin Nelson, *Corp Secy*
Meyer Bolnick, *Vice Pres*
John Fraser, *CFO*
Rob Garber, *IT/INT Sup*
EMP: 42 **EST:** 1990
SQ FT: 25,000
SALES (est): 5MM-9.9MM **Privately Held**
SIC: 4731 4213 Freight forwarding services;
over the road trucking
PA: King Solutions Inc
11011 Holly Ln N
Osseo MN 55369
763 428-5464

(G-3248)
MAPLE GROVE AMBULATORY SURGERY
Also Called: North Mamorial Ambulatory
9855 Hospital Dr Ste 175 (55369-4777)
PHONE..............................763 981-3234
Steven J Kern, *Principal*
Wanda Teply, *Exec Dir*
EMP: 25 **EST:** 2007
SALES (est): 1MM-4.9MM **Privately Held**
SIC: 8062 Medical hospital

(G-3249)
MAPLE GROVE LODGING INVESTORS
Also Called: Hilton Garden Inn Maple Grove
6350 Vinewood Ln N (55311-3639)
PHONE..............................763 509-9500
FAX: 763 509-9501
David A Lenz, *Member*
Kym Myers, *Branch Mgr*
EMP: 38 **EST:** 2002
SALES (est): 1MM-4.9MM **Privately Held**
SIC: 7011 Hotel

(G-3250)
MEYER CONTRACTING INC
11010 93rd Ave N Ste A (55369-4125)
PHONE..............................763 391-5959
Kathleen Meyer, *President*
Paul Meyer, *Finance*
Steph Hanson, *Assistant*
EMP: 48 **EST:** 1987
SALES (est): 10MM-24.9MM **Privately Held**
SIC: 1542 1799 Commercial & institutional
building construction; hospital construction;
building site preparation service

(G-3251)
MORTGAGES UNLIMITED INC
7365 Kirkwood Ct N Ste 300 (55369-4736)
PHONE..............................763 416-2600
Chris Fredin, *CEO*
James Benincasa, *President*
Jody Benincasa, *Vice Pres*
EMP: 70 **EST:** 1991
SQ FT: 2,000
SALES (est): 5MM-9.9MM **Privately Held**
SIC: 6162 Mortgage & loan lending

(G-3252)
QUALITY DRYWALL MIDWEST INC
8620 Monticello Ln N # 100 (55369-4547)
PHONE..............................763 424-5774
Bret Palmer, *President*
Betty Robson, *Manager*
EMP: 35
SALES (est): 1MM-4.9MM **Privately Held**
SIC: 1742 Drywall, plastering & insulation
contractor

(G-3253)
SEARCH AMERICA, A PART OF
6450 Wedgwood Rd N # 100 (55311-3649)
PHONE..............................763 416-1007
Dan Johnson, *President*
Julie Varnam, *Business Mgr*
Bruce Nelson, *VP Sls/Mktg*
Doug Kellar, *Controller*
Scott Osterlie, *Controller*
EMP: 49 **EST:** 2001
SQ FT: 12,000
SALES (est): 5MM-9.9MM **Privately Held**
WEB: www.searchamerica.com
SIC: 7379 Data processing consulting
service

(G-3254)
TILLER CORP (PA)
7200 Hemlock Ln N Ste 200 (55369-5590)
PO Box 1480, Osseo (55311-6480)
PHONE..............................763 425-4191
FAX: 763 425-2324
Gary Sauer, *President*
Gaylen Ghylin, *Exec VP*
Steven Sauer, *Vice Pres*
Keith Sauer, *Human Res Mgr*
Butch Davie, *Manager*
EMP: 83 **EST:** 1953
SQ FT: 15,000 **Privately Held**
WEB: www.tillercorp.com
SIC: 1442 Construction sand & gravel
mining; manufactures paving mixtures

(G-3255)
TOPLINE FEDERAL CREDIT UNION
9353 Jefferson Hwy (55369-4240)
PHONE..............................763 391-9494
FAX: 763 391-7540
Harry Carter, *President*
Kevin Kuntz, *Senior VP*
Vicki Roscoe, *Assistant VP*
Carla Hansen, *Vice Pres*
Mick Olson, *Vice Pres*
EMP: 69 **EST:** 1935
SQ FT: 36,000
SALES (est): 10MM-24.9MM **Privately Held**
WEB: www.toplinecu.com
SIC: 6062 State chartered credit union

(G-3256)
VISTAR CORP
8555 Revere Ln N Ste 100 (55369-4007)
PHONE..............................800 333-3056
Kathy Krause, *Branch Mgr*

(PA)=Parent Co (HQ)=Headquarters (DH)=Div Headquarters
✿ = New business established in last 2 years

2011 Harris Minnesota
Services Directory

© Harris InfoSource 1-866-281-6415
149

EMP: 36
SALES (est): 10MM-24.9MM **Privately Held**
WEB: www.mfdg.com
SIC: 5145 Wholesales confectionery products
PA: Vistar Corp
　　12650 E Arapahoe Rd D
　　Englewood CO 80112
　　303 662-7100

(G-3257)
VSI CONSTRUCTION INC
11751 Troy Ln N　(55369-9279)
PHONE 763 493-3000
FAX: 763 428-3954
Len D Sutherland, *CEO*
Jay D Tutt, *President*
Brent Thompson, *Vice Pres*
Dan Herman, *Vice Pres*
Barbara Rounds, *Vice Pres*
EMP: 50 **EST:** 1987
SQ FT: 10,000
SALES (est): 10MM-24.9MM **Privately Held**
WEB: www.vsiconstruction.com
SIC: 1542 1799 Commercial & office building renovation & repair services; home & office interiors finishing, furnishing & remodeling service

MAPLE LAKE
Wright County

(G-3258)
BOGART & PETERSON & ASSOCIATES
Also Called: Ellestad & Bogart & Peterson
311 Division St W　(55358)
PHONE 763 682-9329
John Bogart, *Owner*
Dennis Peterson, *Co-Owner*
EMP: 40 **EST:** 1996
SALES (est): 1MM-4.9MM **Privately Held**
SIC: 8713 Surveying service

(G-3259)
COURAGE CENTER
Also Called: Camp Courage
8046 83rd St NW　(55358-2454)
PHONE 320 963-3121
FAX: 320 963-3698
Roger Upcraft, *Manager*
Jo Tornell, *Manager*
John Schwartz, *Info Tech Mgr*
Denise Saylor, *Assistant*
EMP: 25
SALES (est): 500-999K **Privately Held**
WEB: www.courage.org
SIC: 7999 8093 Recreation center; outpatient rehabilitation treatment center
PA: Courage Center
　　3915 Golden Valley Rd
　　Minneapolis MN 55422
　　763 588-0811

(G-3260)
LATOUR CONSTRUCTION INC
2134 County Rd Ste 8NW　(55358)
PHONE 320 963-5993
FAX: 320 963-6017
Theodore Latour, *President*
Joseph Latour, *Vice Pres*
Marsha Nixon, *Treasurer*
EMP: 39 **EST:** 1972
SQ FT: 2,400
SALES (est): 5MM-9.9MM **Privately Held**
SIC: 1623 Sewer line construction

(G-3261)
M & P UTILITIES INC
500 County Road 37　(55358-2864)
PHONE 320 963-2400
FAX: 320 478-2465
Larry Pribyl, *President*
Lois Carlson, *Corp Secy*
Emilio Alfonso, *Corp Secy*
Richard Detweiller, *CFO*
Daniel F Harrington, *Treasurer*
EMP: 200 **EST:** 1972
SALES (est): 25MM-49.9MM **Privately Held**
WEB: www.lincnet.com

SIC: 1623 Water & sewer line construction; power & communication transmission tower construction
PA: Lincnet Inc
　　6161 Blue Lagoon Dr # 300
　　Miami FL 33126
　　305 266-7670

(G-3262)
MP NEXLEVEL LLC
500 County Road 37　(55358-2864)
PHONE 320 963-2400
Timothy Pribyl, *Member*
Robbi Pribyl, *Member*
Larry Pribyl, *Member*
EMP: 250 **EST:** 2002
SQ FT: 45,000
SALES (est): 25MM-49.9MM **Privately Held**
WEB: www.mpnexlevel.com
SIC: 1623 Water & sewer line construction

(G-3263)
MP TECHNOLOGIES LLC
501 County Road 37　(55358-2864)
PHONE 320 963-2499
Karen Pribyl, *President*
Pam Pribyl, *Vice Pres*
Rob Pribyl, *Vice Pres*
Lois Carlson, *Treasurer*
Greg Kriese, *VP Finance*
EMP: 50 **EST:** 2004
SQ FT: 8,000
SALES (est): 25MM-49.9MM **Privately Held**
WEB: www.mptech.biz
SIC: 4911 Electric services

(G-3264)
ROGER'S AMOCO INC
Also Called: Amoco
300 State Hwy 55 NW　(55358)
PO Box 267　(55358-0267)
PHONE 320 963-6555
FAX: 320 963-5693
Irene Hudek, *President*
EMP: 26 **EST:** 1968
SQ FT: 4,000
SALES (est): 5MM-9.9MM **Privately Held**
SIC: 7538 Retail gasoline filling station; general automotive repair services; retail independent convenience store

(G-3265)
SUGAR LAKE SUPPORTED LIVING
6523 117th St NW　(55358-2330)
PHONE 320 963-7571
FAX: 320 963-7572
Mike Hilgert, *CEO*
EMP: 30 **EST:** 2001
SALES (est): 1MM-4.9MM **Privately Held**
SIC: 8082 Home health care services

(G-3266)
TL NEXLEVEL CO'S LLC　(PA)
500 County Road 37　(55358-2864)
PHONE 320 963-2400
Larry Pribyl, *Member*
Mike Aydt, *CFO*
Timothy L Pribyl, *Manager*
EMP: 250 **EST:** 2004
SALES (corp-wide): 71.59M **Privately Held**
SIC: 1623 Utility line construction; sewer line construction

(G-3267)
VETERANS OF FOREIGN WARS OF
Also Called: Post 7664
66 Maple Ave N　(55358)
PO Box 392　(55358-0392)
PHONE 320 963-3405
Karen Albrecht, *Manager*
EMP: 30 **Privately Held**
SIC: 8641 Veterans' organization
PA: Veterans of Foreign Wars of
　　406 W 34th St Fl 11
　　Kansas City MO 64111
　　816 756-3390

(G-3268)
WRIGHT AERO INC
Municipal Airport　(55358)
PHONE 320 963-5094
FAX: 320 963-6441

William Mavencamp Jr, *President*
EMP: 26 **EST:** 1982
SQ FT: 20,000
SALES (est): 1MM-4.9MM **Privately Held**
SIC: 4581 4522 Aircraft charter, maintenance & flight training services

MAPLE PLAIN
Hennepin County

(G-3269)
BERG EXTERIORS INC
5145 Industrial St # 101　(55359-8626)
PHONE 763 479-1115
Rob Berg, *Principal*
Eric Finch, *Director*
Todd Hewitt, *Director*
EMP: 26 **EST:** 2004
SALES (est): 1MM-4.9MM **Privately Held**
WEB: www.bergexteriors.com
SIC: 1771 5099 Exterior concrete stucco contractor; wholesales durable goods

(G-3270)
BERGERSON-CASWELL INC
5115 Industrial St　(55359-8610)
PHONE 763 479-3121
FAX: 763 479-2183
John Henrich, *President*
Roberta Henrich, *Corp Secy*
EMP: 40 **EST:** 1948
SQ FT: 15,000
SALES (est): 5MM-9.9MM **Privately Held**
WEB: www.bergersoncaswell.com
SIC: 1781 Water well drilling contractor; water well drilling contractor; retails plumbing & heating supplies

(G-3271)
CAREFREE SERVICES INC
5541 Industrial Blvd　(55359)
PO Box 208　(55359-0208)
PHONE 763 479-2600
FAX: 763 479-2620
Steve Curtis, *President*
EMP: 25 **EST:** 1973
SALES (est): 1MM-4.9MM **Privately Held**
WEB: www.carefreesvs.com
SIC: 4959 0781 7538 Snow plowing services; landscape services; general truck repair services; road, airport & parking lot sweeping services

(G-3272)
COUNTRYSIDE HEATING & COOLING
6511 Highway 12　(55359-9710)
PHONE 763 479-1600
Craig Schumacher, *President*
Barbara Schansberg, *Executive*
EMP: 26 **EST:** 1974
SALES (est): 1MM-4.9MM **Privately Held**
WEB: www.countrysideservices.com
SIC: 1711 Heating & air conditioning contractor

(G-3273)
ELECTRICAL INSTALLATION
Also Called: Eim
1480 County Road 90　(55359-9525)
PHONE 763 479-3744
Ken Pysick, *CEO*
David Pysick, *President*
Maureen Pysick, *Corp Secy*
EMP: 30 **EST:** 1978
SQ FT: 3,600
SALES (est): 1MM-4.9MM **Privately Held**
SIC: 1731 General electrical contractor

(G-3274)
G M CLARK CO'S INC
180 Northshore Dr　(55359-9621)
PO Box 47508, Minneapolis　(55447-0508)
PHONE 763 475-1000
Gerald M Clark III, *President*
EMP: 25 **EST:** 1981
SALES (est): 5MM-9.9MM **Privately Held**
SIC: 1542 Commercial & office building contractor

(G-3275)
HAVEN HOMES INC
Also Called: Bryant House
1520 Wyman Ave　(55359-9639)
PHONE 763 479-1993
Don V Stickney V, *President*
Marie Fair, *Vice Pres*
Jennie Pogreba, *Manager*
Jenny Banitt, *Manager*
Robert Mueller, *Administrator*
EMP: 100
SALES (est): 1MM-4.9MM **Privately Held**
SIC: 8059 8051 Convalescent home; skilled nursing care facility

(G-3276)
HAVEN HOMES OF MAPLE PLAIN
1520 Wyman Ave　(55359-9639)
PHONE 763 479-1993
FAX: 763 479-1996
Robert Muller, *Administrator*
EMP: 100 **EST:** 1965
SQ FT: 17,000
SALES (est): 1MM-4.9MM **Privately Held**
WEB: www.havenhomesinc.com
SIC: 8059 8051 Convalescent home; convalescent home

(G-3277)
HERC-U-LIFT INC　(PA)
5655 Highway 12　(55359-9401)
PO Box 69　(55359-0069)
PHONE 763 479-2501
FAX: 763 479-2296
Lester Nielsen, *CEO*
Tom Showalter, *President*
Dan Showalter, *General Mgr*
June Nielsen, *Corp Secy*
Brad Ellingson, *VP Finance*
EMP: 93 **EST:** 1968
SQ FT: 74,000
SALES (corp-wide): 34.91M **Privately Held**
WEB: www.herculift.com
SIC: 5084 Wholesales industrial lift trucks & parts; wholesales materials handling equipment

(G-3278)
MANOR ELECTRIC INC
5350 Pioneer Creek Dr # 3　(55359-9018)
PHONE 763 479-4170
Timothy Loken, *CEO*
EMP: 30 **EST:** 1989
SQ FT: 5,000
SALES (est): 1MM-4.9MM **Privately Held**
SIC: 1731 General electrical contractor

(G-3279)
NUTRI-DYN MIDWEST INC
Also Called: Nutrition Dynamics Gmp
5414 Highway 12　(55359-8752)
PO Box 219　(55359-0219)
PHONE 763 479-3444
FAX: 763 479-1288
David Peterson, *President*
Gregg Peterson, *Vice Pres*
EMP: 25 **EST:** 1973
SQ FT: 9,000
SALES (est): 25MM-49.9MM **Privately Held**
SIC: 5122 Wholesales vitamins & minerals

(G-3280)
ORONO INDEPENDENT SCHOOL DIST
Also Called: Early Childhood Center
5050 Independence St　(55359-9642)
PHONE 763 479-1530
FAX: 763 479-3633
Erin Anderson, *COO*
Mitzie Overland, *Manager*
Robin Haugen, *Assistant*
EMP: 34
SALES (est): 1MM-4.9MM **Privately Held**
WEB: www.orono.k12.mn.us
SIC: 8322 Community center; public elementary school
PA: Orono Independent School Dist
　　685 N Old Crystal Bay Rd
　　Long Lake MN 55356
　　952 449-8300

▲=Import ▼=Export
◆=Import/Export

GEOGRAPHIC

(G-3281)
WENCK ASSOCIATES INC
1800 Pioneer Creek Ctr (55359-9000)
PO Box 249 (55359-0249)
PHONE..............................763 479-4200
FAX: 763 479-4242
Joseph J Grabowski, *President*
Norman Wenck, *Corp Secy*
Steve Menden, *Vice Pres*
Mollie Wenck, *Vice Pres*
Mark Panian, *Vice Pres*
EMP: 70 **EST:** 1985
SQ FT: 15,000
SALES (est): 5MM-9.9MM **Privately Held**
SIC: 8711 Engineering services

MAPLETON
Blue Earth County

(G-3282)
CHOICE CONNECTIONS LLP
15503 State Highway 22 (56065-9417)
PHONE..............................507 524-4583
FAX: 507 524-4183
Michelle Hislop, *Partner*
Scott Hislop, *Partner*
EMP: 40 **EST:** 1999 **Privately Held**
WEB: www.choiceconnectn.com
SIC: 0213 Hog & pig farming

(G-3283)
MONSANTO CO
310 Main St E (56065-2060)
PHONE..............................507 524-3475
FAX: 507 524-3470
Randy Gettle, *Manager*
EMP: 30
SALES (est): 10MM-24.9MM **Publicly Held**
WEB: www.monsanto.com
SIC: 5191 Wholesales field, garden & flower
seeds; retails nursery stock, seeds & bulbs
PA: Monsanto Co
800 N Lindbergh Blvd
Saint Louis MO 63167
314 694-1000

(G-3284)
PIONEER BANK
301 Main St E (56065-2060)
PHONE..............................507 524-3630
Jerry Benrud, *Principal*
Barb Hofbauer, *CIO*
EST: 2007 **Privately Held**
SIC: 6022 State commercial bank

(G-3285)
ROBERT FITZSIMMONS & SONS LLP
503 Silver St E (56065-2040)
PO Box 308 (56065-0308)
PHONE..............................507 524-4511
William Fitzsimmons, *Partner*
Richard Fitzsimmons, *Partner*
John Fitzsimmons, *Partner*
Paul Fitzsimmons, *Partner*
EMP: 25 **EST:** 1979 **Privately Held**
WEB: www.proteinsources.com
SIC: 0291 Animal specialty farm

MAPLEWOOD
Ramsey County

(G-3286)
NEW STREAMS INTERNATIONAL INC
1686 Village Trl E Unit 4 (55109-5830)
PHONE..............................651 777-8020
Marcus Benson, *President*
Nicole Benson, *Vice Pres*
EST: 2005 **Privately Held**
SIC: 5199 Manufactures carbonated
mineral water; wholesales nondurable
general merchandise

(G-3287)
S & D CLEANING
2371 Linwood Ave E (55119-5824)
PHONE..............................651 558-7336
George Vonbrugger, *Consultant*
EMP: 30 **EST:** 2007
SALES (est): 500-999K **Privately Held**
SIC: 7349 Building cleaning & maintenance
services

(G-3288)
SENIORS CARING COMPANIONS INC
3070 Chisholm Ct N (55109-1749)
PHONE..............................651 770-2288
Paula Carter, *President*
Janis M Lynch, *Administrator*
EMP: 30 **EST:** 2004
SALES (est): 1MM-4.9MM **Privately Held**
WEB: www.seniorscaringcompanions.com
SIC: 8059 8082 Personal care home, with
health care; visiting nurse services

MARINE ON SAINT CROIX
Washington County

(G-3289)
SEAL GUARD SYSTEMS INC
18300 Norell Ave N (55047-8606)
PHONE..............................612 787-0700
Ken Wolfbauer, *President*
Kathi Wolfbauer, *Vice Pres*
EMP: 25 **EST:** 1997
SQ FT: 36,000
SALES (est): 1MM-4.9MM **Privately Held**
WEB: www.sealguardsystems.com
SIC: 1521 1751 1761 Retails wood or metal
storm windows; prefabricated window &
door installation service; skylight installation
service; residential remodeling

MARSHALL
Lyon County

(G-3290)
AFFILIATED COMMUNITY MEDICAL
Also Called: Affilted Cmnty Med Centers-Mar
300 S Bruce St (56258-1934)
PHONE..............................507 532-9631
FAX: 507 532-1176
Shirley Slettedahl, *Office Mgr*
Jon G Vanroekel MD, *Med Doctor*
Jagmeet Sethi MD, *Med Doctor*
Lori Lynner MD, *Med Doctor*
Terry Tone, *Administrator*
EMP: 75
SALES (est): 5MM-9.9MM **Privately Held**
WEB: www.acmc.com
SIC: 8011 Physicians' office & clinic
PA: Affiliated Community Medical
101 Willmar Ave SW
Willmar MN 56201
320 231-5000

(G-3291)
BREMER BANK, NATIONAL ASSN
208 E College Dr (56258-1818)
PHONE..............................507 537-0222
Roger Madison, *President*
Roger Josaas, *Senior VP*
Janet Vandendriessch, *Vice Pres*
Tom Duenow, *Vice Pres*
Steve Jacobson, *IT/INT Sup*
EMP: 43 **EST:** 1935
SQ FT: 8,000
SALES (est): 10MM-24.9MM **Privately Held**
SIC: 6022 Commercial state trust
companies accepting deposits
HQ: Bremer Financial Corp
445 Minnesota St Ste 2000
Saint Paul MN 55101
651 227-7621

(G-3292)
D & G EXCAVATING INC
2324 County Road 30 (56258-1681)
PHONE..............................507 532-2334
Kristin Gruhot, *CEO*
Brian Gruhot, *CFO*
Sharon Gruhot, *Treasurer*
Chris Gruhot, *CTO*
EMP: 45 **EST:** 1979
SQ FT: 20,000
SALES (est): 5MM-9.9MM **Privately Held**
WEB: www.dandgexcavating.com
SIC: 1794 1629 4212 Excavating
contractor; dump truck hauling services;
trenching service

(G-3293)
DOUG BRADLEY TRUCKING INC
1301 W Main St (56258-3080)
PHONE..............................507 532-9681
FAX: 507 532-9682
Kurt Vogt, *Manager*
EMP: 25
SALES (est): 1MM-4.9MM **Privately Held**
SIC: 4213 Over the road trucking
PA: Doug Bradley Trucking Inc
680 E Water Well Rd
Salina KS 67401
785 826-9681

(G-3294)
EICKHOFF ENTERPRISES INC
615 Kathryn Ave (56258-2214)
PHONE..............................507 537-0919
Gary Eickhoff, *President*
Joyce Eickhoff, *Corp Secy*
Janet Chad, *Vice Pres*
EMP: 76 **EST:** 1997
SALES (est): 10MM-24.9MM **Privately Held**
SIC: 4213 Long-distance refrigerated
trucking services

(G-3295)
FIREMENS RELIEF ASSNS
201 E Saratoga St (56258-1715)
PHONE..............................507 532-5141
David Marks, *Principal*
Chief D Marks, *Principal*
Marc Klaith, *Manager*
EMP: 35 **EST:** 1882 **Privately Held**
SIC: 6371 Pension fund

(G-3296)
FLINT HILLS RESOURCES, LP
901 N 7th St (56258-5416)
PO Box 200 (56258-0200)
PHONE..............................507 532-6331
Jeff Wilkes, *Vice Pres*
Mark Bailey, *Plant Mgr*
EMP: 35
SALES (est): 10MM-24.9MM **Privately Held**
WEB: www.flinthillsresources.com
SIC: 1771 Manufactures bituminous road
materials; asphalt contractor
HQ: Flint Hills Resources LLC
2801 Centerville Rd
Wilmington DE 19808
877 446-8478

(G-3297)
FLOYD WILD INC
2521 County Road 7 (56258-5468)
PO Box 1063 (56258-0863)
PHONE..............................507 537-0531
FAX: 507 537-0693
Dennis Wild, *President*
Lenny Wild, *Vice Pres*
Adelyne Wild, *Treasurer*
Arla Cousins, *Office Mgr*
Floyd Wild, *CTO*
EMP: 100 **EST:** 1946
SQ FT: 17,930
SALES (est): 10MM-24.9MM **Privately Held**
SIC: 4213 4212 Over the road trucking;
local trucking without storage services

(G-3298)
GRILL WORKS INC
1609 Halbur Rd (56258-2702)
PO Box 175 (56258-0175)
PHONE..............................507 532-3524
FAX: 507 532-3526
Keith Miller, *President*
Todd Miller, *Corp Secy*
Jerry Okeson, *Mfg Staff*
Dan Vogd, *Executive*
EMP: 25 **EST:** 1986
SQ FT: 17,000
SALES (est): 5MM-9.9MM **Privately Held**
WEB: www.grillworksinc.com
SIC: 5023 Manufactures metal air registers;
wholesales floor coverings

(G-3299)
HABILITATIVE SERVICES INC
109 S 5th St Ste 250 (56258-1296)
PHONE..............................507 532-5366
FAX: 507 532-2998
Donaebill Olson, *President*
EMP: 100
SALES (est): 1MM-4.9MM **Privately Held**
SIC: 8361 Home for the mentally
handicapped
PA: Habilitative Services Inc
220 Milwaukee St Ste 2
Lakefield MN 56150
507 662-5236

(G-3300)
J R & R PARTNERSHIP
911 Michigan Rd (56258-2721)
PHONE..............................507 532-9566
Dennis Reed, *President*
EMP: 100 **EST:** 1988
SALES (est): 25MM-49.9MM **Privately Held**
SIC: 6512 Operators of commercial &
industrial buildings

(G-3301)
JUBILEE ENTERPRISES INC
403 Donita Ave (56258-2252)
PHONE..............................507 532-2332
FAX: 507 532-2882
George Falconer, *President*
Rob Falconer, *Vice Pres*
EMP: 35 **EST:** 1983
SALES (est): 500-999K **Privately Held**
WEB: www.jubileecleaning.com
SIC: 7349 7217 Janitorial & custodial
services; carpet & upholstery cleaning
service on the customers' premises

(G-3302)
KANE TRANSPORT INC
2328 State Highway 19 (56258-5448)
PHONE..............................507 532-2788
Bob Kane, *President*
Clint Rausch, *Manager*
Ann Neubert, *Manager*
EMP: 30
SALES (est): 1MM-4.9MM **Privately Held**
WEB: www.kanetransport.com
SIC: 4213 Over the road trucking
PA: Kane Transport Inc
40925 403rd St
Sauk Centre MN 56378
320 352-2762

(G-3303)
KHC CONSTRUCTION INC
703 Ontario Rd (56258-2729)
PO Box 450 (56258-0450)
PHONE..............................507 532-6768
Kim H Christensen, *President*
EMP: 30 **EST:** 1999
SQ FT: 10,000
SALES (est): 1MM-4.9MM **Privately Held**
WEB: www.khcconstruction.com
SIC: 1611 Concrete road, highway &
sidewalk construction

(G-3304)
LANNERS BROTHERS CONSTRUCTION
2653 County Road 7 (56258-1680)
PHONE..............................507 532-5457
Bob Lanners, *Partner*
Jack Lanners, *Partner*
EST: 1984 **Privately Held**
SIC: 1542 New commercial & office building
construction; farm building construction

(PA)=Parent Co (HQ)=Headquarters (DH)=Div Headquarters
✿ = New business established in last 2 years

2011 Harris Minnesota
Services Directory

© Harris InfoSource 1-866-281-6415
151

(G-3305)

LINCOLN LYON MURRY & PIPESTONE

Also Called: Enviromental Health Lab
607 W Main St (56258-3021)
PHONE...........................507 537-6709
FAX: 507 537-6719
John Schuh, *Principal*
Christopher J Sorensen, *Director*
Sherry M Marks, *Executive Asst*
EMP: 39 EST: 1979
SALES (est): 1MM-4.9MM **Privately Held**
SIC: 8062 8734 Medical hospital; water testing laboratory

(G-3306)

LINCOLN, LYON, & MURRAY HUMAN

Also Called: Human Services
607 W Main St (56258-3021)
PHONE...........................507 532-1239
Carla Swenhaugen, *Principal*
Michelle Buysse, *Supervisor*
Chris Sorenson, *Director*
EMP: 94
SALES (est): 5MM-9.9MM **Privately Held**
SIC: 8322 Individual & family social services

(G-3307)

LYON FINANCIAL SERVICES INC

1310 Madrid St Ste 100 (56258-4001)
PHONE...........................507 532-7763
Dave Verkinderen, *Senior VP*
Tom Landmark, *Senior VP*
Adrian Hebig, *Senior VP*
Joseph H Anderson, *Vice Pres*
Laura F Bednarski, *Vice Pres*
EMP: 150 EST: 1979
SQ FT: 75,000
SALES (est): 50MM-99.9MM **Publicly Held**
WEB: www.firstar.com
SIC: 6159 7359 Equipment & vehicle finance leasing service; office machine & equipment leasing & rental
DH: U S Bancorp Equipment Finance
     13010 SW 68th Pkwy # 100
     Portland OR 97223
     503 797-0200

(G-3308)

LYON LODGING LLC

Also Called: Comfort Inn
1511 E College Dr (56258-2601)
PHONE...........................507 532-3070
FAX: 507 537-9641
Brad Duruyck, *Member*
Julane Coquyt, *Member*
Mark Buff, *Member*
Chuck Bradley, *Member*
John Bornhoft, *Member*
EMP: 28 EST: 1989
SALES (est): 1MM-4.9MM **Privately Held**
SIC: 7011 Traveler accommodations

(G-3309)

MARSHALL ADULT LEARNING CENTER

607 W Main St (56258-3021)
PHONE...........................507 537-7046
Pat Thomas, *Principal*
EMP: 25 EST: 2004
SALES (est): 1MM-4.9MM **Privately Held**
SIC: 8748 Educational consulting services

(G-3310)

MARSHALL GOLF CLUB

800 Country Club Dr 23 (56258-2287)
PO Box 502 (56258-0502)
PHONE...........................507 532-2278
FAX: 507 537-4608
Eric Eben, *President*
Jason Clarin, *Corp Secy*
Tara Plant, *Manager*
Philip Myhrberg, *Exec Dir*
EMP: 50 EST: 1930
SQ FT: 12,000
SALES (est): 1MM-4.9MM **Privately Held**
WEB: www.marshallgolfclub.com
SIC: 7997 7299 Membership golf club; full service independent family restaurant; banquet hall facility

(G-3311)

MARSHALL PUBLIC SCHOOL

1420 E College Dr (56258-2065)
PHONE...........................507 537-6210
FAX: 507 537-7609
Cynthia Celander, *Branch Mgr*
EMP: 25
SALES (est): 500-999K **Privately Held**
WEB: www.marshall.k12.mn.us
SIC: 8351 Child day care service
PA: Marshall Public School
     401 S Saratoga St
     Marshall MN 56258
     507 537-6924

(G-3312)

MATERIAL DISTRIBUTORS INC

Also Called: M D I
211 N 11th St (56258-2750)
PHONE...........................507 532-4463
FAX: 507 532-6938
Steve Sanders, *President*
Juli Sanders, *Corp Secy*
Lori Johnson, *Manager*
EMP: 30
SQ FT: 47,300
SALES (est): 10MM-24.9MM **Privately Held**
WEB: www.buymdi.com
SIC: 5031 Wholesales plywood; wholesales exterior building materials; wholesales interior building materials; wholesales rough, dressed & finished lumber

(G-3313)

MINNESOTA DEPARTMENT OF

607 W Main St Fl 3 (56258-3021)
PHONE...........................507 537-6236
Dan Zimansky, *Director*
EMP: 30 **Privately Held**
WEB: www.state.mn.us
SIC: 7361 Employment agency services; human resource, social work & welfare administration services; state government administration of social & manpower programs
DH: Minnesota Department of
     332 Minnesota St Ste E200
     Saint Paul MN 55101
     651 259-7114

(G-3314)

MINNESOTA DEPARTMENT OF PUBLIC

Also Called: Minesota State Patrol
1800 E College Dr (56258-2619)
PHONE...........................507 537-3664
FAX: 507 537-7310
Brian West, *Branch Mgr*
EMP: 35
SALES (est): 500-999K **Privately Held**
WEB: www.state.mn.us
SIC: 7381 Guard protective service; public order & safety statistics centers; state government public order & safety office
DH: Minnesota Department of Public
     444 Cedar St Ste 126
     Saint Paul MN 55101
     651 201-7000

(G-3315)

MOCCO ENTERPRISES INC

901 Michigan Rd (56258-2721)
PO Box 812 (56258-0812)
PHONE...........................507 537-1421
Gerald Moberg, *Partner*
John H Moberg, *Partner*
EMP: 25 EST: 1960
SALES (est): 5MM-9.9MM **Privately Held**
SIC: 6512 Nonresidential building operator

(G-3316)

MORGAN TIRE & AUTO LLC

Also Called: Team Tires Plus
1100 E Main St (56258-2505)
PHONE...........................507 532-9686
FAX: 507 532-7454
Emmit Thompson, *Manager*
EMP: 30
SALES (est): 1MM-4.9MM **Privately Held**
WEB: www.bfsusa.com
SIC: 7534 Tire recapping & retreading services
HQ: Bfs Retail Operations LLC
     333 E Lake St Ste 300
     Bloomingdale IL 60108
     630 259-9000

(G-3317)

OLSON & JOHNSON BODY SHOP INC

Hwy 59 N (56258)
PHONE...........................507 537-1669
Steve Hatleftad, *President*
EMP: 33 EST: 1948
SALES (est): 1MM-4.9MM **Privately Held**
SIC: 7538 7532 General automotive repair services; automotive body shop

(G-3318)

OLSON & JOHNSON INTERNATIONAL

503 N Highway 59 (56258-2765)
PO Box 410 (56258-0410)
PHONE...........................507 532-5718
FAX: 507 532-3126
Steven Hatlestad, *President*
Tom Fox, *Vice Pres*
Andy Hatlestad, *Manager*
EMP: 36
SQ FT: 14,000
SALES (est): 25MM-49.9MM **Privately Held**
WEB: www.olsonjohnson.com
SIC: 5012 5013 Wholesales commercial trucks; wholesales truck parts & accessories

(G-3319)

PRAIRIE DANCE ALLIANCE

408 N 5th St (56258-1122)
PO Box 83 (56258-0083)
PHONE...........................507 532-3195
Jenniser Danielson, *President*
Chad Kerr, *Vice Pres*
EMP: 25 EST: 1990
SALES (est): 500-999K **Privately Held**
WEB: www.prairiedancealliance.org
SIC: 7911 Dance studio, school & hall

(G-3320)

PRAIRIE PRIDE COOPERATIVE (PA)

1100 E Main St (56258-2505)
PHONE...........................507 532-9686
Al Steffes, *President*
Connie Doom, *Controller*
Jeff Meusburger, *Manager*
EMP: 25 EST: 1924
SQ FT: 35,000
SALES (corp-wide): 25M **Privately Held**
SIC: 5171 Gas station; wholesales petroleum bulk stations; retail independent convenience store; retails automotive accessories; retails automotive parts; retails bottled propane gas

(G-3321)

PRAIRIE RIVER HOME CARE INC

1411 E College Dr Ste 103 (56258-2086)
PHONE...........................507 532-2264
FAX: 507 532-6920
Clair Tettemer, *Branch Mgr*
Deb Bloome, *Branch Mgr*
Becky Bicknase, *Manager*
Lois Boerboom, *Manager*
Sherlyn Dahl, *Exec Dir*
EMP: 93
SALES (est): 1MM-4.9MM **Privately Held**
WEB: www.prhomecare.com
SIC: 8082 Home health care services
PA: Prairie River Home Care Inc
     4432 Highway 25 SE
     Buffalo MN 55313
     507 252-9844

(G-3322)

PRIVATE INDUSTRY COUNCIL

607 W Main St Fl 3 (56258-3021)
PHONE...........................507 537-6236
FAX: 507 537-6362
Juanita Lauritsen, *Director*
EMP: 25 EST: 1984 **Privately Held**
SIC: 7361 Employment agency services

(G-3323)

R & G CONSTRUCTION CO

2694 County Road 6 (56258-5496)
PHONE...........................507 537-1473
Reinhold Mathiowetz, *President*
Constance Mathiowetz, *Corp Secy*
Richard Schaeffer, *Corp Secy*
Greg Mathiowetz, *Vice Pres*
Rick Chaffer, *Office Mgr*
EMP: 50 EST: 1983
SQ FT: 5,000
SALES (est): 5MM-9.9MM **Privately Held**
SIC: 1611 1794 Grading services; excavating contractor

(G-3324)

REINHART FOODSERVICE LLC

702 Fairview St (56258-1180)
PHONE...........................507 537-1451
FAX: 507 537-1724
Marge Reinhart, *President*
Dave Lyon, *Opers Staff*
Myron Green, *Opers Staff*
Julie Geary, *Purch Dir*
Kevin Derynck, *Sales Staff*
EMP: 130
SALES (est): 100MM-499.9MM **Privately Held**
SIC: 5141 Wholesales general line groceries
PA: Reyes Holdings LLC
     9500 Bryn Mawr Ave # 700
     Rosemont IL 60018
     847 227-6500

(G-3325)

SCHWAN FOOD CO (PA)

115 W College Dr (56258-1747)
PHONE...........................507 532-3274
FAX: 507 537-8145
Bernadette Kruk, *President*
Greg Flack, *President*
Brad Botsford, *District Mgr*
John Beadle, *COO*
David Bunnell, *Exec VP*
◆ EMP: 2500 EST: 1956
SQ FT: 50,000 **Privately Held**
WEB: www.theschwanfoodcompany.com
SIC: 6159 Manufactures frozen pizza; manufactures frozen ice cream novelties; manufactures frozen ice milk novelties; manufactures frozen fruit juice concentrates; manufactures frozen ethnic foods; equipment & vehicle finance leasing service

(G-3326)

SCHWAN'S GLOBAL FOOD SERVICE

115 W College Dr (56258-1747)
PHONE...........................507 532-3274
Jim Clough, *President*
Brian Rademacher, *CFO*
▲ EMP: 140 EST: 2002
SALES (est): 25MM-49.9MM **Privately Held**
WEB: www.theschwanfoodcompany.com
SIC: 5142 5143 Manufactures frozen food products; manufactures frozen bakery pies; wholesales frozen dairy desserts; manufactures frozen desserts & novelties; wholesales packaged frozen foods
PA: Schwan Food Co
     115 W College Dr
     Marshall MN 56258
     507 532-3274

(G-3327)

SHOPKO STORES OPERATING CO LLC

1200 E Southview Dr (56258)
PHONE...........................507 532-3266
FAX: 507 537-9646
Mike Moore, *Branch Mgr*
EMP: 150
SALES (est): 10MM-24.9MM **Privately Held**
WEB: www.shopko.com
SIC: 8042 Discount department store; drug store; optometrists' office; retails optical goods
HQ: Shopko Stores Operating Co LLC
     700 Pilgrim Way
     Green Bay WI 54304
     920 429-2211

▲=Import ▼=Export
◆=Import/Export

(G-3328)
SOUTHWEST COACHES INC
2660 State Highway 23 (56258-5458)
PHONE 507 532-4043
FAX: 507 532-9398
Thomas Hey, *President*
Jim Hey, *Vice Pres*
Gary Willink, *Sales Staff*
EMP: 90 **EST:** 1945
SQ FT: 22,000
SALES (est): 5MM-9.9MM **Privately Held**
WEB: www.swcoaches.com
SIC: 4142 4141 4151 Long-distance bus
charter service; school bus service; local
bus charter service

(G-3329)
SOUTHWEST MN PIC
607 W Main St (56258-3021)
PHONE 507 537-6987
FAX: 507 537-6997
Winthro Block, *Chairman*
Juanita Lauritsen, *Director*
EMP: 40 **EST:** 1984
SALES (est): 1MM-4.9MM **Privately Held**
SIC: 8331 Community services employment
training program

(G-3330)
TURKEY VALLEY FARMS LLC
112 S 6th St (56258-3063)
PO Box 200 (56258-0200)
PHONE 507 337-3100
Richard A Peterson, *Member*
Tim Fruin, *Vice Pres*
Kenneth Wilson, *Human Res Mgr*
Mary Berger, *Manager*
Keith Burger, *Manager*
EMP: 350 **EST:** 2003 **Privately Held**
SIC: 0253 Turkey farm

(G-3331)
WEINER MEMORIAL FOUNDATION
1104 E College Dr (56258-4270)
PHONE 507 537-7070
Doris Derynck, *Director*
EMP: 40
SALES (est): 1MM-4.9MM **Privately Held**
SIC: 8082 5047 Home health care services;
wholesales medical equipment & supplies
PA: Weiner Memorial Foundation
300 N Bruce St Apt 1
Marshall MN 56258
507 532-9661

(G-3332)
WEINER MEMORIAL FOUNDATION (PA)
300 N Bruce St Apt 1 (56258-1526)
PHONE 507 532-9661
FAX: 507 537-9259
Bil Bumgarner, *President*
Sharon Williams, *Accountant*
EMP: 410 **EST:** 1944
SQ FT: 150,000
SALES (corp-wide): 43.31M **Privately Held**
SIC: 8051 7991 8062 8082 8322 Skilled
nursing care facility; senior citizen center;
home health care services; medical
hospital; physical fitness center

(G-3333)
WELLS FARGO BANK, NATIONAL
400 W Main St (56258-1315)
PHONE 507 532-4405
Rick Ramert, *Manager*
Stan Finnestad, *Manager*
EMP: 40
SALES (est): 10MM-24.9MM **Publicly Held**
SIC: 6021 National commercial bank
HQ: Wfc Holdings, Corp
420 Montgomery St
San Francisco CA 94104
415 396-7392

(G-3334)
WESTERN COMMUNITY ACTION INC (PA)
1400 S Saratoga St (56258-3114)
PHONE 507 537-1416
FAX: 507 537-1849

Cindy Cevaere, *Corp Secy*
Rachel Wolff, *Corp Secy*
Elenora Monsen, *Corp Secy*
Ginger Kaufman, *Corp Secy*
Jerome Bottelberghe, *Corp Secy*
EMP: 40 **EST:** 1965
SALES (corp-wide): 7.54M **Privately Held**
SIC: 8611 Community affairs & services

(G-3335)
WESTERN MENTAL HEALTH CENTER
1212 E College Dr (56258-2010)
PHONE 507 532-3236
Gloria Sabin, *Principal*
Melissa Louwgie, *Principal*
Jolene Henricksen, *Manager*
Tom Hobbs, *Exec Dir*
Sarah Ackerman, *Director*
EMP: 28 **EST:** 1960
SQ FT: 6,000
SALES (est): 1MM-4.9MM **Privately Held**
SIC: 8093 Outpatient mental health clinic

(G-3336)
ZIEGLER INC
1200 N Highway 59 (56258-2761)
PO Box 1064 (56258-0864)
PHONE 507 532-4403
FAX: 507 537-1519
Tom Larson, *Manager*
Fred Bern, *Manager*
Joe Stefanick, *Manager*
EMP: 29
SALES (est): 10MM-24.9MM **Privately Held**
SIC: 5082 Wholesales road construction &
maintenance machinery
PA: Ziegler Inc
901 W 94th St
Minneapolis MN 55420
952 888-4121

MAYNARD
Chippewa County

(G-3337)
THORSTAD CONSTRUCTION CO INC
467 Spicer Ave (56260)
PO Box 275 (56260-0275)
PHONE 320 367-2159
FAX: 320 367-2160
Larry A Bosch, *President*
Cornelius Beukhof, *Corp Secy*
Royal Ashburn, *Vice Pres*
Keith Levitz, *Vice Pres*
Bruce C Anderson, *Treasurer*
EMP: 30 **EST:** 1958
SQ FT: 16,000
SALES (est): 10MM-24.9MM **Privately Held**
WEB: www.thorstadconstruction.com
SIC: 5083 1542 Wholesales grain elevator
equipment & supplies; new commercial &
office building construction; farm building
construction

MCGREGOR
Aitkin County

(G-3338)
CAMP NEW HOPE INC
53035 Lake Ave (55760-4598)
PHONE 218 426-3560
Lori Czarneski, *Exec Dir*
EMP: 30 **EST:** 1968
SALES (est): 1MM-4.9MM **Privately Held**
SIC: 7032 Recreational & sporting camp

(G-3339)
EAST LAKE COMMUNITY CENTER
3666 State Hwy (55760)
PHONE 218 768-3311
FAX: 218 768-3903
Anita Misquadece, *Administrator*
EMP: 25 **Privately Held**
SIC: 8611 Community affairs & services

(G-3340)
RAVEILL TRUCKING INC
20982 State Highway 210 (55760-4710)
PO Box 10 (55760-0010)
PHONE 218 768-2701
Curt Raveill, *President*
Lisa Farley, *Manager*
EMP: 28 **EST:** 1983
SALES (est): 1MM-4.9MM **Privately Held**
SIC: 4213 Heavy hauling transportation
services

MCINTOSH
Polk County

(G-3341)
FOUNDATION FOR RURAL HEALTH
Also Called: McIntosh Manor Nursing Home
600 Riverside Ave NE (56556-5750)
PHONE 218 563-2715
FAX: 218 563-2300
Roger Miller, *President*
Nick Berg, *Administrator*
Shelley Solberg, *Administrator*
Faith Wilkens, *Director*
EMP: 100 **EST:** 1965
SALES (est): 1MM-4.9MM **Privately Held**
SIC: 8051 Convalescent home

(G-3342)
SENIOR MCINTOSH LIVING
175 N Broadway (56556)
PHONE 218 563-3043
Teresa Syverson, *Treasurer*
Steve Haaven, *Exec Dir*
EMP: 60
SALES (est): 1MM-4.9MM **Privately Held**
SIC: 8051 Skilled nursing care facility

MEDFORD
Steele County

(G-3343)
FABRICATED WOOD PRODUCTS INC
6150 W Frontage Rd (55049)
PO Box 59 (55049-0059)
PHONE 507 451-1019
FAX: 507 451-5103
Charles Spitzack, *Ch of Bd*
Pat Anderson, *President*
Bob Blezek, *Plant Supt*
Richard E Nielson, *Controller*
Dan Branstad, *Finance Mgr*
EMP: 25 **EST:** 1963
SQ FT: 40,000
SALES (est): 1MM-4.9MM **Privately Held**
SIC: 1521 1522 Manufactures wooden floor
trusses; new single-family home
construction service; new multi-family
dwelling construction service

(G-3344)
NILES - WIESE CONSTRUCTION CO
112 S Mn St (55049)
PO Box 419 (55049-0419)
PHONE 507 446-0825
FAX: 507 446-1114
Dan Niles, *President*
Gary Wiese, *Vice Pres*
EMP: 50 **EST:** 2001
SQ FT: 3,000
SALES (est): 5MM-9.9MM **Privately Held**
SIC: 1794 Excavation & grading, building
construction contractor

MELROSE
Stearns County

(G-3345)
CENTRACARE CLINIC
525 W Main St (56352-1043)
PHONE 320 256-4228
James Mohs MD, *President*

Julia Draxten, *Principal*
Carl Melling MD, *Vice Pres*
Sherri Lieble, *Office Mgr*
Dante C Beretta, *Manager*
EMP: 40 **EST:** 1972
SQ FT: 3,000
SALES (est): 1MM-4.9MM **Privately Held**
SIC: 8011 8042 Clinic operated by
physicians; optometrists' office

(G-3346)
CENTRACARE HEALTH SYSTEM
525 W Main St (56352-1043)
PHONE 320 256-4231
James R Davis, *President*
Vern Dingman, *Engineering*
Todd Stordahl, *CFO*
Anita Rademacher, *Marketing Staff*
Janet Kruzel, *Director*
EMP: 195 **EST:** 1997
SQ FT: 140,000
SALES (est): 10MM-24.9MM **Privately Held**
SIC: 8062 Medical hospital

(G-3347)
CENTRAL MINNESOTA FEDERAL (PA)
20 S 4th Ave E (56352-1356)
PO Box 160 (56352-0160)
PHONE 320 256-3669
FAX: 320 256-7686
Rick Odenthal, *CEO*
Bernard Brixius, *COO*
Dennis Waldvogel, *Vice Pres*
Karen Sunderman, *Vice Pres*
Michael Wehlage, *Ch Credit Ofcr*
EMP: 41 **EST:** 1939
SQ FT: 10,000
SALES (corp-wide): 35.32M **Privately Held**
SIC: 6062 State chartered credit union

(G-3348)
COMMERCIAL CONTRACTORS CO OF
Also Called: C C C I
631 S Central Ave (56352-1300)
PO Box 125 (56352-0125)
PHONE 320 256-7422
FAX: 320 256-7699
Jeremy Kraemer, *Owner*
Harry Kraemer, *General Mgr*
EMP: 26 **EST:** 1986
SQ FT: 2,500
SALES (est): 1MM-4.9MM **Privately Held**
SIC: 1771 1741 Flooring contractor;
masonry & stonework contractor

(G-3349)
MELROSE DIVERSICOM TELEPHONE
320 E Main St (56352-1164)
PO Box 100 (56352-0100)
PHONE 320 256-8288
Francis Monroe, *President*
Dean Mohs, *COO*
EMP: 30 **EST:** 2002
SALES (est): 500-999K **Privately Held**
SIC: 7349 Building cleaning & maintenance
services

(G-3350)
MELROSE METALWORKS INC
313 N 8th Ave W (56352-1263)
PO Box 157 (56352-0157)
PHONE 320 256-4170
FAX: 320 256-4175
Scott Kramer, *President*
Troy Dragt, *Engineer*
EMP: 28 **EST:** 1998
SQ FT: 21,000
SALES (est): 10MM-24.9MM **Privately Held**
SIC: 5084 Wholesales industrial metal
refining machinery & equipment

(G-3351)
MELROSE-ALBANY-UPSULA
222 County Road 173 (56352-1602)
PHONE 320 256-4252
Neal Womack, *Principal*
Gerald Lake, *Principal*
Tom Bush, *Principal*
David Thomsche DVM, *Principal*
EMP: 30 **EST:** 1993
SQ FT: 10,000 **Privately Held**
SIC: 0742 Animal hospital services

(PA)=Parent Co (HQ)=Headquarters (DH)=Div Headquarters
✿ = New business established in last 2 years

2011 Harris Minnesota
Services Directory

© Harris InfoSource 1-866-281-6415

153

(G-3352)
STEARNS COOPERATIVE ELECTRIC
900 E Kraft Dr　(56352-1455)
PO Box 40　(56352-0040)
PHONE.............................320 256-4241
FAX: 320 256-3618
Rick Banke, *President*
William Banke, *General Mgr*
Dave Gruenes, *District Mgr*
Arnold Blommel, *Corp Secy*
Gerald Blaine, *Vice Pres*
EMP: 54 EST: 1937
SQ FT: 21,000
SALES (est): 25MM-49.9MM **Privately Held**
WEB: www.stearnselectric.org
SIC: **4911** Electric power distribution service

(G-3353)
STEARNS VETERINARY OUTLET
222 County Road 173　(56352-1602)
PO Box 219　(56352-0219)
PHONE.............................320 256-3303
FAX: 320 256-4014
David Tomsche, *President*
Dick Peifer, *General Mgr*
Daniel Tomsche, *Vice Pres*
Ruth Weitzel, *Marketing Staff*
Charee Pelzer, *Manager*
EMP: 40 EST: 1994
SQ FT: 6,000
SALES (est): 10MM-24.9MM **Privately Held**
WEB: www.stearnsvetoutlet.com
SIC: **5083** 5047 Wholesales dairy machinery & equipment; wholesales veterinarians' equipment & supplies

MENAHGA
Wadena County

(G-3354)
BLUEBERRY PINES GOLF CLUB
39161 US 71　(56464-3228)
PHONE.............................218 564-4657
Curtis Maaf, *Owner*
Dan Miller, *Manager*
EMP: 30 EST: 1991
SALES (est): 1MM-4.9MM **Privately Held**
SIC: **7992** Public golf course

(G-3355)
BLUEBERRY PINES GOLF CLUB INC
39161 US 71　(56464-3228)
PHONE.............................218 564-4653
Wes Renneberg, *CEO*
Arvid Welman, *Chairman*
Lambert Rennaberg, *Corp Secy*
Robert Larson, *Corp Secy*
Dan Miller, *COO*
EMP: 40 EST: 1990
SQ FT: 15,000
SALES (est): 1MM-4.9MM **Privately Held**
SIC: **7997** Membership golf club

(G-3356)
CITY OF MENAHGA
Also Called: Green Pine Acres Nursing Home
427 Main St NE　(56464-8702)
PHONE.............................218 564-4101
FAX: 218 564-5309
Becky Selander, *Bookkeeper*
Clair Erickson, *Manager*
EMP: 100
SALES (est): 1MM-4.9MM **Privately Held**
SIC: **8051** 8322 Convalescent home; adult daycare center
PA: City of Menahga
　　115 2nd St NE
　　Menahga MN 56464
　　218 564-4557

(G-3357)
COOPERATIVE SAMPO INC (PA)
14 Birch Ave SE　(56464)
PO Box 220　(56464-0220)
PHONE.............................218 564-4534
Douglas Koskiniemi, *Chairman*
Dale Hillukka, *Treasurer*
EMP: 68

EST: 1903
SQ FT: 5,000 **Privately Held**
SIC: **5191** 5172 Wholesales animal feeds; retail independent grocery store; wholesales petroleum products

(G-3358)
KOCH INDUSTRIES INC
10632 110th St　(56464)
PHONE.............................218 564-4495
Scott Nier, *Manager*
EMP: 80
SALES (est): 25MM-49.9MM **Privately Held**
WEB: www.kochind.com
SIC: **4612** Crude petroleum pipeline
PA: Koch Industries Inc
　　4111 E 37th St N
　　Wichita KS 67220
　　316 828-5500

(G-3359)
RENNEBERG HARDWOODS INC (PA)
11773 State Highway 87　(56464-2166)
PO Box 188　(56464-0188)
PHONE.............................218 564-4912
FAX: 218 564-5360
Wesley Renneberg, *President*
Jeff Reinhart, *Opers Staff*
Lynn Litzau, *Services*
EMP: 60 EST: 1968
SQ FT: 1,000
SALES (corp-wide): 20M **Privately Held**
WEB: www.thebestwood.com
SIC: **5031** Wholesales rough, dressed & finished lumber

MENDOTA HEIGHTS
Dakota County

(G-3360)
AVIALL SERVICES INC
1355 Mendota Heights Rd　(55120-1199)
PHONE.............................651 452-1680
Duane Larsen, *Branch Mgr*
EMP: 25
SALES (est): 10MM-24.9MM **Publicly Held**
WEB: www.aviall.com
SIC: **5088** Wholesales aircraft equipment & supplies
DH: Aviall Services Inc
　　2750 Regent Blvd
　　Dallas TX 75261
　　972 586-1000

(G-3361)
BITUMINOUS ROADWAYS INC (PA)
1520 Commerce Dr　(55120-1023)
PHONE.............................651 686-7001
Kent Peterson, *President*
John Kittleson, *Corp Secy*
Tom Haller, *Vice Pres*
Sherry Ringberg, *Treasurer*
David Peterson, *CIO*
EMP: 30 EST: 1946
SQ FT: 3,500 **Privately Held**
WEB: www.bitroads.com
SIC: **1611** Manufactures asphalt coatings & sealers; street surfacing & paving construction; manufactures bituminous road materials

(G-3362)
DAKOTA'S ADULTS INC
2031 Victoria Rd S　(55118-4163)
PHONE.............................651 688-8808
Paula Hart, *CEO*
EMP: 34
SALES (est): 1MM-4.9MM **Privately Held**
SIC: **8052** Intermediate care facility

(G-3363)
G P CO'S INC
Also Called: General Pump
1174 Northland Dr　(55120-1167)
PHONE.............................651 454-6500
FAX: 651 454-8015
William Brown, *President*
Scott Grossmann, *Materials Mgr*
Kristin Sanders, *CFO*
Troy Benike, *Marketing Mgr*
Marc Palecek, *Manager*

▲ EMP: 55 EST: 1982
SQ FT: 36,000
SALES (est): 10MM-24.9MM **Privately Held**
WEB: www.eaglepower.com
SIC: **5084** 5087 Wholesales industrial water pumps; wholesales cleaning & maintenance equipment & supplies; manufactures pumps & pumping equipment; manufactures screw machine products

(G-3364)
HEALTHSENSE INC
1191 Northland Dr Ste 100　(55120-1391)
PHONE.............................952 400-7300
Brian J Bischoff, *President*
Bryan W Fuhr, *Vice Pres*
Dan Vatland, *Vice Pres*
Terry Barck, *CFO*
Julie Bischoff, *Manager*
EMP: 25 EST: 2001
SQ FT: 12,000
SALES (est): 1MM-4.9MM **Privately Held**
WEB: www.healthsense.com
SIC: **8742** New products & services consultants

(G-3365)
KENDELL DOORS & HARDWARE INC
2425 Entp Dr Ste 100　(55120)
PHONE.............................651 905-0144
Daniel Zajac, *CFO*
Robert Katter, *Manager*
EMP: 60
SALES (est): 25MM-49.9MM **Privately Held**
SIC: **5072** 5031 Wholesales hardware; wholesales door frames constructed of all materials; wholesales metal doors, sash & trim; wholesales doors & windows
PA: Kendell Doors & Hardware Inc
　　222 E 2nd St
　　Winona MN 55987
　　507 454-1723

(G-3366)
LASER PRINTING TECHNOLOGIES　(PA)
2500 Lexington Ave S　(55120-1260)
PHONE.............................952 888-7375
Sean Carey, *President*
Brad Huda, *Sales Staff*
Camelia Carey, *Manager*
Marshall Swanson, *Info Tech Dir*
EMP: 58 EST: 1987
SQ FT: 20,000
SALES (corp-wide): 19.25M **Privately Held**
SIC: **5044** 7379 Retails computer printers & plotters; computer system consulting services; wholesales office equipment

(G-3367)
MN AIRLINES LLC
Also Called: Sun Country Airlines
1300 Mendota Heights Rd　(55120-1128)
PHONE.............................651 681-3900
FAX: 651 681-3970
John S Fredericksen, *Member*
Stan Gadek, *Member*
Dave Banmiller, *COO*
Jim Olsen, *COO*
Spellman Steve, *COO*
EMP: 650 EST: 2002
SQ FT: 35,000
SALES (est): 100MM-499.9MM **Privately Held**
SIC: **4512** Air freight service; passenger airline services
PA: MN Airline Holdings Inc
　　1300 Mendota Heights Rd
　　Saint Paul MN 55120
　　651 681-3900

(G-3368)
NORTHWESTERN MUTUAL LIFE
1191 Northland Dr　(55120-1390)
PO Box 21309, Saint Paul　(55121-0309)
PHONE.............................651 456-9446
FAX: 651 456-0906
Edward J Zore, *CEO*
Thomas Guay, *Vice Pres*
Julie Dulack, *Opers Mgr*
Michael G Carter, *CFO*
Emmett Wright, *Ch Invest Ofcr*
EMP: 50 EST: 1998
SALES (est): 5MM-9.9MM **Privately Held**
SIC: **6411** Insurance services

(G-3369)
R J RYAN CONSTRUCTION INC
1100 Mendota Heights Rd　(55120-1224)
PHONE.............................651 681-0200
FAX: 651 681-0235
Tom Ryan, *President*
Ashley Brown, *Manager*
EMP: 33 EST: 1978
SQ FT: 10,000
SALES (est): 5MM-9.9MM **Privately Held**
WEB: www.rjryan.com
SIC: **1541** 1542 New industrial building construction; new commercial & office building construction

(G-3370)
RICOH AMERICAS CORP
1110 Cntr Pointe Cur 10　(55120)
PHONE.............................651 294-2600
FAX: 651 294-2660
Ivan Franklin, *Manager*
EMP: 75
SALES (est): 10MM-24.9MM **Privately Held**
WEB: www.ricoh-usa.com
SIC: **5044** 5065 5112 7359 Wholesales photocopy machines; wholesales photocopy supplies; wholesales facsimile or fax equipment; wholesales office supplies; retails office forms & supplies; retails business machines & equipment; retails photocopy machines
PA: Ricoh Americas Corp
　　5 Dedrick Pl
　　West Caldwell NJ 07006
　　973 882-2000

(G-3371)
TAJ TECHNOLOGIES INC
1168 Northland Dr　(55120-1167)
PHONE.............................651 405-7412
FAX: 651 688-8321
K C Sukumar, *President*
Amit Kakatkar, *Project Mgr*
David Yunker, *Opers Staff*
Jeff Monsaas, *CFO*
Lauren Alson, *Controller*
EMP: 95 EST: 1987
SQ FT: 13,000
SALES (est): 10MM-24.9MM **Privately Held**
WEB: www.tajtech.com
SIC: **7373** 7379 Systems software development service; systems integration service; computer system consulting services

MERRIFIELD
Crow Wing County

(G-3372)
WES HANSON BUILDERS INC
13645 N Horseshoe Lake Rd　(56465-4394)
PHONE.............................218 765-4122
FAX: 218 765-3662
Wesley A Hanson, *President*
Marilyn Hanson, *Vice Pres*
EMP: 30 EST: 1985
SALES (est): 5MM-9.9MM **Privately Held**
SIC: **1522** Residential construction

MILACA
Isanti County

(G-3373)
KREGER FARMS INC
40412 Tiger St NW　(56353-4262)
PO Box 59, Pease　(56363-0059)
PHONE.............................320 983-5060
Lawrence Kreger, *President*
EMP: 27 EST: 1994
SQ FT: 4,000 **Privately Held**
SIC: **0115** 0116 Corn farm; soybean farm

▲=Import ▼=Export
◆=Import/Export

G E O G R A P H I C

MILACA
Mille Lacs County

(G-3374)
CENTRAL MINNESOTA DIAGNOSTIC
150 10th St NW (56353-1737)
PO Box 158 (56353-0158)
PHONE..........................320 983-6300
Glenn Erickson, *President*
EMP: 50 **EST:** 1985
SQ FT: 500
SALES (est): 5MM-9.9MM **Privately Held**
SIC: 8071 Testing laboratory

(G-3375)
CHAMBER TRILL PUBLIC TRANSIT
535 8th St NE (56353-1810)
PO Box 7 (56353-0007)
PHONE..........................320 983-5064
Helen Piper, *Director*
EMP: 30 **EST:** 1978
SALES (est): 1MM-4.9MM **Privately Held**
SIC: 4789 Transportation services

(G-3376)
EVANGELICAL FREE CHURCH OF
Also Called: Elim Nursing Home
730 2nd St SE (56353-1307)
PO Box 157 (56353-0157)
PHONE..........................320 983-2185
FAX: 320 983-2190
Laura Broberg, *Vice Pres*
Terri Puffer, *Manager*
Jay Rensenbrink, *Manager*
Jay Rensencrink, *Administrator*
Judy Terhaar, *Asst Director*
EMP: 170
SALES (est): 5MM-9.9MM **Privately Held**
SIC: 8059 8051 Convalescent home; skilled nursing care facility

(G-3377)
FIRST NATIONAL BANK OF MILACA
190 2nd Ave SW (56353-1106)
PO Box 38 (56353-0038)
PHONE..........................320 983-3101
FAX: 320 983-2579
B P Allen Jr, *CEO*
Donald Fox, *President*
Douglas Brink, *President*
Sandra Westling, *Assistant VP*
Barbara Jedicki, *Vice Pres*
EMP: 32 **EST:** 1897
SQ FT: 5,000
SALES (est): 5MM-9.9MM **Privately Held**
WEB: www.fnbmilaca.com
SIC: 6021 National commercial bank

(G-3378)
JOHNSON, CARL E PLUMBING
Also Called: Johnson Carl E Mechanical
12724 160th St (56353-3318)
PO Box 26 (56353-0026)
PHONE..........................320 983-2171
FAX: 320 983-2172
Terry Johnson, *President*
Mary Vanheel, *Bookkeeper*
Mary Fanheel, *Bookkeeper*
EMP: 30 **EST:** 1946
SQ FT: 8,400
SALES (est): 1MM-4.9MM **Privately Held**
WEB: www.carlejohnson.com
SIC: 1711 Process piping contractor; plumbing service

(G-3379)
JOY US CARES
7219 140th St (56353-4633)
PHONE..........................320 983-5708
Joy Klanderude, *Owner*
EMP: 50 **EST:** 1993
SALES (est): 1MM-4.9MM **Privately Held**
SIC: 8082 Home health care services

(G-3380)
MILLE LACS CTY AREA
Also Called: D A C
1st St E (56353)
PO Box 92 (56353-0092)
PHONE..........................320 983-2162
FAX: 320 983-2163
Frederic Hoffman, *Director*
Kety Vesolkmith, *Admin Asst*
EMP: 29 **EST:** 1970
SALES (est): 1MM-4.9MM **Privately Held**
SIC: 8331 Vocational training agency; skill training center; vocational rehabilitation agency

---

MILTONA
Douglas County

(G-3381)
R & R READY MIX INC
13947 State Highway 29 N (56354-8126)
PO Box 197 (56354-0197)
PHONE..........................218 943-4601
FAX: 218 943-5138
David O Luedeke, *President*
Marcia Luedeke, *Corp Secy*
Paul Leudeke, *Vice Pres*
EMP: 28 **EST:** 1964
SALES (est): 1MM-4.9MM **Privately Held**
SIC: 1442 Construction sand & gravel mining; manufactures ready-mixed concrete

---

MINNEAPOLIS
Anoka County

(G-3382)
A & C METALS-SAWING INC
9170 Davenport St NE (55449-4346)
PHONE..........................763 786-1048
FAX: 763 786-2949
David J Girk, *President*
Dan Huseby, *General Mgr*
Jeff Jensen, *Plant Mgr*
Gail Dornbusch, *Purch Mgr*
Joy Dainty, *Manager*
EMP: 38 **EST:** 1982
SQ FT: 37,000
SALES (est): 25MM-49.9MM **Privately Held**
WEB: www.acmetals.com
SIC: 5051 7389 Metal service center; metal cutting service

(G-3383)
A-VEDA CORP (HQ)
Also Called: Aveda Experience Centres
4000 Pheasant Ridge Dr NE (55449-7101)
PHONE..........................763 951-4000
FAX: 763 783-4110
Dominique Consiel, *President*
Sara Moss, *Corp Secy*
Jim Pavlakis, *Vice Pres*
Tom Petrillo, *Vice Pres*
Bob Salem, *Vice Pres*
▲ **EMP:** 300 **EST:** 1965
SQ FT: 275,000
SALES (corp-wide): 7.79B **Publicly Held**
WEB: www.aveda.com
SIC: 7231 Manufactures hair shampoos, rinses & conditioners; manufactures natural or synthetic perfumes; manufactures face creams or lotions; manufactures lipsticks; cosmetology school
PA: Estee Lauder Co's Inc
767 5th Ave Fl 36
New York NY 10153
212 572-4200

(G-3384)
ABRASIVE SPECIALISTS INC
7521 Commerce Ln NE (55432-3123)
PHONE..........................763 571-4111
FAX: 763 571-5026
Dennis L Olsen, *President*
Stacie Tate, *Manager*
Joyce Cargor, *Government Rel*
EMP: 30 **EST:** 1976
SQ FT: 15,000
SALES (est): 10MM-24.9MM **Privately Held**
SIC: 5085 Wholesales industrial tools

(G-3385)
ADMINISTRATION RESOURCES CORP
11490 Zeon St NW Ste 200 (55448)
PO Box 367, Anoka (55303-0367)
PHONE..........................763 421-5510
FAX: 763 421-7628
Ardy Prekker, *President*
Marc Mosiman, *Vice Pres*
EMP: 43 **EST:** 1998
SQ FT: 11,000
SALES (est): 5MM-9.9MM **Privately Held**
SIC: 8748 Employee programs administration consultant
PA: Optum Health
11490 Xeon St NW Ste 200
Minneapolis MN 55448
763 421-5510

(G-3386)
ADT SECURITY SERVICES INC
5910 Rice Crk 700 (55432)
PHONE..........................651 917-0010
Tony Kukuk, *General Mgr*
EMP: 140
SALES (est): 5MM-9.9MM **Privately Held**
WEB: www.adt.com
SIC: 7382 Burglar alarm maintenance & monitoring service
DH: ADT Security Services Inc
1 Town Center Rd
Boca Raton FL 33486
561 988-3600

(G-3387)
AID ELECTRIC CORP
1622 93rd Ln NE (55449-4313)
PHONE..........................763 571-7267
Brian Kovar, *President*
Jesse Skluzacek, *CFO*
Stepanie Hansen, *Manager*
Lisa Clark, *Manager*
EMP: 37 **EST:** 1979
SQ FT: 5,000
SALES (est): 1MM-4.9MM **Privately Held**
WEB: www.aidelectriccorp.com
SIC: 1731 Electrical contractor

(G-3388)
ALEXANDRA HOUSE INC
10065 3rd St NE (55434-1534)
PO Box 490039 (55449-0039)
PHONE..........................763 780-2332
FAX: 763 780-9696
Connie Moore, *Exec Dir*
Margaret Andersen, *Director*
Jenny Haider, *Bd of Directors*
Jenny Green, *Bd of Directors*
EMP: 46 **EST:** 1977 **Privately Held**
WEB: www.alexandrahouse.org
SIC: 8399 8322 Social change association; individual & family social services

(G-3389)
ALL AMERICAN TITLE CO INC
9298 Central Ave NE # 102 (55434-4205)
PHONE..........................763 225-8710
Kevin Webb, *President*
Dave Buelow, *Vice Pres*
EMP: 42
SALES (est): 5MM-9.9MM **Privately Held**
SIC: 6361 Title insurance carrier

(G-3390)
ALL-DATA INC
5400 Main St NE Ste 201 (55421-1132)
PHONE..........................763 571-5719
John C Holman, *CEO*
Susan Holman-Sutich, *Exec VP*
Susan Sutch, *Vice Pres*
Jon Anderson, *Opers Mgr*
Margaret Siluk, *Controller*
EMP: 45 **EST:** 1991
SQ FT: 50,000
SALES (est): 1MM-4.9MM **Privately Held**
SIC: 7389 Document storage service

(G-3391)
ALLEGIS CORP (PA)
8001 Central Ave NE (55432-2110)
PO Box 490007 (55449-0007)
PHONE..........................763 780-4333
Richard F Keister, *President*

Jeff England, *Sales Mgr*
▲ **EMP:** 32 **EST:** 1969
SQ FT: 20,000 **Privately Held**
WEB: www.allegiscorp.com
SIC: 5072 Wholesales hardware

(G-3392)
ALLINA HEALTH SYSTEM
Also Called: Coon Rapids Womens Health Ctr
3960 Coon Rapids Blvd NW (55433-2569)
PHONE..........................763 236-9236
Connie Skeate, *Office Mgr*
Suzette Christensen, *Office Mgr*
Derek B Simonsmd MD, *Med Doctor*
Michelle Lindman-Miller, *Obstetrician*
Casey Sprague, *Obstetrician*
EMP: 60
SALES (est): 5MM-9.9MM **Privately Held**
WEB: www.allina.com
SIC: 8011 Clinic operated by physicians
PA: Allina Health System
2925 Chicago Ave
Minneapolis MN 55407
612 775-5000

(G-3393)
ALLINA HEALTH SYSTEM
Also Called: Mercy Hospital
4050 Coon Rapids Blvd NW (55433-2522)
PHONE..........................763 236-6000
FAX: 763 422-4689
Ric Magnuson, *Vice Pres*
Dennis O'Hare, *Vice Pres*
Cheryl Vogel, *Vice Pres*
Brandi Lunnebord, *VP Opers-Prdtn-*
Christine Southbloom, *Purchasing*
EMP: 1200
SALES (est): 100MM-499.9MM **Privately Held**
WEB: www.allina.com
SIC: 8062 Medical hospital
PA: Allina Health System
2925 Chicago Ave
Minneapolis MN 55407
612 775-5000

(G-3394)
ALLINA HEALTH SYSTEM
9055 Springbrook Dr NW (55433-5841)
PHONE..........................763 780-9155
FAX: 763 783-6054
Duncan P Gallagher, *CFO*
Angela Dee-Ellingson, *Phys Therapist*
Jennifer Yeaton, *Phys Therapist*
Matthew Grigal, *Phys Therapist*
Kari Nelson, *Phys Therapist*

SQ FT: 87,108 **Privately Held**
WEB: www.allina.com
SIC: 8011 Clinic operated by physicians
PA: Allina Health System
2925 Chicago Ave
Minneapolis MN 55407
612 775-5000

(G-3395)
ALLINA HEALTH SYSTEM
500 Osborne Rd NE Ste 200 (55432-2768)
PHONE..........................763 786-6011
FAX: 763 786-7935
Pam Botner, *Business Mgr*
Sue Hauge, *Office Mgr*
Karen Hayes, *Office Mgr*
Carren Haynes, *Branch Mgr*
Pamela J Green, *Obstetrician*
EMP: 30
SALES (est): 1MM-4.9MM **Privately Held**
WEB: www.allina.com
SIC: 8011 Medical center; obstetrician office
PA: Allina Health System
2925 Chicago Ave
Minneapolis MN 55407
612 775-5000

(G-3396)
ALLTEMP DISTRIBUTION CO
5400 Main St NE Ste 101A (55421-1131)
PHONE..........................763 571-0215
FAX: 763 571-0523
John Holman, *President*
EMP: 45 **EST:** 1985
SQ FT: 425,000
SALES (est): 1MM-4.9MM **Privately Held**

SIC: 4225 4222 4731 Warehousing & storage services; cold storage or refrigerated warehousing; truck transportation brokers

(G-3397)
ALTERRA HEALTHCARE CORP
Also Called: Sterling House of Blaine
1005 Paul Pkwy NE (55434-3926)
PHONE..............................763 755-2800
FAX: 763 755-6400
Dana Sexton, *Mktg Dir*
David Jislason, *Manager*
Andrea Schrotke, *Director*
EMP: 25
SALES (est): 500-999K **Publicly Held**
WEB: www.assisted.com
SIC: 8059 Retirement community with nursing
DH: Alterra Healthcare Corp
10000 W Innovation Dr
Milwaukee WI 53226
414 918-5000

(G-3398)
AMERICAN LEGION CLUB 334 INC
Also Called: Coon Rapids Legion Post 334
11640 Crooked Lk Blvd NW (55433-2828)
PHONE..............................763 421-6260
FAX: 763 421-4719
Roger Ruth, *Principal*
Dawn Jabhan, *Corp Secy*
Dave Childs, *Manager*
EMP: 50 EST: 1959
SQ FT: 3,000 **Privately Held**
SIC: 8641 Veterans' organization

(G-3399)
AMERICAN MASONRY RESTORATION
7701 E River Rd (55432-2458)
PHONE..............................763 502-1400
FAX: 763 502-1300
Mike G Hart, *President*
EMP: 35 EST: 1994
SALES (est): 1MM-4.9MM **Privately Held**
WEB: www.americanmasonry.net
SIC: 1741 Masonry & stonework contractor

(G-3400)
AMERICAN PRECLINICAL SERVICES
8945 Evergreen Blvd NW (55433-6043)
PHONE..............................763 717-7990
FAX: 763 784-4810
Pam Conforti, *Member*
EMP: 45 EST: 2005
SQ FT: 43,750 **Privately Held**
SIC: 8731 Commercial medical research services

(G-3401)
AMERICAN WINGS AIR MUSEUM
2141 Rhode Island Ave (55449)
PO Box 490322 (55449-0322)
PHONE..............................763 786-4146
Leonard Bergers, *Director*
EMP: 40
SALES (est): 1MM-4.9MM **Privately Held**
WEB: www.americanwings.org
SIC: 8412 Museum

(G-3402)
AMF BOWLING CENTERS INC
6310 Highway 65 NE (55432-5120)
PHONE..............................763 571-3520
FAX: 763 571-1298
Dave Langer, *Manager*
EMP: 40
SALES (est): 1MM-4.9MM **Privately Held**
WEB: www.kidsports.org
SIC: 7933 Bowling center; cocktail lounge
HQ: AMF Bowling Centers Inc
7313 Bell Creek Rd
Mechanicsville VA 23111
804 417-2008

(G-3403)
ANOKA COUNTY COMMUNITY ACTION
1201 89th Ave NE Ste 345 (55434-3373)
PHONE..............................763 783-4747
Patrick McFarland, *Director*
George Steiner, *Bd of Directors*
Shirley Rolling, *Bd of Directors*
Jill Brown, *Bd of Directors*
EMP: 38 EST: 1965 **Privately Held**
SIC: 8399 Social change association

(G-3404)
ANOKA COUNTY COMMUNITY ACTION
Also Called: Senior Outreach Program
1201 89th Ave NE Ste 345 (55434-3373)
PHONE..............................763 783-4747
Nancy Hendrickson, *General Mgr*
Cherie Hanson, *Corp Secy*
Melissa Daniels, *Corp Secy*
Susan Dennistoun, *Manager*
Jill Sadler, *Manager*
EMP: 220 EST: 1965
SQ FT: 10,000
SALES (est): 10MM-24.9MM **Privately Held**
SIC: 8322 Social services center

(G-3405)
ANOKA COUNTY TRAVELER
2180 108th Ln NE (55449-5246)
PHONE..............................763 323-5222
David Keller, *Manager*
EMP: 50 EST: 2001
SALES (est): 1MM-4.9MM **Privately Held**
SIC: 4131 Bus transit system

(G-3406)
APG CASH DRAWER LLC ✪
5250 Industrial Blvd NE (55421-1012)
PHONE..............................763 571-5000
FAX: 763 571-5771
Mark J Olson, *President*
John Meilahn, *Vice Pres*
Dale Dahlbert, *VP Opers*
Sheila Weber, *Materials Mgr*
Todd Polzin, *Controller*
EMP: 95 EST: 2008
SALES (est): 10MM-24.9MM **Privately Held**
SIC: 7389 Commercial & industrial design service

(G-3407)
APPLE TREE DENTAL
8960 Springbrook Dr NW # 150 (55433-5810)
PHONE..............................763 784-7570
FAX: 763 784-5978
Michael Helgeson DDS, *President*
Thy P Lu, *Manager*
Brenda Marks, *Info Tech Mgr*
Carl Ebert, *Exec Dir*
Jean Drexler, *Exec Dir*
EMP: 40 EST: 1985
SQ FT: 11,700
SALES (est): 1MM-4.9MM **Privately Held**
WEB: www.appletreedental.com
SIC: 8021 Dental practitioners specialist office

(G-3408)
ARAMARK UNIFORM & CAREER
5330 Industrial Blvd NE (55421-1013)
PHONE..............................763 586-0020
FAX: 763 586-1199
Bill Muskee, *General Mgr*
Scott Simmons, *Manager*
Glen Moore, *Manager*
Laura Erickson, *Manager*
EMP: 120
SQ FT: 69,757
SALES (est): 5MM-9.9MM **Privately Held**
WEB: www.aramark-uniform.com
SIC: 7218 7213 Industrial laundry service; uniform supply service
HQ: ARAMARK Uniform & Career
115 N 1st St Ste 203
Burbank CA 91502
818 973-3700

(G-3409)
ARNAGE SECURITY SERVICES LLC ✪
12527 Ctrl Ave NE Ste 312 (55434-4861)
PHONE..............................763 269-8440
Sara Gordon, *Member*
Cheryl Hollman, *Human Res Mgr*
EMP: 99 EST: 2010
SALES (est): 1MM-4.9MM **Privately Held**
SIC: 7381 Security guard service

(G-3410)
ARROW SPRINKLER INC
1011 Osborne Rd NE (55432-2850)
PHONE..............................763 780-2800
FAX: 763 780-2858
John Smoluch, *President*
EMP: 50 EST: 1978
SQ FT: 20,000
SALES (est): 5MM-9.9MM **Privately Held**
SIC: 1711 Fire sprinkler system installation service

(G-3411)
ASSOCIATED SKIN CARE
Also Called: Associted Skin Care Spclists
7205 University Ave NE (55432-3134)
PHONE..............................763 571-4000
FAX: 763 786-5213
Steven Prawer MD, *President*
Frederick Fish MD, *Principal*
Ngo T Hien MD, *Principal*
Harry I Katz MD, *Principal*
Steven Kempers MD, *Principal*
EMP: 50 EST: 1973
SQ FT: 12,000
SALES (est): 5MM-9.9MM **Privately Held**
WEB: www.associatedskincare.com
SIC: 8011 Dermatologist office

(G-3412)
ASSOCIATES PLUS INC
Also Called: Re Max
299 Coon Rapids Blvd NW NW201 (55433-5832)
PHONE..............................763 784-1400
Jane Pithers, *Manager*
Robin Lee, *Manager*
Sheldon Berquist, *Manager*
Dennis Anderson, *Manager*
Chas Campbell, *IT/INT Sup*
EMP: 100
SALES (est): 10MM-24.9MM **Privately Held**
WEB: www.stenvig.com
SIC: 6531 Residential real estate agency
PA: Associates Plus Inc
480 Highway 96 W Ste 200
Saint Paul MN 55126
651 484-8800

(G-3413)
BABCOCK, NEILSON, MANNELLA, LA
408 Northdale Blvd NW (55448-3364)
PHONE..............................763 421-5151
Gary T La Fleur, *Partner*
Thomas A Klint, *Partner*
Jim Neilson, *Partner*
Felix Manella, *Partner*
Robert F Mannella, *Partner*
EMP: 30 EST: 1950
SALES (est): 1MM-4.9MM **Privately Held**
WEB: www.matthewanderson.com
SIC: 8111 General practice attorney's or lawyer's office

(G-3414)
BALLY TOTAL FITNESS CORP
7200 University Ave NE (55432-3170)
PHONE..............................763 574-8888
FAX: 763 574-9821
Sebastian Galindo, *General Mgr*
Kevin Niksic, *Manager*
Addison Johnston, *Manager*
John Kohler, *Manager*
David McWilliams, *Manager*
EMP: 40
SALES (est): 1MM-4.9MM **Publicly Held**
WEB: www.ballyfitnes.com
SIC: 7991 Health club
HQ: Bally Total Fitness Corp
12440 Imperial Hwy # 300
Norwalk CA 90650
562 484-2000

(G-3415)
BARNA GUZY & STEFFEN LTD
400 N Town Fincl Plz 200 (55433)
PHONE..............................763 780-8500
Jeffrey Johnson, *President*
Darell Jensen, *Principal*
Joan M Quade, *Member*
Steven Thorson, *Member*
William Huefner, *Manager*
EMP: 74 EST: 1938
SQ FT: 17,000
SALES (est): 10MM-24.9MM **Privately Held**
SIC: 8111 General practice law office

(G-3416)
BIFF'S BILLIARDS SPORTS BAR
7777 Highway 65 NE (55432-2851)
PHONE..............................763 784-9446
FAX: 763 784-9257
Bob Mullan, *President*
Tom Obert, *Owner*
Mary K Obert, *Vice Pres*
EMP: 50 EST: 1989
SALES (est): 1MM-4.9MM **Privately Held**
SIC: 7999 Limited service grill restaurant; billiard parlor; bar

(G-3417)
BIO-MEDICAL APPLICATIONS OF MN
Also Called: North Suburban Dialysis Center
9144 Springbrook Dr NW (55433-5847)
PHONE..............................763 783-0103
FAX: 763 783-0234
Jim Barsanti, *Manager*
EMP: 29
SALES (est): 1MM-4.9MM **Privately Held**
WEB: www.fmcna.com
SIC: 8092 Kidney dialysis center
PA: Fresenius Medical Care
920 Winter St Ste A
Waltham MA 02451
781 699-9000

(G-3418)
BIZAL MFG INC
7880 Ranchers Rd NE (55432-2522)
PHONE..............................763 571-4030
FAX: 763 571-1467
Michael S Bizal, *President*
Michelle Klemz, *Corp Secy*
Ruth Bizal, *Treasurer*
Pete Magnolo, *Manager*
Bizal Micheal, *CIO*
EMP: 38 EST: 1965
SQ FT: 32,000
SALES (est): 1MM-4.9MM **Privately Held**
WEB: www.bizalmfg.com
SIC: 7692 Machine shop, jobbing & repair services; welding service

(G-3419)
BLAINBROOK ENTERTAINMENT CTR
12000 Central Ave NE (55434-3912)
PHONE..............................763 755-8686
FAX: 763 755-8731
Douglas Thorp, *President*
Don May, *Vice Pres*
EMP: 75 EST: 1976
SALES (est): 1MM-4.9MM **Privately Held**
SIC: 7933 6512 Ten pin center; limited service snack bar; operators of auditoriums & halls

(G-3420)
BLAKE DRILLING CO INC
10604 Radisson Rd NE (55449-5220)
PHONE..............................763 780-9187
FAX: 763 780-8087
Willard R Blake, *President*
Julie Rumreich, *Finance*
EMP: 31 EST: 1965
SQ FT: 7,200
SALES (est): 1MM-4.9MM **Privately Held**
SIC: 1799 Dewatering service; building construction boring service

(G-3421)
BNSF RAILWAY CO
80 44th Ave NE (55421-2501)
PHONE..............................651 298-2121
Tom Packer, *Director*

www.HarrisInfo.com
156

2011 Harris Minnesota
Services Directory

▲=Import ▼=Export
◆=Import/Export

EMP: 230 **Publicly Held**
WEB: www.bnsf.com
SIC: **4011** Long haul railroad
HQ: Burlington Northern Santa Fe
2650 Lou Menk Dr
Fort Worth TX 76131
800 795-2673

(G-3422)
BOILER SERVICES INC
10327 Flanders St NE (55449-5711)
PHONE..............................763 784-8178
Thomas G Marchessault, *President*
Kim Case-Drengman, *Corp Secy*
Nancy Emery, *Corp Secy*
Tera Luby, *Office Mgr*
EMP: 25 EST: 1993
SALES (est): 1MM-4.9MM **Privately Held**
WEB: www.bsimn.com
SIC: **1711** 7699 Boiler maintenance service;
boiler setting contractor; mechanical
contractor; boiler repair shop

(G-3423)
BOWLING BOB'S 13TH FRAME PRO
12000 Central Ave NE (55434-3912)
PHONE..............................763 755-8686
Doug Thorp, *Owner*
EMP: 70 EST: 2000
SALES (est): 1MM-4.9MM **Privately Held**
SIC: **7933** Bowling center

(G-3424)
BRIGHT HORIZONS CHILDREN'S
500 Medtronic Pkwy (55432-5609)
PHONE..............................763 571-2375
Sue Marufic, *Director*
EMP: 35
SALES (est): 500-999K **Privately Held**
WEB: www.atlantaga.ncr.com
SIC: **8351** Child day care service
DH: Bright Horizons Children's
200 Talcott Ave
Watertown MA 02472
617 673-8000

(G-3425)
BROOK HALL BLAINE BROOK
12000 Central Ave NE (55434-3912)
PHONE..............................763 755-8731
FAX: 763 755-2447
Doug Thorpe, *Partner*
Terry Thorpe, *Partner*
EMP: 50 EST: 1975
SALES (est): 1MM-4.9MM **Privately Held**
WEB: www.brookhall.com
SIC: **7299** 7389 Banquet hall facility;
accommodation locating service

(G-3426)
BUNZL USA INC
5301 Industrial Blvd NE (55421-1034)
PHONE..............................763 571-1011
FAX: 763 571-2226
Dave Benson, *General Mgr*
Linda Kortum, *Manager*
John Eifert, *Manager*
EMP: 40
SALES (est): 25MM-49.9MM **Privately Held**
SIC: **5113** Wholesales industrial & personal
service paper
HQ: Bunzl USA Inc
701 Emerson Rd Ste 500
Saint Louis MO 63141
314 997-5959

(G-3427)
CAPITAL BEVERAGE SALES LTD
6982 Highway 65 NE (55432-3324)
PHONE..............................651 298-0800
Pamela Grover, *CIO*
EMP: 34 EST: 1994
SQ FT: 38,000
SALES (est): 10MM-24.9MM **Privately Held**
SIC: **5181** Wholesales beer & ale

(G-3428)
CAPITOL BEVERAGE SALES LP
6982 Highway 65 NE (55432-3324)
PHONE..............................763 571-4115
FAX: 763 571-9785
▲ EMP: 100

EST: 1950
SQ FT: 96,500
SALES (est): 25MM-49.9MM **Privately Held**
SIC: **5181** Wholesales beer & other
fermented malt liquors

(G-3429)
CASTREJON INC
9201 Isanti St NE (55449-4361)
PHONE..............................763 450-2055
Bert Castrejon, *President*
Monica Castrejon, *Office Mgr*
Jane Readding, *Manager*
EMP: 25 EST: 1997
SQ FT: 43,560
SALES (est): 1MM-4.9MM **Privately Held**
SIC: **1623** 1731 Underground utilities
contractor; cable television installation
contractor

(G-3430)
CENAIKO EXPO INC
9697 E River Rd NW (55433-5514)
PHONE..............................763 755-8111
Nicholas Cenaiko Sr, *CEO*
Barry Cenaiko, *President*
EMP: 25 EST: 1965
SQ FT: 20,000
SALES (est): 1MM-4.9MM **Privately Held**
WEB: www.cenaiko.com
SIC: **7389** Trade show arrangement service

(G-3431)
CENTERPOINT ENERGY HOUSTON
9320 Evergreen Blvd NW B (55433-5882)
PHONE..............................763 757-6200
Christe Singleton, *Manager*
Nancy Knox, *Training Super*
EMP: 50
SALES (est): 50MM-99.9MM **Publicly Held**
SIC: **4924** Natural gas distribution to
consumers
HQ: Centerpoint Energy Houston
1111 Louisiana St
Houston TX 77002
713 207-1111

(G-3432)
CENTRAL ROOFING CO
4550 Main St NE (55421-2157)
PHONE..............................763 572-0660
FAX: 763 572-0230
Charels Campman, *President*
Catherine Smith, *Vice Pres*
Mike Arduino, *CFO*
EMP: 50 EST: 1929
SQ FT: 18,000
SALES (est): 5MM-9.9MM **Privately Held**
WEB: www.centralroofing.com
SIC: **1761** Roofing contractor; sheet metal
work contractor
PA: Tecta America Corp
5215 Old Orchard Rd Ste 8
Skokie IL 60077
847 581-3888

(G-3433)
CLASSIC BOWL INC
11707 Round Lake Blvd NW (55433-2516)
PHONE..............................763 421-4402
FAX: 763 421-1842
Mike Anderson, *President*
EMP: 25 EST: 1992
SQ FT: 25,500
SALES (est): 500-999K **Privately Held**
WEB: www.classicbowl.com
SIC: **7933** Bowling center; drinking
establishment

(G-3434)
CLEANING AUTHORITY
1628 County Highway 10 # 15
(55432-2190)
PHONE..............................763 717-9200
Jim Brethorst, *Owner*
Kathy Brethorst, *Co-Owner*
EMP: 30 EST: 2002
SALES (est): 500-999K **Privately Held**
SIC: **7349** Industrial or commercial cleaning
services

(G-3435)
CODE WELDING & MFG INC
3151 101st Ave NE (55449-6922)
PHONE..............................763 792-6632
FAX: 763 792-6635
Charles Lynk, *President*
Curt Simonson, *Vice Pres*
Micheal Roe, *Vice Pres*
Kurt Simons, *Vice Pres*
EMP: 25 EST: 1990
SQ FT: 22,000
SALES (est): 1MM-4.9MM **Privately Held**
WEB: www.codewelding.net
SIC: **7692** 1799 5088 Welding service;
on-site welding contractor; wholesales
marine crafts & supplies

(G-3436)
COLDWELL BANKER BURNET REAL
3495 Northdale Blvd NW # 200
(55448-6714)
PHONE..............................763 754-5400
Peter Rizzo, *Vice Pres*
Keith Maahs, *Sales Mgr*
Mike Stanton, *Manager*
Renee M Patterson, *Office Admin*
Hugh Cha, *Administrator*
EMP: 85
SALES (est): 10MM-24.9MM **Privately Held**
SIC: **6531** Residential real estate agency

(G-3437)
COMMERCIAL AUDITORS CORP
1635 Coon Rapids Blvd NW (55433-4779)
PO Box 48775 (55448-0775)
PHONE..............................763 783-9160
Ken Maltby, *President*
Annastasia Maltby, *General Mgr*
Kim Lewis, *Vice Pres*
Leroy Hoefs Jr, *VP Sales*
Erica Weed, *Management*
EMP: 28 EST: 1992
SQ FT: 3,500
SALES (est): 1MM-4.9MM **Privately Held**
WEB: www.commercialauditors.com
SIC: **8721** 8111 Accounting, auditing &
bookkeeping services; legal services

(G-3438)
COMMERCIAL RECOVERY CORP
Also Called: C R C
9298 Central Ave NE # 310 (55434-4219)
PO Box 490456 (55449-0456)
PHONE..............................763 786-6333
FAX: 763 786-8113
Robert J Nielsen, *President*
Paul Krenik-Sr, *Vice Pres*
Kevin Layne, *Info Tech Dir*
EMP: 44 EST: 1989
SQ FT: 4,500
SALES (est): 1MM-4.9MM **Privately Held**
SIC: **7322** Collection agency

(G-3439)
COON RAPIDS CHRYSLER INC
10541 Woodcrest Dr NW (55433-6535)
PHONE..............................763 421-8000
FAX: 763 421-3187
Mike Hannan, *General Mgr*
Jay Birch, *General Mgr*
Gary Ross, *Manager*
Debbie Aasen, *Manager*
Rick Wolfe, *CIO*
EMP: 125 EST: 1957
SQ FT: 22,000
SALES (est): 50MM-99.9MM **Privately Held**
WEB: www.coonrapidscj.com
SIC: **7515** 7538 New & used car dealer;
general automotive repair services;
passenger car leasing

(G-3440)
COON RAPIDS DAY CARE CENTER
10506 Hanson Blvd NW (55433-4131)
PHONE..............................763 755-2412
FAX: 763 767-4732
Steve Rundgren, *Director*
Cathi Weber, *Administration*
EMP: 25 EST: 1969
SALES (est): 500-999K **Privately Held**
WEB: www.coonrapidsumc.org
SIC: **8351** Child day care service

(G-3441)
COON RAPIDS LIONS
10800 Xavis St NW Ste 1 (55433-4048)
PHONE..............................763 323-1668
FAX: 763 427-3857
John Leggate, *President*
EMP: 28 EST: 1954 **Privately Held**
WEB: www.coonrapidslions.org
SIC: **8641** Civic associations

(G-3442)
COON RAPIDS VFW POST 9625
1919 Coon Rapids Blvd NW (55433-4707)
PHONE..............................763 755-4760
FAX: 763 755-0882
Charles Hawkins, *President*
Robert Faucett, *Manager*
James Peterson, *Manager*
John Staum, *Master*
EMP: 40 EST: 1953
SQ FT: 20,000 **Privately Held**
SIC: **8641** 7997 Veterans' organization;
membership recreation club

(G-3443)
COUNSELOR REALTY INC (PA)
7766 Highway 65 NE Ste 1 (55432-2869)
PHONE..............................763 786-0600
FAX: 763 786-4312
Steve Westmark, *President*
Gregory Stull, *Managing Prtnr*
Steve Crb, *Partner*
Krissan Rollings, *Partner*
Ken Kunzman, *Vice Pres*
EMP: 60 EST: 1963
SQ FT: 6,000 **Privately Held**
WEB: www.counsellorrealty.com
SIC: **6531** Real estate agency & broker

(G-3444)
COUNTY OF ANOKA
Also Called: Job Training Center Anoka Cnty
1201 89th Ave NE Ste 235 (55434-3372)
PHONE..............................763 783-4800
FAX: 763 783-4844
Krista Monsrud, *Office Mgr*
Donna Grendler, *Manager*
Jerry Vitzthum, *Exec Dir*
Jerry Vitzphum, *Director*
David Ahsenmacher, *Coordinator*
EMP: 65
SALES (est): 1MM-4.9MM **Privately Held**
SIC: **8331** Job training & vocational
rehabilitation services; county supervisors'
& executives' office

(G-3445)
COUNTY OF ANOKA
Also Called: Achieve
1201 89th Ave NE Ste 105 (55434-3371)
PHONE..............................763 783-4909
FAX: 763 783-4725
Richard Brow, *Director*
EMP: 50
SQ FT: 136,476
SALES (est): 1MM-4.9MM **Privately Held**
SIC: **8322** Rehabilitation services

(G-3446)
COVENANT HOME SERVICES LLC
11375 Robinson Dr NW Ste 104
(55433-2594)
PHONE..............................763 755-9009
FAX: 763 323-2099
Gloria Klinefelter, *President*
Cheryl Zbaracki, *Exec Dir*
Cynthia Stevens, *Nursing Dir*
EMP: 45 EST: 1987
SALES (est): 1MM-4.9MM **Privately Held**
WEB: www.covcare.com
SIC: **8361** 8082 Residential care facility;
home health care services

(G-3447)
CREST VIEW CORP (PA)
4444 Reservoir Blvd (55421-3255)
PHONE..............................763 782-1611
FAX: 763 788-0012
Shirley Barnes, *CEO*
Ken Svor, *CFO*
Deb Kaminski, *Human Res Mgr*
Kevin Genereux, *Administrator*
Karen Fantlebarn, *Director*

GEOGRAPHIC

EMP: 170 **EST:** 1952
SQ FT: 35,000
SALES (corp-wide): 846.84M **Privately Held**
WEB: www.crestviewcares.com
SIC: 8051 8052 8082 Convalescent home; intermediate care facility; home health care services

(G-3448)
CREST VIEW CORP
Also Called: Royce Place
444 Reservois Blvd (55421)
PHONE 763 788-2020
FAX: 763 789-2313
Karen Fantle, *Manager*
Anita Kottsick, *Manager*
Sharon Panasuk, *Manager*
EMP: 100
SALES (est): 10MM-24.9MM **Privately Held**
WEB: www.crestviewcares.com
SIC: 6513 Apartment building operator
PA: Crest View Corp
    4444 Reservoir Blvd
    Minneapolis MN 55421
    763 782-1611

(G-3449)
CUB FOODS INC
12595 Central Ave NE (55434-4861)
PHONE 763 755-9802
FAX: 763 755-9452
Gary Bacher, *Manager*
Greg Massner, *Manager*
EMP: 300
SALES (est): 100MM-499.9MM **Publicly Held**
WEB: www.supervalu.com
SIC: 5149 Wholesales groceries
HQ: Cub Foods Inc
    421 3rd St S
    Stillwater MN 55082
    651 439-7200

(G-3450)
DAHLKE TRAILER SALES INC
8170 Hickory St NE (55432-1001)
PHONE 763 783-0077
FAX: 763 783-0347
Greg Dahlke, *President*
Greg Welcome, *Corp Secy*
Doug Smitters, *VP Purch*
Brian Dahlke, *Treasurer*
EMP: 30 **EST:** 1967
SQ FT: 10,400
SALES (est): 1MM-4.9MM **Privately Held**
WEB: www.dahlketrailer.com
SIC: 7539 5012 5013 7519 Trailer repair service; wholesales new & used trailers for trucks; wholesales automotive trailer parts & accessories; trailer rental service

(G-3451)
DASCO SYSTEMS INC
7787 Ranchers Rd NE (55432-2524)
PHONE 763 574-2275
FAX: 763 574-2243
Kenneth Schultz, *President*
Holly Schultz, *Vice Pres*
Chad Overgaauw, *Purchasing*
Judi Skoog, *Accounts Mgr*
▼ **EMP:** 27 **EST:** 1954
SQ FT: 9,000
SALES (est): 1MM-4.9MM **Privately Held**
WEB: www.dascolabel.com
SIC: 5131 Commercial printing; wholesales piece goods & notions

(G-3452)
DAVE'S FLOOR SANDING
1451 92nd Ln NE (55449-4332)
PHONE 763 784-3000
Matt Austion, *President*
EMP: 56 **EST:** 1979
SQ FT: 8,500
SALES (est): 5MM-9.9MM **Privately Held**
WEB: www.davesfloorsanding.com
SIC: 1752 Flooring contractor; wood floor installation & refinishing contractor

(G-3453)
DELTA INDUSTRIAL SERVICES INC
11501 Eagle St NW (55448-3062)
PHONE 763 755-7744
David Schiebout, *CEO*
Ronda Schiebout, *Corp Secy*
Victor Schiebout, *Vice Pres*
Toby Fuerst, *Vice Pres*
Michael Kult, *Engineering*
EMP: 75 **EST:** 1977
SQ FT: 70,000
SALES (est): 10MM-24.9MM **Privately Held**
WEB: www.deltaind.com
SIC: 5065 Manufactures assembly machines; wholesales electronic parts; manufactures paper industry machinery; wholesales electronic parts & equipment

(G-3454)
DEPENDABLE INDOOR AIR QUALITY
2619 Coon Rapids Blvd NW # 100 (55433-3663)
PHONE 763 757-5040
FAX: 763 757-5751
Jim Holt, *President*
Jim Odonnell, *Finance*
EMP: 25 **EST:** 1990
SQ FT: 5,600
SALES (est): 1MM-4.9MM **Privately Held**
SIC: 1711 5064 5075 7623 Heating & air conditioning contractor; wholesales household appliance parts; wholesales warm air heating equipment & supplies; air conditioning repair service

(G-3455)
DIESEL CAST WELDING INC
2190 107th Ln NE (55449-5236)
PHONE 763 780-5940
FAX: 763 780-5646
Jerry Ladd, *President*
Kim Ladd, *General Mgr*
M D Ladd, *Corp Secy*
Gerald Mountain, *Controller*
▲ **EMP:** 40 **EST:** 1973
SQ FT: 35,000
SALES (est): 1MM-4.9MM **Privately Held**
SIC: 7692 Welding service; cracked casting repair service

(G-3456)
DIVERSIFIED ADJUSTMENT SERVICE
600 Coon Rapids Blvd NW (55433-5549)
PHONE 763 783-2301
FAX: 763 783-0667
Kathleen Zurek, *President*
Robert A Zurek Sectreas, *Corp Secy*
Robert A Zurek, *Corp Secy*
Kelly Larson, *Vice Pres*
Michael Holtz, *Vice Pres*
EMP: 135 **EST:** 1981
SQ FT: 23,000
SALES (est): 5MM-9.9MM **Privately Held**
WEB: www.diversifiedadjustment.com
SIC: 7322 Collection agency

(G-3457)
DIVERSIFIED DYNAMICS CORP
1681 94th Ln NE (55449-4324)
PHONE 763 780-5440
FAX: 763 780-2958
William L Bruggeman Jr, *CEO*
Steven Bruggeman, *President*
Thomas Bruggeman, *President*
Diane M Erickson, *Senior VP*
Steve Larson, *Engrg Mgr*
▲ **EMP:** 79 **EST:** 1969
SQ FT: 158,582
SALES (est): 10MM-24.9MM **Privately Held**
WEB: www.catpumps.com
SIC: 5084 Manufactures pumps & pumping equipment; wholesales pumps & pumping equipment

(G-3458)
DON'S CAR WASHES OF MINNESOTA
4423 Central Ave NE (55421-2927)
PHONE 763 788-1631
Jerry Koschney, *President*
Peggy A Stordahl, *Corp Secy*

Angie Koschney, *Vice Pres*
Del V Heel, *Manager*
Wade Koschney, *Manager*
EMP: 30 **EST:** 1978
SQ FT: 3,000
SALES (est): 1MM-4.9MM **Privately Held**
SIC: 7542 Automatic carwash service; retail gasoline filling station

(G-3459)
DONLYN MANUFACTURE
Also Called: Impact
1490 94th Ln NE (55449-4319)
PHONE 763 786-1103
Paul Ramberg, *President*
EMP: 30 **EST:** 2007
SALES (est): 5MM-9.9MM **Privately Held**
WEB: www.puckmaster.com
SIC: 1542 1761 Commercial & institutional building construction; sheet metal work contractor

(G-3460)
EAGLE TOOL & DESIGN INC
7979 Central Ave NE (55432-2119)
PHONE 763 784-7400
FAX: 763 784-7702
Ole Christensen, *Ch of Bd*
Mike Tschida, *President*
Chuck Boho, *Vice Pres*
EMP: 36 **EST:** 1966
SQ FT: 44,000
SALES (est): 1MM-4.9MM **Privately Held**
WEB: www.eagletoolinc.com
SIC: 7692 8711 Machine shop, jobbing & repair services; mechanical engineering services; manufactures tools, dies, jigs & fixtures; welding service

(G-3461)
EAR NOSE THROAT SPECIALTY CARE
3960 Coon Rapids Blvd NW # 315 (55433-2598)
PHONE 763 421-8443
FAX: 763 421-2817
Julie Klosterman, *Principal*
Leighton G Siegel MD, *Med Doctor*
Melvin E Sigel MD, *Med Doctor*
Stephen L Liston MD, *Med Doctor*
Gary Garvis MD, *Med Doctor*
EMP: 60 **EST:** 2005
SALES (est): 5MM-9.9MM **Privately Held**
SIC: 8011 Ears, nose & throat specialist office

(G-3462)
ECM PUBLISHERS INC (PA)
4095 Coon Rapids Blvd NW (55433-2523)
PHONE 763 712-2400
FAX: 763 712-2480
Julian L Andersen, *CEO*
Jeff Athmann, *President*
Timothy Enger, *Corp Secy*
Judy Hible, *Corp Secy*
Eleanor J Andersen, *Vice Pres*
EMP: 50 **EST:** 1964
SQ FT: 20,000 **Privately Held**
WEB: www.ecm-inc.com
SIC: 7319 Provides commercial printing & newspaper publishing combined services; book binding service; advertising material distribution services; shopping news publishing & printing; shopping news, advertising & distributing services

(G-3463)
EDINA REALTY HOME SERVICES
3161 Northdale Blvd NW (55433-1756)
PHONE 763 755-1300
FAX: 763 755-8397
Jan Hettwer-Dummer, *Office Mgr*
Jan Hettwer, *Manager*
Jan Dummer, *Manager*
EMP: 75
SALES (est): 10MM-24.9MM **Publicly Held**
WEB: www.ilovetennis.net
SIC: 6531 Real estate agency & broker
HQ: Edina Realty Home Services
    6800 France Ave S Ste 600
    Minneapolis MN 55435
    952 928-5900

(G-3464)
EDINA REALTY HOME SERVICES
2407 109th Ave NE Ste 100 (55449-5769)
PHONE 651 636-2299
Linda Mitchell, *Manager*
Vicki Gay, *Manager*
EMP: 50
SALES (est): 5MM-9.9MM **Publicly Held**
WEB: www.ilovetennis.net
SIC: 6531 Real estate agency & broker
HQ: Edina Realty Home Services
    6800 France Ave S Ste 600
    Minneapolis MN 55435
    952 928-5900

(G-3465)
EPIPHANY ASSISTED LIVING
10955 Hanson Blvd NW 221-1 (55433-3673)
PHONE 763 755-0320
FAX: 763 772-1070
Laurie Anderson, *Director*
EMP: 35 **EST:** 2001
SALES (est): 1MM-4.9MM **Privately Held**
WEB: www.epiphanyal.org
SIC: 8052 Intermediate care facility

(G-3466)
ERICKSON PLUMBING HEATING
1471 92nd Ln NE (55449-4332)
PHONE 763 783-4545
FAX: 763 783-4566
Stacy Erickson, *President*
Ron Erickson, *Vice Pres*
EMP: 30 **EST:** 1983
SQ FT: 10,200
SALES (est): 1MM-4.9MM **Privately Held**
SIC: 1711 1731 Heating & air conditioning contractor; electrical contractor

(G-3467)
EXCEL ENGINEERING INC
500 73rd Ave NE Ste 119 (55432-3271)
PHONE 763 571-5008
Timothy A Rollman, *President*
Richard Gonzalez, *Vice Pres*
Gary L Niedermann, *Treasurer*
Kris Bissener, *Assistant*
Jeff Richardson, *Technician*
EMP: 71 **EST:** 1990
SQ FT: 9,000
SALES (est): 5MM-9.9MM **Privately Held**
WEB: www.exceleng.net
SIC: 8711 Engineering consulting services

(G-3468)
FAMILY LIFE MENTAL HEALTH CTR
1930 Coon Rapids Blvd NW (55433-4708)
PHONE 763 427-7964
FAX: 763 427-7976
Mary Kesser, *Corp Secy*
Katie Olson, *Human Res Mgr*
Rosalin Chrest, *Director*
Yasser E El-Hammamy, *Psychiatry*
Karen K Dickson, *Psychiatry*
EMP: 39 **EST:** 1984
SALES (est): 1MM-4.9MM **Privately Held**
SIC: 8011 Physicians' office & clinic

(G-3469)
FIRST STUDENT INC
2180 108th Ln NE (55449-5246)
PHONE 763 717-9447
FAX: 763 717-9352
David Keller, *Manager*
EMP: 35
SALES (est): 1MM-4.9MM **Privately Held**
WEB: www.firststudentinc.com
SIC: 4151 School bus service
HQ: First Student Inc
    600 Vine St Ste 1400
    Cincinnati OH 45202
    513 241-2200

(G-3470)
FIT PRO LLC
12420 Aberdeen St NE (55449-4721)
PO Box 328, Sartell (56377-0328)
PHONE 763 784-4747
Brad Kloss, *President*
Klint Shepherd, *Manager*

www.HarrisInfo.com
158

2011 Harris Minnesota
Services Directory

▲=Import ▼=Export
◆=Import/Export

EMP: 60 **EST:** 2003
SALES (est): 1MM-4.9MM **Privately Held**
WEB: www.fitpronutrition.com
SIC: 7991 Physical fitness center

(G-3471)
FOLEY DENTAL CLINIC (PA)
11237 Foley Blvd NW (55448-3389)
PHONE 763 757-3120
FAX: 763 757-5161
Roger E Austin, *Partner*
Thomas Anderson, *Partner*
EMP: 30 **EST:** 1974 **Privately Held**
SIC: 8021 Dentists' office & clinic

(G-3472)
FRIDLEY AUTO PARTS INC
Also Called: A-Abco Auto Parts
7300 Old Central Ave NE (55432-3519)
PHONE 763 784-8890
FAX: 763 784-7819
Derek L Haluptzok, *CEO*
Chris Close, *General Mgr*
EMP: 80 **EST:** 1988
SQ FT: 15,000
SALES (est): 5MM-9.9MM **Privately Held**
SIC: 5015 5093 Wholesales used automotive parts & supplies; wholesales junk & scrap; retails automotive parts

(G-3473)
FRIENDLY CHEVROLET, GEO INC
7501 Highway 65 NE (55432-3544)
PHONE 763 786-6100
FAX: 763 786-0914
Loren Holuv, *President*
Andrew Duncanson, *Vice Pres*
Tim Hornig, *Parts Mgr*
Mark Vogtlin, *Parts Mgr*
Ronald Stelter, *Treasurer*
EMP: 145 **EST:** 2007
SQ FT: 69,000
SALES (est): 50MM-99.9MM **Privately Held**
WEB: www.friendlychev.com
SIC: 7515 7532 7538 Retails new & used automobiles; automotive body, paint & interior repair & maintenance services; general automotive repair services; passenger car leasing; used car dealer

(G-3474)
GALE'S AUTO BODY INC
10600 Highway 65 NE (55434-3713)
PHONE 763 786-4110
FAX: 763 786-4593
Troy Westerlund, *President*
Sharon Westerlund, *Corp Secy*
EMP: 42 **EST:** 1973
SQ FT: 11,000
SALES (est): 1MM-4.9MM **Privately Held**
WEB: www.galesautocenter.com
SIC: 7532 Automotive body shop

(G-3475)
GLENN REHBEIN EXCAVATING INC (PA)
8651 Naples St NE (55449-6724)
PHONE 763 784-0657
Glenn R Rehbein, *Ch of Bd*
Bart Rehbein, *President*
Myrna Rehbein, *Corp Secy*
Gennadiy Epshteyn, *Manager*
Mathew Kytonen, *Manager*
EMP: 150 **EST:** 1956
SQ FT: 34,500 **Privately Held**
WEB: www.rehbein.com
SIC: 1794 0181 Excavation & grading, building construction contractor; sod farm

(G-3476)
GRANGER'S INC
10909 Radisson Rd NE (55449-5302)
PHONE 651 429-2524
Daniel Granger, *President*
Corrie Mikkonen, *General Mgr*
Mark Granger, *Vice Pres*
Kenneth Granger, *Shareholder*
Darrell Granger, *Shareholder*
EMP: 25 **EST:** 1954
SQ FT: 2,040
SALES (est): 1MM-4.9MM **Privately Held**
SIC: 7532 7538 Automotive body shop; general automotive repair services; gas station

(G-3477)
GRAPHIC FINISHING SERVICES INC
11490 Xeon St NW Ste 100 (55448-3111)
PHONE 763 767-3026
Rick Olsby, *President*
Diane Olsby, *Vice Pres*
Lisa Olsby, *Accounting Dir*
Carla Dold, *Manager*
Gary Wilson, *CIO*
EMP: 40 **EST:** 1991
SQ FT: 25,000
SALES (est): 1MM-4.9MM **Privately Held**
WEB: www.gfsmn.com
SIC: 7389 Binds books, pamphlets & magazines; folding & collating service for printers

(G-3478)
GREAT GARAGE PRODUCTS INC (PA)
1308 113th Ave NE (55434-3822)
PHONE 763 422-4000
FAX: 763 767-4099
Steve Donahue, *President*
Dwight Bangstad, *Manager*
Rob Hasty, *IT/INT Sup*
EMP: 29 **EST:** 1986 **Privately Held**
WEB: www.greatgaragedoor.com
SIC: 1751 Retails & installs garage doors; garage door contractor

(G-3479)
GRIFFIN PETROLEUM SERVICES INC
8700 Xylite St NE (55449-5005)
PHONE 763 780-6332
FAX: 763 780-5927
Dennis Habisch, *President*
Marty Habisch, *Vice Pres*
Sheila Rogers, *Controller*
Laurel Johnson, *Manager*
Jeff Barry, *Technician*
EMP: 26 **EST:** 1987
SQ FT: 10,000
SALES (est): 1MM-4.9MM **Privately Held**
WEB: www.gpsgc.com
SIC: 1799 7699 Service station equipment contractor; service station equipment installation, maintenance & repair contractor; hydraulic equipment repair services

(G-3480)
GROUNDED AIR INC
7932 Main St NE (55432-1842)
PO Box 490743 (55449-0743)
PHONE 763 780-1443
FAX: 763 780-9231
David Herzog, *President*
Bob Hart, *Manager*
EMP: 53 **EST:** 1984
SQ FT: 1,850
SALES (est): 5MM-9.9MM **Privately Held**
SIC: 4212 4213 4214 Local trucking without storage services; local trucking with storage; over the road trucking

(G-3481)
HANS HAGEN HOMES INC
941 Hillwind Rd NE Ste 300 (55432-5965)
PHONE 763 586-7200
FAX: 763 572-9417
Hans T Hagen Jr, *President*
Jamie Herby, *Corp Secy*
Ted Hagen, *Vice Pres*
Dan Mosow, *Treasurer*
Kevin Bosley, *Manager*
EMP: 35 **EST:** 1965
SQ FT: 5,000
SALES (est): 5MM-9.9MM **Privately Held**
SIC: 1521 Single-family housing construction

(G-3482)
HARCO MOVING & STORAGE INC
11365 Xeon St NW (55448-3148)
PHONE 763 571-6227
Doug Harrison, *President*
EMP: 30
SALES (est): 1MM-4.9MM **Privately Held**
WEB: www.harcomoving.com

SIC: 4214 4212 Local trucking with storage; local moving service

(G-3483)
HARDWIRE TECH INC
7930 University Ave NE (55432-1860)
PHONE 763 783-8111
David Halseth, *Principal*
EMP: 25 **EST:** 2002 **Privately Held**
SIC: 8731 Commercial physical research laboratory

(G-3484)
HEALTHPARTNERS INC
Also Called: Hlthptnrs Coon Rapids Dntl CL
11475 Robinson Dr NW (55433-3746)
PHONE 763 754-0041
FAX: 763 754-4506
Susan Hora, *Principal*
Tammy Robinson, *Manager*
EMP: 48
SALES (est): 1MM-4.9MM **Privately Held**
WEB: www.healthpartners.com
SIC: 8021 Dentists' office & clinic
PA: HealthPartners Inc
8170 33rd Ave S
Bloomington MN 55425
952 883-6000

(G-3485)
HEALTHPARTNERS INC
Also Called: Spring Lake Park Dental Ctr
1415 81st Ave NE (55432-2111)
PHONE 763 780-1292
FAX: 763 785-3232
Joan Slaaten, *Office Mgr*
Julian Chelberg, *Manager*
Susan Hora, *Manager*
EMP: 32
SALES (est): 1MM-4.9MM **Privately Held**
WEB: www.healthpartners.com
SIC: 8021 Dental office
PA: HealthPartners Inc
8170 33rd Ave S
Bloomington MN 55425
952 883-6000

(G-3486)
HEALTHPARTNERS INC
2003 Northdale Blvd NW (55433-3004)
PHONE 763 754-0041
Tom Zyvoloski DDS, *Branch Mgr*
EMP: 400
SALES (est): 25MM-49.9MM **Privately Held**
WEB: www.healthpartners.com
SIC: 8011 Physicians' office & clinic
PA: HealthPartners Inc
8170 33rd Ave S
Bloomington MN 55425
952 883-6000

(G-3487)
HEALTHPARTNERS INC
Also Called: Coon Rapids Dental
11475 Robinson Dr NW (55433-3746)
PHONE 763 754-4600
FAX: 763 754-4614
Liane Davie, *Pharmacist*
Tammy Robinson, *Manager*
Cynthia Herboldt, *Administrator*
EMP: 60
SALES (est): 1MM-4.9MM **Privately Held**
WEB: www.healthpartners.com
SIC: 8021 Dental clinic
PA: HealthPartners Inc
8170 33rd Ave S
Bloomington MN 55425
952 883-6000

(G-3488)
HILLTOP TRAILER SALES INC
7810 University Ave NE (55432-2625)
PHONE 763 571-9103
FAX: 763 571-2536
Richard Pearo, *President*
Gerald Pearo, *Corp Secy*
EMP: 50 **EST:** 1951
SQ FT: 20,000
SALES (est): 10MM-24.9MM **Privately Held**
WEB: www.hilltoptrailers.com
SIC: 7519 Recreational vehicle dealer; recreational vehicle parts & accessories store; travel, camping or recreational trailer rental service

(G-3489)
HOLLENBACK & NELSON INC
1206 114th Ln NW (55448-3127)
PHONE 763 862-7525
FAX: 763 754-1126
Dave Nelson, *CEO*
Tom Parentau, *Vice Pres*
EMP: 40 **EST:** 1963
SQ FT: 1,700
SALES (est): 1MM-4.9MM **Privately Held**
SIC: 1741 1771 Masonry & stonework contractor; concrete contractor

(G-3490)
HOME DEPOT USA INC
3550 124th Ave NW (55433-1000)
PHONE 763 422-1200
FAX: 763 576-5416
Scott Tesmer, *Manager*
Becky Severson, *Manager*
Laura Cook, *Manager*
EMP: 250
SALES (est): 25MM-49.9MM **Publicly Held**
SIC: 7359 Home center store; tool rental
HQ: Home Depot International Inc
2455 Paces Ferry Rd SE
Atlanta GA 30339
770 319-1669

(G-3491)
HOME DEPOT USA INC
4550 Pheasant Ridge Dr NE (55449-4532)
PHONE 763 717-0316
Rich Nelson, *Manager*
EMP: 150
SQ FT: 291,012
SALES (est): 25MM-49.9MM **Publicly Held**
SIC: 7359 Home center store; tool rental
HQ: Home Depot International Inc
2455 Paces Ferry Rd SE
Atlanta GA 30339
770 319-1669

(G-3492)
HOMESTEAD AT COON RAPIDS
1770 113th Ln NW (55433-3019)
PHONE 763 754-2800
FAX: 763 754-4800
Dave Gislason, *Exec Dir*
Jennifer John, *Director*
EMP: 35 **EST:** 2005
SALES (est): 1MM-4.9MM **Privately Held**
SIC: 8361 Residential care facility

(G-3493)
HVH AUTO PARTS INC
Also Called: John's Auto Parts
10506 Central Ave NE (55434-3711)
PHONE 763 784-1711
FAX: 763 784-8132
Harold V Haluptzok V, *President*
Linda Haluptzok, *Vice Pres*
Curt Dolman, *Manager*
EMP: 105 **EST:** 1941
SQ FT: 68,880
SALES (est): 10MM-24.9MM **Privately Held**
WEB: www.johnsauto.com
SIC: 5015 5013 Wholesales used automotive parts & supplies; retails automotive parts; wholesales new motor vehicle parts & supplies

(G-3494)
HYDRAULIC SPECIALTY CO INC
1131 72nd Ave NE (55432-3502)
PHONE 763 571-3072
FAX: 763 571-2330
Richard Haarstad, *President*
Karen Haarstad, *Corp Secy*
Steve Berge, *Opers Mgr*
Lauri Stark, *Purchasing*
Larry Schultz, *Manager*
EMP: 25 **EST:** 1968
SQ FT: 15,000
SALES (est): 1MM-4.9MM **Privately Held**
WEB: www.hydraulicspecialty.com
SIC: 7699 5084 Hydraulic equipment repair services; manufactures motor vehicle cylinder heads; wholesales industrial hydraulic systems equipment & supplies

GEOGRAPHIC

GEOGRAPHIC

(G-3495)
I-STATE TRUCK CENTER
8950 Eldorado St NE (55449-4353)
PHONE...............................651 636-3400
Jim Williams, *General Mgr*
Reid Jaeger, *Manager*
EMP: 73
SALES (est): 25MM-49.9MM **Privately Held**
WEB: www.istatetruck.com
SIC: 5084 Wholesales industrial machinery & equipment
HQ: I-State Truck Center
2601 American Blvd E
Minneapolis MN 55425
952 854-5511

(G-3496)
INDEPENDENT SCHOOL DISTRICT 16
Also Called: Early Childhood Family Educatn
8000 Highway 65 NE (55432-2051)
PHONE...............................763 786-1338
Karen Schaub, *Director*
EMP: 57 EST: 1987
SALES (est): 1MM-4.9MM **Privately Held**
SIC: 8351 Child day care service; educational services

(G-3497)
INDUSTRIAL DOOR CO INC (PA)
360 Coon Rapids Blvd NW (55433-5627)
PHONE...............................763 786-4730
FAX: 763 786-9186
Gerry Sizer, *President*
Donna Luoma, *Corp Secy*
Jeremy Sizer, *Vice Pres*
Jodi S Boldenow, *Treasurer*
Rhys Larson, *Manager*
EMP: 25 EST: 1974
SQ FT: 16,495
SALES (corp-wide): 28M **Privately Held**
WEB: www.inddoor.com
SIC: 1751 Garage door contractor; manufactures spring sash balances

(G-3498)
INDUSTRIAL SYSTEMS ASSOCIATES
1400 73rd Ave NE (55432-3702)
PHONE...............................763 574-5208
Matt Valdez, *Manager*
EMP: 87
SALES (est): 10MM-24.9MM **Privately Held**
WEB: www.sdi.com
SIC: 8748 Business consulting services
DH: Industrial Systems Associates
1414 Radcliffe St Ste 300
Bristol PA 19007
215 633-1900

(G-3499)
INFINITE CAMPUS INC
4321 109th Ave NE (55449-6794)
PHONE...............................651 631-0000
Charles Kratsch, *CEO*
Steve Rutledge, *General Mgr*
Eric Creighton, *CFO*
David V Meter, *Officer*
Brian Page, *Officer*
EMP: 130 EST: 1993
SQ FT: 2,000
SALES (est): 10MM-24.9MM **Privately Held**
WEB: www.infinitecampus.com
SIC: 7371 Computer software development

(G-3500)
INTERNATIONAL ASSOCIATION OF
555 Mill St NE (55421-3822)
PHONE...............................763 706-3650
Gary Gorman, *Director*
EMP: 30 EST: 1907 **Privately Held**
SIC: 8611 Trade association

(G-3501)
INTERNATIONAL TWINS ASSOC
6898 Channel Rd NE (55432-4621)
PHONE...............................763 571-3022
Len Long, *Corp Secy*
Lori Stewart, *Corp Secy*
EMP: 100 EST: 1937 **Privately Held**
SIC: 8399 Social change association

(G-3502)
INTERSTATE POWER SYSTEMS INC
8950 Eldorado St NE (55449-4353)
PHONE...............................952 854-5511
Bob Woodward, *Branch Mgr*
Robert Woodward, *Manager*
Bill Schuster, *Manager*
Tom Gombold, *Manager*
EMP: 70
SALES (est): 25MM-49.9MM **Privately Held**
WEB: www.istate.com
SIC: 5084 5063 Wholesales industrial engines & transportation equipment; wholesales electrical apparatus & equipment; manufactures factory basis rebuilt motor vehicle engines & transmissions
HQ: Interstate Power Systems Inc
2601 American Blvd E
Minneapolis MN 55425
952 854-2044

(G-3503)
J J VANDERSON & CO
Also Called: Beam Central Vacuum Systems
1214 98th Ave NE (55434-3501)
PHONE...............................651 641-1376
Jay Vandermyde, *CEO*
Darlene Vandermyde, *Office Mgr*
Christal Vanderson, *Manager*
EMP: 35 EST: 1985
SQ FT: 6,500
SALES (est): 25MM-49.9MM **Privately Held**
WEB: www.jjvanderson.com
SIC: 5099 5065 5087 Wholesales video & audio equipment; retails vacuum cleaners; wholesales security control equipment & systems; wholesales vacuum cleaning systems; retails radios, televisions & consumer electronics

(G-3504)
JACKSON SPAH DENTAL STUDIO INC
1150 Osborne Rd NE (55432-2836)
PO Box 9659 (55440-9659)
PHONE...............................763 785-2435
FAX: 763 785-9767
Gerald E Jackson, *President*
Jeffrey Jackson, *Corp Secy*
Bruce Spah, *Vice Pres*
Bradley Jackson, *Treasurer*
Denise Stanley, *Officer*
EMP: 35 EST: 1979
SQ FT: 3,500
SALES (est): 1MM-4.9MM **Privately Held**
SIC: 8072 Dental crown & bridge production laboratory; manufactures dental equipment & supplies

(G-3505)
JAMES R HILL INC
1523 94th Ln NE Ste B (55449-4390)
PHONE...............................763 792-1136
FAX: 763 792-1743
Joel Cooper, *President*
EMP: 70 EST: 2005
SALES (est): 5MM-9.9MM **Privately Held**
SIC: 8711 Engineering services

(G-3506)
JEFF'S, BOBBY & STEVES
3701 Central Ave NE (55421-3928)
PHONE...............................763 788-1113
Steve Williams, *Partner*
Bobby Williams, *Partner*
Jeff Bahe, *Partner*
EMP: 40 EST: 1987
SQ FT: 25,000
SALES (est): 1MM-4.9MM **Privately Held**
SIC: 7538 General automotive repair services

(G-3507)
JEWELRY REPAIR CENTERS INC
12031 Ilex St NW (55448-2217)
PO Box 48870 (55448-0870)
PHONE...............................763 370-2511
James Zagaros, *Member*
EMP: 30
SALES (est): 1MM-4.9MM **Privately Held**
SIC: 7631 Jewelry repair service

(G-3508)
KERRY LOGISTICS INC ✪
9124 Isanti St NE (55449-4358)
PO Box 43995 (55443-0995)
PHONE...............................763 717-1400
James Beamon, *President*
Susan Beamon, *COO*
EMP: 25 EST: 2008
SQ FT: 3,490
SALES (est): 1MM-4.9MM **Privately Held**
SIC: 4212 4213 Local trucking without storage services; over the road trucking

(G-3509)
KEYSTONE AUTOMOTIVE INDUSTRIES
Also Called: North Star Bumper
3900 Jackson St NE # 100 (55421-3986)
PHONE...............................763 788-3039
FAX: 763 788-3649
Pat Perchum, *Manager*
EMP: 30
SALES (est): 10MM-24.9MM **Publicly Held**
WEB: www.keystone-auto.com
SIC: 5013 Wholesales new motor vehicle parts & supplies
DH: Keystone Automotive Industries
3615 Marshall St NE
Minneapolis MN 55418
612 789-1919

(G-3510)
KLEINMAN REALTY CO
5301 E River Rd Ste 101 (55421-3779)
PHONE...............................763 572-9400
FAX: 763 572-9404
R J Kleinman Jr, *President*
James N Kleinman, *Vice Pres*
Carolyn Leblanc, *Manager*
EMP: 60 EST: 1937
SQ FT: 2,000
SALES (est): 10MM-24.9MM **Privately Held**
WEB: www.kleinmanrealty.com
SIC: 6531 Real estate management services

(G-3511)
KOLSTAD CO INC
8501 Naples St NE (55449-6702)
PHONE...............................763 792-1033
Robert J Crosson, *CEO*
Paul O'Brien, *President*
Gene Seebeck, *Engineer*
Kathy Wilke, *Human Res Mgr*
David McNeill, *Manager*
EMP: 75 EST: 1947
SQ FT: 68,000
SALES (est): 10MM-24.9MM **Privately Held**
SIC: 5013 7538 Manufactures trailer bodies; manufactures beverage truck bodies; wholesales automotive supplies & parts; truck engine repair service; sheet metal fabricator

(G-3512)
KURT MANUFACTURING CO INC
Also Called: Products Division
9445 E River Rd NW (55433-5510)
PHONE...............................763 572-4592
L Lenz, *General Mgr*
Jeff Lenz, *General Mgr*
Kevin Carlson, *Engineer*
Dan Cooke, *Engineer*
Ken White, *Engineer*
EMP: 35
SALES (est): 5MM-9.9MM **Privately Held**
SIC: 4225 7389 Manufactures switchgear & switchboard apparatus; self storage warehousing; purchasing service; machine tools & accessories; manufactures computers; manufactures process control instruments
PA: Kurt Manufacturing Co Inc
5280 Main St NE
Minneapolis MN 55421
763 572-1500

(G-3513)
L & S ELECTRIC INC
9300 Evergreen Blvd NW (55433-5815)
PHONE...............................763 780-3234
FAX: 763 780-3957
Todd Esala, *Branch Mgr*
EMP: 44
SALES (est): 25MM-49.9MM **Privately Held**
WEB: www.lselectric.com
SIC: 5063 Wholesales electric motors; wholesales electric motor controls, starters & relays
PA: L & S Electric Inc
5101 Mesker St
Schofield WI 54476
715 359-3155

(G-3514)
LANDMARK FINANCIAL GROUP INC
11490 Hanson Blvd NW Ste 2 (55433-3979)
PHONE...............................763 572-8626
FAX: 763 572-8865
William F Ouellette, *President*
Martin L Ouellette, *Corp Secy*
Douglas W Ouellette, *Vice Pres*
EMP: 37 EST: 1998
SQ FT: 1,800
SALES (est): 1MM-4.9MM **Privately Held**
WEB: www.landmarkmortgagecompany.com
SIC: 6163 Mortgage brokers service arranging for loans, using money of others

(G-3515)
LEONARD V ACKERMAN DDS
11441 Osage St NW (55433-3677)
PHONE...............................763 757-7540
FAX: 763 757-7661
Scott Rensch, *Owner*
EMP: 25
SALES (est): 1MM-4.9MM **Privately Held**
WEB: www.williambecker.net
SIC: 8021 Orthodontist
PA: Leonard V Ackerman DDS
402 Monroe St
Anoka MN 55303
763 427-2740

(G-3516)
LEPTOS BIOMEDICAL
452 Northco Dr Ste 100 (55432-3310)
PO Box 32710 (55432-0710)
PHONE...............................763 561-0880
EMP: 30 EST: 2006
SALES (est): 1MM-4.9MM **Privately Held**
SIC: 8099 Health & allied services

(G-3517)
LIBERTY DISPLAY GROUP INC
10087 Goodhue St NE (55449-4431)
PHONE...............................763 785-1593
FAX: 763 785-9852
Robert Cegla, *President*
Mike McDonald, *Vice Pres*
Nancy Ballard, *Sales/Mktg Mgr*
Scott Sims, *Sales Staff*
Gary Britz, *Director*
EMP: 35 EST: 1987
SQ FT: 30,000
SALES (est): 1MM-4.9MM **Privately Held**
WEB: www.libertydisplaygroup.com
SIC: 7389 Manufactures nonwood store fixtures; advertising, promotional & trade show service

(G-3518)
LIFE BY DESIGN INC
7866 University Ave NE (55432-2625)
PHONE...............................763 757-3263
FAX: 763 757-3238
Beth Hawkins, *President*
Linda Zeien, *President*
Jennifer Husom, *Safety Dir*
EMP: 190 EST: 1997 **Privately Held**
WEB: www.lifebydesign-inc.com
SIC: 8399 8082 Community development groups; home health care services

(G-3519)
LIFE TIME FITNESS INC
2100 Northdale Blvd NW (55433-3005)
PHONE...............................763 257-1067
FAX: 763 767-2222
Cary Sutherland, *Manager*
EMP: 150
SALES (est): 1MM-4.9MM **Publicly Held**

www.HarrisInfo.com
160

2011 Harris Minnesota
Services Directory

▲=Import ▼=Export
◆=Import/Export

SIC: 7991 7299 Physical fitness center; personal appearance service
PA: Life Time Fitness Inc
2902 Corporate Pl
Chanhassen MN 55317
952 947-0000

(G-3520)
LIFES COMPANION PCA INC
10307 University Ave NE (55434-8026)
PHONE 763 786-3439
Donna Wilson, *President*
Marilyn Lom, *Vice Pres*
EMP: 250 **EST:** 1991
SQ FT: 4,500
SALES (est): 5MM-9.9MM **Privately Held**
SIC: 8082 Home health care services

(G-3521)
LINDSTROM METRIC LLC (PA)
2950 100th Ct NE (55449-5100)
PHONE 763 780-4200
FAX: 763 780-0554
Shane Longen, *General Mgr*
Adam Bridges, *General Mgr*
Dean Lindahl, *General Mgr*
Paul Kelley, *General Mgr*
Bernie Longen, *General Mgr*
▲ **EMP:** 100 **EST:** 1979
SQ FT: 100,000 **Privately Held**
WEB: www.lindfastgrp.com
SIC: 5072 Wholesales fasteners

(G-3522)
LORENZ BUS SERVICE INC
8600 Xylite St NE (55449-5003)
PHONE 763 784-7196
FAX: 763 784-1077
Jim Canine, *President*
James Cesario, *CFO*
Doug Loos, *Manager*
Dianne Thomas, *Executive*
EMP: 60 **EST:** 1967
SQ FT: 2,000
SALES (est): 1MM-4.9MM **Privately Held**
WEB: www.lorenzbus.com
SIC: 4141 Local bus charter service

(G-3523)
LOWE'S HOME CENTERS INC
11651 Ulysses St NE (55434-3941)
PHONE 763 367-1120
EMP: 158
SALES (est): 25MM-49.9MM **Publicly Held**
WEB: www.lowes.com
SIC: 5031 5064 Retails building products & materials; wholesales exterior building materials; wholesales interior building materials; wholesales electrical appliances; retails household appliances
HQ: Lowe's Home Centers Inc
1605 Curtis Bridge Rd
Wilkesboro NC 28697
336 658-4000

(G-3524)
LOWE'S HOME CENTERS INC
2700 Main St NW (55448-1247)
PHONE 763 367-1340
EMP: 150
SALES (est): 25MM-49.9MM **Publicly Held**
WEB: www.lowes.com
SIC: 5031 5064 Retails building products & materials; wholesales exterior building materials; wholesales interior building materials; wholesales electrical appliances; retails household appliances
HQ: Lowe's Home Centers Inc
1605 Curtis Bridge Rd
Wilkesboro NC 28697
336 658-4000

(G-3525)
MAERTENS-BRENNY CONSTRUCTION
8251 Mn St NE Ste 105 (55432)
PHONE 763 786-4779
FAX: 763 786-6973
Joseph D Maertens, *President*
Irene M Aertens, *Manager*
Linda Wallace, *Manager*
Pat Zehowski, *Manager*
Chris Ratelle, *Manager*
EMP: 40

EST: 1980
SQ FT: 7,500
SALES (est): 10MM-24.9MM **Privately Held**
SIC: 1541 1542 Industrial building & warehouse construction; commercial & office building contractor

(G-3526)
MALTON ELECTRIC CO
7580 Commerce Ln NE (55433-3115)
PHONE 763 571-7758
FAX: 763 571-7921
Brad Bozich, *Manager*
EMP: 25
SALES (est): 1MM-4.9MM **Privately Held**
SIC: 5063 7694 Manufactures switchgear & switchgear accessories; wholesales electric motors; electric motor repair service; manufactures electronic enclosures
PA: Malton Electric Co
1505 Chestnut St W
Virginia MN 55792
218 741-8252

(G-3527)
MANNING TRANSFER INC
2775 101st Ave NE (55449-5704)
PHONE 763 784-4022
FAX: 763 784-7542
Michael J Manning, *President*
Dawn Manning, *Manager*
EMP: 36 **EST:** 1970
SQ FT: 13,420
SALES (est): 1MM-4.9MM **Privately Held**
WEB: www.manningtransfer.com
SIC: 4213 4212 Contract haulers; light local haulage & cartage services; heavy hauling transportation services

(G-3528)
MARTIN-BROWER CO L L C
Also Called: Perlman Rocque Co Fridley
51 52nd Way NE (55421-1004)
PHONE 763 571-6311
FAX: 763 571-6512
Deb Smith, *Manager*
Mike Kokesh, *Manager*
Jim Haley, *Manager*
EMP: 200
SQ FT: 60,744
SALES (est): 100MM-499.9MM **Privately Held**
WEB: www.reyesholdings.com
SIC: 5142 5141 Wholesales packaged frozen foods; wholesales general line groceries
HQ: Martin-Brower Co LLC
9500 Bryn Mawr Ave # 700
Rosemont IL 60018
847 227-6500

(G-3529)
MARY T ASSOCIATES INC
1555 118th Ln NW Ste 1 (55448-7501)
PHONE 763 754-6706
Paula Berger, *Branch Mgr*
EMP: 30
SALES (est): 1MM-4.9MM **Privately Held**
SIC: 8082 Home health care services
PA: Mary T Associates Inc
1555 118th Ln NW Ste 1
Minneapolis MN 55448
763 754-2505

(G-3530)
MARY T INC
1555 118th Ln NW Ste 1 (55448-7501)
PHONE 763 754-2505
Mary M Tjosvold, *CEO*
Teresa Jepma, *Human Res Dir*
Jim Neuswanger, *Administrator*
Roberta Tray, *Info Tech Mgr*
EMP: 36 **EST:** 1985
SALES (est): 1MM-4.9MM **Privately Held**
SIC: 8322 Individual & family social services

(G-3531)
MCCOLLISTER'S TRANSPORTATION
Also Called: Gazda Transportation Mayflower
223 Osborne Rd NE (55432-3168)
PHONE 763 502-2120
FAX: 763 755-2909
Eric Greene, *General Mgr*
EMP: 34

SALES (est): 1MM-4.9MM **Privately Held**
SIC: 4214 4212 4213 Local trucking with storage; over the road trucking; local moving service
HQ: McCollister's Transportation
1800 Route 130 N
Burlington NJ 08016
609 386-0600

(G-3532)
MEDICAL ADVANCED PAIN
2104 Northdale Blvd NW # 220 (55433-3005)
PHONE 763 537-6000
FAX: 763 537-6666
David M Schultz, *President*
Mary Dubel, *Human Resources*
Laurie Curtis, *Office Mgr*
Sue Schneider, *Nursing Mgr*
Lee M Espeland, *Med Doctor*
EMP: 80 **EST:** 1995
SALES (est): 5MM-9.9MM **Privately Held**
WEB: www.painphysicians.com
SIC: 8011 8049 Specialized medical practitioners; physical therapist office

(G-3533)
MEDSTAT SYSTEMS INC
5155 E River Rd Ste 418 (55421-3776)
PHONE 763 586-8146
FAX: 763 586-8147
Scott A Bohm, *President*
Tom Breyen, *General Mgr*
Bob Byrnes, *Vice Pres*
Ann Maddaus, *Manager*
Chris Nguyen, *Info Tech Mgr*
EMP: 49 **EST:** 1996
SQ FT: 4,200
SALES (est): 1MM-4.9MM **Privately Held**
WEB: www.medstatsystems.com
SIC: 4212 Local trucking without storage services

(G-3534)
MEDTRONIC USA INC (HQ)
710 Medtronic Pkwy (55432-5603)
PHONE 763 514-4000
Arthur D Collins Jr, *President*
Philip J Albert, *Corp Secy*
D C Findlay, *Corp Secy*
Keyn P Skeffington, *Corp Secy*
Susan Alpert, *Senior VP*
EMP: 2500 **EST:** 1997
SALES (corp-wide): 15.81B **Publicly Held**
WEB: www.medtronic.com
SIC: 5047 Wholesales medical & hospital equipment
PA: Medtronic Inc
710 Medtronic Pkwy
Minneapolis MN 55432
763 514-4000

(G-3535)
MEDTRONIC WORLD HEADQUARTERS
710 Medtronic Pkwy (55432-5603)
PHONE 763 574-4000
Art Collins, *CEO*
Michael Hegland, *Principal*
Jean Dutel, *Senior VP*
Deborah Denz, *Vice Pres*
Frederick Halverson, *Vice Pres*
EMP: 2500 **EST:** 1974
SALES (est): 1B-9.9B **Publicly Held**
WEB: www.medtronic-inc.com
SIC: 5047 Wholesales medical & hospital equipment
PA: Medtronic Inc
710 Medtronic Pkwy
Minneapolis MN 55432
763 514-4000

(G-3536)
METRO FRAMING INC
1550 91st Ave NE Ste 110 (55449-4388)
PO Box 490368 (55449-0368)
PHONE 763 785-1482
Andy Harrington, *President*
EMP: 50 **EST:** 1994
SQ FT: 2,000
SALES (est): 1MM-4.9MM **Privately Held**
WEB: www.metroframing.com
SIC: 1751 Framing contractor

(G-3537)
METRO HOME HEALTH CARE INC
Also Called: At Home Services
3931 Coon Rapids Blvd NW # 101 (55433-2580)
PHONE 763 323-2099
Robert Loftus, *President*
Mary J Loftus, *Corp Secy*
Thomas Loftus, *Vice Pres*
EMP: 160
SQ FT: 1,600
SALES (est): 5MM-9.9MM **Privately Held**
SIC: 8082 Home health care services

(G-3538)
METRO PACKAGING CORP
7000 Highway 65 NE Ste 1A (55432-3358)
PHONE 763 586-0808
Lawrence R Meuers, *President*
Dan Meuers, *Vice Pres*
Ron Tschida, *Vice Pres*
Virginia Meuers, *Treasurer*
EMP: 50 **EST:** 1971
SQ FT: 40,000 **Privately Held**
SIC: 0723 Vegetable packing services

(G-3539)
METROPLITAN PEDIATRIC DENTAL
500 Osborne Rd NE Ste 345 (55432-2769)
PHONE 763 786-4260
FAX: 763 786-7301
DH Lipschultz, *Principal*
Kathy Keeler, *Manager*
EMP: 25
SALES (est): 1MM-4.9MM **Privately Held**
WEB: www.metropediatricdental.com
SIC: 8021 Dentists' office & clinic
PA: Metroplitan Pediatric Dental
411 Main St Ste 400
Saint Paul MN 55102
651 224-4969

(G-3540)
METROPOLITAN CARDIOLOGY
4040 Coon Rapids Blvd NW 12 (55433-4567)
PHONE 763 427-9980
FAX: 763 427-0904
Steven Remole, *President*
Brian Anderson MD, *Managing Prtnr*
Greg Path MD, *Vice Pres*
Sajad H Mir, *Med Doctor*
Joseph J Garamella, *Manager*
EMP: 120 **EST:** 1986
SQ FT: 10,000
SALES (est): 10MM-24.9MM **Privately Held**
WEB: www.metrocardiology.com
SIC: 8011 Cardiologist & cardio-vascular specialist

(G-3541)
METROPOLITAN TRANSPORTATION
8960 Evergreen Blvd NW (55433-6042)
PHONE 763 571-1541
FAX: 763 780-9211
Tashitaa Tufaa, *CEO*
Gebi Kogi, *Director*
EMP: 97 **EST:** 2004
SALES (est): 5MM-9.9MM **Privately Held**
SIC: 4119 Local rental transportation service

(G-3542)
MIDWEST INTERNAL MEDICINE
3960 Coon Rapids Blvd NW # 100 (55433-2521)
PHONE 763 236-9428
FAX: 763 422-6166
Judy Olstad, *Administrator*
Elizabeth Zaiser, *Internal Med*
EMP: 48 **EST:** 2003
SALES (est): 5MM-9.9MM **Privately Held**
SIC: 8011 Physicians' office & clinic

GEOGRAPHIC

(PA)=Parent Co (HQ)=Headquarters (DH)=Div Headquarters
✿ = New business established in last 2 years

2011 Harris Minnesota
Services Directory

© Harris InfoSource 1-866-281-6415
161

(G-3543)
MIDWEST VETERINARY SPECIALTY
11850 Aberdeen St NE (55449-4786)
PHONE.................................763 754-5000
FAX: 763 754-6002
Norb Epping, *Member*
Jay Epping, *Member*
Lori Cody, *Manager*
EMP: 25 **Privately Held**
WEB: www.nvsg.com
SIC: 0742 Veterinary services

(G-3544)
MILL CITY KENNEL
11247 Foley Blvd NW (55448-3389)
PHONE.................................763 755-3595
Roger I Bari, *Director*
EMP: 33 EST: 1980 **Privately Held**
SIC: 0752 Kennel boarding services

(G-3545)
MORGAN TIRE & AUTO LLC
Also Called: Team Tires Plus
5126 Central Ave NE (55421-1825)
PHONE.................................763 571-4392
Dan Donovan, *Manager*
EMP: 30
SALES (est): 1MM-4.9MM **Privately Held**
WEB: www.bfsusa.com
SIC: 7534 Tire recapping & retreading
services
HQ: Bfs Retail Operations LLC
333 E Lake St Ste 300
Bloomingdale IL 60108
630 259-9000

(G-3546)
MULTICARE ASSOCIATES OF THE (PA)
Also Called: Fridley Medical Center
7675 Madison St NE (55432-2753)
PO Box 86 (55486-0086)
PHONE.................................763 785-4500
FAX: 763 785-3329
Kevin Bailey, *President*
Janis Dimants MD, *Med Doctor*
Kathleen Smith, *Manager*
Jeannine Schlottman, *Administrator*
EMP: 159 EST: 1964
SQ FT: 16,000 **Privately Held**
SIC: 8011 Medical center

(G-3547)
MULTICARE ASSOCIATES OF THE
Also Called: Blaine Medical Center
11855 Ulymnes St NE 100 (55434)
PO Box 86 (55486-0001)
PHONE.................................763 785-4250
Jeannine Schlottman, *CEO*
Jack Stoulil, *Med Doctor*
Suzanne S Teragawamd MD, *Med Doctor*
Liling Lai, *Med Doctor*
Diane Welter, *Administrator*
EMP: 100
SALES (est): 10MM-24.9MM **Privately Held**
SIC: 8011 Medical center
PA: Multicare Associates of The
7675 Madison St NE
Minneapolis MN 55432
763 785-4500

(G-3548)
MURPHY BROS DESIGNERS
1613 93rd Ln NE (55449-4314)
PHONE.................................763 780-3262
John D Murphy, *CEO*
Nathan Murphy, *Opers Mgr*
David Long, *Advt Staff*
Amelia Eskelson, *Manager*
EMP: 25 EST: 1983
SQ FT: 10,000
SALES (est): 5MM-9.9MM **Privately Held**
WEB: www.mbros.com
SIC: 1521 New single-family home
construction service; single-family home
general remodeling service; commercial &
office building renovation & repair services;
retails door & window products

(G-3549)
MURPHY WAREHOUSE CO
4700 Main St NE (55421-2165)
PHONE.................................612 623-1226
Julie Nepine, *Branch Mgr*
EMP: 30
SALES (est): 1MM-4.9MM **Privately Held**
WEB: www.murphywarehouse.com
SIC: 4225 Warehousing & storage services
PA: Murphy Warehouse Co
701 24th Ave SE
Minneapolis MN 55414
612 623-1200

(G-3550)
NATIONAL AUTOMATIC SPRINKLER
10351 Jamestown St NE (55449-4269)
PHONE.................................763 784-8902
FAX: 763 784-5787
Gerald Lind, *CEO*
Bill Wiehle, *Vice Pres*
Jerry Lind, *Vice Pres*
EMP: 50 EST: 1981
SQ FT: 18,000
SALES (est): 5MM-9.9MM **Privately Held**
WEB: www.nationalsprinkler.com
SIC: 1711 Fire sprinkler system installation
service

(G-3551)
NATIONAL SPORTS CENTER FNDTN
1700 105th Ave NE (55449-4500)
PHONE.................................763 785-5600
FAX: 763 785-5699
Curtiss Conkright, *Superintendent*
Steve Olson, *COO*
Roger Stawski, *CFO*
Patti Pallow, *Accountant*
Tee Collins, *Sales Staff*
EMP: 42 EST: 1989
SALES (est): 10MM-24.9MM **Privately Held**
SIC: 7941 Sporting complex providing
services for soccer, field track sports teams

(G-3552)
NEDEGAARD CONSTRUCTION CO INC
1521 94th Ln NE (55449-4322)
PHONE.................................763 757-2926
FAX: 763 757-0649
Bruce Nedegaard, *President*
Jay Norgaard, *Vice Pres*
Kelly Nekole, *Treasurer*
EMP: 25 EST: 1971
SALES (est): 5MM-9.9MM **Privately Held**
WEB: www.norgaardhomes.com
SIC: 1521 New single-family home
construction service

(G-3553)
NEW HORIZON CHILD CARE INC
999 Moore Lake Dr E (55432-5194)
PHONE.................................763 574-7450
FAX: 763 574-7450
Cheryl Faehn, *Director*
EMP: 30
SALES (est): 500-999K **Privately Held**
WEB: www.kidsquest.com
SIC: 8351 Child day care service
HQ: New Horizon Child Care Inc
16355 36th Ave N Ste 700
Plymouth MN 55446
763 557-1111

(G-3554)
NEW HORIZON CHILD CARE INC
2381 108th Ln NE (55449-5222)
PHONE.................................763 757-2604
Amy White, *Sales Mgr*
Becky Strasser, *Director*
EMP: 25
SALES (est): 500-999K **Privately Held**
WEB: www.kidsquest.com
SIC: 8351 Child day care service
HQ: New Horizon Child Care Inc
16355 36th Ave N Ste 700
Plymouth MN 55446
763 557-1111

(G-3555)
NEW MILLENNIUM ✪
7931 6th St NE (55432-1815)
PHONE.................................763 780-9933
John Arndt, *Owner*
EMP: 80 EST: 2008
SALES (est): 5MM-9.9MM **Privately Held**
SIC: 8099 Health & allied services

(G-3556)
NORAN NEUROLOGICAL CLINIC
500 Osborne Rd NE Ste 365 (55432-2769)
PHONE.................................763 786-8406
FAX: 763 786-0607
Craig Weflen, *Manager*
David J Streitz, *Urology*
Agnieszka S Hatfield, *Surgery-Plastic*
Ana P Groeschel, *Neurology*
EMP: 35
SALES (est): 1MM-4.9MM **Privately Held**
SIC: 8011 Neurologist; clinic operated by
physicians
PA: Noran Neurological Clinic
2828 Chicago Ave
Minneapolis MN 55407
612 879-1000

(G-3557)
NORDIC INSULATION INC
1550 93rd Ln NE (55449-4317)
PHONE.................................763 784-7893
FAX: 763 784-6931
Steve Wrolstad, *President*
Donna Wrolstad, *Corp Secy*
Collette Wagner, *Vice Pres*
EMP: 30 EST: 1976
SQ FT: 16,000
SALES (est): 1MM-4.9MM **Privately Held**
WEB: www.nordicinsulation.com
SIC: 1742 Building insulation installation
service

(G-3558)
NORTH AMERICAN FRAMING INC
8411 Center Dr NE (55432-1309)
PO Box 490395 (55449-0395)
PHONE.................................763 784-4855
Steve Hank, *President*
EMP: 35 EST: 1986
SALES (est): 1MM-4.9MM **Privately Held**
SIC: 1751 Framing contractor; finish & trim
carpentry service

(G-3559)
NORTHPARK DENTAL
9120 Baltimore St NE (55449-4337)
PHONE.................................763 786-1560
FAX: 763 786-4390
Paul Chadbourn, *President*
Gregory J Povolny, *Dentist*
Vicki Imholte, *Manager*
Wendy Gulden, *Executive*
EST: 1960 **Privately Held**
WEB: www.northparkdental.com
SIC: 8021 Dental clinic; endodontist office;
oral pathologist office; periodontist office

(G-3560)
ON MOVIN INC
1493 94th Ln NE (55449-4320)
PHONE.................................763 784-7111
FAX: 763 784-7272
Michael V Welton V, *President*
Kevin Walton, *Manager*
EMP: 43 EST: 1984
SQ FT: 260
SALES (est): 1MM-4.9MM **Privately Held**
WEB: www.onmovin.com
SIC: 4119 Local passenger transportation
service

(G-3561)
ON TIME LAWN & SNOW SERVICES
8794 Dunkirk Ct NE (55449-6764)
PHONE.................................763 786-0652
William Murphy, *Owner*
EMP: 30 EST: 2003 **Privately Held**
SIC: 0782 Lawn care services

(G-3562)
ORTHOPEDIC PARTNERS (PA)
8290 University Ave NE # 200
(55432-1873)
PHONE.................................763 786-9543
FAX: 763 786-3320
Becky Anderson, *Principal*
Marge Briggs, *Office Mgr*
Cyril F Kruse, *Surgeon*
Peter D Holmberg, *Surgeon*
Paul R Diekmann, *Surgeon*
EMP: 30 EST: 1991 **Privately Held**
SIC: 8011 Orthopedic physician office

(G-3563)
PARK CONSTRUCTION CO
500 73rd Ave NE Ste 123 (55432-3271)
PHONE.................................763 786-9800
FAX: 763 786-2952
Richard N Carlson, *Ch of Bd*
Verlyn Schoep, *President*
Richard P Southworth, *Corp Secy*
Bruce Carlson, *Vice Pres*
Jeff Carlson, *Vice Pres*
EMP: 100 EST: 1890
SQ FT: 10,000
SALES (est): 10MM-24.9MM **Privately Held**
WEB: www.parkconstructionco.com
SIC: 1611 1622 1629 Grading services;
bridge construction; power plant
construction; land preparation service; dam,
waterway, dock & other marine structure
construction; dam construction

(G-3564)
PARK DENTAL BLAINE
12904 Central Ave NE (55434-4147)
PHONE.................................763 755-1330
FAX: 763 755-4305
Peter Thompson, *Partner*
Levi T Kinsey DDS, *Dentist*
EMP: 55 EST: 1990
SALES (est): 1MM-4.9MM **Privately Held**
SIC: 8021 Dental clinic

(G-3565)
PARSONS ELECTRIC LLC (PA)
5960 Main St NE (55432-5441)
PHONE.................................763 571-8000
FAX: 763 571-5680
Greg Fangel, *Superintendent*
Joel Moryn, *Member*
Mike Northquest, *Member*
Jack Clauson, *Vice Pres*
Steve Jandro, *Vice Pres*
EMP: 140 EST: 1927
SQ FT: 60,000 **Privately Held**
SIC: 1731 7382 8711 Electrical contractor;
security systems services; electrical or
electronic engineers

(G-3566)
PASSE ENGINEERING INC
Also Called: Anderson Land Survey
1611 County Highway 10 # 2
(55432-2158)
PHONE.................................763 780-4100
FAX: 763 780-5200
Derrick Passe, *President*
Mark Maistrovich, *Corp Secy*
Dale Anderson, *Vice Pres*
Brent Roshell, *Treasurer*
EST: 1993 **Privately Held**
SIC: 8711 Civil engineering services

(G-3567)
PC SOLUTIONS INC
5155 E River Rd Ste 409 (55421-1043)
PHONE.................................763 852-1600
Mark Berndt, *President*
Michael Schaaf, *Manager*
Greg Schwartz, *Network Enginr*
Andy Brogan, *Director*
EMP: 35 EST: 1972
SQ FT: 55,000
SALES (est): 1MM-4.9MM **Privately Held**
SIC: 7378 5045 Computer & office machine
maintenance & repair services; wholesales
computers, peripherals & software;
wholesales computers

www.HarrisInfo.com
162

2011 Harris Minnesota
Services Directory

▲=Import ▼=Export
◆=Import/Export

(G-3568)

PERFECT 10 CAR WASH INC
999 Highway 10 NE (55432-1208)
PHONE..............................651 227-9274
FAX: 651 784-9364
Kevin Hanover, *President*
Richard P Hanover, *Purchasing*
Kim Fels, *Supervisor*
EMP: 50 **EST:** 1989
SQ FT: 17,520
SALES (est): 1MM-4.9MM **Privately Held**
SIC: 7542 Car wash

(G-3569)

PERFECT COMPLEMENT LTD
Also Called: Excel Marine & Motorsports
3050 Coon Rapids Blvd NW (55433-3474)
PHONE..............................763 421-8360
Robert Langer, *President*
Dan Patrin, *Vice Pres*
Charles Langer, *Vice Pres*
EMP: 25 **EST:** 1974
SQ FT: 25,000
SALES (est): 5MM-9.9MM **Privately Held**
WEB: www.excelmms.com
SIC: 7699 Boat dealer; snowmobile dealer;
boat repair service

(G-3570)

PGA TOUR INC
Also Called: Tournament Players Club
11444 Tournament Players Pkwy
(55449-5665)
PHONE..............................763 795-0800
FAX: 763 795-0840
Alan Cull, *General Mgr*
Jami Larkin, *Manager*
Ken Lane, *Manager*
EMP: 100
SQ FT: 18,395
SALES (est): 5MM-9.9MM **Privately Held**
WEB: www.pgatour.com
SIC: 7997 7991 Membership golf club;
eating place; physical fitness center;
drinking establishment; retails sporting
goods
PA: PGA Tour Inc
112 PGA Tour Blvd
Ponte Vedra Beach FL 32082
904 285-3700

(G-3571)

POWER SYSTEM ENGINEERING INC
Also Called: Pse
10710 Town Square Dr NE (55449-8102)
PHONE..............................763 755-5122
FAX: 763 755-7028
Dennis Eicher, *President*
Douglas Joens, *Project Engr*
EMP: 50
SALES (est): 5MM-9.9MM **Privately Held**
SIC: 8711 Engineering consulting services
PA: Power System Engineering Inc
1532 W Broadway
Madison WI 53713
608 222-8400

(G-3572)

PRECISION REPAIR & CALIBRATION
9150 Isanti St NE (55449-4358)
PHONE..............................763 784-1704
James Durand, *President*
Michael Tihanyi, *Vice Pres*
Paula Durand, *CFO*
EMP: 25 **EST:** 1986
SALES (est): 1MM-4.9MM **Privately Held**
WEB: www.prcilab.com
SIC: 7699 8734 Tool repair service;
calibrating & certification services; precision
instrument repair service

(G-3573)

PRIDE N'LIVING HOME CARE INC
7691 Central Ave NE Ste 102
(55432-3581)
PHONE..............................763 572-2390
Celestina Waindim, *CEO*
EMP: 30 **EST:** 2004
SALES (est): 1MM-4.9MM **Privately Held**
SIC: 8082 Home health care services

(G-3574)

PRO COURIER INC
8375 Sunset Rd NE (55432-1316)
PHONE..............................763 571-8811
FAX: 763 572-8458
Lizabeth Erickson, *President*
Greg Erickson, *Treasurer*
Jose Arzdorf, *Comptroller*
Edwin Sanville, *IT/INT Sup*
EMP: 35 **EST:** 1996
SQ FT: 4,800
SALES (est): 1MM-4.9MM **Privately Held**
WEB: www.procourierinc.com
SIC: 4215 Ground courier services

(G-3575)

PROEX PHOTO SYSTEMS INC (PA)
12680 Riverdale Blvd NW (55448-6711)
PHONE..............................952 893-1915
David Ritc, *President*
Brayan Engblom, *General Mgr*
Maynard Wagner, *Info Tech Dir*
Laurie Thulien, *Exec Dir*
Shannon Hardner, *Executive*
EMP: 25 **EST:** 1962
SQ FT: 10,000 **Privately Held**
SIC: 7384 7221 Photofinishing laboratory;
portrait studio

(G-3576)

PROFORM THERMAL SYSTEMS INC
10401 Jamestown St NE (55449-5135)
PHONE..............................763 572-2200
FAX: 763 572-2286
Doug Petty, *President*
Bonnie Petty, *Corp Secy*
Ryan Tollander, *Exec Dir*
EMP: 35 **EST:** 1987
SQ FT: 12,000
SALES (est): 5MM-9.9MM **Privately Held**
WEB: www.proformthermal.com
SIC: 1541 Industrial building & warehouse
construction; warehouse construction

(G-3577)

PROSOURCE TECHNOLOGIES INC
9219 E River Rd NW (55433-5722)
PHONE..............................763 786-1445
Wade Carlson, *President*
John Polhan, *Controller*
Jeffery Anderson, *Manager*
Scott Stenger, *Manager*
John Canon, *Manager*
EMP: 49 **EST:** 1997
SQ FT: 2,400
SALES (est): 5MM-9.9MM **Privately Held**
WEB: www.prosourcetech.com
SIC: 8748 Environmental consultant

(G-3578)

PRUDENCIAL SUNDIAL REALTY INC
961 Hillwind Rd NE (55432-5911)
PHONE..............................763 571-9200
FAX: 763 571-5105
Tom Blomberg, *President*
EMP: 38
SQ FT: 3,000
SALES (est): 5MM-9.9MM **Privately Held**
WEB: www.rogerharmon.com
SIC: 6531 Real estate selling agency

(G-3579)

PUBLIC HEALTH SOLUTIONS I
12770 Raven St NW (55448-2576)
PHONE..............................763 754-7427
Shelly Shanterich, *Partner*
Shannon Williams, *Partner*
EMP: 28 **EST:** 2006
SALES (est): 500-999K **Privately Held**
SIC: 8082 Home health care services

(G-3580)

RE MAX REAL ESTATE PROPERTIES
11905 Highway 65 NE (55434-3911)
PHONE..............................763 755-1100
FAX: 763 757-3746
Jeff Tollefson, *President*

Darron Morris, *Manager*
Jessica Johnson, *Exec Dir*
EMP: 80 **EST:** 1996
SALES (est): 10MM-24.9MM **Privately Held**
SIC: 6531 Residential real estate agency

(G-3581)

REESE BROOKS HOSPITALITY INDS
Also Called: Minne Ha Ha Lanes
1737 122nd Ln NW (55448-1957)
PHONE..............................763 767-0754
Harry R Erkenbrabk, *Partner*
Toris J Erkenbrabk, *Partner*
Jean Erkenbrack, *Vice Pres*
Robert Hjort, *Vice Pres*
Jeff Quade, *Manager*
EMP: 45 **EST:** 2001
SALES (est): 1MM-4.9MM **Privately Held**
SIC: 7933 Bowling center

(G-3582)

REFUGE GOLF CLUB
1323 Coon Rapids Blvd NW (55433-5362)
PHONE..............................763 753-7770
Rick Lund, *President*
Al Owens, *Exec Dir*
EMP: 30 **EST:** 1999
SALES (est): 1MM-4.9MM **Privately Held**
SIC: 7992 Public golf course

(G-3583)

RESPONSE FIRE PROTECTION INC
8201 Central Ave NE Ste J (55432-2090)
PHONE..............................763 717-4740
FAX: 763 717-4741
Ronald D Peil, *President*
EMP: 40 **EST:** 1996
SQ FT: 3,600
SALES (est): 1MM-4.9MM **Privately Held**
SIC: 1711 Fire sprinkler system installation
service

(G-3584)

REVIVA INC (PA)
5130 Main St NE (55421-1528)
PHONE..............................763 535-8900
David W Goodwin, *CEO*
R D Estes, *Corp Secy*
Duane M Wanner, *COO*
John Mathisen, *Vice Pres*
Larry E Schmidt, *Vice Pres*
▲ **EMP:** 60 **EST:** 1945
SQ FT: 83,000 **Privately Held**
WEB: www.dealersmfg.com
SIC: 5013 Manufactures motor vehicle
steering systems & components;
wholesales automotive engines & engine
parts

(G-3585)

RISE INC (PA)
8406 Sunset Rd NE (55432-1317)
PHONE..............................763 786-8334
FAX: 763 786-0008
John Barrett, *President*
Jon Pratt, *Managing Dir*
Mary Zins, *Corp Secy*
Tom Carman, *Corp Secy*
Gerald Bauer, *Vice Pres*
EMP: 100 **EST:** 1971
SQ FT: 60,000
SALES (corp-wide): 6.04M **Privately Held**
SIC: 8331 Vocational rehabilitation agency

(G-3586)

RISE INC
1156 114th Ln NW (55448-3127)
PHONE..............................763 784-0900
Steve Larson, *Manager*
Kevin Kelly, *Manager*
EMP: 60
SQ FT: 21,584
SALES (est): 1MM-4.9MM **Privately Held**
SIC: 8331 Vocational rehabilitation agency
PA: Rise Inc
8406 Sunset Rd NE
Minneapolis MN 55432
763 786-8334

(G-3587)

RIVERSIDE AUTO WASH INC
6520 E River Rd (55432-4213)
PHONE..............................763 571-2700
FAX: 763 571-6420
Tony Abena, *President*
EMP: 35 **EST:** 1969
SQ FT: 8,000
SALES (est): 1MM-4.9MM **Privately Held**
SIC: 7542 Self-service carwash service;
truck wash service

(G-3588)

RMR SERVICES LLC
9272 Isanti St NE (55449-4360)
PHONE..............................763 786-7323
Todd Edinger, *Mng Member*
EMP: 52 **EST:** 1990
SQ FT: 3,000
SALES (est): 1MM-4.9MM **Privately Held**
SIC: 7389 1731 Remote meter reading
service; electronic controls installation
service

(G-3589)

ROBERT A WILLIAMS ENTERPRISES (PA)
Also Called: Bobbie Stves Auto Wrld Rchfeld
3701 Central Ave NE (55421-3928)
PHONE..............................763 788-1113
FAX: 763 782-0792
Robert A Williams, *Partner*
Arlan Williams, *Partner*
Jon Junch, *Partner*
Jeff Bahe, *Partner*
Steve Anderson, *Partner*
EMP: 50 **EST:** 1963
SQ FT: 1,000 **Privately Held**
SIC: 6519 Retail gasoline filling station;
landholding offices

(G-3590)

ROCK ELECTRIC CORP
9701 6th St NE (55434-1309)
PHONE..............................763 792-9664
Kristine Shoenrock, *President*
Troy Shoenrock, *Vice Pres*
Troy Schoenrock, *Vice Pres*
Jason Hoeft, *Treasurer*
EMP: 30 **EST:** 2000
SALES (est): 1MM-4.9MM **Privately Held**
SIC: 1731 Electrical contractor

(G-3591)

ROCKINGHAM GROUP
11412 Ivywood St NW (55433-3456)
PHONE..............................763 421-8672
J Miller, *Owner*
EMP: 32 **EST:** 1995
SALES (est): 1MM-4.9MM **Privately Held**
SIC: 8748 Business consulting services

(G-3592)

ROSE CAMILIA CO INC
Also Called: Camilia Rose Convalescent Ctr
11800 Xeon Blvd NW (55448-2061)
PHONE..............................763 755-8400
FAX: 763 755-3130
Mary Tjosvold, *CEO*
Agnes Mallery, *President*
Susan Kemming, *Accounting Mgr*
Norma Brendle, *Administrator*
Sharon Falknor, *Administrator*
EMP: 200 **EST:** 1976
SQ FT: 60,456
SALES (est): 5MM-9.9MM **Privately Held**
WEB: www.camiliarose.com
SIC: 8052 8059 Personal care facility; home
for the mentally retarded

(G-3593)

ROYAL FINANCIAL LLC
4111 Central Ave NE # 201 (55421-2960)
PO Box 7881, Saint Paul (55107-0881)
PHONE..............................763 746-9480
Rafik Mukharemov, *Member*
Nicholas Henkels, *Member*
Ali Mirdamadi, *Office Mgr*
EMP: 30 **EST:** 2002
SQ FT: 500
SALES (est): 1MM-4.9MM **Privately Held**
SIC: 6163 Mortgage brokers service
arranging for loans, using money of others

GEOGRAPHIC

(G-3594)
RUTE AGENCY
9716 Zilla St NW　(55433-5407)
PHONE....................612 240-1795
Drew Rute, *Owner*
EMP: 25 **EST:** 2002
SALES (est): 10MM-24.9MM **Privately Held**
SIC: 6321 Direct accident & health
insurance carrier

(G-3595)
SARA LEE CORP
350 73rd Ave NE Ste 15　(55432-3269)
PHONE....................763 572-2506
FAX: 763 572-3718
Roger Fox, *Branch Mgr*
EMP: 60
SALES (est): 25MM-49.9MM **Publicly Held**
SIC: 5149 Wholesales coffee & tea
PA: Sara Lee Corp
　　3500 Lacey Rd Ste LL1
　　Downers Grove IL 60515
　　630 598-6000

(G-3596)
SAV ENTERPRISES INC
11325 Xeon St NW　(55448-3148)
PO Box 480050　(55448-8050)
PHONE....................763 278-3340
FAX: 763 278-3354
Mike Abbott, *President*
Joe Speltz, *Corp Secy*
Donald Devine, *Vice Pres*
Steven L Morgan, *Opers Staff*
EMP: 30 **EST:** 1987
SQ FT: 12,500
SALES (est): 1MM-4.9MM **Privately Held**
SIC: 4731 8742 Truck transportation
brokers; transportation consultant

(G-3597)
SAV LOGISTICS INC
11325 Xeon St NW　(55448-3148)
PHONE....................763 489-4213
Mike Abbott, *CEO*
EMP: 50
SALES (est): 5MM-9.9MM **Privately Held**
WEB: www.savtrans.com
SIC: 4789 Transportation services

(G-3598)
SCHMIT TOWING INC
92 43rd Ave NE　(55421-2605)
PHONE....................763 253-1568
FAX: 763 253-1569
Stephen Schmit, *President*
Sue Schmit, *CFO*
EMP: 25 **EST:** 1983
SQ FT: 5,000
SALES (est): 1MM-4.9MM **Privately Held**
WEB: www.schmittowing.com
SIC: 7549 Automotive towing service

(G-3599)
SECURITY PRODUCTS CO
4005 Pheasant Ridge Dr NE　(55449-4517)
PHONE....................763 784-6504
Dan Chastanet, *President*
Kelley Rafferty, *Accountant*
Mike Musch, *Manager*
Steve Bradbury, *Info Tech Mgr*
▲ **EMP:** 33 **EST:** 1972
SQ FT: 18,800
SALES (est): 1MM-4.9MM **Privately Held**
WEB: www.securityproductscompany.com
SIC: 1731 6099 8748 Safety & security
specialization contractor; business
consulting services; automated teller
machine network

(G-3600)
SHADDRIC & LE BEAU HOUSING
7365 Central Ave NE　(55432-3520)
PHONE....................763 784-9824
Bob Saltness, *Principal*
Madeleine Saltness, *Manager*
EMP: 25 **EST:** 1995
SALES (est): 5MM-9.9MM **Privately Held**
SIC: 6512 Nonresidential building operator

(G-3601)
**SHORTY'S HEAVY DUTY
WRECKER**
1257 Osborne Rd NE　(55432-2839)
PO Box 32358　(55432-0358)
PHONE....................763 784-1411
FAX: 763 784-1656
Jo A Schuur, *President*
Terra Wilson, *Manager*
EMP: 50 **EST:** 1947
SQ FT: 100,000
SALES (est): 1MM-4.9MM **Privately Held**
SIC: 7549 4212 4213 Automotive towing
service; local trucking without storage
services; over the road trucking

(G-3602)
**SHOWPLACE 16 KERASOTES
THEATRE**
10051 Woodcrest Dr NW　(55433-6516)
PHONE....................763 757-6233
Dean Kerasotes, *President*
EMP: 60 **EST:** 1997
SALES (est): 1MM-4.9MM **Privately Held**
SIC: 7832 Indoor movie theater

(G-3603)
SNG CONSTRUCTION INC
8383 Sunset Rd NE　(55432-1316)
PHONE....................763 795-8496
FAX: 763 784-0126
Peter J Schwieters, *President*
Mike Barrett, *Prdtn Mgr*
Paul Schwieters, *VP Persnl*
Kayle Shuselt, *Info Tech Mgr*
EMP: 55 **EST:** 1994
SQ FT: 700
SALES (est): 5MM-9.9MM **Privately Held**
WEB: www.sngconstruction.com
SIC: 1761 Siding contractor

(G-3604)
SOCON CONSTRUCTION INC
11306 Ibis St NW　(55433-3747)
PHONE....................763 754-4027
Ronald Swanson, *President*
Gerald Swanson, *Treasurer*
Kim Swanson, *Manager*
EMP: 33 **EST:** 1966
SQ FT: 6,000
SALES (est): 5MM-9.9MM **Privately Held**
SIC: 1542 1521 Commercial & office
building renovation & repair services; new
commercial & office building construction;
single-family housing construction

(G-3605)
SONDANCE STUDIO
Also Called: Son Sheim Music School
8301 Sunset Rd NE Ste 6　(55432-1336)
PHONE....................763 784-2920
FAX: 763 784-2800
Liz Gerfshem, *Partner*
Jan Albertson, *Partner*
EMP: 35 **EST:** 1994
SALES (est): 1MM-4.9MM **Privately Held**
SIC: 7911 Dance instructor

(G-3606)
**SPRING LAKE PARK LIONS
CLUB**
8433 Center Dr NE　(55432-1309)
PHONE....................763 784-9179
FAX: 763 784-9167
Bill Larson, *President*
Dean Keller, *Manager*
Shawn Donahue, *Manager*
EMP: 50 **EST:** 1967
SQ FT: 2,400　**Privately Held**
WEB: www.slplions.com
SIC: 8641 6732 Civic associations;
management of charitable trusts

(G-3607)
SPRINT LAKE PARK ALLIANCE
8433 Center Dr NE　(55432-1309)
PHONE....................763 784-9179
Norm McCarthy, *President*
Shawn Donahue, *Manager*
EMP: 45 **EST:** 1956 **Privately Held**
SIC: 8641 Civic & social organization

(G-3608)
**STERICYCLE SPECIALTY
WASTE**
Also Called: Special Waste Disposal Inc
2850 100th Ct NE　(55449-5137)
PHONE....................612 285-9865
Mark C Miller, *President*
Chris Psihos, *General Mgr*
William Jolitz, *Vice Pres*
Jenni Wymer, *Accountant*
EMP: 40 **EST:** 1979
SALES (est): 5MM-9.9MM **Publicly Held**
WEB: www.stericycle.com
SIC: 4953 Refuse collection & disposal
services
PA: Stericycle Inc
　　28161 N Keith Dr
　　Lake Forest IL 60045
　　847 367-5910

(G-3609)
STINSON HOME CARE LLC
Also Called: Continual Feast Companion Care
1425 Coon Rapids Blvd NW # 202
(55433-5390)
PHONE....................763 755-4801
FAX: 763 755-4805
Loretta Stinson, *Member*
Tom Stinson, *Mng Member*
EMP: 25 **EST:** 2002
SALES (est): 500-999K **Privately Held**
WEB: www.continualfeast.com
SIC: 8082 Home health care services
PA: LivHome Inc
　　5900 Wilshire Blvd Ste 705
　　Los Angeles CA 90036
　　323 932-1300

(G-3610)
STREAMFEEDER LLC
103 Osborne Rd NE　(55432-3131)
PHONE....................763 502-0000
Mitch Speicher, *Member*
David Helffrich, *Vice Pres*
Cliff Thompson, *Vice Pres*
Peggy Schempf, *Opers Mgr*
Mark Yeager, *Purchasing*
EMP: 57 **EST:** 1990
SQ FT: 60,000
SALES (est): 5MM-9.9MM **Privately Held**
WEB: www.streamfeeder.com
SIC: 5044 Manufactures electrical
equipment & supplies; wholesales mailing
machines; manufactures current carrying
wiring devices

(G-3611)
**SUBURBAN RADIOLOGIC
CONSLNTS**
8990 Springbrook Dr NW Ste 140
(55433-5880)
PHONE....................763 792-1900
Jerry Board, *Office Mgr*
Brian T Sullivan, *Diag Radio*
Patrick J Juenemann, *Diag Radio*
Ellen L Abeln, *Diag Radio*
Matthew M Schaar, *Diag Radio*
EMP: 50
SALES (est): 5MM-9.9MM **Privately Held**
WEB: www.fibroidinfo.com
SIC: 8011 Radiologist office
PA: Suburban Radiologic Conslnts
　　4801 W 81st St Ste 108
　　Minneapolis MN 55437
　　952 837-9700

(G-3612)
**SUBURBAN RADIOLOGIC
CONSLNTS**
8990 Springbrook Dr NW Ste 125
(55433-5879)
PHONE....................763 786-9460
Sue Kern, *Manager*
EMP: 25
SALES (est): 1MM-4.9MM **Privately Held**
WEB: www.fibroidinfo.com
SIC: 8011 Radiologist office
PA: Suburban Radiologic Conslnts
　　4801 W 81st St Ste 108
　　Minneapolis MN 55437
　　952 837-9700

(G-3613)
SYNERGETIC SOLUTIONS INC
3890 Pheasant Ridge Dr NE　(55449-5854)
PHONE....................763 331-3300
Patrick Charais, *CEO*
EMP: 35 **EST:** 1996
SQ FT: 14,000
SALES (est): 1MM-4.9MM **Privately Held**
SIC: 8742 Compensation & benefits
planning consultant

(G-3614)
**T & J CONCRETE & MASONRY
INC**
9100 Baltimore St NE # 105　(55449-4376)
PO Box 357, Cedar　(55011-0357)
PHONE....................763 413-0988
Timothy Fystrom, *President*
EMP: 60 **EST:** 1995
SQ FT: 1,150
SALES (est): 5MM-9.9MM **Privately Held**
SIC: 1771 Concrete contractor

(G-3615)
TERADYNE INC
5301 E River Rd Ste 106　(55421-3779)
PHONE....................763 586-0725
FAX: 763 586-9001
Teck Shuin, *Engineer*
Teck S Lim, *Engineer*
Thomas Eammons, *Engineer*
Jack Kretchmer, *Engineer*
William Betten, *Engineering*
EMP: 30
SALES (est): 5MM-9.9MM **Publicly Held**
WEB: www.teradyne.com
SIC: 8711 Manufactures test equipment for
electronic & electrical circuits; engineering
services
PA: Teradyne Inc
　　600 Riverpark Dr
　　North Reading MA 01864
　　978 370-2700

(G-3616)
THOR CONSTRUCTION INC
5400 Main St NE Ste 203　(55421-1132)
PHONE....................763 571-2580
FAX: 763 571-2631
Richard Copeland, *Ch of Bd*
Christopher Rowe, *President*
Denise Spanbauer, *General Mgr*
Ravi Norman, *COO*
Jim Lukasiewicz, *Vice Pres*
EMP: 84 **EST:** 1980
SQ FT: 2,800
SALES (est): 10MM-24.9MM **Privately Held**
SIC: 1542 Commercial & office building
contractor

(G-3617)
TOP SECRET HAIR SALON
3925 3rd St NE　(55421-3742)
PHONE....................651 500-9233
Courtney Leak, *Owner*
EMP: 32 **EST:** 2002
SQ FT: 2,700
SALES (est): 500-999K **Privately Held**
SIC: 7231 Unisex hair salon

(G-3618)
TOTAL CONCRETE SERVICES
2699 Rodeo Dr NE　(55449-5906)
PHONE....................763 786-8477
Randall Nissen, *President*
Linda Sides, *Administrator*
EMP: 25 **EST:** 1997
SALES (est): 1MM-4.9MM **Privately Held**
SIC: 1771 Concrete contractor

(G-3619)
**TOURCO'S FIRSTLINE TOURS
INC**
1313 Osborne Rd NE　(55432-2841)
PHONE....................763 780-2985
David R Ebertowski, *CEO*
Naomi Peifzer, *Office Mgr*
EST: 1997 **Privately Held**
WEB: www.tourco.net
SIC: 4725 Tour operator

(G-3620)
TOWN & COUNTRY BUS CO INC
9015 Radisson Rd NE (55449-4268)
PHONE............763 786-2510
FAX: 763 783-4505
Becky Clark, *Finance*
Bonnie Blommer, *Manager*
Carl Saarion, *Manager*
Chris Armbrust, *Manager*
Steve Richter, *Supervisor*
EMP: 60 EST: 1960
SQ FT: 5,000
SALES (est): 1MM-4.9MM **Privately Held**
SIC: 4151 4142 School bus service; long-distance bus charter service

(G-3621)
TRAVEL SUITES OF COON RAPIDS
Also Called: Country Suites By Carlson
155 Coon Rapids Blvd NW (55433-5812)
PHONE............763 780-3797
FAX: 763 780-3797
Susan Jung, *General Mgr*
Andrea Anderjack, *General Mgr*
Rebecca Baird, *Sales Staff*
Van Larson, *Mng Member*
EMP: 45 EST: 1987
SQ FT: 57,000
SALES (est): 1MM-4.9MM **Privately Held**
SIC: 7011 Traveler accommodations

(G-3622)
21ST CENTURY BANK (HQ)
9380 Central Ave NE # 120 (55434-3563)
PHONE............763 767-2178
Thomas P Dolphin, *President*
Becky Lapointe, *Vice Pres*
EMP: 27 EST: 1917 **Privately Held**
WEB: www.21stcenturybank.com
SIC: 6022 State commercial bank
PA: 21st Century Bank
9380 Central Ave NE # 120
Minneapolis MN 55434
763 767-2178

(G-3623)
21ST CENTURY BANK (PA)
9380 Central Ave NE # 120 (55434-3563)
PHONE............763 767-2178
Thomas P Dolphin, *CEO*
EST: 1980 **Privately Held**
WEB: www.21stcenturybank.com
SIC: 6022 State commercial bank

(G-3624)
TWIN CITY CUSTOM RAILINGS & GL
1582 93rd Ln NE (55449-4317)
PHONE............763 780-7314
Paul Johnson, *Owner*
EMP: 25 EST: 2003
SALES (est): 1MM-4.9MM **Privately Held**
WEB: www.twincitycustom.com
SIC: 1799 5031 7539 Manufactures prefabricated metal stairs, staircases & stair treads; fencing dealer; powertrain components repair service; wholesales lumber, plywood & millwork; fence construction contractor

(G-3625)
TWIN CITY SECURITY INC
519 Coon Rapids Blvd NW (55433-5520)
PHONE............763 784-4160
FAX: 763 784-7800
Virginia Nygren, *Office Mgr*
Larry Shrider, *Manager*
EMP: 300
SQ FT: 1,989
SALES (est): 5MM-9.9MM **Privately Held**
SIC: 7381 8748 Security guard service; business consulting services
PA: Twin City Security Inc
105 Garfield St S Ste 100
Cambridge MN 55008
763 689-3888

(G-3626)
TWV LP
12861 Ctrl Ave NE Apt 103 (55434-4800)
PHONE............651 291-1750
Jennifer Wille, *Principal*

EMP: 99 EST: 1992
SALES (est): 10MM-24.9MM **Privately Held**
SIC: 6513 Apartment building operator

(G-3627)
U S INSULATION INC
Also Called: Insulation Midwest
2201 108th Ln NE (55449-5259)
PHONE............763 785-1726
FAX: 763 785-1841
Richard Carmichael, *President*
EMP: 45 EST: 1982
SQ FT: 5,200
SALES (est): 1MM-4.9MM **Privately Held**
SIC: 1742 Building insulation installation service

(G-3628)
U-HAUL CO OF MINNESOTA (DH)
9890 Central Ave NE (55434-3540)
PHONE............763 780-9746
Mike Herron, *Principal*
William Piette, *Manager*
Kris Huwe, *Manager*
EMP: 60 EST: 1945
SQ FT: 100,000
SALES (corp-wide): 2B **Publicly Held**
WEB: www.uhaul.com
SIC: 7513 4225 7359 7519 Truck leasing & rental without drivers; lawn & garden equipment rental service; trailer rental service; warehousing & storage services
HQ: U-Haul International Inc
2727 N Central Ave
Phoenix AZ 85004
602 263-6011

(G-3629)
ULTEIG ENGINEERS INC
5201 E River Rd Ste 308 (55421-1035)
PHONE............763 571-2500
FAX: 763 571-1168
Brian Long, *Vice Pres*
Glenn Gogauer, *Vice Pres*
David Long, *Engineering*
Dan Sargeant, *Branch Mgr*
Jeffrey Schmit, *Manager*
EMP: 89
SALES (est): 10MM-24.9MM **Privately Held**
WEB: www.ulteig.com
SIC: 8711 Ship, boat, machine & product design services
PA: Ulteig Engineers Inc
4776 28th Ave S Ste 202
Fargo ND 58104
701 451-8300

(G-3630)
UNIVERSITY BILLIARDS INC
Also Called: Billards Street Cafe
7178 University Ave NE (55432-3100)
PHONE............763 574-1399
FAX: 763 571-1437
Ty Wilson, *President*
Dean Bradly, *General Mgr*
Nancy Asproth, *Accountant*
EMP: 40 EST: 1988
SQ FT: 13,000
SALES (est): 1MM-4.9MM **Privately Held**
SIC: 7999 Billiard parlor

(G-3631)
VISION WOODWORKING INC
7890 Hickory St NE (55432-2518)
PHONE............763 571-5767
John J Jarrett, *Vice Pres*
Jim Roth, *Engineer*
Marcia Palme, *Human Resources*
David Olson, *Director*
Donald Gamboni, *President*
EMP: 40 EST: 1994
SQ FT: 48,000
SALES (est): 1MM-4.9MM **Privately Held**
WEB: www.visionwoodworking.com
SIC: 5046 Manufactures wood store fixtures; wholesales store fixtures

(G-3632)
VISUAL IMPACT SIGNS INC
8732 W 35W Svc Dr NE (55449-6787)
PHONE............763 783-9411
Terrence Verdick, *President*
David Hood, *Vice Pres*
Jackie Verdick, *Office Mgr*

EMP: 25 EST: 1992
SQ FT: 27,600
SALES (est): 1MM-4.9MM **Privately Held**
SIC: 7389 Graphic layout service for printed circuitry

(G-3633)
VITATRON INC
7000 Central Ave NE (55432-3568)
PHONE............763 574-4000
FAX: 763 514-2209
Thomas S Anderson, *President*
Bob Hanvik, *Managing Dir*
William Stoessel, *Managing Dir*
Michael Demane, *COO*
John Meslow, *Exec VP*
EMP: 25 EST: 1986
SALES (est): 10MM-24.9MM **Publicly Held**
WEB: www.medtronic.com
SIC: 5047 Wholesales medical equipment & supplies
PA: Medtronic Inc
710 Medtronic Pkwy
Minneapolis MN 55432
763 514-4000

(G-3634)
WAGAMON BROTHERS INC
3719 3rd St NE (55421-3737)
PHONE............763 789-7227
Perry Wagamon, *President*
Wallace Wagamon, *Corp Secy*
Michael Knapper, *Manager*
Pat Wagamon, *Supervisor*
Barbie Aamodt, *Info Tech Mgr*
EMP: 25 EST: 1956
SQ FT: 20,000
SALES (est): 1MM-4.9MM **Privately Held**
WEB: www.wagamonbrothers.com
SIC: 7538 General automotive repair services

(G-3635)
WALGREEN CO
Also Called: Walgreens
10686 University Ave NW (55448-6141)
PHONE............763 755-1259
FAX: 763 754-1502
D R Caroon, *Manager*
EMP: 35
SQ FT: 14,924
SALES (est): 5MM-9.9MM **Publicly Held**
WEB: www.walgreens.com
SIC: 7384 Drug store; photofinishing laboratory
PA: Walgreen Co
200 Wilmot Rd
Deerfield IL 60015
847 914-2500

(G-3636)
WALGREEN CO
Also Called: Walgreens
6525 University Ave NE (55432-4331)
PHONE............763 586-0730
FAX: 763 586-0924
Dirk Streuber, *Manager*
Ben Brand, *Manager*
Dave Caroon, *Manager*
EMP: 30
SALES (est): 1MM-4.9MM **Publicly Held**
WEB: www.walgreens.com
SIC: 7384 Drug store; photofinishing laboratory
PA: Walgreen Co
200 Wilmot Rd
Deerfield IL 60015
847 914-2500

(G-3637)
WALTER'S RECYCLING & REFUSE
2830 101st Ave NE (55449-5705)
PO Box 67, Circle Pines (55014-0067)
PHONE............763 780-8464
FAX: 763 780-5620
George Walter, *President*
Greg Walter, *Vice Pres*
John Walter, *Treasurer*
EMP: 40 EST: 1980
SQ FT: 19,848
SALES (est): 5MM-9.9MM **Privately Held**
WEB: www.waltersrecycling.com
SIC: 4953 Rubbish collection & disposal services

(G-3638)
WASHINGTON INVENTORY SERVICE
7978 University Ave NE (55432-1860)
PHONE............763 784-2055
FAX: 763 784-0601
Michael Meyers, *Manager*
Tami Darland, *Manager*
EMP: 50
SALES (est): 1MM-4.9MM **Privately Held**
WEB: www.wisusa.com
SIC: 7389 Inventory computing service
PA: Washington Inventory Service
9265 Sky Park Ct Ste 100
San Diego CA 92123
858 565-8111

(G-3639)
WASTE MANAGEMENT OF WISCONSIN
10050 Naples St NE (55449-6900)
PHONE............952 890-1100
Ginger Kaladas, *Credit Staff*
Linda Trydahl, *Hum Res Coord*
Jennifer Klennert, *Marketing Staff*
Steve Metz, *Manager*
Jim Dillinger, *Manager*
EMP: 200
SALES (est): 25MM-49.9MM **Privately Held**
SIC: 4953 4212 Garbage collecting, destroying & processing services; local trucking without storage services
HQ: Waste Management of Wisconsin
W124N8925 Boundary Rd
Menomonee Falls WI 53051
262 251-4000

(G-3640)
WAYMORE TRANSPORTATION INC
8201 Hickory St NE (55432-1000)
PHONE............763 786-9076
FAX: 763 786-7669
Don Schille, *President*
Curt Carr, *Vice Pres*
Dave Wecker, *Treasurer*
EMP: 40 EST: 1995
SQ FT: 21,000
SALES (est): 1MM-4.9MM **Privately Held**
WEB: www.waymoretransportation.com
SIC: 4212 4213 4731 Local trucking without storage services; long-distance refrigerated trucking services; truck transportation brokers

(G-3641)
WELLS FARGO BANK, NATIONAL
12120 Aberdeen St NE (55449-4716)
PHONE............612 316-3965
FAX: 612 316-3970
Wanda Seiferth, *Manager*
EMP: 32
SALES (est): 5MM-9.9MM **Publicly Held**
SIC: 6021 National commercial bank
HQ: Wfc Holdings, Corp
420 Montgomery St
San Francisco CA 94104
415 396-7392

(G-3642)
WM HEALTHCARE SOLUTIONS INC ✿
Also Called: Wmhs Minnesota Wisconsin
961 73rd Ave NE (55432-3406)
PHONE............763 786-5555
Paul Pistono, *President*
EMP: 99 EST: 2009
SALES (est): 5MM-9.9MM **Privately Held**
SIC: 8099 Health & allied services

(G-3643)
WOODGROUP FIELD SERVICES INC
8010 Ranchers Rd NE (55432-1825)
PHONE............763 785-0650
Jerry Pinneke, *Opers Mgr*
Gary Welfred, *Manager*
EMP: 60 EST: 2006
SALES (est): 1MM-4.9MM **Privately Held**
SIC: 7629 Generator repair service

(G-3644)
YOUNG MEN'S CHRITN ASSOC OF
Also Called: Emma B Howe Family YMCA
8950 Springbrook Dr NW (55433-5848)
PHONE.................................763 785-7882
FAX: 763 785-9133
Jackie Huff, *Member*
Caytie Anderson, *Business Mgr*
Molly Hanson, *Sales Dir*
Chad Lanners, *Exec Dir*
EMP: 125
SALES (est): 5MM-9.9MM **Privately Held**
SIC: 7011 7991 7997 Hotel operated by YMCA/YMHA; membership recreation club; physical fitness center

MINNEAPOLIS
Hennepin County

(G-3645)
A A A MINNEAPOLIS
5400 Auto Club Way (55416-2513)
PHONE.................................952 944-9585
FAX: 952 927-2559
Steven J Frank, *President*
Bryan Miller, *Manager*
EMP: 100 EST: 1902
SQ FT: 40,000
SALES (est): 10MM-24.9MM **Privately Held**
SIC: 8699 4724 Automobile owners' association; travel club; travel agency

(G-3646)
A B E CONSTRUCTION CO
2525 Nevada Ave N Ste 307 (55427-3643)
PHONE.................................763 542-9070
Abraham Thomas, *President*
Abha Thomas, *Treasurer*
EMP: 28 EST: 1980
SQ FT: 2,000
SALES (est): 1MM-4.9MM **Privately Held**
SIC: 1629 Waste water & sewage treatment plant construction

(G-3647)
A CHANCE TO GROW INC
1800 2nd St NE (55418-4306)
PHONE.................................612 789-1236
FAX: 612 706-5555
Ellen Jackson, *CFO*
James Ricketts, *Finance*
Laurel Kelly, *Human Resources*
Christophe Josephes, *Web Proj Mgr*
Paul Cluskey, *Director*
EMP: 99 EST: 1982
SQ FT: 42,000
SALES (est): 1MM-4.9MM **Privately Held**
SIC: 8322 8082 8093 8351 8748 Child & youth services; business consulting services; elementary & secondary school; child day care service; home health care services; specialty outpatient clinic

(G-3648)
A J SPANJERS CO INC
9257 W River Rd (55444-1219)
PHONE.................................763 424-8288
FAX: 763 424-8731
Robert L Spanjers, *President*
Robert A Pe, *Corp Secy*
A Robert, *Corp Secy*
Randall J Spanjers, *Treasurer*
Maynard Eggersgluess, *Manager*
EMP: 40 EST: 1925
SQ FT: 5,000
SALES (est): 10MM-24.9MM **Privately Held**
SIC: 1542 1799 Commercial & office building renovation & repair services; construction caulking contractor

(G-3649)
A T & T CORP
901 Marquette Ave Fl 9 (55402-3205)
PHONE.................................612 376-5401
FAX: 612 376-5356
Brian Coleman, *District Mgr*
Andy Welch, *District Mgr*
David P Honer, *Exec VP*
Cathy Krentz, *Prdtn Mgr*
Larry M Newman, *VP Opers-Prdtn-*
EMP: 500 **Publicly Held**
WEB: www.att.com
SIC: 4813 8741 Wired telecommunications carrier & service; management services
HQ: AT&T Corp
175 E Houston St
San Antonio TX 78205
210 821-4105

(G-3650)
A TO Z INTERNATIONAL INC
8933 Lyndale Ave S (55420-2778)
PHONE.................................612 729-2328
FAX: 612 729-2320
Orville Klemp, *President*
Kevin Moore, *Vice Pres*
Kevin Rumpza, *Manager*
Vern Faber, *Manager*
EMP: 50 EST: 1965
SALES (est): 1MM-4.9MM **Privately Held**
SIC: 7359 Rental center

(G-3651)
A WORLD OF FISH INC
1516 E 66th St (55423-2647)
PHONE.................................612 866-2026
FAX: 612 866-8873
Ted Levin, *President*
Jill Levin, *Corp Secy*
EMP: 25 EST: 1975
SQ FT: 7,000
SALES (est): 1MM-4.9MM **Privately Held**
WEB: www.aworldoffish.com
SIC: 5199 Retails tropical fish; wholesales tropical fish; retails aquarium supplies; retails pet supplies

(G-3652)
A-ABC APPLIANCE & HEATING INC
Also Called: Total Comfort
4000 Winnetka Ave N # 100 (55427-1251)
PHONE.................................763 383-8383
FAX: 763 383-8500
Gary Katz, *President*
Amy Reed, *Manager*
Len Erickson, *Manager*
EMP: 35 EST: 1980
SALES (est): 1MM-4.9MM **Privately Held**
SIC: 1711 Heating & air conditioning contractor

(G-3653)
A1 CONTRACT CLEANING INC
7600 Boone Ave N Ste 71 (55428-1014)
PHONE.................................763 544-3847
Bob Todman, *President*
EMP: 30 EST: 1994
SALES (est): 500-999K **Privately Held**
WEB: www.a1cc.com
SIC: 7349 Building cleaning & maintenance services

(G-3654)
AAA WICKS FURNACE DUCT
12810 54th Ave N (55442-1718)
PHONE.................................651 770-1263
Dave Regan, *President*
EMP: 70 EST: 1999
SQ FT: 4,000
SALES (est): 5MM-9.9MM **Privately Held**
SIC: 7699 Cleaning service

(G-3655)
AAF-MCQUAY INC
13600 Industrial Park Blvd (55441-3743)
PO Box 1551 (55440-1551)
PHONE.................................763 553-5330
FAX: 763 553-1667
Jim Cullen, *General Mgr*
Michael Caolo, *Corp Secy*
Katayama Yoshibumi, *Exec VP*
Anne Awsumb, *Vice Pres*
Claudio Capozio, *Vice Pres*
EMP: 450
SALES (est): 50MM-99.9MM **Privately Held**
WEB: www.aafintl.com
SIC: 1711 5064 7382 Manufactures heating & air conditioning combination units; wholesales household appliance parts; heating & air conditioning contractor; manufactures complete domestic or industrial air conditioning units; security systems services
PA: AAF-McQuay Inc
10300 Ormsby Park Pl # 600
Louisville KY 40223
502 637-0011

(G-3656)
AAFEDT, FORDE, GRAY, & MONSON
150 S 5th St Ste 2600 (55402-4226)
PHONE.................................612 339-8965
FAX: 612 349-6839
Michael Aafedt, *President*
Amie Allison, *Mktg Coord*
Alysa Hannula, *Office Mgr*
Jeff Pricco, *Executive*
Susanne Glasser, *Associate*
EMP: 40 EST: 1920
SALES (est): 5MM-9.9MM **Privately Held**
WEB: www.aafedt.com
SIC: 8111 General practice attorney's or lawyer's office

(G-3657)
AARCEE PARTY & TENT RENTAL
5300 W 35th St (55416-2653)
PHONE.................................952 922-7233
FAX: 952 922-3743
Richard P Nelson, *President*
Charles Nelson, *Vice Pres*
EMP: 30 EST: 1956
SQ FT: 30,000
SALES (est): 1MM-4.9MM **Privately Held**
WEB: www.aarcee.com
SIC: 7359 7299 7389 Party supplies rental services; party & special event planning services; retails gifts & novelties; party supply services

(G-3658)
AARP
228 Mrket St Mall Of Amer (55425)
PHONE.................................952 858-9040
FAX: 952 858-9131
Roni Schultz, *Manager*
Michele Kimball, *Director*
EMP: 51 **Privately Held**
SIC: 8399 Health systems agency
PA: AARP
601 E St NW Ste A1200
Washington DC 20049
202 434-2277

(G-3659)
ABBOT NORTHWESTERN HOSPITAL
Also Called: Piper Breast Center
913 E 26th St Ste 402 (55404-4515)
PHONE.................................612 863-3150
Cystral Schlosser, *Med Doctor*
Daniel H Dunn, *Surgeon*
John F O'Leary, *Surgeon*
Margit L Bretzke, *Surgeon*
Diane K Stoller, *Surgeon*
EMP: 35 EST: 1994
SALES (est): 1MM-4.9MM **Privately Held**
SIC: 8099 Blood bank

(G-3660)
ABBOTT NORTHWESTERN HOSPITAL
800 E 28th St (55407-3723)
PHONE.................................612 863-4000
Gordon M Sprenger, *CEO*
Robert K Spinner, *President*
Mark Miglorie, *Ch of Surgery*
Terry Graner, *Vice Pres*
Ben Bache-Wiig, *Vice Pres*
EST: 1882
SQ FT: 900,000 **Privately Held**
WEB: www.allina.com
SIC: 8062 Medical hospital
PA: Allina Health System
2925 Chicago Ave
Minneapolis MN 55407
612 775-5000

(G-3661)
ABM JANITORIAL SERVICES - NTHN
760 Harding St NE (55413-2817)
PHONE.................................612 378-0646
FAX: 612 378-3934
Ann Fenderson, *VP Admin*
Phil Helper, *Vice Pres*
Jeffory L Southard, *Vice Pres*
Greg Wohlforth, *Manager*
Joan Padal, *Manager*
EMP: 30
SALES (est): 500-999K **Publicly Held**
WEB: www.abm.com
SIC: 7349 Janitorial & custodial services
HQ: ABM Janitorial Services - Nthn
420 Taylor St 200
San Francisco CA 94102
415 733-4000

(G-3662)
ABRA INC (PA)
6601 Shingle Creek Pkwy Ste 20 (55430-1788)
PHONE.................................763 561-7220
FAX: 763 561-7433
Roland Benjamin, *CEO*
Duane Rouse, *President*
Tim Adelmann, *COO*
Julie J Borchert, *Vice Pres*
Kevin Comrie, *Sales Staff*
EMP: 65 EST: 1984
SQ FT: 4,500 **Privately Held**
WEB: www.abraauto.com
SIC: 7532 6794 Automotive body shop; selling or licensing of franchises

(G-3663)
ACA INTERNATIONAL (PA)
Also Called: AMERICAN COLLECTORS ASSOCIATIO
4040 W 70th St (55435-4104)
PO Box 390106 (55439-0106)
PHONE.................................952 926-6547
FAX: 952 926-1624
Rozanne M Andersen, *CEO*
Mike Klippenstein, *Member*
Thomas Rongitsch, *Member*
Lee Brown, *Corp Secy*
Natalie Meyer, *Corp Secy*
EMP: 65 EST: 1939
SQ FT: 30,000
SALES (corp-wide): 7.19M **Privately Held**
SIC: 8611 7389 8743 Trade association; publishes magazines without printing; legal & tax service; nondegree granting continuing education educational services; public relations & publicity services

(G-3664)
ACCENTURE LLP
333 S 7th St Ste 500 (55402-2415)
PHONE.................................612 277-0000
FAX: 612 277-1010
Sheila Babin, *Finance*
Arindam Taran, *Office Mgr*
Michelle Rose, *Manager*
Paul Larsen, *Manager*
Sohanny Schwartz, *Manager*
EMP: 140
SALES (est): 10MM-24.9MM **Privately Held**
WEB: www.wavesecurities.com
SIC: 8742 8748 Management consulting services; business consulting services
DH: Accenture LLP
161 N Clark St Ste 1100
Chicago IL 60601
312 693-0161

(G-3665)
ACCESS COMMUNICATIONS INC
5005 Cheshire Ln N Ste 1 (55446-3719)
PHONE.................................763 545-9998
FAX: 763 545-1494
Randy Herman, *CEO*
Arlyn Birkholz, *President*
Chris Holtman, *Sales Mgr*
Dave Ryan, *Manager*
EMP: 29 EST: 1997
SQ FT: 9,000 **Privately Held**
WEB: www.access-com.net
SIC: 4899 Data communication services

www.HarrisInfo.com
166

2011 Harris Minnesota
Services Directory

▲=Import ▼=Export
◆=Import/Export

(G-3666)
ACCESS INFORMATION SYSTEMS INC
1210 W 96th St Ste A (55431-2602)
PHONE 952 888-8503
FAX: 952 888-5562
W R Allen, *President*
Scott Simonett, *Vice Pres*
Julie Payne, *Controller*
Scott Simmonett, *VP Sales*
Julie Olsen, *Manager*
EMP: 150 EST: 1991
SQ FT: 10,000
SALES (est): 10MM-24.9MM **Privately Held**
SIC: 6531 6541 7389 Real estate appraiser; title & trust company; inspection & testing service

(G-3667)
ACCESSABILITY INC
360 Hoover St NE (55413-2940)
PHONE 612 331-5958
FAX: 612 331-2448
Barbara Arnold, *President*
Bruce Groves, *Corp Secy*
Stephen Dahl, *Prdtn Mgr*
Lewis Leversedge, *Accountant*
Lisa Lundmark, *Manager*
EMP: 77 EST: 1948
SQ FT: 43,000
SALES (est): 5MM-9.9MM **Privately Held**
WEB: www.accessability.org
SIC: 7389 8331 Sewing contractor; skill training center

(G-3668)
ACCLAIM BENEFITS LLC
2905 NW Blvd Ste 220 (55441-2644)
PHONE 763 278-4620
Jeffrey Ackerson, *Member*
Thomas Singsank, *CFO*
EMP: 60 EST: 2006
SQ FT: 55,000
SALES (est): 1MM-4.9MM **Privately Held**
WEB: www.acclaimbenefits.com
SIC: 7389 Financial service
PA: Total Administrative Services
2302 Intl Ln Frnt 1 1 Frnt
Madison WI 53704
608 241-1900

(G-3669)
ACCORD BENEFIT RESOURCES INC
945 Highway 169 N (55441-6405)
PHONE 763 746-9004
Sully Sullivan, *Principal*
EMP: 30 EST: 1999
SALES (est): 1MM-4.9MM **Privately Held**
SIC: 8742 Compensation & benefits planning consultant

(G-3670)
ACE ELECTRICAL CONTRACTORS INC
5465 Highway 169 N (55442-1903)
PHONE 763 694-8800
FAX: 763 694-8888
Larry Palm, *CEO*
Gary Gniffke, *President*
EMP: 85 EST: 1995
SQ FT: 12,000
SALES (est): 5MM-9.9MM **Privately Held**
WEB: www.aceelectrical.net
SIC: 1731 General electrical contractor

(G-3671)
ACE NICOLLET RENTAL PLACE
3805 Nicollet Ave (55409-1303)
PHONE 612 822-3121
FAX: 612 822-4874
Julene Lind, *Owner*
EMP: 25 EST: 2001
SALES (est): Under 500K **Privately Held**
SIC: 7359 Equipment rental & leasing services

(G-3672)
ACE SUPPLY CO INC
3825 Edgewood Ave S (55426-4403)
PHONE 952 929-1618
FAX: 952 929-9716
Bruce Hasselbring, *President*

Darrell Hurd, *Controller*
Cindy Motzko, *Sales Mgr*
Glen Swan, *Manager*
EMP: 32 EST: 1958
SQ FT: 34,000
SALES (est): 10MM-24.9MM **Privately Held**
WEB: www.aircontrolessentials.com
SIC: 5075 Wholesales air conditioning & ventilation equipment & supplies

(G-3673)
ACME COMEDY CO
708 N 1st St Ste G31 (55401-1144)
PHONE 612 338-6393
Luis Lee, *President*
Rick Rice, *Manager*
EMP: 30 EST: 2001
SALES (est): 1MM-4.9MM **Privately Held**
WEB: www.acmecomedycompany.com
SIC: 7929 Entertainment services

(G-3674)
ACOUSTICS ASSOCIATES INC
1250 Zane Ave N (55422-4608)
PHONE 763 544-8901
FAX: 763 544-2928
Rick Dehmer, *President*
Steve Ficocello, *Exec VP*
Alan Schwartz, *Vice Pres*
Dennis Dickson, *Vice Pres*
Gary Carlson, *Vice Pres*
▲ EMP: 120 EST: 1962
SQ FT: 20,000
SALES (est): 10MM-24.9MM **Privately Held**
WEB: www.acousticsassociates.com
SIC: 1742 1771 Acoustical & ceiling work contractor; flooring contractor

(G-3675)
ACRYLIC DESIGN ASSOCIATES INC
6050 Nathan Ln N (55442-1662)
PHONE 763 559-8392
FAX: 763 551-0019
William M Neely Sr, *CEO*
William McNeely Jr, *President*
Stefie J Orth, *Corp Secy*
Tony Hauer, *Engineer*
▲ EMP: 100 EST: 1976
SQ FT: 250,000
SALES (est): 5MM-9.9MM **Privately Held**
WEB: www.acrylicdesign.com
SIC: 5162 Manufactures signs & advertising specialties; manufactures partitions & fixtures; wholesales plastics sheets & rods

(G-3676)
ACTION MAILING SERVICES INC
12811 16th Ave N (55441-4558)
PHONE 763 557-6767
FAX: 763 557-9115
Tony Zirnhelt, *President*
Mike Gilbert, *General Mgr*
Michelle Hansen, *Manager*
Sandra Brew, *Manager*
Todd Kerin, *Manager*
EMP: 80 EST: 1967
SQ FT: 42,000
SALES (est): 5MM-9.9MM **Privately Held**
WEB: www.actionmailingservice.com
SIC: 7331 Direct mail advertising service

(G-3677)
ACTIVAR INC
Also Called: J L Industries
4450 W 78th Street Cir (55435-5416)
PHONE 952 835-6850
Kevin Shephard, *Product Mgr*
Kirby Bayerle, *Branch Mgr*
Greg Kannan, *Manager*
Lex Mike, *Telecom Exec*
EMP: 50
SALES (est): 5MM-9.9MM **Privately Held**
WEB: www.activar.com
SIC: 5063 5087 5099 Manufactures show, display, or storage cabinets; wholesales electrical panelboards; wholesales firefighting equipment; wholesales fire extinguishers
PA: Activar Inc
7808 Creekridge Cir # 200
Minneapolis MN 55439
952 944-3533

(G-3678)
ACTIVSTYLE INC (HQ)
3100 Pacific St (55411-1626)
PHONE 612 520-9333
FAX: 612 520-9300
Keith Trowbridge, *President*
Burt Haigh, *CFO*
Gregg T Anderson, *Treasurer*
Guy White, *Marketing Staff*
Christy Gruba, *Manager*
EMP: 65 EST: 1997
SQ FT: 50,000
SALES (corp-wide): 206.90K **Privately Held**
WEB: www.activstyle.com
SIC: 5047 Wholesales incontinent care products & supplies
PA: Riverside Partners LLC
630 5th Ave Ste 2400
New York NY 10111
212 265-6575

(G-3679)
ACTS OF ST PAUL
3353 Columbus Ave (55407-2032)
PHONE 612 823-4237
Gael Larfen, *Exec Dir*
EMP: 28 **Privately Held**
SIC: 8641 8699 Youth organizations; charitable organization

(G-3680)
ADMINISTRATIVE OFFICE OF THE
Also Called: US District Crt Mnnapolis Bldg
300 S 4th St (55415-1320)
PHONE 612 664-5050
Francis Dosal, *Manager*
Richard Fletten, *Manager*
Sam Kaplin, *Supervisor*
EMP: 60
SALES (est): 5MM-9.9MM **Privately Held**
WEB: www.ao.uscourts.gov
SIC: 8111 Criminal law office
HQ: Administrative Office of The
1 Columbus Cir NE
Washington DC 20002
202 502-3800

(G-3681)
ADMIRAL-MERCHANTS MOTOR
215 S 11th St (55403-2520)
PHONE 612 332-4819
FAX: 612 332-4765
Marion D Short, *President*
Brian P Short, *Exec VP*
Michael Fielding, *Vice Pres*
Penny Lynner, *Vice Pres*
Douglas V Swanson V, *CFO*
EMP: 47 EST: 1945
SQ FT: 2,000
SALES (est): 5MM-9.9MM **Privately Held**
WEB: www.calhouncompanies.com
SIC: 4213 Contract haulers
PA: Calhoun Management Co
215 S 11th St
Minneapolis MN 55403
612 332-4732

(G-3682)
ADOLFSON & PETERSON INC (PA)
6701 W 23rd St (55426-2801)
PO Box 9377 (55440-9377)
PHONE 952 544-1561
FAX: 952 525-2333
Douglas W Jaeger, *CEO*
Scott A Weicht, *President*
Brook Adolfson, *Corp Secy*
Dennis Mulvey, *Senior VP*
Kent Weicht, *Senior VP*
EMP: 200 EST: 1946
SQ FT: 15,000
SALES (corp-wide): 616.02M **Privately Held**
WEB: www.adolfsonpeterson.com
SIC: 1542 New commercial & office building construction; school building construction; institutional building construction

(G-3683)
ADULT HELP & COMPANION CARE
4584 Cedar Lake Rd S # 5 (55416-3733)
PHONE 952 377-0411
Christian Rivard, *President*
Pat Hoehn, *Manager*
EMP: 48 EST: 2003
SALES (est): 1MM-4.9MM **Privately Held**
WEB: www.adulthelpcare.com
SIC: 8082 Home health care services

(G-3684)
ADULTS SAVING KIDS
1901 Portland Ave (55404-2713)
PHONE 612 872-0684
Amy Hartman, *Manager*
Doris Williams, *Exec Dir*
Al Erickson, *Exec Dir*
Phillas Beatty, *Director*
EMP: 75 EST: 2000 **Privately Held**
WEB: www.adultssavingkids.org
SIC: 8641 Youth organizations

(G-3685)
ADVANCE AMERICA SERVICES INC
Also Called: Adam Services
2211 Edgewood Ave S (55426-2822)
PHONE 952 544-7273
FAX: 952 544-7461
Joseph Regan, *President*
▲ EMP: 35
SQ FT: 4,500
SALES (est): 1MM-4.9MM **Privately Held**
WEB: www.advanceamericanloan.com
SIC: 4151 School bus service

(G-3686)
ADVANCED CARE INC
1415 Park Ave (55404-1551)
PHONE 612 721-1957
FAX: 612 721-6522
Victor Ogbuehi, *President*
EMP: 89
SALES (est): 1MM-4.9MM **Privately Held**
SIC: 8082 7361 Home health care services; nurses' registry service

(G-3687)
ADVANCED CONCRETE & MASONRY
Also Called: Acm
9020 Wyoming Ave N (55445-1839)
PHONE 763 424-9365
FAX: 763 424-6511
Tim D Kopen, *President*
EMP: 30 EST: 1989
SALES (est): 1MM-4.9MM **Privately Held**
SIC: 1741 Masonry & stonework contractor

(G-3688)
ADVANCED DUPLICATION SERVICES
2155 Niagara Ln N Ste 120 (55447-4654)
PHONE 763 449-5500
FAX: 763 449-5555
Butch Herzog, *Vice Pres*
Pat Locklear, *Vice Pres*
Greg Schoener, *Vice Pres*
Scott Bartsch, *CFO*
Doug Ostrich, *CFO*
EMP: 200 EST: 1989
SQ FT: 48,000
SALES (est): 10MM-24.9MM **Privately Held**
SIC: 7379 Computer related maintenance service

(G-3689)
ADVANCED INFORMATICS LLC
10 2nd St NE Ste 300 (55413-2270)
PHONE 612 253-0130
FAX: 612 253-0135
Craig Skiem, *CEO*
Karl Hartquist, *CFO*
Paul Welle, *Director*
Quinn Montgomery, *Officer*
EMP: 34 EST: 1998
SQ FT: 1,200
SALES (est): 1MM-4.9MM **Privately Held**
WEB: www.advancedinformatics.com
SIC: 7371 Computer software development

(PA)=Parent Co (HQ)=Headquarters (DH)=Div Headquarters
✿ = New business established in last 2 years

2011 Harris Minnesota
Services Directory

© Harris InfoSource 1-866-281-6415

167

(G-3690)
AEC ENGINEERING INC (PA)
400 1st Ave N Ste 400 (55401-1722)
PHONE..............................612 332-8905
FAX: 612 334-3101
Randal Lipps, *President*
John R Buzek, *Senior VP*
Thomas E Lorentz, *Senior VP*
Roberta S Bean, *CFO*
Beth Harrill, *Manager*
EMP: 38 EST: 1980
SQ FT: 11,000
SALES (corp-wide): 5.10M Privately Held
WEB: www.aecengineering.net
SIC: 8711 Professional engineers

(G-3691)
AECOM TECHNICAL SERVICES INC
3033 Campus Dr Ste 290 (55441-2651)
PHONE..............................763 551-1001
FAX: 763 551-2499
Joe Odegaard, *Manager*
Mike Valentine, *Manager*
EMP: 50
SALES (est): 5MM-9.9MM Privately Held
WEB: www.earthtech.com
SIC: 8711 8742 8748 Engineering services; industrial hygiene consultant; environmental consultant
HQ: Aecom Technical Services Inc
515 S Flower St Fl 4
Los Angeles CA 90071
562 951-2000

(G-3692)
AEG MANAGEMENT TWN LLC
Also Called: Target Center
600 1st Ave N Ste SKY (55403-1400)
PHONE..............................612 673-1300
Steve Mattson, *General Mgr*
Keith Hilsgen, *Finance*
Philip Ansutz, *Mng Member*
EMP: 1500 EST: 2007
SALES (est): 100MM-499.9MM Privately Held
WEB: www.anschutzfilmgroup.com
SIC: 7941 Sports support services
PA: Anschutz Co
555 17th St Ste 2400
Denver CO 80202
303 298-1000

(G-3693)
AEGON USA INC
3600 Amercn Blvd W # 200 (55431-4507)
PHONE..............................952 893-6767
Larry Berhow, *Vice Pres*
Nancy Johnson, *Vice Pres*
Jim Bean, *Manager*
Lisa Bergerson, *Manager*
Jon Fletcher, *Manager*
EMP: 200
SALES (est): 100MM-499.9MM Privately Held
WEB: www.aegonins.com
SIC: 6311 Life insurance carrier
HQ: Aegon USA Inc
1111 N Charles St
Baltimore MD 21201
410 576-4571

(G-3694)
AFFILIATED EMERGENCY
Also Called: Affilted Emrgncy Vtrinary Svcs
4708 Olson Memorial Hwy (55422-5144)
PHONE..............................763 529-6560
FAX: 763 529-1667
Steve Schulberg, *Manager*
EMP: 25 EST: 1979
SQ FT: 3,000 Privately Held
WEB: www.aevs.com
SIC: 0742 Animal hospital services

(G-3695)
AFFILIATED PEDIATRIC DENTISTS
Also Called: Dentistry For Children
7373 France Ave S Ste 402 (55435-4598)
PHONE..............................952 831-4400
FAX: 952 893-3041
Kurt J King DDS, *President*
Mark Greenwood DDS, *Treasurer*
EMP: 28 EST: 1965

SALES (est): 1MM-4.9MM Privately Held
SIC: 8021 Dental office

(G-3696)
AFRICAN AMERICAN FAMILY SVCS (PA)
Also Called: INSTITUTE FOR BLACK CHEMICAL A
2616 Nicollet Ave (55408-1628)
PO Box 8900 (55408-0900)
PHONE..............................612 871-7878
FAX: 612 871-2567
Randy Hager, *Controller*
Danielle Mische, *Sales Staff*
Gwendolyn Velez, *Exec Dir*
Lissa Jones, *Exec Dir*
Richard Newberry, *Bd of Directors*
EMP: 30 EST: 1974
SQ FT: 12,000
SALES (corp-wide): 1.81M Privately Held
SIC: 8322 Nontreatment drug abuse counselor

(G-3697)
AFRICAN AMERICAN FAMILY SVCS
100 W Franklin Ave (55404-2433)
PO Box 8900 (55408-0900)
PHONE..............................612 813-0782
Briana Miller, *Sales Executive*
Lissa Jones, *Manager*
EMP: 25
SALES (est): 1MM-4.9MM Privately Held
SIC: 8322 Nontreatment drug abuse counselor
PA: African American Family Svcs
2616 Nicollet Ave
Minneapolis MN 55408
612 871-7878

(G-3698)
AGAPE 24 HOUR PRESCHOOL
2304 Emerson Ave N (55411-2050)
PHONE..............................612 287-9775
Diane Tipato, *Director*
EMP: 25 EST: 1987
SALES (est): 500-999K Privately Held
SIC: 8351 Preschool center

(G-3699)
AGMOTION INC (PA)
730 2nd Ave S Ste 700 (55402-2480)
PHONE..............................612 486-3800
Rolf Peters, *CEO*
Tim Carlson, *President*
Wint Ritchie, *Vice Pres*
Bill Hren, *CFO*
William F Hren, *CFO*
▲ EMP: 30 EST: 2000
SQ FT: 6,000 Privately Held
SIC: 5153 Wholesales grains

(G-3700)
AGRAMSON ENTERPRISES INC
Also Called: Seniors' Choice At Home
9909 S Shore Dr Ste 1000 (55441-5037)
PHONE..............................763 546-1599
Jim Agramson, *President*
EMP: 90 EST: 1994
SALES (est): 1MM-4.9MM Privately Held
SIC: 8322 Homemakers' services

(G-3701)
AJK CUTTERS INC
Also Called: Great Clips
8136 Highway 7 (55426-3903)
PHONE..............................952 933-7525
Ray Barton, *President*
EMP: 50 EST: 1982
SALES (est): 1MM-4.9MM Privately Held
SIC: 7231 Unisex hair salon

(G-3702)
AL JOHNSON TRUCKING INC
81 Saint Anthony Pkwy Ste 2
(55418-1244)
PHONE..............................612 253-1000
FAX: 612 788-8652
Alvin Johnson, *President*
EMP: 50 EST: 1965
SQ FT: 48,000
SALES (est): 5MM-9.9MM Privately Held
SIC: 4213 4212 Over the road trucking; local trucking without storage services

(G-3703)
ALBINSON REPROGRAPHICS LLC (PA)
1401 Glenwood Ave (55405-1226)
PHONE..............................612 374-1120
Paul Karpinko, *General Mgr*
Rodger Stiger, *General Mgr*
Bryan C Thomas, *Member*
Joe Zmuda, *Sales Mgr*
Lonny L Foote, *Sales Mgr*
EMP: 40 EST: 1946
SQ FT: 38,000 Privately Held
WEB: www.albinson.com
SIC: 5199 7334 Wholesales architect's supplies; blueprinting services; commercial printing; wholesales advertising specialties; retails drafting equipment & supplies; photocopying & duplicating services; plate making services; typesetting service

(G-3704)
ALIGN HEALTH INC ✪
Also Called: Bright Star Healthcare
1516 W Lake St Ste 300 (55408-6601)
PHONE..............................612 821-7909
Perry Burke, *President*
EMP: 74 EST: 2009
SALES (est): 5MM-9.9MM Privately Held
SIC: 8011 Physicians' office & clinic

(G-3705)
ALIGNEX INC
7200 Metro Blvd (55439-2128)
PHONE..............................952 888-6801
Steve Keinath, *President*
Sue Feik, *Accountant*
EMP: 25 EST: 2003
SQ FT: 8,000
SALES (est): 5MM-9.9MM Privately Held
WEB: www.alignex.com
SIC: 7372 Software publisher

(G-3706)
ALIVE PROMO INC
2401 Edgewood Ave S # 100
(55426-2825)
PHONE..............................952 960-3677
Sam Rogers, *CEO*
Paul Demmer, *CFO*
Matt Rogers, *Director*
EMP: 30 EST: 2000
SQ FT: 10,000
SALES (est): 1MM-4.9MM Privately Held
WEB: www.alivepromo.com
SIC: 7319 Display advertising services

(G-3707)
ALL AMERICAN MORTGAGE LENDING
7420 Unity Ave N Ste 308 (55443-3136)
PHONE..............................763 560-5815
Kayode S Ologunde, *President*
EMP: 30 EST: 1999
SALES (est): 1MM-4.9MM Privately Held
WEB: www.allamericanlendinginc.com
SIC: 6163 Mortgage brokers service arranging for loans, using money of others

(G-3708)
ALL ENGLAND ENTERPRISES LTD (PA)
Also Called: Brits
1110 Nicollet Mall (55403-2405)
PHONE..............................612 332-8011
M E Purdy Jr, *Partner*
Stuart Higgins, *Partner*
Richard Stanchik, *Controller*
Ann Mortenson, *Coordinator*
EST: 1989
SQ FT: 6,000
SALES (corp-wide): 7.50M Privately Held
WEB: www.britspub.com
SIC: 8742 Drinking establishment; real estate consultant

(G-3709)
ALL FIRE TEST CO INC
915 Washington Ave N (55401-1030)
PHONE..............................612 332-3473
FAX: 612 321-9177
Michael Stich, *President*
Angie Boettner, *Vice Pres*
EMP: 30

EST: 1976
SQ FT: 10,000
SALES (est): 1MM-4.9MM Privately Held
SIC: 7389 Fire extinguisher services; retails fire extinguishers

(G-3710)
ALL FURNITURE INSTALLATION INC
675 Stinson Blvd Ste 100 (55413-2762)
PHONE..............................763 571-2203
Dion Schilling, *CEO*
EMP: 25 EST: 1995
SQ FT: 1,000
SALES (est): 1MM-4.9MM Privately Held
WEB: www.allfurnitureinc.com
SIC: 4214 1799 Local furniture moving & storage; office furniture installation service

(G-3711)
ALL TEMPORARIES CARING
3638 Central Ave NE (55418-1343)
PHONE..............................612 378-1474
Donna Liveringhoust, *President*
Julie Liveringhouse, *Data Proc Exec*
EMP: 32 EST: 1995
SALES (est): 1MM-4.9MM Privately Held
SIC: 8099 Health & allied services

(G-3712)
ALLERGY & ASTHMA SPECIALISTS (PA)
825 Nicollet Mall Ste 1149 (55402-2750)
PHONE..............................612 338-3333
FAX: 612 349-3838
Harold B Kaiser, *President*
Gary D Berman, *Principal*
Philip Halverson MD, *Vice Pres*
Angela Jensen, *Manager*
Hemalini Mehta, *Allrgy & Immnlg*
EMP: 30 EST: 1974 Privately Held
SIC: 8011 Allergist office

(G-3713)
ALLIANT PRECISION FUSE CO
4700 Nathan Ln N (55442-2512)
PHONE..............................763 744-5000
Blake Larson, *President*
EMP: 99 EST: 1990
SALES (est): 5MM-9.9MM Privately Held
SIC: 7389 Business support services

(G-3714)
ALLIANZ LIFE INSURANCE CO OF (PA)
5701 Golden Hills Dr (55416-1297)
PO Box 59060 (55459-0060)
PHONE..............................763 765-6500
FAX: 763 542-9944
Gary Bhojwani, *President*
David Ottinger, *Partner*
Monica Yeager, *Partner*
Maureen S Philips, *Corp Secy*
Maureen Phillips, *Counsel*
EMP: 1800 EST: 1987 Privately Held
WEB: www.lifetracnetwork.com
SIC: 6311 Life insurance carrier
PA: Allianz AG
K"niginstr. 28
MšNCHEN Germany

(G-3715)
ALLIED ADJUSTERS INC
222 S 9th St Ste 1300 (55402-3332)
PO Box 583479 (55458-3479)
PHONE..............................612 766-3700
Peter J Huber, *President*
Jeff Wanat, *Vice Pres*
Steve Davis, *CFO*
EMP: 25 EST: 1972
SQ FT: 17,800
SALES (est): 1MM-4.9MM Publicly Held
WEB: www.wrbc.com
SIC: 6411 Insurance claim processing
HQ: Berkley Risk Administrators Co
222 S 9th St Ste 1300
Minneapolis MN 55402
612 766-3000

▲=Import ▼=Export
◆=Import/Export

(G-3716)
ALLIED PROFESSIONALS INC
3209 W 76th St Ste 201 (55435-5246)
PHONE..............................952 832-5101
FAX: 952 832-0656
Pat Mulligan, *President*
Robert Pihart, *Human Res Mgr*
Lisa Mulligan, *Info Tech Dir*
EMP: 300 **EST:** 1989
SALES (est): 5MM-9.9MM **Privately Held**
WEB: www.alliedprofessionals.com
SIC: 7363 7361 8049 Temporary help
service; dental hygienists' office;
employment agency services

(G-3717)
ALLINA HEALTH SYSTEM
407 W 66th St (55423-2374)
PHONE..............................612 798-8800
FAX: 612 798-8833
Jean Fish, *Manager*
Goytree Hakim, *Administrator*
Louise Brandt, *Supervisor*
Rebecca Ormsby, *Obstetrician*
Patricia M Pettit, *Obstetrician*
EMP: 60
SALES (est): 5MM-9.9MM **Privately Held**
WEB: www.allina.com
SIC: 8011 Medical center
PA: Allina Health System
      2925 Chicago Ave
      Minneapolis MN 55407
      612 775-5000

(G-3718)
ALLINA HEALTH SYSTEM
Also Called: Abbott Northwestern Hospital
800 E 28th St (55407-3723)
PHONE..............................612 863-4000
Dennis Coulthart, *Financial Analy*
Jay M Hemmila MD, *Med Doctor*
Craig L Bowronmd MD, *Med Doctor*
Richard E Skoog, *Med Doctor*
Candace J Sabers, *Med Doctor*
EMP: 5167
SALES (est): 100MM-499.9MM **Privately
Held**
WEB: www.allina.com
SIC: 8062 8011 Medical hospital;
physicians' office & clinic
PA: Allina Health System
      2925 Chicago Ave
      Minneapolis MN 55407
      612 775-5000

(G-3719)
ALLINA HEALTH SYSTEM
7920 Old Cedar Ave S (55425-1207)
PHONE..............................952 851-1000
Shelley Barton, *Branch Mgr*
EMP: 120
SALES (est): 10MM-24.9MM **Privately Held**
WEB: www.allina.com
SIC: 8011 Clinic operated by physicians
PA: Allina Health System
      2925 Chicago Ave
      Minneapolis MN 55407
      612 775-5000

(G-3720)
ALLINA HEALTH SYSTEM
Also Called: Phillips Eye Institute
2215 Park Ave (55404-3711)
PHONE..............................612 775-8800
FAX: 612 775-8896
Bob Hewitt, *General Mgr*
Mary Foarde, *Corp Secy*
Heather Wermers, *Vice Pres*
Laurel Krause, *Vice Pres*
Rickie Ressler, *Vice Pres*
EMP: 150
SALES (est): 10MM-24.9MM **Privately Held**
WEB: www.allina.com
SIC: 8011 Ophthalmologist office
PA: Allina Health System
      2925 Chicago Ave
      Minneapolis MN 55407
      612 775-5000

(G-3721)
ALLINA HEALTH SYSTEM (PA)
2925 Chicago Ave (55407-1321)
PO Box 43 (55440-0043)
PHONE..............................612 775-5000
Rollin Crawford, *Ch of Bd*
N M Thygeson, *President*
Kenneth Paulus, *President*
Christine A Morrison, *Vice Chairman*
Mark J Peterson, *Opers Mgr*
EMP: 1200 **EST:** 1983
SALES (corp-wide): 2.97B **Privately Held**
WEB: www.allina.com
SIC: 8062 8011 8741 Medical hospital;
hospital management services; medical
center

(G-3722)
ALLINA HEALTH SYSTEM
7500 France Ave S (55435-3400)
PHONE..............................952 835-1311
FAX: 952 835-5279
Linda Toskey, *Office Mgr*
Dawn Sawatzke, *Branch Mgr*
Molly J Magnani, *Chiropractor*
Rochelle Rougier-Maas, *Chiropractor*
Douglas L Pernula, *Chiropractor*
EMP: 35
SALES (est): 1MM-4.9MM **Privately Held**
WEB: www.allina.com
SIC: 8011 Medical center
PA: Allina Health System
      2925 Chicago Ave
      Minneapolis MN 55407
      612 775-5000

(G-3723)
ALLINA HEALTH SYSTEM
2855 Campus Dr Ste 400 (55441-2659)
PHONE..............................763 577-7400
FAX: 763 577-7196
Kathy Ebert, *Office Mgr*
Thomas Holets, *Branch Mgr*
Swarna E Latha MD, *Med Doctor*
Lisa Thelen, *Manager*
EMP: 30
SALES (est): 1MM-4.9MM **Privately Held**
WEB: www.allina.com
SIC: 8011 Medical center
PA: Allina Health System
      2925 Chicago Ave
      Minneapolis MN 55407
      612 775-5000

(G-3724)
ALLINA HEALTH SYSTEM
920 E 28th St Ste 300 (55407-1195)
PHONE..............................612 863-3720
Les Stern, *Director*
EMP: 120
SALES (est): 10MM-24.9MM **Privately Held**
WEB: www.allina.com
SIC: 8011 Cardiologist & cardio-vascular
specialist
PA: Allina Health System
      2925 Chicago Ave
      Minneapolis MN 55407
      612 775-5000

(G-3725)
ALLINA HEALTH SYSTEM
6200 Shingle Creek Pkwy # 480
(55430-2182)
PHONE..............................763 560-6922
Raye Eyrich, *Manager*
EMP: 30
SALES (est): 1MM-4.9MM **Privately Held**
WEB: www.allina.com
SIC: 8011 Clinic operated by physicians
PA: Allina Health System
      2925 Chicago Ave
      Minneapolis MN 55407
      612 775-5000

(G-3726)
ALLINA HEALTH SYSTEM
Also Called: Sister Knny Rhabilitation Inst
800 E 28th St (55407-3723)
PHONE..............................612 863-4466
FAX: 612 863-5485
Linda Kelly, *Marketing Staff*
Lori Eiesland, *Manager*
Bobbie Dressen, *Exec Dir*
Karl Sandin, *Director*

Betty A Olson, *Nursing Dir*
EMP: 560
SALES (est): 50MM-99.9MM **Privately Held**
WEB: www.allina.com
SIC: 8011 Medical center
PA: Allina Health System
      2925 Chicago Ave
      Minneapolis MN 55407
      612 775-5000

(G-3727)
ALLINA SPECIALTY ASSOCIATES
Also Called: Minneapolis Cardiology Assoc
920 E 28th St Ste 300 (55407-1139)
PHONE..............................612 863-3753
Robert V Tassell, *President*
Susie Day, *Corp Secy*
Brad Anderson, *Office Mgr*
Irvin Goldenberg MD, *Med Doctor*
Bjorn P Flygenring MD, *Med Doctor*
EMP: 40 **EST:** 1973
SQ FT: 25,000
SALES (est): 1MM-4.9MM **Privately Held**
WEB: www.allina.com
SIC: 8011 Physical medicine physician or
surgeon office
PA: Allina Health System
      2925 Chicago Ave
      Minneapolis MN 55407
      612 775-5000

(G-3728)
ALLSTATE LEASING CORP
10700 Lyndale Ave S (55420-5641)
PO Box 20087 (55420-0087)
PHONE..............................651 681-4900
William D Larson, *President*
Allen T Ofstehage, *Corp Secy*
Glenn D Evans, *Vice Pres*
Ruth Busta, *CFO*
EMP: 29 **EST:** 1968
SQ FT: 5,000
SALES (est): 5MM-9.9MM **Privately Held**
WEB: www.wdlarson.com
SIC: 7513 Truck leasing service, without
drivers
PA: W D Larson Co's Ltd Inc
      10700 Lyndale Ave S Ste A
      Minneapolis MN 55420
      952 703-3425

(G-3729)
ALLSTATE LEASING LLC
10700 Lyndale Ave S (55420-5641)
PO Box 20087 (55420-0087)
PHONE..............................952 703-3444
William D Larson, *CEO*
Glen D Evans, *President*
Allen T Ofstehage, *Corp Secy*
Ruth Busta, *CFO*
Ricky DOE, *Administrator*
EMP: 29 **EST:** 1996
SQ FT: 5,000
SALES (est): 5MM-9.9MM **Privately Held**
SIC: 7513 Truck leasing service, without
drivers

(G-3730)
ALLY FINANCIAL INC
3500 Amercn Blvd W # 300 (55431-4442)
PHONE..............................800 689-6768
Harvey M Reitinger, *Branch Mgr*
EMP: 30
SALES (est): 10MM-24.9MM **Privately Held**
WEB: www.gmacfs.com
SIC: 6159 Automobile finance leasing
service
DH: Ally Financial Inc
      200 Renaissance Ctr
      Detroit MI 48243
      800 200-4622

(G-3731)
ALOFT HTL MINNEAPOLIS ✿
900 Washington Ave S (55415-1223)
PHONE..............................612 455-8400
EMP: 80 **EST:** 2008
SALES (est): 1MM-4.9MM **Privately Held**
SIC: 7011 Hotel

(G-3732)
ALPHA HUMAN SERVICES INC
2712 Fremont Ave S (55408-1122)
PHONE..............................612 872-8218
FAX: 612 874-8885
Sue Russell, *Business Mgr*
Anita Olson, *Accountant*
Gerald Kaplan, *Director*
EMP: 26 **EST:** 1971 **Privately Held**
WEB: www.alphaservices.org
SIC: 8399 Social change association

(G-3733)
ALPHA VIDEO & AUDIO INC
7711 Computer Ave (55435-5402)
PHONE..............................952 896-9898
FAX: 952 896-9899
Stanley Stanek, *President*
Kevin Groves, *Corp Secy*
Douglas J Freeman, *Engineer*
Nathan Ackerman, *Engineer*
Rick Wessels, *Manager*
EMP: 82 **EST:** 1970
SQ FT: 20,000
SALES (est): 5MM-9.9MM **Privately Held**
WEB: www.newsjet.net
SIC: 7359 5065 7336 7622 Audio-visual
equipment & supply rental service;
wholesales electronic video equipment;
advertisers creative service; graphic arts &
related design service; video repair service

(G-3734)
ALQUEST INC
4050 Olson Memorial Hwy Ste 35
(55422-5342)
PHONE..............................763 287-3830
FAX: 763 287-3836
Linda Alexander, *CEO*
Ann Q Smith, *President*
Elizabeth Kempen, *COO*
Tom Huyck, *Vice Pres*
Marti Charpentier, *CFO*
EMP: 47 **EST:** 1993
SQ FT: 13,000
SALES (est): 5MM-9.9MM **Privately Held**
WEB: www.alquest.com
SIC: 8742 8748 Management consulting
services; business consulting services

(G-3735)
ALSIDE BUILDERS SERVICE
Also Called: Allside Installed Services
400 W 86th St (55420-2708)
PHONE..............................952 888-1339
Mike Caporale, *CEO*
Craig Osberg, *Manager*
Adam Casebere, *Manager*
EMP: 30 **EST:** 2001
SALES (est): 10MM-24.9MM **Privately Held**
SIC: 5031 Wholesales windows

(G-3736)
ALTERNATIVE FOR AUTISTIC
Also Called: Shingle Creek Option
5624 73rd Ave N (55429-1176)
PHONE..............................763 560-3013
FAX: 763 566-8426
Rodney Rosse, *President*
Mary Dalldorf, *Corp Secy*
Betty Rosse, *Vice Pres*
Mike Amon, *Director*
EMP: 51 **EST:** 1980
SQ FT: 12,000
SALES (est): 1MM-4.9MM **Privately Held**
SIC: 8361 Home for the mentally retarded

(G-3737)
ALTERNATIVE FOR PEOPLE WITH
5624 73rd Ave N (55429-1176)
PHONE..............................763 560-5330
Rod Ross, *President*
David Smith, *Program Mgr*
Noel Phillips, *Manager*
Michael Amon, *Director*
EMP: 60 **EST:** 1982
SALES (est): 1MM-4.9MM **Privately Held**
SIC: 8361 Halfway group home for persons
with social or personal problems

(G-3738)
AMALFI CONSULTING LLC ✪
3600 Amercn Blvd W # 110 (55431-4512)
PHONE..............................952 893-6732
Todd Leone, *President*
Miachael Blanchard, *Managing Dir*
Gayle Appelbaum, *Managing Dir*
Stephen Keller, *Vice Pres*
EST: 2008
SQ FT: 7,000 **Privately Held**
SIC: 8748 Business consulting services

(G-3739)
AMANO MCGANN INC
Also Called: McGann Associates
651 Taft St NE (55413-2814)
PHONE..............................612 331-2020
FAX: 612 331-5187
Michael Lee, *Ch of Bd*
Terrence G McGann, *President*
Ronald Gallo, *Corp Secy*
Lawrence Fever, *Vice Pres*
Brian T McGann, *Vice Pres*
EMP: 50 **EST:** 1982
SQ FT: 12,000
SALES (est): 10MM-24.9MM **Privately Held**
SIC: 5046 7371 Wholesales commercial
equipment; computer software development

(G-3740)
**AMB CONSTRUCTION
ENGINEERING**
5730 Duluth St (55422-4000)
PO Box 27714 (55427-0714)
PHONE..............................763 587-4920
Al Hixon, *President*
EMP: 26 **EST:** 1998
SQ FT: 1,300
SALES (est): 5MM-9.9MM **Privately Held**
SIC: 1542 Commercial & office building
renovation & repair services

(G-3741)
AMBIENT CONSULTING LLC
5500 Wayzata Blvd # 1250 (55416-1281)
PHONE..............................763 582-9000
Andrew Grossman, *Member*
David Getz, *Member*
Mallie Kridel, *Member*
Allen Stern, *COO*
Mike Harvath, *Vice Pres*
EMP: 140 **EST:** 2001
SALES (est): 10MM-24.9MM **Privately Held**
WEB: www.ambientconsulting.com
SIC: 7374 7371 Data processing &
preparation services; custom computer
software systems analysis & design service

(G-3742)
AMBRION INC
1660 Highway 100 S Ste 329
(55416-1559)
PHONE..............................952 278-1800
Brian Back, *President*
Amy Mettlach, *Corp Secy*
Brian Carlson, *CFO*
EMP: 25 **EST:** 1999
SQ FT: 3,000 **Privately Held**
WEB: www.ambrion.com
SIC: 7361 Executive placement & search
consulting services

(G-3743)
**AMEC EARTH &
ENVIRONMENTAL INC**
800 Marquette Ave # 1200 (55402-5716)
PHONE..............................612 332-8326
Shalene Thomas, *Manager*
EMP: 45
SALES (est): 5MM-9.9MM **Privately Held**
WEB: www.audioeden.com
SIC: 8711 Engineering services;
engineering consulting services
PA: AMEC Earth & Environmental Inc
502 W Germantown Pike # 850
Plymouth Meeting PA 19462
610 828-8100

(G-3744)
AMERICA'S TPA INC
Also Called: Healthez
7201 W 78th St (55439-2507)
PHONE..............................952 896-1246
Nazie Eftekhari, *CEO*
Mitch Nicholls, *Vice Pres*
EMP: 40 **EST:** 2006
SALES (est): 1MM-4.9MM **Privately Held**
SIC: 7389 Business support services

(G-3745)
**AMERICAN BAPTIST HOMES OF
THE**
512 49th Ave N (55430-3621)
PHONE..............................612 529-7747
FAX: 612 529-5643
Pam Fabel, *Manager*
Ron Gilsrud, *Manager*
Susan Kiley, *Administrator*
Robert Letich, *Administrator*
Sandy Rieschl, *Nursing Dir*
EMP: 100
SALES (est): 1MM-4.9MM **Privately Held**
WEB: www.abhomes.net
SIC: 8059 Nursing home
PA: American Baptist Homes of The
14850 Scenic Heights Rd
Eden Prairie MN 55344
952 941-3175

(G-3746)
**AMERICAN BUILDING
MAINTENANCE**
90 S 7th St Ste 5000 (55402-4103)
PHONE..............................612 344-1758
Kevin Sulivan, *CEO*
EMP: 40 **EST:** 1989
SALES (est): 5MM-9.9MM **Privately Held**
SIC: 6141 Personal credit institution

(G-3747)
**AMERICAN DAIRY QUEEN CORP
(DH)**
7505 Metro Blvd Ste 500 (55439-3042)
PHONE..............................952 830-0200
FAX: 952 830-0301
Charles Mooty, *President*
William M Zucco, *Corp Secy*
Kerry Olson, *VP Legal*
Lee Banbury, *Vice Pres*
Keith Correia, *Vice Pres*
EMP: 350 **EST:** 1962
SQ FT: 48,000
SALES (corp-wide): 112.49B **Publicly Held**
WEB: www.dairyqueen.net
SIC: 6794 Selling or licensing of franchises;
dairy products store; retails packaged ice
cream; eating place; limited service ice
cream stand or dairy bar
HQ: International Dairy Queen Inc
7505 Metro Blvd Ste 500
Minneapolis MN 55439
952 830-0200

(G-3748)
**AMERICAN ENTERPRISE
INVESTMENT**
70400 Axp Financial Ctr (55474-0704)
PHONE..............................612 671-3131
Tim Armbrustmacher, *Director*
EMP: 199 **EST:** 1990
SALES (est): 25MM-49.9MM **Publicly Held**
SIC: 8742 Financial management
consulting services
HQ: Ameriprise Financial Inc
1099 Ameriprise Financial Ctr
Minneapolis MN 55474
612 671-3131

(G-3749)
**AMERICAN FINANCIAL
MARKETING**
400 Highway 169 S Ste 200 (55426-1106)
PHONE..............................763 593-0905
FAX: 763 545-5223
Brad Frene, *President*
Darryl Chouinard, *Vice Pres*
Ronald L Berger, *CFO*
Shawn Brown, *Controller*
Drew Barth, *Corp Comm Staff*
EMP: 60 **EST:** 1993
SALES (est): 5MM-9.9MM **Privately Held**

WEB: www.afmus.com
SIC: 6411 Insurance information &
consulting service

(G-3750)
**AMERICAN HEART
ASSOCIATION INC**
4701 W 77th St (55435-4806)
PHONE..............................952 835-3300
FAX: 952 835-5828
Willaim Sugrue, *Vice Pres*
Dottie Seamans, *Sales Staff*
Tony Lee, *Tech/Comp Coord*
EMP: 50 **Privately Held**
SIC: 8399 Health systems agency

(G-3751)
AMERICAN IMPORTING CO INC
Also Called: Amport Foods
550 Kasota Ave SE (55414-2811)
PHONE..............................612 331-7000
Andrew Stillman, *CEO*
Ralph Stillman, *Ch of Bd*
Jeff Vogel, *Vice Pres*
Dan Mueller, *Controller*
Mike McIvor, *Manager*
▲ **EMP:** 100 **EST:** 1962
SQ FT: 120,000
SALES (est): 50MM-99.9MM **Privately Held**
WEB: www.amportfoods.com
SIC: 5149 5145 Wholesales dried fruits;
wholesales snack foods; wholesales salted
or roasted nuts; wholesales candy;
wholesales bakery products

(G-3752)
AMERICAN INDIAN COMMUNITY
1404 E Franklin Ave (55404-2134)
PHONE..............................612 813-1610
FAX: 612 813-1612
Celeste Demars, *Vice Pres*
Todd Swenson, *Treasurer*
Gordon Thayer, *Exec Dir*
Robert Albee, *Director*
Art Holmes, *Bd of Directors*
EMP: 60 **EST:** 1991
SQ FT: 5,000 **Privately Held**
SIC: 8399 Non-fee basis fund raising
organization

(G-3753)
AMERICAN INDIAN OIC INC
1845 E Franklin Ave (55404-2221)
PHONE..............................612 341-3358
FAX: 612 341-2766
Lee Antel, *CEO*
Clyde Belecourt, *President*
Trisha L Cook, *Corp Secy*
Brenda Starr, *Corp Secy*
Carolyn Deters, *CFO*
EMP: 38 **EST:** 1979
SALES (est): 1MM-4.9MM **Privately Held**
WEB: www.aioic.org
SIC: 8331 Job training & vocational
rehabilitation services; vocational school

(G-3754)
**AMERICAN INVESTMENT
MANAGEMENT**
Also Called: A I M S
2000 Merrimac Ln N # 200 (55447-4920)
PHONE..............................763 533-7193
Gerrad Yaeger, *President*
EMP: 28
SQ FT: 1,200
SALES (est): 5MM-9.9MM **Privately Held**
SIC: 6512 6163 6531 Nonresidential
building operator; mortgage brokers service
arranging for loans, using money of others;
real estate services

(G-3755)
**AMERICAN IRON & STEEL CO
INC**
2800 Pacific St (55411-1624)
PHONE..............................612 529-9221
FAX: 612 529-5863
Fred Isaacs, *Ch of Bd*
Larry Stearns, *Sr Corp Ofcr*
Russell Wakkinen, *CFO*
Linda Klapperich, *Human Res Dir*
Don Kempf, *Manager*
EMP: 50 **EST:** 1885
SQ FT: 6,000
SALES (est): 10MM-24.9MM **Privately Held**

SIC: 5093 Wholesales ferrous metal scrap
& waste; wholesales nonferrous metals
scrap

(G-3756)
**AMERICAN LEGION
MINNEAPOLIS**
6501 Portland Ave (55423-1661)
PHONE..............................612 866-3647
FAX: 612 866-0741
Gene Svendsen, *Manager*
Bob Gilbertson, *Manager*
EMP: 40 **EST:** 1927
SQ FT: 5,000 **Privately Held**
SIC: 8641 Veterans' organization

(G-3757)
**AMERICAN NATIONAL RED
CROSS**
Also Called: Twin City Red Cross
1201 W River Pkwy (55454-1025)
PHONE..............................612 871-7676
Phil Hansen, *President*
Tom Schmidt, *General Mgr*
Bob Siegfred, *CFO*
Jennifer Lu, *Finance*
Leslie Fransen, *Human Resources*
EMP: 50
SALES (est): 1MM-4.9MM **Privately Held**
WEB: www.redcross.org
SIC: 8322 Disaster services

(G-3758)
**AMERICAN REFUGEE
COMMITTEE**
430 Oak Grove St Ste 204 (55403-3234)
PHONE..............................612 872-7060
FAX: 612 872-4309
Daniel Wordsworth, *President*
Joel Charny, *General Mgr*
Walda W Roseman, *Corp Secy*
Vince Sanfuentes, *Corp Secy*
Al Sikes, *Corp Secy*
EMP: 30 **EST:** 1978
SALES (est): 1MM-4.9MM **Privately Held**
WEB: www.archq.org
SIC: 8322 Aid to Families with Dependent
Children or AFDC

(G-3759)
**AMERICAN REPROGRAPHICS
CO LLC**
Also Called: Minnesota Blueprint
2001 E 24th St (55404-4109)
PHONE..............................612 722-2303
FAX: 612 722-2958
Larry Aalberf, *MIS Mgr*
EMP: 75
SALES (est): 5MM-9.9MM **Publicly Held**
SIC: 7334 Photocopying & duplicating
services; blueprinting services;
mimeographing service
PA: American Reprographics Co
1981 N Broadway Ste 385
Walnut Creek CA 94596
925 949-5100

(G-3760)
AMERICAN SWEDISH INSTITUTE
2600 Park Ave (55407-1007)
PHONE..............................612 871-4907
Michael Larson, *President*
Bonnie Nelson, *CFO*
Bruce Karstadt, *Exec Dir*
EMP: 26 **EST:** 1929
SQ FT: 50,000 **Privately Held**
WEB: www.americanswedishinst.org
SIC: 8399 8412 8741 Social change
association; museum; construction
management services

(G-3761)
**AMERICAN TIRE DISTRIBUTORS
INC**
Also Called: Heafner Tires & Products 510
5100 W 35th St (55416-2616)
PHONE..............................952 345-0000
Jay Halvorson, *Manager*
EMP: 40
SALES (est): 10MM-24.9MM **Privately Held**

▲=Import ▼=Export
◆=Import/Export

SIC: **5014** Wholesales tires & tubes
PA: American Tire Distributors
12200 Herbert Wayn Ct # 150
Huntersville NC 28078
704 992-2000

(G-3762)
AMERICAN-RUSSIAN TRADE INC
2214 W 54th St (55419-1516)
PHONE............................612 922-1163
Jay Cherner, *President*
Ilia Turner, *Vice Pres*
Ron Bowman, *VP Sls/Mktg*
EMP: 70 **EST:** 1990
SQ FT: 1,200
SALES (est): 10MM-24.9MM **Privately Held**
SIC: **8742** Foreign trade consultant

(G-3763)
AMERICLEAN JANITORIAL SERVICES
Also Called: Allied National Services
6066 Shingle Creek Pkwy (55430-2316)
PHONE............................763 503-0707
Emile Nguimfack, *President*
EMP: 610 **EST:** 2002
SQ FT: 6,000
SALES (est): 10MM-24.9MM **Privately Held**
SIC: **7349** Janitorial & custodial services

(G-3764)
AMERIPRIDE SERVICES INC
700 Industrial Blvd NE (55413-2906)
PHONE............................612 331-1600
Al Ertz, *Manager*
EMP: 300
SALES (est): 10MM-24.9MM **Privately Held**
WEB: www.ameripride.com
SIC: **7213** 7218 Linen supply service;
industrial laundry service
PA: Ameripride Services Inc
10801 Wayzata Blvd # 100
Hopkins MN 55305
952 738-4200

(G-3765)
AMERIPRISE
3800 Amercn Blvd W Ste 200
(55431-4454)
PHONE............................952 835-8180
EMP: 32
SALES (est): 5MM-9.9MM **Privately Held**
SIC: **6282** Financial investment advice
service

(G-3766)
AMERIPRISE FINANCIAL
1246 Axp Financial Center (55474-0001)
PHONE............................612 671-3131
Steven Roselle, *CEO*
Ward Armstrong, *President*
Neal Maglaque, *Senior VP*
Michael P Koehl, *Project Mgr*
Monica Johnson, *Finance Mgr*
EMP: 85 **EST:** 1985 **Publicly Held**
SIC: **6722** Open-ended investment funds
management services
HQ: Ameriprise Financial Inc
1099 Ameriprise Financial Ctr
Minneapolis MN 55474
612 671-3131

(G-3767)
AMERIPRISE FINANCIAL INC (HQ)
1099 Ameriprise Financial Ctr
(55474-0010)
PHONE............................612 671-3131
James M Cracchiolo, *CEO*
Kelli A Hunter, *Exec VP*
John C Junek, *Exec VP*
Holly Morris, *Senior VP*
Becky Nash, *Senior VP*
EMP: 3300 **EST:** 1894
SQ FT: 897,280
SALES (corp-wide): 26.73B **Publicly Held**

SIC: **6722** 6211 6282 Management of
personal mutual fund sales; securities
dealer; mutual fund management
services; security broker service; security distributing
service; sales of mutual funds by
independent salespeople; investment
advisory service
PA: American Express Co
200 Vesey St
New York NY 10285
212 640-2000

(G-3768)
AMERIPRISE FINANCIAL SERVICES
1001 S 3rd St (55415-1240)
PHONE............................612 671-7536
David Kaercher, *Network Mgr*
EMP: 150
SALES (est): 25MM-49.9MM **Publicly Held**
SIC: **6282** Financial investment advice
service; investment advisory service
HQ: Ameriprise Financial Inc
1099 Ameriprise Financial Ctr
Minneapolis MN 55474
612 671-3131

(G-3769)
AMERIPRISE FINANCIAL SERVICES
50032 Axp Financial Ctr (55402)
PHONE............................612 671-4343
Claire Huang, *VP Sls/Mktg*
Kevin Mahoney, *Controller*
Elizabeth Hanson, *Manager*
John Junek, *General Counsel*
EMP: 150
SALES (est): 25MM-49.9MM **Publicly Held**
SIC: **6282** Financial investment advice
service; investment advisory service
HQ: Ameriprise Financial Inc
1099 Ameriprise Financial Ctr
Minneapolis MN 55474
612 671-3131

(G-3770)
AMERIPRISE FINANCIAL SERVICES
154 Axp Financial Ctr (55474-0001)
PHONE............................612 671-3131
Timothy S Meehan, *Corp Secy*
William Dudley, *Exec VP*
Doug Lennick, *Exec VP*
James A Mitchell, *Exec VP*
Glen Salow, *Exec VP*
EMP: 150
SALES (est): 25MM-49.9MM **Publicly Held**
SIC: **6282** 6411 Investment advisory
service; insurance services
HQ: Ameriprise Financial Inc
1099 Ameriprise Financial Ctr
Minneapolis MN 55474
612 671-3131

(G-3771)
AMF BOWLING CENTERS INC
6440 James Cir N (55430-2102)
PHONE............................763 566-6250
FAX: 763 566-6253
Lynn Roth, *General Mgr*
Dave Cook, *Manager*
EMP: 40
SALES (est): 1MM-4.9MM **Privately Held**
WEB: www.kidsports.org
SIC: **7933** Ten pin center; eating place;
drinking establishment
HQ: AMF Bowling Centers Inc
7313 Bell Creek Rd
Mechanicsville VA 23111
804 417-2008

(G-3772)
ANALYSTS INTERNATIONAL CORP
3601 W 76th St Ste 200 (55435-3002)
PHONE............................952 897-4500
Mike Lavoie, *President*
William W Brittain, *Director*
Russ Littlefield, *Bd of Directors*
EMP: 250
SALES (est): 25MM-49.9MM **Publicly Held**
WEB: www.analysts.com

SIC: **7379** Computer system consulting
services
PA: Analysts International Corp
3601 W 76th St Ste 500
Minneapolis MN 55435
952 835-5900

(G-3773)
ANALYSTS INTERNATIONAL CORP (PA)
3601 W 76th St Ste 500 (55435-3002)
PHONE............................952 835-5900
FAX: 952 897-4555
Brittany McKinney, *CEO*
Bill Bartkowski, *Managing Dir*
David H Jenkins, *Managing Dir*
Ross D Jackson, *Corp Secy*
James D Anderson, *Senior VP*
EMP: 127 **EST:** 1966
SQ FT: 53,000
SALES (corp-wide): 143.16M **Publicly
Held**
WEB: www.analysts.com
SIC: **7371** 7379 Custom computer
programming service; custom computer
software systems analysis & design service;
computer system consulting services

(G-3774)
ANALYTIKS INTERNATIONAL INC
10 S 5th St Ste 720 (55402-1012)
PHONE............................612 305-4312
Rafi Sheikh, *President*
EMP: 25
SALES (est): 1MM-4.9MM **Privately Held**
SIC: **7371** Custom computer software
systems analysis & design service

(G-3775)
ANCHOR BLOCK CO
Also Called: Factory
8201 Brooklyn Blvd # 55445 (55445-2301)
PHONE............................763 425-9779
Wade Medlar, *General Mgr*
John Hogan, *Opers Mgr*
Steve Hewitt, *Sales Mgr*
Glenn Bowles, *Manager*
EMP: 80
SALES (est): 5MM-9.9MM **Privately Held**
SIC: **1442** Manufactures structural bricks &
blocks; manufactures concrete block &
brick; retails masonry materials & supplies;
manufactures concrete products;
construction sand & gravel mining

(G-3776)
ANDERSON DOVE FRETLAND & VAN
5881 Cedar Lake Rd S (55416-1481)
PHONE............................952 545-9000
Joseph Paiement, *Partner*
David Brueggemann, *Partner*
Paul Dove, *Partner*
Jane V Vulkenburg, *Partner*
EMP: 30 **EST:** 1994
SQ FT: 12,000
SALES (est): 1MM-4.9MM **Privately Held**
WEB: www.adfvvlaw.com
SIC: **8111** General practice attorney's or
lawyer's office

(G-3777)
ANDERSON ENGINEERING OF MN LLC
Also Called: Applied Environmental Services
13605 1st Ave N Ste 100 (55441-5463)
PHONE............................763 383-1084
FAX: 763 383-1089
Jack S Bolke, *Partner*
Roger A Anderson, *Partner*
John Lichter, *Principal*
Martha Ferris, *Corp Secy*
Scott Dickerson, *Vice Pres*
EMP: 25 **EST:** 1989
SQ FT: 5,200
SALES (est): 1MM-4.9MM **Privately Held**
SIC: **8711** Civil engineering services

(G-3778)
ANDERSON SWENSON ASSOCIATES
Also Called: Swenson Anderson Fincl Group
1221 Nicollet Ave Ste 400 (55403-2474)
PHONE............................612 347-8600
FAX: 612 347-8664
Dan W Anderson, *President*
Dan May, *Exec VP*
Joe Larkin, *Vice Pres*
Karen Nystrom, *Vice Pres*
Paul Stein, *Opers Mgr*
EMP: 45 **EST:** 1959
SQ FT: 30,000
SALES (est): 10MM-24.9MM **Privately Held**
WEB: www.saanet.com
SIC: **6211** 6411 Security broker & dealer
service; insurance agent

(G-3779)
ANDREW RESIDENCE MANAGEMENT
1215 S 9th St (55404-1710)
PHONE............................612 333-0111
FAX: 612 338-1734
Tim Ryden, *CFO*
Greg Schultz, *Human Resources*
Phyllis Goranson, *Manager*
Karen Foy, *Director*
Gene Seehusen, *Executive*
EMP: 200 **EST:** 2000
SQ FT: 56,000
SALES (est): 10MM-24.9MM **Privately Held**
WEB: www.andrewresidence.com
SIC: **8322** Individual & family social services

(G-3780)
ANIMAL HUMANE SOCIETY
845 Meadow Ln N (55422-4831)
PHONE............................763 522-4325
Kathy Homes, *Accountant*
Mike Petersdorf, *Manager*
Alan T Stensrud, *Director*
Julie Bouholn, *Officer*
Judy Dworkin, *Relations*
EMP: 77 **EST:** 1891
SQ FT: 50,000 **Privately Held**
SIC: **8699** 0752 Animal humane society;
animal specialty services

(G-3781)
ANIMATION SERVICES INC
510 1st Ave N Ste 650 (55403-1616)
PO Box 3450 (55403-0450)
PHONE............................612 379-7117
FAX: 612 252-9017
Mike Brown, *President*
Bob Glamm, *General Mgr*
Kyle Smeby, *General Mgr*
John Emms, *Vice Pres*
Dan Lindhorst, *Marketing Staff*
EMP: 35 **EST:** 1979
SQ FT: 14,500 **Privately Held**
WEB: www.a-s-i.com
SIC: **4899** Data communication services

(G-3782)
ANIXTER INC
6055 Nathan Ln N Ste 14 (55442-1662)
PHONE............................763 559-2417
FAX: 763 559-4422
Steven Maus, *Opers Mgr*
Jairo Pinilla, *Engineer*
Laren Metcalf, *Engineer*
Mark Gabel, *Sales & Mktg St*
Donna Bradbury, *Sales Mgr*
EMP: 40
SALES (est): 25MM-49.9MM **Publicly Held**
WEB: www.anixter.com
SIC: **5063** Wholesales wire & cable
HQ: Anixter Inc
2301 Patriot Blvd
Glenview IL 60026
224 521-8000

(G-3783)
ANTHONY OSTLUND & BAER
90 S 7th St Ste 3600 (55402-4107)
PHONE............................612 349-6969
Joseph W Anthony, *President*
Jonathan Mack, *Corp Secy*
Jason Geer, *Corp Secy*
Norman J Baer, *Vice Pres*
Vince Louwagie, *Vice Pres*

(PA)=Parent Co (HQ)=Headquarters (DH)=Div Headquarters
✿ = New business established in last 2 years

2011 Harris Minnesota
Services Directory

© Harris InfoSource 1-866-281-6415

171

EMP: 46 EST: 1985
SQ FT: 19,356
SALES (est): 5MM-9.9MM **Privately Held**
WEB: www.aoblaw.com
SIC: 8111 General practice attorney's or lawyer's office

(G-3784)
AON BENFIELD
3600 Amercn Blvd W # 700 (55431-4504)
PHONE..............................952 886-8000
Larry Lamere, *General Mgr*
George Dragonetti, *Vice Pres*
Kevin Zakoski, *Assoc VP*
Ellen Itskovich, *Manager*
EMP: 320
SALES (est): 100MM-499.9MM **Publicly Held**
WEB: www.ewb.com
SIC: 6321 Accident & health reinsurance carriers
HQ: AON Benfield
       3600 American Blvd W
       Minneapolis MN 55431
       952 886-8000

(G-3785)
AON BENFIELD (HQ)
3600 American Blvd W (55431-1084)
PHONE..............................952 886-8000
Rod Fox, *President*
Daniel P Keefe, *Corp Secy*
Charles Hewitt, *Exec VP*
Edmund S Lee, *Senior VP*
David Tritton, *Senior VP*
EMP: 45 EST: 1957
SALES (corp-wide): 7.59B **Publicly Held**
WEB: www.ewb.com
SIC: 6321 Accident & health reinsurance carriers
PA: Aon Corp
       200 E Randolph St
       Chicago IL 60601
       312 381-1000

(G-3786)
AON CORP
8300 Norman Center Dr Ste 1000
(55437-1060)
PHONE..............................952 656-8000
FAX: 952 656-8001
Rod Hood, *Manager*
EMP: 200
SALES (est): 10MM-24.9MM **Publicly Held**
SIC: 6411 Insurance broker
PA: Aon Corp
       200 E Randolph St
       Chicago IL 60601
       312 381-1000

(G-3787)
AON RISK SERVICES CENTRAL INC
8300 Norman Center Dr # 1000
(55437-1060)
PHONE..............................952 656-8000
Rod Hood, *President*
Richard Krahl, *Vice Pres*
John Devins, *Vice Pres*
Louise Schrupp, *Office Mgr*
Paula Johnson, *Manager*
EMP: 205 EST: 1992
SALES (est): 10MM-24.9MM **Publicly Held**
SIC: 6411 Insurance broker
PA: Aon Corp
       200 E Randolph St
       Chicago IL 60601
       312 381-1000

(G-3788)
AP MIDWEST LLC
6701 W 23rd St (55426-2801)
PHONE..............................952 544-1561
Mark Pederson, *Member*
Mike Peterson, *Mng Member*
EMP: 175 EST: 2006
SALES (est): 25MM-49.9MM **Privately Held**
WEB: www.adolfsonpeterson.com
SIC: 1542 Commercial & office building contractor
PA: Adolfson & Peterson Inc
       6701 W 23rd St
       Minneapolis MN 55426
       952 544-1561

(G-3789)
API GARAGE DOOR CO
5601 Boone Ave N (55428-3048)
PHONE..............................763 533-3838
FAX: 763 533-0932
Lisa Donabauer, *President*
William M Beadie, *Corp Secy*
Gregory Keup, *Treasurer*
Kathy Carter, *Credit Mgr*
Jeff Whirley, *Info Tech Mgr*
EMP: 25 EST: 1965
SQ FT: 10,000
SALES (est): 1MM-4.9MM **Privately Held**
WEB: www.twincitygaragedoor.com
SIC: 1751 5031 7699 Retails wood or metal storm doors; wholesales metal doors, sash & trim; door & window repair service; carpentry contractor
PA: API Group Inc
       1100 Old Highway 8 NW
       Saint Paul MN 55112
       651 636-4320

(G-3790)
APPLETREE MOTEL PARTNERSHIP
Also Called: Holiday Inn Select Intl
3 Appletree Sq Ste 1B (55425-1669)
PHONE..............................952 854-9000
Rene Logan, *Partner*
Martin Fishman, *Partner*
Erin Hayak, *Human Res Mgr*
EMP: 230 EST: 1981
SALES (est): 10MM-24.9MM **Privately Held**
SIC: 7011 7299 Traveler accommodations; eating place; banquet hall facility

(G-3791)
APPLIANCE RECYCLING CENTERS OF (PA)
Also Called: Appliancesmart
7400 Excelsior Blvd (55426-4502)
PHONE..............................952 930-9000
FAX: 952 930-1800
Edward R Cameron, *President*
Jim Kirwan, *General Mgr*
Joseph M Berta, *Managing Dir*
Denis E Grande, *Corp Secy*
Bruce J Wall, *Vice Pres*
EMP: 33 EST: 1976
SQ FT: 126,000
SALES (corp-wide): 101.26M **Publicly Held**
WEB: www.arcainc.com
SIC: 4953 Retails household appliances; waste material recycling services; retails appliance parts

(G-3792)
APPLIED STATISTICS INC (PA)
Also Called: A S I
2800 Campus Dr Ste 60 (55441-2669)
PHONE..............................763 268-0696
John P Holdahl, *Ch of Bd*
Frank Voigt, *President*
Peter Belsito, *Vice Pres*
William B Oyer, *Finance Mgr*
William B Boyer, *Finance*
EMP: 80 EST: 1986
SQ FT: 20,800 **Privately Held**
SIC: 7373 Computer-aided system service; computer-aided engineering systems service

(G-3793)
APRES INC
7625 Cahill Rd (55439-2747)
PHONE..............................952 942-3399
FAX: 952 942-5118
Charles M Feldbaum, *President*
Willis M Decko, *Vice Pres*
Will Deckel, *Vice Pres*
Pat Little, *Accountant*
Jim Bach, *Consultant*
EMP: 45 EST: 1987
SQ FT: 34,000
SALES (est): 1MM-4.9MM **Privately Held**
SIC: 7359 Party supplies rental services; retails gifts & novelties

(G-3794)
AQUENT LLC
1550 Amrcn Blvd E Ste 750 (55425)
PHONE..............................952 851-3411
Sarah Schuh, *General Mgr*
Bonnie Harris, *Project Mgr*
Mark Peterson, *Project Mgr*
Alex Lou, *Sales Mgr*
Nancy Greene, *Accounts Mgr*
EMP: 85 Privately Held
SIC: 7361 7371 7374 8748 Employment agency services; business consulting services; data processing & preparation services; computer programming service

(G-3795)
ARAMARK CORP
6667 W Old Shakopee Rd # 103
(55438-2643)
PHONE..............................952 946-1438
FAX: 952 946-1531
Karen Toomey, *Manager*
EMP: 50
SALES (est): 10MM-24.9MM **Privately Held**
SIC: 5046 7389 Wholesales coffee brewing equipment & supplies; coffee service
PA: Aramark Holdings Corp
       1101 Market St Ste 45
       Philadelphia PA 19107
       215 238-3000

(G-3796)
ARAZ GROUP INC
7201 W 78th St Ste 100 (55439-2508)
PHONE..............................952 896-1200
Nazie Eftekhari, *CEO*
Lee Marwede, *CFO*
Jim Pipes, *Director*
EMP: 99 EST: 1994
SQ FT: 19,000
SALES (est): 50MM-99.9MM **Privately Held**
WEB: www.healthez.com
SIC: 6324 6411 8742 Hospital & medical insurance carrier; management consulting services; insurance services

(G-3797)
ARC GREATER TWIN CITIES
6528 Penn Ave S (55423-1143)
PHONE..............................612 861-9550
FAX: 612 915-3638
Lora Smith, *Sales Staff*
Erin Geiser, *Manager*
EMP: 85
SALES (est): 1MM-4.9MM **Privately Held**
WEB: www.arcsvaluevillage.com
SIC: 8322 Social services center; retails used merchandise
PA: ARC Greater Twin Cities
       2446 University Ave W # 110
       Saint Paul MN 55114
       952 920-0855

(G-3798)
ARC GREATER TWIN CITIES
Also Called: Value Village Thrift Store
2751 Winnetka Ave N (55427-2830)
PHONE..............................763 544-0006
FAX: 763 535-2046
Erin Geiser, *General Mgr*
Sarah Hoese, *Manager*
EMP: 25
SALES (est): 1MM-4.9MM **Privately Held**
WEB: www.arcsvaluevillage.com
SIC: 8699 Retails used merchandise; charitable organization
PA: ARC Greater Twin Cities
       2446 University Ave W # 110
       Saint Paul MN 55114
       952 920-0855

(G-3799)
ARCANOKA RAMSEY & SUBURBAN ARC
Also Called: ARC of Anoka & Ramsey Counties
4301 Highway 7 Ste 140 (55416-5802)
PHONE..............................952 890-3057
Kim Capril, *CEO*
Marianne Reich, *Principal*
Karen Sabesta, *Corp Secy*
Lora Smith, *Sales Staff*
Terri Srotzewski, *IT Specialist*
EMP: 60 EST: 2000

SALES (est): 1MM-4.9MM **Privately Held**
WEB: www.archennepin.org
SIC: 8322 Individual & family social services

(G-3800)
ARCHDIOCESE OF SAINT PAUL
Also Called: Saint Vncent De Paul Cthlic Ch
9100 93rd Ave N (55445-1407)
PHONE..............................763 425-2210
FAX: 763 425-7898
John M Long, *Pastor*
Gloria Krynski, *Office Mgr*
Norm Olafson, *Manager*
Jean Landman, *Web Proj Mgr*
EMP: 60 Privately Held
WEB: www.archspm.org
SIC: 8322 Religious organization; provides Catholic church services; individual & family social services
PA: Archdiocese of Saint Paul
       226 Summit Ave
       Saint Paul MN 55102
       651 291-4400

(G-3801)
ARCHER-DANIELS-MIDLAND CO
Also Called: ADM
301 4th Ave S Ste 1075 (55415-1039)
PO Box 15226 (55415-0226)
PHONE..............................612 340-5900
FAX: 612 335-2948
Mary K Petersen, *Opers Staff*
Paul Savre, *CFO*
Stacy Meyer, *Human Res Mgr*
Steven Shoemaker, *Branch Mgr*
Larry Neumann, *Branch Mgr*
EMP: 30
SALES (est): 10MM-24.9MM **Publicly Held**
WEB: www.admworld.com
SIC: 6221 Commodity futures broker
PA: Archer Daniels Midland Co
       4666 E Faries Pkwy Ste 1
       Decatur IL 62526
       217 424-5200

(G-3802)
ARCHITECTURAL SALES OF MN
4550 Quebec Ave N (55428-4915)
PHONE..............................763 533-1595
FAX: 763 533-7852
Chuck Tambornino, *President*
John E Dean, *Vice Pres*
Mike Tamborino, *Vice Pres*
Rodney C Hall, *Accounts Mgr*
EMP: 100 EST: 1959
SQ FT: 16,600
SALES (est): 5MM-9.9MM **Privately Held**
WEB: www.archsalesmn.com
SIC: 1742 1752 5039 Drywall, plastering & insulation contractor; acoustical & ceiling work contractor; carpet laying contractor; wholesales ceiling systems & products; flooring contractor

(G-3803)
ARCHIVES PAPER CO INC
3401 Nevada Ave N (55427-2159)
PHONE..............................763 533-0612
John Jerome, *President*
EMP: 40 EST: 1994
SALES (est): 1MM-4.9MM **Privately Held**
SIC: 7389 Document destruction service
PA: Archives Corp
       3401 Nevada Ave N
       Minneapolis MN 55427
       763 533-0612

(G-3804)
ARDEL INC
3650 Annapolis Ln N # 107 (55447-5434)
PO Box 723, Chanhassen (55317-0723)
PHONE..............................763 545-1919
Rosealee M Lee, *CEO*
David J Lee, *Ch of Bd*
John Thurston, *Opers Mgr*
Gregg Warner, *Manager*
Rosealee Bourdeau, *Manager*
EMP: 30 EST: 1975
SQ FT: 2,500
SALES (est): 1MM-4.9MM **Privately Held**
WEB: www.ardel.com
SIC: 7389 8742 Convention & trade show services; business planning & organizing services

▲=Import ▼=Export
◆=Import/Export

(G-3805)
ARDEN STEPHEN SALON INC
3300 Edinbrgh Way Ste 100 (55435-5957)
PHONE............................952 893-1938
Lynnae Zarcardi, *President*
EMP: 30 **EST:** 2000
SALES (est): 500-999K **Privately Held**
SIC: 7231 Beauty salon

(G-3806)
ARKAY CONSTRUCTION CO
620 Mendelssohn Ave N Ste 156
(55427-4386)
PHONE............................763 544-3341
FAX: 763 544-3368
John N Schmidt, *President*
Joseph Abrahamson, *Counsel*
Dan Kristal, *Vice Pres*
Wayne Paskey, *Vice Pres*
Betty Payne, *Office Mgr*
EMP: 30 **EST:** 1964
SQ FT: 1,100
SALES (est): 5MM-9.9MM **Privately Held**
WEB: www.arkayconstruction.net
SIC: 1542 1541 New commercial & office
building construction; new industrial building
construction; industrial building renovating,
remodeling & repair service; commercial &
office building renovation & repair services

(G-3807)
ARKRAY FACTORY USA INC
5182 W 76th St (55439-2900)
PHONE............................952 646-3200
John McCrea, *President*
Jonathan Chapman, *Corp Secy*
Kosuke Nakanishi, *Vice Pres*
Thomas Kampmann, *Safety Mgr*
Craig Brosseau, *VP Finance*
EMP: 54 **EST:** 2004
SALES (est): 5MM-9.9MM **Privately Held**
WEB: www.arkrayusa.com
SIC: 5047 Manufactures medical diagnostic
equipment; wholesales medical diagnostic
equipment

(G-3808)
ARKRAY USA INC
5198 W 76th St (55439-2900)
PHONE............................952 646-3259
FAX: 952 832-0052
Jonathan Chapman, *President*
John McCrea, *Managing Dir*
Craig Brosseau, *Vice Pres*
Kosuke Nakanishi, *Vice Pres*
Michael Khler, *Project Mgr*
EMP: 75 **EST:** 2000
SALES (est): 10MM-24.9MM **Privately Held**
WEB: www.hypoguard.net
SIC: 5047 Manufactures medical diagnostic
equipment; wholesales medical diagnostic
equipment

(G-3809)
ARMOR SECURITY INC
2601 Stevens Ave (55408-1635)
PHONE............................612 870-1572
FAX: 612 870-4789
Margarita Wilson, *Principal*
Douglas Wilson, *Vice Pres*
Robert Gonzalez, *Manager*
Jill Bartyzal, *IT/INT Sup*
Ryan Welshinger, *IT/INT Sup*
EMP: 32 **EST:** 1971
SQ FT: 6,000
SALES (est): 1MM-4.9MM **Privately Held**
WEB: www.armorsecurity.com
SIC: 7699 Retails alarm signal systems;
locksmith service

(G-3810)
ARMSTRONG, TORSETH, SKOLD
8501 Golden Valley Rd # 300
(55427-4472)
PHONE............................763 545-3731
FAX: 763 525-3289
Paul Erickson, *President*
Tammy Magney, *Corp Secy*
Rodney Erickson, *Vice Pres*
Bill Poppe, *Purchasing*
James Lange, *Engineering*
EMP: 80 **EST:** 1944
SALES (est): 5MM-9.9MM **Privately Held**
WEB: www.atsr.com
SIC: 8712 Architectural engineers

(G-3811)
ART HOLDINGS CORP
6210 Wayzata Blvd (55416-1210)
PHONE............................763 567-2200
FAX: 763 567-2201
Greg Hennes, *CEO*
Todd Guelker, *COO*
Leslie Palmer-Ross, *Director*
EMP: 30 **EST:** 1980
SQ FT: 26,000
SALES (est): 10MM-24.9MM **Privately Held**
WEB: www.artholdings.com
SIC: 5199 Wholesales art goods;
wholesales artists' materials

(G-3812)
ART WALKER CENTER
Also Called: Walker Art Center Shop
1750 Hennepin Ave (55403-2115)
PHONE............................612 375-7600
Wendy Lane, *Manager*
Michelle Kleint, *Manager*
Jose Iturrino, *Info Tech Dir*
Olga Viso, *Exec Dir*
Nazie Eftekhari, *Bd of Directors*
▲ **EMP:** 140 **EST:** 1927
SALES (est): 10MM-24.9MM **Privately Held**
SIC: 8412 Museum

(G-3813)
ART WALKER CENTER INC
725 Vineland Pl (55403-1139)
PHONE............................612 375-7600
FAX: 612 375-7671
Olga Viso, *President*
Kirby Smith, *Engineering*
David Galligan, *Treasurer*
Janna Rademacher, *Marketing Mgr*
Paul Schmelzer, *Manager*
▲ **EMP:** 165 **EST:** 1946
SQ FT: 125,000
SALES (est): 10MM-24.9MM **Privately Held**
SIC: 8412 Museum; retails books; eating
place; art school

(G-3814)
ARTHUR J GALLAGHER & CO
7825 Washingtn Ave S Ste 300
(55439-2434)
PHONE............................952 944-8885
FAX: 952 944-9795
Paul F Wasikowski, *Vice Pres*
A Molke, *Vice Pres*
Richard C Cary, *Controller*
Pat Gallagher, *Sales Staff*
Benita Schnebele, *Manager*
EMP: 34
SALES (est): 1MM-4.9MM **Publicly Held**
WEB: www.ajg.com
SIC: 6411 Insurance services
PA: Arthur J Gallagher & Co
2 Pierce Pl
Itasca IL 60143
630 773-3800

(G-3815)
ARTHUR, CHAPMAN, KETTERING
81 S 9th St Ste 500 (55402-3228)
PHONE............................612 339-3500
FAX: 612 339-7655
Robert Kettering, *CEO*
James Pikala, *President*
Jack Chapman, *Principal*
Theodore Smetak, *Principal*
Raymond Benning, *Principal*
EMP: 61 **EST:** 1974
SQ FT: 28,000
SALES (est): 5MM-9.9MM **Privately Held**
SIC: 8111 General practice law office

(G-3816)
AS SOON AS POSSIBLE INC
Also Called: ASAP
3000 France Ave S (55416-4223)
PHONE............................952 564-2727
Ted Politis, *President*
James Parsons, *Vice Pres*
Ken Parsons, *Vice Pres*
George West, *Vice Pres*
Dave Gaudette, *Mfg Staff*
EMP: 70 **EST:** 1983
SQ FT: 25,000
SALES (est): 5MM-9.9MM **Privately Held**

WEB: www.asap.net
SIC: 7379 Commercial printing; book
binding service; online technology
consulting service; computer system
consulting services; commercial lithographic
printing; computer typesetting service

(G-3817)
ASHLAND INC
5201 Post Rd (55450-1158)
PHONE............................612 726-1787
FAX: 612 726-1787
Cliff Fleischmann, *Manager*
Nick Kalal, *Manager*
Rick Roberts, *Manager*
EMP: 25
SALES (est): 10MM-24.9MM **Publicly Held**
WEB: www.ashland.com
SIC: 5169 Wholesales alkalines & chlorine
PA: Ashland Inc
50 E Rivercenter Blvd
Covington KY 41011
859 815-3333

(G-3818)
ASPEN MEDICAL GROUP
3024 Snelling Ave (55406-1911)
PHONE............................612 728-1800
Daniel Rischall, *Chief*
Paula Chesler MD, *Med Doctor*
Daniel R Ischall, *Manager*
EMP: 50 **EST:** 2001
SALES (est): 5MM-9.9MM **Privately Held**
WEB: www.davidberman.com
SIC: 8011 Internal medicine practitioners

(G-3819)
ASPEN WASTE SYSTEMS INC (PA)
2951 Weeks Ave SE (55414-2833)
PHONE............................612 884-8000
FAX: 612 884-8010
Robert E Kircher, *CEO*
Richard Miller, *Vice Pres*
David Absey, *Accounting Dir*
Marv Vikla, *Info Tech Mgr*
Tom Heuer, *Exec Dir*
EMP: 44 **EST:** 1990
SQ FT: 5,000
SALES (corp-wide): 30.50M **Privately Held**
SIC: 4212 4953 Local trucking without
storage services; rubbish collection &
disposal services

(G-3820)
ASPHALT & CONCRETE BUY KNOX
Also Called: B & K Windows
2828 Anthony Ln S Ste 200 (55418-3282)
PHONE............................612 781-1112
FAX: 612 781-9285
Tom Knox, *President*
Jana Litecky, *Manager*
EMP: 30 **EST:** 1997
SALES (est): 1MM-4.9MM **Privately Held**
SIC: 1771 Concrete contractor

(G-3821)
ASSET MANAGEMENT GROUP INC
5353 Wayzata Blvd Ste 602 (55416-1335)
PHONE............................952 546-3385
FAX: 952 546-3440
Tom Chazin, *President*
Julie Johnson, *General Mgr*
Myra L Chazin, *Vice Pres*
Nelson Barb, *Accountant*
EMP: 70 **EST:** 1983
SQ FT: 1,750
SALES (est): 10MM-24.9MM **Privately Held**
WEB: www.amgproperties.com
SIC: 6531 Real estate management
services

(G-3822)
ASSOCIATED ANESTHESIOLOGISTS
14700 28th Ave N Ste 20 (55447-4876)
PHONE............................651 735-0501
Robert Roettger, *President*
EMP: 175 **EST:** 2001
SALES (est): 25MM-49.9MM **Privately Held**
SIC: 8742 Hospital & health services
consultant

(G-3823)
ASSOCIATED BANK MINNESOTA
800 S 8th St (55440)
PHONE............................612 359-4461
EMP: 30
SALES (est): 5MM-9.9MM **Publicly Held**
WEB: www.associatedbank.com
SIC: 6022 State commercial bank
HQ: Associated Bank Minnesota
1801 Riverside Ave
Minneapolis MN 55454
612 341-3505

(G-3824)
ASSOCIATED CLINIC OF
Also Called: Acp
3100 W Lake St Ste 210 (55416-4597)
PHONE............................952 925-6033
FAX: 952 925-8496
John Brose, *Partner*
Charles Evans, *Vice Pres*
Shelley Peterson, *Human Res Mgr*
Marie Olson, *Office Mgr*
Kathy Witte, *Office Mgr*
EMP: 35 **EST:** 1981
SQ FT: 3,000
SALES (est): 1MM-4.9MM **Privately Held**
WEB: www.acp-mn.com
SIC: 8049 8322 Clinical psychologist office;
general counseling services

(G-3825)
ASSOCIATED CLINIC OF
6200 Shingle Creek Pkwy # 455
(55430-2178)
PHONE............................763 503-8560
FAX: 763 503-8563
John Brose, *Owner*
EMP: 75 **EST:** 2002
SALES (est): 5MM-9.9MM **Privately Held**
SIC: 8011 8322 Psychiatrist office; general
counseling services

(G-3826)
ASSOCIATED COURIER INC
1122 16th Ave SE (55414-2499)
PHONE............................612 623-9999
FAX: 612 623-0328
Joe McGraw, *CEO*
EMP: 25 **EST:** 1996
SALES (est): 1MM-4.9MM **Privately Held**
WEB: www.bikex.com
SIC: 4215 Ground courier services

(G-3827)
ASSOCIATES IN WOMENS HEALTH
825 Nicollet Mall Ste 853 (55402-2604)
PHONE............................952 806-0011
Bronagh M Cafferty, *Project Mgr*
Flora M Maccafferty, *Obstetrician*
John C Neadeau, *Obstetrician*
Crista Perkins, *Officer*
EMP: 30
SALES (est): 1MM-4.9MM **Privately Held**
WEB: www.awhpa.com
SIC: 8011 Obstetrician office; gynecologist
office
PA: Associates In Womens Health
6517 Drew Ave S
Minneapolis MN 55435
952 806-0011

(G-3828)
ASSOCIATES IN WOMENS HEALTH (PA)
6517 Drew Ave S (55435-2103)
PHONE............................952 806-0011
Andrew R Agee, *President*
Bronagh Maccafferty, *Manager*
Mac C Bronagh, *Manager*
Rona Maccafferty, *Manager*
Jill H Rusterholz, *Obstetrician*
EMP: 35 **EST:** 1994 **Privately Held**
WEB: www.awhpa.com
SIC: 8011 Obstetrician office; gynecologist
office

(PA)=Parent Co (HQ)=Headquarters (DH)=Div Headquarters
✿ = New business established in last 2 years

2011 Harris Minnesota
Services Directory

© Harris InfoSource 1-866-281-6415
173

(G-3829)
ASSURECARE
13700 Water Twr Cir Ste D (55441-3730)
PHONE..........................763 383-4800
FAX: 763 383-4880
Rich Agar, *President*
Craig Mell, *CFO*
Mary Tomac, *CIO*
Wayne Gilseth, *IT/INT Sup*
EMP: 85 EST: 1994
SQ FT: 6,500
SALES (est): 50MM-99.9MM **Privately Held**
SIC: 6324 Hospital & medical insurance carrier

(G-3830)
AT HOME LTD
1622 Park Ave (55404-1631)
PHONE..........................612 673-9594
FAX: 612 673-9896
Pat Anderson, *Owner*
EMP: 75 EST: 1991
SALES (est): 1MM-4.9MM **Privately Held**
SIC: 8082 Home health care services

(G-3831)
ATLANTIS POOLS INC
4321 68th Ave N (55429-1753)
PHONE..........................763 560-0103
FAX: 763 560-8619
Niece L Hubbard, *President*
Scott Hubbard, *Treasurer*
EMP: 25 EST: 1989
SQ FT: 12,000
SALES (est): 1MM-4.9MM **Privately Held**
WEB: www.atlantispoolsinc.com
SIC: 1799 7389 Swimming pool construction; swimming pool & hot tub cleaning & maintenance services; water softener service

(G-3832)
ATOMIC PLAYPEN INC
701 Xenia Ave S Ste 200 (55416-3597)
PHONE..........................763 231-3400
FAX: 763 231-3401
Troy Venjohn, *President*
Michael Kretsinger, *Corp Secy*
Lisa Paule, *Manager*
Alan Squires, *Administrator*
Matt Anderson, *Prgrmr*
EMP: 30 EST: 1999
SQ FT: 7,500
SALES (est): 1MM-4.9MM **Privately Held**
WEB: www.atomicplaypen.com
SIC: 7374 Computer graphics service

(G-3833)
ATTORNEY'S PROCESS SERVICE LTD
7800 Glenroy Rd (55439-3129)
PHONE..........................952 831-7776
FAX: 952 831-8150
Michael Clements, *CEO*
Kees Blase, *Training Spec*
EMP: 200 EST: 1968
SALES (est): 10MM-24.9MM **Privately Held**
WEB: www.mri-now.com
SIC: 7389 8111 Process serving services; legal services

(G-3834)
AUERBACH POLLOCK FRIEDLANDER
6113 Arctic Way (55436-1844)
PHONE..........................952 930-0818
Len Auerbach, *President*
Steve Pollock, *Vice Pres*
Steve Friedlander, *Vice Pres*
EMP: 45 EST: 1973
SALES (est): 5MM-9.9MM **Privately Held**
SIC: 8748 Business consulting services

(G-3835)
AUGUSTANA CHAPEL VIEW HOMES (HQ)
1007 E 14th St (55404-1314)
PHONE..........................612 333-1551
FAX: 612 238-5055
Tim Tucker, *CEO*
Michael Bastian, *Purch Dir*
Clark Warden, *Chief Engr*
Craig Kittelson, *CFO*

April Hitchcock, *Human Resources*
EMP: 500 EST: 1896
SQ FT: 196,555
SALES (corp-wide): 4.73M **Privately Held**
WEB: www.augustanacare.org
SIC: 8052 6513 8051 8361 Personal care facility; residential care facility; convalescent home; operators of retirement hotels
PA: Augustana Care Corp
    1007 E 14th St
    Minneapolis MN 55404
    612 238-5201

(G-3836)
AUTO BUTLER INC (PA)
Also Called: Broadway Equipment
4701 Humboldt Ave N (55430-3741)
PHONE..........................612 529-3345
FAX: 612 529-0028
Keith Schleeter, *President*
Harry Schleeter, *Vice Pres*
Lon Crotts, *Purch Agent*
Michelle Ogren, *Manager*
EMP: 45 EST: 1969
SQ FT: 90,000 **Privately Held**
WEB: www.autobutler.net
SIC: 5169 Manufactures car wash machinery; wholesales sealants; wholesales surface active agents

(G-3837)
AUTOMATED MAILING CORP
1226 Linden Ave (55403-1213)
PHONE..........................612 333-4477
FAX: 612 333-9194
John C Rosholt, *President*
Firasat Khan, *Manager*
EMP: 65 EST: 1987
SQ FT: 17,000
SALES (est): 5MM-9.9MM **Privately Held**
SIC: 7331 Mailing services

(G-3838)
AUTOMATIC DATA PROCESSING INC
Also Called: ADP
8100 Cedar Ave S 100 (55425-1803)
PHONE..........................952 814-5800
FAX: 952 851-4799
Daniel Semi, *Technical Mgr*
Greg Brust, *Department Mgr*
Dian Sylvester, *Manager*
Cheryl Ryan, *CTO*
Doug Rage, *MIS Dir*
EMP: 350
SALES (est): 25MM-49.9MM **Publicly Held**
WEB: www.adp.com
SIC: 7374 8721 Data processing & preparation services; data processing service; accounting, auditing & bookkeeping services
PA: Automatic Data Processing Inc
    1 Adp Blvd
    Roseland NJ 07068
    973 974-5000

(G-3839)
AUTOMATION FLUID POWER INC
4830 Azelia Ave N Ste 500 (55429-3915)
PHONE..........................763 571-3336
FAX: 763 592-5700
Jeff Bartels, *President*
Shari Fisher, *General Mgr*
Henry O'Donnell, *Vice Pres*
Scott Sorensen, *Vice Pres*
David Moe, *CFO*
EMP: 30 EST: 1981
SQ FT: 4,300
SALES (est): 10MM-24.9MM **Privately Held**
WEB: www.automationinc.com
SIC: 5084 5065 Wholesales industrial pneumatic tools & equipment; wholesales electronic parts

(G-3840)
AUTOMOTIVE RESTYLING CONCEPTS
2731 Nevada Ave N (55427-2806)
PHONE..........................763 535-2181
John Prosser, *President*
Jeremy Luffey, *Opers-Prdtn-Mfg*
Karen Emery, *CFO*
Catherine Juul, *Accounting Dir*
Dave Hiekes, *VP Sales*
EMP: 56

EST: 1985
SQ FT: 14,000
SALES (est): 10MM-24.9MM **Privately Held**
WEB: www.automotiveconceptsonline.com
SIC: 5013 1799 5014 7539 Wholesales new motor vehicle parts & supplies; manufactures motor vehicles & car bodies; architectural & automotive glass tinting service; wholesales truck tires & tubes; retails automotive parts; automotive sound system service & installation

(G-3841)
AVALON FORTRESS SECURITY SVCS
3300 County Road 10 # 512 (55429-3068)
PHONE..........................763 767-9111
Dan Seman, *President*
Julie Schoenecker, *Accounts Mgr*
William Durose, *Manager*
EMP: 250 EST: 1985
SQ FT: 2,900
SALES (est): 5MM-9.9MM **Privately Held**
WEB: www.avalonsecurity.com
SIC: 7381 Security guard service

(G-3842)
AVIS RENT A CAR SYSTEM INC
2407 University Ave SE (55414-3032)
PHONE..........................612 623-3999
Eric Perkins, *General Mgr*
EMP: 40
SALES (est): 5MM-9.9MM **Publicly Held**
WEB: www.avis.com
SIC: 7514 Rent-a-car service
DH: Avis Rent A Car System Inc
    6 Sylvan Way Ste 1
    Parsippany NJ 07054
    973 496-3500

(G-3843)
AVISTA SOLUTIONS INTERNATIONAL
2485 Xenium Ln N (55441-3625)
PHONE..........................952 949-0594
Mark Gartrell, *President*
Dan White, *Corp Secy*
James Cade, *Engineer*
Glory Ernste, *Office Mgr*
EMP: 30 EST: 1987
SQ FT: 5,500
SALES (est): 1MM-4.9MM **Privately Held**
WEB: www.alliancetechnical.com
SIC: 7373 Computer integrated systems design services

(G-3844)
AVIV HEALTH CARE INC
Also Called: Westwood Health Care Center
7500 W 22nd St (55426-2602)
PHONE..........................952 546-4261
Annette Thorson, *Principal*
Charlotte Spiss, *Administrator*
EMP: 150
SALES (est): 5MM-9.9MM **Privately Held**
SIC: 8051 Skilled nursing care facility
PA: Aviv Health Care Inc
    4509 Minnetonka Blvd
    Minneapolis MN 55416
    952 920-4111

(G-3845)
AVIV HEALTH CARE INC
Also Called: Bryn Mawr Health Care Center
275 Penn Ave N (55405-1216)
PHONE..........................612 377-4723
FAX: 612 377-0294
Tony Passell, *Controller*
Ladonna Kane, *Med Doctor*
Donald Calliez, *Med Doctor*
Renee Storbakken, *Med Doctor*
Bryan Benkstein, *Adm Mgr*
EMP: 140
SALES (est): 5MM-9.9MM **Privately Held**
SIC: 8051 8361 Skilled nursing care facility; residential care facility
PA: Aviv Health Care Inc
    4509 Minnetonka Blvd
    Minneapolis MN 55416
    952 920-4111

(G-3846)
AVIV HEALTH CARE INC
Also Called: Westwood Health Care Center
7500 W 22nd St (55426-2602)
PHONE..........................952 546-4261
Charlotte Spiss, *Administrator*
EMP: 150
SALES (est): 5MM-9.9MM **Privately Held**
SIC: 8051 Convalescent home

(G-3847)
AVNET INC
14800 28th Ave N (55447-4873)
PHONE..........................763 559-2211
Rick Nelson, *Manager*
EMP: 26
SALES (est): 10MM-24.9MM **Publicly Held**
WEB: www.avnet.com
SIC: 5065 Wholesales electronic parts & equipment
PA: Avnet Inc
    2211 S 47th St
    Phoenix AZ 85034
    480 643-2000

(G-3848)
AVTEX SOLUTIONS LLC (HQ)
9401 James Ave S Ste 180 (55431-2528)
PHONE..........................952 831-0888
Bob Denman, *President*
Thomas J Denman, *Exec VP*
James E Crutchfild, *Exec VP*
Scott Todd, *Senior VP*
Mike Caslte, *Engineer*
EMP: 48 EST: 1972
SQ FT: 5,000 **Privately Held**
WEB: www.citywatch.com
SIC: 5065 1731 Wholesales telephone equipment; telephone equipment installation; communications contractor services
PA: Pohlad Co's
    60 S 6th St Ste 3700
    Minneapolis MN 55402
    612 661-3700

(G-3849)
AWARE SYSTEMS INC
1660 Highway 100 S # 500 (55416-1551)
PHONE..........................800 783-8919
Jeremy Ziegler, *CEO*
Trevor Olson, *President*
Deb Francis, *Vice Pres*
Scott Olson, *Director*
Dan Miller, *Creative Dir*
EMP: 30 EST: 1998
SALES (est): 1MM-4.9MM **Privately Held**
WEB: www.awaresystems.com
SIC: 7371 Computer software development & applications

(G-3850)
AXA ADVISORS LLC
2 Meridian Xing Ste 450 (55423-3967)
PHONE..........................612 243-3200
Gary Gullo, *General Mgr*
Paul Evans, *Manager*
EMP: 68
SALES (est): 25MM-49.9MM **Publicly Held**
WEB: www.axacs.com
SIC: 6351 Surety reinsurance carrier
HQ: Axa Advisors LLC
    1290 Avenue Of The Americas Fl
    New York NY 10104
    212 314-4600

(G-3851)
AXONOM INC
10860 Nesbitt Ave S (55437-3100)
PHONE..........................952 653-0400
Clark Dircz, *President*
EMP: 26 EST: 2002
SALES (est): 1MM-4.9MM **Privately Held**
WEB: www.axonom.com
SIC: 7371 Computer software development

(G-3852)
B L B INC
Also Called: Bryant-Lake Bowl
1600 W Lake St Ste A (55408-2698)
PHONE..........................612 825-3737
FAX: 612 825-7109
Kim Bartmann, *Owner*

www.HarrisInfo.com
174

2011 Harris Minnesota
Services Directory

▲=Import ▼=Export
◆=Import/Export

EMP: 55 EST: 1939
SALES (est): 1MM-4.9MM **Privately Held**
WEB: www.bryantlakebowl.com
SIC: 7933 7993 Bowling center; video game arcade

(G-3853)
B NELSON JULIUS & SON INC
962 Central Ave NE (55413-2405)
PHONE..............................612 379-3347
FAX: 612 379-7004
Gary Buchert, *President*
Rebecca Biondo, *Corp Secy*
Tim Everson, *Manager*
Stuart Bonniwell, *Director*
EMP: 50 EST: 1940
SQ FT: 10,000
SALES (est): 1MM-4.9MM **Privately Held**
WEB: www.jbnelson.com
SIC: 1721 Interior commercial painting contractor; exterior commercial painting contractor

(G-3854)
B T & A CONSTRUCTION CO
3401 Colfax Ave S Ste A (55408-4030)
PHONE..............................612 825-6811
FAX: 612 825-7662
Theodore Goldman, *President*
Jane Loney, *Vice Pres*
Arnold Goldman, *Vice Pres*
EMP: 100 EST: 1960
SQ FT: 2,000
SALES (est): 10MM-24.9MM **Privately Held**
SIC: 6513 Apartment building operator

(G-3855)
B'NAI EMET SYNAGOGUE INC
3115 Ottawa Ave S (55416-2208)
PHONE..............................952 927-7309
FAX: 952 927-0179
David L Abramson, *Principal*
Howard Siegel, *Rabbi*
Sybil Korengold, *Administrator*
Bruce Freidson, *Administrator*
Ira D Wal, *Webmaster*
EMP: 30 EST: 1854 **Privately Held**
SIC: 8351 Synagogue; preschool center

(G-3856)
BACHMAN'S INC (PA)
6010 Lyndale Ave S (55419-2225)
PHONE..............................612 861-7600
FAX: 612 861-7745
Dale Bachman, *CEO*
Paul Bachman, *President*
Mark Madsen, *Member*
Alan Bachman, *Corp Secy*
Michael Bonk, *Vice Pres*
EMP: 105 EST: 1885
SQ FT: 200,000
SALES (corp-wide): 70M **Privately Held**
SIC: 0181 5193 7359 Retails potted plants; ornamental nursery products; wholesales nursery stock; retails fresh flowers; live plant rental service; retail nursery & garden center

(G-3857)
BADGER ACQUISITION OF MN
5534 Lakeland Ave N (55429-3121)
PHONE..............................763 259-0400
Tim Krause, *President*
EMP: 150 EST: 1998
SALES (est): 100MM-499.9MM **Publicly Held**
WEB: www.omnicare.com
SIC: 5122 5047 8082 8732 8741 Wholesales pharmaceuticals; wholesales medical & hospital equipment; business research services; nursing & personal care facility management services; home health care services
PA: Omnicare Inc
100 E Rivercenter Blvd
Covington KY 41011
859 392-3300

(G-3858)
BAINEY GROUP INC
14700 28th Ave N Ste 30 (55447-4884)
PHONE..............................763 557-6911
Brad Bainey, *President*
Chuck Bainey, *Project Mgr*
Gordy Johnson, *Treasurer*
Steve Oelfke, *VP Persnl*

Gina Esson, *Office Mgr*
EMP: 25 EST: 1994
SQ FT: 7,500
SALES (est): 5MM-9.9MM **Privately Held**
WEB: www.bainey.com
SIC: 1542 8741 Commercial & institutional building construction; construction management services

(G-3859)
BAKER IT INC
137 W 46th St (55419-4965)
PHONE..............................612 822-3664
Randy Baker, *President*
Doug Harvey, *Director*
EMP: 35 EST: 1993
SALES (est): 1MM-4.9MM **Privately Held**
WEB: www.bakerit.com
SIC: 8748 Business consulting services

(G-3860)
BAKER, TILLY, VIRCHOW KRAUSE
225 S 6th St Ste 2300 (55402-4661)
PHONE..............................612 876-4500
FAX: 612 341-9838
Tim Christen, *CEO*
Jeff Deyoung, *Managing Prtnr*
Gretchen Thompson, *Human Res Dir*
Michelle Chambers, *Marketing Mgr*
Cristi Hedtke, *Manager*
EMP: 158
SALES (est): 10MM-24.9MM **Privately Held**
SIC: 8721 Certified public accountant services

(G-3861)
BAKKE KOPP BALLOU & MCFARLIN
5930 Brooklyn Blvd (55429-2518)
PHONE..............................763 843-0420
FAX: 763 843-0421
Thomas J Downs, *President*
Roger Oberg, *Vice Pres*
John Thiesse, *Vice Pres*
Andrew Rauch, *Vice Pres*
Ron Lamere, *Treasurer*
EMP: 33 EST: 1967
SQ FT: 11,500
SALES (est): 1MM-4.9MM **Privately Held**
WEB: www.bkbm.com
SIC: 8711 Civil engineering services; structural engineering services; electrical or electronic engineers; mechanical engineering services

(G-3862)
BAKKEN MUSEUM
3537 Zenith Ave S (55416-4623)
PHONE..............................612 927-6508
FAX: 612 927-7265
Elizabeth Ihrig, *Corp Secy*
John L Powers, *Corp Secy*
Marjorie F Andersen, *Vice Pres*
Cynthia Hartman, *CFO*
Georgine Busch, *Treasurer*
EMP: 35 EST: 1975
SQ FT: 20,000
SALES (est): 1MM-4.9MM **Privately Held**
WEB: www.thebakken.org
SIC: 8412 Museum; specialized libraries

(G-3863)
BAKKEN SECURITIES INC (PA)
5000 W 36th St (55416-2758)
PHONE..............................952 926-6561
FAX: 952 926-7544
Bradley Bakken, *President*
EMP: 40 EST: 1984
SQ FT: 45,000 **Privately Held**
SIC: 6712 Bank holding company

(G-3864)
BALLET ARTS MINNESOTA INC
528 Hennepin Ave Ste 600 (55403-1810)
PHONE..............................612 340-1071
FAX: 612 332-8131
Marcia Chapman, *President*
Bonnie Mathis, *Vice Pres*
EMP: 25 EST: 1989
SQ FT: 10,000
SALES (est): 500-999K **Privately Held**
SIC: 7911 Dance instructor & school service

(G-3865)
BAN-KOE SYSTEMS INC
9100 W Blmgtn Fwy Fwy Ste 195
(55431-2265)
PHONE..............................952 888-6688
FAX: 952 888-3344
William L Bangtson, *President*
Loren Adams, *Corp Secy*
Gina Lombardo, *Counsel*
William Koenig, *Vice Pres*
Brian Kleist, *Human Res Mgr*
EMP: 70 EST: 1981
SQ FT: 15,586
SALES (est): 10MM-24.9MM **Privately Held**
SIC: 5044 5063 5065 Wholesales office equipment; wholesales electrical fire alarm systems; wholesales public address equipment

(G-3866)
BANKERS LIFE & CASUALTY CO
4940 Viking Dr Ste 530 (55435-5300)
PHONE..............................952 835-2611
FAX: 952 835-2320
Carl Parloborne, *Manager*
Steven Meyer, *Manager*
Steve Kattke, *Manager*
Abigail Anderson, *Administrator*
Richard Buteau, *Supervisor*
EMP: 25
SALES (est): 1MM-4.9MM **Publicly Held**
WEB: www.conseco.com
SIC: 6411 Insurance services
DH: Bankers Life & Casualty Co
222 Merchandise Mart Plz # 19
Chicago IL 60654
312 396-6000

(G-3867)
BARBERS HAIRSTYLING FOR MEN (HQ)
7201 Metro Blvd (55439-2130)
PHONE..............................952 947-7777
Paul D Finkelstein, *CEO*
Myron D Kunin, *Ch of Bd*
Mark Kartarik, *President*
Bert Gross, *Corp Secy*
John A Fox, *Senior VP*
▼ EMP: 96 EST: 1963
SQ FT: 100,000
SALES (corp-wide): 2.35B **Publicly Held**
WEB: www.citylookssalons.com
SIC: 6794 5087 5122 7231 Selling or licensing of franchises; unisex hair salon; wholesales cosmetics; wholesales barber shop equipment & supplies; wholesales beauty parlor equipment & supplies; wholesales hair preparations
PA: Regis Corp
7201 Metro Blvd
Minneapolis MN 55439
952 947-7777

(G-3868)
BARNES & THORNBURG LLP ✪
100 S 5th St Ste 1100 (55402-1226)
PHONE..............................612 333-2111
FAX: 612 333-6798
Howard Rubin, *Managing Prtnr*
EMP: 60 EST: 2009
SALES (est): 5MM-9.9MM **Privately Held**
SIC: 8111 Legal services

(G-3869)
BARRY & SEWALL INDUSTRIAL SPLY
2001 Broadway St NE (55413-1714)
PO Box 50 (55440-0050)
PHONE..............................612 331-6170
FAX: 612 378-6340
Steven Olson, *President*
Andy Hoyer, *Manager*
Richard Myers, *Executive*
EMP: 25 EST: 1957
SQ FT: 100,000
SALES (est): 10MM-24.9MM **Privately Held**
WEB: www.barrysewall.com
SIC: 5085 5084 Wholesales industrial supplies; wholesales industrial machinery & equipment

(G-3870)
BASF CORP (DH)
13630 Water Tower Cir (55441-3704)
PHONE..............................763 559-3266
FAX: 763 559-0945
David Dressel, *Principal*
James Andersen, *Principal*
Joel Johnson, *Principal*
Mike Arnold, *Finance*
Bruce Schenke, *Manager*
EMP: 45 EST: 1977
SQ FT: 32,500 **Publicly Held**
WEB: www.foamenterprises.com
SIC: 5169 5084 Wholesales polyurethane products; wholesales industrial plastic products machinery; wholesales synthetic rubber resins
HQ: BASF Corp
100 Campus Dr Ste 301
Florham Park NJ 07932
973 245-6000

(G-3871)
BASILICA OF SAINT MARY OF
88 N 17th St (55403-1201)
PO Box 50010 (55405-0010)
PHONE..............................612 333-1381
FAX: 612 333-7230
Audra Johnson, *Accounting Staf*
Terri Ashmore, *Administrator*
Dave Abbott, *CTO*
Don Stores, *E-Business*
Dave Laurent, *Director*
EMP: 49 EST: 1882
SQ FT: 5,000 **Privately Held**
WEB: www.mary.org
SIC: 7999 Provides Catholic church services; contract ticket sales office for sporting events

(G-3872)
BASSETT CREEK DENTAL
5851 Duluth St Ste 100 (55422-3955)
PHONE..............................763 546-1301
Steven J Nielsen DDS, *President*
Samira S Mahabadi DDS, *Dentist*
Lawrence J Kreuger, *Manager*
Todd Tsuchiya, *VP Systems*
EMP: 35 EST: 1979
SQ FT: 2,500
SALES (est): 1MM-4.9MM **Privately Held**
WEB: www.bassettcreekdental.com
SIC: 8021 Dental office

(G-3873)
BASSFORD REMELE
33 S 6th St Ste 3800 (55402-3707)
PHONE..............................612 333-3000
Greer E Lockhart, *President*
John Degman, *President*
John M Anderson, *Vice Pres*
John Degnan, *Vice Pres*
Maclay R Hyde, *Vice Pres*
EMP: 65 EST: 1940
SALES (est): 5MM-9.9MM **Privately Held**
WEB: www.bassford.com
SIC: 8111 General practice law office

(G-3874)
BAUNE DOSEN & CO LLP
600 Highway 169 S Ste 1750
(55426-1276)
PHONE..............................952 473-2002
James Dosen, *Partner*
Steve Wagner, *Partner*
Stephen Dennis, *Partner*
Lori Simonson, *Administrator*
EMP: 30 EST: 1974
SALES (est): 1MM-4.9MM **Privately Held**
SIC: 8721 Certified public accountant services

(G-3875)
BBDO WORLDWIDE INC
150 S 5th St Ste 3500 (55402-4228)
PHONE..............................612 338-8401
FAX: 612 338-2136
Thomas Keating, *Senior VP*
Wesley Crawford, *Vice Pres*
Evonne Groves, *Vice Pres*
Carolyn Hubbartt, *Vice Pres*
Mark Ludwig, *Vice Pres*
EMP: 50
SALES (est): 5MM-9.9MM **Publicly Held**
WEB: www.bbdo.com

(PA)=Parent Co (HQ)=Headquarters (DH)=Div Headquarters
✪ = New business established in last 2 years
2011 Harris Minnesota
Services Directory
© Harris InfoSource 1-866-281-6415
175

SIC: 7311 Advertising agency
HQ: BBDO Worldwide Inc
   1285 Avenue Of The Americas
   New York NY 10019
   212 459-5000

(G-3876)
BCE DEVELOPMENT CORP
Also Called: Brookfield Properties
4340 Multifoods Tower   (55402)
PHONE.............................612 372-1500
Harold Brandt, *Senior VP*
David Sternberg, *Senior VP*
EMP: 30
SALES (est): 5MM-9.9MM **Privately Held**
WEB: www.onewfc.com
SIC: 6531 6552 Real estate services; land
subdivision & development services
PA: Brookfield Properties Ltd
   181 BAY ST SUITE 4300
   TORONTO Canada
   416 3692300

(G-3877)
BECKETWOOD COOPERATIVE INC
4300 W River Pkwy Apt 212   (55406-3677)
PHONE.............................612 722-4077
FAX: 612 722-1878
Sandy Witz, *Manager*
Tom Johnson, *Manager*
Lisa Boyd, *Assistant*
EMP: 50 **EST:** 1986
SALES (est): 1MM-4.9MM **Privately Held**
WEB: www.becketwood.com
SIC: 6531 Cooperative apartment
managers

(G-3878)
BECKLUND PERSONAL CARE ORG
44005 Quaker Ln   (55441)
PHONE.............................763 546-2030
Rhoda Becklund, *President*
John Becklund, *Vice Pres*
Tom Becklund, *Treasurer*
EMP: 50 **EST:** 2004
SALES (est): 1MM-4.9MM **Privately Held**
SIC: 8059 Personal care home, with health
care

(G-3879)
BEHAVIORAL HLTH CARE PROVIDERS
1405 Lilac Dr N Ste 151   (55422-4528)
PHONE.............................763 525-9919
FAX: 763 525-9918
Fred Ferron MD, *President*
EMP: 40 **EST:** 1995
SALES (est): 1MM-4.9MM **Privately Held**
WEB: www.bhpnet.com
SIC: 8051 Skilled nursing care facility

(G-3880)
BELL ANCILLARY SERVICES INC
7650 Edinbrgh Way Ste 100   (55435-6002)
PHONE.............................952 893-0865
Michael A O'Brien, *Manager*
Kathy Harrison, *Manager*
EMP: 35
SALES (est): 1MM-4.9MM **Privately Held**
WEB: www.bellmortgage.com
SIC: 6162 Mortgage & loan lending
PA: Bell Ancillary Services Inc
   1000 Shelard Pkwy Ste 500
   Minneapolis MN 55426
   952 591-1880

(G-3881)
BELL ANCILLARY SERVICES INC (PA)
1000 Shelard Pkwy Ste 500   (55426-4921)
PHONE.............................952 591-1880
FAX: 952 591-5801
Gary V Kirt V, *CEO*
Karen Beeth-Kirt, *Principal*
Gary Wiome, *Vice Pres*
Karen Jocketty, *Vice Pres*
Bob Strandell, *Manager*
EMP: 40 **EST:** 1880
SQ FT: 10,000 **Privately Held**
WEB: www.bellmortgage.com
SIC: 6162 Mortgage banking service

(G-3882)
BEMIDJI AVIATION SERVICES INC
Also Called: Air Direct
3700 E 70th St   (55450-1167)
PO Box 624, Bemidji   (56619-0624)
PHONE.............................612 726-1500
Cori Rude, *Manager*
EMP: 40
SALES (est): 25MM-49.9MM **Privately Held**
WEB: www.bemidjiaviation.com
SIC: 7359 4513 Aircraft rental service; air
courier services
PA: Bemidji Aviation Services Inc
   4125 Hangar Dr NW
   Bemidji MN 56601
   218 751-1880

(G-3883)
BEMIS CO INC
2705 University Ave NE   (55418-2712)
PHONE.............................612 788-0100
FAX: 612 788-6064
Bill Zenner, *Vice Pres*
Robert Uren, *Plant Engr*
Jenny Schindler, *Human Res Mgr*
Ray Bragg, *Marketing Mgr*
Bob Goldstrand, *Manager*
EMP: 40
SALES (est): 5MM-9.9MM **Publicly Held**
WEB: www.bemis.com
SIC: 5199 Manufactures paper bags;
manufactures plastic bags; manufactures
coated & laminated paper; wholesales
packaging materials; manufactures paper
packaging materials
PA: Bemis Co Inc
   1 Neenah Ctr Ste 400
   Neenah WI 54956
   920 727-4100

(G-3884)
BENESYST INC
800 Washington Ave N # 800
(55401-1173)
PHONE.............................612 746-3100
FAX: 612 338-7969
Robert P Contin, *President*
Trevor Farnum, *Vice Pres*
Irene Holm, *CFO*
EMP: 50 **EST:** 1993
SQ FT: 20,000
SALES (est): 5MM-9.9MM **Privately Held**
WEB: www.benesyst.net
SIC: 8742 Administrative services
consultant

(G-3885)
BENNETT PORTER III DVM
4345 France Ave S   (55410-1371)
PHONE.............................612 925-1121
Bennett Porter, *Owner*
EMP: 45 **EST:** 2001 **Privately Held**
WEB: www.benport.com
SIC: 0742 Animal hospital services

(G-3886)
BERBEE INFORMATION NETWORKS
7145 Boone Ave N Ste 140   (55428-1555)
PHONE.............................763 592-5800
FAX: 763 535-7428
Ben Esselman, *Opers Mgr*
Terry Swanson, *Branch Mgr*
EMP: 80
SALES (est): 10MM-24.9MM **Privately Held**
WEB: www.berbee.com
SIC: 7373 Systems integration service
DH: Berbee Information Networks
   5520 Research Park Dr
   Madison WI 53711
   608 288-3000

(G-3887)
BERKLEY RISK ADMINISTRATORS CO (HQ)
222 S 9th St Ste 1300   (55402-3332)
PHONE.............................612 766-3000
FAX: 612 766-3099
J M Foley, *President*
Jim Walker, *President*
Michael T Elsenpeter, *Member*
Bert Hirschfield, *Corp Secy*
David Daugherty, *Vice Pres*
EMP: 525 **EST:** 1984
SQ FT: 90,000
SALES (corp-wide): 4.43B **Publicly Held**
WEB: www.wrbc.com
SIC: 6411 Insurance agency & broker
PA: W R Berkley Corp
   475 Steamboat Rd
   Greenwich CT 06830
   203 629-3000

(G-3888)
BERNARD L DALSIN CO
Also Called: B L Dalsin Roofing
8824 Wentworth Ave S   (55420-2812)
PHONE.............................952 881-7663
Daniel Dalsin, *President*
James Dalsin, *Vice Pres*
Timothy Dalsin, *Vice Pres*
John Flynn, *Sales Staff*
Mike Dalsin, *Sales Staff*
EMP: 50 **EST:** 1944
SQ FT: 27,000
SALES (est): 5MM-9.9MM **Privately Held**
WEB: www.bldalsinroofing.com
SIC: 1761 Roofing contractor; sheet metal
work contractor

(G-3889)
BERTELSON BROTHERS INC
6645 James Ave N   (55430-4535)
PHONE.............................763 546-4371
Steve Unruh, *President*
Jeff Bertelson, *Corp Secy*
Mark Bertelson, *Vice Pres*
Darrell Bertelson, *Vice Pres*
Mark Shobe, *Vice Pres*
EMP: 35 **EST:** 1906
SQ FT: 18,000
SALES (est): 10MM-24.9MM **Privately Held**
WEB: www.bertelsontos.com
SIC: 5112 5021 Wholesales office supplies;
wholesales office furniture

(G-3890)
BEST & FLANAGAN LLP
225 S 6th St Ste 4000   (55402-4625)
PHONE.............................612 339-7121
FAX: 612 339-5897
Cathy E Gorlin, *Member*
Charles C Berquist, *Member*
Daniel Kaplan, *Member*
N W Graff, *Member*
Paul E Kaminski, *Member*
EMP: 120 **EST:** 1923
SQ FT: 42,070
SALES (est): 10MM-24.9MM **Privately Held**
WEB: www.bestlaw.com
SIC: 8111 General practice law office

(G-3891)
BEST CARE HOME HEALTH INC
3008 University Ave SE   (55414-3316)
PHONE.............................612 378-1040
FAX: 612 378-2850
Nazneen Khatoon, *President*
Hyder Khan, *Vice Pres*
Adil Khan, *CFO*
EMP: 150 **EST:** 1989
SQ FT: 4,000
SALES (est): 5MM-9.9MM **Privately Held**
SIC: 8082 Home health care services

(G-3892)
BEST VENDORS MANAGEMENT INC
4000 Olson Memorial Hwy   (55422-5351)
PHONE.............................763 287-7200
Anthony McDonald, *President*
Lou Sturdivant, *General Mgr*
Laura Borofka, *CTO*
Chris Lilly, *MIS Dir*
Kathleen Beecher, *Exec Dir*
EMP: 102 **EST:** 2003
SALES (est): 5MM-9.9MM **Privately Held**
WEB: www.compass-usa.com
SIC: 8741 Management services
HQ: Compass Group USA Inc
   2400 Yorkmont Rd
   Charlotte NC 28217
   704 329-4000

(G-3893)
BETHANY COVENANT VILLAGE
2309 Hayes St NE   (55418-3934)
PHONE.............................612 781-2691
Paula Sparling, *President*
Tim McAuley, *Accounting Staf*
Janette Harberts, *Human Res Mgr*
Jim Cable, *Manager*
Jon Haugen, *Manager*
EMP: 86 **EST:** 1929
SQ FT: 33,532
SALES (est): 1MM-4.9MM **Privately Held**
SIC: 8052 8361 Intermediate care facility;
residential care facility

(G-3894)
BEVERLY ENTERPRISES - MN
Also Called: St Louis Park Plaza
3201 Virginia Ave S   (55426-3624)
PHONE.............................952 935-0333
Tony Johnson, *Director*
John Defreitas, *Nursing Dir*
EMP: 300
SALES (est): 10MM-24.9MM **Privately Held**
WEB: www.beverlynet.com
SIC: 8051 Skilled nursing care facility
HQ: Beverly Enterprises - MN
   650 Ramer Ave S
   Rush City MN 55069
   320 358-4765

(G-3895)
BEVERLY ENTERPRISES - MN
Also Called: Chateau Nursing Home
2106 2nd Ave S   (55404-2606)
PHONE.............................612 874-1603
Paula Olauson, *Manager*
Chris Kressehch, *Administrator*
Elisa Andersenjung, *Admin Dir*
EMP: 67
SALES (est): 1MM-4.9MM **Privately Held**
WEB: www.beverlynet.com
SIC: 8051 Skilled nursing care facility
HQ: Beverly Enterprises - MN
   650 Ramer Ave S
   Rush City MN 55069
   320 358-4765

(G-3896)
BEVERLY ENTERPRISES - MN
Also Called: Bloomington Care Center
9200 Nicollet Ave S   (55420-3714)
PHONE.............................952 881-8676
FAX: 952 881-1050
Joe Gubbels, *Director*
EMP: 50
SALES (est): 1MM-4.9MM **Privately Held**
WEB: www.beverlynet.com
SIC: 8051 Skilled nursing care facility;
convalescent home
HQ: Beverly Enterprises - MN
   650 Ramer Ave S
   Rush City MN 55069
   320 358-4765

(G-3897)
BEVERLY ENTERPRISES - MN
1215 S 9th St   (55404-1710)
PHONE.............................612 333-0111
Karen Foy, *Exec Dir*
EMP: 140
SALES (est): 5MM-9.9MM **Privately Held**
WEB: www.beverlynet.com
SIC: 8051 8361 Skilled nursing care facility;
residential care facility
HQ: Beverly Enterprises - MN
   650 Ramer Ave S
   Rush City MN 55069
   320 358-4765

(G-3898)
BFG SUPPLY CO LLC
1500 Jackson St NE   (55413-1561)
PHONE.............................612 781-6068
Steave Gullett, *Branch Mgr*
John Wendrof, *Manager*
EMP: 60
SALES (est): 25MM-49.9MM **Privately Held**
SIC: 5191 Wholesales garden supplies
PA: Bfg Supply Co LLC
   14500 Kinsman Rd
   Burton OH 44021
   440 834-1883

(G-3899)

BFI WASTE SYSTEMS OF NORTH

725 44th Ave N (55412-1401)
PHONE..............................612 522-6558
Matt Augustson, *Opers Mgr*
Matt Augustson, *Manager*
EMP: 35
SALES (est): 5MM-9.9MM **Publicly Held**
WEB: www.republicservices.com
SIC: 4953 Refuse collection & disposal services
HQ: Allied Waste Industries Inc
18500 N Allied Way # 100
Phoenix AZ 85054
480 627-2700

(G-3900)

BGD CO'S INC

5323 Lakeland Ave N Ste 100 (55429-3115)
PHONE..............................612 338-6804
Dennis M Diaz, *President*
Angelita Diaz, *Vice Pres*
◆ EMP: 28 EST: 2002
SQ FT: 44,000
SALES (est): 5MM-9.9MM **Privately Held**
SIC: 5021 Wholesales chairs; manufactures metal household furniture; manufactures wood household furniture

(G-3901)

BGM-CERES ENVIRONMENTAL SVCS

3825 85th Ave N (55443-2059)
PHONE..............................800 218-4424
Steven Johnson, *Business Mgr*
EMP: 35 EST: 2007
SQ FT: 1,500
SALES (est): 1MM-4.9MM **Privately Held**
SIC: 8322 Disaster services

(G-3902)

BIG ALE-CAT

Also Called: Alexander's Mobility Services
335 E 78th St (55420-1250)
PHONE..............................952 881-4128
Donald Hill, *CEO*
Clara Smith, *Accounting Mgr*
EMP: 35 EST: 1991
SALES (est): 1MM-4.9MM **Privately Held**
SIC: 4212 Local moving service

(G-3903)

BIGOS PROPERTIES

Also Called: Meadowbrook Manor Apartments
6860 Excelsior Blvd Ofc (55426-4617)
PHONE..............................952 938-6329
FAX: 952 938-2849
Helen Bigos, *Owner*
Ted Bigos, *Partner*
Denn Evans, *Complex Mgr*
EMP: 25 EST: 1989
SALES (est): 1MM-4.9MM **Privately Held**
SIC: 6513 Apartment building operator

(G-3904)

BII DI GAIN DASH ANWEBI ELDER

2410 16th Ave S (55404-3904)
PHONE..............................651 291-1750
Ellen Higgins, *CEO*
EMP: 99
SALES (est): 10MM-24.9MM **Privately Held**
SIC: 6513 Apartment building operator

(G-3905)

BINGO CAROUSEL

7324 Lakeland Ave N Ste A (55428-4546)
PHONE..............................763 493-2111
FAX: 763 493-4620
Christopher Josephes, *Manager*
Deb Schmidt, *Director*
Church of Saint Gerard, *Co-Venturer*
Minnesota National Guard, *Co-Venturer*
EMP: 75 EST: 1988
SALES (est): 5MM-9.9MM **Privately Held**
SIC: 7999 Bingo hall

(G-3906)

BIRCHWOOD CARE HOME INC

715 W 31st St (55408-2915)
PHONE..............................612 823-7286
FAX: 612 823-0518
Janie Schultz, *Facilities Dir*
Orville Satter, *Maint Mgr*
Nancy Myers, *Office Mgr*
Eldora McClure, *Manager*
Deb Koppy, *Manager*
EMP: 29 EST: 1965
SQ FT: 20,000
SALES (est): 500-999K **Privately Held**
WEB: www.birchwoodcare.com
SIC: 8322 Adult daycare center

(G-3907)

BIRKELAND & ASSOCIATES

5912 W 35th St Ste C (55416-2310)
PHONE..............................952 922-1772
Craig Birkeland, *Owner*
EMP: 25
SALES (est): 1MM-4.9MM **Privately Held**
SIC: 7389 Auction, appraisal & exchange service

(G-3908)

BITUMINOUS ROADWAYS INC

2825 Cedar Ave S (55407-1429)
PHONE..............................612 721-2451
FAX: 612 721-6875
Kirk Leabo, *Safety Dir*
Chuck Halvorson, *CFO*
Tom Haller, *Manager*
Mark Lewis, *Info Tech Mgr*
EMP: 40
SALES (est): 5MM-9.9MM **Privately Held**
WEB: www.bitroads.com
SIC: 1611 1771 1799 Heavy highway & street construction; parking lot maintenance service; manufactures asphalt paving mixtures & blocks; concrete contractor
PA: Bituminous Roadways Inc
1520 Commerce Dr
Mendota Heights MN 55120
651 686-7001

(G-3909)

BKV GROUP

Also Called: Boarmen Kroos Vogel Group
222 N 2nd St (55401-1492)
PHONE..............................612 339-3752
Jack Boarmen, *President*
Wendy Peterson, *Manager*
EMP: 55 EST: 1978
SQ FT: 4,500
SALES (est): 5MM-9.9MM **Privately Held**
SIC: 8712 Architectural engineers

(G-3910)

BLACK BOX CORP

7125 Northland Ter N Ste 400 (55428-1535)
PHONE..............................763 971-6260
FAX: 763 971-2300
Mike Ertel, *Manager*
EMP: 55
SALES (est): 25MM-49.9MM **Publicly Held**
WEB: www.blackbox.com
SIC: 5065 Wholesales electronic parts & equipment
PA: Black Box Corp
1000 Park Dr
Lawrence PA 15055
724 746-5500

(G-3911)

BLACKFOREST DEVELOPERS LLC

125 W Broadway Ave # 100 (55411-2246)
PHONE..............................612 872-9200
Don Gerberding, *CEO*
EMP: 30 EST: 2005
SALES (est): 10MM-24.9MM **Privately Held**
WEB: www.masterengr.com
SIC: 6552 Land subdivision & development services

(G-3912)

BLM TECHNOLOGIES INC

14755 27th Ave N Ste 100 (55447-4803)
PHONE..............................763 559-5100
Ronald L Meinhardt, *President*

Katy Bentrott, *Vice Pres*
Gary Beyer, *Vice Pres*
David Dremann, *Info Tech Dir*
Patrick Hickey, *IT/INT Sup*
EMP: 35 EST: 2001
SQ FT: 16,000
SALES (est): 1MM-4.9MM **Privately Held**
SIC: 7379 5045 7378 Computer related maintenance service; wholesales computers, peripherals & software; computer & office machine maintenance & repair services

(G-3913)

BLOOMINGTON ELECTRIC CO

815 American Blvd E (55420-1330)
PHONE..............................952 888-7905
David Dulas, *CEO*
Dorothy Dulas, *Ch of Bd*
Timothy Dulas, *President*
Roger Novotny, *Vice Pres*
Terry Brens, *Office Mgr*
EMP: 50 EST: 1962
SQ FT: 6,000
SALES (est): 5MM-9.9MM **Privately Held**
SIC: 1731 General electrical contractor

(G-3914)

BLOOMINGTON HOSPITALITY LLC

1700 American Blvd E (55425-1216)
PHONE..............................763 367-9200
Jeffrey Wirth, *Member*
Becky Wallace, *Controller*
EMP: 420 EST: 2006
SALES (est): 10MM-24.9MM **Privately Held**
SIC: 7011 Traveler accommodations

(G-3915)

BLOOMINGTON HOTEL ACQUISITION

7770 Johnson Ave S (55435-5418)
PHONE..............................952 893-9999
Tim Olson, *Controller*
Jim Johnson, *Manager*
EMP: 45
SALES (est): 1MM-4.9MM **Privately Held**
SIC: 7011 Hotel
PA: Bloomington Hotel Acquisition
2215 S 6th St
Brainerd MN 56401
218 829-8730

(G-3916)

BLOOMINGTON LAKE CLINIC LTD (PA)

Also Called: Bloomngton Lk Clinic Southtown
3017 Bloomington Ave (55407-1715)
PHONE..............................612 721-6511
FAX: 612 721-0239
John R Bjorklund, *President*
Karen Beckett, *Purch Mgr*
Robert Vogel, *Administrator*
Bob Vogel, *Administrator*
Michael A Schaal, *Surgeon*
EMP: 50 EST: 1930
SQ FT: 25,000 **Privately Held**
WEB: www.bloomingtonlakeclinic.com
SIC: 8011 Physicians' office & clinic

(G-3917)

BLOOMINGTON LINOLEUM & CARPET

9939 Lyndale Ave S (55420-4732)
PHONE..............................952 881-5825
FAX: 952 881-9203
David Pahl, *President*
Rhonda Erickson, *Manager*
EMP: 50 EST: 1955
SQ FT: 4,750
SALES (est): 5MM-9.9MM **Privately Held**
SIC: 1799 Retails floor coverings; countertop installation service

(G-3918)

BLU DOT DESIGN & MANUFACTURING

1323 Tyler St NE (55413-1530)
PHONE..............................612 782-1844
FAX: 612 782-1845
John Christakos, *CEO*
Maurice Blanks, *Vice Pres*
Charles Lazor, *Vice Pres*
Liana Hall, *Manager*

▲ EMP: 30 EST: 1996
SQ FT: 45,000
SALES (est): 5MM-9.9MM **Privately Held**
WEB: www.bludot.com
SIC: 5021 Wholesales furniture

(G-3919)

BNCCORP INC

Also Called: BNC National Bank
333 S 7th St Ste 200 (55402-2408)
PHONE..............................612 305-2200
FAX: 612 305-0089
Jean Anderson, *Assistant VP*
Brad Schulz, *Engineer*
Timothy J Franz, *CFO*
Kur Berelsen, *Manager*
Steven Landberg, *Manager*
EMP: 25
SALES (est): 5MM-9.9MM **Publicly Held**
WEB: www.bnccorp.com
SIC: 6022 State commercial bank
PA: Bnccorp Inc
322 E Main Ave
Bismarck ND 58501
701 250-3040

(G-3920)

BOARD OF PENSIONS OF THE

800 Marquette Ave # 1050 (55402-2892)
PHONE..............................612 333-7651
John G Kapanke, *President*
Ken Cychosz, *Corp Secy*
Kelly L Birch, *Trustee*
Charlotte E Carlson, *Trustee*
Emried D Cole, *Trustee*
EMP: 204 EST: 1987
SQ FT: 35,000 **Privately Held**
SIC: 6371 Provides pensions

(G-3921)

BOARMAN KROOS VOGEL GROUP

222 N 2nd St Ste 2 (55401-1493)
PHONE..............................612 339-3752
Jack Boarman, *President*
David Kroos, *Vice Pres*
Gary Vogel, *Vice Pres*
Jason Hardy, *Info Tech Mgr*
Greg Houle, *Associate*
EMP: 80 EST: 1978
SQ FT: 11,500
SALES (est): 5MM-9.9MM **Privately Held**
WEB: www.bkvgroup.com
SIC: 8712 7389 8711 Architectural service; structural engineering services; electrical or electronic engineers; mechanical engineering services; interior design service

(G-3922)

BOECKERMANN, GRAFSTROM & MAYER

7900 Xerxes Ave S # 1200 (55431-1139)
PHONE..............................952 844-2500
Brad E Mayer, *President*
Alvin Apple, *Accounting Dir*
Neil Lorntson, *Accountant*
Mary J Blood, *Finance*
Alan Kildow, *Manager*
EMP: 35 EST: 1982
SQ FT: 12,000
SALES (est): 1MM-4.9MM **Privately Held**
SIC: 8721 Certified public accountant services

(G-3923)

BOESER INC

2901 4th St SE (55414-3203)
PHONE..............................612 378-1803
Lawrence Boeser, *CEO*
Joan Yontas, *President*
Scott Boeser, *Corp Secy*
Marion Springob, *Vice Pres*
EMP: 50 EST: 1979
SQ FT: 100,000
SALES (est): 5MM-9.9MM **Privately Held**
SIC: 5075 Sheet metal fabricator; wholesales air conditioning & ventilation equipment & supplies

(G-3924)

BOLTON DEVELOPMENT WORLDWIDE

7760 France Ave S Ste 310 (55435-3216)
PHONE..............................952 886-7211
Velma Bolton, *CEO*

(PA)=Parent Co (HQ)=Headquarters (DH)=Div Headquarters
✿ = New business established in last 2 years

2011 Harris Minnesota
Services Directory

© Harris InfoSource 1-866-281-6415
177

La G Bolton, *President*
Houston Bolton, *Vice Pres*
EMP: 49 **EST:** 1999
SQ FT: 1,250
SALES (est): 10MM-24.9MM **Privately Held**
SIC: 1541 Industrial building & warehouse
construction

(G-3925)
BONE ADVENTURE INC
5045 France Ave S (55410-2034)
PHONE..............................612 920-2201
FAX: 612 920-1153
Brian Fulmer, *President*
EMP: 35 **EST:** 1989
SALES (est): 1MM-4.9MM **Privately Held**
SIC: 0752 Retails pet supplies; animal
grooming services

(G-3926)
BONFIRE PARTNERS LLC
Also Called: Denali
100 S 5th St Ste 2000 (55402-1220)
PHONE..............................612 455-7400
Peter Brennan, *Member*
Gary Kanowitz, *Member*
Mark Lacek, *Mng Member*
EMP: 30 **EST:** 2006
SALES (est): 1MM-4.9MM **Privately Held**
SIC: 8742 Marketing consulting service

(G-3927)
BOOK SALES INC
400 1st Ave N Ste 300 (55401-1721)
PHONE..............................732 225-0530
Mel Shapiro, *President*
Cheryl Adamo, *Vice Pres*
Frank Oppel, *Vice Pres*
Deborah Kearney, *Mfg Staff*
Sharon Leone, *Accounting Dir*
▲ **EMP:** 66 **EST:** 1991
SALES (est): 25MM-49.9MM **Privately Held**
WEB: www.booksalesusa.com
SIC: 5192 Wholesales books
PA: Quarto Group Inc
276 5th Ave Rm 205
New York NY 10001
212 779-0700

(G-3928)
BOR-SON BUILDING CORP
2001 Killebrew Dr Ste 400 (55425-1993)
PHONE..............................952 854-8444
Gary Heppelmann, *President*
Roger A Asp, *Corp Secy*
James J Ozek, *Corp Secy*
Raymond Schwartz, *VP Opers-Prdtn-*
Roger Raaum, *VP Opers-Prdtn-*
EMP: 200 **EST:** 1960
SQ FT: 7,500
SALES (est): 50MM-99.9MM **Privately Held**
SIC: 1542 1541 New commercial & office
building construction; industrial building &
warehouse construction

(G-3929)
BOR-SON CONSTRUCTION INC
2001 Killebrew Dr Ste 400 (55425-1993)
PHONE..............................952 854-8444
FAX: 952 854-8910
Wm A Young, *President*
Gary Krocak, *Vice Pres*
James Williams, *Vice Pres*
Roger Raaum, *Vice Pres*
David Walock, *Vice Pres*
EMP: 269 **EST:** 1957
SQ FT: 10,000
SALES (est): 50MM-99.9MM **Privately Held**
WEB: www.borson.com
SIC: 1542 1522 Commercial & institutional
building construction; residential
construction

(G-3930)
BORKON, RAMSTEAD, MARIANI
Also Called: Ramstead, John H
5401 Gamble Dr Ste 100 (55416-1552)
PHONE..............................952 546-6000
Edward H Borkon, *Partner*
John Mariani, *Partner*
John Ramstead, *Corp Secy*
EMP: 26 **EST:** 1971
SQ FT: 5,000
SALES (est): 1MM-4.9MM **Privately Held**
WEB: www.borkonlaw.com

SIC: 8111 General practice attorney's or
lawyer's office

(G-3931)
BORN INFORMATION SERVICES INC
6465 Wayzata Blvd Ste 400 (55426-1721)
PHONE..............................763 404-4000
Paul Kjer, *Manager*
EMP: 70
SALES (est): 5MM-9.9MM **Privately Held**
SIC: 7371 Custom computer programming
service
PA: Fujitsu Consulting Information
110 Cheshire Ln Ste 300
Minnetonka MN 55305
952 258-6000

(G-3932)
BOSSARDT CORP
8300 Norman Center Dr Ste 770
(55437-1061)
PHONE..............................952 837-3346
John Bossardt, *President*
Mark Bosch, *Vice Pres*
Steve Kilmer, *Vice Pres*
Charlene Jasan, *Vice Pres*
Michele Stossel, *VP Sls/Mktg*
EMP: 43 **EST:** 1989
SQ FT: 8,500
SALES (est): 1MM-4.9MM **Privately Held**
WEB: www.bossardt.com
SIC: 8741 8742 Construction management
services; industry specialist consultant;
construction project management consultant

(G-3933)
BOULEVARD COLLISION INC
6901 Laurel Ave (55426-1586)
PHONE..............................763 595-0006
FAX: 763 595-0556
Robert K Londo, *CEO*
Thomas R Londo, *President*
Tim Londo, *Vice Pres*
EMP: 30 **EST:** 1994
SQ FT: 25,000
SALES (est): 1MM-4.9MM **Privately Held**
WEB: www.boulevardcollision.com
SIC: 7532 Automotive collision shop;
automotive paint shop

(G-3934)
BOWMAN & BROOKE LLP (PA)
150 S 5th St Ste 3000 (55402-4207)
PHONE..............................612 339-8682
FAX: 612 627-3200
Edward V Collins V, *Managing Prtnr*
Richard Bowman, *Partner*
Mark Berry, *Partner*
David Graves Jr, *Partner*
Mickey Bailey, *COO*
EMP: 110 **EST:** 1985
SQ FT: 125,000
SALES (corp-wide): 70M **Privately Held**
WEB: www.bowmanandbrooke.com
SIC: 8111 Specialized legal services;
environmental law office; labor &
employment law office

(G-3935)
BOX OFFICE SERVICE & SALES INC
Also Called: Boss
9000 Chicago Ave S (55420-3803)
PHONE..............................952 854-2836
Rick Olsen, *President*
EMP: 70 **EST:** 1993
SALES (est): 5MM-9.9MM **Privately Held**
SIC: 7999 Contract ticket sales office for
sporting events

(G-3936)
BRAEMAR DRIVING RANGE
6364 John Harris Dr (55439-2564)
PHONE..............................952 826-6786
John Vallerie, *Manager*
John Keprios, *Director*
EMP: 35 **EST:** 2002
SALES (est): 1MM-4.9MM **Privately Held**
SIC: 7999 Golf driving range

(G-3937)
BRAIN INJURY ASSOCIATION OF MN
34 13th Ave NE Ste B001 (55413-1005)
PHONE..............................612 378-2742
Kathy Anderson, *Corp Secy*
Mark Han, *Sr Corp Ofcr*
Brad Donaldson, *Opers Staff*
Dave Scott, *Treasurer*
Debbi Ericson, *Manager*
EMP: 42 **EST:** 1984
SQ FT: 1,500
SALES (est): 1MM-4.9MM **Privately Held**
WEB: www.braininjurymn.org
SIC: 8322 Individual & family social services

(G-3938)
BRAUN INTERTEC CORP (PA)
11001 Hampshire Ave S (55438-2424)
PHONE..............................952 995-2000
FAX: 952 995-2020
George D Kluempke, *CEO*
Michelle Bissonnette, *Principal*
Jodi D Norman, *Corp Secy*
Ray A Huber, *Vice Pres*
Gregg R Jandro, *Vice Pres*
EMP: 113 **EST:** 1957
SQ FT: 83,000 **Privately Held**
SIC: 8711 8742 8748 Professional
engineers; industrial hygiene consultant;
energy conservation consultant

(G-3939)
BREAK-THRU HOME CARE
112 N 3rd St Ste 300 (55401-1651)
PHONE..............................612 659-1505
Debra Burke, *President*
EMP: 40 **EST:** 2002
SALES (est): 1MM-4.9MM **Privately Held**
WEB: www.breakthrucare.com
SIC: 8082 Home health care services

(G-3940)
BRECK SCHOOL
123 Ottawa Ave N (55422-5124)
PHONE..............................763 381-8100
FAX: 763 381-8288
Sam Salas, *Superintendent*
Dick Nickel, *Member*
Lynn Casey, *Trustee*
Sue Hage, *Librarian*
Monica Kunkel, *Librarian*
EMP: 134 **EST:** 1886
ADMISSIONS: 1170 **Privately Held**
WEB: www.breckschool.org
SIC: 7999 Private combined elementary &
secondary school; ice skating rink

(G-3941)
BREDE INC
2211 Broadway St NE (55413-1718)
PHONE..............................612 331-4540
FAX: 612 378-6502
William Casey Sr, *President*
Mike Tanski, *Corp Secy*
George F Cahill, *Corp Secy*
Timothy Casey, *Senior VP*
Jay D Trepp, *Vice Pres*
EMP: 125 **EST:** 1898
SQ FT: 65,000
SALES (est): 10MM-24.9MM **Privately Held**
WEB: www.bredeexhibitsplus.com
SIC: 7389 Convention & trade show
services; manufactures window & lobby
displays & cutouts
PA: Casey & Hayes Inc
430 E 1st St
Boston MA 02127
617 269-5900

(G-3942)
BREMNER FOOD GROUP INC
824 6th Ave SE (55414-1326)
PHONE..............................612 331-5908
FAX: 612 331-3212
Lynn Mortenson, *Mfg Staff*
Nick Smith, *Manager*
EMP: 30
SALES (est): 10MM-24.9MM **Publicly Held**
WEB: www.bremnerfoodgroup.com

SIC: 5153 5191 Grain milling; manufactures
animal feed; retails farm supplies;
manufactures cookies & crackers;
wholesales grains; wholesales feed
HQ: Bremner Food Group Inc
800 Market St Ste 2900
Saint Louis MO 63101
314 877-7000

(G-3943)
BRICKMAN GROUP LTD LLC
7204 W 27th St Ste 221 (55426-3113)
PHONE..............................952 922-8777
Pierre Kubesh, *Manager*
Tom Badon, *Manager*
Jake Gregory, *Manager*
EMP: 30 **Privately Held**
SIC: 0781 Landscape services
DH: Brickman Group Ltd LLC
18227 Flower Hill Way
Gaithersburg MD 20879
301 987-9200

(G-3944)
BRIDGE FOR YOUTH
1111 W 22nd St (55405-2705)
PHONE..............................612 377-8800
FAX: 612 377-6426
Peter Loewenson, *Vice Chairman*
Nate Soderberg, *Facilities Mgr*
Todd Jeffers, *CFO*
John March, *Treasurer*
Beth Holger, *Manager*
EMP: 65 **EST:** 1970
SQ FT: 4,000
SALES (est): 1MM-4.9MM **Privately Held**
WEB: www.bridgeforyouth.org
SIC: 8361 8322 Residential care for
children; individual & family social services

(G-3945)
BRIDGEWATER BANCSHARES INC (PA)
3800 Amercn Blvd W # 100 (55431-4416)
PHONE..............................952 893-6868
Rachel Peterson, *CFO*
EST: 2005 **Privately Held**
SIC: 6712 Bank holding company

(G-3946)
BRIGGS & MORGAN PROFESSIONAL
80 S 8th St Ste 2200 (55402-2210)
PHONE..............................612 977-8400
FAX: 612 223-6450
Richard Mark, *President*
William Dolan, *Counsel*
Elizabeth M Brama, *Treasurer*
Andrea M Bond, *Attorney*
Wendy W Citron, *Attorney*
EMP: 300
SALES (est): 25MM-49.9MM **Privately Held**
SIC: 8111 Legal services
PA: Briggs & Morgan Professional
2200 S Ids Cntr 80 8th St St
Minneapolis MN 55402
651 223-6600

(G-3947)
BRIGGS & MORGAN PROFESSIONAL (PA)
2200 S Ids Cntr 80 8th St St (55402)
PHONE..............................651 223-6600
FAX: 651 223-6450
Alan Maclin, *President*
James A Vose, *Corp Secy*
Thomas Gelbmann, *Vice Pres*
Terence N Doyle, *Treasurer*
Lisa Mell, *Human Res Mgr*
EMP: 165 **EST:** 1886
SQ FT: 35,000
SALES (corp-wide): 336.11K **Privately
Held**
SIC: 8111 General practice attorney's or
lawyer's office

(G-3948)
BRIM HEALTHCARE INC
10820 38th Pl N (55441-1409)
PHONE..............................763 546-4801
Dave Woodland, *President*
EMP: 30
SALES (est): 1MM-4.9MM **Privately Held**
WEB: www.brimhealthcare.com

www.HarrisInfo.com
178

2011 Harris Minnesota
Services Directory

▲=Import ▼=Export
◆=Import/Export

SIC: **8741** Hospital management services
HQ: Brim Healthcare Inc
105 Westwood Pl Ste 300
Brentwood TN 37027
615 309-6053

(G-3949)
BRIN GLASS CO (PA)
2300 N 2nd St (55411-2209)
PHONE................................612 529-9671
FAX: 612 529-9670
Douglas M Nelson, *CEO*
Jon Bill, *President*
Tom McColl, *Manager*
Scott Peterson, *Manager*
Stan Mariska, *Director*
▲ EMP: 177 EST: 1912
SQ FT: 60,000 **Privately Held**
SIC: **5039** 1793 Wholesales glass
construction materials; glass & glazing
contractor

(G-3950)
BRINK'S INC
830 Boone Ave N Ste 2 (55427-4589)
PHONE................................763 486-1730
Stewart Ebner, *Manager*
EMP: 53
SALES (est): 1MM-4.9MM **Publicly Held**
WEB: www.brinksinc.com
SIC: **7381** Armored car service
HQ: Brink's Inc
1801 Bayberry Ct Ste 400
Richmond VA 23226
804 289-9600

(G-3951)
BRITE SIGNS LLC
13805 1st Ave N Ste 800 (55441-5461)
PHONE................................763 489-3841
Bruce Friedman, *Member*
Robert Tendergrass, *Controller*
EMP: 55 EST: 2006
SALES (est): 5MM-9.9MM **Privately Held**
WEB: www.britesigns.net
SIC: **7313** Electronic media advertising
representative

(G-3952)
BROADWAY RENTAL EQUIPMENT CO
6800 W Broadway Ave (55428-2308)
PHONE................................763 533-1680
FAX: 763 533-3227
Thomas S Martin, *President*
Guy S Martin, *Vice Pres*
Mike Collins, *Accountant*
Todd Breuer, *Manager*
Steve Kumpf, *Manager*
EMP: 25 EST: 1956
SQ FT: 8,800
SALES (est): 1MM-4.9MM **Privately Held**
SIC: **7359** 7353 Cleaning & maintenance
equipment rental service; party supplies
rental services; tent & tarpaulin rental
service; construction & mining equipment
leasing & rental

(G-3953)
BROADWAY RESOURCE & RECOVERY
2301 N 2nd St (55411-2208)
PHONE................................612 623-8888
Reed Lewis, *Managing Prtnr*
Kyle Reed, *Partner*
EMP: 25 EST: 2006
SALES (est): 1MM-4.9MM **Privately Held**
SIC: **7389** Repossession service

(G-3954)
BROOKDALE CAR WASH INC
5500 Brooklyn Blvd (55429-3054)
PHONE................................763 561-1123
FAX: 763 561-1129
Stephen T Graham, *President*
Rita Graham, *Corp Secy*
EMP: 40 EST: 1967
SQ FT: 3,300
SALES (est): 1MM-4.9MM **Privately Held**
SIC: **7542** Car wash

(G-3955)
BROOKDALE INTEGRATIVE HEALTH
5740 Brooklyn Blvd # 100 (55429-3093)
PHONE................................763 561-4045
Kent Erickson DC, *President*
Thea Killeen, *Med Doctor*
Sara Reiser, *Med Doctor*
Rob Groscop, *Exec Dir*
EMP: 30 EST: 1988
SALES (est): 1MM-4.9MM **Privately Held**
WEB: www.brookdalehealth.com
SIC: **8041** 8049 Chiropractors' office;
physical therapist office

(G-3956)
BROOKDALE MOTOR SALES INC
4301 68th Ave N (55429-1753)
PHONE................................763 561-8161
FAX: 763 561-1429
C D Luther, *President*
R D Luther, *VP Purch*
EMP: 200 EST: 1996
SQ FT: 29,000
SALES (est): 100MM-499.9MM **Privately Held**
SIC: **7513** 7515 7538 Retails new & used
automobiles; general automotive repair
services; retails new & used pickups;
passenger car leasing; used car dealer;
truck leasing & rental without drivers

(G-3957)
BROOKFIELD COMMERCIAL
33 S 6th St Ste 4640 (55402-3718)
PHONE................................612 372-1500
David Sternberg, *Senior VP*
Joel Tauer, *Controller*
Jan Johnson, *Human Resources*
Tina Lacroix, *Office Mgr*
Geeta Vadgama, *Director*
EMP: 225
SALES (est): 50MM-99.9MM **Privately Held**
WEB: www.onewfc.com
SIC: **6512** 6513 6514 Nonresidential
building operator; residential building
leasing services; apartment building
operator
PA: Brookfield Properties Ltd
181 BAY ST SUITE 4300
TORONTO Canada
416 3692300

(G-3958)
BROOKFIELD DEVELOPMENT INC
555 Nicollet Mall Ste 50 (55402-1059)
PHONE................................612 372-1230
David Sternberg, *President*
Amy Coleman, *Manager*
Nathan Reed, *Manager*
EMP: 50 EST: 1999
SALES (est): 10MM-24.9MM **Privately Held**
SIC: **6512** 6531 Shopping center & mall
operator; real estate services

(G-3959)
BROOKLYN CENTER MOTORS LLC
Also Called: Luther Brookdale
6121 Brooklyn Blvd (55429-4033)
PHONE................................763 535-5200
David Luther, *Member*
Scott Spaeth, *Manager*
Bill Love, *Manager*
Scott Hanson, *Manager*
EMP: 75 EST: 2001
SALES (est): 50MM-99.9MM **Privately Held**
SIC: **5012** Wholesales motor vehicles

(G-3960)
BROOKLYN PARK HOSPITALITY LLC
Also Called: Ramada Minneapo
6900 Lakeland Ave N (55428-1615)
PHONE................................763 566-8855
FAX: 763 561-0572
Mark Peregory, *General Mgr*
Angela G Reed, *Member*
Colleen Donahue, *Engineering*
Peggy Counce, *Controller*
Bunnie Gabrielick, *Human Res Dir*

EMP: 99 EST: 2002
SALES (est): 5MM-9.9MM **Privately Held**
WEB: www.grandrios.com
SIC: **7021** Rooming & boarding house

(G-3961)
BROOKPARK GROUP
8525 Edinbrook Xing Ste 101
(55443-1967)
PHONE................................763 424-8525
Robert Schmidt, *President*
Thomas Leroux, *Treasurer*
Bill Gleason, *Manager*
EMP: 25 EST: 1951
SQ FT: 800
SALES (est): 1MM-4.9MM **Privately Held**
SIC: **6531** 6552 Real estate services; land
subdivision & development services

(G-3962)
BROWN & CARLSON
5411 Circle Down 100 (55416-1311)
PHONE................................763 540-1019
Douglas J Brown, *President*
Gina Uhrbom, *Partner*
Jeffrey Carlson, *Partner*
Greg Broos, *Partner*
EMP: 30 EST: 1992
SQ FT: 11,000
SALES (est): 1MM-4.9MM **Privately Held**
WEB: www.brownandcarlson.com
SIC: **8111** General practice attorney's or
lawyer's office

(G-3963)
BRUNBERG BLATT & CO INC
5500 Wayzata Blvd Ste 600 (55416-3576)
PHONE................................763 545-2353
Kathy Diaby, *President*
Steven Thoresen, *Chairman*
Michael Condon, *Corp Secy*
Michael Wachner, *Manager*
Rachel A Otten, *Manager*
EMP: 30 EST: 1991
SQ FT: 9,017
SALES (est): 1MM-4.9MM **Privately Held**
WEB: www.brunberg.net
SIC: **8721** Certified public accountant
services

(G-3964)
BRUSH MASTERS INC
12955 Highway 55 (55441-3841)
PHONE................................763 478-3232
Paul W Luedemann, *President*
Debbie Scully, *CFO*
Jamie Johnson, *Accounting Dir*
Kevin Luedemann, *Manager*
Mark Jones, *Manager*
EMP: 110 EST: 1977
SQ FT: 30,000
SALES (est): 5MM-9.9MM **Privately Held**
SIC: **1742** 1721 Drywall contractor; interior
residential painting contractor; exterior
residential painting contractor

(G-3965)
BRYANT SQUARE APARTMENTS
3115 Aldrich Ave S (55408-2805)
PHONE................................612 825-4379
Lenny Ghistlewood, *President*
EMP: 50 EST: 2006 **Privately Held**
SIC: **8631** Labor organization

(G-3966)
BUCA INC
1204 Harmon Pl Ste C (55403-1923)
PHONE................................612 288-0138
FAX: 612 341-0496
Mike Mussell, *General Mgr*
John Emerson, *Manager*
EMP: 65
SALES (est): 1MM-4.9MM **Privately Held**
WEB: www.bucainc.com
SIC: **7299** Full service Italian restaurant;
banquet hall facility
PA: Buca Inc
1300 Nicollet Ave # 5003
Minneapolis MN 55403
612 225-2382

(G-3967)
BUDGET EXTERIORS INC
8017 Nicollet Ave S (55420-1229)
PHONE................................952 887-1613
FAX: 952 887-1659
Kenneth Thompson, *President*
Cassie Meyer, *Accountant*
Todd Shely, *Info Tech Mgr*
EMP: 40 EST: 1988
SALES (est): 10MM-24.9MM **Privately Held**
SIC: **1521** Single-family housing
construction

(G-3968)
BUFF & SHINE CENTER INC
10820 Bush Lake Rd (55438-2645)
PHONE................................952 944-9033
FAX: 952 253-1921
Robert H Schleeter, *President*
Harry Schleeter, *Corp Secy*
Cory Owen, *Manager*
John Cowell, *Manager*
EMP: 40 EST: 1985
SALES (est): 1MM-4.9MM **Privately Held**
WEB: www.autobutler.net
SIC: **7542** Automotive washing & polishing
service
PA: Auto Butler Inc
4701 Humboldt Ave N
Minneapolis MN 55430
612 529-3345

(G-3969)
BUFFALO WILD WINGS INC (PA)
5500 Wayzata Blvd # 1600 (55416-1237)
PHONE................................952 593-9943
FAX: 952 593-9787
Sally J Smith, *President*
Chip Ackley, *General Mgr*
Rachelle Bellmore, *General Mgr*
Angela Buckley, *General Mgr*
Phil Albanese, *General Mgr*
EMP: 70 EST: 1982
SQ FT: 44,000
SALES (corp-wide): 538.92M **Publicly Held**
WEB: www.buffalowildwings.com
SIC: **6794** Full service chain family
restaurant; selling or licensing of franchises

(G-3970)
BUILDERS & REMODELERS INC
3517 Hennepin Ave S (55408-3830)
PHONE................................612 827-5481
FAX: 612 827-7351
Ken Bressler, *President*
Dean Banderwerf, *Corp Secy*
Dean V Werf, *CFO*
EMP: 32 EST: 1962
SQ FT: 5,000
SALES (est): 1MM-4.9MM **Privately Held**
WEB: www.buildersandremodelers.com
SIC: **1751** 1761 Window & door contractor;
siding contractor

(G-3971)
BUILDERS INC
8100 Wayzata Blvd (55426-1338)
PHONE................................952 545-3217
Craig Moleski, *CEO*
Scott Krinke, *President*
EMP: 25 EST: 1988
SQ FT: 2,200
SALES (est): 5MM-9.9MM **Privately Held**
SIC: **1542** 1522 New commercial & office
building construction; apartment building
construction service

(G-3972)
BUILDING BLOCK CHILD CARE INC
16355 36th Ave N Ste 700 (55446-4601)
PHONE................................763 557-1111
FAX: 763 404-1546
Susan Dunkley, *President*
Maryjo Odriscoll, *Purchasing*
Lorraine Dunkley, *Treasurer*
Nora Kremmel, *VP Persnl*
Sandra Duncan, *Manager*
EST: 1971
SQ FT: 1,200 **Privately Held**
WEB: www.cruzenandassociates.com
SIC: **8351** Nursery school

(PA)=Parent Co (HQ)=Headquarters (DH)=Div Headquarters
✿ = New business established in last 2 years

2011 Harris Minnesota
Services Directory

© Harris InfoSource 1-866-281-6415
179

(G-3973)
BUILDING FASTENERS OF MN (PA)
2827 Anthony Ln S (55418-3269)
PHONE.............................612 706-3300
FAX: 612 788-1914
Loren O'Brien, *CEO*
Robert O'Brien, *President*
Todd Boone, *Vice Pres*
Rick Keranen, *Purch Mgr*
Bob Bridgeman, *VP Sls/Mktg*
EMP: 75 EST: 1984
SQ FT: 24,000 Privately Held
SIC: 5072 5085 Wholesales bolts, nuts & screws; wholesales builders' hardware; wholesales industrial fasteners including nuts, bolts, screws, etc

(G-3974)
BUILDING MAINTENANCE MGT
1724 Douglas Dr N Ste 100 (55422-4313)
PHONE..............................763 541-4886
James Rognlie, *CEO*
Keith Sterner, *Administrator*
Tammy Anderson, *Director*
EMP: 27 EST: 1987
SQ FT: 2,000
SALES (est): 500-999K Privately Held
WEB: www.buildingmaintenancemanagement.com
SIC: 7349 Janitorial & custodial services

(G-3975)
BUILDING RESOURCES INC
2525 E Franklin Ave # 300 (55406-1075)
PHONE..............................612 341-1111
FAX: 612 341-1016
Wayne Nelson, *President*
Rebecca Surmont, *Human Res Mgr*
Sandi Radanke, *Office Mgr*
EMP: 103 EST: 1997
SQ FT: 6,000
SALES (est): 1MM-4.9MM Privately Held
WEB: www.buildingresources.net
SIC: 7349 Janitorial & custodial services

(G-3976)
BURKE BLACKWELL
431 S 7th St Ste 2500 (55415-1808)
PHONE..............................612 343-3200
Jerry Blackwell, *Principal*
EMP: 25 EST: 2006
SALES (est): 1MM-4.9MM Privately Held
SIC: 8111 Legal services

(G-3977)
BURNET REALTY LLC (HQ)
Also Called: Coldwell Banker
7550 France Ave S Ste 300 (55435-4765)
PHONE..............................952 844-6400
FAX: 952 703-8602
Joseph Reis, *CEO*
Ralph Burnet, *Ch of Bd*
Robin Peterson, *President*
Julia Jones, *Purchasing*
Constance McCaffrey, *Comms Dir*
EMP: 350 EST: 1973
SQ FT: 60,000 Privately Held
WEB: www.cburnet.com
SIC: 6531 6361 Real estate agency & broker; title insurance carrier

(G-3978)
BURRELLE'S INFORMATION SVCS
Also Called: Minnesota Clipping Service
12 S 6th St Ste 1150 (55402-1524)
PHONE..............................612 672-9141
FAX: 612 672-9174
Brian Bornfleth, *Branch Mgr*
EMP: 27
SALES (est): 1MM-4.9MM Privately Held
SIC: 7389 Press clipping service
PA: Burrelle's Information Svcs
    75 E Northfield Rd
    Livingston NJ 07039
    973 992-6600

(G-3979)
BYSTROM PRECISION INDUSTRIES
7500 W 27th St (55426-3106)
PHONE.............................952 929-6888
FAX: 952 929-6999
Mikeal Bystrom, *President*
Deb Wangen, *Govt Rel Mgr*
Wayne Houser, *Director*
EMP: 30 EST: 1998
SALES (est): 1MM-4.9MM Privately Held
WEB: www.bystromprecision.com
SIC: 7389 Personal service agents

(G-3980)
C & R ROSS INC
Also Called: City Looks Salon International
2732 Quebec Ave N (55427-2811)
PHONE.............................763 545-7347
Cherie Ross, *President*
EMP: 25 EST: 1981
SALES (est): 1MM-4.9MM Privately Held
WEB: www.young-living.net
SIC: 7231 Direct retail telemarketing; unisex hair salon

(G-3981)
C B RICHARD ELLIS INC
4400 McRthur Blvd Ste 600 (55439)
PHONE.............................952 278-2106
Janet Turner, *President*
EMP: 300
SALES (est): 50MM-99.9MM Publicly Held
WEB: www.cbre.com
SIC: 6531 Real estate services
HQ: CB Richard Ellis Inc
    11150 Santa Monica Blvd
    Los Angeles CA 90025
    310 606-4700

(G-3982)
C C C T INC
Also Called: California Closet Co
5000 W 78th St (55435-5411)
PHONE.............................952 844-0004
FAX: 952 844-0096
Thomas Sweeney, *President*
Michelee Skjei, *Vice Pres*
Zach Larman, *Manager*
EMP: 30 EST: 1989
SQ FT: 10,000
SALES (est): 1MM-4.9MM Privately Held
SIC: 1799 Closet organizer installation & design service; retails closets, interiors & accessories

(G-3983)
C F HAGLIN & SONS INC
3939 W 69th St (55435-2001)
PHONE.............................952 920-6123
FAX: 952 920-5318
Thomas B Roberts, *President*
Doris A Fritzen, *Corp Secy*
Gary J Gunderson, *Vice Pres*
Cliff Reep, *Project Mgr*
EMP: 65 EST: 1873
SALES (est): 10MM-24.9MM Privately Held
SIC: 1542 1541 New commercial & office building construction; new industrial building construction; commercial & office building renovation & repair services; institutional building construction; industrial building & warehouse construction

(G-3984)
C J DUFFEY PAPER CO (PA)
528 Washington Ave N (55401-1226)
PHONE.............................612 338-8701
FAX: 612 338-1320
Mary A Berley, *President*
John P Duffey, *Corp Secy*
David Hewes, *Exec VP*
Bob Margl, *Vice Pres*
John Berget, *Vice Pres*
EMP: 60 EST: 1945
SQ FT: 110,000 Privately Held
SIC: 5111 5087 5113 Wholesales fine paper; wholesales cleaning & maintenance equipment & supplies; wholesales industrial & personal service paper

(G-3985)
C J OLSON MARKET RESEARCH
901 N 3rd St Ste 218 (55401-1051)
PHONE.............................612 378-5040
FAX: 612 339-1788
Tianna Ramaker, *President*
Carolyn J Olson, *President*
Richard Chay, *Senior VP*
Wayne Ramaker, *Vice Pres*
Russell McGuire, *Accounts Exec*
EMP: 40 EST: 1984
SQ FT: 4,500
SALES (est): 1MM-4.9MM Privately Held
WEB: www.cjolson.com
SIC: 8732 Market analysis or research services

(G-3986)
C P P NORTH AMERICA LLC
Also Called: Card Protection Plan
5100 Gamble Dr Ste 600 (55416-1512)
PHONE.............................952 541-5800
Gregory Mazza, *Member*
Eric Woolley, *Member*
Steven H Arlowe, *Corp Secy*
William Anderson, *Vice Pres*
Bev Campbell, *Vice Pres*
EMP: 189 EST: 1995
SQ FT: 45,000
SALES (est): 10MM-24.9MM Privately Held
WEB: www.cppnorthamerica.com
SIC: 8748 Business consulting services

(G-3987)
C S AERO-SPACE INC
9270 Bryant Ave S (55420-3402)
PHONE.............................952 884-4725
FAX: 952 884-5561
Steven R Hanson, *President*
Diane R Hanson, *Corp Secy*
Lawrence A Hruby, *Vice Pres*
Don Bauer, *Sales Mgr*
Brian Hatfield, *Manager*
▲ EMP: 34 EST: 1964
SQ FT: 30,000
SALES (est): 10MM-24.9MM Privately Held
WEB: www.ascs.com
SIC: 5072 5051 5065 Wholesales hardware nuts; wholesales wire cable; wholesales electronic parts; wholesales bolts; wholesales rivets; wholesales screws

(G-3988)
CA INC
7760 France Ave S Ste 500 (55435-5928)
PHONE.............................952 838-1186
Jessica Lukensow, *Pub Rel Mgr*
Lora Romain, *Manager*
John Dolejsi, *Supervisor*
Jeanne Glass, *CTO*
William Lozito, *Web Proj Mgr*
EMP: 170
SALES (est): 25MM-49.9MM Publicly Held
WEB: www.cai.com
SIC: 7372 Application software publishing; business & professional software publishers

(G-3989)
CABINETS BY CHOICE INC
3300 Gorham Ave (55426-4220)
PHONE.............................952 924-8958
Nick Smaby, *President*
John Greely, *Vice Pres*
Andrew Berg, *Manager*
Jim McGrory, *Manager*
Joyce Miller, *Officer*
EMP: 70 EST: 1992
SQ FT: 20,000
SALES (est): 5MM-9.9MM Privately Held
SIC: 1751 Cabinet building & installation service; manufactures wooden kitchen cabinets; manufactures wood partitions & fixtures

(G-3990)
CALABRIO INC
605 Highway 169 N Ste 800 (55441-6533)
PHONE.............................763 592-4600
Tom Goodmanson, *President*
Brett Theisen, *Vice Pres*
Ruth Porter, *Executive Asst*
EMP: 85 EST: 2007
SQ FT: 26,000
SALES (est): 50MM-99.9MM Privately Held
SIC: 5045 Wholesales computer software

(G-3991)
CALCO SPROUTS INC
2751 Minnehaha Ave (55406-1546)
PHONE.............................612 724-0276
FAX: 612 724-1377
Jino Yen, *President*
Linda Yen, *Treasurer*
Linda Yang, *Manager*
EMP: 30 EST: 1987
SQ FT: 17,632 Privately Held
SIC: 0182 Bean sprout farming; manufactures food preparations

(G-3992)
CALHOUN BEACH CLUB OF
2925 Dean Pkwy Ste 300 (55416-7700)
PHONE.............................612 927-9951
FAX: 612 925-8307
Georgia Brown, *General Mgr*
Donald Ardell, *General Mgr*
Bryce Karasiak, *Vice Pres*
Bob Macey, *Finance*
David Schomaker, *Finance*
EMP: 100 EST: 1980
SQ FT: 100,000
SALES (est): 1MM-4.9MM Privately Held
SIC: 7997 Membership recreation club; full service American restaurant

(G-3993)
CALHOUN SHORES APARTMENTS
3101 E Calhoun Pkwy # 107 (55408-2513)
PHONE.............................612 824-7505
Charles Minter, *President*
EMP: 30 EST: 2003
SALES (est): 1MM-4.9MM Privately Held
SIC: 6513 Apartment building operator

(G-3994)
CALIX NETWORKS INC
16305 36th Ave N Ste 300 (55446-4273)
PHONE.............................763 268-3300
FAX: 763 268-3301
Robert Lund, *Vice Pres*
James Stewart, *CFO*
Rick Paal, *Branch Mgr*
EMP: 70
SALES (est): 25MM-49.9MM Publicly Held
WEB: www.calix-networks.com
SIC: 1731 Manufactures fiber optic communication equipment; manufactures pressed & blown glass; electrical contractor
PA: Calix Networks Inc
    1035 N McDowell Blvd
    Petaluma CA 94954
    707 766-3000

(G-3995)
CAMDEN PHYSICIANS LTD
4209 Webber Pkwy (55412-1747)
PHONE.............................612 876-9700
Caryn Carlson, *Corp Secy*
Anita Dextrand, *Office Mgr*
Elaine R Hischfield MD, *Med Doctor*
Yohannes Gebregziabher MD, *Med Doctor*
Jennifer L Woodand MD, *Med Doctor*
EMP: 25
SALES (est): 1MM-4.9MM Privately Held
SIC: 8011 Physicians' office & clinic

(G-3996)
CAMP BUCKSKIN INC
4124 Quebec Ave N Ste 300 (55427-1241)
PHONE.............................952 930-3544
Tom Bauer, *Director*
EMP: 60 EST: 1959
SALES (est): 1MM-4.9MM Privately Held
SIC: 8322 General counseling services

(G-3997)
CAMPBELL MITHUN INC (HQ)
222 S 9th St Ste 2100 (55402-3361)
PHONE.............................612 347-1000
FAX: 612 347-1848
Steve Wehrenberg, *CEO*
Jonathan Hoffman, *President*
Kevin Connolly, *General Mgr*
Lance Crane, *Senior VP*
John Rash, *Senior VP*
EMP: 300 EST: 1933
SQ FT: 100,000
SALES (corp-wide): 6.02B Publicly Held

www.HarrisInfo.com
180

2011 Harris Minnesota
Services Directory

▲=Import ▼=Export
◆=Import/Export

WEB: www.cmithun.com
SIC: 7311 Advertising agency
PA: Interpublic Group of Co's Inc
1114 Avenue Of The Americas
New York NY 10036
212 704-1200

(G-3998)
CANADIAN PACIFIC LTD
615 30th Ave NE (55418-2003)
PHONE..............................612 781-7284
Greg Jones, Manager
EMP: 30
SALES (est): 1MM-4.9MM Privately Held
SIC: 4731 Freight transportation
arrangement services

(G-3999)
CANNON TECHNOLOGIES INC
505 Highway 169 N Ste 1200
(55441-6449)
PHONE..............................763 595-7777
FAX: 763 595-7776
Edward L Cannon, CEO
Terrance V Helz V, Corp Secy
Tobin Sobaski, Engineer
Stephen M Kole, Treasurer
Roberto Itchon, Controller
EMP: 45 EST: 1987
SQ FT: 13,000
SALES (est): 10MM-24.9MM Privately Held
WEB: www.cooperpower.com
SIC: 5084 Wholesales industrial electrical
measuring & testing equipment
HQ: Cooper Power Systems LLC
2300 Badger Dr
Waukesha WI 53188
262 896-2400

(G-4000)
CAPTIONMAX INC
2438 27th Ave S (55406-1308)
PHONE..............................612 341-3566
Max Duckler, President
Robin Miller, Editor
Kendra Riemermann, Editor
Stephanie Hammergren, Prdtn Mgr
Diane Richard, Finance Dir
EMP: 50 EST: 1993
SQ FT: 38,000
SALES (est): 10MM-24.9MM Privately Held
WEB: www.captionmax.com
SIC: 4841 7389 Pay television distribution;
music & broadcasting service

(G-4001)
CARDINAL HEALTH INC
17400 Medina Rd (55447-1339)
PHONE..............................763 398-8321
Jeff Schaff, Data Proc Exec
EMP: 200
SALES (est): 100MM-499.9MM Publicly
Held
WEB: www.cardinal.com
SIC: 5122 Wholesales pharmaceuticals,
drug proprietaries & sundries
PA: Cardinal Health Inc
7000 Cardinal Pl
Dublin OH 43017
614 757-5000

(G-4002)
**CARDIOVASCULAR
CONSULTANTS LTD**
3300 Oakdale Ave N Ste 200
(55422-2926)
PHONE..............................763 520-2000
Pamela Paulsen, President
Andrew McGinn, Principal
Jody Rowland, Principal
David Abrams, Vice Pres
Joseph G Boston, Vice Pres
▲ EMP: 100 EST: 1975
SALES (est): 10MM-24.9MM Privately Held
SIC: 8011 Cardiologist & cardio-vascular
specialist

(G-4003)
CARE PLUS H H A INC
4050 Olson Memorial Hwy (55422-5323)
PHONE..............................763 529-5520
FAX: 763 529-5521
Kathleen Pasqualini, President
Toby Pasqualini, Opers Mgr
Jean Jorlett, Nursing Dir

EST: 1986
SQ FT: 2,200 Privately Held
WEB: www.careplushha.com
SIC: 8082 Home health care services

(G-4004)
CARE TV
8811 Olson Memorial Hwy (55427-4762)
PHONE..............................763 546-1111
John Remes, General Mgr
Mike Amme, Manager
Mike Tamme, Manager
Rita Beatty, Producer
John Storm, IT Specialist
EMP: 150 EST: 1986
SALES (est): 25MM-49.9MM Privately Held
SIC: 4833 Television translator station

(G-4005)
CAREFUSION 203 INC (HQ)
17400 Medina Rd Ste 100 (55447-1341)
PHONE..............................763 398-8300
FAX: 763 398-8400
Gerri Robinson, President
Joe Hicman, Purchasing
Ann McGregor, Manager
Virginia Minter, CTO
Jim Homouth, Director
▲ EMP: 140 EST: 1996
SQ FT: 44,000
SALES (corp-wide): 3.92B Publicly Held
SIC: 5047 Wholesales medical & hospital
equipment
PA: Carefusion Corp
3750 Torrey View Ct
San Diego CA 92130
858 617-2000

(G-4006)
**CARGILL FINANCIAL SERVICES
INT**
405 2nd Ave SE (55414-1101)
PO Box 5657 (55440-5657)
PHONE..............................952 742-7575
EMP: 1990 EST: 1990
SALES (est): 500MM-999.9MM Privately
Held
SIC: 6211 Securities broker & dealer

(G-4007)
CARGILL INC
7650 Edinbrgh Way Ste 600 (55435-6012)
PHONE..............................612 367-3000
Robert Mann, Branch Mgr
Nadia Dawood, Manager
Debbie Blattner, Manager
EMP: 180
SALES (est): 100MM-499.9MM Privately
Held
SIC: 5051 Wholesales steel

(G-4008)
CARGILL INC
15407 Mc Ginty Rd (55440)
PO Box 9300 (55440-9300)
PHONE..............................763 742-5512
Gayl Bunes, Project Mgr
Rod Smoliak, Manager
Peter Price, Director
EMP: 25
SALES (est): 1MM-4.9MM Privately Held
SIC: 8721 Billing & bookkeeping services

(G-4009)
CARGILL INC
12700 Whtwater Dr Fl 2 (55440)
PO Box 5653 (55440-5653)
PHONE..............................952 984-3890
David Maclennen, Manager
Peter Stadick, IT/INT Sup
EMP: 200
SALES (est): 100MM-499.9MM Privately
Held
SIC: 6221 Commodity contracts broker or
dealer

(G-4010)
CARGILL INC
15407 McGnty Rd W Ms 20 (55440)
PO Box 5602 (55440-5602)
PHONE..............................952 742-4417
Shirley Newman, Branch Mgr
EMP: 200
SALES (est): 100MM-499.9MM Privately
Held

SIC: 5153 Wholesales grains

(G-4011)
CARGILL INC
12900 Whtwater Dr MS109 109 Ms
(55440)
PO Box 5614 (55440-5614)
PHONE..............................763 497-2157
Roxanne Vetsch, Branch Mgr
EMP: 85
SALES (est): 25MM-49.9MM Privately Held
SIC: 5191 Manufactures animal feed;
wholesales animal feeds

(G-4012)
CARL CROSBY LEHMANN
Also Called: Gray Plant Mooty
80 S 8th St Ste 500 (55402-5383)
PHONE..............................612 632-3000
FAX: 612 632-4444
Carl C Lehman, Owner
Ashley Ewald, Editor In Chief
In December, Member
Jeffrey Karlin, Member
Thomas Johnson, Member
EMP: 300 EST: 2004
SALES (est): 25MM-49.9MM Privately Held
SIC: 8111 Specialized legal services

(G-4013)
CARLSON CO'S INC
1405 Xenium Ln N (55441-4410)
PHONE..............................763 212-5253
FAX: 763 550-6280
Jack O Neill, COO
Jon V Rentzell, COO
William A Van Brunt, Senior VP
Geri Corrigan, Vice Pres
Koch Isablle, Vice Pres
EMP: 400
SALES (est): 50MM-99.9MM Privately Held
SIC: 8742 Marketing consulting service

(G-4014)
CARLSON HOTELS LP (DH)
Carlson Parkway 701 Twr St (55459)
PO Box 59159 (55459-8200)
PHONE..............................763 212-1000
Marilyn Nelson, Ch of Bd
Curtis C Nelson, President
Gary Hokkanen, COO
Richard Frommeyer, Exec VP
Michael D Nicola, Vice Pres
EMP: 201 EST: 1983
SQ FT: 300,000 Privately Held
WEB: www.carlson.com
SIC: 6794 7011 Selling or licensing of
franchises; bar; full service chain family
restaurant; franchised hotel; franchised
resort hotel
HQ: Carlson Inc
701 Carlson Pkwy
Minnetonka MN 55305
763 212-5000

(G-4015)
**CARLSON HOTELS
MANAGEMENT CORP**
35 S 7th St (55402-1602)
PHONE..............................612 339-4900
Judith Kalson, General Mgr
John Stephens, Engineer
Bob Smith, Controller
Michella Renchin, Human Res Dir
Denise Schultz, Sales Staff
EMP: 175
SALES (est): 10MM-24.9MM Privately Held
WEB: www.radisson.com
SIC: 7011 Traveler accommodations
HQ: Carlson Hotels Management Corp
701 Tower Carlson Pike
Minneapolis MN 55459
763 212-5000

(G-4016)
**CARLSON HOTELS
MANAGEMENT CORP**
Also Called: Radisson Inn
701 Tower Carlson Pike (55459)
PO Box 59159 (55459-8200)
PHONE..............................763 212-5000
Jay Witzel, President
Hubert Joly, President
Trudy Rautio, General Mgr
Andrea Tyler, Business Mgr

Frederic Deschamps, Vice Pres
◆ EMP: 160 EST: 1967
SQ FT: 10,000
SALES (est): 50MM-99.9MM Privately Held
WEB: www.radisson.com
SIC: 6794 6531 6552 Selling or licensing of
franchises; real estate management
services; commercial land subdividers &
developers
HQ: Radisson Hotels International
701 Carlson Pkwy
Minnetonka MN 55305
763 212-5000

(G-4017)
**CARLSON HOTELS WORLDWIDE
INC**
Carlson Parkway 701 Tower St (55459)
PO Box 59159 (55459-8200)
PHONE..............................763 212-5000
Jay Witzel, President
Bjorn Gullaksen, President
Paul Kirwin, President
Judith Kalfon, General Mgr
James Riker, General Mgr
EMP: 40 EST: 1998
SQ FT: 15,000
SALES (est): 1MM-4.9MM Privately Held
WEB: www.carlsonhotels.com
SIC: 7011 6794 Franchised hotel; selling or
licensing of franchises
DH: Carlson Hotels LP
Carlson Parkway 701 Twr St
Minneapolis MN 55459
763 212-1000

(G-4018)
**CARLSON MARKETING
WORLDWIDE**
12805 Highway 55 Ste 311 (55441-3859)
PO Box 59159 (55459-8200)
PHONE..............................763 449-3704
Mike Simpson, Exec VP
Josh Birkel, Manager
Charles Schmid, Manager
Karl Luebbe, Programmer Anys
EMP: 25
SALES (est): 1MM-4.9MM Privately Held
WEB: www.carlsonmarketing.com
SIC: 8742 Marketing consulting service

(G-4019)
**CARLSON, LUNDQUIST & CO
LTD**
7101 Northland Cir N (55428-1525)
PHONE..............................763 535-8150
FAX: 763 535-8154
Rick Riesgraf, President
Melvin Enger, Vice Pres
Joel Henley, Vice Pres
Brian McGrane, Vice Pres
Michael T Niznik, Vice Pres
EMP: 35 EST: 1974
SQ FT: 10,000
SALES (est): 1MM-4.9MM Privately Held
WEB: www.carlson-advisors.com
SIC: 8721 8742 Certified public accountant
services; management consulting services

(G-4020)
CARPET FACTORY OUTLET INC
Also Called: Stone Mountain Crpt Fctry Outl
6363 Highway 7 (55416-2346)
PHONE..............................612 988-0400
Chuck Carlson, President
Catherine Carlson, Office Mgr
EST: 1995
SQ FT: 20,000 Privately Held
SIC: 5023 Retails floor coverings;
wholesales floor coverings

(G-4021)
CARRIER COMMERCIAL
6325 Sandburg Rd Ste 800 (55427-3658)
PHONE..............................763 231-8300
Patrick Kline, Branch Mgr
Steve Rols, Exec Dir
EMP: 45
SALES (est): 5MM-9.9MM Publicly Held
WEB: www.ccr.carrier.com

GEOGRAPHIC

(PA)=Parent Co (HQ)=Headquarters (DH)=Div Headquarters
✿ = New business established in last 2 years
2011 Harris Minnesota
Services Directory
© Harris InfoSource 1-866-281-6415
181

SIC: 1711 5078 Refrigeration contractor; wholesales ice making machines
DH: Carrier Commercial
9300 Harris Corners Pkwy
Charlotte NC 28269
704 494-2500

(G-4022)
CARTIKA MEDICAL INC
9909 S Shore Dr Ste 5 (55441-5037)
PHONE 763 545-5188
Thomas C Carlson, *President*
Sheila A Carlson, *Vice Pres*
EMP: 50 **EST:** 1993
SQ FT: 20,000
SALES (est): 5MM-9.9MM **Publicly Held**
WEB: www.cartikamedical.com
SIC: 8742 Manufactures prosthetic appliances; industry specialist consultant; manufactures medical instruments
PA: Advansource Biomaterials Corp
229 Andover St
Wilmington MA 01887
978 657-0075

(G-4023)
CASCADE MORTGAGE INC
2801 Hennepin Ave (55408-1907)
PHONE 612 252-3333
FAX: 612 252-3366
Kam Talebi, *CEO*
EMP: 30 **EST:** 2005
SALES (est): 10MM-24.9MM **Privately Held**
SIC: 6211 Buying & selling of mortgages

(G-4024)
CASH PLUS INC
222 S 9th St Ste 2100 (55402-3361)
PHONE 612 347-6900
FAX: 612 347-6969
Dick Hurrelbrink, *President*
Pete Engebretson, *Vice Pres*
EMP: 38 **EST:** 1976
SALES (est): 1MM-4.9MM **Publicly Held**
WEB: www.cmithun.com
SIC: 7319 Media buying services
HQ: Campbell Mithun Inc
222 S 9th St Ste 2100
Minneapolis MN 55402
612 347-1000

(G-4025)
CASSERLY MOLZAHN & ASSOC INC
8000 Norman Center Dr Ste 1000
(55437-1177)
PHONE 952 885-1298
Jim Casserly, *President*
EMP: 60 **EST:** 1996
SALES (est): 5MM-9.9MM **Privately Held**
SIC: 8111 Legal services

(G-4026)
CASSIDY TURLEY MIDWEST INC
200 S 6th St Ste 1400 (55402-1434)
PHONE 612 341-4444
Dennis Panzer, *Branch Mgr*
EMP: 60
SALES (est): 10MM-24.9MM **Privately Held**
WEB: www.ctmt.com
SIC: 6531 8742 Real estate agency & broker; commercial real estate agency; real estate consultant
PA: Cassidy Turley Midwest Inc
7701 Forsyth Blvd Ste 500
Saint Louis MO 63105
314 862-7100

(G-4027)
CATALOG MARKETING SERVICES (PA)
Also Called: CMS
6300 Shingle Creek Pkwy (55430-2124)
PHONE 651 636-6265
R K Johnson, *CEO*
Patrick C Minton, *President*
Andy Doscette, *Opers Staff*
John Brand, *CFO*
Jennifer Olesen, *Finance*
EMP: 110 **EST:** 1982
SQ FT: 30,000 **Privately Held**
WEB: www.cmscms.com
SIC: 7374 Computer service bureau

(G-4028)
CATHOLIC CHARITIES OF THE (PA)
1200 2nd Ave S (55403-2513)
PHONE 612 664-8500
FAX: 612 375-9105
John Estrem, *CEO*
J M Dady, *Ch of Bd*
Jack S Jackson, *Corp Secy*
Brian J McGrane, *Senior VP*
Douglas C Cooley, *Vice Pres*
EMP: 49 **EST:** 1869
SQ FT: 10,000
SALES (corp-wide): 30.76M **Privately Held**
SIC: 8322 Social services center

(G-4029)
CATHOLIC CHARITIES OF THE
Also Called: Northside Child Dev Center
1000 Plymouth Ave N (55411-4005)
PHONE 612 529-9107
FAX: 612 529-9294
Helen Jirak, *Branch Mgr*
EMP: 40
SALES (est): 500-999K **Privately Held**
SIC: 8351 Child development center providing Montessori based instruction
PA: Catholic Charities of The
1200 2nd Ave S
Minneapolis MN 55403
612 664-8500

(G-4030)
CATHOLIC CHARITIES OF THE
Also Called: St Joseph's Home For Children
1121 E 46th St (55407-3562)
PHONE 612 827-6241
FAX: 612 827-7954
Nancy Zemel, *Office Mgr*
Edward McBrayer, *Branch Mgr*
Sandra Hestness, *Manager*
Tabatha Johnson, *Manager*
Keith Kozerski, *Administrator*
EMP: 230
SALES (est): 5MM-9.9MM **Privately Held**
SIC: 8059 8093 8322 Home for the mentally retarded; elementary & secondary school; individual & family social services; specialty outpatient clinic
PA: Catholic Charities of The
1200 2nd Ave S
Minneapolis MN 55403
612 664-8500

(G-4031)
CATHOLIC HEALTH INITIATIVES
Also Called: C H I Mnnplis Nat Oprtions Ctr
7650 Edinbrgh Way Ste 200 (55435-5989)
PHONE 952 324-9010
Peter Mannix, *Vice Pres*
Dave Goode, *Manager*
EMP: 500
SALES (est): 25MM-49.9MM **Privately Held**
SIC: 8062 Medical hospital
PA: Catholic Health Initiatives
98 Inverness Dr W Ste 800
Englewood CO 80112
303 298-9100

(G-4032)
CB RICHARD ELLIS INC
7760 France Ave S Ste 770 (55435-3211)
PHONE 952 924-4600
FAX: 952 831-8023
Peter Taffe, *Regional Mgr*
Anthony R Aspholm, *Opers Mgr*
Matt Seguin, *Facilities Mgr*
Whitney Peyton, *VP Sls/Mktg*
Betsy Primeau, *Controller*
EMP: 80
SALES (est): 10MM-24.9MM **Publicly Held**
WEB: www.cbre.com
SIC: 6531 Real estate agency & broker
HQ: CB Richard Ellis Inc
11150 Santa Monica Blvd
Los Angeles CA 90025
310 606-4700

(G-4033)
CBS RADIO INC
625 2nd Ave S Ste 550 (55402-1909)
PHONE 612 339-1029
Mick Anselmo, *Senior VP*
Dick Carlson, *Vice Pres*

Doug Campbell, *Chief Engr*
Craig Walters, *Engineer*
Tom Mooney, *Controller*
EMP: 30
SALES (est): 1MM-4.9MM **Privately Held**
WEB: www.infinityradio.com
SIC: 4832 Radio broadcasting station
DH: CBS Radio Inc
40 W 57th St Fl 14
New York NY 10019
212 846-3939

(G-4034)
CC HOLDINGS INC
712 Ontario Ave W Ste 200 (55403-1158)
PHONE 612 371-8008
FAX: 612 371-8011
Steve Javinsky, *President*
Paige M Nelson, *Manager*
Joe Stanley, *Exec Dir*
EMP: 35 **EST:** 1997
SQ FT: 10,000
SALES (est): 1MM-4.9MM **Privately Held**
WEB: www.fastdisc.com
SIC: 7389 Music & broadcasting service

(G-4035)
CDI CENTRAL FLORIDA LLC
5775 Wayzata Blvd Ste 400 (55416-1271)
PHONE 952 543-6500
Robert Baumgartner, *Member*
Ryan Raschke, *Asst Treas*
EMP: 65 **EST:** 2000
SALES (est): 5MM-9.9MM **Privately Held**
SIC: 8071 Dental & medical X-ray laboratory

(G-4036)
CEDAR RIDGE INC
320 2nd Ave SE Apt 405 (55414-1169)
PHONE 651 426-8983
Paul Cowdery, *President*
EMP: 66 **EST:** 1988
SQ FT: 15,000
SALES (est): 1MM-4.9MM **Privately Held**
WEB: www.cedarridge.com
SIC: 8069 8063 Substance abuse hospital; psychiatric hospital
PA: Twin Town Treatment Center LLC
1706 University Ave W
Saint Paul MN 55104
651 645-3661

(G-4037)
CEDAR TOWING & AUCTION INC
359 Hoover St NE (55413-2941)
PHONE 612 721-6645
FAX: 612 721-6645
Thomas A Rodrigue, *President*
Thomas A Rodriguez, *Principal*
Julie Rodrigue, *Vice Pres*
EMP: 30 **EST:** 1979
SQ FT: 3,000
SALES (est): 1MM-4.9MM **Privately Held**
WEB: www.cedartowing.com
SIC: 7538 7549 General automotive repair services; automotive towing service

(G-4038)
CEDAR-RIVERSIDE PEOPLE'S CTR
425 20th Ave S (55454-4400)
PHONE 612 332-4973
Peggy Metzer, *CEO*
Barry Irving, *Corp Secy*
Betsy David, *COO*
Elaine Wynee, *Manager*
Luciano Mariucci, *IT/INT Sup*
EMP: 38 **EST:** 1970
SALES (est): 1MM-4.9MM **Privately Held**
WEB: www.cedarriverside.com
SIC: 8011 Clinic operated by physicians

(G-4039)
CEDARS OF EDINA APARTMENTS
7340 Gallagher Dr Ste 1 (55435-3705)
PHONE 952 835-3388
Jon K Gura, *General Mgr*
EMP: 35 **EST:** 1974
SALES (est): 5MM-9.9MM **Privately Held**
SIC: 6513 Apartment building operator

(G-4040)
CELLCO PARTNERSHIP
Also Called: Verizon
2510 Mendelssohn Ave N (55427-3119)
PHONE 763 595-5102
Rich Kenny, *General Mgr*
EMP: 30 **Publicly Held**
WEB: www.verizon.com
SIC: 4812 Cellular telephone services
HQ: Cellco Partnership
1 Verizon Way
Basking Ridge NJ 07920
908 559-5490

(G-4041)
CENTENNIAL LAKES DENTAL GROUP
7373 France Ave S Ste 500 (55435-4551)
PHONE 952 831-2800
Alan Mogck, *President*
Judy Salbik, *Business Mgr*
Steven Mahler, *Vice Pres*
EMP: 26 **EST:** 1972
SQ FT: 5,300
SALES (est): 1MM-4.9MM **Privately Held**
WEB: www.centlakedent.com
SIC: 8021 Dental office

(G-4042)
CENTER FOR APPLIED RESEARCH
159 Pillsbury Dr SE # 275 (55455-0228)
PHONE 612 624-0300
FAX: 612 625-3086
Marilyn Johnston, *Administrator*
Mark Yackel-Juleen, *Exec Dir*
Kyla Wahlstrom, *Director*
EMP: 35 **EST:** 2001
SALES (est): 1MM-4.9MM **Privately Held**
WEB: www.centerforappliedresearch.com
SIC: 8733 Educational research agency

(G-4043)
CENTER FOR VICTIMS OF TORTURE (PA)
717 E River Pkwy (55455-0369)
PHONE 612 436-4800
FAX: 612 626-2465
Venetia Kudrle, *Vice Chairman*
Karla Wetherby, *CFO*
Carol White, *Manager*
Martha Meier, *Exec Dir*
Douglas A Johnson, *Exec Dir*
EMP: 60 **EST:** 1985
SQ FT: 4,400
SALES (corp-wide): 8.67M **Privately Held**
SIC: 8011 Specialized medical practitioners; psychiatrist or psychoanalysts office

(G-4044)
CENTERPOINT ENERGY RESOURCES
Also Called: Minnegasco
501 W 61st St (55419-2212)
PHONE 612 861-8450
Rich Becker, *President*
Bruce Soderholm, *Buyer*
EMP: 100
SALES (est): 100MM-499.9MM **Publicly Held**
WEB: www.reliantresources.com
SIC: 4924 Natural gas distribution to consumers
HQ: CenterPoint Energy Resources
1111 Louisiana St
Houston TX 77002
713 207-1111

(G-4045)
CENTERPOINT ENERGY RESOURCES
800 Lasalle Ave Fl 16 (55402-2051)
PO Box 59038 (55459-0038)
PHONE 612 372-4720
FAX: 612 342-5056
Ron Trussell, *Info Tech Mgr*
EMP: 25
SALES (est): 10MM-24.9MM **Publicly Held**
WEB: www.reliantresources.com

---

www.HarrisInfo.com
182
2011 Harris Minnesota
Services Directory
▲=Import ▼=Export
◆=Import/Export

SIC: **4911** Provides electric power
generation services
HQ: CenterPoint Energy Resources
1111 Louisiana St
Houston TX 77002
713 207-1111

(G-4046)
CENTRAL PARKING INC
81 S 9th St Ste 445 (55402-3254)
PHONE...............................612 340-9025
Chris Stekora, *Manager*
EMP: 40 EST: 1981
SALES (est): 1MM-4.9MM **Privately Held**
WEB: www.parking.com
SIC: **7521** Vehicle parking lot or garage
HQ: Central Parking Corp
2401 21st Ave S Ste 200
Nashville TN 37212
615 297-4255

(G-4047)
CENTRAL TERRITORIAL OF THE
Also Called: Adult Rehabilitatioin Center
900 N 4th St (55401-1039)
PHONE...............................612 332-5855
FAX: 612 332-0781
Bill Price, *Administrator*
EMP: 120 **Privately Held**
WEB: www.salarmychicago.org
SIC: **8699** Religious organization; charitable
organization
HQ: Central Territorial of The
10 W Algonquin Rd
Des Plaines IL 60016
847 294-2000

(G-4048)
CENTRO CULTURAL CHICANO
1915 Chicago Ave (55404-1904)
PHONE...............................612 874-1412
FAX: 612 874-8149
Francini Acuna, *Manager*
Tyrone Guzman, *Exec Dir*
Mary J Avendano, *Director*
Tess Vergara, *Director*
Roxana Linares, *Director*
EMP: 27 EST: 1974
SALES (est): 1MM-4.9MM **Privately Held**
SIC: **8322** General counseling services

(G-4049)
CENTURY 21 CARE REALTY
8016 64th Ave N (55428-2103)
PHONE...............................763 862-5690
Ron Colbert, *Owner*
EMP: 40 EST: 1985
SALES (est): 5MM-9.9MM **Privately Held**
SIC: **6531** Real estate agency & broker

(G-4050)
CENTURY 21 LUGER REALTY INC
4536 France Ave S (55410-1368)
PHONE...............................952 925-3901
James Luger, *President*
Judith Luger, *Corp Secy*
James Tice, *Executive*
Rolando Borja-Trujillo, *Real Est Agnt*
Tawn Eikel, *Real Est Agnt*
EMP: 50 EST: 1976
SALES (est): 5MM-9.9MM **Privately Held**
WEB: www.century21luger.com
SIC: **6531** Real estate services

(G-4051)
CERES CARIBE CERES ENVIRON
3825 85th Ave N (55443-2059)
PHONE...............................800 218-4424
John Ulschmid, *Vice Pres*
David A McIntyre, *CFO*
Steven M Johnson, *Director*
EMP: 41 EST: 2007
SQ FT: 1,500
SALES (est): 1MM-4.9MM **Privately Held**
SIC: **8322** Disaster services

(G-4052)
CERIDIAN CORP (HQ)
3311 E Old Shakopee Rd (55425-1361)
PHONE...............................952 853-8100
FAX: 952 548-5100
Lee A Kennedy, *CEO*

Robert H Ewald, *President*
John F Hunter, *General Mgr*
Harry Hurley, *General Mgr*
Ralph Rolen, *General Mgr*
EMP: 635 EST: 1957
SQ FT: 211,000 **Privately Held**
WEB: www.ceridian.com
SIC: **8721** Payroll services
PA: Foundation Holdings Inc
3311 E Old Shakopee Rd
Minneapolis MN 55425
952 853-8100

(G-4053)
CFC TECHNOLOGY CORP
2600 Fernbrook Ln N # 138 (55447-4752)
PO Box 47597 (55447-0597)
PHONE...............................763 235-5300
FAX: 763 235-5301
William Ristvedt, *President*
Richard A Wanke, *COO*
Gregg Thielsen, *CFO*
EMP: 47 EST: 1998
SQ FT: 5,000
SALES (est): 5MM-9.9MM **Privately Held**
WEB: www.cfctechnology.com
SIC: **8742** Banking & finance consultant

(G-4054)
CHANGS INC
3833 Ewing Ave S (55410-1051)
PHONE...............................763 442-9080
Jane Chang, *CEO*
EMP: 25 EST: 2001
SALES (est): 1MM-4.9MM **Privately Held**
SIC: **1721** Painting & wall covering
contractor

(G-4055)
CHANNEL 12
6900 Winnetka Ave N (55428-1669)
PHONE...............................763 533-8196
Mike Johnson, *Opers Mgr*
Greg Moore, *Exec Dir*
EMP: 50 EST: 2001
SALES (est): 10MM-24.9MM **Privately Held**
SIC: **4833** Television broadcasting station

(G-4056)
CHARLES SCHWAB & CO INC
7400 France Ave S Ste 100 (55435-4738)
PHONE...............................952 835-6784
Patrick Moyneur, *Vice Pres*
Polly Pfieffer, *Branch Mgr*
EMP: 76
SALES (est): 10MM-24.9MM **Publicly Held**
WEB: www.schwabrt.com
SIC: **6211** Securities broker & dealer
DH: Charles Schwab & Co Inc
101 Montgomery St Ste 200
San Francisco CA 94104
415 636-7000

(G-4057)
CHECKER MACHINE INC
2701 Nevada Ave N (55427-2806)
PHONE...............................763 544-5000
FAX: 763 544-1272
Steven Lipinski, *CEO*
Margaret Lipinski, *CEO*
Barb Sridgen, *Human Res Dir*
Mike Nesmoe, *Manager*
Brad Schmitt, *Director*
EMP: 40 EST: 1976
SQ FT: 85,000
SALES (est): 1MM-4.9MM **Privately Held**
WEB: www.checkermachine.com
SIC: **7389 7692** Machine shop, jobbing &
repair services; commercial or industrial
precision grinding service; welding service

(G-4058)
CHENEY LLC
14025 23rd Ave N Ste A (55447-4922)
PHONE...............................763 559-1980
Steve Cheney, *Mng Member*
EMP: 25 EST: 1969
SQ FT: 50,000
SALES (est): 5MM-9.9MM **Privately Held**
SIC: **5023** Wholesales carpets

(G-4059)
CHERISHED WINGS TRANSPORTATION
2121 S 9th St Apt 315 (55404-2230)
PHONE...............................763 221-8788
Chad Older, *Principal*
EMP: 26
SALES (est): 1MM-4.9MM **Privately Held**
SIC: **8059** Nursing & personal care facility

(G-4060)
CHESTER E GROTH MUSIC CO
Also Called: Groth Music Co
8056 Nicollet Ave S (55420-1230)
PHONE...............................952 884-4772
FAX: 952 884-1134
Nancy Kersten, *President*
Darrell Kersten, *Vice Pres*
Alan Hager, *Advt Staff*
▲ EMP: 45 EST: 1939
SQ FT: 21,000
SALES (est): 5MM-9.9MM **Privately Held**
WEB: www.grothmusic.com
SIC: **7359** Retails musical instruments &
supplies; retails sheet music; musical
instrument rental service

(G-4061)
CHESTNUT & CAMMBRONE, PROF
222 S 9th St Ste 3700 (55402-3806)
PHONE...............................612 339-7300
FAX: 612 336-2940
Jack L Chestnut, *President*
EMP: 25 EST: 1963
SALES (est): 1MM-4.9MM **Privately Held**
WEB: www.chestnutcambronne.com
SIC: **8111** General practice attorney's or
lawyer's office

(G-4062)
CHEVYS
2251 Killebrew Dr (55425-1881)
PHONE...............................952 814-9555
Greg Komen, *Owner*
Dan Patterson, *Branch Mgr*
Randy Ashbrooke, *Manager*
EMP: 60 EST: 2001
SALES (est): 1MM-4.9MM **Privately Held**
SIC: **7299** Eating place; banquet hall facility

(G-4063)
CHIEF'S SERVICE INC
8610 Harriet Ave S (55420-2728)
PHONE...............................952 881-6404
Robert Schoenborn, *President*
EMP: 32 EST: 1982
SQ FT: 1,200
SALES (est): 1MM-4.9MM **Privately Held**
WEB: www.chiefstowing.com
SIC: **7549** Automotive towing & wrecking
services

(G-4064)
CHIEF'S TOWING INC
8610 Harriet Ave S (55420-2728)
PHONE...............................952 888-2201
Robert Schoenborn, *President*
Jeff Schoenboren, *General Mgr*
Gail Evans, *Accounting Staf*
EMP: 40 EST: 1971
SALES (est): 1MM-4.9MM **Privately Held**
SIC: **7549** Automotive towing service

(G-4065)
CHILDREN'S HEALTH CARE INC (PA)
2525 Chicago Ave (55404-4518)
PHONE...............................612 813-6100
FAX: 612 813-6807
Alan Goldbloom MD, *President*
Joel Aaron, *Member*
Penny Ayim, *Member*
David J Schmeling, *Ch of Surgery*
Mary K Wood, *Purchasing*
▲ EMP: 2340 EST: 1953
SQ FT: 100,000
SALES (corp-wide): 24.23M **Privately Held**
SIC: **8069** Children's hospital

(G-4066)
CHILDREN'S RESPIRATORY
2530 Chicago Ave Ste 400 (55404-4387)
PHONE...............................612 863-3226
William Wheeler MD, *President*
John Fugate, *Principal*
Stephen C Kurachek, *Principal*
John McNamara, *Principal*
David Burton, *CFO*
EMP: 40 EST: 1988
SQ FT: 3,300
SALES (est): 1MM-4.9MM **Privately Held**
WEB: www.crccs.com
SIC: **8011** Physicians' office & clinic;
pulmonary specialist, physician or surgeon;
pediatrician office

(G-4067)
CHILDREN'S THEATRE CO
2400 3rd Ave S (55404-3506)
PHONE...............................612 874-0500
FAX: 612 874-8119
Teresa Eyring, *Managing Dir*
Ann E Gundrson, *Mktg Dir*
Lori Sudit, *Marketing Mgr*
Ken Wik, *Administrator*
Dan Wozney, *Systems Mgr*
EMP: 200 EST: 1962
SQ FT: 80,000
SALES (est): 10MM-24.9MM **Privately Held**
SIC: **7922** Plays, road & stock companies;
music & drama school

(G-4068)
CHOICE COMMUNICATIONS INC
Also Called: Sprint
6808 13th Ave S (55423-2610)
PHONE...............................651 230-7127
Adrienne Awad, *President*
Sammi Awad, *Vice Pres*
EST: 2006 **Privately Held**
SIC: **4812** Wireless telecommunications
carrier & service

(G-4069)
CHOICES PSYCHOTHERAPY LTD
715 Florida Ave S Ste 307 (55426-1759)
PHONE...............................952 544-6806
FAX: 952 545-0098
Susan Davis, *President*
EMP: 30 EST: 1999
SALES (est): 1MM-4.9MM **Privately Held**
WEB: www.choicespsychotherapy.net
SIC: **8049** Psychotherapist office

(G-4070)
CHRISTOFERSEN MEATS CO (PA)
2700 26th Ave S (55406-1527)
PHONE...............................612 721-4411
Mark Mann, *President*
Bob Smith, *Manager*
EST: 1950
SQ FT: 12,500 **Privately Held**
WEB: www.garlandsinc.com
SIC: **5147** Wholesales fresh meat

(G-4071)
CHRISTOPHER MACLENNAN
2 Merrden Crssngs Ste 450 (55423)
PHONE...............................612 243-3302
Thomas Ibsen, *General Mgr*
Edward Balfour, *Exec VP*
William Degnan, *Vice Pres*
Roger Schiffler, *Manager*
Amy Putkonen, *Manager*
EMP: 25 EST: 2004 **Privately Held**
SIC: **6289** Financial reporting service

(G-4072)
CHRISTOPHERSON, JOHN
8009 34th Ave S (55425-1608)
PHONE...............................952 814-7185
Jim Bradley, *Vice Pres*
EMP: 55 EST: 1997
SALES (est): 5MM-9.9MM **Privately Held**
SIC: **7371** Computer software development
& applications

(PA)=Parent Co (HQ)=Headquarters (DH)=Div Headquarters
✿ = New business established in last 2 years

2011 Harris Minnesota
Services Directory

© Harris InfoSource 1-866-281-6415
183

(G-4073)
CHROMATIC CONCEPTS, CO
Also Called: Creative Banners
2730 Nevada Ave N (55427-2807)
PHONE..............................763 566-1118
Dennis J Flaherty, *President*
Keith Kirkland, *COO*
Kim Jackson, *Opers Mgr*
Jim Siesennop, *Research*
George Butkovich, *CFO*
▲ EMP: 75 EST: 1985
SQ FT: 50,000
SALES (est): 5MM-9.9MM **Privately Held**
SIC: 5131 Manufactures fabric banners;
manufactures signs & advertising
specialties; wholesales flags & banners

(G-4074)
CHURCH OF THE NATIVITY OF THE
Also Called: Nativity Mary Catholic School
9901 E Bloomington Fwy (55420-4721)
PHONE..............................952 881-8160
FAX: 952 881-3032
Barb Castagna, *Principal*
Jim Ellison, *Engineer*
Brain Gutzman, *Administrator*
Mike Simon, *Tech/Comp Coord*
EMP: 48
ADMISSIONS: 340 **Privately Held**
WEB: www.nativitybloomington.org
SIC: 8351 Catholic elementary school; child
day care service
PA: Church of The Nativity of The
9900 Lyndale Ave S
Bloomington MN 55420
952 881-8671

(G-4075)
CIN-MAR CORP
Also Called: Central Car Wash
1814 Central Ave NE (55418-4528)
PHONE..............................612 781-6924
FAX: 612 781-4204
Marty Carder, *President*
Cindy Carder, *Corp Secy*
EMP: 30
SQ FT: 13,000
SALES (est): 1MM-4.9MM **Privately Held**
SIC: 7542 Automotive washing & polishing
service

(G-4076)
CINEPLEX ODEAN CORP
9900 Shelard Pkwy (55441-6441)
PHONE..............................763 591-5921
Mike Muller, *Manager*
EMP: 25
SALES (est): 1MM-4.9MM **Privately Held**
SIC: 7832 Indoor movie theater
PA: Cineplex Odeon Corp
1303 Yonge St
Toronto Canada
416 3237216

(G-4077)
CINTAS CORP
Also Called: Minneapolis Rental
2306 Washington Ave N (55411-2223)
PHONE..............................763 588-2701
Ron Nord, *Sales/Mktg Mgr*
EMP: 45
SALES (est): 1MM-4.9MM **Privately Held**
SIC: 7213 Retails formal wear; uniform
supply service
PA: Cintas Corp
6800 Cintas Blvd
Cincinnati OH 45262
513 459-1200

(G-4078)
CIRCLE OF LIFE HOME CARE
1433 E Franklin Ave # 12 (55404-2101)
PHONE..............................612 871-2474
Patricia M Yager, *President*
Josie Sawiers, *Accountant*
EMP: 350 EST: 2006
SQ FT: 1,000
SALES (est): 10MM-24.9MM **Privately Held**
SIC: 8082 Home health care services

(G-4079)
CITIFINANCIAL CREDIT CO
8036 Brooklyn Blvd (55445-2407)
PHONE..............................763 424-6012
Leah Dockman, *Manager*
EMP: 47
SALES (est): 10MM-24.9MM **Publicly Held**
WEB: www.citifinancial.com
SIC: 6153 6141 Short-term business credit
institution; personal credit institution
DH: Citifinancial Credit Co
300 Saint Paul St Fl 3
Baltimore MD 21202
410 332-3000

(G-4080)
CITIGROUP GLOBAL MARKETS INC
333 S 7th St Ste 2600 (55402-2437)
PHONE..............................612 349-4800
FAX: 612 371-8875
Bill Adams, *Vice Pres*
M A Mandile, *Vice Pres*
David Jeffery, *Branch Mgr*
Paul Brunswich, *Manager*
EMP: 50
SALES (est): 10MM-24.9MM **Publicly Held**
WEB: www.salomonsmithbarney.com
SIC: 6211 Stock broker & dealer service
DH: Citigroup Global Markets Inc
388 Greenwich St Fl 18
New York NY 10013
212 816-6000

(G-4081)
CITIGROUP INC
7825 Washington Ave S (55439-2430)
PHONE..............................952 942-9880
FAX: 952 942-0015
Jay Kones, *Manager*
EMP: 175
SALES (est): 100MM-499.9MM **Publicly Held**
WEB: www.citigroup.com
SIC: 6159 6141 Automobile finance leasing
service; personal automobiles & furniture
financing
PA: Citigroup Inc
399 Park Ave
New York NY 10022
212 559-1000

(G-4082)
CITIZENS INDEPENDENT BANK
5000 W 36th St Ste 100 (55416-2759)
PHONE..............................952 926-6561
Brad Bakken, *President*
Constance L Bakken, *Chairman*
Marion Brummer, *Exec VP*
Rifal Manhanson, *Vice Pres*
Jeff Sanderson, *Vice Pres*
EMP: 40 EST: 1950
SALES (est): 10MM-24.9MM **Privately Held**
WEB: www.bankcib.com
SIC: 6022 State commercial bank
PA: Bakken Securities Inc
5000 W 36th St
Minneapolis MN 55416
952 926-6561

(G-4083)
CITY OF BLOOMINGTON
Also Called: Bloomington Port Authority
1800 W Old Shakopee Rd (55431-3071)
PHONE..............................952 563-8920
Larry Lee, *Manager*
EMP: 400
SALES (est): 50MM-99.9MM **Privately Held**
SIC: 8742 Planning consultant
PA: City of Bloomington
1800 W Old Shakopee Rd
Bloomington MN 55431
952 563-8700

(G-4084)
CITY OF BLOOMINGTON
Also Called: Bloomington Cemetery
10340 Lyndale Ave S (55420-5267)
PHONE..............................952 563-4925
FAX: 952 893-9166
Charles J McMurray, *Senior VP*
Mark Bernhardson, *Manager*
EMP: 200
SALES (est): 10MM-24.9MM **Privately Held**
SIC: 6553 Cemetery subdivision &
development services
PA: City of Bloomington
1800 W Old Shakopee Rd
Bloomington MN 55431
952 563-8700

(G-4085)
CITY OF BROOKLYN CENTER
Also Called: Earle Brown Heritage Center
6155 Earle Brown Dr (55430-2138)
PHONE..............................763 569-6300
FAX: 763 569-6320
Anthony Leitz, *General Mgr*
Carson Chemical, *Vice Pres*
Judith Berkland, *Manager*
EMP: 45
SALES (est): 1MM-4.9MM **Privately Held**
SIC: 7389 7299 Convention & trade show
services; banquet hall facility; mayors'
office; caterer

(G-4086)
CITY OF EDINA
7499 France Ave S (55435-4702)
PHONE..............................952 832-6792
Tom Shirley, *Branch Mgr*
EMP: 30
SALES (est): 1MM-4.9MM **Privately Held**
WEB: www.edinabasketball.com
SIC: 7999 Miniature golf course
PA: City of Edina
4801 W 50th St
Minneapolis MN 55424
952 927-8861

(G-4087)
CITY OF EDINA
Also Called: Braemar Golf Course Gar Maint
6364 John Harris Dr (55439-2564)
PHONE..............................952 941-2443
Tom Swenson, *Superintendent*
EMP: 25
SALES (est): 1MM-4.9MM **Privately Held**
WEB: www.edinabasketball.com
SIC: 7992 Public golf course
PA: City of Edina
4801 W 50th St
Minneapolis MN 55424
952 927-8861

(G-4088)
CITY OF MINNEAPOLIS
Also Called: Park & Recreation
3800 Bryant Ave S (55409-1029)
PHONE..............................612 370-4900
FAX: 612 370-4787
Jim Fagrelius, *Opers Mgr*
EMP: 200
SALES (est): 10MM-24.9MM **Privately Held**
WEB: www.ci.minneapolis.mn.us
SIC: 7996 0783 Amusement park;
ornamental shrub & tree service
PA: City of Minneapolis
350 S 5th St Ste 325M
Minneapolis MN 55415
612 673-3000

(G-4089)
CITY OF MINNEAPOLIS
Also Called: Solid Waste & Recycling
309 2nd Ave S Ste 210 (55401-2230)
PHONE..............................612 673-3779
FAX: 612 673-3538
Patrick Todd, *Manager*
Andy Castlene, *Manager*
Susan Young, *Manager*
EMP: 26
SALES (est): 1MM-4.9MM **Privately Held**
WEB: www.ci.minneapolis.mn.us
SIC: 4953 Waste material recycling services
PA: City of Minneapolis
350 S 5th St Ste 325M
Minneapolis MN 55415
612 673-3000

(G-4090)
CITY OF MINNEAPOLIS
Also Called: Hiawatha Golf Course
4553 Longfellow Ave (55407-3681)
PHONE..............................612 724-7715
Dan Stoneburg, *Manager*
Steve Skaar, *Director*
EMP: 40
SALES (est): 1MM-4.9MM **Privately Held**

WEB: www.ci.minneapolis.mn.us
SIC: 7992 Public golf course; mayors' office
PA: City of Minneapolis
350 S 5th St Ste 325M
Minneapolis MN 55415
612 673-3000

(G-4091)
CITY OF MINNEAPOLIS
1301 2nd Ave S (55403-2710)
PHONE..............................612 335-6000
FAX: 612 335-6757
Kim Nelson, *General Mgr*
Gary Fricke, *Vice Pres*
Wayne Mahoney, *Vice Pres*
Mary Kuether, *Vice Pres*
Stephanie Case, *Vice Pres*
EMP: 200
SALES (est): 5MM-9.9MM **Privately Held**
WEB: www.ci.minneapolis.mn.us
SIC: 7299 6512 7389 Banquet hall facility;
nonresidential building operator;
accommodation locating service; mayors'
office
PA: City of Minneapolis
350 S 5th St Ste 325M
Minneapolis MN 55415
612 673-3000

(G-4092)
CITY OF MINNEAPOLIS
Also Called: Francis A Gross Golf Course
2201 Saint Anthony Blvd (55418-3120)
PHONE..............................612 789-2542
Steven Walters, *Manager*
Tim Kuebelbeck, *Exec Dir*
EMP: 35
SALES (est): 1MM-4.9MM **Privately Held**
WEB: www.ci.minneapolis.mn.us
SIC: 7992 Public golf course; mayors' office
PA: City of Minneapolis
350 S 5th St Ste 325M
Minneapolis MN 55415
612 673-3000

(G-4093)
CITY OF MINNEAPOLIS
350 S 5th St Ste 210 (55415-1314)
PHONE..............................612 673-2597
Barbara Sporlein, *Director*
EMP: 50
SALES (est): 5MM-9.9MM **Privately Held**
WEB: www.ci.minneapolis.mn.us
SIC: 8748 Urban planning & consulting
services
PA: City of Minneapolis
350 S 5th St Ste 325M
Minneapolis MN 55415
612 673-3000

(G-4094)
CITY OF MINNEAPOLIS
Also Called: Minneapolis Park Police
2117 W River Rd Ste 1 (55411-2261)
PHONE..............................612 230-6550
Bradley Johnson, *Chief*
EMP: 59 **Privately Held**
WEB: www.ci.minneapolis.mn.us
SIC: 7999 Mayors' office; recreation
services
PA: City of Minneapolis
350 S 5th St Ste 325M
Minneapolis MN 55415
612 673-3000

(G-4095)
CITY OF PLYMOUTH
Also Called: Plymouth Ice Center
3650 Plymouth Blvd (55446-3201)
PHONE..............................763 509-5262
FAX: 763 509-5260
Bill Abel, *Branch Mgr*
EMP: 35
SALES (est): 1MM-4.9MM **Privately Held**
SIC: 7999 Ice skating rink
PA: City of Plymouth
3400 Plymouth Blvd
Plymouth MN 55447
763 509-5000

www.HarrisInfo.com
184

2011 Harris Minnesota
Services Directory

▲=Import ▼=Export
◆=Import/Export

(G-4096)
CITY OF RICHFIELD
Also Called: Richfield Youth Employment Svc
7000 Nicollet Ave (55423-3116)
PHONE..............612 861-9385
FAX: 612 861-9388
Beverly Reid, *Director*
EMP: 39 Privately Held
WEB: www.cityofrichfield.org
SIC: 7361 Employment agency services;
mayors' office
PA: City of Richfield
6700 Portland Ave
Minneapolis MN 55423
612 861-9700

(G-4097)
CITY-COUNTY FEDERAL CREDIT (PA)
6160 Summit Dr N (55430-2100)
PHONE..............763 549-6000
Dean Nelson, *President*
Bryan Bennett, *Exec VP*
Jack Flatley, *Senior VP*
Gail Mills, *Loan Officer*
Jerry Deyo, *Marketing Mgr*
EMP: 170 EST: 1928
SQ FT: 20,000
SALES (corp-wide): 27.24M Privately Held
SIC: 6061 Federally chartered credit union

(G-4098)
CITY-COUNTY FEDERAL CREDIT
6160 Summit Dr N (55430-2118)
PHONE..............763 549-6000
Jerry Dahl, *Branch Mgr*
EMP: 100
SALES (est): 10MM-24.9MM Privately Held
SIC: 6061 Federally chartered credit union
PA: City-County Federal Credit
6160 Summit Dr N
Minneapolis MN 55430
763 549-6000

(G-4099)
CLARE HOUSING
929 Central Ave NE (55413-2404)
PHONE..............612 236-9505
Paul Mellblom, *President*
Kathleen Andrus, *Corp Secy*
Cynthia Wolterding, *Manager*
Lee Haugee, *Manager*
Kathleen M Osf, *Manager*
EMP: 25 EST: 1994
SALES (est): 500-999K Privately Held
WEB: www.clarehousing.org
SIC: 8322 Senior citizen center

(G-4100)
CLARIANT CORP
9101 International Pkwy (55428-3607)
PHONE..............763 535-4511
Jim Brinks, *Vice Pres*
Steve Snow, *Manager*
EMP: 80
SALES (est): 10MM-24.9MM Privately Held
WEB: www.clariant.com
SIC: 5169 Manufactures organic color
pigments; manufactures synthetic organic
dyes; wholesales synthetic resins, rubber &
plastic materials; manufactures inorganic
pigments; manufactures paint
PA: Clariant Corp
4000 Monroe Rd
Charlotte NC 28205
704 331-7000

(G-4101)
CLARITY COVERDALE FURY ADV
120 S 6th St Ste 1300 (55402-1810)
PHONE..............612 339-3902
FAX: 612 359-4399
Timothy B Clarity, *President*
Diane Ethier, *COO*
Gary Hellmer, *Vice Pres*
Jerry Fury, *Vice Pres*
Jeri Quest, *Vice Pres*
EMP: 50 EST: 1979
SQ FT: 13,700
SALES (est): 5MM-9.9MM Privately Held
SIC: 7311 Advertising agency

(G-4102)
CLARK & WAMBERG LLC
Also Called: Integrated Hlth Care Strategy
901 Marquette Ave # 2100 (55402-3713)
PHONE..............612 339-0919
Gary A Van House, *Principal*
Felipe Padilla, *Principal*
Bob Cummings, *Vice Pres*
Julie McCauley, *Vice Pres*
Bob Erra, *Manager*
EMP: 180
SALES (est): 25MM-49.9MM Privately Held
WEB: www.clarkwamberg.co
SIC: 8742 6371 6411 Management
consulting services; pension, health &
welfare funds services; insurance broker
HQ: Clark & Wamberg LLC
102 S Wynstone Park Dr
Barrington IL 60010
847 304-5800

(G-4103)
CLARK ENGINEERING CORP
621 Lilac Dr N (55422-4609)
PHONE..............763 545-9196
Cory Casperson, *President*
Tim Labissoniere, *Corp Secy*
ABI Assadi, *Exec VP*
Don Weigel, *Vice Pres*
Lonnie Anderson, *Vice Pres*
EMP: 36 EST: 1991
SQ FT: 15,000
SALES (est): 1MM-4.9MM Privately Held
WEB: www.clark-eng.com
SIC: 8711 8713 8742 Civil engineering
services; management consulting services;
structural engineering services; surveying
service

(G-4104)
CLASS A VALET INC
120 N 4th St (55401-1774)
PHONE..............612 677-0071
FAX: 612 677-0072
Westy Graves, *President*
EMP: 25 EST: 1985
SALES (est): 1MM-4.9MM Privately Held
SIC: 7299 Valet parking services

(G-4105)
CLEAN WATER ACTION INC
308 E Hennepin Ave (55414-1016)
PHONE..............612 623-3666
FAX: 612 623-3354
Peter Lockwood, *Treasurer*
Marie Zellar, *Manager*
Bill Redding, *Bd of Directors*
Lorry Hautajarvi, *Officer*
EMP: 150
SALES (est): 10MM-24.9MM Privately Held
SIC: 8733 8743 8748 Noncommercial
research organization; lobbying services;
environmental consultant

(G-4106)
CLEANING MANAGEMENT GROUP INC
8120 Penn Ave S Ste 153 (55431-1326)
PHONE..............952 881-8791
Tracy Pearson, *President*
EMP: 48 EST: 1994
SALES (est): 1MM-4.9MM Privately Held
SIC: 7349 Industrial or commercial cleaning
services

(G-4107)
CLEAR CHANNEL COMMUNICATIONS
Also Called: Ktcz FM
1600 Utica Ave S Ste 400 (55416-1480)
PHONE..............952 417-3000
FAX: 952 417-3001
Dan Seeman, *General Mgr*
Peggy Hardie, *General Mgr*
Art Morales, *Managing Dir*
Matt Tell, *Managing Dir*
Barb Hueser, *Managing Dir*
EMP: 200
SALES (est): 10MM-24.9MM Privately Held
SIC: 4832 Radio broadcasting station
HQ: Clear Channel Communications
200 E Basse Rd
San Antonio TX 78209
210 822-2828

(G-4108)
CLEAR CHANNEL OUTDOOR INC
3225 Spring St NE (55413-2908)
PHONE..............612 605-5100
FAX: 612 605-5150
Marvin Kirchberg, *Maint Spvr*
Pam Schauff, *Accounting Staf*
Roy Schroeder, *VP Sales*
Jodi Durdle, *Marketing Staff*
Jeff Fuller, *Manager*
EMP: 56
SALES (est): 5MM-9.9MM Privately Held
WEB: www.clearchanneloutdoor.com
SIC: 7312 Outdoor advertising services;
manufactures signs & advertising
specialties; commercial printing
DH: Clear Channel Outdoor Inc
2201 E Camelbck Rd # 500
Phoenix AZ 85016
602 381-5700

(G-4109)
CLEARONE COMMUNICATIONS INC
901 Marquette Ave Ste 250 (55402-3243)
PHONE..............763 550-2300
Deena Flemmer, *Manager*
Tobin Schroder, *Info Tech Mgr*
EMP: 40
SALES (est): 25MM-49.9MM Publicly Held
WEB: www.clearone.com
SIC: 5065 Wholesales communications
equipment
PA: Clearone Communications Inc
5225 Wiley Post Way Ste 5
Salt Lake City UT 84116
801 975-7200

(G-4110)
CLOVER SUPER FOODS RT 30 INC
2850 Anthony Ln S (55418-3287)
PHONE..............612 465-8900
Craig Cook, *President*
Jodi Cook, *Corp Secy*
EMP: 35 EST: 1979
SQ FT: 60,000
SALES (est): 10MM-24.9MM Privately Held
WEB: www.cloversuperfoods.com
SIC: 5046 Wholesales commercial cooking
& food services equipment

(G-4111)
CLUB KID OF EDINA INC
7541 France Ave S (55435-4704)
PHONE..............952 831-1055
Mayer Berg, *Sales Staff*
Jennifer Clark, *Manager*
EMP: 25
SALES (est): 500-999K Privately Held
SIC: 8351 Child day care service

(G-4112)
CLUB THE CAMPUS INC
300 Washingtn Ave SE # 401
(55455-0371)
PHONE..............612 625-9696
Lee Stauffer, *President*
Barbara Jeppsen, *Principal*
David Jensen, *Systems Staff*
Ann Holt, *Director*
EMP: 40 EST: 1917
SALES (est): 1MM-4.9MM Privately Held
SIC: 7997 Membership recreation club

(G-4113)
CMGRP INC
8400 Norman Ctr Ste 400 (55437)
PHONE..............952 832-5588
R L Bailey, *Managing Dir*
Walter Shadwick, *Manager*
EMP: 200
SALES (est): 25MM-49.9MM Publicly Held
WEB: www.webershandwick.com
SIC: 7311 Advertising agency
HQ: Cmgrp Inc
919 3rd Ave Fl 15
New York NY 10022
212 445-8000

(G-4114)
CNH AMERICA LLC
2626 E 82nd St (55425-1300)
PHONE..............952 854-1443
Bob Atwood, *Branch Mgr*
EMP: 35
SALES (est): 10MM-24.9MM Privately Held
WEB: www.cnh.com
SIC: 5083 Wholesales farm & garden
machinery
HQ: Cnh America LLC
700 State St
Racine WI 53404
262 636-6011

(G-4115)
CNM INC
Also Called: Choice Wood Co
3300 Gorham Ave (55426-4220)
PHONE..............952 924-0043
Nick Smaby, *President*
Chris Jordan, *Vice Pres*
Andy Berg, *CFO*
Mark McClellan, *CFO*
Steve Stromor, *Analyst*
EMP: 65 EST: 1989
SQ FT: 20,000
SALES (est): 10MM-24.9MM Privately Held
WEB: www.choicecompanies.com
SIC: 1521 Residential remodeling

(G-4116)
COLDWELL BANKER BURNET
1501 W 80th St (55431-1401)
PHONE..............952 820-4663
Joe Reis, *CEO*
Robin Peterson, *President*
Ralph Burnet, *Chairman*
Kathy Krause, *Vice Pres*
Sandy Glover, *Sales Associate*
EMP: 50 EST: 1975
SALES (est): 5MM-9.9MM Privately Held
SIC: 6531 Real estate services; real estate
& insurance school

(G-4117)
COLIN CO, LP
800 Lasalle Ave Ste 1750 (55402-2028)
PHONE..............612 375-9670
Vincent Egan, *Partner*
Louis Moriarty, *Ltd Ptnr*
Norwest V Capital, *Ltd Ptnr*
EMP: 38 EST: 1980
SQ FT: 11,600
SALES (est): 1MM-4.9MM Privately Held
SIC: 7999 Concession operator

(G-4118)
COLLABORATIVE DESIGN GROUP INC
100 Portland Ave Ste 100 (55401-2533)
PHONE..............612 332-3654
William D Hickey, *President*
Philip Waugh, *Manager*
Pamela A Gilbert, *Incorporator*
EMP: 32 EST: 2001
SALES (est): 1MM-4.9MM Privately Held
WEB: www.collaborativedesigngroup.com
SIC: 8712 Architectural engineers

(G-4119)
COLLE & MCVOY INC
400 1st Ave N Ste 700 (55401-1725)
PHONE..............612 305-6000
Christine Fruechte, *CEO*
Philip J Johnson, *President*
Riff Yeager, *Managing Dir*
Glenn Gibson, *Corp Secy*
Ralph O Yeager, *Senior VP*
EMP: 160 EST: 1935
SQ FT: 55,000
SALES (est): 10MM-24.9MM Privately Held
WEB: www.collemcvoy.com
SIC: 7311 Advertising agency
PA: MDC Corp Inc
45 HAZELTON AVE
TORONTO Canada
416 9609000

(G-4120)

COLLIERS TOWLE VALUATION

200 S 6th St Ste 1400 (55402-1434)
PHONE..................................612 347-9336
Mark Burkhard, *President*
Eric Wedepohl, *Vice Pres*
Vicky Clement, *HR Admin*
Bradley J Conner, *Info Svcs Mgr*
EST: 1909
SQ FT: 15,000 **Privately Held**
SIC: 6531 6512 8742 Commercial real
estate agency; operators of commercial &
industrial buildings; real estate consultant

(G-4121)

COLLINS ELECTRICAL SYSTEMS INC

Also Called: Collisys
4990 Highway 169 N (55428-4026)
PHONE..................................763 535-6000
FAX: 763 535-6961
Richard W Boe, *Ch of Bd*
Robert Gorg, *President*
Richard Messbarger, *Division Mgr*
Bruce Young, *Exec VP*
Tony Benecke, *Purch Agent*
EMP: 100 **EST:** 1933
SQ FT: 15,000
SALES (est): 10MM-24.9MM **Privately Held**
WEB: www.collisys.com
SIC: 1731 General electrical contractor

(G-4122)

COLONIAL ACRES HOME INC

Also Called: Covenant Manor
5825 Saint Croix Ave N (55422-4419)
PHONE..................................763 546-6125
Katherine Witta, *Principal*
Vicki Gossard, *Nursing Dir*
EMP: 200
SALES (est): 5MM-9.9MM **Privately Held**
SIC: 8051 8361 Skilled nursing care facility;
residential care facility
PA: Colonial Acres Home Inc
5800 Saint Croix Ave N
Golden Valley MN 55422
763 544-1555

(G-4123)

COLOPLAST CORP (PA)

Also Called: Amonea
1601 W River Rd (55411-3431)
PHONE..................................612 337-7800
Don Looney, *President*
Kimberly Herman, *President*
Larry Pless, *Corp Secy*
Jan R Frederickson, *Vice Pres*
Peter Romanot, *Vice Pres*
◆ **EMP:** 270 **EST:** 1978 **Privately Held**
SIC: 5047 Manufactures cosmetic
restorations; wholesales medical & hospital
equipment; manufactures hair shampoos,
rinses & conditioners; manufactures shaving
preparations; manufactures cosmetic
preparations
PA: Coloplast A S
Holtedam 1
HUMLEBAEK Denmark

(G-4124)

COLUMBIA BUILDING SERVICES INC

2020 Broadway St NE (55413-1715)
PHONE..................................612 331-2090
FAX: 612 331-7603
Michael D Le Sage, *President*
Doug James, *MIS Staff*
EMP: 35 **EST:** 1916
SALES (est): 500-999K **Privately Held**
WEB: www.columbiabldgservices.com
SIC: 7349 1794 Building cleaning &
maintenance services; excavating
contractor; fabricates architectural
metalwork

(G-4125)

COLUMNS RESOURCE GROUP

100 Washington Ave S Ste 1200
(55401-2150)
PHONE..................................612 758-7600
FAX: 612 758-7740
Gene Storm, *President*
Mark Heurung, *Managing Dir*

Sandy Callen, *Info Tech Mgr*
Heather Isaackson, *Director*
EMP: 52 **EST:** 1963
SQ FT: 16,000
SALES (est): 5MM-9.9MM **Privately Held**
SIC: 6411 Insurance agent

(G-4126)

COLUMNS RESOURCE OF

3600 Minnesota Dr Ste 300 (55435-7906)
PHONE..................................952 806-9600
FAX: 952 831-0161
Scott Wolf, *Managing Dir*
Cammie Lillehaug, *Office Mgr*
Mark Heurung, *Manager*
Michael Noel, *Technology*
Christa Selness, *Representative*
EMP: 30 **EST:** 2002
SALES (est): 1MM-4.9MM **Privately Held**
SIC: 7389 Financial service

(G-4127)

COMEDYSPORTZ TWIN CITIES

3001 Hennepin Ave E103 (55408-2656)
PO Box 130745, Saint Paul (55113-0007)
PHONE..................................612 870-1230
Mary Strutzel, *President*
Toug Ocar, *Vice Pres*
EMP: 30 **EST:** 1995
SALES (est): 1MM-4.9MM **Privately Held**
WEB: www.comedysportztc.com
SIC: 7922 Theatrical production service

(G-4128)

COMFORT SERVICES LLC

2200 Minnehaha Ave (55404-3152)
PHONE..................................612 871-2160
Gandi Mohamed, *Member*
EMP: 35 **EST:** 2007
SALES (est): 1MM-4.9MM **Privately Held**
SIC: 8082 Home health care services

(G-4129)

COMLINK MIDWEST INC

7308 Aspen Ln N Ste 160 (55428-1027)
PHONE..................................763 391-7483
FAX: 763 425-7467
Cabot Dunham, *President*
James Galloway, *General Mgr*
Roger Alexander, *Vice Pres*
David Ellis, *Project Mgr*
Ron Bundy, *Manager*
EMP: 28 **EST:** 1984
SALES (est): 1MM-4.9MM **Privately Held**
WEB: www.comlink-usa.com
SIC: 1623 Cable television line construction

(G-4130)

COMM-WORKS HOLDINGS LLC (HQ)

1405 Xenium Ln N Ste 120 (55441-4410)
PHONE..................................763 258-5800
Karen Tuleta, *Member*
Alan Lampe, *Member*
Theodore Laufik, *Member*
David Miller, *COO*
Ginger Iglesias, *Project Mgr*
EMP: 100 **EST:** 1995
SQ FT: 65,000 **Privately Held**
SIC: 1731 5065 7373 7622 Telephone
equipment installation; wholesales electrical
telephone & telegraphic equipment; retails
telephone & communication equipment;
local area network systems integration
service; communications equipment repair
& maintenance services
PA: Morgenthaler LLP
50 Public Sq Ste 2700
Cleveland OH 44113
216 416-7500

(G-4131)

COMM-WORKS LLC

1405 Xenium Ln N Ste 120 (55441-4410)
PHONE..................................763 258-5800
Todd Eberhardt, *Member*
Al Lampe, *Member*
Theodore Laufik, *Member*
Karen Tuleta, *Member*
Duane Althoff, *Vice Pres*
EMP: 75 **EST:** 1995
SQ FT: 20,000
SALES (est): 5MM-9.9MM **Privately Held**

SIC: 1731 Telephone equipment installation
HQ: Comm-Works Holdings LLC
1405 Xenium Ln N Ste 120
Minneapolis MN 55441
763 258-5800

(G-4132)

COMMERCIAL PARTNERS TITLE LLC

200 S 6th St Ste 1300 (55402-1439)
PHONE..................................612 337-2470
FAX: 612 337-2471
Tony Winczewski, *Member*
Lynn Gleason, *Vice Pres*
Mark Goodman, *Vice Pres*
Steve Hunt, *Vice Pres*
EMP: 25 **EST:** 1995
SALES (est): 1MM-4.9MM **Privately Held**
WEB: www.cptitle.com
SIC: 6361 Title insurance carrier

(G-4133)

COMMODITY SPECIALISTS CO (PA)

920 2nd Ave S Ste 850 (55402-4002)
PHONE..................................612 330-9120
FAX: 612 330-9110
Philip J Lindau, *Co-President*
O W Mikkelson, *Co-President*
Bill Mikkelson, *CFO*
Lawrence J Dellwo, *Controller*
Wesley Mahlberg, *Manager*
▼ **EMP:** 35 **EST:** 1993 **Privately Held**
WEB: www.csc-world.com
SIC: 5191 Wholesales animal feeds

(G-4134)

COMMON SENSE BUILDING SERVICES

1300 Godward St NE Ste B1 (55413-1882)
PHONE..................................612 379-7106
Dianne McCann, *President*
Harold McCann, *Vice Pres*
EMP: 65 **EST:** 1991
SALES (est): 10MM-24.9MM **Privately Held**
WEB: www.csbsi.com
SIC: 5087 Wholesales janitorial equipment
& supplies

(G-4135)

COMMONWEALTH LAND TITLE INSCE

222 S 9th St Ste 3250 (55402-3808)
PHONE..................................651 227-8571
Antoinette Reichow, *Manager*
Paula Hendrickson, *Manager*
EMP: 32
SALES (est): 5MM-9.9MM **Publicly Held**
WEB: www.laurabarnetthomes.com
SIC: 6361 Provides real estate title
insurance
HQ: Commonwealth Land Title Insce
5600 Cox Rd
Glen Allen VA 23060
804 267-8000

(G-4136)

COMMUNITY ACTION AGENCY

Also Called: Parent & Community Action
8500 Zane Ave N (55443-1810)
PHONE..................................763 425-7422
Diane Hughes, *Director*
EMP: 35
SALES (est): 500-999K **Privately Held**
SIC: 8351 Preschool center

(G-4137)

COMMUNITY ACTION OF

505 E Grant St Ste 1 (55404-1474)
PHONE..................................612 348-8858
William J Davis, *President*
Fay Harrison, *Vice Chairman*
Evelyn A Larue, *Corp Secy*
Ahmed Nimco, *Treasurer*
Jack Bethke, *Manager*
EMP: 42 **EST:** 1992
SALES (est): 1MM-4.9MM **Privately Held**
SIC: 8322 Social services center

(G-4138)

COMMUNITY ACTON OF MINNEAPOLIS

2104 Park Ave (55404-2847)
PHONE..................................612 335-5837
William Davis, *President*
Michael Lieser, *MIS Mgr*
Anthony Spears, *Director*
EMP: 30 **EST:** 2007 **Privately Held**
SIC: 8399 Social services

(G-4139)

COMMUNITY CHILD CARE CENTER

8 W 60th St (55419-2553)
PHONE..................................612 861-4303
FAX: 612 861-2266
Marlwe Ivreson, *Manager*
Coleen Cook, *Director*
EMP: 40 **EST:** 1974
SALES (est): 500-999K **Privately Held**
WEB: www.ccccenter.org
SIC: 8351 Child day care service

(G-4140)

COMMUNITY DEVELOPMENT INC

7100 Madison Ave W (55427-3602)
PHONE..................................763 225-6412
FAX: 763 746-8124
Charles Schneider, *CEO*
Ryan Hall, *Principal*
Mindy Peterson, *Manager*
EMP: 32 **EST:** 1999
SALES (est): 5MM-9.9MM **Privately Held**
SIC: 6531 Real estate services

(G-4141)

COMMUNITY FINANCE GROUP INC

5747 W Broadway Ave (55428-3572)
PHONE..................................763 416-5959
Jacob Vilenchile, *President*
EMP: 50 **EST:** 2007
SALES (est): 5MM-9.9MM **Privately Held**
SIC: 6531 6211 Real estate services;
buying & selling of mortgages

(G-4142)

COMMUNITY HOUSING & SERVICE

Also Called: Knollwood Place Apartments
3630 Phillips Pkwy (55426-3792)
PHONE..................................952 933-1833
FAX: 952 933-1485
Michael Henson, *CEO*
Sherry Greger, *Administrator*
Bruce Khan, *Director*
Katie Sobas, *Executive Asst*
EMP: 25 **EST:** 1971
SQ FT: 450
SALES (est): 1MM-4.9MM **Privately Held**
WEB: www.knollwoodplaceapartments.com
SIC: 6513 Apartment building operator

(G-4143)

COMMUNITY INVOLVEMENT PROGRAMS (PA)

1600 Broadway St NE (55413-2617)
PHONE..................................612 362-4400
FAX: 612 331-4086
John Everett, *Exec Dir*
EMP: 60 **EST:** 1971
SALES (corp-wide): 22.23M **Privately Held**
WEB: www.cipmn.org
SIC: 8331 Vocational rehabilitation agency

(G-4144)

COMMUNITY INVOLVEMENT PROGRAMS

1701 E 79th St Ste 16A (55425-1151)
PHONE..................................952 854-4007
FAX: 952 854-0413
Bob Niemiec, *Branch Mgr*
EMP: 25
SALES (est): 500-999K **Privately Held**
WEB: www.cipmn.org

www.HarrisInfo.com
186

2011 Harris Minnesota
Services Directory

▲=Import ▼=Export
◆=Import/Export

SIC: **8322** Social services for the handicapped
PA: Community Involvement Programs
1600 Broadway St NE
Minneapolis MN 55413
612 362-4400

(G-4145)
COMPANIONCARE INC
Also Called: Companions Home Health Care
4124 Quebec Ave N Ste 304 (55427-1241)
PHONE..............................763 533-1919
FAX: 763 533-1607
Maria Hartlaedge, *President*
EMP: 40 **EST:** 1986
SALES (est): 1MM-4.9MM **Privately Held**
SIC: **8082** Home health care services

(G-4146)
COMPASS AIRLINES INC
7500 Airline Dr Ste 130 (55450-1101)
PHONE..............................612 713-6800
Neal S Cohen, *CEO*
Tim Campbell, *President*
Kristi Luckette, *Assistant*
EMP: 25 **EST:** 2006
SALES (est): 5MM-9.9MM **Publicly Held**
WEB: www.nwairlines.com
SIC: **4512** Scheduled air transportation services
HQ: Northwest Airlines Inc
7500 Airline Dr
Minneapolis MN 55450
612 726-2111

(G-4147)
COMPASS MARKETING INC
251 1st Ave N Fl 2 (55401-1644)
PHONE..............................612 333-5300
FAX: 612 335-9557
Jeffrey Arundel, *President*
Keith Harrison, *Vice Pres*
Alisa Brooks, *Marketing Staff*
Pete Scholovich, *Marketing Staff*
Mat Riccio, *Marketing Staff*
EMP: 70 **EST:** 1985
SQ FT: 18,000
SALES (est): 10MM-24.9MM **Privately Held**
SIC: **5023 7311** Manufactures prerecorded compact laser discs; advertising agency; wholesales home furnishings

(G-4148)
COMPUTER SCIENCES CORP
5500 Wayzata Blvd # 1100 (55416-1244)
PHONE..............................763 593-1122
FAX: 763 593-1135
Ted Tranzelick, *Manager*
EMP: 40
SALES (est): 5MM-9.9MM **Publicly Held**
WEB: www.csc.com
SIC: **7371 7374** Computer programming service; data processing & preparation services
PA: Computer Sciences Corp
3170 Fairview Park Dr
Falls Church VA 22042
703 876-1000

(G-4149)
COMSYS INFORMATION TECHNOLOGY
Also Called: Active Software
1201 Harmon Pl Ste 200 (55403-2044)
PHONE..............................612 630-9100
FAX: 612 630-9104
Perry Wedum, *General Mgr*
Ken Beckwith, *Managing Dir*
Rich Thomas, *Principal*
Ted Schalow, *Manager*
Kim Barnes, *Manager*
EMP: 110
SALES (est): 10MM-24.9MM **Publicly Held**
WEB: www.comsys.com
SIC: **7371 7374** Applications software programming; custom computer software systems analysis & design service; computer software development; data processing service
DH: Comsys Information Technology
2050 E Asu Cir Ste 120
Tempe AZ 85284
877 626-6797

(G-4150)
CONCEPT MACHINE TOOL SALES INC
15625 Medina Rd (55447-1467)
PHONE..............................763 559-1975
FAX: 763 553-7704
Ken Norberg, *President*
Craig Conlon, *President*
Mitzi Sarenpa, *Vice Pres*
Sam Carmichael, *Engineer*
Randy Reed, *Engineer*
EMP: 40 **EST:** 1974
SQ FT: 15,130
SALES (est): 10MM-24.9MM **Privately Held**
WEB: www.conceptmachine.com
SIC: **5084** Wholesales industrial machinery & equipment

(G-4151)
CONCIERGE ENTERPRISES INC
7150 Madison Ave W (55427-3602)
PO Box 669, Osseo (55369-0669)
PHONE..............................763 746-8121
Tim Pearson, *President*
Richard Anderson, *Vice Pres*
Correll Pickerell, *Accountant*
EMP: 25 **EST:** 2000
SQ FT: 8,600 **Privately Held**
WEB: www.concierge-enterprises.com
SIC: **0781** Landscape services

(G-4152)
CONECT PROJECT
15215 18th Ave N Apt 103 (55447-6476)
PHONE..............................763 476-8477
Kris Korsmo, *Director*
EMP: 25 **EST:** 1995
SALES (est): 1MM-4.9MM **Privately Held**
SIC: **8322** Self-help organization

(G-4153)
CONNECTIONS INC
1200 E Old Shakopee Rd (55425-2546)
PHONE..............................952 888-5792
FAX: 952 888-8605
Michael Ferrier, *President*
EMP: 80 **EST:** 1997
SALES (est): 1MM-4.9MM **Privately Held**
WEB: www.connections22.com
SIC: **8059** Home for the mentally retarded

(G-4154)
CONSOLIDATED CONTAINER CO LLC
109 27th Ave NE (55418-2716)
PHONE..............................612 781-0923
FAX: 612 781-0967
William Dworsky, *Member*
Philly J Dworsky, *Member*
Paul Felegy, *Controller*
EMP: 57 **EST:** 2005
SQ FT: 60,000
SALES (est): 25MM-49.9MM **Privately Held**
SIC: **5085** Wholesales commercial containers

(G-4155)
CONSTRUCTION COORDINATORS INC
505 E Grant St (55404-1411)
PHONE..............................612 332-2020
Thomas Horty, *President*
Barbara Kassanchuk, *Treasurer*
Dale Podvin, *Manager*
EMP: 30 **EST:** 1969
SQ FT: 1,500
SALES (est): 1MM-4.9MM **Privately Held**
SIC: **8742** Construction project management consultant

(G-4156)
CONSTRUCTION MIDWEST INC
Also Called: C M I
3531 Nevada Ave N Ste 100 (55427-2181)
PHONE..............................763 536-8336
FAX: 763 536-8530
Walter S Jones, *President*
Dore Antonello, *Treasurer*
EMP: 32 **EST:** 1972
SQ FT: 16,000
SALES (est): 10MM-24.9MM **Privately Held**
WEB: www.constructionmidwest.com

SIC: **5031** Wholesales lumber, plywood & millwork

(G-4157)
CONSULTANTS IN ARTHRITISAND
7250 France Ave S Ste 215 (55435-4312)
PHONE..............................952 832-0246
Kurt Zimmerman, *Partner*
EMP: 41 **EST:** 1987
SALES (est): 1MM-4.9MM **Privately Held**
SIC: **8071** Medical laboratory

(G-4158)
CONSULTING RADIOLOGISTS LTD (PA)
1221 Nicollet Ave Ste 600 (55403-2444)
PHONE..............................612 573-2200
Peter Bartling, *CEO*
David Tubman MD, *President*
Craig Lamp, *COO*
Charles Engmark, *CFO*
Brian Brenedhl, *Office Mgr*
EMP: 127 **EST:** 1920
SQ FT: 3,000 **Privately Held**
WEB: www.consultingradiologists.com
SIC: **8011** Radiologist office

(G-4159)
CONSULTING RADIOLOGISTS LTD
Also Called: Edina Imaging Center
3955 Parklawn Ave Ste 100 (55435-5660)
PHONE..............................952 831-9300
David Tubman MD, *President*
Denise Zimmerman, *Manager*
Julie Weiss, *Manager*
EMP: 75
SALES (est): 5MM-9.9MM **Privately Held**
WEB: www.consultingradiologists.com
SIC: **8011** Radiologist office
PA: Consulting Radiologists Ltd
1221 Nicollet Ave Ste 600
Minneapolis MN 55403
612 573-2200

(G-4160)
CONTACT CARTAGE INC
1912 Broadway St NE (55413-2619)
PHONE..............................612 331-4780
FAX: 612 331-3158
Robert P Black Jr, *President*
Greg Ballanger, *Treasurer*
Ken Mehlhaff, *Mktg Dir*
Troy Bomstad, *Manager*
Neal Gardner, *Manager*
EMP: 49 **EST:** 1965
SQ FT: 16,000
SALES (est): 1MM-4.9MM **Privately Held**
WEB: www.contactcartage.com
SIC: **4212 4731** Local trucking without storage services; freight transportation arrangement services

(G-4161)
COOK & KOFF ENTERPRISES INC
Also Called: Day Spa
7575 France Ave S (55435-4704)
PHONE..............................952 830-0100
FAX: 952 806-0943
Angela Howard, *President*
Dianne Cook, *President*
EMP: 30 **EST:** 1988
SALES (est): 500-999K **Privately Held**
SIC: **7991** Spas

(G-4162)
CORNERSTONE ADVOCACY SERVICE
1000 E 80th St (55420-1424)
PHONE..............................952 884-0376
FAX: 952 884-2135
Janet Simson, *General Mgr*
Sharon Anderson, *Vice Chairman*
Mike Elliot, *Treasurer*
Laurie Langer, *Manager*
Mary Serie, *Director*
EMP: 50 **EST:** 1983
SQ FT: 7,000
SALES (est): 1MM-4.9MM **Privately Held**
WEB: www.cornerstonedv.com
SIC: **8322** Crisis intervention center

(G-4163)
CORPORATE 4 INSURANCE AGENCY
7220 Metro Blvd (55439-2128)
PHONE..............................952 893-9218
FAX: 952 893-9402
Robert Leitschuh, *President*
Jack Hungelmann, *General Mgr*
Glen Carlson, *Vice Pres*
Gary Andren, *Vice Pres*
Peter Gutlovics, *Vice Pres*
EMP: 52 **EST:** 1988
SQ FT: 9,800
SALES (est): 5MM-9.9MM **Privately Held**
WEB: www.corporate4.com
SIC: **6411** Insurance agent

(G-4164)
CORPORATE MECHANICAL INC
5114 Hillsboro Ave N (55428-4030)
PHONE..............................763 533-3070
FAX: 763 533-3464
Jeff Borns, *President*
Rick Potter, *Vice Pres*
EMP: 52 **EST:** 1996
SQ FT: 20,000
SALES (est): 5MM-9.9MM **Privately Held**
WEB: www.corporatemechanical.com
SIC: **1711** Mechanical contractor

(G-4165)
COSMOPOLITAN & ASSOCIATES INC ✪
711 W Lake St (55408-2918)
PHONE..............................612 822-3830
Halimo Said, *CEO*
EMP: 8082 **EST:** 2008
SALES (est): 500MM-999.9MM **Privately Held**
SIC: **7389** Business support services

(G-4166)
COST CUTTERS FAMILY HAIR CARE
2922 W 66th St (55423-1939)
PHONE..............................612 861-0040
Brent Hanson, *Owner*
EMP: 25 **EST:** 1984
SALES (est): 500-999K **Privately Held**
SIC: **7231** Unisex hair salon

(G-4167)
COUNSELOR REALTY INC
7250 France Ave S Ste 300 (55435-4313)
PHONE..............................952 921-0911
Tom Clark, *CFO*
Pat Sholl, *Manager*
Thomas Simonsen, *Manager*
Renato Krsnik, *Real Est Agnt*
Donald Sletten, *Real Est Agnt*
EMP: 40
SALES (est): 5MM-9.9MM **Privately Held**
WEB: www.counselorrealty.com
SIC: **6531** Real estate services
PA: Counselor Realty Inc
7766 Highway 65 NE Ste 1
Minneapolis MN 55432
763 786-0600

(G-4168)
COUNTRY INNS & SUITES BY
210 Carlson Pkwy N (55447-4444)
PHONE..............................763 473-3008
FAX: 763 473-9005
Keith Gartland, *General Mgr*
Joseph Shemon, *General Mgr*
Vickie Anderson, *Manager*
Amy Herberg, *Manager*
EMP: 35
SALES (est): 1MM-4.9MM **Privately Held**
WEB: www.carlsonhotels.com
SIC: **7011** Traveler accommodations
HQ: Country Inns & Suites By
701 Carlson Pkwy
Minneapolis MN 55441
763 212-2525

(G-4169)
COUNTRY INNS & SUITES BY
2221 Killebrew Dr (55425-1881)
PHONE..............................952 854-5555
FAX: 952 854-5564
AVI Nauth, *Accounting Staf*

(PA)=Parent Co (HQ)=Headquarters (DH)=Div Headquarters
✪ = New business established in last 2 years

2011 Harris Minnesota
Services Directory

© Harris InfoSource 1-866-281-6415
187

Nick Duff, *Manager*
Belinda Salden, *Manager*
Lynn Krallman, *Mng Officer*
EMP: 30
SALES (est): 1MM-4.9MM **Privately Held**
WEB: www.carlsonhotels.com
SIC: 7011 Traveler accommodations
HQ: Country Inns & Suites By
　　　701 Carlson Pkwy
　　　Minneapolis MN 55441
　　　763 212-2525

(G-4170)
COUNTRY INNS & SUITES BY
701 Carlson Pkwy　(55441)
PHONE 763 212-2525
Steve Mark, *President*
Steven Mogck, *COO*
Yvonne L Pentotiere, *Exec VP*
Steven A Brown, *Vice Pres*
James H Peterson, *Vice Pres*
EMP: 50 **EST:** 1986
SQ FT: 300,000
SALES (est): 1MM-4.9MM **Privately Held**
WEB: www.carlsonhotels.com
SIC: 7011 6794 Traveler accommodations;
selling or licensing of franchises
HQ: Carlson Hotels Worldwide Inc
　　　Carlson Parkway 701 Tower St
　　　Minneapolis MN 55459
　　　763 212-5000

(G-4171)
COUNTRYWIDE TIRE & RUBBER INC
17200 Medina Rd Ste 100　(55447-1296)
PHONE 763 546-1636
Robert Stone, *CEO*
Ron Bonden, *VP Opers*
Jennifer Benesh, *Manager*
▲ **EMP:** 25 **EST:** 1976
SQ FT: 55,000
SALES (est): 5MM-9.9MM **Privately Held**
WEB: www.innertube.com
SIC: 5014 Wholesales tires & tubes

(G-4172)
COURAGE CENTER (PA)
3915 Golden Valley Rd　(55422-4249)
PHONE 763 588-0811
Jan Malcolm, *CEO*
S Krishnan, *Vice Chairman*
Nancy Larkin, *COO*
Audrey Kintzi, *Vice Pres*
John Tschida, *Vice Pres*
EMP: 450 **EST:** 1928
SQ FT: 200,000
SALES (corp-wide): 33.49M **Privately Held**
WEB: www.courage.org
SIC: 8322 Association for the handicapped

(G-4173)
COUSINEAU MCGUIRE CHARTERED
1550 Utica Ave S Ste 600　(55416-5306)
PHONE 952 546-8400
Barbara Burke, *President*
Mark Kleinschmidt, *Trustee*
Pam Ackerman, *Accountant*
Toni Hammond, *Administrator*
Brose Robert, *Info Tech Mgr*
EMP: 65 **EST:** 1942
SQ FT: 18,000
SALES (est): 5MM-9.9MM **Privately Held**
SIC: 8111 General practice law office

(G-4174)
COVANTA ENERGY GROUP INC
505 6th Ave N　(55405-1503)
PHONE 612 333-7303
FAX: 612 333-7347
Derwin Fitch, *Manager*
EMP: 40
SALES (est): 5MM-9.9MM **Publicly Held**
WEB: www.covantaenergy.com
SIC: 4953 Waste material recycling services
HQ: Covanta Energy Corp
　　　40 Lane Rd
　　　Fairfield NJ 07004
　　　973 882-9000

(G-4175)
COYNE'S & CO INC
Also Called: Gift Connection Minneapolis
7400 Boone Ave N　(55428-1008)
PHONE 763 425-8666
John Coyne, *Ch of Bd*
Michael P Coyne, *President*
Carl Guggenberger, *COO*
▲ **EMP:** 60 **EST:** 1955
SQ FT: 65,000
SALES (est): 25MM-49.9MM **Privately Held**
WEB: www.coynes.com
SIC: 5199 Wholesales gifts & novelties;
retails gifts, novelties & souvenirs

(G-4176)
CRAIG-HALLUM CAPITAL GROUP LLC
222 S 9th St Ste 350　(55402-3380)
PHONE 612 334-6300
FAX: 612 692-8250
Richard J Rinkoff, *Managing Prtnr*
John L Flood, *Managing Prtnr*
Patricia Bartholomew, *Managing Prtnr*
Bradley W Baker, *Managing Prtnr*
John Stevenson, *Managing Dir*
EMP: 65 **EST:** 2002
SALES (est): 10MM-24.9MM **Privately Held**
WEB: www.chlm.com
SIC: 6211 Securities broker & dealer

(G-4177)
CRAWFORD-MERZ CONSTRUCTION CO
2316 4th Ave S　(55404-3626)
PHONE 612 874-9011
FAX: 612 874-9015
Wayne Anderson, *President*
John Merz, *Vice Pres*
Chuck Anderson, *Vice Pres*
EMP: 25 **EST:** 1886
SQ FT: 5,000
SALES (est): 5MM-9.9MM **Privately Held**
SIC: 1541 Industrial building renovating,
remodeling & repair service

(G-4178)
CRE 8 IT INC
3130 Talmage Ave SE　(55414-2715)
PHONE 612 623-8866
Sandy Goldetsky, *President*
Bob Goldetsky, *Vice Pres*
Sue Koehn, *Human Res Dir*
Dave Staehl, *Human Res Mgr*
EMP: 90 **EST:** 1993
SQ FT: 11,000
SALES (est): 25MM-49.9MM **Privately Held**
SIC: 5148 Wholesales fresh fruits &
vegetables

(G-4179)
CREATIS INC
227 Colfax Ave N Ste 200　(55405-1413)
PHONE 612 333-3233
Dodd W Clasen, *CEO*
Charles Swensson, *President*
Pat Adams, *Business Mgr*
Steve Gimmestad, *Mktg Dir*
Dean Flory, *Network Mgr*
EMP: 98 **EST:** 1998
SQ FT: 5,400
SALES (est): 10MM-24.9MM **Privately Held**
WEB: www.creatis.com/
SIC: 8742 Management consulting services

(G-4180)
CREEKRIDGE CAPITAL LLC
7808 Creekridge Cir # 250　(55439-2647)
PHONE 952 996-0270
FAX: 952 920-1135
Jeffrey D Cowan, *President*
Gregory E Larson, *President*
Stephen V Alpeter V, *Member*
Jody Ainley, *Senior VP*
Art Greve, *Senior VP*
EMP: 38 **EST:** 1984
SQ FT: 10,000
SALES (est): Under 500K **Privately Held**
SIC: 7359 Equipment rental & leasing
services

(G-4181)
CREMATION SOCIETY INC
Also Called: Twin City Cremation Supply
4343 Nicollet Ave　(55409-2032)
PHONE 612 825-2435
FAX: 612 827-0370
Mark Waterston, *President*
Kevin Waterson, *Vice Pres*
Kevin Waterson, *Vice Pres*
EST: 1955
SQ FT: 8,000　**Privately Held**
WEB: www.cremationsocietyofmn.com
SIC: 7261 Funeral home & services

(G-4182)
CREW2 INC
2650 Minnehaha Ave　(55406-1500)
PHONE 612 276-1600
FAX: 612 276-1700
Steven Firkus, *President*
Doug Firkus, *President*
Perry Firkus, *Vice Pres*
Cindy Firkus, *VP Human Res*
▲ **EMP:** 75 **EST:** 1985
SQ FT: 53,300
SALES (est): 5MM-9.9MM **Privately Held**
SIC: 1752 Flooring contractor

(G-4183)
CRI SECURITIES INC
2701 University Ave SE # 100
(55414-3231)
PHONE 612 617-6000
Phillip C Richards, *President*
Bardea Huppert, *Vice Pres*
David Vasos, *Vice Pres*
Ann Elliott, *Treasurer*
EMP: 105 **EST:** 1988
SQ FT: 18,000
SALES (est): 25MM-49.9MM **Privately Held**
SIC: 6211 Security broker & dealer service

(G-4184)
CRIMINAL INVESTIGATION DEPT
350 S 5th St Ste 108　(55415-1323)
PHONE 612 673-2941
R Skomra, *Principal*
EMP: 50 **EST:** 2002
SALES (est): 1MM-4.9MM **Privately Held**
SIC: 7381 Private investigator service

(G-4185)
CRITICAL CARE SERVICES INC
Also Called: LIFE LINK III
3010 Broadway St NE　(55413-1708)
PHONE 612 638-4900
Carter McComb, *CEO*
Kelly J Spratt, *COO*
Ashok Sinha, *CFO*
Robert Sannerud, *CFO*
Donald Solberg, *Manager*
EMP: 197 **EST:** 1976
SQ FT: 33,000
SALES (est): 5MM-9.9MM **Privately Held**
WEB: www.lifelinkiii.com
SIC: 4119 4522 Ambulance service; air
ambulance services

(G-4186)
CRONSTROM FURNACE & SHEET
6437 Goodrich Ave　(55426-4405)
PHONE 952 920-3800
Peter Rice, *President*
EMP: 25 **EST:** 1928
SQ FT: 7,500
SALES (est): 1MM-4.9MM **Privately Held**
WEB: www.cronstroms.com
SIC: 1711 Heating & air conditioning
contractor

(G-4187)
CROSSROADS AT PENN APARTMENTS (PA)
7620 Penn Ave S　(55423-3644)
PHONE 612 866-3628
FAX: 612 866-4937
Michael N Garvin, *Vice Pres*
Yamilka Burdier, *Manager*
Donna Seawell, *Manager*
Missy Locy, *Manager*
EMP: 25 **EST:** 1962
SQ FT: 5,000　**Privately Held**

WEB: www.centurycourtapartments.com
SIC: 6513 Apartment building operator

(G-4188)
CROW RIVER TECHNICAL INC
3300 Bass Lake Rd Ste 318　(55429-3066)
PHONE 763 560-6015
FAX: 763 535-9402
Tom Wolden, *President*
EMP: 35 **EST:** 1995 **Privately Held**
WEB: www.crtechnical.com
SIC: 7361 Employment agency services

(G-4189)
CROWN PLASTICS INC
12615 16th Ave N　(55441-4609)
PHONE 763 557-6000
FAX: 763 557-6638
Thomas V Beusekom, *CEO*
EMP: 35 **EST:** 1971
SQ FT: 28,000
SALES (est): 25MM-49.9MM **Privately Held**
WEB: www.crownplasticsinc.com
SIC: 5162 Wholesales plastics sheets &
rods; manufactures plastics sheet packing
materials

(G-4190)
CRYSTAL CARE HOME HEALTH SVCS
6461 Lyndale Ave S　(55423-1405)
PHONE 612 861-4272
FAX: 612 866-2290
Sally Knutson, *President*
Jeamette Mefford, *Vice Pres*
Don Lindstedt, *Human Res Mgr*
Bridgette Culpepper, *Manager*
Jennifer Thompson, *Administrator*
EMP: 325 **EST:** 2000
SALES (est): 10MM-24.9MM **Privately Held**
SIC: 8082 Home health care services

(G-4191)
CSL PLASMA INC
1026 Washington Ave SE　(55414-3038)
PHONE 612 331-9180
FAX: 612 331-5010
David Monte, *General Mgr*
Holt Petterson, *Manager*
EMP: 60
SALES (est): 1MM-4.9MM **Privately Held**
WEB: www.zlbplasma.com
SIC: 8099 Plasmapherous center
PA: Csl Plasma Inc
　　　5201 Congress Ave Ste 220
　　　Boca Raton FL 33487
　　　561 981-3700

(G-4192)
CSM CORP OF MINNESOTA
Also Called: Springhill Suites
5901 Wayzata Blvd　(55416-1204)
PHONE 952 738-7300
Mike Stickler, *Manager*
Lori Molina, *Manager*
EMP: 34
SALES (est): 1MM-4.9MM **Privately Held**
WEB: www.csmcorp.net
SIC: 7011 Traveler accommodations

(G-4193)
CSM CORP OF MINNESOTA
Also Called: Residence Inn By Marriott
425 S 2nd St　(55401-2181)
PHONE 612 340-1300
FAX: 612 340-9800
Anna Ownes, *Sales Dir*
Lori Geiwigz, *Manager*
EMP: 30
SALES (est): 1MM-4.9MM **Privately Held**
WEB: www.csmcorp.net
SIC: 7011 Traveler accommodations

(G-4194)
CSM CORP OF MINNESOTA
Also Called: Renaissance-Depot
225 3rd Ave S　(55401-2524)
PHONE 612 375-1700
Robb Hall, *Branch Mgr*
EMP: 110
SALES (est): 5MM-9.9MM **Privately Held**
WEB: www.csmcorp.net
SIC: 7011 Traveler accommodations

www.HarrisInfo.com
188
　　　2011 Harris Minnesota
　　　Services Directory
　　　▲=Import ▼=Export
　　　◆=Import/Export

(G-4195)
CSM CORP OF MINNESOTA
9960 Wayzata Blvd (55426-1008)
PHONE..............................952 593-1918
Fred Talerico, *General Mgr*
Melissa Gladney, *Accountant*
Robbie Sullivan, *Marketing Staff*
EMP: 100
SALES (est): 5MM-9.9MM Privately Held
WEB: www.csmcorp.net
SIC: 7011 Traveler accommodations

(G-4196)
CSM EQUITIES LLC ✪
500 Washington Ave S # 3000
(55415-1151)
PHONE..............................612 395-7000
Rob Dan, *Member*
Melissa Gladney, *Accountant*
Kathy Pierce, *Accountant*
K Westberg, *Manager*
EMP: 99 EST: 2008
SALES (est): 5MM-9.9MM Privately Held
SIC: 7011 Hotel

(G-4197)
CSM EXECUTIVE LODGING LLC
Also Called: Marriott Execustay
500 Washington Ave S 300 (55415-1149)
PHONE..............................612 395-7195
Dave Carland, *Corp Secy*
Daniel Peterson, *Vice Pres*
Jen Claude, *Mng Member*
Marjorie Smith, *Manager*
EST: 2004 Privately Held
WEB: www.csmcorp.net
SIC: 7021 Rooming & boarding house

(G-4198)
CULLIGAN SOFT WATER SERVICE CO
7165 Boone Ave N Ste 100 (55428-1512)
PO Box 1609 (55440-1609)
PHONE..............................763 535-4545
FAX: 763 535-7686
Phil Fusterisick, *Branch Mgr*
EMP: 31
SALES (est): 10MM-24.9MM Privately Held
WEB: www.uncodata.com
SIC: 5149 Wholesales bottled mineral or spring water; bottled water delivery services
PA: Culligan Soft Water Service Co
6030 Culligan Way
Minnetonka MN 55345
952 933-7200

(G-4199)
CUMMINGS, KEEGAN & CO PLLP
600 Highway 169 S Ste 1625
(55426-1290)
PHONE..............................952 345-2500
Jeffrey Emerick, *Partner*
John Frees, *Partner*
EMP: 31 EST: 1956
SQ FT: 5,000
SALES (est): 1MM-4.9MM Privately Held
WEB: www.ckco-cpa.com
SIC: 8721 Certified public accountant services

(G-4200)
CUNINGHAM GROUP ARCHITECTURE (PA)
201 Main St SE Ste 325 (55414-7025)
PHONE..............................612 379-3400
FAX: 612 379-4400
Timothy Dufault, *President*
Ann Lancaster, *Corp Secy*
Roger Kipp, *Corp Secy*
Harry Hern, *Vice Pres*
Douglas A Lowe, *Vice Pres*
EMP: 117 EST: 1968
SQ FT: 28,000
SALES (corp-wide): 44.88M Privately Held
WEB: www.cuningham.com
SIC: 8712 Architectural service

(G-4201)
CUSHMAN & WAKEFIELD INC
333 S 7th St Ste 320 (55402-2414)
PHONE..............................612 659-1743
Robert Bohnenkamp, *Vice Pres*

Gabriel Rein, *Finance*
George Myers, *Manager*
Paul Larsen, *Manager*
Robert Traeger, *Manager*
EMP: 100
SALES (est): 10MM-24.9MM Privately Held
WEB: www.cushwake.com
SIC: 6531 Real estate services
HQ: Cushman & Wakefield Inc
1290 Avenue Of The Americas
New York NY 10104
212 841-7500

(G-4202)
CUSHMAN & WAKEFIELD INC
1001 S 3rd St (55415-1240)
PHONE..............................612 671-7593
Todd Doering, *Manager*
EMP: 25
SALES (est): 1MM-4.9MM Privately Held
WEB: www.cushwake.com
SIC: 6531 Real estate agency & broker
HQ: Cushman & Wakefield Inc
1290 Avenue Of The Americas
New York NY 10104
212 841-7500

(G-4203)
CUSTOM DOOR SALES INC
5005 Hillsboro Ave N (55428-4020)
PHONE..............................612 332-0357
Ron Fick, *President*
Joann Larson, *Manager*
EMP: 53 EST: 1946
SQ FT: 15,000
SALES (est): 25MM-49.9MM Privately Held
WEB: www.customdoorsales.com
SIC: 5031 Wholesales garage doors; retails & installs garage doors

(G-4204)
CUSTOM ONE PAINTING INC
2543 Marshall St NE (55418-3328)
PHONE..............................612 787-1040
Michael Ellies, *President*
Debra Ellies, *Treasurer*
Heather Bergstrom, *Management*
EMP: 25 EST: 1996
SQ FT: 30,000
SALES (est): 1MM-4.9MM Privately Held
SIC: 1721 Exterior residential painting contractor

(G-4205)
CUSTOM PLASTIC LAMINATES INC
1 E 19th St (55403-3759)
PO Box 8658 (55408-0658)
PHONE..............................612 781-8191
FAX: 612 781-8920
Wayne Rosemius, *President*
Mike Kopet, *Director*
EMP: 35 EST: 1956
SQ FT: 37,000
SALES (est): 1MM-4.9MM Privately Held
SIC: 1799 Manufactures factory furniture & fixtures; countertop installation service

(G-4206)
CUSTOMER TRAAC INC (PA)
3030 Harbor Ln N Ste 132 (55447-5143)
PHONE..............................763 553-2989
Brenda Burg, *President*
Chris Berg, *Info Tech Mgr*
EMP: 32 EST: 1990
SQ FT: 1,200 Privately Held
WEB: www.customertraac.com
SIC: 7389 Telemarketing services

(G-4207)
CVRX INC
9201 W Broadway Ave Ste 650
(55445-1925)
PHONE..............................763 416-2840
Robert S Kieval, *President*
Todd Langevin, *Senior VP*
Dean Bruhn-Ding, *Vice Pres*
Robert Cody MD, *Vice Pres*
Joseph Dupay, *Vice Pres*
EMP: 42 EST: 2000
SQ FT: 11,000
SALES (est): 1MM-4.9MM Privately Held
WEB: www.cvrx.com
SIC: 8732 Business research services

(G-4208)
CYBERTROL ENGINEERING LLC
2950 Xenium Ln N Ste 130 (55441-2623)
PHONE..............................763 559-8660
FAX: 763 519-7800
Merlin Graunke, *Member*
Dan Scott, *Member*
Dean Dobitz, *Engineer*
Britt M Wood, *Controller*
Kelly Hines, *Manager*
EMP: 30 EST: 1996
SQ FT: 10,624
SALES (est): 1MM-4.9MM Privately Held
WEB: www.cybertrol.com
SIC: 8711 Engineering services

(G-4209)
CYGNIA CORP
10800 Lyndale Ave S # 244 (55420-5690)
PHONE..............................952 887-9030
FAX: 952 887-9044
Jack N Hennen, *CEO*
Theresa Hennen, *CFO*
EMP: 30 EST: 1991
SALES (est): 5MM-9.9MM Privately Held
SIC: 7372 Software publisher

(G-4210)
CYNTHIA COOK INC
1701 American Blvd E # 17 (55425-1401)
PHONE..............................952 854-4975
Cynthia Cook, *President*
Thomas J Cook, *Vice Pres*
Dick Grussendorf, *Vice Pres*
EMP: 33 EST: 1988
SQ FT: 4,000
SALES (est): 500-999K Privately Held
WEB: www.j-o-b-s.com
SIC: 7363 Temporary help service

(G-4211)
D A PETERSON
2500 Highway 88 Ste 210 (55418-4228)
PHONE..............................612 782-9860
Douglas Peterson, *Owner*
EMP: 25 EST: 2005 Privately Held
SIC: 8399 Council for social agency

(G-4212)
D C M SERVICES LLC
4150 Olson Memorial Hwy (55422-4800)
PHONE..............................612 332-3700
Gary Becker, *Member*
EMP: 60 EST: 1983
SQ FT: 2,500
SALES (est): 5MM-9.9MM Privately Held
SIC: 8111 General practice attorney's or lawyer's office

(G-4213)
D C SALES CO INC
2700 Minnehaha Ave (55406-4503)
PHONE..............................612 728-8700
John J Dovolis, *President*
Georgia J Dovolis, *Corp Secy*
Jeff Shields, *CFO*
David W Schneider, *Finance Dir*
Michael Boehm, *VP Sales*
EMP: 35 EST: 1947
SQ FT: 50,000
SALES (est): 10MM-24.9MM Privately Held
SIC: 5074 5075 Wholesales hydronic heating equipment; wholesales air conditioning equipment; wholesales plumbing fittings & supplies; wholesales ventilating equipment & supplies

(G-4214)
D L RYAN CO'S LTD
Also Called: Ryan Partnership
10 S 5th St Ste 330 (55402-1029)
PHONE..............................612 204-9790
FAX: 612 204-9851
Joseph Robinson, *Owner*
Tom Brown, *Managing Dir*
EMP: 43
SALES (est): 5MM-9.9MM Privately Held
SIC: 8743 8742 Sales promotion services; marketing consulting service
PA: D L Ryan Co's Ltd
50 Danbury Rd
Wilton CT 06897
203 210-3000

(G-4215)
D M I LLC
Also Called: Bridgz Marketing Group
7831 E Bush Lake Rd # 300 (55439-3154)
PHONE..............................952 841-6200
FAX: 952 521-0690
Michael D Nelson, *Member*
Terryl Olson, *Accountant*
EMP: 80 EST: 1999
SALES (est): 10MM-24.9MM Privately Held
WEB: www.schoeneckers.com
SIC: 8742 New products & services consultants; commercial printing
PA: Schoeneckers Inc
7630 Bush Lake Rd
Edina MN 55439
952 835-4800

(G-4216)
DACON ENGINEERING & SERVICE CO
5101 Olson Memorial Hwy (55422-5149)
PHONE..............................763 544-1686
Rolland R Davis, *CEO*
Marge Brown, *Owner*
EMP: 175 EST: 1965
SQ FT: 4,000
SALES (est): 10MM-24.9MM Privately Held
SIC: 8711 Engineering services

(G-4217)
DAIN RAUSCHER INC
60 S 6th St Ste 700 (55402-4413)
PHONE..............................612 371-2711
FAX: 612 371-2745
Todd Kadrie, *General Mgr*
Irving Weiser, *Ch of Bd*
Peter Armenio, *President*
John C Appel, *President*
Jay Hennen, *General Mgr*
EMP: 1500 EST: 1929
SQ FT: 225,000
SALES (est): 100MM-499.9MM Privately Held
WEB: www.hough.com
SIC: 6211 Security broker service; securities dealer; investment banking service; security underwriting service
PA: Rbc Wealth Management
60 S 6th St Ste 700
Minneapolis MN 55402
612 371-7750

(G-4218)
DAKOTA COOK LLC
1010 Nicollet Mall (55403-2403)
PHONE..............................612 332-1010
FAX: 612 332-7070
Lowell Pickett, *President*
Susan Dennison, *Manager*
EMP: 95 EST: 1991
SQ FT: 8,000
SALES (est): 1MM-4.9MM Privately Held
SIC: 7922 Full service independent family restaurant; cocktail lounge; entertainment promotion service

(G-4219)
DAKOTA GROWERS PASTA CO INC
7300 36th Ave N (55427-2001)
PHONE..............................763 531-5340
FAX: 763 376-9712
Tim Dodd, *Branch Mgr*
EMP: 150
SALES (est): 10MM-24.9MM Privately Held
WEB: www.dakotagrowers.com
SIC: 7389 5149 Personal service agents; wholesales pasta & rice; manufactures pasta
PA: Dakota Growers Pasta Co Inc
1 Pasta Ave
Carrington ND 58421
701 652-2855

(G-4220)
DALCO ROOFING & SHEET METAL
15525 32nd Ave N (55447-1494)
PHONE..............................763 559-0222
FAX: 763 559-3783
David J Dalbec, *CEO*
Daniel Lewis, *President*

(PA)=Parent Co (HQ)=Headquarters (DH)=Div Headquarters
✪ = New business established in last 2 years

2011 Harris Minnesota
Services Directory

© Harris InfoSource 1-866-281-6415
189

Richard Trumble, *Corp Secy*
John McPhillips, *COO*
Terry Aten, *Vice Pres*
EMP: 100 **EST:** 1945
SQ FT: 30,000
SALES (est): 10MM-24.9MM **Privately Held**
WEB: www.dalcoroofing.com
SIC: 1761 Roofing contractor; sheet metal work contractor

(G-4221)
DALE TILE CO
Also Called: Minnesota Tile Supply
8400 89th Ave N Ste 445 (55445-1873)
PHONE 763 488-1880
FAX: 763 488-5216
Alan J Dale, *President*
Bob Keitzman, *General Mgr*
Troy Linville, *Manager*
Lynn Corbett, *Manager*
EMP: 30 **EST:** 1930
SQ FT: 25,000
SALES (est): 5MM-9.9MM **Privately Held**
WEB: www.mntile.com
SIC: 5032 Wholesales tile, clay or other ceramic construction materials; wholesales granite building stone; wholesales marble building stone

(G-4222)
DAN LARSON ENTERPRISES INC
Also Called: Zahl Petroleum Maintenance Co
3101 Spring St NE (55413-2907)
PHONE 612 331-8550
FAX: 612 331-8553
Dan Larson, *CEO*
Tom Manke, *President*
Danny Byrne, *Vice Pres*
Jodi Heinz, *Human Res Mgr*
EMP: 46 **EST:** 1952
SQ FT: 25,000
SALES (est): 10MM-24.9MM **Privately Held**
SIC: 5084 1799 5172 Wholesales industrial machinery & equipment; service station equipment contractor; gasoline pump installation; service station equipment installation, maintenance & repair contractor; wholesales service station petroleum

(G-4223)
DATA RECOGNITION CORP
8900 Wyoming Ave N (55445-1838)
PHONE 763 268-2238
Doyle Kirkeby, *Manager*
Brian Fellegy, *Analyst*
EMP: 50
SALES (est): 5MM-9.9MM **Privately Held**
SIC: 7374 7336 Optical scanning services; graphic arts & related design service
PA: Data Recognition Corp
13490 Bass Lake Rd
Maple Grove MN 55311
763 268-2000

(G-4224)
DAVEY TREE EXPERT CO
2500 Fernbrook Ln N (55447-4733)
PHONE 763 553-9740
FAX: 763 553-2739
Steve Kuefler, *Manager*
EMP: 26 **Privately Held**
SIC: 0783 0782 Ornamental shrub & tree service; lawn services
PA: Davey Tree Expert Co
1500 N Mantua St
Kent OH 44240
330 673-9511

(G-4225)
DAVID KELLOWAY
Also Called: Kelloway Digital
2515 E 26th St (55406-1238)
PHONE 952 944-0739
David Kelloway, *Owner*
▲ **EMP:** 30 **EST:** 1995
SQ FT: 3,500
SALES (est): 1MM-4.9MM **Privately Held**
SIC: 7335 Commercial photography service

(G-4226)
DAVID'S BODY SHOP INC
Also Called: Firm-A Workout Studio
245 Aldrich Ave N Ste 220 (55405-1690)
PHONE 612 377-3003
FAX: 612 377-6136
Kelly L Miyamoto, *President*
EMP: 70 **EST:** 1986
SQ FT: 22,000
SALES (est): 1MM-4.9MM **Privately Held**
SIC: 7991 Aerobic dance & exercise classes; retails dancewear; retails health food products

(G-4227)
DAVIDSON HOTEL CO
Also Called: Hilton
2200 Freeway Blvd (55430-1737)
PHONE 763 566-8000
FAX: 763 566-9286
Frank Adams, *General Mgr*
Amy Utley, *Network Mgr*
Harding Ron, *Webmaster*
EMP: 104
SALES (est): 5MM-9.9MM **Privately Held**
WEB: www.davidsonhotels.com
SIC: 7011 Traveler accommodations; eating place; drinking establishment
PA: Davidson Hotel Co
3340 Players Ste 200
Memphis TN 38125
901 761-4664

(G-4228)
DAVIES CHAPEL
Also Called: Welander Quist
2301 Dupont Ave S (55405-2755)
PHONE 612 377-2203
FAX: 612 377-7306
William McReavy, *Owner*
EMP: 50 **EST:** 2000
SALES (est): 1MM-4.9MM **Privately Held**
SIC: 7261 Funeral home & services

(G-4229)
DAVIS DENTAL LAB
5775 Wayzata Blvd Ste 670 (55416-2665)
PHONE 952 345-6315
EMP: 30 **EST:** 2005
SALES (est): 1MM-4.9MM **Privately Held**
SIC: 8072 Dental laboratory

(G-4230)
DAY S P A AT NAILS ETC
7575 France Ave S (55435-4704)
PHONE 952 830-0100
Diane Cook, *President*
EMP: 45 **EST:** 1989
SALES (est): 1MM-4.9MM **Privately Held**
SIC: 7231 Nail salon

(G-4231)
DAYS INNS & SUITES
6415 James Cir N (55430-2101)
PHONE 763 561-8400
Rochelle Thello, *General Mgr*
Denise Pooniwalla, *General Mgr*
Dinaz Pooniwala, *Principal*
Percy Pooniwala, *Principal*
Robert Johnson, *Maint Mgr*
EMP: 98 **EST:** 2007
SALES (est): 5MM-9.9MM **Privately Held**
SIC: 7011 Hotel

(G-4232)
DAYTON RADISON INC
Also Called: Parking Ramp
24 S 8th St Fl 2 (55402-2007)
PHONE 612 672-0060
James Sanders, *President*
EMP: 50 **EST:** 1997
SALES (est): 1MM-4.9MM **Privately Held**
WEB: www.parkingramp.com
SIC: 7521 Vehicle parking lot or garage

(G-4233)
DAYTON-RADISSON RAMP
1300 Nicollet Ave Ste 3060 (55403-2693)
PHONE 612 333-2293
Albert Tychman, *Partner*
David Sanders, *General Ptnr*
Deera Tychman, *Ltd Ptnr*
Miriam Sanders, *Ltd Ptnr*

EMP: 100 **EST:** 1955
SALES (est): 5MM-9.9MM **Privately Held**
SIC: 7521 Parking structure

(G-4234)
DBI CONSULTING INC
6200 Shingle Creek Pkwy # 5 (55430-2128)
PHONE 763 561-4990
FAX: 763 561-9022
Sophie B Kelley, *President*
Brenda Gucks, *Director*
EMP: 55 **EST:** 1988
SQ FT: 4,000
SALES (est): 5MM-9.9MM **Privately Held**
WEB: www.dbiconsulting.com
SIC: 7379 Computer system consulting services

(G-4235)
DCM SERVICES LLC
4150 Olson Memorial Hwy # 200 (55422-4811)
PHONE 763 852-8440
Steven M Farscht, *Member*
James Balough, *Member*
Gary W Becker, *Member*
Ben Boyum, *Exec VP*
Tom Ryan, *IT/INT Sup*
EMP: 180 **EST:** 2007
SQ FT: 47,000
SALES (est): 10MM-24.9MM **Privately Held**
SIC: 7322 Collection agency

(G-4236)
DEAFBLIND SERVICES MINNESOTA
1936 Lyndale Ave S (55403-3101)
PHONE 612 362-8454
Paul Deeming, *Manager*
Megan Deblin, *Administrator*
Steven Fischer, *Director*
EST: 1986 **Privately Held**
WEB: www.dbsm.org
SIC: 8322 Individual & family social services

(G-4237)
DEALERS CHOICE AUTO CLEAN
8601 73rd Ave N (55428-1507)
PHONE 763 592-9900
Lowel Loelskar, *Partner*
Dave Bartell, *Partner*
EMP: 25
SALES (est): 500-999K **Privately Held**
SIC: 7542 Car wash

(G-4238)
DECEASED CREDIT MANAGEMENT LLC
4150 Olson Memorial Hwy (55422-4800)
PHONE 763 852-8400
Gary Becker, *Member*
James Balogh, *Member*
Clare Chisholm, *Controller*
Mandy Marcelino, *IT/INT Sup*
EST: 2006
SQ FT: 47,000 **Privately Held**
WEB: www.probatefinder.com
SIC: 7322 Collection agency

(G-4239)
DECONSTRUCTION SERVICES
Also Called: Reuse Center
2801 21st Ave S Ste 190 (55407-1283)
PHONE 888 224-2608
Cory Rincamoff, *Exec Dir*
Jamie Heipel, *Director*
Janet Meister, *Program Dir*
EMP: 30 **EST:** 1997
SALES (est): 1MM-4.9MM **Privately Held**
WEB: www.deconstructionservices.com
SIC: 1795 Buildings & other structure demolition contractor

(G-4240)
DEDICATED LOGISTICS INC
8201 54th Ave N (55428-3709)
PHONE 763 504-9229
Eugene M Kasper, *Opers Mgr*
Joel Meier, *Manager*
EMP: 25
SALES (est): 1MM-4.9MM **Privately Held**

SIC: 4225 Warehousing & storage services
PA: Dedicated Logistics Inc
2900 Granada Ln N
Oakdale MN 55128
651 631-5918

(G-4241)
DEDINA EYE PHYSICIANS
7450 France Ave S Ste 100 (55435-4799)
PHONE 952 832-8179
Carter Nicholson, *President*
Eugene Gullinsrud, *Vice Pres*
EMP: 60 **EST:** 1960
SALES (est): 5MM-9.9MM **Privately Held**
SIC: 8011 Ophthalmologist office

(G-4242)
DEFINITY HEALTH CORP (HQ)
1600 Utica Ave S Ste 900 (55416-1465)
PHONE 952 277-5500
FAX: 952 277-5501
Anthony Miller, *CEO*
Forrest G Burke, *Corp Secy*
Timothy Godzich, *Corp Secy*
Brian Ternan, *Vice Pres*
John W Kelly, *Vice Pres*
EMP: 175 **EST:** 1998
SALES (corp-wide): 87.13B **Publicly Held**
WEB: www.unitedhealthgroup.com
SIC: 8011 Medical insurance plan
PA: Unitedhealth Group Inc
9900 Bren Rd E
Minnetonka MN 55343
952 936-1300

(G-4243)
DELANCY BUILDERS INC
2210 44th Ave N (55412-1165)
PHONE 612 354-3724
Kenneth Delancy, *President*
EMP: 100 **EST:** 2001
SQ FT: 2,000
SALES (est): 25MM-49.9MM **Privately Held**
SIC: 1521 New single-family home construction service

(G-4244)
DELOITTE & TOUCHE LLP
10824 Johnson Ave S (55437-2925)
PHONE 612 397-4772
James Copeland, *Branch Mgr*
EMP: 700
SALES (est): 25MM-49.9MM **Privately Held**
WEB: www.deloitte.com
SIC: 8721 Accounting, auditing & bookkeeping services
HQ: Deloitte & Touche LLP
1633 Broadway
New York NY 10019
212 489-1600

(G-4245)
DELTA CO'S LLC
4005 W 65th St Ste 208 (55435-1701)
PHONE 952 929-5005
FAX: 952 929-9526
Kristin Lagaard, *Principal*
Jerry Crow, *Member*
Marc Bowles, *Vice Pres*
Mike Gianas, *Manager*
Delta Crow, *Manager*
EMP: 35 **EST:** 1994
SALES (est): 500-999K **Privately Held**
SIC: 7363 7361 Temporary help service; employment agency services

(G-4246)
DELTA PROTECTIVE SERVICES
1302 2nd St NE (55413-1132)
PHONE 612 331-1885
James Bardon, *President*
Kang Hyejeen, *Vice Pres*
Mark Menter, *Manager*
EMP: 30 **EST:** 1996
SQ FT: 1,000
SALES (est): 500-999K **Privately Held**
SIC: 7381 Security guard service

(G-4247)
DENISON MAILING SERVICE INC
9601 Newton Ave S Ste A (55431-2556)
PHONE 952 888-1460
FAX: 952 888-9641
Donald Hill, *President*

www.HarrisInfo.com
190

2011 Harris Minnesota
Services Directory

▲=Import ▼=Export
◆=Import/Export

Sherrill Flora, *Vice Pres*
Kenton Brings, *Shareholder*
EMP: 45 **EST:** 1876
SQ FT: 34,000
SALES (est): 1MM-4.9MM **Privately Held**
WEB: www.denisonmailing.com
SIC: 7331 Mailing services

(G-4248)

DENNY KEMP INC
605 Central Ave SE (55414-1118)
PHONE 612 676-0300
FAX: 612 676-1766
Denny Kemp, *President*
EMP: 25 **EST:** 1998
SALES (est): 500-999K **Privately Held**
WEB: www.dennykempsalon.com
SIC: 7231 Unisex hair salon

(G-4249)

DESTINEER INC
13755 1st Ave N Ste 500 (55441-5473)
PHONE 763 231-8000
Peter Tamte, *President*
Al Schilling, *General Mgr*
Scott Addyman, *Vice Pres*
Peter Tampe, *Software Dev*
Tony Chiodo, *Director*
EMP: 50 **EST:** 2001
SALES (est): 25MM-49.9MM **Privately Held**
SIC: 5092 Wholesales video games

(G-4250)

DFG INC
Also Called: Dolphin Staffing
17 Washington Ave N (55401-1617)
PHONE 612 343-8936
Kathleen Dolphin, *President*
Dorothy Dolphin, *Chairman*
Jodie Bonk, *Controller*
Cindy Brooks, *Human Res Dir*
Greg Clone, *Manager*
EMP: 55 **EST:** 1969
SQ FT: 15,000
SALES (est): 1MM-4.9MM **Privately Held**
WEB: www.dolphinstaffing.com
SIC: 7363 Temporary help service

(G-4251)

DHM MINNEAPOLIS HOTEL, LP
2200 Freeway Blvd (55430-1737)
PHONE 763 489-2570
Silas Clayton, *Partner*
EMP: 110 **EST:** 2005
SALES (est): 5MM-9.9MM **Privately Held**
SIC: 7011 Traveler accommodations

(G-4252)

DIAMOND WOMEN'S CENTER
6545 France Ave S Ste 540 (55435-2124)
PHONE 952 927-4045
Charles H Haislet, *President*
Joyce Kermmoade, *Human Res Mgr*
Jennifer Depperschm, *Manager*
Pat Burgraff, *Administrator*
Daniel Chow, *Obstetrician*
EMP: 39 **EST:** 2005
SALES (est): 1MM-4.9MM **Privately Held**
SIC: 8011 Physicians' office & clinic

(G-4253)

DIAMONDROCK MINNEAPOLIS TENANT
1001 Marquette Ave (55403-2418)
PHONE 612 376-1000
Nashika Kelly, *CEO*
Mashia Kelly, *Treasurer*
EMP: 99
SALES (est): 5MM-9.9MM **Privately Held**
SIC: 7011 Hotel

(G-4254)

DICKE BILLIG & CZAJA
100 S 5th St Ste 2250 (55402-1235)
PHONE 612 573-2000
FAX: 612 573-2005
Steven Dicke, *Partner*
Philip Fox, *Counsel*
Darla P Fonseca, *Manager*
John Weyrauch, *Officer*
EMP: 25 **EST:** 1998
SALES (est): 1MM-4.9MM **Privately Held**
WEB: www.dbclaw.com
SIC: 8111 Patent, trademark & copyright law office

(G-4255)

DIEBOLD INVESTMENTS LLC (PA)
6530 Cortlawn Cir N 300 (55426-1565)
PHONE 952 960-9600
Anne Loff, *Member*
Chris Diebold, *Member*
EMP: 30 **EST:** 1998 **Privately Held**
SIC: 6719 Investment holding company

(G-4256)

DIGINEER INC
505 Highway 169 N Ste 750 (55441-6449)
PHONE 763 210-2300
Michael Lacey, *CEO*
Chuck Rusch, *Vice Pres*
Jon Whitcomb, *Vice Pres*
Bob Maclean, *Vice Pres*
Tom Brady, *CFO*
EMP: 64 **EST:** 2001
SALES (est): 5MM-9.9MM **Privately Held**
SIC: 8748 Business consulting services

(G-4257)

DINNAKEN PROPERTIES INC
900 Washington Ave SE Apt 216
(55414-3088)
PHONE 612 623-3634
FAX: 612 623-0605
J R Cargill, *President*
Yvonne Grosulak, *Vice Pres*
Ivan Swenson, *Administrator*
Chris Zedell, *Info Tech Mgr*
EMP: 30 **EST:** 1985
SALES (est): 5MM-9.9MM **Privately Held**
WEB: www.dinnaken.com
SIC: 6531 Real estate services

(G-4258)

DIRECT HOME HEALTH CARE INC
1607 Chicago Ave (55404-1605)
PHONE 612 870-8256
Abdullahi Jama, *President*
EMP: 42 **EST:** 2004
SALES (est): 1MM-4.9MM **Privately Held**
SIC: 8082 Home health care services

(G-4259)

DISPLAY SALES CO
10925 Nesbitt Ave S (55437-3125)
PHONE 952 885-0100
Jane Heither, *CEO*
Nancy Peterson, *Vice Pres*
Cheryl Legan, *Sales Mgr*
EMP: 35 **EST:** 1966
SQ FT: 8,000
SALES (est): 10MM-24.9MM **Privately Held**
SIC: 5199 5131 Wholesales Christmas novelties; wholesales flags & banners

(G-4260)

DISTINCTION IN DESIGN INC
14264 23rd Ave N (55447-4910)
PHONE 763 550-1138
FAX: 763 550-1349
Frank Freels, *Ch of Bd*
Rich Larson, *President*
Dave Komula, *Sales Mgr*
Kathy Guggenberger, *Sales Mgr*
Ryan Brown, *Sales Mgr*
EMP: 85 **EST:** 1985
SQ FT: 5,000
SALES (est): 10MM-24.9MM **Privately Held**
WEB: www.distinctionindesign.com
SIC: 8711 Mechanical engineering services; electrical or electronic engineers

(G-4261)

DIVERSIFIED DISTRIBUTION SYSTS (PA)
2828 10th Ave S Ste 200 (55407-5514)
PHONE 612 813-5200
Peter Courtney, *CEO*
Ila Courtney, *Ch of Bd*
Gary Langer, *President*
Wade Wilson, *COO*
Jack Abrahamsen, *Opers Mgr*
◆ **EMP:** 150 **EST:** 1986
SQ FT: 350,000 **Privately Held**
SIC: 5112 Wholesales office supplies

(G-4262)

DIVERSIFIED INDUSTRIES INC
Also Called: Payroll Controls Systems
6040 Earle Brown Dr # 250 (55430-2561)
PHONE 763 513-5951
FAX: 763 513-5968
Joseph Reilly Jr, *President*
Bob Wessel, *VP Opers*
Thomas A Christianson, *Controller*
Bob Willbanks, *Sales Mgr*
Brian Compton, *Administrator*
EMP: 35 **EST:** 1995
SQ FT: 6,000
SALES (est): 1MM-4.9MM **Privately Held**
SIC: 8721 Payroll services

(G-4263)

DIVERSIFIED PHARMACEUTICAL
Also Called: D P S
6225 W 78 St (55439)
PO Box 390842 (55439-0842)
PHONE 952 820-7000
FAX: 952 837-7104
Barrett Toan, *President*
George Paz, *CFO*
EST: 1981
SQ FT: 160,000 **Publicly Held**
WEB: www.express-scripts.com
SIC: 7375 6411 8741 Information retrieval services; contract or fee basis medical insurance claim processing; management services
PA: Express Scripts Inc
1 Express Way
Saint Louis MO 63121
314 996-0900

(G-4264)

DJONT JPM LEASING LLC
Also Called: Embassy Suites - Bloomington
2800 American Blvd W (55431-1205)
PHONE 952 884-4811
FAX: 952 884-8137
Ken Boyles, *General Mgr*
Ken Golder, *Sales Mgr*
EMP: 63
SALES (est): 1MM-4.9MM **Privately Held**
WEB: www.felcor.com
SIC: 7011 Hotel
HQ: Djont Jpm Leasing LLC
6515 International Dr
Orlando FL 32819
407 351-3500

(G-4265)

DJONT OPERATIONS LLC
7901 34th Ave S (55425-1605)
PHONE 952 854-1000
Yvonne Jeziorski, *General Mgr*
David Breen, *General Mgr*
Tim Jerin, *Chief Engr*
Pat Madigan, *Chief Engr*
Heather Rosenfeldt, *Accountant*
EMP: 115
SALES (est): 5MM-9.9MM **Privately Held**
WEB: www.felcor.com
SIC: 7011 Traveler accommodations; eating place; drinking establishment
HQ: Djont Operations LLC
545 E John Carpenter Fwy
Irving TX 75062
972 444-4900

(G-4266)

DLR GROUP KKE
520 Nicollet Mall Ste 200 (55402-1040)
PHONE 612 977-3500
William G Davenport, *President*
Marlene Evenson, *Vice Pres*
Matthew C Johnson, *Vice Pres*
Donald H Horkey, *Vice Pres*
Kelly B Artz, *Vice Pres*
EMP: 37 **EST:** 1992
SQ FT: 32,000
SALES (est): 1MM-4.9MM **Privately Held**
SIC: 8712 8711 Architectural engineers; electrical or electronic engineers

(G-4267)

DMW PROPERTIES INC
Also Called: Multiconcepts
4317 Flag Ave N (55428-4734)
PHONE 763 432-3401
Colleen P Wallin, *CEO*
EMP: 52 **EST:** 1997
SALES (est): 10MM-24.9MM **Privately Held**
WEB: www.dmwproperties.com
SIC: 6512 Nonresidential building operator

(G-4268)

DOBBS TEMPORARY SERVICES INC (PA)
Also Called: Pro Staff
50 S 10th St Ste 500 (55403-2003)
PHONE 612 373-2600
Kevin Roberg, *CEO*
Clay Morel, *President*
Michael E Morris, *Corp Secy*
Todd Dawson, *Vice Pres*
Deanne Schreifels, *Vice Pres*
EMP: 50 **EST:** 1982
SQ FT: 26,000 **Privately Held**
WEB: www.prostaff.com
SIC: 7363 7361 7379 8711 8748 Temporary help service; computer related maintenance service; systems engineering consultant; employment agency services; engineering services

(G-4269)

DOCTORS DIAGNOSTIC CENTER LTD
12805 Highway 55 Ste 111 (55441-3860)
PO Box 19319 (55419-0319)
PHONE 763 550-0707
FAX: 763 550-0705
Alan Divine MD, *President*
Neil Hoffman MD, *Corp Secy*
David Berman MD, *Vice Pres*
Aaron Mark MD, *Vice Pres*
Stuart Borken MD, *Vice Pres*
EMP: 29 **EST:** 1959
SALES (est): 1MM-4.9MM **Privately Held**
SIC: 8011 Internal medicine physician or surgeon

(G-4270)

DOHERTY EMPLOYMENT GROUP INC
7625 Parklawn Ave (55435-5123)
PHONE 952 832-8383
FAX: 952 356-0912
Timothy Doherty, *CEO*
Joe Drake, *Corp Secy*
Valerie K Doherty, *COO*
H R Herring, *Vice Pres*
Barbara Herring, *Treasurer*
EMP: 50 **EST:** 1980
SQ FT: 30,916
SALES (est): 1MM-4.9MM **Privately Held**
WEB: www.dohertyhro.com
SIC: 7363 7361 Help supply services; temporary help service; employment agency services

(G-4271)

DOMESTIC ABUSE PROJECT INC
204 W Franklin Ave (55404-2331)
PHONE 612 874-7063
FAX: 612 874-8445
Ann Moore, *Opers Staff*
Ann Kranz, *Marketing Staff*
Gerrell McBrian, *CIO*
Carol Author, *Exec Dir*
Sonia Palmer, *Director*
EMP: 30 **EST:** 1979
SQ FT: 5,500
SALES (est): 1MM-4.9MM **Privately Held**
WEB: www.domesticabuseproject.com
SIC: 8322 General counseling services; crisis intervention center

(G-4272)

DOMINIUM GROUP INC
2355 Polaris Ln N Ste 100 (55447-4777)
PHONE 763 354-5500
FAX: 763 354-5519
Jack Safar, *Member*
Jon Segner, *Member*
Sue Koch, *Corp Secy*
Lori Warner, *Vice Pres*

(PA)=Parent Co (HQ)=Headquarters (DH)=Div Headquarters
✪ = New business established in last 2 years

2011 Harris Minnesota
Services Directory

© Harris InfoSource 1-866-281-6415

191

Sherry Hatilla, *Office Mgr*
EMP: 70 **EST:** 1972
SQ FT: 27,000
SALES (est): 10MM-24.9MM **Privately Held**
WEB: www.dominiumapartments.com
SIC: 6552 Land subdivision & development services

(G-4273)
DOMINIUM MANAGEMENT SERVICES
5805 73rd Ave N (55429-1104)
PHONE............................763 560-0244
FAX: 763 560-4646
Sue Meyer, *Manager*
EMP: 25
SALES (est): 1MM-4.9MM **Privately Held**
WEB: www.dominiuminc.com
SIC: 6513 Apartment building operator
PA: Dominium Management Services
2355 Polaris Ln N Ste 100
Minneapolis MN 55447
763 354-5500

(G-4274)
DOMINIUM MANAGEMENT SERVICES (PA)
2355 Polaris Ln N Ste 100 (55447-4777)
PHONE............................763 354-5500
David Brierton, *President*
Rita Ahrens, *Regional Mgr*
Sue K Secvp, *Corp Secy*
Sue Koch, *Corp Secy*
Jack Safer, *Vice Pres*
EMP: 128 **EST:** 1980 **Privately Held**
WEB: www.dominiuminc.com
SIC: 6531 Real estate management services

(G-4275)
DON CAMERON & ASSOCIATES INC
396 American Blvd E (55420-1219)
PHONE............................952 884-0070
Don Cameron, *President*
EMP: 50 **EST:** 1987
SQ FT: 5,000
SALES (est): 5MM-9.9MM **Privately Held**
SIC: 4731 Domestic freight forwarding services; foreign freight forwarding services

(G-4276)
DON'S LEATHER CLEANING INC
3713 E Lake St (55406-2149)
PHONE............................612 721-4881
FAX: 612 721-4833
Dart Poach, *President*
Dawn Schumann, *Manager*
Rick Ferwa, *Manager*
EMP: 30 **EST:** 1971
SQ FT: 6,600
SALES (est): 1MM-4.9MM **Privately Held**
SIC: 7699 7219 7251 Leather goods, cleaning & repair service; fur garment cleaning, repairing & storage service; hat cleaning & blocking shop

(G-4277)
DONALD H SEALOCK
Also Called: Four Seasons Eye Care
4455 Highway 169 N # 100 (55442-2898)
PHONE............................763 559-7358
Donald H Sealock OD, *President*
Jason Welle, *General Mgr*
EMP: 60 **EST:** 1987
SALES (est): 5MM-9.9MM **Privately Held**
SIC: 8011 8042 Physicians' office; retail opticians; optometrists' office

(G-4278)
DONNELLY BROTHERS CONSTRUCTION
5928 Portland Ave (55417-3128)
PHONE............................612 866-1204
FAX: 612 866-8662
Dennis Donnelly, *President*
Mark Donnelly, *Vice Pres*
EMP: 25 **EST:** 1987
SALES (est): 1MM-4.9MM **Privately Held**
SIC: 1771 1541 1742 Stucco, gunite & grouting contractor; industrial building renovating, remodeling & repair service; plain or ornamental plastering contractor

(G-4279)
DORAN CONSTRUCTION INC ✪
7803 Glenroy Rd Ste 200 (55439-3126)
PHONE............................763 421-0553
Kelly J Doran, *President*
Ryan Johnson, *Manager*
EMP: 25 **EST:** 2008
SALES (est): 5MM-9.9MM **Privately Held**
SIC: 1542 Commercial & office building contractor

(G-4280)
DORF & STANTON COMMUNICATIONS (HQ)
8000 Norman Center Dr Ste 400 (55437-1180)
PHONE............................952 832-5000
Sara Gavin, *President*
Jessica Niedzielski, *Manager*
EMP: 90 **EST:** 1972
SALES (corp-wide): 6.02B **Publicly Held**
SIC: 8743 Public relations services
PA: Interpublic Group of Co's Inc
1114 Avenue Of The Americas
New York NY 10036
212 704-1200

(G-4281)
DORSEY & WHITNEY LLP (PA)
50 S 6th St Ste 1500 (55402-1498)
PHONE............................612 340-2600
FAX: 612 340-7800
Christopher J Barry, *Ch of Bd*
Marianne Short, *Managing Prtnr*
Peter Bado, *Partner*
Thomas W Tinkham, *Partner*
Marcus Sisk, *Partner*
EMP: 780 **EST:** 1978
SQ FT: 235,000
SALES (corp-wide): 2.27M **Privately Held**
WEB: www.dorsey.com
SIC: 8111 Legal services

(G-4282)
DOUBLETREE CORP
1500 Park Place Blvd (55416-1527)
PHONE............................952 542-8600
Jennifer Ferguson, *Manager*
EMP: 250
SALES (est): 10MM-24.9MM **Publicly Held**
WEB: www.dtwarrenplace.com
SIC: 7011 Traveler accommodations
HQ: Doubletree Corp
9336 Civic Center Dr
Beverly Hills CA 90210
310 278-4321

(G-4283)
DOUGHERTY & CO LLC
90 S 7th St Ste 4300 (55402-4108)
PHONE............................612 376-4000
Thomas Abood, *Member*
David Juran, *Member*
Gerald Kraut, *Member*
Michelle Sandberg, *Member*
Gary Bloauer, *Exec VP*
EMP: 116 **EST:** 1977
SQ FT: 35,000
SALES (est): 25MM-49.9MM **Privately Held**
WEB: www.doughertymarkets.com
SIC: 6211 Security broker service; stock broker & dealer service
PA: Dougherty Financial Group LLC
90 S 7th St Ste 4300
Minneapolis MN 55402
612 376-4000

(G-4284)
DOUGHERTY FINANCIAL GROUP LLC (PA)
90 S 7th St Ste 4300 (55402-4108)
PHONE............................612 376-4000
Robert Pohlad, *Member*
James Pohlad, *Member*
Beth Sanderburg, *Facilities Mgr*
Michelle Sandberg, *CFO*
Michael Dougherty, *Mng Member*
EMP: 143 **EST:** 1977
SQ FT: 37,400 **Privately Held**
WEB: www.dfg-companies.com
SIC: 6211 6163 6221 6282 Investment banking service; commodity contracts broker or dealer; investment advisory service; loan broker

(G-4285)
DOUGLAS DRIVE CAR WASH INC
Also Called: Octopus Car Wash
5301 Douglas Dr N (55429-3105)
PHONE............................763 533-1581
FAX: 763 533-1283
David Richardson, *Manager*
Barbara Brown, *Asst Mgr*
EMP: 31 **EST:** 1973
SQ FT: 21,800
SALES (est): 1MM-4.9MM **Privately Held**
SIC: 7542 Automatic carwash service; retail gasoline filling station; automotive washing & polishing service

(G-4286)
DP PROPERTY ACQUISITION LLC
322 1st Ave N (55401-1618)
PHONE............................612 344-1515
FAX: 612 344-1527
EMP: 30 **EST:** 1993
SALES (est): 5MM-9.9MM **Privately Held**
SIC: 6512 Operators of commercial & industrial buildings

(G-4287)
DS & B LTD
222 S 9th St Ste 3000 (55402-3370)
PHONE............................612 359-9630
FAX: 612 359-0572
Larry Gamst, *President*
Nathan H Wayne, *Corp Secy*
Marvin K Mirsky, *Treasurer*
Dean Dille, *CPA*
Cathy Mate, *CPA*
EMP: 44 **EST:** 1967
SQ FT: 6,145
SALES (est): 1MM-4.9MM **Privately Held**
SIC: 8721 Accounting service

(G-4288)
DSW SHOE WAREHOUSE INC
124 W Market (55425-5521)
PHONE............................952 876-0991
Lynn Sandbeck, *Manager*
Lynn Sanddeck, *Manager*
EMP: 25
SALES (est): 1MM-4.9MM **Privately Held**
SIC: 5139 Retails shoes; wholesales boots
PA: Schottenstein Stores Corp
1800 Moler Rd
Columbus OH 43207
614 221-9200

(G-4289)
DUKE CO'S
Also Called: Halderman Homme
430 Industrial Blvd NE (55413-2931)
PHONE............................612 331-4880
William J Krueger, *Partner*
Mike Propp, *Partner*
EMP: 60 **EST:** 1966
SQ FT: 14,000
SALES (est): 25MM-49.9MM **Privately Held**
SIC: 7515 4225 6512 7359 Passenger car leasing; general warehousing; operators of commercial & industrial buildings; business machine & electronic equipment rental service

(G-4290)
DUKE FINANCIAL GROUP INC (PA)
80 S 8th St Ste 2900 (55402-2250)
PHONE............................612 204-0255
FAX: 612 204-0173
Richard W Perkins, *Vice Pres*
Brenda Coulter, *Vice Pres*
EST: 1982
SALES (corp-wide): 7.60M **Privately Held**
SIC: 6712 Bank holding company

(G-4291)
DUKE REALTY CORP
1600 Utica Ave S Ste 250 (55416-1470)
PHONE............................952 543-2900
FAX: 952 543-2999
Pat Mascia, *Senior VP*
Phil Cobb, *Senior VP*
Bill Deboer, *Senior VP*
Kevin Rogus, *Senior VP*
Rudy Behne, *Vice Pres*
EMP: 60
SALES (est): 10MM-24.9MM **Privately Held**
WEB: www.dukereit.com
SIC: 6512 Operators of commercial & industrial buildings
PA: Duke Realty Corp
600 E 96th St Ste 100
Indianapolis IN 46240
317 808-6000

(G-4292)
DUNCAN CO
425 Hoover St NE (55413-2926)
PHONE............................612 331-1776
FAX: 612 331-4735
Joseph Klick, *President*
Pam Hennager, *General Mgr*
Josh Ralph, *Vice Pres*
Robert Finke, *CFO*
Gary Steichen, *Manager*
EMP: 35 **EST:** 1973
SQ FT: 25,000
SALES (est): 10MM-24.9MM **Privately Held**
WEB: www.duncanco.com
SIC: 5085 Wholesales industrial supplies; wholesales industrial valves & fittings; wholesales industrial brushes; wholesales industrial abrasives

(G-4293)
DUNDEE NURSERY & LANDSCAPING (PA)
16800 Highway 55 (55446-3012)
PHONE............................763 559-4004
FAX: 763 559-8483
Gerald W Theis, *President*
Ken Theis, *Vice Pres*
Elaine Theis, *Treasurer*
Larry Goetzinger, *Controller*
Tom Schirmers, *Retail*
EMP: 30 **EST:** 1946
SQ FT: 12,000 **Privately Held**
WEB: www.dundeenursery.com
SIC: 0781 Retail nursery & garden center; landscape services

(G-4294)
DUNHAM ASSOCIATES INC
50 S 6th St Ste 1100 (55402-1583)
PHONE............................612 465-7550
Katy Kolbeck, *CEO*
Charles Macy, *Corp Secy*
David Kolbeck, *Corp Secy*
David L Kauffman, *Corp Secy*
Stephen Gentilini, *Exec VP*
EMP: 70 **EST:** 1960
SALES (est): 5MM-9.9MM **Privately Held**
WEB: www.dunhamassociates.com
SIC: 8711 Engineering consulting services

(G-4295)
DUNK N JUMP
1500 Jackson St NE # 185 (55413-2859)
PHONE............................612 788-0404
Marijo Greeman, *Owner*
EMP: 82 **EST:** 1986
SALES (est): 10MM-24.9MM **Privately Held**
WEB: www.dunknjump.net
SIC: 7929 5199 Entertainment services; wholesales carnival supplies; retails gifts & novelties

(G-4296)
DUNKLEY & BENNETT
Also Called: Stewart T Chris
701 4th Ave S Ste 700 (55415-1812)
PHONE............................612 339-1290
FAX: 612 339-9545
William Dunkley, *CEO*
Jay Bennett, *President*
EMP: 40 **EST:** 1979
SQ FT: 14,000
SALES (est): 5MM-9.9MM **Privately Held**
SIC: 8111 General practice attorney's or lawyer's office

(G-4297)
DUNN ENTERPRISES INC (PA)
Also Called: Johnson-Williams Auto Livery
302 Industrial Blvd NE (55413-2929)
PHONE............................612 627-5661
FAX: 612 627-5656
Todd P Anderson, *President*
Becky Hoffer, *Business Mgr*
John Delaundreau, *Controller*

www.HarrisInfo.com
192

2011 Harris Minnesota
Services Directory

▲=Import ▼=Export
◆=Import/Export

John Galendreau, *Human Resources*
EMP: 140 **EST:** 1974
SQ FT: 30,000
SALES (corp-wide): 4.50M **Privately Held**
WEB: www.dunnenterprises.com
SIC: 4119 4111 Hearse rental services with driver; passenger transit system; limousine service

(G-4298)
DYMANYK ELECTRIC
1915 Broadway St NE (55413-2627)
PHONE 612 379-4112
FAX: 612 379-0459
Robert Dymanyk, *President*
Debbie Hrbek, *Corp Secy*
Richard Dymanyk, *Vice Pres*
Lola Thomaws, *Manager*
EMP: 35 **EST:** 1946
SQ FT: 9,000
SALES (est): 1MM-4.9MM **Privately Held**
WEB: www.dymanykelectric.com
SIC: 1731 General electrical contractor

(G-4299)
E & C AMEC SERVICES INC
Also Called: Simmons Engineering
800 Marquette Ave Ste 1200 (55402-2876)
PHONE 612 332-8326
Anthony Wedell, *Opers Mgr*
Dewey Thorson, *Opers Staff*
Mike Stokes, *Engineer*
David Smith, *Engineering*
Marie Hopper, *Human Resources*
EMP: 100
SALES (est): 10MM-24.9MM **Privately Held**
SIC: 8711 7389 8742 8748 Engineering services; commercial & industrial design service; automation & robotics consultant; environmental consultant

(G-4300)
E FRAME
6600 France Ave S Ste 670 (55435-1807)
PHONE 952 926-3555
James Folsom, *Owner*
Brad Queck, *Vice Pres*
EMP: 60 **EST:** 2000
SALES (est): 1MM-4.9MM **Privately Held**
SIC: 7389 Personal service agents

(G-4301)
E TECH INC
1401 W River Rd Ste D (55411-3436)
PHONE 612 722-1366
FAX: 612 722-4709
Duane Martinson, *President*
Joseph Schult, *Vice Pres*
Jason Landkamar, *Materials Mgr*
Brian Sckichting, *Engineer*
Todd Sanders, *Engineering*
▲ **EMP:** 70 **EST:** 1970
SALES (est): 25MM-49.9MM **Privately Held**
WEB: www.etechsystems.com
SIC: 5084 Wholesales materials handling equipment

(G-4302)
E W BLANCH INTERNATIONAL INC
3600 Amercn Blvd W # 700 (55431-4504)
PHONE 952 886-8000
Rod Fox, *CEO*
Paul Karon, *Vice Pres*
Shahriar Sahba, *Project Mgr*
EMP: 75 **EST:** 1992
SALES (est): 100MM-499.9MM **Publicly Held**
WEB: www.ewb.com
SIC: 6321 Accident & health reinsurance carriers
HQ: AON Benfield
3600 American Blvd W
Minneapolis MN 55431
952 886-8000

(G-4303)
E WEINBERG SUPPLY CO INC
Also Called: Weinberg Supply & Equipment Co
7434 W 27th St (55426-3104)
PHONE 952 920-0888
FAX: 952 920-2911
David Y Weinberg, *President*
Eugene Weinberg, *Corp Secy*

Gene Weinberg, *Corp Secy*
Moshe Weinberg, *Vice Pres*
Dick Duis, *Controller*
EMP: 30 **EST:** 1938
SQ FT: 30,000
SALES (est): 5MM-9.9MM **Privately Held**
WEB: www.weinbergsupply.com
SIC: 6512 5087 Operators of commercial & industrial buildings; wholesales service establishment equipment & supplies

(G-4304)
E-GROUP INC
901 N 3rd St Ste 195 (55401-1006)
PHONE 612 339-4777
FAX: 612 339-4740
Paul Estenson, *CEO*
Dean Noble, *Vice Pres*
Steve Waletzko, *Vice Pres*
Michelle Bideback, *Opers Mgr*
Jake Dunn, *Manager*
▲ **EMP:** 25 **EST:** 1994
SQ FT: 40,000
SALES (est): 1MM-4.9MM **Privately Held**
SIC: 5199 8742 Wholesales advertising specialties; incentive or award program consultant

(G-4305)
EAGLE LAKE GOLF CENTER
11000 County Road 10 (55442-1611)
PHONE 763 694-7695
FAX: 763 744-1277
Joe L Barrow Jr, *Exec Dir*
Troy Nygaard, *Director*
EMP: 25 **EST:** 2001
SALES (est): 1MM-4.9MM **Privately Held**
SIC: 7992 Public golf course

(G-4306)
EAR NOSE & THROAT (PA)
2211 Park Ave (55404-3711)
PHONE 612 871-1144
FAX: 612 871-2012
Jackie Lee, *Office Mgr*
Kathleen M O'Brien, *Office Mgr*
Michael P Murphy MD, *Med Doctor*
Joann Borders, *Manager*
Carl A Brown, *Otolaryngology*
EMP: 40 **EST:** 1968 **Privately Held**
SIC: 8011 Eyes, ears, nose & throat specialist, physician or surgeon office

(G-4307)
EAST ASIAN TRADING CO INC
Also Called: Top Star Group
405 Brockton Ln N (55447-3335)
PHONE 763 473-3520
Bernard J Resiberg, *CEO*
Charles B Freeburg, *Corp Secy*
▲ **EMP:** 355 **EST:** 1990
SALES (est): 100MM-499.9MM **Privately Held**
SIC: 5199 Wholesales textile bags; manufactures felt nonwoven mats; wholesales art goods

(G-4308)
EAST SIDE NEIGHBORHOOD SVCS
1700 2nd St NE (55413-1139)
PHONE 612 781-6011
FAX: 612 781-9257
Terry Andrew, *Superintendent*
Thomas Spurrier, *CFO*
Grant Thesing, *CFO*
Vern Lovstad, *Human Res Mgr*
Richard Gray, *MIS Staff*
EMP: 80 **EST:** 1916
SQ FT: 45,000 **Privately Held**
WEB: www.esns.org
SIC: 8399 Community development groups

(G-4309)
EBENEZER SOCIETY
2545 Portland Ave (55404-4406)
PHONE 612 879-2262
FAX: 612 879-2316
Mike Sortum, *VP Finance*
Holly Groff, *Manager*
Jody Barney, *Manager*
Joel Prevost, *Administrator*
Lynnann Lloyd, *Info Tech Mgr*
EMP: 130
SALES (est): 5MM-9.9MM **Privately Held**
WEB: www.fairview.org

SIC: 8051 8741 Skilled nursing care facility; management services
HQ: Ebenezer Society
2722 Park Ave
Minneapolis MN 55407
612 874-3460

(G-4310)
EBENEZER SOCIETY
2523 Portland Ave Ste 1 (55404-4443)
PHONE 612 879-1400
Julie Debilzan, *Coordinator*
EMP: 200
SALES (est): 5MM-9.9MM **Privately Held**
WEB: www.fairview.org
SIC: 8051 8741 Skilled nursing care facility; management services
HQ: Ebenezer Society
2722 Park Ave
Minneapolis MN 55407
612 874-3460

(G-4311)
ECOMMERCE NETWORK RESOURCE GRP
3033 Excelsior Blvd # 307 (55416-4675)
PHONE 612 340-1110
Diana Albrecht, *President*
Richard Earley, *Vice Pres*
EMP: 35 **EST:** 1999
SQ FT: 2,490
SALES (est): 1MM-4.9MM **Privately Held**
SIC: 8748 Business consulting services

(G-4312)
ECUMEN HOME CARE INC
Also Called: Meadow Woods
1301 E 100th St Ofc (55425-2635)
PHONE 952 888-1010
FAX: 952 881-4323
Beverly Heise, *Branch Mgr*
EMP: 50
SALES (est): 1MM-4.9MM **Privately Held**
WEB: www.augustanahomes.org
SIC: 7021 8361 Rooming & boarding house; residential care facility
PA: Ecumen
3530 Lexington Ave N
Saint Paul MN 55126
651 766-4300

(G-4313)
EDEN RS
Also Called: WATCHGUARD
1931 W Broadway Ave # 101 (55411-2418)
PHONE 612 287-1600
Daniel Cain, *President*
Amy Holzem, *Sales/Mktg Mgr*
Bill Mordaunt, *Treasurer*
Watchguard T Cushing, *Exec Dir*
Tim Cushing, *Bd of Directors*
EMP: 160 **EST:** 1971
SQ FT: 5,000
SALES (est): 5MM-9.9MM **Privately Held**
SIC: 8361 8322 Halfway home for delinquents & offenders; rehabilitation services; offender rehabilitation agency; probation office

(G-4314)
EDINA COUNTRY CLUB
5100 Wooddale Ave (55424-1334)
PHONE 952 927-7151
FAX: 952 927-7155
Jeff Bohlit, *President*
Kimberly Dalnes, *Purch Mgr*
Rob Bunn, *Engineer*
Kimberly Delaney, *Finance*
Marty Lass, *Director*
EMP: 200 **EST:** 1946
SALES (est): 10MM-24.9MM **Privately Held**
WEB: www.edinacountryclub.org
SIC: 7997 Membership golf club

(G-4315)
EDINA EYE PHYSICIANS
7450 France Ave S Ste 100 (55435-4799)
PHONE 952 831-8811
Thomas F Carroll MD, *President*
Paul O Sanderson MD, *Corp Secy*
John A Nilsen MD, *Vice Pres*
Jeri Jewells, *Office Mgr*
EMP: 25 **EST:** 1965
SALES (est): 1MM-4.9MM **Privately Held**

WEB: www.edinaeye.com
SIC: 8011 Ophthalmologist office

(G-4316)
EDINA FAMILY PHYSICIANS
5301 Vernon Ave S (55436-2303)
PHONE 952 925-2200
John T Beecher MD, *President*
James A Rohde MD, *Vice Pres*
Kerry Thompson, *Office Mgr*
Linda M Odell, *Administrator*
Viseth Minh, *Info Tech Mgr*
EMP: 27 **EST:** 1974
SALES (est): 1MM-4.9MM **Privately Held**
WEB: www.edinafamilyphysicians.com
SIC: 8011 General & family practice physician or surgeon office

(G-4317)
EDINA LAUNDRY CO
4500 France Ave S (55410-1368)
PHONE 952 927-9991
Lee Stotts, *President*
David H Stotts, *VP Persnl*
EMP: 50 **EST:** 1950
SQ FT: 15,000
SALES (est): 1MM-4.9MM **Privately Held**
WEB: www.edinacleaners.com
SIC: 7216 7211 Dry cleaning plant; commercial & family dry cleaning & laundry services

(G-4318)
EDINA PEDIATRICS
3250 W 66th St Ste 210 (55435-2526)
PHONE 952 927-7337
Vicki Thompson MD, *Partner*
Ann Runyon, *Office Mgr*
Katie Graff, *Manager*
Kelly Woods, *Bd of Directors*
Janette Sorensen, *Nurse Practr*
EMP: 25 **EST:** 1985
SALES (est): 1MM-4.9MM **Privately Held**
SIC: 8011 Pediatrician office; surgeon's office

(G-4319)
EDINA PLASTIC SURGERY LTD
6525 France Ave S Ste 300 (55435-2177)
PHONE 952 925-1765
William Carter MD, *President*
Phillip Henderschott, *Managing Dir*
Bradley Childs, *Managing Dir*
Patty Rodningen, *Managing Dir*
Orla McClure, *Office Mgr*
EMP: 25 **EST:** 1977
SQ FT: 7,820
SALES (est): 1MM-4.9MM **Privately Held**
WEB: www.edinaplasticsurgery.com
SIC: 8011 Plastic surgeon office

(G-4320)
EDINA REALTY
5300 Hyland Pl (55437-1927)
PHONE 952 844-5409
FAX: 952 844-5370
Ron Peltier, *President*
EMP: 60
SALES (est): 10MM-24.9MM **Publicly Held**
WEB: www.crosslakeedinarealty.com
SIC: 6531 Real estate services
HQ: Edina Realty
15354 Danielson Rd
Brainerd MN 56401
218 829-7500

(G-4321)
EDINA REALTY HOME SERVICES
4425 Highway 169 N (55442-2856)
PHONE 763 559-2894
FAX: 763 557-4595
Dwayne Coben, *VP Finance*
Patty Rodningen, *Manager*
Vicki Gay, *Manager*
Monica Tucker, *Manager*
Brad Fisher, *Manager*
EMP: 90
SALES (est): 10MM-24.9MM **Publicly Held**
WEB: www.ilovetennis.net
SIC: 6531 Real estate agency & broker
HQ: Edina Realty Home Services
6800 France Ave S Ste 600
Minneapolis MN 55435
952 928-5900

(PA)=Parent Co (HQ)=Headquarters (DH)=Div Headquarters
✪ = New business established in last 2 years
2011 Harris Minnesota
Services Directory
© Harris InfoSource 1-866-281-6415
193

GEOGRAPHIC

GEOGRAPHIC *(vertical left margin)*

(G-4322)
EDINA REALTY HOME SERVICES
5309 Lyndale Ave S (55419-1229)
PHONE............................612 827-3551
FAX: 612 827-0373
Ed Donfrancesco, *Sales/Mktg Mgr*
Christine Murphy-Jones, *Real Est Agnt*
Philip Kirsch, *Real Est Agnt*
Thomas Inskip, *Real Est Agnt*
Carolyn Engelking, *Real Est Agnt*
EMP: 50
SALES (est): 5MM-9.9MM **Publicly Held**
WEB: www.ilovetennis.net
SIC: 6531 Real estate agency & broker
HQ: Edina Realty Home Services
       6800 France Ave S Ste 600
       Minneapolis MN 55435
       952 928-5900

(G-4323)
EDINA REALTY HOME SERVICES
4800 Olson Memorial Hwy # 100
(55422-5171)
PHONE............................763 545-5000
Paul Olson, *Manager*
Christina Matson, *Manager*
Matthew Gilberg, *Real Est Agnt*
Michael Gacek, *Real Est Agnt*
Katherine Fuhrman, *Real Est Agnt*
EMP: 50
SALES (est): 5MM-9.9MM **Publicly Held**
WEB: www.ilovetennis.net
SIC: 6531 Real estate agency & broker
HQ: Edina Realty Home Services
       6800 France Ave S Ste 600
       Minneapolis MN 55435
       952 928-5900

(G-4324)
EDINA REALTY HOME SERVICES
3021 Harbor Ln N (55447-5109)
PHONE............................763 567-7000
Jennifer Cutter, *Manager*
Patrick Manning, *Real Est Agnt*
Tom Loweth, *Real Est Agnt*
Patricia Long, *Real Est Agnt*
Bette Jensen, *Real Est Agnt*
EMP: 40
SALES (est): 5MM-9.9MM **Publicly Held**
WEB: www.ilovetennis.net
SIC: 6531 Real estate services
HQ: Edina Realty Home Services
       6800 France Ave S Ste 600
       Minneapolis MN 55435
       952 928-5900

(G-4325)
EDINA REALTY HOME SERVICES
6800 France Ave S Ste 600 (55435-2017)
PHONE............................952 928-5900
Ronald J Peltier, *CEO*
Greg Mason, *President*
Robert Peltier, *President*
Barb Jandric, *General Mgr*
Phillip Henderschott, *Managing Dir*
EMP: 52 **EST:** 1995
SQ FT: 14,000
SALES (est): 5MM-9.9MM **Publicly Held**
WEB: www.ilovetennis.net
SIC: 6531 6541 Real estate agency &
broker; title abstract service
DH: Homeservices of America Inc
       333 S 7th St Ste 2700
       Minneapolis MN 55402
       888 485-0018

(G-4326)
EDINA REALTY TITLE
6800 France Ave S Ste 160 (55435-2004)
PHONE............................952 928-5181
FAX: 952 928-5160
Diane Thormodsgard, *CEO*
Ron Peltier, *President*
Greg Mason, *Vice Pres*
Matt Gri, *Vice Pres*
Erica Kaiser, *Manager*
EMP: 85 **EST:** 1986
SQ FT: 2,250
SALES (est): 5MM-9.9MM **Publicly Held**
WEB: www.ilovetennis.net

SIC: 6541 Title abstract service
HQ: Edina Realty Home Services
       6800 France Ave S Ste 600
       Minneapolis MN 55435
       952 928-5900

(G-4327)
EDUCATIONAL COOPERATIVE SVC
Also Called: METRO ECSU
3055 Old Highway 8 # 302 (55418-2497)
PHONE............................612 638-1500
FAX: 612 706-0811
Tom Baldwin, *Exec Dir*
Julie Framhansan, *Director*
Sandy Nelson, *Executive Asst*
EMP: 26 **EST:** 1976
SQ FT: 2,400
SALES (est): 1MM-4.9MM **Privately Held**
SIC: 8733 8732 Educational research
agency; elementary & secondary school;
commercial nonphysical research laboratory

(G-4328)
EFI GLOBAL INC
7667 Cahill Rd Ste 350 (55439-2750)
PHONE............................952 942-9812
FAX: 952 942-7002
David Bellis, *Manager*
John Marsh, *Manager*
EMP: 26
SALES (est): 1MM-4.9MM **Publicly Held**
WEB: www.efiglobal.com
SIC: 8711 Engineering services
HQ: Efi Global Inc
       8811 Fm 1960 Byp Rd W
       Humble TX 77338
       281 358-4441

(G-4329)
EGAN, FIELD, & NOWAK INC
Also Called: Egan Field & Nowak Surveyors
1229 Tyler St NE Ste 100 (55413-1529)
PHONE............................612 466-3300
Lee Nord, *President*
Randy Mullins, *Vice Pres*
Richard Smith, *Vice Pres*
Scott Hillestad, *Mktg Dir*
Nancy Miller, *Assistant*
EMP: 40 **EST:** 1872
SQ FT: 11,000
SALES (est): 1MM-4.9MM **Privately Held**
WEB: www.efnsurvey.com
SIC: 8713 Surveying service

(G-4330)
EGGLESTON MEDSCRIBE INC
3501 Douglas Dr N (55422-2415)
PO Box 27108 (55427-0108)
PHONE............................763 971-5000
FAX: 763 971-5050
Lawrence R Eggleston, *President*
EMP: 29 **EST:** 1984
SALES (est): 1MM-4.9MM **Privately Held**
WEB: www.eggleston-medscribe.com
SIC: 7338 Secretarial services;
stenographic service

(G-4331)
EGO SYSTEMS INC
6500 Excelsior Blvd Fl 3 (55426-4702)
PHONE............................952 200-8246
Gerald Pollard, *President*
EMP: 74
SALES (est): 10MM-24.9MM **Privately Held**
SIC: 7379 Online technology consulting
service

(G-4332)
EIDE BAILLY LLP
5601 Green Valley Dr Ste 700
(55437-1145)
PHONE............................952 944-6166
David L Stende, *COO*
William McCue, *CPA*
Anne Warshaw, *Mktg Dir*
Jason Johnson, *Manager*
Randy Dewey, *Manager*
EMP: 115
SALES (est): 10MM-24.9MM **Privately Held**
WEB: www.eide.com

SIC: 8721 Certified public accountant
services
PA: Eide Bailly LLP
       4310 17th Ave S
       Fargo ND 58103
       701 239-8593

(G-4333)
8TH STREET GARAGE INC
800 Marquette Ave Ste 107 (55402-2819)
PHONE............................612 349-5717
FAX: 612 349-5722
Jerry Snyder, *President*
Kim Gruetzmacher, *Business Mgr*
EMP: 40 **EST:** 1991
SALES (est): 1MM-4.9MM **Privately Held**
SIC: 7299 Eating place; banquet hall facility;
drinking establishment

(G-4334)
EIS INC
9210 Wyoming Ave N Ste 215
(55445-1854)
PHONE............................763 493-6800
FAX: 763 391-8170
Rollie Schwanz, *Purch Agent*
Hans Sprandel, *Finance Mgr*
Daniel Erikson, *Manager*
EMP: 40
SALES (est): 25MM-49.9MM **Publicly Held**
WEB: www.eis-inc.com
SIC: 5063 Wholesales electrical insulators
HQ: Eis Inc
       2018 Powers Ferry Rd SE # 500
       Atlanta GA 30339
       678 255-3600

(G-4335)
ELAM INVESTMENTS
Also Called: Pazaaz Hair & Nail Design
7759 Medicine Lake Rd (55427-3501)
PHONE............................763 544-4264
Randy Elam, *Owner*
EMP: 25 **EST:** 1971
SALES (est): 500-999K **Privately Held**
SIC: 7231 7299 Beauty salon; tanning salon

(G-4336)
ELDER-JONES INC
1120 E 80th St Ste 211 (55420-1463)
PHONE............................952 854-2854
FAX: 952 854-2703
John S Elder, *President*
David Brian, *Corp Secy*
Mark Utne, *Senior VP*
David B Perkkio, *Senior VP*
David Good, *Vice Pres*
EMP: 50 **EST:** 1971
SQ FT: 3,700
SALES (est): 10MM-24.9MM **Privately Held**
WEB: www.elderjones.com
SIC: 1542 Commercial & office building
contractor; shopping center & mall
construction; commercial & office building
renovation & repair services

(G-4337)
ELECTRIC MOTOR REPAIR INC
2010 N 4th St (55411-2705)
PHONE............................612 588-4693
FAX: 612 588-1617
Thomas Frickle, *President*
Harlen R Fricke, *President*
Doug Schleifman, *General Mgr*
EMP: 25 **EST:** 1947
SQ FT: 40,000
SALES (est): 10MM-24.9MM **Privately Held**
SIC: 5063 7694 7699 Wholesales electric
motors; wholesales electric motor controls,
starters & relays; electric motor repair
service; motor rebuilding service; pumps &
pumping equipment repair service; welding
equipment repair service

(G-4338)
ELECTRIC RESOURCE CONTRACTORS
4024 Washington Ave N (55412-1742)
PHONE............................612 522-6511
FAX: 612 522-4134
Dana Daniels, *CEO*
David Hennek, *President*
Terry Towey, *Vice Pres*
Jeff Lester, *Vice Pres*
Christian Sides, *Warehouse Mgr*

EMP: 225 **EST:** 1935
SQ FT: 11,000
SALES (est): 25MM-49.9MM **Privately Held**
WEB: www.electricresource.com
SIC: 1731 General electrical contractor

(G-4339)
ELECTRONIC DESIGN CO
Also Called: Edcsolutions
3225 E Hennepin Ave (55413-2942)
PHONE............................612 355-2300
Toby E Marcovich, *CEO*
Daniel Murray, *President*
Paul Zadel, *Engineer*
Adam Hardman, *Software Engr*
EMP: 38 **EST:** 1955
SQ FT: 14,000
SALES (est): 1MM-4.9MM **Privately Held**
WEB: www.edcsolutions.com
SIC: 1731 5065 Sound equipment
installation service; voice, data & video
wiring contractor; closed circuit television
installation; wholesales public address
equipment

(G-4340)
ELIZABETH CHARLES CORP (PA)
Also Called: Spalon Montage
3909 W 49 1/2 St (55424-1201)
PHONE............................952 915-2900
FAX: 952 915-2898
Shelly Engelsma, *CEO*
Mitchell Wherley, *President*
EMP: 127 **EST:** 1992
SQ FT: 10,000 **Privately Held**
SIC: 7991 7231 Spas; unisex hair salon;
cosmetologist; facial salon

(G-4341)
ELLERBE BECKET CO (HQ)
800 Lasalle Ave Ste 400 (55402-2020)
PHONE............................612 376-2000
Rick A Lincicome, *CEO*
Gregory Anderson, *COO*
Anne Shinler, *Office Mgr*
Jerry Donahue, *Manager*
Kim Klingeisen, *Info Tech Mgr*
EMP: 165 **EST:** 1909
SQ FT: 89,000 **Privately Held**
WEB: www.ellerbebecket.com
SIC: 8712 1542 8711 Architectural
engineers; commercial & institutional
building construction; building construction
engineering services

(G-4342)
ELLIOTT CONTRACTING CORP
901 N 3rd St Ste 330 (55401-1005)
PHONE............................612 256-0000
FAX: 612 256-0020
Jack Elliott, *President*
Scott Werrbash, *Purchasing*
Robert F Hosch, *Treasurer*
Deborah Walch, *Accountant*
EMP: 50 **EST:** 1993
SQ FT: 6,000
SALES (est): 5MM-9.9MM **Privately Held**
WEB: www.elliottcontracting.com
SIC: 1731 General electrical contractor

(G-4343)
ELNESS SWENSON GRAHAM
500 Washington Ave S Ste 1080
(55415-1153)
PHONE............................612 339-5508
FAX: 612 339-5382
Mark Swenson, *President*
David Graham, *Vice Pres*
Art Weeks, *Vice Pres*
Steve Larsen, *CFO*
Erin McCleary, *Manager*
EMP: 84 **EST:** 1973
SALES (est): 10MM-24.9MM **Privately Held**
SIC: 8712 7389 Architectural service;
interior design service

(G-4344)
ELSIE'S RESTAURANT LOUNGE
729 Marshall St NE (55413-1815)
PHONE............................612 378-9702
Bob Tuttle, *President*
Tim Tuttle, *President*
EMP: 40 **EST:** 1991
SALES (est): 1MM-4.9MM **Privately Held**

www.HarrisInfo.com
194

2011 Harris Minnesota
Services Directory

▲=Import ▼=Export
◆=Import/Export

SIC: **7933** Bowling center; eating place; drinking establishment

(G-4345)
EMERGE COMMUNITY DEVELOPMENT
1101 W Broadway Ave 200   (55411-2570)
PHONE...............................612 529-9267
Paul Halvorson, *CFO*
Mike Wynne, *Exec Dir*
Dawn Williams, *Director*
EMP: 45 EST: 1996 **Privately Held**
SIC: **7361** Employment agency services

(G-4346)
EMERGENCY PHYSICIANS PROF
Also Called: Emergncy Physicians Prof Associ
7301 Ohms Ln Ste 650   (55439-4000)
PHONE...............................952 835-9880
FAX: 952 892-2670
Donald Brandt MD, *President*
R W Christensen MD, *Med Doctor*
Patricia Dousette, *Manager*
John Husmoe, *Director*
EMP: 110 EST: 1969
SALES (est): 10MM-24.9MM **Privately Held**
WEB: www.eppanet.com
SIC: **8011 8721** Clinic operated by physicians; accounting, auditing & bookkeeping services

(G-4347)
EMILY PROGRAM
1660 Highway 100 S # 141   (55416-1550)
PHONE...............................952 746-5774
FAX: 952 746-5762
Dirk Miller, *Director*
EMP: 50
SALES (est): 1MM-4.9MM **Privately Held**
WEB: www.emilyprogram.com
SIC: **8093** Specialty outpatient clinic

(G-4348)
EMMETT J MCMAHON
800 Lasalle Ave Ste 2800   (55402-2039)
PHONE...............................612 349-8728
Emmett J McMahon, *Principal*
EMP: 50 EST: 1993
SALES (est): 5MM-9.9MM **Privately Held**
SIC: **8111** Legal services

(G-4349)
EMPIRE DOOR & GLASS CO
3415 E 27th St   (55406-1731)
PHONE...............................612 729-4003
FAX: 612 729-4216
Deena Igou, *President*
Tom Igou, *Vice Pres*
Bruce Hegland, *Vice Pres*
EMP: 25 EST: 1987
SALES (est): 1MM-4.9MM **Privately Held**
SIC: **1793** Glass & glazing contractor; glass store; manufactures wooden louver doors; manufactures wooden doors

(G-4350)
EMPLOYER SOLUTIONS GROUP
7301 Ohms Ln Ste 405   (55439-2347)
PHONE...............................952 835-1288
Darryl Peterson, *Partner*
Tom Cherry, *Manager*
Craig Peterson, *Administrator*
EMP: 53 EST: 2005 **Privately Held**
WEB: www.employersolutionsgroup.com
SIC: **7361** Employment agency services

(G-4351)
EMPLOYERS ASSOCIATION INC
9805 45th Ave N   (55442-2568)
PHONE...............................763 253-9100
Tom Ebert, *President*
Meg Steinke, *Human Res Mgr*
Cory Peterson, *Manager*
Bill Porter, *Officer*
EMP: 75 EST: 1936 **Privately Held**
WEB: www.employersinc.com
SIC: **8611** Business association

(G-4352)
EMPO CORP
3100 W Lake St Ste 100   (55416-4596)
PHONE...............................612 285-8707
Alan Reid, *President*
Bob Ringstad, *General Mgr*
Christopher Kelly, *Vice Pres*
Jennifer Robarge, *Asst Controller*
EMP: 31 EST: 1999
SALES (est): 500-999K **Privately Held**
WEB: www.empocorp.com
SIC: **7363 8742** Employee leasing service; human resource consulting services

(G-4353)
ENCLIPSE CORP   (PA)
331 2nd Ave S Ste 703   (55401-2394)
PHONE...............................612 384-6940
Vineet Sinha, *President*
EMP: 25 EST: 2002
SQ FT: 5,500   **Privately Held**
SIC: **7379** Computer system consulting services

(G-4354)
ENDURA FINANCIAL FEDERAL (PA)
820 Lilac Dr N Ste 200   (55422-4789)
PHONE...............................763 287-4630
D P Young, *President*
Larry Monicatti, *Chairman*
John Ferstl, *Vice Pres*
Jeanne L Walkley, *CFO*
EMP: 48 EST: 1929
SALES (corp-wide): 19.94M **Privately Held**
SIC: **6062** State chartered credit union

(G-4355)
ENERGY CONSERVATION INC
1601 67th Ave N   (55430-1743)
PHONE...............................763 569-0069
FAX: 763 569-0095
Paul Sawatzke, *President*
Donald Gaughan, *Vice Pres*
EMP: 30 EST: 1992
SALES (est): 1MM-4.9MM **Privately Held**
SIC: **1799** Pipe & boiler insulating contractor

(G-4356)
ENERGY CONSTRUCTION ✪
7077 Northland Cir N   (55428-1566)
PHONE...............................763 489-7777
Mike Breeze, *Partner*
Keegan Wallace, *Partner*
Cameron Lanyk, *Accountant*
EMP: 30 EST: 2009
SALES (est): 5MM-9.9MM **Privately Held**
SIC: **1521** Single-family housing construction

(G-4357)
ENERGY MANAGEMENT STEAM
3001 Fairmont Ave SE   (55414-2830)
PHONE...............................612 626-7329
EMP: 25 EST: 2003
SALES (est): 10MM-24.9MM **Privately Held**
SIC: **4939 8741** Combination utilities services; management services

(G-4358)
ENGLUND GRAPHICS INC
9100 49th Ave N   (55428-4009)
PO Box 41515   (55441-0515)
PHONE...............................763 536-9100
FAX: 763 536-9950
Edward S Englund, *President*
Robert Stech, *Controller*
Julie Englund, *Personnel*
Mike Nessler, *Manager*
Chris Nelson, *Executive*
▲ EMP: 35 EST: 1972
SQ FT: 18,000
SALES (est): 1MM-4.9MM **Privately Held**
WEB: www.englundgraphics.com
SIC: **7334** Prints lithographed business forms; book binding service; photocopying & duplicating services; typesetting service

(G-4359)
ENTEGEE INC
5620 International Pkwy   (55428-3047)
PHONE...............................763 383-4343
Trista Rehnke, *Human Res Mgr*
Tom Henctges, *Branch Mgr*
Deanna Lenneman, *Executive Asst*
EMP: 40
SALES (est): 500-999K **Publicly Held**
WEB: www.entegee.com

SIC: **7363** Temporary help service
DH: Entegee Inc
128 Corporate Ctr
Burlington MA 01803
781 221-5800

(G-4360)
ENVENTIS TELECOM INC   (HQ)
2950 Xenium Ln N Ste 138   (55441-2623)
PHONE...............................763 577-3900
FAX: 763 577-3999
John Finke, *President*
David A Christensen, *Corp Secy*
Walt Prahl, *COO*
Damon D Dutz, *Vice Pres*
Tom Oliverius, *CFO*
EMP: 75 EST: 1998
SQ FT: 5,000
SALES (corp-wide): 139.10M **Publicly Held**
WEB: www.enventis.com
SIC: **4813** Proprietary online services networks
PA: HickoryTech Corp
221 E Hickory St
Mankato MN 56001
507 386-3636

(G-4361)
ENVIROBATE INC
3301 E 26th St   (55406-1725)
PHONE...............................612 729-1080
FAX: 612 729-1021
Jerry Larson, *CEO*
Rob King, *President*
Carolyn Larson, *Vice Pres*
Scott Larson, *Vice Pres*
Jody Harrison, *Controller*
EMP: 120 EST: 1991
SALES (est): 10MM-24.9MM **Privately Held**
WEB: www.envirobate.com
SIC: **1799** Asbestos removal & encapsulation contractor

(G-4362)
ENVIROMATIC CORP OF AMERICA
Also Called: Blower Balancing & Repair
5936 Pillsbury Ave S   (55419-2327)
PHONE...............................612 861-3330
FAX: 612 861-5578
Donald Pfleiderer, *President*
Larry Pfleiderer, *Chairman*
Mike Gronlund, *Opers Mgr*
Dave Pfleiderer, *Maint Mgr*
Wayne Webb, *Controller*
EMP: 66 EST: 1971
SQ FT: 8,000
SALES (est): 1MM-4.9MM **Privately Held**
WEB: www.enviromatic.com
SIC: **7349 7699** Exhaust hood or fan cleaning service; restaurant equipment repair service

(G-4363)
ENVIRON ELECTRONIC LABS (PA)
9725 Girard Ave S   (55431-2621)
PHONE...............................952 888-7795
Hayes M Mc Callum, *Ch of Bd*
Marcia M Callum, *Manager*
EMP: 34 EST: 1961
SQ FT: 42,000   **Privately Held**
WEB: www.environlab.com
SIC: **8734** Product safety or performance testing laboratory

(G-4364)
EPICOR SOFTWARE CORP
600 Highway 169 S   (55426-1205)
PHONE...............................952 417-1400
Doug Farmer, *Senior VP*
Megan Orstad, *Manager*
Rick Borg, *Manager*
Louise Keppel, *Manager*
Joanne Peter, *Manager*
EMP: 125
SALES (est): 25MM-49.9MM **Publicly Held**
WEB: www.epicor.com
SIC: **7372** Software publisher
PA: Epicor Software Corp
18200 Von Karman Ave
Irvine CA 92612
949 585-4000

(G-4365)
EPREDIX HOLDINGS INC   (HQ)
225 S 6th St Ste 400   (55402-4651)
PHONE...............................612 843-1059
Katrina Dewar, *CEO*
Michael Butler, *COO*
Tony Anello, *Vice Pres*
Nigel Dalton, *Vice Pres*
Shawn Lyndon, *Vice Pres*
▲ EMP: 55 EST: 2000
SQ FT: 26,257   **Privately Held**
WEB: www.previsor.com
SIC: **7375 8742** On-line database information retrieval service; management consulting services
PA: Georgia Previsor Inc
1805 Old Alabama Rd # 150
Roswell GA 30076
770 650-8080

(G-4366)
EQUITY TRANSWESTERN LLC
730 2nd Ave S Ste 400   (55402-2446)
PHONE...............................612 343-4200
Steve Kellogg, *President*
Charles Howard, *Principal*
Michael J Salmen, *Principal*
John Thompson, *Principal*
Douglas Lind, *CFO*
▲ EMP: 35 EST: 1996
SQ FT: 15,000
SALES (est): 5MM-9.9MM **Privately Held**
WEB: www.bakercenter.com
SIC: **6531** Real estate services; commercial real estate agency

(G-4367)
ERNST & YOUNG LLP
220 S 6th St Ste 1400   (55402-4508)
PHONE...............................612 343-1000
FAX: 612 339-1726
Jackie Moser, *Marketing Staff*
Jo Dancik, *Branch Mgr*
Brent Kottinger, *Manager*
Tami R Koosmann, *Manager*
Paul Happe, *Manager*
EMP: 500
SALES (est): 50MM-99.9MM **Privately Held**
WEB: www.ey.com
SIC: **8721 8742** Certified public accountant services; auditing services; business management consultant; management information systems consultant
PA: Ernst & Young LLP
5 Times Sq Fl CONLV1
New York NY 10036
212 773-3000

(G-4368)
EROL T UKE MD
3900 Park Nicollet Blvd   (55416-2503)
PHONE...............................952 993-3190
EMP: 25
SALES (est): 1MM-4.9MM **Privately Held**
SIC: **8011** Physicians' office

(G-4369)
ERS DIGITAL INC   (HQ)
3005 Ranchview Ln N   (55447-1463)
PHONE...............................763 694-5900
Layton Zellman, *President*
Gary Marquardt, *Vice Pres*
Troy Stelton, *Purchasing*
Chris Powers, *Finance Dir*
Jason Hughs, *Manager*
EMP: 75 EST: 1980
SQ FT: 35,000
SALES (corp-wide): 501.54M **Publicly Held**
WEB: www.ersdigital.com
SIC: **5199 7334** Wholesales architect's supplies; blueprinting services; commercial gravure printing
PA: American Reprographics Co
1981 N Broadway Ste 385
Walnut Creek CA 94596
925 949-5100

(G-4370)
ERSTAT & RIEMER
8009 34th Ave S Ste 200   (55425-1634)
PHONE...............................952 854-7638
George Hottinger, *Partner*
Leon Erstad, *Partner*
Richard Riemer, *Partner*

(PA)=Parent Co (HQ)=Headquarters (DH)=Div Headquarters
✪ = New business established in last 2 years

2011 Harris Minnesota
Services Directory

© Harris InfoSource 1-866-281-6415

195

Patrick Riley, *Partner*
Thomas Shaefer, *Partner*
EMP: 29 **EST:** 1991
SALES (est): 1MM-4.9MM **Privately Held**
WEB: www.erstad.com
SIC: 8111 Labor & employment law office

(G-4371)
ESI HOLDING CORP (PA)
8009 34th Ave S Ste 1492 (55425-1794)
PHONE..............................952 853-0924
FAX: 952 853-0295
John West, *Principal*
EMP: 80 **EST:** 2004
SQ FT: 46,000 **Privately Held**
SIC: 6719 Personal holding company
PA: CHAM FOOD PRODUCTS LTD
Meron
Merom Hagalil Israel

(G-4372)
ESSILOR LABORATORIES OF AMER
Also Called: Twin City Optical
5205 Highway 169 N Ste 5 (55442-3900)
PHONE..............................763 551-2000
Mike Browning, *Vice Pres*
Joe Ciochetto, *Vice Pres*
Robert Degregorio, *VP Opers*
Steve Cary, *Engineering*
Mark Tulkki, *Accountant*
EMP: 294
SALES (est): 25MM-49.9MM **Privately Held**
WEB: www.essilor.com
SIC: 5048 Manufactures eyeglasses;
wholesales optometric equipment &
supplies
HQ: Essilor Laboratories of Amer
13515 N Stemmons Fwy
Dallas TX 75234
972 241-4141

(G-4373)
ESTATE JEWELRY & COIN INC
9955 Lyndale Ave S (55420-4779)
PHONE..............................952 881-8862
Daniel Wixon, *President*
Brian Ortale, *Accountant*
David Brenke, *Manager*
EMP: 40 **EST:** 1976
SQ FT: 10,000
SALES (est): 5MM-9.9MM **Privately Held**
SIC: 5094 7631 Retails precious stones &
precious metals jewelry; wholesales
precious metals; wholesales diamond gems;
watch repair service

(G-4374)
EVANGELICAL COVENANT CHURCH
Also Called: Bethany Covenant Home
2309 Hayes St NE (55418-3934)
PHONE..............................612 781-2691
FAX: 612 781-8835
Joel Nyquist, *Sales Staff*
Paula Sparling, *Administrator*
EMP: 80
SALES (est): 1MM-4.9MM **Privately Held**
SIC: 8361 8051 Rest home with health care
incidental; skilled nursing care facility
PA: Evangelical Covenant Church
5101 N Francisco Ave
Chicago IL 60625
773 784-3000

(G-4375)
EVANGELICAL COVENANT CHURCH
Also Called: Covenant Rtrment Cmmnties Minn
5800 Saint Croix Ave N (55422-4446)
PHONE..............................763 546-6125
FAX: 763 546-8529
Jeanne Rothanburg, *Accounting Staf*
Corrine Moore, *Human Resources*
Janet Carlyle, *Marketing Staff*
Paula Sparling, *Administrator*
Gary Gardeen, *Administrator*
EMP: 30
SALES (est): 1MM-4.9MM **Privately Held**

SIC: 8361 Rest home with health care
incidental
PA: Evangelical Covenant Church
5101 N Francisco Ave
Chicago IL 60625
773 784-3000

(G-4376)
EVANGELICAL LUTHERAN CHURCH IN
Also Called: Elca Board of Pension
800 Marquette Ave Ste 1050 (55402-2860)
PHONE..............................612 752-4080
FAX: 612 334-5207
John Kapanki, *President*
Susan Rehwaldt, *Corp Secy*
Kenneth G Mertz, *Trustee*
Yvonne Wells, *Trustee*
Tonya Hedemark, *Vice Pres*
EMP: 200
SALES (est): 10MM-24.9MM **Privately Held**
WEB: www.lordofmercy.org
SIC: 7389 8111 Financial service; legal
services
PA: Evangelical Lutheran Church In
8765 W Higgins Rd
Chicago IL 60631
773 380-2700

(G-4377)
EVANGELICAL LUTHERAN GOOD
Also Called: Good Smrtan
Society-Ambassador
8100 Medicine Lake Rd (55427-3404)
PHONE..............................763 544-4171
FAX: 763 544-5526
Dwayne Milless, *Maint Spvr*
Jennifer Lahti, *Human Resources*
Tina Hellman, *Manager*
Pat Warner, *Manager*
Debi Mamer, *Manager*
EMP: 140
SALES (est): 5MM-9.9MM **Privately Held**
WEB: www.good-sam.com
SIC: 8051 Skilled nursing care facility
PA: Evangelical Lutheran Good
4800 W 57th St
Sioux Falls SD 57108
605 362-3100

(G-4378)
EVANGELICAL LUTHERAN GOOD
Also Called: Good Samtin Scty Univ Spec Ctr
22 27th Ave SE (55414-3102)
PHONE..............................612 332-4262
FAX: 612 673-6270
Charles Huynik, *Administrator*
Pam Haase, *Director*
Lee A Becker, *Food Svc Dir*
EMP: 450
SALES (est): 10MM-24.9MM **Privately Held**
WEB: www.good-sam.com
SIC: 8059 Nursing home
PA: Evangelical Lutheran Good
4800 W 57th St
Sioux Falls SD 57108
605 362-3100

(G-4379)
EVERGREEN AVIATION INC
7550 22nd Ave S (55450-1011)
PHONE..............................612 727-1655
FAX: 612 727-1644
El Smith, *President*
Lois Meger, *Administrator*
EMP: 54 **EST:** 2003
SALES (est): 5MM-9.9MM **Privately Held**
SIC: 8711 Aviation or aeronautical
engineers

(G-4380)
EWING'S ASSOC
10700 Highway 55 Ste 220 (55441-6100)
PHONE..............................763 258-2733
FAX: 763 257-2738
Mathew Ewings, *President*
EMP: 43 **EST:** 2004
SALES (est): 5MM-9.9MM **Privately Held**
WEB: www.ewingsassociates.com
SIC: 8748 Employee programs
administration consultant

(G-4381)
EXACT SOFTWARE ERP-NA INC (HQ)
7701 York Ave S Ste 350 (55435-5832)
PHONE..............................952 831-7182
James Kempt, *Exec VP*
Dan Brewer, *Engineer*
Mitchell Alcon, *CFO*
Steve Kuehne, *VP Sales*
Michelle Schindler, *Marketing Staff*
EMP: 75 **EST:** 1982
SQ FT: 11,500
SALES (corp-wide): 345.79M **Privately Held**
WEB: www.exactamerica.com
SIC: 7371 Computer software development
PA: Exact Software North America
35 Village Rd Ste 602
Middleton MA 01949
978 560-6900

(G-4382)
EXCEL PAINTING PLUS INC
5550 Dunkirk Ln N (55446-1416)
PHONE..............................763 557-2821
John O'Donnell, *President*
EMP: 25 **EST:** 1994
SALES (est): 1MM-4.9MM **Privately Held**
SIC: 1721 Painting & wall covering
contractor

(G-4383)
EXTENDICARE HOMES INC
Also Called: Robbinsdale Rhbltion Care Ctr
3130 Grimes Ave N (55422-3217)
PHONE..............................763 588-0771
FAX: 763 588-8252
Pauline Grogan, *Manager*
Jim Framspad, *Manager*
Matt Schiller, *Administrator*
Kathleen Pankratz, *Administrator*
Cherie Camuel, *Administrator*
EMP: 260
SALES (est): 10MM-24.9MM **Privately Held**
WEB: www.extendacare.com
SIC: 8051 8093 Skilled nursing care facility;
outpatient rehabilitation treatment center
DH: Extendicare Homes Inc
111 W Michigan St
Milwaukee WI 53203
414 908-8000

(G-4384)
EXTENDICARE HOMES INC
Also Called: Golden Vly Rhbltation Care Ctr
7505 Country Club Dr (55427-4501)
PHONE..............................763 545-0416
Julie Liebo, *Principal*
Diane Strobmier, *Manager*
George Paulson, *Exec Dir*
Todd Dickson, *Nursing Dir*
EMP: 260
SALES (est): 10MM-24.9MM **Privately Held**
WEB: www.extendacare.com
SIC: 8051 8093 Skilled nursing care facility;
outpatient rehabilitation treatment center
DH: Extendicare Homes Inc
111 W Michigan St
Milwaukee WI 53203
414 908-8000

(G-4385)
EXTENDICARE HOMES INC
Also Called: Park Nursing & Covalescent Ctr
4415 W 36 1/2 St (55416-4854)
PHONE..............................952 927-9717
Jennifer Kuhn, *Administrator*
Vivian Booker, *Director*
EMP: 100
SALES (est): 1MM-4.9MM **Privately Held**
WEB: www.extendacare.com
SIC: 8051 Skilled nursing care facility
DH: Extendicare Homes Inc
111 W Michigan St
Milwaukee WI 53203
414 908-8000

(G-4386)
EXTENDICARE HOMES INC
Also Called: Park Nrsing An Convasclent Ctr
4415 W 36 1/2 St (55416-4854)
PHONE..............................952 927-4949
Vivian Booker, *General Mgr*
EMP: 115

SALES (est): 1MM-4.9MM **Privately Held**
WEB: www.extendacare.com
SIC: 8059 8051 Nursing home; skilled
nursing care facility
DH: Extendicare Homes Inc
111 W Michigan St
Milwaukee WI 53203
414 908-8000

(G-4387)
EXTENDICARE HOMES INC
Also Called: Texas Terrace Care Center
7900 W 28th St (55426-3011)
PHONE..............................952 920-8380
FAX: 952 920-7866
Sheila Embry, *Vice Pres*
Miriam Burns, *Manager*
Mat Bedard, *Administrator*
Margo Vredenburg, *Nursing Dir*
EMP: 150
SALES (est): 5MM-9.9MM **Privately Held**
WEB: www.extendacare.com
SIC: 8051 8093 Skilled nursing care facility;
outpatient rehabilitation treatment center
DH: Extendicare Homes Inc
111 W Michigan St
Milwaukee WI 53203
414 908-8000

(G-4388)
EYE CARE ASSOCIATES
825 Nicollet Mall # 2000 (55402-2708)
PHONE..............................612 338-4861
Neal Sher, *President*
Dinesh Goyal, *Research*
Mike Foley, *Office Mgr*
Trond A Stockenstrom MD, *Med Doctor*
Autumn Arvidson, *Manager*
EMP: 25 **EST:** 1987
SALES (est): 1MM-4.9MM **Privately Held**
SIC: 8011 Ophthalmologist office

(G-4389)
F-M ASPHALT INC
400 W 61st St (55419-2248)
PHONE..............................612 798-0245
Mark Johnson, *Manager*
EMP: 60
SALES (est): 10MM-24.9MM **Privately Held**
SIC: 1442 Manufactures ready-mixed
concrete; gravel mining; manufactures
standard concrete or cinder blocks
HQ: Camas Minndak Inc
Hwy 10 E
Dilworth MN 56529
218 287-2319

(G-4390)
FABYANSKE, WESTRA, HART
800 Lasalle Ave Ste 1900 (55402-2037)
PHONE..............................612 338-0115
FAX: 612 338-3857
Steve Melpher, *President*
Richard Jensen, *Corp Secy*
Jerry Kearney, *Vice Pres*
Steve Melcher, *Vice Pres*
Dennis Trooien, *Vice Pres*
EMP: 65 **EST:** 1981
SALES (est): 5MM-9.9MM **Privately Held**
WEB: www.fwhlaw.com
SIC: 8111 General practice law office

(G-4391)
FAF ADVISORS INC
800 Nicollet Mall (55402-7000)
PHONE..............................612 303-3381
Thomas Sthreier, *President*
Charles Stone, *Vice Pres*
Joseph M Ulrey, *CFO*
Joe Holinka, *Portfolio Mgr*
Jay Rosenberg, *Portfolio Mgr*
EST: 1999 **Publicly Held**
WEB: www.fafadvisors.com
SIC: 6732 Grantmaking foundation
PA: U S Bancorp
800 Nicollet Mall Ste 800
Minneapolis MN 55402
651 466-3000

(G-4392)
FAIR ISAAC CORP (PA)
901 Marquette Ave Ste 3200 (55402-3232)
PHONE..............................612 758-5200
FAX: 612 758-5202
Mark N Greene, *CEO*

---

www.HarrisInfo.com
196
2011 Harris Minnesota
Services Directory
▲=Import ▼=Export
◆=Import/Export

Robert M Berini, *Partner*
Daniel Dib, *Managing Dir*
Leonard Parkins, *Corp Secy*
Mark Shuster, *Sr Corp Ofcr*
▲ **EMP:** 322 **EST:** 1956
SQ FT: 243,000
SALES (corp-wide): 630.73M **Publicly Held**
WEB: www.fairisaac.com
SIC: 7372 7389 8748 Business & professional software publishers; business consulting services; financial service

(G-4393)
FAIRVIEW HEALTH SERVICES
2020 Minnehaha Ave (55404-3104)
PHONE 612 672-6800
FAX: 612 672-6083
Mike Youso, *Vice Pres*
John Marquardt, *Opers Mgr*
Eileen Eifert, *Opers Staff*
Mike Elton, *Opers Staff*
Jo Milosevic, *Opers Staff*
EMP: 150
SALES (est): 10MM-24.9MM **Privately Held**
WEB: www.fairview.org
SIC: 8741 7374 8062 Hospital management services; data processing & preparation services; medical hospital
PA: Fairview Health Services
2450 Riverside Ave
Minneapolis MN 55454
612 672-6300

(G-4394)
FAIRVIEW HEALTH SERVICES
701 25th Ave S Ste 402 (55454-1443)
PHONE 612 672-2900
FAX: 612 672-2909
Stacia Birkland, *Office Mgr*
Gerald J Cunniff MD, *Med Doctor*
Justin C Hura MD, *Med Doctor*
Leaha Drury, *Manager*
Jill Yungerberg, *Obstetrician*
EMP: 30
SALES (est): 1MM-4.9MM **Privately Held**
WEB: www.fairview.org
SIC: 8011 Gynecologist office
PA: Fairview Health Services
2450 Riverside Ave
Minneapolis MN 55454
612 672-6300

(G-4395)
FAIRVIEW HEALTH SERVICES
3809 42nd Ave S (55406-3503)
PHONE 612 721-5044
FAX: 612 721-1691
Mary L Oglesbee, *Office Mgr*
Regina K Vogt MD, *Med Doctor*
Anne F Lippin MD, *Med Doctor*
Jeffrey Arenson, *Manager*
Kay R Vogt, *Manager*
EMP: 50
SALES (est): 1MM-4.9MM **Privately Held**
WEB: www.fairview.org
SIC: 8093 Family planning clinic
PA: Fairview Health Services
2450 Riverside Ave
Minneapolis MN 55454
612 672-6300

(G-4396)
FAIRVIEW HEALTH SERVICES (PA)
2450 Riverside Ave (55454-1450)
PHONE 612 672-6300
FAX: 612 273-4098
Mark A Eustis, *CEO*
Eric Houle, *President*
Charles W Mooty, *Vice Chairman*
Gladys Christian, *Business Mgr*
Joanell Dyrstad, *Corp Secy*
EMP: 600 **EST:** 1905
SQ FT: 388,000
SALES (corp-wide): 2.74B **Privately Held**
WEB: www.fairview.org
SIC: 8062 Medical hospital

(G-4397)
FAIRVIEW HEALTH SERVICES
6545 France Ave S Ste 150 (55435-2180)
PHONE 952 848-5600
Laurie Azine, *Med Doctor*
Stephanie Patel MD, *Med Doctor*
Karen M Weiler MD, *Med Doctor*

Lina K Swenson MD, *Med Doctor*
Jeanne M Finney, *Manager*
EMP: 40
SALES (est): 1MM-4.9MM **Privately Held**
WEB: www.fairview.org
SIC: 8011 8062 Primary care medical clinic; medical hospital
PA: Fairview Health Services
2450 Riverside Ave
Minneapolis MN 55454
612 672-6300

(G-4398)
FAIRVIEW HEALTH SERVICES
Also Called: Blood Marrow Transplant Clinic
516 Delaware St SE Ste 5B (55455-0356)
PHONE 612 626-2663
FAX: 612 625-0925
Stephanie Lang, *Office Mgr*
Susan Packard-Zutz, *Manager*
Philip B McGlave, *Surgeon*
Margaret L Macmillan, *Hematology*
Linda J Burns, *Hematology*
EMP: 25
SALES (est): 1MM-4.9MM **Privately Held**
WEB: www.fairview.org
SIC: 8741 Hospital management services
PA: Fairview Health Services
2450 Riverside Ave
Minneapolis MN 55454
612 672-6300

(G-4399)
FAIRVIEW HEALTH SERVICES
Also Called: Information Management Svcs
323 Stinson Blvd (55413-2611)
PHONE 612 672-5500
Christine Hill, *District Mgr*
John Benton, *Network Analyst*
Mike Voytovich, *Director*
EMP: 300
SALES (est): 25MM-49.9MM **Privately Held**
WEB: www.fairview.org
SIC: 8741 Hospital management services
PA: Fairview Health Services
2450 Riverside Ave
Minneapolis MN 55454
612 672-6300

(G-4400)
FAIRVIEW HEALTH SERVICES
Also Called: Children's Hospital
500 Harvard St SE (55455-0363)
PHONE 612 273-3000
Marl Hansberry, *VP Mktg*
Mary Dewitt, *Office Mgr*
Marilyn Madsen, *Office Mgr*
David Page, *Branch Mgr*
Kevin Morrison, *Officer*
EMP: 290
SALES (est): 25MM-49.9MM **Privately Held**
WEB: www.fairview.org
SIC: 8741 Hospital management services; nursing & personal care facility management services
PA: Fairview Health Services
2450 Riverside Ave
Minneapolis MN 55454
612 672-6300

(G-4401)
FAIRVIEW HOMECARE & HOSPICE (PA)
2450 26th Ave S (55406-1245)
PHONE 612 721-2491
FAX: 612 728-2400
Carrie Treptow, *Human Res Mgr*
Kate Cummings, *Administrator*
Kathy Lucas, *Exec Dir*
EMP: 500 **EST:** 1982
SQ FT: 13,000 **Privately Held**
SIC: 8082 Home health care services

(G-4402)
FAIRVIEW OXBORO CLINICS INC
600 W 98th St Ste 220 (55420-4710)
PHONE 952 885-6100
FAX: 952 885-6046
Clifford M Phibbs MD, *Ch of Bd*
Robert Olson MD, *Corp Secy*
James M Fox, *Treasurer*
William Schwen, *Branch Mgr*
Brian A Berd, *Manager*
EMP: 270 **EST:** 1952
SQ FT: 26,000
SALES (est): 25MM-49.9MM **Privately Held**

SIC: 8011 Internal medicine practitioners

(G-4403)
FAIRVIEW PHARMACY SERVICES LLC
711 Kasota Ave SE (55414-2842)
PHONE 612 672-5260
FAX: 612 672-5201
Robert Beacher, *President*
Daniel K Anderson, *Member*
David Fasching, *Member*
Michelle Reckinger, *VP Sls/Mktg*
Vickie Stevens, *Human Res Dir*
EMP: 420 **EST:** 2005
SALES (est): 100MM-499.9MM **Privately Held**
WEB: www.fairview.org
SIC: 5122 Wholesales pharmaceuticals, drug proprietaries & sundries
PA: Fairview Health Services
2450 Riverside Ave
Minneapolis MN 55454
612 672-6300

(G-4404)
FAITHFUL & GOULD INC
900 2nd Ave S Ste 500 (55402-3323)
PHONE 612 338-3120
FAX: 612 338-3647
Jonathan Marshall, *Principal*
Jennifer Main, *Human Res Mgr*
Jennifer Neuernberg, *Marketing Staff*
EMP: 27
SALES (est): 1MM-4.9MM **Privately Held**
SIC: 8742 Quality assurance consultant
PA: Faithful+gould Inc
11 E 26th St Fl 18
New York NY 10010
212 252-7070

(G-4405)
FALLON GROUP INC (PA)
901 Marquette Ave # 2400 (55402-3272)
PHONE 612 758-2345
FAX: 612 758-2977
Patrick R Fallon, *CEO*
Robert Senior, *CEO*
Kevin Berigan, *Managing Prtnr*
Roberta D Pace, *Managing Prtnr*
Fred Senn, *Partner*
EMP: 150 **EST:** 1981
SQ FT: 52,000 **Privately Held**
WEB: www.publicis.fr
SIC: 7311 Advertising agency
PA: PUBLICIS GROUPE SA
133 AVENUE DES CHAMPS ELYSEES
PARIS France

(G-4406)
FAMILY & CHILDREN'S SERVICE
4123 E Lake St (55406-2255)
PHONE 612 729-0340
FAX: 612 729-2616
Molly Greenman, *President*
John Till, *Vice Pres*
EMP: 35
SALES (est): 1MM-4.9MM **Privately Held**
WEB: www.fcsmn.org
SIC: 8322 Individual & family social services
PA: Family Partnership
414 S 8th St
Minneapolis MN 55404
612 339-9101

(G-4407)
FAMILY CHILD DEVELOPMENT CTR
100 Nathan Ln N (55441-6308)
PHONE 763 545-7271
FAX: 763 545-3005
Deb Loon, *Exec Dir*
EMP: 26 **EST:** 1990
SALES (est): 1MM-4.9MM **Privately Held**
WEB: www.fcdc.org
SIC: 8322 8351 Child & youth services; child day care service

(G-4408)
FAMILY FOCUS INC
2800 University Ave SE Ste 204 (55414-4205)
PHONE 612 331-4429
FAX: 612 331-3520

Louise Witherspoon, *General Mgr*
Jennifer Olson, *General Mgr*
Amy Larson, *Corp Counsel*
Joseph Waller, *Corp Counsel*
Susan Sloan, *Manager*
EMP: 33 **EST:** 2000
SALES (est): 1MM-4.9MM **Privately Held**
SIC: 8361 Group foster home

(G-4409)
FAMILY HOME HEALTH CARE INC
2525 E Franklin Ave # 300 (55406-1198)
PHONE 612 340-0733
Mohamed Mustafa, *President*
EMP: 120 **EST:** 2000
SALES (est): 1MM-4.9MM **Privately Held**
SIC: 8059 Domiciliary care facility

(G-4410)
FAMILY MEANS
1875 NW Ave S (55401)
PHONE 763 780-4986
Arva D Beck, *President*
EMP: 42 **EST:** 2002
SALES (est): 1MM-4.9MM **Privately Held**
SIC: 8322 8111 Family counseling services; bankruptcy referee

(G-4411)
FAMILY PARTNERSHIP (PA)
414 S 8th St (55404-1025)
PHONE 612 339-9101
FAX: 612 339-9150
Molly Greenman, *President*
Dan Campion, *Vice Pres*
Shane Miller, *Opers Mgr*
Stan Birnbaum, *CFO*
Marit Gladem, *Human Res Mgr*
EMP: 45 **EST:** 1878
SQ FT: 16,000
SALES (corp-wide): 5.47M **Privately Held**
WEB: www.fcsmn.org
SIC: 8322 Individual & family social services

(G-4412)
FAMILY PARTNERSHIP
1101 E 78th St Ste 318 (55420-1402)
PHONE 952 884-7353
Scott Hippert, *Vice Pres*
Shane Miller, *Opers Staff*
Hansen Calah, *Manager*
EMP: 45
SALES (est): 1MM-4.9MM **Privately Held**
WEB: www.fcsmn.org
SIC: 8322 Individual & family social services
PA: Family Partnership
414 S 8th St
Minneapolis MN 55404
612 339-9101

(G-4413)
FAMILY VIOLENCE NETWORK (PA)
3111 1st Ave S (55408-3136)
PHONE 651 770-8544
FAX: 651 770-5506
Beverly Dusso, *President*
Christine Brinkman, *Vice Pres*
Jaclynn L West, *Manager*
EMP: 55 **EST:** 1976
SQ FT: 58,000 **Privately Held**
SIC: 8322 Emergency & relief services

(G-4414)
FAMILY VIOLENCE NETWORK
3111 1st Ave S (55408-3136)
PHONE 612 825-3333
Beverly Dusso, *Branch Mgr*
EMP: 100
SALES (est): 5MM-9.9MM **Privately Held**
SIC: 8322 Emergency & relief services
PA: Family Violence Network
3111 1st Ave S
Minneapolis MN 55408
651 770-8544

(G-4415)
FANTASIA LLC
275 Market St Ste 102 (55405-1622)
PHONE 612 338-5811
FAX: 612 338-7866
Andrea Harrisjohnston, *Member*
Ann Benjamin, *Comptroller*

(PA)=Parent Co (HQ)=Headquarters (DH)=Div Headquarters
✿ = New business established in last 2 years

2011 Harris Minnesota
Services Directory

© Harris InfoSource 1-866-281-6415
197

GEOGRAPHIC

Barb Farrell, *Manager*
EST: 2000
SQ FT: 4,000 **Privately Held**
WEB: www.fantasiashowrooms.com
SIC: 5074 Wholesales plumbing fittings & supplies

(G-4416)
FAST CAB SERVICES LLC
2709 Stevens Ave Apt 3 (55408-1786)
PHONE..............................952 393-8542
James C Prenosil, *Member*
EMP: 75
SALES (est): 1MM-4.9MM **Privately Held**
SIC: 4121 Taxi cab service

(G-4417)
FBS ASSOCIATED PROPERTIES INC
800 Nicollet Mall (55402-7000)
PHONE..............................612 333-2086
Jerry Grundhofer, *President*
EST: 1984
SQ FT: 1,500 **Publicly Held**
WEB: www.usbank.com
SIC: 6531 6552 Real estate services; land subdivision & development services
PA: U S Bancorp
  800 Nicollet Mall Ste 800
  Minneapolis MN 55402
  651 466-3000

(G-4418)
FEDERAL EXPRESS CORP
Also Called: Fedex
9219 Grand Ave S (55420-3603)
PHONE..............................952 884-9212
FAX: 952 881-7580
Mike Dvonak, *Branch Mgr*
Maggie McDonough, *Manager*
Lisa Rudebuck, *Technical Staff*
EMP: 100
SALES (est): 5MM-9.9MM **Publicly Held**
WEB: www.federalexpress.com
SIC: 4513 Provides private air letter delivery services; provides private air package delivery services; provides private air parcel delivery services
HQ: Federal Express Corp
  3610 Hacks Cross Rd
  Memphis TN 38125
  901 369-3600

(G-4419)
FEDERAL EXPRESS CORP
7401 24th Ave S (55450-1039)
PHONE..............................612 794-3100
Tom Rheinick, *Manager*
EMP: 340
SALES (est): 25MM-49.9MM **Publicly Held**
WEB: www.federalexpress.com
SIC: 7389 Packaging & labeling services
HQ: Federal Express Corp
  3610 Hacks Cross Rd
  Memphis TN 38125
  901 369-3600

(G-4420)
FEDERAL EXPRESS CORP
2825 Cargo Rd (55450-1135)
PHONE..............................612 713-8500
Brenda Savage, *Manager*
EMP: 300
SALES (est): 25MM-49.9MM **Publicly Held**
WEB: www.federalexpress.com
SIC: 4522 Nonscheduled air transportation services
HQ: Federal Express Corp
  3610 Hacks Cross Rd
  Memphis TN 38125
  901 369-3600

(G-4421)
FEDERAL RESERVE BANK OF (HQ)
90 Hennepin Ave (55401-1804)
PO Box 291 (55480-0291)
PHONE..............................612 204-5000
FAX: 612 204-5430
David A Koch, *Ch of Bd*
Gary Stern, *President*
Mary K Brainerd, *Vice Chairman*
Luanne Carlson, *Corp Secy*
James M Lyon, *COO*
EMP: 1074 **EST:** 1913 **Privately Held**

WEB: www.mpls.frb.org
SIC: 6035 Federally chartered savings institution
PA: Board of Governors of The
  20th St Cnsttution Ave NW
  Washington DC 20551
  202 452-3000

(G-4422)
FEDERATED MUTUAL INSURANCE CO
7700 France Ave S (55435-5847)
PO Box 390850 (55439-0850)
PHONE..............................952 831-4300
FAX: 952 820-2387
Mike Hatanpa, *Manager*
Lonnie Hindberg, *Supervisor*
EMP: 100
SALES (est): 50MM-99.9MM **Privately Held**
WEB: www.federatedinsurance.com
SIC: 6311 6321 6331 6411 Life insurance carrier; direct accident & health insurance carrier; insurance services; property & casualty insurance carrier
PA: Federated Mutual Insurance Co
  121 E Park Sq
  Owatonna MN 55060
  507 455-5200

(G-4423)
FEDEX OFFICE & PRINT SERVICES
1430 W Lake St (55408-2645)
PHONE..............................612 822-7700
Shalla Wilson, *Sales Mgr*
Johnny Hirschfield, *Branch Mgr*
Dean Schelgel, *Manager*
Rhonda Iverson, *Manager*
EMP: 32
SALES (est): 1MM-4.9MM **Publicly Held**
WEB: www.kinkos.com
SIC: 7334 Photocopying & duplicating services; book binding service; typesetting service
HQ: Fedex Office & Print Services
  13155 Noel Rd Ste 1600
  Dallas TX 75240
  214 550-7000

(G-4424)
FELHABER LARSON FENLON & VOGT (PA)
220 S 6th St Ste 2200 (55402-4504)
PHONE..............................612 339-6321
Thomas J Doyle, *Ch of Bd*
Christopher S Hayhoe, *President*
Steve Pierson, *Comms Dir*
Karen Byck, *Marketing Staff*
Terri Stewart, *Office Mgr*
EMP: 80 **EST:** 1943
SQ FT: 25,754 **Privately Held**
SIC: 8111 General practice attorney's or lawyer's office; general practice law office

(G-4425)
FELTL & CO
600 Highway 169 S Ste 1960 (55426-1223)
PHONE..............................952 546-5018
Maryjo Feltl, *President*
EMP: 30 **EST:** 1975
SALES (est): 5MM-9.9MM **Privately Held**
SIC: 6211 Securities broker & dealer

(G-4426)
FIBERCARE INC
7701 Pillsbury Ave S (55423-4121)
PHONE..............................612 721-5048
Bruce Kienke, *President*
Terri Erker, *Vice Pres*
Tosha Herr, *Accountant*
Ashton L Kienke, *Director*
Bruce W Klenke, *Director*
EMP: 40 **EST:** 1983
SQ FT: 21,000
SALES (est): 1MM-4.9MM **Privately Held**
WEB: www.fibercare.com
SIC: 7217 1711 Carpet & furniture cleaning service on location; upholstery cleaning services; heating systems repair & maintenance service

(G-4427)
FIDELITY BANK
7600 Parklawn Ave Ste 150 (55435-5100)
PO Box 1575 (55480-1575)
PHONE..............................952 831-6600
James W Morton, *Ch of Bd*
Robert Reznick, *Ch of Bd*
Charles Mueller, *President*
EMP: 45 **EST:** 1970
SQ FT: 25,000
SALES (est): 10MM-24.9MM **Privately Held**
WEB: www.fidelitybankmn.com
SIC: 6022 State commercial bank
PA: Fidelity Bank
  7600 Parklawn Ave Ste 150
  Minneapolis MN 55435
  952 831-6600

(G-4428)
FIDELITY BANK (PA)
7600 Parklawn Ave Ste 150 (55435-5100)
PO Box 1575 (55480-1575)
PHONE..............................952 831-6600
Keth Bednarowski, *Ch of Bd*
James W Morton, *President*
Chuck Mueller, *Exec VP*
Marie Marlier, *Vice Pres*
Jo D Kiecker, *Assoc VP*
EMP: 57 **EST:** 1985
SQ FT: 10,000
SALES (corp-wide): 19.63M **Privately Held**
WEB: www.fidelitybankmn.com
SIC: 6029 Commercial bank

(G-4429)
FIDELITY INVESTMENTS ACTUARIAL
7740 France Ave S (55435-5228)
PHONE..............................952 831-8595
Shane Davis, *Manager*
EMP: 50
SALES (est): 5MM-9.9MM **Privately Held**
WEB: www.fidelity.com
SIC: 8999 Actuarial consulting services
PA: Fmr LLC
  82 Devonshire St
  Boston MA 02109
  617 563-7000

(G-4430)
FIELDWORK MINNEAPOLIS INC
7650 Edinbrgh Way Ste 700 (55435-5993)
PHONE..............................952 837-8300
FAX: 952 837-8301
Denice Duncan, *President*
EMP: 25 **EST:** 1999
SALES (est): 1MM-4.9MM **Privately Held**
WEB: www.fieldwork.com
SIC: 8732 Market analysis or research services
PA: Fieldwork Inc
  111 E Wacker Dr Ste 220
  Chicago IL 60601
  312 565-1866

(G-4431)
FINANCE & COMMERCE INC
730 2nd Ave S Ste 100 (55402-2418)
PO Box 86 (55486-0086)
PHONE..............................612 333-4244
James P Dolan, *President*
Joann Barquest, *General Mgr*
Pat Boulay, *Vice Pres*
Steve Jahn, *Vice Pres*
Scott Pollei, *Finance*
EMP: 35 **EST:** 1887
SALES (est): 1MM-4.9MM **Publicly Held**
WEB: www.financeandcommerce.com
SIC: 7375 Newsletter publishing; offset & photolithographic printing service; database information retrieval service
PA: Dolan Co
  222 S 9th St Ste 2300
  Minneapolis MN 55402
  612 317-9420

(G-4432)
FINANCIAL RECOVERY SERVICES (PA)
4640 W 77th St Ste 300 (55435-4906)
PO Box 385908 (55438-5908)
PHONE..............................952 831-4800
FAX: 952 835-5877
Brian Bowers, *CEO*

Paul Dockins, *Vice Pres*
Greg Graff, *Vice Pres*
Wade Davis, *CFO*
EMP: 80 **EST:** 1996
SQ FT: 16,000 **Privately Held**
WEB: www.fin-rec.com
SIC: 7322 Collection agency

(G-4433)
FINANCIAL SYSTEMS SUPPORT
1300 S 2nd St Ste 660 (55454-6003)
PHONE..............................612 625-3493
Marsha Aalseath, *Principal*
Linda Woock, *Director*
EMP: 38 **EST:** 1992
SALES (est): 1MM-4.9MM **Privately Held**
SIC: 8744 7389 Facilities support services; financial service

(G-4434)
FINE ASSOCIATES LLC
80 S 8th St Ste 1916 (55402-2111)
PHONE..............................612 332-2561
FAX: 612 334-3348
Bianca Fine, *Member*
EMP: 45 **EST:** 1972
SQ FT: 3,500
SALES (est): 10MM-24.9MM **Privately Held**
WEB: www.marquetteplace.com
SIC: 6552 6513 Land subdivision & development services; apartment building operator

(G-4435)
FINTEGRA FINANCIAL SOLUTIONS
6120 Earle Brown Dr # 550 (55430-4110)
PHONE..............................763 503-1911
Craig Gould, *Member*
Henri Henriksen, *Sales Dir*
Steven Bullert, *Branch Mgr*
EST: 1997 **Privately Held**
SIC: 6211 8742 Securities broker & dealer; management consulting services

(G-4436)
FIREMEN'S RELIEF ASSOCIATION
7800 Golden Valley Rd (55427-4508)
PHONE..............................763 593-8080
Mark Kuhnly, *Chief*
EMP: 50 **Privately Held**
WEB: www.ci.golden-valley.mn.us
SIC: 8641 Civic & social organization

(G-4437)
FIRENET SYSTEMS INC
6224 Lakeland Ave N Ste 100 (55428-2935)
PHONE..............................763 536-3950
FAX: 763 536-3978
Lee Sloneker, *President*
Edward Schabert, *Corp Secy*
Nathan Sloneker, *Manager*
Mitch Howells, *Manager*
EMP: 25 **EST:** 1993
SQ FT: 7,000
SALES (est): 1MM-4.9MM **Privately Held**
WEB: www.firenetsys.com
SIC: 1731 Fire detection & burglar alarm systems specialization contractor

(G-4438)
FIRST AMERICAN NATIONAL CML
801 Nicollet Mall Ste 1900 (55402-2533)
PHONE..............................612 305-2000
Rod Ive, *Vice Pres*
EMP: 33 **EST:** 1994
SALES (est): 5MM-9.9MM **Privately Held**
WEB: www.fatc.com
SIC: 6361 Title insurance carrier
PA: First American Title Insurance
  1 First American Way
  Santa Ana CA 92707
  714 800-3000

(G-4439)
FIRST AMERICAN REAL ESTATE
Also Called: Vendor Management Services
7900 Intl Dr Ste 500 (55425)
PHONE..............................800 868-8816
Connie Carlson, *Manager*
EMP: 99

www.HarrisInfo.com
198
2011 Harris Minnesota
Services Directory
▲=Import ▼=Export
◆=Import/Export

SALES (est): 5MM-9.9MM **Privately Held**
SIC: 8741 Business management services
PA: First American Real Estate
4 First American Way
Santa Ana CA 92707
714 250-6400

(G-4440)
FIRST AMERICAN TITLE INSURANCE

801 Nicollet Mall # 1900 (55402-5707)
PHONE 612 337-5900
FAX: 612 337-5249
Rod Ives, *Manager*
Christopher Pendleton, *Manager*
Jeff Hawkinson, *Director*
EMP: 50
SALES (est): 1MM-4.9MM **Privately Held**
WEB: www.fatc.com
SIC: 6541 Title search company
PA: First American Title Insurance
1 First American Way
Santa Ana CA 92707
714 800-3000

(G-4441)
1ST AVENUE ENTERTAINMENT GROUP

650 Hennepin Ave (55403-1807)
PHONE 612 337-6700
FAX: 612 338-6777
Joseph A Woods, *President*
Kevin Clover, *Corp Secy*
Bob Walin, *Vice Pres*
Roger Hunt, *Treasurer*
EMP: 30 **EST:** 2003
SQ FT: 8,800 **Privately Held**
WEB: www.theshouthouse.com
SIC: 8641 Members only bar & restaurant for members of organizations only

(G-4442)
FIRST COMMERCIAL BANK

8500 Normandale Lake Blvd (55437-3813)
PHONE 952 903-0777
FAX: 952 903-9365
Bradley Meier, *President*
Jane A Treston, *COO*
Brian R Wagner, *Senior VP*
Kristen Lange, *Vice Pres*
Anthony Page, *Vice Pres*
EST: 1999 **Privately Held**
SIC: 6022 State commercial bank

(G-4443)
FIRST MEMORIAL FUNERAL CHAPEL

7835 Brooklyn Blvd (55445-2716)
PHONE 763 560-4694
Mark Waterson, *Owner*
Steve Hofeck, *Exec Dir*
EMP: 30 **EST:** 1990
SQ FT: 7,500
SALES (est): 1MM-4.9MM **Privately Held**
SIC: 7261 Funeral home & services

(G-4444)
FIRST MINNESOTA CARE INC

1201 E Lake St Ste 1 (55407-1852)
PHONE 612 724-3000
FAX: 612 724-8551
Ahmed M Hussain, *President*
EMP: 80 **EST:** 2003
SQ FT: 1,000
SALES (est): 1MM-4.9MM **Privately Held**
WEB: www.firstmnc.com
SIC: 8082 Home health care services

(G-4445)
FIRST STREET CREDIT CORP

2417 1st Ave S (55404-3446)
PHONE 612 871-4579
FAX: 612 871-2870
Arnold Scholl, *President*
EMP: 25 **EST:** 1980
SALES (est): 1MM-4.9MM **Privately Held**
SIC: 7389 Financial service

(G-4446)
FIRST STUDENT INC

3400 Spring St NE (55413-2910)
PHONE 612 378-7833
FAX: 612 378-5525

John Matthews, *Manager*
Joann Schmidt, *Supervisor*
EMP: 125
SALES (est): 10MM-24.9MM **Privately Held**
WEB: www.firststudentinc.com
SIC: 4729 Carpool or vanpool arrangement services
HQ: First Student Inc
600 Vine St Ste 1400
Cincinnati OH 45202
513 241-2200

(G-4447)
FIRST STUDENT INC

15625 32nd Ave N (55447-1455)
PHONE 763 559-9326
FAX: 763 559-2810
Dan Markiese, *Manager*
Rick Laemo, *Manager*
EMP: 76
SALES (est): 10MM-24.9MM **Privately Held**
WEB: www.firststudentinc.com
SIC: 7513 Truck leasing service, without drivers
HQ: First Student Inc
600 Vine St Ste 1400
Cincinnati OH 45202
513 241-2200

(G-4448)
FIRST TECH INC

2640 Hennepin Ave S (55408-1149)
PHONE 612 374-8000
FAX: 612 374-8080
Arnold Zuckman, *President*
Pete Paulsen, *General Mgr*
H R Zuckman, *Vice Pres*
Harvey Zuckman, *CFO*
Bob Goerne, *Sales Staff*
EMP: 60 **EST:** 1941
SQ FT: 10,000
SALES (est): 25MM-49.9MM **Privately Held**
WEB: www.firsttech.com
SIC: 5045 Wholesales computers, peripherals & software

(G-4449)
FISERV HEALTH INC

5500 Wayzata Blvd (55416-1241)
PHONE 763 549-3359
Jim Cox, *President*
Paul M Buchberger, *Corp Secy*
Forrest G Burke, *Corp Secy*
Juanita B Luis, *Corp Secy*
Ricky M Scheel, *Corp Secy*
EMP: 30 **EST:** 1997
SALES (est): 1MM-4.9MM **Publicly Held**
WEB: www.unitedhealthgroup.com
SIC: 8011 Health maintenance organization or HMO
PA: Unitedhealth Group Inc
9900 Bren Rd E
Minnetonka MN 55343
952 936-1300

(G-4450)
FISERV HEALTH PLAN (HQ)

5500 Wayzata Blvd Ste 500 (55416-3577)
PHONE 262 879-5565
Jay M Anliker, *CEO*
Bruce Czech, *CFO*
EMP: 1000 **EST:** 2006
SALES (corp-wide): 87.13B **Publicly Held**
WEB: www.benesight.com
SIC: 6324 8748 Dental insurance carrier; provides group hospitalization service plans; employee programs administration consultant
PA: Unitedhealth Group Inc
9900 Bren Rd E
Minnetonka MN 55343
952 936-1300

(G-4451)
FISH & RICHARDSON PC

60 S 6th St Ste 3300 (55402-4403)
PHONE 612 335-5070
FAX: 612 288-9696
Jane Smith, *Human Resources*
Sara Ramos, *Marketing Staff*
Carol Varhalla, *Manager*
Neil Fleischhacker, *Info Tech Mgr*
EMP: 150
SALES (est): 10MM-24.9MM **Privately Held**
WEB: www.fr.com

SIC: 8111 Legal services
PA: Fish & Richardson PC
1 Marina Park Dr Ste 1700
Boston MA 02210
617 542-5070

(G-4452)
FISHER PAPER BOX CO

3901 85th Ave N (55443-1907)
PHONE 763 425-7444
Christopher M Kane, *President*
EMP: 30 **EST:** 1892
SQ FT: 25,000
SALES (est): 10MM-24.9MM **Privately Held**
WEB: www.fisherpb.com
SIC: 5113 Wholesales paper & disposable plastic bags

(G-4453)
FIVE STAR H ENTERPRISES INC

3824 Dunbar Ct (55443-1975)
PO Box 14612 (55414-0612)
PHONE 612 867-5373
Won Huh, *President*
EMP: 65 **EST:** 1986
SALES (est): 1MM-4.9MM **Privately Held**
SIC: 7349 Building cleaning & maintenance services

(G-4454)
FLARE HEATING & AIR CONDG

9303 Plymouth Ave N # 104 (55427-3734)
PHONE 763 542-1166
FAX: 763 542-3101
Richard Guerre, *President*
Randy Imker, *Vice Pres*
Craig Schmidtke, *Finance*
EMP: 46 **EST:** 1981
SQ FT: 10,000
SALES (est): 5MM-9.9MM **Privately Held**
WEB: www.flareheating.com
SIC: 1711 Heating & air conditioning contractor; warm air heating & air conditioning contractor

(G-4455)
FLEET WHOLESALE SUPPLY CO INC

Also Called: Mills Fleet Farm
8400 Lakeland Ave N (55445-2163)
PO Box 346, Osseo (55369-0346)
PHONE 763 424-9668
Brad Hoss, *Systems Mgr*
EMP: 200
SALES (est): 100MM-499.9MM **Privately Held**
SIC: 5191 Wholesales farm supplies
PA: Fleet Wholesale Supply Co Inc
1300 S Lynndale Dr
Appleton WI 54914
920 997-8378

(G-4456)
FLINT GROUP LLC (HQ)

15500 28th Ave N (55447-1902)
PHONE 763 559-5911
David Hiserodt, *President*
Chris Berndt, *Purch Mgr*
Martin Coleman, *Finance*
Megan Sawatzke, *Human Res Mgr*
Sue Mozko, *Human Resources*
▲ **EMP:** 80 **EST:** 1990 **Privately Held**
WEB: www.flintink.com
SIC: 5085 Wholesales printer's inks
PA: Flint Group Inc
14909 N Beck Rd
Plymouth MI 48170
734 781-4600

(G-4457)
FLOYD LOCK & SAFE CO (PA)

9036 Grand Ave S (55420-3634)
PHONE 952 881-5625
FAX: 952 881-6524
Michael Karch, *CEO*
Bob Bossert, *President*
Bev Karch, *Corp Secy*
Bob Gibson, *Vice Pres*
David Hanson, *CFO*
EMP: 50 **EST:** 1945
SQ FT: 30,000 **Privately Held**
WEB: www.floydtotalsecurity.com
SIC: 7382 Security systems services

(G-4458)
FLUID INTERIORS

100 N 6th St Ste 100A (55403-1503)
PHONE 612 746-8700
Berk Claiborne, *Member*
Steve Schmaltz, *Member*
Mark Eklund, *Member*
James Effenberger, *Accountant*
EMP: 49 **EST:** 2006
SALES (est): 10MM-24.9MM **Privately Held**
WEB: www.fluidinteriors.com
SIC: 5021 Wholesales furniture

(G-4459)
FOCUS MARKET RESEARCH INC (PA)

2 Meridian Xing Ste 160 (55423-3935)
PHONE 612 869-8181
Judy Opstad, *President*
Stanley E Opstad, *Treasurer*
Bob Yoerg, *Manager*
EMP: 30 **EST:** 1973 **Privately Held**
SIC: 8732 Market analysis or research services

(G-4460)
FOLEY & MANSFIELD LLP (PA)

250 Marquette Ave # 1200 (55401-1874)
PHONE 612 338-8788
Russell D Melton, *Partner*
Frank Dvorall, *Partner*
Kyle Mansfield, *Partner*
Bill Lemire, *Partner*
Carl Heinzerling, *Partner*
EMP: 90 **EST:** 1993 **Privately Held**
SIC: 8111 General practice attorney's or lawyer's office

(G-4461)
FOOD ENGINEERING CORP

Also Called: F E C
1210 Dunkirk Ln N (55447-3166)
PHONE 763 559-5200
FAX: 763 559-4657
Ralph Burgess Jr, *CEO*
Peter Davis, *President*
Suzanne B Jackson, *Vice Pres*
Fred Langschultz, *Vice Pres*
Donald E Lyman, *Vice Pres*
EMP: 130 **EST:** 1965
SQ FT: 120,000
SALES (est): 10MM-24.9MM **Publicly Held**
WEB: www.fec.com
SIC: 1521 1542 Manufactures food products machinery; manufactures pharmaceutical machinery; manufactures tobacco products machinery; single-family housing construction; commercial & institutional building construction; manufactures conveyors & conveying equipment
HQ: Aeroglide Corp
100 Aeroglide Dr
Cary NC 27511
919 851-2000

(G-4462)
FOOD MARKET MERCHANDISING INC

Also Called: FMMI
6401 W 106th St Ste 201 (55438-2696)
PHONE 952 894-0110
Jon Tollefson, *President*
Jeff Willox, *Vice Pres*
Cathy Knoble, *CFO*
Kathy Knobel, *Accounts Mgr*
Tim Winfor, *Manager*
▲ **EMP:** 48 **EST:** 1986
SALES (est): 25MM-49.9MM **Privately Held**
WEB: www.fmmi.net
SIC: 5199 5092 Wholesales nondurable general merchandise; wholesales toys, hobby goods & supplies

(G-4463)
FOOD PERSPECTIVES INC

2880 Vicksburg Ln N (55447-1878)
PHONE 763 553-7787
FAX: 763 553-7789
Merry J Parker, *President*
EMP: 38 **EST:** 1990
SQ FT: 6,000 **Privately Held**
WEB: www.foodperspectives.com

(PA)=Parent Co (HQ)=Headquarters (DH)=Div Headquarters
✿ = New business established in last 2 years

2011 Harris Minnesota
Services Directory

© Harris InfoSource 1-866-281-6415
199

GEOGRAPHIC

SIC: **8731** 8732 8734 8742 Commercial food research services; market analysis or research services; food testing services; food & beverage consultant

(G-4464)
FOOD SYSTEMS DESIGN INC
10640 Lyndale Ave S Ste 1 (55420-5636)
PHONE..............................952 884-4048
FAX: 952 884-4121
Pat Douglas, *CEO*
Lawrence Corless, *CEO*
Patrick Douglass, *President*
Joyce Corless, *Treasurer*
Stephen Bankal, *Controller*
EMP: 45 EST: 1991
SQ FT: 8,000
SALES (est): 1MM-4.9MM **Privately Held**
WEB: www.foodsys.com
SIC: **7389** 8711 Commercial & industrial design service; engineering consulting services

(G-4465)
FORD BOYER TRUCKS INC
2425 Broadway St NE (55413-1730)
PHONE..............................612 378-6000
FAX: 612 627-5551
Tim Blyde, *General Mgr*
Sterling Boyer, *Manager*
George Tillison, *Manager*
Andy Rice, *Exec Dir*
EMP: 55
SALES (est): 5MM-9.9MM **Privately Held**
SIC: **7538** 7532 General automotive repair services; automotive body shop

(G-4466)
FOSS SWIM SCHOOL INC
8332 Highway 7 Ste 954 (55426-3910)
PHONE..............................952 935-8732
John Foss, *President*
Brett Laavos, *VP Mktg*
EMP: 40
SALES (est): 1MM-4.9MM **Privately Held**
SIC: **7999** Swimming instruction

(G-4467)
FOSTER KLIMA & CO LLC
Also Called: Guardian
920 2nd Ave S Ste 1100 (55402-4005)
PHONE..............................612 746-2214
Doug Flink, *Member*
John McGurran, *Member*
Robyn Krohn, *Controller*
EMP: 85 EST: 1981
SQ FT: 22,000
SALES (est): 5MM-9.9MM **Privately Held**
WEB: www.fosterk.com
SIC: **6411** 6282 Pension & retirement plan consulting service; investment advisory service

(G-4468)
FOSTER WHEELER TWIN CITIES INC
2701 University Ave SE # 105 (55414-3231)
PHONE..............................612 379-1885
FAX: 612 379-1980
J T Schroppe, *President*
Liza Freeze-Gardner, *Corp Secy*
David J Roberts, *Vice Pres*
Martin J Karpenski, *Vice Pres*
Richard Lewis, *Engineer*
EMP: 50 EST: 1988
SALES (est): 10MM-24.9MM **Privately Held**
WEB: www.fwc.com
SIC: **4961** Suppliers of steam heat
PA: Foster Wheeler Ltd
    Perryville Corporate Park
    Clinton NJ 08809
    908 730-4000

(G-4469)
FOX CABLE NETWORK SERVICES LLC
90 S 11th St (55403-2414)
PHONE..............................612 330-2468
Kevin Cattoor, *Vice Pres*
Ann Waara, *Manager*
EMP: 80
SALES (est): 25MM-49.9MM **Publicly Held**
WEB: www.fox.com

SIC: **4841** Pay television distribution
DH: Fox Cable Network Services LLC
    10000 Santa Monica Blvd
    Los Angeles CA 90067
    310 369-1000

(G-4470)
FPD POWER DEVELOPMENT LLC
2850 Anthony Ln S (55418-3287)
PHONE..............................612 782-3100
Robert Meyers, *Member*
John B Donnelly, *Member*
Jeff Erygale, *Vice Pres*
EMP: 200 EST: 2004
SQ FT: 5,000
SALES (est): 100MM-499.9MM **Privately Held**
WEB: www.fpdpower.com
SIC: **4911** Provides electric power generation services

(G-4471)
FRANCE AVENUE FAMILY
7250 France Ave S Ste 410 (55435-4314)
PHONE..............................952 831-1551
FAX: 952 831-0725
John L Canfield MD, *President*
Michael Pane, *Partner*
Anthony Smith MD, *Partner*
Rochelle Taube, *Partner*
Ann Kuffel, *Office Mgr*
EMP: 25 EST: 1978
SQ FT: 5,000
SALES (est): 1MM-4.9MM **Privately Held**
WEB: www.fafpedina.com
SIC: **8011** General & family practice physician or surgeon office

(G-4472)
FRANCE AVENUE LLC
3909 Heritage Hills Dr (55437-2655)
PHONE..............................952 831-0343
Robert S Bisanz, *President*
EMP: 150 EST: 1999
SALES (est): 10MM-24.9MM **Privately Held**
SIC: **6513** 6531 Apartment building operator; real estate management services

(G-4473)
FRANKLIN BAKERY LLC
1020 E Franklin Ave (55404-2919)
PHONE..............................612 455-3893
FAX: 612 871-3286
Joann Meyer, *General Mgr*
Pat Siebenaler, *Prdtn Mgr*
Jim Radant, *VP Sls/Mktg*
George Simons, *Controller*
Jack Thompson, *Controller*
EMP: 125 EST: 2003
SQ FT: 20,000
SALES (est): 50MM-99.9MM **Privately Held**
SIC: **5149** Wholesales bakery products

(G-4474)
FRANKLIN CO-OP
Also Called: Riverton Community Housing
2300 E Franklin Ave Ofc (55406-1072)
PHONE..............................612 338-4574
FAX: 612 338-4579
Gary Ellis, *President*
Dianna Tyson, *General Mgr*
Judy Doty, *Manager*
EMP: 30 EST: 1994
SALES (est): 1MM-4.9MM **Privately Held**
SIC: **6513** Apartment building operator

(G-4475)
FRANKLIN CORP
Also Called: PADILLA SPEAR BEARDSLEY
1101 W River Pkwy Ste 400 (55415-1241)
PHONE..............................612 455-1700
Lynn Casey, *CEO*
Marian Briggs, *Senior VP*
David Kistle, *Senior VP*
Thomas Jollie, *Vice Pres*
Barbara Kuklock, *Vice Pres*
EMP: 86 EST: 1957
SQ FT: 10,000
SALES (est): 10MM-24.9MM **Privately Held**
SIC: **8743** Public relations services

(G-4476)
FRANTZ, DONALD R CONCRETE
Also Called: Frantz Donald R Con Cnstr I
3501 Xenwood Ave S (55416-2338)
PHONE..............................952 929-8568
Michael Frantz, *President*
EMP: 30 EST: 1947
SQ FT: 3,000
SALES (est): 1MM-4.9MM **Privately Held**
SIC: **1771** 1741 Concrete contractor; masonry & stonework contractor

(G-4477)
FRANZ REPROGRAPHICS INC
2781 Freeway Blvd Ste 100 (55430-1765)
PHONE..............................763 503-3401
Patricia Franz, *President*
Bruce Franz, *Vice Pres*
Brinda France, *Manager*
EMP: 27 EST: 1965
SQ FT: 2,500
SALES (est): 1MM-4.9MM **Privately Held**
SIC: **7334** 5044 5049 Blueprinting services; wholesales drafting supplies; wholesales blueprinting equipment

(G-4478)
FRASER
2400 W 64th St (55423-1001)
PHONE..............................612 861-1688
FAX: 612 861-6050
Diane Cross, *President*
Jan Luker, *COO*
David Halsey, *CFO*
Carrie Gaske, *Accountant*
Barbara Simmons, *Human Res Mgr*
EMP: 300 EST: 1935
SQ FT: 24,000
SALES (est): 10MM-24.9MM **Privately Held**
WEB: www.fraser.org
SIC: **8322** Community center; special education school

(G-4479)
FRASER CHILD & FAMILY CENTER
3333 University Ave SE (55414-3325)
PHONE..............................612 331-9413
FAX: 612 729-6412
Diane Cross, *CEO*
Karen Carlson, *Govt Rel Mgr*
David Halsey, *CFO*
EMP: 600 EST: 1994
SQ FT: 30,000
SALES (est): 25MM-49.9MM **Privately Held**
SIC: **8322** Individual & family social services

(G-4480)
FRASER-MORRIS ELECTRIC CO INC
250 2nd Ave S Ste 109 (55401-2168)
PHONE..............................612 332-4328
FAX: 612 344-1114
Richard Morris, *President*
Cindy Morris, *Corp Secy*
Tim Tronce, *Project Mgr*
EMP: 50 EST: 1936
SQ FT: 1,700
SALES (est): 5MM-9.9MM **Privately Held**
SIC: **1731** General electrical contractor

(G-4481)
FRED BABCOCK POST NO 5555
Also Called: VFW POST #5555
6715 Lake Shore Dr S (55423-2333)
PHONE..............................612 869-5555
FAX: 612 798-5555
Gin Ng, *General Mgr*
Walt Fix, *Sales Staff*
Sharon Andreas, *Manager*
EMP: 30 EST: 1955 **Privately Held**
SIC: **8641** Veterans' organization

(G-4482)
FRED VOGT & CO
3260 Gorham Ave (55426-4103)
PHONE..............................952 929-6767
FAX: 952 929-1764
Robert Winder, *President*
Bev Wellens-Rudllph, *Manager*
EMP: 70 EST: 1949
SQ FT: 22,000
SALES (est): 5MM-9.9MM **Privately Held**

WEB: www.vogtheating.com
SIC: **1711** Warm air heating & air conditioning contractor

(G-4483)
FREDRICKSON COMMUNICATIONS INC
119 N 4th St Ste 513 (55401-1792)
PHONE..............................612 339-7970
FAX: 612 339-6516
Lola Fredrickson, *CEO*
Joyce Lasecke, *President*
Shannon Russell, *Opers Mgr*
David Lasecke, *CFO*
Molly Emmings, *Accounts Mgr*
EMP: 40 EST: 1985
SALES (est): 5MM-9.9MM **Privately Held**
WEB: www.fredcomm.com
SIC: **8742** Publisher; management consulting services

(G-4484)
FREDRIKSON & BYRON
200 S 6th St Ste 4000 (55402-1431)
PHONE..............................612 492-7000
John Koneck, *President*
John Satorius, *Chairman*
Mary Ranum, *Corp Secy*
John Erhart, *Treasurer*
Robert J Hamilton, *Finance*
EMP: 450 EST: 1948
SQ FT: 150,000
SALES (est): 50MM-99.9MM **Privately Held**
SIC: **8111** General practice law office

(G-4485)
FREEDOM HEALTH CARE INC
2626 E 82nd St Ste 260 (55425-1384)
PHONE..............................952 854-6889
FAX: 952 858-8633
Paul J Fox, *CEO*
Lori Fox, *Exec VP*
EMP: 85 EST: 1993
SQ FT: 3,000
SALES (est): 1MM-4.9MM **Privately Held**
SIC: **8082** Home health care services

(G-4486)
FREEPORT WEST INC
2219 Oakland Ave (55404-3749)
PHONE..............................612 824-3040
Barbara Milon, *Treasurer*
Lisa M McLevis, *Accounts Mgr*
Robert Smith, *Sales Staff*
Leann Brown, *Manager*
Karen Vnuk, *Manager*
EMP: 55 EST: 1970
SQ FT: 2,200
SALES (est): 1MM-4.9MM **Privately Held**
SIC: **8322** 8361 Social services center; residential care facility

(G-4487)
FREEWHEEL BICYCLE COOPERATIVE
1812 S 6th St (55454-1209)
PHONE..............................612 339-2219
FAX: 612 339-8268
Kevin Ishauth, *President*
Ed Neaton, *Purchasing*
EMP: 25 EST: 1974
SQ FT: 10,000
SALES (est): 1MM-4.9MM **Privately Held**
WEB: www.freewheelbike.com
SIC: **7699** Bicycle shop; bicycle repair shop

(G-4488)
FREMONT COMMUNITY HEALTH SVCS
3300 Fremont Ave N (55412-2405)
PHONE..............................612 588-9411
FAX: 612 522-6627
John Skillings, *Finance*
Kenya Dalton, *Office Mgr*
Laura Lipkin, *Office Mgr*
Steve Knutson, *Administrator*
Jennifer Monroe, *Exec Dir*
EMP: 30 EST: 1971
SQ FT: 6,000
SALES (est): 1MM-4.9MM **Privately Held**
WEB: www.fremonthealth.org
SIC: **8011** Clinic operated by physicians

www.HarrisInfo.com
200

2011 Harris Minnesota
Services Directory

▲=Import ▼=Export
◆=Import/Export

(G-4489)

FUJITSU AMERICA INC
605 Highway 169 N Ste 301 (55441-6454)
PHONE..........................763 595-9600
Dan Wisniewski, *Manager*
EMP: 25
SALES (est): 1MM-4.9MM **Privately Held**
WEB: www.fujitsu.com
SIC: 8748 7371 Business consulting services; custom computer software systems analysis & design service
   PA: Fujitsu America Inc
     1250 E Arques Ave
     Sunnyvale CA 94085
     408 746-6000

(G-4490)

FULBRIGHT & JAWORSKI LLP
80 S 8th St Ste 2100 (55402-2112)
PHONE..........................612 321-2800
Karla Billehus, *Manager*
Nicholas Vlietstra, *Manager*
Rebecca B Sanderg, *Sr Associate*
EMP: 50
SALES (est): 5MM-9.9MM **Privately Held**
WEB: www.fulbright.com
SIC: 8111 General practice attorney's or lawyer's office

(G-4491)

FUN SISTERS
5049 Belmont Ave S (55419-1311)
PHONE..........................612 824-9872
Daryl Skiba, *Partner*
Patsy Skiba, *Partner*
EMP: 30 **EST:** 2002
SALES (est): 10MM-24.9MM **Privately Held**
SIC: 5137 Wholesales women's purses

(G-4492)

G&K SERVICES INC
2601 49th Ave N Ste 200 (55430-4530)
PHONE..........................612 521-4771
FAX: 612 521-8271
Robert S Aubin, *General Mgr*
Daniel T Jakubic, *Principal*
Greg Gibson, *Plant Mgr*
Fritz Rademacher, *Manager*
Bob Destaubin, *Manager*
EMP: 188
SALES (est): 10MM-24.9MM **Publicly Held**
WEB: www.gkservices.com
SIC: 7218 7213 Industrial uniform supply services; uniform supply service
   PA: G&K Services Inc
     5995 Opus Pkwy Ste 500
     Minnetonka MN 55343
     952 912-5500

(G-4493)

G&K SERVICES INC
621 Olson Memorial Hwy (55405-1533)
PHONE..........................612 333-2225
FAX: 612 333-2319
Bob Aubin, *General Mgr*
Bob De, *General Mgr*
Bob Destaubin, *Manager*
EMP: 102
SALES (est): 5MM-9.9MM **Publicly Held**
WEB: www.gkservices.com
SIC: 7218 5085 7213 Industrial clothing supply service; wholesales industrial clean room supplies; uniform supply service
   PA: G&K Services Inc
     5995 Opus Pkwy Ste 500
     Minnetonka MN 55343
     952 912-5500

(G-4494)

GABRIEL DEGROOD BENDT LLC
608 2nd Ave S Ste 129 (55402-1910)
PHONE..........................612 547-5000
FAX: 612 547-5090
Doug Degrood, *Member*
Tom Gabriel, *Member*
Marc Razidlo, *CFO*
Crystal Anderson, *Accountant*
Kim Dipprey, *Sales Executive*
▲ **EMP:** 35 **EST:** 1997
SQ FT: 9,000
SALES (est): 1MM-4.9MM **Privately Held**
WEB: www.always-thinking.com
SIC: 7311 Advertising agency

(G-4495)

GAGE GROUP LLC (PA)
10000 Highway 55 Ste 100 (55441-6387)
PHONE..........................763 595-3920
Edwin C Gage, *Member*
Allan Osterud, *Finance Dir*
EMP: 160 **EST:** 1992
SQ FT: 72,500 **Privately Held**
SIC: 8742 7311 7389 7999 8743 Marketing consulting service; telemarketing services; advertising material distribution services; mailing services; mailing list management; operates party type fishing boats; promotion services

(G-4496)

GALLIARD CAPITAL MANAGEMENT
800 Lasalle Ave Ste 1100 (55402-2054)
PHONE..........................612 667-3210
Richard Merriam, *Managing Prtnr*
Karl Tourville, *Managing Prtnr*
John Caswell, *Invest Mgr*
Peter Kiedrowski, *Manager*
Pat Belousek, *Officer*
EMP: 36 **EST:** 1995 **Publicly Held**
WEB: www.galliard.com
SIC: 6722 Open-ended investment funds management services
   HQ: Wfc Holdings, Corp
     420 Montgomery St
     San Francisco CA 94104
     415 396-7392

(G-4497)

GAME FINANCIAL CORP
1550 Utica Ave S Ste 100 (55416-5301)
PHONE..........................800 363-3321
Mary Dutra, *President*
Craig Bongart, *VP Sls/Mktg*
EMP: 200 **EST:** 1990
SALES (est): 10MM-24.9MM **Publicly Held**
WEB: www.goldleaf-tech.com
SIC: 6099 Check cashing services
   HQ: Fidelity National Transaction
     11601 Roosevelt Blvd N
     Saint Petersburg FL 33716
     727 556-9000

(G-4498)

GAMER PACKAGING INC
330 2nd Ave S Ste 895 (55401-2302)
PHONE..........................612 788-4444
FAX: 612 788-9485
Ronald Gamer, *CEO*
Kenneth Gamer, *President*
Mildred Gamer, *Corp Secy*
Tim Kraus, *CFO*
Roberts Richey, *Marketing Mgr*
▲ **EMP:** 26 **EST:** 1988
SQ FT: 12,000
SALES (est): 10MM-24.9MM **Privately Held**
WEB: www.gamerpackaging.com
SIC: 5085 4225 Wholesales industrial storage bins & containers; general warehousing; wholesales industrial glass bottles; wholesales industrial plastic bottles; wholesales industrial bottler supplies

(G-4499)

GARBORGS LLC
Also Called: Garborg's
2060 W 98th St (55431-2505)
PO Box 1010, Siloam Springs AR
(72761-1010)
PHONE..........................612 888-5726
Ralph Garborg, *Principal*
EMP: 30 **EST:** 1987
SQ FT: 18,000
SALES (est): 10MM-24.9MM **Privately Held**
SIC: 5199 Wholesales gifts & novelties

(G-4500)

GARDNER FINANCIAL SERVICES INC
8421 Wayzata Blvd Ste 350 (55426-1352)
PHONE..........................952 935-4601
Larry Bumgardner, *President*
Ryan Carlson, *Vice Pres*
EMP: 35 **EST:** 1987
SALES (est): 5MM-9.9MM **Privately Held**
WEB: www.gardnerfinancialmn.com

SIC: 6211 8742 Security broker & dealer service; financial management consulting services

(G-4501)

GARLAND'S INC (PA)
Also Called: Materials Management Co
2501 26th Ave S (55406-1246)
PHONE..........................612 333-3469
FAX: 612 333-3472
Bob Smith, *President*
Tom Smith, *Corp Secy*
Jerry Smith, *Vice Pres*
Joe Foster, *Manager*
▲ **EMP:** 25 **EST:** 1931
SQ FT: 28,000 **Privately Held**
SIC: 5084 Wholesales materials handling equipment

(G-4502)

GARLOCK FRENCH ROOFING CORP
2301 E 25th St (55406-1220)
PHONE..........................612 722-7129
FAX: 612 722-9754
David Karel, *President*
Steve Karel, *Corp Secy*
Karl Charipar, *Vice Pres*
Bob Dresdack, *Vice Pres*
Glenn Downes, *Vice Pres*
EMP: 50 **EST:** 1932
SQ FT: 17,000
SALES (est): 5MM-9.9MM **Privately Held**
WEB: www.garlock-french.com
SIC: 1761 Roofing contractor; sheet metal work contractor; siding contractor

(G-4503)

GARLOCK-EAST EQUIPMENT CO
2601 Niagara Ln N (55447-4721)
PHONE..........................763 553-1935
Mark Hefty, *President*
Karen Leupold, *Controller*
Corey Scheich, *Manager*
Rick Stoffels, *Manager*
Brad Dunn, *Executive*
▲ **EMP:** 30 **EST:** 1986
SQ FT: 76,000
SALES (est): 10MM-24.9MM **Privately Held**
SIC: 5082 5033 Wholesales road construction equipment; manufactures asphalt coatings & sealers; wholesales asphalt & sheet metal roofing materials
   HQ: Plymouth Industries Inc
     2601 Niagara Ln N
     Minneapolis MN 55447
     763 553-1935

(G-4504)

GB LUMINA INC
Also Called: Lumina Engineering
6120 Earle Brown Dr # 410 (55430-4108)
PO Box 48217 (55448-0217)
PHONE..........................763 797-9036
FAX: 763 797-9626
Steven I Gitelis, *President*
Charles E Savitt, *Counsel*
Gerald Brinba, *Vice Pres*
Amy Larson, *VP Opers*
Kelly Olson, *Opers Staff*
EMP: 40 **EST:** 1991
SQ FT: 2,000
SALES (est): 5MM-9.9MM **Privately Held**
WEB: www.luminaeng.com
SIC: 7373 8711 Systems software development service; engineering services

(G-4505)

GEEK SQUAD INC (HQ)
1213 Washington Ave N (55401-1036)
PHONE..........................612 343-1028
Josh Kappelan, *Administrator*
EMP: 40 **EST:** 1994
SQ FT: 3,000
SALES (corp-wide): 49.69B **Publicly Held**
WEB: www.geeksquad.com
SIC: 7379 Computer system consulting services
   PA: Best Buy Co Inc
     7601 Penn Ave S
     Richfield MN 55423
     612 291-1000

(G-4506)

GEEK SQUAD INC
3724 W 50th St (55410-2016)
PHONE..........................612 922-9288
EMP: 100
SALES (est): 10MM-24.9MM **Publicly Held**
WEB: www.geeksquad.com
SIC: 7379 Computer system consulting services
   HQ: Geek Squad Inc
     1213 Washington Ave N
     Minneapolis MN 55401
     612 343-1028

(G-4507)

GENERAL AVIATION INC
Also Called: Jetways
7100 Northland Cir N Ste 407
(55428-1500)
PHONE..........................763 420-6907
FAX: 763 531-9420
Glen Rudell, *Treasurer*
EMP: 45 **EST:** 1993
SALES (est): 1MM-4.9MM **Privately Held**
SIC: 8741 Management services

(G-4508)

GENERAL DYNAMICS AVIATION SVCS
6925 34th Ave S (55450-1109)
PHONE..........................612 638-2000
Larry Flynn, *President*
Jeff Toline, *Manager*
EMP: 60 **EST:** 2001
SALES (est): 5MM-9.9MM **Publicly Held**
SIC: 7699 Aircraft & heavy equipment repair service
   HQ: General Dynamics Aviation Svcs
     500 Gulfstream Rd
     Savannah GA 31408
     912 965-3000

(G-4509)

GENERAL ELECTRIC CAPITAL CORP
8400 Normandale Lake Blvd (55437-1085)
PHONE..........................952 897-5600
Joanne L Manthe, *Corp Secy*
Bruce Gruys, *Vice Pres*
Michael Hanzel, *Vice Pres*
Thomas F Fanelli, *Vice Pres*
Amy Gross, *Vice Pres*
EMP: 30
SALES (est): 5MM-9.9MM **Publicly Held**
WEB: www.gecapital.com
SIC: 6141 8111 Personal credit institution; legal services
   DH: General Electric Capital Corp
     901 Main Ave
     Norwalk CT 06851
     203 840-6300

(G-4510)

GENERAL ELECTRIC CO
2025 49th Ave N (55430-3739)
PHONE..........................612 529-9502
FAX: 612 520-3737
Dave Grubish, *General Mgr*
Frank Heuckendorf, *Facilities Mgr*
Carol Miller, *Administration*
EMP: 38
SALES (est): 1MM-4.9MM **Publicly Held**
WEB: www.ge.com
SIC: 7699 1731 7694 Industrial machinery repair & maintenance services; armature repairing & rewinding service; electric power systems contractor; electronic controls installation service
   PA: General Electric Co
     3135 Easton Tpke
     Fairfield CT 06828
     203 373-2211

(G-4511)

GENERAL MARKETING SERVICES INC
Also Called: Direct Mail Mktg Specialists
7108 Ohms Ln (55439-2140)
PHONE..........................952 806-5080
James Thomson, *President*
Joan F Thomson, *Corp Secy*
EMP: 52

(PA)=Parent Co (HQ)=Headquarters (DH)=Div Headquarters
✿ = New business established in last 2 years

2011 Harris Minnesota
Services Directory

© Harris InfoSource 1-866-281-6415
201

EST: 1991
SQ FT: 47,000
SALES (est): 5MM-9.9MM **Privately Held**
SIC: 7331 Direct mail advertising service

(G-4512)
GENERAL MILLS INC
3600 Dight Ave   (55406-2613)
PHONE 612 721-6811
FAX: 612 721-3058
Mark Fedje, *Manager*
Mark Feggie, *Manager*
EMP: 100
SALES (est): 10MM-24.9MM **Publicly Held**
WEB: www.generalmills.com
SIC: 4221 Grain elevator with storage only;
manufactures flour mixes
PA: General Mills Inc
    1 General Mills Blvd
    Minneapolis MN 55426
    763 764-7600

(G-4513)
GENERAL MILLS INC
301 4th Ave S Ste 680   (55415-1019)
PO Box 15003   (55415-0003)
PHONE 763 764-3313
Ron Olson, *Branch Mgr*
Margaret Bueltel, *Manager*
Heidi Depuydt, *Manager*
EMP: 30
SALES (est): 50MM-99.9MM **Publicly Held**
WEB: www.generalmills.com
SIC: 5153 Wholesales grains
PA: General Mills Inc
    1 General Mills Blvd
    Minneapolis MN 55426
    763 764-7600

(G-4514)
GENERAL NANOSYSTEMS INC
3014 University Ave SE   (55414-3316)
PHONE 612 331-3690
FAX: 612 331-4082
Khalid Mahmood, *President*
Shahzad Mazhar, *Vice Pres*
Sylvia Lee, *Office Mgr*
EMP: 34 **EST:** 1995
SALES (est): 25MM-49.9MM **Privately Held**
WEB: www.nanosys1.com
SIC: 5045 Wholesales computers,
peripherals & software; wholesales
computer software

(G-4515)
GENERAL PARTS LLC   (PA)
11311 Hampshire Ave S   (55438-2456)
PHONE 952 944-5800
FAX: 952 944-7101
Linnea Chrest, *Member*
Bruce Hodge, *Member*
Jeff Weber, *Vice Pres*
Linnea Crest, *CFO*
John Gardner, *CFO*
EMP: 40 **EST:** 1939 **Privately Held**
WEB: www.generalparts.com
SIC: 7699 Industrial equipment service

(G-4516)
GENERAL PEDIATRIC
717 Delaware St SE Fl 3   (55414-2959)
PHONE 612 626-2820
Rob Super, *Director*
EMP: 40 **EST:** 2001
SALES (est): 1MM-4.9MM **Privately Held**
SIC: 8361 Residential care for children

(G-4517)
GENERAL SECURITY SERVICES CORP   (PA)
9110 Meadowview Rd   (55425-2458)
PHONE 952 858-5000
Whitney Miller, *President*
Jackson Hall, *Vice Pres*
Andrew C Pierucki, *Vice Pres*
Tim Kinsley, *Opers Mgr*
Joel Shanan, *Facilities Mgr*
EMP: 70 **EST:** 1946
SQ FT: 21,000   **Privately Held**
WEB: www.gssc.net
SIC: 7381 Security guard service

(G-4518)
GENERAL SHEET METAL CORP
2330 Louisiana Ave N   (55427-3631)
PHONE 763 544-8747
FAX: 763 544-6580
Jim Wiggem, *President*
Michael Koenik, *Corp Secy*
Jim Krenik, *Treasurer*
Cheryl Fischer, *Manager*
Tom Kost, *Info Tech Mgr*
EMP: 150 **EST:** 1949
SQ FT: 30,000
SALES (est): 10MM-24.9MM **Privately Held**
WEB: www.gsm-hvac.com
SIC: 1711 Heating & air conditioning
contractor; ventilation & duct work
contractor; warm air heating & air
conditioning contractor; sheet metal
fabricator

(G-4519)
GENERATIONS COMMUNITY SUPPORT
2649 Park Ave   (55407-1006)
PHONE 612 676-1604
Katy Gorman, *President*
EMP: 60 **EST:** 2004
SALES (est): 1MM-4.9MM **Privately Held**
WEB: www.generationscss.com
SIC: 8049 Psychotherapist office

(G-4520)
GENERATIONS RESOURCES FOR
2331 University Ave SE   (55414-4002)
PHONE 612 676-1604
FAX: 612 623-4539
Katy Gorman, *Director*
EMP: 50 **EST:** 2000
SALES (est): 1MM-4.9MM **Privately Held**
SIC: 8049 Psychotherapist office

(G-4521)
GENMAR HOLDINGS INC   (HQ)
2900 80 S 8th St   (55402)
PHONE 612 339-7900
Ronald V Purgiel V, *President*
Daniel W Schuette, *President*
Roger R Cloutier II, *President*
Richard Anderson, *General Mgr*
Mary McConnell, *Corp Secy*
▼ **EMP:** 100 **EST:** 1994
SQ FT: 25,000   **Privately Held**
WEB: www.genmar.com
SIC: 8741 Builds & repairs boats; builds &
repairs small lobster, crab or oyster boats;
builds & repairs inboard or outboard
motorboats; builds & repairs yachts;
management services
PA: Platinum Equity LLC
    360 N Crescent Dr Bldg S
    Beverly Hills CA 90210
    310 712-1850

(G-4522)
GENPAK LLC
9611 James Ave S   (55431-2511)
PHONE 952 881-8673
FAX: 952 881-3031
Tom Everett, *Vice Pres*
Russ Snyder, *Plant Supt*
Jerry Zembrycki, *Opers Mgr*
Keith A Puchalski, *Purch Mgr*
Kelli Malecha, *CFO*
EMP: 150
SQ FT: 45,000
SALES (est): 25MM-49.9MM **Privately Held**
WEB: www.genpak.com
SIC: 5162 Manufactures plastic bags made
from purchased materials; manufactures
unsupported plastics film & sheet;
wholesales plastics materials
HQ: Genpak LLC
    68 Warren St
    Glens Falls NY 12801
    518 798-9511

(G-4523)
GENUINE PARTS CO
Also Called: NAPA Auto Parts
7400 W 27th St   (55426-3104)
PHONE 952 925-0188
FAX: 952 922-7809
Ted Webber, *General Mgr*

Jim Badaczewski, *Opers Mgr*
Colette Patterson, *Human Res Mgr*
Chris Wall, *Sales Mgr*
Rick Jensen, *Manager*
EMP: 100
SALES (est): 10MM-24.9MM **Publicly Held**
WEB: www.genpt.com
SIC: 5013 7539 Retails auto & home
supplies; wholesales automotive supplies &
parts; automotive machine shop
PA: Genuine Parts Co
    2999 Circle 75 Pkwy SE
    Atlanta GA 30339
    770 953-1700

(G-4524)
GEORGE KONIK ASSOCIATES INC
7242 Metro Blvd   (55439-2128)
PHONE 952 835-5550
FAX: 952 835-7294
George Konik, *President*
Ila Konik, *Corp Secy*
Brenda Konik, *VP Opers-Prdtn-*
EMP: 70 **EST:** 1974
SQ FT: 1,500
SALES (est): 1MM-4.9MM **Privately Held**
SIC: 7363 7372 7389 8711 Temporary help
service; engineering consulting services;
drafting service; software publisher

(G-4525)
GGNSC MINNEAPOLIS BLOOMINGTON
Also Called: Golden Living Care Center
9200 Nicollet Ave S   (55420-3714)
PHONE 952 881-8676
Mary Jasper, *Member*
EMP: 75
SALES (est): 1MM-4.9MM **Privately Held**
WEB: www.fillmorecap.com
SIC: 8051 Skilled nursing care facility
DH: Ggnsc Holdings LLC
    1000 Fianna Way
    Fort Smith AR 72919
    479 201-2000

(G-4526)
GGNSC MINNEAPOLIS CHATEAU LLC
Also Called: Golden Livingcenter - Chateau
2106 2nd Ave S   (55404-2606)
PHONE 612 874-1603
Chelis Fenner, *Human Res Mgr*
Carole Bonde, *Manager*
Kim Jonhson, *Manager*
Chris Kresbach, *Exec Dir*
EMP: 75 **EST:** 2006
SALES (est): 1MM-4.9MM **Privately Held**
WEB: www.fillmorecap.com
SIC: 8051 Skilled nursing care facility
DH: Ggnsc Holdings LLC
    1000 Fianna Way
    Fort Smith AR 72919
    479 201-2000

(G-4527)
GIERTSEN CO OF MINNESOTA INC   (PA)
8385 10th Ave N   (55427-4420)
PHONE 763 546-1300
FAX: 763 546-0623
K M Giersten, *President*
R I Giersten Sr, *President*
A E Giersten, *Treasurer*
Jim Zondlo, *Marketing Mgr*
Jason Egan, *Administrator*
EMP: 50 **EST:** 1935
SQ FT: 14,000   **Privately Held**
SIC: 1521 Single-family home fire damage
repair service

(G-4528)
GITTLEMAN MANAGEMENT CORP
1801 American Blvd E # 21   (55425-1230)
PHONE 952 277-2700
FAX: 952 277-2739
Melvin C Gittleman, *President*
Rochelle Gittleman, *Corp Secy*
Darlene Edge, *Accountant*
Mike Cleary, *Manager*
Donald Anderson, *Director*
EMP: 50

EST: 1955
SQ FT: 11,000
SALES (est): 1MM-4.9MM **Privately Held**
WEB: www.gittleman.com
SIC: 6531 Condominium managers

(G-4529)
GLENWOOD-INGLEWOOD CO
225 Thomas Ave N   (55405-1040)
PHONE 612 374-2253
FAX: 612 374-2397
Merrill Fie, *Ch of Bd*
Colleen Porterfield, *President*
Doug Oberhamer, *COO*
Roxanne Stillwell, *Asst Treas*
Bill Hansen, *Office Mgr*
EMP: 75 **EST:** 1884
SQ FT: 85,000
SALES (est): 50MM-99.9MM **Privately Held**
WEB: www.deeprockwater.com
SIC: 5149 7359 Wholesales distilled water;
equipment rental & leasing services
PA: Mile-HI Dr LLC
    2640 California St
    Denver CO 80205
    303 292-2020

(G-4530)
GLENWOOD-LYNDALE COMMUNITY CTR
555 Girard Ter Ste 120   (55405-1315)
PHONE 612 342-1500
FAX: 612 342-1575
Calvin Quarles, *Manager*
Linda Tacke, *Exec Dir*
EMP: 52 **EST:** 1978
SALES (est): 1MM-4.9MM **Privately Held**
SIC: 8322 Child guidance services; family
services agency; multi-services center;
self-help organization

(G-4531)
GLOBAL CASE TECHNOLOGY INC
2 Carlson Pkwy N Ste 225   (55447-4485)
PHONE 763 553-1313
Sunil Sharma, *CEO*
EMP: 45 **EST:** 1996
SQ FT: 3,000
SALES (est): 5MM-9.9MM **Privately Held**
SIC: 7371 Computer software development

(G-4532)
GLOBAL TAX NETWORK MINNESOTA
750 Boone Ave N Ste 102   (55427-4464)
PHONE 952 224-2053
Stephen Daas, *Member*
David Kolb, *Member*
EMP: 26 **EST:** 2003
SQ FT: 1,500
SALES (est): Under 500K **Privately Held**
SIC: 7291 8742 Tax return preparation
services; financial management consulting
services

(G-4533)
GOLD GROVES
761 Kasota Ave SE   (55414-2842)
PHONE 612 884-8383
Trisha Hamrin, *Partner*
EMP: 40 **EST:** 2002
SALES (est): 5MM-9.9MM **Privately Held**
SIC: 8742 Marketing consulting service

(G-4534)
GOLD POINTS CORP
1405 Xenium Ln N   (55441-4410)
PHONE 763 212-1000
FAX: 763 212-5747
Murad Velani, *CEO*
Scott Heintzeman, *Corp Secy*
Kenneth Lindeman, *Corp Secy*
Harold Taylor, *Marketing Mgr*
Tia Simonson, *Manager*
EMP: 80 **EST:** 1994
SALES (est): 10MM-24.9MM **Privately Held**
WEB: www.carlson.com
SIC: 8742 Marketing consulting service
HQ: Carlson Inc
    701 Carlson Pkwy
    Minnetonka MN 55305
    763 212-5000

www.HarrisInfo.com
202

2011 Harris Minnesota
Services Directory

▲=Import ▼=Export
◆=Import/Export

G E O G R A P H I C

(G-4535)

GOLDEN VALLEY CLINIC INC
8240 Golden Valley Rd # 200
(55427-4409)
PHONE.............................952 993-8300
Mary Campbell, *Manager*
Bernadette Samuel, *Supervisor*
Louis Millman, *Exec Dir*
Laurie Freier, *Physician Asst*
EMP: 25 **EST:** 1960
SQ FT: 9,000
SALES (est): 1MM-4.9MM **Privately Held**
SIC: 8011 General & family practice
physician or surgeon office

(G-4536)

GOLDEN VALLEY COUNTRY CLUB
7001 Golden Valley Rd (55427-4609)
PHONE.............................763 732-4100
Dennis Wyffls, *CFO*
Craig Surdy, *Manager*
EMP: 100 **EST:** 1974
SALES (est): 10MM-24.9MM **Privately Held**
SIC: 7999 Tennis professional; retails tennis
goods & equipment

(G-4537)

GOLDEN VALLEY VIEW POST 7051
7775 Medicine Lake Rd (55427-3501)
PHONE.............................763 545-9996
FAX: 763 545-5746
Aaron Niznik, *General Mgr*
Daniel Elsness, *Manager*
Chuck Lund, *Exec Dir*
Dennis Westley, *Director*
EMP: 40 **EST:** 1964
SQ FT: 1,500 **Privately Held**
SIC: 8641 Veterans' organization

(G-4538)

GOLDEN VALLEY, CITY OF INC
Also Called: Brookview Golf Course
200 Brookview Pkwy (55426-1361)
PHONE.............................763 593-8000
Greg Spencer, *Superintendent*
Rick Jacobson, *Director*
EMP: 70
SALES (est): 1MM-4.9MM **Privately Held**
SIC: 7992 Public golf course; mayors' office
PA: Golden Valley, City of Inc
7800 Golden Valley Rd
Minneapolis MN 55427
763 593-8010

(G-4539)

GOLDSMITH, AGIO, HELMS
225 S 6th St Fl 46 (55402-4601)
PHONE.............................612 339-0500
FAX: 612 339-0507
Roger Redmond, *General Mgr*
Peter Bennett, *Managing Dir*
Gerald M Caruso Jr, *Managing Dir*
Daniel Confino, *Managing Dir*
Karen Furman, *Managing Dir*
EMP: 72 **EST:** 1980
SQ FT: 30,000
SALES (est): 50MM-99.9MM **Privately Held**
WEB: www.agio.com
SIC: 6211 Investment banking service

(G-4540)

GOODIN CO (PA)
2700 N 2nd St (55411-1602)
PHONE.............................612 588-7811
FAX: 612 588-7820
Greg Skagerberg, *CEO*
Steven Kelly, *President*
Ernest Lindstrom, *Member*
Gerard Melgaard, *Exec VP*
Joel Skagerberg, *Vice Pres*
▲ **EMP:** 134 **EST:** 1937
SQ FT: 400
SALES (corp-wide): 125.33M **Privately Held**
WEB: www.goodinco.com
SIC: 5074 5075 Wholesales plastic pipes &
fittings; wholesales air conditioning
equipment; wholesales hot water heating
boilers; wholesales radiators & parts;
wholesales warm air furnaces

(G-4541)

GOPHER CO INC
2701 36th Ave S (55406-1759)
PHONE.............................612 331-1555
FAX: 612 331-7725
Jason Brouwer, *President*
Stacy Reese, *General Mgr*
Todd McClary, *Manager*
EMP: 45 **EST:** 1992
SQ FT: 5,500
SALES (est): 1MM-4.9MM **Privately Held**
WEB: www.gophercompany.com
SIC: 1761 Roofing, siding & sheet metal
work

(G-4542)

GOPHER NEWS CO
Also Called: St Maries Gopher News
9000 10th Ave N (55427-4322)
PHONE.............................763 546-5300
FAX: 763 525-3100
Don Weber, *President*
R Gary St Marie, *Chairman*
Thomas Moe, *Corp Secy*
Jess Aspenson, *Systems Mgr*
EMP: 85 **EST:** 1906
SQ FT: 90,000
SALES (est): 25MM-49.9MM **Privately Held**
SIC: 5192 5065 5092 Wholesales
magazines; wholesales audio & video
tapes; wholesales toys; wholesales books

(G-4543)

GORDON & FERGUSON OF DELAWARE
830 Decatur Ave N (55427-4324)
PHONE.............................763 559-8300
FAX: 763 559-2871
Ian Schaffer, *President*
Stuart Edelman, *Manager*
EMP: 30 **EST:** 1988
SALES (est): 10MM-24.9MM **Privately Held**
SIC: 5136 Wholesales men's & boys'
clothing

(G-4544)

GRACE MANAGEMENT INC
6225 42nd Ave N (55422-1603)
PHONE.............................763 544-9934
Eugene W Grace, *President*
Craig King, *COO*
Mari Jo Grace CPM, *Exec VP*
Jody Boedigheimer, *Vice Pres*
Mari J Grace, *Vice Pres*
EMP: 650 **EST:** 1984
SQ FT: 5,400
SALES (est): 100MM-499.9MM **Privately Held**
WEB: www.plantationsouth-duluth.com
SIC: 6513 6512 Operators of retirement
hotels; operators of commercial & industrial
buildings; operators of apartment hotels

(G-4545)

GRADSTAFF INC
708 N 1st St Ste 245 (55401-1145)
PHONE.............................612 339-5332
FAX: 612 339-5336
David C Weyerhaeuser, *Principal*
Melanie Groen, *Vice Pres*
Bob Labombard, *Exec Dir*
Robert J Labombard, *Director*
Katie Groves, *Executive Asst*
EMP: 50 **EST:** 1998
SQ FT: 2,500
SALES (est): 1MM-4.9MM **Privately Held**
SIC: 7363 Temporary help service

(G-4546)

GRANT THORNTON LLP
200 S 6th St Ste 500 (55402-1429)
PHONE.............................612 332-0001
FAX: 612 332-8361
Jeremy Welsand, *General Mgr*
Michele Montan, *VP Human Res*
Nicole Denault, *Human Resources*
Lynette Uetz, *VP Mktg*
Tom Walters, *Branch Mgr*
EMP: 100
SALES (est): 5MM-9.9MM **Privately Held**
WEB: www.gt.com

SIC: 8721 Accounting service
PA: Grant Thornton LLP
175 W Jackson Blvd Fl 20
Chicago IL 60604
312 856-0200

(G-4547)

GRAVES HOSPITALITY CORP
601 1st Ave N (55403-1409)
PHONE.............................612 677-1100
FAX: 612 312-1157
James Graves, *CEO*
Scott Huston, *Director*
EMP: 100
SALES (est): 5MM-9.9MM **Privately Held**
WEB: www.graves601hotel.com
SIC: 7011 4724 Traveler accommodations;
travel agency
PA: Graves Hospitality Corp
601 1st Ave N
Minneapolis MN 55403
320 252-6034

(G-4548)

GRAY PLANT MOOTY MOOTY
80 S 8th St Ste 500 (55402-5383)
PHONE.............................612 632-3000
FAX: 612 333-0066
Tamara H Olsen, *President*
Stephen F Grinnel, *Principal*
John W Fitzgerald, *Corp Secy*
David C Bahls, *Vice Pres*
William D Klein, *Treasurer*
EMP: 290 **EST:** 1866
SQ FT: 85,380
SALES (est): 25MM-49.9MM **Privately Held**
WEB: www.gpmlaw.com
SIC: 8111 General practice law office

(G-4549)

GRAYBAR ELECTRIC CO INC
13310 Industrial Park Blvd (55441-3800)
PHONE.............................763 852-6000
FAX: 763 852-6099
Bryan Hughes, *Sales Mgr*
John Priebe, *Manager*
EMP: 62
SALES (est): 25MM-49.9MM **Privately Held**
SIC: 5063 Wholesales electrical apparatus
& equipment

(G-4550)

GRAYBAR ELECTRIC CO INC
2300 E 25th St (55406-1221)
PO Box 160 (55440-0160)
PHONE.............................612 721-3545
FAX: 612 728-2620
R L Nowak, *Vice Pres*
Cindy Paschke, *Human Res Mgr*
Lisa Matuska, *Cust Svc Dir*
Erik Olsen, *Branch Mgr*
Don Moersfelder, *Manager*
EMP: 118
SALES (est): 50MM-99.9MM **Privately Held**
SIC: 5063 Wholesales electrical supplies

(G-4551)

GREAT CLIPS INC
7700 France Ave S Ste 425 (55435-5868)
PHONE.............................952 893-9088
FAX: 952 844-3444
Raymond L Barton, *CEO*
Rhoda Olsen, *President*
Shelby Yastrow, *Managing Dir*
Jay Mitchell, *Business Mgr*
Sandra Trenda, *Corp Secy*
EMP: 85 **EST:** 1982
SQ FT: 25,000
SALES (est): 1MM-4.9MM **Privately Held**
WEB: www.greatclips.com
SIC: 7231 Unisex hair salon

(G-4552)

GREAT HARVEST BREAD CO OF MN
4314 Upton Ave S (55410-1555)
PHONE.............................612 929-2899
FAX: 612 928-9329
Sally Weisman, *President*
Tom Amundson, *Vice Pres*
EMP: 25 **EST:** 1982
SQ FT: 2,700
SALES (est): 1MM-4.9MM **Privately Held**

SIC: 5149 Retails bread; commercial
bakery; manufactures cookies & crackers;
retails cakes; retails cookies; wholesales
bakery products

(G-4553)

GREAT NORTHERN BAKING CO LLC
443 Hoover St NE (55413-2926)
PHONE.............................612 331-1043
FAX: 612 331-1043
Fred Johnson, *Member*
Michelle Keltner, *Manager*
EMP: 50 **EST:** 1994
SQ FT: 25,000
SALES (est): 10MM-24.9MM **Privately Held**
WEB: www.greatnorthernbaking.com
SIC: 5149 Manufactures frozen or
refrigerated doughs from purchased flour;
wholesales groceries

(G-4554)

GREAT NORTHERN CORP
Also Called: Creative Disposal & Packg
8600 Wyoming Ave N (55445-1827)
PHONE.............................763 493-5521
FAX: 763 493-6511
Bill Calenhor, *Vice Pres*
Mike Tschida, *Vice Pres*
EMP: 130
SALES (est): 25MM-49.9MM **Privately Held**
WEB: www.rollguard.com
SIC: 5113 Manufactures corrugated boxes;
wholesales shipping supplies; wholesales
industrial & personal service paper
PA: Great Northern Corp
395 Stroebe Rd
Appleton WI 54914
920 739-3671

(G-4555)

GREAT NORTHERN INSURANCE CO
100 S 5th St Ste 1800 (55402-1225)
PHONE.............................612 373-7300
FAX: 612 373-9779
Randy Miller, *Opers Mgr*
Kim Sandiser, *Human Res Mgr*
Tyrus Czeschin, *Marketing Mgr*
Tim Shannahan, *Manager*
EMP: 78 **EST:** 1952
SALES (est): 25MM-49.9MM **Publicly Held**
WEB: www.federalinsurancecompany.com
SIC: 6331 Property & casualty insurance
carrier
HQ: Federal Insurance Co
15 Mountain View Rd
Warren NJ 07059
908 903-2000

(G-4556)

GREAT NORTHERN RESOURCES INC
3230 Gorham Ave Ste 1 (55426-4295)
PHONE.............................952 848-0984
FAX: 952 929-9672
Wayne Benson, *President*
EMP: 30 **EST:** 1995
SQ FT: 16,500
SALES (est): 1MM-4.9MM **Privately Held**
SIC: 1799 Post disaster renovations service

(G-4557)

GREATAPES CORP
1523 Nicollet Ave (55403-2723)
PHONE.............................612 872-8284
FAX: 612 872-0635
James Woelm, *President*
Diane Woelm, *Vice Pres*
Julie Nwosu, *Sales Mgr*
Susan Gorecki, *Exec Dir*
Robert M McCarthy, *Maintence Staff*
EMP: 30 **EST:** 1970
SQ FT: 15,000
SALES (est): 5MM-9.9MM **Privately Held**
WEB: www.greatapes.com
SIC: 7812 Audio-visual program production
service; manufactures educational aides,
devices & supplies

(PA)=Parent Co (HQ)=Headquarters (DH)=Div Headquarters
✪ = New business established in last 2 years

2011 Harris Minnesota
Services Directory

© Harris InfoSource 1-866-281-6415
203

(G-4558)
GREATER MINNEAPOLIS CONVENTION
250 Marquette Ave Ste 1300 (55401-1875)
PHONE..................612 767-8000
Greg Ortale, *President*
Michelle Manatt, *Sales Associate*
Karyn Gruenberg, *VP Mktg*
Katherine G Hadley, *Exec Dir*
Mary Lawson, *Director*
EMP: 150 EST: 1987
SQ FT: 21,400
SALES (est): 10MM-24.9MM **Privately Held**
WEB: www.minneapolis.org
SIC: 7389 Advertising, promotional & trade show service

(G-4559)
GREATER MINNEAPOLIS COUNCIL OF
1001 E Lake St (55407-1616)
PHONE..................612 721-8687
FAX: 612 722-8669
Dorothy Bridges, *Ch of Bd*
Gary Reierson, *President*
Ford W Bell, *Chairman*
Mary Cederberg, *Corp Secy*
Barbara Coch, *Vice Pres*
EMP: 38 EST: 1905
SQ FT: 20,000
SALES (est): 1MM-4.9MM **Privately Held**
SIC: 8322 Social services center

(G-4560)
GREATER MINNEAPOLIS CRISIS
5400 Glenwood Ave (55422-5120)
PHONE..................763 591-0100
FAX: 763 591-0700
Daniel Collins, *Treasurer*
Kathy Schaaf, *Director*
Trent Blain, *Bd of Directors*
Martha Burnett, *Bd of Directors*
EMP: 65 EST: 1980
SALES (est): 1MM-4.9MM **Privately Held**
WEB: www.crisisnursery.org
SIC: 8322 Child & youth services

(G-4561)
GREATER TWIN CITIES UNITED WAY (PA)
404 S 8th St Ste 100 (55404-1027)
PHONE..................612 340-7400
Sarah Caruso, *Exec Dir*
Kabo Yang, *Relations*
EMP: 120 EST: 1919
SQ FT: 1,000
SALES (corp-wide): 92M **Privately Held**
SIC: 8322 Individual & family social services

(G-4562)
GREATER TWIN CITIES UNITED WAY
Also Called: Incresing Self Sfficiency Fund
404 S 8th St Ste 100 (55404-1027)
PHONE..................612 340-7481
James Colville, *CEO*
Nancy Hartzler, *Sales Mgr*
EMP: 110 **Privately Held**
SIC: 8399 Social change association
PA: Greater Twin Cities United Way
    404 S 8th St Ste 100
    Minneapolis MN 55404
    612 340-7400

(G-4563)
GREENE ESPEL PLLP
200 S 6th St Ste 1200 (55402-1415)
PHONE..................612 373-0830
FAX: 612 373-0929
Clifford M Greene, *Partner*
Larry D Espel, *Partner*
Laura J Shryer, *General Mgr*
Jodeen A Kozlak, *Attorney*
Sarah L Brew, *Attorney*
EMP: 45 EST: 1994
SALES (est): 5MM-9.9MM **Privately Held**
WEB: www.greeneespal.com
SIC: 8111 General practice law office

(G-4564)
GREER & ASSOCIATES INC
905 Park Ave (55404-1138)
PHONE..................612 338-6171
FAX: 612 338-2622
Kenneth D Greer, *CEO*
Jill Greer, *President*
Michele Grossfeld, *CFO*
Jerome Thelia, *Manager*
EMP: 25 EST: 1976
SQ FT: 14,500
SALES (est): 1MM-4.9MM **Privately Held**
WEB: www.thinkgreer.com
SIC: 7336 7335 7812 Graphic arts & related design service; film strip, slide & still film production service; video production service; commercial photography service

(G-4565)
GREG GRUMAN
Also Called: Winkley Co
740 Douglas Dr N (55422-4301)
PHONE..................763 546-1177
Greg Gruman, *Owner*
Tim Hubers, *Controller*
EMP: 45 EST: 1888
SALES (est): 10MM-24.9MM **Privately Held**
SIC: 6512 Nonresidential building operator

(G-4566)
GREINER CONSTRUCTION INC
625 Marquette Ave Ste 840 (55402-2426)
PHONE..................612 338-1696
FAX: 612 338-1892
Todd Heyes, *Vice Pres*
EMP: 60 EST: 1989
SQ FT: 450
SALES (est): 10MM-24.9MM **Privately Held**
WEB: www.greinerconstruction.biz
SIC: 1541 Industrial building renovating, remodeling & repair service

(G-4567)
GREYHOUND LINES INC
950 Hawthorne Ave (55403-1323)
PHONE..................612 371-3325
FAX: 612 371-3302
Stan Turbyfill, *Vice Pres*
Jacque Parker, *Opers Spvr*
James Osterberg, *Opers Spvr*
Clayton Beachmann, *Office Mgr*
Amanda Hunt, *Branch Mgr*
EMP: 70
SALES (est): 5MM-9.9MM **Privately Held**
WEB: www.greyhound.com
SIC: 4513 4212 Air courier services; delivery services by vehicle

(G-4568)
GRIFFIN & CO LOGISTICS
7830 12th Ave S (55425-1001)
PHONE..................952 854-2600
FAX: 952 854-2603
William L Griffin, *President*
Rita Griffin, *Corp Secy*
Brnda Callahan, *Vice Pres*
Dennis Ring, *VP Opers*
Deb Wagner, *VP Mktg*
▲ EMP: 26 EST: 1983
SQ FT: 18,000
SALES (est): 1MM-4.9MM **Privately Held**
WEB: www.wlgriffin.com
SIC: 4731 Customhouse broker; domestic freight forwarding services; foreign freight forwarding services

(G-4569)
GRIFFIN CO'S
615 1st Ave NE Ste 500 (55413-2681)
PHONE..................612 338-2828
Robert Dunbar, *Principal*
Suzette Rettinger, *Member*
Jay Demma, *Vice Pres*
James Grobe, *Vice Pres*
Larry Johnson, *Vice Pres*
EMP: 30 EST: 1969
SQ FT: 3,000
SALES (est): 1MM-4.9MM **Privately Held**
SIC: 6513 Apartment building operator

(G-4570)
GRIFFIN INTERNATIONAL CO'S INC
100 N 6th St Ste 300C (55403-1519)
PHONE..................612 344-4700
Robert Griffin, *President*
Richard Nordvold, *CFO*
Susan Zinkl, *Executive Asst*
▲ EMP: 40 EST: 1999
SQ FT: 15,000
SALES (est): 5MM-9.9MM **Privately Held**
WEB: www.griffinintl.com
SIC: 8742 Management consulting services

(G-4571)
GRIFFIN MARKETING & PROMOTIONS
100 N 6th St Ste 300C (55403-1519)
PHONE..................612 344-4677
Robert J Griffin, *President*
John Griffin, *Vice Pres*
Rick Nordvold, *CFO*
Jennifer Farr, *Accounting Mgr*
▲ EMP: 80 EST: 1998
SQ FT: 60,000
SALES (est): 50MM-99.9MM **Privately Held**
SIC: 5063 Wholesales electrical apparatus & equipment

(G-4572)
GRIFFITHS HOLDING CORP
Also Called: Wrico Stamping of Minnesota
2727 Niagara Ln N (55447-4844)
PHONE..................763 559-2288
FAX: 763 553-7976
Arthur Hahn, *Vice Pres*
Al Brummer, *Plant Mgr*
Vern Lee, *Purchasing*
Wilton Ludwig, *Controller*
Allyn Dickie, *Manager*
EMP: 150
SALES (est): 10MM-24.9MM **Privately Held**
SIC: 7692 Manufactures stamped or pressed metal machine parts; welding service
PA: Griffiths Holding Corp
    2717 Niagara Ln N
    Minneapolis MN 55447
    763 557-8935

(G-4573)
GROCERY SHOPPING NETWORK
10 Bluff Ste 900 (55402)
PHONE..................952 345-3232
Andrew Robinson, *President*
Codi Jays, *CFO*
Duane Kolsrud, *Director*
EMP: 30 EST: 1996
SALES (est): 1MM-4.9MM **Privately Held**
WEB: www.coborns.com
SIC: 7371 Computer programming service

(G-4574)
GROCERY SHOPPING NETWORK INC
10 S 5th St Ste 900 (55402-1035)
PHONE..................612 746-4232
FAX: 612 746-4237
Andy Robinson, *CEO*
EMP: 33 EST: 2007
SALES (est): 1MM-4.9MM **Privately Held**
SIC: 7371 Computer software development; computer software development & applications

(G-4575)
GSR REAL ESTATE SERVICES LLC
615 1st Ave NE Ste 500 (55413-2681)
PHONE..................612 338-2828
Robert Dunbar, *Member*
EMP: 70 EST: 2000
SALES (est): 10MM-24.9MM **Privately Held**
SIC: 6531 Real estate management services

(G-4576)
GUARDIAN BUILDING PRODUCTS
700 24th Ave SE (55414-2604)
PHONE..................612 524-0513
Ashley Cameron, *Branch Mgr*
EMP: 35
SALES (est): 5MM-9.9MM **Privately Held**
WEB: www.cabp.com
SIC: 5087 Wholesales service establishment equipment & supplies
HQ: Guardian Building Products
    979 Batesville Rd
    Greer SC 29651
    864 297-6101

(G-4577)
GUARDIAN LIFE INSURANCE CO OF
920 2nd Ave S Ste 1100 (55402-4005)
PHONE..................952 903-2200
Brad Pumesen, *Manager*
EMP: 100
SALES (est): 50MM-99.9MM **Privately Held**
WEB: www.glic.com
SIC: 6311 Life insurance carrier
PA: Guardian Life Insurance Co of
    7 Hanover Sq Fl 14
    New York NY 10004
    212 598-8000

(G-4578)
GUARDSMARK LLC
7230 Metro Blvd Ste 150 (55439-2176)
PHONE..................952 831-3151
FAX: 952 831-2430
Ben Atkins, *Manager*
Patrick Sweet, *Manager*
EMP: 60
SALES (est): 1MM-4.9MM **Privately Held**
WEB: www.guardsmark.com
SIC: 7381 Security guard service
PA: Guardsmark LLC
    10 Rockefeller Plz # 1250
    New York NY 10020
    212 765-8226

(G-4579)
GUTHRIE THEATER FOUNDATION
818 S 2nd St (55415-1252)
PHONE..................612 225-6000
Charles Zelle, *President*
M J Jundt, *Corp Secy*
Dan Soltys, *Engineer*
Jay Kiedrowski, *Treasurer*
Jean Leuthner, *Human Resources*
EMP: 175 EST: 1963
SQ FT: 76,000
SALES (est): 25MM-49.9MM **Privately Held**
WEB: www.guthrietheater.org
SIC: 7922 Theatrical producers & services

(G-4580)
GUY CARPENTER & CO LLC
3600 Minnesota Dr Ste 400 (55435-7902)
PHONE..................952 920-3300
FAX: 952 920-9382
Thomas Baumann, *Senior VP*
Terry Russell, *Manager*
Robert Stangler, *CIO*
Susan Gongoll, *Executive Asst*
EMP: 140
SALES (est): 100MM-499.9MM **Publicly Held**
WEB: www.marshmac.com
SIC: 6311 Life reinsurance carrier
PA: Marsh & McLennan Co's Inc
    1166 Avenue Of The Americas
    New York NY 10036
    212 345-5000

(G-4581)
GUYS FISH INC
301 Royalston Ave (55405-1535)
PHONE..................612 339-7720
FAX: 612 398-7480
Mike Hagens, *President*
Jim Kuehn, *CFO*
EMP: 35 EST: 1995
SQ FT: 10,000
SALES (est): 10MM-24.9MM **Privately Held**
SIC: 5146 Wholesales fish & seafood

www.HarrisInfo.com
204

2011 Harris Minnesota
Services Directory

▲=Import ▼=Export
◆=Import/Export

SIC: 7231 Hairdresser

(G-4582)

GV HEATING & AIR INC

Also Called: Golden Valley Heating & AC
5182 W Broadway Ave (55429-3506)
PHONE............................763 535-2000
FAX: 763 535-4379
Scott Follese, *President*
Cheri Follese, *Corp Secy*
Brian Follese, *Vice Pres*
EMP: 25 **EST:** 1938
SQ FT: 3,500
SALES (est): 1MM-4.9MM **Privately Held**
SIC: 1711 Heating & air conditioning
contractor

(G-4583)

GWG HOLDINGS LLC ✿

220 S 6th St Ste 1200 (55402-4512)
PHONE............................612 746-6119
Steven Sabes, *Partner*
Jon R Sabes, *Partner*
E G Kendrick Jr, *Corp Secy*
Virginia L Piercy, *Vice Pres*
Paul A Siegert, *Manager*
EMP: 46 **EST:** 2008
SALES (est): 1MM-4.9MM **Privately Held**
SIC: 7389 Financial service

(G-4584)

H & J BLISS ENTERPRISES

2811 Aquila Ave S (55426-2951)
PHONE............................952 988-9302
Harold Bliss, *Owner*
Joan Bliss, *Co-Owner*
EMP: 30 **EST:** 1981
SALES (est): 1MM-4.9MM **Privately Held**
SIC: 7221 5043 7699 8742 Still or video
photographer; wholesales cameras &
photographic equipment; retails cameras;
camera repair shop; business planning &
organizing services

(G-4585)

H I R E D

1200 Plymouth Ave N Ste 2 (55411-4008)
PHONE............................612 529-3342
FAX: 612 529-7131
Edmund Kelley, *Treasurer*
Jackie Craig, *Manager*
Jane Samingria, *Manager*
Judy Swanson, *Manager*
Jim Thibodeau, *Info Tech Dir*
EMP: 56 **EST:** 1968
SQ FT: 7,800
SALES (est): 1MM-4.9MM **Privately Held**
SIC: 8331 Job training & vocational
rehabilitation services; job training services;
job counseling

(G-4586)

H J K S INC

Also Called: Texa-Tonka Lanes
8200 Minnetonka Blvd (55426-3037)
PHONE............................952 935-3427
FAX: 952 933-5682
Steve Trickey, *President*
Bill Johnson, *Vice Pres*
Jeff Kristal, *Treasurer*
EMP: 30
SQ FT: 20,000
SALES (est): 1MM-4.9MM **Privately Held**
WEB: www.hjks.com
SIC: 7997 Bowling league or team; eating
place; beer garden drinking establishment

(G-4587)

HAIGH TODD & ASSOC INC

600 Highway 169 S Ste 655 (55426-1233)
PHONE............................952 252-2100
Barry J Todd, *Partner*
EMP: 26 **EST:** 1991
SALES (est): 1MM-4.9MM **Privately Held**
WEB: www.haightodd.com
SIC: 8748 Telecommunications consulting
services

(G-4588)

HAIR DISTRICT

3925 W 50th St Ste 104 (55424-1262)
PHONE............................952 836-0816
Montey Mosiman, *Owner*
Nicole Mosiman, *Co-Owner*
EMP: 35 **EST:** 1999
SALES (est): 1MM-4.9MM **Privately Held**

(G-4589)

HAJOCA CORP

6601A Parkway Cir (55430-1763)
PHONE............................763 315-0100
Dave Majors, *General Mgr*
Dave Maiers, *Branch Mgr*
EMP: 50
SALES (est): 25MM-49.9MM **Privately Held**
WEB: www.hajoca.com
SIC: 5074 5023 5051 5064 5075 5085
Wholesales plumbing fittings & supplies;
wholesales industrial supplies; wholesales
household appliance parts; wholesales
fireplace equipment & accessories;
wholesales steel pipe & tubing; wholesales
warm air heating equipment & supplies
PA: Hajoca Corp
    127 Coulter Ave
    Ardmore PA 19003
    610 649-1430

(G-4590)

HALDEMAN-HOMME INC

430 Industrial Blvd NE (55413-2979)
PHONE............................612 331-4880
FAX: 612 378-2236
Ernest Stalock, *Ch of Bd*
Mike Propp, *President*
Dan Weinmeyer, *Corp Secy*
Paul Fedji, *Exec VP*
Ron Johnson, *Vice Pres*
EMP: 125 **EST:** 1914
SQ FT: 40,000
SALES (est): 25MM-49.9MM **Privately Held**
SIC: 5021 5084 Wholesales furniture; home
center store; wholesales industrial
machinery, parts & equipment

(G-4591)

HAMMEL, GREEN & ABRAHAMSON INC (PA)

Also Called: H G A
701 Washington Ave N (55401-1180)
PHONE............................612 758-4000
FAX: 612 758-4199
Daniel L Avchen, *CEO*
Joseph Madda, *Principal*
Edward A Towey, *Corp Secy*
Steve A Fiskum, *COO*
James V Heiden, *Vice Pres*
EMP: 350 **EST:** 1953
SQ FT: 65,000
SALES (corp-wide): 98.72M **Privately Held**
WEB: www.hga.com
SIC: 8711 8712 Engineering services;
architectural service

(G-4592)

HAMRE SCHUMANN MUELLER LARSON

Also Called: Hsml
225 S 6th St Ste 2650 (55402-4656)
PHONE............................612 455-3800
M Schumann, *Partner*
D Mueller, *Partner*
C Hamre, *Partner*
EMP: 25 **EST:** 2005
SALES (est): 1MM-4.9MM **Privately Held**
WEB: www.hsml.com
SIC: 8111 Real estate law office

(G-4593)

HANLEY-WOOD CUSTOM PUBLISHING

430 1st Ave N Ste 550 (55401-1753)
PHONE............................612 338-8300
Jeanne Milbrath, *President*
James J Youngblut, *Vice Pres*
Sandy Rumreich, *Engineering*
Michael Wood, *Mng Member*
Janc M Ronuck, *Manager*
EMP: 60 **EST:** 1984
SQ FT: 6,000
SALES (est): 5MM-9.9MM **Privately Held**
WEB: www.hwcp.com
SIC: 8742 8743 8748 Marketing consulting
service; public relations & publicity services;
publishing consultant
PA: Hanley Wood LLC
    1 Thomas Cir NW Ste 600
    Washington DC 20005
    202 452-0800

(G-4594)

HANNAY'S INC

1708 Central Ave NE (55413-1523)
PHONE............................612 781-7411
FAX: 612 781-4325
Kenneth D Hannay, *President*
Patricia Hannay, *Corp Secy*
Paul Harris, *Vice Pres*
Gerald Slanga, *Vice Pres*
Judy Urban, *Office Mgr*
EMP: 25 **EST:** 1941
SQ FT: 28,000
SALES (est): 10MM-24.9MM **Privately Held**
WEB: www.hannaysinc.com
SIC: 5091 Wholesales motorboats; marine
supply dealer; outboard motor dealer;
wholesales outboard motors; retails motor
boats

(G-4595)

HANNON SECURITY SERVICES INC

9036 Grand Ave S (55420-3634)
PHONE............................952 881-5865
Michael Karch, *CEO*
Bev Karch, *President*
Nick Luciano, *Vice Pres*
Dave Hanson, *CFO*
Troy Schmitz, *Manager*
EMP: 350 **EST:** 1901
SQ FT: 30,000
SALES (est): 5MM-9.9MM **Privately Held**
WEB: www.hannonsecurity.com
SIC: 7381 Security guard service

(G-4596)

HANSON, LULIC & KRALL

608 2nd Ave S (55402-1916)
PHONE............................612 333-2530
FAX: 612 392-3675
Jon Hanson, *Partner*
Joseph Lulic, *Partner*
Tony Krall, *Partner*
Kevin J Kennedy, *Partner*
William M Drinane, *Partner*
EMP: 30 **EST:** 1986
SQ FT: 9,200
SALES (est): 1MM-4.9MM **Privately Held**
WEB: www.hlk.com
SIC: 8111 General practice attorney's or
lawyer's office

(G-4597)

HARKRAFT INC

3101 Louisiana Ave N (55427-2918)
PHONE............................763 546-9161
John Hinnenthal, *CEO*
Warren Eck, *President*
John Steuck, *Manager*
EMP: 32 **EST:** 1963
SQ FT: 12,000
SALES (est): 1MM-4.9MM **Privately Held**
WEB: www.harkraft.com
SIC: 5031 5072 Manufactures partitions &
fixtures; wholesales hardware;
manufactures wooden kitchen, bathroom &
household ware; manufactures metal doors,
sash & trim; wholesales molding
constructed of all materials

(G-4598)

HARLEYSVILLE INSURANCE CO

7900 W 78th St Ste 400 (55439-2519)
PHONE............................952 829-4000
Walter Bateman, *Division Mgr*
Alan Faley, *Corp Secy*
David Netz, *Vice Pres*
Robert S Wendt Jr, *Vice Pres*
Frederick Baker, *Vice Pres*
EMP: 70 **EST:** 1930
SQ FT: 22,000
SALES (est): 25MM-49.9MM **Privately Held**
WEB: www.pennlandinsurance.com
SIC: 6331 Provides property damage
insurance; fire, marine & casualty insurance
& carriers
HQ: Harleysville Group Inc
    355 Maple Ave
    Harleysville PA 19438
    215 256-5000

(G-4599)

HARMONY HOMES INC

1120 Winter St NE (55413-2900)
PHONE............................763 434-3439
Del Krusenstjerna, *President*
Daniel Rehbein, *General Mgr*
Rick Lockwood, *Manager*
EMP: 25 **EST:** 1983
SQ FT: 4,800
SALES (est): 1MM-4.9MM **Privately Held**
WEB: www.harmonyhomesinc.net
SIC: 1751 Prefabricated window & door
installation service; retails building products
& materials

(G-4600)

HAROLD CHEVROLET INC

1601 Southtown Dr (55431-1431)
PHONE............................952 884-3333
James Lupient, *Ch of Bd*
Mike Gamber, *Comptroller*
Scott Rosstedt, *Manager*
Mike Nelson, *Manager*
Sharon Labatte, *Manager*
EMP: 123 **EST:** 1934
SQ FT: 54,000
SALES (est): 50MM-99.9MM **Privately Held**
SIC: 7532 7538 Retails new & used
automobiles; general automotive repair
services; automotive body shop

(G-4601)

HAROLD PITMAN M CO

Also Called: Pitman Co
2650 2nd St NE (55418-2724)
PHONE............................612 781-8988
FAX: 612 781-4429
Ron Asleson, *General Mgr*
John Zellner, *Manager*
EMP: 32
SALES (est): 10MM-24.9MM **Privately Held**
SIC: 5084 Wholesales printing machinery,
equipment & supplies

(G-4602)

HARRIET TUBMAN CENTER INC

3111 1st Ave S (55408-3136)
PHONE............................612 825-3333
FAX: 612 825-6666
R Sur, *Corp Secy*
Melissa Peterson, *Vice Pres*
Junauld Presley, *Manager*
David White, *Info Tech Mgr*
Beverly Dusso, *Director*
EMP: 50 **EST:** 1977
SQ FT: 2,000
SALES (est): 1MM-4.9MM **Privately Held**
WEB: www.tubmanfamilyalliance.com
SIC: 8322 Crisis center; family services
agency

(G-4603)

HARRINGTON CO

4248 Park Glen Rd (55416-4758)
PHONE............................952 928-4666
FAX: 952 929-1318
John P Francis, *President*
Gretchen Huetteman, *Senior VP*
Judy Harrington, *Vice Pres*
Mary Deinken, *Controller*
Kate M Cantu, *Exec Dir*
EMP: 32 **EST:** 1978
SQ FT: 14,000
SALES (est): 1MM-4.9MM **Privately Held**
SIC: 8741 Business management services

(G-4604)

HARTFORD LIFE INC

3800 Amercn Blvd W # 675 (55431-4421)
PHONE............................952 893-9236
FAX: 952 893-0053
Pat Swanson, *Manager*
EMP: 79
SALES (est): 50MM-99.9MM **Publicly Held**
WEB: www.hartfordife.com
SIC: 6311 Life insurance carrier
HQ: Hartford Life Inc
    200 Hopmeadow St
    Weatogue CT 06089
    860 547-5000

(PA)=Parent Co (HQ)=Headquarters (DH)=Div Headquarters
✿ = New business established in last 2 years

2011 Harris Minnesota
Services Directory

© Harris InfoSource 1-866-281-6415

205

GEOGRAPHIC

(G-4605)
HARVEY-WINCHELL CO
1801 E 79th St Ste 9 (55425-1230)
PHONE...................................952 881-7964
FAX: 952 881-8059
Donald Lamere, *President*
Thomas Vucicevic, *Vice Pres*
EMP: 30 EST: 1991
SALES (est): 10MM-24.9MM **Privately Held**
SIC: 5145 Wholesales candy

(G-4606)
HAUGEN, JOHN A ASSOCIATES
3250 W 66th St Ste 200 (55435-2526)
PHONE...................................952 927-6561
Ronald Peterson MD, *President*
Amy Seheid, *Persnl Dir*
Allison West, *Obstetrician*
Mary Dahling, *Obstetrician*
Andrea J Flom, *Obstetrician*
EMP: 28
SQ FT: 5,000
SALES (est): 1MM-4.9MM **Privately Held**
WEB: www.mnobgyn.com
SIC: 8011 Gynecologist office; obstetrician office
PA: Haugen, John A Associates
   801 Nicollet Mall Ste 400
   Minneapolis MN 55402
   612 333-2503

(G-4607)
HAUGEN, JOHN A ASSOCIATES (PA)
Also Called: John A Haugen - Edina
801 Nicollet Mall Ste 400 (55402-2520)
PHONE...................................612 333-2503
Edward Beadle, *President*
Ronald Petersen, *President*
Arthur Bearon MD, *Vice Pres*
Andrea Flom MD, *Vice Pres*
Gretchen Vannatta MD, *Vice Pres*
EST: 1969
SQ FT: 5,900 **Privately Held**
WEB: www.mnobgyn.com
SIC: 8011 Gynecologist office; obstetrician office

(G-4608)
HAWKINS INC (PA)
3100 E Hennepin Ave (55413-2922)
PHONE...................................612 331-6910
John R Hawkins, *CEO*
Fritz Wagner, *Business Mgr*
Richard G Erstad, *Corp Secy*
Keenan A Paulson, *Vice Pres*
John Eaton, *Vice Pres*
▲ EMP: 120 EST: 1938
SQ FT: 177,000
SALES (corp-wide): 257.09M **Publicly Held**
WEB: www.hawkinschemical.com
SIC: 5169 5074 Wholesales chemicals & allied products; wholesales water purification equipment; wholesales industrial chemicals; wholesales swimming pool & spa chemicals

(G-4609)
HAWKINS PHARMACEUTICAL GROUP
3000 E Hennepin Ave (55413-2920)
PHONE...................................612 617-8600
FAX: 612 617-8544
John R Hawkins, *Corp Secy*
Angela Wagamon, *Corp Secy*
Daniel Soderlund, *Vice Pres*
Dan Suttherland, *Vice Pres*
Howard M Hawkins, *Treasurer*
EMP: 30 EST: 2001
SALES (est): 25MM-49.9MM **Privately Held**
SIC: 5122 Wholesales pharmaceuticals

(G-4610)
HAWKINS WATER TREATMENT GROUP
3100 E Hennepin Ave (55413-2922)
PHONE...................................612 331-6910
Donald L Shipp, *President*
Fritz Wagner, *Manager*
Mike Clemens, *Manager*
EMP: 56 EST: 1967
SALES (est): 25MM-49.9MM **Publicly Held**
WEB: www.hawkinschemical.com

SIC: 5074 Wholesales water purification equipment
PA: Hawkins Inc
   3100 E Hennepin Ave
   Minneapolis MN 55413
   612 331-6910

(G-4611)
HAWTHORNE HOUSE INC
6931 Country Club Dr (55427-4604)
PO Box 27482 (55427-0482)
PHONE...................................763 525-1000
Rohitha Perera, *Owner*
EMP: 30 EST: 2005
SALES (est): 1MM-4.9MM **Privately Held**
SIC: 8361 Residential care facility

(G-4612)
HAYDEN-MURPHY EQUIPMENT CO
9301 E Bloomington Fwy (55420-3410)
PHONE...................................952 884-2301
FAX: 952 884-2293
Leonard Kirk, *President*
Steve Peterson, *General Mgr*
Don Knackstedt, *Controller*
Brice Knackstedt, *Credit Mgr*
Greg Steege, *VP Sales*
▲ EMP: 43 EST: 1957
SQ FT: 40,000
SALES (est): 10MM-24.9MM **Privately Held**
WEB: www.hayden-murphy.com
SIC: 5082 7699 Wholesales general construction machinery & equipment; construction equipment repair service

(G-4613)
HAYS GROUP INC (PA)
80 S 8th St Ste 700 (55402-2105)
PHONE...................................612 333-3323
FAX: 612 373-7270
James Hays, *President*
William Mershon, *Exec VP*
Barry Peters, *Senior VP*
Eric Rosales, *Senior VP*
Russell Berman, *Senior VP*
EMP: 140 EST: 1994
SQ FT: 23,000 **Privately Held**
WEB: www.hayscompanies.com
SIC: 6411 Insurance agency & broker

(G-4614)
HAZELDEN FOUNDATION
11505 36th Ave N (55441-2304)
PHONE...................................612 559-2022
Val Copeland, *Facilities Mgr*
Linda King, *Office Mgr*
Leslie Adair, *Manager*
Jessica Houlding, *Manager*
Dan Kane, *Info Tech Mgr*
EMP: 77
SALES (est): 1MM-4.9MM **Privately Held**
WEB: www.hazelden.org
SIC: 8361 8069 8093 Residential rehabilitation center with health care incidental; drug addiction rehabilitation hospital; outpatient alcohol treatment clinic

(G-4615)
HDR ENGINEERING INC
701 Xenia Ave S Ste 600 (55416-3636)
PHONE...................................763 591-5400
FAX: 763 591-5413
Ed Liebsch, *Vice Pres*
Marissa Cohen, *Human Res Mgr*
Brett Wolfe, *Manager*
Mark Manoleff, *Manager*
EMP: 101
SALES (est): 10MM-24.9MM **Privately Held**
WEB: www.thehoytco.com
SIC: 8711 8712 8742 Engineering services; architectural service; management consulting services
HQ: HDR Engineering Inc
   8404 Indian Hills Dr
   Omaha NE 68114
   402 399-1000

(G-4616)
HEALTH BILLING SYSTEMS LLC
14700 28th Ave N Ste 20 (55447-4876)
PHONE...................................763 559-3779
FAX: 763 559-3543
Eric Stein MD, *President*
Mark Sperry MD, *Vice Pres*

Gary Baggenstoss MD, *Vice Pres*
Greg Maurer, *Opers Dir*
Brad Schultz, *Info Tech Mgr*
EMP: 60 EST: 1987
SQ FT: 8,400
SALES (est): 1MM-4.9MM **Privately Held**
WEB: www.healthbilling.net
SIC: 8721 Billing & bookkeeping services

(G-4617)
HEALTH CARE CENTER
Also Called: Nile Health Care Center
3720 23rd Ave S (55407-3010)
PHONE...................................612 724-5495
FAX: 612 724-3696
Joel Kelsh, *Administrator*
Deborah L Rose, *Nursing Dir*
EMP: 150 EST: 1955
SALES (est): 5MM-9.9MM **Privately Held**
SIC: 8051 Skilled nursing care facility

(G-4618)
HEALTH CARE PROVIDER SERVICE
Also Called: Copy Service
7800 Glenroy Rd (55439-3129)
PHONE...................................952 831-8114
Stan Johnson, *Manager*
EMP: 25 EST: 1985
SALES (est): 1MM-4.9MM **Privately Held**
SIC: 7334 Photocopying & duplicating services

(G-4619)
HEALTHCARE OPTIONS INC
2738 Winnetka Ave N (55427-2850)
PO Box 41454 (55441-0454)
PHONE...................................763 545-3042
Bennie Perkins, *President*
EMP: 115
SALES (est): 1MM-4.9MM **Privately Held**
WEB: www.rouzer.com
SIC: 7363 Help supply services

(G-4620)
HEALTHIA CONSULTING INC
701 Xenia Ave S Ste 170 (55416-3595)
PHONE...................................763 923-7900
FAX: 763 923-7901
Glenn Galloway, *CEO*
James A Zerwas, *Ch of Bd*
Brad Sparish, *Vice Pres*
Micheal Tressler, *Vice Pres*
Kelly Johnson, *Manager*
EMP: 100 EST: 1998
SQ FT: 5,322
SALES (est): 10MM-24.9MM **Publicly Held**
WEB: www.healthiaconsulting.com
SIC: 8742 New products & services consultants
HQ: Ingenix Inc
   12125 Technology Dr
   Eden Prairie MN 55344
   952 833-7100

(G-4621)
HEALTHPARTNERS INC
Also Called: Healthprtners Rvrside Partners
2220 Riverside Ave (55454-1321)
PHONE...................................612 371-1600
Sherry Olson, *Insur/Bill Sup*
Paula Gabay, *Dentist*
Michael Bauer, *Dentist*
Thomas M Harkcom MD, *Med Doctor*
Mustafa O Ucermd MD, *Med Doctor*
EMP: 400
SALES (est): 50MM-99.9MM **Privately Held**
WEB: www.healthpartners.com
SIC: 8011 Health maintenance organization or HMO
PA: HealthPartners Inc
   8170 33rd Ave S
   Bloomington MN 55425
   952 883-6000

(G-4622)
HEALTHPARTNERS INC
Also Called: Eye Department
5100 Gamble Dr Ste 100 (55416-1588)
PHONE...................................952 593-8777
Robert Seigalman, *Principal*
Freeman E Wong MD, *Med Doctor*
Peter M Hinke, *Manager*
Dorene Krenn, *Supervisor*
Jackie Holsten, *Admin Sec*

EMP: 400
SALES (est): 25MM-49.9MM **Privately Held**
WEB: www.healthpartners.com
SIC: 8011 Eyes, ears, nose & throat specialist, physician or surgeon office
PA: HealthPartners Inc
   8170 33rd Ave S
   Bloomington MN 55425
   952 883-6000

(G-4623)
HEALTHPARTNERS INC
3105 E 80th St (55425-1504)
PHONE...................................612 623-4002
Mary Brainerd, *Branch Mgr*
EMP: 500
SALES (est): 100MM-499.9MM **Privately Held**
WEB: www.healthpartners.com
SIC: 6324 Health insurance maintenance organization
PA: HealthPartners Inc
   8170 33rd Ave S
   Bloomington MN 55425
   952 883-6000

(G-4624)
HEALTHSOUTH CORP
3209 W 76th St Ste 202 (55435-5246)
PHONE...................................952 921-0100
Pamela Spohn, *Administrator*
EMP: 50
SALES (est): 1MM-4.9MM **Publicly Held**
WEB: www.healthsouth.com
SIC: 8062 Medical hospital
PA: HEALTHSOUTH Corp
   3660 Grandview Pkwy
   Birmingham AL 35243
   205 967-7116

(G-4625)
HEARTLAND AUTO GLASS
6975 Washingtn Ave S # 225 (55439-1504)
PHONE...................................952 697-0765
FAX: 952 942-8185
Teri Snider, *Owner*
EMP: 25 EST: 2005
SALES (est): 1MM-4.9MM **Privately Held**
SIC: 7536 Automotive glass replacement service

(G-4626)
HEARTLAND INFORMATION SERVICES
527 Marquette Ave Ste 900 (55402-1312)
PO Box 2918 (55402-0918)
PHONE...................................612 371-9255
FAX: 612 371-9262
Paul A Jaeb, *President*
EMP: 35 EST: 1991
SQ FT: 3,600
SALES (est): 500-999K **Privately Held**
SIC: 7381 7375 Security guard service; information retrieval services

(G-4627)
HEDBERG AGGREGATES INC (PA)
1205 Nathan Ln N (55441-5040)
PHONE...................................763 545-4400
FAX: 763 545-7121
Stephen Hedberg, *President*
Bob Hofstrom, *Corp Secy*
Kathy Hackworthy, *CFO*
George Simons, *Treasurer*
Tammy Bader, *Office Mgr*
EMP: 55 EST: 1987 **Privately Held**
WEB: www.hedbergaggregates.com
SIC: 5032 5083 Wholesales brick, stone & related products; wholesales stucco; wholesales aggregate; wholesales landscaping equipment; retails aquarium supplies

(G-4628)
HEIDELBERG USA INC
7400 Metro Blvd Ste 222 (55439-2321)
PHONE...................................952 831-6501
EMP: 30
SALES (est): 10MM-24.9MM **Privately Held**
WEB: www.heidelbergusa.com

www.HarrisInfo.com
206

2011 Harris Minnesota
Services Directory

▲=Import ▼=Export
◆=Import/Export

SIC: **5084** Wholesales printing machinery,
equipment & supplies
PA: Heidelberg USA Inc
1000 Gutenberg Dr NW
Kennesaw GA 30144
770 419-6500

(G-4629)
HEMPEL PROPERTIES INC
527 Marquette Ave Ste 500 (55402-1309)
PHONE..............................612 355-2600
John Hempel, *President*
Sheri Boyland, *Finance Dir*
Diane Jansen, *Administrator*
EMP: 25 EST: 2002
SQ FT: 8,000
SALES (est): 1MM-4.9MM **Privately Held**
SIC: **6531** Commercial real estate agency

(G-4630)
HENNEPIN BROADWAY SERIES
800 Lasalle Ave ATE120 (55402-2006)
PHONE..............................612 373-5665
Tom Hoch, *President*
EMP: 75
SALES (est): 1MM-4.9MM **Privately Held**
SIC: **7922** Community theater production
service

(G-4631)
HENNEPIN COUNTY
417 N 5th St Ste 320 (55401-3208)
PHONE..............................612 348-9260
FAX: 612 348-9710
Chuck Vallentine, *Director*
EMP: 35 **Privately Held**
WEB: www.westhennepin.com
SIC: **4011** Long haul railroad
PA: Hennepin County
300 S 6th St A-2303G
Minneapolis MN 55487
612 348-3000

(G-4632)
HENNEPIN COUNTY
Also Called: Surveyors Office
300 S 6th St Rm A-703 (55487-0999)
PHONE..............................612 348-3131
FAX: 612 348-2837
Gary Casswell, *Principal*
EMP: 28
SALES (est): 1MM-4.9MM **Privately Held**
WEB: www.westhennepin.com
SIC: **8713** Surveying service
PA: Hennepin County
300 S 6th St A-2303G
Minneapolis MN 55487
612 348-3000

(G-4633)
HENNEPIN COUNTY
Also Called: Community Health Dept
525 Portland Ave (55415-1533)
PHONE..............................612 348-5273
FAX: 612 904-4345
Paula Nelson, *Office Mgr*
Marcia Miller, *Manager*
Sue Zuidema, *Exec Dir*
Dan Engstrum, *Director*
Betty Lone-Gattaz, *Nurse Practr*
EMP: 2800
SALES (est): 50MM-99.9MM **Privately Held**
WEB: www.westhennepin.com
SIC: **8322** Adult daycare center
PA: Hennepin County
300 S 6th St A-2303G
Minneapolis MN 55487
612 348-3000

(G-4634)
HENNEPIN COUNTY
300 S 6th St (55487-0999)
PHONE..............................612 348-3050
EMP: 85 **Privately Held**
WEB: www.westhennepin.com
SIC: **6531** County general government
administration office; real estate agency &
broker
PA: Hennepin County
300 S 6th St A-2303G
Minneapolis MN 55487
612 348-3000

(G-4635)
HENNEPIN COUNTY
1145 Shenandoah Ln N (55447-3201)
PHONE..............................612 596-0071
FAX: 612 475-4266
Kevin Simondet, *Manager*
EMP: 35 **Privately Held**
WEB: www.westhennepin.com
SIC: **7389** Government house of correction;
packaging & labeling services
PA: Hennepin County
300 S 6th St A-2303G
Minneapolis MN 55487
612 348-3000

(G-4636)
HENNEPIN COUNTY
Also Called: Sentencing To Service
3000 N 2nd St Ste C (55411-1627)
PHONE..............................612 348-7137
FAX: 612 348-2025
Robert Hunter, *Branch Mgr*
EMP: 45 **Privately Held**
WEB: www.westhennepin.com
SIC: **8611** Community affairs & services
PA: Hennepin County
300 S 6th St A-2303G
Minneapolis MN 55487
612 348-3000

(G-4637)
HENNEPIN FACULTY ASSOCIATES
914 S 8th St Ste 700 (55404-1230)
PHONE..............................612 347-5110
FAX: 612 347-3571
Donald Jacob, *CEO*
Ray Taylor, *Vice Pres*
Fred Ames, *Facilities Mgr*
Cheryl Kraft, *Opers Staff*
Chuck Crank, *Purchasing*
EMP: 700
SALES (est): 50MM-99.9MM **Privately Held**
SIC: **8011** Medical center
PA: Hennepin Faculty Associates
120 S 6th St Ste 155
Minneapolis MN 55402
612 347-7226

(G-4638)
HENNEPIN HEALTHCARE SYSTEM INC
701 Park Ave (55415-1623)
PHONE..............................612 873-3000
FAX: 612 904-4348
Art Gonzales, *CEO*
Tim Harlin, *COO*
Gretchin S Crary, *Ch Pathology*
Troy Anderson, *Opers Staff*
Katie Moscowitz, *Opers Staff*
EMP: 5000 EST: 2007
SALES (est): 100MM-499.9MM **Privately Held**
WEB: www.westhennepin.com
SIC: **8062** Medical hospital; pharmacy &
drug store
PA: Hennepin County
300 S 6th St A-2303G
Minneapolis MN 55487
612 348-3000

(G-4639)
HENSON & EFRON
220 S 6th St Ste 1800 (55402-4503)
PHONE..............................612 339-2500
FAX: 612 339-6364
Joe Dixon, *President*
Stanley Efron, *President*
Alan C Eidsness, *Corp Secy*
Susan E Vandenberg, *Vice Pres*
Clark D Opdahl, *Vice Pres*
EMP: 54 EST: 1976
SQ FT: 15,287
SALES (est): 5MM-9.9MM **Privately Held**
SIC: **8111** General practice law office

(G-4640)
HERBECK, DAVID J CPA PFS CHFC
7500 Olson Memorial Hwy (55427-4800)
PHONE..............................763 546-6211
FAX: 763 546-2048
David Herbeck, *Partner*

EMP: 35 EST: 2001
SALES (est): 5MM-9.9MM **Privately Held**
WEB: www.bpkz.com
SIC: **8742** 8721 Financial management
consulting services; certified public
accountant services

(G-4641)
HERITAGE OF EDINA INC
3434 Heritage Dr Office (55435-2280)
PHONE..............................952 920-9145
Wayne Field, *President*
Maria Fields, *Vice Pres*
Maria Field, *Vice Pres*
Kathryn Nordberg, *Vice Pres*
Cindy Thienes, *Accountant*
EMP: 130 EST: 1961
SALES (est): 5MM-9.9MM **Privately Held**
WEB: www.heritageofedina.com
SIC: **8051** 8059 Skilled nursing care facility;
retirement community with nursing

(G-4642)
HEWITT ASSOCIATES INC
45 S 7th St Ste 2100 (55402-1616)
PHONE..............................612 339-7501
FAX: 612 339-3517
Jane Alexander, *Manager*
Daniel Duke, *IT Specialist*
EMP: 55
SALES (est): 1MM-4.9MM **Publicly Held**
WEB: www.hewitt.com
SIC: **8741** Management services
HQ: AON Hewitt LLC
100 Half Day Rd
Lincolnshire IL 60069
847 295-5000

(G-4643)
HEY CITY THEATER CO
824 Hennepin Ave (55403-1803)
PHONE..............................612 333-9202
FAX: 612 333-9195
Sandra Hey, *President*
Michael Dunne, *Vice Pres*
EMP: 85 EST: 1994
SQ FT: 20,000
SALES (est): 5MM-9.9MM **Privately Held**
WEB: www.heycity.com
SIC: **7922** Legitimate live theater producers

(G-4644)
HEYER ENGINEERING
123 N 3rd St Ste 600 (55401-1665)
PHONE..............................612 238-3805
Jim Heyer, *Owner*
EMP: 25 EST: 2006
SALES (est): 1MM-4.9MM **Privately Held**
SIC: **8711** Engineering services

(G-4645)
HICKS BILL & CO LTD
15155 23rd Ave N (55447-4751)
PHONE..............................763 476-6200
FAX: 763 476-8963
William W Hicks, *CEO*
Shelly Binstock, *President*
Lanny Smaagard, *CFO*
Beth Olson, *Manager*
Beth Merkle, *Manager*
EMP: 60 EST: 1975
SQ FT: 60,000
SALES (est): 25MM-49.9MM **Privately Held**
WEB: www.billhicksco.com
SIC: **5091** Wholesales hunting equipment &
supplies

(G-4646)
HIGH-TECH INSTITUTE INC
5100 Gamble Dr Ste 200 (55416-1522)
PHONE..............................763 560-9700
Elizabeth Beseke, *President*
Lelah White, *Director*
Hollie Robinson, *Technician*
EMP: 75
ADMISSIONS: 400**Privately Held**
WEB: www.hti-online.net
SIC: **7999** College; provides massage
instruction; medical & dental assistant
school
HQ: High-Tech Institute Inc
16404 N Black Canyon Hwy
Phoenix AZ 85053
602 328-2800

(G-4647)
HIGHLAND MANAGEMENT GROUP INC
5290 Villa Way (55436-2153)
PHONE..............................952 925-1020
FAX: 952 920-2097
Mary Sehwenke, *President*
Mark Z Jones II, *Chairman*
Sandy Mariotti, *Corp Secy*
EMP: 25 EST: 1971
SQ FT: 6,000
SALES (est): 5MM-9.9MM **Privately Held**
SIC: **6512** 6513 Nonresidential building
operator; apartment building operator

(G-4648)
HILLCREST DEVELOPMENT, LLLP (PA)
2424 Kennedy St NE (55413-2806)
PHONE..............................612 371-0123
FAX: 612 371-9784
Gary Tankenoff, *Partner*
James Tankenoff, *Partner*
Scott Tankenoff, *Partner*
Leoda Swanson, *Controller*
Dick Nord, *Manager*
EMP: 30 EST: 1948
SQ FT: 1,000,000 **Privately Held**
WEB: www.hillcrestdevelopment.com
SIC: **6512** Operators of commercial &
industrial buildings

(G-4649)
HILLSIDE CEMETERY ASSOCIATION
Also Called: Peterson Stolberg
2600 19th Ave NE (55418-4823)
PHONE..............................612 781-3391
Russell Peterson, *President*
Mark Stohlberg, *Corp Secy*
Joyce E Peterson, *Vice Pres*
David Parkin, *Bookkeeper*
Dale Carlson, *Manager*
EMP: 40 EST: 1890
SQ FT: 4,200
SALES (est): 1MM-4.9MM **Privately Held**
WEB: www.hillside-cemetery.com
SIC: **6553** 7261 Operators of cemetery real
estate; funeral director

(G-4650)
HILTON HOTELS CORP
1001 Marquette Ave (55403-2418)
PHONE..............................612 376-1000
FAX: 612 397-4875
Stephanie Hoffer, *VP Sls/Mktg*
Devon Sloan, *VP Sls/Mktg*
Felix Hernandez, *Human Res Mgr*
Kim Zoulek, *Sales Dir*
Joanna Fack, *Sales Mgr*
EMP: 900
SALES (est): 50MM-99.9MM **Publicly Held**
WEB: www.esirvine.com
SIC: **7011** Traveler accommodations
HQ: Hilton Hotels Corp
755 Crossover Ln
Memphis TN 38117
901 374-5000

(G-4651)
HILTON HOTELS CORP
2800 W 80th St (55431-1205)
PHONE..............................952 884-4811
EMP: 60
SALES (est): 1MM-4.9MM **Publicly Held**
WEB: www.esirvine.com
SIC: **7011** Hotel; eating place; drinking
establishment
HQ: Hilton Hotels Corp
755 Crossover Ln
Memphis TN 38117
901 374-5000

(G-4652)
HINSHAW & CULBERTSON LLP
333 S 7th St Ste 2000 (55402-2431)
PHONE..............................612 333-3434
Robert J Mignone, *Managing Prtnr*
David Mylrea, *Managing Prtnr*
J W Roberts, *Managing Prtnr*
Kevin Moore, *Financial Analy*
Patricia Middleton, *Manager*
EMP: 60
SALES (est): 5MM-9.9MM **Privately Held**

(PA)=Parent Co (HQ)=Headquarters (DH)=Div Headquarters
✿ = New business established in last 2 years

2011 Harris Minnesota
Services Directory

© Harris InfoSource 1-866-281-6415
207

SIC: 8111 General practice law office
PA: Hinshaw & Culbertson LLP
222 N La Salle St Ste 300
Chicago IL 60601
312 704-3000

(G-4653)
HIRE A HOST INC
10800 Lyndale Ave S # 210 (55420-5689)
PHONE..........................952 346-8800
Melanie Vejdani, *President*
EMP: 100 EST: 1996
SALES (est): 10MM-24.9MM Privately Held
SIC: 8742 Business planning & organizing services

(G-4654)
HIRE THINKING INC
1750 80 South 8th St (55402)
PHONE..........................612 339-0535
Amy Erickson, *Manager*
EMP: 50
SALES (est): 1MM-4.9MM Privately Held
WEB: www.advhr.com
SIC: 7363 Help supply services
HQ: Hire Thinking Inc
855 Main St Fl 7
Bridgeport CT 06604
203 394-5200

(G-4655)
HIRSHFIELD'S INC (PA)
Also Called: Lathrop Paint
725 2nd Ave N (55405-1601)
PHONE..........................612 377-3910
FAX: 612 436-3384
Frank Hirshfield, *Chairman*
Corey Jensen, *Warehouse Mgr*
David Gerber, *Purch Mgr*
Mark Miller, *Purchasing*
Susan Hanner, *Controller*
EMP: 75 EST: 1894
SQ FT: 115,000 Privately Held
SIC: 5198 Wholesales wall coverings; wholesales paint brushes, rollers & sprayers; manufactures paints & paint additives; wholesales paints; wholesales varnishes; retails paint; retails paint brushes, rollers, sprayers & other supplies; retails wallpaper

(G-4656)
HMN MORTGAGE SERVICES INC
7101 Northland Cir N Ste 200 (55428-1517)
PO Box 5887, Rochester (55903-5887)
PHONE..........................952 914-7440
Mark Svihel, *President*
EMP: 25 EST: 1996
SQ FT: 2,000
SALES (est): 1MM-4.9MM Publicly Held
SIC: 6163 Mortgage brokers service arranging for loans, using money of others
PA: Hmn Financial Inc
1016 Civic Center Dr NW
Rochester MN 55901
507 535-1200

(G-4657)
HNP MANAGMENT
18105 31st Ave N (55447-1147)
PHONE..........................763 475-1872
Greg Wacek, *President*
Kay Wacek, *Corp Secy*
Pat Burke, *Vice Pres*
EMP: 50 EST: 1982
SALES (est): 10MM-24.9MM Privately Held
SIC: 1521 Single-family housing construction

(G-4658)
HNTB CORP
7900 Intrntl Dr Ste 600 (55425-8910)
PHONE..........................952 920-4668
FAX: 952 920-0173
Kimberly Daily, *Engineering*
Gregory Albjerg, *Manager*
Martina Holzinger, *Info Tech Mgr*
EMP: 42
SALES (est): 5MM-9.9MM Privately Held
WEB: www.hntb.com

SIC: 8711 Engineering consulting services
HQ: HNTB Corp
715 Kirk Dr
Kansas City MO 64105
816 472-1201

(G-4659)
HOCKENBERGS
701 Kasota Ave SE (55414-2842)
PHONE..........................612 331-1300
Tom Schrock Sr, *President*
Tom Skotnicki, *General Mgr*
EMP: 25 EST: 1989
SALES (est): 5MM-9.9MM Privately Held
SIC: 5046 Wholesales commercial cooking & food services equipment; wholesales bakery equipment & supplies; wholesales commercial restaurant equipment

(G-4660)
HOLIDAY DIVERSIFIED SERVICES
4567 W 80th St (55437)
PO Box 1224 (55440-1224)
PHONE..........................952 830-8700
Brian A Erickson, *President*
C E Pihl, *Treasurer*
EMP: 400 EST: 1989
SQ FT: 150,000
SALES (est): 100MM-499.9MM Privately Held
SIC: 6794 Selling or licensing of franchises

(G-4661)
HOLMES HOOPER INC
Also Called: Portamedic 881
4825 Olson Memorial Hwy (55422-5147)
PHONE..........................763 545-5641
Linda Newman, *Manager*
Sue Burley, *Manager*
Linda Hodges, *Manager*
EMP: 56
SALES (est): 5MM-9.9MM Publicly Held
WEB: www.hooperholmes.com
SIC: 6411 8011 Insurance information bureau; occupational & industrial specialist, physician or surgeon office
PA: Hooper Holmes Inc
170 Mount Airy Rd
Basking Ridge NJ 07920
908 766-5000

(G-4662)
HOLY EMMANUEL LUTHERAN CHURCH
Also Called: Open Arms Christian Pre-School
201 E 104th St (55420-5305)
PHONE..........................952 888-5116
FAX: 952 888-2349
Candy Frein, *Corp Secy*
Dennis Starr, *Pastor*
EMP: 29 EST: 1969 Privately Held
SIC: 8351 Provides Lutheran church services; preschool center

(G-4663)
HOLY LAND BRAND INC
2513 Central Ave NE (55418-3725)
PO Box 18380 (55418-0380)
PHONE..........................612 781-2627
FAX: 612 781-9918
Christine McKee, *Manager*
▲ EMP: 104 EST: 1998
SQ FT: 13,600
SALES (est): 1MM-4.9MM Privately Held
SIC: 5149 Delicatessen; wholesales bakery products

(G-4664)
HOM FURNITURE INC
Also Called: Home Furniture
7800 Dupont Ave S (55420-1043)
PHONE..........................952 884-8800
Bruce Christopherson, *Manager*
EMP: 65
SALES (est): 10MM-24.9MM Privately Held
WEB: www.homfurniture.com
SIC: 5023 Retails waterbeds & accessories; retails spas & hot tubs; wholesales barbecue grills; retails clocks
PA: Hom Furniture Inc
10301 Woodcrest Dr NW
Minneapolis MN 55433
763 767-3600

(G-4665)
HOME CARE & PCA SERVICES LLC
6500 Brooklyn Blvd # 205 (55429-1756)
PHONE..........................763 566-5063
Song Anderson, *Mng Member*
EMP: 90 EST: 2004
SALES (est): 1MM-4.9MM Privately Held
SIC: 8059 Personal care home, with health care

(G-4666)
HOME CARE SOLUTIONS
3390 Annapolis Ln N Ste A (55447-5379)
PHONE..........................952 924-0677
FAX: 952 924-9099
Tamara Sullivan, *President*
EMP: 80 EST: 1996
SALES (est): 1MM-4.9MM Privately Held
SIC: 8082 Home health care services

(G-4667)
HOME DEPOT USA INC
1705 Annapolis Ln N (55441-3716)
PHONE..........................763 509-9590
FAX: 763 519-9497
Mark Rusin, *Manager*
John Tuten, *Manager*
EMP: 200
SALES (est): 25MM-49.9MM Publicly Held
SIC: 7359 Home center store; tool rental
HQ: Home Depot International Inc
2455 Paces Ferry Rd SE
Atlanta GA 30339
770 319-1669

(G-4668)
HOME FREE INC
8100 26th Ave S Ste 125 (55425-1301)
PO Box 20102 (55420-0102)
PHONE..........................952 814-7400
FAX: 952 853-0966
Nancy Walters, *President*
Nick Walters, *Administrator*
Mac Walters, *Administrator*
EMP: 150 EST: 1988
SALES (est): 5MM-9.9MM Privately Held
WEB: www.homefree.com
SIC: 8059 Personal care home, with health care

(G-4669)
HOMECOMINGS FINANCIAL NETWORK
7801 Metro Pkwy Ste 100 (55425-1544)
PHONE..........................952 854-5432
John C Shea, *Vice Pres*
Roy Buchholtz, *Controller*
EMP: 110
SALES (est): 5MM-9.9MM Privately Held
WEB: www.hfwholesale.com
SIC: 7322 Collection agency
HQ: Homecomings Financial Network
2711 N Haskell Ave # 900
Dallas TX 75204
214 874-2500

(G-4670)
HOMES OF MINNESOTA EDUCATIONAL
3001 Metro Dr Ste 300 (55425-1603)
PHONE..........................763 543-6978
Mike Smith, *CEO*
Pam Pessmer, *Principal*
Debbie Randall, *COO*
Lisa Guetzkow, *Training Dir*
EMP: 30 EST: 1973
SALES (est): 1MM-4.9MM Privately Held
SIC: 8331 Skill training center

(G-4671)
HOMESERVICES LENDING LLC (PA)
333 S 7th St Fl 27 (55402-2438)
PHONE..........................952 928-5300
Todd Johnson, *Member*
Micky Sonderman, *Admin Asst*
EMP: 75 EST: 1995 Privately Held
SIC: 6162 Mortgage & loan lending

(G-4672)
HOMESERVICES OF AMERICA INC (DH)
333 S 7th St Ste 2700 (55402-2438)
PHONE..........................888 485-0018
Arne M Rovick, *Vice Ch Bd*
Ronald J Peltier, *President*
R M Knapp, *President*
Joseph J Valenti, *President*
David L Sokol, *Chairman*
EMP: 50 EST: 1998
SALES (corp-wide): 112.49B Publicly Held
WEB: www.homeservices.com
SIC: 6361 6531 Provides real estate title insurance; real estate agency & broker
HQ: MidAmerican Energy Holdings Co
666 Grand Ave Ste 500
Des Moines IA 50309
515 242-4300

(G-4673)
HOMEWARD BOUND INC
7839 Brooklyn Blvd (55445-2716)
PHONE..........................763 566-7860
FAX: 763 566-1819
Donna Wain, *Branch Mgr*
EMP: 90
SALES (est): 1MM-4.9MM Privately Held
SIC: 8361 Residential care facility
PA: Homeward Bound Inc
13895 Industrial Park Blvd
Minneapolis MN 55441
763 525-3186

(G-4674)
HOPE PRESBYTERIAN CHURCH OF
7132 Portland Ave (55423-3264)
PHONE..........................612 866-4055
FAX: 612 866-8226
David Lenz, *Pastor*
Keith Koenig, *Manager*
Bruce Sullivan, *Administrator*
Linda Heaner, *Assistant*
Cindy Forsgren, *Receptionist*
EST: 1954
SQ FT: 50,000 Privately Held
WEB: www.hope-pc.org
SIC: 8351 Provides Presbyterian church services; preschool center; child day care service

(G-4675)
HORNIG PROPERTIES INC
1000 W 22nd St (55405-2701)
PHONE..........................612 874-4400
Barbara Hornig, *President*
Gary Hornig, *Corp Secy*
David Hornig, *Vice Pres*
Sandy Hornig, *Treasurer*
EMP: 25 EST: 1977
SQ FT: 4,000
SALES (est): 1MM-4.9MM Privately Held
SIC: 6514 Residential building leasing services

(G-4676)
HORTY ELVING & ASSOCIATES INC
505 E Grant St Ste 3 (55404-1474)
PHONE..........................612 332-4422
FAX: 612 344-1282
Thomas Horty, *President*
Barbara Kassanchuk, *Corp Secy*
James C Elving, *Vice Pres*
Jennie Eide, *Manager*
Matt Kassanchuk, *IT/INT Sup*
EMP: 30 EST: 1955
SQ FT: 6,000
SALES (est): 1MM-4.9MM Privately Held
WEB: www.hortyelving.com
SIC: 8712 8711 Architectural service; building construction engineering services

(G-4677)
HORWITZ INC
4401 Quebec Ave N (55428-4978)
PHONE..........................763 533-1900
FAX: 763 533-1438
William McKoskey, *President*
Ty Hlavachek, *Corp Secy*
Joe O'Shaughnessy, *Vice Pres*
EMP: 110

www.HarrisInfo.com
208
2011 Harris Minnesota
Services Directory
▲=Import ▼=Export
◆=Import/Export

EST: 1921
SQ FT: 25,000
SALES (est): 10MM-24.9MM **Privately Held**
WEB: www.horwitzinc.com
SIC: 1711 Plumbing service; heating & air conditioning contractor; process piping contractor; mechanical contractor

(G-4678)
HOSPICE OF THE LAKES
Also Called: Health Partners Organization
8170 33rd Ave S (55425-4516)
PO Box 1309 (55440-1309)
PHONE 952 883-6877
FAX: 952 883-5633
Barbara Tretheway, *Senior VP*
David Dziuk, *Vice Pres*
Vinnie Manchanda, *Vice Pres*
Bryan Senn, *Engineer*
Elizabeth Swanson, *Human Res Dir*
EMP: 80 **EST:** 2000
SALES (est): 5MM-9.9MM **Privately Held**
SIC: 8062 Medical hospital

(G-4679)
HOSPICE OF THE TWIN CITIES INC
10405 6th Ave N Ste 250 (55441-6382)
PHONE 763 531-2424
David Briscoe, *Vice Pres*
Joel Barnes, *Controller*
Becky Real, *Human Res Mgr*
Linda Debner, *Manager*
Barbara Koffel, *Manager*
EMP: 70 **EST:** 1993
SALES (est): 1MM-4.9MM **Privately Held**
WEB: www.hospiceofthetwincities.com
SIC: 8082 8322 Home health care services; individual & family social services

(G-4680)
HOSPICE PREFERRED CHOICE INC
Also Called: Aseracare Hospice
5001 Amrcn Blvd W Ste 655 (55437)
PHONE 952 943-0009
Lori Krech, *Exec Dir*
EMP: 27
SALES (est): 500-999K **Privately Held**
WEB: www.fillmorecap.com
SIC: 8082 Home health care services
DH: Hospice Preferred Choice Inc
1000 Fianna Way
Fort Smith AR 72919
479 201-2000

(G-4681)
HOT DISH ADVERTISING LLC
800 Washington Ave N A (55401-1330)
PHONE 612 341-3100
FAX: 612 341-0555
Greg Lindberg, *Member*
Dawn Lawin, *Member*
Jennifer Campbell, *Vice Pres*
Jenn Onnen, *Vice Pres*
Sharmill Silva, *Advt Staff*
EMP: 31 **EST:** 1999
SQ FT: 10,000
SALES (est): 1MM-4.9MM **Privately Held**
SIC: 7311 Advertising agency

(G-4682)
HOTEL IVY ✿
201 S 11th St Unit 400 (55403-2544)
PHONE 612 746-4600
EMP: 80 **EST:** 2008
SALES (est): 1MM-4.9MM **Privately Held**
SIC: 7011 Hotel

(G-4683)
HYATT CORP
1300 Nicollet Ave Ste H (55403-2608)
PHONE 612 370-1234
FAX: 612 370-1233
Katie Warburton, *Vice Pres*
Lou Zanoli, *Engineering*
Michael Menard, *Controller*
Sara Lebens, *Human Resources*
Michael Kosky, *Sales Dir*
EMP: 350
SALES (est): 10MM-24.9MM **Privately Held**
WEB: www.hyatt.com

SIC: 7011 7299 Traveler accommodations; retails gifts, novelties & souvenirs; eating place; banquet hall facility; drinking establishment
HQ: Hyatt Corp
71 S Wacker Dr Ste 1
Chicago IL 60606
312 750-1234

(G-4684)
HYPERION SOLUTIONS CORP
8400 Nrmndl Lk Blvd # 920 (55437-3843)
PHONE 952 837-2680
Brad Beneke, *Branch Mgr*
EMP: 50
SALES (est): 10MM-24.9MM **Publicly Held**
WEB: www.oracle.com
SIC: 7372 Software publisher
HQ: Hyperion Solutions Corp
1001 Sunset Blvd
Rocklin CA 95765
916 315-3500

(G-4685)
I-STATE TRUCK CENTER (HQ)
2601 American Blvd E (55425-1321)
PHONE 952 854-5511
Jeff Caswell, *CEO*
Jim Williams, *President*
EMP: 50 **EST:** 2003 **Privately Held**
WEB: www.istatetruck.com
SIC: 5084 Wholesales industrial machinery & equipment
PA: Interstate Co's Inc
2601 American Blvd E
Minneapolis MN 55425
952 854-2044

(G-4686)
ICONOCULTURE INC
244 1st Ave N Ste 200 (55401-1608)
PHONE 612 377-0087
FAX: 612 642-2299
Mary Meehan, *President*
Phil Sanderson, *Managing Dir*
Vickie Abrahmson, *Principal*
Charlotte Beal, *Editor*
Marianne Thiel, *Business Mgr*
EMP: 30 **EST:** 1992
SALES (est): 1MM-4.9MM **Publicly Held**
WEB: www.iconoculture.com
SIC: 8732 8742 Market analysis or research services; marketing consulting service; periodical publisher
PA: Corporate Executive Board Co
1919 N Lynn St Ste 500
Arlington VA 22209
571 303-3000

(G-4687)
IG INC
212 2nd Ave N (55401-1429)
PHONE 612 338-7581
Gregory Dolphin, *President*
EMP: 99 **EST:** 1991
SQ FT: 15,000
SALES (est): 1MM-4.9MM **Privately Held**
SIC: 7363 Temporary help service

(G-4688)
ILBNC
Also Called: Institute For Low Back & Neck
3001 Metro Dr Ste 330 (55425-2088)
PHONE 612 879-2521
FAX: 612 879-2555
Steven Savers, *President*
Richard Salib, *President*
Thomas Hennessey, *Vice Pres*
Bryan Lynn, *Vice Pres*
Brian Neubauer, *Finance Dir*
EMP: 40 **EST:** 1981
SQ FT: 9,300
SALES (est): 1MM-4.9MM **Privately Held**
WEB: www.ilbnc.com
SIC: 8011 Physicians' office

(G-4689)
IMAGINET LLC
1300 Nicollet Ave # 5005 (55403-2606)
PHONE 612 752-5500
FAX: 612 752-5501
Jay W Thomas, *Member*
Justen Stepka, *Engineer*
Amy Farrington, *Accountant*
Charles Rath, *Manager*

Adina Madrid, *Manager*
EMP: 70 **EST:** 1991
SQ FT: 27,000
SALES (est): 5MM-9.9MM **Privately Held**
WEB: www.imaginetllc.com
SIC: 7374 Computer graphics service
DH: J Walter Thompson Co
466 Lexington Ave Fl 6
New York NY 10017
212 210-7000

(G-4690)
IMAGING ALLIANCE GROUP LLC
2601 Minnehaha Ave (55406-1530)
PHONE 612 588-9944
Corey Tansom, *CEO*
Steve Norenberg, *Vice Pres*
Harold Lederman, *CFO*
EMP: 79 **EST:** 1997
SQ FT: 10,000
SALES (est): 10MM-24.9MM **Privately Held**
WEB: www.imagingpath.com
SIC: 5044 Wholesales copy equipment

(G-4691)
IMMEDIA INC
3311 Broadway St NE Ste A (55413-1891)
PHONE 612 524-3400
FAX: 612 524-3528
John Ledy, *CEO*
Patrick Thielen, *CFO*
Todd Voit, *Manager*
Bill Schrup, *Telecom Exec*
▲ **EMP:** 195 **EST:** 1958
SQ FT: 180,000
SALES (est): 10MM-24.9MM **Privately Held**
WEB: www.immediaretail.com/
SIC: 7336 Screen printing on fabric; commercial art & graphic design services

(G-4692)
IMPACT MAILING OF MINNESOTA
4600 Lyndale Ave N (55412-1441)
PHONE 612 521-6245
FAX: 612 521-1349
Timothy Johnson, *CEO*
George Johnson, *Ch of Bd*
Mark Anderson, *President*
EMP: 90 **EST:** 1978
SQ FT: 88,000
SALES (est): 5MM-9.9MM **Privately Held**
SIC: 7331 7374 7389 Direct mail advertising service; data processing service; magazine & newspaper subscription fulfillment service

(G-4693)
IN HOME PERSONAL CARE INC
8441 Wayzata Blvd Ste 130 (55426-1306)
PHONE 763 546-1000
Kevin Sullivan, *President*
Phyllis Anderson, *Human Res Mgr*
Karen Jensen, *VP Mktg*
Patricia Unterschuetz, *Manager*
EMP: 160 **EST:** 1991
SALES (est): 5MM-9.9MM **Privately Held**
SIC: 8082 Home health care services

(G-4694)
INDELCO PLASTICS CORP
6530 Cambridge St (55426-4402)
PHONE 952 925-5075
Trent L Dore, *President*
Steven B Dore, *Vice Pres*
Greg Smola, *Sales Staff*
Amy Johnson, *Director*
▲ **EMP:** 39 **EST:** 1978
SQ FT: 40,000
SALES (est): 25MM-49.9MM **Privately Held**
WEB: www.indelco.com
SIC: 5162 5084 Wholesales plastics sheets & rods; wholesales plastics products; wholesales pumps & pumping equipment

(G-4695)
INDEPENDENT SCHOOL DISTRICT
Also Called: Normandale Hills Elem School
9501 Toledo Ave S (55437-2052)
PHONE 952 806-7000
FAX: 952 835-9624
Thomas R Lee, *Branch Mgr*
Ade Alabi, *Comp Lab Dir*
Rosalind Anderson, *Comp Lab Dir*
Emily Lambrecht, *Tech/Comp Coord*

EMP: 60 **Privately Held**
WEB: www.bloomington.k12.mn.us
SIC: 8641 Parent teacher association
PA: Independent School District
1350 W 106th St
Minneapolis MN 55431
952 681-6400

(G-4696)
INDIAN HEALTH BOARD OF
1315 E 24th St Ste 1 (55404-3919)
PHONE 612 721-9800
FAX: 612 721-2904
Phillys Johnson, *CFO*
Robert E Conlin Jr, *Dentist*
Jeff Pederson, *Manager*
Teresa Turner, *Manager*
Malina Pop, *Surgeon*
EMP: 71 **EST:** 1971
SQ FT: 20,000
SALES (est): 5MM-9.9MM **Privately Held**
WEB: www.ihb-mpls.org
SIC: 8011 8021 8093 8322 Clinic operated by physicians; dental clinic; outpatient mental health clinic; outreach program

(G-4697)
INDUSTRIAL ELECTRIC CO
660 Taft St NE (55413-2815)
PHONE 612 331-1268
Gary Novak, *President*
Gary Setala, *Vice Pres*
David Raeker, *Purch Mgr*
Nicholas Novak, *Service Mgr*
Judy Johnson, *Manager*
EMP: 65 **EST:** 1919
SQ FT: 13,000
SALES (est): 5MM-9.9MM **Privately Held**
WEB: www.industrialelectricmn.com
SIC: 1731 Electrical contractor

(G-4698)
INDUSTRIAL HELP INC
2110 Lyndale Ave S (55405-3196)
PHONE 612 871-5650
Robert Constant, *President*
EMP: 25 **EST:** 1963
SALES (est): 500-999K **Privately Held**
SIC: 7363 Temporary help service

(G-4699)
INDUSTRIAL SUPPLY CO INC (PA)
12905 Highway 55 (55441-3841)
PHONE 763 559-0033
FAX: 763 559-3148
Mark Koch, *President*
William Nelson, *CFO*
Chris Bursack, *Manager*
Ken Schmidz, *Info Tech Mgr*
Bob Ziegeweid, *Representative*
▲ **EMP:** 40 **EST:** 1939
SQ FT: 25,000
SALES (corp-wide): 20M **Privately Held**
WEB: www.industrialsupplyco.com
SIC: 5085 Wholesales industrial bearings; manufactures motor vehicle parts & accessories; wholesales industrial power transmission equipment & apparatus; manufactures mechanical power transmission equipment

(G-4700)
INDUSTRIAL TOOL INC
9210 52nd Ave N (55428-4021)
PHONE 763 533-7244
FAX: 763 533-1712
Dick Leuck, *CEO*
Ed J McDonald, *Chairman*
Allan Stinn, *Vice Pres*
Constance Donald, *Vice Pres*
Lisa Thorud, *Project Mgr*
EMP: 35 **EST:** 1974
SQ FT: 30,000
SALES (est): 5MM-9.9MM **Privately Held**
SIC: 5084 Manufactures metal cutting machine tools; wholesales industrial machinery & equipment

(G-4701)
INFINITY DIRECT INC
13220 County Road 6 # 200 (55441-8791)
PHONE 763 559-1111
Tom Harding, *CEO*
David Greenblat, *President*

(PA)=Parent Co (HQ)=Headquarters (DH)=Div Headquarters
✿ = New business established in last 2 years

2011 Harris Minnesota
Services Directory

© Harris InfoSource 1-866-281-6415
209

Shawn Harding, *Vice Pres*
Jerry Bentley, *CFO*
Cathie Tietz, *Manager*
EMP: 33 **EST:** 1991
SQ FT: 12,000
SALES (est): 1MM-4.9MM **Privately Held**
WEB: www.infinitydirect.com
SIC: 8742 7331 Merchandising consultant;
direct mail advertising service

(G-4702)
ING FINANCIAL PARTNERS INC
111 Washington Ave S (55401-2106)
PHONE............................612 372-5507
FAX: 612 372-1818
Mike Dubes, *CEO*
Barbara Stewart, *President*
Ken Cameraensi, *President*
Don Picha, *Technical Mgr*
Eugene M Grayson, *VP Sls/Mktg*
EMP: 68 **EST:** 1968
SQ FT: 26,000
SALES (est): 10MM-24.9MM **Privately Held**
WEB: www.culveragency.com
SIC: 6211 Security broker service
PA: Ing America Insurance Holdings
1100 N Market St Ste 780
Wilmington DE 19801
302 658-3302

(G-4703)
ING NORTH AMERICA INSURANCE
20 Washington Ave S (55401-1908)
PHONE............................612 342-7878
FAX: 612 372-1015
Fitz Wickham, *Member*
Eric Anderson, *Member*
Paula Engelke, *Corp Secy*
Joy M Benner, *Corp Secy*
Stephen Buschbom, *Assistant VP*
EMP: 60
SALES (est): 50MM-99.9MM **Privately Held**
SIC: 6311 Life insurance carrier
HQ: Ing North America Insurance
5780 Powers Ferry Rd NW
Atlanta GA 30327
770 980-5100

(G-4704)
INNOVATIVE BUILDING CONCEPTS
849 W 80th St (55420-1027)
PHONE............................952 885-0262
FAX: 952 885-0570
Ray Kangas, *President*
Cheri Kangas, *Vice Pres*
Brent Kangas, *Vice Pres*
EMP: 30 **EST:** 1987
SQ FT: 10,000
SALES (est): 1MM-4.9MM **Privately Held**
SIC: 1761 Roofing contractor

(G-4705)
INNOVATIVE TECHNICAL PERSONNEL
Also Called: Inntech Personnel
4050 Olson Memorial Hwy (55422-5323)
PHONE............................763 591-9191
Mike Bruhn, *Owner*
Bruce Stursa, *Administrator*
EMP: 30 **EST:** 1992
SQ FT: 1,100 **Privately Held**
WEB: www.inntechinc.com
SIC: 7361 8711 Employment placement
services; engineering consulting services

(G-4706)
INSIGNIA SYSTEMS INC
8799 Brooklyn Blvd (55445-2398)
PHONE............................763 392-6200
FAX: 763 392-6222
Scott F Drill, *President*
Larry Mortimer, *Exec VP*
Alan M Jones, *Senior VP*
A T Lucas, *Senior VP*
Scott J Simcox, *Senior VP*
EMP: 77 **EST:** 1990
SQ FT: 41,000
SALES (est): 10MM-24.9MM **Publicly Held**
WEB: www.insigniasystems.com
SIC: 8742 7389 Merchandising consultant;
advertising, promotional & trade show
service

(G-4707)
INSPEC INC
5801 Duluth St Ste 212 (55422-3953)
PHONE............................763 546-3434
Mike Remington, *President*
Pete Nottleson, *Vice Pres*
Trace Knapp, *Accounts Mgr*
Fred King, *Marketing Mgr*
Marla Tangen, *Manager*
EMP: 50 **EST:** 1973
SQ FT: 14,000
SALES (est): 1MM-4.9MM **Privately Held**
WEB: www.inspec.com
SIC: 7389 8711 8712 Inspection & testing
service; architectural service; engineering
services

(G-4708)
INSTITUTE FOR CLINICAL SYSTEMS
8009 34th Ave S (55425-1608)
PHONE............................952 814-7060
FAX: 952 858-9675
Kent Bottles, *President*
John Sakowski, *COO*
Gary Oftedahl, *Director*
EMP: 25 **EST:** 1993 **Privately Held**
WEB: www.icsi.org
SIC: 8621 Medical field association

(G-4709)
INSTITUTE FOR ENVIRONMENTAL
Also Called: I E A
9201 W Broadway Ave Ste 600
(55445-1924)
PHONE............................763 315-7900
Bruce Bomier, *CEO*
Margaret Denlinger, *Corp Secy*
Tom Gapinske, *COO*
Brooklyn Park, *COO*
Chris Dukatz, *Plant Mgr*
EMP: 30 **EST:** 1976
SQ FT: 12,000
SALES (est): 1MM-4.9MM **Privately Held**
WEB: www.ieainstitute.com
SIC: 8748 8641 Environmental consultant;
environmental protection organization

(G-4710)
INSTITUTE OF PRODUCTION
312 Washington Ave N (55401-1315)
PHONE............................612 375-1900
FAX: 612 375-1919
Brian Jacoby, *President*
Lance Sabin, *Vice Pres*
Mike Blair, *Controller*
Stacy Semler, *Human Res Mgr*
EMP: 96 **EST:** 2002
SQ FT: 50,000
SALES (est): 1MM-4.9MM **Privately Held**
SIC: 7389 Music & drama school; music &
broadcasting service

(G-4711)
INTEGRA TELECOM INC
511 11th Ave S (55415-1537)
PHONE............................763 745-8000
Don Olds, *Manager*
EMP: 150 **Privately Held**
SIC: 4813 5065 Local & long distance
telephone communications services;
wholesales electronic parts & equipment
PA: Integra Telecom Inc
1201 NE Lloyd Blvd # 500
Portland OR 97232
503 453-8000

(G-4712)
INTEGRAL 7 INC
100 S 5th St Ste 1725 (55402-1266)
PHONE............................612 436-0701
E C Porter, *CEO*
Carolyn Rose, *President*
Kirk Lundeen, *Vice Pres*
Kurt Waltenbaugh, *Vice Pres*
Steve Hatle, *Manager*
EMP: 30 **EST:** 2001
SQ FT: 8,000
SALES (est): 1MM-4.9MM **Privately Held**
WEB: www.integral7.com
SIC: 7371 Computer software development
& applications

(G-4713)
INTEGRATED MEDICAL REHAB
7250 France Ave S Ste 111 (55435-4311)
PHONE............................952 837-8991
Anthony Krier, *Owner*
Xochill Thalhuber, *Manager*
EMP: 30 **EST:** 2001
SALES (est): 1MM-4.9MM **Privately Held**
SIC: 8093 Specialty outpatient clinic

(G-4714)
INTEGRITY HOME HEALTH CO
2100 Plymouth Ave N (55411-3675)
PHONE............................612 827-1479
FAX: 612 827-1482
Cynthia Buffington, *CEO*
◆ **EMP:** 28 **EST:** 2006
SALES (est): 500-999K **Privately Held**
SIC: 8082 Home health care services

(G-4715)
INTEGRITY LIVING OPTIONS INC
4210 W 44th St (55424-1037)
PHONE............................952 920-9291
Kerry F Keller, *President*
David Kendrick, *CFO*
EMP: 75 **EST:** 2002
SALES (est): 1MM-4.9MM **Privately Held**
WEB: www.integrityliving.com
SIC: 8322 Individual & family social services

(G-4716)
INTEREUM INC
845 Berkshire Ln N (55441-5419)
PHONE............................763 417-3300
Jerry Erickson, *President*
Melissa Nelson, *Corp Secy*
Bret Abbott, *Vice Pres*
Matt Sveen, *Treasurer*
Robert Mattson, *Controller*
EMP: 114 **EST:** 1980
SQ FT: 85,000
SALES (est): 25MM-49.9MM **Privately Held**
WEB: www.intereum.com
SIC: 5021 Wholesales office furniture

(G-4717)
INTERLACHEN COUNTRY CLUB
6200 Interlachen Blvd (55436-1137)
PHONE............................952 929-1661
FAX: 952 929-7720
George Carrol, *General Mgr*
Deeanna M Otvedt, *Human Resources*
Terry Sloggy, *Human Resources*
Robert W Carlson, *Info Tech Mgr*
EMP: 125 **EST:** 1911
SQ FT: 52,000
SALES (est): 5MM-9.9MM **Privately Held**
SIC: 7997 Country club

(G-4718)
INTERLOG USA INC (PA)
2818A Anthony Ln S (55418-3234)
PHONE............................612 789-3456
FAX: 612 789-6708
James Taylor, *President*
Brent Koughan, *Vice Pres*
Clyde Reynolds, *Controller*
Ken Ponn, *Controller*
Allan Matthys, *Finance Dir*
◆ **EMP:** 26 **EST:** 1995
SQ FT: 5,500
SALES (corp-wide): 50M **Privately Held**
WEB: www.interlogusa.com
SIC: 4731 Truck transportation brokers

(G-4719)
INTERMED CONSULTANTS LTD
6363 France Ave S Ste 400 (55435-2142)
PHONE............................952 920-2070
David Bowlan, *President*
Steven Diddis, *Corp Secy*
James Somerville MD, *Treasurer*
Lynn Page, *Office Mgr*
Sandy Walto, *Nursing Dir*
EMP: 25 **EST:** 1981
SALES (est): 1MM-4.9MM **Privately Held**
SIC: 8721 Billing & bookkeeping services

(G-4720)
INTERNATIONAL ASSOCIATION OF
30 S 7th St (55402-1601)
PO Box 600035, Saint Paul (55106-0001)
PHONE............................612 673-3586
Kris Arneson, *Principal*
EMP: 500 **Privately Held**
SIC: 8621 Professional organization

(G-4721)
INTERNATIONAL DAIRY QUEEN INC (HQ)
7505 Metro Blvd Ste 500 (55439-3042)
PHONE............................952 830-0200
FAX: 952 830-0498
Charles W Mooty, *President*
Karen Amundson, *Corp Secy*
Jean Champagne, *COO*
Chuck C Champman III, *COO*
Charles J Chapman III, *COO*
▲ **EMP:** 275 **EST:** 1962
SQ FT: 114,000
SALES (corp-wide): 112.49B **Publicly Held**
WEB: www.berkshirehathaway.com
SIC: 5113 5145 5147 Wholesales
disposable plastic & paper dishes;
wholesales disposable plastic utensils;
wholesales paper napkins; wholesales soda
fountain toppings; wholesales salted or
roasted nuts; wholesales candy; wholesales
fresh meat
PA: Berkshire Hathaway Inc
3555 Farnam St Ste 1440
Omaha NE 68131
402 346-1400

(G-4722)
INTERNATIONAL DIABETES CENTER
3800 Park Nicollet Blvd 6F (55416-2527)
PHONE............................952 993-3393
Mary Miley, *Corp Secy*
David Abelson, *Treasurer*
Nielsen D James, *Director*
Richard Bergenstal, *Director*
Mary L Johnson, *Bd of Directors*
EMP: 102 **EST:** 1969
SALES (est): 10MM-24.9MM **Privately Held**
SIC: 8011 Diabetes specialist, physician or
surgeon

(G-4723)
INTERNATIONAL PACKAGING INC
8921 Wyoming Ave N (55445-1834)
PHONE............................763 315-6200
Jon Butkovich, *Ch of Bd*
Mary J Morales, *Corp Secy*
Anthony Francis, *Engineering*
Steve Cavanaugh, *Sales Mgr*
EMP: 100 **EST:** 1973
SQ FT: 35,000
SALES (est): 5MM-9.9MM **Privately Held**
WEB: www.internationalpackaging.com
SIC: 7389 Packaging & labeling services

(G-4724)
INTERNATIONAL PAPER CO
345 Industrial Blvd NE (55413-2928)
PHONE............................612 781-6611
Anne Dilworth, *Credit Mgr*
Joan Vangeest, *Human Res Mgr*
Curt Hustad, *VP Sales*
Tim Kettler, *Sales Mgr*
John McGuire, *Sales Mgr*
EMP: 150
SALES (est): 100MM-499.9MM **Publicly Held**
WEB: www.internationalpaper.com
SIC: 5111 Wholesales printing & writing
paper
PA: International Paper Co
6400 Poplar Ave
Memphis TN 38197
901 419-7000

(G-4725)
INTERPUBLIC GROUP OF CO'S INC
222 S 9th St Ste 2825 (55402-3347)
PHONE............................612 367-5144
EMP: 60

www.HarrisInfo.com
210

2011 Harris Minnesota
Services Directory

▲=Import ▼=Export
◆=Import/Export

SALES (est): 5MM-9.9MM **Publicly Held**
SIC: **8742** Marketing consulting service
PA: Interpublic Group of Co's Inc
1114 Avenue Of The Americas
New York NY 10036
212 704-1200

(G-4726)

INTERSTATE CO'S INC (PA)

2601 American Blvd E (55425-1321)
PHONE..............................952 854-2044
Gordon D Galarneau, *Ch of Bd*
David Walch, *General Mgr*
Carl Brown, *General Mgr*
Chuck Kitchen, *Vice Pres*
Bruce Haggstrom, *Vice Pres*
EMP: 70 EST: 1957 **Privately Held**
WEB: www.istate.com
SIC: **8741** 4961 7538 Management services; air conditioning supply services; retails new & used trucks, tractors & trailers; automotive diesel engine repair service; administrative management services

---

(G-4727)

INTERSTATE HOTELS & RESORTS

814 American Blvd E (55420-1358)
PHONE..............................952 854-5558
FAX: 952 854-4623
Tim Ronayne, *Branch Mgr*
EMP: 40
SALES (est): 1MM-4.9MM **Publicly Held**
SIC: **7011** Traveler accommodations
PA: Interstate Hotels & Resorts
4501 Fairfax Dr Ste 500
Arlington VA 22203
703 387-3100

(G-4728)

INTERSTATE HOTELS & RESORTS

3800 American Blvd E (55425-1658)
PHONE..............................952 854-2100
Charles Goldberg, *General Mgr*
Mike Brunkow, *General Mgr*
Stu Gerwin, *Chief Engr*
Scott Brotemarkle, *Engineer*
Dean Olevson, *Finance*
EMP: 125
SALES (est): 5MM-9.9MM **Publicly Held**
SIC: **7041** Membership hotel
PA: Interstate Hotels & Resorts
4501 Fairfax Dr Ste 500
Arlington VA 22203
703 387-3100

(G-4729)

INTERSTATE POWER SYSTEMS

2501 American Blvd E (55425-1319)
PHONE..............................952 854-5511
Kim Tuma, *Maintenance Dir*
Dave Heairet, *Accounting Dir*
Nan Yaeger, *Human Res Dir*
Michael Ware, *Sales Staff*
Jim Williams, *Sales Staff*
EMP: 82
SALES (est): 25MM-49.9MM **Privately Held**
WEB: www.istate.com
SIC: **5084** 5063 Wholesales industrial engines & transportation equipment; wholesales electrical apparatus & equipment; manufactures factory basis rebuilt motor vehicle engines & transmissions
HQ: Interstate Power Systems Inc
2601 American Blvd E
Minneapolis MN 55425
952 854-2044

(G-4730)

INTERSTATE POWER SYSTEMS INC (HQ)

2601 American Blvd E (55425-1321)
PHONE..............................952 854-2044
Jeff Gaswell, *CEO*
Travis Penrod, *President*
Gordan Galarneau, *Chairman*
Larry Schwartz, *CFO*
James Sarkkinen, *Credit Mgr*
EMP: 60 EST: 1989
SQ FT: 200,000 **Privately Held**
WEB: www.istate.com

SIC: **5084** Wholesales industrial trucks
PA: Interstate Co's Inc
2601 American Blvd E
Minneapolis MN 55425
952 854-2044

(G-4731)

INTO THE MYSTIC PRODUCTIONS

Also Called: Brave New Workshop
2605 Hennepin Ave (55408-1150)
PHONE..............................612 332-6620
Jeeny Lilledhl, *General Mgr*
John Sweeney, *Principal*
Jenni Lilledahl, *Principal*
Mark Bergren, *Principal*
Lynn Lanners, *Executive*
EMP: 30 EST: 1958
SALES (est): 1MM-4.9MM **Privately Held**
SIC: **7922** Legitimate live theater producers

(G-4732)

INTREPID HOME HEALTH CARE INC

6600 France Ave S Ste 510 (55435-1804)
PHONE..............................952 285-7300
Bronwyn Bamber, *Principal*
EMP: 25 EST: 2005
SALES (est): 500-999K **Privately Held**
WEB: www.intrepidusa.com
SIC: **8082** Home health care services
DH: Intrepid of Texas Inc
6600 France Ave S Ste 510
Minneapolis MN 55435
952 285-7300

(G-4733)

INTREPID OF TEXAS INC (DH)

6600 France Ave S Ste 510 (55435-1804)
PHONE..............................952 285-7300
Todd J Garamella, *CEO*
EMP: 30 EST: 2005
SALES (corp-wide): 120M **Privately Held**
WEB: www.intrepidusa.com
SIC: **8082** Home health care services
HQ: Intrepid Co's Inc
4055 Valley View Ln # 500
Dallas TX 75244
214 455-3750

(G-4734)

INTUITIVE TECHNOLOGY GROUP LLC

2001 Killebrew Dr Ste 305 (55425-1886)
PHONE..............................952 854-1663
FAX: 952 854-3193
Jason Livingston, *President*
Eric Ohlson, *Member*
Wayne Schiferl, *CIO*
EMP: 25 EST: 2006
SQ FT: 1,600
SALES (est): 1MM-4.9MM **Privately Held**
WEB: www.be-intuitive.com
SIC: **7379** Computer system consulting services

(G-4735)

IRON MOUNTAIN INFORMATION MGT

9715 James Ave S (55431-2513)
PHONE..............................952 888-3852
FAX: 952 888-7467
Joseph Strub, *General Mgr*
Dale Busch, *General Mgr*
Damien Darveau, *Opers Mgr*
Kathy Wehking, *Sales Mgr*
Tim Sprau, *Sales Executive*
EMP: 130
SALES (est): 10MM-24.9MM **Publicly Held**
WEB: www.ironmountain.com
SIC: **4226** 8721 Document & office records storage services; accounting, auditing & bookkeeping services
HQ: Iron Mountain Information Mgt
745 Atlantic Ave Fl 10
Boston MA 02111
617 357-4455

(G-4736)

ISGN FULFILLMENT SERVICES INC

5401 Gamble Dr Ste 300 (55416-1502)
PHONE..............................952 512-7400
FAX: 952 512-3009

Kristi Stout, *Senior VP*
EMP: 100
SALES (est): 5MM-9.9MM **Privately Held**
WEB: www.isgn.com
SIC: **6541** 6361 6531 Title search company; title insurance carrier; real estate appraiser
DH: Isgn Fulfillment Services Inc
3220 Tillman Dr Ste 301
Bensalem PA 19020
267 525-9400

(G-4737)

ISLE WEST ASSOCIATES, LLP

Also Called: Nicollet Island Inn
601 Marquette Ave Ste 100 (55402-1707)
PHONE..............................612 331-1800
FAX: 612 331-6528
Howard Bergerud, *Partner*
Larry Abdo, *General Mgr*
Mary Grams, *Manager*
Patrick Boyum, *Manager*
EMP: 90 EST: 1988
SALES (est): 1MM-4.9MM **Privately Held**
WEB: www.nicolletislandinn.com
SIC: **7011** Full service American restaurant; traveler accommodations

---

(G-4738)

ISS FACILITY SERVICES INC ✪

4222 Park Glen Rd (55416-4758)
PHONE..............................763 559-6679
Charlie Klever, *General Mgr*
Julie Lynch, *District Mgr*
Charlie Kleber, *Vice Pres*
Sandi Larsen, *Payroll Mgr*
EMP: 40 EST: 2009
SALES (est): 1MM-4.9MM **Privately Held**
SIC: **7349** Janitorial & custodial services

(G-4739)

ISTATE TRUCK INC (PA)

2601 American Blvd E (55425-1321)
PHONE..............................952 854-2044
Gordon D Galarneau, *CEO*
Jeffrey Caswell, *President*
Larry Schwartz, *Corp Secy*
Dave Heairet, *Accountant*
EST: 2002 **Privately Held**
SIC: **5012** 5013 7539 Wholesales truck tractors; automotive turbocharger & blower repair service; wholesales truck parts & accessories

---

(G-4740)

ITALIAN AMERICAN CLUB OF

Also Called: RUSHFORD HALL-ITALIAN AMERICAN
2223 Central Ave NE (55418-3762)
PHONE..............................612 781-0625
FAX: 612 781-1188
Frank Balma, *Treasurer*
Dorothy Derr, *Sales Staff*
EMP: 60
SALES (est): 10MM-24.9MM **Privately Held**
SIC: **6512** 7389 Operators of auditoriums & halls; accommodation locating service

---

(G-4741)

ITASCA CONSULTING GROUP INC (PA)

111 3rd Ave S Ste 450 (55401-2546)
PHONE..............................612 371-4711
FAX: 612 371-4717
S M Bergman, *President*
J Markham, *President*
Itasca G AB, *Managing Dir*
Charles Fairhurst, *Vice Pres*
Kathy Sikora, *Purchasing*
EMP: 25 EST: 1981
SQ FT: 6,000 **Privately Held**
WEB: www.itascacg.com
SIC: **7373** 8999 Computer systems analysis & design; earth science services

---

(G-4742)

IVO APPLIANCE INC

7825 Washingtn Ave S # 500 (55439-2415)
PHONE..............................650 286-1300
Joseph O'Brien, *CEO*
EMP: 85 EST: 2003
SALES (est): 10MM-24.9MM **Privately Held**
WEB: www.ivoappliance.com
SIC: **7373** Computer integrated systems design services

(G-4743)

J B HUNT TRANSPORT INC

722 Kasota Cir SE (55414-2815)
PHONE..............................612 362-9419
Michael Elliot, *Manager*
EMP: 30
SALES (est): 1MM-4.9MM **Publicly Held**
WEB: www.jbhunt.com
SIC: **4213** Over the road trucking
HQ: JB Hunt Transport Inc
615 Jb Hunt Corporate Dr
Lowell AR 72745
479 820-0000

(G-4744)

J BENSON CONSTRUCTION

3230 Gorham Ave Ste 1 (55426-4295)
PHONE..............................952 920-0717
Wayne Benson, *President*
Janine Kemmer, *Manager*
Jerry Penner, *Manager*
EMP: 30 EST: 1988
SQ FT: 9,000
SALES (est): 5MM-9.9MM **Privately Held**
WEB: www.walkerstreet.net
SIC: **1521** Single-family home general remodeling service; single-family home fire damage repair service

---

(G-4745)

J C PENNEY CO INC

6601 France Ave Fl 3 (55435)
PHONE..............................952 920-8557
Renee Pearlman, *Manager*
EMP: 25
SALES (est): 500-999K **Publicly Held**
WEB: www.jcpenney.com
SIC: **7231** Beauty salon
PA: J C Penney Co Inc
6501 Legacy Dr
Plano TX 75024
972 431-1000

(G-4746)

J D FINGERMAN ENTERPRISES INC

2901 W 66th St (55423-1940)
PHONE..............................612 861-1697
James Fingerman, *President*
EMP: 35 EST: 2001
SALES (est): 1MM-4.9MM **Privately Held**
SIC: **7212** Laundry & drycleaning pickup station

(G-4747)

J L BUCHANAN INC

50 S 10th St Ste 440 (55403-2021)
PHONE..............................612 334-1710
Jeff Buchanan, *President*
Suzy Hoaby, *Vice Pres*
Robin Harris, *Manager*
EST: 1984
SQ FT: 11,500 **Privately Held**
WEB: www.jlbuchanan.com
SIC: **5199** 5112 Wholesales variety store merchandise; wholesales calendars; wholesales Christmas novelties; wholesales stationery & office supplies

---

(G-4748)

J PERZEL & ASSOCIATES

4829 Minnetonka Blvd # 201 (55416-2211)
PHONE..............................612 455-6060
Joe Perzel, *Vice Pres*
EMP: 35 EST: 2005
SALES (est): 1MM-4.9MM **Privately Held**
WEB: www.jperzel.com
SIC: **8748** Business consulting services

(G-4749)

J T MEGA LLC

4020 Minnetonka Blvd # 302 (55416-4157)
PHONE..............................952 929-1370
Melissa Mathei, *Adv Mgr*
Patrick Dupont, *Advt Staff*
Phil Lee, *Mng Member*
Jill J Greenough, *Manager*
Tobi Stern, *Admin Asst*
EMP: 27 EST: 1976
SQ FT: 7,000
SALES (est): 1MM-4.9MM **Privately Held**
WEB: www.jtmega.com

(PA)=Parent Co (HQ)=Headquarters (DH)=Div Headquarters
✪ = New business established in last 2 years

2011 Harris Minnesota
Services Directory

© Harris InfoSource 1-866-281-6415
211

SIC: **7311** 8742 Advertising agency; management consulting services

(G-4750)
JACOBS INVESTORS INC
80 S 8th St Ste 2900 (55402-2250)
PHONE..............................612 339-9500
Irwin Jacobs, *President*
Daniel T Lindsay, *Corp Secy*
Gerald A Schwalbach, *Exec VP*
Kenneth Severinson, *Senior VP*
Roger Cloutier II, *Senior VP*
EMP: 30 EST: 1990
SALES (est): 1MM-4.9MM **Privately Held**
SIC: **8741** Management services

(G-4751)
JAECKLE MINNESOTA
504 Malcolm Ave SE Ste 100
(55414-3354)
PHONE..............................612 676-0388
FAX: 612 676-0388
Fred Jaeckle, *CEO*
Jeffrey Jaeckle, *President*
Torrey Jaeckle, *Vice Pres*
Norma Ducommon, *Credit Mgr*
EMP: 90 EST: 1958
SQ FT: 22,000
SALES (est): 25MM-49.9MM **Privately Held**
SIC: **5072** 5031 Wholesales builders' hardware; wholesales interior building materials

(G-4752)
JAMES A DOSEN
600 Highway 169 S Ste 1750
(55426-1276)
PHONE..............................952 473-2002
James A Dosen, *Partner*
Lori Simonson, *Administration*
EMP: 25
SALES (est): 1MM-4.9MM **Privately Held**
SIC: **8721** Certified public accountant services

(G-4753)
JAMES FORD BELL MUSEUM OF
10 Church St SE (55455-0145)
PHONE..............................612 624-4112
FAX: 612 626-7704
Jennifer Menken, *Manager*
Katie Nyberg, *Exec Dir*
Scott Lanyon, *Director*
Susan Weller, *Director*
EMP: 50 EST: 1875
SALES (est): 1MM-4.9MM **Privately Held**
WEB: www.bellmuseum.org
SIC: **8412** Museum

(G-4754)
JAPS-OLSON CO (PA)
7500 Excelsior Blvd (55426-4503)
PHONE..............................952 932-9393
Michael Beddor, *CEO*
Kevin Beddor, *President*
Michael Murphy, *President*
Robert Murphy, *Chairman*
Vern Langsdorf, *Vice Pres*
EMP: 640 EST: 1907
SQ FT: 512,000 **Privately Held**
WEB: www.japsolson.com
SIC: **7331** Prints lithographed circular or form letters; mailing services; prints lithographed coupons; prints lithographed calendars; commercial printing; addressing service; typesetting service

(G-4755)
JAS APARTMENTS INC
1 E 19th St Ste 100 (55403-3785)
PHONE..............................612 872-4444
Stephen A Frenz, *President*
Jackye Maslach, *Administration*
EMP: 40 EST: 1992
SQ FT: 30,000
SALES (est): 5MM-9.9MM **Privately Held**
WEB: www.jasapartments.com
SIC: **6513** Apartment building operator

(G-4756)
JDE STUDIOS INC
3224 Nicollet Ave (55408-4437)
PHONE..............................612 825-4076
Robin Kukas, *President*
EMP: 48 EST: 2004

SALES (est): 1MM-4.9MM **Privately Held**
SIC: **7299** Apartment locating service

(G-4757)
JEFFERSON PARTNERS LP
2100 E 26th St (55404-4101)
PHONE..............................612 359-3400
FAX: 612 359-3437
Fred E Kaiser, *Partner*
Charles A Zelle, *Partner*
Darin Macdonald, *Corp Secy*
Steve Woelfel, *CFO*
Jeffery D Kruger, *Treasurer*
EMP: 220 EST: 1992
SQ FT: 20,000
SALES (est): 10MM-24.9MM **Privately Held**
SIC: **4131** 4141 4142 Interstate bus line transportation service; local bus charter service; long-distance bus charter service

(G-4758)
JEFFREY SLOCUM & ASSOCIATES
43 Main St SE Ste 300 (55414-1032)
PHONE..............................612 338-7020
FAX: 612 338-7034
Jeffrey C Slocum, *President*
EMP: 85 EST: 1986
SQ FT: 18,000
SALES (est): 10MM-24.9MM **Privately Held**
WEB: www.jslocum.com
SIC: **6282** Investment advisory service

(G-4759)
JEREMIAH PROGRAM
1510 Laurel Ave Ste 100 (55403-1266)
PHONE..............................612 692-8711
FAX: 612 692-8712
Gloria P Jordan, *President*
Sandra Davis, *Bd of Directors*
Toni Carter, *Bd of Directors*
EMP: 26 EST: 1997 **Privately Held**
WEB: www.jeremiahprogram.org
SIC: **8399** Social change association

(G-4760)
JEREMIAH SAINT PAUL LP
1510 Laurel Ave Ste 100 (55403-1266)
PHONE..............................612 259-3001
Gloria Perez, *Partner*
EMP: 43
SALES (est): 5MM-9.9MM **Privately Held**
SIC: **6531** Housing authority operator

(G-4761)
JERRY'S ENTERPRISES INC
5033 Vernon Ave S (55436-2102)
PHONE..............................952 929-4601
FAX: 952 929-2273
John Connolly, *Manager*
Sharon Johnson, *Assistant*
EMP: 25
SALES (est): 1MM-4.9MM **Privately Held**
SIC: **5084** 7699 Hardware store; wholesales industrial engines; lawn mower repair shop; manufactures saws & sawing equipment
PA: Jerry's Enterprises Inc
5101 Vernon Ave S Ste 2A
Minneapolis MN 55436
952 922-8335

(G-4762)
JEWISH COMMUNITY CENTER OF
4330 Cedar Lake Rd S (55416-3700)
PHONE..............................952 381-3400
FAX: 952 381-3401
Stuart Wachs, *Co-Owner*
Jeff Schachtman, *Director*
Annette Weinberg, *Receptionist*
EMP: 175 EST: 1967
SQ FT: 116,000
SALES (est): 5MM-9.9MM **Privately Held**
WEB: www.sabesjcc.com
SIC: **8322** 8641 Community center; civic & social organization

(G-4763)
JILL H RUSTERHOLZ
825 Nicollet Mall (55402-2606)
PHONE..............................952 806-0011
Jill H Rusterholz, *Principal*
EMP: 35 EST: 2001
SALES (est): 1MM-4.9MM **Privately Held**

SIC: **8049** Health practitioners' office

(G-4764)
JIM BERN CO
8162 Bloomington Ave (55425-1108)
PHONE..............................952 854-4141
FAX: 952 854-1877
Diana Howe, *Manager*
Theresa Hodgman, *Manager*
Lisa Clark, *Manager*
EMP: 35
SALES (est): 5MM-9.9MM **Privately Held**
SIC: **6514** Residential building leasing services
PA: Jim Bern Co
1336 W Towne Square Rd
Thiensville WI 53092
262 241-4010

(G-4765)
JJ TAYLOR CO'S INC
Also Called: Eastside Beverage
701 Industrial Blvd NE (55413-2905)
PHONE..............................651 482-1133
Mike Bamonti, *President*
Ken Deackman, *Manager*
EMP: 145
SALES (est): 50MM-99.9MM **Privately Held**
SIC: **5181** Wholesales beer & other fermented malt liquors
PA: JJ Taylor Co's Inc
655 N Highway A1A
Jupiter FL 33477
561 354-2900

(G-4766)
JLM LANDSCAPE LLC
7141 Amundson Ave (55439-2020)
PHONE..............................952 941-9818
FAX: 952 941-1160
Robert Roos, *Member*
EMP: 28 EST: 1998 **Privately Held**
WEB: www.jlmlandscape.com
SIC: **0781** 0782 1521 Garden planning services; patio & deck construction & repair service; landscaping services

(G-4767)
JMS EQUITIES INC
5250 W 74th St Ste 1 (55439-2232)
PHONE..............................952 949-3630
Jeffery Schoenwetter, *President*
EMP: 30 EST: 2001
SALES (est): 5MM-9.9MM **Privately Held**
WEB: www.jms-homes.com
SIC: **6531** Real estate services

(G-4768)
JOHN A DALSIN & SON INC
2830 20th Ave S (55407-1223)
PHONE..............................612 729-9334
FAX: 612 729-9330
Robert M Dalsin, *President*
Barbara Dalsin, *Vice Pres*
Brian Bargsten, *Vice Pres*
EMP: 120 EST: 1912
SQ FT: 24,000
SALES (est): 10MM-24.9MM **Privately Held**
SIC: **1761** Roofing, siding & sheet metal work

(G-4769)
JOHN B COLLINS ASSOCIATES INC
8500 Normandale Ste 2400 (55437)
PHONE..............................952 820-1000
Patrick Denzer, *President*
John B Collins, *Chairman*
Scott Fest, *Senior VP*
Daniel Madsen, *Senior VP*
John Novak, *Senior VP*
▲ EMP: 140 EST: 1987
SQ FT: 14,000
SALES (est): 10MM-24.9MM **Publicly Held**
WEB: www.jbcollins.com
SIC: **6411** Life insurance agent
PA: Marsh & McLennan Co's Inc
1166 Avenue Of The Americas
New York NY 10036
212 345-5000

(G-4770)
JOHN ROBERT POWERS INC
7900 Intrntl Dr Ste 100 (55425-1574)
PHONE..............................952 854-8577
Connie Steckling, *President*
Michael Palance, *Vice Pres*
George Caceres, *Exec Dir*
EMP: 25 EST: 2001
SALES (est): 500-999K **Privately Held**
SIC: **7363** Modeling service

(G-4771)
JOHN RYAN PERFORMANCE INC
700 S 3rd St Ste 300W (55415-1130)
PHONE..............................612 924-7700
John C Ryan, *CEO*
Doug Pearson, *CFO*
Michael Hagberg, *Controller*
Rishi Vajpeyi, *IT/INT Sup*
EMP: 45 EST: 1998
SQ FT: 15,000
SALES (est): 5MM-9.9MM **Privately Held**
SIC: **7336** 8742 Advertisers creative service; marketing consulting service

(G-4772)
JOHN T BEECHER MD
5301 Vernon Ave S (55436-2303)
PHONE..............................952 925-2200
John T Beecher MD, *Owner*
EMP: 30 EST: 2001
SALES (est): 1MM-4.9MM **Privately Held**
SIC: **8011** Physicians' office & clinic

(G-4773)
JOHNSON & CONDON
7401 Metro Blvd Ste 600 (55439-3034)
PHONE..............................952 831-6544
Christopher Celichowski, *President*
Mark Condon, *Principal*
Debra Cramer, *Manager*
Annette Kojetin, *Executive*
Matthew Johnson, *Associate*
EMP: 77 EST: 1982
SALES (est): 10MM-24.9MM **Privately Held**
WEB: www.johnson-condon.com
SIC: **8111** General practice attorney's or lawyer's office

(G-4774)
JOHNSON CONTROLS HOLDING CO
3605 Burnbrook Ln N (55447)
PHONE..............................763 566-7650
Dave Werts, *President*
Scott A Willims, *Facilities Mgr*
E R Compaion, *Manager*
EMP: 50 EST: 1992 **Publicly Held**
WEB: www.jci.com
SIC: **6719** Personal holding company
PA: Johnson Controls Inc
5757 N Green Bay Ave
Milwaukee WI 53209
414 524-1200

(G-4775)
JOHNSON LEWIS NILAN
120 S 6th St (55402-1803)
PHONE..............................612 338-1838
FAX: 612 338-7858
Bryan Johnson, *President*
Matthew E Damon, *Vice Pres*
Michael T Nilan, *Treasurer*
Trish Harris, *Controller*
Jenna Gruen, *Marketing Staff*
EMP: 100 EST: 1996
SALES (est): 10MM-24.9MM **Privately Held**
WEB: www.hlnsj.com
SIC: **8111** Legal services

(G-4776)
JON ENGLISH SALON
1439 W Lake St (55408-2644)
PHONE..............................612 824-2474
Jon E Wiczling, *Partner*
Linda W Wiczling, *Partner*
EMP: 40 EST: 1989
SQ FT: 2,500
SALES (est): 1MM-4.9MM **Privately Held**
SIC: **7231** Beauty salon

2011 Harris Minnesota
Services Directory

▲=Import ▼=Export
◆=Import/Export

(G-4777)
JON S NIELSEN MD
3366 Oakdale Ave N Ste 150
(55422-2961)
PHONE..............763 257-4400
Jon Nielsen MD, *Owner*
EMP: 25 **EST:** 1980
SALES (est): 1MM-4.9MM **Privately Held**
SIC: 8011 Physicians' office & clinic

(G-4778)
JONES-HARRISON RESIDENCE CORP
3700 Cedar Lake Ave   (55416-4240)
PHONE..............612 920-2030
FAX: 612 925-7101
Lowell Berggren, *President*
Cindy Fayder, *Purchasing*
Judy Christopherson, *Human Resources*
Heather Glasso, *Mktg Dir*
Cherrie Zitzlfperger, *Marketing Staff*
EMP: 270 **EST:** 1888
SQ FT: 150,000
SALES (est): 10MM-24.9MM **Privately Held**
WEB: www.jones-harrison.org
SIC: 8051 8361 Skilled nursing care facility;
geriatric residential care

(G-4779)
JORDAN REALTY INC
400 E Lake St Ste 3   (55408-2446)
PHONE..............612 827-3844
FAX: 612 827-3051
Pat Jordan, *President*
EMP: 25 **EST:** 1962
SALES (est): 1MM-4.9MM **Privately Held**
WEB: www.jordanrealty.net
SIC: 6531 Real estate agency & broker

(G-4780)
JOSEPH T RYERSON & SON INC
Also Called: Ryerson Tull Coil Processing
1605 Highway 169 N   (55441-4250)
PO Box 619   (55440-0619)
PHONE..............763 544-4401
FAX: 763 559-6342
Tom Endres, *Div Sub Head*
Bennie Powell, *Opers Mgr*
Tom Eckert, *Mfg Staff*
Ron Rolfes, *Sales Mgr*
John Rich, *Sales Staff*
EMP: 140
SALES (est): 100MM-499.9MM **Privately Held**
WEB: www.ryerson.com
SIC: 5051 Wholesales ferrous iron & steel
products; wholesales aluminum bars, rods,
ingots, sheets, pipes, plates, etc; sheet
metal fabricator; steel fabricator
DH: Joseph T Ryerson & Son Inc
2621 W 15th Pl
Chicago IL 60608
773 762-2121

(G-4781)
JUHL BROKERAGE INC
12700 Industrial Park Blvd Ste
(55441-3947)
PHONE..............763 519-0120
FAX: 763 557-7021
Jim M Kinney, *CEO*
Bryan L Lewis, *President*
Robert C Lang, *Exec VP*
Bob Lang, *Vice Pres*
Bob Dess, *Sales Mgr*
EMP: 25 **EST:** 1955
SQ FT: 8,000
SALES (est): 10MM-24.9MM **Privately Held**
SIC: 5141 Food broker

(G-4782)
JUUT MIDWEST INC (HQ)
201 Main St SE Ste 324   (55414-2139)
PHONE..............612 676-2250
David Wagner, *Ch of Bd*
Thomas Kuhn, *President*
EMP: 25 **EST:** 1965 **Privately Held**
WEB: www.juut.com
SIC: 7231 Cosmetology & personal hygiene
salon
PA: Juut Holdings Inc
201 Main St SE Ste 324
Minneapolis MN 55414
612 676-2250

(G-4783)
JUUT MIDWEST INC
Also Called: Horst Salons
651 Nicollet Mall Ste 247   (55402-1600)
PHONE..............612 332-3512
Chrissy Harris, *Manager*
Dennis Smoyer, *Manager*
EMP: 50
SALES (est): 1MM-4.9MM **Privately Held**
WEB: www.juut.com
SIC: 7231 Beauty salon
HQ: Juut Midwest Inc
201 Main St SE Ste 324
Minneapolis MN 55414
612 676-2250

(G-4784)
K M S MANAGEMENT INC
5801 Cedar Lake Rd S A   (55416-1481)
PHONE..............952 593-9930
FAX: 952 544-0599
Robert Levine, *President*
Brian L Kelley, *Vice Pres*
Keith Kraemer, *Vice Pres*
Lori Goar, *Manager*
EMP: 210 **EST:** 1989
SQ FT: 3,000
SALES (est): 25MM-49.9MM **Privately Held**
WEB: www.kmsapartments.com
SIC: 6531 Real estate management
services

(G-4785)
K O P P FUNDS
7701 France Ave S Ste 500   (55435-3201)
PHONE..............952 841-0480
FAX: 952 841-0411
Leroy Kopp, *President*
Sally Anderson, *Vice Pres*
John Flakne, *CFO*
Ray Holton, *Finance*
Jeffrey Olson, *CIO*
EMP: 34 **EST:** 1990 **Privately Held**
WEB: www.koppfunds.com
SIC: 6211 Sales of mutual funds by
independent salespeople

(G-4786)
K-M BUILDING CO OF MINNEAPOLIS
801 2nd Ave N Ste 1   (55405-1652)
PHONE..............612 977-9060
FAX: 612 977-9061
Steven Faber, *CEO*
John Ryan, *President*
Jim Johnson, *VP Purch*
EMP: 45 **EST:** 1988
SQ FT: 18,000
SALES (est): 10MM-24.9MM **Privately Held**
WEB: www.kmbldg.com
SIC: 1542 New commercial & office building
construction

(G-4787)
K-TEL INTERNATIONAL INC
7600 Wayzata Blvd Ste 2B   (55426-1662)
PHONE..............763 559-5566
Philip Kives, *President*
William McMahon, *General Mgr*
Kimmy Lockwood, *CFO*
Larry Dunmall, *CFO*
Dennis W Ward, *VP Finance*
EST: 1968
SQ FT: 3,000 **Publicly Held**
SIC: 7319 5099 Advertising material
distribution services; wholesales compact
discs or CD's; retail catalog sales

(G-4788)
KANTAR MEDIA INTELLIGENCES INC
Also Called: Wallace Marx & Associates
6750 France Ave S Ste 365   (55435-1905)
PHONE..............952 926-5430
Sandy Giesler, *Human Resources*
Bob Cristofano, *Sales Dir*
Wallace Marx, *Mktg Dir*
Dan Kitiell, *Branch Mgr*
Alan Gramont, *Administrator*
EMP: 40
SALES (est): 5MM-9.9MM **Privately Held**
WEB: www.tnsmi-cmr.com
SIC: 8742 Marketing consulting service
PA: Kantar Media Intelligences Inc
11 Madison Ave Fl 12
New York NY 10010
212 991-6000

(G-4789)
KAPLAN, STRANGIS & KAPLAN
90 S 7th St Ste 5500   (55402-4126)
PHONE..............612 375-1138
FAX: 612 375-1143
Sheldon Kaplan, *Ch of Bd*
Samuel L Kaplan, *President*
Harvey F Kaplan, *Partner*
Bruce J Parker, *Corp Secy*
Andris A Baltens, *Vice Pres*
EMP: 33 **EST:** 1977
SQ FT: 15,000
SALES (est): 1MM-4.9MM **Privately Held**
SIC: 8111 General practice law office

(G-4790)
KARDIA HEALTH SYSTEMS INC
5500 Wayzata Blvd Ste 215   (55416-3586)
PHONE..............763 432-8420
Carl George, *President*
Thomas E Kelly, *CFO*
Diana Dunphy, *Controller*
Greg Gentling, *Director*
Paul Lewis, *Director*
EMP: 25 **EST:** 2007
SALES (est): 1MM-4.9MM **Privately Held**
SIC: 7379 Computer system consulting
services

(G-4791)
KAREN B BJORKMAN
2000 Midwest Plz Bldg W   (55402)
PHONE..............612 904-7401
Karen B Bjorkman, *Principal*
EMP: 50 **EST:** 1951
SALES (est): 5MM-9.9MM **Privately Held**
SIC: 8111 Legal services

(G-4792)
KASA CAPITAL LLC ✿
800 Nicollet Mall # 1180   (55402-7030)
PHONE..............612 524-5460
Arash P Allaei, *Member*
Scott Bostrom, *Controller*
EMP: 35 **EST:** 2008
SALES (est): 10MM-24.9MM **Privately Held**
SIC: 6799 Investor services

(G-4793)
KATUN CORP (HQ)
10951 Bush Lake Rd # 100   (55438-2745)
PHONE..............952 941-9505
FAX: 952 941-4307
Carlyle Singer, *President*
Russell S John, *Senior VP*
Robert Barr, *Vice Pres*
Ronald Eisele, *Vice Pres*
Michael Gierden, *Vice Pres*
▲ **EMP:** 320 **EST:** 1979
SQ FT: 222,000 **Privately Held**
WEB: www.katun.com
SIC: 5112 Wholesales photocopy supplies
PA: Monomoy Capital Partners, LP
142 W 57th St Ste 17
New York NY 10019
212 699-4000

(G-4794)
KAUFMAN CONTAINER CO INC
1227 E Hennepin Ave   (55414-2322)
PHONE..............612 331-8880
FAX: 612 331-2768
Chuck Borowiak, *VP Opers*
Karen Melton, *VP Finance*
Robert Hames, *Accounting Mgr*
Mary Tomczak, *Human Res Mgr*
Rebecca Holland, *Marketing Staff*
EMP: 80
SALES (est): 25MM-49.9MM **Privately Held**
SIC: 5085 Wholesales commercial
containers; wholesales industrial glass
bottles; wholesales industrial plastic bottles
PA: Kaufman Container Co Inc
1000 Keystone Pkwy # 100
Cleveland OH 44135
216 898-2000

(G-4795)
KEANE INC
6700 France Ave S Ste 300   (55435-1908)
PHONE..............952 915-6393
Tim Jensen, *Vice Pres*
Paul Backes, *Manager*
Mark Johnson, *Consultant*
Heather Mickus, *Administrator*
R O Stuart, *Administrator*
EMP: 370
SALES (est): 50MM-99.9MM **Privately Held**
WEB: www.keane.com
SIC: 7379 Data processing consulting
service
HQ: Keane Inc
100 City Sq Ste 1
Boston MA 02129
617 241-9200

(G-4796)
KELBRO CO
2900 5th Ave S   (55408-2412)
PHONE..............612 824-9803
David Kelly, *President*
Steven Kelly, *Vice Pres*
Bob Hansen, *Vice Pres*
Lee Hagun, *Office Mgr*
EMP: 40 **EST:** 1949
SQ FT: 42,000
SALES (est): 10MM-24.9MM **Privately Held**
SIC: 5046 7699 Wholesales commercial
restaurant equipment; manufactures
flavoring syrups; restaurant equipment
repair service; manufactures ice

(G-4797)
KELLINGTON CONSTRUCTION INC
2301 N 2nd St   (55411-2208)
PHONE..............763 416-3200
Reed Lewis, *CEO*
Kyle Lewis, *COO*
EMP: 75 **EST:** 1989
SQ FT: 10,000
SALES (est): 10MM-24.9MM **Privately Held**
WEB:
www.maverickcuttingandbreaking.com
SIC: 1542 1541 Commercial & office
building contractor; industrial building &
warehouse construction

(G-4798)
KELLY & BERENS
80 S 8th St Ste 3720   (55402-2219)
PHONE..............612 392-7032
Timothy Kelly, *President*
Michael Berens, *Corp Secy*
John Ekman, *Manager*
John D Bessler, *Manager*
Nancy Gustafson, *Administrator*
EMP: 25 **EST:** 1988
SQ FT: 6,000
SALES (est): 1MM-4.9MM **Privately Held**
WEB: www.kellyandberens.com
SIC: 8111 Specialized legal services;
general practice law office

(G-4799)
KEMPF PAPER CORP
3145 Columbia Ave NE   (55418-1810)
PHONE..............612 781-9225
FAX: 612 781-9249
Gust Kempf Jr, *President*
Michael Kempf, *Vice Pres*
Susan Kempka, *Human Res Dir*
EMP: 58 **EST:** 1976
SQ FT: 175,000
SALES (est): 50MM-99.9MM **Privately Held**
WEB: www.kempfpaper.com
SIC: 5111 Wholesales printing paper

(G-4800)
KENEXA CORP
901 Marquette Ave # 1900   (55402-3212)
PHONE..............612 332-6383
Mary Mahon, *Manager*
James Donoho, *Manager*
Stephanie Kendall, *Consultant*
Wael Abdel-Ghani, *IT/INT Sup*
Mark Schmit, *Exec Dir*
EMP: 43
SALES (est): 1MM-4.9MM **Publicly Held**
WEB: www.kenexa.com

(PA)=Parent Co (HQ)=Headquarters (DH)=Div Headquarters
✿ = New business established in last 2 years

2011 Harris Minnesota
Services Directory

© Harris InfoSource 1-866-281-6415
213

SIC: 8732 8742 Market analysis, business & economic research services; management consulting services
PA: Kenexa Corp
650 E Swedesford Rd
Wayne PA 19087
610 971-9171

(G-4801)
KENNEDY & GRAVEN CHARTERED
200 S 6th St Ste 470 (55402-1408)
PHONE..................612 337-9300
Steven Duvul Jr, *President*
Paula Callies, *Manager*
Jane Carlsen, *Manager*
Linda Nygard, *Manager*
Susan E Torgrson, *Manager*
EMP: 51 **EST:** 1973
SALES (est): 5MM-9.9MM **Privately Held**
SIC: 8111 General practice attorney's or lawyer's office

(G-4802)
KEYSTONE AUTOMOTIVE INDUSTRIES (DH)
3615 Marshall St NE (55418-1005)
PHONE..................612 789-1919
FAX: 612 789-1886
Joe Hlosten, *President*
Joe Hernandez, *General Mgr*
Rob Wagman, *Principal*
Mary Bodem, *Controller*
Jim Dow, *Manager*
▲ **EMP:** 72 **EST:** 1968
SQ FT: 80,000
SALES (corp-wide): 2.04B **Publicly Held**
WEB: www.keystone-auto.com
SIC: 5013 Wholesales automotive supplies & parts; manufactures wheels; manufactures stamped metal automobile body parts
HQ: Keystone Automotive Industries
700 E Bonita Ave
Pomona CA 91767
909 624-8041

(G-4803)
KFORCE INC
7650 Edinbrgh Way Ste 650 (55435-6006)
PHONE..................952 835-5100
Sheri Beatty, *Branch Mgr*
Shawn O'Brien, *Manager*
EMP: 27 **Publicly Held**
WEB: www.kforce.com
SIC: 7361 Employment agency services
PA: Kforce Inc
1001 E Palm Ave
Tampa FL 33605
813 552-5000

(G-4804)
KHASHI ASSOCIATES LLC
3020 Harbor Ln N Ste 110 (55447-5101)
PHONE..................763 550-0961
Kent Lee, *Member*
Vladimir Frangulov, *Vice Pres*
Jeff Strandberg, *Sales Staff*
EMP: 30 **EST:** 1995
SQ FT: 1,000
SALES (est): 1MM-4.9MM **Privately Held**
SIC: 8742 8748 Management consulting services; environmental consultant

(G-4805)
KHCDII INC
Also Called: Kinderberry Hill Child Dev
3950 W 70th St (55435-4102)
PHONE..................952 925-5881
William M Dunkley, *CEO*
Sue Dunkley, *President*
Heidi Olson, *Exec Dir*
Ediana Olson, *Exec Dir*
Sheila Hendricks, *Exec Dir*
EMP: 35 **EST:** 1990
SALES (est): 500-999K **Privately Held**
SIC: 8351 Group day care center

(G-4806)
KIDNEY SPECIALISTS OF MN
6200 Shingle Creek Pkwy Ste 30 (55430-2168)
PHONE..................763 561-5349
Michael G Somermeyer MD, *President*
Tom Davin MD, *Corp Secy*

Frank J Tycast MD, *Vice Pres*
Arkady Synhazsky MD, *Treasurer*
Jane McGinley, *Office Mgr*
EMP: 49 **EST:** 1977
SQ FT: 2,700
SALES (est): 5MM-9.9MM **Privately Held**
WEB: www.kidney-mn.com
SIC: 8011 Nephrologist

(G-4807)
KILLMER ELECTRIC CO INC
5141 Lakeland Ave N (55429-3556)
PHONE..................763 425-2525
Brian Palmer, *President*
Gordon Johnson, *Vice Pres*
Scott Palmer, *Vice Pres*
Raymond Palmer, *Vice Pres*
Brian Bakk, *CFO*
EMP: 75 **EST:** 1920
SQ FT: 50,000
SALES (est): 5MM-9.9MM **Privately Held**
SIC: 1731 Electrical contractor

(G-4808)
KINDERBERRY HILL
185 Cheshire Ln N (55441-5465)
PHONE..................763 404-1070
Anne Roy, *Exec Dir*
Jodi Valentino, *Director*
EMP: 30 **EST:** 1996
SALES (est): 1MM-4.9MM **Privately Held**
WEB: www.kinderberryhill.com
SIC: 8322 Individual & family social services

(G-4809)
KINDERCARE LEARNING CENTERS
8950 France Ave S (55431-1863)
PHONE..................952 835-4955
EMP: 31
SALES (est): 500-999K **Privately Held**
WEB: www.kindercare.com
SIC: 8351 Group day care center; preschool center
HQ: KinderCare Learning Centers
650 NE Holladay St Ste 1400
Portland OR 97232
503 872-1300

(G-4810)
KINNEY & LANGE
312 S 3rd St Ste 120 (55415-1027)
PHONE..................612 339-1863
FAX: 612 339-6580
David R Fairbairn, *President*
Theodore Neils, *Corp Secy*
Jo Fairbairn, *Treasurer*
Arun Subramaniam, *Manager*
Sandy Wollak, *Info Svcs Mgr*
EMP: 50 **EST:** 1978
SQ FT: 18,000
SALES (est): 5MM-9.9MM **Privately Held**
SIC: 8111 General practice attorney's or lawyer's office

(G-4811)
KINSETH HOTEL CORP
Also Called: Holiday Inn
1201 W 94th St (55431-2334)
PHONE..................952 884-8211
FAX: 952 881-5574
William Hickey, *General Mgr*
Johnson Nate, *Treasurer*
Lisa Thielbar, *Finance*
Scott Chisholm, *Manager*
Evie Walters, *Director*
EMP: 150
SALES (est): 5MM-9.9MM **Privately Held**
WEB: www.fourpointsohare.com
SIC: 7011 8741 Traveler accommodations; hotel or motel management services
PA: Kinseth Hotel Corp
2 Quail Creek Cir
North Liberty IA 52317
319 626-5600

(G-4812)
KIRSCHBAUM-KRUPP METAL
Also Called: K & K METAL RECYCLING
1728 N 2nd St (55411-3408)
PO Box 1863, Fargo ND (58107-1863)
PHONE..................612 521-9212
Jihn H Wang, *Member*
Mitch Gibbs, *Member*
Linda Hull, *CFO*

Dustin Gibbs, *Mng Member*
▼ **EMP:** 45 **EST:** 2006
SQ FT: 100,000
SALES (est): 10MM-24.9MM **Privately Held**
SIC: 5093 Wholesales metal scrap & waste materials

(G-4813)
KIWIKAI IMPORTS INC
Also Called: Paustis & Sons
17300 Medina Rd Ste 100 (55447-5607)
PHONE..................763 550-9545
William Paustis, *President*
Daniel J Paustis Jr, *CFO*
Lisa Beltz, *Controller*
Sherry Meade, *Manager*
▲ **EMP:** 31 **EST:** 1973
SQ FT: 13,000
SALES (est): 10MM-24.9MM **Privately Held**
WEB: www.paustiswine.com
SIC: 5182 5181 Wholesales wine; wholesales beer & ale

(G-4814)
KJ INTERNATIONAL RESOURCES LTD
800 Washington Ave N (55401-1330)
PHONE..................612 288-9494
Zhanetta Lundberg, *CEO*
Janna Lundberg, *Vice Pres*
Kristen Giovanis, *CFO*
Christen Giovanis, *CFO*
Ana Marciniak, *Manager*
EMP: 36 **EST:** 1994
SALES (est): 1MM-4.9MM **Privately Held**
WEB: www.kjinternational.com
SIC: 7389 Translation & interpretation services; document storage service

(G-4815)
KNOCK INC
1315 Glenwood Ave (55405-1434)
PHONE..................612 333-6511
Lili Hall, *President*
Todd Paulson, *Exec VP*
Patrice Bevans, *Manager*
EMP: 32 **EST:** 2001
SQ FT: 10,000
SALES (est): 1MM-4.9MM **Privately Held**
SIC: 7336 Commercial art & graphic design services

(G-4816)
KNOWLEDGE LEARNING CORP
Also Called: Childrens World Lrng Ctr 608
3050 Fernbrook Ln N (55447-5318)
PHONE..................763 553-7960
FAX: 763 383-6993
Elizabeth Patza, *Manager*
EMP: 25
SALES (est): 500-999K **Privately Held**
WEB: www.knowledgelearning.com
SIC: 8351 Child day care service
PA: Knowledge Learning Corp
650 NE Holladay St # 1400
Portland OR 97232
503 872-1300

(G-4817)
KNOWLEDGE LEARNING CORP
Also Called: Childrens World Learning Ctr
525 Huron Blvd SE (55414-3114)
PHONE..................612 623-4642
FAX: 612 623-1901
Hilary Pieri, *Exec Dir*
Jon Woodruss, *Director*
Jon Woodruff, *Director*
EMP: 40
SALES (est): 500-999K **Privately Held**
WEB: www.knowledgelearning.com
SIC: 8351 Child day care service
PA: Knowledge Learning Corp
650 NE Holladay St # 1400
Portland OR 97232
503 872-1300

(G-4818)
KONICA MINOLTA BUSINESS SOLN
7300 Metro Blvd Ste 250 (55439-2364)
PHONE..................952 820-8385
Gwen Fenninger, *Advt Staff*
Lee Kurimay, *Branch Mgr*
David Scholle, *Manager*
Steve Deutsch, *CIO*

Donald Brogan, *CTO*
EMP: 55
SALES (est): 10MM-24.9MM **Privately Held**
WEB: www.konicabt.com
SIC: 5044 Wholesales duplicating machines; retails business machines & equipment; photographic equipment & supplies
PA: Konica Minolta Business Soln
100 Williams Dr
Ramsey NJ 07446
201 825-4000

(G-4819)
KONICA MINOLTA BUSINESS SOLN
5500 Lakeland Ave N (55429-3121)
PHONE..................763 531-1721
EMP: 32
SALES (est): 5MM-9.9MM **Privately Held**
WEB: www.konicabt.com
SIC: 5044 Wholesales office equipment
PA: Konica Minolta Business Soln
100 Williams Dr
Ramsey NJ 07446
201 825-4000

(G-4820)
KPMG LLP
4200 Wells Fargo Ctr (55402)
PHONE..................612 305-5000
FAX: 612 305-5100
Dave Jahnkay, *Managing Prtnr*
Brian Hernandez, *Engineer*
George Kehl, *Manager*
Jennifer Ardella, *Director*
EMP: 40
SALES (est): 1MM-4.9MM **Privately Held**
WEB: www.us.kpmg.com
SIC: 8721 Certified public accountant services
PA: KPMG LLP
345 Park Ave Lowr L-4
New York NY 10154
212 758-9700

(G-4821)
KRAFT FOODS GLOBAL INC
Also Called: Nabisco
749 Stinson Blvd (55413-2621)
PHONE..................612 331-4311
FAX: 612 378-2504
Steven Ricker, *Manager*
EMP: 35
SALES (est): 10MM-24.9MM **Privately Held**
WEB: www.kraftfoods.com
SIC: 5145 Wholesales snack foods
PA: Kraft Foods Global Inc
3 Lakes Dr
Winnetka IL 60093
847 646-2000

(G-4822)
KRAUS-ANDERSON CONSTRUCTION CO
2500 Minnehaha Ave (55404-4118)
PHONE..................612 721-7581
FAX: 612 721-2660
Gordie Ziegelman, *CEO*
EMP: 30
SALES (est): 1MM-4.9MM **Privately Held**
WEB: www.krausanderson.com
SIC: 8741 Business management services
PA: Kraus-Anderson Inc
523 S 8th St
Minneapolis MN 55404
612 332-7281

(G-4823)
KRAUS-ANDERSON INC (PA)
523 S 8th St (55404-1030)
PHONE..................612 332-7281
Bruce Engelsma, *CEO*
Daniel W Engelsma, *President*
Rode Manthe, *Corp Secy*
Dennis G Diessner, *COO*
Al Gerhardt, *COO*
EMP: 47 **EST:** 1937
SQ FT: 25,000 **Privately Held**
WEB: www.krausanderson.com

www.HarrisInfo.com
214

2011 Harris Minnesota
Services Directory

▲=Import ▼=Export
◆=Import/Export

SIC: **1542** 1522 1541 6512 New commercial & office building construction; apartment building construction service; new industrial building construction; operators of commercial & industrial buildings

(G-4824)
KRAUS-ANDERSON REALTY CO
4210 W Old Shakopee Rd (55437-2951)
PHONE 952 881-8166
FAX: 952 881-8114
Daniel Engelsma, *President*
Bruce Engelsma, *Principal*
Janice Goebel, *Corp Secy*
Martin J Beckman, *Vice Pres*
Robert E Goemer, *Property Mgr*
EMP: 40 EST: 1978
SQ FT: 25,000
SALES (est): 5MM-9.9MM **Privately Held**
WEB: www.krausanderson.com
SIC: **6531** Real estate management services; real estate leasing & rental agency
PA: Kraus-Anderson Inc
    523 S 8th St
    Minneapolis MN 55404
    612 332-7281

(G-4825)
KRONICK INDUSTRIES INC
3101 E Hennepin Ave (55413-2921)
PHONE 612 331-8080
FAX: 612 331-8083
Bruce Kronick, *President*
David Kronick, *Vice Pres*
EMP: 26 EST: 1942
SQ FT: 85,000
SALES (est): 10MM-24.9MM **Privately Held**
SIC: **5051** Wholesales nonferrous metal sheets, bars, rods, etc

(G-4826)
KTN ACQUISITION CORP
Also Called: Environmental Bus Solutions
10951 Bush Lake Rd # 100 (55438-2745)
PHONE 952 941-9505
Larry Stroup, *President*
Luke Komarek, *Corp Secy*
Kathleen Pepski, *Director*
Carlyle S Singer, *Director*
EMP: 30 EST: 2002
SALES (est): 5MM-9.9MM **Privately Held**
SIC: **5112** Wholesales office supplies

(G-4827)
L H HENDRICKSON & CO INC
3600 W 80th St Ste 200 (55431-4507)
PHONE 952 896-3456
FAX: 952 893-9797
Richard C Chapman, *President*
Tim Kline, *Vice Pres*
Linette Hinderman, *Manager*
Tim Jinks, *CIO*
EMP: 50 EST: 1978
SALES (est): 5MM-9.9MM **Privately Held**
SIC: **6411** Pension & retirement plan consulting service

(G-4828)
L T T INC
9013 Penn Ave S (55431-2225)
PHONE 952 929-4556
Steven D Lott, *President*
EMP: 27 EST: 1996
SALES (est): 500-999K **Privately Held**
SIC: **7349** Building cleaning service

(G-4829)
LA CRECHE EARLY CHILDHOOD
1800 Olson Memorial Hwy (55411-3835)
PHONE 612 377-1786
FAX: 612 823-7983
Corwyn Johnson, *Exec Dir*
Phyllis J Sloan, *Exec Dir*
Denise Sloan, *Director*
EMP: 30 EST: 1969
SQ FT: 10,000
SALES (est): 500-999K **Privately Held**
SIC: **8351** Group day care center

(G-4830)
LABOR SERVICES CO
55 W 78th St (55420-1110)
PHONE 952 884-0765
Dale B Robinson, *President*

Kristina Robison, *Treasurer*
EMP: 350 EST: 1970
SQ FT: 5,000 **Privately Held**
WEB: www.physicaldistributionservices.com
SIC: **7361** Employment agency services
PA: Physical Distribution Services
    55 W 78th St
    Minneapolis MN 55420
    952 884-0765

(G-4831)
LAB HOLDINGS INC (PA)
7901 Xerxes Ave S Ste 201 (55431-1219)
PHONE 612 607-1700
Rodney Burwell, *CEO*
EST: 1999 **Privately Held**
SIC: **8734** 8731 Hazardous waste testing laboratory; soil analysis laboratory; water testing laboratory; commercial physical research laboratory

(G-4832)
LACEK GROUP
900 2nd Ave S Ste 1800 (55402-3342)
PHONE 612 359-3700
FAX: 612 359-9395
Bill Baker, *President*
Cindy Kangas, *Partner*
James Daley, *Vice Pres*
Robert Daley, *Vice Pres*
Annette Long, *Office Mgr*
EMP: 110 EST: 1987
SALES (est): 10MM-24.9MM **Privately Held**
SIC: **8742** Management consulting services

(G-4833)
LACEK GROUP INC
900 2nd Ave S (55402-3314)
PHONE 612 359-3700
Mark Weninger, *Managing Prtnr*
Tim Lucas, *Senior Partner*
Christine M Hoffman, *Partner*
John Jarvis, *Partner*
Julie Bustos, *Partner*
EMP: 50 EST: 1993
SQ FT: 30,000
SALES (est): 5MM-9.9MM **Privately Held**
SIC: **7311** Advertising consultants
PA: Ogilvy & Mather Worldwide Inc
    636 11th Ave
    New York NY 10036
    212 237-4000

(G-4834)
LAKELAND FLORIST SUPPLY INC
7035 Washington Ave S (55439-1514)
PHONE 952 944-5160
FAX: 952 944-0036
William Heisserer, *President*
Teresa Mahoney, *Controller*
EMP: 25 EST: 1952
SQ FT: 47,000
SALES (est): 1MM-4.9MM **Privately Held**
SIC: **5193** Wholesales florists' supplies

(G-4835)
LAKES AREA REALTY INC
1428 W 28th St (55408-1903)
PHONE 612 874-1916
FAX: 612 870-9774
Steve Havig, *President*
Kai Richards, *Real Est Agnt*
Travis Meldahl, *Real Est Agnt*
Crystal McKinney, *Real Est Agnt*
Susan Hennesy, *Real Est Agnt*
EST: 1996 **Privately Held**
WEB: www.lakesarearealty.com
SIC: **6531** Real estate services

(G-4836)
LAKESIDE HOUSE PAINTERS INC
8800 Highway 7 Ste 224 (55426-3927)
PHONE 952 942-9709
FAX: 952 942-0281
Jeff Theilmann, *President*
Tim Bedughn, *President*
Tim Oxvig, *Vice Pres*
EMP: 100 EST: 1985
SALES (est): 5MM-9.9MM **Privately Held**
SIC: **1721** Residential painting contractor

(G-4837)
LAKEWOOD CEMETERY ASSOCIATION
3600 Hennepin Ave (55408-3847)
PHONE 612 822-2171
FAX: 612 822-0575
Ronald Gjerde, *President*
David Crosby, *Chairman*
Mark Jordan, *IT/INT Sup*
Joel Clough, *Executive*
EMP: 26 EST: 1871
SQ FT: 20,000
SALES (est): 1MM-4.9MM **Privately Held**
WEB: www.lakewoodcemetery.com
SIC: **6553** Operators of cemetery real estate

(G-4838)
LAMBSOFT & LAMB & CO
2429 Nicollet Ave (55404-3450)
PHONE 612 813-3727
Jeffery A Thingvold, *Owner*
EMP: 30 EST: 1980
SALES (est): 1MM-4.9MM **Privately Held**
SIC: **7379** Computer related services

(G-4839)
LANE MEMORY
Also Called: Stardust Lanes
2520 26th Ave S (55406-1247)
PHONE 612 721-6211
FAX: 612 721-7598
Robert L Tuttle, *President*
Richard Tuttle, *Vice Pres*
Keith Hinrichs, *Manager*
EMP: 40 EST: 1961
SQ FT: 15,000
SALES (est): 1MM-4.9MM **Privately Held**
WEB: www.stardustlanes.com
SIC: **7933** Ten pin center; cocktail lounge

(G-4840)
LANG-NELSON ASSOCIATES INC
Also Called: Waterford In Park Apartments
7000 62nd Ave N Ofc (55428-2970)
PHONE 763 533-9389
FAX: 763 537-1761
Mary Biggert, *Manager*
Allen Cox, *Manager*
EMP: 25
SALES (est): 1MM-4.9MM **Privately Held**
WEB: www.langnelson.com
SIC: **6513** Apartment building operator
PA: Lang-Nelson Associates Inc
    4601 Excelsior Blvd # 650
    Minneapolis MN 55416
    952 920-0400

(G-4841)
LANG-NELSON ASSOCIATES INC (PA)
4601 Excelsior Blvd # 650 (55416-4977)
PHONE 952 920-0400
FAX: 952 920-0982
Frank Lang, *President*
Eugene Nelson, *Exec VP*
Karen Walders, *Vice Pres*
Allona Clow, *Finance Mgr*
Sheari Frisk, *Sales Staff*
EMP: 25 EST: 1975
SQ FT: 2,500 **Privately Held**
WEB: www.langnelson.com
SIC: **6531** Real estate management services

(G-4842)
LANSING MALL LP
Also Called: Brookdale Center
1108 Brookdale Ctr (55430-2802)
PHONE 763 566-3373
FAX: 763 560-1827
Jim Fchlesinger, *President*
EMP: 40
SALES (est): 10MM-24.9MM **Publicly Held**
WEB: www.generalgrowth.com
SIC: **6512** Shopping center & mall operator
HQ: Lansing Mall LP
    110 N Wacker Dr
    Chicago IL 60606
    312 960-5000

(G-4843)
LANTERNS HOMEOWNER ASSOCIATION
4075 W 51st St (55424-1452)
PHONE 952 922-4435
Blossom Nathanson, *Partner*
EMP: 44 EST: 1972 **Privately Held**
SIC: **8641** Condominium association

(G-4844)
LARKEN INC
Also Called: Clarion Hotel
5151 American Blvd W (55437-1130)
PHONE 952 830-1300
FAX: 952 830-1535
Natalie Goldstein, *General Mgr*
Cindy Benedict, *Controller*
EMP: 80
SALES (est): 1MM-4.9MM **Privately Held**
SIC: **7011** 8741 Traveler accommodations; hotel or motel management services
PA: Larken Inc
    3330 Southgate Ct SW
    Cedar Rapids IA 52404
    319 366-8201

(G-4845)
LARKIN, HOFFMAN, DALY
7900 Xerxes Ave S Ste 1500 (55431-1128)
PHONE 952 835-3800
FAX: 952 896-3333
Thomas Stoltman, *President*
Jon S Swierzewski, *Corp Secy*
Richard A Knutson, *COO*
Nancy Solberg, *Controller*
Wendi Cline, *Librarian*
EMP: 170 EST: 1958
SQ FT: 48,000
SALES (est): 10MM-24.9MM **Privately Held**
SIC: **8111** Legal services

(G-4846)
LARSEN DESIGN OFFICE INC
7101 York Ave S Ste 120 (55435-4400)
PHONE 952 835-2271
FAX: 952 820-0113
Timothy Larsen, *President*
Jo Davison, *Vice Pres*
Richelle Huff, *Vice Pres*
Paul Wharton, *Vice Pres*
David Shultz, *Vice Pres*
EMP: 45 EST: 1975
SQ FT: 14,000
SALES (est): 5MM-9.9MM **Privately Held**
WEB: www.larsen.com
SIC: **7336** Commercial art & graphic design services; advertisers creative service; graphic arts & related design service

(G-4847)
LARSON TRANSFER & STORAGE CO
55 W 78th St (55420-1110)
PO Box 20061 (55420-0061)
PHONE 952 884-0765
FAX: 952 884-1239
Dale B Robinson, *President*
Joe Ryan, *Vice Pres*
Kristie Robison, *Treasurer*
Kristi Robinson, *Treasurer*
Randy Kos, *Controller*
EMP: 28 EST: 1927
SQ FT: 5,000
SALES (est): 1MM-4.9MM **Privately Held**
WEB:
www.physicaldistributionservices.com
SIC: **4212** 4213 Local trucking without storage services; over the road trucking
PA: Physical Distribution Services
    55 W 78th St
    Minneapolis MN 55420
    952 884-0765

(G-4848)
LARSONALLEN LLP (PA)
220 S 6th St Ste 300 (55402-1418)
PHONE 612 376-4500
Gordon A Viere, *CEO*
Thomas P Koop, *Partner*
Robert Cimasi, *Partner*
Jerry Felicelli, *Partner*
Robert J Norman, *Partner*
EMP: 450

(PA)=Parent Co (HQ)=Headquarters (DH)=Div Headquarters
✿ = New business established in last 2 years

2011 Harris Minnesota
Services Directory

© Harris InfoSource 1-866-281-6415

215

EST: 1953
SQ FT: 60,300 **Privately Held**
SIC: 8742 8721 Sales consulting services;
certified public accountant services;
corporate objectives & policies consultant;
planning consultant

(G-4849)
LAURENCE CUNEO & ASSOCIATES
Also Called: Cuneo & Associates
1401 American Blvd E # 6 (55425-1105)
PHONE............................952 707-1212
Laurence A Cuneo, *President*
Robert Paul, *Vice Pres*
Darrell Schmidth, *CFO*
Patty Mitchell, *VP Sales*
Kelly Olson, *Web Proj Mgr*
EMP: 70 **EST:** 1977
SQ FT: 10,144
SALES (est): 5MM-9.9MM **Privately Held**
SIC: 7311 Advertising agency

(G-4850)
LAWRENCE SERVICE CO
3500 Holly Ln N Ste 10 (55447-1498)
PHONE............................763 383-5700
Steve Birkey, *President*
Cathy Bailly, *Business Mgr*
Cindy Sattler, *COO*
Cindy S Cfocoo, *Vice Pres*
Rile Cherrey, *Vice Pres*
EMP: 45 **EST:** 1997
SQ FT: 19,000
SALES (est): 5MM-9.9MM **Privately Held**
WEB: www.lmsvc.com
SIC: 8742 7319 8743 Merchandising
consultant; sales promotion services;
display advertising services
HQ: Hanover Accessories LLC
3500 Holly Ln N Ste 10
Plymouth MN 55447
763 509-6100

(G-4851)
LBP MECHANICAL INC
315 Royalston Ave (55405-1535)
PHONE............................612 333-1515
FAX: 612 333-6122
Tim Hayes, *President*
Kim Rengo, *Controller*
Douglas Hayes, *Officer*
Walter H White, *Officer*
EMP: 50 **EST:** 1976
SQ FT: 10,000
SALES (est): 5MM-9.9MM **Privately Held**
SIC: 1711 Mechanical contractor

(G-4852)
LEARNING FOR LEADERSHIP
3300 5th St NE (55418-1117)
PHONE............................612 789-9598
Briony Sorum, *President*
Stephanie Dess, *Director*
EMP: 40 **EST:** 2006
SALES (est): 500-999K **Privately Held**
SIC: 8351 Child day care service

(G-4853)
LEEDS PRECISION INSTRUMENTS
800 Boone Ave N (55427-4433)
PHONE............................763 546-8575
John S Crouch, *President*
John Zeiss, *Vice Pres*
Greg R Dvorsak, *Opers Mgr*
Lee Johnson, *Purch Agent*
Mike Heinrich, *Engineer*
EMP: 58 **EST:** 1967
SQ FT: 27,500
SALES (est): 10MM-24.9MM **Privately Held**
SIC: 5049 Wholesales scientific &
engineering equipment & supplies;
manufactures measuring & controlling
devices; manufactures wire & wire products

(G-4854)
LEFTY'S SHOOTING & OUTDOOR
Also Called: Bills Gun Shop
4080 W Broadway Ave # 109
(55422-5602)
PHONE............................763 533-9594
John Monson, *President*

EST: 1982
SQ FT: 25,000 **Privately Held**
WEB: www.billsgs.com
SIC: 4813 5099 Retails hunting equipment;
internet host services; proprietary online
services networks; wholesales firearms &
ammunition; retails firearms; retail catalog
sales

(G-4855)
LEGAL AID SOCIETY OF (PA)
Also Called: MID MINNESOTA LEAGAL
ASSISTANC
430 1st Ave N Ste 300 (55401-1742)
PHONE............................612 332-1441
Glen Oliver, *Vice Pres*
Felino De La Pena, *Treasurer*
Lisa Cohen, *Administrator*
Jerry Lane, *Director*
Jean Lastine, *Director*
EMP: 75 **EST:** 1913
SQ FT: 15,000
SALES (corp-wide): 1.88M **Privately Held**
SIC: 8111 Legal services

(G-4856)
LEGAL AID SOCIETY OF
Also Called: Mid Minnesota Legal
2929 4th Ave S Ste 201 (55408-2460)
PHONE............................612 827-3774
FAX: 612 827-7890
Galen Robinson, *Manager*
EMP: 30
SALES (est): 1MM-4.9MM **Privately Held**
SIC: 8111 Legal services
PA: Legal Aid Society of
430 1st Ave N Ste 300
Minneapolis MN 55401
612 332-1441

(G-4857)
LEGAL RESEARCH CENTER INC
310 4th Ave S Ste 1100 (55415-1005)
PHONE............................612 332-4950
Christopher Ljungkull, *CEO*
James R Seidl, *President*
Paul G Zerby Jr, *Editor*
Robert E Woods, *Member*
Ann Action, *COO*
EMP: 25 **EST:** 1978
SQ FT: 7,958
SALES (est): 1MM-4.9MM **Publicly Held**
WEB: www.lrci.com
SIC: 8111 7379 Legal services; online
technology consulting service; book
publisher

(G-4858)
LEHMAN'S GARAGE INC (PA)
171 American Blvd W (55420-1117)
PHONE............................952 888-8700
FAX: 952 888-7229
Karen Cossette, *Ch of Bd*
Darrell Amberson, *President*
Greg Mann, *Controller*
EMP: 67 **EST:** 1917
SQ FT: 88,000
SALES (corp-wide): 15.90M **Privately Held**
SIC: 7532 7538 Automotive body shop;
general automotive repair services

(G-4859)
LEHMAN'S GARAGE MINNEAPOLIS
5431 Lyndale Ave S (55419-1717)
PHONE............................612 827-5431
FAX: 612 827-0076
Darrell Anderson, *President*
Dan Koralesky, *Vice Pres*
EMP: 25 **EST:** 2001
SALES (est): 1MM-4.9MM **Privately Held**
WEB: www.lehmansgarage.com
SIC: 7538 7532 General automotive repair
services; automotive body, paint & interior
repair & maintenance services

(G-4860)
LEMNA CORP (PA)
2445 Park Ave (55404-3714)
PHONE............................612 253-2000
FAX: 612 253-2003
Viet Ngo, *President*
Dave Anderson, *General Mgr*
Poldi Gerard, *Vice Pres*
David Appel, *Vice Pres*
Elizabeth Gerard, *Vice Pres*

EMP: 25 **EST:** 1983 **Privately Held**
SIC: 5074 Wholesales water purification
equipment

(G-4861)
LEO A DALY CO
730 2nd Ave S Ste 1100 (55402-2455)
PHONE............................612 338-8741
Gene Corogan, *Human Res Mgr*
Shannon Hovey, *Marketing Staff*
Kurt E Rogness, *Branch Mgr*
Bob Ubelhoer, *Administrator*
John Sorbel, *Technical Staff*
EMP: 130
SALES (est): 10MM-24.9MM **Privately Held**
SIC: 8712 8711 Architectural service;
engineering consulting services
PA: Leo A Daly Co
8600 Indian Hills Dr
Omaha NE 68114
402 391-8111

(G-4862)
LEONARD, STREET & DEINARD
150 S 5th St Ste 2300 (55402-4223)
PHONE............................612 335-1500
FAX: 612 335-1657
Lowell Stortz, *President*
Eugene Holderness, *COO*
Wayne Schertler, *CFO*
Molly V Guilder, *Marketing Mgr*
Dennis Wyffels, *Manager*
EMP: 429 **EST:** 1922
SQ FT: 93,289
SALES (est): 50MM-99.9MM **Privately Held**
SIC: 8111 General practice law office

(G-4863)
LES JONES ROOFING INC
Also Called: Architectural Sheet Metal
941 W 80th St (55420-1028)
PHONE............................952 881-2241
FAX: 952 881-7009
Leslie B Jones, *President*
Nancy Jones, *Vice Pres*
Gale Ragen, *Manager*
EMP: 45 **EST:** 1981
SQ FT: 10,000
SALES (est): 1MM-4.9MM **Privately Held**
WEB: www.lesjonesroofing.com
SIC: 1761 1751 Roofing contractor; sheet
metal work contractor; carpentry contractor

(G-4864)
LEUTHOLD ASSET ALLOCATION FUND
33 S 6th St Ste 4600 (55402-3718)
PHONE............................612 332-9141
Jess Leadholm, *CEO*
EMP: 30
SALES (est): 1MM-4.9MM **Privately Held**
SIC: 8742 Management consulting services

(G-4865)
LEVEL BRAND INC
724 N 1st St Ste 500 (55401-2880)
PHONE............................612 338-8000
John R Foley, *CEO*
Lois Dirksen, *President*
Jill Griffiths, *Managing Prtnr*
Kim Thelen, *Vice Pres*
Dean Adams, *Vice Pres*
EMP: 33 **EST:** 1986
SQ FT: 19,500
SALES (est): 1MM-4.9MM **Privately Held**
SIC: 7311 Advertising agency

(G-4866)
LEX A NERENBERG MD
2805 Campus Dr Ste 345 (55441-2679)
PHONE............................763 520-2980
Lex A Nerenberg, *Principal*
Dawn Modahl, *Office Mgr*
Teresa Engel, *Supervisor*
Mark Zelent, *Podiatrist*
Brian G Labine, *Internal Med*
EMP: 25 **EST:** 2001
SALES (est): 1MM-4.9MM **Privately Held**
SIC: 8011 Physicians' office & clinic

(G-4867)
LHB INC
250 3rd Ave N Ste 450 (55401-1674)
PHONE............................612 338-2029
FAX: 612 338-2088
Richard Carter, *Branch Mgr*
Charles Bouschor, *Info Tech Mgr*
Kathy Maciejeski, *IT/INT Sup*
EMP: 33
SALES (est): 1MM-4.9MM **Privately Held**
WEB: www.lhbcorp.com
SIC: 8711 0781 7389 8712 Engineering
services; architectural service; interior
design service; landscape architectural
service
PA: LHB Inc
21 W Superior St Ste 500
Duluth MN 55802
218 727-8446

(G-4868)
LHO BLOOMINGTON ONE LESSEE LLC
Also Called: Sheraton Blmngton Ht Mnnplis S
7800 Normandale Blvd (55439-3147)
PHONE............................952 835-7800
Andy Aldrich, *General Mgr*
Paul Wilson, *Member*
Sam Winterbottom, *Exec VP*
Dan Abel, *Opers Staff*
Steve Johnson, *Purch Mgr*
EMP: 200 **EST:** 1970
SQ FT: 210,000
SALES (est): 10MM-24.9MM **Privately Held**
WEB: www.lasallehotels.com
SIC: 7011 7299 Franchised hotel; cocktail
lounge; full service American restaurant;
facility rental & party planning services
PA: Lasalle Hotel Properties
3 Bethesda Metro Ctr # 1200
Bethesda MD 20814
301 941-1500

(G-4869)
LIBERTY DIVERSIFIED INDUSTRIES (PA)
5600 Highway 169 N (55428-3027)
PHONE............................763 536-6600
Benjamin Fiterman, *Ch of Bd*
Michael Fiterman, *President*
David Lenzen, *CFO*
Ray Christo, *Controller*
Stephen Richardson, *VP Finance*
EMP: 90 **EST:** 1972
SQ FT: 191,000 **Privately Held**
WEB: www.libertydiversified.com
SIC: 5112 Manufactures corrugated boxes;
manufactures nonwood office fixtures;
manufactures nonwood store fixtures;
manufactures nonwood office & store
shelving; manufactures processed plastics;
manufactures plastic containers;
manufactures plastic housewares

(G-4870)
LIBERTY MUTUAL INSURANCE CO
701 Xenia Ave S Ste 400 (55416-1035)
PHONE............................763 546-7550
FAX: 763 595-8618
Dan Bilancia, *Sales & Mktg St*
Adam Weinblatt, *Marketing Staff*
EMP: 250
SALES (est): 100MM-499.9MM **Privately Held**
WEB: www.libertymutual.com
SIC: 6331 Property & casualty insurance
carrier
DH: Liberty Mutual Insurance Co
175 Berkeley St
Boston MA 02116
617 357-9500

(G-4871)
LIBOR MANAGEMENT LLC
2550 Freeway Blvd (55430-1719)
PHONE............................763 561-0900
FAX: 763 566-2921
Stephanie Adams, *Sales Staff*
Ray Assemi, *Manager*
EMP: 25
SALES (est): 1MM-4.9MM **Privately Held**
WEB: www.carlson.com

www.HarrisInfo.com
216

2011 Harris Minnesota
Services Directory

▲=Import ▼=Export
◆=Import/Export

SIC: **7011** Traveler accommodations
HQ: Carlson Inc
701 Carlson Pkwy
Minnetonka MN 55305
763 212-5000

(G-4872)
LIBRA INC
3310 N 2nd St (55412-2604)
PHONE..............................612 522-2600
FAX: 612 522-2606
Lee Liberman, *Principal*
Ziv S Liberman, *Principal*
Gregory Lickteid, *Accounts Mgr*
Mike Molumby, *Manager*
▲ EMP: 33 EST: 1987
SQ FT: 103,000
SALES (est): 10MM-24.9MM **Privately Held**
SIC: **5199** Wholesales nondurable general
merchandise

(G-4873)
LIEBERMAN CO'S INC (PA)
Also Called: Viking Vending
9549 Penn Ave S Ste 100 (55431-2532)
PHONE..............................952 887-5299
FAX: 952 887-5656
Stephen E Lieberman, *Chairman*
Sybil C Etna WY, *Corp Secy*
Marlow B Etna WY, *Vice Pres*
Gene Winstead, *Vice Pres*
Harold I Lieberman, *CFO*
▲ EMP: 65 EST: 1907
SQ FT: 30,000 **Privately Held**
WEB: www.liebermancompanies.com
SIC: **5087 7699** Wholesales vending
machines & supplies; vending machine
repair service

(G-4874)
LIEBERMAN CO'S INC
Also Called: American Amusement Arcade
2100 W 96th St (55431-2538)
PHONE..............................952 887-5200
Tim Zahm, *Branch Mgr*
Gene Winstead, *Manager*
EMP: 25
SALES (est): 1MM-4.9MM **Privately Held**
WEB: www.liebermancompanies.com
SIC: **7993** Arcade
PA: Lieberman Co's Inc
9549 Penn Ave S Ste 100
Minneapolis MN 55431
952 887-5299

(G-4875)
LIESCH ASSOCIATES INC (PA)
13400 15th Ave N Ste A (55441-4532)
PHONE..............................763 489-3100
FAX: 763 559-2202
Brian B Liesch, *CEO*
Jim D Lambert, *President*
Joe McGovern, *Partner*
John Lichter, *Vice Pres*
Ken Olson, *Vice Pres*
EMP: 65 EST: 1968
SQ FT: 20,000 **Privately Held**
WEB: www.liesch.com
SIC: **8711** Civil engineering services;
pollution control engineers

(G-4876)
LIFE SAFETY SYSTEMS INC
3700 74th Ave N (55443-3516)
PHONE..............................763 560-2048
FAX: 763 566-4474
Laurie Klein, *President*
Michael Klein, *President*
Chris Jones, *General Mgr*
Benet Klein, *Corp Secy*
Paul Klein, *Treasurer*
EMP: 25 EST: 1993
SQ FT: 3,000
SALES (est): 1MM-4.9MM **Privately Held**
WEB: www.lifesafetysystemsinc.com
SIC: **1731** Safety & security specialization
contractor; fire detection & burglar alarm
systems specialization contractor

(G-4877)
LIFE TIME FITNESS INC
5250 W 84th St (55437-1308)
PHONE..............................952 835-2222
FAX: 952 835-9500
Lesley Scibora, *Vice Pres*
Paul Stjermaine, *Manager*

EMP: 35
SALES (est): 1MM-4.9MM **Publicly Held**
SIC: **7991 7299** Physical fitness center;
personal appearance service
PA: Life Time Fitness Inc
2902 Corporate Pl
Chanhassen MN 55317
952 947-0000

(G-4878)
LIFE TIME FITNESS INC
Also Called: Cafe Della Vita
615 2nd Ave S (55402-1924)
PHONE..............................612 752-9589
Christopher Fazi, *Manager*
Holly Wirth, *CTO*
Jeff Rosga, *Exec Dir*
EMP: 100
SALES (est): 1MM-4.9MM **Publicly Held**
SIC: **7991 7299** Health club; eating place;
personal appearance service; drinking
establishment
PA: Life Time Fitness Inc
2902 Corporate Pl
Chanhassen MN 55317
952 947-0000

(G-4879)
LIFE TIME FITNESS INC
Also Called: Minneapolis Lifetime Athc CLB
615 2nd Ave S (55402-1924)
PHONE..............................612 339-3655
FAX: 612 339-7923
Tim Maurer, *General Mgr*
Natalie Kuskovski, *Marketing Mgr*
Ann Debacker, *Manager*
Mike Ferguson, *Manager*
Efonda Sproles, *Manager*
EMP: 35 **Publicly Held**
SIC: **8699** Athletic organization
PA: Life Time Fitness Inc
2902 Corporate Pl
Chanhassen MN 55317
952 947-0000

(G-4880)
LIFE TIME FITNESS INC
Also Called: Lifetime Fitness
3600 Plymouth Blvd (55446-3201)
PHONE..............................763 509-0909
FAX: 763 509-9100
Stefani Aloquin, *General Mgr*
Efonda Sproles, *General Mgr*
Stephanie Ewings, *General Mgr*
Joy Lewis, *Sales Executive*
Stephanie Peloquin, *Manager*
EMP: 200
SALES (est): 5MM-9.9MM **Publicly Held**
SIC: **7991 7299** Physical fitness center;
retails health & dietetic foods; personal
appearance service
PA: Life Time Fitness Inc
2902 Corporate Pl
Chanhassen MN 55317
952 947-0000

(G-4881)
LIFETIME RESOURCES INC
9600 Thomas Ave N (55444-1155)
PO Box 43967, Brooklyn Park
(55443-0967)
PHONE..............................612 804-2252
Cheri Zajac, *President*
Margery K Schwab, *Vice Pres*
EMP: 60 EST: 2002
SALES (est): 1MM-4.9MM **Privately Held**
WEB: www.lifetimeresources.net
SIC: **8361** Group foster home

(G-4882)
LIFETOUCH NATIONAL SCHOOL
7800 Picture Dr (55439-3149)
PO Box 46995, Eden Prairie (55344-6995)
PHONE..............................952 826-4500
Paul Harmel, *Div Sub Head*
Cliff Gray, *Plant Mgr*
Ron Wiese, *Engineer*
Louanne Golding, *Human Res Mgr*
Wendy Mortimor, *Manager*
EMP: 250
SALES (est): 10MM-24.9MM **Privately Held**
WEB: www.lifetouch.com

SIC: **7221** School photography services
HQ: Lifetouch National School
11000 Viking Dr Ste 300
Eden Prairie MN 55344
952 826-4000

(G-4883)
LIFEWORKS SERVICES INC
7040 Lakeland Ave N Ste 108
(55428-5615)
PHONE..............................763 746-3330
Mary Hexom, *Manager*
EMP: 30
SALES (est): 500-999K **Privately Held**
SIC: **8322** Social services for the
handicapped

(G-4884)
LIGHTHOUSE1 LLC
9800 Bren Rd E Ste 250 (55437)
PHONE..............................952 852-7099
Jeff Brunsberg, *Member*
Jeff Bakke, *Member*
Jeff Young, *Member*
Jim Williams, *Vice Pres*
Lloyd Nelson, *Controller*
EMP: 120 EST: 2003
SQ FT: 2,500
SALES (est): 10MM-24.9MM **Privately Held**
WEB: www.lighthouse1.com
SIC: **7371** Computer software development

(G-4885)
LIGHTS ON BROADWAY INC
6900 W Broadway Ave (55428-1610)
PHONE..............................763 533-3366
FAX: 763 533-3354
Muriel Wirz, *President*
Dwight Wirz, *Vice Pres*
EMP: 25 EST: 1986
SQ FT: 28,000
SALES (est): 10MM-24.9MM **Privately Held**
WEB: www.lightsonbroadway.com
SIC: **5063 5064** Wholesales lighting
fixtures; wholesales electric household fans;
retails lighting fixtures

(G-4886)
LIGHTS ON INC
61 Bedford St SE (55414-3553)
PHONE..............................612 331-6620
David Boe, *CEO*
Dennis Carlson, *CFO*
Robin Turner, *Controller*
EST: 1981
SQ FT: 7,000 **Privately Held**
WEB: www.lightson.net
SIC: **7819** Motion picture equipment rental
service

(G-4887)
LINCOLN LIFE & ANNUITY CO OF
Also Called: Jefferson-Pilot
200 S 6th St Ste 1000 (55402-1411)
PHONE..............................612 373-7460
FAX: 612 925-6089
Jeff Peterson, *Manager*
EMP: 62
SALES (est): 5MM-9.9MM **Publicly Held**
WEB: www.lincolnlife.com
SIC: **6411** Insurance services
DH: Lincoln Life & Annunity Co of
100 Madison St Ste 1860
Syracuse NY 13202
315 428-8400

(G-4888)
LIND, JENSEN, SULLIVAN
Also Called: Lind Jensen & Sullivan
150 S 5th St Ste 1700 (55402-4217)
PHONE..............................612 333-3637
FAX: 612 333-1030
Paul Peterson, *Partner*
Timothy J O'Conner, *Partner*
Richard A Lind, *Partner*
Brian A Wood, *Partner*
Ted Sullivan, *Partner*
EMP: 30 EST: 1991
SQ FT: 100,000
SALES (est): 1MM-4.9MM **Privately Held**
WEB: www.lindjensen.com
SIC: **8111** General practice attorney's or
lawyer's office

(G-4889)
LINDENBERG & ASSOCIATES - TWIN
105 S 5th St Ste 1850 (55402-1249)
PHONE..............................612 375-0234
Earl Lindenberg, *President*
Kimberley Dunn, *Manager*
EMP: 48 EST: 1997
SALES (est): 5MM-9.9MM **Privately Held**
WEB: www.lindenberg.ae
SIC: **7371** Computer programming service

(G-4890)
LINDQUIST & VENNUM PLLP (PA)
80 S 8th St Ste 4200 (55402-2223)
PHONE..............................612 371-3211
J C Cuneo, *Partner*
Dean R Edstrom, *Partner*
Thomas F Dougherty, *Partner*
James M Lockhart, *Partner*
Daryle Uphoff, *Partner*
EMP: 200 EST: 1968
SQ FT: 90,000 **Privately Held**
SIC: **8111** General practice law office

(G-4891)
LINDSTROM CLEANING & CONSTR
9621 10th Ave N (55441-5016)
PHONE..............................763 544-8761
FAX: 763 544-8766
Dick Lindstrom, *Ch of Bd*
Charles Lindstrom, *President*
Doug Lizotte, *General Mgr*
Richard L Lindstrom, *Director*
EMP: 45 EST: 1972
SQ FT: 11,000
SALES (est): 10MM-24.9MM **Privately Held**
SIC: **1521 1542 7217** Single-family home
fire damage repair service; commercial &
office building renovation & repair services;
carpet & rug cleaning plant

(G-4892)
LINSTROM, SAMUELSON, & HARDTEN
Also Called: Lipham, William J MD
710 E 24th St Ste 106 (55404-3810)
PHONE..............................612 813-3600
Thomas Samuelson, *Partner*
Richard Lindstrom, *Partner*
David R Harten, *Partner*
Lisa Norby, *Manager*
Candy Simerson, *Officer*
▲ EMP: 40 EST: 1989
SALES (est): 1MM-4.9MM **Privately Held**
SIC: **8042** Optometrists' office

(G-4893)
LITIN PAPER CO INC
3003 Pacific St (55411-1625)
PHONE..............................612 333-4331
FAX: 612 522-1265
John Hanson, *President*
Marlan Kuhlmann, *Manager*
Bill Patterson, *Manager*
Michelle Nesbitt, *Data Proc Dir*
▲ EMP: 30 EST: 1948
SQ FT: 115,000
SALES (est): 10MM-24.9MM **Privately Held**
WEB: www.litinparty.com
SIC: **5113 5111 5112** Wholesales wrapping
or coarse paper & products; wholesales
printing & writing paper; wholesales
stationery & office supplies

(G-4894)
LITTLER MENDELSON, PC
1300 Ids Center 80 S 8 St (55402)
PHONE..............................612 630-1000
FAX: 612 630-9626
Charles E Feuss, *Attorney*
Marko Mrkomich, *Attorney*
EMP: 35
SALES (est): 1MM-4.9MM **Privately Held**
SIC: **8111** Legal services
PA: Littler Mendelson, PC
650 California St Fl 20
San Francisco CA 94108
415 433-1940

(PA)=Parent Co (HQ)=Headquarters (DH)=Div Headquarters
✿ = New business established in last 2 years

2011 Harris Minnesota
Services Directory

© Harris InfoSource 1-866-281-6415
217

GEOGRAPHIC

(G-4895)

LIVE NATION WORLDWIDE INC
600 1st Ave N (55403-1400)
PHONE...............................612 673-8308
FAX: 612 673-8090
Dina Warg, *Branch Mgr*
EMP: 50
SALES (est): 5MM-9.9MM **Publicly Held**
WEB: www.sfx.com
SIC: 7922 Entertainment promotion service
HQ: Live Nation Worldwide Inc
　　220 W 42nd St
　　New York NY 10036
　　917 421-5100

(G-4896)

LOCAL GOVERNMENT INFORMATION
Also Called: Logis
5750 Duluth St (55422-4036)
PHONE...............................763 543-2600
FAX: 763 543-2699
Dan Donahue, *President*
Mike Garris, *COO*
Tom Hedges, *Vice Pres*
Jason Stickler, *Administrator*
EMP: 43 EST: 1972
SQ FT: 15,000
SALES (est): 5MM-9.9MM **Privately Held**
WEB: www.logis.org
SIC: 7376 7371 Computer facilities management service; computer programming service

(G-4897)

LOCKRIDGE GRINDAL NAUEN LLP
100 Washington Ave S # 2200 (55401-2179)
PHONE...............................612 339-6900
FAX: 612 339-0981
Robert J Schmit, *Partner*
Patricia Bloodgood, *Partner*
W J Bruckner, *Partner*
H T Grindal, *Partner*
Richard A Lockridge, *Partner*
EMP: 71 EST: 1978
SALES (est): 5MM-9.9MM **Privately Held**
WEB: www.locklaw.com
SIC: 8111 General practice law office

(G-4898)

LOG HOUSE FOODS INC
700 Berkshire Ln N (55441-5403)
PHONE...............................763 546-8395
FAX: 763 546-7339
Alan Kasdan, *Ch of Bd*
Josh Kasdan, *President*
Jean Anderson, *Administration*
EMP: 35 EST: 1948
SQ FT: 76,000
SALES (est): 10MM-24.9MM **Privately Held**
WEB: www.loghousefoods.com
SIC: 5149 Wholesales bakery products; manufactures zwieback

(G-4899)

LOGE GROUP LLC
Also Called: C B C A
10900 Hampshire Ave S (55438-2384)
PHONE...............................952 829-3500
FAX: 952 946-7694
Barbra L Rabinowitz, *Corp Secy*
Adele Kimpell, *Exec VP*
Charles Abrahamson, *Vice Pres*
Michael McKim, *Vice Pres*
Pete Wirski, *Vice Pres*
EMP: 125
SALES (est): 10MM-24.9MM **Privately Held**
SIC: 6411 Contract or fee basis medical insurance claim processing
PA: Loge Group LLC
　　4150 Intl Plaza Ste 900
　　Fort Worth TX 76109
　　800 824-3882

(G-4900)

LOGIC PRODUCT DEVELOPMENT CO
411 Washington Ave N # 400 (55401-1426)
PHONE...............................612 672-9495
FAX: 612 672-9849
Michael Davis, *President*

Troy Kopischke, *Corp Secy*
Danny J Cunagin, *Vice Pres*
Reza Vahedi, *Project Mgr*
Mark Teskey, *VP Eng R&D*
EMP: 85 EST: 2005
SQ FT: 18,000
SALES (est): 10MM-24.9MM **Privately Held**
SIC: 8711 Engineering services

(G-4901)

LOMINGER LIMITED INC
5051 Highway 7 Ste 100 (55416-2291)
PHONE...............................952 345-3600
FAX: 952 345-3601
Robert Eichinger, *CEO*
Cara Raymond, *President*
Michael Lombardo, *Principal*
Dee Gaeddert, *COO*
Bill Ward, *Senior VP*
EMP: 45 EST: 1990
SALES (est): 5MM-9.9MM **Publicly Held**
WEB: www.lominger.com
SIC: 8742 Human resource consulting services
PA: Korn Ferry International
　　1900 Avenue Of The Stars
　　Los Angeles CA 90067
　　310 552-1834

(G-4902)

LOOP PARKING CO
1300 Nicollet Ave # 3060 (55403-2693)
PHONE...............................612 333-2293
Jerel Shapiro, *President*
David Sanders, *Principal*
James Sanders, *Treasurer*
EST: 1923 **Privately Held**
SIC: 7521 Parking lot; parking garage

(G-4903)

LORING TOWERS APTS LP
Also Called: Aimco
15 E Grant St Apt 717 (55403-2627)
PHONE...............................612 871-7202
Leeann Morein, *Principal*
Jennifer Hardee, *Corp Secy*
Clyde Jones, *Sales Staff*
Mike Briefemeifter, *Manager*
EMP: 99 EST: 1970
SALES (est): 10MM-24.9MM **Privately Held**
SIC: 6513 Apartment building operator

(G-4904)

LOWE'S HOME CENTERS INC
3205 Vicksburg Ln N (55447-1317)
PHONE...............................763 367-9000
Paul Czerlanis, *Manager*
EMP: 150
SALES (est): 25MM-49.9MM **Publicly Held**
WEB: www.lowes.com
SIC: 5031 5064 Retails building products & materials; wholesales exterior building materials; wholesales interior building materials; wholesales electrical appliances; retails household appliances
HQ: Lowe's Home Centers Inc
　　1605 Curtis Bridge Rd
　　Wilkesboro NC 28697
　　336 658-4000

(G-4905)

LOYEAR CLEANING & RESTORATION
415 W 60th St (55419-2255)
PHONE...............................952 831-0777
FAX: 952 881-2728
John Loyear, *President*
EMP: 37 EST: 2004
SALES (est): 1MM-4.9MM **Privately Held**
WEB: www.loyearcleaning.com
SIC: 7217 Carpet & upholstery cleaning services

(G-4906)

LQ MANAGEMENT LLC
7815 Nicollet Ave S (55420-1226)
PHONE...............................952 881-7311
Tony Sorrell, *General Mgr*
Chris Engle, *Manager*
Tony Sorrells, *Manager*
David Kamm, *Asst Mgr*
EMP: 50
SALES (est): 1MM-4.9MM **Privately Held**
WEB: www.neubayern.net

SIC: 7011 Franchised motel
PA: Lq Management LLC
　　909 Hidden Rdg Ste 600
　　Irving TX 75038
　　214 492-6600

(G-4907)

LS ACQUISITIONS INC
Also Called: KOEHLER & DRAMM WHOLESALE FLOR
2407 E Hennepin Ave (55413-2704)
PHONE...............................612 331-4141
FAX: 612 331-5066
Lee Spence, *President*
Eugene Brunk, *Corp Secy*
Dev Olson, *Human Res Mgr*
Michael Searles, *Sales Mgr*
EMP: 80 EST: 1955
SQ FT: 65,000
SALES (est): 10MM-24.9MM **Privately Held**
WEB: www.koehlerdramm.com
SIC: 5193 Wholesales flowers & nursery stock; wholesales florists' supplies

(G-4908)

LUBRICATION TECHNOLOGIES INC (PA)
Also Called: Lube-Tech
900 Mendelssohn Ave N (55427-4309)
PHONE...............................763 545-0707
Christian N Bame, *President*
Craig Kellberg, *Managing Dir*
Eric Jackson, *COO*
Rick Schultz, *Vice Pres*
Tom McLeod, *Manager*
EMP: 65 EST: 1946
SQ FT: 90,000 **Privately Held**
WEB: www.lube-tech.com
SIC: 5172 5169 Wholesales lubricating oils & greases; wholesales chemicals & allied products

(G-4909)

LUND-MARTIN CONSTRUCTION INC
3023 Randolph St NE (55418-1824)
PHONE...............................612 782-2250
Willard D Haro, *CEO*
Dennis Mette, *Controller*
EMP: 45 EST: 1952
SQ FT: 5,000
SALES (est): 5MM-9.9MM **Privately Held**
WEB: www.lundmartin.com
SIC: 1541 1542 New industrial building construction; new commercial & office building construction

(G-4910)

LUPIENT OLDSMOBILE CO INC
7100 Wayzata Blvd (55426-1616)
PHONE...............................763 546-2222
James Lupient, *President*
Gary Lehman, *Manager*
Mary Swersfiger, *Administrator*
EMP: 240 EST: 1969
SQ FT: 85,000
SALES (est): 100MM-499.9MM **Privately Held**
SIC: 7538 Retails new & used automobiles; general automotive repair services; used car dealer

(G-4911)

LUTHERAN BROTHERHOOD RESEARCH
625 4th Ave S (55415-1624)
PHONE...............................612 340-7000
Robert P Gandrud, *Ch of Bd*
Rolf F Bjelland, *President*
Bruce Nicholson, *President*
Otis Hilbert, *Corp Secy*
Randall Boashek, *Vice Pres*
EMP: 50 EST: 1987
SQ FT: 438,660 **Privately Held**
WEB: www.thrivent.com
SIC: 6211 Sales of investment certificates; sales of mutual funds by independent salespeople
PA: Thrivent Financial For
　　625 4th Ave S Ste 100
　　Minneapolis MN 55415
　　920 734-5721

(G-4912)

LUTHERAN SOCIAL SERVICE OF MN
2414 Park Ave (55404-3713)
PHONE...............................612 871-0221
FAX: 612 871-0354
Sharon Henderson, *Corp Secy*
Sharon Hendrickson, *Office Mgr*
James Swenson, *Med Doctor*
Nelson Matt, *Manager*
Joel Salzer, *Director*
EMP: 100
SALES (est): 5MM-9.9MM **Privately Held**
WEB: www.lssmn.org
SIC: 8322 Individual & family social services
PA: Lutheran Social Service Of MN
　　2485 Como Ave
　　Saint Paul MN 55108
　　651 642-5990

(G-4913)

M & C HOTEL INTERESTS INC
Also Called: Regal Minneapolis Hotel
1313 Nicollet Ave (55403-2668)
PHONE...............................612 332-6000
FAX: 612 359-2164
Robert Rivers, *General Mgr*
EMP: 185
SALES (est): 10MM-24.9MM **Privately Held**
WEB: www.richfield.com
SIC: 7011 Traveler accommodations; caterer
HQ: M & C Hotel Interests Inc
　　7600 E Orchard Rd 230S
　　Englewood CO 80111
　　303 220-2200

(G-4914)

M & I MARSHALL & ILSLEY BANK
5775 Wayzata Blvd (55416-1222)
PHONE...............................952 544-3100
FAX: 952 544-1552
Dan Roberts, *Branch Mgr*
EMP: 35
SALES (est): 5MM-9.9MM **Publicly Held**
WEB: www.uhb-fl.com
SIC: 6022 State commercial bank
HQ: M & I Marshall & Ilsley Bank
　　770 N Water St
　　Milwaukee WI 53202
　　414 765-7700

(G-4915)

M & I MARSHALL & ILSLEY BANK
651 Nicollet Mall (55402-1636)
PHONE...............................612 904-8000
Kevin Kane, *Senior VP*
Donald Kjonass, *Vice Pres*
William Lewis, *Vice Pres*
Bill Klein, *Manager*
Debra W Riefner, *Manager*
EMP: 75
SALES (est): 10MM-24.9MM **Publicly Held**
WEB: www.uhb-fl.com
SIC: 6022 State commercial bank
HQ: M & I Marshall & Ilsley Bank
　　770 N Water St
　　Milwaukee WI 53202
　　414 765-7700

(G-4916)

M & N EQUIPMENT SERVICES INC
620 Malcolm Ave SE (55414-3314)
PHONE...............................612 379-4147
FAX: 612 379-4263
William G Johnson, *President*
Tom North, *Vice Pres*
Diane Mattaini, *Vice Pres*
EMP: 25 EST: 1986
SQ FT: 2,400
SALES (est): 1MM-4.9MM **Privately Held**
SIC: 7699 4731 Ship boiler & tank cleaning & repair contractors; freight forwarding services

▲=Import ▼=Export
◆=Import/Export

(G-4917)
M A MORTENSON CO (PA)
700 Meadow Ln N (55422-4817)
PO Box 710 (55440-0710)
PHONE..............................763 522-2100
Thomas F Gunkel, *CEO*
Tracy Mathieu, *Managing Dir*
Mark A Mortenson, *Corp Secy*
Daniel L Johnson, *COO*
Robert J Nartonis, *Senior VP*
▲ **EMP:** 500 **EST:** 1954
SQ FT: 55,000 **Privately Held**
WEB: www.mortenson.com
SIC: 1542 1629 Institutional building
construction; power plant construction; new
commercial & office building construction;
industrial plant construction; waste water &
sewage treatment plant construction

(G-4918)
M A MORTENSON CO
Also Called: Construction Division
700 Meadow Ln N (55422-4817)
PHONE..............................763 522-2100
Sharon Blaine, *General Mgr*
Amy Sporre, *General Mgr*
James Lesinski, *Vice Pres*
James Deleo, *Purch Agent*
Antoine Dib, *Engineering*
EMP: 700
SALES (est): 100MM-499.9MM **Privately
Held**
WEB: www.mortenson.com
SIC: 1542 Commercial & institutional
building construction
PA: M A Mortenson Co
    700 Meadow Ln N
    Minneapolis MN 55422
    763 522-2100

(G-4919)
M A PETERSON DESIGNBUILD INC
6161 Wooddale Ave Ste 200 (55424-1807)
PHONE..............................952 925-9455
Mark A Peterson, *President*
Dave G Peterson, *Project Mgr*
David Brooks, *Manager*
Jo Kruger, *Manager*
Martin Hackenmueller, *Manager*
EMP: 67 **EST:** 1981
SQ FT: 9,000
SALES (est): 10MM-24.9MM **Privately Held**
SIC: 1521 Single-family home general
remodeling service

(G-4920)
M D A CONSULTING GROUP INC
150 S 5th St Ste 3300 (55402-4205)
PHONE..............................612 332-8182
FAX: 612 334-3299
Sandra Davis, *President*
Robert Barnett, *Exec VP*
Paul H Batz, *Vice Pres*
Kate Hennessey, *Vice Pres*
Magaly Wieczorek, *Vice Pres*
EMP: 30 **EST:** 1981
SQ FT: 11,492
SALES (est): 1MM-4.9MM **Privately Held**
WEB: www.mdaleadership.com
SIC: 8049 8742 Mental health practitioners'
office; management consulting services

(G-4921)
M L T INC (DH)
4660 76th Ave N (55443-3402)
PHONE..............................952 474-2540
FAX: 952 367-8420
Larry Chestler, *President*
Ken Pomerantz, *President*
Sarah Niva, *Project Mgr*
Jayne Zwakman, *Purch Mgr*
Michael Warnken, *VP Sls/Mktg*
EMP: 200 **EST:** 1969
SQ FT: 70,000
SALES (corp-wide): 28.06B **Publicly Held**
WEB: www.nwa.com
SIC: 4725 Wholesale arrangement of travel
tour packages
HQ: Northwest Airlines Corp
    2700 Lone Oak Pkwy
    Eagan MN 55121
    612 726-2111

(G-4922)
M LITTLE & CO INC
Also Called: Little & Co
920 2nd Ave S Ste 1400 (55402-3318)
PHONE..............................612 375-0077
FAX: 612 375-0423
Monica Little, *President*
Joanne Kuebler, *CFO*
Judy McCollum, *Office Mgr*
Rachel Meier, *Manager*
Bennett Y Lum, *Bd of Directors*
EMP: 30 **EST:** 1979
SQ FT: 17,000
SALES (est): 1MM-4.9MM **Privately Held**
WEB: www.littleco.com
SIC: 7336 Graphic arts & related design
service

(G-4923)
M P JOHNSON CONSTRUCTION INC
50 S 6th St Ste 950 (55402-1552)
PHONE..............................612 339-3733
FAX: 612 339-2410
Michael P Johnson, *President*
Brian Jenson, *Vice Pres*
EMP: 35 **EST:** 1988
SQ FT: 2,000
SALES (est): 5MM-9.9MM **Privately Held**
WEB: www.mpjohnson.com
SIC: 1542 Commercial & office building
contractor

(G-4924)
M S I SERVICES
7825 Washingtn Ave S # 210
(55439-2430)
PHONE..............................763 572-0500
Mary Younggren, *Manager*
EMP: 30 **EST:** 1988
SALES (est): 500-999K **Privately Held**
SIC: 7363 Temporary help service

(G-4925)
MAAX US CORP (PA)
9224 73rd Ave N (55428-1111)
PHONE..............................763 424-3335
Pete McNeil, *President*
Mark Bandrauk, *Corp Secy*
Russell Suchan, *Vice Pres*
Mike Hill, *Purch Agent*
Denis Aubin, *CFO*
◆ **EMP:** 75 **EST:** 1993
SQ FT: 78,000
SALES (corp-wide): 25M **Privately Held**
SIC: 6719 Investment holding company;
manufactures hydrotherapy whirlpool baths;
manufactures plastic bath, shower or
laundry tubs

(G-4926)
MAC ENTERPRISES INC
Also Called: Metro Commercial Maintenance
1535 4th St NE (55413-1266)
PHONE..............................612 789-9392
FAX: 612 788-0450
Mark Cady, *President*
Chris Myers, *Office Mgr*
EMP: 40 **EST:** 1996
SALES (est): 1MM-4.9MM **Privately Held**
WEB: www.metrofixit.com
SIC: 7349 Building cleaning & maintenance
services

(G-4927)
MACKALL CROUNSE & MOORE PLC
901 Marquette Ave # 1400 (55402-3264)
PHONE..............................612 305-1400
FAX: 612 305-1414
Shane Anderson, *Partner*
Timothy D Moratzka, *Partner*
Les Novack, *Partner*
James A Wahl, *Partner*
Elizabeth Cobb, *Counsel*
EMP: 69 **EST:** 1918
SQ FT: 20,000
SALES (est): 5MM-9.9MM **Privately Held**
SIC: 8111 General practice law office

(G-4928)
MACPHAIL CENTER FOR MUSIC
501 S 2nd St (55401-2383)
PHONE..............................612 321-0100
Kathy Holzer, *Business Mgr*
Dennis Erickson, *Facilities Mgr*
Kristen Blue, *Human Res Mgr*
Amy Schutte, *Manager*
Barry Berg, *Exec Dir*
EMP: 170 **EST:** 1906 **Privately Held**
SIC: 8399 Non-fee basis fund raising
organization

(G-4929)
MACRO GROUP INC
100 Portland Ave Ste 250 (55401-2533)
PHONE..............................612 332-7880
FAX: 612 335-3674
Alice Lloyd, *President*
Jeffrey Crawford, *CFO*
John Erickson, *Director*
Dawn Kuzma, *Director*
Justice Page, *Criminal Law*
EMP: 35 **EST:** 1987
SALES (est): 5MM-9.9MM **Privately Held**
SIC: 7379 7371 Data processing consulting
service; computer programming service

(G-4930)
MACY'S RETAIL HOLDINGS INC
81 S 9th St Ste 350 (55402-3226)
PHONE..............................612 343-0868
FAX: 612 332-5733
Joe Speritzer, *Manager*
Jeremy Hawthorne, *Manager*
Jason Lund, *Administrator*
EMP: 100
SALES (est): 25MM-49.9MM **Publicly Held**
SIC: 5021 Wholesales office furniture
HQ: Macy's Retail Holdings Inc
    7 W 7th St Ste 1100
    Cincinnati OH 45202
    513 579-7000

(G-4931)
MAGELLAN MEDICAL TECHNOLOGY
120 S 6th St Ste 2150 (55402-1823)
PHONE..............................612 677-0000
FAX: 612 677-1111
Susan L Johnson, *CEO*
Gary Fox, *Controller*
EMP: 200 **EST:** 1995
SALES (est): 25MM-49.9MM **Privately Held**
WEB: www.magellanmed.com
SIC: 8748 Manufactures medical
instruments; business consulting services

(G-4932)
MAGENIC TECHNOLOGIES INC (PA)
4150 Olson Memorial Hwy (55422-4800)
PHONE..............................763 398-4800
FAX: 763 521-4091
Greg Frankenfield, *CEO*
Paul Fridman, *President*
Keith Franklin, *General Mgr*
Matt Lockhart, *General Mgr*
Dave Meier, *General Mgr*
EMP: 120 **EST:** 1995
SQ FT: 20,000
SALES (corp-wide): 41.34M **Privately Held**
WEB: www.magenic.com
SIC: 7371 Computer programming service

(G-4933)
MAGICAL HISTORY TOUR
125 Main St SE (55414-2143)
PHONE..............................612 331-7171
Wl Neuenschwander, *Managing Prtnr*
EMP: 25 **EST:** 2005
SALES (est): 1MM-4.9MM **Privately Held**
WEB: www.magicalhistorytour.com
SIC: 7999 Tour & guide services

(G-4934)
MAGICCOM INC
925 Boone Ave N (55427-4434)
PHONE..............................763 529-2208
Daniel D Witkowski, *President*
Stephen Winnick, *Corp Secy*
▲ **EMP:** 30 **EST:** 1977
SALES (est): 1MM-4.9MM **Privately Held**
WEB: www.magiccominc.com
SIC: 8742 Merchandising consultant

(G-4935)
MAGNETIC PRODUCTS & SERVICES
7500 Boone Ave N Ste 104 (55428-1026)
PHONE..............................763 424-2700
FAX: 763 493-2295
Kristine Hunter, *President*
Michelle Morey, *Treasurer*
Ed McCumber, *Manager*
Kathleen Prekker, *Executive*
EMP: 31 **EST:** 1989
SQ FT: 15,000
SALES (est): 10MM-24.9MM **Privately Held**
WEB: www.mpsinc.org
SIC: 5045 Wholesales computer software

(G-4936)
MAHONEY, DOUGHERTY & MAHONEY
801 Park Ave (55404-1136)
PHONE..............................612 339-5863
FAX: 612 339-1529
Richard Mahoney, *President*
James M Mahoney, *Vice Pres*
Gregory A Zinn, *Attorney*
Dawn G Atchison, *Attorney*
EMP: 35 **EST:** 1922
SQ FT: 12,500
SALES (est): 1MM-4.9MM **Privately Held**
SIC: 8111 General practice law office

(G-4937)
MALLOY, KARNOWSKI & CO
5353 Wayzata Blvd Ste 410 (55416-3674)
PHONE..............................952 545-0424
FAX: 952 545-0569
Kenneth Malloy, *President*
Paul A Radosevich, *Corp Secy*
Bill Lauer, *Vice Pres*
Jim Eichter, *Vice Pres*
Thomas Montague, *Vice Pres*
EMP: 25 **EST:** 1955
SQ FT: 5,000
SALES (est): 1MM-4.9MM **Privately Held**
SIC: 8721 Certified public accountant
services

(G-4938)
MALMBORGS INC
5120 Lilac Dr N (55429-3414)
PHONE..............................763 535-4695
FAX: 763 535-9834
George A Lucht, *CEO*
Troy Lucht, *President*
Van Cooley, *Manager*
EMP: 42 **EST:** 1902
SQ FT: 75,000
SALES (est): 5MM-9.9MM **Privately Held**
WEB: www.geraniumsbygeorge.com
SIC: 5193 Wholesales potted plants; retails
potted plants

(G-4939)
MALY CO'S LLC
2050 E Center Cir Ste 200 (55441-3858)
PHONE..............................612 788-9688
Lance Maly, *Member*
Maureen Maly, *Member*
Joan Larson, *Accounting Dir*
Harold Radke, *Advt Staff*
Randy Barnes, *Manager*
EMP: 29 **EST:** 1960
SALES (est): 10MM-24.9MM **Privately Held**
SIC: 5031 7299 Wholesales windows; home
improvement & renovation contractor
agency

(G-4940)
MANAGED SERVICES INC
6500 Oxford St (55426-4409)
PHONE..............................952 925-4111
FAX: 952 925-6122
Robert H Engelhart, *President*
John E Engelhart, *General Mgr*
Sharon R Engelhart, *Vice Pres*
EMP: 130 **EST:** 1971
SQ FT: 6,400
SALES (est): 10MM-24.9MM **Privately Held**
WEB: www.managedservicesinc.com
SIC: 1711 7349 Heating & air conditioning
contractor; building cleaning service

(PA)=Parent Co (HQ)=Headquarters (DH)=Div Headquarters
✪ = New business established in last 2 years

2011 Harris Minnesota
Services Directory

© Harris InfoSource 1-866-281-6415
219

GEOGRAPHIC *(vertical side tab)*

(G-4941)
MANCHESTER CO'S INC
80 S 8th St Ste 4700 (55402-2201)
PHONE..................612 436-2818
FAX: 612 338-4723
Mark Sheffert, *CEO*
Kevin Jansen, *President*
Darrell J Tamosuinas, *Managing Prtnr*
Rodney H Peterson Jr, *Managing Dir*
Sara E Braziller, *Managing Dir*
EMP: 30 EST: 1988
SALES (est): 1MM-4.9MM **Privately Held**
WEB: www.manchestercompanies.com
SIC: 8742 Management consulting services

(G-4942)
MANHATTAN GROUP LLC
430 1st Ave N Ste 500 (55401-1744)
PHONE..................612 337-9600
FAX: 612 341-4457
Mike Klein, *President*
Neil O Connor, *Vice Pres*
Phil Radtke, *Warehouse Mgr*
Hugh Kennedy, *VP Sls/Mktg*
Jon Berg, *Controller*
▲ EMP: 60 EST: 1988
SQ FT: 14,000
SALES (est): 25MM-49.9MM **Privately Held**
WEB: www.manhattantoy.com
SIC: 5092 Wholesales toys; retails hobby
supplies, toys & games
PA: H Enterprises International
120 S 6th St Ste 2300
Minneapolis MN 55402
612 340-8849

(G-4943)
MANPOWER INC
7831 Glenroy Rd Ste 400 (55439-3132)
PHONE..................952 831-3338
Carolyn Benjamin, *Manager*
EMP: 40
SALES (est): 500-999K **Publicly Held**
WEB: www.manpower.com
SIC: 7363 Manpower pools
PA: Manpower Inc
100 Manpower Pl
Milwaukee WI 53212
414 961-1000

(G-4944)
MANSFIELD & TANICK
220 S 6th St Ste 1700 (55402-4511)
PHONE..................612 339-4295
Earl Cohen, *President*
Aaron Biber, *COO*
Marshall Tanick, *Vice Pres*
Seymour Mansfield, *Vice Pres*
Denise Y Tataryn, *Bd of Directors*
EMP: 58 EST: 1989
SQ FT: 10,000
SALES (est): 5MM-9.9MM **Privately Held**
WEB: www.mtlawwatch.com
SIC: 8111 General practice law office

(G-4945)
MARATHON GROUP INC
3356 Gorham Ave (55426-4225)
PHONE..................952 929-1990
Steven L Utne, *President*
Richard W O'Connor, *VP Purch*
Bruce Utne, *VP Sls/Mktg*
Mitchell Hayden, *CFO*
Cheryle Berg, *Office Mgr*
EMP: 85 EST: 1982
SQ FT: 12,000
SALES (est): 5MM-9.9MM **Privately Held**
WEB: www.marathon-group.com
SIC: 1799 1742 Home & office interiors
finishing, furnishing & remodeling service;
office furniture installation service; drywall,
plastering & insulation contractor

(G-4946)
MARCUS HOTELS INC
Also Called: Crowne Plaza Northstar Hotel
618 2nd Ave S (55402-1929)
PHONE..................612 338-2288
FAX: 612 338-2288
Katie Neufeld, *General Mgr*
Joanne Knutson, *Controller*
Jim Lynch, *Sales Dir*
EMP: 120
SALES (est): 5MM-9.9MM **Publicly Held**

WEB: www.marcustheatres.com
SIC: 7011 Traveler accommodations
HQ: Marcus Hotels Inc
100 E Wisconsin Ave
Milwaukee WI 53202
414 905-1200

(G-4947)
MARCY CONSTRUCTION CO
2246 Edgewood Ave S (55426-2823)
PHONE..................952 525-9700
Kenneth G Marcy, *President*
Jame R Warzonek, *Vice Pres*
Beverley Born, *Treasurer*
EMP: 100 EST: 1989
SALES (est): 25MM-49.9MM **Privately Held**
SIC: 1541 Industrial building & warehouse
construction

(G-4948)
MARKET RESOURCE ASSOCIATES INC
15 S 5th St Ste 800 (55402-1026)
PHONE..................612 334-3056
FAX: 612 334-3121
John D Cashmore, *CEO*
EMP: 48 EST: 1990
SQ FT: 8,300
SALES (est): 5MM-9.9MM **Privately Held**
WEB: www.mraonline.com
SIC: 8742 Management consulting services

(G-4949)
MARKETING BRIDGE LLC
10000 Highway 55 (55441-6300)
PHONE..................763 504-4610
Frantz Corneille, *Member*
Mike Corneille, *CTO*
EMP: 50 EST: 2001
SALES (est): 10MM-24.9MM **Privately Held**
WEB: www.marketingbridge.com
SIC: 4813 Internet connectivity services

(G-4950)
MARKETLINE RESEARCH INC
1313 5th St SE Ste 309 (55414-4509)
PHONE..................612 767-2580
FAX: 612 379-3831
Michael Gassney, *President*
John Schamber, *Vice Pres*
David Bender, *Vice Pres*
Aron Whirley, *Project Mgr*
Jon Mattson, *Director*
EMP: 32 EST: 1994
SALES (est): 1MM-4.9MM **Privately Held**
WEB: www.mktline.com
SIC: 8732 Market analysis or research
services

(G-4951)
MARKETTOOLS INC
6465 Wayzata Blvd Ste 170 (55426-1722)
PHONE..................952 546-2800
FAX: 952 546-0835
Amal Johnson, *CEO*
Diane Jordan, *Manager*
EMP: 50 EST: 2005
SALES (est): 1MM-4.9MM **Privately Held**
SIC: 8732 Market analysis or research
services

(G-4952)
MARQUETTE FINANCIAL CO'S (PA)
60 S 6th St Ste 3800 (55402-4438)
PHONE..................612 661-3880
FAX: 612 661-3863
Carl Pohlad, *President*
Darren Sloniger, *Partner*
Matthew Carter, *Senior VP*
Andre Hawaux, *Senior VP*
Pam Lampert, *Senior VP*
EMP: 25 EST: 1964
SALES (corp-wide): 259.15M **Privately
Held**
SIC: 6712 6022 6141 Bank holding
company; state commercial bank; personal
credit institution

(G-4953)
MARQUETTE HOTEL
710 Marquette Ave (55402-2305)
PHONE..................612 333-4545
Gerard Viardin, *General Mgr*

Sarah Tromans, *Controller*
Lisa Heller, *Marketing Staff*
Jennifer Blom, *Manager*
Roseann Nurse, *Manager*
EMP: 275 EST: 1973
SALES (est): 10MM-24.9MM **Privately Held**
WEB: www.marquettehotel.com
SIC: 7011 Hotel; eating place

(G-4954)
MARQUETTE TRANSPORTATION
1600 W 82nd St Ste 150 (55431-1485)
PHONE..................952 703-7474
Richard Voreis, *President*
Linda A Vinchattle, *Corp Secy*
Scott Franzen, *Senior VP*
Joni Donohue, *Senior VP*
David R McFarland, *Vice Pres*
EMP: 50 EST: 2002
SALES (est): 10MM-24.9MM **Privately Held**
WEB: www.meridianbank.com
SIC: 6153 Short-term business credit for
factoring services
HQ: Meridian Bank, National Assn
16435 N Scottsdale Rd
Scottsdale AZ 85254
480 998-8995

(G-4955)
MARRIOTT
3400 Edinborough Way (55435-5255)
PHONE..................952 893-9300
Melladee York, *General Mgr*
Lisa Plinski, *General Mgr*
Lyn Anfinson, *Vice Pres*
Andy Zorowski, *Chief Engr*
EMP: 40
SALES (est): 1MM-4.9MM **Privately Held**
SIC: 7011 Traveler accommodations

(G-4956)
MARS, W P & R S CO INC
215 E 78th St (55420-1249)
PHONE..................952 884-9388
FAX: 952 884-1329
Robert Mars III, *President*
Richard Palmer, *VP Persnl*
Charles Grimby, *Manager*
EMP: 50
SALES (est): 10MM-24.9MM **Privately Held**
WEB: www.marssupply.com
SIC: 5084 Wholesales industrial pneumatic
tools & equipment
PA: Mars, W P & R S Co Inc
4319 W 1st St
Duluth MN 55807
218 628-0303

(G-4957)
MARSH HEATING & AIR CONDG
6248 Lakeland Ave N # 110 (55428-2900)
PHONE..................763 536-0667
FAX: 763 536-0226
Larry D Marsh, *President*
Carole L Marsh, *Vice Pres*
Kelly Marsh, *Executive*
EMP: 35 EST: 1974
SQ FT: 20,000
SALES (est): 1MM-4.9MM **Privately Held**
WEB: www.marshheating.com
SIC: 1711 1731 7349 Heating & air
conditioning contractor; ventilation & duct
work contractor; refrigeration contractor;
general electrical contractor; air duct
cleaning service

(G-4958)
MARSH USA INC
333 S 7th St Ste 1600 (55402-2427)
PHONE..................612 692-7848
FAX: 612 692-7936
Bruce Smith, *Sales Mgr*
Sharon Albrecht, *Manager*
Chuck Segner, *MIS Mgr*
Jason Gerken, *IT/INT Sup*
EMP: 200
SALES (est): 10MM-24.9MM **Publicly Held**
WEB: www.marsh.com
SIC: 6411 Insurance services
HQ: Marsh USA Inc
1166 Avenue Of The Americas
New York NY 10036
212 345-6000

(G-4959)
MARTIN FALK PAPER CO
Also Called: Falk Paper & Packaging
618 N 3rd St (55401-1232)
PHONE..................612 332-8626
FAX: 612 338-2524
John Duffey, *President*
Robert Margl, *Vice Pres*
Anna Margl, *CFO*
Maria Brandriete, *Marketing Staff*
Jeff Graunke, *Executive*
EMP: 35 EST: 1888
SQ FT: 300,000
SALES (est): 10MM-24.9MM **Privately Held**
SIC: 5113 5046 5162 Wholesales industrial
& personal service paper; manufactures
paper book covers; wholesales commercial
cooking & food services equipment;
wholesales plastics film

(G-4960)
MARTIN LUTHER MANOR
Also Called: Meadow Woods
1401 E 100th St (55425-2615)
PHONE..................952 888-7751
Howard Paulsen, *President*
Betty J Garvey, *Vice Pres*
Sally Haak, *Personnel*
Kristi Sebey, *Marketing Mgr*
Martin Minari, *Manager*
EMP: 270 EST: 1956
SQ FT: 170,000
SALES (est): 10MM-24.9MM **Privately Held**
WEB: www.martinluthermanor.com
SIC: 8051 8052 8059 8361 Skilled nursing
care facility; intermediate care facility;
personal care home, with health care;
residential rehabilitation center with health
care incidental

(G-4961)
MARTIN-WILLIAMS INC (HQ)
60 S 6th St Ste 2800 (55402-4444)
PHONE..................612 340-0800
FAX: 612 342-9700
Thomas Modry, *CEO*
Tim Frojd, *Ch of Bd*
Mike Gray, *President*
Joe Harrington, *Senior VP*
Lori Yeager-Davis, *Senior VP*
EMP: 195 EST: 1947
SQ FT: 136,000
SALES (corp-wide): 11.72B **Publicly Held**
WEB: www.fameretail.com
SIC: 7311 Advertising agency
PA: Omnicom Group Inc
437 Madison Ave
New York NY 10022
212 415-3600

(G-4962)
MARTIN-WILLIAMS INC
Also Called: Fame
120 S 6th St Ste 200 (55402-1800)
PHONE..................612 746-3263
FAX: 612 746-3333
Wayne Talley, *Senior VP*
Amie Valentine, *Vice Pres*
Renae Debates, *CFO*
Susan Gingery, *Branch Mgr*
Mitch McHenry, *Manager*
EMP: 30
SALES (est): 1MM-4.9MM **Publicly Held**
WEB: www.fameretail.com
SIC: 7311 Advertising consultants
HQ: Martin-Williams Inc
60 S 6th St Ste 2800
Minneapolis MN 55402
612 340-0800

(G-4963)
MASTER COLLISION GROUP LLC (PA)
2980 Empire Ln N (55447-5316)
PHONE..................763 509-0900
FAX: 763 509-9022
Paul Oberstar, *Member*
Debbie Niemela, *Comptroller*
Lori Anderson, *Manager*
Kirk Suchomel, *Manager*
Dennis Kennealy, *Info Tech Mgr*
EMP: 32 EST: 1952
SQ FT: 22,000 **Privately Held**
WEB: www.mastercollisiongroup.com
SIC: 7532 Automotive body shop;
automotive paint shop

www.HarrisInfo.com
220
2011 Harris Minnesota
Services Directory
▲=Import ▼=Export
◆=Import/Export

(G-4964)

MASTER COLLISION GROUP LLC
Also Called: Paramount
224 W Lake St Ste A (55408-4676)
PHONE 612 827-4697
FAX: 612 825-0765
Paul Oberstar, *Branch Mgr*
Lorri Anderson, *Manager*
EMP: 26
SALES (est): 1MM-4.9MM **Privately Held**
WEB: www.mastercollisiongroup.com
SIC: 7532 Automotive body, paint & interior repair & maintenance services
PA: Master Collision Group LLC
2980 Empire Ln N
Minneapolis MN 55447
763 509-0900

(G-4965)

MASTERWORKS OF MINNEAPOLIS INC
1121 N 7th St (55415-1704)
PHONE 612 333-8210
FAX: 612 333-1404
Kurt Swanson, *Manager*
Tim Glader, *Director*
EMP: 30 EST: 1991
SQ FT: 20,000
SALES (est): 1MM-4.9MM **Privately Held**
WEB: www.masterworksonline.org
SIC: 7389 Bottles, cans & cartons labeling service

(G-4966)

MATRIX COMMUNICATIONS INC (PA)
171 Cheshire Ln N Ste 700 (55441-5477)
PHONE 763 475-5500
FAX: 763 745-2602
Mike Ellis, *CEO*
Charlie Eicher, *President*
Steven R Ferry, *Exec VP*
Brian Boche, *Info Tech Mgr*
Karie Timion, *Director*
EMP: 45 EST: 1985
SQ FT: 15,000 **Privately Held**
SIC: 7629 5065 Telecommunication equipment repair service; wholesales electronic parts & equipment

(G-4967)

MAXFIELD RESEARCH INC
615 1st Ave NE Ste 500 (55413-2681)
PHONE 612 338-2828
FAX: 612 904-7979
Mary Bujold, *President*
Jay Thompson, *Vice Pres*
Jay Demma, *Vice Pres*
Sharon Moore, *Controller*
Shirley Holzinger, *Accounting Mgr*
EST: 1990
SQ FT: 12,000 **Privately Held**
WEB: www.maxfieldresearch.com
SIC: 8742 Real estate consultant

(G-4968)

MAYER ELECTRIC CORP
7224 Winnetka Ave N (55428-1622)
PHONE 763 537-9357
Allan Holm, *CEO*
Martin Holm, *President*
EMP: 61 EST: 1946
SQ FT: 5,500
SALES (est): 5MM-9.9MM **Privately Held**
WEB: www.mayerelec.com
SIC: 1731 8748 Electrical contractor; energy conservation consultant

(G-4969)

MC KNIGHT FOUNDATION
710 S 2nd St Ste 400 (55401-2290)
PHONE 612 333-4220
FAX: 612 332-3833
Kate Wolford, *President*
Bernadette Christiansen, *Vice Pres*
Sarah Lovan, *Administrator*
Becky Monnens, *Administrator*
Cynthia B Boynton, *Director*
EMP: 30 EST: 1953
SQ FT: 6,500 **Privately Held**
SIC: 6732 Management of educational trusts

(G-4970)

MCCALLUM TRANSFER INC
3501 Marshall St NE (55418-4653)
PO Box 581789 (55458-1789)
PHONE 651 633-1612
George Wintz, *CEO*
EMP: 50 EST: 1957
SQ FT: 600
SALES (est): 1MM-4.9MM **Privately Held**
SIC: 4214 4212 Local trucking with storage; local trucking without storage services

(G-4971)

MCCOLLUM, CROWLEY, MOSCHET
7900 Xerxes Ave S Ste 700 (55431-1127)
PHONE 952 831-4980
Robert M Collum, *President*
Robin Mochet, *Corp Secy*
Lisa Carlson, *Human Res Dir*
Deborah L Crowley, *Attorney*
Nancy E Lamo, *Attorney*
EMP: 53 EST: 1986
SQ FT: 8,000
SALES (est): 5MM-9.9MM **Privately Held**
WEB: www.mccollumlaw.com
SIC: 8111 General practice law office

(G-4972)

MCDATA SERVICES CORP
6000 Nathan Ln N Ste 200 (55442-1691)
PHONE 763 268-6000
Julie Quintal, *Vice Pres*
Doug Davidson, *Engineer*
Steve Pannier, *Engineer*
Greg Barnum, *CFO*
Jennifer Weidauer, *Pub Rel Dir*
EMP: 300
SALES (est): 25MM-49.9MM **Publicly Held**
WEB: www.mcdata.com
SIC: 7373 Computer integrated systems design services; manufactures computer storage devices
HQ: MCDATA Corp
4 Brocade Pkwy
Broomfield CO 80021
720 558-8000

(G-4973)

MCG ENERGY SOLUTIONS LLC
901 Marquette Ave # 1000 (55402-3205)
PHONE 612 376-7757
Micheal Prickett, *Member*
Patrick Cromer, *CTO*
Peder Sterling, *Network Mgr*
EMP: 32 EST: 1995
SALES (est): 1MM-4.9MM **Privately Held**
SIC: 7371 Computer software development

(G-4974)

MCGLADREY & PULLEN, LLP (PA)
3600 Amercn Blvd W # 300 (55431-4510)
PHONE 952 921-7700
Tony Ceci, *Partner*
David R Scudder, *Partner*
Tom Losey, *Partner*
Frank Compiani, *Partner*
Debra K Lockwood, *General Ptnr*
EMP: 150 EST: 1927
SQ FT: 15,000 **Privately Held**
SIC: 8721 8748 Auditing services; business consulting services

(G-4975)

MCGOVERN & FISHER INSURANCE
8200 Highwood Dr (55438-1008)
PHONE 952 996-8818
FAX: 952 829-0482
Reynolds Fisher, *Owner*
Wayne Mann, *Manager*
Scott Zech, *Administrator*
EMP: 60 EST: 2001
SALES (est): 50MM-99.9MM **Privately Held**
WEB: www.northerncapital-mn.com
SIC: 6311 6411 Life insurance carrier; property & casualty insurance agent

(G-4976)

MCGRANN SHEA ANDERSON CARNIVAL
800 Nicollet Mall Ste 2600 (55402-2041)
PHONE 612 338-2525
William R Mc Grann, *President*
Douglas M Carnival, *Corp Secy*
Kathleen Lamb, *Counsel*
Andrew J Shea, *Vice Pres*
Scott B Cebs, *Attorney*
EMP: 50 EST: 1989
SQ FT: 10,000
SALES (est): 5MM-9.9MM **Privately Held**
WEB: www.mcgrannshea.com
SIC: 8111 General practice law office

(G-4977)

MCKESSON MEDICAL-SURGICAL INC
316 W 86th St (55420-2706)
PHONE 952 881-8040
FAX: 952 881-8324
Steve Willms, *Branch Mgr*
EMP: 28
SALES (est): 10MM-24.9MM **Publicly Held**
WEB: www.gmholdings.com
SIC: 5047 Wholesales surgical equipment & supplies
HQ: McKesson Medical-Surgical Inc
8741 Landmark Rd
Richmond VA 23228
804 264-7500

(G-4978)

MCKESSON MEDICAL-SURGICAL MN
8121 10th Ave N (55427-4401)
PHONE 763 595-6000
Gary Keeler, *President*
William H Brennan, *Corp Secy*
James M Humphrey, *Corp Secy*
Nicole Normansell, *Corp Secy*
Anne J Shuford, *Corp Secy*
EMP: 300 EST: 1975
SALES (est): 100MM-499.9MM **Publicly Held**
WEB: www.imckesson.com
SIC: 5047 Wholesales medical equipment & supplies
PA: McKesson Corp
1 Post St Fl 18
San Francisco CA 94104
415 983-8300

(G-4979)

MCKINSEY & CO INC
80 S 8th St Ste 3800 (55402-2216)
PHONE 612 371-3100
Tim Welsh, *Manager*
Denise Miller, *Manager*
Fred Miller, *Manager*
William Emptage, *Manager*
Dean Briesemeister, *Consultant*
EMP: 53
SALES (est): 5MM-9.9MM **Privately Held**
WEB: www.mckinsey.com
SIC: 8742 Management consulting services

(G-4980)

MEADOWBROOK WOMEN'S CLINIC
825 S 8th St Ste 1018 (55404-1221)
PHONE 612 376-7708
Mark Tanv MD, *President*
Fred Kravitz MD, *Corp Secy*
Brad Kravitz MD, *Corp Secy*
Melvin Frisch MD, *Treasurer*
Jackie Willett, *Office Mgr*
EMP: 25 EST: 1975
SALES (est): 1MM-4.9MM **Privately Held**
WEB: www.meadowbrookclinic.com
SIC: 8093 8011 Abortion clinic; physicians' office & clinic

(G-4981)

MEAGHER & GEER
33 S 6th St Ste 4400 (55402-3710)
PHONE 612 338-0661
FAX: 612 338-8384
Charles E Spevacek, *Managing Prtnr*
Robert E Salmon, *Partner*
Christian J Preus, *Partner*
Thomas Propson, *Partner*
Leatha G Wolter, *Partner*
EMP: 145 EST: 1929
SQ FT: 42,000
SALES (est): 10MM-24.9MM **Privately Held**
WEB: www.meagher.com
SIC: 8111 General practice law office

(G-4982)

MEDAFOR INC
2700 Freeway Blvd Ste 800 (55430-1757)
PHONE 763 571-6300
FAX: 763 571-1035
Gary Slope, *CEO*
Dick Zerban, *Chairman*
Carl Orr, *COO*
Ken Noblet, *Mfg Staff*
EMP: 25 EST: 1999
SQ FT: 6,000
SALES (est): 1MM-4.9MM **Privately Held**
WEB: www.medafor.com
SIC: 5047 Manufactures bandages & dressings; wholesales medical equipment & supplies

(G-4983)

MEDELIGIBLE SERVICES
6160 Summit Dr N Ste 400 (55430-2149)
PHONE 763 585-8400
FAX: 763 585-8426
Jack Roe, *President*
Kari Olson, *MIS Mgr*
Barb Bell, *Director*
EMP: 74 EST: 1993
SALES (est): 1MM-4.9MM **Privately Held**
SIC: 8322 Self-help organization

(G-4984)

MEDIA PRODUCTIONS INC
710 S 2nd St Fl 7 (55401-2294)
PHONE 612 379-4678
Jerrold Gershone, *CEO*
Judith Kessel, *President*
Sandra Uri, *Office Mgr*
Marla Kapperud, *Manager*
EMP: 30 EST: 1973
SQ FT: 8,500
SALES (est): 5MM-9.9MM **Privately Held**
SIC: 7812 Audio-visual program production service

(G-4985)

MEDICAL RECORDS INC
7800 Glenroy Rd (55439-3122)
PHONE 952 831-6778
FAX: 952 831-5966
Michael Clements, *President*
Doug Busch, *Vice Pres*
Luster Smith, *Manager*
EMP: 60 EST: 1983
SQ FT: 2,500 **Privately Held**
SIC: 7375 Information retrieval services

(G-4986)

MENASHA PACKAGING CO LLC
7301 Northland Dr N (55428-1005)
PHONE 763 424-6606
Jim Archambo, *Vice Pres*
Jill Appledorn, *Vice Pres*
Doug Bisel, *Vice Pres*
Kathleen Bonetti, *Vice Pres*
Cheri Cieslak, *Vice Pres*
EMP: 125
SALES (est): 25MM-49.9MM **Privately Held**
WEB: www.menashapackaging.com
SIC: 5113 Manufactures corrugated boxes; wholesales corrugated & solid fiber boxes; paperboard mill
HQ: Menasha Packaging Co LLC
1645 Bergstrom Rd
Neenah WI 54956
920 751-1000

(G-4987)

MENCEPT EPILEPTIC CLINIC
5775 Wayzata Blvd Ste 200 (55416-1227)
PHONE 952 525-2400
EMP: 30 EST: 2004
SALES (est): 1MM-4.9MM **Privately Held**
SIC: 8011 Physicians' office & clinic

(PA)=Parent Co (HQ)=Headquarters (DH)=Div Headquarters
✿ = New business established in last 2 years

2011 Harris Minnesota
Services Directory

© Harris InfoSource 1-866-281-6415

221

GEOGRAPHIC

(G-4988)
MENTAL HEALTH RESOURCES INC
2105 Minnehaha Ave (55404-3107)
PHONE..........................612 337-4021
Don Nevin, *Branch Mgr*
EMP: 25
SALES (est): 1MM-4.9MM **Privately Held**
WEB: www.mhresources.com
SIC: 8093 Specialty outpatient clinic
PA: Mental Health Resources Inc
    1821 University Ave W N464A
    Saint Paul MN 55104
    651 659-2900

(G-4989)
MERCER INC
333 S 7th St Ste 1600 (55402-2427)
PHONE..........................612 642-8600
FAX: 612 341-0232
Madison J Groves, *Principal*
Joy Frevel, *Office Mgr*
Eric Walcher, *Manager*
John Polta, *Manager*
Nancy Lindberg, *Manager*
EMP: 100
SALES (est): 10MM-24.9MM **Publicly Held**
WEB: www.marshmac.com
SIC: 8742 Management consulting services
HQ: Mercer Inc
    1166 Avenue Of The Americas
    New York NY 10036
    212 345-4500

(G-4990)
MERCURY MAILERS OF MINNESOTA
Also Called: Mailers of Minnesota
2500 La Ave N Ste C (55427)
PHONE..........................763 544-1881
FAX: 763 544-0484
John Stamson, *President*
Tony Stamson, *Sales Mgr*
EMP: 25 EST: 1988
SQ FT: 22,000
SALES (est): 1MM-4.9MM **Privately Held**
WEB: www.mailersofmn.com
SIC: 7331 Mailing services

(G-4991)
MERISTAR INVESTMENT PARTNERS L
Also Called: Hilton
3800 E 80th St (55425-1658)
PHONE..........................952 854-2100
Jon Kranock, *Manager*
Mike Brunkow, *Manager*
Bert Couch, *Exec Dir*
Vishwa Ural, *Analyst*
EMP: 100
SALES (est): 5MM-9.9MM **Privately Held**
SIC: 7011 Hotel

(G-4992)
MERITEX ENTERPRISES INC (PA)
24 University Ave NE (55413-2685)
PHONE..........................651 855-9700
H G McNeely III, *CEO*
Keith W Baker, *Corp Secy*
Arvid Povilaitis, *COO*
Greg Johnson, *Senior VP*
Thomas Hotovec, *CFO*
▲ EMP: 31 EST: 1989
SQ FT: 18,000 **Privately Held**
SIC: 6512 4225 6531 Operators of
commercial & industrial buildings; real
estate management services; general
warehousing

(G-4993)
MERRILL LYNCH, PIERCE, FENNER
8300 Norman Center Dr # 1250
(55437-1095)
PHONE..........................952 820-1900
FAX: 952 820-8445
Mark Adkins, *Manager*
Chris Schultz, *Manager*
Alice Safon, *Manager*
Shawn Gresseth, *Manager*
Mark Tekris, *Exec Dir*
EMP: 30

SALES (est): 5MM-9.9MM **Publicly Held**
WEB: www.ml.com
SIC: 6211 Securities broker & dealer
HQ: Merrill Lynch & Co Inc
    4 World Financial Ctr # 4
    New York NY 10080
    212 449-1000

(G-4994)
MERRILL LYNCH, PIERCE, FENNER
225 S 6th St Ste 4400 (55402-4618)
PHONE..........................612 349-7801
FAX: 612 349-7909
Rachael Orvik, *Opers Mgr*
John Randolph, *Sales Executive*
Douglas King, *Manager*
James Wileck, *Manager*
Ke Chen, *Manager*
EMP: 50
SALES (est): 10MM-24.9MM **Publicly Held**
WEB: www.ml.com
SIC: 6211 Securities broker & dealer
HQ: Merrill Lynch & Co Inc
    4 World Financial Ctr # 4
    New York NY 10080
    212 449-1000

(G-4995)
MERWIN HOME MEDICAL
4082 Lakeland Ave N (55422-2236)
PHONE..........................763 535-5335
FAX: 763 536-3590
Dan Steinhauser, *President*
Jeff Pribula, *Manager*
Tom Reilly, *Manager*
Rick Steinhauser, *CIO*
Dyan Harlem, *Officer*
EMP: 100 EST: 2000
SALES (est): 50MM-99.9MM **Privately Held**
WEB: www.merwinmedical.com
SIC: 5047 Wholesales medical equipment & supplies

(G-4996)
MESHBESHER & SPENCE LTD (PA)
1616 Park Ave (55404-1631)
PHONE..........................612 339-9121
Ronald Meshbesher, *President*
Dennis Johnson, *Principal*
Daniel Boivin, *Principal*
Mark Streed, *Corp Secy*
Libby Peterson, *Manager*
EMP: 35 EST: 1966
SQ FT: 15,000
SALES (corp-wide): 10M **Privately Held**
SIC: 8111 Specialized legal services;
criminal law office

(G-4997)
MESSERLI & KRAMER
3405 Annapolis Ln N (55447-5342)
PHONE..........................763 548-7900
Ellen Fleming, *Branch Mgr*
William Hicks, *Manager*
Jeff Fournier, *Manager*
EMP: 100
SALES (est): 10MM-24.9MM **Privately Held**
SIC: 8111 Legal services

(G-4998)
MET-CON METRO INC
10640 Lyndale Ave S Ste 4 (55420-5636)
PO Box 427, Faribault (55021-0427)
PHONE..........................952 884-6250
Thomas M Donough, *President*
EMP: 40 EST: 1986
SQ FT: 5,000
SALES (est): 10MM-24.9MM **Privately Held**
SIC: 1541 1771 Steel building construction;
concrete contractor
PA: Met-Con Construction Inc
    15760 Acorn Trl
    Faribault MN 55021
    507 332-2266

(G-4999)
METES & BOUNDS MANAGEMENT CO
6640 Lyndale Ave S # 100 (55423-2385)
PHONE..........................612 861-8526
Jan H Susee, *CEO*
Duncan Susee, *Vice Pres*

David Lee, *Vice Pres*
Thomas A Berning, *Director*
Robert W Worthington, *Director*
EST: 1978
SQ FT: 2,500 **Privately Held**
SIC: 6531 Real estate management
services

(G-5000)
METRO - SALES INC
1640 E 78th St (55423-4645)
PHONE..........................612 861-4000
Jerry Mathwig, *President*
Karen A Mathwig, *Vice Pres*
Deryl Orthmann, *Facilities Mgr*
Kirk Fezler, *Purchasing*
Dave Brynjulfson, *CFO*
EMP: 200 EST: 1969
SQ FT: 16,000
SALES (est): 50MM-99.9MM **Privately Held**
SIC: 5044 5065 5112 7359 Wholesales
office equipment; wholesales duplicating
machines; wholesales typewriters;
wholesales facsimile or fax equipment;
wholesales computer & photocopying
supplies; office machine & equipment
leasing & rental

(G-5001)
METRO LEGAL SERVICES INC (PA)
330 2nd Ave S Ste 150 (55401-2256)
PHONE..........................612 332-0202
FAX: 612 332-5215
Jeff Budde, *President*
Scott Gray, *Vice Pres*
EMP: 85 EST: 1969
SQ FT: 5,700
SALES (corp-wide): 5.68M **Privately Held**
WEB: www.metrolegal.com
SIC: 7338 7389 8111 Court reporting
service; legal & tax service; legal aid
services

(G-5002)
METRO PARKWAY ASSOC
7800 Metro Pkwy Ste 200 (55425-1506)
PHONE..........................952 854-4244
Thomas Margarit, *Managing Prtnr*
Norlin Boyum, *Partner*
Barbara Kleiter, *Controller*
Dewey Johnson, *Marketing Mgr*
Micki Jubera, *Administrator*
EMP: 50 EST: 1980
SALES (est): 10MM-24.9MM **Privately Held**
SIC: 6512 Nonresidential building operator

(G-5003)
METRO PRODUCE DISTRIBUTORS INC
2700 E 28th St Ste B (55406-1575)
PHONE..........................612 722-5575
FAX: 612 722-3185
Robert Spizman, *President*
Raleigh Spizman, *Corp Secy*
Brad Anderson, *Vice Pres*
EMP: 100 EST: 1986
SQ FT: 40,000
SALES (est): 25MM-49.9MM **Privately Held**
SIC: 5148 Wholesales fresh fruits &
vegetables

(G-5004)
METRO SYSTEMS FURNITURE INC
1101 W River Pkwy Ste 100 (55415-1215)
PHONE..........................952 933-5050
FAX: 952 944-1449
James Harmon, *President*
Dick Nash, *General Mgr*
William Meyers, *CFO*
EMP: 50 EST: 1968
SQ FT: 60,000
SALES (est): 10MM-24.9MM **Privately Held**
SIC: 5021 Wholesales office furniture

(G-5005)
METRODENTALLCARE, PLC
6601 Lyndale Ave S (55423-2477)
PHONE..........................612 861-9123
David Milbrath, *CEO*
Marcus Gustasen, *Member*
EMP: 50 EST: 1995
SALES (est): 1MM-4.9MM **Privately Held**
WEB: www.sentinelpartners.com

SIC: 8021 Dental clinics & offices
PA: Sentinel Capital Partners LLC
    330 Madison Ave Fl 27
    New York NY 10017
    212 688-3100

(G-5006)
METROPOLITAN DENTAL ASSOCIATES (HQ)
Also Called: Metrodentalcare
7400 Lyndale Ave S (55423-4055)
PHONE..........................612 866-0054
FAX: 612 861-9102
David E Milbrath DDS, *President*
Barry P Schwerr, *Director*
EMP: 90 EST: 1968
SQ FT: 4,800 **Privately Held**
WEB: www.sentinelpartners.com
SIC: 8021 Dental office
PA: Sentinel Capital Partners LLC
    330 Madison Ave Fl 27
    New York NY 10017
    212 688-3100

(G-5007)
METROPOLITAN PRODUCTIONS INC
1201 Harmon Pl Ste 300 (55403-2048)
PHONE..........................612 333-1025
FAX: 612 359-3636
Kent Hodder, *CEO*
Nancy Bordson, *Vice Pres*
EMP: 60 EST: 1985
SQ FT: 12,000
SALES (est): 10MM-24.9MM **Privately Held**
SIC: 7812 7819 Television film production
service; video tape or disk reproduction
service; video tape production services

(G-5008)
METROPOLITAN SPORTS FACILITIES
Also Called: Hhh Metrodome
900 S 5th St Ste A (55415-1565)
PHONE..........................612 332-0386
FAX: 612 332-8334
Roy Terwilliger, *Ch of Bd*
William Lester, *Exec Dir*
EMP: 80 EST: 1954
SQ FT: 478,290
SALES (est): 10MM-24.9MM **Privately Held**
WEB: www.hhhmetrodome.com
SIC: 6512 Operators of auditoriums & halls

(G-5009)
METROPOLITAN SPORTS FACILITIES
Also Called: MSFC
900 S 5th St (55415-1563)
PHONE..........................612 332-0386
Roy Terwilliger, *Ch of Bd*
Bonnie Demarce, *Branch Mgr*
Dan Twaddle, *Director*
Nancy Matowitz, *Executive Asst*
EMP: 40 EST: 1995
SQ FT: 478,290 **Privately Held**
WEB: www.msfc.com
SIC: 8699 Charitable organization

(G-5010)
METROPOLITAN TRANSIT COMMN
560 6th Ave N (55411-4332)
PHONE..........................612 341-4287
FAX: 612 349-7503
Thomas Sather, *Administrator*
EMP: 240 EST: 1967
SQ FT: 10,000
SALES (est): 10MM-24.9MM **Privately Held**
SIC: 4111 Bus line operations

(G-5011)
MEYER, BORGMAN & JOHNSON INC
12 S 6th St Ste 810 (55402-1512)
PHONE..........................612 338-0713
FAX: 612 337-5325
Daniel Murphy, *President*
Michael J Ramerth, *Corp Secy*
Laura Martinson, *Corp Secy*
Michael Lozelle, *Vice Pres*
Brion Szwed, *Engineering*
EMP: 30 EST: 1955
SALES (est): 1MM-4.9MM **Privately Held**

www.HarrisInfo.com
222
2011 Harris Minnesota
Services Directory
▲=Import ▼=Export
◆=Import/Export

SIC: **8711** Engineering consulting services; structural engineering services

(G-5012)
MEYER, SCHERER & ROCKCASTLE
710 S 2nd St Ste 800   (55401-2294)
PHONE 612 375-0336
Jack Poling, *President*
Bill Meeker, *Corp Secy*
Garth Rockcastle, *Vice Pres*
Thomas Meyer, *Vice Pres*
Jeff Scherer, *Vice Pres*
EMP: 35 EST: 1981
SQ FT: 11,000
SALES (est): 1MM-4.9MM **Privately Held**
WEB: www.msrltd.com
SIC: **8712 7389** Architectural service; interior design service

(G-5013)
MFRA INC
Also Called: McCombs Frank Roos Associates
14800 28th Ave N Ste 140   (55447-4826)
PHONE 763 476-6010
FAX: 763 476-8532
Sirish Samba, *President*
Steven Janson, *Corp Secy*
Erik Miller, *Vice Pres*
Lisa Mazzipello, *Controller*
Brian Deroo, *Manager*
EMP: 92 EST: 1966
SQ FT: 20,000
SALES (est): 10MM-24.9MM **Privately Held**
WEB: www.mfra.com
SIC: **8711** Civil engineering services
PA: Tonka Bay Equity Partners LLC
301 Carlson Pkwy Ste 325
Hopkins MN 55305
952 345-2030

(G-5014)
MGM HOME CARE INC
325 Cedar Ave S Ste 5   (55454-1080)
PHONE 612 338-3636
Idiris Dira, *Owner*
EMP: 30 EST: 2004
SALES (est): 1MM-4.9MM **Privately Held**
SIC: **8082** Home health care services

(G-5015)
MICHAEL D NORMAN & ASSOCIATES
Also Called: Carnegie, Dale Training
4938 Lincoln Dr   (55436-1071)
PHONE 952 935-0515
FAX: 952 935-0117
Michael D Norman, *President*
Jackie Regan, *Vice Pres*
Nancy Glube, *Manager*
Sonya Carter, *E-Business*
EMP: 50 EST: 1969
SQ FT: 3,600
SALES (est): 5MM-9.9MM **Privately Held**
SIC: **8742** Personal development school; management consulting services

(G-5016)
MICHAEL DAM
Also Called: Alliance Insurance Agency
5241 Viking Dr   (55435-5313)
PHONE 952 831-1928
Michael Dam, *Owner*
EMP: 30 EST: 1972
SALES (est): 1MM-4.9MM **Privately Held**
SIC: **6411** Insurance services

(G-5017)
MICHAUD, COOLEY, ERICKSON
333 S 7th St Ste 1200   (55402-2422)
PHONE 612 339-4941
FAX: 612 339-8354
Dean A Rafferty, *CEO*
Douglas C Cooley, *President*
John Smith, *Vice Pres*
Sean A Tewalt, *Project Mgr*
Douglas A Mutcher, *Project Mgr*
EMP: 122 EST: 1946
SQ FT: 36,000
SALES (est): 10MM-24.9MM **Privately Held**
SIC: **8711** Engineering consulting services

(G-5018)
MICRO ELECTRONICS INC
3710 Highway 100 S   (55416-2512)
PHONE 952 285-4040
FAX: 952 285-4046
Mark Hawes, *General Mgr*
Roger Lewis, *Opers Mgr*
Rebecca Kes, *Branch Mgr*
EMP: 75
SALES (est): 10MM-24.9MM **Privately Held**
WEB: www.microcenter.com
SIC: **5045** Retails personal computers; wholesales computer peripheral equipment; wholesales personal & home entertainment computers & accessories; retails computer software & accessories
PA: Micro Electronics Inc
4119 Leap Rd
Hilliard OH 43026
614 850-3000

(G-5019)
MICROSOFT CORP
8300 Norman Center Dr # 950
(55437-1039)
PHONE 952 832-8000
FAX: 952 832-8388
Dan Stock, *Sales/Mktg Mgr*
Bill Busch, *Sales/Mktg Mgr*
Lynn Wangen, *Sales Staff*
Tess Kavanagh, *Marketing Staff*
Andrew Akridge, *Manager*
EMP: 80
SALES (est): 10MM-24.9MM **Publicly Held**
WEB: www.microsoft.com
SIC: **7372** Software publisher
PA: Microsoft Corp
1 Microsoft Way
Redmond WA 98052
425 882-8080

(G-5020)
MID AMERICAN TRANSPORTATION
7700 24th Ave S   (55450-1004)
PO Box 11615, Saint Paul   (55111-0615)
PHONE 612 726-9162
John Dawson, *President*
EMP: 60 EST: 1996
SALES (est): 5MM-9.9MM **Privately Held**
SIC: **4731** Freight transportation arrangement services

(G-5021)
MID MINNESOTA LEGAL ASSISTANCE
430 1st Ave N Ste 300   (55401-1742)
PHONE 612 332-1441
Jeremy Lane, *President*
EMP: 155 EST: 1981
SQ FT: 17,000
SALES (est): 10MM-24.9MM **Privately Held**
WEB: www.midmnlegal.org
SIC: **8111** Specialized legal services

(G-5022)
MID-AMERICA BUSINESS SYSTEMS
2500 Broadway St NE # 100   (55413-1748)
PHONE 612 378-3800
FAX: 612 378-3100
Gilbert J Roscoe, *President*
Phillip Knutsen, *Exec VP*
Bill Bissonette, *Vice Pres*
Mike Braun, *Vice Pres*
Roger House, *Vice Pres*
EMP: 43 EST: 1976
SQ FT: 12,748
SALES (est): 5MM-9.9MM **Privately Held**
SIC: **8742** Management consulting services

(G-5023)
MID-CONTINENT ENGINEERING INC
405 35th Ave NE Ste 1   (55418-1159)
PHONE 612 781-0260
FAX: 612 782-1320
Charles N Marvin, *CEO*
Sanders Marvin, *President*
Dennis Holtz, *Purch Mgr*
James Johnson, *Purch Mgr*
Jason Thom, *Engineering*
EMP: 80

EST: 1950
SQ FT: 114,000
SALES (est): 5MM-9.9MM **Privately Held**
WEB: www.mid-continent.com
SIC: **7692** Machine shop, jobbing & repair services; manufactures sheet metal specialties; metal products painting service; welding service

(G-5024)
MIDCONTINENT MEDIA INC   (PA)
3600 Minnesota Dr Ste 700   (55435-7918)
PHONE 952 844-2600
N L Bentson, *Ch of Bd*
Mark S Niblick, *President*
Joseph H Floyd, *Vice Chairman*
Steve Groer, *CFO*
Steve Grosser, *CFO*
EMP: 250 EST: 1933
SQ FT: 4,305
SALES (corp-wide): 164.99K **Privately Held**
WEB: www.mmi.net
SIC: **4841 4813 4832** Cable television services; radio broadcasting station; long distance telephone communications services

(G-5025)
MIDLAND PAPER CO
1860 Elm St SE   (55414-2500)
PHONE 612 623-2400
John Johnson, *Branch Mgr*
EMP: 30
SALES (est): 25MM-49.9MM **Privately Held**
WEB: www.midlandpaper.com
SIC: **5111** Wholesales fine paper
PA: Midland Paper Co
101 E Palatine Rd
Wheeling IL 60090
847 777-2700

(G-5026)
MIDWEST CLEANING & RESTORATION
6020 Ensign Ave N   (55428-2616)
PHONE 763 533-3723
Kevin Angel, *President*
Van Heel, *Corp Secy*
EMP: 33 EST: 2006 **Privately Held**
SIC: **8641** Social club

(G-5027)
MIDWEST DRIVER CORP
55 W 78th St   (55420-1110)
PHONE 952 884-0765
Dale B Robison, *President*
Kristie Robison, *Corp Secy*
EMP: 300 EST: 1967
SQ FT: 5,000
SALES (est): 5MM-9.9MM **Privately Held**
WEB:
www.physicaldistributionservices.com
SIC: **7363** Truck driver service
PA: Physical Distribution Services
55 W 78th St
Minneapolis MN 55420
952 884-0765

(G-5028)
MIDWEST FAMILY MUTUAL INSCE
3033 Campus Dr Ste E195   (55441-2624)
PHONE 763 951-7000
FAX: 763 951-7092
Ron Boid, *President*
Richard Habstritt, *Treasurer*
Jeff Blum, *Administrator*
Jeanne Jay, *Supervisor*
Brad Sukut, *Info Tech Dir*
EMP: 80 EST: 1891
SALES (est): 50MM-99.9MM **Privately Held**
SIC: **6311** Life insurance carrier

(G-5029)
MIDWEST HOME HEALTH CARE INC
801 Park Ave   (55404-1136)
PHONE 612 343-3265
Mohamud K Hassan, *President*
Bashir Mohamed, *Vice Pres*
EMP: 400 EST: 2002
SQ FT: 9,000
SALES (est): 10MM-24.9MM **Privately Held**
SIC: **8082** Home health care services

(G-5030)
MIDWEST LATINO ENTERTAINMENT
Also Called: El Nuevo Rodeo
2709 E Lake St   (55406-1927)
PHONE 612 728-0101
FAX: 612 721-6601
Maya Santamaria, *President*
EMP: 50 EST: 1998
SQ FT: 20,000
SALES (est): 1MM-4.9MM **Privately Held**
SIC: **7922** Full service ethnic food restaurant; theatrical talent agent; night club drinking establishment

(G-5031)
MIDWEST MAINTENANCE & MECH
710 Penns Ave S Ste B   (55426-1603)
PHONE 763 544-2700
FAX: 763 591-9559
Jim Lupient, *Ch of Bd*
Terry Siede, *President*
EMP: 50 EST: 1995
SQ FT: 2,000
SALES (est): 5MM-9.9MM **Privately Held**
SIC: **1711** Plumbing, heating & air conditioning contractor

(G-5032)
MIDWEST MECHANICAL SOLUTIONS
5831 Cedar Lake Rd S   (55416-1481)
PHONE 952 525-2003
Matt Jacobsen, *Principal*
Mick Miller, *Principal*
Mark McCollough, *Principal*
Tom Bresesen, *Principal*
Nick Brecht, *Principal*
EMP: 25 EST: 1997
SQ FT: 5,000
SALES (est): 10MM-24.9MM **Privately Held**
SIC: **5075 5064** Wholesales air filters; wholesales electric air conditioning appliances

(G-5033)
MIDWEST MEDICAL INSURANCE (PA)
7650 Edinbrgh Way Ste 400   (55435-5981)
PHONE 952 838-6700
FAX: 952 838-6808
David P Bounk, *CEO*
Wayne F Leebaw, *Vice Chairman*
Elizabeth Lincoln, *Vice Pres*
Debra McBride, *Vice Pres*
Julie Stafford, *Vice Pres*
EMP: 80 EST: 1988
SQ FT: 25,000
SALES (corp-wide): 138.31M **Privately Held**
WEB: www.mitbenefits.com
SIC: **6719** Investment holding company

(G-5034)
MIDWEST MEDICAL INSURANCE CO
7650 Edinbrgh Way Ste 400   (55435-5981)
PHONE 952 838-6700
David Bounk, *President*
Richard Geier, *Chairman*
Jack L Kleven, *COO*
Jeff Pearson, *Assistant VP*
Jay Koepsell, *Assistant VP*
EMP: 86 EST: 1980
SQ FT: 26,000
SALES (est): 25MM-49.9MM **Privately Held**
WEB: www.mitbenefits.com
SIC: **6351** Provides liability insurance
PA: Midwest Medical Insurance
7650 Edinbrgh Way Ste 400
Minneapolis MN 55435
952 838-6700

(G-5035)
MIDWEST MEDICAL SOLUTIONS
7650 Edinbrgh Way Ste 400   (55435-5981)
PHONE 952 838-6700
David Bounk, *President*
Dirk Nelson, *Director*
EMP: 72 EST: 1997
SALES (est): 5MM-9.9MM **Privately Held**
WEB: www.mitbenefits.com

(PA)=Parent Co (HQ)=Headquarters (DH)=Div Headquarters
✪ = New business established in last 2 years

2011 Harris Minnesota
Services Directory

© Harris InfoSource 1-866-281-6415
223

SIC: **8099** Physical examination service for insurance purposes
PA: Midwest Medical Insurance
7650 Edinbrgh Way Ste 400
Minneapolis MN 55435
952 838-6700

(G-5036)
MIDWEST RUBBER SERVICE & SPLY
14307 28th Pl N (55447-4833)
PHONE...............................763 559-2551
FAX: 763 559-4429
H C Anderson, *CEO*
Doug Turk, *President*
Roy Campen, *General Mgr*
Bill Weldon, *General Mgr*
Shirley Ostendorf, *Finance Dir*
▲ EMP: 50 EST: 1976
SQ FT: 40,000
SALES (est): 10MM-24.9MM Privately Held
WEB: www.midwestrubber.com
SIC: **5085** Wholesales industrial hose, belting & packing

(G-5037)
MIDWEST SPECIAL SERVICES INC
7600 Boone Ave N Ste 86 (55428-1015)
PHONE...............................763 557-1231
Kevin McCabel, *Manager*
EMP: 70
SALES (est): 1MM-4.9MM Privately Held
WEB: www.mwsservices.org
SIC: **8331** Job training services; work experience center; vocational rehabilitation agency
PA: Midwest Special Services Inc
900 Ocean St
Saint Paul MN 55106
651 778-1000

(G-5038)
MIKARA CORP
Also Called: National Salon Resources Div
3109 Louisiana Ave N (55427-2918)
PHONE...............................763 541-1000
FAX: 763 541-9164
Michael P Hicks, *CEO*
Robin Sanders, *Office Mgr*
EMP: 35 EST: 1970
SQ FT: 30,000
SALES (est): 5MM-9.9MM Privately Held
WEB: www.nationalsalon.com
SIC: **5087** Wholesales beauty parlor equipment & supplies; wholesales barber shop equipment & supplies; retails hair care products

(G-5039)
MILAVETZ GALLOP MILLAVETZ
6500 France Ave S (55435-1703)
PHONE...............................763 533-1111
Robert Milavetz, *Partner*
EMP: 50 EST: 2005
SALES (est): 5MM-9.9MM Privately Held
WEB: www.milavetzlaw.com
SIC: **8111** Legal services

(G-5040)
MILAVETZ, GALLOP & MILAVETZ
6500 France Ave S (55435-1703)
PHONE...............................612 339-0140
Alam Milavetz, *Partner*
EMP: 25
SALES (est): 1MM-4.9MM Privately Held
SIC: **8111** General practice attorney's or lawyer's office

(G-5041)
MILESTONE SYSTEMS INC
8401 Golden Valley Rd # 300 (55427-4488)
PHONE...............................763 404-6200
Michael Kohler, *President*
Leigh A Kohler, *Corp Secy*
Mark Greer, *COO*
Mark Thompson, *Vice Pres*
Nathan Ladd, *Engineer*
EMP: 33 EST: 2000
SALES (est): 5MM-9.9MM Privately Held
WEB: www.milestonesystems.com

SIC: **7379 8748** Retails computer peripheral equipment; retails computer software & accessories; computer system consulting services; communications consultant

(G-5042)
MILL CITY ELECTRIC INC
2710 E 33rd St (55406-2424)
PHONE...............................612 724-4900
Matthew Cina, *President*
Sheila Cina, *Corp Secy*
Cory Gustafson, *Vice Pres*
Adam Gustafson, *Vice Pres*
EMP: 25 EST: 2003
SALES (est): 1MM-4.9MM Privately Held
SIC: **1731** Electrical contractor

(G-5043)
MILLER DUNWIDDIE ARCHITECTURE
123 N 3rd St Ste 104 (55401-1659)
PHONE...............................612 337-0000
FAX: 612 337-0031
Craig R Lau, *President*
John D Mecum, *Vice Pres*
Mark Miller, *Vice Pres*
Kim Erickson, *Office Mgr*
David Kulich, *Manager*
EMP: 38 EST: 1963
SQ FT: 9,000
SALES (est): 1MM-4.9MM Privately Held
WEB: www.millerdunwiddie.com
SIC: **8711 8712** Engineering services; architectural service

(G-5044)
MILLER MEDI VAN INC
Also Called: Contemporary Transportation
904 19th Ave S (55404-2202)
PHONE...............................612 332-2888
Steve Miller, *President*
Kristine Johnson, *Vice Pres*
EMP: 30 EST: 1978
SQ FT: 600
SALES (est): 1MM-4.9MM Privately Held
SIC: **4131** Intercity highway special transport services

(G-5045)
MILLER ROZEBOOM ARCHITECT INC
244 1st Ave N (55401-1608)
PHONE...............................612 332-2110
FAX: 612 332-2166
Ted Rozeboom, *President*
Steve Miller, *Vice Pres*
Donna Thompson, *Manager*
EMP: 25 EST: 1997
SALES (est): 1MM-4.9MM Privately Held
WEB: www.rmarchitects.com
SIC: **8712** Architectural service

(G-5046)
MILLIMAN INC
8500 Normandale Lake Blvd 18 (55437-3813)
PHONE...............................952 897-5300
FAX: 952 897-5301
Alan Pivec, *Manager*
Sue Isaksson, *Manager*
William Bluhm, *Manager*
Shonn Twight, *Administrator*
EMP: 60
SALES (est): 5MM-9.9MM Privately Held
SIC: **8999 6411** Actuarial consulting services; insurance ratemaking organization

(G-5047)
MILLIONZILLION SOFTWARE INC
3306 Decatur Ln (55426-3717)
PHONE...............................952 932-9048
Zebigniew Karwowski, *President*
Maciej Drozdowski, *Vice Pres*
Ted Osborne, *CIO*
EMP: 30 EST: 1997
SALES (est): 1MM-4.9MM Privately Held
WEB: www.millionzillion.com
SIC: **7371** Computer software development

(G-5048)
MINCEP EPILEPSY CARE
Also Called: Minnesota Comprehensive E
5775 Wayzata Blvd Ste 200 (55416-1227)
PHONE...............................952 525-2400
Robert J Gumnit, *President*
Marie Wolpert, *Corp Secy*
Frances Graham, *COO*
Ronald Randall, *Vice Pres*
Sabina Gapany, *Pharmacist*
EMP: 50 EST: 1986
SALES (est): 5MM-9.9MM Privately Held
WEB: www.mincep.com
SIC: **8011** Physicians' office & clinic

(G-5049)
MINIKAHDA CLUB
3205 Excelsior Blvd (55416-4680)
PHONE...............................952 926-4167
James E Jennings, *General Mgr*
Marcia Adams, *Human Res Mgr*
Suzanne Herrera, *Manager*
Jack Bergeson, *MIS Mgr*
EMP: 100 EST: 1878
SQ FT: 10,000
SALES (est): 5MM-9.9MM Privately Held
WEB: www.minikahdaclub.com
SIC: **7997** Country club; retails golf goods & equipment; retails sports apparel; eating place

(G-5050)
MINNEAPOLIS AMERICAN INDIAN
1530 E Franklin Ave (55404-2136)
PHONE...............................612 871-4555
FAX: 612 879-1795
C Stately, *Manager*
Michael Dashner, *Manager*
Frances Fairbanks, *Exec Dir*
EMP: 32 EST: 1970
SQ FT: 40,000
SALES (est): 1MM-4.9MM Privately Held
SIC: **8331** Community services employment training program

(G-5051)
MINNEAPOLIS CLINIC OF (PA)
4225 Golden Valley Rd (55422-4215)
PHONE...............................763 588-0661
FAX: 763 302-4065
Daniel Randa MD, *Principal*
Ivan Brodsky MD, *Corp Secy*
Frederick Strobl MD, *Treasurer*
Suzanne Kersten, *Finance Dir*
John T Macdonald, *Med Doctor*
EMP: 160 EST: 1946
SQ FT: 30,000 Privately Held
WEB: www.minneapolisclinic.com
SIC: **8011** Neurologist

(G-5052)
MINNEAPOLIS COMMUNITY DEVPT
105 5th Ave S Ste 200 (55401-2521)
PHONE...............................612 673-5095
FAX: 612 673-5138
Mike Chriantenson, *CEO*
Mike Christianson, *CEO*
Scott Benson, *Vice Pres*
Rosanne Jones, *Vice Pres*
Michael Sunderman, *Accounting Staf*
EMP: 130 EST: 1947 Privately Held
SIC: **8399** Community development groups

(G-5053)
MINNEAPOLIS FLORAL CO
2420 Hennepin Ave (55405-2604)
PHONE...............................612 377-8080
FAX: 612 377-6240
Larry B Olson, *President*
Paul A Olson, *Vice Pres*
EMP: 30 EST: 1900
SQ FT: 10,000
SALES (est): 1MM-4.9MM Privately Held
WEB: www.minneapolisfloral.com
SIC: **5193** Retails fresh flowers; wholesales fresh flowers; wholesales potted plants; retails potted plants

(G-5054)
MINNEAPOLIS FOUNDATION
800 Ids Ctr 80 S 8th St (55402)
PHONE...............................612 672-3878
Sandra Vargas, *President*
Jean Adams, *Vice Pres*
Gregary Allen, *Controller*
Christelle Langer, *Marketing Staff*
Donald Flower, *Information Mgr*
EMP: 30 EST: 1915 Privately Held
SIC: **6732** Management of charitable trusts

(G-5055)
MINNEAPOLIS GOLF CLUB
2001 Flag Ave S (55426-2327)
PHONE...............................952 544-4471
Kevin Kelly, *President*
Bill Meyer, *General Mgr*
Ray Clemas, *General Mgr*
Gail Thell, *Human Res Dir*
Felicia Winn, *Hum Res Coord*
EMP: 50 EST: 1916
SQ FT: 30,000
SALES (est): 1MM-4.9MM Privately Held
WEB: www.minneapolisgolfclub.com
SIC: **7997** Membership golf club; eating place

(G-5056)
MINNEAPOLIS GRAIN EXCHANGE
400 S 4th St Ste 130 (55415-1413)
PHONE...............................612 321-7101
Mark Bagan, *CEO*
Tabitha Westberg, *Assistant VP*
William Grindell, *Assistant VP*
James Facente, *Opers Staff*
Layne Carlson, *Treasurer*
EMP: 37 EST: 1881
SQ FT: 250,000
SALES (est): 10MM-24.9MM Privately Held
WEB: www.mgex.com
SIC: **6231** Futures contract exchange service

(G-5057)
MINNEAPOLIS MEDICAL RESEARCH
914 S 8th St Ste 600 (55404-1228)
PHONE...............................612 347-5000
FAX: 612 347-3915
Paul R Pentel MD, *President*
Thomas J Bloss MD, *Corp Secy*
Gaylan Rockswold, *Vice Pres*
Gaylan Rockwold, *Vice Pres*
Megan Crosby, *Accountant*
EMP: 200 EST: 1952
SQ FT: 72,782 Privately Held
SIC: **8731** Commercial medical research services
PA: Hennepin Faculty Associates
120 S 6th St Ste 155
Minneapolis MN 55402
612 347-7226

(G-5058)
MINNEAPOLIS OXYGEN CO
3842 Washington Ave N (55412-2142)
PHONE...............................612 588-8855
FAX: 612 588-3123
Mark Falconer, *CEO*
Lou Ottosen, *Vice Pres*
Jim Warrick, *Vice Pres*
Dave Olson, *CFO*
Brandon Paplow, *Info Tech Mgr*
EMP: 43 EST: 1948
SQ FT: 25,000
SALES (est): 10MM-24.9MM Privately Held
WEB: www.mplso2.com
SIC: **5085 5047 5084 5169** Wholesales welding supplies; wholesales medical & hospital equipment; wholesales compressed & liquefied gases; wholesales welding equipment & supplies

(G-5059)
MINNEAPOLIS PTG
60 S 6th St Ste 2450 (55402-4424)
PHONE...............................612 370-2600
Dave Warzala, *Manager*
EMP: 35 EST: 2001
SALES (est): 1MM-4.9MM Privately Held
WEB: www.mplstmo.org
SIC: **8748** Business consulting services

www.HarrisInfo.com
224

2011 Harris Minnesota
Services Directory

▲=Import ▼=Export
◆=Import/Export

(G-5060)
MINNEAPOLIS RADIO LLC
Also Called: Drive 1057
2000 Elm St SE (55414-2531)
PHONE 612 617-4000
FAX: 612 676-8214
Mark Kalman, *President*
Reed Endersbe, *Managing Dir*
Brook Orourke, *Managing Dir*
Rob Montgomery, *Engineer*
Mary L Koecher, *Finance Mgr*
EMP: 100 EST: 1986
SALES (est): 5MM-9.9MM Publicly Held
WEB: www.kqrs.com
SIC: 4832 Radio broadcasting station with a
rock music format
PA: Citadel Broadcasting Corp
7201 W Lake Mead Blvd
Las Vegas NV 89128
702 804-5200

(G-5061)
MINNEAPOLIS RADIOLOGY ASSOCS
Also Called: Mpls Radiology Assoc Clinic
3366 Oakdale Ave N Ste 604
(55422-5700)
PHONE 763 398-6600
Scott Shultz MD, *President*
Edwin T Farrel, *Treasurer*
Deanna Hollis, *Office Mgr*
William Lisberg, *Director*
EMP: 45 EST: 1970
SALES (est): 5MM-9.9MM Privately Held
SIC: 8011 Radiologist office

(G-5062)
MINNEAPOLIS RADIOLOGY ASSOCS
2800 Campus Dr Ste 10 (55441-2669)
PHONE 763 559-2171
Scott Schultz, *President*
Julie Tusler, *Office Mgr*
Jackie Forrette, *Manager*
Troy Roovers, *Exec Dir*
Jeffrey Groffsky, *Diag Radio*
EMP: 70 EST: 1970
SALES (est): 5MM-9.9MM Privately Held
WEB: www.mplsrad.com
SIC: 8011 Radiologist office

(G-5063)
MINNEAPOLIS REFUSE INC
Also Called: M R I
1609 49th Ave N (55430-3734)
PHONE 612 529-4788
FAX: 612 529-4758
Douglas Kruell, *Corp Secy*
Jacki Smith, *Treasurer*
Gregory Burt, *Director*
EMP: 25 EST: 1970
SQ FT: 3,000
SALES (est): 1MM-4.9MM Privately Held
SIC: 4953 Refuse systems services

(G-5064)
MINNEAPOLIS SOCIETY OF FINE
2400 3rd Ave S (55404-3506)
PHONE 612 870-3046
FAX: 612 870-3004
William M Grifwold, *President*
Kaywin Seldman, *President*
Diane Lilly, *Vice Chairman*
Mary Hele, *Opers Staff*
Pat Grazzini, *CFO*
▲ EMP: 250 EST: 1883
SQ FT: 500,000
SALES (est): 10MM-24.9MM Privately Held
SIC: 8412 Noncommercial art gallery

(G-5065)
MINNEAPOLIS URBAN LEAGUE INC (PA)
Also Called: OUTREACH & ADVOCACY
PROGRAM
2100 Plymouth Ave N (55411-3675)
PHONE 612 302-3100
FAX: 612 521-1444
Clarence Hightower, *CEO*
Tony Oshodi, *CFO*
Savigan Loveless, *Manager*
Sue Johnson, *Executive Asst*
Valesha Beeks, *Executive Asst*
EMP: 35

EST: 1925
SQ FT: 42,000
SALES (corp-wide): 5.12M Privately Held
WEB: www.mul.org
SIC: 8322 Individual & family social services

(G-5066)
MINNESOTA AIDS PROJECT
1400 Park Ave (55404-1550)
PHONE 612 341-2060
FAX: 612 341-4057
Mary Kinder, *CFO*
Justin Johnson, *Corp Comm Staff*
Lorraine Teel, *Director*
EMP: 50 EST: 1983
SALES (est): 1MM-4.9MM Privately Held
WEB: www.mnaidsproject.org
SIC: 8322 8399 Social services center;
health & welfare council

(G-5067)
MINNESOTA AIR INC
6901 W Old Shakopee Rd (55438-2683)
PHONE 952 918-8000
FAX: 952 918-8080
Mike Metzger, *President*
Wade Boelter, *Vice Pres*
Robin Lienke, *Human Res Mgr*
Jennifer Devus, *Manager*
EMP: 70 EST: 1999
SQ FT: 72,000
SALES (est): 25MM-49.9MM Privately Held
WEB: www.minnair.com
SIC: 5074 5075 Wholesales plumbing &
heating equipment & supplies; wholesales
heating & air conditioning equipment &
supplies

(G-5068)
MINNESOTA AQUARIUM LLC
120 E Broadway (55425-5511)
PHONE 952 853-0628
FAX: 952 883-0303
Rod Burwell, *Member*
John Sullwold, *Marketing Staff*
Tod Peterson, *Mng Member*
EMP: 80 EST: 1999
SQ FT: 125,000
SALES (est): 1MM-4.9MM Privately Held
WEB: www.underwateradventures.net
SIC: 8422 Aquariums & zoological gardens

(G-5069)
MINNESOTA ARCHITECTURAL
400 Clifton Ave (55403-3212)
PHONE 612 871-5703
FAX: 612 871-7212
Thomas Deangelo, *President*
Cliff Dunham, *Principal*
Peter Vesterholt, *Principal*
Stephen Thayer, *Engineer*
Vicky Knutson, *Marketing Mgr*
EMP: 80 EST: 1970
SALES (est): 5MM-9.9MM Privately Held
SIC: 8712 Architectural service

(G-5070)
MINNESOTA CARE STAFFING INC
3638 Central Ave NE (55418-1343)
PHONE 612 216-1938
Mark Liveringhouse, *President*
EMP: 150 EST: 1998
SALES (est): 1MM-4.9MM Privately Held
SIC: 7363 Medical help service

(G-5071)
MINNESOTA CHAPTER OF THE NATL
Also Called: Naiop Minnesota Chapter
4248 Park Glen Rd (55416-4758)
PHONE 952 928-4647
James Freytag, *Treasurer*
Anthony Leclerc, *Exec Dir*
EMP: 35 EST: 1980 Privately Held
SIC: 8611 Trade association

(G-5072)
MINNESOTA CONWAY FIRE & SAFETY
314 W 86th St (55420-2706)
PHONE 952 345-3473
Dean Howard, *President*
EMP: 39

EST: 1984
SQ FT: 14,940
SALES (est): 1MM-4.9MM Privately Held
SIC: 1731 5099 Safety & security
specialization contractor; wholesales fire
extinguishers

(G-5073)
MINNESOTA DEPARTMENT OF
Also Called: Minneapolis Veterans Home
5101 Minnehaha Ave (55417-1647)
PHONE 612 721-0600
FAX: 612 721-0604
Diane Oleson, *Envir Svcs Dir*
Carol A Lynch, *Human Res Dir*
Dee Oliver, *Pub Rel Dir*
Sandy Larson, *Marketing Staff*
Dave Tabert, *Manager*
EMP: 50
SALES (est): 1MM-4.9MM Privately Held
WEB: www.sbay.mvh.state.mn.us
SIC: 8051 Skilled nursing care facility;
veterans' affairs administration services;
state government administration of
veterans' affairs
DH: Minnesota Department of
20 12th St W Fl 2
Saint Paul MN 55155
651 296-2562

(G-5074)
MINNESOTA DEPARTMENT OF TRANS
Also Called: Metro Transit Garage
570 6th Ave N (55411-4335)
PHONE 612 349-7332
Michael Stezer, *General Mgr*
EMP: 525
SALES (est): 25MM-49.9MM Privately Held
WEB: www.me.umn.edu
SIC: 4111 4173 Passenger transit system;
transportation program regulation &
administration services; bus terminal &
service facility; state government
transportation program regulation or
administration
DH: Minnesota Department of Trans
395 John Ireland Blvd
Saint Paul MN 55155
651 296-3000

(G-5075)
MINNESOTA DIAGNOSTIC CTR
910 E 26th St Ste LL10 (55404-4512)
PHONE 612 879-1528
FAX: 612 879-0913
Char Auld, *Nursing Spvr*
Mary Mickelson, *Manager*
Jan Koehler, *Director*
Anthony Cook, *Director*
EMP: 25 EST: 1996
SALES (est): 1MM-4.9MM Privately Held
SIC: 8011 Physicians' office & clinic

(G-5076)
MINNESOTA DISABILITY LAW CTR
430 1st Ave N Ste 300 (55401-1742)
PHONE 612 332-1441
Jerry Lane, *Exec Dir*
EMP: 30 EST: 2002
SALES (est): 1MM-4.9MM Privately Held
SIC: 8111 General practice attorney's or
lawyer's office

(G-5077)
MINNESOTA EAR HEAD & NECK CLIN
Also Called: Sajjadi, Hamed MD
701 25th Ave S Ste 200 (55454-1443)
PHONE 612 339-2836
Michael Paparella, *President*
Mark Paparella, *Business Mgr*
Ryan Wessels, *Bookkeeper*
Coleen Shaw, *Administrator*
Sandy Wiczek, *Director*
EMP: 30 EST: 1984
SQ FT: 7,264
SALES (est): 1MM-4.9MM Privately Held
SIC: 8011 Ears, nose & throat specialist
office

(G-5078)
MINNESOTA INDIAN WOMENS
Also Called: Miwrc
2300 15th Ave S (55404-3960)
PHONE 612 728-2000
FAX: 612 728-2039
Suzanne Koepplinger, *Director*
EMP: 37 EST: 1984
SALES (est): 1MM-4.9MM Privately Held
SIC: 8322 Individual & family social services

(G-5079)
MINNESOTA INSTY-PRINTS INC
Also Called: Allegra Print & Imaging
618 2nd Ave S Ste B50 (55402-1930)
PHONE 612 332-8669
FAX: 612 332-8669
Phillip Cheney, *President*
Deborah Temple, *Vice Pres*
Marcia Richards, *Mfg Staff*
Tony Cheney, *Accounting Dir*
Gary Neil, *Info Tech Dir*
EMP: 30 EST: 1986
SQ FT: 10,000
SALES (est): 1MM-4.9MM Privately Held
SIC: 7334 Offset & photolithographic
printing service; photocopying & duplicating
services; offset printing

(G-5080)
MINNESOTA LENDING CO LLC
Also Called: Central Florida Lending
6465 Wayzata Blvd Ste 300 (55426-1730)
PHONE 952 960-9600
FAX: 952 960-9601
Gina Dorethy, *General Mgr*
Ann Loff, *Member*
Chris Diebold, *Member*
EMP: 60 EST: 2002
SQ FT: 3,300
SALES (est): 5MM-9.9MM Privately Held
SIC: 6163 Mortgage brokers service
arranging for loans, using money of others
PA: Diebold Investments LLC
6530 Cortlawn Cir N 300
Minneapolis MN 55426
952 960-9600

(G-5081)
MINNESOTA MASONIC CHARITIES ✪
11501 Masonic Home Dr (55437-3661)
PHONE 952 948-6004
EST: 2009 Privately Held
SIC: 8052 Intermediate care facility

(G-5082)
MINNESOTA MASONIC HOME
11501 Masonic Home Dr # 102
(55437-3604)
PHONE 952 948-7000
FAX: 952 948-6210
Mike Hanson, *COO*
Steve Demorot, *Buyer*
Sue Mork, *CFO*
Robert Taival, *Human Res Mgr*
Deb Bowman, *Manager*
EMP: 510 EST: 1906
SALES (est): 10MM-24.9MM Privately Held
WEB: www.mnmasonic.org
SIC: 8051 8052 Convalescent home;
personal care facility

(G-5083)
MINNESOTA MASONIC HOME NORTH
Also Called: North Ridge Care Center
5430 Boone Ave N (55428-3615)
PHONE 763 592-3000
FAX: 763 592-2665
Eric Neetenbeek, *CEO*
Kyle Johnson, *Purchasing*
Sue Mork, *CFO*
Patti Larue, *Human Res Dir*
Kim Peterson, *Mktg Dir*
EMP: 1000 EST: 1966
SQ FT: 500,000
SALES (est): 100MM-499.9MM Privately
Held
SIC: 6513 8051 Operators of retirement
hotels; skilled nursing care facility

(PA)=Parent Co (HQ)=Headquarters (DH)=Div Headquarters
✪ = New business established in last 2 years
2011 Harris Minnesota
Services Directory
© Harris InfoSource 1-866-281-6415
225

(G-5084)
MINNESOTA MEDICAL ASSOCIATION
1300 Godward St NE # 2500
(55413-1878)
PHONE................612 378-1875
Robert Meiches, *CEO*
May Yang, *IT/INT Sup*
David Luehr, *Exec Dir*
Peter A Larsen, *Bd of Directors*
Scott A Uttley, *Bd of Directors*
EMP: 37 **EST:** 1869
SQ FT: 13,000 **Privately Held**
WEB: www.mmaonline.net
SIC: 8621 Medical field association

(G-5085)
MINNESOTA MONITORING INC
2300 Nevada Ave N Ste 100 (55427-3661)
PHONE................763 253-5401
FAX: 763 253-5405
Karen Burkey, *CEO*
Brent Tilley, *Director*
Melissa Seidlitz, *Director*
EMP: 25 **EST:** 1999
SALES (est): 1MM-4.9MM **Privately Held**
WEB: www.mnmonitoring.com
SIC: 8093 Outpatient substance abuse clinic

(G-5086)
MINNESOTA NEWS SERVICE INC
7836 2nd Ave S (55420-1206)
PHONE................952 703-0075
FAX: 952 703-0728
J W Mandery, *President*
Susan Mandery, *Corp Secy*
Chris Mandery, *Exec VP*
Melissa Mandery, *Vice Pres*
EMP: 60 **EST:** 1975
SQ FT: 10,000
SALES (est): 10MM-24.9MM **Privately Held**
WEB: www.mn-news.com
SIC: 5192 Wholesales newspapers; wholesales periodicals

(G-5087)
MINNESOTA OPERA
620 N 1st St (55401-1225)
PHONE................612 333-2700
FAX: 612 333-0869
Kevin Smith, *President*
Todd Hyde, *Publisher*
Liesl Hyde, *Manager*
Dean Weigel, *Exec Dir*
Sonja Cobb, *Exec Dir*
EMP: 200 **EST:** 1963
SQ FT: 50,000
SALES (est): 10MM-24.9MM **Privately Held**
SIC: 7922 Opera company

(G-5088)
MINNESOTA ORCHESTRAL ASSN (PA)
1111 Nicollet Mall (55403-2406)
PHONE................612 371-5600
Michael Henson, *President*
Holly Duevel, *Vice Pres*
Jan Hoglund, *Human Res Dir*
Gary Nelson, *Marketing Staff*
Karl Reichert, *Marketing Staff*
EMP: 51 **EST:** 1903
SQ FT: 100,000
SALES (corp-wide): 14.96M **Privately Held**
WEB: www.mnorch.org
SIC: 7929 Symphony orchestra

(G-5089)
MINNESOTA ORCHESTRAL ASSN
1111 Nicollet Mall (55403-2406)
PHONE................612 371-5600
Brad Monson, *Manager*
EMP: 50
SALES (est): 5MM-9.9MM **Privately Held**
WEB: www.mnorch.org
SIC: 7929 Symphony orchestra
PA: Minnesota Orchestral Assn
1111 Nicollet Mall
Minneapolis MN 55403
612 371-5600

(G-5090)
MINNESOTA PROFESSIONAL NURSING
Also Called: Minneapolis Prof Nursing Svc
2021 E Hennepin Ave # 408 (55413-1754)
PHONE................612 627-9524
FAX: 612 379-2358
Benjamin Narh, *Vice Pres*
EMP: 90 **EST:** 1995
SALES (est): 1MM-4.9MM **Privately Held**
SIC: 7363 7361 Help supply services; employment agency services

(G-5091)
MINNESOTA RADIATION ONCOLOGY
800 E 28th St (55407-3723)
PHONE................612 863-4060
FAX: 612 863-8586
Katie Schwarzkopf, *Office Mgr*
Carol Grabowski, *Administrator*
Dean Gesme, *Oncology*
Patrick J Flynn, *Oncology*
Stuart H Bloom, *Oncology*
EMP: 26 **EST:** 1991
SALES (est): 1MM-4.9MM **Privately Held**
SIC: 8011 Radiologist office

(G-5092)
MINNESOTA REAL STATE SERVICE
4248 Park Glen Rd (55416-4758)
PHONE................952 928-4640
Jerry Dertfch, *Treasurer*
Gloria Isackson, *Exec Dir*
EMP: 35 **EST:** 1999
SALES (est): 5MM-9.9MM **Privately Held**
SIC: 6531 Real estate services

(G-5093)
MINNESOTA SHREDDING LLC
Also Called: Shred-It
8400 89th Ave N Ste 430 (55445-1878)
PHONE................763 493-3007
James C Gendreau, *Member*
Don Drapeau, *Member*
EMP: 35
SQ FT: 7,500
SALES (est): 10MM-24.9MM **Privately Held**
SIC: 5093 4953 7389 Wholesales waste paper; document destruction service; waste material recycling services

(G-5094)
MINNESOTA SOCIETY OF CERTIFIED
1650 W 82nd St Ste 600 (55431-1458)
PHONE................952 831-2707
Betsy Adrian, *President*
Milan Schmiesing, *Member*
Jackson Hole, *Finance Mgr*
Murray Utra, *Accountant*
Judy Cochran, *Manager*
EMP: 30 **EST:** 1928 **Privately Held**
WEB: www.mncpa.org
SIC: 8621 8721 Professional organization; accounting, auditing & bookkeeping services

(G-5095)
MINNESOTA TEEN CHALLENGE INC
1619 Portland Ave (55404-1507)
PHONE................612 373-3366
FAX: 612 333-4111
Rich Scherber, *CEO*
Ronald Goodman, *CFO*
Ron Goldman, *CFO*
Mary Trigler, *Manager*
John Hodgkins, *Webmaster*
EMP: 50 **EST:** 1984
SQ FT: 1,000
SALES (est): 1MM-4.9MM **Privately Held**
SIC: 8361 Residential rehabilitation center with health care incidental

(G-5096)
MINNESOTA TIMBERWOLVES
600 1st Ave N (55403-1400)
PHONE................612 673-1600
FAX: 612 673-1343
James Stack, *General Mgr*
Roger Griffith, *General Ptnr*
Conrad Smith, *Corp Secy*
Ethan Casson, *Senior VP*
Mary Bombach, *Vice Pres*
EMP: 120 **EST:** 1989
SQ FT: 11,000
SALES (est): 25MM-49.9MM **Privately Held**
SIC: 7941 Basketball club

(G-5097)
MINNESOTA TOBACCO DOCUMENT
Also Called: Smart Legal Asstt
980 E Hennepin Ave (55414-1314)
PHONE................612 378-5707
FAX: 612 378-2796
Tammy Sammon, *Manager*
EMP: 25 **EST:** 1995
SQ FT: 20,000
SALES (est): 1MM-4.9MM **Privately Held**
SIC: 7299 Personal document & information services

(G-5098)
MINNESOTA TWINS BASEBALL CLUB (PA)
1 Twins Way (55403-1418)
PHONE................612 659-3400
FAX: 612 375-7480
Bill Smith, *Senior VP*
Laura Day, *Senior VP*
Kip Elliot, *Senior VP*
Raenell Dorn, *Vice Pres*
Eric Curry, *Vice Pres*
EMP: 80 **EST:** 1905
SQ FT: 10,000 **Privately Held**
SIC: 7941 Baseball club

(G-5099)
MINNESOTA TWINS BASEBALL CLUB
34 Kirby Puckett Pl (55415-1523)
PHONE................612 375-7411
FAX: 612 375-7473
Terry Ryan, *General Mgr*
Kip Elliott, *Senior VP*
Kevin J Mather, *Vice Pres*
Matt Hoy, *Vice Pres*
John Avenson, *VP Eng R&D*
EMP: 525
SALES (est): 100MM-499.9MM **Privately Held**
SIC: 7941 7997 7999 8699 Baseball club; athletic organization; baseball club; contract ticket sales office for sporting events
PA: Minnesota Twins Baseball Club
1 Twins Way
Minneapolis MN 55403
612 659-3400

(G-5100)
MINNESOTA VETERANS RESEARCH
Also Called: Mvri
1 Veterans Dr (55417-2309)
PHONE................612 467-2895
Mary Gannon, *Principal*
Carol Matzek, *Officer*
EMP: 60 **EST:** 1989 **Privately Held**
WEB: www.mvri.com
SIC: 8641 Veterans' organization

(G-5101)
MINNESOTA VISITING NURSE AGCY
Also Called: Mvna
3433 Broadway St NE Ste 300
(55413-1761)
PHONE................612 617-4600
FAX: 612 617-4782
Mary A Blade, *CEO*
Carmen Peota, *General Mgr*
Leroy Meyering, *CFO*
Lori Doehne, *Controller*
Lori Doehnel, *Controller*
EMP: 200 **EST:** 1902
SQ FT: 22,000
SALES (est): 5MM-9.9MM **Privately Held**
WEB: www.mvna.org
SIC: 8082 Visiting nurse services

(G-5102)
MINNETONKA MOCCASIN CO INC (PA)
1113 E Hennepin Ave (55414-2321)
PO Box 529 (55440-0529)
PHONE................612 331-8493
FAX: 612 331-5797
David Miller, *CEO*
Scott Sessa, *President*
Mary Marshik, *Accounting Staf*
Sarah Gunther, *Assistant*
▲ **EMP:** 51 **EST:** 1946
SQ FT: 50,000 **Privately Held**
WEB: www.moccasinhouse.com
SIC: 5139 Wholesales footwear; manufactures moccasins

(G-5103)
MINNPAR LLC
900 6th Ave SE Ste 13 (55414-1378)
PO Box 2526, Chicago IL (60690-2526)
PHONE................612 379-0606
Shirish Pareek, *President*
Dan Argetsinger, *Purch Mgr*
Sean Flynn, *Purch Mgr*
Jerry Schwanke, *Purchasing*
Suzie Prenovost, *Purchasing*
▲ **EMP:** 60 **EST:** 1988
SQ FT: 95,000
SALES (est): 25MM-49.9MM **Privately Held**
WEB: www.minnpar.com
SIC: 5099 Wholesales firearms & ammunition

(G-5104)
MINTER-WEISMAN CO
1035 Nathan Ln N Ste A (55441-5028)
PHONE................763 545-3700
Garry Christianson, *Principal*
Gregory P Antholzner, *Treasurer*
Jeremy Fisher, *Finance*
Deloras Deval, *Manager*
J M Walsh, *Director*
EMP: 30
SALES (est): 1MM-4.9MM **Publicly Held**
WEB: www.core-mark.com
SIC: 8741 Administrative management services
DH: Minter-Weisman Co
1035 Nathan Ln N
Minneapolis MN 55441
763 545-3706

(G-5105)
MINTER-WEISMAN CO (DH)
1035 Nathan Ln N (55441-5002)
PHONE................763 545-3706
J M Walsh, *CEO*
Paul Siegel, *Vice Pres*
Todd Kelly, *Controller*
Gary Christensen, *VP Sales*
Audrey Fujimoto, *VP Mktg*
EMP: 320 **EST:** 1958
SQ FT: 130,000
SALES (corp-wide): 6.53B **Publicly Held**
WEB: www.core-mark.com
SIC: 5194 5013 5122 5145 5149 Wholesales cigarettes; wholesales automotive supplies & parts; wholesales cosmetics, perfumes & hair products; wholesales candy; wholesales groceries
HQ: Core-Mark International Inc
395 Oyster Point Blvd # 415
South San Francisco CA 94080
650 589-9445

(G-5106)
MINUTECLINIC LLC
920 2nd Ave S Ste 400 (55402-4010)
PHONE................612 659-7111
FAX: 612 659-7101
Zenon P Lankowsky, *Corp Secy*
Thomas A Charland, *Senior VP*
Tom Morrison, *Senior VP*
Kathy Heslin, *Vice Pres*
Sara Ratner, *Vice Pres*
EMP: 50 **EST:** 1999
SALES (est): 1MM-4.9MM **Publicly Held**
SIC: 8082 Home health care services
PA: Cvs Caremark Corp
1 Cvs Dr
Woonsocket RI 02895
401 765-1500

www.HarrisInfo.com
226
2011 Harris Minnesota
Services Directory
▲=Import ▼=Export
◆=Import/Export

(G-5107)
MINVALCO INC (PA)
3340 Gorham Ave   (55426-4225)
PHONE 952 920-0131
FAX: 952 920-0236
Mary Delmore, *President*
Rolly Ehrenberg, *Tech/Comp Coord*
EMP: 26 **EST:** 1964
SQ FT: 15,900
SALES (corp-wide): 10M **Privately Held**
 WEB: www.minvalco.com
SIC: 5074 Wholesales plumbing & heating
equipment & supplies

(G-5108)
MIRAMAR INC
Also Called: Regency Point Apartment Homes
3205 Harbor Ln N Ofc OFC   (55447-5238)
PHONE 763 559-2527
FAX: 763 559-6371
Laura Gibson, *President*
Joyce Renoylds, *Office Mgr*
Michelle Morgan, *Property Mgr*
EMP: 25 **EST:** 1996
SALES (est): 1MM-4.9MM **Privately Held**
SIC: 6513 Apartment building operator

(G-5109)
MISSIONS INC PROGRAMS
3409 E Medicine Lake Blvd   (55441-2307)
PHONE 763 559-1883
FAX: 763 559-1195
Allen Cannon, *Maint Mgr*
Don Hill, *Treasurer*
Linda Peter, *Manager*
Pat Murphy, *Exec Dir*
Ruth Modrow, *Executive Asst*
EMP: 83 **EST:** 1890
SALES (est): 1MM-4.9MM **Privately Held**
SIC: 8361 Residential rehabilitation center
with health care incidental

(G-5110)
MISTER CAR WASH
8650 Highway 7   (55426-3913)
PHONE 952 931-9412
FAX: 952 820-0067
Jenny Wallis, *General Mgr*
Dean Ngo, *Manager*
Rich Brousseau, *Manager*
EMP: 30 **EST:** 1982
SALES (est): 1MM-4.9MM **Privately Held**
SIC: 7542 Automotive washing & polishing
service

(G-5111)
MJSK INVESTMENT SECURITIES
5500 Wayzata Blvd Ste 190   (55416-3589)
PHONE 763 542-3700
FAX: 763 542-3717
Roz Brand, *MIS Mgr*
EMP: 33
SALES (est): 25MM-49.9MM **Privately Held**
SIC: 6211 Securities dealer

(G-5112)
MMIC
7650 Edinbrgh Way Ste 400   (55435-5981)
PHONE 952 838-6700
Mark D Odland, *Ch of Bd*
David Bounk, *President*
Jeff Pearson, *Vice Pres*
EMP: 130 **EST:** 1980
SALES (est): 10MM-24.9MM **Privately Held**
SIC: 6411 Insurance services

(G-5113)
MMIC HEALTH IT
7650 Edinbrgh Way Ste 400   (55435-5981)
PHONE 763 201-0300
FAX: 763 553-0364
David Bounk, *President*
Tom Lee, *Vice Pres*
Steve Heimel, *Vice Pres*
Trish Lugtu, *Technical Mgr*
Darrell Tukua, *Treasurer*
EMP: 28 **EST:** 1997
SALES (est): 1MM-4.9MM **Privately Held**
 WEB: www.mmicben.com
SIC: 8748 Business consulting services
PA: Midwest Medical Insurance
   7650 Edinbrgh Way Ste 400
   Minneapolis MN 55435
   952 838-6700

(G-5114)
MOA ENTERTAINMENT CO LLC
Also Called: Camp Snoopy
5000 Center Ct   (55425-5505)
PHONE 952 883-8810
FAX: 952 883-8683
Barb Kanter, *Finance Dir*
Annette Scarllato, *Merchandise Mgr*
Dave Frasier, *Mng Member*
Cora Roelofs, *Manager*
Ed Kormendy, *Manager*
▲ **EMP:** 561 **EST:** 1990
SQ FT: 350,000
SALES (est): 25MM-49.9MM **Privately Held**
 WEB: www.mallofamerica.com
SIC: 7996 7999 Theme park; operates
tourist attractions, amusement park
concessions & rides
PA: Simon Property Group, LP
   225 W Washington St
   Indianapolis IN 46204
   317 636-1600

(G-5115)
MOBILE MEDIA INC
Also Called: Corporate Image Store
9425 Syndicate Ave   (55420-4234)
PO Box 202008   (55420-7008)
PHONE 952 884-6201
FAX: 952 884-6181
John Mogan, *President*
Ryan Mogan, *Vice Pres*
Don Stanton, *Plant Mgr*
Susan Mogan, *Treasurer*
Victor Pikula, *CTO*
EMP: 29 **EST:** 1984
SALES (est): 1MM-4.9MM **Privately Held**
SIC: 7311 Publisher; advertising agency;
commercial lithographic printing; periodical
publisher

(G-5116)
MOBILIAM
8400 Normandale Lake Blvd   (55437-1085)
PHONE 952 921-3997
Timothy Belisle, *President*
Ann Steuart, *VP Sls/Mktg*
Scott Gorden, *CFO*
Nathan Clevenger, *Dir Lvl Other*
EST: 2001
SQ FT: 3,500 **Privately Held**
SIC: 8631 Labor organization

(G-5117)
MODERN CLIMATE INC
800 Hennepin Ave Fl 8   (55403-1862)
PHONE 612 343-8180
FAX: 612 343-8178
Geoff Bremner, *CEO*
Jason Tell, *CFO*
Len Eichten, *Vice Pres*
John Moberg, *CFO*
Keith Wolf, *Ch Credit Ofcr*
EMP: 25 **EST:** 1998
SQ FT: 19,000
SALES (est): 1MM-4.9MM **Privately Held**
SIC: 8742 7311 Marketing consulting
service; advertising agency

(G-5118)
MODERN HEATING & AIR CONDG
2318 1st St NE   (55418-3404)
PHONE 612 781-3358
FAX: 612 781-3428
Mike Renstrom, *President*
Andrew Grham, *Vice Pres*
EMP: 34 **EST:** 1963
SQ FT: 20,000
SALES (est): 1MM-4.9MM **Privately Held**
 WEB: www.modernhtg.com
SIC: 1711 Warm air heating & air
conditioning contractor; ventilation & duct
work contractor

(G-5119)
MOLLY'S INC
Also Called: Broders' Cucina Italiana
2308 W 50th St   (55410-2202)
PHONE 612 925-3113
FAX: 612 925-9737
Molly Broder, *President*
Thomas Broder, *Vice Pres*
EMP: 60

EST: 1982
SQ FT: 3,000
SALES (est): 1MM-4.9MM **Privately Held**
 WEB: www.justpawstraining.com
SIC: 5149 Delicatessen; wholesales
groceries

(G-5120)
MONEY GRAM PAYMENT SYSTEMS INC (HQ)
1550 Utica Ave S Ste 100   (55416-5301)
PHONE 952 591-3000
Pedro Moragriega, *General Mgr*
Anthony Ryan, *COO*
Giovanni Crociani, *Vice Pres*
Theodore L Hill, *Vice Pres*
Daniel J Collins, *Treasurer*
EMP: 550 **EST:** 1940
SQ FT: 140,000
SALES (corp-wide): 1.17B **Publicly Held**
SIC: 6099 7389 Money order issuance
services; electronic funds transfer network,
including switching; financial service
PA: Moneygram International Inc
   1550 Utica Ave S Ste 100
   Minneapolis MN 55416
   952 591-3000

(G-5121)
MONEYGRAM PAYMENT SYSTEMS INC
6601 Shingle Creek Pkwy Ste 14
(55430-1780)
PHONE 763 549-7100
Kathy M Cray, *Manager*
EMP: 100
SALES (est): 10MM-24.9MM **Publicly Held**
SIC: 6099 Money order issuance services
HQ: Money Gram Payment Systems Inc
   1550 Utica Ave S Ste 100
   Minneapolis MN 55416
   952 591-3000

(G-5122)
MONROE KRASS
8000 Norman Center Dr Ste 1000
(55437-1177)
PHONE 952 445-5080
Phillip R Krass, *President*
Richard Gibson, *President*
Dennis L Monroe, *Chairman*
Mark J Moxness, *Corp Secy*
James Casserly, *Vice Pres*
EMP: 70 **EST:** 1969
SALES (est): 5MM-9.9MM **Privately Held**
 WEB: www.krassmonroe.com
SIC: 8111 General practice attorney's or
lawyer's office

(G-5123)
MONTINCELLO FORD-MERCURY INC
500 Ford Rd   (55426-1062)
PO Box 68, Monticello   (55362-0068)
PHONE 763 295-2056
Dennis Hecker, *President*
Jesse Schmeling, *Manager*
Steve Bright, *Manager*
Stewart Almaer, *Manager*
EMP: 120 **EST:** 1976
SALES (est): 10MM-24.9MM **Privately Held**
 WEB: www.monticelloford.com
SIC: 7539 Automotive repair services

(G-5124)
MOORE WALLACE NORTH AMERICA
7400 Metro Blvd Ste 300   (55439-2323)
PHONE 952 844-2000
FAX: 952 844-2110
Bill Deppa, *Manager*
EMP: 30
SALES (est): 5MM-9.9MM **Publicly Held**
 WEB: www.moore.com
SIC: 5112 Wholesales business forms
HQ: Moore Wallace North America
   111 S Wacker Dr
   Chicago IL 60606
   312 326-8000

(G-5125)
MOORE, COSTELLO & HART PLLP
900 2nd Ave S Ste 1500   (55402-3305)
PHONE 612 673-0148
FAX: 612 395-8600
Pat Plunkett, *Partner*
John M Harens, *Attorney*
Joleen Rudeen, *Director*
EMP: 35
SALES (est): 1MM-4.9MM **Privately Held**
 WEB: www.patrickplunkett.com
SIC: 8111 General practice law office
PA: Moore, Costello & Hart Pllp
   55 5th St E Ste 1400
   Saint Paul MN 55101
   651 602-2615

(G-5126)
MOQUIST THORVILSON KAUFMANN
7650 Edinbrgh Way Ste 225   (55435-5921)
PHONE 952 854-5700
Michael Latterell, *Member*
Kevin Moquist, *Member*
Elizabeth Kaplan, *Member*
Julie Swan, *Member*
Kathy Nelson, *Member*
EMP: 65 **EST:** 1988
SQ FT: 10,000
SALES (est): 5MM-9.9MM **Privately Held**
 WEB: www.cmocpa.com
SIC: 8721 Certified public accountant
services

(G-5127)
MORCON CONSTRUCTION CO INC
5905 Golden Valley Rd # 231
(55422-4475)
PHONE 763 546-6066
Jerry Jullie, *President*
Tom Hartwell, *Vice Pres*
Stan Thom, *Vice Pres*
Jeff Roerick, *Project Mgr*
Minga Elftmann, *Marketing Staff*
EMP: 75 **EST:** 1982
SQ FT: 5,000
SALES (est): 10MM-24.9MM **Privately Held**
 WEB: www.morconconstruction.com
SIC: 1542 Commercial & office building
contractor

(G-5128)
MORGAN STANLEY & CO INC
8300 Norman Center Dr Ste 1150
(55437-1032)
PHONE 952 921-1900
FAX: 952 921-1944
Marc Terris, *Publisher*
Shari Parsons, *Opers Mgr*
Chris Ascher, *Branch Mgr*
Gina Bolinske, *Branch Mgr*
Rick Vedova, *Manager*
EMP: 70
SALES (est): 10MM-24.9MM **Publicly Held**
 WEB: www.morganstanley.com
SIC: 6211 Stock broker & dealer service
HQ: Morgan Stanley & Co Inc
   1585 Broadway
   New York NY 10036
   212 761-4000

(G-5129)
MORGAN STANLEY & CO INC
225 S 6th St Ste 5100   (55402-4606)
PHONE 612 340-6700
Mark Gherity, *Div Sub Head*
Richard Lund, *Accounts Exec*
Chad Wolsman, *Accounts Exec*
Chris Ascher, *Manager*
EMP: 90
SALES (est): 10MM-24.9MM **Publicly Held**
 WEB: www.morganstanley.com
SIC: 6211 General brokerage investment
firm
HQ: Morgan Stanley & Co Inc
   1585 Broadway
   New York NY 10036
   212 761-4000

(G-5130)
MORGAN TIRE & AUTO INC
Also Called: Team Tires Plus
500 W 78th St (55423-4002)
PHONE..............................612 861-2278
FAX: 612 861-2529
Steve Hanson, *Manager*
EMP: 30
SALES (est): 1MM-4.9MM **Privately Held**
WEB: www.bfsusa.com
SIC: 7534 7539 Tire recapping & retreading
services; automotive brake repair shop
HQ: Bfs Retail Operations LLC
333 E Lake St Ste 300
Bloomingdale IL 60108
630 259-9000

(G-5131)
MORGAN TIRE & AUTO LLC
Also Called: Team Tires Plus
3520 Winnetka Ave N (55427-2022)
PHONE..............................763 525-1583
FAX: 763 544-7660
Trent Anderson, *Manager*
EMP: 30
SALES (est): 1MM-4.9MM **Privately Held**
WEB: www.bfsusa.com
SIC: 7534 Tire recapping & retreading
services
HQ: Bfs Retail Operations LLC
333 E Lake St Ste 300
Bloomingdale IL 60108
630 259-9000

(G-5132)
MORTON'S OF CHICAGO INC
555 Nicollet Mall (55402-1066)
PHONE..............................612 673-9700
FAX: 612 673-0853
Johanne Schmitt, *Manager*
EMP: 50
SALES (est): 1MM-4.9MM **Publicly Held**
WEB: www.mortons.com
SIC: 7299 Full service steak restaurant;
cocktail lounge; banquet hall facility
HQ: Morton's of Chicago Boca Raton
350 W Hubbard St
Chicago IL 60654
312 923-0030

(G-5133)
MOSAIC CO (HQ)
3033 Campus Dr Ste E490 (55441-2655)
PHONE..............................763 577-2700
James T Prokopanko, *President*
Richard L Mack, *Corp Secy*
Norman B Beug, *Senior VP*
Mort Hart, *Senior VP*
Stephen P Malia, *Senior VP*
EMP: 200 EST: 2004
SALES (corp-wide): 107.88B **Privately
Held**
WEB: www.mosaicco.com
SIC: 1094 1311 1475 1481 Manufactures
phosphatic fertilizers; uranium ore mining;
crude petroleum production; nonmetallic
minerals services; manufactures oleum
sulfuric acid; phosphate rock mining
PA: Cargill Fertilizer Inc
15615 McGinty Rd W
Wayzata MN 55391
952 742-7575

(G-5134)
**MOSAIC GLOBAL HOLDINGS
INC (DH)**
3033 Campus Dr Ste E490 (55441-2655)
PHONE..............................763 577-2700
FAX: 763 559-2860
Douglas A Pertz, *CEO*
C S Hoffman, *President*
Richard L Mack, *Corp Secy*
Mary A Hynes, *Senior VP*
Stephen P Malia, *Senior VP*
EMP: 38 EST: 1988
SQ FT: 67,000
SALES (corp-wide): 107.88B **Privately
Held**
WEB: www.imcglobal.com

SIC: 1474 1475 Manufactures phosphatic
fertilizers; potash mining; manufactures high
purity chemicals refined from technical
grade; manufactures fertilizers; phosphate
rock mining
HQ: Mosaic Co
3033 Campus Dr Ste E490
Minneapolis MN 55441
763 577-2700

(G-5135)
**MOSS & BARNETT, A
PROFESSIONAL**
90 S 7th St Ste 4800 (55402-4119)
PHONE..............................612 877-5000
Thomas J Shroyer, *President*
Dave F Senger, *Chairman*
Jeffrey L Watson, *Attorney*
EMP: 170 EST: 1896
SALES (est): 10MM-24.9MM **Privately Held**
SIC: 8111 Legal services

(G-5136)
MOTION INTERNATIONAL INC
3800 Amrcn Blvd W Ste 425 (55431)
PHONE..............................952 746-5630
Glen Brynteson, *President*
Tracey Sutton, *Finance*
Nantawan Walen, *Manager*
Andrew Sincebaugh, *Recruiter*
EMP: 56 EST: 1997
SALES (est): 5MM-9.9MM **Privately Held**
WEB: www.motioninternational.com
SIC: 7379 Computer system consulting
services

(G-5137)
MOTIVACTION LLC
16355 36th Ave N Ste 100 (55446-4600)
PHONE..............................763 412-3000
Janet North, *General Mgr*
William E Bryson, *Member*
Joseph Keller, *Member*
Sharon Hughes, *Corp Secy*
Jodi Daugherty, *COO*
EMP: 100 EST: 1976
SQ FT: 34,500
SALES (est): 10MM-24.9MM **Privately Held**
WEB: www.motivaction.com
SIC: 8742 5064 5091 Incentive or award
program consultant; wholesales electrical
entertainment equipment; wholesales
sporting & recreational goods & supplies

(G-5138)
MOTIVATIONS FOR FITNESS INC
Also Called: Centerpoint
1313 5th St SE Ste 336 (55414-4502)
PHONE..............................612 617-9090
Carolyn J Pelava, *Principal*
Ed Pelava, *Corp Secy*
John H Petersburg, *Vice Pres*
EMP: 40 EST: 1987
SQ FT: 9,700
SALES (est): 1MM-4.9MM **Privately Held**
SIC: 7999 Vocational school; provides
massage instruction

(G-5139)
**MOUNT OLIVET CAREVIEW
HOME**
5517 Lyndale Ave S (55419-1719)
PHONE..............................612 827-5677
FAX: 612 824-2052
Timothy Hokanson, *President*
David Olson, *Engineer*
Marriane Hamner, *Persnl Mgr*
Mary A Hamer, *Asst Admin*
EMP: 260 EST: 1958
SQ FT: 80,273
SALES (est): 10MM-24.9MM **Privately Held**
SIC: 8051 Skilled nursing care facility

(G-5140)
**MOUNT OLIVET LUTHERAN
CHURCH**
5601 Lyndale Ave S (55419-1721)
PHONE..............................612 861-3305
FAX: 612 861-3376
Ginny Cullen, *Director*
EMP: 35
SALES (est): 1MM-4.9MM **Privately Held**
WEB: www.mtolivet.org

SIC: 8361 8351 Residential care facility;
child day care service
PA: Mount Olivet Lutheran Church
5025 Knox Ave S DOOR3
Minneapolis MN 55419
612 926-7651

(G-5141)
**MOUNT YALE PORTFOLIO
ADVISORS**
8000 Norman Center Dr Ste 630
(55437-1184)
PHONE..............................952 897-5390
John Savor, *Mng Member*
John Sabre, *Mng Member*
Cathy Whelpley, *Administrator*
EMP: 30 EST: 2004 **Privately Held**
SIC: 6722 Open-ended investment funds
management services

(G-5142)
MPLSP HOTEL CORP
Also Called: Comfort Inn
1321 E 78th St (55425-1114)
PHONE..............................952 854-3400
FAX: 952 854-1183
Edward Flaherty, *CEO*
Teerence Allen, *Manager*
EMP: 75 EST: 1989
SALES (est): 1MM-4.9MM **Privately Held**
SIC: 7011 Traveler accommodations

(G-5143)
MQ SOFTWARE INC
1660 Highway 100 S # 400 (55416-1507)
PHONE..............................952 345-8720
Willard Cecchi, *President*
Nancy Wandersee-Walte, *Corp Secy*
Rodney M Schmitt, *COO*
Robert Maas, *Vice Pres*
Hans Adema, *Technical Mgr*
EMP: 100 EST: 1996
SQ FT: 25,000
SALES (est): 10MM-24.9MM **Publicly Held**
WEB: www.mqsoftware.com
SIC: 7372 7379 Educational services;
computer system consulting services;
software publisher
PA: BMC Software Inc
2101 Citywest Blvd Bldg 1
Houston TX 77042
713 918-8800

(G-5144)
MRG MANAGEMENT INC
8601 73rd Ave N Ste 21 (55428-1507)
PHONE..............................763 537-1460
David M Glodowski, *President*
Michael Hoff, *Corp Secy*
EMP: 500 EST: 2001
SALES (est): 25MM-49.9MM **Privately Held**
SIC: 8741 Restaurant management
services

(G-5145)
MSP REAL ESTATE INC
7201 Walker St Ste 20 (55426-4280)
PHONE..............................952 351-4540
Milo Pinkerton, *President*
Doloris Pinkerton, *Corp Secy*
Tess Burnham, *Manager*
EMP: 140 EST: 1988
SQ FT: 1,700
SALES (est): 25MM-49.9MM **Privately Held**
WEB: www.louisianaoaks.com
SIC: 6552 Commercial land subdividers &
developers

(G-5146)
MT YALE CAPITAL GROUP LLC
Also Called: Mount Yale Portfolio Advisors
8000 Norman Center Dr # 630
(55437-1184)
PHONE..............................952 897-5390
John Sabre, *Mng Member*
EMP: 30 EST: 2003 **Privately Held**
SIC: 6719 Investment holding company

(G-5147)
MTEC ELECTRIC INC
3707 50th Ave N (55429-3912)
PHONE..............................763 537-1570
Nick Dang, *CEO*
Paul Archambault, *Vice Pres*

Huong Pham, *Vice Pres*
Troy Madison, *Project Mgr*
EMP: 30 EST: 1999
SQ FT: 6,000
SALES (est): 1MM-4.9MM **Privately Held**
WEB: www.mtecelectric.com
SIC: 1731 Electrical contractor

(G-5148)
MULTIMEDIA HOLDINGS
Also Called: K A R E TV Channel 11
8811 Olson Memorial Hwy (55427-4762)
PHONE..............................763 546-1111
John Remes, *President*
Pamala Flom, *Business Mgr*
Tom Lindner, *Vice Pres*
Sue Reimer, *Human Resources*
Jerry Ness, *Sales Mgr*
EMP: 225 EST: 1983
SALES (est): 50MM-99.9MM **Publicly Held**
WEB: www.kare11.com
SIC: 4833 Television broadcasting station
PA: Gannett Co Inc
7950 Jones Branch Dr
Mc Lean VA 22102
703 854-6000

(G-5149)
MUNICIPAL PARKING INC
1030 2nd Ave S (55403-2502)
PHONE..............................612 673-9644
FAX: 612 673-9640
Ellis Mohammad, *Manager*
EMP: 25
SALES (est): 1MM-4.9MM **Privately Held**
SIC: 7521 Vehicle parking lot or garage

(G-5150)
MUNICIPAL PARKING INC
516 2nd Ave N (55403-1415)
PHONE..............................612 339-2003
FAX: 612 339-7552
Mark Bauer, *Manager*
EMP: 32
SALES (est): 1MM-4.9MM **Privately Held**
SIC: 7521 Parking garage

(G-5151)
MURPHY WAREHOUSE CO (PA)
701 24th Ave SE (55414-2603)
PHONE..............................612 623-1200
Richard T Murphy Jr, *President*
Michael Butchert, *Vice Pres*
Laurie Murphy, *Vice Pres*
Paul Welna, *VP Opers*
D T Griep, *CFO*
▲ EMP: 120 EST: 1956
SQ FT: 800,000 **Privately Held**
WEB: www.murphywarehouse.com
SIC: 4225 General warehousing

(G-5152)
MURRAY'S CO INC
24 S 6th St (55402-1501)
PHONE..............................612 333-2507
FAX: 612 333-6770
Patrick Murray, *CEO*
James A Murray, *Corp Secy*
Timothy P Murray, *Vice Pres*
EMP: 75 EST: 1954
SALES (est): 1MM-4.9MM **Privately Held**
SIC: 6719 Full service American restaurant;
personal holding company

(G-5153)
MYSLAJEK LTD
648 Lowry Ave NE (55418-2850)
PHONE..............................612 781-2771
FAX: 612 781-4517
Tim Myslajek, *CEO*
EMP: 25 EST: 1964
SALES (est): 1MM-4.9MM **Privately Held**
WEB: www.myslajek.com
SIC: 8721 Certified public accountant
services

(G-5154)
**N A TRADING & TECHNOLOGY
INC**
9216 Grand Ave S (55420-3604)
PHONE..............................952 888-7654
FAX: 952 888-7678
Jerry Mathwig, *President*
Theodore Johnson, *General Mgr*

www.HarrisInfo.com
228
2011 Harris Minnesota
Services Directory
▲=Import ▼=Export
◆=Import/Export

Dave Bunde, *Manager*
Liz Madison, *Manager*
Jason Thomas, *Manager*
▲ **EMP:** 50 **EST:** 1883
SQ FT: 26,000
SALES (est): 10MM-24.9MM **Privately Held**
WEB: www.natrading.com
SIC: 5044 Wholesales photocopy
machines; manufactures photographic
reproduction machines & equipment

(G-5155)
N'COMPASS SOLUTIONS INC
718 Washington Ave N # 401
(55401-1162)
PHONE 612 379-2100
Chris Flaherty, *CEO*
Josh Verhelst, *Business Anlyst*
Brad Wampole, *Consultant*
EMP: 38 **EST:** 2000
SALES (est): 1MM-4.9MM **Privately Held**
WEB: www.ncompass-inc.com
SIC: 7389 7373 Purchasing service;
systems integration service

(G-5156)
NALCO CHEMICAL CO
5000 Cheshire Ln N Ste 2 (55446-3716)
PHONE 763 559-3209
FAX: 763 559-4511
Steve Anderson, *Manager*
Joseph Petters, *Manager*
Dave Moench, *Manager*
Bruce Keiser, *CTO*
Hubert Certes, *Info Tech Mgr*
EMP: 25 **EST:** 1942
SALES (est): 10MM-24.9MM **Privately Held**
WEB: www.nalco.com
SIC: 5169 Wholesales chemicals & allied
products
HQ: Nalco Co
1601 W Diehl Rd
Naperville IL 60563
630 305-1000

(G-5157)
NASH FRAME DESIGN INC
10 S 13th St (55403-1917)
PHONE 612 338-9041
FAX: 612 338-5574
Roger Nash, *President*
Montgomery Chavez, *Mfg Staff*
Sandy Stewart, *Sales/Mktg Mgr*
EMP: 28 **EST:** 1974
SALES (est): 1MM-4.9MM **Privately Held**
WEB: www.mediajobsearchcanada.com
SIC: 7699 Custom picture framing service;
retails ready made picture frames

(G-5158)
NATH MIDWEST LODGING LLC
Also Called: Quality Inn
900 E 79th St Ste 300 (55420-1393)
PHONE 952 853-1400
Mahendra Nath, *President*
Moody Arafa, *General Mgr*
Scott Henning, *General Mgr*
Diane Forsberg, *General Mgr*
Dave Walia, *Manager*
EMP: 250 **EST:** 1998
SQ FT: 4,000
SALES (est): 10MM-24.9MM **Privately Held**
SIC: 7011 Traveler accommodations

(G-5159)
NATH MINNESOTA FRANCHISE
GROUP (PA)
900 E 79th St Ste 300 (55420-1393)
PHONE 952 853-1400
Mahendra Nath, *CEO*
Ashok Mehta, *COO*
Asha Nath, *Vice Pres*
Patti Porteous, *CFO*
EMP: 35 **EST:** 1991
SQ FT: 4,000 **Privately Held**
SIC: 8741 Limited service fast-food chain
restaurant; management services

(G-5160)
NATIONAL ARBITRATION
FORUM INC
6465 Wayzata Blvd Ste 500 (55426-1724)
PO Box 50191 (55405-0191)
PHONE 952 516-6400
Edward Anderson, *President*

Micheal Kelly, *COO*
Aaron Rose, *Vice Pres*
Terry Allen, *Accountant*
Alberto Riveros, *Business Anlyst*
EMP: 155 **EST:** 1986
SALES (est): 10MM-24.9MM **Privately Held**
SIC: 7389 Arbitration & conciliation services

(G-5161)
NATIONAL CEMETERY ADMIN
Also Called: Fort Snelling National Cmtry
7601 34th Ave S (55450-1105)
PHONE 612 726-1127
Robert Collum, *Exec Dir*
Robert L McCoun, *Director*
Robert L McCollun, *Director*
EMP: 100
SALES (est): 5MM-9.9MM **Privately Held**
WEB: www.va.gov
SIC: 6553 Cemetery subdivision &
development services; veterans' affairs
administration services; federal government
administration of veterans' affairs
DH: National Cemetery Admin
810 Vermont Ave NW Ste 427
Washington DC 20420
202 273-5146

(G-5162)
NATIONAL DENTEX CORP
Also Called: Saber Dental
6500 Shingle Creek Pkwy (55430-1721)
PO Box 1109 (55440-1109)
PHONE 763 566-0210
Greg Bibro, *President*
EMP: 30
SALES (est): 1MM-4.9MM **Privately Held**
WEB: www.nationaldentex.com
SIC: 8072 Dental laboratory
HQ: National Dentex Corp
2 Vision Dr Ste 2
Natick MA 01760
508 907-7800

(G-5163)
NATIONAL ENGINEERING
RESOURCES
Also Called: Ner
7100 Northland Cir N Ste 301
(55428-1500)
PHONE 763 561-7610
Denise Fountain, *General Mgr*
Douglas Pixley, *Principal*
E Egler, *Vice Pres*
Jay Jauer, *Vice Pres*
Aaron Smith, *Engineer*
EMP: 82 **EST:** 1990
SQ FT: 2,400
SALES (est): 1MM-4.9MM **Privately Held**
WEB: www.nerinc.com
SIC: 7363 7361 Temporary help service;
employment agency services

(G-5164)
NATIONAL INDEPENDENT
BROKERS
Also Called: Goldencare USA
10700 County Road 15 # 450
(55441-6157)
PHONE 763 525-1111
FAX: 763 525-1977
Leonard Anderson, *President*
Lori Fjelstad, *General Mgr*
Ruth A Anderson, *Corp Secy*
C J Pan, *Vice Pres*
Lori Stjelstead, *Vice Pres*
EMP: 60 **EST:** 1974
SALES (est): 5MM-9.9MM **Privately Held**
WEB: www.goldencareusa.com
SIC: 6411 Insurance agent

(G-5165)
NATIONAL INITIATIVES FOR
6125 Virginia Ave N (55428-2738)
PHONE 763 229-2753
Brenda Frye PhD, *Exec Dir*
EMP: 25
SALES (est): 1MM-4.9MM **Privately Held**
SIC: 8999 Miscellaneous services

(G-5166)
NATIONAL MARROW DONOR
PROGRAM
3001 Broadway St NE Ste 500
(55413-2197)
PHONE 612 627-5800
FAX: 612 627-5877
Jeffrey W Chell, *CEO*
Shinichiro Okamoto, *Vice Pres*
Mary Strong, *Vice Pres*
Gordon Bryan, *CFO*
Paul Zyla, *Human Res Dir*
EMP: 250 **EST:** 1987
SQ FT: 90,000
SALES (est): 10MM-24.9MM **Privately Held**
SIC: 8099 Medical services organization

(G-5167)
NATIONAL MULTIPLE
SCLEROSIS
200 12th Ave S (55415-1222)
PHONE 612 335-7900
FAX: 612 335-7997
Maureen Reeder, *President*
Debbie Abarr, *Vice Pres*
Jody Payne, *Manager*
Jill Retzer, *Info Tech Mgr*
Brian Columbus, *Analyst*
EMP: 43 **EST:** 1955
SQ FT: 13,000
SALES (est): 1MM-4.9MM **Privately Held**
WEB: www.nmssga.org
SIC: 8322 Individual & family social services
PA: National Multiple Sclerosis
733 3rd Ave Fl 3
New York NY 10017
212 986-3240

(G-5168)
NATIONAL THEATRE FOR
CHILDREN
2733 Park Ave (55407-1008)
PHONE 612 617-4903
FAX: 612 341-2277
E W Eames III, *President*
Bill Turner, *General Mgr*
Margaret Eames, *Accounting Staf*
Bonnie Bernstrom, *Director*
EMP: 90 **EST:** 1977
SQ FT: 10,000
SALES (est): 5MM-9.9MM **Privately Held**
SIC: 7922 Legitimate live theater producers

(G-5169)
NATIONAL TRUCK
UNDERWRITING
5001 Amrcn Blvd W Ste 801 (55437)
PHONE 952 893-1234
FAX: 952 881-4945
James E Joyce Sr, *CEO*
Susan Overholt, *Vice Pres*
Rolland White, *Vice Pres*
Barbara Davis, *CIO*
EMP: 34 **EST:** 1978
SQ FT: 10,000
SALES (est): 1MM-4.9MM **Privately Held**
WEB: www.ntuminc.com
SIC: 6411 Insurance agent

(G-5170)
NATIONS TITLE AGENCY
6465 Wayzata Blvd Ste 710 (55426-1733)
PHONE 952 545-2808
FAX: 952 545-2816
Chris Likens, *President*
Larry J Likens, *Corp Secy*
Clyde Wagner, *Director*
Randy L Larson, *Director*
EMP: 35
SALES (est): 1MM-4.9MM **Privately Held**
SIC: 6162 Mortgage & loan lending

(G-5171)
NATIONWIDE FINANCIAL
4046 Bryant Ave N (55412-1724)
PHONE 612 723-6375
Floyd Wilson, *Owner*
EMP: 25
SALES (est): 1MM-4.9MM **Privately Held**
SIC: 8748 Business consulting services

(G-5172)
NATURAL RESOURCE GROUP
LLC
1000 Ids Ctr 80 S 8th St (55402)
PHONE 612 347-6789
FAX: 612 347-6780
Thomas E Losey, *CEO*
Joseph C Reinemann, *President*
Georgia Crossing, *General Mgr*
Emily C Grothe, *Principal*
Richard L Skarie, *Principal*
EMP: 107 **EST:** 1992
SQ FT: 46,000
SALES (est): 10MM-24.9MM **Privately Held**
WEB: www.nrginc.com
SIC: 8748 Environmental consultant

(G-5173)
NATURE CONSERVANCY
Also Called: Minnesota Field Office
1101 W River Pkwy Ste 200 (55415-1291)
PHONE 612 331-0700
FAX: 612 331-0770
Tammy Tollefson, *Project Mgr*
Louise Morgan, *Opers Staff*
Julie Muehlberg, *Branch Mgr*
Jon Thompson, *Info Tech Mgr*
Ron Nargang, *Exec Dir*
EMP: 25 **Privately Held**
WEB: www.nature.org
SIC: 8641 Environmental protection
organization
PA: Nature Conservancy
4245 Fairfax Dr Ste 100
Arlington VA 22203
703 841-5300

(G-5174)
NAVARRE CORP (PA)
7400 49th Ave N (55428-4258)
PHONE 763 535-8333
FAX: 763 533-2156
Joyce Fleck, *President*
Cary L Deacon, *President*
Jill Griffin, *President*
Troy Hayes, *President*
Ward Thomas, *President*
▲ **EMP:** 206 **EST:** 1983
SQ FT: 322,000
SALES (corp-wide): 528.33M **Publicly
Held**
WEB: www.navarre.com
SIC: 5045 5099 Wholesales computer
software; wholesales video & audio
equipment

(G-5175)
NAVIGANT INTERNATIONAL
ROCKY
700 Nicollet Mall Ste 550 (55402-2040)
PHONE 612 375-2884
FAX: 612 375-2429
Roger Przytarski, *CFO*
Jenny Johnson, *Human Res Mgr*
Sue Carby, *Manager*
EMP: 30
SALES (est): 1MM-4.9MM **Privately Held**
WEB: www.macystravel.com
SIC: 4724 Travel agency
DH: Navigant International Rocky
10731 E Easter Ave Ste 100
Englewood CO 80112
720 568-4700

(G-5176)
NAVITAIRE INC
333 S 7th St Ste 500 (55402-2415)
PHONE 612 317-7000
John Dabkowski, *President*
Matthew Holt, *Project Mgr*
Robert Lambert, *Opers Mgr*
Frank Kuhar, *CFO*
John Tomlinson, *Controller*
EMP: 175 **EST:** 1997
SALES (est): 25MM-49.9MM **Privately Held**
WEB: www.wavesecurities.com
SIC: 7373 Computer integrated systems
design services
DH: Accenture LLP
161 N Clark St Ste 1100
Chicago IL 60601
312 693-0161

(PA)=Parent Co (HQ)=Headquarters (DH)=Div Headquarters
✪ = New business established in last 2 years
2011 Harris Minnesota
Services Directory
© Harris InfoSource 1-866-281-6415
229

(G-5177)
NCS PEARSON INC   (DH)
5601 Green Valley Dr # 220   (55437-1186)
PO Box 9365   (55440-9365)
PHONE..............................952 681-3000
Marjorie Scardino, *CEO*
Eileen Youds, *COO*
Mary Lany, *Counsel*
Watson Carol, *Exec VP*
Michael C Brewer, *Vice Pres*
▲ **EMP:** 600 **EST:** 1962
SQ FT: 67,000 **Privately Held**
WEB: www.ncspearson.com
SIC: 7372 7374 7379 8748 Manufactures
optical scanning devices; application
software publishing; tabulating service;
computer related maintenance service;
educational or personnel testing consulting
services; optical scanning services
HQ: Pearson Education Inc
        1 Lake St
        Upper Saddle River NJ 07458
        201 236-7000

(G-5178)
NCS PEARSON INC
Also Called: Pearson Vue
5601 Green Valley Dr # 220   (55437-1186)
PHONE..............................952 681-3000
FAX: 952 681-3549
Donna Goldstein, *Managing Dir*
John Fenton, *Corp Secy*
John Harnett, *Exec VP*
William R Brooks, *Vice Pres*
Michael Colucci, *Vice Pres*
EMP: 750
SALES (est): 50MM-99.9MM **Privately Held**
WEB: www.ncspearson.com
SIC: 8733 Educational research agency
DH: Ncs Pearson Inc
        5601 Green Valley Dr # 220
        Minneapolis MN 55437
        952 681-3000

(G-5179)
NEDMAC INC
5410 International Pkwy   (55428-3604)
PHONE..............................763 537-8435
FAX: 763 537-4569
Jim Tilbury, *President*
Ward Tilbury, *Corp Secy*
Dennis Kuss, *Vice Pres*
Gary Hommes, *Treasurer*
Darlene Leininger, *Accounting Dir*
EMP: 26 **EST:** 1954
SQ FT: 18,000
SALES (est): 1MM-4.9MM **Privately Held**
WEB: www.nedmac.com
SIC: 7692 Machine shop, jobbing & repair
services; welding service

(G-5180)
NEIGHBORHOOD INVOLVEMENT
Also Called: Rape & Sexual Abuse Center
2431 Hennepin Ave S   (55405-2605)
PHONE..............................612 374-3125
FAX: 612 374-3323
John Walski, *Personnel*
Jennie Yngsdahl, *Manager*
Patsy Bartley, *Administrator*
Linda Pippin, *Director*
Daniel Haugen, *Director*
EMP: 50 **EST:** 1968
SQ FT: 11,000
SALES (est): 1MM-4.9MM **Privately Held**
SIC: 8322 Multi-services center

(G-5181)
NEIGHBORHOOD RECYCLING CORP
Also Called: Eureka Recycling
2828 Kennedy St NE   (55413)
PHONE..............................651 222-7678
FAX: 651 623-3277
Susan Hubbard, *CEO*
Tim Brownell, *COO*
EMP: 40 **EST:** 2001
SALES (est): 5MM-9.9MM **Privately Held**
WEB: www.eurekarecycling.org
SIC: 4953 Waste material recycling services

(G-5182)
NEPHROLOGY ANALYTICAL SERVICES
914 S 8th St   (55404-1210)
PHONE..............................612 337-7345
FAX: 612 347-5878
Shu-Cheng Chen, *Info Tech Mgr*
Eric Frazier, *Webmaster*
Allan J Collins MD, *Director*
Stephan Dunning, *Analyst*
EMP: 35 **EST:** 1996
SALES (est): 1MM-4.9MM **Privately Held**
SIC: 8011 8731 Nephrologist; commercial
medical research services

(G-5183)
NETWORK COMPUTING SERVICES INC
Also Called: Netaspx Minnesota
1200 Washington Ave S   (55415-1227)
PHONE..............................612 337-0200
FAX: 612 337-3400
John Whiteside, *CEO*
Rick Ross, *Vice Pres*
Steve Desrosier, *Technical Mgr*
Ben Davis, *Sales Staff*
Wes Barris, *Manager*
EMP: 50 **EST:** 1982
SALES (est): 5MM-9.9MM **Publicly Held**
WEB: www.navisite.com
SIC: 7374 Computer time-sharing
PA: NaviSite Inc
        400 Minuteman Rd
        Andover MA 01810
        978 682-8300

(G-5184)
NETWORK DESIGN INC
171 Cheshire Ln N Ste 700   (55441-5477)
PHONE..............................763 475-5500
Charles Eicher, *President*
Steve R Ferry, *General Mgr*
Noelle Palen, *Manager*
EMP: 40 **EST:** 1996
SQ FT: 15,000
SALES (est): 5MM-9.9MM **Privately Held**
SIC: 7373 1731 Computer integrated
systems design services; communications
contractor services
PA: Matrix Communications Inc
        171 Cheshire Ln N Ste 700
        Minneapolis MN 55441
        763 475-5500

(G-5185)
NETWORK SECURITY PROFESSIONALS
Also Called: Netspi
800 Washington Ave N   (55401-1330)
PHONE..............................612 465-8880
FAX: 612 677-3407
Deke George, *President*
Seth Peter, *Vice Pres*
John Waldron, *Administrator*
EMP: 25 **EST:** 2001
SQ FT: 16,000
SALES (est): 1MM-4.9MM **Privately Held**
WEB: www.netspi.com
SIC: 8748 Business consulting services

(G-5186)
NEW BOUNDARY TECHNOLOGIES INC
Also Called: Lanovation
1300 Godward St NE # 3100
(55413-2558)
PHONE..............................612 379-3805
Kim Pearson, *CEO*
Scott Ramacier, *General Mgr*
Jim Rhoda, *Vice Pres*
Julie Lemieux, *Research*
Ken Peters, *VP Sales*
▼ **EMP:** 30 **EST:** 1985
SQ FT: 11,000
SALES (est): 1MM-4.9MM **Privately Held**
WEB: www.newboundary.com
SIC: 7371 Computer software development

(G-5187)
NEW CONCEPTS MANAGEMENT GROUP
5707 Excelsior Blvd   (55416-2827)
PHONE..............................952 922-2500
FAX: 952 922-5400
Gene Sullivan, *President*
Paul Roth, *Vice Pres*
Joy Sundet, *Manager*
Paul Bozonie, *Exec Dir*
EMP: 26 **EST:** 1987
SQ FT: 10,000
SALES (est): 1MM-4.9MM **Privately Held**
WEB: www.ncmgi.com
SIC: 6531 Condominium managers

(G-5188)
NEW FRENCH BAKERY INC
2609 26th Ave S   (55406-1501)
PHONE..............................612 728-0193
Peter Kelsey, *President*
Imme Fernandez, *General Mgr*
Kristina Gill, *Safety Mgr*
Bill Hayes, *Controller*
▲ **EMP:** 125 **EST:** 1995
SQ FT: 25,000
SALES (est): 50MM-99.9MM **Privately Held**
WEB: www.newfrenchbakery.com
SIC: 5149 Wholesales bakery products;
commercial bakery; retail bakery

(G-5189)
NEW HORIZON CHILD CARE INC
4201 Minnesota Dr   (55435-5427)
PHONE..............................952 893-1893
Michelle Goodwin, *Manager*
EMP: 25
SALES (est): 500-999K **Privately Held**
WEB: www.kidsquest.com
SIC: 8351 Child day care service
HQ: New Horizon Child Care Inc
        16355 36th Ave N Ste 700
        Plymouth MN 55446
        763 557-1111

(G-5190)
NEW HORIZON CHILD CARE INC
8547 Edinburgh Center Dr   (55443-3724)
PHONE..............................763 315-3033
FAX: 763 315-3926
Heather Brand, *Manager*
Shannon Greeley, *Exec Dir*
EMP: 30
SALES (est): 500-999K **Privately Held**
WEB: www.kidsquest.com
SIC: 8351 Child day care service
HQ: New Horizon Child Care Inc
        16355 36th Ave N Ste 700
        Plymouth MN 55446
        763 557-1111

(G-5191)
NEW HORIZON CHILD CARE INC
4345 Peony Ln N   (55446-1737)
PHONE..............................763 478-2412
FAX: 763 478-2391
Laura McLellan, *Exec Dir*
Dana Benson, *Director*
EMP: 30
SALES (est): 500-999K **Privately Held**
WEB: www.kidsquest.com
SIC: 8351 Preschool center
HQ: New Horizon Child Care Inc
        16355 36th Ave N Ste 700
        Plymouth MN 55446
        763 557-1111

(G-5192)
NEW PARADIGM PRODUCTIONS INC
Also Called: Edleman Productions
800 Washington Ave N # 506
(55401-1184)
PHONE..............................612 321-9091
FAX: 612 321-9484
Steve Edelman, *Owner*
EMP: 40
SALES (est): 10MM-24.9MM **Privately Held**
WEB: www.edelmanproductions.com

SIC: 7812 Television film production service
PA: New Paradigm Productions Inc
        400 Tamal Plz Ste 420
        Corte Madera CA 94925
        415 924-8000

(G-5193)
NEW YORK LIFE INSURANCE CO
3600 Minnesota Dr Ste 100   (55435-7912)
PHONE..............................952 897-5000
FAX: 952 897-5066
Jim Lusk, *Managing Prtnr*
Frank Lusk, *General Mgr*
David Duchene, *General Mgr*
Gary W Chfc, *General Mgr*
Wallace Foreman, *Opers Staff*
EMP: 50
SALES (est): 25MM-49.9MM **Privately Held**
WEB: www.newyorklife.com
SIC: 6311 Life insurance carriers
PA: New York Life Insurance Co
        51 Madison Ave Rm 504
        New York NY 10010
        212 576-7000

(G-5194)
NEW YORK MINT LTD
5577 W 78th St   (55439-2701)
PHONE..............................952 949-6588
FAX: 952 944-8766
William Gale, *President*
EMP: 25 **EST:** 1996
SQ FT: 12,000
SALES (est): 10MM-24.9MM **Privately Held**
WEB: www.newyorkmint.net
SIC: 5094 5091 Wholesales coins; retails
used merchandise; wholesales sporting &
recreational goods & supplies

(G-5195)
NEWPORT CORP
Also Called: Mikroprecision Division
5480 Nathan Ln N Ste 122   (55442-1995)
PHONE..............................763 593-0722
George Wakileh, *General Mgr*
David Martin, *Engrg Mgr*
Leon Dashevsky, *Engineer*
Theresa Gade, *CFO*
Sue Fries, *Manager*
EMP: 65
SALES (est): 10MM-24.9MM **Publicly Held**
WEB: www.newport.com
SIC: 5049 Manufactures industrial process
measurement equipment; manufactures
laboratory apparatus; wholesales optical
goods; manufactures measuring &
controlling devices
PA: Newport Corp
        1791 Deere Ave
        Irvine CA 92606
        949 863-3144

(G-5196)
NEXPRO PERSONNEL SERVICES INC
5353 Gamble Dr Ste 112   (55416-1539)
PHONE..............................952 224-9855
FAX: 952 224-9859
Julia Zimmer, *President*
Isabelle Muse, *Vice Pres*
Leslie Knutson, *Manager*
EMP: 60 **EST:** 2001
SQ FT: 1,500 **Privately Held**
WEB: www.nexprojobs.com
SIC: 7361 Employment agency services

(G-5197)
NEXTEL COMMUNICATIONS INC
7700 France Ave S Ste 400   (55435-5858)
PHONE..............................952 703-7600
FAX: 952 703-7690
Chay Vue, *Technical Mgr*
Marcia Larsen, *Sales Mgr*
Kevin Flynn, *Manager*
Yony Yang, *MIS Mgr*
EMP: 80 **Publicly Held**
WEB: www.nextel.com

SIC: **4812** 5065 7622 7629 Wireless telecommunications carrier & service; wholesales mobile telephone equipment; retails telephone & communication equipment; radio & television repair services; telecommunication equipment repair service
HQ: Nextel Communications Inc
2001 Edmund Halley Dr
Reston VA 20191
703 433-4000

(G-5198)
NEXTMEDIA OUTDOOR INC
13805 1st Ave N Ste 800 (55441-5461)
PHONE................................763 489-3841
Jim Matalone, *President*
Lisa Bittman, *General Mgr*
EMP: 25
SQ FT: 4,000
SALES (est): 1MM-4.9MM **Privately Held**
WEB: www.nextmediagroup.net
SIC: **7319** Poster advertising service
PA: Nextmedia Operating Inc
6312 S Fiddlers Green Cir # 20
Greenwood Village CO 80111
303 694-9118

(G-5199)
NICO PROPERTIES
2929 1st Ave S (55408-2306)
PHONE................................612 822-2185
Mark Hockley, *President*
Denny Donaldson, *President*
Barb Ahrens, *Purch Agent*
EMP: 100 EST: 1979
SQ FT: 35,000
SALES (est): 25MM-49.9MM **Privately Held**
SIC: **6512** Operators of commercial & industrial buildings

(G-5200)
NIECC INC
Also Called: Northland Inn
7025 Northland Dr N (55428-1506)
PHONE................................763 536-8300
FAX: 763 536-8790
James C Stuebner, *President*
Charles Nehme, *General Mgr*
Charles Naemi, *General Mgr*
William Lowinger, *Purch Mgr*
George Schmidt, *Chief Engr*
EMP: 250 EST: 1986
SALES (est): 10MM-24.9MM **Privately Held**
WEB: www.northlandinn.com
SIC: **7011** 7299 7389 Inn; eating place; banquet hall facility; convention & trade show services; drinking establishment

(G-5201)
NIELSEN CO US LLC
600 Highway 169 S Ste 400 (55426-1216)
PHONE................................763 593-2000
FAX: 763 593-4710
Paul Auleciems, *Manager*
Delrae Eden, *Manager*
EMP: 84
SALES (est): 5MM-9.9MM **Privately Held**
SIC: **8732** Market analysis or research services

(G-5202)
NIGHTINGALE HOME HEALTH CARE
8085 Wayzata Blvd Ste 105 (55426-1456)
PHONE................................763 545-3131
Dev Brar, *President*
EMP: 35 EST: 2005
SALES (est): 1MM-4.9MM **Privately Held**
WEB: www.nghhc.com
SIC: **8082** Home health care services

(G-5203)
NIGHTOWL DOCUMENT MANAGEMENT
724 N 1st St Ste 500 (55401-2880)
PHONE................................612 337-0448
FAX: 612 339-3676
Andrea Wallack, *CEO*
Tom Pelidino, *President*
Herman Jass, *Vice Pres*
Tony Copa, *CFO*
Scott Sterkel, *Director*
EMP: 70

EST: 1991
SQ FT: 12,000
SALES (est): 5MM-9.9MM **Privately Held**
WEB: www.copyowl.com
SIC: **7334** Photocopying & duplicating services

(G-5204)
9900 PROPERTIES
9939 Lyndale Ave S (55420-4732)
PHONE................................952 881-5825
David Fhaal, *Owner*
Arnold Fpahl, *Owner*
EMP: 50 EST: 1974
SQ FT: 4,250
SALES (est): 10MM-24.9MM **Privately Held**
SIC: **6512** Operators of commercial & industrial buildings

(G-5205)
NONVIOLENT PEACEFORCE
425 Oak Grove St (55403-3227)
PHONE................................612 871-0005
FAX: 612 871-0006
Israel Naor, *Member*
Lyn Adamson, *Member*
Joann Morse, *Manager*
Ginny Halloran, *Exec Dir*
Timmon Wallace, *Exec Dir*
EMP: 30 EST: 2002
SALES (est): 1MM-4.9MM **Privately Held**
SIC: **8322** Social services center

(G-5206)
NORAN NEUROLOGICAL CLINIC (PA)
2828 Chicago Ave (55407-1544)
PHONE................................612 879-1000
FAX: 612 879-0722
Soren Ryberg MD, *President*
Robert Jacoby MD, *Corp Secy*
Michael Sethna MD, *Vice Pres*
Susan Evans, *Vice Pres*
David Dorn MD, *Vice Pres*
EMP: 100 EST: 1972
SQ FT: 35,000 **Privately Held**
SIC: **8011** Neurologist

(G-5207)
NORCOSTCO INC
825 Rhode Island Ave S (55426-1611)
PHONE................................763 544-0601
FAX: 763 525-8676
James T Scott, *CEO*
Erik Schindler, *President*
Linda Scott, *Corp Secy*
Debbie Dodge, *Administration*
EMP: 35 EST: 1884
SQ FT: 31,000
SALES (est): 10MM-24.9MM **Privately Held**
WEB: www.norcostco.com
SIC: **5049** 7299 7359 Wholesales Theatrical equipment & supplies; retails masquerade or theatrical costumes; retails formal wear; clothing rental service; costume rental service; tuxedo rental service; equipment rental & leasing services; manufactures draperies & curtains

(G-5208)
NORDQUIST SIGN CO
312 W Lake St (55408-3025)
PHONE................................612 823-7291
FAX: 612 824-6211
Richard A Nordquist III, *President*
Steve Fox, *Vice Pres*
Roger Miller, *Accountant*
Steve Hemmesch, *Manager*
EMP: 50 EST: 1904
SQ FT: 37,000
SALES (est): 1MM-4.9MM **Privately Held**
WEB: www.nordquistsign.com
SIC: **1799** Manufactures signs & advertising specialties; sign installation & maintenance contractor; manufactures electrical signs; manufactures neon signs

(G-5209)
NORMANDALE EVANGELICAL
6100 Normandale Rd (55436-2633)
PHONE................................952 929-1697
FAX: 952 929-2767
David Holm, *Pastor*
Nancy Windels, *Pastor*
Chris Nestad, *Pastor*
Dale Howard, *Pastor*

Dan Atkins, *Finance*
EMP: 50 EST: 1950
SQ FT: 88,000 **Privately Held**
SIC: **8351** Provides Lutheran church services; nursery school

(G-5210)
NORMANDY INN INC
Also Called: Best Western Downtown
405 S 8th St (55404-1026)
PHONE................................612 370-1400
FAX: 612 370-0434
Thomas W Noble, *President*
Randy Sheets, *Human Res Mgr*
EMP: 38 EST: 1943
SALES (est): 1MM-4.9MM **Privately Held**
SIC: **7011** 7299 7389 Traveler accommodations; banquet hall facility; convention & trade show services

(G-5211)
NORTEL NETWORKS INC
8000 Norman Center Dr Ste 650 (55437-1181)
PHONE................................952 897-1150
FAX: 952 897-7410
Pat Smith, *General Mgr*
Angie Anderson, *Engineer*
Ronald Hallback, *Engineering*
Steve Manning, *Manager*
Andrea Motz, *Administrator*
EMP: 32
SALES (est): 5MM-9.9MM **Publicly Held**
WEB: www.nortelnetworks.com
SIC: **7373** Local area network systems integration service
PA: Nortel Networks Inc
2221 Lakeside Blvd
Richardson TX 75082
972 684-1000

(G-5212)
NORTH AMERICAN COMMUNICATIONS
10525 Hampshire Ave S (55438-2594)
PHONE................................952 942-7200
FAX: 952 942-7300
Keven Kiloran, *Finance*
Tom Henrichs, *Manager*
EMP: 30
SALES (est): 10MM-24.9MM **Privately Held**
WEB: www.nacr.com
SIC: **5065** Wholesales electrical telephone & telegraphic equipment; wholesales communications equipment; retails telephone equipment & systems
DH: North American Communications
3344 Highway 149
Eagan MN 55121
651 994-6800

(G-5213)
NORTH AMERICAN SYSTEMS INTL
2901 E 78th St (55425-1501)
PHONE................................952 374-6700
FAX: 952 851-9879
Phil Bettenburg, *President*
John Bettenburg, *Vice Pres*
David Bogie, *Vice Pres*
Margie Bettenburg, *Opers Mgr*
Scott Mapes, *Engineer*
EMP: 55 EST: 1994
SQ FT: 25,000
SALES (est): 25MM-49.9MM **Privately Held**
WEB: www.nasi.com
SIC: **5045** Wholesales computers, peripherals & software

(G-5214)
NORTH COAST PARTNERS LLP
7500 W 78th St (55439-2517)
PHONE................................952 947-3000
Sandra Clark, *Partner*
Ronald E Clark, *Partner*
EMP: 40 EST: 1984
SQ FT: 2,000
SALES (est): 10MM-24.9MM **Privately Held**
WEB: www.ronclark.com
SIC: **6512** Operators of retail property

(G-5215)
NORTH MEMORIAL CLINIC
4080 W Broadway Ave Ste 200 (55422-5606)
PHONE................................763 520-5551
FAX: 763 520-1734
Carol Dextor, *Manager*
EMP: 25 EST: 1994
SALES (est): 1MM-4.9MM **Privately Held**
SIC: **8011** Occupational & industrial specialist, physician or surgeon office

(G-5216)
NORTH MEMORIAL HEALTH CARE
3500 France Ave N Ste 101 (55422-2882)
PHONE................................763 520-3900
Kay Johnson, *Sales Executive*
Karen Persico, *Manager*
Thomas J Guyn, *Manager*
EMP: 100
SALES (est): 1MM-4.9MM **Privately Held**
WEB: www.northmemorial.com
SIC: **8082** 7361 8051 Home health care services; nurses' registry service; skilled nursing care facility
PA: North Memorial Health Care
3300 Oakdale Ave N
Minneapolis MN 55422
763 520-5200

(G-5217)
NORTH MEMORIAL HEALTH CARE (PA)
3300 Oakdale Ave N (55422-2900)
PHONE................................763 520-5200
Scott R Anderson, *President*
Jodi Heurung, *Corp Secy*
Bob Johnson, *Corp Secy*
David W Cress, *COO*
Pamela Lindemoen, *COO*
EMP: 3300 EST: 1940
SQ FT: 270,000 **Privately Held**
WEB: www.northmemorial.com
SIC: **8062** 8011 Medical hospital; medical center

(G-5218)
NORTH SECOND STREET STEEL SPLY
2212 N 2nd St (55411-2207)
PHONE................................612 522-6626
FAX: 612 522-1517
Larry Rosen, *President*
EMP: 27 EST: 1984
SQ FT: 3,000
SALES (est): 10MM-24.9MM **Privately Held**
WEB: www.nssss.com
SIC: **5051** Wholesales steel

(G-5219)
NORTH STAR INTERNATIONAL (HQ)
Also Called: Astle Ford International Trcks
3000 Broadway St NE (55413-1708)
PHONE................................612 378-1660
FAX: 612 378-2646
Scott Dowson, *President*
Mary Brown, *Corp Secy*
Donald Williams, *Vice Pres*
Lane Waters, *CFO*
Scott Loyd, *Controller*
EMP: 65 EST: 1960
SQ FT: 50,000
SALES (corp-wide): 11.56B **Publicly Held**
WEB: www.navistar.com
SIC: **5012** 7538 Wholesales commercial trucks; truck engine repair service
PA: Navistar International Corp
4201 Winfield Rd
Warrenville IL 60555
630 753-5000

(G-5220)
NORTH STAR RAIL INTERMODAL LLC (PA)
7400 Metro Blvd Ste 300 (55439-2323)
PHONE................................952 831-4011
Randall K Schwake, *Member*
Craig Damstrom, *Member*
William Dankbar, *Member*
Rammy Swakee, *CFO*
Shawn Steen, *Accounts Mgr*

GEOGRAPHIC

EST: 2006
SQ FT: 3,500 **Privately Held**
SIC: 4789 Railroad cargo loading & unloading services

(G-5221)
NORTH STAR RESOURCE GROUP (HQ)
2701 University Ave SE Ste 100
(55414-3231)
PHONE.....................612 617-6000
FAX: 612 617-6002
David Vasos, *President*
Edward G Deutschlander, *President*
Phillip C Richards, *President*
Karen Johnson, *Controller*
Jay Pugh, *Manager*
EMP: 110 EST: 1908
SQ FT: 20,000 **Privately Held**
WEB: www.northstarltc.com
SIC: 6411 Insurance services
PA: Securian Financial Network Inc
400 Robert St N Ste A
Saint Paul MN 55101
651 665-3500

(G-5222)
NORTH STAR TITLE INC
5401 Gamble Dr Ste 300 (55416-1502)
PHONE.....................952 512-7400
EMP: 100 EST: 1984
SQ FT: 175,000
SALES (est): 5MM-9.9MM **Privately Held**
SIC: 6541 Title abstract service

(G-5223)
NORTH WEST EYE CLINIC
8401 Golden Valley Rd # 330
(55427-4687)
PHONE.....................763 383-4140
FAX: 763 383-4147
John Berestka, *President*
Rich Freeman, *Treasurer*
Barbara Daiker, *Administrator*
EMP: 105 EST: 1965
SQ FT: 9,500
SALES (est): 5MM-9.9MM **Privately Held**
SIC: 8042 Optometrists' office

(G-5224)
NORTHEAST BANK
77 Broadway St NE (55413-1811)
PHONE.....................612 379-8811
FAX: 612 362-3262
Thomas M Beck, *President*
Belva H Rasmussen, *Chairman*
Michael Collins, *Exec VP*
Larry Crane, *Exec VP*
Susan Johnson, *Exec VP*
EMP: 60 EST: 1947
SQ FT: 30,000
SALES (est): 10MM-24.9MM **Privately Held**
WEB: www.northeastbank-mn.com
SIC: 6022 State commercial bank
PA: Northeast Securities Corp
77 Broadway St NE
Minneapolis MN 55413
612 379-8811

(G-5225)
NORTHEAST SECURITIES CORP (PA)
77 Broadway St NE (55413-1811)
PHONE.....................612 379-8811
Belva Rasmussen, *CEO*
Thomas M Beck, *Vice Pres*
Chris Fitzmorris, *Treasurer*
Sue Johnson, *Human Resources*
EST: 1946
SQ FT: 15,000
SALES (corp-wide): 15.50M **Privately Held**
SIC: 6022 4724 State commercial bank;
tourist agency arranging transport, lodging & car rental

(G-5226)
NORTHERN CAPITAL COMMERCIAL
8200 Highwood Dr (55438-1008)
PO Box 9396 (55440-9396)
PHONE.....................952 996-8818
Steven Leupke, *President*
Pat McGovern, *General Mgr*
Judy Jorissen, *Vice Pres*
Wayne Mann, *Shareholder*

EMP: 56 EST: 1978
SALES (est): 5MM-9.9MM **Privately Held**
SIC: 6411 Insurance services

(G-5227)
NORTHERN LIGHTS MORTGAGE CO
501 Washington Ave S # 300
(55415-1127)
PHONE.....................612 435-3500
FAX: 612 435-3504
Tim Jaynes, *President*
Hannah Nordvall, *Manager*
Faith Suzuka, *Manager*
Nick Gohman, *Manager*
Stephanie Blanda, *Manager*
EST: 2000
SQ FT: 1,550 **Privately Held**
SIC: 6163 Mortgage brokers service
arranging for loans, using money of others

(G-5228)
NORTHERN NATURAL GAS CO
1600 W 82nd St Ste 210 (55431-1437)
PHONE.....................952 887-1700
FAX: 952 887-1740
Tim Johanson, *Account Dir*
EMP: 25
SALES (est): 10MM-24.9MM **Publicly Held**
WEB: www.midamerican.com
SIC: 4922 Natural gas pipeline
DH: Northern Natural Gas Co
1111 S 103rd St
Omaha NE 68124
402 398-7200

(G-5229)
NORTHERN STAR CO
3171 5th St SE (55414-3305)
PHONE.....................612 339-8981
FAX: 612 331-3434
J D Clarkson, *President*
John D Reedy, *Vice Pres*
Pat Hagan, *Opers Mgr*
Joe Piro, *Maint Mgr*
Natalie Muering, *Purch Mgr*
EMP: 240 EST: 1953
SQ FT: 150,000
SALES (est): 50MM-99.9MM **Privately Held**
SIC: 5148 Manufactures canned
vegetables; manufactures food
preparations; wholesales fresh fruits &
vegetables
DH: Michael Foods Group Inc
301 Carlson Pkwy Ste 400
Minnetonka MN 55305
952 258-4000

(G-5230)
NORTHERN X-RAY CO (PA)
Also Called: NXC Imaging
2118 4th Ave S (55404-2642)
PHONE.....................612 870-1561
FAX: 612 870-9220
Steven Miller, *President*
Allen Kremlacek, *Corp Secy*
Dan Koehnen, *Treasurer*
Kevin Mattson, *Sales Mgr*
EMP: 43 EST: 1964
SQ FT: 14,000
SALES (corp-wide): 57.66M **Privately Held**
SIC: 5047 Wholesales X-ray machines &
tubes; wholesales X-ray film & supplies

(G-5231)
NORTHLAND GROUP INC
7831 Glenroy Rd Ste 350 (55439-3108)
PHONE.....................952 831-4005
FAX: 952 831-7356
John M Johnson, *CEO*
Lance Black, *President*
Jodi Swenson, *Vice Pres*
Kevin Swanson, *Controller*
Chad Schaefer, *Manager*
EMP: 100 EST: 1982
SQ FT: 18,000
SALES (est): 5MM-9.9MM **Privately Held**
WEB: www.northlandgroup.com
SIC: 7322 Collection agency

(G-5232)
NORTHLAND MECHANICAL CONTR
9001 Science Center Dr (55428-4561)
PHONE.....................763 544-5100
FAX: 763 544-5764
Mike Tieva, *President*
Ross Hanson, *Warehouse Mgr*
EMP: 110 EST: 1971
SQ FT: 7,500
SALES (est): 10MM-24.9MM **Privately Held**
WEB: www.northlandmechanical.com
SIC: 1711 Plumbing service; heating & air
conditioning contractor

(G-5233)
NORTHMARQ CAPITAL LLC (HQ)
3500 Amercn Blvd W # 500 (55431-4413)
PHONE.....................952 356-0100
FAX: 952 356-0088
Jim Kornick, *Managing Dir*
Jerry Burg, *Managing Dir*
Edward Padilla, *Member*
Peter Armbrust, *Corp Secy*
Larissa Champeau, *Corp Secy*
EMP: 80 EST: 1984
SQ FT: 20,000 **Privately Held**
SIC: 6162 Mortgage banking service
PA: Pohlad Co's
60 S 6th St Ste 3700
Minneapolis MN 55402
612 661-3700

(G-5234)
NORTHMARQ REAL ESTATE SERVICES
3500 Amercn Blvd W # 200 (55431-1096)
PHONE.....................952 831-1000
Boyd Stofer, *Member*
Lisa Dongoske, *Senior VP*
Brian Carey, *Senior VP*
Dale Glowa, *Senior VP*
Keith Ulstad, *Senior VP*
EMP: 40 EST: 1991
SALES (est): 10MM-24.9MM **Privately Held**
SIC: 6799 Real estate investors
PA: Pohlad Co's
60 S 6th St Ste 3700
Minneapolis MN 55402
612 661-3700

(G-5235)
NORTHPOINT HEALTH & WELLNESS ✚
1315 Penn Ave N (55411-3047)
PHONE.....................612 767-9500
Stella Whitney-West, *CEO*
Joseph Kirby, *CFO*
EMP: 48 EST: 2008
SALES (est): 1MM-4.9MM **Privately Held**
SIC: 8322 Individual & family social services

(G-5236)
NORTHSHORE RESOURCES INC
212 3rd Ave N Ste 356 (55401-1437)
PHONE.....................612 375-0315
FAX: 612 375-0316
Tim Peterson, *CEO*
Tina Mueller, *Executive*
EMP: 45 EST: 2000
SALES (est): 5MM-9.9MM **Privately Held**
WEB: www.gonorthshore.com
SIC: 7379 7371 Computer system
consulting services; custom computer
software systems analysis & design service

(G-5237)
NORTHSIDE SERVICE CENTER
1126 44th Ave N (55412-1361)
PHONE.....................612 370-4902
FAX: 612 370-3929
Porky Wiseman, *Manager*
EMP: 30 EST: 1862
SALES (est): 1MM-4.9MM **Privately Held**
SIC: 1799 Parking facility equipment
maintenance service

(G-5238)
NORTHWEST AIRLINES INC (HQ)
7500 Airline Dr (55450-1101)
PHONE.....................612 726-2111
Neal Cohen, *CEO*
Richard Anderson, *Ch of Bd*
Mark Powers, *President*
Douglas M Steenland, *President*
John Watkins Jr, *General Mgr*
EMP: 1000 EST: 1926
SQ FT: 1,000,000
SALES (corp-wide): 28.06B **Publicly Held**
WEB: www.nwairlines.com
SIC: 4512 4513 4522 Passenger airline
services; nonscheduled air transportation
services; air courier services; air freight
service
PA: Delta Air Lines Inc
1030 Delta Blvd
Atlanta GA 30354
404 715-2600

(G-5239)
NORTHWEST AIRLINES INC
7500 Airline Dr Ste 6550C (55450-1101)
PHONE.....................612 726-8000
Chris Collette, *Vice Pres*
John Bendoraitis, *Vice Pres*
Fay Beauchine, *Vice Pres*
Peter Kenney, *Vice Pres*
John Klinkenburg, *Vice Pres*
EMP: 25
SALES (est): 5MM-9.9MM **Publicly Held**
WEB: www.nwairlines.com
SIC: 4512 Passenger airline services
HQ: Northwest Airlines Inc
7500 Airline Dr
Minneapolis MN 55450
612 726-2111

(G-5240)
NORTHWEST AIRLINES INC
7200 34th Ave S (55450-1106)
PHONE.....................612 727-9209
Stuart Johnson, *Manager*
Steve Friedrichs, *Manager*
EMP: 135
SALES (est): 25MM-49.9MM **Publicly Held**
WEB: www.nwairlines.com
SIC: 4512 Passenger airline services
HQ: Northwest Airlines Inc
7500 Airline Dr
Minneapolis MN 55450
612 726-2111

(G-5241)
NORTHWEST ANESTHESIA
2828 Chicago Ave Ste 300 (55407-1573)
PHONE.....................612 871-7639
FAX: 612 872-0302
Jeffrey Shaw MD, *President*
Gary Zupfer, *Corp Secy*
David E Brasl, *Manager*
Michael Wipf, *Manager*
Ofelio D Tiu, *Anesthesiology*
EMP: 90 EST: 1974
SQ FT: 975
SALES (est): 10MM-24.9MM **Privately Held**
SIC: 8011 Anesthesiologist office

(G-5242)
NORTHWEST FAMILY PHYSICIANS
1495 County Road 101 N # 1
(55447-3079)
PHONE.....................763 476-6776
Brenda McNeil, *General Mgr*
Kathryn G Justesen MD, *Med Doctor*
Joy Westerdahl MD, *Med Doctor*
Melanie Hoiland, *Physician Asst*
EMP: 26
SALES (est): 1MM-4.9MM **Privately Held**
SIC: 8011 General & family practice
physician or surgeon office

(G-5243)
NORTHWEST ORTHOPEDIC SURGEONS
3366 Oakdale Ave N Ste 103
(55422-2961)
PHONE.....................763 520-7870
Alan Ness, *Principal*

www.HarrisInfo.com
232

2011 Harris Minnesota
Services Directory

▲=Import ▼=Export
◆=Import/Export

Mark Urban, *Treasurer*
Mary Beseres, *Office Mgr*
Rochelle Williams, *Phys Therapist*
Jay Schindlar, *Phys Therapist*
EMP: 52 **EST:** 1994
SALES (est): 5MM-9.9MM **Privately Held**
WEB: www.nwosmn.com
SIC: 8011 Orthopedic physician office;
surgeon's office

(G-5244)
NORTHWEST SUBURBS COMMUNITY
6900 Winnetka Ave N (55428-1669)
PHONE..............................763 533-8196
FAX: 763 533-1346
Shawn Christie, *Info Tech Mgr*
Michael Johnson, *Exec Dir*
Gregory Moore, *Director*
Mike Johnson, *Director*
EMP: 60 **EST:** 1982
SQ FT: 13,700
SALES (est): 10MM-24.9MM **Privately Held**
SIC: 4833 Television broadcasting station

(G-5245)
NORTHWESTERN CASKET CO INC
4300 Quebec Ave N Ste 100 (55428-4982)
PHONE..............................612 789-4356
William L Shields, *President*
David Koll, *Treasurer*
Reene Roach, *Manager*
Matt Germar, *Manager*
Robert Bishop, *Shareholder*
EMP: 25 **EST:** 1882
SQ FT: 50,000
SALES (est): 1MM-4.9MM **Privately Held**
SIC: 5087 Manufactures casket linings;
wholesales caskets

(G-5246)
NORTHWESTERN MARBLE & GRANITE
7705 Bush Lake Rd (55439-2812)
PHONE..............................952 941-8601
FAX: 952 941-0994
David C Gramling, *President*
John Newe, *Vice Pres*
Mary Haupt, *Controller*
Mary APT, *Accountant*
David Granils, *Manager*
▲ **EMP:** 26 **EST:** 1896
SALES (est): 1MM-4.9MM **Privately Held**
WEB: www.northwesternmarble.com
SIC: 1741 1743 Masonry & stonework
contractor; manufactures wooden kitchen
cabinets; interior marble installation service;
ceramic tile installation service;
manufactures cut stone & stone products

(G-5247)
NORWEST BANK MINNESOTA NORTH
6 Street & Marquette Ave (55479-0001)
PHONE..............................612 667-1234
FAX: 612 667-1535
Richard M Kovacevich, *CEO*
Donald A Carlson, *Senior VP*
Tom Pajak, *CFO*
Cheryl Morse, *Human Res Mgr*
Joe Lefto, *Info Tech Mgr*
EMP: 187 **EST:** 1879
SALES (est): 50MM-99.9MM **Publicly Held**
SIC: 6021 National commercial bank
PA: Wells Fargo & Co
420 Montgomery St
San Francisco CA 94104
866 878-5865

(G-5248)
NORWEST EQUITY CAPITAL LLC
80 S 8th St Ste 3600 (55402-2213)
PHONE..............................612 215-1600
Arthur R Monaghan, *Principal*
Paul A Keel, *Principal*
John Lindahl, *Principal*
John Whaley, *Member*
EMP: 29 **EST:** 1982
SQ FT: 10,000
SALES (est): 10MM-24.9MM **Publicly Held**

SIC: 6799 Venture capital services
PA: Wells Fargo & Co
420 Montgomery St
San Francisco CA 94104
866 878-5865

(G-5249)
NORWEST VENTURE CAPITAL MGT (HQ)
80 S 8th St Ste 3600 (55402-2213)
PHONE..............................612 215-1600
FAX: 612 215-1602
Tim Devries, *President*
Jerry Lester, *Vice Pres*
John Lindahl, *Vice Pres*
John Whaley, *Treasurer*
Darren Herz, *Controller*
◆ **EMP:** 33 **EST:** 1959
SQ FT: 6,000
SALES (corp-wide): 98.63B **Publicly Held**
WEB: www.nep.com
SIC: 6799 Venture capital services
PA: Wells Fargo & Co
420 Montgomery St
San Francisco CA 94104
866 878-5865

(G-5250)
NOVUS MARKETING INC
931 Nicollet Mall (55402-3201)
PHONE..............................612 252-1618
Joanne Capria, *President*
John Hoeft, *Vice Pres*
Susan Peattie, *Vice Pres*
Jennifer Dussman, *Sales/Mktg Mgr*
Jeff Adderson, *Controller*
EMP: 35 **EST:** 1985
SQ FT: 24,300
SALES (est): 1MM-4.9MM **Privately Held**
SIC: 7331 Direct mail advertising service;
mailing list management

(G-5251)
NOVUS MEDIA INC
2 Carlson Pkwy N Ste 400 (55447-4469)
PHONE..............................612 758-8625
FAX: 612 338-8604
David Murphy, *CEO*
Gwendolyn Maass, *President*
Eric Monson, *Managing Prtnr*
Dan Alstrup, *Vice Pres*
Henry Anthony, *Vice Pres*
EMP: 130 **EST:** 1987
SQ FT: 27,000
SALES (est): 10MM-24.9MM **Publicly Held**
WEB: www.novusprintmedia.com
SIC: 7319 Media buying services
HQ: Omnicom Media Group Holdings
195 Broadway Fl 12
New York NY 10007
212 415-3700

(G-5252)
NRG ENERGY INC
Also Called: Energy Center
816 4th Ave S (55404-1005)
PHONE..............................612 349-6087
FAX: 612 349-6106
Henry Hansen, *Manager*
Kathleen Beecher, *Exec Dir*
EMP: 40
SALES (est): 25MM-49.9MM **Publicly Held**
WEB: www.xcelenergy.com
SIC: 4931 Electric & related services
PA: XCEL Energy Inc
414 Nicollet Mall
Minneapolis MN 55401
612 330-5500

(G-5253)
NRG ENERGY PLUS RELOCATION
600 Highway 169 S Ste 500 (55426-1209)
PHONE..............................952 512-5500
Susan Schneider, *President*
EMP: 65 **EST:** 2002
SALES (est): 1MM-4.9MM **Privately Held**
SIC: 7389 Relocation services

(G-5254)
NTERNATIONAL PROJECTS
Also Called: Ipcs
600 Highway 169 S Ste 1595
(55426-1274)
PHONE..............................952 541-4888
Anupa Dhar, *CEO*
James Ahles, *Senior VP*
Todd Bleeker, *Senior VP*
Glenn Carleton, *Senior VP*
Kuldeep K Dhar, *Senior VP*
EMP: 58 **EST:** 1996
SQ FT: 4,900
SALES (est): 5MM-9.9MM **Privately Held**
WEB: www.ipcs.net
SIC: 7379 7371 7372 7373 Computer
system consulting services; computer
software development; computer integrated
systems design services; software publisher

(G-5255)
OAKDALE EAR NOSE & THROAT CLIN
3366 Oakdale Ave N Ste 150
(55422-2961)
PHONE..............................763 520-7840
John Zurek, *President*
Kathleen Obrian, *Project Mgr*
Ric Rowe, *Office Mgr*
Karin M Tansek, *Otolaryngology*
Joseph M Kuderko, *Otolaryngology*
EMP: 34 **EST:** 1971
SQ FT: 4,300
SALES (est): 1MM-4.9MM **Privately Held**
WEB: www.oakdaleent.com
SIC: 8011 Ears, nose & throat specialist
office

(G-5256)
OAKDALE HEALTH ENTERPRISES INC
Also Called: North Ambulance
4501 68th Ave N (55429-1712)
PHONE..............................763 520-5357
David Cress, *CEO*
Rosie Anderson, *Manager*
EMP: 27 **EST:** 1983
SQ FT: 10,000
SALES (est): 1MM-4.9MM **Privately Held**
WEB: www.northmemorial.com
SIC: 4119 Ambulance service
PA: North Memorial Health Care
3300 Oakdale Ave N
Minneapolis MN 55422
763 520-5200

(G-5257)
OAKDALE OBSTETRICS & GYNECOLOG
2855 Campus Dr Ste 600 (55441-2683)
PHONE..............................763 520-2999
FAX: 763 383-2188
John Neilsen, *CEO*
Karen Kiley, *Office Mgr*
Shannon E Harris MD, *Med Doctor*
Jennifer Austin, *Manager*
Doris Roettger, *Manager*
EMP: 55 **EST:** 1972
SALES (est): 5MM-9.9MM **Privately Held**
WEB: www.oakdaleobgyn.com
SIC: 8011 Specialized medical practitioners

(G-5258)
OASIS OF LOVE INC
2304 Emerson Ave N (55411-2050)
PHONE..............................612 529-6055
FAX: 612 522-9148
Diane Thibodeaux, *Manager*
EMP: 50 **EST:** 1986
SALES (est): 1MM-4.9MM **Privately Held**
SIC: 8322 Individual & family social services

(G-5259)
OBJECT PARTNERS INC
100 N 6th St Ste 302A (55403-1503)
PHONE..............................612 746-1580
Chris Spurgat, *President*
Gwen Spurgat, *Vice Pres*
Jacob Foley, *Director*
EMP: 43 **EST:** 1996
SQ FT: 3,000
SALES (est): 5MM-9.9MM **Privately Held**
WEB: www.objectpartners.com

SIC: 7379 Computer system consulting
services

(G-5260)
OBJECTFX CORP
10 2nd St NE Ste 400 (55413-2652)
PHONE..............................612 312-2002
FAX: 612 312-2555
Kermit Stofer, *Ch of Bd*
Barry J Glick, *President*
Nick Thomey, *COO*
Diane Hatfull, *Human Res Mgr*
Mark R Myers, *Marketing Staff*
EMP: 27 **EST:** 1993
SQ FT: 5,000
SALES (est): 5MM-9.9MM **Privately Held**
WEB: www.objectfx.com
SIC: 7372 Software publisher

(G-5261)
OBSTETRICS & GYN
6545 France Ave S Ste 600 (55435-2136)
PHONE..............................952 920-2200
Stephen L Larson MD, *President*
Nancy Bains MD, *Corp Secy*
Aimee Song MD, *Vice Pres*
Bryan Colwell MD, *Treasurer*
Kirk A Shibley MD, *Med Doctor*
EST: 1980
SQ FT: 3,700 **Privately Held**
SIC: 8011 Obstetrician office; gynecologist
office

(G-5262)
OBSTETRICS & GYNECOLOGY
6545 France Ave S Ste 600 (55435-2136)
PHONE..............................952 920-2200
Nancy Brown, *Insur/Bill Sup*
Barbara Cookas, *Human Res Mgr*
Sandy Kayman, *Manager*
Shelly Ramberd, *Supervisor*
Regina Cho, *Obstetrician*
EMP: 50 **EST:** 1980
SALES (est): 5MM-9.9MM **Privately Held**
SIC: 8011 Obstetrician office

(G-5263)
OBSTETRICS, GYNECOLOGY
6405 France Ave S Ste W400
(55435-2165)
PHONE..............................952 920-2730
Philip Marcus, *President*
Frank Czerniecki, *Corp Secy*
Richard Gosen, *Vice Pres*
Stephanie Rice, *Vice Pres*
Lisa Baker, *Treasurer*
EMP: 35 **EST:** 1969
SALES (est): 1MM-4.9MM **Privately Held**
SIC: 8011 Physicians' office

(G-5264)
OCTAGON FINANCIAL GROUP
1650 W 82nd St Ste 850 (55431-1460)
PHONE..............................952 885-2700
Thomas V Lynch V, *President*
Steve Kairies, *Principal*
Samuel Cleveland, *Principal*
John Cleveland, *Principal*
Steve Mars, *Principal*
EMP: 25 **EST:** 1988
SQ FT: 7,600
SALES (est): 1MM-4.9MM **Privately Held**
WEB: www.octagonfinancial.com
SIC: 8741 Financial management services
for business

(G-5265)
OFFICE INFORMATION SYSTEMS INC
10800 Lyndale Ave S (55420-5614)
PHONE..............................952 884-9199
FAX: 952 884-2515
John Lewis, *President*
Ken Sandy, *Vice Pres*
Kevin McGregor, *Vice Pres*
EMP: 25 **EST:** 1982
SQ FT: 1,800 **Privately Held**
WEB: www.1techeng.com
SIC: 7361 8711 Executive placement &
search consulting services; engineering
consulting services

(PA)=Parent Co (HQ)=Headquarters (DH)=Div Headquarters
✿ = New business established in last 2 years

2011 Harris Minnesota
Services Directory

© Harris InfoSource 1-866-281-6415
233

GEOGRAPHIC

G E O G R A P H I C

(G-5266)

OFFICE OF GENERAL COUNCIL
200 Oak St SE Ste 360   (55455-2008)
PHONE..................................612 624-4100
Mark Rotenberg, *Partner*
EMP: 41 EST: 1991
SALES (est): 5MM-9.9MM **Privately Held**
SIC: 8111 General practice attorney's or lawyer's office

(G-5267)

OFFICEMAX NORTH AMERICA INC
8085 Brooklyn Blvd   (55445-2406)
PHONE..................................763 391-6629
Jason Haley, *Manager*
Carl Haverson, *Manager*
EMP: 30
SALES (est): 5MM-9.9MM **Publicly Held**
WEB: www.officemax.com
SIC: 5112 Wholesales stationery & office supplies
HQ: OfficeMax North America Inc
    3462 Mayfield Rd
    Cleveland OH 44118
    216 297-9789

(G-5268)

OLD REPUBLIC NATIONAL TITLE   (DH)
400 2nd Ave S   (55401-2406)
PHONE..................................612 371-1111
FAX: 612 371-1176
Rande K Yeager, *President*
Stephen C Wilson, *Exec VP*
Diane Borris, *Vice Pres*
Joseph A Johnson, *Vice Pres*
Marlene Heesch, *Opers Staff*
EMP: 250 EST: 1907
SQ FT: 60,000
SALES (corp-wide): 3.23B **Publicly Held**
WEB: www.orbitinfo.net
SIC: 6361 Provides real estate title insurance
HQ: Old Republic Title Insurance
    307 N Michigan Ave
    Chicago IL 60601
    312 346-8100

(G-5269)

OLR AMERICA INC
1200 Washington Ave S # 280
(55415-1590)
PHONE..................................612 436-4970
Kenneth Wehr, *President*
Michelle Kerrstenzel, *Human Res Mgr*
EMP: 45 EST: 2002
SQ FT: 7,000
SALES (est): 5MM-9.9MM **Privately Held**
SIC: 7379 Online technology consulting service

(G-5270)

OLSEN FIRE PROTECTION INC
321 Wilson St NE   (55413-2804)
PHONE..................................612 331-3111
FAX: 612 331-1161
Kevin R Olsen, *President*
Tom Marxsen, *Managing Dir*
Tom Johnson, *Vice Pres*
Howard Ropp, *Controller*
Dave Norlander, *Controller*
EMP: 45 EST: 1981
SALES (est): 5MM-9.9MM **Privately Held**
WEB: www.olsenfire.com
SIC: 1711 Fire sprinkler system installation service

(G-5271)

OLSON + CO INC
1625 Hennepin Ave   (55403-1701)
PHONE..................................612 215-9800
FAX: 612 215-9801
John Olson, *President*
Bill Firing, *Managing Dir*
Jennifer Bastain, *Editor*
Steve Hanson, *COO*
Carolyn Aberman, *Vice Pres*
EMP: 130 EST: 1996
SQ FT: 38,000
SALES (est): 10MM-24.9MM **Privately Held**
WEB: www.oco.com
SIC: 7311 Advertising agency

(G-5272)

OLSON GENERAL CONTRACTORS INC
9201 49th Ave N   (55428-4010)
PHONE..................................763 535-1481
Robert Olson, *President*
EMP: 25 EST: 1909
SQ FT: 16,000
SALES (est): 1MM-4.9MM **Privately Held**
WEB: www.olsongc.com
SIC: 1541 1542 New industrial building construction; industrial building renovating, remodeling & repair service; new commercial & office building construction; commercial & office building renovation & repair services

(G-5273)

OLSON, JOCK INTERLACHEN
Also Called: Interlachen Cntry CLB Golf Sp
6200 Interlachen Blvd   (55436-1137)
PHONE..................................952 924-7424
Jock Olson, *Owner*
George Carrol, *General Mgr*
George Carroll, *General Mgr*
Dean Schreiner, *CFO*
Mel Preston, *CIO*
EMP: 120 EST: 1958
SQ FT: 1,000
SALES (est): 5MM-9.9MM **Privately Held**
SIC: 7997 Country club

(G-5274)

OLYMPIA TILE INC   (PA)
Also Called: Alpha Tile Co
701 Berkshire Ln N   (55441-5420)
PHONE..................................763 545-5455
Ralph Reichmann, *President*
Timothy Beaupre, *Vice Pres*
Steve Petersen, *Purch Mgr*
Sarah Gaitan, *Finance*
▲ EMP: 40 EST: 1980
SQ FT: 48,500 **Privately Held**
SIC: 1743 5023 5032 Manufactures farm machinery & equipment; wholesales floor coverings; retails cemetery memorials; ceramic tile installation service; wholesale ceramic floor & wall tiles; wholesales tile, clay or other ceramic construction materials
PA: Olympia Tile International Inc
    1000 Lawrence Ave W
    Toronto Canada
    416 7856666

(G-5275)

OLYMPIC STEEL MINNEAPOLIS INC
13100 15th Ave N   (55441-4537)
PHONE..................................763 544-7100
Michael D Siegel, *President*
Marc H Morgenstern, *Corp Secy*
Richard T Marabito, *CFO*
David A Wolfort, *Director*
EMP: 70 EST: 1996
SALES (est): 50MM-99.9MM **Publicly Held**
WEB: www.olysteel.com
SIC: 5051 Wholesales steel; metal heat treating services
PA: Olympic Steel Inc
    5096 Richmond Rd
    Bedford Heights OH 44146
    216 292-3800

(G-5276)

OMNI WORKSPACE CO
1300 Washington Ave N # 200
(55411-3420)
PHONE..................................612 627-1600
Curt Moe, *Branch Mgr*
Jorge Anaya, *Manager*
EMP: 40
SALES (est): 1MM-4.9MM **Publicly Held**
WEB: www.ambis.com
SIC: 7641 Office furniture repair & maintenance service
HQ: Omni Workspace Co
    1300 Washington Ave N Ste 100
    Minneapolis MN 55411
    612 627-1600

(G-5277)

OMNI WORKSPACE CO   (HQ)
1300 Washington Ave N Ste 100
(55411-3435)
PHONE..................................612 627-1600
Timothy Anderson, *President*
EMP: 120 EST: 1994
SALES (corp-wide): 1.65B **Publicly Held**
WEB: www.ambis.com
SIC: 7641 4212 4226 Office furniture repair & maintenance service; local furniture moving services without storage; furniture storage, without local trucking
PA: Hni Corp
    408 E 2nd St
    Muscatine IA 52761
    563 272-7400

(G-5278)

OMNICARE PHARMACY & SUPPLY   (HQ)
5534 Lakeland Ave N   (55429-3121)
PHONE..................................763 259-0188
Tim Krause, *President*
EMP: 200 EST: 1987
SQ FT: 5,600
SALES (corp-wide): 6.16B **Publicly Held**
WEB: www.omnicare.com
SIC: 5122 Wholesales medicinals & botanicals; wholesales pharmaceuticals
PA: Omnicare Inc
    100 E Rivercenter Blvd
    Covington KY 41011
    859 392-3300

(G-5279)

ONCOLOGIC CONSULTANTS
6363 France Ave S Ste 300   (55435-2141)
PHONE..................................952 928-2900
Valerie Campbell, *Human Res Mgr*
Pam Waldinger, *Manager*
Leah Gillette, *Manager*
Rhonda Henschel, *Administrator*
Heather Gonyer, *Officer*
EMP: 40
SALES (est): 1MM-4.9MM **Privately Held**
SIC: 8011 Hematologist; oncologist
PA: Oncologic Consultants
    2550 University Ave W Ste 110N
    Saint Paul MN 55114
    651 602-5335

(G-5280)

ONE WAY BUILDING SERVICES INC
6811 Washington Ave S   (55439-1500)
PHONE..................................952 942-0412
FAX: 952 942-0526
Gary Bormes, *President*
Lois Bormes, *Corp Secy*
Greg Held, *Sr Project Mgr*
EMP: 35 EST: 1977
SALES (est): 5MM-9.9MM **Privately Held**
SIC: 1542 1731 Commercial & office building renovation & repair services; general electrical contractor

(G-5281)

180 DEGREES INC
300 Clifton Ave   (55403-3226)
PHONE..................................612 813-5010
Tom Zoet, *Branch Mgr*
EMP: 30
SALES (est): 5MM-9.9MM **Privately Held**
SIC: 6512 Nonresidential building operator
PA: 180 Degrees Inc
    236 Clifton Ave
    Minneapolis MN 55403
    612 870-7227

(G-5282)

ONVOY INC   (HQ)
300 Highway 169 S Ste 700   (55426-1137)
PHONE..................................952 230-4100
FAX: 952 362-5899
Janice Aune, *President*
Mary McFetridge, *Partner*
Scott Beer, *Corp Secy*
Doug Carnival, *Corp Secy*
Fritz Hendricks, *COO*
EMP: 160 EST: 1988 **Privately Held**
WEB: www.onvoy.com

SIC: 4813 Wired telecommunications carrier & service
PA: Zayo Bandwidth LLC
    901 Front St Ste 200
    Louisville CO 80027
    303 381-4662

(G-5283)

OPEN ACCESS TECHNOLOGY INTL
2300 Berkshire Ln N Ste F   (55441-4585)
PHONE..................................763 201-2000
Sasan Mochtari, *President*
Ali Ipakchi, *Vice Pres*
Kevin Burns, *Vice Pres*
Joe Sanders, *Accountant*
Behnam Danai, *Manager*
EMP: 323 EST: 1995
SALES (est): 25MM-49.9MM **Privately Held**
WEB: www.oatiinc.com
SIC: 7371 8711 Computer software development; electrical or electronic engineers

(G-5284)

OPEN SYSTEMS INTERNATIONAL INC
3600 Holly Ln N Ste 40   (55447-1286)
PHONE..................................763 551-0559
FAX: 763 551-0750
Bahman Hoveida, *President*
John Chambers, *General Mgr*
Ali Hariri, *Engineer*
Tammy Totz, *Accountant*
David Greene, *Manager*
▲ EMP: 90 EST: 1992
SALES (est): 10MM-24.9MM **Privately Held**
WEB: www.osii.com
SIC: 7371 Computer software development

(G-5285)

OPEN-C SOLUTIONS INC
7300 Metro Blvd Ste 645   (55439-2313)
PHONE..................................952 842-3200
FAX: 952 831-0018
Douglas S Thompson, *CEO*
Anthony Buffa, *General Mgr*
Mark Black, *Vice Pres*
Dennis McMaster, *Vice Pres*
Leonard Mignerey, *Vice Pres*
EMP: 58 EST: 1998
SALES (est): 5MM-9.9MM **Privately Held**
WEB: www.open-c.com
SIC: 7371 Computer software development & applications
PA: NWP Services Corp
    22 Executive Park Ste 200
    Irvine CA 92614
    949 253-2500

(G-5286)

OPHTHALMOLOGY
3100 W 70th St   (55435-4227)
PHONE..................................952 925-3150
Donald P Le Win, *President*
James Mitchell, *President*
Thomas W Purcell, *Principal*
Paul F Bruer, *Ophthalmology*
Donna Holcomb, *Manager*
EMP: 25 EST: 1949
SQ FT: 3,000
SALES (est): 1MM-4.9MM **Privately Held**
SIC: 8011 Ophthalmologist office

(G-5287)

OPPENHEIMER WOLFF DONNELLY LLP
45 S 7th St Ste 3300   (55402-1650)
PHONE..................................612 607-7000
FAX: 612 607-7100
David Potter, *Ch of Bd*
Brad Keil, *Managing Prtnr*
Howard S Booth, *COO*
Robert Jackson, *Accounting Mgr*
Shane Zindel, *CPA*
EMP: 300 EST: 1886
SQ FT: 108,000
SALES (est): 25MM-49.9MM **Privately Held**
WEB: www.oppenheimer.com
SIC: 8111 General practice attorney's or lawyer's office

www.HarrisInfo.com
234

2011 Harris Minnesota
Services Directory

▲=Import ▼=Export
◆=Import/Export

(G-5288)
ORACLE SYSTEMS CORP
950 Nicollet Mall (55403-2532)
PHONE.....................612 587-5000
Gregory A Effertz, *Corp Secy*
Daniel Cooperman, *Corp Secy*
Jim Mattecheck, *Senior VP*
Thomas Carretta, *Vice Pres*
Tom Redd, *Vice Pres*
EMP: 500
SALES (est): 100MM-499.9MM **Publicly Held**
WEB: www.forcecapital.com
SIC: 7372 5045 Software publisher; wholesales computers, peripherals & software
HQ: Oracle Systems Corp
500 Oracle Pkwy
Redwood City CA 94065
650 506-7000

(G-5289)
ORAL & MAXILLOFACIAL SURGICAL
7373 France Ave S Ste 602 (55435-4552)
PHONE.....................952 835-5003
Mark R Omlie, *President*
Debbie Keckhafer, *Office Mgr*
Jennifer L Beaudin, *Surgeon*
Eric F Stich, *Surgeon*
Kyle D Tidstrom, *Surgeon*
EMP: 40 **EST:** 1973
SALES (est): 1MM-4.9MM **Privately Held**
WEB: www.oralmax.net
SIC: 8021 Dental surgeon office; maxillofacial specialist office

(G-5290)
ORION COMMUNICATION SERVICES
15395 31st Ave N Ste 1 (55447-1479)
PHONE.....................763 694-7540
FAX: 763 553-2741
Matt Nelson, *Opers Mgr*
John Braun, *Manager*
Carmella Mays, *Manager*
EMP: 35 **EST:** 1999
SALES (est): 1MM-4.9MM **Privately Held**
SIC: 1731 Fiber optic cable installation contractor

(G-5291)
ORMAN GUIDANCE RESEARCH INC
5001 W 80th St Ste 715 (55437)
PHONE.....................952 831-4911
FAX: 952 831-4913
Rosemary Sundin, *Owner*
Anne Golden, *Exec VP*
EMP: 55 **EST:** 1975
SQ FT: 9,500
SALES (est): 1MM-4.9MM **Privately Held**
WEB: www.ormanguidance.com
SIC: 8732 Research services; market analysis or research services

(G-5292)
ORTHOPAEDIC CONSULTANTS
7373 France Ave S Ste 312 (55435-4549)
PHONE.....................952 832-0076
FAX: 952 832-0477
David Holte MD, *President*
Paula Powell, *Office Mgr*
Jody Keller, *Office Mgr*
Joseph T Teynor, *Surgeon*
Edward W Szalapski, *Surgeon*
EMP: 25
SALES (est): 1MM-4.9MM **Privately Held**
SIC: 8011 Surgeon's office

(G-5293)
ORTHOPEDIC MEDICINE & SURGERY
3250 W 66th St Ste 100 (55435-2500)
PHONE.....................952 920-0970
FAX: 952 922-1605
David Gesensway, *President*
Scott Anseth, *Principal*
John Kearns MD, *Principal*
Gary Pattee, *Principal*
Frank Norberg, *Vice Chairman*
EMP: 30 **EST:** 1989
SALES (est): 1MM-4.9MM **Privately Held**
WEB: www.omsmn.com

SIC: 8011 Orthopedic physician office; surgeon's office

(G-5294)
ORTHOPEDIC RESOURCES MGT
Also Called: Kaleidoscope Health System
7801 E Bush Lake Rd # 320 (55439-3113)
PHONE.....................952 831-5773
FAX: 952 831-7224
Richard Board, *President*
Sandy Rutherford, *COO*
Corinne Abdou, *Vice Pres*
Catherine Maruska, *Vice Pres*
Becky Dalton, *Human Resources*
EMP: 28 **EST:** 1995
SALES (est): 1MM-4.9MM **Privately Held**
SIC: 8741 8721 Administrative management services; billing & bookkeeping services

(G-5295)
ORTHOPEDIC SURGEONS LTD
6363 France Ave S Ste 404 (55435-2142)
PHONE.....................952 927-7565
Joseph T Teynor MD, *Treasurer*
Laurie Johnson, *Bookkeeper*
Joe Bianski, *Med Doctor*
Jill Johnson, *Med Doctor*
Tom Gendron, *Med Doctor*
EMP: 35 **EST:** 1963
SALES (est): 1MM-4.9MM **Privately Held**
SIC: 8011 Orthopedic physician office

(G-5296)
OSBORNE PROPERTIES LP
523 S 8th St (55404-1030)
PHONE.....................952 881-8166
EMP: 30
SALES (est): 5MM-9.9MM **Privately Held**
SIC: 6512 Nonresidential building operator
PA: Osborne Properties LP
420 Gateway Blvd
Burnsville MN 55337
952 707-8200

(G-5297)
OTTO BOCK HEALTHCARE LP (PA)
2 Carlson Pkwy N Ste 100 (55447-4467)
PHONE.....................763 553-9464
Bert Harman, *President*
Milo Arkema, *Corp Secy*
Stephen A Carr, *Corp Secy*
Anna Diiorio, *Corp Secy*
Thorsten Schmitt, *COO*
▲ **EMP:** 110 **EST:** 1958
SQ FT: 120,000 **Privately Held**
WEB: www.healthcare.ottobock.com
SIC: 5047 Wholesales artificial limbs
PA: Otto Bock HealthCare GmbH
Max-Nader-Str 15
Duderstadet Germany 37115

(G-5298)
OTTO BOCK HEALTHCARE NORTH (PA)
2 Carlson Pkwy N Ste 100 (55447-4467)
PHONE.....................763 553-9464
Bert Harman, *President*
John Hendrickson Jr, *Principal*
Daniele Britts, *Corp Secy*
▲ **EMP:** 90 **EST:** 1958
SQ FT: 4,800
SALES (corp-wide): 738.71M **Privately Held**
SIC: 5047 Wholesales orthopedic equipment & supplies

(G-5299)
OTTO BOCK US POLYURETHANE FOAM
2 Carlson Pkwy N Ste 100 (55447-4467)
PHONE.....................763 553-9464
Bert Harmen, *CEO*
Carrie Westwood, *Comptroller*
Diane Vollum, *Marketing Staff*
EMP: 40 **EST:** 1987
SQ FT: 45,000
SALES (est): 25MM-49.9MM **Privately Held**
WEB: www.healthcare.ottobock.com

SIC: 5169 Wholesales polyurethane products
PA: Otto Bock Healthcare LP
2 Carlson Pkwy N Ste 100
Minneapolis MN 55447
763 553-9464

(G-5300)
OUTDOOR ADVENTURE TRAVEL INC
Also Called: Carrousel Travel
6625 Lyndale Ave S 104 (55423-2373)
PHONE.....................612 866-2503
FAX: 612 866-9644
Neal Kraemer, *President*
Robert E Harris Jr, *Vice Pres*
Paul Healy, *Controller*
EMP: 29 **EST:** 1988
SALES (est): 1MM-4.9MM **Privately Held**
WEB: www.carouseltravel.com
SIC: 4724 Travel agency

(G-5301)
OUTSOURCEONE INC
730 2nd Ave S Ste 530 (55402-2424)
PHONE.....................612 436-2740
William Mehus, *President*
Paulette Rickey, *General Mgr*
Paul Walther, *Vice Pres*
Helen Jorgensen, *Finance*
Jim Willard, *Officer*
EMP: 30 **EST:** 1988
SQ FT: 20,000
SALES (est): 10MM-24.9MM **Privately Held**
SIC: 6324 6411 Hospital & medical insurance carrier; insurance services

(G-5302)
OUTSOURCEONE INC
730 2nd Ave S Ste 530 (55402-3400)
PHONE.....................612 338-7940
William P Mehus, *CEO*
Nancy Mehus, *Accountant*
EMP: 25 **EST:** 1988
SQ FT: 10,000
SALES (est): 1MM-4.9MM **Privately Held**
SIC: 6411 Insurance services

(G-5303)
OVAL CLEANING SERVICE INC ✿
1516 W Lake St Ste 200 (55408-2502)
PHONE.....................612 605-3166
Letron Clark, *CEO*
EMP: 50 **EST:** 2009
SALES (est): 1MM-4.9MM **Privately Held**
SIC: 7349 Janitorial & custodial services

(G-5304)
P & L AUTOMOTIVE INC
7449 Cahill Rd Ste 120 (55439-2731)
PHONE.....................952 941-0888
FAX: 952 941-0840
Les Suomala, *President*
Paul Schmelz, *Corp Secy*
EMP: 25 **EST:** 1982
SQ FT: 8,000
SALES (est): 5MM-9.9MM **Privately Held**
WEB: www.pandlauto.com
SIC: 5013 7549 Wholesales automotive supplies & parts; automotive rust proofing & undercoating shop; automotive customizing service, nonfactory basis; automotive glass tinting service

(G-5305)
P KEVIN HICKEY
33 S 6th St (55402-3601)
PHONE.....................612 376-1620
Kevin P Hickey, *Owner*
Valerie Cline, *Opers Mgr*
Daniel Rojas, *Consultant*
Jt Williams, *IT/INT Sup*
EMP: 37 **EST:** 1882
SALES (est): 5MM-9.9MM **Privately Held**
SIC: 8111 General practice law office

(G-5306)
P O S BUSINESS SYSTEMS INC
9905 45th Ave N Ste 200 (55442-2500)
PHONE.....................763 559-1341
FAX: 763 559-3610
Wayne Sharp, *President*
Mike Majarus, *CFO*
Chelsey Paulson, *Human Resources*

Ron Schlicht, *Manager*
Doug Taplin, *Manager*
EMP: 37 **EST:** 1973
SQ FT: 17,000
SALES (est): 5MM-9.9MM **Privately Held**
SIC: 5044 Wholesales cash registers

(G-5307)
P R K INC
225 S 11th St (55403-2520)
PHONE.....................612 341-3300
FAX: 612 341-1174
Esta Goodman, *Vice Pres*
Kevin Koenig, *Manager*
EMP: 32
SALES (est): 1MM-4.9MM **Privately Held**
WEB: www.prk.net
SIC: 7011 Traveler accommodations
PA: P R K Inc
50 Groveland Ter Ste A
Minneapolis MN 55403
612 374-1770

(G-5308)
PACE ANALYTICAL SERVICES INC (HQ)
1700 Elm St SE Ste 200 (55414-2485)
PHONE.....................612 607-1700
FAX: 612 617-6444
Rodney Burwell, *Ch of Bd*
Steve A Vanderboom, *President*
Eric Bullock, *General Mgr*
Laurie Woelfel, *General Mgr*
Janet T Leuman, *Corp Secy*
EMP: 335 **EST:** 1995
SQ FT: 63,000 **Privately Held**
WEB: www.pacelabs.com
SIC: 8734 8731 8748 Hazardous waste testing laboratory; business consulting services; soil analysis laboratory; water testing laboratory; commercial physical research laboratory
PA: Lab Holdings Inc
7901 Xerxes Ave S Ste 201
Minneapolis MN 55431
612 607-1700

(G-5309)
PACER CENTER INC
8161 Normandale Blvd (55437-1044)
PHONE.....................952 838-9000
FAX: 952 827-3065
Debra D Leuchovius, *Manager*
Paula Goldberg, *Director*
Dixie Jordan, *Director*
Debra Jones, *Director*
Susan Abderholen, *Director*
EMP: 80 **EST:** 1976
SQ FT: 36,000
SALES (est): 1MM-4.9MM **Privately Held**
WEB: www.pacer.org
SIC: 8322 8699 8748 Individual & family social services; business consulting services; charitable organization

(G-5310)
PACIFIC MARKETING & COMMS
123 N 3rd St (55401-1657)
PHONE.....................651 967-7135
Mark Beaumont, *President*
EMP: 33 **EST:** 1990
SALES (est): 1MM-4.9MM **Privately Held**
SIC: 8742 Marketing consulting service

(G-5311)
PACKAGING CORP OF AMERICA
4300 Highway 55 (55422-4821)
PHONE.....................763 521-3611
FAX: 763 529-2858
Cully Exsped, *General Mgr*
Patrick Yantes, *Prdtn Mgr*
Ken Gierl, *Mfg Staff*
Mark Devinny, *Controller*
Margurite Einer, *Human Res Dir*
EMP: 78
SALES (est): 10MM-24.9MM **Publicly Held**
WEB: www.packagingcorp.com
SIC: 5113 Manufactures corrugated boxes; wholesales corrugated & solid fiber boxes
PA: Packaging Corp of America
1900 W Field Ct
Lake Forest IL 60045
847 482-3000

(PA)=Parent Co (HQ)=Headquarters (DH)=Div Headquarters
✿ = New business established in last 2 years

2011 Harris Minnesota
Services Directory

© Harris InfoSource 1-866-281-6415

235

(G-5312)
PACKAGING SYSTEMS AUTOMATION
2200 Niagara Ln N (55447-4702)
PHONE..............................763 473-1032
FAX: 763 473-1204
Steven Swanlund, *President*
Frederick Fiebranz, *Vice Pres*
Stephen Kaye, *Engineering*
Steve Bennewitz, *Sales Engr*
Mark Baadsgaard, *Manager*
EMP: 35 EST: 1983
SALES (est): 10MM-24.9MM **Privately Held**
WEB: www.psautomation.com
SIC: 5084 Wholesales industrial packaging machinery & equipment

(G-5313)
PAH-DT MINNEAPOLIS SUITES
1101 Lasalle Ave (55403-2046)
PHONE..............................612 332-6800
FAX: 612 332-8246
Scott Y Blood, *Partner*
Tom Peterka, *General Mgr*
Art Johnson, *Chief Engr*
Pete Clysdale, *Sales Mgr*
Olin Sue, *Sales Executive*
EMP: 100 EST: 1987
SALES (est): 5MM-9.9MM **Privately Held**
WEB: www.sunstoneshopper.com
SIC: 7011 Traveler accommodations; eating place; drinking establishment
PA: Sunstone Hotel Management Inc
    903 Calle Amanecer
    San Clemente CA 92673
    949 369-4000

(G-5314)
PALANISAMI & ASSOCIATES INC
5661 International Pkwy (55428-3046)
PHONE..............................763 533-9403
P Palanisami, *President*
Vallinayaki Palanisami, *Corp Secy*
R Pandian, *Corp Secy*
Michael Anderson, *Vice Pres*
EMP: 27
SQ FT: 7,200
SALES (est): 1MM-4.9MM **Privately Held**
WEB: www.palanisami.com
SIC: 8711 Structural engineering services

(G-5315)
PALMER LAKE POST 3915 VFW INC
2817 Brookdale Dr (55444-1844)
PHONE..............................763 560-3720
Lee Ulferts, *CEO*
EMP: 25 EST: 1965 **Privately Held**
SIC: 8641 Members only bar & restaurant for members of organizations only; veterans' organization; drinking establishment

(G-5316)
PAN-O-GOLD BAKING CO
Also Called: Country Hearth
3200 Ranchview Ln N (55447-1461)
PHONE..............................763 559-1515
FAX: 763 559-4633
James Hanson, *Manager*
EMP: 45
SALES (est): 1MM-4.9MM **Privately Held**
WEB: www.panogold.com
SIC: 4225 Warehousing & storage services
PA: Pan-O-Gold Baking Co
    444 E Saint Germain St
    Saint Cloud MN 56304
    320 251-9361

(G-5317)
PAPER DEPOT INC
221 Border Ave (55405-1609)
PHONE..............................612 333-0512
FAX: 612 333-5830
Mark Pupeza, *President*
Kathy Pupeza, *CFO*
EMP: 30 EST: 1974
SQ FT: 9,000
SALES (est): 5MM-9.9MM **Privately Held**
WEB: www.paperdepotinc.com
SIC: 5112 Office supply & stationery store; wholesales stationery & office supplies

(G-5318)
PAQUETTE MAINTENANCE INC
Also Called: Multi Clean
2224 W 94th St (55431-2313)
PHONE..............................952 888-1801
Bruce Paquette, *President*
Craig Paquette, *Vice Pres*
EMP: 85 EST: 1985
SQ FT: 5,000
SALES (est): 10MM-24.9MM **Privately Held**
WEB: www.multiclean.com
SIC: 5087 7349 Wholesales janitorial equipment & supplies; office cleaning or charring service; floor waxing service

(G-5319)
PARADISE CAR WASH
9201 Lyndale Ave S (55420-3510)
PHONE..............................952 888-5388
FAX: 952 888-1803
Ramsingh Prim, *Manager*
Prim Remsingh, *Manager*
EMP: 30
SALES (est): 1MM-4.9MM **Privately Held**
SIC: 7542 Car wash

(G-5320)
PARADYSZ MATERA CO INC
505 Highway 169 N Fl 8 (55441-4683)
PHONE..............................952 544-5121
FAX: 952 544-6320
Randy Robertson, *Senior VP*
Dennis Erickson, *Vice Pres*
Eric Johnson, *Vice Pres*
Robin Nawrocki, *Accounts Mgr*
Bryn Scott, *Marketing Staff*
EMP: 60
SALES (est): 5MM-9.9MM **Privately Held**
WEB: www.paradysz.com
SIC: 7331 Mailing list broker
PA: Paradysz Matera Co Inc
    5 Hanover Sq
    New York NY 10004
    212 387-0300

(G-5321)
PARAGON STRATEGIC SOLUTIONS
5600 W 83rd St 8200 (55437-1000)
PHONE..............................952 886-8000
FAX: 952 886-8302
Jesper Groenveld, *CEO*
Donna Hamel, *Corp Secy*
Daniel P Keefe, *Corp Secy*
Jennifer L Kraft, *Corp Secy*
Rock Schindler, *COO*
EMP: 122 EST: 2001
SQ FT: 3,000
SALES (est): 10MM-24.9MM **Privately Held**
SIC: 8741 Management services

(G-5322)
PARALLEL TECHNOLOGIES INC
4242 Park Glen Rd (55416-4758)
PHONE..............................952 920-7185
FAX: 952 920-7475
Dale Klein, *President*
Randy Wood, *Vice Pres*
Steve Leanger, *Project Mgr*
Bradley Johnson, *Engineer*
Bennie Boydston, *Engineer*
EMP: 107 EST: 1983
SALES (est): 10MM-24.9MM **Privately Held**
WEB: www.ptnet.com
SIC: 7373 1731 8711 Systems integration service; computer installation service; engineering consulting services; computer systems value-added resellers; communications contractor services

(G-5323)
PARENTS IN COMMUNITY ACTION
4225 3rd Ave S (55409-2105)
PHONE..............................612 823-6361
FAX: 612 827-8712
Ken Macon, *Manager*
Alyce Dillon, *Exec Dir*
EMP: 50
SALES (est): 1MM-4.9MM **Privately Held**
SIC: 8351 Head Start center
PA: Parents In Community Action
    700 Humboldt Ave N
    Minneapolis MN 55411
    612 377-7422

(G-5324)
PARENTS IN COMMUNITY ACTION (PA)
Also Called: Pica Headstart
700 Humboldt Ave N (55411-3931)
PHONE..............................612 377-7422
FAX: 612 374-8340
Brody Burton, *Facilities Mgr*
Shonda Ampey, *Finance*
Sue Melton, *Finance*
Aubrey Tuckett, *Human Resources*
William Donahey, *Exec Dir*
EMP: 100 EST: 1967
SQ FT: 59,000
SALES (corp-wide): 21.83M **Privately Held**
SIC: 8351 Head Start center

(G-5325)
PARENTS IN COMMUNITY ACTION
Also Called: Pica
96 Saint Marys Ave SE (55414-3459)
PHONE..............................612 362-0360
FAX: 612 362-0386
Audrey Heavens, *Manager*
Lee-Ann Murphy, *Administrator*
Ken Magan, *Director*
EMP: 25
SALES (est): 500-999K **Privately Held**
SIC: 8351 Child day care service
PA: Parents In Community Action
    700 Humboldt Ave N
    Minneapolis MN 55411
    612 377-7422

(G-5326)
PAREO INC
120 S 6th St Ste 2550 (55402-1843)
PHONE..............................612 371-0400
FAX: 612 371-0500
Raymond Kuntz, *President*
William Krueger, *Principal*
Amy Kahl, *Office Mgr*
Daree Selby, *Info Tech Mgr*
Jerry Alholm, *Info Tech Mgr*
EMP: 40 EST: 1994
SALES (est): 5MM-9.9MM **Privately Held**
WEB: www.pareoinc.com
SIC: 8742 7371 Management consulting services; custom computer software systems analysis & design service

(G-5327)
PARK 'N FLY INC
3750 American Blvd E (55425-1655)
PHONE..............................952 854-0606
FAX: 952 854-6057
Daryl Anderstron, *Branch Mgr*
Marcia Simning, *Manager*
EMP: 71
SALES (est): 5MM-9.9MM **Privately Held**
WEB: www.parkholding.com
SIC: 7521 Parking lot
DH: Park 'n Fly Inc
    2060 Mount Paran Rd NW # 207
    Atlanta GA 30327
    404 264-1000

(G-5328)
PARK BROOKLYN HOUSING ASSOCS
2355 Polaris Ln N Ste 100 (55447-4777)
PHONE..............................763 354-5500
Armand Brachman, *Partner*
EMP: 60 EST: 2003
SALES (est): 5MM-9.9MM **Privately Held**
SIC: 6513 Apartment building operator

(G-5329)
PARK N' GO OF MINNESOTA LP
7901 International Dr (55425-1513)
PHONE..............................952 854-3386
FAX: 952 854-3086
John Bona, *Partner*
Frank Bona, *Vice Pres*
Keith Bateman, *Manager*
EMP: 64 EST: 1993
SQ FT: 400
SALES (est): 1MM-4.9MM **Privately Held**

SIC: 7521 Parking garage

(G-5330)
PARK NICOLLET CLINIC
Also Called: Airport Clinic
7550 34th Ave S (55450-1124)
PHONE..............................952 993-9700
FAX: 952 993-9725
Sandy Olebitch, *Manager*
Alice Sweeney, *Administrator*
Sandy Olevitch, *Administrator*
Denise Silvers, *Supervisor*
Marsha Brumm, *Supervisor*
EMP: 60
SALES (est): 1MM-4.9MM **Privately Held**
WEB: www.ccopnet.com
SIC: 8049 8111 Occupational therapist office; immigration & naturalization law office
HQ: Park Nicollet Clinic
    3800 Park Nicollet Blvd
    Minneapolis MN 55416
    952 993-3123

(G-5331)
PARK NICOLLET CLINIC
3007 Harbor Ln N (55447-5103)
PHONE..............................952 993-8900
FAX: 952 993-8994
Mubina Lakha, *Office Mgr*
Kathy Christenson, *Branch Mgr*
Ray Jonathan MD, *Med Doctor*
Douglas Lowin MD, *Med Doctor*
Ronald G McOwn MD, *Med Doctor*
EMP: 50
SALES (est): 5MM-9.9MM **Privately Held**
WEB: www.ccopnet.com
SIC: 8011 Physicians' office & clinic
HQ: Park Nicollet Clinic
    3800 Park Nicollet Blvd
    Minneapolis MN 55416
    952 993-3123

(G-5332)
PARK NICOLLET CLINIC (HQ)
3800 Park Nicollet Blvd (55416-2527)
PHONE..............................952 993-3123
David K Wessner, *Exec VP*
Rodney R Dueck MD, *Vice Pres*
William F Telleen, *CFO*
Cathy Engels, *Admin Asst*
EMP: 800 EST: 1950
SQ FT: 270,000 **Privately Held**
WEB: www.ccopnet.com
SIC: 8011 Clinic operated by physicians; drug store; retails medical apparatus & supplies
PA: Park Nicollet Health Services
    3800 Park Nicollet Blvd
    Minneapolis MN 55416
    952 993-9900

(G-5333)
PARK NICOLLET HEALTH SERVICES
6500 Excelsior Blvd (55426-4702)
PHONE..............................952 993-5353
David Wessner, *President*
Terry Ruane, *Marketing Mgr*
Jan Bolster, *Admin Asst*
Catherine Spurr, *Registrd Nurse*
EMP: 120
SALES (est): 10MM-24.9MM **Privately Held**
WEB: www.ccopnet.com
SIC: 8062 Medical hospital
PA: Park Nicollet Health Services
    3800 Park Nicollet Blvd
    Minneapolis MN 55416
    952 993-9900

(G-5334)
PARK NICOLLET HEALTH SERVICES
2001 Blaisdell Ave (55404-2414)
PHONE..............................952 993-8000
FAX: 952 993-9120
Bradley Montgomery, *Vice Pres*
K C Bretzke, *Office Mgr*
Mark L Edson, *Optometrist*
Markle Karlen MD, *Med Doctor*
Dale R Petesen MD, *Med Doctor*
EMP: 200
SALES (est): 10MM-24.9MM **Privately Held**
WEB: www.ccopnet.com

www.HarrisInfo.com
236
2011 Harris Minnesota
Services Directory
▲=Import ▼=Export
◆=Import/Export

SIC: **8011** Clinic operated by physicians
PA: Park Nicollet Health Services
3800 Park Nicollet Blvd
Minneapolis MN 55416
952 993-9900

(G-5335)
PARK NICOLLET HEALTH SERVICES
Also Called: Health System Minnesota
6701 Country Club Dr (55427-4602)
PHONE...................................952 993-5495
Rose Wichmann, *Manager*
EMP: 25
SALES (est): 1MM-4.9MM **Privately Held**
WEB: www.ccopnet.com
SIC: **8741** Hospital management services
PA: Park Nicollet Health Services
3800 Park Nicollet Blvd
Minneapolis MN 55416
952 993-9900

(G-5336)
PARK NICOLLET HEALTH SERVICES (PA)
3800 Park Nicollet Blvd (55416-2527)
PO Box 650 (55440-0650)
PHONE...................................952 993-9900
FAX: 952 993-1392
David K Wessner, *CEO*
Donald M Lewis, *Vice Chairman*
Barbara A Benjamin, *Corp Secy*
John W Herman, *COO*
Michael B Kaupa, *COO*
EMP: 175 EST: 1987 **Privately Held**
WEB: www.ccopnet.com
SIC: **8011** Physicians' office & clinic

(G-5337)
PARK SYSTEMS INC
2727 E 26th St (55406-1313)
PHONE...................................612 822-3180
Gordon Wichterman, *President*
Brad Parkhill, *Vice Pres*
Linda Gutzke, *Manager*
▲ EMP: 40 EST: 1965
SQ FT: 49,000
SALES (est): 10MM-24.9MM **Privately Held**
SIC: **5074** 5064 5072 Wholesales plumbing & heating equipment & supplies; wholesales hardware; wholesales household appliance parts; wholesales hydronic heating equipment

(G-5338)
PARKSHORE SENIOR CAMPUS ✿
3663 Park Center Blvd Ste A (55416-2514)
PHONE...................................952 929-1034
FAX: 952 920-8670
Mike Metzler, *Exec Dir*
EMP: 25 EST: 2008
SALES (est): 500-999K **Privately Held**
SIC: **8361** Geriatric residential care

(G-5339)
PARKWOOD SHORES ASSISTED
3633 Park Center Blvd (55416-2597)
PHONE...................................952 924-0400
Sheila Johnson, *Director*
EMP: 50 EST: 2000
SALES (est): 1MM-4.9MM **Privately Held**
SIC: **8322** 8361 Old age assistance; residential care facility

(G-5340)
PARSONS
60 S 6th St Ste 2450 (55402-4424)
PHONE...................................612 656-7000
FAX: 612 656-7001
Lawrence E Williams, *Engineer*
Brent Ogne, *Manager*
Dince Gestoni, *Manager*
Carol Keturakat, *Admin Asst*
EMP: 30 EST: 2001
SALES (est): 1MM-4.9MM **Privately Held**
SIC: **8742** Management consulting services

(G-5341)
PARTNERS FOR SENIOR
Also Called: Edina Park Plaza
3330 Edinbrgh Way Ste 100 (55435-5257)
PHONE...................................952 831-4084
FAX: 952 831-7171
Mike Long, *Chief Engr*
Angie Whitcomb, *Manager*
Jan Palmer, *Manager*
Anna Wilson, *Exec Dir*
EMP: 55
SALES (est): 5MM-9.9MM **Privately Held**
SIC: **6513** Apartment building operator
PA: Partners For Senior
200 E Randolph St # 2100
Chicago IL 60601
312 726-0083

(G-5342)
PARTNERS FOR SENIOR
Also Called: Kenwood Retirement Community
825 Summit Ave Ofc (55403-3100)
PHONE...................................612 374-8100
FAX: 612 377-3600
EMP: 38
SALES (est): 10MM-24.9MM **Privately Held**
SIC: **6552** Land subdivision & development services
PA: Partners For Senior
200 E Randolph St # 2100
Chicago IL 60601
312 726-0083

(G-5343)
PARTNERS IN PEDIATRICS LTD
8500 Edinbrook Pkwy (55443-3720)
PHONE...................................763 425-1211
FAX: 763 425-6277
Debbie Hecimovich, *General Mgr*
Jeanne Walsh, *Office Mgr*
Gretchen R Felton MD, *Med Doctor*
Jennie Wallis, *Manager*
Karen A Arrett, *Pediatrics*
EMP: 30
SALES (est): 1MM-4.9MM **Privately Held**
SIC: **8011** Pediatrician office

(G-5344)
PARTNERS PEDIATRIC
3145 Hennepin Ave (55408-2620)
PHONE...................................612 827-4055
Mace Goldfarb, *President*
Saralynn Klein, *Med Doctor*
EST: 1969 **Privately Held**
SIC: **8011** Pediatrician office

(G-5345)
PARTNERSHIP RESOURCES INC
950 E Hennepin Ave (55414-1314)
PHONE...................................612 331-2075
FAX: 612 331-2887
Norman Munk, *Director*
EMP: 37 EST: 1960
SALES (est): 500-999K **Privately Held**
SIC: **8322** Social services for the handicapped

(G-5346)
PATHWAYS PSYCHOLOGICAL SVCS
7575 Golden Valley Rd # 230 (55427-4571)
PHONE...................................763 525-8590
FAX: 763 525-8592
Terry Zuehlke Exec Di, *Principal*
Gary D Vikeslan, *Manager*
Jane Cavanaugh, *Info Tech Dir*
Terry Zuehlke, *Exec Dir*
EST: 1993 **Privately Held**
SIC: **8322** 8049 Family or marriage counseling; clinical psychologist office

(G-5347)
PATRIOT HOLDING CORP (PA)
90 S 7th St Ste 3700 (55402-4128)
PHONE...................................612 338-5912
Michael Sweeney, *Managing Prtnr*
EST: 2005
SQ FT: 10,000 **Privately Held**
SIC: **4213** Over the road trucking

(G-5348)
PATTERSON, THUENTE, SKAAR
80 S 8th St Ste 4800 (55402-2208)
PHONE...................................612 349-5764
FAX: 612 349-6416
Jim Patterson, *President*
Douglas J Christensen, *Member*
John Thuente, *Corp Secy*
Randel Skaar, *Treasurer*
Sue Sutton, *Controller*
EMP: 70 EST: 1991
SALES (est): 5MM-9.9MM **Privately Held**
WEB: www.ptslaw.com
SIC: **8111** General practice law office; patent, trademark & copyright law office

(G-5349)
PAUL A SCHMITT MUSIC CO
2400 Freeway Blvd (55430-1709)
PHONE...................................763 566-4560
FAX: 763 566-4763
Bruce Mooty, *Corp Secy*
Jerry Hovey, *Vice Pres*
Robert P Baker, *Treasurer*
Douglas R Schmitt, *Director*
EMP: 50
SALES (est): 5MM-9.9MM **Privately Held**
WEB: www.schmittmusic.com
SIC: **4225** 7699 Retails musical instruments & supplies; musical instrument repair services; general warehousing; retails used musical instruments; music & drama school
PA: Paul A Schmitt Music Co
2400 Freeway Blvd
Minneapolis MN 55430
763 566-4560

(G-5350)
PAUL JOHNSTON
200 Ameriprise Financial Ctr (55474-0002)
PHONE...................................800 862-7919
Paul Johnston, *Owner*
Joan K Wetherille, *Manager*
EMP: 33 EST: 2006 **Privately Held**
SIC: **6722** Open-ended investment funds management services

(G-5351)
PAUL LARSON OB-GYN CLINIC
6525 France Ave S Ste 100 (55435-2158)
PHONE...................................952 927-4021
FAX: 952 927-4026
Martin L Immeran MD, *President*
Kathryn Babage MD, *Principal*
Jancey Eddey, *Principal*
Pat Lahti, *Principal*
Kristin Leipgen, *Principal*
EMP: 51 EST: 1932
SQ FT: 12,000
SALES (est): 5MM-9.9MM **Privately Held**
SIC: **8011** Gynecologist office; obstetrician office

(G-5352)
PAUL LESIEUR
635 Lowry Ave NE (55418-2853)
PHONE...................................612 788-5584
Steve Knowlton, *Partner*
Paul Lesieur, *Partner*
EMP: 35 EST: 2001
SALES (est): 1MM-4.9MM **Privately Held**
SIC: **1751** Carpentry contractor

(G-5353)
PAUL MINNEAPOLIS-ST (PA)
6040 28th Ave S (55450-2701)
PHONE...................................612 726-8100
FAX: 612 726-5296
Bert McKasy, *Vice Chairman*
Richard Biddle, *Project Mgr*
John Ostrom, *Opers Staff*
Brad Johnson, *Purch Mgr*
Larue Lemon, *Technical Mgr*
EMP: 85 EST: 1943
SALES (corp-wide): 241.55M **Privately Held**
SIC: **4581** Airport

(G-5354)
PCR COMPUTER SERVICES
5361 Dallas Ln N (55446-3809)
PHONE...................................763 557-6824
Paul Raymond, *Owner*
EMP: 48

EST: 1988
SQ FT: 6,000
SALES (est): 5MM-9.9MM **Privately Held**
SIC: **7378** 7373 Computer & office machine maintenance & repair services; computer system selling service

(G-5355)
PDHC LTD (HQ)
Also Called: Park Dental
6415 Brooklyn Blvd (55429-2178)
PHONE...................................612 338-4546
Gregory Swenson, *President*
Brian F Murn, *Corp Secy*
Robert R Hoover, *Vice Pres*
Kris Hammann, *Human Res Dir*
Jean Lind DDS, *Dentist*
EMP: 27 EST: 1979
SQ FT: 600
SALES (corp-wide): 274.34M **Publicly Held**
WEB: www.parkdental.com
SIC: **8021** Dental clinic
PA: American Dental Partners Inc
401 Edgewater Pl Ste 430
Wakefield MA 01880
781 224-0880

(G-5356)
PDHC LTD
Also Called: Brookpark Dental Health Center
6437 Brooklyn Blvd (55429-2174)
PHONE...................................763 535-2960
FAX: 763 535-6284
Jacque Chinourd, *General Mgr*
Robert Kadat, *Manager*
Christina Hrypa, *Programmer Anys*
EMP: 70
SALES (est): 5MM-9.9MM **Publicly Held**
WEB: www.parkdental.com
SIC: **8021** Dental clinics & offices
HQ: PDHC Ltd
6415 Brooklyn Blvd
Minneapolis MN 55429
612 338-4546

(G-5357)
PDL BIOPHARMA INC
9450 Winnetka Ave N (55445-1619)
PHONE...................................763 255-5000
FAX: 763 255-5474
Geoffrey Schroeder, *Project Mgr*
Brian Bentler, *Materials Mgr*
Peter Grassam, *VP Opers-Prdtn-*
Karl Reindel, *Enginr/R&D Mgr*
Mary Willig, *Manager*
EMP: 100
SQ FT: 30,000
SALES (est): 25MM-49.9MM **Publicly Held**
WEB: www.pdl.com
SIC: **8731** Manufactures inorganic chemicals; manufactures nondiagnostic biological products; commercial physical research laboratory
PA: Pdl Biopharma Inc
932 Southwood Blvd
Incline Village NV 89451
775 832-8500

(G-5358)
PEACE TRANSPORTATION INC
7500 Wayzata Blvd (55426-1622)
PHONE...................................952 595-9030
Diba Sobhani, *President*
EMP: 75 EST: 2000
SALES (est): 1MM-4.9MM **Privately Held**
SIC: **4119** Local passenger transportation service

(G-5359)
PEAK PERFORMERS NETWORK
7831 E Bush Lake Rd # 200 (55439-3131)
PHONE...................................952 345-3333
FAX: 952 595-0550
Jerry Cox, *President*
Michelle Bensen, *Accounting Mgr*
Kent Walker, *Manager*
EMP: 25
SALES (est): 1MM-4.9MM **Privately Held**
WEB: www.ppnlive.com
SIC: **8742** Training & development consultant

(PA)=Parent Co (HQ)=Headquarters (DH)=Div Headquarters
✿ = New business established in last 2 years

2011 Harris Minnesota
Services Directory

© Harris InfoSource 1-866-281-6415
237

(G-5360)
PELLA PRODUCTS INC (PA)
15300 25th Ave N Ste 100 (55447-1993)
PHONE..................................763 745-1400
Scott Kaufman, *General Mgr*
EMP: 50 **EST:** 1946 **Privately Held**
SIC: 5031 Wholesales doors & windows

(G-5361)
PELLA WINDOWS & DOORS TWIN
15300 25th Ave N Ste 100 (55447-1993)
PHONE..................................763 745-1400
Edwin Brecht, *President*
Scott Kaufman, *General Mgr*
Robert Nixon, *General Mgr*
William Anderson, *Corp Secy*
Richard Johnson, *Vice Pres*
EMP: 55 **EST:** 1997
SALES (est): 25MM-49.9MM **Privately Held**
SIC: 5031 Wholesales doors & windows;
retails door & window products
PA: Pella Corp
102 Main St
Pella IA 50219
641 621-1000

(G-5362)
PENCO LEASING CORP
Also Called: Great Clips
5011 France Ave S (55410-2034)
PHONE..................................612 927-4748
Robert Levine, *President*
EMP: 25 **EST:** 1982
SALES (est): 5MM-9.9MM **Privately Held**
SIC: 6512 0752 Nonresidential building
operator; animal grooming services

(G-5363)
PENHALL CO
850 Mendelssohn Ave N (55427-4308)
PHONE..................................763 542-9999
FAX: 763 545-1141
Dave Blackburg, *Branch Mgr*
EMP: 40
SALES (est): 5MM-9.9MM **Privately Held**
WEB: www.penhall.com
SIC: 7353 5082 Construction & mining
equipment leasing & rental; wholesales
construction & mining machinery
HQ: Penhall Co
320 N Crescent Way
Anaheim CA 92801
714 772-6450

(G-5364)
PEREGRINE CAPITAL MANAGEMENT
800 Lasalle Ave Ste 1850 (55402-2029)
PHONE..................................612 343-7600
FAX: 612 343-7636
Robert B Mersky, *President*
Matthew Scherer, *Managing Prtnr*
Patricia Burns, *Senior VP*
Tasso H Coin, *Senior VP*
John S Dale, *Senior VP*
EMP: 40 **EST:** 1984
SQ FT: 12,000
SALES (est): 5MM-9.9MM **Publicly Held**
WEB: www.peregrinecapital.com
SIC: 6282 Investment advisory service
HQ: Wfc Holdings, Corp
420 Montgomery St
San Francisco CA 94104
415 396-7392

(G-5365)
PERFICIENT INC
100 N 6th St Ste 935C (55403-1589)
PHONE..................................612 752-1700
Jeff Davis, *CEO*
Hari Madamalla, *General Mgr*
Keith Rassin, *General Mgr*
Kathy Henely, *Vice Pres*
Chris Gianattasio, *Vice Pres*
EMP: 65 **EST:** 1996
SQ FT: 20,000
SALES (est): 5MM-9.9MM **Privately Held**
SIC: 8742 Management consulting services

(G-5366)
PERKINS + WILL INC
84 S 10th St Ste 200 (55403-2411)
PHONE..................................612 851-5000
FAX: 612 851-5001
Ted Davis, *Principal*
Joseph Hamilton, *Engineering*
Karen Severson, *Human Res Dir*
Jessica McGaa, *Mktg Dir*
Jessica Buck, *Mktg Dir*
EMP: 92
SALES (est): 10MM-24.9MM **Privately Held**
WEB: www.perkinswill.com
SIC: 8712 Architectural service
HQ: Perkins + Will Inc
330 N Wabash Ave Ste 3600
Chicago IL 60611
312 755-0770

(G-5367)
PERSPECTIVES INC
3381 Gorham Ave Ste 101 (55426-4277)
PHONE..................................952 926-2600
Jeannie Seeleysmith, *Exec Dir*
Jeannie Seeley-Smith, *Exec Dir*
EMP: 35 **EST:** 1976
SQ FT: 22,000 **Privately Held**
SIC: 8399 Health & welfare council

(G-5368)
PETCO ANIMAL SUPPLIES STORES
7625 Jolly Ln (55428-1221)
PHONE..................................763 420-5236
FAX: 763 425-9550
Mark Meyer, *General Mgr*
Walter I Shelstad, *Manager*
EMP: 39
SALES (est): 1MM-4.9MM **Privately Held**
WEB: www.petco.com
SIC: 0752 Retails pet supplies; animal
grooming services
PA: Petco Animal Supplies Inc
9125 Rehco Rd
San Diego CA 92121
858 453-7845

(G-5369)
PETERSEN HOME CARE SERVICES
12800 Industrial Park Blvd 2 (55441-3974)
PHONE..................................763 557-1126
FAX: 763 559-2484
Mary J Petersen, *President*
EMP: 40 **EST:** 1991
SALES (est): 1MM-4.9MM **Privately Held**
SIC: 8082 Home health care services

(G-5370)
PETERSON GROUP MANAGEMENT CORP
7340 Gallagher Dr (55435-4503)
PHONE..................................952 835-9232
Dave Peterson, *President*
Kay Peterson, *Vice Pres*
EMP: 50 **EST:** 1984
SQ FT: 3,000
SALES (est): 5MM-9.9MM **Privately Held**
SIC: 6531 Real estate management
services

(G-5371)
PETRATECH INC
Also Called: Petraflex
4444 W 78th St (55435-5406)
PHONE..................................952 897-0475
Bill Tawson, *President*
EMP: 30 **EST:** 1996
SALES (est): 1MM-4.9MM **Privately Held**
SIC: 1799 Coating, caulking & weather,
water & fireproofing contractor

(G-5372)
PETSMART INC
1100 W 78th St Ste B (55423-3970)
PHONE..................................612 798-3665
Lee Kanuf, *Manager*
EMP: 30
SALES (est): 1MM-4.9MM **Publicly Held**
WEB: www.petsmart.com
SIC: 0752 Retails pet food; animal specialty
services
PA: Petsmart Inc
19601 N 27th Ave
Phoenix AZ 85027
623 580-6100

(G-5373)
PGW AUTO GLASS LLC
316 W 86th St (55420-2706)
PHONE..................................952 888-0413
Jeff Kritta, *General Mgr*
Larry Anderson, *COO*
Doug Bleisdell, *Manager*
EMP: 30
SALES (est): 10MM-24.9MM **Privately Held**
WEB: www.pgwglass.com
SIC: 5013 7536 Wholesales automotive
glass; automotive glass replacement service
DH: Pgw Auto Glass LLC
1 Ppg Pl Fl 6
Pittsburgh PA 15272
412 434-4058

(G-5374)
PHILANTHROFUND FOUNDATION
Also Called: P Fund
1409 Willow St Ste 210 (55403-2269)
PHONE..................................612 870-1806
John Brentenall, *President*
Gary Lau, *Corp Secy*
Susan Cogger, *Vice Pres*
Amy Johnson, *Treasurer*
Greg Grinley, *Exec Dir*
EMP: 25 **EST:** 1987 **Privately Held**
WEB: www.pfundonline.com
SIC: 8699 Charitable organization

(G-5375)
PHILIP'S INVESTMENT CO
Also Called: Park Tavern Bowl & Entrmt Ctr
3401 Louisiana Ave S (55426-4125)
PHONE..................................952 929-6810
Phillip Weber, *President*
Diane Weber, *Corp Secy*
EMP: 55 **EST:** 1957
SQ FT: 25,000
SALES (est): 1MM-4.9MM **Privately Held**
WEB: www.parktavern.net
SIC: 7933 Tavern drinking establishment;
ten pin center

(G-5376)
PHYSICAL DISTRIBUTION SERVICES (PA)
55 W 78th St (55420-1110)
PHONE..................................952 884-0765
Dale B Robison, *President*
Harvey Fox, *Human Resources*
Kristi Olson, *Manager*
Robert Anderman, *Info Tech Mgr*
Glenn Tyler, *Computer Mgr*
EMP: 25 **EST:** 1978
SQ FT: 5,000 **Privately Held**
WEB:
www.physicaldistributionservices.com
SIC: 7363 4212 4213 Truck driver service;
local trucking without storage services; over
the road trucking

(G-5377)
PHYSICAL THERAPY ORTHOPEDIC
Also Called: P T O S I
2800 Chicago Ave Ste 200 (55407-1353)
PHONE..................................612 872-2700
Mark Bookhout, *President*
Donald Darling, *Treasurer*
Becky Ellis, *Manager*
Agnes Schreiner, *Exec Dir*
EMP: 50 **EST:** 1983
SALES (est): 1MM-4.9MM **Privately Held**
SIC: 8049 Physical therapist office

(G-5378)
PILLSBURY CO LLC
2025 Pillsbury Ave (55404-2337)
PHONE..................................612 330-4003
FAX: 612 330-5200
John Lilly, *Branch Mgr*
EMP: 100
SALES (est): 50MM-99.9MM **Privately Held**
SIC: 5149 Wholesales bakery products;
manufactures canned fruits

(G-5379)
PINES
400 W 67th St (55423-3369)
PHONE..................................612 861-3331
FAX: 612 259-2889
Eme Lennick, *Principal*
EMP: 25
SALES (est): 500-999K **Privately Held**
SIC: 8361 8052 Residential care
facility; intermediate care facility; skilled
nursing care facility

(G-5380)
PINNACLE CREDIT SERVICES
7900 Highway 7 (55426-4049)
PHONE..................................952 939-8100
Sandy Salguero, *Office Mgr*
Joyce Rubin, *Manager*
Todd R Striker, *Manager*
EMP: 30 **EST:** 1997
SALES (est): 10MM-24.9MM **Privately Held**
SIC: 7389 Credit card service

(G-5381)
PINNACLE FINANCIAL GROUP INC (PA)
7825 Washingtn Ave S # 410
(55439-2411)
PHONE..................................952 996-0559
FAX: 952 996-0655
Tony Michel, *President*
Mike Raab, *Vice Pres*
Darrin Juve, *Vice Pres*
EMP: 80 **EST:** 1995
SQ FT: 12,000 **Privately Held**
SIC: 7322 8721 Collection agency; billing &
bookkeeping services

(G-5382)
PINNACLE SERVICES INC
724 Central Ave SE (55414-1121)
PHONE..................................612 977-3100
Nicolas Thomley, *President*
Jill Cihlar, *COO*
Nicole Byer, *Accountant*
EMP: 300 **EST:** 2001
SALES (est): 10MM-24.9MM **Privately Held**
WEB: www.pinnacleservices.org
SIC: 8322 Individual & family social services

(G-5383)
PIONEER INDUSTRIES INC (PA)
155 Irving Ave N (55405-1731)
PHONE..................................612 374-2280
FAX: 612 374-5982
James Chafoulias, *CEO*
Wayne Dicastri, *President*
Diana Bradway, *Manager*
▼ **EMP:** 90 **EST:** 1894
SQ FT: 98,500 **Privately Held**
WEB: www.pioneerfiber.com
SIC: 5093 4213 4953 Wholesales waste
paper; over the road trucking; refuse
systems services; wholesales textile waste

(G-5384)
PIPER JAFFRAY CO'S (PA)
800 Nicollet Mall Ste 800 (55402-7020)
PHONE..................................612 303-6000
Andrew S Duff, *CEO*
Thomas P Schnettler, *President*
David Runkle, *General Mgr*
Michelle Bock, *Managing Dir*
Michael Brinkman, *Managing Dir*
▲ **EMP:** 1335 **EST:** 1895
SQ FT: 320,000
SALES (corp-wide): 468.79M **Publicly Held**
SIC: 6211 Security broker & dealer service;
securities dealer; security broker service;
investment banking service

(G-5385)
PITNEY BOWES INC
10800 Lyndale Ave S Fl 3 (55420-5614)
PHONE..................................952 885-7287
FAX: 952 888-6137
Stephen M Smith, *President*
Daniel Minnick, *Vice Pres*
Cindy Smith, *Vice Pres*
Tim Galligan, *CFO*
Vicki Javner, *Comms Dir*
EMP: 75
SALES (est): 10MM-24.9MM **Publicly Held**

www.HarrisInfo.com
238

2011 Harris Minnesota
Services Directory

▲=Import ▼=Export
◆=Import/Export

WEB: www.pb.com
SIC: 7359 Manufactures postage meters; business machine & electronic equipment rental service
PA: Pitney Bowes Inc
1 Elmcroft Rd
Stamford CT 06926
203 356-5000

(G-5386)
PIXEL FARM INC
251 1st Ave N Ste 600 (55401-1654)
PHONE.............................612 339-7644
FAX: 612 339-7644
Mohsen Sadeghi, *President*
Chris Chiabotti, *Manager*
Henry Camacho, *CIO*
Gary Lindberg, *Exec Dir*
EMP: 35 **EST:** 1995
SALES (est): 25MM-49.9MM **Privately Held**
WEB: www.pixelfarm.com
SIC: 5065 Wholesales radio & television or TV equipment & parts

(G-5387)
PL ENTERPRISES INC
Also Called: Rochford Supply
1500 Washington Ave N (55411-3412)
PHONE.............................612 588-9000
FAX: 612 588-3000
Liz Christy, *President*
Tony Mycka, *IT/INT Sup*
EMP: 30
SALES (est): 5MM-9.9MM **Privately Held**
SIC: 5087 Wholesales service establishment equipment & supplies

(G-5388)
PLANNED INVESTMENTS INC
5900 Schaefer Rd (55436-1815)
PHONE.............................952 920-3890
Kenneth A Gere, *President*
Dorothy P Gere, *Vice Pres*
EMP: 50 **EST:** 1982
SQ FT: 3,000
SALES (est): 5MM-9.9MM **Privately Held**
SIC: 6531 Real estate management services

(G-5389)
PLATINUM STAFFING LLC
7710 Brooklyn Blvd # 106 (55443-2966)
PHONE.............................763 560-8430
Jessica Harstad, *Member*
Ebizimo Nagberi, *Member*
Michael Syverson, *Manager*
Zee Nagberi, *Manager*
EMP: 70 **EST:** 2002
SQ FT: 1,000 **Privately Held**
WEB: www.platinumstaffing.net
SIC: 7361 Employment agency services

(G-5390)
PLEKKENPOL BUILDERS INC
401 E 78th St (55420-1251)
PHONE.............................952 888-2225
FAX: 952 888-2259
Craig M Plekkenpol, *CEO*
Sue Hager, *General Mgr*
Gary Orders, *Senior VP*
Reno Lindell, *Vice Pres*
Dave Goodlund, *Vice Pres*
EMP: 30 **EST:** 1970
SQ FT: 10,000
SALES (est): 5MM-9.9MM **Privately Held**
WEB: www.plekkenpol.com
SIC: 1521 Single-family home general remodeling service

(G-5391)
PLUS RELOCATION SERVICES INC (PA)
600 Highway 169 S Ste 500 (55426-1209)
PHONE.............................952 512-5500
Lloyd Lee, *President*
Lee Waage, *Business Mgr*
Sandra Lee, *Vice Pres*
Marvin Hannon, *CFO*
EMP: 75 **EST:** 1970
SQ FT: 18,000 **Privately Held**
WEB: www.plusrelocation.com
SIC: 7389 Relocation services

(G-5392)
PLYMOUTH HEIGHTS PET HOSPITAL
9200 49th Ave N (55428-4011)
PHONE.............................763 544-4141
Pierce Fleming, *President*
Sara Sedgwick, *Exec Dir*
Deb Cameron, *Executive*
EMP: 30 **EST:** 1980 **Privately Held**
WEB: www.phph.net
SIC: 0742 Animal hospital services; veterinarian services

(G-5393)
PLYMOUTH INDUSTRIES INC (HQ)
2601 Niagara Ln N (55447-4721)
PHONE.............................763 553-1935
Larry W Hines, *Ch of Bd*
Mark Hefty, *President*
▲ **EMP:** 75 **EST:** 1990
SQ FT: 76,000 **Privately Held**
SIC: 5082 Manufactures construction machinery; manufactures roofing equipment; wholesales general construction machinery & equipment
PA: Hines Corp
1218 Pontaluna Rd Ste B
Spring Lake MI 49456
231 799-6240

(G-5394)
POPP TELCOM INC
620 Mendelssohn Ave N Ste 101 (55427-4362)
PHONE.............................763 546-9707
William J Popp, *President*
David Ehlers, *Senior Engr*
Karrie Willis, *CFO*
Sarah S Padula, *Treasurer*
Kelly Kienholz, *Controller*
EMP: 75 **EST:** 1981
SQ FT: 25,000 **Privately Held**
WEB: www.popp.com
SIC: 4813 5065 Long distance telephone communications services; wholesales telephone equipment; retails telephone equipment & systems

(G-5395)
POPULAR FRONT STUDIO INC
555 1st Ave NE (55413-2209)
PHONE.............................612 362-0900
FAX: 612 362-0999
Michael J Keefe, *President*
Laurence Bricker, *Exec VP*
Katelin Shea, *Manager*
EMP: 40
SALES (est): 1MM-4.9MM **Privately Held**
WEB: www.popularfront.com
SIC: 7374 4813 7311 Computer graphics service; advertising agency; online services providers

(G-5396)
POSITIVE BODY DYNAMICS INC
4815 Minnetonka Blvd (55416-2214)
PHONE.............................952 920-9514
Patricia Givogre, *President*
EMP: 25 **EST:** 1982
SALES (est): 500-999K **Privately Held**
SIC: 7299 Massage parlor

(G-5397)
POTTER DAVID MD PHD
420 Delaware St SE (55455-0341)
PHONE.............................612 625-8933
David Potter PhD, *Owner*
EMP: 99 **EST:** 2007 **Privately Held**
SIC: 8621 Professional standards review board

(G-5398)
POWERTRACK
200 S 6th St Fl 27 (55402-1579)
PHONE.............................612 973-3170
Kevin M Armstrong, *Principal*
EMP: 25 **EST:** 2007
SALES (est): 1MM-4.9MM **Privately Held**
SIC: 8741 Financial management services for business

(G-5399)
PPL INDUSTRIES INC
1179 15th Ave SE (55414-2439)
PHONE.............................612 332-0664
FAX: 612 332-4291
Doug Jewett, *COO*
Glenn Heisinger, *Prdtn Mgr*
Susan Gunder, *Development*
Ken Ochocki, *Finance*
Judi Willms, *Manager*
EMP: 99 **EST:** 1982
SQ FT: 36,000 **Privately Held**
SIC: 7361 8331 Employment agency services; machine shop, jobbing & repair services; job training & vocational rehabilitation services

(G-5400)
PRAIRIE LODGE
Also Called: Alterra Brooklyn Center
6011 Earle Brown Dr (55430-2532)
PHONE.............................763 566-1495
Gina Oschlager, *Director*
EMP: 50 **EST:** 2001
SALES (est): 1MM-4.9MM **Privately Held**
SIC: 8361 Home for the elderly

(G-5401)
PREFERREDONE ADMINISTRATIVE
6105 Golden Hills Dr (55416-1023)
PHONE.............................763 847-3525
Marcus Merz, *President*
Debra Shoemaker, *Corp Secy*
James M Fox, *Vice Pres*
Tom Johnson, *Treasurer*
Michael Umland, *Treasurer*
EMP: 300 **EST:** 1986
SQ FT: 12,000
SALES (est): 25MM-49.9MM **Privately Held**
SIC: 8742 8011 Business management consultant; health maintenance organization or HMO

(G-5402)
PREMIER RESORTS LTD
7760 France Ave S # 1100 (55435-5930)
PHONE.............................952 253-2500
Angela Phillips, *Corp Secy*
Joseph Cox, *Treasurer*
EMP: 250 **EST:** 1995
SALES (est): 10MM-24.9MM **Privately Held**
SIC: 7011 Resort hotel

(G-5403)
PREMIER RINKS INC
Also Called: Athletica
15300 25th Ave N Ste 600 (55447-2080)
PHONE.............................763 249-7417
Edward P Van Pelt Jr, *President*
Heather Landreville, *Exec Dir*
◆ **EMP:** 25 **EST:** 1993
SQ FT: 18,000
SALES (est): 1MM-4.9MM **Privately Held**
WEB: www.athletica.com
SIC: 7941 Boxing & wrestling arenas; manufactures soccer equipment & supplies

(G-5404)
PRESBYTERIAN HOMES & SERVICES
9889 Penn Ave S (55431-2912)
PHONE.............................952 948-3000
Mary Loew, *Human Res Mgr*
Michelle Seline, *Administrator*
Pam Klingfuss, *Administrator*
Cele Hodgim, *Nursing Dir*
EMP: 500
SALES (est): 10MM-24.9MM **Privately Held**
WEB: www.preshomes.com
SIC: 8051 8052 Skilled nursing care facility; intermediate care facility
PA: Presbyterian Homes & Services
2845 Hamline Ave N # 200
Saint Paul MN 55113
651 631-6100

(G-5405)
PRESBYTERIAN NURSING HOMES INC
9889 Penn Ave S (55431-2912)
PHONE.............................952 888-9461
FAX: 952 888-2117

Steve Winthrop, *Controller*
Pamela Klingfus, *Administrator*
Ann Thorn, *Exec Dir*
EMP: 300 **EST:** 1963
SQ FT: 21,124
SALES (est): 10MM-24.9MM **Privately Held**
SIC: 8051 8052 Skilled nursing care facility; intermediate care facility

(G-5406)
PRESTON KELLY
222 1st Ave NE (55413-2401)
PHONE.............................612 843-4000
Charles Kelly, *President*
Chris Preston, *Exec VP*
Beth Elmore, *Prdtn Mgr*
Dawn Leuer, *Controller*
Stacy Hintermeister, *VP Finance*
EMP: 40 **EST:** 1950
SALES (est): 5MM-9.9MM **Privately Held**
SIC: 7311 Advertising consultants

(G-5407)
PREVISOR INC
650 3rd Ave S Ste 1300 (55402-1947)
PHONE.............................612 843-1059
Noel Sitzmann, *CEO*
Todd Boney, *CFO*
Tabitha Tziac, *Manager*
EMP: 55 **EST:** 2007
SALES (est): 1MM-4.9MM **Privately Held**
SIC: 8331 Job training & vocational rehabilitation services

(G-5408)
PRIMARY CARE CENTER
420 Delaware St SE (55455-0341)
PHONE.............................612 624-9499
Nancy Kulstad, *CFO*
Tami Ballew, *Office Mgr*
Micheal Aylword, *Med Doctor*
Mary Jordeth, *Manager*
Leslie Milteer, *Physician Asst*
EMP: 50 **EST:** 2001
SALES (est): 5MM-9.9MM **Privately Held**
SIC: 8011 Primary care medical clinic

(G-5409)
PRIME INVESTMENTS INC (PA)
Also Called: Nath Co
900 American Blvd E # 300 (55420-1393)
PHONE.............................952 853-1680
Mahendra Nath, *CEO*
Vance Rossell, *Managing Dir*
EMP: 30 **EST:** 1984 **Privately Held**
SIC: 6282 Investment advisory service

(G-5410)
PRIMERICA FINANCIAL SERVICES
400 Highway 169 S Ste 170 (55426-1106)
PHONE.............................763 546-8627
Lynn Gilbertson, *Vice Pres*
Kimberly Pearson, *Info Tech Mgr*
EMP: 42
SALES (est): 1MM-4.9MM **Publicly Held**
WEB: www.primerica.com
SIC: 7389 Financial service
HQ: Primerica Financial Services
3120 Breckinridge Blvd
Duluth GA 30099
800 544-5445

(G-5411)
PRISM MORTGAGE INC
6465 Wayzata Blvd Ste 304 (55426-1730)
PHONE.............................952 546-6272
Timothy J Oliver, *President*
Mary Aldridge, *Member*
Robert Boysen, *Corp Secy*
Jason Myhran, *COO*
EMP: 35 **EST:** 1995
SALES (est): 1MM-4.9MM **Privately Held**
WEB: www.prismmortgageinc.com
SIC: 6163 Mortgage brokers service arranging for loans, using money of others

(G-5412)
PRISMA INTERNATIONAL INC
204 N 1st St (55401-1404)
PHONE.............................612 338-1500
FAX: 612 338-1343
James V Romano V, *CEO*
Richard Farrell, *Vice Pres*

(PA)=Parent Co (HQ)=Headquarters (DH)=Div Headquarters
✿ = New business established in last 2 years

2011 Harris Minnesota
Services Directory

© Harris InfoSource 1-866-281-6415
239

Ben Clark, *Manager*
Michele Trinkle, *Manager*
Brian Anderson, *Manager*
EMP: 35 **EST:** 1982
SQ FT: 4,000
SALES (est): 1MM-4.9MM **Privately Held**
SIC: 7389 8742 Translation & interpretation services; foreign trade consultant

(G-5413)
PRO MOTION MARKETING
222 S 9th St 2210 (55402-3389)
PHONE............................612 347-1490
FAX: 612 347-1990
Les Mouser, *President*
Bob Safford, *President*
Brent Otto, *Info Tech Mgr*
EMP: 28 **EST:** 1978
SQ FT: 3,600
SALES (est): 1MM-4.9MM **Publicly Held**
WEB: www.cmithun.com
SIC: 8743 Promotion services
HQ: Campbell Mithun Inc
222 S 9th St Ste 2100
Minneapolis MN 55402
612 347-1000

(G-5414)
PRO ONE MANAGEMENT
2400 Blaisdell Ave (55404-3331)
PHONE............................612 813-0077
Jim Tindall, *Principal*
EMP: 25 **EST:** 2006
SALES (est): 1MM-4.9MM **Privately Held**
SIC: 8741 Business management services

(G-5415)
PROCON CO'S INC
3100 W Lake St Ste 100 (55416-4596)
PHONE............................952 258-6300
Ralph J Burgess, *CEO*
Chuck Degreeff, *Assistant VP*
Kevin Daly, *CFO*
Helen Soares, *Manager*
EMP: 30 **EST:** 1991
SQ FT: 6,500
SALES (est): 1MM-4.9MM **Privately Held**
SIC: 7371 Computer programming service

(G-5416)
PRODUCT DEVE
333 Washington Ave N (55401-1377)
PHONE............................612 676-1474
Mike Finnegan, *Principal*
EMP: 30
SALES (est): 1MM-4.9MM **Privately Held**
SIC: 8732 Commercial nonphysical research laboratory

(G-5417)
PRODUCTIVITY INC
15150 25th Ave N (55447-1969)
PHONE............................763 476-8600
FAX: 763 476-4092
Greg Buck, *President*
Malcolm Jones, *Managing Prtnr*
Catherine Converset, *Managing Prtnr*
Kevin Timm, *Corp Secy*
Kathy Manemann, *Accounts Mgr*
EMP: 70 **EST:** 1968
SQ FT: 20,000
SALES (est): 25MM-49.9MM **Privately Held**
SIC: 5084 Wholesales industrial machine tools & accessories

(G-5418)
PRODUCTIVITY QUALITY INC
15150 25th Ave N Ste 200 (55447-2069)
PHONE............................763 249-8130
FAX: 763 249-8150
Keith Summers, *President*
Dan Stenoien, *Corp Secy*
Don Narr, *Vice Pres*
Henri Lamoureux, *Engineer*
Joann Linnell, *Manager*
EMP: 35 **EST:** 1992
SQ FT: 11,600
SALES (est): 10MM-24.9MM **Privately Held**
WEB: www.productivityquality.com
SIC: 5084 Wholesales industrial instruments & control equipment

(G-5419)
PROFESSIONAL ASSOCIATION OF (PA)
Also Called: Path
2021 E Hennepin Ave # 100 (55413-1769)
PHONE............................612 259-1600
FAX: 612 645-0891
Mike Peterson, *CEO*
EMP: 40 **EST:** 1972
SQ FT: 12,800
SALES (corp-wide): 1.79M **Privately Held**
WEB: www.pathinc.org
SIC: 8322 8611 Children's aid society; business association

(G-5420)
PROFESSIONAL LITHO-ART CO INC
807 13th Ave S (55404-1747)
PHONE............................612 338-0400
FAX: 612 338-8055
Craig Hanson, *President*
David Lee, *Vice Pres*
Gary Larson, *Prdtn Mgr*
Lori Whittet, *Human Res Mgr*
Mike Lehne, *IT/INT Sup*
EMP: 54 **EST:** 1962
SQ FT: 25,000
SALES (est): 5MM-9.9MM **Privately Held**
WEB: www.prolitho.com
SIC: 7335 Photographic & movie film color separation

(G-5421)
PROFESSIONAL PHYSICAL THERAPY
Also Called: St Louis Park Plaza Nursing HM
3201 Virginia Ave S (55426-3624)
PHONE............................952 935-0333
Tricia Lies, *Office Mgr*
Cindy Seiwert, *Director*
Linda Quam, *Director*
Scott Lichty, *Director*
Julie Gobel, *Director*
EMP: 50 **EST:** 1987
SQ FT: 1,000
SALES (est): 1MM-4.9MM **Privately Held**
SIC: 8049 Physiotherapist office

(G-5422)
PROFESSIONAL RADIOLOGY SVCS
6300 Shingle Creek Pkwy Ste 33 (55430-2184)
PHONE............................763 560-0010
Paul Mueller, *President*
Wallace Anderson, *CFO*
William E Koetz, *MIS Mgr*
EMP: 60 **EST:** 2000
SQ FT: 1,400
SALES (est): 1MM-4.9MM **Privately Held**
SIC: 7363 Temporary help service

(G-5423)
PROGRAM IN HUMAN SEXUALITY
Also Called: Center For Sexual Health
1300 S 2nd St Ste 180 (55454-5000)
PHONE............................612 625-1500
FAX: 612 626-8311
Eli C Dir, *Principal*
Avram Cohen, *Sales Staff*
Jody Christiansen, *Office Mgr*
Bean Robinson, *Exec Dir*
Eli Coleman, *Director*
EMP: 35 **EST:** 1970
SALES (est): 1MM-4.9MM **Privately Held**
SIC: 8322 8049 General counseling services; clinical psychologist office

(G-5424)
PROGRAMMING SOLUTIONS INC
9000 Telford Xing (55443-3836)
PHONE............................763 424-8154
FAX: 763 424-9518
William C Hill III, *President*
Cynthia M Hill, *Vice Pres*
EMP: 28
SALES (est): 1MM-4.9MM **Privately Held**
WEB: www.programmingsolutions.com
SIC: 7371 7361 Computer programming service; employment agency services

(G-5425)
PROGRESS VALLEY INC
308 E 78th St (55423-4315)
PHONE............................612 869-3223
Catherine Swinney, *Manager*
Susanne Lambert, *Exec Dir*
Mike Kline, *Exec Dir*
John Solberg, *Director*
EMP: 25
SALES (est): 1MM-4.9MM **Privately Held**
SIC: 8069 8093 Alcoholism rehabilitation hospital; outpatient drug clinic

(G-5426)
PROGRESSIVE HABILITATIVE SVCS
4900 Highway 169 N (55428-4058)
PHONE............................763 536-8128
Michael Potaczek, *Partner*
EMP: 25
SALES (est): 500-999K **Privately Held**
SIC: 8361 Residential care facility

(G-5427)
PROJECT CONSULTING GROUP INC
510 1st Ave N Ste 400 (55403-1609)
PHONE............................612 330-0123
FAX: 612 330-0121
Greg M Grane, *President*
James Fragola, *COO*
Kevin McGrane, *Vice Pres*
Tim Erickson, *Vice Pres*
Eric Halverson, *Vice Pres*
EMP: 100 **EST:** 1998
SALES (est): 10MM-24.9MM **Privately Held**
WEB: www.projectconsultinggroup.com
SIC: 8742 Management consulting services

(G-5428)
PROJECT FOR PRIDE IN LIVING (PA)
Also Called: P P L
1035 E Franklin Ave (55404-2920)
PHONE............................612 455-5100
FAX: 612 874-6444
Barbara McCormick, *Vice Pres*
Susan Baldwin, *Vice Pres*
Steven Studt, *CFO*
Liz Bovee, *Controller*
Melony Mills, *Office Mgr*
EMP: 65 **EST:** 1972
SQ FT: 27,000
SALES (corp-wide): 14M **Privately Held**
WEB: www.ppl-inc.org
SIC: 8399 Neighborhood development group

(G-5429)
PROJECT FOR PRIDE IN LIVING
1179 15th Ave SE (55414-2439)
PHONE............................612 332-0664
Doug Jewett, *Branch Mgr*
EMP: 65 **Privately Held**
WEB: www.ppl-inc.org
SIC: 8399 Neighborhood development group
PA: Project For Pride In Living
1035 E Franklin Ave
Minneapolis MN 55404
612 455-5100

(G-5430)
PROPERTY SOLUTIONS & SERVICES
708 N 1st St Ste 241 (55401-1145)
PHONE............................612 746-0400
FAX: 612 332-2046
Catherine Breier, *President*
Steven Plotz, *Member*
Susan Hackett, *Member*
Erin Torgersen, *Admin Asst*
EMP: 25 **EST:** 1994
SQ FT: 2,000
SALES (est): 1MM-4.9MM **Privately Held**
SIC: 6531 Residential real estate agency; commercial real estate agency

(G-5431)
PROVATION MEDICAL INC
800 Washington Ave N Ste 400 (55401-1183)
PHONE............................612 313-1500
Arvin Subramanian, *CEO*
Scott Poellinger, *Controller*
Joost Vrakking, *Sales Executive*
Patty Niehus, *Office Mgr*
Rich Maher, *Manager*
EMP: 105 **EST:** 1994
SALES (est): 10MM-24.9MM **Privately Held**
WEB: www.provationmedical.com
SIC: 7371 Computer software development
PA: Wolters Kluwer Health Inc
530 Walnut St Fl 7
Philadelphia PA 19106
215 646-8700

(G-5432)
PROVIDENCE ACADEMY
15100 Schmidt Lake Rd (55446-3722)
PHONE............................763 258-2500
FAX: 763 258-2501
Lori Determan, *Business Mgr*
Richard Brasket, *Vice Pres*
Kurt Jaeger, *Director*
Colleen Carron, *Director*
David Myren, *Director*
EMP: 85 **EST:** 1998
ADMISSIONS: 860 **Privately Held**
SIC: 8351 Private school; child day care service

(G-5433)
PROVIDENCE PLACE
3720 23rd Ave S (55407-3010)
PHONE............................612 724-5495
Delys Golberish, *Vice Pres*
Jack Nugent, *Manager*
Joel Kelsh, *Administrator*
EMP: 235 **EST:** 2002
SALES (est): 5MM-9.9MM **Privately Held**
SIC: 8052 Personal care facility
PA: Senior Care Communities Inc
161 Saint Anthony Ave # 825
Saint Paul MN 55103
651 287-6408

(G-5434)
PROVIDENT MORTGAGE CORP OF MN
3100 W Lake St Ste 100 (55416-4596)
PHONE............................612 285-6275
Alan Reid, *President*
Tim Sheetz, *Sales Mgr*
Susan Armfield, *Manager*
Tim Acheson, *Manager*
Kent Berdahl, *Manager*
EMP: 30 **EST:** 1999
SALES (est): 1MM-4.9MM **Privately Held**
SIC: 6163 Mortgage brokers service arranging for loans, using money of others

(G-5435)
PRUDENTIAL INSURANCE CO OF
3701 Wayzata Blvd (55416-3401)
PO Box 1143 (55440-1143)
PHONE............................612 349-1000
R Thuleen, *Info Tech Mgr*
EMP: 750
SALES (est): 500MM-999.9MM **Publicly Held**
WEB: www.prudential.com
SIC: 6311 Life insurance carrier
HQ: Prudential Insurance Co of
751 Broad St
Newark NJ 07102
973 802-6000

(G-5436)
PRUDENTIAL INSURANCE CO OF
9220 Bass Lake Rd Lowr (55428-3000)
PHONE............................763 553-6056
Doug Gniot, *Analyst*
EMP: 25
SALES (est): 1MM-4.9MM **Publicly Held**
WEB: www.prudential.com

www.HarrisInfo.com
240

2011 Harris Minnesota
Services Directory

▲=Import ▼=Export
◆=Import/Export

SIC: **6411** Independent insurance claim adjusters
HQ: Prudential Insurance Co of
751 Broad St
Newark NJ 07102
973 802-6000

(G-5437)
PUBLIC MARKETS INC
2701 Brunswick Ave N   (55422-2571)
PHONE............................763 546-3139
Amy Essma, *President*
Robert Pagitt, *General Mgr*
Jessie Davies, *Corp Secy*
Alan Leighton, *Treasurer*
EMP: 48 **EST:** 1973
SQ FT: 500
SALES (est): 10MM-24.9MM **Privately Held**
SIC: 6512 6513 Operators of commercial & industrial buildings; apartment building operator

(G-5438)
PUBLIC RADIO INTERNATIONAL INC
401 2nd Ave N Ste 500   (55401-2097)
PHONE............................612 330-9266
FAX: 612 330-9222
Alisa Miller, *President*
Dan Jensen, *Managing Dir*
Deedie Rose, *Vice Chairman*
Cory Vanin, *COO*
Cory Zanen, *Exec VP*
EMP: 54 **EST:** 1982
SQ FT: 17,000
SALES (est): 5MM-9.9MM **Privately Held**
SIC: 7389 Music & broadcasting service

(G-5439)
PUBLIC SAFETY COUNCIL
13120 County Road 6 # 100   (55441-3847)
PHONE............................763 550-9200
Robert Callan, *Managing Prtnr*
EMP: 35 **EST:** 1988
SALES (est): 1MM-4.9MM **Privately Held**
WEB: www.publicsafetycouncil.com
SIC: 7313 Magazine advertising representative

(G-5440)
QRS DIAGNOSTIC LLC
14755 27th Ave N Ste 150   (55447-4847)
PHONE............................763 559-8492
FAX: 763 559-2961
Spencer Lien, *CEO*
Brad Sorenson, *COO*
Peter Gove, *Vice Pres*
Steve Pacicco, *Vice Pres*
Steve Wilhelmy, *Mfg Staff*
EMP: 42 **EST:** 1994
SQ FT: 7,000
SALES (est): 10MM-24.9MM **Privately Held**
WEB: www.qrsdiagnostic.com
SIC: 5047 Wholesales medical equipment & supplies

(G-5441)
QUALITY BUSINESS FORMS OF (PA)
Also Called: Q B F
5097 Nathan Ln N   (55442-3208)
PHONE............................763 559-4330
FAX: 763 559-5730
Thomas Hoerr, *President*
Thomas Lyngdal, *CFO*
Mike Counard, *Sales Mgr*
Matthew Peoplis, *Sales Mgr*
David Daoust, *Sales Mgr*
EMP: 27 **EST:** 1970
SQ FT: 22,000 **Privately Held**
WEB: www.gbf.com
SIC: 5112 5199 Wholesales stationery & office supplies; wholesales business forms; wholesales manifold business forms; wholesale commercial stationer; wholesales advertising specialties

(G-5442)
QUALITY INSULATION INC
3509 Raleigh Ave   (55416-2625)
PHONE............................952 929-6889
Jon Edwards, *President*
EMP: 30 **EST:** 1978
SQ FT: 6,000
SALES (est): 1MM-4.9MM **Privately Held**

SIC: **1742** Building insulation installation service

(G-5443)
QUALITY REFRIGERATION INC
6237 Penn Ave S Ste 1   (55423-1168)
PHONE............................612 861-7350
FAX: 612 861-7366
EMP: 32 **EST:** 1975
SQ FT: 5,000
SALES (est): 1MM-4.9MM **Privately Held**
SIC: 7623 1711 Refrigeration repair service; heating & air conditioning contractor; ventilation & duct work contractor; refrigeration contractor

(G-5444)
QUALITY WINE & SPIRITS CO
7900 Chicago Ave S   (55420-1324)
PO Box 1145   (55440-1145)
PHONE............................952 854-8600
FAX: 952 851-0501
Jacob R Goldenberg, *CEO*
Brian Emerson, *General Mgr*
Arnold Lifson, *Vice Pres*
George Larson, *Purchasing*
Paul Curley, *CFO*
▲ **EMP:** 100 **EST:** 1904
SQ FT: 160,000
SALES (est): 50MM-99.9MM **Privately Held**
SIC: 5182 5149 5181 Wholesales liquor; wholesales bottled mineral or spring water; wholesales beer & other fermented malt liquors; wholesales wine; wholesales alcoholic wine coolers

(G-5445)
QUANTUM CO'S INC
10525 Hampshire Ave S # 100 (55438-2691)
PHONE............................952 943-4357
FAX: 952 826-0696
David Ellings, *President*
A H Nelson Jr, *Vice Pres*
EMP: 30 **EST:** 1987
SQ FT: 19,000
SALES (est): 5MM-9.9MM **Privately Held**
WEB: www.quantumcompanies.com
SIC: 1521 1799 7217 Single-family home fire damage repair service; post disaster renovations service; carpet & furniture cleaning service on location

(G-5446)
QUANTUM RETAIL TECHNOLOGY INC
36 S 9th St   (55402-3113)
PHONE............................612 486-3491
Tarik Taman, *CEO*
Wyndham Albery, *Corp Secy*
Vicki Raport, *Vice Pres*
Morgan Day, *Vice Pres*
Chris Allan, *Director*
EMP: 35 **EST:** 2005
SQ FT: 6,000
SALES (est): 1MM-4.9MM **Privately Held**
SIC: 7371 7379 Computer software development; computer system consulting services

(G-5447)
QUELLO CLINIC
7373 France Ave S Ste 202   (55435-4551)
PHONE............................952 985-8100
FAX: 952 844-1657
Ron Quello MD, *Owner*
Cheryl Kicker, *Office Mgr*
Stephen A Ready MD, *Med Doctor*
Craig R Hildahl MD, *Med Doctor*
Debbie Pelch, *Director*
EMP: 60
SALES (est): 5MM-9.9MM **Privately Held**
SIC: 8011 Physicians' office

(G-5448)
QUEST ENGINEERING INC   (PA)
2300 Edgewood Ave S   (55426-2824)
PHONE............................952 546-4441
FAX: 952 546-7392
Peter T Kinney, *President*
Michael Clemens, *Engineer*
Kim Curtin, *Engineer*
Mike Kleve, *Director*
▲ **EMP:** 34 **EST:** 1971
SQ FT: 15,000 **Privately Held**
WEB: www.questenginc.com

SIC: **5085** 5084 Wholesales industrial fittings; wholesales industrial machinery & equipment

(G-5449)
QUEST MANAGEMENT ASSOCIATES
1313 5th St SE Ste 100   (55414-4523)
PHONE............................612 379-3800
David Jasper, *President*
Sharon Jasper, *Treasurer*
EMP: 50 **EST:** 1979
SALES (est): 10MM-24.9MM **Privately Held**
SIC: 6512 6531 7822 Owners & operators of theater buildings; real estate services; distributes motion pictures

(G-5450)
QUESTAR CAPITAL CORP
5701 Golden Hills Dr   (55416-1297)
PHONE............................888 446-5872
Robert E Boone, *President*
Kevin Bachmann, *President*
Ruth Howell, *Corp Secy*
John Gakenheimer, *Vice Pres*
Jason Kavanaugh, *Vice Pres*
EMP: 35 **EST:** 1997
SQ FT: 6,190
SALES (est): 5MM-9.9MM **Privately Held**
WEB: www.questarcapital.com
SIC: 6211 Securities broker & dealer
PA: Allianz Life Insurance Co of
5701 Golden Hills Dr
Minneapolis MN 55416
763 765-6500

(G-5451)
QUICK TEST INC
300 E Broadway   (55425-5514)
PHONE............................952 854-3535
FAX: 612 854-4375
Elena Johnson, *Manager*
EMP: 35 **Privately Held**
WEB: www.quicktest.com
SIC: 7375 8732 Information retrieval services; market analysis or research services
PA: Quick Test Inc
1061 E Indiantown Rd # 300
Jupiter FL 33477
561 748-0931

(G-5452)
QWEST CORP
150 S 5th St Ste 3300   (55402-4205)
PHONE............................612 663-2073
Long Hoang, *Technical Staff*
Tom Pardun, *Director*
EMP: 200 **Publicly Held**
WEB: www.qwest.com
SIC: 4813 Wired telecommunications carrier & service
DH: Qwest Corp
1801 California St # 3800
Denver CO 80202
303 992-1400

(G-5453)
QWEST CORP
2800 Wayzata Blvd Ste 42   (55405-2124)
PHONE............................612 381-5202
Trent Clausen, *Manager*
EMP: 300 **Publicly Held**
WEB: www.qwest.com
SIC: 4813 Local telephone communications services
DH: Qwest Corp
1801 California St # 3800
Denver CO 80202
303 992-1400

(G-5454)
R & O ELEVATOR CO INC
1801 W River Rd   (55411-3433)
PO Box 20006   (55420-0006)
PHONE............................612 588-7844
FAX: 612 588-8221
Lee C Arnold, *President*
Michael E Stelzmiller, *Officer*
EMP: 56 **EST:** 1926
SQ FT: 24,000
SALES (est): 1MM-4.9MM **Privately Held**
WEB: www.tyssenkrupp.com

SIC: **7699** 1796 Elevators inspection, services & repair; elevator installation & conversion; manufactures elevators, escalators & moving walkways
DH: Thyssenkrupp Elevator Corp
2500 Northwinds Pkwy
Alpharetta GA 30009
678 319-3240

(G-5455)
R A VENTURES INC
Also Called: Expedited Transportation
2500 E 25th St Ste 2   (55406-4126)
PHONE............................612 721-9155
FAX: 612 721-9192
Bob Anderson, *President*
Tom Brazil, *Manager*
Tom Tabaur, *Manager*
Kim Keating, *Manager*
Russ Farmer, *Executive*
EMP: 112 **EST:** 1983
SQ FT: 12,000
SALES (est): 5MM-9.9MM **Privately Held**
WEB: www.raventures.com
SIC: 7389 4212 4215 Courier or messenger service; delivery services by vehicle; ground courier services

(G-5456)
R B C CAPITAL MARKET   (PA)
60 S 6th St   (55402-4400)
PO Box 1510   (55440-1510)
PHONE............................612 371-2711
FAX: 612 371-7767
Irving Weiser, *President*
Doug Strachan, *Senior VP*
Martha Baumbach, *Marketing Staff*
Chris D Guck, *Software Dev*
Paul Cavanor, *Director*
EMP: 4100 **EST:** 1981
SALES (corp-wide): 26.79B **Privately Held**
SIC: 7374 Data processing service

(G-5457)
R E PURVIS & ASSOCIATES INC
6667 W Old Shakopee Rd Ste 107 (55438-2622)
PHONE............................952 829-5532
FAX: 952 829-5838
Melinder Hiepler, *CEO*
Alesa Koppen, *President*
Robert E Purvis, *Chairman*
Drew Syring, *Engineering*
Sally Purvis, *Treasurer*
EMP: 32 **EST:** 1990
SQ FT: 20,000
SALES (est): 10MM-24.9MM **Privately Held**
WEB: www.repurvis.com
SIC: 5085 Wholesales industrial seals

(G-5458)
R J M CONSTRUCTION INC
7003 W Lake St Ste 400   (55426-4448)
PHONE............................952 837-8600
Robert Jossart, *President*
Joseph Maddy, *Vice Pres*
Bruce McCulloch, *Vice Pres*
Donald McDonell, *Vice Pres*
Doug Hoiland, *Safety Dir*
EMP: 40 **EST:** 1996
SQ FT: 10,000
SALES (est): 10MM-24.9MM **Privately Held**
SIC: 1542 Commercial & office building contractor

(G-5459)
R L BROOKDALE MOTORS INC
Also Called: Brookdale Honda
6801 Brooklyn Blvd   (55429-1715)
PHONE............................763 561-8111
FAX: 763 569-6118
Rudy D Luther, *CEO*
Ken Retrum, *Sales Staff*
Katy Radunz, *Manager*
Curt Johnson, *Manager*
Diane Fenske, *CIO*
EMP: 88 **EST:** 1968
SQ FT: 55,000
SALES (est): 25MM-49.9MM **Privately Held**
WEB: www.brookdalehonda.com
SIC: 7513 7515 7538 Retails new & used automobiles; general automotive repair services; passenger car leasing; used car dealer; truck leasing & rental without drivers

(PA)=Parent Co (HQ)=Headquarters (DH)=Div Headquarters
✿ = New business established in last 2 years

2011 Harris Minnesota
Services Directory

© Harris InfoSource 1-866-281-6415
241

GEOGRAPHIC

(G-5460)
RAG MINNEAPOLIS STOCK CO
Also Called: RAGSTOCK STORES
113 27th Ave NE Ste I (55418-2726)
PHONE......................612 333-6576
FAX: 612 333-3467
Michael S Finn, *President*
Howard H Weisskopf, *Corp Secy*
Debbie Finn, *Treasurer*
Jenn Lesfard, *Assistant*
▲ EMP: 87 EST: 1949
SQ FT: 100,000
SALES (est): 5MM-9.9MM **Privately Held**
SIC: 5093 Used clothing store; wholesales
waste rags

(G-5461)
RAILWAY EQUIPMENT CO INC
Also Called: Cragg Railcharger
15400 Medina Rd (55447-1473)
PHONE......................763 537-3702
Robert Degel, *Branch Mgr*
EMP: 50
SALES (est): 25MM-49.9MM **Privately Held**
WEB: www.rwy.com
SIC: 5088 Wholesales railroad equipment &
supplies; manufactures alkaline cell storage
batteries

(G-5462)
**RAIN & HAIL INSURANCE
SERVICE**
2 Carlson Pkwy N Ste 255 (55447-4468)
PHONE......................763 473-2421
FAX: 763 473-2937
Julie Skeie, *Office Mgr*
Mark Classen, *Branch Mgr*
EMP: 27
SALES (est): 10MM-24.9MM **Privately Held**
WEB: www.rainhail.com
SIC: 6311 Provides mutual association life
insurance
PA: Rain & Hail Insurance Service
9200 Northpark Dr Ste 300
Johnston IA 50131
515 559-1000

(G-5463)
RAINBOW INC
7324 36th Ave N (55427-2001)
PHONE......................763 535-4041
FAX: 763 535-0299
Charles M Haagenson, *CEO*
Paul Haagenson, *President*
Jennifer Ordorff, *Vice Pres*
Jim Trousdale, *Project Mgr*
Bonnie Arnold, *Manager*
EMP: 130 EST: 1956
SQ FT: 9,500
SALES (est): 5MM-9.9MM **Privately Held**
WEB: www.rainbow.com
SIC: 1721 Commercial painting contractor;
industrial painting contractor

(G-5464)
RAKHMA INC
4953 Aldrich Ave S (55419-5352)
PHONE......................612 824-2345
FAX: 612 824-2345
Sheila McGuire, *Director*
Jannelle Johnson, *Director*
EMP: 60 EST: 1984
SALES (est): 1MM-4.9MM **Privately Held**
WEB: www.rakhma.org
SIC: 8059 8361 Personal care home, with
health care; residential care facility; religious
organization

(G-5465)
RAMSEY EXCAVATING CO
4060 Washington Ave N (55412-1742)
PHONE......................612 529-0077
Alan Ramsey, *President*
Teri Vickerman, *Manager*
EMP: 32 EST: 1998
SALES (est): 1MM-4.9MM **Privately Held**
WEB: www.ramseyexcavating.com
SIC: 1794 Excavating contractor

(G-5466)
RANDALL J HERMAN
Also Called: New Hall Animal Hospital
13015 38th Pl N (55441-1132)
PHONE......................763 559-3111
Randal Herman, *Owner*
EMP: 30 EST: 1990 **Privately Held**
SIC: 0742 Veterinarian services

(G-5467)
RANDALL, OMLIE, HAAS
7373 France Ave S Ste 602 (55435-4552)
PHONE......................952 835-5003
Mark R Omlie, *President*
EMP: 25 EST: 1994
SALES (est): 1MM-4.9MM **Privately Held**
SIC: 8011 Physicians' office & clinic

(G-5468)
RATWIK, ROSZAK, & MALONEY
730 2nd Ave S Ste 300 (55402-2445)
PHONE......................612 339-0060
FAX: 612 339-0038
Joseph Langel, *Managing Prtnr*
Kevin Rupp, *Managing Prtnr*
Patricia Maloney, *Managing Prtnr*
Paul Ratwik, *Senior Partner*
John Roszak, *Partner*
EMP: 32 EST: 1988
SALES (est): 1MM-4.9MM **Privately Held**
SIC: 8111 General practice attorney's or
lawyer's office

(G-5469)
RAY N WELTER HEATING CO
4637 Chicago Ave (55407-3512)
PHONE......................612 825-6867
FAX: 612 825-2303
Ray N Welter Jr, *President*
Germaine F Welter, *Vice Pres*
EMP: 40 EST: 1912
SQ FT: 1,200
SALES (est): 1MM-4.9MM **Privately Held**
SIC: 1711 Warm air heating & air
conditioning contractor

(G-5470)
RAYCO CONSTRUCTION INC
211 Saint Anthony Pkwy (55418-1139)
PHONE......................612 788-0077
Raymond Ellis, *President*
EMP: 45 EST: 1978
SQ FT: 30,000
SALES (est): 1MM-4.9MM **Privately Held**
SIC: 1799 Waterproofing service

(G-5471)
**RBC GLOBAL ASSET
MANAGEMENT**
100 S 5th St Ste 2300 (55402-1230)
PHONE......................612 376-7000
John Taft, *Ch of Bd*
Lisa D Levey, *Corp Secy*
Esther S Hellwig, *Corp Secy*
Mike Lee, *COO*
Erik Preus, *COO*
EMP: 75 EST: 1997
SALES (est): 5MM-9.9MM **Privately Held**
WEB: www.voyageur.net
SIC: 7389 Financial service
PA: Rbc Wealth Management
60 S 6th St Ste 700
Minneapolis MN 55402
612 371-7750

(G-5472)
**RBC WEALTH MANAGEMENT
(PA)**
60 S 6th St Ste 700 (55402-4413)
PHONE......................612 371-7750
FAX: 612 371-2837
Irving Weiser, *Ch of Bd*
Peter Armenio, *President*
Jim Chapman, *President*
John Taft, *President*
Jay Hennen, *General Mgr*
EMP: 700 EST: 1973
SQ FT: 190,000
SALES (corp-wide): 26.79B **Privately Held**
WEB: www.hough.com

SIC: 6211 6282 6512 6513 Security broker
service; securities dealer; mutual fund
management services; investment banking
service; security underwriting service;
operators of commercial & industrial
buildings; operators of apartment hotels

(G-5473)
RBC WEALTH MANAGMENT
7650 Edinbrgh Way Ste 800 (55435-5991)
PHONE......................952 838-7000
Brandon Wood, *Vice Pres*
Amy Martodam, *Treasurer*
Katie Tobin, *Manager*
Debbie Leslie, *Manager*
Diane Soucheray, *Manager*
EMP: 75
SALES (est): 10MM-24.9MM **Privately Held**
WEB: www.hough.com
SIC: 6211 Security broker service
PA: Rbc Wealth Management
60 S 6th St Ste 700
Minneapolis MN 55402
612 371-7750

(G-5474)
RDLP FINANCIAL CORP
3600 Minnesota Dr (55435-7900)
PHONE......................952 857-1479
Daniel Kuplic, *Principal*
EMP: 30
SALES (est): 1MM-4.9MM **Privately Held**
SIC: 7389 Financial service

(G-5475)
REC INC
Also Called: Clark, Ron Construction
7500 W 78th St (55439-2517)
PHONE......................952 947-3000
FAX: 952 947-3030
Ron Clark, *CEO*
Mike Roebuck, *Vice Pres*
Cynthia A Volkart, *Vice Pres*
Torrey Kjelstad, *Manager*
EMP: 30 EST: 1973
SQ FT: 6,000
SALES (est): 1MM-4.9MM **Privately Held**
SIC: 8741 Construction management
services

(G-5476)
**RECREATIONAL EQUIPMENT
INC**
Also Called: R E I
750 79th St W (55420-1059)
PHONE......................952 884-4315
FAX: 952 884-2887
Richard Ness, *Branch Mgr*
Barbara W Eytinge, *Manager*
EMP: 225
SALES (est): 5MM-9.9MM **Privately Held**
WEB: www.rei.com
SIC: 7999 Recreation center; curling rink;
ice skating rink

(G-5477)
**RED ROOSTER AUTO STORES
LLC (HQ)**
5140 W Broadway Ave (55429-3506)
PHONE......................763 533-4321
FAX: 763 533-1366
Tomm Johnson, *CEO*
Roger D Johnson, *CFO*
Tim McElroy, *MIS/IT Dir*
EMP: 60 EST: 1934
SQ FT: 18,000 **Privately Held**
WEB: www.red-rooster.com
SIC: 5013 7539 Wholesales automotive
supplies & parts; manufactures motor
vehicle parts & accessories; retails
automotive parts; automotive machine shop

(G-5478)
REDBRICK HEALTH CORP
920 2nd Ave S Ste 1000 (55402-4009)
PHONE......................612 659-3000
Kyle Rolfing, *CEO*
David Poole, *Vice Pres*
Gregg Waldon, *CFO*
John Uribe, *CFO*
Greg V ARX, *VP Finance*
EMP: 69 EST: 2006
SALES (est): 5MM-9.9MM **Privately Held**
WEB: www.redbrickhealth.com
SIC: 7389 Financial service

(G-5479)
REDEEMER RESIDENCE INC
625 W 31st St (55408-2922)
PHONE......................612 827-2555
FAX: 612 827-0450
Mariann Hamer, *Administrator*
Linda Letick, *Administrator*
Julie Prinsen, *Director*
EMP: 200 EST: 1946
SALES (est): 5MM-9.9MM **Privately Held**
SIC: 8051 Skilled nursing care facility
PA: Elim Care Inc
7485 Office Ridge Cir
Eden Prairie MN 55344
952 259-4500

(G-5480)
REENTRY HOUSE INC
5812 Lyndale Ave S (55419-2222)
PHONE......................612 869-2411
FAX: 612 869-0313
Terry Schneider, *Exec Dir*
EMP: 30 EST: 1981
SQ FT: 10,000
SALES (est): 1MM-4.9MM **Privately Held**
SIC: 8093 Outpatient rehabilitation
treatment center

(G-5481)
REEVES PARK INC
5050 Lincoln Dr Ste 470 (55436-1168)
PHONE......................952 930-0290
FAX: 952 930-0294
Klaus H Jung, *President*
Sandy McMillan, *Exec VP*
Kelly Swanson, *Accounting Dir*
Martha Glass, *Director*
EMP: 40 EST: 1997
SQ FT: 6,000
SALES (est): 5MM-9.9MM **Privately Held**
WEB: www.reevespark.com
SIC: 5094 Manufactures precious metal
jewel settings & mountings; wholesales
jewelry

(G-5482)
REFERRAL MORTGAGE INC
7505 Metro Blvd Ste 400 (55439-3010)
PHONE......................952 933-4400
Greg Bertagnoli, *President*
Lisa Piazza, *Partner*
Jason Glassen, *Partner*
Jessica Davis, *Partner*
Lindsey Clausen, *Partner*
EMP: 26 EST: 1998
SQ FT: 2,000
SALES (est): 1MM-4.9MM **Privately Held**
SIC: 6163 Mortgage brokers service
arranging for loans, using money of others

(G-5483)
**REGENCY ATHLETIC CLUB &
SPA**
1300 Nicollet Ave Ste 6000 (55403-2675)
PHONE......................612 343-3131
Gary O Benson, *President*
Heidi D Coux, *General Mgr*
Jeffery Laux, *Vice Pres*
Rachell Kellovic, *Manager*
EMP: 45 EST: 1984
SQ FT: 60,000
SALES (est): 1MM-4.9MM **Privately Held**
SIC: 7991 Membership athletic club &
gymnasiums; cocktail lounge; eating place

(G-5484)
REGENCY HOSPITAL CO LLC
Also Called: Valley Hospital
1300 Hidden Lakes Pkwy (55422-4286)
PHONE......................763 588-2750
FAX: 763 521-3805
Ron Hand, *President*
Jovan Brandt, *COO*
Ken Ellis, *Purchasing*
Lolita Price, *Purchasing*
Lori Kingston, *Human Res Dir*
EMP: 125
SALES (est): 50MM-99.9MM **Privately Held**
WEB: www.regencyhospital.com

SIC: **6324** Hospital & medical insurance carrier
HQ: Regency Hospital Co LLC
11175 Cicero Dr Ste 300
Alpharetta GA 30022
678 393-6643

(G-5485)
REGENCY PLYMOUTH HOTEL
Also Called: Radisson Inn
3131 Campus Dr (55441-2620)
PHONE 763 559-9600
FAX: 763 559-7516
Michael Serr, *General Mgr*
Milestone Hotel Investmen, *General Ptnr*
Carla Monson, *Manager*
EMP: 250 **EST:** 1986
SQ FT: 280,000
SALES (est): 10MM-24.9MM **Privately Held**
SIC: **7011** Traveler accommodations

(G-5486)
REGENTS OF THE UNIVERSITY OF
Also Called: Coffman Mem Union
300 Washington Ave S (55415-1043)
PHONE 612 625-4665
FAX: 612 625-0993
Maggy Towle, *Director*
EMP: 170
SALES (est): 10MM-24.9MM **Privately Held**
WEB: www.umn.edu
SIC: **8742** School, college, university consultant; educational program administration services; state government administration of educational programs
PA: Regents of The University of
106 Pleasant St SE # 210
Minneapolis MN 55455
612 625-5000

(G-5487)
REGENTS OF THE UNIVERSITY OF
Also Called: W M M R
300 Washington Ave SE (55455-0371)
PHONE 612 625-3500
Andy Marlow, *Branch Mgr*
EMP: 100
SALES (est): 5MM-9.9MM **Privately Held**
WEB: www.umn.edu
SIC: **4832** Radio broadcasting station; university
PA: Regents of The University of
106 Pleasant St SE # 210
Minneapolis MN 55455
612 625-5000

(G-5488)
REGENTS OF THE UNIVERSITY OF
410 Church St SE (55455-0346)
PO Box 1171 (55440-1171)
PHONE 612 625-1612
FAX: 612 626-6595
Carl Anderson, *Opers Mgr*
Sandra Gardebring, *Marketing Mgr*
Debra L Amudnson, *Manager*
Amy E Fowlr, *Manager*
Gene I Geller, *Manager*
EMP: 200
SALES (est): 10MM-24.9MM **Privately Held**
WEB: www.umn.edu
SIC: **8011** Dispensary operated by physicians; university
PA: Regents of The University of
106 Pleasant St SE # 210
Minneapolis MN 55455
612 625-5000

(G-5489)
REGENTS OF THE UNIVERSITY OF
333 E River Pkwy 200 (55455-0367)
PHONE 612 625-9494
FAX: 612 625-9630
Jang Yeon, *Manager*
Lyndel King, *Director*
EMP: 26
SALES (est): 1MM-4.9MM **Privately Held**
WEB: www.umn.edu

SIC: **8412** Museum; university
PA: Regents of The University of
106 Pleasant St SE # 210
Minneapolis MN 55455
612 625-5000

(G-5490)
REGENTS OF THE UNIVERSITY OF
Also Called: Division of Pulmonary All
Mmc 276 420 Del St SE 276 Mmc (55455)
PHONE 612 624-0999
Kathie Taranto, *Vice Pres*
Munazza Humayun, *Office Mgr*
David Ingber, *Director*
Wayne Siegler, *Hlthcr Dir*
Daniel Mulrooney, *Hematology*
EMP: 30
SALES (est): 1MM-4.9MM **Privately Held**
WEB: www.umn.edu
SIC: **8011** Physicians' office & clinic; college
PA: Regents of The University of
106 Pleasant St SE # 210
Minneapolis MN 55455
612 625-5000

(G-5491)
REGENTS OF THE UNIVERSITY OF
Also Called: Reproductive Medicine Center
606 24th Ave S Ste 500 (55454-1438)
PHONE 612 627-4564
Van Houlson, *Librarian*
Sandy Feuling, *Manager*
Nikki Bous, *Receptionist Se*
Theodore C Nagel, *Endocrinology*
Mohammed Mitwally, *Endocrinology*
EMP: 30
SALES (est): 1MM-4.9MM **Privately Held**
WEB: www.umn.edu
SIC: **8011** Internal medicine practitioners; college
PA: Regents of The University of
106 Pleasant St SE # 210
Minneapolis MN 55455
612 625-5000

(G-5492)
REGENTS OF THE UNIVERSITY OF
Also Called: U of M Parking & Trnsp Svcs
511 Washington Ave SE (55455-0395)
PHONE 612 626-7275
Arzu Altay, *Manager*
Bob Baker, *Director*
EMP: 50 **Privately Held**
WEB: www.umn.edu
SIC: **7521** College; vehicle parking lot or garage
PA: Regents of The University of
106 Pleasant St SE # 210
Minneapolis MN 55455
612 625-5000

(G-5493)
REGENTS OF THE UNIVERSITY OF
1600 Rollins Ave SE (55455-0247)
PHONE 612 627-4014
FAX: 612 627-4101
Tracy Beseman, *Administrator*
Patricia Finstad, *Director*
Mary Berg, *Director*
EMP: 60 **Privately Held**
WEB: www.umn.edu
SIC: **8351** College; child day care service
PA: Regents of The University of
106 Pleasant St SE # 210
Minneapolis MN 55455
612 625-5000

(G-5494)
REGENTS OF THE UNIVERSITY OF
Also Called: Univ of Minnesota Clinical
717 Delaware St SE Ste 1 (55414-2933)
PHONE 612 625-2874
FAX: 612 624-1446
Luong V La, *Manager*
Timothy Tracey, *Director*
Karen Grabau, *Admin Asst*
EMP: 60
SALES (est): 5MM-9.9MM **Privately Held**
WEB: www.umn.edu

SIC: **8062** Hospital with medical school affiliation; colleges & universities
PA: Regents of The University of
106 Pleasant St SE # 210
Minneapolis MN 55455
612 625-5000

(G-5495)
REGENTS OF THE UNIVERSITY OF
Also Called: Fairveiw University Med Ctr
420 Delaware St SE (55455-0341)
PHONE 612 624-9499
FAX: 612 626-3028
Mary Jordan, *Principal*
Selwin Vickers, *Ch of Surgery*
Linda Carson, *Ch OB/GYN*
John Carrico, *Purchasing*
Anne Ogden, *VP Business*
EMP: 30
SALES (est): 100MM-499.9MM **Privately Held**
WEB: www.umn.edu
SIC: **8093** Specialty outpatient clinic; college
PA: Regents of The University of
106 Pleasant St SE # 210
Minneapolis MN 55455
612 625-5000

(G-5496)
REGENTS OF THE UNIVERSITY OF
Also Called: Clinical Dental Research
515 Delaware St SE Rm 1 (55455-0357)
PHONE 612 626-5722
Fred Berchold, *Pub Rel Mgr*
Delores Caldwell, *Med Doctor*
Ellen Delmore, *Med Doctor*
Bryan Michalowicz, *Director*
EMP: 30
SALES (est): 1MM-4.9MM **Privately Held**
WEB: www.umn.edu
SIC: **8021** Dentists' office & clinic; university
PA: Regents of The University of
106 Pleasant St SE # 210
Minneapolis MN 55455
612 625-5000

(G-5497)
REGENTS OF THE UNIVERSITY OF
Also Called: Northrup Memorial Auditorium
84 Church St SE (55455-0281)
PHONE 612 624-2345
FAX: 612 626-1750
Sally Dischinger, *Opers Staff*
EMP: 25 **Privately Held**
WEB: www.umn.edu
SIC: **7832** College; indoor movie theater
PA: Regents of The University of
106 Pleasant St SE # 210
Minneapolis MN 55455
612 625-5000

(G-5498)
REGENTS OF THE UNIVERSITY OF
Also Called: Dermatology Department
516 Delaware St SE (55455-0356)
PO Box 98 (55440-0098)
PHONE 612 625-8625
Maria Hordinsky, *Branch Mgr*
Maria D Horinsky, *Med Doctor*
Garrett T Bayrd, *Med Doctor*
Angie Meillier, *Manager*
EMP: 25
SALES (est): 1MM-4.9MM **Privately Held**
WEB: www.umn.edu
SIC: **8011** Physicians' office & clinic; college
PA: Regents of The University of
106 Pleasant St SE # 210
Minneapolis MN 55455
612 625-5000

(G-5499)
REGENTS OF THE UNIVERSITY OF
Also Called: Center For Urban Rgnal Affairs
330 Hubert Humphrey Ctr (55455)
PHONE 612 625-1551
Thomas Scott, *Director*
EMP: 50 **Privately Held**
WEB: www.umn.edu

SIC: **8733** University; noncommercial economic research organization; educational research agency
PA: Regents of The University of
106 Pleasant St SE # 210
Minneapolis MN 55455
612 625-5000

(G-5500)
REGENTS OF THE UNIVERSITY OF
Also Called: Administrative Computing Off
1300 S 2nd St Ste 300 (55454-1087)
PHONE 612 624-8865
Michael A Berthelsen, *CFO*
Anne Hetletvedt, *Manager*
Joe Zanmiller, *Manager*
Bell Lacitia, *Manager*
Ann C Mertens, *Pediatrics*
EMP: 29 **Privately Held**
WEB: www.umn.edu
SIC: **7231** College; beauty salon
PA: Regents of The University of
106 Pleasant St SE # 210
Minneapolis MN 55455
612 625-5000

(G-5501)
REGENTS OF THE UNIVERSITY OF
Also Called: Center On Resid SVC&comm Lvng
150 Pillsbury Dr SE 204 (55455-0226)
PHONE 612 624-6328
Ruth Robinson, *Manager*
David Johnson, *Director*
Ricki Sabia, *Bd of Directors*
EMP: 30 **Privately Held**
WEB: www.umn.edu
SIC: **8732** College; educational research services
PA: Regents of The University of
106 Pleasant St SE # 210
Minneapolis MN 55455
612 625-5000

(G-5502)
REGENTS OF THE UNIVERSITY OF
2221 University Ave SE Ste 111 (55414-3074)
PHONE 612 626-4515
John Gehan, *Branch Mgr*
EMP: 40
SALES (est): 1MM-4.9MM **Privately Held**
WEB: www.umn.edu
SIC: **8322** Outreach program
PA: Regents of The University of
106 Pleasant St SE # 210
Minneapolis MN 55455
612 625-5000

(G-5503)
REGENTS OF THE UNIVERSITY OF
Also Called: Opthalmology Department
516 Delaware St SE Fl 9 (55455-0356)
PHONE 612 625-4400
FAX: 612 626-3119
Jay Krachmer, *Chairman*
EMP: 100
SALES (est): 10MM-24.9MM **Privately Held**
WEB: www.umn.edu
SIC: **8011** Physicians' office & clinic; university
PA: Regents of The University of
106 Pleasant St SE # 210
Minneapolis MN 55455
612 625-5000

(G-5504)
REGIS CORP (PA)
7201 Metro Blvd (55439-2130)
PHONE 952 947-7777
FAX: 952 947-7600
Paul D Finkelstein, *President*
Don Klensmen, *General Mgr*
Eric A Bakken, *Corp Secy*
David Bortnem, *COO*
Diane Calta, *COO*
▲ **EMP:** 600 **EST:** 1922
SQ FT: 270,000
SALES (corp-wide): 2.35B **Publicly Held**
WEB: www.regiscorp.com

(PA)=Parent Co (HQ)=Headquarters (DH)=Div Headquarters
✿ = New business established in last 2 years

2011 Harris Minnesota
Services Directory

© Harris InfoSource 1-866-281-6415
243

SIC: **7231** 7299 Retails hair care products; unisex hair salon; hair replacement & weaving services

(G-5505)
REGIS CORP
134 W Market (55425-5521)
PHONE.............................952 851-9999
Gale Smith, *Manager*
Kelsey Nordhagen, *Manager*
Jeffrey Ebeling, *Manager*
EMP: 29
SALES (est): 500-999K **Publicly Held**
WEB: www.regiscorp.com
SIC: 7231 Beauty salon
PA: Regis Corp
　　7201 Metro Blvd
　　Minneapolis MN 55439
　　952 947-7777

(G-5506)
REINSURANCE GROUP OF AMERICA
Also Called: Ing Reinsurance
20 Washington Ave S (55401-1908)
PHONE.............................612 372-5432
FAX: 612 342-7634
Ruce Grant, *Corp Secy*
Joy M Benner, *Corp Secy*
James Millikan, *Senior VP*
Philip Ricker, *Vice Pres*
Mark E Jackowitz, *Vice Pres*
EMP: 90
SALES (est): 100MM-499.9MM **Publicly Held**
WEB: www.metlife.com
SIC: 6321 Accident & health reinsurance carriers
HQ: Reinsurance Group of America
　　1370 Timberlake Manor Pkwy
　　Chesterfield MO 63017
　　636 736-7000

(G-5507)
RELIASTAR LIFE INSURANCE CO (HQ)
20 Washington Ave S (55401-1908)
PO Box 20 (55440-0020)
PHONE.............................612 372-5432
FAX: 612 372-1198
Donald W Britton, *President*
Edward Goldman, *Superintendent*
Tom McInerney, *Chairman*
Stephen Halley, *Member*
Mary Fernandez, *Member*
EMP: 768 **EST:** 1885
SQ FT: 201,000
SALES (corp-wide): 21.61K **Privately Held**
WEB: www.specialpayplan.com
SIC: 6311 6321 6324 Life insurance carriers; life reinsurance carrier; accident & health reinsurance carriers; health insurance carrier service; provides group hospitalization service plans
PA: Ing America Insurance Holdings
　　1100 N Market St Ste 780
　　Wilmington DE 19801
　　302 658-3302

(G-5508)
REM CANBY INC
6921 York Ave S (55435-2517)
PHONE.............................952 925-5067
Tom Miller, *President*
EMP: 50 **EST:** 1974
SALES (est): 1MM-4.9MM **Privately Held**
SIC: 8052 Intermediate care facility

(G-5509)
REM HEALTH INC
6800 France Ave S Ste 500 (55435-2006)
PHONE.............................952 926-9808
FAX: 952 926-4002
Jill Weldin, *Office Mgr*
Pam Halvorson, *Manager*
Ann Taly, *Manager*
EMP: 40
SALES (est): 1MM-4.9MM **Privately Held**
SIC: 8082 7361 Home health care services; nurses' registry service

(G-5510)
REM HENNEPIN INC
6600 France Ave S Ste 500 (55435-1878)
PHONE.............................952 925-5067
Thomas Miller, *President*
Douglas Miller, *Vice Pres*
Dave Peterson, *Manager*
Howard Miller, *Director*
EMP: 60 **EST:** 1984
SALES (est): 1MM-4.9MM **Privately Held**
SIC: 8052 Residential mentally handicapped facility

(G-5511)
REM LEADWAY INC
6921 York Ave S (55435-2517)
PHONE.............................952 925-5067
Greg Torres, *CEO*
EMP: 40 **EST:** 1979
SQ FT: 4,000
SALES (est): 1MM-4.9MM **Privately Held**
SIC: 8741 Administrative management services

(G-5512)
REM PILLSBURY INC
2311 Pillsbury Ave (55404-3219)
PHONE.............................612 871-1954
FAX: 612 871-2115
Stacey Eonzen, *Manager*
EMP: 60
SALES (est): 1MM-4.9MM **Privately Held**
SIC: 8361 Residential care for the handicapped

(G-5513)
REM WILLIAMS
Also Called: Mentor Network
5100 William Ave (55436-2127)
PHONE.............................952 925-3292
Skip Sajevick, *President*
Tara Carter, *President*
Melissa Swenson, *Director*
Shelly Calkins, *Director*
EMP: 25 **EST:** 1963
SALES (est): 500-999K **Privately Held**
SIC: 8059 Personal care home, with health care

(G-5514)
REM-RAMSEY INC
6921 York Ave S (55435-2517)
PHONE.............................952 925-5067
David Peterson, *President*
EMP: 600 **EST:** 1970
SALES (est): 10MM-24.9MM **Privately Held**
SIC: 8322 Social services for the handicapped

(G-5515)
REMELE BASSFORD
33 S 6th St Ste 3800 (55402-3707)
PHONE.............................612 333-3000
FAX: 612 333-8829
Lewis Remele, *President*
Greg Bulinski, *COO*
Dale Wagner, *CFO*
Kevin Keenen, *Treasurer*
Jeffery S Brockmann, *Manager*
EMP: 76 **EST:** 1882
SALES (est): 10MM-24.9MM **Privately Held**
SIC: 8111 Legal services

(G-5516)
REMODELER'S CHOICE INC
13605 1st Ave N Ste 200 (55441-5445)
PHONE.............................612 767-7000
Jeffrey L Howe, *President*
David Klun, *VP Sls/Mktg*
Robert D Heurung, *CFO*
EMP: 25 **EST:** 2006
SALES (est): 10MM-24.9MM **Privately Held**
SIC: 5031 Wholesales lumber, plywood & millwork; retails building products & materials
PA: Fullerton Lumber Co
　　13605 1st Ave N Ste 200
　　Minneapolis MN 55441
　　763 543-2723

(G-5517)
RENEW RESOURCES INC
5121 Winnetka Ave N # 150 (55428-4261)
PHONE.............................763 533-9200
FAX: 763 537-6657
Charlie Baker Jr, *President*
Steve Thomas, *Vice Pres*
Tiffany Godfrey, *Manager*
Glenn Seeger, *Manager*
Tim Lindell, *Manager*
EMP: 25 **EST:** 1995
SQ FT: 15,000
SALES (est): 1MM-4.9MM **Privately Held**
WEB: www.range-systems.com
SIC: 7999 Custom compounding of rubber materials; shooting range operation

(G-5518)
RENOVATION SYSTEMS INC
2735 Cheshire Ln N # 100 (55447-4903)
PHONE.............................763 550-9600
FAX: 763 550-1300
Michael Elzufon, *CEO*
Ryan Comer, *President*
Teresa Picha, *Accountant*
EMP: 48 **EST:** 1997
SQ FT: 10,000
SALES (est): 5MM-9.9MM **Privately Held**
WEB: www.renovationsystems.com
SIC: 1752 Access flooring system installation service

(G-5519)
RENOVO SOFTWARE INC
5666 Lincoln Dr Ste 206 (55436-1672)
PHONE.............................952 931-0790
Timothy J Eickhoff, *President*
Timothy J Skaja, *Vice Pres*
EMP: 25 **EST:** 2003
SQ FT: 6,000
SALES (est): 1MM-4.9MM **Privately Held**
WEB: www.renovosoftware.com
SIC: 7373 Systems software development service

(G-5520)
REPRISE ASSOCIATES
Also Called: Brooks Garden Apts
5550 69th Ave N (55429-1554)
PHONE.............................763 566-5416
Bois Clair, *Owner*
EMP: 50 **EST:** 1972
SALES (est): 5MM-9.9MM **Privately Held**
SIC: 6513 Apartment building operator

(G-5521)
RESEARCH INTERNATIONAL USA INC
8040 Old Cedar Ave S # 1 (55425-1209)
PHONE.............................952 853-9400
FAX: 952 853-9401
Bruce Lervoog, *Manager*
Clyde Drees, *Manager*
EMP: 30
SALES (est): 1MM-4.9MM **Privately Held**
WEB: www.riyssc.com
SIC: 8732 Commercial nonphysical research laboratory
DH: Research International USA Inc
　　222 Merchandise Mart Plz Ste 2
　　Chicago IL 60654
　　312 787-4060

(G-5522)
RESHARE CORP
5051 Highway 7 Ste 260 (55416-2423)
PHONE.............................952 908-0818
Adam Southam, *CEO*
EMP: 42 **EST:** 1999
SQ FT: 100
SALES (est): 5MM-9.9MM **Privately Held**
WEB: www.reshare.com
SIC: 7371 6799 Computer software development; investor services

(G-5523)
RESIDENCE INN
45 S 8th St (55402-2001)
PHONE.............................612 677-1000
FAX: 612 677-0500
Aaron Goman, *General Mgr*
Valerie Wittmer, *Sales Dir*
Steve Nelson, *Sales Staff*

Mike Steverson, *Manager*
EMP: 40 **EST:** 1998
SALES (est): 1MM-4.9MM **Privately Held**
SIC: 7011 Traveler accommodations

(G-5524)
RESIDENTIAL FUNDING CO LLC
1 Meridian Xing Ste 100 (55423-3938)
PHONE.............................952 857-8700
Keenen Dammen, *President*
Christopher Nordeen, *President*
Gregory B Schultz, *President*
Dean Dibias, *Managing Dir*
Kathy M Bevis, *Managing Dir*
EMP: 350 **EST:** 1982
SALES (est): 25MM-49.9MM **Privately Held**
WEB: www.rescapholdings.com
SIC: 6162 Mortgage & loan lending
HQ: Residential Capital LLC
　　1 Meridian Xing Ste 100
　　Minneapolis MN 55423
　　952 857-8700

(G-5525)
RESIDENTIAL FUNDING SECURITIES
1 Meridian Xing Ste 100 (55423-3938)
PHONE.............................952 857-7000
Rod McGinniss, *President*
Bruce Paradis, *President*
Jill Horner, *Managing Dir*
Jeffrey Hilligoss, *Managing Dir*
Alta Jones, *Managing Dir*
EMP: 350 **EST:** 1990
SQ FT: 30,000
SALES (est): 25MM-49.9MM **Privately Held**
WEB: www.rescapholdings.com
SIC: 6162 Mortgage & loan lending
HQ: Residential Funding Co LLC
　　1 Meridian Xing Ste 100
　　Minneapolis MN 55423
　　952 857-8700

(G-5526)
RESOURCE INC (PA)
Also Called: Recovery Resource Center
1900 Chicago Ave (55404-1903)
PHONE.............................612 752-8000
Debbie Atterberry, *President*
Gordon Engstrom, *CFO*
Jim Blau, *Manager*
Todd Lacy, *Info Tech Mgr*
Isaac Prehall, *Info Tech Mgr*
EMP: 75 **EST:** 1956
SQ FT: 30,000
SALES (corp-wide): 25.41M **Privately Held**
WEB: www.resource-mn.org
SIC: 8331 Job training & vocational rehabilitation services; community services employment training program; vocational rehabilitation agency

(G-5527)
RESOURCE INC
Also Called: Spectrum Community Mental Hlth
1825 Chicago Ave (55404-1939)
PHONE.............................612 752-8200
FAX: 612 752-8201
Karen Hovland, *Branch Mgr*
EMP: 40
SALES (est): 1MM-4.9MM **Privately Held**
WEB: www.resource-mn.org
SIC: 8093 Outpatient mental health clinic
PA: Resource Inc
　　1900 Chicago Ave
　　Minneapolis MN 55404
　　612 752-8000

(G-5528)
RESOURCE INC
Also Called: Employment Action Center
6715 Minnetonka Blvd # 212 (55426-3469)
PHONE.............................952 925-9195
Jeff Priess, *Sales Staff*
Janis Shearer, *Office Mgr*
Debbie Atterberry, *Manager*
Gordan Engstrom, *CTO*
EMP: 30 **Privately Held**
WEB: www.resource-mn.org
SIC: 7361 Employment agency services
PA: Resource Inc
　　1900 Chicago Ave
　　Minneapolis MN 55404
　　612 752-8000

www.HarrisInfo.com
244

2011 Harris Minnesota
Services Directory

▲=Import ▼=Export
◆=Import/Export

(G-5529)
RESPONSE DELIVERY INC
8657 Pine Hill Rd (55438-1339)
PHONE..............................952 941-6813
Keith Laronge, *President*
EMP: 90 **EST:** 1997
SALES (est): 5MM-9.9MM **Privately Held**
SIC: 4215 Ground courier services

(G-5530)
RESTAURANTS UNLIMITED INC
Also Called: Palmino Bistro
825 Hennepin Ave Ste 825 (55402-1802)
PHONE..............................612 339-3800
FAX: 612 339-1628
Karen Ingram, *Manager*
Jean L Gand, *Manager*
Jeanpierre Legane, *Manager*
EMP: 30
SALES (est): 500-999K **Privately Held**
WEB: www.r-u-i.com
SIC: 7299 Full service ethnic food
restaurant; banquet hall facility; drinking
establishment

(G-5531)
RETAIL EMPLOYEES CREDIT UNION
3670 Aquila Ave S (55426-3901)
PO Box 4280, Hopkins (55343-0495)
PHONE..............................952 930-0700
Pat Haggerty, *President*
Joseph Schmidt, *Corp Secy*
Jan Tait, *Mfg Staff*
Brad Porter, *Info Tech Mgr*
EMP: 30 **EST:** 1933
SQ FT: 5,000
SALES (est): 5MM-9.9MM **Privately Held**
SIC: 6062 State chartered credit union

(G-5532)
REUBEN LINDH FAMILY SERVICES
1501 Xerxes Ave N (55411-2851)
PHONE..............................763 521-3477
FAX: 763 721-3290
Dorothy Moline, *Exec Dir*
Mary Lagard, *Exec Dir*
Dorothy Mollien, *Exec Dir*
Diana Haulcy, *Director*
EMP: 70 **EST:** 1968
SQ FT: 11,000
SALES (est): 1MM-4.9MM **Privately Held**
WEB: www.reubenlindh.org
SIC: 8351 Preschool center

(G-5533)
REVAMP SALON & SPA
2910 Hennepin Ave (55408-1954)
PHONE..............................612 341-0404
FAX: 612 821-0966
Kayvon Talabi, *Owner*
Kam Talabi, *Co-Owner*
EMP: 30 **EST:** 2002
SALES (est): 500-999K **Privately Held**
WEB: www.revampsalonspa.com
SIC: 7231 Beauty salon

(G-5534)
RFG DISTRIBUTING INC
7301 32nd Ave N (55427-2835)
PHONE..............................763 540-0335
FAX: 763 545-4649
Mark Thoeny, *CEO*
Craig C Thoeny, *Ch of Bd*
Steve Thoeny, *President*
Dan Gustafson, *Corp Secy*
EMP: 75 **EST:** 1940
SQ FT: 50,000
SALES (est): 50MM-99.9MM **Privately Held**
WEB: www.rfgdistributing.com
SIC: 5149 Wholesales pet food

(G-5535)
RGIS LLC
2626 E 82nd St (55425-1300)
PHONE..............................952 858-8319
Jim Olsen, *Manager*
EMP: 140
SALES (est): 10MM-24.9MM **Privately Held**
WEB: www.rgisinv.com

SIC: 7389 Inventory computing service
HQ: Rgis LLC
　　2000 Taylor Rd
　　Auburn Hills MI 48326
　　248 651-2511

(G-5536)
RHM RECEIVER 3211 CO LLC ✪
Also Called: Hotel Ivy
201 S 11th St (55403-2536)
PHONE..............................612 746-4600
Jeff Laux, *Mng Member*
Nancy Pogreba, *Manager*
EMP: 99 **EST:** 2008
SALES (est): 5MM-9.9MM **Privately Held**
SIC: 7011 Hotel

(G-5537)
RICHARD R RODENBORN
4722 Perry Ave N (55429-3644)
PHONE..............................763 533-5155
Richard R Rodenborn, *Owner*
EMP: 30 **EST:** 1960
SQ FT: 1,400
SALES (est): 500-999K **Privately Held**
SIC: 7231 Beauty salon

(G-5538)
RICHFIELD BUS CO
9237 Grand Ave S (55420-3603)
PHONE..............................952 881-1111
FAX: 952 884-9190
George C Holter, *President*
Marilyn Holter, *Vice Pres*
EMP: 28 **EST:** 1959
SALES (est): 1MM-4.9MM **Privately Held**
WEB: www.richfieldbus.com
SIC: 4142 Long-distance bus charter
service

(G-5539)
RICSONS INC
333 Harrison St NE (55413-2407)
PHONE..............................612 617-9480
FAX: 612 617-9185
Richard Strese, *President*
Gary Getchell, *Manager*
EMP: 30 **EST:** 1986
SQ FT: 38,000
SALES (est): 1MM-4.9MM **Privately Held**
WEB: www.ricsons.com
SIC: 4212 Delivery services by vehicle

(G-5540)
RIGHT MANAGEMENT CONSULTANTS
3600 Minnesota Dr Ste 850 (55435-7924)
PHONE..............................952 837-0955
FAX: 952 921-9690
Jim Appleton, *Manager*
Mary Kloehn, *Manager*
EMP: 40
SALES (est): 5MM-9.9MM **Publicly Held**
WEB: www.right.com
SIC: 8742 Management consulting services
HQ: Right Management Inc
　　1818 Market St Fl 33
　　Philadelphia PA 19103
　　215 988-1588

(G-5541)
RITCHIE ENGINEERING CO INC
10950 Hampshire Ave S (55438-2306)
PHONE..............................952 943-1300
FAX: 952 943-1605
Thomas Ritchie, *President*
▲ **EMP:** 130 **EST:** 1945
SQ FT: 50,000
SALES (est): 10MM-24.9MM **Privately Held**
SIC: 5085 Manufactures refrigeration &
heating equipment; wholesales industrial
hose, belting & packing; wholesales
industrial mechanical rubber goods

(G-5542)
RIVER CITY MORTGAGE
6700 France Ave S Ste 230 (55435-1907)
PHONE..............................952 915-5300
James E Dewall, *President*
Dianna Tuttle, *Loan Officer*
EMP: 80 **EST:** 1997
SALES (est): 5MM-9.9MM **Privately Held**
SIC: 6163 Mortgage brokers service
arranging for loans, using money of others

(G-5543)
RIVER SERVICES INC
3750 Washington Ave N (55412-2140)
PHONE..............................612 588-8141
FAX: 612 588-6570
Thomas Conlan, *President*
Jerry Christonson, *General Mgr*
EMP: 28 **EST:** 1991
SQ FT: 110,000
SALES (est): 1MM-4.9MM **Privately Held**
SIC: 4491 Marine terminals

(G-5544)
RIVER VALLEY HOSPITALITY LLC
Also Called: Ramada Inn
2300 American Blvd E (55425-1220)
PHONE..............................952 854-1771
Richard Chapman, *Principal*
EMP: 25 **EST:** 2000
SQ FT: 125,000
SALES (est): 1MM-4.9MM **Privately Held**
SIC: 7011 Traveler accommodations

(G-5545)
RIVERSIDE PLAZA LP
Also Called: Admin
1600 S 6th St (55454-1154)
PHONE..............................612 338-8925
Larry M Mem, *Principal*
Larry Mitchell, *Mng Member*
EMP: 25
SALES (est): 1MM-4.9MM **Privately Held**
SIC: 6513 Apartment building operator

(G-5546)
RIVERVIEW APARTMENTS SENIOR
5100 E 54th St (55417-2322)
PHONE..............................651 291-1750
Ellen Higgins, *Principal*
EMP: 350
SALES (est): 25MM-49.9MM **Privately Held**
SIC: 8999 Miscellaneous services

(G-5547)
RIVETT GROUP LLC
7800 2nd Ave S (55420-1206)
PHONE..............................952 888-8800
FAX: 952 888-3469
Tracey Nelson, *Manager*
EMP: 40
SALES (est): 1MM-4.9MM **Privately Held**
WEB: www.riverhorseestates.com
SIC: 7011 Motel
PA: Rivett Group LLC
　　523 Camelot Dr
　　Aberdeen SD 57401
　　605 225-8524

(G-5548)
RJF AGENCIES INC
7225 Northland Dr N Ste 300
(55428-1575)
PHONE..............................763 746-8000
FAX: 763 746-8227
William D Jeatran, *CEO*
Tim Fleming, *President*
Bruce E Humphrey, *Corp Secy*
Kent Martinson, *Vice Pres*
Amy Peterson, *Controller*
EMP: 110 **EST:** 1950
SQ FT: 40,000
SALES (est): 10MM-24.9MM **Privately Held**
SIC: 6411 Property & casualty insurance
agent

(G-5549)
RLJ BLOOMINGTON HOTEL LLC
2261 Killebrew Dr (55425-1881)
PHONE..............................952 854-0900
Katie Smith, *Sales Dir*
Lindsay Sparks, *Manager*
EMP: 37 **EST:** 1998
SALES (est): 1MM-4.9MM **Privately Held**
SIC: 7011 Traveler accommodations

(G-5550)
ROBBINSDALE CLINIC PA INC
3819 W Broadway Ave (55422-2207)
PO Box 22220 (55422-0220)
PHONE..............................763 533-2534
FAX: 763 533-9356
June Fahrmann, *President*
Carrie Siwek, *Corp Secy*
Brooke Eichstadt, *Corp Secy*
Joyce Johnson, *Office Mgr*
Sue Jordan, *Nursing Dir*
EMP: 28 **EST:** 1972
SQ FT: 5,000
SALES (est): 1MM-4.9MM **Privately Held**
WEB: www.robbinsdaleclinic.com
SIC: 8011 8093 Clinic operated by
physicians; abortion clinic

(G-5551)
ROBERT A WILLIAMS ENTERPRISES
Also Called: Bobby & Steve Auto World
1221 Washington Ave S (55415-1247)
PHONE..............................612 333-8900
FAX: 612 333-2145
Steve Williams, *Partner*
EMP: 100
SALES (est): 10MM-24.9MM **Privately Held**
SIC: 7513 Retail gasoline filling station;
truck leasing & rental without drivers
PA: Robert A Williams Enterprises
　　3701 Central Ave NE
　　Minneapolis MN 55421
　　763 788-1113

(G-5552)
ROBERT A WILLIAMS ENTERPRISES
Also Called: Bobby & Steve's Auto World
7920 France Ave S (55435-5232)
PHONE..............................952 831-6250
FAX: 952 831-8862
Bobby Willenson, *Owner*
Steve Williams, *Manager*
EMP: 48
SALES (est): 1MM-4.9MM **Privately Held**
SIC: 7538 7549 General automotive repair
services; automotive towing service
PA: Robert A Williams Enterprises
　　3701 Central Ave NE
　　Minneapolis MN 55421
　　763 788-1113

(G-5553)
ROBERT HALF INTERNATIONAL INC
800 Nicollet Mall Ste 2700 (55402-7040)
PHONE..............................612 339-9001
Susan Cheedle, *Vice Pres*
Linda Gardy, *Project Mgr*
Steve Kenny, *Branch Mgr*
Sarah Tully, *Manager*
James Kwapick, *Manager*
EMP: 88
SALES (est): 1MM-4.9MM **Publicly Held**
WEB: www.rhii.com
SIC: 7363 Help supply services
PA: Robert Half International Inc
　　2884 Sand Hill Rd Ste 200
　　Menlo Park CA 94025
　　650 234-6000

(G-5554)
ROBERT HALF INTERNATIONAL INC
8500 Normandale Lake Blvd (55437-3813)
PHONE..............................952 831-5970
FAX: 952 893-0833
George Dellinger, *Manager*
EMP: 50
SALES (est): 1MM-4.9MM **Publicly Held**
WEB: www.rhii.com
SIC: 7363 Help supply services
PA: Robert Half International Inc
　　2884 Sand Hill Rd Ste 200
　　Menlo Park CA 94025
　　650 234-6000

(G-5555)
ROBINS, KAPLAN, MILLER (PA)
800 Lasalle Ave Ste 2800 (55402-2039)
PHONE..............................612 349-8500
Cole Fauver, *Managing Prtnr*

Kenneth Freeling, *Managing Prtnr*
V R Denham Jr, *Partner*
Robert Auchter, *Partner*
Keith Styles, *Partner*
EMP: 493 **EST:** 1938
SQ FT: 165,000
SALES (corp-wide): 175M **Privately Held**
WEB: www.rkmc.com
SIC: 8111 Legal services

(G-5556)
ROCCO ALTOBELLI INC
3260 Galleria (55435-4226)
PHONE............................952 920-5006
Laura Grant, *Manager*
EMP: 100
SALES (est): 1MM-4.9MM **Privately Held**
WEB: www.roccoaltobelli.com
SIC: 7231 Beauty salon
PA: Rocco Altobelli Inc
14301 W Burnsville Pkwy
Burnsville MN 55306
952 707-1900

(G-5557)
ROCK BOTTOM OF MINNEAPOLIS INC (HQ)
800 Lasalle Ave Ste 125 (55402-2009)
PHONE............................612 332-2739
FAX: 612 332-1508
Frank Day, *Ch of Bd*
Ned R Lidvall, *President*
Brent Campbell, *General Mgr*
Mark Borowiak, *Manager*
Lou Hernandez, *Manager*
EMP: 80 **EST:** 1993 **Privately Held**
SIC: 7299 Manufactures beer; eating place; bar & lounge drinking establishment; banquet hall facility
PA: Rock Bottom Restaurants Inc
248 Centennial Pkwy # 100
Louisville CO 80027
303 664-4000

(G-5558)
ROLLIN B CHILD INC
Also Called: Rbc Tile & Stone
1820 Berkshire Ln N (55441-3723)
PHONE............................763 559-5531
FAX: 763 559-6579
Brian Mark, *President*
David M Lundberg, *CFO*
▲ **EMP:** 30 **EST:** 1959
SQ FT: 50,000
SALES (est): 5MM-9.9MM **Privately Held**
WEB: www.rbctile.com
SIC: 5032 Wholesale ceramic floor & wall tiles

(G-5559)
ROSENQUIST CONSTRUCTION INC
2541 24th Ave S (55406-1218)
PHONE............................612 724-1356
FAX: 612 724-0511
Jeff Rosenquist, *President*
Greg Reiser, *Vice Pres*
Nina Nieman, *Manager*
EMP: 25 **EST:** 1993
SQ FT: 4,000
SALES (est): 1MM-4.9MM **Privately Held**
WEB: www.rosenquistroofing.com
SIC: 1761 Roofing, siding & sheet metal work

(G-5560)
ROSS CAPITAL PMC INC
2710 W Lake St (55416-4499)
PHONE............................612 929-9222
Michael Wagner, *President*
EMP: 25 **EST:** 2003
SALES (est): 10MM-24.9MM **Privately Held**
SIC: 6799 Investor services

(G-5561)
ROTHE DEVELOPMENT INC
760 Military Hwy (55450-2100)
PO Box 17009 (55417-0009)
PHONE............................612 726-1102
FAX: 612 713-1252
Rob McCandless, *Manager*
William Fauver, *Manager*
EMP: 30
SALES (est): 1MM-4.9MM **Privately Held**
WEB: www.rothe.com

SIC: 8742 8748 Management consulting services; communications consultant
PA: Rothe Development Inc
4614 Sinclair Rd
San Antonio TX 78222
210 648-3131

(G-5562)
ROUSE MECHANICAL INC
7320 Oxford St (55426-4513)
PHONE............................952 933-5300
FAX: 952 933-1688
David J Rouse, *President*
Donielle Gatlin, *Manager*
Gary Danzeisen, *Admin Mgr*
Nancy Stevenson, *Shareholder*
EMP: 33 **EST:** 1974
SQ FT: 8,000
SALES (est): 1MM-4.9MM **Privately Held**
WEB: www.rousemech.com
SIC: 1711 Heating & air conditioning contractor

(G-5563)
ROYAL HOME HEALTH CARE
5637 Brooklyn Blvd Ste 300 (55429-3085)
PHONE............................763 504-4559
FAX: 763 504-4564
Roy Belfrey, *Principal*
EMP: 30 **EST:** 1997
SALES (est): 1MM-4.9MM **Privately Held**
WEB: www.rehis.org
SIC: 8082 Home health care services

(G-5564)
RSC EQUIPMENT RENTAL INC
3200 Harbor Ln N Ste 100 (55447-5293)
PHONE............................763 509-2400
Jane McMurdo, *General Mgr*
Jane Sutton, *Manager*
EMP: 38
SALES (est): 5MM-9.9MM **Publicly Held**
WEB: www.rscrental.com
SIC: 7513 7353 Truck leasing & rental without drivers; construction & mining equipment leasing & rental
HQ: RSC Holdings III LLC
6929 E Greenway Pkwy
Scottsdale AZ 85254
480 905-3300

(G-5565)
RSC EQUIPMENT RENTAL INC
2340 Fernbrook Ln N (55447-4727)
PHONE............................763 557-1234
FAX: 763 509-2450
Tom Deveny, *General Mgr*
Jim Peterson, *Principal*
EMP: 50
SALES (est): Under 500K **Publicly Held**
WEB: www.rscrental.com
SIC: 7359 5082 7699 Equipment rental & leasing services; construction equipment repair service; wholesales construction & mining machinery
HQ: RSC Holdings III LLC
6929 E Greenway Pkwy
Scottsdale AZ 85254
480 905-3300

(G-5566)
RSC EQUIPMENT RENTAL INC
3200 Harbor Ln N (55447-5278)
PHONE............................763 509-2423
Jane McMurdo, *General Mgr*
EMP: 38
SALES (est): 5MM-9.9MM **Publicly Held**
WEB: www.rscrental.com
SIC: 7353 7513 Construction & mining equipment leasing & rental; truck rental service, without drivers
HQ: RSC Holdings III LLC
6929 E Greenway Pkwy
Scottsdale AZ 85254
480 905-3300

(G-5567)
RSM MCGLADREY BUSINESS SOLN (HQ)
3600 American Blvd W (55431-1084)
PHONE............................952 921-7700
Steve Tait, *President*
Lawrence M Hirsh, *Managing Dir*
Douglas W Opheim, *COO*
Rene Ordogne, *CFO*

George Jenkins, *Manager*
EMP: 250 **EST:** 1998
SALES (corp-wide): 3.87B **Publicly Held**
WEB: www.hrblock.com
SIC: 6211 8721 8742 Securities broker & dealer; management consulting services; accounting, auditing & bookkeeping services
PA: H&R Block Inc
1 H And R Block Way
Kansas City MO 64105
816 854-3000

(G-5568)
RSM MCGLADREY BUSINESS SVCS
7601 France Ave S Ste 600 (55435-5971)
PHONE............................952 857-1220
Jody Johnson, *Branch Mgr*
EMP: 100
SALES (est): 5MM-9.9MM **Publicly Held**
WEB: www.hrblock.com
SIC: 7389 8721 Financial service; certified public accountant services
HQ: RSM McGladrey Business Soln
3600 American Blvd W
Minneapolis MN 55431
952 921-7700

(G-5569)
RSM MCGLADREY INC (DH)
3600 American Blvd W Fl 3 (55431-1084)
PHONE............................952 921-7700
Shawn Fox, *Partner*
Steve Lafrance, *Partner*
Mike Hallick, *Partner*
Michael Bevilacqua, *Partner*
Michelle Horaney, *Partner*
EMP: 210 **EST:** 1999
SALES (corp-wide): 3.87B **Publicly Held**
WEB: www.hrblock.com
SIC: 8721 Accounting, auditing & bookkeeping services
HQ: RSM McGladrey Business Soln
3600 American Blvd W
Minneapolis MN 55431
952 921-7700

(G-5570)
RSM MCGLADREY INC
801 Nicollet Mall # 1300 (55402-2505)
PHONE............................612 332-4300
Colin Chambers, *CFO*
Galen Vetter, *Manager*
Dun Natenstedt, *Manager*
Richard Miller, *Data Proc Dir*
Fred Brantner, *MIS Mgr*
EMP: 200
SALES (est): 25MM-49.9MM **Publicly Held**
WEB: www.hrblock.com
SIC: 8742 8721 Management consulting services; accounting, auditing & bookkeeping services
DH: RSM McGladrey Inc
3600 American Blvd W Fl 3
Minneapolis MN 55431
952 921-7700

(G-5571)
RSP ARCHITECTS LTD
1220 Marshall St NE (55413-1036)
PHONE............................612 677-7100
FAX: 612 677-7499
David Norback, *Ch of Bd*
Kelly Vincent, *Principal*
Jim Fitzhugh, *Corp Secy*
Kathleen Linderkamp, *Facilities Mgr*
Jeff Sundberg, *Facilities Mgr*
EMP: 230 **EST:** 1977
SQ FT: 100,000
SALES (est): 25MM-49.9MM **Privately Held**
WEB: www.rsparch.com
SIC: 8712 Architectural engineers

(G-5572)
RTW INC
8500 Normandale Lake Blvd (55437-3813)
PHONE............................952 893-0403
Jeffrey B Murphy, *President*
Jessica E Buss, *Corp Secy*
Keith D Krueger, *COO*
Mary Oman, *Vice Pres*
Patricia M Sheveland, *Vice Pres*
EMP: 78 **EST:** 1983
SQ FT: 31,930
SALES (est): 25MM-49.9MM **Publicly Held**

WEB: www.rtwi.com
SIC: 6331 Fire, marine & casualty insurance assessment associations; worker's compensation insurance carrier
DH: Rockhill Holding Co
700 W 47th St Ste 350
Kansas City MO 64112
816 412-2801

(G-5573)
RUBBER SPECIALTIES INC
8117 Pleasant Ave S (55420-1140)
PHONE............................952 888-9225
FAX: 952 888-9226
James L Sifferle, *President*
Michael R Sifferle, *Vice Pres*
William Hill, *Purchasing*
Kathy Barnt, *Manager*
EMP: 25 **EST:** 1949
SQ FT: 14,000
SALES (est): 1MM-4.9MM **Privately Held**
WEB: www.rubberspecialties.com
SIC: 5084 Manufactures molded rubber products; wholesales industrial machinery & equipment; manufactures synthetic rubber; manufactures rubber products for mechanical use

(G-5574)
RUBENSTEIN & ZIFF INC
Also Called: R Z Solutions
1055 E 79th St (55420-1417)
PHONE............................952 854-1460
FAX: 952 854-7254
Dennis Hymanson, *Chairman*
Karen Hennes, *Accounts Mgr*
Rebecca Glick, *Manager*
EMP: 33 **EST:** 1915
SQ FT: 30,000
SALES (est): 10MM-24.9MM **Privately Held**
WEB: www.rzsolutions.com
SIC: 5131 5045 7379 Wholesales woven textiles; wholesales computer software; wholesales sewing supplies & notions; computer system consulting services

(G-5575)
RULE ONE TRASPORTATION
5501 W Old Shakopee Rd (55437-3116)
PHONE............................952 703-7318
FAX: 952 921-5260
John Ruan, *Owner*
EMP: 40 **EST:** 1991
SALES (est): 1MM-4.9MM **Privately Held**
SIC: 7389 Business support services

(G-5576)
RUSCIANO-HYLAND INC
Also Called: ServiceMaster
6314 Cambridge St (55416-2471)
PHONE............................612 871-4434
David Rusciano, *President*
Joe Highland, *Vice Pres*
EMP: 25 **EST:** 1993
SQ FT: 3,500
SALES (est): 500-999K **Privately Held**
SIC: 7349 1799 7217 7363 Building cleaning & maintenance services; upholstery cleaning services; post disaster renovations service; domestic help service

(G-5577)
RUST CONSULTING INC (DH)
625 Marquette Ave Ste 880 (55402-2469)
PHONE............................612 359-2000
FAX: 612 359-2835
James F Balayney, *CEO*
Galen Vetter, *President*
Eric C Hudgens, *Senior VP*
Kyle Coolbroth, *Vice Pres*
Joann Graf, *Project Mgr*
EMP: 135 **EST:** 1995
SQ FT: 50,000 **Privately Held**
WEB: www.rustconsulting.com
SIC: 8741 8111 Administrative management services; legal services
HQ: Sourcecorp Inc
3232 McKinney Ave Ste 1000
Dallas TX 75204
214 740-6500

www.HarrisInfo.com
246
2011 Harris Minnesota
Services Directory
▲=Import ▼=Export
◆=Import/Export

(G-5578)
RUTH'S HOSPITALITY GROUP INC
920 2nd Ave S Ste 100 (55402-4000)
PHONE..............................612 672-9000
FAX: 612 672-9102
Bill Wanner, *Manager*
Jeff Carter, *Manager*
Carolyn Miller, *Manager*
EMP: 70
SALES (est): 1MM-4.9MM **Publicly Held**
WEB: www.ruthschris.com
SIC: 7299 Full service steak restaurant;
banquet hall facility
PA: Ruth's Hospitality Group Inc
    400 International Pkwy
    Heathrow FL 32746
    407 333-7440

(G-5579)
RYAN CO'S US INC (PA)
50 S 10th St Ste 300 (55403-2012)
PHONE..............................612 492-4000
FAX: 612 492-3000
James R Ryan, *CEO*
Francis J Ryan, *Vice Ch Bd*
Patrick G Ryan, *President*
Timothy M Gray, *Vice Chairman*
Bob Goodpaster, *COO*
EMP: 312 **EST:** 1938
SQ FT: 70,000 **Privately Held**
WEB: www.ryancompanies.com
SIC: 1542 1541 6512 6552 New
commercial & office building construction;
nonresidential building operator; hospital
construction; shopping center & mall
construction; new industrial building
construction; commercial land subdividers &
developers

(G-5580)
RYDER TRUCK RENTAL INC
835 Decatur Ave N (55427-4338)
PHONE..............................763 545-9417
FAX: 763 786-8657
Dan Conoryes, *Manager*
Micheal Kelly, *Manager*
EMP: 200
SALES (est): 25MM-49.9MM **Publicly Held**
WEB: www.ryder.com
SIC: 7513 Truck rental service, without
drivers
HQ: Ryder Truck Rental Inc
    11690 NW 105th St
    Miami FL 33178
    305 500-3000

(G-5581)
S & S SALES INC
1866 Berkshire Ln N (55441-3723)
PHONE..............................763 476-9599
FAX: 763 557-6618
Thomas A Nelson, *President*
Amy Stabenow, *Corp Secy*
Heidi Obrien, *Office Mgr*
Wolfgang Schulken, *Manager*
EST: 1980
SQ FT: 1,000 **Privately Held**
SIC: 5072 5083 5091 Wholesales
hardware; wholesales garden machinery &
equipment; wholesales lawn machinery &
equipment; wholesales sporting &
recreational goods & supplies

(G-5582)
S P S CO'S INC (PA)
6363 Highway 7 (55416-2346)
PHONE..............................952 929-1377
FAX: 952 929-1862
Ralph Gross, *President*
Scott Frace, *Purch Mgr*
Ed Myslivecek, *Purch Agent*
Gregg Kapsalis, *Technical Mgr*
Bill Weber, *CFO*
EMP: 110 **EST:** 1951
SQ FT: 110,000 **Privately Held**
WEB: www.spscompanies.com
SIC: 5074 5075 Wholesales plumbing &
heating equipment & supplies; wholesales
air conditioning & ventilation equipment &
supplies; fabricates pipe sections from
purchased pipe; wholesales warm air
heating equipment & supplies;
manufactures fabricated pipe fittings

(G-5583)
SA GROUP PROPERTIES INC
800 Nicollet Mall (55402-7000)
PHONE..............................612 303-7833
David C Larsen, *President*
Thomas Pantalion, *Vice Pres*
EMP: 64
SALES (est): 10MM-24.9MM **Privately Held**
SIC: 6512 Nonresidential building operator

(G-5584)
SABATHANI COMMUNITY CENTER
310 E 38th St Ste 200 (55409-1337)
PHONE..............................612 821-2300
FAX: 612 824-0791
Jesus Dominguez, *Facilities Mgr*
Kim Keilholtz, *Treasurer*
Bethany Taitt, *Accounting Staf*
Mary O'Keefe, *Human Resources*
Bob Lay, *Manager*
EMP: 62 **EST:** 1967
SQ FT: 165,000
SALES (est): 1MM-4.9MM **Privately Held**
WEB: www.sabathani.org
SIC: 8322 Social services center

(G-5585)
SABRE PLUMBING, HEATING & AIR
3062 Ranchview Ln N (55447-1459)
PHONE..............................763 473-2267
FAX: 763 550-0932
Steve Hucovski, *President*
Jacqueline Hucovski, *Controller*
EMP: 57 **EST:** 1997
SQ FT: 1,500
SALES (est): 5MM-9.9MM **Privately Held**
WEB: www.sabreheating.com
SIC: 1711 Heating & air conditioning
contractor

(G-5586)
SADAKA TECHNOLOGY CONSULTANTS
7701 France Ave S 203 (55435-5288)
PHONE..............................952 841-6363
Rodney Brown, *Member*
EMP: 700 **EST:** 2004
SALES (est): 50MM-99.9MM **Privately Held**
WEB: www.sadakatg.com
SIC: 7371 7373 7379 Computer software
development & applications; custom
computer software systems analysis &
design service; computer software
development; applications software
programming; systems software
development service; online technology
consulting service

(G-5587)
SAFARI AIRPORT TAXI SERVICE
Also Called: United Services
6808 Candlewood Cir (55445-2546)
PHONE..............................763 424-9070
FAX: 763 424-9962
James Ledlum, *President*
EMP: 99 **EST:** 1996
SALES (est): 1MM-4.9MM **Privately Held**
SIC: 4111 4581 Airport transportation
services; airport

(G-5588)
SAFCO PRODUCTS CO (HQ)
9300 Research Center Rd W
(55428-3626)
PHONE..............................763 536-6700
FAX: 763 536-6777
Benjamin Fiterman, *Ch of Bd*
Michael Fiterman, *President*
Michael Borton, *Vice Pres*
David Lenzen, *CFO*
Scott Iannazzo, *Accounts Mgr*
EMP: 138 **EST:** 1966
SQ FT: 191,000 **Privately Held**
WEB: www.safcoproducts.com

SIC: 5046 5112 Manufactures office
furniture; wholesales commercial &
industrial shelving; wholesales store fixtures
& display equipment; wholesales office
supplies
PA: Liberty Diversified Industries
    5600 Highway 169 N
    Minneapolis MN 55428
    763 536-6600

(G-5589)
SAFEGATE AIRPORT SYSTEMS INC
7101 Northland Cir N Ste 203
(55428-1517)
PHONE..............................763 535-9299
FAX: 763 535-0233
Thomas Duffy, *President*
Jesper Svensson, *Editor*
Per-Olof Hammarlund, *Chairman*
Michael Leeds, *Corp Secy*
Bengt A Dahl, *Vice Pres*
EMP: 40 **EST:** 1992
SALES (est): 5MM-9.9MM **Privately Held**
WEB: www.safegate.com
SIC: 8711 Engineering services

(G-5590)
SAFETY AWARENESS INC
13120 County Road 6 # 100 (55441-3847)
PHONE..............................763 550-9200
Gordy Struss, *President*
EMP: 99 **EST:** 1999
SALES (est): 5MM-9.9MM **Privately Held**
SIC: 7389 Fundraising services

(G-5591)
SAINT MARY'S UNIVERSITY OF MN
Also Called: Institute For Corp & Indus
2500 Park Ave (55404-4403)
PHONE..............................612 728-5109
FAX: 612 728-5121
Alana Neil, *Marketing Staff*
Bob Conover, *Marketing Staff*
James Bedtke, *Manager*
Lee Amenya, *Administrator*
Dave Garrison, *Info Tech Dir*
EMP: 100
ADMISSIONS: 950
SALES (est): 1MM-4.9MM **Privately Held**
WEB: www.smumn.edu
SIC: 8331 Job training & vocational
rehabilitation services; university
PA: Saint Mary's University of MN
    700 Terrace Hts
    Winona MN 55987
    507 452-4430

(G-5592)
SAINT OLAF RETIREMENT
2912 Fremont Ave N (55411-1313)
PHONE..............................612 522-6561
Dan Colgan, *CEO*
Marnie Anderson, *CFO*
Julie Sich, *Human Res Mgr*
Marianne Mitchell, *Office Mgr*
Susan Taylor, *Exec Dir*
EMP: 150 **EST:** 2000
SALES (est): 5MM-9.9MM **Privately Held**
WEB: www.stolafcommunities.org
SIC: 8051 Skilled nursing care facility

(G-5593)
SALO PROJECT LLC
20 S 13th St (55403-1917)
PHONE..............................612 230-7256
Shelley Dubois, *Principal*
Denise Doll-Kiefer, *Principal*
EMP: 99 **Privately Held**
SIC: 7361 Employment agency services

(G-5594)
SALO SEARCH LLC
20 S 13th St (55403-1917)
PHONE..............................612 230-7256
Denise Doll-Kiefer, *CFO*
Shelley Duboise, *Controller*
EMP: 28 **Privately Held**
SIC: 7361 Employment agency services

(G-5595)
SALON 4862 INC
4710 Humboldt Ave N (55430-3752)
PHONE..............................612 298-8310
Adair Mosey, *CEO*
EMP: 50 **EST:** 1989
SQ FT: 12,000
SALES (est): 1MM-4.9MM **Privately Held**
SIC: 7231 Unisex hair salon

(G-5596)
SALON INTRIGUE
3070 Excelsior Blvd Ste 203 (55416-4609)
PHONE..............................952 922-0588
Jim Hoppenyan, *Owner*
EMP: 30 **EST:** 1989
SALES (est): 500-999K **Privately Held**
WEB: www.salonintrigue.com
SIC: 7231 Beauty salon

(G-5597)
SALON SABELL INC
1609 W Lake St (55408-2550)
PHONE..............................612 866-3679
Rudy Gomez, *President*
EMP: 25 **EST:** 1985
SQ FT: 979
SALES (est): 500-999K **Privately Held**
SIC: 7231 Hairdresser; nail salon

(G-5598)
SALVATION ARMY HARBOR LIGHT
1010 Currie Ave (55403-1309)
PHONE..............................612 338-0113
William Miller, *President*
Lee Morrison, *Opers Staff*
Brian Rogers, *Info Tech Mgr*
EMP: 99 **EST:** 2000
SALES (est): 5MM-9.9MM **Privately Held**
SIC: 8322 Individual & family social services

(G-5599)
SAMARITAN WHOLESALE TIRE CO
5100 W 35th St (55416-2616)
PHONE..............................612 729-8000
Jay K Halvorson, *President*
James W Dick, *Vice Pres*
EMP: 28 **EST:** 1971
SQ FT: 60,000
SALES (est): 10MM-24.9MM **Privately Held**
WEB: www.samaritantire.com
SIC: 5014 Wholesales tires & tubes

(G-5600)
SANDMAN MOTEL LLC
Also Called: Comfort Inn
3000 Harbor Ln N (55447-5101)
PHONE..............................763 559-1222
FAX: 763 559-7819
Craig Tim, *President*
Juston Arnold, *Manager*
EMP: 45 **EST:** 1998
SALES (est): 1MM-4.9MM **Privately Held**
SIC: 7011 7991 Traveler accommodations;
eating place; physical fitness center

(G-5601)
SANOFI PASTEUR INC
3601 Minnesota Dr (55435-5281)
PHONE..............................952 893-8080
FAX: 952 893-8082
Kirk Edwards, *President*
EMP: 45
SALES (est): 50MM-99.9MM **Privately Held**
WEB: www.immunizingpharmacist.com
SIC: 5122 Wholesales drugs & drug
proprietaries
PA: Sanofi Pasteur Inc
    1 Discovery Dr
    Swiftwater PA 18370
    570 957-7187

(G-5602)
SAPPHIRE TECHNOLOGIES, LP
100 N 6th St Ste 405B (55403-1526)
PHONE..............................612 332-8700
Sandi Henrikson, *Branch Mgr*
EMP: 51
SALES (est): 1MM-4.9MM **Privately Held**
WEB: www.sapphire.com

SIC: **7363** 7361 Temporary help service; employment placement services
HQ: Sapphire Technologies, LP
10 Presidential Way # 101
Woburn MA 01801
781 938-1910

(G-5603)
SARTELL GROUP INC
310 4th Ave S Ste 800 (55415-1012)
PHONE..............................612 548-3101
Pam Sartell, *President*
Suzanne Noll, *Managing Dir*
Paul Jacoby, *Info Tech Dir*
Karen Pavlicin, *Web Proj Mgr*
Chas Campbell, *Web Proj Mgr*
EMP: **90** EST: 1997
SALES (est): 10MM-24.9MM **Privately Held**
WEB: www.sartellgroup.com
SIC: **7373** Computer systems analysis & design

(G-5604)
SAVVYSHERPA LLC ✪
6200 Shingle Creek Pkwy (55430-2128)
PHONE..............................763 549-3540
Mark Pollmann, *Managing Dir*
Mark Pollman, *Member*
EMP: **38** EST: 2008
SALES (est): 1MM-4.9MM **Privately Held**
SIC: **8748** Business consulting services

(G-5605)
SAWATDEE INC (PA)
607 Washington Ave S (55415-1100)
PHONE..............................612 338-6451
FAX: 612 338-6498
Sue P Harrison, *President*
Bruce Harrison, *Vice Pres*
EMP: **35**
SQ FT: 3,000 **Privately Held**
SIC: **7299** Full service Thai restaurant; bar; banquet hall facility

(G-5606)
SAWHOSE INC
4740 42nd Ave N (55422-1828)
PHONE..............................763 533-0352
FAX: 763 533-2668
James R Rothbauer, *President*
Tracy Wright, *Business Mgr*
David Dahl, *Vice Pres*
Rob Hammer, *Bookkeeper*
Sharon Schirmers, *Office Mgr*
EMP: **35** EST: 1977
SQ FT: 12,000
SALES (est): 5MM-9.9MM **Privately Held**
WEB: www.sawhorseusa.com
SIC: **1521** Residential remodeling

(G-5607)
SCHECHTER DOKKEN KANTER
100 Washington Ave S Ste 1600 (55401-2154)
PHONE..............................612 332-5500
FAX: 612 332-1529
Lawrence Andrews, *President*
Russell L Andrews, *President*
John Lawson, *COO*
Herbert Schechter, *Vice Pres*
Martin Kanter, *Treasurer*
EMP: **60** EST: 1990
SALES (est): 5MM-9.9MM **Privately Held**
WEB: www.sdkcpa.com
SIC: **8721** Certified public accountant services

(G-5608)
SCHERER BROS LUMBER CO (PA)
9401 73rd Ave N Ste 400 (55428-1022)
PHONE..............................612 379-9633
Peter Scherer, *President*
Ed Scharber, *General Mgr*
Rachael Scherer, *Chairman*
Mark Scherer, *COO*
Dave Olson, *Facilities Mgr*
EMP: **31** EST: 1930
SQ FT: 9,000 **Privately Held**
SIC: **5031** Retails building products & materials; wholesales lumber, plywood & millwork

(G-5609)
SCHNEIDER ELECTRIC USA INC
9220 Bass Lake Rd Ste 230 (55428-3018)
PHONE..............................763 543-5500
FAX: 763 543-8950
Marilyn Carrington, *Corp Secy*
Zach Adams, *Opers Staff*
Tim Burns, *Sales/Mktg Mgr*
Randy Blackorbay, *Manager*
EMP: **35**
SALES (est): 10MM-24.9MM **Privately Held**
WEB: www.squared.com
SIC: **5063** 5065 Wholesales electrical apparatus & equipment; wholesales electronic parts & equipment
PA: Schneider Electric USA Inc
1415 S Roselle Rd
Palatine IL 60067
847 397-2600

(G-5610)
SCHOELL & MADSON INC
14800 28th Ave N Ste 140 (55447-4826)
PHONE..............................763 746-1600
Dana Swindler, *Ch of Bd*
Ken Adolf, *President*
John Karwacki, *Project Mgr*
Steven Janson, *CFO*
Lisa Mazzitello, *Controller*
EMP: **46** EST: 1956
SQ FT: 11,000
SALES (est): 5MM-9.9MM **Privately Held**
SIC: **8711** 0781 8713 8731 8742 Engineering consulting services; management consulting services; landscape services; landscape planning services; environmental research laboratory; surveying service

(G-5611)
SCHOENECKERS INC
7760 Bush Lake Rd (55439-2811)
PHONE..............................952 835-4800
Guy Schoenecker, *Chairman*
EMP: **1000**
SALES (est): 50MM-99.9MM **Privately Held**
WEB: www.schoeneckers.com
SIC: **8721** Billing & bookkeeping services
PA: Schoeneckers Inc
7630 Bush Lake Rd
Edina MN 55439
952 835-4800

(G-5612)
SCHOLARSHIP AMERICA
Also Called: Dollars For Scholars
1550 Amrcn Blvd E Ste 155 (55425)
PHONE..............................952 830-7300
FAX: 952 830-1929
Lauren Segal, *CEO*
Anne Cheney, *Controller*
Michelle Showalter, *Manager*
Patsy Rossow, *Technology*
Brian L Donnelly, *Bd of Directors*
EMP: **150** EST: 1955 **Privately Held**
SIC: **8399** 8748 Non-fee basis fund raising organization; educational consulting services

(G-5613)
SCHOLASTIC BOOK FAIRS INC
9201 Wyoming Ave N Ste 102 (55445-1852)
PHONE..............................763 391-0930
FAX: 763 391-0940
Gail Kelly, *Regional Mgr*
Deann Ruttfish, *Manager*
EMP: **70**
SALES (est): 25MM-49.9MM **Publicly Held**
WEB: www.scholastic.com
SIC: **5192** 5199 Wholesales books; wholesales posters
HQ: Scholastic Book Fairs Inc
1080 Greenwood Blvd
Lake Mary FL 32746
407 829-7300

(G-5614)
SCHROEDER MOVING SYSTEMS INC
2405 Annapolis Ln N # 270 (55441-3633)
PHONE..............................763 694-6070
Linda Schroeder, *Manager*
EMP: **40**
SALES (est): 1MM-4.9MM **Privately Held**
WEB: www.freemovingestimates.com
SIC: **4212** Local moving service
PA: Schroeder Moving Systems Inc
1203 33rd St S
Saint Cloud MN 56301
320 252-2771

(G-5615)
SCHUM DRYWALL CO INC
815 W 106th St (55420-5603)
PHONE..............................952 881-3350
Robert H Schum, *President*
EMP: **70** EST: 1973
SALES (est): 5MM-9.9MM **Privately Held**
WEB: www.schumdrywall.com
SIC: **1742** Drywall contractor

(G-5616)
SCHUMACHER WHOLESALE MEATS INC
Also Called: Bringgold Wholesale Meats
1114 Zane Ave N (55422-4606)
PHONE..............................763 546-3291
FAX: 763 546-0053
John F Schumacher, *President*
Collin Ruch, *General Mgr*
Bob Timm, *Vice Pres*
Paul Tempka, *Human Res Mgr*
EMP: **28** EST: 1957
SQ FT: 20,000
SALES (est): 25MM-49.9MM **Privately Held**
WEB: www.schumeats.com
SIC: **5147** Wholesales meat & meat products

(G-5617)
SCHWEBEL, GOETZ, & SIEBEN
80 S 8th St Ste 5120 (55402-2227)
PHONE..............................612 333-8361
FAX: 612 333-6311
James R Schwebel, *President*
Tammy Offerman, *Marketing Mgr*
Lisa McIntyre, *Administrator*
Chris Hasse, *MIS Mgr*
Paul Godlewski, *Shareholder*
EMP: **74** EST: 1975
SQ FT: 3,100
SALES (est): 10MM-24.9MM **Privately Held**
WEB: www.schwebel.com
SIC: **8111** General practice attorney's or lawyer's office

(G-5618)
SCHWEGMAN, LUNDBERG & WOESSNER
121 S 8th St Ste 1600 (55402-2843)
PHONE..............................612 373-6900
Michael Schwegman, *Ch of Bd*
Steven Lundberg, *President*
Warren Woessner, *Corp Secy*
Catherine Klima, *Vice Pres*
Dan Kluth, *CFO*
EMP: **90** EST: 1993
SQ FT: 22,000
SALES (est): 25MM-49.9MM **Privately Held**
SIC: **6794** Copyright buying & licensing

(G-5619)
SCOTT R MCGARVEY MD
7373 France Ave S Ste 312 (55435-4549)
PHONE..............................952 832-0076
Scott R McGarvey MD, *Principal*
EMP: **50**
SALES (est): 5MM-9.9MM **Privately Held**
SIC: **8011** Physicians' office & clinic

(G-5620)
SCOULAR CO
400 S 4th St (55415-1411)
PHONE..............................612 335-8700
Doug Grennan, *Manager*
EMP: **53**
SALES (est): 100MM-499.9MM **Privately Held**
WEB: www.scoular.com
SIC: **5153** Wholesales grain & field beans
PA: Scoular Co
2027 Dodge St Ste 500
Omaha NE 68102
402 342-3500

(G-5621)
SEABURY GROUP L L C
730 2nd Ave S Ste 730 (55402-2449)
PHONE..............................612 399-0033
Marty Kuehne, *Branch Mgr*
EMP: **30**
SALES (est): 1MM-4.9MM **Privately Held**
SIC: **8742** General management consultant

(G-5622)
SEARCH INSTITUTE
615 1st Ave NE Ste 125 (55413-2677)
PHONE..............................612 376-8955
FAX: 612 376-8956
Peter Benson, *President*
Eugene C Roehlkepartain, *Vice Pres*
Paul Krist, *CFO*
Robert A Rudell, *Treasurer*
Kwenen Nelson, *Marketing Staff*
EMP: **50** EST: 1966
SQ FT: 20,000
SALES (est): 1MM-4.9MM **Privately Held**
WEB: www.search-institute.org
SIC: **8732** Sociological research services

(G-5623)
SEARS LOGISTICS SERVICES INC
2700 Winter St NE Ste 8 (55413-2963)
PHONE..............................612 379-5600
FAX: 612 379-5904
Dennis Helmer, *Manager*
EMP: **25**
SALES (est): 1MM-4.9MM **Publicly Held**
WEB: www.slslogistics.com+%22sears+logistics+servi
SIC: **4731** Shipping agent
DH: Sears Logistics Services Inc
3333 Beverly Rd
Hoffman Estates IL 60192
847 645-5100

(G-5624)
SECOND HARVEST HEARTLAND
3100 California St NE (55418-1808)
PHONE..............................612 209-7980
Craig Hoffman, *Manager*
Dan Harty, *Manager*
R J Brown, *Exec Dir*
EMP: **90** EST: 1984
SALES (est): 1MM-4.9MM **Privately Held**
SIC: **8322** Individual & family social services

(G-5625)
SECURITY AUTO LOANS INC
4900 Highway 169 N # 205 (55428-4017)
PHONE..............................763 559-5892
Richard Bernstein, *CEO*
Bill McGuigan, *Corp Secy*
Dima Kuperman, *Vice Pres*
Vince O'Connell, *Treasurer*
Amber Lebow, *Office Mgr*
EMP: **30** EST: 2003
SALES (est): 10MM-24.9MM **Privately Held**
SIC: **6153** Short-term business credit for factoring services

(G-5626)
SECURITY RESPONSE SERVICES INC
9036 Grand Ave S (55420-3634)
PHONE..............................952 346-8922
Michael Karch, *CEO*
Robert Bossert, *President*
Beverly Karch, *Vice Pres*
Rob Riley, *Technical Staff*
EMP: **25** EST: 1998
SQ FT: 2,800
SALES (est): 1MM-4.9MM **Privately Held**
WEB: www.floydtotalsecurity.com
SIC: **7382** Burglar alarm maintenance & monitoring service
PA: Floyd Lock & Safe Co
9036 Grand Ave S
Minneapolis MN 55420
952 881-5625

(G-5627)
SEELYE PLASTICS INC
9700 Newton Ave S # 9702 (55431-2529)
PHONE..............................952 881-2658
FAX: 952 881-6203

www.HarrisInfo.com
248

2011 Harris Minnesota
Services Directory

▲=Import ▼=Export
◆=Import/Export

Richard F Mc Namara, *CEO*
James Reissner, *President*
Paula Brisson, *Corp Secy*
Corinne Dien, *Purch Mgr*
Kennedy Swanson, *Purch Mgr*
EMP: 100 **EST:** 1994
SQ FT: 50,000
SALES (est): 50MM-99.9MM **Privately Held**
WEB: www.activar.com
SIC: 5074 Wholesales plastic pipes & fittings; manufactures processed plastics; wholesales plumbing fittings & supplies
PA: Activar Inc
7808 Creekridge Cir # 200
Minneapolis MN 55439
952 944-3533

(G-5628)
SEH TECHNOLOGY SOLUTIONS INC
100 N 6th St Ste 710C (55403-1515)
PHONE 612 758-6728
Robert Shevik, *President*
Angela Fischels, *Manager*
EMP: 30 **EST:** 2002
SALES (est): 1MM-4.9MM **Privately Held**
WEB: www.sehts.com
SIC: 7379 Computer system consulting services
PA: Short-Elliott-Hendrickson Inc
3535 Vadnais Center Dr # 200
Saint Paul MN 55110
651 490-2000

(G-5629)
SEL-MOR DISTRIBUTING CO
Also Called: S M D Sel-Mor
6520 W Lake St (55426-4205)
PHONE 952 929-0888
FAX: 952 929-7970
A H Lieberman, *Owner*
EMP: 40
SQ FT: 10,000
SALES (est): 10MM-24.9MM **Privately Held**
SIC: 5044 5065 7629 7699 Wholesales photocopy machines; wholesales telephone equipment; wholesales facsimile or fax equipment; telephone set repair service; photocopy machine repair service

(G-5630)
SELA INVESTMENTS LTD, LLP
4915 W 35th St Ste 201 (55416-2658)
PHONE 952 925-3878
FAX: 952 928-3832
Amy Gonyea, *General Mgr*
Paz Sela, *Member*
EMP: 50 **EST:** 1988
SQ FT: 10,000
SALES (est): 5MM-9.9MM **Privately Held**
WEB: www.selainvestments.com
SIC: 6531 Real estate services

(G-5631)
SELA ROOFING & REMODELING INC (PA)
4100 Excelsior Blvd (55416-4727)
PHONE 612 823-8046
FAX: 612 823-1078
Paz Sela, *President*
Amit Sela, *Vice Pres*
Scott Oaks, *Branch Mgr*
Lance Holk, *Manager*
Debbie Peterson, *Manager*
EMP: 80 **EST:** 1982
SQ FT: 6,000 **Privately Held**
WEB: www.selaroofing.com
SIC: 1521 1761 Single-family home general remodeling service; roofing contractor

(G-5632)
SELA ROOFING & REMODELING INC
3400 48th Ave N (55429-3927)
PHONE 763 592-5420
Deanna Ulick, *Branch Mgr*
EMP: 25
SALES (est): 1MM-4.9MM **Privately Held**
WEB: www.selaroofing.com
SIC: 1761 1521 Roofing contractor; single-family home general remodeling service; siding contractor
PA: Sela Roofing & Remodeling Inc
4100 Excelsior Blvd
Minneapolis MN 55416
612 823-8046

(G-5633)
SELECT COMMUNICATIONS INC
12975 16th Ave N Ste 100 (55441-4549)
PHONE 763 744-0900
FAX: 763 744-0901
Scott Alexander, *CEO*
Robert Alexander Jr, *President*
Chris Hansen, *Vice Pres*
Bob Adams, *CFO*
EMP: 50 **EST:** 2000 **Privately Held**
SIC: 4813 Data telephone communications services

(G-5634)
SELECT INN OF BLOOMINGTON LP
7851 Normandale Blvd (55435-5304)
PHONE 952 835-7400
FAX: 952 835-4124
Spencer Schram, *Partner*
Scott Timmington, *General Ptnr*
EMP: 40 **EST:** 1991
SALES (est): 1MM-4.9MM **Privately Held**
SIC: 7011 Hotel

(G-5635)
SELFTEK
Also Called: Design Systems
2722 Irving Ave S (55408-1049)
PHONE 612 872-1285
Stephen Crook, *Principal*
John Carrol, *Vice Pres*
EMP: 45 **EST:** 1996
SALES (est): 5MM-9.9MM **Privately Held**
WEB: www.selftek.com
SIC: 8742 Marketing consulting service

(G-5636)
SENIOR ASSET MANAGEMENT INC
Also Called: Grace Management
6225 42nd Ave N (55422-1603)
PHONE 763 544-9934
Eugene W Grace, *President*
Marijoe Grace, *Senior VP*
Jody Boedigheimar, *Vice Pres*
EMP: 500 **EST:** 2002
SALES (est): 25MM-49.9MM **Privately Held**
WEB: www.gracemanagement.com
SIC: 8741 Management services

(G-5637)
SENIOR HEALTH & HOME CARE INC
6332 Millers Ln (55424-1849)
PHONE 952 920-9399
Barbara Mahony, *President*
EMP: 25 **EST:** 1992
SALES (est): 500-999K **Privately Held**
SIC: 8082 Home health care services

(G-5638)
SENTAGE CORP
Also Called: Boos Dental Lab
801 12th Ave N (55411-4230)
PHONE 612 529-9655
FAX: 612 529-6918
Matt Beckridge, *General Mgr*
Tom Marynak, *Manager*
EMP: 47
SALES (est): 1MM-4.9MM **Privately Held**
WEB: www.dentalservices.net
SIC: 8072 Dental laboratory
PA: Sentage Corp
5775 Wayzata Blvd Ste 890
Minneapolis MN 55416
952 541-9622

(G-5639)
SETTER LEACH & LINDSTROM INC
730 2nd Ave S Ste 1100 (55402-2455)
PHONE 612 338-8741
Robert Egge, *President*
George Theodore, *Chairman*
Jerome A Ritter, *Corp Secy*
Jerome Rittet, *Corp Secy*
Richard C Speers, *Corp Secy*
EMP: 85 **EST:** 1917
SQ FT: 50,000
SALES (est): 10MM-24.9MM **Privately Held**

SIC: 8712 8711 Architectural service; engineering services

(G-5640)
SEVE ENTERPRISES INC
100 S 5th St Fl 19 (55402-1210)
PHONE 612 605-6230
Syreeta Edwards, *President*
EMP: 25
SALES (est): 500-999K **Privately Held**
SIC: 7991 Spas

(G-5641)
SEVEN CORNERS HOTEL PARTNERS (PA)
Also Called: Holiday Inn
1500 Washington Ave S (55454-1067)
PHONE 612 333-4646
Larry Lamont, *General Ptnr*
Michael Borum, *Sales Dir*
Marilyne Bouteiller, *Marketing Staff*
Erica Hyde, *Manager*
EMP: 105 **EST:** 1984
SQ FT: 190,000
SALES (corp-wide): 7.90M **Privately Held**
WEB: www.metrodome.com
SIC: 7011 Traveler accommodations; bar; eating place

(G-5642)
SEVEN CORNERS HOTEL PARTNERS
Also Called: Holiday Inn
1500 Washington Ave S (55454-1067)
PHONE 612 333-4646
Larry Lamont, *General Mgr*
Barm Michael, *Sales Executive*
Turek Evan, *Manager*
EMP: 35
SALES (est): 1MM-4.9MM **Privately Held**
WEB: www.metrodome.com
SIC: 7011 Traveler accommodations
PA: Seven Corners Hotel Partners
1500 Washington Ave S
Minneapolis MN 55454
612 333-4646

(G-5643)
78TH STREET LEASECO LLC
Also Called: Hotel Sofitel
5601 W 78th St (55439-3105)
PHONE 952 835-1900
FAX: 952 835-7020
David Larson, *Facilities Mgr*
Terri Trodhomme, *Controller*
Abeer Taha, *Credit Mgr*
Michela Renchin, *Human Res Dir*
Amy Lewis, *Marketing Staff*
EMP: 270 **EST:** 1979
SQ FT: 250,000
SALES (est): 10MM-24.9MM **Privately Held**
SIC: 7011 Hotel; bar; cocktail lounge; full service French restaurant

(G-5644)
SEVENTY-FIVE HUNDRED YORK
7500 York Ave S (55435-5633)
PHONE 952 835-1010
FAX: 952 835-2154
Perry Strassman, *General Mgr*
Lex Schoonover, *Principal*
Bill Rosen, *Principal*
Jeff Lantto, *Sales Staff*
EMP: 75 **EST:** 1978 **Privately Held**
WEB: www.7500york.com
SIC: 8641 Dwelling-related associations

(G-5645)
SEWARD CSP
2105 Minnehaha Ave (55404-3107)
PHONE 612 333-0331
FAX: 612 333-5614
Nancy Abramson, *CEO*
EMP: 25 **EST:** 1995 **Privately Held**
SIC: 8399 Social services

(G-5646)
SFN GROUP INC
5601 Green Valley Dr # 200 (55437-1173)
PHONE 952 543-3300
FAX: 952 543-3325
David Bell, *Manager*
EMP: 200
SALES (est): 1MM-4.9MM **Publicly Held**

SIC: 7363 Temporary help service
PA: Sfn Group Inc
2050 Spectrum Blvd
Fort Lauderdale FL 33309
954 308-7600

(G-5647)
SHADE WARREN CO
600 Hoover St NE (55413-2903)
PHONE 612 331-5939
FAX: 612 331-9116
Michael Mann, *President*
Jim Woodworth, *General Mgr*
Bill Mann, *VP Opers-Prdtn-*
Bruce Nelson, *Controller*
EMP: 58 **EST:** 1910
SQ FT: 21,000
SALES (est): 10MM-24.9MM **Privately Held**
WEB: www.warrenshade.com
SIC: 5023 Wholesales window furnishings; manufactures window blinds; wholesales draperies; manufactures draperies & curtains

(G-5648)
SHANER HOTEL GROUP LP
Also Called: Hawthorn Suites
3400 Edinborough Way (55435-5255)
PHONE 952 893-9300
FAX: 952 893-9885
Melodee York, *General Mgr*
EMP: 60
SALES (est): 1MM-4.9MM **Privately Held**
SIC: 7011 Traveler accommodations
PA: Shaner Hotel Group LP
1965 Waddle Rd
State College PA 16803
814 234-4460

(G-5649)
SHARI K BRUNING DDS
Also Called: Basset Creek Dental
5851 Duluth St Ste 100 (55422-3955)
PHONE 763 546-1301
Steve Nelson DDS, *Partner*
EMP: 34 **EST:** 2000
SALES (est): 1MM-4.9MM **Privately Held**
SIC: 8021 Dental clinic

(G-5650)
SHAW ACQUISITION CORP
645 Johnson St NE (55413-2535)
PHONE 612 378-1520
Del Krusenstjerna, *President*
G T Withy, *Chairman*
Ann W Wald, *Corp Secy*
Jim Bradrick, *Opers Mgr*
Dave Pratutsky, *Purch Agent*
EMP: 80 **EST:** 1886
SQ FT: 80,000
SALES (est): 10MM-24.9MM **Privately Held**
WEB: www.shawlumberco.com
SIC: 5031 Retail lumber sales; creosotes wood; wholesales rough, dressed & finished lumber; sawing & planing mill
PA: Shaw Lumber Co
645 Johnson St NE
Minneapolis MN 55413
651 488-2525

(G-5651)
SHAW LUMBER CO (PA)
645 Johnson St NE (55413-2535)
PHONE 651 488-2525
Del Krusenstjerna, *President*
Ann W Wald, *Corp Secy*
Bruce Furness, *CFO*
G T Withy, *Shareholder*
EMP: 114 **EST:** 1886
SQ FT: 100,000 **Privately Held**
WEB: www.shawlumberco.com
SIC: 5031 Retails building products & materials; wholesales lumber, plywood & millwork; millwork

(G-5652)
SHEA INC
100 N 6th St Ste 650C (55403-1594)
PHONE 612 339-2257
FAX: 612 349-2930
Steven E Haasl, *Principal*
David A Shea III, *Principal*
Tanya Spaulding, *Principal*
Jim Ruckel, *Vice Pres*
Jason Dvorak, *Accounting Staf*

(PA)=Parent Co (HQ)=Headquarters (DH)=Div Headquarters
✿ = New business established in last 2 years

2011 Harris Minnesota
Services Directory

© Harris InfoSource 1-866-281-6415
249

EMP: 30 EST: 1978
SQ FT: 13,000
SALES (est): 1MM-4.9MM **Privately Held**
WEB: www.shealink.com
SIC: 8712 7374 8742 Architectural service;
manufactures signs & advertising
specialties; computer graphics service;
construction project management consultant

(G-5653)
SHELTER CARE INC
3103 Columbus Ave (55407-1534)
PHONE..............................612 823-8483
FAX: 612 824-9464
Christine Rickart, *President*
EMP: 25 EST: 1975
SALES (est): 1MM-4.9MM **Privately Held**
WEB: www.sheltercare.com
SIC: 8322 Emergency shelters

(G-5654)
SHERIDAN SHEET METAL CO
4108 Quebec Ave N (55427-1201)
PHONE..............................763 537-3686
Greg C Johnson, *CEO*
Scott R Durant, *President*
Steve Mattson, *Vice Pres*
Andy Tegland, *Office Mgr*
EMP: 25 EST: 1950
SQ FT: 16,000
SALES (est): 1MM-4.9MM **Privately Held**
WEB: www.sheridansheetmetal.com
SIC: 1761 Sheet metal work contractor;
sheet metal fabricator

(G-5655)
SHINGLE CREEK HOSPITALITY LLP
Also Called: AmericInn
2050 Freeway Blvd (55430-1752)
PHONE..............................763 566-7500
Donald J Wold, *Partner*
Steven Hanson, *Partner*
Thomas C Wold, *Partner*
James P Wold, *Partner*
EMP: 25 EST: 1997
SALES (est): 1MM-4.9MM **Privately Held**
SIC: 7011 Traveler accommodations

(G-5656)
SHOLOM COMMUNITY ALLIANCE (PA)
3620 Phillips Pkwy (55426-3700)
PHONE..............................952 935-6311
Bruce Kahn, *CEO*
James Newstrom, *CFO*
Ronald Weisman, *MIS Dir*
EMP: 295 EST: 1920
SALES (corp-wide): 6.54M **Privately Held**
WEB: www.sholom.com
SIC: 8051 Skilled nursing care facility

(G-5657)
SHOLOM COMMUNITY ALLIANCE
3630 Phillips Pkwy (55426-3792)
PHONE..............................952 939-1601
Sherry Gregor, *Branch Mgr*
EMP: 30
SALES (est): 1MM-4.9MM **Privately Held**
WEB: www.sholom.com
SIC: 6513 Operators of retirement hotels
PA: Sholom Community Alliance
3620 Phillips Pkwy
Minneapolis MN 55426
952 935-6311

(G-5658)
SHOLOM COMMUNITY ALLIANCE
3610 Phillips Pkwy (55426-3765)
PHONE..............................952 908-1776
FAX: 952 908-1777
Catherine Johnson, *Branch Mgr*
EMP: 50
SALES (est): 1MM-4.9MM **Privately Held**
WEB: www.sholom.com
SIC: 8059 Personal care home, with health
care
PA: Sholom Community Alliance
3620 Phillips Pkwy
Minneapolis MN 55426
952 935-6311

(G-5659)
SHOLOM HOME WEST INC
3620 Phillips Pkwy (55426-3700)
PHONE..............................952 935-6311
FAX: 952 935-2701
Connie Sandler, *Marketing Staff*
Laurie Skau, *Manager*
Bruce Kahn, *Exec Dir*
Lisa Pater, *Hlthcr Dir*
EMP: 250 EST: 1986
SQ FT: 145,000
SALES (est): 10MM-24.9MM **Privately Held**
WEB: www.sholom.com
SIC: 8051 Skilled nursing care facility
PA: Sholom Community Alliance
3620 Phillips Pkwy
Minneapolis MN 55426
952 935-6311

(G-5660)
SHOULDER & SPORTS MEDICINE
8100 W 78th St Ste 230 (55439-2570)
PHONE..............................612 879-6623
Daniell D Buss, *Owner*
Jennine L Speier, *Med Doctor*
EMP: 30 EST: 1999
SALES (est): 1MM-4.9MM **Privately Held**
SIC: 8011 Physicians' office & clinic

(G-5661)
SHRINERS HOSPITALS FOR
2025 E River Pkwy (55414-3604)
PHONE..............................612 596-6100
FAX: 612 339-5954
Donna Rooker, *Purchasing*
Dennis Campbell, *Engineering*
Ed Tusa, *Finance*
Stephanie Cortney, *Human Res Dir*
Amy Ehrler, *Human Res Dir*
EMP: 235
SALES (est): 10MM-24.9MM **Privately Held**
SIC: 8069 Children's hospital
PA: Shriners Hospitals For
2900 N Rocky Point Dr
Tampa FL 33607
813 281-0300

(G-5662)
SHUETT CO'S INC
620 Mendelssohn Ave N # 107
(55427-4362)
PHONE..............................763 541-9199
John E Schuett, *President*
EST: 1977 **Privately Held**
SIC: 8741 Management services

(G-5663)
SICK MAIHAK INC
6900 W 110th St (55438-2397)
PHONE..............................952 941-6780
Brian Tripoli, *President*
Sue Larson, *Office Mgr*
Debbie Singer, *Manager*
EMP: 34 EST: 2001
SQ FT: 12,000
SALES (est): 1MM-4.9MM **Privately Held**
WEB: www.sickmaihak.com
SIC: 8748 Environmental consultant

(G-5664)
SIEBEN, GROSE, VON HOLTUM
800 Marquette Ave Ste 900 (55402-2858)
PHONE..............................612 333-4500
FAX: 612 333-5970
Harry A Sieben Jr, *Managing Prtnr*
Edward Kranz, *Corp Secy*
Veatch Jeffrey, *Data Proc Exec*
EMP: 50 EST: 1952
SALES (est): 5MM-9.9MM **Privately Held**
SIC: 8111 General practice attorney's or
lawyer's office

(G-5665)
SIEGEL, BRILL, GREUPNER DUFFY
Also Called: Yarosh, James A
100 Washington Ave S Ste 1300
(55401-2151)
PHONE..............................612 339-7131
FAX: 612 339-6591
Sarah Macdonald, *Corp Secy*
Heidi Furlong, *Corp Secy*

Cathy Barton, *Administrator*
Thomas H Goodman, *Mng Officer*
Anthony Gleekel, *Mng Officer*
EMP: 30 EST: 1964
SALES (est): 1MM-4.9MM **Privately Held**
WEB: www.sbgdf.com
SIC: 8111 General practice attorney's or
lawyer's office

(G-5666)
SIEMENS HEARING INC
Also Called: Memsi
5010 Cheshire Ln N Ste 1 (55446-3734)
PHONE..............................763 268-4500
Dan Anderson, *Vice Pres*
Ken Correll, *Accounts Mgr*
F P Ournier, *Data Proc Exec*
EMP: 300 EST: 2000
SALES (est): 50MM-99.9MM **Privately Held**
SIC: 7629 Manufactures hearing aids;
hearing aid repair service

(G-5667)
SIFCO INDUSTRIES INC
2430 Winnetka Ave N (55427-3568)
PHONE..............................763 544-3511
Martin Gonior, *President*
George Satava, *Manager*
EMP: 82
SALES (est): 5MM-9.9MM **Publicly Held**
WEB: www.sifco.com
SIC: 7699 Aircraft & heavy equipment repair
service
PA: SIFCO Industries Inc
970 E 64th St
Cleveland OH 44103
216 881-8600

(G-5668)
SIGHTPATH MEDICAL INC
5775 W Old Shakopee Rd (55437-3173)
PHONE..............................952 881-2500
FAX: 952 881-1700
Jim Tiffany, *President*
Dick Minors, *Vice Pres*
Dan McCarty, *Vice Pres*
Kipp Fesenmaier, *Vice Pres*
Angela Longworth, *Manager*
EMP: 106 EST: 1991
SQ FT: 17,000
SALES (est): 10MM-24.9MM **Privately Held**
WEB: www.tlcv.com
SIC: 7352 5047 Medical equipment leasing
& rental; wholesales surgical equipment &
supplies
PA: TLC Vision Corp
16305 Swingley Ridge Rd # 300
Chesterfield MO 63017
636 534-2300

(G-5669)
SIGMA ALPHA EPSILON FRATERNITY
1815 University Ave SE (55414-2024)
PHONE..............................612 331-5986
Jason Peterson, *Manager*
Skogen Marv, *Manager*
Ben Hazelkorn, *Manager*
Chad Trent, *Info Tech Dir*
EMP: 50 **Privately Held**
SIC: 8641 Fraternal association

(G-5670)
SIGNATURE FLIGHT SUPPORT CORP
3800 E 70th St (55450-1147)
PHONE..............................612 726-5700
Dale Kariya, *General Mgr*
Geoffrey Heck, *Vice Pres*
Jenny Roof, *Human Res Dir*
Jenni Roufs, *Human Resources*
Darryl Volk, *Human Res*
EMP: 388
SALES (est): 25MM-49.9MM **Privately Held**
WEB: www.bba-aviation.com/flightsupport
SIC: 4581 Aircraft maintenance & repair
services
HQ: Signature Flight Support Corp
201 S Orange Ave Ste 1100
Orlando FL 32801
407 648-7200

(G-5671)
SIGNCASTER CORP
Also Called: Johnson Plastics
9240 Grand Ave S Ste A (55420-3694)
PHONE..............................952 888-9507
FAX: 952 888-4997
Thomas Johnson, *CEO*
Mike Johnson, *COO*
Margaret Johnson, *Vice Pres*
Lisa Adams, *Purchasing*
Rob Collins, *Manager*
▲ EMP: 40 EST: 1970
SQ FT: 30,000
SALES (est): 1MM-4.9MM **Privately Held**
WEB: www.johnsonplastics.com
SIC: 5085 Manufactures signs & advertising
specialties; wholesales industrial signmaker
equipment & supplies

(G-5672)
SIHAM SOLUTIONS INC
1421 Park Ave Ste 202 (55404-1579)
PHONE..............................651 274-3640
Mohamed Abieb, *President*
EMP: 31 EST: 2002
SQ FT: 4,000
SALES (est): 1MM-4.9MM **Privately Held**
SIC: 8748 Business consulting services

(G-5673)
SILENT KNIGHT SECURITY SYSTEMS
9057 Lyndale Ave S (55420-3520)
PHONE..............................952 881-0038
Fred Haymer, *President*
Domini Valentine, *Controller*
EMP: 30 EST: 1966
SQ FT: 6,000
SALES (est): 1MM-4.9MM **Privately Held**
WEB: www.silent-knight.com
SIC: 1731 7382 Fire detection & burglar
alarm systems specialization contractor;
retails security & safety equipment; security
systems services

(G-5674)
SILVER KING REFRIGERATION INC
Also Called: Norris Dispenser
13430 County Road 6 (55441-4571)
PHONE..............................763 559-1141
Korey Kohl, *General Mgr*
Kenneth Kreye, *Production*
Paul A Benerson, *Purchasing*
Jerame Powlas, *Engineering*
Joe Rother, *VP Sls/Mktg*
EMP: 130
SALES (est): 25MM-49.9MM **Publicly Held**
WEB: www.silverking.com
SIC: 5046 Wholesales commercial
equipment; wholesales coin-operated
equipment
HQ: Silver King Refrigeration Inc
1600 Xenium Ln N
Minneapolis MN 55441
763 553-1881

(G-5675)
SILVERCROSS PROPERTIES
Also Called: Parkshore Place
3663 Park Center Blvd A (55416-2514)
PHONE..............................952 925-6231
FAX: 952 926-6823
Michael Gould, *Owner*
EMP: 30 EST: 1988
SALES (est): 1MM-4.9MM **Privately Held**
SIC: 6513 Apartment building operator

(G-5676)
SIMPLEXGRINNELL LP
5400 Nathan Ln N Ste 100 (55442-2128)
PHONE..............................763 367-5000
Terri Michurski, *Safety Dir*
Gaston Cerrichio, *Engineer*
Ernie Companion, *Sales Executive*
William Gresko, *Branch Mgr*
Bill Gresko, *Manager*
EMP: 200
SALES (est): 25MM-49.9MM **Privately Held**
WEB: www.simplexgrinnell.com

▲=Import ▼=Export
◆=Import/Export

SIC: **1711** 1731 5087 Manufactures emergency alarms; fire sprinkler system installation service; fire detection & burglar alarm systems specialization contractor; wholesales firefighting equipment
DH: Simplexgrinnell LP
1 Town Center Rd
Boca Raton FL 33486
561 988-7200

(G-5677)
SIMPSON HOUSING SERVICES INC
2100 Pillsbury Ave S (55404-2347)
PHONE 612 874-8683
Julie Manworren, *President*
Kim Mueller, *Corp Secy*
John Mattes, *Treasurer*
Kristin Livdahl, *MIS Staff*
Mirja Hansen, *Bd of Directors*
EMP: 37 EST: 1993 **Privately Held**
WEB: www.simpsonhousing.org
SIC: **8699** Charitable organization

(G-5678)
SIMTEK CORP
4550 W 77th St Ste 125 (55435-5010)
PHONE 952 831-7472
Greg Simon, *President*
EMP: 30 EST: 1994
SQ FT: 3,000
SALES (est): 1MM-4.9MM **Privately Held**
WEB: www.ameret.net
SIC: **7334** Photocopying & duplicating services

(G-5679)
SIS ENTERPRISES INC
6707 Shingle Creek Pkwy # 300
(55430-1438)
PHONE 763 789-0956
FAX: 763 789-1170
Shari Hammer, *President*
Lance Pearson, *Mfg Spvr*
Joe Hammer, *CFO*
Michele Fyten, *Human Resources*
Katharine Gotham, *Marketing Mgr*
▲ EMP: 110 EST: 1987
SALES (est): 10MM-24.9MM **Privately Held**
WEB: www.siscovers.com
SIC: **7389** Manufactures pillowcases made from purchased materials; manufactures bedspreads & bed sets made from purchased materials; sewing contractor

(G-5680)
SIT FIXED INCOME ADVISORS II
80 S 8th St Ste 3300 (55402-2206)
PHONE 612 332-3223
Mike Brilley, *Member*
EMP: 74
SALES (est): 10MM-24.9MM **Privately Held**
SIC: **6282** Investment counseling service

(G-5681)
SIT INVESTMENT ASSOCIATES INC (PA)
80 S 8th St Ste 3300 (55402-2206)
PHONE 612 332-3223
FAX: 612 342-2018
Eugene C Sit, *Ch of Bd*
Carla Rose, *Vice Pres*
Paul Rasmussen, *Vice Pres*
David A Brown, *Marketing Staff*
Chris Sover, *Info Tech Mgr*
EMP: 80 EST: 1981
SQ FT: 19,000 **Privately Held**
WEB: www.sitfunds.com
SIC: **6282** Investment advisory service

(G-5682)
SIT MUTUAL FUNDS INC
3300 Ids Ctr (55402)
PHONE 612 332-3223
Roger J Sit, *President*
EMP: 70 EST: 2006 **Privately Held**
SIC: **6722** Open-ended investment funds management services

(G-5683)
SIX CONTINENTS HOTELS INC
5401 Green Valley Dr (55437-1002)
PHONE 952 831-8000
FAX: 952 831-8426

Jim Saccoman, *General Mgr*
Dhaval Brahnbhatt, *Facilities Mgr*
Kristen Selvedt, *Opers Staff*
Kristina Burks, *Controller*
David Colbern, *Manager*
EMP: 100
SALES (est): 5MM-9.9MM **Privately Held**
WEB: www.sixcontinenthotels.com
SIC: **7011** Traveler accommodations; eating place; drinking establishment
HQ: Six Continents Hotels Inc
3 Ravinia Dr Ste 100
Atlanta GA 30346
770 604-2000

(G-5684)
SIX HUNDRED WASHINGTON
610 Washington Ave SE (55414-2916)
PHONE 612 331-9041
Bill Chan, *Partner*
EMP: 55 EST: 2001
SALES (est): 10MM-24.9MM **Privately Held**
SIC: **6512** Nonresidential building operator

(G-5685)
614 CO
81 S 9th St Ste 220 (55402-3225)
PHONE 612 333-6128
FAX: 612 344-1693
Robert D Greenberg, *President*
Susan B Greenberg, *Corp Secy*
Steven Greenberg, *Vice Pres*
Joe Hoff, *Engineer*
EMP: 48 EST: 1949
SALES (est): 10MM-24.9MM **Privately Held**
WEB: www.614co.com
SIC: **6512** 6531 Operators of commercial & industrial buildings; real estate management services

(G-5686)
675 STINSON LLC
Also Called: All Furniture Installation
675 Stinson Blvd Ste 100 (55413-2762)
PHONE 612 238-3200
Dion Schilling, *Member*
EMP: 52 EST: 2007
SALES (est): 10MM-24.9MM **Privately Held**
SIC: **5087** Wholesales moving equipment & supplies

(G-5687)
SKARNES INC
2100 Niagara Ln N (55447-4700)
PHONE 763 231-3600
FAX: 763 231-3610
Thomas K Wanous, *CEO*
Paul Wanous, *President*
John Henschel, *General Mgr*
Dawn Wanous, *Corp Secy*
David Wanous, *Vice Pres*
EMP: 28 EST: 1923
SQ FT: 26,000
SALES (est): 10MM-24.9MM **Privately Held**
WEB: www.skarnes.com
SIC: **5084** Wholesales materials handling equipment

(G-5688)
SKYCOM INC
9555 James Ave S Ste 215 (55431-2542)
PHONE 952 361-4248
Robert Jefperson, *CEO*
Paul Graves, *President*
Aillen Chen, *Manager*
EMP: 26 EST: 1997 **Privately Held**
WEB: www.skycomnow.com
SIC: **4813** Wired telecommunications carrier & service

(G-5689)
SLUMBERLAND INC
7801 Xerxes Ave S (55431-1241)
PHONE 952 888-6204
FAX: 952 888-9111
Greg Tangen, *Manager*
EMP: 60
SALES (est): 10MM-24.9MM **Privately Held**
SIC: **5047** Retails beds & accessories; wholesales hospital beds
PA: Slumberland Inc
3060 Centerville Rd
Saint Paul MN 55117
651 482-7500

(G-5690)
SMITH MORETON INTERNATIONAL
8400 Normandale Lake Blvd (55437-1085)
PHONE 952 820-4441
Richard Moreton, *President*
Charles Mayhew, *Principal*
Mark Smith, *Regional Mgr*
EMP: 45 EST: 2005
SALES (est): 1MM-4.9MM **Privately Held**
SIC: **8732** Commercial nonphysical research laboratory

(G-5691)
SMURFIT-STONE CONTAINER CORP
50 37th Ave NE (55421-3629)
PHONE 612 789-2485
FAX: 612 782-4260
David Beavens, *Plant Supt*
Richard Radman, *Prdtn Mgr*
Tom Bennington, *Mfg Staff*
Matt Jentjes, *QC Mgr*
Robert Gofer, *Cust Svc Mgr*
EMP: 175
SALES (est): 50MM-99.9MM **Privately Held**
WEB: www.sto.com
SIC: **5113** Manufactures linerboard; wholesales corrugated & solid fiber boxes; manufactures corrugated & solid fiber containers
PA: Smurfit-Stone Container Corp
222 N Lasalle St
Chicago IL 60601
312 346-6600

(G-5692)
SNIPS OF EDEN PRAIRIE INC
5147 W 98th St (55437-2040)
PHONE 952 941-1495
FAX: 952 746-6091
Cynthia M Kee, *President*
Sandra Corcoran, *Corp Secy*
EMP: 40 EST: 1980
SQ FT: 1,250
SALES (est): 1MM-4.9MM **Privately Held**
WEB: www.snips.com
SIC: **7231** Unisex hair salon; nail salon

(G-5693)
SOAP TRANSCRIPTION SERVICES
Also Called: S O A P Medical Transcription
2855 Anthony Ln S Ste 110 (55418-2486)
PHONE 612 706-1588
FAX: 612 706-2195
Faye Thayer, *President*
EMP: 36 EST: 1995
SALES (est): 1MM-4.9MM **Privately Held**
SIC: **7338** Secretarial services

(G-5694)
SOCIETY OF CORPORATE ✪
6500 Barrie Rd Ste 250 (55435-2358)
PHONE 952 405-7925
Royce Snell, *CEO*
EMP: 27 EST: 2008 **Privately Held**
SIC: **8399** Social services

(G-5695)
SOFTBRANDS INC (PA)
800 Lasalle Ave Ste 2100 (55402-2012)
PHONE 612 851-1500
Randal B Tofteland, *President*
Tim Farey, *General Mgr*
Gail Froelicher, *General Mgr*
Doug McGregor, *General Mgr*
Gareth Robinson, *General Mgr*
EMP: 100 EST: 2001
SQ FT: 28,000 **Publicly Held**
WEB: www.softbrands.com
SIC: **7371** Computer software development & applications

(G-5696)
SOFTBRANDS MANUFACTURING INC
800 Lasalle Ave Ste 2100 (55402-2012)
PHONE 612 851-1500
Randy Tofteland, *President*
Larry Kallhoff, *Vice Pres*
Diane Palmquist, *Vice Pres*
Ed Trevisani, *Vice Pres*

James Jenkins, *CFO*
EMP: 120 EST: 2004
SALES (est): 10MM-24.9MM **Publicly Held**
WEB: www.softbrands.com
SIC: **7371** Computer software development & applications
PA: Softbrands Inc
800 Lasalle Ave Ste 2100
Minneapolis MN 55402
612 851-1500

(G-5697)
SOLUTRAN INC
3600 Holly Ln N Ste 60 (55447-1286)
PHONE 763 559-2225
Barry Nordstrand, *President*
Christopher D O'Leary, *Vice Pres*
Carmen Nordstand, *Treasurer*
Kari Hawkins, *Natl Sales Mgr*
Todd Firebaugh, *Manager*
EMP: 85 EST: 1987
SQ FT: 20,000
SALES (est): 25MM-49.9MM **Privately Held**
WEB: www.solutran.com
SIC: **6099** 8742 Bank or check clearinghouse association; financial management consulting services

(G-5698)
SONS OF NORWAY
1455 W Lake St Fl 2 (55408-2648)
PHONE 612 827-3611
John Lund, *CEO*
Lee D Goranson, *Corp Secy*
Thomas Vickman, *Corp Secy*
Jayne Hilde, *Vice Pres*
John Claseman, *Purchasing*
EMP: 42 EST: 1895
SQ FT: 55,000
SALES (est): 25MM-49.9MM **Privately Held**
SIC: **6311** Fraternal life insurance organization

(G-5699)
SONS OF NORWAY FOUNDATION
1455 W Lake St Fl 2 (55408-2648)
PHONE 612 827-3611
John Lund, *CEO*
Ted Fosberg, *President*
Karen Ballor, *Property Mgr*
EMP: 40 EST: 1964
SALES (est): 25MM-49.9MM **Privately Held**
SIC: **6311** Fraternal life insurance organization

(G-5700)
SOO LINE CORP (PA)
Also Called: Canadian Pacific Railway
501 Marquette Ave # 1700 (55402-1201)
PHONE 612 337-5333
Robert J Ritchie, *Ch of Bd*
Edwin V Dodge V, *President*
Cathryn Frankenberg, *Member*
Jan Beisheim, *Corp Secy*
John C Miller, *Vice Pres*
EMP: 100 EST: 1983
SQ FT: 120,000
SALES (corp-wide): 4.02B **Privately Held**
SIC: **4011** Long haul railroad

(G-5701)
SOO LINE RAILROAD CO INC (HQ)
Also Called: Canadian Pacific Railway
501 Marquette Ave # 1500 (55402-1203)
PHONE 800 766-4357
Edwin V Dodge V, *President*
Robert V Horte V, *Corp Secy*
Donald F Barnhardt, *Corp Secy*
Patrick A Pender, *COO*
Darryl Palmer, *Exec VP*
EMP: 400 EST: 1949
SQ FT: 120,000
SALES (corp-wide): 4.02B **Privately Held**
WEB: www.cpa.ca
SIC: **4011** Long haul railroad
PA: Soo Line Corp
501 Marquette Ave # 1700
Minneapolis MN 55402
612 337-5333

(PA)=Parent Co (HQ)=Headquarters (DH)=Div Headquarters
✪ = New business established in last 2 years

2011 Harris Minnesota
Services Directory

© Harris InfoSource 1-866-281-6415

251

(G-5702)
SOPHEON CORP (PA)
3050 Metro Dr Ste 200 (55425-1547)
PHONE 952 851-7555
FAX: 952 851-7599
Andrew L Michuda, *President*
Jefferson Smurfit, *Member*
Jack Johnson, *Corp Secy*
Bob Bottelsen, *Vice Pres*
Edward Herzog, *Vice Pres*
EMP: 35 EST: 1984
SQ FT: 15,000
SALES (corp-wide): 13.71M **Privately Held**
SIC: 7375 7372 8742 Information retrieval services; management consulting services; software publisher

(G-5703)
SOS JANITORIAL INC
6741 Edgewood Ave N (55428-1787)
PHONE 763 560-9611
FAX: 763 566-0459
Francis G Olson, *President*
Kathleen Olson, *Vice Pres*
EMP: 25 EST: 1965
SALES (est): 500-999K **Privately Held**
SIC: 7349 Building & office cleaning service

(G-5704)
SOURCE ONE SALES & MARKETING
Also Called: Advantage Sales & Marketing
6300 W Old Shakopee Rd (55438-2654)
PHONE 952 829-0833
Joann Lavigne, *Purchasing*
Karen Stearley, *Human Res Mgr*
Matt Lawin, *VP Sales*
Tim Brinker, *Sales Staff*
Paul Kemmey, *Marketing Mgr*
EMP: 125
SALES (est): 100MM-499.9MM **Privately Held**
WEB: www.jwchilds.com
SIC: 5141 Food broker
DH: Advantage Sales & Marketing
18100 Von Karman Ave # 900
Irvine CA 92612
949 797-2900

(G-5705)
SOUTHDALE DENTAL ASSOCIATES
7373 France Ave S Ste 600 (55435-4552)
PHONE 952 896-1111
James Raymond DDS, *President*
Steven M Johnson DDS, *Vice Pres*
Thomas Telander DDS, *Vice Pres*
Gary Rene DDS, *Vice Pres*
Mary Schacherer, *Office Mgr*
EMP: 50 EST: 1969
SALES (est): 1MM-4.9MM **Privately Held**
SIC: 8021 Dental office

(G-5706)
SOUTHDALE FAMILY PRACTICE
7428 W Shore Dr (55435-4022)
PHONE 952 927-4235
Linda C Johnson MD, *President*
Robert Thomassen MD, *Principal*
Kenneth Hodges, *Vice Pres*
EMP: 33 EST: 1968
SQ FT: 6,000
SALES (est): 1MM-4.9MM **Privately Held**
SIC: 8011 General & family practice physician or surgeon office

(G-5707)
SOUTHDALE OBSTETRIC
3625 W 65th St Ste 100 (55435-2147)
PHONE 952 920-7001
Deb Davenport, *Principal*
Mary Lanner, *Office Mgr*
Anne M Eschke MD, *Med Doctor*
Heather A Mackay, *Med Doctor*
Dottie Jung, *Administrator*
EMP: 50 EST: 1952
SALES (est): 5MM-9.9MM **Privately Held**
SIC: 8011 Gynecologist office; obstetrician office

(G-5708)
SOUTHDALE PEDIATRICS ASSOCS (PA)
3955 Parklawn Ave Ste 120 (55435-5660)
PHONE 952 831-4454
Paul Blum, *CEO*
C S Hoyt MD, *CEO*
Duane Rommel MD, *President*
Jeffrey W Oseid MD, *Principal*
Joan M Williams MD, *Principal*
EMP: 70 EST: 1970
SQ FT: 10,000
SALES (est): 1MM-4.9MM **Privately Held**
WEB: www.southdalepeds.com
SIC: 8011 Pediatrician office; endocrinologist; allergist office

(G-5709)
SOUTHERN HOSPITALITY INC
5120 American Blvd W (55437-1235)
PHONE 952 831-9595
Ryan Flannery, *CEO*
EMP: 40 EST: 1995
SALES (est): 1MM-4.9MM **Privately Held**
SIC: 7011 Traveler accommodations

(G-5710)
SOUTHSIDE COMMUNITY HEALTH
4730 Chicago Ave Ste 1 (55407-3571)
PHONE 612 822-3186
FAX: 612 822-4979
Natalie Hayes MD, *Med Doctor*
Pam Whit, *Manager*
Jennifer Vagts, *Manager*
Pam Kelley, *Manager*
Pam Evens, *Administrator*
EMP: 30
SALES (est): 1MM-4.9MM **Privately Held**
SIC: 8011 Clinic operated by physicians
PA: Southside Community Health
4243 4th Ave S
Minneapolis MN 55409
612 822-9030

(G-5711)
SOUTHSIDE FAMILY NURTURING CTR
2448 18th Ave S (55404-4006)
PHONE 612 721-2762
FAX: 612 721-1301
David Gapen, *Corp Secy*
Scott Moore, *Treasurer*
Barb Olson, *Exec Dir*
Jean Christie, *Director*
EMP: 29 EST: 1974
SALES (est): 1MM-4.9MM **Privately Held**
WEB: www.ssfnc.org
SIC: 8322 8351 Individual & family social services; child day care service

(G-5712)
SOUTHTOWN FREEWAY TOYOTA INC
1750 W 80th St (55431-1403)
PHONE 952 888-5581
FAX: 952 884-7597
Irving Tesler, *President*
EMP: 42 EST: 1971
SQ FT: 17,000
SALES (est): 10MM-24.9MM **Privately Held**
SIC: 7538 Retails new & used automobiles; general automotive repair services

(G-5713)
SOUTHWEST CASINO & HOTEL CORP (HQ)
2001 Killebrew Dr Ste 350 (55425-1886)
PHONE 952 853-9990
FAX: 952 853-9991
Jim Druck, *CEO*
Thomas Fox, *President*
Jeff Halpern, *Vice Pres*
Tracie L Wilson, *CFO*
Janet Smith, *Administrator*
EMP: 42 EST: 1992
SQ FT: 3,500
SALES (corp-wide): 19.53M **Publicly Held**
WEB: www.southwestcasino.com

SIC: 8741 8742 Business management services; business management consultant
PA: Southwest Casino Corp
20 64th Way NE
Minneapolis MN 55432
763 502-7740

(G-5714)
SPACE150 LLC
212 3rd Ave N Ste 150 (55401-1434)
PHONE 612 332-6458
FAX: 612 332-6469
Marcus Fischer, *Vice Pres*
Dutch Thalhuber, *Opers Staff*
Claire Canavan, *CFO*
Chad Gillard, *Business Anlyst*
William Jurewicz, *Mng Member*
EMP: 63 EST: 2000
SQ FT: 17,777
SALES (est): 5MM-9.9MM **Privately Held**
SIC: 8748 Communications consultant

(G-5715)
SPANLINK COMMUNICATIONS INC
605 Highway 169 N Ste 900 (55441-6422)
PHONE 763 971-2000
Scott Christian, *President*
Andy Summers, *General Mgr*
Paul Martin, *Corp Secy*
Loren A Singer Jr, *Corp Secy*
Anna Sunderman, *Counsel*
EMP: 100 EST: 1987
SQ FT: 27,000
SALES (est): 10MM-24.9MM **Privately Held**
SIC: 7373 7371 Computer systems value-added resellers; computer software development & applications

(G-5716)
SPC COMMUNICATIONS INC
5775 W Old Shakopee Rd Ste 160 (55437-3174)
PHONE 952 912-2800
Scott Colesworthy, *President*
Chris Kumsher, *VP Finance*
EMP: 35 EST: 1987
SQ FT: 10,500
SALES (est): 5MM-9.9MM **Privately Held**
SIC: 7373 Systems integration service; computer systems value-added resellers

(G-5717)
SPECIAL SCHOOL DISTRICT NO 1
Also Called: Shingle Creek Elementary
5034 Oliver Ave N (55430-3355)
PHONE 612 668-1420
FAX: 612 668-1430
Karen Erickson, *Principal*
EMP: 65 **Privately Held**
WEB: www.mpls.k12.mn.us
SIC: 8351 Public elementary school; child day care service
PA: Special School District No 1
807 Broadway St NE
Minneapolis MN 55413
612 668-0000

(G-5718)
SPECTRUM LANES BOWLING ALLEY
3050 Quinwood Ln N (55441-2807)
PHONE 763 553-0333
Mark Mandell, *President*
Mark Mandel, *President*
Ron Rosenzweig, *Vice Pres*
Bruce Mandell, *Vice Pres*
EMP: 110 EST: 1985
SQ FT: 20,000
SALES (est): 1MM-4.9MM **Privately Held**
WEB: www.alleygators.com
SIC: 7933 7299 Bowling center; eating place; banquet hall facility; drinking establishment

(G-5719)
SPECTRUM PROPERTY MANAGEMENT
7800 Metro Pkwy Ste 112 (55425-1528)
PHONE 952 853-0036
Laura Lafranz, *Principal*
Dave Schroeder, *Principal*
EMP: 25 EST: 2002

SALES (est): 1MM-4.9MM **Privately Held**
WEB: www.spectrummgt.com
SIC: 6531 Real estate services

(G-5720)
SPECTRUM SOLUTIONS INC (PA)
7801 E Bush Lake Rd # 210 (55439-3135)
PHONE 952 835-8338
Leon Orr, *President*
Keith Bendict, *COO*
Martin Jerome, *CFO*
Carrey Tessman, *Manager*
Mellissa Vigen, *Administrator*
EMP: 39 EST: 2001 **Privately Held**
SIC: 4899 Manufactures security devices; data communication services

(G-5721)
SPLATBALL INC
2412 University Ave SE # 2 (55414-3188)
PHONE 612 378-0385
Jim Lathrop, *President*
Kathy Lathrop, *Corp Secy*
John Borchert, *Finance*
Brian Emde, *Manager*
EMP: 27 EST: 1984
SQ FT: 1,000
SALES (est): 1MM-4.9MM **Privately Held**
WEB: www.splatball.org
SIC: 7999 5092 Sporting goods rental services; wholesales toys & games; retails sporting goods

(G-5722)
SPORTS & ORTHOPAEDIC
8100 W 78th St Ste 225 (55439-2569)
PHONE 952 946-9777
Bill Evan, *Opers Mgr*
Michael Q Freehill, *Surgeon*
Kimberly Nguyen, *Physician Asst*
Vinh Dang, *Physician Asst*
April M Olson, *Physician Asst*
EMP: 30 EST: 1999
SALES (est): 1MM-4.9MM **Privately Held**
WEB: www.sportsandortho.com
SIC: 8011 Surgeon's office

(G-5723)
SPRUCE CO
9311 Bryant Ave S (55420-3403)
PHONE 952 888-1639
FAX: 952 884-9602
Richard A Russell, *President*
Carol J Russell, *Corp Secy*
EMP: 30 EST: 1965
SQ FT: 15,000
SALES (est): 1MM-4.9MM **Privately Held**
WEB: www.sprucelinen.com
SIC: 7213 Linen supply service; towel supply service

(G-5724)
SPS COMMERCE INC
333 S 7th St Ste 1000 (55402-2421)
PHONE 612 435-9400
James Frome, *CEO*
Archie Black, *CEO*
David Verette, *Partner*
Mike Gray, *COO*
Ray Brons, *Vice Pres*
EMP: 83 EST: 1982
SQ FT: 29,000
SALES (est): 10MM-24.9MM **Publicly Held**
WEB: www.spscommerce.com
SIC: 7374 Data processing & preparation services

(G-5725)
SRF CONSULTING GROUP INC
1 Carlson Pkwy N Ste 150 (55447-4453)
PHONE 763 475-0010
FAX: 763 475-2429
Randall Geerdes, *President*
Patrick Corkle, *Principal*
Marie Cote, *Principal*
Larry Erickson, *Principal*
David Filipiak, *Principal*
EMP: 250 EST: 1961
SQ FT: 38,000
SALES (est): 25MM-49.9MM **Privately Held**
SIC: 8711 8713 8742 Engineering services; management consulting services; engineering consulting services; civil engineering services; surveying service

(G-5726)
SSIT NORTH AMERICA INC
Also Called: Orion Consulting
3900 80th Ave N Ste 1420   (55443-2614)
PHONE............................952 857-1600
FAX: 952 857-1699
Kalpathi Suresh, *Chairman*
Danette Bucsko, *Corp Secy*
Ran Krishnan, *CFO*
Tom Pechman, *Manager*
Mark Besser, *Manager*
EMP: 135 **EST:** 1983
SQ FT: 7,400
SALES (est): 10MM-24.9MM **Privately Held**
SIC: 7371 Applications software
programming

(G-5727)
ST LOUIS PARK TRANSPORTATION
2211 Edgewood Ave S   (55426-2822)
PHONE............................952 591-1538
FAX: 952 512-0820
Joe Regan, *CEO*
Tom Burr, *Manager*
EMP: 50 **EST:** 2000
SALES (est): 1MM-4.9MM **Privately Held**
SIC: 4131 Bus transit system

(G-5728)
ST MICHAELS LUTHERAN CHURCH
9201 Normandale Blvd   (55437-1940)
PHONE............................952 831-5276
FAX: 952 831-5225
Luis Rutgerson, *Corp Secy*
Christopher Dodge, *Pastor*
Aaron Rossow, *Technical Mgr*
Roger Wheeler, *Manager*
EMP: 30 **EST:** 1964 **Privately Held**
WEB: www.stmichaelsbloomington.org
SIC: 8351 Provides Lutheran church
services; preschool center

(G-5729)
ST OLAF RETIREMENT CENTER INC
2912 Fremont Ave N   (55411-1313)
PHONE............................612 522-6561
FAX: 612 522-2921
Marian Mitchell, *Manager*
Dan Colgan, *Administrator*
Joni Scott, *Nursing Dir*
EMP: 150 **EST:** 1962
SQ FT: 90,000
SALES (est): 5MM-9.9MM **Privately Held**
SIC: 8051 Skilled nursing care facility

(G-5730)
ST PAUL FIRE & MARINE INSCE
3600 W 80th St   (55431-1084)
PHONE............................952 893-5602
FAX: 952 893-5980
Robert Soukup, *Branch Mgr*
EMP: 120
SALES (est): 50MM-99.9MM **Publicly Held**
WEB: www.stpaul.com
SIC: 6331 Fire, marine & casualty insurance
& carriers
HQ: St Paul Fire & Marine Insce
385 Washington St
Saint Paul MN 55102
651 221-7911

(G-5731)
ST STEPHEN'S HUMAN SERVICES
2211 Clinton Ave   (55404-3656)
PHONE............................612 874-0311
Gary Ellis, *President*
Cynthia Hill, *Corp Secy*
Dianne Marsh, *Opers Staff*
Elizabeth Michaeelis, *Treasurer*
Mikkel Beckmen, *Exec Dir*
EMP: 45
SALES (est): 1MM-4.9MM **Privately Held**
SIC: 8322 Individual & family social services

(G-5732)
ST THERESE APARTMENTS INC
8008 Bass Lake Rd   (55428-3118)
PHONE............................763 531-5400
FAX: 763 531-5004
Barb Rode, *CEO*
Michael Warden, *CFO*
Jay Pizinger, *CFO*
Rand Brugger, *Human Res Dir*
Bernice Ebner, *Manager*
EMP: 55 **EST:** 1978
SALES (est): 5MM-9.9MM **Privately Held**
SIC: 6513 Apartment building operator

(G-5733)
ST THERESE HOME INC
8000 Bass Lake Rd   (55428-3118)
PHONE............................763 537-4503
Barbara Rode, *President*
Jay Pizinger, *Finance*
Colleen Knutson, *Human Res Mgr*
Stacy Lind, *Manager*
Claudia Motl, *Administrator*
EMP: 525 **EST:** 1968
SALES (est): 10MM-24.9MM **Privately Held**
WEB: www.sttheresenh.org
SIC: 8051 Convalescent home

(G-5734)
STAGING CONCEPTS INC
7008 Northland Dr N # 150   (55428-1561)
PHONE............................763 533-2094
FAX: 763 533-4903
Mike Hayden, *President*
Grant Issacson, *Manager*
John Valines, *Manager*
Sue Schai, *Manager*
John Plohetski, *Director*
EMP: 50 **EST:** 1990
SQ FT: 47,000 **Privately Held**
WEB: www.stagingconcepts.com
SIC: 7922 Manufactures stage hardware &
equipment; manufactures theater furniture;
theatrical equipment rental services;
manufactures wooden floor attached
partitions

(G-5735)
STAHL CONSTRUCTION CO
5755 Wayzata Blvd   (55416-1218)
PHONE............................952 931-9300
Wayne Stahl, *CEO*
Scott Everson, *Vice Pres*
Paul Perzichilli, *Vice Pres*
Dale Sonnichsen, *Project Mgr*
Stephanie Dean, *VP Sls/Mktg*
EMP: 28 **EST:** 1981
SQ FT: 30,000
SALES (est): 5MM-9.9MM **Privately Held**
WEB: www.stahlconstruction.com
SIC: 1542 8741 Specialized public building
contractors; commercial & office building
contractor; construction management
services

(G-5736)
STAN KOCH & SONS TRUCKING INC   (PA)
Also Called: Koch NationaLease
4200 Dahlberg Dr Ste 100   (55422-4842)
PHONE............................763 302-5400
Randy Koch, *President*
Robert Buss, *General Mgr*
James S Koch, *Corp Secy*
Mark Scheffert, *Vice Pres*
Dave Koch, *Vice Pres*
◆ **EMP:** 990 **EST:** 1978
SQ FT: 47,500 **Privately Held**
WEB: www.kochcompanies.com
SIC: 4731 4213 Freight transportation
arrangement services; over the road
trucking

(G-5737)
STANDARD PARKING CORP
50 S 6th St Ste 1320   (55402-5180)
PHONE............................612 371-0938
FAX: 612 371-0254
Anna McCabe, *Manager*
Shatika Amerson, *Manager*
Damon Noga, *Manager*
EMP: 200
SALES (est): 10MM-24.9MM **Publicly Held**
WEB: www.standardparking.com

SIC: 7521 Parking lot
PA: Standard Parking Corp
900 N Michigan Ave # 1600
Chicago IL 60611
312 274-2000

(G-5738)
STANDARD WATER CONTROL SYSTEMS
5337 Lakeland Ave N   (55429-3115)
PHONE............................763 537-4849
FAX: 763 537-1882
Michael W Hogenson, *President*
Patty Baker, *Manager*
EMP: 50 **EST:** 1977
SQ FT: 5,400
SALES (est): 1MM-4.9MM **Privately Held**
WEB: www.standardwater.com
SIC: 1799 Waterproofing service

(G-5739)
STANLEY CONSULTANTS INC
5775 Wayzata Blvd Ste 300   (55416-1235)
PHONE............................952 546-3669
FAX: 952 546-4279
Craig J Johnson, *Vice Pres*
William Holman, *Engineering*
John Prescher, *Engineering*
Rob Darnell, *Manager*
EMP: 30
SALES (est): 1MM-4.9MM **Privately Held**
WEB: www.stanleygroup.com
SIC: 8711 Engineering consulting services
PA: Stanley Consultants Inc
225 Iowa Ave
Muscatine IA 52761
563 264-6600

(G-5740)
STAR TRIBUNE MEDIA CO LLC
800 N 1st St   (55401-1105)
PHONE............................612 673-7100
Kevin Desmond, *Senior VP*
Tom Hardy, *Manager*
Noreen Phillips, *MIS Dir*
Dan Barnes, *Technology*
David Cox, *Systems Mgr*
EMP: 400
SALES (est): 25MM-49.9MM **Privately Held**
SIC: 4225 General warehousing;
newspaper publisher

(G-5741)
STARCHTECH INC   (PA)
720 Florida Ave S   (55426-1704)
PHONE............................763 545-5400
Edward Boehmer, *CEO*
Jim Cesaro, *Controller*
Mary Fuller, *Manager*
Gary Barbo, *Manager*
Matt Niles, *Director*
EMP: 26 **EST:** 1996
SQ FT: 27,000 **Privately Held**
WEB: www.starchtech.com
SIC: 5159 Wholesales cotton merchants

(G-5742)
STARMARK NORTHWEST MANAGEMENT
600 1st Ave N Ste SKY   (55403-1400)
PHONE............................612 673-1200
FAX: 612 673-1215
Duane Harris, *General Mgr*
Terrell Battele, *General Mgr*
Bret Zimmerman, *Opers Staff*
Ted Rijtar, *Branch Mgr*
Steve Mattson, *Exec Dir*
EMP: 30
SALES (est): 500-999K **Privately Held**
SIC: 7997 7991 Membership racquetball
club; physical fitness center

(G-5743)
STARMARK NORTHWEST MANAGEMENT
Also Called: Normandale Tennis Club
6701 W 78th St   (55439-2607)
PHONE............................952 944-2434
FAX: 952 944-7779
Rob Gray, *General Mgr*
Wendy Sevenich, *General Mgr*
Debbie Cusack, *Branch Mgr*
EMP: 100
SALES (est): 1MM-4.9MM **Privately Held**

SIC: 7997 7991 Membership tennis club;
physical fitness center; retails sporting
goods

(G-5744)
STARWOOD HOTELS & RESORTS
1330 Industrial Blvd NE   (55413-1703)
PHONE............................612 331-1900
FAX: 612 331-6827
Paul Durand, *General Mgr*
Mellisa Damerow, *Controller*
Liz Sobolik, *Human Res Mgr*
Jaime Kvasager, *Sales Dir*
Charity Marra, *Sales Dir*
EMP: 120
SALES (est): 5MM-9.9MM **Publicly Held**
WEB: www.starwoodhotels.com
SIC: 7011 7299 Traveler accommodations;
eating place; banquet hall facility
PA: Starwood Hotels & Resorts
1111 Westchester Ave
White Plains NY 10604
914 640-8100

(G-5745)
STARWOOD HOTELS & RESORTS
821 Marquette Ave   (55402-2929)
PHONE............................612 215-3720
Susan Mabry, *Branch Mgr*
EMP: 250
SALES (est): 10MM-24.9MM **Publicly Held**
WEB: www.starwoodhotels.com
SIC: 7011 Traveler accommodations
PA: Starwood Hotels & Resorts
1111 Westchester Ave
White Plains NY 10604
914 640-8100

(G-5746)
STEEN ENGINEERING INC
5430 Douglas Dr N   (55429-3106)
PHONE............................763 585-6742
FAX: 763 585-6757
Mark Brengman, *President*
Eugene A Striefel, *Corp Secy*
Steve Young, *Vice Pres*
Steven M Youngs, *CFO*
Gene Striesel, *Treasurer*
EMP: 27 **EST:** 1993
SALES (est): 1MM-4.9MM **Privately Held**
WEB: www.steeneng.com
SIC: 8711 Engineering consulting services

(G-5747)
STEIN INDUSTRIES INC   (HQ)
7153 Northland Dr N   (55428-1563)
PHONE............................763 504-3500
FAX: 763 531-8384
Thomas Meyers, *CEO*
Norman R Stein, *Ch of Bd*
Michael J Stein, *Co-COB*
Frank J Reiter, *Vice Pres*
Allen Levy, *Credit Staff*
▲ **EMP:** 135 **EST:** 1960
SQ FT: 100,000 **Privately Held**
WEB: www.stein-industries.com
SIC: 5063 5046 Wholesales switches;
wholesales store fixtures & display
equipment; manufactures food products
machinery
PA: Stein Holdings Inc
7153 Northland Dr N
Minneapolis MN 55428
763 504-3500

(G-5748)
STEINE COLD STORAGE INC
2355 Polaris Ln N Ste 130   (55447-4758)
PHONE............................763 416-4681
Nicholas Steine, *President*
Gene Steine Sr, *Principal*
Teri Ernst, *Office Mgr*
EMP: 30 **EST:** 1973
SQ FT: 10,000
SALES (est): 1MM-4.9MM **Privately Held**
WEB: www.steinecoldstorage.com
SIC: 1711 Refrigeration contractor

(PA)=Parent Co (HQ)=Headquarters (DH)=Div Headquarters
✿ = New business established in last 2 years

2011 Harris Minnesota
Services Directory

© Harris InfoSource 1-866-281-6415
253

SIC: **8713** Surveying service

(G-5749)
STEP BY STEP MONTESSORI SCHOOL (PA)
4355 Highway 169 N (55442-2855)
PHONE...........................763 557-6777
FAX: 763 920-3310
Rosalie Minor, *President*
Mark Gerling, *Vice Pres*
Erine Smith, *Office Mgr*
EMP: 29 EST: 1967
SQ FT: 15,000
SALES (corp-wide): 12M **Privately Held**
SIC: **8351** Preschool center; group day care center; child development center providing Montessori based instruction

(G-5750)
STEPHEN DONNELLY CO
5200 W 74th St (55439-2200)
PHONE...........................952 884-1848
Stephen Donnelly, *President*
Greg Dostal, *Vice Pres*
Kay Strand, *Office Mgr*
Bobbie J Dostal, *Manager*
EMP: 60 EST: 1981
SQ FT: 2,000
SALES (est): 5MM-9.9MM **Privately Held**
WEB: www.stuccoman.com
SIC: **1742** Plain or ornamental plastering contractor

(G-5751)
STEPHEN SCOTT MANAGEMENT INC
Also Called: Marina Associates
5402 Parkdale Dr Ste 200 (55416-1610)
PHONE...........................763 540-8600
Scott Bader, *Partner*
EMP: 27 EST: 1994
SALES (est): 1MM-4.9MM **Privately Held**
SIC: **6513** Apartment building operator

(G-5752)
STEVEN CABINETS INC
2211 E Hennepin Ave (55413-2714)
PHONE...........................612 378-1812
FAX: 612 378-0026
Douglas M Steven, *President*
Zach Steven, *Vice Pres*
EMP: 26 EST: 1964
SQ FT: 25,000
SALES (est): 1MM-4.9MM **Privately Held**
WEB: www.stevencabinets.com
SIC: **1521** Retails custom made cabinets; single-family home general remodeling service

(G-5753)
STEVEN FABRICS CO
600 Hoover St NE (55413-2903)
PHONE...........................612 781-6671
FAX: 612 781-2135
Richard M Schommer, *President*
Dick Merhar, *Vice Pres*
Holly Wangsness, *Marketing Mgr*
Ed Lavery, *Marketing Mgr*
Jim Woodworth, *Info Tech Mgr*
EMP: 150 EST: 1946
SQ FT: 48,000
SALES (est): 50MM-99.9MM **Privately Held**
SIC: **5131** 5023 Wholesales woven drapery material; manufactures window blinds; manufactures window shades; wholesales Venetian blinds

(G-5754)
STEVEN SCOTT MANAGEMENT INC
5402 Parkdale Dr Ste 200 (55416-1610)
PHONE...........................952 540-8600
Steven Schachtman, *President*
Scott Bader, *Exec VP*
Sidney Bader, *Vice Pres*
Melissa Klauer, *Human Res Mgr*
David L Paveka, *Manager*
EMP: 30 EST: 1992
SQ FT: 6,000
SALES (est): 5MM-9.9MM **Privately Held**
WEB: www.aaapartments.com
SIC: **6531** 6513 Real estate management services; apartment building operator

(G-5755)
STEVENS FOSTER' FINANCIAL
7901 Xerxes Ave S Ste 325 (55431-1220)
PHONE...........................952 843-4200
FAX: 952 843-4404
William H Stevens, *President*
Lynette E Bollom, *Vice Pres*
Jeffrey A Johnson, *Vice Pres*
Tom Luing, *CFO*
Scott D Neslun, *Manager*
EMP: 25 EST: 1988
SALES (est): Under 500K **Privately Held**
WEB: www.stevensfoster.com
SIC: **7291** Tax return preparation services

(G-5756)
STEWART TITLE OF MINNESOTA (DH)
1700 W 82nd St Ste 100 (55431-1465)
PHONE...........................763 422-1116
Dave Fauth, *President*
Anne Crandall, *Vice Pres*
Sandy Johnson, *Vice Pres*
Janiel Lee, *Vice Pres*
Malissa Johnson, *Project Mgr*
EMP: 45 EST: 1978
SALES (corp-wide): 1.70B **Publicly Held**
WEB: www.stewartmn.com
SIC: **6361** Title insurance carrier
HQ: Stewart Title Guaranty Co
    1980 Post Oak Blvd Fl 8
    Houston TX 77056
    713 625-8100

(G-5757)
STIFEL, NICOLAUS & CO INC
5500 Wayzata Blvd # 1400 (55416-1578)
PHONE...........................763 542-3700
Joe Buska, *Principal*
Victor Greenstein, *Senior VP*
Todd Miller, *CFO*
EMP: 32
SALES (est): 5MM-9.9MM **Publicly Held**
WEB: www.stefel.com
SIC: **6211** Security broker & dealer service
HQ: Stifel, Nicolaus & Co Inc
    501 N Broadway Fl 8
    Saint Louis MO 63102
    314 342-2000

(G-5758)
STRATEGIC TECHNOLOGIES INC
9905 45th Ave N Ste 220 (55442-2500)
PHONE...........................763 559-1959
FAX: 763 557-1400
Carl Thelen, *President*
Gavin Roberson, *Info Tech Mgr*
Claude Wallander, *Software Dev*
EMP: 34 EST: 1994
SALES (est): 1MM-4.9MM **Privately Held**
WEB: www.sti2000.com
SIC: **7371** Computer software development

(G-5759)
STRATIS HEALTH
2901 Metro Dr Ste 400 (55425-1529)
PHONE...........................952 854-3306
FAX: 952 853-8503
Patricia Riley, *President*
Joan Gusafson, *Vice Pres*
Mary Lou, *Vice Pres*
Michael Novak, *CFO*
Francis Kamara, *Controller*
EMP: 57 EST: 1971
SQ FT: 20,293 **Privately Held**
SIC: **8399** 8011 Health systems agency; physicians' office & clinic

(G-5760)
STRUCTURAL RESTORATION INC
811 E 54th St (55417-1728)
PHONE...........................612 825-8614
FAX: 612 825-0996
Charles T Threet, *President*
EMP: 25 EST: 1958
SQ FT: 1,200
SALES (est): 5MM-9.9MM **Privately Held**
WEB: www.structuralrestoration.com
SIC: **1542** 1541 1622 Commercial & office building renovation & repair services; bridge construction; grain elevator construction

(G-5761)
SUBURBAN PLASTIC SURGERY
Also Called: Smith, David O MD
6545 France Ave S Ste 505 (55435-2116)
PHONE...........................952 922-0895
David Smith, *Owner*
Nancy L Kraska, *Office Mgr*
June Nelson, *Office Mgr*
Timothy G Schaefer, *Plastic Surgeon*
Nicole Olson, *Nursing Dir*
EMP: 72 EST: 1988
SALES (est): 5MM-9.9MM **Privately Held**
SIC: **8011** Plastic surgeon office

(G-5762)
SUBURBAN RADIOLOGIC CONSLNTS (PA)
4801 W 81st St Ste 108 (55437-1111)
PHONE...........................952 837-9700
Sue Crook, *CEO*
Mary Allen, *Govt Rel Mgr*
EMP: 75 EST: 1971
SQ FT: 4,000 **Privately Held**
WEB: www.fibroidinfo.com
SIC: **8011** 8741 Radiologist office; management services

(G-5763)
SUMMIT ACADEMY OIC
935 Olson Memorial Hwy (55405-1359)
PHONE...........................612 377-0150
FAX: 612 377-0156
Louis J King II, *President*
James Burroughs, *Vice Pres*
Marc Carrier, *CFO*
Joe Kirby, *Controller*
Leroy West, *Finance Other*
EMP: 55 EST: 1966
SQ FT: 60,000
SALES (est): 1MM-4.9MM **Privately Held**
SIC: **8331** Vocational training agency

(G-5764)
SUMMIT MORTGAGE CORP (PA)
13355 10th Ave N Ste 100 (55441-5554)
PHONE...........................763 390-7200
Robert Carter, *President*
Diana J Clarke Carter, *Corp Secy*
Diana C Carter, *Corp Secy*
Diana L Henson, *Vice Pres*
Larry Henson, *Vice Pres*
EMP: 45 EST: 1992
SQ FT: 13,000
SALES (corp-wide): 31.08M **Privately Held**
WEB: www.summit-mortgage.com
SIC: **6163** Mortgage brokers service arranging for loans, using money of others

(G-5765)
SUNDANCE STAFFING MINNESOTA
12805 Highway 55 Ste 106 (55441-3860)
PHONE...........................763 559-7700
Judith A Allen, *Member*
EMP: 100 EST: 2007
SALES (est): 1MM-4.9MM **Privately Held**
WEB: www.sundancestaffingmn.com
SIC: **7363** Help supply services

(G-5766)
SUNDAY LAND SURVEYING
9001 E Bloomington Fwy # 118
(55420-3487)
PHONE...........................952 881-2455
Scott Soukup, *Partner*
Mark S Hanson, *Partner*
EMP: 35
SALES (est): 1MM-4.9MM **Privately Held**
SIC: **8713** Surveying service

(G-5767)
SUNDE LAND SURVEYING LLC
9001 E Bloomington Fwy # 118
(55420-3439)
PHONE...........................952 881-2455
Scott Soukup, *Partner*
Mark Hanson, *Partner*
John Barnes, *Partner*
EMP: 34 EST: 1975
SQ FT: 5,000
SALES (est): 1MM-4.9MM **Privately Held**
WEB: www.sunde.com

(G-5768)
SUNRISE PAINTING
12975 16th Ave N Ste 400 (55441-4572)
PHONE...........................763 557-0100
FAX: 763 557-0011
Kelly Peifer, *President*
Ross Larson, *Vice Pres*
Kim Larson, *CFO*
Rita Sylte, *Executive*
EMP: 40 EST: 1974
SQ FT: 7,000
SALES (est): 1MM-4.9MM **Privately Held**
WEB:
www.sunrisepaintingandwallcovering.com
SIC: **1721** Commercial painting contractor; wall covering contractor

(G-5769)
SUNRISE SENIOR LIVING INC
7128 France Ave S (55435-4301)
PHONE...........................952 927-8000
FAX: 952 927-6400
M Duncan, *Sales Staff*
Maria Lemcke, *Exec Dir*
Renae Witschem, *Exec Dir*
Ardeth Schmiege, *Director*
EMP: 60
SALES (est): 1MM-4.9MM **Publicly Held**
WEB: www.sunrise.com
SIC: **8361** 8052 Residential care facility; intermediate care facility
PA: Sunrise Senior Living Inc
    7900 Westpark Dr Ste T900
    Mc Lean VA 22102
    703 273-7500

(G-5770)
SUPERCUTS INC (HQ)
7201 Metro Blvd (55439-2131)
PHONE...........................952 947-7777
Paul Finkelstein, *CEO*
Mark Kartaric, *President*
Diane Calta, *COO*
Paul Plate, *CFO*
Randy L Pearce, *CFO*
▲ EMP: 800 EST: 1975
SQ FT: 100,000
SALES (corp-wide): 2.35B **Publicly Held**
WEB: www.supercuts.com
SIC: **7231** Unisex hair salon
PA: Regis Corp
    7201 Metro Blvd
    Minneapolis MN 55439
    952 947-7777

(G-5771)
SUPERIOR FORD INC
9700 56th Ave N (55442-1613)
PHONE...........................763 559-9111
FAX: 763 519-6318
Tom Rebiola, *President*
Grant Osgood, *Manager*
Linda Blom, *Manager*
EMP: 115 EST: 1979
SQ FT: 70,000
SALES (est): 50MM-99.9MM **Privately Held**
WEB: www.superiorford.com
SIC: **7513** 7515 7538 Retails new & used automobiles; general automotive repair services; retails new & used pickups; retails new & used trucks, tractors & trailers; passenger car leasing; used car dealer; truck leasing & rental without drivers

(G-5772)
SURESERVICES INC
7317 39th Ave N (55427-1361)
PHONE...........................763 531-0029
Phyllis Schurz, *President*
Debi Schurz, *Corp Secy*
James Schurz, *Vice Pres*
David Schurz, *Treasurer*
EMP: 45 EST: 1987
SALES (est): 1MM-4.9MM **Privately Held**
SIC: **8331** 7363 Community services employment training program; domestic help service

(G-5773)
SURFACEQUEST INC
7760 France Ave S # 1400 (55435-5800)
PHONE...........................952 361-9431
James R Troutfetter, *CEO*
Thomas Roe, *President*

www.HarrisInfo.com
254

2011 Harris Minnesota
Services Directory

▲=Import ▼=Export
◆=Import/Export

Scott Roth, *Vice Pres*
EST: 1997
SQ FT: 2,300 **Privately Held**
WEB: www.surfacequest.com
SIC: 5169 Wholesales surface active
agents

(G-5774)
SURGICAL CARE AFFILIATES LLC
7373 France Ave S Ste 404 (55435-4549)
PHONE 952 832-9360
FAX: 952 835-6867
Pamela Stohn, *Branch Mgr*
Olga L Pamer, *Manager*
Martin Adson, *Manager*
Pamela Spohn, *Administrator*
EMP: 45
SALES (est): 5MM-9.9MM **Privately Held**
SIC: 8011 Surgeon's office
PA: Surgical Care Affiliates LLC
3000 Riverchase Galleria
Birmingham AL 35244
205 545-2572

(G-5775)
SURGICAL CONSULTANTS PROF (PA)
4570 W 77th St Ste 235 (55435-5092)
PHONE 952 832-0805
FAX: 952 835-9964
Christopher Roland, *President*
Stephanie Kronberg, *Business Mgr*
Cara Ashenbrenner, *Office Mgr*
Jerry Poehling, *Manager*
Paul L Benn, *Surgeon*
EMP: 45 **EST:** 1969
SQ FT: 2,500 **Privately Held**
WEB: www.mnsurg.com
SIC: 8011 Surgeon's office

(G-5776)
SUSTAINABLE RESOURCES CENTER
1081 10th Ave SE (55414-1312)
PHONE 612 870-4255
Margaret Weber, *Principal*
Sue Gunderson, *Director*
EMP: 33 **EST:** 1976
SQ FT: 5,000
SALES (est): 1MM-4.9MM **Privately Held**
SIC: 8748 1799 8322 Energy conservation
consultant; weather stripping contractor;
individual & family social services

(G-5777)
SWANSON MEATS INC
2700 26th Ave S (55406-1527)
PHONE 612 721-4411
Mark Mann, *President*
Fred Williams, *Accounts Mgr*
EMP: 55 **EST:** 1962
SQ FT: 30,000
SALES (est): 50MM-99.9MM **Privately Held**
WEB: www.garlandsinc.com
SIC: 5147 Wholesales meat & meat
products
PA: Christofersen Meats Co
2700 26th Ave S
Minneapolis MN 55406
612 721-4411

(G-5778)
SWENSON NHB INVESTOR RELATIONS
150 S 5th St Ste 1300 (55402-4213)
PHONE 612 371-0000
FAX: 612 371-0707
Curtis Swenson, *Owner*
Vick Crespin, *Vice Pres*
EMP: 26 **EST:** 1999
SALES (est): 1MM-4.9MM **Privately Held**
SIC: 8743 Public relations services

(G-5779)
SYNERGISTIC SOFTWARE SOLN
2 Meridian Xing Ste 310 (55423-3946)
PHONE 612 367-7300
Chuck Wunderlich, *President*
Cindy Olson, *Vice Pres*
Tom Frishberg, *Manager*
Tad Tjornhom, *Manager*
Amy Knust, *Manager*
EMP: 25 **EST:** 2001

SALES (est): 5MM-9.9MM **Privately Held**
WEB: www.jobops.com
SIC: 7372 Software publisher

(G-5780)
SYNICO STAFFING INC
3033 Excelsior Blvd (55416-4688)
PHONE 612 926-6000
Robert Marsh, *President*
Jerry Marsh, *Vice Pres*
William Gilbert, *Controller*
Katherine Dufek, *Manager*
Catherine Dufek, *Manager*
EMP: 800 **EST:** 2006
SQ FT: 3,000
SALES (est): 10MM-24.9MM **Privately Held**
WEB: www.synico.com
SIC: 7363 Temporary help service

(G-5781)
SYSTEM DESIGN ADVANTAGE LLC
9655 Penn Ave S (55431-2520)
PHONE 952 703-3500
Lisa Sahli, *CFO*
Tammy Fhareck, *Accountant*
Jim Sahli, *Mng Member*
EMP: 50 **EST:** 1992
SQ FT: 42,000
SALES (est): 5MM-9.9MM **Privately Held**
WEB: www.sdallc.com
SIC: 7629 5045 7378 Electric business
machine repair service; wholesales
personal & home entertainment computers
& accessories; retails computers &
computer software; computer & office
machine maintenance & repair services

(G-5782)
SYSTEMARMED USACOM INC ✪
5716 Nicollet Ave (55419-2415)
PHONE 877 900-0238
Timothy West, *CEO*
EMP: 542 **EST:** 2010
SALES (est): 25MM-49.9MM **Privately Held**
SIC: 7382 Security systems services

(G-5783)
T C B X INC
1912 Broadway St NE (55413-2619)
PO Box 325, Brainerd (56401-0325)
PHONE 651 644-5547
Pat Obrien, *President*
Tim O Brien, *Vice Pres*
EMP: 30 **EST:** 1911
SALES (est): 1MM-4.9MM **Privately Held**
SIC: 4212 Light local haulage & cartage
services

(G-5784)
TACTILE SYSTEMS TECHNOLOGY INC
1331 Tyler St NE Ste 200 (55413-1638)
PHONE 952 224-4060
FAX: 952 224-4061
Jerry Mattys, *President*
David Idstrom, *Finance*
EMP: 80 **EST:** 2004
SALES (est): 25MM-49.9MM **Privately Held**
SIC: 5047 Wholesales medical & hospital
equipment

(G-5785)
TAILWIND VOICE & DATA INC
15350 25th Ave N Ste 114 (55447-2081)
PHONE 763 577-4000
Paul Sugimura, *CEO*
Andy Siemens, *President*
Sue Jones, *Accountant*
Chirs Swanson, *Manager*
EMP: 40 **EST:** 2002
SQ FT: 10,000 **Privately Held**
WEB: www.tailwindvoiceanddata.com
SIC: 4813 Wired telecommunications carrier
& service

(G-5786)
TALENT TECHNICAL SERVICES INC
5353 Wayzata Blvd Ste 200 (55416-1316)
PHONE 952 417-3600
FAX: 952 417-3636
David Iacarella, *President*
Mike Egland, *VP Opers*

Jeff Bentler, *CFO*
Jerry Bentler, *Manager*
Joe Kanyok, *Manager*
EMP: 133 **EST:** 1987
SQ FT: 4,000
SALES (est): 10MM-24.9MM **Privately Held**
WEB: www.talktotalent.com
SIC: 7371 8742 Custom computer software
systems analysis & design service; general
management consultant

(G-5787)
TALISMAN BROOKDALE LLC
1108 Brookdale Ctr (55430-2802)
PHONE 763 566-3373
Sharon Broin, *General Mgr*
EMP: 40 **EST:** 1997
SALES (est): 10MM-24.9MM **Privately Held**
SIC: 6512 Nonresidential building operator

(G-5788)
TANDEM PRODUCTS INC (PA)
3444 Dight Ave (55406-2620)
PHONE 612 721-2911
FAX: 612 721-1009
Nash Helmy, *President*
EMP: 25 **EST:** 1978
SQ FT: 75,000 **Privately Held**
SIC: 5162 Manufactures molded plastic
products; wholesales plastics sheets & rods

(G-5789)
TARGET BRANDS INC
33 S 6th St (55402-3601)
PHONE 612 304-6073
FAX: 612 304-3731
Erica Street, *President*
Lee Lorquin, *Buyer*
Bill Frauly, *Technical Mgr*
Gary Johnson, *Technical Mgr*
Omar Valencia, *Technical Mgr*
EMP: 28 **EST:** 1998
SALES (est): 1MM-4.9MM **Publicly Held**
WEB: www.target.com
SIC: 7336 Commercial art & graphic design
services
PA: Target Corp
1000 Nicollet Mall
Minneapolis MN 55403
612 304-6073

(G-5790)
TARGET CORP
7000 Target Pkwy N (55445-4301)
PO Box 59251 (55459-0251)
PHONE 763 440-2033
Tammy Albers, *Human Res Mgr*
Sandy Koessler, *Branch Mgr*
Steve Amiot, *Manager*
Thomas Guza, *Analyst*
EMP: 400
SALES (est): 25MM-49.9MM **Publicly Held**
WEB: www.target.com
SIC: 8742 Human resource consulting
services
PA: Target Corp
1000 Nicollet Mall
Minneapolis MN 55403
612 304-6073

(G-5791)
TARGET CORP
33 S 6th St Ste CC1 (55402-3730)
PHONE 612 304-6073
Ralph Salo, *Group*
EMP: 200
SALES (est): 25MM-49.9MM **Publicly Held**
WEB: www.target.com
SIC: 4226 Warehousing & storage facility
PA: Target Corp
1000 Nicollet Mall
Minneapolis MN 55403
612 304-6073

(G-5792)
TASKS UNLIMITED INC (PA)
2419 Nicollet Ave (55404-3450)
PHONE 612 871-3320
FAX: 612 871-0432
Kem Pazdernik, *Corp Secy*
Larry Aldrich, *Controller*
Bruce Chelberg, *Manager*
John K Trepp, *Exec Dir*
Misty Snyder, *Coordinator*
EMP: 38

EST: 1965
SQ FT: 5,200
SALES (corp-wide): 618.37K **Privately
Held**
WEB: www.tasksunlimited.org
SIC: 8361 Residential care for the
handicapped

(G-5793)
TAX-SHELTERED COMPENSATION INC
7300 Metro Blvd Ste 450 (55439-2328)
PHONE 952 806-4300
FAX: 952 806-4330
Gary Zurek, *President*
Mark Foster, *Vice Pres*
Kay Teslow, *Data Proc Dir*
EMP: 32 **EST:** 1969
SALES (est): 1MM-4.9MM **Privately Held**
WEB: www.tsc401k.com
SIC: 6411 Pension & retirement plan
consulting service

(G-5794)
TAYLOR CORP
Also Called: Litho Tech Custom Cover
1600 W 92nd St (55431-2322)
PHONE 952 888-7945
Jeff Olsen, *Branch Mgr*
EMP: 125
SALES (est): 10MM-24.9MM **Privately Held**
WEB: www.lithotechusa.com
SIC: 8742 Management consulting services;
commercial lithographic printing
PA: Taylor Corp
1725 Roe Crest Dr
North Mankato MN 56003
507 625-2828

(G-5795)
TAYLOR LIMOUSINES INC
Also Called: Premier Limousine
4225 Hiawatha Ave (55406-3329)
PHONE 612 722-4467
David Taylor, *President*
Larry Deiman, *General Mgr*
Janet Cherrier, *Vice Pres*
EMP: 125 **EST:** 1983
SQ FT: 12,000
SALES (est): 5MM-9.9MM **Privately Held**
SIC: 4119 4111 Limousine service; airport
transportation services

(G-5796)
TCF EQUIPMENT FINANCE INC (DH)
801 Marquette Ave (55402-2840)
PHONE 952 656-5080
Craig Dahl, *President*
George Johnson, *Managing Dir*
Joseph T Green, *Corp Secy*
Douglas B Hiatt, *Corp Secy*
Bill Henak, *Exec VP*
EMP: 110 **EST:** 1999
SALES (corp-wide): 1.48B **Publicly Held**
WEB: www.merrilliron.com
SIC: 6035 Federal savings bank
HQ: TCF National Bank
801 Marquette Ave
Minneapolis MN 55402
612 661-6500

(G-5797)
TCF NATIONAL BANK
1501 University Ave SE (55414-2039)
PHONE 612 379-8597
Jill Longnecker, *Branch Mgr*
EMP: 35
SALES (est): 10MM-24.9MM **Publicly Held**
WEB: www.merrilliron.com
SIC: 6035 Federal savings & loan
association
HQ: TCF National Bank
801 Marquette Ave
Minneapolis MN 55402
612 661-6500

(G-5798)
TCF NATIONAL BANK
7800 Penn Ave S (55431-1313)
PHONE 952 888-8375
Valeri Parker-Carr, *Finance Other*
Valerie Parker, *Manager*
EMP: 25
SALES (est): 5MM-9.9MM **Publicly Held**

(PA)=Parent Co (HQ)=Headquarters (DH)=Div Headquarters
✪ = New business established in last 2 years

2011 Harris Minnesota
Services Directory

© Harris InfoSource 1-866-281-6415
255

WEB: www.merrilliron.com
SIC: **6035** Federal savings & loan association
HQ: TCF National Bank
801 Marquette Ave
Minneapolis MN 55402
612 661-6500

(G-5799)
TCF NATIONAL BANK (HQ)
801 Marquette Ave (55402-2807)
PHONE................612 661-6500
FAX: 612 661-8598
William Cooper, *CEO*
Robert Scott, *President*
Gregory J Pulles, *Corp Secy*
Sara L Evers, *Exec VP*
Claire Graupmann, *Exec VP*
▲ EMP: 100 EST: 1923
SQ FT: 120,000
SALES (corp-wide): 1.48B **Publicly Held**
WEB: www.merrilliron.com
SIC: **6021** National commercial bank
PA: TCF Financial Corp
200 Lake St E
Wayzata MN 55391
952 745-2760

(G-5800)
TCI GROUP INC
4301 Lyndale Ave S (55409-1815)
PHONE................612 823-6214
Beth Fischer, *President*
Elise Fine, *Director*
EMP: 50 EST: 1952
SALES (est): 1MM-4.9MM **Privately Held**
SIC: **8732** Market analysis or research services

(G-5801)
TCS MORTGAGE INC
Also Called: Discover Mortgage
2801 Wayzata Blvd Ste 101 (55405-2130)
PHONE................612 767-5002
Bruce Claussen, *Manager*
EMP: 25
SALES (est): 1MM-4.9MM **Publicly Held**
WEB: www.whyusa.com
SIC: **6162** Mortgage banking service
HQ: TCS Mortgage Inc
2801 Wayzata Blvd Ste 101
Minneapolis MN 55405
612 767-5002

(G-5802)
TEACHING TEMPS INC
4050 Olson Memorial Hwy (55422-5323)
PHONE................763 797-9000
Joseph T Noonen, *President*
EMP: 50 EST: 1991
SALES (est): 1MM-4.9MM **Privately Held**
SIC: **7363** Temporary help service

(G-5803)
TEAMSTERS LOCAL 2000
Also Called: Local 2000 Airline Attendants
3001 University Ave SE # 510 (55414-3344)
PHONE................612 379-9157
Dottie Malinsky, *President*
Danny Campbell, *President*
Bruce E Retrum, *President*
Lynn Miller, *Treasurer*
Vicki Lehnen, *Manager*
EMP: 30 EST: 1992
SQ FT: 4,600 **Privately Held**
SIC: **8631** Labor union

(G-5804)
TECHNE CORP (PA)
614 McKinley Pl NE (55413-2610)
PHONE................612 379-8854
Thomas E Oland, *President*
Roger C Lucas, *Vice Chairman*
Charles A Dinrello, *Safety Dir*
David Clausen, *Facilities Mgr*
Marcel Veronneau, *VP Opers-Prdtn-*
EMP: 514 EST: 1981
SQ FT: 500,000
SALES (corp-wide): 269.04M **Publicly Held**
WEB: www.techne-corp.com
SIC: **8731** Manufactures microbiology & virology diagnostic products; manufactures hematology diagnostic agents; commercial physical research laboratory

(G-5805)
TECH CENTRAL INC
3300 Edinbrgh Way Ste 204 (55435-5958)
PHONE................952 837-8000
FAX: 952 837-8001
John Jay, *President*
Katheryn Hammond, *Partner*
Judith Niles, *Coordinator*
EMP: 120 EST: 1990
SALES (est): 1MM-4.9MM **Privately Held**
WEB: www.diversitymn.com
SIC: **7363** 7361 Engineering help service; employment agency services

(G-5806)
TECHPOWER INC
9340 James Ave S (55431-2317)
PHONE................952 831-7444
FAX: 952 831-8621
Kent Mueller, *President*
EMP: 25 EST: 1969
SQ FT: 4,000
SALES (est): 1MM-4.9MM **Privately Held**
WEB: www.techpower.com
SIC: **1731** Telephone equipment installation

(G-5807)
TEKSYSTEMS INC
7505 Metro Blvd Ste 450 (55439-3045)
PHONE................952 886-4800
FAX: 952 886-4990
Tom Cody, *Manager*
Ruff Orning, *Manager*
Wendy Medina, *Supervisor*
Darin Brooks, *IT/INT Sup*
Todd Fisher, *Asst Director*
EMP: 40
SALES (est): 5MM-9.9MM **Privately Held**
WEB: www.teksystems.com
SIC: **7379** Computer system consulting services
HQ: TEKsystems Inc
7437 Race Rd
Hanover MD 21076
410 579-3000

(G-5808)
TELECONCEPTS INC
7111 W Broadway Ave Ste 203 (55428-1695)
PHONE................763 566-5360
FAX: 763 566-5460
Sam Riemensnider, *President*
Marcia G Walker, *Vice Pres*
EMP: 25 EST: 1986
SQ FT: 1,942
SALES (est): 500-999K **Privately Held**
SIC: **7389** Telemarketing services

(G-5809)
TELEMARKETING RESULTS INC
Also Called: Tri
3131 Fernbrook Ln N Ste 2 (55447-5321)
PHONE................763 519-0874
EMP: 30 EST: 1999
SALES (est): 1MM-4.9MM **Privately Held**
SIC: **7389** Telemarketing services

(G-5810)
TEN THOUSAND THINGS THEATRE
3153 36th Ave S (55406-2126)
PHONE................612 724-4494
Michelle Henseley, *President*
Teresa Eyring, *Exec Dir*
EMP: 40 EST: 1990
SALES (est): 1MM-4.9MM **Privately Held**
SIC: **7832** 7922 Indoor movie theater; theatrical producers & services

(G-5811)
TENET PAINTING
7435 Washington Ave S (55439-2410)
PHONE................952 914-9550
Terry Marlette, *President*
Scott Allen, *Prdtn Mgr*
Wade Jessop, *Prdtn Mgr*
Mike Kumpula, *Prdtn Mgr*
Nate Hopeman, *Sales & Mktg St*
EMP: 90 EST: 2002
SALES (est): 5MM-9.9MM **Privately Held**
WEB: www.tenetpainting.com

SIC: **1721** Painting & wall covering contractor

(G-5812)
THD AT-HOME SERVICES INC
656 Mendelssohn Ave N (55427-4306)
PHONE................763 542-8826
Brian Ecklund, *Branch Mgr*
EMP: 65
SALES (est): 5MM-9.9MM **Publicly Held**
SIC: **8741** Construction management services
DH: Thd At-Home Services Inc
2690 Cumberland Pkwy SE # 300
Atlanta GA 30339
770 779-1300

(G-5813)
THEISEN VENDING INC
2335 Nevada Ave N (55427-3609)
PHONE................612 827-5588
FAX: 612 827-7543
Thomas N Theisen, *President*
Anita Bennett, *General Mgr*
Daniel Wright, *Controller*
▲ EMP: 55 EST: 1960
SQ FT: 35,000
SALES (est): 5MM-9.9MM **Privately Held**
WEB: www.theisenvending.com
SIC: **5046** 7993 Merchandising machine operator; amusement arcade; wholesales coin-operated vending machines

(G-5814)
THINK EQUITY PARTNERS LLC
80 S 8th St Ste 1200 (55402-2133)
PHONE................612 677-5757
Robert McClanahan, *Managing Dir*
Deborah Quazzo, *Member*
Michael Moe, *Member*
Kim Wiley, *Human Res Mgr*
Charles Vacek, *Info Tech Dir*
EMP: 180 EST: 2002
SALES (est): 100MM-499.9MM **Privately Held**
WEB: www.stinkequity.com
SIC: **6211** Investment banking service

(G-5815)
THIRD WAVE SYSTEMS INC
7900 W 78th St Ste 300 (55439-2577)
PHONE................952 832-5515
FAX: 952 844-0202
Kerry J Marusich, *CEO*
Lisa A Ferris, *COO*
Andrew Grevstad, *Engineer*
David A Stephenson, *VP Eng R&D*
Amanada Taylor, *Manager*
EMP: 25 EST: 1993
SQ FT: 1,200
SALES (est): 1MM-4.9MM **Privately Held**
WEB: www.thirdwavesys.com
SIC: **8711** Engineering services

(G-5816)
THM MASTER TE LLC ✪
Also Called: Hotel Minneapolis
215 S 4th St (55401-1709)
PHONE................612 340-2000
Russ Huhner, *Member*
EMP: 100 EST: 2008
SALES (est): 5MM-9.9MM **Privately Held**
SIC: **7011** Traveler accommodations
PA: H E I Hospitality LLC
101 Merritt 7
Norwalk CT 06851
203 849-8844

(G-5817)
THOMAS CHARLES SALON II INC
4008 Minnetonka Blvd (55416-4127)
PHONE................952 925-4277
Michele Odegaard, *President*
EMP: 30 EST: 1994
SALES (est): 500-999K **Privately Held**
SIC: **7231** Beauty salon

(G-5818)
THOMAS M MEYER ENTERPRISES INC
Also Called: Home Energy Center
2415 Annapolis Ln N # 170 (55441-3674)
PHONE................763 476-1990
FAX: 763 476-1143
Thomas M Meyer, *President*
Rosemary Meyer, *Corp Secy*
J S Woolery, *Vice Pres*
EMP: 42 EST: 1981
SQ FT: 4,000
SALES (est): 5MM-9.9MM **Privately Held**
WEB: www.homeenergycenter.com
SIC: **1711** Warm air heating & air conditioning contractor

(G-5819)
THRIVENT FINANCIAL FOR (PA)
625 4th Ave S Ste 100 (55415-1625)
PHONE................920 734-5721
Bruce J Nicholson, *President*
Teresa J Rasmussen, *Corp Secy*
Jon Stellmacher, *Exec VP*
David Anderson, *Senior VP*
Randy Boushek, *Senior VP*
▲ EMP: 1300 EST: 1902
SQ FT: 438,660 **Privately Held**
WEB: www.thrivent.com
SIC: **6311** 6211 6321 6411 8742 Fraternal life insurance organization; management consulting services; fraternal accident & health insurance organization; insurance services; securities broker & dealer

(G-5820)
THRIVENT LIFE INSURANCE CO
625 4th Ave S Ste 100 (55415-1625)
PHONE................612 340-7000
FAX: 612 340-8436
Bruce Nicholson, *President*
David J Larson, *Corp Secy*
Rolf F Bjelland, *Exec VP*
William H Reichwald, *Exec VP*
Anita Young, *Treasurer*
EMP: 151 EST: 1982
SQ FT: 438,660
SALES (est): 10MM-24.9MM **Privately Held**
WEB: www.thrivent.com
SIC: **6411** Insurance services
PA: Thrivent Financial For
625 4th Ave S Ste 100
Minneapolis MN 55415
920 734-5721

(G-5821)
TIERNEY BROTHERS INC
3300 University Ave SE (55414-3326)
PHONE................612 331-5500
FAX: 612 331-3424
Tom Tierney, *President*
Susan Nelson, *COO*
Tom Gust, *Purchasing*
James Tierney, *CFO*
Neva Zonn, *Controller*
EMP: 80 EST: 1976
SQ FT: 15,000
SALES (est): 25MM-49.9MM **Privately Held**
WEB: www.tierneybrothers.com
SIC: **5049** 5043 Wholesales engineers' equipment & supplies; wholesales motion picture equipment; manufactures household audio & video equipment

(G-5822)
TIFFANY & CO
3624 Galleria (55435-4220)
PHONE................952 922-0066
FAX: 952 922-9191
Kathleen Buchanan, *Director*
EMP: 30
SALES (est): 10MM-24.9MM **Publicly Held**
WEB: www.tiffany.com
SIC: **5094** Wholesales jewelry
PA: Tiffany & Co
727 5th Ave
New York NY 10022
212 755-8000

(G-5823)
TILE BY DESIGN INC
1720 Annapolis Ln N (55441-3701)
PHONE................763 551-5900
FAX: 763 551-5999

www.HarrisInfo.com
256
2011 Harris Minnesota
Services Directory
▲=Import ▼=Export
◆=Import/Export

Delmar Emmel, *CEO*
Gary Haverman, *Manager*
▲ **EMP:** 32 **EST:** 1990
SQ FT: 22,000
SALES (est): 5MM-9.9MM **Privately Held**
WEB: www.tilexdesign.com
SIC: 5032 Wholesales tile, clay or other ceramic construction materials; wholesales building stone

(G-5824)

TILE SHOP INC (PA)

14000 Carlson Pkwy (55441-5305)
PHONE 763 541-1444
Robert A Rucker, *President*
Dan Brester, *Store Mgr*
Joe Kinder, *Purch Mgr*
Jim Beukelman, *Controller*
Dacy Corley, *Manager*
▲ **EMP:** 25 **EST:** 1984
SQ FT: 30,000 **Privately Held**
WEB: www.tileshop.com
SIC: 5023 Retails floor tile; wholesales tile or sheet resilient floor coverings

(G-5825)

TILE SHOP LLC

14000 Carlson Pkwy (55441-5305)
PHONE 763 541-1444
Robert A Rucker, *Member*
◆ **EMP:** 45 **EST:** 1987
SQ FT: 30,000
SALES (est): 10MM-24.9MM **Privately Held**
SIC: 1743 5032 Manufactures paste adhesives; retails cemetery memorials; ceramic tile installation service; manufactures linoleum & tile cement; wholesales marble building stone

(G-5826)

TIMBERLAND GROUP INC

2635 Louisiana Ave S (55426-3107)
PO Box 26721 (55426-0721)
PHONE 952 924-9070
FAX: 952 924-9069
William Hibbs, *President*
EMP: 25 **EST:** 1992
SQ FT: 15,000
SALES (est): 1MM-4.9MM **Privately Held**
SIC: 7389 Packaging & labeling services; book binding service

(G-5827)

TIMBERLAND PARTNERS MANAGEMENT

8000 Norman Center Dr # 830
(55437-1193)
PHONE 952 893-1216
Robert Fransen, *President*
Brian Brink, *E-Business*
EMP: 100 **EST:** 1992
SQ FT: 6,161
SALES (est): 25MM-49.9MM **Privately Held**
SIC: 6512 6531 Nonresidential building operator; commercial real estate agency

(G-5828)

TK ADVISORS LTD

920 2nd Ave S Ste 1550 (55402-4033)
PHONE 612 373-9000
John Thorvilson, *President*
Allen Kaufmann, *Vice Pres*
Julie Swan, *CFO*
Christopher Link, *Treasurer*
Timothy Baranick, *Accounting Mgr*
EMP: 45 **EST:** 1970
SQ FT: 13,500
SALES (est): 1MM-4.9MM **Privately Held**
WEB: www.sotk.com
SIC: 8721 Certified public accountant services

(G-5829)

TOLL CO

3005 Niagara Ln N Ste 1 (55447-4857)
PHONE 763 551-5355
Thomas A Mc Grath, *President*
Tom Litchow, *Vice Pres*
James A Quicksell, *Vice Pres*
Tom Litzkow, *Finance Mgr*
Brian Berg, *Sales Staff*
EMP: 42 **EST:** 1945
SQ FT: 30,000
SALES (est): 25MM-49.9MM **Privately Held**

SIC: 5169 5084 Wholesales compressed & liquefied gases; liquefied petroleum gas dealer; retails tools; wholesales welding equipment & supplies

(G-5830)

TOP NOTCH TREECARE

5505 Highway 169 N # 200 (55442-1975)
PHONE 763 253-8733
David Nordgaard, *Owner*
Christina Nordgaard, *Office Mgr*
Debra Nordgaard, *Office Mgr*
Mike Engelbretson, *Manager*
Don Dehn, *Manager*
EMP: 32 **EST:** 1982
SQ FT: 4,000 **Privately Held**
WEB: www.topnotchtree.com
SIC: 0783 Ornamental shrub & tree service; planting, pruning & trimming services; bracing & surgery services

(G-5831)

TORO CREDIT CO

8111 Lyndale Ave S (55420-1136)
PHONE 952 888-8801
Steve Wolfe, *Chairman*
Colleen Beatty, *Executive Asst*
EMP: 26 **EST:** 1978
SQ FT: 4,500
SALES (est): 10MM-24.9MM **Publicly Held**
WEB: www.toro.com
SIC: 6159 Machinery & equipment finance leasing service
PA: Toro Co
    8111 Lyndale Ave S
    Bloomington MN 55420
    952 888-8801

(G-5832)

TORO LLC

8111 Lyndale Ave S (55420-1136)
PHONE 952 888-8801
Michael Hoffman, *Member*
Linda L Colliander, *Engrg Mgr*
Jim Gabebel, *Electrical Engi*
Steve Wolfe, *CFO*
David M Topos, *Controller*
◆ **EMP:** 4900 **EST:** 1999
SALES (est): 1B-9.9B **Publicly Held**
WEB: www.toro.com
SIC: 5083 Manufactures mowers & accessories; wholesales lawn & garden machinery & equipment
PA: Toro Co
    8111 Lyndale Ave S
    Bloomington MN 55420
    952 888-8801

(G-5833)

TORO RECEIVABLES CO

8111 Lyndale Ave S (55420-1136)
PHONE 952 888-8801
Michael Hoffman, *CEO*
EMP: 30
SALES (est): 1MM-4.9MM **Publicly Held**
WEB: www.toro.com
SIC: 8741 Business management services
PA: Toro Co
    8111 Lyndale Ave S
    Bloomington MN 55420
    952 888-8801

(G-5834)

TOTAL QUALITY MAINTENANCE

1 Westwood Dr N (55422-5256)
PO Box 7604, Rapid City SD
(57709-7604)
PHONE 763 377-6530
Ellen Glood, *CEO*
EMP: 65 **EST:** 2001
SQ FT: 2,000
SALES (est): 1MM-4.9MM **Privately Held**
SIC: 7349 Janitorial & custodial services

(G-5835)

TOTAL RENAL CARE INC

825 S 8th St Ste 400 (55404-1216)
PHONE 612 347-5972
Jeniefer Whipple, *Manager*
EMP: 33
SALES (est): 1MM-4.9MM **Publicly Held**
WEB: www.davita.com

SIC: 8092 Kidney dialysis center
PA: DaVita Inc
    1551 Wewatta St
    Denver CO 80202
    303 405-2100

(G-5836)

TOTAL RENAL CARE INC

Also Called: Davida
825 S 8th St Ste 400 (55404-1216)
PHONE 612 873-6089
Ken Thoery, *CEO*
Joe Melow, *CFO*
Arielle Hart, *Manager*
Gwen Beissel, *Manager*
EMP: 54 **EST:** 2007
SALES (est): 5MM-9.9MM **Publicly Held**
WEB: www.devita.com
SIC: 8011 Internal medicine practitioners
PA: DaVita Inc
    1551 Wewatta St
    Denver CO 80202
    303 405-2100

(G-5837)

TOTAL TRAINING NETWORK INC

7831 E Bush Lake Rd # 200 (55439-3131)
PHONE 952 345-5555
FAX: 952 345-1396
Gerald Cox, *President*
Michelle Bensen, *Accounting Mgr*
Kent Walker, *Sales Mgr*
Tim Tamlyn, *Sales Staff*
Doug McCann, *Manager*
EMP: 30 **EST:** 1997
SALES (est): 1MM-4.9MM **Privately Held**
WEB: www.ttnlearning.com
SIC: 8742 Training & development consultant

(G-5838)

TOURNAMENT CLUB OF IOWA LLC

6800 France Ave S Ste 178 (55435-2004)
PHONE 952 252-4474
Lee West, *Controller*
Jane Enebak, *Mng Member*
EMP: 25 **EST:** 2001
SALES (est): 500-999K **Privately Held**
SIC: 7997 Membership recreation club

(G-5839)

TOWERS WATSON DELAWARE INC

8400 Normandale Lake Blvd (55437-1085)
PHONE 952 842-7000
FAX: 952 842-6800
Marty Walsen, *VP Opers*
Michael Springer, *Engineering*
Robin C Hane, *Sls & Mktg Exec*
Paul Dingman, *Controller*
Skip Hacakney, *Branch Mgr*
EMP: 250
SALES (est): 25MM-49.9MM **Publicly Held**
WEB: www.watsonwyatt.com
SIC: 8742 7371 8999 Compensation & benefits planning consultant; actuarial consulting services; custom computer software systems analysis & design service; computer software development; human resource consulting services
HQ: Towers Watson Delaware
    901 N Glebe Rd Ste 500
    Arlington VA 22203
    703 258-8000

(G-5840)

TOWERS WATSON PENNSYLVANIA INC

7650 Edinbrgh Way Ste 500 (55435-6005)
PHONE 952 842-5600
James A Swanke Jr, *Principal*
Tim Feeser, *Principal*
Ted Lyle, *Vice Pres*
John Naylor, *Branch Mgr*
Jeff Kridler, *Consultant*
EMP: 50
SALES (est): 5MM-9.9MM **Publicly Held**
WEB: www.towers.com

SIC: 8742 6411 Management information systems consultant; pension & retirement plan consulting service; hospital & health services consultant
HQ: Towers Watson Pennsylvania Inc
    263 Tresser Blvd Fl 8
    Stamford CT 06901
    203 326-5400

(G-5841)

TOWN & COUNTRY FENCE INC

8511 Xylon Ave N (55445-1820)
PHONE 763 425-5050
Michael J Bistodeau, *President*
Pam Johnson, *Manager*
Tom Morneau, *Director*
EMP: 30 **EST:** 1983
SQ FT: 6,000
SALES (est): 1MM-4.9MM **Privately Held**
WEB: www.tcfence.com
SIC: 1799 5199 Fence construction contractor; wholesales pets & pet supplies

(G-5842)

TOYOTA CITY INC

7325 Brooklyn Blvd (55443-3302)
PHONE 763 566-0060
FAX: 763 566-0343
C D Luther, *President*
Michael E Sullivan, *Treasurer*
EMP: 93 **EST:** 1949
SQ FT: 24,120
SALES (est): 25MM-49.9MM **Privately Held**
WEB: www.toyota-city.com
SIC: 5013 7538 Retails new & used automobiles; general automotive repair services; wholesales new motor vehicle parts & supplies

(G-5843)

TPG CREDIT MANAGEMENT, LP

4600 Wells Fargo Ctr (55402)
PHONE 612 851-3000
Julie Braun, *Partner*
Jasica Dahl, *Manager*
EMP: 36 **EST:** 2005
SQ FT: 15,000 **Privately Held**
WEB: www.tpgcredit.com
SIC: 6726 Management of closed-end investment funds

(G-5844)

TRADITION DEVELOPMENT

6800 France Ave S Ste 178 (55435-2004)
PHONE 952 920-5100
Jake Enebak, *President*
Scott McMahon, *Director*
EMP: 40 **EST:** 1999
SALES (est): 10MM-24.9MM **Privately Held**
WEB: www.traditionrealty.com
SIC: 6552 Land subdivision & development services

(G-5845)

TRADITION MORTGAGE LLC

6800 France Ave S Ste 178 (55435-2004)
PHONE 952 920-5100
FAX: 952 920-8900
Robert Enebak, *Member*
Erik Hendrikson, *Member*
Jake Enebak, *Member*
Tom Buslee, *Member*
Jason Dario, *Member*
EMP: 40 **EST:** 1999
SALES (est): 1MM-4.9MM **Privately Held**
SIC: 6163 Mortgage brokers service arranging for loans, using money of others

(G-5846)

TRANSCEND COMMUNICATIONS INC

2101 Kennedy St NE (55413-2606)
PHONE 763 463-1000
George Demou, *President*
Crutis Mohr, *COO*
Mark Lindgren, *Vice Pres*
Gary Frieler, *Warehouse Mgr*
Ivan Bonk, *Administrator*
EMP: 50 **EST:** 2000
SQ FT: 2,150
SALES (est): 5MM-9.9MM **Privately Held**
WEB: www.transcendonline.com

(PA)=Parent Co (HQ)=Headquarters (DH)=Div Headquarters
✪ = New business established in last 2 years

2011 Harris Minnesota
Services Directory

© Harris InfoSource 1-866-281-6415

257

SIC: 8748 Telecommunications consulting services
PA: Fastech Integrated Solutions
940 W Sproul Rd Ste 201
Springfield PA 19064
610 359-9200

(G-5847)
TRANSIT TEAM INC
1154 N 5th St   (55411-4304)
PHONE.............................612 332-3323
FAX: 612 332-7075
Joyce Doerffler, *President*
Harland Peterson, *Vice Pres*
EMP: 45 **EST:** 1957
SQ FT: 2,000
SALES (est): 1MM-4.9MM **Privately Held**
SIC: 4119 Vanpool operation

(G-5848)
TRANSPORT LEASING CONTRACT INC   (PA)
Also Called: T L C Co's
6160 Summit Dr N Ste 500   (55430-2252)
PHONE.............................763 585-7000
Ardell Deberg, *CEO*
Gary Binning, *Chairman*
Fred Souza, *Senior VP*
Gary Serdar, *Vice Pres*
Bill Benson, *CFO*
EMP: 25 **EST:** 1987
SQ FT: 13,000 **Privately Held**
WEB: www.tlccompanies.com
SIC: 7363 Truck driver service

(G-5849)
TRAVEL ONE INC
Also Called: B T I Travel One
8009 34th Ave S Ste 1500   (55425-1798)
PHONE.............................952 854-2551
William Numan, *President*
Leann Krenz, *Consultant*
EMP: 25 **EST:** 1970
SALES (est): 1MM-4.9MM **Privately Held**
WEB: www.traveloneinc.com
SIC: 4724 Travel agency

(G-5850)
TREHUS BUILDERS INC
Also Called: Tre Hus Builders
3017 4th Ave S   (55408-2410)
PHONE.............................612 729-2992
FAX: 612 729-3982
David Amundson, *President*
EMP: 25 **EST:** 1982
SQ FT: 1,200
SALES (est): 5MM-9.9MM **Privately Held**
WEB: www.trehusbuilders.com
SIC: 1521 Single-family home general remodeling service

(G-5851)
TRI CITY ENTERPRISES INC
Also Called: Chez Daniel
2800 American Blvd W   (55431-1205)
PHONE.............................952 888-4447
FAX: 952 888-1756
Pierre J Lapriep, *General Mgr*
EMP: 50
SALES (est): 1MM-4.9MM **Privately Held**
WEB: www.embassystpaul.com
SIC: 7299 Full service chain family restaurant; banquet hall facility
PA: Tri City Enterprises Inc
8030 Old Cedar Ave S Ste 110
Minneapolis MN 55425
952 854-7405

(G-5852)
TRI-STATE DRILLING INC
16940 Highway 55   (55446-3014)
PO Box 252, Hamel   (55340-0252)
PHONE.............................763 553-1234
FAX: 763 553-9778
Robert Melcher, *CEO*
James Melcher, *President*
Mark Riethmille, *Vice Pres*
Randolph Eisele, *Vice Pres*
Joyce Eisele, *Vice Pres*
EMP: 75 **EST:** 1955
SQ FT: 26,000
SALES (est): 10MM-24.9MM **Privately Held**
WEB: www.tristatedrilling.com

SIC: 1629 1799 Pier construction; drainage system construction; earthmoving service; dewatering service

(G-5853)
TRIA ORTHOPAEDIC CENTER ASC
8100 Northland Dr   (55431-4800)
PHONE.............................952 831-8742
FAX: 952 831-1626
Mary Johnson, *President*
David Cook, *CFO*
Dennis Tifft, *Insur/Bill Sup*
Kara Duphorn, *Phys Therapist*
Maurie Steinley, *Phys Therapist*
EMP: 100 **EST:** 2005
SQ FT: 94,000
SALES (est): 5MM-9.9MM **Privately Held**
WEB: www.tria.com
SIC: 8069 Orthopedic hospital

(G-5854)
TRIANGLE WAREHOUSE INC
3501 Marshall St NE   (55418-4653)
PO Box 581698   (55458-1698)
PHONE.............................651 633-8912
George Wintz, *President*
Nancy Cook, *Corp Secy*
Julie Lenartz, *Treasurer*
Steve Strom, *Manager*
▲ **EMP:** 75 **EST:** 1998
SALES (est): 5MM-9.9MM **Privately Held**
SIC: 4225 4214 Warehousing & storage services; local trucking with storage

(G-5855)
TRICORD SYSTEMS INC
2905 NW Blvd Ste 20   (55441-2644)
PHONE.............................763 557-9005
FAX: 763 557-8403
Keith T Thorndyke, *President*
Gregory T Barnum, *Corp Secy*
Alexander H Frey, *Senior VP*
Ronald L Brown, *Vice Pres*
Robert Wilson, *Vice Pres*
EMP: 37 **EST:** 1987
SQ FT: 14,834
SALES (est): 10MM-24.9MM **Privately Held**
WEB: www.tricord.com
SIC: 7373 Manufactures minicomputers; local area network systems integration service

(G-5856)
TRIMARK HOTEL CORP
Also Called: Millennium Hotel Minneapolis
1313 Nicollet Ave   (55403-2630)
PHONE.............................612 305-9763
Robert Rivers, *General Mgr*
Rhonda Omodt, *Vice Pres*
Shannon Hannah, *Human Resources*
Karina Gronberg, *Manager*
Dan Little, *Manager*
EMP: 200
SALES (est): 10MM-24.9MM **Privately Held**
SIC: 7011 6512 7299 Hotel; nonresidential building operator; eating place; banquet hall facility; drinking establishment
PA: M&C Management Services Inc
6560 Greenwood Plaza Blvd
Greenwood Village CO 80111
303 779-2000

(G-5857)
TRIMLINE
705 Pennsylvania Ave S   (55426-1602)
PHONE.............................763 540-9737
Jeff Morris, *General Mgr*
Gary Urbanski, *Manager*
EMP: 25
SALES (est): 5MM-9.9MM **Privately Held**
WEB: www.libertydiversified.com
SIC: 5039 Wholesales construction materials
PA: Liberty Diversified Industries
5600 Highway 169 N
Minneapolis MN 55428
763 536-6600

(G-5858)
TRIPLE J ENTERPRISES INC (PA)
Also Called: Johnstone Supply
2680 E 81st St   (55425-1328)
PHONE.............................952 853-9898
Rusty D Mace, *President*
Bart Sederski, *Accounts Mgr*
Daaron Delong, *Program Dir*
EMP: 25 **EST:** 1984
SQ FT: 40,000 **Privately Held**
SIC: 5075 Wholesales warm air heating equipment & supplies; wholesales air conditioning & ventilation equipment & supplies

(G-5859)
TRIPLE J ENTERPRISES INC
Also Called: Johnstone Supply
2680 E 81st St   (55425-1328)
PHONE.............................952 853-9898
Rusty Mace, *Manager*
EMP: 25
SALES (est): 10MM-24.9MM **Privately Held**
SIC: 5075 Wholesales warm air heating equipment & supplies; wholesales air conditioning & ventilation equipment & supplies
PA: Triple J Enterprises Inc
2680 E 81st St
Minneapolis MN 55425
952 853-9898

(G-5860)
TRUST SECURITY
Also Called: ADT
5100 Edina Industrial Blvd   (55439-3000)
PHONE.............................952 914-9300
Margaret Graff, *Partner*
Mary Abeln, *Partner*
EMP: 50
SALES (est): 1MM-4.9MM **Privately Held**
WEB: www.trustsecuritymn.com
SIC: 7382 Security systems services

(G-5861)
TRUSTONE FINANCIAL FEDERAL   (PA)
14601 27th Ave N Ste 104   (55447-4834)
PO Box 1260   (55440-1260)
PHONE.............................763 544-1517
FAX: 763 595-4039
Timothy Keran, *President*
Teri Laufers, *Vice Pres*
Diane Hanson, *Mfg Staff*
Jon F Seeman, *VP Finance*
Michael Weir, *Finance*
EMP: 75 **EST:** 1939
SQ FT: 14,000
SALES (corp-wide): 30.82M **Privately Held**
WEB: www.tfcumn.org
SIC: 6061 Federally chartered credit union

(G-5862)
TRUSTONE FINANCIAL FEDERAL
6681 Country Club Dr   (55427-4601)
PO Box 1260   (55440-1260)
PHONE.............................763 544-1517
Timothy Kearan, *President*
EMP: 60
SALES (est): 10MM-24.9MM **Privately Held**
WEB: www.tfcumn.org
SIC: 6061 Federally chartered credit union
PA: Trustone Financial Federal
14601 27th Ave N Ste 104
Minneapolis MN 55447
763 544-1517

(G-5863)
TUBMAN
Also Called: Chrysalis Center
4432 Chicago Ave Ste 1   (55407-3521)
PHONE.............................612 871-0118
Christine Brinkman, *Manager*
Beverly Dusso, *Exec Dir*
Ruth Stoner, *Bd of Directors*
EMP: 55
SALES (est): 1MM-4.9MM **Privately Held**
WEB: www.chrysaliswomen.org

SIC: 8322 Social services center
PA: Tubman
3111 1st Ave S
Minneapolis MN 55408
612 825-3333

(G-5864)
TUBMAN FAMILY ALLIANCE
3111 1st Ave S   (55408-3136)
PHONE.............................612 825-0000
Beverly Dusso, *Principal*
Manuel Depaz, *Info Tech Mgr*
EMP: 36 **EST:** 2004
SALES (est): 1MM-4.9MM **Privately Held**
SIC: 8322 Crisis intervention center

(G-5865)
TUNHEIM PARTNERS INC
8009 34th Ave S Ste 1100   (55425-1661)
PHONE.............................952 851-1600
FAX: 952 851-1610
Kathryn Tunheim, *President*
Hubert H Humphrey III, *Member*
Ellie Lucas, *Exec VP*
Hubert H Umprey, *Senior VP*
Blois Olson, *Vice Pres*
EMP: 78 **EST:** 1990
SALES (est): 10MM-24.9MM **Privately Held**
WEB: www.tunheim.com
SIC: 8743 8742 Public relations services; management consulting services

(G-5866)
TURNERY PROPERTIES LP
Also Called: Super 8 Motel
6300 Wayzata Blvd   (55416-1212)
PHONE.............................763 546-6277
FAX: 763 546-3431
James D Flannery, *Partner*
Edwin J Turnquist, *Partner*
Taylor Flannery, *General Mgr*
Pogorelov Sergie, *Manager*
Sergey Pogorelov, *Manager*
EMP: 25 **EST:** 1989
SALES (est): 1MM-4.9MM **Privately Held**
SIC: 7011 Traveler accommodations

(G-5867)
TURNING POINT ADMINISTRATIVE
1500 Golden Valley Rd   (55411-3139)
PHONE.............................612 520-4004
Elizabeth Reed, *CEO*
Peter Hayden, *President*
EMP: 30 **EST:** 1997 **Privately Held**
SIC: 8641 Civic & social organization

(G-5868)
TURNING POINT FOUNDATION
1500 Golden Valley Rd   (55411-3139)
PHONE.............................612 520-4004
Vincent Hayden, *President*
Elizabeth Reed, *COO*
EMP: 35 **EST:** 1976 **Privately Held**
SIC: 8399 Social change association

(G-5869)
TURNING POINT INC
1500 Golden Valley Rd   (55411-3139)
PHONE.............................612 520-4004
Peter Hayden, *President*
Elizabeth Reed, *COO*
Faith Brandon, *Human Res Mgr*
EMP: 35 **EST:** 1975
SALES (est): 1MM-4.9MM **Privately Held**
WEB: www.ourturningpoint.org
SIC: 8361 Residential rehabilitation center with health care incidental

(G-5870)
TUTTLE INC
Also Called: Elsies Lounge Rest & Bowl Ctr
729 Marshall St NE   (55413-1815)
PHONE.............................612 378-9701
Robert Tuttle, *President*
Timothy Tuttle, *Vice Pres*
Michael Tuttle, *Treasurer*
EMP: 30 **EST:** 1956
SQ FT: 14,400
SALES (est): 1MM-4.9MM **Privately Held**
SIC: 7933 Cocktail lounge; eating place; bowling center

www.HarrisInfo.com
258

2011 Harris Minnesota
Services Directory

▲=Import ▼=Export
◆=Import/Export

(G-5871)

21ST SERVICES
200 S 6th St Ste 350 (55402-1458)
PO Box 2428 (55402-0428)
PHONE.............................612 371-3008
FAX: 612 371-3009
Paul Kirkman, *Managing Dir*
Steven Walker, *Managing Dir*
Robert Simon, *CFO*
EMP: 30 EST: 1998
SALES (est): 1MM-4.9MM **Privately Held**
WEB: www.21stservices.com
SIC: 8742 Financial management
consulting services

(G-5872)

21ST SERVICES LLC
200 S 6th St Ste 350 (55402-1458)
PHONE.............................612 371-3008
Paul Kirkman, *Member*
Steve Walker, *Member*
Nancy Bohannon, *Member*
Andrew Bowman, *Member*
Henry Blackburn, *Member*
EMP: 58 EST: 1998
SALES (est): 50MM-99.9MM **Privately Held**
SIC: 6311 Life reinsurance carrier

(G-5873)

TWIN CITIES RISE
800 Washington Ave N (55401-1330)
PHONE.............................612 338-0295
FAX: 612 338-0191
Steven Rothschild, *President*
Michael Bingham, *President*
Marilyn Dahl, *Vice Chairman*
Sandra Vargas, *Corp Secy*
Peggy Yusten, *COO*
EMP: 28 EST: 1993
SQ FT: 8,500
SALES (est): 1MM-4.9MM **Privately Held**
WEB: www.twincitiesrise.org
SIC: 8331 Skill training center

(G-5874)

TWIN CITIES SPINE SURGEONS LTD
913 E 26th St Ste 600 (55404-4515)
PHONE.............................612 775-6200
FAX: 612 332-2320
Francis Denis, *President*
Amy Zanow, *Business Mgr*
John E Lonstein MD, *Corp Secy*
E D Ensor, *Corp Secy*
Joseph Perra MD, *Vice Pres*
EMP: 60 EST: 1973
SALES (est): 5MM-9.9MM **Privately Held**
WEB: www.tcspine.com
SIC: 8011 Surgeon's office

(G-5875)

TWIN CITY ACOUSTICS INC
2655 Cheshire Ln N # 100 (55447-4941)
PHONE.............................763 535-6697
FAX: 763 553-1611
David Brinker, *President*
Roger Schmitz, *Vice Pres*
Michael Gibby, *Vice Pres*
Dennis Ward, *CFO*
Scott Gallop, *Treasurer*
EMP: 85 EST: 1973
SQ FT: 15,000
SALES (est): 5MM-9.9MM **Privately Held**
WEB: www.tcacoustics.com
SIC: 1742 Acoustical & ceiling work
contractor

(G-5876)

TWIN CITY AGENCY INC
4500 Park Glen Rd Ste 400 (55416-4892)
PHONE.............................952 924-6900
Mark R Sheehan, *Ch of Bd*
Mark Raderstorf, *Finance*
EMP: 30 EST: 1913
SQ FT: 10,000
SALES (est): 1MM-4.9MM **Privately Held**
WEB: www.twincitygroup.com
SIC: 6411 Insurance services
PA: Twin City Group Inc
    4500 Park Glen Rd # 400
    Minneapolis MN 55416
    952 924-6900

(G-5877)

TWIN CITY AUTO BODY COLLISION
419 W 90th St (55420-3514)
PHONE.............................952 884-9878
Paul Weinhandl, *President*
EST: 1983
SQ FT: 16,000 **Privately Held**
WEB: www.tcautobody.com
SIC: 7532 Automotive body shop

(G-5878)

TWIN CITY FAN CO'S LTD (PA)
5959 Trenton Ln N (55442-3237)
PHONE.............................763 551-7600
FAX: 763 551-7601
Charles L Barry, *CEO*
Zika Srejovic, *Vice Ch Bd*
Michael Barry, *President*
Craig Kornols, *Vice Pres*
James Herrboldt, *Vice Pres*
◆ EMP: 120 EST: 1973
SQ FT: 46,000 **Privately Held**
WEB: www.aerovent.com
SIC: 5084 Manufactures blowers & fans;
wholesales industrial machinery &
equipment

(G-5879)

TWIN CITY FLORIST SUPPLY INC
2308 Humboldt Ave S (55405-2513)
PHONE.............................612 377-7849
FAX: 612 339-9827
Thomas Whalen, *President*
Kathy Bystedt, *Corp Secy*
EMP: 30 EST: 1934
SQ FT: 20,000
SALES (est): 5MM-9.9MM **Privately Held**
SIC: 5193 Wholesales fresh flowers;
wholesales florists' supplies; wholesales
potted plants

(G-5880)

TWIN CITY GROUP INC (PA)
4500 Park Glen Rd # 400 (55416-4892)
PHONE.............................952 924-6900
Mark R Sheehan, *President*
Elaine Mustari, *Controller*
EST: 1983
SQ FT: 14,000 **Privately Held**
SIC: 6411 Insurance agent

(G-5881)

TWIN CITY HARDWARE CO
5650 International Pkwy (55428-3047)
PHONE.............................763 535-4660
FAX: 763 535-2005
Calvin Boomer, *Manager*
EMP: 25
SALES (est): 10MM-24.9MM **Privately Held**
WEB: www.twincityhardware.com
SIC: 5072 5031 5099 Wholesales
hardware; wholesales door frames
constructed of all materials; wholesales
locks & lock sets; retails door & window
products; hardware store
PA: Twin City Hardware Co
    723 Hadley Ave N
    Saint Paul MN 55128
    651 735-2200

(G-5882)

TWIN CITY POULTRY CO
4630 Quebec Ave N Uppr (55428-4973)
PHONE.............................763 592-6500
Steve Cohen, *President*
Helene Roberts, *Corp Secy*
Jay Roberts, *Vice Pres*
Andy Tomaschko, *Manager*
▲ EMP: 43 EST: 1970
SQ FT: 35,000
SALES (est): 25MM-49.9MM **Privately Held**
WEB: www.upscalefoods.com
SIC: 5141 5142 Wholesales general line
groceries; wholesales packaged frozen
foods

(G-5883)

TWIN CITY PRODUCE SUPPLIES INC
744 Kasota Cir SE (55414-2815)
PHONE.............................612 378-1055
FAX: 612 378-1808

Ian Smith, *President*
John Rotondo, *Treasurer*
EMP: 30 EST: 1973
SQ FT: 7,500
SALES (est): 10MM-24.9MM **Privately Held**
SIC: 5148 Wholesales fresh fruits;
wholesales fresh vegetables

(G-5884)

TWIN CITY RISK GROUP INC
4500 Park Glen Rd Ste 400 (55416-4892)
PHONE.............................952 924-6900
Mark R Sheehan, *President*
EMP: 32 EST: 1982
SALES (est): 1MM-4.9MM **Privately Held**
SIC: 6411 Insurance agency & broker; life
insurance agent

(G-5885)

U S BANCORP (PA)
800 Nicollet Mall Ste 800 (55402-7020)
PHONE.............................651 466-3000
Richard K Davis, *Ch of Bd*
William R Bertha, *President*
Bryan R Calder, *President*
Julie Huston, *President*
Jeffrey J Kerr, *President*
◆ EMP: 400 EST: 1929
SQ FT: 700,000
SALES (corp-wide): 19.49B **Publicly Held**
WEB: www.usbank.com
SIC: 6021 6022 6091 6159 6162 6411
National commercial bank; state commercial
bank; agricultural credit institution;
equipment & vehicle finance leasing
service; mortgage banking service;
insurance broker; trusts, fiduciary & custody
services

(G-5886)

U S BANK NATIONAL ASSOCIATION
2800 E Lake St (55406-1930)
PHONE.............................612 728-8300
FAX: 612 872-2874
Sherri Kay, *Persnl Mgr*
Robbin Werrbach, *Sales Mgr*
David Young, *Manager*
EMP: 40
SALES (est): 10MM-24.9MM **Publicly Held**
WEB: www.firstar.com
SIC: 6021 National commercial bank
HQ: U S Bank National Association
    425 Walnut St Fl 1
    Cincinnati OH 45202
    513 632-4234

(G-5887)

U S BANK NATIONAL ASSOCIATION
4100 W 50th St Ste 1 (55424-1265)
PHONE.............................952 925-7333
FAX: 952 925-7350
Marilyn Musolf, *Manager*
Mike Birch, *Manager*
EMP: 25
SALES (est): 5MM-9.9MM **Publicly Held**
WEB: www.firstar.com
SIC: 6021 National commercial bank
HQ: U S Bank National Association
    425 Walnut St Fl 1
    Cincinnati OH 45202
    513 632-4234

(G-5888)

U S COMMODITIES L L C
730 2nd Ave S Ste 700 (55402-2480)
PHONE.............................612 486-3800
Rolf Peters, *Member*
Bill Hren, *CFO*
Ron Hartley, *Credit Mgr*
Barb Obinger, *Manager*
Paul Remillard, *Administrator*
EMP: 55 EST: 2001
SQ FT: 6,000
SALES (est): 25MM-49.9MM **Privately Held**
WEB: www.uscommodities-ag.com
SIC: 5191 Wholesales farm supplies
PA: Agmotion Inc
    730 2nd Ave S Ste 700
    Minneapolis MN 55402
    612 486-3800

(G-5889)

U S FILTER WATERPRO
4570 W 77th St Ste 300 (55435-5008)
PHONE.............................952 893-9130
FAX: 952 893-0343
Harry K Hornish Jr, *President*
Damian C Georgino, *Vice Pres*
Mechelle Slaughter, *Vice Pres*
James W Dierker, *Treasurer*
Randi Erickson, *Credit Staff*
EMP: 25 EST: 1967
SQ FT: 10,000
SALES (est): 10MM-24.9MM **Privately Held**
WEB: www.usfilter.com
SIC: 5074 Wholesales plumbing & heating
equipment & supplies
DH: Siemens Water Technologies
    181 Thorn Hill Rd
    Warrendale PA 15086
    724 772-0044

(G-5890)

U S PROBATION OFFICE
300 S 4th St Ste 406 (55415-2280)
PHONE.............................612 664-5400
Kevin Lowry, *Chief*
EMP: 62 EST: 1935 **Privately Held**
WEB: www.txwd.uscourts.gov
SIC: 8322 Probation office

(G-5891)

UBS FINANCIAL SERVICES INC
8500 Nrmndl Lk Blvd Ste 210
(55437-3815)
PHONE.............................952 921-7900
FAX: 952 921-8465
Charles Gits, *Senior VP*
Colin Fleming, *Manager*
Geri Paquette, *Adm Mgr*
EMP: 50
SALES (est): 10MM-24.9MM **Privately Held**
WEB: www.ubs.com
SIC: 6211 General brokerage investment
firm
PA: UBS Financial Services Inc
    1285 Avenue Of The Americas
    New York NY 10019
    212 713-2000

(G-5892)

UCARE MINNESOTA
500 Stinson Blvd (55413-2615)
PO Box 52 (55440-0052)
PHONE.............................612 676-6500
FAX: 612 676-6501
Nancy Feldman, *President*
Donna Ozaturk, *Publisher*
Mark Traynor, *Senior VP*
Russel J Kuzel, *Senior VP*
Thomas Mahowald, *Senior VP*
EMP: 430 EST: 1987
SQ FT: 90,000
SALES (est): 100MM-499.9MM **Privately Held**
SIC: 6324 Health insurance maintenance
organization

(G-5893)

UDELL DENTAL LABORATORY INC
3361 Gorham Ave (55426-4240)
PHONE.............................952 926-9266
Donald R Udell, *President*
Carolyn Udell, *Corp Secy*
Matthew Russell, *Finance*
EMP: 44 EST: 1946
SALES (est): 1MM-4.9MM **Privately Held**
SIC: 8072 8021 Dental laboratory; dentists'
office & clinic

(G-5894)

UHC - EDINA
Also Called: Purchasing Dept
5901 Lincoln Dr (55436-1611)
PO Box 1459 (55440-1459)
PHONE.............................763 519-1335
Bobbie Dahlgren, *Director*
EMP: 34
SALES (est): 1MM-4.9MM **Privately Held**
SIC: 7389 Purchasing service

(PA)=Parent Co (HQ)=Headquarters (DH)=Div Headquarters
✿ = New business established in last 2 years

2011 Harris Minnesota
Services Directory

© Harris InfoSource 1-866-281-6415
259

GEOGRAPHIC

(G-5895)
ULTIMATE ACQUISITION PARTNERS
7435 France Ave S (55435-4702)
PHONE..................952 830-0010
FAX: 952 920-0940
Cory Tickler, *Opers Mgr*
Guy Roper, *Manager*
EMP: 40
SALES (est): 5MM-9.9MM **Privately Held**
SIC: 7622 Retails high fidelity stereo equipment; retails video recorders, players, disc players & accessories; retails automotive sound equipment; retails television sets; automotive radio repair service; home entertainment repair service
HQ: Ultimate Acquisition Partners
321 W 84th Ave Unit A
Thornton CO 80260
303 412-2500

(G-5896)
ULTRA CREATIVE INC
43 Main St SE Ste 430 (55414-1049)
PHONE..................612 378-0748
FAX: 612 378-1052
David Biebighauser, *President*
Terry Schnipkoweit, *Vice Pres*
EMP: 25 **EST:** 1987
SQ FT: 10,000
SALES (est): 1MM-4.9MM **Privately Held**
WEB: www.ultracreative.com
SIC: 8743 Sales promotion services

(G-5897)
ULYSSES TELEMEDIA NETWORKS INC
1300 Godward St NE # 3100
(55413-2558)
PHONE..................763 225-5000
Rick Bayless, *President*
Jack Hanna, *Principal*
Kevin Frisbie, *CFO*
Brent Bissell, *Manager*
G Bayless, *Manager*
EMP: 100 **EST:** 1994
SALES (est): 10MM-24.9MM **Privately Held**
SIC: 7379 Online technology consulting service

(G-5898)
UM ELECTRIC UTLTS SHOP
319 15th Ave SE Ste 300 (55455-0178)
PHONE..................612 625-8081
Brian Rumble, *Director*
EMP: 40 **EST:** 1996
SALES (est): 1MM-4.9MM **Privately Held**
SIC: 1731 Electrical contractor

(G-5899)
UMI CO INC
2950 Weeks Ave SE (55414-2832)
PHONE..................612 331-2566
FAX: 612 331-1295
David R Carlsen, *President*
Dave Price, *Vice Pres*
EMP: 70
SALES (est): 5MM-9.9MM **Privately Held**
WEB: www.umiinc.com
SIC: 4724 Sheet metal fabricator; travel agency
PA: UMI Co Inc
1520 5th St S
Hopkins MN 55343
952 935-8431

(G-5900)
UNI-SELECT USA INC
6001 78th Ave N (55443-2902)
PHONE..................763 566-1285
EMP: 29
SALES (est): 10MM-24.9MM **Privately Held**
SIC: 5013 Wholesales automotive supplies & parts
PA: UNI-Select USA Inc
20 Hazelwood Dr Ste 100
Amherst NY 14228
716 531-9266

(G-5901)
UNI-SYSTEMS LLC
4600 Lake Road Ave (55422-1800)
PHONE..................763 536-1407
Cyril Silberman, *Member*
Bart Riberich, *Member*
John Lanari, *Member*
Pete Fervoy, *Business Mgr*
Darcy Guenette, *Marketing Staff*
▼ **EMP:** 39 **EST:** 1968
SQ FT: 25,000
SALES (est): 5MM-9.9MM **Privately Held**
SIC: 8742 8711 Construction project management consultant; engineering services

(G-5902)
UNICOM CONSULTING INC
7400 Metro Blvd Ste 400 (55439-2326)
PHONE..................952 698-7600
Hai Ngo, *President*
EMP: 30 **EST:** 1994
SALES (est): 1MM-4.9MM **Privately Held**
SIC: 8742 Management consulting services

(G-5903)
UNIMAX SYSTEMS CORP
430 1st Ave N Ste 790 (55401-1746)
PHONE..................612 341-0946
FAX: 612 338-5436
Tim Butler, *CEO*
Eliot Axelrod, *General Mgr*
Patrick Blahosky, *General Mgr*
Jennifer Berens, *General Mgr*
Anthony Hayes, *General Mgr*
EMP: 30 **EST:** 1985
SQ FT: 10,000
SALES (est): 1MM-4.9MM **Privately Held**
WEB: www.unimax.com
SIC: 7371 Computer software development

(G-5904)
UNION BANK & TRUST CO
312 Central Ave SE (55414-1025)
PHONE..................612 379-3222
FAX: 612 379-8837
Gene Hoelscher, *President*
Joe Ertman, *Vice Pres*
Leroy Moore, *Loan Officer*
Beverly Hanes, *Personnel*
EMP: 32 **EST:** 1976
SQ FT: 7,500
SALES (est): 5MM-9.9MM **Privately Held**
SIC: 6022 State commercial bank

(G-5905)
UNION SECURITY INSURANCE CO
6600 France Ave S Ste 314 (55435-1803)
PHONE..................952 920-8990
Amie Benson, *Principal*
Theresa Dalen, *Vice Pres*
Brain Dawood, *Sales Mgr*
Pamela Johnson, *Office Mgr*
Peggy Peterson, *IT/INT Sup*
EMP: 80
SALES (est): 50MM-99.9MM **Privately Held**
WEB: www.assurantemployeebenefits.com
SIC: 6321 Direct accident & health insurance carrier
DH: Union Security Insurance Co
6941 Vista Dr
West Des Moines IA 50266
651 361-4000

(G-5906)
UNIPOWER INDUSTRIAL CORP
1216 W 96th St (55431-2606)
PHONE..................952 884-2933
Robert Welch, *President*
EMP: 25
SALES (est): 10MM-24.9MM **Privately Held**
WEB: www.unipowercorporation.com
SIC: 5063 Wholesales industrial storage batteries
PA: Unipower Corp
1216 W 96th St Ste B
Minneapolis MN 55431
952 884-2933

(G-5907)
UNITED BUSINESS MAIL INC
405 35th Ave NE Ste 2 (55418-1159)
PHONE..................612 782-2044
FAX: 612 782-2015
Doug Hanson, *President*
Bill Wetzel, *Treasurer*
Molly Lundquist, *Controller*
EMP: 70 **EST:** 1985
SQ FT: 30,000
SALES (est): 5MM-9.9MM **Privately Held**
WEB: www.unitedbusinessmail.com
SIC: 7331 Mailing services

(G-5908)
UNITED CHECK CLEARING CORP
Also Called: Solutran
3600 Holly Ln N Ste 60 (55447-1286)
PHONE..................763 559-2225
FAX: 763 559-8872
Barry Nordstrand, *CEO*
Joe Keller, *President*
Carmen Nordstrand, *CFO*
EMP: 87 **EST:** 1984
SALES (est): 10MM-24.9MM **Privately Held**
SIC: 8742 6099 Financial management consulting services; check cashing services

(G-5909)
UNITED HARDWARE DISTRIBUTING (PA)
5005 Nathan Ln N (55442-3208)
PO Box 410 (55440-0410)
PHONE..................763 559-1800
FAX: 763 557-2799
Steven G Draeger, *President*
David Heider, *Corp Secy*
Chad Ruth, *Vice Pres*
Phil Pflepsen, *Vice Pres*
Lori Long, *Treasurer*
▲ **EMP:** 145 **EST:** 1945
SQ FT: 40,000
SALES (corp-wide): 180.02M **Privately Held**
WEB: www.unitedhardware.com
SIC: 5072 Wholesales hardware

(G-5910)
UNITED NOODLES INC
2015 E 24th St (55404-4109)
PHONE..................612 721-6677
FAX: 612 721-4255
Theodoro Wong, *President*
Ramon Tan, *Corp Secy*
Alice Fung, *Vice Pres*
Sue Lam, *Controller*
EMP: 26 **EST:** 1957
SQ FT: 20,000
SALES (est): 10MM-24.9MM **Privately Held**
WEB: www.unitednoodles.com
SIC: 5149 Wholesales specialty food items; retail gourmet food store

(G-5911)
UNITED OPERATIONS INC OF
5025 Cheshire Ln N Ste 1 (55446-4545)
PHONE..................763 551-0202
FAX: 763 551-0202
Paul Mallory, *President*
Dan Shedlove, *CFO*
Michael Roznowski, *CIO*
Heather Murray, *CIO*
EMP: 39 **EST:** 1988
SQ FT: 10,000
SALES (est): 1MM-4.9MM **Privately Held**
WEB: www.unitedoperations.com
SIC: 7699 Miscellaneous building item repair service

(G-5912)
UNITED PARCEL SERVICE INC
3312 Broadway St NE (55413-1709)
PHONE..................800 742-5877
Uri Camarena, *Pub Rel Mgr*
Ivey Merrow, *Manager*
Jim Meyer, *Manager*
Mike Catler, *Manager*
Jay Wettlaufer, *Supervisor*
EMP: 3500
SALES (est): 100MM-499.9MM **Publicly Held**
WEB: www.ups.com
SIC: 4215 Package delivery services by vehicle; parcel delivery services by vehicle
HQ: United Parcel Service Inc
55 Glenlake Pkwy NE
Atlanta GA 30328
404 828-6000

(G-5913)
UNITED PRODUCTS CORP OF AMER
9800 13th Ave N (55441-5032)
PHONE..................763 545-1273
FAX: 763 545-6632
Dave Shultz, *Manager*
EMP: 30
SALES (est): 5MM-9.9MM **Privately Held**
SIC: 5039 5033 Wholesales sheet metal air ducts; wholesales roofing & siding materials; retails door & window products
PA: United Products Corp of Amer
200 Sycamore St W
Saint Paul MN 55117
651 227-8735

(G-5914)
UNITED PROPERTY INVESTMENT LLC (PA)
3500 Amercn Blvd W # 200 (55431-1096)
PHONE..................952 831-1000
FAX: 952 893-8813
Jason Newell, *General Mgr*
Bea James, *General Mgr*
Laurie Johnson, *General Mgr*
Jeff Eaton, *Member*
Paul Hawkins, *Member*
EMP: 200 **EST:** 1998
SQ FT: 40,000 **Privately Held**
SIC: 6531 Real estate multiple listing service

(G-5915)
UNITED RESIDENTIAL MORTGAGE
7301 Ohms Ln Ste 195 (55439-2327)
PO Box 459, Lakeville (55044-0459)
PHONE..................952 820-0272
Mike Bernett, *Member*
Bill Thompson, *Member*
Pat Levoir, *Mng Member*
Peter Tuckner, *Manager*
EMP: 25 **EST:** 1995
SQ FT: 4,000
SALES (est): 1MM-4.9MM **Privately Held**
WEB: www.urmmortgage.com
SIC: 6163 Mortgage brokers service arranging for loans, using money of others

(G-5916)
UNITED SUGARS CORP
7803 Glenroy Rd Ste 300 (55439-3127)
PHONE..................952 896-0131
Paul Wengronowitz, *Vice Pres*
Janet Beachem, *Sales Staff*
Tom Bond, *Manager*
Rocky Wagendorf, *Project Leader*
Randy Bakken, *IT/INT Sup*
EMP: 50
SALES (est): 50MM-99.9MM **Privately Held**
WEB: www.unitedsugars.com
SIC: 5159 Wholesales raw sugar
HQ: United Sugars Corp
524 Center Ave
Moorhead MN 56560
218 236-4400

(G-5917)
UNITED WATER NEW ROCHELLE INC
701 4th Ave S Ste 1200 (55415-1800)
PHONE..................952 820-1666
Paul Taylor, *President*
Charles A Greenberg, *General Mgr*
Lauri Pierce, *Manager*
EMP: 50
SALES (est): 5MM-9.9MM **Privately Held**
WEB: www.unitedwater.com
SIC: 6531 Commercial real estate agency
DH: United Water New Rochelle Inc
2525 Palmer Ave
New Rochelle NY 10801
914 632-6900

www.HarrisInfo.com
260

2011 Harris Minnesota
Services Directory

▲=Import ▼=Export
◆=Import/Export

(G-5918)

UNITY HEALTHCARE
2221 W 55th St (55419-1517)
PHONE..............................612 285-8743
Beth Balenger, *Owner*
EMP: 30 **EST:** 2004
SALES (est): 1MM-4.9MM **Privately Held**
SIC: 8082 Home health care services

(G-5919)

UNIVERSAL HOSPITAL SERVICES
Also Called: Uhs
2020 E 28th St Ste 103 (55407-1453)
PHONE..............................612 721-3374
FAX: 612 728-3677
Carla Miles, *Manager*
Michelle Gross, *Manager*
Jonathan Werner, *Director*
EMP: 60
SALES (est): 5MM-9.9MM **Privately Held**
WEB: www.uhs.com
SIC: 7352 5047 Invalid supplies rental service; wholesales hospital equipment & supplies
PA: Universal Hospital Services
    7700 France Ave S Ste 275
    Minneapolis MN 55435
    952 893-3200

(G-5920)

UNIVERSAL HOSPITAL SERVICES (PA)
7700 France Ave S Ste 275 (55435-5847)
PHONE..............................952 893-3200
Gary D Blackford, *CEO*
Diana J Bryan, *Corp Secy*
Joseph P Schiesl, *Corp Secy*
Timothy W Kuck, *COO*
Jeffrey L Singer, *Exec VP*
▲ **EMP:** 75 **EST:** 1939
SQ FT: 41,000 **Privately Held**
WEB: www.uhs.com
SIC: 7352 5047 Medical equipment leasing & rental; wholesales medical equipment & supplies

(G-5921)

UNIVERSAL PAINTING & DRYWALL
7308 Aspen Ln N Ste 156 (55428-1027)
PHONE..............................763 315-0095
FAX: 763 493-2816
Rob Kaplan, *President*
Myron Cooper, *Vice Pres*
Laurie Zinmer, *Manager*
EMP: 33 **EST:** 2002
SALES (est): 1MM-4.9MM **Privately Held**
SIC: 1742 1721 Drywall contractor; painting & wall covering contractor

(G-5922)

UNIVERSAL TITLE & FINANCIAL (PA)
7777 Washington Ave S (55439-2449)
PHONE..............................952 829-0899
FAX: 952 944-5007
Melville R Bois, *President*
Rudy Wahlsten, *Vice Pres*
Gregory Lindwall, *Vice Pres*
Roberta Mueller, *Manager*
Michelle Andersen, *Manager*
EMP: 49 **EST:** 1984 **Privately Held**
WEB: www.utfc.net
SIC: 6361 Provides guarantee of titles insurance

(G-5923)

UNIVERSITY AFFILIATED FAMILY
Also Called: Uafp
2615 E Franklin Ave (55406-1103)
PHONE..............................612 333-0770
FAX: 612 333-1986
Kolawole S Okuyemi MD, *Med Doctor*
Teresa C Marthy, *Med Doctor*
Shehbana Mahmood MD, *Med Doctor*
Kristine L Eskuchen MD, *Med Doctor*
Margaret Heff, *Manager*
EMP: 30
SALES (est): 1MM-4.9MM **Privately Held**
SIC: 8011 Physicians' office & clinic

(G-5924)

UNIVERSITY INN ASSOCIATES, A
Also Called: Radisson Univ Ht - Minneapolis
615 Washington Ave SE Ste A (55414-2931)
PHONE..............................612 379-8888
FAX: 612 379-8682
Matt Monchamp, *General Mgr*
Francisco F Barbosa, *Controller*
Ben Riley, *Sales Dir*
Larry Jones, *Marketing Staff*
Kyle Hurwitz, *Manager*
EMP: 200 **EST:** 1985
SQ FT: 240,786
SALES (est): 10MM-24.9MM **Privately Held**
SIC: 7011 Traveler accommodations

(G-5925)

UNIVERSITY INN PROPERTY LLC
615 Washington Ave SE (55414-2931)
PHONE..............................612 379-8888
Larry Jones, *Member*
John Greven, *Member*
EMP: 150 **EST:** 1981
SALES (est): 5MM-9.9MM **Privately Held**
SIC: 7011 Hotel

(G-5926)

UNIVERSITY LANGUAGE CENTER INC
1313 5th St SE Ste 201 (55414-4503)
PHONE..............................612 379-3823
FAX: 612 379-3832
Karen Houle, *President*
John Houle, *CFO*
EMP: 35 **EST:** 1986
SALES (est): 1MM-4.9MM **Privately Held**
WEB: www.ulanguage.com
SIC: 7389 Language school; translation & interpretation services

(G-5927)

UNIVERSITY MENTAL HEALTH
1300 S 2nd St Ste 180 (55454-5000)
PHONE..............................612 626-8100
Eli Coleman, *Director*
Joseph Sullivan, *Director*
EMP: 25 **EST:** 1994
SALES (est): 1MM-4.9MM **Privately Held**
WEB: www.university.fairview.org
SIC: 8049 Clinical psychologist office

(G-5928)

UNIVERSITY NEUROSURGICAL ASSN
Also Called: Fairview University Med Centre
420 Delaware St SE Ste 1 (55455-0374)
PHONE..............................612 624-6666
Margaret V Bree, *COO*
Barbara Bailey, *Office Mgr*
John Lake, *Office Mgr*
Keattiyoat Wattanakit MD, *Med Doctor*
Carmelo J Panetta MD, *Med Doctor*
EMP: 35 **EST:** 1972 **Privately Held**
WEB: www.faieview.org
SIC: 8733 8011 Research institute; physicians' office & clinic

(G-5929)

UNIVERSITY OF MINN ALUMNI ASSN
200 Oak St SE Ste 200 (55455-2040)
PHONE..............................612 624-2323
FAX: 612 626-8167
Margaret Carlson, *CEO*
Curtis Coffer, *CFO*
Maureen Arbogast, *Marketing Mgr*
EMP: 35 **EST:** 1906
SQ FT: 18,725 **Privately Held**
SIC: 8641 Alumni association

(G-5930)

UNIVERSITY OF MINNESOTA
720 Washingtn Ave SE # 200 (55414-2924)
PHONE..............................763 782-6400
Jackie Rathke, *Office Mgr*
Elaine Hallen, *Manager*
Ann Peterson, *Manager*
EMP: 150

SALES (est): 10MM-24.9MM **Privately Held**
SIC: 8011 8721 Physicians' office & clinic; primary care medical clinic; accounting, auditing & bookkeeping services
PA: University of Minnesota
    720 Washingtn Ave SE # 200
    Minneapolis MN 55414
    612 884-0600

(G-5931)

UNIVERSITY WOMENS HEALTH
420 Delaware St SE Rm 520 (55455-0341)
PHONE..............................612 625-6991
FAX: 612 626-3646
EMP: 30 **EST:** 1986
SALES (est): 1MM-4.9MM **Privately Held**
SIC: 8011 Obstetrician office

(G-5932)

UP NORTH CONSULTING INC
9100 W Bloomington Fwy (55431-2251)
PHONE..............................952 224-8656
Diann Albers, *President*
Timothy J Murphy, *Vice Pres*
EMP: 40 **EST:** 1999
SALES (est): 1MM-4.9MM **Privately Held**
WEB: www.upnorthconsulting.com
SIC: 8748 Business consulting services

(G-5933)

UPFRONT PRODUCTIONS INC
761 Kasota Ave SE (55414-2842)
PHONE..............................612 623-4433
FAX: 612 623-4411
Tricia Hamrin, *President*
Chris Hamrin, *Vice Pres*
Gena Zavitkovski, *Accountant*
John Brovack, *Manager*
Mike Reinhart, *Executive*
EMP: 47 **EST:** 1994
SQ FT: 27,000
SALES (est): 5MM-9.9MM **Privately Held**
WEB: www.alwayslead.com
SIC: 7336 Commercial art & graphic design services

(G-5934)

UPI PROPERTY MANAGEMENT GROUP
Also Called: Uptown Classic Properties
800 W Franklin Ave (55405-3122)
PHONE..............................612 870-8500
Spiros G Zorbalas, *Mng Member*
EMP: 62 **EST:** 1999
SQ FT: 3,000
SALES (est): 10MM-24.9MM **Privately Held**
SIC: 6531 Real estate agency & broker

(G-5935)

UPLINK STAFFING
5901 Brooklyn Blvd # 206 (55429-2533)
PHONE..............................763 781-8888
Loveth Amayanvbo, *President*
EMP: 35 **EST:** 2007
SALES (est): 500-999K **Privately Held**
SIC: 7363 Help supply services

(G-5936)

UPPER MIDWEST AMERICAN INDIAN
1035 W Broadway Ave (55411-2503)
PHONE..............................612 522-4436
FAX: 612 522-8855
Joyce Yellowhpumer, *General Mgr*
Joyce Yellowhammer, *Finance*
Kathleen Thompson, *Marketing Staff*
Gertrude Buckanaga, *Exec Dir*
EMP: 32 **EST:** 1937
SQ FT: 40,000
SALES (est): 1MM-4.9MM **Privately Held**
SIC: 8322 Community center

(G-5937)

UPS SUPPLY CHAIN SOLUTIONS INC
7550 22nd Ave S (55450-1011)
PHONE..............................612 726-1680
Marc Lewis, *Sales & Mktg St*
Mark Pierro, *Manager*
EMP: 50
SQ FT: 7,000
SALES (est): 5MM-9.9MM **Publicly Held**
WEB: www.ups-scs.com

SIC: 4731 Customhouse broker; foreign freight forwarding services
HQ: UPS Supply Chain Solutions Inc
    550-1 Eccles Ave
    San Francisco CA 94101
    650 635-2693

(G-5938)

UPTOWN PSYCHIC STUDIO
2617 Hennepin Ave (55408-1150)
PHONE..............................612 374-9906
Michael Smith, *Owner*
EMP: 27 **EST:** 1993
SALES (est): 1MM-4.9MM **Privately Held**
SIC: 7999 Fortune teller

(G-5939)

URBAN VENTURES LEADERSHIP
3041 4th Ave S (55408-2410)
PHONE..............................612 822-1628
FAX: 612 822-2507
Art Erickson, *CEO*
Jill Osborn, *President*
Ed Lucas, *COO*
Mark P Lundquist, *Vice Pres*
Ralph Bruins, *Vice Pres*
EMP: 40 **EST:** 1993
SALES (est): 5MM-9.9MM **Privately Held**
WEB: www.urbanventures.org
SIC: 8748 Urban planning & consulting services

(G-5940)

UROLOGIX INC
14405 21st Ave N Ste 110 (55447-4699)
PHONE..............................763 475-1400
Stryker Warren Jr, *CEO*
Gregory J Fluet, *COO*
Ron A Blsewitz, *COO*
Mark Rosvold, *Opers Mgr*
Charles Lehman, *Opers Staff*
EMP: 90 **EST:** 1991
SQ FT: 26,000
SALES (est): 10MM-24.9MM **Publicly Held**
WEB: www.urologix.com
SIC: 5047 Manufactures electromedical equipment; wholesales medical equipment & supplies

(G-5941)

URS GROUP INC
100 S 5th St Ste 1500 (55402-1254)
PHONE..............................612 370-0700
Craig Amundsen, *Principal*
Jeff Benson, *Vice Pres*
Gary Ehret, *Vice Pres*
Rich Greenlee, *Vice Pres*
Mary Swart, *Human Resources*
EMP: 40
SALES (est): 5MM-9.9MM **Publicly Held**
WEB: www.urscorp.com
SIC: 8711 8712 8741 Engineering services; engineering consulting services; architectural engineers; construction management services
HQ: URS Group Inc
    600 Montgomery St Fl 26
    San Francisco CA 94111
    415 377-0188

(G-5942)

US ASIAN HOME CARE
4124 Quebec Ave N Ste 305 (55427-1241)
PHONE..............................763 533-7750
FAX: 763 533-7776
Maria Hartlege, *Owner*
EMP: 40 **EST:** 1986
SALES (est): 1MM-4.9MM **Privately Held**
SIC: 8082 Home health care services

(G-5943)

US BANCORP INFORMATION SVCS
200 S 6th St (55402-1403)
PHONE..............................800 925-4324
Terry Murphy, *Branch Mgr*
Chris Pieroth, *Manager*
Greg Michelson, *Manager*
Mary J Curtin, *Manager*
EMP: 50
SALES (est): 10MM-24.9MM **Publicly Held**
WEB: www.usbank.com

SIC: **6021** National commercial bank
HQ: US Bancorp Information Svcs
332 Minnesota St Ste A
Saint Paul MN 55101
651 466-3000

(G-5944)
US BANCORP LEGAL DEPARTMENT
2100 US Bancorp Ctr (55402)
PO Box A512 (55480)
PHONE...............................612 303-7879
Thomas Johnson, *Principal*
EMP: 99
SALES (est): 25MM-49.9MM **Privately Held**
SIC: **6021** National commercial bank

(G-5945)
US BANK NATIONAL ASSOCIATION
4000 W Broadway Ave (55422-2212)
PHONE...............................763 536-5328
FAX: 763 536-5359
Marty Shimko, *Vice Pres*
Eric Forstrom, *Manager*
EMP: 30
SALES (est): 5MM-9.9MM **Publicly Held**
WEB: www.firstar.com
SIC: **6021** National commercial bank
HQ: U S Bank National Association
425 Walnut St Fl 1
Cincinnati OH 45202
513 632-4234

(G-5946)
US BANK NATIONAL ASSOCIATION
800 Nicollet Mall Fl 4 (55402-7000)
PHONE...............................612 303-3021
Richard K Davis, *Chairman*
Mary Christenson, *Manager*
EMP: 99
SALES (est): 25MM-49.9MM **Privately Held**
SIC: **6021** National commercial bank

(G-5947)
US ENERGY SERVICES INC
605 Highway 169 N Ste 1200
(55441-6531)
PHONE...............................763 543-4600
William Bathe, *CEO*
Todd Overgard, *President*
Casey Whelan, *Vice Pres*
Gary Swanson, *Vice Pres*
Mary Pinick, *Opers Staff*
EMP: 68 EST: 1993
SQ FT: 30,000
SALES (est): 5MM-9.9MM **Privately Held**
WEB: www.usenergyservices.com
SIC: **8741** Management services

(G-5948)
US FOODSERVICE INC
9605 54th Ave N (55442-1946)
PO Box 421210 (55442-0210)
PHONE...............................763 559-9494
FAX: 763 557-2295
Jay Kvafnicka, *Senior VP*
Hal Lange, *Vice Pres*
John Mueller, *Vice Pres*
Dan Salem, *Vice Pres*
Dave Eshelman, *VP Opers*
EMP: 225
SALES (est): 100MM-499.9MM **Privately Held**
WEB: www.usfoodservice.com
SIC: **5141** 5046 5149 Wholesales general line groceries; wholesales commercial cooking & food services equipment; wholesales groceries
HQ: US Foodservice Inc
9399 W Higgins Rd Ste 500
Rosemont IL 60018
847 720-8000

(G-5949)
US ONCOLOGY INC
800 E 28th St Ste 405 (55407-3723)
PHONE...............................612 863-8585
Julie Niemann, *Office Mgr*
Julie Nieman, *Administrator*
EMP: 40
SALES (est): 1MM-4.9MM **Privately Held**

SIC: **8011** Physicians' office & clinic
DH: US Oncology Inc
10101 Woodloch Forest Dr
Spring TX 77380
281 683-1000

(G-5950)
US VENTURE INC
1105 Xenium Ln N Ste 200 (55441-4404)
PHONE...............................763 591-5827
FAX: 763 591-0799
Jason Kruse, *Manager*
Bob Winer, *Manager*
Greg Brien, *Manager*
Ron Aldrecht, *MIS Dir*
EMP: 60
SALES (est): 100MM-499.9MM **Privately Held**
WEB: www.expressconvenience.com
SIC: **5172** 5013 5169 Wholesales petroleum products; wholesales automotive supplies & parts; wholesales anti-freeze compounds
PA: US Venture Inc
425 Better Way
Appleton WI 54915
920 739-6101

(G-5951)
USG INTERIORS INC
2950 Metro Dr Ste 116 (55425-4502)
PHONE...............................952 853-1233
FAX: 952 853-0166
EMP: 25
SALES (est): 10MM-24.9MM **Publicly Held**
WEB: www.gypsumsolutions.com
SIC: **5031** Wholesales lumber, plywood & millwork
PA: USG Corp
550 W Adams St
Chicago IL 60661
312 436-4000

(G-5952)
VA EMPLOYEE CHILD CARE CENTER
1 Veterans Dr (55417-2309)
PHONE...............................612 725-2000
FAX: 612 725-2248
Stephen L Ewing, *Ch Pathology*
Charles Krenzel, *Ch Radiology*
Bill Bulygo, *Purchasing*
Eugene House, *Envir Svcs Dir*
Ralph Heussner, *Marketing Staff*
EMP: 25 EST: 1991
SALES (est): 500-999K **Privately Held**
SIC: **8351** Child day care service

(G-5953)
VAA LLC
2955 Xenium Ln N Ste 10 (55441-2628)
PHONE...............................763 559-9100
FAX: 763 559-6023
Keith Jacobson, *Member*
Scott Stangeland, *Member*
Kc Harris, *Accounts Mgr*
Nat Schmidt, *Info Tech Mgr*
Richard V Sickle, *Coordinator*
EMP: 76 EST: 1978
SALES (est): 5MM-9.9MM **Privately Held**
WEB: www.vaaeng.com
SIC: **8711** Engineering services

(G-5954)
VAIL PLACE
1412 W 36th St (55408-3812)
PHONE...............................612 824-8061
Tom Seuntjens, *Corp Secy*
Mark McVay, *Vice Pres*
Tom Ratelle, *Treasurer*
Kathie Prieze, *Manager*
Kathy Prieve, *Director*
EST: 1981
SQ FT: 5,000 **Privately Held**
SIC: **8331** 8093 Sheltered workshop; outpatient mental health clinic

(G-5955)
VALLEY DENTAL GROUP
7501 Golden Valley Rd (55427-4563)
PHONE...............................763 544-2213
Hugh E Norsted DDS, *President*
Sandra Fexske, *President*
Brian Evensen DDS, *Corp Secy*
Kris Hall, *Manager*

Chris Hall, *Administrator*
EMP: 54 EST: 1974
SQ FT: 10,000
SALES (est): 1MM-4.9MM **Privately Held**
WEB: www.valleydental.com
SIC: **8021** Dental clinic

(G-5956)
VALUE GARDENS SUPPLY
9100 W Bloomington Fwy (55431-2251)
PHONE...............................952 884-6477
Bill Garvey, *Owner*
EMP: 50 EST: 2000
SALES (est): 10MM-24.9MM **Privately Held**
WEB: www.valuegardens.com
SIC: **5193** Retails lawn & garden supplies; wholesales flowers & florists' supplies

(G-5957)
VANMAN CO'S ARCHITECTS
669 Winnetka Ave N Ste 210
(55427-4576)
PHONE...............................763 541-9552
FAX: 763 541-9857
John Holmes, *President*
Bonnie Jacobsen, *Corp Secy*
Richard Keillor, *Vice Pres*
EMP: 30 EST: 1957
SQ FT: 6,500
SALES (est): Under 500K **Privately Held**
WEB: www.vanmanab.com
SIC: **7359** Equipment rental & leasing services

(G-5958)
VANMAN CONSTRUCTION CO
669 Winnetka Ave N # 210 (55427-4576)
PHONE...............................763 541-9552
John Holmes, *President*
Richard Keillor, *Vice Pres*
Bonnie Jacobsen, *Treasurer*
EMP: 28 EST: 1957
SQ FT: 6,000
SALES (est): 5MM-9.9MM **Privately Held**
WEB: www.vanmancompanies.com
SIC: **1542** 8712 Religious building construction; architectural service; bank construction

(G-5959)
VEE CORP
Also Called: Costumes & Creatures
504 Malcolm Ave SE Ste 200
(55414-3300)
PHONE...............................612 333-2223
FAX: 612 378-2635
Christine Vesper, *Manager*
EMP: 30
SALES (est): 1MM-4.9MM **Privately Held**
WEB: www.vee.com
SIC: **7299** Retails masquerade or theatrical costumes; costume rental service

(G-5960)
VELOCITY EXPRESS MID-WEST INC
6521 James Ave N (55430-1728)
PHONE...............................612 492-2400
Jeff Parell, *CEO*
EMP: 30 EST: 1999
SALES (est): 1MM-4.9MM **Privately Held**
WEB: www.comvest.com
SIC: **4215** Ground courier services
HQ: Velocity Express Corp
1 Morningside Dr N
Westport CT 06880
203 349-4160

(G-5961)
VELOCITY EXPRESS NORTHEAST INC
6521 James Ave N (55430-1728)
PHONE...............................612 492-2400
Jeff Parell, *CEO*
EMP: 128 EST: 1996
SALES (est): 10MM-24.9MM **Privately Held**
WEB: www.comvest.com
SIC: **4215** 4513 Ground courier services; air courier services
HQ: Velocity Express Corp
1 Morningside Dr N
Westport CT 06880
203 349-4160

(G-5962)
VENTURE BANK (PA)
5601 Green Valley Dr # 120 (55437-1175)
PHONE...............................952 830-9999
Michael T Zenk, *President*
EMP: 35 EST: 2001
SALES (corp-wide): 17.09M **Privately Held**
SIC: **6021** National commercial bank

(G-5963)
VERDE LAWN CARE LLC
Also Called: Scotts Salon Svc Minneapolis
15675 Medina Rd (55447-1467)
PHONE...............................763 550-9400
Charles Holscher, *Member*
Donald R Brattain, *Member*
EMP: 27 EST: 2003 **Privately Held**
SIC: **0782** Lawn care services

(G-5964)
VERISAE INC
100 N 6th St Ste 710A (55403-1527)
PHONE...............................612 455-2305
FAX: 612 455-2324
Dan Johnson, *CEO*
Paul Wickberg, *President*
Nick Martin, *Managing Dir*
Jerry Dolinsky, *Opers Staff*
Gregory A Effertz, *CFO*
EMP: 46 EST: 2000
SQ FT: 11,000
SALES (est): 5MM-9.9MM **Privately Held**
WEB: www.verisae.com
SIC: **7371** Computer software development

(G-5965)
VERIZON COMMUNICATIONS INC
5500 Wayzata Blvd Ste 400 (55416-3578)
PHONE...............................763 591-0705
FAX: 763 591-2175
Louise Stich, *General Mgr*
Michael Holland, *Vice Pres*
Brian Dall, *Technical Mgr*
Bob Lafont, *Technical Mgr*
Rick Thome, *Engineer*
▲ EMP: 150 **Publicly Held**
WEB: www.verizon.com
SIC: **4813** 8748 Long distance telephone communications services; business consulting services
PA: Verizon Communications Inc
140 West St
New York NY 10007
212 395-1000

(G-5966)
VET MART INC
5669 Duluth St (55422-4054)
PHONE...............................763 546-4452
Linda Dooly, *Manager*
EMP: 30 EST: 1999 **Privately Held**
WEB: www.vetmart.com
SIC: **0742** Veterinary services; retails pets & pet supplies

(G-5967)
VHA UPPER MIDWEST INC
7601 France Ave S Ste 500 (55435-5988)
PHONE...............................952 837-4700
FAX: 952 837-4701
Kurt Nomomaque, *President*
Patricia Dolan, *Finance*
Theresa Honfey, *Manager*
Greg Daves, *Manager*
Rob Arlandson, *Administrator*
EMP: 30 EST: 1997
SALES (est): 1MM-4.9MM **Privately Held**
SIC: **8742** Hospital & health services consultant

(G-5968)
VIBES TECHNOLOGIES INC
7125 Nrthlnd Trl N Ste 40 (55428)
PHONE...............................763 971-6260
FAX: 763 971-6278
Roxann Kahn, *General Mgr*
Robert Wickoren, *Regional Mgr*
Jason Davis, *Business Mgr*
William Chensey, *Vice Pres*
Sheila Kruesel, *Vice Pres*
EMP: 110 EST: 1994
SQ FT: 50,000 **Publicly Held**

2011 Harris Minnesota
Services Directory

WEB: www.conferencepoint.com
SIC: 4813 Wired telecommunications carrier & service
DH: Norstan Communications Inc
5101 Shady Oak Rd S
Minnetonka MN 55343
952 352-4300

(G-5969)
VICTORY CORPS FLAGS FLOATS
2730 Nevada Ave N (55427-2807)
PHONE..............................763 561-5600
Dennis Flaherty, President
Marie Anderson, Finance
Brian Knoop, Manager
Stacy Handeland, Manager
▲ EMP: 60
SALES (est): 1MM-4.9MM Privately Held
WEB: www.victorycorps.com
SIC: 7389 Float decorating services; manufactures trimming fabrics

(G-5970)
VICTORY HOME CARE INC
7420 Unity Ave N Ste 209 (55443-3136)
PHONE..............................763 566-3318
FAX: 763 560-0250
Davida Israel, President
EMP: 50 EST: 2003
SALES (est): 1MM-4.9MM Privately Held
WEB: www.victoryhci.com
SIC: 8082 Home health care services

(G-5971)
VIKING COUNCIL OF THE BOY
Also Called: Boy Scouts Amer Viking Council
5300 Glenwood Ave (55422-5118)
PHONE..............................763 545-4550
Jo M Dancik, President
Paula Miller, Controller
Doris Longly, Manager
John Andrews, Exec Dir
Clint Andrea, Director
EMP: 60 EST: 1910
SQ FT: 20,000 Privately Held
SIC: 8641 Boy Scout organization

(G-5972)
VIKING DRYWALL INC
8601 2nd Ave S (55420-2924)
PHONE..............................952 888-6442
FAX: 952 888-5807
Roger Zack, President
Steven Zack, Vice Pres
EMP: 35 EST: 1973
SQ FT: 24,000
SALES (est): 1MM-4.9MM Privately Held
SIC: 1742 Drywall contractor

(G-5973)
VIKING ELECTRIC SUPPLY INC (HQ)
451 Industrial Blvd NE # 2 (55413-2967)
PHONE..............................612 627-1300
FAX: 612 627-1310
Greg Hames, President
Dann Myers, COO
Richard Passmore, VP Opers
Stuart Schwenke, Purchasing
John Leppa, CFO
EMP: 150 EST: 1964
SQ FT: 187,000
SALES (corp-wide): 10.14M Privately Held
WEB: www.vikingelectric.com
SIC: 5063 Wholesales electrical apparatus & equipment; wholesales wire & cable
PA: Sonepar USA Holdings Inc
300 Delaware Ave Ste 1704
Wilmington DE 19801
215 399-5900

(G-5974)
VIKING MATERIALS INC
3225 Como Ave SE (55414-2807)
PHONE..............................612 617-5800
FAX: 612 623-9070
Craig Sauer, President
Karla R Lewis, Corp Secy
William Sternard, Vice Pres
Dana Terry, Purch Agent
Bill Sternard, VP Sls/Mktg
EMP: 80 EST: 1973
SQ FT: 120,000
SALES (est): 50MM-99.9MM Publicly Held

WEB: www.rsac.com
SIC: 5051 Wholesales steel
PA: Reliance Steel & Aluminum Co
350 S Grand Ave Ste 5100
Los Angeles CA 90071
213 687-7700

(G-5975)
VILANA FINANCIAL INC
5747 W Broadway Ave (55428-3572)
PHONE..............................763 416-5959
Andrew Vilenchik, CEO
EMP: 50 EST: 2004
SALES (est): 10MM-24.9MM Privately Held
WEB: www.vilanafinancial.com
SIC: 6282 Financial investment advice service

(G-5976)
VISION LOSS RESOURCES INC (PA)
1936 Lyndale Ave S (55403-3101)
PHONE..............................612 871-2222
Kate Grathwol, President
Duane Johnson, Vice Pres
Kimberly Dague, Manager
Ellen Morrow, Manager
Kelly McCrary, Manager
EMP: 104 EST: 1955
SQ FT: 25,000 Privately Held
WEB: www.cmprovhi.com
SIC: 8331 Sheltered workshop

(G-5977)
VISION LOSS RESOURCES INC
1936 Lyndale Ave S (55403-3101)
PHONE..............................612 871-2222
Steve Fisher, Director
EMP: 100
SALES (est): 1MM-4.9MM Privately Held
WEB: www.cmprovhi.com
SIC: 8331 Job training & vocational rehabilitation services
PA: Vision Loss Resources Inc
1936 Lyndale Ave S
Minneapolis MN 55403
612 871-2222

(G-5978)
VISIONSHARE INC
2829 University Ave SE # 800 (55414-3278)
PHONE..............................612 460-4301
Mark R Briggs, CEO
James P Bradley, Ch of Bd
John Fraser, President
Leann Castillo, Senior VP
Amy Coulter, Senior VP
EMP: 30 EST: 2000
SALES (est): 1MM-4.9MM Privately Held
SIC: 7379 Computer system consulting services; online technology consulting service

(G-5979)
VITREAL RETINAL SURGERY
7760 France Ave S Ste 310 (55435-3216)
PHONE..............................952 929-1131
David F Williams, Principal
EMP: 50
SALES (est): 1MM-4.9MM Privately Held
SIC: 8042 Optometrists' office

(G-5980)
VITREORENTINAL SURGERY
7760 France Ave S Ste 310 (55435-3216)
PHONE..............................952 929-1131
Robert Ramnsey MD, Partner
EMP: 30 EST: 2000
SALES (est): 1MM-4.9MM Privately Held
SIC: 8049 Health practitioners' office

(G-5981)
VOA CARE CENTERS MN
Also Called: Crystal Care Center
3245 Vera Cruz Ave N (55422-2708)
PHONE..............................763 535-6260
FAX: 763 535-7772
Charles W Gould, CEO
Lori Fisher, Human Res Dir
David Myren, Administrator
Natalie Lenhart, Supervisor
Hassanatu Kamara, Director
EMP: 99 EST: 1989

SALES (est): 1MM-4.9MM Privately Held
SIC: 8051 Skilled nursing care facility

(G-5982)
VOICE & DATA NETWORKS INC
6981 Washington Ave S (55439-1506)
PHONE..............................952 946-7999
FAX: 952 946-1066
Joseph Hines, CEO
Sharon Brings, Opers Mgr
Dan Fulmek, Engineer
Kurt Bichler, Finance Dir
Cara Vosika, Sales Mgr
EMP: 50 EST: 1995
SQ FT: 17,108
SALES (est): 25MM-49.9MM Privately Held
WEB: www.voicedata.com
SIC: 5065 Wholesales communications equipment

(G-5983)
VOLUNTEERS OF AMERICA CARE
Also Called: Edina Care Center
6200 Xerxes Ave S (55423-1033)
PHONE..............................952 925-8500
FAX: 952 925-8502
Michelle Alm, Human Res Mgr
Jim Feyder, Manager
Lisa Lange, Manager
Todd Carsen, Exec Dir
Jonathan Torralba, Nursing Dir
EMP: 200
SALES (est): 5MM-9.9MM Privately Held
SIC: 8051 Convalescent home
HQ: Volunteers of America Care
7530 Market Place Dr
Eden Prairie MN 55344
952 941-0305

(G-5984)
VOLUNTEERS OF AMERICA INC
7625 Metro Blvd Ste 200 (55439-3057)
PHONE..............................952 945-4000
Robert Lovegrove, CFO
Deb Johnson, Human Res Dir
Dave Bruess, Info Tech Mgr
Michael Weber, Systems Staff
EMP: 75
SALES (est): 1MM-4.9MM Privately Held
WEB: www.voa.org
SIC: 8322 Meal delivery program
PA: Volunteers of America Inc
1660 Duke St Ste 100
Alexandria VA 22314
703 341-5000

(G-5985)
VOYAGEUR CO'S INC
100 S 5th St Ste 2300 (55402-1230)
PHONE..............................612 376-7000
John Taft, President
EMP: 78 EST: 1993
SALES (est): 10MM-24.9MM Privately Held
WEB: www.dfg-companies.com
SIC: 6282 6211 Investment advisory service; mutual fund management services; security broker & dealer service
PA: Dougherty Financial Group LLC
90 S 7th St Ste 4300
Minneapolis MN 55402
612 376-4000

(G-5986)
W B M HOLDING CO (PA)
Also Called: Country Suites By Carlson
5120 American Blvd W (55437-1235)
PHONE..............................952 831-9595
James Flannery, President
Taylor Flannery, General Mgr
Mike Engle, Maint Mgr
Taylor Flanery, Finance
Jami Pogue, Human Res Dir
EMP: 35 EST: 1990 Privately Held
SIC: 7011 Traveler accommodations

(G-5987)
W I C PROGRAM
330 S 12th St Ste 4710 (55404-1011)
PHONE..............................612 348-6258
FAX: 612 348-5435
Lisa Brown, Treasurer
Karen Mayer, Director
EMP: 30 EST: 1998
SALES (est): 1MM-4.9MM Privately Held

SIC: 8322 Individual & family social services

(G-5988)
W W GRAINGER INC
2505 Kennedy St NE (55413-2819)
PHONE..............................612 486-3300
Jeremy Bay, Manager
EMP: 50
SALES (est): 10MM-24.9MM Publicly Held
WEB: www.grainger.com
SIC: 5085 Wholesales industrial supplies
PA: W W Grainger Inc
14441 W Il Route 60
Lake Forest IL 60045
847 535-1000

(G-5989)
W W GRAINGER INC
2450 Annapolis Ln N (55441-3604)
PO Box 41008 (55441-0008)
PHONE..............................763 531-0300
Jeremy Day, Branch Mgr
Curt Norem, Manager
Dan McLelan, Manager
Jeremy Johnson, Manager
Jim Dorion, Management
EMP: 40
SALES (est): 10MM-24.9MM Publicly Held
WEB: www.grainger.com
SIC: 5085 Wholesales industrial supplies
PA: W W Grainger Inc
14441 W Il Route 60
Lake Forest IL 60045
847 535-1000

(G-5990)
W2005 NEW CENTURY HOTEL
4201 American Blvd W (55437-1120)
PHONE..............................952 835-6643
Mike Nachreiner, General Mgr
Rick Loyd, General Mgr
EMP: 30
SALES (est): 1MM-4.9MM Publicly Held
WEB: www.premierhotels.us
SIC: 7011 Traveler accommodations
HQ: Hampton Inns Inc
755 Crossover Ln
Memphis TN 38117
901 374-5000

(G-5991)
W2007 EQUITY INNS REALTY LLC
Also Called: Hyatt Place Minneapolis
7800 International Dr (55425-1508)
PHONE..............................952 854-0700
FAX: 952 854-9109
Debbie Hickman, Manager
Jane Serrano, Manager
EMP: 35
SALES (est): 1MM-4.9MM Publicly Held
WEB: www.goldman.com
SIC: 7011 Traveler accommodations
DH: Archon Hospitality, LP
6011 Connection Dr
Irving TX 75039
972 368-2200

(G-5992)
WADDELL & REED INC
3601 Minnesota Dr Ste 550 (55435-5848)
PHONE..............................952 884-1503
FAX: 952 884-9053
Lori Tauring, Sales & Mktg St
Thomas Cordingly, Branch Mgr
Thomas Miller, Manager
Jim Leffelman, Manager
Thomas Cain, Manager
EMP: 40
SALES (est): 1MM-4.9MM Publicly Held
SIC: 6411 Insurance agent
HQ: Waddell & Reed Inc
6300 Lamar Ave
Shawnee Mission KS 66202
913 236-2000

(G-5993)
WAGNER GREENHOUSES INC
Also Called: Wagner's
6024 Penn Ave S (55419-2033)
PHONE..............................612 922-1262
FAX: 612 927-7126
Nola Wagner, CEO
Ronald J Wagner, Vice Pres
Scott R Wagner, Vice Pres

GEOGRAPHIC

Fred Case, *Systems Staff*
EMP: 40 **EST:** 1901
SQ FT: 250,000 **Privately Held**
WEB: www.wagnergreenhouses.com
SIC: 0181 Ornamental nursery products

(G-5994)
WAIR PRODUCTS INC
11201 Hampshire Ave S B (55438-2739)
PHONE.................................952 881-9449
FAX: 952 881-9356
Gary Kable, *President*
Pete Nelson, *CFO*
Laurie Rockman, *Administration*
EMP: 30 **EST:** 1988
SQ FT: 60,000
SALES (est): 1MM-4.9MM **Privately Held**
WEB: www.wairproducts.com
SIC: 5085 Manufactures industrial valves; wholesales industrial valves & fittings; manufactures valves & pipe fittings

(G-5995)
WALDEN AUTOMOTIVE GROUP INC (PA)
500 Ford Rd (55426-1134)
PO Box 26717 (55426-0717)
PHONE.................................952 512-8800
Dennis E Hecker, *President*
Gregory Smith, *COO*
Erik Dove, *Manager*
Molly Kaplan, *Executive Asst*
EMP: 50 **EST:** 1987 **Privately Held**
WEB: www.dennyhecker.net
SIC: 8741 Business management services

(G-5996)
WALDEN LEASING INC
500 Ford Rd (55426-1134)
PHONE.................................952 512-8924
Dennis Hecker, *President*
Donna Rizner, *Vice Pres*
Richard Page, *CFO*
EMP: 40 **EST:** 1986
SALES (est): 50MM-99.9MM **Privately Held**
SIC: 5012 7515 Automobile wholesaler; passenger car leasing

(G-5997)
WALDORF-NEVENS DRY CLEANERS
7079 Amundson Ave (55439-2017)
PHONE.................................952 914-9755
FAX: 952 914-9809
George Zahhos, *CEO*
John Zahhos, *President*
David Jones, *Manager*
Scott Leslie, *Data Proc Staff*
EMP: 55 **EST:** 1961
SQ FT: 18,000
SALES (est): 1MM-4.9MM **Privately Held**
WEB: www.waldorfnevens.com
SIC: 7216 7211 Dry cleaning plant; commercial & family dry cleaning & laundry services

(G-5998)
WALGREEN CO
Also Called: Walgreens
4200 Winnetka Ave N (55428-4925)
PHONE.................................763 545-6466
FAX: 763 545-8001
Jim Myers, *Store Mgr*
Mark E Tool, *Manager*
Dave Kline, *Manager*
EMP: 25
SALES (est): 1MM-4.9MM **Publicly Held**
WEB: www.walgreens.com
SIC: 7384 Drug store; photofinishing laboratory
PA: Walgreen Co
       200 Wilmot Rd
       Deerfield IL 60015
       847 914-2500

(G-5999)
WALGREEN CO
Also Called: Walgreens
4547 Hiawatha Ave (55406-3926)
PHONE.................................612 722-4249
Jim Webber, *Manager*
EMP: 70
SALES (est): 10MM-24.9MM **Publicly Held**
WEB: www.walgreens.com

SIC: 7384 Drug store; photofinishing laboratory
PA: Walgreen Co
       200 Wilmot Rd
       Deerfield IL 60015
       847 914-2500

(G-6000)
WALGREEN CO
Also Called: Walgreens
4005 Vinewood Ln N (55442-1734)
PHONE.................................763 553-9731
FAX: 763 553-9144
Todd Maidl, *Manager*
EMP: 30
SALES (est): 1MM-4.9MM **Publicly Held**
WEB: www.walgreens.com
SIC: 7384 Drug store; photofinishing laboratory
PA: Walgreen Co
       200 Wilmot Rd
       Deerfield IL 60015
       847 914-2500

(G-6001)
WALGREEN CO
Also Called: Walgreens
200 W Lake St (55408-3023)
PHONE.................................612 827-8902
M T Foy, *Manager*
Matt Warden, *Manager*
EMP: 25
SALES (est): 1MM-4.9MM **Publicly Held**
WEB: www.walgreens.com
SIC: 7384 Drug store; photofinishing laboratory
PA: Walgreen Co
       200 Wilmot Rd
       Deerfield IL 60015
       847 914-2500

(G-6002)
WALGREEN CO
Also Called: Walgreens
6975 York Ave S (55435-2517)
PHONE.................................952 920-3561
Jeff L Cromett, *General Mgr*
EMP: 50
SALES (est): 5MM-9.9MM **Publicly Held**
WEB: www.walgreens.com
SIC: 7384 Drug store; photofinishing laboratory
PA: Walgreen Co
       200 Wilmot Rd
       Deerfield IL 60015
       847 914-2500

(G-6003)
WALGREEN CO
Also Called: Walgreens
4323 Chicago Ave (55407-3152)
PHONE.................................612 822-9712
FAX: 612 827-3989
Steven Wurst, *Owner*
EMP: 25
SALES (est): 1MM-4.9MM **Publicly Held**
WEB: www.walgreens.com
SIC: 7384 Pharmacy & drug store; photofinishing laboratory
PA: Walgreen Co
       200 Wilmot Rd
       Deerfield IL 60015
       847 914-2500

(G-6004)
WALGREEN CO
Also Called: Walgreens
9800 Lyndale Ave S (55420-4731)
PHONE.................................952 884-8246
FAX: 952 884-3878
Kathy Doeden, *Manager*
Kathy Dodden, *Manager*
EMP: 80
SALES (est): 10MM-24.9MM **Publicly Held**
WEB: www.walgreens.com
SIC: 7384 Drug store; photofinishing laboratory
PA: Walgreen Co
       200 Wilmot Rd
       Deerfield IL 60015
       847 914-2500

(G-6005)
WALGREEN CO
Also Called: Walgreens
7700 Brooklyn Blvd (55443-2906)
PHONE.................................763 566-8350
FAX: 763 561-2256
Brian Brackens, *Manager*
EMP: 50
SALES (est): 5MM-9.9MM **Publicly Held**
WEB: www.walgreens.com
SIC: 7384 Drug store; photofinishing laboratory
PA: Walgreen Co
       200 Wilmot Rd
       Deerfield IL 60015
       847 914-2500

(G-6006)
WALGREEN CO
Also Called: Walgreens
12 W 66th St (55423-2316)
PHONE.................................612 861-7276
FAX: 612 798-2296
Deborah Abrogast, *Manager*
Christopher Fritz, *Manager*
EMP: 50
SQ FT: 10,000
SALES (est): 5MM-9.9MM **Publicly Held**
WEB: www.walgreens.com
SIC: 7384 Drug store; photofinishing laboratory
PA: Walgreen Co
       200 Wilmot Rd
       Deerfield IL 60015
       847 914-2500

(G-6007)
WALGREEN CO
Also Called: Walgreens
6390 Brooklyn Blvd (55429-2600)
PHONE.................................763 585-9946
FAX: 763 569-9904
Mark Ferber, *Branch Mgr*
EMP: 30
SALES (est): 1MM-4.9MM **Publicly Held**
WEB: www.walgreens.com
SIC: 7384 Drug store; photofinishing laboratory
PA: Walgreen Co
       200 Wilmot Rd
       Deerfield IL 60015
       847 914-2500

(G-6008)
WALKER ASSISTED LIVING CORP
7400 York Ave S (55435-5628)
PHONE.................................952 835-8351
FAX: 952 835-7453
Janet Lindbo, *President*
Crystal Buckhalton, *Manager*
Donna Slatta, *Administrator*
Sarah Miller, *Administrator*
Lisa Toms, *Exec Dir*
EMP: 30 **EST:** 1992
SALES (est): 1MM-4.9MM **Privately Held**
SIC: 8361 Home for the elderly

(G-6009)
WALKER CARE CORP I
6130 Lyndale Ave S (55419-2261)
PHONE.................................612 827-8390
FAX: 612 866-1851
Jannet Lindbo, *President*
Karen A Struve, *President*
Ken Ward, *Vice Pres*
EMP: 180 **EST:** 1992
SALES (est): 5MM-9.9MM **Privately Held**
SIC: 8051 Convalescent home

(G-6010)
WALKER METHODIST HEALTH CENTER
3737 Bryant Ave S (55409-1019)
PHONE.................................612 827-8517
FAX: 612 827-8385
Lynn Starkovich, *President*
John Hune, *Facilities Mgr*
James Blaha, *CFO*
David Kautto, *Controller*
Dave Kautton, *Asst Controller*
EMP: 170 **EST:** 1915
SQ FT: 318,500
SALES (est): 5MM-9.9MM **Privately Held**

WEB: www.walkermeth.org
SIC: 8051 Convalescent home
PA: Walker Methodist Senior Svcs
       3737 Bryant Ave S
       Minneapolis MN 55409
       612 827-5931

(G-6011)
WALKER METHODIST INC
3737 Bryant Ave S (55409-1019)
PHONE.................................612 827-5931
Linn Starkovich, *President*
John Lundburg, *COO*
Jim Blaha, *CFO*
David Saemrow, *Director*
Bert Winkel, *Director*
EMP: 500 **EST:** 1991
SALES (est): 10MM-24.9MM **Privately Held**
WEB: www.walkermethodist.org
SIC: 8082 Home health care services

(G-6012)
WALKER METHODIST SENIOR SVCS (PA)
3737 Bryant Ave S (55409-1019)
PHONE.................................612 827-5931
Lynn M Starkovich, *CEO*
Norma Larson, *Vice Pres*
Janet Lindbo, *Production*
Will Carroll, *Human Res Dir*
Brian Peloquin, *Manager*
EMP: 752 **EST:** 1915
SQ FT: 318,500 **Privately Held**
WEB: www.walkermeth.org
SIC: 8361 Geriatric residential care

(G-6013)
WALLING & BERG
121 S 8th St Ste 1100 (55402-2823)
PHONE.................................612 340-1150
Dorothy Cleveland, *CEO*
Gary Debele, *President*
Wright S Walling, *Corp Secy*
Jody D Smidt, *Vice Pres*
Nancy Berg, *Treasurer*
EMP: 30 **EST:** 1991
SQ FT: 8,200
SALES (est): 1MM-4.9MM **Privately Held**
WEB: www.walling-berg.com
SIC: 8111 General practice law office

(G-6014)
WALMAN OPTICAL CO (PA)
801 12th Ave N Ste 2 (55411-4230)
PHONE.................................612 520-6000
FAX: 612 522-4351
Martin Bassett, *President*
Bob Drake, *General Mgr*
Douglas Schlauderaff, *Corp Secy*
Bob Gustin, *Vice Pres*
Charles Pillsbury, *Vice Pres*
EMP: 110 **EST:** 1915
SQ FT: 55,000
SALES (corp-wide): 182M **Privately Held**
SIC: 5048 Wholesales optometric equipment & supplies; manufactures artificial eyes

(G-6015)
WALSER COLLISION & GLASS INC
9001 Grand Ave S (55420-3633)
PHONE.................................952 884-8884
FAX: 952 884-8898
Darren Heairet, *President*
EST: 2000 **Privately Held**
SIC: 7532 Automotive collision shop

(G-6016)
WALSH BISHOP ASSOCIATES INC
900 2nd Ave S Ste 300 (55402-3321)
PHONE.................................612 338-8799
FAX: 612 337-5785
Dennis Walsh, *President*
Steven S Restemayer, *Principal*
Micheal Shields, *Corp Secy*
Keith O'Brien, *Vice Pres*
John Schneider, *Vice Pres*
EMP: 55 **EST:** 1984
SQ FT: 20,000
SALES (est): 5MM-9.9MM **Privately Held**
WEB: www.walshbishop.com
SIC: 8712 7389 Architectural service; interior design service

www.HarrisInfo.com
264
2011 Harris Minnesota
Services Directory
▲=Import ▼=Export
◆=Import/Export

(G-6017)

WALSH TITLE & REAL ESTATE SVCS
4820 W 77th St Ste 220 (55435-4817)
PHONE..............................952 835-3320
FAX: 952 835-7731
John F Walsh Sr, *Ch of Bd*
Judy Anderson, *President*
Claire Robinson, *Senior VP*
Steve Ackerman, *Vice Pres*
Vicki Applegate, *Vice Pres*
EMP: 50 EST: 1990
SQ FT: 12,000
SALES (est): 5MM-9.9MM **Privately Held**
SIC: 6531 6361 Real estate services; title insurance carrier

(G-6018)

WALSTAD TILE & STONE CO
3700 Annapolis Ln N # 115 (55447-5435)
PHONE..............................763 519-1444
FAX: 763 519-0808
Michael T Walstad, *President*
Gail Gallus, *Corp Secy*
Jesse Violett, *Manager*
EMP: 50 EST: 1985
SALES (est): 1MM-4.9MM **Privately Held**
WEB: www.walstadtile.com
SIC: 1743 Tile, marble, terrazzo & mosaic contractor; interior marble installation service; ceramic tile installation service

(G-6019)

WALTER PONTIAC BUICK GMC INC
4601 American Blvd W (55437-1124)
PHONE..............................952 888-9800
Greg Davis, *General Mgr*
Dale Snyder, *Manager*
EMP: 76 EST: 1947
SQ FT: 38,000
SALES (est): 25MM-49.9MM **Privately Held**
SIC: 7538 Retails new & used automobiles; general automotive repair services

(G-6020)

WARE TAD & CO INC
716 N 1st St Ste 336 (55401-3106)
PHONE..............................612 338-2311
FAX: 612 338-2344
Tad Ware, *President*
Ann Ware, *Exec VP*
Susan Christian, *Vice Pres*
EMP: 35 EST: 1980
SQ FT: 5,500
SALES (est): 1MM-4.9MM **Privately Held**
SIC: 7311 7335 7336 Advertising agency; commercial photographic studio; graphic arts & related design service

(G-6021)

WAREHOUSE DEPOT LLC
1860 E 28th St (55407-1272)
PHONE..............................612 728-5238
Earl Ward, *General Mgr*
Beverly Morris, *Principal*
Mark Velandra, *Manager*
Jeff Scott, *CTO*
▲ EMP: 50 EST: 2000
SALES (est): 1MM-4.9MM **Publicly Held**
WEB: www.roofdepot.com
SIC: 4225 General warehousing
HQ: North Coast Commercial Roofing
2440 Edison Blvd
Twinsburg OH 44087
330 425-3359

(G-6022)

WASHBURN CHILD GUIDANCE CENTER
2430 Nicollet Ave (55404-3449)
PHONE..............................612 871-1454
FAX: 612 871-1505
Carol Olsen, *Manager*
Steve Lepinski, *Exec Dir*
Adam L Fox, *Psychiatry*
Suzanne L Aoun, *Psychiatry*
EMP: 60 EST: 1882
SQ FT: 20,000
SALES (est): 5MM-9.9MM **Privately Held**
WEB: www.washburn.org
SIC: 8093 Specialty outpatient clinic

(G-6023)

WATSON CENTERS INC (PA)
3100 W Lake St Ste 420 (55416-4599)
PHONE..............................612 920-5034
Stephen M Watson, *President*
Bradley Henning, *Treasurer*
Chad Zimmerman, *Marketing Staff*
Mary C Watson, *Director*
EMP: 60 EST: 1973
SALES (corp-wide): 500K **Privately Held**
SIC: 6531 6552 Real estate management services; commercial land subdividers & developers

(G-6024)

WATSON'S OF MINNEAPOLIS INC
7007 Lakeland Ave N (55428-5612)
PHONE..............................763 560-7727
FAX: 763 560-0793
Kevin Bolden, *President*
Derrick Bolden, *Vice Pres*
Stacey Magsam, *Manager*
Mark Hoffmann, *Manager*
EMP: 25 EST: 2000
SALES (est): 1MM-4.9MM **Privately Held**
SIC: 8748 1799 5091 Business consulting services; retails spas & hot tubs; wholesales billiard equipment & supplies; retails outdoor & garden furniture; swimming pool construction

(G-6025)

WATSON-FORSBERG CO
6465 Wayzata Blvd Ste 110 (55426-1722)
PHONE..............................952 544-7761
Dale Forsberg, *President*
Michael Ashmore, *Vice Pres*
Mike McKim, *Vice Pres*
Cindy Hanson, *Manager*
Don Kohlenberger, *Exec Dir*
EMP: 40 EST: 1965
SQ FT: 2,000
SALES (est): 10MM-24.9MM **Privately Held**
SIC: 1542 New commercial & office building construction; commercial & office building renovation & repair services

(G-6026)

WAYMOUTH FARMS INC
5300 Boone Ave N (55428-4054)
PHONE..............................763 533-5300
FAX: 763 533-9890
Gerard S Knight, *President*
Dean Giroux, *Vice Pres*
Scott Vridell, *Vice Pres*
Him Chesemore, *Mfg Staff*
Todd Arver, *Purchasing*
▲ EMP: 210 EST: 1976
SALES (est): 25MM-49.9MM **Privately Held**
WEB: www.goodsensesnacks.com
SIC: 5145 5149 Manufactures candy & other confectionery products; manufactures chocolate & cocoa products; manufactures dried & dehydrated fruits & vegetables & soup mixes; wholesales dog food; wholesales confectionery products; manufactures nut & seed products

(G-6027)

WAYSIDE HOUSE INC
3705 Park Center Blvd (55416-2504)
PHONE..............................952 926-5626
Anne Mavity, *Corp Secy*
Barb McQuillan, *Treasurer*
Cheryl Davidson, *Manager*
Sharon Johnson, *Exec Dir*
EMP: 45 EST: 1954
SALES (est): 1MM-4.9MM **Privately Held**
WEB: www.waysidehouse.org
SIC: 8093 8069 Specialty outpatient clinic; substance abuse hospital

(G-6028)

WAYZATA PARTNERS LP (PA)
Also Called: Meridian Manor
4601 Excelsior Blvd # 301 (55416-4977)
PHONE..............................952 920-5338
Greg Bronk, *Member*
Gene Nelson, *Member*
Frank Lang, *Member*
Paul Brewer, *Member*
Melissa Christain, *Member*
EMP: 74 EST: 1994 **Privately Held**
SIC: 6513 Apartment building operator

(G-6029)

WCL ASSOCIATES INC
4931 W 35th St Ste 200 (55416-2774)
PHONE..............................952 541-9969
David Clark, *President*
Paul G Dahl, *Vice Pres*
Paul D Anderson, *Vice Pres*
EMP: 25 EST: 1981
SQ FT: 5,000
SALES (est): 1MM-4.9MM **Privately Held**
SIC: 8712 Architectural service

(G-6030)

WE DO-CARE INC
1300 E 66th St Uppr (55423-2684)
PHONE..............................612 866-7800
Janine Yates, *CEO*
Lawrence Swanson, *Office Mgr*
EMP: 160 EST: 2004
SALES (est): 5MM-9.9MM **Privately Held**
SIC: 8082 Home health care services

(G-6031)

WEBMD HEALTH CORP
605 Highway 169 N Fl 10 (55441-6407)
PHONE..............................763 512-2600
Bobby McAdam, *Branch Mgr*
Beth Ofelt-Nelson, *Training Spec*
EMP: 50
SQ FT: 16,000
SALES (est): 5MM-9.9MM **Publicly Held**
WEB: www.wellmed.com
SIC: 7374 Data processing & preparation services
PA: Webmd Health Corp
111 8th Ave
New York NY 10011
212 624-3700

(G-6032)

WEDDING CHAPEL INC
7201 Bass Lake Rd (55428-3824)
PHONE..............................763 533-4228
Diana M Ellingson, *President*
Scott E Ellingson, *Vice Pres*
EMP: 36 EST: 1985
SQ FT: 5,000
SALES (est): 1MM-4.9MM **Privately Held**
SIC: 7299 Bridal shop; tuxedo rental service

(G-6033)

WEIS BUILDERS INC (PA)
7645 Lyndale Ave S # 300 (55423-6008)
PHONE..............................612 243-5000
FAX: 612 243-5010
Jay Weis, *CEO*
Erik Weis, *President*
Ron Kreinbring, *Vice Pres*
Steve Knight, *Vice Pres*
Scott Ewing, *Opers Mgr*
EMP: 180 EST: 1939
SQ FT: 20,000 **Privately Held**
WEB: www.weisbuilders.com
SIC: 1522 1541 1542 Apartment building construction service; new industrial building construction; new commercial & office building construction

(G-6034)

WELLINGTON WINDOW CO (PA)
3938 Meadowbrook Rd (55426-4506)
PHONE..............................952 933-2737
FAX: 952 933-1403
Libby Wyatt, *President*
Cliff Stolp, *Project Engr*
Brad Ost, *Controller*
Heidi Holkestad, *Human Res Mgr*
Mike Novitsky, *Manager*
EMP: 70 EST: 1983
SQ FT: 37,000 **Privately Held**
SIC: 1751 Manufactures plastic windows; manufactures metal doors, sash & trim; carpentry contractor; manufactures glass products; millwork

(G-6035)

WELLS CAPITAL MANAGEMENT INC (HQ)
90 S 7th St Ste 5000 (55402-4103)
PHONE..............................612 667-4230
Robert W Bissell, *President*
EST: 2002
SALES (corp-wide): 98.63B **Publicly Held**

SIC: 6282 Investment advisory service
PA: Wells Fargo & Co
420 Montgomery St
San Francisco CA 94104
866 878-5865

(G-6036)

WELLS FARGO ADVISORS LLC
80 S 8th St Ste 3400 (55402-2113)
PHONE..............................612 332-1212
Anthony Parr, *Manager*
Charlie Zajicek, *Manager*
John Ekman, *Manager*
Bradley Smegal, *Manager*
Peter Ryan, *Manager*
EMP: 30
SALES (est): 5MM-9.9MM **Publicly Held**
WEB: www.wachoviasec.com
SIC: 6211 Securities broker & dealer
HQ: Wells Fargo Advisors LLC
1 N Jefferson Ave
Saint Louis MO 63103
314 955-3000

(G-6037)

WELLS FARGO ADVISORS LLC
8500 Normandale Lake Blvd (55437-3813)
PHONE..............................952 835-3111
Brian Reichenberger, *Opers Mgr*
Benjamin Birk, *Opers Mgr*
Dawn Krysan, *Sales Staff*
Denise Olson, *Branch Mgr*
Rich Miles, *Manager*
EMP: 25
SALES (est): 5MM-9.9MM **Publicly Held**
WEB: www.wachoviasec.com
SIC: 6211 Securities broker & dealer
HQ: Wells Fargo Advisors LLC
1 N Jefferson Ave
Saint Louis MO 63103
314 955-3000

(G-6038)

WELLS FARGO AUDIT SERVICES INC
1200 Norwest Center (55479-0001)
PHONE..............................612 667-1234
Robert R CA, *Senior VP*
Christine Kaehler, *Vice Pres*
John T Thornton, *CFO*
Darlya Mathews, *Accounting Mgr*
Gail J Daddio, *Manager*
EMP: 75 EST: 1971
SQ FT: 1,250
SALES (est): 5MM-9.9MM **Publicly Held**
SIC: 8721 Auditing services
PA: Wells Fargo & Co
420 Montgomery St
San Francisco CA 94104
866 878-5865

(G-6039)

WELLS FARGO BANK, NATIONAL
1455 W Lake St Fl 1 (55408-2648)
PHONE..............................612 667-2753
FAX: 612 667-2721
Gerry Gray, *Division Pres*
EMP: 45
SALES (est): 10MM-24.9MM **Publicly Held**
SIC: 6159 Small business investment service
HQ: Wfc Holdings, Corp
420 Montgomery St
San Francisco CA 94104
415 396-7392

(G-6040)

WELLS FARGO BANK, NATIONAL
7901 Xerxes Ave S Ste 108 (55431-1200)
PHONE..............................952 881-7333
FAX: 952 881-9101
Jeff Worst, *Vice Pres*
Betsie Illum, *Store Mgr*
Jon Maier, *Branch Mgr*
EMP: 25
SALES (est): 1MM-4.9MM **Publicly Held**
SIC: 8721 Payroll services; billing & bookkeeping services
HQ: Wfc Holdings, Corp
420 Montgomery St
San Francisco CA 94104
415 396-7392

(PA)=Parent Co (HQ)=Headquarters (DH)=Div Headquarters
✿ = New business established in last 2 years

2011 Harris Minnesota
Services Directory

© Harris InfoSource 1-866-281-6415

265

(G-6041)

WELLS FARGO BANK, NATIONAL

625 Marquette Ave Fl 16 (55402-2308)
PHONE..........................612 667-1234
L S Nelson, *CEO*
Donald A Crlson, *Senior VP*
Eric Nilon, *Vice Pres*
Jim Negal, *Vice Pres*
K C Idder, *Vice Pres*
EMP: 4000
SALES (est): 500MM-999.9MM **Publicly Held**
SIC: 6162 Mortgage banking service
HQ: Wfc Holdings, Corp
  420 Montgomery St
  San Francisco CA 94104
  415 396-7392

(G-6042)

WELLS FARGO BANK, NATIONAL

733 Marquette Ave (55402-2309)
PHONE..........................612 667-8710
FAX: 612 667-2228
Can Pocrnich, *CFO*
Madhav Goparaju, *Manager*
EMP: 30
SALES (est): 5MM-9.9MM **Publicly Held**
SIC: 6021 National commercial bank
HQ: Wfc Holdings, Corp
  420 Montgomery St
  San Francisco CA 94104
  415 396-7392

(G-6043)

WELLS FARGO BUSINESS CREDIT (DH)

109 S 7th St Ste 400 (55402-2310)
PHONE..........................612 673-8500
FAX: 612 673-8589
Martin J Mc Kinley, *President*
Heidi Zeller, *Corp Secy*
Bruce Grath, *Senior VP*
Keith K Theisen, *Senior VP*
Ken J Kohrs, *Assistant VP*
EMP: 73 **EST:** 1974
SQ FT: 10,000
SALES (corp-wide): 98.63B **Publicly Held**
SIC: 6021 6141 National commercial bank; personal credit institution
HQ: Wfc Holdings, Corp
  420 Montgomery St
  San Francisco CA 94104
  415 396-7392

(G-6044)

WELLS FARGO EQUIPMENT FINANCE (DH)

733 Marquette Ave Ste 700 (55402-2316)
PO Box 1450 (55485-0001)
PHONE..........................612 667-9876
FAX: 612 334-9083
James R Renner, *President*
Diana L Kahle, *Corp Secy*
Lea Kahle, *Corp Secy*
Mark Count, *Vice Pres*
John Lande, *Vice Pres*
▲ **EMP:** 130 **EST:** 1968
SQ FT: 14,000
SALES (corp-wide): 98.63B **Publicly Held**
SIC: 6159 Machinery & equipment finance leasing service; vehicle finance leasing service; truck finance leasing service
HQ: Wfc Holdings, Corp
  420 Montgomery St
  San Francisco CA 94104
  415 396-7392

(G-6045)

WELLS FARGO FINANCIAL (DH)

3101 W 69th St Ste 204 (55435-2507)
PHONE..........................952 920-9270
James R Fisher, *President*
Sharon D Alexander, *Corp Secy*
Deidre A Messenger, *Corp Secy*
Frances Montoya, *Corp Secy*
Margaret M Weber, *Corp Secy*
EMP: 155 **EST:** 1947
SQ FT: 20,500
SALES (corp-wide): 98.63B **Publicly Held**
WEB: www.wellsfargofinancial.com

SIC: 6021 National commercial bank
HQ: Wells Fargo Financial Ca Inc
  800 Walnut St
  Des Moines IA 50309
  515 557-7401

(G-6046)

WELLS FARGO FINANCIAL INDIANA

3101 W 69th St Ste 204 (55435-2520)
PHONE..........................952 920-9270
Steve Wagner, *President*
Fay Kunz, *Corp Secy*
Londa Gomble, *Vice Pres*
Patrick Sheely, *Vice Pres*
Dan Abbot, *Vice Pres*
EMP: 30 **EST:** 1994
SALES (est): 5MM-9.9MM **Publicly Held**
WEB: www.wellsfargofinancial.com
SIC: 6141 Personal consumer finance company
DH: Wells Fargo Financial
  3101 W 69th St 204
  Minneapolis MN 55435
  952 920-9270

(G-6047)

WELLS FARGO FUNDING INC

2701 Wells Fargo Way Fl 5 (55467-8000)
PHONE..........................800 328-5074
Eric P Stoddard, *President*
Daniel T Segersin, *Exec VP*
Thomas Navara, *Senior VP*
Michael S Harter, *Senior VP*
Sherri Thiee, *Senior VP*
EMP: 180 **EST:** 1991
SALES (est): 25MM-49.9MM **Publicly Held**
SIC: 6162 Mortgage banking service
HQ: Wfc Holdings, Corp
  420 Montgomery St
  San Francisco CA 94104
  415 396-7392

(G-6048)

WELLS FARGO HOME MORTGAGE INC

600 Highway 169 S Ste 1950 (55426-1215)
PHONE..........................952 939-9066
Ellen Riggle, *Manager*
Raymond Matz, *Manager*
EMP: 30
SALES (est): 1MM-4.9MM **Publicly Held**
WEB: www.wfhm.com
SIC: 6162 6163 Mortgage & loan lending; loan broker
DH: Wells Fargo Home Mortgage Inc
  1 Home Campus
  Des Moines IA 50328
  800 288-3212

(G-6049)

WELLS FARGO INSURANCE INC

600 W Market (55425-5531)
PHONE..........................952 921-3601
Paul Peterson, *Manager*
EMP: 60
SALES (est): 25MM-49.9MM **Publicly Held**
SIC: 6331 Property & casualty insurance carrier
HQ: Wells Fargo Insurance Inc
  600 Highway 169 S Fl 12
  Minneapolis MN 55426
  612 667-5600

(G-6050)

WELLS FARGO INSURANCE INC (HQ)

600 Highway 169 S Fl 12 (55426-1205)
PHONE..........................612 667-5600
FAX: 612 667-2680
Kathleen Arntson, *Corp Secy*
Steven Veno, *Exec VP*
Kathy Sullivan, *Senior VP*
Mary Pelowski, *Opers Mgr*
Liz Misura, *Finance*
EMP: 40 **EST:** 1904
SALES (corp-wide): 98.63B **Publicly Held**
SIC: 6411 Insurance services
PA: Wells Fargo & Co
  420 Montgomery St
  San Francisco CA 94104
  866 878-5865

(G-6051)

WELLS FARGO INSURANCE SERVICES

4300 Market Pointe Dr # 600 (55435-5455)
PHONE..........................952 830-3000
FAX: 952 830-3007
Polly Franchot, *Senior VP*
John Moore, *Vice Pres*
Joan Reynders, *Asst Treas*
Steve Schmitt, *Manager*
Margaret Pemberton, *Manager*
EMP: 200 **EST:** 1919
SALES (est): 10MM-24.9MM **Publicly Held**
SIC: 6411 Insurance agency & broker; life insurance agent; property & casualty insurance agent

(G-6052)

WELLS FARGO PROPERTIES INC (HQ)

Wells Fargo Ctr # 6 (55402)
PHONE..........................612 667-8690
Thomas Parish, *President*
Harold Richey, *Vice Pres*
Robert Seger, *Vice Pres*
Meeghan McGahan, *Manager*
EMP: 32 **EST:** 1974
SQ FT: 6,000
SALES (corp-wide): 98.63B **Publicly Held**
SIC: 6552 Commercial land subdividers & developers
PA: Wells Fargo & Co
  420 Montgomery St
  San Francisco CA 94104
  866 878-5865

(G-6053)

WELLS FARGO SERVICES INC (HQ)

255 2nd Ave S (55401-2120)
PHONE..........................612 667-1234
C W Edwards, *President*
Scott Grengs, *Project Mgr*
Bruce Sunde, *Engineer*
Dan Kieling, *Manager*
Kenny Lake, *Manager*
EMP: 760 **EST:** 1968
SQ FT: 280,000
SALES (corp-wide): 98.63B **Publicly Held**
SIC: 7374 Data processing service
PA: Wells Fargo & Co
  420 Montgomery St
  San Francisco CA 94104
  866 878-5865

(G-6054)

WELLS FARGO SERVICES INC

255 2nd Ave S (55401-2120)
PHONE..........................612 667-1234
R M Damlo, *Principal*
Joel Taylor, *Network Enginr*
EMP: 760
SALES (est): 50MM-99.9MM **Publicly Held**
SIC: 7374 Data processing service
HQ: Wells Fargo Services Inc
  255 2nd Ave S
  Minneapolis MN 55401
  612 667-1234

(G-6055)

WELLS JEFFERSON INTERNATIONAL

3600 Minnesota Dr Ste 850 (55435-7924)
PHONE..........................612 338-5400
Jim McQuillan, *Manager*
Joy Summers, *Administrator*
EMP: 35
SALES (est): 1MM-4.9MM **Publicly Held**
WEB: www.manpower.com
SIC: 8721 Accounting, auditing & bookkeeping services
HQ: Wells Jefferson International
  100 Manpower Pl Fl 4
  Milwaukee WI 53212
  414 319-3400

(G-6056)

WEST BANK SCHOOL OF MUSIC

1813 S 6th St (55454-1208)
PHONE..........................612 333-6651
David Elderson, *Manager*
Jeanne Papish, *Manager*

Karen Lyu, *Exec Dir*
EMP: 36 **EST:** 1970
SQ FT: 1,680
SALES (est): 1MM-4.9MM **Privately Held**
WEB: www.westbankmusic.org
SIC: 7922 Music & drama school; music school; performing arts center production service; musical instrument lessons

(G-6057)

WESTCO SYSTEMS INC

4655 Juneau Ln N (55446-3402)
PHONE..........................763 559-7046
Jeff Caryl, *President*
EMP: 25 **EST:** 2007
SALES (est): 10MM-24.9MM **Privately Held**
SIC: 5065 7382 Wholesales security control equipment & systems; retails security & safety equipment; security systems services

(G-6058)

WESTERN BANK EDINA

4700 W 77th St Ste 160 (55435-4819)
PHONE..........................952 857-1707
FAX: 952 857-4070
Steve Erdall, *Principal*
Tom Porter, *Vice Pres*
▲ **EMP:** 80 **EST:** 2004 **Privately Held**
SIC: 6712 6099 Bank holding company; bank services

(G-6059)

WESTERN DELIVERY INC

5605 Wentworth Ave (55419-1814)
PHONE..........................651 665-0702
Robert Exner, *President*
Emily E Exner, *Vice Pres*
Fotis Couroutoudis, *Manager*
EMP: 25 **EST:** 1997
SQ FT: 1,000
SALES (est): 1MM-4.9MM **Privately Held**
SIC: 4212 Delivery services by vehicle

(G-6060)

WESTERN NATIONAL MUTUAL INSCE (PA)

5350 W 78th St (55439-3101)
PO Box 1463 (55440-1463)
PHONE..........................952 835-5350
FAX: 952 921-3163
Stuart C Henderson, *President*
Joesph Pingatore, *Corp Secy*
David L Eide, *Exec VP*
Dennis Ballinger, *Vice Pres*
Pat Dibble, *Vice Pres*
EMP: 275 **EST:** 1900
SQ FT: 70,000
SALES (corp-wide): 191.60M **Privately Held**
WEB: www.wnins.com
SIC: 6331 Provides property damage insurance; provides mutual fire, marine & casualty insurance

(G-6061)

WESTERN WATERPROOFING CO INC

111 Lowry Ave NE (55418-3418)
PHONE..........................612 781-7100
FAX: 612 781-7177
Mike Mercier, *Division Mgr*
Al Nelson, *Branch Mgr*
EMP: 40
SALES (est): 1MM-4.9MM **Privately Held**
WEB: www.westerngroup.com
SIC: 1799 Waterproofing service
HQ: Western Waterproofing Co Inc
  1637 N Warson Rd
  Saint Louis MO 63132
  314 427-6733

(G-6062)

WESTWOOD LUTHERAN CHURCH

9001 Cedar Lake Rd S (55426-2354)
PHONE..........................952 545-5623
FAX: 952 545-0251
Tania Haber, *Pastor*
Jan Melchert, *Manager*
Cheryl Stark, *Manager*
Toni Robinson, *Manager*
Cindy Folin, *Administrator*
EMP: 50 **EST:** 1989 **Privately Held**
WEB: www.westwoodlutheran.org

www.HarrisInfo.com
266

2011 Harris Minnesota
Services Directory

▲=Import ▼=Export
◆=Import/Export

SIC: 8351 Provides Lutheran church services; nursery school

(G-6063)
WESTWOOD SPORTS INC
9601 Garfield Ave S (55420-4214)
PHONE...........................952 881-2222
FAX: 952 881-1707
David Benolkin, *President*
Sandra Benolkin, *Vice Pres*
Joe Ann, *Accounts Mgr*
EMP: 60
SQ FT: 5,714
SALES (est): 5MM-9.9MM **Privately Held**
SIC: 5091 Retails sporting goods; retails sports apparel; retails baseball equipment; retails hockey equipment; retails skating equipment; wholesales sporting & recreational goods & supplies

(G-6064)
WHEELER CONSOLIDATED INC
Also Called: Erickson Engineering
9330 James Ave S (55431-2317)
PHONE...........................952 929-6791
FAX: 952 346-0047
Dale Drazes, *Vice Pres*
Dale Draves, *Vice Pres*
Dale Dravef, *Vice Pres*
Kevin Scott, *Purchasing*
Bob Larson, *Office Mgr*
EMP: 30
SALES (est): 1MM-4.9MM **Privately Held**
SIC: 8711 5031 Professional engineers; wholesales rough, dressed & finished lumber; steel fabricator
PA: Wheeler Consolidated Inc
6100 Thornton Ave Ste 200
Des Moines IA 50321
515 223-1584

(G-6065)
WHITEBOX ADVISORS LLC
3033 Excelsior Blvd Ste 300 (55416-4675)
PHONE...........................612 253-6025
Johnathan Wood, *Member*
Andrew Redleas, *Mng Member*
Clint Semm, *Manager*
Amy Borgstrom, *Info Tech Mgr*
Mark M Strefling, *Officer*
EMP: 37 EST: 1999
SQ FT: 8,000
SALES (est): 10MM-24.9MM **Privately Held**
WEB: www.whitebox-advisors.com
SIC: 6799 Investor services

(G-6066)
WHITTIER PLACE
2405 1st Ave S (55404-3412)
PHONE...........................612 872-1926
Vicky Frahm, *Exec Dir*
EMP: 25 EST: 1976
SALES (est): 500-999K **Privately Held**
SIC: 8361 Residential care facility

(G-6067)
WHOLESALE PRODUCE SUPPLY LLC
752 Kasota Cir SE (55414-2815)
PHONE...........................612 378-2025
FAX: 612 378-9547
Brian Hauge, *Member*
Arthur Quiggle, *Member*
Christine Plutowski, *Member*
Val Schaaf, *Human Res Dir*
Reed Sibet, *Sales Mgr*
EMP: 190 EST: 1960
SQ FT: 87,000
SALES (est): 50MM-99.9MM **Privately Held**
WEB: www.wholesaleproducesupply.com
SIC: 5148 Wholesales fresh fruits; wholesales vegetables

(G-6068)
WILKERSON & HEGNA
7300 Metro Blvd Ste 300 (55439-2302)
PHONE...........................952 897-1707
Kyle Hegna, *Partner*
Gary C Wilkerson, *Partner*
EMP: 30 EST: 1979
SQ FT: 5,000
SALES (est): 1MM-4.9MM **Privately Held**
WEB: www.wilkersonhegna.com
SIC: 8111 General practice attorney's or lawyer's office

(G-6069)
WILLIAM LLC
Also Called: Minnesota Conway Fire & Safety
314 W 86th St (55420-2706)
PHONE...........................952 345-3461
William Kresbach, *Member*
EMP: 42 EST: 1996
SALES (est): 1MM-4.9MM **Privately Held**
SIC: 7389 Fire extinguisher services

(G-6070)
WILLIAMS STEEL & HARDWARE CO (PA)
416 35th Ave NE Ste 1 (55418-1161)
PO Box 540 (55440-0540)
PHONE...........................612 588-9800
FAX: 612 588-9875
Tom Young, *CEO*
Jack A Ocenasek, *Ch of Bd*
William Winter, *Vice Pres*
Roger Champa, *Vice Pres*
Deland Richter, *CFO*
EMP: 60 EST: 1860
SQ FT: 57,000
SALES (corp-wide): 9M **Privately Held**
SIC: 5085 Wholesales industrial fasteners including nuts, bolts, screws, etc; wholesales mill supplies

(G-6071)
WILLIS OF MINNESOTA INC
1600 Utica Ave S Ste 600 (55416-3687)
PHONE...........................763 302-7100
Sandy Lofsness, *President*
Al Thomas, *President*
Heather D Naaktgeboren, *Corp Secy*
Mark Sponsler, *COO*
Debra Enderle, *Vice Pres*
EMP: 89 EST: 1980
SQ FT: 20,000
SALES (est): 10MM-24.9MM **Privately Held**
WEB: www.willis.com
SIC: 6411 Insurance services
PA: Willis North America Inc
200 Liberty St
New York NY 10281
212 344-8888

(G-6072)
WILLOW GROUP INC
8201 Norman Center Dr # 210 (55437-3420)
PHONE...........................952 897-3550
Leroy Thydean, *President*
Barbara Gurstelle, *Principal*
Jose Santos, *Principal*
Michael B Gaard, *Vice Pres*
James Brownell, *CFO*
EMP: 30 EST: 1998
SQ FT: 1,200
SALES (est): 1MM-4.9MM **Privately Held**
WEB: www.willowg.com
SIC: 8742 Management consulting services

(G-6073)
WILLOWS
6232 65th Ave N Apt 117 (55429-1931)
PHONE...........................763 533-1883
FAX: 763 533-0767
Maria Poisson, *Manager*
Maria Eoisson, *Manager*
Roberta Stow, *Manager*
EMP: 30 EST: 2003
SALES (est): 1MM-4.9MM **Privately Held**
WEB: www.thewillows.com
SIC: 6513 Apartment building operator

(G-6074)
WILSON - MCSHANE CORP
3001 Metro Dr Ste 500 (55425-1617)
PHONE...........................952 854-0795
FAX: 952 854-1632
Matt Winkel, *President*
Pat McDonnell, *Vice Pres*
Patrick M Mc Shane, *Vice Pres*
Patrick McDoneel, *Human Resources*
Patrick Groves, *Data Proc Dir*
EMP: 110 EST: 1969
SQ FT: 6,000
SALES (est): 10MM-24.9MM **Privately Held**
WEB: www.trust653.com
SIC: 6733 Trusts, estates & agency accounts services

(G-6075)
WILSON LEARNING CORP
8000 W 78th St Ste 200 (55439-2549)
PHONE...........................952 944-2880
Tom Roth, *President*
Ed Emde, *President*
Mike Poulson, *Managing Dir*
Hideaki Sekine, *COO*
David Yesford, *Senior VP*
EMP: 60 EST: 1965
SALES (est): 5MM-9.9MM **Privately Held**
WEB: www.wilsonlearning.com
SIC: 8742 7361 Programmed instruction services; employment agency services

(G-6076)
WINMARK CAPITAL CORP
Also Called: Wirth Business Credit
605 Highway 169 N Ste 400 (55441-6536)
PHONE...........................763 520-8500
John L Morgan, *CEO*
Bill Anderson, *Vice Pres*
Jonathan Walmsley, *Vice Pres*
Brett D Heffes, *CFO*
John Dooley, *Sales Staff*
EMP: 100 EST: 2004
SQ FT: 40,000
SALES (est): Under 500K **Publicly Held**
WEB: www.winmarkcorporation.com
SIC: 7359 Equipment rental & leasing services
PA: Winmark Corp
605 Highway 169 N Ste 400
Minneapolis MN 55441
763 520-8500

(G-6077)
WINMARK CORP (PA)
605 Highway 169 N Ste 400 (55441-6407)
PHONE...........................763 520-8500
John L Morgan, *CEO*
Brett D Heffes, *President*
Stephen A Murphy, *President*
Stephen Briggs, *COO*
Anthony D Ishaug, *CFO*
EMP: 115 EST: 1988
SALES (corp-wide): 37.29M **Publicly Held**
WEB: www.winmarkcorporation.com
SIC: 5137 6153 6794 7359 Wholesales women's & children's clothing; selling or licensing of franchises; equipment rental & leasing services; short-term business credit institution

(G-6078)
WINSTED CORP
10901 Hampshire Ave S Ste A (55438-2731)
PHONE...........................952 944-9050
Randy Smith, *President*
Gerald Hoska, *Chairman*
Stephen Hoska, *Vice Pres*
Joseph Lupo, *Treasurer*
Andriene Johnson, *Shareholder*
EMP: 39 EST: 1963
SQ FT: 76,610
SALES (est): 10MM-24.9MM **Privately Held**
SIC: 5021 Wholesales furniture; manufactures office furniture

(G-6079)
WIPFLI LLP
7601 France Ave S Ste 400 (55435-5969)
PHONE...........................952 548-3400
Lauri Roberts, *Branch Mgr*
Nancy Jacobson, *Consultant*
Bruce Washam, *MIS Dir*
EMP: 87
SALES (est): 5MM-9.9MM **Privately Held**
SIC: 8721 Certified public accountant services
PA: Wipfli LLP
11 Scott St Ste 400
Wausau WI 54403
715 845-3111

(G-6080)
WISE GREENWALD & GREENWALD PC
Also Called: Casker Machines
4800 Lilac Dr N (55429-3924)
PHONE...........................763 535-0501
Steve Wise, *Partner*
Greg Greenwald, *Partner*

Dale Greenwald, *Partner*
EMP: 100 EST: 1945
SALES (est): 25MM-49.9MM **Privately Held**
SIC: 6512 Nonresidential building operator

(G-6081)
WKT PROPERTIES LLC
9201 International Pkwy (55428-3609)
PHONE...........................763 525-4000
Bruce Wallace, *Member*
EMP: 25 EST: 2001
SALES (est): 5MM-9.9MM **Privately Held**
WEB: www.tioga-inc.com
SIC: 6512 Nonresidential building operator

(G-6082)
WOLF SPRINGS RANCHES
7321 Washington Ave S (55439-2407)
PHONE...........................952 942-5566
Thomas Redman, *Owner*
EMP: 32 EST: 2005 **Privately Held**
SIC: 0291 Animal production

(G-6083)
WOLFNET TECHNOLOGIES LLC
211 N 1st St Ste 455 (55401-1476)
PHONE...........................612 342-0088
FAX: 612 342-0087
Christopher Freeman, *Member*
Brian Macintosh, *Member*
Jefferson Petty, *Vice Pres*
Rich Bailey, *Mktg Dir*
Joel Macintosh, *Mng Member*
EMP: 35 EST: 1996
SQ FT: 5,600
SALES (est): 5MM-9.9MM **Privately Held**
SIC: 7379 Computer system consulting services

(G-6084)
WOMAN'S CLUB OF MINNEAPOLIS
410 Oak Grove St (55403-3225)
PHONE...........................612 870-8001
FAX: 612 813-5336
Kevin Ehlert, *General Mgr*
Pam Lehan, *General Mgr*
Sally Heer, *Accountant*
Christine Ebert, *Manager*
EMP: 60 EST: 1913
SQ FT: 75,000 **Privately Held**
SIC: 8641 Social club

(G-6085)
WORKABILITIES INC
7400 Laurel Ave (55426-1578)
PHONE...........................763 541-1844
FAX: 763 541-0415
Bill Lyons, *Exec Dir*
EMP: 50 EST: 1976
SQ FT: 15,000
SALES (est): 1MM-4.9MM **Privately Held**
WEB: www.workabilities.org
SIC: 8361 Residential rehabilitation center with health care incidental

(G-6086)
WORKMAN FINANCIAL GROUP INC
3370 Annapolis Ln N Ste B (55447-5384)
PHONE...........................763 746-9420
Bruce Workman, *President*
Nicole Lier, *Manager*
EMP: 30 EST: 1985
SALES (est): 1MM-4.9MM **Privately Held**
WEB: www.workmansecurities.com
SIC: 6411 6211 8742 Insurance broker; financial management consulting services; general brokerage investment firm; insurance agent

(G-6087)
WORLD WIDE PUBLICATIONS
Also Called: Grason Co
1303 Hennepin Ave (55403-1709)
PO Box 668089, Charlotte NC (28266-8089)
PHONE...........................612 333-0940
George M Wilson, *President*
Joel Aarsvold, *Treasurer*
EMP: 30 EST: 1952
SQ FT: 5,000
SALES (est): 1MM-4.9MM **Privately Held**

(PA)=Parent Co (HQ)=Headquarters (DH)=Div Headquarters
✿ = New business established in last 2 years

2011 Harris Minnesota
Services Directory

© Harris InfoSource 1-866-281-6415
267

GEOGRAPHIC

SIC: **5192** Retails religious books; wholesales books

(G-6088)
WORLDWIDE FISH & SEAFOOD INC
Also Called: Coastal Seafoods
2330 Minnehaha Ave (55404-3153)
PHONE.............................612 724-5911
FAX: 612 724-0689
Suzanne Weinstein, *President*
Tim Lauer, *General Mgr*
EMP: 30 EST: 1981
SQ FT: 4,000
SALES (est): 10MM-24.9MM **Privately Held**
WEB: www.coastalseafoods.com
SIC: **5146** Wholesales fresh fish; wholesales seafood; retail fish market; retail seafood market

(G-6089)
WRECKER SERVICES INC
200 E Lyndale Ave N Ste 1 (55405-1502)
PHONE.............................612 330-0013
FAX: 612 330-9099
Mark Anderson, *President*
Lisa Rose, *Vice Pres*
EMP: 25 EST: 1988
SALES (est): 1MM-4.9MM **Privately Held**
WEB: www.wreckerservices.com
SIC: **7549** Automotive towing service

(G-6090)
WYNDHAM INTERNATIONAL INC
4460 W 78th Street Cir (55435-5416)
PHONE.............................952 831-3131
FAX: 952 831-6372
Patrick Munn, *General Mgr*
Jack Rose, *Vice Pres*
Darren Young, *Controller*
Pete Boese, *Manager*
EMP: 125
SALES (est): 5MM-9.9MM **Publicly Held**
WEB: www.wyndham.com
SIC: **7011** Traveler accommodations
DH: Wyndham International Inc
   1950 N Stemmns Fwy
   Dallas TX 75207
   212 583-5000

(G-6091)
XCELLENCE INC
Also Called: Xact Duplicating
400 2nd Ave S Ste 1000 (55401-2411)
PHONE.............................612 305-1330
FAX: 612 305-1334
Scott Berger, *General Mgr*
Robert Finney, *Manager*
Shea Knorr, *Info Tech Mgr*
EMP: 25
SALES (est): 1MM-4.9MM **Privately Held**
WEB: www.xactduplicating.com
SIC: **7334** Photocopying & duplicating services
PA: Xcellence Inc
   5800 Foxridge Dr Ste 406
   Shawnee Mission KS 66202
   913 362-8662

(G-6092)
XENOPHON CORP (PA)
Also Called: Roller Garden
5622 W Lake St (55416-2107)
PHONE.............................952 929-5518
FAX: 952 920-9628
William Sahly, *President*
Patricia K Sahly, *Corp Secy*
EMP: 25 EST: 1969
SQ FT: 35,000 **Privately Held**
WEB: www.rollergarden.com
SIC: **7999** Roller skating rink; tennis services & professionals

(G-6093)
XEROX CORP
3500 Amercn Blvd W # 400 (55431-4411)
PHONE.............................952 921-1300
FAX: 952 921-1438
Edie Patterson, *VP Sales*
Mark Menard, *Manager*
Susan McCabe, *Manager*
EMP: 140
SALES (est): 10MM-24.9MM **Publicly Held**
WEB: www.xerox.com

SIC: **7334** Photocopying & duplicating services; manufactures computer peripheral equipment; photographic equipment & supplies; manufactures telecommunication systems & equipment
PA: Xerox Corp
   45 Glover Ave
   Norwalk CT 06850
   203 968-3000

(G-6094)
XERXES COMPUTER CORP (PA)
5735 W Old Shakopee Rd Ste 100 (55437-3177)
PHONE.............................952 936-9280
David A Duhaime, *CEO*
Travis Renney, *Corp Secy*
Eric Gustafson, *COO*
Kelly Bennewitz, *CFO*
Roger Grill, *Sales Staff*
▲ EMP: 42 EST: 1981
SQ FT: 60,000 **Privately Held**
WEB: www.xcc.com
SIC: **5045** 7377 Wholesales computers, peripherals & software; computers & equipment leasing & rental

(G-6095)
XPANDABLE TECHNOLOGY INC
Also Called: US Family Net
4050 Olson Memorial Hwy # 100 (55422-5347)
PHONE.............................763 521-0401
Jim Lundberg, *President*
Ron Cleven, *Vice Pres*
Mark Tente, *Manager*
Todd Mueller, *Info Tech Mgr*
Matt Schafer, *Technical Staff*
EMP: 40 EST: 1997
SQ FT: 5,000
SALES (est): 1MM-4.9MM **Privately Held**
WEB: www.usfamily.net
SIC: **7374** 4813 Computer graphics service; internet connectivity services; internet host services

(G-6096)
YAEGER, JUNGBAUER & BARCZAK
745 Kasota Ave SE (55414-2842)
PHONE.............................612 333-6371
William Jungbauer, *President*
Louis Jungbauer, *Member*
Gregory Yaeger, *Member*
Michael L Weiner, *Corp Secy*
Ronald J Barczak, *Vice Pres*
EMP: 72 EST: 1959
SQ FT: 17,000
SALES (est): 5MM-9.9MM **Privately Held**
WEB: www.yjblaw.com
SIC: **8111** Specialized legal services

(G-6097)
YALE MECHANICAL INC
9649 Girard Ave S (55431-2619)
PHONE.............................952 884-1661
John Deblon, *President*
Lori Seegar, *Accountant*
Loree Grudem, *MIS Mgr*
EMP: 150 EST: 2002
SALES (est): 10MM-24.9MM **Privately Held**
WEB: www.yalemechanical.com
SIC: **1711** Mechanical contractor

(G-6098)
YALE MECHANICAL LLC
9649 Girard Ave S (55431-2619)
PHONE.............................952 884-1661
John Deblon, *Mng Member*
Mike Bokenewicz, *Manager*
Jennifer Martindale, *Data Proc Exec*
EMP: 200 EST: 2002
SALES (est): 10MM-24.9MM **Privately Held**
WEB: www.yalemech.com
SIC: **1711** Warm air heating & air conditioning contractor

(G-6099)
YAMAMOTO MOSS MACKENZIE
252 1st Ave N (55401-1608)
PHONE.............................612 375-0180
FAX: 612 342-2424
Shelly Regan, *Owner*
Lise Hansen, *Corp Secy*

Elizabeth Murray, *Project Mgr*
Ben Durrant, *Manager*
Nancy Keller, *Manager*
EMP: 26 EST: 1997 **Privately Held**
WEB: www.yamamoto-moss.com
SIC: **6719** 7515 Investment holding company; passenger car leasing

(G-6100)
YMCA OF GREATER SAINT PAUL (PA)
2125 E Hennepin Ave Ste 100 (55413-1763)
PHONE.............................612 465-0450
Tom Brinsko, *President*
Greg Waibel, *CFO*
Richard Vaughn, *Benefits Mgr*
Tim Orpen, *Director*
EMP: 40 EST: 1856
SQ FT: 5,700
SALES (corp-wide): 44.10M **Privately Held**
WEB: www.ymcastpaul.org
SIC: **8641** Social club; youth organizations

(G-6101)
YOUNG MEN'S CHRITN ASSOC OF
Also Called: Metropolitan Ymca-Northwest
7601 42nd Ave N (55427-1226)
PHONE.............................763 535-4800
FAX: 763 592-5550
David Alexander, *Superintendent*
Colleen Hubner, *Marketing Mgr*
Greg Voss, *Manager*
Sabina Smida, *Manager*
Jason Bergquist, *Exec Dir*
EMP: 150 **Privately Held**
SIC: **8641** 7032 7991 8322 8351 Youth organizations; youth camps; child day care service; individual & family social services; physical fitness center

(G-6102)
YOUNG MEN'S CHRITN ASSOC OF
Also Called: YMCA
3335 Blaisdell Ave (55408-4429)
PHONE.............................612 827-5401
FAX: 612 827-5406
Megan Lindeman, *Manager*
Michael Melstad, *Director*
EMP: 75 **Privately Held**
SIC: **8641** 7032 7991 8322 8351 Youth organizations; youth camps; child day care service; individual & family social services; physical fitness center

(G-6103)
YOUNG MEN'S CHRITN ASSOC OF
Also Called: Y M C A
1711 W Broadway Ave (55411-2450)
PHONE.............................612 588-9484
FAX: 612 588-9488
Mary Britts, *Exec Dir*
EMP: 30 **Privately Held**
SIC: **8641** 7032 7991 8322 8351 Youth organizations; youth camps; child day care service; individual & family social services; physical fitness center

(G-6104)
YOUNG MEN'S CHRITN ASSOC OF
Also Called: Southdale YMCA
7355 York Ave S (55435-4701)
PHONE.............................952 835-2567
FAX: 952 835-0221
Tom Burke, *Manager*
Greg Hanks, *Director*
Mary Felty, *Director*
Heidi Freisinger, *Coordinator*
EMP: 150 **Privately Held**
SIC: **8641** 7032 7991 8322 8351 Youth organizations; youth camps; child day care service; individual & family social services; physical fitness center

(G-6105)
YOUNG, QUINLAN ASSOC LLP
81 S 9th St Ste 210 (55402-3225)
PHONE.............................612 337-5109
FAX: 612 333-6128
Bob Greenburg, *Owner*
EMP: 50 EST: 1994

SALES (est): 1MM-4.9MM **Privately Held**
SIC: **7521** 6531 Vehicle parking lot or garage; commercial real estate agency

(G-6106)
YOUNGBLOOD LUMBER CO
1335 Central Ave NE (55413-1514)
PHONE.............................612 789-3521
FAX: 612 789-9625
Thomas E Youngblood II, *CEO*
Randall R Rudesill, *President*
Jack Thornton, *Corp Secy*
Steve Frenz, *Senior VP*
Tomlin J Greenwood, *Vice Pres*
EMP: 35 EST: 1876
SQ FT: 3,500
SALES (est): 10MM-24.9MM **Privately Held**
WEB: www.youngbloodlumber.com
SIC: **5031** 5162 Wholesales lumber, plywood & millwork; wholesales rough, dressed & finished lumber; wholesales particleboard; wholesales plywood; wholesales plastic materials

(G-6107)
YOUTH FRONTIERS INC
6009 Excelsior Blvd (55416-2844)
PHONE.............................952 922-0222
FAX: 952 922-2122
Joe Cavanuagh, *CEO*
Dennis Peterson, *Superintendent*
Tracy Frank, *Principal*
Dottie Titus, *Accountant*
Debra Grahn, *Manager*
EMP: 26 EST: 1987
SALES (est): 1MM-4.9MM **Privately Held**
WEB: www.youthfrontiers.org
SIC: **8322** 8748 Youth center; educational consulting services

(G-6108)
YOUTHLINK
41 N 12th St (55403-1325)
PHONE.............................612 252-1200
Freddie Davis, *Ch of Bd*
Richard Musser, *Finance*
Tiffany Harmon, *Human Resources*
Heather Huseby, *Exec Dir*
Megan Roach, *Exec Dir*
EMP: 65 EST: 1974
SQ FT: 30,000
SALES (est): 1MM-4.9MM **Privately Held**
WEB: www.youthlinkmn.org
SIC: **8322** Youth center; social services center

(G-6109)
YOUTHWORKS INC
3530 E 28th St (55406-1765)
PHONE.............................612 729-5444
FAX: 612 729-4113
Paul Bertelson, *President*
John Potts, *Vice Pres*
Gordon Druvenga, *Treasurer*
Phil Netolicky, *Accounts Mgr*
Dave Parrin, *Director*
EMP: 43 EST: 1994
SQ FT: 5,000 **Privately Held**
SIC: **8641** Youth organizations

(G-6110)
YWCA OF MINNEAPOLIS
2808 Hennepin Ave (55408-1906)
PHONE.............................612 874-7131
Amy Asche, *Exec Dir*
Karen Scerk, *Director*
EMP: 70
SALES (est): 1MM-4.9MM **Privately Held**
WEB: www.ywca-minneapolis.org
SIC: **8322** 7991 Youth center; health club
PA: YWCA of Minneapolis
   1130 Nicollet Ave
   Minneapolis MN 55403
   612 332-0501

(G-6111)
YWCA OF MINNEAPOLIS (PA)
1130 Nicollet Ave (55403-2405)
PHONE.............................612 332-0501
FAX: 612 332-0500
Becky Roloff, *CEO*
Ann Mathews, *Member*
Laurel Murdock, *Member*
John Fitz, *Engineering*
Kathy Purcell, *CFO*
EMP: 511

www.HarrisInfo.com
268

2011 Harris Minnesota
Services Directory

▲=Import ▼=Export
◆=Import/Export

EST: 1891
SQ FT: 85,000
SALES (corp-wide): 15.06M **Privately Held**
WEB: www.ywca-minneapolis.org
SIC: 8641 7032 7991 8322 8351 Youth organizations; youth camps; child day care service; individual & family social services; physical fitness center

(G-6112)
YWCA OF MINNEAPOLIS
800 E 28th St Ste 15103 (55407-3723)
PHONE 612 863-0970
Nancy Hite, *Exec Dir*
Jim Nicholie, *Director*
EMP: 25 **Privately Held**
WEB: www.ywca-minneapolis.org
SIC: 8641 Civic & social organization; fraternal association
PA: YWCA of Minneapolis
1130 Nicollet Ave
Minneapolis MN 55403
612 332-0501

(G-6113)
ZACHRY CONSTRUCTION CORP
222 S 9th St Ste 1500 (55402-3337)
PHONE 612 215-1300
Brigid M Spicola, *Corp Secy*
Alison Cochran, *Manager*
EMP: 42
SALES (est): 5MM-9.9MM **Privately Held**
WEB: www.ueplaza.com
SIC: 8711 Engineering services
DH: Zachry Construction Corp
12625 Wetmore Rd Ste 301
San Antonio TX 78247
210 871-2700

(G-6114)
ZELLE, HOFMANN, VOELBEL, MASON (PA)
500 Washington Ave S (55415-1149)
PHONE 612 339-2020
Kerry Brown, *Managing Prtnr*
Patricia S Peter, *Partner*
James S Reece, *Partner*
Terrence C Mc REA, *Partner*
Mark J Feinberg, *Partner*
EMP: 90 **EST:** 1988
SQ FT: 32,000 **Privately Held**
WEB: www.zelle.com
SIC: 8111 General practice law office

(G-6115)
ZEMAN CONSTRUCTION CO
8900 10th Ave N (55427-4321)
PHONE 612 521-4300
David Zeman, *President*
Chris Zeman, *Corp Secy*
John Zeman, *Vice Pres*
Mark Zeman, *Treasurer*
Mark Lobdell, *Sales Executive*
EMP: 50 **EST:** 1989
SQ FT: 15,000
SALES (est): 10MM-24.9MM **Privately Held**
WEB: www.zemanconstruction.com
SIC: 1542 1541 New commercial & office building construction; industrial building renovating, remodeling & repair service; stadium construction; industrial building & warehouse construction

(G-6116)
ZENTROPY PARTNERS
222 S 9th St Ste 2955 (55402-3302)
PHONE 612 367-5148
Robert Safford, *Partner*
Heather Lejeune, *Manager*
EMP: 40 **EST:** 1999
SALES (est): 5MM-9.9MM **Privately Held**
SIC: 8742 Management consulting services

(G-6117)
ZIEGLER INC (PA)
Also Called: Caterpillar
901 W 94th St (55420-4236)
PHONE 952 888-4121
FAX: 952 885-8212
Stanley Erickson, *CEO*
Leonard C Hoeft, *Ch of Bd*
William L Hoeft, *President*
Laurie Blanchard, *Corp Secy*
David Johnson, *Vice Pres*
EMP: 790 **EST:** 1914
SQ FT: 200,800 **Privately Held**

SIC: 5082 5084 Wholesales construction & mining machinery; wholesales construction tractors; wholesales front end loaders; wholesales industrial diesel engines & parts

(G-6118)
ZIEM'S CARPET WORKROOM INC
Also Called: Mar's Carpet Sales
9201 Penn Ave S Ste 28 (55431-2326)
PHONE 952 884-0058
FAX: 952 884-2665
Bradley Ziemkowski, *President*
Corey Ziemkowski, *Corp Secy*
Scott Ziemkowski, *Vice Pres*
Ryan Ziemkowski, *Vice Pres*
EMP: 35 **EST:** 1968
SQ FT: 12,600
SALES (est): 1MM-4.9MM **Privately Held**
WEB: www.marscarpet.com
SIC: 1752 Carpet laying contractor

(G-6119)
ZIMMERMAN REED PLLP
651 Nicollet Mall Ste 501 (55402-1634)
PHONE 612 341-0400
FAX: 612 332-0971
Carolyn Anderson, *Partner*
Charles Zimmerman, *Partner*
Ronald Goldser, *Partner*
Robert Hopper, *Partner*
Barry Reed, *Partner*
EMP: 50 **EST:** 1983
SQ FT: 10,000
SALES (est): 5MM-9.9MM **Privately Held**
SIC: 8111 General practice law office

(G-6120)
ZINA'S INC
5101 Vernon Ave S Ste 2B (55436-2166)
PHONE 952 929-0093
FAX: 952 929-0093
Zina Shirl, *President*
EMP: 50 **EST:** 1961
SALES (est): 1MM-4.9MM **Privately Held**
SIC: 7231 Beauty salon

(G-6121)
ZITCO INC
Also Called: Lowell's Paint Plus
5251 W 74th St (55439-2224)
PHONE 952 392-6060
FAX: 952 835-3329
Lowell Zitzloff, *President*
Jeff Zitzloff, *Corp Secy*
Richard Piche, *Vice Pres*
Dave Pierson, *CFO*
EMP: 72 **EST:** 1964
SQ FT: 3,600
SALES (est): 25MM-49.9MM **Privately Held**
SIC: 5013 Wholesales automotive supplies & parts; wholesales automotive body repair or paint shop supplies; retails auto & home supplies; retails automotive parts

(G-6122)
ZUHRAH TEMPLE TRUSTEES INC
2540 Park Ave (55404-4403)
PHONE 612 871-3555
FAX: 612 871-2632
Joan Hanson, *President*
Bill Glas, *President*
Hans Herberg, *General Mgr*
Dave Hanson, *Corp Secy*
Larry Horwedel, *Vice Pres*
EMP: 30 **EST:** 1885
SQ FT: 37,000 **Privately Held**
WEB: www.zuhrah.org
SIC: 8641 7299 Fraternal association; eating place; facility rental & party planning services

MINNEAPOLIS
Ramsey County

(G-6123)
APACHE ANIMAL MEDICINE
2503 37th Ave NE (55421-4214)
PHONE 612 781-2734
FAX: 612 789-2499
Terrence Rapacz, *Owner*
Susan Rapacz, *Office Mgr*

Brenda Baker, *Executive*
EMP: 25 **EST:** 1974
SQ FT: 8,000 **Privately Held**
SIC: 0742 Animal hospital services

(G-6124)
CHANDLER PLACE
3701 Chandler Dr NE Ofc (55421-4481)
PHONE 612 788-7321
FAX: 612 913-5370
Marion Post, *CEO*
Don Johnson, *Finance*
Mark Anderson, *Administrator*
Jodi Saeko, *Exec Dir*
Kristin Lueders, *Director*
EMP: 25 **EST:** 1986
SALES (est): 500-999K **Privately Held**
WEB: www.chandlerplacesenior.com
SIC: 8361 8052 Residential care facility; intermediate care facility

(G-6125)
ENVIROTECH REMEDIATION SVCS
3000 84th Ln NE (55449-7214)
PHONE 763 746-0670
FAX: 763 784-0749
Dave Sobaski, *President*
Jennifer Oreskovich, *Office Mgr*
EMP: 100 **EST:** 2001
SQ FT: 15,000
SALES (est): 5MM-9.9MM **Privately Held**
WEB: www.envirotechrs.com
SIC: 8744 Environmental remediation services

(G-6126)
FINE LINE HAIR INC
3902 Silver Lake Rd NE (55421-4351)
PHONE 952 457-2620
Patti Yaucher, *President*
EMP: 25 **EST:** 2000
SALES (est): 500-999K **Privately Held**
SIC: 7231 Beauty salon

(G-6127)
MIDWEST DIESEL SERVICE INC
8284 W 35W Service Dr NE (55449-7255)
PHONE 763 780-8533
FAX: 763 780-9107
Gerald Reiter, *President*
Karen Reiter, *Treasurer*
Sherly Esch, *Manager*
Shirley Fesch, *Administration*
EMP: 35 **EST:** 1975
SQ FT: 16,400
SALES (est): 25MM-49.9MM **Privately Held**
WEB: www.usedcatparts.com
SIC: 5012 Wholesales commercial trucks

(G-6128)
MOHAWK MOVING & STORAGE INC
8271 W 35W Service Dr NE (55449-7256)
PHONE 763 717-3705
FAX: 763 784-1849
Vernet B Larson III, *CEO*
Gary Trettel, *General Mgr*
Kathleen M Larson, *Vice Pres*
Dirk Stedns, *Sales & Mktg St*
Greg Sundem, *Controller*
EMP: 65 **EST:** 1979
SQ FT: 60,000
SALES (est): 5MM-9.9MM **Privately Held**
SIC: 4213 Over the road trucking; long-distance moving services

(G-6129)
MOHAWK UNITED
8271 W 35W Service Dr NE (55449-7256)
PHONE 651 481-0000
Vern Larson, *Owner*
EMP: 50 **EST:** 1979
SALES (est): 5MM-9.9MM **Privately Held**
SIC: 4212 Local moving service

(G-6130)
MORGAN TIRE & AUTO LLC
Also Called: Team Tires Plus
3805 Silver Lake Rd NE (55421-4226)
PHONE 651 789-4361
Matt Johnson, *Manager*
EMP: 30
SALES (est): 1MM-4.9MM **Privately Held**

WEB: www.bfsusa.com
SIC: 7534 Tire recapping & retreading services
HQ: Bfs Retail Operations LLC
333 E Lake St Ste 300
Bloomingdale IL 60108
630 259-9000

(G-6131)
ST ANTHONY HEALTH CENTER
Also Called: Saint Anthony Health Center
3700 Foss Rd (55421-4512)
PHONE 612 788-9673
FAX: 612 788-0104
John B Goodman, *Managing Prtnr*
Sidney A Goodman, *Managing Prtnr*
Marian Post, *President*
Fay Gilbert, *Chiropractor*
Anthony Self, *Manager*
EMP: 300 **EST:** 1967
SQ FT: 37,000
SALES (est): 10MM-24.9MM **Privately Held**
WEB: www.stanthonyhealthcenter.com
SIC: 8051 8361 Convalescent home; home for the elderly

(G-6132)
VAN MINNEAPOLIS & WAREHOUSE CO
3780 Macalaster Dr NE (55421-4303)
PHONE 651 636-6000
William R Dircks, *President*
Bill Dircks, *General Mgr*
EMP: 51 **EST:** 1910
SQ FT: 25,000
SALES (est): 5MM-9.9MM **Privately Held**
WEB: www.bergertransfer.com
SIC: 4213 4214 Long-distance moving services; local moving service & storage
PA: Berger Transfer & Storage Inc
2950 Long Lake Rd
Saint Paul MN 55113
651 639-2260

(G-6133)
ZEP INC
8490 Coral Sea St NE (55449-7253)
PHONE 763 792-2050
Thomas Tangney, *Manager*
EMP: 65
SALES (est): 50MM-99.9MM **Privately Held**
SIC: 5169 5087 Wholesales industrial & heavy chemicals; wholesales car wash equipment & supplies

MINNEOTA
Lyon County

(G-6134)
LIVING SERVICES FOUNDATION
700 N Monroe St (56264-9237)
PHONE 507 872-5300
Jennifer Kamstra, *Member*
EMP: 160
SALES (est): 5MM-9.9MM **Privately Held**
SIC: 8051 Skilled nursing care facility

(G-6135)
MINNEOTA MANOR HEALTH CARE CTR
700 N Monroe St (56264-9237)
PHONE 507 872-5300
Richard Erickson, *President*
Maryann Full, *QA Mgr*
Mavis Erickson, *Treasurer*
Julie Bottelberghe, *Office Mgr*
Mark King, *Hlthcr Dir*
EMP: 150 **EST:** 1971
SALES (est): 5MM-9.9MM **Privately Held**
SIC: 8051 Skilled nursing care facility

(PA)=Parent Co (HQ)=Headquarters (DH)=Div Headquarters
✪ = New business established in last 2 years
2011 Harris Minnesota
Services Directory
© Harris InfoSource 1-866-281-6415
269

MINNESOTA CITY
Winona County

(G-6136)

MINNESOTA CITY BUS SERVICE INC
32 Wenonah Rd (55959-1114)
PHONE...............................507 454-5871
FAX: 507 454-5123
Kirk Wilkie, *President*
EMP: 50
SALES (est): 1MM-4.9MM **Privately Held**
SIC: 4151 4141 School bus service; local bus charter service

MINNESOTA LAKE
Faribault County

(G-6137)

N A H INC
Also Called: Nordaas Retail
10091 Hwy 22 N (56068)
PHONE...............................507 462-3331
Michael Redig, *President*
Paula Kath, *Accountant*
EMP: 25 EST: 1989
SQ FT: 3,500
SALES (est): 5MM-9.9MM **Privately Held**
SIC: 1521 5031 Single-family housing construction; wholesales lumber, plywood & millwork

MINNETONKA
Hennepin County

(G-6138)

ALLINA HEALTH SYSTEM
5601 Smetana Dr (55343-5000)
PO Box 1469, Minneapolis (55440-1469)
PHONE...............................952 992-2500
FAX: 952 992-3848
EMP: 30
SALES (est): 1MM-4.9MM **Privately Held**
WEB: www.allina.com
SIC: 8062 Medical hospital
PA: Allina Health System
     2925 Chicago Ave
     Minneapolis MN 55407
     612 775-5000

(G-6139)

AMERICAN HARDWARE INSURANCE
Also Called: Ahm Insurance Agency
5605 Green Circle Dr # 100 (55343-4525)
PHONE...............................952 939-4510
Dianne Brummond, *President*
Dave Lemon, *President*
Steven Major, *VP Opers*
Greg Opatz, *Project Mgr*
Michael L Wiseman, *Treasurer*
EMP: 100 EST: 1934
SALES (est): 10MM-24.9MM **Privately Held**
SIC: 6061 6411 Federally chartered credit union; insurance services
PA: American Hardware Mutual Insce
     471 E Broad St Bsmt
     Columbus OH 43215
     614 225-8211

(G-6140)

AMERICAN MEDICAL SYSTEMS INC (HQ)
10700 Bren Rd W (55343-9679)
PHONE...............................952 930-6000
Douglas Kohrs, *President*
Kyle Knauf, *Regional Mgr*
Kathy Koenig, *Regional Mgr*
Joe W Martin, *Senior VP*
Larry Getlin, *Vice Pres*
EMP: 300 EST: 1972
SQ FT: 180,000
SALES (corp-wide): 519.27M **Publicly Held**
WEB: www.visitams.com

SIC: 8011 Manufactures surgical appliances & supplies; manufactures medical instruments; physicians' office & clinic
PA: American Medical Systems
     10700 Bren Rd W
     Minnetonka MN 55343
     952 930-6000

(G-6141)

ANNEX MEDICAL INC
6018 Blue Circle Dr (55343-9104)
PHONE...............................952 942-7576
FAX: 952 942-7590
Stuart Lind, *President*
John Skaaland, *QC Dir*
Dan Dostal, *Engineering*
EMP: 40 EST: 1988
SALES (est): 5MM-9.9MM **Privately Held**
WEB: www.annexmedical.com
SIC: 5047 Manufactures medical & laboratory rubber sundries & related products; wholesales medical & hospital equipment; manufactures electromedical equipment

(G-6142)

APPLIED PRODUCTS INC
6035 Baker Rd (55345-5908)
PHONE...............................952 933-2224
FAX: 952 933-1109
Dan Horner, *CEO*
Brian Webb, *President*
Tammy Alberg, *Administrator*
Elizabeth Forbord, *Officer*
Timothy Sinnett, *Management*
▲ EMP: 35 EST: 1973
SQ FT: 35,000
SALES (est): 10MM-24.9MM **Privately Held**
WEB: www.appliedproducts.com
SIC: 5085 5084 Wholesales industrial tape & plasters adhesives; wholesales industrial controlling instruments & accessories; wholesales industrial pneumatic tools & equipment; wholesales industrial hydraulic systems equipment & supplies

(G-6143)

APRIA HEALTHCARE INC
131 Cheshire Ln Ste 500 (55305-1068)
PO Box 1450, Minneapolis (55485-1450)
PHONE...............................952 404-1700
Sherri Hallmann, *Branch Mgr*
Mike Bailey, *Manager*
Phil Schoephoerster, *MIS Mgr*
EMP: 196
SALES (est): 100MM-499.9MM **Publicly Held**
WEB: www.apria.com
SIC: 5047 7352 Wholesales hospital equipment & furniture; invalid supplies rental service
DH: Apria Healthcare Inc
     26220 Enterprise Ct
     Lake Forest CA 92630
     949 639-2000

(G-6144)

ASSOCIATED FINANCIAL GROUP LLC (DH)
12600 Whitewater Dr # 100 (55343-9437)
PHONE...............................952 945-0200
Eldon Oldre, *President*
Debbie Svihovec, *Corp Secy*
Colin Mackenzie, *COO*
James Berry, *Vice Pres*
Greg Biese, *Vice Pres*
EMP: 45 EST: 1974
SQ FT: 20,000
SALES (corp-wide): 1.33B **Publicly Held**
WEB: www.associatedbank.com
SIC: 6411 Insurance services
HQ: Associated Bank, National Assn
     200 N Adams St
     Green Bay WI 54301
     920 433-3200

(G-6145)

ATIRIX MEDICAL SYSTEMS INC
10201 Wayzata Blvd # 310 (55305-3380)
PHONE...............................952 546-2001
Jerad Hahn, *President*
Scott Hudson, *Vice Pres*
Lance Caven, *Vice Pres*
Gary Mannien, *Vice Pres*
Edward Scott, *Vice Pres*
EMP: 25 EST: 2004

SALES (est): 1MM-4.9MM **Privately Held**
SIC: 8741 Hospital management services; nursing & personal care facility management services

(G-6146)

ATM NETWORK INC
10749 Bren Rd E (55343-9056)
PHONE...............................952 767-2000
Philip Rock, *CEO*
Kurt Duhn, *General Mgr*
EMP: 25 EST: 1996
SQ FT: 10,500
SALES (est): 5MM-9.9MM **Privately Held**
WEB: www.atmnetwork.net
SIC: 5044 Wholesales automatic teller machines

(G-6147)

BELL ANCILLARY SERVICES INC
10301 Wayzatta Blve (55305)
PHONE...............................952 545-1880
Tom Joslyn, *Manager*
EMP: 100
SALES (est): 10MM-24.9MM **Privately Held**
WEB: www.bellmortgage.com
SIC: 6162 Mortgage banking service
PA: Bell Ancillary Services Inc
     1000 Shelard Pkwy Ste 500
     Minneapolis MN 55426
     952 591-1880

(G-6148)

BESTMARK INC
5605 Green Circle Dr # 200 (55343-4524)
PHONE...............................952 922-2205
FAX: 952 922-0237
Ann Jennings, *President*
Emily Ryerse, *Vice Pres*
Lavonna Aulwes, *Treasurer*
Mike Fogelberg, *Manager*
Aramis Brusas, *Database Admin*
EMP: 150 EST: 1986
SQ FT: 4,500
SALES (est): 10MM-24.9MM **Privately Held**
SIC: 8742 Restaurant & food services consultants; marketing consulting service

(G-6149)

BOYER BUILDING CORP
3435 County Road 101 (55345-1017)
PHONE...............................952 475-2097
FAX: 952 475-2005
Robert Boyer, *President*
Joseph Boyer, *Corp Secy*
Paul Boyer, *Vice Pres*
John Boyer, *Treasurer*
Signe Benson, *Manager*
EMP: 25 EST: 1950
SQ FT: 2,500
SALES (est): 5MM-9.9MM **Privately Held**
WEB: www.boyerbuilding.com
SIC: 1521 New single-family home construction service; patio & deck construction & repair service

(G-6150)

CARGILL INC
12900 Whitewater Dr (55343-9443)
PHONE...............................952 742-7575
EMP: 150
SALES (est): 100MM-499.9MM **Privately Held**
SIC: 5191 Wholesales animal feeds; manufactures bone meal animal feed; manufactures feather meal animal feed

(G-6151)

CARGILL POWER MARKETS LLC
12700 Whitewater Dr (55343-9438)
PO Box 5653, Minneapolis (55440-5653)
PHONE...............................952 984-3068
David L Gabriel, *Member*
Gene Becker, *Finance*
EMP: 50
SALES (est): 50MM-99.9MM **Privately Held**
WEB: www.cargillenergy.com
SIC: 4924 Natural gas distribution to consumers

(G-6152)

CARLSON HOLDINGS INC (PA)
701 Carlson Pkwy (55305-5240)
PO Box 59159, Minneapolis (55459-8200)
PHONE...............................763 212-5000
Marilyn C Nelson, *Ch of Bd*
Hubert Joly, *President*
Jean-Marc Busato, *Managing Dir*
Paul Kirwin, *Managing Dir*
Martin Rinck, *Managing Dir*
◆ EMP: 3118 EST: 1938
SQ FT: 300,000 **Privately Held**
SIC: 7011 4724 6794 7389 Traveler accommodations; eating place; promoters of shows & exhibitions; patent owners & lessors; travel agency

(G-6153)

CARLSON HOSPITALITY WORLDWIDE
701 Carlson Pkwy (55305-5240)
PO Box 59159, Minneapolis (55459-8200)
PHONE...............................763 540-5035
Marilyn C Nelson, *Ch of Bd*
Curtis Nelson, *President*
Gary Dreyling, *Vice Pres*
EMP: 45 EST: 1996
SALES (est): 5MM-9.9MM **Privately Held**
WEB: www.careerlink.org
SIC: 8742 Management consulting services
DH: Carlson Hotels LP
     Carlson Parkway 701 Twr St
     Minneapolis MN 55459
     763 212-1000

(G-6154)

CARLSON REAL ESTATE CO, A MN
301 Carlson Pkwy Ste 100 (55305-5358)
PHONE...............................952 404-5050
FAX: 952 404-5001
Matt V Slooten, *President*
Chris Cannon, *General Mgr*
Joe Ihrke, *Vice Pres*
Chris Kirby, *Vice Pres*
Mark Schlitter, *Vice Pres*
EMP: 45 EST: 1985
SQ FT: 130,000
SALES (est): 5MM-9.9MM **Privately Held**
WEB: www.carlsonrealestate.org
SIC: 6531 Real estate leasing & rental agency

(G-6155)

CENTEX HOMES INC
12701 Whitewater Dr Ste 300 (55343-4160)
PHONE...............................952 936-7833
FAX: 952 936-7839
Thomas Boyce, *Exec VP*
Scott Richter, *Vice Pres*
Ann Podolske, *Purch Agent*
Matt O'Connell, *Purchasing*
Mary J Weber, *Controller*
EMP: 50
SALES (est): 10MM-24.9MM **Publicly Held**
WEB: www.centexhomes.com
SIC: 1521 New single-family home construction service
HQ: Centex Homes Inc
     2728 N Harwood St Ste 200
     Dallas TX 75201
     214 981-5000

(G-6156)

COMMUNICATIONS SYSTEMS INC (PA)
10900 Red Circle Dr (55343-9106)
PHONE...............................952 996-1674
Jeffrey K Berg, *President*
Vince J Geraci, *Managing Dir*
Melvin J Albiston, *Vice Pres*
Bruce C Blackwood, *Vice Pres*
John Lenzon, *Maint Mgr*
▲ EMP: 148 EST: 1969
SQ FT: 105,000
SALES (corp-wide): 109.79M **Publicly Held**
WEB: www.commsystems.com

www.HarrisInfo.com
270

2011 Harris Minnesota
Services Directory

▲=Import ▼=Export
◆=Import/Export

SIC: **8748** Manufactures telephone equipment; telecommunications consulting services; manufactures wire telephone station equipment & parts; manufactures telephone cords, jacks & adapters; manufactures transceiver receiver-transmitter units

(G-6157)
CULLIGAN SOFT WATER SERVICE CO (PA)
6030 Culligan Way (55345-5917)
PHONE.............................952 933-7200
John Packard, *President*
Mike Jablonski, *General Mgr*
Joe Beumtrog, *Opers Mgr*
Mark Forsberg, *Treasurer*
Carolyn McCormick, *Human Res Dir*
EMP: 89 **EST:** 1939
SQ FT: 40,000
SALES (corp-wide): 11.82M **Privately Held**
WEB: www.uncodata.com
SIC: 7389 Water softener service; retails water purification equipment

(G-6158)
DATA SOLUTIONS INTERNATIONAL
5900 Baker Rd Ste 100 (55345-5957)
PHONE.............................952 943-8137
FAX: 952 945-7301
Tom Eisma, *President*
Diane Sullivan, *Project Mgr*
Don Eisma, *CFO*
Steve Eisma, *Marketing Staff*
Joel Eisma, *Technology Dir*
EMP: 30 **EST:** 1994
SQ FT: 15,000
SALES (est): 1MM-4.9MM **Privately Held**
WEB: www.datasltn.com
SIC: 7374 Data processing & preparation services

(G-6159)
DATACARD CORP (PA)
11111 Bren Rd W (55343-9015)
PO Box 9355, Minneapolis (55440-9355)
PHONE.............................952 933-1223
FAX: 952 933-7971
Hatim Tyabji, *Ch of Bd*
Todd G Wilkinson, *President*
Kevin V Meter, *General Mgr*
Lisa Tibbits, *Corp Secy*
John D Leo, *Senior VP*
▲ **EMP:** 800 **EST:** 1969
SQ FT: 220,000 **Privately Held**
WEB: www.datacard.com
SIC: 7389 Manufactures embossing machines for store & office use; manufactures addressing machines, plates & plate embossers; manufactures radio & television communications equipment; credit card service; manufactures plastic identification cards

(G-6160)
DATATREND TECHNOLOGIES INC
121 Cheshire Ln Ste 700 (55305-1051)
PHONE.............................952 931-1203
Mark Waldrep, *President*
Jerry Campanella, *Vice Pres*
Charlie Cox, *Vice Pres*
Warner Schlais, *Vice Pres*
Kai Hovde, *Project Mgr*
EMP: 28 **EST:** 1989
SALES (est): 1MM-4.9MM **Privately Held**
WEB: www.dtrend.net
SIC: 7373 Computer integrated systems design services

(G-6161)
EATON CORP
5421 Feltl Rd Ste 190 (55343-3943)
PHONE.............................952 939-5400
Mark Gilk, *General Mgr*
Vicki Rich, *Manager*
Doug Molinari, *Other Executive*
EMP: 30
SALES (est): 10MM-24.9MM **Publicly Held**
WEB: www.eaton.com

SIC: **5063** Wholesales electrical apparatus & equipment
PA: Eaton Corp
1111 Superior Ave E Fl 19
Cleveland OH 44114
216 523-5000

(G-6162)
EATON CORP
5421 Feltl Rd Ste 190 (55343-3943)
PHONE.............................952 912-1330
Banks Sam, *Vice Pres*
Robert Sell, *Vice Pres*
Naveen Halbhavi, *Plant Mgr*
Josette Russell, *Plant Mgr*
Mills Batman, *Project Mgr*
EMP: 26
SALES (est): 1MM-4.9MM **Publicly Held**
WEB: www.eaton.com
SIC: 8711 Engineering services
PA: Eaton Corp
1111 Superior Ave E Fl 19
Cleveland OH 44114
216 523-5000

(G-6163)
EDOCUMENT RESOURCES LLC
6101 Baker Rd Ste 207 (55345-5959)
PHONE.............................952 607-3505
Gordon Peterson, *Member*
Matt Charlson, *Member*
Ken Schempp, *Mng Member*
Renee Selnick, *Member*
Bonnie Blair, *Executive Asst*
EMP: 30 **EST:** 2002
SQ FT: 3,700
SALES (est): 10MM-24.9MM **Privately Held**
SIC: 5045 7379 Wholesales computer software; computer system consulting services

(G-6164)
ELECTRO-SENSORS INC (PA)
6111 Blue Circle Dr (55343-9108)
PHONE.............................952 930-0100
Bradley D Slye, *President*
Peter R Peterson, *Corp Secy*
Hugh Ferguson, *Opers Mgr*
Chris Galas, *Engineer*
Corey Welter, *Human Res Mgr*
EMP: 33 **EST:** 1968
SQ FT: 25,400
SALES (corp-wide): 5.90M **Publicly Held**
WEB: www.electro-sensors.com
SIC: 7372 Manufactures motor controls & accessories; software publisher

(G-6165)
ELECTROSONIC INC (PA)
10320 Bren Rd E (55343-9048)
PHONE.............................952 931-7500
FAX: 952 938-9311
James Bowie, *President*
David Mitchell, *Corp Secy*
Bill Daugherty, *Vice Pres*
Todd Knettel, *Engineering*
Scott Meyer, *CFO*
◆ **EMP:** 35 **EST:** 1972 **Privately Held**
SIC: 8711 7359 7812 Engineering services; audio-visual equipment & supply rental service; audio-visual program production service
PA: Electrosonic LTD
Hawley Mill
DARTFORD England

(G-6166)
ENGINEERED PRODUCTS CO
Also Called: EPCO
5401 Smetana Dr (55343-9060)
PHONE.............................952 767-8780
FAX: 952 935-0233
Duncan Lee, *CEO*
Tom Shear, *General Mgr*
Peter Lee, *Chairman*
Dan Brooks, *Mfg Staff*
Aimee Karrow, *Manager*
▲ **EMP:** 52 **EST:** 1976
SQ FT: 80,000
SALES (est): 5MM-9.9MM **Privately Held**
SIC: 5063 Manufactures electrical equipment & supplies; wholesales electrical apparatus & equipment; manufactures current carrying wiring devices

(G-6167)
FAMOUS DAVE'S OF AMERICA INC (PA)
12701 Whitewater Dr # 200 (55343-4165)
PHONE.............................952 294-1300
FAX: 952 294-1301
Christopher O'Donnell, *President*
Martin J O'Dowd, *Corp Secy*
John A Simpson, *Vice Pres*
Jeffrey Abramson, *Vice Pres*
Victor Salamone, *Vice Pres*
EMP: 50 **EST:** 1995
SQ FT: 26,000
SALES (corp-wide): 136.01M **Publicly Held**
WEB: www.nfbmail.com
SIC: 6794 Full service family restaurant; full service independent family restaurant; selling or licensing of franchises

(G-6168)
FCH MINNETONKA
Also Called: Holiday Inn
10985 Red Circle Dr (55343-9105)
PO Box 9555, Fargo ND (58106-9555)
PHONE.............................952 912-9999
Heidi Wilcox, *Principal*
EMP: 35
SALES (est): 1MM-4.9MM **Privately Held**
SIC: 7011 Traveler accommodations

(G-6169)
FIRST PROTECTION CORP
601 Carlson Pkwy Ste 990 (55305-5218)
PHONE.............................952 473-0114
Janet Hanson, *President*
Terry Farland, *Opers Mgr*
Bret Walling, *Manager*
EMP: 30 **EST:** 1978
SQ FT: 6,000
SALES (est): 10MM-24.9MM **Publicly Held**
WEB: www.protective.com
SIC: 6331 Fire, marine & casualty insurance & carriers
HQ: First Protection Co
601 Carlson Pkwy Ste 550
Hopkins MN 55305
952 473-0114

(G-6170)
FRESH SEASONS MARKET LLC
14400 Excelsior Blvd (55345-5820)
PHONE.............................952 938-5555
Tom Wartman, *Member*
Dale Riley, *Member*
Mary Kage, *Manager*
EMP: 74 **EST:** 2005
SQ FT: 25,000
SALES (est): 10MM-24.9MM **Privately Held**
SIC: 5122 Retail supermarkets; wholesales pharmaceuticals

(G-6171)
FUJITSU CONSULTING INFORMATION (PA)
110 Cheshire Ln Ste 300 (55305-1049)
PHONE.............................952 258-6000
Elmer Baldwin, *CEO*
Paul Catton, *COO*
Joe Kranyak, *Counsel*
Julie Pfeiffer, *Vice Pres*
Pavel Ryzhkov, *Technical Mgr*
EMP: 300 **EST:** 1990
SQ FT: 45,000 **Privately Held**
SIC: 7371 Custom computer programming service; computer software development; applications software programming

(G-6172)
G E YOUNG & CO
11100 Wayzata Blvd # 510 (55305-5501)
PHONE.............................952 847-2388
G E Young, *Principal*
Kim Nyberg, *Manager*
EMP: 50 **EST:** 2004
SALES (est): 1MM-4.9MM **Privately Held**
SIC: 6411 Insurance claims adjusting service

(G-6173)
G&K SERVICES INC (PA)
5995 Opus Pkwy Ste 500 (55343-9078)
PHONE.............................952 912-5500
David Miller, *President*

Douglas A Milroy, *President*
Robert G Wood, *President*
Nick Reaves, *General Mgr*
Lenny Pippin, *Managing Dir*
◆ **EMP:** 220 **EST:** 1902
SQ FT: 45,500
SALES (corp-wide): 833.59M **Publicly Held**
WEB: www.gkservices.com
SIC: 7218 7213 Industrial uniform supply services; towel supply service; apron supply service; mat & rug supply service; mats, rugs, mops & cloths treating service; wiping towel supply service

(G-6174)
GEMM INC
12411 Wayzata Blvd (55305-1925)
PHONE.............................952 591-6730
EMP: 50
SALES (est): 1MM-4.9MM **Privately Held**
WEB: www.premiersalons.com
SIC: 7991 Spas
HQ: Gemm Inc
8341 10th Ave N
Minneapolis MN 55427
763 513-7200

(G-6175)
GENERAL MILLS FEDERAL CREDIT (PA)
9999 Wayzata Blvd (55305-5513)
PHONE.............................763 764-6900
FAX: 763 764-6980
Kent Mogler, *Ch of Bd*
CAM Hoang, *Corp Secy*
Missy Mound, *COO*
Wendy Brostrom, *Vice Pres*
Kelly Fulford, *Vice Pres*
EMP: 63 **EST:** 2001
SALES (corp-wide): 12.14M **Privately Held**
SIC: 6061 Federally chartered credit union

(G-6176)
GLOBAL FINANCIAL PARTNERS CORP
11100 Cedar Hills Blvd (55305-3055)
PHONE.............................952 544-0640
Andrew Farnum, *CEO*
EMP: 37 **EST:** 2004
SQ FT: 4,100
SALES (est): 5MM-9.9MM **Privately Held**
SIC: 6798 Real estate investment trust service

(G-6177)
GLOBAL MARKETS INC
Also Called: Horizontal Integration
9800 Bren Rd E Ste 450 (55343-4740)
PHONE.............................612 392-7580
Sabin Ephrem, *President*
Chris Staley, *Principal*
EMP: 50 **EST:** 1994
SQ FT: 5,500
SALES (est): 5MM-9.9MM **Privately Held**
SIC: 7379 Online technology consulting service

(G-6178)
GULF NORTHERN INC
13911 Ridgedale Dr # 353 (55305-1775)
PHONE.............................952 278-1501
FAX: 952 278-1502
Marc Moore, *President*
Ben Kearney, *CFO*
EMP: 50 **EST:** 2004
SQ FT: 3,000
SALES (est): 1MM-4.9MM **Privately Held**
SIC: 7381 Security guard service

(G-6179)
HSBC CARD SERVICES INC
10900 Wayzata Blvd Fl 1 (55305-5574)
PHONE.............................952 358-4000
C Boll, *Member*
Thomas Lee, *Member*
John Cleary, *Member*
Edward Speno, *Member*
Lee Anderson, *Member*
EMP: 150
SALES (est): 25MM-49.9MM **Privately Held**
WEB: www.household.com

(PA)=Parent Co (HQ)=Headquarters (DH)=Div Headquarters
✿ = New business established in last 2 years

2011 Harris Minnesota
Services Directory

© Harris InfoSource 1-866-281-6415
271

GEOGRAPHIC

SIC: 6141 7389 Personal consumer finance company; financial service
DH: Hsbc Finance Corp
26525 N Riverwoods Blvd
Mettawa IL 60045
224 544-2000

(G-6180)
INNER STATE PROTECTION INC
13911 Ridgedale Dr Ste 353 (55305-1775)
PHONE..............................651 771-1501
Marc Moore, *President*
EMP: 30 EST: 1998
SQ FT: 3,000
SALES (est): 500-999K Privately Held
SIC: 7381 Security guard service

(G-6181)
INTER-TAX INC
13911 Ridgedale Dr # 100 (55305-1773)
PHONE..............................952 512-9000
Tom Rushfeldt, *President*
EMP: 30 EST: 1994
SQ FT: 6,000
SALES (est): Under 500K Privately Held
WEB: www.inter-tax.com
SIC: 7291 Tax return preparation services
HQ: Ceridian Corp
3311 E Old Shakopee Rd
Minneapolis MN 55425
952 853-8100

(G-6182)
JOHN RYAN CO INC
11100 Wayzata Blvd # 350 (55305-5604)
PHONE..............................612 924-7700
John C Ryan, *President*
Bob Steele, *Vice Chairman*
Douglas Pearson, *CFO*
Michael Hagberg, *Controller*
Jim Burbeck, *Manager*
EMP: 50 EST: 1983
SALES (est): 5MM-9.9MM Privately Held
SIC: 7319 Display advertising services

(G-6183)
K T I INC
10301 Wayzata Blvd Ste 100 (55305-1656)
PHONE..............................612 378-9731
Alan Weiner, *CEO*
▲ EMP: 28 EST: 1997
SQ FT: 17,000
SALES (est): 1MM-4.9MM Privately Held
WEB: www.ktitrans.com
SIC: 4731 Freight forwarding services

(G-6184)
KEENAN & SVEIVEN INC
15119 Minnetonka Blvd A (55345-1520)
PHONE..............................952 475-1229
Kevin Keenan, *President*
Tim Sveiven, *Vice Pres*
EMP: 30 EST: 1990 Privately Held
WEB: www.kslandarch.com
SIC: 0781 0782 Landscape architectural service; landscaping services

(G-6185)
KINDERCARE LEARNING CENTERS
17701 Excelsior Blvd (55345-4110)
PHONE..............................952 920-8548
Kathy Plitzuweit, *Branch Mgr*
EMP: 35
SALES (est): 500-999K Privately Held
WEB: www.kindercare.com
SIC: 8351 Child day care service
HQ: KinderCare Learning Centers
650 NE Holladay St Ste 1400
Portland OR 97232
503 872-1300

(G-6186)
L & R SUBURBAN LANDSCAPING INC
11421 47th St W (55343-8889)
PHONE..............................952 935-0389
Lyle Cemenski, *President*
Ron Cemenski, *Vice Pres*
Gloria Rasinski, *Manager*
EMP: 30 EST: 1987 Privately Held
WEB: www.lrsuburbanlandscaping.com

SIC: 0782 7389 Landscaping services; swimming pool & hot tub cleaning & maintenance services

(G-6187)
LIVING BENEFITS FINANCIAL SVCS
10505 Wayzata Blvd Ste 1000 (55305-1522)
PHONE..............................952 903-9800
Paul Moe, *Member*
Michael Fannon, *Treasurer*
EMP: 26 EST: 2001
SALES (est): 1MM-4.9MM Privately Held
SIC: 7389 Financial service

(G-6188)
LJK CO'S INC
Also Called: Lodgex Airline Solutions Div
10225 Yellow Circle Dr Ste 200 (55343-4668)
PHONE..............................952 944-5462
Lisa Wing, *Branch Mgr*
EMP: 150
SALES (est): 5MM-9.9MM Privately Held
WEB: www.ljkco.com
SIC: 4724 Tourist agency arranging transport, lodging & car rental
PA: LJK Co's Inc
10225 Yellow Circle Dr # 2
Minnetonka MN 55343
952 944-5462

(G-6189)
MAC MANAGEMENT INC (PA)
5929 Baker Rd Ste 420 (55345-5940)
PO Box 5477, Hopkins (55343-2477)
PHONE..............................952 938-8048
Blair B Bury, *President*
Blaine M Johnson, *Vice Pres*
Maynard Schuldt, *Treasurer*
EMP: 25 EST: 1992
SQ FT: 4,000
SALES (est): 1MM-4.9MM Privately Held
SIC: 1611 5032 Highway & street paving contractor; highway & street resurfacing contractor; manufactures bituminous road materials; wholesales limestone; wholesales gravel; wholesales construction sand

(G-6190)
MARKETING ARCHITECTS INC
110 Cheshire Ln Ste 200 (55305-1041)
PHONE..............................952 449-2500
FAX: 952 249-8790
Charles M Hengel, *President*
J B Longval, *CFO*
Lindsey Brouwer, *Accounts Mgr*
Kelli Udermann, *Sales Staff*
EMP: 92 EST: 1996
SQ FT: 11,000
SALES (est): 10MM-24.9MM Privately Held
SIC: 8742 7319 Marketing consulting service; media buying services

(G-6191)
MEDNET SOLUTIONS INC
601 Carlson Pkwy Ste 605 (55305-5409)
PHONE..............................763 258-2735
John M Robertson IV, *President*
Marti Pierson, *Business Mgr*
Alan D Sherwood, *Senior VP*
Paul C Fadden, *Vice Pres*
Ryan M Anderson, *VP Eng R&D*
EMP: 70 EST: 2001 Privately Held
SIC: 8731 8733 Commercial medical research services; medical research organization

(G-6192)
MG WALDBAUM CO
301 Carlson Pkwy Ste 400 (55305-5370)
PHONE..............................952 258-4000
Mark D Whitmer, *President*
Carolyn Wolsky, *Corp Secy*
Mark Wesphal, *CFO*
Mark Westther, *CFO*
John E Rddy, *VP Finance*
◆ EMP: 60 EST: 1950
SQ FT: 30,000
SALES (est): 10MM-24.9MM Privately Held

SIC: 5153 5191 Manufactures egg food products; manufactures processed desiccated eggs; manufactures processed frozen eggs; wholesales grains; wholesales feed
DH: Michael Foods Group Inc
301 Carlson Pkwy Ste 400
Minnetonka MN 55305
952 258-4000

(G-6193)
MICHAEL FOODS GROUP INC (DH)
301 Carlson Pkwy Ste 400 (55305-5370)
PHONE..............................952 258-4000
James E Dwyer Jr, *President*
Mark Witmer, *Treasurer*
EMP: 240 EST: 2003 Privately Held
SIC: 0252 5143 5144 5148 6719 Chicken egg farming; wholesales butter; wholesales cheese; wholesales eggs; wholesale egg cleaning, oil treating, packing & grading; wholesales fresh potatoes; investment holding company; manufactures egg food products
HQ: Michael Foods Investors LLC
301 Carlson Pkwy Ste 400
Minnetonka MN 55305
952 258-4000

(G-6194)
MID AMERICAN FINANCIAL GROUP
Also Called: New England Financial
301 Carlson Pkwy Ste 300 (55305-5383)
PHONE..............................952 258-5000
Richard Marooney, *General Mgr*
EMP: 58 EST: 1976
SALES (est): 5MM-9.9MM Privately Held
SIC: 6411 6211 Insurance agent; securities dealer

(G-6195)
MIDCOUNTRY BANK INC (PA)
14617 Highway 7 (55345-3706)
PHONE..............................952 997-5608
Larry Flowers, *CEO*
Robin Roberts, *Senior VP*
Wanda Bender, *Vice Pres*
Bob Calander, *Vice Pres*
Karen Conrad, *Vice Pres*
EST: 1933
SALES (corp-wide): 66.43M Privately Held
WEB: www.midcountrybank.com
SIC: 6035 Federally chartered savings institution

(G-6196)
MINNESOTA AUTISM CENTER
5710 Baker Rd (55345-5901)
PHONE..............................952 767-4200
Ryan Cornelius, *General Mgr*
Kathryn Marshall, *Director*
EMP: 106 EST: 1996
SALES (est): 5MM-9.9MM Privately Held
WEB: www.mnautism.org
SIC: 8322 8082 8741 Individual & family social services; management services; home health care services

(G-6197)
MINNETONKA ASSISTED LIVING COM
14505 Minnetonka Dr (55345-2210)
PHONE..............................952 988-0011
FAX: 952 912-0051
Walker Methodist, *Owner*
EMP: 25 EST: 1984
SALES (est): 1MM-4.9MM Privately Held
SIC: 8741 Management services

(G-6198)
MINNETONKA MINNESOTA HOTEL L P
Also Called: Sheraton Minneapolis West
12201 Ridgedale Dr (55305-1903)
PHONE..............................952 593-0000
FAX: 952 544-2090
Leif Chaffee, *General Mgr*
Monty Bennett, *Vice Pres*
Richard Bauman, *Chief Engr*
Michelle Trudeau, *Human Resources*
Rich Edin, *Marketing Mgr*
EMP: 90

EST: 1993
SQ FT: 104,000
SALES (est): 5MM-9.9MM Privately Held
SIC: 7011 Traveler accommodations

(G-6199)
MINNETONKA TRANSPORTATION INC
5801 Baker Rd (55345-5963)
PHONE..............................952 935-1990
FAX: 952 933-5583
Charles Robinson, *President*
EMP: 80 EST: 1972
SALES (est): 1MM-4.9MM Privately Held
SIC: 4151 4141 School bus service; local bus charter service

(G-6200)
MITEL TECHNOLOGIES INC
5929 Baker Rd Ste 410 (55345-5940)
PHONE..............................952 930-4400
FAX: 952 912-2900
Paul Kady, *Manager*
Peter Jones, *Manager*
Bill Blake, *Manager*
EMP: 44
SALES (est): 25MM-49.9MM Privately Held
WEB: www.inter-tel.com
SIC: 5065 Wholesales electronic parts & equipment
HQ: Mitel Technologies Inc
1016 W Geneva Dr
Tempe AZ 85282
480 449-8900

(G-6201)
NETWORK INSTRUMENTS LLC
10701 Red Circle Dr (55343-9136)
PHONE..............................952 358-3800
Roman Oliynyk, *Member*
Douglas Smith, *Member*
Jane Nichols, *Vice Pres*
Deborah Moore, *CFO*
Jim Kruse, *Accounting Dir*
EMP: 25 EST: 1993
SQ FT: 30,000
SALES (est): 1MM-4.9MM Privately Held
SIC: 7371 7372 Freelance computer software writers; software publisher

(G-6202)
NORSTAN COMMUNICATIONS INC (DH)
5101 Shady Oak Rd S (55343-4100)
PHONE..............................952 352-4300
FAX: 952 352-4949
Paul Baszucki, *Ch of Bd*
Scott Christian, *President*
Alice Vazquez, *Treasurer*
Alan Harkrader, *Manager*
John Heckathorn, *Network Mgr*
EMP: 110 EST: 1974
SALES (corp-wide): 961.39M Publicly Held
WEB: www.conferencepoint.com
SIC: 5065 1731 7629 Wholesales telephone equipment; telephone equipment installation; telecommunication equipment repair service
HQ: Norstan Inc
5101 Shady Oak Rd S
Hopkins MN 55343
952 352-4000

(G-6203)
NORTH AMERICAN AFFINITY CLUBS
12301 Whitewater Dr (55343-9447)
PHONE..............................952 936-9333
Nancy Ezensen, *President*
Les Gage, *Publisher*
Sandy Bergmann, *Manager*
Roy Barnhart, *Senior Editor*
▲ EMP: 409 EST: 1978
SALES (est): 10MM-24.9MM Privately Held
SIC: 7997 Membership recreation club

(G-6204)
NORTH CENTRAL CO'S INC
601 Carlson Pkwy Ste 400 (55305-5226)
PHONE..............................952 449-0885
FAX: 952 449-0785
Larry R Zilverberg, *President*
Deanna Faustgen, *Corp Secy*
David Krier, *Controller*

▲=Import ▼=Export
◆=Import/Export

Jeff Stand, *Manager*
▲ **EMP:** 29 **EST:** 1984
SQ FT: 6,269
SALES (est): 25MM-49.9MM **Privately Held**
WEB: www.northcentralco.com
SIC: 5159 5199 Wholesales raw furs;
wholesales hides; wholesales raw hops;
wholesales animal or vegetable greases;
wholesales animal or vegetable oils

(G-6205)
OFFICE DEPOT INC
1005 Plymouth Rd AD (55305-1056)
PHONE..............................952 525-1919
John Minter, *Branch Mgr*
EMP: 27
SALES (est): 5MM-9.9MM **Publicly Held**
WEB: www.officedepot.com
SIC: 5112 Wholesales stationery & office
supplies; retails personal computers; retails
typewriters & business machines; retails
computers & computer software
PA: Office Depot Inc
6600 N Military Trl
Boca Raton FL 33496
561 438-4800

(G-6206)
OPUS DESIGN BUILD LLC ✪
10350 Bren Rd W (55343-9014)
PHONE..............................952 656-4444
Stephanie McMillan, *Executive Asst*
EMP: 95 **EST:** 2010
SALES (est): 10MM-24.9MM **Privately Held**
SIC: 1542 Commercial & institutional
building construction

(G-6207)
OPUS NATIONAL LLC (HQ)
10350 Bren Rd W (55343-9014)
PHONE..............................952 656-4444
Steve Peranich, *General Mgr*
Mark Rauenhorst, *Member*
Alan Cork, *Vice Pres*
Julie Kimble, *Vice Pres*
Tony Martin, *Vice Pres*
EMP: 130 **EST:** 1995 **Privately Held**
SIC: 8742 6552 Marketing consulting
service; land subdivision & development
services
PA: Opus Corp
10350 Bren Rd W
Hopkins MN 55343
952 656-4444

(G-6208)
OUTSOURCE ADMINISTRATORS INC
10225 Yellow Circle Dr # 2 (55343-4653)
PHONE..............................952 944-5462
Lisa Wing, *CEO*
Larry Gehl, *Ch of Bd*
Dirk Draayer, *President*
Earl Kopriva, *Vice Pres*
David Sumners, *VP Finance*
EMP: 30 **EST:** 1994
SQ FT: 10,000
SALES (est): 1MM-4.9MM **Privately Held**
WEB: www.ljkco.com
SIC: 4729 4724 Carpool or vanpool
arrangement services; travel agency
PA: LJK Co's Inc
10225 Yellow Circle Dr # 2
Minnetonka MN 55343
952 944-5462

(G-6209)
PEOPLENET COMMUNICATIONS CORP
4400 Baker Rd (55343-8668)
PHONE..............................952 908-6200
Ronald Konezny, *CEO*
Brian McLaughlin, *COO*
Beverly Mestelle, *Vice Pres*
Mark Kessler, *Vice Pres*
Mike Goergen, *CFO*
▲ **EMP:** 230 **EST:** 1994
SQ FT: 61,000
SALES (est): 25MM-49.9MM **Privately Held**
WEB: www.peoplenetonline.com
SIC: 7373 4812 Computer related systems
engineering; wireless telecommunications
carrier & service; manufactures radio &
television communications equipment

(G-6210)
PERFORMARK INC
10400 Yellow Circle Dr # 101
(55343-9248)
PHONE..............................952 946-7300
A J Lethert, *Chairman*
Marshall Gage, *Exec VP*
Robert Andersen, *Vice Pres*
Jack Brown, *Vice Pres*
Susan Limoncelli, *Vice Pres*
EMP: 120 **EST:** 1984
SQ FT: 60,000
SALES (est): 10MM-24.9MM **Privately Held**
SIC: 8742 5064 Incentive or award program
consultant; sales consulting services;
wholesales electrical entertainment
equipment

(G-6211)
PET CO
13691 Ridgedale Dr (55305-1766)
PHONE..............................952 541-1981
FAX: 952 541-4720
Harvey Suncold, *Branch Mgr*
Garry Smith, *Manager*
EMP: 30 **EST:** 2003
SALES (est): 1MM-4.9MM **Privately Held**
SIC: 0752 Retails pets & pet supplies;
animal grooming services

(G-6212)
PETTERS AVIATION LLC (PA)
4400 Baker Rd (55343-8684)
PHONE..............................952 936-5000
Jay Salmen, *President*
Susan Geitzenauer, *Vice Pres*
EST: 2006 **Privately Held**
SIC: 4581 Aircraft maintenance & repair
services

(G-6213)
PGI FULFILLMENT INC
11354 K Tel Dr (55343-8868)
PHONE..............................952 933-5745
FAX: 952 933-5864
Jeffory D Brower, *President*
Jim Ripka, *Vice Pres*
Chuck Belland, *Finance Dir*
Jennifer Duda, *Human Res Dir*
Kevin Heise, *Manager*
EMP: 100 **EST:** 1990
SALES (est): 5MM-9.9MM **Privately Held**
SIC: 7331 Commercial printing; book
binding service; direct mail advertising
service; commercial lithographic printing

(G-6214)
PINE RIVER CAPITAL MANAGEMENT
601 Carlson Pkwy Ste 330 (55305-7703)
PHONE..............................612 238-3300
Brian Taylor, *Ltd Ptnr*
Jeff Stolt, *CFO*
Jessica Berg, *Manager*
EMP: 53 **EST:** 2002
SQ FT: 11,000 **Privately Held**
WEB: www.pinerivercapital.com
SIC: 6722 Open-ended investment funds
management services

(G-6215)
POLAROID CONSUMER ELECTRONICS (PA)
4400 Baker Rd Ste 900 (55343-8684)
PHONE..............................952 936-5000
Scott W Hardy, *CEO*
Donald Brewer, *Vice Pres*
Mark Laumann, *Controller*
James C Wehmhoff, *Finance*
Cheryl Hemken, *VP Mktg*
▲ **EMP:** 55 **EST:** 2002
SQ FT: 45,000 **Privately Held**
SIC: 5199 Wholesales nondurable general
merchandise

(G-6216)
POLAROID HOLDINGS LLC (PA)
4350 Baker Rd (55343-8609)
PHONE..............................952 934-9918
Camille Chee-Awai, *Member*
Patricia Hamm, *Vice Pres*
Thomas Hay, *Vice Pres*
Deanna Munson, *Vice Pres*
Rick Engels, *CFO*

EST: 1988 **Privately Held**
SIC: 5199 Wholesales nondurable general
merchandise

(G-6217)
PRIME MORTGAGE CORP
11100 Wayzata Blvd Ste 200
(55305-5543)
PHONE..............................952 544-3181
FAX: 952 544-3233
Tom Olson, *President*
Sally Turrittin, *Corp Secy*
Randall Conte, *Exec VP*
Stacy Vasend, *Controller*
Kathy Junquist, *Manager*
EMP: 40 **EST:** 1985
SALES (est): 5MM-9.9MM **Privately Held**
SIC: 6162 Urban mortgage service

(G-6218)
RADISSON HOTELS INTERNATIONAL
701 Carlson Pkwy (55305-5240)
PHONE..............................763 212-5000
Curtis C Nelson, *President*
James Riker, *General Mgr*
Khamis Kazzaz, *General Mgr*
Judith Kalfon, *General Mgr*
Mike Cowell, *Corp Secy*
EMP: 160 **EST:** 1983
SQ FT: 10,000
SALES (est): 5MM-9.9MM **Privately Held**
WEB: www.carlson.com
SIC: 7011 6531 6552 6794 7389 8742
Traveler accommodations; real estate
management services; marketing consulting
service; commercial land subdividers &
developers; selling or licensing of
franchises; purchasing service; training &
development consultant
DH: Carlson Hotels LP
Carlson Parkway 701 Twr St
Minneapolis MN 55459
763 212-1000

(G-6219)
RELATE COUNSELING CENTER INC
15320 Minnetonka Blvd # 200
(55345-1504)
PHONE..............................952 932-7277
FAX: 952 932-9827
La S Williamson, *Insur/Bill Sup*
Tracee L Welker, *Office Mgr*
Lynda J Barger, *Child Psycholgy*
Suzanne Erickson, *Child Psychology*
Warren O Watson, *Director*
EMP: 30 **EST:** 1969
SALES (est): 1MM-4.9MM **Privately Held**
WEB: www.relatemn.org
SIC: 8093 8063 8069 8322 Outpatient
mental health clinic; mental hospital;
alcoholism rehabilitation hospital; general
counseling services

(G-6220)
RMC PROJECT MANAGEMENT INC
10953 Bren Rd E (55343-9613)
PHONE..............................952 846-4484
Rita Mulcahy, *President*
Jude Tomac, *Manager*
Erica Schmidt, *Coordinator*
EMP: 31 **EST:** 1991
SQ FT: 18,000
SALES (est): 1MM-4.9MM **Privately Held**
WEB: www.rmcproject.com
SIC: 8741 Management services

(G-6221)
ROXBURY CAPITAL MANAGEMENT LLC
6001 Shady Oak Rd S (55343-8912)
PHONE..............................952 230-6140
Lance Simpson, *Controller*
Cory Bassett, *Controller*
Alfred J Lockwood, *Accountant*
John Faust, *Marketing Staff*
Brian C Beh, *Mng Member*
EMP: 30 **EST:** 1986
SQ FT: 12,000
SALES (est): 5MM-9.9MM **Privately Held**
WEB: www.roxcap.com
SIC: 6282 Financial investment advice
service

(G-6222)
RUTH STRICKER'S FITNESS UNLTD
Also Called: MARSH
15000 Minnetonka Blvd (55345-1506)
PHONE..............................952 935-2202
FAX: 952 935-9685
Ruth Stricker, *Chairman*
Michael Johnson, *Finance*
Kent Marsh, *Chiropractor*
Frank Chase, *Manager*
Timothy Mortenson, *Manager*
EMP: 220 **EST:** 1982
SQ FT: 76,000
SALES (est): 5MM-9.9MM **Privately Held**
WEB: www.themarsh.com
SIC: 7991 Health club

(G-6223)
S D Q LTD
4737 County Road 101 # 250
(55345-2634)
PHONE..............................952 929-5263
Marie Bak, *CEO*
Dirk Bak, *President*
Scott Bak, *Vice Pres*
EMP: 148 **EST:** 1982
SQ FT: 20,000
SALES (est): 1MM-4.9MM **Privately Held**
WEB: www.sdq.com
SIC: 7349 Janitorial & custodial services

(G-6224)
SAFENET CONSULTING INC
5810 Baker Rd Ste 100 (55345-5941)
PHONE..............................952 930-3636
Robert Purdy, *CEO*
Martin Miller, *CEO*
Kenneth Helmin, *Project Mgr*
Robert Hiben, *Treasurer*
Chuck Stern, *Info Tech Mgr*
EMP: 80 **EST:** 1989
SALES (est): 10MM-24.9MM **Privately Held**
WEB: www.safenetconsulting.com
SIC: 7371 7373 8742 Custom computer
software systems analysis & design service;
local area network systems integration
service; management information systems
consultant

(G-6225)
SCICOM DATA SERVICES LTD
10101 Bren Rd E (55343-9005)
PHONE..............................952 933-4200
FAX: 952 936-4132
Timothy L Johnson, *CEO*
Dale Carlson, *President*
Richard A Walter, *Chairman*
Tom King, *Corp Secy*
Martin P Kiener, *Senior VP*
EMP: 140 **EST:** 1959
SQ FT: 116,000
SALES (est): 10MM-24.9MM **Privately Held**
WEB: www.scicom.com
SIC: 7331 7374 Mailing services; pamphlet
publishing & printing; data processing
service

(G-6226)
SEBRITE AGENCY INC
5421 Feltl Rd Ste 140 (55343-3945)
PHONE..............................952 563-1234
Richard Randall, *President*
Joyce R Kraft, *Corp Secy*
Mary Magnuson, *Treasurer*
EMP: 25 **EST:** 1990
SQ FT: 3,000
SALES (est): 1MM-4.9MM **Privately Held**
WEB: www.sebritefinancial.com
SIC: 6411 Insurance agency & broker
PA: Sebrite Financial Corp
5421 Feltl Rd Ste 140
Hopkins MN 55343
952 563-1234

(G-6227)
SUNRICH INC
Also Called: Sunopta
5850 Opus Pkwy Ste 150 (55343-4418)
PHONE..............................952 939-3949
Allan Routh, *President*
Ed Ihns, *CFO*
EMP: 300 **EST:** 2004

(PA)=Parent Co (HQ)=Headquarters (DH)=Div Headquarters
✪ = New business established in last 2 years

2011 Harris Minnesota
Services Directory

© Harris InfoSource 1-866-281-6415
273

SALES (est): 100MM-499.9MM **Privately Held**
WEB: www.sunopta.com
SIC: 5149 Wholesales natural & organic foods

(G-6228)
TOMSTEN INC (PA)
Also Called: Archivers
5900 Clearwater Dr # 500 (55343-8961)
PHONE 952 516-3300
John Morgan, *CEO*
Brian Olmstaed, *President*
Ken Kranium, *General Mgr*
Jennifer Bockenstedt, *Vice Pres*
Mike Anderson, *Vice Pres*
EMP: 40 **EST:** 1998
SQ FT: 15,842 **Privately Held**
SIC: 5112 7384 Retails photographic supplies; wholesales photo albums & scrapbooks; photographic service

(G-6229)
TRAMMELL CROW CO
9900 Bren Rd E (55343-9664)
PHONE 952 936-3671
FAX: 952 936-3642
Tom Fourre, *Principal*
EMP: 94
SALES (est): 10MM-24.9MM **Publicly Held**
WEB: www.trammellcrow.com
SIC: 6531 Commercial real estate agency
DH: Trammell Crow Co
2001 Ross Ave Ste 3400
Dallas TX 75201
214 863-3000

(G-6230)
U S INTERNET CORP
12450 Wayzata Blvd Ste 121 (55305-1926)
PHONE 651 222-4638
William J Milota, *Ch of Bd*
Raoul Booton, *Senior VP*
Tracy Nelson, *Senior VP*
Kurt Lange, *Vice Pres*
Joseph Caldwell, *Vice Pres*
EMP: 46 **EST:** 1995
SQ FT: 8,000 **Privately Held**
SIC: 7375 4813 On-line database information retrieval service; online services providers

(G-6231)
UNITED STATES COMPLIANCE CORP
4350 Baker Rd Ste 100 (55343-8609)
PHONE 952 252-3000
Linda Stevenson, *President*
Scott Stevenson, *Vice Pres*
Steve Savard, *Accountant*
Tim Stevenson, *Director*
EMP: 26 **EST:** 1988
SQ FT: 10,000
SALES (est): 1MM-4.9MM **Privately Held**
SIC: 8748 8742 Environmental consultant; industrial consultant

(G-6232)
UNITEDHEALTH GROUP INC (PA)
Also Called: United Healthcare
9900 Bren Rd E (55343-9664)
PO Box 1459, Minneapolis (55440-1459)
PHONE 952 936-1300
FAX: 952 936-7430
Steven Nelson, *CEO*
Kathryn Sullivan, *CEO*
Lois Quam, *President*
Gail K Boudreaux, *President*
David S Wichmann, *President*
▼ **EMP:** 1400 **EST:** 1977
SQ FT: 1,700,000
SALES (corp-wide): 87.13B **Publicly Held**
WEB: www.unitedhealthgroup.com
SIC: 6324 6321 6411 8741 Health insurance maintenance organization; direct accident & health insurance carrier; insurance services; business management services

(G-6233)
VIBRANT TECHNOLOGIES INC
6031 Culligan Way (55345-5918)
PHONE 952 653-1700
Jennifer Larson, *CEO*
David Larson, *President*
Corey Donovan, *VP Sls/Mktg*
Gary Crandall, *CFO*
▲ **EMP:** 30 **EST:** 1998
SQ FT: 17,000
SALES (est): 5MM-9.9MM **Privately Held**
SIC: 7377 Retails computer peripheral equipment; computer peripheral equipment rental & leasing

(G-6234)
VIROMED LABORATORIES INC
6101 Blue Circle Dr (55343-9108)
PHONE 952 563-3300
FAX: 952 939-4215
Candance Carlson, *Principal*
Bradford T Smith, *Corp Secy*
Greg Boemer, *Purch Mgr*
Bob Fogerson, *CFO*
Terry Nistler, *Finance*
EMP: 27 **EST:** 2005
SALES (est): 1MM-4.9MM **Privately Held**
SIC: 8071 8734 Medical laboratory; testing laboratory

(G-6235)
VITAL IMAGES INC
5850 Opus Pkwy Ste 300 (55343-4411)
PHONE 952 487-9500
FAX: 952 852-4110
Michael H Carrel, *President*
Mark Fuchs, *General Mgr*
Aaron Akyuz, *Exec VP*
Steven P Canakes, *Exec VP*
Jim D Litterer, *Vice Pres*
EMP: 105 **EST:** 1988
SQ FT: 72,000
SALES (est): 25MM-49.9MM **Publicly Held**
SIC: 7372 Software publisher

(G-6236)
WELSH CO'S LLC
4350 Baker Rd Ste 400 (55343-8628)
PHONE 952 897-7700
Ed Chan, *General Mgr*
Pat Kriske, *General Mgr*
Don Gonsior, *Superintendent*
Mike Milless, *Superintendent*
Ron Nelsen, *Superintendent*
EMP: 150 **EST:** 1999
SALES (est): 25MM-49.9MM **Privately Held**
SIC: 6531 Commercial real estate agency

(G-6237)
WINTHROP RESOURCES CORP
11100 Wayzata Blvd Ste 800 (55305-5525)
PHONE 952 936-0226
FAX: 952 936-0201
Craig R Dahl, *CEO*
Ronald Palmer, *President*
Paul L Gendler, *Senior VP*
Jeff Ripperton, *Vice Pres*
Matt Geurink, *Project Mgr*
EMP: 65 **EST:** 1982
SQ FT: 43,000
SALES (est): 10MM-24.9MM **Publicly Held**
WEB: www.tcfbank.com
SIC: 6035 Federally chartered savings institution
PA: TCF Financial Corp
200 Lake St E
Wayzata MN 55391
952 745-2760

(G-6238)
WIRELESS RONIN TECHNOLOGIES
5929 Baker Rd Ste 475 (55345-5955)
PHONE 952 564-3500
James C Granger, *CEO*
Scott W Koller, *President*
David Boerlin, *Corp Secy*
John Witham, *Exec VP*
Alan D Buterbaugh, *Senior VP*
EMP: 29 **EST:** 2000
SQ FT: 19,000
SALES (est): 1MM-4.9MM **Publicly Held**
WEB: www.wirelessronin.com

SIC: 7373 Computer integrated systems design services

(G-6239)
WORLD DATA PRODUCTS INC
121 Cheshire Ln Ste 100 (55305-1055)
PHONE 952 476-9000
FAX: 952 943-1131
Neil Vill, *President*
Dave Alrick, *Vice Pres*
Glen Littler, *Vice Pres*
Mark Drews, *VP Finance*
Mike Cunnien, *Sales Staff*
EMP: 100 **EST:** 1987
SQ FT: 40,000
SALES (est): 50MM-99.9MM **Privately Held**
WEB: www.wdpi.com
SIC: 5045 7378 Wholesales computers, peripherals & software; computer & data processing equipment repair & maintenance

(G-6240)
ZANBY LLC
3611 Farmington Rd (55305-4128)
PHONE 952 938-5448
Michael Milkovich, *Member*
Chris Dykstra, *Member*
EMP: 25 **EST:** 2007
SALES (est): 1MM-4.9MM **Privately Held**
SIC: 7389 Business services at a non-commercial site

MINNETONKA BEACH
Hennepin County

(G-6241)
LAFAYETTE CLUB
2800 Northview Rd (55361)
PO Box 128 (55361-0128)
PHONE 952 471-8493
Jack Syenson, *President*
Scott Bremer, *General Mgr*
Mary P Peterson, *Corp Secy*
Richard Adams, *Vice Pres*
Roger Dehring, *Treasurer*
EMP: 130 **EST:** 1899
SQ FT: 80,000
SALES (est): 5MM-9.9MM **Privately Held**
SIC: 7997 Membership golf club; eating place

MINNETRISTA
Hennepin County

(G-6242)
INDOFF INC
6343 Bay Ridge Rd (55364-9523)
PHONE 952 472-1295
Gary Wambold, *Partner*
EMP: 389
SALES (est): 100MM-499.9MM **Privately Held**
WEB: www.indoff.com
SIC: 5084 Wholesales materials handling equipment
PA: Indoff Inc
11816 Lackland Rd Stop 1
Saint Louis MO 63146
314 997-1122

MIZPAH
Koochiching County

(G-6243)
GEMMELL LAKES ASSOCIATION
11141 County Road 25 (56660-9540)
PHONE 218 897-5318
Roger Cook, *Principal*
Connie Nelson, *Principal*
Robert Barrieau, *Director*
EMP: 25 **EST:** 1991 **Privately Held**
SIC: 8611 Community affairs & services

MONTEVIDEO
Chippewa County

(G-6244)
CHIPPEWA COUNTY-MONTEVIDEO
824 N 11th St (56265-1629)
PHONE 320 269-8877
FAX: 320 269-8186
Rebecca Arndt, *Business Mgr*
Kevin Myhre, *Ch Radiology*
Teresa Vogel, *Purchasing*
Darlene Boike, *CFO*
Laurie Hass, *Pub Rel Dir*
EMP: 250 **EST:** 1910
SQ FT: 59,796
SALES (est): 10MM-24.9MM **Privately Held**
WEB: www.montevideomedical.com
SIC: 8062 Medical hospital

(G-6245)
FARMERS UNION OIL CO OF
County Rd 15 73rd Ave SW (56265)
PHONE 320 269-8856
Glen Mole, *Manager*
EMP: 25
SALES (est): 10MM-24.9MM **Privately Held**
SIC: 5191 5171 Wholesales agricultural fertilizer; wholesales agricultural chemicals; wholesales petroleum bulk stations; wholesales field, garden & flower seeds; gas station
PA: Farmers Union Oil Co of
124 W Nichols Ave
Montevideo MN 56265
320 269-8861

(G-6246)
HOMEFRONT
224 N 19th St (56265-2121)
PHONE 320 269-2930
FAX: 320 269-4700
Mary Vein, *Owner*
EMP: 30 **EST:** 2001
SALES (est): 1MM-4.9MM **Privately Held**
SIC: 8052 Intermediate care facility

(G-6247)
J & D CONSTRUCTION INC
1100 Hwy 212WEST (56265)
PHONE 320 269-2101
FAX: 320 269-6253
Douglas Nelson, *President*
Tom Williams, *Purch Agent*
Jerry Pauling, *CFO*
Scott Mitlyng, *Sales Mgr*
Jeanna Schmidt, *Clerk*
EMP: 25 **EST:** 1980
SQ FT: 2,500
SALES (est): 5MM-9.9MM **Privately Held**
WEB: www.jdconstinc.com
SIC: 1541 1796 Grain elevator construction; millwright

(G-6248)
KIBBLE EQUIPMENT INC (PA)
Hwy 7 E (56265)
PO Box 277 (56265-0277)
PHONE 320 269-6466
FAX: 320 269-8395
William Kibble, *President*
John Jorgenson, *Accountant*
EMP: 60 **EST:** 1943
SQ FT: 15,000 **Privately Held**
WEB: www.kibbleeq.com
SIC: 5083 7699 Wholesales farm implements; wholesales farm equipment parts & supplies; farm machinery repair service

(G-6249)
LUTHER HAVEN
1109 E Highway 7 (56265-1711)
PHONE 320 269-6517
FAX: 320 269-6510
Karen Vaske, *Corp Secy*
Linda Broich, *Bookkeeper*
James E Flaherty, *Administrator*
EMP: 150 **EST:** 1964
SQ FT: 74,000
SALES (est): 5MM-9.9MM **Privately Held**
SIC: 8051 Skilled nursing care facility

www.HarrisInfo.com
274
2011 Harris Minnesota
Services Directory
▲=Import ▼=Export
◆=Import/Export

(G-6250)
MINNESOTA VALLEY COOPERATIVE
501 S 1st St (56265-2103)
PO Box 248 (56265-0248)
PHONE..............320 269-2163
FAX: 320 269-2302
Patrick Carruth, *General Mgr*
Robert Walsh, *Member*
Kory Johnson, *Engineering*
Kathryn Christenson, *Comms Mgr*
Barbara Holien, *Office Mgr*
EMP: 30 EST: 1938
SQ FT: 20,000
SALES (est): 10MM-24.9MM **Privately Held**
WEB: www.mnvalleyrec.com
SIC: 4911 Provides electric power transmission services; electric power distribution service

(G-6251)
MINNWEST BANK CENTRAL
107 N 1st St (56265-1401)
PO Box 428 (56265-0428)
PHONE..............320 269-6565
FAX: 320 269-2532
Brian Reinert, *President*
Craig Boysen, *Exec VP*
Chris Jerve, *Vice Pres*
Suzanne Ponsch, *Vice Pres*
Ruth Donais, *Mfg Staff*
EMP: 25 EST: 1930
SQ FT: 7,000
SALES (est): 5MM-9.9MM **Privately Held**
SIC: 6029 6021 6163 Commercial bank; national commercial bank; loan broker
PA: Minnwest Corp
14820 Highway 7 Ste 100
Minnetonka MN 55345
952 545-8815

(G-6252)
MONTEVIDEO CLINIC
908 N 11th St (56265-1631)
PHONE..............320 269-6435
FAX: 320 669-4418
Frank Brachman, *President*
Carol Lietzau MD, *Corp Secy*
Norman Hagberg, *Vice Pres*
Ka Myhre MD, *Med Doctor*
F S Brathen MD, *Med Doctor*
EMP: 26 EST: 1958
SQ FT: 11,500
SALES (est): 1MM-4.9MM **Privately Held**
SIC: 8011 Physicians' office & clinic; general & family practice physician or surgeon office

(G-6253)
MONTEVIDEO COUNTRY CLUB INC
Hwy 212W (56265)
PO Box 217 (56265-0217)
PHONE..............320 269-8600
FAX: 320 269-6828
Sheryl Mann, *CEO*
Vern Taggert, *President*
Tom Blank, *General Mgr*
Dennis Sundlee, *Vice Pres*
Carolyn Agre, *Treasurer*
EMP: 25 EST: 1916
SQ FT: 5,000
SALES (est): 1MM-4.9MM **Privately Held**
WEB: www.montegolf.com
SIC: 7997 Membership golf club

(G-6254)
MONTEVIDEO COUNTRY CLUB INC
Also Called: Crossings The
W Hwy 212 (56265)
PO Box 217 (56265-0217)
PHONE..............320 269-6828
Mark Jasperson, *President*
Mike Spain, *Manager*
Keri Huntley, *Manager*
EMP: 50 EST: 1923
SALES (est): 1MM-4.9MM **Privately Held**
SIC: 7997 Membership recreation club

(G-6255)
MORT'S TRANSPORTATION INC
5010 10th Ave SW (56265-4042)
PHONE..............320 269-7340
Chad R Mortenson, *President*
EMP: 50 EST: 2007
SALES (est): 5MM-9.9MM **Privately Held**
SIC: 4789 Transportation services

(G-6256)
PARKVIEW FORD - MERCURY INC
2207 E Highway 7 (56265-1724)
PO Box 346 (56265-0346)
PHONE..............320 269-5565
FAX: 320 564-4552
Robert Kruse, *President*
Joy Hinrichs, *General Mgr*
Diane Kruse, *Vice Pres*
John Albrecht, *Manager*
EMP: 29 EST: 1960
SQ FT: 6,000
SALES (est): 1MM-4.9MM **Privately Held**
WEB: www.parkviewford.com
SIC: 7538 General automotive repair services; retails new & used automobiles; used car dealer

(G-6257)
PRAIRIE FIVE COMMUNITY ACTION (PA)
7th St & Washington Ave S (56265)
PO Box 159 (56265-0159)
PHONE..............320 269-6578
FAX: 320 269-6570
Deb Larson, *Exec Dir*
EMP: 45 EST: 1965
SQ FT: 7,000
SALES (corp-wide): 6.53M **Privately Held**
WEB: www.prairiefive.com
SIC: 8322 Individual & family social services

(G-6258)
RITALKA INC (PA)
121 N 1st St Ste 201 (56265-1401)
PHONE..............320 269-3227
Kevin R Wald, *President*
EMP: 30 EST: 1997
SALES (corp-wide): 11.80M **Privately Held**
SIC: 6719 Investment holding company

(G-6259)
RVI INC (PA)
121 N 1st St Ste 201 (56265-1401)
PHONE..............320 269-3227
Kevin Wald, *CEO*
EMP: 40 EST: 2007
SALES (corp-wide): 4.09M **Privately Held**
WEB: www.specsys.org
SIC: 7629 Electronic equipment repair service

(G-6260)
SPECSYS INC
Also Called: Specialty Systems Engineering
121 N 1st St Ste 201 (56265-1401)
PHONE..............320 269-3227
FAX: 320 269-7982
Kevin Wald, *President*
Dave Gelhar, *Managing Dir*
Jeff Muhl, *Mfg Spvr*
Evone Hagerman, *CFO*
Todd Osman, *Manager*
EMP: 120 EST: 2000
SQ FT: 110,000
SALES (est): 10MM-24.9MM **Privately Held**
SIC: 8711 Engineering services
PA: Ritalka Inc
121 N 1st St Ste 201
Montevideo MN 56265
320 269-3227

(G-6261)
WESTERN CO-OP TRANSPORT ASSN
4501 72nd St SW (56265)
PO Box 327 (56265-0327)
PHONE..............320 269-5531
FAX: 320 269-5532
Dennis Brandon, *General Mgr*
Jana Running, *Manager*
John Moore, *Manager*
Dennis Dahl, *Manager*
EMP: 100 EST: 1959
SQ FT: 10,000
SALES (est): 10MM-24.9MM **Privately Held**
WEB: www.westerncoop.com
SIC: 4213 long distance liquid petroleum transportation services

MONTEVIDEO
Lac Qui Parle County

(G-6262)
KARIAN PETERSON POWER LINE
4437 Highway 212 (56265-4541)
PO Box 345 (56265-0345)
PHONE..............320 269-6769
Dan Persson, *Sales Staff*
Charles Risen, *Mng Member*
Joe Ecklund, *Manager*
EMP: 46 EST: 2000
SALES (est): 1MM-4.9MM **Privately Held**
WEB: www.karianpeterson.com
SIC: 1623 Electric power line construction

MONTGOMERY
Le Sueur County

(G-6263)
AGING SERVICES FOR COMMUNITIES
212 1st St S Ste 3 (56069-1602)
PHONE..............507 364-5663
Shelly Barnett, *Principal*
EMP: 26
SALES (est): 1MM-4.9MM **Privately Held**
SIC: 4789 Transportation services

(G-6264)
MONTGOMERY GOLF & RECREATION
900 Rogers Dr (56069)
PO Box 71 (56069-0071)
PHONE..............507 364-5602
Dann Segna, *President*
Jake Keohen, *General Mgr*
EMP: 40 EST: 1969
SQ FT: 1,800
SALES (est): 1MM-4.9MM **Privately Held**
WEB: www.montgomerygolfclub.com
SIC: 7997 Membership golf club; bar

MONTICELLO
Wright County

(G-6265)
AA MONTICELLO
2025 W River St (55362-4702)
PHONE..............763 295-5066
Patrick Stone, *President*
EMP: 36 EST: 1971
SALES (est): 1MM-4.9MM **Privately Held**
SIC: 8069 8093 8641 Alcoholism rehabilitation hospital; social club; outpatient alcohol treatment clinic

(G-6266)
CENTRAL MINNESOTA JOBS
106 Pine St Ste 2 (55362-8591)
PO Box 720 (55362-0720)
PHONE..............763 271-3715
FAX: 763 271-3701
Barb Chaffee, *CEO*
Victoria Walz, *Manager*
EMP: 66 **Privately Held**
SIC: 7361 Employment agency services
PA: Central Minnesota Jobs
406 E 7th St
Monticello MN 55362
763 271-3700

(G-6267)
CHIN YUEN SILVER FOX INN INC
1114 Cedar St (55362-8911)
PHONE..............763 295-4000
FAX: 763 295-4303
Marianna Khaub, *President*
Lydia Wang, *Vice Pres*
EMP: 45 EST: 1984
SALES (est): 1MM-4.9MM **Privately Held**
SIC: 7011 Traveler accommodations; full service Chinese restaurant

(G-6268)
DAHLHEIMER DISTRIBUTING CO INC
3360 Chelsea Rd W (55362-4577)
PO Box 336 (55362-0336)
PHONE..............763 295-3347
FAX: 763 295-4947
Gregory Dahlheimer, *President*
Joseph Dahlheimer, *Treasurer*
▲ EMP: 30 EST: 1959
SQ FT: 37,000
SALES (est): 10MM-24.9MM **Privately Held**
SIC: 5181 Wholesales beer & ale

(G-6269)
DAN & JERRY'S GREENHOUSES INC (PA)
2121 90th St NE (55362-3299)
PHONE..............763 271-6594
FAX: 763 271-6594
Dan Totushek, *CEO*
Jerry Quaal, *President*
Martin Johnson, *Manager*
Randy Nuss, *Executive*
▲ EMP: 55 EST: 1974
SALES (corp-wide): 14.60M **Privately Held**
SIC: 0181 Nursery stock production; retails potted plants

(G-6270)
EDINA REALTY HOME SERVICES
9240 State Highway 25 NE (55362-3362)
PHONE..............763 295-3456
FAX: 763 295-5789
Grace V Royen, *Sales Staff*
Jeff Shuman, *Manager*
EMP: 60
SALES (est): 10MM-24.9MM **Publicly Held**
WEB: www.ilovetennis.net
SIC: 6531 Real estate agency & broker
HQ: Edina Realty Home Services
6800 France Ave S Ste 600
Minneapolis MN 55435
952 928-5900

(G-6271)
FIT-PRO II (PA)
Also Called: Gold's Gym
133 Sandberg Rd (55362-8902)
PHONE..............763 295-3002
FAX: 763 295-3306
Janel Swanson, *CEO*
Dean Gagnon, *General Mgr*
EMP: 45 EST: 1989
SQ FT: 36,000 **Privately Held**
WEB: www.lifefitnesscenters.com
SIC: 7991 Membership athletic club & gymnasiums

(G-6272)
FULFILLMENT SYSTEMS INC (PA)
406 E 7th St (55362-8948)
PO Box 636 (55362-0636)
PHONE..............763 295-3400
FAX: 763 271-1241
Jack Peach, *President*
Curtis Johnson, *Vice Pres*
Kevin Deschene, *Engineer*
Kwen Johnson, *VP Finance*
Dian Ziettar, *Administrator*
▲ EMP: 63 EST: 1980
SQ FT: 45,000 **Privately Held**
SIC: 7331 Mailing services

(G-6273)
HOGLUND BUS CO INC
116 Oakwood Dr E (55362-8924)
PO Box 249 (55362-0249)
PHONE..............763 295-5119
FAX: 763 295-4992
Wayne Hoglund, *President*
Lisa Hoglund, *Treasurer*
Jack Potter, *Controller*
EMP: 44 EST: 1947
SQ FT: 10,800
SALES (est): 10MM-24.9MM **Privately Held**
WEB: www.hoglundbus.com

SIC: 5012 5013 New & used car dealer; bus wholesaler; retails new & used trucks, tractors & trailers; wholesales motor vehicles; wholesales new motor vehicle parts & supplies

(G-6274)

HOGLUND TRANSPORTATION INC

119 Oakwood Dr E (55362-8924)
PO Box 70 (55362-0070)
PHONE..............................763 295-3604
FAX: 763 295-0055
Gordon Hoglund, *President*
Joe Kunkel, *General Mgr*
Jenny Hoglund, *Corp Secy*
EMP: 54 EST: 1947
SQ FT: 10,000
SALES (est): 1MM-4.9MM **Privately Held**
SIC: 4151 School bus service

(G-6275)

JME OF MONTICELLO INC (PA)

1401 Fallon Ave NE (55362-8323)
PHONE..............................763 295-3122
Jay Morrell, *President*
Chuck McAmy, *CFO*
EMP: 50 EST: 1984
SQ FT: 50,000 **Privately Held**
SIC: 4212 4953 Dump truck hauling services; manufactures concrete block & brick; manufactures precast concrete products; manufactures ready-mixed concrete; refuse collection & disposal services; retails masonry materials & supplies

(G-6276)

MARQUETTE BANK MONTICELLO

Also Called: Wells Fargo
407 Pine St Ste 200 (55362-4712)
PHONE..............................763 271-2700
FAX: 763 271-2775
Sharon Miros, *President*
Michelle Anderson, *Manager*
Terri Erickson, *Manager*
EMP: 27 EST: 1914
SQ FT: 20,000
SALES (est): 5MM-9.9MM **Privately Held**
SIC: 6021 National commercial bank
PA: Marquette Financial Co's
60 S 6th St Ste 3800
Minneapolis MN 55402
612 661-3880

(G-6277)

MONTICELLO COUNTRY CLUB INC

1209 Golf Course Rd (55362-8751)
PO Box 576 (55362-0576)
PHONE..............................763 295-3323
FAX: 763 497-2662
Rick Traver, *General Mgr*
EMP: 40 EST: 1968
SQ FT: 4,500
SALES (est): 1MM-4.9MM **Privately Held**
WEB: www.montigolf.com
SIC: 7997 Membership golf club; retails golf goods & equipment; eating place

(G-6278)

MONTICELLO-BIG LAKE COMMUNITY

1013 Hart Blvd (55362-8575)
PHONE..............................763 295-2945
FAX: 763 271-2345
Barbara Schwientek, *CEO*
Bruce Hamond, *Chairman*
Mark Philbrook, *Corp Secy*
Bob Dawson, *Treasurer*
Darlene Nyquist, *Human Res Dir*
EMP: 425 EST: 1965
SQ FT: 144,504
SALES (est): 25MM-49.9MM **Privately Held**
SIC: 8062 4119 8051 8093 Medical hospital; outpatient mental health clinic; ambulance service; skilled nursing care facility

(G-6279)

NINTEY FOUR SERVICES INC

Also Called: U Save Auto Auto Rental
119 Oakwood Dr E (55362-8924)
PO Box 70 (55362-0070)
PHONE..............................763 295-3604
Gordon Hoglund, *President*
Jenny Hoglund, *Corp Secy*
Kerry Conco, *Manager*
EMP: 50 EST: 1970
SQ FT: 10,000
SALES (est): 10MM-24.9MM **Privately Held**
SIC: 5012 7514 Used car dealer; wholesales ambulances; rent-a-car service

(G-6280)

NORTHERN STATES POWER CO

Also Called: XCEL Energy
2807 W County Road 75 Bldg 1
(55362-4600)
PHONE..............................763 295-5151
Jack Purkins, *Plant Mgr*
Russell V Dell V, *Opers Mgr*
Alan Wojchowski, *Manager*
Mick Hammer, *Manager*
EMP: 50
SALES (est): 25MM-49.9MM **Publicly Held**
WEB: www.middletownpower.com
SIC: 4911 Electric services
HQ: Northern States Power Co
414 Nicollet Mall
Minneapolis MN 55401
612 330-5500

(G-6281)

NORTHERN STATES POWER CO

Also Called: XCEL Energy
2100 W River St (55362-4700)
PHONE..............................763 295-4141
Shawn Hilbert, *General Mgr*
Byron Day, *Senior Engr*
Nai-Tai Fei, *Senior Engr*
Dan Crofoot, *Manager*
EMP: 50
SALES (est): 25MM-49.9MM **Publicly Held**
WEB: www.middletownpower.com
SIC: 4911 Electric services
HQ: Northern States Power Co
414 Nicollet Mall
Minneapolis MN 55401
612 330-5500

(G-6282)

PATTERN STATIONS INC

Also Called: Riverwood Inn & Conference Ctr
10990 95th St NE (55362-8149)
PHONE..............................763 441-6833
FAX: 763 441-3186
John Cozad, *General Mgr*
Jeff Wermager, *Manager*
EMP: 95 EST: 1979
SALES (est): 5MM-9.9MM **Privately Held**
SIC: 7389 6512 7011 Business support services; traveler accommodations; nonresidential building operator; eating place; drinking establishment

(G-6283)

PINNACLE FINANCIAL GROUP INC

108 Thomas Cir (55362-8923)
PHONE..............................763 295-0113
FAX: 763 271-1318
Eric Gapinski, *Branch Mgr*
EMP: 80
SALES (est): 5MM-9.9MM **Privately Held**
SIC: 7322 Collection agency
PA: Pinnacle Financial Group Inc
7825 Washingtn Ave S # 410
Minneapolis MN 55439
952 996-0559

(G-6284)

RETURN INC

9560 Kalenda Ave NE (55362-4301)
PHONE..............................763 295-4659
Kelli Lenz, *Manager*
EMP: 25
SALES (est): 1MM-4.9MM **Privately Held**

SIC: 7389 Damaged merchandise salvaging service
PA: Rti Services Inc
800 Berkshire Ln N
Plymouth MN 55441
952 475-0242

(G-6285)

RIVER CITY LANES

101 Chelsea Rd (55362-8918)
PO Box 1585 (55362-1585)
PHONE..............................763 295-3390
Mark Parnell, *Partner*
Butch Lindenfelser, *Partner*
EMP: 50 EST: 1957
SQ FT: 10,000
SALES (est): 1MM-4.9MM **Privately Held**
WEB: www.rivercitylanes.com
SIC: 7933 Bowling center; bar

(G-6286)

SAINT BENEDICT'S SENIOR COM

1301 E 7th St Ofc (55362-8823)
PHONE..............................763 295-4051
Sandy Haggerty, *Principal*
EST: 1999
WEB: www.centracare.com
SIC: 8052 Intermediate care facility

(G-6287)

SMA ELEVATOR CONSTRUCTION INC

113 Chelsea Rd (55362-8918)
PO Box 10 (55362-0010)
PHONE..............................763 295-4367
FAX: 763 295-4366
Michael Brey, *President*
Mary Wille, *Corp Secy*
Stanley Brey, *Vice Pres*
Arlan Wille, *Manager*
EMP: 35 EST: 1975
SALES (est): 5MM-9.9MM **Privately Held**
SIC: 1541 Grain elevator construction

(G-6288)

SWAN RIVER MONTESSORI CHARTER

500 Maple St (55362-8878)
PHONE..............................763 271-7926
Sandy Morrow, *Principal*
Cathy Augustson, *Administrator*
EMP: 30 EST: 2005
SALES (est): 500-999K **Privately Held**
SIC: 8351 Child development center providing Montessori based instruction

(G-6289)

TAPPERS INC

Also Called: Genereux Fine Wood Products
212 Chelsea Rd (55362-8919)
PHONE..............................763 295-4222
FAX: 763 295-6379
William Tapper, *President*
Lance Hartkopf, *General Mgr*
Barbara Tapper, *Corp Secy*
Cynthia Faris, *Manager*
Bob Seppala, *Manager*
EMP: 55 EST: 1973
SQ FT: 45,000
SALES (est): 5MM-9.9MM **Privately Held**
WEB: www.westlunddistributing.com
SIC: 5072 Retails custom made cabinets; wholesales hardware; manufactures wooden kitchen cabinets

(G-6290)

THEIN WELL CO

102 Dundas Rd (55362-8915)
PHONE..............................763 271-4200
Dennis Thein, *President*
Pete Thein, *Owner*
Michael Thein, *Manager*
EMP: 40
SALES (est): 5MM-9.9MM **Privately Held**
SIC: 1781 Water well drilling contractor

(G-6291)

WELLS FARGO BANK, NATIONAL

407 Pine St Ste 200 (55362-4712)
PHONE..............................763 295-2290
FAX: 763 295-3773

Terri Erickson, *Manager*
Michelle Anderson, *Manager*
EMP: 45
SALES (est): 10MM-24.9MM **Publicly Held**
SIC: 6029 Commercial bank
HQ: Wfc Holdings, Corp
420 Montgomery St
San Francisco CA 94104
415 396-7392

(G-6292)

WILLI HAHN CORP

Also Called: Wiha Tools
1348 Dundas Cir (55362-8434)
PHONE..............................763 295-0666
Paul Allen, *CEO*
Wilfried Hahn, *President*
Stacey Anderson, *Accountant*
Kelly Ledin, *Marketing Staff*
Rick Pracht, *Manager*
▲ EMP: 26 EST: 1985
SQ FT: 30,000
SALES (est): 10MM-24.9MM **Privately Held**
WEB: www.wihatools.com
SIC: 5072 Wholesales hand tools; retails tools

MOORHEAD
Clay County

(G-6293)

ABBOTT ARNE & SCHWINDT INC

2205 SE Main Ave (56560-5940)
PO Box 427 (56561-0427)
PHONE..............................218 236-5648
Lowell Abbott, *President*
David J Hanson, *Corp Secy*
Earl Magnuson, *VP Persnl*
Engebretson K Orland, *Director*
EMP: 40 EST: 1955
SQ FT: 6,250
SALES (est): 5MM-9.9MM **Privately Held**
SIC: 1623 Water & sewer line construction

(G-6294)

AERIAL CONTRACTORS INC (DH)

Also Called: A C Equipment
3030 24th Ave S (56560-5933)
PHONE..............................218 236-9233
Lauris Molbert, *Ch of Bd*
Kevin Ellenson, *President*
George A Koeck, *Corp Secy*
Kevin Moug, *Treasurer*
John D Erickson, *Director*
EMP: 30 EST: 1969
SQ FT: 21,000
SALES (corp-wide): 1.03B **Privately Held**
SIC: 1623 7699 Electric power line construction; construction equipment repair service
HQ: Aevenia Inc
3030 24th Ave S
Moorhead MN 56560
218 284-9500

(G-6295)

AMERICAN CRYSTAL SUGAR CO (PA)

101 3rd St N (56560-1952)
PHONE..............................218 236-4400
FAX: 218 236-4494
David A Berg, *President*
Bob Vivatson, *Chairman*
Mike Astrup, *Vice Chairman*
Daniel C Mott, *Corp Secy*
Gail Engebretson, *Corp Secy*
▲ EMP: 154 EST: 1973
SQ FT: 30,000
SALES (corp-wide): 1.20B **Privately Held**
SIC: 5191 Manufactures refined sugar beet sugar; manufactures dried beet pulp from refined beet sugar; manufactures sugar beet molasses; wholesales field, garden & flower seeds

(G-6296)

AMERICAN CRYSTAL SUGAR CO

2500 11th St N (56560-1400)
PHONE..............................218 287-3400
FAX: 218 291-5444
Tammy Evenson, *Accounting Staf*

▲=Import ▼=Export
◆=Import/Export

Lana Surrell, *Human Res Mgr*
Steve Rosenau, *Manager*
Richard Eskildsen, *Manager*
Cecelia Holzer, *Director*
EMP: 340
SALES (est): 100MM-499.9MM **Privately Held**
SIC: 5149 Manufactures refined sugar beet sugar; manufactures sugar beet molasses; wholesales industrial molasses; wholesales refined sugar
PA: American Crystal Sugar Co
101 3rd St N
Moorhead MN 56560
218 236-4400

(G-6297)
AMERICAN SECURITY & PROTECTION
1620 26th St S (56560-3840)
PHONE..............................218 236-5180
FAX: 218 236-7382
John Montville, *President*
Virgil Anderson, *President*
Paul Caskey, *Area Mgr*
EMP: 100 **EST:** 1979
SALES (est): 1MM-4.9MM **Privately Held**
SIC: 7381 Armored car service

(G-6298)
BERT'S TRUCK EQUIPMENT OF
Hwy 75 N (56560)
PHONE..............................218 233-8681
FAX: 218 233-9548
Kent Gregoie, *Manager*
EMP: 28
SALES (est): 1MM-4.9MM **Privately Held**
SIC: 5013 Retails truck equipment & parts; wholesales truck parts & accessories

(G-6299)
BEVERLY ENTERPRISES - MN
Also Called: Moorhead Health Care Center
2810 Highway 10 E (56560-2501)
PHONE..............................218 233-7578
FAX: 218 233-8307
Robert Dablow, *Manager*
Bob Dablow, *Manager*
David Erickson, *Manager*
EMP: 100
SALES (est): 1MM-4.9MM **Privately Held**
WEB: www.beverlynet.com
SIC: 8051 Convalescent home
HQ: Beverly Enterprises - MN
650 Ramer Ave S
Rush City MN 55069
320 358-4765

(G-6300)
BRUCE JOHNSON
10 4th St N (56560-1955)
PHONE..............................218 284-6555
Jay Krappenhoft, *Owner*
Bruce Johnson, *Co-Owner*
EMP: 40 **EST:** 1993
SALES (est): 5MM-9.9MM **Privately Held**
SIC: 6531 Real estate services

(G-6301)
C C R INC
725 Center Ave Ste 7 (56560-1972)
PHONE..............................218 236-6730
FAX: 218 236-1481
Cecilia Kapungu, *COO*
Angie Stark, *Case Mgr*
Andrea Bashus, *Manager*
Andrea Strom, *Group*
Susan M Lopez, *Director*
EST: 1977 **Privately Held**
WEB: www.creativecare.org
SIC: 8399 Social change association

(G-6302)
CITY OF MOORHEAD
Also Called: Moorhead Police Department
915 9th Ave N (56560-2070)
PO Box 817 (56561-0817)
PHONE..............................218 299-5120
Dave Ebinger, *Chief*
EMP: 63 **Privately Held**
WEB: www.hjemkomst-center.com

SIC: 8111 Local government police protection; legal services
PA: City of Moorhead
500 Ctr Ave
Moorhead MN 56560
218 299-5166

(G-6303)
CITY OF MOORHEAD
Also Called: Village Green Golf Course
700 15th Ave N (56560-1565)
PO Box 779 (56561-0779)
PHONE..............................218 299-5422
FAX: 218 299-5426
Cliff McLain, *Branch Mgr*
Mark Johnson, *Manager*
Chad Martin, *Manager*
Don Reddin, *Director*
EMP: 54
SALES (est): 1MM-4.9MM **Privately Held**
WEB: www.hjemkomst-center.com
SIC: 7992 Public golf course; mayors' office
PA: City of Moorhead
500 Ctr Ave
Moorhead MN 56560
218 299-5166

(G-6304)
COCA-COLA ENTERPRISES INC
2000 1st Ave N (56560-2309)
PHONE..............................218 236-7165
Jess Retmond, *Manager*
EMP: 60
SALES (est): 25MM-49.9MM **Publicly Held**
WEB: www.cokecce.com
SIC: 5149 Wholesales soft drinks
PA: Coca-Cola Enterprises Inc
2500 Windy Ridge Pkwy SE
Atlanta GA 30339
770 989-3000

(G-6305)
COMMUNICATION SERVICE FOR THE
Also Called: Minnesota Relay
800 Holiday Dr Ste 260 (56560-4400)
PHONE..............................218 291-1120
Nancy Soyring, *General Mgr*
Bill Hoppe, *Manager*
Tim Smith, *Technician*
EMP: 200 **Privately Held**
WEB: www.relaysd.com
SIC: 8399 Community development groups
PA: Communication Service For The
102 N Krohn Pl
Sioux Falls SD 57103
800 713-6071

(G-6306)
CONCORDIA COLLEGE
901 8th St S (56562-0001)
PHONE..............................218 299-4321
Pamela Jolicoeur, *President*
Vern Knight, *Supervisor*
EMP: 600
SALES (est): 25MM-49.9MM **Privately Held**
WEB: www.cord.edu
SIC: 7011 Motel; bar; eating place
PA: Concordia College
901 8th St S
Moorhead MN 56562
218 299-4000

(G-6307)
CONNECTIONS OF MOORHEAD
810 4th Ave S Ste 156 (56560-2862)
PHONE..............................218 233-8657
Ada A Kringler, *Manager*
Tonya Oss, *Director*
Sheila Sartwell, *Director*
EMP: 51 **EST:** 1973
SALES (est): 1MM-4.9MM **Privately Held**
SIC: 8331 Sheltered workshop

(G-6308)
COUNTY OF CLAY
Also Called: West Central Reg Juv Center
919 8th Ave N (56560-2098)
PHONE..............................218 299-5150
FAX: 218 299-7508
Berry Steen, *Director*
EMP: 42
SALES (est): 1MM-4.9MM **Privately Held**

SIC: 8361 Juvenile correctional facilities
PA: County of Clay
807 11th St N
Moorhead MN 56560
218 299-5011

(G-6309)
D & M INDUSTRIES INC
4205 30th Ave S (56560-6024)
PHONE..............................218 287-3100
Michael Mace, *Ch of Bd*
Tom Boyle, *President*
Gail Borowicz, *Corp Secy*
Juli Laflamme, *Credit Mgr*
EMP: 50 **EST:** 1982
SQ FT: 64,000
SALES (est): 25MM-49.9MM **Privately Held**
SIC: 5031 5072 Wholesales Doors, sliding; wholesales hardware; wholesales door frames constructed of all materials; wholesales window frames constructed of all materials; wholesales windows

(G-6310)
D-S BEVERAGES INC
201 17th St N (56560-2331)
PHONE..............................218 233-1343
FAX: 218 233-1118
Donald E Setter Sr, *CEO*
Patricia Setter, *Vice Pres*
Doug Restemayer, *VP Opers-Prdtn*
John Hayes, *Sales Mgr*
EMP: 32 **EST:** 1968
SQ FT: 40,000
SALES (est): 10MM-24.9MM **Privately Held**
WEB: www.d-sbeverages.com
SIC: 5181 Wholesales beer & other fermented malt liquors

(G-6311)
DANIEL J OLSGAARD
441 Clearview Ct (56560-6801)
PHONE..............................218 299-6162
Daniel J Olsgaard, *Owner*
EMP: 50 **EST:** 1985 **Privately Held**
SIC: 0119 Grain farm

(G-6312)
DLM A MN LLP
3300 8th St S (56560-5004)
PHONE..............................218 233-0065
FAX: 218 233-0475
Toby Christensen, *President*
EMP: 40
SALES (est): 10MM-24.9MM **Privately Held**
SIC: 6512 Operators of commercial & industrial buildings

(G-6313)
ELLIOTT TRANSPORT SYSTEMS INC
4101 32nd Ave S (56560-6009)
PO Box 366 (56561-0366)
PHONE..............................218 236-9220
Jim Elliott, *President*
Jack Thornton, *Manager*
EMP: 38 **EST:** 1992
SQ FT: 10,200
SALES (est): 5MM-9.9MM **Privately Held**
WEB: www.elliott-transport.com
SIC: 4213 4212 Long-distance refrigerated trucking services; local trucking without storage services

(G-6314)
EVENTIDE SENIOR LIVING
1405 7th St S (56560-3444)
PHONE..............................218 233-7508
FAX: 218 233-3602
Jon Riewer, *President*
Randy Bach, *Maintenance Dir*
Stacey Honeyman, *CFO*
Natasha Maier, *VP Human Res*
Kerry Conlin, *Mktg Dir*
EMP: 380 **EST:** 1951
SQ FT: 100,000
SALES (est): 10MM-24.9MM **Privately Held**
WEB: www.eventide.org
SIC: 8051 8052 8059 8082 Skilled nursing care facility; intermediate care facility; nursing home; home health care services

(G-6315)
FARMERS UNION OIL CO OF
Also Called: Cenex Petro Serve
1321 Center Ave (56560-2230)
PO Box 369 (56561-0369)
PHONE..............................218 233-2497
FAX: 218 236-0420
Kent Satrang, *General Mgr*
Jody Jonson, *Manager*
EMP: 25 **EST:** 1934
SQ FT: 3,000
SALES (est): 50MM-99.9MM **Privately Held**
SIC: 5172 7538 Wholesales petroleum products; general automotive repair services; retail independent convenience store; retails auto & truck equipment & parts; retail gasoline filling station; tire dealer

(G-6316)
GATEWAY BUILDING SYSTEMS INC
2200 14th Ave S (56560-3804)
PHONE..............................218 236-9336
Kevin Johnson, *President*
Gane Skatvold, *General Mgr*
Spry Doug, *Network Mgr*
EMP: 35
SALES (est): 10MM-24.9MM **Privately Held**
SIC: 5084 Wholesales industrial processing & packaging equipment
PA: Gateway Building Systems Inc
3451 University Dr S
Fargo ND 58104
701 293-7202

(G-6317)
GUNHUS GRINNELL KLINGER
215 30th St N (56560-2546)
PO Box 1077 (56561-1077)
PHONE..............................218 236-6462
Edward S Klinger, *President*
Guy William III, *Attorney*
Bernie E Reynolds, *Attorney*
Paul E Grinnell, *Attorney*
Susan J Drenth, *Attorney*
EMP: 47 **EST:** 1914
SALES (est): 5MM-9.9MM **Privately Held**
SIC: 8111 General practice law office

(G-6318)
HEALTH INDUSTRIES INC
Also Called: All American
3501 US Highway 75 S (56560-5155)
PHONE..............................218 233-1516
FAX: 218 233-4897
Steve Clute, *President*
EMP: 50
SALES (est): 1MM-4.9MM **Privately Held**
SIC: 7991 Membership athletic club & gymnasiums

(G-6319)
INDEPENDENT SCHOOL DISTRICT
Also Called: Early Intervention Service
2410 14th St S (56560-4622)
PHONE..............................218 236-8172
Dan Markert, *Technology*
Sara King, *Director*
EMP: 30
SALES (est): 1MM-4.9MM **Privately Held**
SIC: 8322 Child guidance services
PA: Independent School District
2410 14th St S Ste 1
Moorhead MN 56560
218 284-3330

(G-6320)
JAZZ ARTS GROUP FARGOMOORHEAD
2700 12th Ave S (56560-3958)
PHONE..............................218 236-0421
FAX: 218 236-0516
Diane W Williams, *President*
Rochelle Roesler, *Exec Dir*
Robert C Anderson, *Director*
EMP: 27 **EST:** 1991
SALES (est): 1MM-4.9MM **Privately Held**
WEB: www.jazzartsfm.org
SIC: 7922 Performing arts center production service

(PA)=Parent Co (HQ)=Headquarters (DH)=Div Headquarters
✿ = New business established in last 2 years

2011 Harris Minnesota
Services Directory

© Harris InfoSource 1-866-281-6415
277

(G-6321)

KADRMAS, LEE & JACKSON INC

1505 30th Ave S Ste A (56560-5149)
PO Box 96 (56561-0096)
PHONE..................218 287-0300
FAX: 218 287-6313
Kris Bakkegard, *Manager*
EMP: 30
SALES (est): 1MM-4.9MM **Privately Held**
SIC: 8711 Civil engineering services
PA: Kadrmas, Lee & Jackson Inc
    677 27th Ave E
    Dickinson ND 58601
    701 483-1284

(G-6322)

LAKE COUNTRY LOGISTICS LLC

Also Called: Unishippers of Minnesota
4225 30th Ave S (56560-6024)
PHONE..................218 233-2686
FAX: 218 233-4979
Brent Skillman, *Member*
Sid Jones, *Member*
Mary Teiken, *Accountant*
Carl Loge, *Mng Member*
Tom Berglind, *Manager*
EMP: 30 EST: 1996
SQ FT: 3,800
SALES (est): 1MM-4.9MM **Privately Held**
WEB: www.qsisales.com
SIC: 4731 Freight transportation
arrangement services

(G-6323)

LAKELAND MENTAL HEALTH CENTER

1010 32nd Ave S (56560-5001)
PHONE..................218 233-7524
FAX: 218 233-8627
Jane Speich, *Office Mgr*
Clair Prody, *Branch Mgr*
R D Staton, *Psychiatry*
Paul Michaels, *Psychiatry*
Amador Dizon, *Psychiatry*
EMP: 59
SALES (est): 1MM-4.9MM **Privately Held**
SIC: 8093 Outpatient mental health clinic
PA: Lakeland Mental Health Center
    21081 County Highway 1
    Fergus Falls MN 56537
    218 736-6987

(G-6324)

LAKES & PRAIRIES COMMUNITY

715 11th St N Ste 402 (56560-2071)
PHONE..................218 299-7000
Joe Pederson, *President*
Sherrie Roerick, *CFO*
Danny Miles, *Human Res Dir*
Ken Fredette, *Manager*
Michelle Skoblik, *Manager*
EMP: 50 EST: 1965
SQ FT: 23,000 **Privately Held**
WEB: www.lakesandprairies.net
SIC: 8399 Community action agency

(G-6325)

LAND O'LAKES INC

2103 5th Ave N (56560-2403)
PHONE..................218 233-8609
FAX: 218 233-0240
Charlie Stine, *Sales/Mktg Mgr*
EMP: 30
SALES (est): 10MM-24.9MM **Privately Held**
WEB: www.landolakes.com
SIC: 5143 Wholesales fresh dairy products

(G-6326)

MAC'S INC (PA)

5970 50th Ave S (56560-6011)
PO Box 1118 (56561-1118)
PHONE..................218 233-4600
FAX: 218 233-3363
Chuck McWethy, *President*
Mike McWethy, *Principal*
Marvin Faul, *Corp Secy*
Mary McWethy, *Vice Pres*
Kevin L Campbell, *Accountant*
EMP: 25 EST: 1932
SQ FT: 72,000
SALES (corp-wide): 13.88M **Privately Held**
SIC: 5072 Hardware store; wholesales hardware

(G-6327)

MAGNUM ELECTRIC INC

1810 23rd St S (56560-3824)
PHONE..................218 236-8753
FAX: 218 236-8764
Richard Beaton, *President*
Tammy Junk, *Business Mgr*
Tom Heng, *VP Engrg*
Collette Thoemke, *Office Mgr*
EMP: 26 EST: 1989
SQ FT: 6,000
SALES (est): 1MM-4.9MM **Privately Held**
SIC: 1731 Electrical contractor

(G-6328)

MOOREHEAD YOUTH HOCKEY ASSN

707 SE Main Ave (56560-3898)
PHONE..................218 233-5021
FAX: 218 233-4504
Clay Detrich, *President*
Lori Borgen, *Member*
Tim Czichotzki, *Member*
Joyce Hajostek, *Corp Secy*
Kathy Redfeild, *Corp Secy*
EMP: 25 EST: 1998
SALES (est): 1MM-4.9MM **Privately Held**
WEB: www.moorheadyouthhockey.com
SIC: 7999 Provides jockey instruction school

(G-6329)

MOORHEAD COUNTRY CLUB INC

2101 N River Dr (56560-1445)
PO Box 98 (56561-0098)
PHONE..................218 236-0100
FAX: 218 233-8095
Brad Holm, *President*
Larry Murphy, *Manager*
Gregg Baker, *Manager*
EMP: 45 EST: 1937
SQ FT: 8,000
SALES (est): 1MM-4.9MM **Privately Held**
WEB: www.moorheadcountryclub.com
SIC: 7997 Membership golf club; bar; full service American restaurant

(G-6330)

MOORHEAD ELECTRIC INC (DH)

3030 24th Ave S (56560-5933)
PHONE..................218 284-1963
Shane Waslaski, *President*
Doug Kjellerup, *Corp Secy*
John Erickson, *Corp Secy*
George A Koeck, *Vice Pres*
Kevin G Moug, *Vice Pres*
EMP: 40 EST: 1967
SALES (corp-wide): 1.03B **Privately Held**
SIC: 1731 General electrical contractor; telephone equipment installation
HQ: Aevenia Inc
    3030 24th Ave S
    Moorhead MN 56560
    218 284-9500

(G-6331)

MOORHEAD HOSPITALITY LP

Also Called: Courtyard By Marriott
1080 28th Ave S (56560-4406)
PHONE..................218 284-1000
FAX: 218 284-1200
Paul Hegg, *Partner*
Jennifer Seifert-Brenna, *General Mgr*
John Warwicks, *Supervisor*
EMP: 80 EST: 2000
SALES (est): 1MM-4.9MM **Privately Held**
SIC: 7011 Traveler accommodations

(G-6332)

PC HOTELS LLC

Also Called: Americ Inn Lodge & Suites
600 30th Ave S (56560-4924)
PHONE..................218 233-6171
FAX: 218 233-0945
Paul Cronen, *Member*
Kari Anderson, *Sales Mgr*
Barb Dahme, *Manager*
Mike Adams, *Manager*
EMP: 99 EST: 2005
SALES (est): 5MM-9.9MM **Privately Held**
SIC: 7011 Hotel

(G-6333)

PLAINS CONSTRUCTION & DEVPT

3101 S Frontage Rd # 101 (56560-2545)
PHONE..................218 284-0424
Michael Skatvold, *President*
Allan Willson, *Project Mgr*
Andrew M Skatvold, *CFO*
Julie Giannonttti, *Accountant*
EMP: 150 EST: 2004
SALES (est): 25MM-49.9MM **Privately Held**
SIC: 1542 Commercial & office building contractor

(G-6334)

RDO CONSTRUCTION EQUIPMENT CO

2900 SE Main Ave (56560-5465)
PHONE..................218 282-8440
John Hastings, *Branch Mgr*
EMP: 25
SALES (est): 10MM-24.9MM **Privately Held**
SIC: 5082 5084 Wholesales contractor's materials; manufactures construction machinery; wholesales materials handling equipment
HQ: Rdo Construction Equipment Co
    2829 University Dr S
    Fargo ND 58103
    701 223-5798

(G-6335)

RED RIVER BASIN COMMISSION

119 5th St S Ste 209 (56560-9998)
PO Box 66 (56561-0066)
PHONE..................218 291-0422
Bruce Furness, *Chairman*
Jon Evert, *Treasurer*
Janeen Stenso, *Technology Dir*
EMP: 46 EST: 1996
SALES (est): 5MM-9.9MM **Privately Held**
SIC: 4941 Water supply services

(G-6336)

RED RIVER ELECTRIC INC

2323 16th Ave S Ste 105 (56560-3803)
PHONE..................218 236-0502
FAX: 218 233-3483
Clark Bernard, *CEO*
Mark Moderow, *President*
Tom Moltzan, *Vice Pres*
Joey Johnson, *Vice Pres*
Anne Johnson, *Treasurer*
EMP: 40 EST: 1977
SQ FT: 10,000
SALES (est): 1MM-4.9MM **Privately Held**
WEB: www.redriverelectric.com
SIC: 1731 Electrical contractor

(G-6337)

RED RIVER TRAILS INC

4838 Highway 75 S (56560-7405)
PO Box 474 (56561-0474)
PHONE..................218 236-0300
FAX: 218 236-1445
Greg Nord, *President*
Rodland Atwood, *CTO*
EMP: 50 EST: 1955
SQ FT: 10,000
SALES (est): 1MM-4.9MM **Privately Held**
WEB: www.redrivertrails.com
SIC: 4142 4131 4151 Long-distance bus charter service; school bus service; intercity bus line

(G-6338)

RICHARDS TRANSPORTATION SVC

2139 100th Ave N (56560-7242)
PHONE..................218 233-3404
FAX: 218 233-5769
Mark Richards, *President*
Jay Richards, *Treasurer*
EMP: 40 EST: 1960
SQ FT: 7,000
SALES (est): 1MM-4.9MM **Privately Held**
SIC: 4142 7538 Long-distance bus charter service; general automotive repair services

(G-6339)

RICK ELECTRIC INC

3010 24th Ave S (56560-5933)
PO Box 159 (56561-0159)
PHONE..................218 233-6194
FAX: 218 233-7798
Greg Rick, *President*
Dennis Rick, *Vice Pres*
EMP: 30 EST: 1964
SQ FT: 6,400
SALES (est): 1MM-4.9MM **Privately Held**
WEB: www.rickelectric.com
SIC: 1731 Electrical contractor

(G-6340)

RIGELS INC

609 Main Ave (56560-2750)
PO Box 534 (56561-0534)
PHONE..................218 233-6104
FAX: 218 236-7718
Chuck Matthees, *President*
Marjorie Aakre, *Corp Secy*
Robert Matthees, *Vice Pres*
EMP: 26 EST: 1945
SQ FT: 9,500
SALES (est): 1MM-4.9MM **Privately Held**
WEB: www.rigels.com
SIC: 7699 Retails household appliances; household appliance repair service

(G-6341)

SALAD MAKERS INC

1820 1st Ave N (56560-2306)
PHONE..................218 236-4959
FAX: 218 232-7031
Tom Jacobson, *President*
EMP: 30 EST: 1981 **Privately Held**
SIC: 0139 0182 5148 Alfalfa farm; bean sprout farming; wholesales fresh vegetables

(G-6342)

STATE BANK & TRUST

1333 8th St S (56560-3604)
PHONE..................218 233-3107
FAX: 218 233-3187
Michael Solberg, *Vice Pres*
Neil Qualey, *Manager*
Sharon Kemp, *Manager*
EMP: 56
SALES (est): 10MM-24.9MM **Privately Held**
SIC: 6021 National commercial bank
HQ: State Bank & Trust
    3100 13th Ave S
    Fargo ND 58103
    701 298-1500

(G-6343)

TRANSYSTEMS LLC

2486 11th St N (56560-1451)
PHONE..................218 233-8121
Alan Buchhloz, *Manager*
EMP: 50
SALES (est): 1MM-4.9MM **Privately Held**
SIC: 4212 Local trucking without storage services
PA: Transystems LLC
    1901 Benefis Ct
    Great Falls MT 59405
    406 727-7500

(G-6344)

TRAVELODGE & SUITE

3027 S Frontage Rd (56560-2593)
PO Box 918 (56561-0918)
PHONE..................218 233-5333
FAX: 218 233-5605
Roger Erickson, *Partner*
John Isaacson, *General Mgr*
EMP: 25 EST: 1999
SALES (est): 1MM-4.9MM **Privately Held**
SIC: 7011 Traveler accommodations

(G-6345)

VAL-ED JOINT VENTURE, LLP

Also Called: 702 COMMUNICATIONS
702 Main Ave (56560-2752)
PHONE..................218 284-5702
FAX: 218 284-3297
Jim Walter, *Member*
Jeff Nibbe, *Facilities Mgr*
Brian Crommett, *Engineer*
Jennifer Rice, *Finance*
Kenny Budlist, *Manager*

EMP: 43 **EST:** 1989
SQ FT: 10,000 **Privately Held**
WEB: www.702com.net
SIC: 4813 7375 Local telephone communications services; information retrieval services

(G-6346)
VINCENT HAUGEN
Also Called: Haugen Masonry Contractors
1702 30th Ave S (56560-5265)
PO Box 546 (56561-0546)
PHONE.............................218 233-3776
Vincent Haugen, *Owner*
EMP: 35 **EST:** 1957
SALES (est): 1MM-4.9MM **Privately Held**
SIC: 1741 Masonry & stonework contractor

(G-6347)
WELLS FARGO MINNESOTA WEST (HQ)
730 Center Ave Lbby LBBY (56560-1949)
PO Box 340 (56561-0340)
PHONE.............................218 233-6183
Pete Fullerton, *President*
Paul Kemper, *Corp Secy*
Jill Pagel, *Manager*
Bonnie Whaley, *Manager*
James Deibert, *Officer*
EMP: 77 **EST:** 1929
SALES (corp-wide): 98.63B **Publicly Held**
SIC: 6021 National commercial bank
PA: Wells Fargo & Co
420 Montgomery St
San Francisco CA 94104
866 878-5865

(G-6348)
YEATER HENNINGS RUFF ARCHITECT
420 Main Ave (56560-2641)
PHONE.............................218 233-4422
Dale Ruff, *Partner*
Margaret K Follingstad, *Principal*
Mark D Lundberg, *Principal*
Julie N Rokke, *Principal*
Norma Tessmer, *Accounting Dir*
EMP: 35 **Privately Held**
SIC: 8731 Commercial physical research laboratory

MOOSE LAKE
Carlton County

(G-6349)
DEPARTMENT OF CORRECTIONS MN
Also Called: Minnesota Correction Facility
1000 Lakeshore Dr (55767-9449)
PO Box 1000 (55767-1000)
PHONE.............................218 485-5000
FAX: 218 485-5010
Douglas Probst, *Buyer*
Sandy O'Hara, *Human Res Dir*
John Wolfe, *Supervisor*
James Benson, *Warden*
Terry Carlson, *Warden*
EMP: 395
SALES (est): 25MM-49.9MM **Privately Held**
WEB: www.minncor.com
SIC: 8011 Clinic operated by physicians; correctional institution; state government correctional institution
DH: Department of Corrections MN
1450 Energy Park Dr # 200
Saint Paul MN 55108
651 361-7200

(G-6350)
GATEWAY FAMILY HEALTH CLINIC
4570 County Hwy 61 (55767)
PHONE.............................218 485-4491
FAX: 218 485-4724
Daniel Benzie, *Partner*
Barbara J Bonkoski MD, *Med Doctor*
Dania A Kamp MD, *Med Doctor*
Archived News, *Med Doctor*
Christophe N Thiesse MD, *Med Doctor*
EMP: 74 **EST:** 1991
SALES (est): 5MM-9.9MM **Privately Held**
WEB: www.gatewayclinic.com
SIC: 8011 Physicians' office & clinic

(G-6351)
LAKE STATE FEDERAL CREDIT (PA)
301 Elm Ave (55767)
PO Box 330 (55767-0330)
PHONE.............................218 485-4444
Thomas Olson, *President*
Kevin Thomas, *Senior VP*
Trevor Wills, *VP Opers*
Bob Hylland, *Branch Mgr*
Laly Larson, *Info Tech Mgr*
EMP: 80 **EST:** 1939
SQ FT: 6,500
SALES (corp-wide): 10.14M **Privately Held**
SIC: 6061 Federally chartered credit union

(G-6352)
MERCY HOSPITAL HEALTH CARE CTR
710 S Kenwood Ave (55767-9405)
PHONE.............................218 485-4481
FAX: 218 485-8800
William R Storck, *COO*
Gregg Chartrand, *Finance*
Kathy Brown, *Manager*
Mavis Hartman, *Manager*
Christine Shanda, *Manager*
EMP: 400 **EST:** 1963
SALES (est): 10MM-24.9MM **Privately Held**
WEB: www.mercymooselake.org
SIC: 8051 8062 Skilled nursing care facility; medical hospital

MORA
Kanabec County

(G-6353)
CITY OF MORA
Also Called: Mora Village Garage
461W Maple Ave E (55051-1313)
PHONE.............................320 679-1770
Joel Dyne, *Manager*
EMP: 35
SALES (est): 1MM-4.9MM **Privately Held**
WEB: www.cityofmora.com
SIC: 7538 7521 General automotive repair services; mayors' office; vehicle parking lot or garage
PA: City of Mora
101 Lake St S
Mora MN 55051
320 679-1511

(G-6354)
COBORN'S INC
710 Frankie Ln (55051-1914)
PHONE.............................320 679-4003
FAX: 320 679-1440
Tony Clairs, *Manager*
Shane Theisen, *Manager*
Dean Randt, *Manager*
Dean Rant, *Manager*
EMP: 150
SALES (est): 10MM-24.9MM **Privately Held**
WEB: www.cobornsinc.com
SIC: 7841 Retail chain grocery store; florist; pharmacy & drug store; video tape & disc rental
PA: Coborn's Inc
1445 Highway 23 E Bldg A
Saint Cloud MN 56304
320 252-4222

(G-6355)
COUNTY OF KANABEC
18 Vine St N Ste 261A (55051-1351)
PHONE.............................320 679-6430
Denise Cooper, *Treasurer*
Wendy Thompson, *Manager*
EMP: 40
SALES (est): 1MM-4.9MM **Privately Held**
WEB: www.kanabeccounty.com
SIC: 8322 Individual & family social services; county supervisors' & executives' office
PA: County of Kanabec
18 Vine St N Ste 181
Mora MN 55051
320 679-6440

(G-6356)
CREATIVE MARKETING CONCEPTS
2775 Jade St (55051-6240)
PHONE.............................320 679-4105
FAX: 320 679-3349
Fred Carlson, *CEO*
Josh Carlson, *President*
Lynell Carlson, *Corp Secy*
Rose Dunn, *Vice Pres*
Rhonda Becker, *Prdtn Mgr*
▲ **EMP:** 50 **EST:** 1973
SQ FT: 25,000
SALES (est): 5MM-9.9MM **Privately Held**
SIC: 7389 Commercial lithographic printing; display lettering services

(G-6357)
EAST CENTRAL VETERINARY
2004 Mahogany St (55051-7107)
PHONE.............................320 679-4197
FAX: 320 679-4439
Mary Olson, *President*
EMP: 38 **EST:** 1975 **Privately Held**
SIC: 0741 0742 Livestock veterinarian; veterinarian services

(G-6358)
FEDERATED COOP INC
206 Union St S (55051-1544)
PHONE.............................320 679-2682
FAX: 320 679-5797
Tim Kavanaugh, *President*
Byron Anderson, *Manager*
Jim Gutzwiller, *Manager*
EMP: 35 **EST:** 1927
SQ FT: 10,000
SALES (est): 50MM-99.9MM **Privately Held**
SIC: 5172 5191 Wholesales petroleum products; wholesales agricultural fertilizer; wholesales feed; retail gasoline filling station; manufactures fertilizers; wholesales farm supplies; fuel oil dealer; grocery store

(G-6359)
GORHAM OIEN MECHANICAL INC
841 Forest Ave E (55051-1627)
PHONE.............................320 679-1612
Jon Gorham, *President*
Julie Freeman, *Corp Secy*
Jeffery Gorham, *Vice Pres*
Patrick Gorham, *Vice Pres*
Dan Potter, *Project Mgr*
EMP: 60 **EST:** 1962
SQ FT: 18,000
SALES (est): 5MM-9.9MM **Privately Held**
WEB: www.gorhamoien.com
SIC: 1711 Plumbing service; warm air heating & air conditioning contractor; fabricates pipe sections from purchased pipe

(G-6360)
GREATER MINNESOTA CREDIT UNION
112 Lake St S (55051-1525)
PHONE.............................320 679-8100
FAX: 320 679-3882
Steve Ahlness, *President*
Robert Oehrelin, *Chairman*
Bob Oehrelin, *Corp Secy*
Randy Willert, *Vice Pres*
Rox A Carlson, *CFO*
EMP: 28 **EST:** 1935
SQ FT: 18,000
SALES (est): 5MM-9.9MM **Privately Held**
WEB: www.gmcu.com
SIC: 6062 State credit unions

(G-6361)
INDUSTRIES INC (PA)
500 Walnut St S (55051-1936)
PHONE.............................320 679-2354
Julie L Kunde, *Manager*
Lee Morrison, *Manager*
Joyce Spicer, *Director*
Kris M Nally, *Director*
Pauline Bohachek, *Director*
EMP: 30 **EST:** 1967
SQ FT: 16,000
SALES (corp-wide): 2.04M **Privately Held**
WEB: www.industriesinc.org
SIC: 8331 Skill training center

(G-6362)
KANABEC COUNTY HOSPITAL
301 Highway 65 S (55051-1899)
PHONE.............................320 679-1212
FAX: 320 225-3320
Randy Ulseth, *CEO*
Susan Belford, *Business Mgr*
Chris Kimbler, *COO*
Bill Kellogg, *Facilities Mgr*
Melody Hendrickson, *Facilities Mgr*
EMP: 265 **EST:** 1945
SQ FT: 150,000
SALES (est): 10MM-24.9MM **Privately Held**
WEB: www.kanabechospital.org
SIC: 8062 Medical hospital

(G-6363)
KNIFE LAKE CONCRETE INC
2026 Rowland Rd (55051-7119)
PHONE.............................320 679-4141
FAX: 320 679-3927
Doug Yankowiak, *President*
Kevin Olson, *Vice Pres*
EMP: 27 **EST:** 1977
SALES (est): 1MM-4.9MM **Privately Held**
SIC: 1771 1741 Concrete contractor; masonry & stonework contractor

(G-6364)
KNIGHTS OF COLUMBUS INC
Also Called: Father Herman Schmtz Cncl 5078
26204 Nelsons Rd (55051-6547)
PHONE.............................320 679-4093
Arlon Haupert, *Chairman*
Elmer Davis, *Corp Secy*
EMP: 90 **EST:** 2003 **Privately Held**
SIC: 8641 Fraternal association

(G-6365)
LAKES & PINES COMMUNITY ACTION
1700 Maple Ave E (55051-1227)
PHONE.............................320 679-1800
FAX: 320 679-4139
Debbie Nystrom, *Corp Secy*
Robert Weness, *Finance*
Harold Frerich, *Manager*
Kelly Manley, *Technology Dir*
Robert Benes, *Exec Dir*
EMP: 50 **EST:** 1965
SQ FT: 15,000 **Privately Held**
WEB: www.lakesandpines.org
SIC: 8399 8322 Community action agency; individual & family social services

(G-6366)
LONG TERM CARE ASSOCIATES INC
Also Called: Villa Health Care Center
110 7th St N (55051-1110)
PHONE.............................320 679-1411
FAX: 320 679-5257
Doris Monson, *VP Finance*
Jack L'Heureux, *Administrator*
EMP: 80 **EST:** 1969
SQ FT: 29,915
SALES (est): 1MM-4.9MM **Privately Held**
SIC: 8051 Skilled nursing care facility

(G-6367)
PEOPLES NATIONAL BANK OF MORA
45 Union St N (55051-1327)
PO Box 88 (55051-0088)
PHONE.............................320 679-3100
FAX: 320 679-3109
Doyle Jelsing, *CEO*
Charles E Ptrson, *Vice Chairman*
Kevin Nikodym, *Vice Pres*
David Olson, *CFO*
EMP: 27 **EST:** 1963
SALES (est): 5MM-9.9MM **Privately Held**
WEB: www.pnbmora.com
SIC: 6021 National commercial bank

(G-6368)
R J MECHANICAL INC
510 Highway 65 S (55051-1937)
PO Box 373 (55051-0373)
PHONE.............................320 679-0602
FAX: 320 679-0356
Raymond Ludowese, *President*

(PA)=Parent Co (HQ)=Headquarters (DH)=Div Headquarters
✿ = New business established in last 2 years

2011 Harris Minnesota
Services Directory

© Harris InfoSource 1-866-281-6415
279

Janet Ludowes, *Corp Secy*
Craig Virnig, *Vice Pres*
Sherry Haggberg, *Office Mgr*
EMP: 30 **EST:** 1996
SQ FT: 4,000
SALES (est): 1MM-4.9MM **Privately Held**
SIC: 1711 Plumbing service; heating & air conditioning contractor

MORRIS
Stevens County

(G-6369)
ALLINA HEALTH SYSTEM
Also Called: Stevens Community Medical Ctr
400 E 1st St (56267-1408)
PO Box 660 (56267-0660)
PHONE..............................320 589-1313
John Reu, *Manager*
EMP: 350
SALES (est): 10MM-24.9MM **Privately Held**
WEB: www.allina.com
SIC: 8093 Outpatient mental health clinic
PA: Allina Health System
2925 Chicago Ave
Minneapolis MN 55407
612 775-5000

(G-6370)
BREMER FINANCIAL CORP
701 Atlantic Ave (56267-1137)
PHONE..............................320 589-1026
Jeanne Halbe, *Manager*
EMP: 25
SALES (est): 10MM-24.9MM **Privately Held**
SIC: 6399 Provides deposit insurance
HQ: Bremer Financial Corp
445 Minnesota St Ste 2000
Saint Paul MN 55101
651 227-7621

(G-6371)
DENCO II LLC
227 County Road 22 (56267-4691)
PHONE..............................320 589-2931
Mick Miller, *Member*
EMP: 28
SALES (est): 1MM-4.9MM **Privately Held**
SIC: 8999 Miscellaneous services

(G-6372)
DIVINE HOUSE INC
618 Pacific Ave (56267-1943)
PHONE..............................320 589-3652
FAX: 320 589-1808
Debra Schriver, *President*
Nancy Hoy, *Human Res Dir*
Sue Loose, *Director*
Heidi Olsen, *Director*
EMP: 80
SALES (est): 1MM-4.9MM **Privately Held**
SIC: 8322 Individual & family social services
PA: Divine House Inc
328 5th St SW Ste 5
Willmar MN 56201
320 231-2738

(G-6373)
MEADOW STAR DAIRY, LLP ✪
26406 470th Ave (56267-5370)
PHONE..............................320 392-5609
Brady Janzen, *Partner*
EMP: 40 **EST:** 2008 **Privately Held**
SIC: 0241 Dairy farming

(G-6374)
PRAIRIE COMMUNITY SERVICES
Also Called: Hoffman House
605 W 6th St (56267-2012)
PHONE..............................320 589-2057
Judy Richard, *Administrator*
Cynthia Johnson, *Exec Dir*
EMP: 25
SALES (est): 1MM-4.9MM **Privately Held**
SIC: 8361 8052 Home for the mentally handicapped; intermediate care facility
HQ: Prairie Community Services
801 Nevada Ave Ste 100
Morris MN 56267
320 589-3077

(G-6375)
PRAIRIE MEDICAL
Also Called: West Central Internal Medicine
24 E 7th St (56267-1312)
PO Box 410 (56267-0410)
PHONE..............................320 589-4008
FAX: 320 589-4227
John Stock, *Owner*
Lori Berg, *Office Mgr*
Ramona Maanum, *Manager*
George Fortier IV, *Surgeon*
Michelle Blair, *Asst Office Mgr*
EMP: 30
SALES (est): 1MM-4.9MM **Privately Held**
WEB: www.sfhs.org
SIC: 8011 Physicians' office & clinic; internal medicine physician or surgeon

(G-6376)
RILEY BROS CONSTRUCTION INC
46369 208th St (56267-4684)
PO Box 535 (56267-0535)
PHONE..............................320 589-2500
Joseph E Riley, *President*
Joe Figel, *Opers Mgr*
John Riley, *Treasurer*
Nancy Henrichs, *Accountant*
Craig Smithnitzler, *Manager*
EMP: 50 **EST:** 1973
SQ FT: 8,000
SALES (est): 5MM-9.9MM **Privately Held**
WEB: www.rileybros.com
SIC: 1611 General highway & street construction service; highway & street paving contractor

(G-6377)
RIVERVIEW DAIRY INC
26402 470th Ave (56267-5370)
PHONE..............................320 392-5609
Gary Fehr, *President*
Brady Janzen, *General Ptnr*
Kurt Domnick, *CFO*
Lloyd Fehr, *Shareholder*
EMP: 35 **EST:** 1939 **Privately Held**
SIC: 0241 Dairy farming

(G-6378)
ST FRANCIS HEALTH SERVICES OF (PA)
801 Nevada Ave Ste 100 (56267-1874)
PHONE..............................320 589-2004
Luverne Hoffman, *President*
Evonne Kupke, *Corp Secy*
Carol Raw, *Vice Pres*
Sherry Wagner, *CFO*
Leah Nelson, *Human Res Dir*
EMP: 688 **EST:** 1984
SQ FT: 12,000
SALES (corp-wide): 685.40M **Privately Held**
SIC: 8741 Hospital management services; nursing & personal care facility management services

(G-6379)
STEVENS COMMUNITY MEDICAL CTR
400 E 1st St (56267-1408)
PO Box 660 (56267-0660)
PHONE..............................320 589-1313
John Rau, *President*
Karla Larson, *Human Resources*
Kathy Werk, *Manager*
Kim H Tatsumi, *Manager*
Chandel C Dietz, *Phys Thrpy Dir*
EMP: 250 **EST:** 1952
SQ FT: 55,000
SALES (est): 10MM-24.9MM **Privately Held**
WEB: www.scmcmorris.com
SIC: 8062 8011 8093 Medical hospital; primary care medical clinic; outpatient substance abuse clinic; outpatient mental health clinic; specialty outpatient clinic

(G-6380)
WEST WIND VILLAGE
1001 Scotts Ave (56267-1763)
PHONE..............................320 589-1133
FAX: 320 589-3005
Lu V Hoffman, *President*
Richard Blanchard, *Administrator*
Jodi Hagen, *Director*
EMP: 155 **EST:** 1969
SQ FT: 57,000
SALES (est): 5MM-9.9MM **Privately Held**
WEB: www.wwv.sfhs.org
SIC: 8051 8082 Skilled nursing care facility; home health care services

MORTON
Redwood County

(G-6381)
IYANKA DAKOTA COACHES INC
39411 County Highway 24 (56270-1270)
PHONE..............................507 644-3380
FAX: 507 644-3504
Robert Larsen, *President*
Kathy Linsmeyer, *Corp Secy*
EMP: 40 **EST:** 1991
SALES (est): 1MM-4.9MM **Privately Held**
SIC: 4725 Tour operator

MORTON
Renville County

(G-6382)
ALTIMATE MEDICAL INC
262 W First St (56270)
PO Box 180 (56270-0180)
PHONE..............................507 697-6393
FAX: 507 697-6900
Alan Tholkes, *President*
Todd Tholkes, *Vice Pres*
Chris Yessian, *Vice Pres*
Gabriel Routh, *Engineering*
Patty Rohne, *Manager*
EMP: 40 **EST:** 1986
SQ FT: 30,000
SALES (est): 5MM-9.9MM **Publicly Held**
WEB: www.easystand.com
SIC: 5047 Manufactures surgical appliances & supplies; manufactures orthopedic appliances; wholesales medical equipment & supplies
PA: Invacare Corp
1 Invacare Way
Elyria OH 44035
440 329-6000

MOTLEY
Morrison County

(G-6383)
CAMP SHAMINEAU OF THE
Also Called: Shamineau Ministris
2345 Ridge Rd (56466)
PO Box 244 (56466-0244)
PHONE..............................218 575-2240
FAX: 218 575-2371
Greg Loomis, *Chairman*
Herb Bloomquist, *Director*
Jeff Adamson, *Executive*
EMP: 30 **EST:** 1958
SQ FT: 3,200
SALES (est): 1MM-4.9MM **Privately Held**
WEB: www.shamineau.org
SIC: 7032 Bible camp

MOUND
Hennepin County

(G-6384)
CHURCH OF OUR LADY OF THE LAKE
Also Called: Our Lady of Lk Elementary Schl
2385 Commerce Blvd (55364-1427)
PHONE..............................952 472-1284
FAX: 952 472-1216
Teresa Boser, *Corp Secy*
Stan Mader, *Pastor*
Mary Divinian, *Manager*
James Gannon, *Exec Dir*
Katie Buhl, *Director*
EMP: 30 **EST:** 1909 **Privately Held**
SIC: 8322 Provides Catholic church services; private denominational school; multi-services center; convent

(G-6385)
CITIZENS TELECOMMUNICATIONS CO
2378 Wilshire Blvd (55364-1652)
PHONE..............................952 491-5576
Mary A Wilderotter, *CEO*
Livingston E Ross, *President*
Kenneth L Cohen, *President*
EMP: 30 **EST:** 1999 **Publicly Held**
WEB: www.czn.net
SIC: 4813 Wired telecommunications carrier & service
PA: Frontier Communications Corp
3 High Ridge Park
Stamford CT 06905
203 614-5600

(G-6386)
CONCEPT LANDSCAPING INC
3153 Priest Ln (55364-8563)
PHONE..............................952 472-4118
James H Smith, *President*
EMP: 40 **EST:** 1992 **Privately Held**
SIC: 0781 0782 1741 Landscape services; retaining wall construction; landscaping services

(G-6387)
DAVE TAYLOR CONSTRUCTON INC
5991 Ridgewood Rd (55364-8570)
PHONE..............................952 472-1342
Dave Taylor, *President*
Carmen M Taylor, *Vice Pres*
EMP: 28 **EST:** 1977
SALES (est): 5MM-9.9MM **Privately Held**
SIC: 1521 Single-family home general remodeling service

(G-6388)
INFINITI MARKETING INC
Also Called: Infinity Pdts Design Engrg Ctr
5400 Shoreline Dr (55364-1698)
PHONE..............................612 789-2025
Craig Smith, *President*
Dick Erickson, *CFO*
EMP: 30 **EST:** 1992
SQ FT: 24,000
SALES (est): 10MM-24.9MM **Privately Held**
SIC: 5013 5162 7532 Wholesales new motor vehicle parts & supplies; van conversions; wholesales plastic materials

MOUNDS VIEW
Ramsey County

(G-6389)
MIDWEST MEDICAL SERVICES INC
8400 Coral Sea St NE S (55112-4398)
PHONE..............................763 717-7676
Larry Lindberg, *CEO*
Steve Peterson, *President*
EMP: 100 **EST:** 1995
SQ FT: 31,000
SALES (est): 10MM-24.9MM **Privately Held**
SIC: 5047 Retails hospital equipment & supplies; wholesales medical equipment & supplies

(G-6390)
MIDWEST MOTOR EXPRESS INC
2169 Mustang Dr (55112-1555)
PHONE..............................763 784-0650
Joe Greenstein, *Branch Mgr*
EMP: 65
SALES (est): 5MM-9.9MM **Privately Held**
WEB: www.mmeinc.com
SIC: 4213 Contract haulers
PA: Midwest Motor Express Inc
5015 E Main Ave
Bismarck ND 58501
701 223-1880

(G-6391)
VITRAN EXPRESS INC
2160 Mustang Dr (55112-1553)
PHONE..............................763 913-3450
FAX: 763 913-3456
Mike Drew, *Manager*

Mike Grew, *Manager*
EMP: 150
SALES (est): 5MM-9.9MM **Privately Held**
WEB: www.vitran.com
SIC: 4231 Freight trucking terminal

MOUNTAIN IRON
Saint Louis County

(G-6392)
GENERAL ELECTRIC CO
5521 Mineral Ave (55768)
PO Box 595 (55768-0595)
PHONE 218 749-6100
FAX: 218 749-6100
Steve Ross, *Finance*
EMP: 35
SALES (est): 1MM-4.9MM **Publicly Held**
WEB: www.ge.com
SIC: 7629 7694 7699 Machine shop,
jobbing & repair services; armature
repairing & rewinding service; electrical
equipment repair service; industrial
machinery repair & maintenance services
PA: General Electric Co
3135 Easton Tpke
Fairfield CT 06828
203 373-2211

(G-6393)
LAKE COUNTRY POWER
8535 Park Ridge Dr (55768-2059)
PHONE 218 741-8137
Craig Nordling, *Branch Mgr*
EMP: 50
SALES (est): 25MM-49.9MM **Privately Held**
WEB: www.lakecountrypower.coop
SIC: 4911 Electric services

(G-6394)
UNITED STATES STEEL CORP
Also Called: U S Steel
County Rd 102 (55768)
PO Box 417 (55768-0417)
PHONE 218 749-7200
Shaun Youso, *Area Mgr*
Rick Lanari, *Prdtn Mgr*
Frank Lucchino, *Finance Mgr*
Gary Cooper, *Finance Mgr*
Seth Schofield, *Finance Mgr*
EMP: 170
SALES (est): 25MM-49.9MM **Publicly Held**
WEB: www.uss.com
SIC: 1011 Open pit iron ore mining
PA: United States Steel Corp
600 Grant St
Pittsburgh PA 15219
412 433-1121

MOUNTAIN LAKE
Cottonwood County

(G-6395)
BARGEN INC
606 County Road 1 (56159-1649)
PHONE 507 427-2924
Bradley Bargen, *President*
James L Heltemes Jr, *Vice Pres*
Sherri Bargen, *Treasurer*
EST: 1981
SQ FT: 9,600 **Privately Held**
WEB: www.bargeninc.com
SIC: 1799 1761 Coating, caulking &
weather, water & fireproofing contractor;
roofing & gutter work contractor; parking lot
maintenance service

(G-6396)
EVANGELICAL LUTHERAN
GOOD
Also Called: Eventide Good Samaritan Center
810 3rd Ave (56159-1572)
PHONE 507 427-3221
EMP: 30
SALES (est): 1MM-4.9MM **Privately Held**
WEB: www.good-sam.com
SIC: 8059 Nursing home
PA: Evangelical Lutheran Good
4800 W 57th St
Sioux Falls SD 57108
605 362-3100

(G-6397)
EVANGELICAL LUTHERAN
GOOD
Also Called: Mountain Lk Good Samaritan Vlg
745 Basinger Memorial Dr (56159-1312)
PHONE 507 427-2464
FAX: 507 427-3036
Reva Hulzebos, *Human Resources*
D Bednarek, *Manager*
Misty Karschnik, *Manager*
Timothy Swoboda, *Administrator*
Tim Fwoboda, *Systems Dir*
EMP: 130
SALES (est): 5MM-9.9MM **Privately Held**
WEB: www.good-sam.com
SIC: 8059 8051 Nursing home; skilled
nursing care facility
PA: Evangelical Lutheran Good
4800 W 57th St
Sioux Falls SD 57108
605 362-3100

(G-6398)
EVENTIDE HOME ASSOCIATION
INC
810 3rd Ave (56159-1577)
PHONE 507 427-3221
FAX: 507 427-2654
Tim Swoboda, *CEO*
Tim Sabota, *Manager*
Tim Fwoboda, *Administrator*
Steven Harder, *Director*
EMP: 43 **EST:** 1930
SQ FT: 22,000
SALES (est): 1MM-4.9MM **Privately Held**
SIC: 8059 Nursing home

(G-6399)
MILK SPECIALTIES CO
2204 3rd Ave (56159-1468)
PO Box 578 (56159-0578)
PHONE 507 427-3222
FAX: 507 427-2860
Rick Hagder, *Manager*
Narcello Dermea, *Manager*
EMP: 60
SALES (est): 25MM-49.9MM **Privately Held**
SIC: 5143 Wholesales milk

MURDOCK
Swift County

(G-6400)
DOOLEY'S PETROLEUM INC
304 Main Ave (56271)
PO Box 100 (56271-0100)
PHONE 320 875-2641
FAX: 320 875-2295
Randall Dooley, *President*
Thomas Dooley, *Corp Secy*
Tammy Dooley, *Accountant*
EMP: 60 **EST:** 1959
SQ FT: 24,000
SALES (est): 100MM-499.9MM **Privately
Held**
SIC: 5171 Wholesales petroleum bulk
stations; retail gasoline filling station; retails
bottled propane gas

(G-6401)
GLACIAL PLAINS COOPERATIVE
543 Van Norman Ave (56271-8027)
PO Box 47 (56271-0047)
PHONE 320 760-5647
Thomas Traen, *Principal*
EMP: 55
SALES (est): 100MM-499.9MM **Privately
Held**
SIC: 5153 Wholesales grain & field beans

NERSTRAND
Rice County

(G-6402)
KIELMEYER CONSTRUCTION
INC
86 Main St (55053-3806)
PO Box 158 (55053-0158)
PHONE 507 334-6088
FAX: 507 334-0687
Douglas Kielmeyer, *President*
Geraldyne Kielmeyer, *Corp Secy*
Jack Kielmeyer, *Vice Pres*
EMP: 25 **EST:** 1928
SQ FT: 1,400
SALES (est): 1MM-4.9MM **Privately Held**
SIC: 1442 Construction sand & gravel
mining; sand mining; gravel mining

NETT LAKE
Saint Louis County

(G-6403)
BOIS FORTE MEDICAL CLINIC
13071 Nett Lk (55772)
PHONE 218 757-3650
Jeneal Goggleye, *Director*
EMP: 30 **EST:** 1984
SALES (est): 1MM-4.9MM **Privately Held**
SIC: 8011 Clinic operated by physicians

(G-6404)
BOIS FORTE RESERVATION
TRIBAL
5344 Lakeshore Dr (55772)
PO Box 16 (55772-0016)
PHONE 218 757-3261
Kevin Leecy, *Manager*
EMP: 40
SALES (est): 1MM-4.9MM **Privately Held**
SIC: 8322 Individual & family social services
PA: Bois Forte Reservation Tribal
5344 Lakeshore Dr
Nett Lake MN 55772
218 757-3261

NEVIS
Hubbard County

(G-6405)
PINE MANORS INC
22195 State 34 (56467-5023)
PHONE 218 732-4337
Dennis Anderson, *President*
Leonard Anderson, *Vice Pres*
Rachel Mueller, *Director*
EMP: 28 **EST:** 1969
SQ FT: 3,250
SALES (est): 1MM-4.9MM **Privately Held**
SIC: 8361 Residential rehabilitation center
with health care incidental

NEW BRIGHTON
Ramsey County

(G-6406)
APPLIED BUSINESS COMMS
213 Old Highway 8 SW (55112-7734)
PHONE 651 643-6595
FAX: 651 643-6596
Don Karel, *Member*
Steve Puckney, *Vice Pres*
John Karel, *Vice Pres*
Bert Bongard, *VP Opers*
Dave Olsen, *Controller*
EMP: 60 **EST:** 1995
SQ FT: 10,000
SALES (est): 5MM-9.9MM **Privately Held**
SIC: 1731 Electrical contractor

(G-6407)
FRATRANS INC
587 1st St SW (55112-7753)
PHONE 651 294-3944
Michael Ryan, *President*

EMP: 30 **EST:** 2003
SALES (est): 1MM-4.9MM **Privately Held**
WEB: www.fratrans.com
SIC: 4731 Railroad freight agency

(G-6408)
H BROOKS & CO
600 Lakeview Point Dr (55112-3494)
PHONE 651 635-0126
FAX: 651 676-0944
Phillip Brooks, *President*
Ray Ralston, *Corp Secy*
Scott Schaeppi, *Vice Pres*
Marilyn Sipe, *Manager*
Kelly Kjelden, *MIS Dir*
EMP: 80 **EST:** 1921
SQ FT: 110,000
SALES (est): 25MM-49.9MM **Privately Held**
WEB: www.hbrooks.com
SIC: 5148 Wholesales fresh fruits;
wholesales fresh vegetables

(G-6409)
HANK'S SPECIALTIES INC
2050 Old Highway 8 NW (55112-2308)
PO Box 120150 (55112-0013)
PHONE 651 633-5020
FAX: 651 633-8723
Randy Grachek, *President*
Rick Meissner, *General Mgr*
Bruce Grachek, *Vice Pres*
Patricia Faaberg, *Manager*
EMP: 35 **EST:** 1976
SQ FT: 110,000
SALES (est): 10MM-24.9MM **Privately Held**
WEB: www.hanksspec.com
SIC: 5023 Wholesales floor coverings

(G-6410)
HSNB LLC ✿
Also Called: Homewood Suites
1815 Old Highway 8 NW (55112-1828)
PHONE 651 631-8002
Todd Roy, *General Mgr*
Sheryl Walton, *Principal*
EMP: 40 **EST:** 2009
SALES (est): 1MM-4.9MM **Privately Held**
SIC: 7011 Traveler accommodations

(G-6411)
INNSBRUCK HEALTHCARE
CENTER
1101 Black Oak Dr (55112-8400)
PHONE 651 633-1686
FAX: 651 633-5267
Susan Ager, *CEO*
Debbie Wright, *Manager*
Beth McGarry, *Director*
Eileen Anderson, *Director*
EMP: 65 **EST:** 1965
SALES (est): 1MM-4.9MM **Privately Held**
SIC: 8052 8051 Personal care facility;
convalescent home
PA: Benedictine Health System
503 E 3rd St Ste 400
Duluth MN 55805
218 786-2370

(G-6412)
MERIDIAN BEHAVIORAL
HEALTH LLC
550 Main St Ste 230 (55112-3274)
PHONE 612 326-7600
Leary Atkins, *Member*
Jessica Sierra, *Corp Secy*
Connie Bomberger, *COO*
Rick Dunagan, *Engineering*
Paul Jurewicz, *CFO*
EST: 2006
SQ FT: 4,250 **Privately Held**
SIC: 8062 8093 Medical hospital; outpatient
mental health clinic

(G-6413)
RISDALL MARKETING GROUP
LLC
550 Main St (55112-3271)
PHONE 651 286-6700
John Risdall, *CEO*
Dale Henn, *President*
Rose McKinney, *President*
Glenna Dibrell, *Senior VP*
Eva Keiser, *Senior VP*
EMP: 80

(PA)=Parent Co (HQ)=Headquarters (DH)=Div Headquarters
✿ = New business established in last 2 years

2011 Harris Minnesota
Services Directory

© Harris InfoSource 1-866-281-6415
281

GEOGRAPHIC

EST: 1972
SQ FT: 27,000
SALES (est): 10MM-24.9MM **Privately Held**
WEB: www.risdall.com
SIC: 7311 8742 8743 Advertising agency; marketing consulting service; public relations services

NEW LONDON
Kandiyohi County

(G-6414)
EMERGENCY ENERGY SYSTEMS
6925 County Road 40 NE   (56273-9590)
PHONE...............................320 354-5380
John Edwardson, *Owner*
EMP: 25 **EST:** 1987
SALES (est): 10MM-24.9MM **Privately Held**
SIC: 4931 Electric & related services

(G-6415)
JOHN PULSIFER CONSTRUCTION INC
9338 187th Ave NE   (56273-9518)
PHONE...............................320 354-2602
John Pulsifer, *President*
Jill Pulsifer, *Vice Pres*
EMP: 35 **EST:** 2002
SALES (est): 1MM-4.9MM **Privately Held**
SIC: 1791 Structural steel erection contractor

(G-6416)
JUHL ENTERPRISES INC
Also Called: GLEN OAKS CARE CENTER
100 Glenoaks Dr   (56273-9580)
PHONE...............................320 354-2231
FAX: 320 354-2060
Larry E Juhl, *President*
Kryss Gimse, *Bookkeeper*
Saralyn Olson, *Human Res Mgr*
Barb Bendicksin, *Manager*
Louise Ciemer, *Manager*
EMP: 150 **EST:** 1993
SQ FT: 70,000
SALES (est): 5MM-9.9MM **Privately Held**
SIC: 8059 Nursing home

(G-6417)
MID-STATE TELEPHONE CO
Also Called: TDS Telecommunications
7902 Chapin Dr NE   (56273-8538)
PO Box 609   (56273-0609)
PHONE...............................320 354-7805
FAX: 320 354-7811
David A Wittwer, *President*
Ron Elson, *Vice Pres*
Jim Sandin, *Manager*
Tom Ollig, *Data Proc Dir*
EMP: 2700 **EST:** 1964 **Publicly Held**
WEB: www.teldta.com
SIC: 4813 Wired telecommunications carrier & service
PA: Telephone & Data Systems Inc
30 N Lasalle St Ste 4000
Chicago IL 60602
312 630-1900

(G-6418)
PETERSON BUS SERVICE INC
302 Oak St S   (56273-9575)
PO Box 330   (56273-0330)
PHONE...............................320 354-2414
FAX: 320 354-5544
Michael W Nelson, *General Mgr*
Duane Peterson, *Principal*
Gregory Hult, *Principal*
Bill Blonigan, *Vice Pres*
EMP: 80 **EST:** 1962
SQ FT: 3,600
SALES (est): 1MM-4.9MM **Privately Held**
WEB: www.petersonbusinc.com
SIC: 4151 4142 School bus service; long-distance bus charter service

(G-6419)
RAMBOW INC
1000 Rambow Pkwy   (56273)
PHONE...............................320 354-2570
FAX: 320 354-2580
Steven S Rambow, *President*
Vonnie Loterbauer, *Manager*

Joan Conway, *Manager*
Jamie Iverson, *Director*
Paul Hannig, *Representative*
EMP: 37 **EST:** 1977
SQ FT: 41,000
SALES (est): 1MM-4.9MM **Privately Held**
WEB: www.rambow.com
SIC: 5199 Manufactures embroidery & art needlework; manufactures Swiss loom embroideries; wholesales advertising specialties; screen printing on fabric

NEW MARKET
Scott County

(G-6420)
FRIEDGES DRYWALL INC
430 Webster St   (55054)
PO Box 37, Elko   (55020-0037)
PHONE...............................952 461-3288
FAX: 952 461-3289
Terry Friedges, *President*
Todd Friedges, *Treasurer*
EMP: 50 **EST:** 1976
SQ FT: 1,700
SALES (est): 1MM-4.9MM **Privately Held**
SIC: 1742 Drywall contractor

NEW PRAGUE
Le Sueur County

(G-6421)
AMERICINN MOTEL & SUITES
1200 1st St NE   (56071-2198)
PHONE...............................952 758-7300
FAX: 952 758-7309
Scott McAdam, *Manager*
Mark Pexa, *Data Proc Dir*
EMP: 29 **EST:** 1997
SALES (est): 1MM-4.9MM **Privately Held**
SIC: 7011 Traveler accommodations

(G-6422)
LEGION PAVILION CO INC
Also Called: Park Ballroom
300 Lexington Ave S   (56071-2426)
PO Box 113   (56071-0113)
PHONE...............................952 758-4603
Ralph Eisek, *President*
EMP: 30 **EST:** 1929
SQ FT: 14,400
SALES (est): 1MM-4.9MM **Privately Held**
WEB: www.parkballroom.com
SIC: 7911 Dance hall or ballroom operation

(G-6423)
NEW PRAGUE GOLF CLUB INC
400 Lexington Ave S   (56071-2400)
PHONE...............................952 758-5326
FAX: 952 758-4343
Ken Noland, *General Mgr*
Ken Norland, *General Mgr*
Kurt Ruehling, *Manager*
Chris Heyda, *Manager*
Patty Solheid, *Administration*
EMP: 50 **EST:** 1934
SQ FT: 5,000
SALES (est): 1MM-4.9MM **Privately Held**
SIC: 7992 Public golf course

(G-6424)
STATE BANK OF NEW PRAGUE
1101 1st St SE   (56071-3000)
PHONE...............................952 758-4491
FAX: 952 758-5058
David Hyduke, *Ch of Bd*
Bruce Wolf, *President*
Ross Thompson, *Vice Pres*
Lucille Nickolay, *Vice Pres*
Terry Mattson, *Vice Pres*
EMP: 65 **EST:** 1883
SQ FT: 4,978
SALES (est): 10MM-24.9MM **Privately Held**
WEB: www.statebankofnewprague.com
SIC: 6022 State commercial bank
PA: Duke Financial Group Inc
80 S 8th St Ste 2900
Minneapolis MN 55402
612 204-0255

(G-6425)
WITT DOHM PROPERTIES INC
Also Called: Holiday
102 County Road 37   (56071-2100)
PHONE...............................952 758-5252
FAX: 952 758-5252
Brian Dohm, *Vice Pres*
EMP: 25 **EST:** 1998
SALES (est): 500-999K **Privately Held**
SIC: 7542 Eating place; convenience store; automotive washing & polishing service

NEW PRAGUE
Scott County

(G-6426)
ELECTROMED INC
500 6th Ave NW   (56071-1134)
PHONE...............................952 758-9299
FAX: 952 758-1941
Robert Hansen, *CEO*
Roy Kyndberg, *General Mgr*
Brad Blascziek, *Mfg Mgr*
Terry Belford, *CFO*
Eileen M Manning, *Marketing Staff*
▼ **EMP:** 35 **EST:** 1992
SQ FT: 50,000
SALES (est): 5MM-9.9MM **Privately Held**
WEB: www.electromed-usa.com
SIC: 8011 Manufactures surgical stapling devices; physicians' office & clinic

(G-6427)
GENEX COOPERATIVE INC
412 4th Ave NW   (56071-1118)
PO Box 233   (56071-0233)
PHONE...............................952 758-2561
James Olson, *Vice Pres*
Gary Norton, *Manager*
EMP: 26
SALES (est): 1MM-4.9MM **Privately Held**
SIC: 6531 Real estate agency & broker
PA: Cooperative Resources Intl
100 Mbc Dr
Shawano WI 54166
715 526-2141

(G-6428)
GENEX FARM SYSTEMS
Also Called: Twenty One Centry Farm System
412 4th Ave NW   (56071-1118)
PHONE...............................952 758-2561
Bill Wirth, *Managing Dir*
Rosie Kes, *Corp Secy*
James Olson, *Vice Pres*
EST: 2000 **Privately Held**
SIC: 5083 Wholesales dairy machinery & equipment

(G-6429)
K A WITT CONSTRUCTION INC
1530 W 280th St   (56071-9120)
PHONE...............................952 758-2108
FAX: 952 758-5159
Ken Witt, *CEO*
Jason Witt, *President*
Mark Bartusek, *Superintendent*
Christopher Witt, *Corp Secy*
Paula Novak, *Corp Secy*
EMP: 32 **EST:** 1963
SQ FT: 4,160
SALES (est): 5MM-9.9MM **Privately Held**
WEB: www.kawitt.com
SIC: 1521 1542 1794 New single-family home construction service; new commercial & office building construction; excavating contractor

(G-6430)
KIMMY CLEAN LLC
26881 Naylor Ave   (56071-9750)
PHONE...............................952 758-4238
Michael Delbow, *President*
EMP: 30 **EST:** 1997
SALES (est): 500-999K **Privately Held**
SIC: 7349 Janitorial & custodial services

(G-6431)
MALA STRANA HEALTH CARE CENTER
1001 Columbus Ave N   (56071-2008)
PHONE...............................952 758-2511
FAX: 952 758-2514
John Thro, *Principal*
Josephine Ceplecha, *Bookkeeper*
Mary Whitmer, *Exec Dir*
Patricia Boyle, *Director*
Mary O'Brien, *Director*
EMP: 145 **EST:** 1982
SALES (est): 5MM-9.9MM **Privately Held**
WEB: www.throcompany.com
SIC: 8059 Nursing home
PA: Thro Co
638 Southbend Ave
Mankato MN 56001
507 625-8741

(G-6432)
MCCRADY JANITORIAL INC
25664 Willow Ln   (56071-7800)
PHONE...............................952 758-3097
Stephen McCrady, *President*
EMP: 45 **EST:** 1980
SALES (est): 1MM-4.9MM **Privately Held**
SIC: 7349 Building cleaning service

(G-6433)
MIDWEST ASSISTANCE PROGRAM
212 Lady Slipper Ave NE   (56071-2090)
PHONE...............................952 758-4334
Martha Cashmen, *CEO*
EMP: 35 **EST:** 1981 **Privately Held**
SIC: 8731 Environmental research laboratory

(G-6434)
QUEEN OF PEACE HOSPITAL
301 2nd St NE   (56071-1709)
PHONE...............................952 758-5009
FAX: 952 758-4431
Marry Climp, *CEO*
Anna Herman, *COO*
M Eland, *Ch Radiology*
Gregg Redfield, *CFO*
Mick McGuire, *Treasurer*
EMP: 280 **EST:** 1952
SQ FT: 32,000
SALES (est): 10MM-24.9MM **Privately Held**
WEB: www.qofp.org
SIC: 8062 Medical hospital

(G-6435)
THRO CO
Also Called: Mala Strana Nursing Home
1001 Columbus Ave N   (56071-2008)
PHONE...............................952 758-2511
FAX: 952 758-0171
Larry V Derpoel, *Manager*
Beth Greenwood, *Administrator*
Josie Ceplecha, *Administrator*
Patricia Boyle, *CTO*
EMP: 160
SALES (est): 5MM-9.9MM **Privately Held**
WEB: www.throcompany.com
SIC: 8059 8051 Nursing home; skilled nursing care facility
PA: Thro Co
638 Southbend Ave
Mankato MN 56001
507 625-8741

NEW RICHLAND
Waseca County

(G-6436)
NEW RICHLAND CARE CENTER
312 1st St NE   (56072-2003)
PO Box 477   (56072-0477)
PHONE...............................507 465-3292
FAX: 507 465-3403
Mary Bushlack, *Bookkeeper*
Brenda Laker, *Mng Member*
Kris Young, *Manager*
Dori Mutch, *Administrator*
EMP: 115 **EST:** 1975
SALES (est): 1MM-4.9MM **Privately Held**
SIC: 8051 Skilled nursing care facility

www.HarrisInfo.com
282
2011 Harris Minnesota
Services Directory
▲=Import ▼=Export
◆=Import/Export

NEW ULM
Brown County

(G-6437)
A & J TBA INC
1201 N Front St (56073-1179)
PO Box 197, Eagle Lake (56024-0197)
PHONE..............................507 233-3000
Steve Weber, *President*
Curt Cook, *Vice Pres*
Steve Beltz, *Vice Pres*
EST: 1986
SQ FT: 18,000 **Privately Held**
SIC: 5013 5014 Wholesales automotive
supplies; wholesales tires & tubes

(G-6438)
ALLIANCE BANK (PA)
322 N Minnesota St (56073-1734)
PO Box 757 (56073-0757)
PHONE..............................507 354-3133
FAX: 507 359-1432
John S Wisniewski, *President*
David J Lynn, *Senior VP*
Diane Knopke, *Vice Pres*
Christine Peters, *Vice Pres*
Lisa Lammers, *Manager*
EMP: 50 **EST:** 1914
SQ FT: 10,000
SALES (corp-wide): 39.68M **Privately Held**
SIC: 6022 6021 State commercial bank;
national commercial bank

(G-6439)
ALLINA HEALTH SYSTEM
Also Called: Sioux Valley Hospital
1324 5th St N (56073-1514)
PHONE..............................507 233-1000
FAX: 507 233-1589
Marcham Fischer, *Ch Radiology*
Toby Frier, *Opers-Prdtn-Mfg*
Sheila Proehl, *Finance Dir*
Diane Rasmussen, *Human Res Dir*
Kathy Runck, *VP Mktg*
EMP: 350
SQ FT: 85,000
SALES (est): 25MM-49.9MM **Privately Held**
WEB: www.allina.com
SIC: 8062 Medical hospital
PA: Allina Health System
2925 Chicago Ave
Minneapolis MN 55407
612 775-5000

(G-6440)
ASSOCIATED MILK PRODUCERS INC (PA)
315 N Broadway St (56073-1719)
PO Box 455 (56073-0455)
PHONE..............................507 354-8295
FAX: 507 359-8695
Mark Furth, *CEO*
Paul Toft, *Ch of Bd*
Roger Lyon, *Vice Ch Bd*
Bill Barvitski, *Member*
Roger Culbertson, *Member*
EMP: 60 **EST:** 1969 **Privately Held**
WEB: www.ampi.com
SIC: 5143 Manufactures dry, condensed or
evaporated dairy products; wholesales milk;
manufactures bulk ice cream; manufactures
fermented & cultured milk products;
manufactures butter; manufactures cheese

(G-6441)
ASSOCIATED MILK PRODUCERS INC
312 Center St (56073-3017)
PO Box 98 (56073-0098)
PHONE..............................507 233-4600
FAX: 507 354-1063
William Swan, *Division Mgr*
Dick Wepkey, *Principal*
Ross Sawyer, *Plant Mgr*
Dele Breun, *Maint Mgr*
Mark Hence, *Purch Agent*
EMP: 50
SALES (est): 25MM-49.9MM **Privately Held**
WEB: www.ampi.com

SIC: 5143 Wholesales fresh dairy products;
manufactures butter; manufactures dry,
condensed or evaporated dairy products
PA: Associated Milk Producers Inc
315 N Broadway St
New Ulm MN 56073
507 354-8295

(G-6442)
BEACON PROMOTIONS INC
2121 S Bridge St (56073-3959)
PHONE..............................507 233-3240
FAX: 507 233-3241
Arthur Olsen, *CEO*
Brett Olson, *VP Opers-Prdtn-*
Kevin Poirier, *CFO*
Bruce Walters, *CFO*
▲ **EMP:** 90 **EST:** 2003
SQ FT: 58,000
SALES (est): 10MM-24.9MM **Privately Held**
WEB: www.beaconpromotions.com
SIC: 8743 Promotion services

(G-6443)
BROWN COUNTY EVALUATION CENTER
Also Called: MINNESOTA RIVER VALLEY
JUVENIL
510 N Front St (56073-1634)
PO Box 642 (56073-0642)
PHONE..............................507 359-9111
FAX: 507 359-7726
Shirley Swantz, *Manager*
Royce Wempen, *Manager*
Sharon Rhoades, *Director*
Larry Norland, *Director*
EMP: 40 **EST:** 1995
SALES (est): 1MM-4.9MM **Privately Held**
SIC: 8069 Alcoholism rehabilitation hospital

(G-6444)
BROWN COUNTY PROBATION DEPT
1 S State St (56073-3153)
PHONE..............................507 233-6628
FAX: 507 359-1430
Jonathan J Schiro, *Principal*
Pat Booker, *Manager*
EMP: 26
SALES (est): 1MM-4.9MM **Privately Held**
SIC: 8322 Individual & family social services

(G-6445)
CITIZENS BANK MINNESOTA
105 N Minnesota St (56073-1729)
PO Box 547 (56073-0547)
PHONE..............................507 354-3165
Lou Geistfeld, *President*
Brant Drill, *Assistant VP*
Bill Brennan, *Vice Pres*
Sharon Nordby, *Mfg Spvr*
Linda Kretsch, *Auditor*
EMP: 48 **EST:** 1876
SALES (est): 10MM-24.9MM **Privately Held**
SIC: 6022 6029 State commercial bank;
commercial bank

(G-6446)
COUNTY OF BROWN-NICOLLET
Also Called: Family Planning Services
1117 Center St (56073-3255)
PO Box 543 (56073-0543)
PHONE..............................507 354-4418
Jennifer Snell, *Exec Dir*
Anita Hoffman, *Director*
EMP: 30 **EST:** 1938
SALES (est): 1MM-4.9MM **Privately Held**
SIC: 8093 Family planning center

(G-6447)
CULLIGAN INTERNATIONAL CO
918 S German St (56073-3444)
PHONE..............................507 354-2311
FAX: 507 642-3510
Richard Earl, *Branch Mgr*
EMP: 26
SALES (est): 1MM-4.9MM **Privately Held**
WEB: www.cdr-inc.com
SIC: 7389 Retails water purification
equipment; water softener service
HQ: Culligan International Co
9399 W Higgins Rd # 1100
Rosemont IL 60018
847 430-2800

(G-6448)
ENTERPRISE NORTH INC
2100 N Broadway St (56073-1031)
PHONE..............................507 233-8900
FAX: 507 359-5518
Mary Hippert, *Director*
EMP: 25 **EST:** 1970
SALES (est): 1MM-4.9MM **Privately Held**
SIC: 8331 Job training & vocational
rehabilitation services

(G-6449)
FLYING DUTCHMEN CYCLE CLUB
2317 N Broadway St (56073-1186)
PHONE..............................507 354-2306
Les Stadick, *Member*
EMP: 99 **EST:** 1947 **Privately Held**
SIC: 8641 Recreation association

(G-6450)
GAG SHEET METAL INC
125 3rd St N (56073-1623)
PHONE..............................507 354-3813
FAX: 507 354-7847
John M Gag, *President*
Steve Gag, *Vice Pres*
Kathy Domaire, *Manager*
EMP: 25 **EST:** 1904
SQ FT: 6,500
SALES (est): 1MM-4.9MM **Privately Held**
WEB: www.gagsheetmetal.com
SIC: 1711 1761 Heating & air conditioning
contractor; roofing contractor

(G-6451)
GARY J ASCHENBRENNER TRUCKING
219 12th St S (56073-4402)
PHONE..............................507 233-2539
FAX: 507 354-2513
Gary J Aschenbrenner, *President*
EMP: 25 **EST:** 1976
SALES (est): 1MM-4.9MM **Privately Held**
SIC: 4213 Over the road trucking

(G-6452)
GOLDEN HOME CARE PLUS INC
40 Roslyn Rd (56073-3628)
PHONE..............................507 359-2756
FAX: 507 354-1260
Kenneth Gulden, *Owner*
EMP: 300 **EST:** 1992
SALES (est): 10MM-24.9MM **Privately Held**
SIC: 8082 Home health care services

(G-6453)
HECTOR COMMUNICATIONS CORP (PA)
27 N Minnesota St (56073-1727)
PO Box 697 (56073-0697)
PHONE..............................218 346-5500
FAX: 218 346-8840
Bill Otis, *President*
Robert Weiss, *Corp Secy*
William Eckles, *Corp Secy*
David Arvig, *Treasurer*
Carol Haukebo, *Accountant*
EMP: 57 **EST:** 1990
SALES (corp-wide): 111.35K **Privately Held**
SIC: 4813 4841 Local telephone
communications services; cable television
services; online services providers

(G-6454)
HEYMANN CONSTRUCTION CO
210 3rd South St (56073-3075)
PO Box 606 (56073-0606)
PHONE..............................507 354-3174
FAX: 507 354-3175
John P Heymann, *CEO*
Jerry O'Brien, *President*
Patricia Heymann, *Corp Secy*
Tom Clyne, *Sales Staff*
Janna Tessmer, *Manager*
EMP: 60 **EST:** 1918
SQ FT: 5,600
SALES (est): 10MM-24.9MM **Privately Held**
SIC: 1542 1541 New commercial & office
building construction; commercial & office
building renovation & repair services;
industrial building & warehouse construction

(G-6455)
HIGHLAND MANOR INC
1314 8th St N (56073-1554)
PHONE..............................507 359-2026
FAX: 507 354-2751
Carli Lindemann, *Principal*
Cindy Williams, *Manager*
EMP: 225 **EST:** 1995
SALES (est): 5MM-9.9MM **Privately Held**
SIC: 8051 Skilled nursing care facility

(G-6456)
J & R SCHUGEL TRUCKING INC (PA)
2026 N Broadway St (56073-1030)
PO Box 278 (56073-0278)
PHONE..............................507 359-2037
FAX: 507 354-4366
Jerry Schugel, *Ch of Bd*
Rick Schugel, *President*
James Guldan, *Corp Secy*
Quintin Holmberg, *Info Tech Dir*
Lisa Roeder, *Info Tech Mgr*
EMP: 200 **EST:** 1955
SQ FT: 25,000
SALES (corp-wide): 109M **Privately Held**
WEB: www.jrschugel.com
SIC: 4213 Over the road trucking; contract
haulers

(G-6457)
J K F WAREHOUSE
1823 S Valley St (56073)
PHONE..............................507 354-5528
FAX: 507 354-7044
Ted Marty, *President*
EMP: 40
SALES (est): 1MM-4.9MM **Privately Held**
SIC: 4225 Warehousing & storage services

(G-6458)
KRAFT FOODS GLOBAL INC
2525 S Bridge St (56073-3955)
PHONE..............................507 359-2511
FAX: 507 359-2311
Mark Pollack, *Plant Mgr*
Joe Luetmer, *Plant Mgr*
Gene Abernethy, *Maint Mgr*
Sean Gillespie, *Engrg Mgr*
Steven Anderson, *Plant Engr*
EMP: 50
SALES (est): 5MM-9.9MM **Privately Held**
WEB: www.kraftfoods.com
SIC: 4789 Railroad cargo loading &
unloading services
PA: Kraft Foods Global Inc
3 Lakes Dr
Winnetka IL 60093
847 646-2000

(G-6459)
M B W CO
1200 S Broadway St (56073-3454)
PHONE..............................507 354-3808
FAX: 507 354-2168
Vicki Sieve, *President*
Ginny Miller, *Officer*
EMP: 240 **EST:** 1977
SALES (est): 10MM-24.9MM **Privately Held**
SIC: 8361 8741 Home for the mentally
retarded; management services

(G-6460)
MCP FOODS INC
100 N Valley St (56073-1601)
PHONE..............................507 233-7406
Doug Cook, *General Mgr*
▲ **EMP:** 65 **EST:** 2005
SALES (est): 50MM-99.9MM **Privately Held**
SIC: 5169 Wholesales food additives &
preservatives

(G-6461)
MINNESOTA VALLEY TESTING LABS
Also Called: MVTL Labs
1126 N Front St (56073-1176)
PO Box 249 (56073-0249)
PHONE..............................507 354-8517
FAX: 507 345-6460
Thomas Berg, *CEO*
Jerry Balbach, *President*
Michael Grob, *COO*

(PA)=Parent Co (HQ)=Headquarters (DH)=Div Headquarters
✿ = New business established in last 2 years

2011 Harris Minnesota
Services Directory

© Harris InfoSource 1-866-281-6415
283

Colleen Skillings, *CFO*
Lori Allen, *Finance*
EMP: 100 **EST:** 1951
SQ FT: 28,000
SALES (est): 5MM-9.9MM **Privately Held**
WEB: www.mvtl.com
SIC: 8734 8731 Testing laboratory; food testing services; commercial physical research laboratory

(G-6462)
MINNESOTA VALLEY TRANSPORT INC
301 Water St (56073-1610)
PHONE.............................507 354-3276
FAX: 507 354-7326
Daniel Schumacher, *President*
Marliss Meier, *Corp Secy*
Francis Schumacher, *Vice Pres*
EMP: 34 **EST:** 1984
SQ FT: 10,000
SALES (est): 1MM-4.9MM **Privately Held**
SIC: 4213 Long-distance refrigerated trucking services

(G-6463)
MORGAN TIRE & AUTO LLC
1807 S Broadway St (56073-3748)
PHONE.............................507 354-4972
Donovan Steele, *Manager*
Martin Sellner, *Manager*
Mike Hoeppner, *Manager*
EMP: 30
SALES (est): 1MM-4.9MM **Privately Held**
WEB: www.bfsusa.com
SIC: 7534 Tire recapping & retreading services
HQ: Bfs Retail Operations LLC
    333 E Lake St Ste 300
    Bloomingdale IL 60108
    630 259-9000

(G-6464)
MR PAVING & EXCAVATING INC
1000 N Front St (56073-1174)
PHONE.............................507 354-4171
FAX: 507 359-4156
Tim Rahe, *President*
Glen Mathiowetz, *CFO*
EMP: 80 **EST:** 1994
SALES (est): 10MM-24.9MM **Privately Held**
SIC: 1611 1794 Highway & street resurfacing contractor; excavating contractor

(G-6465)
NEW ULM BUS LINES INC
1400 S Minnesota St (56073-2214)
PHONE.............................507 354-4711
FAX: 507 354-4811
Randall Bennett, *President*
EMP: 50 **EST:** 1966
SQ FT: 5,000
SALES (est): 1MM-4.9MM **Privately Held**
SIC: 4151 4142 School bus service; long-distance bus charter service

(G-6466)
NEW ULM COUNTRY CLUB
1 Golf Dr (56073-3830)
PO Box 576 (56073-0576)
PHONE.............................507 354-8896
FAX: 507 359-5597
Tim Huffman, *Manager*
Tim Huffmenn, *Director*
EMP: 50 **EST:** 1928
SALES (est): 1MM-4.9MM **Privately Held**
SIC: 7997 Membership golf club; bar; eating place

(G-6467)
NEW ULM DENTAL CLINIC
127 N Broadway St (56073-1715)
PO Box 848 (56073-0848)
PHONE.............................507 354-3321
FAX: 507 359-1739
Daniel Drugan, *Owner*
Gregory B Jellberg, *Co-Owner*
Julie Nord, *Manager*
EMP: 25 **EST:** 1980
SALES (est): 1MM-4.9MM **Privately Held**
SIC: 8021 Dental office

(G-6468)
NEW ULM TELECOM INC (PA)
27 N Minnesota St (56073-1727)
PHONE.............................507 354-4111
FAX: 507 354-1982
Bill D Otis, *President*
Patricia L Matthews, *Corp Secy*
Barbara A Bornhoft, *COO*
Cathy Runck, *Vice Pres*
Rick Wegner, *Plant Supt*
EMP: 55 **EST:** 1905
SQ FT: 14,000
SALES (corp-wide): 32.61M **Publicly Held**
SIC: 4813 Local telephone communications services; internet connectivity services; telephone or video communications services; retails telephone equipment & systems

(G-6469)
NEW ULM TURNVEREIN INC
Also Called: Turner Club
102 S State St (56073-3156)
PHONE.............................507 354-4916
Ed Webber, *President*
Richard Runck, *Manager*
EMP: 50 **EST:** 1856
SQ FT: 21,000
SALES (est): 1MM-4.9MM **Privately Held**
SIC: 7999 Gymnastics instruction; bar; limited service lunchroom

(G-6470)
NEW ULM, CITY OF INC
310 1st St N (56073-1675)
PHONE.............................507 359-8264
FAX: 507 359-8208
Chris Manderfeld, *Accountant*
Bryan Gramnetz, *Manager*
Chris Gramentz, *Manager*
Bruce Campbell, *Exec Dir*
Gary Gleifner, *Exec Dir*
EMP: 70
SALES (est): 25MM-49.9MM **Privately Held**
WEB: www.ci.new-ulm.mn.us
SIC: 4939 4952 4953 Combination utilities services; refuse systems services; mayors' office; sewage facility
PA: New Ulm, City of Inc
    100 N Broadway St
    New Ulm MN 56073
    507 359-8233

(G-6471)
NORTH CENTRAL CONTAINER OF NEW
209 3rd South St (56073-3006)
PO Box 505 (56073-0505)
PHONE.............................507 359-3136
FAX: 507 359-3137
Femi Shoge, *President*
EMP: 35
SALES (est): 10MM-24.9MM **Privately Held**
SIC: 5085 Wholesales industrial supplies

(G-6472)
PALMER'S AUTO SUPPLY INC
Also Called: Carquest Auto Parts
426 S Minnesota St (56073-2121)
PHONE.............................507 354-3154
Joanne Wolf, *Ch of Bd*
Gregory Palmer, *President*
Marlyn Sellner, *Corp Secy*
Daniel Palmer, *Vice Pres*
Dan Delaug, *Branch Mgr*
EMP: 26 **EST:** 1963
SQ FT: 16,500
SALES (est): 5MM-9.9MM **Privately Held**
WEB: www.autopartshq.com
SIC: 5013 Wholesales automotive supplies & parts; retails automotive accessories; retails automotive parts
HQ: Aph Stores Inc
    2959 Clearwater Rd
    Saint Cloud MN 56301
    320 252-5411

(G-6473)
RICH SCHMITZ DVM
401 20th St S (56073-3944)
PHONE.............................507 233-2520
Rich Schmitz DVM, *Partner*
EMP: 40 **EST:** 2001 **Privately Held**
SIC: 0742 Animal hospital services

(G-6474)
SHELTER PRODUCTS INC
810 N Front St (56073-1149)
PO Box 174 (56073-0174)
PHONE.............................507 354-4176
FAX: 507 354-6710
Duane Lambrecht, *President*
Barb Stueber, *Manager*
EMP: 32 **EST:** 1969
SQ FT: 60,000
SALES (est): 10MM-24.9MM **Privately Held**
WEB: www.shelterproducts.com
SIC: 5033 5031 Wholesales asphalt & sheet metal roofing materials; wholesales rough, dressed & finished lumber; wholesales millwork; wholesales plywood; wholesales siding; wholesales thermal insulation materials; wholesales doors & windows

(G-6475)
SUE CHAPMAN DVM
401 20th St S (56073-3944)
PHONE.............................507 233-2520
Rick Smith, *President*
EMP: 30 **EST:** 2001 **Privately Held**
SIC: 0742 Animal hospital services

(G-6476)
3M CO
1700 N Minn St Bldg 1 (56073-1216)
PO Box 95 (56073-0095)
PHONE.............................507 354-8271
FAX: 507 359-0111
Eric Benz, *Plant Mgr*
Steve Hall, *Mfg Mgr*
Scott Cooper, *Plant Engr Mgr*
Jackie Schuetzle, *Engineer*
Steve Carlson, *Controller*
EMP: 600
SALES (est): 100MM-499.9MM **Publicly Held**
WEB: www.mmm.com
SIC: 5063 Wholesales electrical supplies
PA: 3M Co
    3M Center Bldg 22011W02
    Saint Paul MN 55144
    651 733-1110

(G-6477)
TORGERSON HOSPITALITY LLC
Also Called: Holiday Inn
2101 S Broadway St (56073-3953)
PO Box 597 (56073-0597)
PHONE.............................507 359-2941
FAX: 507 354-7147
Marti Bennett, *General Mgr*
Sheryl Walton, *Principal*
Thomas R Torgerson, *Member*
Rick Neumann, *Manager*
Jenny Eckstein, *Manager*
EMP: 80 **EST:** 1999
SALES (est): 1MM-4.9MM **Privately Held**
WEB: www.torgersonproperties.com
SIC: 7011 Traveler accommodations
PA: Torgerson Properties Inc
    103 15th Ave NW Ste 200
    Willmar MN 56201
    320 235-7207

NEW YORK MILLS
Otter Tail County

(G-6478)
ELDERS' HOME INC
215 Tousley Ave S (56567-4400)
PO Box 188 (56567-0188)
PHONE.............................218 385-2005
FAX: 218 385-4170
Cal Anderson, *CEO*
Russell Jacobson, *Treasurer*
Sharon McKinley, *Administrator*
Timothy Studer, *Director*
Claudia Stursa, *Nursing Dir*
EMP: 70 **EST:** 1960
SQ FT: 26,000
SALES (est): 1MM-4.9MM **Privately Held**
WEB: www.eldershome.com
SIC: 8059 8051 8052 Nursing home; intermediate care facility; skilled nursing care facility

(G-6479)
MID-STATE AUTO AUCTION INC
100 Bach Ave (56567-4328)
PHONE.............................218 385-3777
FAX: 218 385-3232
Robert Thompson, *President*
John Olson, *Vice Pres*
Jeannie Roggenkamp, *Office Mgr*
Jeanne Rogenkamp, *Office Mgr*
Kelly Moench, *Info Tech Mgr*
EMP: 157 **EST:** 1980
SQ FT: 15,000
SALES (est): 100MM-499.9MM **Privately Held**
SIC: 5012 Automobile auction services; used car dealer

(G-6480)
TIM FLANIGAN TRUCKING
409 Heidi Pkwy (56567-4208)
PHONE.............................218 385-3034
FAX: 218 385-2104
Tim Flanigan, *President*
Patty Flanigan, *Corp Secy*
EMP: 36 **EST:** 1996
SQ FT: 10,000
SALES (est): 1MM-4.9MM **Privately Held**
SIC: 4213 Contract haulers

NEWFOLDEN
Marshall County

(G-6481)
BOB DAHL
28248 130th Ave NW (56738-9655)
PHONE.............................218 874-6321
Bob Dahl, *Owner*
EMP: 27 **EST:** 1970 **Privately Held**
WEB: www.bobdahl.com
SIC: 0111 Wheat farm

(G-6482)
KANE TRANSPORT INC
40925 403rd Ave (56738)
PHONE.............................320 352-5800
Robert Kane, *President*
EMP: 100 **EST:** 1949
SALES (est): 5MM-9.9MM **Privately Held**
SIC: 4212 Local trucking without storage services

NEWPORT
Washington County

(G-6483)
ACURA INC
303 21st St Ste 176 (55055-1094)
PHONE.............................651 967-0607
James Peterka, *CEO*
Mary Larson-Peterka, *President*
Michael Larson, *CFO*
EMP: 28 **EST:** 2001
SALES (est): 1MM-4.9MM **Privately Held**
SIC: 7379 Computer system consulting services

(G-6484)
BAILEY NURSERIES INC (PA)
1325 Bailey Rd (55055-1502)
PHONE.............................651 459-9744
Gordon J Bailey, *Ch of Bd*
Terri McEnaney, *President*
John Bailey, *Treasurer*
Barbara Zilmer, *Human Res Mgr*
Rodney P Bailey, *Director*
EMP: 500 **EST:** 1905
SQ FT: 7,000 **Privately Held**
WEB: www.baileynurseries.com
SIC: 5193 Wholesales flowers & nursery stock

(G-6485)
BRADLEY DISTRIBUTING CO
1912 Hastings Ave (55055-1542)
PHONE.............................651 639-0523
James Fritz, *CEO*
Lorie Lauppe, *Director*
EMP: 30

▲=Import ▼=Export
◆=Import/Export

EST: 1976
SQ FT: 54,200
SALES (est): 10MM-24.9MM **Privately Held**
SIC: 5145 5141 5149 Wholesales snack foods; wholesales bottled mineral or spring water; wholesales green or roasted coffee; wholesales general line groceries

(G-6486)
FRITZ CO INC
1912 Hastings Ave (55055-1542)
PHONE 651 459-9751
FAX: 651 459-7381
James P Fritz, *CEO*
Terry Waldoch, *Vice Pres*
Jim Oslund, *Senior Buyer*
Lori Klein, *Accountant*
Jon Klett, *Sales Mgr*
EMP: 100 **EST:** 1940
SQ FT: 130,000
SALES (est): 50MM-99.9MM **Privately Held**
SIC: 5194 5141 5145 5199 Wholesales tobacco & tobacco products; wholesales candy; wholesales variety store merchandise; wholesales confectionery products; wholesales general line groceries

(G-6487)
METROPOLITAN GRAVEL CO INC
37 21st St (55055-1003)
PO Box 289 (55055-0289)
PHONE 651 458-0170
FAX: 651 458-1168
Laurie K Houle, *President*
West Houle Sr, *Vice Pres*
Tom Anderson, *Agent*
EMP: 55 **EST:** 1965
SALES (est): 5MM-9.9MM **Privately Held**
SIC: 4212 Dump truck hauling services

(G-6488)
PAUL NEWPORT-ST COLD STORAGE
2233 Maxwell Ave (55055-1001)
PO Box 129 (55055-0129)
PHONE 651 459-5555
FAX: 651 459-5951
Andrew Greenberg, *President*
Dean L Greenberg, *Chairman*
Ross Beard, *Mfg Staff*
Steven P Greenberg, *Treasurer*
Bob Franklin, *Accounts Mgr*
EMP: 32 **EST:** 1959
SQ FT: 205,000
SALES (est): 1MM-4.9MM **Privately Held**
WEB: www.newportcold.com
SIC: 4222 Frozen or refrigerated goods storage

(G-6489)
TEN-E PACKAGING SERVICES INC
1666 County Road 74 (55055-1765)
PHONE 651 459-0671
FAX: 651 459-1430
Robert T Eyck, *President*
Patricia L Garin, *Vice Pres*
Bryan Anderson, *Project Mgr*
Robert Gindorff, *CFO*
Bob Gindorff, *Manager*
EMP: 25 **EST:** 1989
SQ FT: 30,000
SALES (est): 1MM-4.9MM **Privately Held**
WEB: www.ten-e.com
SIC: 8734 Testing laboratory

(G-6490)
WILSON LINES OF MINNESOTA INC
155 21st St (55055-1005)
PHONE 651 459-8193
FAX: 651 769-3050
Larry Hofstad, *Branch Mgr*
EMP: 45
SALES (est): 5MM-9.9MM **Privately Held**
SIC: 4213 Over the road trucking

NICOLLET
Nicollet County

(G-6491)
SCHMIDT'S MEAT MARKET INC
319 Pine St (56074-2077)
PO Box 542 (56074-0542)
PHONE 507 232-3438
FAX: 507 225-3408
Bruce Schmidt, *President*
Ryan Schmidt, *Vice Pres*
Ryan Scmidt, *Vice Pres*
EMP: 45 **EST:** 1947
SQ FT: 6,000
SALES (est): 5MM-9.9MM **Privately Held**
WEB: www.schmidtsmeatmarket.com
SIC: 0751 Meat market; custom livestock slaughtering services

---

NISSWA
Cass County

(G-6492)
GUNSBURY ALAN QUARTERDECK
Also Called: Boat House Eatery
9820 Birch Bay Dr SW (56468-2041)
PHONE 218 963-2482
FAX: 218 963-7984
Alan Gunsbury, *Owner*
EMP: 35 **EST:** 1976
SALES (est): 1MM-4.9MM **Privately Held**
SIC: 8742 Sales consulting services; eating place

(G-6493)
QUARTERDECK AT PLEASANT ACRES
9820 Birch Bay Dr SW (56468-2041)
PHONE 218 963-2482
FAX: 218 963-7894
Alan Gunsbury, *President*
Jane Gunsbury, *Corp Secy*
EMP: 30 **EST:** 1960
SALES (est): 1MM-4.9MM **Privately Held**
SIC: 7011 Resort hotel

(G-6494)
QUARTERDECK RESORT & REST
9820 Birch Bay Dr SW (56468-2041)
PHONE 218 963-7537
Alan Gunsbury, *President*
Jane Gunsbury, *Vice Pres*
EMP: 60 **EST:** 1976
SALES (est): 1MM-4.9MM **Privately Held**
SIC: 7011 Night club drinking establishment; ski lodge

NISSWA
Crow Wing County

(G-6495)
AMERICAN LEGION POST 627
Also Called: Billie Brown Post
25807 Main St (56468)
PO Box 427 (56468-0427)
PHONE 218 963-9946
FAX: 218 963-7540
Bob Gronau, *Principal*
Comdr R Perkins, *Principal*
EMP: 28 **EST:** 1997 **Privately Held**
SIC: 8641 Veterans' organization

(G-6496)
ETOC CO INC (PA)
Also Called: Grand View Lodge
23611 S Woodward Ave (56468-9472)
PHONE 218 963-2906
Mark Ronnei, *CEO*
Samuel A Cote, *Vice Pres*
James Olson, *CFO*
Julie Hruben, *Administrator*
Jeff Schulz, *Info Tech Dir*
EMP: 75 **EST:** 1935
SQ FT: 2,000 **Privately Held**
SIC: 7011 7032 7992 Resort hotel; boys' camp; girls' camp; public golf course

---

(G-6497)
ETOC CO INC
Also Called: Pines
23521 Nokomis Ave (56468-2711)
PHONE 218 963-2234
Paul Welch, *General Mgr*
Heidi Skalland, *Finance*
Jim Pinnard, *Manager*
Mark Ronnei, *Manager*
EMP: 25
SALES (est): 1MM-4.9MM **Privately Held**
SIC: 7011 Resort hotel
PA: Etoc Co Inc
23611 S Woodward Ave
Nisswa MN 56468
218 963-2906

(G-6498)
NISSWA MARINE INC
24238 Smiley Rd (56468-2449)
PHONE 218 963-2292
FAX: 218 963-4402
Steve Wiczek, *CEO*
Brent Wiczek, *General Mgr*
Irma Zimmerman, *Corp Secy*
Dennis Zimmerman, *Vice Pres*
Heather Wiczek, *Controller*
EMP: 25 **EST:** 1935
SQ FT: 25,000
SALES (est): 5MM-9.9MM **Privately Held**
WEB: www.nisswamarine.com
SIC: 4491 4493 Marine supply dealer; dock operation & maintenance services, including buildings & facilities; boat yard providing storage & incidental repair services

---

NORTH BRANCH
Chisago County

(G-6499)
CENTRAL MOTORS
Also Called: Chevrolet
5660 392nd St (55056-5201)
PHONE 651 674-7017
Sue Williams, *Manager*
Brady Helseth, *Manager*
Jeff Krapu, *Manager*
EMP: 30 **EST:** 2005
SALES (est): 25MM-49.9MM **Privately Held**
WEB: www.chevrolet.com
SIC: 5012 Wholesales motor vehicles

(G-6500)
GUSTAFSON EXCAVATING INC
6610 410th St 230 (55056-6011)
PO Box 788 (55056-0788)
PHONE 651 674-7430
Dennis Gustafson, *President*
Kevin Gustafson, *VP Opers-Prdtn-*
EMP: 40 **EST:** 1970
SALES (est): 1MM-4.9MM **Privately Held**
SIC: 1794 Excavating contractor

(G-6501)
KARCHER FOSTER SERVICES INC
6551 Main St (55056-7030)
PHONE 651 674-2031
David C Karcher, *President*
Joy E Karcher, *Vice Pres*
Michele Goetz, *Manager*
EMP: 45 **EST:** 1998
SQ FT: 3,000
SALES (est): 1MM-4.9MM **Privately Held**
SIC: 8361 Group foster home

(G-6502)
LAKES REGION EMS INC
39840 Grand Ave (55056-6064)
PO Box 266 (55056-0266)
PHONE 651 277-4911
FAX: 651 674-4628
Todd J Fisk, *CFO*
Aarron Reinert, *Exec Dir*
EMP: 40 **EST:** 1970
SQ FT: 5,400
SALES (est): 1MM-4.9MM **Privately Held**
WEB: www.lrems.com
SIC: 4119 Ambulance service

(G-6503)
OAK INN FAMILY RESTAURANT INC
Jct I 35 And Hwy 95 (55056)
PHONE 651 674-9977
Gloria Berkstrum, *President*
EMP: 45 **EST:** 1987
SALES (est): 1MM-4.9MM **Privately Held**
WEB: www.oakinn.ca
SIC: 7299 Eating place; cocktail lounge; banquet hall facility

(G-6504)
PETERSON'S NORTH BRANCH MILL (PA)
39015 Branch Ave (55056)
PO Box 218 (55056-0218)
PHONE 651 674-4425
FAX: 651 674-7466
Jerome Peterson, *CEO*
Jeff Peterson, *President*
Chris Hamann, *Corp Secy*
Dennis Aulich, *Accountant*
EMP: 40 **EST:** 1956
SQ FT: 28,000
SALES (corp-wide): 13.34M **Privately Held**
WEB: www.petersonscountrymill.com
SIC: 5191 5153 Wholesales farm supplies; manufactures animal feed; wholesales agricultural fertilizer; wholesales agricultural chemicals; wholesales feed; wholesales grain & field beans

(G-6505)
THERMOSKIN
6459 Ash St (55056-5050)
PHONE 651 674-8302
Patrick Win, *Owner*
EMP: 40 **EST:** 2004
SALES (est): 10MM-24.9MM **Privately Held**
WEB: www.thermoskin.com
SIC: 5047 Wholesales medical equipment & supplies

(G-6506)
3R NORTH INC
Also Called: Oak Inn Restaurant
1234 Main St (55056-7019)
PO Box 398 (55056-0398)
PHONE 651 674-9977
Gloria Bergstrom, *President*
EMP: 47 **EST:** 1977
SQ FT: 6,000
SALES (est): 1MM-4.9MM **Privately Held**
SIC: 7011 Full service independent family restaurant; inn

NORTH MANKATO
Nicollet County

(G-6507)
COLOPLAST CORP
1940 Commerce Dr (56003-1700)
PHONE 507 345-6200
Tom Ryan, *President*
Richard Ash, *Vice Pres*
Randy Barranger, *Vice Pres*
Doug Rohlk, *Vice Pres*
Greg Brinkman, *Maint Mgr*
EMP: 100
SALES (est): 25MM-49.9MM **Privately Held**
SIC: 7231 Manufactures cosmetic preparations; manufactures shaving preparations; facial salon; manufactures pharmaceutical preparations
PA: Coloplast Corp
1601 W River Rd
Minneapolis MN 55411
612 337-7800

(G-6508)
LLOYD TRUSS SYSTEMS
1880 Commerce Dr (56003-1800)
PO Box 1118, Mankato (56002-1118)
PHONE 507 387-4250
FAX: 507 625-4528
Kathleen Betrand, *President*
Mike Betrand, *President*
EMP: 45 **EST:** 1943
SALES (est): 5MM-9.9MM **Privately Held**
WEB: www.lloydtruss.com

(PA)=Parent Co (HQ)=Headquarters (DH)=Div Headquarters
✿ = New business established in last 2 years

2011 Harris Minnesota
Services Directory

© Harris InfoSource 1-866-281-6415

285

SIC: **6733** Trusts, estates & agency accounts services

(G-6509)
MASTERPIECE STUDIOS INC (DH)
2080 Lookout Dr　(56003-1713)
PHONE.............................507 388-8788
Dave Humbert, *President*
Doug Faust, *Vice Pres*
Greg Jackson, *Manager*
Marilyn Fitzner, *Manager*
Annie Escalara, *Manager*
▲ **EMP:** 140 **EST:** 2005 **Privately Held**
WEB: www.masterpiecestudios.com
SIC: **5112** Wholesales stationery
HQ:　Occasions Group Inc
　　　1710 Roe Crest Dr
　　　North Mankato MN 56003
　　　507 625-6464

(G-6510)
MAYO CLINIC ROCHESTER
Also Called: Isj Clinic - Northridge
1695 Lor Ray Dr　(56003-2804)
PHONE.............................507 387-8231
FAX: 507 387-5701
Marlene Schroeder, *Office Mgr*
Joseph Y Gee MD, *Branch Mgr*
Cory J Ingram MD, *Med Doctor*
Graham Oxnard MD, *Med Doctor*
Joyce Hancock, *Supervisor*
EMP: 50
SALES (est): 5MM-9.9MM **Privately Held**
SIC: **8011** General & family practice physician or surgeon office
PA:　Mayo Clinic
　　　200 1st St SW
　　　Rochester MN 55905
　　　507 284-2511

(G-6511)
NORTH POINT
Also Called: Welcome Home Management
2135 Lor Ray Dr Apt 218　(56003-1256)
PHONE.............................507 344-0059
FAX: 507 344-1504
Peggy Thompson, *Director*
Veronica Frohling, *Director*
Tracy Simmons, *Director*
EMP: 35
SALES (est): 5MM-9.9MM **Privately Held**
SIC: **6513** Apartment building operator

(G-6512)
NOWDOCS INTERNATIONAL INC
1985 Lookout Dr　(56003-1720)
PHONE.............................888 669-3627
Brian Olsem, *CEO*
EMP: 75 **EST:** 2007
SALES (est): 5MM-9.9MM **Privately Held**
SIC: **7374** 7812 Optical scanning services; motion picture & video production services

(G-6513)
PRAIRIELAND UTILITY
1990 Lookout Dr　(56003-1705)
PHONE.............................507 625-2404
Rich Rients, *Treasurer*
EMP: 25
SALES (est): 1MM-4.9MM **Privately Held**
SIC: **8331** Educational services; skill training center

(G-6514)
TAYLOR CORP (PA)
1725 Roe Crest Dr　(56003-1807)
PHONE.............................507 625-2828
Glen A Taylor, *CEO*
Edward Alvarez, *COO*
Mark Deterding, *Vice Pres*
Al Dutcher, *Vice Pres*
Sreve Singer, *Vice Pres*
◆ **EMP:** 250 **EST:** 1948
SQ FT: 50,000 **Privately Held**
WEB: www.taylorcorp.com
SIC: **8742** Management consulting services; commercial printing; manufactures envelopes; commercial lithographic printing

(G-6515)
UNITED COMMUNICATIONS CORP
Also Called: Keyc-Tv
1570 Lookout Dr　(56003-2502)
PO Box 128, Mankato　(56002-0128)
PHONE.............................507 625-7905
Dennis Wahlstrom, *General Mgr*
EMP: 50
SALES (est): 10MM-24.9MM **Privately Held**
SIC: **4833** Television broadcasting station

NORTHFIELD
Dakota County

(G-6516)
BENJAMIN BUS INC (PA)
32611 Northfield Blvd　(55057-1491)
PHONE.............................507 645-5720
Larry Benjamin, *CEO*
John Benjamin, *President*
Pam Wiliams, *Manager*
EMP: 70 **EST:** 1971
SQ FT: 12,000 **Privately Held**
WEB: www.benjaminbus.com
SIC: **4151** School bus service

(G-6517)
NORTHFIELD HOSPITAL & SKILLED
2000 North Ave　(55057-1498)
PHONE.............................507 646-1000
Ken Bank, *President*
J Meland, *Ch Radiology*
David Oliver, *Vice Pres*
Ann Reuter, *QA Dir*
Kirsten Buedean, *Human Res Dir*
EMP: 500 **EST:** 1910
SALES (est): 25MM-49.9MM **Privately Held**
SIC: **8062** Medical hospital

(G-6518)
NORTHFIELD LINES INC
32611 Northfield Blvd　(55057-1491)
PHONE.............................507 645-5267
FAX: 507 645-5635
Larry Benjamin, *CEO*
John Benjamin, *President*
Wanda Benjamin, *Accountant*
Adam Benjamin, *Administrator*
EMP: 40 **EST:** 1952
SQ FT: 1,500
SALES (est): 1MM-4.9MM **Privately Held**
WEB: www.northfieldlines.com
SIC: **4142** 4724 Long-distance bus charter service; travel agency

(G-6519)
RICK PAVEK CONSTRUCTION
32971 Northfield Blvd　(55057-1492)
PHONE.............................507 663-0804
FAX: 507 663-1195
Rick Pavek, *Owner*
EMP: 36 **EST:** 1984
SQ FT: 6,000
SALES (est): 1MM-4.9MM **Privately Held**
WEB: www.rickpavekconstruction.com
SIC: **1799** Building site preparation service

(G-6520)
TAYLOR TRUCK LINE INC
31485 Northfield Blvd　(55057-5466)
PHONE.............................507 645-4531
FAX: 507 645-9722
Robert Taylor, *President*
Derek Brothers, *CFO*
Brian Tjaden, *CIO*
EMP: 130 **EST:** 1957
SALES (est): 10MM-24.9MM **Privately Held**
SIC: **4213** 4212 Over the road trucking; local trucking without storage services

(G-6521)
THOMAS OAS MD
Also Called: Family Health Medical Clinic
2000 North Ave　(55057-1498)
PHONE.............................507 646-1494
Kathy Burville, *Office Mgr*
Christopher S Nielsen, *Surgeon*
Jose Fulco, *Surgeon*
Ferris Timimi, *Cardiovascular*

Randolph Reister, *Internal Med*
EMP: 40 **EST:** 2007
SALES (est): 1MM-4.9MM **Privately Held**
SIC: **8011** 8031 Physicians' office; osteopathic physicians' office & clinic

(G-6522)
VIKING AUTO SALVAGE INC
26548 Chippendale Ave　(55057-5318)
PHONE.............................651 460-6166
FAX: 651 460-8444
Buford Faust, *President*
Tony Faust, *Vice Pres*
EMP: 49
SQ FT: 62,000
SALES (est): 5MM-9.9MM **Privately Held**
SIC: **5015** 5013 Wholesales used motor vehicle parts; wholesales automotive supplies & parts

NORTHFIELD
Rice County

(G-6523)
AGSTAR FINANCIAL SERVICES, ACA
1260 5th St W　(55057-1668)
PO Box 534　(55057-0534)
PHONE.............................507 645-0552
FAX: 507 645-1728
Andy Huneke, *Manager*
EMP: 25
SALES (est): 10MM-24.9MM **Privately Held**
WEB: www.agstar.com
SIC: **6159** Agricultural loan service
PA:　Agstar Financial Services, Aca
　　　1921 Premier Dr
　　　Mankato MN 56001
　　　507 387-4174

(G-6524)
BAKER LAURA SERVICES ASSN
211 Oak St　(55057-2300)
PHONE.............................507 645-8866
FAX: 507 645-8869
Sara Flom, *General Mgr*
Virginia Lorang, *Principal*
Cheryl Buck, *Vice Pres*
Bill Cowles, *Vice Pres*
Noel Statmoen, *Human Resources*
EMP: 120 **EST:** 1897
SQ FT: 14,000
SALES (est): 1MM-4.9MM **Privately Held**
WEB: www.laurabaker.org
SIC: **8322** Social services for the handicapped

(G-6525)
BIRTHRIGHT INC
500 Water St S Ste 103　(55057-2060)
PO Box 476　(55057-0476)
PHONE.............................507 645-7638
Ginger Larson, *Branch Mgr*
Dorothy Young, *Manager*
EMP: 30
SALES (est): 1MM-4.9MM **Privately Held**
WEB: www.birthright.net
SIC: **8322** Emergency & relief services
PA:　Birthright Inc
　　　3424 Hardee Ave
　　　Atlanta GA 30341
　　　770 451-6336

(G-6526)
COMMUNITY NATIONAL BANK (PA)
1605 Heritage Dr　(55057-3265)
PHONE.............................507 645-4441
FAX: 507 645-3100
Donavon Kuehnast, *President*
Betty Chapman, *Senior VP*
Brian Rykhus, *Vice Pres*
Janice Fernstrom, *Vice Pres*
Julie Cochlin, *Vice Pres*
EMP: 50 **EST:** 1878
SQ FT: 60,000 **Privately Held**
WEB: www.communitynational-bank.com
SIC: **6036** State savings bank

(G-6527)
ENEBAK CONSTRUCTION CO
Hwy 3 N　(55057)
PO Box 458　(55057-0458)
PHONE.............................507 645-8962
FAX: 507 645-9569
Robert H Enebak, *President*
Dennis Berry, *Corp Secy*
Diane Enebak, *Vice Pres*
James Docksteder, *Vice Pres*
Rick Esse, *Info Tech Mgr*
EMP: 40 **EST:** 1950
SQ FT: 9,800
SALES (est): 5MM-9.9MM **Privately Held**
WEB: www.enebak.com
SIC: **1611** General highway & street construction service; grading services; highway & street maintenance service

(G-6528)
FIRST NATIONAL BANK
329 Division St S　(55057-2071)
PO Box 59　(55057-0059)
PHONE.............................507 645-5656
FAX: 507 645-6873
David Shumway, *President*
Pam Galle, *Senior VP*
Kim Paddock, *Assistant VP*
Carolyn Seas, *Assistant VP*
Becky Bareens, *Vice Pres*
EMP: 31 **EST:** 1872
SQ FT: 3,000
SALES (est): 5MM-9.9MM **Privately Held**
WEB: www.firstnationalnfld.com
SIC: **6021** National commercial bank

(G-6529)
HETRICKS CONSTRUCTION INC
1909 Lincoln St S　(55057-3531)
PHONE.............................507 645-8629
Mark Hetrick, *President*
EMP: 25 **EST:** 2002
SALES (est): 1MM-4.9MM **Privately Held**
SIC: **1751** Window & door contractor

(G-6530)
HOLDEN FARMS INC
12346 Hall Ave　(55057-4891)
PO Box 257　(55057-0257)
PHONE.............................507 663-0003
FAX: 507 663-0079
Kent Holden, *President*
EMP: 60 **EST:** 1970 **Privately Held**
SIC: **0213** 0253 Hog & pig farming; turkey farm

(G-6531)
MCLANE MINNESOTA INC
1111 5th St W　(55057-1602)
PHONE.............................507 664-3000
FAX: 507 664-3042
William G Rosier, *CEO*
Mike Youngblood, *President*
Jim Kent, *Senior VP*
Brian N AM, *Warehouse Mgr*
Robert Corley, *Opers Staff*
EMP: 435 **EST:** 2002
SQ FT: 560,000
SALES (est): 100MM-499.9MM **Publicly Held**
WEB: www.mclaneco.com
SIC: **5141** Wholesales general line groceries
HQ:　McLane Co Inc
　　　4747 McLane Pkwy
　　　Temple TX 76504
　　　254 771-7500

(G-6532)
MINNESOTA ODD FELLOWS HOME (PA)
Also Called: Three Links Care Center
815 Forest Ave　(55057-1643)
PHONE.............................507 645-6611
Patricia J Vincent, *CEO*
Jeff King, *CFO*
Marcia Stanton, *Human Res Dir*
Barbara McKeever, *Manager*
Diane Anderson, *Director*
EMP: 175 **EST:** 1891
SQ FT: 69,500
SALES (corp-wide): 10.30M **Privately Held**
WEB: www.threelinks.org
SIC: **8051** Skilled nursing care facility

www.HarrisInfo.com
286
2011 Harris Minnesota
Services Directory
▲=Import ▼=Export
◆=Import/Export

(G-6533)
MINNESOTA ODD FELLOWS HOME
Also Called: Vital Link Three Lnks Care Ctr
815 Forest Ave (55057-1643)
PHONE.............................507 645-6611
Pat Vincent, *Administrator*
EMP: 198
SALES (est): 5MM-9.9MM **Privately Held**
WEB: www.threelinks.org
SIC: 8051 Skilled nursing care facility
PA: Minnesota Odd Fellows Home
815 Forest Ave
Northfield MN 55057
507 645-6611

(G-6534)
NASH-FINCH CO
Also Called: Econofoods Quality Care Phrm
601 Division St S (55057-2426)
PHONE.............................507 645-9514
Ann Blastervold, *Manager*
EMP: 100
SALES (est): 50MM-99.9MM **Publicly Held**
WEB: www.nashfinch.com
SIC: 5141 Wholesales general line groceries
PA: Nash-Finch Co
7600 France Ave S Ste 200
Edina MN 55435
952 832-0534

(G-6535)
NASH-FINCH CO
Also Called: Econofoods Pharmacy 330
603 Division St S (55057-2426)
PHONE.............................507 645-4489
EMP: 95
SALES (est): 100MM-499.9MM **Publicly Held**
WEB: www.nashfinch.com
SIC: 5122 Wholesales pharmaceuticals
PA: Nash-Finch Co
7600 France Ave S Ste 200
Edina MN 55435
952 832-0534

(G-6536)
NORTHFIELD CARE CENTER INC
900 Cannon Valley Dr W (55057-1334)
PHONE.............................507 645-9511
FAX: 507 645-9758
Tom Nielsen, *Opers Mgr*
Mary Thorne, *Manager*
Kyle Nordine, *Exec Dir*
Emelda Rasmussen, *Director*
James Mobert, *Maintence Staff*
EMP: 123 **EST:** 1969
SQ FT: 45,000
SALES (est): 1MM-4.9MM **Privately Held**
SIC: 8052 8051 8361 Intermediate care facility; residential care facility; skilled nursing care facility

(G-6537)
NORTHFIELD CONSTRUCTION CO INC
1600 Riverview Ln (55057-3139)
PHONE.............................507 645-8975
FAX: 507 663-0315
Ray Cox, *President*
Jeff Musehl, *Project Mgr*
EMP: 28 **EST:** 1972
SQ FT: 9,000
SALES (est): 5MM-9.9MM **Privately Held**
WEB: www.northfieldconstruction.net
SIC: 1542 1521 Commercial & institutional building construction; single-family housing construction

(G-6538)
NORTHFIELD MANOR INC
901 Cannon Valley Dr W # 120
(55057-3350)
PHONE.............................507 645-9090
Kyle Nordine, *CEO*
Lois Burgoyne, *Manager*
EST: 1979 **Privately Held**
SIC: 8361 Home for the elderly

(G-6539)
PERKINS MOTOR TRANSPORT INC
1800 Riverview Dr (55057-3292)
PHONE.............................651 463-4600
FAX: 651 463-2317
Neil Perkins, *President*
Roger V Eldhuizen V, *Controller*
▲ **EMP:** 42 **EST:** 1948
SQ FT: 16,000
SALES (est): 5MM-9.9MM **Privately Held**
WEB: www.perkinsonline.com
SIC: 4213 Heavy hauling transportation services

(G-6540)
QSC OF NORTHFIELD INC
450 Armstrong Rd (55057-4912)
PO Box 171 (55057-0171)
PHONE.............................507 366-7149
Danny Ayotte, *President*
EMP: 50 **EST:** 1990
SALES (est): 1MM-4.9MM **Privately Held**
SIC: 7349 Building cleaning & maintenance services

(G-6541)
REESE, WINTER & ASSOCIATES LTD
112 5th St W (55057-2006)
PO Box 76 (55057-0076)
PHONE.............................507 645-4473
FAX: 507 645-4615
Phillip Winter, *President*
George Bultman, *Corp Secy*
Dave Beranek, *Vice Pres*
Bruce Rippenprop, *Vice Pres*
David Sandquist, *Accounting Dir*
EST: 1966
SQ FT: 3,200 **Privately Held**
SIC: 8721 Accounting service

(G-6542)
3 BR'S INC
517 Loomis Ct (55057-1318)
PHONE.............................507 645-8600
Jack Kelly, *CEO*
Scott Kelly, *President*
Ana Kelly, *Member*
EMP: 30 **EST:** 1998
SALES (est): 1MM-4.9MM **Privately Held**
WEB: www.3brs.com
SIC: 7389 5192 Magazine & newspaper subscription fulfillment service; wholesales newspapers

(G-6543)
TOM KELLY
Also Called: Envirotec
204 7th St W (55057-2419)
PHONE.............................507 645-7464
Tom Kelly, *Owner*
EMP: 40 **EST:** 1999
SALES (est): 1MM-4.9MM **Privately Held**
SIC: 7379 Computer related maintenance service

(G-6544)
TRANSWAY EXPRESS INC
812 Water St S (55057-2437)
PHONE.............................651 686-7000
Chuck Allot, *President*
EMP: 42 **EST:** 2004
SALES (est): 5MM-9.9MM **Privately Held**
SIC: 4731 8742 Truck transportation brokers; transportation consultant

(G-6545)
WELLS FARGO BANK, NATIONAL
700 Water St S (55057-2435)
PHONE.............................507 663-7300
FAX: 507 663-7312
Mark Mohlke, *Manager*
EMP: 30
SALES (est): 5MM-9.9MM **Publicly Held**
SIC: 6021 National commercial bank
HQ: Wfc Holdings, Corp
420 Montgomery St
San Francisco CA 94104
415 396-7392

(G-6546)
WILLING PARTNERS INC
Also Called: Willinger's Golf Club
6900 Canby Trl (55057-4735)
PHONE.............................952 652-2500
Howard Samb, *President*
Jordan Kuzma, *Superintendent*
Pete Stauffer, *Principal*
Robert Enbak Jr, *Vice Pres*
EMP: 35 **EST:** 1991
SALES (est): 1MM-4.9MM **Privately Held**
WEB: www.willingpartners.com
SIC: 7992 Public golf course; retails golf goods & equipment

NORTHOME
Koochiching County

(G-6547)
NORTHOME HEALTH CARE INC
Also Called: Tealwood Care Centers
Main St (56661)
PHONE.............................218 897-5235
Leonard Jankowski, *President*
Nick Berg, *Principal*
Joanne Jankowski, *Corp Secy*
William Eckblad, *Administrator*
EMP: 70 **EST:** 1968
SQ FT: 8,000
SALES (est): 1MM-4.9MM **Privately Held**
SIC: 8051 Skilled nursing care facility

NORTHROP
Martin County

(G-6548)
BAARTS TRUCKING INC
206 Von Holst St (56075)
PO Box 85 (56075-0085)
PHONE.............................507 436-5536
Larry E Baarts, *President*
Bonita Baarts, *Corp Secy*
Lynn Pettit, *Vice Pres*
Lee Baarts, *Treasurer*
EMP: 50 **EST:** 1995
SQ FT: 3,000
SALES (est): 5MM-9.9MM **Privately Held**
SIC: 4213 4212 Over the road trucking; local trucking without storage services

OAKDALE
Washington County

(G-6549)
CHRISTOPHER J FALLERT MD
1099 Helmo Ave N Ste 100 (55128-6034)
PHONE.............................651 731-4300
Christophe J Fallert MD, *Owner*
Diane Rauvola, *Manager*
EMP: 40
SALES (est): 1MM-4.9MM **Privately Held**
SIC: 8011 Physicians' office & clinic

(G-6550)
DEDICATED LOGISTICS INC (PA)
2900 Granada Ln N (55128-3607)
PO Box 75784, Saint Paul (55175-0784)
PHONE.............................651 631-5918
Thomas G Wintz, *President*
Dennis J Bierschbach, *Senior VP*
Scott Carlson, *Vice Pres*
Jerry Simpson, *Purchasing*
John Roemer, *Engineer*
▲ **EMP:** 350 **EST:** 1995 **Privately Held**
SIC: 4213 4212 4225 Over the road trucking; local trucking without storage services; warehousing & storage services

(G-6551)
IMATION ENTERPRISES CORP
1 Imation Way (55128-3421)
PHONE.............................651 704-4000
FAX: 651 704-4128
Michael Borowski, *Corp Secy*
John L Sullivan, *Senior VP*
Nobuyoshi Kawasaki, *Vice Pres*
Randy J Christofferson, *Vice Pres*
Subodh K Kulkami, *Vice Pres*
EMP: 550 **EST:** 1996
SQ FT: 1,000,000
SALES (est): 100MM-499.9MM **Publicly Held**
WEB: www.imation.com
SIC: 5112 Manufactures magnetic disks & drums; wholesales data processing supplies; manufactures magnetic tape; manufactures electromedical equipment
PA: Imation Corp
1 Imation Way
Oakdale MN 55128
651 704-4000

(G-6552)
PACE ANALYTICAL LIFE SCIENCES
1281 Helmo Ave N (55128-6022)
PHONE.............................651 738-2728
FAX: 651 733-6196
Steve A Vanderboom, *Member*
Christian Edwardson, *Manager*
Chad Healy, *Manager*
Jim Meyer, *Manager*
Angela Rollag, *Administrator*
EMP: 50 **EST:** 2006 **Privately Held**
SIC: 8731 Commercial research laboratory
PA: Lab Holdings Inc
7901 Xerxes Ave S Ste 201
Minneapolis MN 55431
612 607-1700

ODESSA
Big Stone County

(G-6553)
BITUMINOUS PAVING INC
43153 County Rd 21 (56276)
PO Box 6, Ortonville (56278-0006)
PHONE.............................320 273-2113
FAX: 320 273-2120
Jerry Bajari, *President*
Ann Bajari, *Corp Secy*
Colin Alama, *Vice Pres*
Bill Bajari, *Treasurer*
EMP: 163 **EST:** 1980
SQ FT: 1,960
SALES (est): 10MM-24.9MM **Privately Held**
SIC: 1611 Highway & street paving contractor

OGEMA
Becker County

(G-6554)
INDIAN HEALTH SERVICE
Also Called: White Earth Health Center
40520 County Highway 34 (56569-9612)
PHONE.............................218 983-6317
FAX: 218 983-6396
Fred Koebrick, *Manager*
Loretta Sullivan, *IT Specialist*
John Arthur, *Exec Dir*
John McArthur, *Director*
Zane C Rising Sun, *Director*
EMP: 100
SALES (est): 5MM-9.9MM **Privately Held**
WEB: www.navajo.ihs.gov
SIC: 8093 Specialty outpatient clinic
DH: Indian Health Service
801 Thompson Ave Fl 4
Rockville MD 20852
301 443-1083

(G-6555)
WHITE EARTH RESERVATION
35525 County Highway 34 (56569-9526)
PHONE.............................218 983-3387
Dave Murray, *Principal*
EMP: 90 **Privately Held**
SIC: 8399 Social services

(PA)=Parent Co (HQ)=Headquarters (DH)=Div Headquarters
✿ = New business established in last 2 years

2011 Harris Minnesota
Services Directory

© Harris InfoSource 1-866-281-6415
287

OKABENA
Jackson County

(G-6556)

HARTMAN BANCSHARES INC
Also Called: First State Bank
117 S Minnesota Ave (56161-4003)
PO Box 67 (56161-0067)
PHONE 507 853-4421
Dennis P Hartman, *President*
EST: 1981 **Privately Held**
SIC: 6022 State commercial bank

OKLEE
Red Lake County

(G-6557)

INTER-COUNTY COMMUNITY COUNCIL
207 Main St (56742)
PO Box 189 (56742-0189)
PHONE 218 796-5144
FAX: 218 796-5175
Betty Tangen, *Exec Dir*
Robert Melby, *Director*
EMP: 35 **EST:** 1967 **Privately Held**
SIC: 8399 8322 8351 Social change
association; head Start center; individual &
family social services

(G-6558)

TRIPLE D CONSTRUCTION
Csah 5 (56742)
PHONE 218 465-4249
Gary Duray, *President*
Jeff Duray, *Corp Secy*
Dennis Duray, *Treasurer*
EMP: 25 **EST:** 1984
SQ FT: 5,760
SALES (est): 1MM-4.9MM **Privately Held**
SIC: 1794 Excavation & grading, building
construction contractor

OLIVIA
Renville County

(G-6559)

ADULT CLIENT TRAINING SERVICE
802 E Fairview Ave (56277-1368)
PHONE 320 523-5666
FAX: 320 523-5766
Karen Borden, *Director*
EMP: 50 **EST:** 1967
SQ FT: 15,000
SALES (est): 1MM-4.9MM **Privately Held**
WEB: www.acts-ability.org
SIC: 8322 Individual & family social services

(G-6560)

BEVERLY ENTERPRISES - MN
Also Called: Olivia Healthcare Center
1003 W Maple Ave (56277-1063)
PHONE 320 523-1652
FAX: 320 523-5734
David Herder, *Director*
EMP: 100
SALES (est): 1MM-4.9MM **Privately Held**
WEB: www.beverlynet.com
SIC: 8051 Skilled nursing care facility
HQ: Beverly Enterprises - MN
650 Ramer Ave S
Rush City MN 55069
320 358-4765

(G-6561)

GAUB INC
33102 County Road 17 (56277-2552)
PHONE 320 382-8075
Leroy Gaub, *President*
Paul Gaub, *Corp Secy*
Jacque Gaub, *Vice Pres*
EMP: 48 **EST:** 1949
SALES (est): 5MM-9.9MM **Privately Held**
SIC: 1623 Sewer line construction; water
main construction

(G-6562)

PALMER BUS SERVICE OF BOLD MN
115 S 1st St (56277)
PO Box 2026, Mankato (56002-2026)
PHONE 507 386-0210
Floyd Palmer, *CEO*
Chris Champlin, *CFO*
EMP: 25
SALES (est): 1MM-4.9MM **Privately Held**
SIC: 4119 Local passenger transportation
service

(G-6563)

RENVILLE COUNTY EMERGENCY FOOD
902 W Depue Ave (56277-1247)
PHONE 320 523-5339
Artis Wertish, *President*
Sylvia Welsh, *Corp Secy*
Mary Schropfer, *Treasurer*
Esther Wittenberg, *Administrator*
Valerie Mersch, *Director*
EMP: 36 **EST:** 1983
SALES (est): 1MM-4.9MM **Privately Held**
SIC: 8322 Individual & family social services

(G-6564)

RENVILLE COUNTY HOSPICE INC
611 E Fairview Ave Ste A (56277-4214)
PHONE 320 523-1261
FAX: 320 523-3430
Tim Middendorf, *CEO*
Paul E Buhr, *Ch Cardiology*
James Cosgriff, *Ch Radiology*
Maxine Broderius, *Vice Pres*
Anne Groen, *Purchasing*
EMP: 100 **EST:** 1951
SQ FT: 55,000
SALES (est): 5MM-9.9MM **Privately Held**
SIC: 8062 Medical hospital

(G-6565)

TAYLOR & KATIE INC
2425 W Lincoln Ave (56277-1732)
PHONE 320 523-2833
FAX: 320 523-5000
Traci M Buchtel, *CEO*
Corey Buchgeo, *Corp Secy*
EMP: 50 **EST:** 2005
SALES (est): 1MM-4.9MM **Privately Held**
SIC: 8741 Restaurant management
services

ONAMIA
Mille Lacs County

(G-6566)

BCR REAL ESTATE SERVICES
9648 385th St (56359-7861)
PHONE 320 532-4099
Harold Cook, *Owner*
EMP: 25 **EST:** 1996
SALES (est): 1MM-4.9MM **Privately Held**
SIC: 6531 Real estate agency & broker; real
estate appraiser

(G-6567)

CAMP ONAMIA INC
14202 Shakopee Lake Rd (56359-2203)
PHONE 320 532-3767
FAX: 320 532-5260
Barbara Lewison, *President*
Julie Smith, *Exec Dir*
Jerry Olstead, *Director*
John Pedersen, *Director*
EMP: 50 **EST:** 1949
SALES (est): 1MM-4.9MM **Privately Held**
WEB: www.onomia.org
SIC: 7032 Recreational & sporting camp

(G-6568)

CORPORATE COMMISSION OF THE (HQ)
Also Called: Grand Casino Mille Lacs
777 Grand Ave (56359-4500)
PO Box 343 (56359-0343)
PHONE 320 532-8800
FAX: 320 449-5992

Deron Dunkley, *Principal*
Lon Burr, *Vice Pres*
John Loucas, *Vice Pres*
Vernon Robertson, *Vice Pres*
Ned Weizenegger, *Engineer*
EMP: 1200 **EST:** 1991
SQ FT: 40,000 **Privately Held**
WEB: www.grcasinos.com
SIC: 7993 7011 Gambling establishments
operating coin-operated machines; traveler
accommodations; full service American
restaurant; retail gift shop; drinking
establishment
PA: Mille Lacs Band of Ojibwe
43408 Oodena Dr
Onamia MN 56359
320 532-4181

(G-6569)

CORPORATE COMMISSION OF THE
700 Grand Ave (56359-4500)
PHONE 320 532-8862
Sarah Oquist, *President*
Sam Premo, *Manager*
Bernida Churchhill, *Manager*
EMP: 50 **EST:** 2007
SALES (est): 1MM-4.9MM **Privately Held**
SIC: 8721 Accounting service

(G-6570)

EDDY'S LAKE MILLE LACS RESORT
41334 Shakopee Lake Rd (56359-2230)
PHONE 320 532-3657
David Bentley, *Principal*
David Macarthur, *Manager*
EMP: 35 **EST:** 1991
SALES (est): 1MM-4.9MM **Privately Held**
WEB: www.eddysresort.com
SIC: 7999 7011 Ice skating rink; resort
hotel; pleasure boat rental services;
recreation services

(G-6571)

HILLCO REAL ESTATE HOLDINGS
205 Lindquist St (56359-2553)
PHONE 320 532-3237
William Hill Jr, *Member*
EMP: 30
SALES (est): 5MM-9.9MM **Privately Held**
SIC: 6531 Real estate services

(G-6572)

INDIAN HEALTH SERVICE
Also Called: Ne-Ia-Shing Clinic
43500 Migizi Dr (56359-2241)
PHONE 320 532-4163
Keith Modglin, *MIS Dir*
Sheldon Boyd, *IT/INT Sup*
Sam Moose, *Director*
Roger John, *Nursing Dir*
Ann M Landin, *Officer*
EMP: 60
SALES (est): 5MM-9.9MM **Privately Held**
WEB: www.navajo.ihs.gov
SIC: 8011 Physicians' office & clinic; public
health program services; federal
government administration of public health
programs
DH: Indian Health Service
801 Thompson Ave Fl 4
Rockville MD 20852
301 443-1083

(G-6573)

IZATYS GROUP LLC
40005 85th Ave (56359-7841)
PHONE 320 532-3101
Dave Kramber, *Member*
Mark Graebner, *VP Opers*
Diane Cash, *Controller*
Kenneth C Glasgow, *VP Finance*
Jason Tollette, *Manager*
EMP: 35 **EST:** 1987
SALES (est): 1MM-4.9MM **Privately Held**
WEB: www.izatys.com
SIC: 7011 6531 7992 Resort hotel; retails
golf goods & equipment; eating place; real
estate rental agency; public golf course;
drinking establishment

(G-6574)

MILLE LACS HEALTH SYSTEM
200 Elm St N (56359-7901)
PHONE 320 532-3154
FAX: 320 532-3111
Alice Buckalew, *Superintendent*
Kathy Johnson, *COO*
Tom H Bracken, *Vice Pres*
Patrick Dunleavy, *Purch Mgr*
Gerald Vogtlin, *Engineering*
EMP: 300 **EST:** 1953
SQ FT: 45,000
SALES (est): 25MM-49.9MM **Privately Held**
WEB: www.millelacshealth.com
SIC: 8062 8011 8051 Medical hospital;
skilled nursing care facility; physicians'
office & clinic

(G-6575)

ONMIA MANOR
100 Elm St S Apt 125 (56359-9629)
PHONE 320 982-5405
Brittany Campion, *Manager*
EMP: 75 **EST:** 2006
SALES (est): 5MM-9.9MM **Privately Held**
SIC: 8748 Urban planning & consulting
services

(G-6576)

SASKER MANUFACTURING INC
34769 US Highway 169 (56359-2317)
PO Box 178 (56359-0178)
PHONE 320 532-4268
Cliff Sasker, *President*
Roy Delanney, *Mfg Staff*
EMP: 30 **EST:** 1975
SQ FT: 45,000
SALES (est): 1MM-4.9MM **Privately Held**
SIC: 7692 Manufactures prefabricated
metal buildings & components; welding
service

ORR
Saint Louis County

(G-6577)

BRUNS INC
Also Called: Pelican Bay Foods
4539 Highway 53 (55771-8322)
PO Box 276 (55771-0276)
PHONE 218 757-3232
FAX: 218 757-0141
Paul Bruns, *President*
Zelda Bruns, *Vice Pres*
EMP: 30 **EST:** 1985
SALES (est): 1MM-4.9MM **Privately Held**
SIC: 7538 Retail supermarket chain;
general automotive repair services

ORTONVILLE
Big Stone County

(G-6578)

BIG STONE COMMUNITY HOMES INC
Also Called: Monarch Heights
501 Burdick Ave (56278-1167)
PHONE 320 839-6139
FAX: 320 839-2060
Joyce Hansen, *Corp Secy*
Sara Mathes, *Corp Secy*
Kristen Unruh, *Director*
EMP: 25 **EST:** 1982
SQ FT: 5,000
SALES (est): 1MM-4.9MM **Privately Held**
SIC: 8361 6513 8052 Home for the mentally
handicapped; intermediate care facility;
home for the physically handicapped;
apartment building operator

(G-6579)

CITY OF ORTONVILLE
Also Called: Ortonville Area Health Svcs
450 Eastvold Ave (56278-1252)
PHONE 320 839-2502
FAX: 320 839-2507
Robert S Ross, *Ch of Surgery*
Ranet Shmeichel, *Opers Mgr*
Kim Anderson, *Purchasing*
Marilyn Homrighausen, *Envir Svcs Dir*

Shane Bauer, *Engineer*
EMP: 200
SALES (est): 10MM-24.9MM **Privately Held**
WEB: www.ortonville.net
SIC: 8062 Medical hospital
PA: City of Ortonville
217 3rd St NW 101
Ortonville MN 56278
320 839-3428

(G-6580)
CITY OF ORTONVILLE
Also Called: Northridge Nursing Home
1075 Roy St (56278-1141)
PHONE 320 839-6113
FAX: 320 839-2985
Kim M Crea, *Principal*
Cindy Jorgenson, *Exec Dir*
Marge Dragseth, *Hlthcr Dir*
EMP: 75
SALES (est): 1MM-4.9MM **Privately Held**
WEB: www.ortonville.net
SIC: 8059 8051 Nursing home; skilled
nursing care facility
PA: City of Ortonville
217 3rd St NW 101
Ortonville MN 56278
320 839-3428

(G-6581)
D C C SOLUTIONOLUTIONS
105 2nd St NW (56278-1408)
PO Box 184 (56278-0184)
PHONE 320 839-2058
FAX: 320 839-2095
Kristi Hicks, *Principal*
Dave Buff, *Member*
EMP: 35 **EST:** 2004
SALES (est): 1MM-4.9MM **Privately Held**
SIC: 8999 Communication services

(G-6582)
DALLAS I HANSON CONSTRUCTION
700 US Highway 75 (56278-4084)
PO Box 235 (56278-0235)
PHONE 320 839-3455
FAX: 320 839-2411
Dallas I Hanson, *President*
Marilyn L Hanson, *Corp Secy*
Ron Athey, *Treasurer*
Susan Caggiano, *Manager*
EMP: 45 **EST:** 1986
SQ FT: 4,000
SALES (est): 10MM-24.9MM **Privately Held**
WEB: www.utas.edu.au
SIC: 1542 1541 1771 Commercial & office
building contractor; sidewalk contractor;
concrete contractor; industrial building &
warehouse construction

(G-6583)
HASSLEN CONSTRUCTION CO INC
45 1st St SE (56278-1501)
PO Box 157 (56278-0157)
PHONE 320 839-2529
FAX: 320 839-2339
Dan Hasslen, *President*
Ardell Hasslen, *Corp Secy*
Brent Hasslen, *Exec VP*
Maureen Laughlin, *Manager*
Carol Paffe, *Administration*
EMP: 40 **EST:** 1893
SQ FT: 2,800
SALES (est): 10MM-24.9MM **Privately Held**
WEB: www.hasslenconstruction.com
SIC: 1542 Commercial & office building
contractor

(G-6584)
OCCUPRO INC
820 Roy St (56278-1138)
PHONE 320 839-4090
Roman Taffe, *President*
EMP: 25
SALES (est): 1MM-4.9MM **Privately Held**
SIC: 8049 Occupational therapist office

OSAGE
Becker County

(G-6585)
NORTH STAR NURSING INC
22119 480th Ave (56570-9554)
PHONE 218 573-2238
FAX: 218 573-3778
Heidi Gibson, *President*
Helen Drewes, *CFO*
EMP: 50 **EST:** 2001
SALES (est): 1MM-4.9MM **Privately Held**
SIC: 8051 Skilled nursing care facility

OSAKIS
Douglas County

(G-6586)
COMMUNITY MEMORIAL HOME INC
Also Called: Terrace Hts As Living Apartmnt
410 W Main St (56360-8243)
PHONE 320 859-2111
FAX: 320 859-3288
Brenda Majerus, *Manager*
Heidi Cietielinski, *Manager*
Debbie Walter, *Manager*
Dave Carlson, *Administrator*
Dick Letcher, *MIS Dir*
EMP: 100 **EST:** 1961
SALES (est): 1MM-4.9MM **Privately Held**
SIC: 8051 6513 8052 Skilled nursing care
facility; intermediate care facility; apartment
building operator

(G-6587)
ROLLIE'S SALES & SERVICE INC
Hwy 27 W Ste 13790 (56360)
PO Box E (56360-0605)
PHONE 320 859-4811
FAX: 320 829-3585
Dale A Walsh, *President*
Julie Ferno, *Corp Secy*
Bridgett Melvin, *Office Mgr*
EMP: 25 **EST:** 1988
SQ FT: 44,000
SALES (est): 1MM-4.9MM **Privately Held**
WEB: www.rolliessales.com
SIC: 1799 5084 Gasoline pump installation;
manufactures fabric canopies made from
purchased materials; wholesales industrial
machinery & equipment

OSLO
Marshall County

(G-6588)
GOWAN CONSTRUCTION INC
3596 15th St NE (56744-9108)
PO Box 228 (56744-0228)
PHONE 701 699-5171
FAX: 701 699-3400
Milton Gowan, *President*
Mark Gowan, *Vice Pres*
Raymond Gowan, *Vice Pres*
Erika Martens, *Manager*
Steven Mack, *Manager*
EMP: 50 **EST:** 1962
SQ FT: 15,000
SALES (est): 5MM-9.9MM **Privately Held**
WEB: www.gowanconstruction.com
SIC: 1611 Grading services

OSSEO
Hennepin County

(G-6589)
A D B CONSTRUCTION CO INC
9240 Cottonwood Ln N (55369-3917)
PHONE 763 424-5550
Barry Blazevic, *President*
Nick Blazevic, *Vice Pres*
EMP: 30 **EST:** 1971
SQ FT: 3,000
SALES (est): 1MM-4.9MM **Privately Held**
SIC: 1771 Concrete repair contractor

(G-6590)
ABC MINNEAPOLIS LLC
Also Called: Auction Broadcasting Co
18270 Territorial Rd (55369-9225)
PO Box 360 (55369-0360)
PHONE 763 428-8777
FAX: 763 428-8701
Jay Fahrendorff, *General Mgr*
Chuck Eck, *General Mgr*
Thomas R Miller, *Member*
Daniel R Dunn, *Member*
Heather Alt, *Member*
EMP: 150 **EST:** 1997
SALES (est): 100MM-499.9MM **Privately Held**
SIC: 5012 Automobile auction services;
used car dealer

(G-6591)
AC TRANSPORTATION INC
Also Called: Clinic Cab
11785 Justen Cir (55369-9282)
PHONE 763 235-2222
Matthew Liveringhouse, *CEO*
EMP: 32 **EST:** 1995
SQ FT: 10,000
SALES (est): 1MM-4.9MM **Privately Held**
SIC: 4119 Local passenger transportation
service

(G-6592)
ACI CONSTRUCTION INC
11225 90th Ave N Ste 100 (55369-4531)
PHONE 763 424-9191
FAX: 763 424-9190
James Bebo, *President*
Ted Christian, *COO*
EMP: 35 **EST:** 1991
SQ FT: 12,000
SALES (est): 5MM-9.9MM **Privately Held**
WEB: www.aciasphalt.com
SIC: 1611 Street surfacing & paving
construction

(G-6593)
AERO-METRIC INC
Also Called: Markhurd
13400 68th Ave N (55311-3516)
PHONE 763 420-9606
FAX: 763 420-9584
Pat Olson, *Vice Pres*
Marvin Miller, *Sales/Mktg Mgr*
S Eckert, *Controller*
EMP: 32
SALES (est): 1MM-4.9MM **Privately Held**
WEB: www.aerometric.com
SIC: 8713 7335 7389 Photogrammetric
engineers; aerial photography services;
mapmaking service
PA: AERO-METRIC INC
4020 Technology Pkwy
Sheboygan WI 53083
920 457-3631

(G-6594)
APPOLLO SYSTEMS INC
6250 Sycamore Ln N 500B (55369-6309)
PHONE 763 493-5821
Dave Willis, *CEO*
Matt Thompson, *Corp Secy*
Dan Woody, *Vice Pres*
Bryan Cremeen, *CFO*
Roland Willis, *Treasurer*
EMP: 25 **EST:** 1990
SALES (est): 1MM-4.9MM **Privately Held**
WEB: www.focis.com
SIC: 1731 Fire detection & burglar alarm
systems specialization contractor;
communications contractor services

(G-6595)
ATLANTIS TECHNICAL SERVICES
11230 86th Ave N (55369-4510)
PHONE 763 657-2500
David N Nylender, *President*
EMP: 45 **EST:** 2002
SALES (est): 1MM-4.9MM **Privately Held**
WEB: www.atsmn.com
SIC: 7363 Help supply services

(G-6596)
ATLAS FOUNDATION CO
11730 Brockton Ln N (55369-9326)
PO Box 117, Rogers (55374-0117)
PHONE 763 428-2261
FAX: 763 428-4754
Paul S Weingart, *President*
Elizabeth Gunderson, *Corp Secy*
Mike Morller, *Vice Pres*
David I Peterson, *Treasurer*
George E Stannard, *Consultant*
EMP: 50 **EST:** 1968
SQ FT: 4,000
SALES (est): 5MM-9.9MM **Privately Held**
WEB: www.atlasfoundation.com
SIC: 1629 7699 Pile driving service; caisson
drilling service; rust preventive coating
service; manufactures hot wound helical
springs used in railroad equipment;
miscellaneous building item repair service

(G-6597)
AVIV HEALTH CARE INC
Also Called: Berkshire Residence
501 2nd St SE (55369-1603)
PHONE 763 425-3939
FAX: 763 424-2777
Susan Thompson, *General Mgr*
Patti Lundquist, *Manager*
Dale Armitage, *Administrator*
EMP: 123
SALES (est): 1MM-4.9MM **Privately Held**
SIC: 8059 8052 Nursing home; intermediate
care facility

(G-6598)
BARTON SAND & GRAVEL CO
10633 89th Ave N (55369-4041)
PHONE 763 425-4191
Gary B Sauer, *President*
Dale Blum, *Manager*
EMP: 25
SALES (est): 1MM-4.9MM **Privately Held**
WEB: www.tillercorp.com
SIC: 1442 Construction sand & gravel
mining
PA: Tiller Corp
7200 Hemlock Ln N Ste 200
Maple Grove MN 55369
763 425-4191

(G-6599)
BETTE DICKENSON RESEARCH INC
7468 Mariner Dr (55311-2611)
PHONE 763 420-4385
Bette Dickenson, *President*
EMP: 75 **EST:** 1969
SALES (est): 5MM-9.9MM **Privately Held**
SIC: 8732 Market analysis or research
services

(G-6600)
BROOK WEST FAMILY DENTISTRY
7950 Mainstreet Ste 205 (55369-7170)
PHONE 763 561-8901
David Domass, *President*
John C Smith, *Principal*
Susan K Johnson, *Manager*
EMP: 30 **EST:** 1983
SALES (est): 1MM-4.9MM **Privately Held**
WEB: www.brookwest.com
SIC: 8021 Dental office

(G-6601)
CAMDEN PHYSICIANS LTD
12000 Elm Creek Blvd N # 13
(55369-7073)
PHONE 763 420-5822
Anita Beckstrand, *Site Mgr*
Richard M Gebhart, *Director*
Gay Lentfer, *Physician Asst*
EMP: 33
SALES (est): 1MM-4.9MM **Privately Held**
SIC: 8011 Clinic operated by physicians

(G-6602)
CHAPELWOOD COMMUNITY
16500 92nd Ave N Apt 109 (55311-5468)
PHONE 763 493-5910
Darel Farr, *Owner*
EMP: 30 **EST:** 2001

(PA)=Parent Co (HQ)=Headquarters (DH)=Div Headquarters
✿ = New business established in last 2 years
2011 Harris Minnesota
Services Directory
© Harris InfoSource 1-866-281-6415
289

SALES (est):1MM-4.9MM **Privately Held**
SIC: 6513 Apartment building operator

(G-6603)
CINTAS CORP NO 2
11500 95th Ave N   (55369-5559)
PHONE..............................763 425-6666
Chris Cox, *General Mgr*
Norma Parr, *Manager*
Dan Wagner, *Manager*
Dave Marta, *Manager*
EMP: 200
SALES (est): 10MM-24.9MM **Privately Held**
SIC: 7213 7218 Uniform supply service;
industrial laundry service
PA: Cintas Corp
     6800 Cintas Blvd
     Cincinnati OH 45262
     513 459-1200

(G-6604)
CONNECTIVITY SOLUTIONS INC OF
6250 Sycamore Ln N # 500   (55369-6309)
PHONE..............................763 424-7300
Guy Willis, *President*
Scott Estrem, *Corp Secy*
EMP: 52 EST: 1998
SQ FT: 7,800
SALES (est): 5MM-9.9MM **Privately Held**
SIC: 1623 Telephone & communication line
construction; manufactures data conversion
equipment

(G-6605)
COUNSELOR REALTY INC
13601 80th Cir N Ste 300   (55369-8906)
PHONE..............................763 420-7080
Mike Rotter, *Corp Counsel*
Pete Crema, *Manager*
Terri L Holm, *Office Admin*
EMP: 120
SALES (est): 10MM-24.9MM **Privately Held**
WEB: www.counselorrealty.com
SIC: 6531 Real estate services
PA: Counselor Realty Inc
     7766 Highway 65 NE Ste 1
     Minneapolis MN 55432
     763 786-0600

(G-6606)
CS MCCROSSAN INC (PA)
7865 Jefferson Hwy   (55369-4900)
PO Box 1240   (55311-6240)
PHONE..............................763 425-4167
FAX: 763 425-1255
Charles S Mc Crossan, *President*
Thomas M Crossan, *Corp Secy*
John McCrossan, *Vice Pres*
Tom J Rooney, *Asst Sec*
EMP: 150 EST: 1953
SQ FT: 50,000 **Privately Held**
SIC: 1611 1622 1799 Highway & street
paving contractor; bridge construction; pipe
& boiler insulating contractor

(G-6607)
D M S HEALTH GROUP
11600 96th Ave N   (55369-5554)
PHONE..............................763 315-1947
Mark Doda, *President*
Ben Sanderson, *COO*
Buck Fechik, *Med Doctor*
EMP: 25 EST: 2003
SALES (est): 10MM-24.9MM **Privately Held**
WEB: www.dmshg.com
SIC: 5047 7299 Wholesales hospital
equipment & furniture; personal appearance
service
HQ: DMS Health Technologies Inc
     2101 University Dr N
     Fargo ND 58102
     701 237-9073

(G-6608)
DAYTON FREIGHT LINES INC
10001 89th Ave N   (55369-4033)
PHONE..............................763 493-5841
FAX: 763 493-5870
Matthew Glocke, *Manager*
EMP: 50
SALES (est): 5MM-9.9MM **Privately Held**
WEB: www.daytonfreight.com
SIC: 4213 4731 Contract haulers; freight
transportation arrangement services

(G-6609)
DEHN'S COUNTRY MANOR INC
11281 Fernbrook Ln N   (55369-9356)
PHONE..............................763 420-6460
FAX: 763 420-8619
Allen I Dehn, *President*
Phyllis Dehn, *Vice Pres*
EMP: 29 EST: 1957
SALES (est): 500-999K **Privately Held**
SIC: 7011 Full service independent family
restaurant; traveler accommodations

(G-6610)
DOMAINE SRENE VINEYARDS WINERY
Also Called: Rockblock Cellers
6701 Evenstad Dr N   (55369-6026)
PHONE..............................763 473-4412
Ken Evenstad, *President*
Grace Evenstad, *Vice Pres*
EST: 1989 **Privately Held**
WEB: www.domaineserene.com
SIC: 0762 Vineyard management &
maintenance services

(G-6611)
E & A PRODUCTS INC
Also Called: Beth-Fast
11885 Brockton Ln N   (55369-9319)
PHONE..............................763 493-3222
FAX: 763 493-3214
Mark Engstrom, *President*
EMP: 25 EST: 1977
SQ FT: 80,000
SALES (est): 10MM-24.9MM **Privately Held**
WEB: www.ea-products.com
SIC: 5072 Wholesales hardware;
wholesales bolts; wholesales hardware
nuts; wholesales screws

(G-6612)
EDELWEISS HOME HEALTH CARE
7014 E Fish Lake Rd   (55311-2832)
PHONE..............................763 315-1050
FAX: 763 315-1090
Ethel Austin, *Owner*
EMP: 40 EST: 2003
SALES (est): 1MM-4.9MM **Privately Held**
WEB: www.edelhomecare.com
SIC: 8082 Home health care services

(G-6613)
EFFICIO GROUP INC
15966 71st Pl N   (55311-2543)
PHONE..............................612 805-7288
Pamela A Larson, *President*
Eric Larson, *Director*
EMP: 60 EST: 2003
SALES (est): 5MM-9.9MM **Privately Held**
SIC: 8742 Management consulting services

(G-6614)
ELITE HEALTHCARE STAFFING INC
10650 County Rd 81 Ste 110
(55369-4079)
PHONE..............................763 315-4488
FAX: 763 315-4418
Chris Ostby, *President*
Marlene Ostby, *VP Admin*
EMP: 135 EST: 1983
SQ FT: 1,000
SALES (est): 1MM-4.9MM **Privately Held**
SIC: 7363 Help supply services

(G-6615)
FOSS SWIM SCHOOL INC
9455 Garland Ave   (55311-5480)
PHONE..............................763 416-8993
FAX: 763 416-8474
John Foss, *President*
EMP: 40
SALES (est): 1MM-4.9MM **Privately Held**
SIC: 7999 Swimming instruction

(G-6616)
GANDER MOUNTAIN CO
8030 Wedgewood Ln N   (55369-9406)
PHONE..............................763 420-9800
FAX: 763 420-9880
Darren Cambell, *Principal*

EMP: 50
SALES (est): 5MM-9.9MM **Publicly Held**
WEB: www.gandermountain.com
SIC: 7699 Retails sporting goods;
recreational sporting equipment repair
service
PA: Gander Mountain Co
     180 5th St E 1300
     Saint Paul MN 55101
     651 325-4300

(G-6617)
GLEASON GYMNASTIC SCHOOL
9775 85th Ave N Ste 500   (55369-4525)
PHONE..............................763 493-2526
Bev Pearson, *Manager*
EMP: 30
SALES (est): 1MM-4.9MM **Privately Held**
SIC: 7999 Gymnastics instruction; retails
trampolines & equipment
PA: Gleason Gymnastic School
     2015 Silver Bell Rd Ste 180
     Saint Paul MN 55122
     651 454-6203

(G-6618)
HARTFORD LIFE INC
6820 Wedgwood Rd N   (55311-3574)
PHONE..............................877 952-9222
Lowndes Smith, *Opers Staff*
Mike Keeler, *Manager*
Joann Koski, *MIS Mgr*
EMP: 650
SALES (est): 500MM-999.9MM **Publicly Held**
WEB: www.hartfordife.com
SIC: 6311 Life insurance carrier
HQ: Hartford Life Inc
     200 Hopmeadow St
     Weatogue CT 06089
     860 547-5000

(G-6619)
HEATING & COOLING TWO INC
18550 County Road 81   (55369-9231)
PHONE..............................763 428-3677
FAX: 763 428-3682
Steven Sinkie, *President*
Roxanne Sinkie, *Corp Secy*
Wayne Sinkie, *Vice Pres*
Tim Luhrs, *Manager*
EMP: 60 EST: 1980
SQ FT: 15,000
SALES (est): 5MM-9.9MM **Privately Held**
WEB: www.heatcool2.com
SIC: 1711 Warm air heating & air
conditioning contractor

(G-6620)
HEGMAN MACHINE TOOL INC
8718 Monticello Ln N   (55369-4549)
PHONE..............................763 424-5622
FAX: 763 424-2958
Ralph H Hegman, *President*
Damon Frick, *Engrg Mgr*
Donald E Gerlach, *Controller*
Paul Hickok, *Sales Staff*
Jennifer Pantzke, *Manager*
EMP: 32 EST: 1983
SQ FT: 10,000
SALES (est): 10MM-24.9MM **Privately Held**
WEB: www.hegmanmachine.com
SIC: 5084 Wholesales industrial machine
tools & accessories

(G-6621)
HOMESERVICES LENDING LLC
13603 80th Cir N Fl 1   (55369-8961)
PHONE..............................763 494-8138
Bradley Childs, *Manager*
EMP: 35
SALES (est): 1MM-4.9MM **Privately Held**
SIC: 6162 Mortgage & loan lending
PA: Homeservices Lending LLC
     333 S 7th St Fl 27
     Minneapolis MN 55402
     952 928-5300

(G-6622)
HONEYWELL INTERNATIONAL INC
7550 Meridian Cir N # 100   (55369-4930)
PHONE..............................763 493-6400
FAX: 763 493-6475
John Ellis, *President*

Peter Mkreindler, *Senior VP*
Ronald Sinaikin, *Vice Pres*
Rick Fuchs, *Plant Mgr*
Craig Swandal, *Mfg Mgr*
EMP: 120
SALES (est): 10MM-24.9MM **Publicly Held**
WEB: www.honeywell.com
SIC: 5063 Manufactures burglar alarms;
wholesales electrical apparatus &
equipment
PA: Honeywell International Inc
     101 Columbia Rd
     Morristown NJ 07960
     973 455-2000

(G-6623)
INDEPENDENT PACKING SERVICES
11253 91st Ave N   (55369-3912)
PHONE..............................763 425-7155
FAX: 763 425-0451
Sandra Wallace, *President*
Joseph Wallace, *Vice Pres*
Prince Wallace, *Vice Pres*
Andrea Burns, *Human Res Dir*
John Derung, *Manager*
▲ EMP: 40 EST: 1976
SQ FT: 28,000 **Privately Held**
SIC: 4783 Packing goods for shipping;
manufactures wood pallets & skids; crating
goods for shipping; manufactures paper
packaging materials

(G-6624)
JNR ADJUSTMENT CO
7001 E Fish Lake Rd # 200   (55311-2844)
PO Box 27010, Minneapolis   (55427-0010)
PHONE..............................763 519-2710
Robert A Juve, *President*
Rollie Taylor, *General Mgr*
Michael Hedin, *Exec VP*
Daniel Christianson, *Vice Pres*
Tom Osberg, *Vice Pres*
EMP: 102 EST: 1970
SQ FT: 18,100
SALES (est): 5MM-9.9MM **Privately Held**
WEB: www.jnrcollects.com
SIC: 7322 Collection agency

(G-6625)
JRA FINANCIAL ADVISORS
7373 Kirkwood Ct N # 300   (55369-5214)
PHONE..............................763 315-8000
Kathy Moss, *President*
John Roti, *Manager*
EMP: 25 EST: 1986
SALES (est): 5MM-9.9MM **Privately Held**
WEB: www.jrafinancial.com
SIC: 6282 Investment advisory service

(G-6626)
KING SOLUTIONS INC (PA)
11011 Holly Ln N   (55369-9203)
PO Box 460, Rogers   (55374-0460)
PHONE..............................763 428-5464
Michael Patterson, *President*
Meyer Bolnick, *Vice Pres*
John Didier, *Finance*
EMP: 98 EST: 2000 **Privately Held**
SIC: 6719 4213 4731 Investment holding
company; over the road trucking; freight
forwarding services; freight consolidation
services

(G-6627)
KLICK & ASSOCIATE INC
17003 Weaver Lake Dr   (55311-1437)
PHONE..............................763 420-3296
Elizabeth Klick, *President*
EMP: 30 EST: 1985
SALES (est): 500-999K **Privately Held**
SIC: 7363 Temporary help service

(G-6628)
LIFETECH CORP
8940 Yucca Ln N   (55369-9244)
PHONE..............................612 369-5050
Rob Pearson, *Vice Pres*
EMP: 68 EST: 1987
SALES (est): 5MM-9.9MM **Privately Held**
SIC: 7389 Advertising, promotional & trade
show service

www.HarrisInfo.com
290

2011 Harris Minnesota
Services Directory

▲=Import ▼=Export
◆=Import/Export

(G-6629)

LOWE'S HOME CENTERS INC
11201 Fountains Dr (55369-7201)
PHONE..............................763 488-2001
EMP: 150
SALES (est): 25MM-49.9MM **Publicly Held**
WEB: www.lowes.com
SIC: 5031 5064 Retails building products &
materials; wholesales exterior building
materials; wholesales interior building
materials; wholesales electrical appliances;
retails household appliances
HQ: Lowe's Home Centers Inc
     1605 Curtis Bridge Rd
     Wilkesboro NC 28697
     336 658-4000

(G-6630)

LYNDE GREENHOUSE & NURSERY INC
9293 Pineview Ln N (55369-6519)
PHONE..............................763 420-4400
FAX: 763 420-9529
Edward Lynde, *President*
EMP: 40 EST: 1891
SQ FT: 190,000 **Privately Held**
WEB: www.lyndegreenhouse.com
SIC: 0181 Nursery stock production; potted
plant farming; shrubbery grown under cover;
retails nursery stock, seeds & bulbs

(G-6631)

MAJOR MECHANICAL INC
11201 86th Ave N (55369-4510)
PHONE..............................763 424-6680
FAX: 763 425-2301
Gary Mitsch, *President*
EMP: 80 EST: 1986
SALES (est): 5MM-9.9MM **Privately Held**
SIC: 1711 Plumbing service; heating & air
conditioning contractor

(G-6632)

MALARK MOTOR
17700 113th St N (55369-2500)
PHONE..............................763 428-4880
Doug Malark, *President*
Harold Graczyk, *President*
EMP: 30 EST: 1981
SQ FT: 18,000
SALES (est): 1MM-4.9MM **Privately Held**
SIC: 4212 4213 Local trucking without
storage services; over the road trucking

(G-6633)

MANHEIM AUCTIONS INC
Also Called: Minneapolis Auto Auction
8001 Jefferson Hwy (55369-4902)
PO Box 408 (55369-0408)
PHONE..............................763 425-7653
FAX: 763 493-0310
Scott Keener, *Manager*
EMP: 350
SALES (est): 100MM-499.9MM **Privately Held**
WEB: www.coxenterprises.com
SIC: 5012 Wholesales motor vehicles; used
car dealer
PA: Cox Enterprises Inc
     6205 Pchtree Dnwody Rd NE
     Atlanta GA 30328
     678 645-0000

(G-6634)

MAPLE GROVE URGENT CARE
12000 Elm Creek Blvd N # 1 (55369-7073)
PHONE..............................763 420-5279
FAX: 763 420-7938
Richard Gebhart, *Principal*
Virginia Berney, *Administrator*
EMP: 45 EST: 1984
SALES (est): 5MM-9.9MM **Privately Held**
SIC: 8011 Clinic operated by physicians

(G-6635)

MASTER'S MIRACLE INC
9060 Zachary Ln N Ste 104 (55369-4083)
PHONE..............................763 493-3200
FAX: 763 493-7779
Mike Schlegel, *CEO*
Steve Manske, *General Mgr*
Brad Collin, *Vice Pres*
Barb Bower, *Sales Executive*
EMP: 60 EST: 2002
SALES (est): 50MM-99.9MM **Privately Held**
WEB: www.themastersmiracle.com
SIC: 5122 Wholesales toilet soap;
wholesales toiletries

(G-6636)

MCKESSON MEDICAL-SURGICAL
Also Called: Red Line Medical Supply
8790 Valley Forge Ln N (55369-4089)
PHONE..............................763 424-7201
FAX: 763 424-7450
Jim Anderson, *Regional Mgr*
Ray Taylor, *Branch Mgr*
EMP: 25
SALES (est): 10MM-24.9MM **Publicly Held**
WEB: www.imckesson.com
SIC: 5047 Wholesales medical equipment &
supplies
PA: McKesson Corp
     1 Post St Fl 18
     San Francisco CA 94104
     415 983-8300

(G-6637)

MID-AMERICA CEDAR INC
10285 89th Ave N (55369-4029)
PHONE..............................763 425-0125
FAX: 763 424-9593
Steven Bush, *Systems Mgr*
EMP: 30
SALES (est): 10MM-24.9MM **Privately Held**
WEB: www.abc-kitchens.com
SIC: 5031 Wholesales rough, dressed &
finished lumber
PA: Lyman Lumber Co
     300 Morse Ave
     Excelsior MN 55331
     952 470-3600

(G-6638)

MIDWEST HARDWOOD CORP (PA)
Also Called: Metro Hardwoods
9540 83rd Ave N (55369-4567)
PHONE..............................763 425-8700
FAX: 763 391-6741
Michael D Flynn, *President*
Alan Henriksen, *Corp Secy*
Ben Laski, *Purch Mgr*
Blair Marsh, *Purch Mgr*
Mary Kuta, *Human Res Mgr*
▲ EMP: 60 EST: 1981
SQ FT: 110,000 **Privately Held**
WEB: www.metrohardwoods.com
SIC: 5031 Wholesales rough, dressed &
finished lumber; custom sawmill; wholesales
molding constructed of all materials;
wholesales particleboard; wholesales
plywood; manufactures kiln dried lumber;
sawing & planing mill

(G-6639)

MINNESOTA EXTERIORS INC
8600 Jefferson Hwy (55369-4504)
PO Box 266 (55369-0266)
PHONE..............................763 493-5500
FAX: 763 493-8988
Steven Schiltz, *President*
Zenalou Bennis, *Vice Pres*
Jim Heidemann, *CFO*
Gerald Brenhofer, *CFO*
Heather Brummer, *Controller*
EMP: 120 EST: 1965
SQ FT: 102,000
SALES (est): 10MM-24.9MM **Privately Held**
WEB: www.mnext.com
SIC: 1761 5031 5033 Siding contractor;
wholesales windows; wholesales siding

(G-6640)

MINNESOTA MEDTEC INC
11760 Justen Cir Ste B (55369-9256)
PHONE..............................763 428-3720
FAX: 763 428-3721
Brian Packard, *President*
Joe Wimkelman, *Vice Pres*
EMP: 30 EST: 1996
SQ FT: 19,000
SALES (est): 5MM-9.9MM **Privately Held**
WEB: www.minnesotamedtec.com

SIC: 8731 Manufactures medical
instruments; manufactures unsupported
plastics profile shapes; manufactures
catheters; commercial physical research
laboratory; manufactures surgical
equipment

(G-6641)

MUZAK LLC
6901 E Fish Lake Rd Ste 132
(55369-5455)
PHONE..............................763 424-5533
FAX: 763 424-5242
Mindy Hopp, *General Mgr*
Debbie Eggebraaten, *Pub Rel Mgr*
EMP: 30
SALES (est): 1MM-4.9MM **Privately Held**
WEB: www.musak.com
SIC: 7389 1731 5065 Music & broadcasting
service; sound equipment installation
service; wholesales electronic sound
equipment
DH: Muzak LLC
     3318 Lakemont Blvd
     Fort Mill SC 29708
     803 396-3000

(G-6642)

NORTH CENTRAL MANAGEMENT INC
Also Called: Hilton
6350 Vinewood Ln N (55311-3639)
PHONE..............................763 509-9500
William Pollock, *MIS Mgr*
EMP: 30
SALES (est): 1MM-4.9MM **Privately Held**
SIC: 7011 7299 Traveler accommodations;
banquet hall facility
PA: North Central Management Inc
     1600 Aspen Cmns Ste 200
     Middleton WI 53562
     608 836-6060

(G-6643)

NORTH MEMORIAL HEALTH CARE
12000 Elm Creek Blvd N (55369-7073)
PHONE..............................763 420-7002
FAX: 763 441-1985
Anne Roland, *Manager*
EMP: 2000
SALES (est): 100MM-499.9MM **Privately Held**
WEB: www.northmemorial.com
SIC: 8049 Speech pathologist office
PA: North Memorial Health Care
     3300 Oakdale Ave N
     Minneapolis MN 55422
     763 520-5200

(G-6644)

NORTH MEMORIAL IMAGING CENTER
9855 Hospital Dr Ste 150 (55369-4776)
PHONE..............................763 398-4400
Suzanne Blustein, *General Mgr*
EMP: 25
SALES (est): 1MM-4.9MM **Privately Held**
SIC: 8011 Radiologist office

(G-6645)

NORTHERN STATES POWER CO
Also Called: XCEL Energy
8701 Monticello Ln N (55369-4550)
PHONE..............................763 493-1500
FAX: 763 493-1501
Lon Burris, *Manager*
Larry Bick, *Director*
EMP: 75
SALES (est): 25MM-49.9MM **Publicly Held**
WEB: www.middletownpower.com
SIC: 4911 Electric services
HQ: Northern States Power Co
     414 Nicollet Mall
     Minneapolis MN 55401
     612 330-5500

(G-6646)

ORAL & MAX FACIAL SPECIALIST
13998 Maple Knoll Way LL101
(55369-7004)
PHONE..............................763 494-8825
FAX: 763 494-3269

Kirby C Johnson, *Owner*
Michael W Lehnert, *Manager*
Venetia Laganis, *Manager*
EMP: 30 EST: 2000
SALES (est): 1MM-4.9MM **Privately Held**
SIC: 8021 Dentists' office & clinic

(G-6647)

OSSEO BROOKLYN SCHOOL BUS CO
11800 95th Ave N (55369-5539)
PHONE..............................763 425-2542
FAX: 763 425-5728
Scott Regan, *President*
EMP: 180 EST: 1942
SQ FT: 40,000
SALES (est): 5MM-9.9MM **Privately Held**
WEB: www.osseobus.com
SIC: 4151 4111 4141 School bus service;
local bus charter service; passenger transit
system

(G-6648)

OSSEO GARDENS ASSISTED LIVING
525 2nd St SE Ofc (55369-1658)
PHONE..............................763 315-4869
Dan Paknen, *Owner*
Rich Paknen, *Owner*
EMP: 25 EST: 2001
SALES (est): 1MM-4.9MM **Privately Held**
SIC: 8051 Skilled nursing care facility

(G-6649)

OSSEO MAPLE GROVE AMERICAN
260 4th Ave SE (55369-1521)
PHONE..............................763 425-4858
Ruth Lucht, *CEO*
Dick Kolb, *Manager*
EMP: 30 EST: 2001 **Privately Held**
SIC: 8641 Veterans' organization

(G-6650)

PAKOR INC (PA)
6450 Wedgwood Rd N # 110
(55311-3648)
PHONE..............................763 559-8484
FAX: 763 559-8886
Thomas J Nicoski, *President*
David Asplund, *Vice Pres*
Todd Anderson, *Marketing Mgr*
Marlin Hahn, *Representative*
▲ EMP: 30 EST: 1988
SQ FT: 26,000
SALES (corp-wide): 16.67M **Privately Held**
WEB: www.pakor.com
SIC: 5043 Wholesales photographic
equipment & supplies; wholesales
photographic processing equipment

(G-6651)

PALCO MARKETING INC
8575 Monticello Ln N (55369-4546)
PHONE..............................763 559-5539
FAX: 763 493-3262
James S Paletz, *President*
Jean Koehler, *Controller*
Deb Bina, *Controller*
Don Lies, *Sales Executive*
Earl Kessel, *Administrator*
▲ EMP: 35 EST: 1987
SQ FT: 40,000
SALES (est): 10MM-24.9MM **Privately Held**
SIC: 5091 Wholesales sporting &
recreational goods & supplies

(G-6652)

PHASSE III OF MAPLE GROVE INC
Also Called: Fair's Garden Center
9340 Fair Way (55369-4238)
PHONE..............................763 425-4212
Phillip Phenow, *President*
Angela Spinler, *Bookkeeper*
EMP: 40 EST: 1952
SQ FT: 7,200
SALES (est): 5MM-9.9MM **Privately Held**
SIC: 0781 Retail nursery & garden center;
landscape planning services; florist

(PA)=Parent Co (HQ)=Headquarters (DH)=Div Headquarters
✿ = New business established in last 2 years

2011 Harris Minnesota
Services Directory

© Harris InfoSource 1-866-281-6415
291

(G-6653)
PINE POINT WOOD PRODUCTS INC
19380 County Rd 81 (55369)
PO Box 1900, Dayton (55327-1900)
PHONE..................................763 428-4301
FAX: 763 428-4304
James R Talbot, *President*
Ed Talbot, *Sales Mgr*
EMP: 50 **EST:** 1968
SQ FT: 150,000
SALES (est): 25MM-49.9MM **Privately Held**
SIC: 5031 Wholesales lumber, plywood & millwork; wholesales rough, dressed & finished lumber; wholesales plywood

(G-6654)
QUALITY DRYWALL INC
8620 Monticello Ln N # 100 (55369-4547)
PHONE..................................763 424-5774
Bruce Palmer, *President*
Michael Betchwars, *Vice Pres*
EMP: 30 **EST:** 1986
SQ FT: 1,300
SALES (est): 1MM-4.9MM **Privately Held**
SIC: 1742 Drywall contractor

(G-6655)
RECEIVABLES CONTROL CORP
Also Called: General Auditing Bureau
7373 Kirkwood Ct N # 200 (55369-5264)
PO Box 9658, Minneapolis (55440-9658)
PHONE..................................763 315-9600
FAX: 763 315-8040
Luke Vidor, *President*
Michael Zwach, *Vice Pres*
Kelly Cronan, *Vice Pres*
Jim Fritz, *VP Sales*
Matt Friede, *Manager*
▲ **EMP:** 53 **EST:** 1967
SQ FT: 9,000
SALES (est): 1MM-4.9MM **Privately Held**
WEB: www.receivablescontrol.com
SIC: 7322 Collection agency

(G-6656)
ROSE ARBOR
16500 92nd Ave N Apt 109 (55311-5468)
PHONE..................................763 493-5910
Angie Giflason, *Business Mgr*
Martha Foreman, *Marketing Mgr*
Brenda Gammelgaard, *Manager*
Sheila Clark, *Manager*
Trisha Tolzman, *Exec Dir*
EMP: 85 **EST:** 2001
SALES (est): 10MM-24.9MM **Privately Held**
WEB: www.rosearbor-maplegrove.com
SIC: 6513 8082 Apartment building operator; home health care services

(G-6657)
RUDOLPH PRIEBE AMERICAN LEGION
260 4th Ave SE (55369-1521)
PHONE..................................763 425-4858
Ruth Lucht, *Manager*
EMP: 25 **EST:** 1919 **Privately Held**
SIC: 8641 Fraternal association; members only bar & restaurant for members of organizations only

(G-6658)
RUSH CREEK GOLF CLUB LIMITED
7801 Troy Ln N (55311-1652)
PHONE..................................763 494-8844
FAX: 763 494-4286
Duncan McMillan, *Owner*
Steve Hornig, *Vice Pres*
EMP: 200 **EST:** 1996
SALES (est): 10MM-24.9MM **Privately Held**
SIC: 7992 Public golf course

(G-6659)
S R WEIDEMA INC
17600 113th Ave N (55369-9243)
PHONE..................................763 428-9110
FAX: 763 428-9095
Scott Weidema, *President*
EMP: 70 **EST:** 1985
SALES (est): 5MM-9.9MM **Privately Held**
SIC: 1623 Underground utilities contractor

(G-6660)
SCIMED INC
1 Scimed Pl (55311-1565)
PHONE..................................763 494-1700
FAX: 763 494-2290
Dale A Spencer, *President*
Dan Sullivan, *Vice Pres*
Valerie Seeker, *Manager*
Jennifer Vopatek, *Meeting Planner*
EMP: 150 **EST:** 1990
SALES (est): 50MM-99.9MM **Privately Held**
SIC: 5047 Wholesales medical & hospital equipment

(G-6661)
SEEK HOME INC
100 Central Ave Ste 3 (55369-1204)
PHONE..................................763 494-0870
Ron Seubert, *President*
EMP: 70 **EST:** 1997
SALES (est): 1MM-4.9MM **Privately Held**
WEB: www.seekhome.org
SIC: 8361 Home for the elderly

(G-6662)
SERVICE LIGHTING INC
Also Called: Compact Offer
11621 95th Ave N (55369-5573)
PO Box 1836 (55311-6836)
PHONE..................................763 571-3001
David McLellan, *President*
Paul McLellan, *Vice Pres*
David M Lellan, *CFO*
EMP: 25 **EST:** 1951
SQ FT: 6,000
SALES (est): 10MM-24.9MM **Privately Held**
WEB: www.servicelighting.com
SIC: 5063 Wholesales electrical apparatus & equipment

(G-6663)
SIMONSON VENTURE INC
Also Called: Simonson's
13744 83rd Way N (55369-4645)
PHONE..................................763 494-4863
Katie Troye, *General Mgr*
Theresa Steichen, *Purch Agent*
Lisa Milinkovich, *Manager*
Marilyn Aase, *Education*
EMP: 50
SALES (est): 1MM-4.9MM **Privately Held**
SIC: 7231 7299 Cosmetology & personal hygiene salon; massage parlor & steam bath services
PA: Simonson Venture Inc
     3507 Round Lake Blvd NW S
     Anoka MN 55303
     763 416-7823

(G-6664)
SKYLINE FIRE PROTECTION INC
10900 73rd Ave N Ste 108 (55369-5400)
PHONE..................................763 425-4441
FAX: 763 425-7755
Robert Kokales, *President*
Denise Kokales, *Vice Pres*
EMP: 30 **EST:** 1994
SQ FT: 3,600
SALES (est): 1MM-4.9MM **Privately Held**
SIC: 1711 Fire sprinkler system installation service

(G-6665)
SMITH'S WINTER PRODUCTS
10960 County Road 81 (55369-4094)
PHONE..................................763 493-3332
FAX: 763 425-1107
Larry Smith, *President*
Cindy Smith, *Vice Pres*
EMP: 30 **EST:** 1982
SQ FT: 2,000
SALES (est): 10MM-24.9MM **Privately Held**
SIC: 5013 7539 7699 Wholesales new motor vehicle parts & supplies; automotive repair services; wholesales automotive trailer parts & accessories; trailer repair service; snowmobile repair service; wholesales truck parts & accessories

(G-6666)
SPECIALTY CONTRACTING SERVICES
Also Called: ServiceMaster Osseo
9702 85th Ave N (55369-4537)
PHONE..................................763 424-4100
Denise Hedden, *President*
Darby Bitzan, *Manager*
EMP: 140 **EST:** 1999
SALES (est): 1MM-4.9MM **Privately Held**
SIC: 7349 Building cleaning & maintenance services

(G-6667)
STEP BY STEP MONTESSORI
11601 73rd Ave N (55369-5547)
PHONE..................................763 315-3602
FAX: 763 315-4383
Rose Minor, *Owner*
EMP: 25 **EST:** 2001
SALES (est): 500-999K **Privately Held**
SIC: 8351 Child development center providing Montessori based instruction

(G-6668)
STERILMED INC (PA)
11400 73rd Ave N Ste 100 (55369-5562)
PHONE..................................763 488-3400
FAX: 763 488-9780
Brian Sullivan, *CEO*
John Manning, *Vice Pres*
Brian Newton, *Vice Pres*
Chuck Karpinske, *CFO*
Charlie Pistolis, *Human Res Dir*
◆ **EMP:** 500 **EST:** 1997
SQ FT: 60,000 **Privately Held**
WEB: www.sterilmed.com
SIC: 7699 Hospital equipment repair service

(G-6669)
STS ACQUISITION CO
10900 73rd Ave N Ste 150 (55369-5400)
PHONE..................................763 315-6300
FAX: 763 315-1836
Mike Russell, *Manager*
EMP: 60
SALES (est): 5MM-9.9MM **Privately Held**
WEB: www.stsconsultants.com
SIC: 8711 Engineering consulting services
PA: STS Acquisition Co
     750 Corporate Woods Pkwy
     Vernon Hills IL 60061
     847 279-2500

(G-6670)
SUNDANCE GOLF & BOWL INC
15240 113th Ave N (55369-9320)
PHONE..................................763 420-4700
Robert H Allen, *President*
Brian Allen, *President*
Ron Noyce, *Superintendent*
Dave Leyse, *Director*
EMP: 50 **EST:** 1970
SQ FT: 26,000
SALES (est): 1MM-4.9MM **Privately Held**
SIC: 7992 7933 Public golf course; bowling center

(G-6671)
SUPERIOR CONSTRUCTION SERVICES
9702 85th Ave N (55369-4537)
PHONE..................................763 424-9434
Randy Hedden, *President*
EMP: 25 **EST:** 1992
SQ FT: 18,000
SALES (est): 5MM-9.9MM **Privately Held**
SIC: 1521 Single-family housing construction; single-family home fire damage repair service

(G-6672)
TALBERG LAWN & LANDSCAPE INC
11770 Justen Cir (55369-9282)
PHONE..................................763 428-3550
FAX: 763 428-3419
Mark Talberg, *President*
Robert Hunt, *Vice Pres*
Carolyn Talberg, *CFO*
Nancy Miller, *Administrator*
EMP: 75 **EST:** 1980
SQ FT: 9,000 **Privately Held**
WEB: www.talberg-lawn.com
SIC: 0782 Commercial lawn & landscaping services

(G-6673)
THREE RIVERS PARK DISTRICT
12400 James Tim Pkwy (55369)
PHONE..................................763 694-7894
FAX: 763 424-2446
Wayne Iseri, *Principal*
EMP: 100
SALES (est): 5MM-9.9MM **Privately Held**
WEB: www.hennepinparks.com
SIC: 7033 Recreational vehicle park & campground
PA: Three Rivers Park District
     3000 Xenium Ln N
     Plymouth MN 55441
     763 559-9000

(G-6674)
3WIRE GROUP INC (DH)
101 Broadway St W Ste 300 (55369-1546)
PHONE..................................763 488-3000
FAX: 763 488-3030
Robert Guerra, *President*
John Oshea, *Corp Secy*
James L Etter, *Corp Secy*
Dennis P Whelpley, *Corp Secy*
Steven Bye, *Treasurer*
▲ **EMP:** 65 **EST:** 2001
SALES (corp-wide): 2.97B **Privately Held**
WEB: www.imiremcor.com
SIC: 5078 Wholesales refrigerated beverage dispensers
HQ: Cornelius IMI Inc
     101 Broadway St W Ste 204
     Osseo MN 55369
     763 488-8200

(G-6675)
3WIRE GROUP INC
201 Broadway St W (55369-1566)
PHONE..................................763 488-3000
Andy Thompson, *Project Mgr*
Dave Evans, *Manager*
David Womeldorf, *Info Tech Mgr*
EMP: 25
SALES (est): 5MM-9.9MM **Privately Held**
WEB: www.imiremcor.com
SIC: 5087 Wholesales service establishment equipment & supplies
DH: 3Wire Group Inc
     101 Broadway St W Ste 300
     Osseo MN 55369
     763 488-3000

(G-6676)
TOM LOUCKS & ASSOCIATES INC
Also Called: Loucks & Associates
7200 Hemlock Ln N Ste 300 (55369-5592)
PHONE..................................763 424-5505
FAX: 763 424-5822
Jeff Shopek, *President*
Paul McGinley, *Corp Secy*
Eric Beazley, *Engineer*
Jon Donovan, *Engineer*
Nick Mannel, *Engineer*
EMP: 60 **EST:** 1976
SALES (est): 5MM-9.9MM **Privately Held**
WEB: www.loucksmclagan.com
SIC: 8748 8711 8713 8733 Urban planning & consulting services; archeological expeditions; civil engineering services; surveying service

(G-6677)
TOP NOTCH SIDING CO
Also Called: Siding
8532 Jefferson Hwy (55369-4503)
PHONE..................................612 269-7923
Alex Kutsev, *President*
EMP: 30
SALES (est): 1MM-4.9MM **Privately Held**
SIC: 1761 Roofing, siding & sheet metal work

(G-6678)
TRUGREEN LP
11755 95th Ave N (55369-5521)
PHONE..................................612 493-5035
Mike Larson, *Sales Staff*
Dan Phipps, *Manager*
EMP: 25 **Privately Held**

www.HarrisInfo.com
292
                              2011 Harris Minnesota
                              Services Directory
                                                    ▲=Import ▼=Export
                                                    ◆=Import/Export

WEB: www.trugreen.com
SIC: 0782 Lawn care services
DH: Trugreen LP
860 Ridge Lake Blvd Ste G02
Memphis TN 38120
901 681-1800

(G-6679)
TWIN CITY EXTERIORS CO INC
Also Called: ABC Seamless
9060 Zachary Ln N Ste 108 (55369-4083)
PHONE..............................763 425-4737
FAX: 763 425-6457
Steven Patnode, *President*
Brian Patnode, *Vice Pres*
Guiles Patnode, *Treasurer*
Claudia Sundseth, *Office Mgr*
EMP: 65 EST: 1982
SQ FT: 5,000
SALES (est): 10MM-24.9MM Privately Held
WEB: www.goabcseamless.com
SIC: 1521 Residential remodeling

(G-6680)
UHL CO INC
9065 Zachary Ln N (55369-4004)
PHONE..............................763 425-7226
Timothy R Ley, *President*
Tim Jilek, *Vice Pres*
Brad Jones, *Vice Pres*
John Odom, *Vice Pres*
Brian Werger, *Vice Pres*
EMP: 90 EST: 1921
SQ FT: 14,000
SALES (est): 10MM-24.9MM Privately Held
SIC: 1731 5075 Electronic controls
installation service; wholesales air
conditioning equipment; wholesales warm
air heating equipment & supplies

(G-6681)
UPSHER-SMITH LABORATORIES INC
6701 Evenstad Dr N (55369-6026)
PHONE..............................763 315-2000
FAX: 763 315-2001
Phillips Dritsas, *Vice Pres*
Paul Kravolec, *Vice Pres*
Vickie O'Neill, *Vice Pres*
Steven Roinson, *Vice Pres*
Chuck Woodruff, *Vice Pres*
EMP: 100
SALES (est): 50MM-99.9MM Privately Held
SIC: 8011 Manufactures suppositories;
manufactures druggists' pharmaceutical
preparations; manufactures pharmaceutical
pills; physicians' office & clinic

(G-6682)
VERIFICATIONS INC (PA)
6900 Wedgwood Rd N # 120
(55311-3552)
PHONE..............................763 420-0600
FAX: 763 420-0680
Curtis G Marks, *President*
Terry Bartz, *COO*
James Ferguson, *Vice Pres*
Philip Wolf, *CFO*
Chris Oace, *Manager*
EMP: 106 EST: 1987
SQ FT: 11,000 Privately Held
WEB: www.verificationsinc.com
SIC: 8748 Business consulting services

(G-6683)
VIA BIOMEDICAL INC
6655 Wedgwood Rd N # 150
(55311-3613)
PHONE..............................763 577-9936
Fernando Dicaprio, *President*
Tim Hidani, *Opers Mgr*
Les Parson, *Facilities Mgr*
Bill Norman, *Engineer*
Scott Buttermore, *CFO*
EMP: 37 EST: 2001
SQ FT: 17,500
SALES (est): 5MM-9.9MM Privately Held
WEB: www.viabiomedical.com
SIC: 8711 Manufactures blood & bone work
medical instruments & equipment;
mechanical engineering services

(G-6684)
WILDFLOWER LODGE OF CHAPELWOOD
9251 Black Oaks Ln N (55311-5446)
PHONE..............................763 420-3768
FAX: 763 420-4374
Shelley McDonald, *Manager*
Shelley McDonald, *Exec Dir*
EMP: 85 EST: 2003
SALES (est): 1MM-4.9MM Privately Held
SIC: 8322 Adult daycare center

(G-6685)
WURTH ADAMS NUT & BOLT CO (HQ)
Also Called: Adams Nut & Bolt
10100 85th Ave N (55369-4518)
PHONE..............................763 493-0877
Gary Huck, *CEO*
Jane Anderson, *Corp Secy*
Irma Jaques, *Corp Secy*
Christoph Lange, *Corp Secy*
Jody Frearing-Trende, *CFO*
▲ EMP: 80 EST: 1978
SQ FT: 60,000
SALES (corp-wide): 11.18B Privately Held
WEB: www.wurthadams.com
SIC: 5072 Wholesales fasteners;
wholesales bolts; wholesales hardware
nuts; wholesales rivets
PA: Wurth Group of North America
93 Grant St
Ramsey NJ 07446
201 818-8877

OTTERTAIL
Otter Tail County

(G-6686)
CARRS TREE SERVICE INC
307 Mn Highway 78 S (56571-7010)
PO Box 250 (56571-0250)
PHONE..............................218 367-3355
FAX: 218 367-3355
Brad K Carr, *Vice Pres*
EMP: 45 EST: 1974
SQ FT: 14,200 Privately Held
WEB: www.carrstreeservice.com
SIC: 0783 0781 Utility line tree trimming
services; landscape architectural service

OWATONNA
Steele County

(G-6687)
A G TECHNOLOGIES INTERNATIONAL
403 E Broadway St (55060-2503)
PHONE..............................507 444-4157
Rajiv Tandon, *President*
Rob McClelland, *Vice Pres*
EMP: 30 EST: 2000
SQ FT: 2,000
SALES (est): 5MM-9.9MM Privately Held
SIC: 8748 Educational services; agricultural
consultant

(G-6688)
A J LYSNE CONTRACTING CORP
3249 S County Road 45 (55060-5121)
PO Box 407 (55060-0407)
PHONE..............................507 451-7121
FAX: 507 451-0956
Allen J Lysne, *President*
Judy Meister, *Opers Mgr*
Sarah Zimmerman, *Controller*
EMP: 70 EST: 1978
SQ FT: 5,000
SALES (est): 10MM-24.9MM Privately Held
WEB: www.ajlysne.com
SIC: 1542 1796 New commercial & office
building construction; millwright

(G-6689)
ADVANTAGE CABINETS INC
1040 24th Ave NW (55060-1053)
PHONE..............................507 455-0833
FAX: 507 455-0886

Scott Kubicek, *President*
EMP: 26 EST: 1990
SQ FT: 6,000
SALES (est): 1MM-4.9MM Privately Held
WEB: www.advantagecabinets.com
SIC: 1751 Cabinet building & installation
service; retails kitchen cabinets

(G-6690)
ALLINA HEALTH SYSTEM
Also Called: Owatonna Home Care & Hospice
2350 NW 26th St (55060-5506)
PHONE..............................507 446-0936
FAX: 507 455-2207
Nura Negaard, *Manager*
Kathy Blomquist, *Manager*
EMP: 32
SALES (est): 1MM-4.9MM Privately Held
WEB: www.allina.com
SIC: 8082 Home health care services
PA: Allina Health System
2925 Chicago Ave
Minneapolis MN 55407
612 775-5000

(G-6691)
AMERICAN HOSPITALITY MGT
Also Called: Holiday Inn
2365 NW 43rd St (55060-5647)
PHONE..............................507 446-8900
Mike Bhakata, *Manager*
Paul Feddma, *Manager*
EMP: 50
SALES (est): 1MM-4.9MM Privately Held
SIC: 7011 7299 Traveler accommodations;
banquet hall facility
PA: American Hospitality Mgt
327 Village Rd
Tiverton RI 02878
401 625-5015

(G-6692)
AMERICAS RACKET & FITNESS
1929 S Cedar Ave (55060-4302)
PHONE..............................507 451-8833
FAX: 507 451-0267
David Peceraro, *Owner*
Trent Nelson, *Manager*
EMP: 35 EST: 2000
SALES (est): 1MM-4.9MM Privately Held
SIC: 7991 Physical fitness center

(G-6693)
ANERTEC HOLDINGS LLC
815 Rice Lake St Ste 1 (55060-3275)
PHONE..............................507 451-5430
FAX: 507 444-0093
L G Stoddard, *Member*
Jack Heimerman, *Purch Mgr*
Dale E Gandrud, *Mng Member*
Cindy Banta, *CTO*
EMP: 26 EST: 1993
SALES (est): 1MM-4.9MM Privately Held
WEB: www.anertec.com
SIC: 7373 Computer-aided design systems
service

(G-6694)
BENEVOLENT PROTECTIVE ORDER OF
126 E Vine St (55060-2428)
PO Box 881 (55060-0881)
PHONE..............................507 451-1395
FAX: 507 451-1399
Fred Knudsen, *Corp Secy*
Steve Granquist, *Manager*
EMP: 25 EST: 1920
SQ FT: 7,200 Privately Held
SIC: 8699 Personal interest organization

(G-6695)
BEVERLY ENTERPRISES - MN
Also Called: Owatonna Health Care Center
201 18th St SW (55060-3913)
PHONE..............................507 451-6800
FAX: 507 451-6087
Susan Olson, *Administrator*
Terry Korvel, *Administrator*
Gary Roloag, *Supervisor*
Chris Klemmensen RN, *Nursing Dir*
K Chris, *Nursing Dir*
EMP: 50
SALES (est): 1MM-4.9MM Privately Held
WEB: www.beverlynet.com

SIC: 8051 Convalescent home
HQ: Beverly Enterprises - MN
650 Ramer Ave S
Rush City MN 55069
320 358-4765

(G-6696)
BLAST PRESSURE WASHING
206 W Rose St (55060-2339)
PHONE..............................507 455-2898
Jamie Evans, *Owner*
EMP: 35 EST: 1997
SALES (est): 1MM-4.9MM Privately Held
SIC: 8741 Restaurant management
services

(G-6697)
BROOKS
2480 Saint Paul Rd Ofc (55060-2455)
PHONE..............................507 446-5855
FAX: 507 446-5858
Sue Doty, *Director*
EMP: 30
SALES (est): 1MM-4.9MM Privately Held
SIC: 8059 Retirement community with
nursing

(G-6698)
CEDAR VALLEY SERVICES INC
415 N Grove Ave (55060-2452)
PHONE..............................507 451-5897
FAX: 507 451-5932
Gary Randall, *Prdtn Mgr*
Deb Langer, *Mfg Staff*
Mark Sullivan, *Cust Svc Dir*
David Williams, *Branch Mgr*
Taggert Medgaarden, *Info Tech Dir*
EMP: 100
SALES (est): 1MM-4.9MM Privately Held
SIC: 8331 Sheltered workshop
PA: Cedar Valley Services Inc
2111 4th St NW
Austin MN 55912
507 433-2303

(G-6699)
CENTER FOR REHAB & WELLNESS
903 S Oak Ave (55060-3200)
PHONE..............................507 455-7631
FAX: 507 444-6069
Linda Hoffman, *President*
EMP: 25 EST: 2001
SALES (est): 1MM-4.9MM Privately Held
SIC: 8049 Health practitioners' office

(G-6700)
CENTRAL VALLEY COOPERATIVE (PA)
900 30th Pl NW (55060-5001)
PHONE..............................507 451-1230
Gary Mohr, *CEO*
Dave Seykora, *Ch of Bd*
Marvin Spindler, *Corp Secy*
Maynard Bakken, *Vice Pres*
Glenn Schack, *Controller*
EST: 2005
SQ FT: 2,500 Privately Held
SIC: 5191 5171 Wholesales agricultural
fertilizer; wholesales petroleum bulk
stations; retail gasoline filling station

(G-6701)
CITY OF OWATONNA
Also Called: Owatonna Public Util
208 S Walnut Ave (55060-2940)
PO Box 800 (55060-0800)
PHONE..............................507 451-2480
Stephen Shurts, *Manager*
EMP: 67
SALES (est): 25MM-49.9MM Privately Held
WEB: www.owatonnautilities.com
SIC: 4911 4924 4941 Electric services;
water supply services; natural gas
distribution to consumers
PA: City of Owatonna
540 W Hills Cir
Owatonna MN 55060
507 444-4300

(PA)=Parent Co (HQ)=Headquarters (DH)=Div Headquarters
✿ = New business established in last 2 years

2011 Harris Minnesota
Services Directory

© Harris InfoSource 1-866-281-6415

293

GEOGRAPHIC

(G-6702)
CITY OF OWATONNA
Also Called: Owatonna Senior Place
540 W Hills Cir (55060-4701)
PHONE.............................507 444-4300
Anne Pelskonko, *Director*
EMP: 30
SALES (est): 500-999K Privately Held
WEB: www.owatonnautilities.com
SIC: 8322 Senior citizen center
PA: City of Owatonna
540 W Hills Cir
Owatonna MN 55060
507 444-4300

(G-6703)
CITY OF OWATONNA
Also Called: Owatonna Public Utilities
208 S Walnut Ave (55060-2940)
PO Box 800 (55060-0800)
PHONE.............................507 451-2480
FAX: 507 444-2465
Steve Shurts, *General Mgr*
Terrance Zak, *General Mgr*
Ken Finholdt, *Manager*
Steve Rypka, *Manager*
EMP: 67
SALES (est): 50MM-99.9MM Privately Held
WEB: www.owatonnautilities.com
SIC: 4932 Gas & other combined services
PA: City of Owatonna
540 W Hills Cir
Owatonna MN 55060
507 444-4300

(G-6704)
COCA-COLA ENTERPRISES INC
2505 Alexander St SW (55060-4721)
PHONE.............................800 657-4995
Bonnie Barrer, *Sales/Mktg Mgr*
EMP: 40
SALES (est): 25MM-49.9MM Publicly Held
WEB: www.cokecce.com
SIC: 5149 Wholesales soft drinks;
manufactures nonalcoholic carbonated
beverages
PA: Coca-Cola Enterprises Inc
2500 Windy Ridge Pkwy SE
Atlanta GA 30339
770 989-3000

(G-6705)
CON-WAY FREIGHT INC
1020 28th Ave NW (55060-4941)
PHONE.............................507 451-2865
FAX: 507 451-0691
Robert Tarrant, *Manager*
EMP: 25
SALES (est): 1MM-4.9MM Publicly Held
WEB: www.con-way.com
SIC: 4213 4212 Over the road trucking;
local trucking without storage services
HQ: Con-way Freight Inc
2211 Old Earhart Rd # 100
Ann Arbor MI 48105
734 994-6600

(G-6706)
COUNTRY SIDE EAST LIVING
650 El Dorado St SE (55060-6616)
PHONE.............................507 446-8334
EMP: 25 EST: 2005
SALES (est): 500-999K Privately Held
SIC: 8361 Home for the elderly

(G-6707)
COUNTY OF STEELE
Also Called: Steele Dention Center
630 Florence Ave (55060-4704)
PHONE.............................507 444-7410
Dan Schember, *Administrator*
EMP: 43
SALES (est): 1MM-4.9MM Privately Held
SIC: 8744 Privately operated jail facility
support management services
PA: County of Steele
630 Florence Ave Fl 2
Owatonna MN 55060
507 444-7400

(G-6708)
DELTA KAPPA GAMMA SOCIETY
Also Called: Owatonna Chapter
909 Truman Ave (55060-3536)
PHONE.............................507 451-2523
Jan Lewison, *Treasurer*
EMP: 42 EST: 1989 Privately Held
SIC: 8641 Civic & social organization

(G-6709)
FEDERATED EMPLOYEES CREDIT
1929 S Cedar Ave (55060-4301)
PO Box 328 (55060-0328)
PHONE.............................507 455-5430
Annette Arndt, *Principal*
John Hylle, *Vice Chairman*
Denise Kenow, *Corp Secy*
Marcia Pitzenberger, *Asst Treas*
Tom Mesvig, *Officer*
Privately Held
SIC: 6062 State chartered credit union

(G-6710)
FEDERATED MUTUAL INSURANCE CO (PA)
121 E Park Sq (55060-3046)
PO Box 328 (55060-0328)
PHONE.............................507 455-5200
Albert Annexstad, *President*
Jeffrey E Fetters, *COO*
Sarah L Buxton, *Exec VP*
Paul F Droher, *Exec VP*
Jock Kinnett, *Exec VP*
EMP: 200 EST: 1904
SQ FT: 300,000
SALES (corp-wide): 845.54M Privately
Held
WEB: www.federatedinsurance.com
SIC: 6331 6311 6321 6371 Provides mutual
fire, marine & casualty insurance; life
insurance carriers; mutual accident
association; pension, health & welfare funds
services

(G-6711)
FEDERATED MUTUAL INSURANCE CO
121 E Park Sq (55060-3046)
PO Box 328 (55060-0328)
PHONE.............................507 455-5200
Albert Annexstad, *Ch of Bd*
Raymond R Stawarz, *President*
Jeffrey Fetters, *COO*
Sarah Buxton, *Exec VP*
Paul Droher, *Exec VP*
EMP: 1500 EST: 1958
SQ FT: 40,000
SALES (est): 1B-9.9B Privately Held
WEB: www.federatedinsurance.com
SIC: 6311 Life insurance carriers
PA: Federated Mutual Insurance Co
121 E Park Sq
Owatonna MN 55060
507 455-5200

(G-6712)
FEDERATED SERVICE INSURANCE CO
121 E Park Sq (55060-3046)
PO Box 328 (55060-0328)
PHONE.............................507 455-5200
Jeffrey E Fetters, *President*
Albert Annexstad, *Chairman*
Jarius Meilahn, *Corp Secy*
Raymond R Stawaz, *Senior VP*
Gregory J Stroik, *CFO*
EMP: 175 EST: 1975
SQ FT: 300,000
SALES (est): 50MM-99.9MM Privately Held
WEB: www.federatedinsurance.com
SIC: 6331 Property & casualty insurance
carrier
PA: Federated Mutual Insurance Co
121 E Park Sq
Owatonna MN 55060
507 455-5200

(G-6713)
FEDEX FREIGHT INC
1060 26th Pl NW (55060-5065)
PHONE.............................507 444-0633
FAX: 507 444-0645

Kelly Knutson, *Manager*
EMP: 27
SALES (est): 1MM-4.9MM Publicly Held
WEB: www.fedexfreight.fedex.com
SIC: 4213 Long-distance less than
truckload freight trucking services
DH: Fedex Freight Inc
2200 Forward Dr
Harrison AR 72601
870 741-9000

(G-6714)
FRATERNAL ORDER OF EAGLES CLUB
Also Called: Eagles Club
141 E Rose St (55060-2423)
PHONE.............................507 451-3846
Bob Bishop, *Sr Corp Ofcr*
Levern Enzenauer, *Treasurer*
Ron Ankran, *Manager*
EMP: 30 EST: 1908
SQ FT: 16,800 Privately Held
SIC: 8641 Members only bar & restaurant
for members of organizations only

(G-6715)
FRITO-LAY INC
3401 9th St NW (55060-1185)
PHONE.............................507 446-5888
Darin Graeau, *Manager*
EMP: 500
SALES (est): 100MM-499.9MM Publicly
Held
WEB: www.fritolay.com
SIC: 5145 Wholesales snack foods
DH: Frito-Lay Inc
7701 Legacy Dr
Plano TX 75024
972 334-7000

(G-6716)
G&K SERVICES INC
2624 Park Dr (55060-4919)
PHONE.............................507 451-5710
FAX: 507 451-1811
Steve Dempsey, *General Mgr*
Greg Gibson, *Sales & Mktg St*
EMP: 30
SALES (est): 1MM-4.9MM Publicly Held
WEB: www.gkservices.com
SIC: 7218 7213 Industrial uniform supply
services; uniform supply service
PA: G&K Services Inc
5995 Opus Pkwy Ste 500
Minnetonka MN 55343
952 912-5500

(G-6717)
HOME TOWN FEDERAL CREDIT UNION
2400 W Bridge St (55060-5003)
PHONE.............................507 451-3798
FAX: 507 451-8374
Kim Westphal, *President*
Mitch Myre, *Mfg Staff*
Scott Markman, *Treasurer*
Sara Morris, *Branch Mgr*
Julie Conlin, *Officer*
EMP: 40 EST: 1974
SALES (est): 5MM-9.9MM Privately Held
WEB: www.hometowncu.coop
SIC: 6061 Federally chartered credit union

(G-6718)
INDEPENDENT SCHOOL DISTRICT NO
Also Called: Owatonna Community Education
122 E McKinley St (55060-3326)
PHONE.............................507 444-7900
FAX: 507 444-7999
Debra Johnson, *Director*
EMP: 33
SALES (est): 500-999K Privately Held
WEB: www.owatonna.k12.mn.us
SIC: 8351 Preschool center
PA: Independent School District No
515 W Bridge St
Owatonna MN 55060
507 444-8600

(G-6719)
INTERNATIONAL QUALITY HOMECARE
606 Hoffman Dr (55060-2351)
PHONE.............................507 451-6262
FAX: 507 451-6288
Aderonke Mordi, *President*
EMP: 39 EST: 2003 Privately Held
SIC: 7361 8082 Nurses' registry service;
home health care services

(G-6720)
KID'S KORNER EDUCARE CENTER
600 Florence Ave (55060-4704)
PHONE.............................507 451-0312
Jennifer Buck, *Director*
Daniel W Buck, *Director*
EMP: 30 EST: 1990
SALES (est): 500-999K Privately Held
SIC: 8351 Child day care service

(G-6721)
LAIRD LLC
Also Called: Comfort Inn
2345 NW 43rd St (55060-5647)
PHONE.............................507 444-0818
Krista Buss, *Sales Staff*
Janel Swenson, *Manager*
Don Deruyck, *Manager*
EMP: 25 EST: 1999
SALES (est): 1MM-4.9MM Privately Held
WEB: www.laird.net
SIC: 7011 Traveler accommodations

(G-6722)
LIFE STYLE INC
311 N Cedar Ave (55060-2307)
PHONE.............................507 451-8524
FAX: 507 451-5459
Paul H Arnfelt, *President*
Gail Arnfelt, *Corp Secy*
Joyce Peters, *Director*
Marco Falgiano, *Director*
EMP: 90 EST: 1972
SQ FT: 3,500
SALES (est): 10MM-24.9MM Privately Held
WEB: www.lifestyleinc.net
SIC: 6531 Real estate management
services

(G-6723)
LOWE'S HOME CENTERS INC
1280 21st Ave NW (55060-1397)
PHONE.............................507 446-4900
John Schafer, *Asst Mgr*
EMP: 150
SALES (est): 25MM-49.9MM Publicly Held
WEB: www.lowes.com
SIC: 5031 5064 Retails building products &
materials; wholesales exterior building
materials; wholesales interior building
materials; wholesales electrical appliances;
retails household appliances
HQ: Lowe's Home Centers Inc
1605 Curtis Bridge Rd
Wilkesboro NC 28697
336 658-4000

(G-6724)
MIDWEST RESTAURANT GROUP
Also Called: Timberlodge Steak House
4455 W Frontage Rd (55060-5659)
PHONE.............................507 444-0303
FAX: 507 444-0333
Chris Nelson, *President*
EMP: 100 EST: 2000
SALES (est): 1MM-4.9MM Privately Held
SIC: 7299 Full service steak restaurant;
banquet hall facility

(G-6725)
OWATONNA BUS CO INC
1145 Park Dr (55060-5070)
PO Box 583 (55060-0583)
PHONE.............................507 451-5262
FAX: 507 451-5264
William Regan, *President*
Sally Regan, *Vice Pres*
Katy Kreutter, *Treasurer*
EMP: 65 EST: 1968
SQ FT: 21,400
SALES (est): 1MM-4.9MM Privately Held

SIC: 4151 4142 School bus service; long-distance bus charter service

(G-6726)

OWATONNA CLINIC — MAYO HEALTH

134 Southview St (55060-3241)
PHONE.................507 451-1120
FAX: 507 451-8866
Brian Bunkers, *President*
Joanne Thronson, *Persnl Dir*
Stephanie Olson, *Comms Dir*
Lorraine J Griffin MD, *Med Doctor*
Jack A Felland MD, *Med Doctor*
EMP: 350 **EST:** 1954
SALES (est): 25MM-49.9MM **Privately Held**
SIC: 8011 Clinic operated by physicians
PA: Mayo Clinic
   200 1st St SW
   Rochester MN 55905
   507 284-2511

(G-6727)

OWATONNA COUNTRY CLUB INC

1991 Lemond Rd (55060-2871)
PO Box 446 (55060-0446)
PHONE.................507 451-6120
FAX: 507 451-7004
Dianne Nord, *Human Res Mgr*
Robert Howell, *Manager*
EMP: 75 **EST:** 1919
SQ FT: 22,000
SALES (est): 1MM-4.9MM **Privately Held**
WEB: www.owatonnacc.com
SIC: 7997 Membership golf club; cocktail lounge; eating place; membership swimming club; membership tennis club

(G-6728)

OWATONNA FAIRLANES CORP

Also Called: Southpark Lanes & Lounge
333 18th St SE (55060-4005)
PHONE.................507 451-2524
Mary Staats, *President*
H G Staats, *Corp Secy*
EMP: 50 **EST:** 1951
SQ FT: 38,000
SALES (est): 1MM-4.9MM **Privately Held**
SIC: 7933 7999 Ten pin center; retails bowling equipment & supplies; miniature golf course; limited service snack bar

(G-6729)

OWATONNA HOSPITALITY PARTNERS

Also Called: AmericInn
245 Florence Ave (55060-2774)
PHONE.................507 455-1142
FAX: 507 444-0545
Jack Spitzack, *President*
Renee Mischka, *General Mgr*
Bill Weiss, *Vice Pres*
Karen Luxton, *Manager*
EMP: 30 **EST:** 1992
SALES (est): 1MM-4.9MM **Privately Held**
SIC: 7011 Traveler accommodations

(G-6730)

PROPHET CORP (PA)

Also Called: GOPHER SPORT & PLAY WITH A P
2525 Lemond St (55060-5081)
PO Box 998 (55060-0998)
PHONE.................507 451-7470
Joel Jennings, *CEO*
Todd Jennings, *President*
Scott M Davis, *Senior Partner*
Andy Pierce, *Senior Partner*
Tulin Erdem, *Partner*
EMP: 85 **EST:** 1947
SQ FT: 98,000 **Privately Held**
WEB: www.prophet.com
SIC: 5091 Wholesales exercise equipment; wholesales gymnasium equipment; wholesales athletic goods

(G-6731)

PROPHET CORP

2525 Lemond St (55060-5081)
PHONE.................952 841-0021
Mike Prochaska, *Vice Pres*
EMP: 70
SALES (est): 25MM-49.9MM **Privately Held**
WEB: www.prophet.com

SIC: 5091 Wholesales exercise equipment; wholesales gymnasium equipment; wholesales athletic goods
PA: Prophet Corp
   2525 Lemond St
   Owatonna MN 55060
   507 451-7470

(G-6732)

PROPHET CORP

2525 Lemond St (55060-5081)
PHONE.................800 533-0446
John Moen, *Branch Mgr*
EMP: 125
SALES (est): 50MM-99.9MM **Privately Held**
WEB: www.prophet.com
SIC: 5091 Wholesales exercise equipment
PA: Prophet Corp
   2525 Lemond St
   Owatonna MN 55060
   507 451-7470

(G-6733)

RAINBOW RESIDENCE INC

285 Cedardale Dr SE (55060-4425)
PHONE.................507 451-5327
FAX: 507 451-5354
John Ekelund, *President*
Linda Karkhoff, *Corp Secy*
James Karkhoff, *Director*
EMP: 30 **EST:** 1981
SQ FT: 7,600
SALES (est): 1MM-4.9MM **Privately Held**
WEB: www.rainbowresidence.com
SIC: 8361 8052 8059 Home for the mentally retarded; intermediate care facility; convalescent home

(G-6734)

REM WOODVALE INC

592 Adams Ave NW Ofc (55060-2227)
PHONE.................507 451-1296
FAX: 507 451-1349
Diane Rezac, *Manager*
EMP: 31 **EST:** 1978
SALES (est): 500-999K **Privately Held**
SIC: 8052 8059 Residential mentally handicapped facility; home for the mentally retarded

(G-6735)

SA WOODS INC

Also Called: Casey & Groesbeck Construction
1414 S Oak Ave Ste 6 (55060-3957)
PO Box 305 (55060-0305)
PHONE.................507 451-7084
FAX: 507 451-7103
Samuel Woods, *President*
Ardis Woods, *Vice Pres*
EST: 1954 **Privately Held**
SIC: 1542 1541 Commercial & office building contractor; industrial building & warehouse construction

(G-6736)

SCHWAN'S HOME SERVICE INC

2795 Park Dr (55060-4916)
PHONE.................507 451-8538
Steve Koch, *Manager*
EMP: 30
SALES (est): 1MM-4.9MM **Privately Held**
WEB: www.theschwanfoodcompany.com
SIC: 4212 Delivery services by vehicle; retails packaged ice cream
HQ: Schwan's Home Service Inc
   115 W College Dr
   Marshall MN 56258
   507 532-3274

(G-6737)

SOUTH CENTRAL HUMAN RELATIONS

610 Florence Ave (55060-4704)
PHONE.................507 451-2630
FAX: 507 455-8133
David R Tverberg, *Manager*
Mark Skrien, *Manager*
Kathy Jensen, *Manager*
Debra L Vancleave, *Manager*
Joseph R Wilson, *Manager*
EMP: 65 **EST:** 1964
SALES (est): 1MM-4.9MM **Privately Held**
SIC: 8322 General counseling services

(G-6738)

STEELE COUNTY HUMAN SERVICES

630 Florence Ave (55060-4704)
PHONE.................507 444-7500
FAX: 507 451-5947
Kelly Harder, *Director*
EMP: 55 **EST:** 2003
SALES (est): 1MM-4.9MM **Privately Held**
WEB: www.co.steele.mn.us
SIC: 8322 Individual & family social services

(G-6739)

STEELE-WASECA COOPERATIVE ELEC

2411 W Bridge St (55060-5004)
PO Box 485 (55060-0485)
PHONE.................507 451-7340
FAX: 507 451-7923
Donald Kolb, *President*
Gary W Wilson, *Corp Secy*
Roger Rehman, *Purchasing*
Dave Lundberg, *CTO*
EMP: 30 **EST:** 1937
SQ FT: 48,000
SALES (est): 10MM-24.9MM **Privately Held**
WEB: www.swce.com
SIC: 4911 Provides electric power transmission services; electric power distribution service

(G-6740)

TRADITIONS OF MINNESOTA LLC

195 24th Pl NW (55060-1398)
PHONE.................507 455-0700
Deidra Burke, *Director*
EMP: 40 **EST:** 2005
SALES (est): 1MM-4.9MM **Privately Held**
SIC: 8059 Nursing home

(G-6741)

TRADITIONS OF OWATONNA

150 24th Pl NW (55060-1387)
PHONE.................507 451-0433
EMP: 90 **EST:** 2007
SALES (est): 1MM-4.9MM **Privately Held**
SIC: 8361 Residential care facility

(G-6742)

VINE RIPE INC

Also Called: Bushel Boy Farms
215 32nd Ave SW (55060)
PHONE.................507 451-1999
FAX: 507 451-1999
Jay S Johnson, *President*
▲ **EMP:** 75 **EST:** 1989 **Privately Held**
SIC: 0182 Hydroponic crops grown under cover; tomato farming

(G-6743)

WEE PALS CHILD CARE CENTER INC

560 Dunnell Dr (55060-4710)
PHONE.................507 451-8355
FAX: 507 455-9137
Billie Sayer, *Director*
Marisa Schroht, *Director*
EMP: 25 **EST:** 1970
SALES (est): 500-999K **Privately Held**
SIC: 8351 Child day care service

(G-6744)

WELLS FARGO BANK, NATIONAL

101 N Cedar Ave (55060-2303)
PHONE.................507 451-5670
FAX: 507 451-0366
Brad Peters, *President*
Paula Zincke, *Branch Mgr*
EMP: 30
SALES (est): 5MM-9.9MM **Publicly Held**
SIC: 6021 National commercial bank
HQ: Wfc Holdings, Corp
   420 Montgomery St
   San Francisco CA 94104
   415 396-7392

(G-6745)

WEST CENTRAL CHEMICALS

3925 N County Road 45 (55060-6184)
PO Box 1270, Fargo ND (58107-1270)
PHONE.................507 444-0275
Darrell Hursman, *Manager*
EMP: 50 **EST:** 1996
SALES (est): 25MM-49.9MM **Privately Held**
SIC: 5191 Wholesales farm supplies

(G-6746)

ZUMBRO RIVER BRAND INC (PA)

138 W Front St (55060-2326)
PHONE.................507 446-9097
FAX: 507 444-9308
Pam Sander, *President*
Jim Fischer, *Vice Pres*
Doris Maki, *Info Tech Mgr*
EMP: 32 **EST:** 1985
SQ FT: 28,000 **Privately Held**
WEB: www.zumbroriverbrand.com
SIC: 5087 Wholesales service establishment equipment & supplies

PARK RAPIDS
Hubbard County

(G-6747)

AMERICAN LEGION POST 212 A

900 1st St E (56470-1711)
PO Box 143 (56470-0143)
PHONE.................218 732-5238
FAX: 218 237-3360
John Naylor, *Principal*
Eugene Anderson, *Chief*
EMP: 25 **EST:** 1939 **Privately Held**
SIC: 8641 Veterans' organization

(G-6748)

CAMP WILDERNESS BSA INC

29984 Journey Trl (56470-5370)
PHONE.................218 732-4674
FAX: 218 732-1535
Brad Olson, *Director*
EMP: 75 **EST:** 1949
SALES (est): 1MM-4.9MM **Privately Held**
SIC: 7032 Recreational & sporting camp

(G-6749)

CARING HANDS HOME CARE INC

602 1st St E (56470-1705)
PHONE.................218 732-0088
FAX: 218 732-0086
Pat Johnson, *Manager*
EMP: 60
SALES (est): 1MM-4.9MM **Privately Held**
WEB: www.caringhandshomecare.com
SIC: 8082 Home health care services
PA: Caring Hands Home Care Inc
   113 Minnesota Ave W
   Sebeka MN 56477
   218 837-5572

(G-6750)

CITIZENS NATIONAL BANK INC

300 1st St W (56470-1402)
PO Box 231 (56470-0231)
PHONE.................218 732-3393
FAX: 218 732-9158
R L Gack, *President*
Kathy Henry, *Exec VP*
Steve Johnson, *Senior VP*
Jason McCollum, *Assistant VP*
Cal Storseth, *Vice Pres*
EMP: 48 **EST:** 1933
SQ FT: 5,940
SALES (est): 10MM-24.9MM **Privately Held**
WEB: www.cnbbank.com
SIC: 6021 National commercial bank

(G-6751)

EMMONS & OLIVER RESOURCES

601 1st St E (56470-1765)
PO Box 64 (56470-0064)
PHONE.................218 732-3323
FAX: 218 732-3323
Cecilia Oliver, *Principal*

(PA)=Parent Co (HQ)=Headquarters (DH)=Div Headquarters
✿ = New business established in last 2 years

2011 Harris Minnesota
Services Directory

© Harris InfoSource 1-866-281-6415

295

GEOGRAPHIC

Beth Clubb, *Principal*
Brett Emmons, *Principal*
EMP: 48 **EST:** 1982
SALES (est): 5MM-9.9MM **Privately Held**
SIC: 8711 8713 Civil engineering services; photogrammetric engineers

(G-6752)
HEARTLAND HOMES OPTIONS IN COM
609 7th St W　(56470-1303)
PO Box 214　(56470-0214)
PHONE..............................218 732-4572
FAX: 218 732-8462
Raylene Kimball, *Administrator*
EMP: 50 **EST:** 1976
SALES (est): 1MM-4.9MM **Privately Held**
SIC: 8361 Home for the mentally handicapped

(G-6753)
HOFFMAN CONTROLS INC
2506 Albert Ave S　(56470-2786)
PHONE..............................218 732-8374
Don Hoffman, *President*
EMP: 25 **EST:** 1996
SQ FT: 7,800
SALES (est): 1MM-4.9MM **Privately Held**
SIC: 1731 Electrical contractor

(G-6754)
HUBBARD COUNTY DEVELOPMENTAL
109 Pleasant Ave S　(56470-1414)
PO Box 86　(56470-0086)
PHONE..............................218 732-3358
FAX: 218 732-8082
Ed Ranson, *Director*
Linda Hanson, *Admin Asst*
EMP: 60 **EST:** 1973 **Privately Held**
SIC: 8399 Community development groups

(G-6755)
HUBBARD, COUNTY OF INC
Also Called: Heritage Living Center
619 6th St W　(56470-1301)
PHONE..............................218 732-3329
FAX: 218 732-9125
Teresa Walsh, *Manager*
Kurt Hansen, *Manager*
EMP: 120
SALES (est): 1MM-4.9MM **Privately Held**
SIC: 8051 8322 Skilled nursing care facility; adult daycare center; county supervisors' & executives' office
PA: Hubbard, County of Inc
　　301 Court Ave
　　Park Rapids MN 56470
　　218 732-3196

(G-6756)
INNOVIS HEALTH LLC
Also Called: Park Rapids-Walker Clinic
705 Pleasant Ave S　(56470-1440)
PHONE..............................218 732-2800
FAX: 218 732-2874
Larry M Leadbetter, *Med Doctor*
John Boland, *Administrator*
Maggie Yerkes, *Nursing Dir*
EMP: 55
SALES (est): 5MM-9.9MM **Privately Held**
SIC: 8011 Physicians' office & clinic
PA: Innovis Health LLC
　　3000 32nd Ave SW
　　Fargo ND 58103
　　701 364-8989

(G-6757)
ITASCA-MANTRAP CO-OP ELECTRIC
16930 County 6　(56470-2883)
PO Box 192　(56470-0192)
PHONE..............................218 732-3377
FAX: 218 732-5890
John Roehl, *Ch of Bd*
Patrick E O'Brien, *President*
Melvin Hughes, *Vice Chairman*
Royce Peterson, *Corp Secy*
Charles Andress, *Treasurer*
EMP: 26 **EST:** 1939
SQ FT: 24,000
SALES (est): 10MM-24.9MM **Privately Held**
WEB: www.itascamantrap.com
SIC: 4911 Electric power distribution service

(G-6758)
JONES DW MANAGEMENT
609 8th St W　(56470-1336)
PHONE..............................218 547-3307
Lori Duchesneau, *President*
EMP: 25
SALES (est): 1MM-4.9MM **Privately Held**
SIC: 6531 Real estate services

(G-6759)
L & M SUPPLY INC
1415 1st St E　(56470-1803)
PHONE..............................218 732-4465
FAX: 218 732-9470
Mike Heegard, *Manager*
EMP: 30
SALES (est): 1MM-4.9MM **Privately Held**
SIC: 5013 Hardware store; wholesales automotive supplies & parts; tire dealer
PA: L & M Supply Inc
　　1200 E US Highway 169
　　Grand Rapids MN 55744
　　218 326-9451

(G-6760)
R D OFFUTT CO
15357 US 71　(56470-2855)
PHONE..............................218 732-1461
FAX: 218 732-8369
Allan F Knoll, *Treasurer*
Larry Monico, *Manager*
Tyler R Falk, *Director*
EMP: 50 **Privately Held**
SIC: 0134 Potato farm
PA: Rdo Holdings Co
　　2829 University Dr S
　　Fargo ND 58103
　　701 237-6062

(G-6761)
R D OFFUTT CO
Also Called: Great Northern Nursery
11385 State Hwy 34　(56470)
PHONE..............................218 732-4163
Bruce Krabbenfost, *Manager*
EMP: 25
SALES (est): 1MM-4.9MM **Privately Held**
SIC: 5193 Wholesales nursery stock
PA: Rdo Holdings Co
　　2829 University Dr S
　　Fargo ND 58103
　　701 237-6062

(G-6762)
ST JOSEPH'S AREA HEALTH SVCS
600 Pleasant Ave S　(56470-1431)
PHONE..............................218 732-3311
FAX: 218 732-1368
Dan P Smith, *Ch of Surgery*
Tom Hardacre, *Materials Mgr*
Kevin Farrell, *Facilities Mgr*
Brent Schmidt, *CFO*
Eileen Froleich, *Accounting Staf*
EMP: 375 **EST:** 1946
SQ FT: 64,000
SALES (est): 25MM-49.9MM **Privately Held**
SIC: 8062 Medical hospital
PA: Catholic Health Initiatives
　　98 Inverness Dr W Ste 800
　　Englewood CO 80112
　　303 298-9100

(G-6763)
STATE BANK OF PARK RAPIDS
200 1st St E　(56470-1613)
PO Box 31　(56470-0031)
PHONE..............................218 732-3366
FAX: 218 732-8829
J D Smythe, *President*
Susanne Smythe, *Exec VP*
Susan S Ramstors, *Vice Pres*
Dawn Landstrom, *Vice Pres*
Rose Higgins, *Vice Pres*
EMP: 25 **EST:** 1902
SQ FT: 18,600
SALES (est): 5MM-9.9MM **Privately Held**
WEB: www.statebankofparkrapids.com
SIC: 6022 State commercial bank

(G-6764)
U SAVE LEASE & RENTAL INC
Also Called: Thielen Motors
E Highway 34　(56470)
PO Box 73　(56470-0073)
PHONE..............................218 732-3347
Theodore A Thielen, *President*
EMP: 26 **EST:** 1980
SQ FT: 11,900
SALES (est): 10MM-24.9MM **Privately Held**
SIC: 6159 4119 7514 Automobile finance leasing service; automobile rental with driver service; rent-a-car service

PARKERS PRAIRIE
Otter Tail County

(G-6765)
INTERNATIONAL ASSOCIATION OF
Also Called: Parkers Prairie Lions Club
10653 State Highway 29　(56361-4522)
PHONE..............................218 338-6129
James Arvibson, *President*
Richard Bergqutisg, *Director*
EMP: 34 **Privately Held**
WEB: www.iaopc.com
SIC: 8641 Civic associations
PA: International Association of
　　300 W 22nd St
　　Oak Brook IL 60523
　　630 571-5466

(G-6766)
SAINT WILLIAM'S LIVING CENTER
212 W Soo St　(56361-4404)
PO Box 30　(56361-0030)
PHONE..............................218 338-4671
Paul Bear, *President*
EMP: 80 **EST:** 1963
SALES (est): 1MM-4.9MM **Privately Held**
SIC: 8059 Nursing home

(G-6767)
ST WILLIAMS NURSING HOME INC
212 W Soo St　(56361)
PHONE..............................218 338-4671
FAX: 218 338-5917
Paul Bear, *Administrator*
EMP: 110 **EST:** 1962
SQ FT: 90,000
SALES (est): 1MM-4.9MM **Privately Held**
SIC: 8051 8052 8361 Skilled nursing care facility; residential care facility; intermediate care facility

PAYNESVILLE
Stearns County

(G-6768)
A & C FARM SERVICE INC
412 Bridge St　(56362-1102)
PHONE..............................320 243-3736
Eileen Kern, *President*
Randy Kern, *Finance*
Lori Evans, *Manager*
Larry Kern, *Executive*
EMP: 28 **EST:** 1960
SQ FT: 10,000
SALES (est): 10MM-24.9MM **Privately Held**
SIC: 5083 Wholesales agricultural machinery & equipment

(G-6769)
JENNIE-O TURKEY STORE INC
409 E Hwy 55　(56362)
PHONE..............................320 243-3764
La V Anderson, *Branch Mgr*
EMP: 125 **Publicly Held**
WEB: www.hormel.com
SIC: 0253 Turkey farm
HQ: Jennie-O Turkey Store Inc
　　2505 Willmar Ave SW
　　Willmar MN 56201
　　320 235-2622

(G-6770)
KORONIS HILLS GOLF CLUB
29757 State Hwy 23 W　(56362)
PO Box 55　(56362-0055)
PHONE..............................320 243-4111
Alisa Weiss, *Vice Pres*
Cindy Fox, *Manager*
Jack Binsfeld, *Exec Dir*
EMP: 30 **EST:** 1930
SQ FT: 4,000
SALES (est): 1MM-4.9MM **Privately Held**
SIC: 7997 Membership golf club; retails golf goods & equipment

(G-6771)
LOUIS INDUSTRIES INC
222 Industrial Loop W　(56362-1508)
PO Box 57　(56362-0057)
PHONE..............................320 243-3696
FAX: 320 243-4430
Kevin Wall, *Ch of Bd*
Leo Louis, *President*
Cecil Louis, *Vice Pres*
Lance Louis, *CFO*
Sandy Wall, *Manager*
EMP: 34 **EST:** 1940
SQ FT: 45,000
SALES (est): 25MM-49.9MM **Privately Held**
WEB: www.louisind.com
SIC: 5051 Wholesales metal sheets; wholesales metal rods; wholesales metal tubing; steel mill; manufactures tools, dies, jigs & fixtures

(G-6772)
PAYNESVILLE FARMERS UNION
419 E Hoffman St　(56362-1612)
PHONE..............................320 243-3751
Robert B Hemmesch, *President*
Tim Wagner, *Director*
Dallas Fenske, *Director*
Barry Albright, *Director*
EMP: 25 **EST:** 1953
SQ FT: 3,000
SALES (est): 5MM-9.9MM **Privately Held**
WEB: www.paynesvillepress.com
SIC: 5171 Manufactures fertilizers; liquefied petroleum gas dealer; wholesales petroleum bulk stations; gas station

(G-6773)
PAYNESVILLE MOTOR & TRANSFER
314 Minnie St　(56362-1519)
PHONE..............................320 243-4455
Phyllis Nielsen, *President*
EMP: 25 **EST:** 1938
SALES (est): 1MM-4.9MM **Privately Held**
SIC: 7389 Accommodation locating service

(G-6774)
SAINT MARTIN COMMERCIAL CLUB
27392 Sauk Landing Rd　(56362-9762)
PHONE..............................320 548-3208
Steve Revermann, *Principal*
EMP: 25 **EST:** 1985
SALES (est): 500-999K **Privately Held**
SIC: 7997 Baseball club

(G-6775)
VOSS PLUMBING & HEATING OF
316 E Hoffman St　(56362-1611)
PO Box 77　(56362-0077)
PHONE..............................320 243-3644
FAX: 320 243-3664
Dale Klein, *President*
David Voss, *Vice Pres*
Teff Thielen, *Manager*
Sherri McCorquodale, *Officer*
EMP: 40 **EST:** 1961
SQ FT: 4,500
SALES (est): 1MM-4.9MM **Privately Held**
WEB: www.vossplumbing.com
SIC: 1711 Plumbing service; heating & air conditioning contractor

www.HarrisInfo.com
296
2011 Harris Minnesota
Services Directory
▲=Import ▼=Export
◆=Import/Export

PELICAN RAPIDS
Otter Tail County

(G-6776)
CHRISTIANSON BUS SERVICE INC
Hwy 59 S (56572)
PO Box 362 (56572-0362)
PHONE.............................218 863-7000
James A Christianson, *President*
EMP: 25 **EST:** 1950
SQ FT: 28,000
SALES (est): 500-999K Privately Held
SIC: 4151 School bus service

(G-6777)
ENVIRONMENTAL CONTROL SYSTEMS
22 Industrial Park Dr (56572-4001)
PHONE.............................218 863-1766
Sam Hermann, *President*
Karen Syverson, *Accountant*
EMP: 47 **EST:** 2005
SQ FT: 25,000
SALES (est): 10MM-24.9MM Privately Held
SIC: 5084 Wholesales industrial controlling instruments & accessories

(G-6778)
EVANGELICAL LUTHERAN GOOD
Also Called: Good Samaritan Center
119 N Broadway (56572-4140)
PO Box 646 (56572-0646)
PHONE.............................218 863-2401
FAX: 218 863-5049
Jim Sewick, *Administrator*
Carol Johnson, *Education*
EMP: 82
SALES (est): 1MM-4.9MM Privately Held
WEB: www.good-sam.com
SIC: 8051 Skilled nursing care facility
PA: Evangelical Lutheran Good
4800 W 57th St
Sioux Falls SD 57108
605 362-3100

(G-6779)
GERALD N EVENSON INC
835 1st St SW (56572-4406)
PO Box 629 (56572-0629)
PHONE.............................218 863-7101
Jeanne Hovland, *President*
Paul Evenson, *Vice Pres*
EMP: 30 **EST:** 1946
SQ FT: 14,500
SALES (est): 1MM-4.9MM Privately Held
SIC: 4213 4212 5013 Over the road trucking; local trucking without storage services; wholesales truck parts & accessories

(G-6780)
LAKE REGION ELECTRIC CO-OP
1401 S Brdwy (56572)
PO Box 643 (56572-0643)
PHONE.............................218 863-1171
Tim Thompson, *CEO*
Ken Hendrickx, *President*
Jack Lacey, *Vice Chairman*
Richard Akerman, *Vice Pres*
Dan Elton, *Vice Pres*
EMP: 84 **EST:** 1937
SQ FT: 100,000
SALES (est): 25MM-49.9MM Privately Held
WEB: www.lrec.coop
SIC: 4911 Electric power distribution service

(G-6781)
OTTERTAIL LODGE 284
13 W Mill St (56572-4228)
PHONE.............................218 863-7913
Bill Osborne, *Principal*
Harold Brager, *Principal*
Bob Gard, *Principal*
EMP: 50 **EST:** 1914
SQ FT: 3,000 Privately Held
SIC: 8641 Fraternal association

(G-6782)
PARK REGION COOPERATIVE
120 S Broadway (56572-4225)
PO Box 630 (56572-0630)
PHONE.............................218 863-2811
FAX: 218 863-2825
Galen Teithert, *President*
Cathy Vague, *Office Mgr*
Dave Hebsery, *Manager*
Galen Teichert, *Manager*
Lee Brenna, *Manager*
EST: 1926
SQ FT: 1,875 Privately Held
SIC: 5171 Petroleum bulk station; retails bottled propane gas; gas station

(G-6783)
PELICAN RAPIDS GOOD SAMARITAN
119 N Broadway (56572-4140)
PHONE.............................218 863-2401
Maren Gemar, *Director*
EMP: 60
SALES (est): 1MM-4.9MM Privately Held
SIC: 8059 Nursing home

(G-6784)
WEST CENTRAL TURKEYS LLC
704 N Broadway (56572-4147)
PHONE.............................218 863-1491
FAX: 218 863-3171
Staurt Freeze, *General Mgr*
Jeff Ettinger, *Member*
Mindy R Kejece, *Persnl Mgr*
EMP: 670 **EST:** 1996
SALES (est): 25MM-49.9MM Publicly Held
WEB: www.jennieo.com
SIC: 7299 Butcher service, process only, without sales
PA: Hormel Foods Corp
1 Hormel Pl
Austin MN 55912
507 437-5611

PENGILLY
Itasca County

(G-6785)
SWAN LAKE ASSOCIATION
29215 Kaleva Beach Rd (55775-2110)
PHONE.............................218 885-3225
Walt Petrusic, *President*
Philip Strege, *Accounting Dir*
EMP: 50 **EST:** 2000 Privately Held
SIC: 8641 Citizens union

PEQUOT LAKES
Crow Wing County

(G-6786)
CAMPGROUND MARKETING SERVICES
9252 Breezy Point Dr (56472-3159)
PHONE.............................218 562-4204
Robert Spizzo, *President*
Joyce Bzoskie, *Vice Pres*
EMP: 100 **EST:** 1986
SALES (est): 10MM-24.9MM Privately Held
SIC: 6531 Real estate selling agency; real estate management services

(G-6787)
CITY LIGHTS INC
30694 Olson St (56472-3059)
PO Box 440 (56472-0440)
PHONE.............................218 568-4754
Dennis Peterson, *Owner*
EMP: 60 **EST:** 1996
SALES (est): 5MM-9.9MM Privately Held
SIC: 1623 Utility line construction

(G-6788)
FOREST HILLS GOLF RV RESO
9252 Breezy Point Dr (56472-3159)
PHONE.............................218 562-7585
Joyce Bzoske, *Owner*
EMP: 25 **EST:** 2004
SALES (est): 1MM-4.9MM Privately Held

SIC: 7992 Public golf course

(G-6789)
HUNT TECHNOLOGIES LLC
6436 County Road 11 (56472-3107)
PHONE.............................218 562-4877
FAX: 218 562-4878
Robert McLean, *General Mgr*
Bob Zdebski, *General Mgr*
Jeff Carkhuff, *Member*
Todd Headlee, *Member*
Mark Kodet, *Member*
EMP: 200 **EST:** 1984
SQ FT: 50,000
SALES (est): 25MM-49.9MM Privately Held
WEB: www.turtletech.com
SIC: 8711 Manufactures electric, pocket, portable & panelboard meters; manufactures test equipment for electronic & electrical circuits; ship, boat, machine & product design services

(G-6790)
LAKES STATE BANK
31113 Front St (56472)
PO Box 366 (56472-0366)
PHONE.............................218 568-4473
FAX: 218 568-5358
Richard Tiedeman, *CEO*
David Elsenpeter, *President*
EST: 1997 Privately Held
WEB: www.lakesstatebank.com
SIC: 6022 State commercial bank

(G-6791)
NARVESON MANAGEMENT INC
6810 County Road 11 (56472-3110)
PO Box 285 (56472-0285)
PHONE.............................218 562-6400
Neal Narveson, *President*
Tom Turk, *Vice Pres*
Chris Anderson, *Admin Asst*
EMP: 50 **EST:** 1998
SALES (est): 5MM-9.9MM Privately Held
WEB: www.breezypointtimeshare.com
SIC: 8742 Management consulting services

(G-6792)
SIENNA CORP
Also Called: Deacons Lodge Golf Club
9348 Arnold Palmer Dr (56472-3784)
PHONE.............................218 562-6262
FAX: 218 562-6268
Mark Neva, *Principal*
Jack Barry, *Manager*
EMP: 40 **EST:** 1998
SALES (est): 1MM-4.9MM Privately Held
SIC: 7992 Public golf course

PERHAM
Otter Tail County

(G-6793)
ARVIG ENTERPRISES INC (PA)
Also Called: ACS
160 2nd Ave SW (56573-1409)
PHONE.............................218 346-5500
Allen Arvig, *President*
Carmen Arvig, *Corp Secy*
Donna Ward, *Vice Pres*
Rick Vyskocil, *Treasurer*
Lori Meader, *Exec Dir*
EMP: 150 **EST:** 1984
SQ FT: 20,000 Privately Held
SIC: 4813 4841 Wired telecommunications carrier & service; cable television services

(G-6794)
BAUCK BUSING LTD
43569 Fort Thunder Rd (56573-8918)
PO Box 380 (56573-0380)
PHONE.............................218 346-4599
Kent Zitzow, *President*
Paul Winterfeldt, *Vice Pres*
EMP: 30 **EST:** 1996
SALES (est): 1MM-4.9MM Privately Held
SIC: 4131 Bus transit system

(G-6795)
CC & I ENGINEERING INC
150 2nd St SW (56573-1405)
PHONE.............................218 346-3600
FAX: 218 346-3610
Jason Dale, *President*
David Arvig, *Chairman*
David Pawlowski, *Corp Secy*
Ernest Kawlewski Jr, *CFO*
Nancy Bagne, *Manager*
EMP: 28 **EST:** 1951
SQ FT: 6,000
SALES (est): 1MM-4.9MM Privately Held
WEB: www.cci-eng.com
SIC: 8711 Engineering consulting services
PA: Arvig Enterprises Inc
160 2nd Ave SW
Perham MN 56573
218 346-5500

(G-6796)
EAST OTTER TAIL TELEPHONE CO
150 2nd Ave SW (56573-1409)
PHONE.............................218 346-5500
FAX: 218 346-5510
Allen R Arvig, *President*
David Pratt, *General Mgr*
Carmen Arvig, *Corp Secy*
Lauris Molbert, *COO*
David Arvig, *COO*
EMP: 126 **EST:** 1950
SQ FT: 6,750 Privately Held
SIC: 4813 Local telephone communications services
PA: Arvig Enterprises Inc
160 2nd Ave SW
Perham MN 56573
218 346-5500

(G-6797)
HUDALLA ASSOCIATES INC
47500 County Highway 51 (56573-8122)
PHONE.............................218 346-2734
FAX: 218 346-2741
Bruce Hudalla, *President*
Jared Washburn, *Sales Mgr*
Brian Malone, *Sales Mgr*
Anthony Lopez, *Sales Mgr*
Harry Grim, *Sales Mgr*
EMP: 30 **EST:** 1986
SALES (est): 10MM-24.9MM Privately Held
SIC: 5091 Wholesales hunting equipment & supplies

(G-6798)
L & M INVESTMENT INC
323 4th St SW (56573-1623)
PHONE.............................218 346-2798
Lee J Rogert, *President*
EMP: 70 **EST:** 2001
SALES (est): 25MM-49.9MM Privately Held
SIC: 6799 Investor services

(G-6799)
NEW LIFE FARMS, LLLP
105 Jake St (56573-2107)
PHONE.............................218 346-4959
Ross Mickelson, *Partner*
Wayne Mickelson, *Partner*
EMP: 60 **EST:** 1956 Privately Held
SIC: 0253 Turkey farm

(G-6800)
PERHAM HOSPITAL DISTRICT
665 3rd St SW Bldg 2 (56573-1137)
PHONE.............................218 346-4500
FAX: 218 346-4540
Randel T Stolee, *Ch of Surgery*
Karen Meyer, *Materials Dir*
Tina Becker, *Purchasing*
Brad Wurgler, *CFO*
Kathy Johnson, *Human Res Dir*
EMP: 270 **EST:** 1902
SALES (est): 10MM-24.9MM Privately Held
WEB: www.pmhh.com
SIC: 8062 8051 Medical hospital; skilled nursing care facility

(PA)=Parent Co (HQ)=Headquarters (DH)=Div Headquarters
✿ = New business established in last 2 years

2011 Harris Minnesota
Services Directory

© Harris InfoSource 1-866-281-6415
297

GEOGRAPHIC

(G-6801)
PERHAM LAKESIDE GOLF CLUB INC
2727 450th St　(56573)
PO Box 313　(56573-0313)
PHONE..............................218 346-6070
FAX: 218 346-6049
Nick Anderson, *General Mgr*
EMP: 50 EST: 1962
SQ FT: 2,000
SALES (est): 1MM-4.9MM **Privately Held**
WEB: www.perhamlakeside.com
SIC: 7997 7992 Membership golf club; public golf course

(G-6802)
ROYALE RESOURCES INC
154 1st Ave S　(56573-1401)
PHONE..............................218 346-3000
FAX: 218 346-8201
Connie Mort, *CEO*
EMP: 70 EST: 2001
SALES (est): 1MM-4.9MM **Privately Held**
WEB: www.royaleresources.com
SIC: 7363 Employee leasing service

(G-6803)
UNITED COMMUNITY BANK
155 2nd Ave SW　(56573-1408)
PO Box 249　(56573-0249)
PHONE..............................218 346-5700
FAX: 218 346-5701
Charles L Cavanagh, *President*
Robert Cavanagh, *Vice Pres*
William Cavanagh, *Vice Pres*
Peggy Wilcox, *Mfg Staff*
Sandra Waldon, *Marketing Staff*
EMP: 34 EST: 1911
SQ FT: 6,500
SALES (est): 5MM-9.9MM **Privately Held**
WEB: www.ucbankmn.com
SIC: 6022 State commercial bank

PIERZ
Crow Wing County

(G-6804)
HORIZON HEALTH INC
Also Called: Harmony House
301 1st Ave SE　(56364-4119)
PHONE..............................320 468-2811
FAX: 320 468-6863
Shiela Johnson, *Manager*
Betty Fyten, *Manager*
Jennine Engen, *Program Dir*
EMP: 35
SALES (est): 1MM-4.9MM **Privately Held**
WEB: www.horizonhealth.net
SIC: 8059 Personal care home, with health care
PA: Horizon Health Inc
　　26814 143rd St
　　Pierz MN 56364
　　320 468-6451

(G-6805)
MINN-TEX EXPRESS INC
432 State Highway 25　(56364-4100)
PHONE..............................320 277-3562
Edward L Deason, *President*
EMP: 34 EST: 1992
SALES (est): 1MM-4.9MM **Privately Held**
WEB: www.minn-tex.com
SIC: 4731 Truck transportation brokers

PIERZ
Morrison County

(G-6806)
PIERZ VILLA INC
119 Faust St　(56364-9540)
PO Box 397　(56364-0397)
PHONE..............................320 468-6405
Jim Bircham, *CEO*
Kim Rocheleau, *Administrator*
Paula Rochelu, *Administrator*
Lori Besser, *Administration*
EMP: 25 EST: 1985
SALES (est): 1MM-4.9MM **Privately Held**

WEB: www.pierzvilla.com
SIC: 8059 Nursing home

(G-6807)
RED'S AUTO INC
104 Main St S　(56364-4400)
PO Box 33　(56364-0033)
PHONE..............................320 468-6478
FAX: 320 468-6652
Jim Sitzman, *President*
Pam Sitzman, *Vice Pres*
EMP: 25 EST: 1986
SQ FT: 1,500
SALES (est): 1MM-4.9MM **Privately Held**
SIC: 7538 General automotive repair services; retails bait & tackle; gas station

(G-6808)
RICH PRAIRIE LIVESTOCK
96 Hwy 27 W　(56364)
PO Box 121　(56364-0121)
PHONE..............................320 468-2514
FAX: 320 468-6373
Richard Boser, *President*
Diane Varner, *Corp Secy*
Joseph Varner, *VP Purch*
EMP: 25 EST: 1981
SQ FT: 16,000
SALES (est): 10MM-24.9MM **Privately Held**
SIC: 5154 Wholesales cattle

PILLAGER
Cass County

(G-6809)
HENGEL LANDFILL & SERVICE CORP
12883 Upper Sylvan Rd SW　(56473-2380)
PHONE..............................218 746-3198
Elmer Hengel Jr, *Owner*
Heather Schmit, *General Mgr*
EMP: 32 EST: 1976
SALES (est): 1MM-4.9MM **Privately Held**
SIC: 1795 Wrecking & demolition contractor

(G-6810)
KRUSHE RESIDENTIAL SERVICES
12760 W Sylvan Dr SW　(56473-2342)
PO Box 264　(56473-0264)
PHONE..............................218 746-3117
Angela L Krushe, *President*
EMP: 50 EST: 1997
SALES (est): 1MM-4.9MM **Privately Held**
SIC: 8361 Residential care for children; geriatric residential care

(G-6811)
MANION LUMBER & TRUSS INC
220 River St N　(56473-3000)
PO Box 67　(56473-0067)
PHONE..............................218 746-3200
FAX: 218 746-3994
John Manion, *President*
Bob Dabill, *General Mgr*
Steve Scheffel, *Managing Dir*
Gerald Manion, *Corp Secy*
Mark Manion, *Vice Pres*
EMP: 40 EST: 1992
SQ FT: 24,000
SALES (est): 1MM-4.9MM **Privately Held**
SIC: 5031 Manufactures building & structural wood members; wholesales lumber, plywood & millwork; manufactures wooden roof trusses

PINE CITY
Pine County

(G-6812)
KUTZKE OIL CO INC
Also Called: Rock Creek Motor Stop
9865 Pine Shores Dr　(55063-4574)
PHONE..............................320 629-2075
Warren Dufresne, *President*
Mary Dufresne, *Vice Pres*
Melvin R Kutzke, *Treasurer*
EMP: 40 EST: 1938
SQ FT: 2,500
SALES (est): 50MM-99.9MM **Privately Held**

SIC: 5171 Wholesales petroleum bulk stations; truck stop; fuel oil dealer

(G-6813)
LAKESIDE MEDICAL CENTER INC
129 6th Ave SE　(55063-1913)
PHONE..............................320 629-2542
FAX: 320 629-1093
Max Blaufuss, *President*
Mary Blaufuss, *Vice Pres*
Rick McMahon, *Accountant*
Jan Smuder, *Manager*
John Torseth, *Director*
EMP: 135 EST: 1966
SQ FT: 60,000
SALES (est): 5MM-9.9MM **Privately Held**
SIC: 8051 8062 Skilled nursing care facility; medical hospital

(G-6814)
LEE'S PRO SHOP INC
625 Henriette Rd NW　(55063-5021)
PHONE..............................320 629-7568
Loren Samuelson, *President*
Bradley Samuelson, *Corp Secy*
Jonathan Samuelson, *Vice Pres*
Yvonne Louden, *Treasurer*
Chad Fedder, *Accounting Dir*
EMP: 35 EST: 1973
SQ FT: 12,000
SALES (est): 1MM-4.9MM **Privately Held**
WEB: www.leesproshop.com
SIC: 7299 Screen printing on fabric; manufactures plated metal trophies; retails sports apparel; custom stitching service; retails sporting goods

PINE ISLAND
Goodhue County

(G-6815)
DMC PLUMBING & HEATING INC
301 N Main St　(55963-7510)
PO Box 1085　(55963-1085)
PHONE..............................507 356-4455
FAX: 507 356-8586
Dean Cocker, *President*
Sharin Fisher, *Manager*
EMP: 42 EST: 1983
SQ FT: 10,000
SALES (est): 5MM-9.9MM **Privately Held**
WEB: www.dmcplumbing.com
SIC: 1711 Plumbing service; warm air heating & air conditioning contractor

(G-6816)
FARM COUNTRY CO-OP
417 N Main St　(55963-7533)
PO Box 1037　(55963-1037)
PHONE..............................507 356-8313
FAX: 507 356-8881
Noel Frana, *President*
Tim Clemmon, *Finance Mgr*
Jim Tewalt, *Manager*
Linda K Kelly, *Supervisor*
EMP: 50 EST: 1896
SQ FT: 8,000
SALES (est): 10MM-24.9MM **Privately Held**
WEB: www.farmcountrycoop.com
SIC: 5153 5191 Manufactures fertilizers; manufactures animal feed; wholesales seeds & bulbs; wholesale grain elevator; wholesales feed; wholesales field, garden & flower seeds; wholesales farm supplies

(G-6817)
PINE HAVEN CARE CENTER INC
210 3rd St NW　(55963-9139)
PHONE..............................507 356-8304
FAX: 507 356-4400
Lora Burtsinger, *Finance*
Steve Ziller, *Manager*
John Thompson, *Administrator*
Shelley Sobeck, *Director*
EMP: 100 EST: 1964
SQ FT: 10,000
SALES (est): 1MM-4.9MM **Privately Held**
SIC: 8051 8351 Convalescent home; child day care service

PINE RIVER
Cass County

(G-6818)
EVANGELICAL LUTHERAN GOOD
Also Called: Good Samaritan Soc Pine River
518 Jefferson Ave　(56474)
PO Box 29　(56474-0029)
PHONE..............................218 587-4423
FAX: 218 587-2671
Judy Irons, *Purchasing*
Alan Johnson, *Human Resources*
Roxanne Fredericks, *Office Mgr*
Brian Larsen, *Administrator*
EMP: 110
SALES (est): 1MM-4.9MM **Privately Held**
WEB: www.good-sam.com
SIC: 8051 Extended care facility
PA: Evangelical Lutheran Good
　　4800 W 57th St
　　Sioux Falls SD 57108
　　605 362-3100

(G-6819)
KERSTEN MANAGEMENT GROUP INC
10602 Wabigoniss Shrs　(56474-2559)
PHONE..............................218 543-6977
Keith Kersten, *President*
EMP: 60 EST: 2005
SALES (est): 5MM-9.9MM **Privately Held**
SIC: 8742 Management consulting services

(G-6820)
PINE RIVER GROUP HOME INC
103 5th St　(56474-5002)
PO Box 96　(56474-0096)
PHONE..............................218 587-4888
Bruce Winder, *Administrator*
Edward T Bettino, *Administrator*
EMP: 65 EST: 1977
SQ FT: 3,000
SALES (est): 1MM-4.9MM **Privately Held**
SIC: 8361 Home for the physically handicapped

(G-6821)
PINEY RIDGE LODGE INC
37400 Piney Ridge Rd　(56474-3614)
PHONE..............................218 587-2296
Michael C Mahoney, *President*
EMP: 25 EST: 1998
SALES (est): 1MM-4.9MM **Privately Held**
WEB: www.pineyridge.com
SIC: 7011 Resort hotel; eating place; bar & lounge drinking establishment

(G-6822)
WHISPERING PINES THERAPY CTR
518 Jefferson Ave　(56474)
PHONE..............................218 587-4423
Pat Johnson, *Manager*
Brian Larson, *Administrator*
EMP: 99 EST: 2001
SALES (est): 5MM-9.9MM **Privately Held**
SIC: 8093 Outpatient rehabilitation treatment center

PIPESTONE
Pipestone County

(G-6823)
BANNER & ASSOC
119 2nd Ave SW Ste 5　(56164-1684)
PO Box 243　(56164-0243)
PHONE..............................507 562-2957
Scott Leddy, *Manager*
EMP: 70 EST: 2006
SALES (est): 5MM-9.9MM **Privately Held**
SIC: 8712 Architectural engineers

(G-6824)
DAVID BALT DO
920 4th Ave SW　(56164-1455)
PHONE..............................507 825-3390
EMP: 35 EST: 1996
SALES (est): 1MM-4.9MM **Privately Held**

www.HarrisInfo.com
298

2011 Harris Minnesota
Services Directory

▲=Import ▼=Export
◆=Import/Export

SIC: 8031 Osteopathic physicians' office & clinic

(G-6825)
EMP SERV L L C
1300 S Highway 75 (56164-3211)
PO Box 188 (56164-0188)
PHONE..........................507 825-4211
G F Kennedy, *CEO*
EMP: 35 **EST:** 1997
SALES (est): 500-999K **Privately Held**
WEB: www.emp-serv.com
SIC: 7363 Employee leasing service

(G-6826)
EVANGELICAL LUTHERAN GOOD
Also Called: Pipestone Good Samaritan Vlg
1311 N Hiawatha Ave (56164-2200)
PHONE..........................507 825-5428
FAX: 507 825-5113
Karen Hademan-Snow, *Business Mgr*
Roger Madetzke, *Maint Spvr*
Donna Chmelar, *Human Res Mgr*
Phillip Samuelson, *Administrator*
EMP: 119
SALES (est): 1MM-4.9MM **Privately Held**
WEB: www.good-sam.com
SIC: 8059 8051 Nursing home; skilled nursing care facility
PA: Evangelical Lutheran Good
    4800 W 57th St
    Sioux Falls SD 57108
    605 362-3100

(G-6827)
1ST NATIONAL BANK OF PIPESTONE
Also Called: BANK EASY
101 2nd St NW (56164-1661)
PO Box 5057, Brookings SD (57006-5057)
PHONE..........................507 825-3344
FAX: 507 825-4516
Kevin Paulsen, *President*
Eunice Ailts, *Vice Pres*
Kent Lugt, *Vice Pres*
Allan Woitazewski, *Vice Pres*
Bonnie Haken, *Controller*
EMP: 40 **EST:** 1889
SQ FT: 20,000
SALES (est): 10MM-24.9MM **Privately Held**
SIC: 6021 6163 National commercial bank; loan broker
PA: Fishback Financial Corp
    2220 6th St
    Brookings SD 57006
    605 696-2265

(G-6828)
GLOBAL VENTURES I INC
319 N Hiawatha Ave (56164-1889)
PO Box 708 (56164-0708)
PHONE..........................507 825-5462
Robert Taubert, *Partner*
Steven Perkins, *Treasurer*
Dave Logan, *Finance*
EMP: 60 **EST:** 1992
SQ FT: 6,000
SALES (est): 1MM-4.9MM **Privately Held**
WEB: www.newhorizonfarms.com
SIC: 7389 Personal service agents

(G-6829)
HIAWATHA MANOR INC
107 5th Ave NE (56164-1928)
PO Box 247 (56164-0247)
PHONE..........................507 825-5697
FAX: 507 825-4173
Chris Robinson, *Administrator*
Eldonna Hillard, *Asst Admin*
EMP: 37 **EST:** 1976
SQ FT: 3,850
SALES (est): 1MM-4.9MM **Privately Held**
SIC: 8059 Home for the mentally retarded

(G-6830)
HOPE HAVEN INC
Also Called: Pipestone Adult Sls
913 3rd Ave SW (56164-1423)
PHONE..........................507 825-2379
FAX: 507 825-6532
Kelly Johnson, *Manager*
Diane Peterson, *Manager*
EMP: 31
SALES (est): 1MM-4.9MM **Privately Held**

SIC: 8361 Home for the mentally handicapped
PA: Hope Haven Inc
    1800 19th St
    Rock Valley IA 51247
    712 476-2737

(G-6831)
KOZLOWSKI INSURANCE AGENCY
401 8th Ave SE (56164-2047)
PHONE..........................507 825-3366
FAX: 507 825-3369
Jon Kozlowski, *President*
EST: 1970
SQ FT: 4,000 **Privately Held**
WEB: www.kozlowski-insurance.com
SIC: 6411 Insurance agent

(G-6832)
NATIONAL LODGING CO'S INC
Also Called: Historic Calumet Inn
104 W Main St (56164-1652)
PHONE..........................507 825-5871
FAX: 507 825-4578
Steve Klinkhammer, *Manager*
Steve Klikhammer, *Manager*
EMP: 30
SALES (est): 1MM-4.9MM **Privately Held**
SIC: 7011 Traveler accommodations

(G-6833)
PEPSI COLA BOTTLING CO
1809 Forman Dr (56164-3202)
PO Box 747 (56164-0747)
PHONE..........................507 825-4207
FAX: 507 825-5967
Mary Crockenberg, *President*
Tim Haubrich, *General Mgr*
Tim Haubrick, *Vice Pres*
Mickey Rath, *Shareholder*
Treasa Mahoney, *Shareholder*
EMP: 27 **EST:** 1930
SALES (est): 10MM-24.9MM **Privately Held**
SIC: 5149 Wholesales soft drinks

(G-6834)
PIPESTONE COUNTY MEDICAL CTR
916 4th Ave SW (56164-1890)
PHONE..........................507 825-5811
FAX: 507 825-6145
Bradley Burris, *CEO*
Gladys Paulsen, *Facilities Mgr*
Don Kapher, *CFO*
Don Kapser, *Finance Mgr*
Claudia Krerguer, *Human Res Dir*
EMP: 185 **EST:** 1920
SQ FT: 70,000
SALES (est): 10MM-24.9MM **Privately Held**
SIC: 8062 8051 Medical hospital; convalescent home

(G-6835)
PIPESTONE LIVESTOCK AUCTION
E Hwy 30 One Fourth Mile (56164)
PO Box 185 (56164-0185)
PHONE..........................507 825-3306
FAX: 507 825-3308
Brian Schneider, *President*
Dave Schneider, *CIO*
EMP: 35 **EST:** 1955
SQ FT: 30,000
SALES (est): 25MM-49.9MM **Privately Held**
SIC: 5154 Wholesales livestock

(G-6836)
PIPESTONE MEDICAL GROUP INC
920 4th Ave SW (56164-1455)
PHONE..........................507 825-5700
Janine Hazelton, *Manager*
Laurie Ness, *Administrator*
K T Devaraj, *Surgeon*
Jeanie Peters, *Assistant*
Jan Stratton, *Nurse*
EMP: 40 **EST:** 1994
SALES (est): 1MM-4.9MM **Privately Held**
SIC: 8011 Physicians' office

(G-6837)
PIPESTONE VETERINARY CLINIC
1300 S Highway 75 (56164-3211)
PO Box 188 (56164-0188)
PHONE..........................507 825-4211
FAX: 507 825-3140
Gerald F Kennedy, *Partner*
G D Spronk, *Partner*
Cameron Schmitt, *Partner*
Luke Minion, *Partner*
J D Bobb, *Partner*
EMP: 25 **EST:** 1954
SQ FT: 4,000 **Privately Held**
SIC: 0741 0742 Livestock veterinarian; veterinarian services

PLAINVIEW
Wabasha County

(G-6838)
BENEDICTINE HEALTH SYSTEM
Also Called: St Isidore Help Center
800 2nd Ave NW (55964-1041)
PHONE..........................507 534-3191
Dorothy Baker, *Administrator*
EMP: 125
SALES (est): 1MM-4.9MM **Privately Held**
SIC: 8361 Home for the elderly
PA: Benedictine Health System
    503 E 3rd St Ste 400
    Duluth MN 55805
    218 786-2370

(G-6839)
BRUCE KREOFSKY & SONS INC
865 Enterprise Dr SW (55964-1175)
PHONE..........................507 534-3855
FAX: 507 534-3214
Jim Kreofsky, *President*
Dennis Kreofsky, *President*
Ken Kreofsky, *General Mgr*
Lee Ihrke, *Corp Secy*
Robert Kreofsky, *Treasurer*
EMP: 65 **EST:** 1950
SQ FT: 24,400
SALES (est): 10MM-24.9MM **Privately Held**
SIC: 1542 5031 5083 New commercial & office building construction; retails building products & materials; wholesales agricultural machinery & equipment; farm building construction; wholesales lumber, plywood & millwork

(G-6840)
CITY OF PLAINVIEW AMBULANCE
Also Called: Plainview Ambulance
110 3rd St SW (55964-1349)
PHONE..........................507 534-3980
FAX: 507 534-2888
Julie Jurgenson, *Director*
EMP: 26 **EST:** 1973
SALES (est): 1MM-4.9MM **Privately Held**
WEB: www.plainviewmn.com
SIC: 4119 Ambulance service

(G-6841)
1ST NATIONAL BANK OF PLAINVIEW
138 W Broadway Ste 1 (55964-1286)
PHONE..........................507 534-3131
FAX: 507 534-3966
Dean Harrington, *President*
Jim Seberson, *Senior VP*
Kent Harrington, *Senior VP*
Donna Rother, *Purch Dir*
Pat Therneau, *Mktg Coord*
EMP: 28 **EST:** 1902
SQ FT: 10,000
SALES (est): 5MM-9.9MM **Privately Held**
WEB: www.fnbplainview.com
SIC: 6021 National commercial bank

(G-6842)
HALEY COMFORT SYSTEMS INC
445 W Broadway (55964-1257)
PHONE..........................507 534-2901
FAX: 507 281-8030
Thomas Haley, *CEO*
Joe Haley, *CFO*

Julie Eggerberger, *Office Mgr*
Julie Eggenberger, *Manager*
EMP: 50 **EST:** 1990
SALES (est): 5MM-9.9MM **Privately Held**
WEB: www.haleycomfort.com
SIC: 1711 Warm air heating & air conditioning contractor

(G-6843)
HIGH PLAINS COOPERATIVE
300 W Broadway (55964-1256)
PO Box 636 (55964-0636)
PHONE..........................507 534-3111
Scott Rohlik, *General Mgr*
Rick Hodney, *General Mgr*
Stephanie Ellinghuysen, *Human Res Mgr*
Kathy Braker, *Manager*
Tim Novac, *Info Tech Mgr*
EMP: 59 **EST:** 1931
SQ FT: 4,000
SALES (est): 10MM-24.9MM **Privately Held**
WEB: www.highplainscoop.com
SIC: 5171 5191 Retails fertilizer; wholesales petroleum bulk stations; retail independent convenience store; retail gasoline filling station; wholesales farm supplies; hardware store

---

PLATO
Mcleod County

(G-6844)
PLATO WOODWORK INC
200 3rd St SW (55370-5419)
PO Box 98 (55370-0098)
PHONE..........................320 238-2193
FAX: 320 238-2131
Tim Pinske, *President*
Pinske Marlys, *Vice Pres*
Brian Crown, *Purch Agent*
Lisa Rosenau, *Human Res Mgr*
Larry Tempel, *Corp Comm Staff*
▼ **EMP:** 130 **EST:** 1920
SQ FT: 50,000
SALES (est): 10MM-24.9MM **Privately Held**
WEB: www.platowoodwork.com
SIC: 1751 Manufactures wooden kitchen cabinets; cabinet & finish work carpentry service

---

PLYMOUTH
Hennepin County

(G-6845)
AIRCORPS LLC
3700 Annapolis Ln N Ste 175 (55447-5435)
PHONE..........................763 550-0707
FAX: 763 519-8484
Maggy Kottman, *President*
Lori Brodtmann, *Manager*
EMP: 25 **EST:** 1979
SQ FT: 4,290
SALES (est): 1MM-4.9MM **Privately Held**
WEB: www.aircorps.com
SIC: 1711 Warm air heating & air conditioning contractor; ventilation & duct work contractor

(G-6846)
ALLIED INTERSTATE INC (DH)
12755 Highway 55 Ste 300 (55441-4676)
PHONE..........................952 595-2000
Vikas Kapoor, *President*
Jeff Swedberg, *Senior VP*
Judah Kaplan, *Senior VP*
Steve Lamere, *Vice Pres*
Christine V Lith, *Human Res Mgr*
EMP: 470 **EST:** 1954
SQ FT: 27,000 **Privately Held**
SIC: 7322 Collection agency
HQ: Intellirisk Management Corp
    335 Madison Ave Fl 27
    New York NY 10017
    646 274-3030

(G-6847)
ALLINA MEDICAL CLINIC WEST
2855 Campus Dr Ste 400 (55441-2659)
PHONE..........................763 577-7400
Thomas Holets, *President*
Harold R Ostemd MD, *Med Doctor*

(PA)=Parent Co (HQ)=Headquarters (DH)=Div Headquarters
✿ = New business established in last 2 years

2011 Harris Minnesota
Services Directory

© Harris InfoSource 1-866-281-6415
299

Ann Shyer, *Manager*
EMP: 60 **EST:** 1994
SALES (est): 5MM-9.9MM **Privately Held**
SIC: 8011 Clinic operated by physicians

(G-6848)
ALWAYSBETHERE INC
2905 NW Blvd Ste 230 (55441-2644)
PHONE..............................612 243-9233
Douglas Carey, *President*
Tiffany Grengs, *Manager*
EMP: 50 **EST:** 1998
SQ FT: 4,500
SALES (est): 5MM-9.9MM **Privately Held**
WEB: www.alwaysbethere.com
SIC: 8748 Telecommunications consulting
services

(G-6849)
AUER STEEL & HEATING SUPPLY CO
865 Xenium Ln N (55441-5565)
PHONE..............................763 971-2910
FAX: 763 971-2920
Don M Curtes, *President*
Art Curtes, *Vice Pres*
Kristen Jacobsen, *Director*
EMP: 43 **EST:** 1975
SQ FT: 38,000
SALES (est): 10MM-24.9MM **Privately Held**
SIC: 5075 Wholesales heating & air
conditioning equipment & supplies

(G-6850)
BEAUMONT LEASED HOUSING ASSOCS
2355 Polaris Ln N Ste 100 (55447-4777)
PHONE..............................763 354-5500
Mark S Moorhouse, *Partner*
EMP: 75
SALES (est): 25MM-49.9MM **Privately Held**
SIC: 6552 Land subdivision & development
services

(G-6851)
BEAUMONT LEASED HOUSING ASSOCS
2355 Polaris Ln N Ste 100 (55447-4777)
PHONE..............................763 354-5500
Mark S Moorhouse, *Partner*
EMP: 75
SALES (est): 25MM-49.9MM **Privately Held**
SIC: 6552 Land subdivision & development
services

(G-6852)
BROOKDALE PLASTICS INC
9909 S Shore Dr Ste 3 (55441-5037)
PHONE..............................763 797-1000
Joseph Meixell, *CEO*
Robert Kramer, *Corp Secy*
Jeff Ewert, *Engineering*
Steve Eichten, *CFO*
Lynn Weiss, *Manager*
EMP: 55 **EST:** 1963
SQ FT: 65,944
SALES (est): 10MM-24.9MM **Privately Held**
WEB: www.brookdaleplastics.com
SIC: 7389 Manufactures packaging paper;
packaging & labeling services

(G-6853)
CAMDEN PHYSICIANS LTD
9800 Rockford Rd Ste 100 (55442-2930)
PHONE..............................763 235-4900
FAX: 763 559-9404
Anita Baxter, *Office Mgr*
Judy Anderson, *Nursing Spvr*
Anita Beckstrand, *Manager*
Caryn Carlson, *Receptionist Se*
EMP: 55
SALES (est): 5MM-9.9MM **Privately Held**
SIC: 8011 Clinic operated by physicians

(G-6854)
CHARTER SOLUTIONS INC
3033 Campus Dr Ste 160 (55441-2695)
PHONE..............................763 230-6100
William Leonard, *CEO*
Dee Thibodeau, *President*
Mark Jahn, *Vice Pres*
Joe Golema, *VP Business*
Kristi Herman, *Office Mgr*
EMP: 55

EST: 1997
SQ FT: 5,500
SALES (est): 5MM-9.9MM **Privately Held**
WEB: www.chartersolutions.com
SIC: 7379 Computer system consulting
services

(G-6855)
CHRISTOPHER & BANKS CO
2400 Xenium Ln N (55441-3626)
PHONE..............................763 551-5000
Lorna E Nagler, *President*
Luke Komarek, *Senior VP*
Michael Lyftogt, *VP Finance*
EMP: 100 **EST:** 2001
SQ FT: 210,000
SALES (est): 50MM-99.9MM **Privately Held**
SIC: 5137 Wholesales women's & children's
accessories

(G-6856)
CMC ENTERPRISES INC
Also Called: Quixotic Distribution
9905 13th Ave N (55441-5004)
PHONE..............................763 545-3800
Christopher Carey, *President*
◆ **EMP:** 27 **EST:** 2006
SQ FT: 14,000
SALES (est): 10MM-24.9MM **Privately Held**
SIC: 5013 Retail mail-order automotive
supplies & equipment; wholesales
automotive supplies

(G-6857)
CONSTRUCTION RESULTS CORP
14170 23rd Ave N (55447-4904)
PHONE..............................763 559-1100
Mark Snyder, *President*
EMP: 25 **EST:** 1999
SQ FT: 3,000
SALES (est): 5MM-9.9MM **Privately Held**
WEB: www.constructionresults.com
SIC: 1542 Commercial & office building
contractor

(G-6858)
DAVE OSBORNE CONSTRUCTION
Also Called: OSBORNE CONSTRUCTION
15600 28th Ave N (55447-1903)
PHONE..............................763 540-0232
FAX: 763 540-0239
David Osborne, *President*
Brenda Osborne, *Corp Secy*
James Simpson, *CFO*
Brian Nichols, *CFO*
David Hanson, *CFO*
EMP: 372 **EST:** 1982
SQ FT: 4,000
SALES (est): 25MM-49.9MM **Privately Held**
WEB: www.nfi-usa.com
SIC: 1751 Store fixture installation service

(G-6859)
DECORATORS SERVICE CO OF
14100 21st Ave N Ste B (55447-4645)
PHONE..............................763 383-2955
David H Anderson, *President*
Haidi Miller, *Manager*
EMP: 45 **EST:** 1969
SQ FT: 2,000
SALES (est): 1MM-4.9MM **Privately Held**
SIC: 1721 Residential painting contractor;
wall covering contractor

(G-6860)
DOLPHIN POOLS INC
3405 Highway 169 N (55441-2413)
PHONE..............................763 542-9000
Thomas Paun III, *President*
Kevin Gardner, *CFO*
Eileen Young, *Office Mgr*
EMP: 50 **EST:** 2001
SALES (est): 1MM-4.9MM **Privately Held**
SIC: 1799 Swimming pool construction; spa
& hot tub construction & installation

(G-6861)
EGAN CO
Also Called: Interclad
15255 23rd Ave N (55447-4701)
PHONE..............................763 567-0025
Tom Kallio, *Controller*

William John, *Manager*
EMP: 70
SALES (est): 5MM-9.9MM **Privately Held**
SIC: 1793 Glass & glazing contractor
PA: Egan Co
     7625 Boone Ave N
     Brooklyn Park MN 55428
     763 544-4131

(G-6862)
GARTNER REFRIGERATION & MFG
13205 16th Ave N (55441-4566)
PHONE..............................763 559-5880
FAX: 763 559-5925
John R Hendrickson, *President*
Julie A Malek, *Corp Secy*
Todd Hendrickson, *Vice Pres*
Donald H Faust, *Vice Pres*
EMP: 78 **EST:** 1942
SQ FT: 28,000
SALES (est): 5MM-9.9MM **Privately Held**
WEB: www.gartner-refrig.com
SIC: 1711 Refrigeration contractor

(G-6863)
HANOVER ACCESSORIES LLC
3500 Holly Ln N Ste 10 (55447-1498)
PHONE..............................763 509-6100
FAX: 763 509-6650
Rile Cherrey, *Vice Pres*
Zohar Ziv, *CFO*
Lyla West, *CFO*
Tricia Poppema, *Director*
Jerry Otto, *Executive*
▲ **EMP:** 60 **EST:** 1996
SALES (est): 25MM-49.9MM **Privately Held**
WEB: www.ultrapro.com
SIC: 5094 5137 Wholesales jewelry;
wholesales women's & children's
accessories
DH: Ultra Pro Corp
     6049 E Slauson Ave
     Commerce CA 90040
     323 725-1975

(G-6864)
HONEYWELL INTERNATIONAL INC
12001 Highway 55 (55441-4744)
PHONE..............................763 954-2712
Keith Nootbarr, *General Mgr*
Brian Urke, *General Mgr*
Giannantonio Ferrari, *COO*
Paul Saleh, *Exec VP*
Philip Palazzari, *Vice Pres*
EMP: 100
SALES (est): 5MM-9.9MM **Publicly Held**
WEB: www.honeywell.com
SIC: 8713 Surveying service
PA: Honeywell International Inc
     101 Columbia Rd
     Morristown NJ 07960
     973 455-2000

(G-6865)
HOUSTON LEASED HOUSING ASSOCS
2355 Polaris Ln N Ste 100 (55447-4777)
PHONE..............................763 354-5500
Mark S Moorhouse, *Partner*
EMP: 75
SALES (est): 25MM-49.9MM **Privately Held**
SIC: 6552 Land subdivision & development
services

(G-6866)
INFOSECURE TECHNOLOGY INC
655 Windemere Curv (55441-5758)
PHONE..............................202 898-5790
Teryal E Turner, *President*
EMP: 25
SALES (est): 1MM-4.9MM **Privately Held**
SIC: 7379 Computer related services

(G-6867)
J H LARSON ELECTRICAL CO (PA)
10200 51st Ave N Ste B (55442-4505)
PHONE..............................763 545-1717
FAX: 763 786-5864
Charles E Pahl, *Ch of Bd*
Greg Pahl, *President*
Joy L Pahl, *Corp Secy*

Edward Chesen, *Vice Pres*
Bill Forsark, *Purch Mgr*
EMP: 96 **EST:** 1931
SQ FT: 80,000 **Privately Held**
WEB: www.jhlarson.com
SIC: 5063 Wholesales electrical apparatus
& equipment

(G-6868)
JOHNSON CONTROLS INC
2605 Fernbrook Ln N (55447-4736)
PHONE..............................763 566-7650
Dave Werts, *Branch Mgr*
EMP: 100
SALES (est): 10MM-24.9MM **Publicly Held**
WEB: www.jci.com
SIC: 1731 1711 Environmental controls
installation contractor; manufactures relays
& industrial controls; plumbing, heating & air
conditioning contractor
PA: Johnson Controls Inc
     5757 N Green Bay Ave
     Milwaukee WI 53209
     414 524-1200

(G-6869)
JOHNSON CONTROLS INC
2605 Fernbrook Ln N (55447-4736)
PHONE..............................763 566-7650
Terry Giaferio, *Branch Mgr*
EMP: 100
SALES (est): 25MM-49.9MM **Publicly Held**
WEB: www.jci.com
SIC: 5075 Wholesales air conditioning
equipment; retails self-contained air
conditioning room units
PA: Johnson Controls Inc
     5757 N Green Bay Ave
     Milwaukee WI 53209
     414 524-1200

(G-6870)
LINDSTROM ENVIRONMENTAL INC
9621 10th Ave N (55441-5016)
PHONE..............................763 545-9740
David Sobaski, *President*
Jim Moeller, *Manager*
EMP: 60
SALES (est): 1MM-4.9MM **Privately Held**
SIC: 8744 Environmental remediation
services

(G-6871)
LSA LLC
5015 Cheshire Pkwy N (55446-4100)
PHONE..............................763 744-0246
Steve Welckle, *Member*
Karen Noll, *Member*
Mark Benton, *Engineering*
Shannon Johnson, *Accounts Mgr*
Thomas Noll, *Mng Member*
EMP: 48 **EST:** 1998
SALES (est): 1MM-4.9MM **Privately Held**
WEB: www.lsalaser.com
SIC: 1799 On-site welding contractor;
manufactures medical laser system
equipment

(G-6872)
MARRIOTT
Also Called: Residence Inn By Marriott
2750 Annapolis Cir N (55441-2501)
PHONE..............................763 577-1600
Michelle Rein, *Principal*
EMP: 50
SALES (est): 1MM-4.9MM **Privately Held**
SIC: 7011 Traveler accommodations

(G-6873)
METRO SIDING INC
2750 Niagara Ln N (55447-4843)
PHONE..............................763 557-1808
FAX: 763 557-1125
Michael D Cox, *President*
Mark M Farland, *Vice Pres*
Mark McFarland, *Vice Pres*
Raymond Sayles, *Controller*
Michile Tempel, *Manager*
EMP: 25 **EST:** 1988
SQ FT: 10,300
SALES (est): 1MM-4.9MM **Privately Held**
WEB: www.metrosiding.com

www.HarrisInfo.com
300

2011 Harris Minnesota
Services Directory

▲=Import ▼=Export
◆=Import/Export

SIC: **1761** 1751 Roofing, siding & sheet metal work; prefabricated window & door installation service; gutter & downspout contractor; siding contractor; retails door & window products

(G-6874)
MINNEAPOLIS GLASS CO
14600 28th Ave N (55447-4821)
PHONE.................................763 559-0635
FAX: 763 559-8816
Michael B Horovitz, *CEO*
Arlo Schultz, *Controller*
Adam Bauer, *Manager*
Jessica Schiro, *Manager*
Al Aase, *CIO*
EMP: 60 **EST:** 1937
SQ FT: 40,000
SALES (est): 10MM-24.9MM **Privately Held**
WEB: www.minneapolisglass.com
SIC: 5039 1793 Wholesales plate or window exterior flat glass; wholesales plate or window interior flat glass; manufactures glass products; glass & glazing contractor

(G-6875)
NEW HORIZON CHILD CARE INC (HQ)
16355 36th Ave N Ste 700 (55446-4601)
PHONE.................................763 557-1111
Susan Dunkley, *President*
William M Dunkley, *Chairman*
Lorraine Dunkley, *Corp Secy*
Penny L Allen, *CFO*
Penny L Aen, *CFO*
EMP: 60 **EST:** 1972 **Privately Held**
WEB: www.kidsquest.com
SIC: 8351 Preschool center
PA: New Horizon Enterprises Inc
    16355 36th Ave N Ste 700
    Plymouth MN 55446
    763 557-1111

(G-6876)
NEW HORIZON ENTERPRISES INC (PA)
16355 36th Ave N Ste 700 (55446-4601)
PHONE.................................763 557-1111
William M Dunkley, *CEO*
Lorraine Dunkley, *Corp Secy*
Susan Dunkley, *Vice Pres*
EMP: 200 **EST:** 1976
SQ FT: 22,000 **Privately Held**
WEB: www.kidsquest.com
SIC: 8351 Child day care service

(G-6877)
NILFISK-ADVANCE INC (PA)
Also Called: Euro Clean
14600 21st Ave N (55447-4648)
PHONE.................................763 745-3500
Christian C Knudsen, *CEO*
Shirley Pfeffer, *Corp Secy*
Jeannie Firday, *Corp Secy*
Jeff R Oldenkamp, *Vice Pres*
Lawrence M Doerr, *Vice Pres*
◆ **EMP:** 547 **EST:** 1910
SQ FT: 476,000
SALES (corp-wide): 2.33B **Privately Held**
WEB: www.nilfisk-advance.com
SIC: 5087 Manufactures commercial floor washing & polishing machines; wholesales service establishment equipment & supplies

(G-6878)
NORTH COUNTRY BUSINESS PRDTS
9905 45th Ave N Ste 200 (55442-2500)
PO Box 910, Bemidji (56619-0910)
PHONE.................................800 937-4140
Curt Crotty, *Branch Mgr*
EMP: 35
SALES (est): 10MM-24.9MM **Privately Held**
WEB: www.ncbpinc.com
SIC: 5021 5044 5112 7629 Wholesales office furniture; electric business machine repair service; wholesales office equipment; wholesales stationery & office supplies
PA: North Country Business Prdts
    1112 Railroad St SE
    Bemidji MN 56601
    218 751-4140

(G-6879)
PLYMOUTH SENIOR HOUSING
16205 36th Ave N (55446-3374)
PHONE.................................651 631-6300
Dan Lindh, *Principal*
EMP: 70
SALES (est): 1MM-4.9MM **Privately Held**
SIC: 8059 Nursing & personal care facility

(G-6880)
PRO-TEC DESIGN INC
5005 Cheshire Ln N Ste 3 (55446-3721)
PHONE.................................763 553-1477
FAX: 763 553-0204
Thomas A Hagen, *President*
John Eichten, *Manager*
Sean Conway, *Manager*
EMP: 30 **EST:** 1982
SQ FT: 6,800
SALES (est): 10MM-24.9MM **Privately Held**
WEB: www.pro-tecdesign.com
SIC: 5065 7382 Wholesales electronic parts & equipment; wholesales security control equipment & systems; burglar alarm maintenance & monitoring service; fire alarm maintenance & monitoring service

(G-6881)
QUALITY RESOURCE GROUP INC (PA)
12795 16th Ave N (55441-4556)
PHONE.................................763 478-8636
Dennis Pottebaum, *President*
Larry Ihrke, *Controller*
EMP: 30 **EST:** 1993
SQ FT: 30,000 **Privately Held**
SIC: 5199 Commercial lithographic printing; wholesales advertising specialties; typesetting service

(G-6882)
RTI SERVICES INC (PA)
800 Berkshire Ln N (55441-5404)
PHONE.................................952 475-0242
Dick Rentz, *Ch of Bd*
Albert Trapanese, *President*
Cheryl Trapanese, *CFO*
Patricia Harris, *Marketing Mgr*
Robert Durych, *Manager*
EMP: 38 **EST:** 1986
SQ FT: 10,000 **Privately Held**
SIC: 7389 Damaged merchandise salvaging service

(G-6883)
SECURITY AUTO LOANS INC
12800 Industrial Blvd (55441)
PHONE.................................763 559-5892
Richard Bernstein, *President*
H V O'Connell, *Director*
EMP: 30 **EST:** 2007
SQ FT: 1,500
SALES (est): 25MM-49.9MM **Privately Held**
SIC: 5012 Automobile wholesaler

(G-6884)
STONE SOURCE INC
15831 Highway 55 Ste B (55447-1496)
PHONE.................................763 540-9000
Leonard Lome, *President*
Reena Maheshwari, *Vice Pres*
▲ **EST:** 2004
SQ FT: 20,000 **Privately Held**
SIC: 1799 5023 Retails countertops; countertop installation service; wholesales tile or sheet resilient floor coverings

(G-6885)
SWANSON-FLOSYSTEMS CO
151 Cheshire Ln N Ste 700 (55441-5487)
PHONE.................................763 383-4700
FAX: 763 383-4772
Tom Howe, *President*
Richard Westphal, *Vice Pres*
Don Eschenbacher, *CFO*
▲ **EMP:** 47 **EST:** 1960
SQ FT: 31,000
SALES (est): 10MM-24.9MM **Privately Held**
SIC: 5085 5084 7389 Wholesales industrial supplies; wholesales industrial instruments & control equipment; wholesales industrial controlling instruments & accessories; wholesales industrial valves & fittings; packaging & labeling services

(G-6886)
TFX MEDICAL WIRE PRODUCTS INC
3750 Annapolis Ln N Ste 160 (55447-5496)
PHONE.................................763 559-6414
FAX: 763 559-5474
Steve Swinehart, *General Mgr*
Chuck Chaouch, *Materials Mgr*
Loren J Simer, *Engrg Mgr*
Michelle Vang, *Accountant*
Belisa Musser, *Manager*
EMP: 100 **EST:** 1995
SALES (est): 50MM-99.9MM **Publicly Held**
WEB: www.teleflex.com
SIC: 5047 Wholesales medical & hospital equipment
PA: Teleflex Inc
    155 S Limerick Rd
    Limerick PA 19468
    610 948-5100

(G-6887)
THREE RIVERS PARK DISTRICT (PA)
Also Called: Hennepin Parks
3000 Xenium Ln N (55441-2661)
PHONE.................................763 559-9000
FAX: 763 559-3287
Douglas F Bryant, *Superintendent*
Joan Peters, *Vice Chairman*
Bryan Weinzierl, *Safety Mgr*
Jen Dain, *Manager*
Jonathan Flaming, *Manager*
EMP: 120 **EST:** 1957
SALES (corp-wide): 55.34M **Privately Held**
WEB: www.hennepinparks.com
SIC: 7999 Recreation services

(G-6888)
TOWN & COUNTRY CATERERS INC
3155 Empire Ln N (55447-5332)
PHONE.................................763 559-4461
FAX: 763 559-4461
Jason Heins, *President*
EMP: 60 **EST:** 1953
SQ FT: 13,800
SALES (est): 1MM-4.9MM **Privately Held**
SIC: 7299 Caterer; facility rental & party planning services

(G-6889)
UNIPRISE INC
12755 Highway 55 Ste 100 (55441-4676)
PHONE.................................763 765-0852
Jim Mezzano, *Analyst*
Suzanne Oliver, *Nurse Practr*
EMP: 600
SALES (est): 100MM-499.9MM **Publicly Held**
WEB: www.uniprise.com
SIC: 6324 Hospital & medical insurance carrier
HQ: Uniprise Inc
    9900 Bren Rd E Ste 300W
    Hopkins MN 55343
    952 936-1300

(G-6890)
WEALTH ENHANCEMENT GROUP LLC
505 Highway 169 N Ste 900 (55441-4723)
PHONE.................................763 417-1428
Jeff Dekko, *CEO*
John Castino, *Senior VP*
Brenda Aslyn, *Vice Pres*
Nick Beissel, *Vice Pres*
Rob Burley, *Vice Pres*
EMP: 75 **EST:** 1997
SQ FT: 25,000
SALES (est): 5MM-9.9MM **Privately Held**
WEB: www.wealth-group.com
SIC: 7389 Financial service

(G-6891)
WESTHEALTH INC
2855 Campus Dr Ste 465 (55441-2649)
PHONE.................................763 577-7000
FAX: 763 577-7130
Pamela Lindamoen, *CEO*
Betsy Nichols, *CFO*
Terri Foss, *Human Res Dir*
Amy Schumacher, *Human Res Dir*
Leah Wandersee, *VP Mktg*
EMP: 200 **EST:** 1994
SQ FT: 180,000
SALES (est): 10MM-24.9MM **Privately Held**
WEB: www.westhealth.com
SIC: 8011 Internal medicine practitioners

PONSFORD
Becker County

(G-6892)
PINE POINT PUBLIC SCHOOL DIST
27075 County Road 124 (56575-9300)
PO Box 8 (56575-0008)
PHONE.................................218 573-4100
Bonnie Gurno, *Principal*
Pat Miller, *Librarian*
EMP: 25 **EST:** 1930
ADMISSIONS: 76 **Privately Held**
WEB: www.pinepoint.k12.mn.us
SIC: 8351 Public school; preschool center

PORTER
Yellow Medicine County

(G-6893)
FMI HYDRAULICS INC
401 Lone Tree St (56280-9787)
PO Box 95 (56280-0095)
PHONE.................................507 296-4551
Gary Stoks, *President*
EMP: 45 **EST:** 2006
SALES (est): 25MM-49.9MM **Privately Held**
SIC: 4911 Provides electric power generation services

(G-6894)
SMI & HYDRAULICS INC
401 Lone Tree St (56280-9787)
PHONE.................................507 296-4551
FAX: 507 296-4559
Gary Stoks, *President*
James Stoks, *Corp Secy*
Eric Dybsetter, *Electrical Engi*
Saundra Snobl, *Sales Staff*
▲ **EMP:** 35 **EST:** 1995
SQ FT: 65,000
SALES (est): 1MM-4.9MM **Privately Held**
SIC: 7699 5084 Hydraulic equipment repair services; wholesales industrial hydraulic systems equipment & supplies

---

PRESTON
Fillmore County

(G-6895)
BRENNAVILLE INC
Also Called: Michel Amish Tours
24461 Heron Rd (55965-1173)
PHONE.................................507 467-2512
Douglas Brenna, *President*
Vernon Michel, *President*
Paula Michel, *Corp Secy*
EMP: 25 **EST:** 1986
SQ FT: 12,500
SALES (est): 500-999K **Privately Held**
WEB: www.oldbarnresort.com
SIC: 4725 7033 Full service independent family restaurant; campground; conducts tours

(G-6896)
COUNTY OF FILLMORE
Also Called: Court House
101 Fillmore St (55965)
PHONE.................................507 765-4701
Karen Brown, *Principal*
Terry Schultz, *Maint Spvr*
Shirl Boelter, *Treasurer*
Jeffrey Cooper, *Administrator*
EMP: 180
SALES (est): 10MM-24.9MM **Privately Held**
WEB: www.co.fillmore.mn.us

(PA)=Parent Co (HQ)=Headquarters (DH)=Div Headquarters
✿ = New business established in last 2 years

2011 Harris Minnesota
Services Directory

© Harris InfoSource 1-866-281-6415
301

GEOGRAPHIC

SIC: 8721 Auditing services
PA: County of Fillmore
101 Fillmore St E
Preston MN 55965
507 765-2144

(G-6897)
GEHLING AUCTION CO INC
Hwy 52 No 1/2 Mile (55965)
PHONE 507 765-2131
FAX: 507 765-3672
Ronald Gehling, *President*
Lanna Gehling, *Corp Secy*
EMP: 30 EST: 1974
SQ FT: 7,880
SALES (est): 1MM-4.9MM **Privately Held**
WEB: www.gehlingauction.com
SIC: 7389 5083 Fee basis auctioneer; wholesales agricultural machinery & equipment

(G-6898)
GOOD SAMARITAN HOME CARE INC
608 Winona St NW (55965-1086)
PO Box 607 (55965-0607)
PHONE 507 765-2700
FAX: 507 765-3339
Nancy Weplow, *Administrator*
Vicki Lynch, *Exec Dir*
EMP: 55 EST: 1994
SALES (est): 1MM-4.9MM **Privately Held**
SIC: 8082 Home health care services

(G-6899)
MAPLE LEAF SERVICES INC
Also Called: Fillmore Place
110 Fillmore Pl SE (55965-1113)
PHONE 507 765-3848
FAX: 507 765-2159
Barb Morrison, *Manager*
EMP: 40
SALES (est): 1MM-4.9MM **Privately Held**
WEB: www.fchs.com
SIC: 8361 Home for the physically handicapped
PA: Maple Leaf Services Inc
100 Main St SE
Preston MN 55965
507 765-2107

(G-6900)
ROOT RIVER HARDWOODS INC
1300 Highway 52 N (55965-1143)
PO Box 624 (55965-0624)
PHONE 507 765-2284
Richard Bahl, *President*
Michael Merritt, *Vice Pres*
Jeffrey Wand, *Treasurer*
Carolyn Bahl, *Info Tech Dir*
EMP: 45 EST: 1960
SQ FT: 10,000
SALES (est): 5MM-9.9MM **Privately Held**
WEB: www.rootriverhardwoods.com
SIC: 5031 Retails furniture; manufactures furniture dimension stock softwood lumber; produces resawn small dimension lumber; hardwood dimension & flooring mill; wholesales lumber, plywood & millwork; manufactures hardwood veneer & plywood; millwork

(G-6901)
S E RENTAL
Junction Highway 52 16 E (55965)
PO Box 435 (55965-0435)
PHONE 507 765-3805
Harvey Ille, *Owner*
EMP: 25 EST: 1998
SALES (est): 1MM-4.9MM **Privately Held**
SIC: 7359 Stores & yards equipment rental service

PRINCETON
Isanti County

(G-6902)
HAUBENSCHILD FARM DAIRY INC
7201 349th Ave NW (55371-5212)
PHONE 763 389-2867
Dennis Haubenschild, *President*

Marsha Haubenschild, *Corp Secy*
Bryan Haubenschild, *Vice Pres*
EMP: 31 EST: 1979 **Privately Held**
SIC: 0241 Dairy farming

PRINCETON
Mille Lacs County

(G-6903)
BREMER BANK
202 La Grande Ave S (55371-1829)
PHONE 763 389-2020
FAX: 763 389-6130
Richard D Schneider, *CEO*
Wesley Geurkink, *President*
Brain Werner, *Exec VP*
Betty Parenteau, *Senior VP*
Rita D Sorensen, *Vice Pres*
EMP: 47 EST: 1908
SALES (est): 10MM-24.9MM **Privately Held**
SIC: 6022 State commercial bank

(G-6904)
COUNTY OF MILLE LACS
304 S Rum River Dr (55371-2017)
PHONE 763 389-5828
FAX: 763 631-0128
Fred Hoffman, *Director*
EMP: 50
SALES (est): 1MM-4.9MM **Privately Held**
SIC: 8322 8093 Individual & family social services; outpatient rehabilitation treatment center
PA: County of Mille Lacs
635 2nd St SE
Milaca MN 56353
320 983-8399

(G-6905)
ERDMAN AUTOMATION CORP
1603 14th St S (55371-2320)
PHONE 763 389-9475
FAX: 763 389-9757
Rodney Erdman, *President*
Erin E Cannon, *Controller*
Morgan Donohue, *Sales Mgr*
Troy Erdman, *Manager*
Duane Hess, *Coordinator*
EMP: 85 EST: 1993
SQ FT: 72,250
SALES (est): 10MM-24.9MM **Privately Held**
WEB: www.erdmanautomation.com
SIC: 8711 5031 Mechanical engineering services; manufactures custom machinery; wholesales doors & windows

(G-6906)
EVANGELICAL FREE CHURCH OF
Also Called: Elim Nursing Home
701 1st St (55371)
PHONE 763 389-1171
FAX: 763 389-1171
Marlys Tellinghuisen, *Manager*
Linda Olson, *Exec Dir*
Todd Lundeen, *Director*
Connie Senander, *Director*
EMP: 230
SALES (est): 5MM-9.9MM **Privately Held**
SIC: 8059 8051 Nursing home; skilled nursing care facility

(G-6907)
FAIRVIEW HEALTH SERVICES
1407 4th Ave N (55371-1066)
PHONE 763 389-1313
Peter Jensen, *Principal*
Julie Moren, *Controller*
Mike Riley, *Analyst*
EMP: 240
SALES (est): 10MM-24.9MM **Privately Held**
WEB: www.fairview.org
SIC: 8741 Hospital management services
PA: Fairview Health Services
2450 Riverside Ave
Minneapolis MN 55454
612 672-6300

(G-6908)
FAIRVIEW HOMECARE & HOSPICE
110 6th Ave S Unit LOWER (55371-1869)
PHONE 763 389-1923
FAX: 763 389-7000
Char Jebens, *Manager*
Jeanne Olds, *Manager*
EMP: 50
SALES (est): 1MM-4.9MM **Privately Held**
SIC: 8082 Home health care services
PA: Fairview HomeCare & Hospice
2450 26th Ave S
Minneapolis MN 55406
612 721-2491

(G-6909)
FIRST STUDENT INC
604 S Old Highway 18 (55371-2131)
PHONE 763 389-2342
FAX: 763 389-2110
Tim Wilhelm, *Manager*
Carl Neumann, *Manager*
EMP: 50
SALES (est): 1MM-4.9MM **Privately Held**
WEB: www.firststudentinc.com
SIC: 4151 School bus service
HQ: First Student Inc
600 Vine St Ste 1400
Cincinnati OH 45202
513 241-2200

(G-6910)
KINSHIP YOUTH MENTORING
604 3rd St S Apt 151 (55371-1875)
PHONE 763 631-5967
Jeanne Bromberg, *Director*
EMP: 75 EST: 2007
SALES (est): 5MM-9.9MM **Privately Held**
SIC: 7389 Business services at a non-commercial site

(G-6911)
MYCULL FIXTURES INC
1005 16th Ave S (55371-2326)
PHONE 763 389-4400
FAX: 763 389-5321
Michael Culligan, *President*
Yvonne Culligan, *Vice Pres*
Jeff Haehn, *Treasurer*
▲ EMP: 28 EST: 1999
SQ FT: 22,500
SALES (est): 5MM-9.9MM **Privately Held**
SIC: 5046 Wholesales store fixtures & display equipment

(G-6912)
NORTH MEMORIAL AMBULANCE SVCS
4187 Highway 169 (55371-6528)
PHONE 763 389-2082
Nancy Sundberg, *Corp Secy*
Greg Weinand, *Manager*
Dawn Bidwell, *Manager*
EMP: 52 EST: 2004
SALES (est): 1MM-4.9MM **Privately Held**
SIC: 4119 Ambulance service

(G-6913)
OKAY CONSTRUCTION CO INC
9774 18th St (55371-6118)
PHONE 763 633-8729
Greg Johnson, *President*
EMP: 30 EST: 1910
SALES (est): 1MM-4.9MM **Publicly Held**
WEB: www.quantaservices.com
SIC: 1623 Electric power line construction
PA: Quanta Services Inc
1360 Post Oak Blvd
Houston TX 77056
713 629-7600

(G-6914)
PETERSON BUS PRINCETON
604 S County Road 18 (55371-2131)
PO Box 1002 (55371-4002)
PHONE 763 631-5315
FAX: 763 631-5317
Tim Wilhelm, *Manager*
EMP: 70 EST: 2004
SALES (est): 1MM-4.9MM **Privately Held**
SIC: 4151 School bus service

(G-6915)
PRINCETON SPEEDWAY
Also Called: Mille Lacs Fairgrounds
1400 3rd St N (55371)
PO Box 1008 (55371-4008)
PHONE 763 389-3135
FAX: 763 631-3247
Judy Gerth, *Corp Secy*
Ritz Villebrun, *Manager*
Jay Rittenour, *Manager*
Aron Peterson, *Manager*
EMP: 25 EST: 1956
SALES (est): 1MM-4.9MM **Privately Held**
WEB: www.princetonspeedway.com
SIC: 7948 Racetrack

(G-6916)
STEINBRECHER PAINTING INC
1408 7th St N (55371-2402)
PO Box 159 (55371-0159)
PHONE 763 389-3887
FAX: 763 389-9093
Lee Steinbrecher, *President*
Deb Ulm, *Business Mgr*
Cheryl Steinbrecher, *Corp Secy*
EMP: 40 EST: 1990
SQ FT: 4,800
SALES (est): 1MM-4.9MM **Privately Held**
WEB: www.steinbrecherpainting.com
SIC: 1721 Exterior commercial painting contractor; interior commercial painting contractor; commercial wall covering contractor

(G-6917)
SYLVA CORP INC
900 Airport Rd (55371-2341)
PO Box 219 (55371-0219)
PHONE 763 389-2748
Larry Doose, *President*
Yvonne Doose, *Vice Pres*
EMP: 30 EST: 1997
SQ FT: 10,000
SALES (est): 10MM-24.9MM **Privately Held**
WEB: www.sylvacorp.com
SIC: 5083 Wholesales landscaping equipment

(G-6918)
UNITED STATES DISTILLED PRDTS
Also Called: U S Distilled Products
1607 12th St S (55371-2300)
PHONE 763 389-4903
FAX: 763 389-2549
Bradley P Johnson, *President*
Todd Geisness, *Vice Pres*
Keenan Issendorf, *Vice Pres*
Todd Richard, *Vice Pres*
Paul Rowland, *Maint Mgr*
▲ EMP: 170 EST: 1976
SALES (est): 100MM-499.9MM **Privately Held**
WEB: www.usdp.com
SIC: 5149 5182 Distillery; manufactures wines, brandy & brandy spirits; wholesales beverages; wholesales bottled wines & liquors

(G-6919)
UTILI-TRAX CONTRACTING
9774 18th St (55371-6118)
PHONE 763 323-2800
FAX: 763 633-8736
Darin Peterson, *Member*
Larry Peterson, *Member*
Mike Bash, *Member*
Pam Wilcox, *Director*
EMP: 110 EST: 1997
SALES (est): 10MM-24.9MM **Publicly Held**
WEB: www.quantaservices.com
SIC: 1623 Utility line construction
HQ: Infrasource Services Inc
1360 Post Oak Blvd Ste 2100
Houston TX 77056
713 629-7600

www.HarrisInfo.com
302

2011 Harris Minnesota
Services Directory

▲=Import ▼=Export
◆=Import/Export

PRINCETON
Sherburne County

(G-6920)
DISTINCTIVE DOOR DESIGN INC
32010 126th St (55371-3332)
PHONE 763 389-1631
FAX: 763 389-9427
Terry Sewill, *President*
Tim Patten, *Vice Pres*
EMP: 34 EST: 1986
SQ FT: 30,000
SALES (est): 10MM-24.9MM **Privately Held**
WEB: www.distinctivedoordesigns.com
SIC: 5031 Wholesales kitchen cabinets;
millwork

(G-6921)
DONMAR INC
31337 121st St (55371-3326)
PHONE 763 631-2233
Mark Hanson, *President*
EMP: 30 EST: 2000
SALES (est): 1MM-4.9MM **Privately Held**
SIC: 8742 Restaurant & food services
consultants

(G-6922)
FAIRVIEW NORTHLAND CLINIC
911 Northland Dr (55371-2172)
PHONE 763 389-3344
FAX: 763 389-6620
Roger M Boettcher, *Principal*
David G Bue, *Principal*
Ramesh Chawla, *Principal*
Robin Fischer, *Principal*
G B Gerstenkorn, *Principal*
EMP: 65 EST: 1971
SQ FT: 20,000
SALES (est): 5MM-9.9MM **Privately Held**
WEB: www.fairview.org
SIC: 8011 Clinic operated by physicians
PA: Fairview Health Services
2450 Riverside Ave
Minneapolis MN 55454
612 672-6300

(G-6923)
**LITTLE TIGERS
DEN-EDUCATIONAL**
31426 125th St NW (55371-3328)
PHONE 763 389-5950
FAX: 763 389-5560
Jessica Vrchota, *Owner*
EMP: 25 EST: 2004
SALES (est): 1MM-4.9MM **Privately Held**
SIC: 8748 Educational consulting services

(G-6924)
PRAIRIE RESTORATIONS INC
31922 128th St NW (55371-3304)
PO Box 327 (55371-0327)
PHONE 763 389-4342
FAX: 763 389-4346
Ron Bowen, *President*
John Bowen, *Vice Pres*
Mike Evenocheck, *Marketing Staff*
Chris Strandberg, *Office Mgr*
Becky Porter, *Admin Asst*
EMP: 30 EST: 1973
SQ FT: 1,500 **Privately Held**
WEB: www.prairieresto.com
SIC: 0181 Nursery stock production

PRINSBURG
Kandiyohi County

(G-6925)
DUININCK INC (PA)
208 6th St (56281-9739)
PO Box 208 (56281-0208)
PHONE 320 978-6011
FAX: 320 978-4978
Willis Duininck, *President*
Norman Duininck, *Corp Secy*
Larry Duininck, *Vice Pres*
Harris Duininck, *Vice Pres*
Curtis Duininck, *Treasurer*
EMP: 250 EST: 1940
SQ FT: 20,000
SALES (corp-wide): 4.51M **Privately Held**

WEB: www.dbimn.com
SIC: 1629 1611 Golf course construction;
general highway & street construction
service

(G-6926)
**MARCUS CONSTRUCTION CO
INC**
7360 195th Ave SW (56281-9702)
PO Box 68 (56281-0068)
PHONE 320 978-6616
FAX: 320 978-6626
Ross Marcus, *President*
Bruce Marcus, *Vice Pres*
Melissa Swart, *Purch Agent*
Wayne Stoneberg, *Manager*
Seth Calvin, *Technician*
EMP: 45 EST: 1956
SQ FT: 2,700
SALES (est): 10MM-24.9MM **Privately Held**
WEB: www.marcusconstruction.com
SIC: 1542 New commercial & office building
construction

(G-6927)
PRINSBURG FARMERS CO-OP
401 Railroad Ave (56281-3709)
PHONE 320 978-8040
Calvin Ahrenholz, *Manager*
EMP: 33 **Privately Held**
SIC: 0253 Turkey farm
PA: Prinsburg Farmers Co-Op
404 Railroad Ave
Prinsburg MN 56281
320 978-8100

PRIOR LAKE
Scott County

(G-6928)
**ABOVE ALL HARDWOOD
FLOORS LLC**
16861 Welcome Ave SE (55372-3311)
PHONE 952 440-9663
Chad Lamair, *Member*
EMP: 35 EST: 1998
SALES (est): 1MM-4.9MM **Privately Held**
WEB: www.aboveallhardwoodfloors.com
SIC: 1752 Flooring contractor

(G-6929)
CALMAR GROUP INC
Also Called: 4 Ster Camps
17226 Horizon Trl SE (55372-3939)
PHONE 952 440-8834
Lisa Topple, *CEO*
Mitch Topple, *President*
EMP: 60 EST: 2006
SALES (est): 1MM-4.9MM **Privately Held**
SIC: 7032 Summer camp

(G-6930)
COMMUNITY HOME HEALTH INC
16670 Franklin Trl SE Ste 120A
(55372-2926)
PHONE 952 440-3955
FAX: 952 440-3956
Donna Novak, *President*
EMP: 45 EST: 1994
SALES (est): 1MM-4.9MM **Privately Held**
SIC: 8082 Home health care services

(G-6931)
DAKOTA SPORT & FITNESS
Also Called: Smsc
2100 Trail Of Dreams (55372-1056)
PHONE 952 445-9400
Tad Dunsworth, *Partner*
EMP: 150 EST: 1994
SQ FT: 160,000
SALES (est): 5MM-9.9MM **Privately Held**
WEB: www.shakopeesioux.com
SIC: 7999 7991 Provides ice or roller
skating instruction; health club
PA: Shakopee Mdewakanton Sioux Com
2330 Sioux Trl NW
Prior Lake MN 55372
952 445-8900

(G-6932)
**DAKOTAH SPORT & FITNESS
CENTER**
2100 Trail Of Dreams (55372-1056)
PHONE 952 445-9400
Tad Dunsworth, *Principal*
EMP: 150 EST: 1994
SALES (est): 1MM-4.9MM **Privately Held**
SIC: 7997 7299 7991 7999 8351
Membership recreation club; tanning salon;
provides ice or roller skating instruction;
child day care service; physical fitness
center

(G-6933)
**INSURANCE PARAMEDICAL
SERVICES**
4785 Dakota St SE (55372-1715)
PO Box 302 (55372-0302)
PHONE 952 226-2213
FAX: 952 226-2216
Cynthia Wersal, *Partner*
Gerard Wersal, *Partner*
EMP: 60
SALES (est): 5MM-9.9MM **Privately Held**
SIC: 6411 Insurance services

(G-6934)
**INTEGRA TELECOM HOLDINGS
INC**
4690 Colorado St SE (55372-2418)
PO Box 299 (55372-0299)
PHONE 952 226-7000
Trent S Anderson, *COO*
Carol Wirsbinski, *Senior VP*
Dave Kunde, *Vice Pres*
Rebecca Janisch, *VP Opers*
Tom Moran, *Opers Staff*
EMP: 25 **Privately Held**
SIC: 4813 Wired telecommunications carrier
& service
PA: Integra Telecom Inc
1201 NE Lloyd Blvd # 500
Portland OR 97232
503 453-8000

(G-6935)
KEY-LAND HOMES
Also Called: Minnesota Valley Mill Work
4719 Park Nicollet Ave SE (55372-4019)
PHONE 952 440-9400
Gary Horkey, *President*
Karin Horkey, *Data Proc Dir*
EMP: 30 EST: 1983
SQ FT: 20,200
SALES (est): 5MM-9.9MM **Privately Held**
SIC: 1521 New single-family home
construction service

(G-6936)
**KNIGHT OF COLUMBUS
COMMUNITY**
Also Called: Father John Deer
20135 Lake Ridge Dr (55372-7807)
PHONE 952 492-5170
Dick J Baylow, *Director*
EMP: 30
SALES (est): 500-999K **Privately Held**
SIC: 7299 8322 Eating place; bar; banquet
hall facility; community center

(G-6937)
LEGENDS CLUB LLC
8670 Credit River Blvd (55372-9174)
PHONE 952 226-4777
Tip Enebak, *Member*
Jake Enebak, *Mng Member*
John Beshara, *Systems Staff*
Jeff Hilby, *Officer*
EMP: 100 EST: 2000
SQ FT: 9,745
SALES (est): 5MM-9.9MM **Privately Held**
WEB: www.legendsgc.com
SIC: 7997 Membership golf club

(G-6938)
LITTLE SIX CASINO
2354 Sioux Trl NW (55372-9077)
PHONE 952 445-6000
Tom Polasny, *Manager*
EMP: 400 EST: 2007
SALES (est): 25MM-49.9MM **Privately Held**

SIC: 7999 Gambling establishment

(G-6939)
MECHANICAL CONTRACTORS
5218 Candy Cove Trl SE (55372-1800)
PHONE 952 440-9751
Troy Miller, *Owner*
EMP: 27 EST: 1998
SQ FT: 14,500
SALES (est): 1MM-4.9MM **Privately Held**
SIC: 1711 Plumbing, heating & air
conditioning contractor

(G-6940)
MEDEVENT INC
14195 Badger Cir (55372-3259)
PHONE 952 445-2342
Michelle Rieger, *CEO*
Rick Olson, *CFO*
EMP: 30 EST: 2002
SALES (est): 1MM-4.9MM **Privately Held**
WEB: www.medevent.net
SIC: 8099 Health & allied services

(G-6941)
MEDIACOM INC
14162 Commerce Ave NE Ste 100
(55372-1484)
PHONE 952 440-9650
Barbara Cipolla, *President*
Mike Oja, *Project Mgr*
Oja Michael, *Design Engr*
Chris Farris, *Manager*
Carl Powell, *Manager*
EMP: 40 EST: 1998
SALES (est): 10MM-24.9MM **Privately Held**
SIC: 4841 Pay television distribution

(G-6942)
METRO AIR INC
16980 Welcome Ave SE (55372-3310)
PHONE 952 447-8124
FAX: 952 447-8126
Scott E Scheele, *CEO*
David Scheele, *President*
Nancy Scheele, *Office Mgr*
EMP: 28 EST: 1982
SQ FT: 6,000
SALES (est): 1MM-4.9MM **Privately Held**
WEB: www.metroairmn.com
SIC: 1711 Warm air heating & air
conditioning contractor

(G-6943)
**MINNESOTA HORSE & HUNT
CLUB**
Also Called: Triggers Restaurant
2920 220th St E Ste 1 (55372-4531)
PO Box 482 (55372-0482)
PHONE 952 447-2272
FAX: 952 447-2278
Randy Travalia, *Partner*
William Urseth, *Partner*
EMP: 75 EST: 1985
SQ FT: 1,400 **Privately Held**
WEB: www.horseandhunt.com
SIC: 0971 0752 Hunting preserve; kennel
boarding services; full service independent
family restaurant

(G-6944)
**MINNESOTA VALLEY
MILLWORK INC**
17021 Fish Point Rd SE (55372-3326)
PHONE 952 440-9404
FAX: 952 440-4312
Gary Horkey, *President*
Lori McCarthy, *Bookkeeper*
Steve Baeyen, *Exec Dir*
EMP: 50 EST: 1986
SALES (est): 5MM-9.9MM **Privately Held**
SIC: 5031 Manufactures metal doors, sash
& trim; wholesales millwork; retails millwork
& lumber; wholesales doors & windows

(G-6945)
NOREX INC
5505 Cottonwood Ln SE (55372-3971)
PHONE 952 447-8898
Ronald S Haberkorn, *President*
Sandra J Haberkorn, *Vice Pres*
John Muench, *Vice Pres*
N Phelps, *Manager*
EMP: 50

(PA)=Parent Co (HQ)=Headquarters (DH)=Div Headquarters
✪ = New business established in last 2 years

2011 Harris Minnesota
Services Directory

© Harris InfoSource 1-866-281-6415
303

EST: 1980
SQ FT: 16,000
SALES (est): 5MM-9.9MM **Privately Held**
SIC: 7379 Computer system consulting services

(G-6946)
NORTHLAND TRANSPORTATION
7210 154th St W (55372-9777)
PHONE...............................952 885-0580
FAX: 952 846-0393
Cheri Howard, *Owner*
EMP: 50 **EST:** 1991
SALES (est): 1MM-4.9MM **Privately Held**
SIC: 4119 4212 Ambulance service; local trucking without storage services

(G-6947)
OPTIMIST INTERNATIONAL
Also Called: Prairie Lake Optimist
4627 Parkwood Dr SE (55372-3358)
PHONE...............................952 440-8184
Linda Ringstead, *President*
EMP: 40 **Privately Held**
WEB: www.severnaparkoptimistclub.org
SIC: 8641 Social associations
PA: Optimist International
4494 Lindell Blvd
Saint Louis MO 63108
314 371-6000

(G-6948)
PLAYWORKS DAKOTA
2200 Trail Of Dreams (55372-1057)
PHONE...............................952 445-7529
FAX: 952 496-6820
Michelle Jerick, *Opers Mgr*
Gail Whipple, *VP Mktg*
Susan Perez, *Manager*
Mark Bassiter, *Info Tech Dir*
Amy Donaldson, *Director*
EMP: 100 **EST:** 1995
SALES (est): 1MM-4.9MM **Privately Held**
SIC: 8351 6512 7299 7389 7999 Child day care service; nonresidential building operator; party & special event planning services; operates tourist attractions, amusement park concessions & rides; convention & trade show services

(G-6949)
PRIOR LAKE BUS ASSOCIATION
16245 Northwood Rd NW (55372-1675)
PHONE...............................952 440-1166
Ron D Baere, *CEO*
EMP: 75 **EST:** 1970
SALES (est): 1MM-4.9MM **Privately Held**
SIC: 4151 School bus service

(G-6950)
PRIOR LAKE STATE BANK INC
16677 Duluth Ave SE # 100 (55372-2480)
PO Box 369 (55372-0369)
PHONE...............................952 447-2101
R N Barsness, *President*
John R Breibach, *Senior VP*
Brad Grinnell, *Vice Pres*
Steve Hall, *Vice Pres*
James J Swiontek, *Vice Pres*
EMP: 40 **EST:** 1909
SQ FT: 10,000
SALES (est): 10MM-24.9MM **Privately Held**
SIC: 6022 State commercial bank

(G-6951)
PRIOR LAKE VFW
16306 Main Ave SE (55372-2469)
PO Box 116 (55372-0116)
PHONE...............................952 226-6208
FAX: 952 447-5108
Meryl Mahaney, *President*
Ed Mulken, *Treasurer*
EMP: 30 **EST:** 1946
SQ FT: 6,500 **Privately Held**
SIC: 8641 Veterans' organization

(G-6952)
ROCKING HORSE RANCH
14859 Louisiana Ave S (55372-1535)
PHONE...............................952 440-1777
Marsha Koehn, *Owner*
EMP: 25 **EST:** 1992
SQ FT: 2,826
SALES (est): 500-999K **Privately Held**
SIC: 8351 Child day care service

(G-6953)
SAFE HAVEN SHELTER FOR YOUTH
14544 Glendale Ave SE (55372-1407)
PHONE...............................952 440-5379
FAX: 952 226-1489
Daniel Saad, *Director*
EMP: 39 **EST:** 1997
SQ FT: 1,702
SALES (est): 1MM-4.9MM **Privately Held**
SIC: 8322 Individual & family social services

(G-6954)
SHAKOPEE MDEWAKANTON SIOUX COM (PA)
2330 Sioux Trl NW (55372-9077)
PHONE...............................952 445-8900
FAX: 952 445-8906
Glynn Crooks, *Vice Chairman*
Stanley Crooks, *Chief*
Lori Beaulieu, *Corp Secy*
Ty Yurcina, *Controller*
Scott Galloway, *MIS Dir*
EMP: 75 **EST:** 1973
SQ FT: 12,400 **Privately Held**
WEB: www.ccsmdc.org
SIC: 8322 7999 Individual & family social services; gambling establishment

(G-6955)
SMSC GAMING ENTERPRISE (HQ)
Also Called: Mystic Lake Casino
2400 Mystic Lake Blvd (55372-9004)
PHONE...............................952 445-6000
FAX: 952 496-7299
Edward Stevenson, *CEO*
Kyle Kossol, *Vice Pres*
Kyle Kool, *Vice Pres*
Jeff Isaacson, *Buyer*
Paul Clendening, *Engineering*
▲ **EMP:** 3600 **EST:** 1982
SQ FT: 270,000 **Privately Held**
WEB: www.mysticlake.com
SIC: 7999 7011 Gambling establishment; bingo hall; casino hotel
PA: Shakopee Mdewakanton Sioux Com
2330 Sioux Trl NW
Prior Lake MN 55372
952 445-8900

(G-6956)
SMSC GAMING ENTERPRISE
Also Called: Ffmc Enterprises
2354 Sioux Trl NW (55372-9077)
PHONE...............................952 445-8982
Ed Stevenson, *Chief*
EMP: 4000
SALES (est): 100MM-499.9MM **Privately Held**
WEB: www.mysticlake.com
SIC: 7999 7011 Operates tourist attractions, amusement park concessions & rides; casino hotel
HQ: Smsc Gaming Enterprise
2400 Mystic Lake Blvd
Prior Lake MN 55372
952 445-6000

(G-6957)
TAYLOR MADE CONSTRUCTION OF MN
6648 Rustic Rd SE (55372-1423)
PHONE...............................952 440-8510
David Taylor, *President*
EMP: 50 **EST:** 1984
SALES (est): 1MM-4.9MM **Privately Held**
SIC: 1751 Finish & trim carpentry service

(G-6958)
TEN BROOK PORK LLP
15439 Wood Duck Trl NW (55372-4515)
PHONE...............................952 440-5737
James Nordquist, *Partner*
Roger Koosmann, *Partner*
Lori Thorsland, *Accounting Staf*
EMP: 30 **EST:** 1998 **Privately Held**
SIC: 0213 Hog & pig farming

(G-6959)
TMS CONSTRUCTION INC
5990 Meadowlark Ln (55372-3117)
PHONE...............................952 226-6300
FAX: 952 226-6301
Todd Schmidt, *President*
EMP: 25 **EST:** 1997
SALES (est): 1MM-4.9MM **Privately Held**
SIC: 1794 Excavating contractor

(G-6960)
UNISON INSURANCE
3173 Shady Cove Pt NW # 10901 (55372-1656)
PHONE...............................952 345-2305
Gary Wert, *Manager*
EMP: 40
SALES (est): 1MM-4.9MM **Privately Held**
SIC: 6411 Life insurance agent

(G-6961)
WAYNE BAUMGART DISTRIBUTORS
16677 Duluth Ave SE # 207 (55372-2481)
PHONE...............................952 447-2750
FAX: 952 447-2532
Wayne Baumgart, *Owner*
EST: 1980
SQ FT: 225 **Privately Held**
SIC: 5021 Wholesales household furniture

(G-6962)
WILD GOLF CLUB
Also Called: Wilds
3151 Wilds Ridge Ct NW (55372-3247)
PHONE...............................952 445-3500
FAX: 952 445-6320
Mike Regan, *Member*
Jim Stanton, *Member*
Mary Dreier, *Member*
Karissa Grube, *Controller*
Jim Zons, *Manager*
EMP: 150 **EST:** 1996
SQ FT: 15,820
SALES (est): 5MM-9.9MM **Privately Held**
WEB: www.golfthewilds.com
SIC: 7992 7299 Public golf course; eating place; banquet hall facility

---
PROCTOR
Saint Louis County

(G-6963)
HARTEL'S DBJ DISPOSAL CO'S LLC
930 Highway 2 (55810-1654)
PHONE...............................218 729-5446
FAX: 218 624-4792
Dan Hartel, *Member*
Jeffrey Walstrom, *Member*
Darrel Johnson, *Member*
EMP: 35 **EST:** 1995
SQ FT: 7,500
SALES (est): 5MM-9.9MM **Privately Held**
SIC: 4953 Refuse collection & disposal services

(G-6964)
INNOVATIVE LIVING INC
319 7th St (55810-2837)
PHONE...............................218 624-7005
Matthew J Gannucci, *President*
Rob Gannucci, *Vice Pres*
Richard Wick, *Administrator*
EMP: 34 **EST:** 1997
SALES (est): 1MM-4.9MM **Privately Held**
WEB: www.innovativeliving.net
SIC: 8052 Intermediate care facility

(G-6965)
PROCTOR MOTEL ASSOCIATES (PA)
Also Called: American Motel & Suites
185 Highway 2 (55810-2317)
PHONE...............................218 624-1026
Willard Ogren, *Partner*
Mike Ives, *Partner*
Dave Goldberg, *Partner*
Cheryl Goldberg, *Partner*
Janet Broin, *General Mgr*

EMP: 25 **EST:** 1996 **Privately Held**
SIC: 7011 Motel

RACINE
Mower County

(G-6966)
AG ELECTRICAL SPECIALISTS
202 E Main St (55967)
PO Box 36 (55967-0036)
PHONE...............................507 378-2101
FAX: 507 378-2102
Andy Andrew, *President*
Linda Sauer, *Corp Secy*
Mike Weed, *Engineering*
EMP: 26 **EST:** 1984
SQ FT: 16,000
SALES (est): 1MM-4.9MM **Privately Held**
SIC: 5063 Manufactures electric motor & generator parts; wholesales electric motors; manufactures relays & industrial controls; manufactures electrical equipment for engines

(G-6967)
SMIDT SHEET METAL CO INC
107 Highway 63 S (55967-8825)
PHONE...............................507 378-4080
FAX: 507 378-4609
Ken Smidt, *President*
EMP: 25 **EST:** 1989
SALES (est): 1MM-4.9MM **Privately Held**
SIC: 1761 Roofing, siding & sheet metal work

RAMSEY
Anoka County

(G-6968)
NETWORK OF CONTRACTORS INC ✪
15861 Dolomite St NW (55303-6967)
PHONE...............................763 639-1440
Chris Berry, *President*
Ray Coultor, *Vice Pres*
EMP: 28 **EST:** 2010
SQ FT: 3,500
SALES (est): 5MM-9.9MM **Privately Held**
SIC: 1542 Commercial & office building contractor

RANIER
Koochiching County

(G-6969)
NORTHLAND FISHING TACKLE INC
3441 County Rd 20 (56668)
PO Box 295 (56668-0295)
PHONE...............................218 286-5441
FAX: 218 286-5011
John Peterson, *President*
Pat D Benedet, *Manager*
EMP: 70
SALES (est): 25MM-49.9MM **Privately Held**
WEB: www.northlandtackle.com
SIC: 5091 Wholesales fishing tackle; manufactures sporting goods
PA: Big Fish America LLC
1001 Naylor Dr SE
Bemidji MN 56601
218 751-6723

READING
Nobles County

(G-6970)
READING BUS LINE INC
19771 McCall Ave (56165-2008)
PHONE...............................507 926-5404
FAX: 507 926-5404
Cecil Fritz, *President*
Sharon Fritz, *Corp Secy*
Tony Fritz, *VP Purch*
EMP: 25 **EST:** 1982
SALES (est): 1MM-4.9MM **Privately Held**

www.HarrisInfo.com
304
2011 Harris Minnesota
Services Directory
▲=Import ▼=Export
◆=Import/Export

WEB: www.readingbusline.com
SIC: 4141 Local bus charter service

RED LAKE FALLS
Red Lake County

(G-6971)
HILLCREST NURSING HOME
311 Broadway Ave NE (56750-4224)
PHONE..........................218 253-2157
FAX: 218 253-4676
Carrie Michalski, *Director*
EMP: 80 **EST:** 1975
SALES (est): 1MM-4.9MM **Privately Held**
SIC: 8051 8052 Skilled nursing care facility;
intermediate care facility

(G-6972)
HOMARK CO INC
100 3rd St SW (56750-4524)
PHONE..........................218 253-2777
FAX: 218 253-2116
James Violette, *President*
Robert Knutsen, *General Mgr*
Dave Johnson, *General Mgr*
Robert Kennedy, *Corp Secy*
Kelley J Burthwick, *Vice Pres*
▼ **EMP:** 60 **EST:** 1986
SQ FT: 142,000
SALES (est): 5MM-9.9MM **Privately Held**
WEB: www.homark.com
SIC: 1521 Manufactures mobile homes;
single-family housing construction

(G-6973)
RED LAKE COUNTY COOPERATIVE
Also Called: Cenex
702 12th St (56750)
PO Box 460 (56750-0460)
PHONE..........................218 253-2149
FAX: 218 253-2924
Doug Knott, *Manager*
EMP: 35
SALES (est): 25MM-49.9MM **Privately Held**
WEB: www.redlakecoop.com
SIC: 5191 Wholesales agricultural fertilizer;
manufactures fertilizers
PA: Red Lake County Cooperative
106 Hwy 59S
Brooks MN 56715
218 698-4271

RED WING
Goodhue County

(G-6974)
ASSOCIATED BANC-CORP
222 Bush St (55066-2316)
PHONE..........................651 385-1600
Paul Boller, *Purch Mgr*
Mary J Pittman, *Human Res Mgr*
Dan Massett, *Manager*
EMP: 30
SALES (est): 5MM-9.9MM **Publicly Held**
WEB: www.associatedbank.com
SIC: 6021 National commercial bank
PA: Associated Banc-Corp
1200 Hansen Rd
Green Bay WI 54304
920 491-7000

(G-6975)
BENEDICTINE HEALTH SYSTEM
Also Called: Hi-Park Care Center
213 Pioneer Rd (55066-3921)
PHONE..........................651 388-1234
FAX: 651 388-0347
Michael Schultz, *Partner*
Amber Schacht, *Persnl Dir*
Jennifer Meyer, *Manager*
Mary Collins, *Admin Asst*
EMP: 100
SALES (est): 1MM-4.9MM **Privately Held**

SIC: 8052 8051 Residential mentally
handicapped facility; convalescent home;
extended care facility; mental retardation
hospital; personal care facility
PA: Benedictine Health System
503 E 3rd St Ste 400
Duluth MN 55805
218 786-2370

(G-6976)
BRASCHLER'S BAKERY INC
410 W 3rd St (55066-2309)
PHONE..........................651 388-1589
FAX: 651 388-1580
Robert Braschler, *President*
Nancy Braschler, *Vice Pres*
EMP: 50
SQ FT: 5,600
SALES (est): 1MM-4.9MM **Privately Held**
SIC: 5149 Retail bakery; commercial
bakery; wholesales crackers, cookies &
bakery products

(G-6977)
D L RICCI CORP
5001 Moundview Dr (55066-1138)
PHONE..........................651 388-8661
FAX: 651 388-0002
Steve Earney, *President*
Jeannie Fairbank, *Purchasing*
Raylene Ahlgren, *Controller*
Robert Deter, *Finance*
Joanne Daleiden, *Accounts Mgr*
EMP: 85 **EST:** 1993
SQ FT: 25,000
SALES (est): 5MM-9.9MM **Publicly Held**
WEB: www.dlricci.com
SIC: 7389 Personal service agents;
manufactures metal cutting machine tools
PA: Actuant Corp
13000 W Silver Spring Dr
Milwaukee WI 53201
414 352-4160

(G-6978)
DOVER FLUID MANAGEMENT INC
Also Called: Central Research Laboratories
3965 Pepin Ave (55066-1837)
PO Box 75 (55066-0075)
PHONE..........................651 388-3565
FAX: 651 385-2109
Keith Gernentz, *Mfg Staff*
Darlene Arneson, *Purch Mgr*
Sean Peterson, *Engrg Mgr*
Richard Adams, *Research*
Patricia Kroll, *Accounting Mgr*
EMP: 65
SQ FT: 45,000
SALES (est): 10MM-24.9MM **Publicly Held**
WEB: www.cookmanley.com
SIC: 8731 8748 Manufactures valves & pipe
fittings; business consulting services;
commercial physical research laboratory;
manufactures laboratory apparatus &
furniture
HQ: Dover Fluid Management Inc
1415 W 22nd St Ste 600
Oak Brook IL 60523
630 861-2700

(G-6979)
FAIRVIEW REDWING HEALTH SVCS
701 Fairview Blvd (55066-2848)
PO Box 95 (55066-0095)
PHONE..........................651 267-5000
Scott Wordelman, *CEO*
Jan Graner, *Vice Pres*
Judy Treharne, *Vice Pres*
Kim Steman, *Envir Svcs Dir*
K Madhusoodnan, *Engineer*
EMP: 740 **EST:** 1963
SQ FT: 175,000
SALES (est): 50MM-99.9MM **Privately Held**
WEB: www.fairview.org
SIC: 8062 Medical hospital
PA: Fairview Health Services
2450 Riverside Ave
Minneapolis MN 55454
612 672-6300

(G-6980)
FAIRVIEW SEMINARY HOME INC
906 College Ave (55066-2459)
PHONE..........................651 385-3434
FAX: 651 385-3420
Sue Gerdes, *Accountant*
Laura Teele, *Human Resources*
Lavonne Lommel, *Manager*
Mary J Hill, *Administrator*
EMP: 103 **EST:** 1973
SQ FT: 45,000
SALES (est): 1MM-4.9MM **Privately Held**
SIC: 8051 Skilled nursing care facility

(G-6981)
FINANCIAL CRIMES SERVICES LLC
406 Main St Ste 200 (55066-2334)
PO Box 94 (55066-0094)
PHONE..........................651 388-2569
Scott Adkinson, *Member*
Robert Schmaltz, *Vice Pres*
EMP: 43 **EST:** 2001
SALES (est): 1MM-4.9MM **Privately Held**
WEB: www.financialcrimes.net
SIC: 7299 Consumer buying services

(G-6982)
FIRST STATE BK OF RED WING
3209 S Service Dr (55066-1881)
PHONE..........................651 388-4714
FAX: 651 388-9342
M J Collins, *President*
Elizabeth A Schafer, *Vice Pres*
Jolynn Reglin, *Loan Officer*
Mavis Cass, *Cashier*
EST: 1915
SQ FT: 5,000 **Privately Held**
WEB: www.fsbredwing.com
SIC: 6022 State commercial bank

(G-6983)
GOOD HUE COUNTY PUBLIC HEALTH
512 W 6th St (55066-2855)
PHONE..........................651 385-6100
Karen Main, *President*
EMP: 70 **EST:** 1971
SALES (est): 1MM-4.9MM **Privately Held**
SIC: 8082 Home health care services

(G-6984)
GOODHUE COUNTY PUBLIC HEALTH
512 W 6th St (55066-2637)
PHONE..........................651 385-6100
FAX: 651 388-0115
Karen Main, *Administrator*
EMP: 75 **EST:** 2001
SALES (est): 1MM-4.9MM **Privately Held**
SIC: 8082 Home health care services

(G-6985)
HIAWATHAL HOME CARE
4920 Moundview Dr Ste 2 (55066-4530)
PHONE..........................651 388-2223
Karen Siefert, *Owner*
EMP: 85 **EST:** 1989
SALES (est): 1MM-4.9MM **Privately Held**
SIC: 8082 Home health care services

(G-6986)
INDEPENDENT SCHOOL DISTRICT
Also Called: Carlwood Family Center
269 E 5th St (55066-2717)
PHONE..........................651 385-8000
FAX: 651 385-4780
Wendy Tufto, *Director*
EMP: 35
SALES (est): 500-999K **Privately Held**
WEB: www.redwing.k12.mn.us
SIC: 8351 8322 8748 Preschool center;
business consulting services; individual &
family social services
PA: Independent School District
2451 Eagle Ridge Dr
Red Wing MN 55066
651 385-4500

(G-6987)
INTERSTATE REHABILITATION CTR
204 Mississippi Ave (55066-1807)
PHONE..........................651 388-7108
FAX: 651 388-9223
Aul Rodewald, *Mfg Mgr*
David Leiseth, *Exec Dir*
EMP: 290 **EST:** 1968
SQ FT: 43,000
SALES (est): 25MM-49.9MM **Privately Held**
SIC: 7389 8331 Manufactures wood
partitions & fixtures; manufactures wood
pallets & skids; job training & vocational
rehabilitation services; manufactures
personal leather goods; packaging &
labeling services

(G-6988)
LAYLINE CORP
Also Called: Americ Inn
1819 Old West Main St (55066-2092)
PHONE..........................651 385-9060
FAX: 651 385-8139
Cathy Nichols, *President*
Hill Jean, *Sales Executive*
EMP: 29 **EST:** 1994
SALES (est): 1MM-4.9MM **Privately Held**
SIC: 7011 Traveler accommodations

(G-6989)
LUTHERAN SOCIAL SERVICE OF MN
Also Called: Vasa Lutheran Home
5225 Highway 61 W (55066-1117)
PHONE..........................651 388-8845
FAX: 651 388-8848
Linda Soisakis, *Exec Dir*
EMP: 70
SALES (est): 1MM-4.9MM **Privately Held**
WEB: www.lssmn.org
SIC: 8361 Children's home
PA: Lutheran Social Service Of MN
2485 Como Ave
Saint Paul MN 55108
651 642-5990

(G-6990)
MAPLE HILLS LP
521 Maple St (55066-3377)
PHONE..........................651 291-1750
Joseph Holmberg, *Partner*
EMP: 99
SALES (est): 10MM-24.9MM **Privately Held**
SIC: 6513 Apartment building operator

(G-6991)
MORGAN TIRE & AUTO LLC
Also Called: Team Tires Plus
828 Main St (55066-2229)
PHONE..........................651 388-3266
Tom Pomstock, *Owner*
EMP: 30
SALES (est): 1MM-4.9MM **Privately Held**
WEB: www.bfsusa.com
SIC: 7534 Tire recapping & retreading
services
HQ: Bfs Retail Operations LLC
333 E Lake St Ste 300
Bloomingdale IL 60108
630 259-9000

(G-6992)
NASH-FINCH CO
615 Main St (55066-2249)
PHONE..........................651 388-2869
Michelle Schimbeno, *Manager*
Jeff Mace, *Manager*
EMP: 30
SALES (est): 25MM-49.9MM **Publicly Held**
WEB: www.nashfinch.com
SIC: 5141 Wholesales general line
groceries
PA: Nash-Finch Co
7600 France Ave S Ste 200
Edina MN 55435
952 832-0534

(PA)=Parent Co (HQ)=Headquarters (DH)=Div Headquarters
✿ = New business established in last 2 years

2011 Harris Minnesota
Services Directory

© Harris InfoSource 1-866-281-6415
305

(G-6993)
NEUFELDT INDUSTRIAL SERVICES
2568 Eagle Ridge Dr (55066-7454)
PHONE..............651 388-4347
Roy Neufeldt, *President*
Norma Neufeldt, *Vice Pres*
EMP: 30 **EST:** 1975
SQ FT: 15,000
SALES (est): 1MM-4.9MM **Privately Held**
WEB: www.neufeldtis.com
SIC: 1796 Building equipment & machinery installation contractor; sheet metal fabricator; steel fabricator

(G-6994)
PLAAS INC
1427 Old West Main St (55066-2162)
PHONE..............651 388-8881
FAX: 651 388-1621
Frederick Plaas, *President*
Becky Plaas, *Corp Secy*
Russell Kuykendall, *Corp Secy*
EMP: 120 **EST:** 1975
SQ FT: 5,500
SALES (est): 10MM-24.9MM **Privately Held**
SIC: 1711 Mechanical contractor

(G-6995)
POTTERY RED WINGS
Also Called: Loons & Ladys Slippers
1920 Old West Main St (55066-2071)
PHONE..............651 388-3562
Scott Gilmer, *President*
EMP: 25 **EST:** 1968
SALES (est): 1MM-4.9MM **Privately Held**
SIC: 7999 Retail gift shop; commercial art gallery

(G-6996)
RED WING BRASS BAND INC
365 Oak Hill Dr (55066-1464)
PHONE..............651 388-2656
John Tranter, *President*
Bob Erodie, *Treasurer*
EMP: 31 **EST:** 1989
SALES (est): 1MM-4.9MM **Privately Held**
SIC: 7929 Orchestra & bands

(G-6997)
RED WING HEALTHCARE LLC
1412 W 4th St (55066-2107)
PHONE..............651 388-2843
FAX: 651 388-9502
Paul Contras, *President*
Lisa Peterson, *Vice Pres*
Mike Swaner, *Maint Spvr*
Doug Hauschild, *Opers Staff*
Barb Zilmer, *Human Res Dir*
EMP: 200 **EST:** 1950
SALES (est): 5MM-9.9MM **Privately Held**
SIC: 8051 8069 Skilled nursing care facility; specialty hospital

(G-6998)
RED WING HOTEL CORP
406 Main St Ste A (55066-2334)
PHONE..............651 388-2846
FAX: 651 388-5226
William J Sweasy, *Ch of Bd*
Michael McKay, *General Mgr*
Craig Scott, *General Mgr*
Gene Foster, *Vice Pres*
Jerry Cook, *Chief Engr*
EMP: 172 **EST:** 1914
SALES (est): 5MM-9.9MM **Privately Held**
WEB: www.redwingshoe.com
SIC: 7011 6512 Hotel; full service American restaurant; operators of retail property

(G-6999)
RED WING YOUNG MEN'S CHRISTIAN
434 Main St (55066-2323)
PHONE..............651 388-4724
FAX: 651 388-5340
Gary George, *Superintendent*
Maggie Sloan, *Finance*
Pepins High, *Exec Dir*
Mike Melstad, *Director*
Silas B Foot, *Bd of Directors*
EMP: 120 **EST:** 1944
SALES (est): 1MM-4.9MM **Privately Held**

WEB: www.redwingymca.org
SIC: 7999 7991 Recreation center; physical fitness center; religious organization

(G-7000)
REED ELSEVIER INC
491 Highway 19 Blvd # 102 (55066-1119)
PO Box 114 (55066-0114)
PHONE..............651 385-1895
FAX: 651 385-1896
Clyde Owens, *Vice Pres*
Alice Celt, *Manager*
Alex Aminian, *CTO*
Larry Warrington, *Info Tech Mgr*
EMP: 25
SALES (est): 1MM-4.9MM **Privately Held**
WEB: www.lexis-nexis.com
SIC: 7374 Data processing service
HQ: Reed Elsevier Inc
125 Park Ave Fl 22
New York NY 10017
212 309-8100

(G-7001)
REM GREATLAND INC
2606 Malmquist Ave (55066-3949)
PHONE..............651 388-7158
FAX: 651 388-8243
Lee Randall, *Director*
EMP: 28
SALES (est): 1MM-4.9MM **Privately Held**
SIC: 8361 Home for the mentally handicapped

(G-7002)
RIVER VALLEY LAWNSCAPE INC
3399 S Service Dr (55066-1833)
PHONE..............651 388-7000
John Wooden, *President*
EMP: 50 **EST:** 1995
SQ FT: 3,000 **Privately Held**
WEB: www.rivervalleyinc.com
SIC: 0782 Landscaping services

(G-7003)
RIVERSIDE LODGING
Also Called: Super 8 Motel
232 Withers Harbor Dr (55066-2081)
PHONE..............651 388-0491
FAX: 651 388-1066
Michael Patel, *President*
Sarah Jensen, *Manager*
EMP: 26 **EST:** 1987
SALES (est): 1MM-4.9MM **Privately Held**
WEB: www.riversidelodging.com
SIC: 7011 Traveler accommodations

(G-7004)
SARGENT'S NURSERY INC
3352 N Service Dr (55066-1813)
PHONE..............651 388-3847
FAX: 651 388-6220
Robert D Lewis, *President*
Trisha Hadler, *Corp Secy*
David B Lewis, *Corp Secy*
Julia E Peterson, *Exec VP*
Lloyd Peterson, *Vice Pres*
EMP: 40 **EST:** 1928
SQ FT: 18,000
SALES (est): 5MM-9.9MM **Privately Held**
SIC: 0181 Retails nursery stock, seeds & bulbs; flower farming; retails garden supplies & tools; nursery stock production

(G-7005)
SCHWAN'S TECHNOLOGY GROUP INC (HQ)
5140 Moundview Dr (55066-1100)
PHONE..............651 388-1821
FAX: 651 385-2166
David Paskach, *CEO*
Phil Casey, *General Mgr*
Larry Lautt, *Vice Pres*
Dave Morgan, *Plant Mgr*
Jean Lodermeier, *CFO*
EMP: 80 **EST:** 1986
SQ FT: 35,600 **Privately Held**
WEB: www.schwanstech.com

SIC: 7373 7375 Computer integrated systems design services; information retrieval services; manufactures measuring & dispensing pumps
PA: Schwan Food Co
115 W College Dr
Marshall MN 56258
507 532-3274

(G-7006)
STARTECH COMPUTING INC
1755 Old West Main St (55066-2088)
PHONE..............651 385-0607
FAX: 651 385-0507
Terry Chandler, *CEO*
Kenneth B Arneson, *Corp Secy*
Joseph T Coyle, *CFO*
Lori Stein, *Controller*
Dan Flemke, *Business Anlyst*
EMP: 29 **EST:** 1995
SQ FT: 3,500
SALES (est): 1MM-4.9MM **Privately Held**
WEB: www.startech-comp.com
SIC: 7373 7372 Computer integrated systems design services; software publisher

(G-7007)
STENCIL CUTTING & SUPPLY CO (PA)
310 Cannon River Ave N (55066-1824)
PHONE..............800 783-4633
Donna Anderst, *President*
Scott Anderst, *Vice Pres*
Kevin Rippentrop, *Sales Mgr*
Dick Schaper, *Manager*
EMP: 58 **EST:** 1975 **Privately Held**
SIC: 1791 5099 Metal elevator front installation service; wholesales ammunition

(G-7008)
STRESSTECH INC (PA)
1007 Tile Dr (55066-1977)
PHONE..............651 388-7117
FAX: 651 388-0337
Joel Wittenbaker, *President*
Allen Walker, *COO*
David Schiver, *Vice Pres*
George Richcreek, *Exec Dir*
EMP: 50 **EST:** 1974
SQ FT: 16,000 **Privately Held**
WEB: www.techgroupusa.com
SIC: 7629 Manufactures industrial electric heating units & devices; electrical equipment repair & maintenance services

(G-7009)
UNDER THE RAINBOW CHILD CARE
555 Technology Dr (55066-2849)
PHONE..............651 388-6433
FAX: 651 267-1079
Michelle Suchanek, *President*
EMP: 25 **EST:** 1996
SALES (est): 500-999K **Privately Held**
SIC: 8351 Child day care service

(G-7010)
UNITED PARCEL SERVICE INC
Also Called: UPS
880 Bench St (55066-9502)
PHONE..............651 388-6555
Fred Wienzenberger, *Manager*
EMP: 42
SALES (est): 1MM-4.9MM **Publicly Held**
WEB: www.ups.com
SIC: 4215 Ground courier services
HQ: United Parcel Service Inc
55 Glenlake Pkwy NE
Atlanta GA 30328
404 828-6000

(G-7011)
WELLS FARGO BANK
401 Plum St (55066-2533)
PHONE..............651 388-6751
FAX: 651 385-2322
Chris Terry, *President*
John Berg, *Div Sub Head*
Sandy Sandek, *Store Mgr*
Cyndee Marcus, *Administrator*
EMP: 30 **EST:** 1865
SQ FT: 5,000
SALES (est): 5MM-9.9MM **Publicly Held**

SIC: 6021 National commercial bank
PA: Wells Fargo & Co
420 Montgomery St
San Francisco CA 94104
866 878-5865

(G-7012)
WELLS FARGO BANK, NATIONAL
4th & Plum (55066)
PHONE..............651 385-2328
Chuck R Kind, *Manager*
EMP: 30
SALES (est): 5MM-9.9MM **Publicly Held**
SIC: 6211 Security broker & dealer service
HQ: Wfc Holdings, Corp
420 Montgomery St
San Francisco CA 94104
415 396-7392

(G-7013)
WILSON OIL CO INC
2355 W Main St (55066-1927)
PHONE..............651 388-5783
Michael J Wilson, *President*
Jeannette Wilson, *Corp Secy*
EST: 1949
SQ FT: 1,200 **Privately Held**
SIC: 5171 4212 5172 Wholesales petroleum bulk stations; local trucking without storage services; wholesales liquefied petroleum gas; wholesales gasoline; retail gasoline filling station

(G-7014)
XCEL ENERGY INC
801 E 5th St (55066-2760)
PHONE..............651 385-5604
Charles Kinney, *Plant Mgr*
EMP: 28
SALES (est): 10MM-24.9MM **Publicly Held**
WEB: www.xcelenergy.com
SIC: 4911 Electric services
PA: XCEL Energy Inc
414 Nicollet Mall
Minneapolis MN 55401
612 330-5500

REDLAKE
Beltrami County

(G-7015)
INDIAN HEALTH SERVICE
24760 Hospital Dr (56671)
PO Box 249 (56671-0249)
PHONE..............218 679-3316
Oran D Beaulieu, *Director*
Margo Bahr, *Analyst*
EMP: 160
SALES (est): 10MM-24.9MM **Privately Held**
WEB: www.navajo.ihs.gov
SIC: 8062 Medical hospital; public health program services; federal government administration of public health programs
DH: Indian Health Service
801 Thompson Ave Fl 4
Rockville MD 20852
301 443-1083

(G-7016)
RED LAKE BAND OF CHIPPEWA
Also Called: Jourdain Prpch Extndd Cr Fclty
24856 Hospital Dr (56671)
PO Box 399 (56671-0399)
PHONE..............218 679-3400
FAX: 218 679-3434
Nora Thunder, *General Mgr*
James Williamson, *Administrator*
EMP: 80
SALES (est): 1MM-4.9MM **Privately Held**
WEB: www.redlakenation.org
SIC: 8051 Skilled nursing care facility
PA: Red Lake Band of Chippewa
24200 Council St
Redlake MN 56671
218 679-3341

www.HarrisInfo.com
306

2011 Harris Minnesota
Services Directory

▲=Import ▼=Export
◆=Import/Export

(G-7017)
RED LAKE CHEMICAL HEALTH
Hwy 1 & Main St (56671)
PO Box 114 (56671-0114)
PHONE..............................218 679-3995
FAX: 218 679-3976
Arlene Jones, *Corp Secy*
Celina Branchud, *Program Mgr*
Darla Feather, *Manager*
Rose Barret, *Administrator*
Tom Barett, *Exec Dir*
EMP: 70 **EST:** 2004
SALES (est): 5MM-9.9MM **Privately Held**
SIC: 8093 Outpatient substance abuse clinic

REDWOOD FALLS
Redwood County

(G-7018)
A C M C
1100 E Broadway St (56283-2247)
PHONE..............................507 637-2985
Richard L Schroeder, *President*
G W Kaminski, *President*
Michelle Cilek MD, *Med Doctor*
Melissa Johnson, *Manager*
Kris Gulbrandfen, *Manager*
EMP: 35 **EST:** 1977
SQ FT: 11,000
SALES (est): 1MM-4.9MM **Privately Held**
SIC: 8011 Clinic operated by physicians

(G-7019)
AFFILIATED COMMUNITY MEDICAL
1100 E Broadway St (56283-2247)
PHONE..............................507 637-2985
FAX: 507 697-6666
Melissa Johnson, *Office Mgr*
Scott T Hagen, *Optometrist*
Kris Gulbrandfen, *Manager*
Steven D Medrud, *Director*
Janet L Marti, *Nurse Practr*
EMP: 50
SALES (est): 5MM-9.9MM **Privately Held**
WEB: www.acmc.com
SIC: 8011 Physicians' office & clinic
PA: Affiliated Community Medical
101 Willmar Ave SW
Willmar MN 56201
320 231-5000

(G-7020)
CITY OF REDWOOD FALLS
Also Called: Redwood Area Hospital
100 Fallwood Rd (56283-1828)
PHONE..............................507 637-4500
FAX: 507 697-6029
Miranda Ford, *Corp Secy*
J Lundblad, *Ch of Anesth*
Dennis D Gremel, *Ch Pathology*
Blair Anderson, *Vice Pres*
Brenda Vick, *Project Mgr*
EMP: 130
SQ FT: 62,000
SALES (est): 10MM-24.9MM **Privately Held**
SIC: 8062 8011 Medical hospital; physicians' office & clinic
PA: City of Redwood Falls
333 S Washington St
Redwood Falls MN 56283
507 637-5755

(G-7021)
EVANGELICAL LUTHERAN GOOD
200 S Dekalb St (56283-1913)
PHONE..............................507 637-5711
FAX: 507 637-2132
Brad Stevens, *Maint Spvr*
Kim Arnold, *Purchasing*
Kimberly Bagle, *Human Resources*
Jenny Franklin, *Office Mgr*
Angela Mathiowetz, *Manager*
EMP: 90
SALES (est): 1MM-4.9MM **Privately Held**
WEB: www.good-sam.com

SIC: 8051 Convalescent home
PA: Evangelical Lutheran Good
4800 W 57th St
Sioux Falls SD 57108
605 362-3100

(G-7022)
KIBBLE EQUIPMENT INC
Hwy 19 & 71 E (56283)
PO Box 250 (56283-0250)
PHONE..............................507 644-3571
FAX: 507 644-3425
Karen Meyer, *Controller*
Steve Sandven, *Manager*
EMP: 25
SALES (est): 10MM-24.9MM **Privately Held**
WEB: www.kibbleeq.com
SIC: 5083 Wholesales farm implements; retails lawnmowers & tractors
PA: Kibble Equipment Inc
Hwy 7 E
Montevideo MN 56265
320 269-6466

(G-7023)
LARRY SCHEFUS TRUCKING INC
Hwy 71 S (56283)
PO Box 545 (56283-0545)
PHONE..............................507 644-5588
FAX: 507 644-2116
Ron Hummer, *President*
EMP: 40 **EST:** 1965
SQ FT: 1,800
SALES (est): 5MM-9.9MM **Privately Held**
SIC: 4213 4214 Local & long-distance trucking & storage services

(G-7024)
LOWER SIOUX COMMUNITY COUNCIL
Also Called: Dakota Inn Motel
410 W Park Rd (56283-1429)
PHONE..............................507 637-5933
FAX: 507 644-3214
Lisa Furry, *Manager*
Shannon Blue, *Manager*
EMP: 30
SALES (est): 1MM-4.9MM **Privately Held**
SIC: 7011 Motel
PA: Lower Sioux Community Council
39375 County Highway 24
Morton MN 56270
507 697-6185

(G-7025)
MINNWEST BANK M V
300 S Washington St (56283-1658)
PO Box 439 (56283-0439)
PHONE..............................507 637-5731
FAX: 507 637-4301
Douglas Karsky, *President*
Dan Koster, *Senior VP*
Gail J Ripka, *Senior VP*
Mary Evans, *Assistant VP*
Kirby Josephson, *Vice Pres*
EMP: 35 **EST:** 1928
SQ FT: 18,224
SALES (est): 5MM-9.9MM **Privately Held**
WEB: www.minnwestbankgroup.com
SIC: 6022 State commercial bank

(G-7026)
NORTH MEMORIAL HEALTH CARE
614 S Mill St (56283-1676)
PHONE..............................507 637-5055
Dan Desmit, *Manager*
EMP: 25
SALES (est): 1MM-4.9MM **Privately Held**
WEB: www.northmemorial.com
SIC: 4119 Ambulance service
PA: North Memorial Health Care
3300 Oakdale Ave N
Minneapolis MN 55422
763 520-5200

(G-7027)
RAY DRACHENBERG
29668 US Highway 71 (56283-2481)
PHONE..............................507 644-2108
FAX: 507 644-2475
Ray Drachenberg, *Manager*
EMP: 40 **EST:** 2005

SALES (est): 50MM-99.9MM **Privately Held**
SIC: 5153 Wholesales soybeans

(G-7028)
THIELEN BUS LINES INC
220 W 11th St (56283-2004)
PHONE..............................507 637-3600
Richard Thielen, *President*
Joseph Thielen, *Corp Secy*
EMP: 25 **EST:** 1972
SQ FT: 6,500
SALES (est): 500-999K **Privately Held**
WEB: www.thielencoaches.com
SIC: 4151 4142 School bus service; long-distance bus charter service

(G-7029)
WOOD-DALE HOME INC
Also Called: Wood Dale Nursing Home
600 Sunrise Blvd (56283-1863)
PHONE..............................507 637-3587
FAX: 507 637-2546
Dennis Dirlam, *President*
Judy Sandmann, *Administrator*
EMP: 82 **EST:** 1973
SQ FT: 24,000
SALES (est): 1MM-4.9MM **Privately Held**
SIC: 8051 Skilled nursing care facility

REMER
Cass County

(G-7030)
LUTHERAN BIBLE CAMP
Also Called: Luther Dell Bible Camp
2760 S Boy Lake Dr NE (56672-1015)
PHONE..............................218 566-2329
Loren Teig, *President*
Lindsy Johnson, *Principal*
Al Johnson, *Exec Dir*
EMP: 26 **EST:** 1993
SALES (est): 1MM-4.9MM **Privately Held**
SIC: 7032 Bible camp

RENVILLE
Renville County

(G-7031)
CITY OF RENVILLE
Also Called: Renvilla Nursing Home
205 SE Elm St (56284-1815)
PHONE..............................320 329-8381
FAX: 320 329-3678
Tara Hinderks, *Human Res Mgr*
Jane Dikken, *Mktg Dir*
Sara Brandt, *Manager*
Mary Sunvold, *Manager*
Lorin Lilja, *Manager*
EMP: 100
SALES (est): 1MM-4.9MM **Privately Held**
WEB: www.renvilla.sfhs.org
SIC: 8051 8052 Skilled nursing care facility; intermediate care facility
PA: City of Renville
221 N Main St
Renville MN 56284
320 329-8366

(G-7032)
NEW MIDWEST CO LLC
209 N Main St (56284)
PO Box 615 (56284-0615)
PHONE..............................320 329-3363
Dana Persson, *President*
Paul Wilson, *Corp Secy*
Robert A Harrington, *COO*
Thomas A Powell, *CFO*
EMP: 260 **EST:** 1994
SALES (est): 100MM-499.9MM **Privately Held**
WEB: www.goldenovaleggs.com
SIC: 5144 Wholesales poultry & poultry products; wholesales eggs

---

RICE
Benton County

(G-7033)
OAK HILL GOLF CLUB INC
8852 Indian Rd NW (56367-4902)
PHONE..............................320 259-8969
FAX: 320 202-9550
James Dahl, *President*
Michael Berscheid, *Principal*
Roger Petersen, *Corp Secy*
EMP: 25 **EST:** 1989
SQ FT: 2,500
SALES (est): 1MM-4.9MM **Privately Held**
WEB: www.oakhillgolfclub.com
SIC: 7992 7999 Public golf course; retails golf goods & equipment; golf driving range; limited service snack bar

---

RICHFIELD
Hennepin County

(G-7034)
BUY BEST PURCHASING LLC
7601 Penn Ave S (55423-3645)
PHONE..............................612 291-1000
Joesph Joyce, *Member*
Allen U Lenzmien, *Member*
Bradbury Anderson, *Member*
Mark I Gordon, *Member*
Patrick Pautz, *Manager*
EMP: 5000 **EST:** 2001
SQ FT: 260,000
SALES (est): 1B-9.9B **Publicly Held**
WEB: www.bestbuy.com
SIC: 5065 Wholesales electronic parts & equipment
PA: Best Buy Co Inc
7601 Penn Ave S
Richfield MN 55423
612 291-1000

(G-7035)
EXTENDICARE HOMES INC
7727 Portland Ave (55423-4320)
PHONE..............................612 861-1691
FAX: 612 861-0186
Ben Mallon, *Administrator*
Troy Barrick, *Director*
EMP: 100
SALES (est): 1MM-4.9MM **Privately Held**
WEB: www.extendacare.com
SIC: 8051 8093 Skilled nursing care facility; outpatient rehabilitation treatment center
DH: Extendicare Homes Inc
111 W Michigan St
Milwaukee WI 53203
414 908-8000

(G-7036)
MAINSTREET VILLAGE RETIREMENT
7601 Lyndale Ave S (55423-4073)
PHONE..............................612 869-6584
FAX: 612 869-6843
Jill Shewe, *Director*
EMP: 50 **EST:** 2000
SALES (est): 1MM-4.9MM **Privately Held**
WEB: www.tcchomes.org
SIC: 8361 Residential care facility

(G-7037)
RICHFIELD BLOOMINGTON CREDIT (PA)
345 E 77th St (55423-4312)
PHONE..............................612 798-7100
FAX: 612 798-7131
Pat Brekken, *President*
Dawn Nilsen, *Corp Secy*
Andre Thibault, *Assistant VP*
Karen Hoepponer, *Vice Pres*
Larry Klement, *Vice Pres*
EMP: 36 **EST:** 1957
SQ FT: 12,000
SALES (corp-wide): 12.35M **Privately Held**
SIC: 6062 State chartered credit union

(PA)=Parent Co (HQ)=Headquarters (DH)=Div Headquarters
✪ = New business established in last 2 years

2011 Harris Minnesota
Services Directory

© Harris InfoSource 1-866-281-6415
307

GEOGRAPHIC

(G-7038)
STOREFRONT GROUP
6425 Nicollet Ave Ste 210 (55423-1668)
PHONE..............................612 861-1675
FAX: 612 861-3446
Pat Dale, *CEO*
Karen Mattson, *Sales Staff*
Hal Pickett, *Director*
Jenny Rosgren, *Director*
Mary Schneider, *Bd of Directors*
EMP: 50 **EST:** 1973
SALES (est): 1MM-4.9MM **Privately Held**
WEB: www.storefront.org
SIC: 8322 8093 Youth self-help agency;
outpatient mental health clinic; family or
marriage counseling; general counseling
services

(G-7039)
U ABOUT INC
6702 Penn Ave S (55423-2005)
PHONE..............................612 866-4884
Jim Sipulski, *President*
Wendy Gunderson, *Vice Pres*
EMP: 120 **EST:** 2003
SQ FT: 1,400
SALES (est): 1MM-4.9MM **Privately Held**
SIC: 8082 Home health care services

RICHMOND
Stearns County

(G-7040)
C & D GRANITE INC
767 1st St SE (56368)
PHONE..............................320 597-2398
FAX: 320 597-2391
Curt Steil, *CEO*
Jason Krone, *Manager*
EMP: 25 **EST:** 1994
SALES (est): 1MM-4.9MM **Privately Held**
WEB: www.cdgranite.com
SIC: 1741 Masonry & stonework contractor

(G-7041)
RICHMOND BUS SERVICE INC
718 Main St E (56368-8232)
PHONE..............................320 597-2055
FAX: 320 597-3732
David Feldhege, *President*
Pat Feldhege, *Vice Pres*
EMP: 40 **EST:** 1965
SQ FT: 17,500
SALES (est): 1MM-4.9MM **Privately Held**
SIC: 4151 School bus service

ROCHESTER
Olmsted County

(G-7042)
A B SYSTEMS INC
Also Called: Woodlake Park
209 Woodlake Dr SE (55904-5530)
PHONE..............................507 288-9397
FAX: 507 288-5113
Peter Schuller, *President*
Rita Beltz, *Manager*
EMP: 30 **EST:** 1972
SQ FT: 13,700
SALES (est): 5MM-9.9MM **Privately Held**
WEB: www.absystems.com
SIC: 1542 6552 New commercial & office
building construction; commercial land
subdividers & developers

(G-7043)
ABILITY BUILDING CENTER
(PA)
1911 14th St NW (55901-0756)
PO Box 6938 (55903-6938)
PHONE..............................507 281-6262
FAX: 507 281-6270
Dick Quinn, *Treasurer*
Steve Fuchs, *Controller*
Sami Mohr, *Program Mgr*
Steven Schroeder, *Info Tech Mgr*
Steve Hill, *Exec Dir*
EMP: 250 **EST:** 1956
SQ FT: 60,000
SALES (corp-wide): 11.24M **Privately Held**

WEB: www.abcinc.org
SIC: 8331 Vocational rehabilitation agency;
sheltered workshop

(G-7044)
ADAIR ELECTRIC CO
204 16th St SE (55904-7911)
PHONE..............................507 289-7696
David V Kirk, *President*
Edward V Kirk, *Vice Pres*
Randa V Kirk, *Treasurer*
John Siple, *Accountant*
EMP: 90 **EST:** 1950
SQ FT: 4,000
SALES (est): 10MM-24.9MM **Privately Held**
SIC: 1731 Electrical contractor; general
electrical contractor

(G-7045)
AFFILIATED GROUP INC
3055 41st St NW Ste 100 (55901-6893)
PHONE..............................507 280-7000
Mark Neeb, *President*
Steve Loftin, *Corp Secy*
Paul Skovbroten, *Corp Secy*
Brenda Hays, *Vice Pres*
Amy Jahraus, *Manager*
EMP: 80 **EST:** 1923
SQ FT: 11,200
SALES (est): 10MM-24.9MM **Privately Held**
WEB: www.theaffiliatedgroup.com
SIC: 7323 7322 Consumer credit reporting
bureau; collection agency

(G-7046)
AGVANTAGE SOFTWARE INC
107 Woodlake Dr SE (55904-5534)
PHONE..............................507 282-6353
Michelle Blomberg, *President*
Lisa Sick, *Vice Pres*
Bonnie Fohrman, *Vice Pres*
Paul Hawes, *CFO*
Kari Apenhorsp, *Human Res Mgr*
EMP: 29 **EST:** 1976
SQ FT: 5,000
SALES (est): 10MM-24.9MM **Privately Held**
WEB: www.agvantage.com
SIC: 5045 7372 Wholesales computers;
business & professional software publishers

(G-7047)
ALCHEMIST GENERAL INC (PA)
Also Called: Hunts Hillcrest Drug & Gift
1510 Broadway Ave N (55906-4146)
PHONE..............................507 289-3901
Ronald B Johnson, *President*
David Kohler, *Corp Secy*
EMP: 60 **EST:** 1959
SQ FT: 13,000
SALES (corp-wide): 25M **Privately Held**
SIC: 5047 Drug store; greeting card shop;
wholesales medical equipment & supplies;
retail gift shop

(G-7048)
ALDRICH MEMORIAL NURSERY
SCH
855 Essex Pkwy NW (55901-3422)
PHONE..............................507 289-3097
FAX: 507 280-5877
Bonnie Stauff, *Exec Dir*
Dorey Johnson, *Director*
EMP: 35 **EST:** 1952
SALES (est): 500-999K **Privately Held**
SIC: 8351 Nursery school

(G-7049)
ALIANCE HEALTH CARE INC
3224 6th Ave NE Unit A (55906-3807)
PHONE..............................507 252-9737
Mark Walter, *President*
Cynthia Donney, *Manager*
EMP: 64 **EST:** 1993
SQ FT: 1,150
SALES (est): 1MM-4.9MM **Privately Held**
WEB: www.alliancemedsupply.com
SIC: 8082 7361 Home health care services;
nurses' registry service

(G-7050)
ALL SYSTEMS INSTALLATION
INC
929 37th Ave NW (55901-6645)
PHONE..............................507 281-9466
FAX: 507 281-9266
Brian King, *Manager*
Mark Broagwater, *Manager*
EMP: 60
SALES (est): 5MM-9.9MM **Privately Held**
WEB: www.allsysinst.com
SIC: 1731 Computer installation service
PA: All Systems Installation Inc
8300 10th Ave N Ste A
Minneapolis MN 55427
763 593-1330

(G-7051)
ALLIANCE CONCRETE
CONCEPTS INC
325 Alliance Pl NE (55906-3975)
PHONE..............................507 536-4515
Gerald Price, *President*
Jeff Price, *Vice Pres*
EMP: 25 **EST:** 2001
SALES (est): 1MM-4.9MM **Privately Held**
WEB: www.moderra.com
SIC: 1771 Stucco, gunite & grouting
contractor

(G-7052)
ALLIANCE HEALTH CARE INC
3224 6th Ave NE Unit A (55906-3807)
PHONE..............................507 252-9737
Cynthia Donney, *Manager*
EMP: 25
SALES (est): 500-999K **Privately Held**
SIC: 8082 Home health care services
PA: Alliance Health Care Inc
2260 Cliff Rd
Saint Paul MN 55122
651 895-8030

(G-7053)
ALVIN E BENIKE INC
2960 Highway 14 W (55901-7501)
PHONE..............................507 288-6575
FAX: 507 288-0116
John Benike, *President*
Aaron Benike, *Vice Pres*
Mary Kisilewski, *Vice Pres*
James Benike, *Treasurer*
Ronald Markhan, *Manager*
EMP: 150 **EST:** 1937
SQ FT: 3,125
SALES (est): 25MM-49.9MM **Privately Held**
WEB: www.benike.com
SIC: 1542 New commercial & office building
construction; hospital construction;
commercial & office building renovation &
repair services; specialized public building
contractors

(G-7054)
AMERICAN WRESTLING
ASSOCIATION
4739 14th Ave NW Apt 4 (55901-8208)
PHONE..............................507 281-8842
Dale Gagner, *Owner*
EMP: 25 **EST:** 1996
SALES (est): 1MM-4.9MM **Privately Held**
SIC: 7941 Sports support services

(G-7055)
ANALYSTS INTERNATIONAL
CORP
Also Called: A I C
1530 Greenview Dr SW (55902-4286)
PHONE..............................507 280-6663
FAX: 507 280-9213
Randy Horlocker, *Sales/Mktg Mgr*
EMP: 50
SALES (est): 5MM-9.9MM **Publicly Held**
WEB: www.analysts.com
SIC: 7371 Custom computer programming
service
PA: Analysts International Corp
3601 W 76th St Ste 500
Minneapolis MN 55435
952 835-5900

(G-7056)
ANDERSON'S FORMAL WEAR
INC (HQ)
1945 3rd Ave SE (55904-7935)
PO Box 1145 (55903-1145)
PHONE..............................507 285-1884
FAX: 507 282-3001
David G Frana, *President*
Ken Bunn, *Corp Secy*
Rick Paulson, *Vice Pres*
EMP: 30 **EST:** 1961
SQ FT: 19,512
SALES (corp-wide): 10M **Privately Held**
WEB: www.frana.com
SIC: 7299 5136 Tuxedo rental service;
wholesales men's & boys' suits & trousers;
retails formal wear
PA: Frana & Associates Inc
1945 3rd Ave SE
Rochester MN 55904
507 285-1884

(G-7057)
APOLLO DENTAL CENTER PLC
3000 43rd St NW (55901-5847)
PHONE..............................507 287-8320
FAX: 507 287-9165
Lois Berschied, *Partner*
Lois Berscheid-Brunn, *Dentist*
Tom Cafarella, *Dentist*
Sonya Josephs, *Dentist*
Ray Murray, *Dentist*
EMP: 42 **EST:** 1995
SALES (est): 1MM-4.9MM **Privately Held**
WEB: www.apollodentalcenter.com
SIC: 8021 Dentists' office & clinic

(G-7058)
ARNOLD'S SUPPLY & KLEENIT
CO
Also Called: Arnolds Elite Crpt Uphl Clean
835 38th St NW (55901-6985)
PHONE..............................507 289-2393
FAX: 507 289-2318
Thomas Devinny, *President*
Michael Kanz, *Vice Pres*
Mary A Guhl, *Manager*
EMP: 150 **EST:** 1930
SQ FT: 19,000
SALES (est): 1MM-4.9MM **Privately Held**
WEB: www.arnolds-supply.com
SIC: 7349 Janitorial & custodial services;
retails cleaning equipment & supplies

(G-7059)
ART SEMVA GALLERY
Also Called: Semva Gallery
16 1st St SW (55902-3038)
PHONE..............................507 281-4920
Tom Evans, *Principal*
Mary Sheehan, *Treasurer*
Bill Siggelkow, *Director*
EMP: 71 **EST:** 1992
SALES (est): 1MM-4.9MM **Privately Held**
SIC: 7999 Commercial art gallery; art dealer

(G-7060)
ARTHUR A HIRMAN AGENCY
INC
Also Called: Hirman Insurors
4001 W River Pkwy NW (55901-6971)
PO Box 6887 (55903-6887)
PHONE..............................507 285-3111
FAX: 507 285-0294
Greg Cooper, *Corp Secy*
Kate Staffon, *Corp Secy*
Steve Spohn, *Corp Secy*
Tom Floyd, *Vice Pres*
Mitch Mann, *Branch Mgr*
EMP: 25 **EST:** 1930
SQ FT: 5,500
SALES (est): 1MM-4.9MM **Privately Held**
WEB: www.hirman.com
SIC: 6411 Insurance services

(G-7061)
BCI COCA-COLA BOTTLING CO
OF
Also Called: Coca-Cola
1803 14th St NW (55901-0758)
PHONE..............................507 282-2622
EMP: 45
SALES (est): 25MM-49.9MM **Publicly Held**
WEB: www.cokecce.com

▲=Import ▼=Export
◆=Import/Export

SIC: 5149 Wholesales soft drinks
HQ: BCI Coca-Cola Bottling Co of
1334 S Central Ave
Los Angeles CA 90021
213 746-5555

(G-7062)
BEAR CREEK CARE & REHAB
501 8th Ave SE (55904-4834)
PHONE................507 288-6514
FAX: 507 288-6368
Bill Lindberg, *Administrator*
EMP: 140 EST: 1983
SALES (est): 5MM-9.9MM Privately Held
SIC: 8059 Convalescent home

(G-7063)
BETHANY SAMARITAN INC
1530 Assisi Dr NW (55901-1637)
PHONE................507 289-3336
FAX: 507 289-9207
Susan Wiesner, *Branch Mgr*
EMP: 180
SALES (est): 5MM-9.9MM Privately Held
SIC: 8051 Skilled nursing care facility

(G-7064)
BETHANY SAMARITAN INC
Also Called: Samaritan Bethany HM On
Eighth
24 8th St NW (55901-6817)
PO Box 5947 (55903-5947)
PHONE................507 289-4031
FAX: 507 289-6001
Jason Cronk, *Manager*
Judy Holtz, *Manager*
Sue Knutson, *Exec Dir*
Janet Hofschulte, *Technician*
EMP: 150
SALES (est): 5MM-9.9MM Privately Held
SIC: 8051 Extended care facility

(G-7065)
BEVERLY ENTERPRISES - MN
2215 Highway 52 N (55901-7657)
PHONE................507 288-1818
Sylvia Matheson, *Branch Mgr*
EMP: 65
SALES (est): 1MM-4.9MM Privately Held
WEB: www.beverlynet.com
SIC: 8322 Rehabilitation services
HQ: Beverly Enterprises - MN
650 Ramer Ave S
Rush City MN 55069
320 358-4765

(G-7066)
BIGELOW, JOEL & SONS ENTRPRS
Also Called: Bigelow Enterprises
3428 Lakeridge Pl NW Ste A (55901-6572)
PHONE................507 529-1161
FAX: 507 775-2166
Joel Bigelow, *CEO*
Michael Paradise, *President*
Tony Bigelow, *Corp Secy*
Jeremy Bigelow, *Vice Pres*
Mat Simons, *Vice Pres*
EMP: 25 EST: 1975
SQ FT: 3,000
SALES (est): 5MM-9.9MM Privately Held
SIC: 1521 1542 New single-family home
construction service; new commercial &
office building construction

(G-7067)
BOYS & GIRLS CLUB OF ROCHESTER
1026 E Center St (55904-4658)
PHONE................507 287-2300
FAX: 507 287-2308
Larry Kent, *Principal*
Gale McEvoy, *Sales Staff*
Benjamin Lares, *Manager*
Bobbi Mindy, *Exec Dir*
Jody Millerbernd, *Director*
EMP: 28
SALES (est): 1MM-4.9MM Privately Held
SIC: 8322 Individual & family social services

(G-7068)
BUYONLINENOW INC
4865 19th St NW Ste 110 (55901-8397)
PHONE................507 281-6899
Robert Herman, *President*
Michael Nortung, *CFO*
Julie Dahl, *Web Dvlpr*
Sonja Herman, *Director*
Jeffrey Kraus, *Director*
EMP: 39 EST: 1990
SQ FT: 12,000
SALES (est): 10MM-24.9MM Privately Held
WEB: www.buyonlinenow.com
SIC: 5021 5112 Wholesales furniture;
wholesales office supplies

(G-7069)
C O BROWN AGENCY INC
2048 Superior Dr NW # 100 (55901-5028)
PHONE................507 288-7600
FAX: 507 287-3589
Darwin Olson, *President*
Therese Armstead, *Treasurer*
Beth Morris, *Controller*
Steve Meyer, *Manager*
EMP: 40 EST: 1917
SQ FT: 15,000
SALES (est): 1MM-4.9MM Privately Held
WEB: www.cobrown.com
SIC: 6411 Insurance agent

(G-7070)
CARDINAL OF MINNESOTA LTD
3008 Wellner Dr NE (55906-8427)
PHONE................507 281-1077
FAX: 507 281-1127
Jack M Priggen, *President*
V Sandy V, *Human Res Mgr*
Sandy Vanvieuwenhuyze, *Manager*
Paula McGuine, *Exec Dir*
EMP: 250 EST: 1994
SALES (est): 5MM-9.9MM Privately Held
SIC: 8082 8052 Home health care services;
intermediate care facility

(G-7071)
CARPENTER & TORGERSON II LLC
161 13th Ave SW (55902-0349)
PHONE................507 536-0040
Sheryl Walton, *Senior VP*
Thomas R Torgerson, *Mng Member*
Brandon Rabe, *Manager*
EMP: 45
SALES (est): 1MM-4.9MM Privately Held
WEB: www.torgersonproperties.com
SIC: 7011 Traveler accommodations
PA: Torgerson Properties Inc
103 15th Ave NW Ste 200
Willmar MN 56201
320 235-7207

(G-7072)
CDI CORP
400 S Broadway Ste 203 (55904-6498)
PHONE................507 282-8773
Renee Joys, *Manager*
EMP: 54
SALES (est): 1MM-4.9MM Publicly Held
WEB: www.cdicorp.com
SIC: 7363 Temporary help service
HQ: CDI Corp
1717 Arch St Fl 35
Philadelphia PA 19103
215 569-2200

(G-7073)
CENTRAL TERRITORIAL OF THE
20 1st Ave NE (55906-3706)
PHONE................507 288-3663
FAX: 507 281-8348
Cindy Gove, *Sales Staff*
Tom McCom, *Branch Mgr*
Louise Simons, *Director*
EMP: 52 Privately Held
WEB: www.salarmychicago.org
SIC: 8699 Religious organization; charitable
organization
HQ: Central Territorial of The
10 W Algonquin Rd
Des Plaines IL 60016
847 294-2000

(G-7074)
CHARTER COMMUNICATIONS
3993 Heritage Pl NW (55901-3067)
PHONE................888 438-2427
Sherry Doftal, *Manager*
EMP: 70
SALES (est): 25MM-49.9MM Publicly Held
WEB: www.charter.ordercableonline.com
SIC: 4841 Pay television distribution
HQ: Charter Communications
12405 Powerscourt Dr
Saint Louis MO 63131
314 965-0555

(G-7075)
CHARTERHOUSE INC
211 2nd St NW Ofc (55901-2897)
PHONE................507 266-8572
FAX: 507 266-6827
Thomas Dircks, *Managing Prtnr*
Dick Edward, *Principal*
Allen Kubly, *Manager*
Linda Vansickle, *Admin Asst*
EMP: 225 EST: 1981
SALES (est): 25MM-49.9MM Privately Held
WEB: www.charterhouse-mayo.org
SIC: 6513 8051 8052 Operators of
retirement hotels; intermediate care facility;
skilled nursing care facility
PA: Mayo Clinic
200 1st St SW
Rochester MN 55905
507 284-2511

(G-7076)
CHILD CARE RESOURCE & REFERRAL
126 Woodlake Dr SE (55904-5533)
PHONE................507 287-2020
FAX: 507 287-2411
Ronald Luck, *Finance Dir*
Eve Dieterman, *Human Resources*
Dee Rabehl, *Adm Mgr*
Dale Walston, *CIO*
EMI McCoy, *CTO*
EMP: 70 EST: 1972
SQ FT: 15,000
SALES (est): 1MM-4.9MM Privately Held
WEB: www.childcarenet.org
SIC: 8322 8351 8748 General counseling
services; business consulting services; child
day care service

(G-7077)
CIBER INC
2222 18th Ave NW Ste 100 (55901-7724)
PHONE................507 280-9267
FAX: 507 280-0833
Scott Youngman, *Manager*
Paul Cmiel, *Manager*
EMP: 100
SALES (est): 10MM-24.9MM Publicly Held
WEB: www.ciber.com
SIC: 7379 7371 Data processing consulting
service; custom computer software systems
analysis & design service
PA: CIBER Inc
6363 S Fiddlers Green Cir
Greenwood Village CO 80111
303 220-0100

(G-7078)
CITY OF ROCHESTER
425 W Silver Lake Dr NE (55906-3675)
PHONE................507 280-1657
Larry Koshire, *Manager*
EMP: 40
SALES (est): 25MM-49.9MM Privately Held
WEB: www.rochestercvb.org
SIC: 4931 Electric & related services;
mayors' office
PA: City of Rochester
201 4th St SE Ste 204
Rochester MN 55904
507 328-2860

(G-7079)
CITY OF ROCHESTER
4000 E River Rd NE (55906-3414)
PHONE................507 280-1540
FAX: 507 280-1542
Neil Stiller, *Plant Engr*
Franklin Peterson, *Human Res Dir*
Mike Smith, *Sales Mgr*

Stephanie Yrjo, *Sales Mgr*
Patty Hanson, *Sales Staff*
EMP: 200
SALES (est): 100MM-499.9MM Privately
Held
WEB: www.rochestercvb.org
SIC: 4931 4911 4941 Electric & related
services; electric services; water supply
services; mayors' office
PA: City of Rochester
201 4th St SE Ste 204
Rochester MN 55904
507 328-2860

(G-7080)
CLAREY'S SAFETY EQUIPMENT INC
3555 9th St NW Ste 200 (55901-6762)
PO Box 5827 (55903-5827)
PHONE................507 289-6749
FAX: 507 289-5213
Jay Clarey, *President*
Ann C Lumby, *Corp Secy*
Todd Clarey, *Treasurer*
EMP: 25 EST: 1967
SQ FT: 10,000
SALES (est): 5MM-9.9MM Privately Held
WEB: www.clareys.com
SIC: 5087 Wholesales firefighting
equipment; retails safety supplies &
equipment

(G-7081)
CLEAR CHANNEL COMMUNICATIONS
Also Called: WLOL
1530 Greenview Dr SW (55902-4286)
PHONE................507 288-3888
Tom Gjerdrum, *Manager*
EMP: 30
SALES (est): 1MM-4.9MM Privately Held
SIC: 4832 Radio broadcasting station
HQ: Clear Channel Communications
200 E Basse Rd
San Antonio TX 78209
210 822-2828

(G-7082)
CLEMENTS CHEVROLET-CADILLAC CO
1000 12th St SW (55902-3833)
PO Box 5889 (55903-5889)
PHONE................507 289-0491
FAX: 507 285-4759
Gerald Bridwell, *President*
Jim Orke, *General Mgr*
Chris Noble, *Human Res Mgr*
Floyd Albee, *Human Res Mgr*
Tim McBeain, *Sales Mgr*
EMP: 115 EST: 1926
SQ FT: 46,000
SALES (est): 50MM-99.9MM Privately Held
WEB: www.clementsauto.com
SIC: 7515 Retails new & used automobiles;
retails new & used pickups; retails new &
used vans; passenger car leasing; used car
dealer
PA: F B Clements & Co Ltd
1815 E Madison Ave
Mankato MN 56001
507 625-5641

(G-7083)
CNS MANAGED HEALTH CARE INC
3249 19th St NW Ste 1 (55901-6793)
PHONE................507 289-2411
FAX: 507 289-2411
Pam Maxson, *Controller*
Alice Syverson, *Vice Pres*
EMP: 60 EST: 2002
SALES (est): 1MM-4.9MM Privately Held
SIC: 8082 Home health care services

(G-7084)
COLBY YAGGY ASSOCIATES INC (PA)
717 3rd Ave SE Ste 101 (55904-7373)
PHONE................507 288-6464
FAX: 507 288-5058
Robert Ellis, *President*
Michael Court, *Corp Secy*
Jose Rivas, *Vice Pres*
Scott Samuelson, *Vice Pres*
Brian Pehl, *Senior Engr*

GEOGRAPHIC

EMP: 69 EST: 1970
SQ FT: 15,000
SALES (corp-wide): 16M **Privately Held**
WEB: www.yaggy.com
SIC: 8711 8712 8713 Engineering services; architectural engineers; civil engineering services; surveying service

(G-7085)
COLD WELL BANKER AT YOUR SVC
2510 Superior Dr NW Ste A (55901-8349)
PHONE..............................507 285-9115
James Nelson, *President*
Donald Berg, *Exec Dir*
EMP: 50 EST: 1987
SALES (est): 5MM-9.9MM **Privately Held**
SIC: 6531 Residential real estate agency

(G-7086)
COLONIAL LANES CO
1828 14th St NW (55901-0709)
PHONE..............................507 289-2341
FAX: 507 289-6974
Mike Anderson, *President*
EMP: 31
SQ FT: 19,600
SALES (est): 1MM-4.9MM **Privately Held**
SIC: 7933 Bar; ten pin center; bowling center

(G-7087)
COMFORT HOME HEALTH CARE GROUP
2746 Superior Dr NW # 200 (55901-8343)
PHONE..............................507 281-2332
FAX: 507 281-2632
Christopher Blum, *President*
Lynette Oehlke, *Human Res Dir*
Teresa Pawlina, *Exec Dir*
Bonnie Saponari, *Exec Dir*
Susan Harwood, *Director*
EMP: 250 EST: 1982
SALES (est): 5MM-9.9MM **Privately Held**
SIC: 8082 7361 Home health care services; nurses' registry service

(G-7088)
COMFORT INN & SUITES ✪
5708 Bandel Rd NW (55901-2161)
PHONE..............................507 289-3344
Stephanie Johnson, *Manager*
EMP: 80 EST: 2008
SALES (est): 1MM-4.9MM **Privately Held**
SIC: 7011 Inn

(G-7089)
COUNTY OF OLMSTED
151 4th St SE (55904-3710)
PHONE..............................507 285-8138
Raymond F Schmitz, *Principal*
EMP: 27
SALES (est): 1MM-4.9MM **Privately Held**
WEB: www.olmsteddfl.org
SIC: 8111 Legal services; county supervisors' & executives' office
PA: County of Olmsted
151 4th St SE Ste 11
Rochester MN 55904
507 285-8115

(G-7090)
CUMULUS MEDIA INC
Also Called: Fox Country
1530 Greenview Dr SW Ste 200 (55902-4327)
PHONE..............................507 288-1025
Bob Fox, *General Mgr*
EMP: 35 **Publicly Held**
WEB: www.cumulusmedia.com
SIC: 4812 Wireless telecommunications carrier & service
PA: Cumulus Media Inc
3280 Peachtree Rd NE # 2300
Atlanta GA 30305
404 949-0700

(G-7091)
CUSTOM COMMUNICATIONS INC
1661 Greenview Dr SW (55902-4215)
PHONE..............................507 288-5522
FAX: 507 287-0757
Leigh J Johnson, *President*

Melissa Brinkman, *Corp Secy*
Judy Johnson, *Vice Pres*
Liz M Hauger, *CFO*
Nicole Johnson, *Treasurer*
EMP: 58 EST: 1968
SQ FT: 14,000
SALES (est): 5MM-9.9MM **Privately Held**
WEB: www.custom-alarm.com
SIC: 1731 7389 Fire detection & burglar alarm systems specialization contractor; furnishes music distribution systems; communications contractor services

(G-7092)
D & R STAR INC (PA)
2207 7th St NW (55901-0206)
PHONE..............................507 282-6080
Richard Hawkins, *CEO*
Michael Hawkins, *President*
Chuck Evenson, *General Mgr*
David Hawkins, *Vice Pres*
James Hawkins, *Vice Pres*
EMP: 60 EST: 1963
SQ FT: 10,000 **Privately Held**
WEB: www.dnrstar.com
SIC: 7993 Amusement arcade; retails pool & billiard tables; retails specialty sport supplies; retails vending machine candy & snack food; retails vending machine cigarettes

(G-7093)
DAVE SYVERSON TRUCK CENTER INC
7 County 16 Rd SE (55904-8416)
PHONE..............................507 289-3357
FAX: 507 289-1534
David Syverson, *President*
Aaron Smith, *General Mgr*
Elaine Syverson, *Corp Secy*
EMP: 32 EST: 1971
SQ FT: 22,000
SALES (est): 10MM-24.9MM **Privately Held**
WEB: www.syversontruck.com
SIC: 5013 7538 Retails new & used trucks, tractors & trailers; general truck repair services; retails truck equipment & parts; wholesales truck parts & accessories

(G-7094)
DEE SPEE DELIVERY SERVICE INC
4225 Garden Ct SE (55904-7146)
PHONE..............................507 288-0695
Phil Nicholson, *Manager*
EMP: 38
SALES (est): 1MM-4.9MM **Privately Held**
WEB: www.speedeedelivery.com
SIC: 4226 Warehousing & storage facility
PA: Dee Spee Delivery Service Inc
4101 Clearwater Rd
Saint Cloud MN 56301
320 251-6697

(G-7095)
DEMOCRATIC PARTY OF OLMSTED
2002 2nd St SW (55902-2469)
PHONE..............................507 536-9785
Lynn Wilson, *Ch of Bd*
EMP: 30 EST: 2004 **Privately Held**
SIC: 8651 Political organization

(G-7096)
DISCOVER MAGICAL MOMENTS
5450 Royal Pl NW (55901-1895)
PO Box 7568 (55903-7568)
PHONE..............................507 289-7463
FAX: 507 529-9398
Renae Loth, *CEO*
EMP: 30 EST: 2002
SALES (est): 500-999K **Privately Held**
SIC: 8351 Child day care service

(G-7097)
DISON'S CLEANERS & LAUNDRY INC
214 Broadway Ave N (55906-3646)
PHONE..............................507 289-3944
FAX: 507 288-3512
Mark Dison, *President*
Leland Bierbaun, *Corp Secy*
Greg Dison, *VP Opers-Prdtn-*
EMP: 25 EST: 1919
SALES (est): 500-999K **Privately Held**

SIC: 7216 7211 Dry cleaning plant; commercial & family dry cleaning & laundry services

(G-7098)
DOMAILLE LTD
535 37th St NE (55906-3401)
PHONE..............................507 287-1170
FAX: 507 287-1198
Bruce Domaille, *President*
EMP: 62 EST: 1997
SALES (est): 5MM-9.9MM **Privately Held**
SIC: 7532 Automotive body shop

(G-7099)
DUANE SAUKE
4600 18th Ave NW (55901-0400)
PHONE..............................507 287-7742
Duane Sauke, *Principal*
EMP: 50 EST: 1981
SALES (est): 5MM-9.9MM **Privately Held**
WEB: www.duanesauke.com
SIC: 6531 Real estate services

(G-7100)
DUNLAP & SEEGER
206 S Broadway Ste 505 (55904-6516)
PO Box 549 (55903-0549)
PHONE..............................507 288-9111
FAX: 507 288-9342
Sheri Brandvold, *General Mgr*
Daniel E Berndt, *Treasurer*
Kris Dietz, *Controller*
Milton Rosenblad, *Manager*
Jean Parker, *Technology Dir*
EMP: 70 EST: 1973
SALES (est): 5MM-9.9MM **Privately Held**
WEB: www.dunlaplaw.com
SIC: 8111 General practice attorney's or lawyer's office

(G-7101)
EAGLE TRANSPORT SERVICES INC
2430 Marion Rd SE (55904-6003)
PHONE..............................507 281-9787
Eric Kilen, *President*
Sherry Dohrn, *Manager*
EMP: 30 EST: 1995
SQ FT: 3,000
SALES (est): 1MM-4.9MM **Privately Held**
SIC: 4213 Over the road trucking

(G-7102)
ED LUNN CONSTRUCTION INC
6889 10th Ave SW Ste 200 (55902-2512)
PHONE..............................507 288-4400
Edward Lunn, *President*
EMP: 30 EST: 2006
SALES (est): 5MM-9.9MM **Privately Held**
SIC: 1542 New commercial & office building construction

(G-7103)
EDINA REALTY HOME SERVICES
1301 Salem Rd SW Ste A (55902-4313)
PHONE..............................507 288-7665
Lori Mack, *Manager*
Thoren Mangold, *Manager*
Margret Reiner, *Manager*
Marilyn D Stewart, *Manager*
EMP: 65
SALES (est): 10MM-24.9MM **Publicly Held**
WEB: www.ilovetennis.net
SIC: 6531 Real estate agency & broker
HQ: Edina Realty Home Services
6800 France Ave S Ste 600
Minneapolis MN 55435
952 928-5900

(G-7104)
ELCOR REALTY OF ROCHESTER INC
3552 W River Pkwy NW Ste C (55901-7030)
PHONE..............................507 282-3345
FAX: 507 282-0068
Gary O'Reilly, *President*
Bill Doran, *Vice Pres*
Phil S Martin, *Vice Pres*
Randy Reynolds, *Treasurer*
EMP: 45

EST: 1975
SQ FT: 6,000
SALES (est): 5MM-9.9MM **Privately Held**
WEB: www.elcorrealty.com
SIC: 6531 Real estate services

(G-7105)
ELDER NETWORK
1130 1/2 73 NW Ste 205 (55901)
PHONE..............................507 285-5272
Mary Liberko, *Treasurer*
Joyce G Campion, *Office Mgr*
Mary Doucette, *Director*
Betty Gordon, *Bd of Directors*
Paula Westerlund, *Bd of Directors*
EMP: 150 EST: 1988 **Privately Held**
SIC: 8399 8322 Social change association; individual & family social services

(G-7106)
ESA P PORTFOLIO OPERATING
55 Woodlake Dr SE (55904-5509)
PHONE..............................507 536-7444
Chad Speer, *Manager*
Eric Stewart, *Manager*
EMP: 25
SALES (est): 1MM-4.9MM **Privately Held**
WEB: www.exstay.com
SIC: 7011 Franchised hotel
DH: ESA P Portfolio Operating
100 Dunbar St
Spartanburg SC 29306
864 573-1887

(G-7107)
ESA P PORTFOLIO OPERATING
2814 43rd St NW (55901-6895)
PHONE..............................507 289-7444
Jolin Wait, *Manager*
EMP: 25
SALES (est): 1MM-4.9MM **Privately Held**
WEB: www.exstay.com
SIC: 7011 Franchised hotel
DH: ESA P Portfolio Operating
100 Dunbar St
Spartanburg SC 29306
864 573-1887

(G-7108)
EXCEL BUILDING MAINTENANCE INC
814 11th St NW (55901-6769)
PHONE..............................507 288-0913
Erich Busse, *President*
EMP: 31
SALES (est): 5MM-9.9MM **Privately Held**
SIC: 1521 Single-family housing construction

(G-7109)
EXHIBITOR PUBLICATIONS INC
206 Suth Broadway Ste 745 (55904)
PO Box 368 (55903-0368)
PHONE..............................507 289-6556
FAX: 507 289-5253
Lee Knight, *Owner*
Aaron Wismar, *General Mgr*
Randal Acker, *COO*
David Morrison, *Exec VP*
Lee Burr, *Senior VP*
EMP: 42 EST: 1982
SQ FT: 5,000
SALES (est): 5MM-9.9MM **Privately Held**
WEB: www.exhibitoronline.com
SIC: 7375 7389 Publishes magazines without printing; publishes periodicals without printing; publishes & prints trade journals; on-line database information retrieval service; advertising, promotional & trade show service

(G-7110)
FAMILY SERVICE ROCHESTER INC
1110 6th St NW (55901-1839)
PHONE..............................507 287-2010
FAX: 507 287-7805
Brad Lohrbach, *Director*
Brenda Walker, *Director*
Janice Draxler, *Director*
Jane Buffie, *Director*
Stephan Jennebach, *Bd of Directors*
EMP: 57 EST: 1989
SALES (est): 5MM-9.9MM **Privately Held**
WEB: www.familyservicerochester.org

▲=Import ▼=Export
◆=Import/Export

SIC: 8742 Management consulting services

(G-7111)
FIRST ALLIANCE CREDIT UNION (PA)
320 Alliance Pl NE (55906-3975)
PHONE...........................507 288-0330
FAX: 507 288-7288
Kelly McDonough, *President*
Linda Hull, *Loan Officer*
EMP: 40 EST: 1932
SALES (corp-wide): 5.04M **Privately Held**
WEB: www.firstalliancecu.com
SIC: 6061 Federally chartered credit union

(G-7112)
FIRST ALLIANCE CREDIT UNION
501 16th St SE (55904-5234)
PHONE...........................507 281-7640
FAX: 507 281-7600
Robert McIntosh, *Corp Secy*
Mark Hettinger, *Vice Pres*
Lisett Comai, *VP Sls/Mktg*
Greg Hird, *Manager*
Leanne Trom, *Manager*
Privately Held
WEB: www.firstalliancecu.com
SIC: 6062 State chartered credit union
PA: First Alliance Credit Union
320 Alliance Pl NE
Rochester MN 55906
507 288-0330

(G-7113)
FIRST FEDERAL CAPITAL BANK
Also Called: Associated Bank
206 S Broadway Ste 206 (55904-6525)
PHONE...........................507 285-2600
FAX: 507 285-2601
Michael Bue, *President*
Craig Oslund, *Vice Pres*
EMP: 60
SALES (est): 10MM-24.9MM **Publicly Held**
WEB: www.firstfederalcapitalbank.com
SIC: 6035 Federally chartered savings institution
DH: First Federal Capital Bank
605 State St
La Crosse WI 54601
608 784-8000

(G-7114)
FIRST STUDENT INC
2021 32nd Ave NW (55901-8321)
PHONE...........................507 289-4541
FAX: 507 289-6652
Rick Murphy, *General Mgr*
Jon Goetz, *Manager*
EMP: 150
SALES (est): 1MM-4.9MM **Privately Held**
WEB: www.firststudentinc.com
SIC: 4151 School bus service
HQ: First Student Inc
600 Vine St Ste 1400
Cincinnati OH 45202
513 241-2200

(G-7115)
FIRST SUPPLY LLC (HQ)
3815 Highway 14 W (55901-5911)
PO Box 7157 (55903-7157)
PHONE...........................507 287-0202
Robert Beranek, *Member*
Brian Donarski, *Vice Pres*
Edward J Felten, *Mng Member*
Irene Riley, *Manager*
Bob Beranek, *Manager*
EMP: 51 EST: 1988
SQ FT: 53,890 **Privately Held**
SIC: 5075 5074 Wholesales heating & air conditioning equipment & supplies; wholesales ventilating equipment & supplies; wholesales plumbing & heating equipment & supplies
PA: First Supply LLC
6800 Gisholt Dr
Madison WI 53713
608 222-7799

(G-7116)
FIRST SUPPLY LLC
3815 Highway 14 W (55901-5911)
PO Box 7157 (55903-7157)
PHONE...........................507 287-0202
Bob Beranek, *Branch Mgr*

EMP: 50
SALES (est): 25MM-49.9MM **Privately Held**
SIC: 5074 5075 5078 Wholesales plumbing & heating equipment & supplies; wholesales plumbing fittings & supplies; wholesales plumbers' brass goods & fittings; wholesales plumbing & heating valves; wholesales commercial refrigeration equipment; retails kitchen cabinets
PA: First Supply LLC
6800 Gisholt Dr
Madison WI 53713
608 222-7799

(G-7117)
FLEET WHOLESALE SUPPLY CO INC
481 Main St (55904)
PO Box 6127 (55903-6127)
PHONE...........................507 281-1130
Geary Kline, *Manager*
Tim Giesen, *Manager*
EMP: 72
SALES (est): 50MM-99.9MM **Privately Held**
SIC: 5191 Wholesales farm supplies
PA: Fleet Wholesale Supply Co Inc
1300 S Lynndale Dr
Appleton WI 54914
920 997-8378

(G-7118)
FOSTER ELECTRIC CO
538 6th Ave NW (55901-2634)
PHONE...........................507 289-4571
FAX: 507 289-4572
Ed L Pointe Jr, *President*
Minar Bussell, *Vice Pres*
Steve Bussell, *Vice Pres*
Laura L Pointe, *Treasurer*
EMP: 35 EST: 1916
SQ FT: 960
SALES (est): 1MM-4.9MM **Privately Held**
SIC: 1731 Electrical contractor

(G-7119)
FRANKLIN HEATING STATION
119 3rd St SW (55902-3331)
PHONE...........................507 289-3534
FAX: 507 289-0203
Mayo Fondation, *Principal*
Tom Deboer, *Chief Engr*
Toni Musel, *Accounting Mgr*
Debbie Carlson, *Manager*
EMP: 31 EST: 1928
SQ FT: 66,198
SALES (est): 10MM-24.9MM **Privately Held**
SIC: 4961 Steam supply systems services including geothermal; air conditioning supply services; cooled air supplier; suppliers of steam heat

(G-7120)
FRASER CONSTRUCTION CO
3725 Enterprise Dr SW (55902-2808)
PHONE...........................507 288-6583
FAX: 507 282-1148
Greg Utesch, *Treasurer*
EMP: 30 EST: 1956
SALES (est): 1MM-4.9MM **Privately Held**
SIC: 1629 1623 1794 Earthmoving service; sewer line construction; excavation & grading, building construction contractor

(G-7121)
FRITO-LAY INC
1402 60th Ave NW (55901-2938)
PHONE...........................507 282-1134
Dave Zimprch, *Manager*
EMP: 25
SALES (est): 10MM-24.9MM **Publicly Held**
WEB: www.fritolay.com
SIC: 5145 Wholesales potato chips
DH: Frito-Lay Inc
7701 Legacy Dr
Plano TX 75024
972 334-7000

(G-7122)
GABLES INC
604 5th St SW (55902-3256)
PHONE...........................507 282-2500
FAX: 507 282-6036
June Davis, *President*
Merrill Davis III, *Vice Pres*
EMP: 29

EST: 1983
SQ FT: 10,000
SALES (est): 1MM-4.9MM **Privately Held**
WEB: www.gableshome.info
SIC: 8361 Residential rehabilitation center with health care incidental

(G-7123)
GAC DEVELOPMENT LLC
225 S Broadway (55906-6504)
PO Box 249 (55903-0249)
PHONE...........................507 289-5556
Gus Chatoulias, *Mng Member*
EMP: 40 EST: 1999
SALES (est): 10MM-24.9MM **Privately Held**
SIC: 6512 Nonresidential building operator

(G-7124)
GANDER MOUNTAIN CO
3470 55th St NW (55901-0123)
PHONE...........................507 252-2033
FAX: 507 529-1113
Ron Reitmeier, *Manager*
EMP: 50
SALES (est): 5MM-9.9MM **Publicly Held**
WEB: www.gandermountain.com
SIC: 7699 Retails sporting goods; gun service
PA: Gander Mountain Co
180 5th St E Ste 1300
Saint Paul MN 55101
651 325-4300

(G-7125)
GAUTHIER INDUSTRIES INC
3105 22nd St NW (55901-8319)
PO Box 6700 (55903-6700)
PHONE...........................507 289-0731
FAX: 507 289-6883
Michael Jensen, *CEO*
Dave Kocer, *Ch of Bd*
Terry Grendahl, *Corp Secy*
EMP: 100 EST: 1946
SQ FT: 90,000
SALES (est): 10MM-24.9MM **Privately Held**
WEB: www.gauthind.com
SIC: 7692 Sheet metal fabricator; stamps metal for the trade; welding service

(G-7126)
GLOBAL HOME
1032 15th Ave SE (55904-5159)
PHONE...........................507 282-7471
Mark Abasin, *President*
EMP: 50
SALES (est): 1MM-4.9MM **Privately Held**
SIC: 8082 Home health care services

(G-7127)
GOLD CROSS AMBULANCE SERVICE (PA)
501 6th Ave NW (55901-2673)
PHONE...........................507 255-2230
Paul Anderson, *President*
Bob Perez, *CFO*
Tom Hallisy, *Manager*
EMP: 100 EST: 1962
SQ FT: 8,000
SALES (corp-wide): 26.47M **Privately Held**
WEB: www.gcas-duluth.org
SIC: 4119 Ambulance service; medical training services

(G-7128)
GUEST HOUSE INC
4800 48th St NE (55906-2009)
PO Box 954 (55903-0954)
PHONE...........................507 288-4693
FAX: 507 288-1240
Bill Morgan, *Vice Pres*
William Morgan, *Manager*
EMP: 35
SALES (est): 1MM-4.9MM **Privately Held**
WEB: www.guesthouse.org
SIC: 8093 8069 Outpatient alcohol treatment clinic; alcoholism rehabilitation hospital
PA: Guest House Inc
1601 Joslyn Rd
Lake Orion MI 48360
248 391-4445

(G-7129)
GUS CHAFOULIAS
Also Called: Hilton Grdn Inn Rchster Dwntwn
225 S Broadway (55904-6504)
PHONE...........................507 285-1234
FAX: 507 285-2545
Gus Chafoulias, *Owner*
Kurt Jorgensen, *General Mgr*
Cindy Woolley, *Manager*
EMP: 60 EST: 1999
SALES (est): 1MM-4.9MM **Privately Held**
SIC: 7011 Hotel

(G-7130)
H&R BLOCK INC
Also Called: H & R Block
3120 Wellner Dr NE Ste 1 (55906-4905)
PHONE...........................507 280-8406
Kelly Pearson, *Manager*
EMP: 75
SALES (est): 1MM-4.9MM **Publicly Held**
WEB: www.hrblock.com
SIC: 7291 Tax return preparation services
PA: H&R Block Inc
1 H And R Block Way
Kansas City MO 64105
816 854-3000

(G-7131)
HAMMEL, GREEN & ABRAHAMSON INC
202 1st Ave SW Ste 200 (55902-3129)
PHONE...........................507 281-8601
FAX: 507 281-8688
Hal Henderson, *Vice Pres*
Lori Nierman, *Manager*
EMP: 500
SALES (est): 50MM-99.9MM **Privately Held**
WEB: www.hga.com
SIC: 8711 8712 Engineering consulting services; architectural service
PA: Hammel, Green & Abrahamson Inc
701 Washington Ave N
Minneapolis MN 55401
612 758-4000

(G-7132)
HARDCORE COMPUTER INC
2717 Hwy 14 W Ste D (55901-7598)
PHONE...........................507 285-0101
Al Berning, *CEO*
Daren Klum, *President*
Chad Attlesey, *CTO*
EMP: 25 EST: 2006
SALES (est): 1MM-4.9MM **Privately Held**
WEB: www.hardcorecomputer.com
SIC: 7373 Systems software development service

(G-7133)
HARRIS CONTRACTING CO
Also Called: Quality Mechanical
1400 7th St NW (55901-1735)
PHONE...........................507 282-8128
Al Einberger, *Branch Mgr*
Greg Donley, *Branch Mgr*
EMP: 40
SALES (est): 1MM-4.9MM **Privately Held**
WEB: www.hmcc.com
SIC: 1711 7699 Plumbing service; heating & air conditioning contractor; boiler repair shop
PA: Harris Contracting Co
909 Montreal Cir
Saint Paul MN 55102
651 602-6500

(G-7134)
HAWK & SONS INC
5937 15th St NW (55901)
PO Box 7161 (55903-7161)
PHONE...........................507 285-0508
FAX: 507 289-4336
Dennis Haakenson, *President*
Linda Haakenson, *Manager*
EMP: 40 EST: 1970
SALES (est): 10MM-24.9MM **Privately Held**
SIC: 1521 1791 5082 Prefabricated single-family home construction service; structural iron work contractor; wholesales construction cranes

(PA)=Parent Co (HQ)=Headquarters (DH)=Div Headquarters
✿ = New business established in last 2 years

2011 Harris Minnesota
Services Directory

© Harris InfoSource 1-866-281-6415

311

(G-7135)
HEALING TOUCH AQUAMASSAGE
20 2nd Ave SW Ste B5 (55902-3194)
PHONE.............................507 287-6186
Joyce Krogstad, *Manager*
EMP: 25 EST: 2001
SALES (est): 1MM-4.9MM Privately Held
WEB: www.healingtouch-rochester.com
SIC: 8742 Management consulting services; retails wigs & hairpieces; manufactures electric barber & beauty shop massage machines

(G-7136)
HEARTMAN AGENCY INC
1635 Greenview Dr SW (55902-4215)
PO Box 7008 (55903-7008)
PHONE.............................507 288-3834
George Willson, *President*
Robert Forsyth, *Corp Secy*
Charles Sewich, *Vice Pres*
Frederick D Banfiel, *Manager*
EMP: 26 EST: 1963
SQ FT: 5,000
SALES (est): 1MM-4.9MM Privately Held
WEB: www.heartman.com
SIC: 6411 Insurance agent

(G-7137)
HIAWATHA AVIATION OF ROCHESTER
7300 Brataas Dr SW Ste 2 (55902-1822)
PHONE.............................507 282-1717
FAX: 507 282-9939
Steve Birdseye, *CEO*
Kim Donahoe, *Accounting Mgr*
EMP: 33 EST: 1982
SALES (est): 1MM-4.9MM Privately Held
SIC: 4581 Airport, flying field & services; fixed base operator

(G-7138)
HIMEC INC (PA)
1400 7th St NW (55901-1735)
PHONE.............................507 281-4000
FAX: 507 281-5206
Vic Pietkiewicz, *General Mgr*
Dave Schultz, *Corp Secy*
Joe Beckel, *Senior VP*
Tom Depauw, *Vice Pres*
Greg Donley, *President*
EMP: 150 EST: 1976
SQ FT: 42,000 Privately Held
WEB: www.himec.com
SIC: 1711 Plumbing service; heating & air conditioning contractor; sheet metal fabricator

(G-7139)
HOME FEDERAL SAVINGS BANK (HQ)
1016 Civic Center Dr NW # 1 (55901-1881)
PO Box 6057 (55903-6057)
PHONE.............................507 535-1200
FAX: 507 252-7140
Bradley C Krehbiel, *President*
Kelly Marcus, *Business Mgr*
Thomas Wiedebush, *COO*
Dwain C Jorgensen, *Senior VP*
Susan Kolling, *Senior VP*
EMP: 40 EST: 1934
SALES (corp-wide): 65.85M Publicly Held
SIC: 6035 Federal savings bank
PA: Hmn Financial Inc
    1016 Civic Center Dr NW
    Rochester MN 55901
    507 535-1200

(G-7140)
HOMESTEAD AT ROCHESTER
1900 Ballington Blvd NW (55901-5202)
PHONE.............................507 535-2000
EMP: 36 EST: 2006
SALES (est): 500-999K Privately Held
SIC: 8322 Senior citizen center

(G-7141)
HUNT ELECTRIC CORP
6301 Bandel Rd NW Ste 201 (55901-8657)
PHONE.............................507 281-3226
Dick Jenniges, *Manager*
EMP: 50
SALES (est): 5MM-9.9MM Privately Held
SIC: 1731 General electrical contractor
PA: Hunt Electric Corp
    2300 Territorial Rd Ste 1
    Saint Paul MN 55114
    651 646-2911

(G-7142)
INTERNATIONAL QUALITY HOMECARE
3261 19th St NW (55901-6786)
PHONE.............................507 252-8117
Michael Mordi, *President*
Chris Hansen, *General Mgr*
EMP: 90 EST: 2000
SALES (est): 1MM-4.9MM Privately Held
SIC: 8082 6794 Home health care services; selling or licensing of franchises

(G-7143)
ISLAND FREIGHT BROKERAGE LLC ✪
3270 19th St NW Ste 108 (55901-2950)
PHONE.............................507 288-5758
EMP: 32 EST: 2009
SALES (est): 5MM-9.9MM Privately Held
SIC: 6282 4731 Investment advisory service; transportation agents & brokers

(G-7144)
IT'S ABOUT TIME THEATER
618 23rd St NE (55906-4064)
PHONE.............................507 280-8956
Coralee Grebe, *President*
Bonnie Bills, *Member*
EMP: 40 EST: 1992
SALES (est): 1MM-4.9MM Privately Held
SIC: 7922 Legitimate live theater producers

(G-7145)
J & L NURSING CARE INC
3705 Enterprise Dr SW (55902-2856)
PHONE.............................507 529-0018
FAX: 507 529-0058
Jeannette Wilson, *President*
EMP: 30 EST: 1999
SALES (est): 1MM-4.9MM Privately Held
SIC: 8051 Skilled nursing care facility

(G-7146)
JIM CONWAY
4600 18th Ave NW (55901-0400)
PHONE.............................507 287-7717
Jim Conway, *Principal*
EMP: 50 EST: 1979
SALES (est): 5MM-9.9MM Privately Held
WEB: www.jimconway.com
SIC: 6531 Real estate services

(G-7147)
JONES STANLEY & ASSOCIATES
2746 Superior Dr NW Ste 300 (55901-8378)
PHONE.............................507 288-0064
FAX: 507 288-3993
Pat Hanks, *President*
Lynne McCutcheon, *Vice Pres*
Ronda Lovelace, *Engineer*
Cindy Olson, *Manager*
Stuart Dormody, *Management*
EMP: 38 EST: 1984
SALES (est): 5MM-9.9MM Privately Held
WEB: www.sjatherapyservices.com
SIC: 8111 8049 8082 8093 Legal services; occupational therapist office; outpatient rehabilitation treatment center; home health care services

(G-7148)
K & S HEATING & AIR CONDG
4205 Hwy 14 W (55901-6672)
PHONE.............................507 282-4328
FAX: 507 282-1338
Gary Macmillan, *President*

Richard Keehn, *General Mgr*
EMP: 60 EST: 1988
SQ FT: 39,000
SALES (est): 5MM-9.9MM Publicly Held
WEB: www.lennoxinternational.com
SIC: 1711 Warm air heating & air conditioning contractor
HQ: Service Experts Inc
    2100 Lake Park Blvd
    Richardson TX 75080
    972 497-5000

(G-7149)
K R C H WEB RADIO STATIONS
1530 Greenview Dr SW # 200 (55902-4327)
PHONE.............................507 288-3888
Bob Fox, *General Mgr*
Greg Henn, *Manager*
EMP: 30 EST: 1970
SALES (est): 1MM-4.9MM Privately Held
SIC: 4832 Radio broadcasting station

(G-7150)
KATO DISTRIBUTING INC (PA)
3731 Enterprise Dr SW (55902-2808)
PO Box 6758 (55903-6758)
PHONE.............................507 289-7456
John J Jensen, *President*
Jack Briggs, *CFO*
Nick Gilk, *Manager*
Barb Jensen, *Info Tech Mgr*
EMP: 55 EST: 1958
SQ FT: 6,000 Privately Held
SIC: 5013 Gas station; convenience store; retails auto & truck equipment & parts; wholesales new motor vehicle parts & supplies

(G-7151)
KELLER WILLIAMS PREMIER REALTY
2765 Commerce Dr NW (55901-2262)
PHONE.............................507 424-4422
FAX: 507 424-3773
Stephanie Apsel, *Manager*
Kim Reichel, *Manager*
Kelvin Margan, *Manager*
EMP: 60 EST: 2005
SALES (est): 10MM-24.9MM Privately Held
SIC: 6531 Real estate services

(G-7152)
KIDS COME 1ST CHILDREN'S CTR
3615 15th Ave NW (55901-1463)
PHONE.............................507 281-4421
FAX: 507 281-5557
Karri Schultz, *Director*
EMP: 25 EST: 1996
SALES (est): 500-999K Privately Held
SIC: 8351 Child day care service

(G-7153)
KIDS COME 1ST CORP
1818 Greenview Pl SW (55902-1076)
PHONE.............................507 281-3284
FAX: 507 286-8951
Jeff Brown, *President*
Richard Hexum, *Corp Secy*
Kibby Hanson, *Vice Pres*
EMP: 103 EST: 1988
SALES (est): 1MM-4.9MM Privately Held
SIC: 8351 Group day care center

(G-7154)
KINGSWAY TRANSPORTATION SYSTEM
4515 Highway 63 N (55906-8330)
PO Box 6418 (55903-6418)
PHONE.............................507 288-9375
Alan Koeing, *Owner*
EMP: 75 EST: 1980
SALES (est): 5MM-9.9MM Privately Held
SIC: 4213 Over the road trucking

(G-7155)
KNOWLEDGE LEARNING CORP
Also Called: Children's Beginnings
3089 25th St NW (55901-7823)
PHONE.............................507 529-8455
FAX: 507 529-8415
Leah Matta, *Manager*
EMP: 25

SALES (est): 500-999K Privately Held
WEB: www.knowledgelearning.com
SIC: 8351 Child day care service
PA: Knowledge Learning Corp
    650 NE Holladay St # 1400
    Portland OR 97232
    503 872-1300

(G-7156)
KNOWLEDGE LEARNING CORP
2801 Superior Dr NW (55901-1779)
PHONE.............................507 289-5006
FAX: 507 288-2462
Christina Miles, *Manager*
Chris Schmit, *Exec Dir*
EMP: 34
SALES (est): 500-999K Privately Held
WEB: www.knowledgelearning.com
SIC: 8351 Child day care service
PA: Knowledge Learning Corp
    650 NE Holladay St # 1400
    Portland OR 97232
    503 872-1300

(G-7157)
KNUTSON CONSTRUCTION SERVICES
5985 Bandel Rd NW (55901-8754)
PHONE.............................507 280-9788
FAX: 507 280-9797
David Bastyr, *Vice Pres*
Sharyl Wheeler, *Office Mgr*
EMP: 100
SALES (est): 5MM-9.9MM Privately Held
WEB: www.knutsonconstruction.com
SIC: 8741 1541 1542 8711 Construction management services; industrial building & warehouse construction; commercial & institutional building construction; building construction engineering services

(G-7158)
KORSMO INC
Also Called: Tile Super Store & More
2411 7th St NW (55901-7538)
PHONE.............................507 285-1109
James M Korsmo, *President*
Travis Prigge, *Corp Secy*
Lorrie Swancutt, *CFO*
Kem Flicek, *Sales Mgr*
▲ EMP: 55 EST: 1996
SQ FT: 12,000
SALES (est): 5MM-9.9MM Privately Held
WEB: www.korsmo.com
SIC: 1743 Tile, marble, terrazzo & mosaic contractor; retails floor tile

(G-7159)
KTTC TELEVISION INC
6301 Bandel Rd NW Ste A (55901-8660)
PHONE.............................507 288-4444
FAX: 507 288-6324
Ralph Oakley, *President*
Jerry Watson, *Vice Pres*
Tim Morgan, *Engineering*
Liz Dahlen, *Manager*
Adam Aaro, *Director*
EMP: 56 EST: 1932
SQ FT: 10,500
SALES (est): 10MM-24.9MM Privately Held
WEB: www.kttc.com
SIC: 4833 Television broadcasting station
PA: Quincy Newspapers Inc
    130 S 5th St
    Quincy IL 62301
    217 223-5100

(G-7160)
LARSON'S HOME IMPROVEMENT
6910 38th Ave SE (55904-7121)
PHONE.............................507 288-7111
FAX: 507 288-6702
Timothy J Mayer, *President*
Robert Welp, *Corp Secy*
Don Grewing, *Sales Mgr*
EMP: 35 EST: 1958
SQ FT: 2,900
SALES (est): 1MM-4.9MM Privately Held
WEB: www.larsonsidingandwindows.com
SIC: 1761 1521 1799 Siding contractor; single-family home general remodeling service; window treatment installation service; gutter & downspout contractor

www.HarrisInfo.com
312

2011 Harris Minnesota
Services Directory

▲=Import ▼=Export
◆=Import/Export

(G-7161)
LINDA WATERMAN
Also Called: Re Max
4600 18th Ave NW (55901-0400)
PHONE..............................507 287-7741
Dewayn Sauk, *Director*
EMP: 58 **EST:** 2000
SALES (est): 10MM-24.9MM **Privately Held**
WEB: www.lindawaterman.com
SIC: 6531 Residential real estate agency

(G-7162)
LOWE'S HOME CENTERS INC
4550 Maine Ave SE (55904-6732)
PHONE..............................507 328-8920
EMP: 150
SALES (est): 25MM-49.9MM **Publicly Held**
WEB: www.lowes.com
SIC: 5031 5064 Retails building products &
materials; wholesales exterior building
materials; wholesales interior building
materials; wholesales electrical appliances;
retails household appliances
HQ: Lowe's Home Centers Inc
1605 Curtis Bridge Rd
Wilkesboro NC 28697
336 658-4000

(G-7163)
LTX INC (PA)
1515 Industrial Dr NW (55901-0792)
PO Box 7119 (55903-7119)
PHONE..............................507 282-6715
Steve Lawrence, *CEO*
George C Wilson, *President*
Julie Brown, *Govt Rel Mgr*
Laurie Oehlke, *Office Mgr*
EMP: 120 **EST:** 1949
SQ FT: 6,400
SALES (corp-wide): 40M **Privately Held**
WEB: www.lawrencetrans.com
SIC: 4213 Long-distance refrigerated
trucking services

(G-7164)
MACKS LLC
Also Called: Stoneridge Management Co
401 6th St SW (55902-3223)
PHONE..............................507 288-2677
Myron Salz, *President*
EMP: 120 **EST:** 1959
SQ FT: 7,740
SALES (est): 10MM-24.9MM **Privately Held**
SIC: 8741 Management services

(G-7165)
MACY'S RETAIL HOLDINGS INC
901 Apache Mall (55902-2112)
PHONE..............................507 280-5400
Eric Afforacta, *Manager*
EMP: 50
SALES (est): 1MM-4.9MM **Publicly Held**
SIC: 4225 Warehousing & storage services
HQ: Macy's Retail Holdings Inc
7 W 7th St Ste 1100
Cincinnati OH 45202
513 579-7000

(G-7166)
**MADONNA MEADOWS OF
ROCHESTER**
3035 Salem Meadows Dr SW
(55902-2847)
PHONE..............................507 252-5400
FAX: 507 252-5500
Mark Cairns, *President*
Cheryl Saballa, *Controller*
EST: 2002 **Privately Held**
SIC: 8052 Intermediate care facility
PA: Benedictine Health System
503 E 3rd St Ste 400
Duluth MN 55805
218 786-2370

(G-7167)
**MADONNA TOWERS OF
ROCHESTER**
4001 19th Ave NW Apt 607 (55901-1952)
PHONE..............................507 288-3911
FAX: 507 288-0393
Barry J Halm, *President*
Mark Cairns, *Administrator*
Scott Weatherstone, *Info Tech Mgr*

Sheila Erickson, *Nursing Dir*
EMP: 170 **EST:** 1995
SALES (est): 5MM-9.9MM **Privately Held**
SIC: 8059 Nursing home
PA: Benedictine Health System
503 E 3rd St Ste 400
Duluth MN 55805
218 786-2370

(G-7168)
MAGIC MEDIA INC
1734 15th St NW (55901-0211)
PHONE..............................507 288-1866
Ray Kosis, *General Mgr*
Jay Sauber, *Branch Mgr*
Jenny Brostrom, *Manager*
Alexandra Spencel, *Administration*
EMP: 26
SALES (est): 1MM-4.9MM **Privately Held**
SIC: 7312 Billboard advertising service
PA: Magic Media Inc
420A S 1st St
Bangor PA 18013
610 588-6700

(G-7169)
MATHY CONSTRUCTION CO
Also Called: Rochester Sand & Gravel Div
4105 E River Rd NE (55906-3424)
PHONE..............................507 288-7447
FAX: 507 252-3477
William Fitzgerald, *Corp Secy*
Pat Peterson, *Vice Pres*
Robert Mahon, *Controller*
Suzanne Hidermann, *Director*
EMP: 70
SALES (est): 10MM-24.9MM **Privately Held**
SIC: 1611 Highway & street paving
contractor
PA: Mathy Construction Co
920 10th Ave N
Onalaska WI 54650
608 783-6411

(G-7170)
MAYO CLINIC
200 1st St SW Ste W15A (55905-0002)
PHONE..............................507 284-9077
FAX: 507 284-0538
Joe Butterfield, *Principal*
Melissa Jennings, *Corp Secy*
Robert M Carty, *Manager*
Janet Bartz, *Manager*
Ruth Hix, *Supervisor*
EMP: 50
SALES (est): 5MM-9.9MM **Privately Held**
SIC: 8011 Physicians' office & clinic
PA: Mayo Clinic
200 1st St SW
Rochester MN 55905
507 284-2511

(G-7171)
MAYO CLINIC
200 1st St SW (55905-0002)
PHONE..............................507 266-4808
Madeleine Lowry, *Med Doctor*
Collin Yennie, *Manager*
Alan Schilmoeller, *Administrator*
T J Sorenson, *Radiology*
EMP: 400
SALES (est): 25MM-49.9MM **Privately Held**
SIC: 8099 Medical services organization
PA: Mayo Clinic
200 1st St SW
Rochester MN 55905
507 284-2511

(G-7172)
**MAYO CLINIC EMPLOYEES
CREDIT**
130 23rd Ave SW (55902-0994)
PHONE..............................507 535-1460
Kent Graff, *President*
Kenneth Blazing, *Vice Pres*
Sue Palen, *Mfg Staff*
Mary Andre, *Human Res Mgr*
Elaine May, *Mktg Dir*
EMP: 36 **EST:** 1931
SQ FT: 1,000
SALES (est): 5MM-9.9MM **Privately Held**
SIC: 6062 State chartered credit union

(G-7173)
MAYO CLINIC ROCHESTER
10 3rd Ave NW Fl 3 (55901-2890)
PHONE..............................507 284-5135
Margret Phieffer, *Principal*
EMP: 100
SALES (est): 10MM-24.9MM **Privately Held**
SIC: 8011 Obstetrician office
PA: Mayo Clinic
200 1st St SW
Rochester MN 55905
507 284-2511

(G-7174)
**MAYO FOUNDATION FOR
MEDICAL**
200 1st St SW (55905-0001)
PHONE..............................507 284-2511
FAX: 507 284-1172
Denis Cortese, *President*
Shirley Weis, *Vice Chairman*
Colan Yennie, *Facilities Mgr*
Kurt Naumann, *Engineer*
Joel Felmlee, *Med Doctor*
▲ **EMP:** 29186 **EST:** 1984
SALES (est): 1B-9.9B **Privately Held**
SIC: 8741 Hospital management services
PA: Mayo Clinic
200 1st St SW
Rochester MN 55905
507 284-2511

(G-7175)
**MAYO MANAGEMENT SERVICES
INC**
4001 41st St NW (55901-8901)
PHONE..............................507 538-5508
Paula Menkosky, *President*
Thomas Ferraro, *COO*
Mark Matthias, *CFO*
Bruce Plante, *Finance Dir*
Steven Sobczak, *Manager*
EMP: 200 **EST:** 1986
SALES (est): 10MM-24.9MM **Privately Held**
SIC: 8741 Management services
PA: Mayo Clinic
200 1st St SW
Rochester MN 55905
507 284-2511

(G-7176)
MAYO MIDAIR
1216 2nd St SW (55902-1906)
PHONE..............................507 255-2808
Russell A Keting, *Accountant*
Joseph Akornor MD, *Med Doctor*
Andrea S Burch MD, *Med Doctor*
Margaret A Moutvic MD, *Med Doctor*
Annie Dashow, *Manager*
EMP: 40
SALES (est): 1MM-4.9MM **Privately Held**
WEB: www.mayomedicaltransport.com
SIC: 8062 4119 4522 Medical hospital; air
ambulance services; ambulance service

(G-7177)
MAYOWOOD MANSION TOURS
1195 W Circle Dr (55902-6619)
PHONE..............................507 282-9447
Thomas Moskalik, *Editor*
John Hunciker, *Director*
Lillian Sneve, *Bd of Directors*
EMP: 25 **EST:** 1965
SALES (est): 1MM-4.9MM **Privately Held**
SIC: 8412 Museum

(G-7178)
MC BE CO
Also Called: Spring Valley Health Mart
1814 15th St NW (55901-0214)
PO Box 5877 (55903-5877)
PHONE..............................507 289-1666
C D McDonough, *President*
Lowell Janssen, *Corp Secy*
Scott Berndt, *Vice Pres*
Irv Nehring, *CFO*
Vern Johnson, *Treasurer*
EST: 1914 **Privately Held**
WEB: www.weberjudd.com

SIC: 7384 Drug store; greeting card shop;
non-prescription medicine proprietary store;
retail gift shop; photofinishing laboratory
PA: Weber & Judd Co
1814 15th St NW
Rochester MN 55901
507 289-6047

(G-7179)
MCGHIE & BETTS INC
1648 3rd Ave SE (55904-7920)
PHONE..............................507 289-3919
FAX: 507 289-7333
William E Tointon, *President*
Mark Severtson, *Corp Secy*
David Morrill, *Vice Pres*
Douglas N Betts, *Vice Pres*
EMP: 37 **EST:** 1946
SQ FT: 13,560
SALES (est): 1MM-4.9MM **Privately Held**
WEB: www.mbi-nf.com
SIC: 8713 8711 8748 Surveying service;
environmental consultant; engineering
services

(G-7180)
MCGLADREY & PULLEN, LLP
310 S Broadway Ste 300 (55904-6547)
PHONE..............................507 288-6476
FAX: 507 288-5448
Dave Oeth, *Managing Prtnr*
Janet Peters, *Manager*
Brad O'Connor, *Info Tech Mgr*
Laura Nelson, *Admin Asst*
EMP: 35
SALES (est): 1MM-4.9MM **Privately Held**
SIC: 8721 Certified public accountant
services
PA: McGladrey & Pullen, LLP
3600 Amercn Blvd W # 300
Minneapolis MN 55431
952 921-7700

(G-7181)
**MEADOW LAKES GOLF CLUB
LLC**
70 45th Ave SW (55902-8770)
PHONE..............................507 285-1190
FAX: 507 282-8241
Greg Wenczl, *President*
Paul Pehler, *President*
Greg Wentzell, *Vice Pres*
EMP: 25 **EST:** 1997
SALES (est): 1MM-4.9MM **Privately Held**
SIC: 7992 7299 7999 Public golf course;
eating place; banquet hall facility; golf
services & professionals

(G-7182)
MERIT CONTRACTING INC
4615 Highway 63 N (55906-3900)
PHONE..............................507 281-4317
FAX: 507 281-4689
Ed Stanley, *President*
Mark Stanley, *Vice Pres*
Debbie Schuck, *Office Mgr*
EMP: 54 **EST:** 1981
SQ FT: 2,500
SALES (est): 5MM-9.9MM **Privately Held**
WEB: www.meritquality.com
SIC: 1761 1799 Roofing contractor;
construction caulking contractor

(G-7183)
**MIDSTATES RETREADING &
WHSLE**
6233 Bandel Rd NW (55901-8757)
PO Box 6488 (55903-6488)
PHONE..............................507 288-7752
FAX: 507 288-6502
Timothy Gallagher, *President*
Mary Gallagher, *Vice Pres*
EMP: 48 **EST:** 1981
SQ FT: 48,000
SALES (est): 5MM-9.9MM **Privately Held**
SIC: 7534 5014 Automotive tire rebuilding &
retreading service; wholesales truck tires &
tubes; wholesales automotive tires & tubes

(PA)=Parent Co (HQ)=Headquarters (DH)=Div Headquarters
✿ = New business established in last 2 years

2011 Harris Minnesota
Services Directory

© Harris InfoSource 1-866-281-6415
313

(G-7184)

MIDWEST OF ROCHESTER INC (PA)

Also Called: Ramada Hotel & Conference Ctr
1517 16th St SW (55902-1075)
PHONE...........................507 289-8866
Tom Ashbaugh, *General Mgr*
Terri Penz, *General Mgr*
Deb Nordine, *Manager*
EMP: 100 EST: 1994
SALES (corp-wide): 3M Privately Held
WEB: www.ramadarochester.com
SIC: 7011 7299 Traveler accommodations;
eating place; banquet hall facility

(G-7185)

MIDWEST OF ROCHESTER INC

Also Called: Best Western
1517 16th St SW (55902-1075)
PHONE...........................507 289-8866
FAX: 507 292-0000
Terri Penz, *General Mgr*
William Seitl, *Manager*
EMP: 50
SALES (est): 1MM-4.9MM Privately Held
WEB: www.ramadarochester.com
SIC: 7011 Traveler accommodations
PA: Midwest of Rochester Inc
1517 16th St SW
Rochester MN 55902
507 289-8866

(G-7186)

MIDWEST SPECIALIZED TRANS

4515 Highway 63 N (55906-8330)
PO Box 6418 (55903-6418)
PHONE...........................507 288-5649
FAX: 507 288-6859
Allen I Koenig, *President*
Anne Koenig, *Vice Pres*
Katherine Stevens, *Manager*
EMP: 35 EST: 1967
SQ FT: 4,000
SALES (est): 1MM-4.9MM Privately Held
WEB: www.midspec.com
SIC: 4213 Over the road trucking; heavy
machinery transportation services

(G-7187)

MINNESOTA FIRST CREDIT

Also Called: Loan & Thrift Co of Rochester
1932 Viking Dr NW (55901-2460)
PO Box 6387 (55903-6387)
PHONE...........................507 289-0411
FAX: 507 346-7318
Wayne Wolesky, *President*
Sunny Dorn, *Vice Pres*
Judy Wolesky, *Vice Pres*
Shannon Wolesky, *Vice Pres*
Erik Christenson, *Loan Officer*
EST: 1956 Privately Held
SIC: 6141 Personal credit institution

(G-7188)

MPLS HOTEL MANAGEMENT LTD

150 S Broadway (55904-6507)
PHONE...........................507 281-8000
FAX: 507 284-4280
Robert Thimjon, *Partner*
Kevin Molloy, *General Mgr*
Michael Smith, *Opers Staff*
Bruce Putzier, *Chief Engr*
Debra Knox, *Sales Staff*
EMP: 40
SALES (est): 1MM-4.9MM Privately Held
SIC: 7011 Traveler accommodations

(G-7189)

NELSON CO'S

2829 43rd St NW (55901-5897)
PHONE...........................507 289-6789
FAX: 507 289-6375
Gerald Nelson, *President*
EMP: 30
SALES (est): 5MM-9.9MM Privately Held
WEB: www.thebrittanys.com
SIC: 6531 Real estate services
PA: Nelson Co's
6532 Clarkia Dr NW
Rochester MN 55901
507 289-6789

(G-7190)

NORTH BEVERAGE LLC

2222 32nd Ave NW (55901-8322)
PHONE...........................507 282-5462
FAX: 507 288-1544
Paul Jacobus, *Principal*
Terrance North, *Principal*
EMP: 32 EST: 2000
SALES (est): 10MM-24.9MM Privately Held
SIC: 5181 Wholesales beer & other
fermented malt liquors

(G-7191)

NORTHERN VALLEY ANIMAL CLINIC

3309 Alberta Dr NE (55906-3988)
PHONE...........................507 282-0867
FAX: 507 282-6839
Kevin Nigon, *Partner*
Michael Herman, *Partner*
James Bennett, *Partner*
EST: 1981 Privately Held
SIC: 0741 0742 0752 Livestock animal
hospital; animal hospital services; kennel
boarding services

(G-7192)

NORTHWEST AIRLINES INC

Rochester Municipal Arprt (55902)
PHONE...........................507 282-9425
Barry Hoeppner, *Manager*
EMP: 30
SALES (est): 5MM-9.9MM Publicly Held
WEB: www.nwairlines.com
SIC: 4512 Passenger airline services
HQ: Northwest Airlines Inc
7500 Airline Dr
Minneapolis MN 55450
612 726-2111

(G-7193)

NORTHWEST DENTAL GROUP OF

1615 14th St NW (55901-0257)
PHONE...........................507 282-1271
Steven Sperling DDS, *President*
Katie K Post, *Corp Secy*
Tammi Rushing, *Manager*
EMP: 37 EST: 1964
SALES (est): 1MM-4.9MM Privately Held
SIC: 8021 Dental office

(G-7194)

OLMSTED MEDICAL CENTER

1650 4th St SE (55904-4717)
PHONE...........................507 529-6600
FAX: 507 287-2779
Kevin Pitzer, *Principal*
Donna Shanahan, *Business Mgr*
Thomas J Erbach, *Ch of Surgery*
James A Hoffmann, *Ch OB/GYN*
Vega S Durga, *Ch Pathology*
EMP: 950
SALES (est): 50MM-99.9MM Privately Held
SIC: 8062 8011 Medical hospital; plastic
surgeon office
PA: Olmsted Medical Center
210 9th St SE
Rochester MN 55904
507 288-3443

(G-7195)

OLMSTED MEDICAL CENTER (PA)

210 9th St SE (55904-6425)
PHONE...........................507 288-3443
FAX: 507 287-2777
Roy Yawn, *President*
Michael Dietz, *Member*
Jeanne M Mohler, *Corp Secy*
Marge Klee, *Corp Secy*
Ryan Bjeske, *Opers Mgr*
EMP: 281 EST: 1949
SQ FT: 66,000
SALES (corp-wide): 289.84K Privately
Held
SIC: 8062 Medical hospital

(G-7196)

OLMSTED MEDICAL CENTER

3611 Salem Rd SW (55902-6677)
PO Box 882 (55903-0882)
PHONE...........................507 288-8880
George Hemenway, *President*
EMP: 50
SALES (est): 1MM-4.9MM Privately Held
SIC: 8322 Individual & family social services

(G-7197)

OLMSTED NATIONAL BANK INC

120 Elton Hills Dr NW (55901-3555)
PHONE...........................507 280-0028
Paula Kasey, *Principal*
Diana Taylor, *Vice Pres*
Patrick Stallman, *Vice Pres*
Terry Sorenson, *Vice Pres*
Jennifer Busch, *Mfg Staff*
Privately Held
SIC: 6021 National commercial bank
PA: Olmsted National Bank Inc
975 34th Ave NW
Rochester MN 55901
507 280-0621

(G-7198)

OMNIA FAMILY SERVICES

1635 Greenview Dr SW (55902-4306)
PHONE...........................507 287-2300
FAX: 507 287-2491
Teri Eide, *Office Mgr*
Doug Brink, *Exec Dir*
EMP: 38 EST: 1987
SALES (est): 1MM-4.9MM Privately Held
SIC: 8361 Halfway home for delinquents &
offenders; halfway group home for persons
with social or personal problems

(G-7199)

PACE ELECTRONICS INC

3582 Technology Dr NW (55901-7687)
PO Box 6937 (55903-6937)
PHONE...........................507 288-1853
FAX: 507 288-0831
Patrick J Deutsch, *President*
Sandy Regenier, *Corp Secy*
Michael Berg, *Senior VP*
Michael Anderson, *Vice Pres*
Sam Schell, *Vice Pres*
▲ EMP: 40 EST: 1972
SQ FT: 15,000
SALES (est): 25MM-49.9MM Privately Held
WEB: www.pacemso.com
SIC: 5065 Wholesales electronic parts

(G-7200)

PALMER SODERBERG INC

3730 40th Ave NW (55901-1772)
PO Box 7101 (55903-7101)
PHONE...........................507 288-4213
FAX: 507 288-8208
Daniel Soderberg, *President*
EMP: 50 EST: 1958
SALES (est): 1MM-4.9MM Privately Held
WEB: www.palmersoderberg.com
SIC: 1742 1743 Drywall contractor; ceramic
tile installation service

(G-7201)

PEOPLES COOPERATIVE SERVICES

3935 Highway 14 E (55904-7802)
PO Box 339 (55903-0339)
PHONE...........................507 288-4004
FAX: 507 288-9438
Russell Halgerson, *Engineer*
Rick Garmers, *Engineer*
Keith Dickman, *Manager*
Frank Welter, *Manager*
EMP: 49 EST: 1936
SQ FT: 54,000
SALES (est): 10MM-24.9MM Privately Held
WEB: www.peoplesrec.com
SIC: 4911 Electric power distribution service

(G-7202)

PEPSI COLA BOTTLING CO OF

Also Called: Pepsico
1307 Valleyhigh Dr NW (55901-0213)
PHONE...........................507 288-3772
FAX: 507 288-5073
Norman Gillette Jr, *Ch of Bd*

Donald Gillette, *General Mgr*
Jean Vinger, *Corp Secy*
Norma J Vinger, *Corp Secy*
Mike Nelson, *Warehouse Mgr*
EMP: 106 EST: 1954
SQ FT: 125,000
SALES (est): 25MM-49.9MM Privately Held
SIC: 5149 Manufactures soft drinks;
wholesales groceries

(G-7203)

PHARMACEUTICAL SPECIALTIES INC

1620 Industrial Dr NW (55901-0732)
PO Box 6298 (55903-6298)
PHONE...........................507 288-8500
FAX: 507 288-7603
Conrad O Thompson, *President*
Edward S Mansfield, *Treasurer*
Brian Leary, *Marketing Staff*
Lori Blake, *Director*
EMP: 35 EST: 1974
SQ FT: 45,000
SALES (est): 10MM-24.9MM Privately Held
WEB: www.psico.com
SIC: 7231 Manufactures pharmaceutical
preparations; manufactures cosmetics &
toiletries; beauty salon

(G-7204)

PIEPHO MOVING & STORAGE INC

Also Called: Rochester Transfer & Storage
4121 Hwy 14 W (55901-6609)
PHONE...........................507 289-4515
Lawrence Piepho, *Branch Mgr*
EMP: 40
SALES (est): 1MM-4.9MM Privately Held
WEB: www.piepho.com
SIC: 4214 4213 Local trucking with storage;
contract haulers
PA: Piepho Moving & Storage Inc
1300 Oak Forest Dr
Onalaska WI 54650
608 783-3400

(G-7205)

PIEPHO MOVING & STORAGE INC

Also Called: Rochester Transfer & Storage
4121 Hwy 14 W (55901-6609)
PHONE...........................507 289-4515
Lawrence Piepho, *Manager*
EMP: 40
SALES (est): 1MM-4.9MM Privately Held
WEB: www.piepho.com
SIC: 4214 Local trucking with storage
PA: Piepho Moving & Storage Inc
1300 Oak Forest Dr
Onalaska WI 54650
608 783-3400

(G-7206)

POLLUTION CONTROL AGENCY, MN

Also Called: Rochester Office
18 Woodlake Dr SE (55904-5506)
PHONE...........................507 285-7343
FAX: 507 280-5513
Leo Raudys, *Manager*
EMP: 35
SALES (est): 5MM-9.9MM Privately Held
WEB: www.state.mn.us
SIC: 4953 Refuse systems services; air,
water & solid waste programs administration
services; state government air, water & solid
waste management program administration
DH: Pollution Control Agency, MN
520 Lafayette Rd N
Saint Paul MN 55155
651 296-6300

(G-7207)

POMPEII PAINTING INC

29 9th Ave NE (55906-4619)
PO Box 9107 (55903-9107)
PHONE...........................507 288-8494
FAX: 507 288-8469
Thomas J Pompeii, *President*
Anthony M Joseph, *Vice Pres*
EMP: 62 EST: 1993
SQ FT: 10,000
SALES (est): 1MM-4.9MM Privately Held
WEB: www.pompeiipainting.com

www.HarrisInfo.com
314

2011 Harris Minnesota
Services Directory

▲=Import ▼=Export
◆=Import/Export

SIC: **1721** Exterior commercial painting contractor; interior commercial painting contractor

(G-7208)
POSSABILITIES
1808 3rd Ave SE Ste 5 (55904-7948)
PHONE..............................507 281-6116
John Flanders, *President*
EMP: 70 **EST:** 1961
SALES (est): 1MM-4.9MM **Privately Held**
SIC: 8351 Child day care service

(G-7209)
POSSABILITIES OF SOUTHERN MN
1808 3rd Ave SE (55904-7948)
PHONE..............................507 287-7100
FAX: 507 281-6117
Paul Pedersen, *Sales Executive*
John Flanders, *Director*
Paul Peterson, *Director*
EMP: 75 **EST:** 1966
SALES (est): 5MM-9.9MM **Privately Held**
SIC: 8093 Outpatient rehabilitation treatment center

(G-7210)
PRAIRIE RIVER HOME CARE INC
1907 2nd St SW (55902-0822)
PHONE..............................507 252-9844
Ingrid Oehske, *General Mgr*
Ingrid Oehlke, *Branch Mgr*
Becky Anderson, *Manager*
EMP: 200
SALES (est): 5MM-9.9MM **Privately Held**
WEB: www.prhomecare.com
SIC: 8082 Home health care services
PA: Prairie River Home Care Inc
4432 Highway 25 SE
Buffalo MN 55313
507 252-9844

(G-7211)
PRAIRIE SMOKE
3011 Nelson Ct SE (55904-5969)
PHONE..............................507 292-0063
Jaime Edwards, *Member*
EMP: 40 **EST:** 2004 **Privately Held**
WEB: www.prairiesmoke.com
SIC: 8731 Natural resource research services

(G-7212)
PROFESSIONAL HOSPITALITY LLC
Also Called: Country Suites By Carlson
77 Woodlake Dr SE (55904-5509)
PHONE..............................507 287-6758
Travis Whittle, *General Mgr*
Terri Fiebke, *Vice Pres*
Bryan Buck, *Manager*
Tom Ashbaugh, *Manager*
Michelle Steffl, *Manager*
EMP: 30
SALES (est): 1MM-4.9MM **Privately Held**
WEB: www.prohospitality.com
SIC: 7011 Traveler accommodations
PA: Professional Hospitality LLC
2418 Crossroads Dr Ste 38
Madison WI 53718
608 244-0300

(G-7213)
PRUDENTIAL INSURANCE CO OF
140 Elton Hills Ln NW (55901-3567)
PHONE..............................507 281-4200
FAX: 507 285-1441
Dennis G Dee Tweed, *Manager*
EMP: 50
SALES (est): 25MM-49.9MM **Publicly Held**
WEB: www.prudential.com
SIC: 6311 Life insurance carrier
HQ: Prudential Insurance Co of
751 Broad St
Newark NJ 07102
973 802-6000

(G-7214)
QUALITY BUILDING MAINTENANCE
2002 14th St NW (55901-0711)
PHONE..............................507 289-0603
FAX: 507 289-0603
Tayte Peterson, *President*
Vanessa Peterson, *Corp Secy*
EMP: 94 **EST:** 1990
SQ FT: 17,000
SALES (est): 1MM-4.9MM **Privately Held**
SIC: 7349 Building cleaning & maintenance services

(G-7215)
R&S TRANSPORT INC
1725 Highway 14 E (55904-3118)
PHONE..............................507 289-5080
FAX: 507 289-9208
Steve Elwood, *President*
Robert P Elwood, *Co-Owner*
Dave Gathje, *Info Tech Mgr*
EMP: 75
SALES (est): 5MM-9.9MM **Privately Held**
WEB: www.mackmn.com
SIC: 4111 Passenger transit system

(G-7216)
RACE AUTOMOTIVE OF ROCHESTER
Also Called: Automotive Procare
457 16th Ave NW (55901-1808)
PHONE..............................507 282-5200
FAX: 507 536-0151
John Miller, *President*
EMP: 25 **EST:** 2002
SALES (est): 1MM-4.9MM **Privately Held**
SIC: 7539 Automotive repair services

(G-7217)
RAYMOND MANAGEMENT CO INC
Also Called: Hampton Inn
1755 S Broadway (55904-7960)
PHONE..............................507 287-9050
FAX: 507 287-9139
Dan Nelson, *Branch Mgr*
EMP: 30
SALES (est): 1MM-4.9MM **Privately Held**
SIC: 7011 7991 Traveler accommodations; physical fitness center
PA: Raymond Management Co Inc
8333 Greenway Blvd # 200
Middleton WI 53562
608 833-4100

(G-7218)
RCC LIQUIDATING CORP
710 Apache Mall (55902-2110)
PHONE..............................507 281-0313
FAX: 507 289-8998
Karen Bolin, *Manager*
EMP: 25
SALES (est): 1MM-4.9MM **Privately Held**
SIC: 7384 Retails cameras; retails video cameras & accessories; retails photographic supplies; film processing & finishing laboratory

(G-7219)
RE MAX OF ROCHESTER
4600 18th Ave NW (55901-0400)
PHONE..............................507 287-7735
Bill Towey, *Principal*
EMP: 38 **EST:** 1991
SALES (est): 5MM-9.9MM **Privately Held**
WEB: www.livinginrochester.com
SIC: 6531 Residential real estate agency

(G-7220)
REICHEL FOODS INC
3706 Enterprise Dr SW (55902-1257)
PHONE..............................507 289-7264
Craig A Reichel, *CEO*
Bruce Hady, *Plant Mgr*
Alfonso Cerda, *Opers Staff*
Thomas J Wiechmann, *CFO*
Kristi Gordon, *Persnl Mgr*
EMP: 250 **EST:** 1995
SQ FT: 25,000
SALES (est): 50MM-99.9MM **Privately Held**
WEB: www.reichelfoods.com

SIC: **0723** Meat packing plant; eating place; post harvest crop activities; meat processing

(G-7221)
REM INC
1905 3rd Ave SE Ste B (55904-7935)
PHONE..............................507 287-6824
FAX: 507 282-9563
Jennifer Walsh, *Exec Dir*
Pat Masyga, *Exec Dir*
Richardson Betty, *Exec Dir*
John Gamble, *Director*
EMP: 150
SALES (est): 5MM-9.9MM **Privately Held**
SIC: 8063 8361 Mental hospital; residential care facility

(G-7222)
REM RIVERBLUFF INC
2509 55th St NW (55901-0190)
PHONE..............................507 281-1105
FAX: 507 281-1137
Jane Briggs, *Sales Staff*
Jane Coperski-Briggs, *Director*
EMP: 50 **EST:** 1988
SALES (est): 1MM-4.9MM **Privately Held**
SIC: 8361 8059 Residential care facility; convalescent home

(G-7223)
RGIS LLC
1530 Greenview Dr SW S20 (55902-4286)
PHONE..............................507 281-7665
Chris House, *Manager*
EMP: 95
SALES (est): 5MM-9.9MM **Privately Held**
WEB: www.rgisinv.com
SIC: 7389 Inventory computing service
HQ: Rgis LLC
2000 Taylor Rd
Auburn Hills MI 48326
248 651-2511

(G-7224)
RICHARD HAWKINS
Also Called: D&R Vending
2207 7th St NW (55901-0206)
PHONE..............................507 282-6080
Richard Hawkins, *Owner*
EMP: 50 **EST:** 2003
SQ FT: 25,000
SALES (est): 10MM-24.9MM **Privately Held**
WEB: www.dnrstar.com
SIC: 5046 Wholesales coin-operated vending machines
PA: D & R Star Inc
2207 7th St NW
Rochester MN 55901
507 282-6080

(G-7225)
RICK GENTLING
4600 18th Ave NW (55901-0400)
PHONE..............................507 287-7714
Rick Gentling, *President*
EMP: 40 **EST:** 1978
SALES (est): 5MM-9.9MM **Privately Held**
SIC: 6531 Real estate services

(G-7226)
ROBERT B DIASIO ✪
200 1st St SW GONDA19 (55905-0001)
PHONE..............................507 284-3977
Robert B Diasio, *Owner*
EMP: 99 **EST:** 2008
SALES (est): 5MM-9.9MM **Privately Held**
SIC: 8062 Medical hospital

(G-7227)
ROCCO ALTOBELLI INC
Also Called: Altobelli Hairstyle
400 S Broadway Ste 204 (55904-6498)
PHONE..............................507 288-8582
FAX: 507 288-0807
Jodi Rippentrop, *Persnl Mgr*
Nicole Mulder, *Manager*
Jennifer Hicks, *Manager*
EMP: 30
SALES (est): 500-999K **Privately Held**
WEB: www.roccoaltobelli.com

SIC: **7231** Beauty salon
PA: Rocco Altobelli Inc
14301 W Burnsville Pkwy
Burnsville MN 55306
952 707-1900

(G-7228)
ROCHESTER ATHLETIC CLUB INC
3100 19th St NW (55901-6606)
PO Box 6669 (55903-6669)
PHONE..............................507 282-6000
Jack Remick, *President*
Greg Lappin, *General Mgr*
Matthew Remick, *Corp Secy*
Jeff Brown, *Treasurer*
EMP: 275 **EST:** 1993
SQ FT: 260,000
SALES (est): 5MM-9.9MM **Privately Held**
WEB: www.rochesterathleticclub.com
SIC: 7997 7991 Membership recreation club; physical fitness center

(G-7229)
ROCHESTER CITY DELIVERY INC
Also Called: Belco Express
3101 40th Ave NW (55901-1742)
PHONE..............................507 289-2774
Laverne Kothenbeutel, *President*
Belva Kothenbeutel, *Corp Secy*
Joann Keefe, *Office Mgr*
Irv Keefe, *Office Mgr*
EMP: 42 **EST:** 1923
SQ FT: 30,000
SALES (est): 1MM-4.9MM **Privately Held**
WEB: www.rochestercitydelivery.com
SIC: 4212 Delivery services by vehicle; local furniture moving services without storage

(G-7230)
ROCHESTER CITY LINE CO
1825 N Broadway (55906-4101)
PHONE..............................507 288-4353
FAX: 507 288-9318
George C Holter, *President*
Marilyn Holter, *Corp Secy*
Hugh Fendry, *Human Res Mgr*
Dan Holter, *Manager*
Joe Jacobson, *Administrator*
EMP: 50 **EST:** 1966
SQ FT: 27,000
SALES (est): 1MM-4.9MM **Privately Held**
WEB: www.rochestercitylines.com
SIC: 4111 4131 4142 Bus line operations; bus transit system; long-distance bus charter service

(G-7231)
ROCHESTER FITNESS INC
1112 7th St NW (55901-1732)
PHONE..............................507 282-4445
FAX: 507 282-5016
David Skinner, *President*
Terri Bonner, *VP Finance*
EMP: 50 **EST:** 1980
SQ FT: 24,000
SALES (est): 1MM-4.9MM **Privately Held**
WEB: www.northgatehc.com
SIC: 7991 8049 Health club; dieticians' office

(G-7232)
ROCHESTER GOLF & COUNTRY CLUB
3100 Country Club Rd SW (55902-6661)
PHONE..............................507 282-2708
FAX: 507 536-4490
Jim Orke, *President*
Carol Balm, *Finance Mgr*
Eileen O'Oonoghue, *Manager*
Michael Vento, *Manager*
Karla Baillie, *Exec Dir*
EMP: 50 **EST:** 1917
SQ FT: 38,000
SALES (est): 1MM-4.9MM **Privately Held**
WEB: www.rgcc.org
SIC: 7997 Country club; bar; full service American restaurant

(PA)=Parent Co (HQ)=Headquarters (DH)=Div Headquarters
✪ = New business established in last 2 years
2011 Harris Minnesota
Services Directory
© Harris InfoSource 1-866-281-6415
315

GEOGRAPHIC

(G-7233)
ROCHESTER HEALTH & REHAB WEST
2215 Hwy 52 N (55901-7657)
PHONE..................507 288-1818
FAX: 507 288-5502
Vickie Munson, *Human Res Mgr*
Kori Peterson, *Marketing Mgr*
Sylvia Matheson, *Branch Mgr*
Carrie Huebert, *Administrator*
Marliss Dykstra, *Recruiter*
EMP: 70 EST: 1959
SALES (est): 1MM-4.9MM **Privately Held**
WEB: www.beverlynet.com
SIC: 8059 8051 Retirement community with nursing; skilled nursing care facility
DH: Beverly Enterprises Inc
    1000 Fianna Way
    Fort Smith AR 72919
    479 201-2000

(G-7234)
ROCHESTER JUVENILE HOCKEY
2625 Hwy 14 W Ste AB (55901-7597)
PO Box 237 (55903-0237)
PHONE..................507 280-6345
FAX: 507 280-0531
Joan Cousino, *Manager*
EMP: 26 EST: 1992 **Privately Held**
SIC: 8699 Athletic organization

(G-7235)
ROCHESTER MEATS INC (PA)
1825 7th St NW (55901-0270)
PHONE..................507 289-0701
FAX: 507 289-1864
James R Hanson, *President*
Wayne Courtney, *Vice Pres*
Neal Karels, *VP Opers-Prdtn-*
Bob Jacobson, *Engineer*
Craig Allen, *CFO*
EMP: 240 EST: 1971
SQ FT: 53,000 **Privately Held**
WEB: www.rochestermeat.com
SIC: 5147 Wholesales meat & meat products; meat processing

(G-7236)
ROCHESTER METHODIST HOSPITAL
1216 2nd St SW (55902-1906)
PHONE..................507 255-5123
Glenn Forbes, *President*
EMP: 1400 EST: 1968
SALES (est): 100MM-499.9MM **Privately Held**
SIC: 8062 Hospital with AMA approved residency
PA: Mayo Clinic
    200 1st St SW
    Rochester MN 55905
    507 284-2511

(G-7237)
ROCHESTER METHODIST HOSPITAL
201 W Center St (55902-3003)
PHONE..................507 266-7890
FAX: 507 266-7891
Bradley D Schmidt, *Principal*
Craig Smoldt, *Corp Secy*
Paula J Santrach, *Ch Pathology*
Bernard F King, *Ch Radiology*
Dave Senjem, *Safety Dir*
EST: 1953 **Privately Held**
SIC: 8011 8062 8071 8733 Medical center; medical research organization; medical hospital; medical laboratory
PA: Mayo Clinic
    200 1st St SW
    Rochester MN 55905
    507 284-2511

(G-7238)
ROCHESTER PARKING RAMPS
14 2nd St SE (55904-3736)
PHONE..................507 282-0558
Bob Royston, *Owner*
Wayne Lowe, *Manager*
EMP: 38 EST: 1994
SALES (est): 1MM-4.9MM **Privately Held**
SIC: 7521 Parking garage

(G-7239)
ROCHESTER PLUMBING & HEATING
2840 Wilser Rd NW (55901-5400)
PO Box 7125 (55903-7125)
PHONE..................507 289-1613
Gregory T Nesler, *President*
Scott Wiederhoeft, *Manager*
Sheryl Wegner, *Supervisor*
Rose Loftus, *Director*
EMP: 82 EST: 1921
SQ FT: 8,000
SALES (est): 5MM-9.9MM **Privately Held**
SIC: 1711 Plumbing service; heating & air conditioning contractor

(G-7240)
ROCHESTER SERVICE CO INC
2510 Schuster Ln NW (55901-0749)
PHONE..................507 281-5333
Kraig Durst, *President*
Scott Lamplend, *Vice Pres*
Lorie Washburn, *Manager*
EMP: 30 EST: 2002
SALES (est): 1MM-4.9MM **Privately Held**
SIC: 7389 Personal service agents

(G-7241)
ROCKWOOD RETAINING WALLS INC
325 Alliance Pl NE (55906-3975)
PHONE..................507 529-2871
FAX: 507 529-2879
Raymond Price, *President*
Jerry Price, *Vice Pres*
Gerald Price, *VP Systems*
EMP: 36 EST: 1991
SQ FT: 8,000
SALES (est): 1MM-4.9MM **Privately Held**
SIC: 1741 Retaining wall construction

(G-7242)
RSM MCGLADREY INC
310 S Broadway Ste 300 (55904-6547)
PHONE..................507 288-5363
Laura Nelson, *Office Mgr*
David Oeth, *Manager*
Sheryl Iverson, *Info Tech Mgr*
EMP: 60
SALES (est): 5MM-9.9MM **Publicly Held**
WEB: www.hrblock.com
SIC: 8742 6282 7291 7374 8721 Management consulting services; accounting, auditing & bookkeeping services; data processing & preparation services; financial investment advice service; tax return preparation services
DH: RSM McGladrey Inc
    3600 American Blvd W Fl 3
    Minneapolis MN 55431
    952 921-7700

(G-7243)
S & S MOVING & STORAGE INC
6101 Bandel Rd NW (55901-8756)
PHONE..................507 289-0779
FAX: 507 289-8027
David Senst, *President*
Thomas Senst, *Vice Pres*
EMP: 30 EST: 1950
SQ FT: 40,000
SALES (est): 1MM-4.9MM **Privately Held**
SIC: 4213 4214 Long-distance moving services; local moving service & storage

(G-7244)
S P S S INC
Also Called: Showcase
4115 Hwy 52 N Ste 300 (55901)
PHONE..................507 287-2800
Jack Noonan, *President*
Jay Fischer, *Purchasing*
Jason Heggy, *Engineer*
Alex Cragoe, *Engineer*
Larry Jasperson, *Senior Engr*
EMP: 100
SALES (est): 10MM-24.9MM **Publicly Held**
WEB: www.spss.com
SIC: 7372 Software publisher
HQ: SPSS Inc
    233 S Wacker Dr Ste 1100
    Chicago IL 60606
    312 651-3000

(G-7245)
SAFE HAVEN PET RESCUE
1001 1/2 1st Ave SE (55904-6411)
PO Box 733 (55903-0733)
PHONE..................507 529-4079
Steve Fuller, *Member*
Donna Fisher, *Director*
EMP: 30 EST: 1998
SALES (est): 1MM-4.9MM **Privately Held**
SIC: 8699 Retails pets & pet supplies; animal humane society

(G-7246)
SAINT MARYS HOSPITAL OF
1216 2nd St SW (55902-1906)
PHONE..................507 255-5123
Robert R Waller MD, *Owner*
Phil Johnson, *Facilities Dir*
Eleanor V Roekel, *Facilities Mgr*
Kathy Zarling, *Chief Mktg Ofcr*
Lori Ehlenfeldt, *Manager*
EMP: 3250 EST: 1968
SALES (est): 100MM-499.9MM **Privately Held**
SIC: 8062 Medical hospital
PA: Mayo Clinic
    200 1st St SW
    Rochester MN 55905
    507 284-2511

(G-7247)
SARGENT'S LANDSCAPE NURSERY
7955 18th Ave NW (55901-8841)
PHONE..................507 289-0022
FAX: 507 289-7045
Forrest Sargent, *President*
Faye Sargent, *Treasurer*
Scott Moon, *Manager*
Nina Sargent, *Manager*
Jeff Rosburg, *Manager*
EMP: 25 EST: 1971
SQ FT: 8,200 **Privately Held**
WEB: www.sargentsgardens.com
SIC: 0181 0782 Nursery stock production; flower farming; florist; retail nursery & garden center; landscaping services

(G-7248)
SCHOTT DISTRIBUTING CO INC
6735 Highway 14 E (55904-8679)
PHONE..................507 289-3555
FAX: 507 289-8479
Thomas Schott, *President*
Mary K Peshon, *Corp Secy*
Michael Schott, *Vice Pres*
Bernard Schott, *Vice Pres*
▲ EMP: 50 EST: 1937
SALES (est): 10MM-24.9MM **Privately Held**
SIC: 5181 5145 Wholesales beer & other fermented malt liquors; wholesales snack foods

(G-7249)
SEASONS HOSPICE
5650 Weatherhill Rd SW (55902-8858)
PHONE..................507 285-1930
FAX: 507 288-7251
Pam Schaid, *Administrator*
Pattie Nietz, *Admin Asst*
EMP: 45 EST: 1995
SALES (est): 1MM-4.9MM **Privately Held**
WEB: www.seasonshospice.org
SIC: 8361 Geriatric residential care

(G-7250)
SEMCIL LIVING INC
2720 Broadway Ave N (55906-3980)
PHONE..................507 285-1815
MEI Liu, *Finance Dir*
Andy Arends, *Human Res Mgr*
Vicki D Molle, *Exec Dir*
Vicki Dallemolly, *Director*
EMP: 35
SALES (est): 1MM-4.9MM **Privately Held**
SIC: 8361 8059 Home for the elderly; nursing & personal care facility

(G-7251)
SENIOR CITIZENS SERVICE INC
121 Broadway Ave N (55906-3720)
PHONE..................507 287-1404
FAX: 507 280-4719
Cindy Sogla, *Manager*
Sally Gallaher, *Exec Dir*
Sally Gallagher, *Exec Dir*
EMP: 37 EST: 1961
SQ FT: 27,000
SALES (est): 500-999K **Privately Held**
WEB: www.rochesterseniorcare.com
SIC: 8322 Senior citizen center; geriatric social services

(G-7252)
SHAMROCK ENTERPRISES LLC
6415 Bandel Rd NW (55901-8759)
PO Box 300, Oronoco (55960-0300)
PHONE..................507 288-9494
Carrol Kelley, *Partner*
Micahel Wendel, *Partner*
Sharon Lowe, *Partner*
William Quick, *Mng Member*
EMP: 30 EST: 1970
SQ FT: 4,000
SALES (est): 1MM-4.9MM **Privately Held**
SIC: 1771 Asphalt contractor

(G-7253)
SHOPKO STORES OPERATING CO LLC
3708 Highway 63 N (55906-3902)
PHONE..................507 281-0656
John Geradhty, *Manager*
Marty Heimer, *Manager*
EMP: 151
SALES (est): 10MM-24.9MM **Privately Held**
WEB: www.shopko.com
SIC: 7384 Discount department store; drug store; retails optical goods; photofinishing laboratory
HQ: Shopko Stores Operating Co LLC
    700 Pilgrim Way
    Green Bay WI 54304
    920 429-2211

(G-7254)
SIGNATURE HEALTHCARE INC
501 8th Ave SE (55904-4834)
PHONE..................507 288-6514
Dennis Decosta, *Manager*
Karen Eaker, *Administrator*
EMP: 130
SALES (est): 5MM-9.9MM **Privately Held**
SIC: 8051 8052 Convalescent home; intermediate care facility
PA: Signature Healthcare LLC
    2979 PGA Blvd
    Palm Beach Gardens FL 33410
    561 627-0664

(G-7255)
SMITH SCHAFER & ASSOCIATES LTD
220 S Broadway Ste 102 (55904-6517)
PHONE..................507 288-3277
FAX: 507 288-4571
Alan L Schafer, *President*
Jim Schafer, *Business Mgr*
Kim A Mahanna, *Vice Pres*
Jean L Guyse, *Vice Pres*
Thomas H Wente, *Treasurer*
EMP: 35 EST: 1970
SALES (est): 1MM-4.9MM **Privately Held**
WEB: www.smithschafer.com
SIC: 8721 Certified public accountant services

(G-7256)
SMURFIT-STONE CONTAINER
4165 Hwy 14 W (55901-6609)
PHONE..................507 288-2305
FAX: 507 288-9281
Wes Wilcox, *Mfg Staff*
Lynn Olson, *Production*
Stephen Asher, *Controller*
Angie Bourasa, *Human Res Dir*
Geri Geiselhart, *Human Res Dir*
EMP: 40
SALES (est): 5MM-9.9MM **Privately Held**
WEB: www.sto.com
SIC: 5113 Manufactures corrugated boxes; wholesales corrugated & solid fiber boxes
PA: Smurfit-Stone Container Corp
    222 N Lasalle St
    Chicago IL 60601
    312 346-6600

www.HarrisInfo.com
316

2011 Harris Minnesota
Services Directory

▲=Import ▼=Export
◆=Import/Export

(G-7257)
SONOR HOTEL CORP
Also Called: Holiday Inn
1630 S Broadway (55904-7927)
PHONE..............507 288-1844
FAX: 507 288-1844
Mark Anderson, *President*
Bill File, *General Mgr*
Dean Anderson, *Corp Secy*
Alisa Williams, *Manager*
Bill Seitl, *Manager*
EMP: 130 EST: 1963
SQ FT: 120,000
SALES (est): 5MM-9.9MM **Privately Held**
WEB: www.hisouthrochester.com
SIC: 7011 Traveler accommodations;
cocktail lounge; eating place

(G-7258)
SORENSEN & SORENSEN PAINTING
2515 50th Ave SE (55904-9002)
PHONE..............507 289-5368
FAX: 507 289-6026
Dick Sorensen, *President*
Carole A Sorensen, *Corp Secy*
Sheri Wussow, *Manager*
EMP: 25 EST: 1968
SALES (est): 1MM-4.9MM **Privately Held**
SIC: 1721 Residential painting contractor

(G-7259)
SOUTHERN MINNESOTA MUNICIPAL
Also Called: Smmpa
500 1st Ave SW (55902-3303)
PHONE..............507 285-0478
FAX: 507 292-6414
Raymond A Hayward, *CEO*
Lewis Giesking, *President*
Russell Good, *General Mgr*
David P Geschwind, *COO*
Thomas Kuntz, *Vice Pres*
EMP: 41 EST: 1977
SQ FT: 22,800
SALES (est): 25MM-49.9MM **Privately Held**
WEB: www.smmpa.com
SIC: 4911 Provides electric power
generation services; electric power
distribution service

(G-7260)
SPECTRUM COMMUNITY HEALTH INC
1831 24th St NW Ste B (55901-7924)
PHONE..............507 282-8052
FAX: 507 292-1382
Marylyn Hanson, *Manager*
EMP: 25
SALES (est): 500-999K **Privately Held**
SIC: 8082 Home health care services
PA: Spectrum Community Health Inc
6205 Crossman Ln
Inver Grove Heights MN 55076
612 617-1190

(G-7261)
SPRINT SPECTRUM LP
4400 W Frontage Rd NW (55901-3191)
PHONE..............507 358-4727
Bret Edstron, *Manager*
EMP: 25 **Publicly Held**
WEB: www.sprintpcs.com
SIC: 4812 Cellular telephone services
DH: Sprint Spectrum LP
2001 Edmund Halley Dr
Reston VA 20191
703 433-4000

(G-7262)
SPSS INC
4151 Hwy 52 N Ste 300 (55901-0144)
PHONE..............507 287-2835
Ken Holec, *Branch Mgr*
EMP: 120
SALES (est): 10MM-24.9MM **Publicly Held**
WEB: www.spss.com
SIC: 7371 Computer software development
HQ: SPSS Inc
233 S Wacker Dr Ste 1100
Chicago IL 60606
312 651-3000

(G-7263)
STAR LIMOUSINE SERVICE
420 1st Ave NW Ste A (55901-2987)
PHONE..............507 281-0969
Tim Fliehr, *Owner*
EMP: 30 EST: 1997
SALES (est): 1MM-4.9MM **Privately Held**
WEB: www.starlimousineservice.com
SIC: 4119 Limousine service

(G-7264)
STEPHEN J RUSSELL
200 1st St SW (55905-0001)
PHONE..............507 284-8384
Stephen J Russell, *Owner*
EMP: 96
SALES (est): 10MM-24.9MM **Privately Held**
SIC: 8011 Physicians' office & clinic

(G-7265)
STERLING STATE BANK
102 S Broadway Ste 225 (55904-6509)
PO Box 369 (55903-0369)
PHONE..............507 282-1845
FAX: 507 529-4025
Denzil McNeilus, *CEO*
Thomas Winkels, *President*
Jay Nelson, *Exec VP*
Justin McNeilus, *Vice Pres*
Ann Sand, *Manager*
EMP: 30 EST: 1958
SQ FT: 10,000
SALES (est): 5MM-9.9MM **Privately Held**
SIC: 6022 6163 State commercial bank;
loan broker
PA: Sterling Bancorporation Inc
1419 1st Ave SW
Austin MN 55912
507 433-7325

(G-7266)
STEVE YAGGY SPECIALIZED TRUCK
Also Called: Yaggy Trucking
6978 10th Ave SW (55902-2510)
PHONE..............507 282-1715
FAX: 507 536-0800
Steve Yaggy, *President*
Carol Yaggy, *Corp Secy*
Todd Cooper, *Manager*
EMP: 45 EST: 1992
SALES (est): 5MM-9.9MM **Privately Held**
WEB: www.yaggytrucking.com
SIC: 4213 Over the road trucking

(G-7267)
SUNSTONE HOTEL MANAGEMENT INC
Also Called: Textile Care Services
225 Woodlake Dr SE (55904-5530)
PHONE..............507 252-7500
FAX: 507 252-7550
Robert Alter, *CEO*
Randy Lacey, *General Mgr*
Roger Derby, *QC Mgr*
Deb Cardille, *Human Res Mgr*
Vicky Vessey, *Sales Mgr*
EMP: 25 EST: 1954
SALES (est): 500-999K **Privately Held**
WEB: www.textilecs.com
SIC: 7211 7216 Commercial & family dry
cleaning & laundry services; dry cleaning
plant
PA: Sunstone Hotel Management Inc
903 Calle Amanecer
San Clemente CA 92673
949 369-4000

(G-7268)
SUNSTONE HOTEL MANAGEMENT INC
Also Called: Economy Inn & Executive Ste
9 3rd Ave NW (55901-2891)
PHONE..............507 289-8646
FAX: 507 282-4478
Bill Seitl, *General Mgr*
Diane Ditelvson, *Human Res Dir*
Scott Greer, *Sales Mgr*
Scott Terry, *Manager*
Chris Deguise, *Manager*
EMP: 75
SALES (est): 1MM-4.9MM **Privately Held**
WEB: www.sunstoneshopper.com

SIC: 7011 Traveler accommodations
PA: Sunstone Hotel Management Inc
903 Calle Amanecer
San Clemente CA 92673
949 369-4000

(G-7269)
SUNSTONE HOTEL PROPERTIES INC
Also Called: Kahler Hotel
20 2nd Ave SW Ste G13 (55902-3042)
PHONE..............507 282-2581
Bruce Fairchild, *Manager*
EMP: 28
SALES (est): 1MM-4.9MM **Publicly Held**
WEB: www.sunstonehotelproperties.com
SIC: 7011 Traveler accommodations
HQ: Sunstone Hotel Properties Inc
903 Calle Amanecer
San Clemente CA 92673
949 369-4100

(G-7270)
SUPERIOR MECHANICAL SYSTEMS
1244 60th Ave NW Ste C (55901-2933)
PHONE..............507 289-5126
FAX: 507 281-9807
Robert Jones, *President*
James Gander, *Vice Pres*
EMP: 47 EST: 2000
SQ FT: 7,000
SALES (est): 5MM-9.9MM **Privately Held**
WEB:
www.superiormechanicalsystems.com
SIC: 1711 Heating & air conditioning
contractor

(G-7271)
SUPERIOR WATER CONDITIONING
1244 60th Ave NW (55901-2933)
PHONE..............507 289-0229
FAX: 507 285-6512
James Gander, *President*
Larry Klobassa, *COO*
Dave Oftedahl, *Vice Pres*
Lisa Gander, *Treasurer*
Mark Ku, *Controller*
EMP: 45 EST: 1980
SALES (est): 5MM-9.9MM **Privately Held**
SIC: 1711 Plumbing service; heating & air
conditioning contractor; manufactures
household water filters & softeners

(G-7272)
T S P INC
1500 Highway 52 N (55901-0273)
PHONE..............507 288-8155
FAX: 507 288-7220
Richard Gustaf, *President*
Michele Saack, *Business Mgr*
Robert Cline, *Vice Pres*
Bertil Haglund, *Vice Pres*
William Meschke, *Vice Pres*
EMP: 25 EST: 1969
SQ FT: 8,100
SALES (est): 1MM-4.9MM **Privately Held**
SIC: 8712 Architectural engineers
PA: T S P Inc
1112 N West Ave
Sioux Falls SD 57104
605 336-1160

(G-7273)
THINK MUTUAL BANK (PA)
5200 Members Pkwy NW (55901-8381)
PO Box 5949 (55903-5949)
PHONE..............507 288-3425
Cheryl Schaefer, *Senior VP*
Tom Floyd, *Vice Pres*
Steve Spohn, *Vice Pres*
Kirk Muhlenbruck, *Vice Pres*
Mike Snyder, *Vice Pres*
EMP: 172 EST: 1961
SQ FT: 104,000
SALES (corp-wide): 65.05M **Privately Held**
SIC: 6061 Federally chartered credit union

(G-7274)
300 FINANCIAL INC
2768 Superior Dr NW (55901-3063)
PHONE..............507 424-4799
James Dew, *Principal*
Jeffrey Freburg, *Corp Secy*

Missy Emerich, *CFO*
Michael Kaselnak, *Director*
EMP: 32
SALES (est): 5MM-9.9MM **Privately Held**
SIC: 6282 Financial investment advice
service

(G-7275)
TONNA MECHANICAL INC
2411 7th St NW (55901-7538)
PHONE..............507 288-1908
Steven J Murphy, *President*
Larry Strande, *Purch Agent*
Dahl Crates, *Manager*
EMP: 48 EST: 1976
SQ FT: 2,500
SALES (est): 5MM-9.9MM **Privately Held**
SIC: 1711 Warm air heating & air
conditioning contractor; ventilation & duct
work contractor; sheet metal fabricator

(G-7276)
TRUGREEN LP
Also Called: Tru Green-Chemlawn
6636 10th Ave SW (55902-2509)
PHONE..............507 289-8798
FAX: 507 289-8401
Greg Elmer, *Manager*
Kent Smith, *Manager*
EMP: 30 **Privately Held**
WEB: www.trugreen.com
SIC: 0782 Lawn care services
DH: Trugreen LP
860 Ridge Lake Blvd Ste G02
Memphis TN 38120
901 681-1800

(G-7277)
UNITED PARCEL SERVICE INC
Also Called: UPS
1616 Opportunity Rd NW (55901-0745)
PHONE..............507 281-0468
Lais Houltom, *Manager*
EMP: 70
SALES (est): 1MM-4.9MM **Publicly Held**
WEB: www.ups.com
SIC: 4215 Parcel delivery services by
vehicle
HQ: United Parcel Service Inc
55 Glenlake Pkwy NE
Atlanta GA 30328
404 828-6000

(G-7278)
VACAVA INC
3131 Superior Dr NW Ste B (55901-1999)
PHONE..............507 252-9076
Charlie Harter, *CEO*
Terry Bird, *President*
Mark Burmeister, *Project Mgr*
Buck Pohlmann, *CFO*
Bonnie Robinson, *CIO*
EMP: 39 EST: 1999
SQ FT: 5,000
SALES (est): 1MM-4.9MM **Privately Held**
WEB: www.vacava.com
SIC: 7371 Computer software development
& applications

(G-7279)
VEIT CONTAINER CORP
5920 15th St NW (55901-0710)
PHONE..............507 281-3867
FAX: 507 529-1294
Steve Halgren, *General Mgr*
Jeff Olsgard, *Data Proc Dir*
EMP: 25
SALES (est): 1MM-4.9MM **Privately Held**
SIC: 4953 Hazardous waste collection &
disposal services

(G-7280)
VEOLIA ES SOLID WASTE MIDWEST
4245 Highway 14 E (55904-6643)
PHONE..............507 281-5850
FAX: 507 289-0793
G W Dietrich, *President*
David Schnider, *General Mgr*
Joe Merrill, *General Mgr*
Dawn McMahon, *General Mgr*
George K Farr, *CFO*
EMP: 68 EST: 1984
SALES (est): 10MM-24.9MM **Privately Held**
WEB: www.veoliaes.com

(PA)=Parent Co (HQ)=Headquarters (DH)=Div Headquarters
♣ = New business established in last 2 years

2011 Harris Minnesota
Services Directory

© Harris InfoSource 1-866-281-6415
317

SIC: 4953 Garbage collecting, destroying & processing services; rubbish collection & disposal services; waste material recycling services
HQ: Veolia Es Solid Waste Midwest
125 S 84th St Ste 200
Milwaukee WI 53214
414 479-7800

(G-7281)
VERN COOPER & ASSOCIATES INC
2883 Viola Heights Dr NE (55906-6958)
PHONE..................507 319-4139
Vern Cooper, *President*
EMP: 30 EST: 1972
SALES (est): 1MM-4.9MM **Privately Held**
SIC: 6411 Insurance agent

(G-7282)
VETERANS OF FOREIGN WARS INC
16 6th St SW (55902-3325)
PHONE..................507 289-6299
FAX: 507 289-6299
Marshall Sveska, *Manager*
Lori Westguard, *Manager*
Ron Parish, *Manager*
Lori Westerguurd, *Manager*
Jean Clemmons, *Manager*
EMP: 25 EST: 1924 **Privately Held**
SIC: 8641 Veterans' organization

(G-7283)
VIKING AUTOMATIC SPRINKLER CO
4420 19th St NW (55901-6624)
PHONE..................507 289-8270
FAX: 507 289-0143
Kevin Shea, *Vice Pres*
Tim Brumbaugh, *Manager*
Rich Poole, *Manager*
EMP: 25
SALES (est): 1MM-4.9MM **Privately Held**
WEB: www.vikingsprinkler.com
SIC: 1711 Fire sprinkler system installation service
HQ: Viking Automatic Sprinkler Co
301 York Ave
Saint Paul MN 55130
651 558-3300

(G-7284)
VISION SOLUTIONS INC
3535 40th Ave NW Ste 200 (55901-1769)
PHONE..................507 252-3440
FAX: 507 529-2160
Ken Zaiken, *Branch Mgr*
Denise Dempewolf, *Manager*
G T Vanbenschoten, *Director*
EMP: 46
SALES (est): 5MM-9.9MM **Privately Held**
WEB: www.visionsolutions.com
SIC: 7371 Computer software development & applications; computer software training services
PA: Vision Solutions Inc
15300 Barranca Pkwy
Irvine CA 92618
949 253-6500

(G-7285)
WATER RECLAMATION PLANT
301 37th St NW (55901-3403)
PHONE..................507 281-6190
FAX: 507 287-1389
Walt Allen, *Supervisor*
Lyle Zimmerman, *Director*
EMP: 27 EST: 1997
SALES (est): 1MM-4.9MM **Privately Held**
SIC: 4953 Sewage treatment facility

(G-7286)
WEBER & BARLOW STORES INC
Also Called: Mestad's Wedding World
1171 6th St NW (55901-1824)
PHONE..................507 289-2444
FAX: 507 289-7616
Mike Boysen, *Opers Staff*
EMP: 30
SALES (est): 1MM-4.9MM **Privately Held**

SIC: 7299 Bridal shop; retails formal wear; clothing rental service
PA: Weber & Barlow Stores Inc
1161 6th St NW
Rochester MN 55901
507 288-0296

(G-7287)
WEBER & JUDD CO (PA)
1814 15th St NW (55901-0214)
PO Box 5877 (55903-5877)
PHONE..................507 289-6047
FAX: 507 536-4429
C D McDonough, *President*
Todd Fox, *Vice Pres*
Scott Bennett, *Vice Pres*
Irv Nehring, *CFO*
Anne McDonough, *Accountant*
EMP: 50 EST: 1908 **Privately Held**
WEB: www.weberjudd.com
SIC: 7384 Drug store; greeting card shop; non-prescription medicine proprietary store; retail gift shop; photofinishing laboratory

(G-7288)
WEIS BUILDERS INC
2227 7th St NW (55901-0206)
PHONE..................507 288-2041
FAX: 507 288-7979
Scott Fenske, *Vice Pres*
Ron Kreinbring, *Vice Pres*
Doug Happel, *Manager*
Dale Svoboda, *Manager*
Erik Weis, *Director*
EMP: 40
SALES (est): 10MM-24.9MM **Privately Held**
WEB: www.weisbuilders.com
SIC: 1542 1521 Commercial & institutional building construction; new single-family home construction service
PA: Weis Builders Inc
7645 Lyndale Ave S # 300
Minneapolis MN 55423
612 243-5000

(G-7289)
WELLS FARGO BANK, NATIONAL
940 37th St NW (55901-4208)
PHONE..................507 285-2990
FAX: 507 285-2974
Chris Callahan, *Manager*
Patricia Larson, *Manager*
EMP: 25
SALES (est): 5MM-9.9MM **Publicly Held**
SIC: 6021 National commercial bank
HQ: Wfc Holdings, Corp
420 Montgomery St
San Francisco CA 94104
415 396-7392

(G-7290)
WELLS FARGO BANK, NATIONAL
21 1st St SW Ste 611 (55902-3007)
PO Box 4500 (55903-4500)
PHONE..................507 285-2800
FAX: 507 285-3097
Donald Fink, *Branch Mgr*
Norb Harrington, *Branch Mgr*
Dave Stenhaug, *Manager*
EMP: 50
SALES (est): 10MM-24.9MM **Publicly Held**
SIC: 6021 National commercial bank
HQ: Wfc Holdings, Corp
420 Montgomery St
San Francisco CA 94104
415 396-7392

(G-7291)
WELLS FARGO BANK, NATIONAL
3360 55th St NW (55901-0202)
PHONE..................507 285-3015
FAX: 507 285-3080
Christohher Andersaon, *Sales Staff*
Travos Hodny, *Manager*
Lisa Rank, *Manager*
EMP: 30
SALES (est): 5MM-9.9MM **Publicly Held**
SIC: 6282 Investment advisory service
HQ: Wfc Holdings, Corp
420 Montgomery St
San Francisco CA 94104
415 396-7392

(G-7292)
WESTERN WALLS INC
604 11th Ave NW Ste 100 (55901-1805)
PHONE..................507 282-4624
Robert Dewitz, *President*
Julie Leisen, *Corp Secy*
Charles Dewitz, *Vice Pres*
EMP: 25 EST: 1974
SQ FT: 1,600
SALES (est): 1MM-4.9MM **Privately Held**
SIC: 1794 6552 Excavation & grading, building construction contractor; land subdivision & development services

(G-7293)
WHITING, JIM NURSERY & GARDEN
3430 19th St NW (55901-6601)
PHONE..................507 289-3741
FAX: 507 289-4165
James M Whiting, *President*
Chris Graves, *Manager*
EST: 1973 **Privately Held**
WEB: www.jimwhitingnursery.com
SIC: 0781 0782 Retails nursery stock, seeds & bulbs; retails lawn & garden supplies; landscape architectural service; landscaping services

(G-7294)
WILLOW CREEK GOLF COURSE OF
1700 48th St SW (55902-1503)
PHONE..................507 285-0305
FAX: 507 285-9956
Wendell Pittenger, *President*
Scott Rindahl, *General Mgr*
EMP: 30 EST: 1940
SQ FT: 7,800
SALES (est): 1MM-4.9MM **Privately Held**
SIC: 7992 Public golf course; retails golf goods & equipment; cocktail lounge; retails sports apparel; full service American restaurant

(G-7295)
WOMEN'S SHELTER INC
823 W Center St (55902-6289)
PO Box 457 (55903-0457)
PHONE..................507 285-1938
Judy Miller, *President*
Suzie Christianson, *Director*
EMP: 25 EST: 1978
SALES (est): 1MM-4.9MM **Privately Held**
WEB: www.womens-shelter.org
SIC: 8322 Individual & family social services

(G-7296)
WOODRUFF CO
1524 3rd Ave SE (55904-7919)
PO Box 279 (55903-0279)
PHONE..................507 285-2500
James F Woodruff, *President*
John W Woodruff, *Vice Pres*
EMP: 26 EST: 1947
SQ FT: 90,000
SALES (est): 10MM-24.9MM **Privately Held**
SIC: 5074 Wholesales plumbing & heating equipment & supplies

(G-7297)
XYLO TECHNOLOGIES INC
2434 Superior Dr NW Ste 104 (55901-2591)
PHONE..................507 289-9956
Dharani Ramamoorthy, *President*
Santi Arunachalam, *Opers Mgr*
EMP: 60 EST: 2000
SQ FT: 1,300
SALES (est): 5MM-9.9MM **Privately Held**
WEB: www.xylotechnologies.com
SIC: 8748 Systems engineering consultant

(G-7298)
ZIEGLER INC
Also Called: Caterpillar
6340 Highway 63 S (55904-8414)
PHONE..................507 285-1775
FAX: 507 536-5001
Phil Moser, *Opers-Prdtn-Mfg*
EMP: 30
SALES (est): 10MM-24.9MM **Privately Held**

SIC: 5082 Wholesales construction & mining machinery
PA: Ziegler Inc
901 W 94th St
Minneapolis MN 55420
952 888-4121

(G-7299)
ZUMBRO VALLEY MENTAL HEALTH
343 Woodlake Dr SE (55904-6242)
PHONE..................507 289-2089
Lynn Skinner, *President*
John Carlson, *CFO*
Theresa Sanders, *Accounting Staf*
Tracy Lee, *Human Res Dir*
Stan Kruglikov, *Med Doctor*
EMP: 28 EST: 1960
SQ FT: 43,651
SALES (est): 1MM-4.9MM **Privately Held**
WEB: www.zumbromhc.org
SIC: 8093 Outpatient mental health clinic

ROCKFORD
Hennepin County

(G-7300)
ELASTOMERIC ROOFING SYSTEMS
Also Called: ER Systems
6900 Bleck Dr (55373-5132)
PHONE..................763 565-6900
Tony Leonard, *President*
Timothy Leonard, *CFO*
Sheila Lee, *Controller*
Paul Scally, *Exec Dir*
EMP: 33 EST: 1993
SQ FT: 50,000
SALES (est): 1MM-4.9MM **Privately Held**
SIC: 1761 Roofing, siding & sheet metal work; manufactures asphalt coatings & sealers

(G-7301)
HEARTLAND SERVICES LLC
6800 Electric Dr (55373-9386)
PHONE..................763 477-3000
FAX: 763 477-3054
Mark Vogt, *Ch of Bd*
A Cordt, *General Mgr*
Roger Geckler, *Treasurer*
EMP: 26 EST: 1998
SALES (est): 5MM-9.9MM **Privately Held**
SIC: 4812 Retails mobile telephones & equipment; wireless telecommunications carrier & service

(G-7302)
HOSPITALITY SERVICES CORP
Also Called: Pro-Clean
6540 Sioux Trl (55373-9490)
PO Box 739, Delano (55328-0739)
PHONE..................763 323-3141
Jerry Vlaminck, *President*
EMP: 150 EST: 1988
SALES (est): 1MM-4.9MM **Privately Held**
SIC: 7349 Building cleaning & maintenance services

(G-7303)
PRECISION TURF & CHEMICAL INC
7728 Commerce Cir (55373-9704)
PHONE..................763 477-5885
Glenn Krupp, *President*
Jean Krupp, *Treasurer*
EST: 1990 **Privately Held**
WEB: www.precisionturf.com
SIC: 5191 5083 Wholesales agricultural fertilizer; wholesales agricultural machinery & equipment; wholesales agricultural chemicals

(G-7304)
ROCKFORD BUS GARAGE INC
7700 County Road 50 (55373-9537)
PHONE..................763 477-6100
FAX: 763 477-6100
Bob Myer, *Manager*
EMP: 26 EST: 1992
SALES (est): 1MM-4.9MM **Privately Held**

www.HarrisInfo.com
318
2011 Harris Minnesota
Services Directory
▲=Import ▼=Export
◆=Import/Export

SIC: 7538 General automotive repair services

(G-7305)
WRIGHT-HENNEPIN COOPERATIVE (PA)
6800 Electric Dr (55373-9386)
PO Box 330 (55373-0330)
PHONE.................................763 477-3000
Mark Vogt, *President*
Chris Lantto, *Chairman*
Dale Jans, *Corp Secy*
Alicia Mengelkoch, *Vice Pres*
Angela Pirbyl, *Vice Pres*
EMP: 71 EST: 1937
SALES (corp-wide): 81.40M Privately Held
WEB: www.wrightpartnership.org
SIC: 4911 Electric power distribution service

(G-7306)
WRIGHT-HENNEPIN SECURITY CORP
6800 Electric Dr (55373-9386)
PHONE.................................763 477-3000
Mark Vogt, *President*
Jen Goerke, *Corp Secy*
Lance Hovland, *VP Engrg*
Wayne Bowenschmitt, *Design Engr*
Angie Pirbyl, *CFO*
EMP: 135 EST: 1989
SALES (est): 10MM-24.9MM Privately Held
WEB: www.wrightpartnership.org
SIC: 1731 1711 4911 5063 7382 Fire detection & burglar alarm systems specialization contractor; electric services; wholesales electrical burglar alarm systems; security systems services; plumbing, heating & air conditioning contractor
PA: Wright-Hennepin Cooperative
6800 Electric Dr
Rockford MN 55373
763 477-3000

ROCKFORD
Wright County

(G-7307)
ARGENBRIGHT INC (PA)
7600 69th Ave (55373-5400)
PHONE.................................763 477-7600
A C Perfall, *CEO*
Brian Burke, *CFO*
Amy Hillman, *Financial Analy*
Kevin R Mc Carthy, *Director*
Michael D Long, *Director*
▲ EMP: 35 EST: 1977
SQ FT: 400,000 Privately Held
SIC: 8742 Marketing consulting service

(G-7308)
ARGENBRIGHT INC
Also Called: Skybridge Marketing Group
7600 69th Ave (55373-5400)
PHONE.................................763 477-7600
Ron Schleper, *Manager*
EMP: 210
SALES (est): 25MM-49.9MM Privately Held
SIC: 8742 Marketing consulting service
PA: Argenbright Inc
7600 69th Ave
Rockford MN 55373
763 477-7600

(G-7309)
DESIGN READY CONTROLS INC
6704 Bleck Dr (55373-5123)
PHONE.................................763 565-3000
FAX: 763 565-3001
Troy Schmidtke, *President*
David Peterson, *Vice Pres*
Pete Steil, *VP Mfg*
Dshelly Thielen, *Purchasing*
Tim Grogan, *Manager*
EMP: 81
SQ FT: 18,000
SALES (est): 25MM-49.9MM Privately Held
WEB: www.drc1.com
SIC: 5084 Wholesales industrial environmental air pollution control equipment; wholesales industrial environmental water pollution control equipment; manufactures electrical control panels; manufactures pumps & pumping equipment

(G-7310)
E P A AUDIO VISUAL INC
7910 State Hwy 55 (55373)
PO Box 40 (55373-0040)
PHONE.................................763 477-6931
FAX: 763 477-4395
Eric Ask, *President*
Donald Ask, *Exec VP*
Sherry Kill, *Vice Pres*
EMP: 31 EST: 1974
SQ FT: 10,400
SALES (est): 10MM-24.9MM Privately Held
WEB: www.epaaudio.com
SIC: 5099 Wholesales video & audio equipment

(G-7311)
MCC INC
7900 69th Ave (55373-4554)
PHONE.................................763 477-4774
FAX: 763 477-5174
Jon Walters, *President*
Cortney McCormick, *COO*
Dan Shefland, *Vice Pres*
Craig Rolfes, *Foreman/Supr*
Jeff Kayala, *Foreman/Supr*
EMP: 150 EST: 1992
SQ FT: 18,400
SALES (est): 25MM-49.9MM Privately Held
SIC: 1541 Industrial building & warehouse construction

(G-7312)
PRO-WALL INC
7990 69th Ave (55373)
PO Box 529 (55373-0529)
PHONE.................................763 477-5172
Marilyn Schroeder, *President*
Joann Tollefsrud, *General Mgr*
EMP: 28 EST: 1980
SQ FT: 7,800
SALES (est): 5MM-9.9MM Privately Held
SIC: 5032 Wholesale ceramic floor & wall tiles

(G-7313)
SHARK INDUSTRIES LTD
6700 Bleck Dr (55373-5123)
PHONE.................................763 565-1900
Diana M Mini, *Partner*
Dino Daniel, *Partner*
Dean Daniels, *Vice Pres*
▲ EMP: 25 EST: 1983
SQ FT: 50,000
SALES (est): 10MM-24.9MM Privately Held
WEB: www.sharkind.com
SIC: 5085 Wholesales industrial abrasives

ROCKVILLE
Stearns County

(G-7314)
S J LOUIS CONSTRUCTION INC (PA)
1351 Broadway St W (56369)
PO Box 459 (56369-0459)
PHONE.................................320 253-9291
FAX: 320 253-3533
James L Schueller, *CEO*
Les V Whitman V, *Exec VP*
Michael Swanhorst, *Vice Pres*
Donald Meyer, *CFO*
Jaime Woods, *Controller*
EMP: 234 EST: 1983
SQ FT: 24,000 Privately Held
WEB: www.sjlouis.com
SIC: 1623 Water & sewer line construction

ROGERS
Hennepin County

(G-7315)
ABRAHAM TECHNICAL SERVICES INC (PA)
12560 Fletcher Ln Ste 100 (55374-4709)
PHONE.................................763 428-3170
FAX: 763 428-3166
Steve Schmidt, *CEO*
Charlie Schmidt, *General Mgr*
Troy Norman, *Purch Mgr*

Becky Stumpf, *CFO*
Mary Bergeron, *Human Res Dir*
EMP: 40 EST: 1992
SQ FT: 25,000 Privately Held
WEB: www.abetech.com
SIC: 4812 7374 7389 Manufactures magnetic ink & optical scanning equipment; wireless telecommunications carrier & service; data processing & preparation services; packaging & labeling services

(G-7316)
ARCHWAY MARKETING SERVICES INC (PA)
19850 S Diamond Lake Rd (55374-4571)
PHONE.................................763 428-3300
Clay Perfall, *CEO*
Mike Moroz, *President*
Bob Adkinson, *COO*
Richard Rizzardi, *Senior VP*
Rita Hellewell, *Vice Pres*
EMP: 200 EST: 2005 Privately Held
SIC: 8742 Marketing consulting service

(G-7317)
BALDOR ELECTRIC CO
21080 134th Ave N (55374-9598)
PHONE.................................763 428-3633
Rich Rebella, *Mfg Staff*
Jerry Hernandez, *IT/INT Sup*
Marty Engebretson, *Exec Dir*
EMP: 75
SALES (est): 10MM-24.9MM Publicly Held
WEB: www.baldor.com
SIC: 5063 Manufactures electric motor & generator parts; wholesales electric motors
PA: Baldor Electric Co
5711 Rs Boreham Jr St
Fort Smith AR 72901
479 646-4711

(G-7318)
CABELA'S INC
20200 Rogers Dr (55374-4716)
PHONE.................................763 493-8600
Vicky Kluender, *Manager*
EMP: 120
SALES (est): 10MM-24.9MM Publicly Held
WEB: www.cabelas.com
SIC: 7999 Retails sporting goods; sporting goods rental services
PA: Cabela's Inc
1 Cabela Dr
Sidney NE 69160
308 254-5505

(G-7319)
CAMPING WORLD INC
21200 Rogers Dr (55374-8930)
PHONE.................................763 428-7779
FAX: 763 428-7689
Greg Homers, *Manager*
EMP: 27
SALES (est): 5MM-9.9MM Privately Held
SIC: 7538 Recreational vehicle dealer; recreational vehicle repair services
DH: Camping World Inc
650 Three Springs Rd
Bowling Green KY 42104
270 781-2718

(G-7320)
CBC 202 LP
21001 John Milless Dr Ofc (55374-8400)
PHONE.................................651 291-1750
Joseph Holmberg, *Partner*
Kelly Mechavich, *Manager*
EMP: 99
SALES (est): 10MM-24.9MM Privately Held
SIC: 6513 Apartment building operator

(G-7321)
DAWN FOOD PRODUCTS INC
20195 S Diamond Lake Rd # 200 (55374-4868)
PHONE.................................763 428-8826
Mark Boe, *General Mgr*
Jeff Hill, *Manager*
EMP: 36
SALES (est): 10MM-24.9MM Privately Held
WEB: www.dawnfoods.com

SIC: 5046 Wholesales bakery equipment & supplies
HQ: Dawn Food Products Inc
3333 Sargent Rd
Jackson MI 49201
517 789-4400

(G-7322)
DIGNIFIED ASSISTED LIVING INC
Also Called: Wellstead of Rogers
20600 S Diamond Lake Rd (55374-4515)
PHONE.................................763 428-1981
FAX: 763 428-3792
Thomas A Wiskow, *President*
Tee Jan, *Human Res Dir*
EMP: 70 EST: 1998
SALES (est): 1MM-4.9MM Privately Held
WEB: www.wellsteadofrogers.com
SIC: 8051 Skilled nursing care facility

(G-7323)
G R MECHANICAL PLUMBING
12401 Ironwood Cir Ste 500 (55374-3904)
PHONE.................................763 428-2663
FAX: 763 428-7656
Greg Reinking, *President*
Michael Laplante, *General Mgr*
Lance Duncan, *Corp Secy*
Michele Tousignant, *Vice Pres*
Todd Tousignant, *Vice Pres*
EMP: 35 EST: 1985
SQ FT: 6,000
SALES (est): 1MM-4.9MM Privately Held
SIC: 1711 Plumbing, heating & air conditioning contractor

(G-7324)
GLEN'S TRUCK CENTER INC
21701 John Deere Ln (55374-9489)
PO Box 235 (55374-0235)
PHONE.................................763 428-4331
FAX: 763 428-4050
Glen A Haley, *President*
Phyliss Heidenreich, *Corp Secy*
Clellan Olson, *VP Sls/Mktg*
Terry Ahart, *CFO*
EMP: 25 EST: 1974
SQ FT: 46,000
SALES (est): 25MM-49.9MM Privately Held
WEB: www.glenstruckcenter.com
SIC: 5012 5015 Wholesales commercial trucks; wholesales used automotive parts & supplies

(G-7325)
GOLDEN ACRES GOLF COURSE INC
Also Called: Pheasant Acres Run Golf Club
10705 County Road 116 (55374-9738)
PHONE.................................763 428-8244
FAX: 763 428-8821
Robert Brownawell, *CEO*
Mark Ellington, *Manager*
EMP: 50 EST: 1986
SQ FT: 4,250
SALES (est): 1MM-4.9MM Privately Held
WEB: www.pheasantacresgolf.com
SIC: 7992 Public golf course

(G-7326)
GREAT NORTHERN EQUIPMENT DSTBG
20195 S Diamond Lake Rd (55374-4775)
PHONE.................................763 428-9405
FAX: 763 428-4821
Don Kotula, *CEO*
Matt Clemens, *General Mgr*
Kim Barth, *Accounts Mgr*
Randy Riley, *Manager*
Rodney Nielsen, *Manager*
▲ EMP: 32 EST: 1987
SQ FT: 43,000
SALES (est): 10MM-24.9MM Privately Held
SIC: 5084 5063 Wholesales industrial engines; wholesales generators; retails banners

(G-7327)
INFRASTRUCTURE TECHNOLOGIES
Also Called: Infratech
21040 Commerce Blvd Ste 1 (55374-4593)
PHONE.................................763 428-6488
Richard Quast, *President*

Steve Reed, *Corp Secy*
John Selvog, *Vice Pres*
Matthew Huston, *Treasurer*
Alissa Thorsland, *Controller*
EMP: 50 **EST:** 1994
SALES (est): 5MM-9.9MM **Privately Held**
WEB: www.infratechonline.com
SIC: 1623 7699 Water & sewer line
construction; sewer cleaning & rodding
service

(G-7328)

LOWE'S HOME CENTERS INC

13800 Rogers Dr (55374-4774)
PHONE...............................763 428-5970
EMP: 150
SALES (est): 25MM-49.9MM **Publicly Held**
WEB: www.lowes.com
SIC: 5031 5064 Retails building products &
materials; wholesales exterior building
materials; wholesales interior building
materials; wholesales electrical appliances;
retails household appliances
HQ: Lowe's Home Centers Inc
1605 Curtis Bridge Rd
Wilkesboro NC 28697
336 658-4000

(G-7329)

M & L INDUSTRIES INC

23001 Industrial Blvd (55374-9566)
PHONE...............................763 428-4220
FAX: 763 428-2483
Maurice Kapsner, *President*
Linda Kapsner, *Vice Pres*
Lisa Epsen, *Purchasing*
Patrick Miskavige, *Engineer*
Dan Braegelman, *Finance Mgr*
EMP: 40 **EST:** 1973
SQ FT: 38,000
SALES (est): 1MM-4.9MM **Privately Held**
SIC: 7692 Sheet metal fabricator; machine
shop; welding service; manufactures
weldments

(G-7330)

MELYX CORP

21830 Industrial Blvd (55374-9575)
PHONE...............................763 428-6000
FAX: 763 428-7585
Richard A Johnston, *President*
Mitchell Manoski, *VP Opers-Prdtn-*
Doreen Arlandson, *Manager*
EMP: 25 **EST:** 1978
SQ FT: 6,000
SALES (est): 5MM-9.9MM **Privately Held**
SIC: 7372 Application software publishing

(G-7331)

METRO PAVING INC

14350 Northdale Blvd (55374-9175)
PHONE...............................763 428-4121
FAX: 763 428-4581
Robert Severson, *President*
David Olmscheid, *VP Persnl*
EMP: 50 **EST:** 1988
SQ FT: 20,000
SALES (est): 1MM-4.9MM **Privately Held**
WEB: www.metropavinginc.com
SIC: 1771 1611 Asphalt contractor; street
surfacing & paving construction

(G-7332)

NORTHERN DEWATERING INC

14405 Northdale Blvd (55374-9610)
PHONE...............................763 428-2616
FAX: 763 428-2671
John E Mc Shane, *President*
Mary L Mc Shane, *Corp Secy*
Laura Hayers, *Vice Pres*
Kathy Johnson, *Manager*
Dan Johnson, *Executive*
▲ **EMP:** 60 **EST:** 1982
SQ FT: 1,600
SALES (est): 1MM-4.9MM **Privately Held**
WEB: www.northerndewatering.com
SIC: 1799 7359 7699 Dewatering service;
equipment rental & leasing services; pumps
& pumping equipment repair service

(G-7333)

NORTHSTAR IMAGING INC

19875 S Diamond Lk Rd Ste 10
(55374-4651)
PHONE...............................763 463-5650
FAX: 763 463-5650

Scott Bonnema, *President*
Brian Ruether, *Vice Pres*
Chris Burger, *Service Mgr*
Chris Damhof, *Marketing Mgr*
▼ **EMP:** 50 **EST:** 1986
SQ FT: 30,000
SALES (est): 10MM-24.9MM **Privately Held**
SIC: 5084 Wholesales industrial electrical
measuring & testing equipment

(G-7334)

121 MARKETING SERVICES GROUP

12999 Wilfred Ln N (55374-4585)
PHONE...............................763 428-8123
FAX: 763 428-8124
Robert Schiferli, *President*
Grace Jelle, *Controller*
EMP: 60 **EST:** 2000
SQ FT: 35,000
SALES (est): 5MM-9.9MM **Privately Held**
SIC: 8742 Marketing consulting service

(G-7335)

PALMER WEST CONSTRUCTION CO

14595 James Rd (55374-8668)
PHONE...............................763 428-1867
FAX: 763 428-1873
Ralph Blake, *President*
David Schmeichel, *Vice Pres*
Teresa M Master, *Human Res Mgr*
Teresa McMaster, *Manager*
EMP: 60 **EST:** 1978
SQ FT: 5,000
SALES (est): 5MM-9.9MM **Privately Held**
WEB: www.palmerwest.net
SIC: 1761 Roofing contractor

(G-7336)

PASCHKE PROPERTIES

4611 Palmgren Ln NE (55374)
PO Box 308 (55374-0308)
PHONE...............................763 428-7711
Gerald Paschke, *Owner*
EMP: 30 **EST:** 1960
SALES (est): 5MM-9.9MM **Privately Held**
SIC: 1521 Single-family housing
construction

(G-7337)

PENHALL CO

Also Called: Highway Services
14045 Northdale Blvd (55374-9628)
PHONE...............................763 428-2244
Pete Lewis, *Opers Staff*
Duane Erdman, *Bookkeeper*
Gary Aamold, *Manager*
EMP: 75
SALES (est): 10MM-24.9MM **Privately Held**
WEB: www.penhall.com
SIC: 1611 Heavy highway & street
construction
HQ: Penhall Co
320 N Crescent Way
Anaheim CA 92801
714 772-6450

(G-7338)

PSS WORLD MEDICAL INC

Also Called: Physician Sales & Service
12999 Wilfred Ln N # 250 (55374-4591)
PHONE...............................763 428-2388
Laura Johnson, *Principal*
Rusty Marshall, *Opers Mgr*
Eric Kindgren, *Sales Mgr*
Jodi Ankerfelt, *Cust Mgr*
Ermine Dickie, *Manager*
EMP: 35
SQ FT: 27,000
SALES (est): 10MM-24.9MM **Publicly Held**
WEB: www.pssworldmedical.com
SIC: 5047 Wholesales hospital equipment &
supplies; wholesales physician equipment &
supplies; wholesales surgical equipment &
supplies; wholesales medical diagnostic
equipment
PA: PSS World Medical Inc
4345 Southpoint Blvd
Jacksonville FL 32216
904 332-3000

(G-7339)

REINHART FOODSERVICE LLC

13400 Commerce Blvd (55374-8917)
PHONE...............................763 428-6500
FAX: 763 428-6504
Russell Scott, *Sales Staff*
Wayne Kolberg, *Branch Mgr*
EMP: 300
SALES (est): 100MM-499.9MM **Privately
Held**
WEB: www.reinhartfoodservice.com
SIC: 5141 Wholesales general line
groceries

(G-7340)

REINKING ENTERPRISES INC

Also Called: Advance Response Systems
13175 George Weber Dr (55374-8900)
PHONE...............................763 428-1430
FAX: 763 428-1434
Wayne Reinking, *President*
Tim Marchand, *General Mgr*
Chris Wintheiser, *Data Proc Staff*
EMP: 80 **EST:** 1983
SQ FT: 29,000
SALES (est): 5MM-9.9MM **Privately Held**
WEB: www.advanced-response.com
SIC: 7331 Mailing services

(G-7341)

ROGERS HOSPITALITY LLC

Also Called: Sleep Inn
20930 135th Ave N (55374)
PHONE...............................763 428-3000
Brian Conneran, *Member*
Michael Smith, *Controller*
EMP: 25
SALES (est): 1MM-4.9MM **Privately Held**
SIC: 7011 Traveler accommodations

(G-7342)

TAVIS METAL & FABRICATION CORP

14240 James Rd (55374-9479)
PO Box 299 (55374-0299)
PHONE...............................763 428-8483
FAX: 763 428-7692
Kurt Becken, *President*
Scott Becken, *Vice Pres*
Dan Evans, *Mfg Staff*
Mary Becken, *Office Mgr*
Steve Anderson, *Manager*
EMP: 25 **EST:** 1983
SQ FT: 30,000
SALES (est): 1MM-4.9MM **Privately Held**
SIC: 1799 7692 Machine shop, jobbing &
repair services; on-site welding contractor;
fabricates structural metal for bridges; plate
metal fabricator; sheet metal fabricator;
welding service

(G-7343)

THORPE DISTRIBUTING CO

20240 S Diamond Lake Rd (55374)
PO Box 120 (55374-0120)
PHONE...............................763 463-2000
FAX: 763 463-2001
John Reis, *President*
EMP: 80 **EST:** 1962
SALES (est): 25MM-49.9MM **Privately Held**
WEB: www.thorpedistributing.com
SIC: 5181 Wholesales beer & other
fermented malt liquors

(G-7344)

TWIN CITY HOSE INC

20615 Commerce Blvd (55374-9335)
PHONE...............................763 428-5100
FAX: 763 428-5111
Todd McCoy, *President*
Donna Roden, *Corp Secy*
John McCoy, *Vice Pres*
Bob Pearson, *Vice Pres*
Steve Lloyd, *Manager*
▲ **EMP:** 33 **EST:** 1977
SQ FT: 25,000
SALES (est): 5MM-9.9MM **Privately Held**
WEB: www.twincityhose.com
SIC: 5085 Steel fabricator; wholesales
industrial hose, belting & packing
PA: K L McCoy & Associates Inc
4888 Lakepointe St
Detroit MI 48224
313 882-9565

(G-7345)

TWIN CITY WEST 76 AUTO TRUCK

13400 Rogers Dr (55374-9493)
PO Box 238 (55374-0238)
PHONE...............................763 428-2277
Robert Fulton, *President*
Dave Reding, *Division Mgr*
EMP: 100 **EST:** 1982
SALES (est): 10MM-24.9MM **Privately Held**
SIC: 7538 Retail gasoline filling station;
general automotive repair services; truck
stop; full service independent family
restaurant

(G-7346)

TWIN EXPRESS INC

21840 Industrial Ct # 100 (55374-9114)
PHONE...............................763 428-4969
Brad M Alister, *President*
Tammy Kainz, *Corp Secy*
Jo A Wilson, *Purch Agent*
Dennis Barthel, *Controller*
EMP: 50 **EST:** 1988
SALES (est): 5MM-9.9MM **Privately Held**
WEB: www.twinexpress.com
SIC: 4213 Over the road trucking

(G-7347)

VEIT & CO INC

14000 Veit Pl (55374-9583)
PHONE...............................763 428-2242
Patrick Hockett, *Project Mgr*
Loren Nishek, *Project Mgr*
Rollo Wallmow, *Project Mgr*
Mark Nicolay, *CFO*
Mike Dubois, *Controller*
▲ **EMP:** 250 **EST:** 1928
SQ FT: 40,000
SALES (est): 25MM-49.9MM **Privately Held**
SIC: 1611 1629 1795 4953 Grading
services; construction site preparation
services; golf course construction; buildings
& other structure demolition contractor;
sanitary landfill operation

(G-7348)

ZENITH ROGERS LLC ✪

Also Called: Hampton Inn & Suites Roger's
13550 Commerce Blvd (55374-4905)
PHONE...............................763 425-0044
Marie Ronning, *Principal*
Raija Macheledt, *Member*
Carlyon Bing, *Manager*
EMP: 25 **EST:** 2008
SALES (est): 1MM-4.9MM **Privately Held**
SIC: 7011 Traveler accommodations

ROGERS
Wright County

(G-7349)

MAGNUM CO LLC

14475 Quiram Dr Ste 1 (55374-9067)
PHONE...............................651 255-3000
Ed Kieger, *Manager*
EMP: 40 **EST:** 2003
SALES (est): 10MM-24.9MM **Privately Held**
WEB: www.magnumcompany.com
SIC: 1542 Commercial & office building
contractor

ROSE CREEK
Mower County

(G-7350)

JD DRIVER LTD (PA)

61441 170th St Ste 3 (55970-8696)
PO Box 162 (55970-0162)
PHONE...............................507 437-6050
FAX: 507 437-6151
Dean Bendtsen, *President*
Renae Bendtsen, *Bookkeeper*
EMP: 25 **EST:** 1994
SQ FT: 8,000
SALES (corp-wide): 5.78M **Privately Held**
WEB: www.jddriver.com

www.HarrisInfo.com
320

2011 Harris Minnesota
Services Directory

▲=Import ▼=Export
◆=Import/Export

SIC: **1542** 1742 Commercial & institutional building construction; drywall contractor; manufactures wood nonrefrigerated lockers; manufactures counter & sink tops

ROSEAU
Roseau County

(G-7351)
ACE RENTAL PLACE
1114 3rd St NE (56751-1333)
PO Box 266 (56751-0266)
PHONE.............................218 463-2175
Matt Anderson, *Owner*
Tina Poletes, *Vice Pres*
Darci Hults, *VP Finance*
Bruce Monsrud, *Manager*
EMP: 30 **EST:** 2005
SALES (est): 1MM-4.9MM **Privately Held**
SIC: 7021 Furnished room rental

(G-7352)
AGELESS CARE OPTIONS
702 7th St SW (56751-1498)
PHONE.............................218 463-3695
FAX: 218 463-3708
Karen Loven-Kotc, *President*
Roberta Ryan, *Manager*
Rachel Larson, *Manager*
EMP: 26 **EST:** 2004
SALES (est): 500-999K **Privately Held**
SIC: 8082 Home health care services

(G-7353)
ALTRU CLINIC
711 Delmore Dr (56751-1534)
PHONE.............................218 463-1365
FAX: 218 463-3928
Gregg Geroff, *CEO*
Barb Erickson, *Nursing Spvr*
Marie Anderson, *Med Doctor*
Robert H Clayburg, *Med Doctor*
Glen Y Oshida, *Med Doctor*
EMP: 55 **EST:** 1981
SALES (est): 5MM-9.9MM **Privately Held**
SIC: 8011 General & family practice physician or surgeon office

(G-7354)
CITIZENS STATE BANK OF ROSEAU
118 Main Ave S (56751-1512)
PO Box 160 (56751-0160)
PHONE.............................218 463-2135
FAX: 218 463-2943
Robert J Foley, *President*
Myrna Nelson, *Info Tech Mgr*
Allen Olson, *Officer*
Randy Erdmann, *Cashier*
EMP: 40 **EST:** 1939
SQ FT: 9,000
SALES (est): 10MM-24.9MM **Privately Held**
SIC: 6022 State commercial bank

(G-7355)
LIFECARE MEDICAL CENTER (PA)
715 Delmore Dr (56751-1534)
PHONE.............................218 463-4305
FAX: 218 463-4788
Kelly Hulst, *Corp Secy*
Luis G Jain, *Ch of Surgery*
Brian Garstron, *Maintenance Dir*
Brian Grafstrom, *Engineering*
Carol Klotz, *Human Res Dir*
EMP: 240 **EST:** 1952
SQ FT: 110,000
SALES (corp-wide): 34.92M **Privately Held**
SIC: 8062 8051 8052 Medical hospital; intermediate care facility; skilled nursing care facility

(G-7356)
OCCUPATIONAL DEVELOPMENT CTR
Also Called: Roseau Occupational Dev Ctr
1194 Center St W (56751-1903)
PHONE.............................218 463-1123
FAX: 218 463-3973
Ray Roth, *Branch Mgr*
Virginia Dahl, *Programmer Anys*
Shireley Huiras, *Prgrmr*
EMP: 40

SALES (est): 1MM-4.9MM **Privately Held**
WEB: www.odcmn.com
SIC: 8331 Vocational rehabilitation agency; manufactures canvas products; commercial printing; manmade broadwoven fabric mill
PA: Occupational Development Ctr
1520 Highway 32 S
Thief River Falls MN 56701
218 681-4949

(G-7357)
ROSEAU DIESEL SERVICE INC
112 2nd St SW (56751-1402)
PO Box 357 (56751-0357)
PHONE.............................218 463-1711
FAX: 218 463-1734
Wayne Czeh, *President*
EST: 1968
SQ FT: 15,000 **Privately Held**
SIC: 7538 7539 Truck engine repair service; trailer repair service

(G-7358)
ROSEAU ELECTRIC COOPERATIVE
1107 3rd St NE (56751-1326)
PHONE.............................218 463-1543
FAX: 218 463-3713
Mike Adams, *CEO*
Joel Erickson, *CEO*
Robert Melby, *President*
Basil Stavenes, *Vice Pres*
Randy Spicer, *CFO*
EMP: 27 **EST:** 1940
SQ FT: 2,500
SALES (est): 10MM-24.9MM **Privately Held**
WEB: www.roseauelectric.com
SIC: 4911 Electric power distribution service

(G-7359)
WESTAFF INC
301 5th Ave SW (56751-1440)
PHONE.............................218 463-4418
FAX: 218 463-0432
Shirley Hedlund, *Manager*
Wanda Fuerstenberg, *Manager*
EMP: 120 **Privately Held**
WEB: www.personnel-plus.com
SIC: 7361 Employment agency services
HQ: Westaff Inc
298 N Wiget Ln
Walnut Creek CA 94598
877 937-8233

ROSEMOUNT
Dakota County

(G-7360)
AAA AUTO SALVAGE INC
2871 160th St W (55068-1627)
PHONE.............................651 423-2432
FAX: 651 423-2808
Eric Schulz, *President*
John Anderson, *Corp Secy*
Amy Schulz, *Corp Secy*
Peter Anderson, *Vice Pres*
Christopher Anderson, *Vice Pres*
EMP: 43 **EST:** 1984
SQ FT: 61,500
SALES (est): 5MM-9.9MM **Privately Held**
WEB: www.aaaparts.com
SIC: 5015 Wholesales used automotive parts & supplies; retails auto & truck equipment & parts

(G-7361)
ANDERSON DIESEL TRUCK SERVICE (PA)
3686 140th St E (55068-2758)
PO Box 510 (55068-0510)
PHONE.............................651 480-7991
FAX: 651 480-7965
David Anderson, *President*
Sam Anderson, *Vice Pres*
Scott Stelman, *CFO*
Lois A Anderson, *Treasurer*
EMP: 35 **EST:** 1965
SQ FT: 4,400 **Privately Held**
SIC: 7538 General truck repair services

(G-7362)
BAY & BAY TRANSFER CO INC
3686 140th St E (55068-2758)
PO Box 510 (55068-0510)
PHONE.............................651 480-7991
Lois A Anderson, *President*
David B Anderson, *Vice Pres*
Richard Boone, *Opers Mgr*
Scott Stelman, *CFO*
Jackie Palm, *Administrator*
EMP: 200 **EST:** 1940
SQ FT: 9,000
SALES (est): 25MM-49.9MM **Privately Held**
SIC: 4213 4212 Over the road trucking; local trucking without storage services

(G-7363)
BERG CONSTRUCTION SERVICES INC
3328 151st St W (55068-1753)
PHONE.............................651 423-5531
FAX: 651 423-5532
Darlene Berg, *President*
Pam Featherstone, *Vice Pres*
David Triebel, *Manager*
Kristi Johnson, *Manager*
EMP: 40 **EST:** 1964
SQ FT: 5,500
SALES (est): 10MM-24.9MM **Privately Held**
WEB: www.bergconstructionservices.com
SIC: 1521 1542 Townhouse construction service; new single-family home construction service; new commercial & office building construction

(G-7364)
CARLSON TRACTOR & EQUIPMENT CO
15125 S Robert Trl (55068-1745)
PHONE.............................651 423-2222
Ronald C Carlson, *President*
Richard Carlson, *Corp Secy*
Cory Davidson, *Controller*
Diane McLian, *Manager*
Jim Ochetti, *Info Tech Mgr*
EMP: 30 **EST:** 1952
SQ FT: 21,200
SALES (est): 10MM-24.9MM **Privately Held**
WEB: www.carlsontractorinc.com
SIC: 5082 Wholesales general construction machinery & equipment

(G-7365)
CF INDUSTRIES INC
5300 Pine Bend Trl (55068-2560)
PHONE.............................651 437-6191
FAX: 651 437-7708
Scott Dohman, *Manager*
J D Payne, *Manager*
EMP: 37
SALES (est): 1MM-4.9MM **Publicly Held**
WEB: www.cfindustries.com
SIC: 4225 General warehousing
HQ: CF Industries Inc
4 Parkway N Ste 400
Deerfield IL 60015
847 405-2400

(G-7366)
CONSOLIDATED BUILDING CORP
16935 Gerdine Path W (55068-5113)
PHONE.............................612 759-9313
Todd Seavey, *President*
Cynthia Seavey, *Treasurer*
EMP: 140 **EST:** 1991
SALES (est): 10MM-24.9MM **Privately Held**
SIC: 1751 Carpentry contractor

(G-7367)
DAKOTA COUNTY TRANSPORTATION
2800 160th St W (55068-1628)
PHONE.............................651 423-2101
Kevin Schlangen, *Principal*
EMP: 30 **EST:** 2002
SALES (est): 1MM-4.9MM **Privately Held**
SIC: 1611 Highway & street maintenance service

(G-7368)
DAKOTA UNLIMITED INC
15953 Biscayne Ave W (55068-1601)
PHONE.............................651 423-3995
FAX: 651 423-3996
Thomas E Engelmeier, *President*
Charles Engelmeier, *Vice Pres*
Beth Jackson, *CFO*
Todd Thoennes, *Manager*
Steve Lavigne, *Manager*
EMP: 50 **EST:** 1986
SQ FT: 24,000
SALES (est): 1MM-4.9MM **Privately Held**
WEB: www.dakfence.com
SIC: 1799 Fence construction contractor

(G-7369)
ENDRES SERVICES INC
13420 Court House Blvd (55068-2553)
PHONE.............................651 438-3113
Leon Endres, *CEO*
EMP: 80 **EST:** 2001
SALES (est): 10MM-24.9MM **Privately Held**
WEB: www.endresprocessing.com
SIC: 4953 Waste material recycling services; retails farm supplies
PA: Endres Processing L L C
13420 Court House Blvd
Rosemount MN 55068
651 438-3113

(G-7370)
FIRST STATE BANK OF ROSEMOUNT
3025 145th St W (55068-4944)
PO Box 479 (55068-0479)
PHONE.............................651 423-1121
FAX: 651 423-3091
David H Toombs, *President*
Mark Toombs, *Vice Pres*
EMP: 28 **EST:** 1909
SALES (est): 5MM-9.9MM **Privately Held**
WEB: www.fsbrosemount.com
SIC: 6036 State savings bank

(G-7371)
LUNDA CONSTRUCTION CO
15601 Clayton Ave E (55068-2055)
PHONE.............................651 437-9666
Dennis Behmke, *Vice Pres*
John Stodola, *Manager*
Annette Lambrecht, *Admin Asst*
EMP: 250
SQ FT: 75,800
SALES (est): 25MM-49.9MM **Privately Held**
WEB: www.lundaconstruction.com
SIC: 1622 1611 Bridge construction; heavy highway & street construction
PA: Lunda Construction Co
620 Gebhardt Rd
Black River Falls WI 54615
715 284-9491

(G-7372)
MINNESOTA ENERGY RESOURCES
2665 145th St W (55068-4927)
PHONE.............................651 322-8902
FAX: 651 423-3306
Charles A Cloninger, *President*
Nancy Lilienthal, *Assistant*
EMP: 225 **EST:** 2006
SALES (est): 100MM-499.9MM **Privately Held**
SIC: 4924 Natural gas distribution to consumers

(G-7373)
MURPHY AUTOMOTIVE INC
7358 160th St W (55068-1047)
PHONE.............................952 432-2454
FAX: 952 432-2543
Gene Flickinger, *General Mgr*
Steve Caspers, *Vice Pres*
EMP: 30
SALES (est): 5MM-9.9MM **Privately Held**
SIC: 7539 Gas station; automotive repair services

(PA)=Parent Co (HQ)=Headquarters (DH)=Div Headquarters
✿ = New business established in last 2 years

2011 Harris Minnesota
Services Directory

© Harris InfoSource 1-866-281-6415
321

GEOGRAPHIC

(G-7374)
ROSEMOUNT-APPLE VALLEY & EAGAN
Also Called: District 196
14445 Diamond Path W (55068-4143)
PHONE...............651 423-7700
FAX: 651 423-7633
Jane Berenz, *Superintendent*
Jane Schleisman, *Hlthcr Dir*
Tom Pederstuen, *Teacher Per Dir*
EMP: 5981 EST: 1959
SALES (est): 100MM-499.9MM **Privately Held**
WEB: www.isd196.k12.mn.us
SIC: 7389 Personal service agents

(G-7375)
SPECTRO ALLOYS CORP
13220 Doyle Path E (55068-2510)
PHONE...............651 437-2815
FAX: 651 438-3714
Gregory R Palen, *CEO*
C Wurtele, *Corp Secy*
Kyla Ross, *Safety Dir*
Mitch Kvasnick, *Purchasing*
Don Woessner, *CFO*
▲ EMP: 120 EST: 1964
SQ FT: 55,510
SALES (est): 50MM-99.9MM **Privately Held**
WEB: www.spectroalloys.com
SIC: 5051 Aluminum refining & smelting; manufactures aluminum; wholesales aluminum bars, rods, ingots, sheets, pipes, plates, etc

(G-7376)
TWO RIVERS INC
14345 Conley Ave (55068-4441)
PHONE...............715 262-5292
Mark Siemers, *President*
Curtis M Siemers, *President*
Michael W Siemers, *Corp Secy*
Carl Vedders, *Vice Pres*
Joseph A Eschenbcher, *Finance Mgr*
EMP: 300 EST: 1986
SALES (est): 25MM-49.9MM **Privately Held**
SIC: 4213 Over the road trucking

(G-7377)
VIC'S HEAVY HAUL TRUCKING
3000 145th St E (55068-5916)
PHONE...............651 423-7401
Connie Winzel, *Owner*
Steve Ohmann, *Manager*
EMP: 70 EST: 1951
SALES (est): 5MM-9.9MM **Privately Held**
SIC: 4213 Heavy hauling transportation services

(G-7378)
WALBON & CO INC (PA)
4230 Pine Bend Trl Ste A (55068-3589)
PHONE...............651 437-2011
Darrell R Walbon, *President*
Richard Walbon, *Vice Pres*
Thom Sheridan, *Opers Staff*
Kathy Baggenstoss, *Manager*
EMP: 60 EST: 1975
SQ FT: 11,000 **Privately Held**
SIC: 4213 Over the road trucking; long-distance refrigerated trucking services

(G-7379)
WALBON CO TRUCKING SVCS
4230 Pine Bend Trl Ste A (55068-3589)
PHONE...............651 437-2011
Darrell Walbon, *President*
Richard Walbon, *Vice Pres*
Dick Crawford, *Controller*
Bruce Anderson, *Manager*
Tom Johnson, *Director*
EMP: 75 EST: 1994
SALES (est): 5MM-9.9MM **Privately Held**
SIC: 4212 Local trucking without storage services

(G-7380)
WALBON TRANSPORT INC
4230 Pine Bend Trl Ste A (55068-3589)
PHONE...............651 437-2011
Darrell R Walbon, *President*
Richard Walbon, *Shareholder*
EMP: 129

EST: 1976
SQ FT: 20,000
SALES (est): 10MM-24.9MM **Privately Held**
SIC: 4212 Contract mail carriers
PA: Walbon & Co Inc
4230 Pine Bend Trl Ste A
Rosemount MN 55068
651 437-2011

(G-7381)
WAYNE TRANSPORTS INC (PA)
14345 Conley Ave (55068-4441)
PHONE...............651 437-6422
FAX: 651 438-2618
Curtis M Siemers, *President*
Michael Siemers, *Corp Secy*
Carl Vedders, *Vice Pres*
Joseph Eschenbacher, *Vice Pres*
Brad Guggisberg, *Manager*
EMP: 38 EST: 1951
SQ FT: 50,000 **Privately Held**
WEB: www.waynetransports.com
SIC: 4213 Over the road trucking; long distance liquid petroleum transportation services

(G-7382)
WEBB BUSINESS PROMOTIONS INC
15197 Boulder Ave (55068-1768)
PHONE...............651 322-8200
Alan M Webb, *CEO*
Randy Locke, *President*
Tim Bohmer, *VP Sales*
Deb McGuire, *Cust Svc Dir*
Holly Pribyl, *Director*
▲ EMP: 90 EST: 1986
SQ FT: 73,000
SALES (est): 5MM-9.9MM **Privately Held**
WEB: www.webbcompany.com
SIC: 5199 Commercial printing; wholesales advertising specialties

ROTHSAY
Otter Tail County

(G-7383)
ROTHSAY TRUCK STOP & CAFE
544 Center St N (56579-4207)
PHONE...............218 867-2233
FAX: 218 867-2266
Mark Leighton, *President*
EMP: 44
SALES (est): 10MM-24.9MM **Privately Held**
SIC: 5171 Gas station; café; petroleum bulk station

ROUND LAKE
Nobles County

(G-7384)
FARLEY'S & SATHERS CANDY CO (PA)
1 Sather Plz (56167-4006)
PO Box 28 (56167-0028)
PHONE...............507 945-8181
FAX: 507 945-8181
Liam C Killeen, *CEO*
Dennis J Nemeth, *President*
Lynn Spessard, *General Mgr*
Kevin McElvain, *Vice Pres*
Scott Goetsch, *Transportation*
▲ EMP: 257 EST: 2001
SQ FT: 365,000 **Privately Held**
WEB: www.farleysandsathers.com
SIC: 5145 Wholesales confectionery products

(G-7385)
ROUND LAKE SENIOR CITIZEN CTR
206 Main St (56167)
PO Box 2 (56167-0002)
PHONE...............507 945-8477
Walt Beuthien, *President*
EMP: 25 EST: 1973
SALES (est): 500-999K **Privately Held**
SIC: 8322 Geriatric social services

ROYALTON
Morrison County

(G-7386)
PRIME COUNTRY BANK
412 N Highway 10 (56373-9171)
PO Box 25 (56373-0025)
PHONE...............320 584-5522
Rob Ronning, *President*
EST: 1927
SQ FT: 1,144 **Privately Held**
SIC: 6022 State commercial bank
PA: Royalton Bancshares Inc
412 N Highway 10
Royalton MN 56373
320 584-5522

(G-7387)
ROYALTON BANCSHARES INC (PA)
412 N Highway 10 (56373-9171)
PO Box 25 (56373-0025)
PHONE...............320 584-5522
FAX: 320 584-8385
Rob Ronning, *President*
Roseann Brower, *Principal*
Rodger Bense, *Chairman*
Sue Smieja, *Vice Pres*
Dean Dirkes, *Vice Pres*
EST: 1981 **Privately Held**
SIC: 6712 Bank holding company

(G-7388)
SUNRISE A G REPAIR
4859 State Highway 25 (56373-3311)
PHONE...............320 584-0010
Jack Hales, *General Mgr*
EMP: 40 EST: 1998
SALES (est): 25MM-49.9MM **Privately Held**
SIC: 5143 Wholesales milk

RUSH CITY
Chisago County

(G-7389)
BEVERLY ENTERPRISES - MN
650 Ramer Ave S (55069)
PHONE...............320 358-4765
David R Devereaux, *President*
John G Arena, *Corp Secy*
John R Grobmyer, *Vice Pres*
John R Gobmye, *Vice Pres*
Dwight C Kouri, *Vice Pres*
EMP: 50 EST: 2002
SALES (est): 1MM-4.9MM **Privately Held**
WEB: www.beverlynet.com
SIC: 8051 Skilled nursing care facility
DH: Beverly Enterprises Inc
1000 Fianna Way
Fort Smith AR 72919
479 201-2000

(G-7390)
LA CALHENE INC
1325 S Field Ave (55069-9041)
PHONE...............320 358-4713
FAX: 320 358-3549
Alain Sayag, *President*
Jean Brossard, *Corp Secy*
Mike Furlong, *Engrg Mgr*
Paul Olson, *VP Sls/Mktg*
Linda Clement, *Controller*
EMP: 45 EST: 1984
SQ FT: 75,000
SALES (est): 10MM-24.9MM **Privately Held**
WEB: www.lacalhene.com
SIC: 5049 Wholesales laboratory equipment
PA: LA CALHENE
1 RUE DU COMTE DE DONEGAL
VENDOME France

(G-7391)
UNITY BANK EAST
1180 W 4th St (55069-9075)
PHONE...............320 358-3600
Allen Bertilrud, *Principal*
Kevin Nascene, *CFO*
Dennis Kaufmann, *Loan Officer*
EST: 2005 **Privately Held**

SIC: 6099 Bank services

RUSHFORD
Fillmore County

(G-7392)
SEMCAC
204 N Elm St (55971-9123)
PO Box 549 (55971-0549)
PHONE...............507 864-7741
Terry Erickson, *President*
Gayle Smith, *Accounting Staf*
Valerie Howe, *Accounting Staf*
Pat Georgens, *Human Res Dir*
Gary Musselman, *MIS Dir*
EMP: 40 EST: 1966
SQ FT: 12,000 **Privately Held**
SIC: 8399 Community action agency

(G-7393)
SHEPHERD GOOD LUTHERAN HOME
800 Home St (55971-8836)
PHONE...............507 864-7714
FAX: 507 864-2842
Rhonda Spece, *CFO*
Jody Elton, *Manager*
Tom Lindh, *Exec Dir*
EMP: 161 EST: 1961
SQ FT: 82,000
SALES (est): 5MM-9.9MM **Privately Held**
SIC: 8051 Skilled nursing care facility

(G-7394)
TRI-COUNTY ELECTRIC CO-OP
31110 Cooperative Way (55971)
PO Box B (55971)
PHONE...............507 864-7783
FAX: 507 864-2871
Brian Krambeer, *President*
Yudy Sikkink, *Corp Secy*
Allen Aarsvold, *Corp Secy*
Jenny Sharmer, *Vice Pres*
Glenn Jensen, *Info Tech Dir*
EMP: 55 EST: 1937
SQ FT: 36,000
SALES (est): 25MM-49.9MM **Privately Held**
SIC: 4911 Electric power distribution service

RUSHMORE
Nobles County

(G-7395)
THIER FEEDLOTS INC
23225 County Highway 35 (56168-5237)
PHONE...............507 478-4137
Bernard Thier, *President*
Dave Thier, *Vice Pres*
Privately Held
SIC: 0211 Beef cattle feedlot

SABIN
Clay County

(G-7396)
BENEDICT FARMS INC
7540 50th Ave S (56580-9506)
PHONE...............218 789-7376
Blane Benedict, *President*
Fran Benedict, *Corp Secy*
David Benedict, *Vice Pres*
EMP: 30 EST: 1900 **Privately Held**
SIC: 0191 Crop farming

(G-7397)
FITZGERALD CONSTRUCTION
9 Osborn Ave N (56580-4012)
PO Box 197 (56580-0197)
PHONE...............218 789-7318
FAX: 218 789-7552
Ronald Fitzgerald, *Owner*
Brad Fitzgerald, *Co-Owner*
EMP: 35 EST: 1959
SALES (est): 1MM-4.9MM **Privately Held**
SIC: 1442 1771 Sand mining; asphalt contractor; gravel mining

www.HarrisInfo.com
322
2011 Harris Minnesota
Services Directory
▲=Import ▼=Export
◆=Import/Export

SACRED HEART
Renville County

(G-7398)
CLEARWATER SUITES INC
16176 810th Ave (56285-1173)
PHONE 320 765-8841
John Patock, *President*
EMP: 33 EST: 2000
SQ FT: 30,000
SALES (est): 500-999K **Privately Held**
SIC: 8322 Old age assistance

SAINT BONIFACIUS
Hennepin County

(G-7399)
CHOICE INC
8801 Wildwood Ave (55375-1123)
PO Box 327 (55375-0327)
PHONE 952 446-1475
FAX: 952 446-1411
Charlie Cummins, *Exec Dir*
Micheal Cran, *Director*
EMP: 41 EST: 1968
SALES (est): 1MM-4.9MM **Privately Held**
SIC: 8322 Adult daycare center

(G-7400)
EVERGREEN AIR SERVICES INC
4350 Main St (55375-1157)
PHONE 952 446-8255
Keith Lindley, *Owner*
EMP: 25 EST: 2000
SALES (est): 1MM-4.9MM **Privately Held**
SIC: 8748 Environmental consultant;
manufactures analytical instruments

SAINT CHARLES
Olmsted County

(G-7401)
EXCEL MANUFACTURING INC
778 W 12th St (55972-2069)
PO Box 428 (55972-0428)
PHONE 507 932-4680
FAX: 507 932-4683
Bryan Fisher, *CEO*
Todd Wondrow, *President*
Lyle Dietz, *Prdtn Mgr*
Larry Jackson, *Manager*
Tim Gifford, *Manager*
EMP: 42 EST: 1991
SQ FT: 47,000
SALES (est): 5MM-9.9MM **Privately Held**
SIC: 5051 5084 Manufactures baling
machines, for scrap metal, paper or similar
material; manufactures bulk handling
conveyor systems; wholesales wire bale
ties; wholesales industrial recycling
machinery & equipment

SAINT CHARLES
Winona County

(G-7402)
BEVERLY ENTERPRISES - MN
Also Called: Whitewater Health Care Center
525 Bluff Ave (55972-1325)
PHONE 507 932-3283
FAX: 507 932-4756
Karl Fwedderg, *Exec Dir*
EMP: 100
SQ FT: 23,700
SALES (est): 1MM-4.9MM **Privately Held**
WEB: www.beverlynet.com
SIC: 8051 8069 Skilled nursing care facility;
specialty hospital
HQ: Beverly Enterprises - MN
650 Ramer Ave S
Rush City MN 55069
320 358-4765

(G-7403)
HEIM DRYWALL INC
19485 County Road 39 (55972-4155)
PHONE 507 932-5448
James Heim, *President*
Carla Heim, *Corp Secy*
EMP: 27 EST: 1972
SALES (est): 1MM-4.9MM **Privately Held**
WEB: www.heiminsulation.com
SIC: 1742 Drywall contractor

(G-7404)
HIAWATHA BROADBAND COMMS
1242 Whitewater Ave (55972-1228)
PHONE 507 932-3942
Gary Evans, *President*
Kelly Wobig, *Manager*
EMP: 60 EST: 2003
SALES (est): 10MM-24.9MM **Privately Held**
SIC: 4813 Online services providers

(G-7405)
MAPLE VALLEY GOLF & COUNTRY
Also Called: St Charles Golf Course
1920 Gladiola Dr (55972)
PHONE 507 932-5444
FAX: 507 932-5966
Wayne Idso, *President*
EMP: 30
SALES (est): 500-999K **Privately Held**
WEB: www.maplevalleygolf.com
SIC: 7997 Membership recreation club
PA: Maple Valley Golf & Country
8600 Maple Valley Rd SE
Rochester MN 55904
507 285-9100

SAINT CLOUD
Benton County

(G-7406)
ALPINE CUSTOM WOODWORKING INC
1646 Highway 23 E (56304-9603)
PHONE 320 654-1609
Steve Barthelemy, *CEO*
John Prom, *President*
Heidi Przybilla, *General Mgr*
Steve Prom, *CFO*
Ryan Prom, *Client Mgr*
EMP: 45 EST: 1993
SQ FT: 15,000
SALES (est): 1MM-4.9MM **Privately Held**
SIC: 1751 Cabinet building & installation
service

(G-7407)
ANDY'S TOWING CO
675 Crescent St NE (56304-0517)
PHONE 320 251-5691
Robert Neitzke, *CEO*
Scott Neitzke, *General Mgr*
EMP: 42
SQ FT: 2,000
SALES (est): 1MM-4.9MM **Privately Held**
WEB: www.andys-towing.com
SIC: 7549 Automotive towing service

(G-7408)
CENTRAL MINNESOTA ERDC INC
570 1st St SE (56304-0800)
PHONE 320 202-0992
FAX: 320 252-8569
Roger Schuett, *Opers Mgr*
Jeff Hennen, *Finance*
Windy Naack, *Accounts Mgr*
Tom Downing, *CIO*
Dan Desmarais, *Technical Staff*
EMP: 32 EST: 1966
SQ FT: 48,000
SALES (est): 1MM-4.9MM **Privately Held**
SIC: 7389 5049 Purchasing service;
wholesales school supplies

(G-7409)
CONSUMER DIRECTIONS INC
22 Wilson Ave NE Ste 205 (56304-0440)
PO Box 6128 (56302-6128)
PHONE 320 420-3423
Lisa Walz, *President*
Shantel Jaszcak, *CFO*
EMP: 2000 EST: 2001 **Privately Held**
SIC: 7361 8721 Employment agency
services; payroll services

(G-7410)
CORE PROFESSIONAL SERVICES
451 E Saint Germain St # 400
(56304-0759)
PHONE 320 202-1400
FAX: 320 251-8945
Frank Weber, *Director*
EMP: 25 EST: 2001
SALES (est): 1MM-4.9MM **Privately Held**
SIC: 8049 Clinical psychologist office

(G-7411)
DONLIN CO (PA)
3405 Energy Dr (56304-4647)
PHONE 320 251-3680
FAX: 320 251-2722
Lawrence Donlin, *Ch of Bd*
Timothy O Donlin, *President*
Kevin Swecker, *Vice Pres*
Jim Sattler, *Purchasing*
▲ EMP: 50 EST: 1923
SQ FT: 100,000 **Privately Held**
WEB: www.donlin.com
SIC: 5031 Wholesales doors & windows;
wholesales exterior building materials;
wholesales interior building materials;
wholesales millwork

(G-7412)
DUFFY ENGINEERING & ASSOCIATES
350 Highway 10 S Ste 101 (56304-1244)
PHONE 320 259-6575
Terrance W Duffy, *President*
Sandy Duffy, *CFO*
EMP: 26 EST: 1990
SQ FT: 8,300
SALES (est): 1MM-4.9MM **Privately Held**
SIC: 8711 8713 Structural engineering
services; surveying service

(G-7413)
EL-JAY PLUMBING & HEATING INC
520 Apollo Ave NE (56304-0208)
PHONE 320 251-8330
FAX: 320 251-4133
Andrew Fritz, *President*
Jodi Fritz, *Corp Secy*
Geri Herges, *Manager*
EMP: 80 EST: 1967
SQ FT: 10,000
SALES (est): 5MM-9.9MM **Privately Held**
WEB: www.eljayplumbing.com
SIC: 1711 Plumbing service; heating & air
conditioning contractor

(G-7414)
FOSTER FOUR
Also Called: Opportunity Manor
1708 7th St SE (56304-1353)
PHONE 320 240-0243
Barb Rebischke, *Administrator*
Jim Christensen, *Director*
EMP: 50 EST: 2000
SALES (est): 1MM-4.9MM **Privately Held**
SIC: 8361 Group foster home

(G-7415)
FOUSSARD HOSPITALITY INC
Also Called: Americanna Inn
520 Highway 10 S (56304-1249)
PHONE 320 252-8700
FAX: 320 252-8700
Cathy Paulson, *General Mgr*
EMP: 25
SQ FT: 40,000
SALES (est): 1MM-4.9MM **Privately Held**
SIC: 7011 Hotel
PA: Foussard Hospitality Inc
4940 Highway 61 N
Saint Paul MN 55110
651 429-5393

(G-7416)
GENERAL SECURITY SERVICES CORP
Also Called: Midwest Patrol Div
574 And Half E St Germain (56304)
PHONE 320 252-3794
FAX: 320 252-8298
Whitney Miller, *Branch Mgr*
Mike Arseneau, *Manager*
EMP: 60
SALES (est): 1MM-4.9MM **Privately Held**
WEB: www.gssc.net
SIC: 7381 Guard protective service
PA: General Security Services Corp
9110 Meadowview Rd
Minneapolis MN 55425
952 858-5000

(G-7417)
HEARTLAND HOSPICE SERVICES INC
605 Franklin Ave NE (56304-0225)
PHONE 320 654-1136
Kim Aijala, *Manager*
Laura Scherer, *Director*
EMP: 100
SALES (est): 1MM-4.9MM **Privately Held**
WEB: www.carlyle.com
SIC: 8082 Home health care services
HQ: Heartland Hospice Services LLC
333 N Summit St
Toledo OH 43604
419 252-5500

(G-7418)
MCPHERSON INSULATION INC
810 Mayhew Lake Rd NE (56304-9610)
PHONE 320 259-5735
FAX: 320 259-5236
Brent McPherson, *President*
EMP: 26 EST: 1994
SALES (est): 1MM-4.9MM **Privately Held**
SIC: 1742 Drywall, plastering & insulation
contractor

(G-7419)
MECHANICAL ENERGY SYSTEMS INC
629 Lincoln Ave NE (56304-0249)
PHONE 320 253-4859
FAX: 320 253-4464
Mike Fitch, *President*
Mary Kay, *Manager*
Kevin Johnson, *Manager*
EMP: 25 EST: 1983
SALES (est): 1MM-4.9MM **Privately Held**
WEB: www.mechanicalenergysystems.com
SIC: 1711 Heating & air conditioning
contractor

(G-7420)
MICHAEL'S RESTAURANT
510 Highway 10 S (56304-1249)
PHONE 320 252-7100
FAX: 320 252-0053
Larry Lang, *Owner*
EMP: 30
SALES (est): 1MM-4.9MM **Privately Held**
SIC: 7299 Caterer; banquet hall facility

(G-7421)
PAN-O-GOLD BAKING CO (PA)
Also Called: Country Hearth
444 E Saint Germain St (56304-0749)
PO Box 848 (56302-0848)
PHONE 320 251-9361
FAX: 320 251-6894
Howard R Alton III, *President*
Patricia A Baker, *Corp Secy*
Verlyn Owen, *Senior VP*
Identeter J Rolfzen, *Senior VP*
James K Akervik, *Vice Pres*
▲ EMP: 200 EST: 1911
SQ FT: 190,000
SALES (corp-wide): 163.96M **Privately Held**
WEB: www.panogold.com
SIC: 5149 Wholesales bakery products;
manufactures fresh or frozen bread

GEOGRAPHIC

GEOGRAPHIC (vertical tab)

(G-7422)
PHILLIPS RECYCLING SYSTEMS LLC
119 6th Ave NE (56304-0504)
PHONE 320 251-5980
FAX: 320 251-4711
Michael J Roth, *CEO*
Tony White, *Managing Dir*
Jeff Kenpin, *Vice Pres*
David Wiedl, *Opers Mgr*
Ronald J Roth, *Treasurer*
EMP: 52 **EST:** 1971
SQ FT: 1,800
SALES (est): 10MM-24.9MM **Privately Held**
WEB: www.phillipsrecycling.com
SIC: 5093 4212 Wholesales recyclable scrap & waste materials; garbage collection & transportation services without disposal

(G-7423)
REACH-UP INC
1250 Johnson Rd (56304-1255)
PHONE 320 253-8110
Irene Callahan, *CFO*
Linda Maron, *Exec Dir*
EMP: 40 **EST:** 1979
SQ FT: 8,000
SALES (est): 500-999K **Privately Held**
WEB: www.reachup.com
SIC: 8351 Preschool center

(G-7424)
REGENT BROADCASTING OF ST
640 Lincoln Ave SE (56304-1024)
PHONE 320 251-4422
FAX: 320 251-8060
Terry Jacobs, *President*
Andrea Lambrecht, *Business Mgr*
Mark Young, *Engineer*
Deb Huschle, *Finance Mgr*
Steve Lahr, *Sales Mgr*
EMP: 50 **EST:** 1950
SQ FT: 12,000
SALES (est): 1MM-4.9MM **Privately Held**
WEB: www.regentbroadcasting.com
SIC: 4832 Radio broadcasting station

(G-7425)
REGION COMMUNICATIONS
640 Lincoln Ave SE (56304-1024)
PO Box 220 (56302-0220)
PHONE 320 252-5852
Cal Hall, *Manager*
EMP: 50 **EST:** 1996
SALES (est): 1MM-4.9MM **Privately Held**
SIC: 4832 Radio broadcasting station

(G-7426)
REX GRANITE CO
414 Lincoln Ave NE (56304-0244)
PO Box 924 (56302-0924)
PHONE 320 252-2060
FAX: 320 252-4678
Neil Zniewski, *President*
Earl Zniewski, *Vice Pres*
Carl Zniewski, *Treasurer*
Mike Zniewski, *Office Mgr*
▲ **EMP:** 25 **EST:** 1921
SQ FT: 15,000
SALES (est): 1MM-4.9MM **Privately Held**
WEB: www.granitepetmemorials.com
SIC: 1411 Manufactures monuments & markers; dimension stone mining

(G-7427)
SIMPLEXGRINNELL LP
605 Franklin Ave NE (56304-0225)
PHONE 320 253-8883
Steve Hinson, *Branch Mgr*
EMP: 50
SALES (est): 5MM-9.9MM **Privately Held**
WEB: www.simplexgrinnell.com
SIC: 1711 1731 7382 Fire sprinkler system installation service; fire detection & burglar alarm systems specialization contractor; retails fire extinguishers; security systems services
DH: Simplexgrinnell LP
1 Town Center Rd
Boca Raton FL 33486
561 988-7200

(G-7428)
SPECTRUM COMMUNITY HEALTH INC
Also Called: Saint Cloud Care Free Living
1225 E Division St (56304-0928)
PHONE 320 252-9640
FAX: 320 656-5324
Merle Samson, *CEO*
EMP: 37 **EST:** 2003
SALES (est): 1MM-4.9MM **Privately Held**
SIC: 8082 Home health care services

(G-7429)
ST CLOUD REFRIGERATION INC
604 Lincoln Ave NE (56304-0248)
PHONE 320 251-6861
FAX: 320 251-9390
Mike Fitch, *CEO*
Tom Peck, *Vice Pres*
Pat Welty, *CFO*
EMP: 110 **EST:** 1954
SQ FT: 10,000
SALES (est): 10MM-24.9MM **Privately Held**
WEB: www.stcloudrefrig.com
SIC: 1711 Refrigeration contractor; heating & air conditioning contractor; ventilation & duct work contractor

(G-7430)
TRI COUNTY HUMANE SOCIETY INC
735 8th St NE (56304-0207)
PHONE 320 252-0896
FAX: 320 252-1325
Chris Stewart, *President*
Laurie Gerard, *Manager*
Vicki Davis, *Exec Dir*
EMP: 42 **EST:** 1976 **Privately Held**
WEB: www.tricountyhumanesociety.org
SIC: 8699 Animal humane society

(G-7431)
WEIDNER PLUMBING & HEATING CO
29 Wilson Ave NE (56304-0441)
PO Box 1087 (56302-1087)
PHONE 320 252-3000
FAX: 320 252-3046
Bruce Gohmann, *President*
EMP: 60 **EST:** 1942
SQ FT: 8,000
SALES (est): 5MM-9.9MM **Privately Held**
WEB: www.weidnermech.com
SIC: 1711 Plumbing service; heating & air conditioning contractor; ventilation & duct work contractor

---

SAINT CLOUD
Sherburne County

(G-7432)
ABF FREIGHT SYSTEM INC
2981 Highway 10 SE (56304-9763)
PHONE 320 259-5025
FAX: 320 259-1580
Tony Loele, *Marketing Staff*
Nicole Dockter, *Manager*
EMP: 50
SALES (est): 5MM-9.9MM **Publicly Held**
WEB: www.abfs.com
SIC: 4213 Over the road trucking
HQ: ABF Freight System Inc
3801 Old Greenwood Rd
Fort Smith AR 72903
479 785-6000

(G-7433)
APPERT'S INC
900 Highway 10 SE (56304-1824)
PHONE 320 251-3200
Joseph R Omann, *President*
Timothy Appert, *Chairman*
Chris Appert, *Corp Secy*
Pat Lindstrom, *Opers Mgr*
Wayne Harrison, *Purchasing*
EMP: 190 **EST:** 1966
SQ FT: 140,000
SALES (est): 100MM-499.9MM **Privately Held**
WEB: www.apperts.com

SIC: 5142 5141 Wholesales packaged frozen foods; wholesales frozen fish, meat & poultry; meat & fish market; wholesales general line groceries; manufactures frozen meat products; grocery store

(G-7434)
APPERTS FROZEN FOODS INC
Also Called: Appert Foods
809 Highway 10 SE (56304-1806)
PHONE 320 251-3200
Timothy Appert, *President*
Chris Appert, *Corp Secy*
Jeff Morse, *Vice Pres*
Wayne Harrison, *Purchasing*
Duane Monceaux, *QC Dir*
EMP: 65 **EST:** 1935
SQ FT: 48,000
SALES (est): 50MM-99.9MM **Privately Held**
SIC: 5142 5141 5148 Wholesales packaged frozen foods; wholesales packaged frozen fish; wholesales packaged frozen meats; wholesales fresh fruits & vegetables; fruit & vegetable market; wholesales general line groceries; meat market; fish & seafood market; grocery store

(G-7435)
BRISTOW'S INC
3653 32nd St SE (56304-9719)
PHONE 320 253-7878
FAX: 320 253-1038
Michael Bristow, *President*
Barbara Bristow, *Corp Secy*
EMP: 25 **EST:** 1976
SQ FT: 45,000
SALES (est): 5MM-9.9MM **Privately Held**
WEB: www.bristowsinc.com
SIC: 7699 Motorcycle dealer; snowmobile dealer; retails jet skis; retails dune buggies; recreational vehicle repair service

(G-7436)
GRANITE CITY DENTAL LABORATORY
1109 7th St SE (56304-1505)
PHONE 320 253-4825
FAX: 320 253-6046
William C Young, *President*
Brenda James, *Executive*
EMP: 30 **EST:** 1978
SALES (est): 1MM-4.9MM **Privately Held**
SIC: 8072 Dental laboratory; dental crown & bridge production laboratory; denture production laboratory

(G-7437)
GRANITE CITY READY MIX INC
2450 Highway 10 S (56304-9432)
PO Box 1305 (56302-1305)
PHONE 320 252-4322
Robert C Bogard Sr, *President*
Herb Thielem, *Manager*
Dan Erickson, *Manager*
EMP: 46 **EST:** 1959
SQ FT: 1,500
SALES (est): 5MM-9.9MM **Publicly Held**
WEB: www.mdu.com
SIC: 1442 Manufactures ready-mixed concrete; construction sand & gravel mining
HQ: Knife River Corp
1150 W Century Ave
Bismarck ND 58503
701 530-1400

(G-7438)
GUARDIAN SCHOOL BUS CO
2779 Highway 10 SE (56304-9763)
PHONE 320 259-8225
FAX: 320 259-8279
Jeffrey Larson, *President*
Barbara Larson, *Corp Secy*
EMP: 25 **EST:** 1988
SALES (est): 500-999K **Privately Held**
SIC: 4151 School bus service

(G-7439)
NORTHWEST HEALTH CARE INC
1717 University Dr SE (56304-2023)
PHONE 320 251-9120
Darwin Schwantes, *President*
Raymond Dykhuizen, *Admin Asst*
EMP: 120 **EST:** 1964
SALES (est): 1MM-4.9MM **Privately Held**
WEB: www.northwesthealthcare.com

SIC: 8051 Skilled nursing care facility

(G-7440)
S T C AVIATION INC
Also Called: SAINT CLOUD AVIATION
1544 45th Ave SE (56304-9793)
PO Box 1599 (56302-1599)
PHONE 320 253-1500
FAX: 320 253-8554
William Mavencamp Jr, *President*
Robert Shadduck, *Corp Secy*
Steve Hollingworhth, *Manager*
EMP: 35 **EST:** 1969
SQ FT: 5,500
SALES (est): 1MM-4.9MM **Privately Held**
SIC: 4581 Fixed base operator

(G-7441)
ST BENEDICT'S SENIOR COMMUNITY
Also Called: Benedict Village
1810 Minnesota Blvd # 228 (56304-2438)
PHONE 320 252-0010
FAX: 320 252-8611
Shelley Jacobs, *Purch Agent*
Eric Lohn, *Finance Dir*
Erin Hjort, *Human Resources*
James Hyatt, *Mktg Dir*
Kelly Ojeda, *Pub Rel Dir*
EMP: 530 **EST:** 1976
SQ FT: 108,000
SALES (est): 10MM-24.9MM **Privately Held**
SIC: 8051 8052 Skilled nursing care facility; intermediate care facility

(G-7442)
ST CLOUD TRUCK SALES INC
701 15th Ave SE (56304-1542)
PO Box 1475 (56302-1475)
PHONE 320 251-0931
FAX: 320 255-8859
Harold E Anderson, *President*
Clyde Lewandouski, *President*
Rollis Anderson, *Vice Pres*
Pat Miller, *CFO*
Scott Anderson, *Treasurer*
EMP: 94 **EST:** 1963
SQ FT: 60,000
SALES (est): 5MM-9.9MM **Privately Held**
SIC: 7538 5012 5013 General truck repair services; manufactures truck & bus bodies; wholesales new & used trailers for trucks; wholesales truck tractors; wholesales commercial trucks; recreational vehicle repair services; wholesales truck parts & accessories

(G-7443)
UNITED PARCEL SERVICE OF NEW
Also Called: UPS
3057 Highway 10 SE (56304-9763)
PHONE 320 253-4100
Stephen Anderson, *Manager*
EMP: 150
SALES (est): 5MM-9.9MM **Publicly Held**
WEB: www.martrac.com
SIC: 4215 Parcel delivery services by vehicle
HQ: United Parcel Service of New
55 Glenlake Pkwy NE
Atlanta GA 30328
404 828-6000

(G-7444)
VEOLIA ES SOLID WASTE OF PA
2355 12th St SE (56304-9791)
PHONE 320 251-8919
Rob Holzer, *General Mgr*
EMP: 30
SALES (est): 5MM-9.9MM **Privately Held**
WEB: www.veoliaes.com
SIC: 4953 Rubbish collection & disposal services
DH: Veolia Es Solid Waste of Pa
300 W Washington St
Norristown PA 19401
610 272-2001

www.HarrisInfo.com
324

2011 Harris Minnesota
Services Directory

▲=Import ▼=Export
◆=Import/Export

SAINT CLOUD
Stearns County

(G-7445)

A T S SPECIALIZED INC
725 Opportunity Dr (56301-5886)
PO Box 1377 (56302-1377)
PHONE 320 255-7400
Rollis Anderson, *President*
EMP: 200 **EST:** 1994
SALES (est): 25MM-49.9MM **Privately Held**
SIC: 4213 Over the road trucking

(G-7446)

ALL TEMPORARIES INC
2719 W Division St Ste 11 (56301-3858)
PHONE 320 654-6031
FAX: 320 203-1320
Donna Liveringhouse, *Director*
EMP: 38
SALES (est): 1MM-4.9MM **Privately Held**
SIC: 8082 7361 Home health care services;
nurses' registry service

(G-7447)

AMERICAN HERITAGE NATIONAL
2915 2nd St S (56301-3855)
PO Box 160 (56302-0160)
PHONE 320 654-9555
FAX: 320 654-2759
Lenard Wohlman, *President*
Michelle Lehner, *Cust Mgr*
Clair C Shindler, *Receptionist*
EMP: 29
SALES (est): 5MM-9.9MM **Privately Held**
SIC: 6021 National commercial bank
PA: American Heritage National
　24 2nd St S
　Long Prairie MN 56347
　320 732-6131

(G-7448)

AMERIPRIDE SERVICES INC
Also Called: American Linen Supply
6500 Saukview Dr (56303-0804)
PHONE 320 251-2525
FAX: 320 253-7904
Karen Booen, *Human Res Mgr*
Randy Johnson, *Sales Executive*
John Sultherland, *Manager*
David Narlock, *Manager*
EMP: 75
SALES (est): 1MM-4.9MM **Privately Held**
WEB: www.ameripride.com
SIC: 7213 Linen supply service
PA: Ameripride Services Inc
　10801 Wayzata Blvd # 100
　Hopkins MN 55305
　952 738-4200

(G-7449)

ANDERSON TRUCKING SERVICE INC (PA)
725 Opportunity Dr (56301-5886)
PO Box 1377 (56302-1377)
PHONE 320 255-7400
FAX: 320 255-7412
Rollis H Anderson, *President*
Jeff Potthoff, *Vice Pres*
Scott Fuller, *CFO*
Karen Grosulak, *Human Res Mgr*
Joyce Steucey, *Human Resources*
◆ **EMP:** 250 **EST:** 1943
SQ FT: 29,000 **Privately Held**
WEB: www.besttruckdrivingjob.com
SIC: 4213 Over the road trucking; building
materials transportation; heavy hauling
transportation services

(G-7450)

ANESTHESIA ASSOCIATES OF ST
3701 12th St N Ste 202 (56303-2253)
PO Box 725 (56302-0725)
PHONE 320 258-3090
Craig Johnson, *CEO*
EMP: 38 **EST:** 1965
SALES (est): 1MM-4.9MM **Privately Held**
SIC: 8011 Anesthesiologist office

(G-7451)

ANNA MARIES
500 11th Ave N (56303-3553)
PO Box 367 (56302-0367)
PHONE 320 253-6900
Maxine Barnett, *Director*
EMP: 40 **EST:** 2000
SALES (est): 1MM-4.9MM **Privately Held**
WEB: www.annamaries.com
SIC: 8322 Emergency shelters

(G-7452)

APOLLO INSURANCE AGENCY OF ST
28 11th Ave S (56301-4218)
PHONE 320 253-1122
FAX: 320 253-9969
John Delinsky, *President*
Diane Klitsch, *Supervisor*
EMP: 25 **EST:** 1969
SQ FT: 2,200
SALES (est): 1MM-4.9MM **Privately Held**
WEB: www.apolloinsurance.com
SIC: 6411 Insurance services

(G-7453)

ARIA COMMUNICATIONS CORP
717 W Saint Germain St (56301-3534)
PHONE 320 259-5206
FAX: 320 259-4314
Anthony J Segale, *Ch of Bd*
Charles N Lucas, *President*
Linda C Palmer, *Corp Secy*
Michael Harrington, *COO*
Catherine I Winge, *Vice Pres*
EMP: 245 **EST:** 1985
SQ FT: 24,000
SALES (est): 5MM-9.9MM **Privately Held**
WEB: www.ariacallsandcards.com
SIC: 7389 7331 Telemarketing services;
mailing services

(G-7454)

ARTIC COLD STORAGE INC
4139 Roosevelt Rd (56301-9532)
PHONE 320 253-9979
FAX: 320 253-8025
Jeff Condon, *President*
Julie Condon, *Vice Pres*
EMP: 40 **EST:** 1975
SQ FT: 60,000
SALES (est): 1MM-4.9MM **Privately Held**
SIC: 4222 Refrigerated warehousing &
storage service

(G-7455)

ATS INC
725 Opportunity Dr (56301-5886)
PO Box 1377 (56302-1377)
PHONE 320 255-7400
Rollie Anderson, *President*
Lynette Oneil, *Finance Mgr*
Tanya Garren, *Assistant*
EMP: 200 **EST:** 1983
SQ FT: 15,000
SALES (est): 25MM-49.9MM **Privately Held**
WEB: www.besttruckdrivingjob.com
SIC: 4213 Building materials transportation;
heavy hauling transportation services
PA: Anderson Trucking Service Inc
　725 Opportunity Dr
　Saint Cloud MN 56301
　320 255-7400

(G-7456)

ATS LOGISTICS SERVICES INC (HQ)
Also Called: Sureway Transportation Co
725 Opportunity Dr (56301-5886)
PO Box 7095 (56302-7095)
PHONE 320 255-7488
FAX: 320 255-7480
Rollis Anderson, *President*
Jason Netland, *Vice Pres*
Jodi Nesland, *Credit Mgr*
Tanya Garren, *Government Rel*
◆ **EMP:** 51 **EST:** 1989 **Privately Held**
WEB: www.besttruckdrivingjob.com
SIC: 4731 Freight transportation
arrangement services
PA: Anderson Trucking Service Inc
　725 Opportunity Dr
　Saint Cloud MN 56301
　320 255-7400

(G-7457)

BANCNORTH INVESTMENT GROUP
400 1st St S (56301-3626)
PO Box 283 (56302-0283)
PHONE 320 656-4300
Randall Ciccati, *President*
Randall Ciccatti, *President*
EMP: 30 **EST:** 1992
SQ FT: 20,836
SALES (est): 5MM-9.9MM **Privately Held**
WEB: www.eprimevest.com
SIC: 6282 Financial investment advice
service
HQ: Primevest Financial Services
　400 1st St S Ste 300
　Saint Cloud MN 56301
　320 656-4300

(G-7458)

BINGO EMPORIUM
2820 1st St S (56301-3804)
PHONE 320 252-3607
FAX: 320 255-7390
Bonnie Markling, *President*
EMP: 60 **EST:** 1985
SALES (est): 1MM-4.9MM **Privately Held**
WEB: www.bingoemporium.com
SIC: 7999 Bingo hall

(G-7459)

BIOLIFE PLASMA SERVICES LP
2019 Stearns Way (56303-1359)
PHONE 320 259-6300
FAX: 320 259-6306
Inga Anderson, *Manager*
Dennis Glaser, *Manager*
Angie Ahrens, *Supervisor*
Katy Gustafson, *Asst Mgr*
EMP: 40
SALES (est): 1MM-4.9MM **Publicly Held**
WEB: www.biolifeplasma.com
SIC: 8099 Plasmapherous center
HQ: Biolife Plasma Services LP
　1435 Lake Cook Rd
　Philadelphia PA 19182
　847 940-5559

(G-7460)

BLASCHKO COMPUTERS INC
Also Called: EMR Innovations
3290 33rd St S (56301-9558)
PHONE 320 252-0234
FAX: 320 252-1144
Edward Blaschko, *President*
Jim Svihel, *Maint Mgr*
Shanon Odegaard, *Engineer*
Lori Wirtzfeld, *Controller*
Robin Kermier, *Administrator*
EMP: 50 **EST:** 1984
SALES (est): 5MM-9.9MM **Privately Held**
WEB: www.emrinnov.com
SIC: 7373 7371 Computer integrated
systems design services; custom computer
software systems analysis & design service

(G-7461)

BLOCK E LODGING LLC
404 W Saint Germain St (56301-3612)
PHONE 320 258-2580
Jim Graves, *Mng Member*
EMP: 60 **EST:** 2007
SALES (est): 1MM-4.9MM **Privately Held**
SIC: 7011 Vacation lodge

(G-7462)

BNSF RAILWAY CO
1715 Breckenridge Ave (56303-3970)
PO Box 216 (56302-0216)
PHONE 320 259-3208
FAX: 320 259-3240
Jim Haubrick, *Branch Mgr*
Greg Jaeb, *Master*
EMP: 200
SALES (est): 10MM-24.9MM **Publicly Held**
WEB: www.bnsf.com
SIC: 4013 Railroad terminals
HQ: Burlington Northern Santa Fe
　2650 Lou Menk Dr
　Fort Worth TX 76131
　800 795-2673

(G-7463)

BOYS & GIRLS CLUBS OF CENTRAL
345 30th Ave N (56303-3755)
PHONE 320 252-7616
FAX: 320 252-4471
Devon Williams, *Human Resources*
Carol Keller, *Manager*
Mark Sakry, *Exec Dir*
Debra Nebosis, *Director*
Vicki McKnight, *Director*
EMP: 150 **EST:** 1974 **Privately Held**
SIC: 8641 8322 Youth organizations;
individual & family social services

(G-7464)

BR MOTELS INC
Also Called: Super 8 Motel
50 Park Ave S (56301-3711)
PHONE 320 253-5530
FAX: 320 253-5292
Julie Davis, *General Mgr*
Leon Fischer, *Principal*
Julie Neuhalfen, *Treasurer*
Todd Kerfeld, *Asst Mgr*
Teddy B LLP, *Shareholder*
EMP: 30 **EST:** 1995
SALES (est): 1MM-4.9MM **Privately Held**
SIC: 7011 Traveler accommodations

(G-7465)

BREMER BANK (DH)
1100 W Saint Germain St (56301-3403)
PO Box 847 (56302-0847)
PHONE 320 251-3300
FAX: 320 255-7149
Thomas G Rickars, *President*
Randy Wolf, *Exec VP*
Richard Dinello, *Senior VP*
Mike Mavetz, *Senior VP*
Tom Brasel, *Assistant VP*
EMP: 59 **EST:** 1920
SQ FT: 9,600 **Privately Held**
SIC: 6021 National commercial bank
HQ: Bremer Financial Corp
　445 Minnesota St Ste 2000
　Saint Paul MN 55101
　651 227-7621

(G-7466)

BREMER TRUST NATIONAL ASSN
4150 2nd St S Ste 180 (56301-3996)
PO Box 986 (56302-0986)
PHONE 320 252-3918
Kenneth Nelson, *President*
Natalie Kramer, *Principal*
Beverly A Bownik, *Assistant VP*
Douglas A Holzkamp, *Vice Pres*
David Erickson, *Vice Pres*
EMP: 35 **EST:** 1987
SALES (est): 5MM-9.9MM **Privately Held**
SIC: 6022 8742 Commercial state trust
companies accepting deposits; financial
management consulting services
HQ: Bremer Financial Corp
　445 Minnesota St Ste 2000
　Saint Paul MN 55101
　651 227-7621

(G-7467)

CAMCO CONSTRUCTION INC
3201 Bent Tree Dr (56301-9033)
PO Box 7413 (56302-7413)
PHONE 320 259-1051
FAX: 320 259-9793
Jay Lommel, *President*
Terry Serbus, *Exec VP*
Paul Beseman, *Senior VP*
Steven Croak, *Vice Pres*
Jenny Ahlberg, *Treasurer*
EMP: 25 **EST:** 1992
SQ FT: 9,000
SALES (est): 1MM-4.9MM **Privately Held**
SIC: 1741 1771 Masonry & stonework
contractor; concrete contractor

(G-7468)

CAMERA SHOP OF SAINT CLOUD INC
25 7th Ave S Ste 200 (56301-3670)
PO Box 927 (56302-0927)
PHONE 320 251-2622
FAX: 320 251-2995

(PA)=Parent Co (HQ)=Headquarters (DH)=Div Headquarters
✪ = New business established in last 2 years

2011 Harris Minnesota
Services Directory

© Harris InfoSource 1-866-281-6415
325

Harold R Stanius, *President*
Frank Rangsmuth, *Vice Pres*
EMP: 25 **EST:** 1960
SALES (est): 1MM-4.9MM **Privately Held**
WEB: www.thecamerashop.com
SIC: 7384 Photographic service; film developing & printing service

(G-7469)
CAPITAL GRANITE & MARBLE INC
25325 Hwy 23   (56301)
PO Box 375, Rockville   (56369-0375)
PHONE..............................320 259-7625
FAX: 320 259-0251
Charles Johannes, *President*
Joshua Behling, *Manager*
▲ **EMP:** 30 **EST:** 1991
SQ FT: 65,000
SALES (est): 1MM-4.9MM **Privately Held**
SIC: 1799 5032 Countertop installation service; manufactures cut & shaped building marble; manufactures granite or stone curbing; wholesales granite building stone; wholesales marble building stone

(G-7470)
CARE TRANSPORTATION INC
2600 7th St N   (56303-3100)
PHONE..............................320 253-7729
FAX: 320 251-6261
Dale Victor, *President*
EMP: 25 **EST:** 1944
SQ FT: 4,800
SALES (est): 1MM-4.9MM **Privately Held**
SIC: 4119 4121 Local passenger transportation service; taxi cab service

(G-7471)
CARITAS DEBT COUNSELING
911 18th St N   (56303-1203)
PO Box 2390   (56302-2390)
PHONE..............................320 650-1660
Kathy Sherrard, *Office Mgr*
Theresa Lau, *Med Doctor*
Ann M Kooiker, *Med Doctor*
Mishon Bulson, *Manager*
Nancy String, *Nurse Practr*
EMP: 80 **EST:** 2000
SALES (est): 10MM-24.9MM **Privately Held**
SIC: 8742 Banking & finance consultant

(G-7472)
CASTLE REALTY INC
720 8th Ave N   (56303-3420)
PHONE..............................320 251-1010
FAX: 320 251-0217
Donald Landwehr, *CEO*
Sharon Lesikar, *Corp Secy*
EMP: 30 **EST:** 1982
SQ FT: 3,600
SALES (est): 5MM-9.9MM **Privately Held**
SIC: 6531 Real estate services

(G-7473)
CATHOLIC CHARITIES OF THE (PA)
Also Called: ST CLOUD CHILDREN'S HOME
911 18th St N   (56303-1203)
PO Box 2390   (56302-2390)
PHONE..............................320 650-1550
Reane Struck, *Human Res Mgr*
Karleen K Schmiedt, *Manager*
Charlotte A Dokken, *Manager*
Steve Bresnahan, *Director*
EMP: 325 **EST:** 1955
SALES (corp-wide): 24.11M **Privately Held**
SIC: 8322 Family or marriage counseling; meal delivery program; refugee services

(G-7474)
CATHOLIC CHARITIES OF THE
Also Called: St Cloud Children's Home Sch
1726 7th Ave S   (56301-5711)
PHONE..............................320 251-8811
FAX: 320 251-3198
John Krueger, *Branch Mgr*
Bonnie Schwinghammer, *Librarian*
Gene Huckenpoehler, *Administrator*
Marlo Evans, *Director*
Lon Enerson, *Tech/Comp Coord*
EMP: 110
SALES (est): 1MM-4.9MM **Privately Held**

SIC: 8361 Residential care facility
PA: Catholic Charities of The
911 18th St N
Saint Cloud MN 56303
320 650-1550

(G-7475)
CATHOLIC CHARITIES OF THE
Also Called: Services To Handicapped
205 7th Ave N   (56303-4758)
PHONE..............................320 259-8757
FAX: 320 240-3339
Larry Sell, *Branch Mgr*
EMP: 25
SALES (est): 1MM-4.9MM **Privately Held**
SIC: 8322 Individual & family social services
PA: Catholic Charities of The
911 18th St N
Saint Cloud MN 56303
320 650-1550

(G-7476)
CATHOLIC CHARITIES OF THE DIOC
1730 7th Ave S   (56301-5711)
PHONE..............................320 240-3337
FAX: 320 258-3510
David Schwartz, *Principal*
Steven Bresnahan, *Exec Dir*
EMP: 36 **EST:** 2004
SALES (est): 1MM-4.9MM **Privately Held**
SIC: 8322 Individual & family social services

(G-7477)
CATTON WOLSETH COMO & JACOBS
Also Called: North Way Dental
1500 Northway Dr   (56303-4477)
PO Box 1659   (56302-1659)
PHONE..............................320 253-4778
FAX: 320 253-9271
Tom Como DDS, *President*
EMP: 36 **EST:** 1974
SALES (est): 1MM-4.9MM **Privately Held**
SIC: 8021 Group & corporate practice dentist office

(G-7478)
CENTRACARE CLINIC
1900 Centracare Cir   (56303-5000)
PHONE..............................320 654-3630
FAX: 320 654-3667
Donna Corrigan, *Human Res Mgr*
Oluade A Ajayi MD, *Med Doctor*
Elizabeth Riesgraf MD, *Med Doctor*
Mary Stiles MD, *Med Doctor*
Marilyn Jeanitso, *Med Doctor*
EMP: 150
SALES (est): 10MM-24.9MM **Privately Held**
WEB: www.centracareclinic.com
SIC: 8011 Clinic operated by physicians; drug store
PA: Centracare Clinic
1200 6th Ave N
Saint Cloud MN 56303
320 252-5131

(G-7479)
CENTRACARE CLINIC
1520 Whitney Ct   (56303-1867)
PHONE..............................320 251-1775
FAX: 320 240-3131
Patti Bruggeman, *Office Mgr*
Arlys K Solien MD, *Med Doctor*
Steven N Honebrink MD, *Med Doctor*
Patti Bregaman, *Manager*
Jill Stang, *Nurse Practr*
EMP: 48
SALES (est): 1MM-4.9MM **Privately Held**
WEB: www.centracareclinic.com
SIC: 8011 Medical center; drug store
PA: Centracare Clinic
1200 6th Ave N
Saint Cloud MN 56303
320 252-5131

(G-7480)
CENTRACARE CLINIC (PA)
1200 6th Ave N   (56303-2735)
PHONE..............................320 252-5131
FAX: 320 252-3501
Hallen Horn MD, *President*
Mary J Williamson, *Vice Chairman*
Lanse Lang, *Member*
Scot Hutton MD, *Vice Pres*

Gloria Warzecha, *Vice Pres*
EMP: 456 **EST:** 1995
SQ FT: 76,000
SALES (corp-wide): 125.30M **Privately Held**
WEB: www.centracareclinic.com
SIC: 8011 Medical center

(G-7481)
CENTRACARE HEALTH SYSTEM
1406 6th Ave N   (56303-1900)
PHONE..............................320 251-2700
Terence Pladson, *Principal*
Joni Serena, *Corp Secy*
Charles Dooley, *Vice Pres*
Marvin Kiffmeyer, *Purchasing*
Greg Klugherz, *CFO*
EMP: 500
SALES (est): 5MM-9.9MM **Privately Held**
SIC: 8062 Medical hospital

(G-7482)
CENTRAL GROUP MANAGEMENT CO
215 Park Ave S Ste 200   (56301-3779)
PHONE..............................320 654-6307
Robert H Pace Jr, *CEO*
Jean Pace, *Vice Pres*
Joe Hollenkemp, *Assistant*
EMP: 330 **EST:** 1990
SQ FT: 6,000
SALES (est): 25MM-49.9MM **Privately Held**
SIC: 8741 Management services; hotel or motel management services

(G-7483)
CENTRAL MINNESOTA EMERGENCY
1406 6th Ave N   (56303-1900)
PHONE..............................320 255-5657
FAX: 320 656-7071
Daniel Fark, *President*
Jeanette C Miller, *Physician Asst*
Jennifer K Detert, *Physician Asst*
EMP: 28 **EST:** 1991
SALES (est): 1MM-4.9MM **Privately Held**
SIC: 8011 Physicians' office & clinic

(G-7484)
CENTRAL MINNESOTA GROUP HEALTH
1245 15th St N   (56303-1802)
PHONE..............................320 253-5220
FAX: 320 203-2100
Karen Hoeschen, *Human Resources*
Kathryn Laakso, *Manager*
Jay Ophoven, *Manager*
Timothy R Asmussen, *Manager*
Joan Silbernick, *Manager*
EMP: 150 **EST:** 1998
SALES (est): 10MM-24.9MM **Privately Held**
WEB: www.healthpartners.com
SIC: 8062 Medical hospital
PA: HealthPartners Inc
8170 33rd Ave S
Bloomington MN 55425
952 883-6000

(G-7485)
CENTRAL MINNESOTA MENTAL (PA)
1321 13th St N   (56303-2613)
PHONE..............................320 252-5010
FAX: 320 252-0908
John Greenwaldt, *Opers Mgr*
Brett Gilmore, *CFO*
Randy J Burtzel, *Office Mgr*
Diane E Pagel, *Supervisor*
David Baraga, *Director*
EMP: 80 **EST:** 1959
SQ FT: 15,000
SALES (corp-wide): 18.15M **Privately Held**
SIC: 8093 Outpatient mental health clinic; outpatient detoxification center

(G-7486)
CENTRAL MINNESOTA TASK FORCE (PA)
Also Called: Anna Marie's Alliance
44 28th Ave N Ste E   (56303-4259)
PO Box 367   (56302-0367)
PHONE..............................320 251-7203
Jacque French, *Development*
Maxine Barnett, *Exec Dir*
EMP: 38

EST: 1978
SQ FT: 13,800
SALES (corp-wide): 1.81M **Privately Held**
SIC: 8322 Emergency shelters

(G-7487)
CENTRAL MINNESOTA TASK FORCE
Also Called: Battered Woman
511th Ave N   (56303)
PO Box 367   (56302-0367)
PHONE..............................320 252-1603
FAX: 320 253-5563
Maxine Barnett, *Exec Dir*
EMP: 40 **EST:** 1979
SALES (est): 1MM-4.9MM **Privately Held**
SIC: 8322 Emergency shelters

(G-7488)
CENTRAL MINNESOTA TASK FORCE
Also Called: Anna Marie's Alliance
500 11th Ave N   (56303-3553)
PO Box 367   (56302-0367)
PHONE..............................320 253-6900
Maxine Barnett, *Exec Dir*
Jacqueline French, *Director*
EMP: 35 **EST:** 1979
SALES (est): 1MM-4.9MM **Privately Held**
SIC: 8322 Emergency shelters

(G-7489)
CENTRAL MINNESOTA TASK FORCE
Also Called: Battered Woman
511th Ave N   (56303)
PO Box B   (56302)
PHONE..............................320 252-1603
Maxine Barnett, *Manager*
Jacque French, *MIS Dir*
EMP: 30
SALES (est): 1MM-4.9MM **Privately Held**
SIC: 8322 Emergency shelters
PA: Central Minnesota Task Force
44 28th Ave N Ste E
Saint Cloud MN 56303
320 251-7203

(G-7490)
CENTRAL-MCGOWAN INC
123 Roosevelt Rd   (56301-3873)
PO Box 66   (56302-0066)
PHONE..............................320 252-5292
FAX: 320 252-7807
Cynthia H Francis, *CEO*
Jeff Skumautz, *President*
Leo Henkemeyer, *Chairman*
Jeff Francis, *Vice Pres*
Al Prozinski, *CFO*
EMP: 40 **EST:** 1965
SQ FT: 30,000
SALES (est): 10MM-24.9MM **Privately Held**
SIC: 5085 Wholesales industrial supplies; wholesales industrial gas equipment, parts & supplies

(G-7491)
CHILD CARE CHOICES INC
2901 Clearwater Rd   (56301-5950)
PHONE..............................320 251-5081
Renee Hendricks, *Exec Dir*
Mary Kenning, *Exec Dir*
Brad Gustafson, *Executive*
EMP: 25 **EST:** 1977
SQ FT: 3,000
SALES (est): 1MM-4.9MM **Privately Held**
WEB: www.childcarechoices.net
SIC: 8331 8351 Sheltered workshop; child day care service

(G-7492)
CINEDIGM DIGITAL CINEMA CORP
Also Called: Uniquescreen
4140 Thielman Ln Ste 304   (56301-3897)
PHONE..............................320 654-6578
Bill McGlamery, *Branch Mgr*
EMP: 140
SALES (est): 10MM-24.9MM **Publicly Held**

www.HarrisInfo.com
326
2011 Harris Minnesota
Services Directory
▲=Import ▼=Export
◆=Import/Export

SIC: 7319 7336 Display advertising services; commercial art & graphic design services
PA: Cinedigm Digital Cinema Corp
55 Madison Ave Ste 300
Morristown NJ 07960
973 290-0080

(G-7493)
COBORN CANCER CENTER
1900 Centracare Cir # 1500   (56303-5000)
PHONE..............................320 229-4907
Jane Vortherms, *Office Mgr*
Janet White, *Office Mgr*
Hani S Al Khatib, *Med Doctor*
Gregory E Meyers MD, *Med Doctor*
Nicholas F Reuter, *Oncology*
EMP: 50 **EST:** 2003
SALES (est): 1MM-4.9MM **Privately Held**
SIC: 8049 Health practitioners' office

(G-7494)
COUNTY OF STEARNS
Also Called: Stearns-Bntn Emplymnt Train
3333 W Div St Ste 210   (56301)
PHONE..............................320 202-2100
FAX: 320 202-2199
Joyce Belford, *Manager*
EMP: 30
SALES (est): 1MM-4.9MM **Privately Held**
SIC: 8322 Individual & family social services; county supervisors' & executives' office
PA: County of Stearns
705 Courthouse Sq Rm 148
Saint Cloud MN 56303
320 656-3900

(G-7495)
COUNTY OF STEARNS
Also Called: Stearns County Sheriff Dept
807 Courthouse Sq   (56303-4775)
PO Box 217   (56302-0217)
PHONE..............................320 259-3700
John Sanner, *Sheriff*
Joseph M Kustritz, *Administrator*
EMP: 150 **Privately Held**
SIC: 8734 Sheriffs' office; water testing laboratory
PA: County of Stearns
705 Courthouse Sq Rm 148
Saint Cloud MN 56303
320 656-3900

(G-7496)
DEE SPEE DELIVERY SERVICE INC (PA)
4101 Clearwater Rd   (56301-9635)
PO Box 1417   (56302-1417)
PHONE..............................320 251-6697
FAX: 320 251-1846
Donald Weeres, *President*
David Cashman, *Corp Secy*
Tim Papesch, *Vice Pres*
Curtis Herbes, *Treasurer*
Steve Dombroski, *Manager*
EMP: 400 **EST:** 1978
SQ FT: 120,000 **Privately Held**
WEB: www.speedeedelivery.com
SIC: 4212 Delivery services by vehicle

(G-7497)
DESIGN ELECTRIC INC
4807 Heatherwood Rd   (56301-9539)
PO Box 1252   (56302-1252)
PHONE..............................320 252-1658
FAX: 320 252-4276
Douglas Bischoff, *President*
Harry E Bischoff, *Corp Secy*
Shank Karen, *Human Res Dir*
EMP: 75 **EST:** 1972
SQ FT: 1,500
SALES (est): 5MM-9.9MM **Privately Held**
WEB: www.designelectricinc.com
SIC: 1731 General electrical contractor

(G-7498)
DIG AMERICA UTILITY CONTR (PA)
25135 22nd Ave   (56301-9189)
PHONE..............................320 253-3447
FAX: 320 253-0447
Delroy Scheeler, *President*
Daryle Scheeler, *Vice Pres*
Cheryl Honer, *Manager*

EMP: 25 **EST:** 1989
SQ FT: 16,000
SALES (corp-wide): 5.90M **Privately Held**
WEB: www.digamerica.net
SIC: 1623 Underground utilities contractor; telephone & communication line construction; electric power line construction

(G-7499)
DIOCESE OF ST CLOUD
Also Called: Caritas Family Services
305 7th Ave N Ste 100   (56303-3633)
PO Box 2390   (56302-2390)
PHONE..............................320 252-4121
FAX: 320 252-4508
Joan Collins-Marotte, *Director*
EMP: 45
SALES (est): 1MM-4.9MM **Privately Held**
WEB: www.montessorimn.com
SIC: 8322 Adoption services
PA: Diocese of St Cloud
214 3rd Ave S
Saint Cloud MN 56301
320 251-2340

(G-7500)
E T C ENTERPRISES INC
Also Called: Vision Purchasing
24707 County Road 75   (56301-8782)
PHONE..............................320 240-0567
Rodney L Lindquist, *President*
Donald Tamm, *Manager*
EMP: 33 **EST:** 1994
SQ FT: 6,000
SALES (est): 10MM-24.9MM **Privately Held**
WEB: www.etcenterprisesinc.com
SIC: 5021 6552 7011 Wholesales beds & bedding; traveler accommodations; land subdivision & development services; wholesales household furniture

(G-7501)
EAR, NOSE THROAT, HEAD & NECK
1528 Northway Dr   (56303-1255)
PHONE..............................320 252-0233
Steven Cragle, *CEO*
David Schlough, *Administrator*
EMP: 50 **EST:** 2000
SALES (est): 5MM-9.9MM **Privately Held**
SIC: 8011 Physicians' office & clinic

(G-7502)
EBUREAU LLC
25 6th Ave N   (56303-4729)
PHONE..............................320 534-5000
Chris Maher, *CEO*
Gordy Meyer, *President*
Greg Cruze, *Member*
Nancy Deaton, *Member*
Mark Doman, *Member*
EMP: 27 **EST:** 2003
SQ FT: 40,000
SALES (est): 1MM-4.9MM **Privately Held**
SIC: 7374 Data processing & preparation services

(G-7503)
EICH MOTOR CO
1933 W Division St   (56301-3970)
PO Box 396   (56302-0396)
PHONE..............................320 251-1737
FAX: 320 258-2690
Linda Eich Des Jardin, *President*
Carl Fasen, *General Mgr*
Bryan Carlson, *Parts Mgr*
Mat Sanborn, *Sales Mgr*
John Liber, *Manager*
EMP: 50 **EST:** 1898
SQ FT: 4,560
SALES (est): 25MM-49.9MM **Privately Held**
WEB: www.eichmotor.com
SIC: 7515 Retails new & used automobiles; passenger car leasing

(G-7504)
ENTOCRINOLOGY CLINIC
Also Called: St Cloud Hospital
1900 Centracare Cir # 2500   (56303-5000)
PHONE..............................320 229-5000
FAX: 320 229-5183
Christopher E Balkany, *Principal*
Cheryl A Sauerer, *Office Mgr*
Steven M Vincent, *Director*
Ann Kooiker, *Psychiatry*

Steve Hahn, *Psychiatry*
EMP: 40 **EST:** 2003
SALES (est): 1MM-4.9MM **Privately Held**
SIC: 8049 Health practitioners' office

(G-7505)
ESSILOR LABORATORIES OF AMER
Also Called: Precision Optics
6925 Saukview Dr   (56303-0813)
PO Box 1288   (56302-1288)
PHONE..............................320 251-8520
FAX: 320 251-8591
Tom Gertken, *General Mgr*
Kelly Hanson, *Vice Pres*
Greg Mayer, *Sales Executive*
EMP: 154
SALES (est): 10MM-24.9MM **Privately Held**
WEB: www.essilor.com
SIC: 5049 Manufactures ophthalmic lenses; wholesales optical goods
HQ: Essilor Laboratories of Amer
13515 N Stemmons Fwy
Dallas TX 75234
972 241-4141

(G-7506)
EYE KRAFT OPTICAL INC
8 McLeland Rd   (56303-2049)
PO Box 400   (56302-0400)
PHONE..............................320 251-0141
James T Negaard, *President*
Michael T Moeller, *Corp Secy*
Lawrence Lahr, *Vice Pres*
Alice Spinner, *Accounting Mgr*
EMP: 75 **EST:** 1954
SQ FT: 25,000
SALES (est): 10MM-24.9MM **Privately Held**
SIC: 5049 Provides ophthalmic lens grinding services; wholesales optical goods

(G-7507)
EYE SURGEONS & PHYSICIANS
109 Doctors Park   (56303-1207)
PHONE..............................320 253-3637
FAX: 320 253-5412
Mark T Moberg, *Corp Secy*
Tom Hobday, *Office Mgr*
Cindy L Gellner, *Optometrist*
Christopher McDevitt, *Manager*
Andrea Joplin, *Executive*
EMP: 25 **EST:** 1971
SQ FT: 11,000
SALES (est): 1MM-4.9MM **Privately Held**
WEB:
www.eyesurgeonsandphysicians.com
SIC: 8011 Eyes, ears, nose & throat specialist, physician or surgeon office

(G-7508)
FDC SERVICES INC
720 Anderson Ave   (56303-2047)
PO Box 1151   (56302-1151)
PHONE..............................320 656-8880
Pat Baldwin, *President*
David Baldwin, *Manager*
▲ **EMP:** 150 **EST:** 1998
SALES (est): 10MM-24.9MM **Privately Held**
SIC: 7389 Packaging & labeling services

(G-7509)
FERBER INC
1707 Hillcrest Rd   (56303-1415)
PHONE..............................320 251-4072
FAX: 320 251-1614
Peter Ferber, *President*
Kit Ferber, *Clerk*
EMP: 27 **EST:** 1989
SALES (est): 1MM-4.9MM **Privately Held**
WEB: www.ferber.com
SIC: 1771 Concrete contractor

(G-7510)
FIRST CLASS HOSPITALITY GROUP
Also Called: Comfort Inn
4040 2nd St S   (56301-6504)
PHONE..............................320 251-1500
FAX: 320 251-1111
Rod Lindquist, *President*
Kurt Sieve, *Shareholder*
EMP: 26 **EST:** 1987
SALES (est): 1MM-4.9MM **Privately Held**
SIC: 7011 Traveler accommodations

(G-7511)
FLOYD TOTAL SECURITY
777 Anderson Ave   (56303-2048)
PHONE..............................320 654-9549
FAX: 320 654-9730
Michael Carts, *Owner*
EMP: 40
SALES (est): 1MM-4.9MM **Privately Held**
SIC: 7382 Security systems services

(G-7512)
FORD TENVOORDE INC
185 Roosevelt Rd   (56301-3846)
PO Box 1045   (56302-1045)
PHONE..............................320 251-0540
FAX: 320 251-8918
Michael J Tenvoorde, *President*
Mike Tenvooke, *General Mgr*
David C Tenvoorde, *Corp Secy*
Paul J Tenvoorde, *Vice Pres*
Jim Schall, *Vice Pres*
EMP: 75 **EST:** 1896
SQ FT: 41,000
SALES (est): 25MM-49.9MM **Privately Held**
WEB: www.tenvoordeford.com
SIC: 7515 Retails new & used automobiles; passenger car leasing

(G-7513)
FULFILLMENT DISTRIBUTION CTR
720 Anderson Ave   (56303-2047)
PO Box 1151   (56302-1151)
PHONE..............................320 656-8880
David Baldwin, *President*
Rachel Karolus, *Office Mgr*
▲ **EMP:** 545 **EST:** 1998
SQ FT: 275,000
SALES (est): 25MM-49.9MM **Privately Held**
WEB: www.fdcfulfillment.com
SIC: 4225 Warehousing & storage services

(G-7514)
FULFILLMENT SYSTEMS INC
4001 Clearwater Rd   (56301-9636)
PHONE..............................320 255-0800
FAX: 320 255-1731
Carl Peach, *Manager*
Pamela Palm, *Manager*
Mike Benda, *MIS Mgr*
Douglas Peterson, *Director*
EMP: 70
SALES (est): 5MM-9.9MM **Privately Held**
SIC: 7331 Mailing services
PA: Fulfillment Systems Inc
406 E 7th St
Monticello MN 55362
763 295-3400

(G-7515)
G & K SERVICES INC
1250 Kuhn Dr   (56301-9193)
PHONE..............................320 252-9471
FAX: 320 252-8401
James Kleinke, *Sales Staff*
Alipour CAM, *Sales Executive*
Steve Dempsey, *Manager*
EMP: 150
SALES (est): 5MM-9.9MM **Publicly Held**
WEB: www.gkservices.com
SIC: 7218 7213 7216 Industrial clothing supply service; uniform supply service; dry cleaning plant
PA: G&K Services Inc
5995 Opus Pkwy Ste 500
Minnetonka MN 55343
952 912-5500

(G-7516)
G B & CO HAIR & SKIN CARE
80 37th Ave S   (56301-3723)
PHONE..............................320 253-4832
Grace Berg, *Owner*
Robert Berg, *Co-Owner*
EMP: 25 **EST:** 1980
SALES (est): 500-999K **Privately Held**
SIC: 7231 Beauty salon

(G-7517)
GEO-COMM INC
601 W Saint Germain St   (56301-3665)
PHONE..............................320 240-0040
FAX: 320 240-2389

(PA)=Parent Co (HQ)=Headquarters (DH)=Div Headquarters
✪ = New business established in last 2 years

2011 Harris Minnesota
Services Directory

© Harris InfoSource 1-866-281-6415
327

Tom Grones, *President*
Charles Edwards, *Corp Secy*
Keith Kasselder, *Vice Pres*
Janet E Grones, *Treasurer*
Suzanne Boom, *Manager*
EMP: 65 **EST:** 1995
SQ FT: 15,000
SALES (est): 5MM-9.9MM **Privately Held**
WEB: www.geo-comm.com
SIC: 8742 Industry specialist consultant

(G-7518)
GOLD CROSS AMBULANCE SERVICE
2800 7th St N (56303-3104)
PO Box 1614 (56302-1614)
PHONE......................320 251-2302
FAX: 320 251-8154
Brian Murphy, *Vice Pres*
Lou Murphy, *Treasurer*
Paul Anderson, *Manager*
Jack Hill, *Manager*
EMP: 52
SALES (est): 1MM-4.9MM **Privately Held**
WEB: www.gcas-duluth.org
SIC: 4119 Ambulance service
PA: Gold Cross Ambulance Service
501 6th Ave NW
Rochester MN 55901
507 255-2230

(G-7519)
GOLD'N PLUMP MARKETING INC
4150 2nd St S Ste 200 (56301-3994)
PO Box 1106 (56302-1106)
PHONE..........................320 251-3570
Michael J Helgeson, *President*
Tim Wilhemson, *Chief*
Steven R Jurek, *Exec VP*
Kerri Schramel, *Controller*
Timothy J Wersman, *Director*
EMP: 65 **EST:** 1992
SQ FT: 15,000
SALES (est): 50MM-99.9MM **Privately Held**
SIC: 5144 Wholesales poultry & poultry products

(G-7520)
GOODIN CO
5205 Foundry Cir (56303-2032)
PHONE..........................320 259-6086
FAX: 320 259-4592
Jack Roland, *Manager*
EMP: 38
SALES (est): 10MM-24.9MM **Privately Held**
WEB: www.goodinco.com
SIC: 5074 1711 5051 5064 5075
Wholesales plumbing & heating equipment & supplies; wholesales household appliance parts; heating & air conditioning contractor; wholesales steel pipe & tubing; wholesales warm air heating equipment & supplies; retails plumbing & heating supplies
PA: Goodin Co
2700 N 2nd St
Minneapolis MN 55411
612 588-7811

(G-7521)
GRANITE CITY JOBBING CO INC
2731 Clearwater Rd (56301-5952)
PHONE..........................320 252-1782
FAX: 320 252-1574
Michael Smith, *President*
Susan Leeman, *Manager*
Wayne Kampen, *Manager*
EMP: 45 **EST:** 1948
SQ FT: 32,000
SALES (est): 25MM-49.9MM **Privately Held**
SIC: 5194 5145 Wholesales tobacco & tobacco products; wholesales confectionery products

(G-7522)
GRAVES DEVELOPMENT CORP
14 5th Ave S Ste 300 (56301-3631)
PHONE..........................320 252-6034
James J Graves, *President*
Chriss Wohlleber, *General Mgr*
Tracy Libbesmeir, *Corp Secy*
EMP: 50 **EST:** 1996
SALES (est): 1MM-4.9MM **Privately Held**
SIC: 7011 Hotel

(G-7523)
HEALTHPARTNERS CENTRAL MN
1245 15th St N (56303-1802)
PHONE..........................320 253-5220
Matt Brandtthis, *CFO*
Dave Dziuk, *Treasurer*
Tony Ellingson, *Controller*
Kari Quernemoen, *Cert Phar Tech*
Tammy Schindler, *Cert Phar Tech*
EMP: 120 **EST:** 1979
SQ FT: 50,000
SALES (est): 10MM-24.9MM **Privately Held**
WEB: www.healthpartnerscmc.com
SIC: 8011 Health maintenance organization or HMO
PA: HealthPartners Inc
8170 33rd Ave S
Bloomington MN 55425
952 883-6000

(G-7524)
HEALTHSOUTH CORP
1526 Northway Dr (56303-1255)
PHONE..........................320 251-8385
Jeanette Stack, *Administrator*
Patrice Corrigan, *Admin Asst*
EMP: 174
SALES (est): 10MM-24.9MM **Publicly Held**
WEB: www.healthsouth.com
SIC: 8062 Medical hospital
PA: HEALTHSOUTH Corp
3660 Grandview Pkwy
Birmingham AL 35243
205 967-7116

(G-7525)
HEARTLAND FAMILY PRACTICE INC
1520 Whitney Ct Ste 100 (56303-1867)
PHONE..........................320 251-2042
FAX: 320 240-3164
Shar Wallack, *Office Mgr*
Karin Walz, *Manager*
Patty Burgeman, *Administrator*
EMP: 65 **EST:** 1992
SQ FT: 16,000
SALES (est): 5MM-9.9MM **Privately Held**
WEB: www.centracareclinic.com
SIC: 8011 General & family practice physician or surgeon office
HQ: St Cloud Hospital
1406 6th Ave N
Saint Cloud MN 56303
320 251-2700

(G-7526)
HECLA INC (PA)
600 25th Ave S Ste 105 (56301-4820)
PHONE..........................320 255-9530
Del Sand, *President*
EST: 1984 **Privately Held**
WEB: www.hecla.com
SIC: 8361 8093 Home for the mentally handicapped; outpatient mental health clinic

(G-7527)
HERGES REALTY INC
Also Called: Coldwell Banker
25 11th Ave N (56303-4639)
PO Box 1062 (56302-1062)
PHONE..........................320 253-1366
FAX: 320 495-3801
Paul Herges, *CEO*
EMP: 32 **EST:** 1969
SQ FT: 2,000
SALES (est): 5MM-9.9MM **Privately Held**
SIC: 6531 Residential real estate agency

(G-7528)
HERITAGE PARK ESTATES
3600 W Saint Germain St # 268 (56301-4646)
PHONE..........................320 240-7939
Pat Gorham, *President*
EMP: 27 **EST:** 2003
SALES (est): 1MM-4.9MM **Privately Held**
SIC: 7299 6513 Apartment locating service; apartment building operator

(G-7529)
IKON OFFICE SOLUTIONS INC
400 Great Oak Dr (56387-2504)
PHONE..........................320 251-4566
John Getra, *Manager*
John Detra, *Exec Dir*
EMP: 25
SALES (est): 5MM-9.9MM **Privately Held**
WEB: www.ikon.com
SIC: 5044 5065 Wholesales office equipment; wholesales facsimile or fax equipment
HQ: IKON Office Solutions Inc
70 Valley Stream Pkwy
Malvern PA 19355
610 296-8000

(G-7530)
INDEPENDENT SCHOOL DISTRICT
Also Called: Media Service
115 13th Ave S (56301-4152)
PHONE..........................320 252-8770
FAX: 320 529-4302
Dennis Veigt, *Manager*
Wendy Siemers, *Manager*
Marj Hawkins, *Director*
Brad Johannes, *Technician*
EMP: 40
SALES (est): 5MM-9.9MM **Privately Held**
WEB: www.stcloud.k12.mn.us
SIC: 7336 Graphic arts & related design service
PA: Independent School District
1000 44th Ave N Ste 100
Saint Cloud MN 56303
320 253-9333

(G-7531)
ING BANK FSB
600 W Saint Germain St Ste 200 (56301-3681)
PO Box 7425 (56302-7425)
PHONE..........................320 229-4200
Travis Seiler, *Info Tech Mgr*
EMP: 328
SALES (est): 100MM-499.9MM **Privately Held**
SIC: 6035 Federally chartered savings institution
HQ: Ing Bank Fsb
1 S Orange St
Wilmington DE 19801
302 658-2200

(G-7532)
INTERNATIONAL ASSOCIATION OF
Also Called: Iamaw Dist Lodge 165
1903 4th St N Ste 101 (56303-3803)
PHONE..........................320 251-8732
Joseph W Carlson, *President*
George Jansky, *CFO*
Lewis Neuman Jr, *Agent*
EMP: 40 **EST:** 1942 **Privately Held**
SIC: 8631 Labor union

(G-7533)
J M OIL CO
3341 Southway Dr (56301-9561)
PO Box 1065 (56302-1065)
PHONE..........................320 251-2082
FAX: 320 251-3234
Michael A Moores, *President*
James A Moores, *General Mgr*
Kevin Kiloran, *Controller*
Ruth Zabinski, *Manager*
Brian Ludenbach, *Manager*
EMP: 25 **EST:** 1977
SQ FT: 20,000
SALES (est): 25MM-49.9MM **Privately Held**
WEB: www.jmoil.com
SIC: 5171 Wholesales petroleum bulk stations; convenience store; wholesales petroleum terminals

(G-7534)
J-BERD MECHANICAL CONTRACTORS
3308 Southway Dr (56301-9513)
PHONE..........................320 656-0847
FAX: 320 656-0312
David Berdan, *President*

Helen B White, *Treasurer*
Jeff Bovitz, *Manager*
Stewart Schill, *Technician*
EMP: 100 **EST:** 1992
SQ FT: 18,500
SALES (est): 10MM-24.9MM **Privately Held**
SIC: 1711 Mechanical contractor

(G-7535)
JAMES M SMITH MD
3701 12th St N Ste 100 (56303-2253)
PHONE..........................320 253-7257
James M Smith MD, *Owner*
EMP: 60 **EST:** 2001
SALES (est): 5MM-9.9MM **Privately Held**
SIC: 8011 Plastic surgeon office

(G-7536)
JEFFERSON CAPITAL SYSTEMS LLC
16 McLeland Rd (56303-2198)
PHONE..........................866 417-2561
David M Burton, *Mng Member*
EMP: 250 **EST:** 2003
SALES (est): 10MM-24.9MM **Privately Held**
SIC: 7322 Collection agency

(G-7537)
JOHN SCHMITZ MD
1406 6th Ave N (56303-1900)
PHONE..........................320 255-5777
John Schmitz MD, *Principal*
John C Johnson, *Internal Med*
EMP: 30
SALES (est): 1MM-4.9MM **Privately Held**
SIC: 8011 Physicians' office & clinic

(G-7538)
JON BOWAR MD
1406 6th Ave N (56303-1900)
PHONE..........................320 255-5777
Steve Vincnent MD, *Manager*
EMP: 30
SALES (est): 1MM-4.9MM **Privately Held**
SIC: 8011 Physicians' office & clinic

(G-7539)
KELLY MIDWEST VENTURES LP
100 4th Ave S (56301-3615)
PHONE..........................320 253-0606
FAX: 320 202-0505
Arlene Herzberg, *General Mgr*
Mark Laughlin, *General Mgr*
Mike Wilmes, *General Mgr*
Laurie Theis, *Corp Secy*
Mitch Brutger, *Chief Engr*
EMP: 160
SALES (est): 5MM-9.9MM **Privately Held**
SIC: 7011 Traveler accommodations; eating place

(G-7540)
KENDECO SUPPLY CO
1202 Sun Ridge Dr (56301-9178)
PO Box 1394 (56302-1394)
PHONE..........................320 253-1020
FAX: 320 253-6956
Dan Childers, *President*
Susan Childers, *Corp Secy*
EMP: 38 **EST:** 1969
SQ FT: 16,500
SALES (est): 10MM-24.9MM **Privately Held**
SIC: 5085 Wholesales industrial supplies; wholesales industrial abrasives

(G-7541)
KERN DEWENTER VIERE LTD (PA)
220 Park Ave S (56301-3713)
PO Box 1304 (56302-1304)
PHONE..........................320 251-7010
FAX: 320 251-1784
Robin Nelson, *Partner*
Lorne Viere, *Partner*
Chris Shorba, *Partner*
Duane Dewenter, *Accounting Dir*
Lisa Nolden, *Manager*
EMP: 40 **EST:** 1949 **Privately Held**
SIC: 8721 Accounting service; certified public accountant services

www.HarrisInfo.com
328

2011 Harris Minnesota
Services Directory

▲=Import ▼=Export
◆=Import/Export

(G-7542)
LANDWEHR CONSTRUCTION INC
846 33rd St S (56301-9610)
PO Box 1086 (56302-1086)
PHONE............................320 252-1494
FAX: 320 252-2380
Daniel Landwehr, *President*
Greg Fietek, *Corp Secy*
Jerry Larson, *CIO*
Stacy Bastien, *Admin Asst*
EMP: 25 **EST:** 1936
SQ FT: 2,500
SALES (est): 1MM-4.9MM **Privately Held**
SIC: 1794 1795 Excavating contractor;
buildings & other structure demolition
contractor

(G-7543)
LANSING MALL LP
Also Called: Crossroads Center Mall
4101 W Division St (56301-6600)
PHONE............................320 252-2856
FAX: 320 656-5567
Darcy Eigen, *Manager*
EMP: 87
SALES (est): 10MM-24.9MM **Publicly Held**
WEB: www.generalgrowth.com
SIC: 6512 Shopping center & mall operator
HQ: Lansing Mall LP
110 N Wacker Dr
Chicago IL 60606
312 960-5000

(G-7544)
LEIGHTON ENTERPRISES INC (PA)
619 W Saint Germain St # 1 (56301-3663)
PO Box 1458 (56302-1458)
PHONE............................320 251-1450
FAX: 320 251-8952
Al G Leighton, *CEO*
John Sowada, *President*
Dale Daily, *Chief Engr*
Pat Dotzler, *Controller*
Kathy Carton, *Manager*
EMP: 40
SQ FT: 13,000 **Privately Held**
WEB: www.lite999.com
SIC: 4832 Radio broadcasting station

(G-7545)
LIBERTY SAVINGS BANK FSB
111 7th Ave S Ste 101 (56301-4694)
PO Box 1106 (56302-1106)
PHONE............................320 252-2841
Mark Bragelman, *President*
Bonnie Hermanutz, *Vice Pres*
James Arnold, *Officer*
EMP: 50 **EST:** 1939
SQ FT: 16,000
SALES (est): 10MM-24.9MM **Privately Held**
WEB: www.libertysavings.com
SIC: 6035 Federal savings bank

(G-7546)
M HEATH, PAUL MD
3701 12th St N Ste 100 (56303-2253)
PHONE............................320 253-7257
Paul M Heath MD, *Principal*
EMP: 50 **EST:** 2001
SALES (est): 5MM-9.9MM **Privately Held**
SIC: 8011 Physicians' office & clinic

(G-7547)
MAIERS TRANSPORT & WAREHOUSING
640 54th Ave N Ste B (56303-4301)
PO Box 218 (56302-0218)
PHONE............................320 251-6882
John L Maiers, *President*
Mike Mueller, *Treasurer*
▲ **EMP:** 40 **EST:** 1914
SQ FT: 80,000
SALES (est): 10MM-24.9MM **Privately Held**
SIC: 6512 0783 Operators of commercial &
industrial buildings; planting, pruning &
trimming services

(G-7548)
MAIERS TRANSPORT & WAREHOUSING
5 McLeland Rd Ste A (56303-2095)
PO Box 218 (56302-0218)
PHONE............................320 251-6882
John L Maiers Jr, *President*
Michael Mueller, *Vice Pres*
Shirley Maiers, *Vice Pres*
EMP: 38 **EST:** 1915
SQ FT: 270,000
SALES (est): 1MM-4.9MM **Privately Held**
SIC: 4214 4213 Local trucking with storage;
over the road trucking

(G-7549)
MEDICAL MESSAGING CENTER
1406 6th Ave N (56303-1900)
PHONE............................320 255-5640
FAX: 320 255-5769
Dianna Heinen, *Manager*
Genine Nistler, *Director*
Jenine Nistler, *Director*
EMP: 30 **EST:** 1996
SALES (est): 1MM-4.9MM **Privately Held**
SIC: 8099 7389 Medical services
organization; telemarketing services

(G-7550)
MERIDIAN SERVICES INC
44 28th Ave N Ste D (56303-4259)
PHONE............................320 255-5151
FAX: 320 202-9471
Rebecca Thomely, *CEO*
Marya Hage, *President*
Cheryl Vennerstrom, *COO*
Kim Christen, *Manager*
EMP: 50 **EST:** 1980
SQ FT: 1,600
SALES (est): 1MM-4.9MM **Privately Held**
SIC: 8322 Individual & family social services

(G-7551)
MESHBESHER & SPENCE LTD
1015 W Saint Germain St Ste 51
(56301-5445)
PHONE............................320 656-0484
FAX: 320 656-0845
Jeffrey P Oistad, *Attorney*
Colleen Christianson, *Attorney*
Ronald Meshbesher, *Manager*
EMP: 50
SALES (est): 5MM-9.9MM **Privately Held**
SIC: 8111 Specialized legal services
PA: Meshbesher & Spence Ltd
1616 Park Ave
Minneapolis MN 55404
612 339-9121

(G-7552)
MEYER ASSOCIATES INC
14 7th Ave N (56303-4766)
PHONE............................320 259-4000
FAX: 320 259-4064
Lawrence R Meyer, *President*
Peggy A Meyer, *Corp Secy*
Laurie Brown, *Vice Pres*
Robin Abrahamsom, *Opers Mgr*
Gary Owen, *CFO*
EMP: 150 **EST:** 1976
SQ FT: 32,000
SALES (est): 5MM-9.9MM **Privately Held**
SIC: 7389 8732 Telemarketing services;
survey services, including marketing &
location

(G-7553)
MIDSOTA PLASTIC
3701 12th St N Ste 100 (56303-2253)
PHONE............................320 253-7257
FAX: 320 251-2938
James M Smith, *President*
Thomas L Satterberg MD, *Corp Secy*
Paul M Heath MD, *Vice Pres*
Paul W Schultz MD, *Vice Pres*
Karen Schaefer, *Opers Mgr*
EMP: 25 **EST:** 1983
SALES (est): 1MM-4.9MM **Privately Held**
SIC: 8011 Plastic surgeon office

(G-7554)
MIDSOTA REGIONAL HAND CENTER
3701 12th St N Ste 100 (56303-2253)
PHONE............................320 253-7257
Thomas Satterberg, *Partner*
Paul Heath, *Partner*
Everlyn Erikson, *Partner*
James Smith, *Partner*
Paul Schultz, *Partner*
EMP: 50 **EST:** 2001
SALES (est): 1MM-4.9MM **Privately Held**
SIC: 8049 8093 Health practitioners' office;
outpatient rehabilitation treatment center

(G-7555)
MILLER ARCHITECTS & BUILDERS
3335 W Saint Germain St (56301-4532)
PHONE............................320 251-4109
Dan Miller, *CEO*
Joe Seifert, *President*
Marion Miller, *Vice Pres*
David Jongeward, *CFO*
Stu Bailey, *Treasurer*
EMP: 30 **EST:** 1945
SQ FT: 17,500
SALES (est): 1MM-4.9MM **Privately Held**
SIC: 8712 Architectural service

(G-7556)
MILLER ARCHITECTURE INC
Also Called: Millers Architects & Bldrs
3335 W Saint Germain St (56301-4532)
PO Box 1228 (56302-1228)
PHONE............................320 251-4109
Dan Miller, *President*
Dave Jongeward, *CFO*
Bradley A Torok, *Treasurer*
Stu Bailey, *Treasurer*
EMP: 50 **EST:** 1994
SQ FT: 17,000
SALES (est): 5MM-9.9MM **Privately Held**
SIC: 8712 Architectural service

(G-7557)
MILLER ENTERPRISES INC (PA)
2930 2nd St S (56301-3809)
PO Box 7188 (56302-7188)
PHONE............................320 251-8900
Thomas R Miller, *President*
Daniel R Dunn, *Corp Secy*
Barbara M Miller, *Vice Pres*
Tim Peterson, *Parts Mgr*
Todd Walz, *Parts Mgr*
EMP: 150 **EST:** 1988 **Privately Held**
WEB: www.millerautoplaza.com
SIC: 7514 7515 Retails new & used
automobiles; boat dealer; retails new &
used trucks, tractors & trailers; retails used
automobiles; retails auto & home supplies;
passenger car rental; passenger car leasing

(G-7558)
MILLER PONTIAC-BUICK-GMC INC
2930 2nd St S (56301-3809)
PO Box 7188 (56302-7188)
PHONE............................320 251-1363
FAX: 320 529-4186
Thomas R Miller, *President*
Barbara M Miller, *Vice Pres*
Daniel R Dunn, *Treasurer*
EMP: 90 **EST:** 1933
SQ FT: 38,000
SALES (est): 25MM-49.9MM **Privately Held**
WEB: www.millerautoplaza.com
SIC: 7532 Retails new & used automobiles;
retails new & used trucks, tractors & trailers;
exterior repair service
PA: Miller Enterprises Inc
2930 2nd St S
Saint Cloud MN 56301
320 251-8900

(G-7559)
MINNESOTA LEGAL SERVICES
830 W Saint Germain St (56301-3606)
PO Box 886 (56302-0886)
PHONE............................320 253-0121
Ann C Cofell, *Partner*
EMP: 29
SALES (est): 1MM-4.9MM **Privately Held**
SIC: 8111 Legal services
PA: Minnesota Legal Services
2324 University Ave W Ste 101B
Saint Paul MN 55114
651 228-9105

(G-7560)
MINNESOTA SELECT SIRES CO-OP
6601 Gregory Park Rd S (56301-9287)
PHONE............................320 259-6680
FAX: 320 259-5039
Lyle Kruse, *Exec VP*
EMP: 44 **EST:** 1986 **Privately Held**
WEB: www.mnss.coop
SIC: 0752 0751 Animal specialties artificial
insemination services; livestock breeding &
production

(G-7561)
NASH-FINCH CO
360 Hoffman Ct (56303-0800)
PO Box 1418 (56302-1418)
PHONE............................320 251-3961
FAX: 320 656-4756
Randy Jaeger, *General Mgr*
Jeanette Renstrom, *Buyer*
Kara Swanz, *Controller*
Clint Zovvy, *Controller*
Jeff Soderholm, *Human Resources*
EMP: 200
SALES (est): 100MM-499.9MM **Publicly Held**
WEB: www.nashfinch.com
SIC: 5141 Wholesales general line
groceries
PA: Nash-Finch Co
7600 France Ave S Ste 200
Edina MN 55435
952 832-0534

(G-7562)
NORTHERN STAR THERAPY LTD INC
251 County Road 120 Ste A (56303-4886)
PHONE............................320 240-6955
FAX: 320 240-8089
Darrel Matthews, *Manager*
Paul Tembrock, *Manager*
EMP: 25
SALES (est): 1MM-4.9MM **Privately Held**
SIC: 8093 8049 Outpatient rehabilitation
treatment center; physical therapist office

(G-7563)
NORTHERN STATES POWER CO
Also Called: Northwest Region
3515 3rd St N (56303-4025)
PO Box 808 (56302-0808)
PHONE............................320 255-8601
FAX: 320 255-8607
Jerry Kuennen, *Engineer*
EMP: 120
SALES (est): 50MM-99.9MM **Publicly Held**
WEB: www.middletownpower.com
SIC: 4911 4924 Electric services; natural
gas distribution to consumers
HQ: Northern States Power Co
414 Nicollet Mall
Minneapolis MN 55401
612 330-5500

(G-7564)
NORTHLAND CAPITAL FINANCIAL
333 33rd Ave S Ste 100 (56301-5495)
PO Box 7278 (56302-7278)
PHONE............................320 252-2122
FAX: 320 252-2111
Willis Kleinjan, *Member*
Gabe Jarnot, *Member*
Jerry Baker, *Finance*
Tracy Lewellyn, *Manager*
Barb B Holthaus, *Manager*
EMP: 27 **EST:** 1996
SQ FT: 12,000
SALES (est): Under 500K **Privately Held**
WEB: www.northlandcapital.com
SIC: 7359 Equipment rental & leasing
services

(PA)=Parent Co (HQ)=Headquarters (DH)=Div Headquarters
✿ = New business established in last 2 years

2011 Harris Minnesota
Services Directory

© Harris InfoSource 1-866-281-6415
329

(G-7565)
PARAMOUNT THEATER
913 W Saint Germain St (56301-3460)
PHONE..............................320 259-5463
FAX: 320 257-3111
Antony Goddard, *Exec Dir*
Tony Goddard, *Exec Dir*
EMP: 30 EST: 1998
SALES (est): 1MM-4.9MM **Privately Held**
WEB: www.paramountarts.org
SIC: 7922 Legitimate live theater producers

(G-7566)
PETER'S BODY SHOP INC
205 Osseo Ave N (56303-4452)
PHONE..............................320 252-2993
FAX: 320 252-0137
Roger Bonn, *President*
Mark Schulzetenberge, *Corp Secy*
Glen Sunder, *Treasurer*
EMP: 30 EST: 1966
SQ FT: 9,600
SALES (est): 1MM-4.9MM **Privately Held**
SIC: 7532 Automotive body shop

(G-7567)
PETSMART INC
320 2nd St S (56301-3623)
PHONE..............................320 251-4365
FAX: 320 251-3970
John Cruckson, *Manager*
EMP: 35
SALES (est): 1MM-4.9MM **Publicly Held**
WEB: www.petsmart.com
SIC: 0752 Retails pet food; animal specialty services
PA: Petsmart Inc
　　19601 N 27th Ave
　　Phoenix AZ 85027
　　623 580-6100

(G-7568)
PINEVIEW PARK BMX
6655 Saukview Dr (56303-0807)
PO Box 1956 (56302-1956)
PHONE..............................320 230-7820
Joel Kmitch, *Principal*
EMP: 30 EST: 2004
SALES (est): 1MM-4.9MM **Privately Held**
WEB: www.pineviewparkbmx.com
SIC: 7999 Operates tourist attractions, amusement park concessions & rides

(G-7569)
PLEASURELAND INC (PA)
25064 Augusta Dr (56302)
PO Box 669 (56302-0669)
PHONE..............................320 251-7588
FAX: 320 251-0038
Beatrice Pearson, *Ch of Bd*
Daniel R Pearson, *President*
Will Jarnot, *General Mgr*
Patty Jarnot, *Corp Secy*
Brad Beacon, *CFO*
EMP: 80 EST: 1971 **Privately Held**
SIC: 7538 Recreational vehicle dealer; recreational vehicle repair services

(G-7570)
PREFERRED CREDIT INC
3051 2nd St S Ste 200 (56301-3201)
PO Box 1679 (56302-1679)
PHONE..............................320 202-7000
FAX: 320 253-6247
John Gaetz, *President*
Greg Windfeldt, *Vice Pres*
James Schwan, *Info Tech Dir*
Steve Halvorson, *IT/INT Sup*
Jerry Cool, *Director*
EMP: 225 EST: 1989
SQ FT: 25,000
SALES (est): 100MM-499.9MM **Privately Held**
WEB: www.preferredcredit.com
SIC: 6141 Personal installment sales finance

(G-7571)
PRESCRIPTION OPTICAL
311 S 72nd Ave (56301)
PHONE..............................303 343-0427
Julius Reimer, *Owner*
EMP: 30
SALES (est): 10MM-24.9MM **Privately Held**

SIC: 5049 Wholesales optical goods

(G-7572)
PRIMEVEST FINANCIAL SERVICES (HQ)
400 1st St S Ste 300 (56301-3661)
PO Box 283 (56302-0283)
PHONE..............................320 656-4300
FAX: 320 656-4399
Catherine M Bonneau, *President*
Kaye Allen, *Corp Secy*
Joy M Benner, *Corp Secy*
Diana R Cavender, *Corp Secy*
M C Foster, *Corp Secy*
EMP: 285 EST: 1984
SQ FT: 20,836
SALES (corp-wide): 21.61K **Privately Held**
WEB: www.eprimevest.com
SIC: 6211 Security broker service
PA: Ing America Insurance Holdings
　　1100 N Market St Ste 780
　　Wilmington DE 19801
　　302 658-3302

(G-7573)
PROBUILD CO LLC
Also Called: United Building Centers
2915 Roosevelt Rd (56301-9120)
PHONE..............................320 251-0861
FAX: 320 251-4528
Mark Hansen, *Manager*
EMP: 55
SALES (est): 25MM-49.9MM **Privately Held**
WEB: www.probuild.com
SIC: 5031 1761 Wholesales lumber, plywood & millwork; gutter & downspout contractor
HQ: Probuild Co LLC
　　7595 Tech Way Ste 500
　　Denver CO 80237
　　303 262-8500

(G-7574)
PROFESSIONAL GALLERY INC
24795 County Road 75 (56301-8782)
PHONE..............................320 252-8446
Christian Bertram, *CEO*
Matthew Bertram, *President*
Sue Tobias, *Vice Pres*
Kevin Goldrick, *Vice Pres*
Rick Phillips, *Info Tech Dir*
▲ EMP: 70 EST: 1978
SQ FT: 45,000
SALES (est): 10MM-24.9MM **Privately Held**
WEB: www.professionalgallery.com
SIC: 5199 Wholesales advertising specialties

(G-7575)
PROFESSIONAL HOSPITALITY LLC
Also Called: Country Suites By Carlson
235 Park Ave S (56301-3779)
PHONE..............................320 259-8999
FAX: 320 259-9802
Reed Frasier, *Vice Pres*
Michele Sceesfo, *Branch Mgr*
EMP: 25
SALES (est): 1MM-4.9MM **Privately Held**
WEB: www.prohospitality.com
SIC: 7011 Traveler accommodations
PA: Professional Hospitality LLC
　　2418 Crossroads Dr Ste 38
　　Madison WI 53718
　　608 244-0300

(G-7576)
PRUDENTIAL PLADSON REALTY INC
2680 W Saint Germain St (56301-4713)
PHONE..............................320 253-9074
FAX: 320 253-9915
Sue Pladson, *President*
Terence Pladson, *Vice Pres*
Pamela R Pladson Tar, *Human Res Mgr*
Jan Friedmann, *Office Mgr*
Jim Freidman, *Manager*
EMP: 40 EST: 1986
SQ FT: 4,500
SALES (est): 5MM-9.9MM **Privately Held**
WEB: www.prudentialpladson.com
SIC: 6531 Residential real estate agency

(G-7577)
QUALITY CARE SERVICES INC
3333 W Div St Ste 213 (56301)
PHONE..............................320 230-7275
Mike Zirdes, *President*
Kim Schwartz, *Vice Pres*
EMP: 60 EST: 2006
SALES (est): 1MM-4.9MM **Privately Held**
SIC: 8322 Social services center

(G-7578)
QUINLIVAN & HUGHES
400 1st St S Ste 600 (56301-3006)
PHONE..............................320 251-1414
Dyane Ebert, *CEO*
Ronald Brandenburg, *CEO*
Michael D Lafountaine, *Managing Prtnr*
Marian Steffes, *Corp Secy*
Rachel Pollmann, *Corp Secy*
EMP: 53 EST: 1922
SQ FT: 12,000
SALES (est): 5MM-9.9MM **Privately Held**
SIC: 8111 General practice law office

(G-7579)
R J TOOL CRIB LLC
1202 Sun Ridge Dr (56301-9178)
PO Box 1394 (56302-1394)
PHONE..............................320 253-1020
Lucille Nelson, *General Mgr*
Robert Miller, *Member*
Brad Dullinger, *Engineer*
Thomas Cross, *Manager*
EMP: 48 EST: 2002
SALES (est): 10MM-24.9MM **Privately Held**
WEB: www.kendeco.com
SIC: 5085 Wholesales industrial supplies

(G-7580)
RADIO CITY MARKETING GROUP INC
Also Called: Kzpk FM
619 W Saint Germain St (56301-3640)
PO Box 1458 (56302-1458)
PHONE..............................320 253-6500
Al Leighton, *CEO*
John Sowada, *President*
Ron Under, *Managing Dir*
Dennis Niess, *Sales Executive*
Bob Leighton, *Manager*
EMP: 60 EST: 1975
SALES (est): 5MM-9.9MM **Privately Held**
SIC: 4832 Radio broadcasting station

(G-7581)
RAJKOWSKI HANSMEIER LTD
11 7th Ave N Ste 3 (56303-2093)
PO Box 1433 (56302-1433)
PHONE..............................320 251-1055
FAX: 320 251-5896
Paul Rajkowski, *President*
Jan Phillips, *Office Admin*
EMP: 41 EST: 1970
SQ FT: 8,600
SALES (est): 5MM-9.9MM **Privately Held**
WEB: www.rajhan.com
SIC: 8111 General practice law office

(G-7582)
REGAL CONTRACTORS INC
2133 Julep Rd (56301-9422)
PHONE..............................320 253-1161
Robert Zwack, *President*
Jim Salzog, *Executive*
EMP: 35 EST: 1990
SQ FT: 2,000
SALES (est): 1MM-4.9MM **Privately Held**
SIC: 1742 1721 Plaster & drywall work contractor; painting & wall covering contractor

(G-7583)
REGIONAL DIAGNOSTICS RADIOLOGY
1406 6th Ave N (56303-1900)
PHONE..............................320 255-5619
FAX: 320 762-0282
Bryan Brindley MD, *Partner*
Hoang Nguyen MD, *Partner*
Richard Eiser MD, *Partner*
Ralph Fedor MD, *Partner*
Gregory Haines MD, *Partner*
EMP: 31 EST: 1975

SALES (est): 1MM-4.9MM **Privately Held**
SIC: 8011 Radiologist office

(G-7584)
REGIS CORP
41st & W Division St (56301)
PHONE..............................320 253-5353
FAX: 320 230-2047
Marie Rudolph, *Owner*
EMP: 32
SALES (est): 500-999K **Publicly Held**
WEB: www.regiscorp.com
SIC: 7231 Beauty salon
PA: Regis Corp
　　7201 Metro Blvd
　　Minneapolis MN 55439
　　952 947-7777

(G-7585)
REM CENTRAL LAKES INC
1775 Roosevelt Rd (56301-5166)
PHONE..............................320 253-8134
FAX: 320 253-8597
Lori Wirtzfeld, *General Mgr*
Cathy Miskowic, *Supervisor*
Mary Kral, *Exec Dir*
Janine Hesth, *Director*
Janine Hesch, *Program Dir*
EMP: 58
SALES (est): 1MM-4.9MM **Privately Held**
SIC: 8052 Intermediate care facility

(G-7586)
REM CENTRAL LAKES INC
1506 33rd Ave N (56303-1525)
PHONE..............................320 252-8875
FAX: 320 252-7543
Laurie Wirdzfeld, *Manager*
Janine Hesch, *Exec Dir*
EMP: 25
SALES (est): 1MM-4.9MM **Privately Held**
SIC: 8361 Home for the mentally retarded

(G-7587)
REMAX REALTY SOURCE
405 33rd Ave N (56303-3022)
PHONE..............................320 251-2200
FAX: 320 259-4747
Gary Barnier, *President*
EMP: 45 EST: 1994
SALES (est): 5MM-9.9MM **Privately Held**
WEB: www.homesofstcloud.com
SIC: 6531 Real estate services

(G-7588)
RINKE, NOONAN, GROTE, SMOLEY
1015 W Saint Germain St Ste 30 (56301-5442)
PHONE..............................320 251-6700
FAX: 320 656-3500
Roger Justin, *President*
James Degiovanni, *Corp Secy*
Barrett L Colombo, *Vice Pres*
Kurt A Deter, *Vice Pres*
Sharon G Hobbs, *Vice Pres*
EMP: 60 EST: 1967
SALES (est): 5MM-9.9MM **Privately Held**
WEB: www.rnoon.com
SIC: 8111 7929 Specialized legal services; entertainment services

(G-7589)
ROBERT A KOVELL
Also Called: Miller Wally Heiser & Co
4170 Thielman Ln Ste 101 (56301-3896)
PO Box 159 (56302-0159)
PHONE..............................320 253-9505
FAX: 320 255-8939
Robert A Kovell, *Principal*
EMP: 30 EST: 2001
SALES (est): 1MM-4.9MM **Privately Held**
SIC: 8721 Certified public accountant services

(G-7590)
ROYAL TIRE INC (PA)
3955 Roosevelt Rd (56301-9531)
PO Box 7068 (56302-7068)
PHONE..............................320 258-7070
FAX: 320 252-2437
Patrick Duininck, *President*
Paul Duininck, *Vice Pres*
Jerry Wimer, *Warehouse Mgr*

www.HarrisInfo.com
330

2011 Harris Minnesota
Services Directory

▲=Import ▼=Export
◆=Import/Export

Jermery Sands, *Purch Agent*
Yvonne Cooney, *CFO*
EMP: 75 **EST:** 1960
SQ FT: 50,000 **Privately Held**
SIC: 5014 7534 Wholesales automotive tires & tubes; wholesales truck tires & tubes; retails truck equipment & parts; automotive tire rebuilding & retreading service; tire dealer

(G-7591)
SERVICEMASTER OF ST CLOUD INC

501 17th Ave N (56303-3963)
PO Box 608 (56302-0608)
PHONE............................320 252-4622
FAX: 320 252-2145
Candal Dahlquist, *President*
M G Negaard, *Corp Secy*
Trent Negaard, *COO*
Jon Kopka, *CFO*
EMP: 200 **EST:** 1967
SQ FT: 20,000
SALES (est): 5MM-9.9MM **Privately Held**
WEB: www.servicemastercleanmn.com
SIC: 7349 7217 Building cleaning & maintenance services; housekeeping & maid services; carpet & upholstery cleaning services; building cleaning service

(G-7592)
SERVICEMASTER TOTAL CLEANING

501 17th Ave N (56303-3963)
PO Box 608 (56302-0608)
PHONE............................952 873-6070
Kendall Dahlquist, *Owner*
EMP: 200 **EST:** 1997
SALES (est): 5MM-9.9MM **Privately Held**
SIC: 7349 Building cleaning & maintenance services

(G-7593)
SHORT-ELLIOTT-HENDRICKSON INC

Also Called: Seh Architectural Svcs Group
1200 25th Ave S (56301-4806)
PHONE............................800 572-0617
Missy Dobmeier, *Human Resources*
Scott Lange, *Office Mgr*
Duane Day, *Manager*
Melissa Cook, *Technician*
EMP: 70
SALES (est): 5MM-9.9MM **Privately Held**
WEB: www.sehinc.com
SIC: 8711 8712 Engineering services; architectural service
PA: Short-Elliott-Hendrickson Inc
3535 Vadnais Center Dr # 200
Saint Paul MN 55110
651 490-2000

(G-7594)
SMURFIT-STONE CONTAINER CORP

655 41st Ave N (56303-2029)
PHONE............................320 252-3660
FAX: 320 252-7742
Bob Janorschke, *Maint Mgr*
Pat Checka, *Controller*
Cindy Dockendorf, *Human Res Mgr*
Terri Czech, *Human Res Mgr*
Gary Griggs, *Manager*
EMP: 180
SALES (est): 25MM-49.9MM **Privately Held**
WEB: www.sto.com
SIC: 5113 Manufactures corrugated & solid fiber containers; wholesales corrugated & solid fiber boxes
PA: Smurfit-Stone Container Corp
222 N Lasalle St
Chicago IL 60601
312 346-6600

(G-7595)
SOFT TOUCH CAR CARE OF ST

3104 W Division St Ste 1 (56301-5488)
PHONE............................320 253-4204
FAX: 320 253-3812
Mike Weber, *President*
EMP: 30 **EST:** 1986
SQ FT: 10,000
SALES (est): 1MM-4.9MM **Privately Held**
SIC: 7542 Convenience store; car wash; gas station

(G-7596)
SPANIER BUS SERVICE INC

1310 Sun Ridge Dr (56301-9143)
PHONE............................320 251-3313
FAX: 320 251-0845
Kenneth Spanier, *President*
Ronald Spanier, *Corp Secy*
Tammy Spanier, *Vice Pres*
EMP: 50 **EST:** 1960
SALES (est): 1MM-4.9MM **Privately Held**
WEB: www.rearscope.com
SIC: 4151 School bus service

(G-7597)
ST CLOUD AREA FAMILY YMCA

1530 Northway Dr (56303-1255)
PHONE............................320 253-2664
FAX: 320 253-1252
Jerry Clement, *Superintendent*
Dean Bertsch, *Vice Pres*
Mike Bengtson, *Treasurer*
Scott Adams, *Exec Dir*
EMP: 110 **EST:** 1969
SQ FT: 26,100 **Privately Held**
SIC: 8699 8641 Charitable organization; youth organizations

(G-7598)
ST CLOUD DENOVO

Also Called: Daniel Building
11 7th Ave N Ste 3 (56303-2093)
PO Box 1433 (56302-1433)
PHONE............................320 251-1055
Thomas Jovanovich, *CEO*
George M Dowall, *Partner*
Roger R Schmidt, *Partner*
Frederick L Grunke, *Attorney*
Kevin F Gray, *Attorney*
EMP: 53 **EST:** 1984
SALES (est): 10MM-24.9MM **Privately Held**
SIC: 6512 Operators of commercial & industrial buildings

(G-7599)
ST CLOUD EAR, NOSE, THROAT

1528 Northway Dr (56303-1255)
PHONE............................320 252-0233
FAX: 320 252-1421
Gerald Jurgens MD, *President*
Richard Schlarf MD, *Treasurer*
Jackie Prechal, *Office Mgr*
Douglas Liepert, *Med Doctor*
David Schlough, *Administrator*
EMP: 26 **EST:** 1974
SALES (est): 1MM-4.9MM **Privately Held**
WEB: www.stcloudent.com
SIC: 8011 Ears, nose & throat specialist office

(G-7600)
ST CLOUD FEDERAL EMPLOYEES

3030 1st St S (56301-3867)
PHONE............................320 252-2634
FAX: 320 252-9036
William Winter, *CEO*
Rick Wurst, *Treasurer*
Dennis Raffenbuel, *Loan Officer*
Mark Deminsky, *IT/INT Sup*
EMP: 54 **EST:** 1930
SQ FT: 1,600
SALES (est): 5MM-9.9MM **Privately Held**
SIC: 6061 6163 Federally chartered credit union; loan broker

(G-7601)
ST CLOUD HOSPITAL

1406 6th Ave N (56303-1900)
PHONE............................320 656-7020
FAX: 320 656-7101
Mark Larkin, *Exec Dir*
Robert Johnson, *Director*
EMP: 100
SALES (est): 5MM-9.9MM **Privately Held**
WEB: www.centracareclinic.com
SIC: 8322 Individual & family social services
HQ: St Cloud Hospital
1406 6th Ave N
Saint Cloud MN 56303
320 251-2700

(G-7602)
ST CLOUD HOSPITAL (HQ)

1406 6th Ave N (56303-1900)
PHONE............................320 251-2700
Craig Broman, *President*
Creston Martin, *Ch of Anesth*
John Seckinger, *CFO*
Kathy Parsons, *Finance Dir*
Paul Forsting, *Branch Mgr*
EMP: 456 **EST:** 1928
SALES (corp-wide): 125.30M **Privately Held**
WEB: www.centracareclinic.com
SIC: 8062 Medical hospital
PA: Centracare Clinic
1200 6th Ave N
Saint Cloud MN 56303
320 252-5131

(G-7603)
ST CLOUD HOSPITAL

48 29th Ave N Ste 15 (56303-4203)
PHONE............................320 251-2700
FAX: 320 240-3266
Keith D Larson, *Chief Mktg Ofcr*
Kathleen Murphy, *Branch Mgr*
Gwen Kunkel, *Manager*
Deb Randall, *Manager*
Barbara Burandt, *Manager*
EMP: 150
SALES (est): 5MM-9.9MM **Privately Held**
WEB: www.centracareclinic.com
SIC: 8082 Home health care services
HQ: St Cloud Hospital
1406 6th Ave N
Saint Cloud MN 56303
320 251-2700

(G-7604)
ST CLOUD MEDICAL GROUP (PA)

251 County Road 120 (56303-4872)
PHONE............................320 202-8949
Chris Tacl, *President*
Robert Kramer, *Purchasing*
Patty Kennedy, *CFO*
Celeste Gardener, *Persnl Dir*
Beth A Donnelly MD, *Med Doctor*
EMP: 150 **EST:** 1965
SQ FT: 37,000 **Privately Held**
SIC: 8011 Clinic operated by physicians

(G-7605)
ST CLOUD SUBARU

4110 W Division St (56301-3706)
PO Box 7005 (56302-7005)
PHONE............................320 258-0163
EMP: 30 **EST:** 2001
SALES (est): 25MM-49.9MM **Privately Held**
SIC: 5012 Automobile wholesaler

(G-7606)
ST CLOUD SUITE HOTEL INC

Also Called: Radisson Inn
404 W Saint Germain St (56301-3612)
PHONE............................320 654-1661
James Graves, *Controller*
Chris Wohlleber, *Manager*
Chuck Gibbons, *Manager*
EMP: 90
SALES (est): 5MM-9.9MM **Privately Held**
SIC: 7011 7299 7991 Traveler accommodations; eating place; banquet hall facility; physical fitness center; drinking establishment
PA: St Cloud Suite Hotel Inc
14 5th Ave S Ste 300
Saint Cloud MN 56301
320 252-6034

(G-7607)
ST CLOUD SURGICAL CENTER

1526 Northway Dr (56303-1255)
PHONE............................320 251-8385
FAX: 320 251-1267
Cameron Schroeder, *Maint Spvr*
Brenda Kunstal, *Human Res Dir*
Becky Cannon, *Office Mgr*
Sue Herges, *Manager*
Lisa Moschkau, *Supervisor*
EMP: 200 **EST:** 1971
SQ FT: 27,000
SALES (est): 10MM-24.9MM **Publicly Held**
WEB: www.healthsouth.com

SIC: 8093 8011 Specialty outpatient clinic; physicians' office & clinic
PA: HEALTHSOUTH Corp
3660 Grandview Pkwy
Birmingham AL 35243
205 967-7116

(G-7608)
STEARNS BANK NATIONAL ASSN (HQ)

4191 2nd St S (56301-3761)
PO Box 7338 (56302-7338)
PHONE............................320 253-6607
FAX: 320 253-3051
Norman C Skalicky, *President*
Roger J Voit, *Corp Secy*
Robert S Steuck, *Treasurer*
Gary Kiess, *Credit Staff*
Kelly Gunther, *Manager*
EST: 2003
SALES (corp-wide): 163.22M **Privately Held**
WEB: www.stearnsfs.com
SIC: 6021 National commercial bank
PA: Stearns Financial Services Inc
4191 2nd St S
Saint Cloud MN 56301
320 253-6607

(G-7609)
STEARNS COUNTY NATIONAL ASSN (HQ)

4191 2nd St S (56301-3761)
PO Box 7338 (56302-7338)
PHONE............................320 253-6607
Norman C Skalicky, *CEO*
Roger Voit, *Senior VP*
John Halvorson, *Vice Pres*
Susan Lenke, *Mfg Spvr*
Chris Roforth, *Credit Mgr*
EMP: 41 **EST:** 1912
SALES (corp-wide): 163.22M **Privately Held**
WEB: www.stearns-bank.com
SIC: 6021 7359 National commercial bank; equipment rental & leasing services
PA: Stearns Financial Services Inc
4191 2nd St S
Saint Cloud MN 56301
320 253-6607

(G-7610)
STEARNS COUNTY NATIONAL ASSN

4140 Thielman Ln Ste 101 (56301-3899)
PHONE............................320 253-6607
Norman Skalicky, *CEO*
EMP: 40
SALES (est): 10MM-24.9MM **Privately Held**
WEB: www.stearns-bank.com
SIC: 6021 National commercial bank
HQ: Stearns County National Assn
4191 2nd St S
Saint Cloud MN 56301
320 253-6607

(G-7611)
STEARNS FINANCIAL SERVICES INC (PA)

4191 2nd St S (56301-3761)
PO Box 7338 (56302-7338)
PHONE............................320 253-6607
Norman Skalicky, *President*
John H Halvorson, *Corp Secy*
Harley Vestrum, *Officer*
EMP: 130 **EST:** 1984
SALES (corp-wide): 163.22M **Privately Held**
WEB: www.stearnsfs.com
SIC: 6712 Bank holding company

(G-7612)
STEARNS-BENTON EMPLOYMENT

Also Called: Sbetc
1542 Northway Dr (56303-1240)
PHONE............................320 308-5320
FAX: 320 202-6478
Kathy Zavala, *Principal*
Fritz Hoffman, *Manager*
Brad Johnson, *Manager*
EMP: 35 **EST:** 1986
SQ FT: 11,000
SALES (est): 1MM-4.9MM **Privately Held**
SIC: 8322 Individual & family social services

(PA)=Parent Co (HQ)=Headquarters (DH)=Div Headquarters
✿ = New business established in last 2 years

2011 Harris Minnesota
Services Directory

© Harris InfoSource 1-866-281-6415

331

GEOGRAPHIC

(G-7613)
STEMM TRANSFER & STORAGE INC
2300 6th St N (56303-3206)
PO Box 397 (56302-0397)
PHONE.............................320 251-4080
FAX: 320 251-7741
Kathie Jordahl, *President*
Cheryl Vang, *Accountant*
Rick Jordan, *Manager*
EMP: 31 EST: 1898
SQ FT: 20,000
SALES (est): 1MM-4.9MM Privately Held
SIC: 4213 Over the road trucking

(G-7614)
STRATEGIC EQUIPMENT INC
100 Roosevelt Rd (56301-3823)
PHONE.............................320 252-2977
FAX: 320 252-2511
Jeff Grandy, *President*
Jeffrey Vreeland, *Vice Pres*
James Dworkin, *Controller*
EMP: 54 EST: 1962
SQ FT: 36,000
SALES (est): 10MM-24.9MM Privately Held
WEB: www.strategicequipment.com
SIC: 5046 5087 Wholesales commercial
restaurant equipment; wholesales
restaurant supplies; wholesales janitorial
equipment & supplies
PA: Equipment Equity Holdings Inc
5949 Sherry Ln Ste 835
Dallas TX 75225
214 363-7904

(G-7615)
T W ENTERPRISES LTD
2789 Clearwater Rd (56301-5904)
PHONE.............................320 654-0551
Charlie M Clour, *CEO*
Mark Oflund, *President*
Butch Goldenstein, *Manager*
Jenny Moyryla, *Graphic Designe*
▲ EMP: 67 EST: 1991
SQ FT: 20,000
SALES (est): 50MM-99.9MM Privately Held
WEB: www.jkamerica.us
SIC: 5099 Wholesales tanning salon
equipment & supplies

(G-7616)
TARGET CORP
4201 W Division St Ste 71 (56301-3696)
PHONE.............................320 253-4740
Debe Schaas, *Merchandise Mgr*
Bill Hebner, *Manager*
EMP: 250
SALES (est): 25MM-49.9MM Publicly Held
WEB: www.target.com
SIC: 4226 Warehousing & storage facility
PA: Target Corp
1000 Nicollet Mall
Minneapolis MN 55403
612 304-6073

(G-7617)
TL WYNE
Also Called: Saint Club Medical Group
1301 W Saint Germain St (56301-6271)
PHONE.............................320 240-2180
Wyne Tl, *Principal*
EMP: 50 EST: 2001
SALES (est): 5MM-9.9MM Privately Held
SIC: 8011 Physicians' office & clinic

(G-7618)
TRANSIT TEC LTD
23823 67th Ave (56301-9212)
PHONE.............................320 253-5940
FAX: 320 255-0346
Brenda Randolph, *President*
Kim Kenning, *Principal*
EMP: 80 EST: 1992
SALES (est): 1MM-4.9MM Privately Held
SIC: 7363 Chauffeur service

(G-7619)
TRI-COUNTY ABSTRACT & TITLE
122 12th Ave N (56303-4648)
PO Box 1332 (56302-1332)
PHONE.............................320 253-2096
FAX: 320 685-3205
Mitch Rengel, *President*
Sue Lentner, *COO*
Paula Thompson, *Accounting Dir*
Colleen Danner, *Officer*
Reachel Young, *Assistant*
EMP: 30 EST: 1973
SALES (est): 1MM-4.9MM Privately Held
SIC: 6541 6361 Title abstract service; title
insurance carrier

(G-7620)
TRI-COUNTY PARTS SUPPLY INC
Also Called: NAPA Auto Parts
46 33rd Ave N (56303-4144)
PHONE.............................320 253-5050
FAX: 320 253-5618
Kurt D Owen, *President*
EMP: 26 EST: 1971
SQ FT: 5,000
SALES (est): 5MM-9.9MM Privately Held
SIC: 5013 Wholesales automotive supplies
& parts; retails auto & home supplies

(G-7621)
TRIMPAC INC
Also Called: Stallion Door & Millwork
6380 Saukview Dr (56303-0943)
PHONE.............................320 650-0420
FAX: 320 650-0430
Dory Ecker, *Human Res Dir*
Daniel Wright, *Manager*
Alan Ferche, *Manager*
EMP: 50
SALES (est): 5MM-9.9MM Privately Held
WEB: www.trimpaconline.com
SIC: 5031 Manufactures wooden doors,
door parts & trim; wholesales doors &
windows
PA: Trimpac Inc
1030 Stearns Dr
Sauk Rapids MN 56379
320 202-3200

(G-7622)
TRIPLE CROWN GAMING INC
2769 Clearwater Rd (56301-5952)
PO Box 127 (56302-0127)
PHONE.............................320 251-5373
FAX: 320 251-6404
John Grell, *President*
Victor Grell Jr, *Corp Secy*
EMP: 30 EST: 1989
SALES (est): 1MM-4.9MM Privately Held
SIC: 7999 5092 Gambling establishment;
wholesales bingo games & supplies

(G-7623)
UNIQUESCREEN MEDIA INC
Also Called: Accessit
4140 Thielman Ln Ste 304 (56301-3897)
PHONE.............................320 654-6578
FAX: 320 529-4985
Bud Mayo, *CEO*
Bill McGlamery, *President*
Gary Loffredo, *Corp Secy*
John B Brownson, *CFO*
Brain Pflug, *CFO*
EMP: 149
SQ FT: 5,900
SALES (est): 10MM-24.9MM Publicly Held
WEB: www.uniquescreenmedia.com
SIC: 7311 Advertising agency
PA: Cinedigm Digital Cinema Corp
55 Madison Ave Ste 300
Morristown NJ 07960
973 290-0080

(G-7624)
UNITED ENTERTAINMENT CORP
2700 1st St N Ste 200 (56303-4256)
PO Box 1736 (56302-1736)
PHONE.............................320 203-1003
Michael D Ross, *President*
Robert A Ross, *Corp Secy*
Ross R Allen, *Corp Secy*
Shorba John, *COO*

Les Cooper, *Engineer*
EMP: 325 EST: 1993
SALES (est): 10MM-24.9MM Privately Held
WEB: www.uecmovies.com
SIC: 7841 Video tape & disc rental

(G-7625)
UNIVERSAL POWER MARKETING LLC
3333 W Div St Ste 218 (56301)
PHONE.............................320 202-0243
Jill M Olson, *Member*
Robbi Olson, *Member*
EMP: 140 EST: 1994
SQ FT: 5,000
SALES (est): 5MM-9.9MM Privately Held
SIC: 7389 Telemarketing services

(G-7626)
VOIGT'S BUS SERVICE INC
24243 County Road 7 (56301-7714)
PO Box 1 (56302-0001)
PHONE.............................320 252-1807
FAX: 320 252-1883
Darwin Voigt, *President*
Mary Voigt, *Corp Secy*
EMP: 59 EST: 1960
SQ FT: 5,000
SALES (est): 1MM-4.9MM Privately Held
WEB: www.voigtbus.com
SIC: 4142 Long-distance bus charter
service

(G-7627)
VOIGT'S MOTORCOACH TRAVEL INC
24243 County Road 7 (56301-7714)
PO Box 1 (56302-0001)
PHONE.............................320 253-0510
Darwin Voigt, *President*
Mary Voigt, *Corp Secy*
EMP: 150 EST: 1977
SALES (est): 5MM-9.9MM Privately Held
WEB: www.voigtbuscompanies.com
SIC: 4142 Long-distance bus charter
service

(G-7628)
VUKELICH OIL CO
3267 Roosevelt Rd (56301-9126)
PHONE.............................320 253-6546
Ronald Vukelich, *President*
Leslie Vukelich, *Vice Pres*
EST: 1990 Privately Held
SIC: 5172 Wholesales petroleum products;
convenience store; gas station

(G-7629)
WALGREEN CO
Also Called: Walgreens
2505 W Division St (56301-3837)
PHONE.............................320 251-9433
FAX: 320 251-5007
Craig Divio, *Manager*
EMP: 50
SALES (est): 5MM-9.9MM Publicly Held
WEB: www.walgreens.com
SIC: 7384 Drug store; non-prescription
medicine proprietary store; photofinishing
laboratory
PA: Walgreen Co
200 Wilmot Rd
Deerfield IL 60015
847 914-2500

(G-7630)
WARNERT RACING INC
1203 33rd St S (56301-9627)
PHONE.............................320 251-2882
Robert Warnett, *CEO*
Ron Warnert, *Principal*
Mark Warnert, *Principal*
▲ EMP: 35 EST: 1999
SALES (est): 1MM-4.9MM Privately Held
SIC: 7948 Racetrack

(G-7631)
WEERES PONTOON
1045 33rd St S (56301-9625)
PO Box 98 (56302-0098)
PHONE.............................320 251-3551
Clinton Lee, *President*
EMP: 60 EST: 1982
SALES (est): 10MM-24.9MM Privately Held

SIC: 6512 Nonresidential building operator;
manufactures rubber pontoons

(G-7632)
WELLS FARGO BANK, NATIONAL
400 1st St S Ste 100 (56301-3600)
PO Box 967 (56302-0967)
PHONE.............................320 259-3100
FAX: 320 259-3115
Mark Scehusen, *President*
EMP: 32
SALES (est): 5MM-9.9MM Publicly Held
SIC: 6021 National commercial bank
HQ: Wfc Holdings, Corp
420 Montgomery St
San Francisco CA 94104
415 396-7392

(G-7633)
WILLIAMS FUNERAL HOME INC
1900 Veterans Dr (56303-3338)
PO Box 1495 (56302-1495)
PHONE.............................320 252-2522
FAX: 320 252-7058
Thomas J Williams, *President*
Joel Athmann, *Vice Pres*

SQ FT: 9,600 Privately Held
WEB: www.williamsfuneralhome.net
SIC: 7261 Funeral home

(G-7634)
WOLTERS KLUWER FINANCIAL SVCS (DH)
6815 Saukview Dr (56303-0811)
PO Box 1457 (56302-1457)
PHONE.............................320 251-3060
FAX: 320 251-8110
Patrick Hartford, *Ch of Bd*
Brian Longe, *President*
Ken Newton, *Exec VP*
Randy Mueller, *Senior VP*
John Lockner, *Vice Pres*
EMP: 850 EST: 1952 Privately Held
WEB: www.cch.com
SIC: 7389 Financial service
HQ: CCH Inc
2700 Lake Cook Rd
Riverwoods IL 60015
847 267-7000

(G-7635)
ZIEGLER INC
2225 255th St (56301-8742)
PHONE.............................320 253-2234
FAX: 320 253-2187
Kirk Christopherson, *Manager*
Kelly Korpela, *Receptionist*
EMP: 30
SALES (est): 5MM-9.9MM Privately Held
SIC: 7353 Construction & mining equipment
leasing & rental
PA: Ziegler Inc
901 W 94th St
Minneapolis MN 55420
952 888-4121

SAINT FRANCIS
Anoka County

(G-7636)
PONDS GOLF COURSE LLC
2881 229th Ave NW (55070-9585)
PHONE.............................763 753-1100
Tom Feriancek, *Member*
Dave Schulte, *Member*
EMP: 29 EST: 2000
SALES (est): 1MM-4.9MM Privately Held
SIC: 7992 Public golf course

(G-7637)
ST FRANCIS YOUTH HOCKEY ASSN
4826 232nd Ave NW (55070-9760)
PO Box 181 (55070-0181)
PHONE.............................763 913-7395
Bill Karas, *Exec Dir*
EMP: 250 EST: 2001
SALES (est): 5MM-9.9MM Privately Held
SIC: 7997 Membership recreation club

www.HarrisInfo.com
332
2011 Harris Minnesota
Services Directory
▲=Import ▼=Export
◆=Import/Export

(G-7638)
VILLAGE BANK (PA)
3350 Bridge St NW (55070-9732)
PO Box 257 (55070-0257)
PHONE..............................763 753-3007
FAX: 763 753-6593
Larry Schminski, *President*
Ed Dropps, *Vice Chairman*
Pat Cullen, *Senior VP*
Barbara Nellessen, *Senior VP*
Oliver Darling, *Vice Pres*
EMP: 30 **EST:** 1993
SALES (corp-wide): 17.38M **Privately Held**
SIC: 6022 State commercial bank

SAINT FRANCIS
Isanti County

(G-7639)
COMMERCIAL DRYWALL INC
7040 245th Ave NW (55070-9726)
PHONE..............................763 862-6020
James Leach, *President*
Kathleen Leach, *Vice Pres*
Mike Horsch, *Manager*
EMP: 35 **EST:** 1994
SQ FT: 2,000
SALES (est): 1MM-4.9MM **Privately Held**
WEB: www.commercialdrywall.net
SIC: 1742 Drywall contractor

SAINT HILAIRE
Pennington County

(G-7640)
ST HILAIRE SEED CO INC
415 Hwy 32 S (56754)
PO Box 85 (56754-0085)
PHONE..............................218 964-5407
FAX: 218 964-5415
Ronald Anderson, *President*
Ramona Anderson, *Corp Secy*
Nick Waldal, *Plant Mgr*
Julie Anderson, *Manager*
Craig Anderson, *Program Dir*
EMP: 38 **EST:** 1993
SQ FT: 3,900
SALES (est): 50MM-99.9MM **Privately Held**
SIC: 5153 5191 Wholesales field beans; wholesales field, garden & flower seeds

(G-7641)
ST HILAIRE SUPPLY CO
211 Bdway Way (56754)
PO Box 98 (56754-0098)
PHONE..............................218 964-5222
FAX: 218 964-5242
Joel Sorvig, *President*
Gary W Sorvig, *Corp Secy*
David P Sorvig, *Vice Pres*
Timothy A Sorvig, *Treasurer*
Lori Sorvig, *Manager*
EMP: 26 **EST:** 1956
SQ FT: 35,000
SALES (est): 10MM-24.9MM **Privately Held**
SIC: 5074 Wholesales plumbing & heating equipment & supplies; manufactures standard or custom fabricated metal plated tanks

SAINT JAMES
Watonwan County

(G-7642)
C & B OPERATIONS LLC
Also Called: Tricounty Implement
County Rd 57 W (56081)
PO Box 108 (56081-0108)
PHONE..............................507 375-3144
FAX: 507 375-5533
Rich Raymond, *Manager*
EMP: 26
SALES (est): 10MM-24.9MM **Privately Held**

SIC: 5083 Wholesales farm & garden machinery
PA: C & B Operations LLC
30965 US Highway 212
Gettysburg SD 57442
605 765-2434

(G-7643)
EVANGELICAL LUTHERAN GOOD
Also Called: Pleasntview Good Samaritan Ctr
1000 2nd St S (56081-1826)
PHONE..............................507 375-3286
FAX: 507 375-3288
Samantha Dougherty, *Human Resources*
Judy Jones, *Manager*
Marlene Christman, *Administrator*
Tim Swoboda, *Administrator*
Thomas Schumate, *Administrator*
EMP: 130
SALES (est): 5MM-9.9MM **Privately Held**
WEB: www.good-sam.com
SIC: 8059 8051 Nursing home; skilled nursing care facility
PA: Evangelical Lutheran Good
4800 W 57th St
Sioux Falls SD 57108
605 362-3100

(G-7644)
PIONEER NATIONAL BANK
123 Armstrong Blvd S (56081-1759)
PO Box 107 (56081-0107)
PHONE..............................507 375-3201
FAX: 507 375-3204
EMP: 25
SALES (est): 5MM-9.9MM **Privately Held**
SIC: 6022 State commercial bank
PA: Pioneer National Bank
331 N Central Ave
Duluth MN 55807
218 624-3676

(G-7645)
SAINT JAMES LIONS CLUB INC
116 Sunset Dr (56081-1304)
PHONE..............................507 375-5634
Dwight Kuehl, *President*
Rich Raymond, *Vice Pres*
Jeff Price, *Vice Pres*
EMP: 30 **EST:** 1959 **Privately Held**
SIC: 8641 Civic associations

(G-7646)
ST JAMES BUS SERVICE INC
910 Weston Ave (56081-1644)
PO Box 208 (56081-0208)
PHONE..............................507 375-4181
Fred Lenz, *President*
David Lenz, *Principal*
Tony Lenz, *Vice Pres*
EMP: 25 **EST:** 1976
SQ FT: 5,280
SALES (est): 500-999K **Privately Held**
SIC: 4151 School bus service

(G-7647)
ST JAMES MEDICAL CENTER-MAYO
1101 Moulton And Parsons Dr (56081-5550)
PHONE..............................507 375-3261
Roger A Prsons, *Ch of Anesth*
Joyce Bineke, *Purchasing*
Jennifer Quiring, *Envir Svcs Dir*
Ryan Ashland, *CFO*
Gregory Burkel, *CFO*
EMP: 100 **EST:** 1954
SALES (est): 10MM-24.9MM **Privately Held**
WEB: www.stjmc.org
SIC: 8011 Physicians' office & clinic

(G-7648)
UNITED PARCEL SERVICE INC
Also Called: UPS
423 14th St S (56081-2422)
PHONE..............................507 375-4666
Joe Muller, *Manager*
EMP: 31
SALES (est): 1MM-4.9MM **Publicly Held**
WEB: www.ups.com

SIC: 4215 Package delivery services by vehicle; parcel delivery services by vehicle
HQ: United Parcel Service Inc
55 Glenlake Pkwy NE
Atlanta GA 30328
404 828-6000

(G-7649)
WILCON CONSTRUCTION INC
1512 7th Ave S (56081-2435)
PO Box 502 (56081-0502)
PHONE..............................507 375-5464
FAX: 507 375-4707
William D Freitag, *President*
Kirsten Freitag, *CFO*
Tyler Flohrs, *Accountant*
Deb Jans, *Manager*
Todd Tetzloff, *Administrator*
EMP: 35 **EST:** 1986
SQ FT: 8,500
SALES (est): 5MM-9.9MM **Privately Held**
SIC: 1542 New commercial & office building construction; commercial & office building renovation & repair services

SAINT JOSEPH
Stearns County

(G-7650)
ASPHALT SURFACE TECHNOLOGIES
Also Called: ASTECH
8348 Ridgewood Rd (56374-9402)
PO Box 1025, Saint Cloud (56302-1025)
PHONE..............................320 363-8500
FAX: 320 363-8700
Bruce B Batzer, *President*
Dale R Strandberg, *Vice Pres*
Mary L Popp, *Vice Pres*
EMP: 65 **EST:** 1986
SALES (est): 5MM-9.9MM **Privately Held**
WEB: www.astechus.com
SIC: 1611 4959 Highway & street resurfacing contractor; snow plowing services

(G-7651)
BANGASSER CO
Also Called: Computer Friendly
422 Elena Ln (56374-4407)
PHONE..............................320 256-5100
Aaron J Bangasser, *President*
EST: 1996 **Privately Held**
SIC: 7379 Computer system consulting services

(G-7652)
BRENNY SPECIALIZED INC
8505 Ridgewood Rd (56374-9401)
PO Box 7155, Saint Cloud (56302-7155)
PHONE..............................320 363-6996
Todd Brenny, *President*
Joyce Brenny, *Vice Pres*
Brandy Walder, *Manager*
EMP: 25 **EST:** 1997
SALES (est): 1MM-4.9MM **Privately Held**
SIC: 4731 Truck transportation brokers

(G-7653)
NEXT LEVEL ELECTRONICS INC
30593 Pearl Dr Ste 1A (56374-4682)
PO Box 667 (56374-0667)
PHONE..............................320 363-7716
Marie A Bayless, *President*
George M Bayless, *Vice Pres*
Robert P Symanski, *CFO*
▼ **EMP:** 25 **EST:** 2003
SQ FT: 7,000
SALES (est): 10MM-24.9MM **Privately Held**
WEB: www.nextlevelelectronics.com
SIC: 5063 Wholesales electrical supplies

(G-7654)
SAGINAW CONTRACTING INC WGCC
815 County Road 75 (56374-8650)
PO Box 295 (56374-0295)
PHONE..............................218 348-6000
Steve Erickson, *Partner*
EMP: 26
SALES (est): 5MM-9.9MM **Privately Held**
SIC: 1542 Commercial & institutional building construction

(G-7655)
SCHERER & SONS TRUCKING INC
1007 E Minnesota St (56374-4101)
PO Box 178 (56374-0178)
PHONE..............................320 363-8846
FAX: 320 363-3292
Mike Scherer, *President*
Anne Scherer, *Corp Secy*
Charles Scherer, *Vice Pres*
EMP: 25 **EST:** 1950
SQ FT: 6,000
SALES (est): 1MM-4.9MM **Privately Held**
SIC: 4213 Heavy hauling transportation services; long-distance less than truckload freight trucking services

(G-7656)
W GOHMAN CONSTRUCTION CO
815 County Road 75 (56374-8650)
PO Box 250 (56374-0250)
PHONE..............................320 363-7781
FAX: 320 363-7207
Bruce Gohman, *President*
Diane Gohman, *Corp Secy*
Denis Anderson, *Vice Pres*
Mike Gohman, *Vice Pres*
Maczine Woods, *Manager*
EMP: 28 **EST:** 1950
SQ FT: 13,000
SALES (est): 5MM-9.9MM **Privately Held**
SIC: 1542 1541 Commercial & office building contractor; new industrial building construction

SAINT LOUIS PARK
Hennepin County

(G-7657)
ASTON TECHNOLOGIES INC
7515 Wayzata Blvd Ste 205 (55426-1635)
PHONE..............................952 546-1693
Adrian Ratnayake, *CEO*
Sara Schwan, *Administrator*
EMP: 25 **EST:** 2001
SQ FT: 2,400
SALES (est): 1MM-4.9MM **Privately Held**
SIC: 8748 Business consulting services

(G-7658)
COMMERCIAL FURNITURE SERVICES
4301 Highway 7 Ste 200 (55416-5808)
PHONE..............................952 922-6683
John Sorteberg, *President*
Rick Greywitt, *Vice Pres*
William Sorteberg, *Treasurer*
EMP: 40 **EST:** 1979
SQ FT: 112,000
SALES (est): 1MM-4.9MM **Privately Held**
SIC: 7641 Office furniture repair & maintenance service

(G-7659)
DIVERSIFIED CONSTRUCTION
4931 W 35th St Ste 100 (55416-2774)
PHONE..............................952 929-7233
James J Rowland, *CEO*
Steven F Rowland, *Chairman*
Brian M Petersen, *CFO*
Amy Siebert, *Controller*
Debb Vupan, *Accountant*
EMP: 30 **EST:** 1986
SQ FT: 10,000
SALES (est): 5MM-9.9MM **Privately Held**
SIC: 1542 1521 Commercial & office building renovation & repair services; single-family home general remodeling service

(G-7660)
ENERGY RESOURCES LLC ✿
5000 W 36th St Ste 240 (55416-2761)
PHONE..............................612 889-0447
Kelly Frankenfeld, *Mng Member*
EST: 2009
SQ FT: 2,000 **Privately Held**
SIC: 8742 Management consulting services

(PA)=Parent Co (HQ)=Headquarters (DH)=Div Headquarters
✿ = New business established in last 2 years

2011 Harris Minnesota
Services Directory

© Harris InfoSource 1-866-281-6415

333

GEOGRAPHIC

(G-7661)
ENGLISH, BLEEKER & ASSOCIATES
435 Ford Rd Ste 165 (55426-4935)
PHONE.................................952 230-6500
William English, *President*
Benjamin Curry, *Principal*
Todd Bleeker, *Vice Pres*
Kim Lund, *Manager*
EMP: 25 **EST:** 1993
SQ FT: 7,800
SALES (est): 1MM-4.9MM **Privately Held**
WEB: www.mindsharp.com
SIC: 7379 8748 Computer related maintenance service; business consulting services

(G-7662)
HSSLP LLC
Also Called: Homewood Suites
5305 Wayzata Blvd (55416-1325)
PHONE.................................952 544-0495
Sheryl Walton, *Member*
EMP: 25 **EST:** 2006
SALES (est): 1MM-4.9MM **Privately Held**
SIC: 7011 Traveler accommodations

(G-7663)
INTREPID OF GOLDEN VALLEY INC
5353 Wayzata Blvd Ste 300 (55416-1317)
PHONE.................................952 513-5400
FAX: 952 927-0831
Charles Sweet, *CEO*
EMP: 99
SALES (est): 1MM-4.9MM **Privately Held**
WEB: www.intrepidusa.com
SIC: 8082 Home health care services
PA: Intrepid USA Healthcare Svcs
4055 Valley View Ln # 500
Dallas TX 75244
214 445-3750

(G-7664)
MEDICAL EVALUATIONS INC (PA)
5100 Gamble Dr Ste 540 (55416-1587)
PHONE.................................952 229-8500
Thomas Litman MD, *President*
John Rodning, *COO*
Michael Davis MD, *Vice Pres*
Teresa Koch, *Manager*
John Monno, *Manager*
EMP: 25 **EST:** 1986
SQ FT: 5,000 **Privately Held**
WEB: www.medicalevaluations.com
SIC: 8011 Physicians' office & clinic

(G-7665)
MEDICAL SCANNING CONSULTANTS
5775 Wayzata Blvd Ste 190 (55416-2627)
PHONE.................................952 513-6841
Charles T Cunningham MD, *CEO*
EMP: 36 **EST:** 1981
SALES (est): 1MM-4.9MM **Privately Held**
SIC: 8011 Medical center

(G-7666)
METHODIST HOSPITAL
6500 Excelsior Blvd (55426-4700)
PO Box 650, Minneapolis (55440-0650)
PHONE.................................952 993-5000
FAX: 952 993-5585
David Wessner, *CEO*
Michael B Kaupa, *COO*
John Herman, *Exec VP*
Catherine Lenagh, *Vice Pres*
David Cooke, *CFO*
EMP: 2500 **EST:** 1892
SQ FT: 815,000
SALES (est): 100MM-499.9MM **Privately Held**
SIC: 8062 Medical hospital

(G-7667)
MINNESOTA MEDICAL SCANNING (PA)
Also Called: Center For Diagnostic Imaging
5775 Wayzata Blvd Ste 190 (55416-2627)
PHONE.................................952 541-1840
Ken Heithoff, *Ch of Bd*

Tom Tomlinson, *President*
Don Jacobsen, *Corp Secy*
Tracy Wiese, *Senior VP*
Rick Long, *Senior VP*
EMP: 150 **EST:** 1981 **Privately Held**
WEB: www.cdirad.com
SIC: 8071 Medical laboratory

(G-7668)
MOTORS MANAGEMENT CORP (PA)
3701 Alabama Ave S (55416-5156)
PHONE.................................763 593-5755
C D Luther, *President*
Owen A Parr, *Vice Pres*
EMP: 27 **EST:** 1981
SQ FT: 1,728 **Privately Held**
SIC: 8741 8742 Management services; management consulting services; retails men's & boys' clothing

(G-7669)
SR MECHANICAL INC
7320 Oxford St Ste 200 (55426-4513)
PHONE.................................952 933-6933
Nona Rouse, *President*
EMP: 100 **EST:** 2007
SALES (est): 10MM-24.9MM **Privately Held**
SIC: 1711 Plumbing, heating & air conditioning contractor

(G-7670)
VIRTEVA LLC
5775 Wayzata Blvd Ste 900 (55416-2674)
PHONE.................................952 843-1200
Martha Kiesser, *Finance*
Tom Kiesser, *Mng Member*
EMP: 26 **EST:** 2003
SQ FT: 4,000
SALES (est): 1MM-4.9MM **Privately Held**
SIC: 7371 7379 Computer programming service; computer system consulting services

---

SAINT MARTIN
Stearns County

(G-7671)
MONITOR TIRE DISPOSAL INC
130 Maine St (56376-4400)
PO Box 300 (56376-0300)
PHONE.................................320 548-3496
FAX: 320 548-3515
Art Binsfeld, *CEO*
Mike Oevermann, *President*
EST: 1987
SQ FT: 70,000 **Privately Held**
WEB: www.monitortiredisposal.com
SIC: 4953 Refuse systems services

SAINT MICHAEL
Wright County

(G-7672)
B & D PLUMBING, HEATING & AC
4145 Mackenzie Ct NE (55376-4551)
PHONE.................................763 497-2290
Dennis Daleiden, *President*
Tracy Daleiden, *Vice Pres*
Kate Skogstad, *Manager*
EMP: 36 **EST:** 1982
SQ FT: 10,000
SALES (est): 1MM-4.9MM **Privately Held**
WEB: www.bdplumbers.com
SIC: 1711 Plumbing, heating & air conditioning contractor

(G-7673)
GREAT NORTHERN BANK
12725 43rd St NE Ste 100 (55376-4901)
PHONE.................................763 497-7777
FAX: 763 497-8007
Paul Ederer, *CEO*
Peter Alworth, *Chairman*
Chad Vitzthum, *Vice Pres*
Lynn Olson, *Vice Pres*
Mary Hartner, *Vice Pres*
▲ **EMP:** 25 **EST:** 1999 **Privately Held**
WEB: www.greatnorthernbank.com

SIC: 6712 6022 6163 Bank holding company; state commercial bank; loan broker
PA: Great Northern Corp
12725 43rd St NE
Saint Michael MN 55376
763 497-7777

(G-7674)
J & B GROUP INC (PA)
13200 43rd St NE (55376-8420)
PO Box 212 (55376-0212)
PHONE.................................763 497-3913
Robert Hageman, *CEO*
Michael Hageman, *President*
Jim Chapa, *CFO*
Bill Dettmann, *Info Tech Mgr*
EMP: 320 **EST:** 1979
SQ FT: 200,000 **Privately Held**
SIC: 6719 Investment holding company

(G-7675)
L & K LANDSCAPING INC
3333 Iffert Ave NE (55376-9328)
PHONE.................................763 497-4700
Patrick Little, *President*
Mike Kuka, *Vice Pres*
EMP: 30 **EST:** 1984
SQ FT: 1,600 **Privately Held**
SIC: 0782 Landscaping services

(G-7676)
MANOR CONCRETE CONSTRUCTION
4370 Naber Ave NE (55376-9483)
PHONE.................................763 497-5420
FAX: 763 497-5425
Lee Fischer, *President*
Chet Ritchie, *President*
Dick Fischer Jr, *President*
Josh Ritchie, *Manager*
EMP: 150 **EST:** 1982
SALES (est): 10MM-24.9MM **Privately Held**
WEB: www.manorconcrete.com
SIC: 1741 1771 Masonry & stonework contractor; concrete contractor

(G-7677)
MIDWEST PROTECTION AGENCY INC
3797 Larabee Ave NE (55376-8483)
PHONE.................................763 421-2966
Michael Seman, *CEO*
Kenneth Fox, *CFO*
EMP: 35 **EST:** 2006
SALES (est): 1MM-4.9MM **Privately Held**
SIC: 7389 Business support services

(G-7678)
MINNEAPOLIS ELECTRICAL JATC
13100 Frankfort Pkwy NE (55376-8494)
PHONE.................................763 497-0072
Tony Maghrak, *Human Res Dir*
Tony Magrak, *Director*
Carl Madsen, *Bd of Directors*
Annette Hurtado, *Bd of Directors*
EMP: 45 **EST:** 1990
SALES (est): 1MM-4.9MM **Privately Held**
WEB: www.mplsjatc.org
SIC: 7389 Personal service agents

(G-7679)
PCIROADS LLC ✪
14123 42nd St NE (55376-9564)
PHONE.................................763 497-6100
Thomas Sloan, *President*
Steve Gerster, *Vice Pres*
Ted Durkee, *Treasurer*
EMP: 49 **EST:** 2008
SQ FT: 8,000
SALES (est): 5MM-9.9MM **Privately Held**
WEB: www.progressivecontractors.com
SIC: 1611 Highway & street paving contractor

(G-7680)
PCIROADS, CORP ✪
14123 42nd St NE (55376-9564)
PO Box 416 (55376-0416)
PHONE.................................763 497-6100
Mike McGray, *President*
Steve Weston, *Project Mgr*
Ronald Gibbons, *VP Eng R&D*

Ted Durkee, *CFO*
Bill Rosso, *Human Resources*
EMP: 99 **EST:** 2008
SALES (est): 10MM-24.9MM **Privately Held**
SIC: 1611 Heavy highway & street construction

(G-7681)
RACHEL CONTRACTING LLC
4125 Napier Ct NE (55376-9509)
PHONE.................................763 424-9955
Don Rachel, *Member*
Jerry Rachel, *Member*
Mark Cramer, *Member*
Matt Coz, *Member*
John Kapphahn, *Controller*
EMP: 50 **EST:** 2006
SALES (est): 5MM-9.9MM **Privately Held**
SIC: 1794 1795 Excavating contractor; wrecking & demolition contractor

(G-7682)
ST MICHAEL VETERINARY CLINIC
Also Called: Saint McHael Veterinary Clinic
312 Central Ave E (55376-9518)
PO Box 220 (55376-0220)
PHONE.................................763 497-2424
FAX: 763 497-3856
Kristi McAlpin, *Partner*
David L Bourget, *Partner*
EMP: 25 **EST:** 1957
SQ FT: 4,500 **Privately Held**
SIC: 0741 0742 Livestock animal hospital; animal hospital services

(G-7683)
TC AMERICAN MONORAIL INC
Also Called: Jet Edge
12070 43rd St NE (55376-8427)
PHONE.................................763 497-8700
Paul Lague, *President*
Doreen Dietrich, *Purchasing*
Gary Vangsness, *Engrg Mgr*
Doreen Leppa, *Marketing Staff*
Bill Swanson, *Manager*
EMP: 60
SALES (est): 10MM-24.9MM **Privately Held**
WEB: www.tcamerican.com
SIC: 5084 Manufactures overhead cranes; manufactures mineral cleaning machinery; wholesales industrial machinery & equipment; manufactures monorail systems
PA: TC American Monorail Inc
12070 43rd St NE
Saint Michael MN 55376
763 497-7000

SAINT PAUL
Dakota County

(G-7684)
A & H CARTAGE INC
3275 Mike Collins Dr A (55121-2394)
PHONE.................................651 454-9550
FAX: 651 454-0011
Lowell E Anderson, *President*
Jeff Anderson, *Vice Pres*
EMP: 32 **EST:** 1970
SQ FT: 13,000
SALES (est): 1MM-4.9MM **Privately Held**
WEB: www.ahcartage.com
SIC: 4731 4212 Foreign freight forwarding services; local trucking without storage services

(G-7685)
A S K FINANCIAL LLP
2600 Eagan Woods Dr # 400 (55121-1169)
PHONE.................................651 406-9665
John Siegler, *Partner*
Joseph Hess, *Partner*
EMP: 25 **EST:** 1981
SALES (est): 1MM-4.9MM **Privately Held**
WEB: www.askfinancial.com
SIC: 8111 Specialized legal services

(G-7686)
AACC INTERNATIONAL INC
3340 Pilot Knob Rd (55121-2055)
PHONE.................................651 454-7250
Barbara Mock, *CFO*

www.HarrisInfo.com
334
2011 Harris Minnesota
Services Directory
▲=Import ▼=Export
◆=Import/Export

Chris Nygren, *Human Res Mgr*
Kathleen Koegler, *Manager*
Steven C Nelson, *Exec Dir*
Elizabeth Knight, *Director*
EMP: 65 **EST:** 1915
SQ FT: 24,000 **Privately Held**
SIC: 8621 Professional organization

(G-7687)
ACCREDO HEALTH GROUP INC
2915 Waters Rd Ste 109 (55121-1562)
PHONE...............................651 681-0885
FAX: 651 681-0977
Theresa Maine, *Manager*
Robert Furth, *Manager*
EMP: 40
SALES (est): 25MM-49.9MM **Publicly Held**
WEB: www.accredotx.com
SIC: 5122 Wholesales pharmaceuticals
DH: Accredo Health Group Inc
1640 Century Center Pkwy
Memphis TN 38134
901 385-3688

(G-7688)
ACG INC
Also Called: Gateway
2400 Pilot Knob Rd (55120-1118)
PHONE...............................651 488-0574
Kevin Swanson, *President*
EMP: 72 **EST:** 1992
SQ FT: 20,000
SALES (est): 5MM-9.9MM **Privately Held**
SIC: 1793 Glass & glazing contractor
PA: KAS Investment Co Inc
3121 40th Ave NW Ste 100
Rochester MN 55901
507 280-4314

(G-7689)
AGGREGATE INDUSTRIES INC (DH)
2915 Waters Rd Ste 105 (55121-1562)
PHONE...............................651 683-0600
FAX: 651 683-8108
Norm Jagger, *Branch Mgr*
Pam Johnson, *Data Proc Staff*
EMP: 60 **Privately Held**
SIC: 1442 Manufactures ready-mixed
concrete; manufactures concrete block &
brick; construction sand & gravel mining
HQ: Aggregate Industries Inc
7529 Standish Pl Ste 200
Rockville MD 20855
301 795-1900

(G-7690)
ALL TIME FAVORITES INC
4500 Whitetail Way (55123-2093)
PO Box 21145 (55121-0145)
PHONE...............................651 454-1124
FAX: 651 687-0403
Brian Harrell, *CEO*
EMP: 34 **EST:** 1981
SQ FT: 2,200
SALES (est): 1MM-4.9MM **Privately Held**
SIC: 8742 7389 Planning consultant;
special events decorating service;
convention & trade show services

(G-7691)
ALLEN INTERACTIONS INC
1120 Centre Ste 800 (55120)
PHONE...............................651 203-3700
Michael W Allen, *CEO*
Martin Lipshutz, *President*
R Welsh, *Vice Pres*
Cyndi McDurmott, *Human Res Mgr*
Phil Zuidema, *Regl Sales Mgr*
EMP: 40 **EST:** 1993
SQ FT: 9,000
SALES (est): 5MM-9.9MM **Privately Held**
WEB: www.alleninteractions.com
SIC: 7371 Custom computer software
systems analysis & design service

(G-7692)
ALLIANCE HEALTH CARE INC (PA)
2260 Cliff Rd (55122-2316)
PHONE...............................651 895-8030
FAX: 651 895-8070
Alana Fiala, *President*
Laurie Lamson, *Opers Dir*
Shalon Novak, *Human Resources*

Shalon Fiala, *Director*
Gayle Ericksen, *Director*
EMP: 700 **EST:** 1989 **Privately Held**
SIC: 8082 Home health care services

(G-7693)
ALLTECH ENGINEERING CORP
2515 Pilot Knob Rd (55120-1135)
PHONE...............................651 452-7893
Robert D Lawrence, *President*
Michael R Peterson, *Vice Pres*
Steven Peterson, *Vice Pres*
Greg Merz, *CFO*
Jody Compaign, *Manager*
EMP: 100 **EST:** 1973
SQ FT: 28,000
SALES (est): 10MM-24.9MM **Privately Held**
WEB: www.alltechengineering.com
SIC: 1796 1541 Millwright; new industrial
building construction; industrial building
renovating, remodeling & repair service

(G-7694)
ALTERRA HEALTHCARE CORP
Also Called: Clare Bridge of Eagan
1365 Crestridge Ln (55123-1042)
PHONE...............................651 686-5557
FAX: 651 686-7778
Debbie Kattler, *Manager*
EMP: 50
SALES (est): 1MM-4.9MM **Publicly Held**
WEB: www.assisted.com
SIC: 8051 Extended care facility
DH: Alterra Healthcare Corp
10000 W Innovation Dr
Milwaukee WI 53226
414 918-5000

(G-7695)
AMCON CONSTRUCTION CO LLC
1715 Yankee Doodle Rd (55121-1697)
PHONE...............................651 379-9090
Dennis Cornelius, *Member*
James Winkels, *Member*
Todd Christopherson, *Member*
Gordon Schmitz, *Member*
Patrick Gannon, *Vice Pres*
EMP: 50 **EST:** 1997
SQ FT: 7,000
SALES (est): 10MM-24.9MM **Privately Held**
SIC: 1542 1541 Commercial & institutional
building construction; industrial building &
warehouse construction

(G-7696)
AMERICAN ACCOUNTS & ADVISORS
3904 Cedarvale Dr (55122-1410)
PHONE...............................651 405-9760
FAX: 651 405-9846
Bryan M Groarty, *President*
Philip Fahey, *CFO*
EMP: 25 **EST:** 1985
SQ FT: 6,000
SALES (est): 1MM-4.9MM **Privately Held**
SIC: 7322 Collection agency

(G-7697)
AMERICAN PHYTOPATHOLOGICAL SOC
3340 Pilot Knob Rd (55121-2055)
PHONE...............................651 454-7250
FAX: 651 454-0766
Steven C Nelson, *Vice Pres*
Barbara Mock, *CFO*
Julie Mulligan, *Accounts Mgr*
Linda Gold, *Sales Staff*
EMP: 61 **EST:** 1908
SQ FT: 24,000 **Privately Held**
SIC: 8621 Scientific membership
association

(G-7698)
AMERICAN REGISTRY OF
1255 Northland Dr (55120-1139)
PHONE...............................651 687-0048
William Murtaugh, *CFO*
Shaun Bader, *Technology*
Jerry Reid PhD, *Exec Dir*
Doug Cooper, *Exec Dir*
Gordon Anderson, *Exec Dir*
EMP: 50 **EST:** 1922
SQ FT: 30,000 **Privately Held**
WEB: www.arrt.com

SIC: 8621 Professional organization

(G-7699)
ANCHOR BANK
Also Called: West St Paul Office
66 Thompson Ave E Ste A (55118-3185)
PHONE...............................651 457-1111
Deb Millerbemd, *Vice Pres*
Ed Kennedy, *CFO*
EMP: 30
SALES (est): 5MM-9.9MM **Privately Held**
SIC: 6021 Commercial national trust
companies with deposits
PA: Anchor Bank
1055 Wayzata Blvd E
Wayzata MN 55391
952 473-4606

(G-7700)
APPLE VALLEY AMERICAN LEGION
Also Called: American Legion Club Apple Vly
14521 Granada Dr Ste 1776 (55124-7418)
PHONE...............................952 431-1776
FAX: 952 431-1750
Lowell Huber, *Manager*
Dave Cardinal, *Exec Dir*
EMP: 30 **EST:** 1976
SQ FT: 7,500 **Privately Held**
SIC: 8641 Fraternal association

(G-7701)
APPLE VALLEY GSRS LLC
Also Called: Grandstay Rsidential Suites Ht
7083 153rd St W (55124-7289)
PHONE...............................952 953-6111
Philip Johnson, *General Mgr*
Rodney Lindquist, *Member*
EMP: 30
SALES (est): 1MM-4.9MM **Privately Held**
SIC: 7011 Hotel

(G-7702)
APPLE VALLEY MEDICAL CLINIC
14655 Galaxie Ave (55124-8575)
PHONE...............................952 432-6161
FAX: 952 432-7019
Adam A Berry, *CEO*
Stuart Steichen, *President*
Todd Stolpman, *Corp Secy*
Scott Benson, *Vice Pres*
Susan Berg, *CFO*
EMP: 215 **EST:** 1974
SQ FT: 35,674
SALES (est): 10MM-24.9MM **Privately Held**
WEB: www.applevalleymedicalcenter.com
SIC: 8011 Clinic operated by physicians

(G-7703)
APPLE VALLEY VILLA APARTMENTS
14610 Garrett Ave (55124-8498)
PHONE...............................952 236-2600
Katherine Kopp, *Vice Pres*
EMP: 37 **EST:** 1986
SALES (est): 5MM-9.9MM **Privately Held**
WEB: www.applevalleyvilla.com
SIC: 6513 Apartment building operator

(G-7704)
APPLE VALLEY, CITY OF INC
Also Called: Valleywood Golf Course
4851 125th St W (55124-8704)
PHONE...............................952 953-2323
Rick Dodge, *Manager*
EMP: 40
SALES (est): 1MM-4.9MM **Privately Held**
WEB: www.cityofapplevalley.org
SIC: 7992 Public golf course; mayors' office
PA: City of Apple Valley
7100 147th St W
Saint Paul MN 55124
952 953-2500

(G-7705)
APPLIED POWER PRODUCTS INC (PA)
1240 Trapp Rd (55121-1217)
PHONE...............................651 452-2250
FAX: 651 452-9476
Bruce Lundeen, *CEO*
William Scott, *President*

Eric Volden, *General Mgr*
Michael Madigan, *Corp Secy*
Al Luthi, *Vice Pres*
▲ **EMP:** 75 **EST:** 1988
SQ FT: 65,000 **Privately Held**
WEB: www.appliedpowerproducts.com
SIC: 5085 Wholesales industrial supplies;
wholesales industrial hose, belting &
packing; wholesales industrial power
transmission equipment & apparatus

(G-7706)
APPTEC LABORATORY SERVICES INC (PA)
2540 Executive Dr (55120-1175)
PHONE...............................651 675-2044
FAX: 651 675-2005
Bonita L Baskin, *CEO*
Lisa Olson, *Safety Dir*
Edward T Foster, *CFO*
Jeanne Koky, *Human Res Dir*
Kris Ries, *Human Res Mgr*
EMP: 140 **EST:** 2001
SQ FT: 50,000
SALES (corp-wide): 21.80M **Privately Held**
SIC: 8071 Testing laboratory

(G-7707)
ASSOCIATED MATERIAL HANDLING
935 Blue Gentian Rd (55121-1542)
PHONE...............................651 688-6175
FAX: 651 688-6387
Michael Romano, *Branch Mgr*
Christine Gust, *Manager*
Katie Reynolds, *Receptionist*
EMP: 35
SALES (est): 10MM-24.9MM **Privately Held**
SIC: 5084 Wholesales industrial machinery
& equipment
PA: Associated Material Handling
133 N Swift Rd
Addison IL 60101
630 588-8800

(G-7708)
AUGUSTANA HEALTH CARE CENTER
14650 Garrett Ave (55124-7543)
PHONE...............................952 431-7700
FAX: 952 431-7704
Timothy H Tucker, *President*
Andrea Landry, *Purchasing*
Cathy Quick, *Bookkeeper*
Tricia Hall, *Human Res Dir*
Gloria Linton, *Office Mgr*
EMP: 280 **EST:** 1983
SALES (est): 10MM-24.9MM **Privately Held**
SIC: 8051 Skilled nursing care facility
PA: Augustana Care Corp
1007 E 14th St
Minneapolis MN 55404
612 238-5201

(G-7709)
AWARE INTEGRATED INC
3535 Blue Cross Rd (55122-1154)
PO Box 64560 (55164-0560)
PHONE...............................651 662-8000
Andrew Czajkowski, *CEO*
Mark W Banks MD, *Senior VP*
Mark Durishan, *Senior VP*
Richard M Niemiec, *Senior VP*
Roger W Kleppe, *VP Persnl*
EMP: 3400 **EST:** 1995
SALES (est): 1B-9.9B **Privately Held**
SIC: 6324 Hospital & medical insurance
carrier

(G-7710)
BALD EAGLE ERECTORS INC
3045 Sibley Memorial Hwy # 115
(55121-1782)
PHONE...............................651 405-9050
David L Bice, *President*
Kathleen Meyer, *Vice Pres*
Clifton Boyd, *Treasurer*
EMP: 35 **EST:** 1994
SALES (est): 1MM-4.9MM **Privately Held**
WEB: www.baldeagleerectors.com
SIC: 1791 Structural steel erection
contractor

(PA)=Parent Co (HQ)=Headquarters (DH)=Div Headquarters
✪ = New business established in last 2 years

2011 Harris Minnesota
Services Directory

© Harris InfoSource 1-866-281-6415

335

GEOGRAPHIC (vertical tab)

(G-7711)
BCBSM INC (PA)
Also Called: Blue Cross & Blue Shield
3535 Blue Cross Rd (55122-1154)
PO Box 64560 (55164-0560)
PHONE..............................651 662-8000
FAX: 651 456-8902
Mark W Banks, *CEO*
Kathy Mock, *CEO*
Pat Geraghty, *Ch of Bd*
James Rochat, *Managing Dir*
Pete H McNerney, *Vice Chairman*
EMP: 3000 EST: 1933
SQ FT: 389,000 **Privately Held**
SIC: 6321 6324 Direct accident & health
insurance carrier; hospital & medical
insurance carrier

(G-7712)
BCBSM INC
Also Called: Blue Cross
1305 Corporate Center Dr (55121-1204)
PO Box 64560 (55164-0560)
PHONE..............................651 662-8951
Andrew Czajkowski, *President*
Karen M Kositzke, *Manager*
EMP: 560
SALES (est): 100MM-499.9MM **Privately
Held**
SIC: 6324 Hospital & medical insurance
carrier
PA: Bcbsm Inc
　　3535 Blue Cross Rd
　　Saint Paul MN 55122
　　651 662-8000

(G-7713)
BCBSM INC
1200 Yankee Doodle Rd (55121-2202)
PO Box 64560 (55164-0560)
PHONE..............................651 662-8000
Mark Banks, *CEO*
EMP: 400
SALES (est): 100MM-499.9MM **Privately
Held**
SIC: 6321 Health insurance carrier service
PA: Bcbsm Inc
　　3535 Blue Cross Rd
　　Saint Paul MN 55122
　　651 662-8000

(G-7714)
BCBSM INC
Also Called: Blue Cross
3400 Yankee Dr (55121-1627)
PHONE..............................651 662-8000
Mark Banks, *CEO*
David Pautz, *Manager*
Brian Jones, *Administrator*
Frank C Gilbertson, *Director*
EMP: 250
SALES (est): 100MM-499.9MM **Privately
Held**
SIC: 6324 Hospital & medical insurance
carrier
PA: Bcbsm Inc
　　3535 Blue Cross Rd
　　Saint Paul MN 55122
　　651 662-8000

(G-7715)
BERNARD J MULCAHY CO INC
2700 Blue Waters Rd (55121-1403)
PHONE..............................651 686-8580
FAX: 651 686-8588
Thomas Reilly, *President*
Mark Goetz, *Corp Secy*
Jim Burns, *Vice Pres*
Chris Crotteau, *Vice Pres*
Tara Syring, *Vice Pres*
EMP: 33 EST: 1929
SQ FT: 20,000
SALES (est): 10MM-24.9MM **Privately Held**
WEB: www.mulcahyco.com
SIC: 5074 Wholesales plumbing & heating
equipment & supplies

(G-7716)
BEST BRANDS CORP (DH)
111 Cheshire Ln Ste 100 (55121)
PHONE..............................952 404-7500
Scott Humphrey, *CEO*
Michael Skillingstad, *CFO*
Rositta Pohl, *Human Res Mgr*
Michael L Brooks, *Marketing Staff*

Phillip Cayll, *Marketing Staff*
◆ EMP: 250 EST: 2000
SQ FT: 170,000 **Privately Held**
WEB: www.bestbrandscorp.com
SIC: 5149 Wholesales bakery products;
commercial bakery; manufactures frozen
bakery products; manufactures flour & flour
mixes from purchased flour; manufactures
cookies & crackers; manufactures flour
mixes & doughs
HQ: CSM Bakery Products NA Inc
　　1912 Montreal Rd
　　Tucker GA 30084
　　800 892-3039

(G-7717)
BEST BRANDS CORP
1765 Yankee Doodle Rd (55121-1617)
PHONE..............................651 454-5850
FAX: 651 454-0062
Mike Schultz, *Treasurer*
Lutz Peters, *Treasurer*
Ted Kadrlik, *Manager*
Jesse Bye, *Manager*
Mike Haden, *Information Mgr*
EMP: 300
SALES (est): 100MM-499.9MM **Privately
Held**
WEB: www.bestbrandscorp.com
SIC: 5141 Food broker
DH: Best Brands Corp
　　111 Cheshire Ln Ste 100
　　Saint Paul MN 55121
　　952 404-7500

(G-7718)
BEST WESTERN DAKOTA RIDGE
3450 Washington Dr (55122-1303)
PHONE..............................651 452-0100
Martin F Colon, *General Ptnr*
Roy Utne, *Ltd Ptnr*
John Boss, *Ltd Ptnr*
Daniel Dick, *Manager*
EMP: 48 EST: 1983
SQ FT: 65,000
SALES (est): 1MM-4.9MM **Privately Held**
WEB: www.dakotaridgehotel.com
SIC: 7011 Traveler accommodations

(G-7719)
BFS RETAIL OPERATIONS LLC
Also Called: Firestone
7660 150th St W (55124-7102)
PHONE..............................952 432-9212
FAX: 952 432-9218
Jennifer Gronlund, *General Mgr*
Mike Manarcak, *General Mgr*
EMP: 30
SALES (est): 1MM-4.9MM **Privately Held**
WEB: www.bfsusa.com
SIC: 7538 Tire dealer; general automotive
repair services
HQ: Bfs Retail Operations LLC
　　333 E Lake St Ste 300
　　Bloomingdale IL 60108
　　630 259-9000

(G-7720)
BI CONSULTING GROUP LLC
860 Blue Gentian Rd # 290 (55121-1692)
PHONE..............................651 403-6500
Amy Mayer, *Member*
Katie Mayer, *Opers Mgr*
Nate Nelson, *Manager*
EMP: 60 EST: 2005
SQ FT: 3,000
SALES (est): 5MM-9.9MM **Privately Held**
SIC: 7371 Computer software development

(G-7721)
BI-PHASE TECHNOLOGIES LLC
2945 Lone Oak Dr Ste 150 (55121-1588)
PHONE..............................651 681-4450
Greg Flack, *President*
EMP: 43 EST: 1999
SALES (est): 10MM-24.9MM **Privately Held**
WEB: www.theschwanfoodcompany.com
SIC: 7538 Manufactures motor vehicle fuel
systems & parts; general automotive repair
services
HQ: Schwan's Home Service Inc
　　115 W College Dr
　　Marshall MN 56258
　　507 532-3274

(G-7722)
BIRD & CRONIN INC
1200 Trapp Rd (55121-1217)
PHONE..............................651 683-1111
FAX: 651 688-9855
Timothy C Cronin, *President*
John R Bird, *Vice Pres*
Kerry Gleason, *Human Resources*
Mike Frazer, *Manager*
Angela Murray, *Manager*
◆ EMP: 100 EST: 1968
SQ FT: 90,000
SALES (est): 10MM-24.9MM **Privately Held**
WEB: www.birdcronin.com
SIC: 5047 Manufactures orthopedic
appliances; wholesales orthopedic
equipment & supplies; manufactures house
slippers

(G-7723)
BRANDL ANDERSON HOMES INC
4555 Erin Dr Ste 120 (55122-3334)
PHONE..............................952 898-0231
John D Anderson, *President*
Chris Brandl, *Vice Pres*
Tom Aarestad, *CFO*
Cathy Plof, *Executive Asst*
EMP: 43 EST: 1993
SQ FT: 3,500
SALES (est): 10MM-24.9MM **Privately Held**
SIC: 1521 6531 Single-family housing
construction; real estate services

(G-7724)
BURCHFIELD GROUP INC
1295 Northland Dr Ste 350 (55120-1388)
PHONE..............................651 389-5648
Brian Bullock, *President*
Mary Hartjes, *Accountant*
EMP: 42 EST: 1998
SQ FT: 10,612
SALES (est): 1MM-4.9MM **Privately Held**
WEB: www.burchfieldgroup.com
SIC: 8742 Compensation & benefits
planning consultant

(G-7725)
C N A FINANCIAL CORP
Also Called: CNA Insurance
12044 Gantry Ln 1404 (55124-6286)
PHONE..............................952 285-3300
Tim Morse, *Branch Mgr*
EMP: 100
SALES (est): 10MM-24.9MM **Publicly Held**
WEB: www.cna.com
SIC: 6411 Insurance services
HQ: CNA Financial Corp
　　333 S Wabash Ave Ste 300
　　Chicago IL 60604
　　312 822-5000

(G-7726)
CAPITOL CO'S INC
1270 Eagan Industrial Rd Ste 1
(55121-1368)
PO Box 24781, Minneapolis (55424-0781)
PHONE..............................651 454-4511
Chris Gerkach, *President*
Patricia Awada, *Manager*
EMP: 70 EST: 1995
SALES (est): 1MM-4.9MM **Privately Held**
SIC: 7389 7331 Telephone service; mailing
services

(G-7727)
CAPITOL SALES CO INC
1245 Trapp Rd Ste 130 (55121-1268)
PHONE..............................651 688-6830
FAX: 651 688-0107
Curtis A Hayes, *President*
Jill Zank, *Human Res Mgr*
Linda Mead, *Manager*
Micky Dinatale, *Administrator*
▼ EMP: 72 EST: 1964
SQ FT: 40,000
SALES (est): 50MM-99.9MM **Privately Held**
WEB: www.capitolsales.com
SIC: 5064 5065 8742 Wholesales electrical
entertainment equipment; wholesales
communications equipment; incentive or
award program consultant

(G-7728)
CARLSON TRAVEL GROUP INC
1250 Northland Dr Ste 200 (55120-1174)
PHONE..............................651 406-6000
FAX: 651 406-6001
Jan Ley, *Manager*
Colleen Thomas, *Meeting Planner*
EMP: 50
SALES (est): 1MM-4.9MM **Privately Held**
WEB: www.carlsontravelto.com
SIC: 4724 Travel agency

(G-7729)
CENTENNIAL HOUSE OF APPLE VAL
Also Called: Wovenhearts of Apple Valley
14625 Pennock Ave Apt C1 (55124-3505)
PHONE..............................952 891-2711
FAX: 952 953-3132
Janice Rivers, *Director*
EMP: 40 EST: 1995
SALES (est): 1MM-4.9MM **Privately Held**
SIC: 8361 Residential care facility

(G-7730)
CHEVRON USA INC
2600 Eagan Woods Dr # 300
(55121-1144)
PHONE..............................651 905-5700
Clayton Dumcum, *Manager*
Ken Ornsbee, *Manager*
EMP: 30
SALES (est): 1MM-4.9MM **Publicly Held**
WEB: www.chevron.com
SIC: 8711 Energy conservation engineers
HQ: Chevron USA Inc
　　6001 Bollinger Canyon Rd
　　San Ramon CA 94583
　　925 842-1000

(G-7731)
CHICAGO TUBE & IRON CO OF MN
2940 Eagandale Blvd (55121-1213)
PHONE..............................651 454-6800
FAX: 651 456-9547
Robert Haigh, *Ch of Bd*
Curt Roe, *General Mgr*
Bruce Torgerson, *General Mgr*
Derek Bentson, *Warehouse Mgr*
Derrick Benson, *Mfg Staff*
EMP: 85 EST: 1966
SALES (est): 50MM-99.9MM **Privately Held**
SIC: 5051 5085 Wholesales metal tubing;
wholesales steel pipe & tubing; wholesales
industrial valves & fittings

(G-7732)
CHILDREN'S COUNTRY DAY SCHOOL
Also Called: Summer On The Farm
1588 Victoria Rd S (55118-3658)
PHONE..............................651 454-4000
Ronald D Ettinger, *President*
Phylliss Ettinger, *VP Systems*
EMP: 25 EST: 1968
SQ FT: 8,000
SALES (est): 500-999K **Privately Held**
WEB: www.childrenscountryday.org
SIC: 8351 Preschool center; group day care
center

(G-7733)
CINDY DAY CARE
1996 Chipmunk Ct (55122-2225)
PHONE..............................651 688-7678
Cindy L Dilley, *Owner*
EMP: 27 EST: 1996
SALES (est): 500-999K **Privately Held**
SIC: 8351 Child day care service

(G-7734)
COLE'S SALON
2131 Cliff Rd (55122-2345)
PHONE..............................651 454-1390
FAX: 651 688-0362
Doug Cole, *Owner*
EMP: 45 EST: 2003
SALES (est): 1MM-4.9MM **Privately Held**
SIC: 7231 Unisex hair salon

www.HarrisInfo.com
336
2011 Harris Minnesota
Services Directory
▲=Import ▼=Export
◆=Import/Export

(G-7735)
COMFORTS OF HOME
720 Main St Ste 205 (55118-1800)
PHONE 651 287-0265
EMP: 25
SALES (est): 500-999K Privately Held
SIC: 8361 Home for the elderly

(G-7736)
COMPENDIUM CORP
2905 W Service Rd (55121-1224)
PHONE 952 881-1608
Greg Bjork, President
Thomas Wentworth, Principal
Sandy Hermes, Office Mgr
EMP: 80 EST: 1990
SQ FT: 3,500
SALES (est): 5MM-9.9MM Privately Held
SIC: 8732 Commercial nonphysical
research laboratory

(G-7737)
CORT BUSINESS SERVICES CORP
1279 Trapp Rd Ste 130 (55121-1272)
PHONE 651 405-0009
FAX: 651 405-6766
▲ EMP: 27
SALES (est): 1MM-4.9MM Publicly Held
WEB: www.cort.com
SIC: 7359 Furniture rental services
HQ: CORT Business Services Corp
11250 Waples Mill Rd
Fairfax VA 22030
703 968-8500

(G-7738)
COURTYARD BY MARRIOTT
1352 Northland Dr (55120-1140)
PHONE 952 452-2000
FAX: 952 452-1961
Mary Hargen, General Mgr
Fred Tellerico, Principal
Mary Hargens, Manager
EMP: 80 EST: 1987
SALES (est): 1MM-4.9MM Publicly Held
WEB: www.marriott.com
SIC: 7011 Traveler accommodations
HQ: Courtyard By Marriott II L P
6903 Rockledge Dr Ste 1500
Bethesda MD 20817
240 744-1000

(G-7739)
CRAWFORD DOOR SALES CO TWIN
1641 Oakdale Ave (55118-3503)
PO Box 18143 (55118-0143)
PHONE 651 455-1221
FAX: 651 457-9170
John Carl Jr, President
Steve Rawley, Controller
EMP: 26 EST: 1958
SQ FT: 15,000
SALES (est): 1MM-4.9MM Privately Held
WEB: www.cdsdoor.com
SIC: 1751 5031 Garage door contractor;
wholesales garage doors; wholesales
Doors, sliding; retails & installs garage
doors

(G-7740)
CREATIVE PROMOTIONAL CONCEPTS
1301 Corporate Center Dr # 175
(55121-1274)
PHONE 651 905-9339
FAX: 651 905-9482
Ian Lawrow-Svedvik, President
Greg Meehan, CFO
EMP: 59 EST: 1997
SQ FT: 5,000
SALES (est): 5MM-9.9MM Privately Held
WEB: www.cpcevents.com
SIC: 7929 7922 Disc jockey services;
entertainment promotion service

(G-7741)
CROSSCOUNTRY COURIER INC
1010 Aldrin Dr (55121-2444)
PHONE 651 686-5520
Dewey Tietz, President

EMP: 100
SALES (est): 5MM-9.9MM Privately Held
SIC: 4212 Delivery services by vehicle
PA: Crosscountry Courier Inc
1841 Hancock Dr
Bismarck ND 58501
701 222-8498

(G-7742)
CULLIGAN STORE SOLUTIONS
Also Called: Imperial Bottle Co
1030 Lone Oak Rd Ste 110 (55121-2251)
PHONE 651 681-9000
FAX: 651 688-0616
Dennis Doheny, General Mgr
Jeanie Cantu, General Mgr
Larry Murphy, Technical Mgr
Carl Werner, Controller
Carol McGovern, Manager
EMP: 52 EST: 1989
SQ FT: 20,295
SALES (est): 5MM-9.9MM Privately Held
WEB: www.cdr-inc.com
SIC: 5149 Manufactures household water
purification equipment; manufactures
pasteurized water; wholesales distilled
water; retails distilled, mineral or spring
water
HQ: Culligan International Co
9399 W Higgins Rd # 1100
Rosemont IL 60018
847 430-2800

(G-7743)
CUTTING EDGE CREATIONS INC
920 Apollo Rd Ste 100 (55121-2392)
PHONE 651 209-8600
FAX: 651 209-8630
Brian Field, President
Robert Field, Exec VP
Michael Ellis, Purchasing
Lee Prinkkila, Manager
David Burkholder, Director
◆ EMP: 85 EST: 1986
SALES (est): 10MM-24.9MM Privately Held
SIC: 7699 Manufactures rubber toys;
manufactures air-supported rubber
structures; rubber product repair service

(G-7744)
DAKOTA COUNTY COMMUNITY DEVPT
1228 Town Centre Dr (55123-1066)
PHONE 651 675-4400
Kenneth Bauer, Finance Dir
Mark Ulfers, Exec Dir
Kurt Keena, Director
EMP: 110 EST: 2003
SALES (est): 10MM-24.9MM Privately Held
WEB: www.dakotacda.org
SIC: 8748 Urban planning & consulting
services

(G-7745)
DAKOTA HIGHWAY DEPARTMENT
14955 Galaxie Ave Ste 55 (55124-8579)
PHONE 952 891-7109
Jennifer Cukrowski, Principal
EMP: 25 EST: 1900
SALES (est): 1MM-4.9MM Privately Held
SIC: 1622 Elevated highway construction

(G-7746)
DAKOTA RIDGE LLC
3450 Washington Dr (55122-1303)
PHONE 763 398-1821
Michael Berkopec, Member
Andy Schweizer, Member
EMP: 30 EST: 2004
SQ FT: 61,978
SALES (est): 1MM-4.9MM Privately Held
SIC: 7011 Hotel

(G-7747)
DART TRANSIT CO
800 Lone Oak Rd (55121-2212)
PO Box 64110 (55164-0110)
PHONE 651 688-2000
Donald G Oren, President
James C Hardman, Counsel
Beverly Oren, Vice Pres
Gary Volkman, Vice Pres
Gary Randall, VP Opers
EMP: 340 EST: 1934

SALES (est): 25MM-49.9MM Privately Held
WEB: www.dart.net
SIC: 4213 Over the road trucking; contract
haulers

(G-7748)
DARTS
1645 Marthaler Ln (55118-3517)
PHONE 651 455-1560
FAX: 651 234-2280
Mark Hoisser, President
Kris Hopko, Vice Chairman
Beth Wiggins, Vice Pres
Michael Holland, Finance
Barbara Knutson, Sales Staff
EMP: 160 EST: 1978
SQ FT: 22,000
SALES (est): 10MM-24.9MM Privately Held
WEB: www.darts1.org
SIC: 4111 8322 Passenger transit system;
senior citizen center

(G-7749)
DCA TITLE CO
7373 147th St W Ste 161 (55124-7567)
PHONE 952 432-5600
Richard Welshons, Partner
David Welshons, Exec VP
Karen Johnson, Vice Pres
Lynn Roberts, Assistant
Steph Peterson, Assistant
EMP: 50 EST: 2002
SALES (est): 1MM-4.9MM Privately Held
SIC: 6541 Title & trust company

(G-7750)
DECARE DENTAL LLC
3560 Delta Dental Dr (55122-3166)
PO Box 9304, Minneapolis (55440-9304)
PHONE 800 371-6561
Michael Walsh, Member
Norman C Storbakken, Opers Staff
Norma Porter, VP Finance
Mark A Moksnes, Marketing Staff
Rhonda L Altom, Director
EMP: 400 EST: 1987
SQ FT: 58,800
SALES (est): 100MM-499.9MM Publicly
Held
WEB: www.decare.com
SIC: 6324 8621 Dental insurance carrier;
professional organization
HQ: Anthem Holding Corp
120 Monument Cir Ste 200
Indianapolis IN 46204
317 488-6000

(G-7751)
DECK & DOOR CO
6900 151st St W Ste 100 (55124-7264)
PHONE 952 432-1888
Robert M Heidenreich, President
Cathey Revenon, Sales Mgr
Matt Aune, Manager
EMP: 25 EST: 1980
SALES (est): 5MM-9.9MM Privately Held
SIC: 1521 Single-family housing
construction

(G-7752)
DIGITAL DATAVOICE CORP
1210 Northland Dr Ste 160 (55120-1296)
PHONE 651 452-0300
Marty Gliva, President
Diane Gliva, Corp Secy
Mark Dibble, Accountant
Nelson Berg, Sales Associate
Judy Kattau, Business Anlyst
EMP: 32 EST: 1982
SQ FT: 10,000
SALES (est): 5MM-9.9MM Privately Held
WEB: www.ddvc.com
SIC: 7373 Computer systems value-added
resellers

(G-7753)
DIGITAL IMAGES INC (PA)
2915 Commers Dr Ste 900 (55121-2363)
PHONE 651 688-0888
Sudy Shen, President
Philip Lam, CFO
Wes Hiessen, Manager
Judy Adler, Exec Dir
EST: 1995 Privately Held
SIC: 7373 Systems integration service;
computer systems value-added resellers

(G-7754)
E Z AIR PARK INC
2804 Lexington Ave S (55121-1407)
PHONE 651 454-1302
FAX: 651 681-0710
Charles D Nolan Jr, President
Nancy Oneil, Corp Secy
Elizabeth Nordstrom, Vice Pres
John Nolan, Treasurer
EMP: 30 EST: 1979
SQ FT: 1,000
SALES (est): 1MM-4.9MM Privately Held
WEB: www.ezairpark.com
SIC: 4111 7521 Commuter bus operation;
parking lot

(G-7755)
EAGAN TRANSPORT INC
3101 Sibley Memorial Hwy (55121-1604)
PO Box 21216 (55121-0216)
PHONE 651 452-6268
Brian Furlong, President
John R Mogensen, Corp Secy
EMP: 30 EST: 1996
SQ FT: 24,000
SALES (est): 1MM-4.9MM Privately Held
WEB: www.eagantransport.com
SIC: 4213 Over the road trucking

(G-7756)
EAST METRO GORMAN
234 Wentworth Ave E (55118-3525)
PHONE 651 455-2940
Joanne Toninato MD, Partner
Kathy Barky, Project Mgr
Patrick N Arnold, Med Doctor
EMP: 35
SALES (est): 1MM-4.9MM Privately Held
SIC: 8011 Physicians' office & clinic

(G-7757)
ECLIPSE TRANSPORTATION INC
44 Moreland Ave E (55118-2416)
PHONE 651 293-1111
FAX: 651 222-6375
Bernard G Fautch, President
David Hansen, Corp Secy
EMP: 30 EST: 1999
SQ FT: 2,000
SALES (est): 1MM-4.9MM Privately Held
WEB: www.eclipsecars.com
SIC: 4119 Local passenger transportation
service; limousine service

(G-7758)
ELDREDGE TRADING INC
1408 Northland Dr Ste 104 (55120-1013)
PHONE 651 778-8500
Daniel Eldredge, President
Meghan Q Eldredge, Corp Secy
Benejrman W Eldredge, Treasurer
▲ EST: 1994
SQ FT: 3,000 Privately Held
SIC: 6719 5136 Investment holding
company; wholesales men's & boys'
sportswear & work clothing

(G-7759)
ELECTRONICS FOR IMAGING INC
1340 Corporate Ctr Curv (55121-1233)
PHONE 651 365-5255
Don Hill, Manager
EMP: 45 EST: 1989
SALES (est): 5MM-9.9MM Publicly Held
WEB: www.vutek.com
SIC: 8748 Business consulting services
PA: Electronics For Imaging Inc
303 Velocity Way
Foster City CA 94404
650 357-3500

(G-7760)
EMPLOYERS INSURANCE CO OF
Also Called: Wausau Insurance Co's
860 Blue Gentian Rd # 355 (55121-1564)
PO Box 1357, Minneapolis (55440-1357)
PHONE 651 365-8053
Lorna Lauderdale, Manager
EMP: 60
SALES (est): 25MM-49.9MM Privately Held
WEB: www.employmentspot.com

GEOGRAPHIC

SIC: 6331 Provides mutual fire, marine & casualty insurance
DH: Employers Insurance Co of
2000 Westwood Dr
Wausau WI 54401
715 845-5211

(G-7761)
ENCLOS CORP (HQ)
2770 Blue Waters Rd (55121-1671)
PHONE..............................651 796-6100
FAX: 651 994-6360
Gregg C Sage, *President*
Bruce Bornhurst, *General Mgr*
Tom Kretschmer, *Vice Pres*
E J Kelley, *Vice Pres*
David Coleman, *CFO*
▲ EMP: 75 EST: 1976
SQ FT: 20,000 **Privately Held**
WEB: www.enclos.com
SIC: 1793 Glass & glazing contractor
PA: CH Holdings USA Inc
10733 Sunset Office Dr # 200
Saint Louis MO 63127
314 984-8484

(G-7762)
ENGAGE HEALTH INC
852 Basswood Ln (55123-2292)
PHONE..............................651 994-0510
Patti Engel, *Owner*
EMP: 50 EST: 2003
SALES (est): 5MM-9.9MM **Privately Held**
SIC: 8748 Business consulting services

(G-7763)
ENGINEERED CONCRETE PLACER OF
Also Called: E-Con-Placer
2515 Northland Dr (55120-1006)
PHONE..............................651 452-1183
FAX: 651 688-7820
Richard L Tousignant, *President*
Robert T Tousignant, *Vice Pres*
Judy J Kriby, *Controller*
Jonathan Ceder, *VP Finance*
EMP: 35 EST: 1974
SQ FT: 4,000
SALES (est): 1MM-4.9MM **Privately Held**
SIC: 1771 5082 Concrete pumping contractor; wholesales concrete processing equipment

(G-7764)
ENN LEASING CO II LLC ✪
Also Called: Residence Inn Mrt MN Arpt Egon
3040 Eagandale Pl (55121-2118)
PHONE..............................651 688-0363
Larry Auburn, *General Mgr*
Molly Marose, *Principal*
EMP: 30 EST: 2008
SALES (est): 1MM-4.9MM **Privately Held**
SIC: 7011 Traveler accommodations

(G-7765)
ENN LEASING CO II LLC
3040 Eagandale Pl (55121-2118)
PHONE..............................651 688-0363
Lon Breelove, *Manager*
EMP: 50
SALES (est): 1MM-4.9MM **Publicly Held**
SIC: 7011 Traveler accommodations
PA: Interstate Hotels & Resorts
4501 Fairfax Dr Ste 500
Arlington VA 22203
703 387-3100

(G-7766)
ENTERPRISE LEASING CO OF MN (DH)
2775 Blue Waters Rd (55121-1439)
PHONE..............................651 905-5000
Andrew C Taylor, *President*
EMP: 40 EST: 1986
SQ FT: 5,000 **Privately Held**
WEB: www.enterprise.com
SIC: 7514 Rent-a-car service
HQ: Enterprise Holdings Inc
600 Corporate Park Dr
Saint Louis MO 63105
314 512-5000

(G-7767)
ENVIRONMENTAL SYSTEMS RESEARCH
880 Blue Gentian Rd # 200 (55121-1670)
PHONE..............................651 454-0600
FAX: 651 454-0705
Michael Johnson, *General Mgr*
Walter Potts, *Manager*
EMP: 60
SALES (est): 25MM-49.9MM **Privately Held**
SIC: 5045 Wholesales computer software

(G-7768)
EPIC HOLDINGS INC (PA)
Also Called: Educators Personal Insur Ctr
15025 Glazier Ave Ste 100 (55124-6300)
PO Box 241029 (55124-1029)
PHONE..............................952 997-4900
FAX: 952 997-4901
Reinart O Erdahl, *President*
Patrick R Delmar, *Vice Pres*
Gary L Hetzel, *Vice Pres*
Del Fladwood, *Computers*
EMP: 25 EST: 1997
SQ FT: 5,000 **Privately Held**
SIC: 6331 6411 Automobile insurance carrier; property & casualty insurance agent

(G-7769)
ERGOTRON INC
1181 Trapp Rd Ste 100 (55121-1296)
PHONE..............................651 681-7600
FAX: 651 681-7715
Joel Harzzard, *President*
John Veld, *General Mgr*
Dan Hallberg, *Business Mgr*
Jan Sweere, *Corp Secy*
Marc Woods, *Senior VP*
▲ EMP: 130 EST: 1977
SQ FT: 15,000
SALES (est): 10MM-24.9MM **Privately Held**
WEB: www.ergotron.com
SIC: 7373 Computer integrated systems design services

(G-7770)
ESPECIALLY FOR CHILDREN INC
3370 Coachman Rd (55121-1855)
PHONE..............................651 452-0043
Kris Miller, *Principal*
EMP: 30
SALES (est): 500-999K **Privately Held**
SIC: 8351 Child day care service
PA: Especially For Children Inc
5223 W 73rd St
Minneapolis MN 55439
952 835-6055

(G-7771)
EXPEDITORS INTERNATIONAL OF WA
1245 Trapp Rd Ste 100 (55121-1269)
PHONE..............................651 683-9922
FAX: 651 683-9919
Troy M Donough, *General Mgr*
Todd Hinkle, *District Mgr*
EMP: 60
SALES (est): 5MM-9.9MM **Publicly Held**
WEB: www.expd.com
SIC: 4731 Foreign freight forwarding services
PA: Expeditors International Of WA
1015 3rd Ave Fl 12
Seattle WA 98104
206 674-3400

(G-7772)
F B L FINANCIAL SERVICES INC
Also Called: Farm Bureau Financial Service
3080 Eagandale Pl (55121-2118)
PO Box 64565 (55164-0565)
PHONE..............................651 905-2123
FAX: 651 905-2200
Nancy Petschl, *Treasurer*
Kermit Larson, *Manager*
Matthew Cabe, *Manager*
EMP: 50
SALES (est): 10MM-24.9MM **Privately Held**
WEB: www.fblfinancial.com

SIC: 6211 Securities broker & dealer
HQ: Fbl Financial Group Inc
5400 University Ave
West Des Moines IA 50266
515 225-5400

(G-7773)
FAIRVIEW CLINICS
1440 Duckwood Dr (55122-1451)
PHONE..............................651 688-7860
FAX: 651 688-7855
Karl Parens MD, *Med Doctor*
Mary Danielson, *Manager*
EMP: 30
SALES (est): 1MM-4.9MM **Privately Held**
SIC: 8011 8093 Clinic operated by physicians; outpatient rehabilitation treatment center
PA: Fairview Clinics
2450 Riverside Ave
Minneapolis MN 55454
612 626-6666

(G-7774)
FIRST NATIONAL BANK OF WEST ST (PA)
66 Thompson Ave E (55118-3184)
PHONE..............................651 457-1111
Jeff Hawkins, *President*
Gene Crapser, *President*
Greg Drehmel, *Senior VP*
EMP: 30 EST: 1923
SALES (corp-wide): 61.19M **Privately Held**
SIC: 6021 National commercial bank

(G-7775)
FISCHER SAND & AGGREGATE LLP
14698 Galaxie Ave (55124-8574)
PHONE..............................952 432-7132
Liza Robson, *Partner*
Peter Fischer, *Partner*
EMP: 35 EST: 1978
SALES (est): 1MM-4.9MM **Privately Held**
SIC: 1442 Construction sand & gravel mining

(G-7776)
FOX-1 RESOURCES
4155 Old Sibley Memorial Hwy (55122-1949)
PHONE..............................651 894-3990
Kristen Bartsch, *CEO*
Linda Cole, *Director*
EMP: 42 EST: 2002
SALES (est): 5MM-9.9MM **Privately Held**
SIC: 8711 Engineering consulting services

(G-7777)
FREIGHTMASTERS INC
3703 Kennebec Dr (55122-1055)
PHONE..............................651 688-6800
Ronald A Have, *President*
Lisa Have, *Corp Secy*
Scott Anderson, *Vice Pres*
Ken Klecker, *Vice Pres*
Dennis Steele, *CFO*
EMP: 250 EST: 1975
SQ FT: 155,000
SALES (est): 25MM-49.9MM **Privately Held**
SIC: 4213 4212 4214 4225 4731 Over the road trucking; local trucking with storage; delivery services by vehicle; general warehousing; customs clearance of freight services

(G-7778)
GARY L KEMP AGENCY INC
Also Called: Minnesota Insurance Brokers
60 Marie Ave E Ste 209 (55118-5932)
PO Box 18453 (55118-0453)
PHONE..............................651 457-3070
Gary L Kemp, *President*
Mitch Lowen, *Vice Pres*
Buck Purchaise, *Sales Staff*
Mike Ryan, *Manager*
EST: 1967 **Privately Held**
WEB: www.mninsurance.net
SIC: 6411 Insurance services

(G-7779)
GENERAL RESOURCE TECHNOLOGY
2978 Center Ct (55121-1257)
PHONE..............................651 454-4151
FAX: 651 454-4252
William R Collins III, *President*
Julie Duscher, *Corp Secy*
Steven Hawkins, *Vice Pres*
Jennifer Woolley, *Finance Mgr*
Travis Collins, *Sales Mgr*
EMP: 29 EST: 1992
SQ FT: 18,000
SALES (est): 10MM-24.9MM **Privately Held**
WEB: www.grtinc.com
SIC: 5169 Wholesales concrete additives; manufactures chemical products

(G-7780)
GENESIS HOMECARE INC
13379 Hughes Ct (55124-9462)
PHONE..............................651 686-5910
FAX: 651 686-5920
Michael Kashevatsky, *President*
Michael Kashevastkiy, *Manager*
EMP: 60 EST: 2001
SALES (est): 1MM-4.9MM **Privately Held**
SIC: 8082 Home health care services

(G-7781)
GLADSTONE PARTNERS
234 Wentworth Ave E (55118-3525)
PHONE..............................651 455-2940
FAX: 651 455-3354
Steve Sackett, *Partner*
J O Punderson, *Partner*
T J Hernanadez, *Partner*
T V Elumba V, *Partner*
Patrick Arnold, *Partner*
EMP: 30 EST: 1977
SQ FT: 13,000
SALES (est): 5MM-9.9MM **Privately Held**
SIC: 6512 Operators of commercial & industrial buildings

(G-7782)
GLEASON GYMNASTIC SCHOOL (PA)
2015 Silver Bell Rd Ste 180 (55122-3170)
PHONE..............................651 454-6203
Larry Gleason, *Owner*
Carin Boylan, *Director*
EMP: 45 EST: 1966 **Privately Held**
SIC: 7999 Gymnastics instruction

(G-7783)
GLOBAL SPECIALTY CONTRACTORS (PA)
3220 Terminal Dr (55121-1609)
PHONE..............................651 406-8232
FAX: 651 406-8242
Todd Johnson, *President*
C R Brazier, *Corp Secy*
Joel Ecker, *Vice Pres*
Matthew Berlin, *Administrator*
EST: 1990
SQ FT: 8,000 **Privately Held**
WEB: www.globalspecialty.net
SIC: 1541 1611 1623 1629 Industrial building & warehouse construction; highway guardrail construction; telecommunication transmitting tower construction; dam, waterway, dock & other marine structure construction; street sign installation & maintenance

(G-7784)
GO E BIZCOM
1020 Discovery Rd Ste 145 (55121-2096)
PHONE..............................651 454-0013
Tom Salonek, *President*
Andrew W Troelsen, *VP Eng R&D*
Dave Brenner, *Controller*
Dan McCabe, *Sales Staff*
Doug Laing, *Info Tech Mgr*
EMP: 33 EST: 1999
SALES (est): 1MM-4.9MM **Privately Held**
WEB: www.intertechsoftware.com
SIC: 7374 Computer graphics service

www.HarrisInfo.com
338

2011 Harris Minnesota
Services Directory

▲=Import ▼=Export
◆=Import/Export

(G-7785)

GOGGINS & LAVINTMAN
3140 Neil Armstrong Blvd # 319
(55121-2273)
PHONE 651 209-1825
FAX: 651 688-5920
Michael J Goggins, *Partner*
Joel Lavintman, *Partner*
EMP: 25 **EST:** 1994
SALES (est): 1MM-4.9MM **Privately Held**
SIC: 8111 General practice attorney's or
lawyer's office

(G-7786)

GOLD KEY REALTY
15692 Highview Dr (55124-7198)
PHONE 952 431-5751
Ken Egel, *President*
EMP: 26 **EST:** 1993
SALES (est): 1MM-4.9MM **Privately Held**
SIC: 6531 Real estate agency & broker

(G-7787)

GOODWILL INDUSTRIES INC
Also Called: Applevally Goodwill
7320 153rd St W (55124-7039)
PHONE 952 953-4410
FAX: 952 953-4724
Patrick Siedow, *Branch Mgr*
EMP: 30
SALES (est): 1MM-4.9MM **Privately Held**
WEB: www.goodwilleasterseals.org
SIC: 4953 4226 8322 8331 Waste material
recycling services; retails used
merchandise; family services agency; job
training services; warehousing & storage
facility
PA: Goodwill Industries Inc
553 Fairview Ave N
Saint Paul MN 55104
651 379-5800

(G-7788)

GOPHER STATE ONE CALL INC
Also Called: One Call Concepts
2020 Centre Pointe Blvd (55120-1200)
PHONE 651 454-8388
Susan Volkman, *President*
Tonya Bethke, *General Mgr*
Adam Kramer, *Chairman*
Tammy Gardner, *Office Mgr*
John Gardner, *Manager*
EMP: 75 **EST:** 1988
SQ FT: 20,458
SALES (est): 10MM-24.9MM **Privately Held**
WEB: www.gopherstateonecall.org
SIC: 8742 Site location consultant

(G-7789)

GRAHAM CONSTRUCTION SERVICES
2995 Lone Oak Cir Ste 1 (55121-1431)
PHONE 651 687-0648
FAX: 651 452-9030
Dave Lenss, *President*
Scott Fowler, *Regional Mgr*
Doug Sherrod, *Vice Pres*
Daryl Ferko, *Vice Pres*
Doug Bespalko, *Treasurer*
EMP: 60 **EST:** 2003
SQ FT: 10,000
SALES (est): 10MM-24.9MM **Privately Held**
SIC: 1542 1541 1622 New commercial &
office building construction; bridge
construction; new industrial building
construction

(G-7790)

GRAZZINI BROTHERS & CO
1175 Eagan Industrial Rd (55121-1205)
PHONE 651 452-2700
Eugene E Grazzini Jr, *President*
Greg Grazzini, *President*
Wayne T Grazzim, *Corp Secy*
Allen P Grazzini, *Corp Secy*
Guido Gliori, *Vice Pres*
EMP: 200 **EST:** 1923
SQ FT: 26,000
SALES (est): 10MM-24.9MM **Privately Held**
WEB: www.grazzini.com
SIC: 1743 Terrazzo work installation
service; ceramic tile installation service

(G-7791)

GREGG G HIPPLE
1480 Yankee Doodle Rd (55121-1801)
PHONE 651 452-3333
FAX: 651 452-5237
Greg Hipple, *Owner*
EMP: 25 **EST:** 1992
SALES (est): 1MM-4.9MM **Privately Held**
SIC: 8021 Dentists' office & clinic

(G-7792)

GREGORY'S FOODS INC
1301 Trapp Rd (55121-1247)
PHONE 651 454-0277
FAX: 651 454-2254
Gregory Helland, *President*
Davin Duren, *General Mgr*
Charlie Larsen, *Controller*
Tom Hoebbel, *Director*
EMP: 40 **EST:** 1980
SQ FT: 30,000
SALES (est): 25MM-49.9MM **Privately Held**
WEB: www.gregorysfoods.com
SIC: 5149 Wholesales bakery products;
manufactures frozen bakery products;
wholesale or wholesale & retail combined
bakery; manufactures cookies & crackers;
manufactures flour mixes & doughs;
manufactures frozen food products

(G-7793)

GRESSER CO'S INC
2905 Lexington Ave S (55121-1421)
PHONE 651 454-5976
FAX: 651 454-4850
Michael J Gresser, *President*
George Polusny, *Vice Pres*
Mark Jerstad, *Vice Pres*
Mike Lins, *Opers Mgr*
Elizabeth Spillman, *Controller*
EMP: 240 **EST:** 1969
SQ FT: 25,000
SALES (est): 25MM-49.9MM **Privately Held**
WEB: www.gresserco.com
SIC: 1771 1741 Concrete contractor;
masonry & stonework contractor

(G-7794)

HANCO CORP
3650 Dodd Rd (55123-1305)
PHONE 651 456-5600
Dennis Larson, *President*
Carol Larson, *Vice Pres*
Greg Reylonds, *Purch Agent*
▲ **EMP:** 28 **EST:** 1928
SQ FT: 40,000
SALES (est): 10MM-24.9MM **Privately Held**
WEB: www.hancocorp.com
SIC: 5014 Wholesales tire & tube repair
materials

(G-7795)

HARCO MARKETING GROUP INC
Also Called: Aldata List Co
7000 151st St W (55124-5985)
PHONE 952 432-6900
Michael H Harris, *President*
EST: 1985
SQ FT: 4,500 **Privately Held**
WEB: www.aldata.com
SIC: 7331 Mailing services
PA: Lorton Data Inc
2 Pine Tree Dr
Saint Paul MN 55112
612 362-0200

(G-7796)

HARRISON DENTAL STUDIO INC
5 Wentworth Ave E (55118-3405)
PHONE 651 457-6600
FAX: 651 457-8869
Randy Harrison, *President*
Scott Harrison, *Vice Pres*
EMP: 25 **EST:** 1968
SQ FT: 4,000
SALES (est): 1MM-4.9MM **Privately Held**
WEB: www.harrisondentalstudio.com
SIC: 8072 Dental laboratory

(G-7797)

HEALTHCARE MANAGEMENT
2854 Highway 55 Ste 130 (55121-1447)
PHONE 651 224-4930
Jeff Guenther, *President*

Douglas R Anderson, *Vice Pres*
Robert M Bergstrom, *Vice Pres*
Timothy J Quesnell, *Vice Pres*
EMP: 27 **EST:** 1994
SALES (est): 1MM-4.9MM **Privately Held**
SIC: 8742 Management consulting services

(G-7798)

HEALTHPARTNERS INC
Also Called: Apple Valley Dental Clinic
15290 Pennock Ln (55124-7163)
PHONE 952 431-8500
FAX: 952 431-6966
Jan Minnie, *Corp Secy*
Julie White, *Manager*
Rich Weekf, *Manager*
Nicole Amundson, *Surgeon*
Jessica A Drapcho, *Surgeon*
EMP: 400
SALES (est): 25MM-49.9MM **Privately Held**
WEB: www.healthpartners.com
SIC: 8021 Dental clinic
PA: HealthPartners Inc
8170 33rd Ave S
Bloomington MN 55425
952 883-6000

(G-7799)

HERREGAN DISTRIBUTORS INC
3695 Kennebec Dr (55122-1002)
PHONE 651 452-7200
Kenneth L Herriges, *CEO*
Robert Link, *President*
Thomas Splinter, *Vice Pres*
Todd Laing, *Controller*
Matt Link, *Cust Mgr*
▲ **EMP:** 63 **EST:** 1966
SQ FT: 70,000
SALES (est): 10MM-24.9MM **Privately Held**
WEB: www.herregan.com
SIC: 5023 Wholesales floor coverings;
wholesales carpets; wholesales tile or sheet
resilient floor coverings

(G-7800)

HOME DEPOT USA INC
15101 Flagstaff Ave (55124-4528)
PHONE 952 432-7171
FAX: 952 997-9374
Joseph Warhol, *Manager*
Davis Ruffs, *Manager*
Greg Sherill, *Manager*
EMP: 200
SQ FT: 117,688
SALES (est): 25MM-49.9MM **Publicly Held**
SIC: 7359 Home center store; tool rental
HQ: Home Depot International Inc
2455 Paces Ferry Rd SE
Atlanta GA 30339
770 319-1669

(G-7801)

HOSE CONVEYORS INC
2725 Highway 55 (55121-1404)
PHONE 651 456-0200
David Chase, *President*
Jay Adams, *Vice Pres*
Emely Thompson, *Accounts Mgr*
EMP: 30 **EST:** 1982
SQ FT: 70,000
SALES (est): 10MM-24.9MM **Privately Held**
WEB: www.hoseconveyors.com
SIC: 5085 Wholesales industrial supplies;
wholesales industrial hose, belting &
packing; manufactures fluid power valves &
hose fittings

(G-7802)

IMPERIAL DEVELOPERS INC
1771 Yankee Doodle Rd (55121-1618)
PHONE 651 454-3330
FAX: 651 454-3331
Allen J Schefers, *CEO*
Jay D Hembroff, *President*
Dan Ward, *Manager*
John Brelie, *Manager*
EMP: 60 **EST:** 1950
SQ FT: 9,256
SALES (est): 5MM-9.9MM **Privately Held**
WEB: www.imperialdevelopers.com
SIC: 1794 1611 1623 Excavation & grading;
building construction contractor; grading
services; water & sewer line construction;
heavy highway & street construction

(G-7803)

IMPERIAL LEASING INC
1771 Yankee Doodle Rd (55121-1618)
PHONE 651 454-3330
Allen Schefers, *President*
Brenda Petsch, *Office Mgr*
EMP: 50 **EST:** 1987
SALES (est): Under 500K **Privately Held**
SIC: 7359 Equipment rental & leasing
services

(G-7804)

INTERNATIONAL ASSN FOR
Also Called: IAI
2535 Pilot Knob Rd # 117 (55120-1120)
PHONE 651 681-8566
FAX: 651 681-8593
Candace Murray, *Meeting Planner*
EST: 1915
SQ FT: 1,200 **Privately Held**
SIC: 8621 Scientific membership
association

(G-7805)

INTERNATIONAL ASSOCIATION OF
Also Called: Iam Air Trnspt Dst Lodge 143
2510 Lexington Ave S (55120-1260)
PHONE 651 688-2640
Stephen Gordon, *President*
EMP: 38 **EST:** 1947
SQ FT: 7,800 **Privately Held**
WEB: www.internationalcycling.com
SIC: 8631 Labor union

(G-7806)

INTERTECH INC
1020 Discovery Rd Ste 145 (55121-2096)
PHONE 651 994-8558
Thomas H Salonek, *President*
Michael Colikas, *Sales Mgr*
Celeste Swanson, *Manager*
Peter Owusu-Afriyie, *Manager*
Davin Mickelson, *Training Spec*
EMP: 35 **EST:** 1988
SQ FT: 7,100
SALES (est): 1MM-4.9MM **Privately Held**
WEB: www.intertech.com
SIC: 7371 Custom computer software
systems analysis & design service

(G-7807)

IRON MOUNTAIN INC
950 Apollo Rd (55121-2374)
PHONE 651 452-0169
Steve Elm, *Manager*
EMP: 50
SALES (est): 5MM-9.9MM **Publicly Held**
WEB: www.ironmountain.com
SIC: 4226 Warehousing & storage facility
PA: Iron Mountain Inc
745 Atlantic Ave Fl 6
Boston MA 02111
617 535-4766

(G-7808)

IRON MOUNTAIN INFORMATION MGT
950 Apollo Dock 29 (55121)
PHONE 651 452-6515
Dan Dunlap, *Director*
EMP: 50
SALES (est): 1MM-4.9MM **Publicly Held**
WEB: www.ironmountain.com
SIC: 7389 Document destruction service
HQ: Iron Mountain Information Mgt
745 Atlantic Ave Fl 10
Boston MA 02111
617 357-4455

(G-7809)

JENSEN'S SUPPER CLUB
3840 Sibley Memorial Hwy (55122-1412)
PHONE 651 688-7969
FAX: 651 405-6915
Doron R Jensen, *President*
Troy Smith, *General Mgr*
Kevin Burkart, *Info Tech Dir*
EMP: 42 **EST:** 1996
SQ FT: 9,200
SALES (est): 1MM-4.9MM **Privately Held**
WEB: www.jensenssupperclub.com

(PA)=Parent Co (HQ)=Headquarters (DH)=Div Headquarters
✪ = New business established in last 2 years

2011 Harris Minnesota
Services Directory

© Harris InfoSource 1-866-281-6415
339

GEOGRAPHIC

SIC: 7299 Full service American restaurant; banquet hall facility

(G-7810)
JOHN HENRY FOSTER MINNESOTA

3103 Mike Collins Dr (55121-2220)
PHONE..............................651 452-8452
FAX: 651 681-9368
John Hawkins, *Ch of Bd*
Patti Bogwart, *Purchasing*
Nancy Wickard, *Finance*
Jere Prokes, *Sales Mgr*
Curt Crouse, *MIS Staff*
EMP: 68 EST: 1948
SQ FT: 20,000
SALES (est): 25MM-49.9MM Privately Held
WEB: www.jhfoster.com
SIC: 5084 Wholesales industrial machinery & equipment; wholesales compressors; wholesales industrial pneumatic tools & equipment

(G-7811)
JOMAR INVESTMENTS INC

Also Called: Road Equipment
3275 Dodd Rd (55121-2318)
PHONE..............................651 686-6100
FAX: 651 636-6100
John O'Brien, *Manager*
Don Johnson, *Manager*
EMP: 30
SALES (est): 10MM-24.9MM Privately Held
SIC: 5013 Wholesales truck parts & accessories
PA: Jomar Investments Inc
400 Gordon Indus Ct SW
Grand Rapids MI 49509
616 878-3633

(G-7812)
JUSTMAN FREIGHT LINES INC

4855 S Robert Trl (55123-2124)
PHONE..............................651 423-1024
FAX: 651 423-1236
Michael Neisius, *President*
Shar Neisius, *Manager*
EMP: 40 EST: 1977
SQ FT: 6,000
SALES (est): 5MM-9.9MM Privately Held
SIC: 4213 Contract haulers

(G-7813)
JUSTMAN TRUCKING INC

4855 S Robert Trl (55123-2124)
PHONE..............................651 423-1020
Michael Neisius, *President*
EMP: 50 EST: 1980
SALES (est): 5MM-9.9MM Privately Held
SIC: 4213 Over the road trucking

(G-7814)
K 2 INTERNATIONAL INC

2782 Eagandale Blvd (55121-1377)
PHONE..............................651 209-8770
Christian V Walhof, *Principal*
Orlando Mazzolini, *Exec VP*
Lisa Gustafson, *CFO*
Michael Oconnell, *Advt Staff*
Patty Campisi, *Manager*
EST: 1992
SQ FT: 30,000 Privately Held
WEB: www.k2connect.com
SIC: 4731 Shipping broker

(G-7815)
K N AIR DOMESTIC

980 Lone Oak Rd (55121-2253)
PHONE..............................651 688-7650
Bill Castle, *Senior VP*
Ralph Altorfer, *Manager*
EMP: 40 EST: 1999
SALES (est): 1MM-4.9MM Privately Held
SIC: 4731 Freight forwarding services

(G-7816)
KINDERCARE LEARNING CENTERS

3620 Krestwood Ln (55123-1031)
PHONE..............................651 681-1968
FAX: 651 686-6412
Angie Goettl, *Exec Dir*
EMP: 30
SALES (est): 500-999K Privately Held

WEB: www.kindercare.com
SIC: 8351 Child day care service
HQ: KinderCare Learning Centers
650 NE Holladay St Ste 1400
Portland OR 97232
503 872-1300

(G-7817)
KINDERCARE LEARNING CENTERS

Also Called: Eagan Kindercare
1865 Plaza Dr (55122-2612)
PHONE..............................651 452-1616
FAX: 651 452-8892
Shelly Thone, *Director*
EMP: 25
SALES (est): 500-999K Privately Held
WEB: www.kindercare.com
SIC: 8351 Child day care service
HQ: KinderCare Learning Centers
650 NE Holladay St Ste 1400
Portland OR 97232
503 872-1300

(G-7818)
KNOWLEDGE LEARNING CORP

Also Called: Childrens World Lrng Ctr 246
4194 Pilot Knob Rd (55122-1816)
PHONE..............................952 452-6625
Amy Madager, *Sales Staff*
Sally Everson, *Manager*
Kim Neu, *Manager*
EMP: 25
SALES (est): 500-999K Privately Held
WEB: www.knowledgelearning.com
SIC: 8351 Child day care service
PA: Knowledge Learning Corp
650 NE Holladay St # 1400
Portland OR 97232
503 872-1300

(G-7819)
KNUTSON, FLYNN, DEANS

1155 Centre Pte Dr Ste 10 (55120-1278)
PHONE..............................651 222-2811
Joseph E Flynn, *President*
Steve Knutson, *Partner*
James E Knutson, *Corp Secy*
Thomas S Dean, *Vice Pres*
EMP: 25 EST: 1972
SQ FT: 14,000
SALES (est): 1MM-4.9MM Privately Held
WEB: www.kfdmn.com
SIC: 8111 General practice law office; corporate, partnership & business law office

(G-7820)
KUEHNE + NAGEL INC

980 Lone Oak Rd Ste 128 (55121-2253)
PHONE..............................651 688-6645
FAX: 651 688-6401
Missy Nelson, *Human Res Dir*
Stacy Berg, *Sales Staff*
Brian Jones, *Branch Mgr*
Richard Cox, *Manager*
EMP: 45
SALES (est): 5MM-9.9MM Privately Held
WEB: www.kuehnenagel.com
SIC: 4731 Freight forwarding services
HQ: Kuehne + Nagel Inc
10 Exchange Pl Fl 19
Jersey City NJ 07302
201 413-5500

(G-7821)
LANGER CONSTRUCTION CO INC

54 Moreland Ave E (55118-2416)
PHONE..............................651 457-5993
FAX: 651 457-7068
Thomas Langer, *President*
Russ Gellmer, *Safety Mgr*
Bob Teel, *Treasurer*
Robert Teel, *Treasurer*
Dave Langer, *Sales Mgr*
EMP: 55 EST: 1947
SQ FT: 8,000
SALES (est): 10MM-24.9MM Privately Held
WEB: www.langerconstruction.com
SIC: 1542 Commercial & office building contractor

(G-7822)
LE FEBVRE & SONS INC

6055 150th St W (55124-6951)
PHONE..............................952 432-8228
FAX: 952 432-8188
Paul L Febvre, *President*
EMP: 100
SALES (est): 5MM-9.9MM Privately Held
SIC: 4212 4213 Local trucking without storage services; over the road trucking

(G-7823)
LEHMAN'S GARAGE INC

1979 Seneca Rd (55122-1006)
PHONE..............................651 454-1120
Darrell Amberson, *Sales Staff*
Rick Cassett, *Manager*
EMP: 35
SALES (est): 1MM-4.9MM Privately Held
SIC: 7538 General automotive repair services
PA: Lehman's Garage Inc
171 American Blvd W
Minneapolis MN 55420
952 888-8700

(G-7824)
LESSORS INC

1056 Gemini Rd (55121-2205)
PHONE..............................651 789-9270
James R Shapiro, *President*
Wendy Shapiro, *Corp Secy*
Brian Knudson, *Vice Pres*
EMP: 100 EST: 1983
SQ FT: 16,500
SALES (est): 10MM-24.9MM Privately Held
SIC: 4213 Over the road trucking

(G-7825)
LOVEGREEN INDUSTRIAL SERVICES

2280 Sibley Ct (55122-1998)
PHONE..............................651 890-1166
Vernon J Lovegreen III, *President*
Gerald Johnson, *Vice Pres*
Kevin Lovegreen, *Vice Pres*
Monica Hlavac, *Manager*
Catherine Settanni, *Info Tech Mgr*
EMP: 60 EST: 1948
SQ FT: 42,000
SALES (est): 5MM-9.9MM Privately Held
WEB: www.lovegreen.com
SIC: 1796 Machinery installation service; manufactures industrial trucks & tractors; machine shop, jobbing & repair services

(G-7826)
LOWE'S HOME CENTERS INC

1795 Robert St S (55118-3934)
PHONE..............................763 367-4139
EMP: 150
SALES (est): 25MM-49.9MM Publicly Held
WEB: www.lowes.com
SIC: 5031 5064 Retails building products & materials; wholesales exterior building materials; wholesales interior building materials; wholesales electrical appliances; retails household appliances
HQ: Lowe's Home Centers Inc
1605 Curtis Bridge Rd
Wilkesboro NC 28697
336 658-4000

(G-7827)
LPS DEFAULT SOLUTIONS INC

1270 Northland Dr Ste 200 (55120-1176)
PHONE..............................651 234-3500
FAX: 651 234-3600
Scott Barnes, *President*
Dave Funk, *Vice Pres*
Steve Geths, *Vice Pres*
Jason Draher, *Accountant*
Robert Hegstrom, *Manager*
EMP: 60 EST: 1992
SALES (est): 5MM-9.9MM Publicly Held
WEB: www.lpsvcs.com
SIC: 8111 Bankruptcy referee
PA: Lender Processing Services Inc
601 Riverside Ave
Jacksonville FL 32204
904 854-5100

(G-7828)
M V R HOME CARE INC

3435 Washington Dr # 104 (55122-1339)
PHONE..............................651 994-9583
FAX: 651 994-9581
Vladimir Storchak, *President*
EMP: 25 EST: 2000
SALES (est): 500-999K Privately Held
WEB: www.mvrhomecare.com
SIC: 8082 Home health care services

(G-7829)
MACHINE TOOL SUPPLY CORP

3150 Mike Collins Dr (55121-2221)
PHONE..............................651 452-4400
Todd A Kerin, *President*
Dave Thompson, *Division Mgr*
Troy Karen, *Vice Pres*
Dave Learmann, *Engineer*
Kent Zachman, *Manager*
EMP: 35 EST: 1953
SQ FT: 33,000
SALES (est): 10MM-24.9MM Privately Held
WEB: www.machtool.com
SIC: 5085 5084 Wholesales industrial supplies; wholesales industrial machine tools & accessories

(G-7830)
MAILAND MANAGEMENT CORP

149 Thompson Ave E Ste 210 (55118-3263)
PHONE..............................651 451-9034
FAX: 651 451-9028
Gregory Mailand, *President*
EST: 1980 Privately Held
SIC: 6513 Apartment building operator

(G-7831)
MARATHON MANAGEMENT INC

2303 Waters Dr (55120-1163)
PHONE..............................651 259-4093
John Stevens, *Principal*
EMP: 25
SALES (est): 1MM-4.9MM Privately Held
SIC: 8741 Management services

(G-7832)
MARK MACDONALD DO

Also Called: East Metro Family Practice
234 Wentworth Ave E (55118-3525)
PHONE..............................651 455-2940
Teodoro Elumba, *Vice Pres*
Patrick Arnold, *Med Doctor*
Kathy Bahrke, *Administrator*
EMP: 25 EST: 2001
SALES (est): 1MM-4.9MM Privately Held
SIC: 8011 Physicians' office & clinic

(G-7833)
MARKET SOLUTIONS GROUP INC

3356 Sherman Ct Ste 104 (55121-5001)
PHONE..............................612 332-1574
Mark Detours, *President*
Mark D Tours, *President*
Greg Blevins, *Vice Pres*
Doug Skipper, *Vice Pres*
Hannah Valentine, *Project Mgr*
EMP: 70 EST: 1984
SALES (est): 5MM-9.9MM Privately Held
WEB: www.marketsolutionsgroup.com
SIC: 8732 Market analysis or research services

(G-7834)
MASTER MECHANICAL INC

1027 Gemini Rd Ste A (55121-2453)
PHONE..............................651 905-1600
FAX: 651 905-1238
Gordon Peters, *CEO*
Thomas Palermo, *Vice Pres*
Steven Nelson, *Vice Pres*
Robert Johnson, *CFO*
EMP: 120 EST: 1986
SQ FT: 35,000
SALES (est): 10MM-24.9MM Privately Held
WEB: www.mastermechanical.com
SIC: 1711 Mechanical contractor

www.HarrisInfo.com
340

2011 Harris Minnesota
Services Directory

▲=Import ▼=Export
◆=Import/Export

(G-7835)
MAYFLOWER DISTRIBUTING CO INC
1155 Medallion Dr (55120-1220)
PHONE.............................651 452-4892
FAX: 651 452-9257
Joe Abelovitz, *CEO*
Martin Abelovitz, *President*
Allen Scarsella, *VP Sls/Mktg*
Karole Abelovitz, *Treasurer*
Terry Engel, *Human Res Mgr*
EMP: 110 EST: 1981
SQ FT: 100,000
SALES (est): 50MM-99.9MM **Privately Held**
WEB: www.mayflowerdistributing.com
SIC: 5199 5113 Wholesales party favors, balloons, hats, etc; wholesales industrial & personal service paper

(G-7836)
MAYTAG COIN-OP WASHERS
2430 Enterprise Dr (55120-1143)
PHONE.............................651 688-7000
David Demarsh, *Owner*
Karen Ganter, *Vice Pres*
John Simon, *Manager*
EMP: 45 EST: 1999
SALES (est): 1MM-4.9MM **Privately Held**
SIC: 7359 Laundry equipment leasing service

(G-7837)
MENDAKOTA COUNTRY CLUB INC
2075 Mendakota Dr (55120-1335)
PHONE.............................651 454-2822
FAX: 651 454-9299
R S Watson, *General Mgr*
Bob Howell, *Controller*
Nora Sarrell, *Marketing Staff*
EMP: 110 EST: 1920
SQ FT: 24,000
SALES (est): 5MM-9.9MM **Privately Held**
SIC: 7997 7992 Membership golf club; eating place; public golf course; drinking establishment

(G-7838)
METRISOURCE INC
3140 Neil Armstrong Blvd # 323
(55121-4211)
PHONE.............................651 686-0097
Dennis Winsor, *CEO*
Troy Drahos, *Manager*
EMP: 40 EST: 2001
SQ FT: 1,763
SALES (est): 5MM-9.9MM **Privately Held**
WEB: www.metrisource.com
SIC: 8742 Corporation organizing consultant; human resource consulting services

(G-7839)
MICHAEL E MOLENDA
7300 147th St W Ste 600 (55124-4517)
PHONE.............................952 432-3136
Tim M Dermott, *Manager*
EMP: 35 EST: 1985
SALES (est): 1MM-4.9MM **Privately Held**
SIC: 8111 General practice attorney's or lawyer's office

(G-7840)
MID NORTHERN ELECTRIC INC
1299 Eagan Industrial Rd # 101
(55121-1384)
PHONE.............................651 452-3996
Dennis Wolfe, *President*
Tim Phillips, *Info Tech Mgr*
EMP: 31 EST: 1978
SQ FT: 3,800
SALES (est): 1MM-4.9MM **Privately Held**
WEB: www.mid-northernelectric.com
SIC: 1731 General electrical contractor

(G-7841)
MILLENNIUM CREDIT CONSULTANTS
33 Wentworth Ave E # 220 (55118-3432)
PO Box 18160 (55118-0160)
PHONE.............................651 306-9344
FAX: 651 306-9360
Bruce Jahnke, *CEO*

Terri Master, *Corp Secy*
Mike Peterson, *Vice Pres*
EST: 1997 **Privately Held**
SIC: 7322 Collection agency

(G-7842)
MINNESOTA HOUSEKEEPING SVCS
Also Called: Maid Brigade
2535 Pilot Knob Rd # 118 (55120-1120)
PHONE.............................651 686-0900
Quentin Ritchie, *Member*
EMP: 25 EST: 2003
SALES (est): 500-999K **Privately Held**
SIC: 7349 Building cleaning & maintenance services

(G-7843)
MINNESOTA NETWORK FOR
Also Called: Mnpact
13440 Gunflint Ct (55124-7375)
PHONE.............................952 891-1862
Roxanne Mindeman, *President*
EMP: 37 EST: 2005 **Privately Held**
SIC: 8651 Political organization

(G-7844)
MJM INVESTMENTS INC
Also Called: Kendrick Electric
14540 Pennock Ave (55124-5508)
PHONE.............................952 432-5036
Mark Melander, *President*
EMP: 40 EST: 1970
SQ FT: 6,000
SALES (est): 1MM-4.9MM **Privately Held**
SIC: 1731 General electrical contractor

(G-7845)
MOHAWK INDUSTRIES INC
2359 Waters Dr (55120-1163)
PHONE.............................651 405-8300
FAX: 651 405-9286
Tom Mielcarek, *Manager*
EMP: 35
SALES (est): 10MM-24.9MM **Publicly Held**
WEB: www.mohawkind.com
SIC: 5023 Wholesales floor coverings
PA: Mohawk Industries Inc
160 S Industrial Blvd
Calhoun GA 30701
706 629-7721

(G-7846)
MORGAN TIRE & AUTO INC
Also Called: Team Tires Plus
3595 Krestwood Ln (55123-1018)
PHONE.............................651 452-4091
FAX: 651 452-6608
Ryan Benning, *Manager*
Gabe Lopez, *Manager*
EMP: 25
SALES (est): 1MM-4.9MM **Privately Held**
WEB: www.bfsusa.com
SIC: 7534 Tire recapping & retreading services
HQ: Bfs Retail Operations LLC
333 E Lake St Ste 300
Bloomingdale IL 60108
630 259-9000

(G-7847)
MULTI VENUE PRODUCTION INC
3625 Ashbury Rd (55122-1251)
PHONE.............................952 894-9111
Douglas R Petersen, *President*
Kimberly Kile, *Principal*
EMP: 25 EST: 1996
SALES (est): 1MM-4.9MM **Privately Held**
SIC: 8999 Miscellaneous services

(G-7848)
NATIONAL FLOOR MAINTENANCE INC
1670 Robert St S 292 (55118-3918)
PHONE.............................303 771-0509
Ricardo Nava, *President*
EMP: 60 EST: 2002
SQ FT: 1,000
SALES (est): 5MM-9.9MM **Privately Held**
SIC: 1752 Flooring contractor

(G-7849)
NEW CHALLENGES INC
3513 Widgeon Way (55123-1004)
PHONE.............................651 681-2044
Lee A Metzmaker, *President*
EMP: 41 EST: 1999
SALES (est): 1MM-4.9MM **Privately Held**
SIC: 8361 Self-help group home

(G-7850)
NEW HORIZON CHILD CARE INC
14088 141st St W (55124-6581)
PHONE.............................952 423-6690
FAX: 952 423-2316
Cisa Keller, *Sales Staff*
Leanne Meyers, *Exec Dir*
Kristi Fuller, *Director*
EMP: 25
SALES (est): 500-999K **Privately Held**
WEB: www.kidsquest.com
SIC: 8351 Child day care service
HQ: New Horizon Child Care Inc
16355 36th Ave N Ste 700
Plymouth MN 55446
763 557-1111

(G-7851)
NORTH STAR INTERNATIONAL INC
1060 Lone Oak Rd Ste 112 (55121-2252)
PHONE.............................651 379-5030
Kenneth Schumacher, *President*
Joel Pelletier, *Vice Pres*
Jack Prentice, *Branch Mgr*
◆ EMP: 35 EST: 1969
SQ FT: 15,000
SALES (est): 1MM-4.9MM **Privately Held**
WEB: www.shipnorthstar.com
SIC: 4581 4449 Air freight handling services; freight transportation services on bays & sounds of the ocean

(G-7852)
NORTH STAR WORLD TRADE SVCS
1060 Lone Oak Rd Ste 112 (55121-2252)
PHONE.............................651 379-5030
Kenneth Schumacher, *President*
Joe Pellitier, *Vice Pres*
EMP: 40 EST: 1969
SQ FT: 15,000
SALES (est): 1MM-4.9MM **Privately Held**
WEB: www.north-star.com
SIC: 4731 Customhouse broker

(G-7853)
NORTHSTAR FIRE PROTECTION INC (PA)
875 Blue Gentian Rd # 12 (55121-1592)
PHONE.............................651 456-9111
FAX: 651 456-9222
R C Barnett, *President*
Scott Frater, *Corp Secy*
Doug Dagenais, *Vice Pres*
Catherine James, *Human Res Mgr*
EMP: 40 EST: 1997 **Privately Held**
WEB: www.nsfire.com
SIC: 8711 1731 Fire protection engineers; fire detection & burglar alarm systems specialization contractor

(G-7854)
NORTHWEST AIRCRAFT INC
2700 Lone Oak Pkwy (55121-1546)
PHONE.............................612 726-2331
Douglas Steenland, *President*
Rolf Andresen, *VP Finance*
Libby Petit, *VP Mktg*
EMP: 30 EST: 1984
SQ FT: 1,000,000
SALES (est): 10MM-24.9MM **Publicly Held**
WEB: www.northwestaircraft.com
SIC: 5088 7359 Wholesales aircraft & parts; aircraft rental service
HQ: Northwest Airlines Corp
2700 Lone Oak Pkwy
Eagan MN 55121
612 726-2111

(G-7855)
NORTHWEST AIRLINES INC
1500 Towerview Rd (55121-1346)
PHONE.............................612 726-3896
A D Lee, *Project Mgr*
David Ruddy, *Technical Mgr*
Karin Binder, *Senior Engr*
Robert Anderson, *Senior Engr*
Belinda Quick, *Business Anlyst*
EMP: 700
SALES (est): 100MM-499.9MM **Publicly Held**
WEB: www.nwairlines.com
SIC: 4512 Scheduled air transportation services
HQ: Northwest Airlines Inc
7500 Airline Dr
Minneapolis MN 55450
612 726-2111

(G-7856)
ONE CALL CONCEPTS INC
Also Called: Gopher State One Call
2020 Centre Pointe Blvd (55120-1200)
PHONE.............................651 454-0002
Jerry Bukeleman, *Manager*
EMP: 60 **Privately Held**
WEB: www.occinc.com
SIC: 7375 Information retrieval services
PA: One Call Concepts Inc
7223 Parkway Dr Ste 210
Hanover MD 21076
410 712-0082

(G-7857)
ONLINE FREIGHT SERVICES INC
2275 Waters Dr (55120-1363)
PHONE.............................651 468-6868
Keith Burns, *President*
Jeff Burns, *Vice Pres*
EMP: 50 EST: 1997
SQ FT: 1,800
SALES (est): 5MM-9.9MM **Privately Held**
WEB: www.onlinefreight.com
SIC: 4731 Transportation agents & brokers

(G-7858)
ORBIT SYSTEMS INC
860 Blue Gentian Rd Ste 2 (55121-1564)
PHONE.............................651 767-3322
Stephen J McFarland, *President*
Christa Cargo, *Corp Secy*
Gary Milne, *Exec VP*
Chad Westrum, *Vice Pres*
Philip Palmquist, *CFO*
EMP: 60 EST: 1999
SQ FT: 2,400
SALES (est): 5MM-9.9MM **Privately Held**
WEB: www.orbits.net
SIC: 7379 7373 Computer system consulting services; computer integrated systems design services

(G-7859)
ORTHODONTICS CARE SPECIALIST
14605 Glazier Ave Ste 200 (55124-7545)
PHONE.............................952 432-2682
FAX: 952 891-8638
Karl Biewald, *Exec Dir*
EMP: 35 EST: 1974
SQ FT: 4,803
SALES (est): 1MM-4.9MM **Privately Held**
SIC: 8021 Orthodontist

(G-7860)
ORTHOGONISTIC CARE SPECIALIST
Also Called: Apple Park Associates
14605 Glazier Ave (55124-7545)
PHONE.............................952 432-4941
Greg Serral, *President*
EMP: 85 EST: 2001
SALES (est): 5MM-9.9MM **Privately Held**
SIC: 8011 Medical center

(G-7861)
OSSEL BROOKLYN BUS CO INC
14800 Everest Ave (55124-8181)
PHONE.............................952 891-1031
FAX: 952 891-1643
Scott Regan, *President*
Dick Pryd, *Manager*

(PA)=Parent Co (HQ)=Headquarters (DH)=Div Headquarters
✿ = New business established in last 2 years

2011 Harris Minnesota
Services Directory

© Harris InfoSource 1-866-281-6415
341

Keith Franklin, *Manager*
EMP: 100 **EST:** 1987
SALES (est): 5MM-9.9MM **Privately Held**
SIC: 4142 4151 Long-distance bus charter
service; school bus service

(G-7862)
PACKAGING AUTOMATION CORP
2725 Highway 55 (55121-1404)
PHONE 651 456-0003
David Chase, *President*
Kerry Donley, *Div Sub Head*
Jay Adams, *Sales Executive*
David Swain, *Exec Dir*
EMP: 40 **EST:** 1995
SQ FT: 70,000
SALES (est): 5MM-9.9MM **Privately Held**
SIC: 5084 Manufactures packaging
machinery; manufactures bag opening,
filling & closing machines; wholesales
industrial machinery & equipment

(G-7863)
PARK NICOLLET CLINIC
1885 Plaza Dr (55122-2612)
PHONE 952 993-4001
FAX: 952 993-4095
John Robrock MD, *Med Doctor*
David L Von Weiss MD, *Med Doctor*
Todd H Olm MD, *Med Doctor*
Amber Larson, *Manager*
Mary Tim, *Manager*
EMP: 70
SQ FT: 19,660
SALES (est): 5MM-9.9MM **Privately Held**
WEB: www.ccopnet.com
SIC: 8011 General & family practice
physician or surgeon office
HQ: Park Nicollet Clinic
    3800 Park Nicollet Blvd
    Minneapolis MN 55416
    952 993-3123

(G-7864)
PARKVIEW GOLF ASSOCIATES LLC
1310 Cliff Rd (55123-2107)
PHONE 651 452-5098
FAX: 651 452-7415
Ted Green, *General Mgr*
Shane Korman, *General Mgr*
Tod Geller, *Mng Member*
Donald Larsen, *Manager*
EMP: 25 **EST:** 2001
SQ FT: 1,350
SALES (est): 1MM-4.9MM **Privately Held**
WEB: www.parkviewgolfclub.com
SIC: 7992 7997 Public golf course;
membership recreation club

(G-7865)
PATRICK M DOYLE DR
3450 Oleary Ln (55123-2340)
PHONE 651 454-0114
Patrick Doyle, *Owner*
Arlow W Andersen, *Manager*
Lonny D Auseth, *Manager*
Mary W Kreitz, *Manager*
Leena S Ranade, *Manager*
EMP: 30 **EST:** 2000
SQ FT: 13,490
SALES (est): 1MM-4.9MM **Privately Held**
SIC: 8322 8049 General counseling
services; clinical psychologist office

(G-7866)
PATTERSON CO'S INC (PA)
1031 Mendota Heights Rd (55120-1419)
PHONE 651 686-1600
Peter Frechette, *Ch of Bd*
James W Wiltz, *President*
Travis Nelson, *Business Mgr*
Matthew L Levitt, *Corp Secy*
Daniel H Peckskamp, *VP Opers*
EMP: 185 **EST:** 1877
SALES (corp-wide): 3.23B **Publicly Held**
WEB: www.pattersondental.com
SIC: 5047 5112 7372 7699 Wholesales
dental equipment & supplies; business &
professional software publishers;
wholesales X-ray machines & tubes;
wholesales dentists' professional supplies;
wholesales X-ray film & supplies; dental
instrument repair service

(G-7867)
PATTERSON DENTAL SUPPLY INC
2930 Waters Rd Ste 100 (55121-1668)
PHONE 651 688-6054
FAX: 651 688-2085
Teri Lesher, *Opers Mgr*
Scott Anderson, *VP Mktg*
John Schilling, *Manager*
Mark Pouti, *Manager*
Tim Oshaughnessy, *Manager*
EMP: 50
SALES (est): 25MM-49.9MM **Publicly Held**
WEB: www.pattersondentalsupply.com
SIC: 5047 Wholesales dental equipment &
supplies; wholesales X-ray machines &
tubes; wholesales dentists' professional
supplies; wholesales X-ray film & supplies
HQ: Patterson Dental Supply Inc
    1031 Mendota Heights Rd
    Saint Paul MN 55120
    651 686-1600

(G-7868)
PATTERSON DENTAL SUPPLY INC (HQ)
1031 Mendota Heights Rd (55120-1419)
PHONE 651 686-1600
FAX: 651 686-9331
Scott P Anderson, *President*
Debra A Heim, *Corp Secy*
Matthew L Levitt, *Corp Secy*
Roger A Salava, *Corp Secy*
Steve Armstrong, *Exec VP*
▲ **EMP:** 260 **EST:** 1877
SQ FT: 50,000
SALES (corp-wide): 3.23B **Publicly Held**
WEB: www.pattersondentalsupply.com
SIC: 5047 Wholesales dental equipment &
supplies
PA: Patterson Co's Inc
    1031 Mendota Heights Rd
    Saint Paul MN 55120
    651 686-1600

(G-7869)
PAYCHEX INC
1210 Northland Dr Ste 100 (55120-1181)
PHONE 651 365-5060
Holly Bauers, *Sales Mgr*
Joe Duska, *Branch Mgr*
Diana Schult, *Supervisor*
EMP: 100
SALES (est): 1MM-4.9MM **Publicly Held**
WEB: www.paychex.com
SIC: 8721 Payroll services
PA: Paychex Inc
    911 Panorama Trl S
    Rochester NY 14625
    585 385-6666

(G-7870)
PC PRODUCTIONS INC
Also Called: West Side Lanes
1625 Robert St S (55118-3903)
PHONE 651 451-6222
FAX: 651 529-8981
Juette Holseth, *President*
EMP: 25 **EST:** 1956
SQ FT: 21,000
SALES (est): 500-999K **Privately Held**
SIC: 7933 Ten pin center; cocktail lounge

(G-7871)
PEDIATRIC & ADOLESCENT CARE OF (PA)
1547 Livingston Ave (55118-3411)
PHONE 651 451-8050
FAX: 651 552-1575
Albert Heimel, *President*
James Hocks, *Vice Pres*
Mary Zaspel, *Manager*
Carloyn Dreelan, *Administrator*
Connie Ball, *Supervisor*
EMP: 45 **EST:** 1977 **Privately Held**
WEB: www.pacepediatrics.com
SIC: 8011 Pediatrician office

(G-7872)
PENN-CO CONSTRUCTION INC
2995 Lone Oak Cir Ste 5 (55121-1431)
PHONE 651 687-0648
FAX: 651 687-0947
Ernest Penner, *CEO*

Dave Lenss, *President*
Scott Fowler, *General Mgr*
Victor Friesen, *Corp Secy*
Dave Caron, *CFO*
EMP: 45 **EST:** 1988
SALES (est): 10MM-24.9MM **Privately Held**
SIC: 1542 1541 Commercial & office
building contractor; new industrial building
construction

(G-7873)
PENSKE TRUCK LEASING CO, LP
965 Aldrin Dr (55121-2270)
PHONE 651 454-0000
FAX: 651 686-0476
Justin Honeycutt, *Manager*
Mike Hamerlinck, *Manager*
Leroy Heyda, *Supervisor*
EMP: 40
SALES (est): 5MM-9.9MM **Publicly Held**
WEB: www.pensketruckleasing.com
SIC: 7513 7519 Truck rental service,
without drivers; utility trailer & RV leasing &
rental
HQ: Penske Truck Leasing Co, LP
    Green Hls
    Reading PA 19603
    610 775-6000

(G-7874)
PERMASTEELISA NORTH AMERICA
2060 Centre Pointe Blvd Ste 10
(55120-1271)
PHONE 651 905-1515
FAX: 651 905-1653
Mileah Mott, *Engineering*
Mike Kneeland, *Sales Staff*
Mike Budd, *Manager*
EMP: 25
SALES (est): 5MM-9.9MM **Privately Held**
WEB: www.permasteelisa.com
SIC: 1541 Industrial building & warehouse
construction
PA: Permasteelisa North America
    123 Day Hill Rd
    Windsor CT 06095
    860 298-2000

(G-7875)
PHILLIPPI EQUIPMENT CO (PA)
2875 Highway 55 (55121-1406)
PHONE 651 406-4900
Wendell A Phillippi, *President*
Jerry Corcoran, *Treasurer*
Lease Olson, *Assistant*
▼ **EMP:** 50 **EST:** 1971 **Privately Held**
SIC: 5082 7353 Wholesales general
construction machinery & equipment;
construction & mining equipment leasing &
rental

(G-7876)
PHOENIX RESIDENCE INC (PA)
330 Marie Ave E (55118-4011)
PHONE 651 227-7655
Darlene Scott, *President*
Pam Connolly, *Vice Pres*
Jody Docken, *Vice Pres*
Mary Thirsten, *VP Opers*
Robert Turnquist, *Human Res Dir*
EMP: 130 **EST:** 1975
SQ FT: 32,000
SALES (corp-wide): 192.93K **Privately
Held**
WEB: www.phoenixresidence.org
SIC: 8361 8052 8322 Home for the
physically handicapped; intermediate care
facility; home for the mentally handicapped;
individual & family social services

(G-7877)
PLASTIC PROMOTIONS INC
1286 Trapp Rd (55121-1217)
PHONE 651 686-0660
Thomas P Murphy, *President*
Alan Degrand, *Controller*
Rachel Stibal, *Accountant*
Lee Williams, *Director*
John Whaley, *Director*
EMP: 47 **EST:** 1970
SQ FT: 20,000
SALES (est): 25MM-49.9MM **Privately Held**
SIC: 5162 Wholesales plastics products

(G-7878)
POOL & YACHT CLUB
1600 Lilydale Rd (55118-4902)
PHONE 651 455-3900
FAX: 651 455-3312
James McCarthy, *President*
Lee Nelson, *President*
Casey Getten, *General Mgr*
Susane Mullally, *Bookkeeper*
EMP: 50 **EST:** 1955
SQ FT: 10,000
SALES (est): 1MM-4.9MM **Privately Held**
WEB: www.poolandyachtclub.com
SIC: 7997 Membership recreation club

(G-7879)
POWEL INC
930 Blue Gentian Rd Ste 1 (55121-1674)
PHONE 651 251-3005
Marcie D Mostad, *General Mgr*
Brian Driscoll, *Opers Mgr*
Tom Skramstad, *Opers Mgr*
Chris Walsh, *Engineer*
Jeff Baumer, *VP Sls/Mktg*
EMP: 50 **EST:** 2000
SALES (est): 10MM-24.9MM **Privately Held**
WEB: www.minimax.net
SIC: 7371 Retails computers & computer
software; computer programming service

(G-7880)
POWER SYSTEMS RESEARCH INC
Also Called: Compass Intl RES & Info Svcs
1365 Corporate Center Curv (55121-1265)
PHONE 651 905-8400
George Zirnhelt, *President*
Dennis Huibregtse, *Corp Secy*
Barbara Achterberg, *Controller*
Barbara Dick, *Office Mgr*
Dave Alitz, *Manager*
EMP: 35 **EST:** 1976
SQ FT: 14,000
SALES (est): 1MM-4.9MM **Privately Held**
WEB: www.powersys.com
SIC: 8732 Market analysis or research
services

(G-7881)
PRIME THERAPEUTICS INC
1305 Corporate Center Dr (55121-1204)
PO Box 64812 (55164-0812)
PHONE 651 456-1000
Eric Elliott, *President*
Steve Martin, *Member*
Don Amorosi, *COO*
Kim M Mageau, *COO*
Duane Barnes, *Senior VP*
EMP: 165 **EST:** 1998
SALES (est): 10MM-24.9MM **Privately Held**
SIC: 8741 6411 Management services;
manufactures adrenal pharmaceutical
preparations; insurance services

(G-7882)
PRIMERICA FINANCIAL SERVICES
3410 Federal Dr Ste 110 (55122-1337)
PHONE 651 688-9088
FAX: 651 454-3845
Dan Jerik, *Manager*
Tim Teff, *Manager*
EMP: 60
SALES (est): 1MM-4.9MM **Publicly Held**
WEB: www.primerica.com
SIC: 7389 Financial service
HQ: Primerica Financial Services
    3120 Breckinridge Blvd
    Duluth GA 30099
    800 544-5445

(G-7883)
PRO STOP TRUCK SERVICE INC
1066 Gemini Rd Ste B (55121-2517)
PHONE 651 452-8137
FAX: 651 683-1203
David Oren, *President*
Mike Wurzer, *Manager*
EMP: 100 **EST:** 1994
SALES (est): 5MM-9.9MM **Privately Held**
WEB: www.pro-stop.com
SIC: 7538 Automotive diesel engine repair
service; gas station

GEOGRAPHIC (side tab)

WEB: www.ericksontechnologies.com
SIC: 7372 Software publisher

(G-7884)
PROACT INC
3195 Neil Armstrong Blvd   (55121-2256)
PHONE..............................651 686-0405
Steven Ditschler, *President*
Dave Cavalier, *Prdtn Dir*
Pat McGuire, *Controller*
Jo A Peine, *Hum Res Coord*
Douglas Nord, *Sales Mgr*
EMP: 120 EST: 1972
SQ FT: 63,000
SALES (est): 5MM-9.9MM **Privately Held**
WEB: www.proactinc.org
SIC: 8331 7389 Job training & vocational rehabilitation services; packaging & labeling services

(G-7885)
QUESTAR ASSESSMENT INC
5550 Upper 147th St W   (55124-7273)
PHONE..............................952 997-2700
Ann Cheevers, *Senior VP*
Michael Beck, *Vice Pres*
C Hguyen, *Director*
Don Hughes, *Director*
Steve Berger, *Director*
EMP: 80
SALES (est): 5MM-9.9MM **Publicly Held**
WEB: www.tasa.com
SIC: 8748 Business consulting services
PA: Questar Assessment Inc
     4 Hardscrabble Hts
     Brewster NY 10509
     845 277-8100

(G-7886)
QUESTAR DATA SYSTEMS INC
2905 W Service Rd   (55121-1224)
PHONE..............................651 688-0089
FAX: 651 688-0546
David Ihle, *Ch of Bd*
Theodore Naegeli, *President*
Colleen Larson, *COO*
Joseph Stanton, *Vice Pres*
Steve Kippels, *Vice Pres*
EMP: 129 EST: 1985
SALES (est): 10MM-24.9MM **Privately Held**
SIC: 7374 Data processing service; computer calculating service; tabulating service; optical scanning services

(G-7887)
QUICK SERVICE BATTERY CO INC
1156 Robert St S   (55118-2301)
PHONE..............................651 645-0485
FAX: 651 552-9463
Iowa Glass, *Owner*
Todd Diestler, *Controller*
Todd Dietsler, *Manager*
Michelle Diestler, *Manager*
EMP: 26 EST: 1914
SQ FT: 16,000
SALES (est): 5MM-9.9MM **Privately Held**
SIC: 5013 Wholesales automotive supplies; retails auto & truck equipment & parts

(G-7888)
R L BODEKER & SONS INC (PA)
3330 Mike Collins Dr   (55121-2236)
PHONE..............................651 452-0377
Randy Bodeker, *President*
Bill Wilson, *General Mgr*
Melvin Wilson, *Vice Pres*
Karry Rood, *Human Res Mgr*
Emily Garlough, *Cust Mgr*
EMP: 52 EST: 1971
SQ FT: 17,000
SALES (corp-wide): 3M **Privately Held**
WEB: www.rlbodeker.com
SIC: 7389 Machine shop, jobbing & repair services; manufactures nonwood store fixtures; electroplating & plating service; metal slitting & shearing service

(G-7889)
RC ERICKSON & ASSOCIATES INC
2915 Waters Rd Ste 112   (55121-1562)
PHONE..............................651 452-6758
Roger C Erickson, *President*
Ed Oreilly, *Manager*
EMP: 25 EST: 1992
SALES (est): 5MM-9.9MM **Privately Held**

(G-7890)
RDO MATERIAL HANDLING CO
2985 Lone Oak Cir   (55121-1425)
PHONE..............................651 905-7025
FAX: 651 905-7035
Skip Klinkhammer, *General Mgr*
EMP: 36
SALES (est): 10MM-24.9MM **Privately Held**
SIC: 5084 Wholesales materials handling equipment
HQ: Rdo Material Handling Co
     700 7th St S
     Fargo ND 58103
     701 239-8730

(G-7891)
RECEIVABLES MANAGEMENT SOLN
Also Called: RMS
260 E Wentworth Ave   (55118-3523)
PHONE..............................651 457-1130
FAX: 651 457-3827
Robert Dunham, *President*
Cheryl Fink, *Corp Secy*
Deanna Watson, *Human Res Mgr*
Jason Boyd, *Director*
EMP: 140 EST: 1996
SQ FT: 25,426
SALES (est): 5MM-9.9MM **Privately Held**
WEB: www.rmsmn.com
SIC: 7322 Collection agency

(G-7892)
REGAL CINEMAS INC
Also Called: Eagan Cinema 16
2055 Cliff Rd   (55122-2314)
PHONE..............................651 452-8329
Brad Johnson, *Manager*
EMP: 50
SALES (est): 1MM-4.9MM **Privately Held**
WEB: www.regalcinemas.com
SIC: 7832 Indoor movie theater
HQ: Regal Cinemas Inc
     7132 Regal Ln
     Knoxville TN 37918
     865 922-1123

(G-7893)
REGENTS OF THE UNIVERSITY OF
15650 Cedar Ave Ste 1   (55124-7284)
PHONE..............................952 997-4177
FAX: 952 997-4102
Michelle Stsauber, *General Mgr*
Judy Grimm, *Principal*
Michelle S Sauver, *Office Mgr*
Christophe P Balgobin MD, *Med Doctor*
Angela Birnbaum, *Manager*
EMP: 50
SALES (est): 5MM-9.9MM **Privately Held**
WEB: www.umn.edu
SIC: 8011 Physicians' office & clinic; college
PA: Regents of The University of
     106 Pleasant St SE # 210
     Minneapolis MN 55455
     612 625-5000

(G-7894)
RESTAURANT TECHNOLOGIES INC
3711 Kennebec Dr Ste 100   (55122-1087)
PHONE..............................651 796-1600
FAX: 651 379-4914
Jeffrey R Kiesel, *CEO*
Paul Plooster, *President*
Lisa J Merryfield, *Corp Secy*
Leanne E Branham, *Vice Pres*
Joan Getzinger, *Vice Pres*
EMP: 55 EST: 1997
SQ FT: 20,000
SALES (est): 25MM-49.9MM **Privately Held**
WEB: www.rti-inc.com
SIC: 5149 Wholesales cooking oils

(G-7895)
RICH MGT INC
Also Called: Bogarts
14917 Garrett Ave   (55124-7548)
PHONE..............................952 432-1515
FAX: 952 432-1517
Richard Berry, *President*

EMP: 61 EST: 1987
SQ FT: 30,000
SALES (est): 1MM-4.9MM **Privately Held**
WEB: www.bogartsplace.com
SIC: 7933 Cocktail lounge; limited service grill restaurant; ten pin center

(G-7896)
RIVER CITY MORTGAGE CORP (PA)
1895 Plaza Dr Ste 250   (55122-4602)
PHONE..............................651 406-5000
FAX: 651 406-5010
Louis Olsen, *President*
Blaine Peterson, *Corp Secy*
Nancy I Feckler, *Corp Secy*
Gary Frechette, *Vice Pres*
Jeremy M Berg, *Info Tech Dir*
EMP: 34 EST: 1994
SALES (corp-wide): 3.12M **Privately Held**
SIC: 6162 Mortgage banking service

(G-7897)
SARA LEE BAKERY GROUP INC
3255 Neil Armstrong Blvd   (55121-2279)
PHONE..............................651 688-9275
FAX: 651 994-0659
Brad Meier, *Controller*
Mike Andre, *Manager*
Dave Morgel, *Manager*
Rich Lokken, *Manager*
EMP: 75
SALES (est): 1MM-4.9MM **Publicly Held**
WEB: www.saralee.com
SIC: 5149 Retail bakery; wholesales groceries
HQ: Sara Lee Bakery Group Inc
     3470 Rider Trl S
     Earth City MO 63045
     314 291-5480

(G-7898)
SCHWAN'S TECHNOLOGY GROUP INC
2945 Lone Oak Dr Ste 150   (55121-1588)
PHONE..............................651 681-4450
Brian Sattler, *Corp Secy*
Yuri Dobkin, *Project Engr*
Bernadette M Kruk, *CFO*
Tracy Burr, *CFO*
Doug Olsem, *Manager*
EMP: 50 **Privately Held**
WEB: www.schwanstech.com
SIC: 7375 Information retrieval services
HQ: Schwan's Technology Group Inc
     5140 Moundview Dr
     Red Wing MN 55066
     651 388-1821

(G-7899)
SCOUT INFORMATION SERVICES INC
2980 Commers Dr Ste 400   (55121-2370)
PHONE..............................651 686-4646
Jim Caldwell, *CEO*
John Wood, *COO*
David R Lamm, *Vice Pres*
Reid Ingham, *Engineer*
EMP: 30 EST: 1996
SALES (est): 1MM-4.9MM **Privately Held**
SIC: 7371 Computer software development

(G-7900)
SENIOR SOUTHVIEW LIVING
1984 Oakdale Ave Ofc   (55118-3553)
PHONE..............................651 554-4838
Kelly J Myers, *Principal*
EMP: 25 EST: 2005
SALES (est): 500-999K **Privately Held**
SIC: 8361 Home for the elderly

(G-7901)
SEVERSON SHELDON DOUGHERTY
7300 147th St W Ste 600   (55124-4517)
PHONE..............................952 432-3136
FAX: 952 432-3780
Micheal G Dougherty, *President*
Matthew Schaap, *Corp Secy*
Loren Solfest, *Vice Pres*
Tim McDermott, *Office Mgr*
Sharon K Hills, *Attorney*
EMP: 35

EST: 1988
SQ FT: 10,400
SALES (est): 1MM-4.9MM **Privately Held**
SIC: 8111 General practice law office

(G-7902)
SEXTON PARTNERS
250 Lothenbach Ave   (55118-3508)
PHONE..............................651 457-9255
James P Sexton, *Partner*
Thomas E Sexton, *Partner*
Gerl Sexton, *Partner*
John P Sexton, *Partner*
Tom Kubinski, *Sales & Mktg St*
EMP: 160
SQ FT: 44,870
SALES (est): 25MM-49.9MM **Privately Held**
SIC: 6512 Nonresidential building operator

(G-7903)
SHAW - LUNDQUIST ASSOCIATES
2757 W Service Rd   (55121-1230)
PHONE..............................651 454-0670
FAX: 651 454-7982
Fred Shaw, *President*
Hoyt Hsiao, *Corp Secy*
Thomas Meyers, *Vice Pres*
John Sjoberg, *Finance Other*
Dave Lapree, *Manager*
EMP: 73 EST: 1974
SQ FT: 20,000
SALES (est): 10MM-24.9MM **Privately Held**
WEB: www.shawlundquist.com
SIC: 1542 1541 New commercial & office building construction; new industrial building construction; industrial building renovating, remodeling & repair service; commercial & office building renovation & repair services; institutional building construction

(G-7904)
SIGNAL FINANCIAL CORP
1395 Commerce Dr Ste A   (55120-1015)
PHONE..............................651 905-3100
R S Jones, *President*
John L May, *Exec VP*
Donald Davies, *Exec VP*
Marcia O'Brien, *CFO*
Elaine Scharpen, *Auditor*
EMP: 25 EST: 1980
SQ FT: 1,900
SALES (est): 5MM-9.9MM **Publicly Held**
WEB: www.associatedbank.com
SIC: 6021 National commercial bank
PA: Associated Banc-Corp
     1200 Hansen Rd
     Green Bay WI 54304
     920 491-7000

(G-7905)
SINGLE-PLY SYSTEMS INC
909 Apollo Rd   (55121-2246)
PHONE..............................651 688-7554
Joseph Elder, *President*
Dave Zurn, *Vice Pres*
EMP: 65 EST: 1983
SQ FT: 10,000
SALES (est): 5MM-9.9MM **Privately Held**
WEB: www.singleplysystems.com
SIC: 1761 Roofing contractor

(G-7906)
SMART DATA SOLUTIONS INC
1120 Centre Pointe Dr 100   (55120-1275)
PHONE..............................651 690-3140
John Prange, *President*
Patrick Bollom, *Vice Pres*
EMP: 48 EST: 2000
SQ FT: 2,200
SALES (est): 5MM-9.9MM **Privately Held**
WEB: www.smart-data-solutions.com
SIC: 6411 7371 Contract or fee basis medical insurance claim processing; computer programming service

(G-7907)
SOLIMAR WELLNESS SPA
1121 Town Centre Dr # 105   (55123-1217)
PHONE..............................651 686-6686
FAX: 651 686-8691
Lisa Delton, *General Mgr*
EMP: 27 EST: 2003
SALES (est): 500-999K **Privately Held**
WEB: www.solimarspa.com

(PA)=Parent Co (HQ)=Headquarters (DH)=Div Headquarters
✿ = New business established in last 2 years

2011 Harris Minnesota
Services Directory

© Harris InfoSource 1-866-281-6415
343

SIC: 7991 Spas

(G-7908)
SOUTHVIEW ACRES HEALTH CARE
2000 Oakdale Ave　(55118-4662)
PHONE..............................651 451-1821
James Knight, *Business Mgr*
Anne M Waltzer, *Human Resources*
Tom Goeritz, *Administrator*
Lance Lemieux, *Administrator*
Marshall Blackfelner, *Director*
EMP: 280 EST: 1966
SQ FT: 79,000
SALES (est): 10MM-24.9MM **Privately Held**
WEB: www.southviewacres.com
SIC: 8051 Skilled nursing care facility

(G-7909)
SOUTHVIEW COUNTRY CLUB
239 Mendota Rd E　(55118-4623)
PHONE..............................651 451-6856
FAX: 651 451-0409
Witz Braham, *President*
Mark R Mc Cahey, *General Mgr*
Elaine Guertin, *Manager*
EMP: 60 EST: 1919
SQ FT: 42,000
SALES (est): 1MM-4.9MM **Privately Held**
WEB: www.southviewcc.com
SIC: 7997 Membership golf club; bar; eating place

(G-7910)
SOWLES CO　(PA)
3045 Highway 13 Ste 100　(55121-1782)
PHONE..............................651 287-9700
FAX: 651 257-9710
Daniel Sowles, *President*
Sture Berg, *Corp Secy*
Richard D Vries, *Vice Pres*
Gary Lewerer, *Vice Pres*
Michael Dvorkin, *Vice Pres*
▲ **EMP: 140 EST:** 1962
SQ FT: 16,000　**Privately Held**
WEB: www.sowles.com
SIC: 1791 7353 Concrete reinforcement placing contractor; structural iron work contractor; cranes & aerial lift equipment leasing & rental service

(G-7911)
SPUR INC
Also Called: Lost Spur Country Club
2750 Sibley Memorial Hwy　(55121-1007)
PHONE..............................651 454-2330
FAX: 651 454-4254
Wendell Pittenger, *President*
EMP: 30 EST: 1947
SALES (est): 1MM-4.9MM **Privately Held**
WEB: www.osmanshrine.org
SIC: 7992 Public golf course
PA: Osman Temple Ancient Arabic
　　2750 Sibley Memorial Hwy
　　Saint Paul MN 55121
　　651 452-5662

(G-7912)
STEPHEN M KNUTSON
1155 Centre Pte Dr Ste 10　(55120-1278)
PHONE..............................651 225-0626
Stephen Knutson, *Principal*
EMP: 25 EST: 1948
SALES (est): 1MM-4.9MM **Privately Held**
SIC: 8111 General practice attorney's or lawyer's office

(G-7913)
STONE SYSTEMS & SERVICES INC
2425 Waters Dr　(55120-1147)
PHONE..............................651 683-9672
Roberto Contraras, *President*
Mario Cuevas, *General Mgr*
Carlos Canales, *Controller*
Tera Peterson, *Accountant*
EMP: 55 EST: 1996
SALES (est): 5MM-9.9MM **Privately Held**
SIC: 1799 Manufactures cut & shaped granite; countertop installation service

(G-7914)
STRINGER BUSINESS SYSTEMS INC
Also Called: Toshiba Business Solutions
960 Blue Gentian Rd　(55121-1500)
PHONE..............................651 994-7700
Stephan M Moran, *Vice Pres*
Al Holmsten, *Vice Pres*
Michael Torcaso, *CFO*
Ivan Fercho, *Controller*
John Stringer Jr, *President*
EMP: 99 EST: 2004
SALES (est): 25MM-49.9MM **Privately Held**
WEB: www.levenstein.com
SIC: 5044 Wholesales office equipment
PA: Toshiba America Business Soln
　　2 Musick
　　Irvine CA 92618
　　949 462-6000

(G-7915)
TAPEMARK CHARITY PRO AM
150 Marie Ave E　(55118-4002)
PHONE..............................651 455-1611
FAX: 651 450-8498
Robert Klas Jr, *President*
Dave Plum, *COO*
Jim Maloney, *Opers Mgr*
James T Burmeister, *Treasurer*
EMP: 300 EST: 1972
SQ FT: 39,480
SALES (est): 50MM-99.9MM **Privately Held**
WEB: www.tapemarkproam.org
SIC: 7941 Sports support services

(G-7916)
TAPEMARK CO
1685 Marthaler Ln　(55118-3517)
PHONE..............................651 455-1611
FAX: 651 450-8403
Robert C Klas Jr, *CEO*
Andy Rensink, *President*
Steve Rau, *Vice Pres*
Kim Mueller, *Vice Pres*
Tom Yetter, *Vice Pres*
◆ **EMP: 175 EST:** 1952
SQ FT: 160,000
SALES (est): 10MM-24.9MM **Privately Held**
WEB: www.tapemark.com
SIC: 5084 Label & seal printing service; imprinting service; manufactures surgical dressings; manufactures medicated & non-medicated medical adhesive tapes; wholesales industrial machinery & equipment; commercial flexographic printing

(G-7917)
TAPPE CONSTRUCTION CO
915 Blue Gentian Rd Ste 13　(55121-1565)
PO Box 13, Savage　(55378-0013)
PHONE..............................651 994-0200
FAX: 651 994-0300
Mike Tappe, *President*
Colleen Tappe, *Vice Pres*
Amber Wirtz, *VP Finance*
Jon Johnson, *Human Res Mgr*
Kirk Thurnton, *Manager*
EMP: 400 EST: 1981
SALES (est): 25MM-49.9MM **Privately Held**
WEB: www.tappeconstruction.com
SIC: 1751 Framing contractor; finish & trim carpentry service

(G-7918)
TCBH INC
Also Called: Holiday Inn
2700 Pilot Knob Rd　(55121-1118)
PHONE..............................651 454-3434
FAX: 651 454-4904
Alison Change, *President*
EMP: 100
SALES (est): 5MM-9.9MM **Privately Held**
WEB: www.tcbh.com
SIC: 7011 Traveler accommodations
PA: Tcbh Inc
　　2476 Bolsover Ste 418
　　Houston TX 77005
　　713 665-7776

(G-7919)
TECHNIFAX BUSINESS SYSTEMS INC
Also Called: Tbs Office Automations
1385 Mendota Heights Rd # 100 (55120-1367)
PHONE..............................651 905-7090
FAX: 651 291-1407
Kong Khieu, *CEO*
Justin Butler, *General Mgr*
Charles Bluin, *Director*
EMP: 25 EST: 1988
SQ FT: 18,000
SALES (est): 5MM-9.9MM **Privately Held**
WEB: www.tbsoa.com
SIC: 5044 Wholesales office equipment

(G-7920)
TEMPWORKS SOFTWARE INC
3140 Neil Armstrong Blvd # 205 (55121-3508)
PHONE..............................651 452-0366
FAX: 651 452-0362
Gregg Dourgarian, *President*
Jessie Ultgren, *Vice Pres*
Jack Terrana, *Vice Pres*
Melanie Kramer, *Manager*
Casey Kraus, *Manager*
EMP: 54 EST: 1997
SQ FT: 12,841　**Privately Held**
WEB: www.tempworks.com
SIC: 7361 7372 Employment agency services; software publisher

(G-7921)
THOMPSON LIGHTNING PROTECTION
901 Sibley Memorial Hwy　(55118-1742)
PHONE..............................651 455-7661
FAX: 651 455-2545
Allan P Steffes, *Ch of Bd*
Douglas Franklin, *President*
Melvin Krech, *Controller*
▲ **EMP: 20 EST:** 1910
SQ FT: 40,000
SALES (est): 1MM-4.9MM **Privately Held**
WEB: www.tlpinc.com
SIC: 1731 Manufactures lightning protection equipment; electrical contractor

(G-7922)
TIMOTHY J HERNANDEZ MD
234 Wentworth Ave E　(55118-3525)
PHONE..............................651 455-2940
Timothy J Hernandez, *Owner*
EMP: 35 EST: 2001
SQ FT: 13,310
SALES (est): 1MM-4.9MM **Privately Held**
SIC: 8011 Physicians' office & clinic

(G-7923)
TINY TOTS & LITTLE TYKES PRE
1200 Oakdale Ave　(55118-2601)
PHONE..............................651 457-0042
FAX: 651 457-1633
Sylvia Nelson, *Exec Dir*
Manarae Shaan, *Director*
Kathy Darrow, *Director*
Sylvia Witz, *Director*
EMP: 33 EST: 1985
SALES (est): 500-999K **Privately Held**
WEB: www.tinytotsandlittletykes.com
SIC: 8351 Child day care service

(G-7924)
TIVOLI TOO INC
2444 Enterprise Dr Ste A　(55120-1286)
PHONE..............................651 698-3335
FAX: 651 698-0954
Randi Johnson, *President*
David Gale, *E-Business*
▲ **EMP: 30 EST:** 1980
SALES (est): 5MM-9.9MM **Privately Held**
WEB: www.tivolitoo.com
SIC: 8999 Sculptor's studio

(G-7925)
TMI COATINGS INC
3291 Terminal Dr　(55121-1610)
PHONE..............................651 452-6100
Tracy M Gliori, *President*
John M Anderson, *Corp Secy*
Judy Morgel, *Bookkeeper*

Eileen Steffes, *Human Res Mgr*
Gloria Griefnow, *Administrator*
EMP: 80 EST: 1985
SQ FT: 7,000
SALES (est): 5MM-9.9MM **Privately Held**
WEB: www.tmicoatings.com
SIC: 1799 Coating, caulking & weather, water & fireproofing contractor; construction site metal structure coating service

(G-7926)
TORRINI PLASTERING CO INC
1967 Timber Wolf Trl S　(55122-2230)
PHONE..............................612 332-3933
FAX: 612 332-9592
John Torrini, *President*
Patricia Torrini, *Vice Pres*
Peggy Roberts, *Office Mgr*
EMP: 30 EST: 1961
SALES (est): 1MM-4.9MM **Privately Held**
WEB: www.torrini.net
SIC: 1721 Painting & wall covering contractor

(G-7927)
TRIADVANTAGE CREDIT SERVICES
1160 Centre Pointe Dr Ste 1　(55120-1270)
PHONE..............................651 255-2047
Todd Sobiech, *Principal*
EMP: 494 EST: 1999
SALES (est): 25MM-49.9MM **Privately Held**
WEB: www.allianceoneinc.com
SIC: 7322 Collection agency
HQ: Allianceone Receivables Mgt
　　4850 E Street Rd Ste 300
　　Trevose PA 19053
　　215 354-5500

(G-7928)
TRICOM COMMUNICATIONS INC
2401 Pilot Knob Rd Ste 126　(55120-1355)
PHONE..............................651 686-9000
Gary Evans, *President*
Diane Evans, *Vice Pres*
EMP: 45 EST: 1989
SQ FT: 2,000
SALES (est): 1MM-4.9MM **Privately Held**
WEB: www.tricom1.com
SIC: 8999 Communication services

(G-7929)
TRITON TIRE & BATTERY LLC
1300 Corporate Ctr Curv　(55121-1233)
PHONE..............................651 239-1200
Dale Halladay, *Vice Pres*
Allanen Shafer, *Manager*
Robert Maday, *Manager*
Barb Hubers, *Manager*
EMP: 36 EST: 1997
SQ FT: 120,000
SALES (est): 10MM-24.9MM **Privately Held**
WEB: www.ucoop.com
SIC: 5014 5015 Wholesales tires & tubes; wholesales used automotive batteries
HQ: Universal Cooperatives Inc
　　1300 Corporate Center Curv
　　Saint Paul MN 55121
　　651 239-1000

(G-7930)
TRUCK CRANE SERVICE-ILLINOIS
2875 Highway 55　(55121-1406)
PHONE..............................651 406-4949
Wendell A Phillippi, *CEO*
M A Fors, *Corp Secy*
Jerry Corcoran, *Treasurer*
EMP: 35 EST: 1947
SQ FT: 80,000
SALES (est): 5MM-9.9MM **Privately Held**
SIC: 7353 7389 Cranes & aerial lift equipment leasing & rental service; crane & aerial lift service
PA: Phillippi Equipment Co
　　2875 Highway 55
　　Saint Paul MN 55121
　　651 406-4900

(G-7931)
TRUGREEN LANDCARE LLC
3259 Terminal Dr Ste 100　(55121-1624)
PHONE..............................651 994-9855
FAX: 651 994-9860
John Velander, *Area Mgr*

▲=Import ▼=Export
◆=Import/Export

George Rohde, *Treasurer*
Jodi Peterson, *Office Mgr*
Tom Hougnon, *Manager*
Jon Heinz, *Manager*
EMP: 100 **Privately Held**
WEB: www.landcare.com
SIC: 0781 Landscape services
DH: Trugreen Landcare LLC
860 Ridge Lake Blvd Fl 3
Memphis TN 38120
901 681-1800

(G-7932)
U S WAREHOUSE SUPPLY INC
2861 Eagandale Blvd (55121-1202)
PHONE..............................651 405-3500
Elliott Badzin, *President*
Sheldon Badzin, *Corp Secy*
EMP: 75 **EST:** 1950
SQ FT: 50,000
SALES (est): 25MM-49.9MM **Privately Held**
SIC: 5013 Wholesales automotive supplies
& parts; wholesales automotive servicing
equipment

(G-7933)
ULINE INC
985 Aldrin Dr (55121-2270)
PHONE..............................651 688-3495
FAX: 651 688-6377
Mike Ehrhart, *Manager*
John Daniels, *Manager*
EMP: 60
SALES (est): 25MM-49.9MM **Privately Held**
WEB: www.uline.com
SIC: 5113 Wholesales shipping supplies
PA: Uline Inc
12575 Uline Dr
Pleasant Prairie WI 53158
262 612-4200

(G-7934)
ULINE INC
985 Aldrin Dr (55121-2270)
PHONE..............................651 688-3495
Duke Uihlin, *Branch Mgr*
EMP: 150
SALES (est): 100MM-499.9MM **Privately Held**
WEB: www.uline.com
SIC: 5113 Wholesales shipping supplies
PA: Uline Inc
12575 Uline Dr
Pleasant Prairie WI 53158
262 612-4200

(G-7935)
UNISYS CORP
3199 Pilot Knob Rd (55121)
PHONE..............................651 687-2200
FAX: 651 687-2985
D C Hanson, *Principal*
Gregg Berglund, *Regional Mgr*
James Commander, *Vice Pres*
Don Schlafer, *Facilities Mgr*
Michael Betsinger, *Engineer*
EMP: 700
SQ FT: 316,870
SALES (est): 50MM-99.9MM **Publicly Held**
WEB: www.unisys.com
SIC: 8742 7373 7376 Marketing consulting
service; computer facilities management
service; systems integration service
PA: Unisys Corp
Unisys Way
Blue Bell PA 19424
215 986-4011

(G-7936)
UNITED PARCEL SERVICE INC
3025 Lunar Ln (55121-2445)
PHONE..............................651 367-8200
FAX: 651 367-8210
David Braun, *Manager*
EMP: 50
SALES (est): 1MM-4.9MM **Publicly Held**
WEB: www.ups.com
SIC: 4231 4581 Freight trucking terminal;
airport, flying field & services
PA: United Parcel Service Inc
55 Glenlake Pkwy NE
Atlanta GA 30328
404 828-6000

(G-7937)
UNITED STATIONERS SUPPLY CO
1720 Alexander Rd (55121-1640)
PHONE..............................651 681-1720
FAX: 651 681-9386
Kay Edmondson, *Vice Pres*
Eileen Bloch, *Vice Pres*
Daryl Anderstrom, *Opers Staff*
Wayne Scott, *Manager*
Norm Halverson, *Manager*
EMP: 106
SQ FT: 210,643
SALES (est): 25MM-49.9MM **Publicly Held**
WEB: www.ussco.com
SIC: 5112 Wholesales stationery & office
supplies
HQ: United Stationers Supply Co
1 Parkway N Ste 100
Deerfield IL 60015
847 627-7000

(G-7938)
UNIVERSAL COOPERATIVES INC (HQ)
1300 Corporate Center Curv (55121-2487)
PHONE..............................651 239-1000
FAX: 651 239-1080
Bart Krisle, *Ch of Bd*
Steve Barwick, *Vice Ch Bd*
Terrence J Bohman, *President*
L B Morrison, *Corp Secy*
Robert Ramsdell, *Vice Pres*
▲ **EMP:** 60 **EST:** 1972
SQ FT: 40,000
SALES (corp-wide): 306.01M **Privately Held**
WEB: www.ucoop.com
SIC: 5014 5013 5122 Wholesales tires &
tubes; wholesales automotive batteries;
wholesales automotive supplies & parts;
wholesales automotive air & oil filters;
wholesales truck tires & tubes; wholesales
animal medicines; wholesales chemical
additives
PA: Heritage Trading Co LLC
11020 N Ambassador Dr Ste 200
Kansas City MO 64153
816 394-2200

(G-7939)
UPONOR NORTH AMERICA INC (PA)
5925 148th St W (55124-8197)
PHONE..............................952 891-2000
Jim Bjork, *President*
Jeff Davis, *Vice Pres*
Jon Mendel, *Vice Pres*
Timothy Botten, *Engineer*
Greg Sicora, *Credit Mgr*
EMP: 50 **EST:** 1990 **Privately Held**
WEB: www.wirsbo.com
SIC: 8742 Management consulting services;
manufactures pipes & tubes
PA: Uponor Oyj
Robert Huberin Tie 3B
VANTAA Finland

(G-7940)
US BANK NATIONAL ASSOCIATION
15025 Garrett Ave Ste 100 (55124-6457)
PHONE..............................952 997-9600
EMP: 28
SQ FT: 17,223
SALES (est): 5MM-9.9MM **Publicly Held**
WEB: www.firstar.com
SIC: 6021 National commercial bank
HQ: U S Bank National Association
425 Walnut St Fl 1
Cincinnati OH 45202
513 632-4234

(G-7941)
VALUE REALTY INC
4555 Erin Dr Ste 120 (55122-3334)
PHONE..............................952 898-0230
John D Anderson, *President*
Curtis Sticha, *Real Est Agnt*
Camery Weber, *Real Est Agnt*
Richard Trisko, *Real Est Agnt*
EMP: 25

EST: 1991
SQ FT: 1,800
SALES (est): 1MM-4.9MM **Privately Held**
WEB: www.valuerealty.com
SIC: 6531 Residential real estate agency

(G-7942)
VENTURE BANK
2640 Eagan Woods Dr # 100
(55121-1174)
PHONE..............................651 289-2222
FAX: 651 289-4329
Mike Zenk, *President*
Gwen Stanley, *Manager*
EMP: 45
SALES (est): 10MM-24.9MM **Privately Held**
SIC: 6021 National commercial bank
PA: Venture Bank
5601 Green Valley Dr # 120
Minneapolis MN 55437
952 830-9999

(G-7943)
WAGERS BUSINESS SYSTEMS INC
960 Blue Gentian Rd (55121-1500)
PHONE..............................651 644-3830
John Stainer, *President*
Jim Dearstyne, *General Mgr*
Len Sandstron, *General Mgr*
Gerald Byrns, *Vice Pres*
Steve Back, *Service Mgr*
EMP: 70 **EST:** 1903
SALES (est): 10MM-24.9MM **Privately Held**
WEB: www.sbsfyi.com
SIC: 6519 Real estate property leasing &
rental

(G-7944)
WELLS FARGO BANK, NATIONAL
14325 Cedar Ave (55124-5849)
PHONE..............................952 953-3991
FAX: 952 953-3997
Brenda Kado, *Branch Mgr*
Nona Gibson, *Manager*
EMP: 30
SQ FT: 8,201
SALES (est): 5MM-9.9MM **Publicly Held**
SIC: 6021 National commercial bank
HQ: Wfc Holdings, Corp
420 Montgomery St
San Francisco CA 94104
415 396-7392

(G-7945)
WENZEL PLUMBING & HEATING INC
1710 Alexander Rd (55121-1640)
PHONE..............................651 452-1565
FAX: 651 452-0367
Cary Wenzel, *CEO*
Alfred Hansen, *President*
Jan Hansen, *Corp Secy*
Mike Leininger, *Project Mgr*
Dave Thomas, *Project Mgr*
EMP: 85 **EST:** 1960
SQ FT: 15,676
SALES (est): 10MM-24.9MM **Privately Held**
WEB: www.wenzelphcc
SIC: 1711 Plumbing service; warm air
heating & air conditioning contractor

(G-7946)
WEST PUBLISHING CORP (HQ)
610 Opperman Dr (55123-1340)
PHONE..............................651 687-8000
Michael Wilens, *President*
Robert Daleo, *Exec VP*
David Hanssens, *Exec VP*
Shahir Adams, *Senior VP*
Stephane Bello, *Senior VP*
EMP: 8000 **EST:** 1982
SQ FT: 2,600,000 **Publicly Held**
SIC: 7375 Database information retrieval
service
PA: Thomson Legal & Regulatory Inc
610 Opperman Dr
Saint Paul MN 55123
651 687-7000

(G-7947)
WEST PUBLISHING CORP
610 Opperman Dr (55123-1340)
PO Box 64833 (55164-1801)
PHONE..............................651 687-7000
FAX: 651 687-5827
Peter Warwick, *CEO*
Chris Kibarian, *General Mgr*
Mike Suchsland, *General Mgr*
Brian Douty, *Corp Secy*
Edward A Friedland, *Corp Secy*
EMP: 99 **EST:** 1899
SQ FT: 20,000
SALES (est): 10MM-24.9MM **Privately Held**
SIC: 7375 Publisher; information retrieval
services; book printer; book publisher;
typesetting service

(G-7948)
WINDOW CONCEPTS OF MINNESOTA
990 Lone Oak Rd Ste 114 (55121-2226)
PHONE..............................651 905-0105
FAX: 651 905-1745
Gregory Ramel, *President*
Michael Macnamee, *Treasurer*
Sarah Gangelhoff, *Manager*
EMP: 30 **EST:** 1998
SQ FT: 4,000
SALES (est): 1MM-4.9MM **Privately Held**
SIC: 1751 1761 Prefabricated window &
door installation service; roofing, siding &
sheet metal work

(G-7949)
WINGS FINANCIAL CREDIT UNION (PA)
14985 Glazier Ave Ste 100 (55124-7490)
PHONE..............................952 997-8000
Paul Parish, *CEO*
Michael A Cooper, *Vice Chairman*
Mark S Everson, *COO*
John J Wagner, *Vice Pres*
Paul L Dinger, *Vice Pres*
EMP: 200 **EST:** 1938
SQ FT: 120,000
SALES (corp-wide): 103.10M **Privately Held**
SIC: 6061 Federally chartered credit union

(G-7950)
WORLD DISTRIBUTION SERVICES
3470 Washington Dr Ste 211
(55122-1354)
PHONE..............................651 686-9252
James Fink, *Principal*
EMP: 99 **EST:** 1986
SALES (est): 10MM-24.9MM **Privately Held**
SIC: 7331 Mailing services

(G-7951)
XORA INC
2770 Blue Waters Rd (55121-1671)
PHONE..............................651 209-0350
Rob Davis, *Managing Dir*
EMP: 50
SALES (est): 1MM-4.9MM **Privately Held**
WEB: www.xora.com
SIC: 8999 Communication services
PA: Xora Inc
501 Ellis St
Mountain View CA 94043
650 314-6460

(G-7952)
YMCA OF GREATER SAINT PAUL
Also Called: Southwest YMCA Child Care
550 Opperman Dr (55123-1337)
PHONE..............................651 683-4713
FAX: 651 683-4704
Ann Sellers, *Manager*
EMP: 212
SALES (est): 1MM-4.9MM **Privately Held**
WEB: www.ymcastpaul.org
SIC: 8351 8641 Child day care service;
social club; youth organizations
PA: YMCA of Greater Saint Paul
2125 E Hennepin Ave Ste 100
Minneapolis MN 55413
612 465-0450

(PA)=Parent Co (HQ)=Headquarters (DH)=Div Headquarters
✿ = New business established in last 2 years
2011 Harris Minnesota
Services Directory
© Harris InfoSource 1-866-281-6415
345

(G-7953)
YMCA OF GREATER ST PAUL
Also Called: Healthy Kids
150 Thompson Ave E (55118-3216)
PHONE..............................651 457-0048
FAX: 651 457-0339
Tara Monack, *Business Mgr*
Margi Miller, *Manager*
Patty McGrath, *Exec Dir*
Lara Day, *Director*
Patty McGraff, *Director*
EMP: 115 **Privately Held**
WEB: www.ymcastpaul.org
SIC: 8641 7032 7991 8322 8351 Youth
organizations; youth camps; child day care
service; individual & family social services;
physical fitness center
PA: YMCA of Greater Saint Paul
    2125 E Hennepin Ave Ste 100
    Minneapolis MN 55413
    612 465-0450

(G-7954)
YRC INC
2950 Lone Oak Cir (55121-1425)
PHONE..............................651 452-0338
FAX: 651 452-0889
Rolland Swanson, *Sales/Mktg Mgr*
David Ritzdorf, *Finance Mgr*
Wain Smith, *Persnl Mgr*
Mark Heining, *Branch Mgr*
James Dalsasso, *Systems Mgr*
EMP: 150
SQ FT: 64,850
SALES (est): 10MM-24.9MM **Publicly Held**
WEB: www.yellowcorp.com
SIC: 4213 Contract haulers
HQ: Roadway LLC
    10990 Roe Ave
    Shawnee Mission KS 66211
    913 344-3000

(G-7955)
**ZOOLOGICAL GARDENS,
MINNESOTA**
13000 Zoo Blvd (55124-4621)
PHONE..............................952 431-9299
FAX: 952 431-9452
Jeff Higgins, *Finance*
Lee Ehmke, *Director*
EMP: 165 **EST:** 1978
SQ FT: 500,000
SALES (est): 10MM-24.9MM **Privately Held**
WEB: www.state.mn.us
SIC: 8422 Zoo & botanical garden;
government office; state government
executive offices
HQ: Executive Office of The State
    75 Rev Doc Martin Luther
    Saint Paul MN 55155
    651 296-3391

SAINT PAUL
Hennepin County

(G-7956)
AMERICAN AIRLINES INC
Minneapolis St Paul Arprt (55111)
PHONE..............................612 726-5647
Ben Sparks, *Manager*
EMP: 65
SALES (est): 10MM-24.9MM **Publicly Held**
WEB: www.aa.com
SIC: 4512 Passenger airline services
HQ: American Airlines Inc
    4333 Amon Carter Blvd
    Fort Worth TX 76155
    817 963-1234

(G-7957)
AMERICAN AIRLINES INC
4300 Glumack Dr Ste B27 (55111-3010)
PHONE..............................612 726-5833
Jeff Clements, *Branch Mgr*
Cheryl Gonzalez, *Manager*
Lee Brechtel, *Manager*
EMP: 150
SALES (est): 25MM-49.9MM **Publicly Held**
WEB: www.aa.com

SIC: 4512 Passenger airline services
HQ: American Airlines Inc
    4333 Amon Carter Blvd
    Fort Worth TX 76155
    817 963-1234

(G-7958)
CENTRAX ENTERPRISES INC
4300 Glumack Dr (55111-3002)
PHONE..............................612 726-9500
Benjamin Sahr III, *President*
EMP: 70 **EST:** 1981
SQ FT: 400
SALES (est): 5MM-9.9MM **Privately Held**
SIC: 4215 4212 Ground courier services;
delivery services by vehicle

(G-7959)
CONTINENTAL AIRLINES INC
4300 Glumack Dr Ste E11 (55111-3067)
PHONE..............................612 726-5679
Dave Brink, *Office Mgr*
Gordon Bethone, *Branch Mgr*
Jan Ricos, *Administrator*
EMP: 100
SALES (est): 10MM-24.9MM **Publicly Held**
WEB: www.continental.com
SIC: 4729 4512 Airline ticket office;
passenger airline services
HQ: Continental Airlines Inc
    1600 Smith St
    Houston TX 77002
    713 324-2950

(G-7960)
G2 SECURE STAFF LLC
4300 Glumack Dr Ste 3225 (55111-3058)
PHONE..............................612 725-6423
FAX: 612 725-6425
Angela Benes, *General Mgr*
Diane Schleverl, *Human Res Mgr*
Dan Norman, *Branch Mgr*
EMP: 200
SALES (est): 5MM-9.9MM **Privately Held**
SIC: 7381 Detective & armored car services
PA: G2 Secure Staff LLC
    5010 Riverside Dr Ste 300
    Irving TX 75039
    972 915-6979

(G-7961)
MINNESOTA DEPARTMENT OF
Also Called: 133rd Medical Squadron
642 Hercules Ave (55111-4102)
PHONE..............................612 713-2196
Barb Hudson, *Administrator*
EMP: 72
SALES (est): 5MM-9.9MM **Privately Held**
WEB: www.mn.ngb.army.mil
SIC: 8062 Medical hospital; state
government national security; united States
National Guard
DH: Minnesota Department of
    20 12th St W Fl 4
    Saint Paul MN 55155
    651 268-8924

(G-7962)
PAUL MINNEAPOLIS-ST
Also Called: Police Department
4300 Glumack Dr Ste 3060 (55111-3031)
PHONE..............................612 726-5107
Jeff Hameil, *Branch Mgr*
EMP: 65
SALES (est): 1MM-4.9MM **Privately Held**
SIC: 4581 Airport
PA: Paul Minneapolis-St
    6040 28th Ave S
    Minneapolis MN 55450
    612 726-8100

(G-7963)
SERVICEMASTER INC
4300 Glumack Dr 79 (55111-3002)
PHONE..............................612 794-4100
Steven M Laury, *Manager*
EMP: 60 **EST:** 1997
SALES (est): 10MM-24.9MM **Privately Held**
SIC: 4512 Passenger airline services

SIC: 4512 Passenger airline services
HQ: American Airlines Inc
    4333 Amon Carter Blvd
    Fort Worth TX 76155
    817 963-1234

(G-7964)
SERVISAIR USA INC
Also Called: Servisair Globeground
5398 Northwest Dr (55111-3014)
PHONE..............................612 726-5533
Chris Holden, *General Mgr*
EMP: 200
SALES (est): 10MM-24.9MM **Privately Held**
SIC: 4581 Airport, flying field & services
HQ: Servisair USA Inc
    151 Northpoint Dr
    Houston TX 77060
    281 260-3900

(G-7965)
**SUPERSHUTTLE MINNESOTA
INC** ⊙
4500 Glumack Dr Ste 1300 (55111-3025)
PHONE..............................612 827-7777
R B Wier, *Principal*
EMP: 25 **EST:** 2008
SALES (est): 1MM-4.9MM **Privately Held**
SIC: 4111 Passenger transit system

(G-7966)
VA DEPARTMENTAL OFFICES
Also Called: Debt Management Center
1 Federal Dr Rm 156 (55111-4041)
PHONE..............................612 970-5700
Dan Osendorf, *Director*
EMP: 65
SALES (est): 1MM-4.9MM **Privately Held**
WEB: www.va.gov
SIC: 7322 Collection agency
DH: VA Departmental Offices
    810 Vermont Ave NW
    Washington DC 20420
    202 273-8806

SAINT PAUL
Ramsey County

(G-7967)
**A A METCALF MOVING &
STORAGE**
1255 Highway 36 E (55109-2046)
PHONE..............................651 484-0211
Allen Metcalf, *President*
John Archbold, *President*
Cindy Borup, *Vice Pres*
EMP: 175 **EST:** 1919
SQ FT: 31,000
SALES (est): 10MM-24.9MM **Privately Held**
WEB: www.metcalfmoving.com
SIC: 4213 4212 Long-distance moving
services; local furniture moving services
without storage

(G-7968)
A E I FUND MANAGEMENT INC
30 7th St E Ste 1300 (55101-4939)
PHONE..............................800 328-3519
Robert P Johnson, *President*
Mark E Larson, *CFO*
Kathleen Ring, *Manager*
Patrick W Keene, *Executive*
EMP: 35 **EST:** 1976
SALES (est): 5MM-9.9MM **Privately Held**
WEB: www.aeifunds.com
SIC: 6512 6531 Operators of commercial &
industrial buildings; real estate services

(G-7969)
A'VIANDS LLC
1751 County Road B W Ste 300
(55113-4037)
PHONE..............................651 631-0940
FAX: 651 631-0941
William Benzick, *Member*
Mitch Speicher, *Member*
Rick Sorel, *Member*
Perry Rynders, *Member*
Lil D Martino, *Human Res Dir*
EMP: 1900 **EST:** 2003
SQ FT: 30,000
SALES (est): 100MM-499.9MM **Privately
Held**
WEB: www.aviands.com
SIC: 8742 Restaurant & food services
consultants

(G-7970)
**AAA COOPER
TRANSPORTATION**
50 14th St NW (55112-3567)
PHONE..............................651 638-9288
FAX: 651 639-0170
Sean Callahan, *CFO*
Kelley Potrament, *Office Mgr*
Candy Miller, *Manager*
EMP: 25
SALES (est): 1MM-4.9MM **Privately Held**
WEB: www.aact.com
SIC: 4213 Over the road trucking
PA: AAA Cooper Transportation
    1751 Kinsey Rd
    Dothan AL 36303
    334 793-2284

(G-7971)
**ABBEYCARE INC HOME HEALTH
CARE**
1148 Grand Ave (55105-2628)
PHONE..............................651 690-5352
Faina Kanivetsky, *CEO*
Liliya Gokhberg, *CEO*
EMP: 400 **EST:** 1997
SQ FT: 1,000
SALES (est): 10MM-24.9MM **Privately Held**
WEB: www.abbeycareinc.com
SIC: 8082 Home health care services

(G-7972)
ABBOTT PAINT & CARPET INC
2223 4th St (55110-3012)
PHONE..............................651 429-3316
FAX: 651 426-6792
Kevin Abbott, *President*
EMP: 40
SQ FT: 4,500
SALES (est): 5MM-9.9MM **Privately Held**
SIC: 5198 Retails paint; retails paint
brushes, rollers, sprayers & other supplies;
retails wallpaper; retails floor coverings;
wholesales paints, varnishes & supplies

(G-7973)
ABRASIVES OF ST PAUL INC
1000 Labore Industrial Ct (55110-5114)
PO Box 10747 (55110-0747)
PHONE..............................651 636-3955
Mark Nelson, *CEO*
Ken Kruger, *President*
Dan Imholte, *Corp Secy*
Kevin Aasgaard, *Sales Mgr*
EMP: 75
SQ FT: 25,000
SALES (est): 25MM-49.9MM **Privately Held**
SIC: 5085 Wholesales industrial abrasives

(G-7974)
ACCESSIBLE SPACE INC
Also Called: Montreal I
1085 Montreal Ave Apt 1406 (55116-2332)
PHONE..............................651 690-5216
FAX: 651 690-1653
Robert Garcia, *General Mgr*
EMP: 25
SALES (est): 500-999K **Privately Held**
WEB: www.accessiblespace.org
SIC: 7363 Medical help service
PA: Accessible Space Inc
    2550 University Ave W Ste 330N
    Saint Paul MN 55114
    651 645-7271

(G-7975)
ACCESSIBLE SPACE INC (PA)
Also Called: A S I
2550 University Ave W Ste 330N
(55114-1085)
PHONE..............................651 645-7271
Mark E Hamel, *Ch of Bd*
Kay Knutson, *Vice Ch Bd*
Stephen V Schaaf, *President*
John Adams, *Corp Secy*
Steve Schugal, *Treasurer*
EMP: 38 **EST:** 1979
SQ FT: 10,463
SALES (corp-wide): 19.58M **Privately Held**
WEB: www.accessiblespace.org
SIC: 6531 7363 8322 Real estate
management services; medical help
service; outreach program

▲=Import ▼=Export
◆=Import/Export

(G-7976)
ACCESSIBLE SPACE INC
Also Called: Henry Courts II
2550 University Ave W 330N
(55114-2014)
PHONE..............................651 645-7271
Dora Bauer, *Branch Mgr*
EMP: 50
SALES (est): 1MM-4.9MM **Privately Held**
WEB: www.accessiblespace.org
SIC: 8361 Home for the physically
handicapped
PA: Accessible Space Inc
2550 University Ave W Ste 330N
Saint Paul MN 55114
651 645-7271

(G-7977)
ACCESSIBLE SPACE NORTH INC
Also Called: Winston Courts
2550 University Ave W 330N
(55114-2014)
PHONE..............................651 645-7271
Judy Lamky, *Director*
EMP: 55 **EST:** 2003
SALES (est): 5MM-9.9MM **Privately Held**
SIC: 6513 Apartment building operator

(G-7978)
ACCURATE COMPONENT SALES INC
444 2nd St NW (55112-3257)
PHONE..............................651 639-1881
FAX: 651 639-1288
Jerry Moehnke, *President*
Ken Olson, *Vice Pres*
Ken Chock, *Treasurer*
Amy Friedrich, *Manager*
▲ **EMP:** 37 **EST:** 1986
SQ FT: 30,000
SALES (est): 10MM-24.9MM **Privately Held**
WEB: www.accuratecomp.com
SIC: 5072 Wholesales fasteners;
wholesales bolts; wholesales hardware nuts

(G-7979)
ACE AUTO PARTS & SALVAGE INC
754 Rice St (55117-5433)
PHONE..............................651 224-9479
Marcus Weyandt, *CEO*
Donald C Kloek, *President*
Bard Weyandt, *Vice Pres*
Gloria Kloek, *Treasurer*
EMP: 25 **EST:** 1965
SQ FT: 576
SALES (est): 1MM-4.9MM **Privately Held**
SIC: 5015 Wholesales used automotive
parts & supplies

(G-7980)
ACE BUILDING MAINTENANCE INC
5703 Deer Trl W (55126-4816)
PHONE..............................651 482-1020
FAX: 651 482-8867
Dave C Ko, *President*
Kay Ko, *Vice Pres*
EMP: 25 **EST:** 1992
SALES (est): 500-999K **Privately Held**
SIC: 7349 Building & office cleaning service

(G-7981)
ACS INTEGRATED DOC INC
680 Transfer Rd (55114-1402)
PHONE..............................651 999-5400
Jane Kipp, *Principal*
EMP: 50 **EST:** 2000
SALES (est): 1MM-4.9MM **Privately Held**
SIC: 7389 Microfilm services

(G-7982)
ADOBE SYSTEMS INC
3900 Northwoods Dr Ste 300
(55112-6965)
PHONE..............................651 766-4700
FAX: 651 766-4750
Michele Dahlberg, *Manager*
Brett Storrar, *Manager*
Bob Pappas, *Software Dev*
EMP: 48

SALES (est): 10MM-24.9MM **Publicly Held**
WEB: www.adobe.com
SIC: 7372 Software publisher
PA: Adobe Systems Inc
345 Park Ave
San Jose CA 95110
408 536-6000

(G-7983)
ADONAI CARE HOMES CORP
Also Called: Amy Johnson Residence
89 Virginia St (55102-2113)
PHONE..............................651 227-0574
FAX: 651 227-2862
Donetta Johnson, *President*
EMP: 32 **EST:** 1978
SALES (est): 1MM-4.9MM **Privately Held**
WEB: www.adonaicarehomes.com
SIC: 8052 Residential mentally
handicapped facility

(G-7984)
ADT SECURITY SERVICES INC
5910 Rice Creek Pkwy Ste 700
(55126-5023)
PHONE..............................651 917-0000
Pamela Grimm, *Opers Staff*
Rita Anderson, *Human Res Mgr*
Bruce Logie, *Sales Staff*
Bob Peppe, *Manager*
EMP: 175
SALES (est): 10MM-24.9MM **Privately Held**
WEB: www.adt.com
SIC: 7382 Burglar alarm maintenance &
monitoring service
DH: ADT Security Services Inc
1 Town Center Rd
Boca Raton FL 33486
561 988-3600

(G-7985)
ADUDDELL INDUSTRIES INC
69 Empire Dr (55103-1856)
PHONE..............................651 288-2246
EMP: 26
SALES (est): 1MM-4.9MM **Publicly Held**
SIC: 1771 Concrete contractor
PA: Aduddell Industries Inc
14220 S Meridian Ave
Oklahoma City OK 73173
405 692-2300

(G-7986)
ADULTS & CHILDRENS ALLIANCE
2885 Country Dr Ste 165 (55117-1097)
PHONE..............................651 481-9320
FAX: 651 481-4919
William E Herzog, *Corp Secy*
Bruce Menkes, *Corp Secy*
Daniel V Leary V, *Vice Pres*
Ann Hamilton, *Office Mgr*
Sandra Lee, *Manager*
EMP: 25 **EST:** 1981
SQ FT: 4,500
SALES (est): 1MM-4.9MM **Privately Held**
WEB: www.acainc.org
SIC: 8322 Children's aid society

(G-7987)
ADVANCE EQUIPMENT CO
1400 Jackson St (55117-4614)
PHONE..............................651 489-8881
Terry Haug, *President*
Karen Haug, *Vice Pres*
Andie Rousslang, *Office Mgr*
▲ **EMP:** 49 **EST:** 1969
SQ FT: 27,400
SALES (est): 25MM-49.9MM **Privately Held**
SIC: 5082 7353 Wholesales general
construction machinery & equipment;
wholesales construction cranes; cranes &
aerial lift equipment leasing & rental service;
construction & mining equipment leasing &
rental

(G-7988)
ADVANCE SHORING CO
1400 Jackson St (55117-4614)
PHONE..............................651 489-8881
FAX: 651 489-9416
Karen F Haug, *President*
Terry Haug, *Vice Pres*
Sandy Rousslang, *Manager*
Thomas Martin, *Manager*

EMP: 50 **EST:** 1960
SQ FT: 10,000
SALES (est): 25MM-49.9MM **Privately Held**
WEB: www.advancecos.com
SIC: 5082 7359 Wholesales general
construction machinery & equipment;
wholesales scaffolding; equipment rental &
leasing services

(G-7989)
ADVANCE SPECIALTIES CO
1400 Jackson St (55117-4614)
PHONE..............................651 489-8881
Karen F Haug, *CEO*
Terry Haug, *President*
Sandy Rousslang, *Manager*
David O Carlson, *Director*
EMP: 45 **EST:** 1991
SALES (est): 10MM-24.9MM **Privately Held**
WEB: www.advanceequipment.com
SIC: 5032 5082 Manufactures concrete
curing & hardening compounds; wholesales
brick, stone & related products; wholesales
masonry equipment & supplies

(G-7990)
ADVANCED AUTO TRANSPORT INC
2275 McKnight Rd N Ste 4 (55109-2874)
PHONE..............................651 777-7780
FAX: 651 777-3677
Debra Samuelson, *CEO*
Scott Samuelson, *President*
EMP: 150 **EST:** 1990
SQ FT: 5,000
SALES (est): 1MM-4.9MM **Privately Held**
WEB: www.aatransport.net
SIC: 7363 4213 Help supply services;
automobile carrier services

(G-7991)
ADVANCED MASONRY RESTORATION
2960 Yorkton Blvd Ste A (55117-1041)
PHONE..............................651 766-8080
FAX: 651 766-8016
Tom Kromroy, *President*
Tim Miller, *Vice Pres*
EMP: 25 **EST:** 1998
SQ FT: 2,000
SALES (est): 1MM-4.9MM **Privately Held**
WEB: www.advancedmasonry.com
SIC: 1741 Tuck pointing & restoration
contractor

(G-7992)
AERITAE CONSULTING GROUP LTD
380 Jackson St Ste 750 (55101-4805)
PHONE..............................651 229-0300
Nicholas Hernandez, *Principal*
Michael Finlon, *Corp Secy*
Jonas Jasinski, *Manager*
Aaron Ebertowski, *Manager*
Al Sweeny, *Director*
EMP: 50 **EST:** 2001
SALES (est): 5MM-9.9MM **Privately Held**
WEB: www.aeritae.com
SIC: 7379 Computer system consulting
services

(G-7993)
AERO SYSTEMS ENGINEERING INC (HQ)
358 Fillmore Ave E (55107-1204)
PHONE..............................651 227-7515
FAX: 651 227-0519
Charles Loux, *President*
Peter W Kooman, *Chairman*
Tom Moll, *Vice Pres*
Grant A Radinzel, *Vice Pres*
Michael Browne, *Vice Pres*
▲ **EMP:** 125 **EST:** 1967
SQ FT: 52,000
SALES (est): 25MM-49.9MM **Privately Held**
WEB: www.aerosysengr.com
SIC: 8734 Manufactures testing chambers
for altitude, temperature, ordnance, power;
manufactures measuring & controlling
devices; testing laboratory
PA: Tonka Bay Equity Partners LLC
301 Carlson Pkwy Ste 325
Hopkins MN 55305
952 345-2030

(G-7994)
AFFINITY PLUS CREDIT UNION
2730 Snelling Ave N (55113-1732)
PHONE..............................651 291-3700
Heather Anderson, *Principal*
Mike Koshoshek, *Manager*
Kelly Schaum, *Manager*
EMP: 25 **EST:** 2001
SALES (est): 1MM-4.9MM **Privately Held**
SIC: 6162 Mortgage & loan lending

(G-7995)
AFFINITY PLUS FEDERAL CREDIT (PA)
175 W Lafayette Frontage Rd
(55107-1488)
PHONE..............................651 291-3700
Kyle Markland, *President*
Elizabeth Hayes, *Vice Pres*
Todd Utecht, *Vice Pres*
Brian Volkmann, *Loan Officer*
Sandy Olson, *Marketing Staff*
EMP: 32 **EST:** 1930
SQ FT: 14,000
SALES (corp-wide): 55.93M **Privately Held**
SIC: 6062 State credit unions

(G-7996)
AFFINITY PLUS FEDERAL CREDIT
95 Sherburne Ave (55103-2120)
PHONE..............................651 291-3700
Deb Bujak, *Manager*
Thomas Bouse, *Manager*
Michael Vinar, *Manager*
Eric Banfield, *Systs Prg Mgr*
EMP: 40
SALES (est): 5MM-9.9MM **Privately Held**
SIC: 6062 State chartered credit union
PA: Affinity Plus Federal Credit
175 W Lafayette Frontage Rd
Saint Paul MN 55107
651 291-3700

(G-7997)
AFFINITY PLUS FEDERAL CREDIT
2730 Snelling Ave N (55113-1732)
PHONE..............................651 291-3700
Mike Koshoshek, *Manager*
EMP: 35
SALES (est): 5MM-9.9MM **Privately Held**
SIC: 6062 State chartered credit union
PA: Affinity Plus Federal Credit
175 W Lafayette Frontage Rd
Saint Paul MN 55107
651 291-3700

(G-7998)
AFS INTERCULTURAL PROGRAMS
2356 University Ave W # 424
(55114-1850)
PHONE..............................651 647-6337
FAX: 651 647-6628
Sue Crook, *Finance*
Carolyn Sharratt, *Office Mgr*
Barry Gore, *Director*
Lena Luckritz, *Admin Asst*
EMP: 30 **EST:** 1999 **Privately Held**
WEB: www.ass.org
SIC: 8699 Reading rooms & other cultural
organizations

(G-7999)
AGNES SAINT BAKING CO
644 Olive St (55130-4441)
PHONE..............................651 290-7633
Gary Sande, *President*
Larry Burn, *Vice Pres*
EMP: 30 **EST:** 1995
SALES (est): 1MM-4.9MM **Privately Held**
SIC: 5149 Commercial bakery; wholesales
groceries

(G-8000)
AGRIBANK, FCB
375 Jackson St Ste A (55101-1802)
PHONE..............................651 282-8800
FAX: 651 282-8666
William Collins, *President*
Keri Votruba, *Vice Chairman*

(PA)=Parent Co (HQ)=Headquarters (DH)=Div Headquarters
✪ = New business established in last 2 years
2011 Harris Minnesota
Services Directory
© Harris InfoSource 1-866-281-6415
347

Jayme Winebrenner, *Member*
Joshua Yoder, *Member*
Myron Peters, *Member*
EMP: 252 **EST:** 1917
SQ FT: 250,000
SALES (est): 50MM-99.9MM **Privately Held**
WEB: www.farmcredit.com
SIC: 6111 6162 Federal land credit bank;
mortgage & loan lending

(G-8001)
AIN DAH YUNG CENTER
1089 Portland Ave (55104-7011)
PHONE...............................651 227-4184
FAX: 651 224-5136
Jennifer Martini, *Manager*
Tony Bruws, *Manager*
Chelsea Fairbanks, *MIS Mgr*
Gabrielle Strong, *Exec Dir*
Richard Garland, *Exec Dir*
EMP: 30 **EST:** 1984
SALES (est): 1MM-4.9MM **Privately Held**
WEB: www.aindahyung.com
SIC: 8322 Individual & family social
services; child & youth services

(G-8002)
AIRCRAFT OWNER LLC
121 5th Ave NW Ste 300 (55112-3220)
PHONE...............................651 633-1045
Greg Herrick, *Member*
EMP: 30 **EST:** 2005
SALES (est): 10MM-24.9MM **Privately Held**
WEB: www.aircraftowner.com
SIC: 6153 Short-term business credit for
factors of commercial paper

(G-8003)
ALBERS MECHANICAL
SERVICES INC
200 Plato Blvd W Ste A (55107-2049)
PHONE...............................651 224-3100
FAX: 651 224-5390
George Albers, *President*
Brad Huber, *Project Mgr*
EMP: 50 **EST:** 1990
SALES (est): 1MM-4.9MM **Privately Held**
WEB: www.albersco.com
SIC: 7699 Boiler & heating repair service
PA: Albers Sheetmetal
      200 Plato Blvd W Ste A
      Saint Paul MN 55107
      651 224-5428

(G-8004)
ALBERS SHEETMETAL (PA)
200 Plato Blvd W Ste A (55107-2049)
PHONE...............................651 224-5428
FAX: 651 224-1742
Chuck Albers, *President*
John H Albers, *Vice Pres*
Brad Huber, *Project Mgr*
Todd Gray, *Project Mgr*
Dick Ling, *Human Res Mgr*
EMP: 100 **EST:** 1966
SQ FT: 25,000 **Privately Held**
WEB: www.albersco.com
SIC: 1711 Ventilation & duct work
contractor; boiler maintenance service;
heating systems repair & maintenance
service; mechanical contractor

(G-8005)
ALBERT'S ORGANICS INC
Also Called: Twin Cities Div
5230 Quincy St (55112-1426)
PHONE...............................763 780-0101
Greg Cota, *Branch Mgr*
EMP: 115
SALES (est): 50MM-99.9MM **Publicly Held**
WEB: www.albertsorganics.com
SIC: 5149 Wholesales natural & organic
foods
HQ: Albert's Organics Inc
      200 Eagle Ct
      Bridgeport NJ 08014
      856 241-9090

(G-8006)
ALBRECHT CO'S
1408 County Road C W (55113-3165)
PHONE...............................651 633-4510
FAX: 651 633-1675
Dwayne E Albrecht, *Owner*
EMP: 50

EST: 1968
SQ FT: 10,000
SALES (est): 10MM-24.9MM **Privately Held**
SIC: 5083 Wholesales irrigation equipment

(G-8007)
ALDIN EXPORT & IMPORT
1090 Amble Dr (55126-2268)
PHONE...............................651 483-4184
Aladdin S Hassan, *Owner*
EST: 1974 **Privately Held**
SIC: 5084 5065 8742 Wholesales industrial
machinery & equipment; financial
management consulting services; marketing
consulting service; wholesales industrial
food product manufacturing machinery;
wholesales industrial milk products
manufacturing machinery & equipment

(G-8008)
ALEBRA TECHNOLOGIES INC
550 Main St Ste 250 (55112-3273)
PO Box 120390 (55112-0017)
PHONE...............................651 366-6140
Paul Larson, *CEO*
Bill Yeager, *Senior VP*
Harold Stevenson, *Vice Pres*
Tom Lehn, *CFO*
Tom Dipuma, *VP Sales*
EMP: 25 **EST:** 1998
SQ FT: 3,500
SALES (est): 1MM-4.9MM **Privately Held**
SIC: 7371 Custom computer software
systems analysis & design service

(G-8009)
ALL CITY ELEVATOR INC
2340 Capp Rd (55114-1251)
PHONE...............................651 646-5600
FAX: 651 646-5300
Kevin M Whaley, *CEO*
EMP: 38 **EST:** 1992
SQ FT: 4,850
SALES (est): 1MM-4.9MM **Privately Held**
WEB: www.allcityelevator.com
SIC: 7699 Elevators inspection, services &
repair

(G-8010)
ALL INC
185 Plato Blvd W (55107-2007)
PHONE...............................651 227-6331
FAX: 651 292-0541
James Rutzick, *President*
Mark Rutzick, *Vice Pres*
Sue King, *Controller*
Holly Levery, *Controller*
Holly Rodriguze, *Controller*
EMP: 73 **EST:** 1967
SQ FT: 75,000
SALES (est): 50MM-99.9MM **Privately Held**
WEB: www.allinc.com
SIC: 5064 Wholesales electrical major
appliances; retails custom made cabinets

(G-8011)
ALL POOLSIDE SERVICES INC
Also Called: Poolside
121 County Road C E (55117-1350)
PHONE...............................651 483-6600
FAX: 651 483-4549
Robert Anderson, *President*
Leandra Guptill, *Finance Mgr*
EMP: 45 **EST:** 1960
SQ FT: 6,500
SALES (est): 1MM-4.9MM **Privately Held**
SIC: 1799 7389 Retails swimming pools,
hot tubs & sauna equipment & supplies;
retails spas & hot tubs; retails swimming
pool supplies; swimming pool & hot tub
cleaning & maintenance services; spa & hot
tub construction & installation

(G-8012)
ALLEGIANCE FINANCIAL
GROUP INC
2935 Country Dr Ste 102 (55117-1183)
PHONE...............................651 486-5313
John Seibel, *President*
Mark Spease, *Senior VP*
Leon Perkins, *Vice Pres*
Pat O'Brien, *CFO*
Shelly Anderson, *Controller*
EST: 2001
SQ FT: 3,500 **Privately Held**

SIC: 6159 Equipment & vehicle finance
leasing service

(G-8013)
ALLIED SECURITY LLC
1611 County Road B W Ste 215
(55113-4053)
PHONE...............................651 604-9414
FAX: 651 604-9411
William Beckfeld, *Vice Pres*
Edward Larson, *Branch Mgr*
EMP: 100
SALES (est): 1MM-4.9MM **Publicly Held**
WEB: www.blackstone.com
SIC: 7381 Security guard service
DH: Spectaguard Acquisition LLC
      161 Washington St Ste 600
      Conshohocken PA 19428
      484 351-1300

(G-8014)
ALLINA HEALTH SYSTEM
1850 Beam Ave (55109-1162)
PHONE...............................651 779-2500
FAX: 651 770-8834
Anthony Bauer, *Optometrist*
Kathy Sipple, *Manager*
Julie Ganje, *Manager*
Melvin L Ashford, *Obstetrician*
Maren E Elze, *Podiatrist*
EMP: 250
SALES (est): 5MM-9.9MM **Privately Held**
WEB: www.allina.com
SIC: 8082 Home health care services
PA: Allina Health System
      2925 Chicago Ave
      Minneapolis MN 55407
      612 775-5000

(G-8015)
ALLINA HEALTH SYSTEM
2004 Ford Pkwy (55116-1931)
PHONE...............................651 699-1501
Marilyn Junjblugh, *Branch Mgr*
EMP: 35 **Privately Held**
WEB: www.allina.com
SIC: 8621 Medical field association
PA: Allina Health System
      2925 Chicago Ave
      Minneapolis MN 55407
      612 775-5000

(G-8016)
ALLINA HEALTH SYSTEM
Also Called: Aspen Medical Group
1021 Bandana Blvd E (55108-5113)
PHONE...............................651 642-2700
FAX: 651 642-9441
Thomas Matenaer, *Manager*
EMP: 772 **Privately Held**
WEB: www.allina.com
SIC: 8621 Medical field association
PA: Allina Health System
      2925 Chicago Ave
      Minneapolis MN 55407
      612 775-5000

(G-8017)
ALLINA MEDICAL CENTER
Also Called: United Hospital
333 Smith Ave N (55102-2344)
PHONE...............................651 220-8186
FAX: 651 220-5189
Julian Deutch, *Manager*
Juliann Scott, *Manager*
Bonnie Frisk, *Manager*
EMP: 27
SALES (est): 1MM-4.9MM **Privately Held**
SIC: 8071 Medical laboratory

(G-8018)
ALTERRA HEALTHCARE CORP
Also Called: Clare Bridge of North Oaks
300 Village Center Dr (55127-3021)
PHONE...............................651 482-8111
FAX: 651 482-8333
David Jones, *Manager*
Tom Riedel, *Exec Dir*
EMP: 50
SALES (est): 1MM-4.9MM **Publicly Held**
WEB: www.assisted.com

SIC: 8051 Extended care facility
DH: Alterra Healthcare Corp
      10000 W Innovation Dr
      Milwaukee WI 53226
      414 918-5000

(G-8019)
AMERICAN ACADEMY OF
NEUROLOGY
1080 Montreal Ave Ste 100 (55116-2387)
PHONE...............................651 695-1940
FAX: 651 695-2791
Patricia Baskin, *General Mgr*
Kathleen Pieper, *General Mgr*
Terrence L Cascino, *Corp Secy*
Ray Thibodeau, *Vice Pres*
Michael L Goldstein, *Vice Pres*
EMP: 100 **EST:** 1948
SQ FT: 47,000 **Privately Held**
WEB: www.aan.com
SIC: 8621 Medical field association

(G-8020)
AMERICAN AIR PRODUCTS INC
Also Called: Clayhill 2
141 S Lafayette Rd W (55107)
PHONE...............................651 290-0000
FAX: 651 848-0205
Robert F Simmer, *President*
Mark Bruns, *Vice Pres*
EMP: 25 **EST:** 1965
SQ FT: 30,000
SALES (est): 10MM-24.9MM **Privately Held**
WEB: www.airus.com
SIC: 5084 Wholesales industrial pneumatic
tools & equipment

(G-8021)
AMERICAN BANK OF ST PAUL
(HQ)
1578 University Ave W (55104-3908)
PHONE...............................651 452-1320
Norbert J Conzemius, *Ch of Bd*
Norlin G Boyum, *Vice Ch Bd*
John G Kimball, *President*
David Carlson, *Exec VP*
Laura Gevik, *Vice Pres*
EMP: 60 **EST:** 1972
SQ FT: 25,000
SALES (corp-wide): 4.6M **Privately Held**
SIC: 6022 State commercial bank

(G-8022)
AMERICAN BANK OF ST PAUL
1578 University Ave W (55104-3908)
PHONE...............................651 643-8472
Gary Kluthe, *Vice Pres*
Nate Reinhardt, *Technology Dir*
EMP: 175
SALES (est): 25MM-49.9MM **Privately Held**
SIC: 6021 National commercial bank
HQ: American Bank of St Paul
      1578 University Ave W
      Saint Paul MN 55104
      651 452-1320

(G-8023)
AMERICAN CONSULTING
SERVICES (PA)
550 Cleveland Ave N (55114-1804)
PHONE...............................651 659-9001
Terry Swor, *President*
Richard Stehly, *Principal*
EMP: 120 **EST:** 1989
SQ FT: 43,000
SALES (corp-wide): 22.42M **Privately Held**
SIC: 8711 8734 Engineering services;
pollution testing laboratory; soil analysis
laboratory; water testing laboratory

(G-8024)
AMERICAN DAIRY
ASSOCIATION OF
Also Called: National Dairy Council
2015 Rice St Ste 100 (55113-6800)
PHONE...............................651 488-0261
Michael Kruger, *CEO*
Sherry Noel, *Manager*
Andrew Brogan, *Manager*
EMP: 26 **EST:** 1937
SQ FT: 15,000 **Privately Held**
SIC: 8611 Business association

www.HarrisInfo.com
348

2011 Harris Minnesota
Services Directory

▲=Import ▼=Export
◆=Import/Export

GEOGRAPHIC

(G-8025)
AMERICAN ENGINEERING TESTING (HQ)
550 Cleveland Ave N (55114-1804)
PHONE..............................651 659-9001
FAX: 651 659-1379
Terry E Swor, *President*
Robert Krogsgaard, *Corp Secy*
Richard S Pe, *Senior VP*
Richard Stehly, *Senior VP*
Jeffery Voyen, *Vice Pres*
EMP: 100 EST: 1971
SQ FT: 45,000
SALES (corp-wide): 22.42M **Privately Held**
WEB: www.amengtest.com
SIC: 8711 8734 Engineering services; pollution testing laboratory; soil analysis laboratory; water testing laboratory
PA: American Consulting Services
550 Cleveland Ave N
Saint Paul MN 55114
651 659-9001

(G-8026)
AMERICAN HOME HEALTH
Also Called: Ameri-Health
2502 Manitou Is (55110-3901)
PHONE..............................612 860-7301
Pete Markoe, *Owner*
EMP: 25 EST: 1990
SALES (est): 500-999K **Privately Held**
SIC: 8361 Residential care facility

(G-8027)
AMERICAN INSTITUTE OF
Also Called: Wala Group
245 6th St E (55101-1918)
PHONE..............................651 415-1320
Fazal Tagadawala DVM, *President*
Parvin Daghighian, *Vice Pres*
EMP: 26 EST: 1981
SQ FT: 3,000
SALES (est): 1MM-4.9MM **Privately Held**
SIC: 8732 5045 Economic research services; wholesales computer software

(G-8028)
AMERICAN LUNG ASSOCIATION OF
490 Concordia Ave (55103-2412)
PHONE..............................651 227-8014
Penny Fena, *President*
Penny Semama, *Senior VP*
Mary Cich, *Manager*
James Wickler, *Manager*
EMP: 28 EST: 1903
SQ FT: 18,000
SALES (est): 1MM-4.9MM **Privately Held**
SIC: 8733 Educational research agency

(G-8029)
AMERICAN NATIONAL RED CROSS
176 Robert St S (55107-1421)
PHONE..............................651 291-6789
FAX: 651 290-8993
David Therkelsem, *CEO*
Lynne Weber, *Mktg Dir*
Mary Laustrup, *Manager*
William Murtaugh, *Manager*
Kim Stechar, *CTO*
EMP: 250
SALES (est): 25MM-49.9MM **Privately Held**
WEB: www.redcross.org
SIC: 8099 Blood related health services

(G-8030)
AMERICAN NATIONAL RED CROSS
Also Called: Red Cross
100 Robert St S (55107-1411)
PHONE..............................651 291-4600
FAX: 651 290-8925
Ralph Nordstrom, *General Mgr*
Lisa Rohr, *Human Resources*
Jack Sheeman, *Comms Mgr*
Agnes E Aysola, *Med Doctor*
George Dahlgren, *Manager*
EMP: 240
SALES (est): 25MM-49.9MM **Privately Held**
SIC: 8099 8071 Blood bank; blood analysis laboratory

(G-8031)
AMERICAN PAPER RECYCLING CORP
615 Prior Ave N (55104-1743)
PHONE..............................651 644-7806
FAX: 651 659-9196
Duke Bates, *Finance*
Ronald Smith, *Branch Mgr*
EMP: 25
SALES (est): 5MM-9.9MM **Privately Held**
WEB: www.aprcorp.com
SIC: 4953 Paper mill; waste material recycling services; pulp mill
PA: American Paper Recycling Corp
87 Central St Ste 8
Mansfield MA 02048
508 339-5551

(G-8032)
AMERICAN PUBLIC MEDIA GROUP (PA)
480 Cedar St (55101-2217)
PHONE..............................651 290-1500
FAX: 651 290-1188
William H Kling, *President*
Jeff Engelking, *Finance Mgr*
EMP: 307 EST: 1987
SQ FT: 5,800 **Privately Held**
WEB: www.americanpublicmedia.org
SIC: 4832 Radio broadcasting station

(G-8033)
AMERICAN RESIDENTIAL MORTGAGE
235 Roselawn Ave E Ste 12 (55117-1942)
PHONE..............................651 488-1801
FAX: 651 488-3357
Larry Shedd, *Partner*
Christopher Shedd, *Partner*
Loretta Aymond, *Assistant VP*
Brad Anderson, *Vice Pres*
Renee Rollin, *Manager*
EMP: 60 EST: 1987
SQ FT: 9,000
SALES (est): 5MM-9.9MM **Privately Held**
SIC: 6162 Mortgage & loan lending

(G-8034)
AMERICAN SECURITY LLC (PA)
1717 University Ave W (55104-3613)
PHONE..............................651 644-1155
FAX: 651 641-0523
John Gilje, *Member*
Tony Curtis, *Vice Pres*
Cliff Boudreau, *Safety Dir*
Dan McCarthy, *CFO*
Richard Lubbers, *Treasurer*
EMP: 800 EST: 1959
SQ FT: 55,000 **Privately Held**
SIC: 7381 Guard protective service; armored car service

(G-8035)
AMERICARE STAFFING SERVICE INC
2233 University Ave W Ste 301 (55114-1649)
PHONE..............................651 917-1995
FAX: 651 644-2322
Amare Berhie, *President*
Tefera Kassa, *Vice Pres*
Semret Tekleab, *Manager*
Nellie R Akalp, *Incorporator*
EMP: 60 EST: 1997 **Privately Held**
SIC: 7361 Employment agency services

(G-8036)
AMERICOM INC
308 E Lafayette Rd (55107-1217)
PHONE..............................651 726-2200
FAX: 651 224-7833
Dean Jakubowicz, *President*
Joe Smuda, *General Mgr*
EMP: 30 EST: 1995
SQ FT: 11,000
SALES (est): 1MM-4.9MM **Privately Held**
WEB: www.midwestamericom.com
SIC: 7373 Systems integration service

(G-8037)
AMERIPRISE FINANCIAL SERVICES
900 Long Lake Rd Ste 300 (55112-6439)
PHONE..............................651 631-2208
FAX: 651 635-1894
John Greiber, *Vice Pres*
Jake Dunlap, *Vice Pres*
Darla Jacob, *Human Res Mgr*
Pat Glesener, *CIO*
EMP: 100
SALES (est): 10MM-24.9MM **Publicly Held**
SIC: 6282 Investment advisory service
HQ: Ameriprise Financial Inc
1099 Ameriprise Financial Ctr
Minneapolis MN 55474
612 671-3131

(G-8038)
AMF BOWLING CENTERS INC
61 Little Canada Rd W (55117-1362)
PHONE..............................651 484-6501
FAX: 651 484-4497
Rob Selender, *Manager*
EMP: 25
SALES (est): 500-999K **Privately Held**
WEB: www.kidsports.org
SIC: 7933 Bowling center
HQ: AMF Bowling Centers Inc
7313 Bell Creek Rd
Mechanicsville VA 23111
804 417-2008

(G-8039)
AMF BOWLING CENTERS INC
1955 English St (55109-4301)
PHONE..............................651 774-8787
Jim Gardner, *General Mgr*
Adeline Benjamin, *Treasurer*
D B Deleano, *Manager*
EMP: 30
SALES (est): 1MM-4.9MM **Privately Held**
WEB: www.kidsports.org
SIC: 7933 Bowling center
HQ: AMF Bowling Centers Inc
7313 Bell Creek Rd
Mechanicsville VA 23111
804 417-2008

(G-8040)
AMHERST H WILDER FOUNDATION (PA)
451 Lexington Pkwy N # 1 (55104-4637)
PHONE..............................651 280-2000
Thomas W Kingston, *President*
Kelly Urista, *General Mgr*
Malcolm McDonald, *Corp Secy*
Corey Brinkema, *Treasurer*
Mike McDonald, *Accountant*
EMP: 300 EST: 1906
SQ FT: 50,500
SALES (corp-wide): 51.12M **Privately Held**
SIC: 8322 Multi-services center

(G-8041)
AMHERST H WILDER FOUNDATION
Also Called: Health East Residence
514 Humboldt Ave Ofc (55107-4016)
PHONE..............................651 220-1700
FAX: 651 220-1724
Anne Naithani, *Human Res Mgr*
David Messick, *Manager*
EMP: 135
SALES (est): 10MM-24.9MM **Privately Held**
SIC: 6513 8051 8052 Apartment building operator; intermediate care facility; skilled nursing care facility
PA: Amherst H Wilder Foundation
451 Lexington Pkwy N # 1
Saint Paul MN 55104
651 280-2000

(G-8042)
AMHERST H WILDER FOUNDATION
Also Called: Wilder Research Center
1295 Bandana Blvd N Ste 210 (55108-5115)
PHONE..............................651 647-4600
FAX: 651 642-2050
Paul Mattessich, *Director*
EMP: 35

SALES (est): 1MM-4.9MM **Privately Held**
SIC: 8732 Research services
PA: Amherst H Wilder Foundation
451 Lexington Pkwy N # 1
Saint Paul MN 55104
651 280-2000

(G-8043)
AMHERST H WILDER FOUNDATION
Also Called: Bush Memorial Center
180 Grotto St S (55105-3505)
PHONE..............................651 224-1395
Donald Turvold, *Director*
EMP: 62
SALES (est): 1MM-4.9MM **Privately Held**
SIC: 8322 Multi-services center
PA: Amherst H Wilder Foundation
451 Lexington Pkwy N # 1
Saint Paul MN 55104
651 280-2000

(G-8044)
AMHERST H WILDER FOUNDATION
Also Called: Social Adjsment Prog For SE As
450 Syndicate St N Ste 285 (55104-4127)
PHONE..............................651 647-9676
FAX: 651 999-0267
Linda Walker, *Administrator*
EMP: 35 **Privately Held**
SIC: 8399 Council for social agency
PA: Amherst H Wilder Foundation
451 Lexington Pkwy N # 1
Saint Paul MN 55104
651 280-2000

(G-8045)
AMHERST H WILDER FOUNDATION
Also Called: Adult Day Health-Mlk
650 Marshall Ave (55104-6644)
PHONE..............................651 290-8666
FAX: 651 224-6906
Maryanne Mastel, *Principal*
Art Anderson, *Manager*
Jane Vohs, *Manager*
Kris Gjerdi, *Manager*
Marilyn Darwood, *Director*
EMP: 100
SALES (est): 5MM-9.9MM **Privately Held**
SIC: 8322 Multi-services center
PA: Amherst H Wilder Foundation
451 Lexington Pkwy N # 1
Saint Paul MN 55104
651 280-2000

(G-8046)
AMPRO SERVICES INC
2690 Prior Ave N (55113-1327)
PHONE..............................651 631-5924
Thomas Wintz, *President*
EMP: 40 EST: 1996
SQ FT: 500
SALES (est): 500-999K **Privately Held**
SIC: 7363 Truck driver service

(G-8047)
ANCHOR BANK
2700 7th Ave E (55109-3113)
PHONE..............................651 770-2341
Kevin Kelly, *Branch Mgr*
EMP: 30
SALES (est): 5MM-9.9MM **Privately Held**
SIC: 6021 Commercial national trust companies with deposits
PA: Anchor Bank
1055 Wayzata Blvd E
Wayzata MN 55391
952 473-4606

(G-8048)
ANCHOR BANK HERITAGE
2700 7th Ave E (55109-3113)
PHONE..............................651 770-2341
FAX: 651 770-6843
James Hammond, *CEO*
Carl Jones, *Chairman*
Diane Quinn, *Vice Pres*
Pete Bernaciak, *Vice Pres*
Jeffry Hagen, *Vice Pres*
EMP: 33 EST: 1910
SALES (est): 5MM-9.9MM **Privately Held**
SIC: 6021 National commercial bank

(PA)=Parent Co (HQ)=Headquarters (DH)=Div Headquarters
✪ = New business established in last 2 years

2011 Harris Minnesota
Services Directory

© Harris InfoSource 1-866-281-6415
349

(G-8049)
ANCHOR BLOCK CO
2300 McKnight Rd N (55109-2830)
PHONE.............................651 777-8321
Glenn Bolles, *President*
Don Linbfors, *Plant Mgr*
John Evans, *Manager*
Bryan Leer, *CIO*
Steve Rider, *CIO*
EMP: 55
SALES (est): 5MM-9.9MM **Privately Held**
SIC: 1442 Manufactures standard concrete or cinder blocks; manufactures cut stone & stone products; retails masonry materials & supplies; manufactures concrete products; construction sand & gravel mining

(G-8050)
ANDERSON CLEANERS
718 Cleveland Ave S (55116-1319)
PHONE.............................651 690-9592
Ferrell Anderson, *Owner*
EMP: 50 **EST:** 1990
SALES (est): 1MM-4.9MM **Privately Held**
SIC: 7216 Drapery & curtain drycleaning service

(G-8051)
ANDERSON, NIEBUHR & ASSOCIATES
6 Pine Tree Dr Ste 200 (55112-3784)
PHONE.............................651 486-8712
FAX: 651 483-0536
John F Anderson, *President*
Marsha Niebuhr, *Vice Pres*
Jeff Melsa, *Project Mgr*
Thomas Coleman, *Manager*
Jennifer Koper, *Administration*
EMP: 40 **EST:** 1974
SALES (est): 1MM-4.9MM **Privately Held**
WEB: www.ana-inc.com
SIC: 8732 Market analysis or research services; research services; survey services, including marketing & location

(G-8052)
ANN PEARSON MD
1055 Centerville Cir (55127-5033)
PHONE.............................651 426-4844
Ann Pearson MD, *Principal*
EMP: 30
SALES (est): 1MM-4.9MM **Privately Held**
SIC: 8011 General & family practice physician or surgeon office

(G-8053)
ANSWER AMERICA LLC
Also Called: Able One
1600 University Ave W Ste 208 (55104-3825)
PHONE.............................651 644-7332
FAX: 651 644-8295
Nancy Fontana, *Sales Executive*
Thomas Wright, *Manager*
EMP: 28
SALES (est): 1MM-4.9MM **Privately Held**
SIC: 7389 Telephone answering service

(G-8054)
API GROUP INC (PA)
1100 Old Highway 8 NW (55112-6447)
PHONE.............................651 636-4320
FAX: 651 636-7059
Lee R Anderson Sr, *Ch of Bd*
Bernie M Beliveau, *President*
Russell Becker, *President*
Shane Shipman, *General Mgr*
John McCann, *Managing Dir*
◆ **EMP:** 25 **EST:** 1997 **Privately Held**
WEB: www.apigroupinc.com
SIC: 1711 1742 1799 7699 Boiler maintenance service; building insulation installation service; pipe & boiler insulating contractor; boiler & heating repair service
PA: A P I GROUP PLC
  Second Ave, Poynton Indstl Est
  STOCKPORT England

(G-8055)
APPLEWOOD POINTE SENIOR CO OP
1480 Applewood Ct W # 222 (55113-6292)
PHONE.............................651 636-2161
Don Anderson, *Principal*
Paul Mitchell, *Corp Secy*
John Sweeney, *Treasurer*
Jan Hanson, *Bd of Directors*
EMP: 50 **EST:** 2004
SALES (est): 1MM-4.9MM **Privately Held**
SIC: 8322 Individual & family social services

(G-8056)
APRIA HEALTHCARE INC
1645 Energy Park Dr # 100 (55108-2733)
PHONE.............................651 523-8888
Rex Silber, *Sales Executive*
Serena Shea, *Branch Mgr*
Jeff Trotman, *Manager*
Karen Engels, *Manager*
Betty Reed, *Manager*
EMP: 50
SALES (est): 25MM-49.9MM **Publicly Held**
WEB: www.apria.com
SIC: 5047 Wholesales hospital equipment & furniture
DH: Apria Healthcare Inc
  26220 Enterprise Ct
  Lake Forest CA 92630
  949 639-2000

(G-8057)
ARC GREATER TWIN CITIES (PA)
2446 University Ave W # 110 (55114-1740)
PHONE.............................952 920-0855
Lisette Schlosser, *CFO*
Paula Casmey, *Accountant*
Erin Geiser, *Manager*
Terri Skorczewski, *Manager*
Paul Harder, *Technology Dir*
EMP: 34 **EST:** 1946
SQ FT: 12,000
SALES (corp-wide): 4.42M **Privately Held**
WEB: www.arcsvaluevillage.com
SIC: 8322 Social services center

(G-8058)
ARCH CAPITAL SERVICES
30 7th St E Ste 2270 (55101-4927)
PHONE.............................651 855-7111
Deb Sagisser, *Manager*
EMP: 50 **EST:** 2004
SALES (est): 10MM-24.9MM **Privately Held**
SIC: 6351 Provides liability insurance

(G-8059)
ARCH INSURANCE GROUP INC
30 7th St E Ste 2270 (55101-4927)
PHONE.............................651 855-7100
FAX: 651 855-7171
Mary A Krutheim, *Vice Pres*
Ralph E Jones, *Manager*
EMP: 48
SALES (est): 1MM-4.9MM **Privately Held**
WEB: www.archinsurance.com
SIC: 1799 Construction site cleanup service
HQ: Arch Insurance Group Inc
  3000 Bayport Dr Ste 1060
  Tampa FL 33607
  813 371-3305

(G-8060)
ARCHBOLD ENTERPRISES LLC
Also Called: Metcalf Moving & Storage Co
1255 Highway 36 E (55109-2046)
PHONE.............................651 484-0211
Jon Archbold, *CEO*
Betty Worth, *Controller*
Cindy Borup, *Sales Mgr*
EMP: 35 **EST:** 2003
SQ FT: 35,000
SALES (est): 1MM-4.9MM **Privately Held**
SIC: 4213 4212 Long-distance moving services; local furniture moving services without storage

(G-8061)
ARCHITECTURAL TESTING INC
849 Western Ave N (55117-5245)
PHONE.............................651 636-3835
Dan Braun, *Branch Mgr*
EMP: 25
SALES (est): 1MM-4.9MM **Privately Held**
WEB: www.archtest.com
SIC: 8071 Testing laboratory
PA: Architectural Testing Inc
  130 Derry Ct
  York PA 17406
  717 764-7700

(G-8062)
ARGUS HOMES
418 County Road D E (55117-1218)
PHONE.............................651 294-2160
FAX: 651 294-2171
Mike Moriarty, *Member*
John Dierbeck, *Director*
EMP: 30 **EST:** 2005
SALES (est): 5MM-9.9MM **Privately Held**
SIC: 1521 Single-family housing construction

(G-8063)
ARLINGTON HOUSE
712 Larpenteur Ave E (55117-2528)
PHONE.............................651 771-3040
FAX: 651 771-3040
Gary Gulbrandson, *Director*
Tiffany Allbee, *Program Dir*
EMP: 32 **EST:** 1960
SALES (est): 1MM-4.9MM **Privately Held**
WEB: www.arlingtonhouse.com
SIC: 8322 Emergency shelters

(G-8064)
ARRAN TECHNOLOGIES INC
1901 Oakcrest Ave Ste 1 (55113-2617)
PHONE.............................651 468-0002
Steven E Clark, *President*
Elizabeth Marz, *Vice Pres*
Laura Tyson, *Marketing Mgr*
EMP: 25 **EST:** 1981
SQ FT: 7,167
SALES (est): 1MM-4.9MM **Privately Held**
WEB: www.arranmls.com
SIC: 7371 7379 Computer software development; computer system consulting services

(G-8065)
ARTCO BUILDERS INC
4434 Harbor Place Dr (55126-1939)
PHONE.............................651 486-0761
Kevin Reis, *President*
EMP: 50 **EST:** 1979
SALES (est): 5MM-9.9MM **Privately Held**
SIC: 1761 Siding contractor

(G-8066)
ARTHUR SHUSTER INC
1995 Oakcrest Ave (55113-2605)
PO Box 131115 (55113-0010)
PHONE.............................651 631-9200
FAX: 651 636-3922
Stanford Shuster, *President*
Curt Schaap, *Senior VP*
Christina Stevens, *Senior VP*
Charles Shuster, *Vice Pres*
Timothy McLean, *Vice Pres*
EMP: 40 **EST:** 1959
SQ FT: 23,000
SALES (est): 5MM-9.9MM **Privately Held**
WEB: www.arthurshuster.com
SIC: 7389 Interior design service

(G-8067)
ASI GREAT FALLS INC
Also Called: Southwind Estates
2550 University Ave W 330N (55114-2014)
PHONE.............................651 645-7271
Stephen V Schaaf, *President*
EMP: 50 **EST:** 1993
SALES (est): 5MM-9.9MM **Privately Held**
SIC: 6513 Apartment building operator

(G-8068)
ASI MISSOULA INC
2550 University Ave W 330N (55114-2014)
PHONE.............................651 645-7271
EMP: 50 **EST:** 2000
SALES (est): 5MM-9.9MM **Privately Held**
WEB: www.accessiblespace.org
SIC: 6513 Apartment building operator
PA: Accessible Space Inc
  2550 University Ave W Ste 330N
  Saint Paul MN 55114
  651 645-7271

(G-8069)
ASIAN HOME CARE INC
519 University Ave W # 202 (55103-1938)
PHONE.............................651 999-0268
FAX: 651 999-0269
MEI Yang, *President*
EMP: 40 **EST:** 1997
SALES (est): 1MM-4.9MM **Privately Held**
SIC: 8082 8011 Home health care services; physicians' office & clinic

(G-8070)
ASPEN MEDICAL GROUP
2004 Ford Pkwy (55116-1931)
PHONE.............................651 696-8800
Marilyn Jungbluth, *Manager*
EMP: 35
SALES (est): 1MM-4.9MM **Privately Held**
SIC: 8049 Health practitioners' office

(G-8071)
ASPEN RESEARCH CORP
1700 Buerkle Rd (55110-5249)
PHONE.............................651 264-6000
FAX: 651 232-4972
Roger Worm, *Vice Pres*
Vince Rost, *Facilities Mgr*
Josh Beer, *Finance Dir*
Mark Corbey, *Human Res Mgr*
Patrick Gronlund, *Manager*
EMP: 80 **EST:** 1986
SQ FT: 100,000
SALES (est): 5MM-9.9MM **Privately Held**
WEB: www.aspenresearch.com
SIC: 8734 8731 Testing laboratory; commercial physical research laboratory
PA: Andersen Corp
  100 4th Ave N
  Bayport MN 55003
  651 264-5150

(G-8072)
ASPHALT SPECIALTIES CO
Also Called: Act Specialties
547 County Road E W (55126-7000)
PHONE.............................651 484-1696
Erik Peterson, *President*
Dave Swanson, *Vice Pres*
John Wilson, *Manager*

SQ FT: 6,000 **Privately Held**
SIC: 1771 Driveway, parking lot & blacktop contractor; driveway contractor; parking lot construction

(G-8073)
ASSOCIATED DENTISTS LTD
1371 7th St W (55102-4205)
PHONE.............................651 222-0351
FAX: 651 222-1556
David Miller, *President*
M T Winter DDS, *President*
Paul S Phillipi DDS, *Partner*
Richard Melon, *Partner*
David Resch DDS, *Partner*
EMP: 42 **EST:** 1973
SALES (est): 1MM-4.9MM **Privately Held**
WEB: www.adentists.com
SIC: 8021 Dental office

(G-8074)
ASSOCIATES PLUS INC (PA)
Also Called: Re Max Associates Plus
480 Highway 96 W Ste 200 (55126-1901)
PHONE.............................651 484-8800
FAX: 651 484-6376
Dennis Anderson, *President*
Dwight Denyes, *Vice Pres*
EMP: 36 **EST:** 1990 **Privately Held**
WEB: www.stenvig.com

www.HarrisInfo.com
350

2011 Harris Minnesota
Services Directory

▲=Import ▼=Export
◆=Import/Export

SIC: **6531** Residential real estate agency

(G-8075)

ASSOCIATION FOR THE SOLIDATARY

Wright Bldg 2233 Ste 426 (55114)
PHONE..............................952 456-1751
Mililik H Ibrahim, *President*
Mililik H Idrahim, *President*
EMP: 110
SQ FT: 3,000
SALES (est): 1MM-4.9MM **Privately Held**
SIC: **7363** Help supply services

(G-8076)

ATHENA ASSURANCE CO

385 Washington St (55102-1309)
PHONE..............................651 310-7065
Douglas W Leatherdale, *CEO*
Janet Nelson, *President*
Karen C Abraham, *Corp Secy*
Bruce A Backberg, *Corp Secy*
Jay S Benet, *CFO*
EMP: 30 **EST:** 1983
SALES (est): 10MM-24.9MM **Publicly Held**
WEB: www.wmharvey.com
SIC: **6331** Provides property damage insurance
HQ: St Paul Fire & Marine Insce
       385 Washington St
       Saint Paul MN 55102
       651 221-7911

(G-8077)

ATT HOME HEALTH CARE INC

1543 Como Ave (55108-2544)
PHONE..............................651 646-8771
FAX: 651 646-8910
Tony Wynn, *President*
EMP: 50 **EST:** 2001
SALES (est): 1MM-4.9MM **Privately Held**
SIC: **8082** Home health care services

(G-8078)

AUGEO AFFINITY MARKETING INC

2561 Territorial Rd (55114-1500)
PHONE..............................877 781-2586
David Kristal, *CEO*
Juan Sabater, *Principal*
Bill Gamble, *COO*
EMP: 55 **EST:** 1999
SQ FT: 10,617
SALES (est): 5MM-9.9MM **Privately Held**
WEB: www.augeomarketing.com
SIC: **8742** Marketing consulting service

(G-8079)

AUGEO COMMUNICATIONS LLC

2561 Territorial Rd (55114-1500)
PHONE..............................651 204-5734
David Kristal, *Member*
Robert Warrick, *Member*
Jon Otto, *Member*
Jenifer Cloutier, *Vice Pres*
Mike Egan, *Business Anlyst*
EMP: 27 **EST:** 2004
SALES (est): 1MM-4.9MM **Privately Held**
SIC: **8748** Telecommunications consulting services

(G-8080)

AUTO-OWNERS LIFE INSURANCE CO

2539 County Road E E (55110-4906)
PO Box 64358 (55164-0358)
PHONE..............................651 777-9317
Dale Schnur, *Vice Pres*
Jeff Carr, *Manager*
Jamie Whisnant, *Director*
Jeff Andren, *Technician*
EMP: 75
SALES (est): 50MM-99.9MM **Privately Held**
WEB: www.sheratonlansing.com
SIC: **6311** Life insurance carrier
HQ: Auto-Owners Life Insurance Co
       6101 Anacapri Blvd
       Lansing MI 48917
       517 323-1200

(G-8081)

AVI-SPL INC

Also Called: Spl Integrated Solutions
1427 Energy Park Dr (55108-5204)
PHONE..............................651 287-7000
FAX: 651 287-7001
Mary Strohmayer, *General Mgr*
John Babcock, *General Mgr*
Phil Dalen, *Exec VP*
Howard Haberman, *Opers Mgr*
Stephanie James, *Asst Controller*
EMP: 40
SALES (est): 1MM-4.9MM **Privately Held**
SIC: **1731** Voice, data & video wiring contractor
HQ: AVI-Spl Inc
       6301 Benjamin Rd Ste 101
       Tampa FL 33634
       813 884-7168

(G-8082)

AVIS RENT A CAR SYSTEM INC

2550 Cleveland Ave N (55113-2601)
PHONE..............................651 636-6730
Jack Hartmann, *Manager*
EMP: 30
SALES (est): 1MM-4.9MM **Publicly Held**
WEB: www.avis.com
SIC: **7514** Rent-a-car service
DH: Avis Rent A Car System Inc
       6 Sylvan Way Ste 1
       Parsippany NJ 07054
       973 496-3500

(G-8083)

AXIS MINNESOTA INC

Also Called: Peoples Cmnty Care Residence
2345 Rice St Ste 112 (55113-3745)
PHONE..............................651 774-5940
Dorothy Wrobel, *President*
Ben Nordquist, *Engineer*
Denise Scholljegerdes, *CFO*
EMP: 78 **EST:** 1996
SALES (est): 1MM-4.9MM **Privately Held**
WEB: www.axis-mn.com
SIC: **8361** Residential care facility

(G-8084)

B&D ASSOCIATES INC

255 Como Ave (55103-1801)
PHONE..............................651 489-8001
William C Dentinger III, *President*
Richard Dentinger, *Vice Pres*
EMP: 30 **EST:** 2003
SALES (est): 1MM-4.9MM **Privately Held**
SIC: **1741** Masonry & stonework contractor

(G-8085)

BALLY TOTAL FITNESS CORP

71 Minnesota Ave (55117-1737)
PHONE..............................651 484-4444
FAX: 651 484-8437
Alicia Lovato, *Manager*
Kristen Kaphing, *Manager*
Melissa David, *Manager*
EMP: 39
SALES (est): 1MM-4.9MM **Publicly Held**
WEB: www.ballyfitnes.com
SIC: **7991** Health club
HQ: Bally Total Fitness Corp
       12440 Imperial Hwy # 300
       Norwalk CA 90650
       562 484-2000

(G-8086)

BANKCHEROKEE

607 Smith Ave S (55107-2617)
PHONE..............................651 227-7071
Jim Gesell, *Ch of Bd*
Dennis Passeri, *Vice Ch Bd*
Heidi Gesell, *President*
George Ruth, *Exec VP*
Scott Larsen, *Vice Pres*
EMP: 37 **EST:** 1908
SALES (est): 10MM-24.9MM **Privately Held**
SIC: **6022** State commercial bank
PA: Cherokee Bancshares Inc
       607 Smith Ave S
       Saint Paul MN 55107
       651 227-7071

(G-8087)

BANKRUPTCY SOLUTIONS INC

2740 Arthur St (55113-1303)
PHONE..............................651 367-2000
Lawrence J Fallon, *Exec VP*
EMP: 30 **EST:** 1994
SALES (est): 1MM-4.9MM **Privately Held**
SIC: **8111** Bankruptcy referee

(G-8088)

BANKS BROTHERS CONSTRUCTION

2402 University Ave W # 204 (55114-1745)
PHONE..............................651 644-1723
FAX: 651 644-1299
David Banks, *President*
Dan Myers, *Manager*
Hess Christopher, *Director*
Stephen G Banks, *Director*
EMP: 25 **EST:** 1991
SQ FT: 2,500
SALES (est): 5MM-9.9MM **Privately Held**
SIC: **1542** Commercial & office building renovation & repair services

(G-8089)

BARNETT CHRYSLER JEEP KIA

3610 Highway 61 N (55110-4164)
PHONE..............................651 429-3391
FAX: 651 429-5133
Bruce Barnett, *President*
James Barnett, *Vice Pres*
Nancy Greenberg, *Controller*
Jeff Link, *Manager*
Jerry Ensign, *Manager*
EMP: 100 **EST:** 1962
SQ FT: 46,000
SALES (est): 50MM-99.9MM **Privately Held**
WEB: www.barnettchrysler.com
SIC: **7515** 7538 Retails new & used automobiles; general automotive repair services; passenger car leasing; used car dealer

(G-8090)

BATTLE CREEK HEAD START

2181 Suburban Ave (55119-4610)
PHONE..............................651 730-1663
Nancy Perrin, *Exec Dir*
Selina Gant, *Director*
EMP: 30 **EST:** 2005
SALES (est): 500-999K **Privately Held**
SIC: **8351** Head Start center

(G-8091)

BATTMANN HOLDINGS INC (PA)

2480 Long Lake Rd (55113-2534)
PHONE..............................651 639-2800
Dann Battina, *CEO*
Marc V Kley, *President*
Paul A Zagaria, *Corp Secy*
John Loveland, *Credit Staff*
EMP: 75 **EST:** 2001 **Privately Held**
SIC: **4213** 4214 Over the road trucking; local trucking with storage; local moving service & storage; long-distance moving services

(G-8092)

BAUER BUILT INC

625 Fairview Ave N (55104-1709)
PHONE..............................651 646-1239
Joe Stirmlinger, *Manager*
Joe Weber, *Manager*
EMP: 45
SALES (est): 10MM-24.9MM **Privately Held**
WEB: www.bauerbuilt.com
SIC: **5014** Wholesales automotive tires & tubes; wholesales truck tires & tubes; tire dealer
PA: Bauer Built Inc
       1111 W Prospect St
       Durand WI 54736
       715 672-4295

(G-8093)

BAY WEST INC

5 Empire Dr (55103-1856)
PHONE..............................651 291-0456
Lon S Larson, *CEO*
Edward Bacig, *Vice Pres*
Barry Campbell, *Vice Pres*

Gene Kuppenbender, *Vice Pres*
Jeff Becker, *Facilities Mgr*
EMP: 115 **EST:** 1974
SQ FT: 18,000
SALES (est): 5MM-9.9MM **Privately Held**
WEB: www.baywest.com
SIC: **8744** Facilities support services; environmental remediation services

(G-8094)

BAY WEST-BEM SOLUTIONS LLC

5 Empire Dr (55103-1856)
PHONE..............................651 291-0456
Lon Larson, *Member*
EMP: 99
SALES (est): 5MM-9.9MM **Privately Held**
SIC: **8744** Facilities support services

(G-8095)

BDM CONSULTING ENGINEERS

60 Plato Blvd E Ste 140 (55107-1835)
PHONE..............................612 548-3140
FAX: 612 786-4574
Brian Miller, *President*
John Stewart, *Vice Pres*
Denny Honsa, *Vice Pres*
Bill Chang, *Vice Pres*
EMP: 30 **EST:** 1998
SQ FT: 1,900
SALES (est): 1MM-4.9MM **Privately Held**
SIC: **8711** Engineering consulting services

(G-8096)

BEAMKKO

Also Called: Merry Maids
2275 McKnight Rd N Ste 1 (55109-2813)
PHONE..............................651 770-5661
Bruce Kratky, *President*
Lisa Rawlings, *Office Mgr*
EMP: 25 **EST:** 1981
SALES (est): 500-999K **Privately Held**
SIC: **7349** Housekeeping & maid services

(G-8097)

BECKER BROS INC

825 1st St NW (55112-7354)
PHONE..............................651 633-8604
FAX: 651 633-2122
William B Becker, *CEO*
Greg Tofte, *General Mgr*
Karen Sveiven, *Sales Staff*
Char Cipperly, *Administrator*
EMP: 100 **EST:** 1959
SQ FT: 33,000
SALES (est): 10MM-24.9MM **Privately Held**
SIC: **1752** Flooring contractor; retails floor coverings

(G-8098)

BELL LUMBER & POLE CO (PA)

778 1st St NW (55112-3216)
PO Box 120786 (55112-0024)
PHONE..............................651 633-4334
FAX: 651 633-8852
Tom Bell, *President*
William K Riker, *Corp Secy*
Sue Tankratz, *Corp Secy*
Clarence Westberg, *Vice Pres*
Ruth Lindley, *Director*
EMP: 30 **EST:** 1909
SQ FT: 5,000 **Privately Held**
WEB: www.bellpole.com
SIC: **5099** Wholesales logs, hewn ties, posts & poles; logging

(G-8099)

BELL TELEPHONE INC

Also Called: Time Communications
4444 Centerville Rd (55127-3699)
PHONE..............................651 298-1332
FAX: 651 298-1945
Trisha Stenberg, *President*
Patrick Eastwood, *Vice Pres*
Lisa Barbeau, *Office Mgr*
EMP: 65 **EST:** 1972
SQ FT: 3,000
SALES (est): 1MM-4.9MM **Privately Held**
SIC: **7389** 5065 Telephone answering service; wholesales electronic parts & equipment

(PA)=Parent Co (HQ)=Headquarters (DH)=Div Headquarters
✿ = New business established in last 2 years

2011 Harris Minnesota
Services Directory

© Harris InfoSource 1-866-281-6415

351

GEOGRAPHIC

(G-8100)
BELTMANN GROUP INC (HQ)
2480 Long Lake Rd (55113-2534)
PHONE.............................651 639-2800
Dann Battina, *CEO*
Marc V Kley, *President*
Dave Burns, *General Mgr*
Eric Greene, *General Mgr*
Paul A Zagaria, *Corp Secy*
◆ EMP: 70 EST: 1923
SQ FT: 124,000 **Privately Held**
WEB: www.beltmann.com
SIC: 4213 4214 Over the road trucking;
local trucking with storage; local moving
service & storage; long-distance moving
services
PA: Battmann Holdings Inc
     2480 Long Lake Rd
     Saint Paul MN 55113
     651 639-2800

(G-8101)
BEM - BAY WEST JOINT VENTURE
5 Empire Dr (55103-1856)
PHONE.............................651 291-0456
Lon Larson, *Member*
Bay West, *Member*
EMP: 99
SALES (est): 5MM-9.9MM **Privately Held**
SIC: 8744 Facilities support services

(G-8102)
BENCO DELIVERY SERVICE INC
1144 Larpenteur Ave W # 200
(55113-6322)
PHONE.............................651 486-9999
FAX: 651 486-9991
Kurian Benjamin, *President*
Laly Benjamin, *Vice Pres*
Derek Axell, *Sales Mgr*
EMP: 45 EST: 1989
SQ FT: 40,000
SALES (est): 1MM-4.9MM **Privately Held**
WEB: www.bencods.com
SIC: 7389 Courier or messenger service

(G-8103)
BENHAM CO'S THE LLC
60 Plato Blvd E Ste 300 (55107-1831)
PHONE.............................651 771-2222
John Westerheide, *Engineering*
Blane A Kruse, *Electrical Engi*
Jennifer Olson, *Accountant*
Jennifer Sandstrom, *Accountant*
Greg Schneiderhan, *Mktg Dir*
EMP: 50
SALES (est): 10MM-24.9MM **Privately Held**
WEB: www.benham.com
SIC: 5084 Wholesales industrial machinery
& equipment
HQ: Benham Co's The LLC
     9400 Broadway Ext Ste 300
     Oklahoma City OK 73114
     405 478-5353

(G-8104)
BERGER TRANSFER & STORAGE INC (PA)
2950 Long Lake Rd (55113-1050)
PHONE.............................651 639-2260
William K Dircks, *CEO*
Andrew Clark, *Corp Secy*
Robert J Dircks, *Vice Pres*
Kevin Dunlevy, *Opers Mgr*
Thomas J Boehme, *CFO*
▲ EMP: 100 EST: 1910
SQ FT: 240,000
SALES (corp-wide): 89.92M **Privately Held**
SIC: 4731 4213 4214 Truck transportation
brokers; local trucking with storage;
long-distance moving services

(G-8105)
BERGIN FRUIT & NUT CO INC
2000 Energy Park Dr (55108-1506)
PHONE.............................651 642-1234
Thomas R Bergin Sr, *President*
John Bergin, *Treasurer*
Algirdas Vosylius, *Manager*
EMP: 90 EST: 1951
SQ FT: 30,000
SALES (est): 25MM-49.9MM **Privately Held**
WEB: www.berginfruit.com

SIC: 5145 5148 Wholesales salted or
roasted nuts; wholesales fresh fruits;
wholesales vegetables; manufactures food
preparations; manufactures nut & seed
products

(G-8106)
BERKLEY RISK ADMINISTRATORS CO
145 University Ave W (55103-2044)
PHONE.............................651 281-1200
FAX: 651 281-1297
Jim Miller, *Exec Dir*
EMP: 41
SALES (est): 1MM-4.9MM **Publicly Held**
WEB: www.wrbc.com
SIC: 6411 Insurance agency & broker
HQ: Berkley Risk Administrators Co
     222 S 9th St Ste 1300
     Minneapolis MN 55402
     612 766-3000

(G-8107)
BERWALD ROOFING CO INC (PA)
2440 Charles St N Ste 1 (55109-3050)
PHONE.............................651 777-7411
FAX: 651 777-1371
Eugene R Berwald, *President*
Kenneth Berwald, *Treasurer*
James M Blackford, *Finance Dir*
Collin Prochnow, *Human Res Mgr*
EMP: 150 EST: 1936
SQ FT: 60,000 **Privately Held**
SIC: 1761 Roofing contractor; sheet metal
work contractor; millwork

(G-8108)
BEST WESTERN SOUTH ST PAUL
701 Concord St (55107-2494)
PHONE.............................651 455-3600
Pravin Patel, *President*
Linsey Thompson, *General Mgr*
Ashley Mailheyar, *Sales Executive*
EMP: 40 EST: 2004
SALES (est): 1MM-4.9MM **Privately Held**
SIC: 7011 7299 Hotel; banquet hall facility

(G-8109)
BETHESDA HEALTHY REHAB
559 Capitol Blvd Fl 6 (55103-2101)
PHONE.............................651 232-2000
FAX: 651 221-2235
Timothy Hanson, *President*
Martin Paul, *Vice Pres*
Roger Green, *Vice Pres*
Stephen J Kolar, *Vice Pres*
Robert Gill, *Vice Pres*
EMP: 6700 EST: 1895
SALES (est): 500MM-999.9MM **Privately Held**
SIC: 8062 8069 8741 Medical hospital;
hospital management services; nursing &
personal care facility management services;
specialty hospital

(G-8110)
BETTER BUSINESS BUREAU OF MINN
Also Called: BBB OF MINNESOTA & NORTH DAK
2706 Gannon Rd (55116-2642)
PHONE.............................651 699-1111
FAX: 651 699-7665
Albert Hubtell, *President*
Bennett Weiner, *COO*
Barb Grieman, *Vice Pres*
Debbie Reetz, *Info Tech Mgr*
Maili Frison, *Director*
EMP: 40 EST: 1912
SQ FT: 7,500 **Privately Held**
SIC: 8611 Better Business Bureau

(G-8111)
BEVERLY ENTERPRISES - MN
2727 Victoria St N (55113-3029)
PHONE.............................651 483-5431
Michael Marchant, *Manager*
EMP: 200
SALES (est): 5MM-9.9MM **Privately Held**
WEB: www.beverlynet.com

SIC: 8051 8069 Skilled nursing care facility;
specialty hospital
HQ: Beverly Enterprises - MN
     650 Ramer Ave S
     Rush City MN 55069
     320 358-4765

(G-8112)
BEVERLY ENTERPRISES - MN
Also Called: Lynnhurst
471 Lynnhurst Ave W (55104-3408)
PHONE.............................651 645-6453
Wesley Dolittle, *Exec Dir*
EMP: 60
SALES (est): 1MM-4.9MM **Privately Held**
WEB: www.beverlynet.com
SIC: 8051 Skilled nursing care facility;
convalescent home
HQ: Beverly Enterprises - MN
     650 Ramer Ave S
     Rush City MN 55069
     320 358-4765

(G-8113)
BIG BROTHERS BIG SISTERS OF
2550 University Ave W Ste 410N
(55114-2013)
PHONE.............................651 789-2400
FAX: 651 789-2499
Kari Munson, *CFO*
Berit Griffin, *Marketing Staff*
Barbara Hamson, *Manager*
Terry Haney, *Manager*
Patrick Mohan, *Webmaster*
EMP: 70 EST: 1920
SQ FT: 14,600
SALES (est): 1MM-4.9MM **Privately Held**
SIC: 8322 Helping hand services including
Big Brother & others

(G-8114)
BIOMEDIX VASCULAR SOLUTIONS
4215 White Bear Pkwy (55110-7658)
PHONE.............................651 762-4010
FAX: 651 762-4014
John Romans, *CEO*
Meg Heim, *Vice Pres*
Mike Lobinsky, *Vice Pres*
Peter Crist, *Vice Pres*
Scott Leium, *Engineer*
EMP: 39 EST: 1997
SQ FT: 6,500
SALES (est): 10MM-24.9MM **Privately Held**
SIC: 7371 Manufactures microbiology &
virology diagnostic products; computer
software development

(G-8115)
BIX PRODUCE CO LLC
1415 L Orient St (55117-4067)
PHONE.............................651 487-8000
FAX: 651 489-1310
Troy Wilcox, *Opers Mgr*
Randy Wilcox, *Mng Member*
Beth Knops, *Manager*
EMP: 240 EST: 1930
SQ FT: 58,000
SALES (est): 100MM-499.9MM **Privately Held**
WEB: www.bixproduce.com
SIC: 5148 5143 Wholesales fresh fruits;
wholesales vegetables; wholesales fresh
dairy products

(G-8116)
BNSF RAILWAY CO
176 5th St E Fl 1112 (55101-1606)
PHONE.............................651 298-2121
FAX: 651 298-2574
Sarah Thronsedt, *COO*
Robert Brydges, *Vice Pres*
Doug Sinclair, *Vice Pres*
Roy Dahl, *Manager*
David Morton, *Data Proc Dir*
EMP: 230
SALES (est): 10MM-24.9MM **Publicly Held**
WEB: www.bnsf.com
SIC: 8721 4011 8741 Accounting, auditing
& bookkeeping services; management
services; long haul railroad
HQ: Burlington Northern Santa Fe
     2650 Lou Menk Dr
     Fort Worth TX 76131
     800 795-2673

(G-8117)
BONFE'S PLUMBING & HEATING SVC
505 Randolph Ave (55102-3615)
PHONE.............................651 228-7140
FAX: 651 281-0358
Wally Bonfe, *President*
George Heriot, *Vice Pres*
Charles Vrooman, *Controller*
EMP: 33 EST: 1992
SALES (est): 1MM-4.9MM **Privately Held**
SIC: 1711 Plumbing service

(G-8118)
BOSTON HEALTH CARE SYSTEMS INC
Also Called: Dayton Residence
1865 Old Hudson Rd (55119-4336)
PHONE.............................651 501-2378
Jeffrey Boston, *President*
Lori Lindgren, *Controller*
Erica Reinke, *Asst Controller*
Ann Arrigoni, *Manager*
Scott Boston, *CTO*
EMP: 180 EST: 1981
SALES (est): 5MM-9.9MM **Privately Held**
WEB: www.bhcsystems.org
SIC: 8361 Home for the mentally
handicapped

(G-8119)
BOWL RITE INC
Also Called: Midway Pro Bowl
1556 University Ave W (55104-3908)
PHONE.............................651 646-1396
FAX: 651 646-7372
Al Loth, *President*
Scott Koecholor, *Vice Pres*
EMP: 30
SQ FT: 32,000
SALES (est): 1MM-4.9MM **Privately Held**
WEB: www.midwayprobowl.com
SIC: 7933 Bowling center; cocktail lounge

(G-8120)
BRADSHAW GROUP
1174 Payne Ave (55130-3643)
PHONE.............................651 776-1551
FAX: 651 776-1505
James Bradshaw, *President*
Jane Bradshaw, *Vice Pres*
EMP: 50 EST: 1910
SQ FT: 4,000
SALES (est): 1MM-4.9MM **Privately Held**
WEB: www.thebradshawgroup.com
SIC: 7261 Funeral home

(G-8121)
BRANDT MURNANE
30 7th St E Ste 3200 (55101-4919)
PHONE.............................651 227-9411
Stan Haws, *President*
Thomas M Conlin, *Vice Pres*
John Brandt, *Vice Pres*
Daniel A Haws, *Vice Pres*
C T Koebele, *Vice Pres*
EMP: 70 EST: 1940
SQ FT: 25,000
SALES (est): 5MM-9.9MM **Privately Held**
WEB: www.murnane.com
SIC: 8111 General practice law office

(G-8122)
BRAUN INTERTEC CORP
1826 Buerkle Rd (55110-5245)
PHONE.............................651 487-3245
Robert Janssen, *Engineering*
Scott Bernard, *CFO*
Juli Durda, *Human Res Dir*
Bob Janssen, *Branch Mgr*
Eddie Wells, *Info Tech Dir*
EMP: 50
SALES (est): 5MM-9.9MM **Privately Held**
SIC: 8748 8711 8734 8742 Energy
conservation consultant; industrial hygiene
consultant; engineering services; testing
laboratory
PA: Braun Intertec Corp
     11001 Hampshire Ave S
     Minneapolis MN 55438
     952 995-2000

▲=Import ▼=Export
◆=Import/Export

(G-8123)
BREDEMUS HARDWARE CO INC
1285 Sylvan St (55117-4620)
PHONE..............................651 489-6250
E J Bredemus, *Principal*
Richard Bredemus, *Vice Pres*
Nick Bredemus, *Vice Pres*
EMP: 27 **EST:** 1955
SQ FT: 12,000
SALES (est): 10MM-24.9MM **Privately Held**
WEB: www.bredemus.com
SIC: 5072 Wholesales builders' hardware

(G-8124)
BREMER BANK (DH)
2100 Bremer Tower 445 (55101)
PO Box 107, Amery WI (54001-0107)
PHONE..............................800 908-2265
Dan Draxler, *President*
Brenda Olson, *Manager*
EMP: 40 **EST:** 1918 **Privately Held**
SIC: 6022 6162 State commercial bank;
mortgage & loan lending
HQ: Bremer Financial Corp
445 Minnesota St Ste 2000
Saint Paul MN 55101
651 227-7621

(G-8125)
BREMER FINANCIAL CORP
(HQ)
445 Minnesota St Ste 2000 (55101-2135)
PHONE..............................651 227-7621
Terry M Cummings, *Ch of Bd*
Stan K Dardis, *President*
Mike Palmer, *President*
Ralph Tillman, *President*
Patrick J Donovan, *COO*
EMP: 80 **EST:** 1943
SQ FT: 25,000 **Privately Held**
SIC: 6022 State commercial bank
PA: Otto Bremer Foundation
445 Minnesota St Ste 2250
Saint Paul MN 55101
651 227-8036

(G-8126)
BREMER FINANCIAL SERVICES
INC (DH)
445 Minnesota St Ste 2000 (55101-2135)
PHONE..............................651 227-7621
Stan Dardis, *CEO*
Patrick Donovan, *President*
Greg Chaplin, *Vice Pres*
Ann Hengel, *Vice Pres*
Carla Paulson, *Vice Pres*
EMP: 75 **EST:** 1973 **Privately Held**
SIC: 8741 7374 Management services; data
processing service
HQ: Bremer Financial Corp
445 Minnesota St Ste 2000
Saint Paul MN 55101
651 227-7621

(G-8127)
BRENNTAG GREAT LAKES LLC
2130 Energy Park Dr (55108-1506)
PHONE..............................651 204-4300
Emilio Colomer, *Managing Dir*
Jim Holcomb, *Member*
Jnrgen Buchsteiner, *Senior VP*
Lesley Burchett, *Sales Mgr*
David Haxton, *Manager*
EMP: 50
SALES (est): 25MM-49.9MM **Privately Held**
WEB: www.brenntagnorthamerica.com
SIC: 5169 Wholesales chemicals & allied
products
HQ: Brenntag Great Lakes LLC
4420 N Harley Davidson Ave
Milwaukee WI 53225
262 252-3550

(G-8128)
BRIGHTER BUILDING
MAINTENANCE
444 Pine St (55101-2453)
PHONE..............................651 293-1403
Kenneth Johnson, *President*
EMP: 45
SALES (est): 1MM-4.9MM **Privately Held**
SIC: 7349 Janitorial & custodial services

(G-8129)
BRINGS CO INC
600 Lakeview Point Dr (55112-3494)
PHONE..............................651 484-2666
Patricia Coan, *President*
Rita Willox, *Vice Pres*
Judy Micketts, *Accounts Mgr*
Julie Mitketts, *Director*
EMP: 25 **EST:** 1931
SQ FT: 31,400
SALES (est): 10MM-24.9MM **Privately Held**
WEB: www.bringsco.com
SIC: 5148 Wholesales fresh vegetables

(G-8130)
BRO-TEX CO INC
800 Hampden Ave (55114-1203)
PHONE..............................651 645-5721
FAX: 651 646-1876
Roger H Greenberg, *President*
Myra Greenberg, *Corp Secy*
Ed Freeman, *Vice Pres*
Arlys G Freeman, *Vice Pres*
Greg Conroy, *Plant Mgr*
▲ **EMP:** 98 **EST:** 1923
SQ FT: 200,000
SALES (est): 25MM-49.9MM **Privately Held**
SIC: 5087 Wholesales cleaning &
maintenance equipment & supplies; carpet
& rug mill

(G-8131)
BROCK WHITE CO LLC (HQ)
2575 Kasota Ave (55108-1504)
PHONE..............................651 647-0950
Jeff Leech, *General Mgr*
Richard D Garland, *Member*
Wayne C Brock, *Member*
Ted M Arthur, *Member*
Nora O'Leary, *Member*
EMP: 50 **EST:** 1954
SQ FT: 100,000 **Privately Held**
WEB: www.brockwhite.com
SIC: 5032 8611 Wholesales brick, stone &
related products; retails building products &
materials; wholesales concrete & cinder
building products; wholesales masons'
materials; wholesales concrete building
products; business association
PA: H Enterprises International
120 S 6th St Ste 2300
Minneapolis MN 55402
612 340-8849

(G-8132)
BROWN & BIGELOW INC (PA)
345 Plato Blvd E (55107-1211)
PO Box 64539 (55164-0539)
PHONE..............................651 293-7000
FAX: 651 293-7277
William D Smith Jr, *President*
Craig Smith, *Facilities Mgr*
Donna Atneosen, *Purch Agent*
Garry Hoden, *CFO*
Tom Rebeck, *VP Human Res*
▲ **EMP:** 250 **EST:** 1896
SQ FT: 200,000
SALES (corp-wide): 56.31M **Privately Held**
WEB: www.brownandbigelow.com
SIC: 5199 Wholesales advertising
specialties; prints lithographed calendars

(G-8133)
BROWN-WILBERT INC (PA)
2280 Hamline Ave N (55113-4241)
PHONE..............................651 631-1234
FAX: 651 631-1428
Jerry J Brown, *CEO*
C C Brown, *President*
Jack Ascheman, *Vice Pres*
▲ **EMP:** 30 **EST:** 1922
SQ FT: 45,000 **Privately Held**
SIC: 7261 Manufactures concrete products;
manufactures concrete or precast terrazzo
burial vaults; manufactures monuments &
grave markers; manufactures concrete
monuments; funeral home & services

(G-8134)
BROWNING-FERRIS
INDUSTRIES INC
742 Vandalia St (55114-1303)
PHONE..............................651 641-0009
FAX: 651 437-8488
Steve Shiner, *Manager*

EMP: 30
SALES (est): 5MM-9.9MM **Publicly Held**
WEB: www.republicservices.com
SIC: 4953 Refuse collection & disposal
services
HQ: Allied Waste Industries Inc
18500 N Allied Way # 100
Phoenix AZ 85054
480 627-2700

(G-8135)
BRUEGGER'S BAGEL BAKERY
111 Village Center Dr (55127-3007)
PHONE..............................651 486-7135
FAX: 651 486-7154
Shari Medland, *Manager*
EMP: 25 **EST:** 1996
SALES (est): 1MM-4.9MM **Privately Held**
SIC: 5149 Retails bagels; wholesales
bakery products

(G-8136)
BRUGGEMAN HOMES INC
3564 Rolling View Dr I (55110-7003)
PHONE..............................651 770-2981
FAX: 651 770-9273
Paul Bruggeman, *President*
Steve Laberg, *General Mgr*
Gretchen Bruggeman, *Corp Secy*
Homer F Bruggeman, *Vice Pres*
Gary Nelson, *Safety Dir*
EMP: 25 **EST:** 1957
SQ FT: 2,000
SALES (est): 5MM-9.9MM **Privately Held**
SIC: 1522 1521 Multi-family housing
construction; new single-family home
construction service

(G-8137)
BRYANSTON GROUP INC
Also Called: Days Inn-St Paul Nw Roseville
2550 Cleveland Ave N (55113-2601)
PHONE..............................651 636-6730
Sarah Taft, *Manager*
EMP: 25
SALES (est): 1MM-4.9MM **Privately Held**
SIC: 7011 Traveler accommodations
PA: Bryanston Group Inc
1886 State Route 52 52
Hopewell Junction NY 12533
845 223-3603

(G-8138)
BT AMERICAS INC
2665 Long Lake Rd Ste 300 (55113-2535)
PHONE..............................651 746-8590
Anthony Meger, *Plant Mgr*
Sandra Price, *Project Mgr*
Kathryn Klecker, *Branch Mgr*
Babu Sathyanarayana, *Consultant*
EMP: 100
SALES (est): 50MM-99.9MM **Privately Held**
SIC: 5065 Wholesales electronic parts &
equipment; wholesales electronic video
equipment
PA: BT United States LLC
2160 E Grand Ave
El Segundo CA 90245
310 335-4507

(G-8139)
BUDGET TOWING INC OF ST
PAUL
Also Called: Gus Post Towing
1145 Homer St (55116-3231)
PHONE..............................651 699-5690
FAX: 651 771-7085
Beverly Carlson, *President*
Mike Dorrion, *Vice Pres*
Roy Carlson Sr, *Manager*
EMP: 25 **EST:** 1987
SQ FT: 2,000
SALES (est): 1MM-4.9MM **Privately Held**
SIC: 7549 Automotive towing service

(G-8140)
BUERKLE BUICK LEASING CO
3350 Highway 61 N (55110-5212)
PHONE..............................651 484-0231
David Buerkle, *President*
Mary Buerkle, *Owner*
Jerry Fischer, *Corp Secy*
EMP: 150 **EST:** 1967
SQ FT: 69,000
SALES (est): 10MM-24.9MM **Privately Held**

SIC: 7359 7513 7515 Rental center; truck
leasing service, without drivers; passenger
car leasing

(G-8141)
BURNET HOMESELLING TEAM
4525 White Bear Pkwy # 2 (55110-7652)
PHONE..............................651 653-2520
Pam Steers, *Manager*
Chuck Stout, *Manager*
EMP: 80 **EST:** 1999
SALES (est): 10MM-24.9MM **Privately Held**
SIC: 6531 Real estate services

(G-8142)
BUSINESS DATA RECORD
SERVICES
201 9th Ave SW (55112-3211)
PHONE..............................651 631-8663
Mark Cloucier, *CEO*
Carrie Patee, *Manager*
Patsy Premo, *Manager*
Chris Goffin, *Info Tech Mgr*
Martha Mayer, *Executive*
EMP: 33 **EST:** 1984
SQ FT: 250,000
SALES (est): 1MM-4.9MM **Privately Held**
WEB: www.bdrs.com
SIC: 4226 Document & office records
storage services
PA: B & D Services Inc
2275 County Road C2 W
Saint Paul MN 55113
651 639-0447

(G-8143)
BUSINESS MICROVAR INC
2277 Highway 36 W Ste 300 (55113-3830)
PHONE..............................651 639-0575
John Hendrickson, *CEO*
Miles Longman, *Engineer*
Terry Johnson, *Engineering*
Carol Hendrickson, *Treasurer*
Kristin Rausch, *Mktg Coord*
EMP: 47 **EST:** 1985
SQ FT: 14,000
SALES (est): 5MM-9.9MM **Privately Held**
SIC: 7379 7372 Computer system
consulting services; operating systems
software publishing

(G-8144)
BWBR ARCHITECTS INC
380 Saint Peter St Ste 600 (55102-1316)
PHONE..............................651 222-3701
Stephen P Patrick, *President*
Donald R Thomas, *Corp Secy*
Brian B Buchholz, *Vice Pres*
Richard W Dahl, *Vice Pres*
James Davy, *Vice Pres*
EMP: 144 **EST:** 1922
SQ FT: 24,300
SALES (est): 10MM-24.9MM **Privately Held**
WEB: www.bwbr.com
SIC: 8712 7389 Architectural service;
interior decorating service; interior design
service

(G-8145)
C C SHARROW CO INC
301 County Road E2 W (55112-6859)
PHONE..............................651 489-1341
FAX: 651 489-1534
EMP: 30 **EST:** 1963
SALES (est): 1MM-4.9MM **Privately Held**
SIC: 5051 5072 Manufactures noninsulated
wire cable; wholesales hardware; metal
service center

(G-8146)
C U MORTGAGE SERVICES INC
500 Main St Ste 100 (55112-3269)
PHONE..............................651 631-3111
FAX: 651 746-6400
Brad Crandall, *CEO*
Kathryn Reifenberger, *Manager*
Steve Albers, *Info Tech Dir*
EMP: 52 **EST:** 1987
SALES (est): 5MM-9.9MM **Privately Held**
SIC: 6163 Mortgage brokers service
arranging for loans, using money of others

(PA)=Parent Co (HQ)=Headquarters (DH)=Div Headquarters
✿ = New business established in last 2 years

2011 Harris Minnesota
Services Directory

© Harris InfoSource 1-866-281-6415
353

(G-8147)
C W HOULE INC
1300 County Road I W (55126-5611)
PHONE...................651 484-6077
FAX: 651 484-8895
Bryan Houle, *President*
William Bonczek, *Vice Pres*
C B Donna, *Manager*
Donna CB, *Manager*
EMP: 80 EST: 1956
SQ FT: 4,600
SALES (est): 10MM-24.9MM **Privately Held**
SIC: 1623 1611 Sewer line construction; grading services; water main construction

(G-8148)
CANTEEN VENDING
1091 Pierce Butler Rte (55104-1524)
PHONE...................651 488-0515
Troy Thompson, *Manager*
EMP: 30
SALES (est): 10MM-24.9MM **Privately Held**
SIC: 5046 Wholesales coin-operated vending machines

(G-8149)
CAP REAL ESTATE
954 Minnehaha Ave W (55104-1543)
PHONE...................651 488-5567
FAX: 651 646-0523
Peter Ryan, *Partner*
EMP: 30 EST: 1981
SALES (est): 5MM-9.9MM **Privately Held**
WEB: www.caprealestate.com
SIC: 6512 Nonresidential building operator

(G-8150)
CAPITAL CITY TRAVEL INC
340 Cedar St Ste 1200 (55101-1120)
PHONE...................651 287-4906
FAX: 651 243-2334
Deborah Callahan, *President*
Grace Strangis, *Vice Pres*
Laura Burrow, *Treasurer*
EMP: 39 EST: 1983
SQ FT: 10,000
SALES (est): 1MM-4.9MM **Privately Held**
WEB: www.ctsrst.com
SIC: 4724 Tourist agency arranging transport, lodging & car rental

(G-8151)
CAPITAL EXPRESS INC
601 Campus Dr Ste 12 (55112-3001)
PHONE...................651 631-3595
Jack Johnson, *President*
EMP: 25 EST: 2006
SALES (est): 1MM-4.9MM **Privately Held**
SIC: 7389 Courier or messenger service

(G-8152)
CAPITAL MAINTENANCE SERVICES
3065 Spruce St (55117-1062)
PHONE...................651 773-9777
FAX: 651 773-5567
Nancy Lee, *Member*
Kevin Lee, *Manager*
EMP: 60 EST: 1990
SQ FT: 1,000
SALES (est): 1MM-4.9MM **Privately Held**
SIC: 7349 Building cleaning & maintenance services

(G-8153)
CAPITAL WOOD PRODUCTS CO
735 Olive St (55130-4436)
PHONE...................651 225-5613
FAX: 651 225-9286
Brian Dahl, *President*
James Juris, *Corp Secy*
Richard A Kaster II, *Treasurer*
Bill Juris, *Manager*
Dan Jensen, *Info Tech Mgr*
EMP: 45 EST: 1982
SQ FT: 50,000
SALES (est): 10MM-24.9MM **Privately Held**
WEB: www.capitalwp.com
SIC: 1542 Specialized public building contractors; manufactures partitions & fixtures; manufactures wood partitions & fixtures

(G-8154)
CAPITOL LIEN RECORDS & RES (PA)
Also Called: Minnesota Abstract & Title
1010 Dale St N (55117-5603)
PHONE...................651 488-0100
FAX: 651 488-0200
Tony Magnotta, *President*
Lisa C Magnotta, *Corp Secy*
Ryan Loberg, *Manager*
EMP: 35 EST: 1990
SQ FT: 15,000
SALES (corp-wide): 7M **Privately Held**
WEB: www.capitollien.com
SIC: 8732 6541 Research services; title abstract service

(G-8155)
CAPSTONE SERVICES LLC
1410 Energy Park Dr # 10 (55108-5249)
PHONE...................651 641-0042
Bob Hafdahl, *President*
Steven W Snell, *Vice Pres*
EMP: 175 EST: 1979
SQ FT: 2,500
SALES (est): 5MM-9.9MM **Privately Held**
WEB: www.capstoneservices.net
SIC: 8322 Referral services for personal & social problems

(G-8156)
CARDENAS & REYNOLDS ENTRPRS
Also Called: Quinlan Care Home
391 Pleasant Ave (55102-2333)
PHONE...................651 222-7200
Laura Reynolds, *CFO*
David Reynolds, *Treasurer*
Gwen Harris, *Director*
EMP: 60 EST: 1949
SQ FT: 2,500
SALES (est): 1MM-4.9MM **Privately Held**
SIC: 8059 Nursing home

(G-8157)
CARDINAL HEALTH 414 INC
1045 Westgate Dr Ste 100 (55114-1079)
PHONE...................651 645-9904
Tanya Spillum, *Pharmacist*
Todd Lamb, *Manager*
EMP: 30
SALES (est): 25MM-49.9MM **Publicly Held**
WEB: www.syncor.com
SIC: 5122 Wholesales pharmaceuticals
HQ: Cardinal Health 414 LLC
7000 Cardinal Pl
Dublin OH 43017
614 757-5000

(G-8158)
CARDINAL HEALTH INC
1933 County Rd 2 C (55113)
PHONE...................651 255-1383
Mike Rossman, *Exec Dir*
EMP: 74
SALES (est): 50MM-99.9MM **Publicly Held**
WEB: www.cardinal.com
SIC: 5122 Wholesales pharmaceuticals, drug proprietaries & sundries
PA: Cardinal Health Inc
7000 Cardinal Pl
Dublin OH 43017
614 757-5000

(G-8159)
CARDIODIAGNOSTICS INC
225 Smith Ave N Ste 500 (55102-2545)
PHONE...................651 292-0616
Victor H Tschida MD, *President*
Richard Guthrie MD, *Principal*
Charles Alexander III, *Corp Secy*
K W Baran MD, *Vice Pres*
S Adler MD, *Vice Pres*
EMP: 175 EST: 1978
SQ FT: 5,000
SALES (est): 10MM-24.9MM **Privately Held**
WEB: www.cardiodiagnostics.com
SIC: 8011 Cardiologist & cardio-vascular specialist

(G-8160)
CARE INSTITUTE INC
Also Called: Rosewood Estate
2750 Victoria St N Ofc (55113-2094)
PHONE...................651 482-1611
FAX: 651 482-0429
Julie Pitsenbarger, *General Mgr*
EMP: 50
SALES (est): 1MM-4.9MM **Privately Held**
SIC: 8059 Personal care home, with health care
PA: Care Institute Inc
10401 N Meridian St Ste 122
Indianapolis IN 46290
317 630-3150

(G-8161)
CARE NETWORK INC
2161 University Ave W # 203 (55114-1319)
PHONE...................651 647-5400
Tom Borchardt, *President*
EMP: 30 EST: 1992
SALES (est): 500-999K **Privately Held**
SIC: 7363 Temporary help service

(G-8162)
CARE PLANNERS INC ✪
1919 University Ave W # 114 (55104-3492)
PHONE...................651 645-9887
Elin N Ohlsson, *President*
Chris Hanson, *Manager*
EMP: 87 EST: 2008
SALES (est): 1MM-4.9MM **Privately Held**
SIC: 8052 Residential mentally handicapped facility

(G-8163)
CAREFACTS INFORMATION SYSTEMS
2140 County Road C W (55113-2501)
PHONE...................651 636-3890
FAX: 651 636-3894
Gordon Raup, *President*
Robert Rude, *Corp Secy*
Gregory Floyd, *Vice Pres*
Rob Rue, *Opers Mgr*
Mary Brown, *Accounts Mgr*
EMP: 28 EST: 1991
SQ FT: 4,000
SALES (est): 5MM-9.9MM **Privately Held**
SIC: 7372 Software publisher

(G-8164)
CAREMATE HOME HEALTH CARE INC
2236 Marshall Ave (55104-5799)
PHONE...................651 659-0208
Michael Aderinkomi, *President*
Linda Huebner, *Corp Secy*
Abiodun Odelana, *Marketing Mgr*
Kay Benschop, *Nursing Dir*
EMP: 140 EST: 1990
SALES (est): 1MM-4.9MM **Privately Held**
SIC: 8082 7361 Home health care services; nurses' registry service

(G-8165)
CARL BOLANDER & SONS CO (PA)
251 Starkey St Ste 1 (55107-1824)
PO Box 7216 (55107-0216)
PHONE...................651 224-6299
FAX: 651 223-8197
Mark Ryan, *President*
Richard O'Gara, *Senior VP*
Tom Skluzacek, *Foreman/Supr*
Tim Gillen, *CFO*
Greg G Anklan, *Accounting Mgr*
EMP: 62 EST: 1924
SQ FT: 26,000
SALES (corp-wide): 52.97M **Privately Held**
WEB: www.bolander.com
SIC: 1629 1794 1795 Earthmoving service; pile driving service; buildings & other structure demolition contractor; excavation & grading, building construction contractor

(G-8166)
CARLSON BUILDING MAINTENANCE
1857 Buerkle Rd (55110-5246)
PHONE...................651 481-9970
FAX: 651 481-0095
Roby A Hamme, *CEO*
Corey Maxwell, *President*
Nick Giese, *President*
EMP: 500 EST: 1978
SALES (est): 10MM-24.9MM **Privately Held**
WEB: www.carlsonbuilding.com
SIC: 7349 Floor waxing service; building cleaning service

(G-8167)
CARLSON-LAVINE INC
2965 Partridge Rd (55113-1119)
PHONE...................651 638-9600
FAX: 651 638-9626
Thomas E Shamp, *President*
Lori Baerg, *Accountant*
EMP: 40 EST: 1941
SALES (est): 10MM-24.9MM **Privately Held**
SIC: 1542 New commercial & office building construction; commercial & office building renovation & repair services

(G-8168)
CARMIKE CINEMAS INC
2430 Highway 10 (55112-1406)
PHONE...................763 785-1855
Jerry Bing, *Manager*
EMP: 60
SALES (est): 1MM-4.9MM **Publicly Held**
WEB: www.carmike.com
SIC: 7832 Motion picture itinerant exhibitors
PA: Carmike Cinemas Inc
1301 1st Ave
Columbus GA 31901
706 576-3400

(G-8169)
CARTRIDGE CARE INC
2256 Terminal Rd (55113-2516)
PHONE...................612 331-7757
Charles E Pydych, *President*
Brian K Quinlivan, *Corp Secy*
EMP: 36 EST: 1989
SQ FT: 15,000
SALES (est): 25MM-49.9MM **Privately Held**
WEB: www.cartridgecare.com
SIC: 5045 5084 Wholesales computers, peripherals & software; wholesales industrial machinery & equipment; manufactures computer peripheral equipment; photographic equipment & supplies

(G-8170)
CASA DE ESPERANZA
1821 University Ave W (55104-2801)
PO Box 75177 (55175-0177)
PHONE...................651 646-5553
FAX: 651 772-5407
Maria G Fressia, *Managing Prtnr*
Karen Smith, *Corp Secy*
Rosario Delatorre, *Manager*
Marina Lozano, *Manager*
Miguel Ramos, *Manager*
EMP: 25 EST: 1982
SQ FT: 3,233
SALES (est): 1MM-4.9MM **Privately Held**
WEB: www.casadeesperanza.org
SIC: 8322 General counseling services

(G-8171)
CASH REGISTER SALES INC
4851 White Bear Pkwy (55110-3325)
PHONE...................651 294-2700
FAX: 651 294-2900
David Sanders, *President*
Dave Schwartzbauer, *Division Mgr*
Tara Tracy, *Purchasing*
Bruce Mann, *VP Sls/Mktg*
William Oas, *CFO*
◆ EMP: 59 EST: 1927
SQ FT: 57,000
SALES (est): 10MM-24.9MM **Privately Held**
WEB: www.crs-usa.com
SIC: 5044 5065 Wholesales cash registers; wholesales accounting machines; wholesales electronic parts & equipment

(G-8172)
CASHILL SPAULDING PROPERTIES
616 Lincoln Ave Apt MGR (55102-2827)
PHONE..............651 225-8227
Mike Cashill, *President*
Alan Spaulding, *Corp Secy*
Larry Devore, *CFO*
EMP: 50 **EST:** 1992
SQ FT: 3,000
SALES (est): 5MM-9.9MM **Privately Held**
SIC: 6531 6513 Real estate management services; apartment building operator

(G-8173)
CATHEDRAL HILL HOMES LP
268 Dayton Ave (55102-4325)
PHONE..............651 291-1750
Joseph Holmberg, *Partner*
Kelly Mechavich, *Manager*
EMP: 99
SALES (est): 10MM-24.9MM **Privately Held**
SIC: 6513 Apartment building operator

(G-8174)
CATHOLIC AID ASSOCIATION
3499 Lexington Ave N # 201 (55126-8098)
PHONE..............651 490-0170
FAX: 651 765-6551
Michael G McGovern, *Ch of Bd*
Mary Fitzpatrick, *Corp Secy*
Dennis Olson, *Senior VP*
Deborah Gephart, *Vice Pres*
Cletus Tauer, *Vice Pres*
EMP: 50 **EST:** 1878
SQ FT: 36,000 **Privately Held**
WEB: www.catholicaid.com
SIC: 8641 6411 Fraternal association; life insurance agent

(G-8175)
CATHOLIC CHARITIES OF THE
Also Called: Seton Services
1276 University Ave W (55104-4101)
PHONE..............651 641-1180
FAX: 651 641-1005
Linda Ericson, *Office Mgr*
Mary A Sullivan, *Administrator*
R P Ulland, *Obstetrician*
Stephanie Abel, *Registrd Nurse*
EMP: 26
SALES (est): 1MM-4.9MM **Privately Held**
SIC: 8011 Clinic operated by physicians
PA: Catholic Charities of The
1200 2nd Ave S
Minneapolis MN 55403
612 664-8500

(G-8176)
CATHOLIC CHARITIES OF THE
Also Called: St Paul Offc
215 Old 6th St W (55102-1026)
PHONE..............651 222-3001
Kelly Helland, *Manager*
Linde Gassman, *Manager*
EMP: 50
SALES (est): 1MM-4.9MM **Privately Held**
SIC: 8322 Old age assistance; provides Catholic church services
PA: Catholic Charities of The
1200 2nd Ave S
Minneapolis MN 55403
612 664-8500

(G-8177)
CATHOLIC SERVICES FOR THE
Also Called: Marian Center of St Paul
200 Earl St (55106-6714)
PHONE..............651 793-2100
FAX: 651 771-4509
Sharon Bestland, *Facilities Dir*
Vicki Trobroxen, *Finance Mgr*
Stacey Dove-Jones, *Marketing Staff*
Janna Kovach, *Administrator*
Jeff Thorn, *Administrator*
EMP: 160 **EST:** 1977
SALES (est): 5MM-9.9MM **Privately Held**
SIC: 8051 8052 Skilled nursing care facility; intermediate care facility

(G-8178)
CATHOLIC YOUTH CAMP
2131 Fairview Ave N Ste 200 (55113-5410)
PHONE..............651 636-1645
Robert Nygaard, *President*
Ted Collins, *Corp Secy*
Margie Sandor, *Vice Pres*
John Breon, *Vice Pres*
Eric Schneeman, *Treasurer*
EMP: 40 **EST:** 1946
SALES (est): 1MM-4.9MM **Privately Held**
SIC: 7032 Summer camp

(G-8179)
CELEBRITIES UNLIMITED INC
Also Called: Field of Dreams
5825 Oxford St N (55126-8410)
PHONE..............651 482-9945
David L Phillips, *President*
Connie C Phillips, *Corp Secy*
Mark W Phillips, *Vice Pres*
EST: 1993 **Privately Held**
SIC: 7389 Retails gifts, novelties & souvenirs; business services at a non-commercial site

(G-8180)
CEMSTONE PRODUCTS CO
2058 Energy Park Dr (55108-1506)
PHONE..............651 645-0769
Ken Clark, *Manager*
Ric Ferguson, *Manager*
EMP: 35
SALES (est): 5MM-9.9MM **Privately Held**
WEB: www.cemstone.com
SIC: 5032 Manufactures ready-mixed concrete; wholesales gravel; wholesales construction sand

(G-8181)
CEMSTONE PRODUCTS CO
1520 Minnehaha Ave E (55106-4823)
PHONE..............651 774-7575
Pat Kinsel, *General Mgr*
Rick Torgeson, *General Mgr*
Randy Olson, *Manager*
EMP: 30
SALES (est): 10MM-24.9MM **Privately Held**
WEB: www.cemstone.com
SIC: 1442 Manufactures concrete curing & hardening compounds; manufactures ready-mixed concrete; construction sand & gravel mining

(G-8182)
CENTER FOR VICTIMS OF TORTURE
2356 University Ave W # 430 (55114-1860)
PHONE..............612 436-4800
Douglas A Johnson, *Branch Mgr*
EMP: 60
SALES (est): 5MM-9.9MM **Privately Held**
SIC: 8011 Physicians' office & clinic
PA: Center For Victims of Torture
717 E River Pkwy
Minneapolis MN 55455
612 436-4800

(G-8183)
CENTRAL TERRITORIAL OF THE
Also Called: Salvation Army Booth
1471 Como Ave (55108-2542)
PHONE..............651 646-2601
Jeff Strickler, *Administrator*
EMP: 30 **Privately Held**
WEB: www.salarmychicago.org
SIC: 8322 8699 Religious organization; crisis intervention center; charitable organization
HQ: Central Territorial of The
10 W Algonquin Rd
Des Plaines IL 60016
847 294-2000

(G-8184)
CENTURY 21 JAY BLANK REALTY
1255 Larpenteur Ave E (55109-4333)
PHONE..............651 645-5581
FAX: 651 644-0000
Jim Reiter, *Administrator*
EMP: 30 **EST:** 1964
SALES (est): 5MM-9.9MM **Privately Held**
WEB: www.century21jayblank.com
SIC: 6531 Residential real estate agency

(G-8185)
CENTURY SYSTEMS INC
Also Called: Sentry Systems Alarms
2182 4th St (55110-3013)
PHONE..............651 426-0975
FAX: 651 426-7871
Ron Olinger, *President*
EMP: 40 **EST:** 1963
SALES (est): 25MM-49.9MM **Privately Held**
WEB: www.sentrysystemsinc.com
SIC: 5063 7382 Wholesales electrical burglar alarm systems; security systems services

(G-8186)
CENVEO INC
Also Called: Mail-Well
2520 Como Ave (55108-1217)
PHONE..............651 645-0251
FAX: 651 659-3680
Ron Rebeck, *Vice Pres*
Michael Kuhl, *Controller*
Jim Bettinger, *Marketing Staff*
Kelly Hunstad, *Manager*
Stephanie Pape, *Manager*
EMP: 40
SALES (est): 10MM-24.9MM **Publicly Held**
WEB: www.mail-well.com
SIC: 5112 Wholesales envelopes; manufactures envelopes
PA: Cenveo Inc
1 Canterbury Grn
Stamford CT 06901
203 595-3000

(G-8187)
CHARLES SCHWAB & CO INC
401 Robert St N (55101-2005)
PHONE..............651 222-8600
FAX: 651 310-1339
William Schrader, *Branch Mgr*
Michael Sailbury, *Branch Mgr*
John Ostrand, *Manager*
Ben Fife, *Manager*
EMP: 76
SALES (est): 10MM-24.9MM **Publicly Held**
WEB: www.schwabrt.com
SIC: 6211 Security broker service
DH: Charles Schwab & Co Inc
101 Montgomery St Ste 200
San Francisco CA 94104
415 636-7000

(G-8188)
CHARLES STOUT
Also Called: Coldwell Banker
4525 White Bear Pkwy (55110-7651)
PHONE..............651 426-1671
Charles Stout, *Owner*
EMP: 45 **EST:** 1996
SALES (est): 5MM-9.9MM **Privately Held**
WEB: www.donsavesumoney.com
SIC: 6531 Residential real estate agency

(G-8189)
CHEROKEE BANCSHARES INC (PA)
607 Smith Ave S (55107-2617)
PHONE..............651 227-7071
R J Gesell, *President*
Heidi Gesell, *Chairman*
Mary King, *Manager*
Scott Larsen, *CTO*
EMP: 80 **EST:** 1983
SALES (corp-wide): 178.33K **Privately Held**
SIC: 6022 State commercial bank

(G-8190)
CHEROKEE STATE BANK
607 Smith Ave S (55107-2617)
PHONE..............651 290-6112
FAX: 651 291-6250
Heidi Gesell, *President*
George Ruth, *Exec VP*
EMP: 50 **EST:** 1908
SALES (est): 5MM-9.9MM **Privately Held**
SIC: 6162 6029 Mortgage & loan lending; commercial bank

(G-8191)
CHIANTI GRILL
1611 Larpenteur Ave W (55113-5702)
PHONE..............651 644-2808
Kevin Schloies, *Owner*
Bob Gillen, *Co-Owner*
EMP: 30 **EST:** 2002
SALES (est): 500-999K **Privately Held**
WEB: www.chiantigrill.com
SIC: 7299 Full service Italian restaurant; banquet hall facility

(G-8192)
CHILDREN'S DISCOVERY LEARNING (PA)
3665 Talmage Cir (55110-4160)
PHONE..............651 653-9871
FAX: 651 407-1078
Marty Walsh, *President*
EMP: 60 **EST:** 1980
SQ FT: 10,500 **Privately Held**
WEB:
www.childrensdiscoveryacademy.com
SIC: 8351 Group day care center

(G-8193)
CHILDREN'S HEALTH CARE INC
345 Smith Ave N (55102-2346)
PHONE..............651 220-6000
FAX: 651 220-5147
David J Schmeling, *Ch of Surgery*
Theresa Pesch, *Vice Pres*
Phillip M Kibort, *Vice Pres*
Paul Benassi, *Opers Staff*
Cindy Hammiller, *Envir Svcs Dir*
EMP: 600
SALES (est): 25MM-49.9MM **Privately Held**
SIC: 8069 Chronic disease hospital
PA: Children's Health Care Inc
2525 Chicago Ave
Minneapolis MN 55404
612 813-6100

(G-8194)
CHILDREN'S HEALTH CARE INC
2910 Centre Pointe Dr (55113-1182)
PHONE..............651 855-2800
FAX: 651 855-2850
Julianne Morath, *COO*
Susan Flanagan, *COO*
Keely Johnson, *Buyer*
Dongs Thorson, *Branch Mgr*
Bobbie Docks, *Manager*
EMP: 150
SALES (est): 5MM-9.9MM **Privately Held**
SIC: 8721 Accounting service; payroll services
PA: Children's Health Care Inc
2525 Chicago Ave
Minneapolis MN 55404
612 813-6100

(G-8195)
CHILDREN'S HOME SOCIETY
235 Marshall Ave (55102-1807)
PHONE..............651 228-7707
Wanda Miller, *Branch Mgr*
Karen Svendsen, *Manager*
EMP: 30
SALES (est): 500-999K **Privately Held**
SIC: 8351 Child day care service

(G-8196)
CHILDREN'S HOME SOCIETY
1605 Eustis St (55108-1219)
PHONE..............651 646-7771
FAX: 651 646-8676
Madonna King, *CEO*
David Pilgrim, *Vice Pres*
Daniel Smith, *VP Finance*
Larry Crawford, *Finance*
Pattricia Connelly, *Human Res Dir*
EMP: 330
SALES (est): 10MM-24.9MM **Privately Held**
SIC: 8322 8351 Social services center; child day care service

(G-8197)
CHRIS ELECTRONICS DISTRIBUTORS
2023 County Road C2 W (55113-1211)
PHONE..............651 631-2647
FAX: 651 631-3071

(PA)=Parent Co (HQ)=Headquarters (DH)=Div Headquarters
✪ = New business established in last 2 years

2011 Harris Minnesota
Services Directory

© Harris InfoSource 1-866-281-6415
355

Colleen Christianson, *President*
Gary Christianson, *General Mgr*
EMP: 25 **EST:** 1981
SQ FT: 12,000
SALES (est): 10MM-24.9MM **Privately Held**
WEB: www.chriselectronics.com
SIC: 5065 Wholesales electronic parts

(G-8198)
CHRIST'S HOUSEHOLD OF FAITH (PA)
355 Marshall Ave (55102-1809)
PHONE..............................651 265-3400
FAX: 651 227-9183
Verne H Butler Jr, *CEO*
Donald Alsbury, *President*
Vernon Harms, *Corp Secy*
Mark Alleman, *Treasurer*
Jana Johnston, *Librarian*
EMP: 70 **EST:** 1972
SQ FT: 96,000 **Privately Held**
SIC: 1521 5031 Single-family home general remodeling service; wholesales interior building materials

(G-8199)
CHRIST'S HOUSEHOLD OF FAITH
Also Called: Electronic Easel
23 Empire Dr (55103-1856)
PHONE..............................651 602-5600
FAX: 651 602-5601
Tony Gilewski, *Manager*
Dan Piepkorn, *Manager*
Vladimir Strezhnev, *CIO*
Sara Person, *IT/INT Sup*
EMP: 40
SALES (est): 5MM-9.9MM **Privately Held**
SIC: 7336 Publisher; commercial printing; commercial art & graphic design services; plate making services; typesetting service
PA: Christ's Household of Faith
　　355 Marshall Ave
　　Saint Paul MN 55102
　　651 265-3400

(G-8200)
CHURCH OF ST BERNARD
Also Called: St Bernard Grade School
1160 Woodbridge St (55117-4491)
PHONE..............................651 488-6733
FAX: 651 489-9203
Karen Cronin, *Business Mgr*
Michael Anderson, *Pastor*
Janet Hanson, *Human Res Mgr*
Rita Albert, *IT/INT Sup*
Laura Beltz, *Director*
EMP: 50 **EST:** 1890 **Privately Held**
SIC: 7933 8322 Provides Catholic church services; elementary & secondary school; community center; bowling center

(G-8201)
CHURCH OF ST MATTHEW
Also Called: St Matthews Pre-School
490 Hall Ave (55107-2845)
PHONE..............................651 224-9793
Stephen Adrian, *Pastor*
Ixia Velez, *Sales Staff*
Cindy Hoffman, *Exec Dir*
EMP: 75 **EST:** 1886
SQ FT: 5,000 **Privately Held**
WEB: www.st-matts.org
SIC: 8351 Provides Catholic church services; child day care service

(G-8202)
CITIGROUP GLOBAL MARKETS INC
345 Saint Peter St Ste 1800 (55102-1219)
PHONE..............................651 215-8400
FAX: 651 215-8408
Dennis Rowland, *Manager*
EMP: 43
SALES (est): 10MM-24.9MM **Publicly Held**
WEB: www.salomonsmithbarney.com
SIC: 6211 Securities broker & dealer
DH: Citigroup Global Markets Inc
　　388 Greenwich St Fl 18
　　New York NY 10013
　　212 816-6000

(G-8203)
CITY & COUNTY CREDIT UNION
144 11th St E (55101-2332)
PHONE..............................651 225-2700
FAX: 651 225-2770
Patrick Pierce, *President*
Oliver Walkingstick, *Senior VP*
Tom Coulter, *Vice Pres*
Steven Galarneau, *Vice Pres*
Jack Kennelly, *Vice Pres*
EMP: 50 **EST:** 1928
SQ FT: 16,141
SALES (est): 5MM-9.9MM **Privately Held**
SIC: 6062 State chartered credit union

(G-8204)
CITY OF SAINT PAUL
25 4th St W Ste 400 (55102-2607)
PHONE..............................651 266-6400
FAX: 651 292-7311
Cindy Morrison, *Office Mgr*
Howie Bell, *Manager*
Judy Barr, *Manager*
Bob Bierscheid, *Exec Dir*
Michael Hahm, *Director*
EMP: 45
SALES (est): 1MM-4.9MM **Privately Held**
WEB: www.stpaul.gov
SIC: 7999 Recreation center; general government administration office
PA: City of Saint Paul
　　15 Kellogg Blvd W Ste 390
　　Saint Paul MN 55102
　　651 266-8500

(G-8205)
CITY OF SAINT PAUL
Also Called: Parks & Recreation Dept
1250 Kaufman Dr N (55103-1060)
PHONE..............................651 487-8200
FAX: 651 488-4041
Victor Camp, *Director*
EMP: 40
SALES (est): 1MM-4.9MM **Privately Held**
WEB: www.stpaul.gov
SIC: 8422 Noncommercial zoological garden; local government land, mineral & wildlife conservation administration; government recreational program administration
PA: City of Saint Paul
　　15 Kellogg Blvd W Ste 390
　　Saint Paul MN 55102
　　651 266-8500

(G-8206)
CITY OF SAINT PAUL
Also Called: Public Works Dept
899 Dale St N (55103-1512)
PHONE..............................651 489-8871
John Maczko, *Branch Mgr*
EMP: 70
SALES (est): 10MM-24.9MM **Privately Held**
WEB: www.stpaul.gov
SIC: 1611 Highway & street maintenance service; local government transportation program regulation or administration; nonoperating government transportation department
PA: City of Saint Paul
　　15 Kellogg Blvd W Ste 390
　　Saint Paul MN 55102
　　651 266-8500

(G-8207)
CITY OF SAINT PAUL
Also Called: Street Maintenance Department
873 Dale St N (55103-1512)
PHONE..............................651 292-6600
FAX: 651 488-7847
Gary Erichson, *General Mgr*
Barb Crudo, *Office Mgr*
Kevin Nelson, *Manager*
Gary Ericson, *Manager*
Joe Lee, *Manager*
EMP: 66
SALES (est): 5MM-9.9MM **Privately Held**
WEB: www.stpaul.gov

SIC: 1611 Highway & street maintenance service; general government administration office; local general government administration office
PA: City of Saint Paul
　　15 Kellogg Blvd W Ste 390
　　Saint Paul MN 55102
　　651 266-8500

(G-8208)
CITY OF SAINT PAUL
Also Called: Office of Financial Services
25 4th St W Ste 600 (55102-1675)
PHONE..............................651 266-6789
FAX: 651 292-6421
Elizabeth Swanson, *Opers Mgr*
Kathleen O'Neill, *Office Mgr*
Jim Giebel, *Manager*
Jim Engfer, *Manager*
Joan Hoover, *Consultant*
EMP: 99
SALES (est): 5MM-9.9MM **Privately Held**
WEB: www.stpaul.gov
SIC: 8741 Management services
PA: City of Saint Paul
　　15 Kellogg Blvd W Ste 390
　　Saint Paul MN 55102
　　651 266-8500

(G-8209)
CITY OF SAINT PAUL
1964 Shryer Ave W (55113-5415)
PHONE..............................651 631-0700
EMP: 50
SALES (est): 1MM-4.9MM **Privately Held**
WEB: www.stpaul.gov
SIC: 8999 Information bureau
PA: City of Saint Paul
　　15 Kellogg Blvd W Ste 390
　　Saint Paul MN 55102
　　651 266-8500

(G-8210)
CITY OF SAINT PAUL
Also Called: Parks & Recreation Dept
1840 Edgcumbe Rd (55116-2406)
PHONE..............................651 695-3773
Adam Zirzachsipple, *Branch Mgr*
EMP: 30
SALES (est): 500-999K **Privately Held**
WEB: www.stpaul.gov
SIC: 7999 Non-membership swimming pool; local government land, mineral & wildlife conservation administration; government recreational program administration
PA: City of Saint Paul
　　15 Kellogg Blvd W Ste 390
　　Saint Paul MN 55102
　　651 266-8500

(G-8211)
CITY OF SAINT PAUL
Also Called: Parks & Recreation Dept
1431 Lexington Pkwy N (55103-1052)
PHONE..............................651 488-9673
Michael Hahm, *Branch Mgr*
Bobby Cotie, *Manager*
EMP: 25
SALES (est): 1MM-4.9MM **Privately Held**
WEB: www.stpaul.gov
SIC: 7992 Public golf course; local government land, mineral & wildlife conservation administration; government recreational program administration
PA: City of Saint Paul
　　15 Kellogg Blvd W Ste 390
　　Saint Paul MN 55102
　　651 266-8500

(G-8212)
CITY OF SAINT PAUL
500 Courthouse 15 (55102)
PHONE..............................651 266-8740
John Choi, *Principal*
EMP: 45 **Privately Held**
WEB: www.stpaul.gov
SIC: 8111 Government legal counsel & prosecution office; general practice attorney's or lawyer's office; local government legal counsel & prosecution office
PA: City of Saint Paul
　　15 Kellogg Blvd W Ste 390
　　Saint Paul MN 55102
　　651 266-8500

(G-8213)
CITY OF WHITE BEAR LAKE
Also Called: Department of Public Works
4701 Highway 61 N (55110-3227)
PHONE..............................651 429-8566
FAX: 651 407-5314
Dan Pawlenty, *Superintendent*
Gene Smith, *Manager*
EMP: 25
SALES (est): 1MM-4.9MM **Privately Held**
SIC: 1611 General highway & street construction service
PA: White Bear Lake City of
　　4701 Highway 61 N
　　White Bear Lake MN 55110
　　651 429-8526

(G-8214)
CITY OF WHITE BEAR LAKE
Also Called: White Bear Lake Sports Center
1328 Highway 96 E (55110-3651)
PHONE..............................651 429-8571
FAX: 651 429-8545
Bruce Bates, *Manager*
EMP: 50
SALES (est): 1MM-4.9MM **Privately Held**
SIC: 7991 7999 Health club; skating rink operation services
PA: White Bear Lake City of
　　4701 Highway 61 N
　　White Bear Lake MN 55110
　　651 429-8526

(G-8215)
CITY VIEW ELECTRIC INC
1145 Snelling Ave N (55108-2726)
PHONE..............................651 659-9496
FAX: 651 659-0905
Pat Kinsella, *President*
Wade Galloway, *Vice Pres*
EMP: 60 **EST:** 1986
SQ FT: 7,000
SALES (est): 5MM-9.9MM **Privately Held**
SIC: 1731 Electrical contractor

(G-8216)
CLEAN IMAGE MOBILE TRUCK WASH
497 Burgess St (55117-4701)
PHONE..............................651 484-7776
FAX: 651 481-7020
Randy Peterson, *President*
Gale Peterson, *Vice Pres*
EMP: 25
SALES (est): 500-999K **Privately Held**
SIC: 7542 Truck wash service

(G-8217)
CLUTCH & TRANSMISSION SERVICE (PA)
Also Called: Catco
2785 Long Lake Rd (55113-1131)
PHONE..............................651 636-4311
FAX: 651 636-5420
Harvey M Peterson, *Ch of Bd*
Tom Peterson, *President*
David Ecrdes, *General Mgr*
Joanne Peterson, *Corp Secy*
Dave Goldner, *Vice Pres*
EMP: 50 **EST:** 1949
SQ FT: 44,000 **Privately Held**
WEB: www.catcoparts.com
SIC: 5013 7699 Wholesales truck parts & accessories; wholesales clutches; hydraulic equipment repair services

(G-8218)
CLUTCH & TRANSMISSION SERVICE
Also Called: Catco
60 Sycamore St W (55117-5448)
PHONE..............................651 631-0959
Dave Gerdes, *COO*
Jane Wlazlo, *Vice Pres*
Jeff Merkling, *Manager*
Jim Horn, *Manager*
EMP: 56
SALES (est): 10MM-24.9MM **Privately Held**
WEB: www.catcoparts.com

www.HarrisInfo.com
356

2011 Harris Minnesota
Services Directory

▲=Import ▼=Export
◆=Import/Export

GEOGRAPHIC

SIC: **5013** 7699 Wholesales truck parts & accessories; wholesales clutches; hydraulic equipment repair services
PA: Clutch & Transmission Service
2785 Long Lake Rd
Saint Paul MN 55113
651 636-4311

(G-8219)
COBRA TRANSPORTATION SERVICES
301 Eaton St (55107-1607)
PHONE..............................651 552-1151
Craig Scott, *President*
EMP: 30 EST: 1989
SQ FT: 300
SALES (est): 1MM-4.9MM **Privately Held**
SIC: **4731** Freight transportation arrangement services; railroad freight agency

(G-8220)
COLDER PRODUCTS CO
1001 Westgate Dr (55114-1065)
PHONE..............................651 645-0091
FAX: 651 645-5404
Gary M Rychley, *President*
Jim Shingler, *Vice Pres*
Randy Nelson, *Engineer*
Dave Meyer, *Engineering*
Will Langton, *CFO*
EMP: 195 EST: 1978
SQ FT: 51,482
SALES (est): 25MM-49.9MM **Publicly Held**
WEB: www.dovertechnologies.com
SIC: **5084** Manufactures couplings; manufactures pipe fittings; wholesales industrial machinery & equipment; manufactures mechanical power transmission equipment
HQ: Dover Electronic Technologies
17542 17th St Ste 470
Tustin CA 92780
714 415-4110

(G-8221)
COLDWELL BANKER BURNET INC
1991 Ford Pkwy (55116-2099)
PHONE..............................651 690-8516
Kevin Knudsen, *Manager*
EMP: 50
SALES (est): 5MM-9.9MM **Privately Held**
WEB: www.ginnyandtim.com
SIC: **6531** Residential real estate agency
PA: Coldwell Banker Burnet Inc
190 Cobblestone Ln
Burnsville MN 55337
952 898-5100

(G-8222)
COLDWELL BANKER BURNET REALTY
821 Grand Ave (55105-3311)
PHONE..............................651 227-9144
FAX: 651 452-5481
Tina Gramm, *Principal*
Linda Rogers, *Vice Pres*
Darlene Flicek, *Vice Pres*
Jill Wentland, *Sales Associate*
Victor Wittgenstein, *Sales Associate*
EMP: 80 EST: 2003
SALES (est): 10MM-24.9MM **Privately Held**
WEB: www.stpaulmortgage.com
SIC: **6531** Real estate services

(G-8223)
COLDWELL BANKER BURNETT REAL
1991 Ford Pkwy (55116-1923)
PHONE..............................651 698-2481
Kathy Phillips, *Manager*
EMP: 80
SALES (est): 10MM-24.9MM **Privately Held**
SIC: **6531** Real estate agency & broker

(G-8224)
COLLINS ELECTRICAL CONSTR
Also Called: Convergent Media
278 State St (55107-1611)
PHONE..............................651 224-2833
FAX: 651 292-0392
Raymond M Barry, *CEO*
Leonard Deeg, *President*

Phil Myers, *Vice Pres*
Robert Werden, *Vice Pres*
Kerry V Koens V, *Project Mgr*
EMP: 250 EST: 1930
SQ FT: 18,000
SALES (est): 25MM-49.9MM **Privately Held**
WEB: www.collinselec.com
SIC: **1731** General electrical contractor

(G-8225)
COLLINS, BUCKLEY, SAUNTRY
332 Minnesota St Ste W1100 (55101-1306)
PHONE..............................651 227-0611
FAX: 651 227-0758
Sarah Batzli, *Partner*
Michael J Sauntry, *Partner*
Mark W Gehan Jr, *Partner*
William E Haugh Jr, *Partner*
Dan O'Connell, *Partner*
EMP: 32 EST: 1971
SQ FT: 17,000
SALES (est): 1MM-4.9MM **Privately Held**
WEB: www.cbsh.net
SIC: **8111** General practice attorney's or lawyer's office

(G-8226)
COLON & RECTAL SURGERY ASSOCS
1055 Westgate Dr Ste 190 (55114-1486)
PHONE..............................651 312-1500
FAX: 651 641-1720
Ann Lowry, *President*
Lynn Ganseveld, *Office Mgr*
Shelly Preer, *Office Mgr*
Anders F Mellgren, *Med Doctor*
Jeffrey J Morken, *Med Doctor*
EMP: 25 EST: 1968
SQ FT: 10,000
SALES (est): 1MM-4.9MM **Privately Held**
SIC: **8011** Occupational & industrial specialist, physician or surgeon office

(G-8227)
COMMERCE PARTNERS LLC
185 Plato Blvd W (55107-2007)
PHONE..............................651 292-8777
Jim Rutzick, *Member*
Sherman R Rutzick, *Member*
Mark Rutzick, *Vice Pres*
EMP: 60 EST: 1951
SQ FT: 2,000
SALES (est): 5MM-9.9MM **Privately Held**
SIC: **6513** 6512 Operators of apartment hotels; operators of commercial & industrial buildings

(G-8228)
COMMERCIAL PRODUCTS V H INDS
216 Wabasha St S (55107-1804)
PHONE..............................651 224-2831
FAX: 651 224-7214
Deby Gordy, *Human Res Dir*
James Munkholm, *Manager*
EMP: 30 EST: 2002
SALES (est): 1MM-4.9MM **Privately Held**
SIC: **7389** Business support services

(G-8229)
COMMERCIAL ROOFING INC
221 Ryan Dr (55117-1034)
PHONE..............................651 483-5298
FAX: 651 483-5387
Gene Hollister, *Manager*
Ryan Romer, *Manager*
EMP: 25
SALES (est): 1MM-4.9MM **Privately Held**
SIC: **1761** Roofing contractor
PA: Commercial Roofing Inc
3736 Carlton St
Barnum MN 55707
218 389-6922

(G-8230)
COMMERCIAL TRUCK & TRAILER REP
2275 County Road C2 W (55113-1009)
PHONE..............................651 639-2260
FAX: 651 634-3415
William R Dircks, *President*
EMP: 50 EST: 1988
SALES (est): 1MM-4.9MM **Privately Held**

WEB: www.commercialtrucktrailerrepair.com
SIC: **7538** General automotive repair services
PA: Berger Transfer & Storage Inc
2950 Long Lake Rd
Saint Paul MN 55113
651 639-2260

(G-8231)
COMMONBOND COMMUNITIES (PA)
328 Kellogg Blvd W (55102-1900)
PHONE..............................651 291-1750
Joseph Errigo Jr, *President*
William J Cosgriss, *Corp Secy*
Patrick J Donovan, *COO*
Mark A Scherer, *COO*
Kurt Keena, *Vice Pres*
EMP: 60 EST: 1974
SQ FT: 7,200
SALES (corp-wide): 44.65M **Privately Held**
SIC: **6552** Residential land subdividers & developers

(G-8232)
COMMONBOND HOUSING
328 Kellogg Blvd W (55102-1900)
PHONE..............................651 291-1750
Joseph Errigo Jr, *President*
Anne Kilpatrick, *Office Mgr*
EMP: 50 EST: 1975
SQ FT: 7,200
SALES (est): 5MM-9.9MM **Privately Held**
WEB: www.commonbond.org
SIC: **6531** Real estate management services
PA: Commonbond Communities
328 Kellogg Blvd W
Saint Paul MN 55102
651 291-1750

(G-8233)
COMMONBOND INVESTMENT CORP
328 Kellogg Blvd W (55102-1900)
PHONE..............................651 291-1750
Joseph Holmberg, *President*
EMP: 99
SALES (est): 10MM-24.9MM **Privately Held**
SIC: **6531** Real estate services

(G-8234)
COMMUNICATION MAILING SERVICES
429 Prior Ave N (55104-3793)
PHONE..............................651 645-5280
FAX: 651 641-6161
Ronald S Weislow, *President*
Sandra L Weislow, *Treasurer*
EMP: 40 EST: 1986
SQ FT: 22,000
SALES (est): 1MM-4.9MM **Privately Held**
WEB:
www.communicationmailingservices.com
SIC: **7331** Direct mail advertising service

(G-8235)
COMMUNICATION SERVICE FOR THE
2055 Rice St (55113-6807)
PHONE..............................651 297-6700
FAX: 651 296-2265
Jan Fland, *Exec Dir*
Katie Monroe, *Director*
EMP: 37 **Privately Held**
WEB: www.relaysd.com
SIC: **8399** Advocacy group
PA: Communication Service For The
102 N Krohn Pl
Sioux Falls SD 57103
800 713-6071

(G-8236)
COMMUNITY ACTION PARTNERSHIP
Also Called: Child Dev Ctr Head Start
586 Fuller Ave (55103-2245)
PHONE..............................651 224-4363
FAX: 651 731-6971
Maria Fitzgerald, *Sales Staff*
M Fitsgerald, *Director*
EMP: 50
SALES (est): 1MM-4.9MM **Privately Held**

SIC: **8351** Child day care service
PA: Community Action Partnership
450 Syndicate St N Ste 5
Saint Paul MN 55104
651 645-6445

(G-8237)
COMMUNITY ACTION PARTNERSHIP (PA)
Also Called: Headstart
450 Syndicate St N Ste 5 (55104-4127)
PHONE..............................651 645-6445
FAX: 651 603-5984
Deanna Dorsey, *Corp Secy*
Robert Daniels, *CFO*
Patrick Singel, *Treasurer*
Barry Dean, *Finance*
Kathy Forliti, *Info Tech Mgr*
EMP: 125 EST: 1965
SQ FT: 20,000
SALES (corp-wide): 26.43M **Privately Held**
SIC: **8322** Individual & family social services; meal delivery program; temporary relief services; social services center

(G-8238)
COMMUNITY DENTAL CARE
828 Hawthorne Ave E (55106-3252)
PHONE..............................651 774-2959
Andrew Peterson DDS, *Partner*
Vacharee Peterson DDS, *Partner*
EMP: 25 EST: 1982
SQ FT: 3,200
SALES (est): 1MM-4.9MM **Privately Held**
SIC: **8021** Dental office

(G-8239)
COMMUNITY SERVICES INC
2845 Hamline Ave N (55113-7127)
PHONE..............................651 631-6000
Dan Lindh, *President*
Valerie Alt, *Corp Secy*
EMP: 60 EST: 1958
SQ FT: 21,000
SALES (est): 1MM-4.9MM **Privately Held**
WEB: www.preshomes.com
SIC: **8051** Skilled nursing care facility
PA: Presbyterian Homes & Services
2845 Hamline Ave N # 200
Saint Paul MN 55113
651 631-6100

(G-8240)
COMO SKI CENTER
1431 Lexington Pkwy N (55103-1052)
PHONE..............................651 488-9679
FAX: 651 488-0691
Sandy Robinson, *Manager*
Bobby Cotie, *Manager*
John Schimpach, *Manager*
EMP: 40 EST: 1932
SALES (est): 1MM-4.9MM **Privately Held**
SIC: **7992** Public golf course

(G-8241)
COMPANION HOUSING PROGRAM INC
475 Cleveland Ave N # 101 (55104-5051)
PHONE..............................952 285-5950
Morris Matthews, *President*
EMP: 110 EST: 1996
SALES (est): 1MM-4.9MM **Privately Held**
SIC: **8059** Home for the mentally retarded

(G-8242)
COMPASS GROUP USA INC
1091 Pierce Butler Rte (55104-1524)
PHONE..............................651 488-0515
FAX: 651 488-8014
Sandy Schoenthaler, *Sales/Mktg Mgr*
Gary R Ista, *Manager*
Duane Goulson, *Manager*
EMP: 30
SALES (est): 10MM-24.9MM **Privately Held**
WEB: www.compass-usa.com
SIC: **5046** Wholesales coin-operated vending machines
HQ: Compass Group USA Inc
2400 Yorkmont Rd
Charlotte NC 28217
704 329-4000

(PA)=Parent Co (HQ)=Headquarters (DH)=Div Headquarters
✿ = New business established in last 2 years

2011 Harris Minnesota
Services Directory

© Harris InfoSource 1-866-281-6415

357

(G-8243)
COMPLETE REAL ESTATE SERVICES
3101 Old Highway 8 # 105   (55113-1069)
PHONE..............................651 287-3400
FAX: 651 287-3410
Jon E Helgason, *President*
Bob Villa, *Marketing Staff*
EMP: 34 **EST:** 1995
SQ FT: 6,000
SALES (est): 1MM-4.9MM **Privately Held**
WEB:
www.completerealestateservices.com
SIC: 6163 Loan broker

(G-8244)
COMUNIDADES LATINAS UNIDAS EN
Also Called: Clues
797 7th St E   (55106-5014)
PHONE..............................651 379-4200
FAX: 651 292-0347
Jesse Bethke, *President*
Tony Rodriguez, *Vice Chairman*
Robert Cera, *CFO*
Nichole Parsch, *Human Resources*
Stacy Opitz, *Manager*
EMP: 35 **EST:** 1978
SQ FT: 12,000
SALES (est): 1MM-4.9MM **Privately Held**
WEB: www.clues.org
SIC: 8322 General counseling services

(G-8245)
CONCEPT GROUP INC
190 5th St E Ste 200   (55101-1637)
PHONE..............................651 221-9710
FAX: 651 227-4591
John Ruddy, *President*
Brad Moore, *Exec VP*
Jay Troe, *Vice Pres*
Kevin Maheny, *Manager*
Brad Fairfield, *Info Tech Mgr*
EMP: 26 **EST:** 1972
SQ FT: 6,500
SALES (est): 1MM-4.9MM **Privately Held**
SIC: 7311 Advertising agency

(G-8246)
CONCORDIA CREATIVE LEARNING
930 Geranium Ave E   (55106-2610)
PHONE..............................651 793-6624
Kyle Knudson, *Principal*
EMP: 45
SALES (est): 1MM-4.9MM **Privately Held**
SIC: 8351 Child day care service

(G-8247)
CONESTOGA-ROVERS & ASSOCIATES
1801 Old Highway 8 NW Ste 114
(55112-2307)
PHONE..............................651 639-0913
FAX: 651 639-0923
Frederick Renn, *Engineering*
Brian Boevers, *Branch Mgr*
Kaie Kamm, *Manager*
Krisi Connors, *Manager*
Chuck Arnett, *Manager*
EMP: 37
SALES (est): 1MM-4.9MM **Privately Held**
SIC: 8748 8711 Environmental consultant;
engineering consulting services
PA: Conestoga-Rovers & Associates
       2055 Niagara Falls Blvd Ste 3
       Niagara Falls NY 14304
       716 297-6150

(G-8248)
CONSECO FINANCE CORP
1100 Landmark Towers   (55102)
PHONE..............................651 293-3434
FAX: 651 293-3622
Charles H Cremens, *President*
Mark Shepherd, *COO*
Barbara Didrikson, *Human Resources*
Andrea Willows, *Manager*
EMP: 200 **EST:** 1998
SALES (est): 100MM-499.9MM **Publicly Held**
WEB: www.consecofinance.com

SIC: 6141 Personal automobile & consumer
finance company; personal consumer
finance company; personal automobiles &
furniture financing
PA: Cno Financial Group Inc
       11825 N Penn St
       Carmel IN 46032
       317 817-6100

(G-8249)
CONSOLIDATED ENTERPRISES INC
Also Called: University Display Co
489 Prior Ave N   (55104-3420)
PHONE..............................651 646-7821
FAX: 651 646-1497
Mike Metzger, *Sales Executive*
Anne Vadnads, *Manager*
Tim Delaney, *Manager*
Julie Setter, *Info Tech Mgr*
Bilal Jones, *IT/INT Sup*
EMP: 186
SALES (est): 100MM-499.9MM **Privately Held**
WEB: www.wirtzrealty.com
SIC: 5182 Wholesales liquor
HQ: Consolidated Enterprises Inc
       680 N Lake Shore Dr # 1900
       Chicago IL 60611
       312 943-7000

(G-8250)
COOL AIR MECHANICAL INC
1441 Rice St   (55117-3864)
PHONE..............................651 489-8821
FAX: 651 487-8857
Charles Worms, *President*
Christopher Worms, *Corp Secy*
Mike Worms, *Vice Pres*
▼ **EMP:** 60 **EST:** 1966
SQ FT: 20,000
SALES (est): 5MM-9.9MM **Privately Held**
WEB: www.coolairinc.com
SIC: 1711 Mechanical contractor

(G-8251)
CORPORATE EXPRESS OFFICE PRDTS
1233 County Road E W   (55112-3738)
PHONE..............................651 636-2250
FAX: 651 638-8800
Doug Krysiak, *Vice Pres*
Greg McCleod, *Vice Pres*
Troy Zangs, *Sales Mgr*
Jan Gilbertson, *Chief Mktg Ofcr*
Greg McLeod, *Branch Mgr*
EMP: 150
SALES (est): 25MM-49.9MM **Publicly Held**
WEB: www.corporate-express.com
SIC: 5112 5021 5049 Wholesales stationery
& office supplies; wholesales school
supplies; wholesales office supplies; office
supply & stationery store; wholesales office
furniture
HQ: Corporate Express Office Prdts
       1 Environmental Way
       Broomfield CO 80021
       303 664-2000

(G-8252)
CORPORATE GRAPHICS INTL
1170 Grey Fox Rd   (55112-6908)
PHONE..............................651 494-1740
FAX: 651 494-1750
Tommie Braddock, *President*
Kamau Woodard, *VP Business*
Lorie Roux, *Accounting Staf*
Diane Seed, *Human Res Dir*
Diane Seep, *Human Res Mgr*
EMP: 120
SALES (est): 10MM-24.9MM **Privately Held**
WEB: www.cgintl.com
SIC: 5112 7336 Commercial printing;
wholesales business forms; commercial art
& graphic design services; manifold
business form printing; commercial
lithographic printing
HQ: Corporate Graphics Intl
       1885 Northway Dr
       North Mankato MN 56003
       507 625-2828

(G-8253)
CORPORATE TRAVEL SERVICES INC
340 Cedar St Ste 1200   (55101-1120)
PHONE..............................651 287-4900
Deborah Callahan, *President*
Grace Strangis, *Vice Pres*
Laura Burrow, *Treasurer*
EMP: 75 **EST:** 1974
SALES (est): 10MM-24.9MM **Privately Held**
SIC: 7372 Business & professional software
publishers

(G-8254)
CORRECTIONAL MEDICAL SERVICES
2336 Lexington Ave N   (55113-4336)
PHONE..............................651 631-0065
FAX: 651 631-0096
Dale Poliak, *Manager*
Dean Lee, *Manager*
Tiffany Quant, *Manager*
EMP: 65
SALES (est): 1MM-4.9MM **Privately Held**
SIC: 8099 Physical examination & testing
services
HQ: Correctional Medical Services
       12647 Olive Blvd Ste 400
       Saint Louis MO 63141
       314 919-8501

(G-8255)
CORVAL CONSTRUCTORS INC
1633 Eustis St   (55108-1219)
PHONE..............................651 642-0451
FAX: 651 642-5557
Paul C Jordan, *CEO*
Steven Poser, *Exec VP*
Richard Poser, *Exec VP*
Peter J Jordan, *Exec VP*
Michael Ahern, *Exec VP*
EMP: 110 **EST:** 1921
SQ FT: 40,000
SALES (est): 10MM-24.9MM **Privately Held**
WEB: www.newmech.com
SIC: 1711 1542 1761 1796 Mechanical
contractor; millwright; commercial & office
building contractor; plumbing service; fire
sprinkler system installation service; warm
air heating & air conditioning contractor;
sheet metal work contractor; manufactures
plastic pipe

(G-8256)
COUNSELOR REALTY INC
3580 Linden Ave   (55110-4667)
PHONE..............................651 779-6000
FAX: 651 779-6688
Jim Judge, *Corp Counsel*
EMP: 30
SALES (est): 5MM-9.9MM **Privately Held**
WEB: www.counselorrealty.com
SIC: 6531 Real estate services
PA: Counselor Realty Inc
       7766 Highway 65 NE Ste 1
       Minneapolis MN 55432
       763 786-0600

(G-8257)
COUNTY OF RAMSEY
Also Called: Information Services
50 Kellogg Blvd W Ste 550   (55102-1556)
PHONE..............................651 266-3400
Robert Porter, *Opers Spvr*
Dave Fenner, *Technical Mgr*
Gail Blackstone, *Human Res Dir*
Lora Sempf, *Manager*
Gregg Nelson, *Supervisor*
EMP: 60
SALES (est): 5MM-9.9MM **Privately Held**
WEB: www.rclreads.org
SIC: 7374 Data processing & preparation
services
PA: County of Ramsey
       15 Kellogg Blvd W Ste 270
       Saint Paul MN 55102
       651 266-8044

(G-8258)
COUNTY OF RAMSEY
Also Called: Ramsey County Care Center
2000 White Bear Ave N   (55109-3713)
PHONE..............................651 777-7486
FAX: 651 777-1426

Scott Kirchoff, *Purch Dir*
Chuck Kollasch, *Chief Engr*
Barb Ruza, *Manager*
Mona Ross, *Manager*
Patricia Reller, *Systems Dir*
EMP: 190
SALES (est): 5MM-9.9MM **Privately Held**
WEB: www.rclreads.org
SIC: 8051 Skilled nursing care facility;
county supervisors' & executives' office
PA: County of Ramsey
       15 Kellogg Blvd W Ste 270
       Saint Paul MN 55102
       651 266-8044

(G-8259)
COUNTY OF RAMSEY
Also Called: Park & Recreation Department
2015 Van Dyke St   (55109-3711)
PHONE..............................651 748-2500
FAX: 651 766-4008
William Schnieder, *Opers Staff*
Linda Koesling, *Accountant*
Tim Reynolds, *Manager*
Greg Mack, *Director*
EMP: 100
SALES (est): 1MM-4.9MM **Privately Held**
WEB: www.rclreads.org
SIC: 7999 Golf driving range
PA: County of Ramsey
       15 Kellogg Blvd W Ste 270
       Saint Paul MN 55102
       651 266-8044

(G-8260)
COUNTY OF RAMSEY
Also Called: Public Health Dept
90 Plato Blvd W Ste 200   (55107-2004)
PHONE..............................651 266-2400
FAX: 651 292-7794
Rob Fulton, *Director*
EMP: 160
SALES (est): 10MM-24.9MM **Privately Held**
WEB: www.rclreads.org
SIC: 8093 8322 Specialty outpatient clinic;
county supervisors' & executives' office;
individual & family social services
PA: County of Ramsey
       15 Kellogg Blvd W Ste 270
       Saint Paul MN 55102
       651 266-8044

(G-8261)
COUNTY OF RAMSEY
Also Called: Workforce Solutions
2098 11th Ave E   (55109-5112)
PHONE..............................651 770-4499
FAX: 651 779-5240
Rick Casperson, *Sales Staff*
Patricia Brady, *Director*
EMP: 70
SALES (est): 1MM-4.9MM **Privately Held**
WEB: www.rclreads.org
SIC: 8331 Job training & vocational
rehabilitation services; human resource,
social work & welfare administration
services; county government administration
of social & manpower programs
PA: County of Ramsey
       15 Kellogg Blvd W Ste 270
       Saint Paul MN 55102
       651 266-8044

(G-8262)
COURIER SYSTEMS LLC
1471 1st Ave NW   (55112-1904)
PHONE..............................651 628-0100
FAX: 651 628-9963
Todd Blank, *Member*
Tom Breyen, *VP Sls/Mktg*
Mark Jeglosky, *Manager*
EMP: 85 **EST:** 1998
SQ FT: 3,000
SALES (est): 5MM-9.9MM **Privately Held**
WEB: www.couriersystems.net
SIC: 7389 Courier or messenger service

(G-8263)
CRAMER INVESTMENT CO
775 Vandalia St   (55114-1304)
PHONE..............................612 861-7232
Richard Cramer, *President*
Lawrence Kanning, *Controller*
Nancy Kewitsch, *Mktg Dir*
Cleon Cathcart, *Manager*
Garet Porter, *IT/INT Sup*

▲=Import ▼=Export
◆=Import/Export

▲ **EMP:** 84 **EST:** 1973
SQ FT: 20,000
SALES (est): 25MM-49.9MM **Privately Held**
SIC: 5075 Wholesales heating & air conditioning equipment & supplies

(G-8264)
CRAWFORD & CO
2387 Rosegate (55113-2625)
PO Box 8008 (55108-0008)
PHONE..............................651 631-0055
FAX: 651 631-9414
Randy Malsam, *General Mgr*
Nancy Christensen, *Office Mgr*
Jason Hernesman, *Branch Mgr*
Randy Malsan, *Manager*
EMP: 45
SALES (est): 1MM-4.9MM **Publicly Held**
WEB: www.crawfordandcompany.com
SIC: 6411 Insurance claims adjusting service
PA: Crawford & Co
1001 Summit Blvd Ste 500
Atlanta GA 30319
404 300-1000

(G-8265)
CREATIVE LIGHTING
1728 Concordia Ave (55104-5226)
PHONE..............................651 647-0111
FAX: 651 647-9170
Solomon J Minsberg, *Ch of Bd*
Jonathan Minsberg, *Vice Pres*
Barbara Minsberg, *Treasurer*
EMP: 50 **EST:** 1926
SQ FT: 35,000
SALES (est): 5MM-9.9MM **Privately Held**
WEB: www.creative-lighting.com
SIC: 5063 Retails lighting fixtures; wholesales lighting fixtures

(G-8266)
CREATIVE MARKETING CONSULTING
1600 Gervais Ave Ste 8 (55109-2199)
PHONE..............................952 935-9385
Liz Deitrich, *President*
Bink Semmer, *Accounts Exec*
Lindsai Truebenbach, *Manager*
Molly Zweigle, *Manager*
EMP: 30 **EST:** 1995
SQ FT: 500
SALES (est): 1MM-4.9MM **Privately Held**
SIC: 7311 8742 Advertising consultants; management consulting services

(G-8267)
CREATIVE SUSTAINABLE SOLUTIONS ✪
Also Called: Cssi
909 Montreal Cir (55102-4296)
PHONE..............................651 602-6644
Greg Hosch, *CEO*
Robert Hosh, *Chairman*
Tom Depauw, *CFO*
Melissa Doumbia, *Manager*
EMP: 99 **EST:** 2008
SQ FT: 64,830
SALES (est): 10MM-24.9MM **Privately Held**
SIC: 1711 Plumbing, heating & air conditioning contractor

(G-8268)
CRESTLINE HOTELS & RESORTS INC
411 Minnesota St (55101-1703)
PHONE..............................651 291-8800
Dave Durbin, *President*
Paul Schirmers, *General Mgr*
EMP: 80 **EST:** 2003
SALES (est): 1MM-4.9MM **Privately Held**
SIC: 7011 Traveler accommodations

(G-8269)
CROSSROADS SOUTH METRO INC
Also Called: Re Max
2100 Ford Pkwy Ste 201 (55116-1950)
PHONE..............................651 698-8006
FAX: 651 698-7686
Scott Blanck, *General Mgr*
Brandon K Hedges, *Sales Associate*
Kaishawna Frazier, *Sales Associate*
Colleen Langford, *Sales Associate*
David H Levine, *Sales Associate*

EMP: 45
SALES (est): 5MM-9.9MM **Privately Held**
SIC: 6531 Residential real estate agency

(G-8270)
CROSSTOWN USED AUTO PARTS
218 Pascal St N (55104-6319)
PHONE..............................612 861-3020
Russ Payne, *President*
EMP: 30 **EST:** 1997
SALES (est): 1MM-4.9MM **Privately Held**
WEB: www.crosstownauto.net
SIC: 5015 5093 Wholesales used automotive parts & supplies; wholesales junk & scrap; tire dealer

(G-8271)
CROWN EQUIPMENT CORP
860 Vandalia St (55114-1305)
PHONE..............................651 645-8668
Bill Wade, *Branch Mgr*
EMP: 45
SALES (est): 5MM-9.9MM **Privately Held**
WEB: www.crown.com
SIC: 5084 Manufactures industrial trucks & tractors; wholesales industrial machinery & equipment
PA: Crown Equipment Corp
44 S Washington St
New Bremen OH 45869
419 629-2311

(G-8272)
CSL PLASMA INC
1054 University Ave W (55104-4707)
PHONE..............................651 646-2556
FAX: 651 646-0125
Darin Bargsten, *General Mgr*
Guy Stinson, *Manager*
EMP: 50
SALES (est): 5MM-9.9MM **Privately Held**
WEB: www.zlbplasma.com
SIC: 8099 Blood bank
PA: Csl Plasma Inc
5201 Congress Ave Ste 220
Boca Raton FL 33487
561 981-3700

(G-8273)
CSM CORP OF MINNESOTA
Also Called: Courtyard
2905 Centre Pointe Dr (55113-1105)
PHONE..............................651 746-8000
FAX: 651 746-8001
Elizabeth Feuerborn, *VP Sls/Mktg*
Joel Danko, *Manager*
EMP: 48
SALES (est): 1MM-4.9MM **Privately Held**
WEB: www.csmcorp.net
SIC: 7011 Traveler accommodations

(G-8274)
CUSTOM DRYWALL INC
488 Atwater Cir (55103-4400)
PHONE..............................651 488-0533
FAX: 651 488-8432
Albert W Carlson, *President*
Troy Carlson, *Vice Pres*
Staci Hammond, *Controller*
Jillian Sidler, *Manager*
Rich Furry, *Manager*
EMP: 155 **EST:** 1956
SALES (est): 10MM-24.9MM **Privately Held**
SIC: 1742 Drywall contractor

(G-8275)
CUSTOM MILLWORK INC
2298 2nd St N (55109-2935)
PHONE..............................651 770-2356
FAX: 651 770-0439
Kenneth Berwald, *President*
Mark Enright, *Corp Secy*
Eugene Berwald, *Vice Pres*
Jason Hjelmberg, *Plant Mgr*
Jack Lawrenz, *Credit Mgr*
EMP: 50 **EST:** 1976
SQ FT: 65,000
SALES (est): 25MM-49.9MM **Privately Held**
SIC: 5031 Wholesales millwork
PA: Berwald Roofing Co Inc
2440 Charles St N Ste 1
Saint Paul MN 55109
651 777-7411

(G-8276)
D W JONES TRUCKING INC
33 Acker St E (55117-5504)
PHONE..............................651 227-4854
FAX: 651 227-8187
Delane W Jones, *President*
EMP: 25 **EST:** 1981
SQ FT: 3,600
SALES (est): 1MM-4.9MM **Privately Held**
SIC: 4212 4213 Local farm to market hauling services; long-distance refrigerated trucking services

(G-8277)
DAHL CONSULTING INC
418 County Road D E (55117-1218)
PHONE..............................651 772-9225
FAX: 651 772-9250
Kenneth A Olsen, *CEO*
Kathleen Dahl, *President*
David Zimmel, *Corp Secy*
Tom Zine, *Controller*
Keith Guggenberger, *Marketing Staff*
EMP: 550 **EST:** 1993
SQ FT: 3,000
SALES (est): 50MM-99.9MM **Privately Held**
WEB:
www.recruitingmanagementsolutions.com
SIC: 7371 Applications software programming

(G-8278)
DAIRY QUALITY CONTROL INST (PA)
5205 Quincy St (55112-1438)
PHONE..............................763 785-0484
Paul Nierman, *CEO*
Frank Busta, *Ch of Bd*
Gene Quast, *President*
Donald Berg, *Vice Pres*
Kip Campbell, *Treasurer*
EMP: 34 **EST:** 1936
SQ FT: 6,800 **Privately Held**
WEB: www.dqci.com
SIC: 8071 Testing laboratory

(G-8279)
DAKOTA SUPPLY GROUP INC
475 Minnehaha Ave W (55103-1522)
PHONE..............................651 224-5781
Gregg Miller, *Branch Mgr*
Debbie Joehansen, *Info Tech Mgr*
Nadine D Ioia, *Receptionist*
EMP: 35
SALES (est): 10MM-24.9MM **Privately Held**
WEB: www.dakotasupplygroup.com
SIC: 5063 Wholesales electrical apparatus & equipment; wholesales electrical supplies; wholesales electrical construction materials
PA: Dakota Supply Group Inc
2601 3rd Ave N
Fargo ND 58102
701 237-9440

(G-8280)
DALCO ENTERPRISES INC
300 5th Ave NW (55112-3232)
PHONE..............................651 604-2966
FAX: 651 604-2961
Ted Stark III, *President*
Theodore Stark Jr, *Chairman*
Peter Stark, *Vice Pres*
Larry Tranberg, *Vice Pres*
Rod Dummer, *Vice Pres*
EMP: 80 **EST:** 1959
SQ FT: 77,400
SALES (est): 10MM-24.9MM **Privately Held**
WEB: www.dalconline.com
SIC: 5087 5113 Wholesales janitorial equipment & supplies; wholesales floor maintenance machinery; wholesales industrial & personal service paper

(G-8281)
DANA JOHNSON
Also Called: Johnson Assoc Consulting Group
1396 White Bear Ave N A (55106-2401)
PHONE..............................651 774-5843
FAX: 651 778-2949
Dana Johnson, *Owner*
EMP: 30 **EST:** 1986 **Privately Held**
WEB: www.danamjohnson.com
SIC: 7361 Executive placement & search consulting services

(G-8282)
DEGIDIO INC
Also Called: Degidio's
425 7th St W (55102-2730)
PHONE..............................651 291-7105
John Degidio, *President*
Anthony Degidio, *Corp Secy*
Terry Klatt, *Treasurer*
Joe Humenansky, *Treasurer*
EMP: 34 **EST:** 1935
SQ FT: 3,000
SALES (est): 1MM-4.9MM **Privately Held**
WEB: www.degidios.com
SIC: 7933 Full service barbecue restaurant; ten pin center

(G-8283)
DELL-COMM INC (PA)
4860 Mustang Cir (55112-1548)
PHONE..............................763 783-0035
FAX: 763 784-0097
Jim Freichels, *CEO*
Karen Aho, *President*
Kathleen Freichels, *Corp Secy*
Brad R Anderson, *Senior VP*
David A Marmonti, *Senior VP*
EMP: 78 **EST:** 1990
SQ FT: 18,500 **Privately Held**
WEB: www.dell-comm.com
SIC: 8711 1623 1731 4813 Engineering services; wired telecommunications carrier & service; underground utilities contractor; telephone equipment installation; retails telephone equipment & systems; ship, boat, machine & product design services

(G-8284)
DELTA ENVIRONMENTAL CONSLNTS (PA)
5910 Rice Creek Pkwy # 100 (55126-5023)
PHONE..............................651 639-9449
FAX: 651 639-9473
Gerard Sanderink, *CEO*
Gary M Wisniewski, *CEO*
Lisa A Hartwig, *Corp Secy*
John Platko, *Vice Pres*
Gregory W Drumm, *Project Mgr*
EMP: 88 **EST:** 1986
SQ FT: 16,948 **Privately Held**
WEB: www.deltaenv.com
SIC: 8748 Environmental consultant

(G-8285)
DELUXE CORP (PA)
3680 Victoria St N (55126-2906)
PHONE..............................651 483-7111
FAX: 651 483-7509
Lee J Schram, *CEO*
Katherine L Miller, *President*
S L Peterson, *Corp Secy*
Anthony C Scarfone, *Corp Secy*
David Hemler, *Senior VP*
◆ **EMP:** 500 **EST:** 1915
SQ FT: 160,000
SALES (corp-wide): 1.34B **Publicly Held**
WEB: www.dlx.com
SIC: 7389 Checkbook printing; manifold strip forms printing service; manufactures embossing seals & hand stamps; financial service; charge account service; check validation service; computer form printing; continuous business form printing

(G-8286)
DELUXE FINANCIAL SERVICES INC
3660 Victoria St N (55126-2906)
PHONE..............................651 787-2766
FAX: 651 481-4371
Carrie Larue, *Principal*
Todd Sather, *Technology Dir*
Rex Sand, *Assistant*
Jim Gullickson, *Analyst*
EMP: 100 **EST:** 1997
SALES (est): 10MM-24.9MM **Privately Held**
WEB: www.deluxebusinessforms.com
SIC: 6282 Financial investment advice service; manufactures blankbooks & looseleaf binders

(PA)=Parent Co (HQ)=Headquarters (DH)=Div Headquarters
✪ = New business established in last 2 years

2011 Harris Minnesota
Services Directory

© Harris InfoSource 1-866-281-6415
359

(G-8287)

DENNIS CO'S INC
551 Topping St (55103-1532)
PHONE...............................651 488-4835
FAX: 651 487-1731
Denise Zaske, *President*
Rich Dennis, *Vice Pres*
EMP: 30 EST: 1999
SQ FT: 6,000
SALES (est): 1MM-4.9MM **Privately Held**
SIC: 1799 Asbestos removal &
encapsulation contractor

(G-8288)

DEPENDABLE HOME HEALTH CARE
2984 Rice St (55113-2230)
PHONE...............................651 779-9810
Sarah Mensah, *President*
Jennifer Frantz, *Corp Secy*
Issac Mensah, *Vice Pres*
Thomas Mielke, *Director*
EMP: 40 EST: 1999
SALES (est): 1MM-4.9MM **Privately Held**
SIC: 8082 Home health care services

(G-8289)

DETAILS SALON & SPA
757 Cleveland Ave S Ste 4 (55116-1301)
PHONE...............................651 696-8700
Brian Horst, *President*
EMP: 35 EST: 1999
SALES (est): 1MM-4.9MM **Privately Held**
WEB: www.detailsmn.com
SIC: 7231 Unisex hair salon

(G-8290)

DEVELOPMENT RESOURCE GROUP INC
7295 Silver Lake Rd (55112-4446)
PHONE...............................763 783-7878
FAX: 763 786-8373
Terry Malley, *President*
Joe Williams, *Representative*
EMP: 70 EST: 1985
SQ FT: 2,000
SALES (est): 5MM-9.9MM **Privately Held**
SIC: 7371 Computer programming service

(G-8291)

DEY APPLIANCE PARTS OF CO
1401 Willow Lake Blvd (55110-5220)
PHONE...............................651 490-9191
Denny Dey, *CEO*
Dennis Roach, *Manager*
EMP: 53 EST: 1996
SALES (est): 50MM-99.9MM **Privately Held**
WEB: www.daydistributing.com
SIC: 5064 Wholesales household appliance
parts; retails appliance parts

(G-8292)

DEY APPLIANCE PARTS OF NORTH
1401 Willow Lake Blvd (55110-5220)
PHONE...............................651 490-9191
Denny Dey, *President*
EST: 1996 **Privately Held**
SIC: 5064 Wholesales household appliance
parts; retails appliance parts

(G-8293)

DEY DISTRIBUTING
1401 Willow Lake Blvd (55110-5220)
PHONE...............................651 490-9191
Dennis Dey, *President*
Peter Dey, *Owner*
Chris Cunningham, *Manager*
EMP: 50 EST: 1975
SALES (est): 5MM-9.9MM **Privately Held**
WEB: www.deydistributing.com
SIC: 5064 Retails appliance parts;
wholesales household appliance parts

(G-8294)

DEY DISTRIBUTING INC (PA)
1401 Willow Lake Blvd (55110-5220)
PO Box 10698 (55110-0698)
PHONE...............................651 490-9191
Denny Dey, *President*
Mark Dey, *Corp Secy*
Peter Dey, *Vice Pres*
Michael Elliott, *Manager*
EMP: 40 EST: 1944
SQ FT: 52,000
SALES (corp-wide): 11.86M **Privately Held**
SIC: 5064 Wholesales household appliance
parts

(G-8295)

DEY PROPERTIES
1401 Willow Lake Blvd (55110-5220)
PO Box 10698 (55110-0698)
PHONE...............................651 490-9191
Denny Dey, *President*
Mark Dey, *Corp Secy*
Peter Dey, *Vice Pres*
J Strauss, *Manager*
Dennis Roach, *Manager*
EMP: 80 EST: 1944
SQ FT: 50,000
SALES (est): 50MM-99.9MM **Privately Held**
WEB: www.deyproperties.com
SIC: 5064 Wholesales household appliance
parts; retails appliance parts

(G-8296)

DIGITILITI INC
266 7th St E Fl 4 (55101-2349)
PHONE...............................651 925-3200
Roy A Bauer, *Ch of Bd*
Ehssan Taghizadeh, *President*
William McDonald, *CFO*
Pamela Miner, *Director*
Mark Savage, *Director*
EMP: 45 EST: 2007
SQ FT: 8,736
SALES (est): 5MM-9.9MM **Publicly Held**
SIC: 7374 Data processing & preparation
services

(G-8297)

DIRK MILLER
Also Called: Emily Program
2550 University Ave W Ste 314N
(55114-1903)
PHONE...............................651 645-5323
Dirk Miller, *Owner*
EMP: 27 EST: 1993
SALES (est): 1MM-4.9MM **Privately Held**
WEB: www.dirkmiller.com
SIC: 8049 Clinical psychologist office

(G-8298)

DISABLE HOME HEAKLTH CARE INC
1086 Rice St Ste 2 (55117-4922)
PHONE...............................651 292-8705
FAX: 651 488-7364
Tong P Yang, *President*
MAI Yang, *Corp Secy*
Xolee L Yang, *CFO*
Lee Y Xolee, *CFO*
EMP: 110 EST: 2001
SQ FT: 7,200
SALES (est): 1MM-4.9MM **Privately Held**
SIC: 8059 Personal care home, with health
care

(G-8299)

DISCOVER PROPERTY & CASUALTY
385 Washington St (55102-1309)
PHONE...............................800 878-2660
EST: 2005 **Privately Held**
SIC: 6331 Property & casualty insurance
carrier; fire, marine & casualty insurance &
carriers; provides property damage
insurance

(G-8300)

DISTRICT ENERGY ST PAUL INC
76 Kellogg Blvd W (55102-1611)
PHONE...............................651 297-8955
Anders Rydaker, *President*
Pete Lujan, *Superintendent*
Joyce Anderson, *Vice Pres*
Ken Smith, *VP Opers*
Andrew Cassid, *CFO*
▲ EMP: 40 EST: 1979
SQ FT: 9,000
SALES (est): 5MM-9.9MM **Privately Held**
WEB: www.districtenergy.com
SIC: 4941 Water supply services

(G-8301)

DIVERSE COMPUTER CORP
2353 Rice St Ste 208 (55113-3744)
PHONE...............................651 766-8138
Timothy Proksch, *President*
EMP: 42
SALES (est): 5MM-9.9MM **Privately Held**
SIC: 7371 Computer programming service
PA: Diverse Computer Corp
W229N1433 Westwood Dr # 203
Waukesha WI 53186
262 524-5500

(G-8302)

DIVERSIFIED LABORATORY TESTING
5205 Quincy St (55112-1438)
PHONE...............................763 785-0484
FAX: 763 785-0584
Roy Ginn, *General Mgr*
Thomas Janas, *Member*
Cindy Zurek, *CFO*
Gary Krejcarek, *Manager*
Gretchen Bulthaus, *Manager*
EMP: 30 EST: 1936
SQ FT: 20,000
SALES (est): 5MM-9.9MM **Privately Held**
WEB: www.dqci.com
SIC: 8734 Manufactures standards &
calibrating equipment, laboratory; testing
laboratory
PA: Dairy Quality Control Inst
5205 Quincy St
Saint Paul MN 55112
763 785-0484

(G-8303)

DIVINE HEALTHCARE NETWORK
856 University Ave W (55104-4807)
PHONE...............................651 665-9795
FAX: 651 665-9796
Isaak Holby, *President*
EMP: 60 EST: 2000
SALES (est): 1MM-4.9MM **Privately Held**
WEB: www.divinecorporation.com
SIC: 8082 Home health care services

(G-8304)

DIVISION21 INC
2402 University Ave W Ste 702
(55114-1712)
PHONE...............................651 917-8805
FAX: 651 917-8808
Stephen Banks, *CEO*
Ralph Bartolotta, *President*
Mitch Leff, *Vice Pres*
David Tintes, *CFO*
EMP: 50 EST: 2000
SALES (est): 10MM-24.9MM **Privately Held**
WEB: www.division21.com
SIC: 1542 Store front construction

(G-8305)

DNK MANAGEMENT INC
3080 Centerville Rd Ste 1 (55117-1176)
PHONE...............................651 773-8077
David N Kloeber Jr, *President*
Lois Rehman, *Office Mgr*
EMP: 70 EST: 1988
SALES (est): 1MM-4.9MM **Privately Held**
SIC: 7389 8741 Telephone solicitation
service; management services

(G-8306)

DOLL ENTERPRISES INC
694 County Road B W (55113-4527)
PHONE...............................651 488-0228
FAX: 651 488-7742
John Doll, *President*
Carol R Doll, *Vice Pres*
EMP: 30 EST: 1972
SQ FT: 2,000
SALES (est): 500-999K **Privately Held**
SIC: 7231 Hairdresser; retails cosmetics

(G-8307)

DONATELLE PROPERTIES
501 County Road E2 Ext (55112-6860)
PHONE...............................651 633-4200
Charles S Donatelle, *President*
Michael J Donatelle, *Vice Pres*
Chad Ihle, *Manager*
EMP: 130

EST: 1970
SQ FT: 50,000
SALES (est): 25MM-49.9MM **Privately Held**
WEB: www.donatelleplastics.com
SIC: 6512 Operators of commercial &
industrial buildings

(G-8308)

DONNELLY ELECTRIC INC
1126 Rice St (55117-4924)
PHONE...............................651 487-2877
FAX: 651 487-2879
Edward J Sobanski, *President*
Clay Parks, *President*
Joe Sobanski, *Vice Pres*
EMP: 30 EST: 1945
SQ FT: 3,600
SALES (est): 1MM-4.9MM **Privately Held**
SIC: 1731 Electrical contractor

(G-8309)

DOODY MECHANICAL INC
1301 L Orient St Ste 1 (55117-3999)
PHONE...............................651 487-1061
FAX: 651 487-2637
Jim Torborg, *President*
William Beadie, *Corp Secy*
Richard H Doody, *Corp Secy*
Laurie Abel, *Vice Pres*
Tim Daly, *Vice Pres*
EMP: 50 EST: 1959
SQ FT: 30,000
SALES (est): 5MM-9.9MM **Privately Held**
WEB: www.doody-united.com
SIC: 1711 Mechanical contractor
PA: API Group Inc
1100 Old Highway 8 NW
Saint Paul MN 55112
651 636-4320

(G-8310)

DOWNTOWNER CAR WASH
520 7th St E (55101-2400)
PHONE...............................651 222-7045
FAX: 651 222-5019
Jay Montpetit, *Owner*
Jenny Rouse, *Sales Staff*
Michelle Montpetit, *Manager*
Abigail Goldsmith, *Manager*
EMP: 30 EST: 1975
SQ FT: 37,000
SALES (est): 1MM-4.9MM **Privately Held**
WEB: www.downtownercarwash.com
SIC: 7542 Car wash

(G-8311)

DPRA INC
332 Minnesota St (55101-1314)
PHONE...............................651 227-6500
FAX: 651 227-5522
Billy Hammerly, *Vice Pres*
May Sands, *Sales & Mktg St*
John Clement, *Manager*
Morris Zimmerman, *Manager*
Bob Binder, *Manager*
EMP: 25
SALES (est): 1MM-4.9MM **Privately Held**
SIC: 8748 8711 Economic consultant;
engineering consulting services
PA: DPRA Inc
10215 Tech Dr Ste 201
Knoxville TN 37932
865 777-3772

(G-8312)

DUNGARVIN ILLINOIS INC
690 Cleveland Ave S (55116-1319)
PHONE...............................651 699-6050
Timothy Madden, *President*
Diane Madden, *Vice Pres*
Robert Sannerud, *CFO*
David R Toeniskoetter, *Treasurer*
EMP: 88 EST: 1994
SQ FT: 14,000
SALES (est): 1MM-4.9MM **Privately Held**
SIC: 8322 8361 Individual & family social
services; residential care facility

(G-8313)

DUNGARVIN MINNESOTA INC
690 Cleveland Ave S (55116-1319)
PHONE...............................651 699-6050
Timothy Madden, *President*
Diane Madden, *Vice Pres*
David R Toeniskoetter, *Treasurer*

2011 Harris Minnesota
Services Directory

▲=Import ▼=Export
◆=Import/Export

EMP: 439 **EST:** 1988
SQ FT: 12,000
SALES (est): 10MM-24.9MM Privately Held
SIC: 8322 8361 Individual & family social services; residential care facility

(G-8314)
DUNGARVIN NEW MEXICO INC (PA)
690 Cleveland Ave S (55116-1319)
PHONE..............................651 699-6050
Timothy Madden, *President*
Diane Madden, *Vice Pres*
Robert Sannerud, *CFO*
David R Toeniskoetter, *Treasurer*
EMP: 60 **EST:** 1994
SQ FT: 14,000
SALES (corp-wide): 3.93M Privately Held
SIC: 8322 8361 Individual & family social services; residential care facility

(G-8315)
DUNN BROS COFFEE INC
1569 Grand Ave (55105-2229)
PHONE..............................651 698-0618
FAX: 651 698-9157
Doug Hinderaker, *President*
Kim Plahn, *CFO*
Kim Eickelberg, *Controller*
Lueann Hinderaker, *Controller*
Jody Hodge, *Bookkeeper*
EMP: 25 **EST:** 1987
SQ FT: 3,500
SALES (est): 1MM-4.9MM Privately Held
WEB: www.dunnbrosgrand.com
SIC: 5149 Retails coffee; wholesales green or roasted coffee; limited service coffee shop; retail mail-order house

(G-8316)
DYNAMAX INC
2395 Capp Rd (55114-1258)
PHONE..............................651 644-8787
FAX: 651 659-6415
Richard M Clelland, *President*
Dave Laforte, *Director*
EMP: 191 **EST:** 1978
SQ FT: 37,500
SALES (est): 10MM-24.9MM Privately Held
SIC: 4215 Package delivery services by vehicle
PA: Dynamex Canada Corp
2630 SKYMARK AVE SUITE 610
MISSISSAUGA Canada
905 2386414

(G-8317)
DYNAMEX OPERATIONS EAST INC
2100 Old Highway 8 NW (55112-1802)
PHONE..............................651 644-8787
FAX: 651 638-1802
Richard Barca, *Manager*
Pat Mackey, *Manager*
EMP: 60
SALES (est): 1MM-4.9MM Publicly Held
SIC: 4215 Ground courier services
HQ: Dynamex Operations East Inc
1870 Crown Dr
Dallas TX 75234
214 561-7500

(G-8318)
EAGLE ELEVATOR CORP
600 Fairview Ave N (55104-1710)
PHONE..............................651 645-1543
FAX: 651 645-1369
John Corbo, *President*
Kimberly Nordenstrom, *Vice Pres*
EMP: 33 **EST:** 1970
SQ FT: 4,500
SALES (est): 1MM-4.9MM Privately Held
WEB: www.eagleelevator.com
SIC: 7699 Elevators inspection, services & repair

(G-8319)
EAST METRO ENDOSCOPY CENTER
1997 Sloan Pl Ste 26 (55117-2051)
PO Box 14909, Minneapolis (55414-0909)
PHONE..............................612 870-5482
Peggy Farmer, *Member*
Allison Nestler, *Office Mgr*
Michelle S Kennedy, *Gastroenterlgy*

David A Ferenci, *Gastroenterlgy*
Sundeep Aurora, *Gastroenterlgy*
EMP: 30 **EST:** 1999
SALES (est): 1MM-4.9MM Privately Held
SIC: 8011 Gastronomist

(G-8320)
EAST METRO FAMILY PRACTICE
911 Maryland Ave E Ste 1 (55106-2655)
PHONE..............................651 776-2719
FAX: 651 772-1707
Thomas Lundsen, *Partner*
John Barsanti, *Partner*
Allan M Camy, *Partner*
Kimberly Turinske, *Partner*
Suzette Meyers, *Insur/Bill Sup*
EMP: 25 **EST:** 1952
SQ FT: 5,000
SALES (est): 1MM-4.9MM Privately Held
SIC: 8011 Clinic operated by physicians

(G-8321)
ECOSURE
370 Wabasha St N (55102-1323)
PHONE..............................651 293-4320
Gaetan Lamblise, *President*
David F Duvick, *Corp Secy*
Daria Durick, *Corp Secy*
Patricia Johnson, *Vice Pres*
Michael P Gustafson, *Vice Pres*
EMP: 37 **EST:** 2005
SALES (est): 5MM-9.9MM Privately Held
WEB: www.ecosure.com
SIC: 8742 Quality assurance consultant

(G-8322)
ECUMEN (PA)
3530 Lexington Ave N (55126-8164)
PHONE..............................651 766-4300
FAX: 651 766-4487
Kathryn Roberts, *President*
Nicole Koep, *General Mgr*
Glen Glancy, *Member*
Kathy Bakkenist, *COO*
Lisa Deverell, *Trustee*
EMP: 64 **EST:** 1863
SQ FT: 22,000
SALES (corp-wide): 486.51K Privately Held
WEB: www.augustanahomes.org
SIC: 8051 Skilled nursing care facility

(G-8323)
EDINA REALTY HOME SERVICES
2966 White Bear Ave N Ste 2 (55109-1323)
PHONE..............................651 770-1775
FAX: 651 779-2628
Erik Sjowall, *Sales/Mktg Mgr*
Jim Young, *Manager*
Randy Crosby, *Info Tech Mgr*
EMP: 100
SALES (est): 10MM-24.9MM Publicly Held
WEB: www.ilovetennis.net
SIC: 6531 Real estate agency & broker
HQ: Edina Realty Home Services
6800 France Ave S Ste 600
Minneapolis MN 55435
952 928-5900

(G-8324)
EDINA REALTY HOME SERVICES
4570 Churchill St (55126-2222)
PHONE..............................651 481-6711
Vickie Gay, *Manager*
EMP: 68
SALES (est): 10MM-24.9MM Publicly Held
WEB: www.ilovetennis.net
SIC: 6531 Real estate services
HQ: Edina Realty Home Services
6800 France Ave S Ste 600
Minneapolis MN 55435
952 928-5900

(G-8325)
EDINA REALTY HOME SERVICES
2137 4th St (55110-3037)
PHONE..............................651 426-7172
FAX: 651 653-4178
Joe Benson, *Manager*
Holly Hejda, *Administrator*
EMP: 52

SALES (est): 5MM-9.9MM Publicly Held
WEB: www.ilovetennis.net
SIC: 6531 Real estate agency & broker
HQ: Edina Realty Home Services
6800 France Ave S Ste 600
Minneapolis MN 55435
952 928-5900

(G-8326)
EDINA REALTY HOME SERVICES
735 Cleveland Ave S Ste 1 (55116-1307)
PHONE..............................651 698-2434
FAX: 651 690-8489
Tony Haider, *Sales Mgr*
Sheryl Craven, *Manager*
EMP: 54
SALES (est): 10MM-24.9MM Publicly Held
WEB: www.ilovetennis.net
SIC: 6531 Real estate agency & broker
HQ: Edina Realty Home Services
6800 France Ave S Ste 600
Minneapolis MN 55435
952 928-5900

(G-8327)
EDUCATION MINNESOTA (PA)
41 Sherburne Ave (55103-2119)
PHONE..............................651 227-9541
FAX: 651 292-4802
Dean Johnson, *General Mgr*
Mark Olson, *Vice Chairman*
Paul Mueller, *Vice Pres*
Marky Engler, *CFO*
Denise Specht, *Treasurer*
EMP: 70 **EST:** 1868
SQ FT: 50,000
SALES (corp-wide): 29.81M Privately Held
WEB: www.educationmn.org
SIC: 8621 Education & teacher association

(G-8328)
EHLERS & ASSOCIATES INC
3060 Centre Pointe Dr (55113-1122)
PHONE..............................651 697-8500
FAX: 651 697-8555
Steve F Apfelbacher, *President*
Nikki McDonald, *Member*
Jerry Shannon, *Member*
Melissa Stirn, *Member*
Nancy Demarais, *Corp Secy*
EMP: 30 **EST:** 1955
SQ FT: 14,000
SALES (est): 5MM-9.9MM Privately Held
WEB: www.ehlers-inc.com
SIC: 6282 Investment advisory service

(G-8329)
ELECTRO-WATCHMAN INC
1 Water St W Ste 110 (55107-2097)
PHONE..............................651 227-8461
FAX: 651 312-1296
Brian L Bertram, *CEO*
Darryl Hersrud, *President*
Sandy Bailey, *Corp Secy*
Jay Helseth, *Vice Pres*
Carol Gerlach, *Treasurer*
EMP: 34 **EST:** 1921
SQ FT: 7,000
SALES (est): 1MM-4.9MM Privately Held
SIC: 7382 1731 Burglar alarm maintenance & monitoring service; access control systems specialization contractor; closed circuit television installation; fire detection & burglar alarm systems specialization contractor; fire alarm maintenance & monitoring service

(G-8330)
ELECTRONIC CHECK ALLIANCE
Also Called: Infinity Marketing Group Minn
332 Minnesota St Ste W820 (55101-1378)
PHONE..............................952 445-2888
Steve Robbins, *President*
Kelly Robbins, *Corp Secy*
Ray Robbins, *VP Opers*
EMP: 30 **EST:** 1991
SQ FT: 2,200
SALES (est): 10MM-24.9MM Privately Held
WEB: www.electronic-cap.com
SIC: 7389 Check validation service

(G-8331)
ELECTRONIC COMMUNICATION SYSTS ✿
2300 Territorial Rd (55114-1637)
PHONE..............................651 735-7470
Jerome Hein, *President*
Sherry Banaszewski, *Treasurer*
Kelly Coates, *Manager*
EMP: 69 **EST:** 2009
SALES (est): 5MM-9.9MM Privately Held
SIC: 1731 General electrical contractor

(G-8332)
ELENAS CARE INC
Also Called: Communities of Care Pediatric
500 Highway 96 W Ste 100 (55126-1959)
PHONE..............................651 482-0549
Joan Vaughn, *President*
EMP: 80 **EST:** 1999
SALES (est): 1MM-4.9MM Privately Held
SIC: 8082 8742 Home health care services; business management consultant

(G-8333)
ELLERMEDIA GROUP
8466 Eastwood Rd (55112-4614)
PHONE..............................612 369-5612
Tim Fedarko, *General Mgr*
EMP: 50 **EST:** 2003
SALES (est): 1MM-4.9MM Privately Held
SIC: 7389 Business support services

(G-8334)
EM - TY CORP
Also Called: Days Inn
1964 University Ave W (55104-3432)
PHONE..............................651 645-0311
FAX: 651 645-0243
Michael Berg, *President*
Cy Sheehy, *Principal*
Jack Ritt, *Principal*
EMP: 60 **EST:** 1965
SALES (est): 1MM-4.9MM Privately Held
SIC: 7011 Traveler accommodations

(G-8335)
EMA GROUP INC (PA)
1970 Oakcrest Ave Ste 300 (55113-2630)
PHONE..............................651 639-5600
Terrance E Brueck, *President*
Bruce Bialka, *Corp Secy*
Mark G Wehmeyer, *Vice Pres*
Clyde S Younkin, *Treasurer*
Suzanne Kochevar, *Manager*
EMP: 36 **EST:** 1975
SQ FT: 45,300
SALES (corp-wide): 22.94M Privately Held
SIC: 8711 Engineering consulting services

(G-8336)
EMA INC (HQ)
1970 Oakcrest Ave Ste 300 (55113-2630)
PHONE..............................651 639-5600
Alan Manning, *Ch of Bd*
Terry Brueck, *President*
Clyde Younkin, *COO*
Craig Yokopenic, *Exec VP*
Judithann M Cascio, *Vice Pres*
EMP: 40 **EST:** 1984
SALES (corp-wide): 22.94M Privately Held
WEB: www.ema-inc.com
SIC: 8711 8742 Engineering consulting services; management consulting services
PA: EMA Group Inc
1970 Oakcrest Ave Ste 300
Saint Paul MN 55113
651 639-5600

(G-8337)
EMA INC
1970 Oakcrest Ave Ste 300 (55113-2624)
PHONE..............................651 639-5600
Terry Brueck, *President*
Clyde Younkin, *COO*
Mark Wehmeyer, *Exec VP*
Suzanne Kochevar, *Vice Pres*
Bruce Bailka, *Finance Dir*
EST: 1984
SQ FT: 24,759 Privately Held
SIC: 8711 Engineering consulting services
PA: EMA Group Inc
1970 Oakcrest Ave Ste 300
Saint Paul MN 55113
651 639-5600

(PA)=Parent Co (HQ)=Headquarters (DH)=Div Headquarters
✿ = New business established in last 2 years

2011 Harris Minnesota
Services Directory

© Harris InfoSource 1-866-281-6415

361

GEOGRAPHIC (side tab)

(G-8338)
EMBERS AMERICA LLC (PA)
2561 Territorial Rd (55114-1500)
PHONE.............................651 645-6473
Henry S Kristal, *Ch of Bd*
David Kristal, *President*
Jennifer Translow, *Accounts Mgr*
John Eisenschenk, *Manager*
EMP: 25 EST: 1956 **Privately Held**
SIC: 6794 Selling or licensing of franchises;
full service ethnic food restaurant

(G-8339)
ENCOMPASS GROUP LLC
2609 Territorial Rd (55114-1009)
PHONE.............................651 646-6600
Javier Zamora, *General Mgr*
Don Quaintance, *Purch Agent*
Al Adamson, *Human Res Mgr*
David Huelssbeck, *Branch Mgr*
William Corty, *Manager*
EMP: 73
SALES (est): 10MM-24.9MM **Privately Held**
SIC: 5023 5021 5131 Wholesales textile
sheets; manufactures linen fabrics;
manufactures household furnishings;
wholesales table linens; wholesales
curtains; wholesales carpets; wholesales
woven linen piece goods; wholesales woven
textiles; manmade broadwoven fabric mill
HQ: Encompass Group LLC
615 Macon Rd
McDonough GA 30253
770 957-3981

(G-8340)
ENCOMPASS GROUP LLC
Also Called: Hospitex Lintex
2609 Territorial Rd (55114-1009)
PHONE.............................651 646-6600
Geoff Mayo, *VP Opers*
Craig Jacobson, *VP Mfg*
Don Quaintance, *Purchasing*
Al Adamson, *Human Res Mgr*
William Corty, *Manager*
EMP: 109
SALES (est): 25MM-49.9MM **Privately Held**
SIC: 5023 5021 5131 Wholesales textile
sheets; manufactures linen fabrics;
wholesales table linens; wholesales
curtains; wholesales carpets; wholesales
woven linen piece goods; wholesales woven
textiles; wholesales mattresses
HQ: Encompass Group LLC
615 Macon Rd
McDonough GA 30253
770 957-3981

(G-8341)
ENRICH INC
3754 Rustic Pl (55126-7036)
PHONE.............................651 482-9608
Anthony Jordon, *President*
Jeanee Jordon, *Vice Pres*
EMP: 34 EST: 1990
SALES (est): 1MM-4.9MM **Privately Held**
SIC: 8361 Group foster home

(G-8342)
ENVIRONMENTAL PLANT SVCS INC
2315 Hampden Ave (55114-1204)
PHONE.............................651 644-4301
Ronald Gagnon, *Ch of Bd*
Lance Pickerign, *President*
Peter Gagnon, *Corp Secy*
Gary Jaje, *Vice Pres*
Patty Pietsch, *Accountant*
EMP: 28 EST: 2005
SQ FT: 750
SALES (est): 1MM-4.9MM **Privately Held**
SIC: 1711 Plumbing, heating & air
conditioning contractor

(G-8343)
ENVOY MEDICAL CORP
5000 Township Pkwy (55110-5852)
PHONE.............................651 361-8000
Michael Spearmen, *CEO*
Kurt Hanson, *Opers Mgr*
Kevin Verzal, *Opers Mgr*
Pamela Johnson, *Controller*
EMP: 30 EST: 1995 **Privately Held**
WEB: www.envoymedical.com

SIC: 8733 Research institute; medical
research organization

(G-8344)
EPISCOPAL CHURCH HOME OF MN
1879 Feronia Ave (55104-3549)
PHONE.............................651 646-4061
FAX: 651 646-2079
Bob Rau, *President*
Mark Ladwig, *Manager*
Mike Karel, *Administrator*
J Magili, *Director*
C Fabricuis, *Nursing Dir*
EMP: 175 EST: 1897
SALES (est): 5MM-9.9MM **Privately Held**
SIC: 8051 8052 Skilled nursing care facility;
intermediate care facility

(G-8345)
ESTETICA
165 Western Ave N Ste 3 (55102-4613)
PHONE.............................651 228-9327
Andrew Jergins, *CEO*
Lee A Jergins, *President*
Justin Donegan, *Executive*
EMP: 27 EST: 1987
SQ FT: 4,500
SALES (est): 500-999K **Privately Held**
WEB: www.esteticastpaul.com
SIC: 7231 Beauty salon

(G-8346)
EVALUMED
17 Exchange St W Ste 110 (55102-1034)
PHONE.............................651 767-0220
FAX: 651 767-0221
Stephanie Rozman, *CEO*
Victoria Rudd, *COO*
EMP: 45 EST: 1995
SALES (est): 5MM-9.9MM **Privately Held**
WEB: www.evalumed.com
SIC: 6411 Insurance services

(G-8347)
EVANGELICAL LUTHERAN GOOD
Also Called: Good Samaritan Soc Maplewood
550 Roselawn Ave E (55117-2120)
PHONE.............................651 774-9765
FAX: 651 774-0831
Tassa Nelson, *Human Res Dir*
Cindy Ballis, *Office Mgr*
Susan Jensen, *Administrator*
A Karpinski, *CTO*
Dennis Hoffman, *Director*
EMP: 200
SALES (est): 5MM-9.9MM **Privately Held**
WEB: www.good-sam.com
SIC: 8051 Skilled nursing care facility
PA: Evangelical Lutheran Good
4800 W 57th St
Sioux Falls SD 57108
605 362-3100

(G-8348)
EVANGELICAL LUTHERAN GOOD
Also Called: Whitehouse Health Care Center
563 County Road B W (55113-6509)
PHONE.............................651 489-8851
Steve Forester, *Principal*
EMP: 90
SALES (est): 1MM-4.9MM **Privately Held**
WEB: www.good-sam.com
SIC: 8322 Adult daycare center
PA: Evangelical Lutheran Good
4800 W 57th St
Sioux Falls SD 57108
605 362-3100

(G-8349)
EVER-GREEN ENERGY LLC
345 Saint Peter St # 1350 (55102-4410)
PHONE.............................651 290-2812
Ander Rydacker, *Member*
Ken Smith, *Member*
Mike Burns, *Vice Pres*
Andrew Kasid Sr, *VP Finance*
Brenda Nelson, *VP Human Res*
EMP: 75 EST: 1998
SALES (est): 25MM-49.9MM **Privately Held**
SIC: 4939 Combination utilities services

(G-8350)
EWALD CONSULTING GROUP INC
1000 Westgate Dr Ste 252 (55114-1469)
PHONE.............................651 290-6260
David Ewald, *President*
EMP: 48 EST: 1982
SQ FT: 7,000
SALES (est): 5MM-9.9MM **Privately Held**
SIC: 8742 Management consulting services

(G-8351)
EXCEL AIR SYSTEM INC
2075 Prosperity Rd (55109-3621)
PHONE.............................651 779-9725
FAX: 651 779-7040
Steven D Marcello, *President*
Allen M Swanson, *Vice Pres*
Pamela Pierson, *Manager*
EMP: 60 EST: 1916
SQ FT: 5,000
SALES (est): 5MM-9.9MM **Privately Held**
WEB: www.excelairsystems.com
SIC: 1761 Sheet metal work contractor

(G-8352)
EXHIBITS DEVELOPMENT GROUP LLC ✪
75 W Fifth St Landmark Ct (55102)
PHONE.............................651 222-1121
Ceile Hartleib, *Corp Secy*
Bill Newgren, *Engrg Dir*
Mike Larson, *Info Tech Mgr*
Eric Brandt, *Exec Dir*
Michael Luick-Thrams, *Exec Dir*
EMP: 29 EST: 2008
SALES (est): 1MM-4.9MM **Privately Held**
SIC: 7999 Provides exhibition operation
services

(G-8353)
EXPERIOR ASSESSMENTS LLC (HQ)
1260 Energy Ln (55108-5225)
PHONE.............................651 646-1170
Michael Brannick, *CEO*
Mark Hamburge, *CFO*
Barry Offutt, *Manager*
Mike Fitton, *Manager*
John C McAvliffe, *Manager*
EMP: 130 EST: 1999
SQ FT: 25,000
SALES (corp-wide): 1.22B **Privately Held**
SIC: 8748 Educational consulting services
PA: Educational Testing Service
666 Rosedale Rd Stop 85D
Princeton NJ 08540
609 921-9000

(G-8354)
EXTENDICARE FACILITIES INC
Also Called: Rose of Sharon Manor
1000 Lovell Ave W (55113-4419)
PHONE.............................651 484-3378
FAX: 651 765-8383
Kay Sheumacher, *Manager*
Craig Edinger, *Manager*
Evelyn Webster, *Manager*
Cassie Krusemark, *Manager*
Diane Willette, *Manager*
EMP: 150
SALES (est): 5MM-9.9MM **Privately Held**
WEB: www.extendicare.com
SIC: 8051 Skilled nursing care facility
HQ: Extendicare Health Facility
111 W Michigan St Fl 8
Milwaukee WI 53203
414 908-8000

(G-8355)
EXTENDICARE HOMES INC
Also Called: Health Rhbltation New Brighton
825 1st Ave NW (55112-6846)
PHONE.............................651 633-7875
FAX: 651 628-9335
Donna Mattson, *Business Mgr*
Jerry Meyer, *Maintenance Dir*
Judy McCullough, *Human Resources*
Ben Mussberger, *Marketing Staff*
Karla Konen, *Office Mgr*
EMP: 200
SALES (est): 5MM-9.9MM **Privately Held**
WEB: www.extendacare.com

SIC: 8051 Skilled nursing care facility
DH: Extendicare Homes Inc
111 W Michigan St
Milwaukee WI 53203
414 908-8000

(G-8356)
EXTENDICARE HOMES INC
Also Called: Galtier Health Center
445 Galtier St (55103-2358)
PHONE.............................651 224-1848
FAX: 651 224-9613
Paul Gallagher, *Vice Pres*
Carolyn Yliniemi, *Marketing Mgr*
Shelly Bhola, *Manager*
Thomas Thompson, *Administrator*
Murrae Dochniak, *Supervisor*
EMP: 150
SALES (est): 5MM-9.9MM **Privately Held**
WEB: www.extendacare.com
SIC: 8051 Skilled nursing care facility
DH: Extendicare Homes Inc
111 W Michigan St
Milwaukee WI 53203
414 908-8000

(G-8357)
F B G SERVICE CORP
2161 University Ave W # 112
(55114-1319)
PHONE.............................651 917-8059
Mark Andelt, *Manager*
John Englund, *Manager*
EMP: 96
SALES (est): 1MM-4.9MM **Privately Held**
WEB: www.fbgservices.com
SIC: 7349 Janitorial & custodial services
PA: FBG Service Corp
407 S 27th Ave
Omaha NE 68131
402 346-4422

(G-8358)
F M TRUCKING INC (PA)
Also Called: D-Rock Center
175 Old Hwy A SW (55112)
PHONE.............................651 639-0446
FAX: 651 639-1321
Romana Morrison, *President*
Micheal Morrison, *Corp Secy*
Sue Morrison, *Manager*
John Warren, *Director*
EMP: 27 EST: 1977 **Privately Held**
SIC: 4212 5191 7699 Dump truck hauling
services; wholesales farm supplies; retail
nursery & garden center; agricultural
machinery & equipment repair services

(G-8359)
F M TRUCKING INC
Also Called: D Rock Center & Small Engines
175 Old Highway 8 SW (55112-7743)
PHONE.............................651 639-0446
Romana Morrison, *President*
Sue Morrison, *Manager*
EMP: 25
SALES (est): 1MM-4.9MM **Privately Held**
SIC: 4212 7629 Local trucking without
storage services; electrical equipment repair
& maintenance services; retail nursery &
garden center
PA: F M Trucking Inc
175 Old Hwy A SW
Saint Paul MN 55112
651 639-0446

(G-8360)
F R BIGELOW FOUNDATION INC
55 5th St E Ste 600 (55101-1718)
PHONE.............................651 224-5463
Carleen Rhodes, *President*
Molly Oshaughnessy, *Corp Secy*
John Clymer, *Corp Secy*
Yang Dao, *Corp Secy*
Douglas McMillan, *Corp Secy*
EMP: 65 EST: 1946 **Privately Held**
WEB: www.saintpaulfoundation.org
SIC: 8611 Community affairs & services

(G-8361)
FACE TO FACE HEALTH
1165 Arcade St (55106-2615)
PHONE.............................651 772-5555
FAX: 651 772-2539
Jean Moose, *Insur/Bill Sup*

www.HarrisInfo.com
362

2011 Harris Minnesota
Services Directory

▲=Import ▼=Export
◆=Import/Export

Willie Suttle, *Manager*
Andy Josh, *IT Specialist*
Mary E Planten-Krell, *Exec Dir*
Mary Krell, *Exec Dir*
EMP: 44 **EST:** 1972
SQ FT: 30,000
SALES (est): 1MM-4.9MM **Privately Held**
WEB: www.face2face.org
SIC: 8093 8322 Outpatient mental health
clinic; child & youth services; general
counseling services

(G-8362)
FAIRVIEW HEALTH SERVICES
2577 Territorial Rd (55114-1500)
PHONE.............................651 632-7300
FAX: 651 632-7301
Jeff McNamara, *Manager*
EMP: 25
SALES (est): 1MM-4.9MM **Privately Held**
WEB: www.fairview.org
SIC: 8741 8062 Hospital management
services; medical hospital
PA: Fairview Health Services
2450 Riverside Ave
Minneapolis MN 55454
612 672-6300

(G-8363)
FAIRVIEW HEALTH SERVICES
2200 University Ave W # 110
(55114-1844)
PHONE.............................651 632-9835
Jill McCartney, *Branch Mgr*
EMP: 33
SALES (est): 25MM-49.9MM **Privately Held**
WEB: www.fairview.org
SIC: 5122 Wholesales pharmaceuticals,
drug proprietaries & sundries
PA: Fairview Health Services
2450 Riverside Ave
Minneapolis MN 55454
612 672-6300

(G-8364)
FAIRVIEW HEALTH SERVICES
1151 Silver Lake Rd NW (55112-6324)
PHONE.............................612 706-4500
Hollie James, *Manager*
Jill Yungerberg, *Obstetrician*
Michael A Reid, *Podiatrist*
Lindsey Greenwood, *Physician Asst*
Steven Gilles, *Physician Asst*
EMP: 30
SALES (est): 1MM-4.9MM **Privately Held**
WEB: www.fairview.org
SIC: 8011 Physicians' office & clinic
PA: Fairview Health Services
2450 Riverside Ave
Minneapolis MN 55454
612 672-6300

(G-8365)
FAIRWAY COLLISION CENTER INC
125 County Road F E (55127-6933)
PHONE.............................651 483-4055
FAX: 651 483-5324
Michael Lund, *President*
Jane Lund, *Corp Secy*
Stacie Lund, *Marketing Mgr*
EMP: 35 **EST:** 1975
SALES (est): 1MM-4.9MM **Privately Held**
WEB: www.fairwaycollisioncenter.com
SIC: 7532 Automotive body shop;
automotive paint shop

(G-8366)
FAMILY HEALTH SERVICES OF MN
2025 Sloan Pl Ste 35 (55117-2092)
PHONE.............................651 772-2077
FAX: 651 772-1889
Paul Bererisford, *CEO*
EMP: 50 **EST:** 1995
SQ FT: 5,000
SALES (est): 5MM-9.9MM **Privately Held**
SIC: 8742 Administrative services
consultant

(G-8367)
FAMILY INNOVATIONS INC
2115 County Road D E B100
(55109-5354)
PHONE.............................651 748-5019
Steven Gray, *President*
EMP: 30
SALES (est): 1MM-4.9MM **Privately Held**
SIC: 8322 Family counseling services

(G-8368)
FEDERAL EXPRESS CORP
Also Called: Fedex
1828 Buerkle Rd (55110-5245)
PHONE.............................651 747-4122
Hal Grey, *Branch Mgr*
EMP: 110
SALES (est): 10MM-24.9MM **Publicly Held**
WEB: www.federalexpress.com
SIC: 4213 Over the road trucking
HQ: Federal Express Corp
3610 Hacks Cross Rd
Memphis TN 38125
901 369-3600

(G-8369)
FEDEX FREIGHT INC
2323 Terminal Rd (55113-2527)
PHONE.............................651 697-9342
Mike Bruni, *Manager*
EMP: 70
SALES (est): 5MM-9.9MM **Publicly Held**
WEB: www.fedexfreight.fedex.com
SIC: 4213 Long-distance less than
truckload freight trucking services
DH: Fedex Freight Inc
2200 Forward Dr
Harrison AR 72601
870 741-9000

(G-8370)
FEDEX OFFICE & PRINT SERVICES
58 Snelling Ave S (55105-1901)
PHONE.............................651 699-9671
Dan Johnson, *Manager*
Brian Eveslage, *Manager*
Brian Brom, *Manager*
EMP: 30
SALES (est): 1MM-4.9MM **Publicly Held**
WEB: www.kinkos.com
SIC: 7334 4822 Photocopying & duplicating
services; book binding service; facsimile
transmission services; office supply &
stationery store; commercial lithographic
printing; typesetting service
HQ: Fedex Office & Print Services
13155 Noel Rd Ste 1600
Dallas TX 75240
214 550-7000

(G-8371)
FEIST ANIMAL HOSPITAL
1430 Marshall Ave (55104-6314)
PHONE.............................651 646-7257
FAX: 651 646-2450
William Hultz, *Partner*
Thomas Hufford, *Partner*
Karen Branch, *Manager*
Jeff Schucker, *Manager*
EMP: 25 **EST:** 1911 **Privately Held**
SIC: 0742 Veterinarian services

(G-8372)
FELHABER LARSON FENLON & VOGT
444 Cedar St Ste 2100 (55101-2136)
PHONE.............................651 222-6321
Nancy Vandergort, *Principal*
Grew Up, *Member*
J P Brinkman, *Attorney*
Edward J Bohrer, *Attorney*
James A Blomquist, *Attorney*
EMP: 30
SQ FT: 3,011
SALES (est): 1MM-4.9MM **Privately Held**
SIC: 8111 Legal services
PA: Felhaber Larson Fenlon & Vogt
220 S 6th St Ste 2200
Minneapolis MN 55402
612 339-6321

(G-8373)
FENWAY DEVELOPMENT INC
Also Called: Pratt Homes
3500 Willow Lake Blvd # 100
(55110-5135)
PHONE.............................651 429-8032
Leonard Pratt, *President*
EMP: 60 **EST:** 2004
SALES (est): 10MM-24.9MM **Privately Held**
SIC: 6552 Land subdivision & development
services

(G-8374)
FERGUSON ENTERPRISES INC
2350 County Road C W # 150
(55113-2543)
PHONE.............................651 638-5000
FAX: 651 638-3500
Jerry Quinlan, *Manager*
Ron Weinke, *Manager*
Ken Chricton, *Manager*
EMP: 60
SALES (est): 25MM-49.9MM **Privately Held**
WEB: www.ferguson.com
SIC: 5085 Wholesales industrial supplies;
manufactures fabricated pipe fittings
HQ: Ferguson Enterprises Inc
12500 Jefferson Ave
Newport News VA 23602
757 874-7795

(G-8375)
FESTIVAL EVENTS OF MINNESOTA
Also Called: Taste of Minnesota
1097 Payne Ave (55130-3738)
PO Box 65188 (55165-0188)
PHONE.............................651 772-9980
FAX: 651 772-5089
John Labaski, *President*
EMP: 75 **EST:** 1983
SALES (est): 5MM-9.9MM **Privately Held**
WEB: www.tasteofmn.org
SIC: 7999 Provides festival operation
services; eating place

(G-8376)
FIDUCIARY COUNSELLING INC
30 7th St E Ste 2000 (55101-4930)
PHONE.............................651 228-0935
FAX: 651 228-0776
Carol R Caruthers, *President*
Michael J Giefer, *Corp Secy*
Nicholas C Spika, *Corp Secy*
R G Martin, *Vice Pres*
Richard T Holm, *Treasurer*
▲ **EMP:** 43 **EST:** 1941
SQ FT: 12,000
SALES (est): 5MM-9.9MM **Privately Held**
WEB: www.fidcouns.net
SIC: 6282 Investment advisory service

(G-8377)
FINANCIAL CORP INC
4388 Round Lake Rd W (55112-3923)
PHONE.............................651 407-5770
Dennis Frandsen, *CEO*
Tom Pesek, *President*
EMP: 25 **EST:** 1993
SALES (est): 10MM-24.9MM **Privately Held**
SIC: 6311 Life insurance carrier

(G-8378)
FIREGUARD SPRINKLER SERVICE
Also Called: Fire-Guard Sprinkler Service
575 Minneajaja Ave W (55109)
PHONE.............................651 748-9499
FAX: 651 748-9143
Quing Rubald, *President*
EMP: 50 **EST:** 1990
SALES (est): 5MM-9.9MM **Privately Held**
SIC: 1711 Sprinkler system contractor

(G-8379)
FIRST CHOICE HOME CARE INC
391 Pleasant Ave (55102-2333)
PHONE.............................651 225-4255
FAX: 651 224-0624
David Reynolds, *President*
EMP: 50 **EST:** 1997
SQ FT: 700
SALES (est): 1MM-4.9MM **Privately Held**

SIC: 8082 Home health care services

(G-8380)
FIRST FEDERAL CAPITAL BANK
176 Snelling Ave N (55104-6322)
PHONE.............................651 646-8681
Dennnis Barrett, *Exec VP*
Don Peters, *Senior VP*
Meggie Lesuce, *Manager*
Ralph Mallicoat, *Exec Dir*
EMP: 80
SALES (est): 25MM-49.9MM **Publicly Held**
WEB: www.firstfederalcapitalbank.com
SIC: 6035 Federally chartered savings
institution
DH: First Federal Capital Bank
605 State St
La Crosse WI 54601
608 784-8000

(G-8381)
FIRST STUDENT INC
1717 County Road C W (55113-1322)
PHONE.............................651 628-0046
FAX: 651 628-0211
Kim Ogen, *Manager*
EMP: 200
SALES (est): 10MM-24.9MM **Privately Held**
WEB: www.firststudentinc.com
SIC: 4111 4131 Passenger transit system;
bus transit system
HQ: First Student Inc
600 Vine St Ste 1400
Cincinnati OH 45202
513 241-2200

(G-8382)
FIRST STUDENT INC
1090 Snelling Ave N (55108-2704)
PHONE.............................651 645-1959
FAX: 651 647-1769
Paul Buharin, *Manager*
EMP: 200
SALES (est): 5MM-9.9MM **Privately Held**
WEB: www.firststudentinc.com
SIC: 4151 School bus service
HQ: First Student Inc
600 Vine St Ste 1400
Cincinnati OH 45202
513 241-2200

(G-8383)
FIRST STUDENT INC
3030 Harbor Ln N Ste 124 (55108)
PHONE.............................763 559-8111
Jeff Pearson, *Manager*
EMP: 150
SALES (est): 5MM-9.9MM **Privately Held**
WEB: www.firststudentinc.com
SIC: 4142 4151 Long-distance bus charter
service; school bus service
HQ: First Student Inc
600 Vine St Ste 1400
Cincinnati OH 45202
513 241-2200

(G-8384)
FLANNERY CONSTRUCTION INC
1375 Saint Anthony Ave (55104-4022)
PHONE.............................651 225-1105
Thomas Yardic, *CEO*
Kenneth Allen, *Member*
Joanne Michaud, *Treasurer*
Dannelle Larson, *Office Mgr*
EMP: 30 **EST:** 1983
SALES (est): 5MM-9.9MM **Privately Held**
WEB: www.flanneryconstruction.com
SIC: 1542 1521 Commercial & office
building renovation & repair services; new
single-family home construction service;
new commercial & office building
construction

(G-8385)
FLIPS GYMNASTIC CENTER
3505 Commerce Blvd (55110-4689)
PHONE.............................651 777-4776
FAX: 651 777-9644
Carol Krueger, *Finance Mgr*
Amy Cayford, *Manager*
Shelly Kringen, *Manager*
Kris Klien, *Manager*
Cindy Kindler, *Manager*
EMP: 50 **EST:** 1987
SALES (est): 1MM-4.9MM **Privately Held**

(PA)=Parent Co (HQ)=Headquarters (DH)=Div Headquarters
◐ = New business established in last 2 years

2011 Harris Minnesota
Services Directory

© Harris InfoSource 1-866-281-6415
363

WEB: www.flipsgym.com
SIC: 7999 Gymnastics instruction

(G-8386)
FM 107 W FMP REAL LIFE
3415 University Ave W (55114-1019)
PHONE 651 642-4107
FAX: 651 647-2904
Stanley Hubbard, *CEO*
Ginny Morris, *Vice Pres*
EMP: 100 **EST:** 1923
SALES (est): 5MM-9.9MM **Privately Held**
SIC: 4832 Radio broadcasting station

(G-8387)
FORD NEW BRIGHTEN
1100 Silver Lake Rd NW (55112-6325)
PHONE 651 633-9010
Patilee Yukl-Dinger-Szy, *Finance Mgr*
Rueben Przybilla, *Office Mgr*
Michael W Saxon, *Director*
Ted W Saxon, *Director*
James W Saxon, *Director*
EMP: 100 **EST:** 1929
SQ FT: 64,000
SALES (est): 50MM-99.9MM **Privately Held**
WEB: www.saxonautogroup.com
SIC: 7515 7532 7538 Retails new & used
automobiles; automotive body, paint &
interior repair & maintenance services;
general automotive repair services; retails
new & used trucks, tractors & trailers; retails
auto & home supplies; passenger car
leasing; used car dealer

(G-8388)
FOREST WEEKES PRODUCTS INC (PA)
Also Called: Northstar Forest Materials
2600 Como Ave (55108-1217)
PO Box 14327 (55114-0327)
PHONE 651 644-9807
FAX: 651 644-9520
Steven E Weekes, *President*
Fred Reynolds, *Vice Pres*
Gary Schulz, *CFO*
Diane Barstow, *Controller*
Dennis Fahey, *Sales Staff*
▲ **EMP:** 59 **EST:** 1978
SQ FT: 7,300 **Privately Held**
SIC: 5031 Wholesales lumber, plywood &
millwork

(G-8389)
FORSTROM & TORGERSON HS LLC
Also Called: Hilton
1050 Gramsie Rd (55126-2949)
PHONE 651 415-1956
Julie Johnson, *General Mgr*
Sheryl D Walton, *Senior VP*
Thomas R Torgerson, *Mng Member*
Gary Miller, *Manager*
EMP: 40
SALES (est): 1MM-4.9MM **Privately Held**
WEB: www.torgersonproperties.com
SIC: 7011 Traveler accommodations
PA: Torgerson Properties Inc
103 15th Ave NW Ste 200
Willmar MN 56201
320 235-7207

(G-8390)
FORSTROM & TORGERSON LLP
Also Called: Hampton Inn North St Paul Mpls
1000 Gramsie Rd (55126-2949)
PHONE 651 482-0402
FAX: 651 482-8917
Thomas R Torgerson, *Managing Prtnr*
Julie Fuller, *General Mgr*
Sheryl D Walton, *Senior VP*
EMP: 130 **EST:** 1973
SALES (est): 5MM-9.9MM **Privately Held**
WEB: www.torgersonproperties.com
SIC: 7011 Traveler accommodations
PA: Torgerson Properties Inc
103 15th Ave NW Ste 200
Willmar MN 56201
320 235-7207

(G-8391)
FORSYTHE APPRAISALS LLC
222 Little Canada Rd E Ste 175
(55117-1399)
PHONE 651 486-9550
Timothy Forsythe, *CEO*
John Forsythe, *President*
Al Gottschalk, *Senior VP*
Kitty Garnett, *Vice Pres*
Kity Garret, *Vice Pres*
EMP: 60 **EST:** 1963
SQ FT: 4,872
SALES (est): 5MM-9.9MM **Privately Held**
WEB: www.seattle.forsytheappraisals.com
SIC: 6531 Real estate appraiser

(G-8392)
FPI PAVING CONTRACTORS INC
3230 Rice St (55126-3047)
PHONE 651 484-0385
Chad Nelson, *CEO*
Leroy Jelen, *President*
Timothy Anderly, *Vice Pres*
Jeanne McCann, *Treasurer*
EMP: 42 **EST:** 1995
SQ FT: 2,000
SALES (est): 1MM-4.9MM **Privately Held**
SIC: 1771 Asphalt contractor

(G-8393)
FRANCISCAN HEALTH COMMUNITY (PA)
Also Called: St Mary's Home
1925 Norfolk Ave (55116-2667)
PHONE 651 696-8400
FAX: 651 696-8404
Joseph Stanislav, *President*
Paula Fisher, *Manager*
EMP: 145 **EST:** 1887
SQ FT: 77,130
SALES (corp-wide): 8.91M **Privately Held**
SIC: 8051 Extended care facility

(G-8394)
FRATTALONE CO'S INC
3205 Spruce St (55117-1045)
PHONE 651 484-0448
Frank M Frattalone, *CEO*
Tony Frattalone, *President*
Sue Busse, *Corp Secy*
Nick Frattalone, *CFO*
Sue Kees, *Manager*
EMP: 225 **EST:** 1969
SQ FT: 7,000
SALES (est): 25MM-49.9MM **Privately Held**
WEB: www.fmfrattalone.com
SIC: 1794 1795 Excavating contractor;
wrecking & demolition contractor

(G-8395)
FRATTALONE I LLC
650 Grand Ave (55105-3402)
PHONE 651 292-9800
FAX: 651 292-1740
Larry Frattalone, *Member*
Kent Eernisse, *Manager*
EMP: 30 **EST:** 2005
SALES (est): 10MM-24.9MM **Privately Held**
SIC: 5072 5099 Wholesales hardware;
retails building products & materials;
wholesales durable goods; hardware store

(G-8396)
FRATTALONE TRACTOR CO INC
3205 Spruce St (55117-1045)
PHONE 651 484-0448
Tony Frattalone, *President*
Nick Frattalone, *CFO*
Brian Pogalz, *Manager*
Van Engen, *Manager*
Frank M Frattalone, *Director*
EMP: 160 **EST:** 1970
SALES (est): 50MM-99.9MM **Privately Held**
SIC: 5083 Wholesales farm & garden
machinery

(G-8397)
FRERICHS CONSTRUCTION CO
3600 Labore Rd Ste 8 (55110-4144)
PHONE 651 787-0687
FAX: 651 787-0407
Paul Frerichs, *CEO*
Marvin Kotek, *President*
Chad Olfon, *Vice Pres*

Chris Osbein, *Vice Pres*
Chad Olson, *Project Mgr*
EMP: 50 **EST:** 1983
SQ FT: 3,500
SALES (est): 10MM-24.9MM **Privately Held**
WEB: www.frerichsconstruction.com
SIC: 1542 New commercial & office building
construction

(G-8398)
G&K SERVICES INC
685 Olive St (55130-4434)
PHONE 651 855-7000
FAX: 651 855-7070
John Toddonio, *General Mgr*
Michelle Eccless, *Finance Mgr*
Michelle Halberg, *Manager*
Eric McNaul, *Manager*
Karen Kirwan, *CIO*
EMP: 150
SALES (est): 5MM-9.9MM **Publicly Held**
WEB: www.gkservices.com
SIC: 7218 7213 Industrial uniform supply
services; towel supply service; apron supply
service; mat & rug supply service; mats,
rugs, mops & cloths treating service; wiping
towel supply service
PA: G&K Services Inc
5995 Opus Pkwy Ste 500
Minnetonka MN 55343
952 912-5500

(G-8399)
G4S SECURE SOLUTIONS INC
2610 University Ave W # 210
(55114-1090)
PHONE 651 482-1928
FAX: 651 482-1998
Robert Dineston, *General Mgr*
Robert Dennistoun, *Area Mgr*
Heidie Dolan, *Office Mgr*
John Jacobs, *Branch Mgr*
Heidie Smith, *Manager*
EMP: 400
SALES (est): 5MM-9.9MM **Privately Held**
WEB: www.wackenhut.com
SIC: 7381 Security guard service
HQ: G4s Secure Solutions Inc
4200 Wackenhut Dr 100
Palm Beach Gardens FL 33410
561 622-5656

(G-8400)
GAGNON INC (PA)
2315 Hampden Ave (55114-1204)
PHONE 651 644-4301
Ronald Gagnon, *President*
Peter D Gagnon, *Corp Secy*
Mark J Gagnon, *Vice Pres*
EMP: 32 **EST:** 1938
SQ FT: 3,000 **Privately Held**
SIC: 1711 Boiler maintenance service;
boiler setting contractor; heating systems
repair & maintenance service

(G-8401)
GARDEN GROVE LLC
2177 Youngman Ave Ste 100
(55116-3084)
PHONE 651 699-5300
David Williams, *Principal*
EMP: 30 **EST:** 2007 **Privately Held**
SIC: 0782 Garden services

(G-8402)
GARY HALGRAN
Also Called: Interim Services
2200 University Ave W Ste 160
(55114-1841)
PHONE 651 917-3634
FAX: 651 917-3620
Gary Halgran, *Ch of Bd*
Pat Skogen, *General Mgr*
Kari Jarvi, *Treasurer*
Lea Ebenstwiner, *Manager*
Perri P Dock, *Administrator*
EMP: 350 **EST:** 2001
SQ FT: 7,000
SALES (est): 5MM-9.9MM **Privately Held**
SIC: 7363 Temporary help service

(G-8403)
GAUSMAN & MOORE ASSOCIATES INC
1700 Highway 36 W Ste 700 (55113-4015)
PHONE 651 639-9606
FAX: 651 639-9618
James W Giefer, *President*
Edward L Studniski, *Principal*
James D Manning, *Principal*
Lane Hersey, *Corp Secy*
Robert Full, *Vice Pres*
▲ **EMP:** 52 **EST:** 1935
SQ FT: 12,000
SALES (est): 5MM-9.9MM **Privately Held**
WEB: www.gausman.com
SIC: 8711 Electrical or electronic engineers;
mechanical engineering services

(G-8404)
GEM LAKE HILLS INC
4039 Scheuneman Rd (55110-4114)
PHONE 651 429-8715
FAX: 651 429-1322
Kenneth Wilson, *President*
Tony Carlson, *General Mgr*
EMP: 30 **EST:** 1986
SQ FT: 5,500
SALES (est): 1MM-4.9MM **Privately Held**
WEB: www.gemlakehillsgolf.com
SIC: 7992 Public golf course

(G-8405)
GENERAL SPRINKLER CORP
1863 Buerkle Rd (55110-5246)
PHONE 651 484-5903
FAX: 651 484-9514
Frank M Winiecki, *Ch of Bd*
Michael J Winiecki, *Principal*
Jean A Winiecki, *Senior VP*
Greg Lindholm, *Manager*
EMP: 25 **EST:** 1989
SQ FT: 7,000
SALES (est): 1MM-4.9MM **Privately Held**
WEB: www.generalsprinkler.com
SIC: 1711 Fire sprinkler system installation
service

(G-8406)
GEPHART ELECTRIC CO INC
3550 Labore Rd Ste 11 (55110-5113)
PHONE 651 484-4900
Carol Heinsch, *President*
Donna Berquist, *Corp Secy*
Lawrence Heinsch, *Senior VP*
David Cords, *Vice Pres*
Kenneth L Heinsch, *Director*
EMP: 210 **EST:** 1977
SQ FT: 8,100
SALES (est): 10MM-24.9MM **Privately Held**
WEB: www.gephartsystems.com
SIC: 1731 Electrical contractor

(G-8407)
GEPHART ELECTRICAL CONSTR
3550 Labore Rd Ste 11 (55110-5113)
PHONE 651 484-4900
Carol Heinsch, *President*
Donna Berquist, *Corp Secy*
Gregory L Heinsch, *Vice Pres*
EMP: 25 **EST:** 1997
SQ FT: 25,000
SALES (est): 1MM-4.9MM **Privately Held**
WEB: www.gephartsystems.net
SIC: 1731 Electric power systems
contractor

(G-8408)
GGNSC ST PAUL LAKE RIDGE LLC
Also Called: Golden Livingcenter - Lk Ridge
2727 Victoria St N (55113-3029)
PHONE 651 483-5431
Joan Johnson, *Member*
Ann Lundberg, *Human Resources*
Maxinme McNamara, *Marketing Staff*
Bree Decorsey, *Marketing Staff*
Cathy Nordby, *Office Mgr*
EMP: 99 **EST:** 2006
SALES (est): 1MM-4.9MM **Privately Held**
WEB: www.fillmorecap.com

www.HarrisInfo.com
364

2011 Harris Minnesota
Services Directory

▲=Import ▼=Export
◆=Import/Export

SIC: 8051 Skilled nursing care facility
DH: Ggnsc Holdings LLC
1000 Fianna Way
Fort Smith AR 72919
479 201-2000

(G-8409)

GILLETTE CHILDREN'S SPECIALTY

183 University Ave E (55101-2526)
PHONE............................651 229-3840
Carrie Trygstad, *Manager*
Margaret Perryman, *Exec Dir*
EMP: 50
SALES (est): 5MM-9.9MM **Privately Held**
SIC: 8011 Physical medicine physician or surgeon office
PA: Gillette Children's Specialty
200 University Ave E
Saint Paul MN 55101
651 291-2848

(G-8410)

GILLETTE CHILDREN'S SPECIALTY (PA)

200 University Ave E (55101-2507)
PHONE............................651 291-2848
Margaret Perryman, *President*
James Rechtiene, *Vice Chairman*
Steven Koop, *Member*
Kevin Walker, *Corp Secy*
Amanda Vandoorn, *Corp Secy*
EMP: 390 EST: 1898
SQ FT: 75,000
SALES (corp-wide): 133.31M **Privately Held**
SIC: 8069 Children's hospital

(G-8411)

GIRL SCOUTS OF MINNESOTA & WI

400 Robert St S (55107-2214)
PHONE............................651 227-8835
FAX: 651 227-7533
Steve Burarow, *Manager*
Dan Ursin, *Manager*
Linda Keene, *Director*
EMP: 65 **Privately Held**
SIC: 8641 Girl Scout organization

(G-8412)

GLACIER INTERNATIONAL INC

1901 Oakcrest Ave (55113-2617)
PO Box 130486 (55113-0016)
PHONE............................651 786-9700
FAX: 651 786-9739
Marvin G Cleveland, *President*
EST: 1978
SQ FT: 25,000
WEB: www.glacierintl.com
SIC: 5084 6159 Wholesales industrial machinery & equipment; equipment & vehicle finance leasing service

(G-8413)

GLEN L STOCKMAN

Also Called: Parkview Motel
2845 Hamline Ave N # 200 (55113-7116)
PHONE............................651 636-1171
Michael Stockman, *Owner*
EMP: 45 EST: 1971
SALES (est): 1MM-4.9MM **Privately Held**
SIC: 7011 Motel

(G-8414)

GLOBAL ANESTHESIA BUSINESS

1503 Hamline Ave N (55108-2314)
PHONE............................651 646-3091
Shawn Gauehan, *CEO*
EMP: 25 EST: 1998
SALES (est): 1MM-4.9MM **Privately Held**
WEB: www.gaba-llc.com
SIC: 8049 Registered & practical nurse office

(G-8415)

GLOBAL VOLUNTEERS

375 Little Canada Rd E (55117-1628)
PHONE............................651 407-6100
FAX: 651 482-0915
Burnham J Philbrook, *President*
Todd Lefko, *Trustee*

Sue Laxdal, *Trustee*
Michele Gran, *Vice Pres*
Bonnie Christensen, *Vice Pres*
EMP: 30 EST: 1984
SQ FT: 2,000 **Privately Held**
SIC: 8699 8322 Personal interest organization; individual & family social services

(G-8416)

GNW ACQUISITION CORP

Also Called: Great Northwest Insurance
400 Robert St N Ste 1100 (55101-2035)
PHONE............................651 325-0060
FAX: 651 224-4135
Steven Doucette, *President*
Bob Czerniak, *Manager*
EMP: 73 EST: 2006
SALES (est): 50MM-99.9MM **Privately Held**
SIC: 6311 Life insurance carrier

(G-8417)

GOFF & HOWARD INC

255 Kellogg Blvd E Ste 102 (55101-1431)
PHONE............................651 292-8062
FAX: 651 292-8091
Chris Georgacas, *President*
Lynda Cilstrom, *Prdtn Mgr*
Paula Howard, *Treasurer*
Heidi Larson, *Shareholder*
Patty Dunn, *Shareholder*
EST: 1978 **Privately Held**
WEB: www.goffhoward.com
SIC: 8743 Public relations services

(G-8418)

GOING GOING GONG INC

5 S Owasso Blvd E (55117-1042)
PHONE............................651 482-1000
FAX: 651 481-6138
Roger Dolle Jr, *President*
Robert Dolle Jr, *President*
Erik Vegoe, *Comptroller*
Wanda Svenson, *MIS Staff*
▲ EMP: 25 EST: 1959
SALES (est): 1MM-4.9MM **Privately Held**
WEB: www.dttruck.com
SIC: 4213 Contract haulers

(G-8419)

GOLDEN ERA TRADING LLC

1865 Magnolia Ave E # 303 (55119-3311)
PO Box 600395 (55106-0007)
PHONE............................651 774-4400
Chris Vang, *Member*
Shoua Vang, *Treasurer*
EMP: 100 EST: 2006
SALES (est): 100MM-499.9MM **Privately Held**
SIC: 5139 Wholesales shoes

(G-8420)

GOLF SERVICES CORP

Also Called: MANITOU RIDGE GOLF CLUB
3200 McKnight Rd N (55110-7530)
PHONE............................651 777-1436
FAX: 651 777-7198
Greg Hubbard, *President*
Bonnie Hubbard, *Corp Secy*
Shelley Gras, *Manager*
EMP: 60 EST: 1971
SQ FT: 3,000
SALES (est): 1MM-4.9MM **Privately Held**
WEB: www.manitouridge.com
SIC: 7992 Public golf course; retails golf goods & equipment; bar; limited service snack bar

(G-8421)

GOODWILL INDUSTRIES INC (PA)

Also Called: Easter Seal Minnesota
553 Fairview Ave N (55104-1708)
PHONE............................651 379-5800
FAX: 651 379-5803
Michael Wirth-Davis, *President*
Brian Lassiter, *Vice Chairman*
Jason Siefert, *CFO*
Gary Scroth, *Finance*
Kathy Gerber, *VP Human Res*
EMP: 150 EST: 1919
SQ FT: 165,000
SALES (corp-wide): 27.21M **Privately Held**
WEB: www.goodwilleasterseals.org

SIC: 4953 4226 8322 8331 Waste material recycling services; retails used merchandise; family services agency; job training services; warehousing & storage facility

(G-8422)

GOODWILL INDUSTRIES INC

2505 University Ave W Ste 2 (55114-1537)
PHONE............................651 603-1544
Julia Wagner, *Manager*
EMP: 80
SALES (est): 5MM-9.9MM **Privately Held**
WEB: www.goodwilleasterseals.org
SIC: 4226 8322 8331 Retails used merchandise; family services agency; job training services; warehousing & storage facility
PA: Goodwill Industries Inc
553 Fairview Ave N
Saint Paul MN 55104
651 379-5800

(G-8423)

GOPHER ELECTRONICS CO

222 Little Canada Rd E (55117-2375)
PHONE............................651 490-4900
FAX: 651 490-4911
John W Reinke, *CEO*
Norris Carnes Jr, *President*
Robert Arnold, *Purchasing*
Mike Treece, *Controller*
Laurie Barth, *Accounting Staf*
EMP: 41 EST: 1952
SQ FT: 35,000
SALES (est): 25MM-49.9MM **Privately Held**
WEB: www.gopherelectronics.com
SIC: 5065 Wholesales electronic parts & equipment

(G-8424)

GOV DELIVERY INC

408 Saint Peter St Ste 600 (55102-1122)
PHONE............................866 276-5583
Scott Burns, *CEO*
Brian Allan, *Senior VP*
Bobbie Browning, *Vice Pres*
Darren Gerke, *Controller*
EMP: 65 EST: 1999
SALES (est): 5MM-9.9MM **Publicly Held**
WEB: www.govdelivery.com
SIC: 7374 Computer graphics service
PA: Internet Capital Group Inc
690 Lee Rd Ste 310
Wayne PA 19087
610 727-6900

(G-8425)

GOVERNOR'S INC

959 Arcade St (55106-3850)
PHONE............................651 778-1045
Louis Lentch, *President*
EMP: 30 EST: 1987
SQ FT: 9,000
SALES (est): 1MM-4.9MM **Privately Held**
SIC: 6513 Drinking establishment; eating place; apartment building operator

(G-8426)

GRAND HERITAGE PROPERTIES LLC

1280 Grand Ave Apt 105 (55105-2605)
PHONE............................651 699-3003
Eugene V Sitzmann V, *Member*
Kurt Christensen, *Administration*
EMP: 67 EST: 2001
SALES (est): 10MM-24.9MM **Privately Held**
WEB: www.grandheritage.com
SIC: 6513 Apartment building operator

(G-8427)

GREAT WESTERN RECYCLING INDS

521 Barge Channel Rd (55107-2441)
PHONE............................651 224-4877
FAX: 651 224-4870
Michael Silverman, *CEO*
Andrew Staebell, *President*
Jerold Bader, *Vice Pres*
Melinda Houst, *Vice Pres*
Meli House, *CFO*
EMP: 50 EST: 1987
SQ FT: 45,000
SALES (est): 1MM-4.9MM **Privately Held**

SIC: 4491 5051 5052 Waterfront terminal operation services; metal service center; wholesales coal; manufactures secondary nonferrous metals

(G-8428)

GREAT WESTERN URON & METAL CO

521 Barge Channel Rd (55107-2441)
PHONE............................651 224-4877
Michael Silverman, *Owner*
Melinda House, *Manager*
EMP: 50 EST: 1936
SALES (est): 10MM-24.9MM **Privately Held**
SIC: 5093 Wholesales metal scrap & waste materials

(G-8429)

GREATSTONE LLC

1177 Goose Lake Rd (55110-4140)
PHONE............................651 429-6606
Alice Williamson, *Mng Member*
EMP: 25 EST: 2007
SALES (est): 1MM-4.9MM **Privately Held**
SIC: 1741 7389 Masonry & stonework contractor; business services at a non-commercial site

(G-8430)

GREEN CO'S INC

2550 University Ave W Ste 400N (55114-2015)
PHONE............................651 644-4389
David Raby, *Branch Mgr*
Tom Kaldunski, *Manager*
Todd Stark, *CIO*
Cherie Coughlin, *IT/INT Sup*
EMP: 55
SALES (est): 5MM-9.9MM **Privately Held**
WEB: www.hrgreen.com
SIC: 8711 Engineering services
PA: Green Co's Inc
8710 Earhart Ln SW
Cedar Rapids IA 52404
319 841-4000

(G-8431)

GREEN MILL GROWERS

2582 Long Lake Rd (55113-2526)
PHONE............................651 697-1081
John R Johnson, *Owner*
Nicole Price, *Corp Secy*
Todd Elet, *Treasurer*
EMP: 63 EST: 2003 **Privately Held**
SIC: 0181 Ornamental nursery products

(G-8432)

GREEN TREE INVESTMENT HOLDINGS

345 Saint Peter St Ste 500 (55102-1212)
PHONE............................651 293-3410
Cheryl Collins, *CFO*
Keith Anderson, *Mng Member*
Robert Tolley, *Director*
EMP: 99 EST: 2003
SALES (est): 5MM-9.9MM **Privately Held**
SIC: 7389 Financial service

(G-8433)

GREEN TREE SERVICING LLC (PA)

345 Saint Peter St Ste 300 (55102-1229)
PHONE............................651 293-4800
Brian Corey, *Member*
George Budzynski, *Member*
John Dolphin, *Exec VP*
James R Breakey, *Senior VP*
Don Fuquay, *Sales Staff*
▲ EMP: 50 EST: 2003
SALES (corp-wide): 250.80M **Privately Held**
WEB: www.gtservicing.com
SIC: 6162 Loan correspondence service

(G-8434)

GUADALUPE ALTERNATIVE PROGRAMS

381 Robie St E (55107-2415)
PHONE............................651 222-0757
FAX: 651 290-2703
Allen Selinski, *Director*
Bety Rios-Christens, *Tech/Comp Coord*
Jody Nelson, *Assistant*
EMP: 33

(PA)=Parent Co (HQ)=Headquarters (DH)=Div Headquarters
✿ = New business established in last 2 years

2011 Harris Minnesota
Services Directory

© Harris InfoSource 1-866-281-6415
365

EST: 1969
   ADMISSIONS: 130
   SALES (est): 5MM-9.9MM **Privately Held**
   WEB: www.gapschool.org
   SIC: 8351 Educational services; child day
   care service

(G-8435)
GUARANTEED CLEAN MAINTENANCE
   1565 Como Ave Ste 101 (55108-2509)
   PHONE..................651 644-9919
   FAX: 651 644-0900
   Mark Devine, *President*
   Mark D Vine, *President*
   Ray Devine, *Vice Pres*
   EMP: 80 **EST:** 1972
   SALES (est): 1MM-4.9MM **Privately Held**
   SIC: 7349 Industrial or commercial cleaning
   services

(G-8436)
GUIDANT SALES CORP (HQ)
   4100 Hamline Ave N (55112-5700)
   PHONE..................651 582-4000
   James M Cornelius, *CEO*
   Ray Elliott, *President*
   Mark C Bartell, *President*
   A J Graf, *Chairman*
   Guido J Neels, *COO*
   EMP: 60 **EST:** 1994
   SQ FT: 18,261
   SALES (corp-wide): 8.18B **Publicly Held**
   WEB: www.guidant.com
   SIC: 5047 Manufactures medical
   instruments; wholesales medical & hospital
   equipment; manufactures catheters;
   manufactures microsurgical instruments;
   manufactures retractors; wholesales
   medical equipment & supplies; wholesales
   medical diagnostic equipment
   PA: Boston Scientific Corp
      1 Boston Scientific Pl
      Natick MA 01760
      508 650-8000

(G-8437)
GUILD INC
   130 Wabasha St S Ste 100 (55107-1819)
   PHONE..................651 291-0067
   FAX: 651 291-8555
   Rich Aylward, *General Mgr*
   Don Connors, *Manager*
   Susan Brown, *Exec Dir*
   EMP: 35
   SALES (est): 1MM-4.9MM **Privately Held**
   WEB: www.guildincorporated.org
   SIC: 8093 Specialty outpatient clinic
   HQ: Guild Inc
      1025 Dodd Rd
      Saint Paul MN 55118
      651 450-2220

(G-8438)
HAGE CONCRETE WORKS
   2030 Saint Clair Ave (55105-1650)
   PHONE..................651 690-4243
   Ollie Hage, *Owner*
   Liz Hage, *Manager*
   EMP: 30 **EST:** 2001
   SALES (est): 1MM-4.9MM **Privately Held**
   SIC: 1771 Concrete contractor

(G-8439)
HAMERNICK PAINT CO
   1321 Rice St (55117-4542)
   PHONE..................651 489-7007
   Ted Natus, *President*
   Edmund H Hamernick, *Vice Pres*
   Gerald Hamernick, *Vice Pres*
   Lorraine Hamernick, *Treasurer*
   EMP: 65 **EST:** 1946
   SQ FT: 12,000
   SALES (est): 10MM-24.9MM **Privately Held**
   WEB: www.hamernicks.com
   SIC: 1721 Retails carpet; glass store; retails
   paint; retails wall coverings; painting & wall
   covering contractor

(G-8440)
HANDI MEDICAL SUPPLY INC
   2505 University Ave W # 1 (55114-1537)
   PHONE..................651 644-9770
   FAX: 651 644-0602
   Mary Benhardus, *President*

Edward Barder, *Accountant*
   EMP: 56 **EST:** 1988
   SQ FT: 25,000
   SALES (est): 5MM-9.9MM **Privately Held**
   WEB: www.handimedical.com
   SIC: 7699 Retails medical apparatus &
   supplies; medical equipment repair service

(G-8441)
HANSEN DORDELL BRADT ODLAUG,
   Also Called: Bradt Resolutions Services
   3900 Northwoods Dr Ste 250
   (55112-6991)
   PHONE..................651 482-8900
   FAX: 651 482-8909
   Jean Bradt, *Partner*
   Randall W Sayers, *Partner*
   Gene P Bradt, *Partner*
   James A Schaps, *Partner*
   Mark M Suby, *Partner*
   EMP: 52 **EST:** 1946
   SALES (est): 5MM-9.9MM **Privately Held**
   WEB: www.hdbob.com
   SIC: 8111 General practice law office

(G-8442)
HARBINGER PARTNERS INC
   855 Village Center Dr # 356 (55127-3016)
   PHONE..................651 426-1569
   Scott Grausnick, *CEO*
   Deb Mull, *Info Tech Dir*
   Nathan Bruckelymer, *Prgrmr*
   Tim Tuffs, *Director*
   Kevin McCroskey, *Director*
   EMP: 53 **EST:** 1999
   SALES (est): 5MM-9.9MM **Privately Held**
   SIC: 7379 8742 Computer system
   consulting services; management consulting
   services

(G-8443)
HARMONY NURSING HOMES INC
   135 Geranium Ave E (55117-5007)
   PHONE..................651 488-6658
   FAX: 651 488-7587
   Judy Loomis, *Business Mgr*
   Angela Brown, *Human Resources*
   Trent Carlson, *Administrator*
   EMP: 100 **EST:** 1964
   SQ FT: 60,000
   SALES (est): 1MM-4.9MM **Privately Held**
   SIC: 8051 Skilled nursing care facility
   PA: Elim Care Inc
      7485 Office Ridge Cir
      Eden Prairie MN 55344
      952 259-4500

(G-8444)
HARRIS CONTRACTING CO (PA)
   909 Montreal Cir (55102-4296)
   PHONE..................651 602-6500
   FAX: 651 643-6699
   Greg Hosch, *CEO*
   Robert F Hosch, *Ch of Bd*
   Robert A Latta Jr, *Vice Pres*
   Steven J Peterson, *Vice Pres*
   Randy Stewart, *Vice Pres*
   EMP: 100 **EST:** 1954
   SQ FT: 65,000 **Privately Held**
   WEB: www.hmcc.com
   SIC: 1711 Plumbing service; mechanical
   contractor

(G-8445)
HAYES RESIDENCE INC
   1620 Randolph Ave (55105-2148)
   PHONE..................651 690-1032
   FAX: 651 690-2787
   Helen Jennen, *President*
   Vonnie Bakke, *Manager*
   Andrea Seal, *Manager*
   Sue Singer, *Director*
   H Sharma, *Director*
   EMP: 30 **EST:** 1974
   SALES (est): 1MM-4.9MM **Privately Held**
   WEB: www.hayesresidence.com
   SIC: 8052 Intermediate care facility

(G-8446)
HEACOX, HARTMAN, MATTAINI
   Also Called: Anderson, Autumn L
   408 Saint Peter St Ste 550 (55102-1118)
   PHONE..................651 222-2922
   Ann Tholey, *Bookkeeper*
   Cindy Anderson, *Office Mgr*
   Michael Koshmrl, *Attorney*
   Sharon Pinska, *Manager*
   EMP: 35 **EST:** 1996
   SQ FT: 9,245
   SALES (est): 1MM-4.9MM **Privately Held**
   WEB: www.hhmkcj.com
   SIC: 8111 Specialized legal services

(G-8447)
HEALTH CARE SERVICES INC
   Also Called: NORTH ST PAUL
   TRANSITIONAL CAR
   2375 Skillman Ave E (55109-4047)
   PHONE..................651 777-7435
   FAX: 651 777-8501
   Eugene Sprinkel, *President*
   Albert Eggert, *Division Mgr*
   Karen Sprinkel, *Corp Secy*
   Todd Sprinkel, *Treasurer*
   Julie Hiland, *Office Mgr*
   EMP: 56 **EST:** 1995
   SQ FT: 4,000
   SALES (est): 1MM-4.9MM **Privately Held**
   SIC: 8051 Skilled nursing care facility

(G-8448)
HEALTH EAST CARE CENTER WHITE
   1891 Florence St (55110-3363)
   PHONE..................651 232-1818
   FAX: 651 232-2809
   Tim Hanson, *President*
   Bob Gill, *Vice Pres*
   Vicki Tobroxen, *Controller*
   Barbara Jordahl, *Human Res Mgr*
   EMP: 240 **EST:** 1960
   SALES (est): 5MM-9.9MM **Privately Held**
   SIC: 8051 Skilled nursing care facility
   PA: Healtheast Care System
      1700 University Ave W # 5
      Saint Paul MN 55104
      651 232-1000

(G-8449)
HEALTH EAST MEDICAL LABORATORY
   45 10th St W (55102-1062)
   PHONE..................651 232-3500
   Timothy H Hanson, *Principal*
   EMP: 100 **EST:** 1985
   SALES (est): 10MM-24.9MM **Privately Held**
   SIC: 8071 Medical laboratory
   DH: Healtheast Diversified Svcs
      559 Capitol Blvd
      Saint Paul MN 55103
      651 232-2300

(G-8450)
HEALTH SYSTEMS COOPERATIVE
   55 5th St E Ste 960 (55101-1717)
   PHONE..................651 774-8620
   Brian Knapp, *President*
   Kyle Roberts, *CFO*
   EMP: 60 **EST:** 1996
   SQ FT: 73,000
   SALES (est): 1MM-4.9MM **Privately Held**
   SIC: 7219 Laundry service

(G-8451)
HEALTHEAST
   69 Exchange St W Unit 3AB (55102-1004)
   PHONE..................651 232-3008
   Maxine Baker, *Principal*
   Kori Sawyer, *Telecom Exec*
   EMP: 80
   SALES (est): 1MM-4.9MM **Privately Held**
   SIC: 8082 Home health care services
   PA: Healtheast Care System
      1700 University Ave W # 5
      Saint Paul MN 55104
      651 232-1000

(G-8452)
HEALTHEAST
   481 Front Ave (55117-4704)
   PHONE..................651 232-1717
   FAX: 651 488-2846
   Darlene Schneider, *Human Resources*
   Harlen Dahl, *Director*
   Bradley Anderson, *Director*
   David McGowan, *Executive*
   EMP: 160
   SALES (est): 5MM-9.9MM **Privately Held**
   SIC: 4119 Ambulance service
   PA: Healtheast Care System
      1700 University Ave W # 5
      Saint Paul MN 55104
      651 232-1000

(G-8453)
HEALTHEAST CARE INC
   559 Capitol Blvd (55103-2101)
   PHONE..................651 232-2300
   FAX: 651 232-2178
   Timothy Hanson, *CEO*
   Ann Schrader, *COO*
   Linda Smith, *Vice Pres*
   Maida Gunther, *Facilities Mgr*
   Nancy Spitzack, *Facilities Mgr*
   EMP: 1000 **EST:** 1990
   SALES (est): 50MM-99.9MM **Privately Held**
   SIC: 8741 8721 Hospital management
   services; accounting, auditing &
   bookkeeping services
   PA: Healtheast Care System
      1700 University Ave W # 5
      Saint Paul MN 55104
      651 232-1000

(G-8454)
HEALTHEAST CARE SYSTEM (PA)
   1700 University Ave W # 5 (55104-3727)
   PHONE..................651 232-1000
   Timothy H Hanson, *President*
   Albert E Eggert, *Vice Chairman*
   Maggie Kendall, *Corp Secy*
   Anne Schrader, *COO*
   Scott W Hinrichs, *Vice Pres*
   EMP: 751 **EST:** 1986
   SALES (corp-wide): 1.33M **Privately Held**
   SIC: 8741 7389 8062 Hospital management
   services; document storage service;
   medical hospital

(G-8455)
HEALTHEAST CARE SYSTEM
   69 Exchange St W (55102-1004)
   PHONE..................651 232-3222
   Bill Hosfield, *Partner*
   Eduardo D Trinia, *Med Doctor*
   Dave Hartford, *Exec Dir*
   Vicky Wells, *Director*
   Biljana Capra, *Psychiatry*
   EMP: 30
   SALES (est): 1MM-4.9MM **Privately Held**
   SIC: 8093 8069 Outpatient drug clinic;
   alcoholism rehabilitation hospital
   PA: Healtheast Care System
      1700 University Ave W # 5
      Saint Paul MN 55104
      651 232-1000

(G-8456)
HEALTHEAST CARE SYSTEM
   Also Called: Medical Care For Seniors
   1690 University Ave W Ste 450
   (55104-3731)
   PHONE..................651 232-2002
   Donald S Asp MD, *Med Doctor*
   Candy Damlo, *Manager*
   EMP: 25
   SALES (est): 500-999K **Privately Held**
   SIC: 8361 Geriatric residential care
   PA: Healtheast Care System
      1700 University Ave W # 5
      Saint Paul MN 55104
      651 232-1000

(G-8457)
HEALTHEAST CARE SYSTEM
   Also Called: Cerenity Care Ctr On Dlwood Pl
   753 7th St E (55106-5025)
   PHONE..................651 776-4107
   Jason Dempster, *Human Res Mgr*
   Ted Schmidt, *Manager*

www.HarrisInfo.com
366

2011 Harris Minnesota
Services Directory

▲=Import ▼=Export
◆=Import/Export

EMP: 155
SALES (est): 5MM-9.9MM **Privately Held**
SIC: 8059 Nursing home
PA: Healtheast Care System
1700 University Ave W # 5
Saint Paul MN 55104
651 232-1000

(G-8458)
HEALTHEAST CARE SYSTEM
799 Reaney Ave (55106-4412)
PHONE..............................651 232-1700
Brad Anderson, *Director*
EMP: 250
SALES (est): 25MM-49.9MM **Privately Held**
SIC: 8011 Physicians' office & clinic
PA: Healtheast Care System
1700 University Ave W # 5
Saint Paul MN 55104
651 232-1000

(G-8459)
HEALTHEAST CLINICS INFOLINE
1010 Highway 96 E (55127-2309)
PHONE..............................651 426-4844
FAX: 651 426-8935
Molly Steffen, *Office Mgr*
John Jendron, *Office Mgr*
Nancy Spurndle, *Manager*
EMP: 30 EST: 1996
SALES (est): 1MM-4.9MM **Privately Held**
SIC: 8049 Health practitioners' office

(G-8460)
HEALTHEAST DIVERSIFIED SVCS
Also Called: Rice Street Clinic
980 Rice St (55117-4949)
PHONE..............................651 489-8061
Cheryl McInery, *Office Mgr*
Kelly Nelson, *Manager*
Sarah M Hammes, *Director*
Marissa Battistini, *Physician Asst*
EMP: 37
SALES (est): 1MM-4.9MM **Privately Held**
SIC: 8011 Clinic operated by physicians
DH: Healtheast Diversified Svcs
559 Capitol Blvd
Saint Paul MN 55103
651 232-2300

(G-8461)
HEALTHEAST DIVERSIFIED SVCS (DH)
559 Capitol Blvd (55103-2101)
PHONE..............................651 232-2300
Tim Hanson, *President*
Brian Patty, *Vice Pres*
Mac McClurkan, *Vice Pres*
Judy Devitt, *Facilities Dir*
Jim Vandrasic, *Purch Mgr*
EST: 1980
SQ FT: 20,000
SALES (corp-wide): 1.33M **Privately Held**
SIC: 6512 8011 8062 8082 Nonresidential
building operator; clinic operated by
physicians; home health care services;
medical hospital
HQ: Healtheast Co's Inc
1700 University Ave W
Saint Paul MN 55104
651 232-2300

(G-8462)
HEALTHEAST HOME CARE INC
1700 University Ave W (55104-3727)
PHONE..............................651 232-2800
FAX: 651 232-2898
Lori Langeberg, *Manager*
Kathy Barr, *Director*
EMP: 450 EST: 1984
SQ FT: 2,000
SALES (est): 10MM-24.9MM **Privately Held**
SIC: 8082 Home health care services
HQ: Healtheast Co's Inc
1700 University Ave W
Saint Paul MN 55104
651 232-2300

(G-8463)
HEALTHEAST MAPLEWOOD OUT
Also Called: Maplewood Surgery Center
1655 Beam Ave Ste B (55109-1197)
PHONE..............................651 232-7780
Timothy H Hanson, *President*
EMP: 35 EST: 1982
SALES (est): 1MM-4.9MM **Privately Held**
SIC: 8011 8062 8093 Clinic operated by
physicians; medical hospital; specialty
outpatient clinic
DH: Healtheast Diversified Svcs
559 Capitol Blvd
Saint Paul MN 55103
651 232-2300

(G-8464)
HEALTHEAST MEDICAL RESEARCH
Also Called: Rice Street Clinic
1006 Rice St (55117-4951)
PHONE..............................651 489-8061
FAX: 651 489-0520
Paul Johnson, *Manager*
EMP: 35
SALES (est): 1MM-4.9MM **Privately Held**
SIC: 8011 Clinic operated by physicians
PA: Healtheast Medical Research
1700 University Ave W
Saint Paul MN 55104
651 232-5857

(G-8465)
HEALTHEAST ST JOHN'S HOSPITAL
1575 Beam Ave (55109-1126)
PHONE..............................651 232-7000
FAX: 651 232-7027
Timothy H Hanson, *President*
Diane Ögren, *Ch of Anesth*
Laure Wachbusch, *Ch OB/GYN*
Joseph Leverone, *Ch Pathology*
Paul Mulcahy, *Ch Radiology*
EMP: 713 EST: 1983
SALES (est): 50MM-99.9MM **Privately Held**
SIC: 8062 Medical hospital
PA: Healtheast Care System
1700 University Ave W # 5
Saint Paul MN 55104
651 232-1000

(G-8466)
HEALTHPARTNERS INC
Also Called: White Bear Lake Clinic
1430 Highway 96 E (55110-3653)
PHONE..............................651 653-2100
Patty Kroska, *Site Mgr*
Tom Grzeskowiak, *Dentist*
Don Worley, *Dentist*
Javed M Alik, *Med Doctor*
Gerald Hautman MD, *Med Doctor*
EMP: 120
SALES (est): 10MM-24.9MM **Privately Held**
WEB: www.healthpartners.com
SIC: 8011 Health maintenance organization
or HMO
PA: HealthPartners Inc
8170 33rd Ave S
Bloomington MN 55425
952 883-6000

(G-8467)
HEALTHPARTNERS INC
Also Called: St Paul Clinic
205 Wabasha St S (55107-1805)
PHONE..............................651 293-8100
FAX: 651 293-8116
Deanne Lorehr, *Principal*
Nancy Coleman, *Office Mgr*
Jean Ryon, *Office Mgr*
Kelly Uglen, *Pharmacist*
James D Norin, *Med Doctor*
EMP: 200
SALES (est): 25MM-49.9MM **Privately Held**
WEB: www.healthpartners.com
SIC: 8011 Health maintenance organization
or HMO
PA: HealthPartners Inc
8170 33rd Ave S
Bloomington MN 55425
952 883-6000

(G-8468)
HEALTHPARTNERS INC
Also Called: Stpaul Health Partner Clinic
205 Wabasha St S (55107-1805)
PHONE..............................651 227-3757
FAX: 651 293-8335
Gavin Thorfrud, *Office Mgr*
Jean Ryan, *Manager*
EMP: 40
SALES (est): 1MM-4.9MM **Privately Held**
WEB: www.healthpartners.com
SIC: 8021 Dental clinic
PA: HealthPartners Inc
8170 33rd Ave S
Bloomington MN 55425
952 883-6000

(G-8469)
HEALTHPARTNERS INC
Also Called: Maplewood Clinic
2165 White Bear Ave N (55109-2707)
PHONE..............................651 779-1500
FAX: 651 779-1597
Kate Covar, *Principal*
Mary L Anderson, *Dentist*
Kurtis A Klotzbuecher, *Dentist*
Karen M Raleigh, *Dentist*
Gail M Amundson MD, *Med Doctor*
EMP: 400
SALES (est): 25MM-49.9MM **Privately Held**
WEB: www.healthpartners.com
SIC: 8011 Physicians' office & clinic
PA: HealthPartners Inc
8170 33rd Ave S
Bloomington MN 55425
952 883-6000

(G-8470)
HEALTHPARTNERS INC
2635 University Ave W Ste 160
(55114-1271)
PHONE..............................651 254-3500
Wanda Bridges, *Office Mgr*
Mary J Pechacek, *Office Mgr*
Kristi Martin, *Branch Mgr*
Joanne E Kridr, *Med Doctor*
Kelly Largent MD, *Med Doctor*
EMP: 400
SALES (est): 50MM-99.9MM **Privately Held**
WEB: www.healthpartners.com
SIC: 8011 Health maintenance organization
or HMO
PA: HealthPartners Inc
8170 33rd Ave S
Bloomington MN 55425
952 883-6000

(G-8471)
HEALTHPARTNERS INC
Also Called: Maplewood Dental Clinic
2165 White Bear Ave N (55109-2707)
PHONE..............................651 770-8828
Pam Nuesemeyer, *Manager*
EMP: 50
SQ FT: 53,578
SALES (est): 1MM-4.9MM **Privately Held**
WEB: www.healthpartners.com
SIC: 8021 Dental clinic
PA: HealthPartners Inc
8170 33rd Ave S
Bloomington MN 55425
952 883-6000

(G-8472)
HEALTHPARTNERS INC
451 Dunlap St N (55104-4619)
PHONE..............................651 999-4740
Sharon B Rowe, *Principal*
Tim Lindquist, *Project Mgr*
Sharon Brownrowe, *Office Mgr*
Terrence J Maag MD, *Med Doctor*
Larisa Turin, *Supervisor*
EMP: 90
SALES (est): 5MM-9.9MM **Privately Held**
WEB: www.healthpartners.com
SIC: 8011 Medical center
PA: HealthPartners Inc
8170 33rd Ave S
Bloomington MN 55425
952 883-6000

(G-8473)
HEALTHPARTNERS INC
860 Arcade St (55106-3852)
PHONE..............................651 772-9757
FAX: 651 772-9959
Kathie Culhane-Pere, *Director*
Anthony Giefer, *Director*
Naomie Ramos, *Assistant*
Socorro Marquez, *Receptionist Se*
Xee X Vang, *Assistant*
EMP: 80
SALES (est): 5MM-9.9MM **Privately Held**
WEB: www.healthpartners.com
SIC: 8011 General & family practice
physician or surgeon office
PA: HealthPartners Inc
8170 33rd Ave S
Bloomington MN 55425
952 883-6000

(G-8474)
HEALTHPARTNERS INC
2500 Como Ave (55108-1460)
PHONE..............................651 641-6200
Glenn J Okner, *Optometrist*
Mark Kapphaan, *Optometrist*
Lori Geddes, *Optometrist*
Chad Reil, *Phys Therapist*
Sheryl Henly, *Manager*
EMP: 400
SALES (est): 25MM-49.9MM **Privately Held**
WEB: www.healthpartners.com
SIC: 8011 Pediatrician office
PA: HealthPartners Inc
8170 33rd Ave S
Bloomington MN 55425
952 883-6000

(G-8475)
HEARTLAND HOSPICE SERVICES INC
2250 County Road C W (55113-2504)
PHONE..............................651 633-6522
Judy Heim, *Marketing Mgr*
Emily Roosa, *Manager*
Darlene Casserly, *Manager*
Dan Vlasavijevich, *Manager*
Dan Vlaisavljevich, *Administrator*
EMP: 150
SALES (est): 5MM-9.9MM **Privately Held**
WEB: www.carlyle.com
SIC: 8082 Home health care services
HQ: Heartland Hospice Services LLC
333 N Summit St
Toledo OH 43604
419 252-5500

(G-8476)
HELGESON ENTERPRISES INC
4461 White Bear Pkwy (55110-7626)
PHONE..............................651 762-9700
Thomas Helgeson, *President*
Lisa Artisensi, *Accounts Mgr*
Paul Wright, *Manager*
Lisa Fleming, *Director*
Jeff Vansomeren, *Director*
EMP: 65 EST: 1972
SQ FT: 36,000
SALES (est): 5MM-9.9MM **Privately Held**
WEB: www.helgesonent.com
SIC: 7374 Data entry service

(G-8477)
HERITAGE ESTATES
2040 Wilson Ave Apt 7 (55119-3974)
PHONE..............................651 735-1776
FAX: 651 735-5302
Peter Lavander, *Principal*
Lisa Dack, *Manager*
EMP: 25 EST: 1992
SALES (est): 1MM-4.9MM **Privately Held**
SIC: 6513 Apartment building operator

(G-8478)
HERMES FLORAL CO INC
1790 Larpenteur Ave W (55113-5736)
PHONE..............................651 646-6344
FAX: 651 646-4890
Donald Hermes, *President*
James R Hermes, *Vice Pres*
Bill Bernston, *Manager*
EMP: 68 EST: 1891
SALES (est): 10MM-24.9MM **Privately Held**
WEB: www.hermeswholesale.com

GEOGRAPHIC

SIC: 5193 Wholesales fresh flowers; wholesales florists' supplies; wholesales potted plants; retails fresh flowers; retails potted plants

(G-8479)

HI-TECH EXPRESS INC

1743 County Road C W　(55113-1319)
PHONE..............................763 537-1690
Erwen Siemens, *President*
Jimmy Parranto, *General Mgr*
Darrell Smock, *Safety Dir*
Brian Honrud, *Office Mgr*
EMP: 35 EST: 1986
SALES (est): 1MM-4.9MM **Privately Held**
WEB: www.hi-techexpress.com
SIC: 4213 Heavy hauling transportation services

(G-8480)

HIGHLAND CHATEAU INC

2319 7th St W　(55116-2813)
PHONE..............................651 698-0793
FAX: 651 698-0378
Jerome Sansby, *President*
Peter Wolf, *Corp Secy*
Henry Weiner, *Treasurer*
Marty Denn, *Mktg Dir*
Mary B Lacine, *Administrator*
EMP: 125 EST: 1961
SQ FT: 40,000
SALES (est): 1MM-4.9MM **Privately Held**
WEB: www.highlandchateau.com
SIC: 8051 Convalescent home

(G-8481)

HIGHLAND CHATEAU SUITES LLC

2319 7th St W　(55116-2813)
PHONE..............................651 698-0793
David Briscoe, *Member*
Nancy Weinand, *Manager*
EMP: 99
SALES (est): 1MM-4.9MM **Privately Held**
SIC: 8059 Nursing home

(G-8482)

HIGHLAND NURSERY INC

1742 7th St W　(55116-2347)
PHONE..............................651 698-1708
Susan Hustings, *President*
EMP: 25 EST: 1948
SQ FT: 1,200
SALES (est): 5MM-9.9MM **Privately Held**
SIC: 0782 Retails nursery stock, seeds & bulbs; garden planting services; retails garden supplies & tools; retails natural Christmas trees

(G-8483)

HILL-ROM INC

1020 County Road F W　(55126-2910)
PHONE..............................651 490-1468
Dan Reuvers, *COO*
Chad Boerst, *Vice Pres*
Nick V Brunt, *Vice Pres*
Barry Greenwood, *Facilities Mgr*
Steve Smith, *VP Opers-Prdtn-*
EMP: 95
SALES (est): 25MM-49.9MM **Publicly Held**
WEB: www.hill-rom.com
SIC: 5047 Wholesales hospital equipment & supplies
HQ: Hill-Rom Inc
　　1069 State Route 46 E
　　Batesville IN 47006
　　812 934-7777

(G-8484)

HISTORICAL SOCIETY OF MN (PA)

345 Kellogg Blvd W　(55102-1903)
PHONE..............................651 259-3160
FAX: 651 297-1345
Sharon Avent, *Vice Pres*
William Stoeri, *Vice Pres*
W C Irrgang, *CFO*
Jeannie Richgels, *Marketing Mgr*
Megan Frederick, *Marketing Staff*
EMP: 250 EST: 1849
SQ FT: 430,000
SALES (corp-wide): 33.78M **Privately Held**
WEB: www.historictheatres.org

SIC: 8699 Historical club; general government administration office; state general government administration office

(G-8485)

HISTORICAL SOCIETY OF MN

Also Called: James J Hill House
240 Summit Ave　(55102-2121)
PHONE..............................651 297-2555
FAX: 651 297-5655
Micheal M Ouw, *Manager*
Sue Fair, *Manager*
EMP: 25
SALES (est): 1MM-4.9MM **Privately Held**
WEB: www.historictheatres.org
SIC: 8412 7389 8741 Museum; tourist information bureau; construction management services; state general government administration office
PA: Historical Society of MN
　　345 Kellogg Blvd W
　　Saint Paul MN 55102
　　651 259-3160

(G-8486)

HISTORY THEATRE INC

30 10th St E　(55101-2205)
PHONE..............................651 292-4323
FAX: 651 292-4322
Ron Peluso, *CEO*
John Apitz, *President*
Cathleen Hansen, *Managing Dir*
Kathleen Hansen, *Managing Dir*
Betsy Husting, *Consultant*
EMP: 120 EST: 1978
SQ FT: 250,042
SALES (est): 10MM-24.9MM **Privately Held**
WEB: www.historytheatre.com
SIC: 7922 Theater company

(G-8487)

HIWAY FEDERAL CREDIT UNION

111 Empire Dr　(55103-1860)
PHONE..............................651 291-1515
FAX: 651 291-7769
Jeff Schwalen, *President*
Dale Hovind, *Vice Pres*
Manfred Gabriel, *Human Res Mgr*
Deb Cariveau-Rogers, *Marketing Staff*
Brian White, *Manager*
EMP: 150 EST: 1931
SQ FT: 25,000
SALES (est): 25MM-49.9MM **Privately Held**
WEB: www.hiway.org
SIC: 6061 Federally chartered credit union

(G-8488)

HLB TAUTGES REDPATH

4810 White Bear Pkwy　(55110-3345)
PHONE..............................651 426-7000
Norman Longsdorf, *Member*
Ken George, *Member*
David Mol, *Member*
James S Redpath, *Member*
John Redpath, *Member*
EMP: 80 EST: 1965
SQ FT: 14,000
SALES (est): 1MM-4.9MM **Privately Held**
SIC: 8721 Accounting, auditing & bookkeeping services

(G-8489)

HMONG AMERICAN PARTNERSHIP

1075 Arcade St　(55106-3213)
PHONE..............................651 495-9160
William Ying, *President*
Patrice Tetta, *Manager*
Ed Sriharatsa, *Director*
Bao Yin, *Director*
Fue Heu, *Director*
EMP: 41 EST: 1990
SQ FT: 8,000
SALES (est): 1MM-4.9MM **Privately Held**
SIC: 8322 Individual & family social services

(G-8490)

HMONG HOME HEALTH

933 White Bear Ave N 1　(55106-3014)
PHONE..............................651 488-1680
Nou Her, *President*
EMP: 40 EST: 1993
SALES (est): 1MM-4.9MM **Privately Held**
SIC: 8082 Home health care services

(G-8491)

HOGLUND, CHWIALKOWSKI

1611 County Road B W # 102 (55113-4053)
PHONE..............................651 628-9929
FAX: 651 628-9377
Robert J Hoglund, *General Ptnr*
Jeff Bursell, *Manager*
Andy Oakes, *IT/INT Sup*
EMP: 40 EST: 1990
SALES (est): 5MM-9.9MM **Privately Held**
WEB: www.hoglundlaw.com
SIC: 8111 Bankruptcy law office

(G-8492)

HOM FURNITURE INC

2480 Cleveland Ave N　(55113-2719)
PHONE..............................651 634-6600
FAX: 651 634-6680
Keith Nelson, *Manager*
EMP: 40
SALES (est): 5MM-9.9MM **Privately Held**
WEB: www.homfurniture.com
SIC: 5023 Retails office furniture; retails spas & hot tubs; wholesales barbecue grills; retails clocks
PA: Hom Furniture Inc
　　10301 Woodcrest Dr NW
　　Minneapolis MN 55433
　　763 767-3600

(G-8493)

HOME INSTEAD SENIOR CARE

2580 White Bear Ave N # 104 (55109-5166)
PHONE..............................651 747-8722
FAX: 651 747-8726
Kendra Phillips, *President*
EMP: 120 EST: 1996
SALES (est): 1MM-4.9MM **Privately Held**
WEB: www.zoehomecare.com
SIC: 8082 Home health care services

(G-8494)

HOPE COMMON

Also Called: Familias De Esperanza
550 Vandalia St Ste 1　(55114-1856)
PO Box 14298　(55114-0298)
PHONE..............................651 917-0917
FAX: 651 917-7458
Bill Huesch, *Ch of Bd*
Pete Regnier, *Vice Pres*
Kathleen Lock, *CFO*
Dave Heider, *Treasurer*
Shannon Broderick, *Manager*
EMP: 150 EST: 1986
SQ FT: 4,000
SALES (est): 5MM-9.9MM **Privately Held**
WEB: www.commonhope.org
SIC: 8322 Child & youth services

(G-8495)

HOSPICE OF HEALTHEAST INC

69 Exchange St W　(55102-1004)
PHONE..............................651 232-3312
Beth Spottiswoode, *Director*
EMP: 90 EST: 1980
SALES (est): 1MM-4.9MM **Privately Held**
SIC: 8051 8082 Skilled nursing care facility; home health care services

(G-8496)

HOSPITAL PATHOLOGY ASSOCIATES

2345 Rice St Ste 160　(55113-3769)
PHONE..............................651 483-2033
FAX: 651 776-7845
John G Strickler, *President*
John Reinartz MD, *Corp Secy*
Stanley McCormick MD, *Vice Pres*
Kevin Stieglbauer MD, *Vice Pres*
Michael Trump MD, *Treasurer*
EMP: 47 EST: 1978
SALES (est): 5MM-9.9MM **Privately Held**
WEB: www.hpath.com
SIC: 8011 Pathologist office

(G-8497)

HOUSE OF HOPE PRESBYTERIAN

797 Summit Ave　(55105-3353)
PHONE..............................651 227-6311
FAX: 651 227-9969

John Miller, *Principal*
Linda Loving, *Pastor*
Michelle Freyholtz, *Manager*
Sofia Ardalan, *Director*
Jo Kircher, *Director*
EMP: 55 EST: 1855 **Privately Held**
WEB: www.hohchurch.org
SIC: 8351 Provides Presbyterian church services; child day care service

(G-8498)

HOWRY RESIDENTIAL SERVICES

475 Cleveland Ave N　(55104-5031)
PHONE..............................651 917-9111
Mike Saliga, *Principal*
EMP: 25 EST: 2005
SALES (est): 500-999K **Privately Held**
SIC: 8361 Group foster home

(G-8499)

HUBBARD BROADCASTING INC

Also Called: Kstp TV
3415 University Ave W　(55114-1019)
PHONE..............................651 646-5555
FAX: 651 642-4142
Rob Hubbard, *President*
Mike Smith, *Publisher*
Ada Sosunov, *Editor*
Kateri Wozny, *Editor*
John Mayasich, *Vice Pres*
EMP: 600
SALES (est): 100MM-499.9MM **Privately Held**
SIC: 4833 Television broadcasting station

(G-8500)

HUNT ELECTRIC CORP (PA)

2300 Territorial Rd Ste 1　(55114-1638)
PHONE..............................651 646-2911
FAX: 651 643-6575
Michael Hanson, *President*
John T Elliott, *Corp Secy*
Duane J Grundhoefer, *Corp Secy*
James J Basara, *Vice Pres*
Curtis Southward, *Vice Pres*
EMP: 450 EST: 1965
SQ FT: 75,000
SALES (corp-wide): 321.60M **Privately Held**
SIC: 1731 General electrical contractor

(G-8501)

HYDRALIFT AMCLYDE INC (HQ)

240 Plato Blvd E　(55107-1609)
PHONE..............................651 293-4646
FAX: 651 293-4646
Richard Juelich, *President*
Pierre Delago, *Vice Pres*
Dick Busker, *Purch Agent*
Roger Baumhover, *Human Res Mgr*
◆ EMP: 100 EST: 2002
SQ FT: 38,000
SALES (corp-wide): 12.71B **Publicly Held**
WEB: www.natoil.com
SIC: 8711 Ship, boat, machine & product design services; manufactures cranes & monorail systems
PA: National Oilwell Varco Inc
　　7909 Parkwood Circle Dr
　　Houston TX 77036
　　713 346-7500

(G-8502)

I C SYSTEM INC

1170 Grey Fox Rd　(55112-6908)
PHONE..............................651 486-0118
John Erickson, *CEO*
EMP: 150
SALES (est): 10MM-24.9MM **Privately Held**
SIC: 7331 Direct mail advertising service

(G-8503)

ICON SERVICES CORP

1043 Grand Ave Ste 312　(55105-2689)
PHONE..............................651 695-8778
FAX: 651 644-2976
Elijah Shaw, *President*
EMP: 30 EST: 1998
SALES (est): 1MM-4.9MM **Privately Held**
WEB: www.industry-icon.com
SIC: 7389 6411 Personal investigation service; insurance inspection & investigation service

www.HarrisInfo.com
368
　　　　2011 Harris Minnesota
　　　　Services Directory
▲=Import ▼=Export
◆=Import/Export

(G-8504)
IDEACOM MID-AMERICA INC
Also Called: Communications Mid-America
30 Water St W (55107-2009)
PHONE..............651 292-0102
Laurence E Anderson, *President*
John L Anderson, *Vice Pres*
James Anderson, *Vice Pres*
Myron Anderson, *CFO*
Robert Braun, *CFO*
EMP: 52 EST: 1954
SQ FT: 12,000
SALES (est): 5MM-9.9MM **Privately Held**
WEB: www.idea-ma.com
SIC: 1731 Telephone equipment installation

(G-8505)
IDENTIFIX INC
Also Called: Ais
2714 Patton Rd (55113-1138)
PHONE..............651 633-8007
Robert Pringle, *President*
Aaron Cherrington, *VP Sls/Mktg*
John Dedzj, *Finance Mgr*
David Boyle, *VP Sales*
Thomas Gordon, *Manager*
EMP: 75 EST: 1987
SQ FT: 17,000
SALES (est): 5MM-9.9MM **Privately Held**
SIC: 7549 Automotive maintenance service
PA: Service Repair Solutions Inc
3058 E Sunset Rd Ste 113
Las Vegas NV 89120
702 433-7101

(G-8506)
IMAGO LTD
1190 James Ave (55105-2919)
PHONE..............651 690-9724
Laura Hlavac, *President*
Wayne Hlavac, *Vice Pres*
Beth Poutges, *Accounts Mgr*
Beth Toutges, *Manager*
Benjamin Hlavac, *Manager*
▲ EMP: 60 EST: 1987
SALES (est): 1MM-4.9MM **Privately Held**
WEB: www.imagoltd.com
SIC: 7389 8748 Manufactures men's, youths' & boys' athletic clothing; business consulting services; manufactures women's, misses' & juniors' athletic clothing; manufactures children's & girls' clothing; sewing contractor

(G-8507)
IMPACT PHYSICAL MEDICINE
1600 University Ave W # 10 (55104-3898)
PHONE..............651 641-0688
Stan Babel, *Manager*
Mark Agre, *Director*
EMP: 25 EST: 1995
SALES (est): 1MM-4.9MM **Privately Held**
SIC: 8049 Physical therapist office

(G-8508)
INDEPENDENT DELIVERY SERVICES
440 Minnehaha Ave W (55103-1523)
PHONE..............651 487-1050
FAX: 651 487-1807
Michael Depe, *President*
EMP: 80 EST: 1973
SQ FT: 18,000
SALES (est): 5MM-9.9MM **Privately Held**
WEB: www.independentdel.com
SIC: 4212 7319 Delivery services by vehicle; sample distribution advertising service; shopping news, advertising & distributing services

(G-8509)
INDEPENDENT REPUBLICANS OF MN
525 Park St Ste 250 (55103-2145)
PHONE..............651 222-0022
FAX: 651 224-4122
Barbara Linert, *Office Mgr*
Ben Tolnik, *Manager*
Joel N Cary, *Info Tech Dir*
EMP: 45 EST: 1855
SQ FT: 3,300 **Privately Held**
SIC: 8651 Political organization

(G-8510)
INDEPENDENT SCHOOL DISTRICT
1910 County Road B W (55113-5448)
PHONE..............651 604-3503
FAX: 651 604-3501
Karen Schaub, *Branch Mgr*
EMP: 100
SALES (est): 5MM-9.9MM **Privately Held**
WEB: www.roseville.k12.mn.us
SIC: 8322 Community center
PA: Independent School District
1251 County Road B2 W
Saint Paul MN 55113
651 635-1600

(G-8511)
INDUSTRIAL FABRICS ASSOCIATION
1801 County Road B W (55113-4052)
PHONE..............651 222-2508
FAX: 651 631-9334
Stephen M Warner, *CEO*
Steven Rider, *CFO*
Cindy Stiller, *Accounting Dir*
Kelly Thomalla, *Marketing Mgr*
Juli Case, *Manager*
EMP: 75 EST: 1912
SQ FT: 23,000
SALES (est): 10MM-24.9MM **Privately Held**
WEB: www.ifai.com
SIC: 8611 Publishes & prints trade journals; trade association

(G-8512)
INFORMATION BUILDERS INC
444 Cedar St Ste 2000 (55101-2157)
PHONE..............651 602-9100
FAX: 651 298-9835
Carl Wangberg, *Branch Mgr*
Rich Hall, *Manager*
William Finnegan, *Manager*
Bill Finnegan, *Manager*
EMP: 25
SALES (est): 1MM-4.9MM **Privately Held**
WEB: www.informationbuilders.com
SIC: 7373 Computer systems analysis & design
PA: Information Builders Inc
2 Penn Plz Fl 27
New York NY 10121
212 736-4433

(G-8513)
INFORMATION SECURITY TECH
2550 University Ave W 155S (55114-1098)
PHONE..............651 287-0823
Dave Gustafson, *President*
Pete Venuta, *Exec VP*
Wade Ebert, *Accounts Mgr*
EMP: 34 EST: 1997
SQ FT: 1,200
SALES (est): 25MM-49.9MM **Privately Held**
WEB: www.forsythe.com
SIC: 5045 Wholesales computers, peripherals & software
HQ: Forsythe Solutions Group Inc
7770 Frontage Rd
Skokie IL 60077
847 213-7000

(G-8514)
INTEGRIS GROUP INC
450 Oak Grove Pkwy (55127-8536)
PHONE..............651 490-0000
John Ledy, *President*
Dave Jessen, *Vice Pres*
Patrick Thielen, *Manager*
EMP: 100 EST: 2003 **Privately Held**
SIC: 6719 Public utility holding company

(G-8515)
INTERLINE BRANDS INC
1930 Energy Park Dr (55108-2736)
PHONE..............651 644-7075
EMP: 25
SALES (est): 1MM-4.9MM **Publicly Held**
SIC: 4225 General warehousing
PA: Interline Brands Inc
701 San Marco Blvd
Jacksonville FL 32207
904 421-1400

(G-8516)
INTERNATIONAL INSTITUTE OF MN
Also Called: Instant Passport Photos
1694 Como Ave (55108-2710)
PHONE..............651 647-0191
FAX: 651 647-9268
Jan Borden, *Exec Dir*
Steve Heckler, *Director*
EMP: 55 EST: 1919
SQ FT: 25,000 **Privately Held**
WEB: www.iimn.org
SIC: 8641 Civic & social organization

(G-8517)
INTERNATIONAL PAPER CO
1699 9th St (55110-6717)
PHONE..............651 426-0345
Joe Lenway, *Controller*
Jim Ondich, *Sales Staff*
Donna Luther, *Manager*
Ryan Steen, *Manager*
Faith Miller, *Administration*
EMP: 125
SALES (est): 5MM-9.9MM **Publicly Held**
WEB: www.internationalpaper.com
SIC: 7389 Packaging & labeling services; manufactures corrugated & solid fiber containers; manufactures metal containers
PA: International Paper Co
6400 Poplar Ave
Memphis TN 38197
901 419-7000

(G-8518)
INTERNET BROADCASTING SYSTEMS
355 Randolph Ave (55102-3610)
PHONE..............651 365-4000
FAX: 651 365-4430
Reid Johnson, *President*
Pj Anzalone, *Partner*
Karen Yancey, *Editor*
Casey Tiedens, *Corp Secy*
Lisa Bilcik, *Corp Secy*
EMP: 106 EST: 1996
SQ FT: 5,000 **Privately Held**
WEB: www.ibsys.com
SIC: 7375 Information retrieval services

(G-8519)
INTERPLASTIC CORP (PA)
1225 Willow Lake Blvd (55110-5145)
PHONE..............651 481-6860
James D Wallenfelsz, *CEO*
Rich McDonald, *General Mgr*
Richard T McCabe, *Business Mgr*
Robert D Roma, *Vice Pres*
Ivan Levy, *Vice Pres*
▼ EMP: 50 EST: 1962
SQ FT: 15,000
SALES (corp-wide): 400M **Privately Held**
WEB: www.interplastic.com
SIC: 5169 Wholesales synthetic resins, rubber & plastic materials; manufactures polyesters; manufactures vinyl resins; manufactures plastic molding compounds

(G-8520)
INTERPLASTIC CORP
1219 Willow Lake Blvd (55110-5145)
PHONE..............651 481-6860
James Wallenfelsz, *Branch Mgr*
EMP: 40
SALES (est): 25MM-49.9MM **Privately Held**
WEB: www.interplastic.com
SIC: 5169 Manufactures polyesters; manufactures vinyl resins; wholesales synthetic resins, rubber & plastic materials; manufactures plastic molding compounds
PA: Interplastic Corp
1225 Willow Lake Blvd
Saint Paul MN 55110
651 481-6860

(G-8521)
INTERPRETATION & TRANS
778 University Ave W (55104-4873)
PHONE..............651 292-9701
FAX: 651 292-0208
Yee Lee, *President*
EMP: 30 EST: 1994
SALES (est): 1MM-4.9MM **Privately Held**
SIC: 7389 Translation & interpretation services

(G-8522)
INTERSTATE BRANDS CORP
Also Called: Wonder & Hostess
2404 Rice St (55113-3701)
PHONE..............651 484-6020
FAX: 651 484-6020
Kaylin McFarland, *Manager*
Paul Mueller, *Manager*
EMP: 25
SALES (est): 10MM-24.9MM **Privately Held**
SIC: 5149 Wholesales bakery products
PA: Hostess Brands Inc
6031 Connection Dr
Irving TX 75039
972 532-4500

(G-8523)
INTOUCH INC
2 Pine Tree Dr Ste 307 (55112-3715)
PHONE..............651 255-7700
Brian J Carroll, *CEO*
Brandon Stamschror, *COO*
Michelle Passe, *Vice Pres*
Nikki Lorch, *Human Resources*
Nicolette Dease, *Program Mgr*
EMP: 60 EST: 1995
SQ FT: 11,709
SALES (est): 5MM-9.9MM **Privately Held**
WEB: www.intouch-inc.com
SIC: 7336 Advertisers creative service

(G-8524)
ISAAC FAIR CORP
4295 Lexington Ave N (55126-6164)
PHONE..............651 482-8593
FAX: 651 486-9688
Vickie Miller, *Managing Dir*
Tom McEnery, *Vice Pres*
Charles Knight, *Purch Mgr*
Justin Neudahl, *Engineer*
Richard Deal, *Human Res Dir*
EMP: 350
SQ FT: 33,000
SALES (est): 25MM-49.9MM **Publicly Held**
WEB: www.fairisaac.com
SIC: 7374 Computer service bureau
PA: Fair Isaac Corp
901 Marquette Ave Ste 3200
Minneapolis MN 55402
612 758-5200

(G-8525)
IZAAK WALTON LEAGUE OF AMERICA
1619 Dayton Ave Ste 202 (55104-6276)
PHONE..............651 649-1446
FAX: 651 649-1494
Curt Leitz, *Vice Pres*
Bill Grant, *Exec Dir*
Gary Schwartz, *Bd of Directors*
EMP: 39
SALES (est): 1MM-4.9MM **Privately Held**
WEB: www.iwla.org
SIC: 8748 8699 Environmental consultant; charitable organization

(G-8526)
J & J DISTRIBUTING CO
653 Rice St (55103-1849)
PHONE..............651 221-0560
FAX: 651 221-0570
James H Hannigan, *President*
Deborah A Hannigan, *Vice Pres*
John Wujek, *CFO*
John Wujack, *CFO*
Patty Fyksen, *Accountant*
▲ EMP: 140 EST: 1979
SQ FT: 81,000
SALES (est): 50MM-99.9MM **Privately Held**
WEB: www.jjdst.com
SIC: 5148 Wholesales fresh fruits & vegetables

(G-8527)
JACK & JILL PRESCHOOL
1910 County Road B W (55113-5448)
PHONE..............651 604-3810
FAX: 651 604-3812
Carol Arens, *Director*
EMP: 28 EST: 1987
SALES (est): 500-999K **Privately Held**
WEB: www.jackandjillpreschool.com

SIC: 8351 Child day care service

(G-8528)
JACKSON STREET ASSOCIATES LLC
180 5th St E Ste 160 (55101-1490)
PHONE..............................651 228-9456
Angela Hummelgard, *Principal*
EMP: 25
SALES (est): 1MM-4.9MM **Privately Held**
SIC: 6531 Commercial real estate agency

(G-8529)
JAMES STEELE CONSTRUCTION CO
1410 Sylvan St (55117-4606)
PHONE..............................651 488-6755
FAX: 651 488-4787
Richard Naughton, *President*
Sandra Naughton, *Corp Secy*
Lindey Lutz, *Marketing Mgr*
Randy Waughtal, *Office Mgr*
EMP: 40 EST: 1991
SQ FT: 2,500
SALES (est): 10MM-24.9MM **Privately Held**
WEB: www.jsteeleconstruction.com
SIC: 1542 New commercial & office building construction; commercial & office building renovation & repair services

(G-8530)
JENSON, BEEL, CONVERSE
Also Called: Converse, Mitchell W
1700 Highway 36 W Ste 110 (55113-4093)
PHONE..............................651 223-4999
FAX: 651 223-4987
Willard Converse, *President*
Dori Betts, *Office Mgr*
Walther Kurt, *Attorney*
Roger A Jensen, *Attorney*
James C Erickson, *Attorney*
EMP: 25 EST: 1998
SALES (est): 1MM-4.9MM **Privately Held**
WEB: www.pbcj.com
SIC: 8111 Legal services

(G-8531)
JEWISH COMMUNITY CENTER OF THE
1375 Saint Paul Ave (55116-2828)
PHONE..............................651 698-0751
FAX: 651 698-8591
Matthew Levitt, *COO*
Peter Mansfield, *Development*
Rebecca Nilsestuen, *Accountant*
Curt Prins, *Mktg Dir*
Cathy Armstrong, *Director*
EMP: 99 EST: 1929 **Privately Held**
WEB: www.stpauljcc.org
SIC: 8641 Community membership club

(G-8532)
JEWISH COMMUNITY NURSERY & DAY
1375 Saint Paul Ave (55116-2828)
PHONE..............................651 698-0751
Lisa Rosenfield, *President*
EMP: 40 EST: 1964
SALES (est): 500-999K **Privately Held**
SIC: 8351 Child day care service

(G-8533)
JIMMY'S CONFERENCE & CATERING
3565 Labore Rd (55110-5125)
PHONE..............................651 482-1233
James Proulx, *President*
EMP: 50 EST: 2000
SALES (est): 1MM-4.9MM **Privately Held**
SIC: 7299 Banquet hall facility

(G-8534)
JOHN A KANUTSON
1781 Prior Ave N (55113-5549)
PHONE..............................651 641-1099
Peter Schadegg, *Member*
EMP: 35 EST: 2001
SALES (est): 1MM-4.9MM **Privately Held**
SIC: 8721 Certified public accountant services

(G-8535)
JOHN A KNUTSON & CO
1781 Prior Ave N (55113-5549)
PHONE..............................651 641-1099
Brian Knutson, *Managing Prtnr*
Pete Schadegg, *Partner*
Jeff Meek, *Partner*
Jason Loven, *Partner*
Todd Koch, *Partner*
EMP: 40 EST: 1930
SALES (est): 1MM-4.9MM **Privately Held**
WEB: www.knutson-cpa.com
SIC: 8721 Certified public accountant services

(G-8536)
JOHNSON BROTHERS LIQUOR CO
Also Called: Phillips Wine & Spirits
1999 Shepard Rd (55116-3210)
PHONE..............................651 649-5800
Lynn Johnson, *CEO*
EMP: 400
SALES (est): 100MM-499.9MM **Privately Held**
SIC: 5182 5149 Wholesales wine & distilled alcoholic beverages; wholesales juices

(G-8537)
JOHNSON BROTHERS LIQUOR CO
Also Called: Wine Merchants
1999 Shepard Rd (55116-3210)
PHONE..............................651 649-5800
Kevin Loegering, *CFO*
Lynn Johnson, *Manager*
Mikel Morgan, *Manager*
Haseen Alam, *CIO*
Ester Kauffman, *Administration*
EMP: 200
SALES (est): 100MM-499.9MM **Privately Held**
SIC: 5182 5149 Wholesales wine; wholesales juices

(G-8538)
JUUT MIDWEST INC
857 Grand Ave Ste 3 (55105-3377)
PHONE..............................651 222-4121
Lisa Williams, *Manager*
EMP: 65
SALES (est): 1MM-4.9MM **Privately Held**
WEB: www.juut.com
SIC: 7231 Cosmetology & personal hygiene salon
HQ: Juut Midwest Inc
201 Main St SE Ste 324
Minneapolis MN 55414
612 676-2250

(G-8539)
JUUT MIDWEST INC
2480 Fairview Ave N (55113-2699)
PHONE..............................651 639-0576
Jessica Gulyard, *Manager*
EMP: 30
SALES (est): 500-999K **Privately Held**
WEB: www.juut.com
SIC: 7231 Beauty salon
HQ: Juut Midwest Inc
201 Main St SE Ste 324
Minneapolis MN 55414
612 676-2250

(G-8540)
KARGES-FAULCONBRIDGE INC
670 County Road B W (55113-4527)
PHONE..............................651 771-0880
FAX: 651 771-0878
James Faulconbridge, *President*
Randy Christenson, *Vice Pres*
Gerald Chartrand, *Manager*
Mark Deshaw, *Manager*
Ryan Erickson, *CIO*
EMP: 65 EST: 1996
SQ FT: 34,500
SALES (est): 5MM-9.9MM **Privately Held**
WEB: www.kfieng.com
SIC: 8711 Engineering consulting services

(G-8541)
KATH MANAGEMENT CO
3096 Rice St (55113-2204)
PHONE..............................651 484-3325
Bruce Kath, *President*
Jeff Larson, *Corp Secy*
Steve Dahl, *Vice Pres*
EMP: 90 EST: 1946
SQ FT: 7,000
SALES (est): 10MM-24.9MM **Privately Held**
WEB: www.kathhvac.com
SIC: 5013 5172 Gas station; wholesales automotive supplies & parts; wholesales fuel oil; retail independent convenience store; retails automotive parts; fuel oil dealer; wholesales petroleum products

(G-8542)
KEEBLER CO
1275 Willow Lake Blvd (55110-5158)
PHONE..............................651 484-0833
FAX: 651 484-8833
Steve Cunningham, *Manager*
Erin Eason, *Manager*
EMP: 46
SALES (est): 1MM-4.9MM **Publicly Held**
WEB: www.keebler.com
SIC: 4225 4212 4214 General warehousing; local trucking with storage; local trucking without storage services

(G-8543)
KEHNE ELECTRIC CORP
2330 Wycliff St (55114-1220)
PO Box 16478 (55116-0478)
PHONE..............................651 645-5781
FAX: 651 649-3516
Donald S Kehne, *President*
Richard Kehne, *Vice Pres*
EMP: 50 EST: 1996
SQ FT: 15,000
SALES (est): 5MM-9.9MM **Privately Held**
SIC: 1731 Electrical contractor

(G-8544)
KELLY MIDWEST VENTURES LP
Also Called: Best Western
161 Saint Anthony Ave A (55103-2300)
PHONE..............................651 227-8711
FAX: 651 227-1698
Brian Fannemel, *Manager*
EMP: 70
SALES (est): 1MM-4.9MM **Privately Held**
SIC: 7011 Traveler accommodations; eating place; drinking establishment

(G-8545)
KENNEDY BRISSMAN
1930 Energy Park Dr Ste 2 (55108-2738)
PHONE..............................651 646-7933
FAX: 651 645-6395
Chris A Norgren, *Member*
Derek Pedlar, *Vice Pres*
Marge Hilmanowski, *Human Resources*
Jill Duchene, *Accounts Mgr*
Dale Norgren, *Director*
EMP: 45 EST: 1947
SQ FT: 76,000
SALES (est): 25MM-49.9MM **Publicly Held**
WEB: www.matcrafters.com
SIC: 5169 5087 5113 Wholesales specialty cleaning & sanitation preparations; wholesales cleaning & maintenance equipment & supplies; wholesales sanitation preparations; wholesales industrial & personal service paper
DH: Amsan LLC
5727 S Lewis Ave Ste 705
Tulsa OK 74105
918 743-6030

(G-8546)
KEY MEDICAL SUPPLY INC
5910 Rice Creek Pkwy # 1000
(55126-5023)
PHONE..............................651 792-3860
Jackie Anderson, *President*
Jeff Richards, *General Mgr*
Lori Gelbmann, *Manager*
EMP: 47 EST: 1998
SALES (est): 5MM-9.9MM **Privately Held**
WEB: www.keymedicalsupply.com
SIC: 5047 Retails medical apparatus & supplies; wholesales medical equipment & supplies

(G-8547)
KEYS WELL DRILLING CO INC
1156 Homer St (55116-3232)
PHONE..............................651 646-7871
FAX: 651 641-0216
Jeff Key, *President*
George Keys, *Vice Pres*
Nadine Kelly, *Manager*
EMP: 30 EST: 1890
SQ FT: 21,000
SALES (est): 1MM-4.9MM **Privately Held**
WEB: www.keyswell.com
SIC: 1781 Water well drilling contractor

(G-8548)
KEYSTONE COMMUNITY SERVICES
2000 Saint Anthony Ave (55104-5125)
PHONE..............................651 645-0349
Greg Wandersee, *President*
Eric Nyberg, *Vice Pres*
Dianne Gustafason, *Human Res Mgr*
Dai Thao, *Director*
EMP: 57 EST: 1995
SALES (est): 1MM-4.9MM **Privately Held**
SIC: 8322 Individual & family social services

(G-8549)
KLINE VOLVO INC (PA)
3040 Highway 61 (55109-1081)
PHONE..............................651 379-4300
Rick Kline, *President*
Misti Winscher, *Sales Mgr*
Amber Kasprowicz, *Sales Mgr*
Andrew Fier, *Sales Mgr*
EMP: 60 EST: 1956 **Privately Held**
WEB: www.klinevolvo.com
SIC: 7538 Retails new & used automobiles; general automotive repair services

(G-8550)
KNOWLEDGE LEARNING CORP
Also Called: Children's World
4545 Hamline Ave N (55112-5719)
PHONE..............................651 631-8728
FAX: 651 631-1017
Rachel Robinson, *Sales Staff*
Brenda Cadalbert, *Director*
EMP: 30
SALES (est): 500-999K **Privately Held**
WEB: www.knowledgelearning.com
SIC: 8351 Child day care service
PA: Knowledge Learning Corp
650 NE Holladay St # 1400
Portland OR 97232
503 872-1300

(G-8551)
KSA REAL ESTATE SERVICES INC
740 Linwood Ave (55105-3322)
PHONE..............................651 290-0507
Anthony Vavoulis, *President*
EMP: 50 EST: 1991
SALES (est): 5MM-9.9MM **Privately Held**
SIC: 6531 Real estate services

(G-8552)
KSTP FM LLC
3415 University Ave W (55114-1019)
PHONE..............................651 642-4242
Jenny Morris, *CEO*
Jeff Nelson, *Engineer*
Tom Newberry, *Controller*
EMP: 36 EST: 1979
SALES (est): 1MM-4.9MM **Privately Held**
SIC: 4832 Radio broadcasting station

(G-8553)
L S BLACK CONSTRUCTORS INC
1959 Sloan Pl Ste 140 (55117-2070)
PHONE..............................651 774-8445
FAX: 651 774-9695
Larry S Black, *President*
Sterling Black, *Vice Pres*
Norma Black, *Treasurer*
Mike Pederso, *Office Mgr*
Paul Provenvazano, *Administrator*
EMP: 60 EST: 1977
SQ FT: 1,600
SALES (est): 10MM-24.9MM **Privately Held**
WEB: www.lsblack.com

www.HarrisInfo.com
370

2011 Harris Minnesota
Services Directory

▲=Import ▼=Export
◆=Import/Export

SIC: 1542 1541 New commercial & office building construction; new industrial building construction; industrial building renovating, remodeling & repair service; commercial & office building renovation & repair services

(G-8554)
LAC ENTERPRISES INC
1175 Highway 36 E (55109-2007)
PHONE..............................651 482-0205
FAX: 651 482-7235
Terry Childers, *President*
Lori Childers, *Corp Secy*
Robert Miller, *Manager*
Ralph Buche, *Manager*
EMP: 30 **EST:** 1972
SQ FT: 6,100 **Privately Held**
SIC: 0782 Landscaping services

(G-8555)
LAFAYETTE LITHO INC
285 Florida St (55107-1616)
PHONE..............................651 665-5617
FAX: 651 665-4646
George Fremder, *Ch of Bd*
Tom Neckvatal, *President*
Dan Gieser, *Engineering*
Robert Corey, *Manager*
Mark Kramer, *Manager*
EMP: 40 **EST:** 1989
SQ FT: 22,200
SALES (est): 5MM-9.9MM **Privately Held**
SIC: 7336 Graphic arts & related design service
HQ: Enterprise Holding Corp
400 Robert St N
Saint Paul MN 55101
651 665-3500

(G-8556)
LAKE AREA BANK
1400 Highway 96 E Ste 1 (55110-8500)
PHONE..............................651 653-9619
FAX: 651 653-0468
Kerstin Wellman, *Manager*
Rita Pechman, *Manager*
EMP: 38
SALES (est): 10MM-24.9MM **Privately Held**
WEB: www.lakeareabank.com
SIC: 6029 Commercial bank
HQ: Lake Area Bank
12790 N 1st Ave
Lindstrom MN 55045
651 257-1117

(G-8557)
LAKE AREA MORTGAGE
1400 Highway 96 E Ste 1 (55110-1447)
PHONE..............................651 257-1114
Paula Williams, *Vice Pres*
EMP: 60 **EST:** 1999
SALES (est): 5MM-9.9MM **Privately Held**
SIC: 6162 Mortgage & loan lending

(G-8558)
LAKEVILLE MOTOR EXPRESS INC
500 County Road D W (55112-3520)
PO Box 130280 (55113-0003)
PHONE..............................651 636-8900
FAX: 651 633-7666
John Wren, *CEO*
Peter Martin, *President*
Bill Felle, *Vice Pres*
Karen Vanney, *Vice Pres*
Mike Brown, *Manager*
EMP: 295 **EST:** 1921
SQ FT: 40,000
SALES (est): 25MM-49.9MM **Privately Held**
SIC: 4212 Local trucking without storage services
PA: Wren Corp
2975 Partridge Rd
Saint Paul MN 55113
651 636-8900

(G-8559)
LAMETTRY COLLISION INC
2923 Maplewood Dr (55109-1019)
PHONE..............................651 766-9770
FAX: 651 766-8660
Steve Daniel, *General Mgr*
Sam Lee, *Manager*
EMP: 30
SALES (est): 1MM-4.9MM **Privately Held**

WEB: www.lamettrys.com
SIC: 7532 Exterior repair service; automotive paint shop

(G-8560)
LAND TITLE INC
1900 Silver Lake Rd NW Ste 200 (55112-1789)
PHONE..............................651 638-1900
FAX: 651 638-1994
Jeff Christian, *President*
Greg Booth, *President*
Kristina Duerr, *Vice Pres*
Larry Mountain, *Vice Pres*
Jean Franhold, *Treasurer*
EMP: 52 **EST:** 1985
SALES (est): 5MM-9.9MM **Privately Held**
SIC: 6361 6531 Title insurance carrier; real estate services

(G-8561)
LAO FAMILY COMMUNITY OF MN
320 University Ave W (55103-2015)
PHONE..............................651 221-0069
FAX: 651 221-0276
Kou Vang, *Treasurer*
Laopao Vang, *Corp Counsel*
Margo Cohen, *Manager*
Peggy Thao, *Manager*
Long Yang, *Director*
EST: 1977
SQ FT: 16,000 **Privately Held**
WEB: www.laofamily.org
SIC: 8322 Individual & family social services

(G-8562)
LARKIN INDUSTRIES INC
2020 Energy Park Dr (55108-1506)
PHONE..............................651 645-6000
FAX: 651 645-6082
Michael Larkin, *President*
Chuck Katz, *General Mgr*
Lynnette Larkin, *Corp Secy*
Tom Larkin, *Info Tech Mgr*
EMP: 50 **EST:** 1975
SQ FT: 47,000
SALES (est): 1MM-4.9MM **Privately Held**
SIC: 7389 Folding & collating service for printers

(G-8563)
LARSON ENGINEERING INC (PA)
3524 Labore Rd (55110-5126)
PHONE..............................651 481-9120
FAX: 651 481-9201
Lee Granquist, *President*
Frank D Werner, *Corp Secy*
Kesh Ramdular, *Corp Secy*
John Dastore, *Vice Pres*
John Pastore, *Vice Pres*
EMP: 45 **EST:** 1978
SQ FT: 7,000 **Privately Held**
WEB: www.larsonengr.com
SIC: 8711 Structural engineering services; engineering consulting services

(G-8564)
LARSON KING, LLP
30 7th St E Ste 2800 (55101-4922)
PHONE..............................651 312-6500
FAX: 651 312-6614
Lawrence R King, *Managing Prtnr*
Adam B Leichtling, *Partner*
Douglas L Skor, *Partner*
Deborah Maier, *Accounting Mgr*
Kristo Sween, *Mktg Dir*
EMP: 75 **EST:** 1999
SALES (est): 10MM-24.9MM **Privately Held**
WEB: www.larsonking.com
SIC: 8111 General practice law office

(G-8565)
LASX INDUSTRIES INC
4817 White Bear Pkwy (55110-3325)
PHONE..............................651 407-0011
FAX: 651 407-0110
William R Dinauer, *President*
John A Dillon, *Exec VP*
EMP: 37 **EST:** 1998
SQ FT: 13,000
SALES (est): 1MM-4.9MM **Privately Held**
WEB: www.lasxindustries.com

SIC: 7699 Manufactures laser systems & equipment; machine shop, jobbing & repair services; industrial machinery repair & maintenance services

(G-8566)
LAW ENFORCEMENT LABOR SERVICES
327 York Ave (55130-4039)
PHONE..............................651 293-4424
FAX: 651 293-0203
Marylee Abrams, *Attorney*
Bill Gillespie, *Exec Dir*
Daniel Wells, *Director*
EST: 1977 **Privately Held**
WEB: www.lels.org
SIC: 8631 Labor union

(G-8567)
LAWN PROFESSIONALS & TREASURES
948 Lydia Dr W (55113-1924)
PHONE..............................651 482-1431
Jack Wolkerstorser, *President*
EMP: 30 **EST:** 1996
SALES (est): 1MM-4.9MM **Privately Held**
SIC: 4959 Snow plowing services

(G-8568)
LAWREMAR INC
Also Called: Fresh Paint
2372 Leibel St (55110-2308)
PHONE..............................651 429-4475
FAX: 651 407-8179
Larry Zack, *President*
Giacomo Baglio, *General Mgr*
Barb Ackerley, *Corp Secy*
Dan Pilla, *Exec Dir*
John Delfavero, *Director*
EMP: 26 **EST:** 1985
SALES (est): 1MM-4.9MM **Privately Held**
SIC: 1721 1542 Exterior commercial painting contractor; commercial & office building renovation & repair services; interior residential painting contractor; interior commercial painting contractor; exterior residential painting contractor

(G-8569)
LAWSON SOFTWARE AMERICAS INC (HQ)
380 Saint Peter St Ste 323 (55102-1315)
PHONE..............................651 767-7000
Harry Debes, *President*
Gan Q Bee, *General Mgr*
Sam Bizzarro, *General Mgr*
Roger Bonet, *General Mgr*
Lorraine Coetzee, *General Mgr*
EMP: 900 **EST:** 1975
SQ FT: 307,000
SALES (corp-wide): 736.40M **Publicly Held**
WEB: www.lawson.com
SIC: 7372 7371 Application software publishing; computer programming service
PA: Lawson Software Inc
380 Saint Peter St # 323
Saint Paul MN 55102
651 767-7000

(G-8570)
LAWSON SOFTWARE INC (PA)
380 Saint Peter St # 323 (55102-1315)
PHONE..............................651 767-7000
Harry Debes, *President*
Bruce B McPheeters, *Corp Secy*
James Desocio, *Exec VP*
Scott Swoish, *Exec VP*
William Lawson, *Exec VP*
EMP: 3780 **EST:** 1975
SQ FT: 308,000
SALES (corp-wide): 736.40M **Publicly Held**
SIC: 7372 7371 Application software publishing; computer programming service

(G-8571)
LCOMUITY NATIONAL BANK
845 County Road E E (55127-7116)
PHONE..............................651 483-4656
FAX: 651 483-4883
William Sandison, *CEO*
EMP: 42 **EST:** 1998
SALES (est): 10MM-24.9MM **Privately Held**
SIC: 6111 Federal credit agency

(G-8572)
LE JEUNE INVESTMENT INC
Also Called: Maplewood Imports
2780 Highway 61 (55109-1017)
PHONE..............................651 483-2681
FAX: 651 766-2323
Doug Mulder, *General Mgr*
Dianna Jancik, *Business Mgr*
Denise Boland, *Business Mgr*
Howard Kokaisel, *Parts Mgr*
Sheryl Debruzzi, *Finance*
EMP: 55
SALES (est): 25MM-49.9MM **Privately Held**
WEB: www.carouselautomobiles.com
SIC: 7538 Retails new & used automobiles; general automotive repair services
PA: Le Jeune Investment Inc
9393 Wayzata Blvd
Minneapolis MN 55426
763 744-9100

(G-8573)
LEAGUE OF MINNESOTA CITIES
145 University Ave W (55103-2044)
PHONE..............................651 281-1200
FAX: 651 281-1299
Bob Weisbrod, *General Mgr*
Jeannette Bach, *Research*
Marky Engler, *CFO*
Dave Dubord, *Finance*
Laura Kushner, *Human Resources*
EMP: 90 **EST:** 1913
SQ FT: 60,000 **Privately Held**
SIC: 8611 6321 8743 Business association; lobbying services; direct accident & health insurance carrier; publishes magazines without printing

(G-8574)
LEE F MURPHY INC
2515 Wabash Ave Ste 300 (55114-2000)
PHONE..............................651 644-7200
FAX: 651 644-9137
Robert B Murphy, *President*
Lee Murphy, *Vice Pres*
Marla Murphy-Goodall, *Vice Pres*
Robert Schmitz, *Sales Mgr*
EMP: 44 **EST:** 1977
SQ FT: 7,000
SALES (est): 1MM-4.9MM **Privately Held**
WEB: www.leefmurphy.com
SIC: 6411 Insurance broker

(G-8575)
LEGAL SERVICES ADVOCACY PROJ (PA)
46 4th St E Ste 726 (55101-1112)
PHONE..............................651 222-3749
Privately Held
SIC: 8111 General practice attorney's or lawyer's office

(G-8576)
LEGEND TECHNICAL SERVICES INC
88 Empire Dr (55103-1855)
PHONE..............................651 642-1150
FAX: 651 642-1239
Cheryl A Sykora, *President*
Kim Igo, *General Mgr*
William F Welbes, *Vice Pres*
Keith Giorgi, *Med Doctor*
Paul Kirchberg, *Manager*
EMP: 34 **EST:** 1991
SQ FT: 24,000
SALES (est): 1MM-4.9MM **Privately Held**
WEB: www.legend-group.com
SIC: 8748 8734 Environmental consultant; testing laboratory

(G-8577)
LEMKE DENTAL LABORATORY INC
1420 E County Road D Ct A (55109-2059)
PHONE..............................651 482-9911
FAX: 651 482-9707
Dennis Lemke, *President*
Gary Johnson, *Vice Pres*
Barbara J Lemke, *Treasurer*
Brenda Taylor, *Asst Mgr*
EMP: 40 **EST:** 1996
SQ FT: 2,500
SALES (est): 1MM-4.9MM **Privately Held**
WEB: www.lemkedental.com

(PA)=Parent Co (HQ)=Headquarters (DH)=Div Headquarters
✪ = New business established in last 2 years

2011 Harris Minnesota
Services Directory

© Harris InfoSource 1-866-281-6415
371

SIC: 8072 Dental laboratory

(G-8578)
LEPHERT, SKWIRA, SHULTZ & CO
170 7th Pl E Ste 100　(55101-2361)
PHONE..............651 265-2051
Michael Lethert, *Partner*
James Stevenson, *Partner*
EMP: 33 EST: 1918
SALES (est): 1MM-4.9MM **Privately Held**
SIC: 8721 Certified public accountant services

(G-8579)
LESLIE E FISHMAN INC
Also Called: Pediatric Young Adult Medicine
233 Smith Ave N　(55102-2571)
PHONE..............651 227-7806
Leslie E Fishman, *Principal*
EMP: 27 EST: 1991
SALES (est): 1MM-4.9MM **Privately Held**
SIC: 8011 Physical medicine physician or surgeon office

(G-8580)
LETHERT, SKWIRA, SCHULTZ & CO
170 7th Pl E Ste 100　(55101-2361)
PHONE..............651 224-5721
FAX: 651 227-7767
Robert Schultz, *Partner*
Leo Yurek, *Partner*
Ken Kalina, *Partner*
Jerry Faletti, *Partner*
Michael J Lethert, *Partner*
EMP: 33 EST: 1961
SQ FT: 12,000
SALES (est): 1MM-4.9MM **Privately Held**
WEB: www.lss-cpas.com
SIC: 8721 Certified public accountant services

(G-8581)
LEVERZ SKIRA & SHCULTZ CPA
170 7th Pl E Ste 100　(55101-2361)
PHONE..............651 265-2045
Donna Waller, *Principal*
EMP: 30
SALES (est): 1MM-4.9MM **Privately Held**
SIC: 8721 Certified public accountant services

(G-8582)
LEXION MEDICAL LLC
5000 Township Pkwy　(55110-5852)
PHONE..............651 635-0000
FAX: 651 636-1671
Dan Spearman, *Mng Member*
Lori Larson, *Manager*
▲ EMP: 30 EST: 2000
SALES (est): 5MM-9.9MM **Privately Held**
WEB: www.lexionmed.com
SIC: 8011 Manufactures blood & bone work medical instruments & equipment; physicians' office & clinic

(G-8583)
LIFE TIME FITNESS INC
2480 Fairview Ave N　(55113-2699)
PHONE..............651 633-4444
FAX: 651 633-6033
Jolene Morris, *Branch Mgr*
EMP: 31
SALES (est): 1MM-4.9MM **Publicly Held**
SIC: 7991 Physical fitness center
PA: Life Time Fitness Inc
　2902 Corporate Pl
　Chanhassen MN 55317
　952 947-0000

(G-8584)
LIFE TIME FITNESS INC
2145 Ford Pkwy Bsmt 1　(55116-1913)
PHONE..............651 698-5000
FAX: 651 698-0700
Marco Schisano, *Manager*
Kevin Kulish, *Director*
Samuel Wigersma, *Director*
EMP: 65
SALES (est): 1MM-4.9MM **Publicly Held**

SIC: 7991 Physical fitness center
PA: Life Time Fitness Inc
　2902 Corporate Pl
　Chanhassen MN 55317
　952 947-0000

(G-8585)
LIFE TIME FITNESS INC
Also Called: White Bear Raquet & Swim
4800 White Bear Pkwy　(55110-3345)
PHONE..............651 426-1308
Layne McCleary, *General Mgr*
Robert Ziton, *CFO*
Lisa Janisch, *Accountant*
Dan Kelly, *Personnel*
Matt Bissel, *Sales Staff*
EMP: 200
SALES (est): 5MM-9.9MM **Publicly Held**
SIC: 7991 7997 Health club; membership tennis club
PA: Life Time Fitness Inc
　2902 Corporate Pl
　Chanhassen MN 55317
　952 947-0000

(G-8586)
LIFETRACK RESOURCES INC (PA)
709 University Ave W　(55104-4804)
PHONE..............651 227-8471
FAX: 651 227-0621
Trixie A Golberg, *President*
Cindy Toppin, *Vice Pres*
Barbara Grossman, *Vice Pres*
Rudy Brynolfson, *Vice Pres*
Tom Spurrier, *CFO*
EMP: 100 EST: 1948
SQ FT: 28,000
SALES (corp-wide): 9.63M **Privately Held**
WEB: www.lifetrackresources.org
SIC: 8093 7361 8322 8331 8351 Outpatient rehabilitation treatment center; vocational rehabilitation agency; employment agency services; child day care service; individual & family social services

(G-8587)
LIFETRACK RESOURCES INC
Also Called: Packaging First
341 Chester St　(55107-1202)
PHONE..............651 290-0567
FAX: 651 290-0625
Harry Whatley, *Manager*
Terry Chote, *Manager*
EMP: 50
SALES (est): 1MM-4.9MM **Privately Held**
WEB: www.lifetrackresources.org
SIC: 7389 8331 Packaging & labeling services; job training & vocational rehabilitation services; manufactures packaging machinery; manufactures paper packaging materials
PA: Lifetrack Resources Inc
　709 University Ave W
　Saint Paul MN 55104
　651 227-8471

(G-8588)
LINDER'S GREENHOUSES INC
270 Larpenteur Ave W　(55113-6738)
PHONE..............651 488-1927
FAX: 651 488-9508
Johnny Conce, *Manager*
Craig Corby, *Manager*
EMP: 40
SALES (est): 5MM-9.9MM **Privately Held**
WEB: www.linders.com
SIC: 0782 Retail nursery & garden center; landscaping services
PA: Linder's Greenhouses Inc
　275 Wheelock Pkwy W
　Saint Paul MN 55117
　651 488-6717

(G-8589)
LINDER'S GREENHOUSES INC (PA)
275 Wheelock Pkwy W　(55117-3607)
PHONE..............651 488-6717
Dave Linder, *President*
Craig Corby, *General Mgr*
Peter A Linder, *Vice Pres*
Lillian M Linder, *Vice Pres*
EMP: 110 EST: 1915
SQ FT: 120,000　**Privately Held**
WEB: www.linders.com

SIC: 0181 Ornamental nursery products

(G-8590)
LINN BUILDING MAINTENANCE INC
1899 Rice St　(55113-6803)
PHONE..............651 778-1322
Steve Kissell, *President*
EMP: 100 EST: 1973
SQ FT: 2,200
SALES (est): 1MM-4.9MM **Privately Held**
WEB: www.lbm-janitorial.com
SIC: 7349 Janitorial & custodial services

(G-8591)
LINTEX CORP
2609 Territorial Rd　(55114-1009)
PHONE..............651 646-6600
FAX: 651 646-3210
David Huelssbeck, *President*
Terry Shea, *Corp Secy*
Geoff Mayo, *Vice Pres*
Don Quaintance, *Purchasing*
Thomas A Folz, *CFO*
▲ EMP: 109 EST: 1954
SALES (est): 25MM-49.9MM **Privately Held**
SIC: 5023 5021 5131 Wholesales textile sheets; manufactures linen fabrics; wholesales table linens; wholesales curtains; wholesales carpets; wholesales woven linen piece goods; wholesales woven textiles; wholesales mattresses

(G-8592)
LITTLE SISTERS OF THE POOR OF
Also Called: HOLY FAMILY RESIDENCE
330 Exchange St S　(55102-2311)
PHONE..............651 227-0336
FAX: 651 227-0326
Micheal Mugan, *Corp Secy*
Carolyn Martin, *Treasurer*
Mary Roberts, *Human Resources*
Jane Johnston, *Manager*
Mary S Karl, *Manager*
EMP: 100 EST: 1883
SALES (est): 1MM-4.9MM **Privately Held**
SIC: 8051 8052 8361 Skilled nursing care facility; residential care facility; intermediate care facility

(G-8593)
LKPB ENGINEERS INC
1935 County Road B2 W Ste 300 (55113-2722)
PHONE..............651 633-1223
FAX: 651 633-1355
Peter A Potvin, *President*
John Killeen, *Vice Pres*
Gayland Bender, *Vice Pres*
Michael Westemeier, *Vice Pres*
Laurel R Hofmann, *Controller*
EMP: 42 EST: 1968
SQ FT: 9,000
SALES (est): 5MM-9.9MM **Privately Held**
WEB: www.lkpb.com
SIC: 8711 Engineering consulting services; electrical or electronic engineers; mechanical engineering services

(G-8594)
LOOMIS ARMORED US INC
735 Raymond Ave　(55114-1709)
PHONE..............651 645-4511
FAX: 651 645-8063
Mark Fahning, *General Mgr*
Karen Thomley, *Office Mgr*
Alexander Reynolds, *Manager*
EMP: 50
SALES (est): 1MM-4.9MM **Privately Held**
WEB: www.loomisfargo.com
SIC: 7381 Armored car service
HQ: Loomis Armored Us LLC
　2500 Citywest Blvd Ste 900
　Houston TX 77042
　713 435-6700

(G-8595)
LOVINGCARE NURSING SERVICES
501 Dale St N Ste 205　(55103-1914)
PHONE..............651 848-0061
FAX: 651 848-0079
Rufus Adewola, *President*
EMP: 40 EST: 1999

SALES (est): 1MM-4.9MM **Privately Held**
SIC: 8051 Skilled nursing care facility

(G-8596)
LUBRICATION TECHNOLOGIES INC
2420 County Road C W　(55113-2531)
PHONE..............651 636-7990
James Pittelko, *Manager*
Bob Lashus, *Manager*
Jay Grasto, *Manager*
Matt Thinly, *Manager*
EMP: 60
SALES (est): 100MM-499.9MM **Privately Held**
WEB: www.lube-tech.com
SIC: 5172 5169 Wholesales diesel fuel; wholesales gasoline; wholesales lubricating oils & greases; wholesales anti-freeze compounds; wholesales industrial chemicals; wholesales fuel oil; fuel oil dealer
PA: Lubrication Technologies Inc
　900 Mendelssohn Ave N
　Minneapolis MN 55427
　763 545-0707

(G-8597)
LUNNING WENDE BVH ARCHITECTS
275 4th St E Ste 620　(55101-1684)
PHONE..............651 221-0915
Robert Lunning, *Principal*
EMP: 52
SALES (est): 5MM-9.9MM **Privately Held**
SIC: 8712 Architectural service

(G-8598)
LUTHERAN SOCIAL SERVICE OF MN (PA)
2485 Como Ave　(55108-1445)
PHONE..............651 642-5990
FAX: 651 969-2360
Mark A Peterson, *President*
Jodi Harpstead, *COO*
Eden Fitzgerald, *COO*
Ken Borle, *CFO*
Joyce Norals, *VP Persnl*
EMP: 80 EST: 1865
SQ FT: 34,000
SALES (corp-wide): 86.69M **Privately Held**
WEB: www.lssmn.org
SIC: 8322 Individual & family social services

(G-8599)
LYNGBLOMSTEN
1415 Almond Ave　(55108-2507)
PHONE..............651 646-2941
Paul Mikelson, *President*
Julie Anderson, *Attorney*
Jackie Lyaruu, *Manager*
EMP: 325 EST: 1976
SALES (est): 10MM-24.9MM **Privately Held**
SIC: 8059 8051 8082 8322 8361 Personal care home, with health care; residential care facility; home health care services; skilled nursing care facility; individual & family social services

(G-8600)
M C C A
2550 University Ave W Ste 350S (55114-1907)
PHONE..............651 645-4545
Gayle Kvenvold, *CEO*
Lawrence Massa, *President*
Ken Pazdernik, *Finance*
EMP: 60 EST: 1984 **Privately Held**
WEB: www.mcca.com
SIC: 8631 Trade union

(G-8601)
M C U INTERMODAL INC
380 E Lafayette Frontage Rd (55107-1200)
PHONE..............651 222-2224
FAX: 651 222-1549
William Lundquist, *President*
Mark Myran, *Vice Pres*
Louann Jacobson, *Vice Pres*
EMP: 25 EST: 1988
SQ FT: 2,000
SALES (est): 1MM-4.9MM **Privately Held**
WEB: www.mcucorp.com
SIC: 4731 Freight transportation arrangement services

▲=Import ▼=Export
◆=Import/Export

(G-8602)
M D I GOVERNMENT SERVICES (PA)
1700 Wynne Ave (55108-2708)
PHONE...............651 999-8200
Peter McDermitt, *CEO*
Lloyd Bratland, *CEO*
EMP: 300 EST: 1995
SQ FT: 315,000
SALES (corp-wide): 10.95M Privately Held
SIC: 7389 Packaging & labeling services; manufactures wooden boxes

(G-8603)
M P SYSTEMS INC
Also Called: Pieper Electric
53 S Owasso Blvd W (55117-1029)
PHONE...............651 484-9632
Richard R Pieper Sr, *Chairman*
Jim Findell, *Manager*
EMP: 60 EST: 1998
SALES (est): 5MM-9.9MM Privately Held
WEB: www.donovanline.com
SIC: 1623 Utility line construction

(G-8604)
MACDONALD MONTESSORI CHILD
175 Western Ave S (55102-2942)
PHONE...............651 227-1039
FAX: 651 227-7304
Elizabeth A Macdonald, *Exec Dir*
Beth McDonald, *Exec Dir*
Nichole McDonald, *Director*
Sandy Burwell, *Executive*
EMP: 35 EST: 1986
SALES (est): 500-999K Privately Held
WEB: www.macdonaldmontessori.org
SIC: 8351 Child development center providing Montessori based instruction

(G-8605)
MACQUEEN EQUIPMENT INC
595 Aldine St (55104-2201)
PHONE...............651 645-5726
FAX: 651 645-6668
Curt Steffen, *President*
Robert Garber, *Exec VP*
Dan Gage, *Vice Pres*
Heather Boston, *Manager*
EMP: 35 EST: 1961
SQ FT: 22,000
SALES (est): 10MM-24.9MM Privately Held
WEB: www.macqueeneq.com
SIC: 5082 5084 Wholesales road construction & maintenance machinery; wholesales industrial machinery & equipment

(G-8606)
MAGUIRE AGENCY INC
1935 County Road B2 W Ste 241 (55113-2722)
PO Box 64316 (55164-0316)
PHONE...............651 638-9100
FAX: 651 638-9762
Mathew Clysdale, *President*
EMP: 40 EST: 1928
SQ FT: 10,000
SALES (est): 1MM-4.9MM Privately Held
WEB: www.maguireagency.com
SIC: 6411 Insurance services

(G-8607)
MAHONEY ULBRICH CHRISTIANSEN
30 Plato Blvd E (55107-1809)
PHONE...............651 227-6695
FAX: 651 227-9796
Ronald Ulbrich, *President*
Patrick J Smith, *Corp Secy*
Larry Mahoney, *Vice Pres*
David Christiansen, *Accounting Dir*
Peggy Prall, *Accounting Staf*
EMP: 48 EST: 1989
SQ FT: 10,000
SALES (est): 5MM-9.9MM Privately Held
WEB: www.mucr.com
SIC: 8721 Certified public accountant services

(G-8608)
MAINTENANCE PROFESSIONALS INC
843 7th St E (55106-4515)
PHONE...............651 774-2334
FAX: 651 774-9998
David Seymour, *President*
EMP: 25
SALES (est): 500-999K Privately Held
SIC: 7349 Building cleaning & maintenance services

(G-8609)
MAIRS & POWER BALANCED FUND
332 Minnesota St Ste W1520 (55101-1337)
PHONE...............651 222-8478
William Frels, *CEO*
Jon Theobald, *President*
EMP: 28 Privately Held
SIC: 6722 Open-ended investment funds management services

(G-8610)
MANKATO LUTHERAN HOMES INC
3530 Lexington Ave N (55126-8164)
PHONE...............507 345-4576
Jenniffer Peffer, *Director*
EMP: 150 EST: 1993
SALES (est): 5MM-9.9MM Privately Held
SIC: 8051 Convalescent home

(G-8611)
MAPLE HILLS LP
328 Kellogg Blvd W (55102-1900)
PHONE...............651 291-1750
Joseph Holmberg, *Partner*
EMP: 99
SALES (est): 10MM-24.9MM Privately Held
SIC: 6513 Apartment building operator

(G-8612)
MAPLEWOOD BOWL INC
1955 English St (55109-4301)
PHONE...............651 774-8787
FAX: 651 774-2122
Deleano D Benjamin, *President*
Adeline Benjamin, *Corp Secy*
EMP: 55 EST: 1988
SQ FT: 60,000
SALES (est): 1MM-4.9MM Privately Held
SIC: 7933 Ten pin center; cocktail lounge; full service American restaurant

(G-8613)
MAPLEWOOD DENTAL ASSOCIATES
1736 Cope Ave E Ste 3 (55109-2661)
PHONE...............651 770-3831
William Johnson, *President*
R J Prokosch, *Principal*
EMP: 31 EST: 1972
SALES (est): 1MM-4.9MM Privately Held
WEB: www.maplewooddental.com
SIC: 8021 Dental office

(G-8614)
MAPLEWOOD MOTORS INC
2873 Highway 61 (55109-1082)
PHONE...............651 482-1322
Stephen M Daniels, *President*
Andy Hulcher, *Finance Dir*
Scott Stanko, *Finance*
Don Castle, *Sales Staff*
Brenda Dotsetch, *Manager*
EMP: 100 EST: 1982
SQ FT: 50,000
SALES (est): 50MM-99.9MM Privately Held
WEB: www.maplewoodtoyota.com
SIC: 7538 Retails new & used automobiles; retails automotive parts; automotive engine repair service

(G-8615)
MARSDEN HOLDING LLC (PA)
1717 University Ave W (55104-3613)
PHONE...............651 641-1717
FAX: 651 523-6629
Mary Marsden, *Member*
Adrian Marsden, *Member*
Guy Mingo, *Member*
Greg Theroux, *COO*
Joe Reid, *VP Admin*
EMP: 2100 EST: 1951
SQ FT: 55,000 Privately Held
WEB: www.marsden.com
SIC: 7349 Janitorial & custodial services; window cleaning services

(G-8616)
MARSHALL ASI INC
Also Called: Accessible Space
2550 University Ave W 330N (55114-2014)
PHONE...............651 645-7271
Steve V Shaff, *President*
EMP: 35 EST: 1979
SALES (est): 5MM-9.9MM Privately Held
SIC: 6513 Apartment building operator

(G-8617)
MARUDAS GRAPHICS INC
20 Yorkton Ct (55117-1065)
PHONE...............651 697-7820
FAX: 651 482-1369
Phillip P Marudas, *President*
Alexander Marudas, *Vice Pres*
Tom Ramsdell, *Info Tech Mgr*
EMP: 40 EST: 1983
SQ FT: 35,000
SALES (est): 10MM-24.9MM Privately Held
WEB: www.marudas.com
SIC: 5112 5199 Wholesales business forms; wholesales advertising specialties; commercial lithographic printing

(G-8618)
MAVO SYSTEMS INC
4330 Centerville Rd (55127-3676)
PHONE...............763 788-7713
FAX: 763 788-9560
Dana Sawrey, *President*
Jay Robertson, *COO*
Larry Reese, *CFO*
Shanda Cichon, *Manager*
EMP: 130 EST: 1982
SQ FT: 40,000
SALES (est): 10MM-24.9MM Privately Held
SIC: 1799 Asbestos removal & encapsulation contractor

(G-8619)
MAXANN LLC
Also Called: Sunbelt Business Brokers
3212 Rice St (55126-3047)
PHONE...............651 484-2677
Scott Evert, *Member*
Ben Brickway, *Marketing Staff*
Chris Jones, *Mng Member*
EMP: 27 EST: 2000
SALES (est): 1MM-4.9MM Privately Held
SIC: 8732 Merger, acquisition & reorganization research services

(G-8620)
MB ST PAUL INC
Also Called: Holiday Inn St Paul East
2201 Burns Ave (55119-6667)
PHONE...............651 731-2220
Michael Ridings, *President*
EMP: 99 EST: 2000
SQ FT: 125,000
SALES (est): 5MM-9.9MM Privately Held
SIC: 7011 Traveler accommodations

(G-8621)
MC PHILLIPS BROS ROOFING CO
2590 Centennial Dr (55109-3040)
PHONE...............651 770-2062
FAX: 651 770-2891
Stephen P Johnson, *President*
Steve Peterson, *Superintendent*
Ramona Bandelow, *Corp Secy*
Bridget M Kliewer, *Corp Secy*
John W McPhillips, *Director*
EMP: 30 EST: 1985
SQ FT: 25,000
SALES (est): 1MM-4.9MM Privately Held
SIC: 1761 Roofing contractor

(G-8622)
MC QUILLAN BROTHERS PLUMBING
688 Hague Ave (55104-6605)
PHONE...............651 292-0124
Timothy M Quillan, *President*
Michelle Acciari, *Treasurer*
EMP: 35 EST: 1883
SQ FT: 12,000
SALES (est): 1MM-4.9MM Privately Held
SIC: 1711 Plumbing service; ventilation & duct work contractor; warm air heating & air conditioning contractor

(G-8623)
MCCAREN DESIGN INC
760 Vandalia St Ste 100 (55114-1341)
PHONE...............651 646-4764
FAX: 651 646-8393
Mc R Anderson, *President*
Mary Wilbanks, *Vice Pres*
EMP: 25 EST: 1977
SQ FT: 10,000
SALES (est): 1MM-4.9MM Privately Held
WEB: www.mccaren.com
SIC: 7389 Interior design service; plant care services

(G-8624)
MCGOUGH CONSTRUCTION CO INC (PA)
2737 Fairview Ave N (55113-1307)
PHONE...............651 633-5050
FAX: 651 633-5673
Lawrence J McGough, *Ch of Bd*
Thomas J McGough, *President*
Richard Opitz, *Corp Secy*
Bradley S Wood, *Corp Secy*
John A Shea, *Corp Secy*
EMP: 800 EST: 1956
SQ FT: 16,000 Privately Held
WEB: www.mcgough.com
SIC: 1541 1542 New industrial building construction; school building construction; religious building construction; commercial & institutional building construction

(G-8625)
MCKESSON INFORMATION SOLUTIONS
2700 Snelling Ave N Ste 400 (55113-1783)
PHONE...............651 697-5900
FAX: 651 697-5910
Robert Heim, *Engineer*
Bruce Sielaff, *Engineer*
Gordon Fink, *Engineer*
Debbie Johnson, *Controller*
Melissa Konietzko, *Human Res Mgr*
EMP: 180
SALES (est): 25MM-49.9MM Publicly Held
WEB: www.imckesson.com
SIC: 7373 Systems software development service
HQ: McKesson Information Solutions
5995 Windward Pkwy
Alpharetta GA 30005
404 338-6000

(G-8626)
MCLEODUSA INC
2996 Centre Pointe Dr (55113-1182)
PHONE...............800 593-1177
Thomas Barrera, *Engineer*
Sean Carroll, *Manager*
Dale Schroth, *Administrator*
EMP: 30 Publicly Held
WEB: www.mcleodusa.com
SIC: 4813 Wired telecommunications carrier & service
HQ: MCLEODUSA INC
6400 C St SW
Cedar Rapids IA 52404
319 364-0000

(G-8627)
MDI LP 38
1600 University Ave W # 212 (55104-3825)
PHONE...............651 646-7848
Gary Stenfon, *Partner*
Larry Olsen, *Partner*
EMP: 25 EST: 1982
SALES (est): 5MM-9.9MM Privately Held

(PA)=Parent Co (HQ)=Headquarters (DH)=Div Headquarters
✪ = New business established in last 2 years

2011 Harris Minnesota
Services Directory

© Harris InfoSource 1-866-281-6415

373

SIC: **6552** Land subdivision & development services

(G-8628)
MEAD METALS INC
555 Cardigan Rd (55126-3965)
PHONE...............................651 484-1400
FAX: 651 484-3692
Jon R Holt, *CEO*
John G Allyn, *President*
Jim Bast, *Corp Secy*
Catherine Murray, *Manager*
Jeanette Leuwer, *Assistant*
EMP: 33 EST: 1961
SQ FT: 52,000
SALES (est): 25MM-49.9MM **Privately Held**
WEB: www.meadmetals.com
SIC: **5051** Wholesales flat iron or steel products; wholesales steel pipe & tubing; wholesales copper; wholesales metal sheets

(G-8629)
MECA SPORTSWEAR INC (PA)
3499 Lexington Ave N # 205 (55126-7056)
PHONE...............................651 638-3888
David Bramwell, *Vice Pres*
Thomas D Bramwell Jr, *VP Opers*
Joe Clary, *Purchasing*
Kevin Kirchenwitz, *Purchasing*
Richard Schuster, *CFO*
▼ EMP: 35 EST: 1970
SQ FT: 59,000
SALES (corp-wide): 14.50M **Privately Held**
WEB: www.mecasportswear.com
SIC: **5199** Manufactures men's, youths' & boys' athletic clothing; manufactures work apparel; manufactures men's & boys' industrial garments; manufactures men's & boys' sport jackets; manufactures women's, misses' & juniors' athletic clothing

(G-8630)
MEDICAL LEARNING INC
287 6th St E Ste 400 (55101-1658)
PHONE...............................651 292-3432
FAX: 651 224-4694
Michael Rogge, *President*
Steven Johnson, *Principal*
Clifford Leach, *Principal*
Mathew Juechter, *Corp Secy*
W M Juechter, *Corp Secy*
EMP: 50 EST: 1991
SQ FT: 5,000
SALES (est): 5MM-9.9MM **Privately Held**
WEB: www.medlearn.com
SIC: **8742** Hospital & health services consultant; publishes periodicals without printing; educational services

(G-8631)
MEDTOX LABORATORIES INC
402 County Road D W # 402 (55112-3522)
PHONE...............................651 636-7466
FAX: 651 628-6102
Richard Braun, *CEO*
Steven J Schmidt, *Vice Pres*
Jennifer Collins, *Vice Pres*
Barb Mayer, *Opers Staff*
Gregory C Janis, *Research*
EMP: 282 EST: 1996
SQ FT: 41,000
SALES (est): 25MM-49.9MM **Publicly Held**
WEB: www.medtox.com
SIC: **8071** Testing laboratory; medical bacteriological laboratory; biological laboratory; urinalysis laboratory
PA: MEDTOX Scientific Inc
    402 County Road D W
    Saint Paul MN 55112
    651 636-7466

(G-8632)
MEDTOX SCIENTIFIC INC (PA)
402 County Road D W (55112-3522)
PHONE...............................651 636-7466
FAX: 651 636-7466
Richard J Braun, *President*
James B Lockhart, *Corp Secy*
B M Owens, *COO*
Timothy M Hearne, *Vice Pres*
Mitchell Owens, *Vice Pres*
EMP: 400 EST: 1986
SQ FT: 98,000
SALES (corp-wide): 84.10M **Publicly Held**
WEB: www.medtox.com

SIC: **8071 8734** Medical laboratory; manufactures microbiology & virology diagnostic products; manufactures diagnostic substances; testing laboratory; forensic laboratory

(G-8633)
MEMORIAL BLOOD CENTER (PA)
737 Pelham Blvd (55114-1739)
PHONE...............................651 332-7000
Donald Berglund, *CEO*
John Buske, *CFO*
Barry Hamill, *Management*
EMP: 230 EST: 1947
SQ FT: 25,000
SALES (corp-wide): 49.49M **Privately Held**
WEB: www.mbcm.org
SIC: **8099** Blood bank

(G-8634)
MENTAL HEALTH RESOURCES INC (PA)
1821 University Ave W N464A (55104-2887)
PHONE...............................651 659-2900
FAX: 651 645-7307
Anitabh Tipnic, *CFO*
Miki Bedard, *Manager*
Derek Petersen, *Administrator*
Peg Dubord, *Exec Dir*
Nancy Abramson, *Exec Dir*
EMP: 60 EST: 1975
SQ FT: 7,700
SALES (corp-wide): 13.03M **Privately Held**
WEB: www.mhresources.com
SIC: **8399** Health systems agency

(G-8635)
MERIT DENTAL LAB INC
1630 University Ave W # 102 (55104-3888)
PHONE...............................651 644-4042
FAX: 651 644-9121
David Milbrath DDS, *President*
Marcus Gustafson DDS, *Vice Pres*
John Strutt, *Manager*
EMP: 30 EST: 1969
SALES (est): 1MM-4.9MM **Privately Held**
SIC: **8072** Dental laboratory

(G-8636)
MERITIDE INC
2670 Patton Rd (55113-1136)
PHONE...............................651 255-7300
FAX: 651 255-7299
Patrick Irestone, *CEO*
Joe Massman, *Corp Secy*
Randy Spiess, *Vice Pres*
Richard Peterson, *Vice Pres*
Tom Quanbeck, *Marketing Staff*
EMP: 40 EST: 1999
SQ FT: 12,000
SALES (est): 5MM-9.9MM **Privately Held**
WEB: www.meritide.com
SIC: **7371** Computer software development

(G-8637)
MERMAID INC
2200 Highway 10 (55112-4926)
PHONE...............................763 784-7350
FAX: 763 784-0107
Daniel L Hall, *President*
Janet Bona, *Vice Pres*
EMP: 130 EST: 1960
SQ FT: 33,750
SALES (est): 1MM-4.9MM **Privately Held**
SIC: **7933 7011 7299** Ten pin center; full service independent family restaurant; night club drinking establishment; banquet hall facility; hotel

(G-8638)
MERRICK COMMUNITY SERVICES
1526 6th St E (55106-4806)
PHONE...............................651 771-8821
FAX: 651 771-8465
Francis Ivory, *Director*
EMP: 28 **Privately Held**
WEB: www.merrickcs.org

SIC: **8399** Community development groups
PA: Merrick Community Services
    715 Edgerton St
    Saint Paul MN 55130
    651 771-9339

(G-8639)
MERRICK INC
3210 Labore Rd (55110-5130)
PHONE...............................612 789-6200
John Barker, *CEO*
Rhonda Schwartz, *President*
Jane Peltier, *Human Res Dir*
Sue Waitehanson, *Manager*
Wendy Gervais, *Supervisor*
EST: 1964
SQ FT: 52,000 **Privately Held**
WEB: www.merrickinc.org
SIC: **8331** Vocational rehabilitation agency; manufactures telecommunication systems & equipment

(G-8640)
MERRILL LYNCH, PIERCE, FENNER
30 7th St E Ste 3400 (55101-4918)
PHONE...............................651 298-1700
John Randlph, *Sales Executive*
Henry Crepeau, *Manager*
Michael Putnam, *Manager*
Chad Zawacki, *Manager*
Carole Wheeler, *Manager*
EMP: 55
SALES (est): 10MM-24.9MM **Publicly Held**
WEB: www.ml.com
SIC: **6211** Securities broker & dealer
HQ: Merrill Lynch & Co Inc
    4 World Financial Ctr # 4
    New York NY 10080
    212 449-1000

(G-8641)
METRO LEGAL SERVICES INC
332 Minnesota St Ste N105 (55101-1300)
PHONE...............................651 291-0008
Jeff Budde, *President*
Scott Gray, *Mfg Staff*
Steve Peterson, *Sales/Mktg Mgr*
EMP: 30
SALES (est): 1MM-4.9MM **Privately Held**
WEB: www.metrolegal.com
SIC: **8111 7389** Legal aid services; process serving services
PA: Metro Legal Services Inc
    330 2nd Ave S Ste 150
    Minneapolis MN 55401
    612 332-0202

(G-8642)
METROPLITAN CTR FOR
Also Called: McII
1600 University Ave W Ste 16 (55104-3834)
PHONE...............................651 646-8342
FAX: 651 603-2006
David Hancox, *Exec Dir*
John Goodeve, *Director*
EMP: 100 EST: 1981 **Privately Held**
WEB: www.mcil-mn.org
SIC: **8399 8322** Social services information exchange; general counseling services

(G-8643)
METROPOLITAN COUNCIL, MN
Also Called: Environmental Services Lab
2400 Childs Rd (55106-6724)
PHONE...............................651 602-8393
FAX: 651 602-8846
Leisa Thompson, *Plant Mgr*
Al Roy, *Facilities Mgr*
James Wyzkoowski, *Manager*
John Hubbling, *Manager*
Walter Wessels, *Manager*
EMP: 100
SALES (est): 10MM-24.9MM **Privately Held**
WEB: www.state.mn.us
SIC: **1623** Water & sewer line construction; government waste management program administration office; state government air, water & solid waste management program administration
DH: Metropolitan Council, MN
    390 Robert St N
    Saint Paul MN 55101
    651 602-1629

(G-8644)
METROPOLITAN COUNCIL, MN
Also Called: Metro Construction
2500 Childs Rd (55106-6726)
PHONE...............................651 772-2585
Walter Wessels, *Manager*
EMP: 27
SALES (est): 1MM-4.9MM **Privately Held**
WEB: www.state.mn.us
SIC: **8711** Engineering services; air, water & solid waste programs administration services; state government air, water & solid waste management program administration
DH: Metropolitan Council, MN
    390 Robert St N
    Saint Paul MN 55101
    651 602-1629

(G-8645)
METROPOLITAN COUNCIL, MN
Also Called: Central Office
390 Robert St N (55101-1805)
PHONE...............................612 373-3333
Helen Boyer, *Manager*
Tom Weaver, *Administrator*
EMP: 200
SALES (est): 10MM-24.9MM **Privately Held**
WEB: www.state.mn.us
SIC: **8721** Accounting, auditing & bookkeeping services; air, water & solid waste programs administration services; state government air, water & solid waste management program administration
DH: Metropolitan Council, MN
    390 Robert St N
    Saint Paul MN 55101
    651 602-1629

(G-8646)
METROPOLITAN FINANCIAL MGT
Also Called: Auriton Solutions
1700 Highway 36 W Ste 301 (55113-4015)
PHONE...............................651 631-8000
FAX: 651 697-7989
Tiffany T Worley, *President*
David I Norling, *CFO*
William Boyle, *Director*
Brad McCanna, *Director*
Leisa Irwin, *Director*
EMP: 25 EST: 1991
SQ FT: 7,500
SALES (est): 1MM-4.9MM **Privately Held**
WEB: www.aiccca.com
SIC: **8742** Management consulting services

(G-8647)
METROPOLITAN HAND SURGERY
310 Smith Ave N Ste 370 (55102-2383)
PHONE...............................651 223-5406
FAX: 651 297-6834
Charles J Mac Donald MD, *President*
Melissa Barton, *Principal*
Paul J Donahue MD, *Corp Secy*
Robert O Andersn, *Med Doctor*
Lawren T Donovan, *Med Doctor*
EMP: 40 EST: 1973
SALES (est): 1MM-4.9MM **Privately Held**
WEB: www.metrohandsurgery.com
SIC: **8011 8049** Surgeon's office; physical therapist office

(G-8648)
METROPOLITAN OBSTETRICS & GYN
1655 Beam Ave Ste 206 (55109-1476)
PHONE...............................651 770-1385
Thomas Grande, *Partner*
Kathy Lee, *Project Mgr*
Randy Thompson, *Finance*
Michael Dunn, *Administrator*
Jennifer A Flynn, *Obstetrician*
EMP: 45 EST: 1961
SALES (est): 1MM-4.9MM **Privately Held**
SIC: **8049 8011** Health practitioners' office; physicians' office & clinic

www.HarrisInfo.com
374
2011 Harris Minnesota
Services Directory
▲=Import ▼=Export
◆=Import/Export

(G-8649)
METROPOLITAN UROLOGIC
Also Called: Metro Urology
2550 University Ave W Ste 240N
(55114-2004)
PHONE 651 999-7034
Jeanne Walden, *General Mgr*
Sharon Hoffman, *Corp Secy*
Tina Montbirand, *Div Sub Head*
Wendy Rider, *Office Mgr*
Randall Thompson, *Exec Dir*
EMP: 35 **EST:** 1970
SALES (est): 1MM-4.9MM **Privately Held**
WEB: www.metro-urology.com
SIC: 8011 Urologist office

(G-8650)
MIC SERVICES LLC
Also Called: Mics Construction
1722 Terrace Dr (55113-1315)
PHONE 651 379-9590
Michael K Hudson, *Mng Member*
EMP: 30 **EST:** 2007
SALES (est): 5MM-9.9MM **Privately Held**
SIC: 1521 Single-family housing
construction

(G-8651)
MICHAEL ERPELDING
Also Called: Northwestern Mutl Fincl Netwrk
2550 University Ave W Ste 455S
(55114-1908)
PHONE 651 647-1000
Michael Erpelding, *Owner*
Jane Myogeto, *Officer*
EMP: 30 **EST:** 1971
SALES (est): 1MM-4.9MM **Privately Held**
SIC: 6411 Insurance services

(G-8652)
MID-STATES DISTRIBUTING CO INC
548 Snelling Ave S (55116-1524)
PO Box 64537 (55164-0537)
PHONE 651 698-8831
FAX: 651 698-1504
John W Atkins, *President*
Betsy Hibbard, *Buyer*
Roberta Jensen, *Human Res Mgr*
Heather Jackson, *Manager*
Pam Nord, *Manager*
◆ **EMP:** 25 **EST:** 1954
SQ FT: 12,000
SALES (est): 10MM-24.9MM **Privately Held**
WEB: www.mid-states-dist.com
SIC: 5072 5013 5091 5092 5136 5191
Wholesales hardware; wholesales
automotive supplies & parts; wholesales
toys & games; wholesales farm supplies;
wholesales men's & boys' clothing;
wholesales sporting & recreational goods &
supplies

(G-8653)
MIDCOUNTRY MORTGAGE CORP
1001 Labore Industrial Ct (55110-5167)
PHONE 651 766-7000
FAX: 651 766-7024
Greg Krenz, *President*
Robin Roberts, *Senior VP*
Paul Lohmann, *Vice Pres*
Nancy Albrecht, *Vice Pres*
EMP: 55 **EST:** 1988
SQ FT: 12,000
SALES (est): 5MM-9.9MM **Privately Held**
WEB: www.midcountrybank.com
SIC: 6163 6162 Mortgage brokers service
arranging for loans, using money of others;
mortgage banking service
PA: Midcountry Bank Inc
14617 Highway 7
Minnetonka MN 55345
952 997-5608

(G-8654)
MIDLAND HILLS COUNTRY CLUB
2001 Fulham St (55113-5111)
PHONE 651 631-0440
FAX: 651 633-3043
John Hamburger, *President*
Tim Ivory, *General Mgr*
Sue Sheridan, *Controller*

Kathy Lopez, *Manager*
EMP: 80 **EST:** 1919
SQ FT: 28,000
SALES (est): 1MM-4.9MM **Privately Held**
WEB: www.midlandhillscc.org
SIC: 7997 Country club; bar; limited service
lunch counter

(G-8655)
MIDWAY INDUSTRIAL SUPPLY CO
4759 Old Highway 8 (55112-1529)
PO Box 120417 (55112-0017)
PHONE 763 780-3000
Gregg C Lien, *President*
Laurel Lien, *Corp Secy*
David Lapinski, *Vice Pres*
John Spoolman, *Vice Pres*
EMP: 26 **EST:** 1956
SQ FT: 16,400
SALES (est): 10MM-24.9MM **Privately Held**
WEB: www.midwayis.com
SIC: 5084 Wholesales pumps & pumping
equipment; wholesales industrial paint spray
equipment; wholesales industrial plastic
products machinery; wholesales industrial
safety equipment

(G-8656)
MIDWAY TRAINING SERVICES INC
1246 Unver Ave W 239 (55104)
PHONE 651 641-0709
FAX: 651 641-0976
Robert Brick, *President*
EMP: 64 **EST:** 1965
SQ FT: 2,000
SALES (est): 1MM-4.9MM **Privately Held**
SIC: 8331 8322 Job training services;
vocational rehabilitation agency; individual &
family social services

(G-8657)
MIDWAY UNIVERSITY LLC
1625 Energy Park Dr Ste 100
(55108-2735)
PHONE 651 292-9844
Jim Gilespie, *Member*
Steve Wellington, *Member*
John Pope, *Member*
Terry Waldorf, *Manager*
EMP: 25 **EST:** 2000
SALES (est): 5MM-9.9MM **Privately Held**
SIC: 6799 Real estate investors

(G-8658)
MIDWEST DAIRY ASSOCIATION
2015 Rice St Ste 100 (55113-6800)
PHONE 651 488-0261
FAX: 651 488-0265
Mike Kruger, *CEO*
Kay Henninger, *Corp Secy*
Jeff Fasching, *Treasurer*
Marilyn Calvin, *Treasurer*
John McClerrey, *Info Tech Dir*
EMP: 75 **EST:** 1981 **Privately Held**
WEB: www.midwestdairy.com
SIC: 8611 Business association

(G-8659)
MIDWEST MENTAL HEALTH RESOURCE
2550 University Ave W 435S (55114-1907)
PHONE 651 647-1900
Tim Quesnell, *President*
Catherine Mollner, *Director*
EMP: 27
SALES (est): 1MM-4.9MM **Privately Held**
SIC: 8322 General counseling services

(G-8660)
MIDWEST MOTOR EXPRESS INC
2169 Mustang Dr (55112-1555)
PHONE 763 784-0650
Joseph Greenstein, *VP Sls/Mktg*
EMP: 37
SALES (est): 1MM-4.9MM **Privately Held**
WEB: www.mmeinc.com
SIC: 4231 Freight trucking terminal
PA: Midwest Motor Express Inc
5015 E Main Ave
Bismarck ND 58501
701 223-1880

(G-8661)
MIDWEST SIGN & SCREEN PRINTING (PA)
45 Maryland Ave E (55117-4610)
PHONE 651 489-9999
FAX: 651 489-0101
Nancy Anderson, *CEO*
James Fisher, *President*
Patrick O'Neill, *Corp Secy*
Craig Anderson, *Vice Pres*
Lyle Hanzal, *Vice Pres*
EMP: 80 **EST:** 1943
SQ FT: 120,000 **Privately Held**
WEB: www.midwestsign.com
SIC: 5084 5063 Wholesales printing
machinery, equipment & supplies;
wholesales electrical supplies

(G-8662)
MIDWEST SOUND & LIGHT INC
Also Called: Alentertainment
970 Raymond Ave Ste G70 (55114-1199)
PHONE 651 644-4111
Daniel P Thompson, *President*
EMP: 45 **EST:** 1976
SQ FT: 940
SALES (est): 1MM-4.9MM **Privately Held**
SIC: 7929 Entertainment services

(G-8663)
MIDWEST SPECIAL SERVICES INC
1045 Tomlyn Ave (55126-5865)
PHONE 651 483-3000
Victoria Patterson, *Manager*
Kim Alexzander, *Systems Staff*
EMP: 25
SALES (est): 1MM-4.9MM **Privately Held**
WEB: www.mwservices.org
SIC: 8331 Job training services
PA: Midwest Special Services Inc
900 Ocean St
Saint Paul MN 55106
651 778-1000

(G-8664)
MIDWEST SPECIAL SERVICES INC (PA)
900 Ocean St (55106-3448)
PHONE 651 778-1000
Lyth L Hartz, *President*
Julie Johnson, *Vice Pres*
Ed Selnes, *Plant Mgr*
Barbara Beseth, *VP Finance*
Krista Fitzsimmons, *Accountant*
EMP: 225 **EST:** 1949
SQ FT: 52,000
SALES (corp-wide): 9.02M **Privately Held**
WEB: www.mwservices.org
SIC: 8331 Job training services; work
experience center; vocational rehabilitation
agency

(G-8665)
MIDWEST STONE MANAGEMENT, A MN
1885 County Road C W (55113-1304)
PHONE 651 633-9414
Christopher J Knoedler, *Corp Secy*
Charles Nystrom, *COO*
Roland Ugarte, *Treasurer*
David Katz, *Director*
EMP: 33 **EST:** 1986
SQ FT: 8,620
SALES (est): 1MM-4.9MM **Privately Held**
SIC: 8011 Urologist office

(G-8666)
MIDWEST UROLOGIC STONE UNIT LP
1885 County Road C W (55113-1304)
PHONE 651 633-9414
Charlie Nystrom, *Partner*
EMP: 30 **EST:** 1986
SALES (est): 1MM-4.9MM **Privately Held**
SIC: 8093 Specialty outpatient clinic

(G-8667)
MIKE HALL CHEVROLET INC
3191 Fanum Rd (55110-5234)
PHONE 651 484-4671
Kirt Perkins, *Manager*

EMP: 25
SALES (est): 1MM-4.9MM **Publicly Held**
WEB: www.autonation.com
SIC: 7532 Automotive collision shop
HQ: Mike Hall Chevrolet Inc
8100 Highway 6 S
Houston TX 77083
281 879-2314

(G-8668)
MILWAUKEE INSULATION CO I
2400 Wycliff St (55114-1220)
PHONE 651 659-2211
Clyde Rhodes, *CEO*
EMP: 28 **EST:** 2007
SALES (est): 1MM-4.9MM **Privately Held**
SIC: 1742 Building insulation installation
service

(G-8669)
MINN HEALTH
2716 Upper Afton Rd E (55119-4780)
PHONE 651 739-5050
FAX: 651 739-7393
Cameron McConnell MD, *Principal*
EMP: 35 **EST:** 1992
SALES (est): 1MM-4.9MM **Privately Held**
SIC: 8011 Physicians' office & clinic

(G-8670)
MINN HEALTH CARE UNION LOCAL
Also Called: Seiu Local 113
345 Randolph Ave Ste 100 (55102-3610)
PHONE 612 331-4690
Julie Schnell, *President*
Shane Davis, *Corp Secy*
EMP: 42 **EST:** 1946 **Privately Held**
SIC: 8631 Labor union

(G-8671)
MINNEHAHA BOWLING CENTER INC
955 Seminary Ave (55104-1525)
PHONE 651 488-7208
FAX: 651 488-8145
Dutch Erkenbrack, *Owner*
Jean Erkenbrack, *Vice Pres*
Robert Hjort, *Vice Pres*
Donna Hjort, *Treasurer*
Jeff Quade, *Executive*
EMP: 50 **EST:** 1958
SQ FT: 40,000
SALES (est): 1MM-4.9MM **Privately Held**
WEB: www.mikesproshop.com
SIC: 7933 6512 Bowling center;
nonresidential building operator; bar; eating
place

(G-8672)
MINNESOTA ASSOCIATION OF
1000 Westgate Dr Ste 252 (55114-8679)
PHONE 651 290-7462
Dave Dederichs, *Manager*
Chris Kann, *Exec Dir*
Pamela Eakes, *Exec Dir*
Shannon Pfarrthompson, *Director*
Scott Franzmeier, *Director*
EMP: 30 **EST:** 2006 **Privately Held**
SIC: 8641 Social club

(G-8673)
MINNESOTA ASSOCIATION OF SCH
Also Called: MASA
1884 Como Ave (55108-2715)
PHONE 651 645-6272
Charles Kyte, *Exec Dir*
EMP: 99 **EST:** 1968 **Privately Held**
WEB: www.mnasa.org
SIC: 8621 Professional organization;
education & teacher association

(G-8674)
MINNESOTA BRD OF MED PRAC
2700 University Ave W # 106
(55114-1016)
PHONE 651 642-0538
FAX: 651 642-0393
Rob Leach, *Partner*
EMP: 25 **EST:** 1995
SALES (est): 1MM-4.9MM **Privately Held**
SIC: 8011 General & family practice
physician or surgeon office

(PA)=Parent Co (HQ)=Headquarters (DH)=Div Headquarters
✿ = New business established in last 2 years

2011 Harris Minnesota
Services Directory

© Harris InfoSource 1-866-281-6415
375

GEOGRAPHIC

(G-8675)
MINNESOTA CHAMBER OF COMMERCE
400 Robert St N Ste 1500 (55101-2030)
PHONE..................651 292-4650
FAX: 651 292-4656
Joe Swedberg, Ch of Bd
David C Olson, President
Joseph Otting, Vice Chairman
Audrey Groteboer, Corp Secy
Chad Simons, Corp Secy
EMP: 25 EST: 1909 Privately Held
WEB: www.mnchamber.com
SIC: 8611 6411 Chamber of commerce; insurance services

(G-8676)
MINNESOTA CHEMICAL CO
2285 Hampden Ave (55114-1204)
PHONE..................651 646-7521
Michael F Baker, President
Stephen A Baker, Treasurer
Earl Olson, Controller
Daniel A Baker, VP Persnl
James Garcia, Manager
EMP: 25 EST: 1915
SQ FT: 62,500
SALES (est): 5MM-9.9MM Privately Held
WEB: www.minnesotachemical.com
SIC: 5087 7699 Wholesales dry cleaning plant equipment & supplies; wholesales laundry equipment & supplies; manufactures commercial laundry equipment; manufactures polishes & sanitation agents; manufactures soaps & detergents

(G-8677)
MINNESOTA CHILDREN'S MUSEUM
10 7th St W (55102-1104)
PHONE..................651 225-6000
FAX: 651 225-6062
Carleen K Rhodes, President
Carol Aegerter, Vice Pres
Shawn Longacre, Facilities Mgr
Nancy Lee, CFO
Helen Franzzyk, Marketing Staff
EMP: 90 EST: 1979
SQ FT: 65,000
SALES (est): 5MM-9.9MM Privately Held
WEB: www.mcm.org
SIC: 8412 Museum

(G-8678)
MINNESOTA COMMERCIAL RAILWAY (PA)
508 Cleveland Ave N (55114-1804)
PHONE..................651 646-2010
John Gohmann, President
Joe Richardson, Finance
Tom Whelan, Info Tech Mgr
Becky Kotz, Director
EMP: 75 EST: 1883
SQ FT: 250,000 Privately Held
SIC: 4013 Railroad terminals; railroad switching

(G-8679)
MINNESOTA COUNTIES INSURANCE
100 Empire Dr Ste 100 (55103-1885)
PHONE..................651 209-6400
FAX: 651 209-6495
Denise Hegberk, Chairman
Sharon Anderson, Vice Chairman
Mary Frank, Manager
Jeff Kulas, Info Tech Mgr
Robyn Sykes, Exec Dir
EMP: 37 EST: 1979
SQ FT: 39,000
SALES (est): 1MM-4.9MM Privately Held
SIC: 8742 Compensation & benefits planning consultant

(G-8680)
MINNESOTA CROP IMPROVEMENT
Also Called: MN Crop Improvement Assn
1900 Hendon Ave (55108-1048)
PHONE..................612 625-7766
FAX: 612 625-3748
Gary Beil, President
Cindy Wippler, General Mgr

Marilyn Polsfuss, VP Mktg
Roger Wippler, Manager
Brent Benike, Bd of Directors
EMP: 28 EST: 1903
SQ FT: 15,000
SALES (est): 1MM-4.9MM Privately Held
SIC: 8734 Seed testing laboratory

(G-8681)
MINNESOTA DEPARTMENT OF
Also Called: Radio Talking Book
2200 University Ave W Ste 240 (55114-1840)
PHONE..................651 642-0503
Bonnie Elfey, Commissioner
Charles Hamilton, Director
EMP: 150
SALES (est): 1MM-4.9MM Privately Held
WEB: www.state.mn.us
SIC: 8322 Social services for the handicapped; human resource, social work & welfare administration services; state government administration of social & manpower programs
DH: Minnesota Department of
332 Minnesota St Ste E200
Saint Paul MN 55101
651 259-7114

(G-8682)
MINNESOTA DEPARTMENT OF ADMIN
Also Called: Human Resourses Div
50 Sherburne Ave Ste 114 (55155-1402)
PHONE..................651 296-2600
FAX: 651 296-0579
Ben Benson, IT/INT Sup
Annette Friedl, IT/INT Sup
Kent Allin, Director
Deborah Tomczyk, Director
Brenda Thielin-Willard, Asst Director
EMP: 900
SALES (est): 50MM-99.9MM Privately Held
WEB: www.state.mn.us
SIC: 8741 Personnel management services; economic programs administration services; state government administration of general economic programs
DH: Minnesota Department of Admin
50 Sherburne Ave Ste 200
Saint Paul MN 55155
651 201-2530

(G-8683)
MINNESOTA DEPARTMENT OF HUMAN
Also Called: Provider Call Center
444 Lafayette Rd N (55155-3802)
PHONE..................651 431-2000
Martin Daniels, Opers Staff
Jeff Swason, Purch Mgr
Martin Cammack, Finance
Connie Jones, Human Resources
Ted Gredvig, Manager
EMP: 6000
SALES (est): 100MM-499.9MM Privately Held
WEB: www.state.mn.us
SIC: 8322 Family services agency; human resource, social work & welfare administration services; offender self-help agency
DH: Minnesota Department of Human
540 Cedar St
Saint Paul MN 55101
651 431-2000

(G-8684)
MINNESOTA DIVERSIFIED INDS (PA)
1700 Wynne Ave (55108-2708)
PHONE..................651 999-8200
FAX: 651 999-8200
Betsy Jaros, Vice Pres
Stacy Wentz, Vice Pres
Rod Wood, Vice Pres
Jeff Gervais, Opers Mgr
Lance Novak, CFO
EMP: 42 EST: 1964
SQ FT: 32,000
SALES (corp-wide): 14.87M Privately Held
WEB: www.mdi.org
SIC: 7389 Manufactures plastic corrugated panels; packaging & labeling services

(G-8685)
MINNESOTA EPILEPSY GROUP
225 Smith Ave N Ste 201 (55102-2697)
PHONE..................651 241-5305
John R Gates MD, President
Shannon Lenzen, General Mgr
Michael D Frost MD, Corp Secy
Frank Ritter MD, Vice Pres
Ronald H Spiegel MD, Treasurer
EMP: 117 EST: 1990
SALES (est): 10MM-24.9MM Privately Held
WEB: www.mnepilepsy.org
SIC: 8011 Neurologist

(G-8686)
MINNESOTA FARMERS' MARKET ASSN
625 Robert St N (55155-2538)
PHONE..................320 763-6893
Ronald Branch, Treasurer
EMP: 60 Privately Held
SIC: 8611 Growers' associations

(G-8687)
MINNESOTA FLEXIBLE CORP (PA)
803 Transfer Rd Ste 1 (55114-1424)
PHONE..................651 645-7522
FAX: 651 645-8259
Will Stewart, President
Terry Kelly, Vice Pres
Richard Hering, Warehouse Mgr
Brad Serstan, Purchasing
Patti Sawyer, Controller
▲ EMP: 30 EST: 1969
SQ FT: 90,000 Privately Held
WEB: www.minnesotaflexible.com
SIC: 5085 5162 Wholesales industrial hose, belting & packing; manufactures rubber & plastic hoses & beltings; manufactures plastic hose; manufactures hydraulic or pneumatic hose & tube couplings; manufactures flexible metal hose; manufactures rubber hose

(G-8688)
MINNESOTA GASTROENTEROLOGY PA
2550 University Ave W Ste 423S (55114-8685)
PO Box 14909, Minneapolis (55414-0909)
PHONE..................612 871-1145
Sam Leon, President
Tim Potter, Vice Pres
Marit Brock, Human Resources
Dawn Cowle, Office Mgr
Nancy L Engler, Office Mgr
EMP: 65 EST: 1975
SQ FT: 10,000
SALES (est): 5MM-9.9MM Privately Held
WEB: www.mngastro.com
SIC: 8011 Gastronomist

(G-8689)
MINNESOTA HOSPITAL
2250 University Ave W (55114-1801)
PHONE..................651 641-1121
Bruce Rueben, President
Ken Pazdernik, Controller
EMP: 75 EST: 1993
SALES (est): 5MM-9.9MM Privately Held
SIC: 8741 Hospital management services; nursing & personal care facility management services

(G-8690)
MINNESOTA HOSPITAL ASSOCIATION
2550 University Ave W Ste 350S (55114-1907)
PHONE..................651 641-1121
FAX: 651 659-1477
Bruce Ruben, President
Barbara Averill, VP Mktg
Jeanne Talmadge, VP Mktg
Charles Kronschnable, Programmer Anys
EMP: 50 EST: 1974
SQ FT: 20,767 Privately Held
WEB: www.mhha.com
SIC: 8621 Professional organization

(G-8691)
MINNESOTA INSTITUTE OF PUBLIC
2720 Highway 10 NE (55112-4092)
PHONE..................763 427-5310
Diane Schenkenberg, Accountant
Sherri Lincoln, Administrator
Kevin Spading, Exec Dir
F Jaker, Exec Dir
Gerald F Jaker, Exec Dir
EMP: 39 EST: 1972
SQ FT: 13,000 Privately Held
WEB: www.miph.org
SIC: 8399 Health systems agency; social change association

(G-8692)
MINNESOTA INTERNAL MEDICINE
Also Called: Health Internal Medicine
1690 University Ave W Ste 570 (55104-3795)
PHONE..................651 232-4800
FAX: 651 232-4899
William Brombach, President
Joan Husting, Office Mgr
Michael Leehy, Internal Med
Tammy Chiesa, Internal Med
Samantha J Brown, Internal Med
EMP: 35 EST: 1953
SQ FT: 8,000
SALES (est): 1MM-4.9MM Privately Held
WEB: www.minnesotanaturalmedicine.com
SIC: 8011 Internal medicine physician or surgeon; oncologist; rheumatology specialist, physician or surgeon office

(G-8693)
MINNESOTA LANDMARKS INC
Also Called: LANDMARK CENTER
75 5th St W Ste 404 (55102-1438)
PHONE..................651 292-3233
FAX: 651 292-3272
Negussie Haile-Sblassie, Business Mgr
Amy Mino, Exec Dir
Stephanie Sierleja, Assistant
EMP: 30 EST: 1970
SALES (est): 1MM-4.9MM Privately Held
WEB: www.landmarkcenter.org
SIC: 7922 Performing arts center production service

(G-8694)
MINNESOTA LEAGUE OF CREDIT
555 Wabasha St N Ste 250 (55102-1673)
PHONE..................651 288-5170
MO Commins, President
David Douglas, Exec Dir
EMP: 30 EST: 1939
SQ FT: 7,000 Privately Held
SIC: 8611 6163 Business association; loan broker

(G-8695)
MINNESOTA LEGAL SERVICES (PA)
2324 University Ave W Ste 101B (55114-1854)
PHONE..................651 228-9105
Ann Conroy, Manager
Carmen Goettsch, Administrator
Privately Held
SIC: 8111 Legal services

(G-8696)
MINNESOTA LIONS EYE BANK INC
1000 Westgate Dr Ste 260 (55114-8671)
PHONE..................612 624-6446
Jackie Malling, Director
EMP: 60
SALES (est): 1MM-4.9MM Privately Held
SIC: 8099 Eye banks

(G-8697)
MINNESOTA LIQUOR RETAILERS INC
1983 Sloan Pl Ste 15 (55117-2004)
PHONE..................651 772-0900
FAX: 651 772-0910
Pat Watercott, Vice Pres

Bruce Knowlan, *Vice Pres*
Tony Chesak, *Finance Mgr*
Colin Minehart, *Manager*
Anthony Chesak, *Exec Dir*
EMP: 37 **EST:** 1953 **Privately Held**
SIC: 8611 7011 Business association;
traveler accommodations

(G-8698)
MINNESOTA MAGAZINE & PUBN
1821 University Ave W S256 (55104-2872)
PHONE 651 290-6281
Bill Monn, *Director*
EMP: 25 **EST:** 2005 **Privately Held**
SIC: 8611 Business association

(G-8699)
MINNESOTA MUTUAL CO'S INC
400 Robert St N Ste A (55101-2099)
PHONE 651 665-3500
FAX: 651 665-4128
Robert L Senkler, *CEO*
Joseph Freking, *Project Mgr*
Julianne Pohl, *Manager*
EMP: 2500 **EST:** 1998
SALES (est): 1B-9.9B **Privately Held**
SIC: 6311 Life insurance carriers

(G-8700)
MINNESOTA NURSES' ASSOCIATION
Also Called: Mna
1625 Energy Park Dr # 200 (55108-2735)
PHONE 651 646-4807
FAX: 651 647-5301
Linda Slattengren, *President*
Diane Johnson, *Corp Secy*
Kent Searl, *Vice Pres*
Patricia Dwyer, *Vice Pres*
Deedee Bloch, *Treasurer*
EMP: 40 **EST:** 1920 **Privately Held**
WEB: www.mnnurses.org
SIC: 8621 Nursing association

(G-8701)
MINNESOTA PIPE TRADES ASSN
411 Main St Ste 309 (55102-1031)
PHONE 651 291-8151
FAX: 651 228-0068
David Grefe, *IT/INT Sup*
Carl Crimmins, *Director*
EST: 1992 **Privately Held**
SIC: 8742 Labor & union relations
consultant

(G-8702)
MINNESOTA PUBLIC RADIO (HQ)
480 Cedar St (55101-2217)
PHONE 651 290-1500
William H Kling, *President*
Thomas Kigin, *Managing Dir*
Pamela Moret, *Corp Secy*
Donald Creighton, *Senior VP*
Ralph Hornberger, *Engineer*
EMP: 278 **EST:** 1969
SQ FT: 44,000 **Privately Held**
WEB: www.americanpublicmedia.org
SIC: 4832 Radio broadcasting station
PA: American Public Media Group
480 Cedar St
Saint Paul MN 55101
651 290-1500

(G-8703)
MINNESOTA PUBLIC RADIO
Also Called: K N O W 911 F M
45 7th St E Bldg 100 (55101-2202)
PHONE 651 290-1500
FAX: 651 290-1243
Bill Kling, *President*
Kathryn Eldred, *General Mgr*
Addison L Piper, *Trustee*
Steven M Rothschild, *Trustee*
Anita Kunin, *Trustee*
EMP: 53 **EST:** 1967
SALES (est): 1MM-4.9MM **Privately Held**
SIC: 4832 Radio broadcasting station

(G-8704)
MINNESOTA SALT SERVICE
2500 Walnut St Ste 100 (55113-2553)
PHONE 651 774-6237
Richard Benjamin, *President*
EMP: 30 **EST:** 1970
SALES (est): 10MM-24.9MM **Privately Held**
SIC: 5169 Wholesales industrial salts

(G-8705)
MINNESOTA STATE AGRICULTURAL
1265 Snelling Ave N (55108-3003)
PHONE 651 288-4400
FAX: 651 642-2240
Karen Frost, *General Mgr*
Brian Hudalla, *General Mgr*
Jerry Hammer, *Corp Secy*
Jim Sinclair, *Sales Dir*
Brigid McGough, *Marketing Mgr*
EMP: 70 **EST:** 1855
SALES (est): 1MM-4.9MM **Privately Held**
WEB: www.msffoundation.org
SIC: 7999 6512 Agricultural fair;
nonresidential building operator

(G-8706)
MINNESOTA STATE BAR ASSN
2550 University Ave W 160S (55114-1098)
PHONE 651 227-8266
Frank Harris, *Exec Dir*
Jeffrey Johnson, *Associate Dir*
Johanna Werner, *Executive Asst*
Dannielle Hokanson, *Executive Asst*
EMP: 35
SALES (est): 5MM-9.9MM **Privately Held**
WEB: www.minncle.org
SIC: 7299 Nondegree granting continuing
education educational services; consumer
information service
PA: Minnesota State Bar Assn
600 Nicollet Mall Ste 380
Minneapolis MN 55402
612 333-1183

(G-8707)
MINNESOTA STREET ASSOCIATES
332 Minnesota St Ste W120 (55101-1309)
PHONE 651 225-3666
FAX: 651 222-4158
Guy Labarre, *President*
Cathy Morris, *Manager*
EMP: 90 **EST:** 1985
SQ FT: 1,100,000
SALES (est): 10MM-24.9MM **Privately Held**
SIC: 6531 Real estate management
services

(G-8708)
MINNESOTA SURGICAL ASSOCIATES
Also Called: England, Michael D
1973 Sloan Pl Ste 225 (55117-2094)
PHONE 651 776-0724
FAX: 651 776-0932
Michael Copeland, *Partner*
John Miller MD, *Partner*
Michael England, *Partner*
Jim Tepp, *Office Mgr*
Clarice Huddleson, *Manager*
EMP: 25 **EST:** 1994
SQ FT: 1,200
SALES (est): 1MM-4.9MM **Privately Held**
SIC: 8011 8741 Surgeon's office;
management services

(G-8709)
MINNESOTA VIKINGS FOOD SVCS (HQ)
2830 Fairview Ave N (55113-1314)
PHONE 952 835-5250
Larry Bittinger, *President*
Jeffrey A Cropp, *Vice Pres*
EMP: 150 **EST:** 1962
SQ FT: 50,000 **Privately Held**
WEB: www.informtek.net
SIC: 8741 Merchandising machine operator;
restaurant management services; caterer
PA: Minnesota Vikings Football
9520 Viking Dr
Eden Prairie MN 55344
952 828-6500

(G-8710)
MINNESOTA WATER WELL ASSN
1000 Westgate Dr Ste 252 (55114-1067)
PHONE 651 290-6270
David Ewald, *President*
EMP: 30 **EST:** 1982
SALES (est): 1MM-4.9MM **Privately Held**
SIC: 1781 Water well drilling contractor

(G-8711)
MINNESOTA WILD HOCKEY CLUB LP
317 Washington St (55102-1609)
PHONE 651 602-6000
Craig Leipold, *CEO*
Jack Sperling, *Partner*
Chuck Fletcher, *General Mgr*
Phil Falcone, *General Ptnr*
Matt Majka, *COO*
EMP: 100 **EST:** 2001
SALES (est): 10MM-24.9MM **Privately Held**
WEB: www.minnesotahockey.org
SIC: 7941 Sports support services

(G-8712)
MINNETRONIX INC
1635 Energy Park Dr (55108-2703)
PHONE 651 917-4060
FAX: 651 917-4066
Richard Nazarian, *President*
Joe Renzetti, *COO*
Dirk Smith, *Vice Pres*
Stan Crossett, *VP Opers-Prdtn-*
Lynn Ihlenfeldt, *VP Opers-Prdtn-*
EMP: 135 **EST:** 1996
SQ FT: 45,501
SALES (est): 10MM-24.9MM **Privately Held**
WEB: www.minnetronix.com
SIC: 8711 8731 Manufactures electrical
equipment & supplies; engineering services;
manufactures medical instruments;
manufactures electromedical equipment;
electronic research laboratory

(G-8713)
MINNHEALTH FAMILY PHYSICIANS
1050 Larpenteur Ave W # 2 (55113-6556)
PHONE 651 487-2831
FAX: 651 487-1705
Celeste Gillitzer, *Office Mgr*
Michele Guftson, *Manager*
Tracy Schulke, *Supervisor*
EMP: 30
SALES (est): 1MM-4.9MM **Privately Held**
WEB: www.minnhealth.com
SIC: 8011 General & family practice
physician or surgeon office
PA: Minnhealth Family Physicians
2025 Sloan Pl Ste 35
Saint Paul MN 55117
651 772-1572

(G-8714)
MINNHOUSE
4786 Banning Ave (55110-3264)
PHONE 651 426-6402
P L Richman, *Principal*
EMP: 30 **EST:** 2001
SALES (est): 1MM-4.9MM **Privately Held**
SIC: 8049 Health practitioners' office

(G-8715)
MIRATEC SYSTEMS INC
640 Olive St (55130-4441)
PHONE 651 222-8440
Bert Guinee, *President*
Carol Guinee, *Vice Pres*
Dan Krossehell, *Mfg Staff*
Lisa Tahti, *Sales Staff*
Tim Haskin, *Sales Staff*
EMP: 25 **EST:** 1988
SQ FT: 22,000
SALES (est): 10MM-24.9MM **Privately Held**
WEB: www.miratecsystems.com
SIC: 5199 Wholesales art goods & supplies;
manufactures signs & advertising
specialties

(G-8716)
MISSION HEALTH CARE LLC
Also Called: Bethel Care Center
420 Marshall Ave (55102-1718)
PHONE 651 224-2368
FAX: 651 224-3582
Paul Contis, *Member*
Paul J Contris, *Member*
Thomas E Boerboom, *COO*
Rod Hawkins, *Accountant*
Nancy Watroba, *Accountant*
EMP: 180 **EST:** 1975
SALES (est): 5MM-9.9MM **Privately Held**
SIC: 8059 Convalescent home; nursing
home
PA: Mission Healthcare LLC
7921 S Stephanie Ln
Tempe AZ 85284
480 730-1573

(G-8717)
MODEL CITIES OF ST PAUL INC (PA)
839 University Ave W (55104-4808)
PHONE 651 632-8350
Beverley Hawkins, *CEO*
Brenda Bailey, *Finance Dir*
Annie Oheneswere, *Sales Mgr*
Babette Jamison, *Director*
EST: 1992
SQ FT: 21,800
SALES (corp-wide): 1.79M **Privately Held**
WEB: www.modelcities.org
SIC: 8741 6512 6513 Administrative
management services; nonresidential
building operator; apartment building
operator

(G-8718)
MONTAGE INC (PA)
3050 Centre Pte Dr Ste 50 (55113-1180)
PHONE 651 633-1955
FAX: 651 633-2072
Ken Ehling, *President*
Bill Thomalla, *Vice Pres*
Micki Furlong, *Opers Mgr*
Richard Moberg, *VP Sls/Mktg*
Nancy Kerfeld, *Accounting Mgr*
EMP: 35 **EST:** 1972
SQ FT: 12,000 **Privately Held**
WEB: www.montagenet.com
SIC: 7363 Help supply services

(G-8719)
MOORE, COSTELLO & HART PLLP (PA)
Also Called: Patrick Plunkett
55 5th St E Ste 1400 (55101-1799)
PHONE 651 602-2615
Timothy C Cook, *Partner*
Phyllis Karasov, *Partner*
Patrick Plunkett, *Partner*
Tara D Mattessich, *Partner*
John G Patterson, *Partner*
EMP: 45 **EST:** 1856
SQ FT: 15,634 **Privately Held**
WEB: www.patrickplunkett.com
SIC: 8111 General practice law office

(G-8720)
MORE COSTELLO & HART PLLP
55 5th St E Ste 1400 (55101-1799)
PHONE 651 227-7683
FAX: 651 602-2670
John M Harens, *Partner*
William M Beadie, *Partner*
J P Plunkett, *Partner*
Pat Pounkett, *Partner*
Debra Klintworth, *Accounting Staf*
EMP: 29 **EST:** 1994
SALES (est): 1MM-4.9MM **Privately Held**
SIC: 8111 Corporate, partnership &
business law office

(G-8721)
MORGAN TIRE & AUTO LLC
Also Called: Team Tires Plus
2185 Ford Pkwy (55116-1816)
PHONE 651 690-5007
FAX: 651 690-5059
Thomas Comstock, *Manager*
EMP: 30
SALES (est): 1MM-4.9MM **Privately Held**
WEB: www.bfsusa.com

(PA)=Parent Co (HQ)=Headquarters (DH)=Div Headquarters
✿ = New business established in last 2 years

2011 Harris Minnesota
Services Directory

© Harris InfoSource 1-866-281-6415
377

SIC: 7534 Tire recapping & retreading services
HQ: Bfs Retail Operations LLC
333 E Lake St Ste 300
Bloomingdale IL 60108
630 259-9000

(G-8722)
MORNING STAR HEALTHCARE SVCS
2147 University Ave W # 206
(55114-1327)
PHONE.............................651 209-2950
Precious Ojika, *President*
EMP: 25 **EST:** 2007
SALES (est): 500-999K **Privately Held**
SIC: 8059 Personal care home, with health care

(G-8723)
MORTGAGE & INVESTMENT CONSLNTS
2489 Rice St Ste 202 (55113-3723)
PHONE.............................651 483-0200
FAX: 651 483-0500
James Gale, *President*
Lori H Sandon, *Corp Secy*
Steve Olson, *Controller*
Kevin Kleist, *Controller*
Ed Droel, *Branch Mgr*
EMP: 28 **EST:** 1999
SQ FT: 2,400
SALES (est): 1MM-4.9MM **Privately Held**
WEB: www.minnmortgage.com
SIC: 6163 Mortgage brokers service arranging for loans, using money of others

(G-8724)
MOTHERS & CHILDREN PROGRAM MAC
1140 Gervais Ave (55109-2020)
PHONE.............................651 484-8241
FAX: 651 484-1064
Jan Brown, *Director*
EMP: 50 **EST:** 1974
SALES (est): 1MM-4.9MM **Privately Held**
SIC: 8322 Individual & family social services

(G-8725)
MOUNDSVIEW BANQUET
5394 Edgewood Dr (55112-1402)
PHONE.............................763 717-4041
Matt Bowman, *Manager*
EMP: 25 **EST:** 1998
SALES (est): 500-999K **Privately Held**
SIC: 7299 Banquet hall facility

(G-8726)
MOUNT ZION HEBREW CONGREGATION
1300 Summit Ave (55105-2601)
PHONE.............................651 698-3881
FAX: 651 698-3818
James Steinman, *Principal*
Julie Beckman, *Corp Secy*
Liz Stein, *Treasurer*
Jane Steinman, *Director*
EMP: 40 **EST:** 1856 **Privately Held**
WEB: www.mzion.org
SIC: 8351 Synagogue; preschool center; religious library

(G-8727)
MSP CORP
5910 Rice Creek Pkwy # 300
(55126-5028)
PHONE.............................651 287-8100
Ben Liu, *President*
Janet Rantala, *Assistant VP*
Virgil A Marple PhD, *Vice Pres*
Helen Liu, *Vice Pres*
Kevin Wong, *Technical Mgr*
EMP: 34 **EST:** 1985
SQ FT: 26,000
SALES (est): 5MM-9.9MM **Privately Held**
SIC: 8734 Manufactures measuring & controlling devices; pollution testing laboratory

(G-8728)
MULTICARE ASSOCIATES OF THE
Also Called: Rosedale Medical Center
1835 County Road C W Ste 20
(55113-1343)
PHONE.............................763 785-4300
FAX: 763 785-7716
Janeen Slotum, *CEO*
Susan Turcotte, *Office Mgr*
Diane Rieck, *Administrator*
Jack Stoulil, *Physician Asst*
EMP: 35
SALES (est): 1MM-4.9MM **Privately Held**
SIC: 8011 Medical center
PA: Multicare Associates of The
7675 Madison St NE
Minneapolis MN 55432
763 785-4500

(G-8729)
MURLOWSKI CONSTRUCTION CO INC
2200 Old Highway 8 NW (55112-1894)
PHONE.............................651 786-1300
Mark Murlowski, *CEO*
Gina R Murlowski, *President*
Jennifer L Murlowski, *Vice Pres*
EMP: 25 **EST:** 1995
SQ FT: 20,000
SALES (est): 5MM-9.9MM **Privately Held**
WEB: www.murlowskiconstruction.com
SIC: 1542 1541 New commercial & office building construction; industrial building & warehouse construction

(G-8730)
MUSKA ELECTRIC CO
1985 Oakcrest Ave (55113-2605)
PHONE.............................651 636-5820
FAX: 651 636-0916
Gary D Nelson, *President*
Terry Artmann, *Member*
Randolph C Luhrs, *Corp Secy*
Larry EBY, *Materials Mgr*
Ronald Vonbank, *Manager*
EMP: 190 **EST:** 1919
SQ FT: 19,000
SALES (est): 10MM-24.9MM **Privately Held**
SIC: 1731 General electrical contractor

(G-8731)
MUTUAL SERVICE COOPERATIVE
Also Called: Country Insurance & Fincl Svcs
2 Pine Tree Dr (55112-3715)
PO Box 64035 (55164-0035)
PHONE.............................651 631-7000
John Blackburn, *CEO*
Steve Ricklefs, *Vice Pres*
William Rustad, *Purchasing*
Frank Radermacher, *CFO*
Clark Boatman, *CFO*
EMP: 325 **EST:** 1949
SQ FT: 250,000
SALES (est): 25MM-49.9MM **Privately Held**
SIC: 8741 Administrative management services

(G-8732)
NA CORP (PA)
2230 Albert St N (55113-4206)
PHONE.............................651 636-9654
Michael Bilski, *President*
Brad Huckle, *Exec VP*
EMP: 65 **EST:** 1997 **Privately Held**
WEB: www.pipegrep.net
SIC: 6712 Bank holding company

(G-8733)
NALCO DISTRIBUTING INC
Also Called: North American Abrasives
1000 Labore Industrial Ct (55110-5114)
PO Box 10747 (55110-0747)
PHONE.............................651 636-8124
Ken Kruger, *President*
EMP: 60 **EST:** 2000
SALES (est): 25MM-49.9MM **Privately Held**
SIC: 5085 Wholesales industrial abrasives

(G-8734)
NAOMI FAMILY CENTER
77 9th St E (55101-2263)
PHONE.............................651 222-7962
Bil L Beckstrom, *Treasurer*
Denise Best, *Director*
EMP: 25 **EST:** 1994
SALES (est): 1MM-4.9MM **Privately Held**
SIC: 8322 Individual & family social services; church

(G-8735)
NARDINI FIRE EQUIPMENT CO INC
405 County Road E W (55126-7032)
PHONE.............................651 483-6631
FAX: 651 483-6945
Tom Nardini, *President*
Karl Shoberg, *Vice Pres*
Jocko Frucci, *Purch Mgr*
Daniel Bircher, *Controller*
Brian Youngquist, *Info Tech Mgr*
EMP: 75 **EST:** 1955
SQ FT: 15,000
SALES (est): 50MM-99.9MM **Privately Held**
WEB: www.nardinifire.com
SIC: 5099 7699 Wholesales fire extinguishers; wholesales safety equipment & supplies; fire control equipment repair service for the military

(G-8736)
NATH MANAGEMENT INC
Also Called: Denny's
255 Century Ave N (55119-4101)
PHONE.............................651 739-2377
FAX: 651 739-2377
Fred Fairchild, *General Mgr*
EMP: 40
SALES (est): 1MM-4.9MM **Privately Held**
SIC: 7011 Full service chain family restaurant; vacation lodge
PA: Nath Management Inc
900 American Blvd E # 300
Minneapolis MN 55420
952 853-1400

(G-8737)
NATH MIDWEST LODGING LLC
2540 Cleveland Ave N (55113-2719)
PHONE.............................952 853-1423
Scott Henning, *General Mgr*
EMP: 65 **EST:** 1998
SALES (est): 1MM-4.9MM **Privately Held**
SIC: 7011 Hotel

(G-8738)
NATIONAL AMTELCO EQUIPMENT
Also Called: N A E O
1000 Westgate Dr Ste 252 (55114-8679)
PHONE.............................651 265-7845
Mary Peterson, *Principal*
Shannon Thompson, *Exec Dir*
EMP: 40 **EST:** 2005 **Privately Held**
WEB: www.naeo.org
SIC: 8641 Civic & social organization

(G-8739)
NATIONAL CAMERA EXCHANGE INC
2401 Fairview Ave N # 10 (55113-2708)
PHONE.............................651 636-0693
FAX: 651 604-0830
Marc Gerr, *Store Mgr*
Mark Gere, *Manager*
EMP: 30
SALES (est): 1MM-4.9MM **Privately Held**
SIC: 7384 Retails cameras; retails video cameras, recorders & accessories; retails photographic supplies; retails binoculars; retails telescopes; film processing & finishing laboratory

(G-8740)
NATIONAL OILWELL VARCO INC
240 Plato Blvd E (55107-1609)
PHONE.............................651 293-4699
Bauer Rick, *Controller*
Wayne Long, *VP Sales*
Richard Juelich, *Branch Mgr*
Timothy Connelly, *MIS Mgr*
Cathy Leritz, *Administration*

EMP: 100
SALES (est): 25MM-49.9MM **Publicly Held**
WEB: www.natoil.com
SIC: 5084 Wholesales industrial machinery & equipment
PA: National Oilwell Varco Inc
7909 Parkwood Circle Dr
Houston TX 77036
713 346-7500

(G-8741)
NATUS CORP
1381 Rice St (55117-4545)
PHONE.............................651 487-3211
FAX: 651 487-1514
Lynn Natus, *President*
Ted Natus, *Vice Pres*
EMP: 75 **EST:** 1961
SQ FT: 30,000
SALES (est): 10MM-24.9MM **Privately Held**
SIC: 7389 Interior decorating service

(G-8742)
NB SAINT PAUL INC
Also Called: Holiday Inn Saint Paul East
2201 Burns Ave (55119-6667)
PHONE.............................651 731-2220
Alasdair Cripps, *President*
EMP: 99 **EST:** 1984
SALES (est): 5MM-9.9MM **Privately Held**
SIC: 7011 Traveler accommodations
PA: Larken Inc
3330 Southgate Ct SW
Cedar Rapids IA 52404
319 366-8201

(G-8743)
NEIGHBORHOOD HOUSE
179 Robie St E (55107-2360)
PHONE.............................651 789-2500
Armando Camacho, *President*
Lisa Lane, *Vice Pres*
Sheri Zigan, *Vice Pres*
Bern Lovstad, *Human Resources*
Steve Kean, *Marketing Staff*
EMP: 59 **EST:** 1897
SQ FT: 93,000
SALES (est): 1MM-4.9MM **Privately Held**
SIC: 8322 Neighborhood center

(G-8744)
NELNET INC
180 5th St E Ste 1350 (55101-1677)
PO Box 64692 (55164-0692)
PHONE.............................651 265-7600
FAX: 651 265-7780
Bob Forbrook, *Manager*
EMP: 180
SALES (est): 25MM-49.9MM **Publicly Held**
SIC: 6141 Personal credit institution
PA: Nelnet Inc
121 S 13th St Ste 201
Lincoln NE 68508
402 458-2370

(G-8745)
NELSON, BRUCE PLUMBING
1272 Point Douglas Rd S (55119-5673)
PHONE.............................651 738-9354
Bruce Nelson, *President*
Debra Nelson, *Vice Pres*
EMP: 25 **EST:** 1976
SQ FT: 6,300
SALES (est): 1MM-4.9MM **Privately Held**
WEB: www.landofloons.com
SIC: 1711 Plumbing service; heating & air conditioning contractor; retails plumbing & heating supplies

(G-8746)
NEUROLOGICAL ASSOCIATES OF ST
Also Called: Schanfield, Paul M MD
1650 Beam Ave Ste 200 (55109-1147)
PHONE.............................651 221-9051
Richard Foreman, *Partner*
T D Capistrant MD, *Partner*
Paul Schanfield, *Partner*
Linda G Goldman MD, *Partner*
Kenneth Hoj MD, *Partner*
EMP: 35 **EST:** 1978
SALES (est): 1MM-4.9MM **Privately Held**
WEB: www.neurostpaul.com
SIC: 8011 Neurologist

www.HarrisInfo.com
378
2011 Harris Minnesota
Services Directory
▲=Import ▼=Export
◆=Import/Export

(G-8747)
NEW CONCEPTS MANAGEMENT GROUP
Also Called: Gables At Arbor Pnte Homeownrs
3065 Centre Pointe Dr (55113-1130)
PHONE.............................952 922-2500
Gene Sullivan, *President*
EMP: 30 EST: 2001
SALES (est): 5MM-9.9MM Privately Held
SIC: 6531 Real estate services

(G-8748)
NEW ERA INCENTIVES INC
Also Called: Expedite Drect Mail Fulfilment
3770 Dunlap St N (55112-6907)
PHONE.............................651 486-0252
FAX: 651 482-1782
Donald Klohn, *President*
William Hedahl, *General Mgr*
Bill Bell, *Vice Pres*
Bill Hedahl, *Vice Pres*
Tony Isom, *Vice Pres*
EMP: 50 EST: 1982
SQ FT: 35,000
SALES (est): 5MM-9.9MM Privately Held
WEB: www.expedite-dmf.com
SIC: 7331 Direct mail advertising service

(G-8749)
NEW HORIZON CHILD CARE INC
2360 Lexington Ave N (55113-4337)
PHONE.............................651 481-8069
FAX: 651 481-7030
Julie Stewart, *Exec Dir*
Ann Roy, *Director*
EMP: 30
SALES (est): 500-999K Privately Held
WEB: www.kidsquest.com
SIC: 8351 Child day care service
HQ: New Horizon Child Care Inc
16355 36th Ave N Ste 700
Plymouth MN 55446
763 557-1111

(G-8750)
NORTH AMERICAN BANKING CO
2230 Albert St N (55113-4206)
PHONE.............................651 636-9654
Bradley G Huckle, *President*
Michael Bilski, *Exec VP*
Todd Lovaas, *Vice Pres*
Colleen Fogle, *Loan Officer*
EMP: 50 EST: 1998
SQ FT: 10,000
SALES (est): 10MM-24.9MM Privately Held
WEB: www.pipegrep.net
SIC: 6022 6163 State commercial bank; loan broker
PA: NA Corp
2230 Albert St N
Saint Paul MN 55113
651 636-9654

(G-8751)
NORTH CITIES HEALTH CARE INC
Also Called: New Brighton Care Center
805 6th Ave NW (55112-2717)
PHONE.............................651 633-7200
FAX: 651 697-7377
Corrine Isle, *Nursing Dir*
EMP: 100
SALES (est): 1MM-4.9MM Privately Held
SIC: 8051 8052 Skilled nursing care facility; intermediate care facility

(G-8752)
NORTH OAKS GOLF CLUB INC
54 E Oaks Rd (55127-6430)
PHONE.............................651 484-6311
FAX: 651 484-5411
Thomas Plumb, *President*
Richard Haugen, *General Mgr*
David Stautz, *Corp Secy*
Michael Mulvaney, *Vice Pres*
Allen Bergh, *Manager*
EMP: 40 EST: 1953
SQ FT: 25,000
SALES (est): 1MM-4.9MM Privately Held
SIC: 7997 Membership golf club; bar; full service American restaurant

(G-8753)
NORTH POINT CAPITAL PARTNERS
2299 Territorial Rd (55114-1613)
PHONE.............................651 602-0789
FAX: 651 602-0202
Stacy L Colbert, *Member*
Marshall Johnson, *Member*
Thomas Gujer, *Member*
Cort Jerome, *Member*
Greg Wandschneider, *Sales Mgr*
EMP: 80 EST: 1987
SQ FT: 135,000
SALES (est): 50MM-99.9MM Privately Held
WEB: www.assetrecoverycorp.com
SIC: 5065 7379 8711 Wholesales electronic parts; computer system consulting services; electrical or electronic engineers

(G-8754)
NORTH SUBURBAN YOUTH FNDTN
1970 Oakcrest Ave Ste 118 (55113-2624)
PHONE.............................651 697-9865
Robert Matson, *CEO*
EMP: 25 EST: 1997 Privately Held
WEB: www.nsyf.net
SIC: 8641 Youth organizations

(G-8755)
NORTH WAY INVESTMENT CO
2227 University Ave W (55114-1625)
PHONE.............................651 646-7901
Edward J Paster, *President*
EMP: 30 EST: 1987
SALES (est): 5MM-9.9MM Privately Held
SIC: 6512 Operators of retail property

(G-8756)
NORTHEAST RESIDENCE INC
410 Little Canada Rd E (55117-1629)
PHONE.............................651 765-0217
FAX: 651 765-0212
Lisa Heross, *Finance*
Corrine Schmidt, *Administrator*
Brion Curran, *Assistant*
EMP: 260 EST: 1972
SQ FT: 3,400
SALES (est): 5MM-9.9MM Privately Held
SIC: 8361 8322 Residential care facility; individual & family social services

(G-8757)
NORTHERN AIR CORP
1001 Labore Industrial Ct B (55110-5168)
PHONE.............................651 490-9868
Lynn Bishop, *President*
Anderson Stevea, *Vice Pres*
Steve Anderson, *Vice Pres*
Brenda Sjerven, *Controller*
Mike Bjokne, *Manager*
EMP: 128 EST: 1985
SQ FT: 6,000
SALES (est): 10MM-24.9MM Privately Held
WEB: www.nac-hvac.com
SIC: 1711 Warm air heating & air conditioning contractor; ventilation & duct work contractor; refrigeration contractor

(G-8758)
NORTHERN LIGHT PEDIATRICS
3585 Lexington Ave N # 350 (55126-8056)
PHONE.............................651 484-3942
FAX: 651 787-0519
Sig Culver, *Owner*
Margaret J Hustad, *Owner*
Lisa Swanson, *Principal*
EMP: 27 EST: 2001
SALES (est): 1MM-4.9MM Privately Held
WEB: www.nothernlight.com
SIC: 8011 Pediatrician office

(G-8759)
NORTHERN STAR COUNCIL, BOY (PA)
393 Marshall Ave (55102-1717)
PHONE.............................651 224-1891
Paula Miller, *CFO*
Pam Grayson, *Human Res Mgr*
Kent York, *Marketing Staff*
Marelene Gerdets, *Manager*
Clint Guy, *Manager*
EMP: 52
EST: 1910
SQ FT: 15,000
SALES (corp-wide): 177.63K Privately Held
SIC: 8641 Boy Scout organization

(G-8760)
NORTHERN STATES POWER CO
Also Called: XCEL Energy
3115 Centre Pointe Dr (55113-1130)
PHONE.............................651 639-4470
Gene Westberk, *General Mgr*
Dave Adolphson, *Project Mgr*
Ben Sherman, *Engineer*
Jane Doyon, *Manager*
Lori Kahl, *Manager*
EMP: 235
SALES (est): 100MM-499.9MM Publicly Held
WEB: www.middletownpower.com
SIC: 4911 Provides electric power transmission services
HQ: Northern States Power Co
414 Nicollet Mall
Minneapolis MN 55401
612 330-5500

(G-8761)
NORTHERN STATES POWER CO
Also Called: Metro East Region
825 Rice St (55117-5459)
PHONE.............................612 330-5674
Susan Ganzer, *Principal*
Tony Rude, *Opers Staff*
Mark Nelson, *Engineering*
Kearn Kelley, *Info Tech Mgr*
EMP: 372
SALES (est): 100MM-499.9MM Publicly Held
WEB: www.middletownpower.com
SIC: 4911 Provides electric power transmission services
HQ: Northern States Power Co
414 Nicollet Mall
Minneapolis MN 55401
612 330-5500

(G-8762)
NORTHFIELD INSURANCE CO
385 Washington St (55102-1309)
PO Box 64816 (55164-0816)
PHONE.............................651 688-4100
Randall D Jones, *President*
Gene G Gopon, *Principal*
Bruce A Backberg, *Corp Secy*
Jerome B Simon, *Corp Secy*
David J Brick, *Vice Pres*
EMP: 25 EST: 1972
SQ FT: 85,000
SALES (est): 10MM-24.9MM Publicly Held
WEB: www.stpaul.com
SIC: 6331 Provides property damage insurance
HQ: Northland Insurance Co
385 Washington St
Saint Paul MN 55102
651 688-4100

(G-8763)
NORTHLAND DEALER FINANCE INC
3564 Rolling View Dr (55110-5676)
PHONE.............................651 773-4973
Jim Koivispo, *Principal*
EMP: 25 EST: 1995
SALES (est): 5MM-9.9MM Privately Held
SIC: 6141 Personal credit institution

(G-8764)
NORTHLAND INSURANCE CO (HQ)
385 Washington St (55102-1309)
PHONE.............................651 688-4100
FAX: 651 688-4498
Gene G Gopon, *Ch of Bd*
Randall D Jones, *President*
Bruce A Backberg, *Corp Secy*
Jerome B Simon, *Corp Secy*
Wendy C Skjerven, *Corp Secy*
EMP: 470 EST: 1948
SQ FT: 190,000
SALES (corp-wide): 24.68B Publicly Held
WEB: www.stpaul.com
SIC: 6331 Provides property damage insurance
PA: Travelers Co's Inc
485 Lexington Ave
New York NY 10017
917 778-6000

(G-8765)
NORTHSTAR CAPITAL MARKETS SVCS
444 Cedar St Ste 800 (55101-3154)
PHONE.............................651 290-8781
Taige Thornton, *President*
Lisa Parker, *Opers Mgr*
John Swingler, *Controller*
EMP: 50 EST: 2000
SQ FT: 11,834
SALES (est): 5MM-9.9MM Privately Held
SIC: 6163 Loan broker

(G-8766)
NORTHWEST AREA FOUNDATION
60 Plato Blvd E Ste 400 (55107-1832)
PHONE.............................651 224-9635
FAX: 651 225-7701
Kevin Walker, *President*
Gary Cunningham, *Vice Pres*
Jean Adams, *Opers Staff*
Vicki Itzkowitz, *Finance*
Marie Podratz, *Office Mgr*
EMP: 41 EST: 1934
SQ FT: 20,000
SALES (est): 1MM-4.9MM Privately Held
SIC: 7389 Fundraising services

(G-8767)
NORTHWEST RESPIRATORY SERVICES
716 Prior Ave N Ste 1 (55104-1062)
PHONE.............................651 603-8720
FAX: 651 603-8723
Chris Larson, *Vice Pres*
Dana Brandt, *Vice Pres*
Charles Morgan, *Mng Member*
Ann McBurney, *Manager*
Dana Drandt, *Manager*
EMP: 65 EST: 1977
SALES (est): 5MM-9.9MM Privately Held
WEB: www.nwrespiratory.com
SIC: 7352 Medical equipment leasing & rental

(G-8768)
NORTHWEST SHEET METAL CO OF ST
110 Sycamore St W (55117-5451)
PHONE.............................651 310-0102
FAX: 651 310-0403
Rodney Albers, *President*
Deborah Sawyer, *Corp Secy*
Joseph Albers, *Vice Pres*
Joe Goetz, *Purchasing*
Diane Goetz, *Treasurer*
EMP: 60 EST: 1928
SQ FT: 15,000
SALES (est): 5MM-9.9MM Privately Held
SIC: 1711 Warm air heating & air conditioning contractor; ventilation & duct work contractor

(G-8769)
NORTHWEST TITLE & ESCROW INC
4255 White Bear Pkwy (55110-3383)
PHONE.............................651 490-9056
Frank Greibenow, *President*
Wayne Holstad, *President*
Dale Jacobson, *CFO*
Frederic Knaak, *Attorney*
EMP: 25 EST: 1991
SALES (est): 1MM-4.9MM Privately Held
SIC: 6541 Title abstract service

(G-8770)
NORTHWEST YOUTH & FAMILY SVCS
3490 Lexington Ave N (55126-8074)
PHONE.............................651 486-3808
FAX: 651 486-3858
Jerry Hrmoaka, *President*
Amanda Little, *Vice Chairman*
Ken Pazdernik, *CFO*
Ken Povdenk, *CFO*

(PA)=Parent Co (HQ)=Headquarters (DH)=Div Headquarters
✿ = New business established in last 2 years
2011 Harris Minnesota
Services Directory
© Harris InfoSource 1-866-281-6415
379

Fran Smith, *Office Mgr*
EMP: 80 **EST:** 1976
SALES (est): 1MM-4.9MM **Privately Held**
WEB: www.nyfs.org
SIC: 8322 Individual & family social services

(G-8771)
NORTHWESTERN FRUIT CO
616 Pine St (55130-4493)
PHONE............................651 224-4373
Robert L Meyers, *President*
Daniel Zelle, *COO*
Rita Meyers, *Vice Pres*
EMP: 26 **EST:** 1940
SQ FT: 12,000
SALES (est): 10MM-24.9MM **Privately Held**
WEB: www.northwesternfruit.com
SIC: 5148 Wholesales fresh fruits;
wholesales fresh vegetables

(G-8772)
NOTT CO　(PA)
4480 Round Lake Rd W (55112-1961)
PHONE............................651 415-3400
Edward L Davis, *President*
Mark Segner, *Managing Dir*
Mark Manderfeld, *Corp Secy*
Richard A Rosa, *Corp Secy*
Christy Clark, *Sr Corp Ofcr*
▲ **EMP:** 150 **EST:** 1879
SQ FT: 63,150 **Privately Held**
WEB: www.nottco.com
SIC: 5084 5085 Wholesales materials
handling equipment; wholesales industrial
supplies; manufactures gaskets, packing &
sealing devices; manufactures fluid power
valves & hose fittings

(G-8773)
**NOW CARE MEDICAL CENTERS
INC**
1955 County Road B2 W # 10
(55113-2723)
PHONE............................651 635-0054
FAX: 651 635-0949
John Eibs, *Sales Staff*
Sue E Mollnr MD, *Med Doctor*
Kathryn A Granley MD, *Med Doctor*
Tammy McCreey, *Manager*
Michelle Roubinek, *Physician Asst*
EMP: 27
SALES (est): 1MM-4.9MM **Privately Held**
WEB: www.northmemorial.com
SIC: 8052 Intermediate care facility
HQ: Now Care Medical Centers Inc
　　8301 Golden Valley Rd Ste 300
　　Golden Valley MN 55427
　　763 971-9882

(G-8774)
NOW MICRO INC
1645 Energy Park Dr # 200 (55108-2733)
PHONE............................651 633-9072
FAX: 651 631-9333
Patrick Finn, *President*
Kennen Pflughoeft, *Marketing Staff*
Bridget Beaudry, *Manager*
Brent Stanley, *Info Tech Dir*
Bob Milam, *VP Systems*
EMP: 36 **EST:** 1993
SQ FT: 16,800
SALES (est): 25MM-49.9MM **Privately Held**
WEB: www.nowmicro.com
SIC: 5045 Wholesales computers,
peripherals & software; retails computers &
computer software

(G-8775)
NYSTROM & ASSOCIATES LTD
1900 Silver Lake Rd NW # 110
(55112-1789)
PHONE............................651 628-9566
FAX: 651 628-0411
Brian Nystrom, *President*
Lisa Olson, *Corp Secy*
Mary A Nystrom, *Vice Pres*
Annie Pope, *Office Mgr*
Sue Vanek, *Office Mgr*
EMP: 42 **EST:** 1991
SQ FT: 4,000
SALES (est): 1MM-4.9MM **Privately Held**
SIC: 8322 8093 General counseling
services; outpatient mental health clinic

(G-8776)
O'NEIL ASSOCIATES INC
801 Crestview Dr S (55119-5879)
PHONE............................651 738-2694
Neil Schwartz, *President*
EMP: 50 **EST:** 1997
SALES (est): 10MM-24.9MM **Privately Held**
WEB: www.surfoneil.com
SIC: 1521 Single-family housing
construction

(G-8777)
OAK HOTELS INC
Also Called: Days Inn Roseville
2550 Cleveland Ave N (55113-2601)
PHONE............................651 636-6730
Alisha Ragland, *Vice Pres*
Leanne Lessard, *Director*
EMP: 40
SALES (est): 1MM-4.9MM **Privately Held**
SIC: 7011 Traveler accommodations

(G-8778)
OAKDALE-GRANADA LAKES LP
328 Kellogg Blvd W (55102-1900)
PHONE............................651 291-1750
Ellen Higgins, *Partner*
EMP: 99
SALES (est): 10MM-24.9MM **Privately Held**
SIC: 6513 Apartment building operator

(G-8779)
OKI SYSTEMS LIMITED
860 Vandalia St (55114-1305)
PHONE............................651 645-8668
Bret Meyer, *Controller*
Bill Wade, *Manager*
EMP: 53
SALES (est): 10MM-24.9MM **Privately Held**
WEB: www.okisys.com
SIC: 5084 Wholesales industrial machinery
& equipment
PA: OKI Systems Limited
　　10685 Medallion Dr
　　Cincinnati OH 45241
　　513 874-2600

(G-8780)
OLAFSON, RENAE
Also Called: Caring Companions
2324 University Ave W # 102
(55114-1854)
PHONE............................651 452-6825
FAX: 651 452-7829
Renae Olafson, *Owner*
EMP: 50 **EST:** 1997
SALES (est): 1MM-4.9MM **Privately Held**
WEB: www.touchinghearts.com
SIC: 8082 Home health care services

(G-8781)
**OLSEN THIELEN
TECHNOLOGIES INC**
2675 Long Lake Rd (55113-1117)
PHONE............................651 483-4521
Kenneth Vohs, *President*
Kelly Salwei, *Corp Secy*
Patrick Powers, *Vice Pres*
John Coleman, *Vice Pres*
Dennis Carson, *Vice Pres*
EMP: 120 **EST:** 1921
SQ FT: 25,500
SALES (est): 10MM-24.9MM **Privately Held**
WEB: www.olsen-thielen.com
SIC: 8721 7371 Certified public accountant
services; computer programming service

(G-8782)
OLSON COFFEE ROASTERS INC
Also Called: White Rock Coffee Roasters
2325 Endicott St Ste 207W (55114-1223)
PHONE............................651 645-1729
Bruce Olson, *President*
Greg Schiffer, *Treasurer*
EMP: 25 **EST:** 2003
SQ FT: 1,700
SALES (est): 10MM-24.9MM **Privately Held**
WEB: www.whiterockcoffee.com
SIC: 5149 Wholesales green or roasted
coffee; retail beverage store

(G-8783)
OLSON M D, PETER J
Also Called: Health East
980 Rice St (55117-4949)
PHONE............................651 326-9020
FAX: 651 232-2940
Peter J Olson MD, *Owner*
Laurel M Hansen MD, *Med Doctor*
Anne M Pearson MD, *Med Doctor*
Sarah Hammes MD, *Med Doctor*
Carol Balcome, *Supervisor*
EMP: 30 **EST:** 1985
SALES (est): 1MM-4.9MM **Privately Held**
SIC: 8011 Physical medicine physician or
surgeon office

(G-8784)
**ON ASSIGNMENT STAFFING
SVCS**
2550 University Ave W Ste 315N
(55114-1903)
PHONE............................651 647-1160
FAX: 651 917-3039
Dana Hause, *Branch Mgr*
Tim Michael, *Manager*
EMP: 75
SALES (est): 5MM-9.9MM **Publicly Held**
WEB: www.onassignment.com
SIC: 8071 Testing laboratory
HQ: On Assignment Staffing Svcs
　　9987 Carver Rd Ste 510
　　Blue Ash OH 45242
　　513 936-3468

(G-8785)
ON-SITE SANITATION INC
95 Woodlyn Ave Ste 1 (55117-2091)
PHONE............................651 429-3781
FAX: 651 486-6400
Karen Holm, *CEO*
David Holm, *President*
Molly R Holm, *Vice Pres*
EMP: 50 **EST:** 1989
SQ FT: 20,000
SALES (est): 1MM-4.9MM **Privately Held**
WEB: www.onsitesanitation.com
SIC: 7359 Portable toilet rental

(G-8786)
**ONCOLOGIC CONSULTANTS
(PA)**
2550 University Ave W Ste 110N
(55114-2001)
PHONE............................651 602-5335
Thomas Flynn MD, *President*
Burton Schwartz MD, *Principal*
Mark Sborov MD, *Treasurer*
Eleanor Vasey, *Office Mgr*
Joan Theis, *Manager*
EMP: 27 **EST:** 1985
SQ FT: 13,000 **Privately Held**
SIC: 8011 Hematologist; oncologist

(G-8787)
175 FORT LLC
Also Called: Holiday Inn Saint Paul Dwntwn
175 7th St W (55102-2520)
PHONE............................651 225-1515
FAX: 651 225-1616
Ken Golder, *CEO*
Robert Hjort, *Exec VP*
EMP: 50 **EST:** 2000
SQ FT: 94,000
SALES (est): 1MM-4.9MM **Privately Held**
SIC: 7011 Traveler accommodations

(G-8788)
OPEN CITIES HEALTH CENTER
409 Dunlap St N (55104-4201)
PHONE............................651 290-9200
Dorri G Bolo, *CEO*
Melanie Shipek, *CFO*
Marilyn Campbell, *Office Mgr*
Dawne R Pflughoeft DDS, *Dentist*
Nadia Halimi DDS, *Dentist*
EMP: 99 **EST:** 1967
SQ FT: 10,500
SALES (est): 10MM-24.9MM **Privately Held**
WEB: www.ochealthcenter.com
SIC: 8011 Clinic operated by physicians

(G-8789)
OPTION CARE INC
2750 Arthur St (55113-1303)
PHONE............................651 635-9272
FAX: 651 635-9174
Becky Valvez, *General Mgr*
Becky Valdez, *Manager*
EMP: 145
SALES (est): 1MM-4.9MM **Publicly Held**
WEB: www.walgreens.com
SIC: 8082 Home health care services
HQ: Option Care Inc
　　485 E Half Day Rd Ste 300
　　Buffalo Grove IL 60089
　　847 465-2100

(G-8790)
ORDWAY CENTER FOR THE
345 Washington St Ste 775 (55102-1419)
PHONE............................651 282-3000
Patricia Mitchell, *President*
David Lilly, *Vice Chairman*
Lee Koch, *Vice Pres*
Lynn A Von Eschen, *Vice Pres*
Laura Sweet, *Vice Pres*
EST: 1983
SQ FT: 150,000 **Privately Held**
WEB: www.ordway.org
SIC: 7922 Theatrical production service;
performing arts center production service

(G-8791)
**ORTHODONIC CARE
SPECIALIST**
3930 Northwoods Dr (55112-6963)
PHONE............................651 490-6732
FAX: 651 490-6742
Christopher S Hipp, *Principal*
Chris Nelson, *Manager*
EMP: 100 **EST:** 1980
SALES (est): 5MM-9.9MM **Privately Held**
SIC: 8021 Orthodontist

(G-8792)
**OTTO BREMER FOUNDATION
(PA)**
445 Minnesota St Ste 2250 (55101-2190)
PHONE............................651 227-8036
Viva Yang, *VP Mktg*
Elsa Vegaperez, *VP Mktg*
Lynda Marrone, *VP Mktg*
Mark Lindberg, *VP Mktg*
Stephanie Ottenbacher, *Manager*
EMP: 150 **EST:** 1944 **Privately Held**
SIC: 6732 6022 Grantmaking foundation;
state commercial bank

(G-8793)
**OTTO PACKAGING MIDWEST
LLC**
391 Topping St (55117-5226)
PHONE............................651 488-0474
FAX: 651 488-8616
Jeffrey E Otto, *Managing Prtnr*
David Graff, *Manager*
EMP: 30 **EST:** 1977
SQ FT: 50,000
SALES (est): 1MM-4.9MM **Privately Held**
SIC: 7699 Pallet repair service;
manufactures wood & bark mulch;
manufactures wooden pallets

(G-8794)
**OUR LADY OF GOOD COUNSEL
HOME**
2076 Saint Anthony Ave (55104-5028)
PHONE............................651 646-2797
FAX: 651 646-7884
Ann Maire, *Director*
EMP: 30 **EST:** 1941
SALES (est): 1MM-4.9MM **Privately Held**
SIC: 8051 Skilled nursing care facility

(G-8795)
OUTCOMES INC
3508 Rice St Ste 1 (55126-3171)
PHONE............................651 483-9500
FAX: 651 483-0775
Susan Norton, *Director*
EMP: 45 **EST:** 1985
SALES (est): 1MM-4.9MM **Privately Held**
SIC: 8322 Individual & family social services

www.HarrisInfo.com
380
2011 Harris Minnesota
Services Directory
▲=Import ▼=Export
◆=Import/Export

(G-8796)
OWENS & MINOR INC
2151 County Road H2 (55112-4729)
PHONE 763 785-9100
FAX: 763 785-2615
Jerry Alhquist, *Purch Agent*
Marc Johnson, *Manager*
Jonah Berndt, *Administrator*
EMP: 70
SQ FT: 97,000
SALES (est): 25MM-49.9MM **Publicly Held**
WEB: www.owens-minor.com
SIC: 5047 Wholesales medical equipment &
supplies
PA: Owens & Minor Inc
9120 Lockwood Blvd
Mechanicsville VA 23116
804 723-7000

(G-8797)
OXYGEN SERVICE CO INC
1111 Pierce Butler Rte (55104-1450)
PHONE 651 644-7273
FAX: 651 644-2973
Dave Weigel, *President*
Duane Salberg, *Corp Secy*
Bob Olsson, *CFO*
Randy Anderson, *VP Sales*
EMP: 62 EST: 1955
SQ FT: 33,000
SALES (est): 5MM-9.9MM **Privately Held**
WEB: www.oxyserv.com
SIC: 5084 5085 5169 Retails welding
supplies; wholesales welding supplies;
wholesales compressed gas; wholesales
oxygen; wholesales welding equipment &
supplies

(G-8798)
P H M EAGLECREST INC (PA)
3220 Lake Johanna Blvd (55112-7944)
PHONE 651 631-6009
Donald Davies, *Chairman*
Daniel Lyndh, *Vice Chairman*
Mark Meyer, *CFO*
Marleyen Weston, *Director*
EMP: 60 EST: 1992
SQ FT: 350,000
SALES (corp-wide): 11.72M **Privately Held**
SIC: 8399 Social change association

(G-8799)
P H M EAGLECREST INC
Also Called: Eaglecrest
2945 Lincoln Dr Ofc (55113-1338)
PHONE 651 628-3000
Mary Gillis, *Human Res Mgr*
Suzzanne Heins, *Manager*
EMP: 40
SALES (est): 5MM-9.9MM **Privately Held**
SIC: 6531 Real estate services
PA: P H M Eaglecrest Inc
3220 Lake Johanna Blvd
Saint Paul MN 55112
651 631-6009

(G-8800)
PACIFIC MUTUAL DOOR CO
2655 Fairview Ave N (55113-2616)
PHONE 651 631-2211
Bruce Schneider, *Principal*
EMP: 25
SALES (est): 10MM-24.9MM **Privately Held**
SIC: 5031 Wholesales millwork
PA: Pacific Mutual Door Co Inc
1525 W 31st St
Kansas City MO 64108
816 531-7631

(G-8801)
PAIGE J DONNELLY LTD
325 Cedar St Ste 900 (55101-1162)
PHONE 651 222-2797
Paige J Donnelly, *President*
Marie Donnelly, *Corp Secy*
Vickie Hollenkamp, *Manager*
EMP: 29 EST: 1976
SQ FT: 9,000
SALES (est): 1MM-4.9MM **Privately Held**
WEB: www.paigedonnelly.com
SIC: 8111 General practice attorney's or
lawyer's office

(G-8802)
PAINTING BY NAKASONE INC
1535 Marshall Ave (55104-6316)
PHONE 651 646-6999
FAX: 651 646-6792
John Nakasone, *President*
Michelle Paulsen, *Controller*
EMP: 49 EST: 1978
SQ FT: 6,000
SALES (est): 1MM-4.9MM **Privately Held**
SIC: 1721 Commercial painting contractor;
residential painting contractor; commercial
wall covering contractor; residential wall
covering contractor

(G-8803)
PAINTING PERFECTION LTD
1971 Gateway Blvd (55112-2750)
PHONE 651 762-9011
FAX: 651 634-7878
Judith Sitarz, *President*
EMP: 50 EST: 1995
SQ FT: 15,000
SALES (est): 1MM-4.9MM **Privately Held**
SIC: 1721 Painting & wall covering
contractor

(G-8804)
PALEN KIMBALL LLC
550 Vandalia St Ste 4 (55114-1856)
PHONE 651 646-2800
FAX: 651 642-2564
Linda Ritland, *General Mgr*
Douglas Evink, *Member*
EMP: 42 EST: 1932
SQ FT: 20,000
SALES (est): 1MM-4.9MM **Privately Held**
SIC: 7623 1711 5084 Refrigeration repair
service & repair; boiler & furnace service;
wholesales industrial instruments & control
equipment

(G-8805)
PAR NUCLEAR HOLDING CO INC (DH)
899 Highway 96 W (55126-1912)
PHONE 651 278-0007
Gregory Hott, *President*
F R Coats, *Vice Pres*
Brian C Abbott, *Vice Pres*
Jon B Sakry, *Vice Pres*
Jerald Olsen, *CFO*
▲ EST: 1960
SQ FT: 180,000 **Privately Held**
WEB: www.westinghousenuclear.com
SIC: 1799 Nuclear power refueling service
HQ: Westinghouse Electric Co LLC
1000 Westinghouse Dr
Cranberry Township PA 16066
412 374-4111

(G-8806)
PAR SYSTEMS INC (HQ)
707 County Road E W (55126-7007)
PHONE 651 484-7261
Mark Wrightsman, *CEO*
Brian Behm, *President*
Rick Copas, *General Mgr*
Karen O'Rourke, *Vice Pres*
Albert Sturm, *Vice Pres*
EMP: 270 EST: 2004
SALES (corp-wide): 697M **Publicly Held**
SIC: 8742 Automation & robotics consultant
PA: American Capital Ltd
2 Bethesda Metro Ctr # 14
Bethesda MD 20814
301 951-6122

(G-8807)
PARADIGM PUBLISHING INC
875 Montreal Way (55102-4245)
PHONE 651 290-2800
Steve V Thournout, *President*
▲ EMP: 41 EST: 1989
SALES (est): 10MM-24.9MM **Privately Held**
WEB: www.emcp.com
SIC: 7812 Book publisher; motion picture &
video production services
HQ: Wicks Educational Publishing
875 Montreal Way
Saint Paul MN 55102
651 290-2800

(G-8808)
PARTNERS IN EXCELLENCE
2344 Helen St N (55109-2942)
PHONE 651 773-5988
FAX: 651 773-5978
Debbie Thomas, *CEO*
Keri Taylor, *Superintendent*
John Bohr, *Vice Pres*
Dorsie Mosher, *Vice Pres*
Dick Fosse, *MIS Mgr*
EMP: 40 EST: 2005
SALES (est): 1MM-4.9MM **Privately Held**
SIC: 8322 Association for the handicapped

(G-8809)
PATHWAY HEALTH SERVICES INC
2025 4th St (55110-2762)
PHONE 651 407-8699
FAX: 651 429-8721
Debra Schuna, *President*
Robert K Hysjulien, *Managing Prtnr*
Duncan McBougll, *Principal*
Catherine Baker, *Vice Pres*
Donna Webb, *Vice Pres*
EMP: 100 EST: 1997
SALES (est): 10MM-24.9MM **Privately Held**
WEB: www.pathwayhealth.com
SIC: 8742 8741 Hospital & health services
consultant; management services

(G-8810)
PATZIG TESTING LABORATORIES
Also Called: Stork Twin City Testing
662 Cromwell Ave (55114-1720)
PHONE 651 659-7554
Robert Carter, *Corp Secy*
Michiel Grafwinckel, *Manager*
EMP: 70 EST: 2006
SALES (est): 5MM-9.9MM **Privately Held**
SIC: 7389 Inspection & testing service

(G-8811)
PAYSOURCE INC
2258 Sioux Blvd (55112-7223)
PHONE 651 633-9595
FAX: 651 633-9595
E M Malone, *President*
EMP: 51 EST: 1995
SALES (est): 1MM-4.9MM **Privately Held**
SIC: 8721 Payroll services

(G-8812)
PEDIATRIC & ADOLESCENT CARE OF
Also Called: Pace Pediatrics
3615 Grand Ave (55110-4952)
PHONE 651 770-2124
FAX: 651 770-3701
Sig Colber, *General Mgr*
Sig Culder, *Manager*
Luis Bilasete, *Manager*
EMP: 30
SALES (est): 1MM-4.9MM **Privately Held**
WEB: www.pacepediatrics.com
SIC: 8011 Pediatrician office
PA: Pediatric & Adolescent Care of
1547 Livingston Ave
Saint Paul MN 55118
651 451-8050

(G-8813)
PEDIATRIC & YOUNG ADULT MED
233 Grand Ave (55102-2331)
PHONE 651 227-7806
FAX: 651 256-6710
Stanley Leonard MD, *President*
John R Balfanz MD, *Corp Secy*
Terence J Coyne MD, *Vice Pres*
Terri Joseph, *Office Mgr*
Cynthia L Garr, *Pediatrics*
EMP: 30 EST: 1970
SALES (est): 1MM-4.9MM **Privately Held**
SIC: 8011 Pediatrician office

(G-8814)
PENSKE TRUCK LEASING CO, LP
2460 County Road C W (55113-2531)
PHONE 651 631-3399
FAX: 651 631-1021
Michael Hamerlinck, *Principal*
EMP: 40
SALES (est): 5MM-9.9MM **Publicly Held**
WEB: www.pensketruckleasing.com
SIC: 7513 Truck leasing & rental without
drivers
HQ: Penske Truck Leasing Co, LP
Green Hls
Reading PA 19603
610 775-6000

(G-8815)
PEOPLE ENHANCING PEOPLE
1600 University Ave W # 301
(55104-3800)
PHONE 651 450-5960
Jim Carlisle, *Director*
EMP: 45 EST: 2003 **Privately Held**
SIC: 8399 Health & welfare council

(G-8816)
PEOPLE INC (PA)
317 York Ave (55130-4039)
PHONE 651 774-0011
FAX: 651 774-0006
M T Burkett, *CEO*
Angie A Moris, *Human Res Mgr*
Richard Braun, *Manager*
Carrie Ronken, *Executive Asst*
EMP: 30 EST: 1969
SALES (corp-wide): 24.77M **Privately Held**
WEB: www.peopleincorporated.org
SIC: 8361 Residential rehabilitation center
with health care incidental; home for the
mentally handicapped; home for the
physically handicapped

(G-8817)
PEOPLE INC
Also Called: Apollo Research Center
313 Dale St N Apt 337 (55103-2447)
PHONE 651 227-6321
FAX: 651 215-9857
Maureen Marrin, *Director*
EMP: 50
SALES (est): 1MM-4.9MM **Privately Held**
WEB: www.peopleincorporated.org
SIC: 8322 Individual & family social services
PA: People Inc
317 York Ave
Saint Paul MN 55130
651 774-0011

(G-8818)
PERENNIAL MANAGEMENT LLC
1360 Energy Park Dr # 300 (55108-5300)
PHONE 651 644-9600
Diane F Nelson, *Member*
Sue Whirry, *Manager*
EMP: 25
SALES (est): 1MM-4.9MM **Privately Held**
SIC: 6531 Real estate management
services

(G-8819)
PEROT SYSTEMS CORP
2550 University Ave W # 143
(55114-1052)
PHONE 651 999-5600
Pamela Wiche, *Director*
EMP: 30
SALES (est): 1MM-4.9MM **Publicly Held**
WEB: www.perotsystems.com
SIC: 8721 Billing & bookkeeping services
HQ: Perot Systems Corp
2300 W Plano Pkwy
Plano TX 75075
972 577-0000

(G-8820)
PETERSON BROS ROOFING & CONSTR
481 Burgess St (55117-4701)
PHONE 651 488-5630
FAX: 651 488-9029
Michael Peterson, *CEO*
Jan Peterson, *Manager*

(PA)=Parent Co (HQ)=Headquarters (DH)=Div Headquarters
✿ = New business established in last 2 years

2011 Harris Minnesota
Services Directory

© Harris InfoSource 1-866-281-6415

381

EMP: 35 **EST:** 1951
SQ FT: 12,400
SALES (est): 1MM-4.9MM **Privately Held**
WEB: www.petersonroofing.net
SIC: 1761 Roofing contractor

(G-8821)
PETERSON, FRAM & BERGMAN, A
55 5th St E Ste 800 (55101-1718)
PHONE 651 291-8955
FAX: 651 228-1753
Warren E Peterson, *President*
Witt Fram, *Senior Partner*
Glenn Bergman, *Corp Secy*
Leann Ogilvie, *Opers Mgr*
Daniel Fram, *CFO*
EMP: 30 **EST:** 1972
SALES (est): 1MM-4.9MM **Privately Held**
WEB: www.pfb-pa.com
SIC: 8111 General practice law office

(G-8822)
PHALEN VILLAGE APARTMENTS
1511 Westminster St # 201 (55130-3133)
PHONE 651 771-5625
FAX: 651 771-5532
Doug Samek, *Partner*
Kim Tindall, *Member*
Amy Schulte, *Manager*
EMP: 70 **EST:** 1967
SALES (est): 10MM-24.9MM **Privately Held**
SIC: 6513 Apartment building operator

(G-8823)
PHASE I RICE-MARION
195 Edmund Ave Ofc (55103-1788)
PHONE 763 540-8600
Zollie Baratz, *Owner*
Sidney Bader, *General Ptnr*
EMP: 35 **EST:** 1977
SALES (est): 5MM-9.9MM **Privately Held**
SIC: 6513 Apartment building operator

(G-8824)
PHEASANTS FOREVER INC (PA)
1783 Buerkle Cir (55110-5254)
PHONE 651 773-2000
FAX: 651 481-0715
Howard Vincent, *President*
Robert P Larson, *Corp Secy*
James Koerber, *CFO*
Bruce D Hertzke, *CFO*
Chris Knabusch, *Treasurer*
▲ **EMP:** 50 **EST:** 1982
SQ FT: 33,000
SALES (corp-wide): 27.90M **Privately Held**
SIC: 8699 Animal humane society

(G-8825)
PHOENIX ALTERNATIVES INC
4453 White Bear Pkwy (55110-7626)
PHONE 651 426-2484
FAX: 651 426-3789
Susan Warweg, *President*
Lori Jarratt, *Finance*
Terry Higgs, *Director*
Toni Quirk, *Director*
Denise R McKee, *Director*
EMP: 120 **EST:** 1990
SALES (est): 5MM-9.9MM **Privately Held**
WEB: www.phoenixalternatives.org
SIC: 8322 8331 Individual & family social services; job training & vocational rehabilitation services

(G-8826)
PHOENIX ALTERNATIVES VOCATION
1754 Commerce Ct (55110-4686)
PHONE 651 747-8740
FAX: 651 747-8741
Denise Ryan, *Director*
EMP: 30 **EST:** 2003 **Privately Held**
SIC: 8699 Organization

(G-8827)
PHYSICANS NECK & BACK CLINIC (PA)
3050 Centre Pointe Dr (55113-1102)
PHONE 651 639-9150
FAX: 651 639-9153
Brian Nelson, *President*

Katie Opack, *Office Mgr*
Dietmar J Grentz MD, *Med Doctor*
Brenda Loe, *Administrator*
Charles E Kelly, *Internal Med*
EMP: 25 **EST:** 1990 **Privately Held**
WEB: www.pnbconline.com
SIC: 8049 8011 8093 Physical therapist office; physical medicine physician or surgeon office; outpatient rehabilitation treatment center

(G-8828)
PIONEER POWER INC
570 Hatch Ave (55117-4716)
PHONE 651 488-5561
FAX: 651 488-2652
Mark D Garrison, *President*
Gerald R Siverson, *Corp Secy*
Bryan H Norman, *Corp Secy*
Randall S Olson, *Senior VP*
Scott Wenzel, *Vice Pres*
EMP: 90 **EST:** 1947
SQ FT: 10,700
SALES (est): 10MM-24.9MM **Privately Held**
WEB: www.pioneerpower.com
SIC: 1711 Mechanical contractor

(G-8829)
PIONEER PRESS INC
220 Fillmore Ave E (55107-1418)
PHONE 651 222-8298
FAX: 651 222-2594
Par Ridder, *Publisher*
Jonni Felber, *Human Res Mgr*
Frank Teak, *Manager*
Gregory Schendel, *Manager*
EMP: 60 **EST:** 1926
SQ FT: 10,000
SALES (est): 5MM-9.9MM **Privately Held**
WEB: www.hearstcorp.com
SIC: 4212 4213 Local trucking without storage services; contract haulers
PA: Hearst Corp
    300 W 57th St Fl 42
    New York NY 10019
    212 649-2000

(G-8830)
PLANNED PARENTHOOD OF MN
1965 Ford Pkwy (55116-1923)
PHONE 651 698-2401
FAX: 651 698-2405
Sarah Stoesz, *President*
Margaret Friese, *COO*
Nancy Speer, *Vice Pres*
Alice Johnson, *CFO*
Carolyn Rehn, *Human Res Dir*
EMP: 50 **EST:** 1930
SQ FT: 14,000
SALES (est): 1MM-4.9MM **Privately Held**
WEB: www.ppmsd.org
SIC: 8093 Family planning center

(G-8831)
POPE ASSOCIATES INC
1255 Energy Park Dr (55108-5103)
PHONE 651 642-9200
FAX: 651 642-1101
Paul Holmes, *President*
Dan Clecker, *Vice Pres*
Randal L Peek, *Treasurer*
Lois Rogers, *Accountant*
Ken Wettstein, *Manager*
EMP: 50 **EST:** 1958
SQ FT: 8,000
SALES (est): 5MM-9.9MM **Privately Held**
WEB: www.popearch.com
SIC: 8712 Architectural service

(G-8832)
POWER MATION DIVISION INC (PA)
1310 Energy Ln (55108-5250)
PO Box 8198 (55108-0198)
PHONE 651 605-3300
FAX: 651 605-4400
Jim Landes, *President*
Mike Kazmerski, *Vice Pres*
Amanda Clore, *Opers Staff*
Scott Hurkes, *VP Sls/Mktg*
Daniel Folsom, *CFO*
EMP: 71 **EST:** 1961
SQ FT: 25,000 **Privately Held**
WEB: www.powermation.com

SIC: 5085 5045 5065 5084 Wholesales industrial supplies; wholesales computers, peripherals & software; wholesales industrial power transmission equipment & apparatus; wholesales industrial machinery & equipment; wholesales electronic parts & equipment

(G-8833)
PRATT CONSTRUCTION INC
3500 Willow Lake Blvd # 100 (55110-5135)
PHONE 651 765-0572
Leonard Pratt, *President*
Lowell Pratt, *President*
Tracy Pratt, *Corp Secy*
▲ **EMP:** 50 **EST:** 1973
SALES (est): 10MM-24.9MM **Privately Held**
SIC: 1522 Residential construction

(G-8834)
PRATT CONSTRUCTION INC
3500 Willow Lake Blvd (55110-5124)
PHONE 651 429-8032
Lowell H Pratt, *President*
Leonard W Pratt, *President*
Tracy Pratt, *Corp Secy*
Calvin Anderson, *VP Opers-Prdtn-*
EMP: 30 **EST:** 1973
SQ FT: 10,000
SALES (est): 5MM-9.9MM **Privately Held**
WEB: www.pratthomes.com
SIC: 1521 New single-family home construction service; single-family home general remodeling service; townhouse construction service

(G-8835)
PRATT NEDEGAARD
3500 Willow Lake Blvd # 100 (55110-5135)
PHONE 651 429-8032
Leonard Pratt, *Partner*
Lowell H Pratt, *Partner*
Craig Anderson, *Technology*
EMP: 60 **EST:** 1998
SALES (est): 10MM-24.9MM **Privately Held**
SIC: 6552 Land subdivision & development services

(G-8836)
PRAXAIR INC
2455 Rosegate (55113-2717)
PHONE 651 633-6781
FAX: 651 633-7088
Paul Bilek, *Exec VP*
Stephen Angel, *Exec VP*
Nigel Muir, *Vice Pres*
Sunil Mattoo, *Vice Pres*
Terry Scholl, *Mfg Staff*
EMP: 48
SALES (est): 25MM-49.9MM **Publicly Held**
WEB: www.praxair.com
SIC: 5169 Wholesales chemicals & allied products; manufactures industrial gases
PA: Praxair Inc
    39 Old Ridgebury Rd
    Danbury CT 06810
    203 837-2000

(G-8837)
PREMIER BANK INC
2866 White Bear Ave N (55109-1301)
PHONE 651 777-7700
FAX: 651 777-3761
Donald Regan, *Ch of Bd*
Mark E Novitzki, *President*
Judith Smith, *Vice Pres*
Brigita Celms, *Vice Pres*
Brian Cames, *Vice Pres*
EMP: 59 **EST:** 1974
SQ FT: 16,000
SALES (est): 10MM-24.9MM **Privately Held**
WEB: www.premierbanks.com
SIC: 6022 State commercial bank

(G-8838)
PREMIER TILE INC
Also Called: Select Surfaces
3440 Victoria St N (55126-3862)
PHONE 651 483-1576
FAX: 651 483-1630
Jeremy Otten, *Partner*
Duane Steen, *Partner*
EMP: 29 **EST:** 1996
SALES (est): 1MM-4.9MM **Privately Held**

WEB: www.selectsurfaces.com
SIC: 1743 Tile, marble, terrazzo & mosaic contractor

(G-8839)
PRESBYTERIAN HOMES & SERVICES
1910 County Road D W (55112-3503)
PHONE 651 631-6200
FAX: 651 631-6122
Beth Baldwin, *Purchasing*
Lisa Casanova, *Human Res Mgr*
Scott Welter, *Manager*
Judy Deeb, *Manager*
EMP: 300
SALES (est): 10MM-24.9MM **Privately Held**
WEB: www.preshomes.com
SIC: 8051 Extended care facility
PA: Presbyterian Homes & Services
    2845 Hamline Ave N # 200
    Saint Paul MN 55113
    651 631-6100

(G-8840)
PRESBYTERIAN HOMES & SERVICES (PA)
2845 Hamline Ave N # 200 (55113-7116)
PHONE 651 631-6100
Daniel Lindh, *President*
Mark Meyer, *CFO*
Martha Hurr, *IT/INT Sup*
Phil Hanson, *Systems Staff*
EMP: 77 **EST:** 1953
SQ FT: 253,000
SALES (corp-wide): 7.52M **Privately Held**
WEB: www.preshomes.com
SIC: 8361 Home for the elderly

(G-8841)
PRESBYTERIAN HOMES H & A
Also Called: Mayfield
2850 Market Place Dr (55117-2607)
PHONE 651 631-6659
FAX: 651 482-1315
Dan Bolhouse, *President*
Laura Sheak, *Manager*
EMP: 25 **EST:** 1995
SALES (est): 500-999K **Privately Held**
SIC: 8361 Residential care facility

(G-8842)
PRESBYTERIAN HOMES MANAGEMENT
3220 Lake Johanna Blvd (55112-7944)
PHONE 651 631-6000
Dan Lindh, *President*
Mark Meyer, *CFO*
EMP: 35 **EST:** 1985
SQ FT: 3,500
SALES (est): 5MM-9.9MM **Privately Held**
WEB: www.preshomes.com
SIC: 8742 Management consulting services
PA: Presbyterian Homes & Services
    2845 Hamline Ave N # 200
    Saint Paul MN 55113
    651 631-6100

(G-8843)
PRESBYTERIAN HOMES OF ARDEN
3220 Lake Johanna Blvd (55112-7944)
PHONE 651 631-6000
FAX: 651 631-6036
Daniel Lindh, *President*
Mark Meyer, *CFO*
Katherine Thunborg, *Bookkeeper*
EMP: 540 **EST:** 1982
SQ FT: 230,000
SALES (est): 50MM-99.9MM **Privately Held**
WEB: www.presstaff.com
SIC: 6513 8051 Operators of retirement hotels; skilled nursing care facility
PA: Presbyterian Homes & Services
    2845 Hamline Ave N # 200
    Saint Paul MN 55113
    651 631-6100

(G-8844)
PRESBYTERIAN HOMES, HOUSING
2845 Hamline Ave N # 200 (55113-7116)
PHONE 651 631-6100
Daniel Lindh, *President*
Valerie Alt, *Exec Dir*

▲=Import ▼=Export
◆=Import/Export

EMP: 650 **EST:** 1983
SQ FT: 253,000
SALES (est): 100MM-499.9MM **Privately Held**
WEB: www.preshomes.com
SIC: 6513 8051 8052 Operators of retirement hotels; intermediate care facility; skilled nursing care facility
PA: Presbyterian Homes & Services
2845 Hamline Ave N # 200
Saint Paul MN 55113
651 631-6100

(G-8845)
PRESCRIPTION LANDSCAPE INC
1311 Sylvan St (55117-4605)
PHONE..............................651 488-8965
FAX: 651 488-9195
Colin O'Neill, *CEO*
Michael Teichert, *President*
T J Mattson, *Sales Mgr*
EMP: 34 **EST:** 1981
SQ FT: 6,000 **Privately Held**
WEB: www.rxlandscape.com
SIC: 0782 Landscaping services

(G-8846)
PREWIRE SPECIALISTS INC
401 4th St E (55101-1429)
PHONE..............................651 452-9192
Jim Haugdahl, *President*
Steve Haugdahl, *CFO*
Jeremey Peck, *Manager*
EMP: 155 **EST:** 1998
SQ FT: 10,000
SALES (est): 50MM-99.9MM **Privately Held**
WEB: www.prewirespecialists.com
SIC: 4841 Cable television services

(G-8847)
PRIMERICA FINANCIAL SERVICES
332 Minnesota St Ste E840 (55101-1328)
PHONE..............................651 290-9822
Vickie Nelson, *Regional Mgr*
Nita Whiting, *Finance*
EMP: 100
SALES (est): 50MM-99.9MM **Publicly Held**
WEB: www.primerica.com
SIC: 6311 Life insurance carriers
HQ: Primerica Financial Services
3120 Breckinridge Blvd
Duluth GA 30099
800 544-5445

(G-8848)
PRIMESTAFF INC
3434 Lexington Ave N # 400 (55126-8093)
PHONE..............................651 697-2120
Kathleen Carlsen, *CEO*
Troy Harper, *CFO*
EMP: 102 **EST:** 1997
SQ FT: 1,100
SALES (est): 1MM-4.9MM **Privately Held**
WEB: www.primestaff.com
SIC: 7363 7361 Temporary help service; employment agency services

(G-8849)
PRISM RESEARCH LLC
1000 Westgate Dr Ste 149 (55114-1469)
PHONE..............................651 641-2900
FAX: 651 641-2901
Chuck Halstenson, *Principal*
EMP: 30 **EST:** 2005 **Privately Held**
WEB: www.prismresearchinc.com
SIC: 8731 Commercial medical research services

(G-8850)
PROBUILT AMERICA INC
Also Called: Window World
2211 11th Ave E Ste 130 (55109-5177)
PHONE..............................651 770-5570
FAX: 651 770-5570
Terence Derosier, *President*
EST: 2002
SQ FT: 9,500 **Privately Held**
WEB: www.probuiltam.com
SIC: 1521 Single-family home general remodeling service

(G-8851)
PRODUCT SAFETY RESOURCES INC
Also Called: Prosar
1295 Bandana Blvd N # 335 (55108-5116)
PHONE..............................651 917-6100
Steve Swantek, *President*
Ann Claridge, *Exec VP*
Claude Tolbert, *Senior VP*
Joele Richardson, *Exec Dir*
EMP: 45 **EST:** 1991
SQ FT: 7,347
SALES (est): 1MM-4.9MM **Privately Held**
WEB: www.prosarcorp.com
SIC: 7389 Safety inspection service

(G-8852)
PROEX PHOTO
2130 Ford Pkwy (55116-1863)
PHONE..............................651 699-4394
FAX: 651 695-1355
Emiliano Malroy, *Store Mgr*
Tom Skaelly, *Finance Mgr*
Bill Hursh, *Manager*
William Hursh, *Manager*
EMP: 30 **EST:** 1981
SALES (est): 1MM-4.9MM **Privately Held**
SIC: 7384 Photofinishing laboratory

(G-8853)
PROGRESSIVE CONCRETE & MASONRY
345 Atwater St Ste 1 (55117-5261)
PHONE..............................651 489-2200
FAX: 651 489-2400
Marlin Broberg, *President*
EMP: 35 **EST:** 1985
SQ FT: 11,000
SALES (est): 1MM-4.9MM **Privately Held**
SIC: 1771 1741 Concrete contractor; masonry & stonework contractor

(G-8854)
PROMETRIC INC
1260 Energy Ln (55108-5225)
PHONE..............................651 647-1723
Pradipto Chakrabarty, *Business Mgr*
Chrystal Blow, *Business Anlyst*
Michael Levin, *Administrator*
Gloria Burnell, *Director*
EMP: 89
SALES (est): 5MM-9.9MM **Privately Held**
SIC: 8734 Testing laboratory
HQ: Prometric Inc
1501 S Clinton St # 1200
Baltimore MD 21224
443 455-8000

(G-8855)
PUBLIC EMPLOYEES RETIREMENT
60 Empire Dr Ste 200 (55103-1890)
PHONE..............................651 296-7460
FAX: 651 297-2547
Jim Vanek, *Purch Dir*
Kim Vanvleet, *Human Resources*
Diane Rognrud, *Prgrmr*
Mary M Vanek, *Exec Dir*
Steven L Devich, *Bd of Directors*
EMP: 91 **EST:** 1933 **Privately Held**
WEB: www.state.mn.us
SIC: 6371 Pension fund; government office; state government executive offices
HQ: Executive Office of The State
75 Rev Doc Martin Luther
Saint Paul MN 55155
651 296-3391

(G-8856)
PUBLISHING BUSINESS SYSTEMS
2611 Hamline Ave N Ste 100 (55113-3167)
PHONE..............................651 639-0662
Stephen Smith, *President*
Jeffrey P Gray, *Corp Secy*
Nancy Baumann, *Controller*
Bud Pietto, *Manager*
Todd Armstrong, *Software Engr*
EMP: 90 **EST:** 1989
SQ FT: 16,000
SALES (est): 10MM-24.9MM **Privately Held**

SIC: 7371 Computer software development; manufactures computer peripheral equipment
PA: Niche Software Systems Inc
13 Grand Central Ln
Schaumburg IL 60193
847 895-7525

(G-8857)
PUGLEASA CO INC
1253 Connelly Ave (55112-6937)
PHONE..............................651 636-6442
FAX: 651 636-0995
Dennis J Pietrini, *President*
Pat Tillman, *Treasurer*
Nate Atkins, *Bd of Directors*
Curt Moses, *Executive*
Jeanne Woeltge, *Representative*
EMP: 30 **EST:** 1957
SQ FT: 15,000
SALES (est): 5MM-9.9MM **Privately Held**
WEB: www.pugleasa.com
SIC: 5087 5084 Wholesales moving equipment & supplies; wholesales industrial machinery & equipment

(G-8858)
PULMONARY HEALTH REALTY ASSOCS
255 Smith Ave N Ste 300 (55102-2572)
PHONE..............................651 224-5895
David Bonham MD, *Partner*
James R Flink MD, *Partner*
Stephen Gryzan, *Partner*
Lee Kamman MD, *General Ptnr*
Susan M Achutt, *Manager*
EMP: 26 **EST:** 1979
SALES (est): 1MM-4.9MM **Privately Held**
SIC: 8011 Pulmonary specialist, physician or surgeon

(G-8859)
Q3 CONTRACTING INC
3066 Spruce St (55117-1061)
PHONE..............................651 224-2424
FAX: 651 224-2424
Jay Osborn, *President*
Dennis Mueller, *Exec VP*
Chad Loecher, *Vice Pres*
Mark Grina, *CFO*
Terry Baumgarten, *Exec Dir*
EMP: 485 **EST:** 1991
SQ FT: 10,000
SALES (est): 50MM-99.9MM **Privately Held**
SIC: 1771 0782 Concrete repair contractor; asphalt contractor; lawn seeding services; sodding contractor

(G-8860)
QUALITY METALS INC
2575 Doswell Ave (55108-1520)
PHONE..............................651 645-5875
FAX: 651 645-2877
Benjamin I Silverberg, *President*
I B Silverberg, *Chairman*
David Silverberg, *COO*
Mary Johnson, *Mfg Staff*
Jana Vanek, *Manager*
▼ **EMP:** 50 **EST:** 1941
SQ FT: 100,000
SALES (est): 25MM-49.9MM **Privately Held**
WEB: www.qualitymetalsinc.com
SIC: 5051 Metal service center

(G-8861)
QUALITY UNDERGROUND SERVICES
3066 Spruce St (55117-1061)
PHONE..............................651 224-0413
Jay Osborn, *President*
Douglas J Yetzer, *Corp Secy*
Dennis Mueller, *Exec VP*
Chad Loecher, *Vice Pres*
Mark Grina, *CFO*
EMP: 100 **EST:** 1991
SQ FT: 10,000
SALES (est): 10MM-24.9MM **Privately Held**
WEB: www.millerqualityrestoration.com
SIC: 1623 Underground utilities contractor

(G-8862)
QUANTUM CONSULTING & PLACEMENT
3000 Centre Pointe Dr (55113-1122)
PHONE..............................952 820-0160
William Lloyd, *President*
David Kinney, *Vice Pres*
Tom Engbretson, *Vice Pres*
Dan McLean, *VP Opers*
Colleen Thomas, *Administrator*
EMP: 183 **EST:** 1992
SQ FT: 1,500
SALES (est): 10MM-24.9MM **Privately Held**
SIC: 8748 Systems engineering consultant

(G-8863)
QUEST DIAGNOSTICS CLINICAL
600 County Road D W Ste 11
(55112-3519)
PHONE..............................651 635-1500
FAX: 651 635-1517
Peter Mockridge, *Branch Mgr*
Kyle Roberts, *Manager*
Lisa Canon, *Supervisor*
Diane Murphy, *Executive*
EMP: 140
SALES (est): 10MM-24.9MM **Publicly Held**
WEB: www.questcentrallab.com
SIC: 8071 Medical laboratory
HQ: Quest Diagnostics Clinical
1201 S Collegeville Rd
Collegeville PA 19426
610 454-6000

(G-8864)
QUICKSILVER EXPRESS COURIER (PA)
203 Little Canada Rd E (55117-1681)
PHONE..............................651 484-1111
Michael Crary, *President*
Curt Sloan, *Corp Secy*
Becky Wagner, *Treasurer*
Rick Purkott, *Controller*
Bob Ley, *Persnl Mgr*
EMP: 400 **EST:** 1982
SQ FT: 13,000 **Privately Held**
WEB: www.qec.com
SIC: 4212 Delivery services by vehicle

(G-8865)
QUICKSILVER EXPRESS COURIER OF
203 Little Canada Rd E (55117-1681)
PO Box 64417 (55164-0417)
PHONE..............................651 484-1111
Michael Crary, *President*
Curt Sloan, *Vice Pres*
Angela Averman, *CFO*
Becky Wagner, *Treasurer*
EMP: 296 **EST:** 1986
SQ FT: 13,000
SALES (est): 25MM-49.9MM **Privately Held**
WEB: www.qec.com
SIC: 4212 4215 Delivery services by vehicle; ground courier services
PA: Quicksilver Express Courier
203 Little Canada Rd E
Saint Paul MN 55117
651 484-1111

(G-8866)
R M L S MINNESOTA
2550 University Ave W 259S (55114-1914)
PHONE..............................651 251-5458
FAX: 651 251-5457
John Mosey, *President*
Dorene Donnay, *Accounting Staf*
EMP: 25 **EST:** 2002
SALES (est): 1MM-4.9MM **Privately Held**
SIC: 6531 Real estate multiple listing service

(G-8867)
R TECH LABORATORIES
1150 County Road F W (55112-2911)
PO Box 64101 (55164-0101)
PHONE..............................651 481-2207
Alecia Dotterwich, *General Mgr*
Amy Remes, *Manager*
Robert Jechorek, *Manager*
Debbie McIntyre, *Exec Dir*
EMP: 17 **EST:** 1986 **Privately Held**
SIC: 8733 8734 Scientific research agency; testing laboratory

(PA)=Parent Co (HQ)=Headquarters (DH)=Div Headquarters
✿ = New business established in last 2 years

2011 Harris Minnesota
Services Directory

© Harris InfoSource 1-866-281-6415
383

GEOGRAPHIC

(G-8868)
RADISON HOTEL
Also Called: Ramada Inn
2540 Cleveland Ave N (55113-2719)
PHONE 651 636-4567
FAX: 651 636-7110
George Harbaugh, *President*
Scott Henning, *General Mgr*
Scott Henley, *General Mgr*
Dave Wallia, *Vice Pres*
David Walia, *Project Mgr*
EMP: 135 **EST:** 1995
SALES (est): 5MM-9.9MM **Privately Held**
SIC: 7011 Traveler accommodations

(G-8869)
RADISSON HOTELS INTERNATIONAL
411 Minnesota St (55101-1703)
PHONE 651 291-8800
FAX: 651 291-0679
Luke Musselman, *General Mgr*
Jason Mercord, *General Mgr*
Jeff Wefel, *Controller*
Jane Curtin, *Human Resources*
Alison Harke, *Sales Staff*
EMP: 200
SALES (est): 10MM-24.9MM **Privately Held**
WEB: www.carlson.com
SIC: 7011 Traveler accommodations
HQ: Radisson Hotels International
      701 Carlson Pkwy
      Minnetonka MN 55305
      763 212-5000

(G-8870)
RATNER STEEL SUPPLY CO
2500 County Road B W 1A (55113-3873)
PHONE 651 631-8515
FAX: 651 631-8512
Mark Ratner, *President*
Steve Gottlieb, *Vice Pres*
EMP: 45 **EST:** 1986
SQ FT: 140,000
SALES (est): 1MM-4.9MM **Privately Held**
WEB: www.ratnersteel.com
SIC: 7389 5051 Metal slitting & shearing service; wholesales steel

(G-8871)
RAYMOND AUTO BODY INC
1075 Pierce Butler Rte (55104-1524)
PHONE 651 488-0588
FAX: 651 488-4794
Jerry Slomkowski, *President*
Joel Slomkowski, *Corp Secy*
Richard Slomkowski, *Vice Pres*
Rick Koonce, *Opers Mgr*
Becky Hoffer, *Accountant*
EMP: 35 **EST:** 1949
SQ FT: 17,000
SALES (est): 1MM-4.9MM **Privately Held**
WEB: www.raymondautobody.com
SIC: 7532 Automotive body shop

(G-8872)
RBC WEALTH MANAGEMENT
400 Robert St N Ste 1400 (55101-2027)
PHONE 651 228-6900
Benjamin Storey, *Senior VP*
Greg Anklam, *Manager*
EMP: 40
SALES (est): 10MM-24.9MM **Privately Held**
WEB: www.hough.com
SIC: 6211 Security broker service; investment banking service
PA: Rbc Wealth Management
      60 S 6th St Ste 700
      Minneapolis MN 55402
      612 371-7750

(G-8873)
RBC WEALTH MANAGMENT
520 Highway 96 W Ste 100 (55126-1963)
PHONE 651 766-4920
FAX: 651 766-4925
Byron Ellingson, *Manager*
Dan Croonquist, *Manager*
EMP: 25
SALES (est): 5MM-9.9MM **Privately Held**
WEB: www.hough.com

SIC: 6211 Securities broker & dealer
PA: Rbc Wealth Management
      60 S 6th St Ste 700
      Minneapolis MN 55402
      612 371-7750

(G-8874)
RCB HOLDING CO
1501 County Road C W (55113-3103)
PHONE 651 631-1040
Donald Kuenhast, *President*
EST: 1990 **Privately Held**
SIC: 6712 Bank holding company

(G-8875)
RCC LIQUIDATING CORP
2130 Ford Pkwy (55116-1863)
PHONE 651 699-0988
Bill Hursch, *Manager*
EMP: 30
SALES (est): 1MM-4.9MM **Privately Held**
SIC: 7384 Retails cameras; retails video cameras & accessories; film processing & finishing laboratory

(G-8876)
REAL ESTATE EQUITES INC
345 Saint Peter St Ste 16 (55102-1211)
PHONE 651 227-6925
Bob Bisanz, *President*
Pamela George, *Partner*
EMP: 25 **EST:** 1986
SQ FT: 3,000
SALES (est): 5MM-9.9MM **Privately Held**
SIC: 6512 6513 Operators of commercial & industrial buildings; apartment building operator

(G-8877)
REAL ESTATE EQUITIES INC (PA)
345 Saint Peter St Ste 1600 (55102-1401)
PHONE 651 227-6925
Terrence Troy, *CEO*
Robert S Bisanz, *President*
Craig Brinkman, *CFO*
EMP: 93 **EST:** 1974
SQ FT: 12,000 **Privately Held**
SIC: 6531 Real estate management services

(G-8878)
REAL ESTATE MASTERS INC
312 County Road D E (55117-1275)
PHONE 651 484-4818
FAX: 651 484-5975
Don Newpower, *President*
Robert Sneen, *Vice Pres*
EMP: 115 **EST:** 1992
SALES (est): 10MM-24.9MM **Privately Held**
SIC: 6531 Real estate agency & broker

(G-8879)
REALIFE COOPERATIVE OF MOUNDS
7735 Silver Lake Rd (55112-4347)
PHONE 763 780-9737
Duane Nickerson, *Principal*
EMP: 90 **EST:** 1999
SALES (est): 1MM-4.9MM **Privately Held**
SIC: 8361 Residential care facility

(G-8880)
REBUILD RESOURCES INC
602 Prior Ave N (55104-1740)
PHONE 651 645-7055
FAX: 651 645-2063
Kevin Lynch, *President*
Ed Donoghue, *Superintendent*
Jenny Hill, *Purch Agent*
Anne Johnston, *Finance*
Pete Tanezer, *Finance*
EMP: 35 **EST:** 1980
SQ FT: 40,000
SALES (est): 1MM-4.9MM **Privately Held**
WEB: www.rebuildacademy.com
SIC: 8331 Job counseling; work experience center

(G-8881)
REGENTS OF THE UNIVERSITY OF
Also Called: Bethesda Clinic
580 Rice St Ste 1 (55103-2149)
PHONE 651 227-6551
FAX: 651 227-1804
Melissa Person, *General Mgr*
Nicki Stevens, *Office Mgr*
Ila Harris, *Pharmacist*
Himanshu S Harma MD, *Med Doctor*
Ishani Jhanjee MD, *Med Doctor*
EMP: 50
SALES (est): 5MM-9.9MM **Privately Held**
WEB: www.umn.edu
SIC: 8011 Physicians' office & clinic; college
PA: Regents of The University of
      106 Pleasant St SE # 210
      Minneapolis MN 55455
      612 625-5000

(G-8882)
REGENTS OF THE UNIVERSITY OF
Also Called: Les Bolstold U MN Golf Course
2275 Larpenteur Ave W (55113-5342)
PHONE 612 627-4000
Chris Korbol, *Branch Mgr*
EMP: 25 **Privately Held**
WEB: www.umn.edu
SIC: 7992 College; public golf course
PA: Regents of The University of
      106 Pleasant St SE # 210
      Minneapolis MN 55455
      612 625-5000

(G-8883)
REGIONS HOSPITAL ALCOHOL
445 Etna St Ste 55 (55106-5848)
PHONE 651 254-4804
Charles Misshek, *Director*
EMP: 30 **EST:** 1994
SALES (est): 1MM-4.9MM **Privately Held**
SIC: 8093 Outpatient alcohol treatment clinic

(G-8884)
REGIONS HOSPITAL FOUNDATION
640 Jackson St (55101-2502)
PHONE 651 254-3456
Brock Nelson, *President*
John Solberg, *Vice Chairman*
Keith Hanning, *Corp Secy*
Greg Klugherz, *CFO*
Patricia Pappas, *Treasurer*
EMP: 2900 **EST:** 1869
SQ FT: 773,377
SALES (est): 100MM-499.9MM **Privately Held**
SIC: 8062 Medical hospital

(G-8885)
REGIS CORP
139 Rosedale Ctr (55113-3005)
PHONE 651 636-9966
Steve Kuntson, *Human Res Mgr*
Dana Dropps, *Manager*
Dana Shepard, *Manager*
EMP: 26
SALES (est): 500-999K **Publicly Held**
WEB: www.regiscorp.com
SIC: 7231 Beauty salon
PA: Regis Corp
      7201 Metro Blvd
      Minneapolis MN 55439
      952 947-7777

(G-8886)
REIGSTAD & ASSOCIATES INC
192 9th St W Ste 200 (55102-1027)
PHONE 651 292-1123
FAX: 651 292-8015
Gordon H Reigstad, *President*
Eunice Hopkins, *Treasurer*
Alan Booth, *Manager*
EMP: 25 **EST:** 1978
SQ FT: 5,000
SALES (est): 1MM-4.9MM **Privately Held**
WEB: www.reigstad.com
SIC: 8711 Structural engineering services

(G-8887)
RELS TITLE SERVICES LLC
Also Called: ATI Title Co
2550 University Ave W Ste 135N
(55114-1098)
PHONE 651 647-4855
FAX: 651 647-4887
Ray McMann, *Manager*
EMP: 25
SALES (est): 1MM-4.9MM **Privately Held**
SIC: 6541 Title abstract service
PA: RELS Title Services LLC
      5700 Smetana Dr Ste 400
      Hopkins MN 55343
      952 933-3804

(G-8888)
REM INC (PA)
2266 2nd St N (55109-2914)
PHONE 651 647-9243
Tom Miller, *President*
Craig Miller, *Principal*
Leesa Biermaier, *Director*
EMP: 50 **EST:** 1973 **Privately Held**
SIC: 8361 8052 Home for the mentally retarded; intermediate care facility

(G-8889)
RENEW SERVICES INC
1410 Energy Park Dr Ste 6 (55108-5249)
PHONE 651 699-3504
FAX: 651 644-2557
Michael C Hilborn, *President*
Cindy Hilborn, *Corp Secy*
EMP: 40 **EST:** 1995
SQ FT: 2,500
SALES (est): 1MM-4.9MM **Privately Held**
WEB: www.roofrenew.com
SIC: 1799 Building exterior cleaning services

(G-8890)
RENODIS HOLDINGS INC
476 Robert St N (55101-2238)
PHONE 651 556-1203
Steve Lambros, *COO*
Monica Weimer, *Exec Sec*
EMP: 25 **EST:** 2001
SALES (est): 5MM-9.9MM **Privately Held**
WEB: www.renodis.net
SIC: 4813 Telephone or video communications services

(G-8891)
RENSTROM DENTAL STUDIO INC
4225 White Bear Pkwy Ste 1240
(55110-3349)
PO Box 272200 (55127-1200)
PHONE 651 407-0491
FAX: 651 407-8712
Robert Renstrom, *Ch of Bd*
Randall Renstrom, *President*
Richard Renstrom, *Vice Pres*
Joanne N Renstrom, *Treasurer*
Tammy Meck, *Office Mgr*
EMP: 27 **EST:** 1966
SQ FT: 4,000
SALES (est): 1MM-4.9MM **Privately Held**
WEB: www.renstrom.com
SIC: 8072 Dental laboratory

(G-8892)
RESER'S FINE FOODS INC
2550 Wabash Ave Ste 2 (55114-1088)
PHONE 651 646-1298
FAX: 651 646-6697
Glen Knippenberg, *Manager*
EMP: 25
SALES (est): 10MM-24.9MM **Privately Held**
SIC: 5149 Wholesales groceries
PA: Reser's Fine Foods Inc
      15570 SW Jenkins Rd
      Beaverton OR 97006
      503 643-6431

(G-8893)
RESOURCES FOR CHILD CARING INC
10 Yorkton Ct (55117-1065)
PHONE 651 641-0305
FAX: 651 645-0990
Barbara Yates, *President*

www.HarrisInfo.com
384

2011 Harris Minnesota
Services Directory

▲=Import ▼=Export
◆=Import/Export

Linda Hein, *Publisher*
Jackie Reis, *Vice Chairman*
Carleen Kerttula, *Corp Secy*
B Davies, *Project Mgr*
EMP: 65 **EST:** 1971
SQ FT: 23,000
SALES (est): 1MM-4.9MM **Privately Held**
SIC: 8322 8331 Individual & family social services; pamphlet publishing & printing; textbook publishing & printing; job training & vocational rehabilitation services; publisher

(G-8894)
RESTORATION CONTRACTORS INC
Also Called: Clean Response
480 Prior Ave N (55104-3421)
PHONE 651 646-3408
Joe Nedoroski, *President*
Mark Larson, *Vice Pres*
C H Ona, *Manager*
EMP: 30 **EST:** 1997
SQ FT: 8,000
SALES (est): 1MM-4.9MM **Privately Held**
WEB: www.cleanresponse.com
SIC: 7217 Carpet & upholstery cleaning services

(G-8895)
RESTORATION PROFESSIONALS INC
505 Minnehaha Ave W (55103-1573)
PHONE 651 379-1990
Timothy T Labey, *CEO*
Ed Strom, *President*
EMP: 70 **EST:** 2003
SQ FT: 1,500
SALES (est): 5MM-9.9MM **Privately Held**
WEB: www.restpro.com
SIC: 1799 1522 7217 Coating, caulking & weather, water & fireproofing contractor; residential construction; carpet & upholstery cleaning services

(G-8896)
RETAIL INVENTORY SERVICES LTD
2400 County Road D W Ste 100 (55112-8503)
PHONE 651 631-9081
FAX: 651 631-9149
Lee Neumann, *President*
Sue Eichler, *General Mgr*
Sandra Neumann, *Treasurer*
Steve Koontz, *Manager*
Dave Foag, *Manager*
EMP: 75 **EST:** 1964
SQ FT: 1,500
SALES (est): 5MM-9.9MM **Privately Held**
SIC: 7389 Appraisal services; inventory computing service

(G-8897)
RHJH INC
Also Called: Ecsi
2300 Territorial Rd (55114-1637)
PHONE 651 735-7470
FAX: 651 735-7471
Jerome Hein, *President*
Richard Hanson, *Vice Pres*
Sherry Banaszewski, *Treasurer*
EMP: 35 **EST:** 1997
SQ FT: 4,100
SALES (est): 1MM-4.9MM **Privately Held**
WEB: www.ecsi.cc
SIC: 7382 1731 Fire alarm maintenance & monitoring service; computerized controls installation service; environmental controls installation contractor

(G-8898)
RICHARD F TSCHIDA
5350 Highway 61 N (55110-2472)
PHONE 651 426-7958
Richard Tschida, *Owner*
EMP: 30 **EST:** 2001
SALES (est): 1MM-4.9MM **Privately Held**
SIC: 8742 Manufacturing management consultant

(G-8899)
RICHARD SCALES ADVERTISING
2303 Wycliff St Ste 1E (55114-1278)
PHONE 651 641-0226
FAX: 651 641-1031
Richard Scales, *President*
Bertil Nielsen, *Exec VP*
Walt Larson, *Treasurer*
Tammy Harpel, *CIO*
EMP: 60 **EST:** 1969
SQ FT: 31,000
SALES (est): 5MM-9.9MM **Privately Held**
WEB: www.scalesadvertising.com
SIC: 7311 Advertising agency

(G-8900)
RIENHARDT & ANDERSON
332 Minnesota St Ste E1250 (55101-7541)
PHONE 651 227-9990
FAX: 651 297-6543
Mark Anderson, *Partner*
Jeffery Anderson, *Partner*
Garrett D Blanchfield Jr, *Member*
EMP: 25 **EST:** 1990
SALES (est): 1MM-4.9MM **Privately Held**
SIC: 8111 Legal services

(G-8901)
RIESCO INC
1885 University Ave W # 1 (55104-3403)
PHONE 651 771-8235
Deborah Zahn, *President*
EMP: 48 **EST:** 1985
SALES (est): 1MM-4.9MM **Privately Held**
SIC: 8361 Group foster home

(G-8902)
RIHM MOTOR CO
2108 University Ave W (55114-1820)
PHONE 651 646-7833
John W Rihm, *President*
Mark D Shide, *Corp Secy*
Kady Vanoort, *Accountant*
Pat Duffy, *Sales Mgr*
Bob Koller, *Manager*
EMP: 90 **EST:** 1934
SQ FT: 27,000
SALES (est): 100MM-499.9MM **Privately Held**
SIC: 5012 5013 7538 Wholesales truck tractors; general truck repair services; wholesales truck parts & accessories

(G-8903)
RITA AMBOURN HAIR DESIGNERS
464 Snelling Ave S (55105-2147)
PHONE 651 698-5537
FAX: 651 690-0229
Rita Ambourn, *President*
EMP: 35 **EST:** 1987
SALES (est): 1MM-4.9MM **Privately Held**
SIC: 7231 Retails wigs & hairpieces; retails toiletries, cosmetics & perfumes; retail gift shop; electrolysis & epilatory service

(G-8904)
RIVER OF GOODS INC
2475 Doswell Ave Ste B (55108-1556)
PHONE 651 917-5335
FAX: 651 917-5336
Terrence Commerford, *CEO*
Lavina Lau, *President*
Tatrick Mullins, *COO*
Ruth Hartke, *Bookkeeper*
Dale Peterson, *Manager*
▲ **EMP:** 70 **EST:** 2001
SQ FT: 140,000
SALES (est): 10MM-24.9MM **Privately Held**
WEB: www.riverofgoods.com
SIC: 5021 Wholesales furniture

(G-8905)
RIVERVIEW PACKAGING INC
35 E Pleasant Lake Rd (55127-2116)
PHONE 651 415-1121
FAX: 651 415-1579
Jon Luebstorf, *President*
Eileen Quinlan, *Office Mgr*
EMP: 30 **EST:** 1998
SQ FT: 11,000 **Privately Held**
SIC: 4783 Packing & crating service

(G-8906)
ROBERT GULLICK CPA
170 7th Pl E Ste 100 (55101-2361)
PHONE 651 265-2043
Robert Gullick, *Member*
EMP: 25 **EST:** 2006
SALES (est): 1MM-4.9MM **Privately Held**
SIC: 8721 Certified public accountant services

(G-8907)
ROBERT HALF INTERNATIONAL INC
Also Called: Officeteam
444 Cedar St Ste 1150 (55101-2185)
PHONE 651 293-8033
FAX: 651 293-8074
Debbie Peterson, *Director*
EMP: 40
SALES (est): 500-999K **Publicly Held**
WEB: www.rhii.com
SIC: 7363 Help supply services
PA: Robert Half International Inc
2884 Sand Hill Rd Ste 200
Menlo Park CA 94025
650 234-6000

(G-8908)
ROCCO ALTOBELLI INC
665 Snelling Ave S (55116-2254)
PHONE 651 690-5491
FAX: 651 690-3281
Rocco Atobelli, *Owner*
Mike Vereide, *Manager*
EMP: 40
SALES (est): 1MM-4.9MM **Privately Held**
WEB: www.roccoaltobelli.com
SIC: 7231 Beauty salon
PA: Rocco Altobelli Inc
14301 W Burnsville Pkwy
Burnsville MN 55306
952 707-1900

(G-8909)
ROCK ISLAND CO
30 7th St E Ste 2000 (55101-4930)
PHONE 651 228-0935
W T Weyerhaeuser, *CEO*
E R Titcomb Jr, *President*
Emily Raml, *Exec Sec*
EMP: 25 **EST:** 1940
SALES (est): 10MM-24.9MM **Privately Held**
WEB: www.rock-island.com
SIC: 6799 6282 Investor services; manufactures sensitized diazo or whiteprint cloth or paper; manufactures diazotype or whiteprint reproduction machines & equipment; investment advisory service; photographic equipment & supplies

(G-8910)
ROCK-TENN CO
2250 Wabash Ave (55114-1828)
PHONE 651 641-4874
Jack Greenshaw, *General Mgr*
Peter Helming, *Safety Mgr*
Mike Doschadis, *Traffic Mgr*
Michael Henderson, *Controller*
Mike Hendrickson, *Controller*
EMP: 600
SALES (est): 100MM-499.9MM **Publicly Held**
WEB: www.rocktenn.com
SIC: 4953 5093 5113 Manufactures pulp from waste recycled paper; waste material recycling services; wholesales waste paper; wholesales corrugated & solid fiber boxes
PA: Rock-Tenn Co
504 Thrasher St
Norcross GA 30071
770 448-2193

(G-8911)
ROED ERICKSEN & ASSOCIATES
Also Called: Ericksen Roed Johnston Sahlman
2550 University Ave W Ste 201S (55114-1904)
PHONE 651 251-7570
FAX: 651 251-7578
A G Ericksen, *President*
Thomas E Amundsson, *Corp Secy*
Thomas Amundson, *Vice Pres*

Michael A Desutter, *Vice Pres*
Jim Roed, *Vice Pres*
EMP: 31 **EST:** 1985
SALES (est): 1MM-4.9MM **Privately Held**
WEB: www.ericksen-roed.com
SIC: 8711 Engineering services

(G-8912)
ROHN INDUSTRIES INC-ST PAUL
862 Hersey St (55114-1214)
PHONE 651 647-1300
FAX: 651 647-1208
Ronald V Mason Jr, *President*
Jim Beran, *Vice Pres*
EMP: 31 **EST:** 1989
SQ FT: 24,000
SALES (est): 10MM-24.9MM **Privately Held**
WEB: www.rohnind.com
SIC: 5113 7389 Wholesales wrapping or coarse paper & products; document destruction service; wholesales paper & disposable plastic containers; pulp mill

(G-8913)
ROSEVILLE VFW POST 7555
1145 Woodhill Dr (55113-1807)
PHONE 651 483-5313
FAX: 651 481-7968
Carla Miller, *Manager*
Karla Miller, *Manager*
Marianne Hagman, *Manager*
Sue McMann, *Manager*
Aaron Ellefson, *Manager*
EMP: 31 **EST:** 1948 **Privately Held**
SIC: 8641 Veterans' organization

(G-8914)
ROTTLUND CO INC (PA)
3065 Centre Pointe Dr (55113-1130)
PHONE 651 638-0500
FAX: 651 638-0501
David H Rotter, *President*
Todd M Stutz, *COO*
Timothy M Whitten, *Exec VP*
John Falk, *VP Sls/Mktg*
Steven A Kahn, *CFO*
EMP: 75 **EST:** 1973
SQ FT: 10,000 **Privately Held**
WEB: www.rottlundhomes.com
SIC: 1521 1531 Single-family housing construction; new housing operative builder

(G-8915)
RYDER TRUCK RENTAL INC
2580 Long Lake Rd (55113-2526)
PHONE 651 636-6906
FAX: 651 636-3119
Jim Sypher, *Sales Executive*
Jim Dreesen, *Manager*
Dennis Hillyer, *Manager*
EMP: 30
SALES (est): 5MM-9.9MM **Publicly Held**
WEB: www.ryder.com
SIC: 7513 7514 Truck rental service, without drivers; passenger car rental
HQ: Ryder Truck Rental Inc
11690 NW 105th St
Miami FL 33178
305 500-3000

(G-8916)
RYDER TRUCK RENTAL INC
1901 Lake Valentine Rd (55112-2835)
PHONE 651 631-1755
FAX: 651 631-8035
Michael Peterson, *General Mgr*
Kim Taylor, *Branch Mgr*
Gail Weber, *Manager*
EMP: 25
SALES (est): 5MM-9.9MM **Publicly Held**
WEB: www.ryder.com
SIC: 7513 Truck rental service, without drivers
HQ: Ryder Truck Rental Inc
11690 NW 105th St
Miami FL 33178
305 500-3000

(G-8917)
S & L TEAM CLEANING
1821 University Ave W S321 (55104-4534)
PHONE 612 558-4502
Ninoska S Lallier, *President*
Mitchell Lallier, *Vice Pres*
EMP: 26 **EST:** 1990
SALES (est): 500-999K **Privately Held**

(PA)=Parent Co (HQ)=Headquarters (DH)=Div Headquarters
✿ = New business established in last 2 years
2011 Harris Minnesota
Services Directory
© Harris InfoSource 1-866-281-6415
385

WEB: www.team-cleaning-mn.com
SIC: 7349 Industrial or commercial cleaning services; housekeeping & maid services

(G-8918)

S & T OFFICE PRODUCTS INC
1000 Kristen Ct (55110-5164)
PHONE..................................651 483-4411
FAX: 651 483-3929
Frank G Tschida, *CEO*
Chris Foss, *Corp Secy*
Gerald A Hanggi, *Senior VP*
Pat Crowley, *Vice Pres*
John Palkowitsch, *Vice Pres*
EMP: 135 EST: 1971
SALES (est): 25MM-49.9MM **Privately Held**
WEB: www.stofficeproducts.com
SIC: 5112 5021 Wholesale commercial stationer; wholesales office supplies; wholesales office furniture

(G-8919)

S J C INC
Also Called: Royal Oaks Car Wash
4595 Hodgson Rd (55126-6041)
PHONE..................................651 483-1752
Steven J Cartier, *President*
EMP: 30 EST: 1989
SALES (est): 1MM-4.9MM **Privately Held**
SIC: 7542 Car wash

(G-8920)

S P RICHARDS CO
2416 Maplewood Dr (55109-1912)
PO Box 64078 (55164-0078)
PHONE..................................651 484-8459
FAX: 651 484-2275
Troy Lovas, *General Mgr*
Terry Sherman, *Manager*
Troy Lovaf, *Manager*
EMP: 50
SALES (est): 10MM-24.9MM **Publicly Held**
WEB: www.sprichards.com
SIC: 5112 5021 5044 Wholesales stationery & office supplies; wholesales office equipment; wholesales office furniture
HQ: S P Richards Co
    6300 Highlands Pkwy SE
    Smyrna GA 30082
    770 436-6881

(G-8921)

SAFEZONE LLC
275 4th St E Ste 110 (55101-1628)
PHONE..................................612 716-0856
Don Culver, *Member*
EMP: 99
SALES (est): 5MM-9.9MM **Privately Held**
SIC: 7389 Business support services

(G-8922)

SAGITEC SOLUTIONS LLC
2233 Hamline Ave N # 420 (55113-5006)
PHONE..................................612 235-4122
Rod Sheppard, *Member*
Ranjit Kotcherlakota, *Member*
Deepak Ahuja, *Member*
Bala Venkat, *Member*
Rick Deshler, *Member*
EMP: 67 EST: 2004
SQ FT: 1,000
SALES (est): 5MM-9.9MM **Privately Held**
WEB: www.sagitec.com
SIC: 7371 Computer software development

(G-8923)

SAINT PATRICK'S GUILD INC
1554 Randolph Ave (55105-2538)
PHONE..................................651 690-1506
FAX: 651 696-5133
Tim Doran, *President*
Kenneth Marqwardt, *Vice Pres*
EMP: 40 EST: 1949
SQ FT: 10,000
SALES (est): 10MM-24.9MM **Privately Held**
WEB: www.stpatricksguild.com
SIC: 5049 Wholesales religious supplies; retails religious goods

(G-8924)

SAINT PAUL BURLINGTON LP
180 5th St E Ste 160 (55101-1490)
PHONE..................................651 228-9456
Gary Lindstrom, *Partner*
Angelea Hummelgard, *Principal*

Charles Palmer, *General Ptnr*
David Frauenshuh, *General Ptnr*
Joey Cremers, *Controller*
EMP: 115 EST: 1984
SQ FT: 615,000
SALES (est): 25MM-49.9MM **Privately Held**
WEB: www.frauenshuhcos.com
SIC: 6512 Nonresidential building operator

(G-8925)

SAINT PAUL CHAMBER ORCHESTRA
408 Saint Peter St Fl 3 (55102-1130)
PHONE..................................651 292-3241
FAX: 651 292-4319
Bruce Coppock, *President*
Thomas Brown, *Corp Secy*
Mary McColl, *Vice Pres*
Jon Bacher, *Vice Pres*
Beth Villaume, *Vice Pres*
EMP: 75 EST: 1958
SALES (est): 10MM-24.9MM **Privately Held**
WEB: www.spcomail.org
SIC: 7929 Orchestra & bands

(G-8926)

SAINT PAUL FOUNDATION INC
Also Called: Minnesota Community Foundation
55 5th St E Ste 600 (55101-1718)
PHONE..................................651 224-5463
FAX: 651 224-9502
Carleen Rhodes, *President*
Jack Pohl, *Vice Pres*
Christine Searson, *Vice Pres*
Gregory Kvam, *Attorney*
Mary Shearen, *Attorney*
EMP: 62 EST: 1940
SQ FT: 22,400 **Privately Held**
SIC: 8641 8399 Community membership club; non-fee basis fund raising organization

(G-8927)

SAINT PAUL LUNG CLINIC
225 Smith Ave N Ste 300 (55102-2592)
PHONE..................................651 726-6200
Tom Lorentzen, *CEO*
Val Sharkey, *Corp Secy*
Mary Bloom, *Opers Staff*
Kristen Stang, *Purch Mgr*
Carrie Letendre, *Insur/Bill Sup*
EMP: 60 EST: 1980
SALES (est): 5MM-9.9MM **Privately Held**
SIC: 8011 Physical medicine physician or surgeon office

(G-8928)

SAINT PAUL REGIONAL WATER SVCS
Also Called: Hazel Park
1585 Maryland Ave E (55106-2931)
PHONE..................................651 776-6960
Jim Haugen, *Branch Mgr*
EMP: 31
SALES (est): 5MM-9.9MM **Privately Held**
SIC: 4941 Water supply services
PA: Saint Paul Regional Water Svcs
    1900 Rice St
    Saint Paul MN 55113
    651 266-6274

(G-8929)

SAINT PAUL REGIONAL WATER SVCS
Also Called: McCarron Pump Station
1900 Rice St (55113-6810)
PHONE..................................651 266-1635
Jim Haugen, *Manager*
EMP: 29
SALES (est): 1MM-4.9MM **Privately Held**
SIC: 4941 Water supply services; mayors' office
PA: Saint Paul Regional Water Svcs
    1900 Rice St
    Saint Paul MN 55113
    651 266-6274

(G-8930)

SAINT PAUL RIVERCENTRE CONV
175 Kellogg Blvd W # 501 (55102-1227)
PHONE..................................651 265-4800
FAX: 651 265-4899
Karolyn Kirchgesler, *President*

Jaye Rykunyk, *Vice Chairman*
Char Mason, *Member*
Eric Willems, *CFO*
Ronald L Poworth, *Comms Dir*
EMP: 70 EST: 1929
SALES (est): 10MM-24.9MM **Privately Held**
WEB: www.stpaulcvb.org
SIC: 7389 Authors' agent & broker

(G-8931)

SBC DATACOMM INC
833 3rd St SW Ste 1 (55112-3461)
PHONE..................................763 315-5343
Kim Beamish, *Engrg Mgr*
Ben Schunk, *Design Engr*
Glenn Zerby, *Manager*
EMP: 25 **Publicly Held**
WEB: www.sbc.com
SIC: 4813 4812 5065 Local & long distance telephone communications services; wholesales communications equipment; cellular telephone services; wholesales mobile telephone equipment; wholesales telephone equipment; paging services
PA: AT&T Inc
    208 S Akard St Ste 3700
    Dallas TX 75202
    210 821-4105

(G-8932)

SBS TRANSPORTATION INC
1700 Wynne Ave (55108-2708)
PHONE..................................651 256-1555
Paul Goff, *President*
Lionel Chinelly, *Vice Pres*
Gregory Schomer, *CFO*
◆ EMP: 30 EST: 1994
SQ FT: 1,000
SALES (est): 5MM-9.9MM **Privately Held**
SIC: 4424 Deep sea domestic freight transportation

(G-8933)

SCHAWK INC
Also Called: Creative Source One
2269 County Road C W (55113-2503)
PHONE..................................651 636-0611
FAX: 651 636-0560
Ed Bohl, *General Mgr*
Chris Hauses, *Director*
Dustin Hawkins, *Director*
EMP: 50
SALES (est): 5MM-9.9MM **Publicly Held**
WEB: www.schawk.com
SIC: 7338 Manufactures printing machinery; manufactures printing plates; secretarial & court reporting services; plate making services; typesetting service
PA: Schawk Inc
    1695 S River Rd
    Des Plaines IL 60018
    847 827-9494

(G-8934)

SCHNEIBERG CO (PA)
Also Called: Automation & Process Controls
1259 Gervais Ave Ste 100 (55109-2064)
PHONE..................................651 489-7489
Tom Schneiberg, *President*
Kathy Schneiberg, *Vice Pres*
EST: 1985 **Privately Held**
WEB: www.apc-inc.com
SIC: 5084 Wholesales industrial instruments & control equipment

(G-8935)

SCHWAB-VOLLHABER-LUBRAT T INC
4600 Churchill St Ste 1 (55126-5829)
PHONE..................................651 481-8000
FAX: 651 481-8621
J M Holland, *President*
James Lubratt, *Vice Pres*
Todd Vollhaber, *Treasurer*
Mark Wiggins, *Controller*
EMP: 53 EST: 1967
SQ FT: 20,000
SALES (est): 10MM-24.9MM **Privately Held**
WEB: www.svl.com
SIC: 5075 Wholesales air conditioning & ventilation equipment & supplies; wholesales warm air heating equipment & supplies

(G-8936)

SCIENCE MUSEUM OF MINNESOTA
120 Kellogg Blvd W (55102-1202)
PHONE..................................651 221-9488
FAX: 651 221-4777
Eric Jolly, *President*
Duane Kocik, *Vice Pres*
Kathy Wilson, *Vice Pres*
David Chittenden, *Vice Pres*
Jane Eastwood, *Vice Pres*
EMP: 497 EST: 1907
SQ FT: 400,000
SALES (est): 25MM-49.9MM **Privately Held**
WEB: www.smm.org
SIC: 8412 Museum; retail gift shop

(G-8937)

SCOTT W KAJER DDS
Also Called: Maplewood Dental Associates
1736 Cope Ave E Ste 3 (55109-2661)
PHONE..................................651 770-3831
Scott W Kajer DDS, *Partner*
EMP: 30 EST: 1973
SALES (est): 1MM-4.9MM **Privately Held**
SIC: 8021 Dentists' office & clinic

(G-8938)

SCOTTISH RITE TEMPLE
200 Plato Blvd E (55107-1618)
PHONE..................................651 222-2676
Larry Wert, *CEO*
EMP: 1000 EST: 1859 **Privately Held**
SIC: 8641 Fraternal association

(G-8939)

SEARS, ROEBUCK & CO
425 Rice St (55103-2123)
PHONE..................................651 291-4397
Dennis Russler, *Branch Mgr*
EMP: 426
SALES (est): 50MM-99.9MM **Publicly Held**
SIC: 7629 Department store; retails appliance parts; vacuum cleaner repair service
HQ: Sears, Roebuck & Co
    3333 Beverly Rd
    Hoffman Estates IL 60179
    847 286-2500

(G-8940)

SEBESTA BLOMBERG & ASSOCIATES (PA)
2381 Rosegate (55113-2625)
PHONE..................................651 634-0775
FAX: 651 634-7400
Tony Litton, *CEO*
Randolph Thompson, *Ch of Bd*
Daniel Tollman, *President*
Nathan F Germolus, *Corp Secy*
Janet Flam, *Vice Pres*
EMP: 120 EST: 1994
SQ FT: 40,000
SALES (corp-wide): 35M **Privately Held**
WEB: www.sebesta.com
SIC: 8711 Engineering services

(G-8941)

SECOND HARVEST HEARTLAND
1140 Gervais Ave (55109-2020)
PHONE..................................651 484-5117
Robert Gifford, *Chairman*
Bob Chatmas, *COO*
Kathleen McKown, *Vice Pres*
Karen Anderson, *Human Resources*
Rob Zeaske, *Exec Dir*
EMP: 130 EST: 1974
SQ FT: 78,000
SALES (est): 5MM-9.9MM **Privately Held**
SIC: 8322 Individual & family social services

(G-8942)

SECRUIAN FINANCIAL SERVICES
Also Called: Mimlic Sales Corp
400 Robert St N (55101-2037)
PHONE..................................651 223-4252
FAX: 651 223-5959
Robert Hunstad, *Ch of Bd*
George Connolly, *President*
Dennis Prohofsky, *Corp Secy*
Margaret Milosevich, *Treasurer*
Thomas Clark, *Asst Treas*

www.HarrisInfo.com
386

2011 Harris Minnesota
Services Directory

▲=Import ▼=Export
◆=Import/Export

EST: 1984 **Privately Held**
SIC: 6211 Security broker service

(G-8943)
SECURE COMPUTING CORP
2340 Energy Park Dr (55108-1511)
PHONE.............................651 628-2700
Mary Budge, *Senior VP*
Coey Minear, *Engineer*
Jill Putman, *CFO*
Laura Dirks, *Human Res Dir*
Timothy Roddy, *Marketing Staff*
EMP: 180
SALES (est): 10MM-24.9MM **Publicly Held**
WEB: www.mcafee.com
SIC: 7371 Computer programming service
HQ: Secure Computing Corp
   3965 Freedom Cir 4
   Santa Clara CA 95054
   408 979-2020

(G-8944)
SECURIAN FINANCIAL NETWORK INC (PA)
400 Robert St N Ste A (55101-2099)
PHONE.............................651 665-3500
Robert L Senkler, *CEO*
Randy F Wallake, *President*
Janet M Hill, *Corp Secy*
Allen L Peterson, *Corp Secy*
Jay R Brown, *Corp Secy*
EMP: 100 EST: 2000 **Privately Held**
SIC: 6311 Life insurance carrier

(G-8945)
SECURIAN FINANCIAL SERVICES
401 Robert St N (55101-2005)
PHONE.............................651 665-4244
George Connolly, *CEO*
Jay R Brown, *Corp Secy*
Kimberly K Carpenter, *Corp Secy*
Dean F Czarnetzki, *Corp Secy*
Janet M Hill, *Corp Secy*
EMP: 104 EST: 1984
SALES (est): 10MM-24.9MM **Privately Held**
WEB: www.minnesotalife.com
SIC: 6411 Insurance services

(G-8946)
SERVICEMASTER INC
Also Called: Merry Maids
1350 Highway 96 E (55110-3603)
PHONE.............................651 552-4979
FAX: 651 552-7677
Brett Peterson, *Owner*
Eugene McNamara, *General Mgr*
Stephanie Engen, *Office Mgr*
Jason Vaughn, *Manager*
Kris Cheney, *Manager*
EMP: 25 EST: 1983
SALES (est): 500-999K **Privately Held**
SIC: 7349 Housekeeping & maid services

(G-8947)
SHAVLIK TECHNOLOGIES CORP
2665 Long Lake Rd Ste 400 (55113-2535)
PHONE.............................651 426-6624
Mark Shavlik, *Member*
Rebecca Shavlik, *Member*
Rocco Donnino, *Vice Pres*
Zach Lanore, *Sales Engr*
James Rydbeck, *Manager*
EMP: 95 EST: 1993
SALES (est): 10MM-24.9MM **Privately Held**
WEB: www.shavlik.com
SIC: 7372 Software publisher

(G-8948)
SHAVLIK TECHNOLOGIES LLC
2665 Long Lake Rd Ste 400 (55113-2535)
PHONE.............................651 426-6624
Mark Shavlik, *Member*
Rebecca Shavlik, *Member*
Terry Noonan, *VP Sls/Mktg*
Ed Peek, *VP Sls/Mktg*
Jason Walker, *VP Business*
EMP: 94 EST: 1993
SQ FT: 18,000
SALES (est): 10MM-24.9MM **Privately Held**
WEB: www.shavliktechnologies.com
SIC: 7379 4813 7371 Computer system consulting services; online services providers; custom computer software systems analysis & design service

(G-8949)
SHEEHY CONSTRUCTION CO
360 Larpenteur Ave W (55113-6782)
PO Box 64570 (55164-0570)
PHONE.............................651 488-6691
FAX: 651 488-4992
Michael D Sheehy, *President*
J M Benson, *Corp Secy*
Laurie Zins, *Corp Secy*
Dan Krause, *Vice Pres*
Joseph Schmidt, *Vice Pres*
EMP: 70 EST: 1985
SQ FT: 7,000
SALES (est): 10MM-24.9MM **Privately Held**
WEB: www.sheehyconstruction.com
SIC: 1542 New commercial & office building construction

(G-8950)
SHEET METAL WORKER FEDERAL
Also Called: Smw Federal Credit Union
1691 Cope Ave E (55109-2632)
PHONE.............................651 770-2385
FAX: 651 747-1559
Janice R Peterson, *President*
Sheet Fe, *Coordinator*
EMP: 32
SALES (est): 5MM-9.9MM **Privately Held**
SIC: 6062 State chartered credit union

(G-8951)
SHEFFIELD, OLSON & MCQUEEN INC
2145 Ford Pkwy Ste 200 (55116-1912)
PHONE.............................651 695-2500
Cynthia J Sheffield, *President*
Steve Halvorsen, *Vice Pres*
Thomas Dalsin, *CFO*
Karen Pielow, *Marketing Mgr*
Robert Wollman, *IT/INT Sup*
EMP: 50 EST: 1982
SQ FT: 10,000
SALES (est): 5MM-9.9MM **Privately Held**
WEB: www.somi.com
SIC: 8748 6371 6411 8742 Employee programs administration consultant; pension, health & welfare funds services; insurance services; compensation & benefits planning consultant

(G-8952)
SHOLOM HOME EAST INC
740 K Ave (55102)
PHONE.............................651 646-6311
FAX: 651 646-2740
Bruce Kahn, *CEO*
Michael Klein, *COO*
Charles Glazman, *Vice Pres*
Becky Arnes, *Human Res Mgr*
Sondra Jacobs, *Administrator*
EMP: 700 EST: 1906
SQ FT: 175,000
SALES (est): 25MM-49.9MM **Privately Held**
WEB: www.sholom.com
SIC: 8051 Skilled nursing care facility
PA: Sholom Community Alliance
   3620 Phillips Pkwy
   Minneapolis MN 55426
   952 935-6311

(G-8953)
SHOLOM ST PAUL SENIOR HOUSING
Also Called: Weinberg Apartments
760 Perlman St (55102-6013)
PHONE.............................651 328-2022
Mike Hanson, *CEO*
EMP: 99
SALES (est): 10MM-24.9MM **Privately Held**
SIC: 6513 Apartment building operator

(G-8954)
SHORT-ELLIOTT-HENDRICKSON INC (PA)
Also Called: S E H
3535 Vadnais Center Dr # 200
(55110-5118)
PHONE.............................651 490-2000
FAX: 651 490-2150
Chris Hiniker, *CEO*
Sam L Claassen, *President*
Noel Vogen, *Principal*
Michael W Flippin, *Corp Secy*

June C Nusz, *Corp Secy*
EMP: 208 EST: 1927
SQ FT: 38,000 **Privately Held**
WEB: www.sehinc.com
SIC: 8711 8712 Civil engineering services; engineering consulting services; sanitary engineers; architectural engineers

(G-8955)
SIEMENS INDUSTRY INC
2350 County Road C W Ste 100
(55113-2542)
PHONE.............................651 631-8533
FAX: 651 255-2701
Ryan Urbach, *Manager*
Bill Gresco, *Manager*
Peter Berger, *Manager*
EMP: 75
SALES (est): 25MM-49.9MM **Privately Held**
WEB: www.sibt.com
SIC: 5084 Wholesales industrial controlling instruments & accessories
HQ: Siemens Industry Inc
   1000 Deerfield Pkwy
   Buffalo Grove IL 60089
   847 215-1000

(G-8956)
SIEMENS PRODUCT LIFECYCLE MGT
4233 Lexington Ave N (55126-6159)
PHONE.............................651 482-4219
FAX: 651 482-4348
Nancy Gehrig, *Vice Pres*
Robert Nierman, *Vice Pres*
Kimberly Harff, *Manager*
EMP: 100
SALES (est): 10MM-24.9MM **Privately Held**
WEB: www.sibt.com
SIC: 7372 Software publisher
HQ: Siemens Industry Inc
   1000 Deerfield Pkwy
   Buffalo Grove IL 60089
   847 215-1000

(G-8957)
SIEMENS WATER TECHNOLOGIES
1239 Willow Lake Blvd (55110-5145)
PHONE.............................651 766-2722
David Gardeen, *VP Sls/Mktg*
Chad Kinkead, *Human Res Dir*
David Lee, *Marketing Staff*
Rick Palmgren, *Manager*
Seven Yoer, *Manager*
EMP: 165
SALES (est): 25MM-49.9MM **Privately Held**
SIC: 7374 Manufactures water quality monitoring & control systems; data processing & preparation services
PA: Siemens Water Technologies
   10 Technology Dr
   Lowell MA 01851
   978 934-9349

(G-8958)
SIGNATURE FLIGHT SUPPORT CORP
515 Eaton St (55107-2495)
PHONE.............................651 224-1100
FAX: 651 265-7924
Kelly Ellert, *Accountant*
Greg Mason, *Human Res Mgr*
Christy Orris, *Data Proc Dir*
EMP: 50
SALES (est): 1MM-4.9MM **Privately Held**
WEB: www.bba-aviation.com/flightsupport
SIC: 4581 Airport, flying field & services
HQ: Signature Flight Support Corp
   201 S Orange Ave Ste 1100
   Orlando FL 32801
   407 648-7200

(G-8959)
SILVER LAKE CLINIC AT SHOREVW
4625 Churchill St Ste 110 (55126-3237)
PHONE.............................651 481-0818
FAX: 651 481-0537
Leslie Norton, *Med Doctor*
Rick Rowe, *Manager*
Gerald A Pitzl MD, *Gnrl Med Prac*
D J Dummer MD, *Gnrl Med Prac*
Gerald D Jensen MD, *Gnrl Med Prac*
EMP: 26 EST: 1984

SALES (est): 1MM-4.9MM **Privately Held**
WEB: www.silver-lake-village.com
SIC: 8011 General & family practice physician or surgeon office

(G-8960)
SINCLAIR BROADCASTING GROUP
Also Called: Kmwb
1640 Como Ave (55108-2725)
PHONE.............................651 646-2300
FAX: 651 646-1220
Miles Kennedy, *Controller*
John Degnan, *Sales Staff*
Becki Flanagin, *Advt Staff*
Bob Weinstein, *Advt Staff*
Joe Tracy, *Manager*
EMP: 35 EST: 1991
SQ FT: 23,000
SALES (est): 5MM-9.9MM **Publicly Held**
WEB: www.kmwb.com
SIC: 4833 Television broadcasting station
PA: Sinclair Broadcast Group Inc
   10706 Beaver Dam Rd
   Hunt Valley MD 21030
   410 568-1500

(G-8961)
SISTERS OF THE GOOD SHEPHERD
5100 Hodgson Rd (55126-1229)
PHONE.............................651 484-0221
Marta Ceballos, *President*
Sharon Lezalla, *Facilities Mgr*
Julie Villella, *Accounting Staf*
Maureen Kunz, *Administrator*
Madelin Munday, *Exec Dir*
EMP: 35 EST: 1974
SALES (est): 1MM-4.9MM **Privately Held**
SIC: 8361 Residential rehabilitation center with health care incidental

(G-8962)
SKE SUPPORT SERVICES INC
100 9th Ave SW (55112-3464)
PHONE.............................651 639-6559
Robert Unger, *President*
EMP: 25
SALES (est): 1MM-4.9MM **Privately Held**
SIC: 8742 General management consultant

(G-8963)
SKY MEDIA LLC
Also Called: Historic Aviation
121 5th Ave NW Ste 300 (55112-3220)
PHONE.............................651 635-0100
Gregory Herrick, *Member*
▲ EMP: 31 EST: 1965
SALES (est): 10MM-24.9MM **Privately Held**
WEB: www.historicaviation.com
SIC: 5088 5099 5192 5199 Retail mail-order house; wholesales books; wholesales art goods; wholesales aircraft equipment & supplies; wholesales prerecorded tapes & cassettes

(G-8964)
SKYLIGHT CORP
3003 Snelling Ave N (55113-1501)
PHONE.............................651 631-5000
Dick Becvar, *President*
Dick Beczar, *Branch Mgr*
Neil Stavem, *Exec Dir*
EMP: 32 EST: 1986
SQ FT: 2,500
SALES (est): 1MM-4.9MM **Privately Held**
WEB: www.skylightcorp.com
SIC: 8748 Communications consultant

(G-8965)
SMARTE CARTE INC (HQ)
4455 White Bear Pkwy (55110-7626)
PHONE.............................651 429-3614
FAX: 651 426-0927
Edward Rudis, *President*
Leo Houle, *Vice Pres*
Tom Rock, *Vice Pres*
Randy Xu, *Vice Pres*
Kathy Zeinty, *Vice Pres*
EMP: 80 EST: 1967
SQ FT: 58,000 **Privately Held**
WEB: www.bdcf.com

(PA)=Parent Co (HQ)=Headquarters (DH)=Div Headquarters
✿ = New business established in last 2 years
2011 Harris Minnesota
Services Directory
© Harris InfoSource 1-866-281-6415
387

GEOGRAPHIC

SIC: 7299 Operates scale, shoeshine, locker & blood pressure coin-operated machines; locker rental
PA: Black Diamond Capital Mgt
100 N Field Dr Ste 140300
Lake Forest IL 60045
847 615-9000

(G-8966)
SMITH MICRO TECHNOLOGIES INC
3435 Labore Rd (55110-5147)
PHONE..............................651 482-8718
FAX: 651 482-9727
Patrick C Smith, *President*
Ron Wientjes, *Vice Pres*
Joseph Smith, *Treasurer*
Linda McIvor, *Human Res Dir*
Tim Warrick, *Marketing Staff*
EMP: 135 EST: 1979
SQ FT: 12,000
SALES (est): 10MM-24.9MM **Privately Held**
WEB: www.smithmicrotech.com
SIC: 7629 5044 5045 Electric business machine repair service; wholesales computer software; wholesales computers; wholesales office equipment

(G-8967)
SMYTH CO'S INC (HQ)
1085 Snelling Ave N (55108-2705)
PHONE..............................651 646-4544
FAX: 651 646-8949
John P Hickey, *CEO*
James Lundquist, *President*
Daniel E Hickey, *Vice Pres*
David Buchholz, *Vice Pres*
Bill Weernink, *Opers Staff*
▲ EMP: 40 EST: 1877
SQ FT: 110,000
SALES (corp-wide): 81M **Privately Held**
WEB: www.smythco.com
SIC: 5084 7389 7699 Manufactures paper label from purchased materials; manufactures window & lobby displays & cutouts; wholesales industrial processing & packaging equipment; laminating service; offset printing; industrial machinery repair & maintenance services
PA: G G Mc Guiggan Corp
1085 Snelling Ave N
Saint Paul MN 55108
651 646-4544

(G-8968)
SO MN REGIONAL SERVICE
166 4th St E Ste 200 (55101-1473)
PHONE..............................651 222-5863
Georgia Sherman, *Corp Secy*
Jessie Nicholson, *Director*
EMP: 50 EST: 2002
SALES (est): 5MM-9.9MM **Privately Held**
SIC: 8111 Legal aid services

(G-8969)
SOBRIETY HIGH FOUNDATION
2233 University Ave W # 357 (55114-1600)
PHONE..............................651 773-8378
Lew Moran, *President*
EMP: 50 EST: 2004 **Privately Held**
SIC: 8699 Charitable organization

(G-8970)
SODERBERG INC (HQ)
230 Eva St (55107-1605)
PO Box 64313 (55164-0313)
PHONE..............................651 291-1400
FAX: 651 291-7402
Aloys Willenbring, *CEO*
Craig Giles, *President*
Bernard Bleske, *Mfg Staff*
Robert Grundtner, *Treasurer*
Sue Ebner, *Sales Mgr*
▲ EMP: 110 EST: 1945
SQ FT: 40,000
SALES (corp-wide): 182M **Privately Held**
WEB: www.soseyes.com
SIC: 5048 Manufactures eyeglasses; wholesales optometric equipment & supplies; manufactures contact lenses; wholesales ophthalmic goods
PA: Walman Optical Co
801 12th Ave N Ste 2
Minneapolis MN 55411
612 520-6000

(G-8971)
SOO LINE RAILROAD CO INC
Also Called: CP Rail
1000 Shop Rd (55106-6706)
PHONE..............................651 646-6044
FAX: 651 778-3684
Jerry Knicle, *Manager*
EMP: 550 **Privately Held**
WEB: www.cpa.ca
SIC: 4011 Long haul railroad
HQ: SOO Line Railroad Co Inc
501 Marquette Ave # 1500
Minneapolis MN 55402
800 766-4357

(G-8972)
SOUTH METRO HUMAN SERVICES
Also Called: Community Foundation
796 Capitol Hts (55103-1852)
PHONE..............................651 221-9880
FAX: 651 225-1545
Tom Paul, *Director*
John Hansen, *Director*
EMP: 35
SQ FT: 8,000
SALES (est): 1MM-4.9MM **Privately Held**
WEB: www.south-metro.org
SIC: 8361 Home for the mentally handicapped
PA: South Metro Human Services
400 Sibley St Ste 500
Saint Paul MN 55101
651 291-1979

(G-8973)
SOUTH METRO HUMAN SERVICES (PA)
400 Sibley St Ste 500 (55101-1938)
PHONE..............................651 291-1979
FAX: 651 291-7378
Terry Schneider, *Chairman*
Michele Kornowski, *Human Res Mgr*
Roger Knott, *Technology*
Tom Paul, *Director*
EMP: 65 EST: 1991
SQ FT: 13,000
SALES (corp-wide): 17.92M **Privately Held**
WEB: www.south-metro.org
SIC: 8322 8361 Individual & family social services; home for the mentally handicapped

(G-8974)
SOUTHEAST ASIAN HEALTH SVCS
421 Dale St N Ste B (55103-2225)
PHONE..............................651 222-2889
Shong Yang, *President*
EMP: 180 EST: 1995
SQ FT: 7,000
SALES (est): 5MM-9.9MM **Privately Held**
SIC: 8082 Home health care services

(G-8975)
SP HOTELS LLC
411 Minnesota St (55101-1703)
PHONE..............................651 291-8800
Jelene Drayna, *Manager*
EMP: 50
SALES (est): 1MM-4.9MM **Privately Held**
SIC: 7011 Hostel

(G-8976)
SPECTRUM SOLUTIONS INC
2920 Centre Pointe Dr (55113-1182)
PHONE..............................651 634-1800
FAX: 651 634-1566
John Dargiewicz, *Vice Pres*
Tom Hall, *Vice Pres*
Mark Johnson, *Purch Mgr*
Thomas Brue, *Engineering*
Howard McCoy, *Engineering*
EMP: 30
SALES (est): 10MM-24.9MM **Privately Held**
SIC: 5065 1731 7629 Wholesales telephone equipment; telephone equipment installation; telecommunication equipment repair service
PA: Spectrum Solutions Inc
7801 E Bush Lake Rd # 210
Minneapolis MN 55439
952 835-8338

(G-8977)
SPEEDWAY SUPERAMERICA LLC
390 Maryland Ave E (55130-3624)
PHONE..............................651 774-7270
FAX: 651 776-0683
Jeremy Davis, *Manager*
Keith Edlund, *Manager*
EMP: 25
SQ FT: 35,283
SALES (est): 10MM-24.9MM **Publicly Held**
WEB: www.speedwaynet.com
SIC: 1311 Crude petroleum production
DH: Speedway SuperAmerica LLC
500 Speedway Dr
Enon OH 45323
937 864-3000

(G-8978)
SPIRE FEDERAL CREDIT UNION
2025 Larpenteur Ave W (55113-5512)
PHONE..............................651 215-3500
Daniel Stoltz, *President*
Cheri Komarek, *Accountant*
EMP: 80 EST: 1934
SALES (est): 10MM-24.9MM **Privately Held**
SIC: 6061 Federally chartered credit union

(G-8979)
SPRIGGS PLUMBING & HEATING INC
124 Eva St (55107-1401)
PHONE..............................651 224-5616
FAX: 651 228-9877
Michael R Dobihal, *President*
EMP: 25 EST: 1908
SQ FT: 10,200
SALES (est): 1MM-4.9MM **Privately Held**
SIC: 1711 Plumbing service; heating & air conditioning contractor; process piping contractor

(G-8980)
SSAB ENTERPRISES LLC
2500 County Road B W (55113-3890)
PO Box 64303 (55164-0303)
PHONE..............................651 631-9031
Dayton Barkley, *Sales Mgr*
John Gosack, *Info Tech Dir*
EMP: 50
SALES (est): 25MM-49.9MM **Privately Held**
SIC: 5051 Wholesales steel
HQ: Ssab Enterprises LLC
801 Warrenville Rd Ste 800
Lisle IL 60532
630 810-4800

(G-8981)
ST ANTHONY PARK HOME INC
2237 Commonwealth Ave (55108-1602)
PHONE..............................651 646-7486
FAX: 651 646-7486
John Barker, *President*
EMP: 90 EST: 1991
SQ FT: 35,000
SALES (est): 1MM-4.9MM **Privately Held**
WEB: www.stanthonyparkhome.com
SIC: 8051 Skilled nursing care facility

(G-8982)
ST CROIX VALLEY HARDWOODS INC
4250 Otter Lake Rd (55110-3763)
PHONE..............................651 407-2800
FAX: 651 407-2801
Greg Pendy, *General Mgr*
Paul Staples, *General Mgr*
Richard Johnson, *Vice Pres*
Scott Ross, *Manager*
Jan Frazee, *Manager*
EMP: 35
SALES (est): 10MM-24.9MM **Privately Held**
WEB: www.scvh.com
SIC: 5031 Wholesales rough, dressed & finished lumber; wholesales particleboard; manufactures hardwood furniture stock & parts
PA: St Croix Valley Hardwoods Inc
4250 Otter Lake Rd
Saint Paul MN 55110
651 407-2800

(G-8983)
ST CROIX VALLEY HARDWOODS INC (PA)
4250 Otter Lake Rd (55110-3763)
PO Box 120, Luck WI (54853-0120)
PHONE..............................651 407-2800
Gordon Fick, *President*
Paul Staples, *General Mgr*
EMP: 60 EST: 1981
SQ FT: 77,000 **Privately Held**
WEB: www.scvh.com
SIC: 5031 Manufactures hardwood furniture stock & parts; wholesales particleboard; wholesales plywood; millwork

(G-8984)
ST JAMES CHURCH INC
749 Juno Ave (55102-3819)
PHONE..............................651 293-3945
FAX: 651 227-1881
Dennis Dempsey, *Pastor*
Jennifer Brown, *Sales Executive*
Susan Peterson, *Director*
EMP: 30 EST: 1981
SALES (est): 500-999K **Privately Held**
SIC: 8351 Child day care service

(G-8985)
ST JUDE MEDICAL
1410 Energy Park Dr (55108-5266)
PHONE..............................651 523-6900
FAX: 651 647-9464
Richard Omilanowicz, *Vice Pres*
Ron Johnson, *Facilities Mgr*
Bruce Schmidt, *Purchasing*
Linda Klein, *Accountant*
Kevin Dillion, *Marketing Staff*
EMP: 30
SALES (est): 1MM-4.9MM **Privately Held**
SIC: 8099 Health & allied services

(G-8986)
ST JUDE MEDICAL SC INC
1 Lillehei Plz (55117-1761)
PHONE..............................651 483-2000
Terry L Shepherd, *Ch of Bd*
Pamela S Krop, *Corp Secy*
Daniel J Starks, *COO*
Angela Craig, *Vice Pres*
Ronald Spielberger, *Vice Pres*
EMP: 350 EST: 1976
SALES (est): 100MM-499.9MM **Publicly Held**
WEB: www.sjm.com
SIC: 5047 Wholesales medical equipment & supplies
PA: St Jude Medical Inc
1 Saint Jude Medical Dr
Saint Paul MN 55117
651 756-2000

(G-8987)
ST PAUL CARDIOLOGY
17 Exchange St W Ste 750 (55102-1036)
PHONE..............................651 232-4320
Kim M Loria MD, *Partner*
EMP: 40 EST: 2001
SALES (est): 1MM-4.9MM **Privately Held**
SIC: 8011 Cardiologist & cardio-vascular specialist

(G-8988)
ST PAUL EYE CLINIC
393 Dunlap St N Ste 861 (55104-4204)
PHONE..............................651 641-0457
FAX: 651 641-0704
Stan Nichols, *President*
H J Drannen, *Administrator*
EMP: 35
SALES (est): 1MM-4.9MM **Privately Held**
SIC: 8011 Ophthalmologist office

(G-8989)
ST PAUL FIRE & MARINE INSCE
408 Saint Peter St Ste 300 (55102-1123)
PHONE..............................651 310-5000
Archie Mrkvicka, *Manager*
Archie Kvicka, *Manager*
Jeff Miles, *Consultant*
Dawn Clarin, *Info Tech Mgr*
Cindy Clarin, *Info Tech Mgr*
EMP: 300
SALES (est): 100MM-499.9MM **Publicly Held**

www.HarrisInfo.com
388

2011 Harris Minnesota
Services Directory

▲=Import ▼=Export
◆=Import/Export

WEB: www.stpaul.com
SIC: 6331 6351 Provides property damage insurance; provides liability insurance
HQ: St Paul Fire & Marine Insce
385 Washington St
Saint Paul MN 55102
651 221-7911

(G-8990)
ST PAUL FIRE & MARINE INSCE (HQ)
385 Washington St (55102-1309)
PHONE..................651 221-7911
FAX: 651 223-3247
Douglas Leatherdale, *President*
Sandra Ulsaker-Wiese, *Corp Secy*
Paul Ziccarelli, *Corp Secy*
Tom Bradley, *Exec VP*
Gary Hanson, *Senior VP*
EMP: 6347 EST: 1925
SQ FT: 450,000
SALES (corp-wide): 24.68B Publicly Held
WEB: www.stpaul.com
SIC: 6331 6321 6351 Property & casualty insurance carrier; 6321 6351 Property & casualty insurance carrier; automobile insurance carrier; worker's compensation insurance carrier; accident & health reinsurance carriers; surety reinsurance carrier; accident & health insurance carrier service
PA: Travelers Co's Inc
485 Lexington Ave
New York NY 10017
917 778-6000

(G-8991)
ST PAUL GUARDIAN INSURANCE CO
385 Washington St (55102-1309)
PHONE..................651 221-7911
Jay Fishman, *CEO*
Bruce A Backberg, *Corp Secy*
Edward Gerber, *Corp Secy*
Jerome Simon, *Corp Secy*
Paul Liska, *Exec VP*
EMP: 1000 EST: 1970
SALES (est): 100MM-499.9MM Publicly Held
WEB: www.stpaul.com
SIC: 6331 Provides property damage insurance; fire, marine & casualty insurance & carriers
HQ: St Paul Fire & Marine Insce
385 Washington St
Saint Paul MN 55102
651 221-7911

(G-8992)
ST PAUL HEART CLINIC (PA)
225 Smith Ave N Ste 500 (55102-2545)
PHONE..................651 292-0616
Thomas Johnson, *President*
Thomas Wiberg MD, *COO*
Richard Brody MD, *Vice Pres*
Nazifa Sajady MD, *Vice Pres*
Stuart Adler MD, *Vice Pres*
EMP: 140 EST: 1976 Privately Held
SIC: 8011 Cardiologist & cardio-vascular specialist

(G-8993)
ST PAUL HEART CLINIC
1600 Saint Johns Blvd Ste 200 (55109-1190)
PHONE..................651 779-9449
Dave Rothschiller, *Director*
Spencer H Kubo, *Cardiology*
Tarang Ray, *Cardiology*
Uma Valeti, *Cardiology*
Salima Shafi, *Cardiology*
EMP: 300
SALES (est): 25MM-49.9MM Privately Held
SIC: 8011 Cardiologist & cardio-vascular specialist
PA: St Paul Heart Clinic
225 Smith Ave N Ste 500
Saint Paul MN 55102
651 292-0616

(G-8994)
ST PAUL MERCURY INSURANCE CO
385 Washington St (55102-1309)
PHONE..................651 221-7911
Douglas W Leatherdale, *Ch of Bd*
James Gustafson, *President*
Bruce A Backberg, *Corp Secy*

Thomas Bradley, *Senior VP*
Gary P Hanson, *Senior VP*
EST: 1964 Publicly Held
WEB: www.stpaul.com
SIC: 6331 Provides property damage insurance; automobile insurance carrier; fire, marine & casualty insurance & carriers
HQ: St Paul Fire & Marine Insce
385 Washington St
Saint Paul MN 55102
651 221-7911

(G-8995)
ST PAUL PLUMBERS JOINT ✪
235 Marshall Ave (55102-1807)
PHONE..................651 846-1389
Rick Gale, *Principal*
Robert Widerski, *Principal*
EMP: 25 EST: 2008
SALES (est): 1MM-4.9MM Privately Held
SIC: 1711 Plumbing service

(G-8996)
ST PAUL PLUMBING & HEATING CO
Also Called: Minneapolis Plumbing & Heating
640 Grand Ave (55105-3402)
PHONE..................651 228-9200
David Smith, *President*
Wayne Johnson, *Business Mgr*
Tamera Mathews, *Manager*
EMP: 50 EST: 1918
SQ FT: 3,000
SALES (est): 5MM-9.9MM Privately Held
WEB: www.stpaulplumbing.com
SIC: 1711 Warm air heating & air conditioning contractor; plumbing service

(G-8997)
ST PAUL POSTAL EMPLOYEES
Also Called: Postal Credit Union
2401 McKnight Rd N (55109-2211)
PHONE..................651 770-7000
FAX: 651 773-2901
Russell Plunkett, *President*
Daniel Blees, *Corp Secy*
D Nelson, *Corp Secy*
Dennis R Bauer, *Vice Pres*
Sue Miggler, *Manager*
EMP: 47 EST: 1926
SQ FT: 22,000
SALES (est): 5MM-9.9MM Privately Held
SIC: 6062 State credit unions

(G-8998)
ST PAUL RADIOLOGY (PA)
166 4th St E Ste 100 (55101-1474)
PHONE..................651 292-2000
Mark Kleinschmidt, *CEO*
Fred Sparks, *Facilities Mgr*
Martha Olzenak, *Purchasing*
Gerald Gehling, *Controller*
Theresa Hazen, *Insur/Bill Sup*
EMP: 100 EST: 1967
SQ FT: 5,000
SALES (corp-wide): 50M Privately Held
SIC: 8011 Radiologist office

(G-8999)
ST PAUL RADIOLOGY
Also Called: Midwest MRI
250 Thompson St (55102-2370)
PHONE..................651 297-6504
FAX: 651 297-6510
Shane Kim, *General Mgr*
Mark Tleinschmidt, *Sales & Mktg St*
Michael M Uel, *Med Doctor*
Linda Meinke, *Info Tech Mgr*
Brion Fornshell, *IT/INT Sup*
EMP: 60
SQ FT: 7,000
SALES (est): 5MM-9.9MM Privately Held
SIC: 8071 Dental & medical X-ray laboratory
PA: St Paul Radiology
166 4th St E Ste 100
Saint Paul MN 55101
651 292-2000

(G-9000)
ST PAUL YOUTH SERVICES
2100 Wilson Ave (55119-4034)
PHONE..................651 771-1301
Anita Keyes, *Corp Secy*
Chuck Hoistad, *Treasurer*

Colleen Mold, *Manager*
David Wilmes, *Director*
Mary Hartman, *Director*
EMP: 26 EST: 1972
SQ FT: 3,000
SALES (est): 1MM-4.9MM Privately Held
SIC: 8322 Child & youth services

(G-9001)
ST PAUL'S CHILDHOOD CENTER
900 Summit Ave (55105-3029)
PHONE..................651 224-4749
FAX: 651 224-9981
Stephanie West, *Manager*
Kelly Sadlovsky, *Exec Dir*
Tara Hollberg, *Exec Dir*
EMP: 45 EST: 1970
SALES (est): 1MM-4.9MM Privately Held
WEB: www.stpaulschildhoodcenter.com
SIC: 8351 Child day care service

(G-9002)
ST PAULS SAINTS BASEBALL CLUB
1771 Energy Park Dr (55108-2720)
PHONE..................651 644-6659
Michael Beck, *President*
Bill Fanning, *General Mgr*
Leesa Anderson, *Business Mgr*
Derek Sharrer, *Vice Pres*
Thomas Whaley, *Vice Pres*
EMP: 150 EST: 1996
SQ FT: 10,000
SALES (est): 25MM-49.9MM Privately Held
SIC: 7941 Baseball club

(G-9003)
STAN KOCH & SONS TRUCKING INC
Also Called: Koch Logistics
2230 Energy Park Dr (55108-1511)
PHONE..................651 999-8500
Carrie Torreson, *Opers Mgr*
Mark Davis, *Opers Mgr*
Tom Torreson, *Branch Mgr*
Paul Grothe, *Info Tech Dir*
Bruce Waslie, *Info Tech Mgr*
EMP: 50
SALES (est): 5MM-9.9MM Privately Held
WEB: www.kochcompanies.com
SIC: 4213 4731 Over the road trucking; freight transportation arrangement services
PA: Stan Koch & Sons Trucking Inc
4200 Dahlberg Dr Ste 100
Minneapolis MN 55422
763 302-5400

(G-9004)
STANLEY SECURITY SOLUTIONS INC
Also Called: Best Access Systems
537 Phalen Blvd (55130-5303)
PHONE..................952 894-3830
Marta Vosberg, *Manager*
Jim Zinsmaster, *Exec Dir*
EMP: 30 Publicly Held
WEB: www.bestlock.com
SIC: 5072 5099 Manufactures locks; wholesales hardware; wholesales locks & lock sets
HQ: Stanley Security Solutions Inc
6161 E 75th St
Indianapolis IN 46250
317 849-2250

(G-9005)
STERICYCLE INC
742 Vandalia St (55114-1303)
PHONE..................651 641-0009
Jim Welch, *Project Mgr*
Jason Ritt, *Facilities Mgr*
Neal Beenenga, *Manager*
EMP: 50
SALES (est): 5MM-9.9MM Publicly Held
WEB: www.stericycle.com
SIC: 4953 Refuse systems services
PA: Stericycle Inc
28161 N Keith Dr
Lake Forest IL 60045
847 367-5910

(G-9006)
STOCKBRIDGE INSURANCE CO (PA)
2 Pine Tree Dr (55112-3715)
PHONE..................651 631-7000
John Blockburn, *President*
Joe Pingatone, *Vice Pres*
Stephen L Rohde, *Treasurer*
Lisa Cortez, *Property Mgr*
EMP: 566 EST: 1919
SQ FT: 240,000
SALES (corp-wide): 259K Privately Held
WEB: www.msi-insurance.com
SIC: 6411 Insurance services

(G-9007)
STOCKMAN HOTEL CORP
Also Called: Matagorda Ht & Conference Ctr
4730 White Bear Pkwy (55110-3483)
PHONE..................651 636-1171
Kevin Ali, *President*
Terry R Stockman, *President*
Michael Stockman, *Corp Secy*
EMP: 50 EST: 1991
SALES (est): 1MM-4.9MM Privately Held
SIC: 7011 Hotel

(G-9008)
STOLTZ DRY CLEANERS INC
1580 Grand Ave (55105-2227)
PHONE..................651 698-0120
FAX: 651 696-1118
Joel Tracey, *President*
Lynn Tracey, *Vice Pres*
EMP: 25 EST: 1961
SQ FT: 6,000
SALES (est): 500-999K Privately Held
SIC: 7216 7219 Dry cleaning plant; tailor shop

(G-9009)
STORK UNITED CORP
662 Cromwell Ave (55114-1720)
PHONE..................651 645-3601
FAX: 651 659-7207
Matt Horton, *COO*
J Doehring, *Manager*
Brian Provan, *Exec Dir*
EMP: 90
SALES (est): 5MM-9.9MM Privately Held
WEB: www.storkgroup.com
SIC: 7389 8734 Personal service agents; testing laboratory
PA: Stork Materials Technology
Czaar Peterstraat 229
Amsterdam Netherlands

(G-9010)
STRUCTURAL WOOD CORP
4000 Labore Rd (55110-4168)
PHONE..................651 426-8111
Vernon G Schumacher, *CEO*
James G Schumacher, *President*
Curtis Erickson, *Corp Secy*
Kent Smith, *Maint Mgr*
Kim Pechman, *Purchasing*
EMP: 46 EST: 1966
SQ FT: 72,000
SALES (est): 10MM-24.9MM Privately Held
WEB: www.structural-wood.com
SIC: 6512 5031 5033 Nonresidential building operator; manufactures building & structural wood members; treats wood structural lumber & timber; wholesales rough, dressed & finished lumber; wholesales roofing & siding materials

(G-9011)
SUBURBAN AUTO BODY INC
Also Called: Saxons
1100 Silver Lake Rd NW (55112-6325)
PHONE..................651 983-4438
Mike Edrick, *Branch Mgr*
EMP: 25
SALES (est): 1MM-4.9MM Privately Held
SIC: 7532 Automotive body shop; automotive paint shop
PA: Suburban Auto Body Inc
2989 Country Dr
Saint Paul MN 55117
651 633-8900

(G-9012)
SUMMIT FIRE PROTECTION CO (PA)
575 Minnehaha Ave W (55103-1573)
PHONE..............................651 251-1880
John J Evrard, *CEO*
Quintin Rubald, *President*
Summit Fire, *Vice Pres*
Paul C Rascher, *Vice Pres*
Lonny J Binder, *CFO*
EMP: 170 **EST:** 1999
SQ FT: 50,000 **Privately Held**
WEB: www.summitfire.com
SIC: 1711 Fire sprinkler system installation service

(G-9013)
SUMMIT LANDMARK ORTHOPEDICS
17 Exchange St W Ste 307 (55102-1223)
PHONE..............................651 842-5200
Jack Drogt MD, *Principal*
Paul T Yellin, *Vice Pres*
Howard Mamstead, *Manager*
Howard Malmestad, *Manager*
Emily Engler, *Admin Mgr*
EMP: 140 **EST:** 1988
SQ FT: 7,400
SALES (est): 10MM-24.9MM **Privately Held**
SIC: 8011 Orthopedic physician office

(G-9014)
SUN BEAR SPA & TAN INC
2207 3rd St (55110-3212)
PHONE..............................651 426-5884
FAX: 651 426-5069
Christina Rauch, *President*
Emily Knieff, *Manager*
EMP: 50 **EST:** 1996
SALES (est): 1MM-4.9MM **Privately Held**
SIC: 7991 Spas

(G-9015)
SUNRISE HAIR STYLING&TANNING
2043 County Road E E (55110-4751)
PHONE..............................651 777-2344
FAX: 651 777-2344
Mark Danielson, *Owner*
Terri Andrews, *General Mgr*
EMP: 25 **EST:** 1996
SALES (est): 500-999K **Privately Held**
SIC: 7231 7241 Beauty salon; barber shop

(G-9016)
SUPERIOR BROKERAGE SERVICES
1700 Wynne Ave (55108-2708)
PHONE..............................651 256-1555
Paul Goff, *President*
Mark Kittel, *Vice Pres*
Gregory Schomer, *CFO*
James Hilgert, *VP Finance*
EMP: 45 **EST:** 1998
SQ FT: 15,000
SALES (est): 5MM-9.9MM **Privately Held**
WEB: www.sbs-intl.com
SIC: 4731 Foreign freight forwarding services

(G-9017)
SUR LA RUE INC
1174 Breen St (55106-2909)
PHONE..............................651 772-4957
Steve Kruc, *Manager*
Mary Suek, *Manager*
EMP: 30
SALES (est): 1MM-4.9MM **Privately Held**
WEB: www.surlarue.com
SIC: 8361 Home for the mentally handicapped
PA: Sur La Rue Inc
    305 Roselawn Ave E # 1200
    Saint Paul MN 55117
    651 772-4957

(G-9018)
SUZANNE'S CUISINE
1046 Portland Ave (55104-7010)
PHONE..............................651 726-2535
Harry Pihl, *President*
EMP: 40 **EST:** 1976
SALES (est): 1MM-4.9MM **Privately Held**

SIC: 7299 Caterer; banquet hall facility

(G-9019)
SWEATSHOP INC
167 Snelling Ave N (55104-6747)
PHONE..............................651 646-8418
Gayle Winegar, *President*
Katherine Kline, *Personnel*
Kathy Nordstrom, *Manager*
Sarah McKim, *Manager*
Jill Winegar, *Director*
EMP: 29 **EST:** 1987
SQ FT: 13,000
SALES (est): 500-999K **Privately Held**
WEB: www.sweatshopfitness.com
SIC: 7991 Health club

(G-9020)
SYMANTEC CORP
2815 Cleveland Ave N (55113-1124)
PHONE..............................651 746-7000
FAX: 651 746-7010
Doug Paunsch, *Vice Pres*
Brice Avila, *Engineer*
Steve Mackey, *Engineering*
Michael Stagg, *Branch Mgr*
Dick Goter, *Manager*
EMP: 500
SALES (est): 100MM-499.9MM **Publicly Held**
WEB: www.symantec.com
SIC: 7372 Business & professional software publishers
PA: Symantec Corp
    350 Ellis St
    Mountain View CA 94043
    650 527-8000

(G-9021)
SYSCO ASIAN FOODS INC
1300 L Orient St (55117-3995)
PHONE..............................651 558-2400
FAX: 651 724-1377
Frank Hamel, *President*
Mike Neira, *General Mgr*
Brian Neumueller, *General Mgr*
Twila M Day, *Assistant VP*
Jerry Barash, *Vice Pres*
▲ **EMP:** 200 **EST:** 1985
SQ FT: 60,000
SALES (est): 100MM-499.9MM **Publicly Held**
SIC: 5149 Wholesales groceries
PA: SYSCO Corp
    1390 Enclave Pkwy
    Houston TX 77077
    281 584-1390

(G-9022)
T C FIELD & CO
530 Robert St N (55101-2210)
PO Box 64016 (55164-0016)
PHONE..............................651 227-8405
FAX: 651 227-0507
Litton Field Jr, *President*
Wendy A Demotts, *Corp Secy*
Julie R Cain, *Corp Secy*
Susan C Converse, *Vice Pres*
Marjorie A Jones, *Vice Pres*
EMP: 32 **EST:** 1912
SQ FT: 9,750
SALES (est): 1MM-4.9MM **Privately Held**
WEB: www.tcfield.com
SIC: 6411 Insurance agent; life insurance agent; property & casualty insurance agent

(G-9023)
T C SWEATSHOP INC
167 Snelling Ave N (55104-6747)
PHONE..............................651 646-8418
Gayle Winegar, *President*
EMP: 30 **EST:** 1983
SQ FT: 250
SALES (est): 1MM-4.9MM **Privately Held**
SIC: 7041 8741 Residence club for organizations; business management services

(G-9024)
T DISTRIBUTION INC (PA)
1880 Oakcrest Ave (55113-2602)
PHONE..............................651 636-6367
Richard Thompson, *CEO*
Tracy Goldman, *Manager*
Heidi Schotzko, *Manager*
Dale Goetzke, *MIS Mgr*

EMP: 30 **EST:** 2004
SQ FT: 500,000 **Privately Held**
WEB: www.tcmoulding.com
SIC: 5023 Wholesales frames & framing; wholesales decorative home furnishings & supplies; retails art, picture frames & decorations

(G-9025)
T GEORGE & ASSOCIATES
411 Lexington Pkwy N Ste G (55104-4615)
PO Box 22066 (55122-0066)
PHONE..............................651 647-0900
Tom George, *Owner*
EMP: 25 **EST:** 1996
SALES (est): 500-999K **Privately Held**
WEB: www.tgeorge.net
SIC: 7381 Detective services

(G-9026)
TALON INVESTIGATION LTD
1538 White Bear Ave N Ste 206 (55106-1612)
PO Box 600058 (55106-0001)
PHONE..............................651 774-6977
FAX: 651 771-1576
Scott Hielsberg, *Partner*
Carlos Baires, *Partner*
EMP: 30 **EST:** 1995
SALES (est): 500-999K **Privately Held**
WEB: www.taloninvestigation.com
SIC: 7381 8111 Security guard service; legal services

(G-9027)
TCF NATIONAL BANK
405 Robert St N Ste 220 (55101-2005)
PHONE..............................651 291-4095
FAX: 651 291-4048
Shannon Hatch, *Manager*
EMP: 42
SALES (est): 10MM-24.9MM **Publicly Held**
WEB: www.merrilliron.com
SIC: 6035 Federal savings & loan association
HQ: TCF National Bank
    801 Marquette Ave
    Minneapolis MN 55402
    612 661-6500

(G-9028)
TCF NATIONAL BANK
1988 Suburban Ave (55119-7001)
PHONE..............................651 735-6510
FAX: 651 735-8050
Robert Anderson, *Manager*
Renee Wollin, *Manager*
EMP: 25
SALES (est): 5MM-9.9MM **Publicly Held**
WEB: www.merrilliron.com
SIC: 6035 Federal savings & loan association
HQ: TCF National Bank
    801 Marquette Ave
    Minneapolis MN 55402
    612 661-6500

(G-9029)
TCF NATIONAL BANK
2989 White Bear Ave N (55109-1314)
PHONE..............................651 770-2273
FAX: 651 770-7035
Cecilia Jaap, *Finance Other*
Brian Schulte, *Manager*
EMP: 28
SALES (est): 5MM-9.9MM **Publicly Held**
WEB: www.merrilliron.com
SIC: 6035 Federal savings & loan association
HQ: TCF National Bank
    801 Marquette Ave
    Minneapolis MN 55402
    612 661-6500

(G-9030)
TEAM INFORMATICS INC (PA)
3900 Northwoods Dr Ste 350 (55112-6971)
PHONE..............................651 222-8326
Dave Shannon, *CEO*
George Wilson, *Opers Mgr*
Craig Johnson, *CFO*
Tami Balfanz, *Finance Mgr*
Nora Lee, *Office Mgr*

EMP: 35 **EST:** 2001
SQ FT: 4,000 **Privately Held**
WEB: www.teaminformatics.com
SIC: 7371 Computer software development

(G-9031)
TEAM USA MORTGAGE LLC
546 Rice St Ste 200 (55103-2164)
PHONE..............................651 848-0484
Lon Firchau, *Member*
EMP: 75 **EST:** 2003
SALES (est): 5MM-9.9MM **Privately Held**
SIC: 6162 Mortgage & loan lending

(G-9032)
TECH-PRO INC
3000 Centre Pointe Dr (55113-1122)
PHONE..............................651 634-1400
FAX: 651 634-1499
Dave Vadis, *President*
Jim Ericson, *Vice Pres*
Stacy Case, *Accountant*
David Jadwin, *MIS Mgr*
Hari Venkatachalam, *Programmer Anys*
EMP: 300 **EST:** 1989
SQ FT: 12,000
SALES (est): 25MM-49.9MM **Privately Held**
WEB: www.tech-pro.com
SIC: 7379 7371 Computer system consulting services; custom computer software systems analysis & design service

(G-9033)
TECHNOLOGY & INFORMATION
Also Called: T I E S
1667 Snelling Ave N (55108-2131)
PHONE..............................651 999-6001
FAX: 651 999-6099
Mike Turritto, *Transportation*
Del Jentz, *Accountant*
Scott Morton, *Manager*
Kathy Johnson, *Manager*
Lee Whitcraft, *Exec Dir*
EMP: 90 **EST:** 1967
SQ FT: 125,000
SALES (est): 10MM-24.9MM **Privately Held**
WEB: www.juit.ac.in
SIC: 7371 Computer software development & applications

(G-9034)
TECH RESTORATION SERVICES INC
192 9th St W Ste 200 (55102-1027)
PHONE..............................651 292-9638
Gordon H Reigstad, *President*
Eunice Hopkins, *Treasurer*
Alan Booth, *Director*
EMP: 30 **EST:** 1987
SQ FT: 2,000
SALES (est): 1MM-4.9MM **Privately Held**
WEB: www.techrestoration.com
SIC: 1771 1799 Parking lot construction; parking lot maintenance service

(G-9035)
TECHSCAN CORP
Also Called: Densei USA
85 2nd Ave SE Ste G (55112-7813)
PHONE..............................651 636-3030
Richard Sawyer, *President*
Kuniyoshi Koba, *General Mgr*
Alicia Sawyer, *CFO*
EST: 1998
SQ FT: 4,400 **Privately Held**
WEB: www.techscancorp.com
SIC: 5065 Wholesales electronic parts & equipment

(G-9036)
TEMPLE OF AARON SISTERHOOD
616 Mississippi River Blvd S (55116-1062)
PHONE..............................651 698-8874
FAX: 651 698-3000
Gary Schurtz, *President*
Barbara Gitlin, *President*
Marilyn Fink, *President*
Etta Lambright, *Treasurer*
EMP: 40 **EST:** 1912 **Privately Held**
SIC: 8399 Non-fee basis fund raising organization; retail gift shop

▲=Import ▼=Export
◆=Import/Export

(G-9037)

TENA CO'S INC
251 W Lafayette Frontage Rd
(55107-1628)
PHONE...........................651 293-1234
FAX: 651 293-4400
Terry Schopfer, *President*
Jerry Bothun, *Senior VP*
Tomas M Donough, *Senior VP*
Diane O'Leary, *Senior VP*
Jerome Ree, *Senior VP*
EMP: 130 **EST:** 1981
SQ FT: 14,070
SALES (est): 10MM-24.9MM **Privately Held**
WEB: www.tenaco.com
SIC: 8742 7323 Real estate consultant; credit reporting services

(G-9038)

TENACIOUS HOLDINGS INC
1021 Bandana Blvd E (55108-5113)
PHONE...........................651 642-9889
Thomas F Votel, *CEO*
Mark B Lindstrom, *Vice Pres*
Richard C McNeely, *Vice Pres*
Gregg Schrab, *Opers-Prdtn-Mfg*
Howard Huber, *Sales/Mktg Mgr*
EMP: 250 **EST:** 1983
SQ FT: 15,000
SALES (est): 100MM-499.9MM **Privately Held**
WEB: www.ergodyne.com
SIC: 5099 Wholesales safety equipment & supplies

(G-9039)

TERMINAL TRANSPORT INC
2982 Cleveland Ave N (55113-1101)
PHONE...........................651 407-6200
FAX: 651 407-6300
Brent B Coatney, *President*
Michelle Willkoom, *Human Resources*
EMP: 70 **EST:** 1961
SQ FT: 11,000
SALES (est): 5MM-9.9MM **Privately Held**
WEB: www.trmnl.com
SIC: 4213 Over the road trucking

(G-9040)

TERRACON CONSULTANTS INC
3535 Hoffman Rd E (55110-5376)
PHONE...........................651 770-1500
FAX: 651 770-1657
David Wolfgram, *Project Mgr*
Tom Gapinske, *Manager*
Jere Strickland, *Manager*
Karen Martinez, *Admin Asst*
EMP: 30
SALES (est): 1MM-4.9MM **Privately Held**
SIC: 8711 Engineering services
PA: Terracon Consultants Inc
   18001 W 106th St Ste 300
   Olathe KS 66061
   913 599-6886

(G-9041)

THERMO KING SALES & SERVICE
1951 Old Highway 8 NW (55112-1826)
PHONE...........................651 633-2820
FAX: 651 633-5113
Jerry Berg, *General Mgr*
Loren Lorig, *General Mgr*
Daniel T Santarsiero, *Chairman*
Gayle Santarsiero, *Corp Secy*
Lynn Ostlund, *Controller*
◆ **EMP:** 29 **EST:** 1962
SQ FT: 32,000
SALES (est): 10MM-24.9MM **Privately Held**
SIC: 5078 7623 Wholesales motor vehicle refrigeration units; refrigeration repair service

(G-9042)

THOMSON REUTERS LLC
30 7th St E Ste 2900 (55101-2988)
PHONE...........................651 846-2000
FAX: 651 846-2022
Christopher Moran, *Manager*
EMP: 45
SALES (est): 5MM-9.9MM **Publicly Held**
WEB: www.reuters.com

SIC: 7371 Computer programming service
HQ: Thomson Reuters LLC
   3 Times Sq
   New York NY 10036
   646 223-4000

(G-9043)

3608 PARK STREET LLC (DH)
Also Called: St Paul Hotel
385 Washington St (55102-1309)
PHONE...........................651 221-7911
James C Adams, *President*
Mark R Hagen, *Vice Pres*
Wayne Hoeschen, *Vice Pres*
William R Insea, *Vice Pres*
R W Inserra, *Vice Pres*
EST: 2002
SALES (corp-wide): 24.68B **Publicly Held**
WEB: www.stpaul.com
SIC: 7011 Hotel; cocktail lounge; eating place
HQ: St Paul Fire & Marine Insce
   385 Washington St
   Saint Paul MN 55102
   651 221-7911

(G-9044)

3M CO
3M Center Bldg 223SW08 (55144-1000)
PHONE...........................651 733-2147
Kevin Kuck, *Branch Mgr*
EMP: 240
SALES (est): 100MM-499.9MM **Publicly Held**
WEB: www.mmm.com
SIC: 5045 5065 Wholesales computers, peripherals & software; wholesales electronic parts & equipment
PA: 3M Co
   3M Center Bldg 22011W02
   Saint Paul MN 55144
   651 733-1110

(G-9045)

3M CO
690 Bayfield St (55107-1002)
PHONE...........................651 778-5302
Donald Thune, *Engrg Mgr*
Daniel Brunsvold, *Manager*
EMP: 60
SALES (est): 10MM-24.9MM **Publicly Held**
WEB: www.mmm.com
SIC: 4522 Nonscheduled passenger air transportation services
PA: 3M Co
   3M Center Bldg 22011W02
   Saint Paul MN 55144
   651 733-1110

(G-9046)

3M CO
3M Ctr Bldg 2756SW01 (55144-0001)
PO Box 33275 (55133-3275)
PHONE...........................651 736-3490
Charles Reich, *Div Sub Head*
Herman Mauwaerts, *Vice Pres*
Robert Harms, *Purch Dir*
Rj Haggerty, *Mktg Dir*
S L O'Donne, *Manager*
EMP: 110
SALES (est): 10MM-24.9MM **Publicly Held**
WEB: www.mmm.com
SIC: 8021 Manufactures surgical appliances & supplies; dentists' office & clinic
PA: 3M Co
   3M Center Bldg 22011W02
   Saint Paul MN 55144
   651 733-1110

(G-9047)

3M CO
3M Center Bldg 223 (55144-1000)
PHONE...........................651 733-5300
S Landwehr, *Vice Pres*
EMP: 80
SALES (est): 10MM-24.9MM **Publicly Held**
WEB: www.mmm.com
SIC: 5013 8732 Manufactures stamped automotive products; commercial nonphysical research laboratory; wholesales new motor vehicle parts & supplies
PA: 3M Co
   3M Center Bldg 22011W02
   Saint Paul MN 55144
   651 733-1110

(G-9048)

3M CO
3M Center Bldg 2755E01 (55144-1000)
PHONE...........................651 733-1110
Brandon Cordts, *Project Mgr*
Brian Hoovestol, *Project Mgr*
Bonnie Lemere, *Project Mgr*
Al Darpa, *Project Mgr*
Barbara Kruzic, *Project Mgr*
EMP: 25
SALES (est): 1MM-4.9MM **Publicly Held**
WEB: www.mmm.com
SIC: 8742 Management consulting services
PA: 3M Co
   3M Center Bldg 22011W02
   Saint Paul MN 55144
   651 733-1110

(G-9049)

3M CO
3 M Ctr Bldg 2233N05 (55144-0001)
PHONE...........................651 733-8432
J J Maskas, *Branch Mgr*
Brian Palkovich, *Manager*
Scott McClure, *IT/INT Sup*
EMP: 31
SALES (est): 5MM-9.9MM **Publicly Held**
WEB: www.mmm.com
SIC: 5113 Manufactures coated & laminated paper; wholesales industrial & personal service paper
PA: 3M Co
   3M Center Bldg 22011W02
   Saint Paul MN 55144
   651 733-1110

(G-9050)

3M CO
3M Center (55144-1000)
PHONE...........................651 733-2008
H C Shin, *Manager*
EMP: 50
SALES (est): 10MM-24.9MM **Publicly Held**
WEB: www.mmm.com
SIC: 5085 Manufactures abrasive products; wholesales industrial abrasives
PA: 3M Co
   3M Center Bldg 22011W02
   Saint Paul MN 55144
   651 733-1110

(G-9051)

3M CO
3M Center Bldg 2253S05 (55144-1000)
PHONE...........................651 733-3929
C E Harstad, *Principal*
Tom Framer, *Manager*
EMP: 200
SALES (est): 10MM-24.9MM **Publicly Held**
WEB: www.mmm.com
SIC: 8732 Market analysis or research services
PA: 3M Co
   3M Center Bldg 22011W02
   Saint Paul MN 55144
   651 733-1110

(G-9052)

3M CO
3M Center (55144-1000)
PO Box 33225 (55133-3225)
PHONE...........................651 736-9682
J B Seropian, *Manager*
Ej Anderson, *Manager*
Lanny Moyer, *Manager*
N J Bidermann, *Manager*
EMP: 140
SALES (est): 100MM-499.9MM **Publicly Held**
WEB: www.mmm.com
SIC: 5099 Wholesales safety equipment & supplies
PA: 3M Co
   3M Center Bldg 22011W02
   Saint Paul MN 55144
   651 733-1110

(G-9053)

3M CO
3M Center Bldg 2232N21 (55144-1000)
PHONE...........................651 733-4740
Gaby Sabongi, *Manager*
Bob Higgard, *Manager*
M Krasky, *Manager*

EMP: 50
SALES (est): 25MM-49.9MM **Publicly Held**
WEB: www.mmm.com
SIC: 5113 Wholesales industrial & personal service paper
PA: 3M Co
   3M Center Bldg 22011W02
   Saint Paul MN 55144
   651 733-1110

(G-9054)

3M CO
3M Center Bldg 2232N26 (55144-1000)
PHONE...........................651 733-5000
Les Odegaard, *Research*
EMP: 25
SALES (est): 1MM-4.9MM **Publicly Held**
WEB: www.mmm.com
SIC: 8711 Engineering services
PA: 3M Co
   3M Center Bldg 22011W02
   Saint Paul MN 55144
   651 733-1110

(G-9055)

3M CO
3M Center Bldg 223 (55144-1000)
PHONE...........................651 733-1941
J L Walker, *Branch Mgr*
EMP: 90
SALES (est): 25MM-49.9MM **Publicly Held**
WEB: www.mmm.com
SIC: 5043 Photographic processing chemicals; manufactures sensitized motion picture, X-ray & still camera film; wholesales photographic developing apparatus
PA: 3M Co
   3M Center Bldg 22011W02
   Saint Paul MN 55144
   651 733-1110

(G-9056)

3M CO
3M Center Bldg 2900402 (55144-1001)
PHONE...........................651 736-1792
James J Schramel, *Manager*
K J Wallace, *Manager*
Pamela Kukacka, *Analyst*
EMP: 200
SALES (est): 25MM-49.9MM **Publicly Held**
WEB: www.mmm.com
SIC: 8711 Engineering services
PA: 3M Co
   3M Center Bldg 22011W02
   Saint Paul MN 55144
   651 733-1110

(G-9057)

3M CO
3M Center Bldg 223 (55144-1000)
PO Box 33223 (55133-3223)
PHONE...........................651 736-2326
FAX: 651 736-8643
Kirk C Graves, *Vice Pres*
M C Harnetty, *Branch Mgr*
Gregory Ehlert, *Exec Dir*
EMP: 40
SALES (est): 10MM-24.9MM **Publicly Held**
WEB: www.mmm.com
SIC: 5169 Manufactures inorganic chemicals; wholesales chemicals & allied products
PA: 3M Co
   3M Center Bldg 22011W02
   Saint Paul MN 55144
   651 733-1110

(G-9058)

3M CO
3M Center (55144-1000)
PHONE...........................651 733-5623
Thomas Boardman, *Corp Secy*
Richard Ziegler, *Senior VP*
Herman Mauwaerts, *Vice Pres*
Glen Copeland, *Engineering*
Kenneth Larock, *Engineering*
EMP: 50
SALES (est): 25MM-49.9MM **Publicly Held**
WEB: www.mmm.com
SIC: 5169 Wholesales chemicals & allied products
PA: 3M Co
   3M Center Bldg 22011W02
   Saint Paul MN 55144
   651 733-1110

(PA)=Parent Co (HQ)=Headquarters (DH)=Div Headquarters
✿ = New business established in last 2 years

2011 Harris Minnesota
Services Directory

© Harris InfoSource 1-866-281-6415

391

(G-9059)
3M CO
3M Center Bldg 2208E05　(55144-1000)
PHONE 651 733-6678
A J Theunissen, *Branch Mgr*
EMP: 400
SALES (est): 100MM-499.9MM **Publicly Held**
WEB: www.mmm.com
SIC: 5169 Manufactures adhesives; wholesales chemical adhesives
PA: 3M Co
　　3M Center Bldg 22011W02
　　Saint Paul MN 55144
　　651 733-1110

(G-9060)
3M CO
3M Center Bldg 2255S08　(55144-1000)
PO Box 33225　(55133-3225)
PHONE 651 733-1110
FAX: 651 736-3094
Larry Lair, *Principal*
Kay Grenz, *Vice Pres*
David A Verlo, *Vice Pres*
Ken Hammerschmidt, *Branch Mgr*
W Brown, *Branch Mgr*
EMP: 200
SALES (est): 25MM-49.9MM **Publicly Held**
WEB: www.mmm.com
SIC: 8743 Manufactures motor vehicle parts & accessories; promotion services
PA: 3M Co
　　3M Center Bldg 22011W02
　　Saint Paul MN 55144
　　651 733-1110

(G-9061)
3M CO
3M Center Bldg 216　(55144-1000)
PHONE 651 733-5562
Harold Laskin, *Branch Mgr*
EMP: 300
SALES (est): 10MM-24.9MM **Publicly Held**
WEB: www.mmm.com
SIC: 8721 Accounting, auditing & bookkeeping services
PA: 3M Co
　　3M Center Bldg 22011W02
　　Saint Paul MN 55144
　　651 733-1110

(G-9062)
3M CO
1024 Hazel St N Bldg 424　(55119-4857)
PHONE 651 733-3154
EMP: 90
SALES (est): 50MM-99.9MM **Publicly Held**
WEB: www.mmm.com
SIC: 5063 Wholesales electrical apparatus & equipment
PA: 3M Co
　　3M Center Bldg 22011W02
　　Saint Paul MN 55144
　　651 733-1110

(G-9063)
3M CO
3 M Ctr Bldg 2234NE13　(55144-0001)
PHONE 651 736-3828
Ed Shivitz, *Manager*
EMP: 50
SALES (est): 5MM-9.9MM **Publicly Held**
WEB: www.mmm.com
SIC: 8742 Marketing consulting service
PA: 3M Co
　　3M Center Bldg 22011W02
　　Saint Paul MN 55144
　　651 733-1110

(G-9064)
3M CO
-07 Bldg 216-2N　(55106)
PHONE 651 733-5094
EMP: 81
SALES (est): 25MM-49.9MM **Publicly Held**
WEB: www.mmm.com
SIC: 5112 Wholesales stationery & office supplies
PA: 3M Co
　　3M Center Bldg 22011W02
　　Saint Paul MN 55144
　　651 733-1110

(G-9065)
3M CO
3 M Ctr Bldg 2254512　(55144-0001)
PHONE 651 733-0963
EMP: 81
SALES (est): 25MM-49.9MM **Publicly Held**
WEB: www.mmm.com
SIC: 5047 Wholesales medical & hospital equipment
PA: 3M Co
　　3M Center Bldg 22011W02
　　Saint Paul MN 55144
　　651 733-1110

(G-9066)
3M CO
3M Center Bldg 5492N18　(55144-1000)
PHONE 651 733-6611
Joellen Fanchez, *Manager*
EMP: 81
SALES (est): 50MM-99.9MM **Publicly Held**
WEB: www.mmm.com
SIC: 5063 Wholesales electrical apparatus & equipment
PA: 3M Co
　　3M Center Bldg 22011W02
　　Saint Paul MN 55144
　　651 733-1110

(G-9067)
3M INNOVATIVE PROPERTIES CO
3M Center Bldg 2254N14　(55144-1001)
PO Box 33427　(55133-3427)
PHONE 651 733-8904
Gary Griswold, *President*
Robert W Sprague, *Corp Secy*
Harold Laskin, *COO*
Ronald A Weber, *Exec VP*
Paul Baril, *Vice Pres*
EST: 1999 **Publicly Held**
WEB: www.mmm.com
SIC: 8111 Legal services
PA: 3M Co
　　3M Center Bldg 22011W02
　　Saint Paul MN 55144
　　651 733-1110

(G-9068)
TIMBERLAND TRANSPORTATION INC
Also Called: Priority Courier Experts
3545 Hoffman Rd E　(55110-5376)
PHONE 651 748-4477
Stephan R Cossack, *CEO*
Edward Burchell, *President*
Jeff Kammerud, *Vice Pres*
EMP: 35 **EST:** 1996
SQ FT: 10,000
SALES (est): 1MM-4.9MM **Privately Held**
WEB: www.shipwithpriority.com
SIC: 7389 Courier or messenger service

(G-9069)
TLC NURSING SERVICES OF
1255 Larpenteur Ave E　(55109-4333)
PHONE 651 647-0017
FAX: 651 647-3423
Solomon Mulugeta, *President*
EMP: 80 **EST:** 1988
SQ FT: 2,000
SALES (est): 1MM-4.9MM **Privately Held**
WEB: www.1homehealthcarecenter.com
SIC: 8082 Home health care services

(G-9070)
TOM JOHNSON
1045 Westgate Dr Ste 100　(55114-1079)
PHONE 651 645-3000
FAX: 651 645-4654
Tom Johnson, *Principal*
EMP: 40 **EST:** 2005
SALES (est): 1MM-4.9MM **Privately Held**
SIC: 8049 Health practitioners' office

(G-9071)
TOP-ALL ROOFING INC
291 Eva St　(55107-1614)
PHONE 651 291-7663
FAX: 651 291-9136
David Welsh, *Vice Pres*
EMP: 50
EST: 1980
SQ FT: 23,000
SALES (est): 5MM-9.9MM **Privately Held**
WEB: www.top-all.com
SIC: 1761 Roofing contractor; architectural sheet metal work contractor

(G-9072)
TOTAL RENAL CARE INC
Also Called: Arden Hills Dialysis Unit
3900 Northwoods Dr Ste 110 (55112-6911)
PHONE 651 483-3159
FAX: 651 483-9156
Wendy McNamara, *Office Mgr*
Rozanna Nelson, *Branch Mgr*
David Bowlin, *Director*
Raja Shah, *Nephrology*
EMP: 30
SALES (est): 1MM-4.9MM **Publicly Held**
WEB: www.davita.com
SIC: 8092 Kidney dialysis center
PA: DaVita Inc
　　1551 Wewatta St
　　Denver CO 80202
　　303 405-2100

(G-9073)
TOTAL TOOL SUPPLY INC
315 Pierce St N Ste A　(55104-5244)
PO Box 4069　(55104-0069)
PHONE 651 646-4055
FAX: 651 646-8610
R D Jordan, *CEO*
Andy Jordan, *President*
Mark Smith, *General Mgr*
Kim Koniar, *Vice Pres*
Scott Richardson, *CFO*
▲ **EMP:** 65 **EST:** 1977
SQ FT: 40,000
SALES (est): 5MM-9.9MM **Privately Held**
SIC: 7359 7699 Tool rental; manufactures cartridge-activated hand power tools; tool repair service; power tool repair service; manufactures iron or steel forgings; manufactures wire & wire products

(G-9074)
TOTAL TRANSPORTATION CORP
3565 Hoffman Rd E　(55110-5376)
PHONE 651 770-5668
David Murray, *President*
Gigi Capaul, *Manager*
Nick Murray, *Manager*
EMP: 50 **EST:** 1987
SALES (est): 1MM-4.9MM **Privately Held**
WEB: www.totallimo.com
SIC: 4119 Limousine service

(G-9075)
TOWN & COUNTRY CLUB OF ST
300 Mississippi River Blvd N　(55104-4927)
PHONE 651 646-7121
FAX: 651 646-7126
Vincent Tracy, *General Mgr*
Richard Mogenson, *Principal*
Leo Nagel, *Controller*
Faith Jamnik, *Manager*
Joe Kramlinger, *Info Tech Mgr*
EMP: 90 **EST:** 1888
SQ FT: 41,000
SALES (est): 5MM-9.9MM **Privately Held**
SIC: 7997 Country club

(G-9076)
TRANSPORTATION MANAGEMENT CORP
1907 Charles Ave　(55104-1745)
PHONE 651 642-9292
Carol Lessingwell, *Vice Pres*
EMP: 80 **EST:** 2005
SALES (est): 5MM-9.9MM **Privately Held**
SIC: 8741 Management services

(G-9077)
TRANSUNION LLC
2780 Snelling Ave N Ste 309 (55113-7125)
PHONE 651 639-0007
FAX: 651 639-0705
Jeff Lahey, *Vice Pres*
EMP: 30
SALES (est): 1MM-4.9MM **Privately Held**
WEB: www.transunion.com
SIC: 7323 Consumer credit reporting bureau
HQ: Transunion LLC
　　555 W Adams St Fl 10
　　Chicago IL 60661
　　312 258-1717

(G-9078)
TRAVELODGE TOWER
1870 Old Hudson Rd　(55119-4307)
PHONE 651 735-2333
FAX: 651 735-1953
Wayne Mitchell, *Owner*
Belle Hicke, *General Mgr*
EMP: 101 **EST:** 1978
SALES (est): 5MM-9.9MM **Privately Held**
WEB: www.travel.times-square-nyc.com
SIC: 7011 Traveler accommodations; eating place; drinking establishment

(G-9079)
TREE OF LIFE LLC
601 Campus Dr Ste 11　(55112-3001)
PHONE 612 752-6300
Jim Schorvmann, *VP Sls/Mktg*
Doug Rotchadl, *Manager*
Janet Carpenter, *Admin Asst*
EMP: 200
SALES (est): 100MM-499.9MM **Privately Held**
WEB: www.treeoflife.com
SIC: 5149 Wholesales groceries
HQ: Tree of Life LLC
　　405 Golfway West Dr
　　Saint Augustine FL 32095
　　904 940-2100

(G-9080)
TRI CITY AMERICAN LEGION
Also Called: Post 513
400 Old Highway 8 NW　(55112-3221)
PHONE 651 631-1124
Comdr Stachowski, *President*
Karen Schwalbe, *Bd of Directors*
EMP: 40 **EST:** 1968
SALES (est): 1MM-4.9MM **Privately Held**
SIC: 6512 7299 Eating place; operators of auditoriums & halls; banquet hall facility

(G-9081)
TRI CITY POST 513
Also Called: American Legion 513
400 Old Highway 8 NW　(55112-3221)
PHONE 651 631-1124
Norb Stachowski, *CEO*
Edwin Linquist, *Corp Secy*
EMP: 30 **EST:** 1949 **Privately Held**
SIC: 8641 7299 7389 Veterans' organization; banquet hall facility; accommodation locating service

(G-9082)
TRIANGLE SERVICES INC
1611 County Road B W # 320 (55113-4053)
PHONE 651 294-0020
FAX: 651 872-9707
Brian Westphal, *Manager*
EMP: 215
SALES (est): 5MM-9.9MM **Privately Held**
SIC: 7349 Building cleaning & maintenance services

(G-9083)
TRIMIN SYSTEMS INC
2277 Highway 36 W 101E　(55113-3830)
PHONE 651 636-7667
Bill Metzger, *President*
Bill Mori, *Vice Pres*
Jay Kratt, *Controller*
Donna Nixon, *Sales Staff*
Sherry L Macom, *Mktg Dir*
EMP: 40 **EST:** 1986
SALES (est): 25MM-49.9MM **Privately Held**
SIC: 5045 7372 7379 Wholesales computer software; wholesales computers; data processing consulting service; computer training school; software publisher

(G-9084)
TRUCK UTILITIES INC　(PA)
2370 English St　(55109-2098)
PHONE 651 484-3305
FAX: 651 484-0076
Leo J Capeder, *President*

▲=Import ▼=Export
◆=Import/Export

Paul Capeder, *Corp Secy*
Jay Langer, *Corp Secy*
Craig Capeder, *Vice Pres*
Dave Claussen, *VP Sls/Mktg*
EMP: 72 **EST:** 1963
SQ FT: 12,000
SALES (corp-wide): 21.94M **Privately Held**
SIC: 7532 7353 Truck body shop; cranes & aerial lift equipment leasing & rental service

(G-9085)
TRUGREEN LTD PTN
Also Called: Tru Green-Chemlawn
4240 Centerville Rd (55127-7813)
PO Box 271090 (55127-1090)
PHONE..............................651 407-3400
FAX: 651 407-6456
Scott Elmer, *Sales Mgr*
Scott Towner, *Sales Staff*
Sheila Marik, *Office Mgr*
EMP: 75 **Privately Held**
WEB: www.trugreen.com
SIC: 0782 Lawn care services
DH: Trugreen LP
860 Ridge Lake Blvd Ste G02
Memphis TN 38120
901 681-1800

(G-9086)
TUV SUD AMERICA INC
1775 Old Highway 8 NW Ste 104
(55112-1891)
PHONE..............................651 631-2487
FAX: 651 638-0285
Judy Haider, *Human Res Dir*
Amy Bahauddin, *Sales Mgr*
Gene Panger, *Marketing Mgr*
Stefan Butz, *Manager*
Theresa Leffler, *Manager*
EMP: 40
SALES (est): 1MM-4.9MM **Privately Held**
WEB: www.tuvamerica.com
SIC: 8734 8071 Testing laboratory; medical laboratory
PA: Tuv Sud America Inc
10 Centennial Dr Fl 2A
Peabody MA 01960
978 573-2500

(G-9087)
TWIN CITIES MACK VOLVO TRUCKS
2195 County Road C2 W (55113-1009)
PHONE..............................651 633-4810
Ronald D Offutt, *President*
Dick Klick, *Manager*
Angie Warner, *Manager*
EMP: 85 **EST:** 1989
SQ FT: 60,000
SALES (est): 25MM-49.9MM **Privately Held**
SIC: 7538 Retails new & used automobiles; retails automotive parts; truck engine repair service

(G-9088)
TWIN CITIES PUBLIC TELEVISION
172 4th St E (55101-1492)
PHONE..............................651 222-1717
James R Pagliarini, *President*
Lawrence T Bell, *Vice Chairman*
Dan Thomas, *COO*
Judith Titcomb, *Trustee*
David C Weyerhaeuser, *Trustee*
EMP: 180 **EST:** 1955
SQ FT: 100,000
SALES (est): 25MM-49.9MM **Privately Held**
WEB: www.tpt.org
SIC: 4833 Television broadcasting station

(G-9089)
TWIN CITIES TRANSPORT
1396 Concordia Ave (55104-5309)
PHONE..............................651 642-1446
FAX: 651 642-0010
Ron Gardas, *Manager*
EMP: 40
SALES (est): 1MM-4.9MM **Privately Held**
SIC: 7549 Automotive towing service
PA: Twin Cities Transport
274 N1 Geneva Ave
Saint Paul MN 55128
651 770-0816

(G-9090)
TWIN CITIES TREE TRUST
2350 Wycliff St Ste 200 (55114-1331)
PHONE..............................651 644-6237
FAX: 651 644-1469
David Hawes, *CEO*
EMP: 40 **EST:** 2004
SALES (est): 1MM-4.9MM **Privately Held**
WEB: www.treetrust.org
SIC: 8331 Job training & vocational rehabilitation services

(G-9091)
TWIN CITY CONCRETE PRODUCTS CO
1351 Trout Brook Cir (55117-4619)
PHONE..............................651 489-8095
Thomas Becken, *CEO*
Mike Fritz, *Manager*
Tom Schuett, *Manager*
EMP: 40
SALES (est): 10MM-24.9MM **Privately Held**
SIC: 5032 Wholesales concrete mixtures; manufactures concrete products
PA: Twin City Concrete Products Co
2025 Centre Pointe Blvd # 300
Saint Paul MN 55120
651 688-9116

(G-9092)
TWIN CITY GLASS CONTRACTORS
520 Atwater Cir (55103-4401)
PHONE..............................651 746-0650
FAX: 651 765-2423
Dan Welty, *CEO*
Sue Wohlk, *Manager*
EMP: 40
SALES (est): 1MM-4.9MM **Privately Held**
SIC: 1793 Glass & glazing contractor

(G-9093)
TWIN CITY LIMOUSINE
Also Called: Headerson Limousine
584 Stryker Ave Fl 13 (55107-2815)
PHONE..............................651 222-8553
John Henderson, *President*
EMP: 200 **EST:** 1979
SALES (est): 10MM-24.9MM **Privately Held**
SIC: 4119 Limousine service

(G-9094)
TWIN CITY TILE & MARBLE CO INC
900 Montreal Way (55102-4247)
PHONE..............................651 602-5800
Jim Hidding, *President*
Mark Lindholm, *Division Mgr*
Alfred Hoedeman, *Corp Secy*
Sara Nikkel, *Corp Secy*
Edward Robichaud, *Vice Pres*
EMP: 99 **EST:** 1911
SQ FT: 40,000
SALES (est): 5MM-9.9MM **Privately Held**
SIC: 1743 Tile, marble, terrazzo & mosaic contractor

(G-9095)
TWIN TOWN TREATMENT CENTER LLC (PA)
1706 University Ave W (55104-3614)
PHONE..............................651 645-3661
FAX: 651 645-0959
Paul Cowdery, *President*
Michael Bundy, *CFO*
EMP: 43 **EST:** 1974
SQ FT: 14,400 **Privately Held**
SIC: 8069 Substance abuse hospital

(G-9096)
TWV LP
422 Concord St (55107-2478)
PHONE..............................651 291-1750
Joseph Holmberg, *Partner*
Kelly Mechavich, *Manager*
EMP: 99
SALES (est): 10MM-24.9MM **Privately Held**
SIC: 6513 Apartment building operator

(G-9097)
TYMPANY LLC
5000 Township Pkwy (55110-5852)
PHONE..............................866 316-3606
Michael Spearman, *Manager*
Daniel Spearman, *Manager*
EMP: 25 **EST:** 2001
SALES (est): 10MM-24.9MM **Publicly Held**
WEB: www.tympany.net
SIC: 5047 Wholesales medical & hospital equipment
PA: Otix Global Inc
4246 Riverboat Rd Ste 300
Salt Lake City UT 84123
801 312-1700

(G-9098)
U S BANK NATIONAL ASSOCIATION
4700 Clark Ave (55110-3220)
PHONE..............................651 426-8266
FAX: 651 426-8282
Darcy Frederickson, *Manager*
EMP: 25
SALES (est): 5MM-9.9MM **Publicly Held**
WEB: www.firstar.com
SIC: 6021 National commercial bank
HQ: U S Bank National Association
425 Walnut St Fl 1
Cincinnati OH 45202
513 632-4234

(G-9099)
U S FILTER RECOVERY SERVICES
2430 Rose Pl (55113-2511)
PHONE..............................651 638-1300
FAX: 651 633-5074
Brent Hillien, *General Mgr*
Gary Turman, *Managing Dir*
Deborah M Newell, *Corp Secy*
Jennifer Kleist, *Vice Pres*
Leo Sharkey, *Plant Mgr*
EMP: 45 **EST:** 1986
SQ FT: 80,000
SALES (est): 5MM-9.9MM **Privately Held**
WEB: www.usfilter.com
SIC: 4953 Hazardous waste collection & disposal services
DH: Siemens Water Technologies
181 Thorn Hill Rd
Warrendale PA 15086
724 772-0044

(G-9100)
UBS FINANCIAL SERVICES INC
444 Cedar St Ste 2200 (55101-2136)
PHONE..............................651 298-1616
Mary Retzlaff, *Manager*
Mike Hatlestad, *Manager*
David Hammer, *Manager*
Colleen Bollom, *Manager*
George Anastos, *Manager*
EMP: 65
SALES (est): 10MM-24.9MM **Privately Held**
WEB: www.ubs.com
SIC: 6211 General brokerage investment firm
PA: UBS Financial Services Inc
1285 Avenue Of The Americas
New York NY 10019
212 713-2000

(G-9101)
ULS OF NEW ENGLAND LLC (PA)
55 5th St E Ste 960 (55101-1717)
PHONE..............................651 227-9855
Timothy Montague, *Member*
Phillip Foussard, *Member*
Darrell Charboneau, *CFO*
EMP: 100 **EST:** 2007
SQ FT: 95,000 **Privately Held**
SIC: 7211 Commercial & family dry cleaning & laundry services

(G-9102)
UNION GOSPEL MISSION ASSN
435 University Ave E (55130-4437)
PHONE..............................651 292-1721
FAX: 651 292-9207
George Verley, *Superintendent*
Larry Grabow, *Human Res Dir*

Dave Benson, *Info Tech Mgr*
Ken Cooper, *Exec Dir*
Nick Gisi, *Director*
EMP: 80 **EST:** 1902
SQ FT: 20,000
SALES (est): 5MM-9.9MM **Privately Held**
SIC: 8322 Emergency shelters

(G-9103)
UNISYS CORP
2470 Highcrest Rd (55113-2509)
PHONE..............................651 635-7777
FAX: 651 635-7523
David E Carpentier, *Principal*
Tom Devries, *Principal*
Frank King, *Principal*
John A Klug, *Principal*
Ann Thureen, *Vice Pres*
EMP: 1200 **Publicly Held**
WEB: www.unisys.com
SIC: 8731 7371 Computer hardware development services; computer programming service
PA: Unisys Corp
Unisys Way
Blue Bell PA 19424
215 986-4011

(G-9104)
UNITED FAMILY PRACTICE HEALTH
1026 7th St W (55102-3828)
PHONE..............................651 241-1000
FAX: 651 293-5889
Melissa Parker, *Business Mgr*
Steve Ficks, *CFO*
Stephanie Rosener MD, *Med Doctor*
Dana D Brian MD, *Med Doctor*
Janet Dailey, *Exec Dir*
EMP: 70 **EST:** 1994
SALES (est): 5MM-9.9MM **Privately Held**
WEB: www.ufphc.org
SIC: 8011 General & family practice physician or surgeon office

(G-9105)
UNITED GLASS INC
1480 County Road C W (55113-3159)
PHONE..............................651 633-2529
FAX: 651 633-3839
David Radcliffe, *CEO*
Michael Drake, *President*
Kathy Larson, *Officer*
EMP: 40 **EST:** 1984
SQ FT: 4,500
SALES (est): 1MM-4.9MM **Privately Held**
WEB: www.unitedglassinc.com
SIC: 1793 Glass & glazing contractor

(G-9106)
UNITED HEALTHCARE OF WYOMING
2550 University Ave W Ste 401S
(55114-1907)
PHONE..............................651 603-8515
FAX: 651 646-1161
Mark Ward, *Manager*
EMP: 60
SALES (est): 1MM-4.9MM **Publicly Held**
WEB: www.unitedhealthgroup.com
SIC: 8099 Medical services organization
PA: Unitedhealth Group Inc
9900 Bren Rd E
Minnetonka MN 55343
952 936-1300

(G-9107)
UNITED LINEN SERVICES INC
55 5th St E Ste 960 (55101-1717)
PHONE..............................651 227-9855
Phillip C Foussard, *President*
Timothy P Montague, *COO*
Darrell Charboneau, *CFO*
EMP: 315 **EST:** 1993
SQ FT: 5,000
SALES (est): 10MM-24.9MM **Privately Held**
SIC: 7211 7218 Commercial & family dry cleaning & laundry services; industrial laundry service

(PA)=Parent Co (HQ)=Headquarters (DH)=Div Headquarters
✿ = New business established in last 2 years

2011 Harris Minnesota
Services Directory

© Harris InfoSource 1-866-281-6415

393

(G-9108)
UNITED PRODUCTS CORP OF AMER (PA)
200 Sycamore St W (55117-5349)
PHONE..................651 227-8735
FAX: 651 227-2417
M A Hatfield, *Ch of Bd*
Charlene Hatfield, *President*
Kim Swanson, *Vice Pres*
Pat Marcy, *Sales Staff*
EMP: 80 **EST:** 1926
SQ FT: 50,000 **Privately Held**
SIC: 5033 5031 Wholesales roofing & siding materials; wholesales windows

(G-9109)
UNITED STATES POSTAL SERVICE
Also Called: US Post Office
314 Eva St (55107-1619)
PHONE..................651 293-3172
Steve Peterson, *Manager*
EMP: 100
SALES (est): 5MM-9.9MM **Privately Held**
WEB: www.usps.gov
SIC: 7538 General automotive repair services
PA: United States Postal Service
475 Lenfant Plz SW
Washington DC 20260
202 268-2000

(G-9110)
UNITED WAY INFO & REFERRAL
Also Called: Emergency Social Svc Program
176 Robert St S (55107-1421)
PHONE..................651 291-6795
Bette Undis, *Director*
EMP: 50 **Privately Held**
SIC: 8399 United fund councils

(G-9111)
UNIVAR USA INC
845 Terrace Ct (55130-4237)
PHONE..................651 774-9400
FAX: 651 774-0850
Philip Eason, *VP Sales*
Kerry Cipra, *Manager*
Don Woznik, *Manager*
Jim Johnson, *Director*
Nancy Minehart, *Administration*
EMP: 50
SALES (est): 25MM-49.9MM **Privately Held**
WEB: www.univarusa.com
SIC: 5169 Wholesales chemicals & allied products
HQ: Univar USA Inc
17425 NE Union Hill Rd
Redmond WA 98052
425 889-3400

(G-9112)
UNIVERSITY CLUB OF ST PAUL
420 Summit Ave (55102-2624)
PHONE..................651 222-1751
FAX: 651 222-3336
John Rupp, *President*
Peggy Faricy, *Corp Secy*
Peggy Rupp, *Corp Secy*
Sharon Kurtt, *Director*
EMP: 60 **EST:** 1907
SQ FT: 30,000 **Privately Held**
WEB: www.universityclubofstpaul.com
SIC: 8641 7991 Social club; membership athletic club & gymnasiums

(G-9113)
UNIVERSITY NATIONAL BANK
200 University Ave W # 100 (55103-2075)
PHONE..................651 265-5600
David Reiling, *President*
John Bennett, *Vice Pres*
Lamey Colleen, *VP Finance*
EMP: 35 **EST:** 1962
SQ FT: 15,000
SALES (est): 5MM-9.9MM **Privately Held**
WEB: www.universitybank.com
SIC: 6021 Commercial national trust companies with deposits
PA: University Financial Corp
200 University Ave W # 200
Saint Paul MN 55103
651 265-5600

(G-9114)
UPPER MIDWEST ORGAN
2550 University Ave W Ste 315S (55114-1909)
PHONE..................651 603-7800
FAX: 651 603-7801
Susan Gunderson, *CEO*
EMP: 80 **EST:** 1987
SQ FT: 15,000
SALES (est): 5MM-9.9MM **Privately Held**
WEB: www.organdonation.org
SIC: 8099 Organ bank

(G-9115)
UPPER RIVER SERVICES LLC
40 State St (55107-1429)
PHONE..................651 292-9293
FAX: 651 227-8456
Lee Nelson, *President*
Robert J Keith Jr, *Co-COB*
Andrew M Hunter III, *Co-COB*
Robert Horstman, *Corp Secy*
Eric Knutson, *Safety Mgr*
EMP: 25 **EST:** 1984
SQ FT: 2,200
SALES (est): 1MM-4.9MM **Privately Held**
WEB: www.ursi.net
SIC: 4491 Docks, piers & terminals

(G-9116)
US ARMY CORPS OF ENGINEERS
190 5th St E Ste 401 (55101-1623)
PHONE..................651 290-5698
FAX: 651 290-4497
Jon Christensen, *Commander*
Jeffry Bailey, *Corp Secy*
Byron Nelson, *Electrical Engi*
Linda A Krueger, *Personnel*
Randal C Brunete, *Manager*
EMP: 750
SALES (est): 50MM-99.9MM **Privately Held**
WEB: www.sac.usace.army.mil
SIC: 8711 Engineering services; federal government national security; united States Army
HQ: US Army Corps of Engineers
441 G St NW Gao Bldg Fl 3
Washington DC 20314
804 435-9362

(G-9117)
US BANCORP INFORMATION SVCS (HQ)
332 Minnesota St Ste A (55101-1311)
PHONE..................651 466-3000
Phil Heasley, *Ch of Bd*
Shannon Rantz, *Vice Pres*
Tammy Schultz-Fugh, *Vice Pres*
Toby Robillard, *Vice Pres*
Paul Rennerfeldt, *Manager*
EMP: 848 **EST:** 1966
SQ FT: 111,000
SALES (corp-wide): 19.49B **Publicly Held**
WEB: www.usbank.com
SIC: 6411 Insurance broker
PA: U S Bancorp
800 Nicollet Mall Ste 800
Minneapolis MN 55402
651 466-3000

(G-9118)
US BANK NATIONAL ASSOCIATION
1071 Grand Ave (55105-3002)
PHONE..................651 229-6123
FAX: 651 229-6168
Marty Long, *Manager*
Ryan Hale, *Manager*
EMP: 26
SALES (est): 5MM-9.9MM **Publicly Held**
WEB: www.firstar.com
SIC: 6021 National commercial bank
HQ: U S Bank National Association
425 Walnut St Fl 1
Cincinnati OH 45202
513 632-4234

(G-9119)
US BANK TRUST NATIONAL ASSN
180 5th St E Ste 200 (55101-1835)
PHONE..................800 934-6802
Terry McRoberts, *President*
Tony Piclamini, *Principal*
Elizabeth Becker, *Corp Secy*
J R Hoffmann, *Exec VP*
Kent C Larson, *Exec VP*
EMP: 765 **EST:** 1903
SALES (est): 100MM-499.9MM **Publicly Held**
WEB: www.usbank.com
SIC: 6091 Trusts, fiduciary & custody services
PA: U S Bancorp
800 Nicollet Mall Ste 800
Minneapolis MN 55402
651 466-3000

(G-9120)
US FOODSERVICE INC
708 Cleveland Ave SW (55112-3500)
PHONE..................651 634-4380
Steve Trebisovfsky, *Branch Mgr*
EMP: 150
SALES (est): 100MM-499.9MM **Privately Held**
WEB: www.usfoodservice.com
SIC: 5149 Wholesales dried or canned foods
HQ: US Foodservice Inc
9399 W Higgins Rd Ste 500
Rosemont IL 60018
847 720-8000

(G-9121)
UTC FIRE & SECURITY AMERICA
1275 Red Fox Rd (55112-6943)
PHONE..................651 777-2690
Kevin Cassidy, *General Mgr*
Michael Guest, *General Mgr*
Pat Kelly, *General Mgr*
John V Osch, *General Mgr*
Emmanuel Amato, *Vice Pres*
EMP: 100
SALES (est): 10MM-24.9MM **Publicly Held**
WEB: www.gesecurity.com
SIC: 5065 Manufactures burglar alarms; manufactures fire alarms; manufactures fire detection systems; wholesales electronic parts & equipment
HQ: UTC Fire & Security America
8985 Town Center Pkwy
Bradenton FL 34202
941 739-4200

(G-9122)
V CARE HOME HEALTH INC
1049 Payne Ave (55130-3840)
PHONE..................651 793-7635
FAX: 651 793-7659
MAI Vang, *President*
EMP: 90 **EST:** 2001
SALES (est): 1MM-4.9MM **Privately Held**
SIC: 8059 Nursing & personal care facility

(G-9123)
VALLEY NATIONAL GASES INC
305 2nd St NW Ste 125 (55112-3279)
PHONE..................651 628-4848
FAX: 651 628-4894
Jim Hart, *President*
Mark Gildea, *Vice Pres*
Keith Bottge, *Vice Pres*
Bill Reynolds, *Vice Pres*
Vernon Vietanen, *Buyer*
EMP: 32 **EST:** 1963
SQ FT: 20,000
SALES (est): 1MM-4.9MM **Privately Held**
WEB: www.vngas.com
SIC: 5084 5169 Retails medical apparatus & supplies; wholesales industrial gases; wholesales industrial machinery & equipment
HQ: Valley National Gases Wv LLC
6500 Rockside Rd Ste 200
Independence OH 44131
216 573-9909

(G-9124)
VEOLIA ENVIRONMENTAL SERVICES
309 Como Ave (55103-1803)
PHONE..................651 774-0916
Mayo Rude, *General Mgr*
Paul Lebing, *Principal*
Brian Kagan, *Sales Executive*
Coral Pierson, *Administrator*
EMP: 26 **EST:** 1968
SQ FT: 5,400
SALES (est): 5MM-9.9MM **Privately Held**
WEB: www.veoliaes.com
SIC: 4953 Rubbish collection & disposal services
HQ: Veolia Es Solid Waste Midwest
125 S 84th St Ste 200
Milwaukee WI 53214
414 479-7800

(G-9125)
VEOLIA ES SOLID WASTE MIDWEST
309 Como Ave (55103-1803)
PHONE..................651 459-3029
Mayo Rude, *Principal*
EMP: 50
SALES (est): 5MM-9.9MM **Privately Held**
WEB: www.veoliaes.com
SIC: 4953 Refuse collection & disposal services
HQ: Veolia Es Solid Waste Midwest
125 S 84th St Ste 200
Milwaukee WI 53214
414 479-7800

(G-9126)
VERICENTER MINNESOTA INC
1125 Energy Park Dr Ste 100 (55108-5032)
PHONE..................952 918-2000
Tom Kieffer, *President*
Brian Lee, *Opers Mgr*
Dan Moldenhauer, *Controller*
Jeffrey Vierzba, *IT/INT Sup*
EMP: 55 **EST:** 1998
SALES (est): 5MM-9.9MM **Privately Held**
SIC: 7371 Applications software programming

(G-9127)
VIETNAMESE SOCIAL SERVICES OF
1159 University Ave W Ste 100 (55104-4614)
PHONE..................651 644-1317
Yen Bham, *Director*
EMP: 32 **EST:** 1987
SALES (est): 1MM-4.9MM **Privately Held**
WEB: www.vssmn.org
SIC: 8322 Social services center

(G-9128)
VIKING AUTOMATIC SPRINKLER CO (HQ)
301 York Ave (55130-4039)
PHONE..................651 558-3300
Lee R Anderson Sr, *Ch of Bd*
Ryan Johnston, *President*
William M Beadie, *Corp Secy*
Rich Poole, *Vice Pres*
Kevin Shea, *Vice Pres*
EMP: 40 **EST:** 1924
SQ FT: 50,000 **Privately Held**
WEB: www.vikingsprinkler.com
SIC: 1711 Fire sprinkler system installation service; manufactures plumbing fixtures
PA: API Group Inc
1100 Old Highway 8 NW
Saint Paul MN 55112
651 636-4320

(G-9129)
VILLAGE GREEN LAWN MAINTENANCE
520 Front Ave (55117-4707)
PO Box 601120 (55106-0019)
PHONE..................651 488-2733
FAX: 651 642-9865
Jerry Ford, *President*
EMP: 28 **EST:** 1999
SQ FT: 4,500 **Privately Held**
WEB: www.villagegreenlandscapes.com

www.HarrisInfo.com
394

2011 Harris Minnesota
Services Directory

▲=Import ▼=Export
◆=Import/Export

SIC: **0782** Landscaping services

(G-9130)
VINTAGE INC
1419 Arona St (55108-2428)
PHONE..............................651 487-6878
Troy D Witt, *President*
Anthony Hulsebus, *Corp Secy*
Vicki D Witt, *Treasurer*
EMP: 30 **EST:** 1996
SQ FT: 6,000
SALES (est): 500-999K **Privately Held**
SIC: **7299** Eating place; banquet hall facility; drinking establishment

(G-9131)
VISION LOSS RESOURCES
216 Wabasha St S (55107-1804)
PHONE..............................651 224-7662
James Munkholm, *Manager*
Steven Fischer, *Exec Dir*
EMP: 50 **EST:** 1990
SALES (est): 1MM-4.9MM **Privately Held**
WEB: www.visionlossresources.com
SIC: **8322** Individual & family social services

(G-9132)
VOMELA SPECIALTY CO (PA)
274 Fillmore Ave E (55107-1417)
PHONE..............................651 228-2200
FAX: 651 228-2295
Thomas Auth, *CEO*
Mark Auth, *President*
Mark Evp, *Exec VP*
David Peterson, *Vice Pres*
Kevin Kuznar, *Vice Pres*
EMP: 136 **EST:** 1946 **Privately Held**
SIC: **7336** Graphic arts & related design service; manufactures trimming fabrics

(G-9133)
VOTEL, ANDERSON & MCEACHRON
444 Cedar St Ste 1250 (55101-2156)
PHONE..............................651 228-1770
FAX: 651 228-1780
Pam Dorege, *Manager*
Terrance Votel, *Manager*
EMP: 35 **EST:** 1992
SALES (est): 1MM-4.9MM **Privately Held**
SIC: **8111** General practice attorney's or lawyer's office

(G-9134)
W E NELSON STUCCO CO
768 Rice St (55117-5433)
PHONE..............................763 377-3631
Jim Geisen, *President*
EMP: 30
SALES (est): 1MM-4.9MM **Privately Held**
SIC: **1771** 1742 Exterior concrete stucco contractor; interior stucco contractor

(G-9135)
WADDELL & REED INC
6 Pine Tree Dr Ste 380 (55112-3766)
PHONE..............................651 483-1411
John Jacobs, *Sales & Mktg St*
Barbara Kirby, *Manager*
Steven Kautz, *Manager*
Gordon Heruth, *Manager*
Marilyn Broussard, *Manager*
EMP: 40
SALES (est): 10MM-24.9MM **Publicly Held**
SIC: **6211** 8742 General brokerage investment firm; financial management consulting services
HQ: Waddell & Reed Inc
6300 Lamar Ave
Shawnee Mission KS 66202
913 236-2000

(G-9136)
WALKER ROOFING CO
2274 Capp Rd (55114-1210)
PHONE..............................651 251-0910
FAX: 651 251-0916
Michael J Kohler, *President*
Stacey Reese, *Corp Secy*
Sandra Kohler, *Vice Pres*
EMP: 40 **EST:** 1938
SQ FT: 45,000
SALES (est): 1MM-4.9MM **Privately Held**

SIC: **1761** Roofing contractor; roofing & gutter work contractor

(G-9137)
WALKER WEST MUSIC ACADEMY
777 Selby Ave (55104-6619)
PHONE..............................651 224-2929
FAX: 651 602-9305
David Buck, *Corp Secy*
Samuel Richardson, *Treasurer*
Jean Nelson, *Accountant*
Clarence White, *Exec Dir*
Marcus Walker, *Exec Dir*
EMP: 37 **EST:** 1988
SALES (est): 1MM-4.9MM **Privately Held**
SIC: **8641** Music school; civic & social organization

(G-9138)
WALLY MC CARTHYS OLDSMOBILE
2325 Prior Ave N (55113-2714)
PHONE..............................651 636-6060
Wallace J Mc Carthy, *President*
Maurice Johnson, *Controller*
EMP: 70 **EST:** 1963
SALES (est): 5MM-9.9MM **Privately Held**
SIC: **7311** 7542 Advertising agency; car wash

(G-9139)
WALLY MCCARTHY'S CADILLAC
2325 Prior Ave N (55113-2714)
PHONE..............................651 636-6060
Wallace J McCarthy, *President*
Maurice Johnson, *Office Mgr*
Steve Hedin, *Manager*
Richard Kinsey, *Info Tech Dir*
EMP: 85
SQ FT: 58,000
SALES (est): 25MM-49.9MM **Privately Held**
SIC: **7513** 7515 7532 7538 Retails new & used automobiles; automotive body, paint & interior repair & maintenance services; general automotive repair services; passenger car leasing; used car dealer; truck leasing & rental without drivers

(G-9140)
WARNERS' STELLIAN CO INC
550 Atwater Cir (55103-4401)
PHONE..............................651 222-0011
Jeffrey D Warner, *President*
Bob Warner, *COO*
Carla Warner, *Vice Pres*
Robert Warner, *Vice Pres*
William Warner, *Vice Pres*
EMP: 60 **EST:** 1954
SQ FT: 60,000
SALES (est): 10MM-24.9MM **Privately Held**
WEB: www.warnersstellian.com
SIC: **5064** Retails electric household appliances; wholesales electric household appliances; retails self-contained air conditioning room units; retails major electric household appliances; retails small electric household appliances

(G-9141)
WASHINGTON POST CO
1295 Bandana Blvd N (55108-5126)
PHONE..............................651 523-1094
Patrick O'Brian, *Branch Mgr*
EMP: 50
SALES (est): 1MM-4.9MM **Publicly Held**
SIC: **7389** Vocational school; financial service; business school
PA: Washington Post Co
1150 15th St NW
Washington DC 20071
202 334-6000

(G-9142)
WEBER ELECTRIC INC
577 Shoreview Park Rd (55126-7014)
PHONE..............................651 490-1333
FAX: 651 490-0670
Stephen Weber, *CEO*
Robert Weber, *President*
Brian Kirkman, *Info Tech Mgr*
EMP: 80 **EST:** 1960
SQ FT: 10,000
SALES (est): 5MM-9.9MM **Privately Held**
WEB: www.weberelectric.com

SIC: **1731** 4899 General electrical contractor; communication signal enhancement network services

(G-9143)
WEBSTER DENTAL LABORATORY INC
1380 Frost Ave (55109-4421)
PO Box 64152 (55164-0152)
PHONE..............................651 779-9160
FAX: 651 779-9039
Doug Carlson, *President*
Rosalie Carlson, *Vice Pres*
Dave Wohlberg, *CFO*
EMP: 48 **EST:** 1977
SALES (est): 1MM-4.9MM **Privately Held**
WEB: www.dentalemodels.com
SIC: **8072** Dental laboratory
PA: Geodigm Corp
1630 Lake Dr W
Chanhassen MN 55317
952 556-5657

(G-9144)
WELLINGTON MANAGEMENT INC
Also Called: Valley Creek Mall
1625 Energy Park Dr # 100 (55108-2727)
PHONE..............................651 292-9844
Steve Wellington, *President*
Nicholas Adams, *Partner*
David Schwebel, *Member*
Don Menier, *Member*
Rachel Sykes, *Business Mgr*
EMP: 30 **EST:** 1994
SQ FT: 6,000
SALES (est): 5MM-9.9MM **Privately Held**
SIC: **6512** Operators of community shopping centers, between 100,000-300,000 sq. ft.

(G-9145)
WELLS FARGO BANK
1815 N Saint Paul Rd (55109-4707)
PHONE..............................651 205-8839
FAX: 651 205-8888
Awale Rage, *Manager*
EMP: 26
SALES (est): 5MM-9.9MM **Publicly Held**
SIC: **6022** State commercial bank
HQ: Wfc Holdings, Corp
420 Montgomery St
San Francisco CA 94104
415 396-7392

(G-9146)
WELLS FARGO BANK, NATIONAL
430 Wabasha St N (55101-4438)
PHONE..............................651 205-7583
FAX: 651 205-8896
Peter A Grretson, *Vice Pres*
Nels Hoplin, *Vice Pres*
Amala Thakkar, *Branch Mgr*
Linda Harmon, *Manager*
EMP: 40
SALES (est): 10MM-24.9MM **Publicly Held**
SIC: **6211** Security broker & dealer service
HQ: Wfc Holdings, Corp
420 Montgomery St
San Francisco CA 94104
415 396-7392

(G-9147)
WESCO DISTRIBUTION INC
601 Lakeview Point Dr (55112-3494)
PHONE..............................651 582-3945
Deb Treanor, *Purch Mgr*
Kurt Hanson, *CFO*
Joan Follmer, *Credit Staff*
Rob Olson, *Sales Mgr*
Dave Talen, *Sales Staff*
EMP: 100
SALES (est): 50MM-99.9MM **Publicly Held**
WEB: www.wesco.com
SIC: **5063** 5065 5085 Wholesales electrical apparatus & equipment; wholesales industrial supplies; wholesales electronic parts & equipment
HQ: WESCO Distribution Inc
225 W Station Square Dr # 700
Pittsburgh PA 15219
412 454-2200

(G-9148)
WEST SIDE COMMUNITY HEALTH
153 Cesar Chavez St (55107-2226)
PHONE..............................651 222-1816
FAX: 651 602-7514
Heidi Conrad, *Vice Chairman*
Kathi Cairns, *Treasurer*
Lourdes R Borges MD, *Med Doctor*
Gisele S Bouroncle MD, *Med Doctor*
Nemera F Weyessa, *Med Doctor*
EMP: 100 **EST:** 1972
SQ FT: 42,000
SALES (est): 10MM-24.9MM **Privately Held**
WEB: www.westsidechs.org
SIC: **8011** 8021 General & family practice physician or surgeon office; dental clinic

(G-9149)
WESTERN BANK (HQ)
663 University Ave W (55104-4802)
PO Box 64689 (55164-0689)
PHONE..............................651 290-8100
Julie Causey, *Ch of Bd*
Stephen C Erdall, *President*
Tony Lemaire, *Senior VP*
James J Kuhn, *Senior VP*
Chris Dressel, *Vice Pres*
EMP: 30 **EST:** 1915
SALES (corp-wide): 23.89M **Privately Held**
SIC: **6022** 6411 State commercial bank; insurance services
PA: Western Bank
663 University Ave W
Saint Paul MN 55104
651 290-8100

(G-9150)
WESTERN BANK (PA)
663 University Ave W (55104-4802)
PO Box 64689 (55164-0689)
PHONE..............................651 290-8100
Tony Lemaire, *President*
James J Kuhn, *Senior VP*
Nicole O Cnnell, *Manager*
Jason Neuerburg, *Director*
EMP: 35 **EST:** 1979
SQ FT: 3,000
SALES (corp-wide): 23.89M **Privately Held**
SIC: **6411** 6512 Insurance agent; operators of commercial & industrial buildings

(G-9151)
WESTWAY EXTERIORS INC
2274 Capp Rd (55114-1210)
PHONE..............................651 251-0910
Michael J Kohler, *President*
Sandy Kohler, *Corp Secy*
Stacey Reese, *Manager*
EMP: 30 **EST:** 1988
SALES (est): 1MM-4.9MM **Privately Held**
SIC: **1761** Roofing & gutter work contractor; siding contractor

(G-9152)
WEYERHAEUSER CO
Also Called: St Paul Customer Service Ctr
700 Emerald St (55114-1010)
PHONE..............................651 645-0811
FAX: 651 645-9512
Ron Geister, *Opers Mgr*
Scott Mitchell, *Controller*
C Usak, *Marketing Mgr*
Jim Anderson, *Manager*
Bob Grandis, *Manager*
EMP: 50
SALES (est): 25MM-49.9MM **Publicly Held**
WEB: www.weyerhaeuser.com
SIC: **5031** Wholesales lumber, plywood & millwork
PA: Weyerhaeuser Co
33663 Weyerhaeuser Way S
Federal Way WA 98001
253 924-2345

(G-9153)
WHEELER HARDWARE CO
2645 Fairview Ave N (55113-2616)
PHONE..............................651 645-4501
FAX: 651 645-9943
Paul M Culloch, *President*
Richard Fenno, *Vice Pres*
Lois Heinz, *Bookkeeper*
EMP: 31

(PA)=Parent Co (HQ)=Headquarters (DH)=Div Headquarters
✿ = New business established in last 2 years

2011 Harris Minnesota
Services Directory

© Harris InfoSource 1-866-281-6415
395

EST: 1944
SQ FT: 10,000
SALES (est): 10MM-24.9MM **Privately Held**
WEB: www.wheelerhardware.com
SIC: 5072 5031 Wholesales builders' hardware; manufactures metal doors, sash & trim; wholesales door frames constructed of all materials; wholesales metal doors, sash & trim; manufactures hardware

(G-9154)
WHITE BEAR ANIMAL HOSPITAL
1909 County Road E E (55110-7332)
PHONE................651 777-1393
Wayne Scanlan, *President*
Stuart Dalton, *Manager*
EST: 1976 **Privately Held**
SIC: 0742 Animal hospital services

(G-9155)
WHITE BEAR DODGE INC
3430 Highway 61 N (55110-5236)
PHONE................651 482-6100
Larry Reid, *President*
Lisa Birkeland, *Controller*
EMP: 90 **EST:** 1986
SQ FT: 40,000
SALES (est): 25MM-49.9MM **Privately Held**
WEB: www.whitebeardodge.com
SIC: 7515 New & used car dealer; retails new & used automobiles; retails new & used pickups; retails new & used vans; passenger car leasing
PA: Reid Enterprises Inc
8000 Penn Ave S
Minneapolis MN 55431
952 888-9541

(G-9156)
WHITE BEAR RACQUET & SWIM LP
4800 White Bear Pkwy (55110-3345)
PHONE................651 426-1308
Robert J Ziton, *Partner*
Paul Steinhauser, *Partner*
Layne McCleary, *General Mgr*
Mandy Ritchie, *Corp Comm Staff*
Corey Lemzmeizier, *Manager*
EMP: 200 **EST:** 1988
SQ FT: 113,000
SALES (est): 5MM-9.9MM **Privately Held**
WEB: www.wbfit.com
SIC: 7997 7991 Membership tennis club; health club

(G-9157)
WILKERSON, GUTHMANN & JOHNSON
55 5th St E Ste 1300 (55101-1787)
PHONE................651 222-1801
FAX: 651 297-6929
Roger A Katzenmaier, *CEO*
Darwin Benz, *Principal*
Barbara Buckley, *Principal*
Marc Hadley, *Vice Pres*
Greg Carlson, *Vice Pres*
EMP: 26 **EST:** 1923
SQ FT: 6,533
SALES (est): 1MM-4.9MM **Privately Held**
SIC: 8721 Certified public accountant services

(G-9158)
WINFIELD SOLUTIONS LLC (HQ)
1080 County Road F W (55126-2910)
PO Box 64589 (55164-0589)
PHONE................651 481-2222
Ruth Reynolds, *Corp Secy*
Billie J Landberg, *Vice Pres*
Norm Mabbit, *Treasurer*
Christopher Policinski, *Mng Member*
Peter S Janzen, *Incorporator*
EMP: 125 **EST:** 2007
SALES (corp-wide): 5.84B **Privately Held**
WEB: www.landolakes.com
SIC: 0721 Crop planting & protection services

(G-9159)
WIPFLI LLP
4000 Lexington Ave N # 201 (55126-8200)
PHONE................651 636-6468
Christina Fasbender, *Office Mgr*
Grant Young, *Branch Mgr*

Christina Susbender, *Officer*
EMP: 28
SALES (est): 1MM-4.9MM **Privately Held**
SIC: 8721 Certified public accountant services
PA: Wipfli LLP
11 Scott St Ste 400
Wausau WI 54403
715 845-3111

(G-9160)
WIRTZ BEVERAGE MINNESOTA BEER
475 Prior Ave N (55104-3420)
PHONE................651 646-6063
FAX: 651 646-6036
William R Wirtz, *President*
Mike Amagliani, *Senior VP*
Kevin Ryan, *Vice Pres*
Judy Anderson, *Purch Agent*
Mark Schmidt, *Controller*
▲ **EMP:** 130 **EST:** 1962
SQ FT: 40,000
SALES (est): 50MM-99.9MM **Privately Held**
WEB: www.delucaliquor.com
SIC: 5181 5149 Wholesales beer & other fermented malt liquors; wholesales beverages; wholesales juices; wholesales soft drinks
PA: Monarch Beverage Co
1849 W Cheyenne Ave
North Las Vegas NV 89032
702 731-1040

(G-9161)
WISCONSIN CENTRAL LTD
Also Called: Canadian National
669 1st St NW (55112-3212)
PHONE................651 633-8771
FAX: 651 633-8763
Marty Carlson, *Principal*
EMP: 25
SALES (est): 1MM-4.9MM **Privately Held**
WEB: www.cn.ca
SIC: 4013 Railroad switching & terminal services
PA: Wisconsin Central Ltd
17641 Ashland Ave
Homewood IL 60430
708 332-3500

(G-9162)
WISE ESSENTIALS INC
716 Mount Curve Blvd (55116-1159)
PHONE................651 699-4468
Melinda Bonk, *CEO*
EMP: 30 **EST:** 1994
SALES (est): 25MM-49.9MM **Privately Held**
WEB: www.wiseessentials.com
SIC: 5122 Wholesales cosmetics, perfumes & hair products

(G-9163)
WOMEN OF NATIONS
Also Called: Eagles Nest Shelter
73 Leech St (55102-2719)
PHONE................651 222-5830
Ann Gaasch, *Corp Secy*
Pat Johnston, *Treasurer*
Michelle Thompson-Tuttle, *Exec Dir*
Joan Myricklewis, *Exec Dir*
Norma Renniville, *Exec Dir*
EMP: 32 **EST:** 1982
SALES (est): 1MM-4.9MM **Privately Held**
SIC: 8322 Crisis center

(G-9164)
WOMEN'S ADVOCATES INC
588 Grand Ave (55102-2610)
PHONE................651 227-9966
Sheila Ellis, *Human Res Mgr*
Lisbet Wolf, *Exec Dir*
Jane Kilian, *Exec Dir*
Raeone Loscalzo, *Exec Dir*
EMP: 50 **EST:** 1972
SQ FT: 11,000
SALES (est): 1MM-4.9MM **Privately Held**
WEB: www.wadvocates.org
SIC: 8322 Crisis center

(G-9165)
WOMENS LIFE CARE CENTER
2870 Middle St (55117-1411)
PHONE................651 777-0350
Mary Kayfchmitt, *Principal*

EMP: 41 **EST:** 1982
SQ FT: 871
SALES (est): 1MM-4.9MM **Privately Held**
SIC: 8322 Individual & family social services

(G-9166)
WOODS EQUIPMENT CO
Also Called: Tisco
2340 County Road C W Ste 120 (55113-2545)
PHONE................651 455-6681
Jim Wisconski, *Vice Pres*
Mark Martheler, *Purch Agent*
Susan Dezenski, *Human Res Mgr*
Don Kemp, *Manager*
Jon Smart, *MIS Mgr*
EMP: 100
SALES (est): 25MM-49.9MM **Privately Held**
SIC: 5083 Wholesales farm equipment parts & supplies
PA: Genstar Capital, LP
4 Embarcadero Ctr # 1500
San Francisco CA 94111
415 834-2350

(G-9167)
WOODY'S REBAR CO
3580 Centerville Rd (55127-7104)
PHONE................651 592-5038
Gayre F Woodbury, *Vice Pres*
Larry L Woodbury, *Vice Pres*
EMP: 30 **EST:** 1998
SALES (est): 1MM-4.9MM **Privately Held**
SIC: 1731 Electrical contractor

(G-9168)
WORLD ARCHITECTS INC
305 Saint Peter St (55102-1607)
PHONE................651 227-7773
FAX: 651 223-5646
Mike Cox, *President*
Matthew Mooney, *CFO*
EMP: 100 **EST:** 1968
SQ FT: 25,000
SALES (est): 10MM-24.9MM **Privately Held**
WEB: www.woldae.com
SIC: 8712 7389 8711 Architectural service; interior designing service; electrical or electronic engineers; mechanical engineering services

(G-9169)
WREN CORP (PA)
2975 Partridge Rd (55113-1119)
PO Box 130280 (55113-0003)
PHONE................651 636-8900
John Wren, *CEO*
Peter Martin, *President*
Karen Vanney, *Vice Pres*
EMP: 295 **EST:** 1985
SQ FT: 40,000 **Privately Held**
SIC: 4212 Local trucking without storage services

(G-9170)
XMALPHA TECHNOLOGIES
Also Called: Legislative Solutions
935 Arbogast St (55126-3825)
PHONE................651 484-0471
Devan Shepherd, *CEO*
Katherine Shepherd, *COO*
EMP: 30 **EST:** 1977
SQ FT: 2,000
SALES (est): 1MM-4.9MM **Privately Held**
WEB: www.xmalpha.com
SIC: 8748 Business consulting services

(G-9171)
Y M C A INFANT CENTER
1761 University Ave W (55104-3509)
PHONE................651 646-4557
David Doninick, *Exec Dir*
EMP: 25 **EST:** 2005 **Privately Held**
SIC: 8641 7032 7991 8322 8351 Youth organizations; youth camps; child day care service; individual & family social services; physical fitness center

(G-9172)
YADA SYSTEMS INC
2717 Lincoln Dr (55113-1334)
PHONE................651 631-3237
FAX: 651 631-3241
Robert Yauk, *President*
Kelly Dixon, *General Mgr*

Peter Santrach, *Vice Pres*
Barb Birchem, *Manager*
Deb Remillard, *Info Tech Mgr*
EMP: 65 **EST:** 1985
SQ FT: 25,000
SALES (est): 25MM-49.9MM **Privately Held**
WEB: www.yadasystems.com
SIC: 5045 Wholesales computers, peripherals & software

(G-9173)
YMCA CHILDREN'S CENTER
Also Called: Northeast Family YMCA
2100 Orchard Ln (55110-5447)
PHONE................651 777-8103
Jenny Byron, *Business Mgr*
Tim Opren, *Vice Pres*
Tom Holland, *Exec Dir*
Shane Hoefer, *Exec Dir*
Keith Stout, *Exec Dir*
EMP: 50 **Privately Held**
SIC: 8641 7032 7991 8322 8351 Youth organizations; youth camps; child day care service; individual & family social services; physical fitness center

(G-9174)
YMCA OF GREATER SAINT PAUL
Also Called: Eastside YMCA
875 Arcade St (55106-3800)
PHONE................651 771-8881
FAX: 651 793-3565
Jon Bryan, *Business Mgr*
Maggie Staiger, *Data Proc Exec*
Leroy West, *Exec Dir*
Michelle Ocasio, *Exec Dir*
Scott Miller, *Director*
EMP: 50 **Privately Held**
WEB: www.ymcastpaul.org
SIC: 8641 8351 Social club; youth organizations; child day care service
PA: YMCA of Greater Saint Paul
2125 E Hennepin Ave Ste 100
Minneapolis MN 55413
612 465-0450

(G-9175)
YMCA OF GREATER SAINT PAUL
Also Called: Camp Wigiwagen
2 E Hennepin Ste 150 (55108)
PHONE................651 645-6605
Tom Kranz, *Exec Dir*
EMP: 50 **Privately Held**
WEB: www.ymcastpaul.org
SIC: 8641 7032 7991 8322 8351 Youth organizations; youth camps; child day care service; individual & family social services; physical fitness center
PA: YMCA of Greater Saint Paul
2125 E Hennepin Ave Ste 100
Minneapolis MN 55413
612 465-0450

(G-9176)
YMCA OF GREATER ST PAUL
Also Called: Northwest YMCA
3760 Lexington Ave N (55126-2915)
PHONE................651 483-2671
Susan Faus, *Sales Staff*
Pat Riemersma, *Manager*
Chad Turner, *Maintence Staff*
EMP: 197 **Privately Held**
WEB: www.ymcastpaul.org
SIC: 8641 7032 7991 8322 8351 Youth organizations; youth camps; child day care service; individual & family social services; physical fitness center
PA: YMCA of Greater Saint Paul
2125 E Hennepin Ave Ste 100
Minneapolis MN 55413
612 465-0450

(G-9177)
YMCA OF GREATER ST PAUL
Also Called: Midway Family YMCA
1761 University Ave W (55104-3509)
PHONE................651 646-4557
FAX: 651 644-4692
Jessica Henry, *Member*
Gabriel Blott, *Business Mgr*
Greg Weibel, *Vice Pres*
David Dominick, *Engrg Dir*
Phil Imsdahl, *Engineering*
EMP: 76 **Privately Held**

▲=Import ▼=Export
◆=Import/Export

WEB: www.ymcastpaul.org
SIC: 8641 7032 7991 8322 8351 Youth organizations; youth camps; child day care service; individual & family social services; physical fitness center
PA: YMCA of Greater Saint Paul
2125 E Hennepin Ave Ste 100
Minneapolis MN 55413
612 465-0450

(G-9178)
YMCA OF GREATER ST PAUL
Also Called: Skyway YMCA
194 6th St E (55101-1911)
PHONE............................651 292-4143
FAX: 651 292-4148
Robbie William, *Business Mgr*
Tom Eaton, *Office Mgr*
Peg Schmoll, *Info Tech Mgr*
Darwin Miles, *Exec Dir*
Stephanie Sweet, *Exec Dir*
EMP: 100 **Privately Held**
WEB: www.ymcastpaul.org
SIC: 8641 7032 7991 8322 8351 Youth organizations; youth camps; child day care service; individual & family social services; physical fitness center
PA: YMCA of Greater Saint Paul
2125 E Hennepin Ave Ste 100
Minneapolis MN 55413
612 465-0450

(G-9179)
YOCUM OIL CO INC
2719 Stillwater Rd E (55119-3619)
PHONE..............................651 739-9141
Tim Yocum, *President*
Jon Yoccum, *Exec VP*
Tricia Palm, *Human Res Dir*
John Halberg, *Manager*
Dane Copic, *Manager*
EMP: 131 **EST:** 1959
SQ FT: 8,000
SALES (est): 100MM-499.9MM **Privately Held**
SIC: 5172 Wholesales fuel oil; liquefied petroleum gas dealer; wholesales gasoline; wholesales lubricating oils & greases; retail independent convenience store; retail gasoline filling station

(G-9180)
YORKDALE TOWNHOMES INC
328 Kellogg Blvd W (55102-1900)
PHONE..............................651 291-1750
Joseph Holmberg, *President*
Jennifer Wille, *Principal*
EMP: 99
SALES (est): 10MM-24.9MM **Privately Held**
SIC: 6513 Apartment building operator

(G-9181)
YOUNG WOMEN'S CHRISTIAN ASSN
Also Called: Y W C A of Saint Paul
375 Selby Ave (55102-1822)
PHONE..............................651 222-3741
Stephen Bates, *Controller*
Brad Enderle, *IT/INT Sup*
Tara Anderson, *Exec Dir*
William L Collins Jr, *Exec Dir*
EMP: 105 **EST:** 1907 **Privately Held**
SIC: 8641 Youth organizations; recreation association

SAINT PAUL
Washington County

(G-9182)
ADVANCED AUTOMOTIVE INDUSTRIES
7161 55th St N (55128-1706)
PHONE..............................651 777-5420
James Harley III, *President*
EMP: 50 **EST:** 1985
SQ FT: 28,000
SALES (est): 10MM-24.9MM **Privately Held**
SIC: 5013 Wholesales new motor vehicle parts & supplies

(G-9183)
AMERICAN EXPRESS TRAVEL
1811 Weir Dr Ste 340 (55125-2273)
PHONE..............................651 731-9396
Lynn Abbott, *Manager*
Ann Hucksted, *Manager*
EMP: 30
SALES (est): 1MM-4.9MM **Publicly Held**
SIC: 4724 Tourist agency arranging transport, lodging & car rental
PA: American Express Co
200 Vesey St
New York NY 10285
212 640-2000

(G-9184)
ANIMAL EMERGENCY CLINIC
7166 10th St N Ste 1 (55128-5950)
PHONE..............................651 501-3766
Jenny Rafmanson, *Manager*
EMP: 35 **EST:** 2001 **Privately Held**
WEB: www.aec-tc.com
SIC: 0742 Animal hospital services

(G-9185)
ATOMIC PROPS & EFFECTS LTD
895 Hale Ave N (55128-7549)
PHONE..............................612 331-1335
Patricia Punch, *Partner*
Michael Pearson, *Partner*
David Dunn, *General Mgr*
Kim Kuklok, *Exec Dir*
▲ **EMP:** 35 **EST:** 1980
SQ FT: 35,000
SALES (est): 1MM-4.9MM **Privately Held**
WEB: www.atomicprops.com
SIC: 1799 Theatrical prop, set & scenery construction

(G-9186)
AUTOMOTIVE COOLING PRODUCTS (PA)
8934 Springwood Cir (55125-4913)
PHONE..............................651 731-2414
Shawn Lewis, *President*
Dick Hoel, *Chairman*
Edward Drenttel, *Vice Chairman*
Larry Gamst, *Treasurer*
EMP: 35 **EST:** 1980
SQ FT: 35,000 **Privately Held**
SIC: 5075 5013 Wholesales heating & air conditioning equipment & supplies; wholesales automotive supplies & parts; wholesales automotive radiators

(G-9187)
BBJ INC
Also Called: Heppners Woodbury Auto Wash
7776 Hudson Rd (55125-1439)
PHONE..............................651 730-7808
Bonnie Kluge, *President*
EMP: 25 **EST:** 1993
SALES (est): 500-999K **Privately Held**
SIC: 7542 Automotive washing & polishing service

(G-9188)
BRIGHTKEYS BUILDING & DEVPT
Also Called: Countryvilla Builders
707 Commerce Dr Ste 410 (55125-7741)
PHONE..............................651 501-6500
Linda Petersen, *President*
Paul Hamblin, *Purchasing*
Kerry Mulcrone, *Human Res Mgr*
EMP: 40 **EST:** 1996
SALES (est): 10MM-24.9MM **Privately Held**
WEB: www.brightkeys.com
SIC: 1522 Condominium construction service

(G-9189)
BROWN TANK LLC
6995 55th St N (55128-1725)
PHONE..............................651 747-0100
Bob Sumter, *Member*
Mike Mitchell, *Vice Pres*
Jack Sudbeck, *Manager*
Michael Peterson, *Manager*
Barbarra Demars, *Manager*
EMP: 59 **EST:** 2000
SQ FT: 25,000
SALES (est): 5MM-9.9MM **Privately Held**

WEB: www.browntank-mn.com
SIC: 1791 Metal storage tank erection; plate metal fabricator

(G-9190)
BRUCE B CUNNINGHAM
Also Called: Minnhealth Family Physicians
8325 City Centre Dr (55125-3323)
PHONE..............................651 731-0859
FAX: 651 731-0976
Bruce B Cunningham DO, *Principal*
Nancy Montdrianz, *Officer*
EMP: 25
SALES (est): 1MM-4.9MM **Privately Held**
SIC: 8031 Osteopathic physicians' office & clinic

(G-9191)
BT AMERICAS HOLDINGS LTD
7007 55th St N (55128-1729)
PHONE..............................651 746-8739
Mike Cooper, *Branch Mgr*
EMP: 35
SALES (est): 1MM-4.9MM **Privately Held**
SIC: 7389 Teleconferencing services

(G-9192)
CARDINAL POINTE OF OAKDALE
1201 Hadley Ave N (55128-5930)
PHONE..............................651 578-0650
EMP: 25 **EST:** 2007
SALES (est): 500-999K **Privately Held**
SIC: 8361 Geriatric residential care

(G-9193)
CARVER LAKE VETERINARY CENTER
2201 Ventura Dr (55125-4337)
PHONE..............................651 578-3290
FAX: 651 578-3261
Kate Anhunter, *Owner*
EMP: 25 **EST:** 1996 **Privately Held**
SIC: 0742 Veterinary services

(G-9194)
CENTRAL REGIONAL PATHOLOGY LAB
1875 Woodwinds Dr Ste 220 (55125-2502)
PHONE..............................651 264-1611
FAX: 651 264-1661
John Uecker, *President*
Renee Simmons, *Business Mgr*
Joseph Leverone, *Vice Pres*
David M Cartwright, *Pathologist*
Yap Y Chong, *Pathologist*
EMP: 28 **EST:** 1970
SQ FT: 1,000
SALES (est): 1MM-4.9MM **Privately Held**
WEB: www.crplab.com
SIC: 8071 8733 Medical pathology laboratory; medical research organization

(G-9195)
CHESLEY TRUCK SALES INC
370 Quail Rd (55110-1422)
PHONE..............................651 636-3400
FAX: 651 636-8456
George Chesley, *President*
Steve Chesley, *Corp Secy*
EMP: 111 **EST:** 1984
SQ FT: 35,000
SALES (est): 100MM-499.9MM **Privately Held**
SIC: 5012 7699 Wholesales commercial trucks; industrial truck repair service

(G-9196)
CHEX SYSTEMS INC
7805 Hudson Rd Ste 100 (55125-1595)
PHONE..............................651 361-2000
Juliet A Lim, *Branch Mgr*
EMP: 350
SALES (est): 50MM-99.9MM **Publicly Held**
WEB: www.goldleaf-tech.com
SIC: 7323 7322 Credit reporting services; collection agency
PA: Fidelity National Information
601 Riverside Ave
Jacksonville FL 32204
904 854-5000

(G-9197)
CHILDREN'S HEALTH CARE INC
1825 Woodwinds Dr (55125-2202)
PHONE..............................651 232-6800
FAX: 651 232-0059
Kelly Micolichek, *Co-Director*
EMP: 120
SALES (est): 10MM-24.9MM **Privately Held**
SIC: 8011 Physicians' office
PA: Children's Health Care Inc
2525 Chicago Ave
Minneapolis MN 55404
612 813-6100

(G-9198)
COMPUTER INTEGRATION TECHS
Also Called: CIT
2375 Ventura Dr Ste A (55125-4406)
PHONE..............................651 450-0333
FAX: 651 450-0300
Christopher J Taylor, *President*
Mark Wagner, *Vice Pres*
Mark Sellner, *Purchasing*
William T Lehner, *CFO*
Andrew Fjeld, *Accounts Mgr*
EMP: 65 **EST:** 1992
SQ FT: 20,000
SALES (est): 10MM-24.9MM **Privately Held**
WEB: www.cit-net.com
SIC: 7373 Computer integrated systems design services; local area network systems integration service

(G-9199)
CON SPEC CORP
707 Commerce Dr Ste 410 (55125-7741)
PHONE..............................651 501-6500
Clement R Hackworthy, *CEO*
Donna Caywood, *Treasurer*
EMP: 35 **EST:** 1982
SQ FT: 3,000
SALES (est): 5MM-9.9MM **Privately Held**
SIC: 1522 1542 New multi-family dwelling construction service; multi-family home remodeling service; new commercial & office building construction; commercial & office building renovation & repair services

(G-9200)
DANIEL P KHOURY
Also Called: Central Pediatrics
7803 Afton Rd (55125-4412)
PHONE..............................651 738-0470
FAX: 651 738-8915
Wendy Teralje, *General Mgr*
Daniel Khoury, *Principal*
Dale Asterman, *Office Mgr*
Mike Fishbein, *Administrator*
Laura Benjamin, *Nursing Dir*
EMP: 62 **EST:** 2001
SALES (est): 5MM-9.9MM **Privately Held**
SIC: 8011 Pediatrician office

(G-9201)
DASCOM SYSTEMS GROUP LLC
2415 Ventura Dr (55125-3930)
PHONE..............................651 578-1200
FAX: 651 578-1200
Daniel Takkunen, *Member*
Scott Apfelbacher, *Member*
Mark Sturm, *Exec Dir*
EMP: 32 **EST:** 1995
SQ FT: 6,900 **Privately Held**
WEB: www.dascom-systems.com
SIC: 4899 Communication signal enhancement network services; manufactures radio & television communications equipment

(G-9202)
DAVID G MCALPHIE MD
8325 City Centre Dr (55125-3323)
PHONE..............................651 731-0859
David G McAlpine MD, *President*
EMP: 25 **EST:** 1996
SALES (est): 1MM-4.9MM **Privately Held**
SIC: 8011 General & family practice physician or surgeon office

(PA)=Parent Co (HQ)=Headquarters (DH)=Div Headquarters
✿ = New business established in last 2 years

2011 Harris Minnesota
Services Directory

© Harris InfoSource 1-866-281-6415
397

(G-9203)

DELLWOOD HILLS GOLF CLUB
29 Highway 96 E (55110-1407)
PHONE..............................651 426-3218
FAX: 651 426-0484
Ken Galloway, *General Mgr*
Jack Grengs, *Finance Mgr*
Dianna Lemire, *Manager*
David Macias, *Manager*
Jenell Levender, *Manager*
EMP: 80 EST: 1974
SQ FT: 19,000
SALES (est): 1MM-4.9MM **Privately Held**
WEB: www.dellwoodhillsgc.org
SIC: 7997 Membership golf club; eating place

(G-9204)

DELWIN TRANSFER INC
7500 Hudson Blvd N Ste 620
(55128-7056)
PHONE..............................651 731-0510
Robert Apmang, *President*
Robert Apman, *President*
Sherry Little, *General Mgr*
Barbara Apman, *Principal*
EMP: 28 EST: 1960
SQ FT: 8,500
SALES (est): 1MM-4.9MM **Privately Held**
SIC: 4212 Local trucking without storage services

(G-9205)

DUKE & KING ACQUISITION CORP
Also Called: Burger King
1501 Vly Creek Rd Wier Dr (55125)
PHONE..............................651 731-8720
Mark Forneris, *General Mgr*
Watters Mike, *Sales Executive*
EMP: 30
SALES (est): 10MM-24.9MM **Privately Held**
SIC: 6794 Selling or licensing of franchises
PA: Duke & King Acquisition Corp
12252 Nicollet Ave
Burnsville MN 55337
952 288-2300

(G-9206)

ECOWATER SYSTEMS LLC (DH)
1890 Woodlane Dr (55125-2913)
PO Box 64420 (55164-0420)
PHONE..............................651 739-5330
FAX: 651 739-4547
Russ Patterson, *President*
Robert Webb, *Corp Secy*
Steve Dakolios, *VP Opers*
Dave Kell, *Plant Mgr*
Steve Webb, *VP Sls/Mktg*
▲ EMP: 300 EST: 1925
SQ FT: 275,000
SALES (corp-wide): 112.49B **Publicly Held**
WEB: www.ecowater.com
SIC: 5074 Wholesales water softening equipment; manufactures household water filters & softeners; manufactures industrial water treatment equipment; wholesales water purification equipment
HQ: Marmon Holdings Inc
181 W Madison St Ste 2500
Chicago IL 60602
312 372-9500

(G-9207)

EDDIE BAUER INC
10150 Hudson Rd Ste 106 (55129-8633)
PHONE..............................651 738-8653
Deborah Marine, *Manager*
EMP: 30
SALES (est): 1MM-4.9MM **Privately Held**
WEB: www.eddiebauer.com
SIC: 4226 Warehousing & storage facility
HQ: Eddie Bauer Inc
10401 NE 8th St Ste 500
Bellevue WA 98004
425 755-6100

(G-9208)

EDGEWOOD MANAGEMENT INC
Also Called: Woodbury Estates
2825 Woodlane Dr Apt 224 (55125-2970)
PHONE..............................651 714-1000
FAX: 651 476-6794
Kit McGuire, *CFO*

Mary A Wiebusch, *Manager*
Larson Allen, *Director*
EMP: 30 EST: 1998
SALES (est): 1MM-4.9MM **Privately Held**
WEB: www.leanoncarleen.com
SIC: 8052 Intermediate care facility

(G-9209)

EDUCATIONAL CREDIT MANAGEMENT
Also Called: Ecmc
1 Imation Pl (55128-3422)
PHONE..............................651 221-0566
Richard J Boyle, *President*
John Depodesta, *Member*
Bob McGowan, *CFO*
Kathleen King, *CFO*
Amy Spartz, *VP Human Res*
EMP: 200 EST: 1994
SALES (est): 50MM-99.9MM **Privately Held**
SIC: 6111 Federal credit agency

(G-9210)

EFUNDS CORP
7805 Hudson Rd Ste 100 (55125-1595)
PHONE..............................651 361-2000
Coleen Abstedt, *Vice Pres*
Bernie Ortt, *Engineer*
Sandy Lien, *Marketing Mgr*
Mike Dado, *Manager*
Brian Jacques, *Manager*
EMP: 800
SALES (est): 50MM-99.9MM **Publicly Held**
WEB: www.goldleaf-tech.com
SIC: 7374 Data processing & preparation services
PA: Fidelity National Information
601 Riverside Ave
Jacksonville FL 32204
904 854-5000

(G-9211)

ELITE COMMUNICATIONS & CONSTR
651 Hayward Ave N (55128-7152)
PHONE..............................651 739-1366
Fernando Huerta, *Member*
Val Huerta, *Member*
EMP: 25 EST: 2005
SALES (est): 5MM-9.9MM **Privately Held**
SIC: 1521 Single-family housing construction

(G-9212)

ELIZABETH CHARLES CORP
Also Called: Spalon Montage Woodbury
8375 Seasons Pkwy (55125-9110)
PHONE..............................952 915-2900
Todd Schroeder, *Manager*
EMP: 79
SALES (est): 1MM-4.9MM **Privately Held**
SIC: 7231 7991 Unisex hair salon; cosmetologist; facial salon; spas
PA: Elizabeth Charles Corp
3909 W 49 1/2 St
Minneapolis MN 55424
952 915-2900

(G-9213)

EMMONS & OLIVIER RESOURCES INC
651 Hale Ave N (55128-7534)
PHONE..............................651 770-8448
Brett Emmons, *President*
Cecilio Olivier, *Vice Pres*
Elizabeth Clubb, *Treasurer*
Jennifer Olson, *Info Tech Mgr*
Gary Oberts, *Exec Dir*
EMP: 37 EST: 1996
SQ FT: 11,000
SALES (est): 1MM-4.9MM **Privately Held**
WEB: www.bcwd.org
SIC: 8748 Environmental consultant

(G-9214)

ENGINEERING AMERICA INC
647 Hale Ave N (55128-7534)
PHONE..............................651 777-4041
Anthony Belden, *President*
Andrew Cunningham, *Vice Pres*
Travis Hackworthy, *Vice Pres*
Mark Lindgren, *CFO*
EMP: 36 EST: 1980
SQ FT: 17,000
SALES (est): 1MM-4.9MM **Privately Held**

WEB: www.engamerica.com
SIC: 1791 5084 Metal storage tank erection; wholesales industrial machinery & equipment

(G-9215)

ENTEGEE INC
6053 Hudson Rd Ste 350 (55125-1099)
PHONE..............................651 739-7366
Scott Nelson, *Manager*
EMP: 40
SALES (est): 500-999K **Publicly Held**
WEB: www.entegee.com
SIC: 7363 Temporary help service
DH: Entegee Inc
128 Corporate Ctr
Burlington MA 01803
781 221-5800

(G-9216)

FAMILY RESOURCES DEVELOPMENT
Also Called: Oak Meadows
8131 4th St N (55128-7078)
PHONE..............................651 578-0676
FAX: 651 578-1431
Connie Dow, *Exec Dir*
▲ EMP: 35 EST: 1995
SALES (est): 5MM-9.9MM **Privately Held**
SIC: 6513 Apartment building operator

(G-9217)

FEDEX OFFICE & PRINT SERVICES
8300 City Centre Dr (55125-3331)
PHONE..............................612 578-9000
Kerry Banston, *Managing Dir*
John Guftsaon, *Branch Mgr*
Rhonda Iverson, *Branch Mgr*
Richard Fauver, *Manager*
EMP: 30
SALES (est): 1MM-4.9MM **Publicly Held**
WEB: www.kinkos.com
SIC: 7334 Photocopying & duplicating services
HQ: Fedex Office & Print Services
13155 Noel Rd Ste 1600
Dallas TX 75240
214 550-7000

(G-9218)

FIRSTMARK SERVICES LLC
2101 Wooddale Dr Ste B (55125-4442)
PHONE..............................651 265-7600
Robert Beiersdorf, *Member*
EMP: 60 EST: 2002
SQ FT: 10,000
SALES (est): 10MM-24.9MM **Privately Held**
SIC: 6141 Personal credit institution

(G-9219)

GENESIS CORP
7650 Currell Blvd Ste 260 (55125-8209)
PHONE..............................651 702-3300
Jim Kelly, *Branch Mgr*
EMP: 525
SALES (est): 50MM-99.9MM **Privately Held**
SIC: 7379 8742 Computer system consulting services; management consulting services
PA: Genesis Corp
950 3rd Ave Ste 2702
New York NY 10022
212 688-5522

(G-9220)

GIANNETTI PROPERTIES LLC
2899 Hudson Rd (55128-7100)
PHONE..............................651 738-2168
Tom Gianetti, *Co-Owner*
EMP: 115 EST: 1998
SALES (est): 25MM-49.9MM **Privately Held**
SIC: 6512 Nonresidential building operator

(G-9221)

GOLDWOOD KENNELS INC
9500 Dellwood Rd N (55115-2118)
PHONE..............................651 429-0648
FAX: 651 429-5397
Joan Hilton, *Principal*
Cliff Hilton, *Principal*
EMP: 25
SQ FT: 10,000 **Privately Held**
WEB: www.goldwoodkennels.com

SIC: 0752 Kennel boarding services

(G-9222)

HARTFORD LIFE INC
500 Bielenberg Dr (55125-4401)
PHONE..............................651 738-4516
Ryan Knaup, *Senior VP*
Kevin Harnetiaux, *Senior VP*
Matt Shulman, *Vice Pres*
Jilene Christenson, *Manager*
Phil Eldredge, *Manager*
EMP: 100
SALES (est): 50MM-99.9MM **Publicly Held**
WEB: www.hartfordlife.com
SIC: 6321 Direct accident & health insurance carrier
HQ: Hartford Life Inc
200 Hopmeadow St
Weatogue CT 06089
860 547-5000

(G-9223)

HARVEST FACILITY HOLDINGS LP
Also Called: Lodge At White Bear
3666 E County Line N # 126 (55110-1864)
PHONE..............................651 779-9255
FAX: 651 762-2531
Annette Murray, *Manager*
Jim Murray, *Manager*
EMP: 31
SALES (est): 1MM-4.9MM **Publicly Held**
WEB: www.holidaytouch.com
SIC: 6513 Apartment building operator
HQ: Harvest Facility Holdings LP
2250 McGilchrist St SE
Salem OR 97302
503 370-7070

(G-9224)

HAVEN CHEMICAL HEALTH SYSTEM
2042 Wooddale Dr Ste 220 (55125-4421)
PHONE..............................651 734-9633
Robert Haven, *Director*
EMP: 35
SALES (est): 1MM-4.9MM **Privately Held**
WEB:
www.havenchemicalhealthsystems.com
SIC: 8093 Outpatient rehabilitation treatment center

(G-9225)

HEALTHEAST CO'S INC
Also Called: Woodwinds Health Campus
1925 Woodwinds Dr (55125-2270)
PHONE..............................651 232-4000
Julie Schmidt, *CEO*
Kathleen Killeen, *General Mgr*
EMP: 400
SALES (est): 25MM-49.9MM **Privately Held**
SIC: 8062 Medical hospital
HQ: Healtheast Co's Inc
1700 University Ave W
Saint Paul MN 55104
651 232-2300

(G-9226)

HEALTHPARTNERS INC
Also Called: Woodbury Clinic
8450 Seasons Pkwy (55125-4402)
PHONE..............................651 702-5300
FAX: 651 702-3505
Pam Morben, *Principal*
Sonia M Hely, *Med Doctor*
Karen R Steine, *Med Doctor*
David A Baram, *Obstetrician*
Buvana R Reddy, *Obstetrician*
EMP: 80
SALES (est): 5MM-9.9MM **Privately Held**
WEB: www.healthpartners.com
SIC: 8011 Physicians' office & clinic
PA: HealthPartners Inc
8170 33rd Ave S
Bloomington MN 55425
952 883-6000

(G-9227)

HEALTHPARTNERS INC
Also Called: Healthprtners Wodbury Eye Dntl
8325 Seasons Pkwy Ste 103
(55125-3602)
PHONE..............................651 702-5871
Kirk Kluegel, *Optometrist*

www.HarrisInfo.com
398

2011 Harris Minnesota
Services Directory

▲=Import ▼=Export
◆=Import/Export

Katherine Spencer, *Optometrist*
David Busch, *Manager*
EMP: 25
SALES (est): 1MM-4.9MM **Privately Held**
WEB: www.healthpartners.com
SIC: 8021 Dental clinic
PA: HealthPartners Inc
  8170 33rd Ave S
  Bloomington MN 55425
  952 883-6000

(G-9228)
HIGHER DIMENSION MATERIALS INC (PA)
570 Hale Ave N (55128-7548)
PHONE 651 730-6203
Young H Kim, *CEO*
▲ **EMP:** 40 **EST:** 1996
SQ FT: 60,000 **Privately Held**
WEB: www.superfabric.com
SIC: 8731 Commercial physical research laboratory

(G-9229)
HIGHER DIMENSION RESEARCH INC
570 Hale Ave N (55128-7548)
PHONE 651 730-6203
Young-Hwa Kim PhD, *CEO*
Joel T Nelson, *Ch of Bd*
Linda Burrell, *Human Resources*
EMP: 48 **EST:** 1992 **Privately Held**
WEB: www.hdri.com
SIC: 8731 5045 Commercial biotechnology research laboratory; wholesales computer software; commercial food research services; chemical laboratory
PA: Higher Dimension Materials Inc
  570 Hale Ave N
  Saint Paul MN 55128
  651 730-6203

(G-9230)
HILTON GARDEN INN - ST PAUL
420 Inwood Ave N (55128-7095)
PHONE 651 735-4100
FAX: 651 735-4101
Christpher Hutchinson, *Principal*
Stephen Schwartz, *Member*
Chris Ruage, *Manager*
EMP: 65 **EST:** 2005
SALES (est): 1MM-4.9MM **Privately Held**
SIC: 7011 Traveler accommodations

(G-9231)
HOHENSTEINS INC
2330 Ventura Dr (55125-3929)
PHONE 651 735-4978
FAX: 651 735-4987
Karl Hohenstein, *President*
Lorraine Hohenstein, *Vice Pres*
▲ **EMP:** 28 **EST:** 1972
SQ FT: 100,000
SALES (est): 10MM-24.9MM **Privately Held**
WEB: www.hohensteins.com
SIC: 5181 5149 Wholesales beer & other fermented malt liquors; wholesales beverages

(G-9232)
HOHENWALD PROPERTIES
Also Called: Spartan Commercial Group
711 Hale Ave N (55128-7545)
PHONE 651 735-1333
Phyllis Hohenwald, *Owner*
EMP: 80 **EST:** 1995
SALES (est): 10MM-24.9MM **Privately Held**
SIC: 6512 Nonresidential building operator

(G-9233)
HUMAN SERVICES INC IN WA (PA)
7066 Stillwater Blvd N (55128-3937)
PHONE 651 777-5222
FAX: 651 251-5111
Mark Kuppe, *CEO*
Naomi Bakke, *Purchasing*
Steve Hunt, *CFO*
Kathy Bendenburg, *Human Resources*
Cathy Korich, *Office Mgr*
EMP: 150 **EST:** 1970
SQ FT: 38,432
SALES (corp-wide): 15.39M **Privately Held**
SIC: 8322 Social services center

(G-9234)
KATE ANNE HUNTER
2201 Ventura Dr (55125-4337)
PHONE 651 578-3290
Kate A Hunter, *Owner*
EMP: 30 **EST:** 1996 **Privately Held**
SIC: 0742 Animal hospital services

(G-9235)
KILTIE CORP
Also Called: Versa-Lok Retaining Wall Sys
6348 Highway 36 Blvd N Ste 1 (55128-1407)
PHONE 651 770-3166
FAX: 651 770-4089
Terri Jungquist, *CEO*
Todd Strand, *President*
Joe Glidden, *Vice Pres*
Tom Olson, *Vice Pres*
Matt Singer, *Sales Executive*
EMP: 42 **EST:** 1984
SQ FT: 12,000
SALES (est): 10MM-24.9MM **Privately Held**
WEB: www.versalok.com
SIC: 6794 Patent buying, licensing & leasing

(G-9236)
KIM KUNWOOK
2820 White Eagle Dr (55129-4291)
PHONE 651 578-7627
Kim Kunwood, *President*
EMP: 25 **EST:** 1995
SALES (est): 500-999K **Privately Held**
SIC: 7349 Janitorial & custodial services

(G-9237)
KINDERCARE LEARNING CENTERS
8425 City Centre Dr (55125-3380)
PHONE 651 735-0037
FAX: 651 730-6632
Susan Knutson, *Director*
EMP: 30
SALES (est): 500-999K **Privately Held**
WEB: www.kindercare.com
SIC: 8351 Child day care service
HQ: KinderCare Learning Centers
  650 NE Holladay St Ste 1400
  Portland OR 97232
  503 872-1300

(G-9238)
KINDERCARE LEARNING CENTERS
Also Called: Oakdale Kindercare
7380 10th St N (55128-5395)
PHONE 651 735-3711
FAX: 651 738-0097
Bria Walters, *Manager*
EMP: 25
SALES (est): 500-999K **Privately Held**
WEB: www.kindercare.com
SIC: 8351 Child day care service
HQ: KinderCare Learning Centers
  650 NE Holladay St Ste 1400
  Portland OR 97232
  503 872-1300

(G-9239)
KINDERCARE LEARNING CENTERS
8425 City Centre Dr (55125-3380)
PHONE 651 386-6672
Susan Knutson, *Manager*
EMP: 35
SALES (est): 500-999K **Privately Held**
WEB: www.kindercare.com
SIC: 8351 Group day care center
HQ: KinderCare Learning Centers
  650 NE Holladay St Ste 1400
  Portland OR 97232
  503 872-1300

(G-9240)
LANDFALL TERRACE INC
50 Aspen Way (55128-7112)
PHONE 651 739-8284
FAX: 651 702-6067
Jim Heltzer, *President*
EMP: 30 **EST:** 1995
SALES (est): 1MM-4.9MM **Privately Held**

SIC: 6515 Mobile home site leasing & rental

(G-9241)
LE CLAIR INSURANCE SERVICES
6701 Upper Afton Rd (55125-2154)
PHONE 651 739-2010
Edward J Le Clair, *President*
John E Leclair, *Corp Secy*
Lela Schmitt, *Corp Secy*
Brian Leclair, *Vice Pres*
Rick Lyrek, *Vice Pres*
EMP: 30 **EST:** 1925
SQ FT: 12,000
SALES (est): 1MM-4.9MM **Privately Held**
SIC: 6411 Insurance services

(G-9242)
LIFE TIME FITNESS INC
675 Commons Dr (55125-8880)
PHONE 651 730-6000
FAX: 651 730-8877
Shawn Severson, *Dept Chairman*
Robert Kubij, *Department Mgr*
Kroll Lee, *Manager*
Dan Blustin, *Manager*
EMP: 150
SALES (est): 1MM-4.9MM **Publicly Held**
SIC: 7991 Physical fitness center
PA: Life Time Fitness Inc
  2902 Corporate Pl
  Chanhassen MN 55317
  952 947-0000

(G-9243)
LIQUORS PLUS INC
9887 Norma Ln (55125-4916)
PHONE 651 501-1199
Bruce Knowlin, *President*
EMP: 50 **EST:** 1999
SALES (est): 25MM-49.9MM **Privately Held**
SIC: 5182 Wholesales alcoholic wine coolers; retails hard liquor

(G-9244)
LONG TERM CARE GROUP INC
7805 Hudson Rd Ste 180 (55125-1591)
PHONE 651 501-4000
FAX: 651 516-6706
Ted Duley, *Manager*
Kelly Bjerkeng, *Manager*
Tim McClure, *Info Tech Mgr*
EMP: 250
SALES (est): 100MM-499.9MM **Privately Held**
SIC: 6321 6324 Health insurance carrier service; hospital & medical insurance carrier
PA: Long Term Care Group Inc
  11000 Prairie Lakes Dr
  Eden Prairie MN 55344
  952 516-6829

(G-9245)
M DM RUBICON INC
6053 Hudson Rd Ste 175 (55125-1095)
PHONE 651 731-8621
FAX: 651 731-8726
Diana Golden, *President*
Mary Johnson, *Manager*
Becky Bass, *Manager*
EMP: 50 **EST:** 1993
SQ FT: 1,200
SALES (est): 1MM-4.9MM **Privately Held**
WEB: www.mdmrubicon.com
SIC: 8322 Individual & family social services

(G-9246)
MAPLEWOOD OAKDALE SCHOOL DIST
Also Called: Tartan Arena
740 Greenway Ave N (55128-6232)
PHONE 651 714-9251
FAX: 651 714-9252
Lee Alger, *Exec Dir*
Brad Martinson, *Director*
EMP: 25 **EST:** 1996
SALES (est): 1MM-4.9MM **Privately Held**
SIC: 7999 Provides ice or roller skating instruction

(G-9247)
METRO COMMUNICATION SERVICES
7250 Hudson Blvd N Ste 160 (55128-9000)
PHONE 651 702-3100
FAX: 651 702-3107
Gene Johnson, *CEO*
John Walek, *President*
Eva Mach, *Vice Pres*
Jan Illies, *Advt Staff*
Jason Sandifer, *Advt Staff*
EMP: 60 **EST:** 1989
SQ FT: 9,600
SALES (est): 5MM-9.9MM **Privately Held**
WEB: www.metrocommserv.com
SIC: 1731 Communications contractor services

(G-9248)
MIDWEST SURGERY CENTER
2080 Woodwinds Dr Ste 200 (55125-2524)
PHONE 651 642-9199
Carol Mursid, *Vice Pres*
Maryjo Katzenmaier, *Nursing Spvr*
Jenna Hobbs, *Manager*
Mary J Katzenmaie, *Manager*
Randy Gruber, *Administrator*
EMP: 48 **EST:** 1986
SQ FT: 7,000
SALES (est): 5MM-9.9MM **Privately Held**
SIC: 8011 Ambulatory surgical center

(G-9249)
MINNESOTA BENEFIT ASSOCIATION
Also Called: MBA
6701 Upper Afton Rd (55125-2154)
PHONE 651 739-4550
FAX: 651 739-3265
Edward L Clair, *President*
Jim Harrison, *Exec Dir*
EMP: 30 **EST:** 1929
SALES (est): 1MM-4.9MM **Privately Held**
SIC: 6411 Insurance broker

(G-9250)
MINNESOTA DEPARTMENT OF TRANS
3485 Hadley Ave N (55128-3307)
PHONE 651 582-1364
FAX: 651 779-5109
Carol Molnau, *Commissioner*
EMP: 4800
SALES (est): 500MM-999.9MM **Privately Held**
WEB: www.me.umn.edu
SIC: 1611 Heavy highway & street construction; transportation program regulation & administration services; state government transportation program regulation or administration
DH: Minnesota Department of Trans
  395 John Ireland Blvd
  Saint Paul MN 55155
  651 296-3000

(G-9251)
MO-TECH CORP
2920 Granada Ave N (55128-3534)
PHONE 651 770-1515
FAX: 651 770-8926
Thomas Nielsen, *President*
Richard Hesse, *Owner*
Wendy Arnhols, *Finance*
Karen Gorski, *Manager*
EMP: 43 **EST:** 1969
SQ FT: 27,000
SALES (est): 25MM-49.9MM **Privately Held**
SIC: 5031 Wholesales molding constructed of all materials

(G-9252)
MOTION TECH AUTOMATION INC
7166 4th St N (55128-7082)
PHONE 651 730-9010
FAX: 651 730-9039
Steven C Vilks, *President*
Cindy Vilks, *Corp Secy*
Joyce Fernandez, *Accountant*
Janny Lee, *Accountant*
EMP: 30

(PA)=Parent Co (HQ)=Headquarters (DH)=Div Headquarters
✿ = New business established in last 2 years

2011 Harris Minnesota
Services Directory

© Harris InfoSource 1-866-281-6415
399

EST: 1987
SQ FT: 40,000
SALES (est): 10MM-24.9MM **Privately Held**
WEB: www.motiontech.com
SIC: 5063 Wholesales electric motor controls, starters & relays

(G-9253)
OAK DALE HEALTHEAST
1099 Helmo Ave N Ste 100 (55128-6034)
PHONE 651 326-5300
FAX: 651 232-5085
Diane Sweeney, *Office Mgr*
Hanson Andrew MD, *Med Doctor*
Rosemarie Delorey MD, *Med Doctor*
Christophe Fallert MD, *Med Doctor*
Debra E Casprs MD, *Med Doctor*
EMP: 30 **EST:** 2006
SALES (est): 1MM-4.9MM **Privately Held**
SIC: 8011 Physicians' office & clinic

(G-9254)
OAKRIVER TECHNOLOGY INC
640 Hayward Ave N (55128-5396)
PHONE 651 770-8710
Rick Shand, *President*
John M Carsello, *Corp Secy*
Paul Angeli, *Vice Pres*
Dan Bartlett, *Vice Pres*
Karen Miller, *Opers Mgr*
EMP: 50 **EST:** 1998
SQ FT: 32,000
SALES (est): 5MM-9.9MM **Privately Held**
WEB: www.oakrivertechnology.com
SIC: 8711 Industrial engineers

(G-9255)
ONEKA RIDGE LLC
5610 120th St N (55110-1154)
PHONE 651 429-2390
Rosemary Arcand, *Partner*
Scott Arcand, *Partner*
Agnus Arcand, *Partner*
Fern Anderson, *Member*
Harley Anderson, *Member*
EMP: 60 **EST:** 1995
SALES (est): 1MM-4.9MM **Privately Held**
WEB: www.onekaridgegc.com
SIC: 7992 Public golf course

(G-9256)
PACE DEIS CORP
403 Hayward Ave N (55128-5374)
PHONE 651 702-2900
Richard Pace, *President*
Timothy Deis, *Vice Pres*
Shelby Myszewski, *Director*
EMP: 35 **EST:** 1988
SQ FT: 24,600
SALES (est): 1MM-4.9MM **Privately Held**
WEB: www.goeastdesign.com
SIC: 7336 Graphic arts & related design service; commercial printing

(G-9257)
PEACE OF MIND DAY CARE INC
9025 Tamarack Rd (55125-9225)
PHONE 651 731-2608
FAX: 651 731-9766
Nicole J Robbins, *President*
EMP: 65 **EST:** 1993
SALES (est): 1MM-4.9MM **Privately Held**
WEB: www.peaceofminddaycare.com
SIC: 8351 Child day care service

(G-9258)
PEDIATRICIANS FOR HEALTH
Also Called: Health East Woodbury Clinic
1875 Woodwinds Dr WL200 (55125-2506)
PHONE 651 232-6700
FAX: 651 232-7826
Pat Hallen, *Office Mgr*
Apeksha Tripathi MD, *Med Doctor*
Lillie Lynne MD, *Med Doctor*
Thomas Scheider MD, *Med Doctor*
Stephan G Bureson, *Med Doctor*
EMP: 40 **EST:** 1999
SALES (est): 1MM-4.9MM **Privately Held**
SIC: 8011 Pediatrician office

(G-9259)
PERFORMANCE POOL & SPA INC
Also Called: P P S
1890 Wooddale Dr Ste 800 (55125-1900)
PHONE 651 731-3440
FAX: 651 731-8370
Michael J Pearson, *President*
Brett McNally, *General Mgr*
Terry B Moody, *Vice Pres*
Podd Follis, *Manager*
EMP: 26 **EST:** 1989
SQ FT: 4,000
SALES (est): 1MM-4.9MM **Privately Held**
WEB: www.performancepools.com
SIC: 1799 7389 Retails swimming pools, hot tubs & sauna equipment & supplies; swimming pool & hot tub cleaning & maintenance services; spa & hot tub construction & installation; swimming pool construction

(G-9260)
PERPETUAL MOTION CHILDREN'S
257 Rivertown Dr (55125-7726)
PHONE 651 459-5837
FAX: 651 731-0839
Mike Flavin, *President*
EMP: 25 **EST:** 1991
SALES (est): 1MM-4.9MM **Privately Held**
SIC: 7999 Gymnastics instruction

(G-9261)
PHYSICIANS EXAMONE INC
436 Hayward Ave N (55128-5379)
PHONE 651 731-2949
FAX: 651 731-0081
Kessea Moses, *President*
EMP: 35 **EST:** 2000
SALES (est): 1MM-4.9MM **Privately Held**
WEB: www.phexamone.com
SIC: 8099 Physical examination & testing services

(G-9262)
PINNACLE TECHNOLOGIES INC
680 Hale Ave N Ste 120 (55128-7560)
PHONE 651 735-3239
Patrick Kasper, *President*
EMP: 35 **EST:** 2004
SQ FT: 1,082
SALES (est): 10MM-24.9MM **Privately Held**
SIC: 5082 Wholesales general construction machinery & equipment

(G-9263)
PORTFOLIO DESIGN SERVICES INC
Also Called: Rosewood Construction
752 Stillwater Rd (55115-2060)
PHONE 651 631-1300
FAX: 651 631-1500
Rebecca Hilger, *Ch of Bd*
Peter Hilger, *President*
Bill Bartolic, *Principal*
Brenda C Carlson, *CFO*
Peter Thurmes, *Manager*
EMP: 25 **EST:** 1991
SALES (est): 1MM-4.9MM **Privately Held**
WEB: www.rosewoodportfolio.com
SIC: 8712 Architectural service

(G-9264)
PRESTWICK GOLF CLUB INC
9372 Bailey Rd (55129-9684)
PHONE 651 459-0288
Dave Kavmierczak, *Manager*
EMP: 37
SALES (est): 1MM-4.9MM **Privately Held**
SIC: 7992 Public golf course
PA: Prestwick Golf Club Inc
    9555 Wedgewood Dr
    Saint Paul MN 55125
    651 731-4779

(G-9265)
PRINCIPAL LIFE INSURANCE CO
7300 Hudson Blvd N # 245 (55128-7141)
PHONE 651 227-7717
Gerry Boggesser, *Sales/Mktg Mgr*
Nicholas Halvorson, *Exec Dir*
EMP: 25

SALES (est): 1MM-4.9MM **Privately Held**
WEB: www.ccmaui.net
SIC: 6411 Insurance agent
HQ: Principal Life Insurance Co
    711 High St
    Des Moines IA 50392
    515 247-5111

(G-9266)
RED ROOF INNS INC
1806 Wooddale Dr (55125-2902)
PHONE 651 738-7160
FAX: 651 738-1869
Jeremy Dowd, *General Mgr*
Scott Pokorany, *Branch Mgr*
Jason Johnson, *Executive*
EMP: 26
SALES (est): 1MM-4.9MM **Privately Held**
WEB: www.redroof.com
SIC: 7011 Traveler accommodations
HQ: Red Roof Inns Inc
    605 S Front St Ste 150
    Columbus OH 43215
    614 744-2600

(G-9267)
REPRODUCTIVE MEDICINE
2101 Woodwinds Dr Ste 100 (55125-2526)
PHONE 651 221-4620
Jack Stassart, *CEO*
Amy Vinar, *Corp Secy*
Grant Wilson, *CFO*
Chuck Gooder, *Office Mgr*
Daniel A Dumesic, *Med Doctor*
EMP: 30 **EST:** 1998
SALES (est): 1MM-4.9MM **Privately Held**
SIC: 8011 Fertility specialist or physician office

(G-9268)
RICK S SHAND
6400 Hayward Ave (55128)
PHONE 651 770-8710
Rick S Shand, *Owner*
EMP: 40 **EST:** 1994
SALES (est): 10MM-24.9MM **Privately Held**
SIC: 7812 Motion picture & video production services

(G-9269)
RMIA
2101 Woodwinds Dr Ste 100 (55125-2526)
PHONE 651 221-4600
Jaques Stassart, *CEO*
EMP: 35 **EST:** 2004
SALES (est): 1MM-4.9MM **Privately Held**
SIC: 8099 Childbirth preparation clinic

(G-9270)
ROCCO ALTOBELLI INC
Also Called: Salon
8390 Tamarack Vlg Ste 515 (55125-3391)
PHONE 651 730-7077
FAX: 651 730-7110
Kim Stumm, *Manager*
EMP: 50
SALES (est): 1MM-4.9MM **Privately Held**
WEB: www.roccoaltobelli.com
SIC: 7231 Beauty salon
PA: Rocco Altobelli Inc
    14301 W Burnsville Pkwy
    Burnsville MN 55306
    952 707-1900

(G-9271)
ROTO-ROOTER SERVICES CO
7041 6th St N (55128-6157)
PHONE 651 738-8355
FAX: 651 519-3932
Eddy Gillus, *Manager*
EMP: 30
SALES (est): 1MM-4.9MM **Publicly Held**
WEB: www.chemed.com
SIC: 7699 Sewer cleaning & rodding service
HQ: Roto-Rooter Development Co
    2600 Chemed Ct 255 E 5th 255
    Cincinnati OH 45202
    513 762-6690

(G-9272)
SFN GROUP INC
585 Hale Ave N (55128-7558)
PHONE 651 501-5037
FAX: 651 501-5067

Tracy Collins, *Manager*
EMP: 100
SALES (est): 1MM-4.9MM **Publicly Held**
SIC: 7363 Temporary help service
PA: Sfn Group Inc
    2050 Spectrum Blvd
    Fort Lauderdale FL 33309
    954 308-7600

(G-9273)
SHERATON ST PAUL-WOODBURY ✪
676 Bielenberg Dr (55125-1414)
PHONE 651 209-3280
Gerald Trooien, *Principal*
EMP: 80 **EST:** 2008
SALES (est): 1MM-4.9MM **Privately Held**
SIC: 7011 Hotel

(G-9274)
SMITHS MEDICAL ASD INC
3350 Granada Ave N Ste 100 (55128-3553)
PHONE 651 628-7030
Phillip Sumo, *Branch Mgr*
EMP: 30
SALES (est): 1MM-4.9MM **Privately Held**
WEB: www.smiths-group.com
SIC: 4225 General warehousing
HQ: Smith's Medical Asd Inc
    1265 Grey Fox Rd
    Saint Paul MN 55112
    651 633-2556

(G-9275)
SPARTAN PROMOTIONAL GROUP INC
711 Hale Ave N (55128-7545)
PHONE 651 735-1333
FAX: 651 735-0506
Allen Hohenwald, *CEO*
Phyllis Hohenwald, *President*
Michael Hohenwald, *Exec VP*
Greg Michael, *Controller*
Emmett Taylor, *VP Mktg*
EMP: 68 **EST:** 1966
SQ FT: 24,000
SALES (est): 5MM-9.9MM **Privately Held**
WEB: www.spartanpromo.com
SIC: 5199 Wholesales advertising specialties; manufactures signs & advertising specialties; manufactures trimming fabrics; pleating & stitching service

(G-9276)
SPINEOLOGY INC
7800 3rd St N Ste 600 (55128-5451)
PHONE 651 256-8500
John Booth, *CEO*
Don Kennedy, *Vice Pres*
Daniel McPhillips, *Vice Pres*
Timothy R Walnofer, *Vice Pres*
Cindy Peck, *Accounting Mgr*
EMP: 48 **EST:** 1997
SQ FT: 5,000
SALES (est): 1MM-4.9MM **Privately Held**
WEB: www.spineology.com
SIC: 8733 Medical research organization

(G-9277)
ST PAUL HARLEY DAVIDSON INC
2899 Hudson Rd (55128-7100)
PHONE 651 738-2168
FAX: 651 739-6185
Thomas Giannetti, *President*
Tim Bonniwell, *Publisher*
Melanie Giannetti, *Vice Pres*
Marcy Vail, *Marketing Mgr*
Kurt Harder, *Exec Dir*
EMP: 80 **EST:** 1945
SQ FT: 25,000
SALES (est): 10MM-24.9MM **Privately Held**
WEB: www.stpaulhd.com
SIC: 7699 Motorcycle dealer; motorcycle parts & accessories dealer; motorcycle repair shop

(G-9278)
STONECREST ✪
Also Called: Presbyterian Homes & Svcs
8725 Promenade Ln (55125-9622)
PHONE 651 264-3200
FAX: 651 264-3202
Stacy Carlsrud, *Director*

www.HarrisInfo.com
400

2011 Harris Minnesota
Services Directory

▲=Import ▼=Export
◆=Import/Export

EMP: 73 **EST:** 2008
SALES (est): 1MM-4.9MM **Privately Held**
SIC: 8361 1521 Geriatric residential care;
new single-family home construction service

(G-9279)
SUMMIT EMPLOYMENT INC
3894 Homestead Dr (55125-8417)
PHONE.............................651 501-0531
Doug Hendricks, *President*
EMP: 100 **EST:** 2000
SALES (est): 1MM-4.9MM **Privately Held**
SIC: 7363 Help supply services

(G-9280)
TAMARACK VILLAGE SHOPPING CENT
8278 Tamarack Vlg Ste 311 (55125-5361)
PHONE.............................651 702-6308
FAX: 651 702-6308
Robert Muir, *Manager*
Robert Miller, *Manager*
EMP: 25 **EST:** 2003
SALES (est): 5MM-9.9MM **Privately Held**
SIC: 6512 Shopping center & mall operator

(G-9281)
THEODORE F BOLLES
Also Called: Dairy Queen
7249 Courtly Rd (55125-4003)
PHONE.............................651 731-9436
Theodore F Bolles, *Owner*
EMP: 75 **EST:** 1990
SALES (est): 1MM-4.9MM **Privately Held**
SIC: 6519 Limited service ice cream stand
or dairy bar; real estate property leasing &
rental

(G-9282)
TLC ELECTRONICS
18 Long Lake Rd (55115-6824)
PHONE.............................651 488-2933
FAX: 651 488-3246
Richard Crofford, *President*
Jill McCorkel, *Human Res Dir*
Terri Crofford, *Human Res Mgr*
Steve Olson, *Sales Mgr*
Joel Root, *Manager*
EMP: 72 **EST:** 1984
SQ FT: 38,000
SALES (est): 5MM-9.9MM **Privately Held**
SIC: 5065 Manufactures electronic cable &
wire harness assemblies; wholesales
electronic parts

(G-9283)
TWIN CITIES TRANSPORT (PA)
274 N1 Geneva Ave (55128)
PHONE.............................651 770-0816
Ron Gardas, *President*
EMP: 30 **EST:** 1988
SQ FT: 600 **Privately Held**
SIC: 7549 Automotive towing service

(G-9284)
TWIN CITY HARDWARE CO (PA)
723 Hadley Ave N (55128-6205)
PHONE.............................651 735-2200
FAX: 651 735-1800
George H Boomer, *President*
Mike Schultz, *Corp Secy*
Calvin B Boomer, *Vice Pres*
Jim Colburn, *Purch Agent*
David Shroyer, *CFO*
EMP: 40 **EST:** 1883
SQ FT: 92,000 **Privately Held**
WEB: www.twincityhardware.com
SIC: 5072 5031 Wholesales hardware;
wholesales door frames constructed of all
materials; wholesales Doors, sliding;
wholesales metal doors, sash & trim;
wholesales millwork; wholesales builders'
hardware; retails builders' hardware;
hardware store

(G-9285)
TWO MEN & TRUCK
670 Commerce Dr Ste 240 (55125-9248)
PHONE.............................651 645-1279
Mike Goergen, *Owner*
EMP: 60 **EST:** 2004
SALES (est): 5MM-9.9MM **Privately Held**
SIC: 4213 Over the road trucking

(G-9286)
UNIFIED THEORY INC
Also Called: Uti
1811 Weir Dr Ste 365 (55125-2293)
PHONE.............................651 578-8100
FAX: 651 578-8200
Michael Herron, *President*
Timothy Herron, *Vice Pres*
Marie Lindpeck, *Office Mgr*
David Herron, *Manager*
EST: 2004 **Privately Held**
WEB: www.unifiedtheory.net
SIC: 8711 Engineering services

(G-9287)
USP HOTEL SERVICES LLC
Also Called: Wingate Inn Oakdale
970 Helena Ave N (55128-5388)
PHONE.............................651 578-2563
FAX: 651 578-0763
Dan Wright, *Member*
Heather Osmundsom, *Manager*
EMP: 25 **EST:** 1999
SALES (est): 1MM-4.9MM **Privately Held**
SIC: 7011 Traveler accommodations

(G-9288)
WINROC CORP (PA)
5262 Glenbrook Ave N (55128-1328)
PHONE.............................651 777-8222
FAX: 651 777-4375
Paul Vanderberg, *President*
James Empey, *VP Finance*
Karen Gille, *Accountant*
Allan Miller, *Manager*
EMP: 65 **EST:** 1972
SQ FT: 16,800 **Privately Held**
SIC: 5032 5031 Wholesales drywall
materials; wholesales wallboard; wholesales
stucco; wholesales cement
PA: Winroc Corp
5824 2 St SW Suite 300
Calgary Canada
403 2365383

(G-9289)
WOODBURY FINANCIAL SERVICES (HQ)
500 Bielenberg Dr (55125-1416)
PO Box 64284 (55164-0284)
PHONE.............................651 738-4000
FAX: 651 738-4001
Brian Murphy, *Ch of Bd*
Patrick McEvoy, *President*
Richard G Costello, *Corp Secy*
Scott A Carlson, *Senior VP*
John N Giamalis, *Vice Pres*
EMP: 200 **EST:** 1968
SQ FT: 17,000
SALES (corp-wide): 24.70B **Publicly Held**
WEB: www.thehartford.com
SIC: 6722 Open-ended investment funds
management services; management of
personal mutual fund sales
PA: Hartford Financial Services
1 Hartford Plz
Hartford CT 06115
860 547-5000

(G-9290)
WOODWINDS HEALTH CAMPUS
1925 Woodwinds Dr (55125-2270)
PHONE.............................651 232-0100
Tom Scmith, *CEO*
Timothy Hanson, *President*
Thomas Bravo, *Manager*
Carol Meehan, *Asst Sec*
EMP: 700 **EST:** 1998
SALES (est): 50MM-99.9MM **Privately Held**
SIC: 8069 Specialty hospital

(G-9291)
XENOPHON CORP
Also Called: Wooddale Recreation Center
2122 Wooddale Dr (55125-2905)
PHONE.............................651 735-6214
Kevin Fahly, *Manager*
Kevin Sahly, *Manager*
EMP: 35
SALES (est): 1MM-4.9MM **Privately Held**
WEB: www.rollergarden.com

SIC: 7999 Tennis services & professionals;
roller skating rink
PA: Xenophon Corp
5622 W Lake St
Minneapolis MN 55416
952 929-5518

(G-9292)
YMCA OF GREATER ST PAUL
Also Called: Southeast Area YMCA
2175 Radio Dr (55125-9453)
PHONE.............................651 731-9507
FAX: 651 731-1534
Kathy Barton, *Business Mgr*
Stephanie Chauhss, *VP Opers*
Kelly Raglim, *Sales Staff*
Heidi Bardwell, *Marketing Mgr*
Stephanie Sweet, *Manager*
EMP: 133 **Privately Held**
WEB: www.ymcastpaul.org
SIC: 8641 Social club; youth organizations
PA: YMCA of Greater Saint Paul
2125 E Hennepin Ave Ste 100
Minneapolis MN 55413
612 465-0450

(G-9293)
ZUMBRO HOUSE INC
1103 Weir Dr Ste 100 (55125-1313)
PHONE.............................651 264-1000
Christopher Onken, *CEO*
EMP: 80 **EST:** 2004
SALES (est): 1MM-4.9MM **Privately Held**
SIC: 8361 Group foster home

SAINT PAUL PARK
Washington County

(G-9294)
D & A TRUCK LINE INC
700 Broadway Ave (55071-1520)
PHONE.............................651 769-1045
Florence Dittrich, *President*
EMP: 48
SALES (est): 5MM-9.9MM **Privately Held**
SIC: 4213 Over the road trucking

(G-9295)
MARATHON PETROLEUM CO LP
301 St (55071)
PHONE.............................651 459-9771
George Shaffner, *Plant Mgr*
George Schaffner, *Plant Mgr*
Mark Videtich, *Engineer*
Bill Miller, *Sales Staff*
Mike Gamlen, *Manager*
EMP: 400
SALES (est): 1B-9.9B **Publicly Held**
WEB: www.mapllc.com
SIC: 5172 Wholesales petroleum products
HQ: Marathon Petroleum Co LP
539 S Main St
Findlay OH 45840
419 422-2121

(G-9296)
MARATHON PETROLEUM CO LP
459 3rd St (55071-1872)
PO Box 9 (55071-0009)
PHONE.............................651 459-9771
FAX: 651 458-2699
Steve Hood, *Maint Mgr*
Jay Gieseke, *Safety Mgr*
Tom Johnson, *Human Res Mgr*
Kirk Gomanger, *Manager*
Marty Elzea, *Manager*
EMP: 270
SALES (est): 500MM-999.9MM **Publicly Held**
WEB: www.mapllc.com
SIC: 5172 Wholesales petroleum products;
manufactures asphalt paving mixtures &
blocks; petroleum refining
HQ: Marathon Petroleum Co LP
539 S Main St
Findlay OH 45840
419 422-2121

(G-9297)
MYSEEKS INC
356 9th Ave Ste 304 (55071-1898)
PHONE.............................651 967-4150
Michael Larson, *President*

EMP: 27 **EST:** 2007
SALES (est): 1MM-4.9MM **Privately Held**
SIC: 7371 Computer software development

(G-9298)
TENNIS SANITATION LLC
720 4th St (55071-1827)
PO Box 62 (55071-0062)
PHONE.............................651 459-1887
William Tennis, *Member*
Greg Tennis, *Member*
EMP: 30 **EST:** 1966
SQ FT: 1,200
SALES (est): 1MM-4.9MM **Privately Held**
SIC: 4212 4953 Garbage collection &
transportation services without disposal;
garbage collecting, destroying & processing
services

SAINT PETER
Le Sueur County

(G-9299)
MINNESOTA DEPARTMENT OF HUMAN
2100 Sheppard Dr (56082-2527)
PHONE.............................507 931-7137
FAX: 507 931-7703
Ron Weyl, *Manager*
Larry Debrach, *Deputy Dir*
Nancy Petersen, *Risk Mgmt Dir*
Denise Roggow, *Admin Asst*
EMP: 300
SALES (est): 10MM-24.9MM **Privately Held**
WEB: www.state.mn.us
SIC: 8063 Mental hospital
DH: Minnesota Department of Human
540 Cedar St
Saint Paul MN 55101
651 431-2000

(G-9300)
SAINT PETER COUNSELING CENTER
1711 Sheppard Dr (56082-2539)
PHONE.............................507 934-9612
Dave Compton, *Director*
EMP: 90 **EST:** 1983
SALES (est): 1MM-4.9MM **Privately Held**
SIC: 8322 Individual & family social services

SAINT PETER
Nicollet County

(G-9301)
COUNSELING SERVICES OF STHN
116 S 3rd St (56082-2043)
PHONE.............................507 931-8040
FAX: 507 931-8060
Natalee Anderson, *President*
Candice Mattoks, *Corp Secy*
Kelly Hulke, *Corp Secy*
EMP: 35 **EST:** 1997
SALES (est): 1MM-4.9MM **Privately Held**
WEB: www.counseling-services.org
SIC: 7389 Personal service agents

(G-9302)
EVANGELICAL LUTHERAN GOOD
Also Called: Grandview Good Samaritan
830 Sunrise Dr (56082-1203)
PHONE.............................507 931-9021
Teresa Hildenbrandt, *Principal*
EMP: 90
SALES (est): 1MM-4.9MM **Privately Held**
WEB: www.good-sam.com
SIC: 8051 Skilled nursing care facility
PA: Evangelical Lutheran Good
4800 W 57th St
Sioux Falls SD 57108
605 362-3100

(PA)=Parent Co (HQ)=Headquarters (DH)=Div Headquarters
✪ = New business established in last 2 years

2011 Harris Minnesota
Services Directory

© Harris InfoSource 1-866-281-6415
401

GEOGRAPHIC

(G-9303)
FIRST NATIONAL BANK OF ST (HQ)
226 Nassau St (56082-2056)
PHONE..............................507 931-4000
Paul Dumdei, *President*
Anderson Marie, *Purch Agent*
Michael O'Gaard, *CIO*
Tim Grabow, *VP Systems*
Horn Jill, *Data Proc Exec*
EMP: 32 **EST:** 1857
SALES (corp-wide): 10.37M **Privately Held**
WEB: www.fnbmn.com
SIC: 6022 Commercial state trust companies accepting deposits
PA: Bancommunity Services Inc
226 Nassau St
Saint Peter MN 56082
507 931-4000

(G-9304)
GELDNER CONSTRUCTION INC
101 Locust St (56082-2115)
PO Box 416 (56082-0416)
PHONE..............................507 931-4230
FAX: 507 931-6576
Robert L Geldner, *President*
EMP: 30 **EST:** 1965
SQ FT: 4,600
SALES (est): 1MM-4.9MM **Privately Held**
SIC: 1623 1794 Telephone & communication line construction; excavating contractor

(G-9305)
GRANDVIEW GOOD SAMARITAN CTR
830 Sunrise Dr (56082-1203)
PHONE..............................507 931-9021
Kirstin Adkins, *Financial Analy*
Teresa Hildidrantt, *Administrator*
Theresa Hildebrandt, *Director*
EMP: 55 **EST:** 1967
SQ FT: 8,000
SALES (est): 1MM-4.9MM **Privately Held**
WEB: www.good-sam.org
SIC: 8051 Skilled nursing care facility
PA: Good Samaritan Society Inc
4800 W 57th St
Sioux Falls SD 57108
605 362-3100

(G-9306)
HOPE SHILOHS INC
1746 Riggs Rd (56082-1640)
PHONE..............................507 934-2094
Randy Frey-Hawkins, *President*
Patty Pearson, *Principal*
EMP: 40
SALES (est): 1MM-4.9MM **Privately Held**
SIC: 8361 Home for the elderly

(G-9307)
INTELESERVE INC
419 S Minnesota Ave (56082-2547)
PHONE..............................800 390-4851
Greg Saer, *President*
EMP: 200 **EST:** 1980
SALES (est): 5MM-9.9MM **Privately Held**
SIC: 7389 Telemarketing services

(G-9308)
MAYO CLINIC
622 Sunrise Dr (56082-1201)
PHONE..............................507 931-2110
FAX: 507 931-9409
Terri Karau, *Corp Secy*
Carol Rosenthal, *Branch Mgr*
Kevin G Hardesty, *Chiropractor*
Curtis N Stolee MD, *Med Doctor*
K Engelhardt MD, *Med Doctor*
EMP: 28
SALES (est): 1MM-4.9MM **Privately Held**
SIC: 8011 Clinic operated by physicians
PA: Mayo Clinic
200 1st St SW
Rochester MN 55905
507 284-2511

(G-9309)
NASH-FINCH CO
Also Called: Econo Foods
612 S Minnesota Ave (56082-2100)
PHONE..............................507 931-5541
FAX: 507 931-6623
Marilyn Kluntz, *Manager*
Steve Ginond, *Manager*
EMP: 100
SALES (est): 50MM-99.9MM **Publicly Held**
WEB: www.nashfinch.com
SIC: 5141 Wholesales general line groceries
PA: Nash-Finch Co
7600 France Ave S Ste 200
Edina MN 55435
952 832-0534

(G-9310)
NICOLLET COUNTY BANK OF SAINT
220 S 3rd St (56082-2045)
PO Box 420 (56082-0420)
PHONE..............................507 931-3310
FAX: 507 931-2418
Samuel B Gault, *President*
Zuriel S Gault, *Chairman*
Lisa Gault, *Vice Pres*
Douglas D Miller, *Vice Pres*
Gary Miller, *Vice Pres*
EMP: 32 **EST:** 1883
SQ FT: 8,000
SALES (est): 5MM-9.9MM **Privately Held**
WEB: www.nicolletcountybank.com
SIC: 6022 State commercial bank
PA: Saint Peter Agency Inc
220 S 3rd St
Saint Peter MN 56082
507 931-3310

(G-9311)
PALMER BUS SERVICE OF ST
43336 371st Ave (56082-4003)
PHONE..............................507 931-1811
FAX: 507 931-1822
Floyd Palmer, *President*
Lois Palmer, *Corp Secy*
Mike Hennek, *Manager*
EMP: 25 **EST:** 1988
SQ FT: 5,000
SALES (est): 500-999K **Privately Held**
SIC: 4151 School bus service

(G-9312)
SAINT PETER AGENCY INC (PA)
220 S 3rd St (56082-2045)
PO Box 420 (56082-0420)
PHONE..............................507 931-3310
Samuel B Gault, *President*
EMP: 32
SQ FT: 8,000 **Privately Held**
SIC: 6712 Bank holding company

(G-9313)
SCHOLARSHIP AMERICA INC
1 Scholarship Way (56082-1693)
PO Box 297 (56082-0297)
PHONE..............................507 931-1682
David Bach, *COO*
Terrance Kraling, *COO*
Donald Lassere, *Senior VP*
Barb Weber, *Assistant VP*
Barbara Arnold, *Vice Pres*
EMP: 120 **EST:** 1961
SQ FT: 32,450 **Privately Held**
WEB: www.vantagescholar.com
SIC: 8399 Non-fee basis fund raising organization

(G-9314)
ST PETER, CITY OF INC
1900 Sunrise Dr (56082-5376)
PHONE..............................507 931-7354
FAX: 507 931-7651
Colleen Spike, *CEO*
Stan Schimke, *Vice Pres*
Roxanne Reese, *Purchasing*
Tom Wilcox, *Engineering*
Tammie Hudstith, *Human Res Dir*
EMP: 103
SALES (est): 5MM-9.9MM **Privately Held**

SIC: 8062 4119 8051 Medical hospital; ambulance service; skilled nursing care facility
PA: St Peter, City of Inc
227 S Front St
Saint Peter MN 56082
507 934-4840

(G-9315)
TENNIS & LIFE CAMPS INC
800 W College Ave (56082-1485)
PHONE..............................507 931-1614
Stephen L Wilkinson, *Owner*
Neal Hagberg, *Corp Secy*
EMP: 38 **EST:** 1977
SALES (est): 1MM-4.9MM **Privately Held**
SIC: 7999 Tennis services & professionals

(G-9316)
WILDS OF SAN PRAIRIE
700 Knight St Apt 221 (56082-1745)
PHONE..............................507 931-4375
FAX: 507 934-5346
Mary Olson, *Manager*
Shelia Snider, *Director*
EMP: 25 **EST:** 1999
SALES (est): 500-999K **Privately Held**
SIC: 8059 Personal care home, with health care

SAINT STEPHEN
Stearns County

(G-9317)
TROBEC'S BUS SERVICE INC
413 County Road 2 S (56375-9644)
PHONE..............................320 251-1202
FAX: 320 252-7756
Betty Trobec, *President*
Tim Sherbet, *Treasurer*
EMP: 65 **EST:** 1938
SQ FT: 2,000
SALES (est): 1MM-4.9MM **Privately Held**
WEB: www.trobecbus.com
SIC: 4151 4141 4142 School bus service; local bus charter service; long-distance bus charter service

---

SANBORN
Redwood County

(G-9318)
L & S CONSTRUCTION
12226 Knox Ave (56083-3059)
PHONE..............................507 648-3382
Herb Scheffler, *President*
Donna L Scheffler, *Corp Secy*
Terry Roiger, *Vice Pres*
EMP: 25 **EST:** 1970
SALES (est): 1MM-4.9MM **Privately Held**
SIC: 4212 1794 Dump truck hauling services; excavation & grading, building construction contractor

---

SANDSTONE
Kanabec County

(G-9319)
CARLSON TIMBER PRODUCTS INC
53778 Fir Ln (55072-2836)
PHONE..............................320 245-2920
FAX: 320 245-2933
Dave Carlson, *President*
Sue Carlson, *Vice Pres*
Missy Jorgenson, *Manager*
EMP: 80 **EST:** 1988
SQ FT: 5,824 **Privately Held**
SIC: 0811 Timber tract operation

SANDSTONE
Pine County

(G-9320)
COMMUNITY INVOLVEMENT PROGRAMS
206 Commercial Ave N (55072-5139)
PO Box 278 (55072-0278)
PHONE..............................320 245-5362
FAX: 320 245-5105
Ludwig Deedree, *Manager*
Mae Delaney, *Director*
EMP: 40
SALES (est): 1MM-4.9MM **Privately Held**
WEB: www.cipmn.org
SIC: 8361 8052 Residential care facility; intermediate care facility
PA: Community Involvement Programs
1600 Broadway St NE
Minneapolis MN 55413
612 362-4400

(G-9321)
FIRST NATIONAL BANK OF THE N
510 Main Ave (55072)
PO Box 9 (55072-0009)
PHONE..............................320 245-5261
William P Loew, *President*
John O'Brien, *Chairman*
Dave Dewitt, *COO*
Judy A Nelson, *Senior VP*
EMP: 27 **EST:** 1902
SQ FT: 5,000
SALES (est): 5MM-9.9MM **Privately Held**
WEB: www.jdob.com
SIC: 6021 National commercial bank
PA: Jdob Inc
510 Main
Sandstone MN 55072
320 245-5261

(G-9322)
LAKE STATE FEDERAL CREDIT
406 N Commercial (55072)
PO Box 659 (55072-0659)
PHONE..............................320 245-5251
FAX: 320 245-5510
EMP: 80
SALES (est): 10MM-24.9MM **Privately Held**
WEB: www.lakestatefederalcreditunion.com
SIC: 6061 Federally chartered credit union
PA: Lake State Federal Credit
301 Elm Ave
Moose Lake MN 55767
218 485-4444

(G-9323)
NATIONAL ASSOC OF RETIRED
222 Court Ave S (55072-5112)
PO Box 311 (55072-0311)
PHONE..............................320 245-2629
Marilyn Jokela, *President*
EMP: 45 **EST:** 1984 **Privately Held**
SIC: 8641 Alumni association

(G-9324)
PINE COUNTY HEALTH & HUMAN SVC
130 Oriole St E Ste 1 (55072-5134)
PHONE..............................320 245-3020
FAX: 320 245-3060
Richard Ebnet, *Manager*
Linda Cassman, *Director*
EMP: 40 **EST:** 2002
SALES (est): 1MM-4.9MM **Privately Held**
SIC: 8322 Public welfare center

(G-9325)
PINE HABILITATION & SUPPORTED (PA)
106 Main St (55072-6503)
PO Box 126 (55072-0126)
PHONE..............................320 245-2246
FAX: 320 245-0431
Marian Lewis, *Office Mgr*
Timothy Schmupzer, *Director*
EMP: 31 **EST:** 1970
SQ FT: 5,000
SALES (corp-wide): 2.49M **Privately Held**
SIC: 8331 Vocational counseling; job training services; sheltered workshop

www.HarrisInfo.com
402

2011 Harris Minnesota
Services Directory

▲=Import ▼=Export
◆=Import/Export

(G-9326)

SANDSTONE AREA NURSING HOME
109 Court Ave S (55072-5120)
PHONE..............................320 245-2212
FAX: 320 245-2359
Chris Johnson, *CFO*
Chris Storebo, *Manager*
Jim Koppen, *Administrator*
Micheal Hedricks, *Analyst*
EMP: 180 EST: 1956
SQ FT: 37,300
SALES (est): 5MM-9.9MM **Privately Held**
SIC: 8051 Extended care facility

(G-9327)

SANDSTONE RIDERS HORSE CLUB
52803 County Rd 61 (55072)
PO Box 36 (55072-0036)
PHONE..............................320 245-0370
Keith Carlson, *President*
Harold Bonnin, *Corp Secy*
EMP: 50 EST: 1987 **Privately Held**
SIC: 8699 Personal interest organization

SARTELL
Benton County

(G-9328)

FOUNDATION FOR HEALTHCARE
Also Called: Country Manor
520 1st St NE Ste 1 (56377-2449)
PHONE..............................320 253-1920
FAX: 320 253-2848
Brian Kelm, *CEO*
Kevin Harguth, *CFO*
Judy Waletski, *Asst Controller*
Audrey Twit, *Manager*
Ryan Salner, *Info Tech Mgr*
EMP: 392 EST: 1968
SALES (est): 10MM-24.9MM **Privately Held**
WEB: www.countrymanorcampus.org
SIC: 8051 6513 8082 Skilled nursing care facility; drug store; home health care services; apartment building operator

---

SARTELL
Stearns County

(G-9329)

ADULT & PEDIATRIC UROLOGY
2351 Connecticut Ave S # 200 (56377-2477)
PHONE..............................320 259-1411
FAX: 320 259-8967
Henri P Lanctin MD, *Managing Prtnr*
Gregory S Parries MD, *Managing Prtnr*
Benjamin K Rhee MD, *Managing Prtnr*
Jerome P Keating MD, *Managing Prtnr*
John K Matsuura MD, *Managing Prtnr*
EMP: 40 EST: 1981
SALES (est): 1MM-4.9MM **Privately Held**
WEB: www.adultandpediatricurology.com
SIC: 8011 Neurosurgeon

(G-9330)

ALLERGY & ASTHMA SPECIALISTS
1350 Lesauk Dr Ste 1149 (56377-2127)
PHONE..............................320 654-6565
Mary E Schaefer, *Manager*
EMP: 30
SALES (est): 1MM-4.9MM **Privately Held**
SIC: 8011 Specialized medical practitioners
PA: Allergy & Asthma Specialists
    825 Nicollet Mall Ste 1149
    Minneapolis MN 55402
    612 338-3333

(G-9331)

ARRAY SERVICES GROUP INC
Also Called: Carecall
205 14th Ave E (56377-4500)
PHONE..............................320 534-3401
Jerry Lange, *Facilities Mgr*
Charles Engebretson, *CFO*
Sue Roberts, *Human Res Dir*
Mark Kottke, *Sales Staff*
Lisa Drew, *Marketing Staff*
EMP: 120
SALES (est): 5MM-9.9MM **Privately Held**
SIC: 7322 Collection agency

(G-9332)

BALYLE INC
208 2nd St S (56377-1918)
PHONE..............................320 253-2910
FAX: 320 253-2910
Lyle Mathiasen, *CEO*
Barbara Mathiasen, *CFO*
Bob Beltz, *Manager*
EMP: 32 EST: 1983
SQ FT: 17,000
SALES (est): 1MM-4.9MM **Privately Held**
WEB: www.greatriverbowl.com
SIC: 7933 Ten pin center; cocktail lounge; eating place

(G-9333)

BLACKBERRY RIDGE GOLF CLUB LLC
3125 Clubhouse Rd (56377)
PO Box 264 (56377-0264)
PHONE..............................320 257-4653
FAX: 320 257-0515
Don Fenlenson, *Member*
Verle Fenlenson, *Member*
Gary Gillian, *Manager*
EMP: 25 EST: 2001
SQ FT: 8,000
SALES (est): 1MM-4.9MM **Privately Held**
WEB: www.blackberryridgegolf.com
SIC: 7992 Public golf course

(G-9334)

CARECALL INC
200 14th Ave E (56377-4500)
PHONE..............................320 253-0800
James C Christensen, *CEO*
Matthew A Schmit, *President*
Mark A Kottke, *Vice Pres*
Lee Harris, *Dir Ops-Prd-Mfg*
Charles Engebretson, *CFO*
▲ EMP: 72 EST: 1994
SQ FT: 8,000
SALES (est): 5MM-9.9MM **Privately Held**
SIC: 7389 Telephone service

(G-9335)

CDI CORP
166 19th St S Ste 100 (56377-2154)
PHONE..............................320 251-0609
Kaye Barthelemy, *Branch Mgr*
Rosemarie Imgrund, *Supervisor*
Kate Bartholemu, *Exec Dir*
Vibhu Kapoor, *Diag Radio*
Hayley I Sheldon, *Diag Radio*
EMP: 40
SALES (est): 1MM-4.9MM **Publicly Held**
WEB: www.cdicorp.com
SIC: 8011 Radiologist office
HQ: CDI Corp
    1717 Arch St Fl 35
    Philadelphia PA 19103
    215 569-2200

(G-9336)

CENTER FOR PAIN MANAGEMENT
166 19th St S Ste 101 (56377-2154)
PHONE..............................320 230-7788
Samir M Elghor, *Principal*
Mark Janiger, *Vice Pres*
Renee Jansky, *Office Mgr*
Jason S Wolff, *Pain Mangement*
James B Parmele, *Pain Mangement*
EMP: 25 EST: 2007
SALES (est): 1MM-4.9MM **Privately Held**
SIC: 8011 Medical center

(G-9337)

J C CHRISTENSEN & ASSOCIATES
200 14th Ave E (56377-4500)
PHONE..............................320 534-3629
Chad Lemke, *Principal*
EMP: 80
SALES (est): 5MM-9.9MM **Privately Held**
SIC: 7322 Collection agency

(G-9338)

MARK DOMAN
Also Called: X Tex
621 17th St N (56377-1684)
PHONE..............................320 203-9004
Mark Doman, *President*
EMP: 50
SALES (est): 5MM-9.9MM **Privately Held**
SIC: 7374 Data processing & preparation services

(G-9339)

OPPORTUNITY MANOR INC
1908 Kruchten Ct S (56377-4645)
PHONE..............................320 240-1900
Arn Reagan, *CEO*
EMP: 70
SALES (est): 1MM-4.9MM **Privately Held**
WEB: www.opportunitymanor.com
SIC: 8351 Child day care service
PA: Opportunity Manor Inc
    1908 Kruchten Ct S
    Sartell MN 56377
    320 240-1900

(G-9340)

PACE INTERNATIONAL UNION
Also Called: Local 7-274
100 E Sartell St (56377-1947)
PHONE..............................320 240-7274
FAX: 320 240-7244
Lyle Flyck, *President*
Judith Lueck, *Purchasing*
David Zimmer, *Engineering*
Al Voit, *Engineering*
EMP: 434 **Privately Held**
SIC: 8631 Labor union
PA: Pace International Union
    5 Gateway Ctr
    Pittsburgh PA 15222
    412 562-2400

(G-9341)

W3I HOLDINGS LLC
1900 Medical Arts Ave S (56377-4646)
PHONE..............................320 257-7500
Andy Johnson, *CEO*
Joe Bergstrom, *Member*
Robert Weber, *Vice Pres*
Ryan Ranweiler, *Vice Pres*
Hayden Creque, *Vice Pres*
EMP: 63 EST: 2000
SQ FT: 11,000
SALES (est): 10MM-24.9MM **Privately Held**
WEB: www.freeze.com
SIC: 4813 Online services providers

SAUK CENTRE
Stearns County

(G-9342)

CENTRE ELECTRIC INC
43543 County Road 17 (56378-8200)
PHONE..............................320 352-0160
Michael A Froseth, *President*
EMP: 26 EST: 2002
SALES (est): 1MM-4.9MM **Privately Held**
WEB: www.centreelectric.com
SIC: 1731 Electrical contractor

(G-9343)

DRS ACQUISITIONS INC
833 Main St S (56378-1646)
PHONE..............................320 351-8100
FAX: 320 351-8080
Dennis Schulte, *President*
Richard Fisher, *Vice Pres*
Chad Fruchiti, *Vice Pres*
Kimberly Ahrens, *Manager*
EMP: 75 EST: 2002
SALES (est): 1MM-4.9MM **Privately Held**
SIC: 7389 Telemarketing services

(G-9344)

ECM PUBLISHERS INC
Also Called: Dairyland Peac
601 Sinclair Lewis Ave (56378-1247)
PO Box 285 (56378-0285)
PHONE..............................320 352-6569
Brian McCory, *President*
Annette Gruber, *Manager*
EMP: 25
SALES (est): 1MM-4.9MM **Privately Held**
WEB: www.ecm-inc.com
SIC: 8748 Publishing consultant
PA: ECM Publishers Inc
    4095 Coon Rapids Blvd NW
    Minneapolis MN 55433
    763 712-2400

(G-9345)

FIRST STATE BANK OF SAUK
423 Main St S (56378-1508)
PO Box 266 (56378-0266)
PHONE..............................320 352-5771
FAX: 320 352-2246
Loren Beste, *CEO*
Roger Beuning, *President*
David D Bois, *Senior VP*
Michael Bick, *Vice Pres*
Pat Arnzen, *Vice Pres*
EMP: 27 EST: 1879
SQ FT: 9,600
SALES (est): 5MM-9.9MM **Privately Held**
SIC: 6022 State commercial bank
PA: Dubois Bankshares Inc
    423 Main St S
    Sauk Centre MN 56378
    320 352-5771

(G-9346)

GENE BUECKERS
Also Called: City Sanitation Service
39864 US Highway 71 (56378-8431)
PO Box 109 (56378-0109)
PHONE..............................320 352-2876
FAX: 320 351-2876
Gene Bueckers, *President*
Janine Kutter, *Sales Executive*
Donna Bueckers, *Manager*
Chad Bueckers, *Manager*
EMP: 25 EST: 1974
SQ FT: 9,800
SALES (est): 5MM-9.9MM **Privately Held**
SIC: 4953 Garbage collecting, destroying & processing services

(G-9347)

I D D D INC
Also Called: Truckers Inn
1420 Main St S (56378-1699)
PO Box 48 (56378-0048)
PHONE..............................320 352-5241
Dan Lundy, *Manager*
Lowell Helgeson, *Manager*
EMP: 75
SALES (est): 1MM-4.9MM **Privately Held**
SIC: 7011 Full service diner; traveler accommodations
PA: I D D D Inc
    6162 US Highway 51
    De Forest WI 53532
    608 246-3040

(G-9348)

INDEPENDENT COMMUNITY BANKERS
Also Called: I C B A
518 Lincoln Rd (56378-2001)
PO Box 267 (56378-0267)
PHONE..............................320 352-6546
FAX: 320 352-5766
William C Rosacker, *Corp Secy*
Joel Maertens, *Corp Secy*
Camden R Fine, *CFO*
Larry W Winum, *CFO*
Greg Martinson, *Branch Mgr*
EMP: 57 **Privately Held**
WEB: www.icba.org
SIC: 8611 Banker's organization providing advisory services
PA: Independent Community Bankers
    1615 L St NW Ste 900
    Washington DC 20036
    202 659-8111

(G-9349)

KANE TRANSPORT INC (PA)
40925 403rd St (56378)
PO Box 126 (56378-0126)
PHONE..............................320 352-2762
FAX: 320 352-6141
Robert Kane, *President*
Paul Kane, *President*
Steve Hostle, *Manager*
EMP: 50 EST: 1949
SQ FT: 15,000 **Privately Held**

(PA)=Parent Co (HQ)=Headquarters (DH)=Div Headquarters
✿ = New business established in last 2 years

2011 Harris Minnesota
Services Directory

© Harris InfoSource 1-866-281-6415
403

WEB: www.kanetransport.com
SIC: 4213 4212 long distance liquid petroleum transportation services; local liquid hauling services; local petroleum hauling services

(G-9350)
LAKEVIEW MEDICAL CLINIC
433 Elm St N (56378-1052)
PHONE.................................320 352-6591
FAX: 320 352-5164
Keith J Olson DO, *Partner*
Mary Thomas, *Partner*
James Sayovitz, *Partner*
Larry Okerlund, *Partner*
Terry Wolff DO, *Partner*
EMP: 35 EST: 1976
SALES (est): 1MM-4.9MM Privately Held
WEB: www.lakeviewclinic.org
SIC: 8031 8011 Osteopathic physicians' office & clinic; general & family practice physician or surgeon office

(G-9351)
RENT A FORD CAR
203 10th St S (56378-1616)
PHONE.................................320 352-6561
John Wiese, *Manager*
EMP: 40 EST: 1975
SALES (est): 5MM-9.9MM Privately Held
WEB: www.johnwieseford.com
SIC: 7514 Passenger car rental

(G-9352)
ROBERT CHAPIN
Also Called: N F P Transportation
39465 415th St Ste A (56378-8388)
PHONE.................................320 351-8901
FAX: 320 351-8905
Robert Chapin, *Owner*
Roger Nordvedt, *General Mgr*
EMP: 70 EST: 2001
SALES (est): 5MM-9.9MM Privately Held
WEB: www.robertchapin.com
SIC: 4213 Over the road trucking

(G-9353)
STEARNS DAIRY HERD IMPROVEMENT
825 12th St S (56378-1744)
PO Box 227 (56378-0227)
PHONE.................................320 352-2028
FAX: 320 352-6163
Lois Vanbeck, *Principal*
Mark Heidgerken, *Principal*
Dan Hanson, *Chairman*
Paul Reitsma, *Corp Secy*
Amundson Dave, *Sales Executive*
EMP: 30 EST: 1958
SQ FT: 6,000
SALES (est): 1MM-4.9MM Privately Held
WEB: www.stearnsdhialab.com
SIC: 8734 Testing laboratory

(G-9354)
WALTERS TRUCKING INC
411 Lincoln Loop (56378-2007)
PHONE.................................320 352-2207
FAX: 320 352-5362
David K Walters, *President*
Mike Foster, *Managing Dir*
Mary Walters, *Corp Secy*
Mary Classman, *Purch Agent*
EMP: 27 EST: 1982
SQ FT: 16,000
SALES (est): 1MM-4.9MM Privately Held
SIC: 4212 4213 Local trucking without storage services; over the road trucking

SAUK RAPIDS
Benton County

(G-9355)
A A A COURIER INC
1 Industrial Blvd (56379-1270)
PO Box 70 (56379-0070)
PHONE.................................320 259-9292
FAX: 320 259-0959
Drew Austin, *President*
EMP: 25 EST: 1991
SALES (est): 1MM-4.9MM Privately Held
SIC: 4212 Delivery services by vehicle

(G-9356)
ALL STATE COMMUNICATIONS INC
800 Industrial Dr S Ste 204 (56379-1244)
PHONE.................................320 203-1511
FAX: 320 203-1510
Jared Gapinski, *President*
Jim Gapinksi, *Vice Pres*
Richard Shapiro, *CFO*
Tracy Johnson, *Finance*
EMP: 40 EST: 1996
SQ FT: 5,000
SALES (est): 1MM-4.9MM Privately Held
WEB: www.allstatecom.com
SIC: 1731 Communications contractor services

(G-9357)
ARRAY SERVICES GROUP INC
Also Called: Prosource Billing
217 N Benton Dr (56379-1530)
PHONE.................................320 534-3680
Gerry Gilbertson, *Vice Pres*
Mark Kottke, *Vice Pres*
Roberta Kelash, *Manager*
Troy Kutzera, *Info Tech Dir*
EMP: 125
SALES (est): 5MM-9.9MM Privately Held
SIC: 7322 Collection agency

(G-9358)
BAUERLY DYNAMICS INC
Also Called: Short Stop Service Station
4787 Shadowwood Dr NE (56379-9431)
PHONE.................................320 251-9472
Mark Bauerly, *President*
Brian Bauerly, *Corp Secy*
Michael Bauerly, *Vice Pres*
David Bauerly, *Vice Pres*
Denny Hennon, *Finance*
EMP: 28 EST: 1940
SQ FT: 5,000
SALES (est): 5MM-9.9MM Privately Held
SIC: 1521 Gas station; delicatessen; townhouse construction service; retail independent convenience store

(G-9359)
BOSER CONSTRUCTION INC
7135 5th Ave NE (56379-9558)
PHONE.................................320 393-3185
FAX: 320 393-3186
Douglas Boser, *President*
Tanya Boser, *Vice Pres*
Scott Keho, *Foreman/Supr*
Robert Brinkman, *Foreman/Supr*
EMP: 31 EST: 1996
SQ FT: 8,500
SALES (est): 5MM-9.9MM Privately Held
WEB: www.boserconstruction.com
SIC: 1542 1742 Commercial & office building contractor; drywall contractor

(G-9360)
CARLSON & LYTER DISTRIBUTING (PA)
1020 Industrial Dr S (56379-1241)
PO Box 457 (56379-0457)
PHONE.................................320 251-7375
FAX: 320 259-7981
Bernadette Perryman, *President*
Mike Bengtson, *CFO*
Pete Benson, *Manager*
EMP: 65 EST: 1980
SQ FT: 55,000 Privately Held
WEB: www.budtime.com
SIC: 5181 Wholesales beer & other fermented malt liquors

(G-9361)
CSI SPORTS PROPERTIES LLC
360 Industrial Blvd (56379-9785)
PO Box 360 (56379-0360)
PHONE.................................320 252-4193
FAX: 320 252-7177
Al Dehler, *General Mgr*
Adrian Holler, *Member*
Jay Samuels, *VP Persnl*
Dosha Renick, *Human Res Mgr*
Marie Weinand, *Manager*
EMP: 120 EST: 1963
SQ FT: 83,000
SALES (est): 50MM-99.9MM Privately Held
WEB: www.mt-sports.com

SIC: 5091 Wholesales fishing tackle; wholesales hunting equipment & supplies; wholesales boat accessories & parts
PA: Big Rock Sports LLC
173 Hankison Dr
Newport NC 28570
252 808-3500

(G-9362)
DMZ TRUCKING INC
3635 Quail Rd NE 1 (56379-9444)
PHONE.................................320 252-0313
FAX: 320 252-0635
Douglas Moulzolf, *President*
Leann Moulzolf, *Corp Secy*
EMP: 30 EST: 1992
SALES (est): 1MM-4.9MM Privately Held
SIC: 4212 Local trucking without storage services

(G-9363)
GOLF INC
Also Called: Wapicada Golf Course
4498 15th St NE (56379-9612)
PO Box 454 (56379-0454)
PHONE.................................320 251-7804
FAX: 320 251-0329
Thom Bailey, *General Mgr*
Jan Neils, *Manager*
Brad Deyak, *Manager*
EMP: 40 EST: 1957
SQ FT: 6,000
SALES (est): 1MM-4.9MM Privately Held
WEB: www.wapicada.com
SIC: 7997 Membership golf club

(G-9364)
GRANITE CITY ARMORED CAR INC
1026 13th Ave N (56379-2504)
PO Box 295 (56379-0295)
PHONE.................................320 252-0708
FAX: 320 252-2309
Tim Kosloske, *CEO*
Joyce Kosloske, *Corp Secy*
Debbie Kosloske, *Vice Pres*
William L Kosloske Jr, *Treasurer*
EMP: 32 EST: 1971
SQ FT: 25,000
SALES (est): 1MM-4.9MM Privately Held
SIC: 7381 4226 Armored car service; document & office records storage services

(G-9365)
GREAT RIVER FEDERAL CREDIT
Also Called: T & L Credit Union Sauk Rapids
4 2nd Ave N (56379-1604)
PHONE.................................320 252-3507
FAX: 320 252-0500
Barbara Oconnell, *Vice Pres*
Becky Nelson, *Human Res Dir*
R Vaccaro, *Manager*
Steve Lovejoy, *Manager*
Inesc Bevans, *Manager*
EMP: 50
SALES (est): 5MM-9.9MM Privately Held
WEB: www.greatriverfcu.org
SIC: 6061 Federally chartered credit union

(G-9366)
HEALTHCARE OPTIONS MINNESOTA
Also Called: Option Care
1000 S Benton Dr Unit 405 (56379-1228)
PO Box 578, Saint Cloud (56302-0578)
PHONE.................................320 252-5666
FAX: 320 252-5073
Stephen Mareck, *President*
Joe Bauer, *Sales Executive*
Jon Richey, *Manager*
Jim Dewaard, *Administrator*
EMP: 38 EST: 1988
SQ FT: 2,800
SALES (est): 1MM-4.9MM Privately Held
SIC: 8099 Nutrition services

(G-9367)
HUISKEN MEAT CO OF SAUK RAPIDS
245 Industrial Blvd (56379-1238)
PHONE.................................320 259-0305
James R Hanson, *President*
Cliff Albertson, *General Mgr*
Jenny Molitor, *Director*
Neil Bueckers, *Director*

EMP: 80 EST: 2002
SQ FT: 50,000
SALES (est): 50MM-99.9MM Privately Held
SIC: 5147 Wholesales meat & meat products

(G-9368)
KNIFE RIVER CORP - NORTH (DH)
4787 Shadowwood Dr NE (56379-9431)
PHONE.................................320 251-9472
Michael Bauerly, *Vice Pres*
Brian Bauerly, *Vice Pres*
Ray Matheney, *Purchasing*
Nancy K Christenson, *Treasurer*
Mike Hoffman, *Controller*
EMP: 375 EST: 1960
SQ FT: 5,000
SALES (corp-wide): 4.17B Publicly Held
WEB: www.mdu.com
SIC: 1611 1442 Highway & street paving contractor; gravel mining; manufactures asphalt paving mixtures & blocks; manufactures ready-mixed concrete
HQ: Knife River Corp
1150 W Century Ave
Bismarck ND 58503
701 530-1400

(G-9369)
MARSON CONTRACTORS INC
3636 Quail Rd NE (56379-9444)
PHONE.................................320 255-5506
FAX: 320 255-5506
Jeff Hanson, *President*
Mark Hanson, *Vice Pres*
EMP: 30 EST: 1990
SALES (est): 1MM-4.9MM Privately Held
SIC: 4212 Local trucking without storage services

(G-9370)
NORTH CREST GYMNASTICS & DANCE
1009 Industrial Dr S (56379-1241)
PHONE.................................320 251-3416
FAX: 320 251-7533
Tom Maiers, *President*
Nadine Maiers, *President*
Laura Dvorak, *Exec Dir*
Megan Rogholt, *Exec Dir*
Austin Kelly, *Director*
EMP: 39 EST: 1993
SQ FT: 22,700
SALES (est): 1MM-4.9MM Privately Held
WEB: www.northcrestgym.com
SIC: 7911 7991 7999 Dance studio, school & hall; martial arts instruction; health club
PA: North Crest Enterprises Inc
1009 Industrial Dr S
Sauk Rapids MN 56379
320 253-6498

(G-9371)
RIDGEVIEW PLACE LP
1009 10th Ave NE Ofc (56379-9689)
PHONE.................................320 251-5228
FAX: 320 259-8964
Brenda Eggerth, *VP Finance*
Angie Vanbeek, *Manager*
Patty Campbell, *Manager*
Tina Roering, *Manager*
EMP: 25 EST: 1998
SQ FT: 50,000
SALES (est): 1MM-4.9MM Privately Held
SIC: 8059 Nursing home

(G-9372)
RON'S CABINETS INC
380 Industrial Blvd (56379-9785)
PO Box 515 (56379-0515)
PHONE.................................320 252-7667
FAX: 320 257-0158
John Packert, *President*
Elizabeth Packert, *Vice Pres*
Nancy March, *Accounting Dir*
James Dockendorf, *Manager*
EMP: 40 EST: 2000
SQ FT: 21,000
SALES (est): 1MM-4.9MM Privately Held
SIC: 1751 5031 Millwork; manufactures wooden kitchen cabinets; wholesales kitchen cabinets; cabinet & finish work carpentry service; manufactures wood office furniture

www.HarrisInfo.com
404

2011 Harris Minnesota
Services Directory

▲=Import ▼=Export
◆=Import/Export

(G-9373)
SCENIC SIGN CORP
828 5th St S (56379-1352)
PO Box 881, Saint Cloud (56302-0881)
PHONE 320 252-9400
FAX: 320 252-4260
Marc Ree, *President*
Bob Gruber Jr, *CFO*
Jessica Orton, *Accounting Dir*
Joan Nicoll, *Manager*
EMP: 28 EST: 1957
SQ FT: 7,500
SALES (est): 1MM-4.9MM Privately Held
WEB: www.scenicsign.com
SIC: 7389 Manufactures signs & advertising
specialties; sign painting & lettering shop;
manufactures electrical signs; manufactures
neon signs

(G-9374)
SHEPHERD GOOD LUTHERAN HOME (PA)
1115 4th Ave N (56379-2201)
PHONE 320 252-6525
FAX: 320 259-3463
Bruce Glanzer, *CEO*
Inez Smallwood, *Corp Secy*
Krista Martini, *CFO*
Rhonda Pohl, *Hum Res Coord*
Jodi Speicher, *Mktg Dir*
EMP: 240 EST: 1962
SQ FT: 87,300
SALES (corp-wide): 17.22M Privately Held
SIC: 8051 6513 Skilled nursing care facility;
operators of retirement hotels

(G-9375)
SHEPHERD GOOD LUTHERAN HOME
Also Called: Good Shepherd Cottages
307 11th St N (56379-2184)
PHONE 320 258-8665
Jane Bloom, *Manager*
EMP: 30
SALES (est): 1MM-4.9MM Privately Held
SIC: 8051 6513 Skilled nursing care facility;
operators of retirement hotels
PA: Shepherd Good Lutheran Home
1115 4th Ave N
Sauk Rapids MN 56379
320 252-6525

(G-9376)
ST CLOUD HOSPITAL
Also Called: Journey Home Halfway House
1485 10th Ave NE (56379-9838)
PHONE 320 259-9149
FAX: 320 259-4565
Carol Belling, *Branch Mgr*
EMP: 25
SALES (est): 1MM-4.9MM Privately Held
WEB: www.centracareclinic.com
SIC: 8093 8361 Outpatient drug clinic;
residential care facility
HQ: St Cloud Hospital
1406 6th Ave N
Saint Cloud MN 56303
320 251-2700

(G-9377)
STRACK CONSTRUCTION CO INC
1139 Franklin Ave Ste 2 (56379-1230)
PO Box 668, Saint Cloud (56302-0668)
PHONE 320 251-5933
FAX: 320 251-3123
Bob Stack, *CEO*
Mary Faust, *Corp Secy*
EMP: 25 EST: 1938
SQ FT: 3,421
SALES (est): 5MM-9.9MM Privately Held
SIC: 1542 1541 New commercial & office
building construction; industrial building
renovating, remodeling & repair service;
commercial & office building renovation &
repair services; industrial building &
warehouse construction

(G-9378)
TRIMPAC INC (PA)
1030 Stearns Dr (56379-2503)
PO Box 277, Saint Cloud (56302-0277)
PHONE 320 202-3200
FAX: 320 202-3202
Daniel Wright, *President*
Forrest Loven, *Purch Mgr*
Craig Lambrecht, *CFO*
Bill Stevens, *Marketing Mgr*
EMP: 70 EST: 1945
SQ FT: 45,000 Privately Held
WEB: www.trimpaconline.com
SIC: 5031 5072 Wholesales millwork;
manufactures wooden doors, door parts &
trim; wholesales windows; wholesales
builders' hardware

(G-9379)
VETERANS OF FOREIGN WARS OF
901 N Benton Dr (56379-1547)
PHONE 320 252-3617
David Bonit, *Principal*
Janet Essery, *Manager*
EMP: 275 Privately Held
SIC: 8641 Veterans' organization
PA: Veterans of Foreign Wars of
406 W 34th St Fl 11
Kansas City MO 64111
816 756-3390

(G-9380)
WALGREEN CO
Also Called: Walgreens
10 S Benton Dr (56379-1416)
PHONE 320 253-6601
FAX: 320 253-7858
David King, *Manager*
EMP: 25
SALES (est): 1MM-4.9MM Publicly Held
WEB: www.walgreens.com
SIC: 7384 Drug store; photofinishing
laboratory
PA: Walgreen Co
200 Wilmot Rd
Deerfield IL 60015
847 914-2500

SAUK RAPIDS
Stearns County

(G-9381)
FAIRVIEW GARDENS
1080 35th St NE (56379-9778)
PHONE 320 229-2281
Chanda Gebhardt, *Owner*
EMP: 30 EST: 2006 Privately Held
SIC: 0782 Landscaping services

SAVAGE
Scott County

(G-9382)
ADVANTAGE TRAVEL & INCENTIVES
7447 Egan Dr Ste 300 (55378-2396)
PHONE 952 447-1333
FAX: 952 447-1334
Mary S Leathers, *President*
Christopher Lund, *Exec VP*
Jennifer Rohne, *Purchasing*
Ray Leathers, *CFO*
Julie Farrell, *Human Res Mgr*
▼ EMP: 73 EST: 1995
SQ FT: 37,000
SALES (est): 5MM-9.9MM Privately Held
WEB:
www.advantageperformancenetwork.com
SIC: 8742 Incentive or award program
consultant
PA: Altour International Inc
1270 Ave Of T Flr 15
New York NY 10020
212 897-5000

(G-9383)
ASSOCIATED PARTNERSHIP LTD
6591 Highway 13 W (55378-1177)
PHONE 952 890-7851
Du N Wade Harris, *President*
Michael Harris, *Senior VP*
Mike Polis, *Purch Agent*
Debbie Willeford, *Purchasing*
Craig Elison, *Engineering*

▼ EMP: 120 EST: 1971
SQ FT: 65,000
SALES (est): 10MM-24.9MM Privately Held
WEB: www.rollxvans.com
SIC: 7532 5012 7515 Van conversions;
wholesales noncommercial vans; retails
new & used vans; manufactures motor
homes; passenger car leasing

(G-9384)
CATO CONSTRUCTION INC
6707 Highway 13 W (55378-3129)
PHONE 952 736-8134
FAX: 952 894-0646
Ron Hill, *Partner*
Jeff Hagen, *Partner*
Sharon Lindborg, *Manager*
EMP: 50 EST: 2000
SALES (est): 5MM-9.9MM Privately Held
WEB: www.catoconstruction.com
SIC: 1761 Roof repair contractor

(G-9385)
CHAMPION COATINGS
7385 W 126th St (55378-1105)
PHONE 952 707-9000
Gary Johnson, *Principal*
EMP: 25
SALES (est): 1MM-4.9MM Privately Held
SIC: 1721 Residential painting contractor

(G-9386)
COLE'S SALON MANAGEMENT INC
8160 W County Road 42 Ste 100
(55378-2130)
PHONE 952 226-5310
FAX: 952 226-5315
Tim Cole, *Branch Mgr*
EMP: 36
SALES (est): 1MM-4.9MM Privately Held
WEB: www.colessalon.com
SIC: 7231 Unisex hair salon
PA: Cole's Salon Management Inc
14150 Nicollet Ave Ste 11
Burnsville MN 55337
952 435-8585

(G-9387)
CURBSIDE LAWN CARE
9084 Windsor Ct (55378-2160)
PHONE 952 403-9012
FAX: 952 403-9282
David Leffler, *President*
Al King, *Vice Pres*
Sharon King, *Manager*
EMP: 60 EST: 1998
SALES (est): 5MM-9.9MM Privately Held
WEB: www.curbsidelawn.com
SIC: 1711 0782 Plumbing, heating & air
conditioning contractor; landscaping
services

(G-9388)
DCI ENVIRONMENTAL INC
7217 W 128th St (55378-1162)
PHONE 952 894-0012
Larry D Johnson, *President*
Kathleen L Johnson, *Treasurer*
Pete Haqlluska, *Controller*
Pete Halluska, *Controller*
EMP: 35 EST: 1977
SQ FT: 2,000
SALES (est): 5MM-9.9MM Privately Held
SIC: 1611 Gravel or dirt road construction

(G-9389)
DUSTCOATING INC
7217 W 128th St (55378-1162)
PHONE 952 894-0012
FAX: 952 894-0126
Larry Johnson, *President*
Kathleen Johnson, *Corp Secy*
Wade Johnson, *Vice Pres*
Shane Johnson, *Human Res Mgr*
EMP: 25 EST: 1971
SQ FT: 1,120
SALES (est): 1MM-4.9MM Privately Held
WEB: www.dustcoating.com
SIC: 1799 1611 Decontamination service;
heavy highway & street construction

(G-9390)
FABCON INC (PA)
6111 Highway 13 W (55378-1235)
PHONE 952 890-4444
Michael L Lejeune, *President*
Mark Hansen, *Vice Pres*
Richard K Wessen, *Vice Pres*
James O Hasse, *Vice Pres*
James Houtman, *Vice Pres*
EMP: 200 EST: 1970
SQ FT: 65,000 Privately Held
WEB: www.fabcon-usa.com
SIC: 1771 Manufactures prefabricated
concrete panels & sections; manufactures
precast concrete floor slabs & tiles;
manufactures concrete wall & ceiling
squares; concrete contractor

(G-9391)
INTERNATIONAL ASSOCIATION OF
6917 Connelly Cir (55378-5629)
PHONE 952 447-0413
Dave Moen, *President*
EMP: 30 Privately Held
WEB: www.iaopc.com
SIC: 8641 Civic associations
PA: International Association of
300 W 22nd St
Oak Brook IL 60523
630 571-5466

(G-9392)
KEINATH LEASING CO
12800 Hwy 13 S Ste 500 (55378-1266)
PHONE 952 944-8000
Allan Dmore, *President*
Keith Bevzriege, *President*
EMP: 30
SQ FT: 42,000
SALES (est): Under 500K Privately Held
SIC: 7359 Equipment rental & leasing
services

(G-9393)
KINDERCARE LEARNING CENTERS
Also Called: Savage Kindercare
5710 Loftus Dr (55378-3902)
PHONE 952 440-9890
FAX: 952 440-9870
Kim Anderson, *Manager*
Lisa Kasper, *Manager*
EMP: 26
SALES (est): 500-999K Privately Held
WEB: www.kindercare.com
SIC: 8351 Child day care service
HQ: KinderCare Learning Centers
650 NE Holladay St Ste 1400
Portland OR 97232
503 872-1300

(G-9394)
KNOWLEDGE LEARNING CORP
14014 Hwy 13 S (55378-2191)
PHONE 952 440-2677
FAX: 952 440-2679
Susan Hannesson, *Manager*
EMP: 25
SALES (est): 500-999K Privately Held
WEB: www.knowledgelearning.com
SIC: 8351 Child day care service
PA: Knowledge Learning Corp
650 NE Holladay St # 1400
Portland OR 97232
503 872-1300

(G-9395)
LAPP TANNEHILL INC
8675 Eagle Creek Pkwy (55378-1284)
PHONE 952 881-6700
Andrea Lapp, *President*
Marc Mackin, *Corp Secy*
Mark Babcock, *Exec VP*
Bartta Bokamp, *Treasurer*
Lisa O'Malley, *Credit Mgr*
EMP: 30 EST: 1958
SQ FT: 32,000
SALES (est): 10MM-24.9MM Privately Held

SIC: 5063 Wholesales electrical apparatus & equipment; wholesales electrical supplies; wholesales electrical insulators; wholesales electronic wire & cable
PA: Lapp Holding North America
29 Hanover Rd
Florham Park NJ 07932
973 660-9634

(G-9396)
LEHMAN'S GARAGE INC
8533 Highway 101 W   (55378-1029)
PHONE..............................952 888-8700
FAX: 952 890-7067
Richard Cossette, *President*
Greg Mann, *Controller*
Mike Seger, *Finance*
Dan Olson, *Manager*
EMP: 45
SALES (est): 1MM-4.9MM **Privately Held**
SIC: 7532 Automotive body, paint & interior repair & maintenance services
PA: Lehman's Garage Inc
171 American Blvd W
Minneapolis MN 55420
952 888-8700

(G-9397)
LLOYDS CONSTRUCTION SERVICES
7207 W 128th St   (55378-1162)
PHONE..............................952 746-5832
Stephanie Lloyd, *President*
Amanda Lloyd, *Corp Secy*
John Lloyd, *Vice Pres*
Jeff Stocker, *Opers Mgr*
Allie Lloyd, *Treasurer*
EMP: 50 **EST:** 1983
SQ FT: 30,000
SALES (est): 5MM-9.9MM **Privately Held**
WEB: www.lloyds-construction.com
SIC: 1795 1799 Wrecking & demolition contractor; construction site cleanup service

(G-9398)
MASTER ELECTRIC CO INC
8555 W 123rd St   (55378-1150)
PHONE..............................952 890-3555
FAX: 952 890-3095
Jeff Loftsgaarden, *President*
Kim Loftsgaarden, *Vice Pres*
Darren Dickenson, *Project Mgr*
John Bradley, *Opers Mgr*
Ted Hansen, *Safety Mgr*
EMP: 65 **EST:** 1973
SQ FT: 16,000
SALES (est): 5MM-9.9MM **Privately Held**
WEB: www.masterelectric.com
SIC: 1731 Communications contractor services; fiber optic cable installation contractor; telephone equipment installation; retails consumer electronic equipment; retails radios, televisions & consumer electronics

(G-9399)
MASTER TECHNOLOGY GROUP INC
8555 W 123rd St   (55378-1150)
PHONE..............................952 960-1212
Ryan Blundell, *President*
Kim Loftsgaarden, *Principal*
Jeff Loftsgaarden, *Principal*
Carla Downer, *Manager*
Roger Beissel, *Manager*
EMP: 48 **EST:** 2005
SALES (est): 5MM-9.9MM **Privately Held**
SIC: 1731 Voice, data & video wiring contractor

(G-9400)
NEWTOWN SOLUTIONS INC
8608 Eagle Creek Pkwy   (55378-1284)
PHONE..............................952 440-4400
Christine Smith, *CEO*
EMP: 26 **EST:** 2002 **Privately Held**
WEB: www.newtownsolutions.com
SIC: 7361 Employment agency services

(G-9401)
NOVUS FRANCHISING INC
12800 Hwy 13 S Ste 500   (55378-1266)
PHONE..............................952 944-8000
Keith A Beveridge, *Vice Pres*
Murad Meraly, *Info Tech Dir*

EMP: 26 **EST:** 1973
SQ FT: 40,000
SALES (est): 10MM-24.9MM **Privately Held**
SIC: 6794 Selling or licensing of franchises
PA: TCG International Inc
4710 Kingsway Suite 2700
Burnaby Canada
604 4381000

(G-9402)
NOVUS INC
12800 Hwy 13 S Ste 500   (55378-1266)
PHONE..............................952 944-8152
Keith Beveridge, *President*
Leo Cyr, *Vice Pres*
David Osland, *Vice Pres*
Jim Pascale, *Vice Pres*
Jim Dufresne, *Mfg Staff*
EMP: 30 **EST:** 1972
SQ FT: 42,000
SALES (est): 10MM-24.9MM **Privately Held**
WEB: www.novuspolish.com
SIC: 7359 7536 Manufactures polishing preparations & related products; automotive glass replacement service; manufactures plastics materials & resins; equipment rental & leasing services
PA: TCG International Inc
4710 Kingsway Suite 2700
Burnaby Canada
604 4381000

(G-9403)
OUTDOOR ENVIRONMENTS INC
12488 Xenwood Ave   (55378-1231)
PHONE..............................952 496-1000
FAX: 952 496-1800
Hugh Kramber, *President*
Eric Lint, *Opers Mgr*
Mita Wagner, *Controller*
Steve Mortland, *Controller*
Kollen Parsons, *Accounts Mgr*
EMP: 25 **EST:** 1975 **Privately Held**
WEB: www.outdoor-environments.com
SIC: 0782 0781 4959 Lawn care services; landscape planning services; snow plowing services

(G-9404)
R & S HEATING & AIR CONDG
12600 Creek View Ave   (55378-2369)
PHONE..............................952 894-0376
Brett Thielen, *CEO*
Jessica Thielen, *President*
Robert Theilen, *Vice Pres*
EMP: 35 **EST:** 1978
SQ FT: 15,000
SALES (est): 1MM-4.9MM **Privately Held**
SIC: 1711 Heating & air conditioning contractor

(G-9405)
ROAD MACHINERY & SUPPLIES CO (PA)
5633 Highway 13 W   (55378-1215)
PHONE..............................952 895-9595
FAX: 952 895-9564
David Johnson, *CEO*
Michael M Sill II, *President*
Mark Rossi, *General Mgr*
Mike Mencel, *Vice Pres*
John Ruud, *VP Opers-Prdtn-*
◆ **EMP:** 80 **EST:** 1926
SQ FT: 40,000 **Privately Held**
WEB: www.rmseq.com
SIC: 5082 Wholesales general construction machinery & equipment; wholesales road construction equipment; wholesales logging equipment & supplies; wholesales mining machinery & equipment

(G-9406)
SAFE STEP INC
12400 Princeton Ave Ste C   (55378-1366)
PHONE..............................952 229-8282
Suzanne Wallskog, *CEO*
Mark Wallskog, *President*
EMP: 44 **EST:** 2001
SQ FT: 8,300
SALES (est): 1MM-4.9MM **Privately Held**
WEB: www.safestep.com
SIC: 1799 Bathtub refinishing contractor

(G-9407)
SOMERSET HOSPITALITY LLC
Also Called: Comfort Inn
4601 Highway 13 W   (55378-1365)
PHONE..............................952 894-6124
FAX: 952 894-6124
Salman Rizvi, *Member*
Sabeena Rizvi, *Member*
Joyce Senthens, *Manager*
EMP: 25 **EST:** 2001
SQ FT: 11,892
SALES (est): 1MM-4.9MM **Privately Held**
SIC: 7011 Traveler accommodations

(G-9408)
STOCKER EXCAVATING INC
12336 Boone Ave   (55378-2316)
PHONE..............................952 890-4241
Donald Stocker, *President*
Curt Stocker, *Vice Pres*
EMP: 25 **EST:** 1970
SQ FT: 4,000
SALES (est): 1MM-4.9MM **Privately Held**
SIC: 1794 Excavating contractor

(G-9409)
STS OPERATING INC
Also Called: Sunsource Fauver
12800 Hwy 13 S Ste 100   (55378-1262)
PHONE..............................952 563-1700
FAX: 952 563-1817
Al Roland, *COO*
David Sacher, *COO*
Kim Shearer, *Vice Pres*
Bill Valdmanis, *Vice Pres*
Cheryl Isensee, *Purch Agent*
EMP: 100
SALES (est): 25MM-49.9MM **Privately Held**
WEB: www.sun-source.com
SIC: 5084 5085 Wholesales industrial hydraulic systems equipment & supplies; wholesales industrial supplies
HQ: STS Operating Inc
2301 W Windsor Ct
Addison IL 60101
630 317-2700

(G-9410)
TURNER EXCAVATING CO
12520 Nevada Ave   (55378-1116)
PHONE..............................952 890-1645
FAX: 952 890-3187
John H Turner Jr, *President*
Helen Turner, *Treasurer*
EMP: 60 **EST:** 1963
SQ FT: 18,000
SALES (est): 5MM-9.9MM **Privately Held**
SIC: 1794 1629 Excavation & grading, building construction contractor; earthmoving service

(G-9411)
WALGREEN CO
Also Called: Walgreens
8100 W County Road 42   (55378-2193)
PO Box 16   (55378-0016)
PHONE..............................952 226-1283
FAX: 952 226-1289
Katina Petty, *General Mgr*
EMP: 40
SALES (est): 5MM-9.9MM **Publicly Held**
WEB: www.walgreens.com
SIC: 7384 Drug store; photofinishing laboratory
PA: Walgreen Co
200 Wilmot Rd
Deerfield IL 60015
847 914-2500

(G-9412)
WASTE MANAGEMENT OF WISCONSIN
12448 Pennsylvania Ave   (55378-1118)
PHONE..............................952 890-1100
FAX: 952 890-5143
Ginger Kaladas, *Credit Staff*
Ron Moeing, *Branch Mgr*
Bruce Oulette, *Manager*
Ron Moeing, *Manager*
EMP: 120
SALES (est): 10MM-24.9MM **Privately Held**

SIC: 4212 Garbage collection & transportation services without disposal
HQ: Waste Management of Wisconsin
W124N8925 Boundary Rd
Menomonee Falls WI 53051
262 251-4000

SAWYER
Carlton County

(G-9413)
MINNESOTA INDIAN PRIMARY
1150 Mission Rd   (55780)
PO Box 66   (55780-0066)
PHONE..............................218 879-6731
FAX: 218 879-6734
Jeffrey D Johnson, *Business Mgr*
Giles Hart, *Vice Pres*
Gordon Adams, *Treasurer*
Deborah Kamunen, *Manager*
Elwin Benton, *Administrator*
EMP: 34 **EST:** 1977
SQ FT: 11,500
SALES (est): 1MM-4.9MM **Privately Held**
SIC: 8361 Residential rehabilitation center with health care incidental

SEBEKA
Wadena County

(G-9414)
CARING HANDS HOME CARE INC (PA)
113 Minnesota Ave W   (56477-6004)
PO Box 197   (56477-0197)
PHONE..............................218 837-5572
FAX: 218 837-6155
Gary Johnson, *President*
Beth Johnson, *Vice Pres*
EMP: 50 **EST:** 1994
SALES (corp-wide): 1.30M **Privately Held**
WEB: www.caringhandshomecare.com
SIC: 8082 Home health care services

SHAFER
Chisago County

(G-9415)
SHAFER CONTRACTING CO INC
30405 Regal Ave   (55074-2307)
PO Box 128   (55074-0128)
PHONE..............................651 257-5019
FAX: 651 462-7319
George Mattson, *President*
Brad Mattson, *Vice Pres*
EMP: 40 **EST:** 1968
SQ FT: 3,000
SALES (est): 5MM-9.9MM **Privately Held**
WEB: www.shafercontracting.com
SIC: 1611 General highway & street construction service

SHAKOPEE
Scott County

(G-9416)
'Q' CARRIERS INC
1415 Maras St   (55379-8800)
PHONE..............................952 445-8718
FAX: 952 445-8796
Greg Gorvin, *President*
Traci Culver, *Vice Pres*
Bruce Bruchman, *Vice Pres*
Renee Loney, *Accountant*
Cindy Kalal, *Director*
EMP: 30 **EST:** 1981
SQ FT: 16,265
SALES (est): 1MM-4.9MM **Privately Held**
WEB: www.qcarriers.com
SIC: 4213 Over the road trucking
PA: Summit Holdings Corp
1415 Maras St
Shakopee MN 55379
952 445-8718

www.HarrisInfo.com
406

2011 Harris Minnesota
Services Directory

▲=Import ▼=Export
◆=Import/Export

(G-9417)
A-SCAPE INC
690 Industrial Cir S (55379-1842)
PHONE..............................952 496-1178
FAX: 952 496-0204
Anthony Newman, *President*
Anne Newman, *Vice Pres*
EMP: 30 EST: 1981
SQ FT: 5,000 **Privately Held**
WEB: www.a-scape.com
SIC: 0781 0782 4959 Landscape planning services; lawn care services; snow plowing services

(G-9418)
AMERICINN SHAKOPEE
4100 12th Ave E (55379-1945)
PHONE..............................952 445-6775
FAX: 952 277-1100
EMP: 80 EST: 2006
SQ FT: 18,238
SALES (est): 1MM-4.9MM **Privately Held**
SIC: 7011 Traveler accommodations; hotel

(G-9419)
ARTEKA CO'S LLC
8810 13th Ave E (55379-8804)
PHONE..............................952 934-2000
FAX: 952 934-3067
Stewart Hanson, *Member*
Mike Hammel, *Project Mgr*
Kathy Maleck, *CFO*
Hugh Kramber, *Manager*
EMP: 110 EST: 1970
SQ FT: 10,000 **Privately Held**
WEB: www.artekacompanies.com
SIC: 0782 Lawn services

(G-9420)
BENEDICTINE HEALTH SYSTEM
Also Called: St Francis Regional Med Ctr
1455 Saint Francis Ave (55379-3374)
PHONE..............................952 403-3000
EMP: 854
SALES (est): 25MM-49.9MM **Privately Held**
SIC: 8059 Personal care home, with health care
PA: Benedictine Health System
    503 E 3rd St Ste 400
    Duluth MN 55805
    218 786-2370

(G-9421)
BETASEED INC (PA)
1788 Marschall Rd (55379-3308)
PO Box 195 (55379-0195)
PHONE..............................952 445-8090
FAX: 952 496-0205
Kurt Wickstrom, *CEO*
John Enright, *CFO*
Donald Weiman, *CFO*
Connie Ginsbach, *Human Res Mgr*
Paul Seminari, *Manager*
▲ EMP: 25 EST: 1969
SQ FT: 10,500
SALES (corp-wide): 976.92M **Privately Held**
WEB: www.betaseed.com
SIC: 8731 0181 5191 Commercial agricultural research services; vegetable seed farming; wholesales field, garden & flower seeds

(G-9422)
BIFFS BOXES LLC
8610 Hansen Ave (55379-3723)
PHONE..............................952 403-1221
FAX: 952 403-1220
Derek Pauling, *Member*
Michael Pauling, *Member*
Heather Pauling, *Member*
Diana Pauling, *Member*
Sharon Wailks, *Office Mgr*
EMP: 40 EST: 1986
SQ FT: 9,000
SALES (est): 1MM-4.9MM **Privately Held**
SIC: 7359 Portable toilet rental

(G-9423)
BITUMINOUS ROADWAYS INC
6898 Highway 101 E (55379-9056)
PHONE..............................952 233-1660
FAX: 952 233-0686
John Kittleson, *Manager*

EMP: 25
SALES (est): 1MM-4.9MM **Privately Held**
WEB: www.bitroads.com
SIC: 1611 1771 1799 Street surfacing & paving construction; asphalt contractor; parking lot maintenance service
PA: Bituminous Roadways Inc
    1520 Commerce Dr
    Mendota Heights MN 55120
    651 686-7001

(G-9424)
BUG INC
Also Called: Total Rental
441 1st Ave W (55379-1205)
PHONE..............................952 445-1022
FAX: 952 445-9505
William L Michaelson, *President*
Bill Michaelson, *Manager*
Chris Sellner, *Administrator*
EMP: 25 EST: 1968
SQ FT: 7,000
SALES (est): Under 500K **Privately Held**
WEB: www.mbl2000.com
SIC: 7359 Equipment rental & leasing services

(G-9425)
C A P SCOTT-CARVER-DAKOTA INC
Also Called: Cap Agency
712 Canterbury Rd S (55379-1840)
PHONE..............................952 496-2125
FAX: 952 402-9815
Diane Weckman, *Manager*
Vincent Loesch, *Info Tech Mgr*
Mary F Sullivan, *Director*
Mary Riley, *Deputy Dir*
EMP: 30 EST: 1965
SQ FT: 6,400
SALES (est): 500-999K **Privately Held**
SIC: 8351 8322 Head Start center; old age assistance; general counseling services

(G-9426)
CANARD AEROSPACE CORP
250 Fuller St S Ste 201 (55379-1324)
PHONE..............................952 944-7990
FAX: 952 944-9149
Tim Millard, *President*
Dave Sindelar, *Vice Pres*
Roxanne Malott, *Manager*
Joann Sindelar, *Assistant*
EMP: 25 EST: 1991
SQ FT: 8,000
SALES (est): 1MM-4.9MM **Privately Held**
WEB: www.canardaero.com
SIC: 8711 5088 Aviation or aeronautical engineers; wholesales aircraft engines & engine parts; wholesales aircraft equipment & supplies

(G-9427)
CANTERBURY PARK HOLDING CORP
1100 Canterbury Rd S (55379-1867)
PHONE..............................952 445-7223
Randall D Sampson, *President*
Claire Lundgren, *Corp Secy*
Logan Foreman, *Corp Secy*
Mark A Erickson, *Vice Pres*
Eric Haslstrom, *Vice Pres*
EMP: 40 EST: 1994
SALES (est): 1MM-4.9MM **Publicly Held**
SIC: 7948 7999 Racetrack; provides card & game services

(G-9428)
CARNAHAN CITY-WIDE INSULATION
Also Called: City-Wide Insulation
1725 3rd Ave W (55379-1018)
PO Box 298 (55379-0298)
PHONE..............................952 445-1387
FAX: 952 445-0677
Linda Carnahan, *President*
Denny Tienter, *Exec Dir*
EMP: 55 EST: 1971
SQ FT: 5,000
SALES (est): 1MM-4.9MM **Privately Held**
WEB: www.citywideinsul.com
SIC: 1742 Building insulation installation service

(G-9429)
CARVER-SCOTT COOPERATIVE
792 Canterbury Rd S Ste 231 (55379-1825)
PHONE..............................952 445-7524
FAX: 952 403-7673
Diane Weckman, *Manager*
Marge Neil, *Manager*
EMP: 40 EST: 1993
SALES (est): 10MM-24.9MM **Privately Held**
SIC: 6512 Shopping center & mall operator

(G-9430)
CEDAR FAIR, LP
Also Called: Valleyfair Amusement Park
1 Valleyfair Dr (55379-3012)
PHONE..............................952 445-7600
FAX: 952 445-9333
Larry McKenzie, *General Mgr*
Dave Vosejpka, *Opers Staff*
Allen Schwartz, *VP Finance*
Lyle Jaeger, *Finance*
Pam Amundson, *Mktg Dir*
EMP: 71
SALES (est): 1MM-4.9MM **Publicly Held**
WEB: www.cedarfair.com
SIC: 7996 Amusement park
PA: Cedar Fair, LP
    1 Cedar Point Dr
    Sandusky OH 44870
    419 626-0830

(G-9431)
COKEM INTERNATIONAL LTD
3880 4th Ave E (55379-1773)
PHONE..............................952 358-6000
Chuck Bond, *President*
Dave Stark, *Credit Mgr*
John Simenson, *Manager*
EMP: 64 EST: 2000
SQ FT: 110,000
SALES (est): 25MM-49.9MM **Privately Held**
SIC: 5045 Wholesales computer software

(G-9432)
CONCRETE MOBILITY LLC
2917 133rd St W Ste 2 (55379-9219)
PHONE..............................952 746-5887
FAX: 952 492-3463
Brenda Flood, *Mng Member*
EMP: 26 EST: 2004
SALES (est): 1MM-4.9MM **Privately Held**
SIC: 1771 Concrete contractor

(G-9433)
CONTECH CONSTRUCTION PRODUCTS
11155 Chaparral Ave (55379-9210)
PHONE..............................952 496-1050
FAX: 952 496-1152
Bob Moore, *Vice Pres*
Elwin Coe, *Manager*
EMP: 40
SALES (est): 10MM-24.9MM **Privately Held**
WEB: www.contech-cpi.com
SIC: 5082 Wholesales construction & mining machinery
HQ: Contech Construction Products
    9025 Centre Pointe Dr # 400
    West Chester OH 45069
    513 645-7000

(G-9434)
CRYSTAL MARINE INC
12720 Chestnut Blvd (55379-9319)
PHONE..............................952 233-3437
Matt Ness, *Manager*
EMP: 25 EST: 2001
SALES (est): 10MM-24.9MM **Privately Held**
WEB: www.crystalpierz.com
SIC: 5091 Wholesales boats, canoes, watercrafts & equipment

(G-9435)
DANNY'S CONSTRUCTION CO INC
Also Called: Dcci
1066 3rd Ave W Ste 4 (55379-1105)
PO Box 11 (55379-0011)
PHONE..............................952 445-4143
FAX: 952 445-4337
Keiran W O'Brien, *CEO*
William Mizell, *President*

Alysa Schneider, *Exec VP*
Larry Bunston, *Safety Dir*
William Heggelman, *Treasurer*
EMP: 144 EST: 1970
SQ FT: 15,200
SALES (est): 10MM-24.9MM **Privately Held**
WEB: www.dannysconstruction.com
SIC: 1791 Structural steel erection contractor

(G-9436)
DEM-CON LANDFILL LLC
13020 Dem Con Dr (55379-7200)
PHONE..............................952 445-5755
FAX: 952 445-8288
Mark Pahl, *Principal*
EMP: 30 EST: 2007
SALES (est): 1MM-4.9MM **Privately Held**
SIC: 4953 Waste material recycling services

(G-9437)
ELANDER MECHANICAL INC
591 Citation Dr (55379-1888)
PHONE..............................952 445-4692
FAX: 952 445-7487
Thomas E Elander, *President*
Richard Elander, *Vice Pres*
Todd Wedin, *Manager*
EMP: 25 EST: 1983
SQ FT: 5,000
SALES (est): 1MM-4.9MM **Privately Held**
SIC: 1711 Plumbing service

(G-9438)
EMERALD CREST OF SHAKOPEE
1855 10th Ave W (55379-2021)
PHONE..............................952 233-8811
FAX: 952 233-8855
Stacy Jorgenson, *Exec Dir*
Janet Berglind, *Director*
EMP: 30 EST: 2003
SALES (est): 1MM-4.9MM **Privately Held**
SIC: 8059 Personal care home, with health care

(G-9439)
EVERGREEN CHILD CARE CENTER
712 Canterbury Rd S (55379-1840)
PHONE..............................952 402-0303
Judi Moonen, *Director*
EMP: 25 EST: 2000
SALES (est): 500-999K **Privately Held**
SIC: 8351 Child day care service

(G-9440)
GAGE & GAGE INC
4950 12th Ave E (55379-1810)
PHONE..............................952 403-1193
Robert D Gage, *President*
Barbara A Gage, *Exec VP*
Tracy Reimann, *CIO*
▲ EMP: 26 EST: 1953
SQ FT: 25,000
SALES (est): 10MM-24.9MM **Privately Held**
WEB: www.gage-gage.com
SIC: 5113 Wholesales paper & disposable plastic bags; wholesales paperboard & disposable plastic boxes; wholesales wrapping or coarse paper & products

(G-9441)
GLH SEEDS INC
1788 Marschall Rd (55379-3308)
PO Box 195 (55379-0195)
PHONE..............................952 445-8090
Don Weaver, *Ch of Bd*
Michael F Stephenson, *President*
Dan Peacock, *Finance*
Ramon Molinary, *Station Mgr*
Mark Bullen, *Administrator*
EST: 1966
SQ FT: 120,000 **Privately Held**
WEB: www.glh-seeds.com
SIC: 5191 Wholesales farm supplies

(G-9442)
GRL INVESTMENT CO LLC
100 Fuller St S Ste 200 (55379-1354)
PHONE..............................952 445-6745
Gary Laurent, *Principal*
Randy Laurent, *Member*
Joann Homyak, *Manager*

(PA)=Parent Co (HQ)=Headquarters (DH)=Div Headquarters
✿ = New business established in last 2 years

2011 Harris Minnesota
Services Directory

© Harris InfoSource 1-866-281-6415
407

GEOGRAPHIC

EMP: 25 EST: 1999
SALES (est): 5MM-9.9MM **Privately Held**
SIC: **1521** 7992 New single-family home
construction service; townhouse
construction service; public golf course

(G-9443)
HELLER DRYWALL LTD
1480 3rd Ave W (55379-1013)
PHONE..............................952 496-2525
Stephen Heller, *President*
Barb Malinski, *Manager*
EMP: 25 EST: 1988
SQ FT: 5,000
SALES (est): 1MM-4.9MM **Privately Held**
WEB: www.hellerdrywall.com
SIC: **1742** Drywall contractor

(G-9444)
HOME DEPOT USA INC
1701 County Road 18 (55379-8119)
PHONE..............................952 496-3076
FAX: 952 233-6974
Darse Ayers, *Branch Mgr*
EMP: 150
SALES (est): 25MM-49.9MM **Publicly Held**
SIC: **7359** Home center store; tool rental
HQ: Home Depot International Inc
2455 Paces Ferry Rd SE
Atlanta GA 30339
770 319-1669

(G-9445)
INTERNATIONAL SEAL CO INC (DH)
1087 Park Pl (55379-1889)
PHONE..............................952 894-8400
John Rice, *President*
Jerry Norcia, *Vice Pres*
Jerry Johnson, *Vice Pres*
Bill Hansen, *Accounts Mgr*
Katie Ilinkovich, *Manager*
▲ EMP: 60 EST: 1978
SQ FT: 38,000
SALES (corp-wide): 6.24B **Privately Held**
WEB: www.tcmseals.com
SIC: **5085** Wholesales industrial seals;
wholesales industrial bearings
HQ: Freudenberg-Nok General
47690 E Anchor Ct
Plymouth MI 48170
734 451-0020

(G-9446)
INTERPLX INC
1157 Valley Park Dr # 115 (55379-1925)
PO Box 800 (55379-0800)
PHONE..............................952 403-7180
Chuck Buckner, *CEO*
Robert Rayca, *Vice Pres*
Michael Jones, *Manager*
EMP: 30 EST: 1994
SQ FT: 13,000
SALES (est): 5MM-9.9MM **Privately Held**
WEB: www.interplx.com
SIC: **7372** Business & professional software
publishers

(G-9447)
JOHNSON ANDERSON & ASSOCIATES
5010 Valley Ind Blvd S (55379-1823)
PHONE..............................952 496-6699
FAX: 952 496-9760
Neil Johnson, *President*
Jon Anderson, *Vice Pres*
Jon Laurent, *Vice Pres*
Mike Glidden, *Maint Mgr*
Kjersten Johnson, *Manager*
EMP: 85 EST: 1983
SQ FT: 60,000
SALES (est): 25MM-49.9MM **Privately Held**
WEB: www.johnsonanderson.com
SIC: **5112** Wholesales envelopes; book
binding service; commercial printing;
commercial lithographic printing; typesetting
service

(G-9448)
KINDERCARE LEARNING CENTERS
Also Called: Shakopee Valley Kindercare
1308 Greenwood Ct (55379-4452)
PHONE..............................952 403-6862
FAX: 952 496-0728

Donna Gainor, *Exec Dir*
Corrie Backus, *Director*
EMP:
SALES (est): 500-999K **Privately Held**
WEB: www.kindercare.com
SIC: **8351** Group day care center
HQ: KinderCare Learning Centers
650 NE Holladay St Ste 1400
Portland OR 97232
503 872-1300

(G-9449)
KMART CORP
901 Canterbury Rd S (55379-1803)
PHONE..............................952 445-2936
FAX: 952 445-0341
Steve Mayfield, *Human Resources*
William Finkel, *Manager*
Keith Morton, *Manager*
Gary Hellmers, *Manager*
Michael Beckman, *Manager*
EMP: 400
SALES (est): 25MM-49.9MM **Publicly Held**
WEB: www.kmart.com
SIC: **4225** Warehousing & storage services
DH: Kmart Corp
3333 Beverly Rd
Hoffman Estates IL 60179
847 286-2500

(G-9450)
LAURENT BUILDERS INC
100 Fuller St S Ste 200 (55379-1354)
PHONE..............................952 445-6745
FAX: 952 445-9727
Gary Laurent, *President*
Randy Laurent, *Vice Pres*
Joann Homyak, *Manager*
EMP: 25 EST: 1975
SQ FT: 4,000
SALES (est): 5MM-9.9MM **Privately Held**
WEB: www.laurentcompanies.com
SIC: **1521** New single-family home
construction service; townhouse
construction service

(G-9451)
LOGISTICS INTERNATIONAL LLC
Also Called: Trans Group
1150 Gateway Dr W (55379-3819)
PHONE..............................952 697-4800
Glen Hasse, *Mng Member*
Bob Hall, *Manager*
EMP: 77 EST: 2007
SQ FT: 180,000
SALES (est): 5MM-9.9MM **Privately Held**
SIC: **4731** Freight transportation
arrangement services

(G-9452)
LOWE'S HOME CENTERS INC
4270 Dean Lakes Blvd (55379-2828)
PHONE..............................952 367-9000
EMP: 150
SALES (est): 25MM-49.9MM **Publicly Held**
WEB: www.lowes.com
SIC: **5031** 5064 Retails building products &
materials; wholesales exterior building
materials; wholesales interior building
materials; wholesales electrical appliances;
retails household appliances
HQ: Lowe's Home Centers Inc
1605 Curtis Bridge Rd
Wilkesboro NC 28697
336 658-4000

(G-9453)
LUMA CORP
5200 12th Ave E (55379-1948)
PHONE..............................952 995-6500
Gerald Strand, *President*
Carianne Maki, *Vice Pres*
Leanne Jones, *Office Mgr*
EMP: 27 EST: 1970
SQ FT: 18,000
SALES (est): 10MM-24.9MM **Privately Held**
WEB: www.lumasales.com
SIC: **5063** Wholesales electrical apparatus
& equipment; wholesales electrical
commercial & industrial lighting fixtures;
manufactures lighting equipment;
manufactures current carrying wiring
devices

(G-9454)
LUNDELL ENTERPRISES LLC
1838 Westchester Ln (55379-4566)
PHONE..............................952 261-7617
Brent Lundell, *Principal*
EMP: 70 EST: 2005
SALES (est): 1MM-4.9MM **Privately Held**
SIC: **7011** Hotel

(G-9455)
METROPOLITAN PEDIATRIC
1515 Saint Francis Ave # 230
(55379-4383)
PHONE..............................952 445-6700
Thomas R Stealey, *President*
Kelly Rockhold, *Office Mgr*
Sally Vissers, *Administrator*
Judy Hutter, *Nursing Dir*
Timothy D Johanson, *Pediatrics*
EMP: 70 EST: 2001
SALES (est): 5MM-9.9MM **Privately Held**
SIC: **8011** Pediatrician office

(G-9456)
MID-AMERICA FESTIVALS CORP
Also Called: Minnesota Renaissance Festival
1244 Canterbury Rd S # 306 (55379-8944)
PHONE..............................952 445-7361
FAX: 952 445-3120
James Peterson, *President*
Bonnie Jacobson, *General Mgr*
Jeff Holbrook, *Finance*
Katie Kline, *Sales Dir*
Mary Strussert, *Payroll Mgr*
EMP: 25 EST: 1970
SQ FT: 1,200
SALES (est): 1MM-4.9MM **Privately Held**
WEB: www.help-net.com
SIC: **7999** Provides festival operation
services

(G-9457)
MINNESOTA VINYL & ALUMINUM
Also Called: MN Vinyl & Aluminum Systems
12820 Emery Way (55379-8300)
PHONE..............................952 403-0805
FAX: 952 403-0822
Wendy Anderson, *President*
Bradley Anderson, *VP Opers-Prdtn-*
EMP: 35 EST: 1993
SQ FT: 7,929
SALES (est): 10MM-24.9MM **Privately Held**
WEB: www.mvas.com
SIC: **5031** Wholesales lumber, plywood &
millwork

(G-9458)
MIRUMI INC
Also Called: Holiday Inn
511 Marschall Rd (55379-2612)
PHONE..............................952 445-9779
FAX: 952 445-9725
Harem Shroff, *President*
Bharti Shroff, *General Mgr*
EMP: 25 EST: 2002
SQ FT: 3,800
SALES (est): 1MM-4.9MM **Privately Held**
SIC: **7011** Traveler accommodations

(G-9459)
NORTH AMERICAN MEMBERSHIP GRP
5555 12th Ave E Ste 170 (55379-1966)
PHONE..............................952 988-7451
David High, *Branch Mgr*
EMP: 100
SALES (est): 1MM-4.9MM **Privately Held**
WEB: www.northamericanmediagroup.com
SIC: **7997** 7331 Membership recreation
club; publishes & prints magazines; retail
mail-order fishing, hunting & camping
equipment & supplies; membership hunting
club; direct mail advertising service
HQ: North American Membership Grp
12301 Whitewater Dr
Hopkins MN 55343
952 936-9333

(G-9460)
NORTH STAR AUTO AUCTION
4908 Valley Ind Blvd N (55379-1861)
PO Box 257 (55379-0257)
PHONE..............................952 445-5544
FAX: 952 445-6773
Jerry Aman, *General Mgr*
Jackie Lovo, *Purch Agent*
Gregory Choate, *Controller*
Jeff Starn, *Human Res Dir*
Sue Samuelson, *Sales Mgr*
EMP: 150 EST: 1971
SQ FT: 50,000
SALES (est): 100MM-499.9MM **Privately Held**
WEB: www.coxenterprises.com
SIC: **5012** Automobile auction services;
used car dealer

(G-9461)
NORTHWEST ASPHALT INC
1451 Stagecoach Rd (55379-8045)
PHONE..............................952 445-1003
FAX: 952 445-1056
Michael B Pfeiffer, *President*
Debra Hendrickson, *Vice Pres*
Michael H Sand, *CFO*
Kent Skonseng, *Asst Controller*
EMP: 30 EST: 1978
SQ FT: 10,000
SALES (est): 1MM-4.9MM **Privately Held**
WEB: www.nwasphalt.net
SIC: **1771** Driveway, parking lot & blacktop
contractor; asphalt contractor; parking lot
construction

(G-9462)
NSL HOLDINGS INC
1157 Valley Park Dr # 130 (55379-1964)
PHONE..............................952 943-8474
FAX: 952 496-2495
Michael Amundson, *President*
Janice Holvorsen, *Controller*
▲ EMP: 25 EST: 2002
SQ FT: 150,000
SALES (est): 10MM-24.9MM **Privately Held**
SIC: **5199** Wholesales art goods;
wholesales gifts & novelties

(G-9463)
OPEN SYSTEMS HOLDINGS CORP (PA)
4301 Dean Lakes Blvd (55379-2994)
PHONE..............................952 403-5700
Michael Bertini, *CEO*
Dave Link, *Vice Pres*
Craig Faulds, *Vice Pres*
Jody Flatebo, *Finance Other*
Kurt Busher, *Manager*
EMP: 50 EST: 1990
SQ FT: 25,000 **Privately Held**
SIC: **7372** Business & professional software
publishers; application software publishing

(G-9464)
OPEN SYSTEMS INC
4301 Dean Lakes Blvd (55379-2994)
PHONE..............................952 403-5700
Michael Bertini, *President*
Brian Bartos, *Vice Pres*
Carla Alarcon, *CIO*
Jim Stolis, *Info Tech Dir*
Gary Long, *Info Tech Dir*
EMP: 100 EST: 1976
SQ FT: 25,000
SALES (est): 10MM-24.9MM **Privately Held**
SIC: **7372** Business & professional software
publishers
PA: Open Systems Holdings Corp
4301 Dean Lakes Blvd
Shakopee MN 55379
952 403-5700

(G-9465)
PALMER BUS SERVICES
730 3rd Ave W (55379-1152)
PHONE..............................952 445-1166
FAX: 952 445-9632
Floyd Palmer, *President*
Patricia Huber, *Regional Mgr*
William Schmitt, *Vice Pres*
EMP: 30 EST: 1962
SALES (est): 500-999K **Privately Held**

www.HarrisInfo.com
408

2011 Harris Minnesota
Services Directory

▲=Import ▼=Export
◆=Import/Export

SIC: **4151** 4953 School bus service; garbage collecting, destroying & processing services

(G-9466)
QLOGIC CORP
4601 Dean Lakes Blvd   (55379-2720)
PHONE..............................952 932-4000
Terry Kolodjski, *Principal*
Cheryl Puelston, *Purch Agent*
Skip Andersen, *Engineer*
Jim Herkenhoff, *Engineer*
Steve Carter, *Manager*
EMP: 180
SALES (est): 10MM-24.9MM **Publicly Held**
WEB: www.qlogic.com
SIC: **8711** Manufactures electronic circuits; engineering services
PA: QLogic Corp
     26650 Aliso Viejo Pkwy
     Aliso Viejo CA 92656
     949 389-6000

(G-9467)
QUALITY FORKLIFT SALES & SVC
587 Citation Dr   (55379-1888)
PHONE..............................952 445-6607
FAX: 952 895-9036
Todd Doege, *President*
Mark Stack, *Vice Pres*
Bob Gerdes, *Sales Staff*
Matt Malone, *Sales Staff*
Colleen Wright, *Executive*
EMP: 40 EST: 1989
SQ FT: 38,000
SALES (est): 5MM-9.9MM **Privately Held**
WEB: www.qualityforklift.com
SIC: **7699** Manufactures fork, platform or straddle industrial lift trucks; industrial equipment service

(G-9468)
QUALITY LIFE STYLES INC
Also Called: Shakopee Friendship Manor
1340 3rd Ave W   (55379-1011)
PHONE..............................952 445-4155
FAX: 952 445-9367
Timothy A Riffe, *President*
Terry A Riffe, *Vice Pres*
Rosena Moore RN, *Nursing Dir*
EMP: 100 EST: 1965
SQ FT: 30,000
SALES (est): 1MM-4.9MM **Privately Held**
SIC: **8051** Skilled nursing care facility

(G-9469)
RELIAKOR SERVICES INC   (PA)
8600 Hansen Ave   (55379-3723)
PHONE..............................952 403-1440
FAX: 952 403-1441
William Pilla, *President*
Nancy Brick, *Executive Asst*
EMP: 30 EST: 1959
SQ FT: 21,000   **Privately Held**
SIC: **1799** 4953 4959 Parking lot maintenance service; snow plowing services; garbage collecting, destroying & processing services

(G-9470)
RTL CONSTRUCTION INC
4000 Valley Ind Blvd S   (55379-1855)
PHONE..............................952 934-4695
Mike Larson, *President*
Robyn Larson, *Human Res Mgr*
Troy R Moore, *Manager*
EMP: 83 EST: 1992
SQ FT: 3,600
SALES (est): 10MM-24.9MM **Privately Held**
WEB: www.rtlconstruction.com
SIC: **1521** Single-family housing construction

(G-9471)
RYAN CONTRACTING CO
8700 13th Ave E   (55379-8806)
PO Box 246, Elko   (55020-0246)
PHONE..............................952 894-3200
Thomas J Ryan, *President*
Kari B Priewe, *Corp Secy*
Scott Enright, *Vice Pres*
Tyler Enright, *Vice Pres*
Rochelle D Dacar, *Vice Pres*
▼ EMP: 150

EST: 1991
SQ FT: 12,700
SALES (est): 10MM-24.9MM **Privately Held**
SIC: **1623** 1611 1771 Sewer line construction; grading services; water main construction; curb construction; concrete contractor

(G-9472)
SAFE HAVEN SHELTER FOR YOUTH
13780 McKenna Rd NW Ofc   (55379-3398)
PHONE..............................952 288-2680
EMP: 25 EST: 1995
SALES (est): 1MM-4.9MM **Privately Held**
SIC: **8361** Self-help group home

(G-9473)
SHAKOPEE CHEVROLET INC
Also Called: Canterbury Collision
1220 1st Ave E   (55379-1611)
PHONE..............................952 445-4148
George McGuire, *President*
EMP: 40 EST: 2004
SALES (est): 1MM-4.9MM **Privately Held**
SIC: **7532** Automotive body shop

(G-9474)
SHAKOPEE PUBLIC UTILITIES
255 Sarazin St   (55379-3942)
PO Box 470   (55379-0470)
PHONE..............................952 233-1505
Lou Vanhout, *Manager*
Lou V Hout, *Manager*
Joseph Adams, *Director*
EMP: 45 EST: 2005
SQ FT: 65,191
SALES (est): 25MM-49.9MM **Privately Held**
SIC: **4931** Electric & related services

(G-9475)
SHOCK CITY CELLULAR
205 Lewis St S   (55379-1459)
PHONE..............................952 233-5281
Don Breding, *Member*
Robb Breding, *Member*
EMP: 50 EST: 1999 **Privately Held**
SIC: **4812** Cellular telephone services

(G-9476)
ST FRANCIS REGIONAL MEDICAL
1455 Saint Francis Ave   (55379-3374)
PHONE..............................952 403-3000
Kathy Tyler, *Corp Secy*
Alan Lem, *Vice Pres*
Anita K Nystrom, *Human Res Mgr*
Greg Schuer, *Lab Dir*
Brad Handahl, *Radiology Dir*
◆ EMP: 840 EST: 1938
SQ FT: 85,000
SALES (est): 50MM-99.9MM **Privately Held**
WEB: www.stfrancis-shakopee.com
SIC: **8062** Medical hospital
PA: Allina Health System
     2925 Chicago Ave
     Minneapolis MN 55407
     612 775-5000

(G-9477)
ST GERTRUDE'S HEALTH CENTER
1850 Sarazin St Ofc OFC   (55379-4615)
PHONE..............................952 233-4400
FAX: 952 403-3431
Denise Moen, *Manager*
Roxy Helm, *Manager*
Lee Larson, *Administrator*
Jane Goebel, *Nursing Dir*
EMP: 75 EST: 1996
SALES (est): 1MM-4.9MM **Privately Held**
SIC: **8051** Skilled nursing care facility
PA: Benedictine Health System
     503 E 3rd St Ste 400
     Duluth MN 55805
     218 786-2370

(G-9478)
ST JOSEPH EQUIPMENT INC
6340 Highway 101 E   (55379-9052)
PHONE..............................952 445-5400
FAX: 952 445-0365
Bill Brikid, *General Mgr*

Sam Weatherhead, *Controller*
Bill Burket, *Manager*
EMP: 40
SQ FT: 19,100
SALES (est): 10MM-24.9MM **Privately Held**
WEB: www.stjosephequipment.com
SIC: **5082** Wholesales general construction machinery & equipment
PA: St Joseph Equipment Inc
     N1626 Wuensch Rd
     La Crosse WI 54601
     608 788-1775

(G-9479)
SUMMIT HOLDINGS CORP   (PA)
1415 Maras St   (55379-8800)
PHONE..............................952 445-8718
Greg Gorvin, *President*
EMP: 40 EST: 1999 **Privately Held**
WEB: www.qcarriers.com
SIC: **6719** 4213 Personal holding company; over the road trucking

(G-9480)
SYNERA SOLUTIONS
1674 Sage Ln   (55379-3487)
PHONE..............................952 403-9911
Jeff Gunhus, *Owner*
EMP: 100 EST: 1999
SALES (est): 1MM-4.9MM **Privately Held**
SIC: **7349** Housekeeping & maid services

(G-9481)
TRUDEAU HOLDINGS LLC
Also Called: Stone Gate Foods
4218 Valley Ind Blvd S   (55379-1851)
PHONE..............................952 445-1350
Vicki Evans, *Branch Mgr*
EMP: 70
SALES (est): 50MM-99.9MM **Privately Held**
WEB: www.trudeaudistributing.com
SIC: **5142** 5147 Wholesales packaged frozen foods; wholesales packaged frozen meats; wholesales packaged frozen poultry; wholesales meat & meat products
PA: Trudeau Holdings LLC
     25 Cliff Rd W Ste 115
     Burnsville MN 55337
     952 882-8295

(G-9482)
ZIEGLER INC
Also Called: Caterpillar
8050 Highway 101 E   (55379-9764)
PHONE..............................952 445-4292
FAX: 952 496-1864
R G Rick, *Manager*
Sue Clough, *Manager*
Ricardo Paloma, *Manager*
Curt Bailey, *Manager*
EMP: 80
SALES (est): 25MM-49.9MM **Privately Held**
SIC: **5082** Wholesales construction & mining machinery
PA: Ziegler Inc
     901 W 94th St
     Minneapolis MN 55420
     952 888-4121

SILVER BAY
Lake County

(G-9483)
MINNESOTA DEPARTMENT OF
Also Called: Silver Bay Veterans Home
45 Banks Blvd   (55614-1337)
PHONE..............................218 226-6300
FAX: 218 226-6336
Gina Thompson, *Persnl Dir*
Lindsey Klegstad, *Personnel*
Jeff Brown, *Manager*
Wayne Frame, *Manager*
Michael Bond, *Manager*
EMP: 50
SALES (est): 1MM-4.9MM **Privately Held**
WEB: www.sbay.mvh.state.mn.us
SIC: **8361** Residential care facility; veterans' affairs administration services; state government administration of veterans' affairs
DH: Minnesota Department of
     20 12th St W Fl 2
     Saint Paul MN 55155
     651 296-2562

(G-9484)
NORTHSHORE MINING CO
10 Outer Dr   (55614-1401)
PO Box 207, Babbitt   (55706-0207)
PHONE..............................218 226-4125
Don Prahl, *General Mgr*
William A Brake Jr, *Vice Pres*
Kimbell Alvey, *Safety Mgr*
Terry Severn, *Safety Mgr*
Hubert Garland, *Purch Agent*
EMP: 120
SALES (est): 25MM-49.9MM **Publicly Held**
WEB: www.cci-northshore.com
SIC: **1011** Iron ore mining
HQ: Northshore Mining Co
     1100 Superior Ave E Fl 15
     Cleveland OH 44114
     216 694-5700

SLAYTON
Murray County

(G-9485)
BEVERLY ENTERPRISES - MN
Also Called: Slayton Manor Care Center
2957 Redwood Ave   (56172-1549)
PHONE..............................507 836-6135
FAX: 507 836-8746
Linda Nelson, *Office Mgr*
Brooke Shriver, *Manager*
Trina Cooper, *Administrator*
EMP: 70
SALES (est): 1MM-4.9MM **Privately Held**
WEB: www.beverlynet.com
SIC: **8051** Skilled nursing care facility
HQ: Beverly Enterprises - MN
     650 Ramer Ave S
     Rush City MN 55069
     320 358-4765

(G-9486)
COUNTY OF MURRAY
2042 Juniper Ave   (56172-1017)
PHONE..............................507 836-6111
FAX: 507 836-6700
Renee Logan, *CFO*
Mel Snow, *Branch Mgr*
Daniel Woldt, *Med Doctor*
Sue Jensen, *Supervisor*
EMP: 131
SALES (est): 5MM-9.9MM **Privately Held**
SIC: **8069** 8062 Specialty hospital; medical hospital
PA: County of Murray
     2500 28th St
     Slayton MN 56172
     507 836-6148

(G-9487)
FINLEY ENGINEERING CO
1981 Engebretson Ave   (56172-2006)
PO Box 259   (56172-0259)
PHONE..............................507 836-8515
FAX: 507 777-2200
Ken Knuth, *President*
Ben Humphrey, *Sales & Mktg St*
Steve Leek, *Manager*
EMP: 30
SALES (est): 1MM-4.9MM **Privately Held**
WEB: www.fecinc.com
SIC: **8711** Engineering consulting services
PA: Finley Engineering Co Inc
     104 E 11th St
     Lamar MO 64759
     417 682-5531

(G-9488)
LRN ASSOCIATES MANAGEMENT INC
Also Called: Prairie View
2220 27th St   (56172-1212)
PHONE..............................507 836-8955
FAX: 507 836-8957
Lewis Nelson, *President*
EMP: 26 EST: 1985
SALES (est): 1MM-4.9MM **Privately Held**
SIC: **8322** 8361 Individual & family social services; residential care facility

(PA)=Parent Co (HQ)=Headquarters (DH)=Div Headquarters
✪ = New business established in last 2 years

2011 Harris Minnesota
Services Directory

© Harris InfoSource 1-866-281-6415
409

(G-9489)
MINNWEST BANK SOUTH
2565 King Ave (56172-1264)
PO Box 27 (56172-0027)
PHONE..............507 836-6141
FAX: 507 836-6143
Ivan Vansvssen, *President*
Brad Oeltjenbruns, *Exec VP*
Neal Everson, *Senior VP*
EMP: 27 **EST:** 1987
SALES (est): 5MM-9.9MM **Privately Held**
SIC: 6021 6141 National commercial bank; personal credit institution

(G-9490)
RUPP CONSTRUCTION CO INC
Highway 59 N (56172)
PO Box 1 (56172-0001)
PHONE..............507 836-8555
FAX: 507 836-8888
Douglas A Rupp, *President*
Larry Dargen, *Vice Pres*
Richard Klawitter, *Treasurer*
EMP: 85 **EST:** 1934
SQ FT: 4,850
SALES (est): 10MM-24.9MM **Privately Held**
SIC: 1611 1442 Heavy highway & street construction; gravel mining

(G-9491)
UNITED PARCEL SERVICE OF NEW
Also Called: UPS
1930 Engebretson Ave (56172-2006)
PHONE..............507 836-6671
Eric Stevenson, *Manager*
EMP: 35
SALES (est): 1MM-4.9MM **Publicly Held**
WEB: www.martrac.com
SIC: 4215 Parcel delivery services by vehicle
HQ: United Parcel Service of New
55 Glenlake Pkwy NE
Atlanta GA 30328
404 828-6000

SLEEPY EYE
Brown County

(G-9492)
CHRISTENSEN FARMS & FEEDLOTS (PA)
23971 County Road 10 (56085-4700)
PHONE..............507 794-5310
Bob Christensen, *President*
Glen D Christensen, *Corp Secy*
Lynn Christensen, *Corp Secy*
Candace Lee, *COO*
Shawne Johnson, *Manager*
EMP: 147 **EST:** 1991 **Privately Held**
SIC: 0213 Hog feedlot

(G-9493)
CHRISTENSEN FARMS MIDWEST LLC
23971 County Road 10 (56085-4700)
PHONE..............507 794-5310
Bob Christensen, *Mng Member*
Adam Reinhart, *Manager*
EMP: 99 **EST:** 2004 **Privately Held**
SIC: 0213 Hog & pig farming

(G-9494)
DIVINE PROVIDENCE COMMUNITY
700 3rd Ave NW (56085-1036)
PHONE..............507 794-3011
FAX: 507 794-3020
Rhonda Brown, *Administrator*
Linda Willette, *Administrator*
Sharon S Williams, *Director*
EMP: 85 **EST:** 1960
SQ FT: 61,000
SALES (est): 1MM-4.9MM **Privately Held**
SIC: 8051 Skilled nursing care facility

(G-9495)
FIRST SECURITY BANK - SLEEPY (HQ)
100 Main St E (56085-1353)
PO Box 1270, Sioux Falls SD (57101-1270)
PHONE..............507 794-3911
Lloyd Amundson, *Ch of Bd*
Blair Folken, *President*
David Carr, *Vice Pres*
EMP: 38 **EST:** 1969
SQ FT: 5,000 **Privately Held**
SIC: 6022 State commercial bank
PA: First Sleepy Eye
629 S Minnesota Ave Ste 203
Sioux Falls SD 57104
605 335-1508

(G-9496)
HOFFMAN CONSTRUCTION CO
24214 220th St (56085)
PHONE..............507 794-5230
Butch Hoffman, *President*
EMP: 35 **EST:** 1971
SALES (est): 1MM-4.9MM **Privately Held**
SIC: 1794 Excavating contractor

(G-9497)
MATHIOWETZ ENTERPRISES INC
30676 County Road 24 (56085-4359)
PHONE..............507 794-6953
FAX: 507 794-3514
Brian J Mathiowetz, *President*
Ronda Mathiowetz, *Corp Secy*
Julie A Anderson, *Vice Pres*
Randy Huiras, *Vice Pres*
David Domm, *Vice Pres*
EMP: 180 **EST:** 1924
SQ FT: 9,600
SALES (est): 25MM-49.9MM **Privately Held**
WEB: www.mathiowetzconst.com
SIC: 1611 Heavy highway & street construction

(G-9498)
MILLER SELLNER IMPLEMENT INC (PA)
22024 State Highway 4 (56085-5060)
PO Box 409 (56085-0409)
PHONE..............507 794-2131
FAX: 507 794-3056
Doug Miller, *President*
Michael S Miller, *Corp Secy*
Gerald Sellner, *Vice Pres*
Wayne Redman, *Vice Pres*
David Sellner, *Treasurer*
EMP: 40 **EST:** 1920
SQ FT: 38,840
SALES (corp-wide): 20M **Privately Held**
WEB: www.millersellner.com
SIC: 5083 Wholesales farm implements

(G-9499)
SCHWARTZ BROS INC
32296 190th St (56085)
PHONE..............507 794-5779
FAX: 507 794-5572
Joe Schwartz, *CEO*
John Schwartz, *President*
Matthew Lux, *Controller*
EMP: 50 **Privately Held**
WEB: www.schwartzbros.com
SIC: 0213 Hog & pig farming

(G-9500)
SLEEPY EYE AREA HOME HEALTH
1100 1st Ave S (56085-1856)
PHONE..............507 794-3594
Karen Braulick, *Exec Dir*
EST: 1994 **Privately Held**
SIC: 8082 Home health care services

(G-9501)
SOUTHPOINT FEDERAL CREDIT
Also Called: Saint Marys Parish Credit Un
920 Main St E (56085-4380)
PO Box 406 (56085-0406)
PHONE..............877 794-6712
Richard Nesvold, *CEO*
Miki Schultz, *Vice Pres*
Patrice Gohl, *Vice Pres*
Michelle Strate, *Loan Officer*
Mary Berdan, *CIO*
EMP: 40 **EST:** 1936
SALES (est): 5MM-9.9MM **Privately Held**
SIC: 6062 State chartered credit union

(G-9502)
ST MARY'S SCHOOL
104 Saint Marys St NW (56085-1024)
PHONE..............507 794-6141
FAX: 507 794-4841
Mary Ganglehoff, *Principal*
Kathy Goblirsch, *Business Mgr*
Gail Bromenschenkel, *Manager*
Mary Berdan, *Supervisor*
Chris Heiderscheidt, *Director*
EMP: 50 **EST:** 1892
ADMISSIONS: 213 **Privately Held**
SIC: 8351 Private denominational school; child day care service

(G-9503)
VOLUNTEERS OF AMERICA CARE
Also Called: Sleepy Eye Care Center
1105 3rd Ave SW (56085-1857)
PHONE..............507 794-7995
Gary Halmsted, *Systems Staff*
EMP: 140
SALES (est): 5MM-9.9MM **Privately Held**
SIC: 8051 Skilled nursing care facility
HQ: Volunteers of America Care
7530 Market Place Dr
Eden Prairie MN 55344
952 941-0305

SOUDAN
Saint Louis County

(G-9504)
MINNESOTA DEPARTMENT OF
Also Called: Soudan Undgrd Mine State Pk
1379 Stuntz Bay Rd (55782)
PO Box 335 (55782-0335)
PHONE..............218 753-2245
FAX: 218 753-2246
Paul Wannarka, *Manager*
Jim Essig, *Manager*
EMP: 32
SALES (est): 1MM-4.9MM **Privately Held**
WEB: www.guessmail.com
SIC: 7999 Commercial tourist attraction; conservation programs administration services; state government land, mineral & wildlife conservation administration
DH: Minnesota Department of
500 Lafayette Rd N
Saint Paul MN 55155
651 296-6157

SOUTH HAVEN
Stearns County

(G-9505)
FAIRHAVEN FARM
13835 51st Ave (55382-9092)
PHONE..............320 236-7685
David M Gregor, *Owner*
EMP: 27 **EST:** 1988 **Privately Held**
SIC: 0191 Crop farming

SOUTH HAVEN
Wright County

(G-9506)
CLEAR WATER CLEANERS INC
9616 140th St NW (55382-2859)
PHONE..............320 558-6691
Sonja Dahlberg, *CEO*
EMP: 75 **EST:** 2005
SQ FT: 2,500
SALES (est): 1MM-4.9MM **Privately Held**
SIC: 7349 Building cleaning & maintenance services

SOUTH SAINT PAUL
Dakota County

(G-9507)
AFSCME BUILDING CORP
300 Hardman Ave S Ste 3 (55075-2471)
PHONE..............651 451-7678
Kim Bunce, *Vice Pres*
Ellen Goedel, *Treasurer*
Robin Madsen, *Treasurer*
Duane Johnson, *Accounting Mgr*
Coleman Peral, *Manager*
EMP: 38 **EST:** 1946
SQ FT: 17,224 **Privately Held**
SIC: 8631 Labor organization

(G-9508)
ALLSTATE SALES & LEASING CORP (HQ)
558 Villuame Ave (55075-2445)
PO Box 268 (55075-0268)
PHONE..............651 455-6500
William D Larson, *CEO*
Jeff Banthournout, *President*
Glenn D Evans, *General Mgr*
Paula Sanders, *Corp Secy*
Allen Ofstehage, *Senior VP*
EMP: 82 **EST:** 1967
SQ FT: 5,000 **Privately Held**
WEB: www.wdlarson.com
SIC: 5012 5013 7538 Wholesales commercial trucks; wholesales new & used trailers for trucks; truck engine repair service; wholesales new motor vehicle parts & supplies
PA: W D Larson Co's Ltd Inc
10700 Lyndale Ave S Ste A
Minneapolis MN 55420
952 703-3425

(G-9509)
AMERICAN BOTTLING CO
270 Bridgepoint Dr (55075-2425)
PHONE..............651 552-3400
FAX: 651 457-3854
Tom Dahill, *Opers Mgr*
Mark Lad, *Manager*
Bruce Westerburg, *Manager*
Rick Heuertz, *Manager*
EMP: 125
SALES (est): 50MM-99.9MM **Publicly Held**
SIC: 5149 Manufactures bottled & canned soft drinks; wholesales groceries
PA: Dr Pepper Snapple Group Inc
5301 Legacy Dr
Plano TX 75024
972 673-7000

(G-9510)
AWM ENTERPRISES INC
Also Called: Stockmen's Truck Stop
501 Farwell Ave (55075-2473)
PHONE..............651 455-3044
FAX: 651 455-1193
A W McGuire, *President*
EMP: 45 **EST:** 1967
SQ FT: 6,500
SALES (est): 10MM-24.9MM **Privately Held**
SIC: 7215 7299 7999 Truck stop; coin operated laundry facility; retail independent convenience store; full service independent family restaurant; station operation service; provides card & game services

(G-9511)
BELDE BUILDING MAINTENANCE
450 Southview Blvd (55075-2395)
PO Box 626 (55075-0626)
PHONE..............651 457-6337
FAX: 651 457-6330
Gregory Belde, *President*
Judith Belde, *Corp Secy*
EMP: 52 **EST:** 1970
SALES (est): 1MM-4.9MM **Privately Held**
SIC: 7349 Building cleaning service

(G-9512)
BESTER BROS TRANSFER & STORAGE
260 Hardman Ave S (55075-2454)
PHONE..............651 451-1018
Douglas Bester, *President*

www.HarrisInfo.com
410

2011 Harris Minnesota
Services Directory

▲=Import ▼=Export
◆=Import/Export

Paul Lentz, *President*
Joe Gullered, *Vice Pres*
Kathryn Bester, *Treasurer*
EMP: 45 **EST:** 1917
SQ FT: 17,500
SALES (est): 1MM-4.9MM **Privately Held**
WEB: www.besterbros.com
SIC: 4214 Local moving service & storage;
local furniture moving & storage

(G-9513)
BFI WASTE SYSTEMS OF NORTH
Also Called: Site R47
2795 117th St E (55077-5925)
PHONE..............................651 437-8101
Karen Franson, *Manager*
Michael Ayers, *Manager*
Scott Stelman, *Manager*
EMP: 25
SALES (est): 1MM-4.9MM **Publicly Held**
WEB: www.republicservices.com
SIC: 4953 Waste material recycling services
HQ: Allied Waste Industries Inc
18500 N Allied Way # 100
Phoenix AZ 85054
480 627-2700

(G-9514)
BNSF RAILWAY CO
1312 Kassan Dr (55075-1026)
PHONE..............................651 451-1312
William S Purdy, *Manager*
EMP: 200 **Publicly Held**
WEB: www.bnsf.com
SIC: 4011 Long haul railroad
HQ: Burlington Northern Santa Fe
2650 Lou Menk Dr
Fort Worth TX 76131
800 795-2673

(G-9515)
BREMER BANK NATIONAL ASSN
633 Concord St N (55075-1114)
PHONE..............................651 451-6822
FAX: 651 457-9093
Steven Meads, *President*
Tom Naughtin, *Exec VP*
David Faust, *Senior VP*
Douglas Rued, *Senior VP*
Christopher Vosbeek, *Senior VP*
EMP: 92 **EST:** 1912
SQ FT: 20,250
SALES (est): 25MM-49.9MM **Privately Held**
SIC: 6021 National commercial bank
HQ: Bremer Financial Corp
445 Minnesota St Ste 2000
Saint Paul MN 55101
651 227-7621

(G-9516)
CENEX INC
5500 Cenex Dr (55077-1733)
PO Box 64089, Saint Paul (55164-0089)
PHONE..............................800 232-3639
John Johnson, *President*
Mary Banaszewski, *Manager*
Al Czapski, *Manager*
David E Sortland, *Manager*
EMP: 2500 **EST:** 1965
SALES (est): 1B-9.9B **Privately Held**
SIC: 1311 4213 4613 4789 4922 Crude
petroleum production; pipeline terminal
facility; natural gas production;
manufactures refinery gas; manufactures
lubricating greases; heavy hauling
transportation services; provides natural gas
storage services; manufactures liquefied
gases

(G-9517)
CENTERPOINT ENERGY RESOURCES
Also Called: Minnegasco
201 Concord Exc N Ste 100 (55075-1165)
PHONE..............................651 554-3000
Mike Donegan, *General Mgr*
Siu Lee, *Manager*
EMP: 40
SALES (est): 50MM-99.9MM **Publicly Held**
WEB: www.reliantresources.com

SIC: 4932 Gas & other combined services
HQ: CenterPoint Energy Resources
1111 Louisiana St
Houston TX 77002
713 207-1111

(G-9518)
CENTURY CONSTRUCTION CO INC
820 Concord St N Ste 101 (55075-1100)
PHONE..............................651 451-1020
FAX: 651 451-2745
Joe Baumann, *President*
Mike Holmes, *Vice Pres*
Lory Haugen, *Manager*
EMP: 30 **EST:** 1994
SQ FT: 4,200
SALES (est): 5MM-9.9MM **Privately Held**
WEB: www.centuryconstruct.com
SIC: 1542 1795 Commercial & office
building renovation & repair services;
wrecking & demolition contractor

(G-9519)
CERENITY SR CARE CENTER
724 19th Ave N (55075-1301)
PHONE..............................651 232-6000
Robert W Reif MD, *Vice Pres*
Sergei Shvetzoff, *Vice Pres*
Eugene Bolster, *Engineering*
Stephen C Spring, *VP Sls/Mktg*
Heather Kerl, *Marketing Mgr*
EMP: 200 **EST:** 1983
SALES (est): 5MM-9.9MM **Privately Held**
SIC: 8051 Extended care facility
PA: Benedictine Health System
503 E 3rd St Ste 400
Duluth MN 55805
218 786-2370

(G-9520)
CHEROKEE MANUFACTURING INC (PA)
501 Richmond St E (55075-5942)
PHONE..............................651 451-6568
FAX: 651 256-1146
John Gunderman, *President*
Judy Gunderman, *Corp Secy*
Jerry Gunderman, *Vice Pres*
James Gunderman, *Vice Pres*
Rick French, *Opers Mgr*
▲ **EMP:** 50 **EST:** 1940
SQ FT: 14,000
SALES (corp-wide): 15M **Privately Held**
SIC: 5193 Manufactures steel wire baskets;
manufactures textile bags; manufactures
canvas products; manufactures fiber cans,
drums & similar products; manufactures
insulated or armored steel wire;
manufactures metal containers

(G-9521)
CHS INC
Also Called: C H S
11600 Courthouse Blvd (55077-5912)
PHONE..............................651 306-8088
James Rossbach, *Plant Mgr*
Ralph Sanders, *Manager*
EMP: 70
SALES (est): 5MM-9.9MM **Publicly Held**
WEB: www.cenexharveststates.com
SIC: 4225 Warehousing & storage services
PA: CHS Inc
5500 Cenex Dr
Inver Grove Heights MN 55077
651 355-6000

(G-9522)
CITY AUTO GLASS
116 Concord Exchange S (55075-2446)
PO Box 629 (55075-0629)
PHONE..............................651 552-1000
Phillis Stratman, *Manager*
EMP: 40 **EST:** 1990
SQ FT: 3,200
SALES (est): 5MM-9.9MM **Privately Held**
SIC: 7699 Professional instrument repair
service

(G-9523)
COMMEMORATIVE AIR FORCE
Also Called: Southern Minnesota Wing
310 Airport Rd (55075-3551)
PHONE..............................651 455-6942
Bob Granbin, *Manager*

EMP: 200 **Privately Held**
WEB: www.cafwi.org
SIC: 8699 8412 Historical club; museum
PA: Commemorative Air Force
9600 Wright Dr
Midland TX 79706
432 563-1000

(G-9524)
COMMON SENSE SERVICES FOR
724 19th Ave N Ste 100 (55075-1301)
PHONE..............................651 552-0288
FAX: 651 552-0192
Lynne Zimmerman, *President*
Nancy Dahlin, *Vice Pres*
Kim Galles, *Bd of Directors*
Julie Williams, *Bd of Directors*
EMP: 25 **EST:** 1992
SALES (est): 1MM-4.9MM **Privately Held**
WEB: www.commonsenseservices.com
SIC: 8322 Individual & family social services

(G-9525)
COTTONWOOD TRUCK SERVICE INC
100 Slockman Rd Ste 206 (55075)
PO Box 652 (55075-0652)
PHONE..............................651 451-7320
Julianne Lenertz, *President*
Fred Lenertz, *Officer*
EMP: 25 **EST:** 1991
SALES (est): 1MM-4.9MM **Privately Held**
SIC: 4212 Local trucking without storage
services

(G-9526)
DROVER'S INN & RESTAURANT INC
Also Called: Best Western
701 Concord St S (55075-2411)
PHONE..............................320 252-6034
James J Graves, *President*
Scott Henning, *Manager*
EMP: 50 **EST:** 1984
SQ FT: 57,155
SALES (est): 1MM-4.9MM **Privately Held**
SIC: 7011 Traveler accommodations; tavern
drinking establishment

(G-9527)
FURY MOTORS INC
1000 Concord St S (55075-5913)
PHONE..............................651 451-1313
FAX: 651 251-8234
Harold T Leonard, *President*
Thomas J Leonard, *Vice Pres*
Geraldine I Leonard, *Vice Pres*
James P Leonard, *Vice Pres*
Steve Lee, *Manager*
EMP: 80 **EST:** 1963
SQ FT: 65,000
SALES (est): 25MM-49.9MM **Privately Held**
WEB: www.furymotors.com
SIC: 7532 New & used car dealer;
automotive body shop

(G-9528)
HEALTHPARTNERS INC
5625 Cenex Dr (55077-1724)
PHONE..............................651 552-1720
Caroline Mason, *Branch Mgr*
EMP: 75
SALES (est): 5MM-9.9MM **Privately Held**
WEB: www.healthpartners.com
SIC: 8011 Physicians' office & clinic
PA: HealthPartners Inc
8170 33rd Ave S
Bloomington MN 55425
952 883-6000

(G-9529)
HEARTSTONE OF MINNESOTA
222 Grand Ave W Ste 200 (55075-4000)
PHONE..............................651 457-2629
Jan G Talbot, *President*
Virginia Justice, *Manager*
EMP: 50 **EST:** 1993
SALES (est): 1MM-4.9MM **Privately Held**
WEB: www.hearthstonemn.org
SIC: 8361 Home for the emotionally
disturbed

(G-9530)
HOLTKOETTER INTERNATIONAL INC
155 Hardman Ave S (55075-2456)
PO Box 623 (55075-0623)
PHONE..............................651 552-8776
Paul W Eusterbrock, *President*
Brad Baker, *General Mgr*
▲ **EMP:** 50 **EST:** 1983
SQ FT: 110,000
SALES (est): 5MM-9.9MM **Privately Held**
WEB: www.holtkoetter.com
SIC: 5063 Manufactures residential lighting
fixtures; wholesales electrical residential
lighting fixtures

(G-9531)
IRISH GENEALOGICAL SOCIETY
1185 Concord St N Ste 218 (55075-1150)
PO Box 16585, Saint Paul (55116-0585)
PHONE..............................763 574-1436
Valerie Morrison, *President*
Marge Sobotka, *Exec Dir*
EMP: 30
SALES (est): 1MM-4.9MM **Privately Held**
SIC: 7299 Genealogical investigation
service

(G-9532)
KAMISH EXCAVATING INC
1301 Concord St S (55075-5944)
PHONE..............................651 457-3600
Angela Kamish, *Principal*
EMP: 25 **EST:** 2006
SALES (est): 1MM-4.9MM **Privately Held**
SIC: 1794 Excavating contractor

(G-9533)
MAIN STREET BANK (PA)
835 Southview Blvd (55075-2237)
PHONE..............................651 451-2133
Bruce Soma, *President*
Laura Brandt, *Senior VP*
Rita Drury, *Personnel*
Gus Briguet, *Manager*
EMP: 35 **EST:** 1964 **Privately Held**
WEB: www.localbankers.com
SIC: 6036 State savings bank

(G-9534)
MINNESOTA AFSCME COUNCIL 5
300 Hardman Ave S (55075-2471)
PHONE..............................651 455-0773
Cliff Poehler, *President*
Kim Bunce, *Vice Pres*
Lois McEwen, *Office Mgr*
Laureen Karnick, *Manager*
EMP: 25 **EST:** 1990 **Privately Held**
WEB: www.afscme14.org
SIC: 8631 Labor organization

(G-9535)
MINNESOTA STATE EMPLOYEES
300 Hardman Ave S Ste 3 (55075-2471)
PHONE..............................651 450-4990
Lois McEwen, *Sales Staff*
Elliott Seide, *Director*
EMP: 35 **EST:** 1946
SQ FT: 10,000 **Privately Held**
SIC: 8631 Labor union

(G-9536)
O & S CATTLE CO
100 Stockyards Rd Ste 106 (55075-5584)
PHONE..............................651 455-1102
FAX: 651 455-8394
Fred O'Harrow, *President*
Todd Anne, *Corp Secy*
Ann Todd, *Corp Secy*
Stewart Harold, *Treasurer*
Ed Helgesen, *Controller*
EMP: 28 **EST:** 1972
SQ FT: 1,000
SALES (est): 25MM-49.9MM **Privately Held**
SIC: 5154 Wholesales livestock

(PA)=Parent Co (HQ)=Headquarters (DH)=Div Headquarters
✿ = New business established in last 2 years

2011 Harris Minnesota
Services Directory

© Harris InfoSource 1-866-281-6415
411

(G-9537)
PROTOUCH PAINTING INC
139 Concord Exchange S (55075-2402)
PHONE 651 457-5628
FAX: 651 457-5991
James R Hoffman, *President*
Georgia Hoffman, *Vice Pres*
EMP: 30 **EST:** 1983
SQ FT: 3,000
SALES (est): 1MM-4.9MM Privately Held
WEB: www.protouchpainting.com
SIC: 1721 Painting & wall covering contractor

(G-9538)
RIES ELECTRIC CO
777 Concord St N (55075-1116)
PHONE 651 451-2238
John Ries, *President*
C M Ries, *Corp Secy*
Ron Schendel, *Vice Pres*
EMP: 25 **EST:** 1952
SALES (est): 1MM-4.9MM Privately Held
WEB: www.rieselectric.com
SIC: 1731 General electrical contractor

(G-9539)
S & S TREE & HORTICULTURAL
405 Hardman Ave S (55075-2415)
PHONE 651 451-8907
Steve Sylvester, *President*
Charlie Ruegemer, *Accountant*
EMP: 35 **EST:** 1976
SQ FT: 16,000 Privately Held
SIC: 0783 Ornamental tree bracing services; ornamental tree surgery services; arborist services; bush & tree removal services

(G-9540)
S & S TREE SPECIALISTS INC
405 Hardman Ave S (55075-2415)
PHONE 612 872-3901
Steven Sylvester, *President*
Dave Swanson, *Vice Pres*
Charlie Ruegemer, *Vice Pres*
EMP: 30 **EST:** 1976
SQ FT: 20,000 Privately Held
SIC: 0783 Utility line tree trimming services; bush & tree removal services; ornamental tree spraying services

(G-9541)
SCHADEGG MECHANICAL INC
225 Bridgepoint Dr (55075-2433)
PHONE 651 292-9933
Daniel Schadegg, *President*
Keith Larson, *Vice Pres*
Katie Bromert, *Manager*
EMP: 90 **EST:** 1997
SQ FT: 30,000
SALES (est): 10MM-24.9MM Privately Held
WEB: www.schadegg-mech.com
SIC: 1711 Mechanical contractor

(G-9542)
SCHADEGG PROPERTIES LLC
225 Bridgepoint Dr (55075-2433)
PHONE 651 292-9933
Daniel Schadegg, *Member*
EMP: 100 **EST:** 2000
SQ FT: 30,000
SALES (est): 25MM-49.9MM Privately Held
SIC: 6512 Operators of commercial & industrial buildings

(G-9543)
SEIU LOCAL 284
450 Southview Blvd Ste 101 (55075-2349)
PHONE 651 256-9102
FAX: 651 256-9119
Jan Hirsch, *Office Mgr*
Shane Allers, *Exec Dir*
EMP: 27 **EST:** 2005 Privately Held
WEB: www.seiu284.com
SIC: 8631 Labor organization

(G-9544)
STOCK YARDS MEAT PACKING CO
Also Called: Westlund's
280 Grand Ave E (55075-1133)
PHONE 651 450-6000
FAX: 651 450-9809
Larry Benjamin, *Member*
Frank Roedl, *Member*
David Ickes, *Senior VP*
Mike Kinne, *Purchasing*
Doug Keller, *VP Finance*
EMP: 165 **EST:** 1965
SQ FT: 30,000
SALES (est): 100MM-499.9MM Privately Held
WEB: www.usfoodservice.com
SIC: 5147 5143 5146 5148 Wholesales meat & meat products; wholesales seafood; wholesales fresh dairy products; wholesales fresh fruits & vegetables
HQ: US Foodservice Inc
    9399 W Higgins Rd Ste 500
    Rosemont IL 60018
    847 720-8000

(G-9545)
2020 PROMOTIONS LLC
135 Grand Ave E (55075-1134)
PHONE 651 451-3850
FAX: 651 455-8507
James McCarthy, *Member*
James Ryan, *Member*
James Stute, *Corp Secy*
Jim Guarnera, *Vice Pres*
Mandy Shearer, *Accounting Mgr*
▲ **EMP:** 41 **EST:** 1984
SQ FT: 22,000
SALES (est): 5MM-9.9MM Privately Held
WEB: www.cpimarketing.com
SIC: 5199 8742 8743 Wholesales advertising specialties; marketing consulting service; wholesales nondurable general merchandise; incentive or award program consultant; sales promotion services

(G-9546)
UNION PACIFIC RAILROAD CO INC
301 Hardman Ave N (55075-2417)
PHONE 651 552-3925
Stan Brenke, *Principal*
EMP: 103 Publicly Held
WEB: www.uprr.com
SIC: 4011 Long haul railroad
HQ: Union Pacific Railroad Co Inc
    1400 Douglas St
    Omaha NE 68179
    402 544-5000

(G-9547)
US FOODSERVICE INC
280 Grand Ave E (55075-1133)
PHONE 651 450-6000
EMP: 156
SALES (est): 100MM-499.9MM Privately Held
WEB: www.usfoodservice.com
SIC: 5149 Wholesales groceries
HQ: US Foodservice Inc
    9399 W Higgins Rd Ste 500
    Rosemont IL 60018
    847 720-8000

(G-9548)
US UNION TOOL INC
953 Concord St S (55075-5912)
PHONE 651 552-0440
FAX: 651 552-0435
Dale Knealing, *Manager*
EMP: 25
SALES (est): 1MM-4.9MM Privately Held
WEB: www.usuniontool.com
SIC: 7629 Circuit board repair service
PA: US Union Tool Inc
    1260 N Fee Ana St
    Anaheim CA 92807
    714 521-6242

(G-9549)
VETERINARY HOSPITALS ASSN
370 Bridgepoint Dr (55075-2486)
PHONE 651 451-6669
FAX: 651 451-6788
John Lillie, *President*
Dave Perry, *General Mgr*
Jim Wood, *Corp Secy*
Bruce Schnabel, *Vice Pres*
Kate Schmitt, *CFO*
EMP: 38 **EST:** 1984
SQ FT: 13,500
SALES (est): 10MM-24.9MM Privately Held
WEB: www.veterinaryha.org
SIC: 5047 8621 Wholesales veterinarians' equipment & supplies; medical field association

(G-9550)
VFW GALLAGHER-HANSON POST 295
Also Called: Veterans of Foreign Wars
111 Concord Exchange St S (55075-2402)
PHONE 651 455-1505
FAX: 651 455-1159
Tyson Taniya, *Manager*
Bernie Bidinger, *Manager*
Rory Anderson, *Manager*
EMP: 31 **EST:** 1948
SQ FT: 14,000 Privately Held
SIC: 8641 7299 Veterans' organization; bar; banquet hall facility

(G-9551)
WELLS FARGO BANK, NATIONAL
161 Concord Exchange N (55075-1144)
PHONE 651 450-4054
FAX: 651 205-8011
Jenny Leno, *Accounts Mgr*
Lennie M Kaufman, *Manager*
Denise Lasse, *Manager*
Richard Dargis, *Manager*
Jeff Helmquist, *MIS Mgr*
EMP: 240 Publicly Held
SIC: 6289 Stock transfer agent
HQ: Wfc Holdings, Corp
    420 Montgomery St
    San Francisco CA 94104
    415 396-7392

(G-9552)
WELLS LANES INC
365 Concord Exchange N (55075-1106)
PHONE 651 455-3220
FAX: 651 450-7729
Dan Keefe, *General Mgr*
EMP: 25 **EST:** 1978
SQ FT: 10,000
SALES (est): 500-999K Privately Held
SIC: 7933 Bowling center; eating place; bar & lounge drinking establishment

(G-9553)
WIPAIRE INC
1700 Henry Ave (55075-3500)
PHONE 651 451-1205
FAX: 651 457-7858
Robert Wiplinger, *CEO*
Razia Meer, *Vice Pres*
Bernard Winkleman, *Plant Mgr*
Pat Garfield, *Plant Mgr*
Charlie Wiplinger, *Design Engr*
EMP: 79 **EST:** 1974
SQ FT: 22,000
SALES (est): 10MM-24.9MM Privately Held
WEB: www.wipaire.com
SIC: 5088 7699 Manufactures aircraft pontoons; wholesales aircraft & space vehicle supplies & parts; aircraft & heavy equipment repair service

---

SPICER
Kandiyohi County

(G-9554)
ALTERNATIVE MICROGRAPHICS INC
Also Called: AMI
12011 Highway 71 NE (56288-9420)
PO Box 506 (56288-0506)
PHONE 320 796-2599
FAX: 320 796-2599
Mike Baker, *President*
EMP: 25 **EST:** 1982
SQ FT: 8,000
SALES (est): 1MM-4.9MM Privately Held
WEB: www.alternativemicrographics.net
SIC: 7389 Microfilm services; manufactures magnetic & optical recording media

(G-9555)
AMERICAN LEGION 545
155 Lake Ave S (56288-4614)
PO Box 296 (56288-0296)
PHONE 320 796-5542
FAX: 320 796-6023
Robert Pinske, *President*
Dennis Blumke, *Vice Pres*
Tammy Kragbring, *Manager*
EMP: 40 **EST:** 1930 Privately Held
SIC: 8641 Members only bar & restaurant for members of organizations only; fraternal association

(G-9556)
KANDIYOHI POWER COOPERATIVE
8605 47th St NE (56288-4617)
PO Box 40 (56288-0040)
PHONE 320 796-1155
David George, *President*
Darrell Fostervold, *Vice Chairman*
Scott Froemming, *CFO*
Loel Larson, *Manager*
EMP: 32 **EST:** 2007
SALES (est): 10MM-24.9MM Privately Held
SIC: 4911 Electric services

(G-9557)
MARKETING CONCEPTS OF MN
130 Lake Ave N (56288-9616)
PO Box 152 (56288-0152)
PHONE 320 796-6245
Diane Buzzeo, *President*
Lora Nelson, *Finance Dir*
Melissa Winsoow, *Marketing Mgr*
Kate Tucker, *Manager*
Michele Okuly, *Manager*
EMP: 125 **EST:** 1986
SQ FT: 15,000
SALES (est): 10MM-24.9MM Privately Held
WEB: www.marketingconcepts.com
SIC: 7336 Graphic arts & related design service

(G-9558)
PRAIRIE COMMUNITY SERVICES
Also Called: Lake Wood Home
256 Lake Ave N (56288-9512)
PHONE 320 796-6999
FAX: 320 796-6522
Diane Stearns, *Manager*
EMP: 30
SALES (est): 1MM-4.9MM Privately Held
SIC: 8052 Intermediate care facility
HQ: Prairie Community Services
    801 Nevada Ave Ste 100
    Morris MN 56267
    320 589-3077

(G-9559)
SUPPORTIVE LIFESTYLES INC
5465 132nd Ave NE (56288-9343)
PO Box 487 (56288-0487)
PHONE 320 796-5900
Tim Helgeson, *CEO*
EMP: 50 **EST:** 1994
SALES (est): 1MM-4.9MM Privately Held
SIC: 8744 Facilities support services

SPRING GROVE
Houston County

(G-9560)
CENTRAL BANK
126 W Main St (55974-1444)
PHONE 507 498-5589
EMP: 25
SALES (est): 5MM-9.9MM Privately Held
WEB: www.centralbnk.com
SIC: 6022 State commercial bank
PA: Central Bank
    2270 Frontage Rd W
    Stillwater MN 55082
    651 439-3050

www.HarrisInfo.com
412

2011 Harris Minnesota
Services Directory

▲=Import ▼=Export
◆=Import/Export

(G-9561)

KNIFE RIVER MIDWEST LLC
601 E Main St (55974-1431)
PO Box 248, Saint Cloud (56302-0248)
PHONE............................507 498-3377
FAX: 507 498-5835
Curt Roverud, *Branch Mgr*
EMP: 70
SALES (est): 10MM-24.9MM **Privately Held**
SIC: 1611 General highway & street
construction service; street surfacing &
paving construction

(G-9562)

TWEETEN-LUTHERAN HEALTH CARE
125 5th Ave SE (55974-1318)
PHONE............................507 498-3211
FAX: 507 498-3228
Tim Rieck, *COO*
Carl Magers, *Engineering*
Chris Loppnow, *Human Res Dir*
Chuck Hazzard, *Manager*
Mike Mayer, *Administrator*
EMP: 120 **EST:** 1916
SQ FT: 53,400
SALES (est): 1MM-4.9MM **Privately Held**
SIC: 8051 8062 Skilled nursing care facility;
medical hospital

SPRING PARK
Hennepin County

(G-9563)

FITZCO INC
4300 Shoreline Dr (55384-9722)
PHONE............................952 471-1185
FAX: 952 471-0787
June Fitz, *CEO*
Christine Fitz, *Vice Pres*
Todd Fitz, *CFO*
Betsy Fitz, *Office Mgr*
Scott Miller, *Manager*
EMP: 35 **EST:** 1987
SQ FT: 42,000
SALES (est): 1MM-4.9MM **Privately Held**
WEB: www.fitzcoinc.com
SIC: 8734 Forensic laboratory

(G-9564)

RESTAURANTS NO LIMIT INC
Also Called: Lord Fletcher's Old Lake Lodge
3746 Sunset Dr (55384-9630)
PHONE............................952 471-8513
Tom Emer, *Manager*
EMP: 90
SALES (est): 1MM-4.9MM **Privately Held**
WEB: www.lordfletchers.com
SIC: 7299 Full service seafood restaurant;
café; full service steak & barbecue
restaurant; banquet hall facility
PA: Restaurants No Limit Inc
4300 Baker Rd Ste 1
Hopkins MN 55343
952 938-3000

(G-9565)

RIDGEVIEW MEDICAL CLINIC
4695 Shoreline Dr (55384-9715)
PHONE............................952 471-2585
FAX: 952 442-7893
Robert Stevens, *President*
Anita Lang, *Office Mgr*
Christy Besse, *Manager*
Robert E Heeter, *Surgeon*
D D Rotenberg, *Surgeon*
EMP: 40 **EST:** 1954
SALES (est): 1MM-4.9MM **Privately Held**
SIC: 8011 Physicians' office & clinic;
internal medicine practitioners; pediatrician
office

(G-9566)

SCS DIALARIDE
4140 Shoreline Dr (55384-9629)
PHONE............................952 474-7441
FAX: 952 471-9002
Ron Bloch, *Manager*
EMP: 30 **EST:** 1992
SALES (est): 1MM-4.9MM **Privately Held**
SIC: 4729 Passenger travel arrangement
services

(G-9567)

UPPER MINNETONKA YACHT CLUB
Also Called: Umyc
4165 Shoreline Dr Ste 10 (55384-9653)
PHONE............................952 471-8783
FAX: 952 404-1638
Bill Miller, *Exec Dir*
EMP: 100 **EST:** 1963
SALES (est): 1MM-4.9MM **Privately Held**
WEB: www.umyc.org
SIC: 7997 7991 Membership recreation
club; physical fitness center

SPRING VALLEY
Fillmore County

(G-9568)

COMMUNITY MEMORIAL HOSPITAL
800 Memorial Dr (55975-1024)
PHONE............................507 346-7381
FAX: 507 346-7903
Penny Solberg, *Vice Pres*
Janell Kraut, *Exec Dir*
EMP: 100 **EST:** 1968
SQ FT: 60,324
SALES (est): 1MM-4.9MM **Privately Held**
SIC: 8051 Skilled nursing care facility

(G-9569)

DAN-AM CO
1 Sata Dr (55975-8566)
PO Box 46 (55975-0046)
PHONE............................507 346-7102
FAX: 507 633-7282
Knud Jorgensen, *President*
Bent Jorgensen, *Vice Pres*
Tammy Wolfgram, *Officer*
▲ **EMP:** 30 **EST:** 1976
SQ FT: 16,000
SALES (est): 10MM-24.9MM **Privately Held**
WEB: www.satausa.com
SIC: 5099 Wholesales safety equipment &
supplies

(G-9570)

SPRING VALLEY AREA AMBULANCE
201 S Broadway St (55975-1301)
PHONE............................507 346-7414
James Cooper, *Director*
EMP: 29 **EST:** 1992
SALES (est): 1MM-4.9MM **Privately Held**
SIC: 4119 Ambulance service

SPRINGFIELD
Brown County

(G-9571)

FARMERS & MERCHANTS STATE BANK
101 N Marshall Ave (56087-1520)
PHONE............................507 723-4234
FAX: 507 723-4228
Daniel Olson, *Senior VP*
Richard Loomis, *Vice Pres*
Shelly Anderson, *Marketing Staff*
G Pieschel, *Branch Mgr*
Richard S Loomi, *Manager*
EMP: 30
SALES (est): 5MM-9.9MM **Privately Held**
SIC: 6022 State commercial bank
PA: Farmers & Merchants State Bank
80 Main St N
Pierz MN 56364
320 468-6422

(G-9572)

FARMERS & MERCHANTS STATE BANK
101 N Marshall Ave (56087-1520)
PHONE............................507 723-4800
R S Loomi, *Vice Pres*
Linda L Fredin, *Manager*
Privately Held
SIC: 6022 State commercial bank

(G-9573)

MAYO CLINIC
602 N Jackson Ave (56087-1715)
PHONE............................507 723-4231
FAX: 507 723-6522
Do M Schmitz DO, *Principal*
EMP: 80
SALES (est): 5MM-9.9MM **Privately Held**
SIC: 8011 Physicians' office & clinic
PA: Mayo Clinic
200 1st St SW
Rochester MN 55905
507 284-2511

(G-9574)

SALONEK CONCRETE & CONSTR
12 W Lincoln St (56087-1301)
PO Box 127 (56087-0127)
PHONE............................507 723-4218
FAX: 507 723-6355
Urban Salonek, *CEO*
Judy Rubey, *President*
Rose Salonek, *Vice Pres*
Rodney Salonek, *Vice Pres*
Kent Salonek, *Vice Pres*
EMP: 26 **EST:** 1939
SQ FT: 3,750
SALES (est): 5MM-9.9MM **Privately Held**
SIC: 1542 1771 7389 Commercial &
institutional building construction;
manufactures ready-mixed concrete; crane
& aerial lift service; concrete contractor

(G-9575)

SPRINGFIELD MEDICAL CENTER
625 N Jackson Ave (56087-1714)
PHONE............................507 723-6201
FAX: 507 723-6447
Maryanne Schoper, *Corp Secy*
Greg Smith, *Engineering*
Linda L Walin, *Manager*
Fred Probe, *Anesthesiology*
Craig Curry, *Director*
EMP: 90 **EST:** 1958
SQ FT: 24,000
SALES (est): 5MM-9.9MM **Privately Held**
SIC: 8062 8011 Medical hospital;
physicians' office & clinic
PA: Mayo Clinic
200 1st St SW
Rochester MN 55905
507 284-2511

(G-9576)

ST JOHN LUTHERAN HOME INC
201 S County Road 5 (56087-2102)
PHONE............................507 723-3200
FAX: 507 723-6429
J M Jansen, *CEO*
Dale Potter, *Opers Staff*
Dawn Buddensiek, *Manager*
Chris Stark, *Exec Dir*
Patricia Schulte, *Officer*
EMP: 275 **EST:** 1901
SQ FT: 74,000
SALES (est): 10MM-24.9MM **Privately Held**
WEB: www.sjlhome.com
SIC: 8051 Convalescent home

SQUAW LAKE
Itasca County

(G-9577)

HELEN ANDRESEN
64037 County Road 149 (56681-2085)
PHONE............................218 659-4491
Helen Andresen, *Owner*
EMP: 40 **EST:** 1972 **Privately Held**
SIC: 0211 Beef cattle feedlot

STACY
Anoka County

(G-9578)

SUNRISE HEALTH SERVICES
22350 Sunrise Rd NE (55079-9383)
PHONE............................651 462-9331
FAX: 651 462-5761

Sue Anderson, *Owner*
Paul Anderson, *Executive*
EMP: 60 **EST:** 1999
SALES (est): 1MM-4.9MM **Privately Held**
WEB: www.sunrisehealthservices.com
SIC: 8082 Home health care services

STACY
Chisago County

(G-9579)

GREAT NORTHERN GOLF CO OF MN
Also Called: Falcon Ridge Golf Course
33942 Falcon Ave (55079-9581)
PO Box 477 (55079-0477)
PHONE............................651 462-5797
FAX: 651 462-5027
Patrick Smith, *President*
EMP: 35 **EST:** 1998
SQ FT: 4,096
SALES (est): 1MM-4.9MM **Privately Held**
WEB: www.falconridgegolf.net
SIC: 7999 Golf services & professionals

(G-9580)

PROMOTION MANAGEMENT CENTER
31205 Falcon Ave (55079-9555)
PO Box 245 (55079-0245)
PHONE............................651 462-1213
FAX: 651 462-4118
Devere Monson, *CEO*
Deann Monson, *President*
Bonita Monson, *Vice Pres*
Deb Stone, *Marketing Staff*
Rose Conway, *Info Tech Mgr*
EMP: 75 **EST:** 1983
SQ FT: 66,000
SALES (est): 5MM-9.9MM **Privately Held**
WEB: www.promotionmailing.com
SIC: 7331 Mailing services

(G-9581)

SUNRISE ESTATES MOBILE HOME
5335 Stacy Trl (55079-9487)
PO Box 165 (55079-0165)
PHONE............................651 462-4047
FAX: 651 462-7707
John Ulvin, *Owner*
Kathy Holtz, *Manager*
EMP: 28 **EST:** 1976
SQ FT: 12,000
SALES (est): 1MM-4.9MM **Privately Held**
SIC: 6515 7033 Retail independent grocery
store; recreational vehicle park &
campground; retail gasoline filling station;
mobile home site leasing & rental

STANTON
Goodhue County

(G-9582)

SYNGENTA SEEDS INC
317 330th St (55018-7228)
PHONE............................507 645-5621
FAX: 507 645-7519
Bruce A Wiese, *Manager*
EMP: 70 **Publicly Held**
WEB: www.syngenta.com
SIC: 8731 Commercial agricultural research
services
HQ: Syngenta Seeds Inc
11055 Wayzata Blvd
Minnetonka MN 55305
612 656-8600

STAPLES
Todd County

(G-9583)

ESSILOR LABORATORIES OF AMER
605 4th St SW (56479-2672)
PO Box 190 (56479-0190)
PHONE............................218 894-3385
FAX: 218 328-9403

(PA)=Parent Co (HQ)=Headquarters (DH)=Div Headquarters
✿ = New business established in last 2 years

2011 Harris Minnesota
Services Directory

© Harris InfoSource 1-866-281-6415

413

Allan Barrow, *General Mgr*
Jean Miller, *Sales Executive*
EMP: 35
SALES (est): 1MM-4.9MM **Privately Held**
WEB: www.essilor.com
SIC: 5049 Retails optical goods; wholesales optical goods
HQ: Essilor Laboratories of Amer
13515 N Stemmons Fwy
Dallas TX 75234
972 241-4141

(G-9584)
FIRST INTEGRITY BANK (PA)
111 4th St NE (56479-2545)
PO Box 40 (56479-0040)
PHONE 218 894-1522
FAX: 218 894-3858
K P Kruchten, *CEO*
David Duhn, *President*
Marvin Rothstein, *Senior VP*
Richard Gallahue, *Vice Pres*
Demian Kurchten, *Vice Pres*
EMP: 35 **EST:** 1920
SQ FT: 8,000
SALES (corp-wide): 4.13M **Privately Held**
SIC: 6036 6163 State savings bank; loan broker

(G-9585)
LITTLE MORAN HUNTING CLUB
44357 Red Oak Rd (56479-5048)
PHONE 218 894-3852
Steve Grossman, *Owner*
EMP: 30 **EST:** 1984
SALES (est): 500-999K **Privately Held**
WEB: www.littlemoran.com
SIC: 7997 Membership recreation club

STAPLES
Wadena County

(G-9586)
LAKEWOOD HEALTH SYSTEM
49725 County 83 (56479-5280)
PHONE 218 894-1515
Tim Rice, *President*
Jim Dregney, *CFO*
Gretchen Bestland, *Admin Asst*
EMP: 500 **EST:** 1973
SQ FT: 219,016
SALES (est): 25MM-49.9MM **Privately Held**
WEB: www.lakewoodhealthsystem.com
SIC: 8062 8051 Medical hospital; extended care facility

(G-9587)
UNITED HOSPITAL DISTRICT ✪
49725 County 83 (56479-5280)
PHONE 218 894-8610
Tim Rice, *Principal*
EMP: 99 **EST:** 2008
SALES (est): 5MM-9.9MM **Privately Held**
SIC: 8062 Medical hospital

STARBUCK
Pope County

(G-9588)
WEST CENTRAL IRRIGATION INC
810 Industrial Dr (56381-9775)
PHONE 320 239-2230
Tim Vandestreek, *Principal*
EMP: 27 **EST:** 2006
SALES (est): 1MM-4.9MM **Privately Held**
SIC: 4971 Irrigation water supply services

(G-9589)
WESTERN POPE COUNTY HOSPITAL
Also Called: Minnewaska District Hospital
610 W 6th St (56381-9782)
PHONE 320 239-2201
FAX: 320 239-4214
Jeff Kuhn, *Ch of Bd*
Jerry Holten, *Vice Chairman*
David Tollifson, *Corp Secy*
Kay Lagred, *Director*
EMP: 60

EST: 1937
SQ FT: 22,500
SALES (est): 5MM-9.9MM **Privately Held**
SIC: 8062 Medical hospital

STEWARTVILLE
Olmsted County

(G-9590)
ALL-AMERICAN CO-OP (PA)
113 4th St SE (55976-1329)
PO Box 125 (55976-0125)
PHONE 507 533-4222
FAX: 507 280-0066
Mickeal Hims, *President*
Ronald Nelson, *General Mgr*
James R Hunter, *Controller*
Beth Pagel, *Cust Svc Dir*
Steve Sturm, *Sales Staff*
EMP: 26 **EST:** 1908
SQ FT: 4,000 **Privately Held**
WEB: www.allamericancoop.com
SIC: 5153 Wholesales grains; manufactures livestock feeds; wholesales corn; wholesales oats; wholesales soybeans

(G-9591)
ED LUNN CONSTRUCTION INC
901 2nd Ave SW (55976-8287)
PHONE 507 533-6565
FAX: 507 533-6266
Edward Lunn, *President*
EMP: 25 **EST:** 1971
SALES (est): 1MM-4.9MM **Privately Held**
SIC: 1751 Framing contractor

(G-9592)
FAMILY TREE LANDSCAPE NURSERY
1735 Highway 30 SW (55976-8002)
PHONE 507 533-8558
Margaret Hinz, *President*
Russell Hinz, *Vice Pres*
EMP: 30 **EST:** 2005 **Privately Held**
SIC: 0781 Landscape services

(G-9593)
MPS GROUP PROPERTIES INC
Also Called: Stewartville Bowl
101 10th St NW (55976-1629)
PHONE 507 533-8330
Morris Schutz, *President*
Phyllis Schutz, *Vice Pres*
EMP: 38 **EST:** 1978
SQ FT: 10,000
SALES (est): 1MM-4.9MM **Privately Held**
WEB: www.strikerscorner.com
SIC: 7933 Ten pin center; liquor store; cocktail lounge; limited service independent fast-food restaurant

(G-9594)
STEWARTVILLE NURSING HOME INC
120 4th St NE (55976-1212)
PHONE 507 533-4288
FAX: 507 533-4829
Marcie B Smith, *Manager*
Eugene Gustason, *Administrator*
EMP: 125 **EST:** 1969
SQ FT: 44,343
SALES (est): 1MM-4.9MM **Privately Held**
WEB: www.stewartvillecarecenter.com
SIC: 8051 6513 Convalescent home; apartment building operator

STILLWATER
Washington County

(G-9595)
AMTECH LIGHTING SERVICES CO
6077 Lake Elmo Ave N (55082-9373)
PHONE 651 439-7440
FAX: 651 439-7521
Nat McGinn, *Manager*
EMP: 30
SALES (est): 500-999K **Privately Held**
WEB: www.sibt.com

SIC: 7349 1799 Lighting maintenance service; sign installation & maintenance contractor
HQ: Amtech Lighting Services
2390 E Orangewood Ave
Anaheim CA 92806
714 940-4000

(G-9596)
AND SEW ON INC
10850 62nd St N (55082-8362)
PHONE 651 439-9311
Deborah Gangnon, *President*
EST: 1990
SQ FT: 2,300 **Privately Held**
SIC: 7699 Retails sewing machines; retails custom made dresses; retails electric household appliances; retails fabric remnants; retails sewing & needlework; sewing machine repair shop

(G-9597)
APPLEWOOD HILLS INC
11840 60th St N (55082-9312)
PHONE 651 439-7276
FAX: 651 439-6545
Kenneth Wilson, *President*
Ruth Wilson, *Vice Pres*
EMP: 30
SALES (est): 1MM-4.9MM **Privately Held**
WEB: www.applewoodhills.com
SIC: 7992 Public golf course; retails golf goods & equipment

(G-9598)
ASSOCIATED EYE CARE LTD (PA)
2950 Curve Crest Blvd W (55082-5085)
PHONE 651 439-8500
FAX: 651 439-5106
Douglas Carlson MD, *President*
Rachel Keogh, *CFO*
Jacob R Lang, *Optometrist*
Ann H Hickson, *Optometrist*
David Peroceshi, *Manager*
EMP: 40 **EST:** 1970
SQ FT: 6,000 **Privately Held**
WEB: www.associatedeyecare.com
SIC: 8011 Ophthalmologist office; surgeon's office

(G-9599)
ASSOCIATED EYE CARE LTD
Also Called: Assocted Eye Physcans Surgeons
1719 Tower Dr W (55082-7512)
PHONE 651 275-3013
Ron Klemz, *Branch Mgr*
Crystal A Rogers, *Optometrist*
Jacob R Lang, *Optometrist*
Anne M Hixon, *Optometrist*
Sue King, *Manager*
EMP: 30
SALES (est): 1MM-4.9MM **Privately Held**
WEB: www.associateeyecare.com
SIC: 8742 Business planning & organizing services
PA: Associated Eye Care Ltd
2950 Curve Crest Blvd W
Stillwater MN 55082
651 439-8500

(G-9600)
AXDAHL FARMS INC
17120 116th St N (55082-8911)
PHONE 651 439-3134
Brian Axdahl, *President*
Leslie Axdahl, *Principal*
EMP: 35 **EST:** 1994 **Privately Held**
SIC: 0161 Pumpkin farm

(G-9601)
BAKER COLBERG & REALTY
2020 Washington Ave S (55082-7527)
PHONE 651 430-7745
Bob Nicholson, *Vice Pres*
EMP: 45
SALES (est): 10MM-24.9MM **Privately Held**
SIC: 1521 Single-family housing construction

(G-9602)
BEVERLY ENTERPRISES - MN
Also Called: Greeley Healthcare Ctr
313 Greeley St S (55082-7007)
PHONE 651 439-5775
FAX: 651 439-1936
David Banks, *Branch Mgr*
Kerry Otteson, *Manager*
Sue Tennis, *Exec Dir*
EMP: 100
SALES (est): 1MM-4.9MM **Privately Held**
WEB: www.beverlynet.com
SIC: 8051 Skilled nursing care facility
HQ: Beverly Enterprises - MN
650 Ramer Ave S
Rush City MN 55069
320 358-4765

(G-9603)
BURNET REALTY INC
2020 Washington Ave S (55082-7527)
PHONE 651 430-2100
FAX: 651 430-0212
Bob Nickelson, *President*
Gordon Spray, *Member*
Paula Winter, *Finance*
EMP: 40 **EST:** 2003
SALES (est): 5MM-9.9MM **Privately Held**
SIC: 6531 Real estate services

(G-9604)
CENTRAL BANK (PA)
2270 Frontage Rd W (55082-2165)
PO Box 225 (55082-0225)
PHONE 651 439-3050
Kurt Weise, *Ch of Bd*
Larry Albert, *President*
Bonnie Warren, *Vice Pres*
Sheryl Carlson, *Vice Pres*
Ken Junker, *Vice Pres*
EMP: 32 **EST:** 1974
SALES (corp-wide): 26.30M **Privately Held**
WEB: www.centralbnk.com
SIC: 6022 State commercial bank

(G-9605)
COUNTY OF WASHINGTON
14949 62nd St N (55082-6132)
PO Box 30 (55082-0030)
PHONE 651 430-6800
FAX: 651 430-6947
Jon Larson, *Manager*
Edison Vizuete, *Manager*
James Schug, *Manager*
Dan Papin, *Director*
EMP: 275
SALES (est): 10MM-24.9MM **Privately Held**
SIC: 8322 Individual & family social services
PA: County of Washington
14949 62nd St N
Stillwater MN 55082
651 439-3220

(G-9606)
COUNTY OF WASHINGTON
Also Called: Washington County Sheriffs Off
15015 62nd St N (55082-6804)
PHONE 651 439-9381
William Huttom, *Sheriff*
James Frank, *Manager*
EMP: 300 **Privately Held**
SIC: 4119 Sheriffs' office; county general government administration office; ambulance service
PA: County of Washington
14949 62nd St N
Stillwater MN 55082
651 439-3220

(G-9607)
COURAGE CENTER
1460 Curve Crest Blvd W (55082-6070)
PHONE 651 439-8283
FAX: 651 439-0576
Carol Lombard, *Office Mgr*
Lori Martin, *Supervisor*
Patty Radoc, *Exec Dir*
Peter Ploga, *Director*
Jeff Dingee, *Director*
EMP: 101
SALES (est): 5MM-9.9MM **Privately Held**
WEB: www.courage.org

www.HarrisInfo.com
414

2011 Harris Minnesota
Services Directory

▲=Import ▼=Export
◆=Import/Export

SIC: 8093 Outpatient rehabilitation treatment center
PA: Courage Center
3915 Golden Valley Rd
Minneapolis MN 55422
763 588-0811

(G-9608)
CROIX OIL CO
1749 Greeley St S (55082-6008)
PO Box 15 (55082-0015)
PHONE............................651 439-5755
FAX: 651 439-1051
Mark Ogren, *President*
EMP: 45 **EST:** 1964
SQ FT: 7,000
SALES (est): 100MM-499.9MM **Privately Held**
SIC: 5172 Wholesales gasoline; wholesales diesel fuel; wholesales fuel oil

(G-9609)
CURB MASTERS INC
500 Poplar St W (55082-4243)
PHONE............................651 351-9200
FAX: 651 351-9300
Randall Callies, *President*
Margaret Callies, *Corp Secy*
EMP: 30 **EST:** 1988
SALES (est): 1MM-4.9MM **Privately Held**
WEB: www.curbmasters.info
SIC: 1771 Curb construction

(G-9610)
DIVERSIFIED CONSULTING ASSOCS
915 Nordic Ct N (55082-1935)
PHONE............................651 436-1330
Thomas Wasserman, *Member*
Marsha McBreen, *Member*
EMP: 25 **EST:** 1996
SALES (est): 1MM-4.9MM **Privately Held**
WEB: www.dcallc.com
SIC: 8742 Hospital & health services consultant

(G-9611)
EAST SUBURBAN RESOURCES INC (PA)
1754 Washington Ave S (55082-7561)
PHONE............................651 351-0190
FAX: 651 351-0192
Chris Baker, *Finance*
Cindy Parent, *Personnel*
Jeane Buhr, *Manager*
Ed Boeve, *Exec Dir*
Sara Hasslen, *Director*
EMP: 32 **EST:** 1964
SQ FT: 7,600
SALES (corp-wide): 4.78M **Privately Held**
WEB: www.esrworks.com
SIC: 7361 8322 Employment agency services; general counseling services

(G-9612)
EAST SUBURBAN RESOURCES INC
1754 Washington Ave S (55082-7561)
PHONE............................651 464-5137
Sara Hasslen, *Opers Staff*
Ed Boeve, *Branch Mgr*
Shakiru Momoh, *Supervisor*
EMP: 75
SALES (est): 1MM-4.9MM **Privately Held**
WEB: www.esrworks.com
SIC: 8322 Individual & family social services
PA: East Suburban Resources Inc
1754 Washington Ave S
Stillwater MN 55082
651 351-0190

(G-9613)
EDINA REALTY HOME SERVICES
14430 60th St N (55082-6313)
PHONE............................651 430-3200
FAX: 651 430-7575
Jim Young, *Manager*
Lisa Meyer, *Manager*
Sue Saxon, *Office Admin*
Susan Fenton, *Office Admin*
Michele Martineau, *Director*
EMP: 65
SALES (est): 10MM-24.9MM **Publicly Held**

WEB: www.ilovetennis.net
SIC: 6531 Real estate agency & broker
HQ: Edina Realty Home Services
6800 France Ave S Ste 600
Minneapolis MN 55435
952 928-5900

(G-9614)
ELERT & ASSOCIATES NETWORKING
140 3rd St S (55082-4902)
PHONE............................651 430-2772
FAX: 651 430-2661
Gary Elert, *President*
Tom Tavek, *Vice Pres*
Felix Fayngersh, *Senior Engr*
Mark Quade, *Accountant*
Janice Colbeth, *Manager*
EMP: 25 **EST:** 1984
SQ FT: 6,000
SALES (est): 1MM-4.9MM **Privately Held**
WEB: www.elert.com
SIC: 8748 Telecommunications consulting services

(G-9615)
EVANGELICAL LUTHERAN GOOD
Also Called: Good Smrtan Society-Stillwater
1119 Owens St N (55082-4316)
PHONE............................651 439-7180
FAX: 651 439-4502
Troy Duncanson, *Maintenance Dir*
Linda Otteson, *Office Mgr*
Pam Trudeau, *Manager*
Art Schmitz, *Manager*
Nathan Pearson, *Administrator*
EMP: 145
SALES (est): 5MM-9.9MM **Privately Held**
WEB: www.good-sam.com
SIC: 8051 8052 Skilled nursing care facility; intermediate care facility
PA: Evangelical Lutheran Good
4800 W 57th St
Sioux Falls SD 57108
605 362-3100

(G-9616)
FAMILY MEANS
1875 Northwestern Ave S (55082-7534)
PHONE............................651 439-4840
Karen Reier, *CFO*
McGowan Maren, *Sales Executive*
Arba-Della Beck, *Exec Dir*
Pat Rogers, *Director*
Patrick R Stokes, *Psychiatry*
EMP: 30 **EST:** 1963
SQ FT: 11,000
SALES (est): 1MM-4.9MM **Privately Held**
WEB: www.familymeans.org
SIC: 8322 Individual & family social services

(G-9617)
FAMILYMEANS INC
1875 Northwestern Ave S (55082-7534)
PHONE............................612 874-8164
EMP: 40 **EST:** 1969
SQ FT: 6,000
SALES (est): 5MM-9.9MM **Privately Held**
SIC: 8742 Management consulting services

(G-9618)
FEDA RIDGE INC
11400 Julianne Ave N (55082-9436)
PHONE............................651 426-3300
FAX: 651 426-0419
Paul Cowdery, *President*
Amy Christiansen, *Manager*
Stephanie Gilquist, *Program Dir*
Terry Moffit, *Coordinator*
EMP: 40 **EST:** 2004
SALES (est): 1MM-4.9MM **Privately Held**
SIC: 8093 Specialty outpatient clinic

(G-9619)
GARTNER STUDIOS INC (PA)
220 Myrtle St E (55082-5033)
PHONE............................651 351-7700
FAX: 651 351-1408
Gregory Gartner, *President*
Carl Monty, *Vice Pres*
David Hinker, *Controller*
Kathy Lindeen, *Controller*
Jorge Allen, *Incorporator*
EMP: 40

EST: 1995
SQ FT: 11,500 **Privately Held**
WEB: www.gartnerstudios.com
SIC: 5112 Wholesales stationery & office supplies

(G-9620)
GOODWILL INDUSTRIES INC
5899 Nova Scotia Ave N (55082-6793)
PHONE............................651 439-4207
FAX: 651 439-4207
Terry Wehking, *Manager*
EMP: 26
SALES (est): 1MM-4.9MM **Privately Held**
WEB: www.goodwilleasterseals.org
SIC: 4953 4226 8322 8331 Waste material recycling services; retails used merchandise; family services agency; job training services; warehousing & storage facility
PA: Goodwill Industries Inc
553 Fairview Ave N
Saint Paul MN 55104
651 379-5800

(G-9621)
HOLIDAY INN EXPRESS & SUITES
2000 Washington Ave S (55082-7527)
PHONE............................651 275-1401
FAX: 651 275-1402
Jan Bergstron, *Owner*
Bill Costa, *General Mgr*
Jan Bergstrom, *Manager*
EMP: 26 **EST:** 1999
SALES (est): 1MM-4.9MM **Privately Held**
SIC: 7011 Traveler accommodations

(G-9622)
HSI HUMAN SERVICES INC
5650 Memorial Ave N (55082-1087)
PHONE............................651 275-4302
Mark Kuppg, *CEO*
EMP: 30 **EST:** 2007
SALES (est): 1MM-4.9MM **Privately Held**
SIC: 8999 Miscellaneous services

(G-9623)
HUMAN SERVICES INC
Also Called: Chemical Dependency
375 Orleans St E (55082-5830)
PHONE............................651 430-2720
Robert Butler, *Director*
EMP: 30 **EST:** 1969
SALES (est): 1MM-4.9MM **Privately Held**
SIC: 8093 8069 Outpatient drug clinic; alcoholism rehabilitation hospital

(G-9624)
INTERNATIONAL ASSOCIATION OF
Also Called: Stillwater Lions Clubs
2397 Driftwood Ln (55082-5367)
PHONE............................651 439-4659
Tom Phillips, *Corp Secy*
EMP: 128 **Privately Held**
WEB: www.iaopc.com
SIC: 8641 Civic associations
PA: International Association of
300 W 22nd St
Oak Brook IL 60523
630 571-5466

(G-9625)
LAKEVIEW MEMORIAL HOSPITAL
927 Churchill St W (55082-6605)
PHONE............................651 439-5330
FAX: 651 430-4528
Debb Marshall, *CEO*
Jeffrey Robertson, *CEO*
C A Brookman, *Corp Secy*
Nancy Dokkestul, *Corp Secy*
Kelly Riemenschneider, *Vice Pres*
EMP: 500 **EST:** 1958
SQ FT: 100,000
SALES (est): 25MM-49.9MM **Privately Held**
SIC: 8062 Medical hospital

(G-9626)
LOWE'S HOME CENTERS INC
5888 Nova Scotia Ave N (55082-6763)
PHONE............................651 275-9910
EMP: 150
SALES (est): 25MM-49.9MM **Publicly Held**
WEB: www.lowes.com
SIC: 5031 5064 Retails building products & materials; wholesales exterior building materials; wholesales interior building materials; wholesales electrical appliances; retails household appliances
HQ: Lowe's Home Centers Inc
1605 Curtis Bridge Rd
Wilkesboro NC 28697
336 658-4000

(G-9627)
MERRILL LYNCH, PIERCE, FENNER
219 Main St N Ste 4 (55082-5057)
PHONE............................651 275-8040
FAX: 651 275-9002
Jeffrey Wegge, *Manager*
Allen Chaves, *Manager*
EMP: 25
SALES (est): 5MM-9.9MM **Publicly Held**
WEB: www.ml.com
SIC: 6211 Securities broker & dealer
HQ: Merrill Lynch & Co Inc
4 World Financial Ctr # 4
New York NY 10080
212 449-1000

(G-9628)
MIDWEST MEDICAL MANAGEMENT LLC
1950 Curve Crest Blvd W Ste 10 (55082-6062)
PHONE............................651 430-3892
Greg Maurer, *President*
Gail Grainger, *Office Mgr*
Shari Ohland, *Administrator*
Glenn R Butterman, *Surgeon*
Glenn R Buttermann, *Surgeon*
EMP: 30 **EST:** 1998
SALES (est): 10MM-24.9MM **Privately Held**
SIC: 5047 Wholesales medical equipment & supplies

(G-9629)
MINNESOTA RESIDENTIAL AQUATICS
Also Called: Aautomated Pool & Patio
263 Pineridge Ln (55082-7102)
PHONE............................651 439-8467
FAX: 651 777-2973
Todd Wilson, *President*
EST: 1992 **Privately Held**
WEB: www.poolproductsdirect.com
SIC: 1799 7389 Retails swimming pools, hot tubs & sauna equipment & supplies; swimming pool & hot tub cleaning & maintenance services; spa & hot tub construction & installation; swimming pool construction

(G-9630)
MISSISSIPPI TRANSPORT INC
2930 Quant Ave N (55082-1626)
PHONE............................651 439-5773
FAX: 651 439-6887
Lanny Wilhem, *President*
Christopher Ogren, *VP Systems*
Deb V Dinburg V, *Data Proc Staff*
EMP: 60 **EST:** 1980
SALES (est): 5MM-9.9MM **Privately Held**
WEB: www.mississippitransport.com
SIC: 4212 4231 Local petroleum hauling services; freight trucking terminal

(G-9631)
NOAH INSURANCE GROUP
5795 Morning Dove Ave N # 101 (55082-1280)
PHONE............................651 430-0085
John Noah, *President*
Mitchell Noah, *Manager*
EMP: 35 **EST:** 2004
SALES (est): 1MM-4.9MM **Privately Held**
SIC: 6411 Insurance services

(PA)=Parent Co (HQ)=Headquarters (DH)=Div Headquarters
✪ = New business established in last 2 years
2011 Harris Minnesota
Services Directory
© Harris InfoSource 1-866-281-6415
415

(G-9632)
NORTHLAND PAINTING
15260 15th St N (55082-1864)
PHONE.............................651 645-9791
FAX: 651 646-6349
Christopher Keith, *President*
Patricia Keith, *Vice Pres*
EMP: 50 EST: 1980
SQ FT: 6,000
SALES (est): 1MM-4.9MM **Privately Held**
WEB: www.northlandpaintingsupplies.com
SIC: 1721 Painting & wall covering
contractor

(G-9633)
OAK GLEN LLC
1599 McKusick Rd N (55082-4166)
PHONE.............................651 439-6981
FAX: 651 439-7971
Ken Wilson, *Owner*
Mark Larson, *Manager*
EMP: 70 EST: 1993
SQ FT: 18,000
SALES (est): 1MM-4.9MM **Privately Held**
WEB: www.oakglengolf.com
SIC: 7997 7299 Country club; limited
service snack shop; banquet hall facility

(G-9634)
ORTHOPEDIC SPORTS INC
Also Called: OSI Physical Therapy
1700 Tower Dr W (55082-7511)
PHONE.............................651 439-8540
Michael Ripley, *President*
Jim Hyome, *Vice Pres*
Mandy Honnett, *Manager*
Roger Harrison, *CIO*
EMP: 70 EST: 1978
SQ FT: 6,500
SALES (est): 5MM-9.9MM **Privately Held**
SIC: 8011 Orthopedic physician office

(G-9635)
ROBERT C MEISTERLING MD
1701 Curve Crest Blvd W (55082-6044)
PHONE.............................651 439-8807
Robert Meisterling MD, *Owner*
EMP: 60 EST: 1976
SALES (est): 5MM-9.9MM **Privately Held**
SIC: 8011 Physicians' office & clinic

(G-9636)
ROOF TECH INC
14520 61st Street Ct N (55082-6170)
PHONE.............................651 351-7302
Robert Poutre, *President*
Teri Poutre, *Vice Pres*
Ted Buttweiller, *Manager*
EMP: 26 EST: 1993
SQ FT: 4,200
SALES (est): 1MM-4.9MM **Privately Held**
SIC: 1761 Roofing, siding & sheet metal
work

(G-9637)
ROSE FLORAL & GREENHOUSE INC
14298 60th St N (55082-6309)
PHONE.............................651 439-3765
FAX: 651 439-1250
Glenn Rose, *President*
Lawrence Rose, *Vice Pres*
Richard Rose, *Treasurer*
Dick Rose, *Accountant*
EMP: 40 EST: 1949
SQ FT: 30,000
SALES (est): 1MM-4.9MM **Privately Held**
SIC: 0181 Florist; ornamental nursery
products

(G-9638)
RUDISILL ADVERTISING
501 Main St N Ste 402 (55082-6615)
PHONE.............................651 636-0345
Lynn Rudisill, *President*
Lynn Beseth, *President*
EMP: 30
SQ FT: 8,400
SALES (est): 1MM-4.9MM **Privately Held**
WEB: www.mirageadvertising.com
SIC: 7311 Advertising agency

(G-9639)
SIMPER LOWELL LLC
Also Called: Lowell Inn
102 2nd St N (55082-5003)
PHONE.............................651 439-1100
FAX: 651 439-4686
Dick Anderson, *President*
Kent Lagoon, *Manager*
Krisin V Puen, *Manager*
Brian Anderson, *Info Tech Mgr*
EMP: 50 EST: 1927
SALES (est): 1MM-4.9MM **Privately Held**
SIC: 7011 Eating place; hotel

(G-9640)
SOLUTIA CONSULTING INC
1241 Amundson Cir (55082-4132)
PHONE.............................651 351-0123
Richard Kuula, *President*
Susan Moschkau, *Consultant*
Gloria Sharp, *Director*
Laura Dockery, *Director*
Dean Swan, *Director*
EMP: 44 EST: 1997
SALES (est): 5MM-9.9MM **Privately Held**
WEB: www.solutia-consulting.com
SIC: 7379 Data processing consulting
service

(G-9641)
SOUTHHILL DENTAL
2850 Curve Crest Blvd W # 200
(55082-4073)
PHONE.............................651 439-9400
Phil Flodin, *Partner*
Cheryl Lindgren, *Partner*
Donna Kobs, *Manager*
EMP: 25 EST: 1979
SQ FT: 3,000
SALES (est): 1MM-4.9MM **Privately Held**
SIC: 8021 Dental office

(G-9642)
ST CROIX BOAT & PACKET INC
301 2nd St S (55082-5135)
PO Box 406 (55082-0406)
PHONE.............................651 430-1234
Dick Anderson, *President*
Bob Anderson, *Vice Pres*
EMP: 75 EST: 1983
SALES (est): 5MM-9.9MM **Privately Held**
SIC: 4489 Excursion boat operator

(G-9643)
ST CROIX ORTHOPAEDICS
1991 Northwestern Ave S (55082-7536)
PHONE.............................651 439-8807
Robert Nuffort, *CEO*
Robert C Meisterling, *President*
David H Palmer, *Corp Secy*
Bruce J Bartie, *Vice Pres*
Glenn W Ciegler, *Vice Pres*
EMP: 80 EST: 1977
SALES (est): 5MM-9.9MM **Privately Held**
WEB: www.stcroixortho.com
SIC: 8011 Orthopedic physician office

(G-9644)
ST CROIX PRESERVATION CO INC
Also Called: Lumber Baron's Hotel Resta
101 Water St S (55082-5150)
PHONE.............................651 439-6000
FAX: 651 430-9393
Chuck Dourthgery, *President*
Martha Hubbs, *Manager*
EMP: 50 EST: 1994
SALES (est): 1MM-4.9MM **Privately Held**
WEB: www.waterstreetinn.us
SIC: 7011 7299 Hotel; banquet hall facility

(G-9645)
STILLWATER COUNTRY CLUB INC
1421 4th St N (55082-4379)
PHONE.............................651 439-7979
FAX: 651 439-2434
Mike Adams, *President*
Marlin Murphy, *Manager*
Lynn Johnson, *Manager*
EMP: 45 EST: 1925
SQ FT: 5,000
SALES (est): 1MM-4.9MM **Privately Held**

SIC: 7997 Country club; cocktail lounge; full
service American restaurant

(G-9646)
STILLWATER FITNESS CLUB INC
110 Greeley St S (55082-5664)
PHONE.............................651 430-1584
Heidi Rosebud, *President*
EMP: 40 EST: 1990
SALES (est): 1MM-4.9MM **Privately Held**
WEB: www.stillwaterfitness.com
SIC: 7991 8011 Health club; physicians'
office & clinic

(G-9647)
STILLWATER MEDICAL CLINIC
1500 Curve Crest Blvd W (55082-6040)
PHONE.............................651 439-1234
Gwen Moore, *Finance Dir*
Jen Farring, *Human Res Dir*
Rob Turnquist, *Human Res Dir*
Susan Rockwood, *Manager*
Gary Bowery, *MIS Dir*
EMP: 200
SALES (est): 10MM-24.9MM **Privately Held**
SIC: 8011 Clinic operated by physicians
PA: Water Medical Group
1500 Curve Crest Blvd W
Stillwater MN 55082
651 439-1234

(G-9648)
STILLWATER MEDICAL GROUP
1500 Curve Crest Blvd W (55082-6040)
PHONE.............................651 439-1234
Joan Ptacek, *Vice Pres*
Vicki Voorhees, *Opers Mgr*
Kathleen M De Manivel MD, *Med Doctor*
Susan M Aschd MD, *Med Doctor*
Gwen Moore, *Manager*
EMP: 220 EST: 1995
SALES (est): 10MM-24.9MM **Privately Held**
SIC: 8011 Medical center

(G-9649)
STUDENT ASSURANCE SERVICES INC
333 Main St N Ste 300 (55082-5098)
PO Box 196 (55082-0196)
PHONE.............................651 439-7098
Mark Desch, *President*
Gloria Desch, *Corp Secy*
Tom Miller, *Vice Pres*
Ryan E Desch, *CFO*
David Desch, *Treasurer*
EMP: 38 EST: 1971
SQ FT: 15,000
SALES (est): 1MM-4.9MM **Privately Held**
WEB: www.sas-mn.com
SIC: 6411 Insurance education service

(G-9650)
SUMMIT MANAGEMENT LLC
122 Water St S (55082-5154)
PHONE.............................651 689-2200
EMP: 25 EST: 2006
SALES (est): 1MM-4.9MM **Privately Held**
SIC: 8741 Management services

(G-9651)
TECHBARNCOM INC
270 Main St N Ste 300 (55082-5022)
PO Box 368 (55082-0368)
PHONE.............................651 275-8300
FAX: 651 275-8301
Melissa Uppgren, *President*
John Upgren, *Vice Pres*
EMP: 35 EST: 2000
SQ FT: 6,000 **Privately Held**
WEB: www.techbarn.com
SIC: 7375 Information retrieval services

(G-9652)
THOMAS GRACE CONSTRUCTION INC
1912 Greeley St S (55082-3305)
PHONE.............................651 342-1298
Don Harvieux, *President*
Janine Harvieux, *Vice Pres*
Donna Caywood, *Controller*
Kathy Lundberg, *Accounting Mgr*
EMP: 25

EST: 2002
SQ FT: 4,200
SALES (est): 1MM-4.9MM **Privately Held**
WEB: www.thomas-grace.com
SIC: 1751 Store fixture installation service

(G-9653)
VALLEY DENTAL ARTS INC
1745 Northwestern Ave S (55082-7502)
PO Box 205 (55082-0205)
PHONE.............................651 439-2855
FAX: 651 439-9027
Charles N Maragos, *President*
Pete Hemstock, *Vice Pres*
Rick Aeziman, *Vice Pres*
Mavis Peterson, *Project Mgr*
Mia Walker, *Technical Mgr*
EMP: 65 EST: 1974
SQ FT: 21,000
SALES (est): 1MM-4.9MM **Privately Held**
WEB: www.valleydentalarts.com
SIC: 8072 8021 Dental laboratory; dentists'
office & clinic

(G-9654)
W ZINTL CONSTRUCTION INC
Also Called: Zintl W
5670 Memorial Ave N Ste 1 (55082-2186)
PHONE.............................651 439-7973
FAX: 651 439-7758
William Zintl, *President*
Ann Zintl, *Corp Secy*
EMP: 168 EST: 1980
SALES (est): 10MM-24.9MM **Privately Held**
SIC: 1742 Drywall contractor; plain or
ornamental plastering contractor

(G-9655)
WATER MEDICAL GROUP (PA)
1500 Curve Crest Blvd W (55082-6040)
PHONE.............................651 439-1234
Charles Hipp, *President*
Gene C Stringer MD, *Corp Secy*
Brian Cress MD, *Med Doctor*
Craig Howard MD, *Med Doctor*
Stephen Danaher MD, *Med Doctor*
EMP: 200 EST: 1970
SQ FT: 2,500 **Privately Held**
SIC: 8011 Clinic operated by physicians

STORDEN
Cottonwood County

(G-9656)
HEARTLAND STATE BANK
Also Called: First State Agency of Storden
311 America St (56174-2074)
PHONE.............................507 445-3417
FAX: 507 445-3259
Ronald Terkilson, *President*
Ernest Iverson, *Cashier*
EST: 1904
SQ FT: 2,400 **Privately Held**
SIC: 6022 State commercial bank

STURGEON LAKE
Pine County

(G-9657)
DULUTH AREA FAMILY Y M C A
Also Called: YMCA Camp Miller
89382 E Frontage Rd (55783-3422)
PHONE.............................218 372-3188
FAX: 218 372-3188
Greg Burns, *Manager*
Travis Fountaine, *Director*
EMP: 35
SALES (est): 1MM-4.9MM **Privately Held**
WEB: www.duluthymca.org
SIC: 7032 8641 Recreational & sporting
camp; youth organizations
PA: Duluth Area Family YMCA
302 W 1st St
Duluth MN 55802
218 722-4745

www.HarrisInfo.com
416

2011 Harris Minnesota
Services Directory

▲=Import ▼=Export
◆=Import/Export

SWANVILLE
Morrison County

(G-9658)

GESSELL FEED MILL INC
302 Degraff Ave (56382-4400)
PO Box 158 (56382-0158)
PHONE..............................320 547-2994
FAX: 320 547-2994
Joe Gessell, *CEO*
John Gessell, *President*
Frank C Gessell, *Corp Secy*
EMP: 35 **EST:** 1935
SQ FT: 5,000
SALES (est): 25MM-49.9MM **Privately Held**
SIC: 5191 Wholesales feed; manufactures animal feed

(G-9659)

SONNY PETERSON TRUCKING INC
Hwy 28 N (56382)
PO Box 276 (56382-0276)
PHONE..............................320 547-2489
FAX: 320 547-2195
Sonny Peterson, *President*
EMP: 40 **EST:** 1987
SQ FT: 5,376
SALES (est): 1MM-4.9MM **Privately Held**
SIC: 4214 Local trucking with storage

TAYLORS FALLS
Chisago County

(G-9660)

DENNIS RAEDEKE INC
Also Called: Wild Mountain
37350 Wild Mountain Rd (55084-1890)
PO Box 235 (55084-0235)
PHONE..............................651 465-6365
Dennis Raedeke, *President*
Amanda Raedeke, *President*
Amanda R Frischmon, *Vice Pres*
Jim Koski, *Manager*
EMP: 100 **EST:** 1972
SQ FT: 10,000
SALES (est): 10MM-24.9MM **Privately Held**
SIC: 7999 Amusement or scenic aerial tramway or ski lift; amusement ride services; go-cart raceway operation & rental services; waterslide operation

(G-9661)

MULLER BOAT CO
Also Called: Taylors Falls Boats & Canoes
37350 Wild Mountain Rd (55084-1890)
PO Box 235 (55084-0235)
PHONE..............................651 465-6315
Dan Raedeke, *President*
Amy Frischmon, *Exec VP*
Julie Johnson, *Office Mgr*
EMP: 30 **EST:** 1960
SALES (est): 1MM-4.9MM **Privately Held**
WEB: www.wildmountain.com
SIC: 4489 7999 Excursion boat operator; builds & repairs boats; pleasure boat rental services

TENSTRIKE
Beltrami County

(G-9662)

ELDER MEADOWLAND CARE HOMES
21368 Gull Lake Loop Rd NE (56683-2121)
PHONE..............................218 586-3740
FAX: 218 586-3740
Lynn Bedell, *President*
Donna Stephens, *Vice Pres*
Delores Bradshaw, *Vice Pres*
EMP: 25 **EST:** 1996
SQ FT: 36,000
SALES (est): 1MM-4.9MM **Privately Held**
SIC: 8051 Skilled nursing care facility

THIEF RIVER FALLS
Pennington County

(G-9663)

BEST WESTERN OF THIEF RIVER
1060 Highway 32 S (56701-3902)
PO Box 573 (56701-0573)
PHONE..............................218 681-7555
FAX: 218 681-7721
Sami Haj, *President*
Abdul Chamma, *General Mgr*
Norris Melander, *Corp Secy*
Richard L Evans, *Treasurer*
EMP: 90 **EST:** 1975
SQ FT: 18,000
SALES (est): 5MM-9.9MM **Privately Held**
SIC: 7011 Traveler accommodations; cocktail lounge; eating place

(G-9664)

COUNTY OF PENNINGTON
Also Called: Intercounty Nursing Service
318 Knight Ave N (56701-1929)
PHONE..............................218 681-0876
FAX: 218 681-5341
Susan Olsen, *Director*
EMP: 35
SALES (est): 1MM-4.9MM **Privately Held**
SIC: 8049 Registered & practical nurse office
PA: County of Pennington
County Court House
Thief River Falls MN 56701
218 683-7017

(G-9665)

COUNTY OF PENNINGTON
Also Called: Oakland Park Nursing Home
123 Baken St (56701-3903)
PHONE..............................218 681-1675
FAX: 218 681-1037
Kathy Wentz, *Office Mgr*
Angela Malone, *Administrator*
EMP: 75
SALES (est): 1MM-4.9MM **Privately Held**
SIC: 8051 8052 Skilled nursing care facility; intermediate care facility
PA: County of Pennington
County Court House
Thief River Falls MN 56701
218 683-7017

(G-9666)

DIGI-KEY CORP
701 Brooks Ave S (56701-2757)
PO Box 677 (56701-0677)
PHONE..............................218 681-6674
FAX: 218 681-3380
Ronald Stordahl, *CEO*
Mark Larson, *President*
Marie Finney, *Senior VP*
Chris Beeson, *Vice Pres*
Kevin Brown, *Vice Pres*
▲ **EMP:** 1150 **EST:** 1971
SQ FT: 600,000
SALES (est): 500MM-999.9MM **Privately Held**
WEB: www.digikey.com
SIC: 5065 Wholesales electronic parts

(G-9667)

FALLS ELECTRIC INC
720 Dawn Ave (56701-1049)
PHONE..............................218 681-7299
FAX: 218 681-6288
Chad Lian, *President*
Shannon Lia, *Corp Secy*
EMP: 30 **EST:** 2002
SALES (est): 1MM-4.9MM **Privately Held**
WEB: www.fallselectric.com
SIC: 1731 Electrical contractor

(G-9668)

FRATERNAL ORDER OF EAGLES INC
Also Called: Eagles Club Rooms
305 Red Lake Blvd (56701-2103)
PHONE..............................218 681-2406
Greg Dalley, *President*
Kay Nelson, *Branch Mgr*
Ken Bakke, *Manager*
EMP: 33 **Privately Held**
WEB: www.fraternalorderofeagles.tribe.net
SIC: 8641 Fraternal association
HQ: Fraternal Order of Eagles Inc
1623 Gateway Cir
Grove City OH 43123
614 883-2200

(G-9669)

HARTZ TRUCK LINE INC
124 State Ave S (56701-2837)
PO Box 618 (56701-0618)
PHONE..............................218 681-3295
FAX: 218 681-6487
Keith Higginbotham, *President*
Ryan Barth, *Corp Secy*
Tim Carlson, *Vice Pres*
Steve Olson, *Treasurer*
Paul Nelson, *Manager*
EMP: 40 **EST:** 1982
SQ FT: 2,400
SALES (est): 5MM-9.9MM **Privately Held**
WEB: www.hartztruckline.com
SIC: 4213 Over the road trucking

(G-9670)

INGSTAD BROADCASTING INC
Also Called: Kkdq
Hwy 32 N (56701)
PHONE..............................218 681-4900
Tom Ingstad, *Owner*
Jon Praska, *Sales Executive*
EMP: 30 **EST:** 1977
SQ FT: 800
SALES (est): 1MM-4.9MM **Privately Held**
SIC: 4832 Radio broadcasting station

(G-9671)

JOHNSON'S RIVERSIDE BOARDING
16117 160th St NE (56701-8490)
PHONE..............................218 681-1278
FAX: 218 681-1295
Genneil Johnson, *Corp Secy*
Paul Johnson, *Administrator*
EST: 1964
SQ FT: 200 **Privately Held**
SIC: 8052 Residential mentally handicapped facility

(G-9672)

KKAQ AM 1460
1433 N Main St (56701)
PO Box 40 (56701-0040)
PHONE..............................218 681-4900
FAX: 218 681-6311
Jon Praska, *General Mgr*
EMP: 30
SALES (est): 1MM-4.9MM **Privately Held**
SIC: 4832 Radio broadcasting stations with a country music format

(G-9673)

LEGAL SERVICE NORTHWEST MN
220 Pennington Ave B (56701-2904)
PHONE..............................218 681-7710
Mary Schneider, *Director*
EMP: 25
SALES (est): 1MM-4.9MM **Privately Held**
SIC: 8111 Legal services

(G-9674)

MINN-DAK ASPHALT INC
423 W Zea St (56701)
PHONE..............................218 281-6840
Robert Herkenhoff, *CEO*
EMP: 40 **EST:** 1995
SALES (est): 1MM-4.9MM **Privately Held**
SIC: 1771 1611 Asphalt contractor; street surfacing & paving construction

(G-9675)

MINNESOTA STATE COLLEGES
1101 Highway 1 E (56701-2528)
PHONE..............................218 681-2181
James Haviland, *Principal*
EMP: 31 **Privately Held**
WEB: www.msus.edu
SIC: 8399 Social change association
DH: Minnesota State Colleges
30 7th St E Ste 350
Saint Paul MN 55101
651 296-8012

(G-9676)

NORTHWEST MEDICAL CENTER
120 Labree Ave S Ste A (56701-2819)
PO Box 531 (56701-0531)
PHONE..............................218 681-4240
FAX: 218 681-5614
Chris Harff, *CEO*
Wallace A Sprby, *Vice Chairman*
Cindy Dally, *Corp Secy*
Michelle Paulson, *Manager*
Rob Lovejoy, *COO*
EMP: 296 **EST:** 1950
SQ FT: 220,000
SALES (est): 25MM-49.9MM **Privately Held**
SIC: 8062 Medical hospital

(G-9677)

OCCUPATIONAL DEVELOPMENT CTR (PA)
Also Called: O D C
1520 Highway 32 S (56701-4508)
PO Box 730 (56701-0730)
PHONE..............................218 681-4949
FAX: 218 681-7635
Peter J Lavalier, *President*
Kevin Iverson, *COO*
Ron Reierson, *CFO*
Joanne Olson, *Manager*
EMP: 100 **EST:** 1971
SQ FT: 20,000
SALES (corp-wide): 15.51M **Privately Held**
WEB: www.odcmn.com
SIC: 8331 Vocational rehabilitation agency

(G-9678)

THIEF RIVER GOLF CLUB
Hwy 32 N (56701)
PO Box 481 (56701-0481)
PHONE..............................218 681-2955
Chuck Tuthill, *Director*
EMP: 35 **EST:** 1922
SALES (est): 1MM-4.9MM **Privately Held**
SIC: 7997 Membership golf club

(G-9679)

THYGESON CONSTRUCTION CO
17913 US Highway 59 NE (56701-8545)
PHONE..............................218 681-1924
FAX: 218 681-7723
Duwayne Thygeson, *President*
Wenda Thygeson, *Corp Secy*
Monty Thygeson, *Vice Pres*
Mike Thygeson, *Vice Pres*
Bruce Thygeson, *Vice Pres*
EMP: 40 **EST:** 1951
SQ FT: 8,000
SALES (est): 1MM-4.9MM **Privately Held**
SIC: 1794 4213 Excavation & grading, building construction contractor; over the road trucking

(G-9680)

TITAN MACHINERY INC
17108 US Highway 59 NE (56701-8545)
PHONE..............................218 681-1423
Cecil D Anderson, *Manager*
Jennifer Davis, *Officer*
EMP: 34
SALES (est): 1MM-4.9MM **Publicly Held**
SIC: 5072 5083 Hardware store; wholesales hardware; wholesales farm implements

(G-9681)

VALLEY HOME SOCIETY
523 Arnold Ave S (56701-3599)
PHONE..............................218 681-3286
FAX: 218 681-3287
Arlene Solheil, *Administrator*
Arden Solheim, *Director*
EMP: 55 **EST:** 1955
SALES (est): 1MM-4.9MM **Privately Held**
SIC: 8059 Retirement community with nursing

(G-9682)

WELLS FARGO BANK
208 Main Ave N (56701-1904)
PHONE..............................218 681-1930
Oneae Iverson, *Manager*
Desirae Iverson, *Manager*
Lenae Iverson, *Mng Officer*
EMP: 25
SALES (est): 5MM-9.9MM **Publicly Held**

GEOGRAPHIC

(PA)=Parent Co (HQ)=Headquarters (DH)=Div Headquarters
✪ = New business established in last 2 years

2011 Harris Minnesota
Services Directory

© Harris InfoSource 1-866-281-6415
417

SIC: **6021** National commercial bank
HQ: Wfc Holdings, Corp
420 Montgomery St
San Francisco CA 94104
415 396-7392

(G-9683)
WELLS FARGO MINNESOTA WEST
110 3rd St E (56701-2006)
PHONE...............................218 681-1930
FAX: 218 681-4871
Lenee Iverson, *President*
EMP: 26
SALES (est): 5MM-9.9MM **Publicly Held**
SIC: **6021** National commercial bank
HQ: Wells Fargo Minnesota West
730 Center Ave Lbby LBBY
Moorhead MN 56560
218 233-6183

TOFTE
Cook County

(G-9684)
TOFTE MANAGEMENT CO LLC
Also Called: BLUEFIN RESORT
7198 W Highway 61 (55615-8615)
PO Box 2125 (55615-2125)
PHONE...............................218 663-7296
FAX: 218 663-7130
Robert A Buntz Jr, *Member*
Dennis Rysdahl, *Member*
Steve Nelson, *Manager*
Mary Henry, *Manager*
EMP: 105 **EST:** 1984
SQ FT: 10,000
SALES (est): 5MM-9.9MM **Privately Held**
SIC: **8741** 6512 7011 Hotel or motel
management services; traveler
accommodations; nonresidential building
operator; eating place

TOGO
Itasca County

(G-9685)
DEPARTMENT OF CORRECTIONS MN
Also Called: Thistledew Camp
62741 County Road 551 (55723-4509)
PHONE...............................218 376-4411
FAX: 218 376-4489
David M Hegg, *Superintendent*
EMP: 55 **Privately Held**
WEB: www.minncor.com
SIC: **8748** Correctional institution; business
consulting services; state government
correctional institution
DH: Department of Corrections MN
1450 Energy Park Dr # 200
Saint Paul MN 55108
651 361-7200

TOWER
Saint Louis County

(G-9686)
BOIS FORTE ENTERPRISES
Also Called: FORTUNE BAY RESORT CASINO
1430 Bois Forte Rd (55790-8111)
PHONE...............................218 753-6400
FAX: 218 753-6404
William B Tibbetts, *President*
Norman G Adams, *General Mgr*
John Monacelli, *Vice Pres*
Joe Wisocki, *Facilities Dir*
Joe Wisoki, *Facilities Mgr*
▲ **EMP:** 480 **EST:** 1986
SQ FT: 32,000
SALES (est): 25MM-49.9MM **Privately Held**
WEB: www.fortunebay.com
SIC: **7999** 7011 Gambling establishment;
traveler accommodations; eating place;
drinking establishment

(G-9687)
GULL WAY LTD ✪
Also Called: Stealth Muffler Co
5776 Lake Ave S (55790-8350)
PHONE...............................218 753-1210
Terry Anderson, *President*
Marlene Rustad, *Corp Secy*
▲ **EMP:** 30 **EST:** 2008
SALES (est): 25MM-49.9MM **Privately Held**
SIC: **5012** Automotive brokers; motorcycle
wholesaler

(G-9688)
STATE BANK OF TOWER INC
415 Main St (55790)
PO Box 499 (55790-0499)
PHONE...............................218 753-6100
FAX: 218 753-2334
Peter Pichetti, *President*
Peter M Kinney, *Vice Pres*
Diane Meehan, *Loan Officer*
EST: 1969 **Privately Held**
SIC: **6022** 6411 State commercial bank;
insurance agent

TRACY
Lyon County

(G-9689)
AM & S TRUCKING INC
2901 190th St (56175-2146)
PHONE...............................507 629-3224
Samuel Hedge, *President*
Annette Hedge, *Vice Pres*
Matthew Hedge, *Treasurer*
EMP: 45 **EST:** 1986
SQ FT: 30,000
SALES (est): 5MM-9.9MM **Privately Held**
SIC: **4213** Over the road trucking

(G-9690)
PRARIE VIEW HEALTHCARE CENTER
250 5th St E (56175-1537)
PHONE...............................507 629-3331
FAX: 507 629-3086
Steven L Harl, *Vice Pres*
Marlene Torkelson, *Facilities Dir*
Tim Byrne, *Administrator*
Jackie Lanoue, *Director*
EMP: 68 **EST:** 1966
SALES (est): 1MM-4.9MM **Privately Held**
SIC: **8051** Skilled nursing care facility

(G-9691)
SANFORD HEALTH NETWORK
Also Called: Tracy Area Medical Services
251 5th St E (56175-1536)
PHONE...............................507 674-2932
Rick Nordahl, *Principal*
Gordy Kopperud, *COO*
Ali Jasmin, *Ch Pathology*
Deb Ohman, *Purchasing*
David Buysse, *Engineering*
EMP: 107
SALES (est): 5MM-9.9MM **Privately Held**
SIC: **8741** 8011 Hospital management
services; physicians' office & clinic
PA: Sanford Health Network
1305 W 18th St
Sioux Falls SD 57105
605 328-2929

(G-9692)
TRACY HEALTHCARE CENTER INC
250 5th St E (56175-1537)
PHONE...............................507 629-3331
Howard Groff, *President*
Gail Sheridan, *Corp Secy*
Steven L Harl, *Vice Pres*
Gregory V ARX, *Treasurer*
EMP: 58 **EST:** 1989
SQ FT: 32,000
SALES (est): 1MM-4.9MM **Privately Held**
SIC: **8051** Skilled nursing care facility
PA: Tealwood Care Centers Inc
9031 Penn Ave S
Minneapolis MN 55431
952 888-2923

TRIMONT
Martin County

(G-9693)
CENEX NUWAY CO OP INC
620 2nd Ave S (56176)
PO Box Q (56176-0370)
PHONE...............................507 375-4291
Jim Lorenz, *Administrator*
EMP: 70 **EST:** 1995
SALES (est): 50MM-99.9MM **Privately Held**
SIC: **6111** National consumer cooperative
bank credit agency

(G-9694)
TRIMONT HEALTH CARE CENTER
303 Broadway St S (56176-9732)
PHONE...............................507 639-2381
FAX: 507 639-2142
Leilani Eickman, *Principal*
Michele Hagen, *Manager*
EMP: 80 **EST:** 1959
SQ FT: 100,000
SALES (est): 5MM-9.9MM **Privately Held**
SIC: **8011** Physicians' office & clinic

TRUMAN
Martin County

(G-9695)
LUTHERAN RETIREMENT HOME OF
400 N 4th Ave E (56088-1108)
PHONE...............................507 776-2031
FAX: 507 776-2032
James Birchem, *President*
Arnold Bentz, *Chairman*
EMP: 130 **EST:** 1963
SQ FT: 50,000
SALES (est): 5MM-9.9MM **Privately Held**
SIC: **8051** Skilled nursing care facility

(G-9696)
PROFINIUM FINANCIAL INC (HQ)
414 N 5th Ave E (56088-1116)
PO Box 400 (56088-0400)
PHONE...............................507 776-2311
Oev Oren, *President*
Brenda Stockwell, *Mfg Spvr*
Ron Kopischke, *Marketing Staff*
Jeff Frey, *Manager*
Gary Hoehn, *Officer*
EMP: 35 **EST:** 1916 **Privately Held**
SIC: **6022** State commercial bank
PA: Profinium Financial Holdings
102 E Ciro St
Truman MN 56088
507 776-2311

(G-9697)
TRUMAN SR LIVING INC
400 N 4th Ave E (56088-1108)
PHONE...............................507 776-2031
Jacquelyn M Edwards, *Principal*
Vickie Lewis, *Office Mgr*
EMP: 25 **EST:** 2007
SALES (est): 500-999K **Privately Held**
SIC: **8361** Home for the elderly

(G-9698)
TYSON FRESH MEATS INC
2241 State Highway 15 (56088-2025)
PHONE...............................507 776-2828
Brian Mohn, *Manager*
EMP: 25
SALES (est): 10MM-24.9MM **Publicly Held**
WEB: www.tyson.com
SIC: **5154** Wholesales hogs
HQ: Tyson Fresh Meats Inc
800 Stevens Port Dr
North Sioux City SD 57049
605 235-2061

(G-9699)
WATONWAN FARM SERVICE INC (PA)
233 W Ciro St (56088-2018)
PO Box 68 (56088-0068)
PHONE...............................507 776-2831
FAX: 507 776-9114
Todd Ludwig, *President*
Bruce Stofferan, *General Mgr*
Ed Bosanko, *General Mgr*
Doug Kuhlman, *Vice Chairman*
Larry Olsen, *Corp Secy*
EMP: 35 **EST:** 1937
SQ FT: 12,000
SALES (corp-wide): 483.99M **Privately Held**
WEB: www.wfsag.com
SIC: **5172** 5153 5191 Wholesales
petroleum products; wholesales agricultural
fertilizer; wholesales agricultural chemicals;
wholesales grains; wholesales feed;
wholesales field, garden & flower seeds

TWIN VALLEY
Norman County

(G-9700)
ARVIG ENTERPRISES INC
Also Called: Tekstar Cablevision
204 Main Ave W (56584)
PO Box 189 (56584-0189)
PHONE...............................218 584-5119
Dave Schornack, *General Mgr*
John Burnse, *Controller*
David Arvig, *Manager*
Mary Lowden, *Manager*
EMP: 30
SALES (est): 10MM-24.9MM **Privately Held**
SIC: **4841** Pay television distribution
PA: Arvig Enterprises Inc
160 2nd Ave SW
Perham MN 56573
218 346-5500

(G-9701)
CENTROL INC
102 Main Ave E (56584)
PO Box 367 (56584-0367)
PHONE...............................218 584-5107
FAX: 218 584-5100
Dennis Berglund, *CEO*
Belynda Metz, *Bookkeeper*
Bryan Smith, *Manager*
Paul Baukol, *Manager*
Rob Hauger, *Advisor*
EMP: 30 **EST:** 1980
SQ FT: 3,000 **Publicly Held**
WEB: www.cenexharveststates.com
SIC: **0762** 8748 Farm management
services; agricultural consultant
PA: CHS Inc
5500 Cenex Dr
Inver Grove Heights MN 55077
651 355-6000

(G-9702)
LUTHERAN MEMORIAL HOME (PA)
208 Oppegard Ave NW (56584)
PO Box 480 (56584-0480)
PHONE...............................218 584-5181
Dennis Thorson, *President*
Gary Lunde, *Vice Pres*
Cheryl Anderson, *Office Mgr*
Dwight Fuglie, *Exec Dir*
EMP: 150 **EST:** 1950
SQ FT: 42,000
SALES (corp-wide): 6.94M **Privately Held**
WEB: www.lutheranlivingcenter.com
SIC: **8051** 8059 Convalescent home;
retirement community with nursing

(G-9703)
LUTHERAN MEMORIAL HOME
205 3rd St NW Apt 302 (56584-4024)
PO Box 480 (56584-0480)
PHONE...............................218 584-5181
Dwight Fuglie, *General Mgr*
EMP: 125
SALES (est): 1MM-4.9MM **Privately Held**
WEB: www.lutheranlivingcenter.com

SIC: 8051 Convalescent home
PA: Lutheran Memorial Home
208 Oppegard Ave NW
Twin Valley MN 56584
218 584-5181

TWO HARBORS
Lake County

(G-9704)
API OUTSOURCING INC
320 7th Ave (55616-1448)
PHONE..............................218 834-8007
FAX: 218 834-2888
Jake Yates, *Prdtn Mgr*
Stephanie Schmit, *Persnl Mgr*
Kirk Dresen, *Branch Mgr*
Matt Coffell, *Administrator*
EMP: 50
SALES (est): 5MM-9.9MM Privately Held
SIC: 7371 Computer programming service
PA: API Outsourcing Inc
2975 Lone Oak Rd
Eagan MN 55121
651 675-2600

(G-9705)
BLUE WATERS DEVELOPMENT CORP
1521 Superior Shores Dr (55616-2000)
PO Box 470, Nisswa (56468-0470)
PHONE..............................800 242-1988
Dale Jensen, *President*
Darren Young, *Manager*
EMP: 80 EST: 1994
SALES (est): 1MM-4.9MM Privately Held
WEB: www.superiorshores.com
SIC: 7011 Hotel; eating place; drinking establishment

(G-9706)
ECUMEN
Also Called: Sunrise Nursing Home
402 3rd Ave (55616-1629)
PHONE..............................218 834-8374
FAX: 218 834-8461
Sue Johnson, *Manager*
Karen Foebe, *Exec Dir*
EMP: 96
SALES (est): 1MM-4.9MM Privately Held
WEB: www.augustanahomes.org
SIC: 8051 Skilled nursing care facility
PA: Ecumen
3530 Lexington Ave N
Saint Paul MN 55126
651 766-4300

(G-9707)
FIRST SOLUTIONS
Also Called: Superior Health Community Care
1010 4th St (55616-1200)
PHONE..............................218 834-7205
Louise Anderson, *Director*
EMP: 30
SALES (est): 1MM-4.9MM Privately Held
SIC: 8051 Skilled nursing care facility
PA: First Solutions
525 S Lake Ave Ste 222
Duluth MN 55802
218 740-2330

(G-9708)
HISTORICAL SOCIETY OF MN
Also Called: Split Rock Lighthouse
3713 Split Rock Lighthouse Rd
(55616-2020)
PHONE..............................218 226-6372
FAX: 218 226-6373
Gloria Rosenau-Stern, *Store Mgr*
Terry Tobey, *Program Mgr*
Lee Radzak, *Manager*
EMP: 30
SALES (est): 1MM-4.9MM Privately Held
WEB: www.historictheatres.org
SIC: 8412 Museum; general government administration office; state general government administration office
PA: Historical Society of MN
345 Kellogg Blvd W
Saint Paul MN 55102
651 259-3160

(G-9709)
LAKE BANK NATIONAL ASSOCIATION (PA)
613 1st Ave (55616-1505)
PHONE..............................218 834-2111
Peter Jeronimus, *President*
Mary Turnquist, *Corp Secy*
Edna Ulrich, *Vice Pres*
Debbie Ruberg, *Purch Agent*
Christine Jackson, *Finance Mgr*
EMP: 27 EST: 1981
SALES (corp-wide): 6.39M Privately Held
SIC: 6022 6411 State commercial bank; insurance services

(G-9710)
LAKE COUNTY AMBULANCE
421 20th Ave (55616-1364)
PHONE..............................218 834-7110
Gina Heinzen, *Director*
EMP: 25 EST: 2005
SALES (est): 1MM-4.9MM Privately Held
SIC: 4119 Ambulance service

(G-9711)
PARK GOOSEBERRY MOTEL CABINS
Also Called: Rustic Inn Gifts
2778 Highway 61 (55616-2002)
PHONE..............................218 834-3751
James Sullivan, *Owner*
EMP: 32 EST: 1974
SALES (est): 1MM-4.9MM Privately Held
SIC: 7011 Eating place; snowmobile dealer; traveler accommodations; retails gifts & novelties

TYLER
Lincoln County

(G-9712)
REM & TYLER INC
303 Highland Ct (56178-9783)
PHONE..............................507 247-5568
Tyler Mennett, *Director*
EMP: 30 EST: 1978
SALES (est): 500-999K Privately Held
SIC: 8059 Home for the mentally retarded

(G-9713)
SCHAK TRUCKING INC
201 E Highway 14 (56178-9310)
PHONE..............................507 247-5204
Daniel Schak, *President*
EMP: 50 EST: 1946
SQ FT: 3,200
SALES (est): 5MM-9.9MM Privately Held
SIC: 4213 4731 Long-distance refrigerated trucking services; truck transportation brokers

(G-9714)
SUNRISE MANOR NURSING HOME
208 Highland Ct (56178-9311)
PHONE..............................507 247-5839
Doug Schweikhart, *Director*
EMP: 75 EST: 1950
SALES (est): 1MM-4.9MM Privately Held
SIC: 8059 Convalescent home

(G-9715)
TYLER AREA COMMUNITY CLUB
151 N Tyker St (56178)
PHONE..............................507 247-3905
Sharon Jacobsen, *President*
Lynn Pohlman, *Principal*
Diane Sartell, *Corp Secy*
Donna Marr, *Vice Pres*
EMP: 65 Privately Held
SIC: 8611 Business association

(G-9716)
TYLER HEALTHCARE CENTER INC
Also Called: Sunrise Manor
240 Willow St (56178-1166)
PHONE..............................507 247-5521
FAX: 507 247-5972

Dale Kruger, *CEO*
Kathe Miranowski, *Corp Secy*
James Rotert, *Vice Pres*
Kathe Mironosowski, *QA Dir*
Owen Hansen, *Chief Engr*
EMP: 190 EST: 1957
SQ FT: 15,000
SALES (est): 5MM-9.9MM Privately Held
WEB: www.tylerhealthcare.org
SIC: 8051 8062 Skilled nursing care facility; medical hospital

ULEN
Clay County

(G-9717)
CITY OF ULEN
Also Called: Northern Lghts Assisted Living
317 1st St NW (56585-4010)
PHONE..............................218 596-8847
Todd Kjos, *Finance Other*
Sandy Braseth, *Manager*
EMP: 75
SALES (est): 1MM-4.9MM Privately Held
SIC: 8059 Nursing home

UNDERWOOD
Otter Tail County

(G-9718)
PARK REGION MUTUAL TELEPHONE
100 Main St N (56586-7124)
PO Box 277 (56586-0277)
PHONE..............................218 826-6161
FAX: 218 826-6298
Dave Bickett, *CEO*
Mary J Biegler, *Controller*
Karen Thompson, *Human Res Dir*
Scott Toso, *Sales Mgr*
Katie Johnson, *Pub Rel Dir*
EMP: 25 EST: 1906
SQ FT: 22,000 Privately Held
WEB: www.prtel.com
SIC: 4813 Local telephone communications services

VADNAIS HEIGHTS
Ramsey County

(G-9719)
AREA MECHANICAL INC
3276 Fanum Rd Ste 800 (55110-5295)
PHONE..............................651 451-9356
FAX: 651 451-8676
Sandra K Schaefer, *President*
Jill Omodt, *Vice Pres*
EMP: 40 EST: 1989
SQ FT: 2,000
SALES (est): 1MM-4.9MM Privately Held
SIC: 1711 Plumbing service; heating & air conditioning contractor

(G-9720)
BOREAL ENERGY INC (PA)
1058 Centerville Cir (55127-6344)
PHONE..............................651 762-1200
Greg Jaunich, *CEO*
Greg Boreal, *Consultant*
Jolene Altman, *Director*
EST: 2005
SQ FT: 2,178 Privately Held
WEB: www.borealenergy.com
SIC: 8731 Energy research services

(G-9721)
WKS VADNAIS HEIGHTS LLC
Also Called: Holiday Inn
1100 County Road E E (55110-5122)
PHONE..............................651 484-2400
FAX: 651 486-0033
Mary Simon, *Principal*
EMP: 40 EST: 2000
SALES (est): 1MM-4.9MM Privately Held
SIC: 7011 Traveler accommodations

VERGAS
Otter Tail County

(G-9722)
HANSON'S PLUMBING & HEATING
99 Railway Ave (56587)
PO Box 99 (56587-0099)
PHONE..............................218 342-2422
FAX: 218 342-2290
Robin Hanson, *President*
Jolin Priem, *Corp Secy*
Jeffrey Hanson, *Vice Pres*
EMP: 25 EST: 1933
SQ FT: 3,200
SALES (est): 1MM-4.9MM Privately Held
WEB: www.hansonsplumbing.com
SIC: 1711 Plumbing service; warm air heating & air conditioning contractor

VERMILLION
Dakota County

(G-9723)
VERMILLION STATE BANK
107 Main St E (55085-4503)
PO Box 28 (55085-0028)
PHONE..............................651 437-4433
FAX: 651 437-1842
Frances J Poepl, *President*
Mike Ogaard, *COO*
Kevin Pedelty, *Vice Pres*
Brenda Ratgen, *Manager*
Steve Fluegel, *Consultant*
EMP: 35 EST: 1918
SALES (est): 5MM-9.9MM Privately Held
SIC: 6022 State commercial bank

VERNDALE
Wadena County

(G-9724)
BNSF RAILWAY CO
10 Eastside Dr (56481-2004)
PHONE..............................218 894-1676
Wallace Thompson, *Manager*
EMP: 75 Publicly Held
WEB: www.bnsf.com
SIC: 4011 Long haul railroad
HQ: Burlington Northern Santa Fe
2650 Lou Menk Dr
Fort Worth TX 76131
800 795-2673

VICTORIA
Carver County

(G-9725)
BROADBAND AMERICA, CORP
1772 Steiger Lake Ln (55386-7723)
PO Box 146 (55386-0146)
PHONE..............................952 941-7900
FAX: 952 941-7916
Mark Wegscheid, *President*
Richard Bennetts, *Manager*
EMP: 28 EST: 2002 Privately Held
WEB: www.ba-corp.com
SIC: 4813 1731 Wired telecommunications carrier & service; voice, data & video wiring contractor

(G-9726)
COMMUNITY LIVING INC
1600 Arboretum Blvd (55386-7705)
PHONE..............................952 443-2048
FAX: 952 443-2371
Gerald D Gross, *Principal*
Bill Martancik, *Principal*
EMP: 60 EST: 1970
SALES (est): 1MM-4.9MM Privately Held
SIC: 8059 8361 Home for the mentally retarded; residential care facility

(PA)=Parent Co (HQ)=Headquarters (DH)=Div Headquarters
✿ = New business established in last 2 years

2011 Harris Minnesota
Services Directory

© Harris InfoSource 1-866-281-6415
419

(G-9727)

DEER RUN GOLF CLUB LLC

8661 Deer Run Dr (55386-9520)
PHONE..............................952 443-2351
FAX: 952 443-3358
Tom Abts, *Member*
Troy Malo, *Manager*
EMP: 45 **EST:** 1987
SALES (est): 1MM-4.9MM **Privately Held**
SIC: 7992 Public golf course

(G-9728)

EMERALD CREST

8150 Bavaria Rd (55386-9702)
PHONE..............................952 856-7510
Gregg Getchelle, *Owner*
Joe Guertin, *Co-Owner*
EMP: 25 **EST:** 2007
SALES (est): 500-999K **Privately Held**
SIC: 8361 Home for the elderly

(G-9729)

HARTMAN CO'S INC

8011 Bavaria Rd (55386-9702)
PHONE..............................952 443-2958
FAX: 952 443-3452
Jeff Hartman, *President*
Sandy Proscek, *Product Mgr*
Kathy Ebel, *Office Mgr*
EMP: 40 **EST:** 1972
SQ FT: 20,000 **Privately Held**
WEB: www.hartmancompanies.com
SIC: 0782 1629 1794 Landscaping
services; golf course construction;
excavating contractor

(G-9730)

MID-AMERICAN BAPTIST SOCIAL

7600 Victoria Dr (55386-9792)
PO Box 330 (55386-0330)
PHONE..............................952 443-2024
Charlie Lawler, *Exec Dir*
EMP: 40 **Privately Held**
SIC: 8399 Regional planning organization
PA: Mid American Baptist Social
2160 Arboretum Blvd
Victoria MN 55386
952 443-5002

(G-9731)

MOUNT OLIVET ROLLING ACRES INC

7200 Rolling Acres Rd (55386)
PO Box 220 (55386-0220)
PHONE..............................952 474-5974
FAX: 952 474-3652
Paul Youngdahl, *Ch of Bd*
Cathy Cunningham, *Corp Secy*
Thomas Macnally, *Vice Pres*
Gary Rindahl, *Treasurer*
Kari Dose, *Manager*
EMP: 400 **EST:** 1966
SQ FT: 4,500
SALES (est): 10MM-24.9MM **Privately Held**
SIC: 8361 Children's home; home for the
mentally retarded

VIRGINIA
Saint Louis County

(G-9732)

AEOA HEADSTART

702 S 3rd Ave (55792-2775)
PHONE..............................218 749-5856
Kim Hustad, *Manager*
Charisse Salo, *Manager*
Harlan Tardy, *Exec Dir*
Norman Ferris, *Director*
Laura Wassenaar, *Director*
EMP: 85 **EST:** 1965
SALES (est): 1MM-4.9MM **Privately Held**
SIC: 8351 Head Start center

(G-9733)

ARROWHEAD CENTER INC

505 S 12th Ave Ste 1 (55792-2001)
PHONE..............................218 749-2877
FAX: 218 741-1719
Rick Goodman, *Exec Dir*

EST: 1969
SQ FT: 1,420 **Privately Held**
SIC: 8093 Outpatient alcohol treatment
clinic

(G-9734)

ARROWHEAD ECONOMIC OPPORTUNITY

Also Called: Virginia Workforce Center
820 9th St N Ste 240 (55792-2300)
PHONE..............................218 742-9187
Harlan Tardy, *Manager*
EMP: 25
SALES (est): 1MM-4.9MM **Privately Held**
WEB: www.northlandrides.com
SIC: 8331 Community services employment
training program
PA: Arrowhead Economic Opportunity
702 S 3rd Ave
Virginia MN 55792
218 749-2912

(G-9735)

ARROWHEAD ECONOMIC OPPORTUNITY (PA)

Also Called: A E O A
702 S 3rd Ave (55792-2775)
PHONE..............................218 749-2912
Howard Ankrum, *QC Mgr*
Laura L Wassenaar, *Manager*
Harlan Tardy, *Exec Dir*
Steve Rauker, *Director*
Jack Larsen, *Director*
EMP: 100 **EST:** 1966
SQ FT: 18,000
SALES (corp-wide): 24.25M **Privately Held**
WEB: www.northlandrides.com
SIC: 8399 Community action agency

(G-9736)

BCBSM INC

Also Called: Blue Shield
1301 Chestnut St W (55792-3442)
PHONE..............................218 748-2700
Cassandra Beardsly, *COO*
Annette Geroy, *Director*
EMP: 150
SALES (est): 10MM-24.9MM **Privately Held**
SIC: 6411 Insurance services
PA: Bcbsm Inc
3535 Blue Cross Rd
Saint Paul MN 55122
651 662-8000

(G-9737)

CONVEYOR BELT SERVICE INC

400 S 1st Ave (55792-2770)
PO Box 1023 (55792-1023)
PHONE..............................218 741-5939
FAX: 218 741-5953
Ted Fossum, *Purchasing*
Joe Anderson, *Manager*
Janice Horton, *MIS/IT Dir*
EMP: 30
SALES (est): 1MM-4.9MM **Privately Held**
WEB: www.cbsrubber.com
SIC: 7699 5084 Industrial machinery repair
& maintenance services; manufactures
conveyors & conveying equipment;
wholesales industrial machinery &
equipment
HQ: Conveyor Belt Service Inc
4319 W 1st St
Duluth MN 55807
218 628-0303

(G-9738)

EDWARDS OIL CO INC

Also Called: Trimark Industrial
820 Hoover Rd N (55792-2353)
PHONE..............................218 741-9634
Edward P Skalko, *President*
Bob Skalko, *Vice Pres*
Marion Skalko, *Vice Pres*
R Skalko, *Manager*
EMP: 35 **EST:** 1969
SQ FT: 3,500
SALES (est): 50MM-99.9MM **Privately Held**
SIC: 5171 5084 Wholesales petroleum bulk
stations; retail independent convenience
store; retail gasoline filling station; fuel oil
dealer; wholesales industrial machinery &
equipment

(G-9739)

GROVE CHESTNUT INC

1204 Chestnut St W (55792-3445)
PHONE..............................218 749-6846
Randy Schroetter, *Principal*
EMP: 25 **EST:** 2001
SALES (est): 500-999K **Privately Held**
SIC: 8361 8322 Residential care facility;
adult daycare center

(G-9740)

IDEA DRILLING LLC

1997 N 9th Ave (55792-2162)
PHONE..............................218 741-9287
Richard Backstrom, *Member*
Brian M Cabe, *Member*
Tammy Lillo, *Business Mgr*
EMP: 70 **EST:** 2007
SQ FT: 13,500
SALES (est): 5MM-9.9MM **Privately Held**
SIC: 1799 Core drilling & cutting service

(G-9741)

IDEA INC

115 S 14th Ave (55792-3403)
PHONE..............................218 741-9287
FAX: 218 741-9288
Richard Backstrom, *President*
EMP: 30 **EST:** 1997
SQ FT: 8,000
SALES (est): 1MM-4.9MM **Privately Held**
WEB: www.ideadrilling.com
SIC: 1799 Core drilling & cutting service

(G-9742)

IRON RANGE LEARNING & DEVPT

Also Called: Apple Tree Learning Center
409 1st St N (55792-2517)
PHONE..............................218 741-7441
Whitney Cretoll, *President*
Kristine Norberg, *Director*
EMP: 25 **EST:** 1985
SALES (est): 500-999K **Privately Held**
SIC: 8351 Child day care service

(G-9743)

IRON RANGE REHABILITATION CTR

901 9th St N Ste 100 (55792-2374)
PHONE..............................218 741-2147
FAX: 218 749-9407
Henry J Tamminen, *Director*
EMP: 42 **EST:** 1954
SQ FT: 8,000
SALES (est): 1MM-4.9MM **Privately Held**
SIC: 8093 Outpatient rehabilitation
treatment center

(G-9744)

LAURENTIAN LEASING INC

501 9th St N (55792-2301)
PHONE..............................218 741-6000
Ken Waschke, *President*
EMP: 50 **EST:** 1981
SQ FT: 32,000
SALES (est): 10MM-24.9MM **Privately Held**
SIC: 7515 Passenger car leasing

(G-9745)

LENCI ENTERPRISES INC

1021 S 2nd Ave (55792-2878)
PO Box 6 (55792-0006)
PHONE..............................218 741-3482
FAX: 218 741-3483
Michael Ralston, *President*
Dale J Hansen, *Corp Secy*
EMP: 32 **EST:** 1939
SQ FT: 2,000
SALES (est): 5MM-9.9MM **Privately Held**
SIC: 1542 New commercial & office building
construction

(G-9746)

MESABI FAMILY YMCA

Also Called: Y M C A
8367 Unity Dr (55792-4005)
PHONE..............................218 749-8020
FAX: 218 749-0921
Boyd Carlblom, *President*
Wanda McGillivray, *Bookkeeper*
Nancy Hendersonkorp, *Manager*

Karlena Graff, *Supervisor*
Darlene Simonson, *Supervisor*
EMP: 75 **EST:** 1985
SQ FT: 18,000 **Privately Held**
SIC: 8699 7999 Athletic organization;
recreation center

(G-9747)

NORTH RIDGE COMMUNITY CREDIT

921 17th St S (55792-3705)
PHONE..............................218 741-1222
FAX: 218 748-6866
Don Werdick, *President*
Sharon Nelson, *Assistant VP*
Trish Matthews, *Assistant VP*
Marrilou Kuitunen, *Assistant VP*
EMP: 28 **EST:** 2004
SALES (est): 5MM-9.9MM **Privately Held**
SIC: 6061 Federally chartered credit union

(G-9748)

NORTHEAST MINNESOTA OFFICE OF

820 9th St N Ste 250 (55792-2346)
PO Box 1028 (55792-1028)
PHONE..............................218 748-2200
FAX: 218 749-1673
Dennis Wain, *Exec Dir*
Michelle Ufford, *Director*
Robert Marconett, *Director*
Renee Marconett, *Assistant*
EMP: 43 **EST:** 1974
SALES (est): 1MM-4.9MM **Privately Held**
WEB: www.jobtrainingmn.org
SIC: 8331 Job training & vocational
rehabilitation services

(G-9749)

NORTHEAST TECHNICAL SERVICES

315 Chestnut St (55792-2523)
PO Box 1142 (55792-1142)
PHONE..............................218 741-4290
FAX: 218 741-4291
Tom Lucas, *President*
Mike Applewick, *Vice Pres*
Thomas Wagner, *Controller*
Laura Lubahn, *Med Doctor*
Russ Smith, *Planning Mgr*
EMP: 39 **EST:** 1985
SQ FT: 9,000
SALES (est): 1MM-4.9MM **Privately Held**
WEB: www.netechnical.com
SIC: 8748 8734 Environmental consultant;
soil analysis laboratory

(G-9750)

OPERATING ENGINEER NO 49

8381 Enterprise Dr NE (55792-4001)
PHONE..............................218 741-8190
Butch Pariseau, *Owner*
Butch Pariscau, *Manager*
EMP: 40 **EST:** 1949 **Privately Held**
SIC: 8631 Labor organization

(G-9751)

PUBLIC WORKS HIGHWAY MAINT

7823 Highway 135 (55792-2934)
PHONE..............................218 742-9800
FAX: 218 741-7832
Bob Lloyd, *Superintendent*
Dave Skelton, *Director*
EMP: 60
SALES (est): 5MM-9.9MM **Privately Held**
SIC: 1611 Highway & street maintenance
service

(G-9752)

QUEEN CITY FEDERAL SAVINGS

501 Chestnut St (55792-2531)
PO Box 1147 (55792-1147)
PHONE..............................218 741-2040
FAX: 218 741-2042
Kevin E Pietrini, *President*
Judie Kauchick, *Vice Pres*
Gerry McKenna, *Vice Pres*
Daniel F Schultz, *CFO*
Ronda Harvey, *Sales Dir*
EST: 1960
SQ FT: 16,000 **Privately Held**
WEB: www.qcfb.com

www.HarrisInfo.com
420

2011 Harris Minnesota
Services Directory

▲=Import ▼=Export
◆=Import/Export

SIC: 6035 Federal savings & loan association
PA: QCF Bancorp Inc
501 Chestnut St
Virginia MN 55792
218 741-2040

(G-9753)
RANGE CO OPERATIVES INC
102 Hoover Rd S (55792-3415)
PHONE..............................218 741-7393
FAX: 218 741-7396
John Briski, *President*
EST: 1933
SQ FT: 7,000 **Privately Held**
SIC: 7261 Retails bottled propane gas; retail independent grocery store; funeral home

(G-9754)
RANGE MENTAL HEALTH CENTER INC (PA)
624 13th St S (55792-3149)
PO Box 1188 (55792-1188)
PHONE..............................218 749-2881
FAX: 218 749-3806
Gordon Hoelscher, *CEO*
Wanda Taray, *CFO*
Rosalyn Barker, *Manager*
Shawna M Benson, *Manager*
Daniel J Lofgren, *Manager*
EMP: 30 **EST:** 1962
SQ FT: 10,000
SALES (corp-wide): 13.39M **Privately Held**
WEB: www.rangementalhealth.org
SIC: 8063 8093 Mental hospital; outpatient alcohol treatment clinic; outpatient detoxification center

(G-9755)
SENIOR LAURENTIAN CITIZEN CTR
RR Box 2374 (55792)
PHONE..............................218 749-3688
Sue Rikala, *President*
EMP: 55 **EST:** 1979
SALES (est): 1MM-4.9MM **Privately Held**
SIC: 8322 Senior citizen center

(G-9756)
ST LOUIS COUNTY PUBLIC WORKS
Also Called: Bridge Const Div North
7823 Highway 135 (55792-2934)
PHONE..............................218 742-9804
John Gaus, *Principal*
Bob Martimo, *Manager*
Keith Mickelson, *Manager*
EMP: 50 **EST:** 1984
SALES (est): 10MM-24.9MM **Privately Held**
SIC: 1521 Single-family housing construction

(G-9757)
ST MICHAEL'S HEALTH & REHAB
1201 8th St S (55792-3349)
PHONE..............................218 748-7800
FAX: 218 741-9241
Dale Thomposon, *President*
Shirley High, *Director*
Cheri High, *Director*
Cindy Green, *Nursing Dir*
EMP: 150 **EST:** 1968
SQ FT: 88,000
SALES (est): 5MM-9.9MM **Privately Held**
SIC: 8051 Skilled nursing care facility
PA: Benedictine Health System
503 E 3rd St Ste 400
Duluth MN 55805
218 786-2370

(G-9758)
TRENTI LAW FIRM INC
1000 Lincoln Bldg (55792)
PO Box 958 (55792-0958)
PHONE..............................218 749-1962
FAX: 218 749-4308
Sam A Aluni, *President*
Patrick J Roche, *Treasurer*
EMP: 30 **EST:** 1960
SQ FT: 8,000
SALES (est): 1MM-4.9MM **Privately Held**
WEB: www.trentilaw.com

SIC: 8111 General practice attorney's or lawyer's office

(G-9759)
VIRGINIA COOP CREDIT UNION INC
307 1st St N Ste 1 (55792-2543)
PO Box 1225 (55792-1225)
PHONE..............................218 741-5644
FAX: 218 749-4359
Victor Rovich, *President*
Nancy Edman, *Corp Secy*
Karen Sicola, *Vice Pres*
EST: 1937 **Privately Held**
WEB: www.vccu.org
SIC: 6062 State credit unions

(G-9760)
VIRGINIA, CITY OF INC
Also Called: Virginia Regional Medical Ctr
901 9th St N (55792-2325)
PHONE..............................218 741-3340
FAX: 218 749-9443
Sheryl Leoni, *Corp Secy*
Sue A Brinkman, *Corp Secy*
Kathleen Sulentich, *Ch of Surgery*
Leah Becika, *Ch OB/GYN*
Kent Froberg, *Ch Pathology*
EMP: 550
SALES (est): 50MM-99.9MM **Privately Held**
WEB: www.vpuc.com
SIC: 8011 8062 Medical center; mayors' office; medical hospital
PA: Virginia, City of Inc
327 1st St S
Virginia MN 55792
218 748-7500

(G-9761)
VIRGINIA, CITY OF INC
Also Called: Department of Public Utilities
620 2nd St S (55792-3002)
PO Box 1048 (55792-1048)
PHONE..............................218 748-7540
FAX: 218 748-7544
Teri Leoni, *General Mgr*
Doug Ganoe, *Opers Staff*
EMP: 75
SALES (est): 10MM-24.9MM **Privately Held**
WEB: www.vpuc.com
SIC: 4941 4911 4924 Water supply services; mayors' office; electric power distribution service; natural gas distribution to consumers
PA: Virginia, City of Inc
327 1st St S
Virginia MN 55792
218 748-7500

(G-9762)
WALKER, GIROUX, HAHNE LTD
225 1st St N Ste 2400 (55792-2457)
PO Box 960 (55792-0960)
PHONE..............................218 749-4880
FAX: 218 749-8528
Gary Giroux, *President*
Michael Hahne, *Corp Secy*
Steven Jarvi, *Accounting Staf*
Patricia Axelsen, *Accounting Staf*
Thomas Teasck, *Accounting Staf*
EMP: 25 **EST:** 1979
SALES (est): 1MM-4.9MM **Privately Held**
WEB: www.wghcpas.com
SIC: 8721 Accounting, auditing & bookkeeping services

(G-9763)
WALTER W CULBERT JR
Also Called: Culbert Realty
601 S 5th Ave (55792-2737)
PHONE..............................218 741-8026
Walter Culbert, *Owner*
Christine Culbert, *Manager*
EMP: 30
SALES (est): 1MM-4.9MM **Privately Held**
SIC: 6531 Real estate appraiser

(G-9764)
WAYNE TRANSPORTS INC
1917 S 15th Ave (55792-3746)
PHONE..............................218 749-6050
FAX: 218 749-8812
Jeff Hill, *Manager*
EMP: 62
SALES (est): 5MM-9.9MM **Privately Held**

WEB: www.waynetransports.com
SIC: 4213 Over the road trucking
PA: Wayne Transports Inc
14345 Conley Ave
Rosemount MN 55068
651 437-6422

(G-9765)
WELLS FARGO BANK, NATIONAL
401 Chestnut St (55792-2525)
PHONE..............................218 749-5920
FAX: 218 749-6864
Brent Hanson, *District Mgr*
Debra Ehrich, *Store Mgr*
John Oltmanns, *Info Tech Mgr*
Annette Knutson, *Admin Asst*
EMP: 35
SALES (est): 5MM-9.9MM **Publicly Held**
SIC: 6021 National commercial bank
HQ: Wfc Holdings, Corp
420 Montgomery St
San Francisco CA 94104
415 396-7392

WABASHA
Wabasha County

(G-9766)
FIRST STATE BANK OF WABASHA
111 Main St W (55981-1236)
PO Box 28 (55981-0028)
PHONE..............................651 565-3331
John E Doffing, *President*
Christ Christopherson, *Vice Pres*
Richard Vaplon, *Vice Pres*
Christ Opherson, *Vice Pres*
Doreen Brunner, *Mfg Staff*
EMP: 25 **EST:** 1881
SALES (est): 5MM-9.9MM **Privately Held**
WEB: www.fsbwabasha.com
SIC: 6022 State commercial bank

(G-9767)
HIAWATHA VALLEY MENTAL HEALTH
611 Broadway Ave Ste 100 (55981-1988)
PHONE..............................651 565-2234
FAX: 651 565-2890
Kristina Wright, *Corp Secy*
Laura L Bloomquist MD, *Med Doctor*
Julie Hanson, *Director*
George Planavsky, *Psychiatry*
EMP: 100
SALES (est): 5MM-9.9MM **Privately Held**
SIC: 8093 Outpatient mental health clinic
PA: Hiawatha Valley Mental Health
166 Main St
Winona MN 55987
507 454-4341

(G-9768)
MAYO CLINIC
Also Called: Wabasha Community Clinic
1202 Grant Blvd W (55981-1042)
PHONE..............................651 565-4571
Anne Barklage, *Manager*
Phil Malley, *Manager*
EMP: 50
SALES (est): 5MM-9.9MM **Privately Held**
SIC: 8011 Clinic operated by physicians
PA: Mayo Clinic
200 1st St SW
Rochester MN 55905
507 284-2511

(G-9769)
MISSISSIPPI EAGLES LLC
Also Called: AmericInn Lodge Suites Wabasha
150 Commerce St (55981-2300)
PHONE..............................651 565-5366
FAX: 651 565-5367
Carolynn Klees, *Member*
EMP: 28 **EST:** 2002
SALES (est): 1MM-4.9MM **Privately Held**
SIC: 7011 Motel

(G-9770)
SAINT ELIZABETH'S HOSPITAL (PA)
1200 Grant Blvd W (55981-1042)
PHONE..............................651 565-4531
FAX: 651 565-2482
Tom Crowley, *President*
Phillip Schwend, *Ch of Surgery*
John Wolfe, *CFO*
Pat Grainer, *Accounting Mgr*
Val Runions, *Persnl Dir*
▼ **EMP:** 220 **EST:** 1898
SQ FT: 89,000
SALES (corp-wide): 776.79K **Privately Held**
SIC: 8062 8051 8082 Medical hospital; home health care services; skilled nursing care facility

(G-9771)
SAINT ELIZABETH'S HOSPITAL OF
626 Shields Ave (55981-1142)
PHONE..............................651 565-4581
FAX: 651 565-3414
Jim Root, *Human Res Dir*
Rita Fox, *Manager*
Mark Suilmann, *Info Tech Dir*
EMP: 120
SALES (est): 1MM-4.9MM **Privately Held**
SIC: 8051 Skilled nursing care facility
PA: Saint Elizabeth's Hospital
1200 Grant Blvd W
Wabasha MN 55981
651 565-4531

(G-9772)
TYCO ELECTRONICS CORP
Also Called: Unipatch
1313 Grant Blvd W (55981-1058)
PHONE..............................651 565-2601
Ron Schurhammer, *Plant Mgr*
Seth Kersten, *QC Mgr*
Jennifer Bauer, *Controller*
Michelle Gosse, *Med Doctor*
Brian Wolfe, *Manager*
EMP: 200
SALES (est): 25MM-49.9MM **Privately Held**
SIC: 5047 Manufactures electromedical equipment; wholesales electromedical equipment
HQ: Tyco Electronics Corp
1050 Westlakes Dr
Berwyn PA 19312
717 564-0100

(G-9773)
WABASHA CITY AMBULANCE SVC
129 Hiawatha Dr E (55981-1550)
PHONE..............................651 565-2633
FAX: 651 565-0160
Darren Sheeley, *Exec Dir*
Erisha Chelly, *Director*
EMP: 25 **EST:** 2002
SALES (est): 1MM-4.9MM **Privately Held**
SIC: 4119 Ambulance service

(G-9774)
WABASHA CLINIC MAYO HEALTH
1202 Grant Blvd W (55981-1042)
PHONE..............................651 565-4571
Thomas Witt MD, *President*
J V Magrath V, *Trustee*
Karen D Vrchota MD, *Med Doctor*
Ann C Mc Kenzie MD, *Med Doctor*
Phil Malley, *Manager*
EMP: 28 **EST:** 1962
SQ FT: 2,500
SALES (est): 1MM-4.9MM **Privately Held**
SIC: 8011 General & family practice physician or surgeon office

(G-9775)
WABASHA COUNTY HIGHWAY
821 Hiawatha Dr W (55981-1175)
PHONE..............................651 565-3366
David Shanahan, *Chief*
David Shamahan, *Engineer*
Dietrich Flesch, *Manager*
Corey Schmidt, *Manager*
EMP: 25 **EST:** 1999

(PA)=Parent Co (HQ)=Headquarters (DH)=Div Headquarters
✿ = New business established in last 2 years

2011 Harris Minnesota
Services Directory

© Harris InfoSource 1-866-281-6415
421

SALES (est): 1MM-4.9MM **Privately Held**
SIC: 1611 Highway & street maintenance service

WABASSO
Redwood County

(G-9776)
BEVERLY ENTERPRISES - MN
Also Called: Wabasso Healthcare Center
660 Maple St (56293-1614)
PO Box 129 (56293-0129)
PHONE..........................507 342-5166
FAX: 507 342-5136
Dru Fishgrabe, *Exec Dir*
Mat Bebard, *Exec Dir*
Kim Nott, *Director*
EMP: 60
SALES (est): 1MM-4.9MM **Privately Held**
WEB: www.beverlynet.com
SIC: 8051 8093 Skilled nursing care facility; convalescent home; outpatient drug clinic
HQ: Beverly Enterprises - MN
650 Ramer Ave S
Rush City MN 55069
320 358-4765

(G-9777)
REDWOOD LONG DISTANCE CO
731 Main St (56293-1600)
PHONE..........................507 644-3844
Steve Chambers, *President*
EMP: 47
SALES (est): 10MM-24.9MM **Privately Held**
SIC: 4813 Telephone & other directory publishing; wired telecommunications carrier & service

WACONIA
Carver County

(G-9778)
AUBURN WEST INC
594 S Cherry Dr (55387-4578)
PHONE..........................952 442-2546
Fritz J Bost, *President*
John Boughton, *President*
Gary Brandenburg, *Vice Pres*
Christy Olmanson, *Administrator*
EMP: 48 EST: 1963
SQ FT: 9,000
SALES (est): 1MM-4.9MM **Privately Held**
SIC: 8051 Skilled nursing care facility

(G-9779)
BROADSTON CONSULTING SERVICES
400 E 10th St (55387-4552)
PHONE..........................952 442-9770
Lee Broadston, *President*
Rhonda Broadston, *Vice Pres*
Margie Westergaard, *Manager*
EMP: 35 EST: 1986
SALES (est): 1MM-4.9MM **Privately Held**
SIC: 8721 Billing & bookkeeping services

(G-9780)
BUNN WILLIAM MASONRY INC
219 E Frontage Rd Ste F (55387-1849)
PHONE..........................952 292-2685
FAX: 952 442-8562
William Bunn, *President*
Brenda Bunn, *Corp Secy*
Michael Bunn, *Vice Pres*
Edna Bunn, *Vice Pres*
Marla Peterson, *Manager*
EMP: 40 EST: 1979
SALES (est): 1MM-4.9MM **Privately Held**
SIC: 1741 Masonry & stonework contractor

(G-9781)
CARVER COUNTY AGRICULTURAL SOC
501 W 3rd St (55387)
PO Box 208 (55387-0208)
PHONE..........................952 442-2333
FAX: 952 442-2996
Janice Albrecht, *Exec Sec*
EMP: 30 EST: 1912
SALES (est): 1MM-4.9MM **Privately Held**

SIC: 7999 Fair; newspaper publisher

(G-9782)
CHECKPOINT SECURITY
4250 Norex Dr (55387)
PHONE..........................952 227-5353
Rob V Demier, *President*
EMP: 30
SALES (est): 500-999K **Privately Held**
SIC: 7381 Guard service

(G-9783)
CITY OF WACONIA
Also Called: Safari Island Community Center
1600 Community Dr (55387-1157)
PHONE..........................952 442-0695
Chad Storley, *Manager*
Tim Litfin, *Exec Dir*
EMP: 36
SALES (est): 1MM-4.9MM **Privately Held**
WEB: www.waconia.org
SIC: 8322 Community center
PA: City of Waconia
201 S Vine St
Waconia MN 55387
952 442-2184

(G-9784)
CUSTOM HBC CORP
888 Industrial Blvd Ste 1 (55387-1083)
PHONE..........................952 442-8241
FAX: 952 442-1084
Larry J Wilhelm, *President*
Sarah Manley, *Manager*
▲ EMP: 60 EST: 2000
SQ FT: 20,000
SALES (est): 50MM-99.9MM **Privately Held**
WEB: www.customhbc.com
SIC: 5122 Wholesales cosmetics, perfumes & hair products

(G-9785)
EVANGELICAL LUTHERAN GOOD
Also Called: Waconia Good Samaritan Center
333 W 5th St (55387-1720)
PHONE..........................952 442-5111
Barb Schank, *Med Doctor*
James P Duchene, *Manager*
Teresa Boon, *Manager*
Sharon Zender, *Nursing Dir*
EMP: 150
SALES (est): 5MM-9.9MM **Privately Held**
WEB: www.good-sam.com
SIC: 8051 Skilled nursing care facility
PA: Evangelical Lutheran Good
4800 W 57th St
Sioux Falls SD 57108
605 362-3100

(G-9786)
HUBERT MELCHERT SJODIN PLLP
121 W Main St Ste 200 (55387-1005)
PHONE..........................952 442-5155
Paul Melchert, *Partner*
Dave Hubert, *Partner*
Keith Djodin, *Partner*
Mary L Reiner, *Office Admin*
EMP: 30
SALES (est): 1MM-4.9MM **Privately Held**
WEB: www.mhslaw.com
SIC: 8111 General practice law office

(G-9787)
KLEINBANK
53 W Main St (55387-1021)
PO Box 85 (55387-0085)
PHONE..........................952 442-4471
Susan Johnson, *Manager*
EMP: 25
SALES (est): 5MM-9.9MM **Privately Held**
SIC: 6021 Commercial national trust companies with deposits

(G-9788)
LAKEVIEW CLINIC (PA)
424 W Highway 5 (55387-1723)
PHONE..........................952 442-4461
FAX: 952 442-2970
Molly Johnston, *Med Doctor*
Barbara A Stedmn, *Med Doctor*
John E Bithon MD, *Med Doctor*
Heidi Wuerger, *Med Doctor*

Joseph V Kirk, *Manager*
EMP: 127 EST: 1979 **Privately Held**
SIC: 8011 Primary care medical clinic

(G-9789)
LIGHTHOUSE VILLAGES
500 S Cherry St Apt 207 (55387-4518)
PHONE..........................952 442-1261
FAX: 952 442-1209
Tina Duvall, *Principal*
Barb Zebell, *Manager*
EMP: 90 EST: 2006
SALES (est): 1MM-4.9MM **Privately Held**
SIC: 8361 Geriatric residential care

(G-9790)
PROGRESSIVE INTERIORS INC
10450 Knight Ave (55387-9401)
PHONE..........................612 718-1868
Brian Root, *President*
EMP: 29 EST: 2003
SQ FT: 5,000
SALES (est): 1MM-4.9MM **Privately Held**
SIC: 7389 Interior designing service

(G-9791)
RIDGEVIEW HOME SUPPORT SERVICE
501 S Maple St Ste 1 (55387-0096)
PHONE..........................952 442-6032
EMP: 50 EST: 2007
SALES (est): 1MM-4.9MM **Privately Held**
SIC: 8051 Skilled nursing care facility

(G-9792)
RIDGEVIEW MEDICAL CENTER
500 S Maple St (55387-1752)
PHONE..........................952 442-2191
FAX: 952 442-5295
Bob Stevens, *President*
Gordon Gablenz, *Corp Secy*
Doug Kleam, *COO*
Tom R Hallin, *Ch Pathology*
Mike Phelps, *Vice Pres*
EMP: 1000 EST: 1990
SQ FT: 213,000
SALES (est): 50MM-99.9MM **Privately Held**
SIC: 8062 Medical hospital

(G-9793)
VALLEY SALES INC
1320 Mill Ln (55387-1000)
PHONE..........................952 314-8560
FAX: 952 442-7900
Dave Bacon, *General Mgr*
Darrin Bert, *Finance Mgr*
Frank Kerkhoff, *Sales Executive*
Elizabeth Schmitt, *Office Mgr*
Corey Polifka, *Manager*
EMP: 30
SQ FT: 16,833
SALES (est): 1MM-4.9MM **Privately Held**
WEB: www.valleyautomotivegroup.com
SIC: 7538 7514 General automotive repair services; retails new & used automobiles; rent-a-car service
PA: Valley Sales Inc
7500 145th St W
Saint Paul MN 55124
952 432-9500

(G-9794)
VOIGT'S OF WACONIA
308 S Birch St (55387-1808)
PO Box 1, Saint Cloud (56302-0001)
PHONE..........................952 442-2818
TOLL FREE: 800 468-6480
FAX: 952 442-2665
Darwin Voigt, *President*
EMP: 26 EST: 1963
SQ FT: 10,000
SALES (est): 1MM-4.9MM **Privately Held**
SIC: 4142 Long-distance bus charter service

(G-9795)
WESTERN OB GYNE LTD
560 S Maple St Ste 130 (55387-1753)
PHONE..........................952 442-2137
FAX: 952 442-5960
Robert Nordland, *President*
Jenny Bebo, *Corp Secy*
Tony Werner, *Office Mgr*
Cheryl A Hnsen, *Med Doctor*

Karen Karn, *Manager*
EMP: 29 EST: 1975
SALES (est): 1MM-4.9MM **Privately Held**
SIC: 8011 Gynecologist office; obstetrician office

WADENA
Otter Tail County

(G-9796)
AGRELIANT GENETICS LLC
Also Called: Wensman Seed Co
63585 Highway 10 (56482-4710)
PHONE..........................218 631-2954
Jeff Wensman, *Manager*
Mark Vorthems, *Exec Dir*
EMP: 30
SALES (est): 10MM-24.9MM **Privately Held**
WEB: www.agreliant.com
SIC: 5191 Wholesales farm supplies; retail nursery & garden center
HQ: Agreliant Genetics LLC
1122 E 169th St
Westfield IN 46074
317 896-5551

WADENA
Wadena County

(G-9797)
A SHARE HOME INC
840 Sunnybrook Rd (56482-2413)
PHONE..........................218 631-1853
Karen Crandall, *Director*
EMP: 40 EST: 1986
SALES (est): 1MM-4.9MM **Privately Held**
SIC: 8361 Home for the mentally retarded

(G-9798)
BELL HILL RECOVERY CENTER INC
12213 200th St (56482)
PO Box 206 (56482-0206)
PHONE..........................218 631-3610
FAX: 218 631-3917
Ross Olson, *Exec Dir*
EMP: 30 EST: 1973
SQ FT: 3,000
SALES (est): 1MM-4.9MM **Privately Held**
SIC: 8361 8069 Residential rehabilitation center with health care incidental; alcoholism rehabilitation hospital

(G-9799)
CARMAN BERRY FARM
19168 145th Ave (56482-4051)
PHONE..........................218 631-4613
Darren Rohr, *President*
EMP: 25 EST: 2001 **Privately Held**
WEB: www.carmanberryfarm.com
SIC: 0191 Crop farming

(G-9800)
DAVIS RUSS WHOLESALE INC
266 4th St NE (56482-1205)
PO Box 272 (56482-0272)
PHONE..........................218 631-3070
FAX: 218 631-9024
Gary B Davis, *President*
James Lehr, *Corp Secy*
James Rosender, *Manager*
Neal Juers, *Manager*
Steve Brown, *Manager*
EMP: 100 EST: 1947
SQ FT: 90,000
SALES (est): 25MM-49.9MM **Privately Held**
SIC: 5148 Wholesales fresh fruits; wholesales fresh vegetables

(G-9801)
FAIR OAKS LODGE INC
201 Shady Lane Dr (56482-3093)
PHONE..........................218 631-1391
Dennis C Miley, *President*
Joel Beiswenger, *CFO*
Michael Gibson, *Administrator*
EMP: 115 EST: 2004
SQ FT: 45,000
SALES (est): 1MM-4.9MM **Privately Held**
WEB: www.fairoakslodge.com

www.HarrisInfo.com
422

2011 Harris Minnesota
Services Directory

▲=Import ▼=Export
◆=Import/Export

SIC: 8051 Skilled nursing care facility

(G-9802)
1ST NATIONAL BANK IN WADENA
25 Bryant Ave SW (56482-1405)
PO Box 111 (56482-0111)
PHONE..............................218 631-1590
FAX: 218 631-4020
Scott J Pettit, *President*
Jamie Pettit, *Exec VP*
Larry Hahn, *Assistant VP*
Jonell Asfeld, *Assistant VP*
Scott Loween, *Assistant VP*
EMP: 25 EST: 1892
SALES (est): 5MM-9.9MM **Privately Held**
SIC: 6021 National commercial bank

(G-9803)
HOMECREST OUTDOOR LIVING LLC
1250 Homecrest Ave SE (56482-1877)
PO Box 350 (56482-0350)
PHONE..............................218 631-1000
FAX: 218 631-2609
Mark Sillhouer, *Member*
Bruce Gorghuber, *Plant Mgr*
John Markeson, *VP Purch*
Clarence Frauedienft, *Purch Agent*
John Markenson, *Purch Agent*
EMP: 75 EST: 2007
SQ FT: 200,000
SALES (est): 10MM-24.9MM **Privately Held**
SIC: 5023 Wholesales home furnishings

(G-9804)
J MAAS CO
Also Called: Uptown Cafe
224 Jefferson St S (56482-1532)
PHONE..............................218 631-3498
FAX: 218 631-4680
James Maas, *President*
Kimberly Maas, *Corp Secy*
EMP: 30 EST: 1976
SALES (est): 500-999K **Privately Held**
SIC: 7299 Eating place; banquet hall facility

(G-9805)
MID-CENTRAL FEDERAL SAINGS
520 Jefferson St S (56482-1844)
PHONE..............................218 631-1414
FAX: 218 631-1444
Gary Sellman, *President*
Janice Aagard, *Corp Secy*
Robert Iken, *Exec VP*
Leone Rowan, *Marketing Staff*
Dan Jarvi, *Director*
EMP: 28 EST: 1957
SQ FT: 4,200
SALES (est): 5MM-9.9MM **Privately Held**
WEB: www.midcentralbank.com
SIC: 6035 Federal savings & loan association

(G-9806)
MINNESOTA VALLEY IRRIGATION
12317 150th St (56482-2376)
PO Box 509 (56482-0509)
PHONE..............................218 631-9271
FAX: 218 631-9277
Ron Offutt, *President*
Allan Knoll, *Corp Secy*
Robert Kempenich, *Vice Pres*
EMP: 25 EST: 1991
SALES (est): 10MM-24.9MM **Privately Held**
SIC: 5083 Wholesales irrigation equipment

(G-9807)
NEIGHBORHOOD COUNSELING CENTER
11 2nd St SW Ste 1 (56482-1417)
PHONE..............................218 631-1714
FAX: 218 631-4228
James Kramer, *Principal*
Lisa Sack, *Office Mgr*
Lisa Fack, *Office Mgr*
Sarah Yetter, *Director*
Robert B Jones, *Psychiatry*
EMP: 25 EST: 1987
SALES (est): 1MM-4.9MM **Privately Held**
SIC: 8322 8093 General counseling services; outpatient mental health clinic

(G-9808)
PEOPLE'S EXPRESS INC
15578 Shady Acres Dr (56482-3017)
PHONE..............................218 631-2909
FAX: 218 631-2800
Jan Roers, *President*
Michael Roers, *Treasurer*
Debbie Sanders, *Manager*
EMP: 43 EST: 1992
SALES (est): 500-999K **Privately Held**
WEB: www.peoplesexpressmn.com
SIC: 7363 Medical help service

(G-9809)
POLMAN TRANSFER INC
63254 Hwy 10W (56482)
PO Box 470 (56482-0470)
PHONE..............................218 631-1753
Nick Polman, *President*
Hank Larson, *General Mgr*
Duane J Polman, *Treasurer*
EMP: 70 EST: 1953
SQ FT: 8,400
SALES (est): 5MM-9.9MM **Privately Held**
WEB: www.polmantransfer.com
SIC: 4213 Over the road trucking

(G-9810)
PROBUILD CO LLC
Also Called: United Building Centers
1000 Jefferson St N (56482-2311)
PO Box 109 (56482-0109)
PHONE..............................218 631-2607
FAX: 218 631-2513
Don Scheller, *Asst Mgr*
EMP: 70
SALES (est): 25MM-49.9MM **Privately Held**
WEB: www.probuild.com
SIC: 5031 Wholesales lumber, plywood & millwork; manufactures building & structural wood members; sawing & planing mill
HQ: Probuild Co LLC
7595 Tech Way Ste 500
Denver CO 80237
303 262-8500

(G-9811)
SHADY LANE NURSING HOME
201 Shady Lane Dr (56482-3093)
PHONE..............................218 631-1391
FAX: 218 631-1528
Terry Ratzell, *Mayor*
Chris Perks, *Engineer*
Edward Phelps, *Manager*
Michael M Gibson, *Administrator*
EMP: 115 EST: 1952
SALES (est): 1MM-4.9MM **Privately Held**
SIC: 8052 8051 Intermediate care facility; skilled nursing care facility

(G-9812)
TODD WADENA ELECTRIC CO-OP
550 Ash Ave NE (56482-2421)
PO Box 431 (56482-0431)
PHONE..............................218 631-3120
FAX: 218 631-4188
Dale Hendrickson, *General Mgr*
Norman Krause, *Corp Secy*
Dan Skogen, *Vice Pres*
Mark Grieme, *Controller*
Tim Pavek, *Manager*
EMP: 28 EST: 1940
SQ FT: 26,700
SALES (est): 10MM-24.9MM **Privately Held**
SIC: 4911 Electric power distribution service

(G-9813)
TRI-COUNTY HOSPITAL INC
Also Called: Otteraial Area Medical
415 Jefferson St N (56482-1264)
PHONE..............................218 631-3510
FAX: 218 631-7496
Joel Beiswenger, *CEO*
Dan Sartell, *Corp Secy*
Leo Kempf, *Facilities Mgr*
Cindy Collison, *Purchasing*
Betty Klingman, *Envir Svcs Dir*
EMP: 318 EST: 1935
SQ FT: 100,000
SALES (est): 25MM-49.9MM **Privately Held**
SIC: 8062 Medical hospital

(G-9814)
WADENA MEDICAL CENTER LTD
4 Deerwood Ave NW (56482-1253)
PHONE..............................218 631-1360
FAX: 218 631-7571
Tim Schmitt MD, *President*
Matthe Yelle MD, *Corp Secy*
Shaneen Schmidt MD, *Med Doctor*
Bobbijo D Adams MD, *Med Doctor*
Judy White, *Administrator*
EMP: 40 EST: 1912
SALES (est): 1MM-4.9MM **Privately Held**
SIC: 8011 General & family practice physician or surgeon office

---

WAITE PARK
Stearns County

(G-9815)
AGSTAR FINANCIAL SERVICES, ACA
806 3rd St S (56387-2318)
PO Box 608 (56387-0608)
PHONE..............................320 203-4613
Steven Shaler, *Vice Pres*
Bernie Quist, *Branch Mgr*
EMP: 50
SALES (est): 1MM-4.9MM **Privately Held**
WEB: www.agstar.com
SIC: 7389 Financial service
PA: Agstar Financial Services, Aca
1921 Premier Dr
Mankato MN 56001
507 387-4174

(G-9816)
ANTONS INC
2001 Frontage Rd N (56387-1070)
PHONE..............................320 253-3611
FAX: 320 253-1173
David Gates, *President*
Elizabeth Gates, *Manager*
Basil Anton, *Exec Dir*
EMP: 50 EST: 2001
SALES (est): 1MM-4.9MM **Privately Held**
WEB: www.antons.net
SIC: 7212 Garment pressing & cleaners' agent services; eating place

(G-9817)
BERNICK'S FULL-LINE VENDING (PA)
801 Sundial Dr (56387-1533)
PHONE..............................320 656-2131
FAX: 320 616-2160
Richard Bernick, *Ch of Bd*
Mike Heinen, *President*
John Togerson, *Senior VP*
Susan Pederson, *Human Res Dir*
Richard Grandquist, *CIO*
EMP: 30 EST: 1981
SQ FT: 5,000 **Privately Held**
SIC: 5149 5145 5194 Wholesales soft drinks; wholesales candy; wholesales specialty food items; wholesales cigarettes

(G-9818)
BUTTWEILER ENVIRONMENTAL INC
250 Sundial Dr Ste 1 (56387-1523)
PO Box 931, Saint Cloud (56302-0931)
PHONE..............................320 251-4385
FAX: 320 251-6357
Tim Buttweiler, *President*
EMP: 110 EST: 1970
SALES (est): 1MM-4.9MM **Privately Held**
SIC: 7349 Janitorial & custodial services

(G-9819)
CHAS A BERNICK INC
Also Called: Bernick's Sports Unlimited
801 Sundial Dr (56387-1533)
PO Box 7008, Saint Cloud (56302-7008)
PHONE..............................320 252-6441
FAX: 320 656-2111
Dean Bernick, *CEO*
Richard Bernick, *President*
▲ EMP: 50 EST: 1915
SQ FT: 200,000
SALES (est): 10MM-24.9MM **Privately Held**

SIC: 5181 Manufactures soft drinks; manufactures flavoring extracts & syrups; wholesales beer & other fermented malt liquors

(G-9820)
CON-WAY FREIGHT INC
301 33rd Ave S (56387-4523)
PHONE..............................320 259-0245
FAX: 320 259-0670
Glenn McKeon, *Branch Mgr*
Chris Meers, *Manager*
EMP: 41
SALES (est): 5MM-9.9MM **Publicly Held**
WEB: www.con-way.com
SIC: 4213 Over the road trucking
HQ: Con-way Freight Inc
2211 Old Earhart Rd # 100
Ann Arbor MI 48105
734 994-6600

(G-9821)
COORDINATED BUSINESS SYSTEMS
624 1st St S (56387-1865)
PHONE..............................320 251-1212
Jim Oricchio, *Owner*
EMP: 60 EST: 2003
SALES (est): 10MM-24.9MM **Privately Held**
SIC: 5044 Wholesales blueprinting equipment; retails computer modems, monitors, terminals & disk drives

(G-9822)
ESCO INDUSTRIES INC (PA)
Also Called: Performance Seed
115 4th St N (56387-1283)
PO Box 7126, Saint Cloud (56302-7126)
PHONE..............................320 259-9470
FAX: 320 259-6043
Sheldon Sturgis, *President*
Mary Hinkemeyer, *Controller*
Ron Klein, *Manager*
Lloyd Batien, *Manager*
EMP: 35 EST: 1991
SQ FT: 70,000 **Privately Held**
SIC: 5191 Wholesales grass seed; manufactures prepared bird food

(G-9823)
GREAT RIVER FEDERAL CREDIT
206 1st St S (56387-1306)
PHONE..............................320 258-5393
FAX: 320 258-5394
Cloudnet Hostmaster, *Manager*
Sara Burnett, *Manager*
EMP: 75
SALES (est): 10MM-24.9MM **Privately Held**
WEB: www.greatriverfcu.org
SIC: 6061 Federally chartered credit union

(G-9824)
HORIZON ROOFING INC
2010 County Road 137 (56387-2091)
PHONE..............................320 252-1608
FAX: 320 252-6939
Kurt Scepaniak, *President*
Kurk Scepaniak, *President*
Daniel Scepaniak, *Corp Secy*
Greg Scepaniak, *Vice Pres*
EMP: 25
SQ FT: 6,000
SALES (est): 1MM-4.9MM **Privately Held**
WEB: www.horizonroofinginc.com
SIC: 1761 Roofing contractor

(G-9825)
L S STARRETT CO
Also Called: Tru-Stone Technologies
1101 Prosper Dr (56387-1762)
PHONE..............................320 251-7171
FAX: 320 259-5073
Carlo Schwinn, *General Mgr*
Melissa Beckman, *Principal*
Joe Erkens, *Vice Pres*
Pat Nowacki, *Human Res Mgr*
Julie Tibben, *Persnl Mgr*
EMP: 50
SALES (est): 1MM-4.9MM **Publicly Held**
WEB: www.starrett.com

(PA)=Parent Co (HQ)=Headquarters (DH)=Div Headquarters
✿ = New business established in last 2 years

2011 Harris Minnesota
Services Directory

© Harris InfoSource 1-866-281-6415

423

SIC: **1411** Manufactures cut & shaped granite; dimension stone mining
PA: L S Starrett Co
121 Crescent St
Athol MA 01331
978 249-3551

(G-9826)
LADY WELLNESS MANAGEMENT INC
136 Division St (56387-1330)
PHONE 320 253-3371
FAX: 320 259-6334
Carla Smetana, *Manager*
EMP: 30
SALES (est): 500-999K **Privately Held**
WEB: www.ladywellness.com
SIC: **7991** Physical fitness clubs with training equipment
PA: Lady Wellness Management Inc
1525 32nd Ave S
Fargo ND 58103
701 234-9080

(G-9827)
LARSON ELLEN WEISHARIR CO LLP
818 2nd St S Ste 320 (56387-1887)
PO Box 1067, Saint Cloud (56302-1067)
PHONE 320 253-8616
Jerome L Mc Carter, *Partner*
Donald A Kinzer, *Partner*
Thomas Bosl, *Partner*
John M Amundson, *Partner*
Mark Krebsbach, *Partner*
EMP: 44 EST: 1963
SQ FT: 20,000
SALES (est): 1MM-4.9MM **Privately Held**
SIC: **8721** Certified public accountant services

(G-9828)
MARTIN MARIETTA MATERIALS INC
1450 Division St (56387-1062)
PO Box 7517, Saint Cloud (56302-7517)
PHONE 320 251-7141
FAX: 320 251-2336
Joe Michels, *Regional Mgr*
Mike Rienert, *Manager*
EMP: 40
SALES (est): 5MM-9.9MM **Publicly Held**
WEB: www.martinmarietta.com
SIC: **1423** Crushed & broken granite mining
PA: Martin Marietta Materials Inc
2710 Wycliff Rd
Raleigh NC 27607
919 781-4550

(G-9829)
MCDOWALL CO
1431 Prosper Dr (56387)
PO Box 606 (56387-0606)
PHONE 320 251-8640
John W Mc Dowall, *President*
Peter Dowall, *Corp Secy*
Cheryl M Dowall, *Vice Pres*
Lawrence M Dowall, *Treasurer*
Rita Barrett, *Manager*
EMP: 60 EST: 1948
SQ FT: 14,000
SALES (est): 5MM-9.9MM **Privately Held**
SIC: **1711 1761 7623** Heating & air conditioning contractor; ventilation & duct work contractor; architectural sheet metal work contractor; air conditioning repair service; roofing contractor

(G-9830)
PARK WAITE MANUFACTURING INC
430 7th Ave N (56387-1168)
PHONE 320 251-8616
FAX: 320 251-4926
Paul Lague, *President*
Jude Lague, *Vice Pres*
Karen Rothanburg, *Accounting Dir*
Wayne Flury, *Manager*
▲ EMP: 150 EST: 1990
SQ FT: 120,000
SALES (est): 10MM-24.9MM **Privately Held**
WEB: www.tcamerican.com

SIC: **1799** Machine shop, jobbing & repair services; on-site welding contractor; manufactures hoists, cranes & monorails; manufactures industrial trucks & tractors; steel fabricator
PA: TC American Monorail Inc
12070 43rd St NE
Saint Michael MN 55376
763 497-7000

(G-9831)
PARKWOOD 18 THEATRES
1533 Frontage Rd N (56387-1809)
PHONE 320 251-1188
Marcus Theatres, *President*
Darcy Eigen, *General Mgr*
EMP: 50 EST: 2005
SALES (est): 1MM-4.9MM **Privately Held**
SIC: **7832** Indoor movie theater

(G-9832)
PETCO ANIMAL SUPPLIES STORES
35 Waite Ave N (56387-1270)
PHONE 320 253-1004
FAX: 320 253-7645
Cynthia L Hullett, *Manager*
EMP: 29
SALES (est): 1MM-4.9MM **Privately Held**
WEB: www.petco.com
SIC: **0752** Retails pet food; animal grooming services; retails pet supplies
PA: Petco Animal Supplies Inc
9125 Rehco Rd
San Diego CA 92121
858 453-7845

(G-9833)
PETSMART INC
320 2nd St S Ste 1 (56387-2314)
PHONE 320 251-4459
John Cruckson, *Branch Mgr*
EMP: 28
SALES (est): 1MM-4.9MM **Publicly Held**
WEB: www.petsmart.com
SIC: **0752** Retails pet supplies; animal grooming services
PA: Petsmart Inc
19601 N 27th Ave
Phoenix AZ 85027
623 580-6100

(G-9834)
PLAZA PARK STATE BANK INC
131 6th Ave S Ste 100 (56387-1360)
PO Box 337 (56387-0337)
PHONE 320 252-4200
FAX: 320 252-0981
Thomas Eickhoff, *President*
John Gallus, *Exec VP*
Dan Hagan, *Vice Pres*
Bill Eickhoff, *Info Tech Mgr*
EMP: 28 EST: 1910
SALES (est): 5MM-9.9MM **Privately Held**
WEB: www.plazaparkbank.com
SIC: **6022** Commercial state trust companies accepting deposits

(G-9835)
SAINT CLOUD AUTO CENTER LLC
Also Called: Kia of St Cloud
903 2nd St S (56387-1396)
PO Box 797 (56387-0797)
PHONE 320 259-4542
Amado Espinosa, *Member*
EMP: 50 EST: 2006
SALES (est): 25MM-49.9MM **Privately Held**
SIC: **7549** New & used car dealer; retails automotive parts; automotive maintenance service

(G-9836)
SAND CO'S INC
366 10th Ave S (56387-1400)
PO Box 727 (56387-0727)
PHONE 320 202-3100
Jamie J Thelen, *CEO*
Leo M Sand, *Ch of Bd*
Joyce Winter, *Corp Secy*
Dave Thelen, *Project Mgr*
Jerry Burau, *Manager*
EMP: 45 EST: 1991
SQ FT: 10,000
SALES (est): 10MM-24.9MM **Privately Held**

WEB: www.sandcompanies.com
SIC: **1522 1542** New multi-family dwelling construction service; new commercial & office building construction

(G-9837)
SEARS, ROEBUCK & CO
Also Called: Sears Product Services
41 Division St (56387-1349)
PHONE 800 882-5351
Shelley Ostendorf, *Manager*
R J Grieman, *Manager*
EMP: 80
SALES (est): 5MM-9.9MM **Publicly Held**
SIC: **7699** Household appliance repair service
HQ: Sears, Roebuck & Co
3333 Beverly Rd
Hoffman Estates IL 60179
847 286-2500

(G-9838)
SIMPLEXGRINNELL LP
820 Sundial Dr (56387-1529)
PHONE 320 253-8883
Leo Rehmann, *Branch Mgr*
EMP: 200
SALES (est): 10MM-24.9MM **Privately Held**
WEB: www.simplexgrinnell.com
SIC: **1711** Sprinkler system contractor
DH: Simplexgrinnell LP
1 Town Center Rd
Boca Raton FL 33486
561 988-7200

(G-9839)
SLUMBERLAND INC
2121 Frontage Rd N (56387-1071)
PHONE 320 251-1024
FAX: 320 650-2080
Gayle Frolek, *Manager*
EMP: 35
SALES (est): 5MM-9.9MM **Privately Held**
SIC: **5047** Retails beds & accessories; wholesales hospital beds
PA: Slumberland Inc
3060 Centerville Rd
Saint Paul MN 55117
651 482-7500

(G-9840)
SPACE ALIENS GRILL & BAR
700 2nd St S (56387-1696)
PHONE 320 259-7670
Chris Lind, *Owner*
Eric Rognedy, *Owner*
Amanda Egerman, *Manager*
EMP: 75 EST: 2002 **Privately Held**
WEB: www.spacealiens.com
SIC: **8641** Members only bar & restaurant for members of organizations only

(G-9841)
STERLING PARK HEALTH CARE CTR
142 1st St N (56387-1273)
PHONE 320 252-9595
Jeanne Jaeckels, *Sales Staff*
Brenda Eggerth, *Manager*
Fred Jusick, *Administrator*
EMP: 1300 EST: 1999
SALES (est): 50MM-99.9MM **Privately Held**
WEB: www.tealwoodcc.com
SIC: **8051** Skilled nursing care facility
PA: Tealwood Care Centers Inc
9031 Penn Ave S
Minneapolis MN 55431
952 888-2923

(G-9842)
TEALWOOD CARE CENTERS INC
142 1st St N (56387-1273)
PHONE 320 252-9595
Fred Strzke, *Manager*
EMP: 99
SALES (est): 1MM-4.9MM **Privately Held**
SIC: **8051** Skilled nursing care facility
PA: Tealwood Care Centers Inc
9031 Penn Ave S
Minneapolis MN 55431
952 888-2923

(G-9843)
THOELE DENTAL LABORATORIES INC
540 Progress Rd (56387-1718)
PHONE 320 252-2070
FAX: 320 252-9868
Robert Schoenberg, *President*
Terry Lenz, *Corp Secy*
Debra Mensing, *Administrator*
Don Waletzko, *Executive*
EMP: 42 EST: 1922
SQ FT: 8,000
SALES (est): 1MM-4.9MM **Privately Held**
WEB: www.thoeledental.com
SIC: **8072** Denture production laboratory; artificial teeth production laboratory; manufactures dental equipment & supplies
HQ: National Dentex Corp
2 Vision Dr Ste 2
Natick MA 01760
508 907-7800

(G-9844)
TRI CAP TRI COUNTY ACTION
2341 County Road 137 (56387-2012)
PO Box 683 (56387-0683)
PHONE 320 255-0769
Mike Fisher, *General Mgr*
Janey Palmer, *General Mgr*
Marney Curfman, *Administrator*
Angie Lieser, *CTO*
Marilee Blais, *IT/INT Sup*
EMP: 28 EST: 2001
SALES (est): 5MM-9.9MM **Privately Held**
SIC: **1521** Single-family housing construction

(G-9845)
TRI-COUNTY ACTION PROGRAM INC (PA)
1210 23rd Ave S (56387-4527)
PO Box 683 (56387-0683)
PHONE 320 251-1612
FAX: 320 251-7786
Angie Leiser, *Finance*
Char Christiansen, *Human Resources*
Angela Theisen, *Exec Dir*
EMP: 25 EST: 1965
SQ FT: 5,000
SALES (corp-wide): 6.28M **Privately Held**
WEB: www.tricap.org
SIC: **8399** Community action agency

(G-9846)
TRI-COUNTY ACTION PROGRAM INC
2341 County Road 137 (56387-2012)
PHONE 320 255-0705
Mike Fisher, *Manager*
EMP: 25 **Privately Held**
WEB: www.tricap.org
SIC: **8399** Community action agency
PA: Tri-County Action Program Inc
1210 23rd Ave S
Waite Park MN 56387
320 251-1612

(G-9847)
VERIZON WIRELESS INC
126 Division St (56387-1330)
PHONE 320 241-5433
William Casto, *Branch Mgr*
EMP: 60 **Publicly Held**
WEB: www.verizonwireless.com
SIC: **4812** Cellular telephone services
HQ: Verizon Wireless Inc
1 Verizon Way
Basking Ridge NJ 07920
908 559-7000

(G-9848)
WACOSA
320 Sundial Dr (56387-1524)
PO Box 757 (56387-0757)
PHONE 320 251-0087
Jennifer Johnson, *Corp Secy*
Brad Schwieger, *Vice Pres*
Jan Matvick, *Controller*
Ann Roesler, *Marketing Staff*
Michael Struffert, *Manager*
EMP: 100 EST: 1963
SQ FT: 32,000
SALES (est): 1MM-4.9MM **Privately Held**
WEB: www.wacosa.org

www.HarrisInfo.com
424

2011 Harris Minnesota
Services Directory

▲=Import ▼=Export
◆=Import/Export

SIC: 8322 Social services for the handicapped

WALKER
Cass County

(G-9849)
COUNTY OF CASS
Also Called: Cass County Child Support Svcs
400 Michigan Ave W (56484)
PO Box 519 (56484-0519)
PHONE..............................218 547-1346
FAX: 218 547-1448
Kim Minton, *Office Spvr*
Kay Ahlef, *Director*
EMP: 80
SALES (est): 1MM-4.9MM **Privately Held**
SIC: 8322 Child & youth services

(G-9850)
FIRST NATIONAL BANK OF WALKER
600 Minnesota Ave W (56484)
PO Box 520 (56484-0520)
PHONE..............................218 547-1160
FAX: 218 547-2474
Michael Elsenpeter, *President*
Richard J Tiedeman, *Exec VP*
Cyrill Drier, *Vice Pres*
Jeanette J Goehring, *Assoc VP*
Todd Schoeck, *Loan Officer*
EMP: 35 EST: 1902
SALES (est): 5MM-9.9MM **Privately Held**
SIC: 6021 National commercial bank

(G-9851)
HEAD START PROGRAM ONIGUM
8825 Onigum Rd NW (56484-2673)
PHONE..............................218 547-1420
Windy Whitebird, *Principal*
EMP: 78 EST: 2001
SALES (est): 1MM-4.9MM **Privately Held**
SIC: 8351 Child day care service

(G-9852)
HUDDLE'S SOUTH SHORE RESORT
1696 Whipholt Beach Rd NW (56484-2711)
PHONE..............................218 836-2420
FAX: 218 836-2422
Roy Huddle, *President*
Kay Huddle, *Corp Secy*
EMP: 30 EST: 1928
SALES (est): 1MM-4.9MM **Privately Held**
WEB: www.huddlesresort.com
SIC: 7011 Resort hotel; retails sporting goods

(G-9853)
LEECH LAKE DISTRIBUTORS INC
Also Called: Reed's Sporting Goods
522 Minnesota Ave NW (56484)
PO Box 490 (56484-0490)
PHONE..............................218 547-1505
FAX: 218 547-3162
Adam Arnold, *President*
Kathryn Arnold, *Corp Secy*
EMP: 25 EST: 1971
SQ FT: 25,000
SALES (est): 1MM-4.9MM **Privately Held**
WEB: www.muskiefever.com
SIC: 5091 Retails sporting goods; wholesales fishing equipment & supplies; wholesales hunting equipment & supplies; retails fishing equipment; retails hunting equipment; retail mail-order fitness & sporting goods

(G-9854)
LEECH LAKE RESERVATION
Also Called: Northern Lights Casino
6800 Y Frontage Rd NW (56484-2123)
PHONE..............................218 547-2744
FAX: 218 335-3101
Kevin Lewis, *General Mgr*
Larry Hanks, *General Mgr*
Bob Whipple, *Manager*
Lawrence Baylark, *Manager*
Guy Beaulieu, *Info Tech Dir*
EMP: 530
SALES (est): 25MM-49.9MM **Privately Held**
SIC: 7999 7011 7997 Gambling establishment; eating place; membership recreation club; drinking establishment; casino hotel
PA: Leech Lake Reservation
425 7th St NW
Cass Lake MN 56633
218 335-8206

(G-9855)
NO NAME
Hwy 371 (56484)
PO Box 843 (56484-0843)
PHONE..............................218 547-3334
James K Kellogg, *President*
David Kellogg, *Corp Secy*
Jeff Kellog, *Treasurer*
EMP: 30 EST: 1978
SQ FT: 3,200
SALES (est): 500-999K **Privately Held**
SIC: 7011 Full service independent family restaurant; franchised motel

(G-9856)
NORTH STOP INC
Also Called: Food-N-Fuel
Hwy 34SOUTH (56484)
PHONE..............................218 547-1859
FAX: 218 547-3197
Marianne Johnson, *President*
EMP: 26 EST: 1972
SQ FT: 5,000
SALES (est): 50MM-99.9MM **Privately Held**
WEB: www.northstop.com
SIC: 5172 Wholesales petroleum products; retail gasoline filling station

(G-9857)
NORTHERN CASS DAC INC
8059 County Rd 12 (56484)
PO Box B (56484)
PHONE..............................218 547-1121
Glen Gitchel, *Ch of Bd*
Merle Johnson, *Vice Chairman*
Jeannie Nelson, *Corp Secy*
Gene Johnson, *Treasurer*
David Terdan, *Exec Dir*
EMP: 29 EST: 1976
SALES (est): 1MM-4.9MM **Privately Held**
SIC: 8331 Vocational rehabilitation agency

(G-9858)
TIANNA COUNTRY CLUB INC
7470 State 34 NW (56484)
PO Box 177 (56484-0177)
PHONE..............................218 547-1712
FAX: 218 547-1710
Frank Lamb Jr, *President*
John Johnson, *Corp Secy*
Joe Fletcher, *Treasurer*
John Johnson, *Manager*
EMP: 50 EST: 1933
SQ FT: 1,600
SALES (est): 1MM-4.9MM **Privately Held**
WEB: www.tianna.com
SIC: 7997 Country club; membership golf club; retails sporting goods

(G-9859)
TRAPPER'S LANDING LODGE
1812 Merit Rd NW (56484-2536)
PHONE..............................218 836-2500
EMP: 30 EST: 2007
SALES (est): 1MM-4.9MM **Privately Held**
SIC: 7011 Resort hotel

(G-9860)
WALKER AMBULANCE SERVICE
205 Minnesota Ave W (56484)
PO Box 207 (56484-0207)
PHONE..............................218 547-5500
Mark Kimmerle, *Manager*
Christy Johnson, *Director*
Norma Grassmen, *Director*
Mona Glassmann, *Director*
EMP: 25 EST: 1975
SALES (est): 1MM-4.9MM **Privately Held**
SIC: 4119 Ambulance service

(G-9861)
WOODREST HEALTH CARE CENTER
Also Called: Beverly Outpatient Therapy
209 Birchwood Ave (56484)
PO Box 700 (56484-0700)
PHONE..............................218 547-1855
FAX: 218 547-3949
Shirley Kureth, *President*
Kathy Sandell, *Manager*
Cathaline Tankratz, *Manager*
EMP: 52 EST: 1967
SALES (est): 1MM-4.9MM **Privately Held**
SIC: 8051 Skilled nursing care facility

WALNUT GROVE
Redwood County

(G-9862)
KIWANIS INTERNATIONAL INC
810 Clark St (56180-9323)
PHONE..............................507 859-2635
Mary K McVenes, *Corp Secy*
EMP: 39 **Privately Held**
SIC: 8641 Civic associations
PA: Kiwanis International Inc
3636 Woodview Trce
Indianapolis IN 46268
317 875-8755

WANAMINGO
Goodhue County

(G-9863)
HADER FARMS
41905 Highway 57 Blvd (55983-3410)
PHONE..............................507 824-2327
Herbert Fredrickson, *Owner*
EMP: 30 EST: 1973 **Privately Held**
SIC: 0116 Soybean farm

(G-9864)
MAPLE ISLAND INC
25 Main St 57 (55983-1465)
PHONE..............................507 824-2224
FAX: 507 824-2711
Roger Furgeson, *Maint Mgr*
Harry Drager, *Research*
Ron Zirbel, *Research*
Greg Johnson, *Finance*
Jim Kelleher, *Sales Staff*
EMP: 30
SALES (est): 10MM-24.9MM **Privately Held**
WEB: www.maple-island.com
SIC: 0241 Manufactures powdered milk; milk production
PA: Maple Island Inc
2497 7th Ave E Ste 105
Saint Paul MN 55109
651 773-1000

(G-9865)
NORTHSTAR GENETICS LTD
104 Main St (55983-3847)
PO Box 40 (55983-0040)
PHONE..............................507 824-2878
FAX: 507 824-3208
Dan Hogstad, *President*
Kelly Steberg, *Manager*
EST: 1996 **Privately Held**
SIC: 5153 Wholesales soybeans

(G-9866)
RIVERVIEW MANOR INC
400 Hillcrest Ave (55983-1464)
PHONE..............................507 824-2091
FAX: 507 824-2249
Eileen Bjorngaard, *Chairman*
Joanne Flom, *Vice Chairman*
Phyllis Carlson, *Treasurer*
Nancy Adams, *Administrator*
EMP: 50 EST: 1978
SALES (est): 1MM-4.9MM **Privately Held**
SIC: 8059 8052 Home for the mentally retarded; intermediate care facility

(G-9867)
VERTICAL LIMIT CONSTRUCTION
811 3rd Ave (55983-1479)
PHONE..............................507 824-1222
FAX: 507 824-1223
Eric Bicknese, *Member*
Scott Shepard, *Member*
Jonathan Schroeder, *Member*
Corey Nihart, *Member*
Jody Bickley, *Administrator*
EMP: 70 EST: 2002
SQ FT: 1,200
SALES (est): 5MM-9.9MM **Privately Held**
WEB: www.verticallimit.com
SIC: 1623 Power & communication transmission tower construction

WANNASKA
Roseau County

(G-9868)
MINNESOTA DEPARTMENT OF
Also Called: Wannaska Forestry Office
16945 State Highway 89 (56761-9721)
PHONE..............................218 425-7793
Bob Wennerstrand, *Manager*
Gary Johnson, *Manager*
Nancy Calder, *Manager*
EMP: 25 **Privately Held**
WEB: www.guessmail.com
SIC: 0851 Forestry services; government wildlife conservation agency
DH: Minnesota Department of
500 Lafayette Rd N
Saint Paul MN 55155
651 296-6157

WARREN
Marshall County

(G-9869)
WARREN COMMUNITY HOSPITAL INC
Also Called: North Valley Health Center
109 S Minnesota St Ste 4 (56762-1420)
PHONE..............................218 745-4211
FAX: 218 745-4204
Kevin Smith, *President*
Sadie Bring, *Purchasing*
Dan Olson, *Engineering*
Mitch Kotrba, *CFO*
Jill Lysford, *Human Res Dir*
EMP: 60 EST: 1965
SQ FT: 23,585
SALES (est): 5MM-9.9MM **Privately Held**
WEB: www.nvhc.net
SIC: 8011 8062 8082 Medical center; home health care services; medical hospital

WARROAD
Roseau County

(G-9870)
FROLANDER ISLAND RESORT
59473 330th St (56763-9505)
PHONE..............................218 386-3019
Timothy Anacabe, *Manager*
EMP: 99 EST: 1994
SALES (est): 5MM-9.9MM **Privately Held**
SIC: 7011 Traveler accommodations

(G-9871)
LAKEVIEW RETIREMENT APARTMENTS
611 Lake St NE (56763-2311)
PHONE..............................218 386-1235
Rod Kutter, *President*
EMP: 70 EST: 2001
SALES (est): 5MM-9.9MM **Privately Held**
SIC: 8741 Nursing & personal care facility management services

(PA)=Parent Co (HQ)=Headquarters (DH)=Div Headquarters
✪ = New business established in last 2 years

2011 Harris Minnesota
Services Directory

© Harris InfoSource 1-866-281-6415
425

GEOGRAPHIC

(G-9872)
WARROAD CARE CENTER INC
611 Lake St NE (56763-2311)
PHONE.....................218 386-1235
FAX: 218 386-3548
Carla Wolf, *CFO*
Yaneth Janzen, *Manager*
Rod Cutter, *Administrator*
EMP: 60 EST: 1979
SALES (est): 1MM-4.9MM **Privately Held**
SIC: 8051 6513 8052 Extended care facility; intermediate care facility; apartment building operator

WASECA
Waseca County

(G-9873)
ARABIAN HORSE TIMES INC
299 Johnson Ave SW # 150 (56093-2534)
PHONE.....................800 248-4637
Walter Mishek, *President*
Mike Villasenor, *General Mgr*
Robin Matejcek, *Purchasing*
Bruce Pehn, *Rsch/Dvlpt Dir*
EMP: 25 EST: 1970
SQ FT: 6,000
SALES (est): 5MM-9.9MM **Privately Held**
SIC: 5192 Wholesales magazines

(G-9874)
CLEMONS BUS LINE INC
213 19th Ave NE (56093-2619)
PHONE.....................507 833-4438
FAX: 507 835-2065
Michael Clemons, *President*
EMP: 25 EST: 1974
SALES (est): 500-999K **Privately Held**
SIC: 4151 School bus service

(G-9875)
DAKOTA, MINNESOTA & EASTERN
Also Called: D M & E
308 State St S (56093-3047)
PHONE.....................507 835-4185
FAX: 507 835-3940
Dave Dunn, *Manager*
EMP: 55 **Privately Held**
WEB: www.dmerail.com
SIC: 4011 Long haul railroad
HQ: Dakota, Minnesota & Eastern
140 N Phillips Ave # 300
Sioux Falls SD 57104
605 782-1200

(G-9876)
ELM NORTH INC
104 22nd Ave NE (56093-2610)
PO Box 489 (56093-0489)
PHONE.....................507 835-1146
Eugene L Miller, *President*
Bonnie J Miller, *Vice Pres*
Stew Miller, *Manager*
EMP: 28 EST: 1984
SALES (est): 500-999K **Privately Held**
SIC: 8052 Residential mentally handicapped facility

(G-9877)
ELM RESIDENCE INC
204 2nd St (56093)
PHONE.....................507 835-1146
Eugene Miller, *President*
Bonnie Miller, *Vice Pres*
Tammy Marsolek, *Supervisor*
Mavis Klien, *Exec Sec*
EMP: 500 EST: 1981
SALES (est): 10MM-24.9MM **Privately Held**
SIC: 8361 8052 Residential care facility; intermediate care facility

(G-9878)
1ST NATIONAL BANK OF WASECA
Also Called: First National Bank
101 State St N (56093-2928)
PHONE.....................507 835-2740
FAX: 507 835-2040
R P Sankovitz, *CEO*

Bernard Gaytko, *President*
Michael Halvorson, *President*
Marty Armstrong, *Senior VP*
Tom Sankovitz, *CFO*
EMP: 44 EST: 1875
SQ FT: 14,000
SALES (est): 10MM-24.9MM **Privately Held**
WEB: www.fnbwaseca.com
SIC: 6021 National commercial bank

(G-9879)
GARKAT INC
Also Called: Colony Court
200 22nd Ave NE Ofc (56093-2657)
PHONE.....................507 835-8227
FAX: 507 835-5734
Gary Worke, *President*
Kathy Worke, *Vice Pres*
Adam Worke, *Manager*
Eric Worke, *Administrator*
Brenda Paterson, *Supervisor*
EMP: 28 EST: 1991
SALES (est): 1MM-4.9MM **Privately Held**
SIC: 8361 Home for the elderly

(G-9880)
I C A N INC
100 State St N Ste 1 (56093-2964)
PHONE.....................507 835-9140
Tracy Jevning, *President*
Linda Ebnet, *Principal*
EMP: 70 EST: 2004
SALES (est): 1MM-4.9MM **Privately Held**
SIC: 8082 Home health care services

(G-9881)
LAKE SHORE INN NURSING HOME
108 8th St NW (56093-1912)
PHONE.....................507 835-2800
FAX: 507 833-1391
Raymond P Madel Jr, *President*
Jo Poyser, *Bookkeeper*
Audrey Gehrke, *Office Mgr*
Amy Fessel, *Manager*
Tom Zensen, *Director*
EMP: 125 EST: 1964
SQ FT: 25,000
SALES (est): 5MM-9.9MM **Privately Held**
WEB: www.lsiwaseca.com
SIC: 8051 8059 Skilled nursing care facility; nursing home

(G-9882)
MEDIACOM LLC
1504 2nd St SE (56093-3101)
PO Box 110 (56093-0110)
PHONE.....................507 835-5975
FAX: 507 835-4567
Lisa Bruhl, *Vice Pres*
William Jensen, *VP Opers-Prdtn-*
Barb Baedke, *Human Resources*
Charlie King, *Manager*
Bill Jenson, *Manager*
EMP: 26
SALES (est): 10MM-24.9MM **Publicly Held**
WEB: www.mediacommcc.com
SIC: 4841 Cable television services
HQ: Mediacom LLC
100 Crystal Run Rd # 103
Middletown NY 10941
845 695-2600

(G-9883)
NORSEMEN INC
Also Called: STI
32960 State Highway 13 (56093-5129)
PHONE.....................507 835-5060
FAX: 507 835-5196
David A Steffens, *President*
Roger Christianson, *General Mgr*
Jean Steffens, *Treasurer*
Stephanie Steffens, *Sales Staff*
Bev Byer, *Data Proc Exec*
EMP: 30 EST: 1985
SQ FT: 7,000
SALES (est): 1MM-4.9MM **Privately Held**
WEB: www.norsemen.com
SIC: 4213 4212 Contract haulers; local trucking without storage services

(G-9884)
NUTRITION SERVICES INC
812 4th Ave NE (56093-3333)
PO Box 369 (56093-0369)
PHONE.....................507 835-5697
Larry Kroeger, *President*
Nena Schumacher, *Vice Pres*
EMP: 250 EST: 1996
SALES (est): 10MM-24.9MM **Privately Held**
WEB: www.smail.rasmussen.edu
SIC: 8099 8322 Nutrition services; individual & family social services

(G-9885)
RICHARD SANKOVITZ
101 Clear Lake Dr (56093)
PHONE.....................507 835-4836
Richard Sankovitz, *President*
EMP: 50 EST: 2005
SALES (est): 10MM-24.9MM **Privately Held**
SIC: 6029 Commercial bank

(G-9886)
ROUNDBANK
200 2nd St NE (56093-2904)
PO Box 667 (56093-0667)
PHONE.....................507 835-4220
Larry Thompson, *President*
Beth Hintz, *Vice Pres*
Kevin Neuharth, *Vice Pres*
Carol Raimann, *Manager*
Kate Johanningmeier, *Director*
EMP: 36 EST: 1881
SALES (est): 10MM-24.9MM **Privately Held**
WEB: www.roundbank.com
SIC: 6022 6163 State commercial bank; loan broker

(G-9887)
SHADY OAKS NURSERY
400 15th Ave SE (56093-3110)
PO Box 708 (56093-0708)
PHONE.....................507 835-5033
FAX: 507 835-8772
Gordon J Oslund, *Owner*
EMP: 25 EST: 1995 **Privately Held**
SIC: 0181 Ornamental nursery products

(G-9888)
TAS ADVENTURES INC
905 9th Ave SE (56093-3914)
PHONE.....................507 833-8164
Jay Dulas, *Principal*
EMP: 43 EST: 2001
SALES (est): 10MM-24.9MM **Privately Held**
SIC: 5087 Wholesales service establishment equipment & supplies

(G-9889)
WASECA MEDICAL CENTER — MAYO
501 State St N (56093-2811)
PHONE.....................507 835-1210
Amy Fossen, *Corp Secy*
Donald Lucek, *Ch of Surgery*
Michael Milbrath, *Exec VP*
Jodi Dykema, *Purchasing*
Roy Miller, *Engineering*
EMP: 150 EST: 1922
SQ FT: 30,000
SALES (est): 10MM-24.9MM **Privately Held**
WEB: www.isj-mhs.net
SIC: 8062 Medical hospital
HQ: Immanuel-St Joseph's Hospital
1025 Marsh St
Mankato MN 56001
507 625-4031

WATERTOWN
Carver County

(G-9890)
ELIM HOMES INC
409 Jefferson Ave SW (55388-9250)
PHONE.....................952 955-2691
FAX: 952 955-2692
Abigail M Donald, *General Mgr*
Cory Allen RN, *Nursing Dir*
Denise Heile, *Hlthcr Dir*
EMP: 100
SALES (est): 1MM-4.9MM **Privately Held**

SIC: 8059 8051 Nursing home; skilled nursing care facility

(G-9891)
LAKEVIEW CLINIC
309 Jefferson Ave SW (55388-9266)
PHONE.....................952 955-1921
FAX: 952 955-3115
Robert Wilcox, *Principal*
Kathy M Sweetman, *Pediatrics*
Paul E Brown, *Internal Med*
Tom Bowman, *Asst Admin*
EMP: 25
SQ FT: 7,849
SALES (est): 1MM-4.9MM **Privately Held**
SIC: 8011 Clinic operated by physicians
PA: Lakeview Clinic
424 W Highway 5
Waconia MN 55387
952 442-4161

(G-9892)
MIDWEST MOTOR & EQUIPMENT INC
601 Lewis Ave N (55388-8351)
PHONE.....................952 955-1962
Todd E Hendricks, *President*
EMP: 25 EST: 1974
SQ FT: 10,000
SALES (est): 500-999K **Privately Held**
SIC: 4151 School bus service

(G-9893)
TIMBER CREEK GOLF COURSE INC
9750 County Road 24 (55388-9326)
PHONE.....................952 955-3600
FAX: 952 955-3332
Timothy O'Connor, *President*
EMP: 25 EST: 1985
SQ FT: 8,878
SALES (est): 1MM-4.9MM **Privately Held**
SIC: 7992 Public golf course

WATERVILLE
Le Sueur County

(G-9894)
EVANGELICAL LUTHERAN GOOD
205 1st St N (56096-1156)
PHONE.....................507 362-4245
FAX: 507 362-8631
Teresa Hildidrantt, *Principal*
Carolyn Gothier, *Office Mgr*
Debra Jacobs, *Manager*
Teresa Hildebrandt, *Administrator*
Tamara Vendt, *Coordinator*
EMP: 81
SALES (est): 1MM-4.9MM **Privately Held**
WEB: www.good-sam.com
SIC: 8051 Skilled nursing care facility
PA: Evangelical Lutheran Good
4800 W 57th St
Sioux Falls SD 57108
605 362-3100

(G-9895)
LCS PRECISION MOLDING INC
Also Called: Lake Country Sales
119 2nd St S (56096-1440)
PHONE.....................507 362-8685
FAX: 507 362-8893
Reed Hart, *President*
Julie Kaplan, *Corp Secy*
Pete Olmanson, *Engineer*
Rachael Douglas, *CFO*
Maureen Kaplan, *Manager*
EMP: 38 EST: 1973
SQ FT: 30,000
SALES (est): 1MM-4.9MM **Privately Held**
WEB: www.lcsplastics.com
SIC: 5072 Manufactures finished injection molded plastic products; wholesales hardware; manufactures plastic hardware

www.HarrisInfo.com
426
2011 Harris Minnesota
Services Directory
▲=Import ▼=Export
◆=Import/Export

(G-9896)

LE SUEUR COUNTY DEVELOPMENTAL
519 Paquin St W (56096-1388)
PO Box 47 (56096-0047)
PHONE............................507 362-8560
FAX: 507 362-4372
Bruce Bahlmann, *Director*
Doug Scharfe, *Director*
EMP: 30 **EST:** 1966
SALES (est): 1MM-4.9MM **Privately Held**
SIC: 8331 Job training & vocational rehabilitation services; manufactures plastic bags

---

WATKINS
Meeker County

(G-9897)

EVANGELICAL LUTHERAN GOOD
Also Called: Hilltop Good Samaritan Center
410 Luella St (55389-1012)
PHONE............................320 764-2300
FAX: 320 764-2665
Annette Schroeder, *Director*
EMP: 80
SALES (est): 1MM-4.9MM **Privately Held**
WEB: www.good-sam.com
SIC: 8051 Convalescent home
PA: Evangelical Lutheran Good
  4800 W 57th St
  Sioux Falls SD 57108
  605 362-3100

(G-9898)

MIES EQUIPMENT INC
720 State Highway 55 (55389-4507)
PO Box 436 (55389-0436)
PHONE............................320 764-5310
FAX: 320 764-7900
Steve Mies, *President*
Anthony Mies, *Principal*
Jeff Mies, *VP Purch*
EMP: 50 **EST:** 1947
SQ FT: 35,000
SALES (est): 10MM-24.9MM **Privately Held**
WEB: www.miesoutland.com
SIC: 5083 Wholesales farm equipment parts & supplies; wholesales farm implements; recreational vehicle dealer

(G-9899)

RANDY KRAMER EXCAVATING INC
Also Called: Stearns Aggregate
67962 State Highway 55 (55389-5902)
PO Box 498 (55389-0498)
PHONE............................320 764-6871
Randy Kramer, *President*
EMP: 50 **EST:** 1978
SQ FT: 1,500
SALES (est): 5MM-9.9MM **Privately Held**
SIC: 1623 1794 5032 Water & sewer line construction; wholesales gravel; excavating contractor

---

WAUBUN
Becker County

(G-9900)

LADUE CONSTRUCTION INC
2354 340th St (56589-9004)
PHONE............................218 846-9865
Mike Ladue, *President*
EMP: 50 **EST:** 1992
SALES (est): 1MM-4.9MM **Privately Held**
SIC: 1742 Drywall contractor

(G-9901)

WHITE EARTH HOUSING AUTHORITY
3303 US Highway 59 (56589-9001)
PHONE............................218 473-4663
Robert Durant, *Exec Dir*
Robert Durantz, *Director*
EMP: 31 **EST:** 1965
SALES (est): 5MM-9.9MM **Privately Held**

SIC: 6531 Real estate services; housing authority operator

WAVERLY
Wright County

(G-9902)

CARPENTRY CONTRACTORS CORP
1791 Estes Ave SW (55390-5007)
PHONE............................763 658-4000
Brian Balcer, *Treasurer*
Scott Gertjejansen, *Controller*
Kathy Dooher, *Accountant*
EMP: 80 **EST:** 1980
SALES (est): 5MM-9.9MM **Privately Held**
WEB: www.carpentrycontractors.com
SIC: 1751 Carpentry contractor

(G-9903)

CITIZENS STATE BANK OF
609 Pacific Ave (55390)
PHONE............................763 675-2265
Brian Matzke, *Manager*
EMP: 30
SALES (est): 5MM-9.9MM **Privately Held**
SIC: 6029 6022 Commercial bank; state commercial bank
PA: Citizens State Bank of
  216 1st Ave NE
  Hayfield MN 55940
  507 477-2212

(G-9904)

NEW BEGINNINGS AT WAVERLY LLC
109 N Shore Dr (55390-5517)
PHONE............................763 658-5800
FAX: 763 658-4128
Jan Broll, *Purchasing*
Chuck Anderson, *Envir Svcs Dir*
Brenda Griffin, *CFO*
Kathy Berscheid, *Marketing Mgr*
Char Gilchrist, *Marketing Staff*
EMP: 60 **EST:** 1981
SALES (est): 1MM-4.9MM **Privately Held**
WEB: www.newbeginningsatwaverly.com
SIC: 8361 Residential rehabilitation center with health care incidental

---

WAYZATA
Hennepin County

(G-9905)

ANCHOR BANK (PA)
1055 Wayzata Blvd E (55391-1856)
PHONE............................952 473-4606
FAX: 952 476-5219
Jay Hammond, *President*
Patricia A Diedrich, *Corp Secy*
Teresa Tembreull, *Senior VP*
Tony Berthlaume, *Vice Pres*
Jane Dilley, *Vice Pres*
EMP: 40 **EST:** 1963
SALES (corp-wide): 61.19M **Privately Held**
SIC: 6021 Commercial national trust companies with deposits

(G-9906)

BEVERLY ENTERPRISES - MN
Also Called: Hillcrest Rehab Hlth Care Ctr
15409 Wayzata Blvd (55391-1402)
PHONE............................952 473-5466
FAX: 952 249-0804
Margaret Owens, *Manager*
Mark Chouanard, *IT/INT Sup*
Lisa Herrel, *Exec Dir*
Lisa Harrell, *Exec Dir*
Debe Neubauer, *Hlthcr Dir*
EMP: 300
SALES (est): 10MM-24.9MM **Privately Held**
WEB: www.beverlynet.com
SIC: 8051 Skilled nursing care facility
HQ: Beverly Enterprises - MN
  650 Ramer Ave S
  Rush City MN 55069
  320 358-4765

(G-9907)

CARGILL INC
2301 Crosby Rd (55391-2313)
PO Box 5699, Minneapolis (55440-5699)
PHONE............................952 742-6437
Steven McCurry, *Manager*
Gene McCaherty, *Manager*
Kendra K Gruman, *Manager*
Audrey Coleman, *Manager*
Kim Bonin, *Manager*
EMP: 100
SALES (est): 5MM-9.9MM **Privately Held**
SIC: 8734 8731 Food testing services; commercial physical research laboratory

(G-9908)

CARGILL INC
15407 McGinty Rd W (55391-2365)
PHONE............................763 742-7237
Diane Schanhaar, *Principal*
Rita J Heise, *VP Info Sys*
EMP: 50
SALES (est): 1MM-4.9MM **Privately Held**
SIC: 8721 Billing & bookkeeping services

(G-9909)

CARGILL INC
156151 McGinty Rd W (55391)
PHONE............................952 742-7575
David Braden, *Branch Mgr*
EMP: 2000
SALES (est): 1B-9.9B **Privately Held**
SIC: 5153 Wholesales grain & field beans; manufactures meal corn oil; manufactures refined corn oil; manufactures high fructose corn syrup; manufactures gluten meal; manufactures soybean oil, cake or meal; wholesales corn; wholesales wheat; wholesales soybeans

(G-9910)

CHARLES SCHWAB & CO INC
130 Lake St W (55391-1599)
PHONE............................952 404-0398
Brian Wagenbach, *Manager*
EMP: 25
SALES (est): 5MM-9.9MM **Publicly Held**
WEB: www.schwab.com
SIC: 6211 Securities broker & dealer
DH: Charles Schwab & Co Inc
  101 Montgomery St Ste 200
  San Francisco CA 94104
  415 636-7000

(G-9911)

COLEMANBRANDWORX WORLDWIDE
18258 Minnetonka Blvd B (55391-3321)
PHONE............................763 390-1100
FAX: 763 390-1111
Heather Kruger, *Office Mgr*
Nancy Brown, *Branch Mgr*
EMP: 25
SALES (est): 1MM-4.9MM **Privately Held**
WEB: www.colemanbrandworx.com
SIC: 7389 Design services
PA: Colemanbrandworx Worldwide
  35 E 21st St
  New York NY 10010
  212 404-7970

(G-9912)

COUNSELOR REALTY INC
Also Called: Conselor Realty
3622 County Road 101 S # 100
(55391-3424)
PHONE............................952 475-9500
FAX: 952 473-5530
Barb Solyst, *Manager*
Tom Selseph, *Manager*
John Butler, *Manager*
John Grotting, *Manager*
EMP: 25
SALES (est): 10MM-24.9MM **Privately Held**
WEB: www.counselorrealty.com
SIC: 6531 Real estate services
PA: Counselor Realty Inc
  7766 Highway 65 NE Ste 1
  Minneapolis MN 55432
  763 786-0600

(G-9913)

DAVIES PRINTING CO
16507 Holdridge Rd W (55391-2050)
PHONE............................952 473-6924
Tom Davies, *Owner*
EMP: 50 **EST:** 1999
SALES (est): 1MM-4.9MM **Privately Held**
SIC: 7389 Printing broker

(G-9914)

DKS SYSTEMS LLC
725 Ferndale Rd N (55391-1010)
PHONE............................952 476-7443
Mike Sowada, *CEO*
EST: 2001
SQ FT: 1,700 **Privately Held**
SIC: 8748 7379 Business consulting services; computer system consulting services

(G-9915)

DONALD A DRIGGS
2925 Casco Point Rd (55391-9412)
PHONE............................952 471-9500
Donald Driggs, *Principal*
EMP: 30 **EST:** 2004
SALES (est): 5MM-9.9MM **Privately Held**
SIC: 6531 Real estate services

(G-9916)

ENGLISH ROSEAT SUITES INC
1708 Pondview Ter (55391-2251)
PHONE............................952 983-0412
Brent Longtin, *President*
Jayne Clairmont, *Vice Pres*
EMP: 50 **EST:** 1996
SALES (est): 1MM-4.9MM **Privately Held**
WEB: www.englishrosesuites.com
SIC: 8361 Residential care facility

(G-9917)

FLAGSHIP BANK MINNESOTA
445 Lake St E Ste 110 (55391-1670)
PHONE............................952 473-1959
Roy Terwilliger, *CEO*
Don Kleinschmidt, *Senior VP*
Patricia Lehn, *Senior VP*
Elaine Eckstein, *Vice Pres*
Eden Praine, *Loan Officer*
EST: 1933 **Privately Held**
SIC: 6022 State commercial bank

(G-9918)

GGNSC WAYZATA LLC
Also Called: Golden Livingcenter-Wayzata
15409 Wayzata Blvd (55391-1402)
PHONE............................952 473-5466
Tara Heisler, *Mktg Dir*
William Gould, *Exec Dir*
Allison Murkowski, *Exec Dir*
Troy Field, *Maintence Staff*
EMP: 99 **EST:** 2006
SALES (est): 1MM-4.9MM **Privately Held**
WEB: www.fillmorecap.com
SIC: 8051 Skilled nursing care facility
DH: Ggnsc Holdings LLC
  1000 Fianna Way
  Fort Smith AR 72919
  479 201-2000

(G-9919)

HAMMER RESIDENCES INC
1909 Wayzata Blvd (55391-2047)
PHONE............................763 473-1261
Tim Nelson, *CEO*
James Landt, *CFO*
Stefanie Miller, *Manager*
Sharon Knodel, *Director*
Tim Eshelman, *Director*
EMP: 125 **EST:** 1923
SALES (est): 1MM-4.9MM **Privately Held**
WEB: www.hammer.org
SIC: 8361 Residential care for the handicapped; home for the mentally handicapped; home for the physically handicapped

(G-9920)

HARMONY HOLDINGS INC
15500 Wayzata Blvd # 604221
(55391-1438)
PHONE............................952 925-8840
Gary Horowitz, *CEO*

G
E
O
G
R
A
P
H
I
C

GEOGRAPHIC

Harvey Bibicoff, *Chairman*
Fujiko Yamashita, *Vice Pres*
Brian Rackohn, *CFO*
James M Kelvey, *Info Tech Mgr*
EMP: 63 **EST:** 1991
SALES (est): 10MM-24.9MM **Publicly Held**
WEB: www.intelefilm.com
SIC: 7812 Tape or film television
commercial production service
PA: Intelefilm Corp
3500 Vicksburg Ln N 405
Minneapolis MN 55447
952 925-8840

(G-9921)
INTRAN MEDIA LLC
294 Grove Ln E Ste 400 (55391-1682)
PHONE..............................952 646-0036
FAX: 952 646-0337
Mark Spaniol, *Member*
McG Capital, *Member*
Jim Arabanos, *Member*
EMP: 35 **EST:** 2001
SQ FT: 1,500
SALES (est): 1MM-4.9MM **Privately Held**
WEB: www.intranmedia.com
SIC: 7311 Advertising agency

(G-9922)
JAMES W COPELAND
Also Called: Copeland Buhl & Co
800 Wayzata Blvd E # 300 (55391-1766)
PHONE..............................952 476-7100
James W Copeland, *Principal*
EMP: 50 **EST:** 2001
SALES (est): 5MM-9.9MM **Privately Held**
WEB: www.copelandbuhl.com
SIC: 8721 Certified public accountant
services

(G-9923)
**L L BRUSTAD & ASSOCIATES
INC**
3309 Casco Cir (55391-9718)
PHONE..............................952 842-1142
Lawrence Brustad, *President*
EST: 1981 **Privately Held**
WEB: www.llbrustad.com
SIC: 6411 Insurance agency & broker

(G-9924)
**LAKE MINNETONKA SAILING
SCHOOL**
3645 Laurel Dr (55391-3228)
PHONE..............................952 404-1645
Gordy Bowers, *Owner*
John Reed, *General Mgr*
Tom Bowers, *Vice Pres*
Tom McGrath, *Info Tech Dir*
Cappy Capper, *Exec Dir*
EMP: 30 **EST:** 2000
SALES (est): 1MM-4.9MM **Privately Held**
WEB:
www.lakeminnetonkasailingschool.org
SIC: 7999 Provides sailing instruction

(G-9925)
LITTLE ACORNS DAY SCHOOL
1865 Wayzata Blvd (55391-2048)
PHONE..............................952 475-0828
Mary Male, *President*
EMP: 35 **EST:** 2006
SALES (est): 500-999K **Privately Held**
SIC: 8351 Child day care service

(G-9926)
**MERRILL LYNCH, PIERCE,
FENNER**
308 Walker Ave S Fl 2 (55391-1726)
PHONE..............................952 476-5600
FAX: 952 476-5695
Greg Rohard, *Manager*
Ann Olson, *Manager*
Donald Hutson, *Manager*
Margaret Harper, *Manager*
Barbara Bencini, *Manager*
EMP: 30
SALES (est): 5MM-9.9MM **Publicly Held**
WEB: www.ml.com
SIC: 6211 Security broker service
HQ: Merrill Lynch & Co Inc
4 World Financial Ctr # 4
New York NY 10080
212 449-1000

(G-9927)
METROPOLIS SALON SPA
18166 Minnetonka Blvd (55391-3327)
PHONE..............................952 473-8664
Mark Melter, *Owner*
EMP: 29 **EST:** 1994
SALES (est): 500-999K **Privately Held**
WEB: www.metropolissalonspa.com
SIC: 7231 Beauty salon

(G-9928)
MIRO MANAGEMENT INC
1001 Twelve Oaks Ctr Ste D (55391-4301)
PHONE..............................952 404-8267
Robert Wood, *President*
EMP: 45 **EST:** 1967
SALES (est): 5MM-9.9MM **Privately Held**
WEB: www.miromanagement.com
SIC: 8742 Management consulting services

(G-9929)
**MOHAGEN HANSEN
ARCHITECTURAL**
1000 Twelve Oaks Ste 200 (55391)
PHONE..............................952 426-7400
Todd Mohagen, *Member*
Janet Sullivan, *Manager*
EMP: 30 **EST:** 2007
SALES (est): 5MM-9.9MM **Privately Held**
SIC: 1542 Nonresidential building design &
construction service

(G-9930)
MORGAN STANLEY
701 Lake St E (55391-1712)
PHONE..............................763 475-4100
John Gehlhaart, *Div Sub Head*
Chris Ascher, *Manager*
Barney Smith, *Manager*
EMP: 35
SALES (est): 5MM-9.9MM **Publicly Held**
WEB: www.morganstanley.com
SIC: 6211 Securities broker & dealer
PA: Morgan Stanley
1585 Broadway
New York NY 10036
212 761-4000

(G-9931)
NATHAN J LILLEODDEN CPA
Also Called: Copeland Buhl
800 Wayzata Blvd E # 300 (55391-1766)
PHONE..............................952 476-7107
Nathan J Lilleodden, *Owner*
EMP: 60
SALES (est): 5MM-9.9MM **Privately Held**
SIC: 8721 Certified public accountant
services

(G-9932)
NORTECH SYSTEMS INC (PA)
1120 Wayzata Blvd E 201 (55391-1984)
PHONE..............................952 345-2244
FAX: 952 449-0442
Michael J Degen, *President*
Bud Brown, *General Mgr*
Michael Jepsen, *General Mgr*
Jeff Kinney, *General Mgr*
Bert M Gross, *Corp Secy*
▲ **EMP:** 150 **EST:** 1981
SQ FT: 5,000
SALES (corp-wide): 79.93M **Publicly Held**
WEB: www.nortechsys.com
SIC: 7378 Manufactures computer
terminals, monitors & components;
computer & office machine maintenance &
repair services

(G-9933)
**NORTHERN ALTERNATIVE
ENERGY**
15600 Wayzta Blvd Ste 209 (55391-1437)
PHONE..............................612 370-1061
Gregory J Jaunich, *CEO*
John Jaunich, *President*
Alfredo Cahuas, *CFO*
EMP: 28 **EST:** 1992
SQ FT: 7,000
SALES (est): 10MM-24.9MM **Privately Held**
SIC: 4911 Provides electric power
generation services

(G-9934)
NORTHERN OIL & GAS INC
315 Manitoba Ave Ste 200 (55391-1660)
PHONE..............................952 476-9800
FAX: 952 476-9801
Michael Reger, *CEO*
Ryan Gilbertson, *CFO*
Lisa Meier, *CFO*
Carter Stewart, *Director*
Loren O'Toole, *Director*
EMP: 25 **EST:** 2006
SALES (est): 10MM-24.9MM **Privately Held**
SIC: 1311 Crude petroleum & natural gas
production

(G-9935)
PIPER JAFFRAY CO'S
Also Called: US Bank
681 Lake St E Ste 354 (55391-1758)
PHONE..............................952 476-3939
EMP: 40
SALES (est): 10MM-24.9MM **Publicly Held**
SIC: 6211 Security floor trader service
PA: Piper Jaffray Co's
800 Nicollet Mall Ste 800
Minneapolis MN 55402
612 303-6000

(G-9936)
**PROFESSIONAL ALTERNATIVES
L L**
15600 Wayzata Blvd Ste 300
(55391-1447)
PHONE..............................952 404-2600
Dave Dodge, *Member*
Faith Williams, *Senior VP*
Faith Williamson, *Vice Pres*
EMP: 35 **EST:** 1991
SQ FT: 3,500 **Privately Held**
SIC: 7361 Executive placement & search
consulting services

(G-9937)
**QUALITY CAR WASH OPS LTD
INC**
1405 Wayzata Blvd E (55391-1949)
PHONE..............................952 473-4535
FAX: 952 473-4237
Steven Gerring, *President*
Marty Gerring, *President*
EMP: 30 **EST:** 1992
SALES (est): 1MM-4.9MM **Privately Held**
SIC: 7542 Automatic carwash service

(G-9938)
RBA INC
100 Lake St W (55391-1691)
PHONE..............................952 404-2676
Rick Born, *CEO*
Mike Reinhart, *President*
Adam Grocholski, *IT/INT Sup*
EMP: 70 **EST:** 2005
SQ FT: 6,000
SALES (est): 5MM-9.9MM **Privately Held**
SIC: 8748 Business consulting services

(G-9939)
**SAWHORSE DESIGNER'S &
BUILDERS**
239 Lake St E (55391-1608)
PHONE..............................952 475-4477
Jim Rothbauer, *Owner*
EMP: 36 **EST:** 2001
SALES (est): 5MM-9.9MM **Privately Held**
SIC: 1521 Single-family home general
remodeling service

(G-9940)
SPRING HILL GOLF CLUB
725 Spring Hill Rd (55391-9551)
PHONE..............................952 473-1500
Jeff Kringen, *General Mgr*
Tim Ivory, *General Mgr*
Tim Johnson, *Superintendent*
EMP: 69 **EST:** 1999
SALES (est): 1MM-4.9MM **Privately Held**
SIC: 7997 Membership recreation club

(G-9941)
SPRING HILL GOLF CLUB
725 County Road 6 (55391-7600)
PHONE..............................952 473-1500
FAX: 952 473-3341
Tim Johnson, *Superintendent*
Tim Ivory, *Manager*
Tom Dalum, *Manager*
EMP: 48 **EST:** 1998
SALES (est): 1MM-4.9MM **Privately Held**
WEB: www.springhillgolfclub.com
SIC: 7997 Membership golf club

(G-9942)
STEVEN N ARENDT
800 Wayzata Blvd E (55391-1764)
PHONE..............................952 476-7143
Steven Arendt, *Partner*
EMP: 60 **EST:** 1971
SALES (est): 1MM-4.9MM **Privately Held**
SIC: 8721 Accounting, auditing &
bookkeeping services

(G-9943)
STREETER & ASSOCIATES INC
18312 Minnetonka Blvd (55391-3232)
PHONE..............................952 449-9448
FAX: 952 449-4987
Steven Streeter, *President*
Kevin Streeter, *Vice Pres*
Kathy Slowter, *Administrator*
Justin Streeter, *Shareholder*
Don Streeter, *Shareholder*
EMP: 39 **EST:** 1979
SQ FT: 4,800
SALES (est): 10MM-24.9MM **Privately Held**
WEB: www.streeterhomes.com
SIC: 1521 New single-family home
construction service; single-family home
general remodeling service

(G-9944)
T M B CONSULTING INC
18305 Minnetonka Blvd (55391-3276)
PHONE..............................952 249-1223
Darel Gustafson, *President*
Steve Dwyer, *Corp Secy*
Wally Vogtmann, *CFO*
EMP: 80 **EST:** 1994
SQ FT: 500
SALES (est): 10MM-24.9MM **Privately Held**
SIC: 7371 Custom computer software
systems analysis & design service

(G-9945)
TCF FINANCIAL CORP (PA)
200 Lake St E (55391-1690)
PHONE..............................952 745-2760
William A Cooper, *CEO*
Neil W Brown, *President*
Timothy B Meyer, *President*
Ronald J Palmer, *President*
Mark L Jeter, *Managing Dir*
EMP: 914 **EST:** 1987
SALES (corp-wide): 1.48B **Publicly Held**
WEB: www.tcfbank.com
SIC: 6021 National commercial bank

(G-9946)
TRUSTEE GROUP LLP
3610 County Road 101 S (55391-3424)
PHONE..............................952 473-5650
David Kordonowi, *Managing Prtnr*
Richard Lang, *Partner*
Tom Kordonowi, *Partner*
Vishal Dutt, *Controller*
EMP: 25 **EST:** 1998
SALES (est): 1MM-4.9MM **Privately Held**
SIC: 8742 Real estate consultant

(G-9947)
**VILLAGE CHEVROLET CO -
WAYZATA**
16200 Wayzata Blvd (55391-2018)
PHONE..............................952 473-5444
FAX: 952 473-0720
Grant Osgood, *General Mgr*
Geraldine Bloomer, *Corp Secy*
Steve Bennett, *Vice Pres*
Steve Davis, *Parts Mgr*
John Varner, *Sales Staff*
EMP: 138 **EST:** 1949
SQ FT: 47,000
SALES (est): 50MM-99.9MM **Privately Held**

www.HarrisInfo.com
428

2011 Harris Minnesota
Services Directory

▲=Import ▼=Export
◆=Import/Export

WEB: www.villagechev.com
SIC: 7538 Retails new & used automobiles; general automotive repair services; retails automotive parts

(G-9948)
WAYZATA COUNTRY CLUB INC
200 Wayzata Blvd W (55391-1557)
PHONE 952 473-8846
Jeanne Clellan, *General Mgr*
Jeffrey Kreafle, *General Mgr*
R Fazendin, *Member*
Jeanne McClellan, *Manager*
Kurt Charter, *IT/INT Sup*
EMP: 90 **EST:** 1956
SQ FT: 48,000
SALES (est): 5MM-9.9MM **Privately Held**
SIC: 7997 Country club; bar; eating place; retails golf, tennis & ski equipment

(G-9949)
WAYZATA PARTNERS LP
Also Called: Meridian Manor
163 Wayzata Blvd W Ofc (55391-1562)
PHONE 763 473-3200
Cheri Smith, *Sales Mgr*
Grace Willenbirg, *Administrator*
Gerald Fenstad, *Exec Dir*
Jennifer Anderson, *Director*
EMP: 40
SALES (est): 5MM-9.9MM **Privately Held**
SIC: 6513 Apartment building operator
PA: Wayzata Partners LP
    4601 Excelsior Blvd # 301
    Minneapolis MN 55416
    952 920-5338

(G-9950)
WIKEN PROMOTION & ADVERTISING
681 Lake St E Ste 262 (55391-1757)
PO Box 664 (55391-0664)
PHONE 952 476-2002
Lawrence Wiken, *President*
Gail Severson, *CFO*
EMP: 50 **EST:** 1995
SQ FT: 4,500
SALES (est): 5MM-9.9MM **Privately Held**
WEB: www.wiken.com
SIC: 8742 7311 Marketing consulting service; advertising consultants

(G-9951)
WOODHILL COUNTRY CLUB
200 Woodhill Rd (55391-9388)
PHONE 952 473-7333
FAX: 952 473-0113
Kirt Pitcher, *General Mgr*
EMP: 100 **EST:** 1915
SQ FT: 20,000
SALES (est): 5MM-9.9MM **Privately Held**
SIC: 7997 Country club; full service independent family restaurant; membership swimming club; membership tennis club; membership golf club

(G-9952)
WUOLLET BAKERY INC
771 Lake St E (55391-1712)
PHONE 763 473-8621
Nicole Jacobson, *General Mgr*
Jo Genten, *Sales Staff*
Jim Jurmu, *Branch Mgr*
Lori V Ada, *Manager*
EMP: 25
SQ FT: 4,800
SALES (est): 1MM-4.9MM **Privately Held**
WEB: www.wuollet.com
SIC: 5149 Retail bakery; commercial bakery; manufactures cookies & crackers; wholesales groceries
PA: Wuollet Bakery Inc
    2447 Hennepin Ave S
    Minneapolis MN 55405
    612 381-9400

WEBSTER
Rice County

(G-9953)
RUD CONSTRUCTION INC
4275 Bagley Ave (55088-2430)
PO Box 85 (55088-0085)
PHONE 952 652-2886
FAX: 952 652-2896
Rodney Rud, *President*
Tim Rud, *Vice Pres*
EMP: 50 **EST:** 1973
SALES (est): 5MM-9.9MM **Privately Held**
SIC: 1611 General highway & street construction service

WELCH
Goodhue County

(G-9954)
NORTHERN STATES POWER CO
Also Called: Prairie Island Nuclear Generat
1717 Wakonade Dr E (55089-9642)
PHONE 612 330-6349
Mike Wadley, *Plant Mgr*
Len Clewitt, *Plant Mgr*
George Andrews, *Engineer*
Ken Slingsby, *Engineer*
Mark Aeling, *Accounting Mgr*
EMP: 50
SALES (est): 25MM-49.9MM **Publicly Held**
WEB: www.middletownpower.com
SIC: 4911 Electric services
HQ: Northern States Power Co
    414 Nicollet Mall
    Minneapolis MN 55401
    612 330-5500

(G-9955)
PRAIRIE ISLAND INDIAN COM (PA)
5636 Sturgeon Lake Rd (55089-9635)
PO Box 75, Red Wing (55066-0075)
PHONE 651 388-0083
FAX: 651 385-2750
Audrey Kohnen, *President*
Darelynn Lehto, *Corp Secy*
Mason Pacini, *Vice Pres*
Allen Childs Sr, *Treasurer*
Ryan Veenendaal, *Human Res Mgr*
EMP: 165 **EST:** 1934 **Privately Held**
SIC: 7999 7011 Bingo hall; eating place; casino hotel

(G-9956)
PRAIRIE ISLAND TRIBAL COUNCIL
5636 Sturgeon Lake Rd (55089-9635)
PHONE 651 385-2554
FAX: 651 385-4110
Audrey Bennett, *President*
Johny Jackson, *Corp Secy*
Victoria Winfrey, *Vice Pres*
Eleanore Bartell, *Opers Mgr*
Alan Childs II, *Treasurer*
EMP: 100 **EST:** 1934 **Privately Held**
WEB: www.prairieisland.org
SIC: 8399 Social change association

(G-9957)
TREASURE ISLAND CASINO & BINGO
5734 Sturgeon Lake Rd (55089-9647)
PO Box 75, Red Wing (55066-0075)
PHONE 651 388-6300
FAX: 651 385-2558
Mike Heavner, *General Mgr*
Allan Kronberg, *General Mgr*
Kim Pang, *General Mgr*
Holli Hoesli, *Corp Secy*
Johny Jackson, *Corp Secy*
EMP: 1500 **EST:** 1984
SALES (est): 100MM-499.9MM **Privately Held**
WEB: www.treasureislandcasino.com
SIC: 7999 7011 Bingo hall; eating place; game parlor; hotel
PA: Prairie Island Indian Com
    5636 Sturgeon Lake Rd
    Welch MN 55089
    651 388-0083

WELCOME
Martin County

(G-9958)
EASY AUTOMATION INC
102 Mill St (56181)
PO Box 412 (56181-0412)
PHONE 507 728-8214
Mark Gaalswyk, *President*
Rod Olson, *Business Mgr*
Michael Johnson, *Director*
Leslie Truesdell, *Assistant*
EMP: 50 **EST:** 2001
SQ FT: 50,000
SALES (est): 10MM-24.9MM **Privately Held**
SIC: 5084 7372 Wholesales industrial machinery & equipment; software publisher

(G-9959)
MARTIN COUNTY WEST SCHOOL DIST
Also Called: Small Treasures Pre School
308 4th St (56181)
PO Box 268 (56181-0268)
PHONE 507 728-8609
Dale Herbitz, *Principal*
EMP: 32
SALES (est): 500-999K **Privately Held**
WEB: www.westwoodpublicschools.com
SIC: 8351 Child day care service
HQ: Martin County West School Dist
    77 Beech St W
    Trimont MN 56176
    507 639-2071

WELLS
Faribault County

(G-9960)
ALBERT LEE MEDICAL CENTER INC
Also Called: Naeve Parkview Home
55 10th St SE (56097-1814)
PHONE 507 553-3115
FAX: 507 553-6060
Scott Rafferty, *Manager*
Jerry Ehn, *Manager*
EMP: 80
SALES (est): 1MM-4.9MM **Privately Held**
SIC: 8059 8011 Nursing home; clinic operated by physicians
PA: Albert Lee Medical Center Inc
    404 W Fountain St
    Albert Lea MN 56007
    507 373-2384

(G-9961)
BLUE EARTH VALLEY TELEPHONE CO
Also Called: Easton Telephone
191 2nd St SE (56097-1610)
PHONE 507 787-2222
FAX: 507 553-6700
Neil Eckles, *President*
EMP: 30 **Privately Held**
SIC: 4813 Wired telecommunications carrier & service

(G-9962)
HERMAN MANUFACTURING CO
295 3rd St NE (56097-1530)
PHONE 507 553-5256
FAX: 507 553-6062
John F Herman, *President*
Mark Herman, *Partner*
Diane Morgan, *Corp Secy*
EMP: 30 **EST:** 1973
SALES (est): 1MM-4.9MM **Privately Held**
SIC: 7692 Machine shop, jobbing & repair services; manufactures sewing machines & hat & zipper making machinery; welding service

(G-9963)
WELLS FEDERAL BANK FSB
53 1st St SW (56097-1912)
PO Box 310 (56097-0310)
PHONE 507 553-3151
FAX: 507 553-6295
Lonnie Trasamar, *President*

William Cotter, *General Mgr*
Wiget Lane, *General Mgr*
Michael Marino, *General Mgr*
John McKinny, *General Mgr*
EMP: 37 **EST:** 1934
SALES (est): 10MM-24.9MM **Publicly Held**
WEB: www.wellsfinancialcorp.com
SIC: 6035 Federal savings bank
PA: Wells Financial Corp
    53 1st St SW
    Wells MN 56097
    507 553-3151

WEST CONCORD
Dodge County

(G-9964)
ELLINGSON DRAINAGE INC
56113 State Highway 56 (55985-6066)
PO Box 68 (55985-0068)
PHONE 507 527-2294
FAX: 507 527-2128
Roger Ellingson, *President*
Kevin Ellingson, *Vice Pres*
Leonard Binstock, *Human Res Dir*
EMP: 60 **EST:** 1970
SALES (est): 5MM-9.9MM **Privately Held**
WEB: www.ellingsondrainage.com
SIC: 1629 Waterway construction; golf course construction

(G-9965)
FARMERS STATE BANK OF WEST
181 Main St (55985-2040)
PO Box 245 (55985-0245)
PHONE 507 527-2236
FAX: 507 527-2164
Allan Organ, *President*
Dan Rabe, *Loan Officer*
EMP: 30 **EST:** 1930
SALES (est): 5MM-9.9MM **Privately Held**
SIC: 6022 State commercial bank

WESTBROOK
Cottonwood County

(G-9966)
EVANGELICAL LUTHERAN GOOD
149 1st Ave (56183-1102)
PO Box 218 (56183-0218)
PHONE 507 274-6155
FAX: 507 274-6156
Gordon Kopperud, *COO*
Jerry Thompson, *CFO*
Becky Foster, *Human Res Dir*
Carol Corman, *Pub Rel Dir*
Geana Hamilton, *Manager*
EMP: 65
SALES (est): 1MM-4.9MM **Privately Held**
WEB: www.good-sam.com
SIC: 8051 8059 Convalescent home; nursing home
PA: Evangelical Lutheran Good
    4800 W 57th St
    Sioux Falls SD 57108
    605 362-3100

(G-9967)
SANFORD WESTBROOK MEDICAL CTR
920 Bell Ave (56183-9669)
PHONE 507 274-6802
Gene Lindaman, *Principal*
EMP: 50
SALES (est): 1MM-4.9MM **Privately Held**
SIC: 8099 Health & allied services

(G-9968)
WESTBROOK HEALTH CENTER
920 Bell Ave (56183-9669)
PO Box 158 (56183-0158)
PHONE 507 274-6121
Stacey Baarstead, *President*
Joni Lohre, *Ch Radiology*
Rick Nordahl, *CFO*
Joy Christans, *Accountant*
Kathie Christians, *Manager*
EMP: 35

(PA)=Parent Co (HQ)=Headquarters (DH)=Div Headquarters
✿ = New business established in last 2 years

2011 Harris Minnesota
Services Directory

© Harris InfoSource 1-866-281-6415
429

EST: 1951
SQ FT: 5,000
SALES (est): 1MM-4.9MM **Privately Held**
SIC: 8062 8069 Medical hospital; specialty hospital

WHEATON
Traverse County

(G-9969)
TRAVERSE CARE CENTER
303 7th St S (56296-1740)
PHONE.............................320 563-8124
FAX: 320 563-4133
William Gibson, *Principal*
Clarence Zimmel, *Principal*
David Naatz, *Principal*
Norman Holtz, *Principal*
Chere Rikimoto, *Administrator*
EMP: 85 **EST:** 1959
SQ FT: 23,421
SALES (est): 1MM-4.9MM **Privately Held**
SIC: 8051 8052 Skilled nursing care facility; intermediate care facility; extended care facility

(G-9970)
WHEATON COMMUNITY HOSPITAL
401 12th St N (56296-1070)
PO Box 868 (56296-0868)
PHONE.............................320 563-8226
Perry Engstrom, *Ch of Surgery*
David Brandell, *QA Dir*
Ralth Mahler, *CFO*
Shane Ayres, *CFO*
James Talley, *Administrator*
EMP: 54 **EST:** 1950
SQ FT: 36,916
SALES (est): 1MM-4.9MM **Privately Held**
WEB: www.wheatonhealthcare.org
SIC: 8062 Medical hospital
PA: City of Wheaton
104 9th St N
Wheaton MN 56296
320 563-4110

(G-9971)
WHEATON HEAD START
710 4th Ave N (56296-1424)
PHONE.............................320 563-8191
Ranae Nelson, *Principal*
EMP: 35 **EST:** 1997
SALES (est): 500-999K **Privately Held**
SIC: 8351 Head Start center

(G-9972)
WHEATON LIQUOR
920 Broadway (56296-1302)
PHONE.............................320 563-4155
Kevin Olson, *Owner*
EMP: 26 **EST:** 1994
SALES (est): 10MM-24.9MM **Privately Held**
SIC: 5182 Wholesales wine & distilled alcoholic beverages; retails hard liquor

WHITE BEAR LAKE
Ramsey County

(G-9973)
ADVANCED RESEARCH CORP
4459 White Bear Pkwy (55110-7626)
PHONE.............................651 789-9000
Judith Dugas, *President*
Matthew Dugas, *Vice Pres*
Brant Zielinski, *Electrical Engi*
Sandra Alexandra, *Manager*
EMP: 25 **EST:** 1985
SQ FT: 36,000
SALES (est): 1MM-4.9MM **Privately Held**
WEB: www.arcnano.com
SIC: 8711 Engineering consulting services

(G-9974)
COMFORTS OF HOME
1235 Gun Club Rd (55110-3313)
PHONE.............................651 426-1036
Andrea Leech, *Manager*
EMP: 25 **EST:** 2007
SALES (est): 500-999K **Privately Held**

SIC: 8361 Home for the elderly

(G-9975)
HALLBERG ENGINEERING INC
1750 Commerce Ct (55110-4686)
PHONE.............................651 748-1100
FAX: 651 748-9370
Joe Hallberg, *President*
Jennifer Farr, *Controller*
Larry Jensen, *Info Tech Dir*
EMP: 45 **EST:** 2007
SALES (est): 5MM-9.9MM **Privately Held**
WEB: www.hallbergengineering.com
SIC: 8711 Mechanical engineering services

(G-9976)
MINNHEALTH FAMILY PHYSICIANS
4786 Banning Ave (55110-3264)
PHONE.............................651 426-6402
FAX: 651 429-3402
Deb Dox, *Office Mgr*
Paula Schmitzer, *Manager*
Andrea Connell, *Assistant*
EMP: 30
SALES (est): 1MM-4.9MM **Privately Held**
WEB: www.minnhealth.com
SIC: 8011 Physical medicine physician or surgeon office
PA: Minnhealth Family Physicians
2025 Sloan Pl Ste 35
Saint Paul MN 55117
651 772-1572

(G-9977)
SENTRY SYSTEMS INC
2182 4th St (55110-3013)
PHONE.............................651 426-4627
Ron Olinger, *President*
Bill Delmonico, *General Mgr*
Curt Olinger, *Manager*
EMP: 45 **EST:** 1963
SQ FT: 5,200
SALES (est): 1MM-4.9MM **Privately Held**
SIC: 7382 5063 Security systems services; wholesales electrical alarms & signaling equipment; retails alarm signal systems

(G-9978)
THANE HAWKINS POLAR CHEVROLET
1801 County Road F E (55110-3882)
PHONE.............................651 429-7791
FAX: 651 426-9267
Thane Hawkins, *President*
R W Krouse, *Vice Pres*
Tom Greenberg, *Controller*
Jim Lapadat, *Manager*
EMP: 130 **EST:** 1963
SQ FT: 50,000
SALES (est): 50MM-99.9MM **Privately Held**
WEB: www.polarchev.com
SIC: 7532 Retails new & used automobiles; retails new & used pickups; automotive body shop

(G-9979)
VALERE LLC
1988 Oak Knoll Dr (55110-4263)
PO Box 10589 (55110-0589)
PHONE.............................763 390-9286
Sandra Dischinger, *Member*
Debra Womack, *Mng Member*
EMP: 25 **EST:** 2006
SALES (est): 1MM-4.9MM **Privately Held**
SIC: 7379 7361 Computer system consulting services; employment agency services

WILLMAR
Kandiyohi County

(G-9980)
AFFILIATED COMMUNITY MEDICAL (PA)
101 Willmar Ave SW (56201-3556)
PHONE.............................320 231-5000
Ron Holmgren, *President*
Tom Rozendaal, *CFO*
Sherri Klaers, *Marketing Staff*
Lawrence Jedlicka MD, *Med Doctor*
James P Zwach MD, *Med Doctor*

EMP: 500 **EST:** 1971
SQ FT: 140,000 **Privately Held**
WEB: www.acmc.com
SIC: 8011 Clinic operated by physicians

(G-9981)
AGRI TEMPS INC
1701 2nd Ave SE (56201-3823)
PO Box 27 (56201-0027)
PHONE.............................320 235-5230
FAX: 320 231-1704
Les Shermack, *President*
EMP: 50
SALES (est): 1MM-4.9MM **Privately Held**
WEB: www.employment-plus.com
SIC: 7363 Help supply services
PA: Agri Temps Inc
920 Litchfield Ave SW
Willmar MN 56201
320 235-1707

(G-9982)
AGRI TEMPS INC (PA)
920 Litchfield Ave SW (56201-3115)
PHONE.............................320 235-1707
FAX: 320 235-8510
Les Chermak, *President*
Mary Warszynski, *Vice Pres*
Renae Chermak, *Treasurer*
EMP: 100 **EST:** 1986
SQ FT: 3,000 **Privately Held**
WEB: www.employment-plus.com
SIC: 7363 7361 Temporary help service; employment agency services

(G-9983)
AMERICAN WELDING & GAS
1909 Highway 12 W (56201-5843)
PO Box 30118, Billings MT (59107-0118)
PHONE.............................320 235-4774
Alvina Henrickson, *Principal*
Odee Hendrickson, *Principal*
Ron Adkins, *Principal*
Brian Henrickson, *Principal*
Tammy Gran, *Controller*
EMP: 25 **EST:** 1960
SALES (est): 10MM-24.9MM **Privately Held**
SIC: 5084 5169 Wholesales welding equipment & supplies; wholesales oxygen; wholesales industrial gases

(G-9984)
ARNOLD'S OF WILLMAR INC
4773 Highway 71 S (56201-9501)
PHONE.............................320 235-4898
Kraig Dejong, *Manager*
EMP: 28
SALES (est): 10MM-24.9MM **Privately Held**
SIC: 5083 Wholesales agricultural machinery & equipment

(G-9985)
BENNETT OFFICE TECHNOLOGIES
Also Called: Computerland
312 24th Ave SW (56201-5210)
PHONE.............................320 235-6425
Russell S Bennett, *President*
Nyla Fifield, *Purch Agent*
Jeff Jensen, *Manager*
Steve Gardner, *Consultant*
Mike Hawkenson, *Consultant*
EMP: 30 **EST:** 1969
SQ FT: 7,500
SALES (est): 10MM-24.9MM **Privately Held**
WEB: www.bennettoffice.com
SIC: 5045 5021 5044 7629 Wholesales computers, peripherals & software; electric business machine repair service; wholesales office equipment; wholesales office furniture

(G-9986)
BERNICK'S PEPSI COLA OF
Also Called: Pepsico
2400 19th Ave SW (56201-5808)
PO Box 7008, Saint Cloud (56302-7008)
PHONE.............................320 235-1370
Dean Bernick, *CEO*
Richard Bernick, *President*
EMP: 50 **EST:** 1970
SALES (est): 25MM-49.9MM **Privately Held**
SIC: 5149 Wholesales soft drinks

(G-9987)
BETHESDA
1012 3rd St SE (56201-4554)
PHONE.............................320 235-3924
Anhony Ogdahl, *Administrator*
EMP: 200
SALES (est): 5MM-9.9MM **Privately Held**
SIC: 8051 Skilled nursing care facility

(G-9988)
BETHESDA
1604 1st St S Ste 16 (56201-4243)
PHONE.............................320 235-8364
FAX: 320 235-6968
Pam Adam, *Administrator*
Jason Christopher, *IT/INT Sup*
Jana Smith, *Director*
Marlys Gustafson, *Nursing Dir*
EMP: 25
SALES (est): 1MM-4.9MM **Privately Held**
SIC: 8051 Skilled nursing care facility

(G-9989)
BETHESDA HERITAGE CENTER
1012 3rd St SE (56201-4554)
PHONE.............................320 235-3924
Anthony Ogdahl, *President*
Becki Kallevig, *Manager*
EMP: 99 **EST:** 2004
SALES (est): 1MM-4.9MM **Privately Held**
SIC: 8051 Convalescent home

(G-9990)
BNSF RAILWAY CO
400 Pacific Ave SW (56201-3252)
PO Box 1177 (56201-1177)
PHONE.............................320 231-5555
Jan Ruby, *Manager*
Tom Longanecker, *Manager*
Mike Babik, *Manager*
A J Cawson, *Manager*
EMP: 215
SALES (est): 25MM-49.9MM **Publicly Held**
WEB: www.bnsf.com
SIC: 4731 Railroad freight agency
HQ: Burlington Northern Santa Fe
2650 Lou Menk Dr
Fort Worth TX 76131
800 795-2673

(G-9991)
BOLTON & MENK INC
2040 Highway 12 E (56201-5818)
PHONE.............................320 231-3956
FAX: 320 231-9710
Malcom Tilberg, *Manager*
Keith Muetzel, *Manager*
Brad Dewolf, *Manager*
EMP: 28
SALES (est): 1MM-4.9MM **Privately Held**
WEB: www.bolton-menk.com
SIC: 8711 8713 Civil engineering services; surveying service
PA: Bolton & Menk Inc
1960 Premier Dr
Mankato MN 56001
507 625-4171

(G-9992)
BORDER STATES ELECTRIC SUPPLY
1209 Highway 12 E (56201-3742)
PHONE.............................320 214-4237
Lex Silbernagel, *Vice Pres*
Barry Nelson, *Vice Pres*
Gerald Buck, *Vice Pres*
Brian Becker, *Vice Pres*
Robert Burdette, *Vice Pres*
EMP: 136
SALES (est): 50MM-99.9MM **Privately Held**
WEB: www.bseweb.com
SIC: 5063 Wholesales electrical supplies
HQ: Border States Electric Supply
105 25th St N
Fargo ND 58102
701 293-5834

(G-9993)
BREMER BANK
500 Willmar Ave SE (56201-4590)
PHONE.............................320 235-1111
Greg Hilding, *President*
Roger Madison, *Senior VP*

www.HarrisInfo.com
430

2011 Harris Minnesota
Services Directory

▲=Import ▼=Export
◆=Import/Export

Kevin Dahl, *CFO*
Steve Jacobson, *IT/INT Sup*
Debra Zinda-Hanson, *Officer*
EMP: 50 **EST:** 1884
SALES (est): 10MM-24.9MM **Privately Held**
SIC: 6022 6021 State commercial bank;
national commercial bank
HQ: Bremer Financial Corp
445 Minnesota St Ste 2000
Saint Paul MN 55101
651 227-7621

(G-9994)
BUREAU OF COLLECTION RECOVERY
1009 16th St SW (56201-2821)
PHONE 320 214-8747
Mark Neal, *Finance Mgr*
Brenda McNichols, *Manager*
EMP: 40
SALES (est): 1MM-4.9MM **Privately Held**
WEB: www.nvars.com
SIC: 7322 Collection agency
HQ: Bureau of Collection Recovery
7575 Corporate Way
Eden Prairie MN 55344
952 934-7777

(G-9995)
CENTRAL ALLIED ENTERPRISES INC
Also Called: Willmar Readymix
605 Lakeland Dr NE (56201-2608)
PO Box 1317 (56201-1317)
PHONE 320 235-5846
Mary Grindy, *Division Mgr*
Gene Bertram, *Managing Dir*
Eugene Bertram, *Sales Staff*
John A Woodhall III, *Branch Mgr*
Curt Hirman, *Manager*
EMP: 68
SALES (est): 10MM-24.9MM **Privately Held**
SIC: 1611 General highway & street
construction service; manufactures
ready-mixed concrete

(G-9996)
CHAD MONSON EXCAVATING LLC
7600 Highway 71 S (56201-9628)
PHONE 320 995-6703
Joanne Monson, *Member*
Chad L Monson, *Mng Member*
Lisa Nelson, *Manager*
EMP: 70 **EST:** 2004
SALES (est): 5MM-9.9MM **Privately Held**
SIC: 1794 Excavating contractor

(G-9997)
CHAPIN ENTERPRISES INC
320 Becker Ave SW (56201-3341)
PO Box 934 (56201-0934)
PHONE 320 235-4386
John Chapin, *President*
Justin Chapin, *Corp Secy*
Frank E Chapin, *Vice Pres*
David Chapin, *Treasurer*
Butch Mellon, *Director*
EMP: 250 **EST:** 1920
SQ FT: 10,000
SALES (est): 25MM-49.9MM **Privately Held**
SIC: 1731 General electrical contractor

(G-9998)
CHYRSALIS OF KANDIYOHI COUNTY
1208 9th St SE (56201-5407)
PO Box 665 (56201-0665)
PHONE 320 231-1480
Louanne Kruger, *President*
EMP: 25 **EST:** 1992 **Privately Held**
SIC: 8399 Social services

(G-9999)
CONWAY, DEUTH & SCHMIESING
331 3rd St SW Ste 2 (56201-3322)
PHONE 320 235-3311
FAX: 320 235-7071
Brett Aamot, *Partner*
Milan Schmiesing CPA, *Partner*
Mark Olson, *Partner*
James Gilman, *Partner*
Larry Stulen, *Partner*

EMP: 25 **EST:** 1979
SQ FT: 8,000
SALES (est): 1MM-4.9MM **Privately Held**
SIC: 8721 Certified public accountant
services

(G-10000)
DIVERSIFIED LIFESTYLES INC
1111 6th St SE (56201-4637)
PHONE 320 235-0270
Beata Erickson, *CEO*
Tim Helgeson, *CEO*
EMP: 50 **EST:** 1991
SALES (est): 1MM-4.9MM **Privately Held**
SIC: 8361 Residential care facility

(G-10001)
FAMILY PRACTICE MEDICAL CENTER
502 2nd St SW Ste 1 (56201-3365)
PO Box 957 (56201-0957)
PHONE 320 235-7232
FAX: 320 231-8602
Mike Morris MD, *President*
Barbara Swenson, *Business Mgr*
Kevin Switzer, *Corp Secy*
Andrew Hoffmann, *Vice Pres*
Alan Roiseland, *Vice Pres*
EMP: 43 **EST:** 1984
SALES (est): 1MM-4.9MM **Privately Held**
SIC: 8011 General & family practice
physician or surgeon office; physicians'
office

(G-10002)
G&S STAFFING SERVICES INC
305 7th St SW Ste 4 (56201-2790)
PHONE 320 235-3949
FAX: 320 235-0993
Sandra K Nielsen, *President*
EMP: 600 **EST:** 1991
SQ FT: 1,000
SALES (est): 10MM-24.9MM **Privately Held**
SIC: 7389 Telemarketing services

(G-10003)
GREATER MINNESOTA FAMILY SVCS
513 5th St SW (56201-3216)
PO Box 1810 (56201-1810)
PHONE 320 214-9692
FAX: 320 214-9924
George Dubie, *CEO*
Steve Michaud, *President*
Thomas Belcher, *CFO*
Jeff Hess, *Director*
Jaci Finneman, *Director*
EMP: 75 **EST:** 1996
SQ FT: 2,200
SALES (est): 1MM-4.9MM **Privately Held**
WEB: www.greaterminnesota.org
SIC: 8322 Family counseling services

(G-10004)
GREATER MINNESOTA FAMILY SVCS
3619 15th Ave SW (56201-9706)
PHONE 320 235-3664
Steve Mashad, *Exec Dir*
George Dubie, *Director*
EMP: 70 **EST:** 1993
SALES (est): 1MM-4.9MM **Privately Held**
SIC: 8322 General counseling services

(G-10005)
HANSON COMMUNICATIONS INC (PA)
1700 Technology Dr NE (56201-2284)
PO Box 800, Clara City (56222-0800)
PHONE 320 235-2260
FAX: 320 847-2736
Mark Hanson, *President*
Angela Hanson, *Corp Secy*
Bruce Hanson, *Treasurer*
Jamie Shaffer, *Bookkeeper*
EMP: 28 **EST:** 1952
SQ FT: 7,500 **Privately Held**
SIC: 4813 Wired telecommunications carrier
& service

(G-10006)
HAUG IMPLEMENT CO (PA)
3711 Highway 12 E (56201-5809)
PO Box 1055 (56201-1055)
PHONE 320 235-8115
FAX: 320 214-9824
Donald Haug Jr, *President*
Caryl Haug, *Corp Secy*
Gunder Haug, *Vice Pres*
EMP: 25 **EST:** 1930
SQ FT: 29,000 **Privately Held**
WEB: www.haugimp.com
SIC: 5083 Wholesales agricultural
machinery & equipment; wholesales lawn &
garden machinery & equipment

(G-10007)
HEARTLAND COMMUNITY ACTION
409 19th Ave SW (56201-5246)
PO Box 1359 (56201-1359)
PHONE 320 235-0850
FAX: 320 235-7703
Paula Holstrom, *Corp Secy*
Bridgett Ouren, *Corp Secy*
Jay Kieft, *Director*
Linda Lacey, *Executive Asst*
EMP: 25 **EST:** 1966
SQ FT: 8,000 **Privately Held**
SIC: 8399 Community action agency

(G-10008)
HERITAGE BANK
310 1st St S (56201-3304)
PO Box 1124 (56201-1124)
PHONE 320 235-5720
Wayne Nelson, *President*
Jeff Asche, *Vice Pres*
Vera Novak, *Vice Pres*
Duaine Amundson, *Vice Pres*
Robert Krattenmaker, *CFO*
EMP: 50 **EST:** 1912
SQ FT: 2,500
SALES (est): 10MM-24.9MM **Privately Held**
SIC: 6022 State commercial bank

(G-10009)
HINW LLC
Also Called: Holiday Inn Arbor Lakes
103 15th Ave NW Ste 200 (56201-2195)
PO Box 1020 (56201-1020)
PHONE 763 425-3800
Patrick Bisson, *General Mgr*
EMP: 120 **EST:** 2001
SALES (est): 5MM-9.9MM **Privately Held**
SIC: 7011 Traveler accommodations

(G-10010)
HOME DEPOT USA INC
300 28th Ave SE (56201-4259)
PHONE 320 235-1975
FAX: 320 231-0174
Jody Bjerke, *Human Res Mgr*
Chris Loxtercamp, *Manager*
EMP: 150
SALES (est): 25MM-49.9MM **Publicly Held**
SIC: 7359 Home center store; tool rental
HQ: Home Depot International Inc
2455 Paces Ferry Rd SE
Atlanta GA 30339
770 319-1669

(G-10011)
JENNIE-O TURKEY STORE INC (HQ)
2505 Willmar Ave SW (56201-2711)
PO Box 778 (56201-0778)
PHONE 320 235-2622
FAX: 320 231-7100
Mike Tolbert, *President*
Jeff Ehinger, *COO*
Gary Matthyf, *Senior VP*
Gary Matthys, *Senior VP*
David Dohman, *Vice Pres*
▼ **EMP:** 240 **EST:** 1949
SQ FT: 250,000
SALES (corp-wide): 6.53B **Publicly Held**
WEB: www.hormel.com
SIC: 0253 Turkey processing &
slaughtering; turkey farm
PA: Hormel Foods Corp
1 Hormel Pl
Austin MN 55912
507 437-5611

(G-10012)
KANDI ENTERTAINMENT CENTER INC
Also Called: 19th Ave Grill & Lounge
500 19th Ave SE (56201-5300)
PHONE 320 235-3800
FAX: 320 235-0575
Keith Pattison, *President*
Kent Larson, *General Mgr*
EMP: 52 **EST:** 1950
SQ FT: 36,000
SALES (est): 1MM-4.9MM **Privately Held**
WEB: www.k-e-c.com
SIC: 7933 Eating place; cocktail lounge;
bowling center

(G-10013)
KANDIYOHI COUNTY ECONOMIC
Also Called: Kandihyohi Cnty Rrl Dvl Financ
333 Litchfield Ave SW # 100 (56201-3352)
PO Box 1783 (56201-1783)
PHONE 320 235-7370
FAX: 320 231-2320
Steve Renquist, *Director*
EMP: 30 **EST:** 1989
SALES (est): 1MM-4.9MM **Privately Held**
SIC: 8748 8611 Economic consultant;
business association

(G-10014)
KANDIYOHI POWER COOPERATIVE
1311 Highway 71 NE (56201-2174)
PO Box 40, Spicer (56288-0040)
PHONE 320 235-4155
David J George, *CEO*
EMP: 32 **EST:** 1935
SQ FT: 12,000
SALES (est): 10MM-24.9MM **Privately Held**
WEB: www.kpcoop.com
SIC: 4911 Electric power distribution service

(G-10015)
KEVIN SWITZER
502 2nd St SW (56201-3337)
PHONE 320 231-8888
Kevin Switzer, *Principal*
EMP: 50 **EST:** 1976
SALES (est): 1MM-4.9MM **Privately Held**
WEB: www.kevinswitzer.com
SIC: 8049 Health practitioners' office

(G-10016)
LAKELAND BROADCASTING CO INC
Also Called: Kwlm-AM
1340 N 7th St (56201)
PHONE 320 235-1340
Stephen W Linder, *President*
Doug Loy, *General Mgr*
Paul Linder, *Vice Pres*
Michael Schroeder, *Engineering*
EMP: 32 **EST:** 1939
SQ FT: 22,000
SALES (est): 1MM-4.9MM **Privately Held**
WEB: www.kwlm.com
SIC: 4832 Radio broadcasting station

(G-10017)
LAND O'LAKES PURINA FEED LLC
22nd St SW (56201)
PO Box 1297 (56201-1297)
PHONE 320 235-6000
FAX: 320 235-6007
Steve Reuvers, *Plant Mgr*
Steve Reuvrf, *Manager*
Val Jenson, *Manager*
EMP: 25
SALES (est): 10MM-24.9MM **Privately Held**
WEB: www.landolakes.com
SIC: 5191 Wholesales feed
HQ: Land O'Lakes Purina Feed LLC
1080 County Rd Fw Fw
Saint Paul MN 55126
800 851-8810

(G-10018)
LARRY A LARSON
5479 15th St SE (56201-9515)
PHONE 320 235-1294
Larry A Larson, *Owner*

(PA)=Parent Co (HQ)=Headquarters (DH)=Div Headquarters
✪ = New business established in last 2 years

2011 Harris Minnesota
Services Directory

© Harris InfoSource 1-866-281-6415

431

EMP: 50 EST: 1976 **Privately Held**
SIC: 0762 0116 Farm management services; soybean farm

(G-10019)
LIFE-SCIENCE INNOVATIONS LLC
1800 Technology Dr NE (56201-2280)
PO Box 753 (56201-0753)
PHONE..............................320 222-9750
Joellen Rosendahl, *Mng Member*
EMP: 50 EST: 2005
SALES (est): 5MM-9.9MM **Privately Held**
SIC: 8742 Administrative services consultant

(G-10020)
LUTHERAN SOCIAL SERVICE OF MN
1601 Highway 12 E Ste 6 (56201-5817)
PHONE..............................320 235-5411
Jerry Gustafson, *Manager*
Cherish Holland, *Manager*
Tim Johnson, *Manager*
EMP: 25
SALES (est): 1MM-4.9MM **Privately Held**
WEB: www.lssmn.org
SIC: 8322 Social services center
PA: Lutheran Social Service Of MN
2485 Como Ave
Saint Paul MN 55108
651 642-5990

(G-10021)
MAGNUSON HUISINGA & SONS INC (PA)
2020 5th St SW (56201-5204)
PHONE..............................320 599-4474
Donald Magnuson, *President*
Craig Aurand, *Vice Pres*
Jerry Magnuson, *Vice Pres*
Pat Walter, *Foreman/Supr*
EST: 1978 **Privately Held**
SIC: 1711 Warm air heating & air conditioning contractor

(G-10022)
MICHAEL J MORRIS
502 2nd St SW (56201-3337)
PHONE..............................320 231-8888
Michael J Morris, *Principal*
Gary McDowell, *Administrator*
EMP: 45 EST: 1976
SALES (est): 1MM-4.9MM **Privately Held**
SIC: 8049 Health practitioners' office

(G-10023)
MIDWEST DATA INC
3735 County Road 5 SW (56201-9712)
PHONE..............................320 235-8880
FAX: 320 235-8889
Glenn Miller, *General Mgr*
Rayburn Norling, *Vice Pres*
Chris Goldenstein, *Manager*
EMP: 25 EST: 1969
SQ FT: 3,000
SALES (est): 1MM-4.9MM **Privately Held**
WEB: www.mwd-inc.com
SIC: 7374 5045 Data processing service; wholesales computer software; wholesales personal & home entertainment computers & accessories

(G-10024)
MILLS PONTIAC, BUICK (HQ)
Also Called: Manley Toyota
2000 1st St S (56201-4200)
PO Box 1118 (56201-1118)
PHONE..............................320 231-1160
Stewart C Mills Jr, *President*
Thomas W Green, *Vice Pres*
Wayne Hanson, *Manager*
EMP: 45 EST: 1947
SQ FT: 20,000 **Privately Held**
WEB: www.millsauto.com
SIC: 5013 Retails new & used automobiles; wholesales automotive supplies & parts; retails new & used pickups; retails new & used vans
PA: Mills Motor Inc
512 Laurel St
Brainerd MN 56401
218 829-3521

(G-10025)
MILLS PONTIAC, BUICK
2000 1st S (56201-4200)
PHONE..............................320 231-1160
Rick Hess, *General Mgr*
EMP: 30
SALES (est): 10MM-24.9MM **Privately Held**
WEB: www.millsauto.com
SIC: 5013 Retails new & used automobiles; wholesales automotive supplies & parts; retails new & used pickups; retails new & used vans
HQ: Mills Pontiac, Buick
2000 1st St S
Willmar MN 56201
320 231-1160

(G-10026)
MINNESOTA DEPARTMENT OF
Also Called: Prairie Lakes Youth Program
1808 Civic Center Dr (56201-9446)
PO Box 894 (56201-0894)
PHONE..............................320 231-1729
FAX: 320 231-1166
Barb Aginen, *Exec Dir*
Darin Blaken, *Director*
Barb Heinen, *Director*
EMP: 50 **Privately Held**
WEB: www.minncor.com
SIC: 8641 Youth organizations; business persons club
DH: Department of Corrections MN
1450 Energy Park Dr # 200
Saint Paul MN 55108
651 361-7200

(G-10027)
MONSON CORP ✪
7600 Highway 71 S (56201-9628)
PHONE..............................320 995-6703
Chad Monson, *CEO*
Joanne Monson, *Corp Secy*
EMP: 60 EST: 2008
SQ FT: 12,725
SALES (est): 10MM-24.9MM **Privately Held**
SIC: 1542 Commercial & office building contractor

(G-10028)
MORGAN TIRE & AUTO LLC
Also Called: Team Tires Plus
1801 1st St S (56201-4225)
PHONE..............................320 235-1073
FAX: 320 235-7720
Jarrett Mohr, *Manager*
EMP: 30
SALES (est): 1MM-4.9MM **Privately Held**
WEB: www.bfsusa.com
SIC: 7534 Tire recapping & retreading services
HQ: Bfs Retail Operations LLC
333 E Lake St Ste 300
Bloomingdale IL 60108
630 259-9000

(G-10029)
NELSON LEASING INC (PA)
2700 Highway 12 E (56201-5830)
PO Box 993 (56201-0993)
PHONE..............................320 235-2770
FAX: 320 235-7780
Dale Nelson, *President*
Roxanne Nelson, *Corp Secy*
Ryan Nelson, *Vice Pres*
Gordon J Herdman, *CFO*
Roxanne Wittman, *Treasurer*
EMP: 50 EST: 1964
SQ FT: 26,000
SALES (corp-wide): 30M **Privately Held**
WEB: www.nelsonleasing.com
SIC: 7513 5012 7538 Truck leasing service, without drivers; general truck repair services; wholesales commercial trucks; retails auto & home supplies

(G-10030)
NORTHERN FACTORY SALES INC
2701 4th Ave SW (56201-2778)
PO Box 660 (56201-0660)
PHONE..............................320 235-2288
FAX: 320 235-2297
Roger Gauquie, *President*
Brent Wessels, *General Mgr*
Chuck McKaige, *General Mgr*
Nathan Rohne, *Corp Secy*
Paul Freed, *VP Sls/Mktg*
▲ EMP: 38 EST: 1971
SQ FT: 100,000
SALES (est): 10MM-24.9MM **Privately Held**
WEB: www.northernfactorysales.com
SIC: 5013 Wholesales automotive supplies & parts; wholesales automotive heaters; wholesales automotive radiators; wholesales automotive tools & equipment

(G-10031)
NORTHERN STATES SUPPLY INC
Also Called: Kato Tool
600 Industrial Dr SW (56201-2717)
PO Box 1057 (56201-1057)
PHONE..............................320 235-0555
FAX: 320 235-0981
Robert Dols, *President*
Tina Erpenbach, *Vice Pres*
Don Nelson, *Vice Pres*
Doug Gilbertson, *Vice Pres*
Jackie Cunningham, *Human Res Dir*
EMP: 50 EST: 1960
SQ FT: 40,000
SALES (est): 10MM-24.9MM **Privately Held**
WEB: www.northernstatessupply.com
SIC: 5085 Wholesales industrial supplies; wholesales industrial fasteners including nuts, bolts, screws, etc; wholesales industrial tools

(G-10032)
NOVA-TECH ENGINEERING LLC
1705 Engineering Ave (56201-2282)
PHONE..............................320 231-9660
FAX: 320 231-9668
James Sieben, *General Mgr*
Vanda Heuring, *Member*
Jim Sensieben, *Vice Pres*
Matt Erickson, *Engineering*
Marc Gorans, *Mng Member*
EMP: 75 EST: 1992
SALES (est): 5MM-9.9MM **Privately Held**
SIC: 8711 Engineering services

(G-10033)
ORSTEN TURKEYS INC
8481 15th St NW (56201-8709)
PHONE..............................320 235-5751
Ray Orsten, *President*
Marge Orsten, *Treasurer*
EMP: 28 EST: 1970 **Privately Held**
SIC: 0253 Turkey egg farm

(G-10034)
PACT FOR FAMILIES
Also Called: Putting All Cmmnities Together
2200 23rd St NE (56201-6605)
PHONE..............................320 231-7030
FAX: 320 231-7033
Jolene Borka, *Principal*
Debb Sheehan, *Director*
EMP: 28 EST: 2004
SALES (est): 1MM-4.9MM **Privately Held**
WEB: www.co.kandiyohi.mn.us
SIC: 8322 Individual & family social services
PA: County of Kandiyohi
400 Benson Ave SW
Willmar MN 56201
320 231-6202

(G-10035)
PALS INC (PA)
3735 1st Ave W (56201-4374)
PO Box 753 (56201-0753)
PHONE..............................320 235-8860
Theodore Huisinga, *Ch of Bd*
Richard Huisinga, *President*
Ronald R Hanson, *Corp Secy*
Scott Norling, *Vice Pres*
Pam Schlagel, *Manager*
▲ EMP: 72 EST: 1951
SQ FT: 22,000 **Privately Held**
WEB: www.willmarpoultry.com
SIC: 5083 0253 0254 5191 8741 Wholesales poultry equipment; turkey farm; manufactures animal feed; wholesales animal feeds; wholesales livestock equipment; poultry hatchery; management services

(G-10036)
PALS INC
3735 County Road 5 SW (56201-9712)
PO Box 753 (56201-0753)
PHONE..............................320 235-8860
Theodre Huisinga, *CEO*
Rayburn Norling, *President*
Ronald R Hanson, *Treasurer*
Joellen Rosendhal, *Assistant*
EMP: 50 EST: 1965
SALES (est): 10MM-24.9MM **Privately Held**
SIC: 5083 Wholesales poultry & livestock equipment

(G-10037)
PERKINS LUMBER CO INC
1010 Benson Ave SW (56201-3109)
PO Box 508 (56201-0508)
PHONE..............................320 235-9420
John R Teigland, *President*
EMP: 30
SALES (est): 5MM-9.9MM **Privately Held**
WEB: www.perkinslumberco.com
SIC: 1542 Commercial & institutional building construction
PA: Perkins Lumber Co Inc
100 10th St NW
Willmar MN 56201
320 235-3242

(G-10038)
PRODUCTION CREDIT ASSOCIATION
Also Called: Farm Credit Services Minn Vly
3881 Abbott Dr (56201-9560)
PO Box 1560 (56201-1560)
PHONE..............................320 235-1771
Marcus L Knisely, *CEO*
Kevin J Foley, *Senior VP*
Ronald Fake, *CFO*
Jeffrey Schmidt, *Ch Credit Ofcr*
Lynda Hauge, *Manager*
EMP: 60 EST: 1933
SQ FT: 7,000
SALES (est): 25MM-49.9MM **Privately Held**
SIC: 6159 Farm mortgage service
PA: United Fcs
3881 Abbott Dr
Willmar MN 56201
320 235-1771

(G-10039)
REM SOUTHWEST SERVICES INC
903 Highway 71 NE (56201-2654)
PHONE..............................320 235-9174
Peg Dallman, *Manager*
EMP: 115
SALES (est): 1MM-4.9MM **Privately Held**
SIC: 8361 Home for the mentally handicapped
HQ: REM Southwest Services Inc
6600 France Ave S Ste 500
Edina MN 55435
952 925-5067

(G-10040)
RICE HOME MEDICAL LLC
Also Called: Home Medical
1033 19th Ave SW (56201-5005)
PHONE..............................320 235-8434
FAX: 320 235-6855
Paul Prokosch, *Finance*
Lisa Ziehl, *Branch Mgr*
Carol Laumer, *Exec Dir*
EMP: 37 EST: 1988
SQ FT: 4,500
SALES (est): 5MM-9.9MM **Privately Held**
WEB: www.ricehomemedical.com
SIC: 7352 5047 Medical equipment leasing & rental; wholesales medical & hospital equipment; retails medical apparatus & supplies

(G-10041)
RICE MEMORIAL HOSPITAL (HQ)
301 Becker Ave SW (56201-3302)
PHONE..............................320 235-4543
FAX: 320 231-4869
Michael Schramm, *CEO*
Troy Barrick, *Corp Secy*
Kevin W Unger, *Ch of Surgery*

Sharon H Banister, *Ch Pathology*
Nihar S Shah, *Ch Radiology*
EMP: 150 **EST:** 1937
SQ FT: 300,000 **Privately Held**
WEB: www.ricehospital.com
SIC: 8062 Medical hospital
PA: Willmar, City of Inc
333 6th St SW Ste 1
Willmar MN 56201
320 235-4913

(G-10042)
RICE MEMORIAL HOSPITAL
2200 23rd St NE (56201-6600)
PHONE..............................320 231-7077
Jean Urban, *Director*
EMP: 50
SALES (est): 1MM-4.9MM **Privately Held**
WEB: www.ricehospital.com
SIC: 8082 Home health care services
HQ: Rice Memorial Hospital
301 Becker Ave SW
Willmar MN 56201
320 235-4543

(G-10043)
RICE MEMORIAL HOSPITAL
311 3rd St SW (56201-3322)
PHONE..............................320 231-4175
FAX: 320 231-4575
Lynn Stier, *Branch Mgr*
EMP: 30
SALES (est): 1MM-4.9MM **Privately Held**
WEB: www.ricehospital.com
SIC: 8049 8093 Physical therapist office;
outpatient rehabilitation treatment center
HQ: Rice Memorial Hospital
301 Becker Ave SW
Willmar MN 56201
320 235-4543

(G-10044)
SHELTER HOUSE
804 Willmar Ave SE (56201-4603)
PO Box 568 (56201-0568)
PHONE..............................320 235-0962
Connie Schmoll, *Director*
EMP: 30 **EST:** 1998
SQ FT: 10,000
SALES (est): 1MM-4.9MM **Privately Held**
WEB: www.willmarshelter.com
SIC: 8322 Emergency shelters

(G-10045)
SPECTRUM COMMUNITY HEALTH INC
Also Called: Nursing Enterprise
1415 1st St S Ste 1C (56201-6403)
PHONE..............................320 235-5684
FAX: 320 214-0896
Shawn Franklin, *Manager*
Terry King, *Manager*
EMP: 40
SALES (est): 1MM-4.9MM **Privately Held**
SIC: 8082 Home health care services
PA: Spectrum Community Health Inc
6205 Crossman Ln
Inver Grove Heights MN 55076
612 617-1190

(G-10046)
STACY'S NURSERY INC
2305 Highway 12 E (56201-5823)
PO Box 229 (56201-0229)
PHONE..............................320 235-6010
FAX: 320 235-6010
Stacy Fladeboe, *President*
EMP: 25 **EST:** 1978
SALES (est): 5MM-9.9MM **Privately Held**
WEB: www.stacysnursery.com
SIC: 0781 Retail nurseries; landscape
planning services

(G-10047)
SWENSON MOTOR CO
1301 Highway 12 E (56201-3744)
PO Box 814 (56201-0814)
PHONE..............................320 235-3434
FAX: 320 214-3433
Roland E Swenson, *President*
Marguerite Swenson, *Treasurer*
Alan Peterson, *Finance Mgr*
Kevin Reineke, *Sales Mgr*
James Jacobson, *Manager*
EMP: 41

EST: 1946
SQ FT: 23,100
SALES (est): 10MM-24.9MM **Privately Held**
WEB: www.swensonmotors.com
SIC: 7532 7538 Retails new & used
automobiles; general automotive repair
services; retails new & used pickups; retails
new & used vans; automotive body shop

(G-10048)
TPI CORE INC
Also Called: Green Mill
2100 Highway 12 E (56201-5819)
PHONE..............................320 231-2301
Thomas R Torgerson, *CEO*
Andy Pirrotta, *General Mgr*
Sheryl D Walton, *Senior VP*
Traci Buchtel, *Manager*
Mike Lamouriex, *Manager*
EMP: 99
SALES (est): 5MM-9.9MM **Privately Held**
WEB: www.torgersonproperties.com
SIC: 7011 Traveler accommodations
PA: Torgerson Properties Inc
103 15th Ave NW Ste 200
Willmar MN 56201
320 235-7207

(G-10049)
UNITED FCS (PA)
3881 Abbott Dr (56201-9560)
PO Box 1560 (56201-1560)
PHONE..............................320 235-1771
Marc Knisley, *CEO*
Ronald Fake, *CFO*
Darrell Busselman, *Technician*
Sharon Eckhart, *Admin Asst*
EMP: 28 **EST:** 1918 **Privately Held**
SIC: 6111 Federal credit agency

(G-10050)
UNITED PARCEL SERVICE INC
Also Called: UPS
2200 Trott Ave SW (56201-2723)
PHONE..............................320 235-6615
Ran Betzler, *Branch Mgr*
EMP: 45
SALES (est): 1MM-4.9MM **Publicly Held**
WEB: www.ups.com
SIC: 4215 Package delivery services by
vehicle
HQ: United Parcel Service Inc
55 Glenlake Pkwy NE
Atlanta GA 30328
404 828-6000

(G-10051)
VALLEY NATIONAL GASES WV LLC
1501 Highway 12 E (56201-3748)
PHONE..............................320 235-3430
EMP: 27
SALES (est): 1MM-4.9MM **Privately Held**
WEB: www.vngas.com
SIC: 5172 Retails medical apparatus &
supplies; wholesales gases
HQ: Valley National Gases Wv LLC
6500 Rockside Rd Ste 200
Independence OH 44131
216 573-9909

(G-10052)
WELDERS SUPPLY CO INC
1501 Highway 12 E (56201-3748)
PO Box 1073 (56201-1073)
PHONE..............................320 235-3430
Thomas Reynolds, *President*
David Reed, *Manager*
Reynolds William, *Director*
Bill Reynolds, *Director*
EMP: 33 **EST:** 1947
SQ FT: 12,000
SALES (est): 10MM-24.9MM **Privately Held**
WEB: www.welderssupplycoinc.com
SIC: 5085 5084 Wholesales welding
supplies; retails welding supplies;
wholesales welding equipment & supplies

(G-10053)
WEST CENTRAL INC
2700 Trott Ave SW (56201-2777)
PO Box 897 (56201-0897)
PHONE..............................320 235-8518
FAX: 320 235-7929
Robert V Diest, *Ch of Bd*

Bruce Moen, *President*
Mike Fiebelkorn, *Corp Secy*
Pat Maiers, *Vice Pres*
Dale Engan, *Treasurer*
EMP: 30 **EST:** 1974
SQ FT: 40,000
SALES (est): 10MM-24.9MM **Privately Held**
SIC: 5191 Wholesales agricultural
chemicals; wholesales agricultural fertilizer

(G-10054)
WEST CENTRAL INDUSTRIES INC (PA)
1300 22nd St SW (56201-2728)
PHONE..............................320 235-5310
FAX: 320 235-5376
Darrell Ruch, *Vice Pres*
Steve Byers, *CFO*
Charles N Oakes, *Exec Dir*
Renee Nolting, *Director*
Oliver Krage, *Director*
EMP: 61 **EST:** 1963
SQ FT: 63,000
SALES (corp-wide): 4.23M **Privately Held**
WEB: www.westcentralindustries.com
SIC: 8331 Job training services; work
experience center

(G-10055)
WEST CENTRAL STEEL INC
110 19th St NW (56201-2427)
PO Box 1178 (56201-1178)
PHONE..............................320 235-4070
Delbert A Allinder, *Ch of Bd*
Jeffrey D Pattison, *President*
Jeffrey Allinder, *Corp Secy*
Dave Runke, *Mfg Staff*
Barb Zwagerman, *Purchasing*
EMP: 125 **EST:** 1961
SQ FT: 150,000
SALES (est): 100MM-499.9MM **Privately Held**
WEB: www.wcsteel.com
SIC: 5051 Metal service center

(G-10056)
WILLMAR, CITY OF INC
Also Called: Willmar Municpl Utilities Comm
700 Litchfield Ave SW (56201-3111)
PO Box 937 (56201-0937)
PHONE..............................320 235-4422
FAX: 320 235-3980
Bruce Gomm, *General Mgr*
Steve Wearda, *Purch Agent*
Tess Stoffel, *Accounting Staf*
Larry Heinen, *Manager*
Michael Sangren, *Programmer Anys*
EMP: 57
SALES (est): 25MM-49.9MM **Privately Held**
SIC: 4939 4911 4941 Combination utilities
services; electric services; water supply
services
PA: Willmar, City of Inc
333 6th St SW Ste 1
Willmar MN 56201
320 235-4913

(G-10057)
WILPRO INC
3735 County Road 5 SW (56201-9712)
PO Box 753 (56201-0753)
PHONE..............................320 235-8850
Theodore Huisinga, *CEO*
Rayburn Norling, *President*
Ronald R Hanson, *Corp Secy*
Richard Huisinga, *Exec VP*
EMP: 70 **EST:** 1988
SALES (est): 10MM-24.9MM **Privately Held**
SIC: 7389 Brokers on a contract basis

(G-10058)
WOODLAND CENTERS (PA)
1125 6th St SE (56201-4675)
PO Box 787 (56201-0787)
PHONE..............................320 235-4613
FAX: 320 231-9140
Paulette Hentz, *Facilities Mgr*
Linda Hocm, *Invest Mgr*
Donna Rupp, *Bookkeeper*
Scott Nelson, *Human Res Dir*
Jane Bonynge, *Accounts Mgr*
EMP: 100 **EST:** 1957
SQ FT: 15,000
SALES (corp-wide): 9.79M **Privately Held**
WEB: www.woodlandcenters.com

SIC: 8049 8093 8322 Mental health
practitioners' office; individual & family
social services; specialty outpatient clinic

(G-10059)
YMCA
1000 Lakeland Dr SE (56201-4708)
PHONE..............................320 222-9622
Karen Carlson, *Principal*
EMP: 80 **EST:** 1998 **Privately Held**
WEB: www.kandiymca.org
SIC: 8641 7032 7991 8322 8351 Youth
organizations; youth camps; child day care
service; individual & family social services;
physical fitness center

WILLOW RIVER
Pine County

(G-10060)
DANELSKI CONSTRUCTION CO INC
8087 County Highway 61 (55795-9786)
PO Box 126 (55795-0126)
PHONE..............................218 372-3236
FAX: 218 372-3236
Gary Danelski, *President*
EMP: 25 **EST:** 1960
SQ FT: 5,000
SALES (est): 1MM-4.9MM **Privately Held**
SIC: 1623 Telephone & communication line
construction

(G-10061)
MLASKOCH EXCAVATING INC
8060 Park Dr (55795-9782)
PO Box 185 (55795-0185)
PHONE..............................218 372-4067
FAX: 218 372-4242
Bradd L Mlaskoch, *Owner*
Danielle Mlaskoch, *Vice Pres*
Linda Hyska, *Executive*
EMP: 70 **EST:** 1993
SALES (est): 5MM-9.9MM **Privately Held**
SIC: 1623 Underground utilities contractor

(G-10062)
MLASKOCH UTILITY CONSTRUCTION
3006 County Road 43 (55795-9746)
PO Box 65 (55795-0065)
PHONE..............................218 372-3977
FAX: 218 372-4190
Ron Mlaskoch, *President*
Amy Johonson, *Corp Secy*
Gordon Eaton, *Vice Pres*
EMP: 40 **EST:** 1980
SALES (est): 5MM-9.9MM **Privately Held**
SIC: 1623 Underground utilities contractor

(G-10063)
WRIGHT'S GENERAL CONSTRUCTION
8098 County Highway 61 (55795-9786)
PO Box 127 (55795-0127)
PHONE..............................218 372-3329
FAX: 218 372-3558
Terry Wright, *President*
Linda Wright, *Corp Secy*
John Bonk, *Vice Pres*
EMP: 30 **EST:** 1962
SALES (est): 1MM-4.9MM **Privately Held**
SIC: 1623 Cable laying service

WILMONT
Nobles County

(G-10064)
WILMONT FARMERS ELEVATOR CO
101 N 4th Ave (56185-9762)
PO Box 219 (56185-0219)
PHONE..............................507 926-5131
Russ Crawford, *President*
EMP: 32 **EST:** 1912
SALES (est): 50MM-99.9MM **Privately Held**

(PA)=Parent Co (HQ)=Headquarters (DH)=Div Headquarters
✪ = New business established in last 2 years

2011 Harris Minnesota
Services Directory

© Harris InfoSource 1-866-281-6415
433

GEOGRAPHIC

SIC: 5153 5191 Wholesales grains; wholesales agricultural fertilizer; wholesales agricultural chemicals; wholesales corn; wholesales oats; wholesales soybeans; wholesales feed; wholesales field, garden & flower seeds

WINDOM
Cottonwood County

(G-10065)
BANK MIDWEST
245 9th St (56101-1642)
PO Box 189 (56101-0189)
PHONE..............................507 831-1322
Juhl Erickson, *Manager*
EMP: 30
SALES (est): 5MM-9.9MM **Privately Held**
SIC: 6022 State commercial bank
PA: Bank Midwest
118 Downtown Plz
Fairmont MN 56031
507 235-3327

(G-10066)
BANK MIDWEST
245 9th St (56101-1642)
PO Box 189 (56101-0189)
PHONE..............................507 831-1322
Juhl Erickson, *Branch Mgr*
EMP: 30
SALES (est): 5MM-9.9MM **Privately Held**
SIC: 6021 National commercial bank
PA: Bank Midwest
118 Downtown Plz
Fairmont MN 56031
507 235-3327

(G-10067)
EVANGELICAL LUTHERAN GOOD
Also Called: Good Smrtan Communities Windom
705 6th St (56101-1814)
PHONE..............................507 831-1788
FAX: 507 831-0844
Margaret Horkey, *Mktg Dir*
Pat Bierman, *Manager*
Paula Sturm, *Administrator*
Nancy Wepplo, *Administrator*
Ken Marshal, *Administrator*
EMP: 125
SALES (est): 1MM-4.9MM **Privately Held**
WEB: www.good-sam.com
SIC: 8051 Convalescent home
PA: Evangelical Lutheran Good
4800 W 57th St
Sioux Falls SD 57108
605 362-3100

(G-10068)
HOME FOR CREATIVE LIVING INC
108 9th St (56101-1746)
PHONE..............................507 831-5033
FAX: 507 831-2612
Douglas Teigen, *President*
D W Olson, *Vice Chairman*
Larry Anderson, *Facilities Mgr*
Brenda Schenk, *Manager*
EMP: 95 **EST:** 1977
SALES (est): 1MM-4.9MM **Privately Held**
SIC: 8361 8052 Home for the mentally retarded; intermediate care facility

(G-10069)
MINNESOTA DEPARTMENT OF TRANS
Also Called: District 7b
180 County Road 26 (56101-1868)
PHONE..............................507 831-1200
FAX: 507 831-1232
Keith Bloomgren, *Engineer*
Pat Spencer, *Personnel*
George Welk, *Manager*
Gordon Regenscheid, *Manager*
Donna Gravely, *Supervisor*
EMP: 90
SALES (est): 10MM-24.9MM **Privately Held**
WEB: www.me.umn.edu

SIC: 1542 Commercial & institutional building construction; transportation program regulation & administration services; state government transportation program regulation or administration
DH: Minnesota Department of Trans
395 John Ireland Blvd
Saint Paul MN 55155
651 296-3000

(G-10070)
PRAIRIE ARTS CONTINUUM
183 1/2 10th St (56101-1553)
PHONE..............................507 831-4862
Tamara Bell, *President*
EMP: 40 **EST:** 2001
SALES (est): 1MM-4.9MM **Privately Held**
SIC: 7389 Business services at a non-commercial site

(G-10071)
SCHWALBACH HARDWARE INC
193 9th St (56101-1770)
PHONE..............................507 831-2523
FAX: 507 831-5343
Michael Schwalbach, *President*
Rich Eisder, *Corp Secy*
Steve Beihoffer, *Manager*
EMP: 26 **EST:** 1946
SQ FT: 31,000
SALES (est): 1MM-4.9MM **Privately Held**
SIC: 1711 Plumbing service; warm air heating & air conditioning contractor; hardware store

(G-10072)
WINDOM, CITY OF INC
2150 Hospital Dr (56101-1287)
PO Box 339 (56101-0339)
PHONE..............................507 831-2400
Marcia Fast, *Corp Secy*
Jane Polz, *Corp Secy*
Monica Maurer, *Purchasing*
Randy Johnson, *Engineering*
Kim Armstrong, *CFO*
EMP: 100
SALES (est): 5MM-9.9MM **Privately Held**
WEB: www.windom-mn.com
SIC: 8062 Medical hospital
PA: Windom, City of Inc
444 9th St
Windom MN 56101
507 831-6129

WINDOM
Jackson County

(G-10073)
FORTUNE TRANSPORTATION CO
93702 470th Ave (56101-4201)
PHONE..............................507 831-2335
FAX: 507 831-5861
Donavan J Olson, *President*
Sharon Olson, *Corp Secy*
EMP: 95 **EST:** 1980
SQ FT: 9,800
SALES (est): 10MM-24.9MM **Privately Held**
WEB: www.fortunetransportation.com
SIC: 4213 Over the road trucking

WINGER
Polk County

(G-10074)
ULTIMA BANK MINNESOTA (PA)
Main St (56592)
PO Box 9 (56592-0009)
PHONE..............................218 938-4144
Arnold K Skeie, *President*
Peggy Ystenes, *Senior VP*
Ronald Lemer, *Manager*
EST: 1904
SALES (corp-wide): 4.84M **Privately Held**
SIC: 6022 State commercial bank

WINNEBAGO
Faribault County

(G-10075)
AMERICAN BAPTIST HOMES OF THE
Also Called: Parker Oaks
211 6th St NW (56098-1067)
PHONE..............................507 893-3171
FAX: 507 893-3174
Penny Hummer, *Finance Dir*
Linda Henry, *Human Res Mgr*
Lynette Dorfner, *Mktg Dir*
Sonya Prange, *Manager*
Deb Barnes, *Administrator*
EMP: 80
SALES (est): 1MM-4.9MM **Privately Held**
WEB: www.abhomes.net
SIC: 8051 8052 Skilled nursing care facility; intermediate care facility
PA: American Baptist Homes of The
14850 Scenic Heights Rd
Eden Prairie MN 55344
952 941-3175

(G-10076)
J-M MANUFACTURING CO INC
743 Main St S (56098-1062)
PO Box 6 (56098-0006)
PHONE..............................507 893-3121
FAX: 507 893-3569
Harvey Dontje, *Plant Mgr*
Jane Myers, *Manager*
Larry Sicker, *Manager*
David Schnieder, *MIS/IT Dir*
▲ **EMP:** 55
SALES (est): 10MM-24.9MM **Privately Held**
WEB: www.fpcusa.com
SIC: 5162 Manufactures plastic pipe; wholesales plastics products
HQ: J-M Manufacturing Co Inc
5200 W Century Blvd
Los Angeles CA 90045
800 621-4404

(G-10077)
MINNESOTA ELECTRIC TECHNOLOGY
352 Main St S (56098-2102)
PO Box 716 (56098-0716)
PHONE..............................507 893-3181
FAX: 507 893-3881
John Kvamme, *Vice Pres*
Melanie Phillips, *Purchasing*
Bruce Boulester, *Accounting Dir*
Kurt Whibeck, *Manager*
EMP: 30
SQ FT: 15,000
SALES (est): 1MM-4.9MM **Privately Held**
WEB: www.metmotors.com
SIC: 5063 Manufactures electric motors; wholesales electric motors
PA: Minnesota Electric Technology
1507 1st Ave
Mankato MN 56001
507 625-6117

(G-10078)
WEERTS CONSTRUCTION INC
Also Called: Blue Valley Sod
524 Main St S (56098-1060)
PHONE..............................507 893-3313
Robert D Weerts, *President*
Gerry Eick, *CFO*
Mike Swenson, *Sales Staff*
Mike Sjursen, *Manager*
EMP: 30 **EST:** 1987
SQ FT: 10,000 **Privately Held**
WEB: www.weertsconstruction.com
SIC: 0782 Lawn seeding services; sodding contractor

WINONA
Winona County

(G-10079)
ALLERGY & ASTHMA CLINIC
420 E Sarnia St Ste 1600 (55987-6413)
PHONE..............................507 474-7830
Marie Luhman, *Manager*
Linda Lindsey, *CTO*

Tweetie Ovaring, *Nursing Dir*
Terry Donnal, *Allrgy & Immnlg*
Robert T Giese, *Physician Asst*
EMP: 30 **EST:** 2007
SALES (est): 1MM-4.9MM **Privately Held**
SIC: 8011 Allergist office

(G-10080)
BENEDICTINE HEALTH SYSTEM
Also Called: Callista Court
1455 W Broadway St Ofc (55987-2385)
PHONE..............................507 457-0280
FAX: 507 494-5117
Marie Bunde, *Manager*
EMP: 40
SALES (est): 1MM-4.9MM **Privately Held**
SIC: 8051 Skilled nursing care facility
PA: Benedictine Health System
503 E 3rd St Ste 400
Duluth MN 55805
218 786-2370

(G-10081)
BEST WESTERN RIVERPORT INN
Also Called: Expresss Sweets Customer's
900 Bruski Dr (55987-6206)
PHONE..............................507 452-0606
FAX: 507 289-3987
Dave Gensen, *General Mgr*
Mike Rivers, *Principal*
EMP: 40 **EST:** 1992
SALES (est): 1MM-4.9MM **Privately Held**
SIC: 7011 Traveler accommodations

(G-10082)
BIESANZ STONE CO
4600 Goodview Rd (55987-6141)
PHONE..............................507 454-4336
FAX: 507 454-8140
Charles W Biesanz Jr, *President*
Barbara Pozanc, *Corp Secy*
EMP: 25 **EST:** 1902
SQ FT: 2,400
SALES (est): 1MM-4.9MM **Privately Held**
WEB: www.biesanzstone.com
SIC: 1411 Dimension travertine quarrying

(G-10083)
BLUFFVIEW MONTESSORI SCHOOL
1321 Gilmore Ave (55987-2459)
PHONE..............................507 452-2807
FAX: 507 452-6869
Leslie Hittner, *President*
Diana Price, *Librarian*
EMP: 50 **EST:** 1987
SQ FT: 33,100
SALES (est): 1MM-4.9MM **Privately Held**
WEB: www.bms.winona.k12.mn.us
SIC: 8351 Child development center providing Montessori based instruction

(G-10084)
BOB BRINK INC
165 Steuben St (55987-4636)
PHONE..............................507 452-1568
FAX: 507 452-8366
James L Brink, *CEO*
Robert W Brink, *President*
Joseph Matejka, *Controller*
Mary A Martin, *Agent*
EMP: 72 **EST:** 1963
SQ FT: 8,540
SALES (est): 5MM-9.9MM **Privately Held**
SIC: 4213 Over the road trucking

(G-10085)
BUB'S BREWING CO INC
65 E 4th St (55987-3577)
PHONE..............................507 457-3121
FAX: 507 453-0372
Bill Leaf, *President*
EMP: 25 **EST:** 1992
SALES (est): 500-999K **Privately Held**
SIC: 7299 Limited service food bars; banquet hall facility

(G-10086)
CATHOLIC CHARITIES OF THE
111 Market St Ste 2 (55987-5532)
PO Box 379 (55987-0379)
PHONE..............................507 454-2270
FAX: 507 457-3027

www.HarrisInfo.com
434

2011 Harris Minnesota
Services Directory

▲=Import ▼=Export
◆=Import/Export

Robert Tereba, *President*
Loyd Lenarz, *Director*
Jennifer Halberg, *Bd of Directors*
Valerie Cunningham, *Bd of Directors*
EMP: 50
SALES (est): 1MM-4.9MM **Privately Held**
 WEB: www.ccwinona.org
 SIC: 8322 General counseling services
 PA: Catholic Charities of The
   55 W Sanborn St
   Winona MN 55987
   507 454-4643

(G-10087)

CEDAR VALLEY GOLF COURSE INC

County Rd 9 (55987)
PO Box 1148 (55987-7148)
PHONE...............................507 457-3241
FAX: 507 457-3241
Vera Miller, *CEO*
Hugh L Miller, *President*
EMP: 35 **EST:** 1991
SQ FT: 5,000
SALES (est): 1MM-4.9MM **Privately Held**
 WEB: www.cedarvalleymn.com
 SIC: 7992 7999 Public golf course; retails
golf goods & equipment; cocktail lounge;
golf driving range; eating place

(G-10088)

CLC CHILDCARE CENTER

259 W Wabasha St (55987-3259)
PHONE...............................507 452-5493
Judy Manges, *Director*
EMP: 25 **EST:** 2005
SALES (est): 500-999K **Privately Held**
 SIC: 8351 Child day care service

(G-10089)

COUNTY OF WINONA

60 W 3rd St (55987-3431)
PHONE...............................507 457-6400
Lyn Theurer, *Administrator*
EMP: 50
SALES (est): 1MM-4.9MM **Privately Held**
 SIC: 8082 Home health care services;
county supervisors' & executives' office
 PA: County of Winona
   177 Main St
   Winona MN 55987
   507 457-6350

(G-10090)

COUNTY OF WINONA

Also Called: Winona County Dept Humn Svc
202 W 3rd St (55987-3146)
PHONE...............................507 457-6200
FAX: 507 457-6469
Craig Brooks, *Branch Mgr*
Christian R Gunderson, *Attorney*
Michael J Krage, *Attorney*
Dale E Meyer, *Attorney*
Steve Johnson, *Manager*
EMP: 75
SALES (est): 1MM-4.9MM **Privately Held**
 SIC: 8322 Individual & family social services
 PA: County of Winona
   177 Main St
   Winona MN 55987
   507 457-6350

(G-10091)

COUNTY OF WINONA

60 W 3rd St (55987-3431)
PHONE...............................507 457-6410
Lyn Theurer, *Manager*
EMP: 50
SALES (est): 1MM-4.9MM **Privately Held**
 SIC: 8322 Individual & family social
services; county supervisors' & executives'
office
 PA: County of Winona
   177 Main St
   Winona MN 55987
   507 457-6350

(G-10092)

DIGITAL TELECOMMUNICATIONS INC

Also Called: D T I
111 Riverfront Ste 305 (55987-3456)
PO Box 107 (55987-0107)
PHONE...............................507 452-2303
FAX: 507 452-2598
Daniel H Arnold, *Ch of Bd*
Thomas Siewert, *President*
Christopher Arnold, *Corp Secy*
Kirsten Herrick, *Vice Pres*
David A Watkins, *VP Sales*
EMP: 28 **EST:** 1998
SQ FT: 6,500 **Privately Held**
 WEB: www.pickdti.com
 SIC: 4813 Long distance telephone
communications services

(G-10093)

DISTRIBUTED WEBSITE CORP

60 Oakwood Ct (55987-6011)
PHONE...............................507 453-5164
FAX: 507 453-5166
Debra McClella, *Business Mgr*
Wil Andreasen, *Corp Secy*
Mark Kevitt, *COO*
Ray Dretske, *Manager*
Deborah McClellan, *Info Tech Dir*
EMP: 50 **EST:** 1993
SQ FT: 3,800
SALES (est): 10MM-24.9MM **Privately Held**
 WEB: www.dwebsite.com
 SIC: 7812 7371 8742 Motion picture &
video production services; management
consulting services; computer programming
service

(G-10094)

FARLEY'S & SATHERS CANDY CO

1000 W 5th St (55987-5123)
PHONE...............................507 452-3433
Rande Clerk, *Branch Mgr*
EMP: 223
SALES (est): 100MM-499.9MM **Privately Held**
 WEB: www.farleysandsathers.com
 SIC: 5145 Wholesales confectionery
products
 PA: Farley's & Sathers Candy Co
   1 Sather Plz
   Round Lake MN 56167
   507 945-8181

(G-10095)

FASTENAL CO (PA)

2001 Theurer Blvd (55987-1500)
PHONE...............................507 454-5374
FAX: 507 454-6542
Willard D Oberton, *President*
Brenton Cashman, *General Mgr*
Anthony Derricks, *General Mgr*
Adam Hans, *General Mgr*
Kevin Kehoe, *General Mgr*
▼ **EMP:** 400 **EST:** 1967
SQ FT: 213,000
SALES (corp-wide): 1.93B **Publicly Held**
 WEB: www.fastenal.com
 SIC: 5085 5063 5072 Wholesales industrial
fasteners & fastening equipment;
wholesales flashlights; wholesales bolts,
nuts & screws; wholesales power tools &
accessories; wholesales chains; wholesales
industrial tools; wholesales industrial rope,
cord & thread

(G-10096)

FASTENAL CO PURCHASING

2001 Theurer Blvd (55987-1500)
PHONE...............................507 454-5374
Wiliard Oberton, *CEO*
Amy Domuyer, *Accountant*
Kim Brackey, *Manager*
Gene Dudois, *Executive Asst*
▲ **EMP:** 35 **EST:** 1997
SALES (est): 10MM-24.9MM **Publicly Held**
 WEB: www.fastenal.com
 SIC: 5085 Wholesales industrial fasteners
including nuts, bolts, screws, etc;
wholesales industrial tools
 PA: Fastenal Co
   2001 Theurer Blvd
   Winona MN 55987
   507 454-5374

(G-10097)

FLATLINER SPEED SOCIETY

1418 Brookview Dr (55987-4190)
PHONE...............................507 452-8917
Fred Prudell, *President*
EMP: 30 **EST:** 2001
SALES (est): 1MM-4.9MM **Privately Held**
 SIC: 7948 Racetrack

(G-10098)

GEOSPATIAL SERVICES

360 Vila St (55987-2440)
PHONE...............................507 457-8723
Steve Lubahn, *President*
Barry Drazkowski, *Exec Dir*
Lane Urtel, *Director*
EMP: 25 **EST:** 2004
SALES (est): 1MM-4.9MM **Privately Held**
 WEB: www.geospatialservices.com
 SIC: 8748 Business consulting services

(G-10099)

GREAT RIVER SHAKESPEARE

79 E 3rd St (55987-3447)
PHONE...............................507 474-7900
Jeff Stevenson, *General Mgr*
Ryan Frederick, *Principal*
Juliet Johnson, *Exec Dir*
EMP: 50 **EST:** 2007
SALES (est): 1MM-4.9MM **Privately Held**
 SIC: 7922 Theatrical production service

(G-10100)

HEALTH ORIENTATED POOL

1897 W 4th St (55987-1840)
PHONE...............................507 452-1646
FAX: 507 452-1706
Elizabeth Motz, *President*
EMP: 25 **EST:** 2000
SALES (est): 500-999K **Privately Held**
 SIC: 7363 Medical help service

(G-10101)

HIAWATHA BROADBAND COMMS

58 Johnson St (55987-3420)
PHONE...............................507 474-4000
FAX: 507 454-5878
Robert Kierlin, *Ch of Bd*
Gary Evans, *President*
Kent Gernander, *Corp Secy*
Bob Bartz, *Vice Pres*
Daniel Pecarina, *Vice Pres*
EMP: 62 **EST:** 1997
SQ FT: 25,000 **Privately Held**
 WEB: www.hbci.com
 SIC: 4899 4813 4841 7375 Data
communication services; cable television
services; online services providers;
information retrieval services

(G-10102)

HIAWATHA VALLEY MENTAL HEALTH (PA)

166 Main St (55987-3405)
PHONE...............................507 454-4341
Kevin Kelleher, *Vice Chairman*
Tricia Hodgdon, *Corp Secy*
Richard Zabel, *Treasurer*
Jennifer Klinger, *Finance Dir*
Mike Fahui, *Sales Staff*
EMP: 45 **EST:** 1965 **Privately Held**
 SIC: 8361 8093 8322 Home for the mentally
handicapped; outpatient mental health
clinic; general counseling services

(G-10103)

HOME & COMMUNITY OPTIONS INC

Also Called: PCA RC Programs
66 E 3rd St Ste 101 (55987-3466)
PHONE...............................507 452-9311
Paul Adams, *Data Proc Staff*
Dennis Theede, *Exec Dir*
Diane Marley, *Officer*
EMP: 30
SALES (est): 1MM-4.9MM **Privately Held**
 WEB: www.hco.org
 SIC: 8361 Residential care facility
 PA: Home & Community Options Inc
   66 E 3rd St Ste 102
   Winona MN 55987
   507 452-1021

(G-10104)

HOME & COMMUNITY OPTIONS INC

721 Main St (55987-3333)
PHONE...............................507 454-5690
Mary Jansen, *Manager*
EMP: 30
SALES (est): 1MM-4.9MM **Privately Held**
 WEB: www.hco.org
 SIC: 8322 Individual & family social services
 PA: Home & Community Options Inc
   66 E 3rd St Ste 102
   Winona MN 55987
   507 452-1021

(G-10105)

INTERNATIONAL ASSOCIATION OF

24094 Spillway Ln (55987-5952)
PHONE...............................507 454-7643
Jack Krage, *President*
EMP: 40 **Privately Held**
 WEB: www.iaopc.com
 SIC: 8641 Civic associations
 PA: International Association of
   300 W 22nd St
   Oak Brook IL 60523
   630 571-5466

(G-10106)

K A G E INC

752 Bluffview Cir (55987-2515)
PO Box 767 (55987-0767)
PHONE...............................507 452-2867
Jerry Papenfuss, *President*
Dean T Papenfuss, *COO*
Marcia Hamernik, *Vice Pres*
Jean Rispow, *CFO*
Bob Sebo, *Program Dir*
EMP: 33 **EST:** 1961
SQ FT: 2,000
SALES (est): 1MM-4.9MM **Privately Held**
 SIC: 4832 Radio broadcasting station

(G-10107)

KENDELL DOORS & HARDWARE INC (PA)

222 E 2nd St (55987-5525)
PHONE...............................507 454-1723
FAX: 507 454-1833
Jack Cornwell, *CEO*
John Catter, *President*
Kathy Blasko, *General Mgr*
Dan Thompson, *Vice Pres*
EMP: 30 **EST:** 1981
SQ FT: 8,400 **Privately Held**
 SIC: 5072 1751 5031 Wholesales
hardware; wholesales door frames
constructed of all materials; wholesales
metal doors, sash & trim; carpentry
contractor; wholesales doors & windows

(G-10108)

KOHNER REALTY CO INC

4980 W 6th St (55987-1208)
PHONE...............................507 454-5093
Steven Kohner, *President*
Roger Kohner, *Partner*
EMP: 25 **EST:** 1967
SQ FT: 600
SALES (est): 1MM-4.9MM **Privately Held**
 SIC: 6519 Landholding offices

(G-10109)

LAKE CENTER INDUSTRIES TRANS

Also Called: T R W
5676 Industrial Park Rd (55987-1420)
PO Box 649 (55987-0649)
PHONE...............................507 457-3750
FAX: 507 452-5051
Ken Kaiser, *General Mgr*
Lisa Voelker, *Engineer*
Doug Bloemke, *Engineering*
Anthony Fielek, *Sales Staff*
F Tryan, *Program Mgr*
▲ **EMP:** 50 **EST:** 1948
SQ FT: 20,000
SALES (est): 5MM-9.9MM **Publicly Held**

(PA)=Parent Co (HQ)=Headquarters (DH)=Div Headquarters
✿ = New business established in last 2 years

2011 Harris Minnesota
Services Directory

© Harris InfoSource 1-866-281-6415
435

SIC: **4213** Over the road trucking
HQ: Kelsey-Hayes Co
12001 Tech Center Dr
Livonia MI 48150
734 855-2600

(G-10110)
LANDSCAPE BRANDS INC
1101 E Sanborn St (55987-4926)
PHONE..............................507 452-1112
James Glende, *Principal*
Troy Knipping, *Corp Secy*
Carla Russo, *Vice Pres*
David Stark, *Purch Mgr*
Matt St St Onge, *Engrg Mgr*
EMP: **30** EST: **2007 Privately Held**
SIC: **0781** Landscape services

(G-10111)
LAWRENCE TRANSPORTATION
Also Called: Hiawatha Transport
6830 Martina Rd (55987)
PO Box 618 (55987-0618)
PHONE..............................507 454-3911
Eric Lawrence, *President*
George Wilson, *Principal*
EMP: **100** EST: **2000**
SALES (est): 10MM-24.9MM Privately Held
SIC: **4213** 4212 4731 Long-distance
refrigerated trucking services; local trucking
without storage services; freight
transportation arrangement services

(G-10112)
LTX INC
Also Called: Freight Plus
6830 Martina Rd (55987-1457)
PO Box 327 (55987-0327)
PHONE..............................507 452-4738
Gene Schultz, *Branch Mgr*
EMP: **40**
SALES (est): 5MM-9.9MM Privately Held
WEB: www.lawrencetrans.com
SIC: **4213** 4214 Long-distance refrigerated
trucking services; local trucking with storage
PA: Ltx Inc
1515 Industrial Dr NW
Rochester MN 55901
507 282-6715

(G-10113)
MATHY CONSTRUCTION CO
24206 Highway 43 (55987-4989)
PHONE..............................507 932-3200
Mike Voeller, *General Mgr*
Steve Beach, *VP Mngmt*
EMP: **35**
SALES (est): 5MM-9.9MM Privately Held
SIC: **1429** Crushed & broken igneous rock
quarrying
PA: Mathy Construction Co
920 10th Ave N
Onalaska WI 54650
608 783-6411

(G-10114)
MAXWELL WSU CHILDREN
CENTER
1010 E 7th St (55987-4742)
PO Box 5838 (55987-0838)
PHONE..............................507 457-5368
Judith Ramley, *President*
Scott Ellinghuysen, *Vice Pres*
Jun Reineke, *Director*
EMP: **60** EST: **2005**
SALES (est): 1MM-4.9MM Privately Held
SIC: **8351** Child day care service

(G-10115)
MERCHANTS BANK, NATIONAL
ASSN (HQ)
102 E 3rd St (55987-3416)
PO Box 248 (55987-0248)
PHONE..............................507 457-1100
Rodney Nelson, *President*
R L Mahoney, *Exec VP*
Mark M Grory, *Senior VP*
Gerald E Neal, *Senior VP*
James Orlikowski, *Senior VP*
EMP: **108** EST: **1875**
SQ FT: **5,000**
SALES (corp-wide): 78.72M Privately Held

SIC: **6021** National commercial bank
PA: Merchants Financial Group Inc
102 E 3rd St
Winona MN 55987
507 457-1100

(G-10116)
MERCHANTS NATIONAL BANK
OF
102 E 3rd St (55987-3416)
PO Box 248 (55987-0248)
PHONE..............................507 457-1100
FAX: 507 457-1101
R P Roehl, *CEO*
Rod Nelson, *President*
Mike Speltz, *Senior VP*
Kip Bolstad, *Info Tech Mgr*
EMP: **126** EST: **1875**
SALES (est): 25MM-49.9MM Privately Held
SIC: **6021** National commercial bank

(G-10117)
MICHAELS' LIGHTING INC
2 Kansas St (55987)
PO Box 192 (55987-0192)
PHONE..............................507 454-5560
FAX: 507 452-1212
Michael Conway, *President*
Lisa Conway, *Project Mgr*
EMP: **40** EST: **1989**
SQ FT: **20,000**
SALES (est): 5MM-9.9MM Privately Held
WEB: www.michaelslighting.com
SIC: **5063** Manufactures industrial &
commercial lighting fixtures; wholesales
electrical apparatus & equipment;
manufactures residential lighting fixtures;
manufactures lighting equipment

(G-10118)
MISSISSIPPI WELDERS SUPPLY
CO (PA)
5150 W 6th St (55987-1248)
PO Box 1036 (55987-7036)
PHONE..............................507 454-5231
FAX: 507 454-8104
Bradley Peterson, *President*
Donald Peterson, *Corp Secy*
Scott Myran, *Opers Mgr*
John Wiseman, *Purch Mgr*
Meg Krinke, *Human Res Mgr*
EMP: **30** EST: **1939**
SQ FT: **18,000 Privately Held**
SIC: **5084** Wholesales welding equipment &
supplies; retails welding supplies

(G-10119)
OMNI CONTROL SYSTEMS INC
370 W 2nd St Ste 100 (55987-2969)
PO Box 132 (55987-0132)
PHONE..............................507 454-5293
James Kiekbusch, *President*
Richard Pflughoeft, *Vice Pres*
Richard Wunsch, *CFO*
EMP: **25** EST: **2000**
SALES (est): 1MM-4.9MM Privately Held
SIC: **8748** Business consulting services;
manufactures security control equipment &
systems

(G-10120)
QUALITY LIVING HOME HEALTH
164 E 4th St Ste 4 (55987-3583)
PHONE..............................507 454-6800
Gary Poblocki, *Owner*
Justus Fry, *Manager*
EMP: **35** EST: **2000**
SALES (est): 1MM-4.9MM Privately Held
SIC: **8082** Home health care services

(G-10121)
RIVERS HOTEL CO INC (PA)
Also Called: Holiday Inn
356 E Sarnia St Ste 2 (55987-3803)
PHONE..............................507 457-0977
FAX: 507 457-0146
Michael J Rivers, *President*
EMP: **60** EST: **1992**
SQ FT: **70,000 Privately Held**
SIC: **7011** Traveler accommodations

(G-10122)
RIVERSTAR INC
1705 Wilkie Dr (55987-6203)
PHONE..............................507 452-5109
FAX: 507 453-6180
Stephen Craney, *President*
Regina Craney, *Corp Secy*
Mandy Weilandt, *Controller*
Erin Craney, *Director*
Sean Craney, *Director*
EMP: **42** EST: **1995**
SQ FT: **43,000**
SALES (est): 10MM-24.9MM Privately Held
WEB: www.riverstarinc.com
SIC: **1541** Industrial building & warehouse
construction

(G-10123)
SAINT ANNE OF WINONA
1347 W Broadway St (55987-2327)
PHONE..............................507 454-3621
FAX: 507 452-2556
Joan Hittner, *COO*
Karen Urbick, *Purchasing*
Matt Peterson, *CFO*
Dana Marquardt, *Human Res Dir*
Carol Ehlinger, *Manager*
EMP: **195** EST: **1978**
SQ FT: **100,000**
SALES (est): 5MM-9.9MM Privately Held
SIC: **8051** Skilled nursing care facility
PA: Benedictine Health System
503 E 3rd St Ste 400
Duluth MN 55805
218 786-2370

(G-10124)
SAUER MEMORIAL HOME (PA)
1635 W Service Dr (55987-2186)
PHONE..............................507 454-5540
Kenneth Bittner, *CEO*
EMP: **128** EST: **1955**
SQ FT: **49,000**
SALES (corp-wide): 4.96M Privately Held
SIC: **8051** Skilled nursing care facility

(G-10125)
SAUER MEMORIAL HOME
Also Called: Knopp Valley Apartments
1635 W Service Dr (55987-2186)
PHONE..............................507 454-5540
Kenneth Bittner, *Branch Mgr*
EMP: **45**
SALES (est): 5MM-9.9MM Privately Held
SIC: **6513** Apartment building operator
PA: Sauer Memorial Home
1635 W Service Dr
Winona MN 55987
507 454-5540

(G-10126)
SEVERSON OIL CO
508 Louisa St (55987-4902)
PHONE..............................507 452-4743
Tom Severson, *President*
EMP: **25**
SALES (est): 50MM-99.9MM Privately Held
SIC: **5172** Wholesales petroleum products
PA: Severson Oil Co
508 Louisa St
Winona MN 55987
507 452-4743

(G-10127)
SEVERSON TRANSPORT INC
508 Louisa St (55987-4902)
PO Box 736 (55987-0736)
PHONE..............................507 454-5090
Tom Serverson, *President*
EMP: **27** EST: **1987**
SALES (est): 500-999K Privately Held
SIC: **7363** Truck driver service
PA: Severson Oil Co
508 Louisa St
Winona MN 55987
507 452-4743

(G-10128)
SOCIETY FOR PRESERVATION
Also Called: Winona Area Barber Shoppers
163 E Howard St (55987-3643)
PHONE..............................507 452-4425
Mike Carston, *President*

Richard Moe, *Treasurer*
EMP: **31** EST: **1951 Privately Held**
SIC: **8641** Singing society

(G-10129)
SOUTHWESTERN MINNESOTA
RADIO
Also Called: Winona Radio
752 Bluffview Cir (55987-2515)
PHONE..............................507 452-4000
Jerry Papenfuss, *President*
EMP: **25** EST: **1961**
SALES (est): 1MM-4.9MM Privately Held
WEB: www.winonaradio.com
SIC: **4832** Radio broadcasting station

(G-10130)
SPRINT COMMUNICATIONS CO
LP
166 W 3rd St (55987-3101)
PO Box 49 (55987-0049)
PHONE..............................507 454-8386
FAX: 507 453-4393
Linda Hazelton, *Manager*
Kip Bolstad, *Manager*
Kevin Goede, *MIS Mgr*
Thomas Gotzinger, *Technical Staff*
EMP: **150** EST: **Publicly Held**
WEB: www.sprint.com
SIC: **4813** Long distance telephone
communications services
PA: Sprint Nextel Corp
6200 Sprint Pkwy
Overland Park KS 66251
800 829-0965

(G-10131)
ST TERESA CAMPUS SCHOOLS
360 Vila St Ste A (55987-2582)
PHONE..............................507 453-5555
Dave Ansell, *Administrator*
Pat Knee, *Administrator*
EMP: **40** EST: **1991 Privately Held**
SIC: **7999** Private school; tennis services &
professionals

(G-10132)
THERAPY NETWORK INC
1635 W Service Dr (55987-2186)
PHONE..............................507 454-6724
FAX: 507 457-0020
Robert Schrupp, *President*
EMP: **35** EST: **1988**
SALES (est): 1MM-4.9MM Privately Held
SIC: **8093** Outpatient rehabilitation
treatment center

(G-10133)
TIMBER ROOTS LLC ✪
125 W 5th St (55987-3557)
PHONE..............................507 452-2361
Dale Kukowski, *Member*
Steve Badciong, *Credit Mgr*
EMP: **150** EST: **2008**
SALES (est): 50MM-99.9MM Privately Held
SIC: **5031** Wholesales exterior building
materials

(G-10134)
UNION PACIFIC RAILROAD CO
50 Harvester Ave (55987-2245)
PHONE..............................507 452-4337
FAX: 507 452-9211
Tim Fox, *Manager*
Steve Forseth, *Manager*
EMP: **500**
SALES (est): 50MM-99.9MM Publicly Held
WEB: www.uprr.com
SIC: **4013** 4011 Railroad switching &
terminal services; long haul railroad
HQ: Union Pacific Railroad Co Inc
1400 Douglas St
Omaha NE 68179
402 544-5000

(G-10135)
UNITED PARCEL SERVICE INC
Also Called: UPS
1157 E Broadway St (55987-4630)
PHONE..............................507 454-2307
FAX: 507 454-8739
Michael Wills, *Opers Spvr*
Gary Langerud, *Manager*
Gary Langer, *Manager*

www.HarrisInfo.com
436

2011 Harris Minnesota
Services Directory

▲=Import ▼=Export
◆=Import/Export

EMP: 50
SALES (est): 1MM-4.9MM **Publicly Held**
WEB: www.ups.com
SIC: 4215 Parcel delivery services by vehicle
HQ: United Parcel Service Inc
55 Glenlake Pkwy NE
Atlanta GA 30328
404 828-6000

(G-10136)
VALLEY SECURITY SERVICE INC
110 Gould St Ste 100 (55987-2211)
PO Box 1528 (55987-7528)
PHONE...........................507 454-2233
Paul Sweazey, *President*
Sharon Sweazey, *Vice Pres*
Randy Aspenson, *Accountant*
Steve Fobcek, *Manager*
Lois Wolisteman, *Data Proc Exec*
EMP: 150 EST: 1975
SQ FT: 48,000
SALES (est): 1MM-4.9MM **Privately Held**
SIC: 7381 Guard service; retails police supplies

(G-10137)
WAPASHA CONSTRUCTION CO INC
927 E King St (55987-4717)
PO Box 556 (55987-0556)
PHONE...........................507 454-2707
FAX: 507 454-8689
Thomas M Peplinski, *President*
Klean Peplinski, *Corp Secy*
Brian Beulow, *Vice Pres*
EMP: 30 EST: 1985
SQ FT: 2,200
SALES (est): 5MM-9.9MM **Privately Held**
SIC: 1542 New commercial & office building construction

(G-10138)
WATKINS INC (HQ)
150 Liberty St (55987-3707)
PO Box 5570 (55987-0570)
PHONE...........................507 457-3300
FAX: 507 452-6723
Irwin Jacobs, *Ch of Bd*
Mark Jacobs, *President*
Delores Antunes, *Vice Pres*
J R Rigley, *Vice Pres*
James Yenish, *Vice Pres*
▲ EMP: 240 EST: 1868
SQ FT: 450,000 **Privately Held**
WEB: www.jrwatkins.com
SIC: 5122 Manufactures spices; manufactures flavoring extracts; manufactures dry seasoning mixes; manufactures synthetic organic or inorganic alkaline detergents,; manufactures scouring compounds; wholesales pharmaceuticals, drug proprietaries & sundries
PA: Jacobs Industries Inc
80 S 8th St Ste 2900
Minneapolis MN 55402
612 339-9500

(G-10139)
WATKINS INC
730 W 3rd St (55987-2215)
PHONE...........................507 457-6136
Frank Laylan, *Manager*
EMP: 40
SALES (est): 1MM-4.9MM **Privately Held**
WEB: www.jrwatkins.com
SIC: 4225 Warehousing & storage services
HQ: Watkins Inc
150 Liberty St
Winona MN 55987
507 457-3300

(G-10140)
WESTFIELD GOLF CLUB INC
1460 W 5th St (55987-2333)
PHONE...........................507 452-8700
FAX: 507 452-8700
Tom Gunn, *President*
John Kosidowski, *Vice Pres*
Lyle Jacobson, *Manager*
Don Boynton, *Manager*
EMP: 35 EST: 1948
SQ FT: 2,500
SALES (est): 1MM-4.9MM **Privately Held**
WEB: www.westfieldgolfclub.com

SIC: 7997 Membership golf club; bar; eating place

(G-10141)
WILLET HAUSER ARCHITECTURAL
1685 Wilkie Dr (55987-6203)
PHONE...........................507 457-3500
FAX: 507 457-0554
Michael F Hauser, *President*
Richard Brang, *General Mgr*
James A Hauser, *Exec VP*
Art Glass, *Executive*
EMP: 25 EST: 1946
SQ FT: 17,500
SALES (est): 1MM-4.9MM **Privately Held**
WEB: www.willethauser.com
SIC: 1793 Glass & glazing contractor; manufactures stained glass

(G-10142)
WINGFOOT COMMERCIAL TIRE SYSTS
5110 Service Dr (55987-1304)
PHONE...........................507 454-5181
FAX: 507 454-1868
Ric Lofgren, *Manager*
Dian Biesanz, *Administration*
EMP: 40
SALES (est): 5MM-9.9MM **Publicly Held**
WEB: www.wingfootct.com
SIC: 5014 7534 Tire dealer; tire recapping & retreading services; wholesales automotive tires & tubes
HQ: Wingfoot Commercial Tire Systs
1000 S 21st St
Fort Smith AR 72901
479 788-6400

(G-10143)
WINONA AGENCY INC
174 Center St (55987-3423)
PO Box 919 (55987-0919)
PHONE...........................507 452-3366
FAX: 507 452-2597
Ken Mogren, *President*
Mary Moham, *Corp Secy*
Jan Northam, *Vice Pres*
Barb Lautenberg, *Vice Pres*
Gary Watts, *Vice Pres*
EMP: 43 EST: 1893
SQ FT: 8,000
SALES (est): 1MM-4.9MM **Privately Held**
WEB: www.winonaagency.com
SIC: 6411 Insurance agent

(G-10144)
WINONA CLINIC LTD
859 Mankato Ave (55987-4868)
PHONE...........................507 454-3680
Richard Ferris MD, *President*
Doug Seberg, *Controller*
Mike Skroch, *Human Res Dir*
Carol Rice, *Office Mgr*
Daniel Ramer, *Pharmacist*
EMP: 180 EST: 1920
SQ FT: 50,000
SALES (est): 10MM-24.9MM **Privately Held**
SIC: 8011 Physicians' office & clinic

(G-10145)
WINONA COMMUNITY MEMORIAL HOSP (PA)
855 Mankato Ave (55987-5377)
PO Box 5600 (55987-0600)
PHONE...........................507 454-3650
FAX: 507 453-3732
Rachelle Schultz, *CEO*
Diane Coates, *Corp Secy*
Matthew J Broghammer, *Ch of Surgery*
Scott D Birdsall, *Ch OB/GYN*
Carl J Szczesiank, *Ch Pathology*
EMP: 850 EST: 1894
SQ FT: 193,000 **Privately Held**
SIC: 8062 8051 Medical hospital; skilled nursing care facility

(G-10146)
WINONA COUNTRY CLUB
22852 County Road 17 (55987-5483)
PHONE...........................507 454-3767
FAX: 507 454-0197
Tin Virgal, *Owner*
EMP: 30 EST: 1997
SALES (est): 1MM-4.9MM **Privately Held**

SIC: 7999 Golf professionals

(G-10147)
WINONA DEVELOPMENTAL
1721 W Service Dr (55987-2186)
PHONE...........................507 452-1798
FAX: 507 452-7504
Mary J Hewett, *Director*
Lynda Tillman, *Coordinator*
EMP: 25 EST: 1966
SALES (est): 1MM-4.9MM **Privately Held**
WEB: www.winonadac.org
SIC: 8093 Specialty outpatient clinic

(G-10148)
WINONA HEALTH
175 E Wabasha St (55987-3594)
PHONE...........................507 457-4468
Don Meierant, *Branch Mgr*
Sylvia Tenlitz, *Manager*
Robin Hoeg, *Director*
Scott Biesanz, *Bd of Directors*
EMP: 25
SALES (est): 1MM-4.9MM **Privately Held**
SIC: 8051 Skilled nursing care facility
PA: Winona Community Memorial Hosp
855 Mankato Ave
Winona MN 55987
507 454-3650

(G-10149)
WINONA HEATING & VENTILATING
374 E 2nd St (55987-3901)
PO Box 77 (55987-0077)
PHONE...........................507 452-2064
FAX: 507 452-6320
Michael Gostomski, *President*
B T Plachecki, *Vice Pres*
Joel V Haden, *Vice Pres*
Wanda Stolpa, *Safety Mgr*
Steve Roberts, *Controller*
▲ EMP: 130 EST: 1902
SQ FT: 8,000
SALES (est): 10MM-24.9MM **Privately Held**
WEB: www.whvr.com
SIC: 1761 1711 Roofing contractor; ventilation & duct work contractor; warm air heating & air conditioning contractor; fabricates architectural metalwork; sheet metal fabricator; steel fabricator

(G-10150)
WINONA INN LP
Also Called: Quality Inn
956 Mankato Ave (55987-4869)
PHONE...........................507 454-4390
FAX: 507 452-2187
Kelli Kronebusch, *General Mgr*
Heather Stowe, *General Mgr*
Nita Trim, *Sales Staff*
Peggy Blank, *Manager*
Mark Hugunin, *Manager*
EMP: 50 EST: 1966
SALES (est): 1MM-4.9MM **Privately Held**
SIC: 7011 Traveler accommodations; cocktail lounge

(G-10151)
WINONA LIGHTING INC
3760 W 4th St (55987-1823)
PHONE...........................507 454-5113
FAX: 507 452-8528
J T Biesanz Sr, *Ch of Bd*
Philip Conway, *Vice Ch Bd*
Steven T Biesanz, *President*
Barb Jabrosky, *Vice Pres*
Ted Biesanz Jr, *Vice Pres*
▲ EMP: 185 EST: 1949
SQ FT: 50,000
SALES (est): 25MM-49.9MM **Privately Held**
WEB: www.winonalighting.com
SIC: 5063 Manufactures industrial & commercial lighting fixtures; wholesales electrical apparatus & equipment

(G-10152)
WINONA NATIONAL HOLDING CO INC
204 Main St (55987-3554)
PO Box 499 (55987-0499)
PHONE...........................507 454-4320
Jack Rickter, *President*
Linda Foss, *Corp Secy*
Thom Kieffer, *Senior VP*

David Vaselaar, *Senior VP*
Mark Every, *Assistant VP*
EMP: 55 EST: 1985 **Privately Held**
SIC: 6712 6163 Bank holding company; loan broker

(G-10153)
WINONA ORC INDUSTRIES INC
1053 E Mark St (55987-4765)
PHONE...........................507 452-1855
FAX: 507 452-1857
Ron Wenzel, *Vice Chairman*
Sonja Shugart, *Vice Pres*
Michael Bellesbach, *Finance*
Jayne Grupa, *Human Resources*
Courtland Humble, *Human Resources*
EMP: 360 EST: 1973
SQ FT: 27,000
SALES (est): 10MM-24.9MM **Privately Held**
WEB: www.worcind.org
SIC: 8331 Vocational rehabilitation agency

WINSTED
Carver County

(G-10154)
VITRAN EXPRESS INC
1300 County Road 1 (55395-6542)
PHONE...........................320 485-2101
FAX: 320 913-3341
Michael McPhee, *Corp Secy*
Bob Stachon, *Manager*
Betty Wrastir, *Manager*
Eric Poncius, *Manager*
EMP: 50
SALES (est): 5MM-9.9MM **Privately Held**
WEB: www.vitran.com
SIC: 4213 Long-distance less than truckload freight trucking services
PA: Vitran Corp Inc
185 The West Mall
Toronto Canada
416 5967664

WINSTED
Mcleod County

(G-10155)
ADULT TRAINING & HABILITATION
Also Called: ATHC
311 Fairlawn Ave W (55395-7839)
PHONE...........................320 485-4191
FAX: 320 485-4763
Jeannie Decker, *Accounts Mgr*
Jason Telander, *Director*
EMP: 25 EST: 1966
SQ FT: 300
SALES (est): 1MM-4.9MM **Privately Held**
SIC: 8331 Job training & vocational rehabilitation services

(G-10156)
AMERICAN LEGION CLUB
Also Called: Martin Kruger Post 407
161 1st St N (55395)
PHONE...........................320 485-4366
Jeff Sterner, *President*
Irene Kegler, *Manager*
Dick Genty, *Director*
EMP: 35 **Privately Held**
SIC: 8641 Civic & social organization

(G-10157)
AWI MANUFACTURING INC
3902 230th St (55395-6518)
PO Box 909 (55395-0909)
PHONE...........................320 485-2471
Gary Scherping, *President*
Dennis Scherping, *Vice Pres*
Tom Scherping, *Vice Pres*
Terry Scherping, *Vice Pres*
Debbie Travis, *CFO*
EMP: 30 EST: 1981
SQ FT: 23,000
SALES (est): 5MM-9.9MM **Privately Held**
WEB: www.awimfg.com
SIC: 1799 Manufactures dairy equipment; on-site welding contractor; manufactures milking machines

---

(PA)=Parent Co (HQ)=Headquarters (DH)=Div Headquarters
✿ = New business established in last 2 years

2011 Harris Minnesota
Services Directory

© Harris InfoSource 1-866-281-6415

437

(G-10158)
BENEDICTINE HEALTH SYSTEM
Also Called: Senior Living Center
551 4th St N Ste 101 (55395-4524)
PHONE................................320 485-2151
Jill J Hesskollasch, *Human Res Mgr*
Sandra Peterson, *Human Resources*
Andy Opsahl, *Administrator*
Lamae Engel, *Director*
EMP: 100
SALES (est): 1MM-4.9MM **Privately Held**
SIC: 8051 Skilled nursing care facility
PA: Benedictine Health System
    503 E 3rd St Ste 400
    Duluth MN 55805
    218 786-2370

(G-10159)
BLUE NOTE OF WINSTED INC
320 3rd St S (55395-7759)
PHONE................................320 485-9698
Neil Schlagel, *President*
EMP: 40 **EST:** 1973
SALES (est): 1MM-4.9MM **Privately Held**
WEB: www.bluenoteofwinsted.com
SIC: 7911 Eating place; liquor store; dance hall or ballroom operation

(G-10160)
D B DIRECT MAIL
351 Lewis Ave W (55395)
PO Box 850 (55395-0850)
PHONE................................320 485-7827
Ick Burrell, *Owner*
Joe Brimmer, *Owner*
EMP: 40 **EST:** 2006
SALES (est): 1MM-4.9MM **Privately Held**
SIC: 7331 Direct mail advertising service

(G-10161)
K-WAY EXPRESS INC
323 Main Ave W (55395)
PO Box 266 (55395-0266)
PHONE................................320 485-2325
FAX: 320 485-2446
James Koch, *President*
Marietta Koch, *Corp Secy*
Jeffrey Koch, *Vice Pres*
Bruce Koch, *Vice Pres*
EMP: 52 **EST:** 1983
SQ FT: 3,400
SALES (est): 5MM-9.9MM **Privately Held**
WEB: www.kwaytrucking.com
SIC: 4213 4214 Contract haulers; local trucking with storage

(G-10162)
LIVING SERVICES FOUNDATION
Also Called: St Mary's Care Center
551 4th St N (55395-4523)
PHONE................................320 485-2151
Dennis Kamstra, *Member*
Liz Kiecker, *Purch Mgr*
Lamae Engel, *Office Mgr*
Andy Opsahl, *Administrator*
Anita Hoese, *Assistant*
EMP: 99 **EST:** 2007
SALES (est): 1MM-4.9MM **Privately Held**
SIC: 8051 Skilled nursing care facility

(G-10163)
MIDLAND CORPORATE BENEFIT SVCS
131 6th St N (55395-7778)
PO Box 99 (55395-0099)
PHONE................................320 485-3821
FAX: 320 485-2199
David A Sherman, *President*
EST: 1984
SQ FT: 3,000 **Privately Held**
SIC: 6411 8742 Insurance information & consulting service; compensation & benefits planning consultant

(G-10164)
RAM BUILDINGS INC
592 Industrial Blvd (55395-4513)
PO Box 660 (55395-0660)
PHONE................................320 485-2844
FAX: 320 485-3625
Rawelin Radtke, *President*
Craig Jackson, *General Mgr*
Todd Ide, *Safety Mgr*

Greg Machemehel, *CFO*
EMP: 45 **EST:** 1999
SQ FT: 7,000
SALES (est): 10MM-24.9MM **Privately Held**
WEB: www.rambuildings.com
SIC: 1542 Specialized public building contractors

(G-10165)
SJF MATERIAL HANDLING INC
211 Baker Ave W (55395-7722)
PO Box 70 (55395-0070)
PHONE................................320 485-2824
FAX: 320 485-2832
Frank Sterner, *CEO*
Stafford Sterner, *President*
Veronica R Sterner, *Corp Secy*
James Sterner, *Vice Pres*
Jim Laliberte, *Engineer*
◆ **EMP:** 53 **EST:** 1977
SQ FT: 52,000
SALES (est): 10MM-24.9MM **Privately Held**
SIC: 5084 Wholesales materials handling equipment

(G-10166)
VITRAN EXPRESS INC
1300 6th St S (55395)
PHONE................................320 485-2333
Eric Poncius, *Manager*
EMP: 40
SALES (est): 1MM-4.9MM **Privately Held**
WEB: www.vitran.com
SIC: 4231 4785 Freight trucking terminal; inspection facility

WINTHROP
Sibley County

(G-10167)
EVANGELICAL LUTHERAN GOOD
506 W High St (55396-9798)
PHONE................................507 647-5391
FAX: 507 647-2035
Linda Messerli, *Human Res Mgr*
Fran Ziegler, *Manager*
Lori Bussler, *Administrator*
EMP: 70
SALES (est): 1MM-4.9MM **Privately Held**
WEB: www.good-sam.com
SIC: 8051 Skilled nursing care facility
PA: Evangelical Lutheran Good
    4800 W 57th St
    Sioux Falls SD 57108
    605 362-3100

(G-10168)
MIDWEST FINANCIAL PROCESSING
204 N Carver St (55396)
PO Box 41 (55396-0041)
PHONE................................507 647-2856
David Gohl, *Principal*
EMP: 32 **EST:** 2006
SALES (est): 5MM-9.9MM **Privately Held**
SIC: 6282 Financial investment advice service

(G-10169)
WINTHROP HONOR GUARD
27076 541st Ave (55396-2253)
PHONE................................507 647-5608
Ron Trebelhorn, *Principal*
EMP: 30 **EST:** 2001 **Privately Held**
SIC: 8641 Veterans' organization

WOOD LAKE
Yellow Medicine County

(G-10170)
BLACK JACK EXPRESS & REPAIR
330 6th St (56297)
PHONE................................507 485-3437
Russ Davis, *Owner*
Jim Rosenau, *Manager*
EMP: 30 **EST:** 1992
SQ FT: 1,600
SALES (est): 1MM-4.9MM **Privately Held**

SIC: 7538 7549 Truck engine repair service; automotive trailer maintenance service

WOODBURY
Washington County

(G-10171)
CHAMPION SERVICE CORP
6043 Hudson Rd Ste 375 (55125-1020)
PHONE................................651 731-9137
Jinmahn Kim, *President*
Myungja Kim, *Corp Secy*
EMP: 34 **EST:** 1984
SQ FT: 540
SALES (est): 500-999K **Privately Held**
SIC: 7349 Janitorial & custodial services; retail mobile food service

(G-10172)
K M L DESIGN STUDIO LLC
731 Bielenberg Dr Ste 105 (55125-1700)
PHONE................................651 731-6672
David Frosch, *Mng Member*
EMP: 40
SALES (est): 5MM-9.9MM **Privately Held**
SIC: 7389 Interior design service

(G-10173)
PERCY NELSON ENTERPRISES INC
7616 Currell Blvd Ste 200 (55125-2296)
PHONE................................651 209-6360
Percy Nelson, *President*
EMP: 30
SALES (est): 1MM-4.9MM **Privately Held**
SIC: 8082 Home health care services

(G-10174)
PETSMART INC
8460 Tamarack Vlg (55125-3383)
PHONE................................800 702-9779
Kathy Lutheran, *Exec Dir*
EMP: 30
SALES (est): 1MM-4.9MM **Publicly Held**
WEB: www.petsmart.com
SIC: 0752 Retails pet food; animal specialty services
PA: Petsmart Inc
    19601 N 27th Ave
    Phoenix AZ 85027
    623 580-6100

(G-10175)
SUPER BOWL ◗
6720 Riverdale Dr (55125)
PHONE................................763 421-7779
Mike Anderson, *Owner*
Mark Garen, *Manager*
EMP: 30 **EST:** 2008 **Privately Held**
SIC: 8699 Bowling club

WOODSTOCK
Pipestone County

(G-10176)
NEW LIFE TREATMENT CENTER
130 Dakota St S (56186)
PO Box 38 (56186-0038)
PHONE................................507 777-4321
FAX: 507 777-4284
Wes Vanessen, *Director*
EMP: 30 **EST:** 1977
SQ FT: 22,500
SALES (est): 1MM-4.9MM **Privately Held**
SIC: 8361 Residential rehabilitation center with health care incidental

WORTHINGTON
Nobles County

(G-10177)
AGSTAR FINANCIAL SERVICES, ACA
1791 Diagonal Rd (56187-1089)
PO Box 579 (56187-0579)
PHONE................................507 376-4144
Dave Jueneman, *Principal*
EMP: 33
SALES (est): 10MM-24.9MM **Privately Held**
WEB: www.agstar.com
SIC: 6159 Farm mortgage service
PA: Agstar Financial Services, Aca
    1921 Premier Dr
    Mankato MN 56001
    507 387-4174

(G-10178)
ATCHISON ENTERPRISES INC (PA)
Also Called: South Shore Care Center
1307 S Shore Dr (56187-1344)
PO Box 69 (56187-0069)
PHONE................................507 376-3175
FAX: 507 376-9709
Richard Atchison, *President*
Barbara Atchison, *VP Persnl*
EMP: 100 **EST:** 1954
SQ FT: 20,000
SALES (corp-wide): 4.20M **Privately Held**
SIC: 8051 Skilled nursing care facility

(G-10179)
ATCHISON ENTERPRISES INC
Also Called: Crossroads Care Center
965 McMillan St (56187-2261)
PHONE................................507 376-5312
FAX: 507 337-6953
Barbara Atchison, *President*
EMP: 65
SALES (est): 1MM-4.9MM **Privately Held**
SIC: 8059 Nursing home
PA: Atchison Enterprises Inc
    1307 S Shore Dr
    Worthington MN 56187
    507 376-3175

(G-10180)
CITY OF WORTHINGTON
Also Called: Worthington Regional Hospital
1018 6th Ave (56187-2202)
PO Box 997 (56187-0997)
PHONE................................507 372-2941
FAX: 507 372-7686
Jeff J Rotert, *COO*
Roger Lester, *Purchasing*
Terry Bramel, *Envir Svcs Dir*
Linda Wagner, *CFO*
Holly Sieve, *Marketing Staff*
EMP: 160
SALES (est): 10MM-24.9MM **Privately Held**
SIC: 8062 Medical hospital
PA: City of Worthington
    303 9th St
    Worthington MN 56187
    507 372-8600

(G-10181)
CLIENT COMMUNITY SERVICES INC
Also Called: Ridgewood
1381 Knollwood Dr (56187-1407)
PHONE................................507 376-6095
FAX: 507 376-5117
Kathy Thurston, *Branch Mgr*
Patricia Cowdin, *Director*
EMP: 40
SALES (est): 1MM-4.9MM **Privately Held**
WEB: www.clientcommserv.com
SIC: 8361 Residential care for the handicapped
PA: Client Community Services Inc
    826 5th Ave
    Worthington MN 56187
    507 376-3171

▲=Import ▼=Export
◆=Import/Export

G E O G R A P H I C

(G-10182)

DAVIS TYPEWRITER CO INC
1158 Oxford St (56187-1666)
PO Box 416 (56187-0416)
PHONE 507 343-2001
FAX: 507 376-4012
Larry M Davis, *President*
Sharon Davis, *Vice Pres*
Mike Kuhle, *Finance Mgr*
EMP: 40 **EST:** 1946
SQ FT: 11,000
SALES (est): 10MM-24.9MM **Privately Held**
WEB: www.davistype.com
SIC: 5044 7629 Wholesales office
equipment; retails office furniture; retails
office forms & supplies; electric business
machine repair service

(G-10183)

FIRST RUSHMORE BANCSHARES INC (PA)
1433 Oxford St (56187-1763)
PO Box 725 (56187-0725)
PHONE 507 376-9747
FAX: 507 478-4321
Alvin Kooiman, *President*
Connie Lonneman, *Corp Secy*
Greg Raymo, *Exec VP*
Randy Thompson, *Vice Pres*
Allan Woitaszewski, *Vice Pres*
EMP: 52 **EST:** 1982
SQ FT: 20,000 **Privately Held**
WEB: www.firststatebanksw.com
SIC: 6022 Commercial state trust
companies accepting deposits

(G-10184)

FIRST STATE BANK SOUTH WEST
1433 Oxford St (56187-1763)
PO Box 725 (56187-0725)
PHONE 507 376-9747
EMP: 28
SALES (est): 5MM-9.9MM **Privately Held**
WEB: www.firststatebanksw.com
SIC: 6022 State commercial bank
HQ: First State Bank South West
1433 Oxford St
Worthington MN 56187
507 376-9747

(G-10185)

FIRST STATE BANK SOUTH WEST (HQ)
1433 Oxford St (56187-1763)
PO Box 725 (56187-0725)
PHONE 507 376-9747
FAX: 507 376-5263
Elvin Kooiman, *President*
Marjorie Buss, *Principal*
Greg Raymo, *Exec VP*
Eunice Ailts, *Vice Pres*
Randy Thompson, *CIO*
EST: 1903 **Privately Held**
WEB: www.firststatebanksw.com
SIC: 6022 6411 State commercial bank;
insurance agent
PA: First Rushmore Bancshares Inc
1433 Oxford St
Worthington MN 56187
507 376-9747

(G-10186)

HIGHLAND MANUFACTURING CO LLC
1660 Rowe Ave (56187-9700)
PO Box 427 (56187-0427)
PHONE 507 376-9460
FAX: 507 376-5915
Greg D Groot, *Member*
Tim Bedries, *Member*
Dick Dobler, *Vice Pres*
Kim Kerry, *Purchasing*
Ron Totten, *Manager*
EMP: 200 **EST:** 1998
SQ FT: 110,000
SALES (est): 50MM-99.9MM **Privately Held**
SIC: 1521 Single-family housing
construction; manufactures mobile homes

(G-10187)

LARRY DAVIS
Also Called: L D Properties
1158 Oxford St (56187-1666)
PO Box 416 (56187-0416)
PHONE 507 372-7774
FAX: 507 372-7816
Larry M Davis, *Owner*
EMP: 25 **EST:** 1984
SQ FT: 4,800
SALES (est): 1MM-4.9MM **Privately Held**
WEB: www.larrydavis.net
SIC: 6513 Operators of apartment hotels

(G-10188)

NATIONAL SERVICE CO OF IOWA
1016 Oxford St (56187-1664)
PHONE 507 372-2276
FAX: 507 372-2276
Garry Murphy, *Manager*
EMP: 90 **Privately Held**
SIC: 7361 Employment agency services
PA: National Service Co of Iowa
1010 E Washington St Ste 202
Mount Pleasant IA 52641
319 385-2614

(G-10189)

NOBLES ROCK PUBLIC HEALTH
315 10th St (56187-2315)
PO Box 757 (56187-0757)
PHONE 507 372-8256
FAX: 507 372-8380
Mel Ruppert, *Principal*
EMP: 38 **EST:** 1969
SALES (est): 1MM-4.9MM **Privately Held**
SIC: 8082 Home health care services

(G-10190)

PRECISION NUTRITION INC
727 Oxford St (56187-1661)
PHONE 507 372-4723
Phil Hooge, *President*
EMP: 50 **EST:** 1998
SALES (est): 25MM-49.9MM **Privately Held**
WEB: www.precisionnutrition.com
SIC: 5191 Wholesales animal feeds

(G-10191)

PRODUCTION HEALTH ASSOCIATES
727 Oxford St (56187-1661)
PO Box 158 (56187-0158)
PHONE 507 372-2957
FAX: 507 372-5578
Keith Wilson, *President*
Erik Nankivil, *Corp Secy*
Craig Pfeifer, *Shareholder*
Rj Leiting, *Shareholder*
Wayne Freese, *Shareholder*
EMP: 25 **EST:** 1998
SQ FT: 2,000
SALES (est): 1MM-4.9MM **Privately Held**
WEB: www.productionhealth.com
SIC: 8741 Hospital management services;
nursing & personal care facility
management services

(G-10192)

ROBERT ABY MD
508 10th St (56187-2343)
PHONE 507 372-1840
Robert Aby MD, *Principal*
EMP: 70
SALES (est): 5MM-9.9MM **Privately Held**
SIC: 8011 Physicians' office & clinic

(G-10193)

SCHAAP SANITATION INC
27008 US Highway 59 (56187-8420)
PO Box 698 (56187-0698)
PHONE 507 376-9218
FAX: 507 376-5773
Eric Joens, *District Mgr*
Shirley Boom, *Manager*
EMP: 28 **EST:** 1973
SALES (est): 5MM-9.9MM **Publicly Held**
WEB: www.wcnx.org

SIC: 4953 Garbage collecting, destroying &
processing services; waste material
recycling services
PA: Waste Connections Inc
2295 Iron Point Rd # 200
Folsom CA 95630
916 608-8200

(G-10194)

SMITH TRUCKING INC
1451 Joosten Rd (56187-1995)
PO Box 249 (56187-0249)
PHONE 507 376-5080
FAX: 507 372-4641
Phillip P Smith, *President*
Mike Smith, *General Mgr*
Rita Smith, *Corp Secy*
Pat Smith, *Vice Pres*
EMP: 100 **EST:** 1946
SQ FT: 10,000
SALES (est): 10MM-24.9MM **Privately Held**
WEB: www.smithtruckinginc.com
SIC: 4213 Over the road trucking

(G-10195)

SOUTHWESTERN MENTAL HEALTH CTR
1024 7th Ave (56187-2287)
PO Box 175 (56187-0175)
PHONE 507 376-4141
FAX: 507 376-4494
Scott Johnson, *Manager*
Dennis Gybert, *Manager*
EMP: 50
SALES (est): 1MM-4.9MM **Privately Held**
SIC: 8322 8069 8093 General counseling
services; alcoholism rehabilitation hospital;
outpatient mental health clinic
PA: Southwestern Mental Health Ctr
216 E Luverne St
Luverne MN 56156
507 283-9511

(G-10196)

SOUTHWESTERN MINNESOTA
1106 3rd Ave (56187-2475)
PO Box 787 (56187-0787)
PHONE 507 376-4195
FAX: 507 376-3636
Kathy Carlson, *Finance Dir*
Brent Groen, *MIS Staff*
Neal Steffl, *Director*
EMP: 25 **EST:** 1965
SQ FT: 4,000 **Privately Held**
WEB: www.smoc.us
SIC: 8399 Community action agency

(G-10197)

VETERINARY MEDICAL CENTER PROF
Also Called: Worthington Small Animal Clinic
600 Oxford St (56187-1660)
PO Box 785 (56187-0785)
PHONE 507 372-2957
FAX: 507 372-2950
Craig W Pfeifer, *President*
Rweed Leiting, *Corp Secy*
Bradley Shaffer, *Corp Secy*
Wein R Freesam, *Vice Pres*
Erik Mankivil, *Treasurer*
EMP: 33 **EST:** 1960
SQ FT: 17,000 **Privately Held**
WEB: www.vmcclinic.com
SIC: 0741 0742 Veterinary services;
livestock; livestock veterinarian; veterinary
services

(G-10198)

WORTHINGTON TRACTOR PARTS INC
27170 US Highway 59 (56187-8419)
PHONE 507 372-2911
FAX: 507 372-5669
Larry Frodermann, *Sales Staff*
Lavonne V Weerd, *Manager*
EMP: 25
SALES (est): 10MM-24.9MM **Privately Held**
WEB: www.worthingtonagparts.com
SIC: 5083 Wholesales farm & garden
machinery
HQ: Worthington Tractor Parts Inc
6901 E Fish Lake Rd Ste 156
Maple Grove MN 55369
763 488-9955

(G-10199)

YMCA OF WORTHINGTON, MINNESOTA
Also Called: Worthington Area YMCA
1501 Collegeway (56187-3028)
PHONE 507 376-6197
FAX: 507 376-5624
Jodi Landgaard, *Corp Secy*
Nancy Antoine, *Corp Secy*
Andy Johnson, *Exec Dir*
Beth V Hove, *Bd of Directors*
Mark Shepherd, *Bd of Directors*
EMP: 30 **EST:** 1944
SQ FT: 18,000 **Privately Held**
SIC: 8641 7032 7991 8322 8351 Youth
organizations; youth camps; child day care
service; individual & family social services;
physical fitness center

WYKOFF
Fillmore County

(G-10200)

THOMPSON MOTORS OF WYKOFF INC
125 Gold St S (55990-8710)
PO Box 38 (55990-0038)
PHONE 507 352-2435
FAX: 507 352-4912
Richard Thompson, *CEO*
Roderick Thompson, *President*
Judith Thompson, *Corp Secy*
Christine Thompson, *Manager*
EMP: 26 **EST:** 1940
SQ FT: 22,000
SALES (est): 10MM-24.9MM **Privately Held**
WEB: www.thompsontrucks.com
SIC: 5012 Retails new & used trucks,
tractors & trailers; wholesales commercial
trucks

WYOMING
Chisago County

(G-10201)

CU RECOVERY INC
26263 Forest Blvd (55092-8033)
PHONE 651 462-4400
FAX: 651 462-7043
Kelly Becker, *President*
Terrence Brelje, *Vice Pres*
Elizabeth A Smith, *Vice Pres*
Karen A Smith, *Treasurer*
EMP: 25 **EST:** 1990
SALES (est): 1MM-4.9MM **Privately Held**
WEB: www.curecovery.com
SIC: 7322 Collection agency

(G-10202)

FAIRVIEW HEALTH SERVICES
5200 Fairview Blvd (55092-8013)
PHONE 651 982-7000
FAX: 651 982-7570
Dave Devosenski, *COO*
Shirley Singh, *Vice Pres*
Deb Stumm, *Vice Pres*
Dan Anderson, *Vice Pres*
John Mollner, *Facilities Mgr*
EMP: 270
SALES (est): 10MM-24.9MM **Privately Held**
WEB: www.fairview.org
SIC: 8741 8051 8062 8082 Hospital
management services; retails hearing aids;
home health care services; medical
hospital; skilled nursing care facility
PA: Fairview Health Services
2450 Riverside Ave
Minneapolis MN 55454
612 672-6300

(G-10203)

FIRST STATE BANK OF WYOMING
26741 Felton Ave (55092-8426)
PO Box 308 (55092-0308)
PHONE 651 462-7611
FAX: 651 462-4966
Myles K Giese, *President*
Kristi S Nelon, *Assistant VP*
M A Zrub, *Vice Pres*

GEOGRAPHIC

(PA)=Parent Co (HQ)=Headquarters (DH)=Div Headquarters
✿ = New business established in last 2 years

2011 Harris Minnesota
Services Directory

© Harris InfoSource 1-866-281-6415
439

Beatrice Zaruba, *Vice Pres*
Stacy Frahs, *Branch Mgr*
EMP: 30 **EST:** 1914
SALES (est): 5MM-9.9MM **Privately Held**
WEB: www.wyoming-bank.com
SIC: 6022 State commercial bank

(G-10204)
FOREST LAKE SANITATION INC
6320 E Viking Blvd (55092-9320)
PO Box 564 (55092-0564)
PHONE 651 464-2321
Cameron Strand, *President*
Marge Strand, *Vice Pres*
EMP: 30 **EST:** 1964
SALES (est): 5MM-9.9MM **Privately Held**
SIC: 4953 Refuse collection & disposal services

(G-10205)
GENERAL SAFETY EQUIPMENT LLC
5181 260th St (55092-8018)
PO Box 549 (55092-0549)
PHONE 651 462-1000
Kevin M Kirvida, *Member*
Jeff Boyd, *Purchasing*
Dixie Olson, *Human Res Dir*
Shannon Huberty, *Human Res Mgr*
Dennis Berry, *Sales Staff*
EMP: 60 **EST:** 1930
SQ FT: 30,000
SALES (est): 10MM-24.9MM **Privately Held**
SIC: 7699 Manufactures specialty motor vehicle bodies; manufactures motor vehicles & car bodies; aircraft & heavy equipment repair service

(G-10206)
PATRIOT BANK MINNESOTA (PA)
26727 Faxton St (55092-9105)
PHONE 651 462-8854
John Milbauer, *President*
Rob Pascavage, *Vice Pres*
EST: 2007
SALES (corp-wide): 7.57M **Privately Held**
SIC: 6021 National commercial bank

(G-10207)
RIVERBANK MN
26777 Fallbrook Ave (55092)
PO Box 188, Osceola WI (54020-0188)
PHONE 651 408-9203
Doug Wynveen, *President*
EMP: 69 **EST:** 1908
SQ FT: 9,600
SALES (est): 10MM-24.9MM **Privately Held**
SIC: 6036 State savings bank
HQ: Riverbank
204 3rd Ave W
Osceola WI 54020
715 294-2183

(G-10208)
ROSENBAUER MOTORS LLC
5181 260th St (55092-8018)
PO Box 549 (55092-0549)
PHONE 651 462-1000
Kevin Kirvida, *Member*
Mary Kay, *Treasurer*
Dennis Berry, *Director*
▲ **EMP:** 60 **EST:** 1995 **Privately Held**
SIC: 6719 Personal holding company

YOUNG AMERICA
Carver County

(G-10209)
KLEIN BANK
800 Faxon Rd (55397-9329)
PO Box 839, Nya (55368-0839)
PHONE 952 467-2313
Roger Zellmann, *Vice Pres*

Darlene Mondor, *Manager*
Jerry Tiggelaar, *Manager*
Jim Jeffrey, *VP Systems*
EMP: 25
SQ FT: 7,002
SALES (est): 5MM-9.9MM **Privately Held**
SIC: 6022 State commercial bank

(G-10210)
SFN GROUP INC
717 Faxon Rd (55397-9304)
PHONE 952 467-1770
John Oswald, *Branch Mgr*
EMP: 400 **Publicly Held**
SIC: 7361 Employment agency services
PA: Sfn Group Inc
2050 Spectrum Blvd
Fort Lauderdale FL 33309
954 308-7600

(G-10211)
YOUNG AMERICA CORP (PA)
717 Faxon Rd (55397-9304)
PHONE 800 533-4529
Mark Shipley, *President*
Paul Hanson, *Senior VP*
Tim Crank, *Vice Pres*
Mark Pearson, *Vice Pres*
Joseph Custer, *CFO*
EMP: 500 **EST:** 1997
SQ FT: 259,000 **Privately Held**
WEB: www.young-america.com
SIC: 7389 Advertising, promotional & trade show service; coupon redemption service

ZIMMERMAN
Sherburne County

(G-10212)
DARAN INC
12280 255th Ave NW Ste 2 (55398-8445)
PO Box 134 (55398-0134)
PHONE 763 856-4000
FAX: 763 856-4444
John Nord, *President*
Bonni Cook, *Corp Secy*
Julie Ericson, *Exec Officer*
Randy Hanson, *CFO*
Julie Bollig-Ericson, *Manager*
EMP: 32 **EST:** 1974
SQ FT: 100
SALES (est): 1MM-4.9MM **Privately Held**
SIC: 4213 4212 Over the road trucking; local trucking without storage services

(G-10213)
FAIRVIEW HEALTH SERVICES
25945 Gateway Dr Ste 2 (55398-5301)
PHONE 763 856-6900
Jim Moore, *Branch Mgr*
EMP: 30
SALES (est): 1MM-4.9MM **Privately Held**
WEB: www.fairview.org
SIC: 8011 Clinic operated by physicians
PA: Fairview Health Services
2450 Riverside Ave
Minneapolis MN 55454
612 672-6300

(G-10214)
NELSON NURSERY INC
25834 Main St (55398-9342)
PHONE 763 856-2441
FAX: 763 856-2440
Michael Lemke, *President*
Jacqueline Lemke, *Corp Secy*
Laura Schroer, *Vice Pres*
Bonnie Cook, *Office Mgr*
EMP: 75 **EST:** 1957
SQ FT: 7,000
SALES (est): 10MM-24.9MM **Privately Held**
SIC: 0181 Retail nurseries; bedding plant farm; shrubbery field nursery; retails nursery stock, seeds & bulbs; nursery stock production

(G-10215)
RP SCHROEDER CONSTRUCTION INC
26657 146th St NW (55398-9309)
PHONE 763 856-2230
Patti Schroeder, *President*
Rick Schroeder, *Vice Pres*
Mike Jacobs, *Manager*
EMP: 30 **EST:** 1985
SALES (est): 1MM-4.9MM **Privately Held**
SIC: 1623 Underground utilities contractor

ZUMBROTA
Goodhue County

(G-10216)
ATLAS COLD STORAGE MIDWEST
1000 Arctic Ave (55992)
PHONE 507 732-4224
FAX: 507 732-5355
Patrick Gouveia, *President*
Jamie Kleis, *General Mgr*
EMP: 30 **EST:** 1996
SQ FT: 131,000
SALES (est): 1MM-4.9MM **Privately Held**
SIC: 4222 Cold storage or refrigerated warehousing

(G-10217)
BANK OF ZUMBROTA
1440 S Main St (55992-1460)
PO Box 8 (55992-0008)
PHONE 507 732-7555
FAX: 507 732-8713
Andrea Kienholtz, *Exec VP*
Sherry Goplen, *Loan Officer*
Jeffrey Perra, *Branch Mgr*
Mindi Arendt, *Manager*
Bretta Damson, *Director*
EMP: 40
SALES (est): 10MM-24.9MM **Privately Held**
WEB: www.bankofzumbrota.com
SIC: 6022 State commercial bank

(G-10218)
DAIRY FARMERS OF AMERICA INC
1313 Northstar Dr (55992-1092)
PHONE 507 732-5124
FAX: 507 732-8609
Tony Jones, *Vice Pres*
Brian Kesler, *Plant Supt*
Ron Collett, *Plant Mgr*
Scott Kleinschmidt, *Warehouse Mgr*
Ruben Cogswell, *Maint Spvr*
EMP: 50
SALES (est): 25MM-49.9MM **Privately Held**
WEB: www.dfamilk.com
SIC: 5083 Manufactures butter; wholesales milking machinery & equipment; manufactures cheese; manufactures frozen desserts & novelties; manufactures dry, condensed or evaporated dairy products; manufactures fluid milk
PA: Dairy Farmers of America Inc
10220 N Ambassador Dr
Kansas City MO 64153
816 801-6455

(G-10219)
HADER FARMS INC
40890 Highway 57 Blvd (55992-5060)
PHONE 507 824-2543
FAX: 507 824-2172
David Frederickson, *President*
Bradley Frederickson, *Treasurer*
EMP: 26 **EST:** 1943
SQ FT: 25,000
SALES (est): 1MM-4.9MM **Privately Held**
SIC: 4213 0115 0116 Heavy hauling transportation services; corn farm; soybean farm

(G-10220)
THREE RIVERS COMMUNITY ACTION
1414 Northstar Dr (55992-1091)
PHONE 507 732-7391
FAX: 507 732-8547
Mollie A Moyer, *Finance*
Jo Mahn, *Manager*
Darlene Highet, *Webmaster*
Michael Thorsteinson, *Exec Dir*
EMP: 27 **EST:** 1965
SQ FT: 7,600
SALES (est): 1MM-4.9MM **Privately Held**
SIC: 8322 8111 Individual & family social services; legal services

(G-10221)
ZUMBROTA AREA AMBULANCE ASSN
1450 Jefferson Dr (55992-1179)
PHONE 507 732-7845
Darren Pahl, *Corp Secy*
Rae Rusnak, *Treasurer*
Danielle Hrstka, *Director*
Sally Houg-Massaro, *Bd of Directors*
EMP: 29 **EST:** 1970
SALES (est): 1MM-4.9MM **Privately Held**
SIC: 4119 Ambulance service

(G-10222)
ZUMBROTA FORD SALES LLC
1660 S Main St (55992-1416)
PO Box 128 (55992-0128)
PHONE 507 732-5127
Steve Johnson, *Member*
Marie Busson, *Corp Secy*
EMP: 32 **EST:** 1954
SQ FT: 14,000
SALES (est): 10MM-24.9MM **Privately Held**
WEB: www.zumbrotaford.com
SIC: 7513 7515 7539 Retails new & used automobiles; automotive repair services; retails automotive parts; passenger car leasing; used car dealer; truck leasing & rental without drivers

(G-10223)
ZUMBROTA NURSING HOME
433 Mill St (55992-1634)
PHONE 507 732-8400
FAX: 507 732-8430
Lynn Werth, *Corp Secy*
Kari Everson, *Administrator*
EMP: 80 **EST:** 1983
SALES (est): 1MM-4.9MM **Privately Held**
SIC: 8051 Skilled nursing care facility

(G-10224)
ZUMBROTA VETERINARY CLINIC, PA
1412 Northstar Dr (55992-1091)
PHONE 507 732-7301
FAX: 507 732-5714
Kory Bigalk, *President*
Bill Erickson, *Office Mgr*
Bill Ericson, *Office Mgr*
Jeff Smith, *Manager*
EMP: 25 **EST:** 1953
SQ FT: 4,000 **Privately Held**
SIC: 0741 0742 Livestock veterinarian; veterinarian services

www.HarrisInfo.com
440

2011 Harris Minnesota
Services Directory

▲=Import ▼=Export
◆=Import/Export

SIC INDEX

SIC NO — PRODUCT

A

6321 Accident & Health Insurance
8721 Accounting, Auditing & Bookkeeping Svcs
7322 Adjustment & Collection Svcs
7311 Advertising Agencies
7319 Advertising, NEC
4513 Air Courier Svcs
4522 Air Transportation, Nonscheduled
4512 Air Transportation, Scheduled
4581 Airports, Flying Fields & Terminal Svcs
7999 Amusement & Recreation Svcs, NEC
7996 Amusement Parks
0291 Animal Production, NEC
0752 Animal Specialty Svcs, Exc Veterinary
1231 Anthracite Mining
8422 Arboreta, Botanical & Zoological Gardens
8712 Architectural Services
7694 Armature Rewinding Shops
7521 Automobile Parking Lots & Garages
5012 Automobiles & Other Motor Vehicles Wholesale
7536 Automotive Glass Replacement Shops
7539 Automotive Repair Shops, NEC
7549 Automotive Svcs, Except Repair & Car Washes
7537 Automotive Transmission Repair Shops

B

7929 Bands, Orchestras, Actors & Entertainers
7241 Barber Shops
7231 Beauty Shops
0211 Beef Cattle Feedlots
0212 Beef Cattle, Except Feedlots
5181 Beer & Ale Wholesale
1221 Bituminous Coal & Lignite: Surface Mining
5192 Books, Periodicals & Newspapers Wholesale
7933 Bowling Centers
5032 Brick, Stone & Related Construction Mtrls Wholesale
1622 Bridge, Tunnel & Elevated Hwy Construction
7349 Building Cleaning & Maintenance Svcs, NEC
4142 Bus Charter Service, Except Local
4173 Bus Terminal & Svc Facilities
8611 Business Associations
8748 Business Consulting Svcs, NEC
7389 Business Svcs, NEC

C

4841 Cable & Other Pay TV Svcs
7542 Car Washes
1751 Carpentry Work
7217 Carpet & Upholstery Cleaning
0119 Cash Grains, NEC
6553 Cemetery Subdividers & Developers
5169 Chemicals & Allied Prdts, NEC Wholesale
0252 Chicken Egg Farms
8351 Child Day Care Svcs
8641 Civic, Social & Fraternal Associations
5052 Coal & Other Minerals & Ores Wholesale
7215 Coin Operated Laundries & Cleaning
7993 Coin-Operated Amusement Devices & Arcades
4939 Combination Utilities, NEC
7336 Commercial Art & Graphic Design
6029 Commercial Banks, NEC
8732 Commercial Economic, Sociological & Educational Research
5046 Commercial Eqpt, NEC Wholesale
7335 Commercial Photography
8731 Commercial Physical & Biological Research
6221 Commodity Contracts Brokers & Dealers
4899 Communication Svcs, NEC
7376 Computer Facilities Management Svcs
7373 Computer Integrated Systems Design
7378 Computer Maintenance & Repair
7379 Computer Related Svcs, NEC
7377 Computer Rental & Leasing
5045 Computers & Peripheral Eqpt & Software Wholesale
1771 Concrete Work
5145 Confectionery Wholesale
5082 Construction & Mining Mach & Eqpt Wholesale
5039 Construction Materials, NEC Wholesale
1442 Construction Sand & Gravel
1021 Copper Ores
0115 Corn
4215 Courier Svcs, Except Air
6159 Credit Institutions, Misc Business
6153 Credit Institutions, Short-Term Business
7323 Credit Reporting Svcs
0191 Crop Farming, Misc

D

0722 Crop Harvesting By Machine
0723 Crop Preparation, Except Cotton Ginning
1311 Crude Petroleum & Natural Gas
4612 Crude Petroleum Pipelines
1423 Crushed & Broken Granite
1422 Crushed & Broken Limestone
1429 Crushed & Broken Stone, NEC
7371 Custom Computer Programming Svcs

D

0241 Dairy Farms
5143 Dairy Prdts, Except Dried Or Canned Wholesale
7911 Dance Studios, Schools & Halls
7374 Data & Computer Processing & Preparation
0175 Deciduous Tree Fruits
4424 Deep Sea Domestic Transportation Of Freight
8072 Dental Laboratories
7381 Detective & Armored Car Svcs
1411 Dimension Stone
7331 Direct Mail Advertising Svcs
7342 Disinfecting & Pest Control Svcs
5122 Drugs, Drug Proprietaries & Sundries Wholesale
7216 Dry Cleaning Plants, Except Rug Cleaning
5099 Durable Goods: NEC Wholesale

E

6732 Education, Religious & Charitable Trusts
4931 Electric & Other Svcs Combined
4911 Electric Svcs
7629 Electrical & Elex Repair Shop, NEC
5064 Electrical Appliances, TV & Radios Wholesale
1731 Electrical Work
5063 Electrl Apparatus, Eqpt, Wiring Splys Wholesale
5065 Electronic Parts & Eqpt Wholesale
7361 Employment Agencies
8711 Engineering Services
7359 Equipment Rental & Leasing, NEC
1794 Excavating & Grading Work

F

8744 Facilities Support Mgmt Svcs
5083 Farm & Garden Mach & Eqpt Wholesale
0762 Farm Management Svcs
4221 Farm Product Warehousing & Storage
5191 Farm Splys Wholesale
5159 Farm-Prdt Raw Mtrls, NEC Wholesale
6111 Federal Credit Agencies
6061 Federal Credit Unions
6035 Federal Savings Institutions
0139 Field Crops, Except Cash Grains, NEC
6331 Fire, Marine & Casualty Insurance
5146 Fish & Seafood Wholesale
4785 Fixed Facilities, Inspection, Weighing Svcs Transptn
1752 Floor Laying & Other Floor Work, NEC
5193 Flowers, Nursery Stock & Florists' Splys Wholesale
0182 Food Crops Grown Under Cover
5139 Footwear Wholesale
0831 Forest Prdts
0851 Forestry Svcs
4731 Freight Forwarding & Arrangement
5148 Fresh Fruits & Vegetables Wholesale
6099 Functions Related To Deposit Banking, NEC
7261 Funeral Svcs & Crematories
5021 Furniture Wholesale

G

7212 Garment Pressing & Cleaners' Agents
4932 Gas & Other Svcs Combined
4925 Gas Production &/Or Distribution
7538 General Automotive Repair Shop
1541 General Contractors, Indl Bldgs & Warehouses
1542 General Contractors, Nonresidential & Non-indl Bldgs
1522 General Contractors, Residential Other Than Single Family
1521 General Contractors, Single Family Houses
8062 General Medical & Surgical Hospitals
4225 General Warehousing & Storage
1793 Glass & Glazing Work
1041 Gold Ores
5153 Grain & Field Beans Wholesale
5149 Groceries & Related Prdts, NEC Wholesale
5141 Groceries, General Line Wholesale

H

5072 Hardware Wholesale
8099 Health & Allied Svcs, NEC

5075 Heating & Air Conditioning Eqpt & Splys Wholesale
7353 Heavy Construction Eqpt Rental & Leasing
1629 Heavy Construction, NEC
7363 Help Supply Svcs
1611 Highway & Street Construction
0213 Hogs
5023 Home Furnishings Wholesale
8082 Home Health Care Svcs
0272 Horse & Other Equine Production
6324 Hospital & Medical Svc Plans Carriers
7011 Hotels, Motels & Tourist Courts
0971 Hunting & Trapping

I

8322 Individual & Family Social Svcs
5113 Indl & Personal Svc Paper Wholesale
7218 Industrial Launderers
5084 Industrial Mach & Eqpt Wholesale
1446 Industrial Sand
5085 Industrial Splys Wholesale
7375 Information Retrieval Svcs
1796 Installation Or Erection Of Bldg Eqpt & Machinery, NEC
6411 Insurance Agents, Brokers & Svc
6399 Insurance Carriers, NEC
4131 Intercity & Rural Bus Transportation
8052 Intermediate Care Facilities
6282 Investment Advice
6799 Investors, NEC
0134 Irish Potatoes
1011 Iron Ores
4971 Irrigation Systems

J

5094 Jewelry, Watches, Precious Stones Wholesale
8331 Job Training & Vocational Rehabilitation Svcs

K

8092 Kidney Dialysis Centers

L

8631 Labor Unions & Similar Organizations
6552 Land Subdividers & Developers
0781 Landscape Counseling & Planning
7219 Laundry & Garment Svcs, NEC
0782 Lawn & Garden Svcs
8111 Legal Svcs
6519 Lessors Of Real Estate, NEC
6311 Life Insurance Carriers
7213 Linen Sply
0751 Livestock Svcs, Except Veterinary
5154 Livestock Wholesale
6163 Loan Brokers
4111 Local & Suburban Transit
4141 Local Bus Charter Svc
4119 Local Passenger Transportation: NEC
4214 Local Trucking With Storage
4212 Local Trucking Without Storage
5031 Lumber, Plywood & Millwork Wholesale

M

8742 Management Consulting Services
6722 Management Investment Offices
8741 Management Services
4493 Marinas
4491 Marine Cargo Handling
1741 Masonry & Other Stonework
5147 Meats & Meat Prdts Wholesale
7352 Medical Eqpt Rental & Leasing
8071 Medical Laboratories
5047 Medical, Dental & Hospital Eqpt & Splys Wholesale
8699 Membership Organizations, NEC
7997 Membership Sports & Recreation Clubs
7041 Membership-Basis Hotels
5136 Men's & Boys' Clothing & Furnishings Wholesale
1081 Metal Mining Svcs
5051 Metals Service Centers
1499 Miscellaneous Nonmetallic Mining
7299 Miscellaneous Personal Svcs, NEC
6162 Mortgage Bankers & Loan Correspondents
7822 Motion Picture & Video Tape Distribution
7812 Motion Picture & Video Tape Production
7832 Motion Picture Theaters, Except Drive-In
5015 Motor Vehicle Parts, Used Wholesale
5013 Motor Vehicle Splys & New Parts Wholesale
8412 Museums & Art Galleries

S
I
C

SIC NO	PRODUCT

N

6021 National Commercial Banks
4924 Natural Gas Distribution
1321 Natural Gas Liquids
4922 Natural Gas Transmission
8733 Noncommercial Research Organizations
6091 Nondeposit Trust Facilities
5199 Nondurable Goods, NEC Wholesale
1481 Nonmetallic Minerals Svcs, Except Fuels
8059 Nursing & Personal Care Facilities, NEC

O

5044 Office Eqpt Wholesale
8041 Offices & Clinics Of Chiropractors
8021 Offices & Clinics Of Dentists
8011 Offices & Clinics Of Doctors Of Medicine
8031 Offices & Clinics Of Doctors Of Osteopathy
8049 Offices & Clinics Of Health Practitioners, NEC
8042 Offices & Clinics Of Optometrists
6712 Offices Of Bank Holding Co's
6719 Offices Of Holding Co's, NEC
1389 Oil & Gas Field Svcs, NEC
1531 Operative Builders
6513 Operators Of Apartment Buildings
6514 Operators Of Dwellings, Except Apartments
6512 Operators Of Nonresidential Bldgs
6515 Operators of Residential Mobile Home Sites
5048 Ophthalmic Goods Wholesale
0181 Ornamental Floriculture & Nursery Prdts
0783 Ornamental Shrub & Tree Svc
7312 Outdoor Advertising Svcs

P

5142 Packaged Frozen Foods Wholesale
4783 Packing & Crating Svcs
1721 Painting & Paper Hanging Contractors
5198 Paints, Varnishes & Splys Wholesale
7515 Passenger Car Leasing
7514 Passenger Car Rental
4729 Passenger Transportation Arrangement, NEC
6794 Patent Owners & Lessors
6371 Pension, Health & Welfare Funds
6141 Personal Credit Institutions
5172 Petroleum & Petroleum Prdts Wholesale
5171 Petroleum Bulk Stations & Terminals
1475 Phosphate Rock
7334 Photocopying & Duplicating Svcs
7384 Photofinishing Labs
5043 Photographic Eqpt & Splys Wholesale
7221 Photographic Studios, Portrait
7991 Physical Fitness Facilities
5131 Piece Goods, Notions & Dry Goods Wholesale
1742 Plastering, Drywall, Acoustical & Insulation Work
5162 Plastics Materials & Basic Shapes Wholesale
5074 Plumbing & Heating Splys Wholesale
1711 Plumbing, Heating & Air Conditioning Contractors
8651 Political Organizations
1474 Potash, Soda & Borate Minerals
5144 Poultry & Poultry Prdts Wholesale
0254 Poultry Hatcheries

7211 Power Laundries, Family & Commercial
7372 Prepackaged Software
5111 Printing & Writing Paper Wholesale
5049 Professional Eqpt & Splys, NEC Wholesale
8621 Professional Membership Organizations
7941 Professional Sports Clubs & Promoters
8063 Psychiatric Hospitals
7992 Public Golf Courses
8743 Public Relations Svcs

R

7948 Racing & Track Operations
7622 Radio & TV Repair Shops
4832 Radio Broadcasting Stations
7313 Radio, TV & Publishers Adv Reps
4812 Radiotelephone Communications
4011 Railroads, Line-Hauling Operations
6531 Real Estate Agents & Managers
6798 Real Estate Investment Trusts
4613 Refined Petroleum Pipelines
4222 Refrigerated Warehousing & Storage
7623 Refrigeration & Air Conditioning Svc & Repair Shop
5078 Refrigeration Eqpt & Splys Wholesale
4953 Refuse Systems
7699 Repair Shop & Related Svcs, NEC
8361 Residential Care
7641 Reupholstery & Furniture Repair
0112 Rice
5033 Roofing, Siding & Insulation Mtrls Wholesale
1761 Roofing, Siding & Sheet Metal Work
7021 Rooming & Boarding Houses

S

4959 Sanitary Svcs, NEC
6036 Savings Institutions, Except Federal
4151 School Buses
5093 Scrap & Waste Materials Wholesale
7338 Secretarial & Court Reporting Svcs
6231 Security & Commodity Exchanges
6289 Security & Commodity Svcs, NEC
6211 Security Brokers & Dealers
7382 Security Systems Svcs
5087 Service Establishment Eqpt & Splys Wholesale
7819 Services Allied To Motion Picture Prdtn
8999 Services Not Elsewhere Classified
4952 Sewerage Systems
7251 Shoe Repair & Shoeshine Parlors
8051 Skilled Nursing Facilities
8399 Social Services, NEC
0711 Soil Preparation Svcs
0721 Soil Preparation, Planting & Cultivating Svc
0116 Soybeans
1799 Special Trade Contractors, NEC
4226 Special Warehousing & Storage, NEC
8069 Specialty Hospitals, Except Psychiatric
8093 Specialty Outpatient Facilities, NEC
7032 Sporting & Recreational Camps
5091 Sporting & Recreational Goods & Splys Wholesale
6022 State Commercial Banks
6062 State Credit Unions

5112 Stationery & Office Splys Wholesale
4961 Steam & Air Conditioning Sply
1791 Structural Steel Erection
6351 Surety Insurance Carriers
8713 Surveying Services
4013 Switching & Terminal Svcs

T

7291 Tax Return Preparation Svcs
4121 Taxi Cabs
4822 Telegraph & Other Message Communications
4813 Telephone Communications, Except Radio
4833 Television Broadcasting Stations
4231 Terminal & Joint Terminal Maint Facilities
1743 Terrazzo, Tile, Marble & Mosaic Work
8734 Testing Laboratories
7922 Theatrical Producers & Misc Theatrical Svcs
0811 Timber Tracts
7534 Tire Retreading & Repair Shops
5014 Tires & Tubes Wholesale
6541 Title Abstract Offices
6361 Title Insurance
5194 Tobacco & Tobacco Prdts Wholesale
7532 Top, Body & Upholstery Repair & Paint Shops
4725 Tour Operators
5092 Toys & Hobby Goods & Splys Wholesale
7033 Trailer Parks & Camp Sites
5088 Transportation Eqpt & Splys, Except Motor Vehicles Wholesale
4789 Transportation Svcs, NEC
4724 Travel Agencies
7513 Truck Rental & Leasing, Without Drivers
4213 Trucking, Except Local
6733 Trusts Except Educational, Religious & Charitable
0253 Turkey & Turkey Egg Farms

U

6726 Unit Investment Trusts, Face-Amount Certificate Offices
1094 Uranium, Radium & Vanadium Ores
7519 Utility Trailers & Recreational Vehicle Rental

V

0161 Vegetables & Melons
0742 Veterinary Animal Specialties
0741 Veterinary Livestock Svcs
7841 Video Tape Rental

W

7631 Watch, Clock & Jewelry Repair
4941 Water Sply
4489 Water Transport Of Passengers, NEC
4449 Water Transportation Of Freight, NEC
1781 Water Well Drilling
1623 Water, Sewer & Utility Line Construction
7692 Welding Repair
0111 Wheat
5182 Wine & Distilled Alcoholic Beverages Wholesale
5137 Women's, Children's & Infants Clothing Wholesale
1795 Wrecking & Demolition Work

SIC

SIC INDEX

SIC NO	PRODUCT

01 AGRICULTURAL PRODUCTION CROPS

0111 Wheat
0112 Rice
0115 Corn
0116 Soybeans
0119 Cash Grains, NEC
0134 Irish Potatoes
0139 Field Crops, Except Cash Grains, NEC
0161 Vegetables & Melons
0175 Deciduous Tree Fruits
0181 Ornamental Floriculture & Nursery Prdts
0182 Food Crops Grown Under Cover
0191 Crop Farming, Misc

02 AGRICULTURAL PRODUCTION LIVESTOCK

0211 Beef Cattle Feedlots
0212 Beef Cattle, Except Feedlots
0213 Hogs
0241 Dairy Farms
0252 Chicken Egg Farms
0253 Turkey & Turkey Egg Farms
0254 Poultry Hatcheries
0272 Horse & Other Equine Production
0291 Animal Production, NEC

07 AGRICULTURAL SERVICES

0711 Soil Preparation Svcs
0721 Soil Preparation, Planting & Cultivating Svc
0722 Crop Harvesting By Machine
0723 Crop Preparation, Except Cotton Ginning
0741 Veterinary Livestock Svcs
0742 Veterinary Animal Specialties
0751 Livestock Svcs, Except Veterinary
0752 Animal Specialty Svcs, Exc Veterinary
0762 Farm Management Svcs
0781 Landscape Counseling & Planning
0782 Lawn & Garden Svcs
0783 Ornamental Shrub & Tree Svc

08 FORESTRY

0811 Timber Tracts
0831 Forest Prdts
0851 Forestry Svcs

09 FISHING, HUNTING & TRAPPING

0971 Hunting & Trapping

10 METAL MINING

1011 Iron Ores
1021 Copper Ores
1041 Gold Ores
1081 Metal Mining Svcs
1094 Uranium, Radium & Vanadium Ores

12 COAL MINING

1221 Bituminous Coal & Lignite: Surface Mining
1231 Anthracite Mining

13 OIL & GAS EXTRACTION

1311 Crude Petroleum & Natural Gas
1321 Natural Gas Liquids
1389 Oil & Gas Field Svcs, NEC

14 MINING & QUARRYING

1411 Dimension Stone
1422 Crushed & Broken Limestone
1423 Crushed & Broken Granite
1429 Crushed & Broken Stone, NEC
1442 Construction Sand & Gravel
1446 Industrial Sand
1474 Potash, Soda & Borate Minerals
1475 Phosphate Rock
1481 Nonmetallic Minerals Svcs, Except Fuels
1499 Miscellaneous Nonmetallic Mining

15 BUILDING CONSTRUCTION, GEN'L CONTRACTORS

1521 General Contractors, Single Family Houses
1522 General Contractors, Residential Other Than Single Family
1531 Operative Builders
1541 General Contractors, Indl Bldgs & Warehouses
1542 General Contractors, Nonresidential & Non-indl Bldgs

16 HEAVY CONSTRUCTION OTHER THAN BUILDING

1611 Highway & Street Construction
1622 Bridge, Tunnel & Elevated Hwy Construction
1623 Water, Sewer & Utility Line Construction
1629 Heavy Construction, NEC

17 CONSTRUCTION-SPECIAL TRADE CONTRACTORS

1711 Plumbing, Heating & Air Conditioning Contractors
1721 Painting & Paper Hanging Contractors
1731 Electrical Work
1741 Masonry & Other Stonework
1742 Plastering, Drywall, Acoustical & Insulation Work
1743 Terrazzo, Tile, Marble & Mosaic Work
1751 Carpentry Work
1752 Floor Laying & Other Floor Work, NEC
1761 Roofing, Siding & Sheet Metal Work
1771 Concrete Work
1781 Water Well Drilling
1791 Structural Steel Erection
1793 Glass & Glazing Work
1794 Excavating & Grading Work
1795 Wrecking & Demolition Work
1796 Installation Or Erection Of Bldg Eqpt & Machinery, NEC
1799 Special Trade Contractors, NEC

40 RAILROAD TRANSPORTATION

4011 Railroads, Line-Hauling Operations
4013 Switching & Terminal Svcs

41 LOCAL & SUBURBAN TRANSIT & HIGHWAY TRANSPORTATION

4111 Local & Suburban Transit
4119 Local Passenger Transportation: NEC
4121 Taxi Cabs
4131 Intercity & Rural Bus Transportation
4141 Local Bus Charter Svc
4142 Bus Charter Service, Except Local
4151 School Buses
4173 Bus Terminal & Svc Facilities

42 MOTOR FREIGHT TRANSPORTATION & WAREHOUSING

4212 Local Trucking Without Storage
4213 Trucking, Except Local
4214 Local Trucking With Storage
4215 Courier Svcs, Except Air
4221 Farm Product Warehousing & Storage
4222 Refrigerated Warehousing & Storage
4225 General Warehousing & Storage
4226 Special Warehousing & Storage, NEC
4231 Terminal & Joint Terminal Maint Facilities

44 WATER TRANSPORTATION

4424 Deep Sea Domestic Transportation Of Freight
4449 Water Transportation Of Freight, NEC
4489 Water Transport Of Passengers, NEC
4491 Marine Cargo Handling
4493 Marinas

45 TRANSPORTATION BY AIR

4512 Air Transportation, Scheduled
4513 Air Courier Svcs
4522 Air Transportation, Nonscheduled
4581 Airports, Flying Fields & Terminal Svcs

46 PIPELINES, EXCEPT NATURAL GAS

4612 Crude Petroleum Pipelines
4613 Refined Petroleum Pipelines

47 TRANSPORTATION SERVICES

4724 Travel Agencies
4725 Tour Operators
4729 Passenger Transportation Arrangement, NEC
4731 Freight Forwarding & Arrangement
4783 Packing & Crating Svcs
4785 Fixed Facilities, Inspection, Weighing Svcs Transptn
4789 Transportation Svcs, NEC

48 COMMUNICATIONS

4812 Radiotelephone Communications
4813 Telephone Communications, Except Radio
4822 Telegraph & Other Message Communications
4832 Radio Broadcasting Stations
4833 Television Broadcasting Stations
4841 Cable & Other Pay TV Svcs
4899 Communication Svcs, NEC

49 ELECTRIC, GAS & SANITARY SVC

4911 Electric Svcs
4922 Natural Gas Transmission
4924 Natural Gas Distribution
4925 Gas Production &/Or Distribution
4931 Electric & Other Svcs Combined
4932 Gas & Other Svcs Combined
4939 Combination Utilities, NEC
4941 Water Sply
4952 Sewerage Systems
4953 Refuse Systems
4959 Sanitary Svcs, NEC
4961 Steam & Air Conditioning Sply
4971 Irrigation Systems

50 WHOLESALE TRADE-DURABLE GOODS

5012 Automobiles & Other Motor Vehicles Wholesale
5013 Motor Vehicle Splys & New Parts Wholesale
5014 Tires & Tubes Wholesale
5015 Motor Vehicle Parts, Used Wholesale
5021 Furniture Wholesale
5023 Home Furnishings Wholesale
5031 Lumber, Plywood & Millwork Wholesale
5032 Brick, Stone & Related Construction Mtrls Wholesale
5033 Roofing, Siding & Insulation Mtrls Wholesale
5039 Construction Materials, NEC Wholesale
5043 Photographic Eqpt & Splys Wholesale
5044 Office Eqpt Wholesale
5045 Computers & Peripheral Eqpt & Software Wholesale
5046 Commercial Eqpt, NEC Wholesale
5047 Medical, Dental & Hospital Eqpt & Splys Wholesale
5048 Ophthalmic Goods Wholesale
5049 Professional Eqpt & Splys, NEC Wholesale
5051 Metals Service Centers
5052 Coal & Other Minerals & Ores Wholesale
5063 Electrl Apparatus, Eqpt, Wiring Splys Wholesale
5064 Electrical Appliances, TV & Radios Wholesale
5065 Electronic Parts & Eqpt Wholesale
5072 Hardware Wholesale
5074 Plumbing & Heating Splys Wholesale
5075 Heating & Air Conditioning Eqpt & Splys Wholesale
5078 Refrigeration Eqpt & Splys Wholesale
5082 Construction & Mining Mach & Eqpt Wholesale
5083 Farm & Garden Mach & Eqpt Wholesale
5084 Industrial Mach & Eqpt Wholesale
5085 Industrial Splys Wholesale
5087 Service Establishment Eqpt & Splys Wholesale
5088 Transportation Eqpt & Splys, Except Motor Vehicles Wholesale
5091 Sporting & Recreational Goods & Splys Wholesale
5092 Toys & Hobby Goods & Splys Wholesale
5093 Scrap & Waste Materials Wholesale
5094 Jewelry, Watches, Precious Stones Wholesale
5099 Durable Goods: NEC Wholesale

51 WHOLESALE TRADE-NONDURABLE GOODS

5111 Printing & Writing Paper Wholesale
5112 Stationery & Office Splys Wholesale
5113 Indl & Personal Svc Paper Wholesale
5122 Drugs, Drug Proprietaries & Sundries Wholesale
5131 Piece Goods, Notions & Dry Goods Wholesale
5136 Men's & Boys' Clothing & Furnishings Wholesale
5137 Women's, Children's & Infants Clothing Wholesale
5139 Footwear Wholesale
5141 Groceries, General Line Wholesale
5142 Packaged Frozen Foods Wholesale
5143 Dairy Prdts, Except Dried Or Canned Wholesale
5144 Poultry & Poultry Prdts Wholesale
5145 Confectionery Wholesale
5146 Fish & Seafood Wholesale
5147 Meats & Meat Prdts Wholesale
5148 Fresh Fruits & Vegetables Wholesale
5149 Groceries & Related Prdts, NEC Wholesale
5153 Grain & Field Beans Wholesale
5154 Livestock Wholesale
5159 Farm-Prdt Raw Mtrls, NEC Wholesale
5162 Plastics Materials & Basic Shapes Wholesale
5169 Chemicals & Allied Prdts, NEC Wholesale
5171 Petroleum Bulk Stations & Terminals
5172 Petroleum & Petroleum Prdts Wholesale
5181 Beer & Ale Wholesale
5182 Wine & Distilled Alcoholic Beverages Wholesale
5191 Farm Splys Wholesale
5192 Books, Periodicals & Newspapers Wholesale

S I C

SIC NO	PRODUCT

5193 Flowers, Nursery Stock & Florists' Splys Wholesale
5194 Tobacco & Tobacco Prdts Wholesale
5198 Paints, Varnishes & Splys Wholesale
5199 Nondurable Goods, NEC Wholesale

60 DEPOSITORY INSTITUTIONS

6021 National Commercial Banks
6022 State Commercial Banks
6029 Commercial Banks, NEC
6035 Federal Savings Institutions
6036 Savings Institutions, Except Federal
6061 Federal Credit Unions
6062 State Credit Unions
6091 Nondeposit Trust Facilities
6099 Functions Related To Deposit Banking, NEC

61 NONDEPOSITORY INSTITUTIONS

6111 Federal Credit Agencies
6141 Personal Credit Institutions
6153 Credit Institutions, Short-Term Business
6159 Credit Institutions, Misc Business
6162 Mortgage Bankers & Loan Correspondents
6163 Loan Brokers

62 SECURITY & COMMODITY BROKERS & DEALERS

6211 Security Brokers & Dealers
6221 Commodity Contracts Brokers & Dealers
6231 Security & Commodity Exchanges
6282 Investment Advice
6289 Security & Commodity Svcs, NEC

63 INSURANCE CARRIERS

6311 Life Insurance Carriers
6321 Accident & Health Insurance
6324 Hospital & Medical Svc Plans Carriers
6331 Fire, Marine & Casualty Insurance
6351 Surety Insurance Carriers
6361 Title Insurance
6371 Pension, Health & Welfare Funds
6399 Insurance Carriers, NEC

64 INSURANCE AGENTS, BROKERS & SVCS

6411 Insurance Agents, Brokers & Svc

65 REAL ESTATE

6512 Operators Of Nonresidential Bldgs
6513 Operators Of Apartment Buildings
6514 Operators Of Dwellings, Except Apartments
6515 Operators of Residential Mobile Home Sites
6519 Lessors Of Real Estate, NEC
6531 Real Estate Agents & Managers
6541 Title Abstract Offices
6552 Land Subdividers & Developers
6553 Cemetery Subdividers & Developers

67 HOLDING & OTHER INVESTMENT OFFICES

6712 Offices Of Bank Holding Co's
6719 Offices Of Holding Co's, NEC
6722 Management Investment Offices
6726 Unit Investment Trusts, Face-Amount Certificate Offices
6732 Education, Religious & Charitable Trusts
6733 Trusts Except Educational, Religious & Charitable
6794 Patent Owners & Lessors
6798 Real Estate Investment Trusts
6799 Investors, NEC

70 HOTELS & OTHER LODGING PLACES

7011 Hotels, Motels & Tourist Courts
7021 Rooming & Boarding Houses
7032 Sporting & Recreational Camps
7033 Trailer Parks & Camp Sites
7041 Membership-Basis Hotels

72 PERSONAL SERVICES

7211 Power Laundries, Family & Commercial
7212 Garment Pressing & Cleaners' Agents

SIC NO	PRODUCT

7213 Linen Sply
7215 Coin Operated Laundries & Cleaning
7216 Dry Cleaning Plants, Except Rug Cleaning
7217 Carpet & Upholstery Cleaning
7218 Industrial Launderers
7219 Laundry & Garment Svcs, NEC
7221 Photographic Studios, Portrait
7231 Beauty Shops
7241 Barber Shops
7251 Shoe Repair & Shoeshine Parlors
7261 Funeral Svcs & Crematories
7291 Tax Return Preparation Svcs
7299 Miscellaneous Personal Svcs, NEC

73 BUSINESS SERVICES

7311 Advertising Agencies
7312 Outdoor Advertising Svcs
7313 Radio, TV & Publishers Adv Reps
7319 Advertising, NEC
7322 Adjustment & Collection Svcs
7323 Credit Reporting Svcs
7331 Direct Mail Advertising Svcs
7334 Photocopying & Duplicating Svcs
7335 Commercial Photography
7336 Commercial Art & Graphic Design
7338 Secretarial & Court Reporting Svcs
7342 Disinfecting & Pest Control Svcs
7349 Building Cleaning & Maintenance Svcs, NEC
7352 Medical Eqpt Rental & Leasing
7353 Heavy Construction Eqpt Rental & Leasing
7359 Equipment Rental & Leasing, NEC
7361 Employment Agencies
7363 Help Supply Svcs
7371 Custom Computer Programming Svcs
7372 Prepackaged Software
7373 Computer Integrated Systems Design
7374 Data & Computer Processing & Preparation
7375 Information Retrieval Svcs
7376 Computer Facilities Management Svcs
7377 Computer Rental & Leasing
7378 Computer Maintenance & Repair
7379 Computer Related Svcs, NEC
7381 Detective & Armored Car Svcs
7382 Security Systems Svcs
7384 Photofinishing Labs
7389 Business Svcs, NEC

75 AUTOMOTIVE REPAIR SERVICES & PARKING

7513 Truck Rental & Leasing, Without Drivers
7514 Passenger Car Rental
7515 Passenger Car Leasing
7519 Utility Trailers & Recreational Vehicle Rental
7521 Automobile Parking Lots & Garages
7532 Top, Body & Upholstery Repair & Paint Shops
7534 Tire Retreading & Repair Shops
7536 Automotive Glass Replacement Shops
7537 Automotive Transmission Repair Shops
7538 General Automotive Repair Shop
7539 Automotive Repair Shops, NEC
7542 Car Washes
7549 Automotive Svcs, Except Repair & Car Washes

76 MISCELLANEOUS REPAIR SERVICES

7622 Radio & TV Repair Shops
7623 Refrigeration & Air Conditioning Svc & Repair Shop
7629 Electrical & Elex Repair Shop, NEC
7631 Watch, Clock & Jewelry Repair
7641 Reupholstery & Furniture Repair
7692 Welding Repair
7694 Armature Rewinding Shops
7699 Repair Shop & Related Svcs, NEC

78 MOTION PICTURES

7812 Motion Picture & Video Tape Production
7819 Services Allied To Motion Picture Prdtn
7822 Motion Picture & Video Tape Distribution
7832 Motion Picture Theaters, Except Drive-In
7841 Video Tape Rental

SIC NO	PRODUCT

79 AMUSEMENT & RECREATION SERVICES

7911 Dance Studios, Schools & Halls
7922 Theatrical Producers & Misc Theatrical Svcs
7929 Bands, Orchestras, Actors & Entertainers
7933 Bowling Centers
7941 Professional Sports Clubs & Promoters
7948 Racing & Track Operations
7991 Physical Fitness Facilities
7992 Public Golf Courses
7993 Coin-Operated Amusement Devices & Arcades
7996 Amusement Parks
7997 Membership Sports & Recreation Clubs
7999 Amusement & Recreation Svcs, NEC

80 HEALTH SERVICES

8011 Offices & Clinics Of Doctors Of Medicine
8021 Offices & Clinics Of Dentists
8031 Offices & Clinics Of Doctors Of Osteopathy
8041 Offices & Clinics Of Chiropractors
8042 Offices & Clinics Of Optometrists
8049 Offices & Clinics Of Health Practitioners, NEC
8051 Skilled Nursing Facilities
8052 Intermediate Care Facilities
8059 Nursing & Personal Care Facilities, NEC
8062 General Medical & Surgical Hospitals
8063 Psychiatric Hospitals
8069 Specialty Hospitals, Except Psychiatric
8071 Medical Laboratories
8072 Dental Laboratories
8082 Home Health Care Svcs
8092 Kidney Dialysis Centers
8093 Specialty Outpatient Facilities, NEC
8099 Health & Allied Svcs, NEC

81 LEGAL SERVICES

8111 Legal Svcs

83 SOCIAL SERVICES

8322 Individual & Family Social Svcs
8331 Job Training & Vocational Rehabilitation Svcs
8351 Child Day Care Svcs
8361 Residential Care
8399 Social Services, NEC

84 MUSEUMS, BOTANICAL, ZOOLOGICAL GARDENS

8412 Museums & Art Galleries
8422 Arboreta, Botanical & Zoological Gardens

86 MEMBERSHIP ORGANIZATIONS

8611 Business Associations
8621 Professional Membership Organizations
8631 Labor Unions & Similar Organizations
8641 Civic, Social & Fraternal Associations
8651 Political Organizations
8699 Membership Organizations, NEC

87 ENGINEERING, RESEARCH, MANAGEMENT & RELATED SVCS

8711 Engineering Services
8712 Architectural Services
8713 Surveying Services
8721 Accounting, Auditing & Bookkeeping Svcs
8731 Commercial Physical & Biological Research
8732 Commercial Economic, Sociological & Educational Research
8733 Noncommercial Research Organizations
8734 Testing Laboratories
8741 Management Services
8742 Management Consulting Services
8743 Public Relations Svcs
8744 Facilities Support Mgmt Svcs
8748 Business Consulting Svcs, NEC

89 SERVICES, NEC

8999 Services Not Elsewhere Classified

SIC SECTION

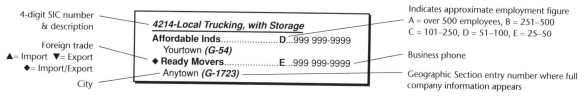

4-digit SIC number & description

4214-Local Trucking, with Storage
Affordable Inds......................D...999 999-9999
Yourtown *(G-54)*
◆ **Ready Movers**......................E...999 999-9999
Anytown *(G-1723)*

Foreign trade
▲= Import ▼= Export
◆= Import/Export
City

Indicates approximate employment figure
A = over 500 employees, B = 251–500
C = 101–250, D = 51–100, E = 25–50

Business phone

Geographic Section entry number where full company information appears

See footnotes for symbols and codes identification.

- The SIC codes used in this section are from the latest Standard Industrial Classification manual published by the U.S. Government's Office of Management and Budget. For more information regarding SICs, see the Explanatory Notes.
- Companies may be listed under multiple classifications.

01 AGRICULTURAL PRODUCTION CROPS

0111 Wheat
Bob Dahl ....E...218 874-6321
Newfolden *(G-6481)*

0112 Rice
Riviana International Inc......................D...218 776-3118
Clearbrook *(G-1040)*

0115 Corn
Bigstone Hutterian Brethren ....E...320 748-7916
Graceville *(G-2252)*
Eldon Potthoff ....E...507 695-2784
Dunnell *(G-1513)*
Gorans Brothers Inc ....E...320 995-6564
Blomkest *(G-475)*
Hader Farms Inc ....E...507 824-2543
Zumbrota *(G-10219)*
Kreger Farms Inc. ....E...320 983-5060
Milaca *(G-3373)*

0116 Soybeans
Eldon Potthoff ....E...507 695-2784
Dunnell *(G-1513)*
Gorans Brothers Inc ....E...320 995-6564
Blomkest *(G-475)*
Hader Farms ....E...507 824-2327
Wanamingo *(G-9863)*
Hader Farms Inc ....E...507 824-2543
Zumbrota *(G-10219)*
Kreger Farms Inc. ....E...320 983-5060
Milaca *(G-3373)*
Larry A Larson ....E...320 235-1294
Willmar *(G-10018)*

0119 Cash Grains, NEC
Bigstone Hutterian Brethren ....E...320 748-7916
Graceville *(G-2252)*
Daniel J Olsgaard ....E...218 299-6162
Moorhead *(G-6311)*

0134 Irish Potatoes
R D Offutt Co ....E...218 732-1461
Park Rapids *(G-6760)*

0139 Field Crops, Except Cash Grains, NEC
Dehn's Gardens Inc ....E...763 753-2806
Anoka *(G-173)*
Salad Makers Inc ....E...218 236-4959
Moorhead *(G-6341)*

0161 Vegetables & Melons
Axdahl Farms Inc ....E...651 439-3134
Stillwater *(G-9600)*

0175 Deciduous Tree Fruits
Apple Jack Inc ....E...763 972-6673
Delano *(G-1181)*
Morris-Walker Ltd ....C...952 873-4334
Belle Plaine *(G-368)*
▲ **Wescott Agri-Products Inc** ....E...507 876-2891
Elgin *(G-1857)*

0181 Ornamental Floriculture & Nursery Prdts
Anderson Florists ....E...320 763-5115
Alexandria *(G-83)*

Bachman's Inc......................C...612 861-7600
Minneapolis *(G-3856)*
Bachman's Inc......................E...952 469-2102
Farmington *(G-2040)*
Baudora State Forest Nursery ....D...218 652-2385
Akeley *(G-25)*
▲ **Betaseed Inc**......................E...952 445-8090
Shakopee *(G-9421)*
Blue Valley Sod Co ....E...218 927-4557
Aitkin *(G-17)*
Central Turf Farms ....E...651 464-2130
Forest Lake *(G-2144)*
Contract Sod Services Inc.......................E...651 457-6037
Inver Grove Heights *(G-2745)*
▲ **Dan & Jerry's Greenhouses Inc** ....D...763 271-6594
Monticello *(G-6269)*
Donahues' Greenhouses Inc.......................E...507 334-8404
Faribault *(G-2001)*
Glenn R Rehbein Excavating Inc ....E...651 674-7937
Harris *(G-2373)*
Glenn Rehbein Excavating Inc.......................C...763 784-0657
Minneapolis *(G-3475)*
Great River Garden ....E...218 927-2521
Aitkin *(G-19)*
Green Mill Growers ....D...651 697-1081
Saint Paul *(G-8431)*
Kowsary Turf Inc ....E...763 862-4646
Elk River *(G-1882)*
Linder's Greenhouses Inc ....C...651 488-6717
Saint Paul *(G-8589)*
Lynde Greenhouse & Nursery Inc ....E...763 420-4400
Osseo *(G-6630)*
Nelson Nursery Inc ....D...763 856-2441
Zimmerman *(G-10214)*
Pinehurst Development Inc......................E...952 469-3202
Farmington *(G-2057)*
Prairie Restorations Inc......................E...763 389-4342
Princeton *(G-6924)*
Richard Koberski 507 642-8380
Madelia *(G-3074)*
Rose Floral & Greenhouse Inc......................E...651 439-3765
Stillwater *(G-9637)*
Sargent's Landscape Nursery ....E...507 289-0022
Rochester *(G-7247)*
Sargent's Nursery Inc.......................E...651 388-3847
Red Wing *(G-7004)*
Shady Oaks Nursery ....E...507 835-5033
Waseca *(G-9887)*
Syngenta Seeds Inc ....E...507 674-3320
Amboy *(G-132)*
Wagner Greenhouses Inc.......................E...612 922-1262
Minneapolis *(G-5993)*
Wagner Sod Co Inc ....E...651 457-6037
Inver Grove Heights *(G-2773)*
Wilson's Nursery Inc......................E...952 445-3630
Chanhassen *(G-946)*
Wolcyn Tree Farms ....E...763 689-3346
Cambridge *(G-847)*
Wright Tree Service Inc......................C...507 625-6950
Mankato *(G-3220)*

0182 Food Crops Grown Under Cover
Calco Sprouts Inc.......................E...612 724-0276
Minneapolis *(G-3991)*
Salad Makers Inc ....E...218 236-4959
Moorhead *(G-6341)*
▲ **Vine Ripe Inc** ....D...507 451-5692
Owatonna *(G-6742)*

0191 Crop Farming, Misc
Altona Hutterian Brethren Inc ....E...507 248-3191
Henderson *(G-2428)*
Benedict Farms Inc ....E...218 789-7376
Sabin *(G-7396)*
Carman Berry Farm ....E...218 631-4613
Wadena *(G-9799)*
Durst Brothers ....E...507 635-5588
Mantorville *(G-3233)*
Fairhaven Farm ....E...320 236-7685
South Haven *(G-9505)*

Lismore Hutterian Brethren......................D...320 325-5485
Clinton *(G-1044)*
Son-D-Farms Inc......................E...507 483-2245
Adrian *(G-5)*
Spring Prairie Hutterian ....C...218 498-0222
Hawley *(G-2423)*

02 AGRICULTURAL PRODUCTION LIVESTOCK

0211 Beef Cattle Feedlots
Helen Andresen ....E...218 659-4491
Squaw Lake *(G-9577)*
Thier Feedlots Inc......................507 478-4137
Rushmore *(G-7395)*

0212 Beef Cattle, Except Feedlots
Lismore Hutterian Brethren......................D...320 325-5485
Clinton *(G-1044)*

0213 Hogs
Altona Hutterian Brethren Inc ....E...507 248-3191
Henderson *(G-2428)*
Choice Connections LLP ....E...507 524-4583
Mapleton *(G-3282)*
Christensen Farms & Feedlots......................C...507 794-5310
Sleepy Eye *(G-9492)*
Christensen Farms Midwest LLC ....D...507 794-5310
Sleepy Eye *(G-9493)*
Eldon Potthoff ....E...507 695-2784
Dunnell *(G-1513)*
Holden Farms Inc ....D...507 663-0003
Northfield *(G-6530)*
New Fashion Pork Inc ....C...507 847-4610
Jackson *(G-2797)*
North Dakota Pigs Co-Op ....E...218 685-6888
Elbow Lake *(G-1854)*
Schwartz Bros Inc ....E...507 794-5779
Sleepy Eye *(G-9499)*
Son-D-Farms Inc......................E...507 483-2245
Adrian *(G-5)*
Ten Brook Pork LLP ....E...952 440-5737
Prior Lake *(G-6958)*
Wakefield Pork Inc.......................D...507 237-5581
Gaylord *(G-2202)*

0241 Dairy Farms
Daley Farm of Lewiston LLP ....E...507 523-3687
Lewiston *(G-2965)*
Diamond K Dairy Inc ....E...507 689-2058
Altura *(G-131)*
Durst Brothers ....E...507 635-5588
Mantorville *(G-3233)*
Haubenschild Farm Dairy Inc ....E...763 389-2867
Princeton *(G-6902)*
Maple Island Inc ....E...507 824-2224
Wanamingo *(G-9864)*
Meadow Star Dairy, LLP ....E...320 392-5609
Morris *(G-6373)*
Rck Inc ....E...320 693-7422
Litchfield *(G-2990)*
Riverview Dairy Inc.......................E...320 392-5609
Morris *(G-6377)*

0252 Chicken Egg Farms
Luoma Egg Ranch Inc ....E...320 233-6122
Finlayson *(G-2130)*
Michael Foods Group Inc......................C...952 258-4000
Minnetonka *(G-6193)*
Michael Foods Inc......................C...507 665-8851
Le Sueur *(G-2962)*

S I C

0253 Turkey & Turkey Egg Farms

AG Forte LLC ....E....507 847-5110
Jackson (G-2785)
Burkel Turkey Farms Inc ....E....218 334-2833
Frazee (G-2183)
Gorans Brothers Inc ....E....320 995-6564
Blomkest (G-475)
Holden Farms Inc ....D....507 663-0003
Northfield (G-6530)
◆ Hormel Foods Corp ....A....507 437-5611
Austin (G-275)
▼ Jennie-O Turkey Store Inc ....C....320 235-2622
Willmar (G-10011)
Jennie-O Turkey Store Inc ....E....320 974-8891
Atwater (G-252)
Jennie-O Turkey Store Inc ....E....218 736-6931
Fergus Falls (G-2079)
Jennie-O Turkey Store Inc ....E....507 334-0087
Faribault (G-2015)
Jennie-O Turkey Store Inc ....E....218 583-2204
Henning (G-2432)
Jennie-O Turkey Store Inc ....C....320 243-3764
Paynesville (G-6769)
Mickelson Farms ....E....218 346-3876
Frazee (G-2185)
New Life Farms LLP ....D....218 346-7587
Frazee (G-2186)
New Life Farms, Lllp ....D....218 346-4959
Perham (G-6799)
Orsten Turkeys Inc ....E....320 235-5751
Willmar (G-10033)
▲ Pals Inc ....D....320 235-8860
Willmar (G-10035)
Prinsburg Farmers Co-Op ....E....320 978-8040
Prinsburg (G-6927)
Turkey Valley Farms LLC ....B....507 337-3100
Marshall (G-3330)

0254 Poultry Hatcheries

▲ Pals Inc ....D....320 235-8860
Willmar (G-10035)
Peterson Turkey Hatchery Inc ....E....507 263-2352
Cannon Falls (G-862)
Willmar Poultry Farms Inc ....E....320 968-6211
Foley (G-2142)

0272 Horse & Other Equine Production

Northstar Arabian Breeders Inc ....E....507 947-3541
Lake Crystal (G-2862)

0291 Animal Production, NEC

Robert Fitzsimmons & Sons LLP ....E....507 524-4511
Mapleton (G-3285)
Spring Prairie Hutterian ....C....218 498-0222
Hawley (G-2423)
Wolf Springs Ranches ....E....952 942-5566
Minneapolis (G-6082)

07 AGRICULTURAL SERVICES

0711 Soil Preparation Svcs

Fountain Centers ....E....507 377-6411
Albert Lea (G-51)
Plaisted Co's Inc ....E....763 441-1100
Elk River (G-1890)

0721 Soil Preparation, Planting & Cultivating Svc

Agrimax LLC 218 281-1441
Fisher (G-2133)
Winfield Solutions LLC ....C....651 481-2222
Saint Paul (G-9158)

0722 Crop Harvesting By Machine

Mike Wingard ....E....763 441-8247
Elk River (G-1884)

0723 Crop Preparation, Except Cotton Ginning

Cargill Freshwater ....E....952 742-3050
Excelsior (G-1941)
▼ Dahlgren & Co Inc ....C....218 281-2985
Crookston (G-1123)
Deer River Wild Rice ....D....218 246-2713
Deer River (G-1170)
Dehn's Gardens Inc ....E....763 753-2806
Anoka (G-173)
Farmers Co-Operative Elevator ....D....507 768-3448
Hanley Falls (G-2368)
Hull Co ....E....763 262-4855
Big Lake (G-447)
J & J Packing Inc ....E....763 263-2296
Big Lake (G-448)
Metro Packaging Corp ....E....763 586-0808
Minneapolis (G-3538)
Mississippi Valley Fruit LLC ....E....507 876-2891
Elgin (G-1856)
Reichel Foods Inc ....C....507 289-7264
Rochester (G-7220)
Sunrich LLC ....D....218 643-8467
Breckenridge (G-602)
Syngenta Seeds Inc ....E....507 674-3320
Amboy (G-132)

0741 Veterinary Livestock Svcs

East Central Veterinary ....E....320 679-4197
Mora (G-6357)
Northern Valley Animal Clinic 507 282-0867
Rochester (G-7191)
Pipestone Veterinary Clinic ....E....507 825-4211
Pipestone (G-6837)
St Michael Veterinary Clinic ....E....763 497-2424
Saint Michael (G-7682)
Veterinary Medical Center Prof ....E....507 372-2957
Worthington (G-10197)
Zumbrota Veterinary Clinic, PA ....E....507 732-7301
Zumbrota (G-10224)

0742 Veterinary Animal Specialties

Affiliated Emergency ....E....763 529-6560
Minneapolis (G-3694)
Affiliated Emergency ....E....952 942-8272
Eden Prairie (G-1585)
Animal Emergency Clinic ....E....651 501-3766
Saint Paul (G-9184)
Anoka Equine Veterinary Svcs ....E....763 441-3797
Elk River (G-1898)
Apache Animal Medicine ....E....612 781-2734
Minneapolis (G-6123)
Bennett Porter III Dvm ....E....612 925-1121
Minneapolis (G-3885)
Carver Lake Veterinary Center ....E....651 578-3290
Saint Paul (G-9193)
East Central Veterinary ....E....320 679-4197
Mora (G-6357)
Feist Animal Hospital ....E....651 646-7257
Saint Paul (G-8371)
Kate Anne Hunter ....E....651 578-3290
Saint Paul (G-9234)
Melrose-Albany-Upsula ....E....320 256-4252
Melrose (G-3351)
Midwest Veterinary Specialty ....E....763 754-5000
Minneapolis (G-3543)
Northern Valley Animal Clinic 507 282-0867
Rochester (G-7191)
Pipestone Veterinary Clinic ....E....507 825-4211
Pipestone (G-6837)
Plymouth Heights Pet Hospital ....E....763 544-4141
Minneapolis (G-5392)
Prime Ridge Pet Care ....E....763 427-2220
Anoka (G-217)
Randall J Herman ....E....763 559-3111
Minneapolis (G-5466)
Rich Schmitz Dvm ....E....507 233-2520
New Ulm (G-6473)
St Michael Veterinary Clinic ....E....763 497-2424
Saint Michael (G-7682)
Sue Chapman Dvm ....E....507 233-2520
New Ulm (G-6475)
VCA Animal Hospitals Inc ....E....952 884-3228
Bloomington (G-524)
Vet Mart Inc ....E....763 546-4452
Minneapolis (G-5966)
Veterinary Medical Center Prof ....E....507 372-2957
Worthington (G-10197)
White Bear Animal Hospital 651 777-1393
Saint Paul (G-9154)
Zumbrota Veterinary Clinic, PA ....E....507 732-7301
Zumbrota (G-10224)

0751 Livestock Svcs, Except Veterinary

Lorentz Etc Inc ....D....507 263-3618
Cannon Falls (G-857)
Minnesota Select Sires Co-Op ....E....320 259-6680
Saint Cloud (G-7560)
Schmidt's Meat Market Inc ....E....507 232-3438
Nicollet (G-6491)

0752 Animal Specialty Svcs, Exc Veterinary

Animal Humane Society ....D....763 522-4325
Minneapolis (G-3780)
Bone Adventure Inc ....E....612 920-2201
Minneapolis (G-3925)
Circle R Ranch Inc ....E....320 547-2176
Long Prairie (G-3039)
Goldwood Kennels Inc ....E....651 429-0648
Saint Paul (G-9221)
Mill City Kennel ....E....763 755-3595
Minneapolis (G-3544)
Minnesota Horse & Hunt Club ....D....952 447-2272
Prior Lake (G-6943)
Minnesota Select Sires Co-Op ....E....320 259-6680
Saint Cloud (G-7560)
Northern Valley Animal Clinic 507 282-0867
Rochester (G-7191)
Penco Leasing Corp ....E....612 927-4748
Minneapolis (G-5362)
Pet Co ....E....952 541-1981
Minnetonka (G-6211)
Petco Animal Supplies Stores ....E....320 253-1004
Waite Park (G-9832)
Petco Animal Supplies Stores ....E....763 420-5236
Minneapolis (G-5368)
Petsmart Inc ....E....320 251-4459
Waite Park (G-9833)
Petsmart Inc ....D....952 941-4660
Eden Prairie (G-1746)
Petsmart Inc ....E....612 798-3665
Minneapolis (G-5372)
Petsmart Inc ....E....320 251-4365
Saint Cloud (G-7567)
Petsmart Inc ....E....800 702-9779
Woodbury (G-10174)

0762 Farm Management Svcs

Centrol Inc ....E....218 584-5107
Twin Valley (G-9701)
Centrol Inc Cottonwood, MN ....E....507 423-5423
Cottonwood (G-1111)
Domaine Srene Vineyards Winery 763 473-4412
Osseo (G-6610)
Larry A Larson ....E....320 235-1294
Willmar (G-10018)

0781 Landscape Counseling & Planning

A-Scape Inc ....E....952 496-1178
Shakopee (G-9417)
AAA All American Lawn ....E....763 537-5733
Anoka (G-145)
Brickman Group Ltd LLC ....E....952 922-8777
Minneapolis (G-3943)
Butler Brothers Enterprises ....E....651 554-9888
Inver Grove Heights (G-2739)
Carefree Services Inc ....E....763 479-2600
Maple Plain (G-3271)
Carrs Tree Service Inc ....E....218 367-3355
Ottertail (G-6686)
Concept Landscaping Inc ....E....952 472-4118
Mound (G-6386)
Concierge Enterprises Inc ....E....763 746-8121
Minneapolis (G-4151)
Dundee Nursery & Landscaping ....E....763 559-4004
Minneapolis (G-4293)
Family Tree Landscape Nursery ....E....507 533-8558
Stewartville (G-9592)
Hough Inc of Detroit Lakes ....E....218 847-7391
Detroit Lakes (G-1199)
Jackson Landscape Supply Inc ....E....952 435-6927
Lakeville (G-2913)
Jlm Landscape LLC ....E....952 941-9818
Minneapolis (G-4766)
Jordan Ray Sons ....E....763 434-1644
Cedar (G-881)
Keenan & Sveiven Inc ....E....952 475-1229
Minnetonka (G-6184)
Landscape Brands Inc ....E....507 452-1112
Winona (G-10110)
Lawn Ranger Inc ....D....952 937-6076
Eden Prairie (G-1706)
Lhb Inc ....E....612 338-2029
Minneapolis (G-4867)
Metro Home Services Network ....E....612 827-0643
Cedar (G-882)
Outdoor Environments Inc ....E....952 496-1000
Savage (G-9403)
Phasse III of Maple Grove Inc ....E....763 425-4212
Osseo (G-6652)
Schoell & Madson Inc ....E....763 746-1600
Minneapolis (G-5610)
Stacy's Nursery Inc ....E....320 235-6010
Willmar (G-10046)
Trugreen Landcare LLC ....D....651 994-9855
Saint Paul (G-7931)
Whiting, Jim Nursery & Garden 507 289-3741
Rochester (G-7293)

0782 Lawn & Garden Svcs

A-Scape Inc ....E....952 496-1178
Shakopee (G-9417)
Alex Irrigation Inc ....E....320 852-7595
Carlos (G-866)
Arrowhead Tree Service Inc ....E....218 729-9203
Duluth (G-1245)
Arteka Co's LLC ....C....952 934-2000
Shakopee (G-9419)
Bauer's Market & Nursery Inc ....E....507 895-4583
La Crescent (G-2839)
Bever & Sons Inc ....E....651 426-7733
Forest Lake (G-2150)
Bloomers Garden Center ....E....218 326-0668
Grand Rapids (G-2270)
Concept Landscaping Inc ....E....952 472-4118
Mound (G-6386)
Craig G Braun Turf Farms ....D....651 463-2302
Hampton (G-2365)
Curbside Lawn Care ....D....952 403-9012
Savage (G-9387)
Dakota Turf Inc ....E....651 460-8873
Farmington (G-2048)
Davey Tree Expert Co ....E....763 553-9740
Minneapolis (G-4224)
Fairview Gardens ....E....320 229-2281
Sauk Rapids (G-9381)

Friedges Landscaping Inc ....E....952 469-2996
Lakeville (G-2908)
Garden Grove LLC ....E....651 699-5300
Saint Paul (G-8401)
Great Northern Landscapes Inc ....E....763 274-2678
Elk River (G-1876)
Greenworks Inc ....E....763 498-7696
Loretto (G-3048)
Hartman Co's Inc ....E....952 443-2958
Victoria (G-9729)
Highland Nursery Inc ....E....651 698-1708
Saint Paul (G-8482)
Hough Inc ....E....218 847-7391
Detroit Lakes (G-1198)
Jirik Sod Farm Inc ....E....651 460-6555
Farmington (G-2052)
Jlm Landscape LLC ....E....952 941-9818
Minneapolis (G-4766)
Keenan & Sveiven Inc ....E....952 475-1229
Minnetonka (G-6184)
Kowsary Turf Inc ....E....763 862-4646
Elk River (G-1882)
L & K Landscaping Inc ....E....763 497-4700
Saint Michael (G-7675)
L & R Suburban Landscaping Inc ....E....952 935-0389
Minnetonka (G-6186)
Lac Enterprises Inc ....E....651 482-0205
Saint Paul (G-8554)
Landscape Renovations Inc ....E....651 769-0010
Afton (G-9)
Landstyle Design & Constr ....E....763 479-1200
Loretto (G-3050)
Lawn King Inc ....E....763 420-2909
Hamel (G-2346)
Linder's Greenhouses Inc ....E....651 488-1927
Saint Paul (G-8588)
Little Yukon Greenhouse Inc ....D....218 692-3536
Crosslake (G-1152)
Metro Home Services Network ....E....612 827-0643
Cedar (G-882)
Midland Nursery Inc ....E....763 478-6122
Buffalo (G-651)
Midwest Landscapes Inc ....E....763 241-1320
Elk River (G-1902)
Natures Garden World Inc ....E....218 739-9641
Fergus Falls (G-2101)
North Metro Landscaping Inc ....E....763 497-4898
Hanover (G-2369)
On Time Lawn & Snow Services............E....763 786-0652
Minneapolis (G-3561)
Outdoor Environments Inc ....E....952 496-1000
Savage (G-9403)
Outdoor Images Inc ....E....651 480-2000
Hastings (G-2397)
Prescription Landscape Inc ....E....651 488-8965
Saint Paul (G-8845)
Q3 Contracting Inc ....B....651 224-2424
Saint Paul (G-8859)
River Valley Lawnscape Inc ....E....651 388-7000
Red Wing (G-7002)
Sargent's Landscape Nursery ....E....507 289-0022
Rochester (G-7247)
Steve's Elk River Nursery Inc ....E....763 441-3090
Elk River (G-1894)
Talberg Lawn & Landscape Inc ....D....763 428-3550
Osseo (G-6672)
TPC Landscape Inc ....E....952 898-7600
Burnsville (G-809)
Trugreen LP ....E....507 289-8798
Rochester (G-7276)
Trugreen LP ....E....612 493-5035
Osseo (G-6678)
Trugreen LP ....D....952 933-7360
Hopkins (G-2648)
Trugreen Ltd Ptn ....D....651 407-3400
Saint Paul (G-9085)
Trugreen Ltd Ptn ....E....952 895-3400
Burnsville (G-814)
Verde Lawn Care LLC ....E....763 550-9400
Minneapolis (G-5963)
Village Green Lawn Maintenance ....E....651 488-2733
Saint Paul (G-9129)
Wagner Sod Co Inc ....E....651 457-6037
Inver Grove Heights (G-2773)
Weerts Construction Inc ....E....507 893-3313
Winnebago (G-10078)
Whiting, Jim Nursery & Garden 507 289-3741
Rochester (G-7293)
Willow Creek Concrete Products...........E....320 398-5415
Kimball (G-2835)
Winco Landscape Inc ....E....651 455-3070
Inver Grove Heights (G-2774)

0783 Ornamental Shrub & Tree Svc

Arrowhead Tree Service Inc ....E....218 729-9203
Duluth (G-1245)
Asplundh Tree Expert Co ....C....763 785-2300
Circle Pines (G-1002)
Carrs Tree Service Inc ....E....218 367-3355
Ottertail (G-6686)
City of Minneapolis ....C....612 370-4900
Minneapolis (G-4088)
Dakota Turf Inc ....E....651 460-8873
Farmington (G-2048)
Davey Tree Expert Co ....E....763 553-9740
Minneapolis (G-4224)

Lake States Tree Service Inc.................D....218 326-5872
Grand Rapids (G-2290)
▲ Maiers Transport & Warehousing ....E....320 251-6882
Saint Cloud (G-7547)
S & S Tree & Horticultural ....E....651 451-8907
South Saint Paul (G-9539)
S & S Tree Specialists Inc ....E....612 872-3901
South Saint Paul (G-9540)
Top Notch Treecare ....E....763 253-8733
Minneapolis (G-5830)
Wright Tree Service Inc ....C....507 625-6950
Mankato (G-3220)

08 FORESTRY

0811 Timber Tracts

Carlson Timber Products Inc ....D....320 245-2920
Sandstone (G-9319)
Wolcyn Tree Farms ....E....763 689-3346
Cambridge (G-847)

0831 Forest Prdts

Fafard Inc ....E....218 476-3022
Floodwood (G-2135)

0851 Forestry Svcs

First Strike of Duluth Inc ....E....218 721-5081
Duluth (G-1324)
Forestry Field Station ....E....651 345-3216
Lake City (G-2853)
Minnesota Department of ....E....218 425-7793
Wannaska (G-9868)

09 FISHING, HUNTING & TRAPPING

0971 Hunting & Trapping

Fergus Falls Fish & Game Club ....D....320 630-0607
Dalton (G-1155)
Minnesota Horse & Hunt Club ....D....952 447-2272
Prior Lake (G-6943)

10 METAL MINING

1011 Iron Ores

Cliffs Natural Resources Inc ....A....218 262-5917
Hibbing (G-2441)
Erie L Cliffs L C ....E....218 225-3127
Hoyt Lakes (G-2669)
Hibbing Taconite Co ....A....218 262-5950
Hibbing (G-2452)
Northshore Mining Co ....C....218 226-4125
Silver Bay (G-9484)
United States Steel Corp ....D....218 778-8700
Keewatin (G-2826)
United States Steel Corp ....C....218 749-7200
Mountain Iron (G-6394)
United Taconite LLC ....B....218 744-7800
Eveleth (G-1933)

1021 Copper Ores

Ames Construction Inc ....B....952 435-7106
Burnsville (G-676)

1041 Gold Ores

Ames Construction Inc ....B....952 435-7106
Burnsville (G-676)

1081 Metal Mining Svcs

DH Blattner & Sons Inc ....D....320 356-7351
Avon (G-294)

1094 Uranium, Radium & Vanadium Ores

Mosaic Co ....C....763 577-2700
Minneapolis (G-5133)

12 COAL MINING

1221 Bituminous Coal & Lignite: Surface Mining

Pengo Corp ....E....320 286-5581
Cokato (G-1078)

1231 Anthracite Mining

Allete Inc ....C....218 279-5000
Duluth (G-1235)

13 OIL & GAS EXTRACTION

1311 Crude Petroleum & Natural Gas

Cenex Inc ....A....800 232-3639
South Saint Paul (G-9516)
◆ CHS Inc ....A....651 355-6000
Inver Grove Heights (G-2742)
I D D D Inc ....E....507 334-3333
Faribault (G-2012)
Mosaic Co ....C....763 577-2700
Minneapolis (G-5133)
Northern Oil & Gas Inc ....E....952 476-9800
Wayzata (G-9934)
Speedway Superamerica LLC ....E....651 774-7270
Saint Paul (G-8977)

1321 Natural Gas Liquids

Heron Lake Bioenergy LLC ....E....507 793-0077
Heron Lake (G-2434)

1389 Oil & Gas Field Svcs, NEC

CHS Inc ....E....507 238-8900
Fairmont (G-1960)

14 MINING & QUARRYING

1411 Dimension Stone

Biesanz Stone Co ....E....507 454-4336
Winona (G-10082)
L S Starrett Co ....E....320 251-7171
Waite Park (G-9825)
▲ Rex Granite Co ....E....320 252-2060
Saint Cloud (G-7426)

1422 Crushed & Broken Limestone

Northland Constructors of ....E....218 722-8170
Duluth (G-1406)

1423 Crushed & Broken Granite

Martin Marietta Materials Inc ....E....320 251-7141
Waite Park (G-9828)

1429 Crushed & Broken Stone, NEC

DH Blattner & Sons Inc ....D....320 356-7351
Avon (G-294)
Mathy Construction Co ....E....507 932-3200
Winona (G-10113)

1442 Construction Sand & Gravel

Aggregate Industries Inc ....D....651 683-0600
Saint Paul (G-7689)
Anchor Block Co ....D....651 777-8321
Saint Paul (G-8049)
Anchor Block Co ....E....763 425-9779
Minneapolis (G-3775)
Barton Sand & Gravel Co ....E....763 425-4191
Osseo (G-6598)
Cemstone Products Co ....E....651 774-7575
Saint Paul (G-8181)
Dennis Fehn Gravel ....E....763 497-2428
Albertville (G-73)
F-M Asphalt Inc ....D....612 798-0245
Minneapolis (G-4389)
Fischer Sand & Aggregate LLP ....E....952 432-7132
Saint Paul (G-7775)
Fitzgerald Construction ....E....218 789-7318
Sabin (G-7397)
Granite City Ready Mix Inc ....E....320 252-4322
Saint Cloud (G-7437)
Kielmeyer Construction Inc ....E....507 334-6088
Nerstrand (G-6402)
Knife River Corp - North ....E....320 251-9472
Sauk Rapids (G-9368)
R & R Ready Mix Inc ....E....218 943-4601
Miltona (G-3381)
Rupp Construction Co Inc ....D....507 836-8555
Slayton (G-9490)
Thull Construction ....E....320 987-3432
Greenwald (G-2327)
Tiller Corp ....D....763 425-4191
Maple Grove (G-3254)

1446 Industrial Sand

Unimin Corp ....D....507 665-3386
Le Sueur (G-2960)

1474 Potash, Soda & Borate Minerals

Mosaic Global Holdings Inc..................E....763 577-2700
Minneapolis (G-5134)

1475 Phosphate Rock

Mosaic Co ....C....763 577-2700
Minneapolis (G-5133)

Employment codes: A=Over 500 employees, B=251-500
C=101-250, D=51-100, E=25-50

2011 Harris Minnesota
Services Directory

© Harris InfoSource 1-866-281-6415
447

Mosaic Global Holdings Inc ....E....763 577-2700
  Minneapolis *(G-5134)*

1481 Nonmetallic Minerals Svcs, Except Fuels

Mosaic Co ....C....763 577-2700
  Minneapolis *(G-5133)*

1499 Miscellaneous Nonmetallic Mining

Pioneer Peat Inc 701 746-4300
  East Grand Forks *(G-1573)*

15 BUILDING CONSTRUCTION, GEN'L CONTRACTORS

1521 General Contractors, Single Family Houses

Argus Homes ....E....651 294-2160
  Saint Paul *(G-8062)*
Arnzen Construction Inc ....E....320 836-2284
  Freeport *(G-2187)*
Baker Colberg & Realty ....E....651 430-7745
  Stillwater *(G-9601)*
Bauerly Dynamics Inc ....E....320 251-9472
  Sauk Rapids *(G-9358)*
Berg Construction Services Inc ....E....651 423-5531
  Rosemount *(G-7363)*
Bigelow, Joel & Sons Entrprs ....E....507 529-1161
  Rochester *(G-7066)*
Bigelow-Lennon Construction ....E....507 775-7068
  Byron *(G-822)*
Billman Construction Inc ....E....218 729-7570
  Duluth *(G-1253)*
Boyer Building Corp ....E....952 475-2097
  Minnetonka *(G-6149)*
Brandl Anderson Homes Inc ....E....952 898-0231
  Saint Paul *(G-7723)*
Bruggeman Homes Inc ....E....651 770-2981
  Saint Paul *(G-8136)*
Budget Exteriors Inc ....E....952 887-1613
  Minneapolis *(G-3967)*
Centex Homes Inc ....E....952 936-7833
  Minnetonka *(G-6155)*
Christ's Household of Faith ....D....651 265-3400
  Saint Paul *(G-8198)*
Christians Inc ....E....952 470-2001
  Chanhassen *(G-916)*
CNM Inc ....D....952 924-0043
  Minneapolis *(G-4115)*
Comstock Construction Inc, of ....E....218 739-5365
  Fergus Falls *(G-2071)*
Custom Remodelers Inc ....C....651 784-2646
  Circle Pines *(G-1009)*
Dave Taylor Constructn Inc ....E....952 472-1342
  Mound *(G-6387)*
Deck & Door Co ....E....952 432-1888
  Saint Paul *(G-7751)*
Deerwood Builders Inc ....E....218 534-5408
  Deerwood *(G-1176)*
Delancy Builders Inc ....D....612 354-3724
  Minneapolis *(G-4243)*
Diversified Construction ....E....952 929-7233
  Saint Louis Park *(G-7659)*
Doug Speedling Builders Inc ....D....651 437-3658
  Hastings *(G-2384)*
Elite Communications & Constr ....E....651 739-1366
  Saint Paul *(G-9211)*
Energy Construction ....E....763 489-7777
  Minneapolis *(G-4356)*
Evenson Concrete Systems ....E....507 243-3660
  Madison Lake *(G-3079)*
Excel Building Maintenance Inc ....E....507 288-0913
  Rochester *(G-7108)*
Fabricated Wood Products Inc ....E....507 451-1019
  Medford *(G-3343)*
FCA Construction Co LLC ....C....952 229-7521
  Chanhassen *(G-923)*
Flannery Construction Inc ....E....651 225-1105
  Saint Paul *(G-8384)*
Food Engineering Corp ....C....763 559-5200
  Minneapolis *(G-4461)*
Frontier Enterprises Corp ....E....763 434-6913
  Cedar *(G-878)*
Giertsen Co of Minnesota Inc ....E....763 546-1300
  Minneapolis *(G-4527)*
Greystone Masonry Inc ....E....763 413-9633
  Anoka *(G-185)*
Grl Investment Co LLC ....E....952 445-6745
  Shakopee *(G-9442)*
Hans Hagen Homes Inc ....E....763 586-7200
  Minneapolis *(G-3481)*
Hawk & Sons Inc ....E....507 285-0508
  Rochester *(G-7134)*
Highland Manufacturing Co LLC ....C....507 376-9460
  Worthington *(G-10186)*
Hnp Managment ....E....763 475-1872
  Minneapolis *(G-4657)*
Holmquist Lumber Co 320 857-2031
  Grove City *(G-2329)*
▼ Homark Co Inc ....D....218 253-2777
  Red Lake Falls *(G-6972)*

J Benson Construction ....E....952 920-0717
  Minneapolis *(G-4744)*
Jlm Landscape LLC ....E....952 941-9818
  Minneapolis *(G-4766)*
K A Witt Construction Inc ....E....952 758-2108
  New Prague *(G-6429)*
Key-Land Homes ....E....952 440-9400
  Prior Lake *(G-6935)*
Krl Exterior Inc ....D....612 296-0222
  Burnsville *(G-743)*
Kuepers Construction Inc ....E....888 829-0707
  Baxter *(G-334)*
Lake Country Builders Ltd ....E....952 474-7121
  Excelsior *(G-1944)*
Lakehead Constructors Inc ....E....218 328-5429
  Cohasset *(G-1071)*
Lang Builders Inc ....E....763 780-9090
  Circle Pines *(G-1014)*
Larson's Home Improvement ....E....507 288-7111
  Rochester *(G-7160)*
Laurent Builders Inc ....E....952 445-6745
  Shakopee *(G-9450)*
Lecy Construction ....E....952 944-9499
  Hopkins *(G-2569)*
Lemaster Restoration Inc ....E....952 707-1256
  Burnsville *(G-748)*
Lindstrom Cleaning & Constr ....E....763 544-8761
  Minneapolis *(G-4891)*
Lipe Brothers Construction Inc ....E....218 525-3364
  Duluth *(G-1384)*
Lumber One, Avon Inc ....D....320 356-7342
  Avon *(G-296)*
Lumber One, Cold Spring Inc ....E....320 685-3631
  Cold Spring *(G-1087)*
M A Peterson Designbuild Inc ....D....952 925-9455
  Minneapolis *(G-4919)*
McDonald Homes Inc ....E....651 455-5142
  Inver Grove Heights *(G-2761)*
Mic Services LLC ....E....651 379-9590
  Saint Paul *(G-8650)*
Minnesota Structures Inc ....E....952 401-3820
  Excelsior *(G-1948)*
Murphy Bros Designers ....E....763 780-3262
  Minneapolis *(G-3548)*
N A H Inc ....E....507 462-3331
  Minnesota Lake *(G-6137)*
Nedegaard Construction Co Inc ....E....763 757-2926
  Minneapolis *(G-3552)*
Nor-Son Inc ....C....218 828-1722
  Baxter *(G-339)*
Northfield Construction Co Inc ....E....507 645-8975
  Northfield *(G-6537)*
O'Neil Associates Inc ....E....651 738-2694
  Saint Paul *(G-8776)*
Paschke Properties ....E....763 428-7711
  Rogers *(G-7336)*
Plekkenpol Builders Inc ....E....952 888-2225
  Minneapolis *(G-5390)*
Pratt Construction Inc ....E....651 429-8032
  Saint Paul *(G-8834)*
Probuilt America Inc 651 770-5570
  Saint Paul *(G-8850)*
Pulte Homes of Minnesota LLC ....D....651 452-5200
  Eagan *(G-1546)*
Quantum Co's Inc ....E....952 943-4357
  Minneapolis *(G-5445)*
Richard Larson Builders Inc ....E....320 587-5555
  Hutchinson *(G-2711)*
Ron Boelter Window & Siding ....E....507 243-4354
  Madison Lake *(G-3081)*
Rottlund Co Inc ....D....651 638-0500
  Saint Paul *(G-8914)*
Rtl Construction Inc ....E....952 934-4695
  Shakopee *(G-9470)*
Ryland Group Inc ....C....952 949-0013
  Eden Prairie *(G-1769)*
Sawhorse Designer's & Builders ....E....952 475-4477
  Wayzata *(G-9939)*
Sawhose Inc ....E....763 533-0352
  Minneapolis *(G-5606)*
Seal Guard Systems Inc ....E....612 787-0700
  Marine On Saint Croix *(G-3289)*
Sela Roofing & Remodeling Inc ....D....612 823-8046
  Minneapolis *(G-5631)*
Sela Roofing & Remodeling Inc ....E....763 592-5420
  Minneapolis *(G-5632)*
Siewert Construction Co Inc 651 437-1728
  Hastings *(G-2405)*
Socon Construction Inc ....E....763 754-4027
  Minneapolis *(G-3604)*
St Louis County Public Works ....E....218 742-9804
  Virginia *(G-9756)*
Steven Cabinets Inc ....E....612 378-1812
  Minneapolis *(G-5752)*
Stonecrest ....D....651 264-3200
  Saint Paul *(G-9278)*
Streeter & Associates Inc ....E....952 449-9448
  Wayzata *(G-9943)*
Superior Construction Services ....E....763 424-9434
  Osseo *(G-6671)*
Swanson's Repair Rental Center ....E....218 847-7487
  Detroit Lakes *(G-1219)*
Tes Construction Inc ....E....763 783-2496
  Anoka *(G-233)*
Trehus Builders Inc ....E....612 729-2992
  Minneapolis *(G-5850)*
Tri Cap Tri County Action ....E....320 255-0769
  Waite Park *(G-9844)*

Twin City Exteriors Co Inc ....D....763 425-4737
  Osseo *(G-6679)*
Wb Enterprises of America Inc ....E....507 324-5050
  Le Roy *(G-2955)*
Weis Builders Inc ....E....507 288-2041
  Rochester *(G-7288)*
Wilcon Construction Inc ....E....507 345-6653
  Mankato *(G-3218)*
Yerigan Construction Co ....E....763 444-5353
  Isanti *(G-2782)*

1522 General Contractors, Residential Other Than Single Family

Advance Wall Systems Inc ....E....763 263-8512
  Big Lake *(G-444)*
Bor-Son Construction Inc ....B....952 854-8444
  Minneapolis *(G-3929)*
Brightkeys Building & Devpt ....E....651 501-6500
  Saint Paul *(G-9188)*
Bruggeman Homes Inc ....E....651 770-2981
  Saint Paul *(G-8136)*
Build All Installed Inc ....E....218 692-5115
  Crosslake *(G-1150)*
Builders Inc ....E....952 545-3217
  Minneapolis *(G-3971)*
Con Spec Corp ....E....651 501-6500
  Saint Paul *(G-9199)*
Ebert Inc ....E....763 498-7844
  Loretto *(G-3047)*
Fabricated Wood Products Inc ....E....507 451-1019
  Medford *(G-3343)*
Johnson-Wilson Constructors ....D....218 628-0202
  Duluth *(G-1363)*
Keystone Bluffs ....E....218 727-2800
  Duluth *(G-1370)*
Klingelhutz Co's Inc ....D....952 448-6776
  Chaska *(G-973)*
Kraus-Anderson Inc ....E....612 332-7281
  Minneapolis *(G-4823)*
Kuepers Construction Inc ....E....888 829-0707
  Baxter *(G-334)*
Lemaster Restoration Inc ....E....952 707-1256
  Burnsville *(G-748)*
Lipe Brothers Construction Inc ....E....218 525-3364
  Duluth *(G-1384)*
Lumber One, Avon Inc ....D....320 356-7342
  Avon *(G-296)*
Lumber One, Cold Spring Inc ....E....320 685-3631
  Cold Spring *(G-1087)*
Patriot Builders Inc ....E....763 434-1702
  Anoka *(G-213)*
▲ Pratt Construction Inc ....E....651 765-0572
  Saint Paul *(G-8833)*
Restoration Professionals Inc ....D....651 379-1990
  Saint Paul *(G-8895)*
Sand Co's Inc ....E....320 202-3100
  Waite Park *(G-9836)*
Schwieters' Co's Inc ....D....651 407-1618
  Hugo *(G-2673)*
Siewert Construction Co Inc ....E....651 437-1728
  Hastings *(G-2405)*
Weis Builders Inc ....C....612 243-5000
  Minneapolis *(G-6033)*
Wes Hanson Builders Inc ....E....218 765-4122
  Merrifield *(G-3372)*

1531 Operative Builders

Auburn Woods Clubhomes Assn ....D....952 922-5575
  Edina *(G-1825)*
Lecy Construction ....E....952 944-9499
  Hopkins *(G-2569)*
Pulte Homes ....D....763 241-9001
  Elk River *(G-1891)*
Rottlund Co Inc ....D....651 638-0500
  Saint Paul *(G-8914)*
Ryland Group Inc ....D....952 229-6000
  Edina *(G-1843)*

1541 General Contractors, Indl Bldgs & Warehouses

Alltech Engineering Corp ....D....651 452-7893
  Saint Paul *(G-7693)*
Amcon Construction Co LLC ....E....651 379-9090
  Saint Paul *(G-7695)*
Arkay Construction Co ....C....763 544-3341
  Minneapolis *(G-3806)*
Boldt Co ....C....218 879-1293
  Cloquet *(G-1047)*
Bolton Development Worldwide ....E....952 886-7211
  Minneapolis *(G-3924)*
Bor-Son Building Corp ....C....952 854-8444
  Minneapolis *(G-3928)*
Breitbach Construction Co ....D....320 697-5525
  Elrosa *(G-1909)*
C F Haglin & Sons Inc ....D....952 920-6123
  Minneapolis *(G-3983)*
CM Construction Co Inc ....E....952 895-8223
  Burnsville *(G-699)*
Comstock Construction Inc, of ....E....218 739-5365
  Fergus Falls *(G-2071)*
Continental Bridge Inc ....D....320 852-7500
  Alexandria *(G-89)*

(G-00000) Company's Geographic Section entry number
448

2011 Harris Minnesota
Services Directory

▲=Import ▼=Export
◆=Import/Export

Crawford-Merz Construction Co ....E.....612 874-9011
Minneapolis *(G-4177)*
Dallas I Hanson Construction ....E.....320 839-3455
Ortonville *(G-6582)*
Donnelly Brothers Construction ....E.....612 866-1204
Minneapolis *(G-4278)*
Fagen Inc ....D.....320 564-3324
Granite Falls *(G-2314)*
Global Specialty Contractors 651 406-8232
Saint Paul *(G-7783)*
Graham Construction Services ....D.....651 687-0648
Saint Paul *(G-7789)*
Greiner Construction Inc ....D.....612 338-1696
Minneapolis *(G-4566)*
Hawk Construction Inc ....E.....218 327-0069
Grand Rapids *(G-2284)*
Heymann Construction Co ....D.....507 354-3174
New Ulm *(G-6454)*
Hy-TEC Construction of ....E.....218 829-8529
Brainerd *(G-570)*
Ibberson Inc 952 938-7007
Hopkins *(G-2555)*
J & D Construction Inc ....E.....320 269-2101
Montevideo *(G-6247)*
Joseph Co Inc ....E.....507 437-3284
Austin *(G-279)*
Kellington Construction Inc ....D.....763 416-3200
Minneapolis *(G-4797)*
Knutson Construction Services ....D.....507 280-9788
Rochester *(G-7157)*
Kraus-Anderson Inc ....E.....612 332-7281
Minneapolis *(G-4823)*
L S Black Constructors Inc ....D.....651 774-8445
Saint Paul *(G-8553)*
Lund-Martin Construction Inc ....E.....612 782-2250
Minneapolis *(G-4909)*
Maertens-Brenny Construction ....E.....763 786-4779
Minneapolis *(G-3525)*
Malark Logistics Inc ....D.....763 428-3564
Brooklyn Park *(G-616)*
Marcy Construction Co ....D.....952 525-9700
Minneapolis *(G-4947)*
Max Gray Construction Inc ....E.....218 262-6622
Hibbing *(G-2461)*
McC Inc ....C.....763 477-4774
Rockford *(G-7311)*
McGough Construction Co Inc ....A.....651 633-5050
Saint Paul *(G-8624)*
Met-Con Construction Inc 507 332-2266
Faribault *(G-2022)*
Met-Con Metro Inc ....E.....952 884-6250
Minneapolis *(G-4998)*
Murlowski Construction Co Inc ....E.....651 786-1300
Saint Paul *(G-8729)*
Nor-Son Inc ....C.....218 828-1722
Baxter *(G-339)*
Oakwood Builders Inc ....E.....952 941-9730
Eden Prairie *(G-1735)*
Olson General Contractors Inc ....E.....763 535-1481
Minneapolis *(G-5272)*
Opus Northwest Construction ....C.....952 656-4444
Hopkins *(G-2598)*
Penn-Co Construction Inc ....E.....651 687-0648
Saint Paul *(G-7872)*
Permasteelisa North America ....E.....651 905-1515
Saint Paul *(G-7874)*
Proform Thermal Systems Inc ....E.....763 572-2200
Minneapolis *(G-3576)*
R J Ryan Construction Inc ....E.....651 681-0200
Mendota Heights *(G-3369)*
Ray Riihiluoma Inc ....E.....218 879-3317
Cloquet *(G-1064)*
Riverstar Inc ....E.....507 452-5109
Winona *(G-10122)*
Ryan Co's US Inc ....B.....612 492-4000
Minneapolis *(G-5579)*
SA Woods Inc 507 451-7084
Owatonna *(G-6735)*
Shaw - Lundquist Associates ....D.....651 454-0670
Saint Paul *(G-7903)*
SMA Elevator Construction Inc ....E.....763 295-4367
Monticello *(G-6287)*
Strack Construction Co Inc ....E.....320 251-5933
Sauk Rapids *(G-9377)*
Structural Restoration Inc ....E.....612 825-8614
Minneapolis *(G-5760)*
Vigen Construction Inc ....E.....218 773-1159
East Grand Forks *(G-1580)*
Vinco Inc ....D.....651 982-4642
Forest Lake *(G-2171)*
W Gohman Construction Co ....E.....320 363-7781
Saint Joseph *(G-7656)*
Weis Builders Inc ....C.....612 243-5000
Minneapolis *(G-6033)*
Ww Constructors Inc ....E.....763 420-4177
Hamel *(G-2362)*
Zeman Construction Co ....E.....612 521-4300
Minneapolis *(G-6115)*

1542 General Contractors, Nonresidential & Non-indl Bldgs

A B Systems Inc ....E.....507 288-9397
Rochester *(G-7042)*
A J Lysne Contracting Corp ....D.....507 451-7121
Owatonna *(G-6688)*
A J Spanjers Co Inc ....E.....763 424-8288
Minneapolis *(G-3648)*
Adolfson & Peterson Inc ....C.....952 544-1561
Minneapolis *(G-3682)*
All Agape Construction Co LLC ....E.....763 205-1313
Anoka *(G-149)*
Alvin E Benike Inc ....C.....507 288-6575
Rochester *(G-7053)*
Amb Construction Engineering ....E.....763 587-4920
Minneapolis *(G-3740)*
Amcon Construction Co LLC ....E.....651 379-9090
Saint Paul *(G-7695)*
AP Midwest LLC ....C.....952 544-1561
Minneapolis *(G-3788)*
Arkay Construction Co ....E.....763 544-3341
Minneapolis *(G-3806)*
Arnzen Construction Inc ....E.....320 836-2284
Freeport *(G-2187)*
Bainey Group Inc ....E.....763 557-6911
Minneapolis *(G-3858)*
Banks Brothers Construction ....E.....651 644-1723
Saint Paul *(G-8088)*
Berg Construction Services Inc ....E.....651 423-5531
Rosemount *(G-7363)*
Bigelow, Joel & Sons Entrprs ....E.....507 529-1161
Rochester *(G-7066)*
Billman Construction Inc ....E.....218 729-7570
Duluth *(G-1253)*
Boldt Co ....C.....218 879-1293
Cloquet *(G-1047)*
Bor-Son Building Corp ....C.....952 854-8444
Minneapolis *(G-3928)*
Bor-Son Construction Inc ....B.....952 854-8444
Minneapolis *(G-3929)*
Boser Construction Inc ....E.....320 393-3185
Sauk Rapids *(G-9359)*
Brehmer Contracting Inc ....E.....952 938-1171
Hopkins *(G-2520)*
Breitbach Construction Co ....D.....320 697-5525
Elrosa *(G-1909)*
Bruce Kreofsky & Sons Inc ....D.....507 534-3855
Plainview *(G-6839)*
Builders Inc ....E.....952 545-3217
Minneapolis *(G-3971)*
C F Haglin & Sons Inc ....D.....952 920-6123
Minneapolis *(G-3983)*
Capital Wood Products Co ....E.....651 225-5613
Saint Paul *(G-8153)*
Carlson-Lavine Inc ....E.....651 638-9600
Saint Paul *(G-8167)*
Century Construction Co Inc ....E.....651 451-1020
South Saint Paul *(G-9518)*
Christians Inc ....E.....952 470-2001
Chanhassen *(G-916)*
Con Spec Corp ....E.....651 501-6500
Saint Paul *(G-9199)*
Construction Results Corp ....E.....763 559-1100
Plymouth *(G-6857)*
Corval Constructors Inc ....C.....651 642-0451
Saint Paul *(G-8255)*
Dallas I Hanson Construction ....E.....320 839-3455
Ortonville *(G-6582)*
Diversified Construction ....E.....952 929-7233
Saint Louis Park *(G-7659)*
Division21 Inc ....E.....651 917-8805
Saint Paul *(G-8304)*
Donald Holm Construction Co ....E.....218 628-2257
Duluth *(G-1295)*
Donlyn Manufacture ....E.....763 786-1103
Minneapolis *(G-3459)*
Doran Construction Inc ....E.....763 421-0553
Minneapolis *(G-4279)*
Eagle Construction Co Inc ....E.....320 632-5429
Little Falls *(G-3001)*
Ebert Inc ....E.....763 498-7844
Loretto *(G-3047)*
Ed Lunn Construction Inc ....E.....507 288-4400
Rochester *(G-7102)*
Elder-Jones Inc ....E.....952 854-2854
Minneapolis *(G-4336)*
Ellerbe Becket Co ....C.....612 376-2000
Minneapolis *(G-4341)*
Flannery Construction Inc ....E.....651 225-1105
Saint Paul *(G-8384)*
Food Engineering Corp ....C.....763 559-5200
Minneapolis *(G-4461)*
Frerichs Construction Co ....E.....651 787-0687
Saint Paul *(G-8397)*
G M Clark Co's Inc ....E.....763 475-1000
Maple Plain *(G-3274)*
Gateway Building Systems Inc ....E.....218 685-4420
Elbow Lake *(G-1853)*
Gordon Construction Inc ....E.....218 935-2191
Mahnomen *(G-3086)*
Graham Construction Services ....D.....651 687-0648
Saint Paul *(G-7789)*
Hasslen Construction Co Inc ....E.....320 839-2529
Ortonville *(G-6583)*
Haztran Inc ....E.....218 327-1116
Grand Rapids *(G-2285)*
Heymann Construction Co ....D.....507 354-3174
New Ulm *(G-6454)*
Hy-TEC Construction of ....E.....218 829-8529
Brainerd *(G-570)*
J E Dunn Construction Co ....C.....952 830-9000
Eden Prairie *(G-1700)*
James Steele Construction Co ....E.....651 488-6755
Saint Paul *(G-8529)*
JD Driver Ltd ....E.....507 437-6050
Rose Creek *(G-7350)*
Johnson-Wilson Constructors ....D.....218 628-0202
Duluth *(G-1363)*
Joseph Co Inc ....E.....507 437-3284
Austin *(G-279)*
Joshco Construction Inc ....D.....952 361-8000
Chaska *(G-971)*
K A Witt Construction Inc ....E.....952 758-2108
New Prague *(G-6429)*
K-M Building Co of Minneapolis ....E.....612 977-9060
Minneapolis *(G-4786)*
Kalway Construction Co Inc ....E.....651 746-0179
Anoka *(G-195)*
Kellington Construction Inc ....D.....763 416-3200
Minneapolis *(G-4797)*
Knutson Construction Services ....D.....507 280-9788
Rochester *(G-7157)*
Kraus-Anderson Construction Co ....D.....763 786-7711
Circle Pines *(G-1013)*
Kraus-Anderson Construction Co ....E.....218 759-0596
Bemidji *(G-400)*
Kraus-Anderson Inc ....E.....612 332-7281
Minneapolis *(G-4823)*
Kuepers Construction Inc ....E.....888 829-0707
Baxter *(G-334)*
L S Black Constructors Inc ....D.....651 774-8445
Saint Paul *(G-8553)*
Langer Construction Co Inc ....D.....651 457-5993
Saint Paul *(G-7821)*
Lanners Brothers Construction 507 532-5457
Marshall *(G-3304)*
Larson Contracting Inc ....D.....507 373-6645
Albert Lea *(G-59)*
Lawremar Inc ....E.....651 429-4475
Saint Paul *(G-8568)*
Lee's Construction Inc ....D.....320 762-0325
Alexandria *(G-111)*
Lenci Enterprises Inc ....E.....218 741-3482
Virginia *(G-9745)*
Lester Buildings LLC ....C.....320 395-2531
Lester Prairie *(G-2963)*
Lindstrom Cleaning & Constr ....E.....763 544-8761
Minneapolis *(G-4891)*
Lodermeiers ....D.....651 923-4441
Goodhue *(G-2250)*
Lund-Martin Construction Inc ....E.....612 782-2250
Minneapolis *(G-4909)*
▲ **M A Mortenson Co** ....B.....763 522-2100
Minneapolis *(G-4917)*
M A Mortenson Co ....A.....763 522-2100
Minneapolis *(G-4918)*
M P Johnson Construction Inc ....E.....612 339-3733
Minneapolis *(G-4923)*
Maertens-Brenny Construction ....E.....763 786-4779
Minneapolis *(G-3525)*
Magnum Co LLC ....E.....651 255-3000
Rogers *(G-7349)*
Marcus Construction Co Inc ....E.....320 978-6616
Prinsburg *(G-6926)*
Max Gray Construction Inc ....E.....218 262-6622
Hibbing *(G-2461)*
McDonald Homes Inc ....E.....651 455-5142
Inver Grove Heights *(G-2761)*
McGough Construction Co Inc ....A.....651 633-5050
Saint Paul *(G-8624)*
Met Con Kato Inc ....C.....507 332-2266
Faribault *(G-2021)*
Met-Con Construction Inc 507 332-2266
Faribault *(G-2022)*
Meyer Contracting Inc ....E.....763 391-5959
Maple Grove *(G-3250)*
Minnesota Department of Trans ....D.....507 831-1200
Windom *(G-10069)*
Mohagen Hansen Architectural ....E.....952 426-7400
Wayzata *(G-9929)*
Monson Corp ....D.....320 995-6703
Willmar *(G-10027)*
Morcon Construction Co Inc ....D.....763 546-6066
Minneapolis *(G-5127)*
Murlowski Construction Co Inc ....E.....651 786-1300
Saint Paul *(G-8729)*
Murphy Bros Designers ....E.....763 780-3262
Minneapolis *(G-3548)*
Network of Contractors Inc ....E.....763 639-1440
Ramsey *(G-6968)*
Nor-Son Inc ....C.....218 828-1722
Baxter *(G-339)*
Northfield Construction Co Inc ....E.....507 645-8975
Northfield *(G-6537)*
Oakwood Builders Inc ....E.....952 941-9730
Eden Prairie *(G-1735)*
Olson General Contractors Inc ....E.....763 535-1481
Minneapolis *(G-5272)*
One Way Building Services Inc ....E.....952 942-0412
Minneapolis *(G-5280)*
Opus Corp ....C.....952 656-4444
Hopkins *(G-2597)*
Opus Design Build LLC ....D.....952 656-4444
Minnetonka *(G-6206)*
Opus Northwest Construction ....C.....952 656-4444
Hopkins *(G-2598)*
PCL Construction Services Inc ....E.....952 882-9600
Burnsville *(G-778)*
PCL Construction Services Inc ....D.....952 882-9600
Burnsville *(G-779)*
Penn-Co Construction Inc ....E.....651 687-0648
Saint Paul *(G-7872)*

SIC

Perkins Lumber Co Inc ....E....320 235-9420 Willmar (G-10037)
Plains Construction & Devpt ....C....218 284-0424 Moorhead (G-6333)
Prestige Drywall Inc ....E....763 506-0030 Anoka (G-216)
Pump & Meter Service Inc ....E....952 933-4800 Hopkins (G-2608)
R J M Construction Inc ....E....952 837-8600 Minneapolis (G-5458)
R J Ryan Construction Inc ....E....651 681-0200 Mendota Heights (G-3369)
Ram Buildings Inc ....E....320 485-2844 Winsted (G-10164)
Raske Building Systems Inc ....E....320 877-7221 Cosmos (G-1095)
Ray Riihiluoma Inc ....E....218 879-3317 Cloquet (G-1064)
Reiner Contracting Inc ....E....320 587-9886 Hutchinson (G-2710)
Reshetar Systems Inc ....E....763 421-1152 Anoka (G-220)
Retail Construction Services ....C....651 704-9000 Lake Elmo (G-2876)
Ryan Co's US Inc ....B....612 492-4000 Minneapolis (G-5579)
SA Woods Inc ....507 451-7084 Owatonna (G-6735)
Saginaw Contracting Inc Wgcc ....E....218 348-6000 Saint Joseph (G-7654)
Salonek Concrete & Constr ....E....507 723-4218 Springfield (G-9574)
Sand Co's Inc ....E....320 202-3100 Waite Park (G-9836)
Shaw - Lundquist Associates ....D....651 454-0670 Saint Paul (G-7903)
Sheehy Construction Co ....D....651 488-6691 Saint Paul (G-8949)
Siwek Lumber & Millwork Inc ....E....952 492-6666 Jordan (G-2810)
Socon Construction Inc ....E....763 754-4027 Minneapolis (G-3604)
Stahl Construction Co ....E....952 931-9300 Minneapolis (G-5735)
Stellar Contractors Inc ....C....952 469-0900 Lakeville (G-2935)
Strack Construction Co Inc ....E....320 251-5933 Sauk Rapids (G-9377)
Structural Restoration Inc ....E....612 825-8614 Minneapolis (G-5760)
Thor Construction Inc ....D....763 571-2580 Minneapolis (G-3616)
Thorstad Construction Co Inc ....E....320 367-2159 Maynard (G-3337)
Trout Enterprises Inc of Nthn ....E....218 246-8165 Deer River (G-1174)
Vanman Construction Co ....E....763 541-9552 Minneapolis (G-5958)
Vinco Inc ....D....651 982-4642 Forest Lake (G-2171)
VSI Construction Inc ....E....763 493-3000 Maple Grove (G-3257)
W Gohman Construction Co ....E....320 363-7781 Saint Joseph (G-7656)
Wapasha Construction Co Inc ....E....507 454-2707 Winona (G-10137)
Watson-Forsberg Co ....E....952 544-7761 Minneapolis (G-6025)
Web Construction Co Inc ....E....507 387-1667 Mankato (G-3214)
Weis Builders Inc ....C....612 243-5000 Minneapolis (G-6033)
Weis Builders Inc ....E....507 288-2041 Rochester (G-7288)
Wilcon Construction Inc ....E....507 375-5464 Saint James (G-7649)
Zeman Construction Co ....E....612 521-4300 Minneapolis (G-6115)

16 HEAVY CONSTRUCTION OTHER THAN BUILDING

1611 Highway & Street Construction

Aci Construction Inc ....E....763 424-9191 Osseo (G-6592)
Aitkin County ....E....218 927-3741 Aitkin (G-14)
Al Minnerath Inc ....C....320 762-7289 Alexandria (G-79)
Allied Blacktop Co ....D....763 425-0575 Maple Grove (G-3234)
Ames Construction Inc ....B....952 435-7106 Burnsville (G-676)
Anderson Brothers Construction ....C....218 829-1768 Brainerd (G-549)
Asphalt Surface Technologies ....D....320 363-8500 Saint Joseph (G-7650)
B H Heselton Co ....D....507 334-3901 Faribault (G-1990)
Bituminous Materials LLC ....D....507 334-3901 Faribault (G-1993)
Bituminous Paving Inc ....C....320 273-2113 Odessa (G-6553)
Bituminous Roadways Inc ....E....651 686-7001 Mendota Heights (G-3361)
Bituminous Roadways Inc ....E....612 721-2451 Minneapolis (G-3908)
Bituminous Roadways Inc ....E....952 233-1660 Shakopee (G-9423)
Bnr Excavating Inc ....E....651 438-8692 Hampton (G-2363)
C R Fischer & Sons Inc ....E....651 463-7300 Farmington (G-2042)
C W Houle Inc ....D....651 484-6077 Saint Paul (G-8147)
Caterpillar Paving Products ....E....763 712-3000 Champlin (G-891)
Central Allied Enterprises Inc ....D....320 235-5846 Willmar (G-9995)
Central Specialties Inc ....D....320 762-7289 Alexandria (G-88)
Christiansen Industrial ....E....218 751-4663 Bemidji (G-384)
City of Saint Paul ....D....651 489-8871 Saint Paul (G-8206)
City of Saint Paul ....D....651 292-6600 Saint Paul (G-8207)
City of White Bear Lake ....E....651 429-8566 Saint Paul (G-8213)
Cone Corp ....E....218 245-2313 Bovey (G-540)
County of Carver ....D....952 466-5200 Cologne (G-1091)
CS McCrossan Inc ....C....763 425-4167 Osseo (G-6606)
D L R Excavating Inc ....D....651 437-3128 Hastings (G-2380)
Dakota County Transportation ....E....651 423-2101 Rosemount (G-7367)
Davidson Ready Mix Inc ....E....218 449-4865 Holt (G-2495)
DCI Environmental Inc ....E....952 894-0012 Savage (G-9388)
DH Blattner & Sons Inc ....D....320 356-7351 Avon (G-294)
Dresel Contracting Inc ....E....651 257-9469 Chisago City (G-990)
Duininck Inc ....C....320 978-6011 Prinsburg (G-6925)
Duluth Superior Erection Inc ....E....218 626-1112 Duluth (G-1305)
Dustcoating Inc ....E....952 894-0012 Savage (G-9389)
Enebak Construction Co ....E....507 645-8962 Northfield (G-6527)
Forby Contracting Inc ....E....320 384-6061 Hinckley (G-2484)
Gladen Construction Inc ....D....218 224-2237 Laporte (G-2948)
Global Specialty Contractors ....651 406-8232 Saint Paul (G-7783)
Gowan Construction Inc ....E....701 699-5171 Oslo (G-6588)
H & R Const Co ....E....218 589-8707 Dalton (G-1156)
Hardrives Inc ....E....218 744-2913 Forbes (G-2143)
Hardrives Inc ....D....651 436-8444 Lakeland (G-2885)
Imperial Developers Inc ....D....651 454-3330 Saint Paul (G-7802)
Interstate Removal Co ....E....651 765-0765 Forest Lake (G-2152)
K G M Contractors Inc ....E....218 666-5698 Angora (G-133)
Khc Construction Inc ....E....507 532-6768 Marshall (G-3303)
Knife River Corp - North ....B....320 251-9472 Sauk Rapids (G-9368)
Knife River Corp - North ....E....218 829-4726 Baxter (G-333)
Knife River Midwest LLC ....D....507 498-3377 Spring Grove (G-9561)
Ktm Paving Inc ....E....218 628-7025 Duluth (G-1374)
Lunda Construction Co ....C....651 437-9666 Rosemount (G-7371)
Mac Management Inc ....E....952 938-8048 Minnetonka (G-6189)
Mark Sand & Gravel Co ....D....218 736-7523 Fergus Falls (G-2092)
Mathiowetz Enterprises Inc ....C....507 794-6953 Sleepy Eye (G-9497)
Mathy Construction Co ....D....507 288-7447 Rochester (G-7169)
Metro Paving Inc ....E....763 428-4121 Rogers (G-7331)
Midwest Asphalt Corp ....E....952 937-8033 Hopkins (G-2582)
Minn-Dak Asphalt Inc ....E....218 281-6840 Thief River Falls (G-9674)
Minnerath Construction Inc ....320 685-3162 Cold Spring (G-1088)
Minnesota Department of Trans ....D....507 389-6351 Mankato (G-3170)
Minnesota Department of Trans ....A....651 582-1364 Saint Paul (G-9250)
MR Paving & Excavating Inc ....D....507 354-4171 New Ulm (G-6464)
Nels Nelson & Sons Inc ....C....218 879-4561 Cloquet (G-1058)
Northland Constructors of ....E....218 722-8170 Duluth (G-1406)
Northwest Bituminous Inc ....E....952 890-3005 Burnsville (G-767)
Park Construction Co ....D....763 786-9800 Minneapolis (G-3563)
PCiRoads LLC ....E....763 497-6100 Saint Michael (G-7679)
Pciroads, Corp ....D....763 497-6100 Saint Michael (G-7680)
Penhall Co ....D....763 428-2244 Rogers (G-7337)
Pine Bend Paving Inc ....E....651 437-2333 Hastings (G-2398)
Polk County Highway Shop ....E....218 945-6952 Fertile (G-2127)
Public Works Highway Maint ....D....218 742-9800 Virginia (G-9751)
R & G Construction Co ....E....507 537-1473 Marshall (G-3323)
R J Zavoral & Sons Inc ....E....218 773-0586 East Grand Forks (G-1574)
Riley Bros Construction Inc ....E....320 589-2500 Morris (G-6376)
Rud Construction Inc ....E....952 652-2886 Webster (G-9953)
Rupp Construction Co Inc ....D....507 836-8555 Slayton (G-9490)
▼ Ryan Contracting Co ....C....952 894-3200 Shakopee (G-9471)
Sellin Brothers Inc ....E....218 483-3522 Hawley (G-2422)
Shafer Contracting Co Inc ....E....651 257-5019 Shafer (G-9415)
Starry Construction Co Inc ....E....320 762-7289 Alexandria (G-123)
Tenson Construction Inc ....E....218 743-3874 Bigfork (G-465)
Ulland Brothers Inc ....E....507 373-1960 Albert Lea (G-68)
Ulland Brothers Inc ....E....218 262-3406 Hibbing (G-2478)
▲ Veit & Co Inc ....C....763 428-2242 Rogers (G-7347)
Wabasha County Highway ....E....651 565-3366 Wabasha (G-9775)
Wieser Brothers General Contr ....D....507 895-8903 La Crescent (G-2845)

1622 Bridge, Tunnel & Elevated Hwy Construction

CS McCrossan Inc ....C....763 425-4167 Osseo (G-6606)
Dakota Highway Department ....E....952 891-7109 Saint Paul (G-7745)
DH Blattner & Sons Inc ....D....320 356-7351 Avon (G-294)
Graham Construction Services ....D....651 687-0648 Saint Paul (G-7789)
Lunda Construction Co ....C....651 437-9666 Rosemount (G-7371)
Minnowa Construction Inc ....D....507 886-6162 Harmony (G-2372)
Park Construction Co ....D....763 786-9800 Minneapolis (G-3563)
Structural Restoration Inc ....E....612 825-8614 Minneapolis (G-5760)
Swenke Co Inc ....E....507 634-7778 Kasson (G-2824)
Swenke Properties Inc ....E....507 634-7778 Kasson (G-2825)

1623 Water, Sewer & Utility Line Construction

A & A Electric & Underground ....E....507 634-7453 Kasson (G-2818)
A W Kuettel & Sons Inc ....D....218 722-3901 Duluth (G-1231)
Abbott Arne & Schwindt Inc ....E....218 236-5648 Moorhead (G-6293)
Aerial Contractors Inc ....E....218 236-9233 Moorhead (G-6294)
B H Heselton Co ....D....507 334-3901 Faribault (G-1990)
BCM Construction Inc ....E....507 333-1155 Faribault (G-1991)
Bnr Excavating Inc ....E....651 438-8692 Hampton (G-2363)
C & G Construction Inc of ....D....218 776-3080 Clearbrook (G-1036)
C W Houle Inc ....D....651 484-6077 Saint Paul (G-8147)
Castrejon Inc ....E....763 450-2055 Minneapolis (G-3429)
City Lights Inc ....D....218 568-4754 Pequot Lakes (G-6787)
Comlink Midwest Inc ....E....763 391-7483 Minneapolis (G-4129)
Connectivity Solutions Inc of ....D....763 424-7300 Osseo (G-6604)
Cooperative Development LLC ....D....218 444-1143 Bemidji (G-385)
Danelski Construction Co Inc ....E....218 372-3236 Willow River (G-10060)
Dell-Comm Inc ....D....763 783-0035 Saint Paul (G-8283)

(G-00000) Company's Geographic Section entry number
450
2011 Harris Minnesota Services Directory
▲=Import ▼=Export ◆=Import/Export

Dig America Utility Contr....E....320 253-3447
Saint Cloud *(G-7498)*
Duluth Superior Erection Inc....E....218 626-1112
Duluth *(G-1305)*
E J M Pipe Services Inc....E....651 786-8041
Circle Pines *(G-1011)*
Energy Economics Inc....D....507 374-2557
Dodge Center *(G-1227)*
Fraser Construction Co....E....507 288-6583
Rochester *(G-7120)*
Friedges Landscaping Inc....E....952 469-2996
Lakeville *(G-2908)*
Gaub Inc....E....320 382-8075
Olivia *(G-6561)*
Geldner Construction Inc....E....507 931-4230
Saint Peter *(G-9304)*
Global Specialty Contractors....651 406-8232
Saint Paul *(G-7783)*
Hammerlund Construction Inc....E....218 326-1881
Grand Rapids *(G-2283)*
Hibbing, City of Inc....E....218 263-5264
Hibbing *(G-2453)*
Imperial Developers Inc....D....651 454-3330
Saint Paul *(G-7802)*
Infrastructure Technologies....E....763 428-6488
Rogers *(G-7327)*
Karian Peterson Power Line....E....320 269-6769
Montevideo *(G-6262)*
Kuechle Underground Inc....E....320 398-8888
Kimball *(G-2834)*
Lametti & Sons Inc....E....651 426-1380
Hugo *(G-2678)*
Latour Construction Inc....E....320 963-5993
Maple Lake *(G-3260)*
M & P Utilities Inc....C....320 963-2400
Maple Lake *(G-3261)*
M P Systems Inc....D....651 484-9632
Saint Paul *(G-8603)*
Metropolitan Council, MN....D....651 602-8393
Saint Paul *(G-8643)*
Minnesota Limited Inc....D....763 428-4444
Big Lake *(G-451)*
Mlaskoch Excavating Inc....D....218 372-4067
Willow River *(G-10061)*
Mlaskoch Utility Construction....E....218 372-3977
Willow River *(G-10062)*
Mp Nexlevel LLC....C....320 963-2400
Maple Lake *(G-3262)*
Nels Nelson & Sons Inc....C....218 879-4561
Cloquet *(G-1058)*
Nodland Construction Co....D....320 763-5159
Alexandria *(G-114)*
Northland Constructors of....E....218 722-8170
Duluth *(G-1406)*
Npl Construction Co....E....218 327-9467
Grand Rapids *(G-2303)*
Okay Construction Co Inc....E....763 633-8729
Princeton *(G-6913)*
Quality Underground Services....D....651 224-0413
Saint Paul *(G-8861)*
Randy Kramer Excavating Inc....E....320 764-6871
Watkins *(G-9899)*
Rp Schroeder Construction Inc....E....763 856-2230
Zimmerman *(G-10215)*
▼ Ryan Contracting Co....C....952 894-3200
Shakopee *(G-9471)*
S J Louis Construction Inc....C....320 253-9291
Rockville *(G-7314)*
S R Weidema Inc....D....763 428-9110
Osseo *(G-6659)*
Sellin Brothers Inc....E....218 483-3522
Hawley *(G-2422)*
State Mechanical Inc....E....651 463-8220
Farmington *(G-2060)*
Swenke Co Inc....E....507 634-7778
Kasson *(G-2824)*
T D & I Cable Maintenance Inc....E....651 436-3383
Lakeland *(G-2887)*
T Ray Construction Co Inc....D....763 757-6859
Anoka *(G-231)*
Telcom Construction Inc....D....320 558-9485
Clearwater *(G-1041)*
Tl Nexlevel Co's LLC....C....320 963-2400
Maple Lake *(G-3266)*
United Piping Inc....E....218 727-7676
Duluth *(G-1492)*
Utili-Trax Contracting....C....763 323-2800
Princeton *(G-6919)*
Vertical Limit Construction....D....507 824-1222
Wanamingo *(G-9867)*
Voson Plumbing Inc....E....952 938-3143
Hopkins *(G-2654)*
Wright's General Construction....E....218 372-3329
Willow River *(G-10063)*

1629 Heavy Construction, NEC

A B E Construction Co....E....763 542-9070
Minneapolis *(G-3646)*
Aqua Engineering Inc....E....952 941-1138
Eden Prairie *(G-1594)*
Atlas Foundation Co....E....763 428-2261
Osseo *(G-6596)*
Carl Bolander & Sons Co....D....651 224-6299
Saint Paul *(G-8165)*
Chard Tiling & Excavating Inc....D....952 873-6152
Belle Plaine *(G-372)*
Cherne Co Inc....D....952 944-4300
Eden Prairie *(G-1623)*
D & G Excavating Inc....E....507 532-2334
Marshall *(G-3292)*
DH Blattner & Sons Inc....D....320 356-7351
Avon *(G-294)*
Doboszenski & Sons Inc....E....763 478-6945
Loretto *(G-3046)*
Duininck Inc....C....320 978-6011
Prinsburg *(G-6925)*
Ellingson Drainage Inc....D....507 527-2294
West Concord *(G-9964)*
Fraser Construction Co....E....507 288-6583
Rochester *(G-7120)*
Global Specialty Contractors....651 406-8232
Saint Paul *(G-7783)*
Hartman Co's Inc....E....952 443-2958
Victoria *(G-9729)*
L H Bolduc Co Inc....D....763 427-4330
Anoka *(G-196)*
▲ M A Mortenson Co....B....763 522-2100
Minneapolis *(G-4917)*
Mini-Dredge Inc....218 773-3331
East Grand Forks *(G-1572)*
Nels Nelson & Sons Inc....C....218 879-4561
Cloquet *(G-1058)*
Park Construction Co....D....763 786-9800
Minneapolis *(G-3563)*
Premier Irrigation Inc....E....651 480-8857
Hastings *(G-2401)*
Railworks Track Systems Inc....D....952 469-4907
Lakeville *(G-2928)*
Rivard Contracting Inc....E....763 753-7888
Cedar *(G-884)*
Traxler Construction Inc....E....507 357-2235
Le Center *(G-2954)*
Tri-State Drilling Inc....D....763 553-1234
Minneapolis *(G-5852)*
Turner Excavating Co....D....952 890-1645
Savage *(G-9410)*
▲ Veit & Co Inc....C....763 428-2242
Rogers *(G-7347)*

17 CONSTRUCTION-SPECIAL TRADE CONTRACTORS

1711 Plumbing, Heating & Air Conditioning Contractors

A G O'Brien Plumbing & Heating....E....218 729-9662
Hermantown *(G-2433)*
A W Kuettel & Sons Inc....D....218 722-3901
Duluth *(G-1231)*
A-ABC Appliance & Heating Inc....E....763 383-8383
Minneapolis *(G-3652)*
AAF-Mcquay Inc....B....763 553-5330
Minneapolis *(G-3655)*
Advance Wall Systems Inc....E....763 263-8512
Big Lake *(G-444)*
Air Mechanical Inc....C....763 434-7747
Anoka *(G-147)*
Aircorps LLC....E....763 550-0707
Plymouth *(G-6845)*
Albers Sheetmetal....D....651 224-5428
Saint Paul *(G-8004)*
Allan Mechanical Inc....E....952 934-3999
Eden Prairie *(G-1587)*
◆ API Group Inc....E....651 636-4320
Saint Paul *(G-8054)*
Area Mechanical Inc....E....651 451-9356
Vadnais Heights *(G-9719)*
Arrow Sprinkler Inc....E....763 780-2800
Minneapolis *(G-3410)*
B & D Plumbing, Heating & AC....E....763 497-2290
Saint Michael *(G-7672)*
Boiler Services Inc....E....763 784-8178
Minneapolis *(G-3422)*
Bonfe's Plumbing & Heating Svc....E....651 228-7140
Saint Paul *(G-8117)*
Brothers Fire Protection Co....D....763 441-2290
Elk River *(G-1864)*
Carrier Commercial....E....763 231-8300
Minneapolis *(G-4021)*
Centraire Heating & Air Condg....E....952 941-1044
Eden Prairie *(G-1619)*
Commercial Plumbing & Heating....D....651 464-2988
Forest Lake *(G-2151)*
▼ Cool Air Mechanical Inc....D....651 489-8821
Saint Paul *(G-8250)*
Corporate Mechanical Inc....D....763 533-3070
Minneapolis *(G-4164)*
Corval Constructors Inc....C....651 642-0451
Saint Paul *(G-8255)*
Countryside Heating & Cooling....E....763 479-1600
Maple Plain *(G-3272)*
County of Douglas....D....320 763-6018
Alexandria *(G-92)*
Creative Sustainable Solutions....D....651 602-6644
Saint Paul *(G-8267)*
Cronstrom Furnace & Sheet....E....952 920-3800
Minneapolis *(G-4186)*
Curbside Lawn Care....D....952 403-9012
Savage *(G-9387)*
D J'S Heating & Air Condg....E....763 421-5313
Elk River *(G-1871)*
Dependable Indoor Air Quality....E....763 757-5040
Minneapolis *(G-3454)*
Diversified Contracting Inc....E....763 712-8087
Anoka *(G-175)*
DMC Plumbing & Heating Inc....E....507 356-4455
Pine Island *(G-6815)*
Doody Mechanical Inc....E....651 487-1061
Saint Paul *(G-8309)*
E & H Enterprises of....D....320 762-8645
Alexandria *(G-97)*
Egan Co....C....763 544-4131
Brooklyn Park *(G-609)*
El-Jay Plumbing & Heating Inc....D....320 251-8330
Saint Cloud *(G-7413)*
Elander Mechanical Inc....E....952 445-4692
Shakopee *(G-9437)*
Environmental Plant Svcs Inc....E....651 644-4301
Saint Paul *(G-8342)*
Erickson Plumbing Heating....E....763 783-4545
Minneapolis *(G-3466)*
Fagen Inc....D....320 564-3324
Granite Falls *(G-2314)*
Faribo Plumbing & Heating Inc....E....507 334-6409
Faribault *(G-2007)*
Fibercare Inc....E....612 721-5048
Minneapolis *(G-4426)*
Fireguard Sprinkler Service....E....651 748-9499
Saint Paul *(G-8378)*
Flare Heating & Air Condg....E....763 542-1166
Minneapolis *(G-4454)*
Fred Vogt & Co....D....952 929-6767
Minneapolis *(G-4482)*
G R Mechanical Plumbing....E....763 428-2663
Rogers *(G-7323)*
Gag Sheet Metal Inc....E....507 354-3813
New Ulm *(G-6450)*
Gagnon Inc....E....651 644-4301
Saint Paul *(G-8400)*
Gartner Refrigeration & Mfg....D....763 559-5880
Plymouth *(G-6862)*
Gartner Refrigeration Co....E....218 722-4439
Duluth *(G-1332)*
Gemini 26 Inc....E....507 334-7951
Faribault *(G-2009)*
General Sheet Metal Corp....C....763 544-8747
Minneapolis *(G-4518)*
General Sprinkler Corp....E....651 484-5903
Saint Paul *(G-8405)*
Genz-Ryan Plumbing & Heating....C....952 882-1144
Burnsville *(G-728)*
Gilbert Mechanical Contractors....C....952 835-3810
Edina *(G-1831)*
Goodin Co....E....320 259-6086
Saint Cloud *(G-7520)*
Gorham Oien Mechanical Inc....D....320 679-1612
Mora *(G-6359)*
Gv Heating & Air Inc....E....763 535-2000
Minneapolis *(G-4582)*
Haley Comfort Systems Inc....E....507 534-2901
Plainview *(G-6842)*
Hanson's Plumbing & Heating....E....218 342-2422
Vergas *(G-9722)*
Harbor City Oil Co....E....218 624-3633
Duluth *(G-1348)*
Harris Contracting Co....D....651 602-6500
Saint Paul *(G-8444)*
Harris Contracting Co....E....507 282-8128
Rochester *(G-7133)*
Harty Mechanical Inc....E....507 437-8201
Austin *(G-273)*
Heating & Cooling Two Inc....D....763 428-3677
Osseo *(G-6619)*
HiMec Inc....C....507 281-4000
Rochester *(G-7138)*
Horwitz Inc....C....763 533-1900
Minneapolis *(G-4677)*
J-Berd Mechanical Contractors....D....320 656-0847
Saint Cloud *(G-7534)*
Johnson Controls Inc....D....763 566-7650
Plymouth *(G-6868)*
Johnson, Carl E Plumbing....E....320 983-2171
Milaca *(G-3378)*
K & S Heating & Air Condg....D....507 282-4328
Rochester *(G-7148)*
Kusske Mechanical Inc....E....651 437-8404
Hastings *(G-2394)*
Laney's Mechanical Inc....E....218 847-1309
Detroit Lakes *(G-1207)*
Larson Plumbing Inc....E....763 427-7680
Anoka *(G-198)*
Lbp Mechanical Inc....E....612 333-1515
Minneapolis *(G-4851)*
Magnuson Huisinga & Sons Inc....320 599-4474
Willmar *(G-10021)*
Maintenance Team....E....952 942-5000
Eden Prairie *(G-1715)*
Major Mechanical Inc....D....763 424-6680
Osseo *(G-6631)*
Managed Services Inc....C....952 925-4111
Minneapolis *(G-4940)*
Marsh Heating & Air Condg....E....763 536-0667
Minneapolis *(G-4957)*
Master Mechanical Inc....C....651 905-1600
Saint Paul *(G-7834)*
Mc Guire Mechanical Services....E....952 469-4988
Lakeville *(G-2916)*
Mc Quillan Brothers Plumbing....E....651 292-0124
Saint Paul *(G-8622)*

S
I
C

Employment codes: A=Over 500 employees, B=251-500
C=101-250, D=51-100, E=25-50
2011 Harris Minnesota
Services Directory
© Harris InfoSource 1-866-281-6415
451

McDowall Co	D	320 251-8640	Waite Park (G-9829)
Mechanical Contractors	E	952 440-9751	Prior Lake (G-6939)
Mechanical Energy Systems Inc	E	320 253-4859	Saint Cloud (G-7419)
Metro Air Inc	E	952 447-8124	Prior Lake (G-6942)
Metro Fire Protection Inc	E	651 784-0417	Lino Lakes (G-2974)
Metropolitan Mechanical Contr	B	952 941-7010	Eden Prairie (G-1722)
Midwest Maintenance & Mech	E	763 544-2700	Minneapolis (G-5031)
Modern Heating & Air Condg	E	612 781-3358	Minneapolis (G-5118)
National Automatic Sprinkler	E	763 784-8902	Minneapolis (G-3550)
Nelson, Bruce Plumbing	E	651 738-9354	Saint Paul (G-8745)
Northern Air Corp	C	651 490-9868	Saint Paul (G-8757)
Northland Mechanical Contr	C	763 544-5100	Minneapolis (G-5232)
Northwest Sheet Metal Co of St	D	651 310-0102	Saint Paul (G-8768)
Olsen Fire Protection Inc	E	612 331-3111	Minneapolis (G-5270)
Owens Co's Inc	D	952 854-3800	Bloomington (G-509)
Paape Distributing Co	E	507 345-8057	Mankato (G-3181)
Palen Kimball LLC	E	651 646-2800	Saint Paul (G-8804)
Pearson Mechanical Services	E	651 275-1100	Hugo (G-2681)
Pioneer Power Inc	D	651 488-5561	Saint Paul (G-8828)
Plaas Inc	C	651 388-8881	Red Wing (G-6994)
Pro-Temp Inc	E	651 460-6022	Farmington (G-2058)
Quality Refrigeration Inc	E	612 861-7350	Minneapolis (G-5443)
R & S Heating & Air Condg	E	952 894-0376	Savage (G-9404)
R J Mechanical Inc	E	320 679-0602	Mora (G-6368)
Range Cornice & Roofing Co Inc	E	218 262-4581	Hibbing (G-2471)
Ray N Welter Heating Co	E	612 825-6867	Minneapolis (G-5469)
Response Fire Protection Inc	E	763 717-4740	Minneapolis (G-3583)
Rochester Plumbing & Heating	D	507 289-1613	Rochester (G-7239)
Rouse Mechanical Inc	E	952 933-5300	Minneapolis (G-5562)
Sabre Plumbing, Heating & Air	D	763 473-2267	Minneapolis (G-5585)
Schadegg Mechanical Inc	D	651 292-9933	South Saint Paul (G-9541)
Schwalbach Hardware Inc	E	507 831-2523	Windom (G-10071)
Schwickert Co	D	507 387-3101	Mankato (G-3193)
Schwickert Inc	D	507 387-3106	Mankato (G-3194)
Shannon-Peterson Inc	E	218 751-4502	Bemidji (G-427)
Simplexgrinnell LP	E	320 253-8883	Saint Cloud (G-7427)
Simplexgrinnell LP	C	763 367-5000	Minneapolis (G-5676)
Simplexgrinnell LP	C	320 253-8883	Waite Park (G-9838)
Skyline Fire Protection Inc	E	763 425-4441	Osseo (G-6664)
SPI Group Inc	D	218 283-9397	International Falls (G-2731)
Spriggs Plumbing & Heating Inc	E	651 224-5616	Saint Paul (G-8979)
Sr Mechanical Inc	D	952 933-6933	Saint Louis Park (G-7669)
St Cloud Refrigeration Inc	C	320 251-6861	Saint Cloud (G-7429)
St Paul Plumbers Joint	E	651 846-1389	Saint Paul (G-8995)
St Paul Plumbing & Heating Co	E	651 228-9200	Saint Paul (G-8996)
State Mechanical Inc	E	651 463-8220	Farmington (G-2060)
Steine Cold Storage Inc	E	763 416-4681	Minneapolis (G-5748)
Steinkraus Plumbing Inc	E	952 361-0128	Chaska (G-981)
Summit Fire Protection Co	C	651 251-1880	Saint Paul (G-9012)
Superior Fire Protection Inc	E	763 263-1929	Big Lake (G-458)
Superior Mechanical Systems	E	507 289-5126	Rochester (G-7270)
Superior Water Conditioning	E	507 289-0229	Rochester (G-7271)
Thomas M Meyer Enterprises Inc	E	763 476-1990	Minneapolis (G-5818)
Thompson Plumbing Co Inc	E	952 933-7717	Hopkins (G-2645)
Tonna Mechanical Inc	E	507 288-1908	Rochester (G-7275)
United States Mechanical Inc	E	763 780-9030	Circle Pines (G-1022)
Valley Plumbing Co Inc	C	952 492-2121	Jordan (G-2812)
Viking Automatic Sprinkler Co	E	651 558-3300	Saint Paul (G-9128)
Viking Automatic Sprinkler Co	E	218 628-2150	Duluth (G-1495)
Viking Automatic Sprinkler Co	E	218 733-0962	Duluth (G-1496)
Viking Automatic Sprinkler Co	E	507 289-8270	Rochester (G-7283)
Voson Plumbing Inc	E	952 938-3143	Hopkins (G-2654)
Voss Plumbing & Heating of	E	320 243-3644	Paynesville (G-6775)
Weidner Plumbing & Heating Co	D	320 252-3000	Saint Cloud (G-7431)
Wenzel Plumbing & Heating Inc	D	651 452-1565	Saint Paul (G-7945)
▲ Winona Heating & Ventilating	C	507 452-2064	Winona (G-10149)
Wright-Hennepin Security Corp	C	763 477-3000	Rockford (G-7306)
Ww Constructors Inc	E	763 420-4177	Hamel (G-2362)
Yale Mechanical Inc	C	952 884-1661	Minneapolis (G-6097)
Yale Mechanical LLC	C	952 884-1661	Minneapolis (G-6098)

1721 Painting & Paper Hanging Contractors

B Nelson Julius & Son Inc	E	612 379-3347	Minneapolis (G-3853)
Brush Masters Inc	C	763 478-3232	Minneapolis (G-3964)
Champion Coatings	E	952 707-9000	Savage (G-9385)
Changs Inc	E	763 442-9080	Minneapolis (G-4054)
Cityscape Contractors Inc	D	952 882-0020	Burnsville (G-698)
Custom One Painting Inc	E	612 787-1040	Minneapolis (G-4204)
Decorators Service Co of	E	763 383-2955	Plymouth (G-6859)
Excel Painting Plus Inc	E	763 557-2821	Minneapolis (G-4382)
Final Coat Painting Inc	D	651 789-0790	Eagan (G-1527)
Fresh Start Enterprises Inc	E	952 903-0262	Eden Prairie (G-1670)
Geo's Paint & Finish LLC	E	320 692-2027	Brainerd (G-567)
Hamernick Paint Co	D	651 489-7007	Saint Paul (G-8439)
Lakeside House Painters Inc	D	952 942-9709	Minneapolis (G-4836)
Lawremar Inc	E	651 429-4475	Saint Paul (G-8568)
Maciej Paint Corp	E	651 407-8000	Hugo (G-2679)
MCI Paint & Drywall Inc	E	952 985-7778	Lakeville (G-2917)
Northland Painting	E	651 645-9791	Stillwater (G-9632)
Painting By Nakasone Inc	E	651 646-6999	Saint Paul (G-8802)
Painting Perfection Ltd	E	651 762-9011	Saint Paul (G-8803)
Pompeii Painting Inc	D	507 288-8494	Rochester (G-7207)
▲ Prefinishing Specialists Inc	E	320 356-2217	Avon (G-297)
Prism Commercial & Industrial	E	763 420-4080	Hamel (G-2354)
Protouch Painting Inc	E	651 457-5628	South Saint Paul (G-9537)
Rainbow Inc	C	763 535-4041	Minneapolis (G-5463)
Regal Contractors Inc	E	320 253-1161	Saint Cloud (G-7582)
▲ Safety Signs Inc	E	952 469-6700	Lakeville (G-2930)
Sorensen & Sorensen Painting	E	507 289-5368	Rochester (G-7258)
Steinbrecher Painting Inc	E	763 389-3887	Princeton (G-6916)
Sunrise Painting	E	763 557-0100	Minneapolis (G-5768)
Tenet Painting	D	952 914-9550	Minneapolis (G-5811)
Torrini Plastering Co Inc	E	612 332-3933	Saint Paul (G-7926)
Treb, Dan Painting	E	952 476-8163	Long Lake (G-3034)
Universal Painting & Drywall	E	763 315-0095	Minneapolis (G-5921)

1731 Electrical Work

A & A Electric & Underground	E	507 634-7453	Kasson (G-2818)
Ace Electrical Contractors Inc	D	763 694-8800	Minneapolis (G-3670)
Adair Electric Co	D	507 289-7696	Rochester (G-7044)
Aid Electric Corp	E	763 571-7267	Minneapolis (G-3387)
All State Communications Inc	E	320 203-1511	Sauk Rapids (G-9356)
All Systems Installation Inc	D	507 281-9466	Rochester (G-7050)
API Electric Co	D	218 628-3323	Duluth (G-1239)
Applied Business Comms	D	651 643-6595	New Brighton (G-6406)
Appollo Systems Inc	E	763 493-5821	Osseo (G-6594)
Augusta Electric Inc	E	320 398-2189	Kimball (G-2831)
AVI-Spl Inc	E	651 287-7000	Saint Paul (G-8081)
Avtex Solutions LLC	E	952 831-0888	Minneapolis (G-3848)
Ben Franklin Electric Inc	D	952 888-2210	Burnsville (G-685)
Bloomington Electric Co	E	952 888-7905	Minneapolis (G-3913)
Broadband America, Corp	E	952 941-7900	Victoria (G-9725)
Calix Networks Inc	D	763 268-3300	Minneapolis (G-3994)
Castrejon Inc	E	763 450-2055	Minneapolis (G-3429)
Cedar Lake Electric Inc	E	507 334-9546	Faribault (G-1998)
Centre Electric Inc	E	320 352-0160	Sauk Centre (G-9342)
Chapin Enterprises Inc	C	320 235-4386	Willmar (G-9997)
Checkpoint Security Systems	C	952 942-9431	Chanhassen (G-914)
Checkpoint Systems Inc	E	952 227-5350	Chaska (G-958)
Checkpoint Systems Inc	C	952 943-3853	Chanhassen (G-915)
Cities Electric Inc	D	651 463-3810	Farmington (G-2044)
City View Electric Inc	D	651 659-9496	Saint Paul (G-8215)
Collins Electrical Constr	C	651 224-2833	Saint Paul (G-8224)
Collins Electrical Systems Inc	D	763 535-6000	Minneapolis (G-4121)
Comm-Works Holdings LLC	D	763 258-5800	Minneapolis (G-4130)
Comm-Works LLC	D	763 258-5800	Minneapolis (G-4131)
Convergeone Holdings Corp	C	651 796-6411	Eagan (G-1522)
Custom Communications Inc	D	507 288-5522	Rochester (G-7091)
Dell-Comm Inc	D	763 783-0035	Saint Paul (G-8283)
Design Electric Inc	D	320 252-1658	Saint Cloud (G-7497)
Dewar Electric Inc	E	507 235-6677	Fairmont (G-1962)
Donnelly Electric Inc	E	651 487-2877	Saint Paul (G-8308)
Dymanyk Electric	E	612 379-4112	Minneapolis (G-4298)
Egan Co	C	763 544-4131	Brooklyn Park (G-609)
Electric Resource Contractors	C	612 522-6511	Minneapolis (G-4338)
Electrical Installation	E	763 479-3744	Maple Plain (G-3273)
Electrical Visions Inc	E	763 425-1153	Dayton (G-1165)
Electro-Watchman Inc	E	651 227-8461	Saint Paul (G-8329)
Electronic Communication Systs	D	651 735-7470	Saint Paul (G-8331)
Electronic Design Co	E	612 355-2300	Minneapolis (G-4339)
Elliott Contracting Corp	E	612 256-0000	Minneapolis (G-4342)
Enhanced Home Systems Inc	E	952 941-5289	Eden Prairie (G-1657)
Erickson Plumbing Heating	E	763 783-4545	Minneapolis (G-3466)
Fagen Inc	D	320 564-3324	Granite Falls (G-2314)
Falls Electric Inc	E	218 681-7299	Thief River Falls (G-9667)
Firenet Systems Inc	E	763 536-3950	Minneapolis (G-4437)
Fishel Information Systems Inc	E	952 544-1108	Hopkins (G-2543)
Foster Electric Co	E	507 289-4571	Rochester (G-7118)
Fox Electrical Co	E	507 433-7184	Austin (G-271)
Fraser-Morris Electric Co Inc	E	612 332-4328	Minneapolis (G-4480)
General Electric Co	E	612 529-9502	Minneapolis (G-4510)
Gephart Electric Co Inc	C	651 484-4900	Saint Paul (G-8406)

S I C

(G-00000) Company's Geographic Section entry number
452
2011 Harris Minnesota Services Directory
▲=Import ▼=Export ◆=Import/Export

Gephart Electrical Constr ....E....651 484-4900
Saint Paul *(G-8407)*
Gilbert Mechanical Contractors ....C....952 835-3810
Edina *(G-1831)*
Hanson Electric Of Bemidji Inc ....E....218 751-5833
Bemidji *(G-397)*
Hoffman Controls Inc ....E....218 732-8374
Park Rapids *(G-6753)*
Honda Electric Inc ....E....763 498-8433
Loretto *(G-3049)*
Hunt Electric Corp ....B....651 646-2911
Saint Paul *(G-8500)*
Hunt Electric Corp ....E....507 281-3226
Rochester *(G-7141)*
Ideacom Mid-America Inc ....D....651 292-0102
Saint Paul *(G-8504)*
Industrial Commercial Farm 218 377-4485
International Falls *(G-2722)*
Industrial Electric Co ....D....612 331-1268
Minneapolis *(G-4697)*
J T Electric Service Inc ....E....320 845-4789
Albany *(G-27)*
JC Custom Welding Inc ....E....218 444-9353
Bemidji *(G-398)*
Johnson Controls Inc ....D....763 566-7650
Plymouth *(G-6868)*
Kehne Electric Corp ....E....651 645-5781
Saint Paul *(G-8543)*
Killmer Electric Co Inc ....D....763 425-2525
Minneapolis *(G-4807)*
Lea Albert Electric Co ....E....507 373-6650
Albert Lea *(G-60)*
Life Safety Systems Inc ....E....763 560-2048
Minneapolis *(G-4876)*
Magnum Electric Inc ....E....218 236-8753
Moorhead *(G-6327)*
Manor Electric Inc ....E....763 479-4170
Maple Plain *(G-3278)*
Marsh Heating & Air Condg ....E....763 536-0667
Minneapolis *(G-4957)*
Master Electric Co Inc ....D....952 890-3555
Savage *(G-9398)*
Master Technology Group Inc ....E....952 960-1212
Savage *(G-9399)*
Mayer Electric Corp ....D....763 537-9357
Minneapolis *(G-4968)*
Medina Electric Inc ....C....763 478-6828
Hamel *(G-2351)*
Metro Communication Services ......D....651 702-3100
Saint Paul *(G-9247)*
Mid Northern Electric Inc ....E....651 452-3996
Saint Paul *(G-7840)*
Mill City Electric Inc ....E....612 724-4900
Minneapolis *(G-5042)*
Minnesota Conway Fire & Safety .....E....952 345-3473
Minneapolis *(G-5072)*
MJM Investments Inc ....E....952 432-5036
Saint Paul *(G-7844)*
Moorhead Electric Inc ....E....218 284-1963
Moorhead *(G-6330)*
Mtec Electric Inc ....E....763 537-1570
Minneapolis *(G-5147)*
Muska Electric Co ....C....651 636-5820
Saint Paul *(G-8730)*
Muzak LLC ....E....763 424-5533
Osseo *(G-6641)*
Naylor Electrical Construction ....E....218 751-2620
Bemidji *(G-405)*
Network Design Inc ....E....763 475-5500
Minneapolis *(G-5184)*
Norstan Communications Inc ....C....952 352-4300
Minnetonka *(G-6202)*
North American Communications ....D....651 994-6800
Eagan *(G-1542)*
North Central Service Inc ....C....218 776-3855
Clearbrook *(G-1039)*
Northstar Fire Protection Inc ....E....651 456-9111
Saint Paul *(G-7853)*
One Way Building Services Inc ....E....952 942-0412
Minneapolis *(G-5280)*
Orion Communication Services ......E....763 694-7540
Minneapolis *(G-5290)*
Otter Tail Corp 866 410-8780
Fergus Falls *(G-2105)*
Parallel Technologies Inc ....C....952 920-7185
Minneapolis *(G-5322)*
Parsons Electric LLC ....C....763 571-8000
Minneapolis *(G-3565)*
Pat S Electric ....E....507 483-2857
Adrian *(G-4)*
Polyphase Electric Co ....D....218 723-1413
Duluth *(G-1428)*
Prairie Electric Co Inc ....E....952 949-0074
Eden Prairie *(G-1752)*
Prairie Technologies Inc of MN ......E....763 255-3200
Elk River *(G-1904)*
Premier Electrical Corp ....C....763 424-6551
Brooklyn Park *(G-617)*
Red River Electric Inc ....E....218 236-0502
Moorhead *(G-6336)*
Rhjh Inc ....E....651 735-7470
Saint Paul *(G-8897)*
Rick Electric Inc ....E....218 233-6194
Moorhead *(G-6339)*
Ridgedale Electric Inc ....E....952 473-2714
Long Lake *(G-3031)*
Ries Electric Co ....E....651 451-2238
South Saint Paul *(G-9538)*

RMR Services LLC ....D....763 786-7323
Minneapolis *(G-3588)*
Rock Electric Corp ....E....763 792-9664
Minneapolis *(G-3590)*
Scheid Electric Inc ....E....507 388-9305
Mankato *(G-3192)*
▲ Security Products Co ....E....763 784-6504
Minneapolis *(G-3599)*
Silent Knight Security Systems ....E....952 881-0038
Minneapolis *(G-5673)*
Simplexgrinnell LP ....E....320 253-8883
Saint Cloud *(G-7427)*
Simplexgrinnell LP ....C....763 367-5000
Minneapolis *(G-5676)*
South Side Electric Inc ....D....952 888-5500
Bloomington *(G-517)*
Spectrum Solutions Inc ....E....651 634-1800
Saint Paul *(G-8976)*
Superior Fire Protection Inc ....E....763 263-1929
Big Lake *(G-458)*
Techpower Inc ....E....952 831-7444
Minneapolis *(G-5806)*
▲ Thompson Lightning Protection ....E....651 455-7661
Saint Paul *(G-7921)*
Trans-Alarm Inc ....D....952 894-1700
Burnsville *(G-810)*
Uhl Co Inc ....D....763 425-7226
Osseo *(G-6680)*
Um Electric Utlts Shop ....E....612 625-8081
Minneapolis *(G-5898)*
Weber Electric Inc ....D....651 490-1333
Saint Paul *(G-9142)*
Winco Landscape Inc ....E....651 455-3070
Inver Grove Heights *(G-2774)*
Woody's Rebar Co ....E....651 592-5038
Saint Paul *(G-9167)*
Wright-Hennepin Security Corp ......C....763 477-3000
Rockford *(G-7306)*

1741 Masonry & Other Stonework

Abfalter Brothers Concrete LLC ......E....763 635-8088
Elk River *(G-1859)*
Advanced Concrete & Masonry ......E....763 424-9365
Minneapolis *(G-3687)*
Advanced Masonry Restoration ......E....651 766-8080
Saint Paul *(G-7991)*
American Masonry Restoration ......E....763 502-1400
Minneapolis *(G-3399)*
B&D Associates Inc ....E....651 489-8001
Saint Paul *(G-8084)*
Bob Pankan & Sons Concrete ....E....763 444-5720
Isanti *(G-2778)*
Bunn William Masonry Inc ....E....952 292-2685
Waconia *(G-9780)*
C & D Granite Inc ....E....320 597-2398
Richmond *(G-7040)*
Camco Construction Inc ....E....320 259-1051
Saint Cloud *(G-7467)*
Classic Construction of Cedar ....E....763 434-8870
Cedar *(G-877)*
▲ Cold Spring Granite Co Inc ....A....320 685-3621
Cold Spring *(G-1083)*
Commercial Contractors Co of ....E....320 256-7422
Melrose *(G-3348)*
Concept Landscaping Inc ....E....952 472-4118
Mound *(G-6386)*
▲ Coughlan Co's Inc ....C....507 385-8295
Mankato *(G-3120)*
Crosstown Masonry Inc ....E....763 434-6371
Anoka *(G-171)*
Dakota Rhoads Masonry Inc ....E....651 437-2100
Hastings *(G-2383)*
Dayco Concrete Co Inc ....D....952 556-0278
Chanhassen *(G-918)*
Frantz, Donald R Concrete ....E....952 929-8568
Minneapolis *(G-4476)*
Greatstone LLC ....E....651 429-6606
Saint Paul *(G-8429)*
Gresser Co's Inc ....C....651 454-5976
Saint Paul *(G-7793)*
Greystone Masonry Inc ....E....763 413-9633
Anoka *(G-185)*
Harbor City Masonry Inc ....D....218 628-3686
Duluth *(G-1347)*
Hicks Concrete Construction ....E....763 420-7755
Hamel *(G-2344)*
Hollenback & Nelson Inc ....E....763 862-7525
Minneapolis *(G-3489)*
Knife Lake Concrete Inc ....E....320 679-4141
Mora *(G-6363)*
Manor Concrete Construction ....C....763 497-5420
Saint Michael *(G-7676)*
Metro Home Services Network ....E....612 827-0643
Cedar *(G-882)*
Michael Nelson Masonry Inc ....E....952 496-0217
Excelsior *(G-1946)*
Northland Concrete & Masonry ......D....952 890-1650
Burnsville *(G-765)*
▲ Northwestern Marble & Granite ....E....952 941-8601
Minneapolis *(G-5246)*
Peck Construction Inc ....D....763 421-2201
Anoka *(G-214)*
Progressive Concrete & Masonry .....E....651 489-2200
Saint Paul *(G-8853)*
Rockwood Retaining Walls Inc ....E....507 529-2871
Rochester *(G-7241)*

Steenberg Watrud Construction ......E....651 457-2291
Inver Grove Heights *(G-2770)*
Stretar Masonry & Concrete Inc .....E....218 624-4824
Duluth *(G-1476)*
Superior Masonry & Concrete ....E....651 786-0884
Anoka *(G-230)*
Valley Masonry LLC ....D....218 498-2244
Glyndon *(G-2235)*
Vincent Haugen ....E....218 233-3776
Moorhead *(G-6346)*
Willow Creek Concrete Products ......E....320 398-5415
Kimball *(G-2835)*
Winco Landscape Inc ....E....651 455-3070
Inver Grove Heights *(G-2774)*
Yerigan Construction Co ....E....763 444-5353
Isanti *(G-2782)*

1742 Plastering, Drywall, Acoustical & Insulation Work

▲ Acoustics Associates Inc ....C....763 544-8901
Minneapolis *(G-3674)*
◆ API Group Inc ....E....651 636-4320
Saint Paul *(G-8054)*
Architectural Sales of MN ....D....763 533-1595
Minneapolis *(G-3802)*
Berg Drywall LLC ....C....952 448-3130
Chaska *(G-953)*
Boser Construction Inc ....E....320 393-3185
Sauk Rapids *(G-9359)*
Brush Masters Inc ....C....763 478-3232
Minneapolis *(G-3964)*
Build All Installed Inc ....E....218 692-5115
Crosslake *(G-1150)*
Carl Hanson Drywall Inc ....E....763 753-4112
Cedar *(G-874)*
Carnahan City-Wide Insulation ......D....952 445-1387
Shakopee *(G-9428)*
Ceiling Pro Interior Inc ....E....952 947-0007
Eden Prairie *(G-1617)*
Commercial Drywall Inc ....E....763 862-6020
Saint Francis *(G-7639)*
Cullen's Home Center of ....D....320 762-1249
Alexandria *(G-93)*
Custom Drywall Inc ....C....651 488-0533
Saint Paul *(G-8274)*
Davis Drywall Inc ....E....218 444-2532
Bemidji *(G-387)*
Donnelly Brothers Construction ......E....612 866-1204
Minneapolis *(G-4278)*
Dual Temp Inc ....E....763 494-9358
Hamel *(G-2339)*
Friedges Drywall Inc ....E....952 461-3288
New Market *(G-6420)*
Heim Drywall Inc ....E....507 932-5448
Saint Charles *(G-7403)*
Heller Drywall Ltd ....E....952 496-2525
Shakopee *(G-9443)*
Installed Building Products ....D....763 441-2313
Elk River *(G-1900)*
J & D Drywall Inc ....E....952 461-4078
Elko *(G-1905)*
JD Driver Ltd ....E....507 437-6050
Rose Creek *(G-7350)*
Ladue Construction Inc ....E....218 846-9865
Waubun *(G-9900)*
Marathon Group Inc ....D....952 929-1990
Minneapolis *(G-4945)*
MCI Paint & Drywall Inc ....E....952 985-7778
Lakeville *(G-2917)*
McPherson Insulation Inc ....E....320 259-5735
Saint Cloud *(G-7418)*
Metro Home Insulation Inc ....E....763 441-2313
Elk River *(G-1901)*
MG Kraus Construction LLC ....E....952 895-5300
Burnsville *(G-755)*
Milwaukee Insulation Co I ....E....651 659-2211
Saint Paul *(G-8668)*
Mulcahy Inc ....C....651 770-5250
Mahtomedi *(G-3095)*
N P D Inc ....E....218 720-3324
Duluth *(G-1398)*
Nordic Insulation Inc ....E....763 784-7893
Minneapolis *(G-3557)*
Northern Industrial Insulation ....E....218 624-0574
Duluth *(G-1404)*
Nyco Inc ....D....651 457-4069
Inver Grove Heights *(G-2764)*
Palmer Soderberg Inc ....E....507 288-4213
Rochester *(G-7200)*
Prestige Drywall Inc ....E....763 506-0030
Anoka *(G-216)*
Quality Drywall Inc ....E....763 424-5774
Osseo *(G-6654)*
Quality Drywall Midwest Inc ....E....763 424-5774
Maple Grove *(G-3252)*
Quality Insulation Inc ....E....952 929-6889
Minneapolis *(G-5442)*
Regal Contractors Inc ....E....320 253-1161
Saint Cloud *(G-7582)*
Russnick Contractors Inc ....E....763 420-3737
Hamel *(G-2356)*
Schum Drywall Co Inc ....D....952 881-3350
Minneapolis *(G-5615)*
Signature Stucco Concepts Inc ......E....763 241-4110
Elk River *(G-1893)*

Employment codes: A=Over 500 employees, B=251-500
C=101-250, D=51-100, E=25-50

2011 Harris Minnesota
Services Directory

© Harris InfoSource 1-866-281-6415

453

SIC

Stephen Donnelly Co ....D....952 884-1848
Minneapolis *(G-5750)*
Superl Inc ....E....763 571-7464
Lino Lakes *(G-2976)*
Twin City Acoustics Inc ....D....763 535-6697
Minneapolis *(G-5875)*
U S Insulation Inc ....E....763 785-1726
Minneapolis *(G-3627)*
Universal Painting & Drywall ....E....763 315-0095
Minneapolis *(G-5921)*
Viking Drywall Inc ....E....952 888-6442
Minneapolis *(G-5972)*
W E Nelson Stucco Co ....E....763 377-3631
Saint Paul *(G-9134)*
W Zintl Construction Inc ....C....651 439-7973
Stillwater *(G-9654)*
Young & Davis Drywall Inc ......E....218 751-6048
Bemidji *(G-434)*

1743 Terrazzo, Tile, Marble & Mosaic Work

Grazzini Brothers & Co ....C....651 452-2700
Saint Paul *(G-7790)*
▲ Korsmo Inc ....D....507 285-1109
Rochester *(G-7158)*
▲ Northwestern Marble & Granite ....E....952 941-8601
Minneapolis *(G-5246)*
▲ Olympia Tile Inc ....E....763 545-5455
Minneapolis *(G-5274)*
Palmer Soderberg Inc ....E....507 288-4213
Rochester *(G-7200)*
Premier Tile Inc ....E....651 483-1576
Saint Paul *(G-8838)*
◆ Tile Shop LLC ....E....763 541-1444
Minneapolis *(G-5825)*
Twin City Tile & Marble Co Inc ....D....651 602-5800
Saint Paul *(G-9094)*
Vinge Tile ....E....952 431-1000
Farmington *(G-2062)*
Walstad Tile & Stone Co ....E....763 519-1444
Minneapolis *(G-6018)*

1751 Carpentry Work

Advantage Cabinets Inc ....E....507 455-0833
Owatonna *(G-6689)*
Al's Cabinets Inc ....D....952 890-3500
Burnsville *(G-674)*
Alpine Custom Woodworking Inc ....E....320 654-1609
Saint Cloud *(G-7406)*
API Garage Door Co ....E....763 533-3838
Minneapolis *(G-3789)*
Builders & Remodelers Inc ......E....612 827-5481
Minneapolis *(G-3970)*
Cabinets By Choice Inc ....D....952 924-8958
Minneapolis *(G-3989)*
Carpentry Contractors Corp ....D....763 658-4000
Waverly *(G-9902)*
Consolidated Building Corp ....C....612 759-9313
Rosemount *(G-7366)*
Crawford Door Sales Co Twin ....E....651 455-1221
Saint Paul *(G-7739)*
Dave Osborne Construction ....B....763 540-0232
Plymouth *(G-6858)*
Deerwood Builders Inc ....E....218 534-5408
Deerwood *(G-1176)*
Designed Cabinets Inc ....D....952 469-2700
Lakeville *(G-2902)*
Doug Speedling Builders Inc ....D....651 437-3658
Hastings *(G-2384)*
Dura-Supreme Inc ....A....320 543-3872
Howard Lake *(G-2666)*
Ed Lunn Construction Inc ....E....507 533-6565
Stewartville *(G-9591)*
Great Garage Products Inc ......E....763 422-4000
Minneapolis *(G-3478)*
Harmony Homes Inc ....E....763 434-3439
Minneapolis *(G-4599)*
Hetricks Construction Inc ....E....507 645-8629
Northfield *(G-6529)*
Industrial Door Co Inc ....E....763 786-4730
Minneapolis *(G-3497)*
J & L Schwieters Construction ....C....651 762-1110
Hugo *(G-2677)*
J Eiden Construction Inc ....E....651 450-5978
Inver Grove Heights *(G-2756)*
Kendell Doors & Hardware Inc ....E....507 454-1723
Winona *(G-10107)*
L L Hage Seamless Gutters Inc ....E....507 433-1158
Austin *(G-280)*
Les Jones Roofing Inc ....E....952 881-2241
Minneapolis *(G-4863)*
Lipe Brothers Construction Inc ....E....218 525-3364
Duluth *(G-1384)*
Metro Framing Inc ....E....763 785-1482
Minneapolis *(G-3536)*
Metro Siding Inc ....E....763 557-1808
Plymouth *(G-6873)*
North American Framing Inc ....E....763 784-4855
Minneapolis *(G-3558)*
Northside Construction Inc ......E....651 426-2632
Hugo *(G-2680)*
Paul Lesieur ....E....612 788-5584
Minneapolis *(G-5352)*
▼ Plato Woodwork Inc ....C....320 238-2193
Plato *(G-6844)*

Richard Larson Builders Inc ....E....320 587-5555
Hutchinson *(G-2711)*
Ron Boelter Window & Siding ....E....507 243-4354
Madison Lake *(G-3081)*
Ron's Cabinets Inc ....E....320 252-7667
Sauk Rapids *(G-9372)*
Russnick Contractors Inc ....E....763 420-3737
Hamel *(G-2356)*
Seal Guard Systems Inc ....E....612 787-0700
Marine On Saint Croix *(G-3289)*
Sierra Corp of Shoreview ....E....763 783-9616
Anoka *(G-226)*
Swedberg Wood Products Inc ....E....320 762-0738
Alexandria *(G-126)*
Tappe Construction Co ....B....651 994-0200
Saint Paul *(G-7917)*
Taylor Made Construction of MN ....E....952 440-8510
Prior Lake *(G-6957)*
Thomas Grace Construction Inc ....E....651 342-1298
Stillwater *(G-9652)*
Welle Construction Inc ....E....763 427-5830
Anoka *(G-240)*
Wellington Window Co ....D....952 933-2737
Minneapolis *(G-6034)*
Window Concepts of Minnesota ....E....651 905-0105
Saint Paul *(G-7948)*
Wood Products Unlimited Inc ....E....218 829-4353
Brainerd *(G-589)*

1752 Floor Laying & Other Floor Work, NEC

Above All Hardwood Floors LLC ....E....952 440-9663
Prior Lake *(G-6928)*
Architectural Sales of MN ....D....763 533-1595
Minneapolis *(G-3802)*
Becker Bros Inc ....D....651 633-8604
Saint Paul *(G-8097)*
C L T Floor Coverings Inc ....E....651 451-0069
Inver Grove Heights *(G-2740)*
▲ Crew2 Inc ....D....612 276-1600
Minneapolis *(G-4182)*
Dave's Floor Sanding ....D....763 784-3000
Minneapolis *(G-3452)*
Johnson's Carpet Tile ....E....218 628-2249
Duluth *(G-1362)*
Lee's Ceramic Contracting Inc ....D....612 720-1653
Hastings *(G-2395)*
National Floor Maintenance Inc ....E....303 771-0509
Saint Paul *(G-7848)*
Renovation Systems Inc ....E....763 550-9600
Minneapolis *(G-5518)*
St Paul Linoleum & Carpet Co ....D....651 686-7770
Eagan *(G-1553)*
Ziem's Carpet Workroom Inc ....E....952 884-0058
Minneapolis *(G-6118)*

1761 Roofing, Siding & Sheet Metal Work

A W Kuettel & Sons Inc ....D....218 722-3901
Duluth *(G-1231)*
Artco Builders Inc ....E....651 486-0761
Saint Paul *(G-8065)*
B & B Sheet Metal & Roofing ....E....763 682-4233
Buffalo *(G-635)*
Bargen Inc 507 427-2924
Mountain Lake *(G-6395)*
Bernard L Dalsin Inc ....E....952 881-7663
Minneapolis *(G-3888)*
Berwald Roofing Co Inc ....C....651 777-7411
Saint Paul *(G-8107)*
Builders & Remodelers Inc ......E....612 827-5481
Minneapolis *(G-3970)*
Cato Construction Inc ....E....952 736-8134
Savage *(G-9384)*
Central Roofing Inc ....E....763 572-0660
Minneapolis *(G-3432)*
Commercial Roofing Inc ....E....651 483-5298
Saint Paul *(G-8229)*
Corval Constructors Inc ....C....651 642-0451
Saint Paul *(G-8255)*
Cullen's Home Center of ....D....320 762-1249
Alexandria *(G-93)*
Dalbec Roofing Inc ....E....952 473-8080
Long Lake *(G-3023)*
Dalco Roofing & Sheet Metal ....D....763 559-0222
Minneapolis *(G-4220)*
Donlyn Manufacture ....E....763 786-1103
Minneapolis *(G-3459)*
E H Lawrence Co ....E....218 254-5705
Chisholm *(G-996)*
Elastomeric Roofing Systems ....E....763 565-6900
Rockford *(G-7300)*
Excel Air System Inc ....D....651 779-9725
Saint Paul *(G-8351)*
Gag Sheet Metal Inc ....E....507 354-3813
New Ulm *(G-6450)*
Garlock French Roofing Corp ....E....612 722-7129
Minneapolis *(G-4502)*
Gemini 26 Inc ....E....507 334-7951
Faribault *(G-2009)*
Gopher Co Inc ....E....612 331-1555
Minneapolis *(G-4541)*
Herzog Roofing Inc ....E....218 847-1121
Detroit Lakes *(G-1195)*
Horizon Roofing Inc ....E....320 252-1608
Waite Park *(G-9824)*

Innovative Building Concepts ....E....952 885-0262
Minneapolis *(G-4704)*
Installed Building Products ......D....763 441-2313
Elk River *(G-1900)*
John A Dalsin & Son Inc ....C....612 729-9334
Minneapolis *(G-4768)*
L L Hage Seamless Gutters Inc ....E....507 433-1158
Austin *(G-280)*
Larson's Home Improvement ....E....507 288-7111
Rochester *(G-7160)*
Les Jones Roofing Inc ....E....952 881-2241
Minneapolis *(G-4863)*
Lifetime Siding & Remodeling ....E....651 458-0844
Hastings *(G-2417)*
Mc Phillips Bros Roofing Co ....E....651 770-2062
Saint Paul *(G-8621)*
McDowall Co ....D....320 251-8640
Waite Park *(G-9829)*
Merit Contracting Inc ....D....507 281-4317
Rochester *(G-7182)*
Metro Siding Inc ....E....763 557-1808
Plymouth *(G-6873)*
Millers Roofing ....E....218 263-4406
Canyon *(G-865)*
Millers Roofing & Siding Co ....E....218 751-4337
Cotton *(G-1110)*
Minnesota Exteriors Inc ....E....763 493-5500
Osseo *(G-6639)*
Nu-Look Exteriors Inc ....E....952 882-8787
Burnsville *(G-769)*
Palmer West Construction Co ....D....763 428-1867
Rogers *(G-7335)*
Peterson Bros Roofing & Constr ....E....651 488-5630
Saint Paul *(G-8820)*
Probuild Co LLC ....D....320 251-0861
Saint Cloud *(G-7573)*
Range Cornice & Roofing Co ....E....218 263-8812
Hibbing *(G-2470)*
Range Cornice & Roofing Co Inc ....E....218 262-4581
Hibbing *(G-2471)*
Ron Boelter Window & Siding ....E....507 243-4354
Madison Lake *(G-3081)*
Roof Tech Inc ....E....651 351-7302
Stillwater *(G-9636)*
Rosenquist Construction Inc ....E....612 724-1356
Minneapolis *(G-5559)*
Schwickert Co ....D....507 387-3101
Mankato *(G-3193)*
Schwickert Inc ....D....507 387-3106
Mankato *(G-3194)*
Schwickert's of Rochester Inc ....E....507 387-3106
Mankato *(G-3195)*
Seal Guard Systems Inc ....E....612 787-0700
Marine On Saint Croix *(G-3289)*
Sela Roofing & Remodeling Inc ....D....612 823-8046
Minneapolis *(G-5631)*
Sela Roofing & Remodeling Inc ....E....763 592-5420
Minneapolis *(G-5632)*
Sgo Roofing & Construction LLC ....E....952 469-8560
Lakeville *(G-2934)*
Sheridan Sheet Metal Co ....E....763 537-3686
Minneapolis *(G-5654)*
Single-Ply Systems Inc ....D....651 688-7554
Saint Paul *(G-7905)*
Smidt Sheet Metal Co Inc ....E....507 378-4080
Racine *(G-6967)*
SNG Construction Inc ....D....763 795-8496
Minneapolis *(G-3603)*
Top Notch Siding Co ....E....612 269-7923
Osseo *(G-6677)*
Top-All Roofing Inc ....E....651 291-7663
Saint Paul *(G-9071)*
Walker Roofing Co ....E....651 251-0910
Saint Paul *(G-9136)*
Westway Exteriors Inc ....E....651 251-0910
Saint Paul *(G-9151)*
Window Concepts of Minnesota ....E....651 905-0105
Saint Paul *(G-7948)*
▲ Winona Heating & Ventilating ....C....507 452-2064
Winona *(G-10149)*

1771 Concrete Work

A D B Construction Co Inc ......E....763 424-5550
Osseo *(G-6589)*
▲ Acoustics Associates Inc ......C....763 544-8901
Minneapolis *(G-3674)*
Aduddell Industries Inc ....E....651 288-2246
Saint Paul *(G-7985)*
Al Minnerath Inc ....C....320 762-7289
Alexandria *(G-79)*
Alliance Concrete Concepts Inc ....E....507 536-4515
Rochester *(G-7051)*
Anderson Brothers Construction ....C....218 829-1768
Brainerd *(G-549)*
Asphalt & Concrete Buy Knox ....E....612 781-1112
Minneapolis *(G-3820)*
Asphalt Specialties Co 651 484-1696
Saint Paul *(G-8072)*
Berg Exteriors Inc ....E....763 479-1115
Maple Plain *(G-3269)*
Bituminous Roadways Inc ....E....612 721-2451
Minneapolis *(G-3908)*
Bituminous Roadways Inc ....E....952 233-1660
Shakopee *(G-9423)*
Bob Pankan & Sons Concrete ....E....763 444-5720
Isanti *(G-2778)*

(G-00000) Company's Geographic Section entry number
454

2011 Harris Minnesota
Services Directory

▲=Import ▼=Export
◆=Import/Export

C R Fischer & Sons Inc E 651 463-7300 Farmington *(G-2042)*

Camco Construction Inc E 320 259-1051 Saint Cloud *(G-7467)*

Collin Garvey E 651 463-4825 Farmington *(G-2045)*

Commercial Contractors Co of E 320 256-7422 Melrose *(G-3348)*

Concrete Mobility LLC E 952 746-5887 Shakopee *(G-9432)*

Cone Corp E 218 245-2313 Bovey *(G-540)*

Crosstown Masonry Inc E 763 434-6371 Anoka *(G-171)*

Curb Masters Inc E 651 351-9200 Stillwater *(G-9609)*

Dallas I Hanson Construction E 320 839-3455 Ortonville *(G-6582)*

Dayco Concrete Co Inc D 952 556-0278 Chanhassen *(G-918)*

DH Blattner & Sons Inc D 320 356-7351 Avon *(G-294)*

Donnelly Brothers Construction E 612 866-1204 Minneapolis *(G-4278)*

Duluth Superior Erection Inc E 218 626-1112 Duluth *(G-1305)*

Duracoat Inc E 320 587-3135 Hutchinson *(G-2696)*

Engineered Concrete Placer of E 651 452-1183 Saint Paul *(G-7763)*

Evenson Concrete Systems E 507 243-3660 Madison Lake *(G-3079)*

Fabcon Inc C 952 890-4444 Savage *(G-9390)*

Ferber Inc E 320 251-4072 Saint Cloud *(G-7509)*

Fitzgerald Construction E 218 789-7318 Sabin *(G-7397)*

Flint Hills Resources, LP E 507 532-6331 Marshall *(G-3296)*

FPI Paving Contractors Inc E 651 484-0385 Saint Paul *(G-8392)*

Frantz, Donald R Concrete E 952 929-8568 Minneapolis *(G-4476)*

Gordon Lund E 320 275-2006 Dassel *(G-1161)*

Gresser Co's Inc C 651 454-5976 Saint Paul *(G-7793)*

Hage Concrete Works E 651 690-4243 Saint Paul *(G-8438)*

Halverson Concrete Inc E 763 434-0318 Anoka *(G-186)*

Harbor City Masonry Inc D 218 628-3686 Duluth *(G-1347)*

Hi-Tech Floors Inc E 952 895-1602 Burnsville *(G-731)*

Hicks Concrete Construction E 763 420-7755 Hamel *(G-2344)*

Hollenback & Nelson Inc E 763 862-7525 Minneapolis *(G-3489)*

Inside Edge Commercial E 651 389-3900 Eagan *(G-1531)*

Kelleher Construction Corp E 952 890-6772 Burnsville *(G-740)*

Knife Lake Concrete Inc E 320 679-4141 Mora *(G-6363)*

Manor Concrete Construction C 763 497-5420 Saint Michael *(G-7676)*

Met-Con Metro Inc E 952 884-6250 Minneapolis *(G-4998)*

Metro Paving Inc E 763 428-4121 Rogers *(G-7331)*

Minn-Dak Asphalt Inc E 218 281-6840 Thief River Falls *(G-9674)*

North Country Concrete Inc D 763 576-8602 Anoka *(G-209)*

Northland Concrete & Masonry D 952 890-1650 Burnsville *(G-765)*

Northland Constructors of E 218 722-8170 Duluth *(G-1406)*

Northwest Asphalt Inc E 952 445-1003 Shakopee *(G-9461)*

O'Malley Construction Inc E 507 357-6330 Le Center *(G-2953)*

Peck Construction Inc D 763 421-2201 Anoka *(G-214)*

Pine Bend Paving Inc E 651 437-2333 Hastings *(G-2398)*

Progressive Concrete & Masonry E 651 489-2200 Saint Paul *(G-8853)*

Q3 Contracting Inc B 651 224-2424 Saint Paul *(G-8859)*

▼ Ryan Contracting Co C 952 894-3200 Shakopee *(G-9471)*

Salonek Concrete & Constr E 507 723-4218 Springfield *(G-9574)*

Shamrock Enterprises LLC E 507 288-9494 Rochester *(G-7252)*

Stockness Construction Inc E 651 484-1286 Hugo *(G-2683)*

Strongform Inc E 218 462-2607 Deer Creek *(G-1166)*

Superior Masonry & Concrete E 651 786-0884 Anoka *(G-230)*

T & J Concrete & Masonry Inc D 763 413-0988 Minneapolis *(G-3614)*

Tech Restoration Services Inc E 651 292-9638 Saint Paul *(G-9034)*

Themescapes Inc E 651 778-1784 Forest Lake *(G-2170)*

Total Concrete Services E 763 786-8477 Minneapolis *(G-3618)*

Truseal America LLC E 952 895-9197 Eagan *(G-1558)*

W E Nelson Stucco Co E 763 377-3631 Saint Paul *(G-9134)*

Web Construction Co Inc E 507 387-1667 Mankato *(G-3214)*

Winco Landscape Inc E 651 455-3070 Inver Grove Heights *(G-2774)*

Young & Davis Drywall Inc E 218 751-6048 Bemidji *(G-434)*

1781 Water Well Drilling

Bergerson-Caswell Inc E 763 479-3121 Maple Plain *(G-3270)*

Keys Well Drilling Co Inc E 651 646-7871 Saint Paul *(G-8547)*

Minnesota Water Well Assn E 651 290-6270 Saint Paul *(G-8710)*

Thein Well Co E 763 271-4200 Monticello *(G-6290)*

1791 Structural Steel Erection

Advanced Process Technologies D 320 286-5060 Cokato *(G-1074)*

Bald Eagle Erectors Inc E 651 405-9050 Saint Paul *(G-7710)*

Brown Tank LLC D 651 747-0100 Saint Paul *(G-9189)*

Danny's Construction Co Inc C 952 445-4143 Shakopee *(G-9435)*

Engineering America Inc E 651 777-4041 Saint Paul *(G-9214)*

Hawk & Sons Inc E 507 285-0508 Rochester *(G-7134)*

John Pulsifer Construction Inc E 320 354-2602 New London *(G-6415)*

Northern Industrial Erectors D 218 326-8466 Grand Rapids *(G-2300)*

▲ Sowles Co C 651 287-9700 Saint Paul *(G-7910)*

Stencil Cutting & Supply Co D 800 783-4633 Red Wing *(G-7007)*

Strongform Inc E 218 462-2607 Deer Creek *(G-1166)*

Web Construction Co Inc E 507 387-1667 Mankato *(G-3214)*

Western Steel Erection Inc E 952 473-4344 Long Lake *(G-3035)*

Ww Constructors Inc E 763 420-4177 Hamel *(G-2362)*

1793 Glass & Glazing Work

ACG Inc D 651 488-0574 Saint Paul *(G-7688)*

▲ Brin Glass Co C 612 529-9671 Minneapolis *(G-3949)*

Egan Co D 763 567-0025 Plymouth *(G-6861)*

Empire Door & Glass Co E 612 729-4003 Minneapolis *(G-4349)*

▲ Enclos Corp D 651 796-6100 Saint Paul *(G-7761)*

Minneapolis Glass Co D 763 559-0635 Plymouth *(G-6874)*

Mulcahy Inc C 651 770-5250 Mahtomedi *(G-3095)*

St Germain's Glass Inc E 218 628-0221 Duluth *(G-1461)*

Superior Glass Duluth E 218 722-7400 Duluth *(G-1478)*

Twin City Glass Contractors E 651 746-0650 Saint Paul *(G-9092)*

United Glass Inc E 651 633-2529 Saint Paul *(G-9105)*

Willet Hauser Architectural E 507 457-3500 Winona *(G-10141)*

1794 Excavating & Grading Work

Ames Construction Inc B 952 435-7106 Burnsville *(G-676)*

BCM Construction Inc E 507 333-1155 Faribault *(G-1991)*

Billington Contracting Inc E 218 722-1213 Duluth *(G-1252)*

Bnr Excavating Inc E 651 438-8692 Hampton *(G-2363)*

Carl Bolander & Sons Co D 651 224-6299 Saint Paul *(G-8165)*

Chad Monson Excavating LLC D 320 995-6703 Willmar *(G-9996)*

Chard Tiling & Excavating Inc D 952 873-6152 Belle Plaine *(G-372)*

Christiansen Industrial E 218 751-4663 Bemidji *(G-384)*

Columbia Building Services Inc E 612 331-2090 Minneapolis *(G-4124)*

D & G Excavating Inc E 507 532-2334 Marshall *(G-3292)*

D L R Excavating Inc D 651 437-3128 Hastings *(G-2380)*

Davidson Construction Inc E 218 449-4865 Holt *(G-2494)*

Dennis Fehn Gravel E 763 497-2428 Albertville *(G-73)*

Dlo Excavating & Poured Walls E 651 480-8457 Hastings *(G-2414)*

Doboszenski & Sons Inc E 763 478-6945 Loretto *(G-3046)*

Engstrom Excavating Inc E 651 437-2782 Hastings *(G-2386)*

Ferguson Brothers Excavating E 320 762-0622 Alexandria *(G-101)*

Fraser Construction Co E 507 288-6583 Rochester *(G-7120)*

Frattalone Co's Inc C 651 484-0448 Saint Paul *(G-8394)*

Friedges Landscaping Inc E 952 469-2996 Lakeville *(G-2908)*

Frontier Construction Co Inc E 218 246-9512 Deer River *(G-1172)*

Geldner Construction Inc E 507 931-4230 Saint Peter *(G-9304)*

Glenn Rehbein Excavating Inc C 763 784-0657 Minneapolis *(G-3475)*

Gordon Construction Inc E 218 935-2191 Mahnomen *(G-3086)*

Gustafson Excavating Inc E 651 674-7430 North Branch *(G-6500)*

Hammerlund Construction Inc E 218 326-1881 Grand Rapids *(G-2283)*

Hartman Co's Inc E 952 443-2958 Victoria *(G-9729)*

Hoffman Construction Co E 507 794-5230 Sleepy Eye *(G-9496)*

Imperial Developers Inc D 651 454-3330 Saint Paul *(G-7802)*

Ingram Excavating Inc D 952 934-0917 Eden Prairie *(G-1693)*

Jay Bros Inc E 651 464-6400 Forest Lake *(G-2147)*

K A Witt Construction Inc E 952 758-2108 New Prague *(G-6429)*

Kamish Excavating Inc E 651 457-3600 South Saint Paul *(G-9532)*

L & S Construction E 507 648-3382 Sanborn *(G-9318)*

Lakehead Trucking Inc E 218 721-3521 Duluth *(G-1379)*

Landwehr Construction Inc E 320 252-1494 Saint Cloud *(G-7542)*

M M Miller Brothers Excavating E 763 420-9170 Hamel *(G-2349)*

MR Paving & Excavating Inc D 507 354-4171 New Ulm *(G-6464)*

Nadeau Excavating Inc E 651 438-8628 Hampton *(G-2366)*

Nedeau Inc E 651 438-8628 Hampton *(G-2367)*

Niles - Wiese Construction Co E 507 446-0825 Medford *(G-3344)*

North Pine Aggregate Inc D 651 464-6802 Forest Lake *(G-2149)*

R & G Construction Co E 507 537-1473 Marshall *(G-3323)*

R J Zavoral Ed's Construction D 218 773-0586 East Grand Forks *(G-1575)*

Rachel Contracting LLC E 763 424-9955 Saint Michael *(G-7681)*

Ramsey Excavating Co E 612 529-0077 Minneapolis *(G-5465)*

Randy Kramer Excavating Inc E 320 764-6871 Watkins *(G-9899)*

Stocker Excavating Inc E 952 890-4241 Savage *(G-9408)*

Thygeson Construction Co E 218 681-1924 Thief River Falls *(G-9679)*

Tms Construction Inc E 952 226-6300 Prior Lake *(G-6959)*

Trentroy Corp D 952 445-3820 Jordan *(G-2811)*

Triple D Construction E 218 465-4249 Oklee *(G-6558)*

Trout Enterprises Inc of Nthn E 218 246-8165 Deer River *(G-1174)*

Turner Excavating Co D 952 890-1645 Savage *(G-9410)*

Western Walls Inc E 507 282-4624 Rochester *(G-7292)*

1795 Wrecking & Demolition Work

Carl Bolander & Sons Co D 651 224-6299 Saint Paul *(G-8165)*

Century Construction Co Inc E 651 451-1020 South Saint Paul *(G-9518)*

Deconstruction Services E 888 224-2608 Minneapolis *(G-4239)*

Frattalone Co's Inc C 651 484-0448 Saint Paul *(G-8394)*

Hengel Landfill & Service Corp E 218 746-3198 Pillager *(G-6809)*

Landwehr Construction Inc E 320 252-1494 Saint Cloud *(G-7542)*

Lloyds Construction Services E 952 746-5832 Savage *(G-9397)*

Employment codes: A=Over 500 employees, B=251-500
C=101-250, D=51-100, E=25-50

2011 Harris Minnesota
Services Directory

© Harris InfoSource 1-866-281-6415

455

Rachel Contracting LLC ....E....763 424-9955
Saint Michael *(G-7681)*
▲ Veit & Co Inc ....C....763 428-2242
Rogers *(G-7347)*

1796 Installation Or Erection Of Bldg Eqpt & Machinery, NEC

A J Lysne Contracting Corp....D....507 451-7121
Owatonna *(G-6688)*
Alltech Engineering Corp....D....651 452-7893
Saint Paul *(G-7693)*
Corval Constructors Inc....C....651 642-0451
Saint Paul *(G-8255)*
Godbout's Viking Intallation....E....218 879-2199
Cloquet *(G-1054)*
J & D Construction Inc....E....320 269-2101
Montevideo *(G-6247)*
K & S Millwrights Inc....E....320 833-2228
Buffalo Lake *(G-665)*
Lovegreen Industrial Services....D....651 890-1166
Saint Paul *(G-7825)*
◆ Minnesota Elevator Inc....C....507 245-3060
Mankato *(G-3171)*
Neufeldt Industrial Services....E....651 388-4347
Red Wing *(G-6993)*
Northern Industrial Erectors....D....218 326-8466
Grand Rapids *(G-2300)*
Pump & Meter Service Inc....E....952 933-4800
Hopkins *(G-2608)*
R & O Elevator Co Inc....D....612 588-7844
Minneapolis *(G-5454)*

1799 Special Trade Contractors, NEC

A J Spanjers Co Inc....E....763 424-8288
Minneapolis *(G-3648)*
All Furniture Installation Inc....E....763 571-2203
Minneapolis *(G-3710)*
All Poolside Services Inc....E....651 483-6600
Saint Paul *(G-8011)*
Amtech Lighting Services Co....E....651 439-7440
Stillwater *(G-9595)*
◆ API Group Inc....E....651 636-4320
Saint Paul *(G-8054)*
Arch Insurance Group Inc....E....651 855-7100
Saint Paul *(G-8059)*
Atlantis Pools Inc....E....763 560-0103
Minneapolis *(G-3831)*
▲ Atomic Props & Effects Ltd....E....612 331-1335
Saint Paul *(G-9185)*
Automotive Restyling Concepts....D....763 535-2181
Minneapolis *(G-3840)*
AWI Manufacturing Inc....E....320 485-2471
Winsted *(G-10157)*
Bargen Inc....507 427-2924
Mountain Lake *(G-6395)*
Bituminous Roadways Inc....E....612 721-2451
Minneapolis *(G-3908)*
Bituminous Roadways Inc....E....952 233-1660
Shakopee *(G-9423)*
Blake Drilling Co Inc....E....763 780-9187
Minneapolis *(G-3420)*
Bloomington Linoleum & Carpet....E....952 881-5825
Minneapolis *(G-3917)*
C C C T Inc....E....952 844-0004
Minneapolis *(G-3982)*
▲ Capital Granite & Marble Inc....E....320 259-7625
Saint Cloud *(G-7469)*
Ceco Concrete Construction DE....D....763 434-4637
Anoka *(G-162)*
Ceiling Pro Interior Inc....E....952 947-0007
Eden Prairie *(G-1617)*
Code Welding & Mfg Inc....E....763 792-6632
Minneapolis *(G-3435)*
Construction Labor Force Inc....E....651 786-0550
Circle Pines *(G-1006)*
CS McCrossan Inc....C....763 425-4167
Osseo *(G-6606)*
Custom Plastic Laminates Inc....E....612 781-8191
Minneapolis *(G-4205)*
Dakota Unlimited Inc....E....651 423-3995
Rosemount *(G-7368)*
Dan Larson Enterprises Inc....E....612 331-8550
Minneapolis *(G-4222)*
Dennis Co's Inc....E....651 488-4835
Saint Paul *(G-8287)*
Diversified Contracting Inc....E....763 712-8087
Anoka *(G-175)*
Dolphin Pools Inc....E....763 542-9000
Plymouth *(G-6860)*
Dustcoating Inc....E....952 894-0012
Savage *(G-9389)*
Dvcm ServiceMaster of The....E....320 763-5551
Alexandria *(G-96)*
E H Lawrence Co....E....218 254-5705
Chisholm *(G-996)*
Energy Conservation Inc....E....763 569-0069
Minneapolis *(G-4355)*
Envirobate Inc....C....612 729-1080
Minneapolis *(G-4361)*
Friedges Contracting Co LLC....E....952 469-2121
Lakeville *(G-2907)*
Great Northern Resources Inc....E....952 848-0984
Minneapolis *(G-4556)*
Griffin Petroleum Services Inc....E....763 780-6332
Minneapolis *(G-3479)*
H & R Const Co....E....218 589-8707
Dalton *(G-1156)*
Heat & Frost Insulators Asbes....D....218 724-3223
Duluth *(G-1350)*
Idea Drilling LLC....D....218 741-9287
Virginia *(G-9740)*
Idea Inc....E....218 741-9287
Virginia *(G-9741)*
Innovative Surfaces Inc....E....651 437-1004
Hastings *(G-2393)*
Kusske Mechanical Inc....E....651 437-8404
Hastings *(G-2394)*
Larson's Home Improvement....E....507 288-7111
Rochester *(G-7160)*
Lemaster Restoration Inc....E....952 707-1256
Burnsville *(G-748)*
Lloyds Construction Services....E....952 746-5832
Savage *(G-9397)*
Lsa LLC....E....763 744-0246
Plymouth *(G-6871)*
Maciej Paint Corp....E....651 407-8000
Hugo *(G-2679)*
Marathon Group Inc....D....952 929-1990
Minneapolis *(G-4945)*
Mavo Systems Inc....C....763 788-7713
Saint Paul *(G-8618)*
Merit Contracting Inc....D....507 281-4317
Rochester *(G-7182)*
Meyer Contracting Inc....E....763 391-5959
Maple Grove *(G-3250)*
Minnesota Department of....E....320 384-6591
Hinckley *(G-2487)*
Minnesota Residential Aquatics....651 439-8467
Stillwater *(G-9629)*
Mulcahy Inc....C....651 770-5250
Mahtomedi *(G-3095)*
Nordquist Sign Co....E....612 823-7291
Minneapolis *(G-5208)*
▲ Northern Dewatering Inc....D....763 428-2616
Rogers *(G-7332)*
Northside Service Center....E....612 370-4902
Minneapolis *(G-5237)*
▲ Par Nuclear Holding Co Inc....651 278-0007
Saint Paul *(G-8805)*
▲ Park Waite Manufacturing Inc....C....320 251-8616
Waite Park *(G-9830)*
Performance Pool & Spa Inc....E....651 731-3440
Saint Paul *(G-9259)*
Petratech Inc....E....952 897-0475
Minneapolis *(G-5371)*
Premier Electrical Corp....C....763 424-6551
Brooklyn Park *(G-617)*
Pump & Meter Service Inc....E....952 933-4800
Hopkins *(G-2608)*
Quantum Co's Inc....E....952 943-4357
Minneapolis *(G-5445)*
Ram Construction Services of....E....651 765-1950
Little Canada *(G-2997)*
Rayco Construction Inc....E....612 788-0077
Minneapolis *(G-5470)*
Regional Home Services of Minn....E....763 416-5607
Hamel *(G-2355)*
Reliakor Services Inc....E....952 403-1440
Shakopee *(G-9469)*
Renew Services Inc....E....651 699-3504
Saint Paul *(G-8889)*
Restoration Professionals Inc....D....651 379-1990
Saint Paul *(G-8895)*
Rick Pavek Construction....E....507 663-0804
Northfield *(G-6519)*
Rollie's Sales & Service Inc....E....320 859-4811
Osakis *(G-6587)*
Ron Boelter Window & Siding....E....507 243-4354
Madison Lake *(G-3081)*
Rusciano-Hyland Inc....E....612 871-4434
Minneapolis *(G-5576)*
Safe Step Inc....E....952 229-8282
Savage *(G-9406)*
▲ Safety Signs Inc....E....952 469-6700
Lakeville *(G-2930)*
Secoa Inc....D....763 506-8800
Champlin *(G-900)*
St Germain's Cabinet Inc....E....218 624-1234
Duluth *(G-1460)*
Standard Water Control Systems....E....763 537-4849
Minneapolis *(G-5738)*
Sterling Systems Inc....E....952 697-1060
Long Lake *(G-3033)*
▲ Stone Source Inc....763 540-9000
Plymouth *(G-6884)*
Stone Systems & Services Inc....D....651 683-9672
Saint Paul *(G-7913)*
Sustainable Resources Center....E....612 870-4255
Minneapolis *(G-5776)*
Tavis Metal & Fabrication Corp....E....763 428-8483
Rogers *(G-7342)*
Tech Restoration Services Inc....E....651 292-9638
Saint Paul *(G-9034)*
TMI Coatings Inc....D....651 452-6100
Saint Paul *(G-7925)*
Town & Country Fence Inc....E....763 425-5050
Minneapolis *(G-5841)*
Tri-State Drilling Inc....D....763 553-1234
Minneapolis *(G-5852)*
Twin City Custom Railings & GL....E....763 780-7314
Minneapolis *(G-3624)*
VSI Construction Inc....E....763 493-3000
Maple Grove *(G-3257)*
Waterproofing By Experts Inc....E....651 786-5042
Circle Pines *(G-1025)*
Watson's of Minneapolis Inc....E....763 560-7727
Minneapolis *(G-6024)*
Western Waterproofing Co Inc....E....612 781-7100
Minneapolis *(G-6061)*
Westside Equipment Installers....E....763 478-9572
Hamel *(G-2360)*

40 RAILROAD TRANSPORTATION

4011 Railroads, Line-Hauling Operations

Bnsf Railway Co....D....218 894-1676
Verndale *(G-9724)*
Bnsf Railway Co....C....651 298-2121
Saint Paul *(G-8116)*
Bnsf Railway Co....C....651 451-1312
South Saint Paul *(G-9514)*
Bnsf Railway Co....C....651 298-2121
Minneapolis *(G-3421)*
Canadian Pacific Railroad....E....320 634-3307
Glenwood *(G-2220)*
CP Rail System SOO Line....E....320 634-3307
Glenwood *(G-2221)*
Dakota, Minnesota & Eastern....D....507 835-4185
Waseca *(G-9875)*
Greg Haug....E....218 727-8578
Duluth *(G-1344)*
Hennepin County....E....612 348-9260
Minneapolis *(G-4631)*
Minnesota Dakota & Western....E....218 285-5690
International Falls *(G-2727)*
Minnesota Northern Railroad....E....218 281-4704
Crookston *(G-1128)*
Red River Valley & Western....E....218 643-4994
Breckenridge *(G-599)*
Soo Line Corp....D....612 337-5333
Minneapolis *(G-5700)*
SOO Line Railroad Co Inc....A....651 646-6044
Saint Paul *(G-8971)*
SOO Line Railroad Co Inc....E....320 634-3012
Glenwood *(G-2233)*
SOO Line Railroad Co Inc....B....800 766-4357
Minneapolis *(G-5701)*
Twin Cities & Western Railroad....E....320 864-7200
Glencoe *(G-2216)*
Union Pacific Railroad Co....B....507 452-4337
Winona *(G-10134)*
Union Pacific Railroad Co Inc....C....651 552-3925
South Saint Paul *(G-9546)*

4013 Switching & Terminal Svcs

Bnsf Railway Co....C....320 259-3208
Saint Cloud *(G-7462)*
Bnsf Railway Co....E....218 727-8194
Duluth *(G-1255)*
Ibt Consolidated Inc....E....218 285-5290
International Falls *(G-2721)*
Minnesota Commercial Railway....D....651 646-2010
Saint Paul *(G-8678)*
Minnesota Dakota & Western....E....218 285-5690
International Falls *(G-2727)*
Minnesota Prairie Line Inc....E....320 864-7200
Glencoe *(G-2211)*
Twin Cities & Western Railroad....E....320 864-7200
Glencoe *(G-2216)*
Union Pacific Railroad Co....B....507 452-4337
Winona *(G-10134)*
Wisconsin Central Ltd....E....651 633-8771
Saint Paul *(G-9161)*

41 LOCAL & SUBURBAN TRANSIT & HIGHWAY TRANSPORTATION

4111 Local & Suburban Transit

Darts....C....651 455-1560
Saint Paul *(G-7748)*
Duluth Transit Authority....D....218 722-7283
Duluth *(G-1306)*
Dunn Enterprises Inc....C....612 627-5661
Minneapolis *(G-4297)*
E Z Air Park Inc....E....651 454-1302
Saint Paul *(G-7754)*
First Student Inc....C....651 628-0046
Saint Paul *(G-8381)*
Metropolitan Transit Commn....C....612 341-4287
Minneapolis *(G-5010)*
Minnesota Department of Trans....A....612 349-7332
Minneapolis *(G-5074)*
Osseo Brooklyn School Bus Co....C....763 425-2542
Osseo *(G-6647)*
R&S Transport Inc....D....507 289-5080
Rochester *(G-7215)*
Robert Lemieur & Sons Inc....E....320 632-9141
Little Falls *(G-3018)*
Rochester City Line Co....E....507 288-4353
Rochester *(G-7230)*
Safari Airport Taxi Service....D....763 424-9070
Minneapolis *(G-5587)*

(G-00000) Company's Geographic Section entry number
456
2011 Harris Minnesota Services Directory
▲=Import ▼=Export ◆=Import/Export

S I C

Supershuttle Minnesota Inc ....E....612 827-7777
Saint Paul (G-7965)
Taylor Limousines Inc ....C....612 722-4467
Minneapolis (G-5795)

4119 Local Passenger Transportation: NEC

AC Transportation Inc ....E....763 235-2222
Osseo (G-6591)
Care Transportation Inc ....E....320 253-7729
Saint Cloud (G-7470)
City of Plainview Ambulance ....E....507 534-3980
Plainview (G-6840)
County of Washington ....B....651 439-9381
Stillwater (G-9606)
Critical Care Services Inc ....C....612 638-4900
Minneapolis (G-4185)
Crosby Ironton Transportation ....E....218 546-6156
Crosby (G-1146)
Dodge Center Ambulance Svcs ....E....507 374-2600
Dodge Center (G-1226)
Dunn Enterprises Inc ....C....612 627-5661
Minneapolis (G-4297)
Eclipse Transportation Inc ....E....651 293-1111
Saint Paul (G-7757)
Gold Cross Ambulance Service ....D....320 251-2302
Saint Cloud (G-7518)
Gold Cross Ambulance Service ....D....218 628-2885
Duluth (G-1336)
Gold Cross Ambulance Service ....D....507 255-2230
Rochester (G-7127)
Gold Cross Ambulance Service ....E....507 345-7540
Mankato (G-3130)
Grove Cottage Emergency Med ....D....651 458-2865
Cottage Grove (G-1103)
Healtheast ....C....651 232-1717
Saint Paul (G-8452)
International Falls, City of ....E....218 283-3500
International Falls (G-2723)
Jackson City Ambulance ....E....507 847-5306
Jackson (G-2794)
Kittson Memorial Hospital Assn ....C....218 843-3612
Hallock (G-2333)
Lake County Ambulance ....E....218 834-7110
Two Harbors (G-9710)
Lake of Woods Ambulance ....E....218 634-2100
Baudette (G-316)
Lakes Medi-Van Inc ....C....218 847-1729
Detroit Lakes (G-1204)
Lakes Region EMS Inc ....E....651 277-4911
North Branch (G-6502)
Le Center Volunteer Ambulance ....E....507 357-4844
Le Center (G-2951)
Mahnomen County Heartland ....E....218 935-2560
Mahnomen (G-3088)
Mayo Midair ....E....507 255-2808
Rochester (G-7176)
Meds 1 Ambulance Service Inc ....E....218 326-0020
Grand Rapids (G-2293)
Metropolitan Transportation ....D....763 571-1541
Minneapolis (G-3541)
Monticello-Big Lake Community ....B....763 295-2945
Monticello (G-6278)
Norman County Ambulance Garage ....C....218 784-5000
ADA (G-2)
North Ambulance Faribault ....E....507 334-6031
Faribault (G-2023)
North Memorial Ambulance ....E....651 464-6738
Forest Lake (G-2166)
North Memorial Ambulance Svcs ....D....763 389-2082
Princeton (G-6912)
North Memorial Health Care ....E....320 763-6160
Alexandria (G-115)
North Memorial Health Care ....D....218 829-8767
Brainerd (G-577)
North Memorial Health Care ....E....507 637-5055
Redwood Falls (G-7026)
Northland Transportation ....E....952 885-0580
Prior Lake (G-6946)
Northland Transportation Inc ....E....952 922-6876
Burnsville (G-766)
Oakdale Health Enterprises Inc ....E....763 520-5357
Minneapolis (G-5256)
On Movin Inc ....E....763 784-7111
Minneapolis (G-3560)
Palmer Bus Service of Bold MN ....E....507 386-0210
Olivia (G-6562)
Peace Transportation Inc ....D....952 595-9030
Minneapolis (G-5358)
Ready Bus Line Co Inc ....D....507 895-2349
La Crescent (G-2843)
Shubat Transportation Co ....E....218 262-1042
Hibbing (G-2475)
Spring Valley Area Ambulance ....E....507 346-7414
Spring Valley (G-9570)
St Peter, City of Inc ....C....507 931-7354
Saint Peter (G-9314)
Star Limousine Service ....E....507 281-0969
Rochester (G-7263)
Taylor Limousines Inc ....C....612 722-4467
Minneapolis (G-5795)
Total Transportation Corp ....E....651 770-5668
Saint Paul (G-9074)
Transit Team Inc ....E....612 332-3323
Minneapolis (G-5847)
Tri County Ambulance Service ....E....218 436-2230
Karlstad (G-2816)
Twin City Limousine ....C....651 222-8553
Saint Paul (G-9093)
U Save Lease & Rental Inc ....E....218 732-3347
Park Rapids (G-6764)
Wabasha City Ambulance Svc ....E....651 565-2633
Wabasha (G-9773)
Walker Ambulance Service ....E....218 547-5500
Walker (G-9860)
Zumbrota Area Ambulance Assn ....E....507 732-7845
Zumbrota (G-10221)

4121 Taxi Cabs

Care Transportation Inc ....E....320 253-7729
Saint Cloud (G-7470)
Fast Cab Services LLC ....D....952 393-8542
Minneapolis (G-4416)

4131 Intercity & Rural Bus Transportation

Anoka County Traveler ....E....763 323-5222
Minneapolis (G-3405)
Bauck Busing Ltd ....E....218 346-4599
Perham (G-6794)
First Student Inc ....C....651 628-0046
Saint Paul (G-8381)
Jefferson Partners LP ....C....612 359-3400
Minneapolis (G-4757)
Miller Medi Van Inc ....E....612 332-2888
Minneapolis (G-5044)
Red River Trails Inc ....E....218 236-0300
Moorhead (G-6337)
Rochester City Line Co ....E....507 288-4353
Rochester (G-7230)
St Louis Park Transportation ....E....952 591-1538
Minneapolis (G-5727)

4141 Local Bus Charter Svc

Albert Lea Bus Co Inc ....E....507 373-1467
Albert Lea (G-30)
Austin Coaches Inc ....E....507 433-5358
Austin (G-259)
Jefferson Partners LP ....C....612 359-3400
Minneapolis (G-4757)
Lorenz Bus Service Inc ....D....763 784-7196
Minneapolis (G-3522)
Manske Bus Service Inc ....E....507 243-3282
Madison Lake (G-3080)
Minnesota City Bus Service Inc ....E....507 454-5871
Minnesota City (G-6136)
Minnetonka Transportation Inc ....D....952 935-1990
Minnetonka (G-6199)
Osseo Brooklyn School Bus Co ....C....763 425-2542
Osseo (G-6647)
Palmer Charter Service Inc ....E....320 632-1555
Little Falls (G-3017)
Reading Bus Line Inc ....E....507 926-5404
Reading (G-6970)
Ready Bus Line Co Inc ....D....507 895-2349
La Crescent (G-2843)
Reichert Enterprises Inc ....C....218 829-6955
Brainerd (G-584)
Southwest Coaches Inc ....D....507 532-4043
Marshall (G-3328)
Trobec's Bus Service Inc ....D....320 251-1202
Saint Stephen (G-9317)

4142 Bus Charter Service, Except Local

Brainerd Bus Lines Inc ....D....218 829-6955
Baxter (G-321)
Crystal Lake Bus Service Inc ....E....507 243-3282
Madison Lake (G-3078)
Faribault Transportation Co ....E....507 334-5121
Faribault (G-2005)
First Student Inc ....C....763 559-8111
Saint Paul (G-8383)
Jefferson Partners LP ....C....612 359-3400
Minneapolis (G-4757)
L C S Coaches Inc ....E....218 879-3391
Cloquet (G-1055)
Marschall Bus Service Inc ....D....952 463-8689
Farmington (G-2054)
Metropolitan School & Charter ....C....218 724-1707
Duluth (G-1392)
Minn-Dakota Coaches Inc ....E....218 739-3393
Fergus Falls (G-2095)
New Ulm Bus Lines Inc ....E....507 354-4711
New Ulm (G-6465)
Northfield Lines Inc ....E....507 645-5267
Northfield (G-6518)
Ossel Brooklyn Bus Co Inc ....D....952 891-1031
Saint Paul (G-7861)
Ottertail Coaches Inc ....D....218 739-3393
Fergus Falls (G-2112)
Owatonna Bus Co Inc ....D....507 451-5262
Owatonna (G-6725)
Palmer Bus Service Inc ....E....320 634-3272
Glenwood (G-2229)
Palmer Bus Service of Mankato ....E....507 386-0210
Mankato (G-3230)
Palmer Bus Service of N ....E....320 632-1555
Little Falls (G-3016)
Palmer Charter Service Inc ....E....320 632-1555
Little Falls (G-3017)
Peterson Bus Service Inc ....D....320 354-2414
New London (G-6418)
Ready Bus Line Co Inc ....D....507 895-2349
La Crescent (G-2843)
Red River Trails Inc ....E....218 236-0300
Moorhead (G-6337)
Richards Transportation Svc ....E....218 233-3404
Moorhead (G-6338)
Richfield Bus Co ....E....952 881-1111
Minneapolis (G-5538)
Rochester City Line Co ....E....507 288-4353
Rochester (G-7230)
Shubat Transportation Co ....E....218 262-1042
Hibbing (G-2475)
Southwest Coaches Inc ....D....507 532-4043
Marshall (G-3328)
Thielen Bus Lines Inc ....E....507 637-3600
Redwood Falls (G-7028)
Town & Country Bus Co Inc ....D....763 786-2510
Minneapolis (G-3620)
Trobec's Bus Service Inc ....D....320 251-1202
Saint Stephen (G-9317)
Voigt's Bus Service Inc ....D....320 252-1807
Saint Cloud (G-7626)
Voigt's Motorcoach Travel Inc ....C....320 253-0510
Saint Cloud (G-7627)
Voigt's of Waconia ....E....952 442-2818
Waconia (G-9794)

4151 School Buses

▲ Advance America Services Inc ....E....952 544-7273
Minneapolis (G-3685)
Albert Lea Bus Co Inc ....E....507 373-1467
Albert Lea (G-30)
Anderson Bus & Coach Inc ....D....218 334-3171
Frazee (G-2182)
Benjamin Bus Inc ....D....507 645-5720
Northfield (G-6516)
Bernard Bus Service Inc ....E....507 867-3410
Chatfield (G-987)
Brown Transportation Inc ....E....218 744-2888
Eveleth (G-1929)
Christianson Bus Service Inc ....E....218 863-7000
Pelican Rapids (G-6776)
Clemons Bus Line Inc ....E....507 833-4438
Waseca (G-9874)
Cloquet Transit Co Inc ....E....218 879-3391
Cloquet (G-1049)
Don's Bus Service Inc ....E....763 497-2585
Albertville (G-74)
Faribault Transportation Co ....E....507 334-5121
Faribault (G-2005)
First Student Inc ....C....507 289-4541
Rochester (G-7114)
First Student Inc ....E....763 389-2342
Princeton (G-6909)
First Student Inc ....D....763 421-5785
Champlin (G-893)
First Student Inc ....D....763 682-5530
Buffalo (G-644)
First Student Inc ....E....763 717-9447
Minneapolis (G-3469)
First Student Inc ....C....651 645-1959
Saint Paul (G-8382)
First Student Inc ....C....763 559-8111
Saint Paul (G-8383)
First Student Inc ....C....763 421-3199
Anoka (G-182)
First Student Inc ....E....952 475-0038
Long Lake (G-3024)
Guardian School Bus Co ....E....320 259-8225
Saint Cloud (G-7438)
Hoglund Transportation Inc ....D....763 295-3604
Monticello (G-6274)
Independent School District ....D....320 762-2148
Alexandria (G-105)
Isensee Bus Service ....E....320 732-2795
Long Prairie (G-3043)
Luverne Ind School Dist 2184 ....E....507 283-8197
Luverne (G-3061)
M & M Bus Service Inc ....E....320 274-8313
Annandale (G-142)
Manske Bus Service Inc ....E....507 243-3282
Madison Lake (G-3080)
Metropolitan School & Charter ....C....218 724-1707
Duluth (G-1392)
Midwest Motor & Equipment Inc ....E....952 955-1962
Watertown (G-9892)
Minnesota City Bus Service Inc ....E....507 454-5871
Minnesota City (G-6136)
Minnesota Motor Bus Inc ....E....507 238-4454
Fairmont (G-1977)
Minnetonka Transportation Inc ....D....952 935-1990
Minnetonka (G-6199)
New Ulm Bus Lines Inc ....E....507 354-4711
New Ulm (G-6465)
Ossel Brooklyn Bus Co Inc ....D....952 891-1031
Saint Paul (G-7861)
Osseo Brooklyn School Bus Co ....C....763 425-2542
Osseo (G-6647)
Ottertail Coaches Inc ....D....218 739-3393
Fergus Falls (G-2112)
Owatonna Bus Co Inc ....D....507 451-5262
Owatonna (G-6725)
Palmer Bus Service ....E....320 847-3109
Clara City (G-1032)

S I C

Employment codes: A=Over 500 employees, B=251-500
C=101-250, D=51-100, E=25-50
2011 Harris Minnesota
Services Directory
© Harris InfoSource 1-866-281-6415
457

Palmer Bus Service....E....320 528-2670
Barrett (G-309)

Palmer Bus Service Inc....E....507 477-3014
Hayfield (G-2425)

Palmer Bus Service of St....E....507 931-1811
Saint Peter (G-9311)

Palmer Bus Services....E....952 445-1166
Shakopee (G-9465)

Palmer Charter Service Inc....E....320 632-1555
Little Falls (G-3017)

Peterson Bus Princeton....D....763 631-5315
Princeton (G-6914)

Peterson Bus Service Inc....D....320 354-2414
New London (G-6418)

Prior Lake Bus Association....D....952 440-1166
Prior Lake (G-6949)

Ready Bus Line Co Inc....D....507 895-2349
La Crescent (G-2843)

Red River Trails Inc....E....218 236-0300
Moorhead (G-6337)

Rehbein Transit Inc....C....651 484-1809
Circle Pines (G-1021)

Reichert Enterprises Inc....C....218 829-6955
Brainerd (G-584)

Richmond Bus Service Inc....E....320 597-2055
Richmond (G-7041)

Safe-Way Bus Co....D....651 451-1375
Inver Grove Heights (G-2767)

Shubat Transportation Co....E....218 262-1042
Hibbing (G-2475)

Southwest Coaches Inc....D....507 532-4043
Marshall (G-3328)

Spanier Bus Service Inc....E....320 251-3313
Saint Cloud (G-7596)

St James Bus Service Inc....E....507 375-4181
Saint James (G-7646)

Stahlke Bus Service Inc....E....763 972-3991
Delano (G-1183)

Stier Transport Services Inc....E....952 873-2362
Belle Plaine (G-371)

Thielen Bus Lines Inc....E....507 637-3600
Redwood Falls (G-7028)

Town & Country Bus Co Inc....D....763 786-2510
Minneapolis (G-3620)

Trobec's Bus Service Inc....D....320 251-1202
Saint Stephen (G-9317)

Vision of Elk River Inc....C....763 441-4420
Elk River (G-1895)

Yaeger Bus Service Inc....E....507 345-5470
Mankato (G-3221)

4173 Bus Terminal & Svc Facilities

Minnesota Department of Trans....C....218 828-2678
Baxter (G-337)

Minnesota Department of Trans....A....612 349-7332
Minneapolis (G-5074)

42 MOTOR FREIGHT TRANSPORTATION & WAREHOUSING

4212 Local Trucking Without Storage

A & H Cartage Inc....E....651 454-9550
Saint Paul (G-7684)

A A A Courier Inc....E....320 259-9292
Sauk Rapids (G-9355)

A A Metcalf Moving & Storage....C....651 484-0211
Saint Paul (G-7967)

Ace Solid Waste Inc....D....763 427-3110
Anoka (G-146)

Al Johnson Trucking Inc....E....612 253-1000
Minneapolis (G-3702)

Archbold Enterprises LLC....E....651 484-0211
Saint Paul (G-8060)

Aspen Waste Systems Inc....E....612 884-8000
Minneapolis (G-3819)

Baarts Trucking Inc....E....507 436-5536
Northrop (G-6548)

Baumgartner Trucking Inc....E....507 895-8490
La Crescent (G-2840)

Bay & Bay Transfer Co Inc....C....651 480-7991
Rosemount (G-7362)

Bayer Trucking LLC....E....320 254-3651
Belgrade (G-361)

Beskau Trucking Inc....E....651 437-9737
Hastings (G-2377)

Big Ale-Cat....E....952 881-4128
Minneapolis (G-3902)

Billington Contracting Inc....E....218 722-1213
Duluth (G-1252)

Bob Fischer Trucking....E....507 263-0384
Hampton (G-2364)

C D Haugen Inc....E....218 751-2738
Bemidji (G-383)

Centrax Enterprises Inc....D....612 726-9500
Saint Paul (G-7958)

Con-Way Freight Inc....E....507 451-2865
Owatonna (G-6705)

Con-Way Freight Inc....E....651 686-2868
Eagan (G-1521)

Contact Cartage Inc....E....612 331-4780
Minneapolis (G-4160)

Cottonwood Truck Service Inc....E....651 451-7320
South Saint Paul (G-9525)

Crosscountry Courier Inc....D....651 686-5520
Saint Paul (G-7741)

D & G Excavating Inc....E....507 532-2334
Marshall (G-3292)

D W Jones Trucking Inc....E....651 227-4854
Saint Paul (G-8276)

Daran Inc....E....763 856-4000
Zimmerman (G-10212)

▲ Dedicated Logistics Inc....B....651 631-5918
Oakdale (G-6550)

Dee Spee Delivery Service Inc....B....320 251-6697
Saint Cloud (G-7496)

Delwin Transfer Inc....E....651 731-0510
Saint Paul (G-9204)

Dmz Trucking Inc....E....320 252-0313
Sauk Rapids (G-9362)

Duane Kottke Trucking Corp....E....320 833-5385
Buffalo Lake (G-663)

Elliott Transport Systems Inc....E....218 236-9220
Moorhead (G-6313)

F M Trucking Inc....E....651 639-0446
Saint Paul (G-8358)

F M Trucking Inc....E....651 639-0446
Saint Paul (G-8359)

Floyd Wild Inc....D....507 537-0531
Marshall (G-3297)

Foodliner Inc....D....651 345-2860
Lake City (G-2852)

Freightmasters Inc....C....651 688-6800
Saint Paul (G-7777)

Gerald N Evenson Inc....E....218 863-7101
Pelican Rapids (G-6779)

Greyhound Lines Inc....D....612 371-3325
Minneapolis (G-4567)

Grounded Air Inc....D....763 780-1443
Minneapolis (G-3480)

Harco Moving & Storage Inc....E....763 571-6227
Minneapolis (G-3482)

Independent Delivery Services....D....651 487-1050
Saint Paul (G-8508)

Istate Truck Center....D....651 455-9775
Inver Grove Heights (G-2755)

JME Of Monticello Inc....E....763 295-3122
Monticello (G-6275)

Kane Transport Inc....E....320 352-2762
Sauk Centre (G-9349)

Kane Transport Inc....D....320 352-5800
Newfolden (G-6482)

Keebler Co....E....651 484-0833
Saint Paul (G-8542)

Keith Carlson Trucking Inc....E....651 923-4822
Goodhue (G-2249)

Kerry Logistics Inc....E....763 717-1400
Minneapolis (G-3508)

L & S Construction....E....507 648-3382
Sanborn (G-9318)

Lakehead Trucking Inc....E....218 721-3521
Duluth (G-1379)

Lakeville Motor Express Inc....B....651 636-8900
Saint Paul (G-8558)

Larson Transfer & Storage Co....E....952 884-0765
Minneapolis (G-4847)

Lawrence Transportation....D....507 454-3911
Winona (G-10111)

Le Febvre & Sons Inc....D....952 432-8228
Saint Paul (G-7822)

Malark Motor....E....763 428-4880
Osseo (G-6632)

Manning Transfer Inc....E....763 784-4022
Minneapolis (G-3527)

Marson Contractors Inc....E....320 255-5506
Sauk Rapids (G-9369)

Mats Inc....E....651 406-8300
Eagan (G-1535)

Max Johnson Trucking Inc....E....507 357-6313
Le Center (G-2952)

Mc Donough Truck Line Inc....D....507 334-9374
Faribault (G-2020)

McCallum Transfer Inc....E....651 633-1612
Minneapolis (G-4970)

McCollister's Transportation....E....763 502-2120
Minneapolis (G-3531)

Medstat Systems Inc....E....763 586-8146
Minneapolis (G-3533)

Metropolitan Gravel Co Inc....D....651 458-0170
Newport (G-6487)

Mississippi Transport Inc....D....651 439-5773
Stillwater (G-9630)

Mohawk United....E....651 481-0000
Minneapolis (G-6129)

Norsemen Inc....E....507 835-5060
Waseca (G-9883)

Northland Transportation....E....952 885-0580
Prior Lake (G-6946)

Omni Workspace Co....C....612 627-1600
Minneapolis (G-5277)

P H Selly & Co Inc....E....507 334-3251
Faribault (G-2025)

Paradis Mail Service Inc....E....218 698-4613
Brooks (G-622)

Paradis Mail Service Inc....E....218 698-4613
Brooks (G-623)

Phillips Recycling Systems LLC....D....320 251-5980
Saint Cloud (G-7422)

Physical Distribution Services....E....952 884-0765
Minneapolis (G-5376)

Pioneer Press Inc....D....651 222-8298
Saint Paul (G-8829)

Quicksilver Express Courier....B....651 484-1111
Saint Paul (G-8864)

Quicksilver Express Courier of....B....651 484-1111
Saint Paul (G-8865)

R & E Enterprises of Mankato....E....507 388-3364
Mankato (G-3184)

R A Ventures Inc....C....612 721-9155
Minneapolis (G-5455)

Ricsons Inc....E....612 617-9480
Minneapolis (G-5539)

Rochester City Delivery Inc....E....507 289-2774
Rochester (G-7229)

Schroeder Moving Systems Inc....E....763 694-6070
Minneapolis (G-5614)

Schwan's Home Service Inc....E....507 451-8538
Owatonna (G-6736)

Shorty's Heavy Duty Wrecker....E....763 784-1411
Minneapolis (G-3601)

T C B X Inc....E....651 644-5547
Minneapolis (G-5783)

Taylor Truck Line Inc....C....507 645-4531
Northfield (G-6520)

Tennis Sanitation LLC....E....651 459-1887
Saint Paul Park (G-9298)

Transystems LLC....C....218 773-8813
East Grand Forks (G-1576)

Transystems LLC....E....218 233-8121
Moorhead (G-6343)

Trout Enterprises Inc of Nthn....E....218 246-8165
Deer River (G-1174)

Volk Transfer Inc....E....507 388-1683
Mankato (G-3213)

Wagner Trucking Inc....320 524-2250
Brandon (G-592)

Walbon Co Trucking Svcs....D....651 437-2011
Rosemount (G-7379)

Walbon Transport Inc....C....651 437-2011
Rosemount (G-7380)

Walters Trucking Inc....E....320 352-2207
Sauk Centre (G-9354)

Waste Management of Wisconsin....C....952 890-1100
Savage (G-9412)

Waste Management of Wisconsin....C....952 890-1100
Minneapolis (G-3639)

Waste Management of Wisconsin....E....507 665-3096
Le Sueur (G-2961)

Waymore Transportation Inc....E....763 786-9076
Minneapolis (G-3640)

Western Delivery Inc....E....651 665-0702
Minneapolis (G-6059)

Wilson Oil Co Inc....651 388-5783
Red Wing (G-7013)

Wren Corp....B....651 636-8900
Saint Paul (G-9169)

4213 Trucking, Except Local

'Q' Carriers Inc....E....952 445-8718
Shakopee (G-9416)

A A Metcalf Moving & Storage....C....651 484-0211
Saint Paul (G-7967)

A T S Specialized Inc....C....320 255-7400
Saint Cloud (G-7445)

AAA Cooper Transportation....E....651 638-9288
Saint Paul (G-7970)

ABF Freight System Inc....E....320 259-5025
Saint Cloud (G-7432)

Action Moving Services Inc....D....952 894-8888
Burnsville (G-672)

Admiral-Merchants Motor....E....612 332-4819
Minneapolis (G-3681)

Advanced Auto Transport Inc....C....651 777-7780
Saint Paul (G-7990)

Al Johnson Trucking Inc....E....612 253-1000
Minneapolis (G-3702)

Allied Systems Ltd....C....651 458-3005
Cottage Grove (G-1096)

Am & S Trucking Inc....E....507 629-3224
Tracy (G-9689)

◆ Anderson Trucking Service Inc....C....320 255-7400
Saint Cloud (G-7449)

Archbold Enterprises LLC....E....651 484-0211
Saint Paul (G-8060)

Ats Inc....C....320 255-7400
Saint Cloud (G-7455)

B J Transport Inc....E....651 436-4300
Afton (G-7)

Baarts Trucking Inc....E....507 436-5536
Northrop (G-6548)

Barole Trucking Inc....E....651 209-1104
Hugo (G-2670)

Barrett Moving & Storage Co....D....952 944-6550
Eden Prairie (G-1602)

Battmann Holdings Inc....D....651 639-2800
Saint Paul (G-8091)

Bay & Bay Transfer Co Inc....C....651 480-7991
Rosemount (G-7362)

Becker HI-Way Frate....E....507 373-8513
Albert Lea (G-41)

◆ Beltmann Group Inc....D....651 639-2800
Saint Paul (G-8100)

▲ Berger Transfer & Storage Inc....D....651 639-2260
Saint Paul (G-8104)

Beskau Trucking Inc....E....651 437-9737
Hastings (G-2377)

Bob Brink Inc....D....507 452-1568
Winona (G-10084)

(G-00000) Company's Geographic Section entry number
458
2011 Harris Minnesota Services Directory
▲=Import ▼=Export ◆=Import/Export

Bob Fischer Trucking ....E....507 263-0384
Hampton *(G-2364)*
C D Haugen Inc ....E....218 751-2738
Bemidji *(G-383)*
Caledonia Haulers LLC ....C....507 725-9000
Caledonia *(G-826)*
Cenex Inc ....A....800 232-3639
South Saint Paul *(G-9516)*
Chalich Trucking Inc ....E....763 421-1095
Anoka *(G-165)*
Cliff Viessman Inc ....E....507 625-1435
Mankato *(G-3223)*
Con-Way Freight Inc ....E....507 451-2865
Owatonna *(G-6705)*
Con-Way Freight Inc ....C....763 783-7123
Fridley *(G-2192)*
Con-Way Freight Inc ....E....320 259-0245
Waite Park *(G-9820)*
Conzemius Family LP ....E....651 437-2107
Hastings *(G-2379)*
Crysteel Truck Equipment Inc ....E....507 726-6041
Lake Crystal *(G-2857)*
Custom Transfer Inc ....E....320 732-3013
Long Prairie *(G-3041)*
D & A Truck Line Inc ....E....651 769-1045
Saint Paul Park *(G-9294)*
D & E Transport Inc ....D....763 878-2880
Clearwater *(G-1043)*
D W Jones Trucking Inc ....E....651 227-4854
Saint Paul *(G-8276)*
Daggett Truck Line Inc ....D....218 334-3711
Frazee *(G-2184)*
Daran Inc ....E....763 856-4000
Zimmerman *(G-10212)*
Dart Transit Co ....B....651 688-2000
Saint Paul *(G-7747)*
Dayton Freight Lines Inc ....E....763 493-5841
Osseo *(G-6608)*
▲ **Dedicated Logistics Inc** ....B....651 631-5918
Oakdale *(G-6550)*
Doug Bradley Trucking Inc ....E....507 532-9681
Marshall *(G-3293)*
Eagan Transport Inc ....E....651 452-6268
Saint Paul *(G-7755)*
Eagle Transport Services Inc ....E....507 281-9787
Rochester *(G-7101)*
Eickhoff Enterprises Inc ....D....507 537-0919
Marshall *(G-3294)*
Elliott Transport Systems Inc ....E....218 236-9220
Moorhead *(G-6313)*
Federal Express Corp ....C....651 747-4122
Saint Paul *(G-8368)*
Fedex Freight Inc ....E....507 444-0633
Owatonna *(G-6713)*
Fedex Freight Inc ....D....651 697-9342
Saint Paul *(G-8369)*
Fedex Freight Inc ....E....218 751-9122
Bemidji *(G-393)*
Fedex Ground Package System ....B....651 748-8636
Mahtomedi *(G-3094)*
Figgins Transport Ltd ....D....218 326-9477
Grand Rapids *(G-2277)*
Filmor Express Inc ....C....507 263-2608
Cannon Falls *(G-856)*
Floyd Wild Inc ....D....507 537-0531
Marshall *(G-3297)*
Foodliner Inc ....D....651 345-2860
Lake City *(G-2852)*
Fortune Transportation Co ....D....507 831-2335
Windom *(G-10073)*
Freerksen Trucking Inc ....E....507 374-6708
Dodge Center *(G-1228)*
Freightmasters Inc ....C....651 688-6800
Saint Paul *(G-7777)*
Gary J Aschenbrenner Trucking ....E....507 233-2539
New Ulm *(G-6451)*
Gerald N Evenson Inc ....E....218 863-7101
Pelican Rapids *(G-6779)*
▲ **Going Going Gong Inc** ....E....651 482-1000
Saint Paul *(G-8418)*
Grounded Air Inc ....D....763 780-1443
Minneapolis *(G-3480)*
Hader Farms Inc ....E....507 824-2543
Zumbrota *(G-10219)*
Hartz Truck Line Inc ....E....218 681-3295
Thief River Falls *(G-9669)*
Hi-Tech Express Inc ....E....763 537-1690
Saint Paul *(G-8479)*
Hicks Trucking Co of ....E....320 693-3292
Litchfield *(G-2985)*
J & R Schugel Trucking Inc ....C....507 359-2037
New Ulm *(G-6456)*
J B Hunt Transport Inc ....E....612 362-9419
Minneapolis *(G-4743)*
J C Trux Inc 218 927-4450
Aitkin *(G-20)*
Justman Freight Lines Inc ....E....651 423-1024
Saint Paul *(G-7812)*
Justman Trucking Inc ....E....651 423-1020
Saint Paul *(G-7813)*
K-Way Express Inc ....D....320 485-2325
Winsted *(G-10161)*
Kane Transport Inc ....E....320 352-2762
Sauk Centre *(G-9349)*
Kane Transport Inc ....E....507 532-2788
Marshall *(G-3302)*
Kerry Logistics Inc ....E....763 717-1400
Minneapolis *(G-3508)*
King Shipping Inc ....E....763 428-5464
Maple Grove *(G-3247)*
King Solutions Inc ....D....763 428-5464
Osseo *(G-6626)*
Kingsway Transportation System ....D....507 288-9375
Rochester *(G-7154)*
Kottke Trucking Inc ....E....320 833-5385
Buffalo Lake *(G-666)*
Kwik Kargo Inc Trucking ....E....320 743-2021
Clear Lake *(G-1035)*
▲ **Lake Center Industries Trans** ....E....507 457-3750
Winona *(G-10109)*
Lakehead Trucking Inc ....E....218 721-3521
Duluth *(G-1379)*
Larry Schefus Trucking Inc ....E....507 644-5588
Redwood Falls *(G-7023)*
Larson Transfer & Storage Co ....E....952 884-0765
Minneapolis *(G-4847)*
Lawrence Transportation ....D....507 454-3911
Winona *(G-10111)*
Le Febvre & Sons Inc ....D....952 432-8228
Saint Paul *(G-7822)*
Lessors Inc ....D....651 789-9270
Saint Paul *(G-7824)*
Long Haul Trucking Inc ....D....763 497-3727
Albertville *(G-75)*
Ltx Inc ....C....507 282-6715
Rochester *(G-7163)*
Ltx Inc ....E....507 452-4738
Winona *(G-10112)*
Maiers Transport & Warehousing ....E....320 251-6882
Saint Cloud *(G-7548)*
Malark Motor ....E....763 428-4880
Osseo *(G-6632)*
Manning Transfer Inc ....E....763 784-4022
Minneapolis *(G-3527)*
Mathy Trucking Inc ....D....507 777-4395
Edgerton *(G-1824)*
Mats Inc ....E....651 406-8300
Eagan *(G-1535)*
Mc Kimm Milk Transit Inc ....E....320 587-3167
Hutchinson *(G-2706)*
McCollister's Transportation ....E....763 502-2120
Minneapolis *(G-3531)*
Midwest Motor Express Inc ....D....763 784-0650
Mounds View *(G-6390)*
Midwest Specialized Trans ....E....507 288-5649
Rochester *(G-7186)*
Minnesota Valley Transport Inc ....E....507 354-3276
New Ulm *(G-6462)*
Mohawk Moving & Storage Inc ....D....763 717-3705
Minneapolis *(G-6128)*
Morrell Transfer Inc ....E....763 441-2011
Elk River *(G-1885)*
Norsemen Inc ....E....507 835-5060
Waseca *(G-9883)*
Northwest Dairy Forwarding Co ....D....763 434-6654
Anoka *(G-211)*
Paradis Mail Service Inc ....E....218 698-4613
Brooks *(G-623)*
◆ **Paragon Moving & Storage Inc** ....E....952 936-9122
Hopkins *(G-2601)*
Patriot Holding Corp 612 338-5912
Minneapolis *(G-5347)*
▲ **Perkins Motor Transport Inc** ....E....651 463-4600
Northfield *(G-6539)*
Physical Distribution Services ....E....952 884-0765
Minneapolis *(G-5376)*
Piepho Moving & Storage Inc ....E....507 289-4515
Rochester *(G-7204)*
▼ **Pioneer Industries Inc** ....D....612 374-2280
Minneapolis *(G-5383)*
Pioneer Press Inc ....D....651 222-8298
Saint Paul *(G-8829)*
Plaisted Co's Inc ....E....763 441-1100
Elk River *(G-1890)*
Polman Transfer Inc ....D....218 631-1753
Wadena *(G-9809)*
R & E Enterprises of Mankato ....E....507 388-3364
Mankato *(G-3184)*
R & R Transportation Inc ....D....218 439-6144
Audubon *(G-255)*
Ramler Trucking Inc ....E....320 845-4500
Albany *(G-28)*
Raveill Trucking Inc ....E....218 768-2701
McGregor *(G-3340)*
Robert Chapin ....D....320 351-8901
Sauk Centre *(G-9352)*
Root River Valley Transfer Inc ....D....507 388-7670
Mankato *(G-3231)*
S & S Moving & Storage Inc ....E....507 289-0779
Rochester *(G-7243)*
Schak Trucking Inc ....E....507 247-5204
Tyler *(G-9713)*
Scherer & Sons Trucking Inc ....E....320 363-8846
Saint Joseph *(G-7655)*
Shaw Trucking Inc ....E....763 434-3300
Anoka *(G-225)*
Shorty's Heavy Duty Wrecker ....E....763 784-1411
Minneapolis *(G-3601)*
Smith Trucking Inc ....D....507 376-5080
Worthington *(G-10194)*
Stagecoach Express Inc ....E....651 437-8138
Hastings *(G-2407)*
◆ **Stan Koch & Sons Trucking Inc** ....A....763 302-5400
Minneapolis *(G-5736)*
Stan Koch & Sons Trucking Inc ....E....651 999-8500
Saint Paul *(G-9003)*
Stemm Transfer & Storage Inc ....E....320 251-4080
Saint Cloud *(G-7613)*
Steve Yaggy Specialized Truck ....E....507 282-1715
Rochester *(G-7266)*
Styer Transportation Co ....E....952 469-4491
Lakeville *(G-2936)*
Summit Holdings Corp ....E....952 445-8718
Shakopee *(G-9479)*
Supervalu Transportation Inc ....A....952 828-4000
Eden Prairie *(G-1789)*
Swift Transportation Corp ....E....651 480-7850
Inver Grove Heights *(G-2771)*
Taylor Truck Line Inc ....C....507 645-4531
Northfield *(G-6520)*
Terminal Transport Inc ....D....651 407-6200
Saint Paul *(G-9039)*
Thygeson Construction Co ....E....218 681-1924
Thief River Falls *(G-9679)*
Tim Flanigan Trucking ....E....218 385-3034
New York Mills *(G-6480)*
Transport Corp Of America Inc ....B....651 686-2500
Eagan *(G-1557)*
Transport Designs Inc ....E....952 894-8242
Burnsville *(G-811)*
Transystems LLC ....E....218 281-7514
Crookston *(G-1138)*
Trout Enterprises Inc of Nthn ....E....218 246-8165
Deer River *(G-1174)*
Twin Express Inc ....E....763 428-4969
Rogers *(G-7346)*
Two Men & Truck ....D....651 645-1279
Saint Paul *(G-9285)*
Two Rivers Inc ....B....715 262-5292
Rosemount *(G-7376)*
UPS Ground Freight Inc ....D....763 780-9800
Circle Pines *(G-1023)*
USF Holland Inc ....E....507 847-2625
Jackson *(G-2800)*
Valley Transportation ....D....507 754-5558
Grand Meadow *(G-2265)*
Van Minneapolis & Warehouse Co ....D....651 636-6000
Minneapolis *(G-6132)*
Vic's Heavy Haul Trucking ....D....651 423-7401
Rosemount *(G-7377)*
Vitran Express Inc ....E....320 485-2101
Winsted *(G-10154)*
Wagner Trucking Inc 320 524-2250
Brandon *(G-592)*
Walbon & Co Inc ....D....651 437-2011
Rosemount *(G-7378)*
Walters Trucking Inc ....E....320 352-2207
Sauk Centre *(G-9354)*
Waymore Transportation Inc ....E....763 786-9076
Minneapolis *(G-3640)*
Wayne Transports Inc ....D....218 749-6050
Virginia *(G-9764)*
Wayne Transports Inc ....E....651 437-6422
Rosemount *(G-7381)*
Western Co-Op Transport Assn ....D....320 269-5531
Montevideo *(G-6261)*
Wille Transport Inc ....D....218 999-0900
Cohasset *(G-1073)*
Wilson Lines of Minnesota Inc ....E....651 459-8193
Newport *(G-6490)*
Yrc Inc ....C....651 452-0338
Saint Paul *(G-7954)*

4214 Local Trucking With Storage

Action Moving Services Inc ....D....952 894-8888
Burnsville *(G-672)*
All Furniture Installation Inc ....E....763 571-2203
Minneapolis *(G-3710)*
American Logistics Services ....D....651 451-1349
Cottage Grove *(G-1099)*
Battmann Holdings Inc ....D....651 639-2800
Saint Paul *(G-8091)*
◆ **Beltmann Group Inc** ....D....651 639-2800
Saint Paul *(G-8100)*
▲ **Berger Transfer & Storage Inc** ....D....651 639-2260
Saint Paul *(G-8104)*
Bester Bros Transfer & Storage ....E....651 451-1018
South Saint Paul *(G-9512)*
C D Haugen Inc ....E....218 751-2738
Bemidji *(G-383)*
C W Logistics LLC 651 209-6814
Eagan *(G-1518)*
Dakt Enterprises Inc ....C....952 474-6683
Eden Prairie *(G-1640)*
Freightmasters Inc ....C....651 688-6800
Saint Paul *(G-7777)*
Grounded Air Inc ....D....763 780-1443
Minneapolis *(G-3480)*
Harco Moving & Storage Inc ....E....763 571-6227
Minneapolis *(G-3482)*
K-Way Express Inc ....D....320 485-2325
Winsted *(G-10161)*
Keebler Co ....E....651 484-0833
Saint Paul *(G-8542)*
Kj & E Properties ....E....218 727-8811
Duluth *(G-1372)*
Larry Schefus Trucking Inc ....E....507 644-5588
Redwood Falls *(G-7023)*
Ltx Inc ....E....507 452-4738
Winona *(G-10112)*
Magnum Ltl Inc ....E....763 795-9534
Circle Pines *(G-1015)*

SIC

Employment codes: A=Over 500 employees, B=251-500
C=101-250, D=51-100, E=25-50
2011 Harris Minnesota
Services Directory
© Harris InfoSource 1-866-281-6415
459

Maiers Transport & Warehousing.............E...320 251-6882
  Saint Cloud *(G-7548)*
McCallum Transfer Inc.............E...651 633-1612
  Minneapolis *(G-4970)*
McCollister's Transportation.............E...763 502-2120
  Minneapolis *(G-3531)*
P H Selly & Co Inc.............E...507 334-3251
  Faribault *(G-2025)*
◆ Paragon Moving & Storage Inc.............E...952 936-9122
  Hopkins *(G-2601)*
Piepho Moving & Storage Inc.............E...507 289-4515
  Rochester *(G-7204)*
Piepho Moving & Storage Inc.............E...507 289-4515
  Rochester *(G-7205)*
S & S Moving & Storage Inc.............E...507 289-0779
  Rochester *(G-7243)*
Sonny Peterson Trucking Inc.............E...320 547-2489
  Swanville *(G-9659)*
Stockman Transfer Inc.............E...320 864-2381
  Glencoe *(G-2215)*
Transystems LLC.............C...218 773-8813
  East Grand Forks *(G-1576)*
▲ Triangle Warehouse Inc.............E...651 633-8912
  Minneapolis *(G-5854)*
Van Minneapolis & Warehouse Co.............D...651 636-6000
  Minneapolis *(G-6132)*

4215 Courier Svcs, Except Air

Associated Courier Inc.............E...612 623-9999
  Minneapolis *(G-3826)*
Centrax Enterprises Inc.............D...612 726-9500
  Saint Paul *(G-7958)*
Dynamax Inc.............C...651 644-8787
  Saint Paul *(G-8316)*
Dynamex Operations East Inc.............D...651 644-8787
  Saint Paul *(G-8317)*
Fedex Ground Package System.............B...651 748-8636
  Mahtomedi *(G-3094)*
Pro Courier Inc.............E...763 571-8811
  Minneapolis *(G-3574)*
Quicksilver Express Courier of.............B...651 484-1111
  Saint Paul *(G-8865)*
R A Ventures Inc.............C...612 721-9155
  Minneapolis *(G-5455)*
Response Delivery Inc.............D...952 941-6813
  Minneapolis *(G-5529)*
Twin Courier Corp.............C...763 576-1133
  Champlin *(G-904)*
United Parcel Service Inc.............C...218 722-0150
  Duluth *(G-1491)*
United Parcel Service Inc.............E...507 373-4392
  Albert Lea *(G-69)*
United Parcel Service Inc.............E...218 847-4439
  Detroit Lakes *(G-1221)*
United Parcel Service Inc.............E...507 375-4666
  Saint James *(G-7648)*
United Parcel Service Inc.............E...320 762-2746
  Alexandria *(G-127)*
United Parcel Service Inc.............D...218 829-6240
  Brainerd *(G-588)*
United Parcel Service Inc.............E...320 235-6615
  Willmar *(G-10050)*
United Parcel Service Inc.............D...507 281-0468
  Rochester *(G-7277)*
United Parcel Service Inc.............E...507 454-2307
  Winona *(G-10135)*
United Parcel Service Inc.............A...800 742-5877
  Minneapolis *(G-5912)*
United Parcel Service Inc.............E...651 388-6555
  Red Wing *(G-7010)*
United Parcel Service of New.............C...320 253-4100
  Saint Cloud *(G-7443)*
United Parcel Service of New.............E...218 751-9109
  Bemidji *(G-430)*
United Parcel Service of New.............E...507 836-6671
  Slayton *(G-9491)*
United Parcel Service of New.............E...218 739-4910
  Fergus Falls *(G-2122)*
United Parcel Service of New.............E...507 334-7924
  Faribault *(G-2036)*
United Parcel Service of New.............E...218 326-8520
  Grand Rapids *(G-2310)*
Velocity Express Mid-West Inc.............E...612 492-2400
  Minneapolis *(G-5960)*
Velocity Express Northeast Inc.............C...612 492-2400
  Minneapolis *(G-5961)*

4221 Farm Product Warehousing & Storage

General Mills Inc.............D...612 721-6811
  Minneapolis *(G-4512)*
General Mills Operations LLC.............E...218 722-7759
  Duluth *(G-1335)*
Northern Grain Design & Constr.............E...320 367-2881
  Clara City *(G-1031)*
Western Consolidated Co-op.............E...320 394-2171
  Holloway *(G-2493)*

4222 Refrigerated Warehousing & Storage

Alltemp Distribution Co.............E...763 571-0215
  Minneapolis *(G-3396)*
Artic Cold Storage Inc.............E...320 253-9979
  Saint Cloud *(G-7454)*
Atlas Cold Storage Midwest.............E...507 732-4224
  Zumbrota *(G-10216)*

Cloverleaf Cold Storage Co.............E...952 469-1221
  Lakeville *(G-2896)*
Cloverleaf Cold Storage Co.............E...507 238-4211
  Fairmont *(G-1961)*
Fairmont Refrigerated Service.............E...507 238-4211
  Fairmont *(G-1966)*
Paul Newport-St Cold Storage.............E...651 459-5555
  Newport *(G-6488)*

4225 General Warehousing & Storage

Alltemp Distribution Co.............E...763 571-0215
  Minneapolis *(G-3396)*
CF Industries Inc.............E...651 437-6191
  Rosemount *(G-7365)*
CHS Inc.............D...651 306-8088
  South Saint Paul *(G-9521)*
▲ Dedicated Logistics Inc.............B...651 631-5918
  Oakdale *(G-6550)*
Dedicated Logistics Inc.............E...763 504-9229
  Minneapolis *(G-4240)*
Duke Co's.............D...612 331-4880
  Minneapolis *(G-4289)*
▲ Falls Distribution Inc.............E...320 632-3999
  Little Falls *(G-3004)*
Freightmasters Inc.............C...651 688-6800
  Saint Paul *(G-7777)*
▲ Fulfillment Distribution Ctr.............A...320 656-8880
  Saint Cloud *(G-7513)*
▲ Gamer Packaging Inc.............E...612 788-4444
  Minneapolis *(G-4498)*
Interline Brands Inc.............E...651 644-7075
  Saint Paul *(G-8515)*
J K F Warehouse.............E...507 354-5528
  New Ulm *(G-6457)*
Keebler Co.............E...651 484-0833
  Saint Paul *(G-8542)*
Kmart Corp.............B...952 445-2936
  Shakopee *(G-9449)*
Kurt Manufacturing Co Inc.............E...763 572-4592
  Minneapolis *(G-5574)*
Macy's Retail Holdings Inc.............E...507 280-5400
  Rochester *(G-7165)*
▲ Meritex Enterprises Inc.............E...651 855-9700
  Minneapolis *(G-4992)*
▲ Murphy Warehouse Co.............C...612 623-1200
  Minneapolis *(G-5151)*
Murphy Warehouse Co.............E...612 623-1226
  Minneapolis *(G-3549)*
Pan-O-Gold Baking Co.............E...763 559-1515
  Minneapolis *(G-5316)*
Paul A Schmitt Music Co.............E...763 566-4560
  Minneapolis *(G-5349)*
Smiths Medical Asd Inc.............E...651 628-7030
  Saint Paul *(G-9274)*
Star Tribune Media Co LLC.............B...612 673-7100
  Minneapolis *(G-5740)*
Supervalu Inc.............A...952 238-3400
  Eden Prairie *(G-1786)*
▲ Triangle Warehouse Inc.............D...651 633-8912
  Minneapolis *(G-5854)*
U-Haul Co of Minnesota.............D...763 780-9746
  Minneapolis *(G-3628)*
Uponor Inc.............E...952 891-2000
  Lakeville *(G-2939)*
▲ Warehouse Depot LLC.............E...612 728-5238
  Minneapolis *(G-6021)*
Watkins Inc.............E...507 457-6136
  Winona *(G-10139)*
Young America Holdings Inc.............E...320 864-6125
  Glencoe *(G-2217)*

4226 Special Warehousing & Storage, NEC

Auto Warehousing Co Inc.............E...651 769-8383
  Cottage Grove *(G-1100)*
Business Data Record Services.............E...651 631-8663
  Saint Paul *(G-8142)*
Dee Spee Delivery Service Inc.............E...507 288-0695
  Rochester *(G-7094)*
Eddie Bauer Inc.............E...651 738-8653
  Saint Paul *(G-9207)*
Goodwill Industries Inc.............C...651 379-5800
  Saint Paul *(G-8421)*
Goodwill Industries Inc.............E...952 953-4410
  Saint Paul *(G-7787)*
Goodwill Industries Inc.............E...651 439-4207
  Stillwater *(G-9620)*
Goodwill Industries Inc.............D...651 603-1544
  Saint Paul *(G-8422)*
Granite City Armored Car Inc.............E...320 252-0708
  Sauk Rapids *(G-9364)*
Iron Mountain Inc.............E...651 452-0169
  Saint Paul *(G-7807)*
Iron Mountain Information MGT.............C...952 888-3852
  Minneapolis *(G-4735)*
Omni Workspace Co.............E...612 627-1600
  Minneapolis *(G-5277)*
Target Corp.............C...320 253-4740
  Saint Cloud *(G-7616)*
Target Corp.............C...612 304-6073
  Minneapolis *(G-5791)*
Xiotech Corp.............E...952 983-3000
  Eden Prairie *(G-1819)*

4231 Terminal & Joint Terminal Maint Facilities

Malark Logistics Inc.............D...763 428-3564
  Brooklyn Park *(G-616)*
Midwest Motor Express Inc.............E...763 784-0650
  Saint Paul *(G-8660)*
Mississippi Transport Inc.............E...651 439-5773
  Stillwater *(G-9630)*
United Parcel Service Inc.............E...651 367-8200
  Saint Paul *(G-7936)*
Vitran Express Inc.............E...320 485-2333
  Winsted *(G-10166)*
Vitran Express Inc.............C...763 913-3450
  Mounds View *(G-6391)*

44 WATER TRANSPORTATION

4424 Deep Sea Domestic Transportation Of Freight

◆ SBS Transportation Inc.............E...651 256-1555
  Saint Paul *(G-8932)*

4449 Water Transportation Of Freight, NEC

◆ North Star International Inc.............E...651 379-5030
  Saint Paul *(G-7851)*

4489 Water Transport Of Passengers, NEC

Afton St Croix Co.............E...651 436-8883
  Afton *(G-6)*
Muller Boat Co.............E...651 465-6315
  Taylors Falls *(G-9661)*
St Croix Boat & Packet Inc.............D...651 430-1234
  Stillwater *(G-9642)*

4491 Marine Cargo Handling

Cargill Inc.............D...218 727-1594
  Duluth *(G-1262)*
Great Western Recycling Inds.............E...651 224-4877
  Saint Paul *(G-8427)*
Nisswa Marine Inc.............E...218 963-2292
  Nisswa *(G-6498)*
River Services Inc.............E...612 588-8141
  Minneapolis *(G-5543)*
Upper River Services LLC.............E...651 292-9293
  Saint Paul *(G-9115)*

4493 Marinas

Gunflint Lodge Inc.............E...218 388-2294
  Grand Marais *(G-2261)*
J & K Marina.............E...218 847-7291
  Detroit Lakes *(G-1201)*
Nisswa Marine Inc.............E...218 963-2292
  Nisswa *(G-6498)*
Rainy Lake Houseboats Inc.............E...218 286-5391
  International Falls *(G-2729)*

45 TRANSPORTATION BY AIR

4512 Air Transportation, Scheduled

American Airlines Inc.............C...612 726-5833
  Saint Paul *(G-7957)*
American Airlines Inc.............D...612 726-5647
  Saint Paul *(G-7956)*
Chisholm-Hibbing Airport.............E...218 262-3451
  Hibbing *(G-2440)*
Compass Airlines Inc.............E...612 713-6800
  Minneapolis *(G-4146)*
Continental Airlines Inc.............D...612 726-5679
  Saint Paul *(G-7959)*
Mesaba Airlines.............E...651 367-5000
  Eagan *(G-1537)*
Mesaba Aviation Inc.............A...651 367-5000
  Eagan *(G-1538)*
MN Airlines LLC.............A...651 681-3900
  Mendota Heights *(G-3367)*
Northwest Airlines Corp.............A...612 726-2111
  Eagan *(G-1543)*
Northwest Airlines Inc.............A...612 726-2111
  Minneapolis *(G-5238)*
Northwest Airlines Inc.............E...507 282-9425
  Rochester *(G-7192)*
Northwest Airlines Inc.............A...612 726-3896
  Saint Paul *(G-7855)*
Northwest Airlines Inc.............E...218 254-7575
  Chisholm *(G-999)*
Northwest Airlines Inc.............E...612 726-8000
  Minneapolis *(G-5239)*
Northwest Airlines Inc.............C...612 727-9209
  Minneapolis *(G-5240)*
Servicemaster Inc.............D...612 794-4100
  Saint Paul *(G-7963)*

4513 Air Courier Svcs

Bemidji Aviation Services Inc.............E...612 726-1500
  Minneapolis *(G-3882)*

(G-00000) Company's Geographic Section entry number
460

2011 Harris Minnesota
Services Directory

▲=Import ▼=Export
◆=Import/Export

Federal Express Corp .... D 952 884-9212
Minneapolis *(G-4418)*
Greyhound Lines Inc .... D 612 371-3325
Minneapolis *(G-4567)*
Northwest Airlines Inc .... A 612 726-2111
Minneapolis *(G-5238)*
Northwest Airlines Inc .... E 218 727-8791
Duluth *(G-1409)*
United Parcel Service Inc .... C 218 722-0150
Duluth *(G-1491)*
Velocity Express Northeast Inc .... C 612 492-2400
Minneapolis *(G-5961)*

4522 Air Transportation, Nonscheduled

Aviation Charter Inc .... D 952 943-1519
Eden Prairie *(G-1600)*
Critical Care Services Inc .... C 612 638-4900
Minneapolis *(G-4185)*
Federal Express Corp .... B 612 713-8500
Minneapolis *(G-4420)*
Mayo Midair .... E 507 255-2808
Rochester *(G-7176)*
Northwest Airlines Inc .... A 612 726-2111
Minneapolis *(G-5238)*
3M Co .... D 651 778-5302
Saint Paul *(G-9045)*
Wright Aero Inc .... E 320 963-5094
Maple Lake *(G-3268)*

4581 Airports, Flying Fields & Terminal Svcs

Aviation Charter Inc .... D 952 943-1519
Eden Prairie *(G-1600)*
Bemidji Aviation Services Inc .... E 218 751-1880
Bemidji *(G-377)*
Elliott Aviation Inc .... D 952 944-1200
Eden Prairie *(G-1654)*
Freight Office For North West .... E 218 727-8747
Duluth *(G-1328)*
Hiawatha Aviation of Rochester .... E 507 282-1717
Rochester *(G-7137)*
Mankato Airport .... E 507 625-2511
Mankato *(G-3159)*
Millian Air Executive Aviation .... E 952 943-1519
Eden Prairie *(G-1724)*
Modern Aero Inc .... D 952 941-2595
Eden Prairie *(G-1729)*
◆ North Star International Inc .... E 651 379-5030
Saint Paul *(G-7851)*
Paul Minneapolis-St .... D 612 726-5107
Saint Paul *(G-7962)*
Paul Minneapolis-St .... D 612 726-8100
Minneapolis *(G-5353)*
Petters Aviation LLC 952 936-5000
Minnetonka *(G-6212)*
S T C Aviation Inc .... E 320 253-1500
Saint Cloud *(G-7440)*
Safari Airport Taxi Service .... D 763 424-9070
Minneapolis *(G-5587)*
Safe Air Repair Inc .... D 507 373-7129
Albert Lea *(G-63)*
Servisair USA Inc .... C 612 726-5533
Saint Paul *(G-7964)*
Signature Flight Support Corp .... B 612 726-5700
Minneapolis *(G-5670)*
Signature Flight Support Corp .... E 651 224-1100
Saint Paul *(G-8958)*
Thunderbird Aviation Inc .... E 952 941-1212
Eden Prairie *(G-1793)*
United Parcel Service Inc .... E 651 367-8200
Saint Paul *(G-7936)*
Wright Aero Inc .... E 320 963-5094
Maple Lake *(G-3268)*

46 PIPELINES, EXCEPT NATURAL GAS

4612 Crude Petroleum Pipelines

Koch Industries Inc .... D 218 564-4495
Menahga *(G-3358)*

4613 Refined Petroleum Pipelines

Cenex Inc .... A 800 232-3639
South Saint Paul *(G-9516)*

47 TRANSPORTATION SERVICES

4724 Travel Agencies

A A A Minneapolis .... D 952 944-9585
Minneapolis *(G-3645)*
American Express Travel .... E 651 731-9396
Saint Paul *(G-9183)*
Blue Green Vacation Corp .... E 888 456-0412
Bloomington *(G-490)*
Capital City Travel Inc .... E 651 287-4906
Saint Paul *(G-8150)*
◆ Carlson Holdings Inc .... A 763 212-5000
Minnetonka *(G-6152)*
Carlson Travel Group Inc .... E 651 406-6000
Saint Paul *(G-7728)*
Emerald Travel Management Co 507 345-8797
Mankato *(G-3126)*
Graves Hospitality Corp .... D 612 677-1100
Minneapolis *(G-4547)*
Ljk Co's Inc .... C 952 944-5462
Minnetonka *(G-6188)*
Navigant International Rocky .... E 612 375-2884
Minneapolis *(G-5175)*
Northeast Securities Corp 612 379-8811
Minneapolis *(G-5225)*
Northfield Lines Inc .... E 507 645-5267
Northfield *(G-6518)*
Ottertail Coaches Inc .... D 218 739-3393
Fergus Falls *(G-2112)*
Outdoor Adventure Travel Inc .... E 612 866-2503
Minneapolis *(G-5300)*
Outsource Administrators Inc .... E 952 944-5462
Minnetonka *(G-6208)*
Rica Costa Ventures Inc .... E 651 426-9262
Hugo *(G-2682)*
Travel Leaders 952 941-8900
Eden Prairie *(G-1796)*
Travel Leaders Group LLC .... A 952 914-6500
Eden Prairie *(G-1797)*
Travel One Inc .... E 952 854-2551
Minneapolis *(G-5849)*
Travelnet Solutions Inc .... E 651 757-4905
Cottage Grove *(G-1108)*
Umi Co Inc .... D 612 331-2566
Minneapolis *(G-5899)*

4725 Tour Operators

Brennaville Inc .... E 507 467-2512
Preston *(G-6895)*
Iyanka Dakota Coaches Inc .... E 507 644-3380
Morton *(G-6381)*
M L T Inc .... C 952 474-2540
Minneapolis *(G-4921)*
Tourco's Firstline Tours Inc 763 780-2985
Minneapolis *(G-3619)*
Travel Leaders Group LLC .... A 952 914-6500
Eden Prairie *(G-1797)*

4729 Passenger Transportation Arrangement, NEC

Continental Airlines Inc .... D 612 726-5679
Saint Paul *(G-7959)*
First Student Inc .... C 612 378-7833
Minneapolis *(G-4446)*
Outsource Administrators Inc .... E 952 944-5462
Minnetonka *(G-6208)*
Scs Dialaride .... E 952 474-7441
Spring Park *(G-9566)*

4731 Freight Forwarding & Arrangement

A & H Cartage Inc .... E 651 454-9550
Saint Paul *(G-7684)*
Advanced Service Management .... E 763 201-1451
Hamel *(G-2337)*
Alltemp Distribution Co .... E 763 571-0215
Minneapolis *(G-3396)*
◆ Ats Logistics Services Inc .... D 320 255-7488
Saint Cloud *(G-7456)*
▲ Berger Transfer & Storage Inc .... D 651 639-2260
Saint Paul *(G-8104)*
Bnsf Railway Co .... C 320 231-5555
Willmar *(G-9990)*
Brenny Specialized Inc .... E 320 363-6996
Saint Joseph *(G-7652)*
◆ C H Robinson Worldwide Inc .... A 952 937-8500
Eden Prairie *(G-1615)*
Canadian Pacific Ltd .... E 612 781-7284
Minneapolis *(G-3998)*
Ceva Freight LLC .... D 651 675-4000
Eagan *(G-1520)*
CH Robinson International Inc .... E 952 937-8500
Eden Prairie *(G-1621)*
CH Robinson International Inc .... D 952 937-2914
Eden Prairie *(G-1622)*
Cobra Transportation Services .... E 651 552-1151
Saint Paul *(G-8219)*
Contact Cartage Inc .... E 612 331-4780
Minneapolis *(G-4160)*
Dayton Freight Lines Inc .... E 763 493-5841
Osseo *(G-6608)*
Don Cameron & Associates Inc .... E 952 884-0070
Minneapolis *(G-4275)*
Expeditors International Of WA .... D 651 683-9922
Saint Paul *(G-7771)*
Fratrans Inc .... E 651 294-3944
New Brighton *(G-6407)*
Freightmasters Inc .... C 651 688-6800
Saint Paul *(G-7777)*
▲ Griffin & Co Logistics .... E 952 854-2600
Minneapolis *(G-4568)*
Hicks Trucking Co of .... E 320 693-3292
Litchfield *(G-2985)*
◆ Interlog USA Inc .... E 612 789-3456
Minneapolis *(G-4718)*
Island Freight Brokerage LLC .... E 507 288-5758
Rochester *(G-7143)*
K 2 International Inc 651 209-8770
Saint Paul *(G-7814)*
K N Air Domestic .... E 651 688-7650
Saint Paul *(G-7815)*
▲ K T I Inc .... E 612 378-9731
Minnetonka *(G-6183)*
King Shipping Inc .... E 763 428-5464
Maple Grove *(G-3247)*
King Solutions Inc .... D 763 428-5464
Osseo *(G-6626)*
Kuehne + Nagel Inc .... E 651 688-6645
Saint Paul *(G-7820)*
Lake Country Logistics LLC .... E 218 233-2686
Moorhead *(G-6322)*
Lawrence Transportation .... D 507 454-3911
Winona *(G-10111)*
Logistics International LLC .... D 952 697-4800
Shakopee *(G-9451)*
M & N Equipment Services Inc .... E 612 379-4147
Minneapolis *(G-4916)*
M C U Intermodal Inc .... E 651 222-2224
Saint Paul *(G-8601)*
Mid American Transportation .... D 612 726-9162
Minneapolis *(G-5020)*
Minn-Tex Express Inc .... E 320 277-3562
Pierz *(G-6805)*
Morrell Transfer Inc .... E 763 441-2011
Elk River *(G-1885)*
North Star World Trade Svcs .... E 651 379-5030
Saint Paul *(G-7852)*
Online Freight Services Inc .... E 651 468-6868
Saint Paul *(G-7857)*
Promises + Inc 763 497-3727
Albertville *(G-76)*
Rubenstein Logistics Services .... E 763 542-1121
Golden Valley *(G-2244)*
SAV Enterprises Inc .... E 763 278-3340
Minneapolis *(G-3596)*
Schak Trucking Inc .... E 507 247-5204
Tyler *(G-9713)*
Schenker Inc .... D 651 367-2500
Eagan *(G-1551)*
Sears Logistics Services Inc .... E 612 379-5600
Minneapolis *(G-5623)*
◆ Stan Koch & Sons Trucking Inc .... A 763 302-5400
Minneapolis *(G-5736)*
Stan Koch & Sons Trucking Inc .... E 651 999-8500
Saint Paul *(G-9003)*
Superior Brokerage Services .... E 651 256-1555
Saint Paul *(G-9016)*
Telin Transportation Group LLC .... E 763 262-3328
Becker *(G-359)*
Transway Express Inc .... E 651 686-7000
Northfield *(G-6544)*
UPS Supply Chain Solutions Inc .... E 612 726-1680
Minneapolis *(G-5937)*
Volk Transfer Inc .... E 507 388-1683
Mankato *(G-3213)*
Waymore Transportation Inc .... E 763 786-9076
Minneapolis *(G-3640)*

4783 Packing & Crating Svcs

▲ Business Impact Group LLC .... D 952 278-7800
Chanhassen *(G-911)*
▲ Independent Packing Services .... E 763 425-7155
Osseo *(G-6623)*
Innovative Packaging .... E 763 488-9708
Maple Grove *(G-3246)*
Riverview Packaging Inc .... E 651 415-1121
Saint Paul *(G-8905)*
Sunopta Aseptic Inc .... D 320 763-9822
Alexandria *(G-124)*
Visual Packaging Corp .... E 952 938-1575
Hopkins *(G-2653)*

4785 Fixed Facilities, Inspection, Weighing Svcs Transptn

Ibt Consolidated Inc .... E 218 285-5290
International Falls *(G-2721)*
Minnesota Dakota & Western .... E 218 285-5690
International Falls *(G-2727)*
Vitran Express Inc .... E 320 485-2333
Winsted *(G-10166)*

4789 Transportation Svcs, NEC

Aging Services For Communities .... E 507 364-5663
Montgomery *(G-6263)*
America Midwest Transportation .... E 507 359-4450
Courtland *(G-1115)*
Cenex Inc .... A 800 232-3639
South Saint Paul *(G-9516)*
Chamber Trill Public Transit .... E 320 983-5064
Milaca *(G-3375)*
Duluth Missabe & Iron Range .... A 218 723-2016
Duluth *(G-1302)*
Johnson Co Inc, R M .... E 320 398-6080
Kimball *(G-2832)*
Kraft Foods Global Inc .... E 507 359-2511
New Ulm *(G-6458)*
Loram Rail Services LLC .... B 763 478-6014
Hamel *(G-2348)*
Mort's Transportation Inc .... E 320 269-7340
Montevideo *(G-6255)*

S I C

North Star Rail Intermodal LLC 952 831-4011
Minneapolis (G-5220)
Progressive Rail Inc .... E 952 985-7245
Lakeville (G-2927)
Sav Logistics Inc .... E 763 489-4213
Minneapolis (G-3597)

48 COMMUNICATIONS

4812 Radiotelephone Communications

Abraham Technical Services Inc .... E 763 428-3170
Rogers (G-7315)
American Cellular Corp .... D 218 727-4700
Duluth (G-1238)
American Cellular Corp .... E 218 828-8000
Baxter (G-319)
Cellco Partnership .... E 763 595-5102
Minneapolis (G-4040)
Choice Communications Inc 651 230-7127
Minneapolis (G-4068)
Cumulus Media Inc .... E 507 288-1025
Rochester (G-7090)
Embarq Minnesota Inc .... D 952 556-5679
Chaska (G-964)
Heartland Services LLC .... E 763 477-3000
Rockford (G-7301)
Hickory Tech Information Soln .... D 507 625-1691
Mankato (G-3139)
Hickory Tech Information Soln .... D 507 625-1691
Mankato (G-3140)
Hutchinson Telephone Co .... D 320 587-2323
Hutchinson (G-2702)
Midwest Wireless Comms .... B 507 385-2396
Mankato (G-3169)
Motorola Inc .... C 952 895-7800
Burnsville (G-760)
Nextel Communications Inc .... D 952 703-7600
Minneapolis (G-5197)
▲ PeopleNet Communications Corp .... C 952 908-6200
Minnetonka (G-6209)
Rural Cellular Corp .... C 320 762-2000
Alexandria (G-122)
SBC Datacomm Inc .... E 763 315-5343
Saint Paul (G-8931)
Shock City Cellular .... E 952 233-5281
Shakopee (G-9475)
Sprint Spectrum LP .... E 507 358-4727
Rochester (G-7261)
USA Mobility Wireless Inc .... E 952 996-0400
Eden Prairie (G-1801)
Verizon Business Network Svcs .... E 612 607-1116
Cologne (G-1093)
Verizon Wireless Inc .... D 320 241-5433
Waite Park (G-9847)

4813 Telephone Communications, Except Radio

A T & T Corp .... B 612 376-5401
Minneapolis (G-3649)
Ace Communications Group .... D 507 896-3111
Houston (G-2661)
Arvig Enterprises Inc .... C 218 346-5500
Perham (G-6793)
Bevcomm Inc .... E 507 526-3252
Blue Earth (G-529)
Bhi Advanced Internet Inc .... E 952 361-5557
Eden Prairie (G-1605)
Bishop Communications Corp .... D 320 274-8201
Annandale (G-138)
Blue Earth Valley Telephone Co .... E 507 787-2222
Wells (G-9961)
Broadband America, Corp .... E 952 941-7900
Victoria (G-9725)
Citizens Telecommunications Co .... E 952 491-5576
Mound (G-6385)
Convergeone Holdings Corp .... C 651 796-6411
Eagan (G-1522)
Dell-Comm Inc .... D 763 783-0035
Saint Paul (G-8283)
Digital Telecommunications Inc .... E 507 452-2303
Winona (G-10092)
Earthlink Inc .... E 507 847-2700
Jackson (G-2790)
East Otter Tail Telephone Co .... C 218 346-5500
Perham (G-6796)
Eckles Telephone Co Inc .... E 507 526-3252
Blue Earth (G-534)
Embarq Minnesota Inc .... D 952 556-5679
Chaska (G-964)
Enventis Telecom Inc .... D 763 577-3900
Minneapolis (G-4360)
Focalpoint Inc .... D 952 944-0932
Eden Prairie (G-1666)
Four51 Inc .... E 952 294-0451
Eden Prairie (G-1668)
Frontier Communications of MN .... C 952 898-6422
Burnsville (G-725)
Garden Valley Telephone Co .... D 218 687-2400
Erskine (G-1920)
Hanson Communications Inc .... E 320 235-2260
Willmar (G-10005)
Hector Communications Corp .... D 218 346-5500
New Ulm (G-6453)
Hiawatha Broadband Comms .... D 507 474-4000
Winona (G-10101)
Hiawatha Broadband Comms .... D 507 932-3942
Saint Charles (G-7404)
Hickory Tech Information Soln .... D 507 625-1691
Mankato (G-3139)
Hickory Tech Information Soln .... D 507 625-1691
Mankato (G-3140)
HickoryTech Corp .... B 507 386-3636
Mankato (G-3141)
Hutchinson Telephone Co .... D 320 587-2323
Hutchinson (G-2702)
Integra Telecom Holdings Inc .... E 952 226-7000
Prior Lake (G-6934)
Integra Telecom Inc .... C 763 745-8000
Minneapolis (G-4711)
Integra Telecom of Minnesota .... D 952 746-7100
Golden Valley (G-2242)
K N R Communication Services .... E 763 478-2058
Brooklyn Park (G-612)
Kasson & Mantorville Telephone .... E 507 634-2511
Kasson (G-2821)
Lakedale Telephone Co .... D 320 274-8201
Annandale (G-140)
Larson Utilities Inc 507 557-2275
Franklin (G-2181)
Lefty's Shooting & Outdoor 763 533-9594
Minneapolis (G-4854)
Link Lakedale Inc .... E 320 274-7777
Annandale (G-141)
Marketing Bridge LLC .... E 763 504-4610
Minneapolis (G-4949)
McLeodusa Inc .... E 800 593-1177
Saint Paul (G-8626)
Mid-State Telephone Co .... A 320 354-7805
New London (G-6417)
Midcontinent Media Inc .... C 952 844-2600
Minneapolis (G-5024)
New Ulm Telecom Inc .... D 507 354-4111
New Ulm (G-6468)
North American Communications .... D 651 994-6800
Eagan (G-1542)
Northstar Access .... E 763 691-0885
Cambridge (G-844)
Onvoy Inc .... C 952 230-4100
Minneapolis (G-5282)
Onvoy Inc .... E 320 324-7530
Chokio (G-1001)
Otter Tail Telcom LLC .... E 218 998-2000
Fergus Falls (G-2111)
Park Region Mutual Telephone .... E 218 826-6161
Underwood (G-9718)
Paul Bunyan Rural Telephone .... D 218 444-1234
Bemidji (G-420)
Popp Telcom Inc .... D 763 546-9707
Minneapolis (G-5394)
Popular Front Studio Inc .... E 612 362-0900
Minneapolis (G-5395)
Qwest Corp .... C 612 663-2073
Minneapolis (G-5452)
Qwest Corp .... B 612 381-5202
Minneapolis (G-5453)
Redwood Long Distance Co .... E 507 644-3844
Wabasso (G-9777)
Renodis Holdings Inc .... E 651 556-1203
Saint Paul (G-8890)
SBC Datacomm Inc .... E 763 315-5343
Saint Paul (G-8931)
Select Communications Inc .... E 763 744-0900
Minneapolis (G-5633)
Shavlik Technologies LLC .... D 651 426-6624
Saint Paul (G-8948)
Sherburne County Rural .... E 763 262-4100
Big Lake (G-455)
Sherburne Tele Systems Inc .... E 763 262-4100
Big Lake (G-456)
Skycom Inc .... E 952 361-4248
Minneapolis (G-5688)
▲ Skyvision Inc .... E 218 739-5231
Fergus Falls (G-2119)
Sprint Communications Co LP .... C 507 454-8386
Winona (G-10130)
Tailwind Voice & Data Inc .... E 763 577-4000
Minneapolis (G-5785)
TW Telecom Inc .... E 952 351-2300
Hopkins (G-2650)
U S Internet Corp .... E 651 222-4638
Minnetonka (G-6230)
Val-Ed Joint Venture, LLP .... E 218 284-5702
Moorhead (G-6345)
Verizon Business Network Svcs .... E 612 607-1116
Cologne (G-1093)
▲ Verizon Communications Inc .... C 763 591-0705
Minneapolis (G-5965)
Vibes Technologies Inc .... C 763 971-6260
Minneapolis (G-5968)
W3i Holdings LLC .... D 320 257-7500
Sartell (G-9341)
Wikstrom Telephone Co Inc .... D 218 436-2121
Karlstad (G-2817)
Xpandable Technology Inc .... E 763 521-0401
Minneapolis (G-6095)

4822 Telegraph & Other Message Communications

Fedex Office & Print Services .... E 651 699-9671
Saint Paul (G-8370)
Fedex Office & Print Services .... E 952 892-0200
Burnsville (G-721)
Hutchinson Telephone Co .... D 320 587-2323
Hutchinson (G-2702)

4832 Radio Broadcasting Stations

American Public Media Group .... B 651 290-1500
Saint Paul (G-8032)
CBS Radio Inc .... E 612 339-1029
Minneapolis (G-4033)
Clear Channel Communications .... C 952 417-3000
Minneapolis (G-4107)
Clear Channel Communications .... E 507 288-3888
Rochester (G-7081)
Clear Channel Communications .... E 218 727-4500
Duluth (G-1277)
Cumulus Media Inc .... E 507 334-0061
Faribault (G-2000)
FM 107 W Fmp Real Life .... D 651 642-4107
Saint Paul (G-8386)
Ingstad Broadcasting Inc .... E 218 681-4900
Thief River Falls (G-9670)
K A G E Inc .... E 507 452-2867
Winona (G-10106)
K L L Z F M .... E 218 444-1500
Bemidji (G-399)
K R C H Web Radio Stations .... E 507 288-3888
Rochester (G-7149)
Kkaq AM 1460 .... E 218 681-4900
Thief River Falls (G-9672)
Kliz FM Powerloon 107 5 .... E 218 822-4440
Baxter (G-332)
Kstp FM LLC .... E 651 642-4242
Saint Paul (G-8552)
Lakeland Broadcasting Co Inc .... E 320 235-1340
Willmar (G-10016)
Leighton Enterprises Inc .... E 320 251-1450
Saint Cloud (G-7544)
Midcontinent Media Inc .... C 952 844-2600
Minneapolis (G-5024)
Midwest Communication Inc .... E 218 749-3000
Hibbing (G-2466)
Minneapolis Radio LLC .... D 612 617-4000
Minneapolis (G-5060)
Minnesota Public Radio .... D 651 290-1500
Saint Paul (G-8703)
Minnesota Public Radio .... B 651 290-1500
Saint Paul (G-8702)
Northern Lights Broadcasting .... E 952 842-7200
Edina (G-1840)
Paul Bunyan Broadcasting Co .... E 218 444-1011
Bemidji (G-418)
Radio City Marketing Group Inc .... D 320 253-6500
Saint Cloud (G-7580)
Regent Broadcasting of St .... E 320 251-4422
Saint Cloud (G-7424)
Regents of The University of .... D 612 625-3500
Minneapolis (G-5487)
Region Communications .... E 320 252-5852
Saint Cloud (G-7425)
Result Radio Inc .... E 218 736-7596
Fergus Falls (G-2118)
Southwestern Minnesota Radio .... E 507 452-4000
Winona (G-10129)
Woodward Broadcasting Inc .... E 507 235-5595
Fairmont (G-1984)
Wwtc .... E 651 289-4404
Eagan (G-1561)

4833 Television Broadcasting Stations

Care TV .... C 763 546-1111
Minneapolis (G-4004)
Channel 12 .... E 763 533-8196
Minneapolis (G-4055)
Duluth Superior Area .... E 218 724-8567
Duluth (G-1304)
Fox Television Stations Inc .... C 952 946-1234
Eden Prairie (G-1669)
Granite Broadcasting Corp .... D 218 720-9666
Duluth (G-1341)
Granite Broadcasting Corp .... D 218 720-9642
Duluth (G-1342)
Hubbard Broadcasting Inc .... A 651 646-5555
Saint Paul (G-8499)
Kbjr Inc .... D 218 727-8484
Duluth (G-1366)
KDLH News Channel .... D 218 733-0303
Duluth (G-1368)
Kttc Television Inc .... D 507 288-4444
Rochester (G-7159)
Midwest Kaal Corp .... E 507 437-6666
Austin (G-283)
Multimedia Holdings .... C 763 546-1111
Minneapolis (G-5148)
Northern Minnesota Public .... E 218 751-3407
Bemidji (G-413)
Northwest Suburbs Community .... D 763 533-8196
Minneapolis (G-5244)
Quincy Newspapers Inc .... D 507 895-9969
La Crescent (G-2842)

S I C

(G-00000) Company's Geographic Section entry number
462
2011 Harris Minnesota Services Directory
▲=Import ▼=Export ◆=Import/Export

Sinclair Broadcasting Group ....E....651 646-2300
Saint Paul *(G-8960)*
Twin Cities Public Television ....C....651 222-1717
Saint Paul *(G-9088)*
United Communications Corp ....E....507 625-7905
North Mankato *(G-6515)*
United Communications Corp ....E....507 625-7905
Mankato *(G-3232)*

4841 Cable & Other Pay TV Svcs

Arvig Enterprises Inc ....C....218 346-5500
Perham *(G-6793)*
Arvig Enterprises Inc ....E....218 584-5119
Twin Valley *(G-9700)*
Captionmax Inc ....E....612 341-3566
Minneapolis *(G-4000)*
Charter Communications ....D....888 438-2427
Rochester *(G-7074)*
Fox Cable Network Services LLC ....D....612 330-2468
Minneapolis *(G-4469)*
Hector Communications Corp ....D....218 346-5500
New Ulm *(G-6453)*
Hiawatha Broadband Comms ....D....507 474-4000
Winona *(G-10101)*
Kasson & Mantorville Telephone ....E....507 634-2511
Kasson *(G-2821)*
Mediacom Inc ....E....952 440-9650
Prior Lake *(G-6941)*
Mediacom LLC ....E....507 835-5975
Waseca *(G-9882)*
Midcontinent Media Inc ....C....952 844-2600
Minneapolis *(G-5024)*
Prewire Specialists Inc ....C....651 452-9192
Saint Paul *(G-8846)*

4899 Communication Svcs, NEC

Access Communications Inc ....E....763 545-9998
Minneapolis *(G-3665)*
Animation Services Inc ....E....612 379-7117
Minneapolis *(G-3781)*
Dascom Systems Group LLC ....E....651 578-1200
Saint Paul *(G-9201)*
Hiawatha Broadband Comms ....D....507 474-4000
Winona *(G-10101)*
Spectrum Solutions Inc ....E....952 835-8338
Minneapolis *(G-5720)*
Thomas Koll ....E....763 323-9797
Anoka *(G-235)*
Weber Electric Inc ....D....651 490-1333
Saint Paul *(G-9142)*

49 ELECTRIC, GAS & SANITARY SVC

4911 Electric Svcs

Agralite Electric Cooperative ....E....320 843-4150
Benson *(G-437)*
Allete Inc ....C....218 279-5000
Duluth *(G-1235)*
Allete Inc ....D....320 632-2311
Little Falls *(G-2999)*
Allete Inc ....B....218 328-5711
Cohasset *(G-1070)*
Allete Inc ....E....218 628-3627
Duluth *(G-1236)*
Allete Inc ....E....218 722-2641
Duluth *(G-1237)*
Beltrami Electric Co-Op Inc ....D....218 444-2540
Bemidji *(G-375)*
Ben Co Electric ....E....507 387-7963
Mankato *(G-3110)*
Centerpoint Energy Resources ....E....612 372-4720
Minneapolis *(G-4045)*
Central Minnesota Municipal 507 526-2193
Blue Earth *(G-531)*
City of Elk River ....E....763 441-2020
Elk River *(G-1867)*
City of Grand Rapids ....D....218 326-7604
Grand Rapids *(G-2273)*
City of Owatonna ....D....507 451-2480
Owatonna *(G-6701)*
City of Rochester ....C....507 280-1540
Rochester *(G-7079)*
Connexus Energy ....C....763 323-2600
Anoka *(G-169)*
Crow Wing Cooperative Power ....D....218 829-2827
Brainerd *(G-562)*
Dakota Electric Association ....C....651 463-6212
Farmington *(G-2047)*
East Central Energy ....C....320 396-3351
Braham *(G-541)*
FMI Hydraulics Inc ....E....507 296-4551
Porter *(G-6893)*
Fpd Power Development LLC ....C....612 782-3100
Minneapolis *(G-4470)*
General Electric Co ....E....507 368-9222
Lake Benton *(G-2848)*
▲ **Great River Energy** ....B....763 445-5000
Maple Grove *(G-3243)*
Great River Energy ....C....763 441-3121
Elk River *(G-1877)*
Interstate Power & Light Co ....D....507 373-2371
Albert Lea *(G-58)*

Itasca-Mantrap Co-Op Electric ....E....218 732-3377
Park Rapids *(G-6757)*
Kandiyohi Power Cooperative ....E....320 235-4155
Willmar *(G-10014)*
Kandiyohi Power Cooperative ....E....320 796-1155
Spicer *(G-9556)*
Lake Country Power ....E....218 741-8137
Mountain Iron *(G-6393)*
Lake Region Electric Co-op ....D....218 863-1171
Pelican Rapids *(G-6780)*
McLeod Cooperative Power Assn ....E....320 864-3148
Glencoe *(G-2208)*
Mille Lacs Electric Co-op ....D....218 927-2191
Aitkin *(G-22)*
Minnesota Valley Cooperative ....E....320 269-2163
Montevideo *(G-6250)*
Minnesota Valley Electric ....D....952 492-2313
Jordan *(G-2807)*
Mp Technologies LLC ....E....320 963-2499
Maple Lake *(G-3263)*
Northern Alternative Energy ....E....612 370-1061
Wayzata *(G-9933)*
Northern States Power Co ....D....763 441-3800
Elk River *(G-1887)*
Northern States Power Co ....E....763 295-5151
Monticello *(G-6280)*
Northern States Power Co ....B....763 261-4100
Becker *(G-357)*
Northern States Power Co ....E....763 295-4141
Monticello *(G-6281)*
Northern States Power Co ....B....612 330-5674
Saint Paul *(G-8761)*
Northern States Power Co ....C....320 255-8601
Saint Cloud *(G-7563)*
Northern States Power Co ....C....651 639-4470
Saint Paul *(G-8760)*
Northern States Power Co ....E....612 330-6349
Welch *(G-9954)*
Northern States Power Co ....C....507 387-9629
Mankato *(G-3176)*
Northern States Power Co ....D....651 731-5701
Bayport *(G-350)*
Northern States Power Co ....D....763 493-1500
Osseo *(G-6645)*
Otter Tail Corp ....E....218 739-8100
Fergus Falls *(G-2104)*
Otter Tail Corp 866 410-8780
Fergus Falls *(G-2105)*
◆ **Otter Tail Power Co** ....C....866 410-8780
Fergus Falls *(G-2109)*
Otter Tail Power Co ....E....218 281-3632
Crookston *(G-1132)*
Otter Tail Power Co ....B....218 736-6947
Fergus Falls *(G-2108)*
Otter Tail Power Co ....B....218 739-8200
Fergus Falls *(G-2110)*
Peoples Cooperative Services ....E....507 288-4004
Rochester *(G-7201)*
Rice Wild Electric Cooperative ....E....218 935-2517
Mahnomen *(G-3090)*
Roseau Electric Cooperative ....E....218 463-1543
Roseau *(G-7358)*
Runestone Electric Association ....E....320 763-6641
Alexandria *(G-121)*
Southern Minnesota Municipal ....E....507 285-0478
Rochester *(G-7259)*
Stearns Cooperative Electric ....D....320 256-4241
Melrose *(G-3352)*
Steele-Waseca Cooperative Elec ....E....507 451-7340
Owatonna *(G-6739)*
Telepak Industries Inc ....E....507 332-0012
Faribault *(G-2034)*
Todd Wadena Electric Co-op ....E....218 631-3120
Wadena *(G-9812)*
Tri-County Electric Co-op ....D....507 864-7783
Rushford *(G-7394)*
Virginia, City of Inc ....D....218 748-7540
Virginia *(G-9761)*
Willmar, City of Inc ....D....320 235-4422
Willmar *(G-10056)*
Wisconsin Public Service Corp ....E....218 879-1571
Cloquet *(G-1069)*
Wright-Hennepin Cooperative ....D....763 477-3000
Rockford *(G-7305)*
Wright-Hennepin Security Corp ....C....763 477-3000
Rockford *(G-7306)*
XCEL Energy Inc ....E....651 385-5604
Red Wing *(G-7014)*

4922 Natural Gas Transmission

Cenex Inc ....A....800 232-3639
South Saint Paul *(G-9516)*
Northern Natural Gas Co ....E....952 887-1700
Minneapolis *(G-5228)*

4924 Natural Gas Distribution

Allete Inc ....C....218 279-5000
Duluth *(G-1235)*
Cargill Power Markets LLC ....E....952 984-3068
Minnetonka *(G-6151)*
Centerpoint Energy Houston ....E....763 757-6200
Minneapolis *(G-3431)*
Centerpoint Energy Resources ....D....612 861-8450
Minneapolis *(G-4044)*

City of Owatonna ....D....507 451-2480
Owatonna *(G-6701)*
MDU Resources Group Inc ....E....218 736-6935
Fergus Falls *(G-2093)*
Minnesota Energy Resources ....C....651 322-8902
Rosemount *(G-7372)*
Northern States Power Co ....C....320 255-8601
Saint Cloud *(G-7563)*
Virginia, City of Inc ....D....218 748-7540
Virginia *(G-9761)*

4925 Gas Production &/Or Distribution

▲ **Hearth & Home Technologies Inc** ....C....952 985-6000
Lakeville *(G-2909)*

4931 Electric & Other Svcs Combined

Austin Utilities ....D....507 433-8886
Austin *(G-262)*
City of Rochester ....C....507 280-1540
Rochester *(G-7079)*
City of Rochester ....E....507 280-1657
Rochester *(G-7078)*
Cottage Grove, City of Inc ....E....651 458-2808
Cottage Grove *(G-1101)*
Emergency Energy Systems ....E....320 354-5380
New London *(G-6414)*
Hibbing Public Utilities Commn ....D....218 262-7700
Hibbing *(G-2451)*
NRG Energy Inc ....E....612 349-6087
Minneapolis *(G-5252)*
Shakopee Public Utilities ....E....952 233-1505
Shakopee *(G-9474)*

4932 Gas & Other Svcs Combined

Centerpoint Energy Resources ....E....651 554-3000
South Saint Paul *(G-9517)*
City of Owatonna ....D....507 451-2480
Owatonna *(G-6703)*
Otter Tail Energy Services Co ....A....218 739-8888
Fergus Falls *(G-2107)*

4939 Combination Utilities, NEC

Energy Management Steam ....E....612 626-7329
Minneapolis *(G-4357)*
Ever-Green Energy LLC ....D....651 290-2812
Saint Paul *(G-8349)*
New Ulm, City of Inc ....D....507 359-8264
New Ulm *(G-6470)*
Willmar, City of Inc ....D....320 235-4422
Willmar *(G-10056)*

4941 Water Sply

Allete Inc ....C....218 279-5000
Duluth *(G-1235)*
City of Duluth ....A....218 730-5230
Duluth *(G-1276)*
City of Owatonna ....D....507 451-2480
Owatonna *(G-6701)*
City of Rochester ....C....507 280-1540
Rochester *(G-7079)*
▲ **District Energy St Paul Inc** ....E....651 297-8955
Saint Paul *(G-8300)*
Red River Basin Commission ....E....218 291-0422
Moorhead *(G-6335)*
Saint Paul Regional Water Svcs ....E....651 776-6960
Saint Paul *(G-8928)*
Saint Paul Regional Water Svcs ....E....651 266-1635
Saint Paul *(G-8929)*
Virginia, City of Inc ....D....218 748-7540
Virginia *(G-9761)*
Willmar, City of Inc ....D....320 235-4422
Willmar *(G-10056)*

4952 Sewerage Systems

New Ulm, City of Inc ....D....507 359-8264
New Ulm *(G-6470)*
Western Lake Superior Sanitary ....D....218 722-3336
Duluth *(G-1502)*

4953 Refuse Systems

Allied Waste Industries Inc ....D....952 941-5174
Eden Prairie *(G-1588)*
American Paper Recycling Corp ....E....651 644-7806
Saint Paul *(G-8031)*
Appliance Recycling Centers of ....E....952 930-9000
Minneapolis *(G-3791)*
Aspen Waste Systems Inc ....E....612 884-8000
Minneapolis *(G-3819)*
BFI Waste Systems of North ....E....612 522-6558
Minneapolis *(G-3899)*
BFI Waste Systems of North ....E....651 437-8101
South Saint Paul *(G-9513)*
BFI Waste Systems of North ....C....763 259-5570
Circle Pines *(G-1003)*
Browning-Ferris Industries Inc ....E....651 641-0009
Saint Paul *(G-8134)*
City of Minneapolis ....E....612 673-3779
Minneapolis *(G-4089)*

S I C

Employment codes: A=Over 500 employees, B=251-500
C=101-250, D=51-100, E=25-50
2011 Harris Minnesota
Services Directory
© Harris InfoSource 1-866-281-6415
463

Covanta Energy Group Inc....E....612 333-7303
Minneapolis (G-4174)
Darrell B Johnson Disposal Co....E....218 729-5446
Duluth (G-1291)
Deer River Hired Hands Inc....E....218 246-8182
Deer River (G-1169)
Dem-Con Landfill LLC....E....952 445-5755
Shakopee (G-9436)
Dick's Sanitation Service Inc....D....952 469-2239
Lakeville (G-2903)
Employment Enterprises Inc....D....320 632-9251
Little Falls (G-3002)
Endres Services Inc....D....651 438-3113
Rosemount (G-7369)
Forest Lake Sanitation Inc....E....651 464-2321
Wyoming (G-10204)
Gene Bueckers....E....320 352-2876
Sauk Centre (G-9346)
Goodwill Industries Inc....C....651 379-5800
Saint Paul (G-8421)
Goodwill Industries Inc....E....952 953-4410
Saint Paul (G-7787)
Goodwill Industries Inc....E....651 439-4207
Stillwater (G-9620)
Hartel's Dbj Disposal Co's LLC....E....218 729-5446
Proctor (G-6963)
Jmdl Inc....E....952 873-2636
Belle Plaine (G-373)
JME Of Monticello Inc....E....763 295-3122
Monticello (G-6275)
Liberty Paper Inc....D....763 261-6100
Becker (G-356)
M & M Sanitation Inc....E....320 358-4078
Cambridge (G-841)
Mid-State Reclamation Inc....E....952 985-5555
Lakeville (G-2919)
Minneapolis Refuse Inc....E....612 529-4788
Minneapolis (G-5063)
Minnesota Dakota Generating Co....218 739-8200
Fergus Falls (G-2096)
Minnesota Shredding LLC....E....763 493-3007
Minneapolis (G-5093)
Monitor Tire Disposal Inc....320 548-3496
Saint Martin (G-7671)
Neighborhood Recycling Corp....E....651 222-7678
Minneapolis (G-5181)
New Ulm, City of Inc....D....507 359-8264
New Ulm (G-6470)
Palmer Bus Services....E....952 445-1166
Shakopee (G-9465)
▼ Pioneer Industries Inc....D....612 374-2280
Minneapolis (G-5383)
Pollution Control Agency, MN....E....507 285-7343
Rochester (G-7206)
Pollution Control Agency, MN....D....218 723-4660
Duluth (G-1427)
Pope Douglas Solid Waste Mgt....E....320 763-9340
Alexandria (G-117)
Randt Recycling Technologies....E....763 417-1370
Litchfield (G-2989)
Reliakor Services Inc....E....952 403-1440
Shakopee (G-9469)
Rock-Tenn Co....A....651 641-4874
Saint Paul (G-8910)
S KB Environmental....E....507 433-8131
Austin (G-285)
Safety-Kleen Systems Inc....E....952 469-8356
Lakeville (G-2931)
Schaap Sanitation Inc....E....507 376-9218
Worthington (G-10193)
Schwartzman Co Inc....E....763 421-1187
Anoka (G-224)
Stericycle Inc....E....651 641-0009
Saint Paul (G-9005)
Stericycle Specialty Waste....E....612 285-9865
Minneapolis (G-3608)
Tennis Sanitation LLC....E....651 459-1887
Saint Paul Park (G-9298)
Tires To Fuel LLC....218 624-5009
Duluth (G-1485)
U S Filter Recovery Services....E....651 638-1300
Saint Paul (G-9099)
▲ Veit & Co Inc....C....763 428-2242
Rogers (G-7347)
Veit Container Corp....E....507 281-3867
Rochester (G-7279)
Veolia Environmental Services....E....651 774-0916
Saint Paul (G-9124)
Veolia Es Solid Waste Midwest....D....507 281-5850
Rochester (G-7280)
Veolia Es Solid Waste Midwest....E....651 459-3029
Saint Paul (G-9125)
Veolia Es Solid Waste of Pa....E....320 251-8919
Saint Cloud (G-7444)
Walter's Recycling & Refuse....E....763 780-8464
Minneapolis (G-3637)
Waste Management of Minnesota....E....507 826-3610
Albert Lea (G-70)
Waste Management of Minnesota....E....952 736-2428
Burnsville (G-820)
Waste Management of North MN....D....218 624-7838
Duluth (G-1498)
Waste Management of Wisconsin....C....952 890-1100
Minneapolis (G-3639)
Water Reclamation Plant....E....507 281-6190
Rochester (G-7285)

4959 Sanitary Svcs, NEC

A-Scape Inc....E....952 496-1178
Shakopee (G-9417)
AAA All American Lawn....E....763 537-5733
Anoka (G-145)
Asphalt Surface Technologies....D....320 363-8500
Saint Joseph (G-7650)
Carefree Services Inc....E....763 479-2600
Maple Plain (G-3271)
Ferguson Brothers Excavating....E....320 762-0622
Alexandria (G-101)
Heikes Enterprises Inc....E....651 437-3847
Hastings (G-2391)
Lawn Professionals & Treasures....E....651 482-1431
Saint Paul (G-8567)
Outdoor Environments Inc....E....952 496-1000
Savage (G-9403)
Premier Co's Inc....E....218 348-1991
Duluth (G-1429)
Reliakor Services Inc....E....952 403-1440
Shakopee (G-9469)
Wagner Sod Co Inc....E....651 457-6037
Inver Grove Heights (G-2773)

4961 Steam & Air Conditioning Sply

Foster Wheeler Twin Cities Inc....E....612 379-1885
Minneapolis (G-4468)
Franklin Heating Station....E....507 289-3534
Rochester (G-7119)
Interstate Co's Inc....D....952 854-2044
Minneapolis (G-4726)

4971 Irrigation Systems

West Central Irrigation Inc....E....320 239-2230
Starbuck (G-9588)

50 WHOLESALE TRADE-DURABLE GOODS

5012 Automobiles & Other Motor Vehicles Wholesale

▲ ABC Bus Co's Inc....D....507 334-1871
Faribault (G-1985)
▲ ABC Bus Inc....D....507 334-1871
Faribault (G-1986)
ABC Minneapolis LLC....C....763 428-8777
Osseo (G-6590)
ABM Equipment & Supply Inc....952 938-5451
Hopkins (G-2498)
ABM Equipment & Supply LLC....E....952 938-5451
Hopkins (G-2499)
Allstate Sales & Leasing Corp....D....651 455-6500
South Saint Paul (G-9508)
▼ Associated Partnership Ltd....C....952 890-7851
Savage (G-9383)
Astleford Equipment Co Inc....E....952 894-9200
Burnsville (G-681)
Brooklyn Center Motors LLC....D....763 535-5200
Minneapolis (G-3959)
Central Motors....E....651 674-7017
North Branch (G-6499)
Chesley Truck Sales Inc....C....651 636-3400
Saint Paul (G-9195)
Crossroads Trailer Sales & Svc....E....507 373-4443
Albert Lea (G-45)
Dahlke Trailer Sales Inc....E....763 783-0077
Minneapolis (G-3450)
Glen's Truck Center Inc....E....763 428-4331
Rogers (G-7324)
▲ Gull Way Ltd....E....218 753-1210
Tower (G-9687)
Hoglund Bus Co Inc....E....763 295-5119
Monticello (G-6273)
Istate Truck Inc....952 854-2044
Minneapolis (G-4739)
Manders Diesel Repair Inc....E....952 469-1800
Lakeville (G-2915)
Manheim Auctions Inc....B....763 425-7653
Osseo (G-6633)
Mid-State Auto Auction Inc....C....218 385-3777
New York Mills (G-6479)
Midwest Diesel Service Inc....E....763 780-8533
Minneapolis (G-6127)
Midwest Motors LLC....D....651 455-6000
Inver Grove Heights (G-2763)
Nelson Leasing Inc....E....320 235-2770
Willmar (G-10029)
Nintey Four Services Inc....E....763 295-3604
Monticello (G-6279)
North Star Auto Auction....C....952 445-5544
Shakopee (G-9460)
North Star International....D....612 378-1660
Minneapolis (G-5219)
▲ Northern Wholesale Supply Inc....D....651 429-1515
Hugo (G-2672)
Nuss Truck Group Inc....E....507 345-6225
Mankato (G-3178)
Olson & Johnson International....E....507 532-5718
Marshall (G-3318)
Rihm Motor Co....D....651 646-7833
Saint Paul (G-8902)
River Valley Truck Centers Inc....D....507 345-1129
Mankato (G-3187)
Riverbend Auto Sales Inc....E....507 345-8967
Mankato (G-3188)
Security Auto Loans Inc....E....763 559-5892
Plymouth (G-6883)
St Cloud Subaru....E....320 258-0163
Saint Cloud (G-7605)
St Cloud Truck Sales Inc....D....320 251-0931
Saint Cloud (G-7442)
Thompson Motors of Wykoff Inc....E....507 352-2435
Wykoff (G-10200)
Titan Machinery Inc....E....218 281-4668
Crookston (G-1137)
Trudell Trailers of Minnesota....E....763 497-7084
Albertville (G-77)
Walden Leasing Inc....E....952 512-8924
Minneapolis (G-5996)
Westman Freightliner Inc....E....507 625-4118
Mankato (G-3217)

5013 Motor Vehicle Splys & New Parts Wholesale

A & J Tba Inc....507 233-3000
New Ulm (G-6437)
ABM Equipment & Supply Inc....952 938-5451
Hopkins (G-2498)
ABM Equipment & Supply LLC....E....952 938-5451
Hopkins (G-2499)
Advanced Automotive Industries....E....651 777-5420
Saint Paul (G-9182)
Allstate Sales & Leasing Corp....D....651 455-6500
South Saint Paul (G-9508)
Astleford Equipment Co Inc....E....952 894-9200
Burnsville (G-681)
Automotive Cooling Products....E....651 731-2414
Saint Paul (G-9186)
Automotive Restyling Concepts....D....763 535-2181
Minneapolis (G-3840)
Bell Industries Inc....C....651 203-2300
Eagan (G-1517)
Bert's Truck Equipment of....E....218 233-8681
Moorhead (G-6298)
Best Oil Co....E....218 879-4666
Cloquet (G-1046)
Clutch & Transmission Service....E....651 636-4311
Saint Paul (G-8217)
Clutch & Transmission Service....D....651 631-0959
Saint Paul (G-8218)
◆ CMC Enterprises Inc....E....763 545-3800
Plymouth (G-6856)
▲ Como Lube & Supplies Inc....E....218 722-2920
Duluth (G-1280)
Crookston Welding Machine Co....E....218 281-6911
Crookston (G-1122)
Crysteel Truck Equipment Inc....E....952 469-5678
Lakeville (G-2899)
Dahlke Trailer Sales Inc....E....763 783-0077
Minneapolis (G-3450)
Dave Syverson Truck Center Inc....E....507 289-3357
Rochester (G-7093)
Forbes, John....E....320 693-3287
Litchfield (G-2984)
Genuine Parts Co....D....952 925-0188
Minneapolis (G-4523)
Gerald N Evenson Inc....E....218 863-7101
Pelican Rapids (G-6779)
Graffco Inc....E....651 464-1079
Forest Lake (G-2146)
Grossman Chevrolet Co Inc....C....952 435-8501
Burnsville (G-730)
Grove Cottage Auto Parts Inc....952 469-2801
Lakeville (G-2942)
Hance Distributing Inc....E....952 935-6429
Hopkins (G-2548)
Hoglund Bus Co Inc....E....763 295-5119
Monticello (G-6273)
Hvh Auto Parts Inc....C....763 784-1711
Minneapolis (G-3493)
Infiniti Marketing Inc....E....612 789-2025
Mound (G-6388)
Innovance Inc....E....507 373-5152
Albert Lea (G-55)
Istate Truck Inc....952 854-2044
Minneapolis (G-4739)
J B Distributing Co Inc....E....952 934-7354
Eden Prairie (G-1699)
Jomar Investments Inc....E....651 686-6100
Saint Paul (G-7811)
Kath Management Co....D....651 484-3325
Saint Paul (G-8541)
Kato Distributing Inc....D....507 289-7456
Rochester (G-7150)
Keystone Automotive Industries....E....763 788-3039
Minneapolis (G-3509)
▲ Keystone Automotive Industries....D....612 789-1919
Minneapolis (G-4802)
Kolstad Co Inc....D....763 792-1033
Minneapolis (G-3511)
Kunz Oil Co....D....952 352-8600
Hopkins (G-2567)
L & M Supply Inc....C....218 326-9451
Grand Rapids (G-2289)
L & M Supply Inc....D....218 751-3237
Bemidji (G-401)

(G-00000) Company's Geographic Section entry number
464
2011 Harris Minnesota
Services Directory
▲=Import ▼=Export
◆=Import/Export

L & M Supply Inc ....E....218 732-4465
Park Rapids (G-6759)
▲ Lakeview Industries Inc ....E....952 368-3500
Chaska (G-974)
◆ Mid-States Distributing Co Inc ....E....651 698-8831
Saint Paul (G-8652)
Mills Pontiac, Buick ....E....320 231-1160
Willmar (G-10024)
Mills Pontiac, Buick ....E....320 231-1160
Willmar (G-10025)
Minter-Weisman Co ....B....763 545-3706
Minneapolis (G-5105)
▲ Napco International LLC ....E....952 931-2400
Hopkins (G-2587)
▲ Northern Factory Sales Inc ....E....320 235-2288
Willmar (G-10030)
▲ Northern Wholesale Supply Inc ....D....651 429-1515
Hugo (G-2672)
Olson & Johnson International ....E....507 532-5718
Marshall (G-3318)
P & L Automotive Inc ....E....952 941-0888
Minneapolis (G-5304)
Palmer's Auto Supply Inc ....E....507 354-3154
New Ulm (G-6472)
Pgw Auto Glass LLC ....E....952 888-0413
Minneapolis (G-5373)
Quick Service Battery Co Inc ....E....651 645-0485
Saint Paul (G-7887)
Red Rooster Auto Stores LLC ....D....763 533-4321
Minneapolis (G-5477)
▲ Reviva Inc ....D....763 535-8900
Minneapolis (G-3584)
Rihm Motor Co ....D....651 646-7833
Saint Paul (G-8902)
River Valley Truck Centers Inc ....D....507 345-1129
Mankato (G-3187)
Smith's Winter Products ....E....763 493-3332
Osseo (G-6665)
St Cloud Truck Sales Inc ....D....320 251-0931
Saint Cloud (G-7442)
3M Co ....D....651 733-5300
Saint Paul (G-9047)
◆ Total Automotive Inc ....E....952 448-7750
Chanhassen (G-944)
Toyota City Inc ....D....763 566-0060
Minneapolis (G-5842)
Tri-County Parts Supply Inc ....E....320 253-5050
Saint Cloud (G-7620)
Trudell Trailers of Minnesota ....E....763 497-7084
Albertville (G-77)
Twinco Romax LLC ....E....763 478-2360
Hamel (G-2358)
U S Warehouse Supply Inc ....D....651 405-3500
Saint Paul (G-7932)
UNI-Select USA Inc ....E....952 352-8603
Eden Prairie (G-1800)
UNI-Select USA Inc ....E....763 566-1285
Minneapolis (G-5900)
▲ Universal Cooperatives Inc ....D....651 239-1000
Saint Paul (G-7938)
US Venture Inc ....D....763 591-5827
Minneapolis (G-5950)
Valley Truck Parts & Service ....E....218 773-3486
East Grand Forks (G-1578)
Viking Auto Salvage Inc ....E....651 460-6166
Northfield (G-6522)
Von Ruden Manufacturing Inc ....D....763 682-3122
Buffalo (G-659)
Westman Freightliner Inc ....E....507 625-4118
Mankato (G-3217)
Zitco Inc ....D....952 392-6060
Minneapolis (G-6121)

5014 Tires & Tubes Wholesale

A & J Tba Inc 507 233-3000
New Ulm (G-6437)
American Tire Distributors Inc ....E....952 345-0000
Minneapolis (G-3761)
Automotive Restyling Concepts ....D....763 535-2181
Minneapolis (G-3840)
Bauer Built Inc ....E....651 646-1239
Saint Paul (G-8092)
▲ Countrywide Tire & Rubber Inc ....E....763 546-1636
Minneapolis (G-4171)
▲ Hanco Corp ....E....651 456-5600
Saint Paul (G-7794)
Midstates Retreading & Whsle ....E....507 288-7752
Rochester (G-7183)
Royal Tire Inc ....D....320 258-7070
Saint Cloud (G-7590)
Samaritan Wholesale Tire Co ....E....612 729-8000
Minneapolis (G-5599)
Tire Associates Warehouse Inc ....E....507 625-2975
Mankato (G-3207)
Triton Tire & Battery LLC ....E....651 239-1200
Saint Paul (G-7929)
▲ Universal Cooperatives Inc ....D....651 239-1000
Saint Paul (G-7938)
◆ Westside Wholesale Tire Inc ....E....763 420-2100
Hamel (G-2361)
Wingfoot Commercial Tire Systs ....E....507 454-5181
Winona (G-10142)

5015 Motor Vehicle Parts, Used Wholesale

AAA Auto Salvage Inc ....E....651 423-2432
Rosemount (G-7360)
Ace Auto Parts & Salvage Inc ....E....651 224-9479
Saint Paul (G-7979)
Crosstown Used Auto Parts ....E....612 861-3020
Saint Paul (G-8270)
Erickson Truck Sales & Salvage ....E....507 847-3664
Jackson (G-2791)
Fridley Auto Parts Inc ....D....763 784-8890
Minneapolis (G-3472)
Glen's Truck Center Inc ....E....763 428-4331
Rogers (G-7324)
Hvh Auto Parts Inc ....C....763 784-1711
Minneapolis (G-3493)
Triton Tire & Battery LLC ....E....651 239-1200
Saint Paul (G-7929)
Viking Auto Salvage Inc ....E....651 460-6166
Northfield (G-6522)

5021 Furniture Wholesale

Alternative Business Furniture ....D....952 937-7688
Eden Prairie (G-1589)
Bennett Office Technologies ....E....320 235-6425
Willmar (G-9985)
Bertelson Brothers Inc ....E....763 546-4371
Minneapolis (G-3889)
◆ Bgd Co's Inc ....E....612 338-6804
Minneapolis (G-3900)
▲ Blu DOT Design & Manufacturing ....E....612 782-1844
Minneapolis (G-3918)
Buyonlinenow Inc ....E....507 281-6899
Rochester (G-7068)
Corporate Express Office Prdts ....C....651 636-2250
Saint Paul (G-8251)
E T C Enterprises Inc ....E....320 240-0567
Saint Cloud (G-7500)
Ecm Publishers Inc ....E....763 689-1981
Cambridge (G-837)
Encompass Group LLC ....D....651 646-6600
Saint Paul (G-8339)
Encompass Group LLC ....C....651 646-6600
Saint Paul (G-8340)
Fluid Interiors ....E....612 746-8700
Minneapolis (G-4458)
Haldeman-Homme Inc ....C....612 331-4880
Minneapolis (G-4590)
Innovative Office Solutions ....D....952 808-9900
Burnsville (G-736)
Intereum Inc ....C....763 417-3300
Minneapolis (G-4716)
Jacobs Trading LLC ....E....763 843-2066
Hopkins (G-2561)
▲ Lintex Corp ....C....651 646-6600
Saint Paul (G-8591)
Macy's Retail Holdings Inc ....D....612 343-0868
Minneapolis (G-4930)
Metro Systems Furniture Inc ....E....952 933-5050
Minneapolis (G-5004)
North Country Business Prdts ....D....218 751-4140
Bemidji (G-408)
North Country Business Prdts ....E....800 937-4140
Plymouth (G-6878)
▲ Northern Business Products Inc ....E....218 726-0167
Duluth (G-1402)
▲ River of Goods Inc ....D....651 917-5335
Saint Paul (G-8904)
S & T Office Products Inc ....C....651 483-4411
Saint Paul (G-8918)
S P Richards Co ....E....651 484-8459
Saint Paul (G-8920)
Wayne Baumgart Distributors 952 447-2750
Prior Lake (G-6961)
Winsted Corp ....E....952 944-9050
Minneapolis (G-6078)

5023 Home Furnishings Wholesale

C L T Floor Coverings Inc ....E....651 451-0069
Inver Grove Heights (G-2740)
Carpet Factory Outlet Inc 612 988-0400
Minneapolis (G-4020)
Cheney LLC ....E....763 559-1980
Minneapolis (G-4058)
Compass Marketing Inc ....D....612 333-5300
Minneapolis (G-4147)
Encompass Group LLC ....D....651 646-6600
Saint Paul (G-8339)
Encompass Group LLC ....C....651 646-6600
Saint Paul (G-8340)
Floor Store Inc ....E....952 401-0955
Excelsior (G-1943)
Gordy's Glass Inc ....E....651 437-5356
Hastings (G-2416)
Grill Works Inc ....E....507 532-3524
Marshall (G-3298)
Hajoca Corp ....E....763 315-0100
Minneapolis (G-4589)
Hank's Specialties Inc ....E....651 633-5020
New Brighton (G-6409)
▲ Herregan Distributors Inc ....D....651 452-7200
Saint Paul (G-7799)
Hom Furniture Inc ....D....952 884-8800
Minneapolis (G-4664)
Hom Furniture Inc ....E....651 634-6600
Saint Paul (G-8492)
Homecrest Outdoor Living LLC ....D....218 631-1000
Wadena (G-9803)
▲ Impact Innovations Inc ....D....320 847-1210
Clara City (G-1028)
Jacobs Trading LLC ....E....763 843-2066
Hopkins (G-2561)
Lenox Group Inc ....C....952 943-4100
Eden Prairie (G-1708)
▲ Lintex Corp ....C....651 646-6600
Saint Paul (G-8591)
Mohawk Industries Inc ....E....651 405-8300
Saint Paul (G-7845)
▲ Olympia Tile Inc ....E....763 545-5455
Minneapolis (G-5274)
Shade Warren Co ....D....612 331-5939
Minneapolis (G-5647)
Steven Fabrics Co ....C....612 781-6671
Minneapolis (G-5753)
▲ Stone Source Inc 763 540-9000
Plymouth (G-6884)
T Distribution Inc ....E....651 636-6367
Saint Paul (G-9024)
▲ Tile Shop Inc ....E....763 541-1444
Minneapolis (G-5824)
▲ Wild Wings LLC ....D....651 345-5355
Lake City (G-2856)

5031 Lumber, Plywood & Millwork Wholesale

Alside Builders Service ....E....952 888-1339
Minneapolis (G-3735)
API Garage Door Co ....E....763 533-3838
Minneapolis (G-3789)
Arrowhead Concrete Works Inc ....E....218 729-8274
Duluth (G-1240)
Automated Building Components ....E....952 474-4374
Excelsior (G-1938)
Bayer Built Woodworks Inc ....C....320 254-3651
Belgrade (G-360)
Bruce Kreofsky & Sons Inc ....D....507 534-3855
Plainview (G-6839)
Christ's Household of Faith ....D....651 265-3400
Saint Paul (G-8198)
Construction Midwest Inc ....E....763 536-8336
Minneapolis (G-4156)
Contract Hardware Co Inc ....E....651 780-0010
Circle Pines (G-1007)
Crawford Door Sales Co Twin ....E....651 455-1221
Saint Paul (G-7739)
Custom Door Sales Inc ....D....612 332-0357
Minneapolis (G-4203)
Custom Millwork Inc ....E....651 770-2356
Saint Paul (G-8275)
D & M Industries Inc ....E....218 287-3100
Moorhead (G-6309)
Distinctive Door Design Inc ....E....763 389-1631
Princeton (G-6920)
▲ Donlin Co ....E....320 251-3680
Saint Cloud (G-7411)
Erdman Automation Corp ....D....763 389-9475
Princeton (G-6905)
Extreme Panel Technologies Inc ....E....507 423-5530
Cottonwood (G-1112)
▲ Forest Weekes Products Inc ....D....651 644-9807
Saint Paul (G-8388)
Gordy's Glass Inc ....E....651 437-5356
Hastings (G-2416)
Harkraft Inc ....E....763 546-9161
Minneapolis (G-4597)
Heritage Millwork Inc ....E....763 323-7501
Anoka (G-190)
Jaeckle Minnesota ....D....612 676-0388
Minneapolis (G-4751)
Kendell Doors & Hardware Inc ....E....507 454-1723
Winona (G-10107)
Kendell Doors & Hardware Inc ....D....651 905-0144
Mendota Heights (G-3365)
Lake States Lumber Inc ....E....218 927-2125
Aitkin (G-21)
Lake States Lumber Inc ....E....763 425-0204
Brooklyn Park (G-613)
Lowe's Home Centers Inc ....C....763 367-1340
Minneapolis (G-3524)
Lowe's Home Centers Inc ....C....507 446-4900
Owatonna (G-6723)
Lowe's Home Centers Inc ....C....763 367-9000
Minneapolis (G-4904)
Lowe's Home Centers Inc ....C....952 367-9000
Shakopee (G-9452)
Lowe's Home Centers Inc ....C....763 428-5970
Rogers (G-7328)
Lowe's Home Centers Inc ....C....763 488-2001
Osseo (G-6629)
Lowe's Home Centers Inc ....C....218 262-7460
Hibbing (G-2459)
Lowe's Home Centers Inc ....C....651 275-9910
Stillwater (G-9626)
Lowe's Home Centers Inc ....C....507 328-8920
Rochester (G-7162)
Lowe's Home Centers Inc ....C....507 385-3560
Mankato (G-3158)
Lowe's Home Centers Inc ....C....763 367-4139
Saint Paul (G-7826)

S
I
C

Employment codes: A=Over 500 employees, B=251-500
C=101-250, D=51-100, E=25-50
2011 Harris Minnesota
Services Directory
© Harris InfoSource 1-866-281-6415
465

Lowe's Home Centers Inc ....C....763 367-1120
Minneapolis (G-3523)
Lowe's Home Centers Inc ....C....763 691-6040
Cambridge (G-840)
Lumber Mart Inc ....E....218 773-1151
East Grand Forks (G-1571)
Lyman Lumber Co ....B....952 470-3600
Excelsior (G-1945)
Lyman Lumber Co ....D....952 470-4800
Chanhassen (G-931)
Maly Co's LLC ....E....612 788-9688
Minneapolis (G-4939)
Manion Lumber & Truss Inc ....E....218 746-3200
Pillager (G-6811)
Material Distributors Inc ....E....507 532-4463
Marshall (G-3312)
Menard Inc ....C....218 722-0078
Duluth (G-1390)
Menard Inc ....C....952 941-4400
Eden Prairie (G-1719)
Mid-America Cedar Inc ....E....763 425-0125
Osseo (G-6637)
▲ Midwest Hardwood Corp ....D....763 425-8700
Osseo (G-6638)
Minnesota Exteriors Inc ....C....763 493-5500
Osseo (G-6639)
Minnesota Valley Millwork Inc ....E....952 440-9404
Prior Lake (G-6944)
Minnesota Vinyl & Aluminum ....E....952 403-0805
Shakopee (G-9457)
Mo-Tech Corp ....E....651 770-1515
Saint Paul (G-9251)
N A H Inc ....E....507 462-3331
Minnesota Lake (G-6137)
Northland Hardwood Lumber Co ....E....218 751-0550
Bemidji (G-414)
Pacific Mutual Door Co ....E....651 631-2211
Saint Paul (G-8800)
Pella Products Inc ....E....763 745-1400
Minneapolis (G-5360)
Pella Windows & Doors Twin ....D....763 745-1400
Minneapolis (G-5361)
Pine Point Wood Products Inc ....E....763 428-4301
Osseo (G-6653)
Plastic Products Co Inc ....E....651 257-3143
Lindstrom (G-2970)
Probuild Co LLC ....D....218 631-2607
Wadena (G-9810)
Probuild Co LLC ....D....320 251-0861
Saint Cloud (G-7573)
Probuild Co LLC ....E....952 469-2116
Lakeville (G-2925)
Probuild Co LLC ....D....952 469-3466
Lakeville (G-2926)
Remodeler's Choice Inc ....E....612 767-7000
Minneapolis (G-5516)
Renneberg Hardwoods Inc ....D....218 564-4912
Menahga (G-3359)
▲ Rice Lake Lumber Inc ....E....218 727-3213
Duluth (G-1437)
Ron's Cabinets Inc ....E....320 252-7667
Sauk Rapids (G-9372)
Root River Hardwoods Inc ....E....507 765-2284
Preston (G-6900)
Scherer Bros Lumber Co ....E....612 379-9633
Minneapolis (G-5608)
Shaw Acquisition Corp ....D....612 378-1520
Minneapolis (G-5650)
Shaw Lumber Co ....C....651 488-2525
Minneapolis (G-5651)
Shelter Products Inc ....E....507 354-4176
New Ulm (G-6474)
St Croix Valley Hardwoods Inc ....D....651 407-2800
Saint Paul (G-8983)
St Croix Valley Hardwoods Inc ....E....651 407-2800
Saint Paul (G-8982)
Structural Wood Corp ....E....651 426-8111
Saint Paul (G-9010)
Timber Roots LLC ....C....507 452-2361
Winona (G-10133)
Trimpac Inc ....D....320 202-3200
Sauk Rapids (G-9378)
Trimpac Inc ....E....320 650-0420
Saint Cloud (G-7621)
Twin City Custom Railings & GL ....E....763 780-7314
Minneapolis (G-3624)
Twin City Hardware Co ....E....651 735-2200
Saint Paul (G-9284)
Twin City Hardware Co ....E....763 535-4660
Minneapolis (G-5881)
United Products Corp of Amer ....D....651 227-8735
Saint Paul (G-9108)
USG Interiors Inc ....B....218 878-4000
Cloquet (G-1068)
USG Interiors Inc ....E....952 853-1233
Minneapolis (G-5951)
◆ Viking Forest Products LLC ....E....952 941-6512
Eden Prairie (G-1805)
W L Hall Co ....E....952 937-8400
Hopkins (G-2655)
Weyerhaeuser Co ....E....651 645-0811
Saint Paul (G-9152)
Weyerhaeuser Co ....C....218 546-8114
Deerwood (G-1180)
Wheeler Consolidated Inc ....E....952 929-6791
Minneapolis (G-6064)
Wheeler Hardware Co ....E....651 645-4501
Saint Paul (G-9153)

Winroc Corp ....D....651 777-8222
Saint Paul (G-9288)
Woodline Manufacturing Inc ....D....218 744-5966
Eveleth (G-1934)
Youngblood Lumber Co ....E....612 789-3521
Minneapolis (G-6106)

5032 Brick, Stone & Related Construction Mtrls Wholesale

Advance Specialties Co ....E....651 489-8881
Saint Paul (G-7989)
Brock White Co LLC ....E....651 647-0950
Saint Paul (G-8131)
▲ Capital Granite & Marble Inc ....E....320 259-7625
Saint Cloud (G-7469)
Cemstone Products Co ....E....651 645-0769
Saint Paul (G-8180)
Dale Tile Co ....E....763 488-1880
Minneapolis (G-4221)
Hancor Inc ....E....507 238-4791
Fairmont (G-1970)
Hedberg Aggregates Inc ....D....763 545-4400
Minneapolis (G-4627)
K&G Enterprises Inc ....E....763 263-7997
Big Lake (G-450)
L&W Supply Corp ....E....952 890-0828
Burnsville (G-745)
Mac Management Inc ....E....952 938-8048
Minnetonka (G-6189)
▲ Maxxon Corp ....E....763 478-6000
Hamel (G-2350)
Midwest Asphalt Corp ....E....952 937-8033
Hopkins (G-2582)
▲ Olympia Tile Inc ....E....763 545-5455
Minneapolis (G-5274)
Pro-Wall Inc ....E....763 477-5172
Rockford (G-7312)
Randy Kramer Excavating Inc ....E....320 764-6871
Watkins (G-9899)
▲ Rollin B Child Inc ....E....763 559-5531
Minneapolis (G-5558)
▲ Rubble Stone Co Inc ....E....952 938-2599
Hopkins (G-2623)
▲ Tile By Design Inc ....E....763 551-5900
Minneapolis (G-5823)
◆ Tile Shop LLC ....E....763 541-1444
Minneapolis (G-5825)
Twin City Concrete Products Co ....E....651 489-8095
Saint Paul (G-9091)
Winroc Corp ....D....651 777-8222
Saint Paul (G-9288)

5033 Roofing, Siding & Insulation Mtrls Wholesale

▲ Garlock-East Equipment Co ....E....763 553-1935
Minneapolis (G-4503)
Insulation Distributors Inc ....E....952 937-2000
Chanhassen (G-927)
Minnesota Exteriors Inc ....C....763 493-5500
Osseo (G-6639)
Shelter Products Inc ....E....507 354-4176
New Ulm (G-6474)
Structural Wood Corp ....E....651 426-8111
Saint Paul (G-9010)
United Products Corp of Amer ....D....651 227-8735
Saint Paul (G-9108)
United Products Corp of Amer ....E....763 545-1273
Minneapolis (G-5913)
Wausau Supply Co ....D....952 469-2500
Lakeville (G-2941)

5039 Construction Materials, NEC Wholesale

Architectural Sales of MN ....D....763 533-1595
Minneapolis (G-3802)
▲ Brin Glass Co ....C....612 529-9671
Minneapolis (G-3949)
▲ Harmon Inc ....E....952 944-5700
Eden Prairie (G-1677)
Menard Inc ....C....763 684-0830
Buffalo (G-650)
Minneapolis Glass Co ....D....763 559-0635
Plymouth (G-6874)
St Germain's Glass Inc ....E....218 628-0221
Duluth (G-1461)
St Paul Linoleum & Carpet Co ....D....651 686-7770
Eagan (G-1553)
Stylepointe LLC ....E....651 437-5356
Hastings (G-2418)
Trimline ....E....763 540-9737
Minneapolis (G-5857)
United Products Corp of Amer ....E....763 545-1273
Minneapolis (G-5913)

5043 Photographic Eqpt & Splys Wholesale

H & J Bliss Enterprises ....E....952 988-9302
Minneapolis (G-4584)
▲ Pakor Inc ....E....763 559-8484
Osseo (G-6650)
3M Co ....D....651 733-1941
Saint Paul (G-9055)
Tierney Brothers Inc ....D....612 331-5500
Minneapolis (G-5821)

5044 Office Eqpt Wholesale

Advanced Imaging Solutions Inc ....E....952 930-1882
Hopkins (G-2501)
AMI Imaging Systems Inc ....E....952 828-0080
Bloomington (G-485)
Atm Network Inc ....E....952 767-2000
Minnetonka (G-6146)
Ban-Koe Systems Inc ....D....952 888-6688
Minneapolis (G-3865)
Bennett Office Technologies ....E....320 235-6425
Willmar (G-9985)
◆ Cash Register Sales Inc ....D....651 294-2700
Saint Paul (G-8171)
Coordinated Business Systems ....D....952 894-9460
Burnsville (G-703)
Coordinated Business Systems ....D....320 251-1212
Waite Park (G-9821)
Data Systems Inc ....E....952 934-4001
Eden Prairie (G-1642)
Davis Typewriter Co Inc ....E....507 343-2001
Worthington (G-10182)
Ecm Publishers Inc ....E....763 689-1981
Cambridge (G-837)
Franz Reprographics Inc ....E....763 503-3401
Minneapolis (G-4477)
IKON Office Solutions Inc ....E....320 251-4566
Saint Cloud (G-7529)
Imaging Alliance Group LLC ....D....612 588-9944
Minneapolis (G-4690)
Konica Minolta Business Soln ....D....952 820-8385
Minneapolis (G-4818)
Konica Minolta Business Soln ....E....763 531-1721
Minneapolis (G-4819)
Laser Printing Technologies ....E....952 888-7375
Mendota Heights (G-3366)
Metro - Sales Inc ....C....612 861-4000
Minneapolis (G-5000)
▲ N A Trading & Technology Inc ....E....952 888-7654
Minneapolis (G-5154)
National Business Systems Inc ....D....651 688-0202
Eagan (G-1540)
North Country Business Prdts ....D....218 751-4140
Bemidji (G-408)
North Country Business Prdts ....E....800 937-4140
Plymouth (G-6878)
P O S Business Systems Inc ....E....763 559-1341
Minneapolis (G-5306)
Ricoh Americas Corp ....D....651 294-2600
Mendota Heights (G-3370)
Ricoh Americas Corp ....E....866 856-3000
Eden Prairie (G-1765)
S P Richards Co ....E....651 484-8459
Saint Paul (G-8920)
Sel-Mor Distributing Co ....E....952 929-0888
Minneapolis (G-5629)
Smith Micro Technologies Inc ....C....651 482-8718
Saint Paul (G-8966)
Streamfeeder LLC ....D....763 502-0000
Minneapolis (G-3610)
Stringer Business Systems Inc ....D....651 994-7700
Saint Paul (G-7914)
Technifax Business Systems Inc ....E....651 905-7090
Saint Paul (G-7919)
▲ Wand Corp ....C....952 361-6200
Eden Prairie (G-1813)

5045 Computers & Peripheral Eqpt & Software Wholesale

Agvantage Software Inc ....E....507 282-6353
Rochester (G-7046)
American Institute of ....E....651 415-1320
Saint Paul (G-8027)
Avionte LLC ....E....651 556-2121
Eagan (G-1516)
Beckhoff Automation LLC ....E....952 890-0000
Burnsville (G-683)
Bennett Office Technologies ....E....320 235-6425
Willmar (G-9985)
Blm Technologies Inc ....E....763 559-5100
Minneapolis (G-3912)
Calabrio Inc ....D....763 592-4600
Minneapolis (G-3990)
Cartridge Care Inc ....E....612 331-7757
Saint Paul (G-8169)
Cokem International Ltd ....D....952 358-6000
Shakopee (G-9431)
Consan Inc ....D....952 949-0053
Eden Prairie (G-1635)
Data Sales Co Inc ....D....952 890-8838
Burnsville (G-710)
Direct Source Inc ....D....952 934-8000
Chanhassen (G-920)
Edocument Resources LLC ....E....952 607-3505
Minnetonka (G-6163)
Environmental Systems Research ....D....651 454-0600
Saint Paul (G-7767)
Evolving Solutions Inc ....E....763 516-6500
Hamel (G-2340)
▲ Expresspoint Technology Svcs ....C....763 543-6000
Golden Valley (G-2240)
Facet Technology Corp ....E....952 944-1839
Eden Prairie (G-1660)
First Tech Inc ....D....612 374-8000
Minneapolis (G-4448)

(G-00000) Company's Geographic Section entry number
466

2011 Harris Minnesota
Services Directory

▲=Import ▼=Export
◆=Import/Export

▲ G C M Inc....E....952 882-8500
Burnsville (G-726)
General Nanosystems Inc....E....612 331-3690
Minneapolis (G-4514)
Healthland Inc....C....320 634-5331
Glenwood (G-2226)
Hickory Tech Information Soln....D....507 625-1691
Mankato (G-3139)
Hickory Tech Information Soln....D....507 625-1691
Mankato (G-3140)
Higher Dimension Research Inc....E....651 730-6203
Saint Paul (G-9229)
Information Security Tech....E....651 287-0823
Saint Paul (G-8513)
▲ J D L Technologies Inc....E....952 946-1810
Hopkins (G-2559)
Knowledge Computers Inc....E....952 249-9940
Long Lake (G-3026)
▲ MacDermid ColorSpan Inc....C....952 944-9457
Hopkins (G-2573)
Magnetic Products & Services....E....763 424-2700
Minneapolis (G-4935)
Micro Electronics Inc....D....952 285-4040
Minneapolis (G-5018)
Midwave Corp....C....952 279-5600
Eden Prairie (G-1723)
Midwest Data Inc....E....320 235-8880
Willmar (G-10023)
▲ Navarre Corp....C....763 535-8333
Minneapolis (G-5174)
North American Systems Intl....D....952 374-6700
Minneapolis (G-5213)
Northern Computer Technologies....E....952 808-1000
Burnsville (G-763)
Now Micro Inc....E....651 633-9072
Saint Paul (G-8774)
Oracle Systems Corp....B....612 587-5000
Minneapolis (G-5288)
PC Solutions Inc....E....763 852-1600
Minneapolis (G-3567)
Power Mation Division Inc....D....651 605-3300
Saint Paul (G-8832)
Regents of The University of....E....218 281-8376
Crookston (G-1135)
Rorke Data Inc....D....952 829-0300
Eden Prairie (G-1767)
Rubenstein & Ziff Inc....E....952 854-1460
Minneapolis (G-5574)
Rural Computer Consultants Inc....E....320 365-4027
Bird Island (G-468)
Sirius Computer Solutions Inc....D....952 470-6144
Chanhassen (G-940)
Smith Micro Technologies Inc....C....651 482-8718
Saint Paul (G-8966)
System Design Advantage LLC....E....952 703-3500
Minneapolis (G-5781)
Telvent Dtn Inc....E....952 941-6628
Eden Prairie (G-1791)
3M Co....C....651 733-2147
Saint Paul (G-9044)
TriMin Systems Inc....E....651 636-7667
Saint Paul (G-9083)
World Data Products Inc....D....952 476-9000
Minnetonka (G-6239)
▲ Xerxes Computer Corp....E....952 936-9280
Minneapolis (G-6094)
Yada Systems Inc....D....651 631-3237
Saint Paul (G-9172)

5046 Commercial Eqpt, NEC Wholesale

Amano McGann Inc....E....612 331-2020
Minneapolis (G-3739)
Aramark Corp....E....952 946-1438
Minneapolis (G-3795)
Bakemark USA LLC....E....952 937-9495
Eden Prairie (G-1601)
C & S Vending Co Inc....D....507 334-8414
Faribault (G-1994)
Canteen Vending....E....651 488-0515
Saint Paul (G-8148)
Clover Super Foods Rt 30 Inc....E....612 465-8900
Minneapolis (G-4110)
Compass Group USA Inc....E....651 488-0515
Saint Paul (G-8242)
Data Systems Inc....E....952 934-4001
Eden Prairie (G-1642)
Dawn Food Products Inc....E....763 428-8826
Rogers (G-7321)
Direct Source Inc....D....952 934-8000
Chanhassen (G-920)
Don Stevens Inc....E....651 452-0872
Eagan (G-1525)
Exactec Inc....E....952 448-7722
Chaska (G-966)
5 K Enterprises Inc....E....612 216-6292
Mankato (G-3127)
Hockenbergs....E....612 331-1300
Minneapolis (G-4659)
Kelbro Co....E....612 824-9803
Minneapolis (G-4796)
Kristico Inc....E....507 625-2900
Mankato (G-3155)
Martin Falk Paper Co....E....612 332-8626
Minneapolis (G-4959)
▲ Midwest Fixture Group Inc....E....763 712-9637
Anoka (G-204)
▲ Mycull Fixtures Inc....E....763 389-4400
Princeton (G-6911)
Paragon Store Fixtures Inc....E....763 263-0660
Big Lake (G-453)
Retailer Services Corp....E....763 421-6868
Anoka (G-221)
Richard Hawkins....E....507 282-6080
Rochester (G-7224)
Safco Products Co....C....763 536-6700
Minneapolis (G-5588)
Silver King Refrigeration Inc....C....763 559-1141
Minneapolis (G-5674)
Skyline Displays Midwest Inc....E....952 895-6000
Burnsville (G-798)
▲ Stein Industries Inc....C....763 504-3500
Minneapolis (G-5747)
Strategic Equipment Inc....D....320 252-2977
Saint Cloud (G-7614)
Supervalu Equipment Services....E....952 828-4000
Eden Prairie (G-1785)
▲ Theisen Vending Inc....D....612 827-5588
Minneapolis (G-5813)
Upper Lakes Foods Inc....C....218 879-1265
Cloquet (G-1066)
US Foodservice Inc....C....763 559-9494
Minneapolis (G-5948)
Vision Woodworking Inc....E....763 571-5767
Minneapolis (G-3631)
Zumbro River Brand Inc....E....507 377-9776
Albert Lea (G-72)

5047 Medical, Dental & Hospital Eqpt & Splys Wholesale

Activstyle Inc....D....612 520-9333
Minneapolis (G-3678)
Alchemist General Inc....D....507 289-3901
Rochester (G-7047)
Altimate Medical Inc....E....507 697-6393
Morton (G-6382)
American Hearing Systems Inc....C....763 404-1122
Bloomington (G-483)
Annex Medical Inc....E....952 942-7576
Minnetonka (G-6141)
Apria Healthcare Inc....E....651 523-8888
Saint Paul (G-8056)
Apria Healthcare Inc....C....952 404-1700
Minnetonka (G-6143)
▲ Arizant Healthcare Inc....C....952 947-1200
Eden Prairie (G-1596)
Arkray Factory USA Inc....D....952 646-3200
Minneapolis (G-3807)
Arkray USA Inc....D....952 646-3259
Minneapolis (G-3808)
Augustine Medical Inc....D....952 947-1288
Eden Prairie (G-1599)
Badger Acquisition of MN....C....763 259-0400
Minneapolis (G-3857)
◆ Bird & Cronin Inc....D....651 683-1111
Saint Paul (G-7722)
Cardinal Health 200 Inc....D....763 323-9666
Champlin (G-890)
▲ Carefusion 203 Inc....C....763 398-8300
Minneapolis (G-4005)
Carpe Diem Medical Inc....E....507 399-0262
Fairmont (G-1959)
Cold Spring St Joseph....E....320 685-3237
Cold Spring (G-1084)
◆ Coloplast Corp....B....612 337-7800
Minneapolis (G-4123)
D M S Health Group....E....763 315-1947
Osseo (G-6607)
General Pet Supply Inc....E....952 890-2300
Burnsville (G-727)
Global Medical Instrumentation....E....763 712-8717
Anoka (G-183)
Guidant Sales Corp....D....651 582-4000
Saint Paul (G-8436)
Gyrus Acmi, LP....D....763 416-3000
Maple Grove (G-3244)
▲ Harris Communications Inc....E....952 906-1180
Eden Prairie (G-1678)
Healthline Inc....E....218 262-6981
Hibbing (G-2450)
Healthworks Home Medical....D....507 238-9200
Fairmont (G-1974)
Hill-Rom Inc....D....651 490-1468
Saint Paul (G-8483)
▲ Keomed Inc....E....952 933-3940
Hopkins (G-2563)
Key Medical Supply Inc....E....651 792-3860
Saint Paul (G-8546)
Kruse Family Enterprises LLC....E....507 345-5926
Mankato (G-3156)
McKesson Medical-Surgical....E....763 424-7201
Osseo (G-6636)
McKesson Medical-Surgical Inc....E....952 881-8040
Minneapolis (G-4977)
McKesson Medical-Surgical MN....B....763 595-6000
Minneapolis (G-4978)
Medafor Inc....E....763 571-6300
Minneapolis (G-4982)
Medtronic USA Inc....A....763 514-4000
Minneapolis (G-3534)
Medtronic World Headquarters....A....763 574-4000
Minneapolis (G-3535)
Merwin Home Medical....D....763 535-5335
Minneapolis (G-4995)
Midwest Medical Equipment....E....218 722-3420
Duluth (G-1393)
Midwest Medical Management LLC....E....651 430-3892
Stillwater (G-9628)
Midwest Medical Services Inc....D....763 717-7676
Mounds View (G-6389)
Midwest Veterinary Supply Inc....E....952 894-4350
Burnsville (G-759)
Minneapolis Oxygen Co....E....612 588-8855
Minneapolis (G-5058)
Northern X-Ray Co....E....612 870-1561
Minneapolis (G-5230)
Otter Tail Corp....866 410-8780
Fergus Falls (G-2105)
▲ Otto Bock Healthcare LP....C....763 553-9464
Minneapolis (G-5297)
▲ Otto Bock Healthcare North....D....763 553-9464
Minneapolis (G-5298)
Owens & Minor Inc....D....763 785-9100
Saint Paul (G-8796)
Patterson Co's Inc....C....651 686-1600
Saint Paul (G-7866)
Patterson Co's Inc....D....651 688-9265
Eagan (G-1545)
Patterson Dental Supply Inc....E....651 688-6054
Saint Paul (G-7867)
▲ Patterson Dental Supply Inc....B....651 686-1600
Saint Paul (G-7868)
PSS World Medical Inc....E....763 428-2388
Rogers (G-7338)
Qrs Diagnostic LLC....E....763 559-8492
Minneapolis (G-5440)
Reliable Medical Supply Inc....D....763 255-3800
Brooklyn Park (G-618)
Rice Home Medical LLC....E....320 235-8434
Willmar (G-10040)
Scimed Inc....C....763 494-1700
Osseo (G-6660)
Sightpath Medical Inc....C....952 881-2500
Minneapolis (G-5668)
Slumberland Inc....E....320 251-1024
Waite Park (G-9839)
Slumberland Inc....D....952 888-6204
Minneapolis (G-5689)
St Jude Medical SC Inc....B....651 483-2000
Saint Paul (G-8986)
Stearns Veterinary Outlet....E....320 256-3303
Melrose (G-3353)
Tactile Systems Technology Inc....D....952 224-4060
Minneapolis (G-5784)
Tfx Medical Wire Products Inc....D....763 559-6414
Plymouth (G-6886)
Thermoskin....E....651 674-8302
North Branch (G-6505)
3M Co....D....651 733-0963
Saint Paul (G-9065)
Tyco Electronics Corp....C....651 565-2601
Wabasha (G-9772)
Tympany LLC....E....866 316-3606
Saint Paul (G-9097)
Unimed-Midwest Inc....E....952 469-9400
Lakeville (G-2938)
▲ Universal Hospital Services....D....952 893-3200
Minneapolis (G-5920)
Universal Hospital Services....D....612 721-3374
Minneapolis (G-5919)
Urologix Inc....D....763 475-1400
Minneapolis (G-5940)
Veterinary Hospitals Assn....E....651 451-6669
South Saint Paul (G-9549)
Vitatron Inc....E....763 574-4000
Minneapolis (G-3633)
Weiner Memorial Foundation....E....507 537-7070
Marshall (G-3331)

5048 Ophthalmic Goods Wholesale

Essilor Laboratories of Amer....B....763 551-2000
Minneapolis (G-4372)
▲ Soderberg Inc....C....651 291-1400
Saint Paul (G-8970)
Walman Optical Co....C....612 520-6000
Minneapolis (G-6014)

5049 Professional Eqpt & Splys, NEC Wholesale

Base Eight Inc....952 941-5888
Chaska (G-951)
Central Minnesota Erdc Inc....E....320 202-0992
Saint Cloud (G-7408)
Corporate Express Office Prdts....C....651 636-2250
Saint Paul (G-8251)
Essilor Laboratories of Amer....C....320 251-8591
Saint Cloud (G-7505)
Essilor Laboratories of Amer....E....218 894-3385
Staples (G-9583)
Eye Kraft Optical Inc....D....320 251-0141
Saint Cloud (G-7506)
▲ Foss North America Inc....E....952 974-9892
Eden Prairie (G-1667)
Franz Reprographics Inc....E....763 503-3401
Minneapolis (G-4477)
GPM Inc....E....218 722-9904
Duluth (G-1339)

S I C

Hysitron Inc ....D....952 835-6366
Eden Prairie *(G-1689)*
La Calhene Inc....E....320 358-4713
Rush City *(G-7390)*
Leeds Precision Instruments....D....763 546-8575
Minneapolis *(G-4853)*
Newport Corp....D....763 593-0722
Minneapolis *(G-5195)*
Norcostco Inc....E....763 544-0601
Minneapolis *(G-5207)*
▲ Omicron Associates....C....952 345-5240
Eden Prairie *(G-1737)*
Prescription Optical....E....303 343-0427
Saint Cloud *(G-7571)*
Saint Patrick's Guild Inc....E....651 690-1506
Saint Paul *(G-8923)*
Tierney Brothers Inc....D....612 331-5500
Minneapolis *(G-5821)*

5051 Metals Service Centers

A & C Metals-Sawing Inc....E....763 786-1048
Minneapolis *(G-3382)*
C C Sharrow Co Inc....E....651 489-1341
Saint Paul *(G-8145)*
▲ C S Aero-Space Inc....E....952 884-4725
Minneapolis *(G-3987)*
Cargill Inc....C....612 367-3000
Minneapolis *(G-4007)*
Cargill Inc....E....952 984-3377
Hopkins *(G-2526)*
Chicago Tube & Iron Co of MN....D....651 454-6800
Saint Paul *(G-7731)*
Donner Industries Inc....E....651 429-0890
Hugo *(G-2676)*
Excel Manufacturing Inc....E....507 932-4680
Saint Charles *(G-7401)*
▲ Firestone Metal Products LLC....C....763 576-9595
Anoka *(G-181)*
Goodin Co....E....320 259-6086
Saint Cloud *(G-7520)*
Great Western Recycling Inds....E....651 224-4877
Saint Paul *(G-8427)*
Hajoca Corp....E....763 315-0100
Minneapolis *(G-4589)*
Hd Supply Waterworks Ltd....E....952 937-9666
Eden Prairie *(G-1680)*
Joseph T Ryerson & Son Inc....C....763 544-4401
Minneapolis *(G-4780)*
Kronick Industries Inc....E....612 331-8080
Minneapolis *(G-4825)*
Louis Industries Inc....E....320 243-3696
Paynesville *(G-6771)*
▼ McNeilus Steel Inc....C....507 374-6336
Dodge Center *(G-1229)*
Mead Metals Inc....E....651 484-1400
Saint Paul *(G-8628)*
North Second Street Steel Sply....E....612 522-6626
Minneapolis *(G-5218)*
Olympic Steel Minneapolis Inc....D....763 544-7100
Minneapolis *(G-5275)*
▼ Quality Metals Inc....E....651 645-5875
Saint Paul *(G-8860)*
Ratner Steel Supply Co....E....651 631-8515
Saint Paul *(G-8870)*
Russel Metals Williams Bahcall....E....651 688-8138
Little Canada *(G-2998)*
▲ Spectro Alloys Corp....C....651 437-2815
Rosemount *(G-7375)*
Ssab Enterprises LLC....E....651 631-9031
Saint Paul *(G-8980)*
Two Rivers Enterprises Inc....E....320 746-3156
Holdingford *(G-2491)*
Viking Materials Inc....D....612 617-5800
Minneapolis *(G-5974)*
Voyager Aluminum Inc....E....320 834-4940
Brandon *(G-591)*
West Central Steel Inc....C....320 235-4070
Willmar *(G-10055)*

5052 Coal & Other Minerals & Ores Wholesale

Great Western Recycling Inds....E....651 224-4877
Saint Paul *(G-8427)*

5063 Electrl Apparatus, Eqpt, Wiring Splys Wholesale

Activar Inc....E....952 835-6850
Minneapolis *(G-3677)*
AG Electrical Specialists....E....507 378-2101
Racine *(G-6966)*
Anixter Inc....E....763 559-2417
Minneapolis *(G-3782)*
Anixter Inc....E....952 887-8191
Bloomington *(G-486)*
Arrowhead Security Systems Inc....E....218 722-1234
Duluth *(G-1243)*
Baldor Electric Co....D....763 428-3633
Rogers *(G-7317)*
Ban-Koe Systems Inc....D....952 888-6688
Minneapolis *(G-3865)*
Border States Electric Supply....C....320 214-4237
Willmar *(G-9992)*
Border States Industries Inc....D....763 425-5500
Brooklyn Park *(G-606)*
Cable Connection & Supply Co....E....507 334-6417
Faribault *(G-1995)*
Century Systems Inc....E....651 426-0975
Saint Paul *(G-8185)*
Checkpoint Systems Inc....E....952 227-5350
Chaska *(G-958)*
Creative Lighting....E....651 647-0111
Saint Paul *(G-8265)*
Dakota Supply Group....D....952 890-3811
Burnsville *(G-708)*
Dakota Supply Group Inc....E....651 224-5781
Saint Paul *(G-8279)*
Eaton Corp....E....952 939-5400
Minnetonka *(G-6161)*
Eis Inc....E....763 493-6800
Minneapolis *(G-4334)*
Electric Motor Repair Inc....E....612 588-4693
Minneapolis *(G-4337)*
▲ Engineered Products Co....D....952 767-8780
Minnetonka *(G-6166)*
▼ Fastenal Co....B....507 454-5374
Winona *(G-10095)*
Graybar Electric Co Inc....C....612 721-3545
Minneapolis *(G-4550)*
Graybar Electric Co Inc....E....218 722-6685
Duluth *(G-1343)*
Graybar Electric Co Inc....D....763 852-6000
Minneapolis *(G-4549)*
▲ Great Northern Equipment Dstbg....E....763 428-9405
Rogers *(G-7326)*
▲ Griffin Marketing & Promotions....D....612 344-4677
Minneapolis *(G-4571)*
▲ Holtkoetter International Inc....E....651 552-8776
South Saint Paul *(G-9530)*
Honeywell International Inc....C....763 493-6400
Osseo *(G-6622)*
Interstate Power Systems....D....952 854-5511
Minneapolis *(G-4729)*
Interstate Power Systems Inc....D....952 854-5511
Minneapolis *(G-3502)*
J H Larson Electrical Co....D....763 545-1717
Plymouth *(G-6867)*
L & S Electric Inc....E....763 780-3234
Minneapolis *(G-3513)*
Lapp Tannehill Inc....E....952 881-6700
Savage *(G-9395)*
Lights On Broadway Inc....E....763 533-3366
Minneapolis *(G-4885)*
Luma Corp....E....952 995-6500
Shakopee *(G-9453)*
Malton Electric Co....E....763 571-7758
Minneapolis *(G-3526)*
Menstar Technologies Inc....D....218 326-5566
Grand Rapids *(G-2294)*
Michaels' Lighting Inc....E....507 454-5560
Winona *(G-10117)*
Midwest Sign & Screen Printing....D....651 489-9999
Saint Paul *(G-8661)*
Mielke Electric Works Inc....E....218 727-7411
Duluth *(G-1394)*
Minnesota Electric Technology....E....507 893-3181
Winnebago *(G-10077)*
Motion Tech Automation Inc....E....651 730-9010
Saint Paul *(G-9252)*
▼ Next Level Electronics Inc....E....320 363-7716
Saint Joseph *(G-7653)*
◆ R & D Batteries Inc....E....952 890-0629
Burnsville *(G-783)*
Schneider Electric USA Inc....E....763 543-5500
Minneapolis *(G-5609)*
Secoa Inc....D....763 506-8800
Champlin *(G-900)*
Sentry Systems Inc....E....651 426-4627
White Bear Lake *(G-9977)*
Service Lighting Inc....E....763 571-3001
Osseo *(G-6662)*
Southern Lighting Inc....E....952 890-8977
Burnsville *(G-802)*
▲ Stein Industries Inc....C....763 504-3500
Minneapolis *(G-5747)*
3M Co....A....507 354-8271
New Ulm *(G-6476)*
3M Co....D....651 733-3154
Saint Paul *(G-9062)*
3M Co....D....651 733-6611
Saint Paul *(G-9066)*
Trico Tcwind Inc....E....320 693-6200
Litchfield *(G-2991)*
Unipower Industrial Corp....E....952 884-2933
Minneapolis *(G-5906)*
Viking Electric Supply Inc....C....612 627-1300
Minneapolis *(G-5973)*
Viking Electric Supply Inc....E....952 890-8420
Duluth *(G-1497)*
Werner Electric Ventures LLC....C....651 769-6841
Cottage Grove *(G-1109)*
Wesco Distribution Inc....D....651 582-3945
Saint Paul *(G-9147)*
▲ Winona Lighting Inc....C....507 454-5113
Winona *(G-10151)*
Wright-Hennepin Security Corp....C....763 477-3000
Rockford *(G-7306)*
▲ Yale Materials Handling - MN....D....763 434-3832
Anoka *(G-241)*

5064 Electrical Appliances, TV & Radios Wholesale

AAF-Mcquay Inc....B....763 553-5330
Minneapolis *(G-3655)*
All Inc....D....651 227-6331
Saint Paul *(G-8010)*
▼ Capitol Sales Co Inc....D....651 688-6830
Saint Paul *(G-7727)*
Curry Sales Inc....E....952 351-4200
Hopkins *(G-2534)*
Dependable Indoor Air Quality....E....763 757-5040
Minneapolis *(G-3454)*
Dey Appliance Parts of CO....D....651 490-9191
Saint Paul *(G-8291)*
Dey Appliance Parts of North....651 490-9191
Saint Paul *(G-8292)*
Dey Distributing....E....651 490-9191
Saint Paul *(G-8293)*
Dey Distributing Inc....E....651 490-9191
Saint Paul *(G-8294)*
Dey Properties....D....651 490-9191
Saint Paul *(G-8295)*
Goodin Co....E....320 259-6086
Saint Cloud *(G-7520)*
Hajoca Corp....E....763 315-0100
Minneapolis *(G-4589)*
Lights On Broadway Inc....E....763 533-3366
Minneapolis *(G-4885)*
▲ Lindhaus USA Inc....E....952 707-1131
Burnsville *(G-749)*
Lowe's Home Centers Inc....C....763 367-1340
Minneapolis *(G-3524)*
Lowe's Home Centers Inc....C....507 446-4900
Owatonna *(G-6723)*
Lowe's Home Centers Inc....C....763 367-9000
Minneapolis *(G-4904)*
Lowe's Home Centers Inc....C....952 367-9000
Shakopee *(G-9452)*
Lowe's Home Centers Inc....C....763 428-5970
Rogers *(G-7328)*
Lowe's Home Centers Inc....C....763 488-2001
Osseo *(G-6629)*
Lowe's Home Centers Inc....C....218 262-7460
Hibbing *(G-2459)*
Lowe's Home Centers Inc....C....651 275-9910
Stillwater *(G-9626)*
Lowe's Home Centers Inc....C....507 328-8920
Rochester *(G-7162)*
Lowe's Home Centers Inc....C....507 385-3560
Mankato *(G-3158)*
Lowe's Home Centers Inc....C....763 367-4139
Saint Paul *(G-7826)*
Lowe's Home Centers Inc....C....763 367-1120
Minneapolis *(G-3523)*
Lowe's Home Centers Inc....C....763 691-6040
Cambridge *(G-840)*
Midwest Mechanical Solutions....E....952 525-2003
Minneapolis *(G-5032)*
Motivaction LLC....D....763 412-3000
Minneapolis *(G-5137)*
▲ Park Systems Inc....E....612 822-3180
Minneapolis *(G-5337)*
Performark Inc....C....952 946-7300
Minnetonka *(G-6210)*
Warners' Stellian Co Inc....D....651 222-0011
Saint Paul *(G-9140)*

5065 Electronic Parts & Eqpt Wholesale

Advanced Imaging Solutions Inc....E....952 930-1882
Hopkins *(G-2501)*
Aldin Export & Import....651 483-4184
Saint Paul *(G-8007)*
Alpha Video & Audio Inc....D....952 896-9898
Minneapolis *(G-3733)*
American Communications Supply....507 334-2268
Faribault *(G-1989)*
Arrow Electronics Inc....E....952 949-0053
Eden Prairie *(G-1597)*
Asml Us Inc....E....952 876-0713
Bloomington *(G-488)*
Automation Fluid Power Inc....E....763 571-3336
Minneapolis *(G-3839)*
Avnet Inc....E....763 559-2211
Minneapolis *(G-3847)*
Avnet Inc....E....952 346-3000
Bloomington *(G-489)*
Avtex Solutions LLC....E....952 831-0888
Minneapolis *(G-3848)*
Ban-Koe Systems Inc....D....952 888-6688
Minneapolis *(G-3865)*
Bell Telephone Inc....D....651 298-1332
Saint Paul *(G-8099)*
▲ Bergquist Co....C....952 835-2322
Chanhassen *(G-909)*
Best Source Electronics Corp....E....763 502-7847
Fridley *(G-2191)*
Black Box Corp....D....763 971-6260
Minneapolis *(G-3910)*
BT Americas Inc....D....651 746-8590
Saint Paul *(G-8138)*
Buy Best Purchasing LLC....A....612 291-1000
Richfield *(G-7034)*
▲ C S Aero-Space Inc....E....952 884-4725
Minneapolis *(G-3987)*

(G-00000) Company's Geographic Section entry number
468
2011 Harris Minnesota Services Directory
▲=Import ▼=Export
◆=Import/Export

C-1 Holdings LLC ....D....651 994-6800
Eagan *(G-1519)*

▼ Capitol Sales Co Inc ....D....651 688-6830
Saint Paul *(G-7727)*

◆ Cash Register Sales Inc ....D....651 294-2700
Saint Paul *(G-8171)*

Chris Electronics Distributors ....E....651 631-2647
Saint Paul *(G-8197)*

Clearone Communications Inc ....E....763 550-2300
Minneapolis *(G-4109)*

Comm-Works Holdings LLC ....D....763 258-5800
Minneapolis *(G-4130)*

▲ Crest Electronics Inc ....D....320 275-3382
Dassel *(G-1160)*

Cross Telecom Corp ....D....952 983-3500
Bloomington *(G-493)*

Delta Industrial Services Inc ....D....763 755-7744
Minneapolis *(G-3453)*

▲ Digi-Key Corp ....A....218 681-6674
Thief River Falls *(G-9666)*

Electronic Design Co ....E....612 355-2300
Minneapolis *(G-4339)*

Gopher Electronics Co ....E....651 490-4900
Saint Paul *(G-8423)*

Gopher News Co ....D....763 546-5300
Minneapolis *(G-4542)*

Graybar Electric Co Inc ....E....218 722-6685
Duluth *(G-1343)*

Graybow Communications Group ....E....952 544-5555
Golden Valley *(G-2241)*

IKON Office Solutions Inc ....E....320 251-4566
Saint Cloud *(G-7529)*

Integra Telecom Inc ....C....763 745-8000
Minneapolis *(G-4711)*

Ironwood Electronics Inc ....E....952 229-8200
Burnsville *(G-737)*

J J Vanderson & Co ....E....651 641-1376
Minneapolis *(G-3503)*

▲ Kgp Logistics Inc ....A....507 334-2268
Faribault *(G-2017)*

Kgp Telecommunications Inc ....D....507 334-2268
Faribault *(G-2018)*

Matrix Communications Inc ....E....763 475-5500
Minneapolis *(G-4966)*

Metro - Sales Inc ....C....612 861-4000
Minneapolis *(G-5000)*

Mitel Technologies Inc ....E....952 930-4400
Minnetonka *(G-6200)*

Muzak LLC ....E....763 424-5533
Osseo *(G-6641)*

▲ Napco International LLC ....E....952 931-2400
Hopkins *(G-2587)*

Nextel Communications Inc ....D....952 703-7600
Minneapolis *(G-5197)*

Norstan Communications Inc ....C....952 352-4300
Minnetonka *(G-6202)*

North American Communications ....E....952 942-7200
Minneapolis *(G-5212)*

North Point Capital Partners ....D....651 602-0789
Saint Paul *(G-8753)*

▲ Pace Electronics Inc ....E....507 288-1853
Rochester *(G-7199)*

Pixel Farm Inc ....E....612 339-7644
Minneapolis *(G-5386)*

Popp Telcom Inc ....D....763 546-9707
Minneapolis *(G-5394)*

Power Mation Division Inc ....D....651 605-3300
Saint Paul *(G-8832)*

Pro-TEC Design Inc ....E....763 553-1477
Plymouth *(G-6880)*

Ricoh Americas Corp ....D....651 294-2600
Mendota Heights *(G-3370)*

SBC Datacomm Inc ....E....763 315-5343
Saint Paul *(G-8931)*

Schneider Electric USA Inc ....E....763 543-5500
Minneapolis *(G-5609)*

Sel-Mor Distributing Co ....E....952 929-0888
Minneapolis *(G-5629)*

Shopjimmycom LLC ....E....952 881-6492
Bloomington *(G-515)*

Spectrum Solutions Inc ....E....651 634-1800
Saint Paul *(G-8976)*

Techscan Corp 651 636-3030
Saint Paul *(G-9035)*

3M Co ....C....651 733-2147
Saint Paul *(G-9044)*

TLC Electronics ....D....651 488-2933
Saint Paul *(G-9282)*

▲ Unicon Inc ....D....763 424-7892
Hamel *(G-2359)*

UTC Fire & Security America ....D....651 777-2690
Saint Paul *(G-9121)*

Voice & Data Networks Inc ....E....952 946-7999
Minneapolis *(G-5982)*

Waytek Inc ....E....952 949-0765
Chanhassen *(G-945)*

Wesco Distribution Inc ....D....651 582-3945
Saint Paul *(G-9147)*

Westco Systems Inc ....E....763 559-7046
Minneapolis *(G-6057)*

5072 Hardware Wholesale

▲ Accurate Component Sales Inc ....E....651 639-1881
Saint Paul *(G-7978)*

▲ Allegis Corp ....E....763 780-4333
Minneapolis *(G-3391)*

Bredemus Hardware Co Inc ....E....651 489-6250
Saint Paul *(G-8123)*

Building Fasteners of MN ....D....612 706-3300
Minneapolis *(G-3973)*

C C Sharrow Co Inc ....E....651 489-1341
Saint Paul *(G-8145)*

▲ C S Aero-Space Inc ....E....952 884-4725
Minneapolis *(G-3987)*

Cable Connection & Supply Co ....E....507 334-6417
Faribault *(G-1995)*

Contract Hardware Co Inc ....E....651 780-0010
Circle Pines *(G-1007)*

Curry Sales Inc ....E....952 351-4200
Hopkins *(G-2534)*

D & M Industries Inc ....E....218 287-3100
Moorhead *(G-6309)*

E & A Products Inc ....E....763 493-3222
Osseo *(G-6611)*

Enderes Tool Co Inc ....E....507 373-2396
Albert Lea *(G-48)*

▼ Fastenal Co ....B....507 454-5374
Winona *(G-10095)*

Frattalone I LLC ....E....651 292-9800
Saint Paul *(G-8395)*

Harkraft Inc ....E....763 546-9161
Minneapolis *(G-4597)*

Holmquist Lumber Co 320 857-2031
Grove City *(G-2329)*

▲ Import Specialties Inc ....C....952 361-3640
Chaska *(G-969)*

Jaeckle Minnesota ....D....612 676-0388
Minneapolis *(G-4751)*

Kendell Doors & Hardware Inc ....E....507 454-1723
Winona *(G-10107)*

Kendell Doors & Hardware Inc ....D....651 905-0144
Mendota Heights *(G-3365)*

L&M Fleet Supply True Value ....E....218 847-1171
Detroit Lakes *(G-1202)*

Lcs Precision Molding Inc ....E....507 362-8685
Waterville *(G-9895)*

▲ Lindstrom Metric LLC ....D....763 780-4200
Minneapolis *(G-3521)*

Mac's Inc ....E....218 233-4600
Moorhead *(G-6326)*

▲ Malco Products Inc ....C....320 274-8246
Annandale *(G-143)*

◆ Mid-States Distributing Co Inc ....E....651 698-8831
Saint Paul *(G-8652)*

▲ Park Systems Inc ....E....612 822-3180
Minneapolis *(G-5337)*

S & S Sales Inc 763 476-9599
Minneapolis *(G-5581)*

Stanley Security Solutions Inc ....E....952 894-3830
Saint Paul *(G-9004)*

Tappers Inc ....D....763 295-4222
Monticello *(G-6289)*

Titan Machinery Inc ....E....218 681-1423
Thief River Falls *(G-9680)*

Trimpac Inc ....D....320 202-3200
Sauk Rapids *(G-9378)*

True Value Co ....C....507 625-6021
Mankato *(G-3209)*

Twin City Hardware Co ....E....651 735-2200
Saint Paul *(G-9284)*

Twin City Hardware Co ....E....763 535-4660
Minneapolis *(G-5881)*

▲ United Hardware Distributing ....C....763 559-1800
Minneapolis *(G-5909)*

Wheeler Hardware Co ....E....651 645-4501
Saint Paul *(G-9153)*

▲ Willi Hahn Corp ....E....763 295-0666
Monticello *(G-6292)*

▲ Wurth Adams Nut & Bolt Co ....D....763 493-0877
Osseo *(G-6685)*

5074 Plumbing & Heating Splys Wholesale

AAA-American Co ....E....507 894-4156
Hokah *(G-2490)*

Bernard J Mulcahy Co Inc ....E....651 686-8580
Saint Paul *(G-7715)*

▲ Central Boiler Inc ....C....218 782-2575
Greenbush *(G-2325)*

D C Sales Co Inc ....E....612 728-8700
Minneapolis *(G-4213)*

D J'S Heating & Air Condg ....E....763 421-5313
Elk River *(G-1871)*

▲ Ecowater Systems LLC ....B....651 739-5330
Saint Paul *(G-9206)*

Fantasia LLC 612 338-5811
Minneapolis *(G-4415)*

Ferguson Enterprises Inc ....E....218 628-2844
Duluth *(G-1321)*

First Supply LLC ....D....507 287-0202
Rochester *(G-7115)*

First Supply LLC ....E....507 287-0202
Rochester *(G-7116)*

▲ Goodin Co ....C....612 588-7811
Minneapolis *(G-4540)*

Goodin Co ....E....320 259-6086
Saint Cloud *(G-7520)*

Hajoca Corp ....E....763 315-0100
Minneapolis *(G-4589)*

▲ Hawkins Inc ....C....612 331-6910
Minneapolis *(G-4608)*

Hawkins Water Treatment Group ....D....612 331-6910
Minneapolis *(G-4610)*

Lemna Corp ....E....612 253-2000
Minneapolis *(G-4860)*

Marketing Focus Inc ....E....952 939-9880
Hopkins *(G-2576)*

▲ Maxxon Corp ....E....763 478-6000
Hamel *(G-2350)*

Minnesota Air Inc ....D....952 918-8000
Minneapolis *(G-5067)*

Minvalco Inc ....E....952 920-0131
Minneapolis *(G-5107)*

Northern Sales & Consulting ....D....651 429-5757
Lino Lakes *(G-2975)*

▲ Northern Wholesale Supply Inc ....D....651 429-1515
Hugo *(G-2672)*

▲ Park Systems Inc ....E....612 822-3180
Minneapolis *(G-5337)*

Pipeline Supply Inc ....D....952 935-0445
Hopkins *(G-2603)*

S P S Co's Inc ....C....952 929-1377
Minneapolis *(G-5582)*

S P S Co's Inc ....E....507 387-5691
Mankato *(G-3190)*

Seelye Plastics Inc ....D....952 881-2658
Minneapolis *(G-5627)*

St Hilaire Supply Co ....E....218 964-5222
Saint Hilaire *(G-7641)*

U S Filter Waterpro ....E....952 893-9130
Minneapolis *(G-5889)*

Woodruff Co ....E....507 285-2500
Rochester *(G-7296)*

5075 Heating & Air Conditioning Eqpt & Splys Wholesale

Ace Supply Co Inc ....E....952 929-1618
Minneapolis *(G-3672)*

Auer Steel & Heating Supply Co ....E....763 971-2910
Plymouth *(G-6849)*

Automotive Cooling Products ....E....651 731-2414
Saint Paul *(G-9186)*

Boeser Inc ....E....612 378-1803
Minneapolis *(G-3923)*

▲ Cramer Investment Co ....D....612 861-7232
Saint Paul *(G-8263)*

Crystal Distribution Inc ....D....763 391-7790
Elk River *(G-1870)*

D C Sales Co Inc ....E....612 728-8700
Minneapolis *(G-4213)*

Dependable Indoor Air Quality ....E....763 757-5040
Minneapolis *(G-3454)*

Don Stevens Inc ....E....651 452-0872
Eagan *(G-1525)*

First Supply LLC ....D....507 287-0202
Rochester *(G-7115)*

First Supply LLC ....E....507 287-0202
Rochester *(G-7116)*

▲ Goodin Co ....C....612 588-7811
Minneapolis *(G-4540)*

Goodin Co ....E....320 259-6086
Saint Cloud *(G-7520)*

Hajoca Corp ....E....763 315-0100
Minneapolis *(G-4589)*

Harbor City Oil Co ....E....218 624-3633
Duluth *(G-1348)*

Johnson Controls Inc ....D....763 566-7650
Plymouth *(G-6869)*

Johnson Controls Interiors LLC ....E....218 727-8996
Duluth *(G-1361)*

◆ Mammoth-Webco Inc ....B....952 361-2711
Eden Prairie *(G-1717)*

Midwest Mechanical Solutions ....E....952 525-2003
Minneapolis *(G-5032)*

Minnesota Air Inc ....D....952 918-8000
Minneapolis *(G-5067)*

Munters Corp ....B....952 831-9418
Burnsville *(G-761)*

Paape Distributing Co ....E....507 345-8057
Mankato *(G-3181)*

S P S Co's Inc ....C....952 929-1377
Minneapolis *(G-5582)*

Schwab-Vollhaber-Lubratt Inc ....D....651 481-8000
Saint Paul *(G-8935)*

Triple J Enterprises Inc ....E....952 853-9898
Minneapolis *(G-5858)*

Triple J Enterprises Inc ....E....952 853-9898
Minneapolis *(G-5859)*

Uhl Co Inc ....D....763 425-7226
Osseo *(G-6680)*

5078 Refrigeration Eqpt & Splys Wholesale

Carrier Commercial ....E....763 231-8300
Minneapolis *(G-4021)*

Crossroads Trailer Sales & Svc ....E....507 373-4443
Albert Lea *(G-45)*

Don Stevens Inc ....E....651 452-0872
Eagan *(G-1525)*

First Supply LLC ....E....507 287-0202
Rochester *(G-7116)*

◆ Thermo King Sales & Service ....E....651 633-2820
Saint Paul *(G-9041)*

▲ 3Wire Group Inc ....D....763 488-3000
Osseo *(G-6674)*

S I C

Employment codes: A=Over 500 employees, B=251-500
C=101-250, D=51-100, E=25-50

2011 Harris Minnesota
Services Directory

© Harris InfoSource 1-866-281-6415
469

5082 Construction & Mining Mach & Eqpt Wholesale

ABM Equipment & Supply Inc.......952 938-5451
Hopkins (G-2498)
ABM Equipment & Supply LLC.......E.....952 938-5451
Hopkins (G-2499)
▲ Advance Equipment Co.......E.....651 489-8881
Saint Paul (G-7987)
Advance Shoring Co.......E.....651 489-8881
Saint Paul (G-7988)
Advance Specialties Co.......E.....651 489-8881
Saint Paul (G-7989)
Ballantine Inc.......E.....763 427-3959
Anoka (G-158)
Carlson Tractor & Equipment Co.......E.....651 423-2222
Rosemount (G-7364)
Contech Construction Products.......E.....952 496-1050
Shakopee (G-9433)
◆ Dom-Ex LLC.......E.....218 262-6116
Hibbing (G-2442)
Engineered Concrete Placer of.......E.....651 452-1183
Saint Paul (G-7763)
▲ Garlock-East Equipment Co.......E.....763 553-1935
Minneapolis (G-4503)
Hawk & Sons Inc.......E.....507 285-0508
Rochester (G-7134)
▲ Hayden-Murphy Equipment Co.......E.....952 884-2301
Minneapolis (G-4612)
Macqueen Equipment Inc.......E.....651 645-5726
Saint Paul (G-8605)
Nortrax Equipment Co SE.......E.....218 759-1996
Bemidji (G-415)
Penhall Co.......E.....763 542-9999
Minneapolis (G-5363)
▼ Phillippi Equipment Co.......E.....651 406-4900
Saint Paul (G-7875)
Pinnacle Technologies Inc.......E.....651 735-3239
Saint Paul (G-9262)
▲ Plymouth Industries Inc.......D.....763 553-1935
Minneapolis (G-5393)
RDO Construction Equipment Co.......D.....952 890-8880
Burnsville (G-784)
Rdo Construction Equipment Co.......E.....218 282-8440
Moorhead (G-6334)
Rdo Equipment Co.......E.....218 483-3353
Hawley (G-2421)
◆ Road Machinery & Supplies Co.......D.....952 895-9595
Savage (G-9405)
RSC Equipment Rental Inc.......E.....763 557-1234
Minneapolis (G-5565)
St Joseph Equipment Inc.......E.....952 445-5400
Shakopee (G-9478)
Sweeney Brothers Tractor Co.......E.....952 894-9595
Burnsville (G-805)
Tri State Machinery Co.......E.....952 224-1500
Burnsville (G-812)
Ziegler Inc.......D.....218 258-3232
Buhl (G-669)
Ziegler Inc.......A.....952 888-4121
Minneapolis (G-6117)
Ziegler Inc.......D.....952 445-4292
Shakopee (G-9482)
Ziegler Inc.......E.....218 722-6628
Duluth (G-1509)
Ziegler Inc.......E.....507 285-1775
Rochester (G-7298)
Ziegler Inc.......E.....507 532-4403
Marshall (G-3336)

5083 Farm & Garden Mach & Eqpt Wholesale

A & C Farm Service Inc.......E.....320 243-3736
Paynesville (G-6768)
▲ AG Systems Inc.......E.....320 587-4030
Hutchinson (G-2684)
▲ Agriliance LLC.......C.....651 451-5000
Inver Grove Heights (G-2736)
Albrecht Co's.......E.....651 633-4510
Saint Paul (G-8006)
Alex Irrigation Inc.......E.....320 852-7595
Carlos (G-866)
Arnold's of Mankato Inc.......E.....320 398-3800
Kimball (G-2830)
Arnold's of Willmar Inc.......E.....320 235-4898
Willmar (G-9984)
Arnzen Construction Inc.......E.....320 836-2284
Freeport (G-2187)
◆ Avery Weigh-Tronix LLC.......A.....507 238-4461
Fairmont (G-1957)
Bruce Kreofsky & Sons Inc.......D.....507 534-3855
Plainview (G-6839)
C & B Operations LLC.......E.....507 375-3144
Saint James (G-7642)
Cnh America LLC.......E.....952 854-1443
Minneapolis (G-4114)
Dairy Farmers Of America Inc.......E.....507 732-5124
Zumbrota (G-10218)
Frattalone Tractor Co Inc.......C.....651 484-0448
Saint Paul (G-8396)
Gateway Building Systems Inc.......E.....218 685-4420
Elbow Lake (G-1853)
Gehling Auction Co Inc.......E.....507 765-2131
Preston (G-6897)
Genex Farm Systems.......952 758-2561
New Prague (G-6428)
Hance Distributing Inc.......E.....952 935-6429
Hopkins (G-2548)
Haug Implement Co.......E.....320 235-8115
Willmar (G-10006)
Hedberg Aggregates Inc.......D.....763 545-4400
Minneapolis (G-4627)
Interstate Service of Fergus.......E.....218 739-3284
Fergus Falls (G-2077)
Kibble Equipment Inc.......D.....320 269-6466
Montevideo (G-6248)
Kibble Equipment Inc.......E.....507 644-3571
Redwood Falls (G-7022)
Lee Hydra-Mac Sales.......E.....218 574-2237
Fertile (G-2126)
Lodermeiers.......D.....651 923-4441
Goodhue (G-2250)
Mies Equipment Inc.......E.....320 764-5310
Watkins (G-9898)
Miller Manufacturing Co Inc.......D.....320 864-4039
Glencoe (G-2209)
Miller Sellner Equipment Inc.......E.....507 831-1106
Bingham Lake (G-467)
Miller Sellner Implement Inc.......E.....507 794-2131
Sleepy Eye (G-9498)
Minnesota Valley Irrigation.......E.....218 631-9271
Wadena (G-9806)
▲ Pals Inc.......D.....320 235-8860
Willmar (G-10035)
Pals Inc.......E.....320 235-8860
Willmar (G-10036)
Pinehurst Development Inc.......E.....952 469-3202
Farmington (G-2057)
Power Systems LLC.......E.....952 361-6800
Chanhassen (G-935)
Precision Turf & Chemical Inc.......763 477-5885
Rockford (G-7303)
Rdo Agriculture Equipment Co.......E.....218 643-2601
Breckenridge (G-597)
RDO Construction Equipment Co.......D.....952 890-8880
Burnsville (G-784)
Rdo Equipment Co.......E.....218 483-3353
Hawley (G-2421)
Red River Implement Co Inc.......E.....218 643-2601
Breckenridge (G-598)
S & S Sales Inc.......763 476-9599
Minneapolis (G-5581)
Smith's Mill Implement Inc.......E.....507 234-5191
Janesville (G-2803)
Stearns Veterinary Outlet.......E.....320 256-3303
Melrose (G-3353)
Sylva Corp Inc.......E.....763 389-2748
Princeton (G-6917)
Tandem Products Inc.......D.....507 583-7222
Blooming Prairie (G-479)
Thorstad Construction Co Inc.......E.....320 367-2159
Maynard (G-3337)
▲ Tilton Equipment Co.......D.....763 783-7030
Lindstrom (G-2971)
Titan Machinery Inc.......E.....218 281-4668
Crookston (G-1137)
Titan Machinery Inc.......E.....218 681-1423
Thief River Falls (G-9680)
◆ Toro LLC.......A.....952 888-8801
Minneapolis (G-5832)
Woods Equipment Co.......D.....651 455-6681
Saint Paul (G-9166)
Worthington Tractor Parts Inc.......E.....507 372-2911
Worthington (G-10198)
Ziegler AG Equipment.......E.....507 847-7600
Jackson (G-2801)

5084 Industrial Mach & Eqpt Wholesale

Ace Label Systems Inc.......E.....763 450-3202
Golden Valley (G-2236)
Aeration Industries Intl.......E.....952 448-6789
Chaska (G-947)
Airgas - North Central Inc.......E.....763 712-5100
Anoka (G-148)
Aldin Export & Import.......651 483-4184
Saint Paul (G-8007)
Almco Inc.......E.....507 377-2102
Albert Lea (G-36)
American Air Products Inc.......E.....651 290-0000
Saint Paul (G-8020)
American Welding & Gas.......E.....320 235-4774
Willmar (G-9983)
▲ Applied Products Inc.......E.....952 933-2224
Minnetonka (G-6142)
Associated Material Handling.......E.....651 688-6175
Saint Paul (G-7707)
Automation Fluid Power Inc.......E.....763 571-3336
Minneapolis (G-3839)
Barrett Automatic Products Co.......E.....320 528-2512
Barrett (G-307)
Barry & Sewall Industrial Sply.......E.....612 331-6170
Minneapolis (G-3869)
BASF Corp.......E.....763 559-3266
Minneapolis (G-3870)
Benham Co's The LLC.......E.....651 771-2222
Saint Paul (G-8103)
Bennett Material Handling Inc.......E.....952 933-5544
Hopkins (G-2517)
Boedecker Co.......E.....952 279-5205
Chanhassen (G-910)
Braas Co.......D.....952 937-8902
Eden Prairie (G-1611)
Cable Connection & Supply Co.......E.....507 334-6417
Faribault (G-1995)
Cannon Technologies Inc.......E.....763 595-7777
Minneapolis (G-3999)
Cartridge Care Inc.......E.....612 331-7757
Saint Paul (G-8169)
▲ Central Power Distributors Inc.......E.....763 576-0901
Anoka (G-164)
Colder Products Co.......C.....651 645-0091
Saint Paul (G-8220)
Concept Machine Tool Sales Inc.......E.....763 559-1975
Minneapolis (G-4150)
Conveyor Belt Service Inc.......E.....218 741-5939
Virginia (G-9737)
Crown Equipment Corp.......E.....651 645-8668
Saint Paul (G-8271)
Crysteel Truck Equipment Inc.......E.....507 726-6041
Lake Crystal (G-2857)
Dan Larson Enterprises Inc.......E.....612 331-8550
Minneapolis (G-4222)
Delkor Systems Inc.......D.....763 783-0855
Circle Pines (G-1010)
Design Ready Controls Inc.......D.....763 565-3000
Rockford (G-7309)
▲ Diversified Dynamics Corp.......D.....763 780-5440
Minneapolis (G-3457)
▲ E Tech Inc.......D.....612 722-1366
Minneapolis (G-4301)
Easy Automation Inc.......E.....507 728-8214
Welcome (G-9958)
Eaton Corp.......B.....952 937-9800
Eden Prairie (G-1648)
Edwards Oil Co Inc.......E.....218 741-9634
Virginia (G-9738)
Engineering America Inc.......E.....651 777-4041
Saint Paul (G-9214)
Environmental Control Systems.......E.....218 863-1766
Pelican Rapids (G-6777)
Excel Manufacturing Inc.......E.....507 932-4680
Saint Charles (G-7401)
First Supply LLC.......E.....507 287-0202
Rochester (G-7116)
5 K Enterprises Inc.......E.....612 216-6292
Mankato (G-3127)
▲ Force America Inc.......E.....952 707-1300
Burnsville (G-722)
▲ G P Co's Inc.......D.....651 454-6500
Mendota Heights (G-3363)
▲ Garland's Inc.......E.....612 333-3469
Minneapolis (G-4501)
Gateway Building Systems Inc.......E.....218 236-9336
Moorhead (G-6316)
Glacier International Inc.......651 786-9700
Saint Paul (G-8412)
▲ Great Northern Equipment Dstbg.......E.....763 428-9405
Rogers (G-7326)
Greenlee Textron Inc.......D.....507 238-4357
Fairmont (G-1969)
Haldeman-Homme Inc.......C.....612 331-4880
Minneapolis (G-4590)
Harold Pitman M Co.......E.....612 781-8988
Minneapolis (G-4601)
Harriston-Mayo LLC.......E.....218 773-1234
East Grand Forks (G-1568)
Hartfiel Co.......D.....952 974-2500
Eden Prairie (G-1679)
Hegman Machine Tool Inc.......E.....763 424-5622
Osseo (G-6620)
Heidelberg USA Inc.......E.....952 831-6501
Minneapolis (G-4628)
Herc-U-Lift Inc.......D.....763 479-2501
Maple Plain (G-3277)
Hydraulic Headquarters Inc.......E.....763 478-6220
Hamel (G-2345)
Hydraulic Specialty Co Inc.......E.....763 571-3072
Minneapolis (G-3494)
I-State Truck Center.......E.....651 455-9775
Inver Grove Heights (G-2754)
I-State Truck Center.......E.....952 854-5511
Minneapolis (G-4685)
I-State Truck Center.......D.....651 636-3400
Minneapolis (G-3495)
▲ Indelco Plastics Corp.......E.....952 925-5075
Minneapolis (G-4694)
Indoff Inc.......B.....952 472-1295
Minnetrista (G-6242)
Industrial Tool Inc.......E.....763 533-7244
Minneapolis (G-4700)
Interstate Power Systems.......D.....952 854-5511
Minneapolis (G-4729)
Interstate Power Systems Inc.......D.....952 854-5511
Minneapolis (G-3502)
Interstate Power Systems Inc.......D.....952 854-2044
Minneapolis (G-4730)
J A Swenson & Assoc Inc.......E.....952 469-3585
Lakeville (G-2912)
JEM Technical Marketing Co Inc.......D.....952 473-5012
Long Lake (G-3025)
Jerry's Enterprises Inc.......E.....952 929-4601
Minneapolis (G-4761)
John Henry Foster Minnesota.......D.....651 452-8452
Saint Paul (G-7810)
Lofton Label Inc.......D.....651 457-8118
Inver Grove Heights (G-2759)
Machine Tool Supply Corp.......E.....651 452-4400
Saint Paul (G-7829)
Macqueen Equipment Inc.......E.....651 645-5726
Saint Paul (G-8605)

- Marketing Focus Inc ... E ... 952 939-9880 — Hopkins *(G-2576)*
- Mars, W P & R S Co Inc ... E ... 952 884-9388 — Minneapolis *(G-4956)*
- ▲ Mate Precision Tooling Inc ... B ... 763 421-0230 — Anoka *(G-203)*
- Mechanical Systems Inc ... E ... 507 645-5675 — Dundas *(G-1512)*
- Melrose Metalworks Inc ... E ... 320 256-4170 — Melrose *(G-3350)*
- Mhc Material Handling ... E ... 320 634-4593 — Glenwood *(G-2228)*
- Midway Industrial Supply Co ... E ... 763 780-3000 — Saint Paul *(G-8655)*
- Midwest Sign & Screen Printing ... D ... 651 489-9999 — Saint Paul *(G-8661)*
- Minneapolis Oxygen Co ... E ... 612 588-8855 — Minneapolis *(G-5058)*
- ▲ Minnesota Supply Co ... D ... 952 828-7300 — Eden Prairie *(G-1726)*
- Mississippi Welders Supply Co ... E ... 507 454-5231 — Winona *(G-10118)*
- National Oilwell Varco Inc ... D ... 651 293-4699 — Saint Paul *(G-8740)*
- ▼ Northstar Imaging Inc ... E ... 763 463-5650 — Rogers *(G-7333)*
- ▲ Nott Co ... C ... 651 415-3400 — Saint Paul *(G-8772)*
- Novaspect Inc ... E ... 952 934-5100 — Eden Prairie *(G-1733)*
- ▲ Oil-Air Products LLC ... E ... 763 478-8744 — Hamel *(G-2353)*
- Oki Systems Limited ... D ... 651 645-8668 — Saint Paul *(G-8779)*
- Oxygen Service Co Inc ... D ... 651 644-7273 — Saint Paul *(G-8797)*
- Packaging Automation Corp ... E ... 651 456-0003 — Saint Paul *(G-7862)*
- Packaging Systems Automation ... E ... 763 473-1032 — Minneapolis *(G-5312)*
- Palen Kimball LLC ... E ... 651 646-2800 — Saint Paul *(G-8804)*
- Parker-Hannifin Corp ... E ... 952 469-5000 — Lakeville *(G-2924)*
- Power Mation Division Inc ... D ... 651 605-3300 — Saint Paul *(G-8832)*
- Ppt Vision Inc ... C ... 952 942-5747 — Eden Prairie *(G-1751)*
- Premier Technologies Inc ... D ... 952 475-2317 — Long Lake *(G-3030)*
- Prima Laserdyne Inc ... E ... 763 433-3700 — Champlin *(G-898)*
- Productivity Inc ... D ... 763 476-8600 — Minneapolis *(G-5417)*
- Productivity Quality Inc ... E ... 763 249-8130 — Minneapolis *(G-5418)*
- Pugleasa Co Inc ... E ... 651 636-6442 — Saint Paul *(G-8857)*
- ▲ Quest Engineering Inc ... E ... 952 546-4441 — Minneapolis *(G-5448)*
- ▲ Rapid Packaging Inc ... E ... 763 404-8900 — Champlin *(G-899)*
- Rdo Construction Equipment Co ... E ... 218 282-8440 — Moorhead *(G-6334)*
- Rdo Equipment Co ... E ... 218 483-3353 — Hawley *(G-2421)*
- Rdo Material Handling Co ... E ... 651 905-7025 — Saint Paul *(G-7890)*
- Rollie's Sales & Service Inc ... E ... 320 859-4811 — Osakis *(G-6587)*
- ▲ Rosemount Inc ... A ... 952 949-7000 — Chanhassen *(G-939)*
- Rubber Specialties Inc ... E ... 952 888-9225 — Minneapolis *(G-5573)*
- ▲ Safety Signs Inc ... E ... 952 469-6700 — Lakeville *(G-2930)*
- Schneiberg Co ... 651 489-7489 — Saint Paul *(G-8934)*
- Siemens Industry Inc ... D ... 651 631-8533 — Saint Paul *(G-8955)*
- ◆ Sjf Material Handling Inc ... D ... 320 485-2824 — Winsted *(G-10165)*
- Skarnes Inc ... E ... 763 231-3600 — Minneapolis *(G-5687)*
- ▲ SMI & Hydraulics Inc ... E ... 507 296-4551 — Porter *(G-6894)*
- ▲ Smyth Co's Inc ... E ... 651 646-4544 — Saint Paul *(G-8967)*
- Source Fluid Power Inc ... E ... 952 448-4440 — Chaska *(G-980)*
- STS Operating Inc ... D ... 952 563-1700 — Savage *(G-9409)*
- STS Operating Inc ... E ... 320 564-3057 — Granite Falls *(G-2320)*
- ▲ Swanson-Flosystems Co ... E ... 763 383-4700 — Plymouth *(G-6885)*
- ◆ Tapemark Co ... C ... 651 455-1611 — Saint Paul *(G-7916)*
- Tc American Monorail Inc ... D ... 763 497-8700 — Saint Michael *(G-7683)*
- Tc American Monorail Inc ... E ... 320 634-4531 — Glenwood *(G-2234)*
- ▲ Tilton Equipment Co ... D ... 763 783-7030 — Lindstrom *(G-2971)*
- Toll Co ... E ... 763 551-5355 — Minneapolis *(G-5829)*
- Toyota-Lift of Minnesota Inc ... D ... 763 425-9066 — Brooklyn Park *(G-619)*
- ◆ Twin City Fan Co's Ltd ... C ... 763 551-7600 — Minneapolis *(G-5878)*
- Vac System Industries of MN ... E ... 952 808-1616 — Burnsville *(G-816)*
- Valley Craft Inc ... C ... 651 345-3386 — Lake City *(G-2855)*
- Valley National Gases Inc ... E ... 651 628-4848 — Saint Paul *(G-9123)*
- Welders Supply Co Inc ... E ... 320 235-3430 — Willmar *(G-10052)*
- Westside Equipment Installers ... E ... 763 478-9572 — Hamel *(G-2360)*
- ▲ Yale Materials Handling - MN ... D ... 763 434-3832 — Anoka *(G-241)*
- Ziegler Inc ... A ... 952 888-4121 — Minneapolis *(G-6117)*

5085 Industrial Splys Wholesale

- Abrasive Specialists Inc ... E ... 763 571-4111 — Minneapolis *(G-3384)*
- Abrasives of St Paul Inc ... D ... 651 636-3955 — Saint Paul *(G-7973)*
- Applied Power Products Inc ... E ... 952 985-5100 — Lakeville *(G-2891)*
- ▲ Applied Power Products Inc ... D ... 651 452-2250 — Saint Paul *(G-7705)*
- Applied Power Products Inc ... D ... 952 985-5100 — Lakeville *(G-2892)*
- ▲ Applied Products Inc ... E ... 952 933-2224 — Minnetonka *(G-6142)*
- Barry & Sewall Industrial Sply ... E ... 612 331-6170 — Minneapolis *(G-3869)*
- Belcourt Corp ... E ... 952 894-0406 — Burnsville *(G-684)*
- Building Fasteners of MN ... D ... 612 706-3300 — Minneapolis *(G-3973)*
- Carbide Tool Services Inc ... E ... 763 421-2210 — Anoka *(G-161)*
- Central-Mcgowan Inc ... E ... 320 252-5292 — Saint Cloud *(G-7490)*
- Chicago Tube & Iron Co of MN ... D ... 651 454-6800 — Saint Paul *(G-7731)*
- Cone Corp ... E ... 218 245-2313 — Bovey *(G-540)*
- Consolidated Container Co LLC ... D ... 612 781-0923 — Minneapolis *(G-4154)*
- Diamond Drilling & Supply Inc ... 218 628-3671 — Duluth *(G-1293)*
- Duncan Co ... E ... 612 331-1776 — Minneapolis *(G-4292)*
- ▼ Fastenal Co ... B ... 507 454-5374 — Winona *(G-10095)*
- ▲ Fastenal Co Purchasing ... E ... 507 454-5374 — Winona *(G-10096)*
- Ferguson Enterprises Inc ... D ... 651 638-5000 — Saint Paul *(G-8374)*
- ▲ Flint Group LLC ... D ... 763 559-5911 — Minneapolis *(G-4456)*
- G&K Services Inc ... C ... 612 333-2225 — Minneapolis *(G-4493)*
- ▲ Gamer Packaging Inc ... E ... 612 788-4444 — Minneapolis *(G-4498)*
- Hajoca Corp ... E ... 763 315-0100 — Minneapolis *(G-4589)*
- Hose Conveyors Inc ... E ... 651 456-0200 — Saint Paul *(G-7801)*
- ▲ Industrial Supply Co Inc ... E ... 763 559-0033 — Minneapolis *(G-4699)*
- ▲ International Seal Co Inc ... D ... 952 894-8400 — Shakopee *(G-9445)*
- JEM Technical Marketing Co Inc ... D ... 952 473-5012 — Long Lake *(G-3025)*
- Kaufman Container Co Inc ... D ... 612 331-8880 — Minneapolis *(G-4794)*
- Kendeco Supply Co ... E ... 320 253-1020 — Saint Cloud *(G-7540)*
- ▲ MacDermid ColorSpan Inc ... C ... 952 944-9457 — Hopkins *(G-2573)*
- Machine Tool Supply Corp ... E ... 651 452-4400 — Saint Paul *(G-7829)*
- Matrix Adhesives Inc ... E ... 952 912-2452 — Hopkins *(G-2578)*
- ▲ Midwest Rubber Service & Sply ... E ... 763 559-2551 — Minneapolis *(G-5036)*
- Minneapolis Oxygen Co ... E ... 612 588-8855 — Minneapolis *(G-5058)*
- ▲ Minnesota Flexible Corp ... E ... 651 645-7522 — Saint Paul *(G-8687)*
- Nalco Distributing Inc ... D ... 651 636-8124 — Saint Paul *(G-8733)*
- North Central Container of New ... E ... 507 359-3136 — New Ulm *(G-6471)*
- Northern States Supply Inc ... E ... 320 235-0555 — Willmar *(G-10031)*
- ▲ Nott Co ... C ... 651 415-3400 — Saint Paul *(G-8772)*
- Oxygen Service Co Inc ... D ... 651 644-7273 — Saint Paul *(G-8797)*
- Power Mation Division Inc ... D ... 651 605-3300 — Saint Paul *(G-8832)*
- ▲ Quest Engineering Inc ... E ... 952 546-4441 — Minneapolis *(G-5448)*
- R E Purvis & Associates Inc ... E ... 952 829-5532 — Minneapolis *(G-5457)*
- R J Tool Crib LLC ... E ... 320 253-1020 — Saint Cloud *(G-7579)*
- Replenex ... D ... 952 941-9150 — Eden Prairie *(G-1762)*
- ▲ Ritchie Engineering Co Inc ... C ... 952 943-1300 — Minneapolis *(G-5541)*
- Safeway Hydraulics Inc ... E ... 952 466-6220 — Chaska *(G-979)*
- ▲ Shark Industries Ltd ... E ... 763 565-1900 — Rockford *(G-7313)*
- ▲ Signcaster Corp ... E ... 952 888-9507 — Minneapolis *(G-5671)*
- STS Operating Inc ... D ... 952 563-1700 — Savage *(G-9409)*
- ▲ Swanson-Flosystems Co ... E ... 763 383-4700 — Plymouth *(G-6885)*
- 3M Co ... E ... 651 733-2008 — Saint Paul *(G-9050)*
- ▲ Twin City Hose Inc ... E ... 763 428-5100 — Rogers *(G-7344)*
- W W Grainger Inc ... E ... 763 531-0300 — Minneapolis *(G-5989)*
- W W Grainger Inc ... E ... 612 486-3300 — Minneapolis *(G-5988)*
- Wair Products Inc ... E ... 952 881-9449 — Minneapolis *(G-5994)*
- Welders Supply Co Inc ... E ... 320 235-3430 — Willmar *(G-10052)*
- Wells Technology Inc ... E ... 218 751-5117 — Bemidji *(G-432)*
- Wells Technology Inc ... E ... 218 751-1412 — Bemidji *(G-433)*
- Wesco Distribution Inc ... D ... 651 582-3945 — Saint Paul *(G-9147)*
- Williams Steel & Hardware Co ... D ... 612 588-9800 — Minneapolis *(G-6070)*

5087 Service Establishment Eqpt & Splys Wholesale

- A-1 Maintenance Service Corp ... E ... 952 891-3711 — Lakeville *(G-2888)*
- Activar Inc ... E ... 952 835-6850 — Minneapolis *(G-3677)*
- Altobella Hair Products Inc ... E ... 952 707-1900 — Burnsville *(G-675)*
- ▼ Barbers Hairstyling For Men ... D ... 952 947-7777 — Minneapolis *(G-3867)*
- Beauty Craft Supply & Eqpt ... E ... 952 935-4420 — Hopkins *(G-2515)*
- ▲ Bro-Tex Co Inc ... D ... 651 645-5721 — Saint Paul *(G-8130)*
- C J Duffey Paper Co ... D ... 612 338-8701 — Minneapolis *(G-3984)*
- Ceiling Pro Interior Inc ... E ... 952 947-0007 — Eden Prairie *(G-1617)*
- Clarey's Safety Equipment Inc ... E ... 507 289-6749 — Rochester *(G-7080)*
- Common Sense Building Services ... D ... 612 379-7106 — Minneapolis *(G-4134)*
- Dalco Enterprises Inc ... D ... 651 604-2966 — Saint Paul *(G-8280)*
- E Weinberg Supply Co Inc ... E ... 952 920-0888 — Minneapolis *(G-4303)*
- Four Seasons Services Inc ... E ... 507 373-9666 — Albert Lea *(G-53)*
- ▲ G P Co's Inc ... D ... 651 454-6500 — Mendota Heights *(G-3363)*
- Guardian Building Products ... E ... 612 524-0513 — Minneapolis *(G-4576)*
- J J Vanderson & Co ... E ... 651 641-1376 — Minneapolis *(G-3503)*
- Kennedy Brissman ... E ... 651 646-7933 — Saint Paul *(G-8545)*
- ▲ Lieberman Co's Inc ... D ... 952 887-5299 — Minneapolis *(G-4873)*
- Mikara Corp ... E ... 763 541-1000 — Minneapolis *(G-5038)*
- Minnesota Chemical Co ... E ... 651 646-7521 — Saint Paul *(G-8676)*
- ◆ Nilfisk-Advance Inc ... A ... 763 745-3500 — Plymouth *(G-6877)*
- Northwestern Casket Co Inc ... E ... 612 789-4356 — Minneapolis *(G-5245)*
- Osland Janitorial Supply Inc ... E ... 952 894-4815 — Burnsville *(G-773)*
- Paquette Maintenance Inc ... D ... 952 888-1801 — Minneapolis *(G-5318)*
- PI Enterprises Inc ... E ... 612 588-9000 — Minneapolis *(G-5387)*
- Pugleasa Co Inc ... E ... 651 636-6442 — Saint Paul *(G-8857)*
- Pump & Meter Service Inc ... E ... 952 933-4800 — Hopkins *(G-2608)*
- Simplexgrinnell LP ... C ... 763 367-5000 — Minneapolis *(G-5676)*
- 675 Stinson LLC ... D ... 612 238-3200 — Minneapolis *(G-5686)*
- Strategic Equipment Inc ... D ... 320 252-2977 — Saint Cloud *(G-7614)*
- TAS Adventures Inc ... E ... 507 833-8164 — Waseca *(G-9888)*
- 3Wire Group Inc ... E ... 763 488-3000 — Osseo *(G-6675)*
- Zep Inc ... D ... 763 792-2050 — Minneapolis *(G-6133)*
- Zumbro River Brand Inc ... E ... 507 446-9097 — Owatonna *(G-6746)*

S I C

5088 Transportation Eqpt & Splys, Except Motor Vehicles Wholesale

Aviall Services Inc	E	651 452-1680
Mendota Heights *(G-3360)*		
Bemidji Aviation Services Inc	E	218 751-1880
Bemidji *(G-377)*		
Canard Aerospace Corp	E	952 944-7990
Shakopee *(G-9426)*		
Code Welding & Mfg Inc	E	763 792-6632
Minneapolis *(G-3435)*		
Harsco Corp	E	507 235-7127
Fairmont *(G-1971)*		
Modern Aero Inc	D	952 941-2595
Eden Prairie *(G-1729)*		
Northwest Aircraft Inc	E	612 726-2331
Saint Paul *(G-7854)*		
Railway Equipment Co Inc	E	763 537-3702
Minneapolis *(G-5461)*		
Safe Air Repair Inc	D	507 373-7129
Albert Lea *(G-63)*		
▲ Sky Media LLC	E	651 635-0100
Saint Paul *(G-8963)*		
Thunderbird Aviation Inc	E	952 941-1212
Eden Prairie *(G-1793)*		
Wipaire Inc	D	651 451-1205
South Saint Paul *(G-9553)*		

5091 Sporting & Recreational Goods & Splys Wholesale

Bell Industries Inc	C	651 203-2300
Eagan *(G-1517)*		
Crystal Marine Inc	E	952 233-3437
Shakopee *(G-9434)*		
Csi Sports Properties LLC	C	320 252-4193
Sauk Rapids *(G-9361)*		
H & G Marketing Inc	E	763 263-8998
Big Lake *(G-446)*		
Hannay's Inc	E	612 781-7411
Minneapolis *(G-4594)*		
Heelside Inc	E	612 508-0887
Anoka *(G-189)*		
Hicks Bill & Co Ltd	D	763 476-6200
Minneapolis *(G-4645)*		
Hudalla Associates Inc	E	218 346-2734
Perham *(G-6797)*		
Johnson Outdoors Inc	C	507 345-4623
Mankato *(G-3154)*		
Josuda Inc	E	763 263-0313
Big Lake *(G-449)*		
Leech Lake Distributors Inc	E	218 547-1505
Walker *(G-9853)*		
◆ Mid-States Distributing Co Inc	E	651 698-8831
Saint Paul *(G-8652)*		
Motivaction LLC	D	763 412-3000
Minneapolis *(G-5137)*		
▲ N C Holdings	E	952 933-7060
Hopkins *(G-2586)*		
New York Mint Ltd	E	952 949-6588
Minneapolis *(G-5194)*		
▲ Normark Corp	D	952 933-7060
Hopkins *(G-2589)*		
▲ Northern Wholesale Supply Inc	D	651 429-1515
Hugo *(G-2672)*		
Northland Fishing Tackle Inc	D	218 286-5441
Ranier *(G-6969)*		
▲ Palco Marketing Inc	E	763 559-5539
Osseo *(G-6651)*		
Prophet Corp	D	507 451-7470
Owatonna *(G-6730)*		
Prophet Corp	D	952 841-0021
Owatonna *(G-6731)*		
Prophet Corp	E	800 533-0446
Owatonna *(G-6732)*		
S & S Sales Inc	E	763 476-9599
Minneapolis *(G-5581)*		
▲ Saunatec Inc	D	320 286-5584
Cokato *(G-1079)*		
Watson's of Minneapolis Inc	E	763 560-7727
Minneapolis *(G-6024)*		
Westwood Sports Inc	D	952 881-2222
Minneapolis *(G-6063)*		

5092 Toys & Hobby Goods & Splys Wholesale

Destineer Inc	E	763 231-8000
Minneapolis *(G-4249)*		
▲ Food Market Merchandising Inc	E	952 894-0110
Minneapolis *(G-4462)*		
Gopher News Co	D	763 546-5300
Minneapolis *(G-4542)*		
H Enterprises International	E	320 453-2626
Eden Valley *(G-1821)*		
▲ Manhattan Group LLC	D	612 337-9600
Minneapolis *(G-4942)*		
◆ Mid-States Distributing Co Inc	E	651 698-8831
Saint Paul *(G-8652)*		
Midwest Craft Distributors Inc	E	952 252-7043
Excelsior *(G-1947)*		
Splatball Inc	E	612 378-0385
Minneapolis *(G-5721)*		
Triple Crown Gaming Inc	E	320 251-5373
Saint Cloud *(G-7622)*		

5093 Scrap & Waste Materials Wholesale

Alter Trading Corp	E	507 387-6504
Mankato *(G-3103)*		
American Iron & Steel Co Inc	E	612 529-9221
Minneapolis *(G-3755)*		
Crosstown Used Auto Parts	E	612 861-3020
Saint Paul *(G-8270)*		
Fridley Auto Parts Inc	D	763 784-8890
Minneapolis *(G-3472)*		
Great Western Uron & Metal Co	E	651 224-4877
Saint Paul *(G-8428)*		
▼ Kirschbaum-Krupp Metal	E	612 521-9212
Minneapolis *(G-4812)*		
Minnesota Shredding LLC	E	763 493-3007
Minneapolis *(G-5093)*		
Phillips Recycling Systems LLC	D	320 251-5980
Saint Cloud *(G-7422)*		
▼ Pioneer Industries Inc	D	612 374-2280
Minneapolis *(G-5383)*		
▲ Rag Minneapolis Stock Co	D	612 333-6576
Minneapolis *(G-5460)*		
Rock-Tenn Co	A	651 641-4874
Saint Paul *(G-8910)*		
Schwartzman Co Inc	E	763 421-1187
Anoka *(G-224)*		

5094 Jewelry, Watches, Precious Stones Wholesale

Estate Jewelry & Coin Inc	E	952 881-8862
Minneapolis *(G-4373)*		
Fred Meyer Jewelers Inc	E	952 892-6374
Burnsville *(G-723)*		
▲ Hanover Accessories LLC	D	763 509-6100
Plymouth *(G-6863)*		
New York Mint Ltd	E	952 949-6588
Minneapolis *(G-5194)*		
Reeves Park Inc	E	952 930-0290
Minneapolis *(G-5481)*		
Tiffany & Co	E	952 922-0066
Minneapolis *(G-5822)*		

5099 Durable Goods: NEC Wholesale

AAA-American Co	E	507 894-4156
Hokah *(G-2490)*		
Activar Inc	E	952 835-6850
Minneapolis *(G-3677)*		
Bell Lumber & Pole Co	E	651 633-4334
Saint Paul *(G-8098)*		
Berg Exteriors Inc	E	763 479-1115
Maple Plain *(G-3269)*		
Central Wood Products	E	763 753-7374
Cedar *(G-876)*		
▲ Dan-AM Co	E	507 346-7102
Spring Valley *(G-9569)*		
Dima Corp	E	507 373-6969
Albert Lea *(G-47)*		
E P A Audio Visual Inc	E	763 477-6931
Rockford *(G-7310)*		
Elvin Safety LLC	E	952 829-2950
Eden Prairie *(G-1655)*		
Frattalone I LLC	E	651 292-9800
Saint Paul *(G-8395)*		
J J Vanderson & Co	E	651 641-1376
Minneapolis *(G-3503)*		
K-Tel International Inc		763 559-5566
Minneapolis *(G-4787)*		
Lefty's Shooting & Outdoor		763 533-9594
Minneapolis *(G-4854)*		
Minnesota Conway Fire & Safety	E	952 345-3473
Minneapolis *(G-5072)*		
▲ Minnpar LLC	D	612 379-0606
Minneapolis *(G-5103)*		
Nardini Fire Equipment Co Inc	D	651 483-6631
Saint Paul *(G-8735)*		
▲ Navarre Corp	C	763 535-8333
Minneapolis *(G-5174)*		
Potlatch Corp	D	218 751-6144
Bemidji *(G-435)*		
▲ Seaver Co	D	507 665-3321
Le Sueur *(G-2959)*		
▲ Sky Media LLC	E	651 635-0100
Saint Paul *(G-8963)*		
Skyline Displays Midwest Inc	E	952 895-6000
Burnsville *(G-798)*		
Stanley Security Solutions Inc	E	952 894-3830
Saint Paul *(G-9004)*		
Stencil Cutting & Supply Co	D	800 783-4633
Red Wing *(G-7007)*		
▲ T W Enterprises Ltd	D	320 654-0551
Saint Cloud *(G-7615)*		
Tenacious Holdings Inc	C	651 642-9889
Saint Paul *(G-9038)*		
3M Co	C	651 736-9682
Saint Paul *(G-9052)*		
Twin City Hardware Co	E	763 535-4660
Minneapolis *(G-5881)*		

51 WHOLESALE TRADE-NONDURABLE GOODS

5111 Printing & Writing Paper Wholesale

C J Duffey Paper Co	D	612 338-8701
Minneapolis *(G-3984)*		
Henry's Foods Inc	C	320 763-3194
Alexandria *(G-104)*		
International Paper Co	C	612 781-6611
Minneapolis *(G-4724)*		
Kempf Paper Corp	D	612 781-9225
Minneapolis *(G-4799)*		
▲ Litin Paper Co Inc	E	612 333-4331
Minneapolis *(G-4893)*		
Midland Paper Co	E	612 623-2400
Minneapolis *(G-5025)*		
Unisource Worldwide Inc	B	763 488-7200
Brooklyn Park *(G-620)*		
▲ Wilcox Paper LLC	E	763 404-8400
Champlin *(G-906)*		

5112 Stationery & Office Splys Wholesale

American Business Forms Inc	C	320 634-5471
Glenwood *(G-2219)*		
Bertelson Brothers Inc	E	763 546-4371
Minneapolis *(G-3889)*		
Buyonlinenow Inc	E	507 281-6899
Rochester *(G-7068)*		
Cenveo Inc	E	651 645-0251
Saint Paul *(G-8186)*		
Corporate Express Office Prdts	C	651 636-2250
Saint Paul *(G-8251)*		
Corporate Graphics Intl	C	651 494-1740
Saint Paul *(G-8252)*		
Curry Sales Inc	E	952 351-4200
Hopkins *(G-2534)*		
◆ Diversified Distribution Systs	C	612 813-5200
Minneapolis *(G-4261)*		
Gartner Studios Inc	E	651 351-7700
Stillwater *(G-9619)*		
Help Systems LLC	D	952 933-0609
Eden Prairie *(G-1683)*		
Imation Enterprises Corp	A	651 704-4000
Oakdale *(G-6551)*		
Innovative Office Solutions	D	952 808-9900
Burnsville *(G-736)*		
J L Buchanan Inc		612 334-1710
Minneapolis *(G-4747)*		
Johnson Anderson & Associates	D	952 496-6699
Shakopee *(G-9447)*		
▲ Katun Corp	B	952 941-9505
Minneapolis *(G-4793)*		
Ktn Acquisition Corp	E	952 941-9505
Minneapolis *(G-4826)*		
Liberty Diversified Industries	D	763 536-6600
Minneapolis *(G-4869)*		
▲ Litin Paper Co Inc	E	612 333-4331
Minneapolis *(G-4893)*		
Marudas Graphics Inc	E	651 697-7820
Saint Paul *(G-8617)*		
▲ Masterpiece Studios Inc	C	507 388-8788
North Mankato *(G-6509)*		
Metro - Sales Inc	C	612 861-4000
Minneapolis *(G-5000)*		
Moore Wallace North America	E	952 844-2000
Minneapolis *(G-5124)*		
North Country Business Prdts	D	218 751-4140
Bemidji *(G-408)*		
North Country Business Prdts	E	800 937-4140
Plymouth *(G-6878)*		
▲ Northern Business Products Inc	E	218 726-0167
Duluth *(G-1402)*		
Office Depot Inc	E	952 525-1919
Minnetonka *(G-6205)*		
OfficeMax North America Inc	E	218 287-3755
Dilworth *(G-1224)*		
OfficeMax North America Inc	E	763 391-6629
Minneapolis *(G-5267)*		
OfficeMax North America Inc	E	651 686-6606
Eagan *(G-1544)*		
Paper Depot Inc	E	612 333-0512
Minneapolis *(G-5317)*		
Patterson Co's Inc	C	651 686-1600
Saint Paul *(G-7866)*		
Quality Business Forms of	E	763 559-4330
Minneapolis *(G-5441)*		
Ricoh Americas Corp	D	651 294-2600
Mendota Heights *(G-3370)*		
S & T Office Products Inc	C	651 483-4411
Saint Paul *(G-8918)*		
S P Richards Co	E	651 484-8459
Saint Paul *(G-8920)*		
Safco Products Co	C	763 536-6700
Minneapolis *(G-5588)*		
3M Co	D	651 733-5094
Saint Paul *(G-9064)*		
Tomsten Inc	E	952 516-3300
Minnetonka *(G-6228)*		
Unisource Worldwide Inc	B	763 488-7200
Brooklyn Park *(G-620)*		
United Stationers Supply Co	C	651 681-1720
Saint Paul *(G-7937)*		

(G-00000) Company's Geographic Section entry number

472

2011 Harris Minnesota
Services Directory

▲=Import ▼=Export
◆=Import/Export

Victor Lundeen Co ....E....218 736-5433
Fergus Falls (G-2123)

5113 Indl & Personal Svc Paper Wholesale

Berry Coffee Co ....E....952 937-8697
Eden Prairie (G-1604)
Bunzl USA Inc ....E....763 571-1011
Minneapolis (G-3426)
C J Duffey Paper Co ....D....612 338-8701
Minneapolis (G-3984)
Dalco Enterprises Inc ....D....651 604-2966
Saint Paul (G-8280)
Fisher Paper Box Co ....E....763 425-7444
Minneapolis (G-4452)
▲ Gage & Gage Inc ....E....952 403-1193
Shakopee (G-9440)
Great Northern Corp ....C....763 493-5521
Minneapolis (G-4554)
Henry's Foods Inc ....C....320 763-3194
Alexandria (G-104)
▲ International Dairy Queen Inc ....B....952 830-0200
Minneapolis (G-4721)
International Paper Co ....C....507 433-3467
Austin (G-278)
Kennedy Brissman ....E....651 646-7933
Saint Paul (G-8545)
▲ Litin Paper Co Inc ....E....612 333-4331
Minneapolis (G-4893)
Martin Falk Paper Co ....E....612 332-8626
Minneapolis (G-4959)
Mayflower Distributing Co Inc ....C....651 452-4892
Saint Paul (G-7835)
Menasha Packaging Co LLC ....C....763 424-6606
Minneapolis (G-4986)
Menasha Packaging Co LLC ....C....952 469-4451
Lakeville (G-2918)
Packaging Corp of America ....D....763 521-3611
Minneapolis (G-5311)
Procter & Gamble Distributing ....C....952 942-1857
Eden Prairie (G-1754)
▲ Rapid Packaging Inc ....E....763 404-8900
Champlin (G-899)
Rock-Tenn Co ....A....651 641-4874
Saint Paul (G-8910)
▲ Rohlfing of Brainerd Inc ....E....218 829-0303
Brainerd (G-585)
Rohn Industries Inc-St Paul ....E....651 647-1300
Saint Paul (G-8912)
Smurfit-Stone Container ....E....507 288-2305
Rochester (G-7256)
Smurfit-Stone Container Corp ....C....612 789-2485
Minneapolis (G-5691)
Smurfit-Stone Container Corp ....C....320 252-3660
Saint Cloud (G-7594)
3M Co ....E....651 733-8432
Saint Paul (G-9049)
3M Co ....E....651 733-4740
Saint Paul (G-9053)
Uline Inc ....D....651 688-3495
Saint Paul (G-7933)
Uline Inc ....C....651 688-3495
Saint Paul (G-7934)
Unisource Worldwide Inc ....B....763 488-7200
Brooklyn Park (G-620)
V-TEK Inc ....D....507 387-2039
Mankato (G-3211)
Watson Co Inc ....E....763 689-3722
Cambridge (G-846)

5122 Drugs, Drug Proprietaries & Sundries Wholesale

Accredo Health Group Inc ....E....651 681-0885
Saint Paul (G-7687)
Amerisourcebergen Corp ....B....952 903-7600
Eden Prairie (G-1592)
▲ Apothecary Products Inc ....C....952 890-1940
Burnsville (G-679)
Badger Acquisition of MN ....C....763 259-0400
Minneapolis (G-3857)
▼ Barbers Hairstyling For Men ....D....952 947-7777
Minneapolis (G-3867)
Cardinal Health 414 Inc ....E....651 645-9904
Saint Paul (G-8157)
Cardinal Health Inc ....C....763 398-8321
Minneapolis (G-4001)
Cardinal Health Inc ....D....651 255-1383
Saint Paul (G-8158)
Contract Hardware Co Inc ....E....651 780-0010
Circle Pines (G-1007)
Curry Sales Inc ....E....952 351-4200
Hopkins (G-2534)
▲ Custom Hbc Corp ....D....952 442-8241
Waconia (G-9784)
Eniva Corp ....E....763 795-8870
Anoka (G-177)
Fairview Health Services ....E....651 632-9835
Saint Paul (G-8363)
Fairview Pharmacy Services LLC ....B....612 672-5260
Minneapolis (G-4403)
Fresh Seasons Market LLC ....D....952 938-5555
Minnetonka (G-6170)
Hawkins Pharmaceutical Group ....E....612 617-8600
Minneapolis (G-4609)
Instymeds Corp ....E....952 653-2525
Eden Prairie (G-1696)
Kruse Family Enterprises LLC ....E....507 345-5926
Mankato (G-3156)
Master's Miracle Inc ....D....763 493-3200
Osseo (G-6635)
McKesson Corp ....D....651 484-4811
Little Canada (G-2996)
Midwest Veterinary Supply Inc ....E....952 894-4350
Burnsville (G-759)
Minter-Weisman Co ....B....763 545-3706
Minneapolis (G-5105)
Nash-Finch Co ....D....507 645-4489
Northfield (G-6535)
Nutri-Dyn Midwest Inc ....E....763 479-3444
Maple Plain (G-3279)
Omnicare Pharmacy & Supply ....C....763 259-0188
Minneapolis (G-5278)
Procter & Gamble Distributing ....C....952 942-1857
Eden Prairie (G-1754)
Redpharm Drug ....E....952 653-2525
Eden Prairie (G-1760)
Sanofi Pasteur Inc ....E....952 893-8080
Minneapolis (G-5601)
▲ Universal Cooperatives Inc ....D....651 239-1000
Saint Paul (G-7938)
Walgreen Co ....E....952 938-1168
Hopkins (G-2657)
▲ Watkins Inc ....C....507 457-3300
Winona (G-10138)
Wise Essentials Inc ....E....651 699-4468
Saint Paul (G-9162)

5131 Piece Goods, Notions & Dry Goods Wholesale

▲ Chromatic Concepts, Co ....D....763 566-1118
Minneapolis (G-4073)
▼ Dasco Systems Inc ....E....763 574-2275
Minneapolis (G-3451)
Display Sales Co ....E....952 885-0100
Minneapolis (G-4259)
Encompass Group LLC ....D....651 646-6600
Saint Paul (G-8339)
Encompass Group LLC ....C....651 646-6600
Saint Paul (G-8340)
▲ Lintex Corp ....C....651 646-6600
Saint Paul (G-8591)
Rubenstein & Ziff Inc ....E....952 854-1460
Minneapolis (G-5574)
Steven Fabrics Co ....C....612 781-6671
Minneapolis (G-5753)
▲ Stone Fabrics Inc ....E....952 941-2303
Eden Prairie (G-1783)

5136 Men's & Boys' Clothing & Furnishings Wholesale

Anderson's Formal Wear Inc ....E....507 285-1884
Rochester (G-7056)
▲ Eldredge Trading Inc 651 778-8500
Saint Paul (G-7758)
Gordon & Ferguson of Delaware ....E....763 559-8300
Minneapolis (G-4543)
◆ Mid-States Distributing Co Inc ....E....651 698-8831
Saint Paul (G-8652)
▲ River's End Holdings LLC 952 912-2543
Hopkins (G-2618)
▲ Rivers End Trading Co ....D....952 912-2500
Hopkins (G-2619)

5137 Women's, Children's & Infants Clothing Wholesale

Christopher & Banks Co ....D....763 551-5000
Plymouth (G-6855)
Fun Sisters ....E....612 824-9872
Minneapolis (G-4491)
▲ Hanover Accessories LLC ....D....763 509-6100
Plymouth (G-6863)
▲ River's End Holdings LLC 952 912-2543
Hopkins (G-2618)
▲ Rivers End Trading Co ....D....952 912-2500
Hopkins (G-2619)
Winmark Corp ....C....763 520-8500
Minneapolis (G-6077)

5139 Footwear Wholesale

Dsw Shoe Warehouse Inc ....E....952 876-0991
Minneapolis (G-4288)
Golden ERA Trading LLC ....D....651 774-4400
Saint Paul (G-8419)
▲ Minnetonka Moccasin Co Inc ....D....612 331-8493
Minneapolis (G-5102)

5141 Groceries, General Line Wholesale

Appert's Inc ....C....320 251-3200
Saint Cloud (G-7433)
Apperts Frozen Foods Inc ....D....320 251-3200
Saint Cloud (G-7434)
Belgrade Cooperative Assn ....E....320 254-8231
Belgrade (G-363)
Best Brands Corp ....B....651 454-5850
Saint Paul (G-7717)
Bradley Distributing Co ....E....651 639-0523
Newport (G-6485)
Curry Sales Inc ....E....952 351-4200
Hopkins (G-2534)
Fraboni's Wholesale Distrs ....E....218 263-8991
Hibbing (G-2445)
Fritz Co Inc ....D....651 459-9751
Newport (G-6486)
Hawkeye Foodservice Distbn ....E....507 238-4721
Fairmont (G-1972)
Henry's Foods Inc ....C....320 763-3194
Alexandria (G-104)
Jerry's Enterprises Inc ....C....952 941-9050
Eden Prairie (G-1701)
Juhl Brokerage Inc ....E....763 519-0120
Minneapolis (G-4781)
Key Sales Group Inc ....E....952 979-1531
Hopkins (G-2564)
Martin-Brower Co L L C ....C....763 571-6311
Minneapolis (G-3528)
McLane Minnesota Inc ....B....507 664-3000
Northfield (G-6531)
▲ Nash-Finch Co ....B....952 832-0534
Edina (G-1838)
Nash-Finch Co ....D....507 931-5541
Saint Peter (G-9309)
Nash-Finch Co ....E....651 388-2869
Red Wing (G-6992)
Nash-Finch Co ....C....218 739-5272
Fergus Falls (G-2100)
Nash-Finch Co ....D....651 463-3404
Farmington (G-2055)
Nash-Finch Co ....D....507 645-9514
Northfield (G-6534)
Nash-Finch Co ....C....320 251-3961
Saint Cloud (G-7561)
Nash-Finch Co ....E....320 587-8233
Hutchinson (G-2708)
Nash-Finch Co ....D....507 263-3643
Cannon Falls (G-861)
Reinhart Foodservice LLC ....C....507 537-1451
Marshall (G-3324)
Reinhart Foodservice LLC ....B....763 428-6500
Rogers (G-7339)
Roisum Elite Rosium Foods ....E....952 227-3199
Chanhassen (G-938)
Source One Sales & Marketing ....C....952 829-0833
Minneapolis (G-5704)
▲ SUPERVALU Inc ....A....952 828-4000
Eden Prairie (G-1787)
SUPERVALU Inc ....C....952 932-4300
Hopkins (G-2640)
Supervalu Inc ....C....952 906-6260
Chanhassen (G-941)
Supervalu Inc ....C....952 380-9900
Excelsior (G-1937)
Supervalu Inc ....C....952 906-6600
Chanhassen (G-942)
Supervalu Inc ....C....952 947-3700
Eden Prairie (G-1788)
▲ Twin City Poultry Co ....E....763 592-6500
Minneapolis (G-5882)
Upper Lakes Foods Inc ....C....218 879-1265
Cloquet (G-1066)
US Foodservice Inc ....C....763 559-9494
Minneapolis (G-5948)
US Foodservice Inc ....B....651 454-6580
Eagan (G-1559)
Watson Co Inc ....E....763 689-3722
Cambridge (G-846)
Wincom Systems Inc ....B....952 828-4000
Eden Prairie (G-1816)

5142 Packaged Frozen Foods Wholesale

A H Hermel Candy & Tobacco Co ....D....507 387-5634
Mankato (G-3098)
American Fish & Seafood Inc ....D....952 935-3474
Hopkins (G-2509)
Appert's Inc ....C....320 251-3200
Saint Cloud (G-7433)
Apperts Frozen Foods Inc ....D....320 251-3200
Saint Cloud (G-7434)
▲ E A Sween Deli Express ....C....952 937-9440
Eden Prairie (G-1647)
5 K Enterprises Inc ....E....612 216-6292
Mankato (G-3127)
Hawkeye Foodservice Distbn ....E....507 238-4721
Fairmont (G-1972)
Martin-Brower Co L L C ....C....763 571-6311
Minneapolis (G-3528)
▲ Nash-Finch Co ....B....952 832-0534
Edina (G-1838)
Royal Foods Inc ....E....952 936-0336
Hopkins (G-2622)
Schwan's Consumer Brands North ....C....952 832-4300
Bloomington (G-513)
▲ Schwan's Global Food Service ....C....507 532-3274
Marshall (G-3326)
Schwan's Home Service Inc ....E....218 879-5470
Esko (G-1923)
▲ SUPERVALU Inc ....A....952 828-4000
Eden Prairie (G-1787)
Supervalu Inc ....C....952 906-6260
Chanhassen (G-941)
Trudeau Holdings LLC ....C....952 882-8295
Burnsville (G-813)

SIC

Employment codes: A=Over 500 employees, B=251-500
C=101-250, D=51-100, E=25-50
2011 Harris Minnesota
Services Directory
© Harris InfoSource 1-866-281-6415
473

Trudeau Holdings LLC	D	952 445-1350	Shakopee *(G-9481)*
▲ Twin City Poultry Co	E	763 592-6500	Minneapolis *(G-5882)*
Upper Lakes Foods Inc	C	218 879-1265	Cloquet *(G-1066)*

5143 Dairy Prdts, Except Dried Or Canned Wholesale

Associated Milk Producers Inc	E	507 233-4600	New Ulm *(G-6441)*
Associated Milk Producers Inc	E	320 864-5561	Glencoe *(G-2204)*
Associated Milk Producers Inc	D	507 354-8295	New Ulm *(G-6440)*
Associated Milk Producers Inc	D	320 769-2994	Dawson *(G-1163)*
Bix Produce Co LLC	C	651 487-8000	Saint Paul *(G-8115)*
Dairy Farmers of America Inc	D	218 736-5691	Fergus Falls *(G-2073)*
Davisco Foods International	E	952 914-0400	Eden Prairie *(G-1643)*
Franklin Foods	D	218 727-6651	Duluth *(G-1327)*
Land O'Lakes Inc	E	218 233-8609	Moorhead *(G-6325)*
Michael Foods Group Inc	C	952 258-4000	Minnetonka *(G-6193)*
Milk Specialties Co	D	507 427-3222	Mountain Lake *(G-6399)*
Polka Dot Dairy Inc	E	651 438-2793	Hastings *(G-2400)*
▲ Schwan's Global Food Service	C	507 532-3274	Marshall *(G-3326)*
Stock Yards Meat Packing Co	C	651 450-6000	South Saint Paul *(G-9544)*
Sunrise A G Repair	E	320 584-0010	Royalton *(G-7388)*
Sunrise AG Cooperative	E	320 468-6433	Buckman *(G-632)*
▲ SUPERVALU Inc	A	952 828-4000	Eden Prairie *(G-1787)*
Supervalu Inc	C	952 906-6260	Chanhassen *(G-941)*
West Plains Dairy LLC	E	651 258-4666	Goodhue *(G-2251)*

5144 Poultry & Poultry Prdts Wholesale

American Fish & Seafood Inc	D	952 935-3474	Hopkins *(G-2509)*
Daybreak Foods Inc	D	320 732-2966	Long Prairie *(G-3042)*
Gold'n Plump Marketing Inc	D	320 251-3570	Saint Cloud *(G-7519)*
Michael Foods Group Inc	C	952 258-4000	Minnetonka *(G-6193)*
Michael Foods Inc	E	507 237-2429	Gaylord *(G-2200)*
New Midwest Co LLC	B	320 329-3363	Renville *(G-7032)*

5145 Confectionery Wholesale

A H Hermel Candy & Tobacco Co	D	507 387-5634	Mankato *(G-3098)*
Abdallah Inc	D	952 890-4770	Burnsville *(G-671)*
▲ American Importing Co Inc	D	612 331-7000	Minneapolis *(G-3751)*
Bergin Fruit & Nut Co Inc	D	651 642-1234	Saint Paul *(G-8105)*
Bernick's Full-Line Vending	E	320 656-2131	Waite Park *(G-9817)*
Bradley Distributing Co	E	651 639-0523	Newport *(G-6485)*
Debbie Bolen	E	218 722-0912	Duluth *(G-1292)*
▲ Farley's & Sathers Candy Co	B	507 945-8181	Round Lake *(G-7384)*
Farley's & Sathers Candy Co	C	507 452-3433	Winona *(G-10094)*
Frito-Lay Inc	E	507 282-1134	Rochester *(G-7121)*
Frito-Lay Inc	B	507 446-5888	Owatonna *(G-6715)*
Fritz Co Inc	D	651 459-9751	Newport *(G-6486)*
Granite City Jobbing Co Inc	E	320 252-1782	Saint Cloud *(G-7521)*
Harvey-Winchell Co	E	952 881-7964	Minneapolis *(G-4605)*
Henry's Foods Inc	C	320 763-3194	Alexandria *(G-104)*
▲ International Dairy Queen Inc	B	952 830-0200	Minneapolis *(G-4721)*
Jerky Snack Brands Inc	D	507 388-1661	Mankato *(G-3153)*
Kraft Foods Global Inc	E	612 331-4311	Minneapolis *(G-4821)*
Minter-Weisman Co	B	763 545-3706	Minneapolis *(G-5105)*
▲ Sandstrom's Inc	D	218 326-0567	Grand Rapids *(G-2307)*
▲ Schott Distributing Co Inc	E	507 289-3555	Rochester *(G-7248)*
Vistar Corp	E	800 333-3056	Maple Grove *(G-3256)*
Watson Co Inc	E	763 689-3722	Cambridge *(G-846)*
▲ Waymouth Farms Inc	C	763 533-5300	Minneapolis *(G-6026)*

5146 Fish & Seafood Wholesale

American Fish & Seafood Inc	D	952 935-3474	Hopkins *(G-2509)*
Chin Leeann Inc	E	952 890-9012	Burnsville *(G-697)*
Guys Fish Inc	E	612 339-7720	Minneapolis *(G-4581)*
Stock Yards Meat Packing Co	C	651 450-6000	South Saint Paul *(G-9544)*
Sushi Avenue Inc	D	651 294-7000	Eagan *(G-1555)*
Worldwide Fish & Seafood Inc	E	612 724-5911	Minneapolis *(G-6088)*

5147 Meats & Meat Prdts Wholesale

Cargill Inc	E	763 262-1900	Big Lake *(G-445)*
Christofersen Meats Co		612 721-4411	Minneapolis *(G-4070)*
Hormel Foods Corporate Svcs	E	952 931-9030	Eden Prairie *(G-1688)*
Hormel Foods Corporate Svcs	D	507 437-5611	Austin *(G-276)*
Hormel Foods International	D	507 437-5611	Austin *(G-277)*
Huisken Meat Co of Sauk Rapids	D	320 259-0305	Sauk Rapids *(G-9367)*
▲ International Dairy Queen Inc	B	952 830-0200	Minneapolis *(G-4721)*
Interstate Meat Service Inc	E	507 377-2228	Albert Lea *(G-56)*
▲ Nash-Finch Co	B	952 832-0534	Edina *(G-1838)*
Rochester Meats Inc	C	507 289-0701	Rochester *(G-7235)*
Royal Foods Inc	E	952 936-0336	Hopkins *(G-2622)*
Schumacher Wholesale Meats Inc	E	763 546-3291	Minneapolis *(G-5616)*
Stock Yards Meat Packing Co	C	651 450-6000	South Saint Paul *(G-9544)*
▲ SUPERVALU Inc	A	952 828-4000	Eden Prairie *(G-1787)*
Supervalu Inc	C	952 906-6260	Chanhassen *(G-941)*
Swanson Meats Inc	D	612 721-4411	Minneapolis *(G-5777)*
Trudeau Holdings LLC	C	952 882-8295	Burnsville *(G-813)*
Trudeau Holdings LLC	D	952 445-1350	Shakopee *(G-9481)*
Upper Lakes Foods Inc	C	218 879-1265	Cloquet *(G-1066)*

5148 Fresh Fruits & Vegetables Wholesale

A & L Potato Co	E	218 773-0123	East Grand Forks *(G-1564)*
Apperts Frozen Foods Inc	D	320 251-3200	Saint Cloud *(G-7434)*
Bergin Fruit & Nut Co Inc	D	651 642-1234	Saint Paul *(G-8105)*
Bix Produce Co LLC	C	651 487-8000	Saint Paul *(G-8115)*
Brings Co Inc	E	651 484-2666	Saint Paul *(G-8129)*
Cre 8 It Inc	D	612 623-8866	Minneapolis *(G-4178)*
Cut Fruit Express Inc	D	651 438-8834	Inver Grove Heights *(G-2747)*
Davis Russ Wholesale Inc	D	218 631-3070	Wadena *(G-9800)*
H Brooks & Co	D	651 635-0126	New Brighton *(G-6408)*
Hollandale Marketing Assn	E	507 889-3181	Hollandale *(G-2492)*
Hull Co	E	763 262-4855	Big Lake *(G-447)*
▲ J & J Distributing Co	C	651 221-0560	Saint Paul *(G-8526)*
Jerry's Farm Market	A	320 968-7001	Foley *(G-2140)*
Metro Produce Distributors Inc	D	612 722-5575	Minneapolis *(G-5003)*
Michael Foods Group Inc	C	952 258-4000	Minnetonka *(G-6193)*
▲ Nash-Finch Co	B	952 832-0534	Edina *(G-1838)*
Northern Star Co	C	612 339-8981	Minneapolis *(G-5229)*
Northwestern Fruit Co	E	651 224-4373	Saint Paul *(G-8771)*
Salad Makers Inc	E	218 236-4959	Moorhead *(G-6341)*
Stock Yards Meat Packing Co	C	651 450-6000	South Saint Paul *(G-9544)*
▲ SUPERVALU Inc	A	952 828-4000	Eden Prairie *(G-1787)*
Supervalu Inc	C	952 906-6260	Chanhassen *(G-941)*
Twin City Produce Supplies Inc	E	612 378-1055	Minneapolis *(G-5883)*
▲ Wescott Agri-Products Inc	E	507 876-2891	Elgin *(G-1857)*
Wholesale Produce Supply LLC	C	612 378-2025	Minneapolis *(G-6067)*
Wingard Farms	E	763 263-2635	Elk River *(G-1896)*

5149 Groceries & Related Prdts, NEC Wholesale

Agnes Saint Baking Co	E	651 290-7633	Saint Paul *(G-7999)*
Albert's Organics Inc	C	763 780-0101	Saint Paul *(G-8005)*
▲ American Agco Inc	D	651 451-1349	Cottage Grove *(G-1098)*
American Bottling Co	C	651 552-3400	South Saint Paul *(G-9509)*
American Crystal Sugar Co	B	218 287-3400	Moorhead *(G-6296)*
▲ American Importing Co Inc	D	612 331-7000	Minneapolis *(G-3751)*
American Logistics Services	D	651 451-1349	Cottage Grove *(G-1099)*
Bakemark USA LLC	E	952 937-9495	Eden Prairie *(G-1601)*
BCI Coca-Cola Bottling Co of	E	507 282-2622	Rochester *(G-7061)*
Bernick's Full-Line Vending	E	320 656-2131	Waite Park *(G-9817)*
Bernick's Pepsi Cola of	E	320 235-1370	Willmar *(G-9986)*
Berry Coffee Co	E	952 937-8697	Eden Prairie *(G-1604)*
◆ Best Brands Corp	C	952 404-7500	Saint Paul *(G-7716)*
Bradley Distributing Co	E	651 639-0523	Newport *(G-6485)*
Braschler's Bakery Inc	E	651 388-1589	Red Wing *(G-6976)*
Bruegger's Bagel Bakery	E	651 486-7135	Saint Paul *(G-8135)*
Cargill Inc	D	952 984-8280	Hopkins *(G-2525)*
Coca-Cola Bottling	C	218 736-5661	Fergus Falls *(G-2067)*
Coca-Cola Enterprises Inc	E	800 657-4995	Owatonna *(G-6704)*
Coca-Cola Enterprises Inc	E	218 628-2311	Duluth *(G-1278)*
Coca-Cola Enterprises Inc	D	218 236-7165	Moorhead *(G-6304)*
Cub Foods Inc	B	763 755-9802	Minneapolis *(G-3449)*
Culligan Soft Water Service Co	E	763 535-4545	Minneapolis *(G-4198)*
Culligan Store Solutions	D	651 681-9000	Saint Paul *(G-7742)*
Dakota Growers Pasta Co Inc	C	763 531-5340	Minneapolis *(G-4219)*
Deer River Wild Rice	D	218 246-2713	Deer River *(G-1170)*
Don Stevens Inc	E	651 452-0872	Eagan *(G-1525)*
Dunn Bros Coffee Inc	E	651 698-0618	Saint Paul *(G-8315)*
Emily's Bakery & Deli Inc	E	651 437-3338	Hastings *(G-2385)*
5 K Enterprises Inc	E	612 216-6292	Mankato *(G-3127)*
Franklin Bakery LLC	C	612 455-3893	Minneapolis *(G-4473)*
Glenwood-Inglewood Co	D	612 374-2253	Minneapolis *(G-4529)*
Gordy's Inc	E	507 847-2074	Jackson *(G-2793)*
Great Harvest Bread Co of MN	E	612 929-2899	Minneapolis *(G-4552)*
Great Northern Baking Co LLC	E	612 331-1043	Minneapolis *(G-4553)*
Gregory's Foods Inc	E	651 454-0277	Saint Paul *(G-7792)*
▲ Hohensteins Inc	E	651 735-4978	Saint Paul *(G-9231)*
▲ Holy Land Brand Inc	C	612 781-2627	Minneapolis *(G-4663)*
Horizon Milling LLC	E	507 388-1680	Mankato *(G-3145)*
Interstate Brands Corp	E	651 484-6020	Saint Paul *(G-8522)*
Interstate Brands Corp	D	952 935-3034	Hopkins *(G-2558)*
Javaology Enterprises LLC	D	952 943-3990	Chaska *(G-970)*
Johnson Brothers Liquor Co	C	651 649-5800	Saint Paul *(G-8537)*
Johnson Brothers Liquor Co	B	651 649-5800	Saint Paul *(G-8536)*
Log House Foods Inc	E	763 546-8395	Minneapolis *(G-4898)*

Lund Food Holdings Inc D 952 915-4888
Eden Prairie *(G-1713)*
Minnesota Dehydrated D 218 435-1997
Fosston *(G-2178)*
Minter-Weisman Co B 763 545-3706
Minneapolis *(G-5105)*
Molly's Inc D 612 925-3113
Minneapolis *(G-5119)*
Nei Bottling Inc E 218 751-3847
Bemidji *(G-407)*
▲ New French Bakery Inc C 612 728-0193
Minneapolis *(G-5188)*
Olson Coffee Roasters Inc E 651 645-1729
Saint Paul *(G-8782)*
▲ Pan-O-Gold Baking Co C 320 251-9361
Saint Cloud *(G-7421)*
Pepsi Cola Bottling Co E 507 825-4207
Pipestone *(G-6833)*
Pepsi Cola Bottling Co of C 507 288-3772
Rochester *(G-7202)*
Pepsi Cola Bottling Co of E 218 628-0276
Duluth *(G-1421)*
Pepsi-Cola Metropolitan Btlng E 218 326-1271
Grand Rapids *(G-2306)*
Pepsi-Cola Metropolitan Btlng E 218 829-4196
Brainerd *(G-580)*
Perfect Pickle E 651 779-6129
Forest Lake *(G-2153)*
Pillsbury Co LLC E 952 903-5262
Eden Prairie *(G-1748)*
Pillsbury Co LLC D 612 330-4003
Minneapolis *(G-5378)*
Procter & Gamble Distributing C 952 942-1857
Eden Prairie *(G-1754)*
▲ Quality Wine & Spirits Co D 952 854-8600
Minneapolis *(G-5444)*
Reser's Fine Foods Inc E 651 646-1298
Saint Paul *(G-8892)*
Restaurant Technologies Inc D 651 796-1600
Saint Paul *(G-7894)*
Rfg Distributing Inc D 763 540-0335
Minneapolis *(G-5534)*
▲ Rohlfing of Brainerd Inc E 218 829-0303
Brainerd *(G-585)*
Royal Foods Inc E 952 936-0336
Hopkins *(G-2622)*
Sara Lee Bakery Group Inc D 651 688-9275
Saint Paul *(G-7897)*
Sara Lee Corp D 763 572-2506
Minneapolis *(G-3595)*
Sunopta Food Group LLC 320 763-5977
Alexandria *(G-125)*
Sunrich Inc B 952 939-3949
Minnetonka *(G-6227)*
SUPERVALU Inc C 952 932-4300
Hopkins *(G-2640)*
▲ Sysco Asian Foods Inc C 651 558-2400
Saint Paul *(G-9021)*
Tech Investments Inc E 218 733-0214
Duluth *(G-1481)*
Tree of Life LLC C 612 752-6300
Saint Paul *(G-9079)*
United Noodles Inc E 612 721-6677
Minneapolis *(G-5910)*
▲ United States Distilled Prdts C 763 389-4903
Princeton *(G-6918)*
US Foodservice Inc C 763 559-9494
Minneapolis *(G-5948)*
US Foodservice Inc C 651 634-4380
Saint Paul *(G-9120)*
US Foodservice Inc C 651 450-6000
South Saint Paul *(G-9547)*
Viking Coca Cola Bottling Co E 218 829-2204
Baxter *(G-344)*
▲ Waymouth Farms Inc C 763 533-5300
Minneapolis *(G-6026)*
▲ Wirtz Beverage Minnesota Beer C 651 646-6063
Saint Paul *(G-9160)*
Wuollet Bakery Inc E 763 473-8621
Wayzata *(G-9952)*

5153 Grain & Field Beans Wholesale

AG Partners Coop E 651 923-4496
Goodhue *(G-2248)*
▲ Agmotion Inc E 612 486-3800
Minneapolis *(G-3699)*
All-American Co-Op E 507 533-4222
Stewartville *(G-9590)*
Anheuser-Busch Co's Inc E 218 326-0571
Grand Rapids *(G-2268)*
Bremner Food Group Inc E 612 331-5908
Minneapolis *(G-3942)*
Cargill Inc C 952 742-4417
Minneapolis *(G-4010)*
Cargill Inc A 952 742-7575
Wayzata *(G-9909)*
◆ CHS Inc A 651 355-6000
Inver Grove Heights *(G-2742)*
CHS Inc C 507 345-2253
Mankato *(G-3116)*
Coop Audubon Elevator Assn 218 439-6111
Audubon *(G-254)*
Coop FCA E 507 847-4160
Jackson *(G-2789)*
Crystal Valley Coop E 507 642-8837
La Salle *(G-2846)*
Farm Country Co-Op E 507 356-8313
Pine Island *(G-6816)*
Farmers Co-Operative of Hanska E 507 439-6244
Hanska *(G-2370)*
General Mills Inc E 763 764-3313
Minneapolis *(G-4513)*
Glacial Plains Cooperative D 320 760-5647
Murdock *(G-6401)*
Glaciel Plans Coop E 320 843-2563
Benson *(G-440)*
Greenway Co-Operative Service E 507 775-2900
Byron *(G-824)*
Greenway Co-Operative Service E 507 287-6676
Byron *(G-823)*
M & B Enterprise of Freeport 320 836-2145
Freeport *(G-2188)*
◆ MG Waldbaum Co D 952 258-4000
Minnetonka *(G-6192)*
Minn-Kota AG Products Inc E 218 643-8464
Breckenridge *(G-595)*
Minnesota Soybean Processors D 507 842-6677
Brewster *(G-605)*
Northstar Genetics Ltd 507 824-2878
Wanamingo *(G-9865)*
Peterson's North Branch Mill E 651 674-4425
North Branch *(G-6504)*
Ray Drachenberg E 507 644-2108
Redwood Falls *(G-7027)*
Scoular Co D 612 335-8700
Minneapolis *(G-5620)*
South Central Grain & Energy D 507 426-8263
Fairfax *(G-1955)*
St Hilaire Seed Co Inc E 218 964-5407
Saint Hilaire *(G-7640)*
Sunrich Inc D 507 451-3316
Hope *(G-2496)*
▲ Sunrich LLC D 507 451-4724
Hope *(G-2497)*
United Farmers Cooperative E 507 228-8224
Lafayette *(G-2847)*
Wagner Trucking Inc 320 524-2250
Brandon *(G-592)*
Watonwan Farm Service Inc E 507 776-2831
Truman *(G-9699)*
Western Consolidated Co-op E 320 394-2171
Holloway *(G-2493)*
Wilmont Farmers Elevator Co E 507 926-5131
Wilmont *(G-10064)*

5154 Livestock Wholesale

Lanesboro Sales Commission Inc E 507 467-2192
Lanesboro *(G-2947)*
Northstar Ethanol LLC E 507 726-2645
Lake Crystal *(G-2863)*
O & S Cattle Co E 651 455-1102
South Saint Paul *(G-9536)*
Pipestone Livestock Auction E 507 825-3306
Pipestone *(G-6835)*
Rich Prairie Livestock E 320 468-2514
Pierz *(G-6808)*
Tyson Fresh Meats Inc E 507 776-2828
Truman *(G-9698)*

5159 Farm-Prdt Raw Mtrls, NEC Wholesale

Darling International Inc D 507 526-3296
Blue Earth *(G-533)*
▲ North Central Co's Inc E 952 449-0885
Minnetonka *(G-6204)*
Starchtech Inc E 763 545-5400
Minneapolis *(G-5741)*
United Sugars Corp E 952 896-0131
Minneapolis *(G-5916)*

5162 Plastics Materials & Basic Shapes Wholesale

▲ Acrylic Design Associates Inc D 763 559-8392
Minneapolis *(G-3675)*
AEP Industries Inc D 507 625-3011
Mankato *(G-3100)*
AEP Industries Inc D 507 386-4420
Mankato *(G-3101)*
Crown Plastics Inc E 763 557-6000
Minneapolis *(G-4189)*
Genpak LLC C 952 881-8673
Minneapolis *(G-4522)*
▲ Indelco Plastics Corp E 952 925-5075
Minneapolis *(G-4694)*
Infiniti Marketing Inc E 612 789-2025
Mound *(G-6388)*
▲ J-M Manufacturing Co Inc D 507 893-3121
Winnebago *(G-10076)*
Martin Falk Paper Co E 612 332-8626
Minneapolis *(G-4959)*
▲ Minnesota Flexible Corp E 651 645-7522
Saint Paul *(G-8687)*
▲ North American Composites Co C 651 481-6860
Circle Pines *(G-1019)*
Plastic Promotions Inc E 651 686-0660
Saint Paul *(G-7877)*
Plastics International Inc E 952 934-2303
Eden Prairie *(G-1750)*
Spray Control Systems Inc E 507 583-2112
Blooming Prairie *(G-478)*
Tandem Products Inc E 612 721-2911
Minneapolis *(G-5788)*
Youngblood Lumber Co E 612 789-3521
Minneapolis *(G-6106)*

5169 Chemicals & Allied Prdts, NEC Wholesale

Airgas - North Central Inc E 763 712-5100
Anoka *(G-148)*
American Welding & Gas E 320 235-4774
Willmar *(G-9983)*
Arkema Inc E 507 583-6641
Blooming Prairie *(G-476)*
Ashland Inc E 612 726-1787
Minneapolis *(G-3817)*
Auto Butler Inc E 612 529-3345
Minneapolis *(G-3836)*
BASF Corp E 763 559-3266
Minneapolis *(G-3870)*
Brenntag Great Lakes LLC E 651 204-4300
Saint Paul *(G-8127)*
Clariant Corp D 763 535-4511
Minneapolis *(G-4100)*
General Resource Technology E 651 454-4151
Saint Paul *(G-7779)*
▲ Hawkins Inc C 612 331-6910
Minneapolis *(G-4608)*
Healthline Inc E 218 262-6981
Hibbing *(G-2450)*
▼ Interplastic Corp E 651 481-6860
Saint Paul *(G-8519)*
Interplastic Corp E 651 481-6860
Saint Paul *(G-8520)*
Kennedy Brissman E 651 646-7933
Saint Paul *(G-8545)*
Lubrication Technologies Inc D 763 545-0707
Minneapolis *(G-4908)*
Lubrication Technologies Inc D 651 636-7990
Saint Paul *(G-8596)*
▲ MCP Foods Inc D 507 233-7406
New Ulm *(G-6460)*
Minneapolis Oxygen Co E 612 588-8855
Minneapolis *(G-5058)*
Minnesota Salt Service E 651 774-6237
Saint Paul *(G-8704)*
Nalco Chemical Co E 763 559-3209
Minneapolis *(G-5156)*
Otto Bock US Polyurethane Foam E 763 553-9464
Minneapolis *(G-5299)*
Oxygen Service Co Inc D 651 644-7273
Saint Paul *(G-8797)*
Praxair Inc E 651 633-6781
Saint Paul *(G-8836)*
Surfacequest Inc 952 361-9431
Minneapolis *(G-5773)*
3M Co B 651 733-6678
Saint Paul *(G-9059)*
3M Co E 651 733-5623
Saint Paul *(G-9058)*
3M Co E 651 736-2326
Saint Paul *(G-9057)*
Toll Co E 763 551-5355
Minneapolis *(G-5829)*
Univar USA Inc E 651 774-9400
Saint Paul *(G-9111)*
▲ Universal Cooperatives Inc D 651 239-1000
Saint Paul *(G-7938)*
US Venture Inc D 763 591-5827
Minneapolis *(G-5950)*
Valley National Gases Inc E 651 628-4848
Saint Paul *(G-9123)*
Viking Explosives & Supply Inc E 218 263-8845
Hibbing *(G-2479)*
Zep Inc D 763 792-2050
Minneapolis *(G-6133)*

5171 Petroleum Bulk Stations & Terminals

Anderson-Gilyard E 763 261-5161
Becker *(G-354)*
Belgrade Cooperative Assn E 320 254-8231
Belgrade *(G-363)*
Best Oil Co E 218 879-4666
Cloquet *(G-1046)*
Central Valley Cooperative 507 451-1230
Owatonna *(G-6700)*
Consumers Cooperative Assn E 320 693-2821
Litchfield *(G-2981)*
Coop FCA E 507 847-4160
Jackson *(G-2789)*
Coop Northern Star D 218 246-8660
Deer River *(G-1167)*
Country Pride Services Co-op E 507 831-2580
Bingham Lake *(G-466)*
Crystal Valley Coop E 507 642-8837
La Salle *(G-2846)*
Dooley's Petroleum Inc D 320 875-2641
Murdock *(G-6400)*
Edwards Oil Co Inc E 218 741-9634
Virginia *(G-9738)*
Egan Oil Co LLC E 763 421-0410
Anoka *(G-176)*
Farmers Co-Op Oil Co of Clara 320 847-2318
Clara City *(G-1027)*
Farmers Co-Operative of Hanska E 507 439-6244
Hanska *(G-2370)*

S I C

Employment codes: A=Over 500 employees, B=251-500
C=101-250, D=51-100, E=25-50

2011 Harris Minnesota
Services Directory

© Harris InfoSource 1-866-281-6415
475

Farmers Co-Operative Oil Co of E 507 925-4114
Echo (G-1581)
Farmers Union Oil Co of E 320 269-8856
Montevideo (G-6245)
Greenway Co-Operative Service E 507 775-2900
Byron (G-824)
High Plains Cooperative D 507 534-3111
Plainview (G-6843)
J M Oil Co E 320 251-2082
Saint Cloud (G-7533)
Kutzke Oil Co Inc E 320 629-2075
Pine City (G-6812)
Lake Region Co-Op Oil Assn E 763 682-1431
Buffalo (G-648)
Mille Lacs Oil Co E 320 396-2693
Braham (G-543)
Multi-County AG LLC E 507 223-5634
Canby (G-850)
Park Region Cooperative 218 863-2811
Pelican Rapids (G-6782)
Paynesville Farmers Union E 320 243-3751
Paynesville (G-6772)
Prairie Pride Cooperative E 507 532-9686
Marshall (G-3320)
Rothsay Truck Stop & Cafe E 218 867-2233
Rothsay (G-7383)
United Farmers Co Op E 507 237-2281
Gaylord (G-2201)
Wilson Oil Co Inc 651 388-5783
Red Wing (G-7013)

5172 Petroleum & Petroleum Prdts Wholesale

Adium Oil Co Inc E 320 356-7350
Avon (G-293)
Aviation Charter Inc D 952 943-1519
Eden Prairie (G-1600)
Belle Plaine Cooperative E 952 873-4244
Belle Plaine (G-367)
Bemidji Cooperative Assn E 218 751-4260
Bemidji (G-379)
Best Oil Co E 218 879-4666
Cloquet (G-1046)
Border States Cooperative E 320 695-2575
Browns Valley (G-626)
Chamberlain Oil Co Inc E 320 843-3434
Clontarf (G-1045)
▲ Como Lube & Supplies Inc E 218 722-2920
Duluth (G-1280)
Cooperative Sampo Inc D 218 564-4534
Menahga (G-3357)
Croix Oil Co E 651 439-5755
Stillwater (G-9608)
Crookston Fuel Co E 218 281-2157
Crookston (G-1121)
Curtis Oil & Tire E 218 729-8241
Duluth (G-1288)
Dan Larson Enterprises Inc E 612 331-8550
Minneapolis (G-4222)
Egan Oil Co LLC E 763 421-0410
Anoka (G-176)
Farmers Union Oil Co of E 218 233-2497
Moorhead (G-6315)
Federated Coop Inc E 320 679-2682
Mora (G-6358)
Graffco Inc E 651 464-1079
Forest Lake (G-2146)
Inter City Oil Co Inc E 218 728-3641
Duluth (G-1358)
Kath Management Co D 651 484-3325
Saint Paul (G-8541)
Kunz Oil Co D 952 352-8600
Hopkins (G-2567)
Lubrication Technologies Inc D 763 545-0707
Minneapolis (G-4908)
Lubrication Technologies Inc D 651 636-7990
Saint Paul (G-8596)
Marathon Petroleum Co LP B 651 459-9771
Saint Paul Park (G-9296)
Marathon Petroleum Co LP B 651 459-9771
Saint Paul Park (G-9295)
Monaco Air Duluth LLC E 218 727-2911
Duluth (G-1396)
North Stop Inc E 218 547-1859
Walker (G-9856)
Olson Oil Co Inc E 218 736-2786
Fergus Falls (G-2103)
Severson Oil Co E 507 452-4743
Winona (G-10126)
US Venture Inc D 763 591-5827
Minneapolis (G-5950)
Valley National Gases WV LLC E 320 235-3430
Willmar (G-10051)
Vukelich Oil Co 320 253-6546
Saint Cloud (G-7628)
Watonwan Farm Service Inc E 507 776-2831
Truman (G-9699)
Wilson Oil Co Inc 651 388-5783
Red Wing (G-7013)
Yocum Oil Co Inc C 651 739-9141
Saint Paul (G-9179)

5181 Beer & Ale Wholesale

Beverage Wholesalers D 320 759-9009
Alexandria (G-84)
Capital Beverage Sales Ltd E 651 298-0800
Minneapolis (G-3427)
▲ Capitol Beverage Sales LP D 763 571-4115
Minneapolis (G-3428)
Carlson & Lyter Distributing D 320 251-7375
Sauk Rapids (G-9360)
Carlson & Lyter Distributing E 218 829-2978
Baxter (G-322)
▲ Chas A Bernick Inc E 320 252-6441
Waite Park (G-9819)
College City Beverage Inc D 507 645-4106
Dundas (G-1510)
D-S Beverages Inc E 218 233-1343
Moorhead (G-6310)
▲ Dahlheimer Distributing Co Inc E 763 295-3347
Monticello (G-6268)
▲ Hohensteins Inc E 651 735-4978
Saint Paul (G-9231)
JJ Taylor Co's Inc C 651 482-1133
Minneapolis (G-4765)
▲ Kiwikai Imports Inc E 763 550-9545
Minneapolis (G-4813)
Locher Bros Inc E 507 625-4198
Mankato (G-3227)
Locher Bros Inc E 507 326-5471
Green Isle (G-2323)
North Beverage LLC E 507 282-5462
Rochester (G-7190)
▲ Quality Wine & Spirits Co D 952 854-8600
Minneapolis (G-5444)
▲ Rohlfing of Brainerd Inc E 218 829-0303
Brainerd (G-585)
▲ Schott Distributing Co Inc E 507 289-3555
Rochester (G-7248)
Thorpe Distributing Co D 763 463-2000
Rogers (G-7343)
Tow Distributing Corp E 507 388-2931
Mankato (G-3208)
▲ Wirtz Beverage Minnesota Beer C 651 646-6063
Saint Paul (G-9160)

5182 Wine & Distilled Alcoholic Beverages Wholesale

Consolidated Enterprises Inc C 651 646-7821
Saint Paul (G-8249)
Johnson Brothers Liquor Co C 651 649-5800
Saint Paul (G-8537)
Johnson Brothers Liquor Co B 651 649-5800
Saint Paul (G-8536)
▲ Kiwikai Imports Inc E 763 550-9545
Minneapolis (G-4813)
Liquors Plus Inc E 651 501-1199
Saint Paul (G-9243)
▲ Quality Wine & Spirits Co D 952 854-8600
Minneapolis (G-5444)
▲ United States Distilled Prdts C 763 389-4903
Princeton (G-6918)
Wheaton Liquor E 320 563-4155
Wheaton (G-9972)
▲ World Class Wines Inc E 952 941-8795
Eden Prairie (G-1817)

5191 Farm Splys Wholesale

AG Partners Coop E 651 923-4496
Goodhue (G-2248)
Agreliant Genetics LLC E 218 631-2954
Wadena (G-9796)
Aitkin Agri-Peat Inc E 763 441-8387
Elk River (G-1860)
Albert Lea Seed House Inc E 507 373-3161
Albert Lea (G-33)
▲ American Agco Inc D 651 451-1349
Cottage Grove (G-1098)
▲ American Crystal Sugar Co C 218 236-4400
Moorhead (G-6295)
Archer Daniels Midland Co D 507 625-7949
Mankato (G-3106)
Belgrade Cooperative Assn E 320 254-8231
Belgrade (G-363)
Belle Plaine Cooperative E 952 873-4244
Belle Plaine (G-367)
Bemidji Cooperative Assn E 218 751-4260
Bemidji (G-379)
▲ Betaseed Inc E 952 445-8090
Shakopee (G-9421)
Bfg Supply Co LLC D 612 781-6068
Minneapolis (G-3898)
Border States Cooperative E 320 695-2575
Browns Valley (G-626)
Bremner Food Group Inc E 612 331-5908
Minneapolis (G-3942)
Cargill Inc D 763 497-2157
Minneapolis (G-4011)
Cargill Inc D 763 441-6508
Elk River (G-1866)
Cargill Inc C 952 742-7575
Minnetonka (G-6150)
Central Valley Cooperative 507 451-1230
Owatonna (G-6700)
▼ Commodity Specialists Co E 612 330-9120
Minneapolis (G-4133)
Coop Audubon Elevator Assn 218 439-6111
Audubon (G-254)
Coop FCA E 507 847-4160
Jackson (G-2789)
Cooperative Sampo Inc D 218 564-4534
Menahga (G-3357)
Country Pride Services Co-op E 507 831-2580
Bingham Lake (G-466)
Crystal Valley Coop E 507 642-8837
La Salle (G-2846)
Esco Industries Inc E 320 259-9470
Waite Park (G-9822)
F M Trucking Inc E 651 639-0446
Saint Paul (G-8358)
Faribo Farm & Home Supply Inc E 507 334-3232
Faribault (G-2006)
Farm Country Co-Op E 507 356-8313
Pine Island (G-6816)
Farmers Co-Op Oil Co of Clara 320 847-2318
Clara City (G-1027)
Farmers Co-Operative of Hanska E 507 439-6244
Hanska (G-2370)
Farmers Co-Operative Oil Co of E 507 925-4114
Echo (G-1581)
Farmers Union Oil Co of E 320 763-6557
Alexandria (G-100)
Farmers Union Oil Co of E 320 269-8856
Montevideo (G-6245)
Federated Coop Inc E 320 679-2682
Mora (G-6358)
Fleet Wholesale Supply Co Inc D 507 281-1130
Rochester (G-7117)
Fleet Wholesale Supply Co Inc C 763 424-9668
Minneapolis (G-4455)
Gessell Feed Mill Inc E 320 547-2994
Swanville (G-9658)
Glacial Plains Cooperative D 320 843-4820
Benson (G-439)
Glh Seeds Inc 952 445-8090
Shakopee (G-9441)
Greenway Co-Operative Service E 507 775-2900
Byron (G-824)
High Plains Cooperative D 507 534-3111
Plainview (G-6843)
Hollandale Marketing Assn E 507 889-3181
Hollandale (G-2492)
Jirik Sod Farm Inc E 651 460-6555
Farmington (G-2052)
Kristico Inc E 507 625-2900
Mankato (G-3155)
Kruse Family Enterprises LLC E 507 345-5926
Mankato (G-3156)
Land O'Lakes Inc E 320 543-2566
Howard Lake (G-2668)
Land O'Lakes Purina Feed LLC E 320 235-6000
Willmar (G-10017)
Land O'Lakes Purina Feed LLC E 651 681-5917
Inver Grove Heights (G-2757)
Land O'Lakes Purina Feed LLC E 218 847-3176
Detroit Lakes (G-1206)
Land O'Lakes Purina Feed LLC E 651 437-7762
Inver Grove Heights (G-2758)
◆ MG Waldbaum Co D 952 258-4000
Minnetonka (G-6192)
Michael Foods Inc C 507 665-8851
Le Sueur (G-2962)
◆ Mid-States Distributing Co Inc E 651 698-8831
Saint Paul (G-8652)
Minn-Kota AG Products Inc E 218 643-8464
Breckenridge (G-595)
Monsanto Co E 507 524-3475
Mapleton (G-3283)
Multi-County AG LLC E 507 223-5634
Canby (G-850)
National Tack North Inc E 651 464-7733
Forest Lake (G-2165)
▲ Pals Inc D 320 235-8860
Willmar (G-10035)
Peterson Biddick Co E 218 631-2954
Crookston (G-1133)
Peterson's North Branch Mill E 651 674-4425
North Branch (G-6504)
Precision Nutrition Inc E 507 372-4723
Worthington (G-10190)
Precision Turf & Chemical Inc 763 477-5885
Rockford (G-7303)
Red Lake County Cooperative E 218 253-2149
Red Lake Falls (G-6973)
Rosen's Diversified Inc E 507 238-4201
Fairmont (G-1980)
▲ Seeds 2000 Inc E 218 643-2410
Breckenridge (G-600)
St Hilaire Seed Co Inc E 218 964-5407
Saint Hilaire (G-7640)
Sunrich Inc D 507 451-3316
Hope (G-2496)
Sunrich LLC D 218 643-8467
Breckenridge (G-602)
Sunrise AG Cooperative E 320 468-6433
Buckman (G-632)
Syngenta Seeds Inc E 320 286-5511
Cokato (G-1081)
U S Commodities L L C D 612 486-3800
Minneapolis (G-5888)
United Farmers Co Op E 507 237-2281
Gaylord (G-2201)
▲ Universal Cooperatives Inc D 651 239-1000
Saint Paul (G-7938)
Watonwan Farm Service Inc E 507 776-2831
Truman (G-9699)
West Central Chemicals E 507 444-0275
Owatonna (G-6745)

S I C

(G-00000) Company's Geographic Section entry number
476
2011 Harris Minnesota Services Directory
▲=Import ▼=Export ◆=Import/Export

West Central Inc....E....320 235-8518
Willmar (G-10053)
Western Consolidated Co-op....E....320 394-2171
Holloway (G-2493)
Wilmont Farmers Elevator Co....E....507 926-5131
Wilmont (G-10064)
▼ Zinpro Animal Nutrition Inc....E....952 944-2736
Eden Prairie (G-1820)

5192 Books, Periodicals & Newspapers Wholesale

Arabian Horse Times Inc....E....800 248-4637
Waseca (G-9873)
▲ Book Sales Inc....D....732 225-0530
Minneapolis (G-3927)
East View Information Services....E....952 252-1201
Hopkins (G-2536)
Gopher News Co....D....763 546-5300
Minneapolis (G-4542)
Lakeland Distribution Services....E....320 762-8385
Alexandria (G-109)
Mackin Book Co....B....952 895-9540
Burnsville (G-750)
Minnesota News Service Inc....D....952 703-0075
Minneapolis (G-5086)
Scholastic Book Fairs Inc....D....763 391-0930
Minneapolis (G-5613)
▲ Sky Media LLC....E....651 635-0100
Saint Paul (G-8963)
3 Br's Inc....E....507 645-8600
Northfield (G-6542)
Valley News Co....D....507 345-4819
Mankato (G-3212)
World Wide Publications....E....612 333-0940
Minneapolis (G-6087)

5193 Flowers, Nursery Stock & Florists' Splys Wholesale

Bachman's Inc....C....612 861-7600
Minneapolis (G-3856)
Bachman's Inc....E....651 463-3288
Farmington (G-2041)
Bailey Nurseries Inc....B....651 459-9744
Newport (G-6484)
Bergen's Greenhouses Inc....E....218 847-2138
Detroit Lakes (G-1188)
▲ Cherokee Manufacturing Inc....E....651 451-6568
South Saint Paul (G-9520)
Donahues' Greenhouses Inc....E....507 334-8404
Faribault (G-2001)
▲ Gerten Greenhouses & Garden....B....651 450-1501
Inver Grove Heights (G-2751)
Great River Garden....E....218 927-2521
Aitkin (G-19)
▲ Green Valley Greenhouse Inc....D....763 753-1621
Anoka (G-184)
Hermes Floral Co Inc....D....651 646-6344
Saint Paul (G-8478)
Lakeland Florist Supply Inc....E....952 944-5160
Minneapolis (G-4834)
Little Yukon Greenhouse Inc....D....218 692-3536
Crosslake (G-1152)
Ls Acquisitions Inc....D....612 331-4141
Minneapolis (G-4907)
Malmborgs Inc....E....763 535-4695
Minneapolis (G-4938)
Midland Nursery Inc....E....763 478-6122
Buffalo (G-651)
Minneapolis Floral Co....E....612 377-8080
Minneapolis (G-5053)
Pinehurst Development Inc....E....952 469-3202
Farmington (G-2057)
R D Offutt Co....E....218 732-4163
Park Rapids (G-6761)
Twin City Florist Supply Inc....E....612 377-7849
Minneapolis (G-5879)
Value Gardens Supply....E....952 884-6477
Minneapolis (G-5956)

5194 Tobacco & Tobacco Prdts Wholesale

A H Hermel Candy & Tobacco Co....D....507 387-5634
Mankato (G-3098)
Bernick's Full-Line Vending....E....320 656-2131
Waite Park (G-9817)
Fritz Co Inc....D....651 459-9751
Newport (G-6486)
Granite City Jobbing Co Inc....E....320 252-1782
Saint Cloud (G-7521)
Henry's Foods Inc....C....320 763-3194
Alexandria (G-104)
Hermel Coffee Service....E....507 387-5634
Mankato (G-3138)
Minter-Weisman Co....B....763 545-3706
Minneapolis (G-5105)
▲ Sandstrom's Inc....D....218 326-0567
Grand Rapids (G-2307)
Watson Co Inc....E....763 689-3722
Cambridge (G-846)

5198 Paints, Varnishes & Splys Wholesale

Abbott Paint & Carpet Inc....E....651 429-3316
Saint Paul (G-7972)

▼ Fastenal Co....B....507 454-5374
Winona (G-10095)
Hirshfield's Inc....D....612 377-3910
Minneapolis (G-4655)

5199 Nondurable Goods, NEC Wholesale

A World of Fish Inc....E....612 866-2026
Minneapolis (G-3651)
Albinson Reprographics LLC....E....612 374-1120
Minneapolis (G-3703)
American Business Forms Inc....C....320 634-5471
Glenwood (G-2219)
Art Holdings Corp....E....763 567-2200
Minneapolis (G-3811)
Atlas Pet Supply Inc....E....763 753-4818
Anoka (G-157)
Belcourt Corp....E....952 894-0406
Burnsville (G-684)
Bemis Co Inc....E....612 788-0100
Minneapolis (G-3883)
Berry Coffee Co....E....952 937-8697
Eden Prairie (G-1604)
▲ Brown & Bigelow Inc....C....651 293-7000
Saint Paul (G-8132)
Cac Retail Inc....D....952 944-5600
Eden Prairie (G-1616)
▲ Coyne's & Co Inc....D....763 425-8666
Minneapolis (G-4175)
Curry Sales Inc....E....952 351-4200
Hopkins (G-2534)
Delkor Systems Inc....D....763 783-0855
Circle Pines (G-1010)
Display Sales Co....E....952 885-0100
Minneapolis (G-4259)
Doug Thorson Sales Co Inc....E....218 736-2249
Fergus Falls (G-2074)
Dunk N Jump....D....612 788-0404
Minneapolis (G-4295)
▲ E-Group Inc....E....612 339-4777
Minneapolis (G-4304)
▲ East Asian Trading Co Inc....B....763 473-3520
Minneapolis (G-4307)
Ers Digital Inc....D....763 694-5900
Minneapolis (G-4369)
5 K Enterprises Inc....E....612 216-6292
Mankato (G-3127)
Foam Industries Inc....E....763 503-9265
Champlin (G-894)
▲ Food Market Merchandising Inc....E....952 894-0110
Minneapolis (G-4462)
Fritz Co Inc....D....651 459-9751
Newport (G-6486)
Garborgs LLC....E....612 888-5726
Minneapolis (G-4499)
General Pet Supply Inc....E....952 890-2300
Burnsville (G-727)
GWS Inc....E....763 551-1700
Hamel (G-2343)
J L Buchanan Inc....612 334-1710
Minneapolis (G-4747)
Lenox Group Inc....C....952 943-4100
Eden Prairie (G-1708)
▲ Libra Inc....E....612 522-2600
Minneapolis (G-4872)
Marudas Graphics Inc....E....651 697-7820
Saint Paul (G-8617)
Mayflower Distributing Co Inc....C....651 452-4892
Saint Paul (G-7835)
▼ Meca Sportswear Inc....E....651 638-3888
Saint Paul (G-8629)
Midwest - Cbk Inc....E....320 847-1210
Clara City (G-1029)
Midwest - Cbk Inc....D....507 263-4261
Cannon Falls (G-858)
Miller Manufacturing Co Inc....D....320 864-4189
Glencoe (G-2210)
Miratec Systems Inc....E....651 222-8440
Saint Paul (G-8715)
New Streams International Inc....651 777-8020
Maplewood (G-3286)
▲ North Central Co's Inc....E....952 449-0885
Minnetonka (G-6204)
▲ Nsl Holdings Inc....E....952 943-8474
Shakopee (G-9462)
▲ Ovp Inc....C....952 944-5600
Eden Prairie (G-1740)
▲ Polaroid Consumer Electronics....D....952 936-5000
Minnetonka (G-6215)
Polaroid Holdings LLC....952 934-9918
Minnetonka (G-6216)
▲ Professional Gallery Inc....D....320 252-8446
Saint Cloud (G-7574)
Quality Business Forms of....E....763 559-4330
Minneapolis (G-5441)
Quality Resource Group Inc....E....763 478-8636
Plymouth (G-6881)
Rambow Inc....E....320 354-2570
New London (G-6419)
Scholastic Book Fairs Inc....D....763 391-0930
Minneapolis (G-5613)
▲ Seasonal Specialties LLC....E....952 942-6555
Eden Prairie (G-1773)
▲ Sky Media LLC....E....651 635-0100
Saint Paul (G-8963)
Spartan Promotional Group Inc....D....651 735-1333
Saint Paul (G-9275)

Tandem Printing Inc....E....651 289-2970
Eagan (G-1556)
Town & Country Fence Inc....E....763 425-5050
Minneapolis (G-5841)
▲ 2020 Promotions LLC....E....651 451-3850
South Saint Paul (G-9545)
▲ Webb Business Promotions Inc....D....651 322-8200
Rosemount (G-7382)

60 DEPOSITORY INSTITUTIONS

6021 National Commercial Banks

Alliance Bank....E....507 354-3133
New Ulm (G-6438)
American Bank of St Paul....C....651 643-8472
Saint Paul (G-8022)
American Heritage National....E....320 732-6131
Long Prairie (G-3036)
American Heritage National....E....320 654-9555
Saint Cloud (G-7447)
Anchor Bank....E....952 473-4606
Wayzata (G-9905)
Anchor Bank....E....651 770-2341
Saint Paul (G-8047)
Anchor Bank....E....651 457-1111
Saint Paul (G-7699)
Anchor Bank Heritage....E....651 770-2341
Saint Paul (G-8048)
Associated Banc-Corp....E....651 385-1600
Red Wing (G-6974)
Bank Midwest....E....507 847-3010
Jackson (G-2786)
Bank Midwest....E....507 235-3327
Fairmont (G-1958)
Bank Midwest....E....507 831-1322
Windom (G-10066)
Bremer Bank....D....320 251-3300
Saint Cloud (G-7465)
Bremer Bank....E....320 235-1111
Willmar (G-9993)
Bremer Bank National Assn....D....651 451-6822
South Saint Paul (G-9515)
Center National Bank....E....320 693-3255
Litchfield (G-2980)
Citizens National Bank Inc....E....218 732-3393
Park Rapids (G-6750)
Farmers State B of Hartland....507 845-2233
Hartland (G-2374)
First American Bank Valley....E....218 281-4182
Crookston (G-1124)
First Minnesota Bank National....320 864-3161
Glencoe (G-2206)
First National Bank....E....507 645-5656
Northfield (G-6528)
First National Bank....E....218 254-3371
Chisholm (G-997)
First National Bank In....E....218 935-5251
Mahnomen (G-3085)
1st National Bank In Wadena....E....218 631-1590
Wadena (G-9802)
1st National Bank Inc....E....218 534-3111
Deerwood (G-1177)
First National Bank of Bemidji....D....218 751-2430
Bemidji (G-394)
First National Bank of Cold....E....320 685-8611
Cold Spring (G-1085)
First National Bank of Deer....218 246-8221
Deer River (G-1171)
First National Bank of Milaca....E....320 983-3101
Milaca (G-3377)
1st National Bank of Pipestone....E....507 825-3344
Pipestone (G-6827)
1st National Bank of Plainview....E....507 534-3131
Plainview (G-6841)
First National Bank of The N....E....320 245-5261
Sandstone (G-9321)
First National Bank of Walker....E....218 547-1160
Walker (G-9850)
1st National Bank of Waseca....E....507 835-2740
Waseca (G-9878)
First National Bank of West St....E....651 457-1111
Saint Paul (G-7774)
Kleinbank....E....763 682-1142
Buffalo (G-647)
Kleinbank....E....952 442-4471
Waconia (G-9787)
Marquette Bank Monticello....E....763 271-2700
Monticello (G-6276)
Merchants Bank, National Assn....C....507 457-1100
Winona (G-10115)
Merchants National Bank of....C....507 457-1100
Winona (G-10116)
Midcountry Bank Inc....E....320 234-4500
Hutchinson (G-2707)
Minnstar Bank....E....507 726-2137
Lake Crystal (G-2861)
Minnwest Bank Central....E....320 269-6565
Montevideo (G-6251)
Minnwest Bank Luverne....E....507 283-2366
Luverne (G-3066)
Minnwest Bank South....E....507 836-6141
Slayton (G-9489)
Norwest Bank Minnesota North....C....612 667-1234
Minneapolis (G-5247)

S I C

- **Olmsted National Bank Inc** .... 507 280-0028 — Rochester *(G-7197)*
- **Patriot Bank Minnesota** .... 651 462-8854 — Wyoming *(G-10206)*
- **Peoples National Bank of Mora** .... E .... 320 679-3100 — Mora *(G-6367)*
- **Pioneer National Bank** .... E .... 218 624-3676 — Duluth *(G-1424)*
- **Pioneer National Bank** .... E .... 218 728-1172 — Duluth *(G-1425)*
- **Profinium Financial Inc** .... D .... 507 235-5538 — Fairmont *(G-1978)*
- **Riverwood Bank** .... E .... 218 751-5120 — Bemidji *(G-423)*
- **Security Bank & Trust Co Inc** .... E .... 320 864-3171 — Glencoe *(G-2213)*
- **Signal Financial Corp** .... E .... 651 905-3100 — Saint Paul *(G-7904)*
- **State Bank & Trust** .... D .... 218 233-3107 — Moorhead *(G-6342)*
- **Stearns Bank National Assn** .... 320 253-6607 — Saint Cloud *(G-7608)*
- **Stearns County National Assn** .... E .... 320 253-6607 — Saint Cloud *(G-7609)*
- **Stearns County National Assn** .... E .... 320 253-6607 — Saint Cloud *(G-7610)*
- **TCF Financial Corp** .... A .... 952 745-2760 — Wayzata *(G-9945)*
- ▲ **TCF National Bank** .... D .... 612 661-6500 — Minneapolis *(G-5799)*
- ◆ **U S Bancorp** .... B .... 651 466-3000 — Minneapolis *(G-5885)*
- **U S Bank National Association** .... E .... 612 728-8300 — Minneapolis *(G-5886)*
- **U S Bank National Association** .... E .... 952 925-7333 — Minneapolis *(G-5887)*
- **U S Bank National Association** .... E .... 651 426-8266 — Saint Paul *(G-9098)*
- **Unity Bank North** .... D .... 952 465-3000 — Edina *(G-1849)*
- **University National Bank** .... E .... 651 265-5600 — Saint Paul *(G-9113)*
- **US Bancorp Information Svcs** .... E .... 800 925-4324 — Minneapolis *(G-5943)*
- **US Bancorp Legal Department** .... D .... 612 303-7879 — Minneapolis *(G-5944)*
- **US Bank National Association** .... E .... 651 229-6123 — Saint Paul *(G-9118)*
- **US Bank National Association** .... E .... 763 536-5328 — Minneapolis *(G-5945)*
- **US Bank National Association** .... E .... 952 997-9600 — Saint Paul *(G-7940)*
- **US Bank National Association** .... E .... 218 878-7878 — Cloquet *(G-1067)*
- **US Bank National Association** .... D .... 612 303-3021 — Minneapolis *(G-5946)*
- **Venture Bank** .... E .... 952 830-9999 — Minneapolis *(G-5962)*
- **Venture Bank** .... E .... 651 289-2222 — Saint Paul *(G-7942)*
- **Wells Fargo Bank** .... E .... 651 388-6751 — Red Wing *(G-7011)*
- **Wells Fargo Bank** .... E .... 320 762-2181 — Alexandria *(G-129)*
- **Wells Fargo Bank** .... E .... 218 681-1930 — Thief River Falls *(G-9682)*
- **Wells Fargo Bank, National** .... E .... 218 326-8521 — Grand Rapids *(G-2311)*
- **Wells Fargo Bank, National** .... E .... 507 373-1423 — Albert Lea *(G-71)*
- **Wells Fargo Bank, National** .... E .... 218 749-5920 — Virginia *(G-9765)*
- **Wells Fargo Bank, National** .... E .... 507 285-2800 — Rochester *(G-7290)*
- **Wells Fargo Bank, National** .... E .... 507 285-2990 — Rochester *(G-7289)*
- **Wells Fargo Bank, National** .... E .... 507 387-9254 — Mankato *(G-3215)*
- **Wells Fargo Bank, National** .... E .... 612 316-3965 — Minneapolis *(G-3641)*
- **Wells Fargo Bank, National** .... E .... 507 663-7300 — Northfield *(G-6545)*
- **Wells Fargo Bank, National** .... E .... 507 451-5670 — Owatonna *(G-6744)*
- **Wells Fargo Bank, National** .... E .... 507 532-4405 — Marshall *(G-3333)*
- **Wells Fargo Bank, National** .... E .... 320 259-3100 — Saint Cloud *(G-7632)*
- **Wells Fargo Bank, National** .... D .... 507 625-1872 — Mankato *(G-3216)*
- **Wells Fargo Bank, National** .... E .... 952 953-3991 — Saint Paul *(G-7944)*
- **Wells Fargo Bank, National** .... E .... 218 847-1361 — Detroit Lakes *(G-1222)*
- **Wells Fargo Bank, National** .... E .... 612 667-8710 — Minneapolis *(G-6042)*
- **Wells Fargo Business Credit** .... D .... 612 673-8500 — Minneapolis *(G-6043)*
- **Wells Fargo Financial** .... C .... 952 920-9270 — Minneapolis *(G-6045)*
- **Wells Fargo Minnesota West** .... E .... 218 736-7391 — Fergus Falls *(G-2124)*
- **Wells Fargo Minnesota West** .... E .... 218 681-1930 — Thief River Falls *(G-9683)*
- **Wells Fargo Minnesota West** .... D .... 218 233-6183 — Moorhead *(G-6347)*
- **Wf National Bank South Central** .... E .... 507 334-5546 — Faribault *(G-2037)*

6022 State Commercial Banks

- **Alliance Bank** .... E .... 507 354-3133 — New Ulm *(G-6438)*
- **Alliance Bank** .... E .... 651 345-3311 — Lake City *(G-2850)*
- **American Bank of St Paul** .... D .... 651 452-1320 — Saint Paul *(G-8021)*
- **American Bank of St Paul** .... E .... 507 377-7000 — Albert Lea *(G-38)*
- **Annandale State Bank Inc** .... E .... 320 274-8216 — Annandale *(G-136)*
- **Arlington State Bank Inc** .... E .... 507 964-2256 — Arlington *(G-248)*
- **Associated Bank Minnesota** .... E .... 612 359-4461 — Minneapolis *(G-3823)*
- **Bank Midwest** .... E .... 507 831-1322 — Windom *(G-10065)*
- **Bank of Elk River** .... E .... 763 441-1000 — Elk River *(G-1863)*
- **Bank of Zumbrota** .... E .... 507 732-7555 — Zumbrota *(G-10217)*
- **Bankcherokee** .... E .... 651 227-7071 — Saint Paul *(G-8086)*
- **Beacon Bank** .... E .... 952 474-7309 — Excelsior *(G-1939)*
- **Bnccorp Inc** .... E .... 612 305-2200 — Minneapolis *(G-3919)*
- **Border State Bank** .... E .... 218 782-2151 — Greenbush *(G-2324)*
- **Bremer Bank** .... E .... 800 908-2265 — Saint Paul *(G-8124)*
- **Bremer Bank** .... E .... 218 847-9292 — Detroit Lakes *(G-1189)*
- **Bremer Bank** .... E .... 763 389-2020 — Princeton *(G-6903)*
- **Bremer Bank** .... E .... 320 235-1111 — Willmar *(G-9993)*
- **Bremer Bank, National Assn** .... E .... 507 537-0222 — Marshall *(G-3291)*
- **Bremer Financial Corp** .... D .... 651 227-7621 — Saint Paul *(G-8125)*
- **Bremer Trust National Assn** .... E .... 320 252-3918 — Saint Cloud *(G-7466)*
- **Bremmer Bank** .... D .... 320 763-6622 — Alexandria *(G-86)*
- **Business Bank** .... E .... 952 847-1100 — Hopkins *(G-2521)*
- **Central Bank** .... E .... 651 439-3050 — Stillwater *(G-9604)*
- **Central Bank** .... E .... 507 498-5589 — Spring Grove *(G-9560)*
- **Cherokee Bancshares Inc** .... D .... 651 227-7071 — Saint Paul *(G-8189)*
- **Citizens Bank & Trust Co** .... E .... 320 587-2233 — Hutchinson *(G-2693)*
- **Citizens Bank Minnesota** .... E .... 507 354-3165 — New Ulm *(G-6445)*
- **Citizens Independent Bank** .... E .... 952 926-6561 — Minneapolis *(G-4082)*
- **Citizens State Bank of** .... E .... 763 675-2265 — Waverly *(G-9903)*
- **Citizens State Bank of Roseau** .... E .... 218 463-2135 — Roseau *(G-7354)*
- **Community Bank Vernon Center** .... E .... 507 625-1551 — Mankato *(G-3118)*
- **Community of Red River Valley** .... D .... 218 773-2451 — East Grand Forks *(G-1567)*
- **Crow River State Bank** .... E .... 763 972-3385 — Delano *(G-1182)*
- **Elmo Lake Bank** .... E .... 651 777-8365 — Lake Elmo *(G-2870)*
- **Faribault Bancshares Inc** .... D .... 507 332-7401 — Faribault *(G-2003)*
- **Farmers & Merchants State Bank** .... E .... 507 723-4234 — Springfield *(G-9571)*
- **Farmers & Merchants State Bank** .... 507 723-4800 — Springfield *(G-9572)*
- **Farmers State Bank of Elkton** .... 507 584-6441 — Elkton *(G-1906)*
- **Farmers State Bank of Hamel** .... E .... 763 478-6611 — Hamel *(G-2341)*
- **Farmers State Bank of West** .... E .... 507 527-2236 — West Concord *(G-9965)*
- **Fidelity Bank** .... E .... 952 831-6600 — Minneapolis *(G-4427)*
- **First Aid & Trust** .... E .... 651 439-5195 — Bayport *(G-348)*
- **First Commercial Bank** .... 952 903-0777 — Minneapolis *(G-4442)*
- **First Farmers & Merchants** .... 507 567-2219 — Brownsdale *(G-629)*
- **First National Bank** .... 507 425-2575 — Fulda *(G-2194)*
- **First National Bank of St** .... E .... 507 931-4000 — Saint Peter *(G-9303)*
- **First Rushmore Bancshares Inc** .... D .... 507 376-9747 — Worthington *(G-10183)*
- **First Security Bank** .... 218 948-2259 — Evansville *(G-1927)*
- **First Security Bank - Sleepy** .... E .... 507 794-3911 — Sleepy Eye *(G-9495)*
- **First State Bank & Trust** .... D .... 651 439-5195 — Bayport *(G-349)*
- **First State Bank of Ashby** .... 218 747-2235 — Ashby *(G-251)*
- **First State Bank of Sauk** .... E .... 320 352-5771 — Sauk Centre *(G-9345)*
- **First State Bank of Wabasha** .... E .... 651 565-3331 — Wabasha *(G-9766)*
- **First State Bank of Wyoming** .... E .... 651 462-7611 — Wyoming *(G-10203)*
- **First State Bank South West** .... E .... 507 376-9747 — Worthington *(G-10184)*
- **First State Bank South West** .... 507 376-9747 — Worthington *(G-10185)*
- **First State Bk of Red Wing** .... 651 388-4714 — Red Wing *(G-6982)*
- **Flagship Bank Minnesota** .... 952 473-1959 — Wayzata *(G-9917)*
- **FNB Bank of Blue Earth** .... E .... 507 526-3241 — Blue Earth *(G-535)*
- **Frandsen Bank & Trust** .... E .... 507 744-2361 — Lonsdale *(G-3044)*
- **Frandsen Bank & Trust** .... E .... 320 968-6293 — Foley *(G-2138)*
- ▲ **Great Northern Bank** .... E .... 763 497-7777 — Saint Michael *(G-7673)*
- **Hartman Bancshares Inc** .... 507 853-4421 — Okabena *(G-6556)*
- **Heartland State Bank** .... 507 445-3417 — Storden *(G-9656)*
- **Heritage Bank** .... E .... 320 235-5720 — Willmar *(G-10008)*
- **Hometown Community Bank** .... 320 795-2533 — Cyrus *(G-1154)*
- **Klein Bank** .... E .... 952 467-2313 — Young America *(G-10209)*
- **Lake Area Bank** .... 651 257-1117 — Lindstrom *(G-2969)*
- **Lake Bank National Association** .... E .... 218 834-2111 — Two Harbors *(G-9709)*
- **Lake Community Bank** .... E .... 952 473-7347 — Long Lake *(G-3027)*
- **Lakes State Bank** .... 218 568-4473 — Pequot Lakes *(G-6790)*
- **M & I Marshall & Ilsley Bank** .... E .... 952 544-3100 — Minneapolis *(G-4914)*
- **M & I Marshall & Ilsley Bank** .... D .... 612 904-8000 — Minneapolis *(G-4915)*
- **Marquette Financial Co's** .... E .... 612 661-3880 — Minneapolis *(G-4952)*
- **Midwest Bank** .... E .... 218 847-4771 — Detroit Lakes *(G-1211)*
- **Minnwest Bank Luverne** .... E .... 507 283-2366 — Luverne *(G-3066)*
- **Minnwest Bank M V** .... E .... 507 637-5731 — Redwood Falls *(G-7025)*
- **Nicollet County Bank of Saint** .... E .... 507 931-3310 — Saint Peter *(G-9310)*
- **North American Banking Co** .... E .... 651 636-9654 — Saint Paul *(G-8750)*
- **North American State Bank** .... E .... 320 254-8271 — Belgrade *(G-365)*
- **North American State Bank** .... E .... 320 697-5533 — Elrosa *(G-1910)*
- **North Shore Bank of Commerce** .... D .... 218 722-4784 — Duluth *(G-1399)*
- **North Shore Financial Corp** .... D .... 218 722-4784 — Duluth *(G-1400)*
- **Northeast Bank** .... D .... 612 379-8811 — Minneapolis *(G-5224)*
- **Northeast Securities Corp** .... 612 379-8811 — Minneapolis *(G-5225)*
- **Northview Bank** .... E .... 320 233-7575 — Finlayson *(G-2131)*
- **Northview Bank** .... 320 233-7575 — Finlayson *(G-2132)*
- **Northwestern Bank** .... D .... 218 287-2311 — Dilworth *(G-1223)*
- **Otto Bremer Foundation** .... C .... 651 227-8036 — Saint Paul *(G-8792)*
- **Peoples Bank of Commerce** .... E .... 763 689-1212 — Cambridge *(G-845)*
- **Peoples State Bank of Madison** .... 507 257-3544 — Eagle Lake *(G-1563)*
- **Pioneer Bank** .... 507 524-3630 — Mapleton *(G-3284)*
- **Pioneer National Bank** .... E .... 507 375-3201 — Saint James *(G-7644)*
- **Plaza Park State Bank Inc** .... E .... 320 252-4200 — Waite Park *(G-9834)*
- **Premier Bank Inc** .... D .... 651 777-7700 — Saint Paul *(G-8837)*
- **Prime Country Bank** .... 320 584-5522 — Royalton *(G-7386)*
- **Prior Lake State Bank Inc** .... E .... 952 447-2101 — Prior Lake *(G-6950)*
- **Profinium Financial Inc** .... E .... 507 776-2311 — Truman *(G-9696)*
- **Republic Bancshares Inc** .... E .... 218 722-3445 — Duluth *(G-1435)*
- **Roundbank** .... E .... 507 835-4220 — Waseca *(G-9886)*
- **Security Bank & Trust Co Inc** .... E .... 320 864-3171 — Glencoe *(G-2213)*
- **Security Bank Minnesota** .... E .... 507 373-1481 — Albert Lea *(G-65)*
- **Security Bank USA** .... E .... 218 751-1510 — Bemidji *(G-426)*
- **Security Bankshares Co Inc** .... E .... 320 864-3171 — Glencoe *(G-2214)*
- **Security State Bank of Kenyon** .... E .... 507 789-6123 — Kenyon *(G-2829)*

S I C

(G-00000) Company's Geographic Section entry number
478
2011 Harris Minnesota Services Directory
▲=Import ▼=Export ◆=Import/Export

Sherburne State Bank....E....763 261-4200
Becker *(G-358)*

Signature Bank....952 936-7800
Hopkins *(G-2633)*

State Bank of Belle Plaine....E....952 873-2296
Belle Plaine *(G-370)*

State Bank of Cokato....E....320 286-2146
Cokato *(G-1080)*

State Bank of Delano....E....763 972-2935
Delano *(G-1184)*

State Bank of Faribault....E....507 332-7401
Faribault *(G-2033)*

State Bank of New Prague....D....952 758-4491
New Prague *(G-6424)*

State Bank of Park Rapids....E....218 732-3366
Park Rapids *(G-6763)*

State Bank of Tower Inc....218 753-6100
Tower *(G-9688)*

Stearns County National Assn....D....320 845-2149
Albany *(G-29)*

Sterling State Bank....E....507 282-1845
Rochester *(G-7265)*

Tradition Capital Bank....952 806-6600
Edina *(G-1847)*

21st Century Bank....E....763 479-1901
Loretto *(G-3053)*

21st Century Bank....E....763 767-2178
Minneapolis *(G-3622)*

21st Century Bank....763 767-2178
Minneapolis *(G-3623)*

◆ U S Bancorp....B....651 466-3000
Minneapolis *(G-5885)*

Ultima Bank Minnesota....218 938-4144
Winger *(G-10074)*

Union Bank & Trust Co....E....612 379-3222
Minneapolis *(G-5904)*

United Community Bank....E....218 346-5700
Perham *(G-6803)*

Vermillion State Bank....E....651 437-4433
Vermillion *(G-9723)*

Village Bank....E....763 753-3007
Saint Francis *(G-7638)*

Wells Fargo Bank....E....651 205-8839
Saint Paul *(G-9145)*

Wells Fargo Bank....E....651 464-3334
Forest Lake *(G-2172)*

Western Bank....E....651 290-8100
Saint Paul *(G-9149)*

White Rock Bank....C....507 263-3030
Cannon Falls *(G-864)*

6029 Commercial Banks, NEC

Bremer Bank....E....320 763-6622
Alexandria *(G-85)*

Cherokee State Bank....E....651 290-6112
Saint Paul *(G-8190)*

Citizens Bank Minnesota....E....507 354-3165
New Ulm *(G-6445)*

Citizens State Bank of....E....763 675-2265
Waverly *(G-9903)*

Community Bank Chaska....E....952 361-2265
Chaska *(G-960)*

Fidelity Bank....D....952 831-6600
Minneapolis *(G-4428)*

Frandsen Bank & Trust....E....320 968-6293
Foley *(G-2138)*

Lake Area Bank....E....651 653-9619
Saint Paul *(G-8556)*

Landmark Community Bank....E....763 444-7787
Anoka *(G-197)*

Minnwest Bank Central....E....320 269-6565
Montevideo *(G-6251)*

Peoples Bank of Commerce....E....763 689-1212
Cambridge *(G-845)*

Richard Sankovitz....E....507 835-4836
Waseca *(G-9885)*

Wells Fargo Bank, National....E....763 295-2290
Monticello *(G-6291)*

Wells Fargo Bank, National....E....218 726-9325
Duluth *(G-1500)*

6035 Federal Savings Institutions

Bremer Bank....E....218 847-9292
Detroit Lakes *(G-1189)*

Federal Reserve Bank of....A....612 204-5000
Minneapolis *(G-4421)*

First Federal Capital Bank....D....507 285-2600
Rochester *(G-7113)*

First Federal Capital Bank....D....651 646-8681
Saint Paul *(G-8380)*

1st United Bank....E....507 334-2201
Faribault *(G-2008)*

Home Federal Savings Bank....E....507 535-1200
Rochester *(G-7139)*

Home Savings of America....E....320 632-5461
Little Falls *(G-3006)*

Ing Bank Fsb....B....320 229-4200
Saint Cloud *(G-7531)*

Inter Savings Bank Fsb....E....952 920-6700
Edina *(G-1834)*

Liberty Savings Bank Fsb....E....320 252-2841
Saint Cloud *(G-7545)*

Mid-Central Federal Saings....E....218 631-1414
Wadena *(G-9805)*

Midcountry Bank Inc....952 997-5608
Minnetonka *(G-6195)*

Queen City Federal Savings....218 741-2040
Virginia *(G-9752)*

TCF Equipment Finance Inc....C....952 656-5080
Minneapolis *(G-5796)*

TCF Equipment Finance Inc....E....952 934-4404
Hopkins *(G-2642)*

TCF National Bank....E....651 770-2273
Saint Paul *(G-9029)*

TCF National Bank....E....612 379-8597
Minneapolis *(G-5797)*

TCF National Bank....E....651 735-6510
Saint Paul *(G-9028)*

TCF National Bank....E....952 888-8375
Minneapolis *(G-5798)*

TCF National Bank....E....651 291-4095
Saint Paul *(G-9027)*

TCF National Bank....E....763 546-5637
Hopkins *(G-2643)*

Viking Savings Association....E....320 762-0236
Alexandria *(G-128)*

Voyager Bank....E....952 345-7600
Eden Prairie *(G-1811)*

Wells Federal Bank Fsb....E....507 553-3151
Wells *(G-9963)*

Winthrop Resources Corp....D....952 936-0226
Minnetonka *(G-6237)*

6036 Savings Institutions, Except Federal

American National Bank of MN....E....218 824-7900
Brainerd *(G-548)*

American National Bank of MN....D....218 829-1484
Baxter *(G-320)*

Bremer Bank....D....218 829-8781
Brainerd *(G-555)*

Citizens Bank & Trust Co....E....320 587-2233
Hutchinson *(G-2693)*

Community National Bank....E....507 645-4441
Northfield *(G-6526)*

First Integrity Bank....E....218 894-1522
Staples *(G-9584)*

First State Bank of Rosemount....E....651 423-1121
Rosemount *(G-7370)*

1st United Bank....E....507 334-2201
Faribault *(G-2008)*

Main Street Bank....E....651 451-2133
South Saint Paul *(G-9533)*

Riverbank MN....D....651 408-9203
Wyoming *(G-10207)*

Security State Bank of Kenyon....E....507 789-6123
Kenyon *(G-2829)*

6061 Federal Credit Unions

American Hardware Insurance....D....952 939-4510
Minnetonka *(G-6139)*

Anoka Hennepin School District....E....651 255-7000
Forest Lake *(G-2157)*

City-County Federal Credit....C....763 549-6000
Minneapolis *(G-4097)*

City-County Federal Credit....D....763 549-6000
Minneapolis *(G-4098)*

First Alliance Credit Union....E....507 288-0330
Rochester *(G-7111)*

General Mills Federal Credit....D....763 764-6900
Minnetonka *(G-6175)*

Great River Federal Credit....E....320 252-3507
Sauk Rapids *(G-9365)*

Great River Federal Credit....D....320 258-5393
Waite Park *(G-9823)*

Hiway Federal Credit Union....C....651 291-1515
Saint Paul *(G-8487)*

Home Town Federal Credit Union....E....507 451-3798
Owatonna *(G-6717)*

Lake State Federal Credit....D....218 485-4444
Moose Lake *(G-6351)*

Lake State Federal Credit....D....320 245-5251
Sandstone *(G-9322)*

Mid Minnesota Federal Credit....E....218 829-0371
Brainerd *(G-574)*

North Ridge Community Credit....E....218 741-1222
Virginia *(G-9747)*

Spire Federal Credit Union....D....651 215-3500
Saint Paul *(G-8978)*

St Cloud Federal Employees....D....320 252-2634
Saint Cloud *(G-7600)*

Think Mutual Bank....C....507 288-3425
Rochester *(G-7273)*

Trustar Federal Credit Union....E....218 283-2000
International Falls *(G-2733)*

Trustone Financial Federal....D....763 544-1517
Minneapolis *(G-5861)*

Trustone Financial Federal....D....763 544-1517
Minneapolis *(G-5862)*

Wings Financial Credit Union....E....612 726-2073
Bloomington *(G-526)*

Wings Financial Credit Union....C....952 997-8000
Saint Paul *(G-7949)*

6062 State Credit Unions

Accentra Credit Union....E....507 433-1829
Austin *(G-258)*

Affinity Plus Federal Credit....E....651 291-3700
Saint Paul *(G-7995)*

Affinity Plus Federal Credit....E....651 291-3700
Saint Paul *(G-7996)*

Affinity Plus Federal Credit....E....651 291-3700
Saint Paul *(G-7997)*

Central Minnesota Federal....E....320 256-3669
Melrose *(G-3347)*

City & County Credit Union....E....651 225-2700
Saint Paul *(G-8203)*

Endura Financial Federal....E....763 287-4630
Minneapolis *(G-4354)*

Federated Employees Credit....507 455-5430
Owatonna *(G-6709)*

First Alliance Credit Union....507 281-7640
Rochester *(G-7112)*

Greater Minnesota Credit Union....E....320 679-8100
Mora *(G-6360)*

Mayo Clinic Employees Credit....E....507 535-1460
Rochester *(G-7172)*

Members Cooperative Credit....D....218 879-3304
Cloquet *(G-1057)*

Minnco Credit Union....D....763 689-1071
Cambridge *(G-843)*

Northern Communities Credit....218 279-3200
Duluth *(G-1403)*

Retail Employees Credit Union....E....952 930-0700
Minneapolis *(G-5531)*

Richfield Bloomington Credit....E....612 798-7100
Richfield *(G-7037)*

Sheet Metal Worker Federal....E....651 770-2385
Saint Paul *(G-8950)*

Southpoint Federal Credit....E....877 794-6712
Sleepy Eye *(G-9501)*

St Paul Postal Employees....E....651 770-7000
Saint Paul *(G-8997)*

Topline Federal Credit Union....D....763 391-9494
Maple Grove *(G-3255)*

Virginia Coop Credit Union Inc....218 741-5644
Virginia *(G-9759)*

6091 Nondeposit Trust Facilities

◆ U S Bancorp....B....651 466-3000
Minneapolis *(G-5885)*

US Bank Trust National Assn....A....800 934-6802
Saint Paul *(G-9119)*

6099 Functions Related To Deposit Banking, NEC

Game Financial Corp....C....800 363-3321
Minneapolis *(G-4497)*

Money Gram Payment Systems Inc....A....952 591-3000
Minneapolis *(G-5120)*

Moneygram Payment Systems Inc....D....763 549-7100
Minneapolis *(G-5121)*

New Unbank Co LLC....D....952 544-5155
Hopkins *(G-2588)*

▲ Security Products Co....E....763 784-6504
Minneapolis *(G-3599)*

Solutran Inc....D....763 559-2225
Minneapolis *(G-5697)*

T-Chek Systems Inc....D....952 934-3413
Eden Prairie *(G-1790)*

United Check Clearing Corp....D....763 559-2225
Minneapolis *(G-5908)*

Unity Bank East....320 358-3600
Rush City *(G-7391)*

Vanco Services LLC....E....952 983-8660
Eden Prairie *(G-1803)*

▲ Western Bank Edina....D....952 857-1707
Minneapolis *(G-6058)*

61 NONDEPOSITORY INSTITUTIONS

6111 Federal Credit Agencies

Agribank, Fcb....B....651 282-8800
Saint Paul *(G-8000)*

Agstar Financial Services, Aca....C....507 387-4174
Mankato *(G-3102)*

Agstar Financial Services, Aca....E....507 526-7366
Blue Earth *(G-528)*

Cenex Nuway Co Op Inc....D....507 375-4291
Trimont *(G-9693)*

City of Jackson....E....507 847-4410
Jackson *(G-2788)*

Educational Credit Management....C....651 221-0566
Saint Paul *(G-9209)*

Lcomuity National Bank....E....651 483-4656
Saint Paul *(G-8571)*

United Fcs....E....320 235-1771
Willmar *(G-10049)*

6141 Personal Credit Institutions

American Building Maintenance....E....612 344-1758
Minneapolis *(G-3746)*

Citifinancial Credit Co....E....763 424-6012
Minneapolis *(G-4079)*

Citigroup Inc....C....952 942-9880
Minneapolis *(G-4081)*

Conseco Finance Corp....C....651 293-3434
Saint Paul *(G-8248)*

S
I
C

Employment codes: A=Over 500 employees, B=251-500
C=101-250, D=51-100, E=25-50

2011 Harris Minnesota
Services Directory

© Harris InfoSource 1-866-281-6415

479

Firstmark Services LLC ... D ... 651 265-7600
Saint Paul *(G-9218)*

General Electric Capital Corp ... E ... 952 897-5600
Minneapolis *(G-4509)*

Hsbc Card Services Inc ... C ... 952 358-4000
Minnetonka *(G-6179)*

Marquette Financial Co's ... E ... 612 661-3880
Minneapolis *(G-4952)*

▲ Metris Co's Inc ... A ... 952 358-4000
Hopkins *(G-2580)*

Minnesota First Credit ... 507 289-0411
Rochester *(G-7187)*

Minnwest Bank South ... E ... 507 836-6141
Slayton *(G-9489)*

Mortgages Unlimited ... E ... 763 633-0576
Elk River *(G-1886)*

Nelnet Inc ... C ... 651 265-7600
Saint Paul *(G-8744)*

Northland Dealer Finance Inc ... E ... 651 773-4973
Saint Paul *(G-8763)*

Payday America LLC ... E ... 952 646-1793
Burnsville *(G-777)*

Preferred Credit Inc ... C ... 320 202-7000
Saint Cloud *(G-7570)*

Wells Fargo Business Credit ... D ... 612 673-8500
Minneapolis *(G-6043)*

Wells Fargo Financial Indiana ... E ... 952 920-9270
Minneapolis *(G-6046)*

6153 Credit Institutions, Short-Term Business

Aircraft Owner LLC ... E ... 651 633-1045
Saint Paul *(G-8002)*

Business Funding Group LLC ... E ... 952 697-0202
Eden Prairie *(G-1614)*

Citifinancial Credit Co ... E ... 763 424-6012
Minneapolis *(G-4079)*

Marquette Transportation ... E ... 952 703-7474
Minneapolis *(G-4954)*

Security Auto Loans Inc ... E ... 763 559-5892
Minneapolis *(G-5625)*

TCI Business Capital Inc ... D ... 952 656-3400
Burnsville *(G-806)*

◆ Toro Co ... A ... 952 888-8801
Bloomington *(G-519)*

Total Card Inc ... C ... 507 449-6401
Luverne *(G-3071)*

Winmark Corp ... C ... 763 520-8500
Minneapolis *(G-6077)*

6159 Credit Institutions, Misc Business

▲ ABC Bus Co's Inc ... D ... 507 334-1871
Faribault *(G-1985)*

Agstar Financial Services, Aca ... E ... 507 376-4144
Worthington *(G-10177)*

Agstar Financial Services, Aca ... E ... 507 526-7366
Blue Earth *(G-528)*

Agstar Financial Services, Aca ... E ... 507 645-0552
Northfield *(G-6523)*

Allegiance Financial Group Inc ... 651 486-5313
Saint Paul *(G-8012)*

Ally Financial Inc ... E ... 800 689-6768
Minneapolis *(G-3730)*

Citigroup Inc ... C ... 952 942-9880
Minneapolis *(G-4081)*

Geneva Capital LLC ... E ... 320 762-8400
Alexandria *(G-102)*

Glacier International Inc ... 651 786-9700
Saint Paul *(G-8412)*

Lyon Financial Services Inc ... C ... 507 532-7763
Marshall *(G-3307)*

Production Credit Association ... D ... 320 235-1771
Willmar *(G-10038)*

◆ Schwan Food Co ... A ... 507 532-3274
Marshall *(G-3325)*

Toro Credit Co ... E ... 952 888-8801
Minneapolis *(G-5831)*

◆ U S Bancorp ... B ... 651 466-3000
Minneapolis *(G-5885)*

U Save Lease & Rental Inc ... E ... 218 732-3347
Park Rapids *(G-6764)*

Wells Fargo Bank, National ... E ... 612 667-2753
Minneapolis *(G-6039)*

▲ Wells Fargo Equipment Finance ... C ... 612 667-9876
Minneapolis *(G-6044)*

6162 Mortgage Bankers & Loan Correspondents

Advisors Mortgage LLC ... E ... 763 753-8133
Cedar *(G-873)*

Affinity Plus Credit Union ... E ... 651 291-3700
Saint Paul *(G-7994)*

Agribank, Fcb ... B ... 651 282-8800
Saint Paul *(G-8000)*

American Residential Mortgage ... E ... 763 784-2022
Champlin *(G-889)*

American Residential Mortgage ... D ... 651 488-1801
Saint Paul *(G-8033)*

Bell Ancillary Services Inc ... E ... 952 893-0865
Minneapolis *(G-3880)*

Bell Ancillary Services Inc ... E ... 952 591-1880
Minneapolis *(G-3881)*

Bell Ancillary Services Inc ... D ... 952 545-1880
Minnetonka *(G-6147)*

Bremer Bank ... E ... 800 908-2265
Saint Paul *(G-8124)*

Cherokee State Bank ... E ... 651 290-6112
Saint Paul *(G-8190)*

D H I Mortgage ... E ... 952 985-7850
Lakeville *(G-2900)*

▲ Green Tree Servicing LLC ... E ... 651 293-4800
Saint Paul *(G-8433)*

Home Savings of America ... E ... 320 632-5461
Little Falls *(G-3006)*

Homeservices Lending LLC ... D ... 952 928-5300
Minneapolis *(G-4671)*

Homeservices Lending LLC ... E ... 763 494-8138
Osseo *(G-6621)*

Lake Area Mortgage ... D ... 651 257-1114
Saint Paul *(G-8557)*

Lyman Lumber Co ... B ... 952 470-3600
Excelsior *(G-1945)*

Midcountry Mortgage Corp ... D ... 651 766-7000
Saint Paul *(G-8653)*

Mortgage Assurance ... E ... 507 388-8140
Mankato *(G-3174)*

Mortgages Unlimited ... E ... 763 633-0576
Elk River *(G-1886)*

Mortgages Unlimited Inc ... D ... 763 416-2600
Maple Grove *(G-3251)*

Nations Title Agency ... E ... 952 545-2808
Minneapolis *(G-5170)*

Northland Mortgage Corp ... E ... 507 388-8600
Mankato *(G-3177)*

Northmarq Capital LLC ... D ... 952 356-0100
Minneapolis *(G-5233)*

Prime Mortgage Corp ... E ... 952 544-3181
Minnetonka *(G-6217)*

Residential Funding Co LLC ... B ... 952 857-8700
Minneapolis *(G-5524)*

Residential Funding Securities ... B ... 952 857-7000
Minneapolis *(G-5525)*

River City Mortgage Corp ... E ... 651 406-5000
Saint Paul *(G-7896)*

Ryland Group Inc ... D ... 952 229-6000
Edina *(G-1843)*

State Bank of Belle Plaine ... E ... 952 873-2296
Belle Plaine *(G-370)*

TCS Mortgage Inc ... E ... 612 767-5002
Minneapolis *(G-5801)*

Team USA Mortgage LLC ... D ... 651 848-0484
Saint Paul *(G-9031)*

Trustcorp Mortgage Co ... E ... 218 444-5626
Bemidji *(G-429)*

◆ U S Bancorp ... B ... 651 466-3000
Minneapolis *(G-5885)*

U S Bank Home Mortgage ... 952 851-5494
Bloomington *(G-522)*

Vision Financial & Home Mtge ... E ... 952 224-3370
Hopkins *(G-2652)*

Wells Fargo Bank, National ... E ... 320 587-2122
Hutchinson *(G-2718)*

Wells Fargo Bank, National ... E ... 952 890-1424
Burnsville *(G-821)*

Wells Fargo Bank, National ... A ... 612 667-1234
Minneapolis *(G-6041)*

Wells Fargo Funding Inc ... C ... 800 328-5074
Minneapolis *(G-6047)*

Wells Fargo Home Mortgage Inc ... E ... 952 939-9066
Minneapolis *(G-6048)*

Western National Bank ... E ... 218 723-5152
Duluth *(G-1503)*

Westner National Bank Inc ... E ... 218 723-5100
Duluth *(G-1504)*

6163 Loan Brokers

All American Mortgage Lending ... E ... 763 560-5815
Minneapolis *(G-3707)*

American Investment Management ... E ... 763 533-7193
Minneapolis *(G-3754)*

C U Mortgage Services Inc ... D ... 651 631-3111
Saint Paul *(G-8146)*

Commonsense Mortgage Inc ... E ... 952 942-8502
Eden Prairie *(G-1633)*

Complete Real Estate Services ... E ... 651 287-3400
Saint Paul *(G-8243)*

Dougherty Financial Group LLC ... C ... 612 376-4000
Minneapolis *(G-4284)*

First Integrity Bank ... E ... 218 894-1522
Staples *(G-9584)*

1st National Bank of Pipestone ... E ... 507 825-3344
Pipestone *(G-6827)*

Global Lending Corp ... E ... 651 438-7976
Hastings *(G-2388)*

▲ Great Northern Bank ... E ... 763 497-7777
Saint Michael *(G-7673)*

Hmn Mortgage Services Inc ... E ... 952 914-7440
Minneapolis *(G-4656)*

Lake Community Bank ... E ... 952 473-7347
Long Lake *(G-3027)*

Landmark Community Bank ... E ... 763 444-7787
Anoka *(G-197)*

Landmark Financial Group Inc ... E ... 763 572-8626
Minneapolis *(G-3514)*

Midcountry Mortgage Corp ... D ... 651 766-7000
Saint Paul *(G-8653)*

Minnesota League of Credit ... E ... 651 288-5170
Saint Paul *(G-8694)*

Minnesota Lending Co LLC ... D ... 952 960-9600
Minneapolis *(G-5080)*

Minnwest Bank Central ... E ... 320 269-6565
Montevideo *(G-6251)*

Mortgage & Investment Conslnts ... E ... 651 483-0200
Saint Paul *(G-8723)*

North American Banking Co ... E ... 651 636-9654
Saint Paul *(G-8750)*

Northern Lights Mortgage Co ... 612 435-3500
Minneapolis *(G-5227)*

Northstar Capital Markets Svcs ... E ... 651 290-8781
Saint Paul *(G-8765)*

Northwestern Bank ... D ... 218 287-2311
Dilworth *(G-1223)*

Prism Mortgage Inc ... E ... 952 546-6272
Minneapolis *(G-5411)*

Provident Mortgage Corp of MN ... E ... 612 285-6275
Minneapolis *(G-5434)*

Referral Mortgage Inc ... E ... 952 933-4400
Minneapolis *(G-5482)*

Residential Mortgage Group Inc ... E ... 952 593-1169
Hopkins *(G-2616)*

River City Mortgage ... D ... 952 915-5300
Minneapolis *(G-5542)*

Roundbank ... E ... 507 835-4220
Waseca *(G-9886)*

Royal Financial LLC ... E ... 763 746-9480
Minneapolis *(G-3593)*

Security Bank USA ... E ... 218 751-1510
Bemidji *(G-426)*

St Cloud Federal Employees ... D ... 320 252-2634
Saint Cloud *(G-7600)*

Sterling State Bank ... E ... 507 282-1845
Rochester *(G-7265)*

Summit Mortgage Corp ... E ... 763 390-7200
Minneapolis *(G-5764)*

Tradition Mortgage LLC ... E ... 952 920-5100
Minneapolis *(G-5845)*

United Residential Mortgage ... E ... 952 820-0272
Minneapolis *(G-5915)*

Wells Fargo Home Mortgage Inc ... E ... 952 939-9066
Minneapolis *(G-6048)*

Winona National Holding Co Inc ... D ... 507 454-4320
Winona *(G-10152)*

62 SECURITY & COMMODITY BROKERS & DEALERS

6211 Security Brokers & Dealers

A G Edwards & Sons Inc ... D ... 952 832-1600
Bloomington *(G-480)*

Ameriprise Financial Inc ... A ... 612 671-3131
Minneapolis *(G-3767)*

Anderson Swenson Associates ... E ... 612 347-8600
Minneapolis *(G-3778)*

Cargill Financial Services ... C ... 952 742-7575
Hopkins *(G-2524)*

Cargill Financial Services Int ... A ... 952 742-7575
Minneapolis *(G-4006)*

Cascade Mortgage Inc ... E ... 612 252-3333
Minneapolis *(G-4023)*

Charles Schwab & Co Inc ... D ... 952 835-6784
Minneapolis *(G-4056)*

Charles Schwab & Co Inc ... E ... 952 404-0398
Wayzata *(G-9910)*

Charles Schwab & Co Inc ... D ... 651 222-8600
Saint Paul *(G-8187)*

Citigroup Derivatives Markets ... D ... 952 475-5500
Hopkins *(G-2531)*

Citigroup Global Markets Inc ... E ... 612 349-4800
Minneapolis *(G-4080)*

Citigroup Global Markets Inc ... E ... 651 215-8400
Saint Paul *(G-8202)*

Community Finance Group Inc ... E ... 763 416-5959
Minneapolis *(G-4141)*

Craig-Hallum Capital Group LLC ... D ... 612 334-6300
Minneapolis *(G-4176)*

Cri Securities Inc ... C ... 612 617-6000
Minneapolis *(G-4183)*

Dain Rauscher Inc ... A ... 612 371-2711
Minneapolis *(G-4217)*

Dougherty & Co LLC ... C ... 612 376-4000
Minneapolis *(G-4283)*

Dougherty Financial Group LLC ... C ... 612 376-4000
Minneapolis *(G-4284)*

F B L Financial Services Inc ... E ... 651 905-2123
Saint Paul *(G-7772)*

Feltl & Co ... E ... 952 546-5018
Minneapolis *(G-4425)*

Fintegra Financial Solutions ... 763 503-1911
Minneapolis *(G-4435)*

Gardner Financial Services Inc ... E ... 952 935-4601
Minneapolis *(G-4500)*

Goldsmith, Agio, Helms ... D ... 612 339-0500
Minneapolis *(G-4539)*

Ing Financial Partners Inc ... D ... 612 372-5507
Minneapolis *(G-4702)*

K O P P Funds ... E ... 952 841-0480
Minneapolis *(G-4785)*

Knight Financial Products LLC ... D ... 952 249-5500
Hopkins *(G-2565)*

Lutheran Brotherhood Research ... E ... 612 340-7000
Minneapolis *(G-4911)*

Merrill Lynch, Pierce, Fenner ... D ... 651 298-1700
Saint Paul *(G-8640)*

(G-00000) Company's Geographic Section entry number
480
2011 Harris Minnesota Services Directory
▲=Import ▼=Export ◆=Import/Export

Merrill Lynch, Pierce, Fenner E 218 726-3140
Duluth *(G-1391)*
Merrill Lynch, Pierce, Fenner E 952 820-1900
Minneapolis *(G-4993)*
Merrill Lynch, Pierce, Fenner E 612 349-7801
Minneapolis *(G-4994)*
Merrill Lynch, Pierce, Fenner E 952 476-5600
Wayzata *(G-9926)*
Merrill Lynch, Pierce, Fenner E 651 275-8040
Stillwater *(G-9627)*
Mid American Financial Group D 952 258-5000
Minnetonka *(G-6194)*
Mid Coutry Bank C 952 931-2200
Hopkins *(G-2581)*
Mjsk Investment Securities E 763 542-3700
Minneapolis *(G-5111)*
Morgan Stanley E 763 475-4100
Wayzata *(G-9930)*
Morgan Stanley & Co Inc D 612 340-6700
Minneapolis *(G-5129)*
Morgan Stanley & Co Inc D 952 921-1900
Minneapolis *(G-5128)*
▲ **Piper Jaffray Co's** A 612 303-6000
Minneapolis *(G-5384)*
Piper Jaffray Co's E 952 476-3939
Wayzata *(G-9935)*
Primevest Financial Services B 320 656-4300
Saint Cloud *(G-7572)*
Questar Capital Corp E 888 446-5872
Minneapolis *(G-5450)*
Rbc Wealth Management E 651 228-6900
Saint Paul *(G-8872)*
Rbc Wealth Management A 612 371-7750
Minneapolis *(G-5472)*
Rbc Wealth Managment E 651 766-4920
Saint Paul *(G-8873)*
Rbc Wealth Managment D 952 838-7000
Minneapolis *(G-5473)*
Rbc Wealth Managment E 218 724-2100
Duluth *(G-1431)*
Rbc Wealth Managment E 763 476-3700
Hopkins *(G-2610)*
RSM McGladrey Business Soln C 952 921-7700
Minneapolis *(G-5567)*
Secruian Financial Services 651 223-4252
Saint Paul *(G-8942)*
Stifel, Nicolaus & Co Inc E 763 542-3700
Minneapolis *(G-5757)*
Think Equity Partners LLC C 612 677-5757
Minneapolis *(G-5814)*
▲ **Thrivent Financial For** A 920 734-5721
Minneapolis *(G-5819)*
Thrivent Financial For E 952 894-6772
Burnsville *(G-808)*
UBS Financial Services Inc E 952 921-7900
Minneapolis *(G-5891)*
UBS Financial Services Inc D 651 298-1616
Saint Paul *(G-9100)*
Voyageur Co's Inc D 612 376-7000
Minneapolis *(G-5985)*
Waddell & Reed Inc E 651 483-1411
Saint Paul *(G-9135)*
Wells Fargo Advisors LLC E 952 835-3111
Minneapolis *(G-6037)*
Wells Fargo Advisors LLC E 612 332-1212
Minneapolis *(G-6036)*
Wells Fargo Bank, National E 507 373-1423
Albert Lea *(G-71)*
Wells Fargo Bank, National E 651 385-2328
Red Wing *(G-7012)*
Wells Fargo Bank, National E 651 205-7583
Saint Paul *(G-9146)*
Workman Financial Group Inc E 763 746-9420
Minneapolis *(G-6086)*

6221 Commodity Contracts Brokers & Dealers

Archer-Daniels-Midland Co E 612 340-5900
Minneapolis *(G-3801)*
Cargill Inc C 952 984-3890
Minneapolis *(G-4009)*
Country Hedging Inc E 651 355-6500
Inver Grove Heights *(G-2746)*
Dougherty Financial Group LLC C 612 376-4000
Minneapolis *(G-4284)*

6231 Security & Commodity Exchanges

Minneapolis Grain Exchange E 612 321-7101
Minneapolis *(G-5056)*

6282 Investment Advice

Alliance Benefit Group D 507 377-9344
Albert Lea *(G-35)*
Ameriprise E 952 835-8180
Minneapolis *(G-3765)*
Ameriprise Financial Inc A 612 671-3131
Minneapolis *(G-3767)*
Ameriprise Financial Services E 952 368-3100
Chaska *(G-948)*
Ameriprise Financial Services D 651 631-2208
Saint Paul *(G-8037)*
Ameriprise Financial Services C 612 671-7536
Minneapolis *(G-3768)*
Ameriprise Financial Services C 612 671-4343
Minneapolis *(G-3769)*
Ameriprise Financial Services C 612 671-3131
Minneapolis *(G-3770)*
Bancnorth Investment Group E 320 656-4300
Saint Cloud *(G-7457)*
Deluxe Financial Services Inc D 651 787-2766
Saint Paul *(G-8286)*
Dougherty Financial Group LLC C 612 376-4000
Minneapolis *(G-4284)*
Ebf & Associates LP E 952 476-7200
Hopkins *(G-2537)*
Ehlers & Associates Inc E 651 697-8500
Saint Paul *(G-8328)*
▲ **Fiduciary Counselling Inc** E 651 228-0935
Saint Paul *(G-8376)*
Foster Klima & Co LLC D 612 746-2214
Minneapolis *(G-4467)*
Island Freight Brokerage LLC E 507 288-5758
Rochester *(G-7143)*
Jeffrey Slocum & Associates D 612 338-7020
Minneapolis *(G-4758)*
Jra Financial Advisors E 763 315-8000
Osseo *(G-6625)*
Knight Financial Products LLC D 952 249-5500
Hopkins *(G-2565)*
Midwest Financial Processing E 507 647-2856
Winthrop *(G-10168)*
Oshkosh, McNeilus Financia E 507 775-3310
Byron *(G-825)*
Peregrine Capital Management E 612 343-7600
Minneapolis *(G-5364)*
Prime Investments Inc E 952 853-1680
Minneapolis *(G-5409)*
Primerica Financial Services D 952 895-1091
Burnsville *(G-782)*
Rbc Wealth Management A 612 371-7750
Minneapolis *(G-5472)*
Rock Island Co E 651 228-0935
Saint Paul *(G-8909)*
Roxbury Capital Management LLC E 952 230-6140
Minnetonka *(G-6221)*
RSM McGladrey Inc D 507 288-5363
Rochester *(G-7242)*
Sit Fixed Income Advisors II D 612 332-3223
Minneapolis *(G-5680)*
Sit Investment Associates Inc D 612 332-3223
Minneapolis *(G-5681)*
300 Financial Inc E 507 424-4799
Rochester *(G-7274)*
Vilana Financial Inc E 763 416-5959
Minneapolis *(G-5975)*
Voyageur Co's Inc D 612 376-7000
Minneapolis *(G-5985)*
Wells Capital Management Inc 612 667-4230
Minneapolis *(G-6035)*
Wells Fargo Bank, National E 507 285-3015
Rochester *(G-7291)*

6289 Security & Commodity Svcs, NEC

Christopher Maclennan E 612 243-3302
Minneapolis *(G-4071)*
Wells Fargo Bank, National C 651 450-4054
South Saint Paul *(G-9551)*

63 INSURANCE CARRIERS

6311 Life Insurance Carriers

Aegon USA Inc C 952 893-6767
Minneapolis *(G-3693)*
Allianz Life Insurance Co of A 763 765-6500
Minneapolis *(G-3714)*
Auto-Owners Life Insurance Co D 651 777-9317
Saint Paul *(G-8080)*
Employers Mutual Casualty Co E 952 938-4646
Hopkins *(G-2539)*
Federated Mutual Insurance Co C 507 455-5200
Owatonna *(G-6710)*
Federated Mutual Insurance Co D 952 831-4300
Minneapolis *(G-4422)*
Federated Mutual Insurance Co A 507 455-5200
Owatonna *(G-6711)*
Financial Corp Inc E 651 407-5770
Saint Paul *(G-8377)*
General Casualty Co of WI D 952 941-0980
Eden Prairie *(G-1673)*
Gnw Acquisition Corp D 651 325-0060
Saint Paul *(G-8416)*
Guardian Life Insurance Co of D 952 903-2200
Minneapolis *(G-4577)*
Guy Carpenter & Co LLC C 952 920-3300
Minneapolis *(G-4580)*
Hartford Life Inc D 952 893-9236
Minneapolis *(G-4604)*
Hartford Life Inc A 877 952-9222
Osseo *(G-6618)*
Ing North America Insurance D 612 342-7878
Minneapolis *(G-4703)*
McGovern & Fisher Insurance D 952 996-8818
Minneapolis *(G-4975)*
Midwest Family Mutual Insce D 763 951-7000
Minneapolis *(G-5028)*
Minnesota Mutual Co's Inc A 651 665-3500
Saint Paul *(G-8699)*
New York Life Insurance Co E 952 897-5000
Minneapolis *(G-5193)*
Primerica Financial Services D 651 290-9822
Saint Paul *(G-8847)*
Principal Life Insurance Co E 952 277-4300
Hopkins *(G-2605)*
Prudential Insurance Co of A 612 349-1000
Minneapolis *(G-5435)*
Prudential Insurance Co of E 507 281-4200
Rochester *(G-7213)*
Rain & Hail Insurance Service E 763 473-2421
Minneapolis *(G-5462)*
Reliastar Life Insurance Co A 612 372-5432
Minneapolis *(G-5507)*
Securian Financial Network Inc D 651 665-3500
Saint Paul *(G-8944)*
Security American Financial E 952 544-2121
Hopkins *(G-2628)*
Security Life Insurance Co of D 952 544-2121
Hopkins *(G-2629)*
Sons of Norway E 612 827-3611
Minneapolis *(G-5698)*
Sons of Norway Foundation E 612 827-3611
Minneapolis *(G-5699)*
▲ **Thrivent Financial For** A 920 734-5721
Minneapolis *(G-5819)*
21st Services LLC D 612 371-3008
Minneapolis *(G-5872)*

6321 Accident & Health Insurance

Allina Self-Insured D 952 992-2500
Hopkins *(G-2507)*
AON Benfield B 952 886-8000
Minneapolis *(G-3784)*
AON Benfield E 952 886-8000
Minneapolis *(G-3785)*
Bcbsm Inc A 651 662-8000
Saint Paul *(G-7711)*
Bcbsm Inc E 218 722-3371
Duluth *(G-1248)*
Bcbsm Inc B 651 662-8000
Saint Paul *(G-7713)*
E W Blanch International Inc D 952 886-8000
Minneapolis *(G-4302)*
Employers Mutual Casualty Co E 952 938-4646
Hopkins *(G-2539)*
Federated Mutual Insurance Co C 507 455-5200
Owatonna *(G-6710)*
Federated Mutual Insurance Co D 952 831-4300
Minneapolis *(G-4422)*
First Solutions D 218 740-2330
Duluth *(G-1323)*
Hartford Life Inc D 651 738-4516
Saint Paul *(G-9222)*
League of Minnesota Cities D 651 281-1200
Saint Paul *(G-8573)*
Long Term Care Group Inc C 651 501-4000
Saint Paul *(G-9244)*
Medical Network Inc E 763 595-3208
Golden Valley *(G-2243)*
Reinsurance Group of America D 612 372-5432
Minneapolis *(G-5506)*
Reliastar Life Insurance Co A 612 372-5432
Minneapolis *(G-5507)*
Rute Agency E 612 240-1795
Minneapolis *(G-3594)*
Security American Financial E 952 544-2121
Hopkins *(G-2628)*
Security Life Insurance Co of D 952 544-2121
Hopkins *(G-2629)*
St Paul Fire & Marine Insce A 651 221-7911
Saint Paul *(G-8990)*
▲ **Thrivent Financial For** A 920 734-5721
Minneapolis *(G-5819)*
Union Security Insurance Co D 952 920-8990
Minneapolis *(G-5905)*
▼ **Unitedhealth Group Inc** A 952 936-1300
Minnetonka *(G-6232)*

6324 Hospital & Medical Svc Plans Carriers

ARAZ Group Inc D 952 896-1200
Minneapolis *(G-3796)*
Assurecare D 763 383-4800
Minneapolis *(G-3829)*
Aware Integrated Inc A 651 662-8000
Saint Paul *(G-7709)*
Bcbsm Inc A 651 662-8000
Saint Paul *(G-7711)*
Bcbsm Inc A 651 662-8951
Saint Paul *(G-7712)*
Bcbsm Inc C 651 662-8000
Saint Paul *(G-7714)*
Cigna Behavioral Health Inc B 952 996-2000
Eden Prairie *(G-1626)*
Decare Dental LLC B 800 371-6561
Saint Paul *(G-7750)*
Department of Health Minnesota D 218 335-3200
Cass Lake *(G-871)*
Fiserv Health Plan A 262 879-5565
Minneapolis *(G-4450)*
HealthPartners Inc A 952 883-6000
Bloomington *(G-500)*
Healthpartners Inc D 952 944-0432
Eden Prairie *(G-1681)*

SIC

Employment codes: A=Over 500 employees, B=251-500
C=101-250, D=51-100, E=25-50
2011 Harris Minnesota
Services Directory
© Harris InfoSource 1-866-281-6415
481

Healthpartners Inc ....B....612 623-4002 Minneapolis (G-4623)
Long Term Care Group Inc ....C....651 501-4000 Saint Paul (G-9244)
Outsourceone Inc ....E....612 436-2740 Minneapolis (G-5301)
Ovations Inc ....A....952 936-1300 Hopkins (G-2600)
Regency Hospital Co LLC ....C....763 588-2750 Minneapolis (G-5484)
Reliastar Life Insurance Co ....A....612 372-5432 Minneapolis (G-5507)
Ucare Minnesota ....B....612 676-6500 Minneapolis (G-5892)
Uniprise Inc ....A....763 765-0852 Plymouth (G-6889)
United Healthcare of Wyoming ....A....952 992-5450 Edina (G-1848)
▼ Unitedhealth Group Inc ....A....952 936-1300 Minnetonka (G-6232)

6331 Fire, Marine & Casualty Insurance

AAA Minnesota Iowa ....C....952 707-4222 Burnsville (G-670)
Athena Assurance Co ....E....651 310-7065 Saint Paul (G-8076)
Austin Mutual Insurance Co ....D....800 328-4628 Maple Grove (G-3237)
Discover Property & Casualty ....800 878-2660 Saint Paul (G-8299)
Employers Insurance Co of ....D....651 365-8053 Saint Paul (G-7760)
Employers Mutual Casualty Co ....E....952 938-4646 Hopkins (G-2539)
EPIC Holdings Inc ....E....952 997-4900 Saint Paul (G-7768)
Federated Mutual Insurance Co ....C....507 455-5200 Owatonna (G-6710)
Federated Mutual Insurance Co ....D....952 831-4300 Minneapolis (G-4422)
Federated Service Insurance Co ....C....507 455-5200 Owatonna (G-6712)
First Protection Corp ....E....952 473-0114 Minnetonka (G-6169)
General Casualty Co of WI ....D....952 941-0980 Eden Prairie (G-1673)
Great Northern Insurance Co ....D....612 373-7300 Minneapolis (G-4555)
Harleysville Insurance Co ....D....952 829-4000 Minneapolis (G-4598)
Liberty Mutual Insurance Co ....C....763 546-7550 Minneapolis (G-4870)
Mendota Insurance Co ....800 422-0792 Eagan (G-1536)
Midwest Family Mutual Insce ....D....952 545-6000 Hopkins (G-2583)
Northfield Insurance Co ....E....651 688-4100 Saint Paul (G-8762)
Northland Insurance Co ....B....651 688-4100 Saint Paul (G-8764)
Ram Mutual Insurance Co Inc ....D....218 879-3321 Esko (G-1922)
Rtw Inc ....D....952 893-0403 Minneapolis (G-5572)
SFM Mutual Insurance Co ....C....952 838-4200 Bloomington (G-514)
St Paul Fire & Marine Insce ....B....651 310-5000 Saint Paul (G-8989)
St Paul Fire & Marine Insce ....A....651 221-7911 Saint Paul (G-8990)
St Paul Fire & Marine Insce ....C....952 893-5602 Minneapolis (G-5730)
St Paul Guardian Insurance Co ....A....651 221-7911 Saint Paul (G-8991)
St Paul Mercury Insurance Co ....651 221-7911 Saint Paul (G-8994)
Wells Fargo Insurance Inc ....D....952 921-3601 Minneapolis (G-6049)
Western National Mutual Insce ....B....952 835-5350 Minneapolis (G-6060)

6351 Surety Insurance Carriers

Arch Capital Services ....E....651 855-7111 Saint Paul (G-8058)
Axa Advisors LLC ....D....612 243-3200 Minneapolis (G-3850)
Midwest Medical Insurance Co ....D....952 838-6700 Minneapolis (G-5034)
St Paul Fire & Marine Insce ....B....651 310-5000 Saint Paul (G-8989)
St Paul Fire & Marine Insce ....A....651 221-7911 Saint Paul (G-8990)

6361 Title Insurance

All American Title Co Inc ....E....763 225-8710 Minneapolis (G-3389)
Burnet Realty LLC ....B....952 844-6400 Minneapolis (G-3977)
Burnet Title LLC ....D....952 844-6200 Edina (G-1827)
Commercial Partners Title LLC ....E....612 337-2470 Minneapolis (G-4132)
Commonwealth Land Title Insce ....E....651 227-8571 Minneapolis (G-4135)
Complete Title Services LLC ....E....218 828-9611 Baxter (G-326)
Consolidated Title & Abstract ....E....218 722-1495 Duluth (G-1281)
First American National Cml ....E....612 305-2000 Minneapolis (G-4438)
Homeservices of America Inc ....E....888 485-0018 Minneapolis (G-4672)
Isgn Fulfillment Services Inc ....D....952 512-7400 Minneapolis (G-4736)
Land Title Inc ....D....651 638-1900 Saint Paul (G-8560)
Old Republic National Title ....C....612 371-1111 Minneapolis (G-5268)
Registered Abstractors Inc ....E....763 427-3012 Anoka (G-219)
RELS Title Services LLC ....D....952 933-8804 Hopkins (G-2614)
Stewart Title of Minnesota ....E....763 422-1116 Minneapolis (G-5756)
Tri-County Abstract & Title ....E....320 253-2096 Saint Cloud (G-7619)
Universal Title & Financial ....E....952 829-0899 Minneapolis (G-5922)
Walsh Title & Real Estate Svcs ....E....952 835-3320 Minneapolis (G-6017)

6371 Pension, Health & Welfare Funds

Alliance Benefit Group ....D....507 377-9344 Albert Lea (G-35)
Board of Pensions of The ....C....612 333-7651 Minneapolis (G-3920)
Clark & Wamberg LLC ....C....612 339-0919 Minneapolis (G-4102)
Federated Mutual Insurance Co ....C....507 455-5200 Owatonna (G-6710)
Firemens Relief Assns ....E....507 532-5141 Marshall (G-3295)
Public Employees Retirement ....D....651 296-7460 Saint Paul (G-8855)
Sheffield, Olson & McQueen Inc ....E....651 695-2500 Saint Paul (G-8951)

6399 Insurance Carriers, NEC

Bremer Financial Corp ....E....320 589-1026 Morris (G-6370)

64 INSURANCE AGENTS, BROKERS & SVCS

6411 Insurance Agents, Brokers & Svc

AG States Agency LLC ....E....651 355-6000 Inver Grove Heights (G-2735)
Allied Adjusters Inc ....E....612 766-3700 Minneapolis (G-3715)
American Financial Marketing ....D....763 593-0905 Minneapolis (G-3749)
American Hardware Insurance ....D....952 939-4510 Minnetonka (G-6139)
Ameriprise Financial Services ....C....612 671-3131 Minneapolis (G-3770)
Anderson Swenson Associates ....E....612 347-8600 Minneapolis (G-3778)
AON Corp ....C....952 656-8000 Minneapolis (G-3786)
AON Risk Services Central Inc ....C....952 656-8000 Minneapolis (G-3787)
Apollo Insurance Agency of St ....E....320 253-1122 Saint Cloud (G-7452)
ARAZ Group Inc ....D....952 896-1200 Minneapolis (G-3796)
Arthur A Hirman Agency Inc ....E....507 285-3111 Rochester (G-7060)
Arthur J Gallagher & Co ....E....952 944-8885 Minneapolis (G-3814)
Associated Financial Group LLC ....E....952 945-0200 Minnetonka (G-6144)
Bankers Life & Casualty Co ....E....952 835-2611 Minneapolis (G-3866)
Bcbsm Inc ....C....218 748-2700 Virginia (G-9736)
Berkley Risk Administrators Co ....E....651 281-1200 Saint Paul (G-8106)
Berkley Risk Administrators Co ....A....612 766-3000 Minneapolis (G-3887)
C N A Financial Corp ....D....952 285-3300 Saint Paul (G-7725)
C O Brown Agency Inc ....E....507 288-7600 Rochester (G-7069)
Catholic Aid Association ....E....651 490-0170 Saint Paul (G-8174)
Cedar Valley Conservation Club ....B....507 433-4937 Austin (G-264)
Christensen Group Inc ....D....952 653-1000 Hopkins (G-2530)
Citi Investor Services Inc ....B....218 825-5000 Baxter (G-324)
Citi Investor Services Inc ....B....218 829-4781 Baxter (G-325)
Citi Investor Services Inc ....E....218 825-0552 Brainerd (G-557)
Citizens Bancshares of ....E....320 587-2233 Hutchinson (G-2692)
Ciu ....E....952 469-5520 Lakeville (G-2895)
Clark & Wamberg LLC ....C....612 339-0919 Minneapolis (G-4102)
Columns Resource Group ....D....612 758-7600 Minneapolis (G-4125)
Combined Insurance Co of Amer ....D....952 933-2133 Eden Prairie (G-1632)
Corporate 4 Insurance Agency ....D....952 893-9218 Minneapolis (G-4163)
Crawford & Co ....E....651 631-0055 Saint Paul (G-8264)
D D P Marketing Inc ....D....952 808-7615 Burnsville (G-707)
Direct Response Insurance ....D....952 556-5600 Chanhassen (G-919)
Diversified Pharmaceutical ....952 820-7000 Minneapolis (G-4263)
EPIC Holdings Inc ....E....952 997-4900 Saint Paul (G-7768)
Erickson-Larsen Inc ....E....763 535-0055 Maple Grove (G-3240)
Evalumed ....E....651 767-0220 Saint Paul (G-8346)
Federated Mutual Insurance Co ....D....952 831-4300 Minneapolis (G-4422)
First McLeod Agency Inc ....320 864-5581 Glencoe (G-2205)
First State Bank South West ....507 376-9747 Worthington (G-10185)
Foster Klima & Co LLC ....D....612 746-2214 Minneapolis (G-4467)
Freedom Services Inc ....E....952 890-6524 Burnsville (G-724)
G E Young & Co ....E....952 847-2388 Minnetonka (G-6172)
Gary L Kemp Agency Inc ....651 457-3070 Saint Paul (G-7778)
Groebner Insurance Agency ....507 243-3102 Madison Lake (G-3082)
H C C Life Insurance Co ....E....877 843-5743 Hopkins (G-2547)
Hays Group Inc ....C....612 333-3323 Minneapolis (G-4613)
Heartman Agency Inc ....E....507 288-3834 Rochester (G-7136)
Holmes Hooper Inc ....D....763 545-5641 Minneapolis (G-4661)
Horizon Agency Inc ....E....952 944-2929 Eden Prairie (G-1687)
Icon Services Corp ....E....651 695-8778 Saint Paul (G-8503)
Insurance Paramedical Services ....D....952 226-2213 Prior Lake (G-6933)
▲ John B Collins Associates Inc ....C....952 820-1000 Minneapolis (G-4769)
Knw Group LLC ....E....952 593-0265 Hopkins (G-2566)
Kozlowski Insurance Agency ....507 825-3366 Pipestone (G-6831)
L H Hendrickson & Co Inc ....E....952 896-3456 Minneapolis (G-4827)
L L Brustad & Associates Inc ....952 842-1142 Wayzata (G-9923)
Lake Bank National Association ....E....218 834-2111 Two Harbors (G-9709)
Le Clair Insurance Services ....E....651 739-2010 Saint Paul (G-9241)
Lee F Murphy Inc ....E....651 644-7200 Saint Paul (G-8574)
Leneave Financial Group ....E....952 542-0777 Hopkins (G-2570)
Lincoln Financial Advisors ....E....952 933-8000 Hopkins (G-2571)
Lincoln Life & Annunity Co of ....D....612 373-7460 Minneapolis (G-4887)
Loge Group LLC ....C....952 829-3500 Minneapolis (G-4899)
Long Term Care Group Inc ....B....952 516-6829 Eden Prairie (G-1712)
Maguire Agency Inc ....E....651 638-9100 Saint Paul (G-8606)
Marsh USA Inc ....C....612 692-7848 Minneapolis (G-4958)
McGovern & Fisher Insurance ....D....952 996-8818 Minneapolis (G-4975)
Michael Dam ....E....952 831-1928 Minneapolis (G-5016)
Michael Erpelding ....E....651 647-1000 Saint Paul (G-8651)
Mid American Financial Group ....D....952 258-5000 Minnetonka (G-6194)
Midland Corporate Benefit Svcs ....320 485-3821 Winsted (G-10163)
Milliman Inc ....D....952 897-5300 Minneapolis (G-5046)
Minnesota Benefit Association ....E....651 739-4550 Saint Paul (G-9249)
Minnesota Chamber of Commerce ....E....651 292-4650 Saint Paul (G-8675)
Mmic ....C....952 838-6700 Minneapolis (G-5112)
Mmk International Marine Svcs ....E....507 263-0975 Cannon Falls (G-860)
N Bruce Christense ....D....952 653-1000 Hopkins (G-2585)
National Independent Brokers ....D....763 525-1111 Minneapolis (G-5164)

S I C

National Truck Underwriting....E....952 893-1234
Minneapolis (G-5169)
Noah Insurance Group....E....651 430-0085
Stillwater (G-9631)
North Star General Insurance....D....507 423-6262
Cottonwood (G-1114)
North Star Resource Group....C....612 617-6000
Minneapolis (G-5221)
North Western Research....E....218 327-4615
Grand Rapids (G-2299)
Northern Capital Commercial....D....952 996-8818
Minneapolis (G-5226)
Northwestern Mutual Life....E....651 456-9446
Mendota Heights (G-3368)
Novologix....E....952 826-2500
Eden Prairie (G-1734)
Osborne Properties LP....D....952 890-0414
Burnsville (G-771)
Osborne Properties LP....D....952 707-8200
Burnsville (G-772)
Otis-Magie Insurance Agency....E....218 722-7753
Duluth (G-1415)
Outsourceone Inc....E....612 436-2740
Minneapolis (G-5301)
Outsourceone Inc....E....612 338-7940
Minneapolis (G-5302)
Prime Therapeutics Inc....C....651 456-1000
Saint Paul (G-7881)
Prime West Central County....C....320 763-4135
Alexandria (G-118)
Primerica Financial Services....D....952 895-1091
Burnsville (G-782)
Principal Life Insurance Co....E....651 227-7717
Saint Paul (G-9265)
Prudential Insurance Co of....E....763 553-6056
Minneapolis (G-5436)
R J Ahmann Co....D....952 947-9761
Eden Prairie (G-1757)
Ram Mutual Insurance Co Inc....D....218 879-3321
Esko (G-1922)
RELS Title Services LLC....D....952 933-8804
Hopkins (G-2614)
Rjf Agencies Inc....C....763 746-8000
Minneapolis (G-5548)
Robert A Schneider Agency Inc....E....952 938-0655
Hopkins (G-2621)
Ross Nesbit Agencies Inc....E....952 941-9418
Eden Prairie (G-1768)
Rural Community Insurance Agcy....C....763 427-0290
Anoka (G-223)
Sandra Hamer....E....651 254-0116
Inver Grove Heights (G-2768)
Sebrite Agency Inc....E....952 563-1234
Minnetonka (G-6226)
Securian Financial Services....C....651 665-4244
Saint Paul (G-8945)
Sheffield, Olson & McQueen Inc....E....651 695-2500
Saint Paul (G-8951)
Signature Title Co....E....952 942-5155
Eden Prairie (G-1778)
Smart Data Solutions Inc....E....651 690-3140
Saint Paul (G-7906)
State Bank of Tower Inc....218 753-6100
Tower (G-9688)
State Farm Mutual Automobile....E....952 895-3900
Burnsville (G-803)
Stockbridge Insurance Co....A....651 631-7000
Saint Paul (G-9006)
Student Assurance Services Inc....E....651 439-7098
Stillwater (G-9649)
T C Field & Co....E....651 227-8405
Saint Paul (G-9022)
Tax-Sheltered Compensation Inc....E....952 806-4300
Minneapolis (G-5793)
▲ Thrivent Financial For....A....920 734-5721
Minneapolis (G-5819)
Thrivent Financial For....E....952 894-6772
Burnsville (G-808)
Thrivent Life Insurance Co....C....612 340-7000
Minneapolis (G-5820)
Towers Watson Pennsylvania Inc....E....952 842-5600
Minneapolis (G-5840)
Twin City Agency Inc....E....952 924-6900
Minneapolis (G-5876)
Twin City Group Inc....952 924-6900
Minneapolis (G-5880)
Twin City Risk Group Inc....E....952 924-6900
Minneapolis (G-5884)
◆ U S Bancorp....B....651 466-3000
Minneapolis (G-5885)
Unison Insurance....E....952 345-2305
Prior Lake (G-6960)
▼ Unitedhealth Group Inc....A....952 936-1300
Minnetonka (G-6232)
US Bancorp Information Svcs....A....651 466-3000
Saint Paul (G-9117)
Vern Cooper & Associates Inc....E....507 319-4139
Rochester (G-7281)
Waddell & Reed Inc....E....952 884-1503
Minneapolis (G-5992)
Wells Fargo Insurance Inc....E....612 667-5600
Minneapolis (G-6050)
Wells Fargo Insurance Services....C....952 830-3000
Minneapolis (G-6051)
Western Bank....E....651 290-8100
Saint Paul (G-9149)
Western Bank....E....651 290-8100
Saint Paul (G-9150)

Willis of Minnesota Inc....D....763 302-7100
Minneapolis (G-6071)
Winona Agency Inc....E....507 452-3366
Winona (G-10143)
Workman Financial Group Inc....E....763 746-9420
Minneapolis (G-6086)
Zurich North American Insce....D....952 229-3600
Edina (G-1850)

65 REAL ESTATE

6512 Operators Of Nonresidential Bldgs

A E I Fund Management Inc....E....800 328-3519
Saint Paul (G-7968)
American Investment Management....E....763 533-7193
Minneapolis (G-3754)
Arrowhead Town Hall....E....218 879-6916
Brookston (G-624)
Birchwood Lab Associates LLP....D....952 937-7900
Eden Prairie (G-1607)
Blainbrook Entertainment Ctr....D....763 755-8686
Minneapolis (G-3419)
Brookfield Commercial....C....612 372-1500
Minneapolis (G-3957)
Brookfield Development Inc....E....612 372-1230
Minneapolis (G-3958)
Cap Real Estate....E....651 488-5567
Saint Paul (G-8149)
Carver-Scott Cooperative....E....952 445-7524
Shakopee (G-9429)
Chem Vestments Inc....E....952 469-4965
Lakeville (G-2894)
City of Minneapolis....C....612 335-6000
Minneapolis (G-4091)
Colliers Towle Valuation....612 347-9336
Minneapolis (G-4120)
Commerce Partners LLC....D....651 292-8777
Saint Paul (G-8227)
Diversified Motel Properties....C....218 728-3601
Duluth (G-1294)
DLM A MN LLP....E....218 233-0065
Moorhead (G-6312)
DMW Properties Inc....D....763 432-3401
Minneapolis (G-4267)
Donatelle Properties....C....651 633-4200
Saint Paul (G-8307)
Dp Property Acquisition LLC....E....612 344-1515
Minneapolis (G-4286)
Duke Co's....D....612 331-4880
Minneapolis (G-4289)
Duke Realty Corp....D....952 543-2900
Minneapolis (G-4291)
Duluth 10 Theater....E....218 722-1573
Duluth (G-1296)
Duluth Entertainment Conv....A....218 722-5573
Duluth (G-1298)
E Weinberg Supply Co Inc....E....952 920-0888
Minneapolis (G-4303)
Fitgers On The Lake LLC....C....218 727-9077
Duluth (G-1325)
Gac Development LLC....E....507 289-5556
Rochester (G-7123)
Giannetti Properties LLC....C....651 738-2168
Saint Paul (G-9220)
Gladstone Partners....E....651 455-2940
Saint Paul (G-7781)
Grace Management Inc....A....763 544-9934
Minneapolis (G-4544)
Greg Gruman....E....763 546-1177
Minneapolis (G-4565)
Happy Chef Systems Inc....E....507 345-4571
Mankato (G-3134)
Healtheast Diversified Svcs....651 232-2300
Saint Paul (G-8461)
Highland Management Group Inc....E....952 925-1020
Minneapolis (G-4647)
Hillcrest Development, Lllp....E....612 371-0123
Minneapolis (G-4648)
Hohenwald Properties....D....651 735-1333
Saint Paul (G-9232)
Holly Properties....D....507 388-6265
Mankato (G-3142)
IFP Inc....D....507 334-2730
Faribault (G-2013)
Italian American Club of....D....612 781-0625
Minneapolis (G-4740)
J R & R Partnership....D....507 532-9566
Marshall (G-3300)
Kraus-Anderson Inc....E....612 332-7281
Minneapolis (G-4823)
Lansing Mall LP....E....763 566-3373
Minneapolis (G-4842)
Lansing Mall LP....D....320 252-2856
Saint Cloud (G-7543)
Luthern Brothern School Inc....D....218 739-3375
Fergus Falls (G-2091)
▲ Maiers Transport & Warehousing....E....320 251-6882
Saint Cloud (G-7547)
▲ Meritex Enterprises Inc....E....651 855-9700
Minneapolis (G-4992)
Metro Parkway Assoc....E....952 854-4244
Minneapolis (G-5002)
Metropolitan Sports Facilities....D....612 332-0386
Minneapolis (G-5008)
Minnehaha Bowling Center Inc....E....651 488-7208
Saint Paul (G-8671)

Minnesota State Agricultural....D....651 288-4400
Saint Paul (G-8705)
Moac Mall Holdings LLC....A....952 883-8810
Bloomington (G-507)
Mocco Enterprises Inc....E....507 537-1421
Marshall (G-3315)
Model Cities of St Paul Inc....651 632-8350
Saint Paul (G-8717)
Nico Properties....D....612 822-2185
Minneapolis (G-5199)
9900 Properties....E....952 881-5825
Minneapolis (G-5204)
North Coast Partners LLP....E....952 947-3000
Minneapolis (G-5214)
North Way Investment Co....E....651 646-7901
Saint Paul (G-8755)
180 Degrees Inc....E....612 813-5010
Minneapolis (G-5281)
Oneida Realty Co Inc....D....218 722-0816
Duluth (G-1413)
Osborne Properties LP....D....952 707-8200
Burnsville (G-772)
Osborne Properties LP....E....952 881-8166
Minneapolis (G-5296)
Osborne Properties LP....E....952 881-8166
Bloomington (G-508)
Pattern Stations Inc....D....763 441-6833
Monticello (G-6282)
Penco Leasing Corp....E....612 927-4748
Minneapolis (G-5362)
Playworks Dakota....D....952 445-7529
Prior Lake (G-6948)
Public Markets Inc....E....763 546-3139
Minneapolis (G-5437)
Quest Management Associates....E....612 379-3800
Minneapolis (G-5449)
Rbc Wealth Management....A....612 371-7750
Minneapolis (G-5472)
Real Estate Equites Inc....E....651 227-6925
Saint Paul (G-8876)
Red Wing Hotel Corp....C....651 388-2846
Red Wing (G-6998)
Ryan Co's US Inc....B....612 492-4000
Minneapolis (G-5579)
SA Group Properties Inc....D....612 303-7833
Minneapolis (G-5583)
Saint Paul Burlington LP....C....651 228-9456
Saint Paul (G-8924)
Schadegg Properties LLC....D....651 292-9933
South Saint Paul (G-9542)
Sexton Partners....C....651 457-9255
Saint Paul (G-7902)
Shaddric & Le Beau Housing....E....763 784-9824
Minneapolis (G-3600)
Shelard Group Inc....E....952 941-7493
Eden Prairie (G-1777)
Siewert Construction Co Inc....651 437-1728
Hastings (G-2405)
Six Hundred Washington....D....612 331-9041
Minneapolis (G-5684)
614 Co....E....612 333-6128
Minneapolis (G-5685)
St Cloud Denovo....D....320 251-1055
Saint Cloud (G-7598)
Structural Wood Corp....E....651 426-8111
Saint Paul (G-9010)
Talisman Brookdale LLC....E....763 566-3373
Minneapolis (G-5787)
Tamarack Village Shopping Cent....E....651 702-6311
Saint Paul (G-9280)
Timberland Partners Management....D....952 893-1216
Minneapolis (G-5827)
Tofte Management Co LLC....C....218 663-7296
Tofte (G-9684)
Tri City American Legion....E....651 631-1124
Saint Paul (G-9080)
Trimark Hotel Corp....C....612 305-9763
Minneapolis (G-5856)
Weeres Pontoon....D....320 251-3551
Saint Cloud (G-7631)
Wellington Management Inc....E....651 292-9844
Saint Paul (G-9144)
Western Bank....E....651 290-8100
Saint Paul (G-9150)
Wise Greenwald & Greenwald PC....D....763 535-0501
Minneapolis (G-6080)
Wkt Properties LLC....E....763 525-4000
Minneapolis (G-6081)

6513 Operators Of Apartment Buildings

Accessible Space North Inc....D....651 645-7271
Saint Paul (G-7977)
Amherst H Wilder Foundation....C....651 220-1700
Saint Paul (G-8041)
Annandale Congregate Housing....D....320 274-3737
Annandale (G-135)
Apple Valley Villa Apartments....E....952 236-2600
Saint Paul (G-7703)
Asi Great Falls Inc....E....651 645-7271
Saint Paul (G-8067)
Asi Missoula Inc....E....651 645-7271
Saint Paul (G-8068)
Augustana Chapel View Homes....B....612 333-1551
Minneapolis (G-3835)
Augustana Chapel View Homes....C....952 938-2761
Hopkins (G-2512)

SIC

Employment codes: A=Over 500 employees, B=251-500
C=101-250, D=51-100, E=25-50
2011 Harris Minnesota
Services Directory
© Harris InfoSource 1-866-281-6415
483

Augustana Dassel Lakeside Com....D....320 275-3308
Dassel (G-1159)
Augustana Regent At Burnsville....D....952 898-1910
Burnsville (G-682)
B T & A Construction Co....D....612 825-6811
Minneapolis (G-3854)
Big Stone Community Homes Inc....E....320 839-6139
Ortonville (G-6578)
Bigos Properties....E....952 938-6329
Minneapolis (G-3903)
Bii Di Gain Dash Anwebi Elder....D....651 291-1750
Minneapolis (G-3904)
Brookfield Commercial....C....612 372-1500
Minneapolis (G-3957)
Calhoun Shores Apartments....E....612 824-7505
Minneapolis (G-3993)
Carefree Living of America....E....952 988-0011
Brainerd (G-556)
Cashill Spaulding Properties....E....651 225-8227
Saint Paul (G-8172)
Cathedral Hill Homes LP....D....651 291-1750
Saint Paul (G-8173)
Cbc 202 LP....D....651 291-1750
Rogers (G-7320)
Cedars of Edina Apartments....E....952 835-3388
Minneapolis (G-4039)
Centennial Villa Apartments....E....320 274-3737
Annandale (G-139)
Chapelwood Community....E....763 493-5910
Osseo (G-6602)
Charterhouse Inc....C....507 266-8572
Rochester (G-7075)
Chosen Valley Care Center Inc....C....507 867-4220
Chatfield (G-986)
Colonial Village Apartments....E....218 739-3795
Fergus Falls (G-2068)
Commerce Partners LLC....D....651 292-8777
Saint Paul (G-8227)
Community Housing & Service....E....952 933-1833
Minneapolis (G-4142)
Community Memorial Home Inc....D....320 859-2111
Osakis (G-6586)
Crest View Corp....D....763 788-2020
Minneapolis (G-3448)
Croixdale Apts....D....651 275-4800
Bayport (G-347)
Crossroads At Penn Apartments....E....612 866-3628
Minneapolis (G-4187)
Dominium Management Services....E....763 560-0244
Minneapolis (G-4273)
Edgebrook Care Center....D....507 442-7121
Edgerton (G-1823)
▲ Family Resources Development....E....651 578-0676
Saint Paul (G-9216)
Fine Associates LLC....E....612 332-2561
Minneapolis (G-4434)
Foundation For Healthcare....B....320 253-1920
Sartell (G-9328)
France Avenue LLC....C....952 831-0343
Minneapolis (G-4472)
Franklin Co-Op....E....612 338-4574
Minneapolis (G-4474)
Governor's Inc....E....651 778-1045
Saint Paul (G-8425)
Grace Management Inc....A....763 544-9934
Minneapolis (G-4544)
Grand Heritage Properties LLC....D....651 699-3003
Saint Paul (G-8426)
Grandview Manor HRA Office....D....218 529-6300
Duluth (G-1340)
Griffin Co's....E....612 338-2828
Minneapolis (G-4569)
Guardian Angels Health Svcs....C....763 441-1213
Elk River (G-1880)
Gunflint Lodge Inc....E....218 388-2294
Grand Marais (G-2261)
Harvest Facility Holdings LP....E....651 779-9255
Saint Paul (G-9223)
Heritage Estates....E....651 735-1776
Saint Paul (G-8477)
Heritage Park Estates....E....320 240-7939
Saint Cloud (G-7528)
Highland Management Group Inc....E....952 925-1020
Minneapolis (G-4647)
Isle View Apartments....E....320 676-8624
Isle (G-2783)
JAS Apartments Inc....E....612 872-4444
Minneapolis (G-4755)
Joshco Construction Inc....D....952 361-8000
Chaska (G-971)
Lang-Nelson Associates Inc....E....763 533-9389
Minneapolis (G-4840)
Larry Davis....E....507 372-7774
Worthington (G-10187)
Lloyd Management Inc....D....507 625-5573
Mankato (G-3157)
Loring Towers Apts LP....D....612 871-7202
Minneapolis (G-4903)
Mailand Management Corp....651 451-9034
Saint Paul (G-7830)
Maple Hills LP....D....651 291-1750
Saint Paul (G-8611)
Maple Hills LP....D....651 291-1750
Red Wing (G-6990)
Marshall Asi Inc....E....651 645-7271
Saint Paul (G-8616)
Mill Street Residence Inc....E....218 739-2900
Fergus Falls (G-2094)
Minnesota Masonic Home North....A....763 592-3000
Minneapolis (G-5083)
Miramar Inc....E....763 559-2527
Minneapolis (G-5108)
Model Cities of St Paul Inc....651 632-8350
Saint Paul (G-8717)
North Point....E....507 344-0059
North Mankato (G-6511)
Northern Itasca Hospital Dist....C....218 743-3177
Bigfork (G-461)
Oakdale-Granada Lakes LP....D....651 291-1750
Saint Paul (G-8778)
Park Brooklyn Housing Assocs....D....763 354-5500
Minneapolis (G-5328)
Partners For Senior....D....952 831-4084
Minneapolis (G-5341)
Phalen Village Apartments....D....651 771-5625
Saint Paul (G-8822)
Phase I Rice-Marion....E....763 540-8600
Saint Paul (G-8823)
Pioneer Home Inc....C....218 739-7701
Fergus Falls (G-2113)
Presbyterian Homes of Arden....A....651 631-6000
Saint Paul (G-8843)
Presbyterian Homes, Housing....A....651 631-6100
Saint Paul (G-8844)
Public Markets Inc....E....763 546-3139
Minneapolis (G-5437)
Rbc Wealth Management....A....612 371-7750
Minneapolis (G-5472)
Real Estate Equites Inc....E....651 227-6925
Saint Paul (G-8876)
Reprise Associates....E....763 566-5416
Minneapolis (G-5520)
Richard Sigert....D....218 444-1875
Bemidji (G-422)
Riverside Plaza LP....E....612 338-8925
Minneapolis (G-5545)
Rose Arbor....D....763 493-5910
Osseo (G-6656)
Sauer Memorial Home....E....507 454-5540
Winona (G-10125)
Shepherd Good Lutheran Home....C....320 252-6525
Sauk Rapids (G-9374)
Shepherd Good Lutheran Home....E....320 258-8665
Sauk Rapids (G-9375)
Sholom Community Alliance....E....952 939-1601
Minneapolis (G-5657)
Sholom St Paul Senior Housing....D....651 328-2022
Saint Paul (G-8953)
Siewert Construction Co Inc....651 437-1728
Hastings (G-2405)
Silvercross Properties....E....952 925-6231
Minneapolis (G-5675)
St Therese Apartments Inc....D....763 531-5400
Minneapolis (G-5732)
St Therese South West Inc....E....952 933-3333
Hopkins (G-2637)
Stephen Scott Management Inc....E....763 540-8600
Minneapolis (G-5751)
Steven Scott Management Inc....E....952 540-8600
Minneapolis (G-5754)
Stewartville Nursing Home Inc....C....507 533-4288
Stewartville (G-9594)
Tuff Memorial Homes Inc....D....507 962-3275
Hills (G-2482)
Twv LP....D....651 291-1750
Minneapolis (G-3626)
Twv LP....D....651 291-1750
Saint Paul (G-9096)
United Properties Investment....E....952 893-8272
Bloomington (G-523)
Walker Plaza....E....763 422-1226
Anoka (G-239)
Warroad Care Center Inc....D....218 386-1235
Warroad (G-9872)
Wayzata Partners LP....D....952 920-5338
Minneapolis (G-6028)
Wayzata Partners LP....E....763 473-3200
Wayzata (G-9949)
Willows....E....763 533-1883
Minneapolis (G-6073)
Yorkdale Townhomes Inc....D....651 291-1750
Saint Paul (G-9180)

6514 Operators Of Dwellings, Except Apartments

Brookfield Commercial....C....612 372-1500
Minneapolis (G-3957)
Hornig Properties Inc....E....612 874-4400
Minneapolis (G-4675)
Jim Bern Co....E....952 854-4141
Minneapolis (G-4764)

6515 Operators of Residential Mobile Home Sites

Hometown America LLC....E....651 436-2790
Lake Elmo (G-2873)
Landfall Terrace Inc....E....651 739-8284
Saint Paul (G-9240)
Sunrise Estates Mobile Home....E....651 462-4047
Stacy (G-9581)

6519 Lessors Of Real Estate, NEC

Coop Tricounty....E....320 748-7187
Graceville (G-2253)
Employers Mutual Casualty Co....E....952 938-4646
Hopkins (G-2539)
Kohner Realty Co Inc....E....507 454-5093
Winona (G-10108)
Robert A Williams Enterprises....E....763 788-1113
Minneapolis (G-3589)
Theodore F Bolles....D....651 731-9436
Saint Paul (G-9281)
Thomas Furlong....E....651 437-2518
Hastings (G-2408)
Upper Minnesota Properties Inc....E....218 722-2641
Duluth (G-1494)
Wagers Business Systems Inc....D....651 644-3830
Saint Paul (G-7943)

6531 Real Estate Agents & Managers

A E I Fund Management Inc....E....800 328-3519
Saint Paul (G-7968)
AAA-American Co....E....507 894-4156
Hokah (G-2490)
Access Information Systems Inc....C....952 888-8503
Minneapolis (G-3666)
Accessible Space Inc....E....651 645-7271
Saint Paul (G-7975)
American Investment Management....E....763 533-7193
Minneapolis (G-3754)
Asset Management Group Inc....D....952 546-3385
Minneapolis (G-3821)
Associates Plus Inc....E....651 484-8800
Saint Paul (G-8074)
Associates Plus Inc....D....763 784-1400
Minneapolis (G-3412)
Associates Plus Inc....C....763 323-8080
Anoka (G-156)
Atlas Pet Supply Inc....E....763 753-4818
Anoka (G-157)
Atwood Land Co Inc....507 388-9375
Mankato (G-3107)
Bce Development Corp....E....612 372-1500
Minneapolis (G-3876)
Bcr Real Estate Services....E....320 532-4099
Onamia (G-6566)
Becker Meggy Rl Est....E....507 388-8469
Mankato (G-3109)
Becketwood Cooperative Inc....E....612 722-4077
Minneapolis (G-3877)
Belgrade Commerical Club....E....320 254-8271
Belgrade (G-362)
Brandl Anderson Homes Inc....E....952 898-0231
Saint Paul (G-7723)
Brookfield Development Inc....E....612 372-1230
Minneapolis (G-3958)
Brookpark Group....E....763 424-8525
Minneapolis (G-3961)
Bruce Johnson....E....218 284-6555
Moorhead (G-6300)
Burnet Homeselling Team....D....651 653-2520
Saint Paul (G-8141)
Burnet Realty Inc....E....651 430-2100
Stillwater (G-9603)
Burnet Realty LLC....B....952 844-6400
Minneapolis (G-3977)
C B Richard Ellis Inc....B....952 278-2106
Minneapolis (G-3981)
Campground Marketing Services....D....218 562-4204
Pequot Lakes (G-6786)
◆ Carlson Hotels Management Corp....C....763 212-5000
Minneapolis (G-4016)
Carlson Real Estate Co, A MN....E....952 404-5050
Minnetonka (G-6154)
Cashill Spaulding Properties....E....651 225-8227
Saint Paul (G-8172)
Cassidy Turley Midwest Inc....D....612 341-4444
Minneapolis (G-4026)
Castle Realty Inc....E....320 251-1010
Saint Cloud (G-7472)
CB Richard Ellis Inc....D....952 924-4600
Minneapolis (G-4032)
Center City Housing Corp....E....218 722-7161
Duluth (G-1264)
Century 21 Care Realty....E....763 862-5690
Minneapolis (G-4049)
Century 21 Jay Blank Realty....E....651 645-5581
Saint Paul (G-8184)
Century 21 Luger Realty Inc....E....952 925-3901
Minneapolis (G-4050)
Charles Stout....E....651 426-1671
Saint Paul (G-8188)
Cold Well Banker At Your Svc....E....507 285-9115
Rochester (G-7085)
Coldwell Banker Burnet....E....952 820-4663
Minneapolis (G-4116)
Coldwell Banker Burnet Inc....D....952 920-1224
Eden Prairie (G-1630)
Coldwell Banker Burnet Inc....D....952 474-2525
Excelsior (G-1942)
Coldwell Banker Burnet Inc....D....952 898-5100
Burnsville (G-700)
Coldwell Banker Burnet Inc....E....651 690-8516
Saint Paul (G-8221)
Coldwell Banker Burnet Real....D....763 754-5400
Minneapolis (G-3436)

S I C

(G-00000) Company's Geographic Section entry number
484
2011 Harris Minnesota Services Directory
▲=Import ▼=Export ◆=Import/Export

Coldwell Banker Burnet Realty ....D 651 227-9144
Saint Paul (G-8222)
Coldwell Banker Burnet Realty ....E 763 682-2882
Buffalo (G-643)
Coldwell Banker Burnett Real ....D 651 698-2481
Saint Paul (G-8223)
Coldwell Banker Vision ....D 763 241-0155
Elk River (G-1868)
Colliers Towle Valuation 612 347-9336
Minneapolis (G-4120)
Collopy & Saunders Real Estate 952 829-2900
Eden Prairie (G-1631)
Commonbond Housing ....E 651 291-1750
Saint Paul (G-8232)
Commonbond Investment Corp ....D 651 291-1750
Saint Paul (G-8233)
Community Development Inc ....E 763 225-6412
Minneapolis (G-4140)
Community Finance Group Inc ....E 763 416-5959
Minneapolis (G-4141)
Counselor Realty Inc ....D 763 786-0600
Minneapolis (G-3443)
Counselor Realty Inc ....C 763 420-7080
Osseo (G-6605)
Counselor Realty Inc ....D 952 475-9500
Wayzata (G-9912)
Counselor Realty Inc ....E 952 921-0911
Minneapolis (G-4167)
Counselor Realty Inc ....E 651 779-6000
Saint Paul (G-8256)
Crossroads South Metro Inc ....E 651 698-8006
Saint Paul (G-8269)
Cushman & Wakefield Inc ....D 612 659-1743
Minneapolis (G-4201)
Cushman & Wakefield Inc ....E 612 671-7593
Minneapolis (G-4202)
Cushman & Wakefield Inc ....E 763 450-3600
Eden Prairie (G-1639)
Dakota County Abstract & Title ....E 651 437-5600
Hastings (G-2381)
Dinnaken Properties Inc ....E 612 623-3634
Minneapolis (G-4257)
Dominium Management Services ....C 763 354-5500
Minneapolis (G-4274)
Donald A Driggs ....E 952 471-9500
Wayzata (G-9915)
Duane Sauke ....E 507 287-7742
Rochester (G-7099)
Edina Realty ....D 952 844-5409
Minneapolis (G-4320)
Edina Realty ....D 651 450-6876
Eagan (G-1526)
Edina Realty Home Services ....E 763 567-7000
Minneapolis (G-4324)
Edina Realty Home Services ....D 651 481-6711
Saint Paul (G-8324)
Edina Realty Home Services ....D 763 755-1300
Minneapolis (G-3463)
Edina Realty Home Services ....E 612 827-3551
Minneapolis (G-4322)
Edina Realty Home Services ....D 763 295-3456
Monticello (G-6270)
Edina Realty Home Services ....D 952 928-5900
Minneapolis (G-4325)
Edina Realty Home Services ....D 651 770-1775
Saint Paul (G-8323)
Edina Realty Home Services ....E 763 545-5000
Minneapolis (G-4323)
Edina Realty Home Services ....D 651 430-3200
Stillwater (G-9613)
Edina Realty Home Services ....E 651 636-2299
Minneapolis (G-3464)
Edina Realty Home Services ....D 763 559-2894
Minneapolis (G-4321)
Edina Realty Home Services ....D 507 288-7665
Rochester (G-7103)
Edina Realty Home Services ....D 952 892-7000
Lakeville (G-2904)
Edina Realty Home Services ....D 651 426-7172
Saint Paul (G-8325)
Edina Realty Home Services ....E 320 762-8181
Alexandria (G-99)
Edina Realty Home Services ....D 651 698-2434
Saint Paul (G-8326)
Edina Realty Home Services ....D 952 442-1700
Chanhassen (G-921)
Edina Realty Home Services ....D 952 944-7107
Eden Prairie (G-1651)
Elcor Realty of Rochester Inc ....E 507 282-3345
Rochester (G-7104)
▲ Equity Transwestern LLC ....E 612 343-4200
Minneapolis (G-4366)
Execu Systems Inc ....E 218 444-1021
Bemidji (G-391)
Fbs Associated Properties Inc 612 333-2086
Minneapolis (G-4417)
First Realty GMAC ....E 218 751-2511
Bemidji (G-395)
Forsythe Appraisals LLC ....D 651 486-9550
Saint Paul (G-8391)
France Avenue LLC ....C 952 831-0343
Minneapolis (G-4472)
Gary Thaler ....E 651 464-5555
Forest Lake (G-2145)
Gassen Co Inc ....E 952 922-5575
Eden Prairie (G-1671)
Genex Cooperative Inc ....E 952 758-2561
New Prague (G-6427)
Gittleman Management Corp ....E 952 277-2700
Minneapolis (G-4528)
Gold Key Realty ....E 952 431-5751
Saint Paul (G-7786)
Greencastle Condominium Assn ....E 320 587-4040
Hutchinson (G-2697)
Gsr Real Estate Services LLC ....D 612 338-2828
Minneapolis (G-4575)
Hempel Properties Inc ....E 612 355-2600
Minneapolis (G-4629)
Hennepin County ....D 612 348-3050
Minneapolis (G-4634)
Herges Realty Inc ....E 320 253-1366
Saint Cloud (G-7527)
Hillco Real Estate Holdings ....E 320 532-3237
Onamia (G-6571)
Home Smart Realty & Logo Dsgn ....E 763 421-0481
Anoka (G-191)
Homeservices of America Inc ....E 888 485-0018
Minneapolis (G-4672)
Hometown America LLC ....E 651 436-2790
Lake Elmo (G-2873)
Isgn Fulfillment Services Inc ....D 952 512-7400
Minneapolis (G-4736)
Izatys Group LLC ....E 320 532-3101
Onamia (G-6573)
Jackson Street Associates LLC ....E 651 228-9456
Saint Paul (G-8528)
Jeremiah Saint Paul LP ....E 612 259-3001
Minneapolis (G-4760)
Jim Conway ....E 507 287-7717
Rochester (G-7146)
JMS Equities Inc ....E 952 949-3630
Minneapolis (G-4767)
Jones Dw Management ....E 218 547-3307
Park Rapids (G-6758)
Jordan Realty Inc ....E 612 827-3844
Minneapolis (G-4779)
K M S Management Inc ....C 952 593-9930
Minneapolis (G-4784)
Keller Williams Premier Realty ....D 507 424-4422
Rochester (G-7151)
Keller Williams Realty Inc ....E 952 746-9696
Lakeville (G-2914)
Kit Fucile ....D 952 435-3030
Burnsville (G-742)
Kleinman Realty Co ....D 763 572-9400
Minneapolis (G-3510)
Kraus-Anderson Realty Co ....E 952 881-8166
Minneapolis (G-4824)
KSA Real Estate Services Inc ....E 651 290-0507
Saint Paul (G-8551)
Lakes Area Realty Inc 612 874-1916
Minneapolis (G-4835)
Land Title Inc ....D 651 638-1900
Saint Paul (G-8560)
Lang-Nelson Associates Inc ....E 952 920-0400
Minneapolis (G-4841)
Leinvestors Inc ....E 952 854-1114
Bloomington (G-503)
Life Style Inc ....D 507 451-8524
Owatonna (G-6722)
Linda Waterman ....D 507 287-7741
Rochester (G-7161)
▲ Meritex Enterprises Inc ....E 651 855-9700
Minneapolis (G-4992)
Metes & Bounds Management Co 612 861-8526
Minneapolis (G-4999)
Minnesota Dakota Generating Co 218 739-8200
Fergus Falls (G-2096)
Minnesota Real State Service ....E 952 928-4640
Minneapolis (G-5092)
Minnesota Street Associates ....D 651 225-3666
Saint Paul (G-8707)
MLS Online ....D 763 427-0539
Champlin (G-896)
Nelson Co's ....E 507 289-6789
Rochester (G-7189)
New Concepts Management Group ....E 952 922-2500
Minneapolis (G-5187)
New Concepts Management Group ....E 952 922-2500
Saint Paul (G-8747)
New Homes Realty Inc ....E 952 469-6003
Lakeville (G-2921)
New Life Multi-Family Mgt ....C 952 831-0866
Edina (G-1839)
Nuvo Network Management ....D 952 933-4600
Hopkins (G-2592)
Oneida Realty Co Inc ....D 218 722-0816
Duluth (G-1413)
Opus Corp ....C 952 656-4444
Hopkins (G-2597)
P D Management, LLP ....E 612 281-1464
Lakeville (G-2943)
P H M Eaglecrest Inc ....E 651 628-3000
Saint Paul (G-8799)
Pederson Team ....E 218 692-5253
Crosslake (G-1153)
Perennial Management LLC ....E 651 644-9600
Saint Paul (G-8818)
Peterson Group Management Corp ....E 952 835-9232
Minneapolis (G-5370)
Pine Ridge Homes Inc ....D 218 879-1257
Cloquet (G-1059)
Planned Investments Inc ....E 952 920-3890
Minneapolis (G-5388)
Positive Realty & Investment ....E 218 829-1777
Brainerd (G-582)
Property Solutions & Services ....E 612 746-0400
Minneapolis (G-5430)
Prudential Sundial Realty Inc ....E 763 571-9200
Minneapolis (G-3578)
Prudential Pladson Realty Inc ....E 320 253-9074
Saint Cloud (G-7576)
Prudential Truscott Realtors ....E 218 726-1255
Duluth (G-1430)
Quest Management Associates ....E 612 379-3800
Minneapolis (G-5449)
R M L S Minnesota ....E 651 251-5458
Saint Paul (G-8866)
Radisson Hotels International ....C 763 212-5000
Minnetonka (G-6218)
RE Max Advisors ....E 952 898-1112
Burnsville (G-785)
RE MAX of Rochester ....E 507 287-7735
Rochester (G-7219)
RE Max Real Estate Properties ....D 763 755-1100
Minneapolis (G-3580)
Real Estate Equities Inc ....D 651 227-6925
Saint Paul (G-8877)
Real Estate Masters Inc ....C 651 484-4818
Saint Paul (G-8878)
Real Services Inc ....E 218 728-5161
Duluth (G-1432)
RELS LLC ....A 952 933-8804
Hopkins (G-2613)
Remax Northern Properties ....E 218 263-8877
Hibbing (G-2474)
Remax Realty Source ....E 320 251-2200
Saint Cloud (G-7587)
Rick Gentling ....E 507 287-7714
Rochester (G-7225)
Roger Illies Realtor ....E 320 685-8119
Cold Spring (G-1090)
Sela Investments Ltd, LLP ....E 952 925-3878
Minneapolis (G-5630)
Shelard Group Inc ....E 952 941-7493
Eden Prairie (G-1777)
614 Co ....E 612 333-6128
Minneapolis (G-5685)
Spectrum Property Management ....E 952 853-0036
Minneapolis (G-5719)
Steven Scott Management Inc ....E 952 540-8600
Minneapolis (G-5754)
Timberland Partners Management ....D 952 893-1216
Minneapolis (G-5827)
Tower Hill Association ....E 763 682-2321
Buffalo (G-658)
Trammell Crow Co ....D 952 936-3671
Minnetonka (G-6229)
United Property Investment LLC ....C 952 831-1000
Minneapolis (G-5914)
United Water New Rochelle Inc ....E 952 820-1666
Minneapolis (G-5917)
Upi Property Management Group ....D 612 870-8500
Minneapolis (G-5934)
Value Realty Inc ....E 952 898-0230
Saint Paul (G-7941)
Walsh Title & Real Estate Svcs ....E 952 835-3320
Minneapolis (G-6017)
Walter W Culbert Jr ....E 218 741-8026
Virginia (G-9763)
Watson Centers Inc ....D 612 920-5034
Minneapolis (G-6023)
Welsh Co's LLC ....C 952 897-7700
Minnetonka (G-6236)
White Earth Housing Authority ....E 218 473-4663
Waubun (G-9901)
Young, Quinlan Assoc LLP ....E 612 337-5109
Minneapolis (G-6105)
Zweber LLC ....E 952 440-4653
Lakeville (G-2944)

6541 Title Abstract Offices

Access Information Systems Inc ....C 952 888-8503
Minneapolis (G-3666)
Burnet Title LLC ....D 952 844-6200
Edina (G-1827)
Capitol Lien Records & Res ....E 651 488-0100
Saint Paul (G-8154)
Collopy & Saunders Real Estate 952 829-2900
Eden Prairie (G-1631)
Consolidated Title & Abstract ....E 218 722-1495
Duluth (G-1281)
Dakota County Abstract & Title ....E 651 437-5600
Hastings (G-2381)
DCA Title Co ....E 952 432-5600
Saint Paul (G-7749)
Edina Realty Home Services ....D 952 928-5900
Minneapolis (G-4325)
Edina Realty Title ....D 952 928-5181
Minneapolis (G-4326)
First American Title Insurance ....E 612 337-5900
Minneapolis (G-4440)
Isgn Fulfillment Services Inc ....D 952 512-7400
Minneapolis (G-4736)
Lutheran Trust ....E 218 998-4058
Fergus Falls (G-2090)
North Star Title Inc ....D 952 512-7400
Minneapolis (G-5222)
Northwest Title & Escrow Inc ....E 651 490-9056
Saint Paul (G-8769)
Registered Abstractors Inc ....E 763 427-3012
Anoka (G-219)

SIC

Employment codes: A=Over 500 employees, B=251-500
C=101-250, D=51-100, E=25-50
2011 Harris Minnesota
Services Directory
© Harris InfoSource 1-866-281-6415
485

Rels Title Services LLC ....E..651 647-4855
  Saint Paul *(G-8887)*
RELS Title Services LLC ....D..952 933-8804
  Hopkins *(G-2614)*
Tri-County Abstract & Title ....E..320 253-2096
  Saint Cloud *(G-7619)*

6552 Land Subdividers & Developers

A B Systems Inc ....E..507 288-9397
  Rochester *(G-7042)*
Allete Inc ....C..218 279-5000
  Duluth *(G-1235)*
Bce Development Corp ....E..612 372-1500
  Minneapolis *(G-3876)*
Beaumont Leased Housing Assocs ....D..763 354-5500
  Plymouth *(G-6851)*
Beaumont Leased Housing Assocs ....D..763 354-5500
  Plymouth *(G-6850)*
Blackforest Developers LLC ....E..612 872-9200
  Minneapolis *(G-3911)*
Brookpark Group ....E..763 424-8525
  Minneapolis *(G-3961)*
◆ Carlson Hotels Management Corp ...C..763 212-5000
  Minneapolis *(G-4016)*
Commonbond Communities ....D..651 291-1750
  Saint Paul *(G-8231)*
Dominium Group Inc ....D..763 354-5500
  Minneapolis *(G-4272)*
E T C Enterprises Inc ....E..320 240-0567
  Saint Cloud *(G-7500)*
Fbs Associated Properties Inc 612 333-2086
  Minneapolis *(G-4417)*
Fenway Development Inc ....D..651 429-8032
  Saint Paul *(G-8373)*
Fine Associates LLC ....E..612 332-2561
  Minneapolis *(G-4434)*
Houston Leased Housing Assocs .....D..763 354-5500
  Plymouth *(G-6865)*
Keystone Bluffs ....E..218 727-2800
  Duluth *(G-1370)*
Liberty Property Trust ....E..952 947-1100
  Eden Prairie *(G-1709)*
Mdi LP 38 ....E..651 646-7848
  Saint Paul *(G-8627)*
MSP Real Estate Inc ....C..952 351-4540
  Minneapolis *(G-5145)*
Odyssey Development Inc ....E..218 728-8060
  Duluth *(G-1412)*
Opus Corp ....C..952 656-4444
  Hopkins *(G-2597)*
Opus National LLC ....C..952 656-4444
  Minnetonka *(G-6207)*
Opus Northwest Construction ....C..952 656-4444
  Hopkins *(G-2598)*
Partners For Senior ....E..612 374-8100
  Minneapolis *(G-5342)*
Pratt Nedegaard ....D..651 429-8032
  Saint Paul *(G-8835)*
Radisson Hotels International ....C..763 212-5000
  Minnetonka *(G-6218)*
Ryan Co's US Inc ....B..612 492-4000
  Minneapolis *(G-5579)*
Tradition Development ....E..952 920-5100
  Minneapolis *(G-5844)*
Watson Centers Inc ....D..612 920-5034
  Minneapolis *(G-6023)*
Wells Fargo Properties Inc ....E..612 667-8690
  Minneapolis *(G-6052)*
Western Walls Inc ....E..507 282-4624
  Rochester *(G-7292)*

6553 Cemetery Subdividers & Developers

City of Bloomington ....C..952 563-4925
  Minneapolis *(G-4084)*
Hillside Cemetery Association ....E..612 781-3391
  Minneapolis *(G-4649)*
Lakewood Cemetery Association ......E..612 822-2171
  Minneapolis *(G-4837)*
National Cemetery Admin ....D..612 726-1127
  Minneapolis *(G-5161)*

67 HOLDING & OTHER INVESTMENT OFFICES

6712 Offices Of Bank Holding Co's

Bakken Securities Inc ....E..952 926-6561
  Minneapolis *(G-3863)*
Belle Plaine Bancorporation ....E..952 873-2296
  Belle Plaine *(G-366)*
Bridgewater Bancshares Inc 952 893-6868
  Minneapolis *(G-3945)*
Deerwood Bancshares Inc ....D..218 534-3111
  Deerwood *(G-1175)*
Duke Financial Group Inc 612 204-0255
  Minneapolis *(G-4290)*
▲ Great Northern Bank ....E..763 497-7777
  Saint Michael *(G-7673)*
Marquette Financial Co's ....E..612 661-3880
  Minneapolis *(G-4952)*
Minn Star Bank ....E..507 726-2137
  Lake Crystal *(G-2860)*
NA Corp ....D..651 636-9654
  Saint Paul *(G-8732)*

Rcb Holding Co 651 631-1040
  Saint Paul *(G-8874)*
Riverwood Bank ....E..218 751-5120
  Bemidji *(G-423)*
Royalton Bancshares Inc 320 584-5522
  Royalton *(G-7387)*
Saint Peter Agency Inc ....E..507 931-3310
  Saint Peter *(G-9312)*
Stearns Financial Services Inc ....C..320 253-6607
  Saint Cloud *(G-7611)*
Sterling Bancorporation Inc ....E..507 433-7325
  Austin *(G-289)*
▲ Western Bank Edina ....D..952 857-1707
  Minneapolis *(G-6058)*
Winona National Holding Co Inc .....D..507 454-4320
  Winona *(G-10152)*

6719 Offices Of Holding Co's, NEC

C & G Holding Co of Clearbrook .....D..218 776-3080
  Clearbrook *(G-1037)*
Diebold Investments LLC ....E..952 960-9600
  Minneapolis *(G-4255)*
▲ Eldredge Trading Inc 651 778-8500
  Saint Paul *(G-7758)*
Esi Holding Corp ....D..952 853-0924
  Minneapolis *(G-4371)*
Hayworth Partners LP ....E..952 476-7200
  Hopkins *(G-2549)*
Integris Group Inc ....D..651 490-0000
  Saint Paul *(G-8514)*
J & B Group Inc ....B..763 497-3913
  Saint Michael *(G-7674)*
Johnson Controls Holding Co ....E..763 566-7650
  Minneapolis *(G-4774)*
King Solutions Inc ....D..763 428-5464
  Osseo *(G-6626)*
◆ Maax US Corp ....D..763 424-3335
  Minneapolis *(G-4925)*
Michael Foods Group Inc ....C..952 258-4000
  Minnetonka *(G-6193)*
Midwest Medical Insurance ....D..952 838-6700
  Minneapolis *(G-5033)*
Mt Yale Capital Group LLC ....E..952 897-5390
  Minneapolis *(G-5146)*
Murray's Co Inc ....E..612 333-2507
  Minneapolis *(G-5152)*
Ritalka Inc ....E..320 269-3227
  Montevideo *(G-6258)*
▲ Rosenbauer Motors LLC ....D..651 462-1000
  Wyoming *(G-10208)*
Summit Holdings Corp ....E..952 445-8718
  Shakopee *(G-9479)*
Yamamoto Moss Mackenzie ....E..612 375-0180
  Minneapolis *(G-6099)*

6722 Management Investment Offices

Ameriprise Financial ....D..612 671-3131
  Minneapolis *(G-3766)*
Ameriprise Financial Inc ....A..612 671-3131
  Minneapolis *(G-3767)*
Galliard Capital Management ....E..612 667-3210
  Minneapolis *(G-4496)*
Knight Financial Products LLC ....D..952 249-5500
  Hopkins *(G-2565)*
Mairs & Power Balanced Fund ....E..651 222-8478
  Saint Paul *(G-8609)*
Mount Yale Portfolio Advisors ....E..952 897-5390
  Minneapolis *(G-5141)*
Paul Johnston ....E..800 862-7919
  Royalton *(G-5350)*
Pine River Capital Management ....D..612 238-3300
  Minnetonka *(G-6214)*
Sit Mutual Funds Inc ....E..612 332-3223
  Minneapolis *(G-5682)*
Woodbury Financial Services ....E..651 738-4000
  Saint Paul *(G-9289)*

6726 Unit Investment Trusts, Face-Amount Certificate Offices

Ameriprise Financial Inc ....A..612 671-3131
  Minneapolis *(G-3767)*
Tpg Credit Management, LP ....E..612 851-3000
  Minneapolis *(G-5843)*

6732 Education, Religious & Charitable Trusts

Faf Advisors Inc 612 303-3381
  Minneapolis *(G-4391)*
Mc Knight Foundation ....E..612 333-4220
  Minneapolis *(G-4969)*
Minneapolis Foundation 612 672-3878
  Minneapolis *(G-5054)*
Otto Bremer Foundation ....C..651 227-8036
  Saint Paul *(G-8792)*
Spring Lake Park Lions Club ....E..763 784-9179
  Minneapolis *(G-3606)*

6733 Trusts Except Educational, Religious & Charitable

Lloyd Truss Systems ....E..507 387-4250
  North Mankato *(G-6508)*
Wilson - McShane Corp ....C..952 854-0795
  Minneapolis *(G-6074)*

6794 Patent Owners & Lessors

Abra Inc ....D..763 561-7220
  Minneapolis *(G-3662)*
American Dairy Queen Corp ....B..952 830-0200
  Minneapolis *(G-3747)*
▼ Barbers Hairstyling For Men ....D..952 947-7777
  Minneapolis *(G-3867)*
Buffalo Wild Wings Inc ....D..952 593-9943
  Minneapolis *(G-3969)*
◆ Carlson Holdings Inc ....A..763 212-5000
  Minnetonka *(G-6152)*
Carlson Hotels LP ....C..763 212-1000
  Minneapolis *(G-4014)*
◆ Carlson Hotels Management Corp ...C..763 212-5000
  Minneapolis *(G-4016)*
Carlson Hotels Worldwide Inc ....E..763 212-5000
  Minneapolis *(G-4017)*
Country Inns & Suites By ....E..763 212-2525
  Minneapolis *(G-4170)*
Duke & King Acquisition Corp ....A..952 288-2300
  Burnsville *(G-713)*
Duke & King Acquisition Corp ....E..651 731-8720
  Saint Paul *(G-9205)*
Embers America LLC ....E..651 645-6473
  Saint Paul *(G-8338)*
Famous Dave's Of America Inc ....E..952 294-1300
  Minnetonka *(G-6167)*
Holiday Diversified Services ....B..952 830-8700
  Minneapolis *(G-4660)*
▲ International Dairy Queen Inc ....B..952 830-0200
  Minneapolis *(G-4721)*
International Quality Homecare ....D..507 252-8117
  Rochester *(G-7142)*
Kiltie Corp ....E..651 770-3166
  Saint Paul *(G-9235)*
Novus Franchising Inc ....E..952 944-8000
  Savage *(G-9401)*
Radisson Hotels International ....C..763 212-5000
  Minnetonka *(G-6218)*
Schwegman, Lundberg & Woessner ...D..612 373-6900
  Minneapolis *(G-5618)*
Winmark Corp ....C..763 520-8500
  Minneapolis *(G-6077)*

6798 Real Estate Investment Trusts

Global Financial Partners Corp ....E..952 544-0640
  Minnetonka *(G-6176)*
Hospitality Investors LLC ....B..218 729-5616
  Duluth *(G-1353)*
Opus Properties Inc ....D..952 656-4444
  Hopkins *(G-2599)*

6799 Investors, NEC

Elim Care Foundation ....E..952 259-4500
  Eden Prairie *(G-1652)*
Kasa Capital LLC ....E..612 524-5460
  Minneapolis *(G-4792)*
L & M Investment Inc ....D..218 346-2798
  Perham *(G-6798)*
Midway University LLC ....E..651 292-9844
  Saint Paul *(G-8657)*
Minnesota Vikings Football ....C..952 828-6500
  Eden Prairie *(G-1727)*
Northmarq Real Estate Services ......E..952 831-1000
  Minneapolis *(G-5234)*
Norwest Equity Capital LLC ....E..612 215-1600
  Minneapolis *(G-5248)*
◆ Norwest Venture Capital Mgt ....E..612 215-1600
  Minneapolis *(G-5249)*
Reshare Corp ....E..952 908-0818
  Minneapolis *(G-5522)*
Rock Island Co ....E..651 228-0935
  Saint Paul *(G-8909)*
Ross Capital Pmc Inc ....E..612 929-9222
  Minneapolis *(G-5560)*
Whitebox Advisors LLC ....E..612 253-6025
  Minneapolis *(G-6065)*

70 HOTELS & OTHER LODGING PLACES

7011 Hotels, Motels & Tourist Courts

Adrian's Resort Inc ....D..218 634-1985
  Baudette *(G-313)*
Afton Alps Inc ....A..651 436-5245
  Hastings *(G-2412)*
Afton St Croix Co ....E..651 436-8883
  Afton *(G-6)*
Aloft Htl Minneapolis ....D..612 455-8400
  Minneapolis *(G-3731)*
Americ Inn of Ham Lake ....E..763 755-2100
  Anoka *(G-151)*

(G-00000) Company's Geographic Section entry number

486

2011 Harris Minnesota
Services Directory

▲=Import ▼=Export
◆=Import/Export

American Hospitality Mgt E 507 446-8900
Owatonna *(G-6691)*
AmericInn Motel & Suites E 952 758-7300
New Prague *(G-6421)*
AmericInn Shakopee D 952 445-6775
Shakopee *(G-9418)*
Ameriprise Financial Services E 952 368-3100
Chaska *(G-948)*
Apple Valley Gsrs LLC E 952 953-6111
Saint Paul *(G-7701)*
Appletree Motel Partnership C 952 854-9000
Minneapolis *(G-3790)*
Ashford Trs Nickel, LP D 952 854-2100
Bloomington *(G-487)*
Beltrami's Tally Inc E 218 243-2231
Bemidji *(G-376)*
Best Western Chaska River Inn E 952 448-7877
Chaska *(G-955)*
Best Western Dakota Ridge E 651 452-0100
Saint Paul *(G-7718)*
Best Western of Thief River D 218 681-7555
Thief River Falls *(G-9663)*
Best Western Riverport Inn E 507 452-0606
Winona *(G-10081)*
Best Western South St Paul E 651 455-3600
Saint Paul *(G-8108)*
Block E Lodging LLC D 320 258-2580
Saint Cloud *(G-7461)*
Bloomington Hospitality LLC B 763 367-9200
Minneapolis *(G-3914)*
Bloomington Hotel Acquisition E 952 893-9999
Minneapolis *(G-3915)*
Blue Waters Development Corp D 800 242-1988
Two Harbors *(G-9705)*
▲ **Bois Forte Enterprises** B 218 753-6400
Tower *(G-9686)*
BR Motels Inc E 320 253-5530
Saint Cloud *(G-7464)*
Briggs Hennum Inc E 218 634-2168
Baudette *(G-314)*
Brutger Equities Inc E 218 727-3110
Duluth *(G-1257)*
Bryanston Group Inc E 651 636-6730
Saint Paul *(G-8137)*
Buck Hill Inc 952 435-7174
Burnsville *(G-688)*
Buena Vista E 218 728-3533
Duluth *(G-1258)*
Buffalo Lodging E 763 682-5660
Buffalo *(G-639)*
Burnsville Development Ltd D 952 435-2100
Burnsville *(G-689)*
C H Suites of Chanhassen MN E 952 937-2424
Chanhassen *(G-912)*
Campbells Cabins & Trading E 218 993-2361
Crane Lake *(G-1116)*
Canadian Border Outfitters Inc E 218 365-5847
Ely *(G-1911)*
Canal Park Lodge D 218 279-6000
Duluth *(G-1260)*
Canal Properties Inc E 218 720-3000
Duluth *(G-1261)*
◆ **Carlson Holdings Inc** A 763 212-5000
Minnetonka *(G-6152)*
Carlson Hotels LP C 763 212-1000
Minneapolis *(G-4014)*
Carlson Hotels Management Corp C 612 339-4900
Minneapolis *(G-4015)*
Carlson Hotels Worldwide Inc E 763 212-5000
Minneapolis *(G-4017)*
Carpenter & Torgerson II LLC E 507 536-0040
Rochester *(G-7071)*
Causeway & Gull Associates E 218 963-3675
Lake Hubert *(G-2879)*
Central Lakes Lodging LLC E 218 828-0629
Baxter *(G-323)*
Chin Yuen Silver Fox Inn Inc E 763 295-4000
Monticello *(G-6267)*
City of Duluth B 218 628-2891
Duluth *(G-1275)*
Comfort Inn & Suites D 507 289-3344
Rochester *(G-7088)*
Concordia College A 218 299-4321
Moorhead *(G-6306)*
Corporate Commission of The A 320 532-8800
Onamia *(G-6568)*
Corporate Commission of The A 320 384-7101
Hinckley *(G-2483)*
Country Inn & Suites By E 651 982-9799
Forest Lake *(G-2159)*
Country Inn & Suites By E 763 241-6990
Elk River *(G-1869)*
Country Inn & Suites Duluth D 218 740-4500
Duluth *(G-1282)*
Country Inns & Suites By E 952 854-5555
Minneapolis *(G-4169)*
Country Inns & Suites By E 763 473-3008
Minneapolis *(G-4168)*
Country Inns & Suites By E 763 212-2525
Minneapolis *(G-4170)*
Courtyard By Marriott D 952 942-9100
Eden Prairie *(G-1636)*
Courtyard By Marriott D 952 452-2000
Saint Paul *(G-7738)*
Cove Point Lodge E 218 226-3221
Beaver Bay *(G-352)*
CP Saddle Brook LLC C 952 854-7441
Bloomington *(G-492)*

Crestline Hotels & Resorts Inc D 651 291-8800
Saint Paul *(G-8268)*
CSM Corp of Minnesota E 651 746-8000
Saint Paul *(G-8273)*
CSM Corp of Minnesota E 952 738-7300
Minneapolis *(G-4192)*
CSM Corp of Minnesota E 952 829-0033
Eden Prairie *(G-1638)*
CSM Corp of Minnesota E 612 340-1300
Minneapolis *(G-4193)*
CSM Corp of Minnesota C 612 375-1700
Minneapolis *(G-4194)*
CSM Corp of Minnesota D 952 593-1918
Minneapolis *(G-4195)*
CSM Equities LLC D 612 395-7000
Minneapolis *(G-4196)*
Cynw LLC E 763 425-5355
Maple Grove *(G-3238)*
D D D Motel Corp D 507 625-9333
Mankato *(G-3224)*
D D D Motel Corp C 507 345-1234
Mankato *(G-3121)*
Dakota Ridge LLC E 763 398-1821
Saint Paul *(G-7746)*
Davidson Hotel Co C 763 566-8000
Minneapolis *(G-4227)*
Days Inns & Suites D 763 561-8400
Minneapolis *(G-4231)*
Dehn's Country Manor Inc E 763 420-6460
Osseo *(G-6609)*
Dhm Minneapolis Hotel, LP C 763 489-2570
Minneapolis *(G-4251)*
Diamondrock Minneapolis Tenant D 612 376-1000
Minneapolis *(G-4253)*
Diversified Motel Properties C 218 728-3601
Duluth *(G-1294)*
Djont Jpm Leasing LLC D 952 884-4811
Minneapolis *(G-4264)*
Djont Operations LLC C 952 854-1000
Minneapolis *(G-4265)*
Dl-Dw Holdings LLC E 952 942-6818
Eden Prairie *(G-1646)*
Doubletree Corp C 952 542-8600
Minneapolis *(G-4282)*
Drover's Inn & Restaurant Inc E 320 252-6034
South Saint Paul *(G-9526)*
Duluth Lodging Inc E 218 628-1464
Duluth *(G-1300)*
Duluth Lodging Inc E 218 628-1464
Duluth *(G-1301)*
E T C Enterprises Inc E 320 240-0567
Saint Cloud *(G-7500)*
Eagan Lodging Group LLC E 651 450-1100
Inver Grove Heights *(G-2748)*
East Bay Hotel Corp E 218 387-2800
Grand Marais *(G-2259)*
Eddy's Lake Mille Lacs Resort E 320 532-3657
Onamia *(G-6570)*
Eden Fch Prairie LLC E 952 952-9000
Eden Prairie *(G-1649)*
Eden Prairie Hhp-II LLC E 952 942-9000
Eden Prairie *(G-1650)*
Edgewater Management LLC E 218 751-3603
Bemidji *(G-389)*
Em - Ty Corp D 651 645-0311
Saint Paul *(G-8334)*
Enn Leasing Co II LLC E 651 688-0363
Saint Paul *(G-7765)*
Enn Leasing Co II LLC E 651 688-0363
Saint Paul *(G-7764)*
ESA P Portfolio Operating E 507 289-7444
Rochester *(G-7107)*
ESA P Portfolio Operating E 507 536-7444
Rochester *(G-7106)*
Etoc Co Inc D 218 963-2906
Nisswa *(G-6496)*
Etoc Co Inc E 218 963-2234
Nisswa *(G-6497)*
Fairfield Inn D 218 723-8607
Duluth *(G-1317)*
Fch Minnetonka E 952 912-9999
Minnetonka *(G-6168)*
First Class Hospitality Group E 320 251-1500
Saint Cloud *(G-7510)*
Fitgers On The Lake LLC C 218 727-9077
Duluth *(G-1325)*
Fond Du Lac Reservation A 218 878-2327
Carlton *(G-867)*
Fond Dulac Development Corp D 218 722-8633
Carlton *(G-868)*
Forstrom & Torgerson Hnw LLC E 763 494-4498
Maple Grove *(G-3241)*
Forstrom & Torgerson Hs LLC E 651 415-1956
Saint Paul *(G-8389)*
Forstrom & Torgerson LLP C 651 482-0402
Saint Paul *(G-8390)*
Forstrom & Torgerson Ssnw LLC E 763 494-8856
Maple Grove *(G-3242)*
Foussard Hospitality Inc E 320 252-8700
Saint Cloud *(G-7415)*
Frolander Island Resort D 218 386-3019
Warroad *(G-9870)*
G G Tucson Inc D 218 723-8433
Duluth *(G-1330)*
Glen L Stockman E 651 636-1171
Saint Paul *(G-8413)*
Grand Marais Hotel Co Inc E 218 387-2448
Grand Marais *(G-2260)*

Grand Rapids Development Corp D 218 326-8501
Grand Rapids *(G-2281)*
Graves Development Corp E 320 252-6034
Saint Cloud *(G-7522)*
Graves Hospitality Corp D 612 677-1100
Minneapolis *(G-4547)*
Gunflint Lodge Inc E 218 388-2294
Grand Marais *(G-2261)*
Gus Chafoulias D 507 285-1234
Rochester *(G-7129)*
Hgib LLC E 952 831-1012
Bloomington *(G-501)*
Hie LLC E 651 681-9266
Eagan *(G-1528)*
Hilton Garden Inn E 651 686-4605
Eagan *(G-1529)*
Hilton Garden Inn - St Paul D 651 735-4100
Saint Paul *(G-9230)*
Hilton Hotels Corp D 952 884-4811
Minneapolis *(G-4651)*
Hilton Hotels Corp A 612 376-1000
Minneapolis *(G-4650)*
Hinw LLC C 763 425-3800
Willmar *(G-10009)*
Hinw LLC C 763 425-3800
Maple Grove *(G-3245)*
Holiday Inn Express & Suites E 651 275-1401
Stillwater *(G-9621)*
Holiday Inn Sunspree Resort E 218 365-6565
Ely *(G-1914)*
Holland Lodging Inc D 218 847-6997
Detroit Lakes *(G-1196)*
Hotel Ivy D 612 746-4600
Minneapolis *(G-4682)*
Hsnb LLC E 651 631-8002
New Brighton *(G-6410)*
Hsslp LLC E 952 544-0495
Saint Louis Park *(G-7662)*
Huddle's South Shore Resort E 218 836-2420
Walker *(G-9852)*
Hyatt Corp B 612 370-1234
Minneapolis *(G-4683)*
I D D D Inc D 320 352-5241
Sauk Centre *(G-9347)*
Improvement LP D 218 262-3481
Hibbing *(G-2456)*
Infinity Motel Holdings LLC E 320 763-9900
Alexandria *(G-106)*
Inn Hampton & Suites D 763 746-7999
Lino Lakes *(G-2972)*
International Management Co D 218 283-4451
International Falls *(G-2724)*
Interstate Hotels & Resorts E 952 854-5558
Minneapolis *(G-4727)*
Isle West Associates, LLP D 612 331-1800
Minneapolis *(G-4737)*
Izatys Group LLC E 320 532-3101
Onamia *(G-6573)*
J & L Hennum Inc D 218 634-1342
Baudette *(G-315)*
Kavco Inc 218 829-5226
Brainerd *(G-545)*
Kelly Midwest Ventures LP D 651 227-8711
Saint Paul *(G-8544)*
Kelly Midwest Ventures LP C 320 253-0606
Saint Cloud *(G-7539)*
Kinseth Hotel Corp C 952 884-8211
Minneapolis *(G-4811)*
L Jireh Inc E 218 387-2688
Grand Marais *(G-2262)*
Laird LLC E 507 444-0818
Owatonna *(G-6721)*
Lakeland Lodging LP D 218 829-8730
Alexandria *(G-110)*
Lakeside Hospitality LLP D 218 847-2121
Brainerd *(G-572)*
Land & Cabins LLC D 320 384-6488
Hinckley *(G-2485)*
Larken Inc D 952 830-1300
Minneapolis *(G-4844)*
Layline Corp E 651 385-9060
Red Wing *(G-6988)*
Leech Lake Palace & Casino A 218 335-7000
Cass Lake *(G-872)*
Leech Lake Reservation A 218 547-2744
Walker *(G-9854)*
Lho Bloomington One Lessee LLC C 952 835-7800
Minneapolis *(G-4868)*
Libor Management LLC E 763 561-0900
Minneapolis *(G-4871)*
Lino Lake Lodging LLC E 763 746-9500
Lino Lakes *(G-2973)*
Lodge At Brainerd Lake D 218 822-5634
Brainerd *(G-573)*
Lodge At Giants Ridge D 218 865-7170
Biwabik *(G-470)*
Lodge At Sugar Lake Inc E 218 327-1462
Cohasset *(G-1072)*
Lonesome Pine Restaurant E 218 678-2874
Deerwood *(G-1178)*
Lower Sioux Community Council E 507 637-5933
Redwood Falls *(G-7024)*
Lq Management LLC E 952 881-7311
Minneapolis *(G-4906)*
Lundell Enterprises LLC D 952 261-7617
Shakopee *(G-9454)*
Lutsen Resort Co E 218 663-7212
Lutsen *(G-3056)*

SIC

Employment codes: A=Over 500 employees, B=251-500
C=101-250, D=51-100, E=25-50
2011 Harris Minnesota
Services Directory
© Harris InfoSource 1-866-281-6415
487

Lyon Lodging LLC ....E....507 532-3070
Marshall *(G-3308)*
Lyric Block Development Corp ....C....218 722-1202
Duluth *(G-1386)*
M & C Hotel Interests Inc ....C....612 332-6000
Minneapolis *(G-4913)*
Madden Brothers Inc ....E....218 829-2811
Brainerd *(G-546)*
Madison Properties Inc ....D....218 847-2121
Detroit Lakes *(G-1208)*
Madison Properties Inc ....D....320 763-2498
Alexandria *(G-112)*
Mankato Fairfield Inn ....E....507 386-1220
Mankato *(G-3161)*
Mankato Lodging LLC ....D....507 388-8555
Mankato *(G-3163)*
Maple Grove Lodging Investors ....E....763 509-9500
Maple Grove *(G-3249)*
Marcus Hotels Inc ....C....612 338-2288
Minneapolis *(G-4946)*
Marquette Hotel ....B....612 333-4545
Minneapolis *(G-4953)*
Marriott ....E....952 893-9300
Minneapolis *(G-4955)*
Marriott ....E....763 577-1600
Plymouth *(G-6872)*
MB St Paul Inc ....D....651 731-2220
Saint Paul *(G-8620)*
Medina Inn ....D....763 478-6661
Hamel *(G-2352)*
Meristar Investment Partners L ....D....952 854-2100
Minneapolis *(G-4991)*
Mermaid Inc ....C....763 784-7350
Saint Paul *(G-8637)*
Midwest Heritage Inn of ....C....952 858-8475
Bloomington *(G-505)*
Midwest of Rochester Inc ....D....507 289-8866
Rochester *(G-7184)*
Midwest of Rochester Inc ....E....507 289-8866
Rochester *(G-7185)*
Minnesota Liquor Retailers Inc ....E....651 772-0910
Saint Paul *(G-8697)*
Minnetonka Minnesota Hotel L P ....D....952 593-0000
Minnetonka *(G-6198)*
Mirumi Inc ....E....952 445-9779
Shakopee *(G-9458)*
Mississippi Eagles LLC ....E....651 565-5366
Wabasha *(G-9769)*
Moorhead Hospitality LP ....D....218 284-1000
Moorhead *(G-6331)*
Mpls Hotel Management Ltd ....E....507 281-8000
Rochester *(G-7188)*
Mplsp Hotel Corp ....D....952 854-3400
Minneapolis *(G-5142)*
Murray Williamson ....E....218 751-8481
Bemidji *(G-404)*
Nath Management Inc ....E....651 739-2377
Saint Paul *(G-8736)*
Nath Midwest Lodging LLC ....C....952 853-1400
Minneapolis *(G-5158)*
Nath Midwest Lodging LLC ....D....952 853-1423
Saint Paul *(G-8737)*
National Lodging Co's Inc ....E....507 825-5871
Pipestone *(G-6832)*
Nb Saint Paul Inc ....D....651 731-2220
Saint Paul *(G-8742)*
Niecc Inc ....C....763 536-8300
Minneapolis *(G-5200)*
No Name ....E....218 547-3334
Walker *(G-9855)*
Normandy Inn Inc ....E....612 370-1400
Minneapolis *(G-5210)*
North Central Management Inc ....E....763 509-9500
Osseo *(G-6642)*
Northcott Hospitality Intl ....D....952 294-5000
Chanhassen *(G-934)*
Northcott Hospitality Intl ....E....952 934-3888
Chanhassen *(G-933)*
Northland Inn of Crookston ....D....218 281-5210
Crookston *(G-1129)*
Oak Hotels Inc ....E....651 636-6730
Saint Paul *(G-8777)*
175 Fort LLC ....E....651 225-1515
Saint Paul *(G-8787)*
Orchard Park LLC ....E....952 873-6017
Belle Plaine *(G-369)*
Owatonna Hospitality Partners ....E....507 455-1142
Owatonna *(G-6729)*
P R K Inc ....E....612 341-3300
Minneapolis *(G-5307)*
Pah-Dt Minneapolis Suites ....D....612 332-6800
Minneapolis *(G-5313)*
Park Gooseberry Motel Cabins ....E....218 834-3751
Two Harbors *(G-9711)*
Pattern Stations Inc ....D....763 441-6833
Monticello *(G-6282)*
PC Hotels LLC ....D....218 233-6171
Moorhead *(G-6332)*
Piney Ridge Lodge Inc ....E....218 587-2296
Pine River *(G-6821)*
Prairie Island Indian Com ....C....651 388-0083
Welch *(G-9955)*
Premier Resorts Ltd ....C....952 253-2500
Minneapolis *(G-5402)*
Proctor Motel Associates ....E....218 624-1026
Proctor *(G-6965)*
Professional Hospitality LLC ....E....320 259-8999
Saint Cloud *(G-7575)*
Professional Hospitality LLC ....E....507 287-6758
Rochester *(G-7212)*
Quarterdeck At Pleasant Acres ....E....218 963-2482
Nisswa *(G-6493)*
Quarterdeck Resort & Rest ....D....218 963-7537
Nisswa *(G-6494)*
Radison Hotel ....C....651 636-4567
Saint Paul *(G-8868)*
Radisson Hotels International ....C....763 212-5000
Minnetonka *(G-6218)*
Radisson Hotels International ....C....651 291-8800
Saint Paul *(G-8869)*
Raymond Management Co Inc ....E....507 287-9050
Rochester *(G-7217)*
Red Roof Inns Inc ....E....651 738-7160
Saint Paul *(G-9266)*
Red Roof Inns Inc ....E....952 890-1420
Burnsville *(G-787)*
Red Wing Hotel Corp ....C....651 388-2846
Red Wing *(G-6998)*
Regency Midwest Ventures LP ....C....320 762-1124
Alexandria *(G-119)*
Regency Plymouth Hotel ....C....763 559-6600
Minneapolis *(G-5485)*
Residence Inn ....E....612 677-1000
Minneapolis *(G-5523)*
Rhm Receiver 3211 Co LLC ....D....612 746-4600
Minneapolis *(G-5536)*
Rica Costa Ventures Inc ....E....651 426-9262
Hugo *(G-2682)*
Richard Sigert ....D....218 444-1875
Bemidji *(G-422)*
River Valley Hospitality LLC ....E....952 854-1771
Minneapolis *(G-5544)*
Rivers Hotel Co Inc ....D....507 457-0977
Winona *(G-10121)*
Riverside Lodging ....E....651 388-0491
Red Wing *(G-7003)*
Rivett Group LLC ....E....952 888-8800
Minneapolis *(G-5547)*
Rlj Bloomington Hotel LLC ....E....952 854-0900
Minneapolis *(G-5549)*
Rogers Hospitality LLC ....E....763 428-3000
Rogers *(G-7341)*
Ruttger's Birchmont Lodge Inc ....E....218 751-4131
Bemidji *(G-425)*
Sand Co Inc ....E....507 388-8555
Mankato *(G-3191)*
Sandman Motel LLC ....E....763 559-1222
Minneapolis *(G-5600)*
Sandman Motels LLC ....E....952 932-9987
Hopkins *(G-2626)*
Sanford Hospitality LLC 952 854-3411
Bloomington *(G-512)*
Sbse LLC ....E....651 994-7810
Eagan *(G-1549)*
Select Hotels Group LLC ....E....952 944-9700
Eden Prairie *(G-1774)*
Select Inn of Bloomington LP ....E....952 835-7400
Minneapolis *(G-5634)*
Seven Corners Hotel Partners ....C....612 333-4646
Minneapolis *(G-5641)*
Seven Corners Hotel Partners ....E....612 333-4646
Minneapolis *(G-5642)*
78th Street Leaseco LLC ....B....952 835-1900
Minneapolis *(G-5643)*
Shady Oak Hospitality LP ....E....952 995-9000
Eden Prairie *(G-1776)*
Shaner Hotel Group LP ....D....952 893-9300
Minneapolis *(G-5648)*
Sheraton Duluth ....D....218 733-5660
Duluth *(G-1449)*
Sheraton St Paul-Woodbury ....D....651 209-3280
Saint Paul *(G-9273)*
Shingle Creek Hospitality LLP ....E....763 566-7500
Minneapolis *(G-5655)*
Simper Lowell LLC ....E....651 439-1100
Stillwater *(G-9639)*
Six Continents Hotels Inc ....D....952 831-8000
Minneapolis *(G-5683)*
▲ Smsc Gaming Enterprise ....A....952 445-6000
Prior Lake *(G-6955)*
Smsc Gaming Enterprise ....A....952 445-8982
Prior Lake *(G-6956)*
Somerset Hospitality LLC ....E....952 894-6124
Savage *(G-9407)*
Sonor Hotel Corp ....C....507 288-1844
Rochester *(G-7257)*
Southern Hospitality Inc ....E....952 831-9595
Minneapolis *(G-5709)*
Sp Hotels LLC ....E....651 291-8800
Saint Paul *(G-8975)*
Spirit Mountain Travel Lodge ....E....218 628-3691
Duluth *(G-1457)*
Ssb LLC ....E....952 831-7900
Bloomington *(G-518)*
St Cloud Suite Hotel Inc ....D....320 654-1661
Saint Cloud *(G-7606)*
St Croix Preservation Co Inc ....E....651 439-6000
Stillwater *(G-9644)*
Starwood Hotels & Resorts ....C....612 331-1900
Minneapolis *(G-5744)*
Starwood Hotels & Resorts ....C....612 215-3720
Minneapolis *(G-5745)*
Stockman Hotel Corp ....E....651 636-1171
Saint Paul *(G-9007)*
Sunstone Hotel Management Inc ....D....507 289-8646
Rochester *(G-7268)*
Sunstone Hotel Properties Inc ....E....507 282-2581
Rochester *(G-7269)*
Tb Duluth LLC ....C....218 727-8981
Duluth *(G-1479)*
Tcbh Inc ....D....651 454-3434
Saint Paul *(G-7918)*
Thm Master Te LLC ....D....612 340-2000
Minneapolis *(G-5816)*
3608 Park Street LLC 651 221-7911
Saint Paul *(G-9043)*
3R North Inc ....E....651 674-9977
North Branch *(G-6506)*
Thunderbird Lodge Inc ....D....218 286-3151
International Falls *(G-2732)*
Tofte Management Co LLC ....C....218 663-7296
Tofte *(G-9684)*
Torgerson Hospitality LLC ....D....507 359-2941
New Ulm *(G-6477)*
Torgerson Properties LP ....D....507 238-4771
Fairmont *(G-1983)*
Torgerson Properties LP ....D....507 433-6720
Austin *(G-290)*
Townhomes At Lutsen Mountains ....E....218 663-7241
Lutsen *(G-3058)*
Tpi Core Inc ....D....320 231-2301
Willmar *(G-10048)*
Tpi Core Inc ....D....507 433-1000
Austin *(G-291)*
Trapper's Landing Lodge ....E....218 836-2500
Walker *(G-9859)*
Travel Suites of Coon Rapids ....E....763 780-3797
Minneapolis *(G-3621)*
Travelodge & Suite ....E....218 233-5333
Moorhead *(G-6344)*
Travelodge Tower ....C....651 735-2333
Saint Paul *(G-9078)*
Treasure Island Casino & Bingo ....A....651 388-6300
Welch *(G-9957)*
Trimark Hotel Corp ....C....612 305-9763
Minneapolis *(G-5856)*
Turney Properties LP ....E....763 546-6277
Minneapolis *(G-5866)*
University Inn Associates, A ....C....612 379-8888
Minneapolis *(G-5924)*
University Inn Property LLC ....C....612 379-8888
Minneapolis *(G-5925)*
USP Hotel Services LLC ....E....651 578-2563
Saint Paul *(G-9287)*
Victoria Inn ....D....320 587-6030
Hutchinson *(G-2716)*
Villa ....E....218 865-4155
Biwabik *(G-472)*
W B M Holding Co ....E....952 831-9595
Minneapolis *(G-5986)*
W2005 Fargo Hotels Realty, LP ....E....952 854-1687
Bloomington *(G-525)*
W2005 New Century Hotel ....E....952 835-6643
Minneapolis *(G-5990)*
W2005 New Century Hotel ....E....763 541-1094
Hopkins *(G-2656)*
W2007 Equity Inns Realty LLC ....E....952 854-0700
Minneapolis *(G-5991)*
Waterfront Plaza Hotel Co LLC ....E....218 727-4663
Duluth *(G-1499)*
White Earth Band of Chippewa ....A....218 935-2711
Mahnomen *(G-3091)*
Winona Inn LP ....E....507 454-4390
Winona *(G-10150)*
Wks Vadnais Heights LLC ....E....651 484-2400
Vadnais Heights *(G-9721)*
Wsi - Rwp LLC ....D....901 821-4117
Bloomington *(G-527)*
Wyndham International Inc ....C....952 831-3131
Minneapolis *(G-6090)*
Young Men's Chritn Assoc of ....C....763 785-7882
Minneapolis *(G-3644)*
Z M C Hotels Inc ....E....218 726-1111
Duluth *(G-1506)*
Zenith Rogers LLC ....E....763 425-0044
Rogers *(G-7348)*

7021 Rooming & Boarding Houses

Ace Rental Place ....E....218 463-2175
Roseau *(G-7351)*
Brooklyn Park Hospitality LLC ....D....763 566-8855
Minneapolis *(G-3960)*
CSM Executive Lodging LLC 612 395-7195
Minneapolis *(G-4197)*
Ecumen Home Care Inc ....E....952 888-1010
Minneapolis *(G-4312)*
Minnesota Pipestone ....D....952 294-5100
Chanhassen *(G-932)*

7032 Sporting & Recreational Camps

Albert Lea Family YMCA ....E....507 373-8228
Albert Lea *(G-31)*
Calmar Group Inc ....D....952 440-8834
Prior Lake *(G-6929)*
Camp Buckskin ....D....218 365-2121
Isabella *(G-2776)*
Camp Greenwood Girl Scout ....E....763 684-4243
Buffalo *(G-640)*
Camp New Hope Inc ....E....218 426-3560
McGregor *(G-3338)*

Camp Onamia Inc ... E ... 320 532-3767 — Onamia *(G-6567)*
Camp Shamineau of The ... E ... 218 575-2240 — Motley *(G-6383)*
Camp Widji Wagan ... E ... 218 365-2117 — Ely *(G-1912)*
Camp Wilderness Bsa Inc ... D ... 218 732-4674 — Park Rapids *(G-6748)*
Catholic Youth Camp ... E ... 651 636-1645 — Saint Paul *(G-8178)*
Circle R Ranch Inc ... E ... 320 547-2176 — Long Prairie *(G-3039)*
Concordia Language Villages ... E ... 218 758-3068 — Dent *(G-1186)*
Courage Center ... D ... 218 266-3658 — Lake George *(G-2878)*
Duluth Area Family Y M C A ... E ... 218 372-3188 — Sturgeon Lake *(G-9657)*
Duluth Area Family YMCA ... E ... 218 722-4745 — Duluth *(G-1297)*
Etoc Co Inc ... D ... 218 963-2906 — Nisswa *(G-6496)*
Hastings YMCA ... E ... 651 480-8887 — Hastings *(G-2390)*
Itasca County Family Young ... D ... 218 327-1161 — Grand Rapids *(G-2287)*
Little Elk Youth Ranch Inc ... E ... 320 594-2750 — Browerville *(G-625)*
Lutheran Bible Camp ... E ... 218 566-2329 — Remer *(G-7030)*
North Star Camp ... E ... 218 829-6631 — Brainerd *(G-578)*
Peters Sunset Beach Inc ... E ... 320 634-4501 — Glenwood *(G-2230)*
Y M C A Infant Center ... E ... 651 646-4557 — Saint Paul *(G-9171)*
Ymc Camp Dunord ... E ... 218 365-3681 — Ely *(G-1918)*
YMCA ... D ... 320 222-9622 — Willmar *(G-10059)*
YMCA Children's Center ... E ... 651 777-8103 — Saint Paul *(G-9173)*
YMCA of Greater Saint Paul ... E ... 651 645-6605 — Saint Paul *(G-9175)*
YMCA of Greater St Paul ... D ... 218 365-2117 — Ely *(G-1919)*
YMCA of Greater St Paul ... D ... 651 292-4143 — Saint Paul *(G-9178)*
YMCA of Greater St Paul ... D ... 651 646-4557 — Saint Paul *(G-9177)*
YMCA of Greater St Paul ... C ... 651 483-2671 — Saint Paul *(G-9176)*
YMCA of Greater St Paul ... C ... 651 457-0048 — Saint Paul *(G-7953)*
YMCA of Worthington, Minnesota ... E ... 507 376-6197 — Worthington *(G-10199)*
Young Men's Chrltn Assoc of ... C ... 763 535-4800 — Minneapolis *(G-6101)*
Young Men's Chrltn Assoc of ... D ... 612 827-5401 — Minneapolis *(G-6102)*
Young Men's Chrltn Assoc of ... E ... 612 588-9484 — Minneapolis *(G-6103)*
Young Men's Chrltn Assoc of ... C ... 952 835-2567 — Minneapolis *(G-6104)*
Young Women's Christian Assn ... D ... 218 722-7425 — Duluth *(G-1505)*
YWCA of Minneapolis ... A ... 612 332-0501 — Minneapolis *(G-6111)*

7033 Trailer Parks & Camp Sites

Brennaville Inc ... E ... 507 467-2512 — Preston *(G-6895)*
Buffalo Junction ... E ... 218 624-9901 — Duluth *(G-1259)*
Corporate Commission of The ... A ... 320 384-7101 — Hinckley *(G-2483)*
Pathfinder Village St Croix ... E ... 320 384-7726 — Hinckley *(G-2488)*
Sunrise Estates Mobile Home ... E ... 651 462-4047 — Stacy *(G-9581)*
Three Rivers Park District ... D ... 763 694-7894 — Osseo *(G-6673)*

7041 Membership-Basis Hotels

Interstate Hotels & Resorts ... C ... 952 854-2100 — Minneapolis *(G-4728)*
T C Sweatshop Inc ... E ... 651 646-8418 — Saint Paul *(G-9023)*

72 PERSONAL SERVICES

7211 Power Laundries, Family & Commercial

Dison's Cleaners & Laundry Inc ... E ... 507 289-3944 — Rochester *(G-7097)*
Edina Laundry Co ... E ... 952 927-9991 — Minneapolis *(G-4317)*
Sunstone Hotel Management Inc ... E ... 507 252-7500 — Rochester *(G-7267)*
Uls of New England LLC ... D ... 651 227-9855 — Saint Paul *(G-9101)*
United Linen Services Inc ... B ... 651 227-9855 — Saint Paul *(G-9107)*
Waldorf-Nevens Dry Cleaners ... D ... 952 914-9755 — Minneapolis *(G-5997)*

7212 Garment Pressing & Cleaners' Agents

Antons Inc ... E ... 320 253-3611 — Waite Park *(G-9816)*
J D Fingerman Enterprises Inc ... E ... 612 861-1697 — Minneapolis *(G-4746)*

7213 Linen Sply

▲ Ameripride Services Inc ... D ... 952 738-4200 — Hopkins *(G-2510)*
Ameripride Services Inc ... D ... 320 251-2525 — Saint Cloud *(G-7448)*
Ameripride Services Inc ... D ... 507 345-1039 — Mankato *(G-3105)*
Ameripride Services Inc ... E ... 218 751-5150 — Bemidji *(G-374)*
Ameripride Services Inc ... B ... 612 331-1600 — Minneapolis *(G-3764)*
ARAMARK Uniform & Career ... C ... 763 586-0020 — Minneapolis *(G-3408)*
Buffalo Drycleaners ... E ... 763 682-1061 — Buffalo *(G-638)*
Cintas Corp ... E ... 763 588-2701 — Minneapolis *(G-4077)*
Cintas Corp No 2 ... C ... 763 425-6666 — Osseo *(G-6603)*
G & K Services Inc ... C ... 320 252-9471 — Saint Cloud *(G-7515)*
◆ G&K Services Inc ... C ... 952 912-5500 — Minnetonka *(G-6173)*
G&K Services Inc ... C ... 651 855-7000 — Saint Paul *(G-8398)*
G&K Services Inc ... C ... 612 521-4771 — Minneapolis *(G-4492)*
G&K Services Inc ... C ... 612 333-2225 — Minneapolis *(G-4493)*
G&K Services Inc ... E ... 507 451-5710 — Owatonna *(G-6716)*
Spruce Co ... E ... 952 888-1639 — Minneapolis *(G-5723)*

7215 Coin Operated Laundries & Cleaning

Awm Enterprises Inc ... E ... 651 455-3044 — South Saint Paul *(G-9510)*

7216 Dry Cleaning Plants, Except Rug Cleaning

Anderson Cleaners ... E ... 651 690-9592 — Saint Paul *(G-8050)*
Buffalo Drycleaners ... E ... 763 682-1061 — Buffalo *(G-638)*
Dison's Cleaners & Laundry Inc ... E ... 507 289-3944 — Rochester *(G-7097)*
Edina Laundry Co ... E ... 952 927-9991 — Minneapolis *(G-4317)*
G & K Services Inc ... C ... 320 252-9471 — Saint Cloud *(G-7515)*
Pilgrim Cleaners & Launderers ... E ... 952 937-9391 — Eden Prairie *(G-1747)*
Stoltz Dry Cleaners Inc ... E ... 651 698-0120 — Saint Paul *(G-9008)*
Sunstone Hotel Management Inc ... E ... 507 252-7500 — Rochester *(G-7267)*
Waldorf-Nevens Dry Cleaners ... D ... 952 914-9755 — Minneapolis *(G-5997)*

7217 Carpet & Upholstery Cleaning

A S T Inc ... E ... 952 888-7340 — Eden Prairie *(G-1582)*
Christians Inc ... E ... 952 470-2001 — Chanhassen *(G-916)*
Fibercare Inc ... E ... 612 721-5048 — Minneapolis *(G-4426)*
Jubilee Enterprises Inc ... E ... 507 532-2332 — Marshall *(G-3301)*
Lindstrom Cleaning & Constr ... E ... 763 544-8761 — Minneapolis *(G-4891)*
Loyear Cleaning & Restoration ... E ... 952 831-0777 — Minneapolis *(G-4905)*
Quantum Co's Inc ... E ... 952 943-4357 — Minneapolis *(G-5445)*
Restoration Contractors Inc ... E ... 651 646-3408 — Saint Paul *(G-8894)*
Restoration Professionals Inc ... D ... 651 379-1990 — Saint Paul *(G-8895)*
Rick L Schoenrock ... E ... 320 763-7144 — Alexandria *(G-120)*
Rug & Carpet Caretakers ... E ... 507 388-5384 — Mankato *(G-3189)*
Rusciano-Hyland Inc ... E ... 612 871-4434 — Minneapolis *(G-5576)*
Servicemaster of St Cloud Inc ... C ... 320 252-4622 — Saint Cloud *(G-7591)*
Shine-Way Janitorial Service ... D ... 507 388-7439 — Mankato *(G-3197)*

7218 Industrial Launderers

▲ Ameripride Services Inc ... D ... 952 738-4200 — Hopkins *(G-2510)*
Ameripride Services Inc ... D ... 218 263-3611 — Hibbing *(G-2436)*
Ameripride Services Inc ... D ... 507 345-1039 — Mankato *(G-3105)*
Ameripride Services Inc ... B ... 612 331-1600 — Minneapolis *(G-3764)*
ARAMARK Uniform & Career ... C ... 763 586-0020 — Minneapolis *(G-3408)*
Cintas Corp No 2 ... C ... 763 425-6666 — Osseo *(G-6603)*
G & K Services Inc ... C ... 320 252-9471 — Saint Cloud *(G-7515)*
◆ G&K Services Inc ... C ... 952 912-5500 — Minnetonka *(G-6173)*
G&K Services Inc ... C ... 651 855-7000 — Saint Paul *(G-8398)*
G&K Services Inc ... C ... 612 521-4771 — Minneapolis *(G-4492)*
G&K Services Inc ... C ... 612 333-2225 — Minneapolis *(G-4493)*
G&K Services Inc ... E ... 507 451-5710 — Owatonna *(G-6716)*
United Linen Services Inc ... B ... 651 227-9855 — Saint Paul *(G-9107)*

7219 Laundry & Garment Svcs, NEC

Don's Leather Cleaning Inc ... E ... 612 721-4881 — Minneapolis *(G-4276)*
Health Systems Cooperative ... D ... 651 774-8620 — Saint Paul *(G-8450)*
Small Change Diaper Service ... E ... 507 895-8625 — La Crescent *(G-2844)*
Stoltz Dry Cleaners Inc ... E ... 651 698-0120 — Saint Paul *(G-9008)*

7221 Photographic Studios, Portrait

H & J Bliss Enterprises ... E ... 952 988-9302 — Minneapolis *(G-4584)*
In Fisherman Inc ... E ... 218 829-1648 — Baxter *(G-330)*
JC Penney Corp Inc ... C ... 218 727-8111 — Duluth *(G-1360)*
Lifetouch National School ... C ... 952 826-4500 — Minneapolis *(G-4882)*
Lifetouch National School ... B ... 952 826-4000 — Eden Prairie *(G-1710)*
Lifetouch Portrait Studios Inc ... D ... 952 826-5000 — Eden Prairie *(G-1711)*
Proex Photo Systems Inc ... E ... 952 893-1915 — Minneapolis *(G-3575)*

7231 Beauty Shops

▲ A-Veda Corp ... B ... 763 951-4000 — Minneapolis *(G-3383)*
AJK Cutters Inc ... E ... 952 933-7525 — Minneapolis *(G-3701)*
Arden Stephen Salon Inc ... E ... 952 893-1938 — Minneapolis *(G-3805)*
▼ Barbers Hairstyling For Men ... D ... 952 947-7777 — Minneapolis *(G-3867)*
Bixby Inc ... 952 448-6520 — Chaska *(G-956)*
C & R Ross Inc ... E ... 763 545-7347 — Minneapolis *(G-3980)*
Cole's Salon ... E ... 651 454-1390 — Saint Paul *(G-7734)*
Cole's Salon Management Inc ... E ... 952 226-5310 — Savage *(G-9386)*
Coloplast Corp ... D ... 507 345-6200 — North Mankato *(G-6507)*
Cost Cutters Family Hair Care ... E ... 612 861-0040 — Minneapolis *(G-4166)*
Day S P A At Nails Etc ... E ... 952 830-0100 — Minneapolis *(G-4230)*
Denny Kemp Inc ... E ... 612 676-0300 — Minneapolis *(G-4248)*
Details Salon & Spa ... E ... 651 696-8700 — Saint Paul *(G-8289)*
Doll Enterprises Inc ... E ... 651 488-0228 — Saint Paul *(G-8306)*
Elam Investments ... E ... 763 544-4264 — Minneapolis *(G-4335)*
Elizabeth Charles Corp ... C ... 952 915-2900 — Minneapolis *(G-4340)*
Elizabeth Charles Corp ... D ... 952 915-2900 — Saint Paul *(G-9212)*
Elizabeth Charles Corp ... D ... 952 915-2900 — Chanhassen *(G-922)*
Estetica ... E ... 651 228-9327 — Saint Paul *(G-8345)*
Fine Line Hair Inc ... E ... 952 457-2620 — Minneapolis *(G-6126)*
Flagship Athletic Club Inc ... B ... 952 941-2000 — Eden Prairie *(G-1665)*
G B & Co Hair & Skin Care ... E ... 320 253-4832 — Saint Cloud *(G-7516)*
Great Clips Inc ... D ... 952 893-9088 — Minneapolis *(G-4551)*
Hair District ... E ... 952 836-0816 — Minneapolis *(G-4588)*
Image Shoppe Inc ... E ... 952 949-1313 — Eden Prairie *(G-1690)*
Indulge Salon & Tanning LLP ... E ... 507 345-3400 — Mankato *(G-3226)*
J C Penney Co Inc ... E ... 952 920-8557 — Minneapolis *(G-4745)*

S I C

Employment codes: A=Over 500 employees, B=251-500
C=101-250, D=51-100, E=25-50
2011 Harris Minnesota Services Directory
© Harris InfoSource 1-866-281-6415
489

JC Penney Corp Inc ....C....218 727-8111 Duluth (G-1360)
JC Penney Corp Inc ....D....507 625-1606 Mankato (G-3152)
Jon English Salon ....E....612 824-2474 Minneapolis (G-4776)
Justin Paul Inc ....E....218 727-0034 Duluth (G-1365)
Juut Midwest Inc ....E....612 676-2250 Minneapolis (G-4782)
Juut Midwest Inc ....D....651 222-4121 Saint Paul (G-8538)
Juut Midwest Inc ....E....612 332-3512 Minneapolis (G-4783)
Juut Midwest Inc ....E....651 639-0576 Saint Paul (G-8539)
La Grande' Salon Ltd ....E....651 464-4371 Forest Lake (G-2163)
Metropolis Salon Spa ....E....952 473-8664 Wayzata (G-9927)
Pharmaceutical Specialties Inc ....E....507 288-8500 Rochester (G-7203)
Regents of The University of ....E....612 624-8865 Minneapolis (G-5500)
▲ Regis Corp ....A....952 947-7777 Minneapolis (G-5504)
Regis Corp ....E....320 253-5353 Saint Cloud (G-7584)
Regis Corp ....E....952 435-5545 Burnsville (G-789)
Regis Corp ....E....952 851-9999 Minneapolis (G-5505)
Regis Corp ....E....651 636-9966 Saint Paul (G-8885)
Revamp Salon & Spa ....E....612 341-0404 Minneapolis (G-5533)
Richard R Rodenborn ....E....763 533-5155 Minneapolis (G-5537)
Rita Ambourn Hair Designers ....E....651 698-5537 Saint Paul (G-8903)
Rocco Altobelli Inc ....C....952 707-1900 Burnsville (G-793)
Rocco Altobelli Inc ....E....507 288-8582 Rochester (G-7227)
Rocco Altobelli Inc ....E....651 690-5491 Saint Paul (G-8908)
Rocco Altobelli Inc ....E....651 730-7077 Saint Paul (G-9270)
Rocco Altobelli Inc ....D....952 920-5006 Minneapolis (G-5556)
Sakada ....E....952 938-9400 Hopkins (G-2625)
Salon 2000 & Day Spa ....E....952 942-8444 Eden Prairie (G-1770)
Salon 4862 Inc ....E....612 298-8310 Minneapolis (G-5595)
Salon Intrigue ....E....952 922-0588 Minneapolis (G-5596)
Salon Sabell Inc ....E....612 866-3679 Minneapolis (G-5597)
Seaco Inc ....C....952 470-7400 Excelsior (G-1953)
Simonson Venture Inc ....E....763 416-7823 Anoka (G-228)
Simonson Venture Inc ....E....763 494-4863 Osseo (G-6663)
Snips of Eden Prairie Inc ....E....952 941-1495 Minneapolis (G-5692)
Sunrise Hair STYling&tanning ....E....651 777-2344 Saint Paul (G-9015)
▲ Supercuts Inc ....A....952 947-7777 Minneapolis (G-5770)
Thomas Charles Salon II Inc ....E....952 925-4277 Minneapolis (G-5817)
Top Secret Hair Salon ....E....651 500-9233 Minneapolis (G-3617)
Zina's Inc ....E....952 929-0093 Minneapolis (G-6120)

7241 Barber Shops

Sunrise Hair STYling&tanning ....E....651 777-2344 Saint Paul (G-9015)

7251 Shoe Repair & Shoeshine Parlors

Don's Leather Cleaning Inc ....E....612 721-4881 Minneapolis (G-4276)

7261 Funeral Svcs & Crematories

Bradshaw Group ....E....651 776-1551 Saint Paul (G-8120)
▲ Brown-Wilbert Inc ....E....651 631-1234 Saint Paul (G-8133)
Cremation Society Inc ....612 825-2435 Minneapolis (G-4181)
Davies Chapel ....E....612 377-2203 Minneapolis (G-4228)
First Memorial Funeral Chapel ....E....763 560-4694 Minneapolis (G-4443)
Hillside Cemetery Association ....E....612 781-3391 Minneapolis (G-4649)
Range Co Operatives Inc ....218 741-7393 Virginia (G-9753)
Williams Funeral Home Inc ....320 252-2522 Saint Cloud (G-7633)

7291 Tax Return Preparation Svcs

Global Tax Network Minnesota ....E....952 224-2053 Minneapolis (G-4532)
H&R Block Inc ....E....507 345-1040 Mankato (G-3132)
H&R Block Inc ....D....507 280-8406 Rochester (G-7130)
Inter-Tax Inc ....E....952 512-9000 Minnetonka (G-6181)
Larsonallen LLP ....E....218 692-5750 Crosslake (G-1151)
RSM McGladrey Inc ....D....507 288-5363 Rochester (G-7242)
Stevens Foster' Financial ....E....952 843-4200 Minneapolis (G-5755)

7299 Miscellaneous Personal Svcs, NEC

Aarcee Party & Tent Rental ....E....952 922-7233 Minneapolis (G-3657)
American Hospitality Mgt ....E....507 446-8900 Owatonna (G-6691)
American Legion Club ....E....651 460-9909 Farmington (G-2039)
American Legion Club ....E....763 421-0883 Anoka (G-152)
Anderson's Formal Wear Inc ....E....507 285-1884 Rochester (G-7056)
▲ Apex International Mfg Inc ....C....952 227-3000 Chaska (G-949)
Appletree Motel Partnership ....C....952 854-9000 Minneapolis (G-3790)
Awm Enterprises Inc ....E....651 455-3044 South Saint Paul (G-9510)
Best Western South St Paul ....E....651 455-3600 Saint Paul (G-8108)
Brook Hall Blaine Brook ....E....763 755-8731 Minneapolis (G-3425)
Bub's Brewing Co Inc ....E....507 457-3121 Winona (G-10085)
Buca Inc ....D....612 288-0138 Minneapolis (G-3966)
Buca Inc ....D....952 892-7272 Burnsville (G-687)
C E C Entertainment Inc ....E....952 892-7786 Burnsville (G-694)
Chanhassen Theatre LLC ....C....952 934-1500 Chanhassen (G-913)
Chevys ....D....952 814-9555 Minneapolis (G-4062)
Chevys Inc ....E....507 345-1446 Mankato (G-3115)
Chianti Grill ....E....651 644-2808 Saint Paul (G-8191)
City of Brooklyn Center ....E....763 569-6300 Minneapolis (G-4085)
City of Minneapolis ....C....612 335-6000 Minneapolis (G-4091)
Class A Valet Inc ....E....612 677-0071 Minneapolis (G-4104)
D M S Health Group ....E....763 315-1947 Osseo (G-6607)
Dakotah Sport & Fitness Center ....C....952 445-9400 Prior Lake (G-6932)
Dependable Care Inc ....E....763 438-2811 Brooklyn Park (G-608)
Diggers Bar & Grill Inc ....D....507 634-7400 Kasson (G-2819)
8th Street Garage Inc ....E....612 349-5717 Minneapolis (G-4333)
Elam Investments ....E....763 544-4264 Minneapolis (G-4335)
Financial Crimes Services LLC ....E....651 388-2569 Red Wing (G-6981)
Heritage Park Estates ....E....320 240-7939 Saint Cloud (G-7528)
Hidden Haven Golf Course Inc ....E....763 434-6867 Cedar (G-879)
Hyatt Corp ....B....612 370-1234 Minneapolis (G-4683)
▲ Impact Innovations Inc ....D....320 847-1210 Clara City (G-1028)
Irish Genealogical Society ....E....763 574-1436 South Saint Paul (G-9531)
J Maas Co ....E....218 631-3498 Wadena (G-9804)
Jade Catering Inc ....E....763 767-3336 Anoka (G-193)
Jala Contracting Co ....E....763 434-4626 Cedar (G-880)
Jde Studios Inc ....E....612 825-4076 Minneapolis (G-4756)
Jensen's Supper Club ....E....651 688-7969 Saint Paul (G-7809)
Jimmy's Conference & Catering ....E....651 482-1233 Saint Paul (G-8533)
Keep In Touch of Burnsville ....E....952 953-3313 Burnsville (G-739)
Knight of Columbus Community ....E....952 492-5170 Prior Lake (G-6936)
Lee's Pro Shop Inc ....E....320 629-7568 Pine City (G-6814)
Lho Bloomington One Lessee LLC ....C....952 835-7800 Minneapolis (G-4868)
Life Time Fitness Inc ....D....612 752-9589 Minneapolis (G-4878)
Life Time Fitness Inc ....E....952 835-2222 Minneapolis (G-4877)
Life Time Fitness Inc ....C....763 576-3000 Champlin (G-895)
Life Time Fitness Inc ....C....763 509-0909 Minneapolis (G-4880)
Life Time Fitness Inc ....C....763 257-1067 Minneapolis (G-3519)
Links On The Mississippi Inc ....E....651 768-7611 Cottage Grove (G-1104)
Madison Properties Inc ....D....218 847-2121 Detroit Lakes (G-1208)
Maly Co's LLC ....E....612 788-9688 Minneapolis (G-4939)
Marshall Golf Club ....E....507 532-2278 Marshall (G-3310)
Meadow Lakes Golf Club LLC ....E....507 285-1190 Rochester (G-7181)
Mermaid Inc ....C....763 784-7350 Saint Paul (G-8637)
Michael's Restaurant ....E....320 252-7100 Saint Cloud (G-7420)
Midwest of Rochester Inc ....D....507 289-8866 Rochester (G-7184)
Midwest Restaurant Group ....D....507 444-0303 Owatonna (G-6724)
Minnesota State Bar Assn ....E....651 227-8266 Saint Paul (G-8706)
Minnesota Tobacco Document ....E....612 378-5707 Minneapolis (G-5097)
Morton's of Chicago Inc ....E....612 673-9700 Minneapolis (G-5132)
Moundsview Banquet ....E....763 717-4041 Saint Paul (G-8725)
Niecc Inc ....C....763 536-8300 Minneapolis (G-5200)
Norcostco Inc ....E....763 544-0601 Minneapolis (G-5207)
Normandy Inn Inc ....E....612 370-1400 Minneapolis (G-5210)
North Central Management Inc ....E....763 509-9500 Osseo (G-6642)
O K Corral Inc ....D....952 492-6700 Jordan (G-2808)
Oak Glen LLC ....D....651 439-6981 Stillwater (G-9633)
Oak Inn Family Restaurant Inc ....E....651 674-9977 North Branch (G-6503)
Playworks Dakota ....D....952 445-7529 Prior Lake (G-6948)
Positive Body Dynamics Inc ....E....952 920-9514 Minneapolis (G-5396)
▲ Regis Corp ....A....952 947-7777 Minneapolis (G-5504)
Restaurants No Limit Inc ....D....952 471-8513 Spring Park (G-9564)
Restaurants Unlimited Inc ....E....612 339-3800 Minneapolis (G-5530)
Rock Bottom of Minneapolis Inc ....D....612 332-2739 Minneapolis (G-5557)
Ruth's Hospitality Group Inc ....D....612 672-9000 Minneapolis (G-5578)
S & S Spa Salon Inc ....E....651 464-6612 Forest Lake (G-2168)
Sawatdee Inc ....E....612 338-6451 Minneapolis (G-5605)
Simonson Venture Inc ....E....763 494-4863 Osseo (G-6663)
Smarte Carte Inc ....D....651 429-3614 Saint Paul (G-8965)
Speak Easy Restaurant ....E....218 844-1326 Detroit Lakes (G-1216)
Spectrum Lanes Bowling Alley ....C....763 553-0333 Minneapolis (G-5718)
St Cloud Suite Hotel Inc ....D....320 654-1661 Saint Cloud (G-7606)
St Croix Preservation Co Inc ....E....651 439-6000 Stillwater (G-9644)
Starwood Hotels & Resorts ....C....612 331-1900 Minneapolis (G-5744)
Superior Concepts Inc ....D....952 892-7555 Burnsville (G-804)
Suzanne's Cuisine ....E....651 726-2535 Saint Paul (G-9018)
Town & Country Caterers Inc ....D....763 559-4461 Plymouth (G-6888)
Tri City American Legion ....E....651 631-1124 Saint Paul (G-9080)
Tri City Enterprises Inc ....E....952 888-4447 Minneapolis (G-5851)
Tri City Post 513 ....E....651 631-1124 Saint Paul (G-9081)
Trimark Hotel Corp ....C....612 305-9763 Minneapolis (G-5856)
Vee Corp ....E....612 333-2223 Minneapolis (G-5959)
VFW Gallagher-Hanson Post 295 ....E....651 455-1505 South Saint Paul (G-9550)
Victoria Inn ....D....320 587-6030 Hutchinson (G-2716)
Vintage Inc ....E....651 487-6878 Saint Paul (G-9130)
Weber & Barlow Stores Inc ....E....507 289-2444 Rochester (G-7286)
Wedding Chapel Inc ....E....763 533-4228 Minneapolis (G-6032)
West Central Turkeys LLC ....A....218 863-1491 Pelican Rapids (G-6784)

S I C

(G-00000) Company's Geographic Section entry number
490

2011 Harris Minnesota Services Directory

▲=Import ▼=Export ◆=Import/Export

Wild Golf Club ....C....952 445-3500
Prior Lake (G-6962)

Zuhrah Temple Trustees Inc ....E....612 871-3555
Minneapolis (G-6122)

73 BUSINESS SERVICES

7311 Advertising Agencies

Bbdo Worldwide Inc ....E....612 338-8401
Minneapolis (G-3875)

Campbell Mithun Inc ....B....612 347-1000
Minneapolis (G-3997)

Clarity Coverdale Fury Adv ....E....612 339-3902
Minneapolis (G-4101)

Cmgrp Inc ....C....952 832-5588
Minneapolis (G-4113)

Colle & McVoy Inc ....C....612 305-6000
Minneapolis (G-4119)

Compass Marketing Inc ....D....612 333-5300
Minneapolis (G-4147)

Concept Group Inc ....E....651 221-9710
Saint Paul (G-8245)

Creative Marketing Consulting ....E....952 935-9385
Saint Paul (G-8266)

Fallon Group Inc ....C....612 758-2345
Minneapolis (G-4405)

▲ Gabriel Degrood Bendt LLC ....E....612 547-5000
Minneapolis (G-4494)

H T Klatzky & Associates Inc ....E....218 728-3651
Duluth (G-1345)

Hot Dish Advertising LLC ....E....612 341-3100
Minneapolis (G-4681)

Intran Media LLC ....E....952 646-0036
Wayzata (G-9921)

J T Mega LLC ....E....952 929-1370
Minneapolis (G-4749)

Lacek Group Inc ....E....612 359-3700
Minneapolis (G-4833)

Laurence Cuneo & Associates ....D....952 707-1212
Minneapolis (G-4849)

Level Brand Inc ....E....612 338-8000
Minneapolis (G-4865)

Martin-Williams Inc ....C....612 340-0800
Minneapolis (G-4961)

Martin-Williams Inc ....E....612 746-3263
Minneapolis (G-4962)

Mobile Media Inc ....E....952 884-6201
Minneapolis (G-5115)

Modern Climate Inc ....E....612 343-8180
Minneapolis (G-5117)

Olson + Co Inc ....C....612 215-9800
Minneapolis (G-5271)

Popular Front Studio Inc ....E....612 362-0900
Minneapolis (G-5395)

Preston Kelly ....E....612 843-4000
Minneapolis (G-5406)

Richard Scales Advertising ....D....651 641-0226
Saint Paul (G-8899)

Risdall Marketing Group LLC ....D....651 286-6700
New Brighton (G-6413)

Rudisill Advertising ....E....651 636-0345
Stillwater (G-9638)

Uniquescreen Media Inc ....C....320 654-6578
Saint Cloud (G-7623)

Verified Credentials Inc ....D....952 985-2335
Lakeville (G-2940)

Wally Mc Carthys Oldsmobile ....D....651 636-6060
Saint Paul (G-9138)

Ware Tad & Co Inc ....E....612 338-2311
Minneapolis (G-6020)

Wiken Promotion & Advertising ....E....952 476-2002
Wayzata (G-9950)

7312 Outdoor Advertising Svcs

Clear Channel Outdoor Inc ....D....612 605-5100
Minneapolis (G-4108)

Magic Media Inc ....E....507 288-1866
Rochester (G-7168)

7313 Radio, TV & Publishers Adv Reps

Brite Signs LLC ....D....763 489-3841
Minneapolis (G-3951)

K J Country 965 ....E....218 736-7596
Fergus Falls (G-2080)

Kbmx Mix 108 Studio ....E....218 740-2649
Duluth (G-1367)

Public Safety Council ....E....763 550-9200
Minneapolis (G-5439)

Result Radio Inc ....E....218 736-7596
Fergus Falls (G-2118)

7319 Advertising, NEC

Alive Promo Inc ....E....952 960-3677
Minneapolis (G-3706)

Cash Plus Inc ....E....612 347-6900
Minneapolis (G-4024)

Cinedigm Digital Cinema Corp ....C....320 654-6578
Saint Cloud (G-7492)

ECM Publishers Inc ....E....763 712-2400
Minneapolis (G-3462)

Gage Group LLC ....C....763 595-3920
Minneapolis (G-4495)

Independent Delivery Services ....D....651 487-1050
Saint Paul (G-8508)

John Ryan Co Inc ....E....612 924-7700
Minnetonka (G-6182)

K-Tel International Inc 763 559-5566
Minneapolis (G-4787)

Lakeland Distribution Services ....E....320 762-8385
Alexandria (G-109)

Lawrence Service Co ....E....763 383-5700
Minneapolis (G-4850)

Marketing Architects Inc ....D....952 449-2500
Minnetonka (G-6190)

Nextmedia Outdoor Inc ....E....763 489-3841
Minneapolis (G-5198)

Novus Media Inc ....C....612 758-8625
Minneapolis (G-5251)

7322 Adjustment & Collection Svcs

Affiliated Group Inc ....D....507 280-7000
Rochester (G-7045)

Allied Interstate Inc ....B....952 595-2000
Plymouth (G-6846)

American Accounts & Advisors ....E....651 405-9760
Saint Paul (G-7696)

Array Services Group Inc ....C....320 534-3401
Sartell (G-9331)

Array Services Group Inc ....C....320 534-3680
Sauk Rapids (G-9357)

Bureau of Collection Recovery ....E....952 934-7777
Eden Prairie (G-1613)

Bureau of Collection Recovery ....E....320 214-8747
Willmar (G-9994)

Central Portfolio Control Inc ....E....952 944-5440
Eden Prairie (G-1620)

Chex Systems Inc ....B....651 361-2000
Saint Paul (G-9196)

Commercial Recovery Corp ....E....763 786-6333
Minneapolis (G-3438)

CU Recovery Inc ....E....651 462-4400
Wyoming (G-10201)

Dcm Services LLC ....C....763 852-8440
Minneapolis (G-4235)

Deceased Credit Management LLC 763 852-8400
Minneapolis (G-4238)

Diversified Adjustment Service ....C....763 783-2301
Minneapolis (G-3456)

Financial Recovery Services ....D....952 831-4800
Minneapolis (G-4432)

Homecomings Financial Network ....C....952 854-5432
Minneapolis (G-4669)

J C Christensen & Associates ....D....320 534-3629
Sartell (G-9337)

Jefferson Capital Systems LLC ....C....866 417-2561
Saint Cloud (G-7536)

Jnr Adjustment Co ....C....763 519-2710
Osseo (G-6624)

MCC Group Inc ....E....952 941-0552
Eden Prairie (G-1718)

Millennium Credit Consultants 651 306-9344
Saint Paul (G-7841)

National Recoveries Inc ....E....763 754-1931
Anoka (G-207)

Northland Group Inc ....D....952 831-4005
Minneapolis (G-5231)

Pinnacle Financial Group Inc ....D....952 996-0559
Minneapolis (G-5381)

Pinnacle Financial Group Inc ....D....763 295-0113
Monticello (G-6283)

▲ Receivables Control Corp ....D....763 315-9600
Osseo (G-6655)

Receivables Management Soln ....C....651 457-1130
Saint Paul (G-7891)

Triadvantage Credit Services ....B....651 255-2047
Saint Paul (G-7927)

VA Departmental Offices ....D....612 970-5700
Saint Paul (G-7966)

Viking Collection Service Inc ....B....952 944-7575
Eden Prairie (G-1804)

7323 Credit Reporting Svcs

Affiliated Group Inc ....D....507 280-7000
Rochester (G-7045)

Chex Systems Inc ....B....651 361-2000
Saint Paul (G-9196)

Dun & Bradstreet Inc ....E....952 841-9961
Bloomington (G-494)

MCC Group Inc ....E....952 941-0552
Eden Prairie (G-1718)

RELS LLC ....A....952 933-8804
Hopkins (G-2613)

Rental Research Services Inc ....E....952 935-5700
Hopkins (G-2615)

Tena Co's Inc ....C....651 293-1234
Saint Paul (G-9037)

Transunion LLC ....E....651 639-0007
Saint Paul (G-9077)

7331 Direct Mail Advertising Svcs

Action Mailing Services Inc ....D....763 557-6767
Minneapolis (G-3676)

Advanstar Holdings Corp 218 740-7200
Duluth (G-1232)

Air Park Dt & H ....E....218 723-4631
Duluth (G-1234)

Argenbright Inc ....C....320 543-3737
Howard Lake (G-2665)

Aria Communications Corp ....C....320 259-5206
Saint Cloud (G-7453)

▲ Arrowhead Promotion ....B....218 327-1165
Grand Rapids (G-2269)

Automated Mailing Corp ....D....612 333-4477
Minneapolis (G-3837)

Capitol Co's Inc ....D....651 454-4511
Saint Paul (G-7726)

Communication Mailing Services ....E....651 645-5280
Saint Paul (G-8234)

D B Direct Mail ....E....320 485-7827
Winsted (G-10160)

Denison Mailing Service Inc ....E....952 888-1460
Minneapolis (G-4247)

▲ Fulfillment Systems Inc ....D....763 295-3400
Monticello (G-6272)

Fulfillment Systems Inc ....D....320 255-0800
Saint Cloud (G-7514)

Gage Group LLC ....C....763 595-3920
Minneapolis (G-4495)

General Marketing Services Inc ....D....952 806-5080
Minneapolis (G-4511)

Harco Marketing Group Inc 952 432-6900
Saint Paul (G-7795)

I C System Inc ....C....651 486-0118
Saint Paul (G-8502)

Impact Mailing Of Minnesota ....D....612 521-6245
Minneapolis (G-4692)

Infinity Direct Inc ....E....763 559-1111
Minneapolis (G-4701)

Instant Web Inc ....A....320 616-5100
Little Falls (G-3008)

Japs-Olson Co ....A....952 932-9393
Minneapolis (G-4754)

Kandi-Works Developmental ....E....320 382-6156
Kandiyohi (G-2814)

Mail Handling Inc ....C....952 975-5000
Eden Prairie (G-1714)

Mercury Mailers Of Minnesota ....E....763 544-1881
Minneapolis (G-4990)

New ERA Incentives Inc ....E....651 486-0252
Saint Paul (G-8748)

North American Membership Grp ....D....952 988-7451
Shakopee (G-9459)

Novus Marketing Inc ....E....612 252-1618
Minneapolis (G-5250)

Paradysz Matera Co Inc ....D....952 544-5121
Minneapolis (G-5320)

Pgi Fulfillment Inc ....D....952 933-5745
Minnetonka (G-6213)

Professional Reproductions Inc ....E....952 946-1200
Edina (G-1841)

Promotion Management Center ....D....651 462-1213
Stacy (G-9580)

Rebs Supply Inc ....E....952 942-5457
Eden Prairie (G-1758)

Reinking Enterprises Inc ....D....763 428-1430
Rogers (G-7340)

Scicom Data Services Ltd ....C....952 933-4200
Minnetonka (G-6225)

United Business Mail Inc ....D....612 782-2044
Minneapolis (G-5907)

World Distribution Services ....D....651 686-9252
Saint Paul (G-7950)

7334 Photocopying & Duplicating Svcs

Albinson Reprographics LLC ....E....612 374-1120
Minneapolis (G-3703)

American Reprographics Co LLC ....D....612 722-2303
Minneapolis (G-3759)

▲ Bernard Group Inc ....D....952 934-1900
Chaska (G-954)

▲ Englund Graphics Inc ....E....763 536-9100
Minneapolis (G-4358)

Ers Digital Inc ....D....763 694-5900
Minneapolis (G-4369)

Fedex Office & Print Services ....E....651 699-9671
Saint Paul (G-8370)

Fedex Office & Print Services ....C....952 593-1143
Hopkins (G-2542)

Fedex Office & Print Services ....E....952 892-0200
Burnsville (G-721)

Fedex Office & Print Services ....E....612 822-7700
Minneapolis (G-4423)

Fedex Office & Print Services ....E....612 578-9000
Saint Paul (G-9217)

Fedex Office & Print Services ....E....952 943-4000
Eden Prairie (G-1664)

Franz Reprographics Inc ....E....763 503-3401
Minneapolis (G-4477)

Health Care Provider Service ....E....952 831-8114
Minneapolis (G-4618)

Minnesota Insty-Prints Inc ....E....612 332-8669
Minneapolis (G-5079)

National Business Systems Inc ....D....651 688-0202
Eagan (G-1540)

Nightowl Document Management ....D....612 337-0448
Minneapolis (G-5203)

Professional Reproductions Inc ....E....952 946-1200
Edina (G-1841)

Shel Don Group Inc ....E....218 727-2817
Duluth (G-1448)

Simtek Corp ....E....952 831-7472
Minneapolis (G-5678)

S I C

Xcellence Inc ....E....612 305-1330
Minneapolis (G-6091)
Xerox Corp....C....952 921-1300
Minneapolis (G-6093)

7335 Commercial Photography

Aero-Metric Inc....E....763 420-9606
Osseo (G-6593)
▲ David Kelloway ....E....952 944-0739
Minneapolis (G-4225)
Greer & Associates Inc....E....612 338-6171
Minneapolis (G-4564)
Professional Litho-Art Co Inc ....D....612 338-0400
Minneapolis (G-5420)
Ware Tad & Co Inc ....E....612 338-2311
Minneapolis (G-6020)

7336 Commercial Art & Graphic Design

Alpha Video & Audio Inc ....D....952 896-9898
Minneapolis (G-3733)
Christ's Household of Faith ....E....651 602-5600
Saint Paul (G-8199)
Cinedigm Digital Cinema Corp ....C....320 654-6578
Saint Cloud (G-7492)
Corporate Graphics Intl....C....651 494-1740
Saint Paul (G-8252)
Data Recognition Corp....E....763 268-2238
Minneapolis (G-4223)
Greer & Associates Inc....E....612 338-6171
Minneapolis (G-4564)
▲ Immedia Inc....C....612 524-3400
Minneapolis (G-4691)
Independent School District ....E....320 252-8770
Saint Cloud (G-7530)
International Paper Co....C....507 433-3467
Austin (G-278)
Intouch Inc....D....651 255-7700
Saint Paul (G-8523)
John Ryan Performance Inc....E....612 924-7700
Minneapolis (G-4771)
Knock Inc....E....612 333-6511
Minneapolis (G-4815)
Lafayette Litho Inc ....E....651 665-5617
Saint Paul (G-8555)
▼ Lakeshirts Inc ....B....218 847-2171
Detroit Lakes (G-1205)
Larsen Design Office Inc....E....952 835-2271
Minneapolis (G-4846)
Logos Productions Inc....E....651 451-9945
Inver Grove Heights (G-2760)
M Little & Co Inc....E....612 375-0077
Minneapolis (G-4922)
Marketing Concepts of MN....C....320 796-6245
Spicer (G-9557)
Media Relations Inc....E....612 798-7200
Burnsville (G-752)
Pace Deis Corp....E....651 702-2900
Saint Paul (G-9256)
Signsearch Inc....E....952 960-4470
Burnsville (G-797)
Target Brands Inc....E....612 304-6073
Minneapolis (G-5789)
Upfront Productions Inc....E....612 623-4433
Minneapolis (G-5933)
Visions Inc....D....763 425-4251
Brooklyn Park (G-621)
Vomela Specialty Co....C....651 228-2200
Saint Paul (G-9132)
Ware Tad & Co Inc ....E....612 338-2311
Minneapolis (G-6020)

7338 Secretarial & Court Reporting Svcs

Eggleston Medscribe Inc....E....763 971-5000
Minneapolis (G-4330)
Fedex Office & Print Services....C....952 593-1143
Hopkins (G-2542)
Jpg & Associates Inc....E....651 779-1072
Lake Elmo (G-2875)
Metro Legal Services Inc....D....612 332-0202
Minneapolis (G-5001)
Minnesota Clerical Inc....C....763 753-7243
Anoka (G-205)
Northern Counties Secretarial ....D....763 427-0166
Anoka (G-210)
Schawk Inc....E....651 636-0611
Saint Paul (G-8933)
7 West Secretarial Answering....E....952 936-4000
Eden Prairie (G-1775)
Soap Transcription Services....E....612 706-1588
Minneapolis (G-5693)

7342 Disinfecting & Pest Control Svcs

Adam's Pest Control Inc....E....763 478-9810
Hamel (G-2336)

7349 Building Cleaning & Maintenance Svcs, NEC

A-1 Maintenance Service Corp ....E....952 891-3711
Lakeville (G-2888)
A1 Contract Cleaning Inc ....E....763 544-3847
Minneapolis (G-3653)
ABM Janitorial Services - Nthn....E....612 378-0646
Minneapolis (G-3661)
Ace Building Maintenance Inc ....E....651 482-1020
Saint Paul (G-7980)
Americlean Janitorial Services....A....763 503-0707
Minneapolis (G-3763)
Amtech Lighting Services Co ....E....651 439-7440
Stillwater (G-9595)
Arnold's Supply & Kleenit Co ....C....507 289-2393
Rochester (G-7058)
Assured Decontamination Svcs ....D....651 998-0922
Lake Elmo (G-2865)
Beamkko....E....651 770-5661
Saint Paul (G-8096)
Belde Building Maintenance ....D....651 457-6337
South Saint Paul (G-9511)
Brighter Building Maintenance....E....651 293-1403
Saint Paul (G-8128)
Brunskill Enterprises....E....763 477-4546
Buffalo (G-636)
Building Maintenance Mgt....E....763 541-4886
Minneapolis (G-3974)
Building Material Supply Inc....E....763 252-5555
Golden Valley (G-2237)
Building Resources Inc....C....612 341-1111
Minneapolis (G-3975)
Burnsville Commercial Cleaning....E....952 469-5423
Lakeville (G-2893)
Buttweiler Environmental Inc....C....320 251-4385
Waite Park (G-9818)
Capital Maintenance Services....D....651 773-9777
Saint Paul (G-8152)
Carlson Building Maintenance....B....651 481-9970
Saint Paul (G-8166)
Ceda Inc ....E....763 434-4403
Anoka (G-163)
Ceiling Pro Interior Inc....E....952 947-0007
Eden Prairie (G-1617)
Champion Service Corp ....E....651 731-9137
Woodbury (G-10171)
Christians Inc ....E....952 470-2001
Chanhassen (G-916)
City Heights Inc....E....763 421-3345
Anoka (G-166)
Citywide Window Services Inc....E....763 421-3345
Anoka (G-168)
Clean-It Group Inc....C....952 943-1911
Hopkins (G-2532)
Cleaning Authority....E....763 717-9200
Minneapolis (G-3434)
Cleaning Management Group Inc ....E....952 881-8791
Minneapolis (G-4106)
Clear Water Cleaners Inc....D....320 558-6691
South Haven (G-9506)
Columbia Building Services Inc ....E....612 331-2090
Minneapolis (G-4124)
Deer River Hired Hands Inc....E....218 246-8182
Deer River (G-1169)
Dvcm ServiceMaster of The ....E....320 763-5551
Alexandria (G-96)
Enviromatic Corp of America....D....612 861-3330
Minneapolis (G-4362)
Epic Enterprise Inc....E....507 645-6800
Dundas (G-1511)
Ermc II LP....E....952 435-8182
Burnsville (G-719)
F B G Service Corp ....D....651 917-8059
Saint Paul (G-8357)
Fidelity Building Services Inc ....B....952 854-1447
Bloomington (G-497)
Five Star H Enterprises Inc ....D....612 867-5373
Minneapolis (G-4453)
Four TS Inc ....E....320 685-7407
Cold Spring (G-1086)
General Cleaning Corp....D....218 727-4513
Duluth (G-1333)
Guaranteed Clean Maintenance....D....651 644-9919
Saint Paul (G-8435)
Hanson McFarland Inc....D....763 421-9554
Anoka (G-188)
Hospitality Services Corp....C....763 323-3141
Rockford (G-7302)
Huber Bros Building Maintence....E....952 224-7000
Burnsville (G-733)
Independent School District ....E....218 723-4119
Duluth (G-1356)
ISS Facility Services Inc....E....763 559-6679
Minneapolis (G-4738)
Jubilee Enterprises Inc....E....507 532-2332
Marshall (G-3301)
Kim Kunwook....E....651 578-7627
Saint Paul (G-9236)
Kimmy Clean LLC ....E....952 758-4238
New Prague (G-6430)
L T T Inc ....E....952 929-4556
Minneapolis (G-4828)
Leone Enterprises Inc....C....763 427-9657
Anoka (G-199)
Linn Building Maintenance Inc ....D....651 778-1322
Saint Paul (G-8590)
Mac Enterprises Inc....E....612 789-9392
Minneapolis (G-4926)
Maintenance Professionals Inc....E....651 774-2334
Saint Paul (G-8608)
Maintenance Team....E....952 942-5000
Eden Prairie (G-1715)
Managed Services Inc....C....952 925-4111
Minneapolis (G-4940)
Marsden Holding LLC ....A....651 641-1717
Saint Paul (G-8615)
Marsh Heating & Air Condg....E....763 536-0667
Minneapolis (G-4957)
McCrady Janitorial Inc ....E....952 758-3097
New Prague (G-6432)
Melrose Diversicom Telephone....E....320 256-8288
Melrose (G-3349)
Minnesota Housekeeping Svcs....E....651 686-0900
Saint Paul (G-7842)
Multi-Services Inc ....D....952 944-4000
Eden Prairie (G-1732)
Osland Janitorial Supply Inc ....E....952 894-4815
Burnsville (G-773)
Oval Cleaning Service Inc....E....612 605-3166
Minneapolis (G-5303)
Paquette Maintenance Inc ....D....952 888-1801
Minneapolis (G-5318)
Picture Perfect Cleaning....E....612 865-4522
Farmington (G-2056)
Qsc of Northfield Inc ....E....507 366-7149
Northfield (G-6540)
Quality Building Maintenance ....D....507 289-0603
Rochester (G-7214)
Rbm Services Inc....D....952 361-0897
Chaska (G-978)
Retka Enterprises Inc....E....218 829-4076
Baxter (G-340)
Rick L Schoenrock ....E....320 763-7144
Alexandria (G-120)
Rusciano-Hyland Inc....E....612 871-4434
Minneapolis (G-5576)
S & D Cleaning....E....651 558-7336
Maplewood (G-3287)
S & L Team Cleaning....E....612 558-4502
Saint Paul (G-8917)
S D Q Ltd....C....952 929-5263
Minnetonka (G-6223)
ServiceMaster Inc....E....651 552-4979
Saint Paul (G-8946)
Servicemaster of St Cloud Inc....C....320 252-4622
Saint Cloud (G-7591)
ServiceMaster Total Cleaning ....C....952 873-6070
Saint Cloud (G-7592)
Shine-Way Janitorial Service ....D....507 388-7439
Mankato (G-3197)
SOS Janitorial Inc....E....763 560-9611
Minneapolis (G-5703)
Specialty Contracting Services....C....763 424-4100
Osseo (G-6666)
Sulco Cleaning Service....E....952 937-8777
Eden Prairie (G-1784)
Supreme Building Maintenance ....E....763 972-8425
Delano (G-1185)
Synera Solutions ....D....952 403-9911
Shakopee (G-9480)
Tidy Clean LLC ....D....507 344-1742
Mankato (G-3206)
Tidy Service of Minnesota Inc....E....612 332-5461
Hopkins (G-2646)
TLC Cleaning Specialists....E....218 263-4778
Hibbing (G-2477)
Total Quality Maintenance ....D....763 377-6530
Minneapolis (G-5834)
Triangle Services Inc....C....651 294-0020
Saint Paul (G-9082)
U M D Facilities Management....E....218 726-8262
Duluth (G-1488)
Vac System Industries of MN ....E....952 808-1616
Burnsville (G-816)
Woodfam Inc....E....218 283-4775
International Falls (G-2734)

7352 Medical Eqpt Rental & Leasing

Apria Healthcare Inc....C....952 404-1700
Minnetonka (G-6143)
Northwest Respiratory Services ....D....651 603-8720
Saint Paul (G-8767)
Rice Home Medical LLC....E....320 235-8434
Willmar (G-10040)
Sightpath Medical Inc....C....952 881-2500
Minneapolis (G-5668)
▲ Universal Hospital Services....D....952 893-3200
Minneapolis (G-5920)
Universal Hospital Services ....D....612 721-3374
Minneapolis (G-5919)

7353 Heavy Construction Eqpt Rental & Leasing

▲ Advance Equipment Co....E....651 489-8881
Saint Paul (G-7987)
Broadway Rental Equipment Co ....E....763 533-1680
Minneapolis (G-3952)
K R Wagner Inc....E....218 283-3700
International Falls (G-2725)
Penhall Co....E....763 542-9999
Minneapolis (G-5363)
▼ Phillippi Equipment Co....E....651 406-4900
Saint Paul (G-7875)
RSC Equipment Rental Inc ....E....763 509-2423
Minneapolis (G-5566)
RSC Equipment Rental Inc ....E....763 509-2400
Minneapolis (G-5564)
▲ Sowles Co....C....651 287-9700
Saint Paul (G-7910)

(G-00000) Company's Geographic Section entry number
492
2011 Harris Minnesota Services Directory
▲=Import ▼=Export ◆=Import/Export

Tri State Machinery Co ....E....952 224-1500
Burnsville *(G-812)*
Truck Crane Service-Illinois ....E....651 406-4949
Saint Paul *(G-7930)*
Truck Utilities Inc ....D....651 484-3305
Saint Paul *(G-9084)*
Ziegler Inc ....E....320 253-2234
Saint Cloud *(G-7635)*

7359 Equipment Rental & Leasing, NEC

A H Hermel Candy & Tobacco Co....D....507 387-5634
Mankato *(G-3098)*
A To Z International Inc ....E....612 729-2328
Minneapolis *(G-3650)*
Aarcee Party & Tent Rental ....E....952 922-7233
Minneapolis *(G-3657)*
Ace Nicollet Rental Place ....E....612 822-3121
Minneapolis *(G-3671)*
Advance Shoring Co....E....651 489-8881
Saint Paul *(G-7988)*
Alpha Video & Audio Inc ....D....952 896-9898
Minneapolis *(G-3733)*
Apres Inc....E....952 942-3399
Minneapolis *(G-3793)*
Bachman's Inc....C....612 861-7600
Minneapolis *(G-3856)*
Bemidji Aviation Services Inc ....E....612 726-1500
Minneapolis *(G-3882)*
Biffs Boxes LLC ....E....952 403-1221
Shakopee *(G-9422)*
Broadway Rental Equipment Co....E....763 533-1680
Minneapolis *(G-3952)*
Buerkle Buick Leasing Co....C....651 484-0231
Saint Paul *(G-8140)*
Bug Inc....E....952 445-1022
Shakopee *(G-9424)*
▲ Chester E Groth Music Co ....E....952 884-4772
Minneapolis *(G-4060)*
▲ CORT Business Services Corp ....E....651 405-0009
Saint Paul *(G-7737)*
Creekridge Capital LLC ....E....952 996-0270
Minneapolis *(G-4180)*
Duke Co's....D....612 331-4880
Minneapolis *(G-4289)*
◆ Electrosonic Inc....E....952 931-7500
Minnetonka *(G-6165)*
Elliott Aviation Inc....D....952 944-1200
Eden Prairie *(G-1654)*
Farnam Street Financial Inc ....E....952 908-0850
Hopkins *(G-2541)*
Geneva Capital LLC ....E....320 762-8400
Alexandria *(G-102)*
Glenwood-Inglewood Co....D....612 374-2253
Minneapolis *(G-4529)*
Home Depot USA Inc ....C....218 829-0341
Baxter *(G-329)*
Home Depot USA Inc ....C....763 422-1200
Minneapolis *(G-3490)*
Home Depot USA Inc ....C....763 509-9590
Minneapolis *(G-4667)*
Home Depot USA Inc ....C....651 452-2323
Eagan *(G-1530)*
Home Depot USA Inc ....C....763 717-0316
Minneapolis *(G-3491)*
Home Depot USA Inc ....C....952 432-7171
Saint Paul *(G-7800)*
Home Depot USA Inc ....C....320 235-1975
Willmar *(G-10010)*
Home Depot USA Inc ....C....952 496-3076
Shakopee *(G-9444)*
IFP Inc ....D....507 334-2730
Faribault *(G-2013)*
Imperial Leasing Inc....E....651 454-3330
Saint Paul *(G-7803)*
Information Systems Sciences ....E....507 754-4405
Elkton *(G-1907)*
Keinath Leasing Co....E....952 944-8000
Savage *(G-9392)*
Lpl LLC....E....952 345-8240
Edina *(G-1835)*
Lyon Financial Services Inc ....C....507 532-7763
Marshall *(G-3307)*
Maytag Coin-Op Washers....E....651 688-7000
Saint Paul *(G-7836)*
McDonald Rentals Inc....E....218 879-9060
Cloquet *(G-1056)*
Metro - Sales Inc....C....612 861-4000
Minneapolis *(G-5000)*
▲ Minnesota Supply Co ....D....952 828-7300
Eden Prairie *(G-1726)*
Modern Aero Inc....D....952 941-2595
Eden Prairie *(G-1729)*
Monaco Air Duluth LLC ....E....218 727-2911
Duluth *(G-1396)*
Norcostco Inc ....E....763 544-0601
Minneapolis *(G-5207)*
▲ Northern Dewatering Inc....D....763 428-2616
Rogers *(G-7332)*
Northland Capital Financial....E....320 252-2122
Saint Cloud *(G-7564)*
Northwest Aircraft Inc....E....612 726-2331
Saint Paul *(G-7854)*
Novus Inc....E....952 944-8152
Savage *(G-9402)*
On-Site Sanitation Inc....E....651 429-3781
Saint Paul *(G-8785)*
Pitney Bowes Inc....D....952 885-7287
Minneapolis *(G-5385)*
Pitney Bowes Inc....E....952 983-1600
Eden Prairie *(G-1749)*
Ricoh Americas Corp....D....651 294-2600
Mendota Heights *(G-3370)*
RSC Equipment Rental Inc....E....763 557-1234
Minneapolis *(G-5565)*
S E Rental ....E....507 765-3805
Preston *(G-6901)*
▲ Safety Signs Inc....E....952 469-6700
Lakeville *(G-2930)*
Sky Blue Leasing Inc ....E....320 692-2027
Brainerd *(G-586)*
Stearns County National Assn....E....320 253-6607
Saint Cloud *(G-7609)*
Temp-Air Inc ....D....952 707-5203
Burnsville *(G-807)*
Thunderbird Aviation Inc....E....952 941-1212
Eden Prairie *(G-1793)*
▲ Total Tool Supply Inc ....D....651 646-4055
Saint Paul *(G-9073)*
U-Haul Co of Minnesota....D....763 780-9746
Minneapolis *(G-3628)*
Vanman Co's Architects ....E....763 541-9552
Minneapolis *(G-5957)*
Winmark Capital Corp....D....763 520-8500
Minneapolis *(G-6076)*
Winmark Corp....C....763 520-8500
Minneapolis *(G-6077)*

7361 Employment Agencies

Advanced Care Inc....D....612 721-1957
Minneapolis *(G-3686)*
Advanced Practice Solutions....E....651 439-8484
Lake Elmo *(G-2864)*
Agri Temps Inc....D....320 235-1707
Willmar *(G-9982)*
Aliance Health Care Inc ....D....507 252-9737
Rochester *(G-7049)*
All Temporaries Inc....E....320 654-6031
Saint Cloud *(G-7446)*
Alliancenet Inc....E....952 934-4104
Chanhassen *(G-907)*
Allied Professionals Inc....B....952 832-5101
Minneapolis *(G-3716)*
Ambrion Inc ....E....952 278-1800
Minneapolis *(G-3742)*
Americare Staffing Service Inc ....D....651 917-1995
Saint Paul *(G-8035)*
Applied Staffing Inc ....E....763 502-1388
Fridley *(G-2190)*
Aquent LLC....D....952 851-3411
Minneapolis *(G-3794)*
Caremate Home Health Care Inc....C....651 659-0208
Saint Paul *(G-8164)*
Central Minnesota Jobs....D....763 271-3715
Monticello *(G-6266)*
Choice Unlimited Inc....D....218 724-5869
Duluth *(G-1270)*
City of Richfield....E....612 861-9385
Minneapolis *(G-4096)*
Comfort Home Health Care Group ....C....507 281-2332
Rochester *(G-7087)*
Consumer Directions Inc....A....320 420-3423
Saint Cloud *(G-7409)*
Contingent Work Force Soln....C....651 636-5624
Little Canada *(G-2995)*
County of Beltrami ....D....218 333-8206
Bemidji *(G-386)*
Crow River Technical Inc ....E....763 560-6015
Minneapolis *(G-4188)*
Dana Johnson ....E....651 774-5843
Saint Paul *(G-8281)*
Delta Co's LLC....E....952 929-5005
Minneapolis *(G-4245)*
Dobbs Temporary Services Inc ....E....612 373-2600
Minneapolis *(G-4268)*
Doherty Employment Group Inc ....E....952 832-8383
Minneapolis *(G-4270)*
East Suburban Resources Inc ....E....651 351-0190
Stillwater *(G-9611)*
Emerge Community Development....E....612 529-9267
Minneapolis *(G-4345)*
Employer Solutions Group....D....952 835-1288
Minneapolis *(G-4350)*
Fairview Health Line Home Care ....D....218 262-6982
Hibbing *(G-2443)*
Infosoft Group ....D....952 806-0631
Edina *(G-1833)*
Innovative Technical Personnel ....E....763 591-9191
Minneapolis *(G-4705)*
International Quality Homecare....E....507 451-6262
Owatonna *(G-6719)*
Jpg & Associates Inc....E....651 779-1072
Lake Elmo *(G-2875)*
Kforce Inc....E....952 835-5100
Minneapolis *(G-4803)*
Labor Services Co....B....952 884-0765
Minneapolis *(G-4830)*
Lifetrack Resources Inc....D....651 227-8471
Saint Paul *(G-8586)*
McKinley Group Inc ....E....952 476-2107
Hopkins *(G-2579)*
Minnesota Department of....E....507 537-6236
Marshall *(G-3313)*
Minnesota Professional Nursing....D....612 627-9524
Minneapolis *(G-5090)*
National Engineering Resources ....D....763 561-7610
Minneapolis *(G-5163)*
National Service Co of Iowa ....D....507 372-2276
Worthington *(G-10188)*
Newtown Solutions Inc ....E....952 440-4400
Savage *(G-9400)*
Nexpro Personnel Services Inc....D....952 224-9855
Minneapolis *(G-5196)*
Norman County Education Assoc ....E....218 356-8773
Gary *(G-2198)*
North Memorial Health Care ....D....763 520-3900
Minneapolis *(G-5216)*
Office Information Systems Inc....E....952 884-9199
Minneapolis *(G-5265)*
Platinum Staffing LLC....D....763 560-8430
Minneapolis *(G-5389)*
PPL Industries Inc ....D....612 332-0664
Minneapolis *(G-5399)*
Precision Design Inc ....E....952 933-6550
Hopkins *(G-2604)*
Primestaff Inc....C....651 697-2120
Saint Paul *(G-8848)*
Private Industry Council ....E....507 537-6236
Marshall *(G-3322)*
Professional Alternatives L L ....E....952 404-2600
Wayzata *(G-9936)*
Programming Solutions Inc....E....763 424-8154
Minneapolis *(G-5424)*
REM Health Inc ....E....952 926-9808
Minneapolis *(G-5509)*
Resource Group Inc ....E....952 974-9225
Chanhassen *(G-937)*
Resource Inc....E....952 925-9195
Minneapolis *(G-5528)*
Resources For You Inc ....D....320 864-5871
Glencoe *(G-2212)*
Rural Minnesota Cep Inc....E....218 755-4458
Bemidji *(G-424)*
Salo Project LLC....D....612 230-7256
Minneapolis *(G-5593)*
Salo Search LLC ....E....612 230-7256
Minneapolis *(G-5594)*
Sapphire Technologies, LP ....D....612 332-8700
Minneapolis *(G-5602)*
Sfn Group Inc....B....952 467-1770
Young America *(G-10210)*
Spectrum Community Health Inc ....E....218 326-4202
Grand Rapids *(G-2308)*
Talus Group Inc ....E....952 544-2526
Excelsior *(G-1954)*
Tech Central Inc....C....952 837-8000
Minneapolis *(G-5805)*
Tempworks Software Inc ....D....651 452-0366
Saint Paul *(G-7920)*
Valere LLC....E....763 390-9286
White Bear Lake *(G-9979)*
Vantro Systems LLC ....E....952 890-2080
Burnsville *(G-817)*
Westaff Inc ....C....218 463-4418
Roseau *(G-7359)*
Wilson Learning Corp ....D....952 944-2880
Minneapolis *(G-6075)*
Work Connection Inc....D....320 693-8871
Litchfield *(G-2994)*

7363 Help Supply Svcs

Accessible Space Inc....E....651 645-7271
Saint Paul *(G-7975)*
Accessible Space Inc....E....651 690-5216
Saint Paul *(G-7974)*
Advanced Auto Transport Inc ....C....651 777-7780
Saint Paul *(G-7990)*
Agri Temps Inc....D....320 235-1707
Willmar *(G-9982)*
Agri Temps Inc....E....320 235-5230
Willmar *(G-9981)*
Allied Professionals Inc....B....952 832-5101
Minneapolis *(G-3716)*
▼ American Telecare Inc....E....952 897-0000
Eden Prairie *(G-1591)*
Ampro Services Inc....E....651 631-5924
Saint Paul *(G-8046)*
Association For The Solidatary....C....952 456-1751
Saint Paul *(G-8075)*
Atlantis Technical Services ....E....763 657-2500
Osseo *(G-6595)*
Care Network Inc....E....651 647-5400
Saint Paul *(G-8161)*
CDI Corp....D....507 282-8773
Rochester *(G-7072)*
Cynthia Cook Inc ....E....952 854-4975
Minneapolis *(G-4210)*
Delta Co's LLC....E....952 929-5005
Minneapolis *(G-4245)*
Dfg Inc ....D....612 343-8936
Minneapolis *(G-4250)*
Dobbs Temporary Services Inc....E....612 373-2600
Minneapolis *(G-4268)*
Doherty Employment Group Inc ....E....952 832-8383
Minneapolis *(G-4270)*
Doherty Staffing Solutions ....D....952 832-8300
Edina *(G-1829)*
Elite Healthcare Staffing Inc....C....763 315-4488
Osseo *(G-6614)*

S I C

Employment codes: A=Over 500 employees, B=251-500
C=101-250, D=51-100, E=25-50

2011 Harris Minnesota
Services Directory

© Harris InfoSource 1-866-281-6415
493

Emp Serv L L C ....E....507 825-4211
Pipestone (G-6825)
Empo Corp ....E....612 285-8707
Minneapolis (G-4352)
Entegee Inc ....E....763 383-4343
Minneapolis (G-4359)
Entegee Inc ....E....651 739-7366
Saint Paul (G-9215)
Executive Services Midwest LLC ....E....952 469-4755
Lakeville (G-2905)
Gary Halgran ....B....651 917-3634
Saint Paul (G-8402)
George Konik Associates Inc ....D....952 835-5550
Minneapolis (G-4524)
Gradstaff Inc ....E....612 339-5332
Minneapolis (G-4545)
Health Orientated Pool ....E....507 452-1646
Winona (G-10100)
Healthcare Options Inc ....C....763 545-3042
Minneapolis (G-4619)
Hicks Trucking Inc ....E....320 693-3292
Litchfield (G-2986)
Hire Thinking Inc ....E....612 339-0535
Minneapolis (G-4654)
IG Inc ....D....612 338-7581
Minneapolis (G-4687)
Industrial Help Inc ....E....612 871-5650
Minneapolis (G-4698)
Interim Healthcare Of Lake ....B....218 722-0053
Duluth (G-1359)
J-I-T Services Inc ....E....763 545-6991
Hopkins (G-2560)
John Robert Powers Inc ....E....952 854-8577
Minneapolis (G-4770)
Jpg & Associates Inc ....E....651 779-1072
Lake Elmo (G-2875)
Klick & Associate Inc ....E....763 420-3296
Osseo (G-6627)
M S I Services ....E....763 572-0500
Minneapolis (G-4924)
Manpower Inc ....E....952 831-3338
Minneapolis (G-4943)
Midwest Driver Corp ....B....952 884-0765
Minneapolis (G-5027)
Minnesota Care Staffing Inc ....C....612 216-1938
Minneapolis (G-5070)
Minnesota Professional Nursing ....D....612 627-9524
Minneapolis (G-5090)
Minnesota Prophy Power Inc ....D....952 898-1594
Lakeville (G-2920)
Montage Inc ....E....651 633-1955
Saint Paul (G-8718)
National Engineering Resources ....D....763 561-7610
Minneapolis (G-5163)
Northern Counties Secretarial ....D....763 427-0166
Anoka (G-210)
People's Express Inc ....E....218 631-2909
Wadena (G-9808)
Physical Distribution Services ....E....952 884-0765
Minneapolis (G-5376)
Pride Institute Inc ....E....952 934-7554
Eden Prairie (G-1753)
Primestaff Inc ....C....651 697-2120
Saint Paul (G-8848)
Professional Radiology Svcs ....D....763 560-0010
Minneapolis (G-5422)
Right Staff Inc ....E....952 546-1100
Hopkins (G-2617)
Robert Half International Inc ....D....612 339-9001
Minneapolis (G-5553)
Robert Half International Inc ....E....952 831-5970
Minneapolis (G-5554)
Robert Half International Inc ....E....651 293-8033
Saint Paul (G-8907)
Royale Resources Inc ....D....218 346-3000
Perham (G-6802)
Rusciano-Hyland Inc ....E....612 871-4434
Minneapolis (G-5576)
Sapphire Technologies, LP ....D....612 332-8700
Minneapolis (G-5602)
SAR Inc ....E....507 373-7129
Albert Lea (G-64)
Severson Transport Inc ....E....507 454-5090
Winona (G-10127)
Sfn Group Inc ....C....952 543-3300
Minneapolis (G-5646)
Sfn Group Inc ....C....952 469-7583
Lakeville (G-2933)
Sfn Group Inc ....D....651 501-5037
Saint Paul (G-9272)
Summit Employment Inc ....D....651 501-0531
Saint Paul (G-9279)
Sundance Staffing Minnesota ....D....763 559-7700
Minneapolis (G-5765)
Sureservices Inc ....E....763 531-0029
Minneapolis (G-5772)
Synico Staffing Inc ....A....612 926-6000
Minneapolis (G-5780)
Teaching Temps Inc ....E....763 797-9000
Minneapolis (G-5802)
Tech Central Inc ....C....952 837-8000
Minneapolis (G-5805)
Transit TEC Ltd ....D....320 253-5940
Saint Cloud (G-7618)
Transport Leasing Contract Inc ....E....763 585-7000
Minneapolis (G-5848)
Trueblue Inc ....C....218 624-6222
Duluth (G-1487)
Uplink Staffing ....E....763 781-8888
Minneapolis (G-5935)

7371 Custom Computer Programming Svcs

Acuo Technologies LLC ....E....952 905-3440
Bloomington (G-481)
Advanced Informatics LLC ....E....612 253-0130
Minneapolis (G-3689)
Ahles & Associates LLC ....E....952 935-8554
Hopkins (G-2504)
Alebra Technologies Inc ....E....651 366-6140
Saint Paul (G-8008)
Allen Interactions Inc ....E....651 203-3700
Saint Paul (G-7691)
Amano McGann Inc ....E....612 331-2020
Minneapolis (G-3739)
Ambient Consulting LLC ....C....763 582-9000
Minneapolis (G-3741)
Analysts International Corp ....C....952 835-5900
Minneapolis (G-3773)
Analysts International Corp ....E....507 280-6663
Rochester (G-7055)
Analytiks International Inc ....E....612 305-4312
Minneapolis (G-3774)
API Outsourcing Inc ....E....651 675-2600
Eagan (G-1515)
API Outsourcing Inc ....E....218 834-8007
Two Harbors (G-9704)
Aquent LLC ....D....952 851-3411
Minneapolis (G-3794)
Architecture Technology Corp ....E....952 829-5864
Eden Prairie (G-1595)
Arran Technologies Inc ....E....651 468-0002
Saint Paul (G-8064)
Avantgard ....E....952 935-3300
Hopkins (G-2514)
Avionte LLC ....E....651 556-2121
Eagan (G-1516)
Aware Systems Inc ....E....800 783-8919
Minneapolis (G-3849)
Axonom Inc ....E....952 653-0400
Minneapolis (G-3851)
Bi Consulting Group LLC ....D....651 403-6500
Saint Paul (G-7720)
Biomedix Vascular Solutions ....E....651 762-4010
Saint Paul (G-8114)
Blaschko Computers Inc ....E....320 252-0234
Saint Cloud (G-7460)
Born Information Services Inc ....D....763 404-4000
Minneapolis (G-3931)
Christopherson, John ....D....952 814-7185
Minneapolis (G-4072)
Ciber Inc ....D....507 280-9267
Rochester (G-7077)
Citi Investor Services Inc ....E....218 825-0552
Brainerd (G-557)
Computer Sciences Corp ....E....763 593-1122
Minneapolis (G-4148)
Comsys Information Technology ....C....612 630-9100
Minneapolis (G-4149)
Csi International ....E....952 882-9115
Burnsville (G-704)
Dahl Consulting Inc ....A....651 772-9225
Saint Paul (G-8277)
Dayport Inc ....E....507 344-3000
Mankato (G-3122)
Development Resource Group Inc ....D....763 783-7878
Saint Paul (G-8290)
Distributed Website Corp ....E....507 453-5164
Winona (G-10093)
Diverse Computer Corp ....E....651 766-8138
Saint Paul (G-8301)
Exact Software Erp-Na Inc ....D....952 831-7182
Minneapolis (G-4381)
▲ Fargo Electronics Inc ....C....952 941-9470
Eden Prairie (G-1663)
Fpx LLC ....E....866 826-6344
Mankato (G-3129)
Fujitsu America Inc ....E....763 595-9600
Minneapolis (G-4489)
Fujitsu Consulting Information ....B....952 258-6000
Minnetonka (G-6171)
Global Case Technology Inc ....E....763 553-1313
Minneapolis (G-4531)
Global Communication Services ....E....952 890-3911
Burnsville (G-729)
Grocery Shopping Network ....E....952 345-3232
Minneapolis (G-4573)
Grocery Shopping Network Inc ....E....612 746-4232
Minneapolis (G-4574)
Icentera Inc ....E....952 898-0888
Burnsville (G-734)
Imagetrend Inc ....C....952 469-1589
Lakeville (G-2910)
Infinite Campus Inc ....C....651 631-0000
Minneapolis (G-3499)
Ingenix Inc ....B....952 833-7100
Eden Prairie (G-1692)
Innovative Computer Systems ....E....952 934-5665
Eden Prairie (G-1694)
Integral 7 Inc ....E....612 436-0701
Minneapolis (G-4712)
Intertech Inc ....E....651 994-8558
Saint Paul (G-7806)
Lake Superior Software Inc ....C....952 941-1000
Eden Prairie (G-1705)
Lancet Software Development ....E....952 230-7360
Burnsville (G-747)
Lawson Software Americas Inc ....A....651 767-7000
Saint Paul (G-8569)
Lawson Software Inc ....A....651 767-7000
Saint Paul (G-8570)
Lighthouse1 LLC ....C....952 852-7099
Minneapolis (G-4884)
Lindenberg & Associates - Twin ....E....612 375-0234
Minneapolis (G-4889)
Local Government Information ....E....763 543-2600
Minneapolis (G-4896)
Macro Group Inc ....E....612 332-7880
Minneapolis (G-4929)
Magenic Technologies Inc ....C....763 398-4800
Minneapolis (G-4932)
Marix Technologies Inc ....E....952 582-9100
Hopkins (G-2575)
McG Energy Solutions LLC ....E....612 376-7757
Minneapolis (G-4973)
Media Relations Inc ....E....612 798-7200
Burnsville (G-752)
Meritide Inc ....E....651 255-7300
Saint Paul (G-8636)
Mhc Software Inc ....D....952 882-0884
Burnsville (G-756)
Millionzillion Software Inc ....E....952 932-9048
Minneapolis (G-5047)
Mortgage Resource Center Inc ....E....651 683-9705
Eagan (G-1539)
Myseeks Inc ....E....651 967-4150
Saint Paul Park (G-9297)
Network Instruments LLC ....E....952 358-3800
Minnetonka (G-6201)
▼ New Boundary Technologies Inc ....E....612 379-3805
Minneapolis (G-5186)
Northshore Resources Inc ....E....612 375-0315
Minneapolis (G-5236)
Nternational Projects ....D....952 541-4888
Minneapolis (G-5254)
Olsen Thielen Technologies Inc ....C....651 483-4521
Saint Paul (G-8781)
Open Access Technology Intl ....B....763 201-2000
Minneapolis (G-5283)
▲ Open Systems International Inc ....D....763 551-0559
Minneapolis (G-5284)
Open-C Solutions Inc ....D....952 842-3200
Minneapolis (G-5285)
Pareo Inc ....E....612 371-0400
Minneapolis (G-5326)
Powel Inc ....E....651 251-3005
Saint Paul (G-7879)
Procon Co's Inc ....E....952 258-6300
Minneapolis (G-5415)
Programming Solutions Inc ....E....763 424-8154
Minneapolis (G-5424)
Provation Medical Inc ....C....612 313-1500
Minneapolis (G-5431)
Publishing Business Systems ....D....651 639-0662
Saint Paul (G-8856)
Quantum Retail Technology Inc ....E....612 486-3491
Minneapolis (G-5446)
Quest Software Inc ....E....952 229-3500
Eden Prairie (G-1756)
Reshare Corp ....E....952 908-0818
Minneapolis (G-5522)
Rjs Software Systems Inc ....E....952 736-5800
Burnsville (G-792)
Rural Computer Consultants Inc ....E....320 365-4027
Bird Island (G-468)
Sadaka Technology Consultants ....A....952 841-6363
Minneapolis (G-5586)
SafeNet Consulting Inc ....D....952 930-3636
Minnetonka (G-6224)
Sagitec Solutions LLC ....D....612 235-4122
Saint Paul (G-8922)
Scout Information Services Inc ....E....651 686-4646
Saint Paul (G-7899)
Secure Computing Corp ....C....651 628-2700
Saint Paul (G-8943)
Shavlik Technologies LLC ....D....651 426-6624
Saint Paul (G-8948)
Sierra Bravo Corp ....C....952 948-1211
Bloomington (G-516)
Smart Data Solutions Inc ....E....651 690-3140
Saint Paul (G-7906)
Softbrands Inc ....D....612 851-1500
Minneapolis (G-5695)
Softbrands Manufacturing Inc ....C....612 851-1500
Minneapolis (G-5696)
Solid Logic Computer Solutions ....E....952 949-0140
Eden Prairie (G-1780)
Spanlink Communications Inc ....D....763 971-2000
Minneapolis (G-5715)
Spss Inc ....C....507 287-2835
Rochester (G-7262)
SSIT North America Inc ....C....952 857-1600
Minneapolis (G-5726)
Sterling Commerce Inc ....D....952 294-1800
Eden Prairie (G-1782)
Strategic Technologies Inc ....E....763 559-1959
Minneapolis (G-5758)
Sudhko Inc ....E....952 595-8500
Hopkins (G-2638)
T M B Consulting Inc ....D....952 249-1223
Wayzata (G-9944)
Talent Technical Services Inc ....C....952 417-3600
Minneapolis (G-5786)

(G-00000) Company's Geographic Section entry number
494
2011 Harris Minnesota
Services Directory
▲=Import ▼=Export
◆=Import/Export

Team Informatics Inc ....E....651 222-8326
Saint Paul (G-9030)
Tech-Pro Inc ....B....651 634-1400
Saint Paul (G-9032)
Technology & Information....D....651 999-6001
Saint Paul (G-9033)
Testquest Inc....E....952 936-7887
Chanhassen (G-943)
Thomson Reuters LLC....E....651 846-2000
Saint Paul (G-9042)
3-D CNC Inc....E....320 587-5923
Hutchinson (G-2713)
Towers Watson Delaware Inc....C....952 842-7000
Minneapolis (G-5839)
Unimax Systems Corp....E....612 341-0946
Minneapolis (G-5903)
Unisys Corp....A....651 635-7777
Saint Paul (G-9103)
Vacava Inc....E....507 252-9076
Rochester (G-7278)
Vericenter Minnesota Inc....D....952 918-2000
Saint Paul (G-9126)
Verisae Inc....E....612 455-2305
Minneapolis (G-5964)
Virtelligence Inc....C....952 746-9220
Eden Prairie (G-1806)
Virteva LLC....E....952 843-1200
Saint Louis Park (G-7670)
Vision Solutions Inc....E....507 252-3440
Rochester (G-7284)
Visions Inc....D....763 425-4251
Brooklyn Park (G-621)
▲ Wand Corp....C....952 361-6200
Eden Prairie (G-1813)
Warecorp....D....952 938-5448
Hopkins (G-2658)
Weidt Group Inc....E....952 938-1588
Hopkins (G-2659)

7372 Prepackaged Software

Adobe Systems Inc....E....651 766-4700
Saint Paul (G-7982)
Agvantage Software Inc....E....507 282-6353
Rochester (G-7046)
Alignex Inc....E....952 888-6801
Minneapolis (G-3705)
Amcom Software Inc....D....952 230-5200
Hopkins (G-2508)
Architecture Technology Corp....E....952 829-5864
Eden Prairie (G-1595)
Business Microvar Inc....E....651 639-0575
Saint Paul (G-8143)
Ca Inc....C....952 838-1186
Minneapolis (G-3988)
Carefacts Information Systems....E....651 636-3890
Saint Paul (G-8163)
Corporate Travel Services Inc....D....651 287-4900
Saint Paul (G-8253)
Cygnia Corp....E....952 887-9030
Minneapolis (G-4209)
Digital River Inc....B....952 253-1234
Eden Prairie (G-1645)
Easy Automation Inc....E....507 728-8214
Welcome (G-9958)
Ecologic Analytics LLC....E....952 843-6000
Bloomington (G-495)
Educational Biometric Tech....E....507 724-5773
Caledonia (G-827)
Electro-Sensors Inc....E....952 930-0100
Minnetonka (G-6164)
EMC Corp....C....952 828-9005
Eden Prairie (G-1656)
Epicor Software Corp....C....952 417-1400
Minneapolis (G-4364)
Expert Software Inc....E....952 918-9400
Eden Prairie (G-1659)
▲ Fair Isaac Corp....B....612 758-5200
Minneapolis (G-4392)
Fishel Information Systems Inc....E....952 544-1108
Hopkins (G-2543)
Four51 Inc....E....952 294-0451
Bloomington (G-498)
Fpx LLC....D....507 388-5000
Mankato (G-3128)
Fpx LLC....E....866 826-6344
Mankato (G-3129)
George Konik Associates Inc....D....952 835-5550
Minneapolis (G-4524)
Hyperion Solutions Corp....E....952 837-2680
Minneapolis (G-4684)
Innovative Computer Systems....E....952 934-5665
Eden Prairie (G-1694)
Interplx Inc....E....952 403-7180
Shakopee (G-9446)
Kroll Ontrack Inc....C....952 937-1107
Eden Prairie (G-1704)
Lawson Software Americas Inc....A....651 767-7000
Saint Paul (G-8569)
Lawson Software Inc....A....651 767-7000
Saint Paul (G-8570)
Makemusic Inc....D....952 937-9611
Eden Prairie (G-1716)
Melyx Corp....E....763 428-6000
Rogers (G-7330)
Microsoft Corp....D....952 832-8000
Minneapolis (G-5019)
MQ Software Inc....D....952 345-8720
Minneapolis (G-5143)
▲ Ncs Pearson Inc....A....952 681-3000
Minneapolis (G-5177)
Network Instruments LLC....E....952 358-3800
Minnetonka (G-6201)
Nternational Projects....D....952 541-4888
Minneapolis (G-5254)
ObjectFX Corp....E....612 312-2002
Minneapolis (G-5260)
Open Systems Holdings Corp....E....952 403-5700
Shakopee (G-9463)
Open Systems Inc....D....952 403-5700
Shakopee (G-9464)
Oracle Systems Corp....B....612 587-5000
Minneapolis (G-5288)
Paisley Consulting Inc....C....320 286-5870
Cokato (G-1077)
Patterson Co's Inc....C....651 686-1600
Saint Paul (G-7866)
Plato Learning Inc....C....952 832-1000
Bloomington (G-510)
Quest Software Inc....E....952 229-3500
Eden Prairie (G-1756)
RC Erickson & Associates Inc....E....651 452-6758
Saint Paul (G-7889)
Rural Computer Consultants Inc....E....320 365-4027
Bird Island (G-468)
S P S S Inc....D....507 287-2800
Rochester (G-7244)
◆ Scantron Corp....C....651 683-6000
Eagan (G-1550)
Shavlik Technologies Corp....D....651 426-6624
Saint Paul (G-8947)
Siemens Product Lifecycle Mgt....D....651 482-4219
Saint Paul (G-8956)
Sisu Medical Solutions LLC....D....218 529-7900
Duluth (G-1451)
▲ Smead Manufacturing Co Inc....B....651 437-4111
Hastings (G-2406)
Sopheon Corp....E....952 851-7555
Minneapolis (G-5702)
Startech Computing Inc....E....651 385-0607
Red Wing (G-7006)
Sungard Financial Systems LLC....B....952 935-3300
Hopkins (G-2639)
Symantec Corp....B....651 746-7000
Saint Paul (G-9020)
Synergistic Software Soln....E....612 367-7300
Minneapolis (G-5779)
Tempworks Software Inc....D....651 452-0366
Saint Paul (G-7920)
Testquest Inc....E....952 936-7887
Chanhassen (G-943)
TMC Enterprises Inc....E....952 943-9077
Eden Prairie (G-1794)
TriMin Systems Inc....E....651 636-7667
Saint Paul (G-9083)
Virtelligence Inc....C....952 746-9220
Eden Prairie (G-1806)
Vital Images Inc....C....952 487-9500
Minnetonka (G-6235)
XATA Corp....C....952 707-5600
Eden Prairie (G-1818)

7373 Computer Integrated Systems Design

Advanced Communication Design....E....952 854-4000
Bloomington (G-482)
Americom Inc....E....651 726-2200
Saint Paul (G-8036)
Anertec Holdings LLC....E....507 451-5430
Owatonna (G-6693)
Applied Statistics Inc....D....763 268-0696
Minneapolis (G-3792)
Architecture Technology Corp....E....952 829-5864
Eden Prairie (G-1595)
Avista Solutions International....E....952 949-0594
Minneapolis (G-3843)
Berbee Information Networks....D....763 592-5800
Minneapolis (G-3886)
Blaschko Computers Inc....E....320 252-0234
Saint Cloud (G-7460)
Citon Computer Corp....E....218 720-4435
Duluth (G-1274)
Comm-Works Holdings LLC....D....763 258-5800
Minneapolis (G-4130)
Computer Integration Techs....D....651 450-0333
Saint Paul (G-9198)
Datalink Corp....D....952 944-3462
Chanhassen (G-917)
Datatrend Technologies Inc....E....952 931-1203
Minnetonka (G-6160)
Digital Datavoice Corp....E....651 452-0300
Saint Paul (G-7752)
Digital Images Inc....651 688-0888
Saint Paul (G-7753)
Digital River Inc....B....952 253-1234
Eden Prairie (G-1645)
Dynixa Corp....B....651 436-8800
Lakeland (G-2884)
▲ Ergotron Inc....C....651 681-7600
Saint Paul (G-7769)
Evolving Systems Inc....E....763 516-6500
Hamel (G-2340)
Gb Lumina Inc....E....763 797-9036
Minneapolis (G-4504)
Hardcore Computer Inc....E....507 285-0101
Rochester (G-7132)
Healthland Inc....C....320 634-5331
Glenwood (G-2226)
High Wire Networks Inc....952 934-9080
Eden Prairie (G-1685)
Highjump Software Inc....D....952 947-4088
Eden Prairie (G-1686)
Information Builders Inc....E....651 602-9100
Saint Paul (G-8512)
Intercim LLC....E....651 289-5700
Eagan (G-1532)
Itasca Consulting Group Inc....E....612 371-4711
Minneapolis (G-4741)
Ivo Appliance Inc....D....650 286-1300
Minneapolis (G-4742)
McData Services Corp....B....763 268-6000
Minneapolis (G-4972)
McKesson Information Solutions....C....651 697-5900
Saint Paul (G-8625)
N'Compass Solutions Inc....E....612 379-2100
Minneapolis (G-5155)
Navitaire Inc....C....612 317-7000
Minneapolis (G-5176)
Network Design Inc....E....763 475-5500
Minneapolis (G-5184)
Nortel Networks Inc....E....952 897-1150
Minneapolis (G-5211)
Nternational Projects....D....952 541-4888
Minneapolis (G-5254)
Nuvo Network Management....D....952 933-4600
Hopkins (G-2592)
ORBIT Systems Inc....D....651 767-3322
Saint Paul (G-7858)
Parallel Technologies Inc....C....952 920-7185
Minneapolis (G-5322)
Pcr Computer Services....E....763 557-6824
Minneapolis (G-5354)
▲ PeopleNet Communications Corp....C....952 908-6200
Minnetonka (G-6209)
Renovo Software Inc....E....952 931-0790
Minneapolis (G-5519)
Sadaka Technology Consultants....A....952 841-6363
Minneapolis (G-5586)
SafeNet Consulting Inc....D....952 930-3636
Minnetonka (G-6224)
Sartell Group Inc....D....612 548-3101
Minneapolis (G-5603)
Schwan's Technology Group Inc....D....651 388-1821
Red Wing (G-7005)
Sovran Inc....E....651 686-0515
Eagan (G-1552)
Spanlink Communications Inc....D....763 971-2000
Minneapolis (G-5715)
Spc Communications Inc....E....952 912-2800
Minneapolis (G-5716)
Startech Computing Inc....E....651 385-0607
Red Wing (G-7006)
TAJ Technologies Inc....D....651 405-7412
Mendota Heights (G-3371)
Tricord Systems Inc....E....763 557-9005
Minneapolis (G-5855)
Unisys Corp....A....651 687-2200
Saint Paul (G-7935)
Virtelligence Inc....C....952 746-9220
Eden Prairie (G-1806)
Visions Inc....D....763 425-4251
Brooklyn Park (G-621)
Wireless Ronin Technologies....E....952 564-3500
Minnetonka (G-6238)
Wyde Corp....D....651 882-2400
Eagan (G-1562)

7374 Data & Computer Processing & Preparation

Abraham Technical Services Inc....E....763 428-3170
Rogers (G-7315)
Adapt Inc....E....952 939-0538
Hopkins (G-2500)
Ambient Consulting LLC....C....763 582-9000
Minneapolis (G-3741)
AMI Imaging Systems Inc....E....952 828-0080
Bloomington (G-485)
Aquent LLC....D....952 851-3411
Minneapolis (G-3794)
▲ Arrowhead Promotion....B....218 327-1165
Grand Rapids (G-2269)
Atomic Playpen Inc....E....763 231-3400
Minneapolis (G-3832)
Automatic Data Processing Inc....B....952 814-5800
Minneapolis (G-3838)
Bremer Financial Services Inc....D....651 227-7621
Saint Paul (G-8126)
Bremer Financial Services Inc....C....651 734-4040
Lake Elmo (G-2866)
Catalog Marketing Services....C....651 636-6265
Minneapolis (G-4027)
Computer Sciences Corp....E....763 593-1122
Minneapolis (G-4148)
Comsys Information Technology....C....612 630-9100
Minneapolis (G-4149)
County of Ramsey....D....651 266-3400
Saint Paul (G-8257)
Data Recognition Corp....E....763 268-2238
Minneapolis (G-4223)

S I C

Data Solutions International....E....952 943-8137
Minnetonka (G-6158)
Digitiliti Inc....E....651 925-3200
Saint Paul (G-8296)
Ebureau LLC....E....320 534-5000
Saint Cloud (G-7502)
Efunds Corp....A....651 361-2000
Saint Paul (G-9210)
Fairview Health Services....C....612 672-6800
Minneapolis (G-4393)
Fidelity National Information....D....651 855-6500
Lake Elmo (G-2871)
Fifty Below Sales & Marketing....C....218 720-4828
Duluth (G-1322)
Go E Bizcom....E....651 454-0013
Saint Paul (G-7784)
Gov Delivery Inc....D....866 276-5583
Saint Paul (G-8424)
Helgeson Enterprises Inc....D....651 762-9700
Saint Paul (G-8476)
Hickory Tech Information Soln....D....507 625-1691
Mankato (G-3139)
Hickory Tech Information Soln....D....507 625-1691
Mankato (G-3140)
Imaginet LLC....D....612 752-5500
Minneapolis (G-4689)
Impact Mailing Of Minnesota....D....612 521-6245
Minneapolis (G-4692)
Isaac Fair Corp....B....651 482-8593
Saint Paul (G-8524)
Klein Financial Inc....D....952 448-2924
Chaska (G-972)
Kroll Ontrack Inc....C....952 937-1107
Eden Prairie (G-1704)
Mail Handling Inc....C....952 975-5000
Eden Prairie (G-1714)
Mark Doman....E....320 203-9004
Sartell (G-9338)
Midwest Data Inc....E....320 235-8880
Willmar (G-10023)
Mortgage Resource Center Inc....E....651 683-9705
Eagan (G-1539)
National Business Systems Inc....D....651 688-0202
Eagan (G-1540)
▲ Ncs Pearson Inc....A....952 681-3000
Minneapolis (G-5177)
Network Computing Services Inc....E....612 337-0200
Minneapolis (G-5183)
Nowdocs International Inc....D....888 669-3627
North Mankato (G-6512)
Popular Front Studio Inc....E....612 362-0900
Minneapolis (G-5395)
Questar Data Systems Inc....C....651 688-0089
Saint Paul (G-7886)
R B C Capital Market....A....612 371-2711
Minneapolis (G-5456)
Reed Elsevier Inc....E....651 385-1895
Red Wing (G-7000)
Rev Solutions Inc....E....952 746-6005
Eden Prairie (G-1764)
RSM McGladrey Inc....D....507 288-5363
Rochester (G-7242)
Scicom Data Services Ltd....C....952 933-4200
Minnetonka (G-6225)
Second Data Enterprises Inc....D....612 326-6833
Edina (G-1845)
Shea Inc....E....612 339-2257
Minneapolis (G-5652)
Siemens Water Technologies....C....651 766-2722
Saint Paul (G-8957)
SPS Commerce Inc....D....612 435-9400
Minneapolis (G-5724)
Sungard Financial Systems LLC....B....952 935-3300
Hopkins (G-2639)
Webmd Health Corp....E....763 512-2600
Minneapolis (G-6031)
Wells Fargo Services Inc....A....612 667-1234
Minneapolis (G-6053)
Wells Fargo Services Inc....A....612 667-1234
Minneapolis (G-6054)
Xpandable Technology Inc....E....763 521-0401
Minneapolis (G-6095)

7375 Information Retrieval Svcs

C & C Business Solutions....D....612 875-9488
Burnsville (G-693)
Diversified Pharmaceutical....952 820-7000
Minneapolis (G-4263)
▲ Epredix Holdings Inc....D....612 843-1059
Minneapolis (G-4365)
Exhibitor Publications Inc....E....507 289-6556
Rochester (G-7109)
Finance & Commerce Inc....E....612 333-4244
Minneapolis (G-4431)
Heartland Information Services....E....612 371-9255
Minneapolis (G-4626)
Hiawatha Broadband Comms....D....507 474-4000
Winona (G-10101)
Hickory Tech Information Soln....D....507 625-1691
Mankato (G-3139)
Hickory Tech Information Soln....D....507 625-1691
Mankato (G-3140)
Ingenix Inc....B....952 833-7100
Eden Prairie (G-1692)
Internet Broadcasting Systems....C....651 365-4000
Saint Paul (G-8518)
Medical Records Inc....D....952 831-6778
Minneapolis (G-4985)
One Call Concepts Inc....D....651 454-0002
Saint Paul (G-7856)
Ontrack Data Recovery Inc....A....952 937-1107
Eden Prairie (G-1739)
Quick Test Inc....E....952 854-3535
Minneapolis (G-5451)
Schwan's Technology Group Inc....D....651 388-1821
Red Wing (G-7005)
Schwan's Technology Group Inc....E....651 681-4450
Saint Paul (G-7898)
Sopheon Corp....E....952 851-7555
Minneapolis (G-5702)
Techbarncom Inc....E....651 275-8300
Stillwater (G-9651)
U S Internet Corp....E....651 222-4638
Minnetonka (G-6230)
Val-Ed Joint Venture, LLP....E....218 284-5702
Moorhead (G-6345)
West Publishing Corp....A....651 687-8000
Saint Paul (G-7946)
West Publishing Corp....D....651 687-7000
Saint Paul (G-7947)

7376 Computer Facilities Management Svcs

I B Industries Inc....D....507 567-2701
Brownsdale (G-630)
Local Government Information....E....763 543-2600
Minneapolis (G-4896)
Unisys Corp....A....651 687-2200
Saint Paul (G-7935)

7377 Computer Rental & Leasing

Data Sales Co Inc....D....952 890-8838
Burnsville (G-710)
▲ Vibrant Technologies Inc....E....952 653-1700
Minnetonka (G-6233)
▲ Xerxes Computer Corp....E....952 936-9280
Minneapolis (G-6094)

7378 Computer Maintenance & Repair

All Systems Go....E....651 628-0000
Hopkins (G-2505)
Blm Technologies Inc....E....763 559-5100
Minneapolis (G-3912)
Citon Computer Corp....E....218 720-4435
Duluth (G-1274)
▲ Expresspoint Technology Svcs....C....763 543-6000
Golden Valley (G-2240)
National Communications Svcs....E....763 576-9977
Anoka (G-206)
▲ Nortech Systems Inc....C....952 345-2244
Wayzata (G-9932)
PC Solutions Inc....E....763 852-1600
Minneapolis (G-3567)
Pcr Computer Services....E....763 557-6824
Minneapolis (G-5354)
Solbrekk Inc....E....763 404-4712
Golden Valley (G-2246)
Sovran Inc....E....651 686-0515
Eagan (G-1552)
System Design Advantage LLC....E....952 703-3500
Minneapolis (G-5781)
World Data Products Inc....D....952 476-9000
Minnetonka (G-6239)

7379 Computer Related Svcs, NEC

Acura Inc....E....651 967-0607
Newport (G-6483)
Advanced Duplication Services....C....763 449-5500
Minneapolis (G-3688)
Aeritae Consulting Group Ltd....E....651 229-0300
Saint Paul (G-7992)
Analysts International Corp....C....952 835-5900
Minneapolis (G-3773)
Analysts International Corp....C....952 897-4500
Minneapolis (G-3772)
Arran Technologies Inc....E....651 468-0002
Saint Paul (G-8064)
As Soon As Possible Inc....D....952 564-2727
Minneapolis (G-3816)
Bailiwick Data Systems Inc....D....952 556-5502
Chaska (G-950)
Bangasser Co....320 256-5100
Saint Joseph (G-7651)
Blm Technologies Inc....E....763 559-5100
Minneapolis (G-3912)
Business Microvar Inc....E....651 639-0575
Saint Paul (G-8143)
Charter Solutions Inc....D....763 230-6100
Plymouth (G-6854)
Ciber Inc....D....507 280-9267
Rochester (G-7077)
Concord Inc....D....952 697-5500
Hopkins (G-2533)
CS Solutions Inc....E....651 603-8288
Eagan (G-1523)
Dbi Consulting Inc....D....763 561-4990
Minneapolis (G-4234)
Digital River Inc....B....952 253-1234
Eden Prairie (G-1645)
Dks Systems LLC....952 476-7443
Wayzata (G-9914)
Dobbs Temporary Services Inc....E....612 373-2600
Minneapolis (G-4268)
Edocument Resources LLC....E....952 607-3505
Minnetonka (G-6163)
Ego Systems Inc....D....952 200-8246
Minneapolis (G-4331)
Enclipse Corp....E....612 384-6940
Minneapolis (G-4353)
English, Bleeker & Associates....E....952 230-6500
Saint Louis Park (G-7661)
▲ Expresspoint Technology Svcs....C....763 543-6000
Golden Valley (G-2240)
Facet Technology Corp....E....952 944-1839
Eden Prairie (G-1660)
Fishel Information Systems Inc....E....952 544-1108
Hopkins (G-2543)
Geek Squad Inc....E....612 343-1028
Minneapolis (G-4505)
Geek Squad Inc....D....612 922-9288
Minneapolis (G-4506)
Genesis Corp....A....651 702-3300
Saint Paul (G-9219)
Global Markets Inc....E....612 392-7580
Minnetonka (G-6177)
Gnazzo Technical Services Inc....E....952 949-1026
Eden Prairie (G-1675)
Harbinger Partners Inc....D....651 426-1569
Saint Paul (G-8442)
Ilm Professional Services Inc....E....952 960-2220
Edina (G-1832)
Infosecure Technology Inc....E....202 898-5790
Plymouth (G-6866)
Intuitive Technology Group LLC....E....952 854-1663
Minneapolis (G-4734)
▲ J D L Technologies Inc....E....952 946-1810
Hopkins (G-2559)
Kardia Health Systems Inc....E....763 432-8420
Minneapolis (G-4790)
Keane Inc....B....952 915-6393
Minneapolis (G-4795)
Lambsoft & Lamb & Co....E....612 813-3727
Minneapolis (G-4838)
Laser Printing Technologies....D....952 888-7375
Mendota Heights (G-3366)
Legal Research Center Inc....E....612 332-4950
Minneapolis (G-4857)
Macro Group Inc....E....612 332-7880
Minneapolis (G-4929)
Midwave Corp....C....952 279-5600
Eden Prairie (G-1723)
Milestone Systems Inc....E....763 404-6200
Minneapolis (G-5041)
Motion International Inc....D....952 746-5630
Minneapolis (G-5136)
MQ Software Inc....D....952 345-8720
Minneapolis (G-5143)
▲ Ncs Pearson Inc....A....952 681-3000
Minneapolis (G-5177)
Nemadji Research Corp....E....320 838-3838
Bruno (G-631)
Norex Inc....E....952 447-8898
Prior Lake (G-6945)
Norstan Inc....C....952 352-4000
Hopkins (G-2590)
North Point Capital Partners....D....651 602-0789
Saint Paul (G-8753)
Northshore Resources Inc....E....612 375-0315
Minneapolis (G-5236)
Nternational Projects....D....952 541-4888
Minneapolis (G-5254)
Object Partners Inc....E....612 746-1580
Minneapolis (G-5259)
Olr America Inc....E....612 436-4970
Minneapolis (G-5269)
ORBIT Systems Inc....D....651 767-3322
Saint Paul (G-7858)
Quantum Retail Technology Inc....E....612 486-3491
Minneapolis (G-5446)
RCM Technologies Inc....E....952 841-1188
Hopkins (G-2612)
Rubenstein & Ziff Inc....E....952 854-1460
Minneapolis (G-5574)
Sadaka Technology Consultants....A....952 841-6363
Minneapolis (G-5586)
Search America, A Part of....E....763 416-1007
Maple Grove (G-3253)
Seh Technology Solutions Inc....E....612 758-6728
Minneapolis (G-5628)
Shavlik Technologies LLC....D....651 426-6624
Saint Paul (G-8948)
Skamp Corp....E....952 937-8990
Eden Prairie (G-1779)
Solid Logic Computer Solutions....E....952 949-0140
Eden Prairie (G-1780)
Solutia Consulting Inc....E....651 351-0123
Stillwater (G-9640)
TAJ Technologies Inc....D....651 405-7412
Mendota Heights (G-3371)
Talus Group Inc....E....952 544-2526
Excelsior (G-1954)
Tech-Pro Inc....B....651 634-1400
Saint Paul (G-9032)
Teksystems Inc....E....952 886-4800
Minneapolis (G-5807)
Tom Kelly....E....507 645-7464
Northfield (G-6543)

(G-00000) Company's Geographic Section entry number
496
2011 Harris Minnesota Services Directory
▲=Import ▼=Export ◆=Import/Export

TriMin Systems Inc ....E....651 636-7667
Saint Paul *(G-9083)*
Tuesday Networking Inc ....E....952 942-7378
Eden Prairie *(G-1798)*
Ulysses Telemedia Networks Inc ......D....763 225-5000
Minneapolis *(G-5897)*
Valere LLC ....E....763 390-9286
White Bear Lake *(G-9979)*
Virtelligence Inc ....C....952 746-9220
Eden Prairie *(G-1806)*
Virteva LLC ....E....952 843-1200
Saint Louis Park *(G-7670)*
Visionshare Inc ....E....612 460-4301
Minneapolis *(G-5978)*
Wolfnet Technologies LLC ....E....612 342-0088
Minneapolis *(G-6083)*

7381 Detective & Armored Car Svcs

Allied Security LLC ....D....651 604-9414
Saint Paul *(G-8013)*
American Security & Protection ....D....218 236-5180
Moorhead *(G-6297)*
American Security LLC ....A....651 644-1155
Saint Paul *(G-8034)*
Arnage Security Services LLC ....D....763 269-8440
Minneapolis *(G-3409)*
Avalon Fortress Security Svcs ....C....763 767-9111
Minneapolis *(G-3841)*
Brink's Inc ....D....763 486-1730
Minneapolis *(G-3950)*
Checkpoint Security ....E....952 227-5353
Waconia *(G-9782)*
Criminal Investigation Dept ....E....612 673-2941
Minneapolis *(G-4184)*
Deco Inc ....A....763 576-9572
Champlin *(G-892)*
Delta Protective Services ....E....612 331-1885
Minneapolis *(G-4246)*
G2 Secure Staff LLC ....C....612 725-6423
Saint Paul *(G-7960)*
G4s Secure Solutions Inc ....B....651 482-1928
Saint Paul *(G-8399)*
General Security Services Corp ....D....952 858-5000
Minneapolis *(G-4517)*
General Security Services Corp ....D....320 252-3794
Saint Cloud *(G-7416)*
Granite City Armored Car Inc ....E....320 252-0708
Sauk Rapids *(G-9364)*
Guardsmark LLC ....D....952 831-3151
Minneapolis *(G-4578)*
Gulf Northern Inc ....E....952 278-1501
Minnetonka *(G-6178)*
Hannon Security Services Inc ....B....952 881-5865
Minneapolis *(G-4595)*
Heartland Information Services ....E....612 371-9255
Minneapolis *(G-4626)*
Inner State Protection Inc ....E....651 771-1501
Minnetonka *(G-6180)*
Loomis Armored Us Inc ....E....651 645-4511
Saint Paul *(G-8594)*
Minnesota Department of Public ....E....507 537-3664
Marshall *(G-3314)*
Securitas Security Services ....C....218 727-7870
Duluth *(G-1446)*
T George & Associates ....E....651 647-0900
Saint Paul *(G-9025)*
Talon Investigation Ltd ....E....651 774-6977
Saint Paul *(G-9026)*
Twin City Security Inc ....B....763 784-4160
Minneapolis *(G-3625)*
Valley Security Service Inc ....C....507 454-2233
Winona *(G-10136)*

7382 Security Systems Svcs

AAF-Mcquay Inc ....B....763 553-5330
Minneapolis *(G-3655)*
ADT Security Services Inc ....C....651 917-0000
Saint Paul *(G-7984)*
ADT Security Services Inc ....C....651 917-0010
Minneapolis *(G-3386)*
Arrowhead Security Systems Inc ......E....218 722-1234
Duluth *(G-1243)*
Century Systems Inc ....E....651 426-0975
Saint Paul *(G-8185)*
Checkpoint Security Systems ....C....952 942-9431
Chanhassen *(G-914)*
Checkpoint Systems Inc ....E....952 227-5350
Chaska *(G-958)*
Checkpoint Systems Inc ....C....952 943-3853
Chanhassen *(G-915)*
Electro-Watchman Inc ....E....651 227-8461
Saint Paul *(G-8329)*
Floyd Lock & Safe Co ....E....952 881-5625
Minneapolis *(G-4457)*
Floyd Total Security ....E....320 654-9549
Saint Cloud *(G-7511)*
Parsons Electric LLC ....C....763 571-8000
Minneapolis *(G-3565)*
Pro-TEC Design Inc ....E....763 553-1477
Plymouth *(G-6880)*
Rhjh Inc ....E....651 735-7470
Saint Paul *(G-8897)*
Security Response Services Inc ......E....952 346-8922
Minneapolis *(G-5626)*

Sentry Systems Inc ....E....651 426-4627
White Bear Lake *(G-9977)*
Silent Knight Security Systems ....E....952 881-0038
Minneapolis *(G-5673)*
Simplexgrinnell LP ....E....320 253-8883
Saint Cloud *(G-7427)*
Systemarmed Usacom Inc ....A....877 900-0238
Minneapolis *(G-5782)*
Trans-Alarm Inc ....D....952 894-1700
Burnsville *(G-810)*
Trust Security ....E....952 914-9300
Minneapolis *(G-5860)*
Videotronix Inc ....D....952 894-5343
Burnsville *(G-818)*
Westco Systems Inc ....E....763 559-7046
Minneapolis *(G-6057)*
Wright-Hennepin Security Corp ....C....763 477-3000
Rockford *(G-7306)*

7384 Photofinishing Labs

Camera Shop of Saint Cloud Inc ......E....320 251-2622
Saint Cloud *(G-7468)*
Falk's Woodland Pharmacy Inc ....E....218 728-4242
Duluth *(G-1318)*
Falk's Woodland Pharmacy Inc ....E....218 740-2650
Duluth *(G-1319)*
Mc Be Co ....E....507 289-1666
Rochester *(G-7178)*
National Camera Exchange Inc ....E....651 636-0693
Saint Paul *(G-8739)*
National Camera Exchange Inc ....E....952 898-4888
Burnsville *(G-762)*
Proex Photo ....E....651 699-4394
Saint Paul *(G-8852)*
Proex Photo Systems Inc ....E....952 893-1915
Minneapolis *(G-3575)*
Proex Photo Systems Inc ....E....952 941-5232
Eden Prairie *(G-1755)*
Rcc Liquidating Corp ....E....507 281-0313
Rochester *(G-7218)*
Rcc Liquidating Corp ....E....651 699-0988
Saint Paul *(G-8875)*
Rcc Liquidating Corp ....E....763 546-3771
Hopkins *(G-2611)*
Shopko Stores Operating Co LLC ......C....507 281-0656
Rochester *(G-7253)*
Snyder's Drug Stores Inc ....E....763 427-8111
Champlin *(G-901)*
Snyder's Drug Stores Inc ....E....507 345-1002
Mankato *(G-3198)*
Tomsten Inc ....E....952 516-3300
Minnetonka *(G-6228)*
Walgreen Co ....E....320 251-9433
Saint Cloud *(G-7629)*
Walgreen Co ....E....952 448-1180
Chaska *(G-984)*
Walgreen Co ....E....763 427-6389
Champlin *(G-905)*
Walgreen Co ....E....612 822-9712
Minneapolis *(G-6003)*
Walgreen Co ....E....952 226-1283
Savage *(G-9411)*
Walgreen Co ....E....763 566-8350
Minneapolis *(G-6005)*
Walgreen Co ....E....952 938-1168
Hopkins *(G-2657)*
Walgreen Co ....E....612 861-7276
Minneapolis *(G-6006)*
Walgreen Co ....E....612 827-8902
Minneapolis *(G-6001)*
Walgreen Co ....E....763 755-1259
Minneapolis *(G-3635)*
Walgreen Co ....E....320 253-6601
Sauk Rapids *(G-9380)*
Walgreen Co ....E....763 576-0388
Anoka *(G-238)*
Walgreen Co ....E....763 545-6466
Minneapolis *(G-5998)*
Walgreen Co ....E....763 783-7005
Circle Pines *(G-1024)*
Walgreen Co ....D....612 722-4249
Minneapolis *(G-5999)*
Walgreen Co ....E....763 553-9731
Minneapolis *(G-6000)*
Walgreen Co ....D....952 884-8246
Minneapolis *(G-6004)*
Walgreen Co ....E....952 920-3561
Minneapolis *(G-6002)*
Walgreen Co ....E....952 882-7998
Burnsville *(G-819)*
Walgreen Co ....E....763 586-0730
Minneapolis *(G-3636)*
Walgreen Co ....E....952 941-8666
Eden Prairie *(G-1812)*
Walgreen Co ....E....763 585-9946
Minneapolis *(G-6007)*
Weber & Judd Co ....E....507 289-6047
Rochester *(G-7287)*
White House Custom Colour Inc ......C....651 646-8263
Eagan *(G-1560)*

7389 Business Svcs, NEC

A & C Metals-Sawing Inc ....E....763 786-1048
Minneapolis *(G-3382)*

A G Edwards & Sons Inc ....D....952 832-1600
Bloomington *(G-480)*
A G O'Brien Plumbing & Heating ......E....218 729-9662
Hermantown *(G-2433)*
AAA-American Co ....E....507 894-4156
Hokah *(G-2490)*
Aarcee Party & Tent Rental ....E....952 922-7233
Minneapolis *(G-3657)*
Abraham Technical Services Inc ......E....763 428-3170
Rogers *(G-7315)*
Aca International ....D....952 926-6547
Minneapolis *(G-3663)*
Access Information Systems Inc ......C....952 888-8503
Minneapolis *(G-3666)*
Accessability Inc ....D....612 331-5958
Minneapolis *(G-3667)*
Acclaim Benefits LLC ....D....763 278-4620
Minneapolis *(G-3668)*
ACS Integrated Doc Inc ....E....651 999-5400
Saint Paul *(G-7981)*
Advanced Cellular LLC ....D....952 469-4200
Lakeville *(G-2889)*
Advanstar Holdings Corp 218 740-7200
Duluth *(G-1232)*
Aero-Metric Inc ....E....763 420-9606
Osseo *(G-6593)*
Agstar Financial Services, Aca ....E....320 203-4613
Waite Park *(G-9815)*
All Fire Test Co Inc ....E....612 332-3473
Minneapolis *(G-3709)*
All Poolside Services Inc ....E....651 483-6600
Saint Paul *(G-8011)*
All Time Favorites Inc ....E....651 454-1124
Saint Paul *(G-7690)*
All-Data Inc ....E....763 571-5719
Minneapolis *(G-3390)*
Alliant Precision Fuse Co ....D....763 744-5000
Minneapolis *(G-3713)*
Alternative Micrographics Inc ....E....320 796-2599
Spicer *(G-9554)*
America's Tpa Inc ....E....952 896-1246
Minneapolis *(G-3744)*
American Legion Club ....E....763 421-0883
Anoka *(G-152)*
Answer America LLC ....E....651 644-7332
Saint Paul *(G-8053)*
Apg Cash Drawer LLC ....D....763 571-5000
Minneapolis *(G-3406)*
Aramark Corp ....E....952 946-1438
Minneapolis *(G-3795)*
Archives Paper Co Inc ....E....763 533-0612
Minneapolis *(G-3803)*
Ardel Inc ....E....763 545-1919
Minneapolis *(G-3804)*
Argenbright Inc ....C....320 543-3737
Howard Lake *(G-2665)*
Aria Communications Corp ....C....320 259-5206
Saint Cloud *(G-7453)*
▲ Arrowhead Promotion ....B....218 327-1165
Grand Rapids *(G-2269)*
Arthur Shuster Inc ....E....651 631-9200
Saint Paul *(G-8066)*
Atlantis Pools Inc ....E....763 560-0103
Minneapolis *(G-3831)*
Attorney's Process Service Ltd ....C....952 831-7776
Minneapolis *(G-3833)*
Bell Telephone Inc ....D....651 298-1332
Saint Paul *(G-8099)*
Benco Delivery Service Inc ....E....651 486-9999
Saint Paul *(G-8102)*
▼ Birchwood Laboratories Inc ....D....952 937-7900
Eden Prairie *(G-1608)*
Birkeland & Associates ....E....952 922-1772
Minneapolis *(G-3907)*
Boarman Kroos Vogel Group ....D....612 339-3752
Minneapolis *(G-3921)*
Brede Inc ....E....612 331-4540
Minneapolis *(G-3941)*
Broadway Resource & Recovery ......E....612 623-8888
Minneapolis *(G-3953)*
Brook Hall Blaine Brook ....E....763 755-8731
Minneapolis *(G-3425)*
Brookdale Plastics Inc ....D....763 797-1000
Plymouth *(G-6852)*
BT Americas Holdings Ltd ....E....651 746-8739
Saint Paul *(G-9191)*
Burrelle's Information Svcs ....E....612 672-9141
Minneapolis *(G-3978)*
Bwbr Architects Inc ....C....651 222-3701
Saint Paul *(G-8144)*
Bystrom Precision Industries ....E....952 929-6888
Minneapolis *(G-3979)*
Canby Concerned Citizens ....E....507 223-7061
Canby *(G-849)*
Capital Express Inc ....E....651 631-3595
Saint Paul *(G-8151)*
Capitol Co's Inc ....D....651 454-4511
Saint Paul *(G-7726)*
Captionmax Inc ....E....612 341-3566
Minneapolis *(G-4000)*
Carbide Tool Services Inc ....E....763 421-2210
Anoka *(G-161)*
▲ CareCall Inc ....D....320 253-0800
Sartell *(G-9334)*
◆ Carlson Holdings Inc ....A....763 212-5000
Minnetonka *(G-6152)*
Cash Pass Network ....E....952 358-7080
Burnsville *(G-695)*

Employment codes: A=Over 500 employees, B=251-500
C=101-250, D=51-100, E=25-50

2011 Harris Minnesota
Services Directory

© Harris InfoSource 1-866-281-6415
497

Castle Danger LP ....D....218 728-8060
Duluth *(G-1263)*
CC Holdings Inc ....E....612 371-8008
Minneapolis *(G-4034)*
Celebrities Unlimited Inc 651 482-9945
Saint Paul *(G-8179)*
Cenaiko Expo Inc ....E....763 755-8111
Minneapolis *(G-3430)*
Central Minnesota Erdc Inc ....E....320 202-0992
Saint Cloud *(G-7408)*
Checker Machine Inc ....E....763 544-5000
Minneapolis *(G-4057)*
City of Beaver Creek ....E....507 673-2266
Beaver Creek *(G-353)*
City of Brooklyn Center ....E....763 569-6300
Minneapolis *(G-4085)*
City of Minneapolis ....C....612 335-6000
Minneapolis *(G-4091)*
Colemanbrandworx Worldwide ....E....763 390-1100
Wayzata *(G-9911)*
Columns Resource of ....E....952 806-9600
Minneapolis *(G-4126)*
Commercial Products V H Inds ....E....651 224-2831
Saint Paul *(G-8228)*
Cooperative Response Center ....D....507 437-2400
Austin *(G-267)*
Cosmopolitan & Associates Inc ....A....612 822-3830
Minneapolis *(G-4165)*
Counseling Services of Sthn ....E....507 931-8040
Saint Peter *(G-9301)*
Courier Systems LLC ....D....651 628-0100
Saint Paul *(G-8262)*
▲ Creative Marketing Concepts ....E....320 679-4105
Mora *(G-6356)*
Culligan International Co ....E....507 354-2311
New Ulm *(G-6447)*
Culligan Soft Water Service Co ....D....952 933-7200
Minnetonka *(G-6157)*
Custom Communications Inc ....D....507 288-5522
Rochester *(G-7091)*
Customer Traac Inc ....E....763 553-2989
Minneapolis *(G-4206)*
Customer Traac Inc ....E....218 435-2600
Fosston *(G-2175)*
Customerlink LLC ....C....218 722-2800
Duluth *(G-1289)*
Cygnus Expositions ....D....952 894-8007
Burnsville *(G-705)*
D & G Packaging Co ....E....952 890-7525
Burnsville *(G-706)*
D L Ricci Corp ....D....651 388-8661
Red Wing *(G-6977)*
Dakota Growers Pasta Co Inc ....C....763 531-5340
Minneapolis *(G-4219)*
Data Listing Services LLC ....D....952 948-5488
Burnsville *(G-709)*
▲ Datacard Corp ....A....952 933-1223
Minnetonka *(G-6159)*
Davies Printing Co ....E....952 473-6924
Wayzata *(G-9913)*
◆ Deluxe Corp ....B....651 483-7111
Saint Paul *(G-8285)*
Devicix LLC ....E....952 368-0073
Eden Prairie *(G-1644)*
Dnk Management Inc ....D....651 773-8077
Saint Paul *(G-8305)*
Dolce International ....E....952 368-3100
Chaska *(G-961)*
Drs Acquisitions Inc ....D....320 351-8100
Sauk Centre *(G-9343)*
Duluth Entertainment Conv ....A....218 722-5573
Duluth *(G-1298)*
E & C Amec Services Inc ....D....612 332-8326
Minneapolis *(G-4299)*
E Frame ....D....952 926-3555
Minneapolis *(G-4300)*
Electronic Check Alliance ....E....952 445-2888
Saint Paul *(G-8330)*
Ellermedia Group ....E....612 369-5612
Saint Paul *(G-8333)*
Elness Swenson Graham ....D....612 339-5508
Minneapolis *(G-4343)*
Enventis Telecom Inc ....E....218 720-2686
Duluth *(G-1313)*
Environments Inc ....E....952 933-9981
Hopkins *(G-2540)*
Evangelical Lutheran Church In ....C....612 752-4080
Minneapolis *(G-4376)*
Exhibitor Publications Inc ....E....507 289-6556
Rochester *(G-7109)*
▲ Expresspoint Technology Svcs ....C....763 543-6000
Golden Valley *(G-2240)*
▲ Fair Isaac Corp ....B....612 758-5200
Minneapolis *(G-4392)*
▲ FDC Services Inc ....C....320 656-8880
Saint Cloud *(G-7508)*
Feather, Larson & Synhorst ....D....651 480-0123
Hastings *(G-2415)*
Federal Express Corp ....B....612 794-3100
Minneapolis *(G-4419)*
Fedex Office & Print Services ....E....952 892-0200
Burnsville *(G-721)*
Financial Systems Support ....E....612 625-3493
Minneapolis *(G-4433)*
First Financial USA Ltd ....D....763 231-8120
Hamel *(G-2342)*
1st National Repossessioncom ....E....763 241-5212
Elk River *(G-1874)*

First Street Credit Corp ....E....612 871-4579
Minneapolis *(G-4445)*
Food Systems Design Inc ....E....952 884-4048
Minneapolis *(G-4464)*
G&S Staffing Services Inc ....A....320 235-3949
Willmar *(G-10002)*
Gage Group LLC ....C....763 595-3920
Minneapolis *(G-4495)*
Games People Play Inc ....E....507 433-7593
Austin *(G-272)*
Gehling Auction Co Inc ....E....507 765-2131
Preston *(G-6897)*
Gelco Information Network Inc ....C....952 947-1500
Eden Prairie *(G-1672)*
George Konik Associates Inc ....D....952 835-5550
Minneapolis *(G-4524)*
Glenmore Foundation ....E....218 281-3123
Crookston *(G-1125)*
Global Ventures I Inc ....D....507 825-5462
Pipestone *(G-6828)*
Gold Country Inc ....E....952 935-9887
Hopkins *(G-2546)*
Goldberg Bail Bonds ....D....218 847-8122
Detroit Lakes *(G-1194)*
Graphic Finishing Services Inc ....E....763 767-3026
Minneapolis *(G-3477)*
Greater Minneapolis Convention ....C....612 767-8000
Minneapolis *(G-4558)*
Greatstone LLC ....E....651 429-6606
Saint Paul *(G-8429)*
Green Tree Investment Holdings ....D....651 293-3410
Saint Paul *(G-8432)*
Gwg Holdings LLC ....E....612 746-6119
Minneapolis *(G-4583)*
Healtheast Care System ....A....651 232-1000
Saint Paul *(G-8454)*
Hennepin County ....E....612 596-0071
Minneapolis *(G-4635)*
Hickey Thorstenson Grover Ltd ....E....952 278-8880
Eden Prairie *(G-1684)*
Historical Society of MN ....E....651 297-2555
Saint Paul *(G-8485)*
Homelink Mortgage Corp ....E....952 935-1986
Hopkins *(G-2552)*
Hsbc Card Services Inc ....C....952 358-4000
Minnetonka *(G-6179)*
Icon Services Corp ....E....651 695-8778
Saint Paul *(G-8503)*
Image Sea Co's Inc ....D....952 882-0884
Burnsville *(G-735)*
▲ Imago Ltd ....D....651 690-9724
Saint Paul *(G-8506)*
Impact Mailing Of Minnesota ....D....612 521-6245
Minneapolis *(G-4692)*
Insignia Systems Inc ....D....763 392-6200
Minneapolis *(G-4706)*
Inspec Inc ....E....763 546-3434
Minneapolis *(G-4707)*
Institute of Production ....D....612 375-1900
Minneapolis *(G-4710)*
Inteleserve Inc ....C....800 390-4851
Saint Peter *(G-9307)*
International Packaging Inc ....D....763 315-6200
Minneapolis *(G-4723)*
International Paper Co ....C....651 426-0345
Saint Paul *(G-8517)*
Interpoll Laboratories Inc ....E....763 786-6020
Circle Pines *(G-1012)*
Interpretation & Trans ....E....651 292-9701
Saint Paul *(G-8521)*
Interscope Records Inc ....E....952 828-6060
Eden Prairie *(G-1697)*
Interstate Rehabilitation Ctr ....B....651 388-7108
Red Wing *(G-6987)*
Iron Mountain Information Mgt ....E....651 452-6515
Saint Paul *(G-7808)*
Italian American Club of ....D....612 781-0625
Minneapolis *(G-4740)*
J&M Co ....E....218 998-4062
Fergus Falls *(G-2078)*
Jacobs Trading LLC ....E....763 843-2066
Hopkins *(G-2561)*
K M L Design Studio LLC ....E....651 731-6672
Woodbury *(G-10172)*
Kinship Youth Mentoring ....D....763 631-5967
Princeton *(G-6910)*
Kj International Resources Ltd ....E....612 288-9494
Minneapolis *(G-4814)*
Kraus-Anderson Construction Co ....E....218 759-0596
Bemidji *(G-400)*
Kurt Manufacturing Co Inc ....E....763 572-4592
Minneapolis *(G-3512)*
L & R Suburban Landscaping Inc ....E....952 935-0389
Minnetonka *(G-6186)*
Lake Carlos Villas ....E....320 846-1784
Alexandria *(G-108)*
Lake Crystal Fire Department ....E....507 726-2440
Lake Crystal *(G-2859)*
Larkin Industries Inc ....E....651 645-6000
Saint Paul *(G-8562)*
Leisure Inc ....E....952 401-8440
Eden Prairie *(G-1707)*
Lhb Inc ....E....612 338-2029
Minneapolis *(G-4867)*
Liberty Display Group Inc ....E....763 785-1593
Minneapolis *(G-3517)*
Lifetech Corp ....D....612 369-5050
Osseo *(G-6628)*

Lifetrack Resources Inc ....E....651 290-0567
Saint Paul *(G-8587)*
Lighthouse On Homestead Inc ....E....218 525-4525
Duluth *(G-1383)*
Living Benefits Financial Svcs ....E....952 903-9800
Minnetonka *(G-6187)*
▲ Lonsdale Packaging ....D....507 744-2376
Lonsdale *(G-3045)*
Lower Saint Croix Valley Fire ....E....651 436-7033
Lakeland *(G-2886)*
M D I Government Services ....E....218 326-9544
Grand Rapids *(G-2292)*
M D I Government Services ....C....218 263-3663
Hibbing *(G-2460)*
M D I Government Services ....B....651 999-8200
Saint Paul *(G-8602)*
Mahnomen County Sheriff's ....E....218 935-2255
Mahnomen *(G-3089)*
Masterworks Of Minneapolis Inc ....E....612 333-8210
Minneapolis *(G-4965)*
McCaren Design Inc ....E....651 646-4764
Saint Paul *(G-8623)*
Medical Messaging Center ....E....320 255-5640
Saint Cloud *(G-7549)*
Metro Legal Services Inc ....D....612 332-0202
Minneapolis *(G-5001)*
Metro Legal Services Inc ....E....651 291-0008
Saint Paul *(G-8641)*
Meyer Associates Inc ....C....320 259-4000
Saint Cloud *(G-7552)*
Meyer, Scherer & Rockcastle ....E....612 375-0336
Minneapolis *(G-5012)*
Midwest Protection Agency Inc ....E....763 421-2966
Saint Michael *(G-7677)*
Midwest Recreational ....D....507 263-9234
Cannon Falls *(G-859)*
Minneapolis Electrical Jatc ....E....763 497-0072
Saint Michael *(G-7678)*
Minneapolis Jewish Federation ....E....952 593-2600
Hopkins *(G-2584)*
Minnesota Diversified Inds ....E....651 999-8200
Saint Paul *(G-8684)*
Minnesota Diversified Inds ....E....218 263-3663
Hibbing *(G-2468)*
Minnesota Residential Aquatics 651 439-8467
Stillwater *(G-9629)*
Minnesota Shredding LLC ....E....763 493-3007
Minneapolis *(G-5093)*
Money Gram Payment Systems Inc ....A....952 591-3000
Minneapolis *(G-5120)*
Muzak LLC ....E....763 424-5533
Osseo *(G-6641)*
N'Compass Solutions Inc ....E....612 379-2100
Minneapolis *(G-5155)*
National Arbitration Forum Inc ....C....952 516-6400
Minneapolis *(G-5160)*
National Business Systems Inc ....D....651 688-0202
Eagan *(G-1540)*
National Retirement Plan Inc ....D....651 789-1037
Eagan *(G-1541)*
Natus Corp ....D....651 487-3211
Saint Paul *(G-8741)*
Ndn Mulcahy LLC ....E....651 747-4201
Mahtomedi *(G-3096)*
Niecc Inc ....C....763 536-8300
Minneapolis *(G-5200)*
Normandy Inn Inc ....E....612 370-1400
Minneapolis *(G-5210)*
Norstan Inc ....C....952 352-4000
Hopkins *(G-2590)*
Northern Tool & Equipment Co ....E....952 894-0326
Burnsville *(G-764)*
Northwest Area Foundation ....E....651 224-9635
Saint Paul *(G-8766)*
NRG Energy Plus Relocation ....D....952 512-5500
Minneapolis *(G-5253)*
1 Micro LLC ....E....952 767-1010
Eden Prairie *(G-1738)*
Pattern Stations Inc ....D....763 441-6833
Monticello *(G-6282)*
Patzig Testing Laboratories ....D....651 659-7554
Saint Paul *(G-8810)*
Paynesville Motor & Transfer ....E....320 243-4455
Paynesville *(G-6773)*
Performance Pool & Spa Inc ....E....651 731-3440
Saint Paul *(G-9259)*
Pinnacle Credit Services ....E....952 939-8100
Minneapolis *(G-5380)*
Playworks Dakota ....D....952 445-7529
Prior Lake *(G-6948)*
Plus Relocation Services Inc ....D....952 512-5500
Minneapolis *(G-5391)*
Pouchtec Industries LLC ....D....320 968-4868
Foley *(G-2141)*
Prairie Arts Continuum ....E....507 831-4862
Windom *(G-10070)*
Primerica Financial Services ....E....763 546-8627
Minneapolis *(G-5410)*
Primerica Financial Services ....D....651 688-9088
Saint Paul *(G-7882)*
Prisma International Inc ....E....612 338-1500
Minneapolis *(G-5412)*
ProAct Inc ....C....651 686-0405
Saint Paul *(G-7884)*
Product Safety Resources Inc ....E....651 917-6100
Saint Paul *(G-8851)*
Progressive Interiors Inc ....E....612 718-1868
Waconia *(G-9790)*

(G-00000) Company's Geographic Section entry number
498
2011 Harris Minnesota Services Directory
▲=Import ▼=Export ◆=Import/Export

Public Radio International Inc .... D 612 330-9266
Minneapolis *(G-5438)*
R A Ventures Inc .... C 612 721-9155
Minneapolis *(G-5455)*
R J M Enterprises of Minnesota .... C 763 323-8389
Anoka *(G-218)*
R L Bodeker & Sons Inc .... D 651 452-0377
Saint Paul *(G-7888)*
Radisson Hotels International .... C 763 212-5000
Minnetonka *(G-6218)*
Ratner Steel Supply Co .... E 651 631-8515
Saint Paul *(G-8870)*
Rbc Global Asset Management .... D 612 376-7000
Minneapolis *(G-5471)*
Rdlp Financial Corp .... E 952 857-1479
Minneapolis *(G-5474)*
Red Rock Fire Inc .... E 651 765-0765
Forest Lake *(G-2154)*
Redbrick Health Corp .... D 612 659-3000
Minneapolis *(G-5478)*
Retail Inventory Services Ltd .... D 651 631-9081
Saint Paul *(G-8896)*
Return Inc .... E 763 295-4659
Monticello *(G-6284)*
Rgis LLC .... D 507 281-7665
Rochester *(G-7223)*
Rgis LLC .... C 952 858-8319
Minneapolis *(G-5535)*
RMR Services LLC .... D 763 786-7323
Minneapolis *(G-3588)*
Rochester Service Co Inc .... E 507 281-5333
Rochester *(G-7240)*
Roghard Financial LLC .... C 952 351-8300
Edina *(G-1842)*
Rohn Industries Inc-St Paul .... E 651 647-1300
Saint Paul *(G-8912)*
Rosemount-Apple Valley & Eagan .... A 651 423-7700
Rosemount *(G-7374)*
RSM McGladrey Business Svcs .... D 952 857-1220
Minneapolis *(G-5568)*
Rti Services Inc .... E 952 475-0242
Plymouth *(G-6882)*
Rule One Trasportation .... E 952 703-7318
Minneapolis *(G-5575)*
Ryt-Way Industries LLC .... A 952 469-1417
Lakeville *(G-2929)*
S KB Environmental .... E 507 433-8131
Austin *(G-285)*
Safety Awareness Inc .... D 763 550-9200
Minneapolis *(G-5590)*
Safezone LLC .... D 612 716-0856
Saint Paul *(G-8921)*
Saint Paul Rivercentre Conv .... D 651 265-4800
Saint Paul *(G-8930)*
Salonek Concrete & Constr .... E 507 723-4218
Springfield *(G-9574)*
Scenic Sign Corp .... E 320 252-9400
Sauk Rapids *(G-9373)*
Schmid & Son Packaging Inc .... D 651 452-0588
Cottage Grove *(G-1107)*
Schneiderman Furniture Inc .... E 952 435-3399
Lakeville *(G-2932)*
Schwieters' Co's Inc .... D 651 407-1618
Hugo *(G-2673)*
7 West Secretarial Answering .... E 952 936-4000
Eden Prairie *(G-1775)*
▲ Sign-Zone Inc .... C 763 746-1350
Anoka *(G-227)*
▲ SIS Enterprises Inc .... C 763 789-0956
Minneapolis *(G-5679)*
Skyline Displays Midwest Inc .... E 952 895-6000
Burnsville *(G-798)*
▲ Smyth Co's Inc .... E 651 646-4544
Saint Paul *(G-8967)*
South Bend Township Fire Dept .... E 507 345-4863
Mankato *(G-3199)*
Stork United Corp .... D 651 645-3601
Saint Paul *(G-9009)*
Sunfish Express Inc .... E 763 433-8383
Anoka *(G-229)*
Sunshine Readers Inc .... E 763 433-2534
Champlin *(G-902)*
▲ Swanson-Flosystems Co .... E 763 383-4700
Plymouth *(G-6885)*
Synergy Advantage Group Inc .... D 320 695-2000
Browns Valley *(G-628)*
Tele Resources Inc .... D 218 724-2026
Duluth *(G-1482)*
Tele Resources Inc .... C 218 724-2026
Duluth *(G-1483)*
Teleconcepts Inc .... E 763 566-5360
Minneapolis *(G-5808)*
Telemarketing Results Inc .... E 763 519-0874
Minneapolis *(G-5809)*
Tembua Inc .... E 952 435-8178
Lakeville *(G-2937)*
3 Br's Inc .... E 507 645-8600
Northfield *(G-6542)*
Timberland Group Inc .... E 952 924-9070
Minneapolis *(G-5826)*
Timberland Transportation Inc .... E 651 748-4477
Saint Paul *(G-9068)*
Tri City Post 513 .... E 651 631-1124
Saint Paul *(G-9081)*
Truck Crane Service-Illinois .... E 651 406-4949
Saint Paul *(G-7930)*
Uhc - Edina .... E 763 519-1335
Minneapolis *(G-5894)*
Universal Marketing .... E 218 722-1698
Duluth *(G-1493)*
Universal Power Marketing LLC .... C 320 202-0243
Saint Cloud *(G-7625)*
University Language Center Inc .... E 612 379-3823
Minneapolis *(G-5926)*
V-TEK Inc .... D 507 387-2039
Mankato *(G-3211)*
▲ Victory Corps Flags Floats .... D 763 561-5600
Minneapolis *(G-5969)*
Visual Impact Signs Inc .... E 763 783-9411
Minneapolis *(G-3632)*
Walsh Bishop Associates Inc .... D 612 338-8799
Minneapolis *(G-6016)*
Washington Inventory Service .... E 763 784-2055
Minneapolis *(G-3638)*
Washington Post Co .... E 651 523-1094
Saint Paul *(G-9141)*
Wealth Enhancement Group LLC .... D 763 417-1428
Plymouth *(G-6890)*
Western Steel Erection Inc .... E 952 473-4344
Long Lake *(G-3035)*
William LLC .... E 952 345-3461
Minneapolis *(G-6069)*
Wilpro Inc .... D 320 235-8850
Willmar *(G-10057)*
Wolters Kluwer Financial Svcs .... A 320 251-3060
Saint Cloud *(G-7634)*
World Architects Inc .... D 651 227-7773
Saint Paul *(G-9168)*
Young America Corp .... B 800 533-4529
Young America *(G-10211)*
Zanby LLC .... E 952 938-5448
Minnetonka *(G-6240)*

75 AUTOMOTIVE REPAIR SERVICES & PARKING

7513 Truck Rental & Leasing, Without Drivers

Allstate Leasing Corp .... E 651 681-4900
Minneapolis *(G-3728)*
Allstate Leasing LLC .... E 952 703-3444
Minneapolis *(G-3729)*
Brookdale Motor Sales Inc .... C 763 561-8161
Minneapolis *(G-3956)*
Buerkle Buick Leasing Co .... C 651 484-0231
Saint Paul *(G-8140)*
Coop Tricounty .... E 320 748-7187
Graceville *(G-2253)*
Dave Syverson Inc .... D 507 373-1438
Albert Lea *(G-46)*
First Student Inc .... D 763 559-9326
Minneapolis *(G-4447)*
Nelson Leasing Inc .... E 320 235-2770
Willmar *(G-10029)*
Penske Truck Leasing Co, LP .... E 651 631-3399
Saint Paul *(G-8814)*
Penske Truck Leasing Co, LP .... E 651 454-0000
Saint Paul *(G-7873)*
R & R Transportation Inc .... D 218 439-6144
Audubon *(G-255)*
R L Brookdale Motors Inc .... D 763 561-8111
Minneapolis *(G-5459)*
Robert A Williams Enterprises .... D 612 333-8900
Minneapolis *(G-5551)*
RSC Equipment Rental Inc .... E 763 509-2423
Minneapolis *(G-5566)*
RSC Equipment Rental Inc .... E 763 509-2400
Minneapolis *(G-5564)*
Ryder Truck Rental Inc .... C 763 545-9417
Minneapolis *(G-5580)*
Ryder Truck Rental Inc .... E 651 636-6906
Saint Paul *(G-8915)*
Ryder Truck Rental Inc .... E 651 631-1755
Saint Paul *(G-8916)*
Superior Ford Inc .... C 763 559-9111
Minneapolis *(G-5771)*
U-Haul Co of Minnesota .... D 763 780-9746
Minneapolis *(G-3628)*
Wally McCarthy's Cadillac .... D 651 636-6060
Saint Paul *(G-9139)*
Zumbrota Ford Sales LLC .... E 507 732-5127
Zumbrota *(G-10222)*

7514 Passenger Car Rental

Avis Rent A Car System Inc .... E 612 623-3999
Minneapolis *(G-3842)*
Avis Rent A Car System Inc .... E 651 636-6730
Saint Paul *(G-8082)*
Brookman Motor Sales Inc .... E 651 777-1316
Lake Elmo *(G-2867)*
Chisholm-Hibbing Airport .... E 218 262-3451
Hibbing *(G-2440)*
Clusiau Sales & Rental Inc .... E 218 326-9421
Grand Rapids *(G-2275)*
Enterprise Leasing Co of MN .... E 651 905-5000
Saint Paul *(G-7766)*
General Electric Fleet Svcs .... B 952 828-1000
Eden Prairie *(G-1674)*
Metropolitan Corp .... D 952 943-9000
Eden Prairie *(G-1721)*
Miller Enterprises Inc .... C 320 251-8900
Saint Cloud *(G-7557)*
Montavon Motors Inc .... E 218 326-0551
Grand Rapids *(G-2297)*
National Car Rental System Inc .... E 218 283-8486
International Falls *(G-2728)*
Nintey Four Services Inc .... E 763 295-3604
Monticello *(G-6279)*
Rent A Ford Car .... E 320 352-6561
Sauk Centre *(G-9351)*
Ryder Truck Rental Inc .... E 651 636-6906
Saint Paul *(G-8915)*
U Save Lease & Rental Inc .... E 218 732-3347
Park Rapids *(G-6764)*
Valley Sales Inc .... E 952 314-8560
Waconia *(G-9793)*

7515 Passenger Car Leasing

A & R Leasing Inc .... D 218 829-4787
Baxter *(G-318)*
▼ Associated Partnership Ltd .... C 952 890-7851
Savage *(G-9383)*
Barnett Chrysler Jeep Kia .... D 651 429-3391
Saint Paul *(G-8089)*
Brookdale Motor Sales Inc .... C 763 561-8161
Minneapolis *(G-3956)*
Buerkle Buick Leasing Co .... C 651 484-0231
Saint Paul *(G-8140)*
Clements Chevrolet-Cadillac Co .... C 507 289-0491
Rochester *(G-7082)*
Coon Rapids Chrysler Inc .... C 763 421-8000
Minneapolis *(G-3439)*
Duke Co's .... D 612 331-4880
Minneapolis *(G-4289)*
Eich Motor Co .... E 320 251-1737
Saint Cloud *(G-7503)*
Ford New Brighten .... D 651 633-9010
Saint Paul *(G-8387)*
Ford Tenvoorde Inc .... D 320 251-0540
Saint Cloud *(G-7512)*
Friendly Chevrolet, Geo Inc .... C 763 786-6100
Minneapolis *(G-3473)*
Interstate Motor Trucks Inc .... E 507 373-0653
Albert Lea *(G-57)*
Laurentian Leasing Inc .... E 218 741-6000
Virginia *(G-9744)*
Miller Enterprises Inc .... C 320 251-8900
Saint Cloud *(G-7557)*
Montavon Motors Inc .... E 218 326-0551
Grand Rapids *(G-2297)*
R L Brookdale Motors Inc .... D 763 561-8111
Minneapolis *(G-5459)*
Superior Ford Inc .... C 763 559-9111
Minneapolis *(G-5771)*
Trail Dodge Inc .... D 651 455-2201
Inver Grove Heights *(G-2772)*
Walden Leasing Inc .... E 952 512-8924
Minneapolis *(G-5996)*
Wally McCarthy's Cadillac .... D 651 636-6060
Saint Paul *(G-9139)*
White Bear Dodge Inc .... D 651 482-6100
Saint Paul *(G-9155)*
Yamamoto Moss Mackenzie .... E 612 375-0180
Minneapolis *(G-6099)*
Zumbrota Ford Sales LLC .... E 507 732-5127
Zumbrota *(G-10222)*

7519 Utility Trailers & Recreational Vehicle Rental

Brookman Motor Sales Inc .... E 651 777-1316
Lake Elmo *(G-2867)*
Dahlke Trailer Sales Inc .... E 763 783-0077
Minneapolis *(G-3450)*
Hilltop Trailer Sales Inc .... E 763 571-9103
Minneapolis *(G-3488)*
Penske Truck Leasing Co, LP .... E 651 454-0000
Saint Paul *(G-7873)*
Thermo Leasing Corp .... E 763 421-2505
Anoka *(G-234)*
U-Haul Co of Minnesota .... D 763 780-9746
Minneapolis *(G-3628)*

7521 Automobile Parking Lots & Garages

Central Parking Inc .... E 612 340-9025
Minneapolis *(G-4046)*
City of Mora .... E 320 679-1770
Mora *(G-6353)*
Dayton Radison Inc .... E 612 672-0060
Minneapolis *(G-4232)*
Dayton-Radisson Ramp .... D 612 333-2293
Minneapolis *(G-4233)*
E Z Air Park Inc .... E 651 454-1302
Saint Paul *(G-7754)*
Loop Parking Co 612 333-2293
Minneapolis *(G-4902)*
Municipal Parking Inc .... E 612 339-2003
Minneapolis *(G-5150)*
Municipal Parking Inc .... E 612 673-9644
Minneapolis *(G-5149)*
Oneida Realty Co Inc .... D 218 722-0816
Duluth *(G-1413)*
Park 'n Fly Inc .... D 952 854-0606
Minneapolis *(G-5327)*
Park N' Go of Minnesota LP .... D 952 854-3386
Minneapolis *(G-5329)*

SIC

Regents of The University of .... E 612 626-7275
Minneapolis (G-5492)
Rochester Parking Ramps .... E 507 282-0558
Rochester (G-7238)
Standard Parking Corp .... C 612 371-0938
Minneapolis (G-5737)
Young, Quinlan Assoc LLP .... E 612 337-5109
Minneapolis (G-6105)

7532 Top, Body & Upholstery Repair & Paint Shops

A & R Leasing Inc .... D 218 829-4787
Baxter (G-318)
Abra Inc .... D 763 561-7220
Minneapolis (G-3662)
▼ Associated Partnership Ltd .... C 952 890-7851
Savage (G-9383)
Boulevard Collision Inc .... E 763 595-0006
Minneapolis (G-3933)
Crystal Lake Automotive Inc .... E 952 892-3377
Lakeville (G-2897)
Domaille Ltd .... D 507 287-1170
Rochester (G-7098)
Fairway Collision Center Inc .... E 651 483-4055
Saint Paul (G-8365)
Ford Boyer Trucks Inc .... D 612 378-6000
Minneapolis (G-4465)
Ford New Brighten .... D 651 633-9010
Saint Paul (G-8387)
Friendly Chevrolet, Geo Inc .... C 763 786-6100
Minneapolis (G-3473)
Fury Motors Inc .... D 651 451-1313
South Saint Paul (G-9527)
Gale's Auto Body Inc .... E 763 786-4110
Minneapolis (G-3474)
Granger's Inc .... E 651 429-2524
Minneapolis (G-3476)
Harold Chevrolet Inc .... C 952 884-3333
Minneapolis (G-4600)
Hutchinson Auto Center .... E 320 587-4748
Hutchinson (G-2699)
Infiniti Marketing Inc .... E 612 789-2025
Mound (G-6388)
Jay Malone Motors .... E 320 587-4748
Hutchinson (G-2704)
Lamettry Collision Inc .... E 952 898-1636
Burnsville (G-746)
Lamettry Collision Inc .... E 651 766-9770
Saint Paul (G-8559)
Lehman's Garage Inc .... D 952 888-8700
Minneapolis (G-4858)
Lehman's Garage Inc .... E 952 888-8700
Savage (G-9396)
Lehman's Garage Minneapolis .... E 612 827-5431
Minneapolis (G-4859)
Lenzen Chevrolet Buick Inc .... E 952 448-2850
Chaska (G-975)
Lewiston Auto Co Inc .... E 507 523-2164
Lewiston (G-2967)
Master Collision Group LLC .... E 763 509-0900
Minneapolis (G-4963)
Master Collision Group LLC .... E 612 827-4697
Minneapolis (G-4964)
Metropolitan Corp .... C 952 944-2438
Eden Prairie (G-1720)
Mgmt Five Inc .... D 651 451-2201
Inver Grove Heights (G-2762)
Mike Hall Chevrolet Inc .... E 651 484-4671
Saint Paul (G-8667)
Miller Pontiac-Buick-Gmc Inc .... D 320 251-1363
Saint Cloud (G-7558)
Nelson Chrysler Dodge GMC Inc .... E 218 739-2283
Fergus Falls (G-2102)
Olson & Johnson Body Shop Inc .... E 507 537-1669
Marshall (G-3317)
Peter's Body Shop Inc .... E 320 252-2993
Saint Cloud (G-7566)
Raymond Auto Body Inc .... E 651 488-0588
Saint Paul (G-8871)
Rudy Hopkins Luther's Motors .... C 952 938-1717
Hopkins (G-2624)
Shakopee Chevrolet Inc .... E 952 445-4148
Shakopee (G-9473)
Suburban Auto Body Inc .... E 651 983-4438
Saint Paul (G-9011)
Swenson Motor Co .... E 320 235-3434
Willmar (G-10047)
Thane Hawkins Polar Chevrolet .... C 651 429-7791
White Bear Lake (G-9978)
Truck Utilities Inc .... D 651 484-3305
Saint Paul (G-9084)
Twin City Auto Body Collision 952 884-9878
Minneapolis (G-5877)
Wally McCarthy's Cadillac .... D 651 636-6060
Saint Paul (G-9139)
Walser Collision & Glass Inc 952 884-8884
Minneapolis (G-6015)
Wolf Motors Co Inc .... E 952 492-2340
Jordan (G-2813)

7534 Tire Retreading & Repair Shops

Dickson Enterprises Inc .... E 218 759-2000
Bemidji (G-388)
First State Tire Disposal Inc .... E 763 434-0578
Isanti (G-2779)
Marco Investments LLC .... E 763 795-8145
Circle Pines (G-1016)
Midstates Retreading & Whsle .... E 507 288-7752
Rochester (G-7183)
Morgan Tire & Auto Inc .... E 651 452-4091
Saint Paul (G-7846)
Morgan Tire & Auto Inc .... E 507 388-6461
Mankato (G-3173)
Morgan Tire & Auto Inc .... E 612 861-2278
Minneapolis (G-5130)
Morgan Tire & Auto Inc .... E 218 828-8552
Baxter (G-338)
Morgan Tire & Auto LLC .... E 952 944-0458
Eden Prairie (G-1730)
Morgan Tire & Auto LLC .... E 763 682-4979
Buffalo (G-653)
Morgan Tire & Auto LLC .... E 763 571-4392
Minneapolis (G-3545)
Morgan Tire & Auto LLC .... E 651 458-1812
Cottage Grove (G-1105)
Morgan Tire & Auto LLC .... E 651 690-5007
Saint Paul (G-8721)
Morgan Tire & Auto LLC .... E 651 388-3266
Red Wing (G-6991)
Morgan Tire & Auto LLC .... E 507 354-4972
New Ulm (G-6463)
Morgan Tire & Auto LLC .... E 763 525-1583
Minneapolis (G-5131)
Morgan Tire & Auto LLC .... E 507 532-9686
Marshall (G-3316)
Morgan Tire & Auto LLC .... E 320 235-1073
Willmar (G-10028)
Morgan Tire & Auto LLC .... E 651 789-4361
Minneapolis (G-6130)
Royal Tire Inc .... D 320 258-7070
Saint Cloud (G-7590)
Tire Associates Warehouse Inc .... E 507 625-2975
Mankato (G-3207)
Wingfoot Commercial Tire Systs .... E 507 454-5181
Winona (G-10142)

7536 Automotive Glass Replacement Shops

Heartland Auto Glass .... E 952 697-0765
Minneapolis (G-4625)
Novus Inc .... E 952 944-8152
Savage (G-9402)
Pgw Auto Glass LLC .... E 952 888-0413
Minneapolis (G-5373)

7537 Automotive Transmission Repair Shops

Mankato Auto Mall Owners Inc .... E 507 387-7877
Mankato (G-3228)
Norseman Motors Inc .... E 218 847-4415
Detroit Lakes (G-1212)

7538 General Automotive Repair Shop

A & R Leasing Inc .... D 218 829-4787
Baxter (G-318)
Allstate Sales & Leasing Corp .... D 651 455-6500
South Saint Paul (G-9508)
Anderson Diesel Truck Service .... E 952 890-1580
Burnsville (G-678)
Anderson Diesel Truck Service .... E 651 480-7991
Rosemount (G-7361)
Astleford Equipment Co Inc .... E 952 894-9200
Burnsville (G-681)
Barnett Chrysler Jeep Kia .... D 651 429-3391
Saint Paul (G-8089)
Bfs Retail Operations LLC .... E 952 432-9212
Saint Paul (G-7719)
Bi-Phase Technologies LLC .... E 651 681-4450
Saint Paul (G-7721)
Black Jack Express & Repair .... E 507 485-3437
Wood Lake (G-10170)
Brookdale Motor Sales Inc .... C 763 561-8161
Minneapolis (G-3956)
Brookman Motor Sales Inc .... E 651 777-1316
Lake Elmo (G-2867)
Bruns Inc .... E 218 757-3232
Orr (G-6577)
Burnsville Volkswagen Inc .... D 952 892-9400
Burnsville (G-692)
Caledonia Haulers LLC .... C 507 725-9000
Caledonia (G-826)
Camping World Inc .... E 763 428-7779
Rogers (G-7319)
Carefree Services Inc .... E 763 479-2600
Maple Plain (G-3271)
Cedar Towing & Auction Inc .... E 612 721-6645
Minneapolis (G-4037)
City of Mora .... E 320 679-1770
Mora (G-6353)
▲ Clearwater Truck Center Inc .... E 320 558-6565
Clearwater (G-1042)
Coates Rv Center Inc .... E 651 488-0234
Hugo (G-2674)
Commercial Truck & Trailer Rep .... E 651 639-2260
Saint Paul (G-8230)
Coon Rapids Chrysler Inc .... C 763 421-8000
Minneapolis (G-3439)
Crystal Lake Automotive Inc .... E 952 892-3377
Lakeville (G-2897)
Dahl Trucking Inc .... D 507 773-4226
Granada (G-2256)
Dave Syverson Truck Center Inc .... E 507 289-3357
Rochester (G-7093)
Dick's Valley Service Inc .... E 952 891-4431
Apple Valley (G-243)
Dodge of Burnsville Inc .... E 952 894-9000
Burnsville (G-712)
Dondelinger Chevrolet .... D 218 829-4787
Baxter (G-327)
Farmers Union Oil Co of .... E 218 233-2497
Moorhead (G-6315)
Forbes, John .... E 320 693-3287
Litchfield (G-2984)
Ford Boyer Trucks Inc .... D 612 378-6000
Minneapolis (G-4465)
Ford New Brighten .... D 651 633-9010
Saint Paul (G-8387)
Friendly Chevrolet, Geo Inc .... C 763 786-6100
Minneapolis (G-3473)
Granger's Inc .... E 651 429-2524
Minneapolis (G-3476)
Harold Chevrolet Inc .... C 952 884-3333
Minneapolis (G-4600)
Hawkins Chevrolet-Cadillac Inc .... E 507 238-4786
Fairmont (G-1973)
Hilligoss Chevrolet Inc .... E 218 263-7578
Hibbing (G-2454)
Hutchinson Auto Center .... E 320 587-4748
Hutchinson (G-2699)
Independent School District .... E 218 773-0476
East Grand Forks (G-1569)
Interstate Co's Inc .... D 952 854-2044
Minneapolis (G-4726)
Jeff's, Bobby & Steves .... E 763 788-1113
Minneapolis (G-3506)
Kline Volvo Inc .... D 651 379-4300
Saint Paul (G-8549)
Kolstad Co Inc .... D 763 792-1033
Minneapolis (G-3511)
Le Jeune Investment Inc .... D 651 483-2681
Saint Paul (G-8572)
Lehman's Garage Inc .... D 952 888-8700
Minneapolis (G-4858)
Lehman's Garage Inc .... E 651 454-1120
Saint Paul (G-7823)
Lehman's Garage Minneapolis .... E 612 827-5431
Minneapolis (G-4859)
Lewiston Auto Co Inc .... E 507 523-2164
Lewiston (G-2967)
Lupient Oldsmobile Co Inc .... C 763 546-2222
Minneapolis (G-4910)
Manders Diesel Repair Inc .... E 952 469-1800
Lakeville (G-2915)
Maplewood Motors Inc .... D 651 482-1322
Saint Paul (G-8614)
McK of Austin Ltd .... D 507 437-6702
Austin (G-282)
Metropolitan Corp .... C 952 944-2438
Eden Prairie (G-1720)
Metropolitan Corp .... D 952 943-9000
Eden Prairie (G-1721)
Morries New Buffalo Chrysler .... E 763 682-1800
Buffalo (G-654)
Nelson Chrysler Dodge GMC Inc .... E 218 739-2283
Fergus Falls (G-2102)
Nelson Leasing Inc .... E 320 235-2770
Willmar (G-10029)
Norseman Motors Inc .... E 218 847-4415
Detroit Lakes (G-1212)
Norseman Motors Inc .... E 218 847-1639
Detroit Lakes (G-1213)
North Star International .... D 612 378-1660
Minneapolis (G-5219)
Nuss Truck Group Inc .... E 507 345-6225
Mankato (G-3178)
Olson & Johnson Body Shop Inc .... E 507 537-1669
Marshall (G-3317)
Parkview Ford - Mercury Inc .... E 320 269-5565
Montevideo (G-6256)
Pleasureland Inc .... D 320 251-7588
Saint Cloud (G-7569)
Pro Stop Truck Service Inc .... D 651 452-8137
Saint Paul (G-7883)
R L Brookdale Motors Inc .... D 763 561-8111
Minneapolis (G-5459)
Red's Auto Inc .... E 320 468-6478
Pierz (G-6807)
Richards Transportation Svc .... E 218 233-3404
Moorhead (G-6338)
Rihm Motor Co .... D 651 646-7833
Saint Paul (G-8902)
River Valley Truck Centers Inc .... D 507 345-1129
Mankato (G-3187)
Robert A Williams Enterprises .... E 952 831-6250
Minneapolis (G-5552)
Rockford Bus Garage Inc .... E 763 477-6100
Rockford (G-7304)
Roger's Amoco Inc .... E 320 963-6555
Maple Lake (G-3264)
Roseau Diesel Service Inc 218 463-1711
Roseau (G-7357)
Rudy Hopkins Luther's Motors .... C 952 938-1717
Hopkins (G-2624)
Southtown Freeway Toyota Inc .... E 952 888-5581
Minneapolis (G-5712)
St Cloud Truck Sales Inc .... D 320 251-0931
Saint Cloud (G-7442)

S I C

(G-00000) Company's Geographic Section entry number
500
2011 Harris Minnesota Services Directory
▲=Import ▼=Export
◆=Import/Export

Superior Ford Inc C 763 559-9111 Minneapolis (G-5771)
Swenson Motor Co E 320 235-3434 Willmar (G-10047)
Thermo Leasing Corp E 763 421-2505 Anoka (G-234)
Toyota City Inc D 763 566-0060 Minneapolis (G-5842)
Twin Cities Mack Volvo Trucks D 651 633-4810 Saint Paul (G-9087)
Twin City West 76 Auto Truck D 763 428-2277 Rogers (G-7345)
United States Postal Service D 651 293-3172 Saint Paul (G-9109)
Valley Sales Inc E 952 314-8560 Waconia (G-9793)
Valley Sales of Hutchinson Inc E 320 587-2240 Hutchinson (G-2714)
Valley Truck Parts & Service E 218 773-3486 East Grand Forks (G-1578)
Village Chevrolet Co - Wayzata C 952 473-5444 Wayzata (G-9947)
Wagamon Brothers Inc E 763 789-7227 Minneapolis (G-3634)
Wally McCarthy's Cadillac D 651 636-6060 Saint Paul (G-9139)
Walter Pontiac Buick GMC Inc D 952 888-9800 Minneapolis (G-6019)
Westman Freightliner Inc E 507 625-4118 Mankato (G-3217)
Wolf Motors Co Inc E 952 492-2340 Jordan (G-2813)

7539 Automotive Repair Shops, NEC

Automotive Restyling Concepts D 763 535-2181 Minneapolis (G-3840)
Crossroads Trailer Sales & Svc E 507 373-4443 Albert Lea (G-45)
Dahlke Trailer Sales Inc E 763 783-0077 Minneapolis (G-3450)
Genuine Parts Co D 952 925-0188 Minneapolis (G-4523)
Istate Truck Inc 952 854-2044 Minneapolis (G-4739)
Jay Malone Motors E 320 587-4748 Hutchinson (G-2704)
Montincello Ford-Mercury Inc C 763 295-2056 Minneapolis (G-5123)
Morgan Tire & Auto Inc E 612 861-2278 Minneapolis (G-5130)
Murphy Automotive Inc E 952 432-2454 Rosemount (G-7373)
Race Automotive of Rochester E 507 282-5200 Rochester (G-7216)
Red Rooster Auto Stores LLC D 763 533-4321 Minneapolis (G-5477)
Roseau Diesel Service Inc 218 463-1711 Roseau (G-7357)
Schwieters Chevrolet of E 320 634-4507 Glenwood (G-2232)
Smith's Winter Products E 763 493-3332 Osseo (G-6665)
Spring Prairie Hutterian C 218 498-0222 Hawley (G-2423)
Twin City Custom Railings & GL E 763 780-7314 Minneapolis (G-3624)
Zumbrota Ford Sales LLC E 507 732-5127 Zumbrota (G-10222)

7542 Car Washes

Bbj Inc E 651 730-7808 Saint Paul (G-9187)
Brookdale Car Wash Inc E 763 561-1123 Minneapolis (G-3954)
Buff & Shine Center Inc E 952 944-9033 Minneapolis (G-3968)
Cin-Mar Corp E 612 781-6924 Minneapolis (G-4075)
Clean Image Mobile Truck Wash E 651 484-7776 Saint Paul (G-8216)
Dealers Choice Auto Clean E 763 592-9900 Minneapolis (G-4237)
Don's Car Washes of Minnesota E 763 788-1631 Minneapolis (G-3458)
Douglas Drive Car Wash Inc E 763 533-1581 Minneapolis (G-4285)
Downtowner Car Wash E 651 222-7045 Saint Paul (G-8310)
Fast Lane Car Wash E 218 444-9130 Bemidji (G-392)
London Road Car Wash Inc E 218 728-4201 Duluth (G-1385)
Mankato Auto Mall Owners Inc E 507 387-7877 Mankato (G-3228)
Mister Car Wash E 952 931-9412 Minneapolis (G-5110)
Norseman Motors Inc E 218 847-4415 Detroit Lakes (G-1212)
Northland Power Washing E 320 763-6593 Alexandria (G-116)
Paradise Car Wash E 952 888-5388 Minneapolis (G-5319)
Perfect 10 Car Wash Inc E 651 227-9274 Minneapolis (G-3568)
Quality Car Wash Ops Ltd Inc E 952 473-4535 Wayzata (G-9937)
Riverside Auto Wash Inc E 763 571-2700 Minneapolis (G-3587)
S J C Inc E 651 483-1752 Saint Paul (G-8919)
Soft Touch Car Care of St E 320 253-4204 Saint Cloud (G-7595)
Wally Mc Carthys Oldsmobile D 651 636-6060 Saint Paul (G-9138)
Witt Dohm Properties Inc E 952 758-5252 New Prague (G-6425)

7549 Automotive Svcs, Except Repair & Car Washes

Andy's Towing Co E 320 251-5691 Saint Cloud (G-7407)
Black Jack Express & Repair E 507 485-3437 Wood Lake (G-10170)
Brandl Motor Sports E 320 632-2908 Little Falls (G-3000)
Budget Towing Inc of St Paul E 651 699-5690 Saint Paul (G-8139)
Cedar Towing & Auction Inc E 612 721-6645 Minneapolis (G-4037)
Chief's Service Inc E 952 881-6404 Minneapolis (G-4063)
Chief's Towing Inc E 952 888-2201 Minneapolis (G-4064)
Identifix Inc D 651 633-8007 Saint Paul (G-8505)
McDonald Rentals Inc E 218 879-9060 Cloquet (G-1056)
P & L Automotive Inc E 952 941-0888 Minneapolis (G-5304)
Robert A Williams Enterprises E 952 831-6250 Minneapolis (G-5552)
Saint Cloud Auto Center LLC E 320 259-4542 Waite Park (G-9835)
Schmit Towing Inc E 763 253-1568 Minneapolis (G-3598)
Shorty's Heavy Duty Wrecker E 763 784-1411 Minneapolis (G-3601)
Thorco Inc E 320 564-3086 Granite Falls (G-2321)
Twin Cities Transport E 651 770-0816 Saint Paul (G-9283)
Twin Cities Transport E 651 642-1446 Saint Paul (G-9089)
Wrecker Services Inc E 612 330-0013 Minneapolis (G-6089)

76 MISCELLANEOUS REPAIR SERVICES

7622 Radio & TV Repair Shops

Alpha Video & Audio Inc D 952 896-9898 Minneapolis (G-3733)
Comm-Works Holdings LLC D 763 258-5800 Minneapolis (G-4130)
National Camera Exchange Inc E 952 898-4888 Burnsville (G-762)
Nextel Communications Inc D 952 703-7600 Minneapolis (G-5197)
Phoenix Distributing Inc E 952 882-9949 Burnsville (G-781)
Ultimate Acquisition Partners E 952 830-0010 Minneapolis (G-5895)

7623 Refrigeration & Air Conditioning Svc & Repair Shop

Dependable Indoor Air Quality E 763 757-5040 Minneapolis (G-3454)
Egan Co C 763 544-4131 Brooklyn Park (G-609)
McDowall Co D 320 251-8640 Waite Park (G-9829)
Naylor Heating & Refrigeration E 218 444-4328 Bemidji (G-406)
Palen Kimball LLC E 651 646-2800 Saint Paul (G-8804)
Quality Refrigeration Inc E 612 861-7350 Minneapolis (G-5443)
◆ Thermo King Sales & Service E 651 633-2820 Saint Paul (G-9041)

7629 Electrical & Elex Repair Shop, NEC

Andy's Electrical Service Inc E 507 378-2101 Grand Meadow (G-2263)
▲ Artesyn North America Inc C 952 941-1100 Eden Prairie (G-1598)
Bennett Office Technologies E 320 235-6425 Willmar (G-9985)
Davis Typewriter Co Inc E 507 343-2001 Worthington (G-10182)
F M Trucking Inc E 651 639-0446 Saint Paul (G-8359)
General Electric Co E 218 749-6100 Mountain Iron (G-6392)
Jordan Transformer LLC D 952 492-2720 Jordan (G-2805)
Matrix Communications Inc E 763 475-5500 Minneapolis (G-4966)
Nextel Communications Inc D 952 703-7600 Minneapolis (G-5197)
Norstan Communications Inc C 952 352-4300 Minnetonka (G-6202)
North Country Business Prdts D 218 751-4140 Bemidji (G-408)
North Country Business Prdts E 800 937-4140 Plymouth (G-6878)
Party Music Inc E 952 941-3830 Eden Prairie (G-1744)
Phoenix Distributing Inc E 952 882-9949 Burnsville (G-781)
Rvi Inc E 320 269-3227 Montevideo (G-6259)
Sears, Roebuck & Co B 651 291-4397 Saint Paul (G-8939)
Sears, Roebuck & Co D 952 944-4911 Eden Prairie (G-1772)
Sears, Roebuck & Co B 952 435-2380 Burnsville (G-795)
Sel-Mor Distributing Co E 952 929-0888 Minneapolis (G-5629)
Siemens Hearing Inc B 763 268-4500 Minneapolis (G-5666)
Smith Micro Technologies Inc C 651 482-8718 Saint Paul (G-8966)
Spectrum Solutions Inc E 651 634-1800 Saint Paul (G-8976)
ST Cotter Turbine Services Inc C 763 263-5611 Big Lake (G-457)
Stresstech Inc E 651 388-7117 Red Wing (G-7008)
System Design Advantage LLC E 952 703-3500 Minneapolis (G-5781)
US Union Tool Inc E 651 552-0440 South Saint Paul (G-9548)
Woodgroup Field Services Inc D 763 785-0650 Minneapolis (G-3643)

7631 Watch, Clock & Jewelry Repair

Estate Jewelry & Coin Inc E 952 881-8862 Minneapolis (G-4373)
Jewelry Repair Centers Inc E 763 370-2511 Minneapolis (G-3507)

7641 Reupholstery & Furniture Repair

Commercial Furniture Services E 952 922-6683 Saint Louis Park (G-7658)
Omni Workspace Co C 612 627-1600 Minneapolis (G-5277)
Omni Workspace Co E 612 627-1600 Minneapolis (G-5276)

7692 Welding Repair

Aitkin Iron Works Inc D 218 927-2400 Aitkin (G-24)
Alexandria Pro-Fab Co Inc D 320 852-7918 Alexandria (G-82)
American Manufacturing Inc E 763 444-9225 Isanti (G-2777)
Bizal Mfg Inc E 763 571-4030 Minneapolis (G-3418)
Checker Machine Inc E 763 544-5000 Minneapolis (G-4057)
Code Welding & Mfg Inc E 763 792-6632 Minneapolis (G-3435)
▲ Diesel Cast Welding Inc E 763 780-5940 Minneapolis (G-3455)
Eagle Tool & Design Inc E 763 784-7400 Minneapolis (G-3460)
Falls Fabricating C 320 632-2322 Little Falls (G-3005)
Furin & Shea Welding & Fabctg E 218 262-5271 Hibbing (G-2446)
Gauthier Industries Inc D 507 289-0731 Rochester (G-7125)
Griffiths Holding Corp C 763 559-2288 Minneapolis (G-4572)
Herman Manufacturing Co E 507 553-5256 Wells (G-9962)
Industrial Welders E 218 628-1011 Duluth (G-1357)
Lowry Manufacturing Co E 320 283-5450 Lowry (G-3055)
M & L Industries Inc E 763 428-4220 Rogers (G-7329)
▲ Machinewell Inc D 218 294-6101 Grygla (G-2330)
Mid-Continent Engineering Inc D 612 781-0260 Minneapolis (G-5023)
Nedmac Inc E 763 537-8435 Minneapolis (G-5179)
Nobel Welding & Manufacturing E 651 426-1511 Hugo (G-2671)
Par Piping & Fabrication LLC E 320 564-2173 Granite Falls (G-2317)
Remmele Engineering Inc D 763 263-3650 Big Lake (G-454)
Sasker Manufacturing Inc E 320 532-4268 Onamia (G-6576)
Tavis Metal & Fabrication Corp E 763 428-8483 Rogers (G-7342)

S I C

Employment codes: A=Over 500 employees, B=251-500 C=101-250, D=51-100, E=25-50
2011 Harris Minnesota Services Directory
© Harris InfoSource 1-866-281-6415
501

Whirl-Air-Flow Corp ....E....763 262-1200
Big Lake (G-459)

7694 Armature Rewinding Shops

Electric Motor Repair Inc ....E....612 588-4693
Minneapolis (G-4337)
General Electric Co ....E....612 529-9502
Minneapolis (G-4510)
General Electric Co ....E....218 749-6100
Mountain Iron (G-6392)
Malton Electric Co ....E....763 571-7758
Minneapolis (G-3526)
Mielke Electric Works Inc ....E....218 727-7411
Duluth (G-1394)
Spring Prairie Hutterian ....C....218 498-0222
Hawley (G-2423)
Trico Tcwind Inc ....E....320 693-6200
Litchfield (G-2991)

7699 Repair Shop & Related Svcs, NEC

AAA Wicks Furnace Duct ....D....651 770-1263
Minneapolis (G-3654)
Aerial Contractors Inc ....E....218 236-9233
Moorhead (G-6294)
Albers Mechanical Services Inc ....E....651 224-3100
Saint Paul (G-8003)
All City Elevator Inc ....E....651 646-5600
Saint Paul (G-8009)
and Sew On Inc 651 439-9311
Stillwater (G-9596)
API Garage Door Co ....E....763 533-3838
Minneapolis (G-3789)
◆ API Group Inc ....E....651 636-4320
Saint Paul (G-8054)
Armor Security Inc ....E....612 870-1572
Minneapolis (G-3809)
Atlas Foundation Co ....E....763 428-2261
Osseo (G-6596)
Bentley Instruments Inc ....E....952 448-7600
Chaska (G-952)
Boiler Services Inc ....E....763 784-8178
Minneapolis (G-3422)
Brainerd Sports & Marine LLC 218 828-4728
Brainerd (G-554)
Bristow's Inc ....E....320 253-7878
Saint Cloud (G-7435)
Chesley Truck Sales Inc ....C....651 636-3400
Saint Paul (G-9195)
City Auto Glass ....E....651 552-1000
South Saint Paul (G-9522)
Clutch & Transmission Service ....E....651 636-4311
Saint Paul (G-8217)
Clutch & Transmission Service ....D....651 631-0959
Saint Paul (G-8218)
Conveyor Belt Service Inc ....E....218 741-5939
Virginia (G-9737)
Crysteel Truck Equipment Inc ....E....952 469-5678
Lakeville (G-2899)
◆ Cutting Edge Creations Inc ....D....651 209-8600
Saint Paul (G-7743)
Don's Leather Cleaning Inc ....E....612 721-4881
Minneapolis (G-4276)
Eagle Elevator Corp ....E....651 645-1543
Saint Paul (G-8318)
Electric Motor Repair Inc ....E....612 588-4693
Minneapolis (G-4337)
Enviromatic Corp of America ....D....612 861-3330
Minneapolis (G-4362)
▲ Expresspoint Technology Svcs ....C....763 543-6000
Golden Valley (G-2240)
F M Trucking Inc ....E....651 639-0446
Saint Paul (G-8358)
Faribault Harley Davidson Inc ....E....507 334-5130
Faribault (G-2004)
Freewheel Bicycle Cooperative ....E....612 339-2219
Minneapolis (G-4487)
Gander Mountain Co ....E....507 252-2033
Rochester (G-7124)
Gander Mountain Co ....E....763 420-9800
Osseo (G-6616)
General Cleaning Specialists ....D....218 727-4513
Duluth (G-1334)
General Dynamics Aviation Svcs ....D....612 638-2000
Minneapolis (G-4508)
General Electric Co ....E....612 529-9502
Minneapolis (G-4510)
General Electric Co ....E....218 749-6100
Mountain Iron (G-6392)
General Parts LLC ....E....952 944-5800
Minneapolis (G-4515)
General Safety Equipment LLC ....D....651 462-1000
Wyoming (G-10205)
Griffin Petroleum Services Inc ....E....763 780-6332
Minneapolis (G-3479)
H & J Bliss Enterprises ....E....952 988-9302
Minneapolis (G-4584)
Hance Distributing Inc ....E....952 935-6429
Hopkins (G-2548)
Handi Medical Supply Inc ....D....651 644-9770
Saint Paul (G-8440)
Harris Contracting Co ....E....507 282-8128
Rochester (G-7133)
Havco Inc ....E....320 746-2781
Avon (G-295)
▲ Hayden-Murphy Equipment Co ....E....952 884-2301
Minneapolis (G-4612)
Hydraulic Specialty Co Inc ....E....763 571-3072
Minneapolis (G-3494)
Infrastructure Technologies ....E....763 428-6488
Rogers (G-7327)
Instrument & Valve Services Co ....E....800 654-7768
Eden Prairie (G-1695)
Jerry's Enterprises Inc ....E....952 929-4601
Minneapolis (G-4761)
K & S Millwrights Inc ....E....320 833-2228
Buffalo Lake (G-665)
Kelbro Co ....E....612 824-9803
Minneapolis (G-4796)
Kibble Equipment Inc ....D....320 269-6466
Montevideo (G-6248)
Kone Inc ....D....952 688-6827
Eagan (G-1533)
LasX Industries Inc ....E....651 407-0011
Saint Paul (G-8565)
▲ Lieberman Co's Inc ....D....952 887-5299
Minneapolis (G-4873)
M & N Equipment Services Inc ....E....612 379-4147
Minneapolis (G-4916)
Minnesota Chemical Co ....E....651 646-7521
Saint Paul (G-8676)
◆ Minnesota Elevator Inc ....C....507 245-3060
Mankato (G-3171)
Minnesota Prophy Power Inc ....D....952 898-1594
Lakeville (G-2920)
▲ Minnesota Supply Co ....D....952 828-7300
Eden Prairie (G-1726)
Monaco Air Duluth LLC ....E....218 727-2911
Duluth (G-1396)
Nardini Fire Equipment Co Inc ....D....651 483-6631
Saint Paul (G-8735)
Nash Frame Design Inc ....E....612 338-9041
Minneapolis (G-5157)
Northern Belt & Conveyor Inc ....E....218 744-9950
Eveleth (G-1932)
▲ Northern Dewatering Inc ....D....763 428-2616
Rogers (G-7332)
Otto Packaging Midwest LLC ....E....651 488-0474
Saint Paul (G-8793)
Patterson Co's Inc ....C....651 686-1600
Saint Paul (G-7866)
Paul A Schmitt Music Co ....E....763 566-4560
Minneapolis (G-5349)
Perfect Complement Ltd ....E....763 421-8360
Minneapolis (G-3569)
Precision Repair & Calibration ....E....763 784-1704
Minneapolis (G-3572)
Quality Forklift Sales & Svc ....E....952 445-6607
Shakopee (G-9467)
R & O Elevator Co Inc ....D....612 588-7844
Minneapolis (G-5454)
Rigels Inc ....E....218 233-6104
Moorhead (G-6340)
Rosemount Aerospace Inc ....C....651 681-8900
Eagan (G-1548)
Roto-Rooter Services Co ....E....651 738-8355
Saint Paul (G-9271)
RSC Equipment Rental Inc ....E....763 557-1234
Minneapolis (G-5565)
Sears, Roebuck & Co ....D....800 882-5351
Waite Park (G-9837)
Sel-Mor Distributing Co ....E....952 929-0888
Minneapolis (G-5629)
Sifco Industries Inc ....D....763 544-3511
Minneapolis (G-5667)
▲ SMI & Hydraulics Inc ....E....507 296-4551
Porter (G-6894)
Smith's Winter Products ....E....763 493-3332
Osseo (G-6665)
▲ Smyth Co's Inc ....E....651 646-4544
Saint Paul (G-8967)
St Paul Harley Davidson Inc ....D....651 738-2168
Saint Paul (G-9277)
◆ Sterilmed Inc ....B....763 488-3400
Osseo (G-6668)
Sweeney Brothers Tractor Co ....E....952 894-9595
Burnsville (G-805)
▲ Total Tool Supply Inc ....D....651 646-4055
Saint Paul (G-9073)
Twin City Container Inc ....E....651 480-3786
Hastings (G-2409)
Ulland Brothers Inc ....E....218 262-3406
Hibbing (G-2478)
United Operations Inc of ....E....763 551-0202
Minneapolis (G-5911)
Winter Truck Line Inc ....E....218 935-2236
Mahnomen (G-3092)
Wipaire Inc ....D....651 451-1205
South Saint Paul (G-9553)
▲ Yale Materials Handling - MN ....D....763 434-3832
Anoka (G-241)
Zylstra Harley Davidson Inc ....E....763 241-2000
Elk River (G-1897)

78 MOTION PICTURES

7812 Motion Picture & Video Tape Production

Charthouse International ....E....952 890-1800
Burnsville (G-696)
Distributed Website Corp ....E....507 453-5164
Winona (G-10093)
◆ Electrosonic Inc ....E....952 931-7500
Minnetonka (G-6165)
Greatapes Corp ....E....612 872-8284
Minneapolis (G-4557)
Greer & Associates Inc ....E....612 338-6171
Minneapolis (G-4564)
Harmony Holdings Inc ....D....952 925-8840
Wayzata (G-9920)
Hometime Video Publishing Inc ....E....952 448-3812
Chaska (G-968)
In Fisherman Inc ....E....218 829-1648
Baxter (G-330)
Media Productions Inc ....E....612 379-4678
Minneapolis (G-4984)
Metropolitan Productions Inc ....D....612 333-1025
Minneapolis (G-5007)
New Paradigm Productions Inc ....E....612 321-9091
Minneapolis (G-5192)
Nowdocs International Inc ....D....888 669-3627
North Mankato (G-6512)
▲ Paradigm Publishing Inc ....E....651 290-2800
Saint Paul (G-8807)
Rick S Shand ....E....651 770-8710
Saint Paul (G-9268)
Ten Dollar Trophy LLC ....E....952 912-9972
Hopkins (G-2644)

7819 Services Allied To Motion Picture Prdtn

Duplication Factory LLC ....D....952 448-9912
Chaska (G-962)
Lights On Inc 612 331-6620
Minneapolis (G-4886)
Metropolitan Productions Inc ....D....612 333-1025
Minneapolis (G-5007)

7822 Motion Picture & Video Tape Distribution

Quest Management Associates ....E....612 379-3800
Minneapolis (G-5449)

7832 Motion Picture Theaters, Except Drive-In

AMC Entertainment Inc ....E....763 494-0379
Maple Grove (G-3236)
American Multi-Cinema Inc ....E....952 851-0073
Bloomington (G-484)
Andover Cinema ....E....763 767-8401
Anoka (G-153)
Canam Theatres Moa LLC ....E....952 883-8810
Bloomington (G-491)
Carmike Cinemas Inc ....D....763 785-1855
Saint Paul (G-8168)
Cinema Entertainment Corp ....E....218 729-0334
Duluth (G-1272)
Cinema Entertainment Corp ....E....218 529-1636
Duluth (G-1273)
Cinemark U S A Inc ....E....507 625-1929
Mankato (G-3117)
Cineplex Odean Corp ....E....763 591-5921
Minneapolis (G-4076)
Climb Theater Inc ....D....651 453-9275
Inver Grove Heights (G-2743)
Mann Theaters Inc ....E....952 931-3191
Hopkins (G-2574)
Marcus Theatres Corp ....E....763 441-1234
Elk River (G-1883)
Parkwood 18 Theatres ....E....320 251-1188
Waite Park (G-9831)
Premiere Theatres ....E....218 879-7985
Cloquet (G-1061)
Regal Cinemas Inc ....E....651 452-8329
Saint Paul (G-7892)
Regal Cinemas Inc ....E....952 435-8080
Burnsville (G-788)
Regents of The University of ....E....612 624-2345
Minneapolis (G-5497)
Showplace 16 Kerasotes Theatre ....D....763 757-6233
Minneapolis (G-3602)
Ten Thousand Things Theatre ....E....612 724-4494
Minneapolis (G-5810)

7841 Video Tape Rental

Coborn's Inc ....C....320 679-4003
Mora (G-6354)
McDonald Rentals Inc ....E....218 879-9060
Cloquet (G-1056)
United Entertainment Corp ....B....320 203-1003
Saint Cloud (G-7624)

79 AMUSEMENT & RECREATION SERVICES

7911 Dance Studios, Schools & Halls

Ballet Arts Minnesota Inc ....E....612 340-1071
Minneapolis (G-3864)
Blue Note of Winsted Inc ....E....320 485-9698
Winsted (G-10159)

S I C

(G-00000) Company's Geographic Section entry number
502
2011 Harris Minnesota Services Directory
▲=Import ▼=Export
◆=Import/Export

Dance Art Centre ....E....952 937-2618
Eden Prairie *(G-1641)*
Legion Pavilion Co Inc ....E....952 758-4603
New Prague *(G-6422)*
North Crest Gymnastics & Dance ....E....320 251-3416
Sauk Rapids *(G-9370)*
Prairie Dance Alliance ....E....507 532-3195
Marshall *(G-3319)*
Sondance Studio ....E....763 784-2920
Minneapolis *(G-3605)*

7922 Theatrical Producers & Misc Theatrical Svcs

Chanhassen Theatre LLC ....C....952 934-1500
Chanhassen *(G-913)*
Children's Theatre Co ....C....612 874-0500
Minneapolis *(G-4067)*
Climb Theater Inc ....D....651 453-9275
Inver Grove Heights *(G-2743)*
Climb Theatre Inc ....D....651 453-9275
Inver Grove Heights *(G-2744)*
Comedysportz Twin Cities ....E....612 870-1230
Minneapolis *(G-4127)*
Commonweal Theatre Co ....E....507 467-2905
Lanesboro *(G-2946)*
Creative Promotional Concepts ....D....651 905-9339
Saint Paul *(G-7740)*
Dakota Cook LLC ....D....612 332-1010
Minneapolis *(G-4218)*
Great River Shakespeare ....E....507 474-7900
Winona *(G-10099)*
Guthrie Theater Foundation ....C....612 225-6000
Minneapolis *(G-4579)*
Hennepin Broadway Series ....D....612 373-5665
Minneapolis *(G-4630)*
Hey City Theater Co ....D....612 333-9202
Minneapolis *(G-4643)*
History Theatre Inc ....C....651 292-4323
Saint Paul *(G-8486)*
Holmes Center Inc ....D....218 844-4221
Detroit Lakes *(G-1197)*
Into The Mystic Productions ....E....612 332-6620
Minneapolis *(G-4731)*
It's About Time Theater ....E....507 280-8956
Rochester *(G-7144)*
Jazz Arts Group Fargomoorhead ....E....218 236-0421
Moorhead *(G-6320)*
Live Nation Worldwide Inc ....E....612 673-8308
Minneapolis *(G-4895)*
Midwest Latino Entertainment ....E....612 728-0101
Minneapolis *(G-5030)*
Mini Kix Inc ....C....218 829-7107
Baxter *(G-336)*
Minnesota Landmarks Inc ....E....651 292-3233
Saint Paul *(G-8693)*
Minnesota Opera ....C....612 333-2700
Minneapolis *(G-5087)*
National Theatre For Children ....D....612 617-4903
Minneapolis *(G-5168)*
Old Log Theater Ltd ....E....952 474-5951
Excelsior *(G-1951)*
Ordway Center For The 651 282-3000
Saint Paul *(G-8790)*
Paramount Theater ....E....320 259-5463
Saint Cloud *(G-7565)*
Paul Bunyan Community Theater ....E....218 751-7270
Bemidji *(G-419)*
Staging Concepts Inc ....E....763 533-2094
Minneapolis *(G-5734)*
Ten Thousand Things Theatre ....E....612 724-4494
Minneapolis *(G-5810)*
West Bank School of Music ....E....612 333-6651
Minneapolis *(G-6056)*

7929 Bands, Orchestras, Actors & Entertainers

Acme Comedy Co ....E....612 338-6393
Minneapolis *(G-3673)*
Anoka Brass Band Assoc Inc ....E....763 427-2790
Anoka *(G-154)*
Creative Promotional Concepts ....D....651 905-9339
Saint Paul *(G-7740)*
Dunk N Jump ....D....612 788-0404
Minneapolis *(G-4295)*
Mankato Symphony Orchestra ....D....507 625-8880
Mankato *(G-3167)*
Midwest Sound & Light Inc ....E....651 644-4111
Saint Paul *(G-8662)*
Mini Kix Inc ....C....218 829-7107
Baxter *(G-336)*
Minnesota Orchestral Assn ....E....612 371-5600
Minneapolis *(G-5088)*
Minnesota Orchestral Assn ....E....612 371-5600
Minneapolis *(G-5089)*
Party Music Inc ....E....952 941-3830
Eden Prairie *(G-1744)*
Red Wing Brass Band Inc ....E....651 388-2656
Red Wing *(G-6996)*
Rinke, Noonan, Grote, Smoley ....D....320 251-6700
Saint Cloud *(G-7588)*
Saint Paul Chamber Orchestra ....D....651 292-3241
Saint Paul *(G-8925)*

7933 Bowling Centers

AMF Bowling Centers Inc ....E....763 566-6250
Minneapolis *(G-3771)*
AMF Bowling Centers Inc ....E....651 484-6501
Saint Paul *(G-8038)*
AMF Bowling Centers Inc ....E....763 571-3520
Minneapolis *(G-3402)*
AMF Bowling Centers Inc ....E....651 774-8787
Saint Paul *(G-8039)*
B L B Inc ....D....612 825-3737
Minneapolis *(G-3852)*
Balyle Inc ....E....320 253-2910
Sartell *(G-9332)*
Blainbrook Entertainment Ctr ....D....763 755-8686
Minneapolis *(G-3419)*
Bowl Rite Inc ....E....651 646-1396
Saint Paul *(G-8119)*
Bowling Bob's 13th Frame Pro ....D....763 755-8686
Minneapolis *(G-3423)*
Brunswick Bowling & Billiards ....E....952 941-0445
Eden Prairie *(G-1612)*
CB & L Inc ....E....651 257-8047
Chisago City *(G-988)*
Cernick Enterprises ....D....651 552-9005
Inver Grove Heights *(G-2741)*
Church of St Bernard ....E....651 488-6733
Saint Paul *(G-8200)*
Classic Bowl Inc ....E....763 421-4402
Minneapolis *(G-3433)*
Colonial Lanes Co ....E....507 289-2341
Rochester *(G-7086)*
Country Lanes-North Inc ....E....218 722-1741
Duluth *(G-1283)*
Dan Dahlin Inc ....E....763 434-6010
Anoka *(G-172)*
Degidio Inc ....E....651 291-7105
Saint Paul *(G-8282)*
Elsie's Restaurant Lounge ....E....612 378-9702
Minneapolis *(G-4344)*
Jack's House ....E....218 824-5225
Brainerd *(G-571)*
Kalk-Young Inc ....E....218 864-5265
Battle Lake *(G-311)*
Kandi Entertainment Center Inc ....D....320 235-3800
Willmar *(G-10012)*
Kegler's Inc ....E....218 722-0671
Duluth *(G-1369)*
Lane Memory ....E....612 721-6211
Minneapolis *(G-4839)*
Liberty Lanes Inc ....E....218 773-3477
East Grand Forks *(G-1570)*
Maplewood Bowl Inc ....D....651 774-8787
Saint Paul *(G-8612)*
Mermaid Inc ....C....763 784-7350
Saint Paul *(G-8637)*
Minnehaha Bowling Center Inc ....E....651 488-7208
Saint Paul *(G-8671)*
MPS Group Properties Inc ....E....507 533-8330
Stewartville *(G-9593)*
Owatonna Fairlanes Corp ....E....507 451-2524
Owatonna *(G-6728)*
PC Productions Inc ....E....651 451-6222
Saint Paul *(G-7870)*
Philip's Investment Co ....D....952 929-6810
Minneapolis *(G-5375)*
Reese Brooks Hospitality Inds ....E....763 767-0754
Minneapolis *(G-3581)*
Rich Mgt Inc ....D....952 432-1515
Saint Paul *(G-7895)*
River City Lanes ....E....763 295-3390
Monticello *(G-6285)*
Rothgarn Enterprise Inc ....E....651 345-2324
Lake City *(G-2854)*
Skyline Bowling Lanes Inc ....E....218 727-8555
Duluth *(G-1452)*
Spare Times Lanes & Lounge ....E....507 477-3492
Hayfield *(G-2426)*
Spectrum Lanes Bowling Alley ....C....763 553-0333
Minneapolis *(G-5718)*
Sundance Golf & Bowl Inc ....E....763 420-4700
Osseo *(G-6670)*
Tuttle Inc ....E....612 378-9701
Minneapolis *(G-5870)*
Tuttle's Bowling Bar & Grill ....E....952 938-4090
Hopkins *(G-2649)*
Twin Town Bowl Inc ....E....507 387-3439
Mankato *(G-3210)*
Wells Lanes Inc ....E....651 455-3220
South Saint Paul *(G-9552)*

7941 Professional Sports Clubs & Promoters

AEG Management Twn LLC ....A....612 673-1300
Minneapolis *(G-3692)*
American Wrestling Association ....E....507 281-8842
Rochester *(G-7054)*
Dam Lake Sportmens Club ....E....218 927-6263
Aitkin *(G-18)*
Minnesota Timberwolves ....C....612 673-1600
Minneapolis *(G-5096)*
Minnesota Twins Baseball Club ....D....612 659-3400
Minneapolis *(G-5098)*
Minnesota Twins Baseball Club ....A....612 375-7411
Minneapolis *(G-5099)*
Minnesota Vikings Football ....C....952 828-6500
Eden Prairie *(G-1727)*
Minnesota Vikings Football LLC 952 828-6500
Eden Prairie *(G-1728)*
Minnesota Wild Hockey Club LP ....D....651 602-6000
Saint Paul *(G-8711)*
National Sports Center Fndtn ....E....763 785-5600
Minneapolis *(G-3551)*
◆ Premier Rinks Inc ....E....763 249-7417
Minneapolis *(G-5403)*
Soccer Blast Minnesota ....E....952 895-1962
Burnsville *(G-799)*
St Pauls Saints Baseball Club ....C....651 644-6659
Saint Paul *(G-9002)*
Tapemark Charity Pro AM ....B....651 455-1611
Saint Paul *(G-7915)*

7948 Racing & Track Operations

Canterbury Park Holding Corp ....E....952 445-7223
Shakopee *(G-9427)*
Flatliner Speed Society ....E....507 452-8917
Winona *(G-10097)*
North Metro Harness Initiative ....B....651 925-4600
Forest Lake *(G-2148)*
Princeton Speedway ....E....763 389-3135
Princeton *(G-6915)*
▲ Warnert Racing Inc ....E....320 251-2882
Saint Cloud *(G-7630)*

7991 Physical Fitness Facilities

Albert Lea Family YMCA ....E....507 373-8228
Albert Lea *(G-31)*
America's Racquet & Fitness ....E....320 234-7148
Hutchinson *(G-2686)*
America's Racquet & Fitness ....E....320 234-7148
Hutchinson *(G-2687)*
Americas Racket & Fitness ....E....507 451-8833
Owatonna *(G-6692)*
Anytime Fitness LLC ....D....651 438-5000
Hastings *(G-2413)*
Bally Total Fitness Corp ....E....763 574-8888
Minneapolis *(G-3414)*
Bally Total Fitness Corp ....E....651 484-4444
Saint Paul *(G-8085)*
Bemidji Town & Country Club ....D....218 751-9215
Bemidji *(G-380)*
C H Suites of Chanhassen MN ....E....952 937-2424
Chanhassen *(G-912)*
Camp Widji Wagan ....E....218 365-2117
Ely *(G-1912)*
Center For Personal Fitness ....E....218 725-5400
Duluth *(G-1267)*
City of White Bear Lake ....E....651 429-8571
Saint Paul *(G-8214)*
Cook & Koff Enterprises Inc ....E....952 830-0100
Minneapolis *(G-4161)*
D D D Motel Corp ....D....507 625-9333
Mankato *(G-3224)*
Dakota Sport & Fitness ....C....952 445-9400
Prior Lake *(G-6931)*
Dakotah Sport & Fitness Center ....C....952 445-9400
Prior Lake *(G-6932)*
David's Body Shop Inc ....D....612 377-3003
Minneapolis *(G-4226)*
Duluth Area Family YMCA ....E....218 722-4745
Duluth *(G-1297)*
Elizabeth Charles Corp ....C....952 915-2900
Minneapolis *(G-4340)*
Elizabeth Charles Corp ....D....952 915-2900
Saint Paul *(G-9212)*
Elizabeth Charles Corp ....D....952 915-2900
Chanhassen *(G-922)*
Fit Pro LLC ....D....763 784-4747
Minneapolis *(G-3470)*
Fit-Pro II ....E....763 295-3002
Monticello *(G-6271)*
Fitness 19 ....E....952 380-9919
Excelsior *(G-1935)*
Flagship Athletic Club Inc ....B....952 941-2000
Eden Prairie *(G-1665)*
Full Present Inc ....E....763 441-5999
Elk River *(G-1875)*
Gemm Inc ....E....952 591-6730
Minnetonka *(G-6174)*
Georgie's Fitness Inc ....E....507 238-9422
Fairmont *(G-1967)*
Grove Aquatic Fitness Center ....B....651 450-2480
Inver Grove Heights *(G-2752)*
Hastings YMCA ....E....651 480-8887
Hastings *(G-2390)*
Health Fitness Corp ....E....952 831-6830
Bloomington *(G-499)*
Health Industries Inc ....E....218 233-1516
Moorhead *(G-6318)*
Holmes Center Inc ....D....218 844-4221
Detroit Lakes *(G-1197)*
Improvement LP ....D....218 262-3481
Hibbing *(G-2456)*
Itasca County Family Young ....D....218 327-1161
Grand Rapids *(G-2287)*
L A Fitness International LLC ....E....952 392-4400
Burnsville *(G-744)*
Lady Wellness Management Inc ....E....320 253-3371
Waite Park *(G-9826)*
▲ Life Time Fitness Inc ....A....952 947-0000
Chanhassen *(G-929)*

S I C

Employment codes: A=Over 500 employees, B=251-500
C=101-250, D=51-100, E=25-50
2011 Harris Minnesota
Services Directory
© Harris InfoSource 1-866-281-6415
503

Life Time Fitness Inc .... D ... 612 752-9589
Minneapolis *(G-4878)*
Life Time Fitness Inc .... E ... 952 835-2222
Minneapolis *(G-4877)*
Life Time Fitness Inc .... D ... 651 698-5000
Saint Paul *(G-8584)*
Life Time Fitness Inc .... C ... 651 730-6000
Saint Paul *(G-9242)*
Life Time Fitness Inc .... E ... 651 633-4444
Saint Paul *(G-8583)*
Life Time Fitness Inc .... C ... 763 576-3000
Champlin *(G-895)*
Life Time Fitness Inc .... C ... 763 509-0909
Minneapolis *(G-4880)*
Life Time Fitness Inc .... C ... 651 426-1308
Saint Paul *(G-8585)*
Life Time Fitness Inc .... C ... 763 257-1067
Minneapolis *(G-3519)*
Ltf Club Operations Co Inc .... D ... 952 229-7427
Chanhassen *(G-930)*
Maax US Corp .... D ... 763 424-3335
Brooklyn Park *(G-614)*
Moondance Enterprises .... E ... 651 464-1875
Forest Lake *(G-2164)*
North Crest Gymnastics & Dance .... E ... 320 251-3416
Sauk Rapids *(G-9370)*
P & D Klitzke Enterprises Inc .... E ... 320 275-3555
Darwin *(G-1158)*
Pga Tour Inc .... D ... 763 795-0800
Minneapolis *(G-3570)*
Raymond Management Co Inc .... E ... 507 287-9050
Rochester *(G-7217)*
Red Wing Young Men's Christian .... C ... 651 388-4724
Red Wing *(G-6999)*
Regency Athletic Club & Spa .... E ... 612 343-3131
Minneapolis *(G-5483)*
Rochester Athletic Club Inc .... B ... 507 282-6000
Rochester *(G-7228)*
Rochester Fitness Inc .... E ... 507 282-4445
Rochester *(G-7231)*
Ruth Stricker's Fitness Unltd .... C ... 952 935-2202
Minnetonka *(G-6222)*
S & S Spa Salon Inc .... E ... 651 464-6612
Forest Lake *(G-2168)*
Sandman Motel LLC .... E ... 763 559-1222
Minneapolis *(G-5600)*
Seve Enterprises Inc .... E ... 612 605-6230
Minneapolis *(G-5640)*
Solimar Wellness Spa .... E ... 651 686-6686
Saint Paul *(G-7907)*
St Cloud Suite Hotel Inc .... D ... 320 654-1661
Saint Cloud *(G-7606)*
Starmark Northwest Management .... D ... 952 944-2434
Minneapolis *(G-5743)*
Starmark Northwest Management .... E ... 612 673-1200
Minneapolis *(G-5742)*
Stillwater Fitness Club Inc .... E ... 651 430-1584
Stillwater *(G-9646)*
Sun Bear Spa & Tan Inc .... E ... 651 426-5884
Saint Paul *(G-9014)*
Sweatshop Inc .... E ... 651 646-8418
Saint Paul *(G-9019)*
University Club of St Paul .... D ... 651 222-1751
Saint Paul *(G-9112)*
Upper Minnetonka Yacht Club .... D ... 952 471-8783
Spring Park *(G-9567)*
Weiner Memorial Foundation .... B ... 507 532-9661
Marshall *(G-3332)*
White Bear Racquet & Swim LP .... C ... 651 426-1308
Saint Paul *(G-9156)*
Y M C A Infant Center .... E ... 651 646-4557
Saint Paul *(G-9171)*
YMCA .... D ... 320 222-9622
Willmar *(G-10059)*
YMCA Children's Center .... E ... 651 777-8103
Saint Paul *(G-9173)*
YMCA of Greater Saint Paul .... E ... 651 645-6605
Saint Paul *(G-9175)*
YMCA of Greater St Paul .... D ... 218 365-2117
Ely *(G-1919)*
YMCA of Greater St Paul .... D ... 651 292-4143
Saint Paul *(G-9178)*
YMCA of Greater St Paul .... D ... 651 646-4557
Saint Paul *(G-9177)*
YMCA of Greater St Paul .... C ... 651 483-2671
Saint Paul *(G-9176)*
YMCA of Greater St Paul .... C ... 651 457-0048
Saint Paul *(G-7953)*
YMCA of Worthington, Minnesota .... E ... 507 376-6197
Worthington *(G-10199)*
Young Men's Chritn Assoc of .... C ... 763 785-7882
Minneapolis *(G-3644)*
Young Men's Chritn Assoc of .... C ... 763 535-4800
Minneapolis *(G-6101)*
Young Men's Chritn Assoc of .... D ... 612 827-5401
Minneapolis *(G-6102)*
Young Men's Chritn Assoc of .... E ... 612 588-9484
Minneapolis *(G-6103)*
Young Men's Chritn Assoc of .... C ... 952 835-2567
Minneapolis *(G-6104)*
Young Women's Christian Assn .... D ... 218 722-7425
Duluth *(G-1505)*
YWCA of Minneapolis .... D ... 612 874-7131
Minneapolis *(G-6110)*
YWCA of Minneapolis .... A ... 612 332-0501
Minneapolis *(G-6111)*

7992 Public Golf Courses

Afton Alps Golf Course .... E ... 651 436-1320
Hastings *(G-2411)*
Apple Valley, City of Inc .... E ... 952 953-2323
Saint Paul *(G-7704)*
Applewood Hills Inc .... E ... 651 439-7276
Stillwater *(G-9597)*
Bemidji Town & Country Club .... D ... 218 751-9215
Bemidji *(G-380)*
Blackberry Ridge Golf Club LLC .... E ... 320 257-4653
Sartell *(G-9333)*
Blueberry Pines Golf Club .... E ... 218 564-4657
Menahga *(G-3354)*
Cedar Valley Golf Course Inc .... E ... 507 457-3241
Winona *(G-10087)*
City of Becker .... E ... 763 261-4656
Becker *(G-355)*
City of Chaska .... E ... 952 443-3748
Chaska *(G-959)*
City of Edina .... E ... 952 941-2443
Minneapolis *(G-4087)*
City of Grand Rapids .... D ... 218 326-3444
Grand Rapids *(G-2272)*
City of Minneapolis .... E ... 612 724-7715
Minneapolis *(G-4090)*
City of Minneapolis .... E ... 612 789-2542
Minneapolis *(G-4092)*
City of Moorhead .... D ... 218 299-5422
Moorhead *(G-6303)*
City of Saint Paul .... E ... 651 488-9673
Saint Paul *(G-8211)*
Como Ski Center .... E ... 651 488-9679
Saint Paul *(G-8240)*
County of Anoka .... E ... 651 482-8484
Circle Pines *(G-1008)*
Cragun Enterprises Inc .... E ... 218 825-2800
Brainerd *(G-544)*
Crystal Lake Country Club Inc .... E ... 952 432-6566
Lakeville *(G-2898)*
Deer Run Golf Club LLC .... E ... 952 443-2351
Victoria *(G-9727)*
Eagle Lake Golf Center .... E ... 763 694-7695
Minneapolis *(G-4305)*
Eagle's Landing Golf Club Inc .... D ... 320 632-5721
Fort Ripley *(G-2173)*
Etoc Co Inc .... D ... 218 963-2906
Nisswa *(G-6496)*
Fond Du Lac Reservation .... A ... 218 878-2327
Carlton *(G-867)*
Forest Hills Golf Rv Reso .... E ... 218 562-7585
Pequot Lakes *(G-6788)*
Furlong Golf Inc .... E ... 651 480-8558
Hastings *(G-2387)*
Gem Lake Hills Inc .... E ... 651 429-8715
Saint Paul *(G-8404)*
Golden Acres Golf Course Inc .... E ... 763 428-8244
Rogers *(G-7325)*
Golden Valley, City of Inc .... D ... 763 593-8000
Minneapolis *(G-4538)*
Golf Services Corp .... D ... 651 777-1436
Saint Paul *(G-8420)*
Gopher Hills Inc .... E ... 507 263-2507
Cannon Falls *(G-854)*
Grl Investment Co LLC .... E ... 952 445-6745
Shakopee *(G-9442)*
Hawley Golf & Country Club Inc .... E ... 218 483-4808
Hawley *(G-2419)*
Hidden Greens Inc .... E ... 651 437-3085
Hastings *(G-2392)*
Hidden Haven Golf Course Inc .... E ... 763 434-6867
Cedar *(G-879)*
Izatys Group LLC .... E ... 320 532-3101
Onamia *(G-6573)*
Jala Contracting Co .... E ... 763 434-4626
Cedar *(G-880)*
Kimball Golf Club Inc .... E ... 320 398-2285
Kimball *(G-2833)*
Legacy Golf Corp .... E ... 507 332-0777
Faribault *(G-2019)*
Links At Northfork LLP .... E ... 763 241-0506
Anoka *(G-200)*
Links On The Mississippi Inc .... E ... 651 768-7611
Cottage Grove *(G-1104)*
Little Falls Golf Association .... E ... 320 616-5520
Little Falls *(G-3011)*
Madden Brothers Inc .... E ... 218 829-2811
Brainerd *(G-546)*
Malone Golf Inc .... D ... 952 492-2644
Jordan *(G-2806)*
Meadow Lakes Golf Club LLC .... E ... 507 285-1190
Rochester *(G-7181)*
Mendakota Country Club Inc .... C ... 651 454-2822
Saint Paul *(G-7837)*
New Prague Golf Club Inc .... E ... 952 758-5326
New Prague *(G-6423)*
Oak Hill Golf Club Inc .... E ... 320 259-8969
Rice *(G-7033)*
Oakdale Country Club Inc .... E ... 320 833-5518
Buffalo Lake *(G-667)*
Oneka Ridge LLC .... D ... 651 429-2390
Saint Paul *(G-9255)*
Parkview Golf Associates LLC .... E ... 651 452-5098
Saint Paul *(G-7864)*
Perham Lakeside Golf Club Inc .... E ... 218 346-6070
Perham *(G-6801)*
Ponds Golf Course LLC .... E ... 763 753-1100
Saint Francis *(G-7636)*
Prestwick Golf Club Inc .... E ... 651 459-0288
Saint Paul *(G-9264)*
Quarry At Giants Ridge .... E ... 218 865-3092
Biwabik *(G-471)*
Refuge Golf Club .... E ... 763 753-7770
Minneapolis *(G-3582)*
Regents of The University of .... E ... 612 627-4000
Saint Paul *(G-8882)*
Rush Creek Golf Club Limited .... C ... 763 494-8844
Osseo *(G-6658)*
Shadowbrooke Golf Course Inc .... E ... 320 395-4251
Lester Prairie *(G-2964)*
Sienna Corp .... E ... 218 562-6262
Pequot Lakes *(G-6792)*
Spur Inc .... E ... 651 454-2330
Saint Paul *(G-7911)*
Sundance Golf & Bowl Inc .... E ... 763 420-4700
Osseo *(G-6670)*
Superior National At Lutsen .... E ... 218 663-7865
Lutsen *(G-3057)*
Tanners Brook Golf Club LLP .... D ... 651 464-2300
Forest Lake *(G-2169)*
Three Rivers Park District .... D ... 763 694-7670
Hamel *(G-2357)*
Timber Creek Golf Course Inc .... E ... 952 955-3600
Watertown *(G-9893)*
Viking Meadows Inc .... E ... 763 434-4205
Cedar *(G-885)*
Wild Golf Club .... C ... 952 445-3500
Prior Lake *(G-6962)*
Wild Marsh Golf Club LLC .... E ... 763 682-4476
Buffalo *(G-660)*
Willing Partners Inc .... E ... 952 652-2500
Northfield *(G-6546)*
Willow Creek Golf Course of .... E ... 507 285-0305
Rochester *(G-7294)*

7993 Coin-Operated Amusement Devices & Arcades

B L B Inc .... D ... 612 825-3737
Minneapolis *(G-3852)*
Corporate Commission of The .... A ... 320 532-8800
Onamia *(G-6568)*
Corporate Commission of The .... A ... 320 384-7101
Hinckley *(G-2483)*
D & R Star Inc .... D ... 507 282-6080
Rochester *(G-7092)*
Lieberman Co's Inc .... E ... 952 887-5200
Minneapolis *(G-4874)*
Prairie's Edge Casino Resort .... B ... 320 564-2121
Granite Falls *(G-2318)*
▲ **Theisen Vending Inc** .... D ... 612 827-5588
Minneapolis *(G-5813)*

7996 Amusement Parks

Cedar Fair, LP .... D ... 952 445-7600
Shakopee *(G-9430)*
City of Minneapolis .... C ... 612 370-4900
Minneapolis *(G-4088)*
County of Anoka .... D ... 763 767-2871
Anoka *(G-170)*
Grand Portage National .... E ... 218 475-2202
Grand Portage *(G-2266)*
▲ **Moa Entertainment Co LLC** .... A ... 952 883-8810
Minneapolis *(G-5114)*

7997 Membership Sports & Recreation Clubs

Alexandria Golf Club .... E ... 320 762-1093
Alexandria *(G-81)*
America's Raquette & Fitness .... E ... 507 345-8833
Mankato *(G-3104)*
Anytime Fitness LLC .... D ... 651 438-5000
Hastings *(G-2413)*
Arrowhead Tennis Inc .... E ... 218 722-0810
Duluth *(G-1244)*
Auburn Woods Clubhomes Assn .... D ... 952 922-5575
Edina *(G-1825)*
Austin Country Club Inc .... D ... 507 437-7631
Austin *(G-260)*
Bearpath Golf & Country Club .... D ... 952 975-0123
Eden Prairie *(G-1603)*
Bemidji Town & Country Club .... D ... 218 751-9215
Bemidji *(G-380)*
Bemidji Town & Country Club .... E ... 218 751-4535
Bemidji *(G-381)*
Blueberry Pines Golf Club Inc .... E ... 218 564-4653
Menahga *(G-3355)*
Burnsville Hockey Club .... E ... 952 890-2333
Burnsville *(G-691)*
Calhoun Beach Club of .... D ... 612 927-9951
Minneapolis *(G-3992)*
Chisago Lakes Golf Estates Inc .... E ... 651 257-1484
Lindstrom *(G-2968)*
City of Blue Earth .... E ... 507 526-2715
Blue Earth *(G-532)*
Cloquet Country Club .... E ... 218 879-8858
Cloquet *(G-1048)*
Club The Campus Inc .... E ... 612 625-9696
Minneapolis *(G-4112)*

S I C

Coon Rapids VFW Post 9625..........E.....763 755-4760
Minneapolis *(G-3442)*
Crow River Country Club..........E.....320 587-3070
Hutchinson *(G-2695)*
Dakotah Sport & Fitness Center..........C.....952 445-9400
Prior Lake *(G-6932)*
Dellwood Hills Golf Club..........D.....651 426-3218
Saint Paul *(G-9203)*
Eagles Hall..........E.....218 847-5267
Detroit Lakes *(G-1192)*
Edina Country Club..........C.....952 927-7151
Minneapolis *(G-4314)*
Elk River Country Club Inc..........E.....763 441-4111
Elk River *(G-1872)*
Fergus Falls Area Family Young..........D.....218 739-4489
Fergus Falls *(G-2075)*
Flagship Athletic Club Inc..........B.....952 941-2000
Eden Prairie *(G-1665)*
Forest Hills Golf Club Inc..........D.....651 464-3097
Forest Lake *(G-2160)*
Golf Inc..........E.....320 251-7804
Sauk Rapids *(G-9363)*
Gonvick American Legion..........C.....218 487-5214
Gonvick *(G-2247)*
H J K S Inc..........E.....952 935-3427
Minneapolis *(G-4586)*
Hastings Country Club Inc..........D.....651 437-4612
Hastings *(G-2389)*
Hidden Haven Golf Course Inc..........E.....763 434-6867
Cedar *(G-879)*
Interlachen Country Club..........C.....952 929-1661
Minneapolis *(G-4717)*
Koronis Hills Golf Club..........E.....320 243-4111
Paynesville *(G-6770)*
Kraus-Anderson Construction Co..........E.....218 759-0596
Bemidji *(G-400)*
Lafayette Club..........C.....952 471-8493
Minnetonka Beach *(G-6241)*
Le Sueur Country Club..........E.....507 665-8839
Le Sueur *(G-2956)*
Leech Lake Reservation..........A.....218 547-2744
Walker *(G-9854)*
Legends Club LLC..........D.....952 226-4777
Prior Lake *(G-6937)*
Life Time Fitness Inc..........C.....651 426-1308
Saint Paul *(G-8585)*
Litchfield Golf Club..........E.....320 693-6059
Litchfield *(G-2987)*
Little Moran Hunting Club..........E.....218 894-3852
Staples *(G-9585)*
Madden Brothers Inc..........E.....218 829-2811
Brainerd *(G-546)*
Mankato Golf Club Inc..........E.....507 387-5676
Mankato *(G-3162)*
Mannanah Snow Blazers..........E.....320 693-6658
Litchfield *(G-2988)*
Maple Valley Golf & Country..........E.....507 932-5444
Saint Charles *(G-7405)*
Marshall Golf Club..........E.....507 532-2278
Marshall *(G-3310)*
Mendakota Country Club Inc..........C.....651 454-2822
Saint Paul *(G-7837)*
Mesaba Country Club..........E.....218 262-2851
Hibbing *(G-2465)*
Midland Hills Country Club..........D.....651 631-0440
Saint Paul *(G-8654)*
Minikahda Club..........D.....952 926-4167
Minneapolis *(G-5049)*
Minneapolis Golf Club..........E.....952 544-4471
Minneapolis *(G-5055)*
Minnesota Twins Baseball Club..........A.....612 375-7411
Minneapolis *(G-5099)*
Minnesota Valley Country Club..........D.....612 884-2409
Bloomington *(G-506)*
Minnetonka Country Club..........E.....952 474-5222
Excelsior *(G-1949)*
Montevideo Country Club Inc..........E.....320 269-8600
Montevideo *(G-6253)*
Montevideo Country Club Inc..........E.....320 269-6828
Montevideo *(G-6254)*
Montgomery Golf & Recreation..........E.....507 364-5602
Montgomery *(G-6264)*
Monticello Country Club Inc..........E.....763 295-3323
Monticello *(G-6277)*
Moorhead Country Club Inc..........E.....218 236-0100
Moorhead *(G-6329)*
New Ulm Country Club..........E.....507 354-8896
New Ulm *(G-6466)*
▲ North American Affinity Clubs..........B.....952 936-9333
Minnetonka *(G-6203)*
North American Membership Grp..........D.....952 988-7451
Shakopee *(G-9459)*
▲ North American Membership Grp..........B.....952 936-9333
Hopkins *(G-2591)*
North Oaks Golf Club Inc..........E.....651 484-6311
Saint Paul *(G-8752)*
Northern Gopher Enterprises..........C.....952 435-7600
Lakeville *(G-2923)*
Northland Country Club Inc..........E.....218 525-1941
Duluth *(G-1407)*
Oak Glen LLC..........D.....651 439-6981
Stillwater *(G-9633)*
Oak Ridge Country Club..........C.....952 935-7721
Hopkins *(G-2593)*
Oaks Country Club Inc..........E.....507 477-3233
Hayfield *(G-2424)*
Olson, Jock Interlachen..........C.....952 924-7424
Minneapolis *(G-5273)*
Olympic Hills Corp..........E.....952 941-6262
Eden Prairie *(G-1736)*
Owatonna Country Club Inc..........D.....507 451-6120
Owatonna *(G-6727)*
Parkview Golf Associates LLC..........E.....651 452-5098
Saint Paul *(G-7864)*
Pequaywan Area Trail Blazers..........E.....218 848-2510
Duluth *(G-1422)*
Perham Lakeside Golf Club Inc..........E.....218 346-6070
Perham *(G-6801)*
Pezhekee Lounge Inc..........E.....320 634-4502
Glenwood *(G-2231)*
Pga Tour Inc..........D.....763 795-0800
Minneapolis *(G-3570)*
Pool & Yacht Club..........E.....651 455-3900
Saint Paul *(G-7878)*
Rich-Spring Golf Club Inc..........E.....320 685-8810
Cold Spring *(G-1089)*
Ridgeview Country Club Inc..........E.....218 728-5128
Duluth *(G-1438)*
Rochester Athletic Club Inc..........B.....507 282-6000
Rochester *(G-7228)*
Rochester Golf & Country Club..........E.....507 282-2708
Rochester *(G-7232)*
Saint Martin Commercial Club..........E.....320 548-3208
Paynesville *(G-6774)*
Southview Country Club..........D.....651 451-6856
Saint Paul *(G-7909)*
Spring Hill Golf Club..........D.....952 473-1500
Wayzata *(G-9940)*
Spring Hill Golf Club..........E.....952 473-1500
Wayzata *(G-9941)*
St Francis Youth Hockey Assn..........C.....763 913-7395
Saint Francis *(G-7637)*
Starmark Northwest Management..........D.....952 944-2434
Minneapolis *(G-5743)*
Starmark Northwest Management..........E.....612 673-1200
Minneapolis *(G-5742)*
Stillwater Country Club Inc..........E.....651 439-7979
Stillwater *(G-9645)*
Swampsiders Snowmobile Club..........C.....218 245-3222
Bigfork *(G-464)*
Thief River Golf Club..........E.....218 681-2955
Thief River Falls *(G-9678)*
3 M Club of St Paul Inc..........D.....651 733-3466
Lake Elmo *(G-2877)*
Tianna Country Club Inc..........E.....218 547-1712
Walker *(G-9858)*
Tournament Club of Iowa LLC..........E.....952 252-4474
Minneapolis *(G-5838)*
Town & Country Club of St..........D.....651 646-7121
Saint Paul *(G-9075)*
Upper Minnetonka Yacht Club..........D.....952 471-8783
Spring Park *(G-9567)*
Valley Golf Association..........E.....218 773-1207
East Grand Forks *(G-1577)*
Valley High Golf Club..........E.....507 896-3239
Houston *(G-2663)*
Wayzata Country Club Inc..........D.....952 473-8846
Wayzata *(G-9948)*
Westfield Golf Club Inc..........E.....507 452-8700
Winona *(G-10140)*
White Bear Racquet & Swim LP..........C.....651 426-1308
Saint Paul *(G-9156)*
Wild Marsh Golf Club LLC..........E.....763 682-4476
Buffalo *(G-660)*
Woodhill Country Club..........D.....952 473-7333
Wayzata *(G-9951)*
Young Men's Chritn Assoc of..........C.....763 785-7882
Minneapolis *(G-3644)*

7999 Amusement & Recreation Svcs, NEC

Adventure Zone..........E.....952 890-7961
Burnsville *(G-673)*
Afton Alps Inc..........A.....651 436-5245
Hastings *(G-2412)*
Art Semva Gallery..........D.....507 281-4920
Rochester *(G-7059)*
Awm Enterprises Inc..........E.....651 455-3044
South Saint Paul *(G-9510)*
Basilica of Saint Mary of..........E.....612 333-1381
Minneapolis *(G-3871)*
Bemidji Town & Country Club..........D.....218 751-9215
Bemidji *(G-380)*
Biff's Billiards Sports Bar..........E.....763 784-9446
Minneapolis *(G-3416)*
Bingo Carousel..........D.....763 493-2111
Minneapolis *(G-3905)*
Bingo Emporium..........D.....320 252-3607
Saint Cloud *(G-7458)*
▲ Bois Forte Enterprises..........B.....218 753-6400
Tower *(G-9686)*
Box Office Service & Sales Inc..........D.....952 854-2836
Minneapolis *(G-3935)*
Braemar Driving Range..........E.....952 826-6786
Minneapolis *(G-3936)*
Breck School..........C.....763 381-8100
Minneapolis *(G-3940)*
Briggs Hennum Inc..........E.....218 634-2168
Baudette *(G-314)*
Buck Hill Inc..........952 435-7174
Burnsville *(G-688)*
Cabela's Inc..........C.....763 493-8600
Rogers *(G-7318)*
Canadian Border Outfitters Inc..........E.....218 365-5847
Ely *(G-1911)*
Canterbury Park Holding Corp..........E.....952 445-7223
Shakopee *(G-9427)*
Carlton County Fair Assn..........E.....218 389-6737
Barnum *(G-306)*
Carver County Agricultural Soc..........E.....952 442-2333
Waconia *(G-9781)*
Cedar Valley Golf Course Inc..........E.....507 457-3241
Winona *(G-10087)*
City of Chaska..........E.....952 443-3748
Chaska *(G-959)*
City of Duluth..........B.....218 628-2891
Duluth *(G-1275)*
City of Edina..........E.....952 832-6792
Minneapolis *(G-4086)*
City of Minneapolis..........D.....612 230-6550
Minneapolis *(G-4094)*
City of Plymouth..........E.....763 509-5262
Minneapolis *(G-4095)*
City of Saint Paul..........E.....651 266-6400
Saint Paul *(G-8204)*
City of Saint Paul..........E.....651 695-3773
Saint Paul *(G-8210)*
City of White Bear Lake..........E.....651 429-8571
Saint Paul *(G-8214)*
Climb Theater Inc..........D.....651 453-9275
Inver Grove Heights *(G-2743)*
Colin Co, LP..........E.....612 375-9670
Minneapolis *(G-4117)*
Community Charities of MN..........E.....507 386-1934
Mankato *(G-3119)*
County of Ramsey..........D.....651 748-2500
Saint Paul *(G-8259)*
Courage Center..........E.....320 963-3121
Maple Lake *(G-3259)*
Dakota Sport & Fitness..........C.....952 445-9400
Prior Lake *(G-6931)*
Dakotah Sport & Fitness Center..........C.....952 445-9400
Prior Lake *(G-6932)*
Dennis Raedeke Inc..........D.....651 465-6365
Taylors Falls *(G-9660)*
Dkg Management..........E.....214 776-1155
Burnsville *(G-711)*
Eddy's Lake Mille Lacs Resort..........E.....320 532-3657
Onamia *(G-6570)*
Exhibits Development Group LLC..........E.....651 222-1121
Saint Paul *(G-8352)*
Family Swim School..........E.....952 435-1898
Lakeville *(G-2906)*
Festival Events of Minnesota..........D.....651 772-9980
Saint Paul *(G-8375)*
Flips Gymnastic Center..........E.....651 777-4776
Saint Paul *(G-8385)*
Fond Du Lac Management Inc..........D.....218 879-4593
Cloquet *(G-1052)*
Forest Lake Flyaways..........E.....651 464-8648
Forest Lake *(G-2161)*
Foss Swim School Inc..........E.....763 416-8993
Osseo *(G-6615)*
Foss Swim School Inc..........E.....952 935-8732
Minneapolis *(G-4466)*
Freeborn Country Fair Assn..........E.....507 373-6965
Albert Lea *(G-54)*
Funcity..........E.....763 441-8365
Elk River *(G-1899)*
Gage Group LLC..........C.....763 595-3920
Minneapolis *(G-4495)*
Gleason Gymnastic School..........E.....651 454-6203
Saint Paul *(G-7782)*
Gleason Gymnastic School..........E.....763 493-2526
Osseo *(G-6617)*
Golden Valley Country Club..........D.....763 732-4100
Minneapolis *(G-4536)*
Great Northern Golf Co of MN..........E.....651 462-5797
Stacy *(G-9579)*
Hardwood Golf Resort..........E.....320 692-4325
Garrison *(G-2197)*
Haunted LLC..........E.....507 388-7966
Mankato *(G-3136)*
High-Tech Institute Inc..........D.....763 560-9700
Minneapolis *(G-4646)*
Jam Hops Gymnastics Factory..........E.....763 413-0647
Anoka *(G-194)*
Lake Crystal Area Recreation..........E.....507 726-6730
Lake Crystal *(G-2858)*
Lake Minnetonka Sailing School..........E.....952 404-1645
Wayzata *(G-9924)*
Lake Superior Center..........E.....218 740-3474
Duluth *(G-1375)*
Le Sueur, City of Inc..........E.....507 665-3325
Le Sueur *(G-2957)*
Leech Lake Reservation..........A.....218 547-2744
Walker *(G-9854)*
Little Six Casino..........B.....952 445-6000
Prior Lake *(G-6938)*
Luverne, City of Inc..........E.....507 449-5036
Luverne *(G-3063)*
Madden Brothers Inc..........E.....218 829-2811
Brainerd *(G-546)*
Magical History Tour..........E.....612 331-7171
Minneapolis *(G-4933)*
Maintenance Building..........E.....320 384-7084
Hinckley *(G-2486)*
Maplewood Oakdale School Dist..........E.....651 714-9251
Saint Paul *(G-9246)*
Meadow Lakes Golf Club LLC..........E.....507 285-1190
Rochester *(G-7181)*
Mesaba Country Club..........E.....218 262-2851
Hibbing *(G-2464)*

S I C

Employment codes: A=Over 500 employees, B=251-500
C=101-250, D=51-100, E=25-50
2011 Harris Minnesota
Services Directory
© Harris InfoSource 1-866-281-6415
505

Mesabi Family YMCA....D....218 749-8020
Virginia *(G-9746)*
Mid-America Festivals Corp....E....952 445-7361
Shakopee *(G-9456)*
Minnesota Department of....E....218 753-2245
Soudan *(G-9504)*
Minnesota State Agricultural....D....651 288-4400
Saint Paul *(G-8705)*
Minnesota Twins Baseball Club....A....612 375-7411
Minneapolis *(G-5099)*
▲ Moa Entertainment Co LLC....A....952 883-8810
Minneapolis *(G-5114)*
Moorehead Youth Hockey Assn....E....218 233-5021
Moorhead *(G-6328)*
Motivations For Fitness Inc....E....612 617-9090
Minneapolis *(G-5138)*
Muller Boat Co....E....651 465-6315
Taylors Falls *(G-9661)*
New Ulm Turnverein Inc....E....507 354-4916
New Ulm *(G-6469)*
North Crest Gymnastics & Dance....E....320 251-3416
Sauk Rapids *(G-9370)*
Oak Hill Golf Club Inc....E....320 259-8969
Rice *(G-7033)*
Owatonna Fairlanes Corp....E....507 451-2524
Owatonna *(G-6728)*
Paul Schintz Inc....E....218 525-0828
Duluth *(G-1419)*
Perpetual Motion Children's....E....651 459-5837
Saint Paul *(G-9260)*
Pineview Park Bmx....E....320 230-7820
Saint Cloud *(G-7568)*
Playworks Dakota....D....952 445-7529
Prior Lake *(G-6948)*
Pottery Red Wings....E....651 388-3562
Red Wing *(G-6995)*
Prairie Island Indian Com....C....651 388-0083
Welch *(G-9955)*
Rainy Lake Houseboats Inc....E....218 286-5391
International Falls *(G-2729)*
Recreational Equipment Inc....C....952 884-4315
Minneapolis *(G-5476)*
Red Wing Young Men's Christian....C....651 388-4724
Red Wing *(G-6999)*
Renew Resources Inc....E....763 533-9200
Minneapolis *(G-5517)*
River Boat Bingo....E....507 388-6086
Mankato *(G-3186)*
Rock 'n Water....E....218 439-6400
Detroit Lakes *(G-1215)*
Shakopee Mdewakanton Sioux Com....D....952 445-8900
Prior Lake *(G-6954)*
Shooters Billiard Club & Pro....E....952 894-1100
Burnsville *(G-796)*
▲ Smsc Gaming Enterprise....A....952 445-6000
Prior Lake *(G-6955)*
Smsc Gaming Enterprise....A....952 445-8982
Prior Lake *(G-6956)*
Splatball Inc....E....612 378-0385
Minneapolis *(G-5721)*
St Teresa Campus Schools....E....507 453-5555
Winona *(G-10131)*
Tennis & Life Camps Inc....E....507 931-1614
Saint Peter *(G-9315)*
Three Rivers Park District....D....763 694-7670
Hamel *(G-2357)*
Three Rivers Park District....C....763 559-9000
Plymouth *(G-6887)*
Treasure Island Casino & Bingo....A....651 388-6300
Welch *(G-9957)*
Triple Crown Gaming Inc....E....320 251-5373
Saint Cloud *(G-7622)*
Twin City Twisters Inc....E....763 421-3046
Champlin *(G-903)*
University Billiards Inc....E....763 574-1399
Minneapolis *(G-3630)*
Uptown Psychic Studio....E....612 374-9906
Minneapolis *(G-5938)*
White Earth Band of Chippewa....A....218 935-2711
Mahnomen *(G-3091)*
Winona Country Club....E....507 454-3767
Winona *(G-10146)*
Wintergreen Dogsled Lodge Inc....E....218 365-6602
Ely *(G-1917)*
Xenophon Corp....E....952 929-5518
Minneapolis *(G-6092)*
Xenophon Corp....E....651 735-6214
Saint Paul *(G-9291)*
Young Men's Christian Assn....C....507 387-8255
Mankato *(G-3222)*

80 HEALTH SERVICES

8011 Offices & Clinics Of Doctors Of Medicine

A C M C....E....507 637-2985
Redwood Falls *(G-7018)*
Adult & Pediatric Urology....E....320 259-1411
Sartell *(G-9329)*
Advancements In Allergy....E....952 546-6866
Hopkins *(G-2502)*
Affiliated Community Medical....B....320 231-5000
Willmar *(G-9980)*
Affiliated Community Medical....D....507 532-9631
Marshall *(G-3290)*
Affiliated Community Medical....E....320 564-2511
Granite Falls *(G-2313)*
Affiliated Community Medical....E....507 637-2985
Redwood Falls *(G-7019)*
Affiliated Community Medical....B....320 693-3233
Litchfield *(G-2977)*
Affiliated Medical Center....E....320 843-2030
Benson *(G-436)*
Albert Lea Medical Center-Mayo....A....507 373-2384
Albert Lea *(G-32)*
Albert Lee Medical Center Inc....D....507 553-3115
Wells *(G-9960)*
Alexandria Clinic Properties....C....320 763-5123
Alexandria *(G-80)*
Align Health Inc....D....612 821-7909
Minneapolis *(G-3704)*
All True Clinic Crookston Inc....D....218 281-9100
Crookston *(G-1118)*
Allergy & Asthma Clinic....E....507 474-7830
Winona *(G-10079)*
Allergy & Asthma Specialists....E....612 338-3333
Minneapolis *(G-3712)*
Allergy & Asthma Specialists....E....320 654-6565
Sartell *(G-9330)*
Allina Health System....A....612 775-5000
Minneapolis *(G-3721)*
Allina Health System....D....651 458-1884
Cottage Grove *(G-1097)*
Allina Health System....E....763 427-9620
Champlin *(G-888)*
Allina Health System....E....763 427-7180
Anoka *(G-150)*
Allina Health System....D....763 236-9236
Minneapolis *(G-3392)*
Allina Health System....D....612 798-8800
Minneapolis *(G-3717)*
Allina Health System....C....651 464-7100
Forest Lake *(G-2155)*
Allina Health System....A....612 863-4000
Minneapolis *(G-3718)*
Allina Health System....C....952 851-1000
Minneapolis *(G-3719)*
Allina Health System....E....952 936-5600
Hopkins *(G-2506)*
Allina Health System....E....651 450-8000
Inver Grove Heights *(G-2737)*
Allina Health System....763 780-9155
Minneapolis *(G-3394)*
Allina Health System....C....612 775-8800
Minneapolis *(G-3720)*
Allina Health System....E....952 835-1311
Minneapolis *(G-3722)*
Allina Health System....E....763 786-6011
Minneapolis *(G-3395)*
Allina Health System....E....763 577-7400
Minneapolis *(G-3723)*
Allina Health System....C....651 438-1800
Hastings *(G-2375)*
Allina Health System....E....763 236-0414
Elk River *(G-1861)*
Allina Health System....D....507 334-3921
Faribault *(G-1988)*
Allina Health System....E....763 236-0200
Maple Grove *(G-3235)*
Allina Health System....A....763 689-7700
Cambridge *(G-831)*
Allina Health System....C....612 863-3720
Minneapolis *(G-3724)*
Allina Health System....E....952 463-7181
Farmington *(G-2038)*
Allina Health System....E....763 560-6922
Minneapolis *(G-3725)*
Allina Health System....A....612 863-4466
Minneapolis *(G-3726)*
Allina Medical Clinic West....D....763 577-7400
Plymouth *(G-6847)*
Allina Self-Insured....D....952 992-2500
Hopkins *(G-2507)*
Allina Specialty Associates....E....612 863-3753
Minneapolis *(G-3727)*
Altru Clinic....D....218 463-1365
Roseau *(G-7353)*
American Medical Systems Inc....B....952 930-6000
Minnetonka *(G-6140)*
Anderson McDonald Ltd....E....952 469-3937
Lakeville *(G-2890)*
Anesthesia Associates of St....E....320 258-3090
Saint Cloud *(G-7450)*
Ann Pearson MD....E....651 426-4844
Saint Paul *(G-8052)*
Apple Valley Medical Clinic....C....952 432-6161
Saint Paul *(G-7702)*
Appleton Area Health Services....C....320 289-2422
Appleton *(G-244)*
Asian Home Care Inc....E....651 999-0268
Saint Paul *(G-8069)*
Aspen Medical Group....E....612 728-1800
Minneapolis *(G-3818)*
Associated Clinic of....D....763 503-8560
Minneapolis *(G-3825)*
Associated Eye Care Ltd....E....651 439-8500
Stillwater *(G-9598)*
Associated Skin Care....E....763 571-4000
Minneapolis *(G-3411)*
Associates In Womens Health....E....952 806-0011
Minneapolis *(G-3827)*
Associates In Womens Health....E....952 806-0011
Minneapolis *(G-3828)*
Bemidji Clinic Merit Care Inc....D....218 333-5000
Bemidji *(G-378)*
Bloomington Lake Clinic Ltd....E....612 721-6511
Minneapolis *(G-3916)*
Bois Forte Medical Clinic....E....218 757-3650
Nett Lake *(G-6403)*
Brainerd Medical Center....C....218 828-7100
Brainerd *(G-552)*
Broadway Medical Center Ltd....C....320 762-0399
Alexandria *(G-87)*
Buffalo Clinic....D....763 682-1313
Buffalo *(G-637)*
Burnsville Family Physicians....E....952 435-0303
Burnsville *(G-690)*
Camden Physicians Ltd....E....612 876-9700
Minneapolis *(G-3995)*
Camden Physicians Ltd....E....763 420-5822
Osseo *(G-6601)*
Camden Physicians Ltd....D....763 235-4900
Plymouth *(G-6853)*
Cannon Valley Clinic Mayo....D....507 333-3300
Faribault *(G-1997)*
Cardiodiagnostics Inc....C....651 292-0616
Saint Paul *(G-8159)*
▲ Cardiovascular Consultants Ltd....D....763 520-2000
Minneapolis *(G-4002)*
Catholic Charities of The....E....651 641-1180
Saint Paul *(G-8175)*
CDI Corp....E....320 251-0609
Sartell *(G-9335)*
Cedar-Riverside People's Ctr....E....612 332-4973
Minneapolis *(G-4038)*
Center For Pain Management....E....320 230-7788
Sartell *(G-9336)*
Center For Victims of Torture....D....612 436-4800
Minneapolis *(G-4043)*
Center For Victims of Torture....D....612 436-4800
Saint Paul *(G-8182)*
Centracare Clinic....B....320 252-5131
Saint Cloud *(G-7480)*
Centracare Clinic....C....320 654-3630
Saint Cloud *(G-7478)*
Centracare Clinic....E....320 251-1775
Saint Cloud *(G-7479)*
Centracare Clinic....E....320 732-2131
Long Prairie *(G-3037)*
Centracare Clinic....E....320 256-4228
Melrose *(G-3345)*
Central Lakes Medical Clinic....D....218 546-8375
Crosby *(G-1145)*
Central Minnesota Emergency....E....320 255-5657
Saint Cloud *(G-7483)*
Chaska Medical Center....E....952 448-2050
Chaska *(G-957)*
Children's Health Care Inc....E....952 930-8600
Hopkins *(G-2527)*
Children's Health Care Inc....C....651 232-6800
Saint Paul *(G-9197)*
Children's Respiratory....E....612 863-3226
Minneapolis *(G-4066)*
Christopher J Fallert MD....E....651 731-4300
Oakdale *(G-6549)*
City of Littlefork....D....218 278-6634
Littlefork *(G-3022)*
City of Redwood Falls....C....507 637-4500
Redwood Falls *(G-7020)*
Colon & Rectal Surgery Assocs....E....651 312-1500
Saint Paul *(G-8226)*
Consulting Radiologists Ltd....C....612 573-2200
Minneapolis *(G-4158)*
Consulting Radiologists Ltd....D....952 831-9300
Minneapolis *(G-4159)*
Cook Area Health Services Inc....E....218 666-5941
Cook *(G-1094)*
Cook Area Health Services Inc....E....218 743-3232
Bigfork *(G-460)*
County of Douglas....D....320 763-6018
Alexandria *(G-92)*
Craig L Gilbertson MD....E....218 722-6613
Duluth *(G-1286)*
Dakota Pediatric Clinic....E....952 997-2572
Lakeville *(G-2901)*
Daniel P Khoury....D....651 738-0470
Saint Paul *(G-9200)*
David G McAlphie MD....E....651 731-0859
Saint Paul *(G-9202)*
Dawson Area Hospital District....C....320 769-4323
Dawson *(G-1164)*
Dedina Eye Physicians....D....952 832-8179
Minneapolis *(G-4241)*
Definity Health Corp....C....952 277-5500
Minneapolis *(G-4242)*
Department of Corrections MN....B....218 485-5000
Moose Lake *(G-6349)*
Diamond Women's Center....E....952 927-4045
Minneapolis *(G-4252)*
Doctors Diagnostic Center Ltd....E....763 550-0707
Minneapolis *(G-4269)*
Donald H Sealock....D....763 559-7358
Minneapolis *(G-4277)*
Dr Peter Schmitz Inc....E....218 829-7812
Brainerd *(G-564)*
Duluth Clinc- Ely Inc....E....218 365-7900
Ely *(G-1913)*
Duluth Clinic International....D....218 283-9431
International Falls *(G-2719)*
Duluth Graduate Medical Educn....E....218 529-9105
Duluth *(G-1299)*

(G-00000) Company's Geographic Section entry number
506
2011 Harris Minnesota Services Directory
▲=Import ▼=Export
◆=Import/Export

Ear Nose & Throat.....E.....612 871-1144
Minneapolis *(G-4306)*
Ear Nose Throat Specialty Care.....D.....763 421-8443
Minneapolis *(G-3461)*
Ear, Nose Throat, Head & Neck.....E.....320 252-0233
Saint Cloud *(G-7501)*
East Metro Asc LLC.....D.....651 702-7400
Lake Elmo *(G-2869)*
East Metro Endoscopy Center.....E.....612 870-5482
Saint Paul *(G-8319)*
East Metro Family Practice.....E.....651 776-2719
Saint Paul *(G-8320)*
East Metro Family Practice.....E.....651 457-2748
Inver Grove Heights *(G-2749)*
East Metro Gorman.....E.....651 455-2940
Saint Paul *(G-7756)*
Edgar Saldana Dr.....E.....218 249-7910
Duluth *(G-1310)*
Edina Eye Physicians.....E.....952 831-8811
Minneapolis *(G-4315)*
Edina Family Physicians.....E.....952 925-2200
Minneapolis *(G-4316)*
Edina Pediatrics.....E.....952 927-7337
Minneapolis *(G-4318)*
Edina Plastic Surgery Ltd.....E.....952 925-1765
Minneapolis *(G-4319)*
▼ Electromed Inc.....E.....952 758-9299
New Prague *(G-6426)*
Emergency Physicians Prof.....C.....952 835-9880
Minneapolis *(G-4346)*
Erol T Uke MD.....E.....952 993-3190
Minneapolis *(G-4368)*
Eye Care Associates.....E.....612 338-4861
Minneapolis *(G-4388)*
Eye Surgeons & Physicians.....E.....320 253-3637
Saint Cloud *(G-7507)*
Fairmont Medical Center Mayo.....A.....507 238-4263
Fairmont *(G-1964)*
Fairmont Orthopedics & Sports.....D.....507 238-4949
Fairmont *(G-1965)*
Fairview Clinics.....E.....651 688-7860
Saint Paul *(G-7773)*
Fairview Health Services.....E.....612 672-2900
Minneapolis *(G-4394)*
Fairview Health Services.....E.....952 826-6500
Eden Prairie *(G-1662)*
Fairview Health Services.....E.....952 848-5600
Minneapolis *(G-4397)*
Fairview Health Services.....E.....612 706-4500
Saint Paul *(G-8364)*
Fairview Health Services.....E.....763 856-6900
Zimmerman *(G-10213)*
Fairview Northland Clinic.....D.....763 389-3344
Princeton *(G-6922)*
Fairview Oxboro Clinics Inc.....B.....952 885-6100
Minneapolis *(G-4402)*
Family Health Services of MN.....E.....651 457-2748
Inver Grove Heights *(G-2750)*
Family Life Mental Health Ctr.....E.....763 427-7964
Minneapolis *(G-3468)*
Family Practice Medical Center.....E.....320 235-7232
Willmar *(G-10001)*
Fergus Falls Medical Group.....C.....218 739-2221
Fergus Falls *(G-2076)*
Fiserv Health Inc.....E.....763 549-3359
Minneapolis *(G-4449)*
Fond Du Lac Reservation.....C.....218 879-1227
Cloquet *(G-1053)*
France Avenue Family.....E.....952 831-1551
Minneapolis *(G-4471)*
Fremont Community Health Svcs.....E.....612 588-9411
Minneapolis *(G-4488)*
Gateway Family Health Clinic.....D.....218 485-4491
Moose Lake *(G-6350)*
Gillette Children's Specialty.....E.....651 229-3840
Saint Paul *(G-8409)*
Glacial Ridge Hospital Fndtn.....C.....320 634-4521
Glenwood *(G-2223)*
Glencoe Regional Health Svcs.....B.....320 864-3121
Glencoe *(G-2207)*
Golden Valley Clinic Inc.....E.....952 993-8300
Minneapolis *(G-4535)*
Grand Itasca Clinic & Hospital.....C.....218 326-5000
Grand Rapids *(G-2279)*
Grand Itasca Clinic & Hospital.....B.....218 326-7024
Grand Rapids *(G-2280)*
Haugen, John A Associates.....E.....952 927-6561
Minneapolis *(G-4606)*
Haugen, John A Associates.....612 333-2503
Minneapolis *(G-4607)*
Health Activation Management.....D.....763 398-8888
Hopkins *(G-2550)*
Healtheast Care System.....C.....651 232-1700
Saint Paul *(G-8458)*
Healtheast Diversified Svcs.....E.....651 489-8061
Saint Paul *(G-8460)*
Healtheast Diversified Svcs.....651 232-2300
Saint Paul *(G-8461)*
Healtheast Maplewood Out.....E.....651 232-7780
Saint Paul *(G-8463)*
Healtheast Medical Research.....E.....651 489-8061
Saint Paul *(G-8464)*
HealthPartners Central MN.....C.....320 253-5220
Saint Cloud *(G-7523)*
HealthPartners Inc.....A.....952 883-6000
Bloomington *(G-500)*
Healthpartners Inc.....B.....612 371-1600
Minneapolis *(G-4621)*
Healthpartners Inc.....C.....651 653-2100
Saint Paul *(G-8466)*
Healthpartners Inc.....C.....651 293-8100
Saint Paul *(G-8467)*
HealthPartners Inc.....E.....952 546-2500
Hopkins *(G-2551)*
Healthpartners Inc.....B.....651 641-6200
Saint Paul *(G-8474)*
Healthpartners Inc.....D.....651 702-5300
Saint Paul *(G-9226)*
Healthpartners Inc.....B.....952 593-8777
Minneapolis *(G-4622)*
Healthpartners Inc.....D.....651 552-1720
South Saint Paul *(G-9528)*
Healthpartners Inc.....B.....651 779-1500
Saint Paul *(G-8469)*
Healthpartners Inc.....B.....763 754-0041
Minneapolis *(G-3486)*
Healthpartners Inc.....B.....651 254-3500
Saint Paul *(G-8470)*
Healthpartners Inc.....D.....651 772-9757
Saint Paul *(G-8473)*
Healthpartners Inc.....D.....651 999-4740
Saint Paul *(G-8472)*
Heartland Family Practice Inc.....D.....320 251-2042
Saint Cloud *(G-7525)*
Heartland Orthopedic.....E.....320 762-1144
Alexandria *(G-103)*
Hennepin Faculty Associates.....A.....612 347-5110
Minneapolis *(G-4637)*
Hermantown Clinic.....E.....218 786-3540
Duluth *(G-1351)*
Holmes Hooper Inc.....D.....763 545-5641
Minneapolis *(G-4661)*
Hospital Pathology Associates.....E.....651 483-2033
Saint Paul *(G-8496)*
Ilbnc.....E.....612 879-2521
Minneapolis *(G-4688)*
Indian Health Board of.....D.....612 721-9800
Minneapolis *(G-4696)*
Indian Health Service.....D.....320 532-4163
Onamia *(G-6572)*
Innovis Health LLC.....D.....218 732-2800
Park Rapids *(G-6756)*
Innovis Health LLC.....C.....218 844-2300
Detroit Lakes *(G-1200)*
International Diabetes Center.....C.....952 993-3393
Minneapolis *(G-4722)*
Jackson Municipal Clinic.....E.....507 847-2200
Jackson *(G-2796)*
James M Smith MD.....D.....320 253-7257
Saint Cloud *(G-7535)*
John L Bonner Eye Clinic Ltd.....E.....218 326-3433
Grand Rapids *(G-2288)*
John Schmitz MD.....E.....320 255-5777
Saint Cloud *(G-7537)*
John T Beecher MD.....E.....952 925-2200
Minneapolis *(G-4772)*
Jon Bowar MD.....E.....320 255-5777
Saint Cloud *(G-7538)*
Jon S Nielsen MD.....E.....763 257-4400
Minneapolis *(G-4777)*
Kidney Specialists of MN.....E.....763 561-5349
Minneapolis *(G-4806)*
Lake City Medical Center-Mayo.....B.....651 345-3321
Lake City *(G-2849)*
Lakeview Clinic.....C.....952 442-4461
Waconia *(G-9788)*
Lakeview Clinic.....E.....952 955-1921
Watertown *(G-9891)*
Lakeview Medical Clinic.....E.....320 352-6591
Sauk Centre *(G-9350)*
Lakewalk Surgery Center Inc.....E.....218 728-0650
Duluth *(G-1380)*
Leslie E Fishman Inc.....E.....651 227-7806
Saint Paul *(G-8579)*
Lex A Nerenberg MD.....E.....763 520-2980
Minneapolis *(G-4866)*
▲ Lexion Medical LLC.....E.....651 635-0000
Saint Paul *(G-8582)*
M Heath, Paul MD.....E.....320 253-7257
Saint Cloud *(G-7546)*
Mankato Clinic Ltd.....B.....507 625-1811
Mankato *(G-3160)*
Mankato Clinic Ltd.....E.....507 625-5027
Mankato *(G-3229)*
Maple Grove Urgent Care.....E.....763 420-5279
Osseo *(G-6634)*
Mark Macdonald Do.....E.....651 455-2940
Saint Paul *(G-7832)*
Mayo Clinic.....E.....507 931-2110
Saint Peter *(G-9308)*
Mayo Clinic.....D.....507 723-4231
Springfield *(G-9573)*
Mayo Clinic.....E.....651 565-4571
Wabasha *(G-9768)*
Mayo Clinic.....E.....507 284-9077
Rochester *(G-7170)*
Mayo Clinic Rochester.....E.....507 377-5900
Albert Lea *(G-61)*
Mayo Clinic Rochester.....D.....507 284-5135
Rochester *(G-7173)*
Mayo Clinic Rochester.....E.....507 634-4744
Kasson *(G-2822)*
Mayo Clinic Rochester.....E.....507 387-8231
North Mankato *(G-6510)*
Meadowbrook Women's Clinic.....E.....612 376-7708
Minneapolis *(G-4980)*
Medical Advanced Pain.....D.....763 537-6000
Minneapolis *(G-3532)*
Medical Center.....D.....320 632-6611
Little Falls *(G-3013)*
Medical Evaluations Inc.....E.....952 229-8500
Saint Louis Park *(G-7664)*
Medical Scanning Consultants.....E.....952 513-6841
Saint Louis Park *(G-7665)*
Mencept Epileptic Clinic.....E.....952 525-2400
Minneapolis *(G-4987)*
Meritcare Health System.....E.....218 846-2000
Detroit Lakes *(G-1210)*
Mesaba Clinic.....C.....218 263-9426
Hibbing *(G-2463)*
Metropolitan Cardiology.....C.....763 427-9980
Minneapolis *(G-3540)*
Metropolitan Hand Surgery.....E.....651 223-5406
Saint Paul *(G-8647)*
Metropolitan Obstetrics & Gyn.....E.....651 770-1385
Saint Paul *(G-8648)*
Metropolitan Pediatric.....E.....952 435-2450
Burnsville *(G-754)*
Metropolitan Pediatric.....D.....952 445-6700
Shakopee *(G-9455)*
Metropolitan Urologic.....E.....651 999-7034
Saint Paul *(G-8649)*
Michael C Magnuson.....E.....952 435-0303
Burnsville *(G-757)*
Midsota Plastic.....E.....320 253-7257
Saint Cloud *(G-7553)*
Midwest Internal Medicine.....E.....763 236-9428
Minneapolis *(G-3542)*
Midwest Spine Institute LLC.....E.....651 430-3800
Burnsville *(G-758)*
Midwest Stone Management, A MN.....E.....651 633-9414
Saint Paul *(G-8665)*
Midwest Surgery Center.....E.....651 642-9199
Saint Paul *(G-9248)*
Mille Lacs Health System.....B.....320 532-3154
Onamia *(G-6574)*
Mincep Epilepsy Care.....E.....952 525-2400
Minneapolis *(G-5048)*
Minn Health.....E.....651 739-5050
Saint Paul *(G-8669)*
Minneapolis Clinic of.....C.....763 588-0661
Minneapolis *(G-5051)*
Minneapolis Radiology Assocs.....E.....763 398-6600
Minneapolis *(G-5061)*
Minneapolis Radiology Assocs.....D.....763 559-2171
Minneapolis *(G-5062)*
Minnesota Brd of Med Prac.....E.....651 642-0538
Saint Paul *(G-8674)*
Minnesota Diagnostic Ctr.....E.....612 879-1528
Minneapolis *(G-5075)*
Minnesota Ear Head & Neck Clin.....E.....612 339-2836
Minneapolis *(G-5077)*
Minnesota Epilepsy Group.....C.....651 241-5305
Saint Paul *(G-8685)*
Minnesota Gastroenterology PA.....D.....612 871-1145
Saint Paul *(G-8688)*
Minnesota Heart Clinic Inc.....D.....952 836-3700
Edina *(G-1837)*
Minnesota Internal Medicine.....E.....651 232-4800
Saint Paul *(G-8692)*
Minnesota Radiation Oncology.....E.....612 863-4060
Minneapolis *(G-5091)*
Minnesota Rural Health Co-op.....D.....507 423-5300
Cottonwood *(G-1113)*
Minnesota Surgical Associates.....E.....651 776-0724
Saint Paul *(G-8708)*
Minnesota Valley Memorial Hosp.....C.....507 665-3375
Le Sueur *(G-2958)*
Minnhealth Family Physicians.....E.....651 426-6402
White Bear Lake *(G-9976)*
Minnhealth Family Physicians.....E.....651 487-2831
Saint Paul *(G-8713)*
Montevideo Clinic.....E.....320 269-6435
Montevideo *(G-6252)*
Multicare Associates of The.....C.....763 785-4500
Minneapolis *(G-3546)*
Multicare Associates of The.....D.....763 785-4250
Minneapolis *(G-3547)*
Multicare Associates of The.....E.....763 785-4300
Saint Paul *(G-8728)*
Nephrology Analytical Services.....E.....612 337-7345
Minneapolis *(G-5182)*
Neurological Associates of St.....E.....651 221-9051
Saint Paul *(G-8746)*
Noran Neurological Clinic.....D.....612 879-1000
Minneapolis *(G-5206)*
Noran Neurological Clinic.....E.....763 786-8406
Minneapolis *(G-3556)*
North Memorial Clinic.....E.....763 520-5551
Minneapolis *(G-5215)*
North Memorial Health Care.....A.....763 520-5200
Minneapolis *(G-5217)*
North Memorial Imaging Center.....E.....763 398-4400
Osseo *(G-6644)*
Northern Light Pediatrics.....E.....651 484-3942
Saint Paul *(G-8758)*
Northern Pines Mental Health.....320 632-6647
Little Falls *(G-3015)*
Northland Ob Gyn Associates.....E.....218 722-5629
Duluth *(G-1408)*
Northwest Anesthesia.....D.....612 871-7639
Minneapolis *(G-5241)*
Northwest Family Physicians.....E.....763 476-6776
Minneapolis *(G-5242)*

SIC

Employment codes: A=Over 500 employees, B=251-500
C=101-250, D=51-100, E=25-50
2011 Harris Minnesota
Services Directory
© Harris InfoSource 1-866-281-6415
507

Northwest Orthopedic Surgeons....D....763 520-7870
Minneapolis (G-5243)
Oak Dale Healtheast....E....651 326-5300
Saint Paul (G-9253)
Oakdale Ear Nose & Throat Clin....E....763 520-7840
Minneapolis (G-5255)
Oakdale Obstetrics & Gynecolog....D....763 520-2999
Minneapolis (G-5257)
Obstetrics & Gyn....952 920-2200
Minneapolis (G-5261)
Obstetrics & Gynecology....E....952 920-2200
Minneapolis (G-5262)
Obstetrics, Gynecology....E....952 920-2730
Minneapolis (G-5263)
Olmsted Medical Center....A....507 529-6600
Rochester (G-7194)
Olson M D, Peter J....E....651 326-9020
Saint Paul (G-8783)
Oncologic Consultants....E....651 602-5335
Saint Paul (G-8786)
Oncologic Consultants....E....952 928-2900
Minneapolis (G-5279)
Open Cities Health Center....D....651 290-9200
Saint Paul (G-8788)
Open Door Health Center....E....507 388-2120
Mankato (G-3179)
Ophthalmology....E....952 925-3150
Minneapolis (G-5286)
Orthogonistic Care Specialist....D....952 432-4941
Saint Paul (G-7860)
Orthopaedic Consultants....E....952 832-0076
Minneapolis (G-5292)
Orthopedic & Fracture Clinic....D....507 386-6600
Mankato (G-3180)
Orthopedic Associates of....E....218 722-5513
Duluth (G-1414)
Orthopedic Medicine & Surgery....E....952 920-0970
Minneapolis (G-5293)
Orthopedic Partners....E....763 786-9543
Minneapolis (G-3562)
Orthopedic Sports Inc....D....651 439-8540
Stillwater (G-9634)
Orthopedic Surgeons Ltd....E....952 927-7565
Minneapolis (G-5295)
Owatonna Clinic — Mayo Health....B....507 451-1120
Owatonna (G-6726)
P S Rudie & Associates Ltd....E....218 722-6613
Duluth (G-1417)
Park Nicollet Clinic....E....952 993-7400
Eden Prairie (G-1742)
Park Nicollet Clinic....A....952 993-3123
Minneapolis (G-5332)
Park Nicollet Clinic....E....952 993-8900
Minneapolis (G-5331)
Park Nicollet Clinic....B....952 993-8700
Burnsville (G-775)
Park Nicollet Clinic....D....952 993-4001
Saint Paul (G-7863)
Park Nicollet Health Services....C....952 993-9900
Minneapolis (G-5336)
Park Nicollet Health Services....C....952 993-8000
Minneapolis (G-5334)
Partners In Pediatrics Ltd....E....763 425-1211
Minneapolis (G-5343)
Partners Pediatric....612 827-4055
Minneapolis (G-5344)
Paul Larson Ob-Gyn Clinic....D....952 927-4021
Minneapolis (G-5351)
Pavilion Surgery Center LLC....E....218 279-6200
Duluth (G-1420)
Pediatric & Adolescent Care of....E....651 770-2124
Saint Paul (G-8812)
Pediatric & Adolescent Care of....E....651 451-8050
Saint Paul (G-7871)
Pediatric & Young Adult Med....E....651 227-7806
Saint Paul (G-8813)
Pediatricians For Health....E....651 232-6700
Saint Paul (G-9258)
Physicans Neck & Back Clinic....E....651 639-9150
Saint Paul (G-8827)
Pipestone Medical Group Inc....E....507 825-5700
Pipestone (G-6836)
Prairie Medical....E....320 589-4008
Morris (G-6375)
Preferredone Administrative....B....763 847-3525
Minneapolis (G-5401)
Pride Institute Inc....E....952 934-7554
Eden Prairie (G-1753)
Primary Care Center....E....612 624-9499
Minneapolis (G-5408)
Psychiatric Clinic of Mankato....E....507 387-3195
Mankato (G-3183)
Pulmonary Health Realty Assocs....E....651 224-5895
Saint Paul (G-8858)
Quello Clinic....D....952 985-8100
Minneapolis (G-5447)
Raiper Clinic....D....218 879-1271
Cloquet (G-1062)
Raiter Clinic Ltd....E....218 879-1271
Cloquet (G-1063)
Randall, Omlie, Haas....E....952 835-5003
Minneapolis (G-5467)
Range Mental Health Center Inc....E....218 263-9237
Hibbing (G-2472)
Regents of The University of....E....952 997-4177
Saint Paul (G-7893)
Regents of The University of....E....651 227-6551
Saint Paul (G-8881)
Regents of The University of....C....612 625-1612
Minneapolis (G-5488)
Regents of The University of....E....612 624-0999
Minneapolis (G-5490)
Regents of The University of....E....612 627-4564
Minneapolis (G-5491)
Regents of The University of....D....612 625-4400
Minneapolis (G-5503)
Regents of The University of....E....612 625-8625
Minneapolis (G-5498)
Regina Medical Center....A....651 480-4100
Hastings (G-2402)
Regina Medical Center....E....651 480-4200
Hastings (G-2403)
Regional Diagnostics Radiology....E....320 255-5619
Saint Cloud (G-7583)
Reproductive Medicine....E....651 221-4620
Saint Paul (G-9267)
Ridgeview Medical Clinic....E....952 471-2585
Spring Park (G-9565)
Riverway Clinic....C....763 712-6000
Anoka (G-222)
Robbinsdale Clinic PA Inc....E....763 533-2534
Minneapolis (G-5550)
Robert Aby MD....D....507 372-1840
Worthington (G-10192)
Robert C Meisterling MD....D....651 439-8807
Stillwater (G-9635)
Rochester Methodist Hospital....507 266-7890
Rochester (G-7237)
Royal Medical Center....E....218 249-8800
Duluth (G-1439)
Saint Luke's Outpatient Mental....E....218 249-7000
Duluth (G-1442)
Saint Lukes Cardiology Assocs....E....218 249-3057
Duluth (G-1443)
Saint Paul Lung Clinic....D....651 726-6200
Saint Paul (G-8927)
Sanford Health Network....B....507 223-7272
Canby (G-852)
Sanford Health Network....D....507 847-2420
Jackson (G-2799)
Sanford Health Network....C....507 674-2932
Tracy (G-9691)
Scott R McGarvey MD....E....952 832-0076
Minneapolis (G-5619)
Shoulder & Sports Medicine....E....612 879-6623
Minneapolis (G-5660)
Silver Lake Clinic At Shorevw....E....651 481-0818
Saint Paul (G-8959)
Sioux Valley Canby Campus....C....507 223-7221
Canby (G-853)
Sioux Valley Physician....E....507 283-4476
Luverne (G-3069)
Skemp Walk In Clinic....E....507 724-3353
Caledonia (G-829)
Smdc Health System....A....218 786-8364
Duluth (G-1454)
Smdc Health System....E....218 365-3151
Ely (G-1915)
Smdc Health System....E....218 786-3500
Duluth (G-1453)
Smdc Health System....D....218 285-6222
International Falls (G-2730)
Smdc Health System....E....218 246-8275
Deer River (G-1173)
South Central Surgical Center....E....507 235-3939
Fairmont (G-1981)
South Lake Pediatrics....E....952 401-8300
Hopkins (G-2635)
Southdale Family Practice....E....952 927-4235
Minneapolis (G-5706)
Southdale Ob Gyn Consultants....E....952 435-9505
Burnsville (G-800)
Southdale Obstetric....E....952 920-7001
Minneapolis (G-5707)
Southdale Pediatrics Assocs....D....952 831-4454
Minneapolis (G-5708)
Southdale Pediatrics Assocs....E....952 898-5900
Burnsville (G-801)
Southside Community Health....E....612 822-3186
Minneapolis (G-5710)
Sports & Orthopaedic....E....952 946-9777
Minneapolis (G-5722)
Springfield Medical Center....D....507 723-6201
Springfield (G-9575)
St Cloud Ear, Nose, Throat....E....320 252-0233
Saint Cloud (G-7599)
St Cloud Medical Group....C....320 202-8949
Saint Cloud (G-7604)
St Cloud Surgical Center....C....320 251-8385
Saint Cloud (G-7607)
St Croix Orthopaedics....D....651 439-8807
Stillwater (G-9643)
St James Medical Center-Mayo....D....507 375-3261
Saint James (G-7647)
St Luke's Clinics....D....218 249-5555
Duluth (G-1467)
St Luke's Hospital of Duluth....A....218 726-5555
Duluth (G-1469)
St Luke's Hospital of Duluth....E....218 249-8800
Duluth (G-1468)
St Luke's Hospital of Duluth....E....218 362-7100
Hibbing (G-2476)
St Luke's Hospital of Duluth....E....218 249-4600
Duluth (G-1470)
St Luke's Internal Medicine....E....218 249-7960
Duluth (G-1472)
St Mary's Duluth Clinic Health....A....218 786-4000
Duluth (G-1473)
St Paul Cardiology....E....651 232-4320
Saint Paul (G-8987)
St Paul Eye Clinic....E....651 641-0457
Saint Paul (G-8988)
St Paul Heart Clinic....C....651 292-0616
Saint Paul (G-8992)
St Paul Heart Clinic....B....651 779-9449
Saint Paul (G-8993)
St Paul Radiology....D....651 292-2000
Saint Paul (G-8998)
Stephen J Russell....D....507 284-8384
Rochester (G-7264)
Stevens Community Medical Ctr....C....320 589-1313
Morris (G-6379)
Stillwater Fitness Club Inc....E....651 430-1584
Stillwater (G-9646)
Stillwater Medical Clinic....C....651 439-1234
Stillwater (G-9647)
Stillwater Medical Group....C....651 439-1234
Stillwater (G-9648)
Stratis Health....D....952 854-3306
Minneapolis (G-5759)
Suburban Plastic Surgery....D....952 922-0895
Minneapolis (G-5761)
Suburban Radiologic Conslnts....D....952 837-9700
Minneapolis (G-5762)
Suburban Radiologic Conslnts....E....763 792-1900
Minneapolis (G-3611)
Suburban Radiologic Conslnts....E....763 786-9460
Minneapolis (G-3612)
Summit Landmark Orthopedics....C....651 842-5200
Saint Paul (G-9013)
Surgical Care Affiliates LLC....E....952 832-9360
Minneapolis (G-5774)
Surgical Consultants Prof....E....952 832-0805
Minneapolis (G-5775)
Thomas Oas MD....E....507 646-1494
Northfield (G-6521)
Timothy J Hernandez MD....E....651 455-2940
Saint Paul (G-7922)
Tl Wyne....E....320 240-2180
Saint Cloud (G-7617)
Total Renal Care Inc....D....612 873-6089
Minneapolis (G-5836)
Trimont Health Care Center....D....507 639-2381
Trimont (G-9694)
Twin Cities Spine Surgeons Ltd....D....612 775-6200
Minneapolis (G-5874)
United Clinic of Faribault....E....507 526-7388
Blue Earth (G-538)
United Family Practice Health....D....651 241-1000
Saint Paul (G-9104)
United Healthcare of Wyoming....A....218 279-5642
Duluth (G-1490)
University Affiliated Family....E....612 333-0770
Minneapolis (G-5923)
University Neurosurgical Assn....E....612 624-6666
Minneapolis (G-5928)
University of Minnesota....C....763 782-6400
Minneapolis (G-5930)
University Womens Health....E....612 625-6991
Minneapolis (G-5931)
Upsher-Smith Laboratories Inc....D....763 315-2000
Osseo (G-6681)
US Oncology Inc....E....612 863-8585
Minneapolis (G-5949)
Virginia, City of Inc....A....218 741-3340
Virginia (G-9760)
Virtual Radiologic Corp....C....952 595-1100
Eden Prairie (G-1807)
Wabasha Clinic Mayo Health....E....651 565-4571
Wabasha (G-9774)
Wadena Medical Center Ltd....E....218 631-1360
Wadena (G-9814)
Wal-Mart Stores Inc....B....320 587-1020
Hutchinson (G-2717)
Warren Community Hospital Inc....D....218 745-4211
Warren (G-9869)
Water Medical Group....C....651 439-1234
Stillwater (G-9655)
West Side Community Health....D....651 222-1816
Saint Paul (G-9148)
Western Eastern Ob Gyn Limited....E....952 556-0071
Chaska (G-985)
Western Ob Gyne Ltd....E....952 442-2137
Waconia (G-9795)
Westhealth Inc....C....763 577-7000
Plymouth (G-6891)
Winona Clinic Ltd....C....507 454-3680
Winona (G-10144)

8021 Offices & Clinics Of Dentists

Affliated Pediatric Dentists....E....952 831-4400
Minneapolis (G-3695)
Apollo Dental Center PLC....E....507 287-8320
Rochester (G-7057)
Apple Tree Dental....E....763 784-7570
Minneapolis (G-3407)
Associated Dentists Ltd....E....651 222-0351
Saint Paul (G-8073)
Bassett Creek Dental....E....763 546-1301
Minneapolis (G-3872)
Blue Ridge Dental....E....952 938-4767
Hopkins (G-2519)

S I C

(G-00000) Company's Geographic Section entry number
508
2011 Harris Minnesota Services Directory
▲=Import ▼=Export
◆=Import/Export

Brook West Family Dentistry ....E....763 561-8901
Osseo (G-6600)
Catton Wolseth Como & Jacobs ....E....320 253-4778
Saint Cloud (G-7477)
Centennial Lakes Dental Group ....E....952 831-2800
Minneapolis (G-4041)
Charles R Babst ....E....218 722-8377
Duluth (G-1269)
Community Dental Care ....E....651 774-2959
Saint Paul (G-8238)
Cook Area Health Services Inc ....E....218 666-5941
Cook (G-1094)
Dental Specialists ....E....952 926-2763
Lake Elmo (G-2868)
Dentistry At The Center Inc ....E....320 762-5216
Alexandria (G-94)
Falls Court Dentists ....E....320 632-6621
Little Falls (G-3003)
Foley Dental Clinic ....E....763 757-3120
Minneapolis (G-3471)
Gregg G Hipple ....E....651 452-3333
Saint Paul (G-7791)
Healthpartners Inc ....E....763 780-1292
Minneapolis (G-3485)
Healthpartners Inc ....E....763 754-0041
Minneapolis (G-3484)
Healthpartners Inc ....E....651 227-3757
Saint Paul (G-8468)
Healthpartners Inc ....E....651 770-8828
Saint Paul (G-8471)
Healthpartners Inc ....E....651 702-5871
Saint Paul (G-9227)
Healthpartners Inc ....B....952 431-8500
Saint Paul (G-7798)
Healthpartners Inc ....D....763 754-4600
Minneapolis (G-3487)
Indian Health Board of ....D....612 721-9800
Minneapolis (G-4696)
Lake Minnetonka Orthodontics ....E....952 938-1443
Hopkins (G-2568)
Lake Superior Dental ....E....218 728-6445
Duluth (G-1376)
Leonard V Ackerman DDS ....E....763 757-7540
Minneapolis (G-3515)
Maplewood Dental Associates ....E....651 770-3831
Saint Paul (G-8613)
Metro Dental Care ....E....952 435-8525
Burnsville (G-753)
Metrodentallcare, PLC ....E....612 861-9123
Minneapolis (G-5005)
Metroplitan Pediatric Dental ....E....763 786-4260
Minneapolis (G-3539)
Metropolitan Dental Associates ....D....612 866-0054
Minneapolis (G-5006)
New Ulm Dental Clinic ....E....507 354-3321
New Ulm (G-6467)
Northpark Dental 763 786-1560
Minneapolis (G-3559)
Northwest Dental Group of ....E....507 282-1271
Rochester (G-7193)
Nyberg & Assoc PA Inc ....E....763 441-9181
Elk River (G-1888)
Oral & Max Facial Specialist ....E....763 494-8825
Osseo (G-6646)
Oral & Maxillofacial Surgical ....E....952 835-5003
Minneapolis (G-5289)
Orthodontic Care Specialist ....D....651 490-6732
Saint Paul (G-8791)
Orthodontics Care Specialist ....E....952 432-2682
Saint Paul (G-7859)
Park Dental Blaine ....D....763 755-1330
Minneapolis (G-3564)
Park Dental Eden Prairie ....E....952 949-2536
Eden Prairie (G-1741)
Parkway Dental ....E....952 937-2137
Eden Prairie (G-1743)
Pdhc Ltd ....E....952 949-2536
Eden Prairie (G-1745)
Pdhc Ltd ....D....763 535-2960
Minneapolis (G-5356)
PDHC Ltd ....E....612 338-4546
Minneapolis (G-5355)
Pdhc Ltd ....E....952 545-8603
Hopkins (G-2602)
Pdhc Ltd ....E....763 421-5206
Champlin (G-897)
Piedmont Heights Dental Assocs ....E....218 722-0823
Duluth (G-1423)
Rangerland Dental Group Inc ....E....218 534-3141
Deerwood (G-1179)
Regents of The University of ....E....612 626-5722
Minneapolis (G-5496)
Scott A Polzin DDS ....E....218 728-6445
Duluth (G-1445)
Scott W Kajer DDS ....E....651 770-3831
Saint Paul (G-8937)
Shari K Bruning DDS ....E....763 546-1301
Minneapolis (G-5649)
Southdale Dental Associates ....E....952 896-1111
Minneapolis (G-5705)
Southern Minnesota Oral ....E....507 625-9330
Mankato (G-3201)
Southhill Dental ....E....651 439-9400
Stillwater (G-9641)
3M Co ....C....651 736-3490
Saint Paul (G-9046)
Twin City Oral & Maxillofacial ....E....651 437-3262
Hastings (G-2410)
Udell Dental Laboratory Inc ....E....952 926-9266
Minneapolis (G-5893)
Valley Dental Arts Inc ....D....651 439-2855
Stillwater (G-9653)
Valley Dental Group ....D....763 544-2213
Minneapolis (G-5955)
West Side Community Health ....D....651 222-1816
Saint Paul (G-9148)
Westlund Dental Studio Inc ....E....952 942-9464
Eden Prairie (G-1814)

8031 Offices & Clinics Of Doctors Of Osteopathy

Bruce B Cunningham ....E....651 731-0859
Saint Paul (G-9190)
David Balt Do ....E....507 825-3390
Pipestone (G-6824)
Eleah Medical Center ....E....218 685-4406
Elbow Lake (G-1851)
Family Health Services of MN ....E....651 457-2748
Inver Grove Heights (G-2750)
Lakeview Medical Clinic ....E....320 352-6591
Sauk Centre (G-9350)
Thomas Oas MD ....E....507 646-1494
Northfield (G-6521)

8041 Offices & Clinics Of Chiropractors

Brookdale Integrative Health ....E....763 561-4045
Minneapolis (G-3955)
P H Selly & Co Inc ....E....507 334-3251
Faribault (G-2025)

8042 Offices & Clinics Of Optometrists

Centracare Clinic ....E....320 256-4228
Melrose (G-3345)
Donald H Sealock ....D....763 559-7358
Minneapolis (G-4277)
▲ Linstrom, Samuelson, & Hardten ....E....612 813-3600
Minneapolis (G-4892)
North West Eye Clinic ....C....763 383-4140
Minneapolis (G-5223)
Richie Eye Clinic ....E....507 332-9900
Faribault (G-2028)
Shopko Stores Operating Co LLC ....C....507 532-3266
Marshall (G-3327)
Shopko Stores Operating Co LLC ....C....507 437-7785
Austin (G-287)
Vitreal Retinal Surgery ....E....952 929-1131
Minneapolis (G-5979)

8049 Offices & Clinics Of Health Practitioners, NEC

Advanced Spine Associates ....E....763 577-1877
Champlin (G-887)
Allied Professionals Inc ....B....952 832-5101
Minneapolis (G-3716)
Allina Health System ....E....763 427-7180
Anoka (G-150)
Aspen Medical Group ....E....651 696-8800
Saint Paul (G-8070)
Associated Clinic of ....E....952 925-6033
Minneapolis (G-3824)
Brookdale Integrative Health ....E....763 561-4045
Minneapolis (G-3955)
Capernaum Pediatric Therapy ....E....952 938-5348
Hopkins (G-2522)
Center For Independent Living ....B....218 262-6675
Hibbing (G-2439)
Center For Rehab & Wellness ....E....507 455-7631
Owatonna (G-6699)
Choices Psychotherapy Ltd ....E....952 544-6806
Minneapolis (G-4069)
Coborn Cancer Center ....E....320 229-4907
Saint Cloud (G-7493)
Cook Area Health Services Inc ....E....218 666-5941
Cook (G-1094)
Core Professional Services ....E....320 202-1400
Saint Cloud (G-7410)
County of Douglas ....A....320 762-1511
Alexandria (G-91)
County of Pennington ....E....218 681-0876
Thief River Falls (G-9664)
Dirk Miller ....E....651 645-5323
Saint Paul (G-8297)
Entocrinology Clinic ....E....320 229-5000
Saint Cloud (G-7504)
Evangelical Lutheran Good ....D....320 634-4552
Glenwood (G-2222)
Family Focus Inc ....E....218 740-3146
Duluth (G-1320)
Generations Community Support ....D....612 676-1604
Minneapolis (G-4519)
Generations Resources For ....E....612 676-1604
Minneapolis (G-4520)
Global Anesthesia Business ....E....651 646-3091
Saint Paul (G-8414)
Healtheast Clinics Infoline ....E....651 426-4844
Saint Paul (G-8459)
Impact Physical Medicine ....E....651 641-0688
Saint Paul (G-8507)
J C Penny Beauty Salon ....E....507 625-5630
Mankato (G-3151)
Jill H Rusterholz ....E....952 806-0011
Minneapolis (G-4763)
Jones Stanley & Associates ....E....507 288-0064
Rochester (G-7147)
Kevin Switzer ....E....320 231-8888
Willmar (G-10015)
M D A Consulting Group Inc ....E....612 332-8182
Minneapolis (G-4920)
Medical Advanced Pain ....D....763 537-6000
Minneapolis (G-3532)
Metropolitan Hand Surgery ....E....651 223-5406
Saint Paul (G-8647)
Metropolitan Obstetrics & Gyn ....E....651 770-1385
Saint Paul (G-8648)
Michael J Morris ....E....320 231-8888
Willmar (G-10022)
Midsota Regional Hand Center ....E....320 253-7257
Saint Cloud (G-7554)
Minnhouse ....E....651 426-6402
Saint Paul (G-8714)
North Memorial Health Care ....A....763 420-7002
Osseo (G-6643)
Northern Star Therapy Ltd Inc ....E....320 240-6955
Saint Cloud (G-7562)
Occupro Inc ....E....320 839-4090
Ortonville (G-6584)
Park Nicollet Clinic ....D....952 993-9700
Minneapolis (G-5330)
Pathways Psychological Svcs 763 525-8590
Minneapolis (G-5346)
Patrick M Doyle Dr ....E....651 454-0114
Saint Paul (G-7865)
Physical Therapy Orthopedic ....E....612 872-2700
Minneapolis (G-5377)
Physicans Neck & Back Clinic ....E....651 639-9150
Saint Paul (G-8827)
Professional Physical Therapy ....E....952 935-0333
Minneapolis (G-5421)
Program In Human Sexuality ....E....612 625-1500
Minneapolis (G-5423)
Range Mental Health Center Inc ....E....218 263-9237
Hibbing (G-2472)
Rice Memorial Hospital ....E....320 231-4175
Willmar (G-10043)
Rochester Fitness Inc ....E....507 282-4445
Rochester (G-7231)
Tom Johnson ....E....651 645-3000
Saint Paul (G-9070)
University Mental Health ....E....612 626-8100
Minneapolis (G-5927)
Vitreorentinal Surgery ....E....952 929-1131
Minneapolis (G-5980)
Woodland Centers ....D....320 235-4613
Willmar (G-10058)

8051 Skilled Nursing Facilities

A R I Inc ....E....763 689-1162
Cambridge (G-830)
Aicota Healthcare Center ....C....218 927-2164
Aitkin (G-12)
Albert Lea Medical Center-Mayo ....A....507 373-2384
Albert Lea (G-32)
Alternative Continum of Care ....D....507 373-5600
Albert Lea (G-37)
Alterra Healthcare Corp ....E....651 482-8111
Saint Paul (G-8018)
Alterra Healthcare Corp ....E....651 686-5557
Saint Paul (G-7694)
American Baptist Homes of The ....E....507 373-9656
Albert Lea (G-40)
American Baptist Homes of The ....D....507 893-3171
Winnebago (G-10075)
American Baptist Homes of The ....E....952 941-3175
Eden Prairie (G-1590)
Amherst H Wilder Foundation ....C....651 220-1700
Saint Paul (G-8041)
Annandale Care Center ....C....320 274-3737
Annandale (G-134)
Appleton Area Health Services ....C....320 289-2422
Appleton (G-244)
Assumption Home Inc ....C....320 685-3693
Cold Spring (G-1082)
Atchison Enterprises Inc ....D....507 376-3175
Worthington (G-10178)
Auburn West Inc ....E....952 442-2546
Waconia (G-9778)
Augustana Chapel View Homes ....B....612 333-1551
Minneapolis (G-3835)
Augustana Chapel View Homes ....C....952 938-2761
Hopkins (G-2512)
Augustana Dassel Lakeside Com ....D....320 275-3308
Dassel (G-1159)
Augustana Health Care Center ....C....651 437-6176
Hastings (G-2376)
Augustana Health Care Center ....B....952 431-7700
Saint Paul (G-7708)
Augustana Lutheran Homes Inc ....E....320 693-2430
Litchfield (G-2979)
Aviv Health Care Inc ....C....612 377-4723
Minneapolis (G-3845)
Aviv Health Care Inc ....C....952 546-4261
Minneapolis (G-3844)
Aviv Health Care Inc ....C....952 546-4261
Minneapolis (G-3846)
Barrett Care Center Inc ....D....320 528-2527
Barrett (G-308)

S I C

Employment codes: A=Over 500 employees, B=251-500
C=101-250, D=51-100, E=25-50
2011 Harris Minnesota
Services Directory
© Harris InfoSource 1-866-281-6415
509

Bay Shore Health Center ....C....218 727-8651 Duluth *(G-1247)*

Behavioral Hlth Care Providers ....E....763 525-9919 Minneapolis *(G-3879)*

Belgrade Nursing Home Inc ....D....320 254-8215 Belgrade *(G-364)*

Benedictine Health Center ....C....218 723-6408 Duluth *(G-1249)*

Benedictine Health System ....D....320 485-2151 Winsted *(G-10158)*

Benedictine Health System ....E....507 457-0280 Winona *(G-10080)*

Benedictine Health System ....D....651 388-1234 Red Wing *(G-6975)*

Bethany Samaritan Inc ....C....507 289-4031 Rochester *(G-7064)*

Bethany Samaritan Inc ....C....507 289-3336 Rochester *(G-7063)*

Bethesda ....C....320 235-3924 Willmar *(G-9987)*

Bethesda ....E....320 235-8364 Willmar *(G-9988)*

Bethesda Heritage Center ....D....320 235-3924 Willmar *(G-9989)*

Beverly Enterprises - MN ....D....507 932-3283 Saint Charles *(G-7402)*

Beverly Enterprises - MN ....E....507 557-2211 Franklin *(G-2180)*

Beverly Enterprises - MN ....D....507 334-3918 Faribault *(G-1992)*

Beverly Enterprises - MN ....E....952 881-8676 Minneapolis *(G-3896)*

Beverly Enterprises - MN ....C....651 483-5431 Saint Paul *(G-8111)*

Beverly Enterprises - MN ....D....651 439-5775 Stillwater *(G-9602)*

Beverly Enterprises - MN ....D....320 523-1652 Olivia *(G-6560)*

Beverly Enterprises - MN ....D....218 583-2965 Henning *(G-2431)*

Beverly Enterprises - MN ....B....952 935-0333 Minneapolis *(G-3894)*

Beverly Enterprises - MN ....D....612 874-1603 Minneapolis *(G-3895)*

Beverly Enterprises - MN ....D....320 843-2225 Benson *(G-438)*

Beverly Enterprises - MN ....C....952 474-5488 Excelsior *(G-1940)*

Beverly Enterprises - MN ....C....952 935-3338 Hopkins *(G-2518)*

Beverly Enterprises - MN ....D....218 233-7578 Moorhead *(G-6299)*

Beverly Enterprises - MN ....E....507 451-6800 Owatonna *(G-6695)*

Beverly Enterprises - MN ....D....507 895-4445 La Crescent *(G-2841)*

Beverly Enterprises - MN ....D....507 836-6135 Slayton *(G-9485)*

Beverly Enterprises - MN ....D....651 645-6453 Saint Paul *(G-8112)*

Beverly Enterprises - MN ....E....320 358-4765 Rush City *(G-7389)*

Beverly Enterprises - MN ....D....507 342-5166 Wabasso *(G-9776)*

Beverly Enterprises - MN ....C....612 333-0111 Minneapolis *(G-3897)*

Beverly Enterprises - MN ....B....952 473-5466 Wayzata *(G-9906)*

Birchwood Health Care Center ....C....651 464-5600 Forest Lake *(G-2158)*

Browns Valley Health Center ....D....320 695-2165 Browns Valley *(G-627)*

Cambridge Nursing Home Inc ....C....763 689-2323 Cambridge *(G-835)*

Catholic Services For The ....C....651 793-2100 Saint Paul *(G-8177)*

Central Health Care Of Le Ctr ....D....507 357-2275 Le Center *(G-2950)*

Central Todd County Care Ctr ....C....218 756-3636 Clarissa *(G-1033)*

Cerenity Sr Care Center ....C....651 232-6000 South Saint Paul *(G-9519)*

Charterhouse Inc ....C....507 266-8572 Rochester *(G-7075)*

Chisholm Health Center ....C....218 254-5765 Chisholm *(G-995)*

Chosen Valley Care Center Inc ....C....507 867-4220 Chatfield *(G-986)*

Christian Grandview Home ....C....763 689-1474 Cambridge *(G-836)*

City of Adams ....D....507 582-3263 Adams *(G-3)*

City of Clarkfield ....C....320 669-7561 Clarkfield *(G-1034)*

City of Fertile ....C....218 945-6194 Fertile *(G-2125)*

City of Heron Lake ....D....507 793-2349 Heron Lake *(G-2435)*

City of Lakefield ....D....507 662-6646 Lakefield *(G-2881)*

City of Lamberton ....E....507 752-7346 Lamberton *(G-2945)*

City of Menahga ....D....218 564-4101 Menahga *(G-3356)*

City of Ortonville ....D....320 839-6113 Ortonville *(G-6580)*

City of Renville ....D....320 329-8381 Renville *(G-7031)*

Clara City Community Nursing ....D....320 847-2221 Clara City *(G-1026)*

Clearwater County Memorial ....C....218 694-6501 Bagley *(G-300)*

Cokato Charitable Trust ....C....320 286-2158 Cokato *(G-1076)*

Colonial Acres Home Inc ....C....763 544-1555 Golden Valley *(G-2239)*

Colonial Acres Home Inc ....C....763 546-6125 Minneapolis *(G-4122)*

Colonial Manor of Balaton ....D....507 734-3511 Balaton *(G-304)*

Community Memorial Home Inc ....D....320 859-2111 Osakis *(G-6586)*

Community Memorial Hospital ....D....507 346-7381 Spring Valley *(G-9568)*

Community Services Inc ....D....651 631-6000 Saint Paul *(G-8239)*

Cook County North Shore Hosp ....C....218 387-3040 Grand Marais *(G-2257)*

County of Dodge ....D....507 374-2578 Dodge Center *(G-1225)*

County of Mahnomen ....D....218 935-2511 Mahnomen *(G-3084)*

County of Pennington ....D....218 681-1675 Thief River Falls *(G-9665)*

County of Ramsey ....C....651 777-7486 Saint Paul *(G-8258)*

Crest View Corp ....C....763 782-1611 Minneapolis *(G-3447)*

Crestview Manor Inc ....D....218 948-2219 Evansville *(G-1924)*

Cuyuna Range Hospital Inc ....B....218 546-7000 Crosby *(G-1147)*

Dawson Area Hospital District ....C....320 769-4323 Dawson *(G-1164)*

Deer River Healthcare Center ....C....218 246-2900 Deer River *(G-1168)*

Deloughery Home LP ....D....507 523-2123 Lewiston *(G-2966)*

Dignified Assisted Living Inc ....D....763 428-1981 Rogers *(G-7322)*

Divine Providence Community ....D....507 794-3011 Sleepy Eye *(G-9494)*

Divine Providence Health Ctr ....C....507 694-1414 Ivanhoe *(G-2784)*

Ebenezer Ridges Inc ....C....952 898-8400 Burnsville *(G-715)*

Ebenezer Society ....C....612 879-2262 Minneapolis *(G-4309)*

Ebenezer Society ....C....612 879-1400 Minneapolis *(G-4310)*

Ebenezer Society ....D....952 435-8116 Burnsville *(G-716)*

Ecumen ....C....507 345-4576 Mankato *(G-3124)*

Ecumen ....C....320 762-1567 Alexandria *(G-98)*

Ecumen ....D....651 766-4300 Saint Paul *(G-8322)*

Ecumen ....C....651 257-0575 Chisago City *(G-991)*

Ecumen ....D....218 834-8374 Two Harbors *(G-9706)*

Ecumen Home Care Inc ....B....952 888-7751 Bloomington *(G-496)*

Ecumen Home Care Inc ....C....218 847-4486 Detroit Lakes *(G-1193)*

Ecumen Home Care Inc ....C....218 525-1951 Duluth *(G-1309)*

Edgebrook Care Center ....D....507 442-7121 Edgerton *(G-1823)*

Elder Care of Bemidji Inc ....C....218 444-1745 Bemidji *(G-390)*

Elder Meadowland Care Homes ....E....218 586-3740 Tenstrike *(G-9662)*

Elders' Home Inc ....D....218 385-2005 New York Mills *(G-6478)*

Elim Care Inc ....E....952 259-4500 Eden Prairie *(G-1653)*

Elim Homes Inc ....D....952 955-2691 Watertown *(G-9890)*

Episcopal Church Home Of MN ....C....651 646-4061 Saint Paul *(G-8344)*

Evangelical Covenant Church ....D....612 781-2691 Minneapolis *(G-4374)*

Evangelical Free Church of ....C....763 389-1171 Princeton *(G-6906)*

Evangelical Free Church of ....C....320 983-2185 Milaca *(G-3376)*

Evangelical Lutheran Good ....C....218 587-4423 Pine River *(G-6818)*

Evangelical Lutheran Good ....D....507 437-4526 Austin *(G-270)*

Evangelical Lutheran Good ....C....952 442-5111 Waconia *(G-9785)*

Evangelical Lutheran Good ....C....507 847-3100 Jackson *(G-2792)*

Evangelical Lutheran Good ....D....320 543-3800 Howard Lake *(G-2667)*

Evangelical Lutheran Good ....D....218 863-2401 Pelican Rapids *(G-6778)*

Evangelical Lutheran Good ....D....320 764-2300 Watkins *(G-9897)*

Evangelical Lutheran Good ....D....218 864-5231 Battle Lake *(G-310)*

Evangelical Lutheran Good ....C....651 439-7180 Stillwater *(G-9615)*

Evangelical Lutheran Good ....D....507 283-2375 Luverne *(G-3059)*

Evangelical Lutheran Good ....D....507 964-2251 Arlington *(G-249)*

Evangelical Lutheran Good ....C....507 375-3286 Saint James *(G-7643)*

Evangelical Lutheran Good ....D....218 776-3157 Clearbrook *(G-1038)*

Evangelical Lutheran Good ....C....507 831-1788 Windom *(G-10067)*

Evangelical Lutheran Good ....D....218 835-4218 Blackduck *(G-474)*

Evangelical Lutheran Good ....D....507 637-5711 Redwood Falls *(G-7021)*

Evangelical Lutheran Good ....C....651 774-9765 Saint Paul *(G-8347)*

Evangelical Lutheran Good ....D....507 647-5391 Winthrop *(G-10167)*

Evangelical Lutheran Good ....D....507 362-4245 Waterville *(G-9894)*

Evangelical Lutheran Good ....D....320 986-2048 Hoffman *(G-2489)*

Evangelical Lutheran Good ....D....507 274-6155 Westbrook *(G-9966)*

Evangelical Lutheran Good ....E....218 728-6600 Duluth *(G-1315)*

Evangelical Lutheran Good ....B....218 829-1407 Brainerd *(G-565)*

Evangelical Lutheran Good ....C....218 829-1429 Brainerd *(G-566)*

Evangelical Lutheran Good ....C....507 427-2464 Mountain Lake *(G-6397)*

Evangelical Lutheran Good ....C....763 544-4171 Minneapolis *(G-4377)*

Evangelical Lutheran Good ....C....507 825-5428 Pipestone *(G-6826)*

Evangelical Lutheran Good ....D....320 634-4552 Glenwood *(G-2222)*

Evangelical Lutheran Good ....C....507 379-2707 Albert Lea *(G-49)*

Evangelical Lutheran Good ....D....218 283-4768 International Falls *(G-2720)*

Evangelical Lutheran Good ....D....507 931-9021 Saint Peter *(G-9302)*

Evangelical Lutheran Good ....B....507 373-0683 Albert Lea *(G-50)*

Evangelical Lutheran Good ....C....763 421-2311 Anoka *(G-178)*

Evansville Care Campus LLC ....E....218 948-2219 Evansville *(G-1926)*

Eveleth Hospital Corp ....E....218 744-1950 Eveleth *(G-1931)*

Eventide Senior Living ....B....218 233-7508 Moorhead *(G-6314)*

Evergreen Terrace ....C....218 326-3431 Grand Rapids *(G-2276)*

Extendicare Facilities Inc ....C....651 484-3378 Saint Paul *(G-8354)*

Extendicare Homes Inc ....C....651 224-1848 Saint Paul *(G-8356)*

Extendicare Homes Inc ....C....651 633-7875 Saint Paul *(G-8355)*

Extendicare Homes Inc ....B....763 588-0771 Minneapolis *(G-4383)*

Extendicare Homes Inc ....D....612 861-1691 Richfield *(G-7035)*

Extendicare Homes Inc ....B....763 545-0416 Minneapolis *(G-4384)*

Extendicare Homes Inc ....C....952 927-4949 Minneapolis *(G-4386)*

Extendicare Homes Inc ....C....952 920-8380 Minneapolis *(G-4387)*

Extendicare Homes Inc ....D....952 927-9717 Minneapolis *(G-4385)*

Fair Oaks Lodge Inc ....C....218 631-1391 Wadena *(G-9801)*

Fairmont Community Hospital ....A....507 238-8100 Fairmont *(G-1963)*

Fairview Health Services ....B....651 982-7000 Wyoming *(G-10202)*

Fairview Seminary Home Inc ....C....651 385-3434 Red Wing *(G-6980)*

Farmington Health Service ....E....651 463-7818 Farmington *(G-2051)*

Field Crest Care Center ....C....507 477-3266 Hayfield *(G-2427)*

First Care Medical Services ....C....218 435-1133 Fosston *(G-2176)*

First Solutions ....E....218 834-7205 Two Harbors *(G-9707)*

Foley Health Care Inc ....D....320 968-6201 Foley *(G-2137)*

Foundation For Healthcare ....B....320 253-1920 Sartell *(G-9328)*

Foundation For Rural Health ....D....218 563-2715 McIntosh *(G-3341)*

Franciscan Health Center Inc ....D....218 727-8933 Duluth *(G-1326)*

Franciscan Health Community ....C....651 696-8400 Saint Paul *(G-8393)*

Ggnsc Minneapolis Bloomington ....D....952 881-8676 Minneapolis *(G-4525)*

Ggnsc Minneapolis Chateau LLC ....D....612 874-1603 Minneapolis *(G-4526)*

Ggnsc St Paul Lake Ridge LLC ....D....651 483-5431 Saint Paul *(G-8408)*

Ggnsc Wayzata LLC ....D....952 473-5466 Wayzata *(G-9918)*

Glenwood Village Care Center	C	320 634-5131	Glenwood *(G-2225)*
Goldfinch Estates	E	507 235-9405	Fairmont *(G-1968)*
Grand Village	C	218 326-0543	Grand Rapids *(G-2282)*
Grandview Good Samaritan Ctr	D	507 931-9021	Saint Peter *(G-9305)*
Guardian Angels Health & Rehab	C	218 263-7583	Hibbing *(G-2448)*
Guardian Angels Health Svcs	C	763 441-1213	Elk River *(G-1880)*
Harmony Community Healthcare	D	507 886-6544	Harmony *(G-2371)*
Harmony Nursing Homes Inc	D	651 488-6658	Saint Paul *(G-8443)*
Haven Homes Inc	D	763 479-1993	Maple Plain *(G-3275)*
Haven Homes Of Maple Plain	D	763 479-1993	Maple Plain *(G-3276)*
Health Care Center	C	612 724-5495	Minneapolis *(G-4617)*
Health Care Services Inc	D	651 777-7435	Saint Paul *(G-8447)*
Health East Care Center White	C	651 232-1818	Saint Paul *(G-8448)*
Hendricks Community Hospital	C	507 275-3134	Hendricks *(G-2429)*
Heritage of Edina Inc	C	952 920-9145	Minneapolis *(G-4641)*
Highland Chateau Inc	C	651 698-0793	Saint Paul *(G-8480)*
Highland Manor Inc	C	507 359-2026	New Ulm *(G-6455)*
Hillcrest Nursing Home	D	218 253-2157	Red Lake Falls *(G-6971)*
Hospice of Healtheast Inc	D	651 232-3312	Saint Paul *(G-8495)*
Hubbard, County of Inc	C	218 732-3329	Park Rapids *(G-6755)*
Hutchinson Health Care	D	320 234-4906	Hutchinson *(G-2701)*
Innsbruck Healthcare Center	D	651 633-1686	New Brighton *(G-6411)*
Interfaith Care Center Inc	C	218 384-4258	Carlton *(G-869)*
J & L Nursing Care Inc	E	507 529-0018	Rochester *(G-7145)*
Jackson Cottonwood Community	E	507 847-2366	Jackson *(G-2795)*
Janesville Nursing Home Inc	D	507 231-5113	Janesville *(G-2802)*
Jones-Harrison Residence Corp	B	612 920-2030	Minneapolis *(G-4778)*
Joshco Construction Inc	D	952 361-8000	Chaska *(G-971)*
Kenyon Sunset Home	D	507 789-6134	Kenyon *(G-2828)*
Knute Nelson	B	320 763-6653	Alexandria *(G-107)*
Lake Ridge Care Center of	C	763 682-1434	Buffalo *(G-649)*
Lake Shore Inn Nursing Home	C	507 835-2800	Waseca *(G-9881)*
Lakeland Hospice & Home Care	C	218 998-1400	Fergus Falls *(G-2082)*
Lakeside Medical Center Inc	C	320 629-2542	Pine City *(G-6813)*
Lakeview Methodist Health Care	C	507 235-6606	Fairmont *(G-1976)*
Lakewood Health Center	C	218 634-2120	Baudette *(G-317)*
Lakewood Health System	B	218 894-1515	Staples *(G-9586)*
Lifecare Medical Center	D	218 782-2131	Greenbush *(G-2326)*
Lifecare Medical Center	C	218 463-4305	Roseau *(G-7355)*
Little Sisters of The Poor of	D	651 227-0336	Saint Paul *(G-8592)*
Living Services Foundation	D	320 485-2151	Winsted *(G-10162)*
Living Services Foundation	C	507 872-5300	Minneota *(G-6134)*
Long Term Care Associates Inc	D	320 679-1411	Mora *(G-6366)*
Lovingcare Nursing Services	E	651 848-0061	Saint Paul *(G-8595)*
Luther Haven	C	320 269-6517	Montevideo *(G-6249)*
Lutheran Brethren Retirement	C	218 736-5441	Fergus Falls *(G-2088)*
Lutheran Care Center Inc	D	320 632-9211	Little Falls *(G-3012)*
Lutheran Memorial Home	C	218 584-5181	Twin Valley *(G-9702)*
Lutheran Memorial Home	D	218 456-2105	Halstad *(G-2335)*
Lutheran Memorial Home	C	218 584-5181	Twin Valley *(G-9703)*
Lutheran Retirement Home of	C	507 776-2031	Truman *(G-9695)*
Lyngblomsten	B	651 646-2941	Saint Paul *(G-8599)*
Madison Lutheran Home	B	320 598-7536	Madison *(G-3076)*
Mankato Lutheran Homes Inc	C	507 345-4576	Saint Paul *(G-8610)*
Maple Lawn Nursing Home	C	507 425-2571	Fulda *(G-2195)*
Martin Luther Manor	B	952 888-7751	Minneapolis *(G-4960)*
Mercy Hospital Health Care Ctr	B	218 485-4481	Moose Lake *(G-6352)*
Midway Care Center Inc	E	218 435-1272	Fosston *(G-2177)*
Mille Lacs Health System	B	320 532-3154	Onamia *(G-6574)*
Minneota Manor Health Care Ctr	C	507 872-5300	Minneota *(G-6135)*
Minnesota Department of	C	507 283-1100	Luverne *(G-3065)*
Minnesota Department of	E	612 721-0600	Minneapolis *(G-5073)*
Minnesota Department of	E	218 736-0400	Fergus Falls *(G-2097)*
Minnesota Masonic Home	A	952 948-7000	Minneapolis *(G-5082)*
Minnesota Masonic Home North	A	763 592-3000	Minneapolis *(G-5083)*
Minnesota Odd Fellows Home	C	507 645-6611	Northfield *(G-6532)*
Minnesota Odd Fellows Home	C	507 645-6611	Northfield *(G-6533)*
Minnesota Valley Memorial Hosp	C	507 665-3375	Le Sueur *(G-2958)*
Mission Healthcare LLC	C	218 326-3431	Grand Rapids *(G-2296)*
Monticello-Big Lake Community	B	763 295-2945	Monticello *(G-6278)*
Moravian Care Ministries	C	952 448-9303	Chaska *(G-976)*
Mount Olivet Careview Home	B	612 827-5677	Minneapolis *(G-5139)*
New Richland Care Center	C	507 465-3292	New Richland *(G-6436)*
North Cities Health Care Inc	D	651 633-7200	Saint Paul *(G-8751)*
North Country Hospital	C	218 751-0220	Bemidji *(G-409)*
North Country Hospital	A	218 751-5430	Bemidji *(G-410)*
North Memorial Health Care	D	763 520-3900	Minneapolis *(G-5216)*
North Star Nursing Inc	E	218 573-2238	Osage *(G-6585)*
Northern Itasca Hospital Dist	C	218 743-3177	Bigfork *(G-461)*
Northfield Care Center Inc	C	507 645-9511	Northfield *(G-6536)*
Northome Health Care Inc	D	218 897-5235	Northome *(G-6547)*
Northwest Health Care Inc	C	320 251-9120	Saint Cloud *(G-7439)*
Northwest Investors Inc	E	952 894-7795	Burnsville *(G-768)*
Osseo Gardens Assisted Living	E	763 315-4869	Osseo *(G-6648)*
Otter Tail Nursing Home	D	218 495-2993	Battle Lake *(G-312)*
Our Lady of Good Counsel Home	E	651 646-2797	Saint Paul *(G-8794)*
Park View Care Center Inc	C	763 682-1131	Buffalo *(G-656)*
Parkview Manor Inc	D	507 967-2482	Ellsworth *(G-1908)*
Perham Hospital District	B	218 346-4500	Perham *(G-6800)*
Pine Haven Care Center Inc	D	507 356-8304	Pine Island *(G-6817)*
Pines	E	612 861-3331	Minneapolis *(G-5379)*
Pioneer Home Inc	C	218 739-7701	Fergus Falls *(G-2113)*
Pioneer Memorial Care Center	D	218 687-2365	Erskine *(G-1921)*
Pipestone County Medical Ctr	C	507 825-5811	Pipestone *(G-6834)*
Pleasant Manor Inc	D	507 334-3558	Faribault *(G-2026)*
Prairie Manor Nursing Home	C	507 583-4434	Blooming Prairie *(G-477)*
Prarie View Healthcare Center	D	507 629-3331	Tracy *(G-9690)*
Presbyterian Home Farm Stead	E	763 712-7000	Anoka *(G-215)*
Presbyterian Homes & Services	B	651 631-6200	Saint Paul *(G-8839)*
Presbyterian Homes & Services	B	952 948-3000	Minneapolis *(G-5404)*
Presbyterian Homes of Arden	A	651 631-6000	Saint Paul *(G-8843)*
Presbyterian Homes, Housing	A	651 631-6100	Saint Paul *(G-8844)*
Presbyterian Nursing Homes Inc	B	952 888-9461	Minneapolis *(G-5405)*
Quality Life Styles Inc	D	952 445-4155	Shakopee *(G-9468)*
Red Lake Band of Chippewa	D	218 679-3400	Redlake *(G-7016)*
Red Wing Healthcare LLC	C	651 388-2843	Red Wing *(G-6997)*
Redeemer Residence Inc	C	612 827-2555	Minneapolis *(G-5479)*
Regina Medical Center	A	651 480-4100	Hastings *(G-2402)*
Ridgeview Home Support Service	E	952 442-6032	Waconia *(G-9791)*
Rochester Health & Rehab West	D	507 288-1818	Rochester *(G-7233)*
Sacred Heart Care Center	C	507 433-1808	Austin *(G-286)*
Saint Anne of Winona	C	507 454-3621	Winona *(G-10123)*
▼ Saint Elizabeth's Hospital	C	651 565-4531	Wabasha *(G-9770)*
Saint Elizabeth's Hospital of	C	651 565-4581	Wabasha *(G-9771)*
Saint Olaf Retirement	C	612 522-6561	Minneapolis *(G-5592)*
Sandstone Area Nursing Home	C	320 245-2212	Sandstone *(G-9326)*
Sauer Memorial Home	C	507 454-5540	Winona *(G-10124)*
Senior Epoch Living Inc	E	952 473-3330	Hopkins *(G-2630)*
Senior Hutchinson Care Svcs	D	320 234-4751	Hutchinson *(G-2712)*
Senior McIntosh Living	D	218 563-3043	McIntosh *(G-3342)*
Shady Lane Nursing Home	C	218 631-1391	Wadena *(G-9811)*
Shepherd Good Lutheran Home	C	320 252-6525	Sauk Rapids *(G-9374)*
Shepherd Good Lutheran Home	C	507 864-7714	Rushford *(G-7393)*
Shepherd Good Lutheran Home	E	320 258-8665	Sauk Rapids *(G-9375)*
Sholom Community Alliance	B	952 935-6311	Minneapolis *(G-5656)*
Sholom Home East Inc	A	651 646-6311	Saint Paul *(G-8952)*
Sholom Home West Inc	C	952 935-6311	Minneapolis *(G-5659)*
Signature Healthcare Inc	C	507 288-6514	Rochester *(G-7254)*
Sioux Valley Canby Campus	C	507 223-7221	Canby *(G-853)*
Southview Acres Health Care	B	651 451-1821	Saint Paul *(G-7908)*
St Anthony Health Center	B	612 788-9673	Minneapolis *(G-6131)*
St Anthony Park Home Inc	D	651 646-7486	Saint Paul *(G-8981)*
St Benedict's Senior Community	A	320 252-0010	Saint Cloud *(G-7441)*
St Francis Health Services of	C	218 727-8801	Duluth *(G-1459)*
St Francis Medical Center	B	218 643-3000	Breckenridge *(G-601)*
St Gertrude's Health Center	D	952 233-4400	Shakopee *(G-9477)*
St John Lutheran Home Inc	B	507 723-3200	Springfield *(G-9576)*
St Johns Lutheran Home	B	507 373-8226	Albert Lea *(G-67)*
St Louis, County of Inc	B	218 720-1500	Duluth *(G-1463)*
St Lucas Care Center	C	507 332-5100	Faribault *(G-2032)*
St Luke's Lutheran Care Center	C	507 526-2184	Blue Earth *(G-537)*
St Mark's Lutheran Home Inc	C	507 437-4594	Austin *(G-288)*
St Mary's Regional Health Ctr	C	218 847-5611	Detroit Lakes *(G-1217)*
St Mary's Regional Health Ctr	C	218 847-5611	Detroit Lakes *(G-1218)*
St Michael's Health & Rehab	C	218 748-7800	Virginia *(G-9757)*
St Olaf Retirement Center Inc	C	612 522-6561	Minneapolis *(G-5729)*
St Peter, City of Inc	C	507 931-7354	Saint Peter *(G-9314)*
St Therese Home Inc	A	763 537-4503	Minneapolis *(G-5733)*
St Williams Nursing Home Inc	C	218 338-4671	Parkers Prairie *(G-6767)*
Sterling Park Health Care Ctr	A	320 252-9595	Waite Park *(G-9841)*
Stewartville Nursing Home Inc	C	507 533-4288	Stewartville *(G-9594)*
Sunnyside Care Center	D	218 238-5944	Lake Park *(G-2880)*
Sunrise Cottage of Mankato	E	507 345-8787	Mankato *(G-3202)*
Sunrise Senior Living Inc	E	763 682-5489	Buffalo *(G-657)*
Tealwood Care Centers Inc	D	218 436-2161	Karlstad *(G-2815)*
Tealwood Care Centers Inc	D	320 252-9595	Waite Park *(G-9842)*
Thro Co	C	507 387-3491	Mankato *(G-3203)*
Thro Co	C	507 345-4631	Mankato *(G-3204)*
Thro Co	C	952 758-2511	New Prague *(G-6435)*
Thro Co	D	507 388-2913	Mankato *(G-3205)*
Tracy Healthcare Center Inc	D	507 629-3331	Tracy *(G-9692)*
Traverse Care Center	D	320 563-8124	Wheaton *(G-9969)*

SIC

Employment codes: A=Over 500 employees, B=251-500
C=101-250, D=51-100, E=25-50
2011 Harris Minnesota
Services Directory
© Harris InfoSource 1-866-281-6415
511

Tuff Memorial Homes Inc....D....507 962-3275
Hills (G-2482)
Tweeten-Lutheran Health Care....C....507 498-3211
Spring Grove (G-9562)
Twin City Christian Homes Inc....D....952 944-8982
Eden Prairie (G-1799)
Tyler Healthcare Center Inc....C....507 247-5521
Tyler (G-9716)
Valley View Nursing Home of....D....507 896-3125
Houston (G-2664)
Villa St Vincent Inc....C....218 281-3424
Crookston (G-1143)
Voa Anoka Care Center Inc....D....952 941-0305
Eden Prairie (G-1808)
Voa Care Centers MN....D....763 535-6260
Minneapolis (G-5981)
Voans Health Services Corp....D....507 263-4658
Cannon Falls (G-863)
Volunteers of America Care....C....507 794-7995
Sleepy Eye (G-9503)
Volunteers of America Care....C....952 925-8500
Minneapolis (G-5983)
Volunteers of America National....E....952 941-0305
Eden Prairie (G-1810)
Walker Care Corp I....C....612 827-8390
Minneapolis (G-6009)
Walker Methodist Health Center....C....612 827-8517
Minneapolis (G-6010)
Warroad Care Center Inc....D....218 386-1235
Warroad (G-9872)
Weiner Memorial Foundation....B....507 532-9661
Marshall (G-3332)
West Wind Village....C....320 589-1133
Morris (G-6380)
White Community Hospital Corp....C....218 229-2211
Aurora (G-257)
Winona Community Memorial Hosp....A....507 454-3650
Winona (G-10145)
Winona Health....E....507 457-4468
Winona (G-10148)
Wood-Dale Home Inc....D....507 637-3587
Redwood Falls (G-7029)
Woodland Heights Health Care....C....651 451-1881
Inver Grove Heights (G-2775)
Woodrest Health Care Center....D....218 547-1855
Walker (G-9861)
Zumbrota Nursing Home....D....507 732-8400
Zumbrota (G-10223)

8052 Intermediate Care Facilities

Adonai Care Homes Corp....E....651 227-0574
Saint Paul (G-7983)
Almond House....E....218 825-9255
Brainerd (G-547)
AME Community Service Inc....320 286-6421
Cokato (G-1075)
American Baptist Homes of The....D....507 893-3171
Winnebago (G-10075)
American Baptist Homes of The....E....952 941-3175
Eden Prairie (G-1590)
Amherst H Wilder Foundation....C....651 220-1700
Saint Paul (G-8041)
Arbors At Ridges....E....952 898-4005
Burnsville (G-680)
Augustana Chapel View Homes....B....612 333-1551
Minneapolis (G-3835)
Aviv Health Care Inc....C....763 425-3939
Osseo (G-6597)
Barrett Care Center Inc....D....320 528-2527
Barrett (G-308)
Belgrade Nursing Home Inc....D....320 254-8215
Belgrade (G-364)
Benedictine Health System....D....651 388-1234
Red Wing (G-6975)
Bethany Covenant Village....D....612 781-2691
Minneapolis (G-3893)
Big Stone Community Homes Inc....E....320 839-6139
Ortonville (G-6578)
Cardinal of Minnesota Ltd....C....507 281-1077
Rochester (G-7070)
Care Planners Inc....D....651 645-9887
Saint Paul (G-8162)
Catholic Services For The....C....651 793-2100
Saint Paul (G-8177)
Cedar Crest Estate....E....320 587-7077
Hutchinson (G-2691)
Cenneidigh Inc....C....507 334-4347
Faribault (G-1999)
Chandler Place....E....612 788-7321
Minneapolis (G-6124)
Charterhouse Inc....C....507 266-8572
Rochester (G-7075)
Christian Grandview Home....C....763 689-1474
Cambridge (G-836)
City of Lakefield....D....507 662-6646
Lakefield (G-2881)
City of Renville....D....320 329-8381
Renville (G-7031)
Community Involvement Programs....E....320 245-5362
Sandstone (G-9320)
Community Memorial Home Inc....D....320 859-2111
Osakis (G-6586)
County of Pennington....D....218 681-1675
Thief River Falls (G-9665)
Crest View Corp....C....763 782-1611
Minneapolis (G-3447)
Dakota's Adults Inc....E....651 688-8808
Mendota Heights (G-3362)
Ecumen....C....507 345-4576
Mankato (G-3124)
Edgewood Management Inc....E....651 714-1000
Saint Paul (G-9208)
Elders' Home Inc....D....218 385-2005
New York Mills (G-6478)
Elm North Inc....E....507 835-1146
Waseca (G-9876)
Elm Residence Inc....B....507 835-1146
Waseca (G-9877)
Emerald Crest of Burnsville....E....952 736-0766
Burnsville (G-718)
Emerald Crest of Minnetonka....C....952 933-9903
Hopkins (G-2538)
Epiphany Assisted Living....E....763 755-0320
Minneapolis (G-3465)
Episcopal Church Home Of MN....C....651 646-4061
Saint Paul (G-8344)
Evangelical Lutheran Good....C....651 439-7180
Stillwater (G-9615)
Eventide Senior Living....B....218 233-7508
Moorhead (G-6314)
Franciscan Health Center Inc....D....218 727-8933
Duluth (G-1326)
Goldfinch Estates....E....507 235-9405
Fairmont (G-1968)
Graceville Health Center Inc....C....320 748-7223
Graceville (G-2254)
Guardian Angels By The Lake....E....763 241-7682
Elk River (G-1878)
Hallett Cottages....E....218 546-6265
Crosby (G-1149)
Harry Meyering Center Inc....B....507 388-3551
Mankato (G-3135)
Hawley Retirement Inc....E....218 483-3337
Hawley (G-2420)
Hayes Residence Inc....E....651 690-1032
Saint Paul (G-8445)
Hillcrest Nursing Home....D....218 253-2157
Red Lake Falls (G-6971)
Home For Creative Living Inc....D....507 831-5033
Windom (G-10068)
Homefront....E....320 269-2930
Montevideo (G-6246)
Innovative Living Inc....E....218 624-7005
Proctor (G-6964)
Innsbruck Healthcare Center....D....651 633-1686
New Brighton (G-6411)
Johnson's Riverside Boarding....218 681-1278
Thief River Falls (G-9671)
Kenyon Sunset Home....D....507 789-6134
Kenyon (G-2828)
Lifecare Medical Center....D....218 782-2131
Greenbush (G-2326)
Lifecare Medical Center....C....218 463-4305
Roseau (G-7355)
Linnea Residential Home Inc....E....651 257-2211
Chisago City (G-992)
Little Sisters of The Poor of....D....651 227-0336
Saint Paul (G-8592)
Lutheran Memorial Home....D....218 456-2105
Halstad (G-2335)
Luverne Residential Advantage....D....507 283-4088
Luverne (G-3062)
Madonna Meadows of Rochester....507 252-5400
Rochester (G-7166)
Marshall County Group Homes....D....218 437-6695
Argyle (G-247)
Martin Luther Manor....B....952 888-7751
Minneapolis (G-4960)
Minnesota Department of....C....507 283-1100
Luverne (G-3065)
Minnesota Masonic Charities....952 948-6004
Minneapolis (G-5081)
Minnesota Masonic Home....A....952 948-7000
Minneapolis (G-5082)
Minnetonka Health Care Center....E....952 474-4474
Excelsior (G-1950)
North Cities Health Care Inc....D....651 633-7200
Saint Paul (G-8751)
Northfield Care Center Inc....C....507 645-9511
Northfield (G-6536)
Now Care Medical Centers Inc....E....651 635-0054
Saint Paul (G-8773)
Phoenix Residence Inc....C....651 227-7655
Saint Paul (G-7876)
Pine Ridge Homes Inc....D....218 879-1257
Cloquet (G-1059)
Pines....E....612 861-3331
Minneapolis (G-5379)
Prairie Community Services....E....320 589-2057
Morris (G-6374)
Prairie Community Services....E....320 796-6999
Spicer (G-9558)
Presbyterian Homes & Services....B....952 948-3000
Minneapolis (G-5404)
Presbyterian Homes of Inver....E....651 451-5959
Inver Grove Heights (G-2765)
Presbyterian Homes, Housing....A....651 631-6100
Saint Paul (G-8844)
Presbyterian Nursing Homes Inc....B....952 888-9461
Minneapolis (G-5405)
Providence Place....C....612 724-5495
Minneapolis (G-5433)
Rainbow Residence Inc....E....507 451-5327
Owatonna (G-6733)
REM Canby Inc....E....952 925-5067
Minneapolis (G-5508)
REM Central Lakes Inc....D....320 253-8134
Saint Cloud (G-7585)
REM Central Lakes Inc....E....507 238-4751
Fairmont (G-1979)
REM Hennepin Inc....D....952 925-5067
Minneapolis (G-5510)
REM Inc....E....651 647-9243
Saint Paul (G-8888)
REM Inc....D....507 387-3181
Mankato (G-3185)
REM Woodvale Inc....E....507 451-1296
Owatonna (G-6734)
Residential Advantages Inc....D....507 831-3804
Lakefield (G-2883)
Reverence For Life & Concern....D....320 564-4911
Granite Falls (G-2319)
Rison Homes Administrative....E....507 332-0547
Faribault (G-2029)
Riverview Manor Inc....E....507 824-2091
Wanamingo (G-9866)
Rose Camilia Co Inc....C....763 755-8400
Minneapolis (G-3592)
Saint Benedict's Senior Com....763 295-4051
Monticello (G-6286)
Shady Lane Nursing Home....C....218 631-1391
Wadena (G-9811)
Signature Healthcare Inc....C....507 288-6514
Rochester (G-7254)
St Benedict's Senior Community....A....320 252-0010
Saint Cloud (G-7441)
St Williams Nursing Home Inc....C....218 338-4671
Parkers Prairie (G-6767)
Sunrise Senior Living Inc....D....952 927-8000
Minneapolis (G-5769)
Swift County Homes Inc....E....320 843-3509
Benson (G-442)
Traverse Care Center....D....320 563-8124
Wheaton (G-9969)
Twin City Christian Homes Inc....D....952 944-8982
Eden Prairie (G-1799)
Villa St Vincent Inc....C....218 281-3424
Crookston (G-1143)
Vista Villa Inc....E....218 644-3331
Cromwell (G-1117)
Volunteers of America National....E....952 941-0305
Eden Prairie (G-1810)
Warroad Care Center Inc....D....218 386-1235
Warroad (G-9872)
Washington County Association....D....651 439-4946
Bayport (G-351)

8059 Nursing & Personal Care Facilities, NEC

Aitkin Health Services....D....218 927-5545
Aitkin (G-15)
Albert Lee Medical Center Inc....D....507 553-3115
Wells (G-9960)
Alterra Healthcare Corp....E....763 755-2800
Minneapolis (G-3397)
American Baptist Homes of The....D....612 529-7747
Minneapolis (G-3745)
Atchison Enterprises Inc....D....507 376-5312
Worthington (G-10179)
Augustana Health Care Center....C....651 437-6176
Hastings (G-2376)
Aviv Health Care Inc....C....763 425-3939
Osseo (G-6597)
B L E A Inc....E....507 896-3040
Houston (G-2662)
Bear Creek Care & Rehab....C....507 288-6514
Rochester (G-7062)
Becklund Personal Care Org....E....763 546-2030
Minneapolis (G-3878)
Benedictine Health System....D....218 786-2370
Duluth (G-1250)
Benedictine Health System....A....952 403-3000
Shakopee (G-9420)
Brooks....E....507 446-5855
Owatonna (G-6697)
Cardenas & Reynolds Entrprs....D....651 222-7200
Saint Paul (G-8156)
Care Institute Inc....E....651 482-1611
Saint Paul (G-8160)
Catholic Charities of The....C....612 827-6241
Minneapolis (G-4030)
Cherished Wings Transportation....E....763 221-8788
Minneapolis (G-4059)
City of Adams....D....507 582-3263
Adams (G-3)
City of Clarkfield....C....320 669-7561
Clarkfield (G-1034)
City of Fertile....C....218 945-6194
Fertile (G-2125)
City of Ortonville....D....320 839-6113
Ortonville (G-6580)
City of Ulen....D....218 596-8847
Ulen (G-9717)
Class Act Estates Senior....D....612 229-3881
Buffalo (G-642)
Community Living Inc....D....952 443-2048
Victoria (G-9726)
Companion Housing Program Inc....C....952 285-5950
Saint Paul (G-8241)

(G-00000) Company's Geographic Section entry number
512
2011 Harris Minnesota Services Directory
▲=Import ▼=Export
◆=Import/Export

Connections Inc ....D....952 888-5792
Minneapolis *(G-4153)*
Cuyuna Range Hospital Inc....C....218 546-7000
Crosby *(G-1148)*
Disable Home Heaklth Care Inc ....C....651 292-8705
Saint Paul *(G-8298)*
Elder Care of Bemidji Inc....C....218 444-1745
Bemidji *(G-390)*
Elders' Home Inc....D....218 385-2005
New York Mills *(G-6478)*
Elim Homes Inc ....D....952 955-2691
Watertown *(G-9890)*
Emerald Crest of Shakopee ....E....952 233-8811
Shakopee *(G-9438)*
Evangelical Free Church of....C....763 389-1171
Princeton *(G-6906)*
Evangelical Free Church of....C....320 983-2185
Milaca *(G-3376)*
Evangelical Lutheran Good....C....507 847-3100
Jackson *(G-2792)*
Evangelical Lutheran Good....D....320 543-3800
Howard Lake *(G-2667)*
Evangelical Lutheran Good....B....612 332-4262
Minneapolis *(G-4378)*
Evangelical Lutheran Good....D....507 964-2251
Arlington *(G-249)*
Evangelical Lutheran Good....C....507 375-3286
Saint James *(G-7643)*
Evangelical Lutheran Good....D....218 354-2254
Barnesville *(G-305)*
Evangelical Lutheran Good....D....507 274-6155
Westbrook *(G-9966)*
Evangelical Lutheran Good....E....507 427-3221
Mountain Lake *(G-6396)*
Evangelical Lutheran Good....B....218 829-1407
Brainerd *(G-565)*
Evangelical Lutheran Good....C....507 427-2464
Mountain Lake *(G-6397)*
Evangelical Lutheran Good....C....507 825-5428
Pipestone *(G-6826)*
Eventide Home Association Inc....E....507 427-3221
Mountain Lake *(G-6398)*
Eventide Senior Living ....B....218 233-7508
Moorhead *(G-6314)*
Extendicare Homes Inc....C....952 927-4949
Minneapolis *(G-4386)*
Family Home Health Care Inc....C....612 340-0733
Minneapolis *(G-4409)*
Glenwood Village Care Center....C....320 634-5131
Glenwood *(G-2225)*
Grand Village....C....218 326-0543
Grand Rapids *(G-2282)*
Griffin Housing Services Inc....E....507 388-6434
Mankato *(G-3131)*
Haven Homes Inc....D....763 479-1993
Maple Plain *(G-3275)*
Haven Homes Of Maple Plain....D....763 479-1993
Maple Plain *(G-3276)*
Healtheast Care System....C....651 776-4107
Saint Paul *(G-8457)*
Heritage of Edina Inc....C....952 920-9145
Minneapolis *(G-4641)*
Hiawatha Manor Inc....E....507 825-5697
Pipestone *(G-6829)*
Highland Chateau Suites LLC....D....651 698-0793
Saint Paul *(G-8481)*
Home Care & PCA Services LLC....D....763 566-5063
Minneapolis *(G-4665)*
Home Free Inc....C....952 814-7400
Minneapolis *(G-4668)*
Horizon Health Inc....E....320 468-2811
Pierz *(G-6804)*
Janesville Nursing Home Inc....D....507 231-5113
Janesville *(G-2802)*
Juhl Enterprises Inc....C....320 354-2231
New London *(G-6416)*
Kaska Inc....D....320 632-9281
Little Falls *(G-3009)*
Kittson Memorial Hospital Assn....C....218 843-3612
Hallock *(G-2333)*
Lake Ridge Care Center of....C....763 682-1434
Buffalo *(G-649)*
Lake Shore Inn Nursing Home....C....507 835-2800
Waseca *(G-9881)*
Lakeview Ranch Inc....E....320 275-4027
Darwin *(G-1157)*
Lutheran Brethren Retirement....C....218 736-5441
Fergus Falls *(G-2088)*
Lutheran Memorial Home....C....218 584-5181
Twin Valley *(G-9702)*
Lutheran Memorial Home....D....218 456-2105
Halstad *(G-2335)*
Luverne Residential Advantage....D....507 283-4088
Luverne *(G-3062)*
Lyngblomsten....B....651 646-2941
Saint Paul *(G-8599)*
Madonna Towers of Rochester....C....507 288-3911
Rochester *(G-7167)*
Mala Strana Health Care Center....C....952 758-2511
New Prague *(G-6431)*
Martin Luther Manor....B....952 888-7751
Minneapolis *(G-4960)*
Mission Health Care LLC....C....651 224-2368
Saint Paul *(G-8716)*
Mission Healthcare LLC....C....218 326-3431
Grand Rapids *(G-2296)*
Morning Star Healthcare Svcs....E....651 209-2950
Saint Paul *(G-8722)*

North Country Hospital....C....218 751-0220
Bemidji *(G-409)*
Northern Itasca Hospital Dist....D....218 743-3177
Bigfork *(G-462)*
Pelican Rapids Good Samaritan....D....218 863-2401
Pelican Rapids *(G-6783)*
Pierz Villa Inc....E....320 468-6405
Pierz *(G-6806)*
Pioneer Senior Cottages....E....218 998-9678
Fergus Falls *(G-2114)*
Plymouth Senior Housing....D....651 631-6300
Plymouth *(G-6879)*
R E M North Star Inc....E....218 435-6088
Fosston *(G-2179)*
Rainbow Residence Inc....E....507 451-5327
Owatonna *(G-6733)*
Rakhma Inc....D....612 824-2345
Minneapolis *(G-5464)*
Regina Medical Center....A....651 480-4100
Hastings *(G-2402)*
REM & Tyler Inc....E....507 247-5568
Tyler *(G-9712)*
REM Riverbluff Inc....E....507 281-1105
Rochester *(G-7222)*
REM Williams....E....952 925-3292
Minneapolis *(G-5513)*
REM Woodvale Inc....E....507 451-1296
Owatonna *(G-6734)*
Ridgeview Place LP....E....320 251-5228
Sauk Rapids *(G-9371)*
Riverview Manor Inc....E....507 824-2091
Wanamingo *(G-9866)*
Rochester Health & Rehab West....D....507 288-1818
Rochester *(G-7233)*
Rose Camilia Co Inc....C....763 755-8400
Minneapolis *(G-3592)*
Saint William's Living Center....D....218 338-4671
Parkers Prairie *(G-6766)*
Semcil Living Inc....E....507 285-1815
Rochester *(G-7250)*
Senior Epoch Living Inc....E....952 473-3330
Hopkins *(G-2630)*
Senior Management Inc....D....507 725-3351
Caledonia *(G-828)*
Seniors Caring Companions Inc....E....651 770-2288
Maplewood *(G-3288)*
Sholom Community Alliance....E....952 908-1776
Minneapolis *(G-5658)*
St Ann's Home....D....218 727-8831
Duluth *(G-1458)*
Sunrise Manor Nursing Home....D....507 247-5839
Tyler *(G-9714)*
Thro Co....C....507 345-4631
Mankato *(G-3204)*
Thro Co....C....952 758-2511
New Prague *(G-6435)*
Thro Co....D....507 388-2913
Mankato *(G-3205)*
Traditions of Minnesota LLC....E....507 455-0700
Owatonna *(G-6740)*
V Care Home Health Inc....D....651 793-7635
Saint Paul *(G-9122)*
Valley Home Society....D....218 681-3286
Thief River Falls *(G-9681)*
Washington County Association....D....651 439-4946
Bayport *(G-351)*
Wilds of San Prairie....E....507 931-4375
Saint Peter *(G-9316)*

8062 General Medical & Surgical Hospitals

Abbott Northwestern Hospital....612 863-4000
Minneapolis *(G-3660)*
Aitkin Community Hospital Inc....B....218 927-2121
Aitkin *(G-23)*
Albert Lea Medical Center-Mayo....A....507 373-2384
Albert Lea *(G-32)*
Allina Health System....A....612 775-5000
Minneapolis *(G-3721)*
Allina Health System....A....763 236-6000
Minneapolis *(G-3393)*
Allina Health System....A....612 863-4000
Minneapolis *(G-3718)*
Allina Health System....E....952 992-2500
Minnetonka *(G-6138)*
Allina Health System....A....763 236-5000
Fridley *(G-2189)*
Allina Health System....B....763 682-1212
Buffalo *(G-633)*
Allina Health System....B....507 233-1000
New Ulm *(G-6439)*
Appleton Area Health Services....C....320 289-2422
Appleton *(G-244)*
Bethesda Healthy Rehab....A....651 232-2000
Saint Paul *(G-8109)*
Canby Community Hospital Dist....C....507 223-7277
Canby *(G-848)*
Cannon Falls Medical Center....C....507 263-4221
Cannon Falls *(G-855)*
Catholic Health Initiatives....B....952 324-9010
Minneapolis *(G-4031)*
Centracare Health Services of....320 732-2131
Long Prairie *(G-3038)*
Centracare Health System....C....320 256-4231
Melrose *(G-3346)*
Centracare Health System....D....320 251-2700
Saint Cloud *(G-7481)*

Central Minnesota Group Health....C....320 253-5220
Saint Cloud *(G-7484)*
Chippewa County-Montevideo....C....320 269-8877
Montevideo *(G-6244)*
City of Ada....C....218 784-5000
Ada *(G-1)*
City of Jackson....D....507 847-2420
Jackson *(G-2787)*
City of Ortonville....C....320 839-2502
Ortonville *(G-6579)*
City of Redwood Falls....C....507 637-4500
Redwood Falls *(G-7020)*
City of Worthington....C....507 372-2941
Worthington *(G-10180)*
Clearwater County Memorial....C....218 694-6501
Bagley *(G-300)*
Community Health Network....C....320 845-2121
Albany *(G-26)*
Community Memorial Hospital....B....218 879-4641
Cloquet *(G-1050)*
Cook County North Shore Hosp....C....218 387-3040
Grand Marais *(G-2257)*
County of Douglas....A....320 762-1511
Alexandria *(G-91)*
County of Mahnomen....D....218 935-2511
Mahnomen *(G-3084)*
County of Meeker....C....320 693-3242
Litchfield *(G-2982)*
County of Murray....C....507 836-6111
Slayton *(G-9486)*
Cuyuna Range Hospital Inc....B....218 546-7000
Crosby *(G-1147)*
Dawson Area Hospital District....C....320 769-4323
Dawson *(G-1164)*
Deer River Healthcare Center....C....218 246-2900
Deer River *(G-1168)*
Divine Providence Health Ctr....C....507 694-1414
Ivanhoe *(G-2784)*
Essentia Health....218 786-8376
Duluth *(G-1314)*
Fairmont Community Hospital....A....507 238-8100
Fairmont *(G-1963)*
Fairview Health Services....A....612 672-6300
Minneapolis *(G-4396)*
Fairview Health Services....C....612 672-6800
Minneapolis *(G-4393)*
Fairview Health Services....B....651 982-7000
Wyoming *(G-10202)*
Fairview Health Services....E....952 848-5600
Minneapolis *(G-4397)*
Fairview Health Services....B....952 892-2910
Burnsville *(G-720)*
Fairview Health Services....C....218 262-4881
Hibbing *(G-2444)*
Fairview Health Services....E....651 632-7300
Saint Paul *(G-8362)*
Fairview Redwing Health Svcs....A....651 267-5000
Red Wing *(G-6979)*
First Care Medical Services....C....218 435-1133
Fosston *(G-2176)*
Glacial Ridge Hospital Fndtn....C....320 634-4521
Glenwood *(G-2223)*
Graceville Health Center Inc....C....320 748-7223
Graceville *(G-2254)*
Graceville Missionary....D....320 748-7223
Graceville *(G-2255)*
Grand Itasca Clinic & Hospital....B....218 326-7024
Grand Rapids *(G-2280)*
Harmony Community Healthcare....D....507 886-6544
Harmony *(G-2371)*
Healthcare & Wellness Fndtn....D....218 643-0410
Breckenridge *(G-594)*
Healtheast Care System....A....651 232-1000
Saint Paul *(G-8454)*
Healtheast Co's Inc....B....651 232-4000
Saint Paul *(G-9225)*
Healtheast Diversified Svcs....651 232-2300
Saint Paul *(G-8461)*
Healtheast Maplewood Out....E....651 232-7780
Saint Paul *(G-8463)*
Healtheast St John's Hospital....A....651 232-7000
Saint Paul *(G-8465)*
HealthSouth Corp....E....952 921-0100
Minneapolis *(G-4624)*
HealthSouth Corp....C....320 251-8385
Saint Cloud *(G-7524)*
Hendricks Community Hospital....C....507 275-3134
Hendricks *(G-2429)*
Hennepin Healthcare System Inc....A....612 873-3000
Minneapolis *(G-4638)*
Hospice Of The Lakes....D....952 883-6877
Minneapolis *(G-4678)*
Hutchinson Area Health Care....A....320 234-5000
Hutchinson *(G-2698)*
Immanuel-St Joseph's Hospital....A....507 625-4031
Mankato *(G-3148)*
Indian Health Service....C....218 679-3316
Redlake *(G-7015)*
Kanabec County Hospital....B....320 679-1212
Mora *(G-6362)*
Kittson Memorial Hospital Assn....C....218 843-3612
Hallock *(G-2333)*
Kittson Memorial Hospital Assn....C....218 843-3612
Hallock *(G-2334)*
Lake Rainy Medical Center....C....218 283-4481
International Falls *(G-2726)*
Lake Region Healthcare Corp....A....218 736-8000
Fergus Falls *(G-2081)*

S I C

Employment codes: A=Over 500 employees, B=251-500
C=101-250, D=51-100, E=25-50

2011 Harris Minnesota
Services Directory

© Harris InfoSource 1-866-281-6415
513

Lakeside Medical Center Inc ......C....320 629-2542
Pine City (G-6813)
Lakeview Memorial Hospital ......B....651 439-5330
Stillwater (G-9625)
Lakewood Health Center ......C....218 634-2120
Baudette (G-317)
Lakewood Health System ......B....218 894-1515
Staples (G-9586)
Lifecare Medical Center ......C....218 463-4305
Roseau (G-7355)
Lincoln Lyon Murry & Pipestone ......E....507 537-6709
Marshall (G-3305)
Madelia Community Hospital Inc ......D....507 642-3255
Madelia (G-3073)
Mankato Surgical Center LLC ......E....507 388-6000
Mankato (G-3166)
Maple Grove Ambulatory Surgery ......E....763 981-3234
Maple Grove (G-3248)
Mayo Midair ......E....507 255-2808
Rochester (G-7176)
Memorial Hospital Association ......A....763 689-7700
Cambridge (G-842)
Mercy Hospital Health Care Ctr ......B....218 485-4481
Moose Lake (G-6352)
Meridian Behavioral Health LLC 612 326-7600
New Brighton (G-6412)
Methodist Hospital ......A....952 993-5000
Saint Louis Park (G-7666)
Mille Lacs Health System ......B....320 532-3154
Onamia (G-6574)
Minnesota Department of ......D....612 713-2196
Saint Paul (G-7961)
Minnesota Department of Human ......B....218 739-7200
Fergus Falls (G-2099)
Minnesota Valley Memorial Hosp ......C....507 665-3375
Le Sueur (G-2958)
Monticello-Big Lake Community ......B....763 295-2945
Monticello (G-6278)
North Country Hospital ......A....218 751-5430
Bemidji (G-410)
North Country Regional Hosp ......B....218 751-5430
Bemidji (G-412)
North Memorial Health Care ......A....763 520-5200
Minneapolis (G-5217)
Northern Itasca Hospital Dist ......C....218 743-3177
Bigfork (G-461)
Northfield Hospital & Skilled ......B....507 646-1000
Northfield (G-6517)
Northwest Medical Center ......B....218 681-4240
Thief River Falls (G-9676)
Olmsted Medical Center ......B....507 288-3443
Rochester (G-7195)
Olmsted Medical Center ......A....507 529-6600
Rochester (G-7194)
Park Nicollet Health Services ......C....952 993-5353
Minneapolis (G-5333)
Perham Hospital District ......B....218 346-4500
Perham (G-6800)
Pipestone County Medical Ctr ......C....507 825-5811
Pipestone (G-6834)
Queen of Peace Hospital ......B....952 758-4431
New Prague (G-6434)
Range Regional Health Services ......A....218 262-4881
Hibbing (G-2473)
Regents of The University of ......D....612 625-2874
Minneapolis (G-5494)
Regina Medical Center ......A....651 480-4100
Hastings (G-2402)
Regions Hospital Foundation ......A....651 254-3456
Saint Paul (G-8884)
Renville County Hospice Inc ......D....320 523-1261
Olivia (G-6564)
Rice County District One Hosp ......B....507 334-6451
Faribault (G-2027)
Rice Memorial Hospital ......C....320 235-4543
Willmar (G-10041)
Ridgeview Medical Center ......A....952 442-2191
Waconia (G-9792)
Robert B Diasio ......D....507 284-3977
Rochester (G-7226)
Rochester Methodist Hospital ......A....507 255-5123
Rochester (G-7236)
Rochester Methodist Hospital 507 266-7890
Rochester (G-7237)
S M D C St Mary's Duluth Clin ......A....218 786-4020
Duluth (G-1441)
▼ Saint Elizabeth's Hospital ......C....651 565-4531
Wabasha (G-9770)
Saint Marys Hospital of ......A....507 255-5123
Rochester (G-7246)
Sanford Health ......C....507 283-2321
Luverne (G-3067)
Sanford Health ......E....507 847-2420
Jackson (G-2798)
Sanford Health Network ......C....507 283-2321
Luverne (G-3068)
Sibley Medical Center ......C....507 964-2271
Arlington (G-250)
Sioux Valley Canby Campus ......C....507 223-7221
Canby (G-853)
Smdc Medical Center ......A....218 727-8762
Duluth (G-1455)
Springfield Medical Center ......D....507 723-6201
Springfield (G-9575)
St Cloud Hospital ......B....320 251-2700
Saint Cloud (G-7602)
St Francis Medical Center ......B....218 643-3000
Breckenridge (G-601)
◆ St Francis Regional Medical ......A....952 403-3000
Shakopee (G-9476)
St Joseph's Area Health Svcs ......B....218 732-3311
Park Rapids (G-6762)
St Joseph's Medical Center ......A....218 829-2861
Brainerd (G-587)
St Luke's Hospital of Duluth ......A....218 726-5555
Duluth (G-1469)
St Mary's Duluth Clinic Health ......A....218 786-4000
Duluth (G-1473)
St Mary's Medical Center ......A....218 786-4000
Duluth (G-1474)
St Mary's Regional Health Ctr ......C....218 847-5611
Detroit Lakes (G-1217)
St Peter, City of Inc ......C....507 931-7354
Saint Peter (G-9314)
Stevens Community Medical Ctr ......C....320 589-1313
Morris (G-6379)
Swift County-Benson Hospital ......D....320 843-4232
Benson (G-443)
Tri-County Hospital Inc ......B....218 631-3510
Wadena (G-9813)
Tweeten-Lutheran Health Care ......C....507 498-3211
Spring Grove (G-9562)
Tyler Healthcare Center Inc ......C....507 247-5521
Tyler (G-9716)
United Hospital District ......C....507 526-3273
Blue Earth (G-539)
United Hospital District ......D....218 894-8610
Staples (G-9587)
Unity Family Health Care ......A....320 632-5441
Little Falls (G-3021)
Virginia, City of Inc ......A....218 741-3340
Virginia (G-9760)
Warren Community Hospital Inc ......D....218 745-4211
Warren (G-9869)
Waseca Medical Center — Mayo ......C....507 835-1210
Waseca (G-9889)
Weiner Memorial Foundation ......B....507 532-9661
Marshall (G-3332)
Westbrook Health Center ......E....507 274-6121
Westbrook (G-9968)
Western Pope County Hospital ......D....320 239-2201
Starbuck (G-9589)
Wheaton Community Hospital ......D....320 563-8226
Wheaton (G-9970)
White Community Hospital Corp ......C....218 229-2211
Aurora (G-257)
Windom, City of Inc ......D....507 831-2400
Windom (G-10072)
Winona Community Memorial Hosp ......A....507 454-3650
Winona (G-10145)

8063 Psychiatric Hospitals

Albert Lea Medical Center-Mayo ......A....507 373-2384
Albert Lea (G-32)
Cedar Ridge Inc ......D....651 426-8983
Minneapolis (G-4036)
County of Douglas ......E....320 762-2400
Alexandria (G-90)
Minnesota Department of Human ......B....507 931-7137
Saint Peter (G-9299)
Northwestern Mental Health Ctr ......D....218 281-3940
Crookston (G-1131)
Range Mental Health Center Inc ......E....218 749-2881
Virginia (G-9754)
Relate Counseling Center Inc ......E....952 932-7277
Minnetonka (G-6219)
REM Inc ......C....507 287-6824
Rochester (G-7221)
Southwestern Mental Health Ctr 507 283-9511
Luverne (G-3070)

8069 Specialty Hospitals, Except Psychiatric

AA Monticello ......E....763 295-5066
Monticello (G-6265)
Albert Lea Medical Center-Mayo ......A....507 373-2384
Albert Lea (G-32)
Bell Hill Recovery Center Inc ......E....218 631-3610
Wadena (G-9798)
Bethesda Healthy Rehab ......A....651 232-2000
Saint Paul (G-8109)
Beverly Enterprises - MN ......D....507 932-3283
Saint Charles (G-7402)
Beverly Enterprises - MN ......C....651 483-5431
Saint Paul (G-8111)
Brown County Evaluation Center ......E....507 359-9111
New Ulm (G-6443)
Cedar Ridge Inc ......D....651 426-8983
Minneapolis (G-4036)
Children's Health Care Inc ......A....651 220-6000
Saint Paul (G-8193)
▲ Children's Health Care Inc ......A....612 813-6100
Minneapolis (G-4065)
County of Mahnomen ......D....218 935-2511
Mahnomen (G-3084)
County of Murray ......C....507 836-6111
Slayton (G-9486)
Evangelical Lutheran Good ......D....218 776-3157
Clearbrook (G-1038)
Fountain Centers ......E....507 377-6411
Albert Lea (G-51)
Gillette Children's Specialty ......B....651 291-2848
Saint Paul (G-8410)
Guest House Inc ......E....507 288-4693
Rochester (G-7128)
Hazelden Foundation ......D....612 559-2022
Minneapolis (G-4614)
Healtheast Care System ......E....651 232-3222
Saint Paul (G-8455)
Human Services Inc ......E....651 430-2720
Stillwater (G-9623)
Lifecare Medical Center ......D....218 782-2131
Greenbush (G-2326)
Minnesota Department of Human ......B....218 739-7200
Fergus Falls (G-2099)
Northland Counseling Center ......E....218 326-1274
Grand Rapids (G-2301)
Northland Counseling Center ......E....218 327-1105
Grand Rapids (G-2302)
Progress Valley Inc ......E....612 869-3223
Minneapolis (G-5425)
Red Wing Healthcare LLC ......C....651 388-2843
Red Wing (G-6997)
Relate Counseling Center Inc ......E....952 932-7277
Minnetonka (G-6219)
Shriners Hospitals For ......C....612 596-6100
Minneapolis (G-5661)
Skemp Walk In Clinic ......E....507 724-3353
Caledonia (G-829)
Southwestern Mental Health Ctr ......E....507 376-4141
Worthington (G-10195)
Tria Orthopaedic Center Asc ......D....952 831-8742
Minneapolis (G-5853)
Twin Town Treatment Center LLC ......E....651 645-3661
Saint Paul (G-9095)
Unitedhealth Group Inc ......A....952 936-1300
Hopkins (G-2651)
Wayside House Inc ......E....952 926-5626
Minneapolis (G-6027)
Westbrook Health Center ......E....507 274-6121
Westbrook (G-9968)
Woodwinds Health Campus ......A....651 232-0100
Saint Paul (G-9290)

8071 Medical Laboratories

Allina Medical Center ......E....651 220-8186
Saint Paul (G-8017)
American National Red Cross ......C....651 291-4600
Saint Paul (G-8030)
Apptec Laboratory Services Inc ......C....651 675-2044
Saint Paul (G-7706)
Architectural Testing Inc ......E....651 636-3835
Saint Paul (G-8061)
CDI Central Florida LLC ......D....952 543-6500
Minneapolis (G-4035)
Central Minnesota Diagnostic ......E....320 983-6300
Milaca (G-3374)
Central Regional Pathology Lab ......E....651 264-1611
Saint Paul (G-9194)
Consultants In Arthritisand ......E....952 832-0246
Minneapolis (G-4157)
Dairy Quality Control Inst ......E....763 785-0484
Saint Paul (G-8278)
Health East Medical Laboratory ......D....651 232-3500
Saint Paul (G-8449)
Isj Regional Women's Imaging ......D....507 304-7770
Mankato (G-3150)
Marynole Genetics & Energy ......D....612 275-2518
Dassel (G-1162)
Medtox Laboratories Inc ......B....651 636-7466
Saint Paul (G-8631)
MEDTOX Scientific Inc ......B....651 636-7466
Saint Paul (G-8632)
Minnesota Medical Scanning ......C....952 541-1840
Saint Louis Park (G-7667)
On Assignment Staffing Svcs ......D....651 647-1160
Saint Paul (G-8784)
Quest Diagnostics Clinical ......C....651 635-1500
Saint Paul (G-8863)
Rochester Methodist Hospital 507 266-7890
Rochester (G-7237)
Silliker Inc ......E....952 932-2800
Hopkins (G-2634)
St Luke's Hospital of Duluth ......E....218 249-5564
Duluth (G-1471)
St Paul Radiology ......D....651 297-6504
Saint Paul (G-8999)
Tuv Sud America Inc ......E....651 631-2487
Saint Paul (G-9086)
Viromed Laboratories Inc ......E....952 563-3300
Minnetonka (G-6234)

8072 Dental Laboratories

Davis Dental Lab ......E....952 345-6315
Minneapolis (G-4229)
Dexterity Dental Arts Inc ......E....651 463-4444
Farmington (G-2049)
Granite City Dental Laboratory ......E....320 253-4825
Saint Cloud (G-7436)
Harrison Dental Studio Inc ......E....651 457-6600
Saint Paul (G-7796)
Jackson Spah Dental Studio Inc ......E....763 785-2435
Minneapolis (G-3504)
Lemke Dental Laboratory Inc ......E....651 482-9911
Saint Paul (G-8577)
Merit Dental Lab Inc ......E....651 644-4042
Saint Paul (G-8635)

(G-00000) Company's Geographic Section entry number
514
2011 Harris Minnesota Services Directory
▲=Import ▼=Export ◆=Import/Export

National Dentex Corp ....E....763 566-0210
Minneapolis *(G-5162)*
National Dentex Corp ....E....507 625-5079
Mankato *(G-3175)*
Renstrom Dental Studio Inc ....E....651 407-0491
Saint Paul *(G-8891)*
Sentage Corp ....E....612 529-9655
Minneapolis *(G-5638)*
Thoele Dental Laboratories Inc ....E....320 252-2070
Waite Park *(G-9843)*
Udell Dental Laboratory Inc ....E....952 926-9266
Minneapolis *(G-5893)*
Valley Dental Arts Inc ....D....651 439-2855
Stillwater *(G-9653)*
Webster Dental Laboratory Inc ....E....651 779-9160
Saint Paul *(G-9143)*
Westlund Dental Studio Inc ....E....952 942-9464
Eden Prairie *(G-1814)*

8082 Home Health Care Svcs

A Chance To Grow Inc ....D....612 789-1236
Minneapolis *(G-3647)*
Abbeycare Inc Home Health Care ....B....651 690-5352
Saint Paul *(G-7971)*
Access Health Care Inc ....D....218 326-0004
Grand Rapids *(G-2267)*
Adult Help & Companion Care ....E....952 377-0411
Minneapolis *(G-3683)*
Advanced Care Inc ....D....612 721-1957
Minneapolis *(G-3686)*
Affordable Professionals Inc ....C....218 682-3351
Hackensack *(G-2331)*
Ageless Care Options ....E....218 463-3695
Roseau *(G-7352)*
Albert Lee Medical Center Inc ....C....507 377-6393
Albert Lea *(G-34)*
Aliance Health Care Inc ....D....507 252-9737
Rochester *(G-7049)*
All Temporaries Inc ....E....320 654-6031
Saint Cloud *(G-7446)*
Alliance Health Care Inc ....A....651 895-8030
Saint Paul *(G-7692)*
Alliance Health Care Inc ....E....507 252-9737
Rochester *(G-7052)*
Allina Health System ....C....651 779-2500
Saint Paul *(G-8014)*
Allina Health System ....E....507 446-0936
Owatonna *(G-6690)*
Asian Home Care Inc ....E....651 999-0268
Saint Paul *(G-8069)*
At Home Ltd ....D....612 673-9594
Minneapolis *(G-3830)*
ATT Home Health Care Inc ....E....651 646-8771
Saint Paul *(G-8077)*
Avalon Home Care ....D....763 753-8658
Elk River *(G-1862)*
B'S Homecare Inc ....E....763 689-8984
Cambridge *(G-832)*
Badger Acquisition of MN ....C....763 259-0400
Minneapolis *(G-3857)*
Barnabas Health Care Services ....C....218 829-0901
Brainerd *(G-551)*
Best Care Home Health Inc ....C....612 378-1040
Minneapolis *(G-3891)*
Break-Thru Home Care ....E....612 659-1505
Minneapolis *(G-3939)*
C J'S Home Health Care Inc ....E....320 833-2253
Buffalo Lake *(G-662)*
Cardinal of Minnesota Ltd ....C....507 281-1077
Rochester *(G-7070)*
Care 2000 Home Healthcare Svcs ....E....218 736-0246
Fergus Falls *(G-2064)*
Care Plus H H A Inc 763 529-5520
Minneapolis *(G-4003)*
Caregivers's Network Inc ....C....952 935-5581
Hopkins *(G-2523)*
Caremate Home Health Care Inc ....C....651 659-0208
Saint Paul *(G-8164)*
Caring Hands Home Care Inc ....E....218 837-5572
Sebeka *(G-9414)*
Caring Hands Home Care Inc ....D....218 732-0088
Park Rapids *(G-6749)*
Choices For Children Inc ....D....952 935-3515
Hopkins *(G-2529)*
Circle of Life Home Care ....B....612 871-2474
Minneapolis *(G-4078)*
Clearwater Hospice ....E....218 694-6581
Bagley *(G-301)*
Cns Managed Health Care Inc ....D....507 289-2411
Rochester *(G-7083)*
Cokato Charitable Trust ....C....320 286-2158
Cokato *(G-1076)*
Comfort Home Health Care Group ....C....507 281-2332
Rochester *(G-7087)*
Comfort Services LLC ....E....612 871-2160
Minneapolis *(G-4128)*
Community Home Health Inc ....E....952 440-3955
Prior Lake *(G-6930)*
Companioncare Inc ....E....763 533-1919
Minneapolis *(G-4145)*
Connectcare ....E....320 234-5031
Hutchinson *(G-2694)*
County of Cook ....C....218 387-3265
Grand Marais *(G-2258)*
County of Winona ....E....507 457-6400
Winona *(G-10089)*
Covenant Home Services LLC ....E....763 755-9009
Minneapolis *(G-3446)*
Crannys 4 Care LLC ....E....218 824-0077
Brainerd *(G-561)*
Crest View Corp ....C....763 782-1611
Minneapolis *(G-3447)*
Crystal Care Home Health Svcs ....B....612 861-4272
Minneapolis *(G-4190)*
Dependable Home Health Care ....E....651 779-9810
Saint Paul *(G-8288)*
Direct Home Health Care Inc ....E....612 870-8256
Minneapolis *(G-4258)*
Divine Healthcare Network ....D....651 665-9795
Saint Paul *(G-8303)*
Edelweiss Home Health Care ....E....763 315-1050
Osseo *(G-6612)*
Elderly Care Services LLC ....D....952 882-9300
Burnsville *(G-717)*
Elenas Care Inc ....D....651 482-0549
Saint Paul *(G-8332)*
Evangelical Lutheran Good ....C....218 829-1429
Brainerd *(G-566)*
Eventide Senior Living ....B....218 233-7508
Moorhead *(G-6314)*
Extended Family Health Care ....E....218 727-0446
Duluth *(G-1316)*
Fairview Health Line Home Care ....D....218 262-6982
Hibbing *(G-2443)*
Fairview Health Services ....B....651 982-7000
Wyoming *(G-10202)*
Fairview HomeCare & Hospice ....B....612 721-2491
Minneapolis *(G-4401)*
Fairview Homecare & Hospice ....E....763 389-1923
Princeton *(G-6908)*
First Care Medical Services ....C....218 435-1133
Fosston *(G-2176)*
First Choice Home Care Inc ....E....651 225-4255
Saint Paul *(G-8379)*
First Minnesota Care Inc ....D....612 724-3000
Minneapolis *(G-4444)*
Foundation For Healthcare ....B....320 253-1920
Sartell *(G-9328)*
Freedom Health Care Inc ....D....952 854-6889
Minneapolis *(G-4485)*
Galil Medical USA ....D....877 639-2796
Arden Hills *(G-246)*
Genesis Homecare Inc ....D....651 686-5910
Saint Paul *(G-7780)*
Global Home ....E....507 282-7471
Rochester *(G-7126)*
Golden Home Care Plus Inc ....B....507 359-2756
New Ulm *(G-6452)*
Good Hue County Public Health ....D....651 385-6100
Red Wing *(G-6983)*
Good Neighbor Home Health Care ....C....218 829-9238
Baxter *(G-328)*
Good Samaritan Home Care Inc ....D....507 765-2700
Preston *(G-6898)*
Goodhue County Public Health ....D....651 385-6100
Red Wing *(G-6984)*
Grove City Lah BNP ....D....320 857-2274
Grove City *(G-2328)*
Guardian Angels Evan Home Care ....C....763 441-1213
Elk River *(G-1879)*
Guardian Angels Health Svcs ....C....763 441-1213
Elk River *(G-1880)*
Harry Meyering Center Inc ....B....507 388-3551
Mankato *(G-3135)*
Healtheast ....D....651 232-3008
Saint Paul *(G-8451)*
Healtheast Diversified Svcs 651 232-2300
Saint Paul *(G-8461)*
Healtheast Home Care Inc ....B....651 232-2800
Saint Paul *(G-8462)*
Healthline Inc ....E....218 362-6760
Hibbing *(G-2449)*
Healthline Inc ....E....218 262-6981
Hibbing *(G-2450)*
Healthworks Home Medical ....D....507 238-9200
Fairmont *(G-1974)*
Healthworks Home Medical Inc ....E....507 344-8500
Mankato *(G-3137)*
Heartland Hospice Services Inc ....C....651 633-6522
Saint Paul *(G-8475)*
Heartland Hospice Services Inc ....D....320 654-1136
Saint Cloud *(G-7417)*
Hiawathal Home Care ....D....651 388-2223
Red Wing *(G-6985)*
Hmong Home Health ....E....651 488-1680
Saint Paul *(G-8490)*
Home Care Solutions ....D....952 924-0677
Minneapolis *(G-4666)*
Home Health Inc ....C....218 262-5887
Hibbing *(G-2455)*
Home Instead Senior Care ....C....651 747-8722
Saint Paul *(G-8493)*
Homewatch Home Care ....E....507 388-5589
Mankato *(G-3143)*
Hospice of Healtheast Inc ....D....651 232-3312
Saint Paul *(G-8495)*
Hospice of The Twin Cities Inc ....D....763 531-2424
Minneapolis *(G-4679)*
Hospice Preferred Choice Inc ....E....952 943-0009
Minneapolis *(G-4680)*
I C A N Inc ....D....507 835-9140
Waseca *(G-9880)*
Immanuel St Joseph Mayo Health ....A....507 625-4031
Mankato *(G-3147)*
In Home Personal Care Inc ....C....763 546-1000
Minneapolis *(G-4693)*
Independence Plus Inc ....C....218 281-3506
Crookston *(G-1126)*
Integra Health Care Inc ....E....952 985-7290
Lakeville *(G-2911)*
◆ **Integrity Home Health Co** ....E....612 827-1479
Minneapolis *(G-4714)*
International Quality Homecare ....E....507 451-6262
Owatonna *(G-6719)*
International Quality Homecare ....D....507 252-8117
Rochester *(G-7142)*
Intrepid Home Health Care Inc ....E....952 285-7300
Minneapolis *(G-4732)*
Intrepid of Golden Valley Inc ....D....952 513-5400
Saint Louis Park *(G-7663)*
Intrepid of Texas Inc ....E....952 285-7300
Minneapolis *(G-4733)*
Jones Stanley & Associates ....E....507 288-0064
Rochester *(G-7147)*
Joy US Cares ....E....320 983-5708
Milaca *(G-3379)*
Julie's Helping Hands ....C....320 833-6082
Buffalo Lake *(G-664)*
Kittson Memorial Hospital Assn ....C....218 843-3612
Hallock *(G-2333)*
Lakeland Hospice & Home Care ....C....218 998-1400
Fergus Falls *(G-2082)*
Life By Design Inc ....C....763 757-3263
Minneapolis *(G-3518)*
Life's Companion PCA Inc ....D....218 326-1179
Grand Rapids *(G-2291)*
Lifes Companion PCA Inc ....C....763 786-3439
Minneapolis *(G-3520)*
Lyngblomsten ....B....651 646-2941
Saint Paul *(G-8599)*
M V R Home Care Inc ....E....651 994-9583
Saint Paul *(G-7828)*
Mary T Associates Inc ....E....763 754-6706
Minneapolis *(G-3529)*
Metro Home Health Care Inc ....C....763 323-2099
Minneapolis *(G-3537)*
MGM Home Care Inc ....E....612 338-3636
Minneapolis *(G-5014)*
Midwest Home Health Care Inc ....B....612 343-3265
Minneapolis *(G-5029)*
Minnesota Autism Center ....C....952 767-4200
Minnetonka *(G-6196)*
Minnesota Visiting Nurse Agcy ....C....612 617-4600
Minneapolis *(G-5101)*
Minuteclinic LLC ....E....612 659-7111
Minneapolis *(G-5106)*
Montevideo Hospital Home Care ....E....320 367-2877
Clara City *(G-1030)*
Morgan Business Trust ....E....218 348-1359
Duluth *(G-1397)*
Morning Star Home Health ....E....507 373-0201
Albert Lea *(G-62)*
Nightingale Home Health Care ....E....763 545-3131
Minneapolis *(G-5202)*
Nobles Rock Public Health ....E....507 372-8256
Worthington *(G-10189)*
North Country Hospital ....E....218 333-5665
Bemidji *(G-411)*
North Memorial Health Care ....D....763 520-3900
Minneapolis *(G-5216)*
Nurses That Care ....E....218 724-2800
Duluth *(G-1411)*
Olafson, Renae ....E....651 452-6825
Saint Paul *(G-8780)*
Option Care Inc ....C....651 635-9272
Saint Paul *(G-8789)*
Our Circle of Friends ....E....507 334-4346
Faribault *(G-2024)*
Percy Nelson Enterprises Inc ....E....651 209-6360
Woodbury *(G-10173)*
Petersen Home Care Services ....E....763 557-1126
Minneapolis *(G-5369)*
Prairie River Home Care Inc ....D....507 345-8591
Mankato *(G-3182)*
Prairie River Home Care Inc ....C....507 252-9844
Rochester *(G-7210)*
Prairie River Home Care Inc ....D....507 532-2264
Marshall *(G-3321)*
Pride N'Living Home Care Inc ....E....763 572-2390
Minneapolis *(G-3573)*
Public Health Solutions I ....E....763 754-7427
Minneapolis *(G-3579)*
Quality Living Home Health ....E....507 454-6800
Winona *(G-10120)*
REM Health Inc ....E....952 926-9808
Minneapolis *(G-5509)*
Rice Memorial Hospital ....E....320 231-7077
Willmar *(G-10042)*
River Valley Home Care ....C....651 460-4201
Farmington *(G-2059)*
Riverview Healthcare Assn ....E....218 281-9478
Crookston *(G-1136)*
Rose Arbor ....D....763 493-5910
Osseo *(G-6656)*
Royal Home Health Care ....E....763 504-4559
Minneapolis *(G-5563)*
Sacred Heart Care Center ....C....507 433-1808
Austin *(G-286)*
▼ **Saint Elizabeth's Hospital** ....C....651 565-4531
Wabasha *(G-9770)*
Senior Friend ....E....218 878-0990
Cloquet *(G-1065)*

S I C

Employment codes: A=Over 500 employees, B=251-500
C=101-250, D=51-100, E=25-50
2011 Harris Minnesota
Services Directory
© Harris InfoSource 1-866-281-6415
515

Senior Friend Associates Inc....C....218 727-1111
Duluth (G-1447)
Senior Health & Home Care Inc....E....952 920-9399
Minneapolis (G-5637)
Senior Home Living MN LLC....D....952 935-0789
Hopkins (G-2631)
Seniors Caring Companions Inc....E....651 770-2288
Maplewood (G-3288)
Sleepy Eye Area Home Health....507 794-3594
Sleepy Eye (G-9500)
Southeast Asian Health Svcs....C....651 222-2889
Saint Paul (G-8974)
Spectrum Community Health....E....507 332-7471
Faribault (G-2031)
Spectrum Community Health Inc....E....507 282-8052
Rochester (G-7260)
Spectrum Community Health Inc....E....320 235-5684
Willmar (G-10045)
Spectrum Community Health Inc....E....218 326-4202
Grand Rapids (G-2308)
Spectrum Community Health Inc....E....320 252-9640
Saint Cloud (G-7428)
St Cloud Hospital....C....320 251-2700
Saint Cloud (G-7603)
St Mary's Medical Center....A....218 786-4000
Duluth (G-1474)
Stinson Home Care LLC....E....763 755-4801
Minneapolis (G-3609)
Student Experience Inc....E....218 728-8009
Duluth (G-1477)
Sugar Lake Supported Living....E....320 963-7571
Maple Lake (G-3265)
Sunrise Health Services....D....651 462-9331
Stacy (G-9578)
Tgp Inc....E....218 694-2378
Bagley (G-303)
TLC Home Health Care Inc....E....218 326-3555
Grand Rapids (G-2309)
TLC Nursing Services of....D....651 647-0017
Saint Paul (G-9069)
Transformation House Inc....E....763 427-7155
Anoka (G-236)
U About Inc....C....612 866-4884
Richfield (G-7039)
United Homecare Inc....E....952 898-9780
Burnsville (G-815)
Unity Healthcare....E....612 285-8743
Minneapolis (G-5918)
US Asian Home Care....E....763 533-7750
Minneapolis (G-5942)
Victory Home Care Inc....E....763 566-3318
Minneapolis (G-5970)
Village Health Care Inc....952 361-8000
Chaska (G-983)
Walker Methodist Inc....B....612 827-5931
Minneapolis (G-6011)
Warren Community Hospital Inc....D....218 745-4211
Warren (G-9869)
We Do-Care Inc....C....612 866-7800
Minneapolis (G-6030)
Weiner Memorial Foundation....B....507 532-9661
Marshall (G-3332)
Weiner Memorial Foundation....E....507 537-7070
Marshall (G-3331)
West Wind Village....C....320 589-1133
Morris (G-6380)

8092 Kidney Dialysis Centers

Bio-Medical Applications of MN....E....218 624-7787
Duluth (G-1254)
Bio-Medical Applications of MN....E....763 783-0103
Minneapolis (G-3417)
Total Renal Care Inc....E....612 347-5972
Minneapolis (G-5835)
Total Renal Care Inc....E....651 483-3159
Saint Paul (G-9072)

8093 Specialty Outpatient Facilities, NEC

A Chance To Grow Inc....D....612 789-1236
Minneapolis (G-3647)
AA Monticello....E....763 295-5066
Monticello (G-6265)
Allina Health System....C....651 464-7100
Forest Lake (G-2155)
Allina Health System....B....320 589-1313
Morris (G-6369)
Allina Health System....E....320 234-4664
Hutchinson (G-2685)
American Baptist Homes of The....D....507 373-0188
Albert Lea (G-39)
Arrowhead Center Inc....218 749-2877
Virginia (G-9733)
Behavioral Dimensions Inc....E....952 814-0207
Hopkins (G-2516)
Behavioral Health Services Inc....E....763 689-7887
Cambridge (G-833)
Benedictine Health System....C....218 744-9800
Eveleth (G-1928)
Beverly Enterprises - MN....D....507 342-5166
Wabasso (G-9776)
Capernaum Pediatric Therapy....E....952 938-5348
Hopkins (G-2522)
Capernaum Pediatric Therapy....E....612 922-2009
Edina (G-1828)
Catholic Charities of The....C....612 827-6241
Minneapolis (G-4030)
Center For Alcohol & Drug....E....218 723-8444
Duluth (G-1265)
Center For Alcohol & Drug....D....218 723-8444
Duluth (G-1266)
Center For Independent Living....B....218 262-6675
Hibbing (G-2439)
Central Minnesota Mental....E....763 682-4400
Buffalo (G-641)
Central Minnesota Mental....D....320 252-5010
Saint Cloud (G-7485)
Children's Health Care Inc....E....952 930-8630
Hopkins (G-2528)
Children's Mental Health Svcs....E....218 327-4886
Grand Rapids (G-2271)
Chrestomathy Inc....D....952 974-0339
Eden Prairie (G-1624)
Cokato Charitable Trust....C....320 286-2158
Cokato (G-1076)
Core Professional Services....E....218 829-7140
Brainerd (G-560)
County of Brown-Nicollet....E....507 354-4418
New Ulm (G-6446)
County of Douglas....A....320 762-1511
Alexandria (G-91)
County of Mahnomen....D....218 935-2511
Mahnomen (G-3084)
County of Mille Lacs....E....763 389-5828
Princeton (G-6904)
County of Ramsey....C....651 266-2400
Saint Paul (G-8260)
Courage Center....C....651 439-8283
Stillwater (G-9607)
Courage Center....E....320 963-3121
Maple Lake (G-3259)
Dakota County Receiving Center....D....651 437-4209
Hastings (G-2382)
Emily Program....E....952 746-5774
Minneapolis (G-4347)
Extendicare Homes Inc....B....763 588-0771
Minneapolis (G-4383)
Extendicare Homes Inc....D....612 861-1691
Richfield (G-7035)
Extendicare Homes Inc....B....763 545-0416
Minneapolis (G-4384)
Extendicare Homes Inc....C....952 920-8380
Minneapolis (G-4387)
Face To Face Health....E....651 772-5555
Saint Paul (G-8361)
Fairview Clinics....E....651 688-7860
Saint Paul (G-7773)
Fairview Health Services....E....612 721-5044
Minneapolis (G-4395)
Feda Ridge Inc....E....651 426-3300
Stillwater (G-9618)
Five County Mental Health Ctr....E....320 396-3333
Braham (G-542)
Gillette Children's Specialty....E....952 936-0977
Hopkins (G-2544)
Guardian Angels Health & Rehab....C....218 263-7583
Hibbing (G-2448)
Guest House Inc....E....507 288-4693
Rochester (G-7128)
Guild Inc....E....651 291-0067
Saint Paul (G-8437)
Habilitative Services Inc....C....507 625-6047
Mankato (G-3133)
Haven Chemical Health System....E....651 734-9633
Saint Paul (G-9224)
Hazelden Foundation....D....612 559-2022
Minneapolis (G-4614)
Healtheast Care System....E....651 232-3222
Saint Paul (G-8455)
Healtheast Maplewood Out....E....651 232-7780
Saint Paul (G-8463)
Healthpartners Inc....D....651 552-2600
Inver Grove Heights (G-2753)
Hecla Inc....320 255-9530
Saint Cloud (G-7526)
Hiawatha Valley Mental Health....E....507 454-4341
Winona (G-10102)
Hiawatha Valley Mental Health....D....651 565-2234
Wabasha (G-9767)
Human Development Center....D....218 728-5192
Duluth (G-1355)
Human Services Inc....E....651 430-2720
Stillwater (G-9623)
Immanuel-St Joseph's Hospital....D....507 385-4700
Mankato (G-3149)
Indian Health Board of....D....612 721-9800
Minneapolis (G-4696)
Indian Health Service....D....218 983-6317
Ogema (G-6554)
Integrated Medical Rehab....E....952 837-8991
Minneapolis (G-4713)
Iron Range Rehabilitation Ctr....E....218 741-2147
Virginia (G-9743)
Jones Stanley & Associates....E....507 288-0064
Rochester (G-7147)
Lakeland Mental Health Center....D....218 736-6987
Fergus Falls (G-2083)
Lakeland Mental Health Center....D....218 233-7524
Moorhead (G-6323)
Lifespan of Minnesota Inc....D....651 681-0616
Eagan (G-1534)
Lifetrack Resources Inc....D....651 227-8471
Saint Paul (G-8586)
Mayo Clinic Rochester....E....507 377-5900
Albert Lea (G-61)
Meadowbrook Women's Clinic....E....612 376-7708
Minneapolis (G-4980)
Mental Health Resources Inc....E....612 337-4021
Minneapolis (G-4988)
Meridian Behavioral Health LLC....612 326-7600
New Brighton (G-6412)
Midsota Regional Hand Center....E....320 253-7257
Saint Cloud (G-7554)
Midwest Urologic Stone Unit LP....E....651 633-9414
Saint Paul (G-8666)
Minnesota Department of Human....B....218 739-7200
Fergus Falls (G-2099)
Minnesota Monitoring Inc....E....763 253-5401
Minneapolis (G-5085)
Monticello-Big Lake Community....B....763 295-2945
Monticello (G-6278)
Neighborhood Counseling Center....E....218 631-1714
Wadena (G-9807)
Northern Star Therapy Ltd Inc....E....320 240-6955
Saint Cloud (G-7562)
Northland Counseling Center....E....218 326-1274
Grand Rapids (G-2301)
Northland Counseling Center....E....218 327-1105
Grand Rapids (G-2302)
Northwestern Mental Health Ctr....D....218 281-3940
Crookston (G-1130)
Nystrom & Associates Ltd....E....651 628-9566
Saint Paul (G-8775)
Occupational Development Ctr....C....218 326-8574
Grand Rapids (G-2305)
Omegon Inc....E....952 541-4738
Hopkins (G-2594)
Partners In Excellence Inc....D....952 746-5350
Burnsville (G-776)
Physicans Neck & Back Clinic....E....651 639-9150
Saint Paul (G-8827)
Planned Parenthood of MN....E....651 698-2401
Saint Paul (G-8830)
Polinsky Rehabilitation Center....C....218 786-5360
Duluth (G-1426)
Possabilities of Southern MN....D....507 287-7100
Rochester (G-7209)
Progress Valley Inc....E....612 869-3223
Minneapolis (G-5425)
Range Mental Health Center Inc....E....218 749-2881
Virginia (G-9754)
Red Lake Chemical Health....D....218 679-3995
Redlake (G-7017)
ReEntry House Inc....E....612 869-2411
Minneapolis (G-5480)
Regents of The University of....A....612 624-9499
Minneapolis (G-5495)
Regions Hospital Alcohol....E....651 254-4804
Saint Paul (G-8883)
Relate Counseling Center Inc....E....952 932-7277
Minnetonka (G-6219)
Resource Inc....E....612 752-8200
Minneapolis (G-5527)
Rice Memorial Hospital....E....320 231-4175
Willmar (G-10043)
Robbinsdale Clinic PA Inc....E....763 533-2534
Minneapolis (G-5550)
Skemp Walk In Clinic....E....507 724-3353
Caledonia (G-829)
Southwestern Mental Health Ctr....E....507 376-4141
Worthington (G-10195)
Southwestern Mental Health Ctr....507 283-9511
Luverne (G-3070)
St Cloud Hospital....E....320 259-9149
Sauk Rapids (G-9376)
St Cloud Surgical Center....C....320 251-8385
Saint Cloud (G-7607)
St Mary's Duluth Clinic Health....A....218 786-4000
Duluth (G-1473)
Stevens Community Medical Ctr....C....320 589-1313
Morris (G-6379)
Storefront Group....E....612 861-1675
Richfield (G-7038)
Therapy Network Inc....E....507 454-6724
Winona (G-10132)
Upper Mississippi Mental....D....218 751-3280
Bemidji (G-431)
Vail Place....612 824-8061
Minneapolis (G-5954)
Washburn Child Guidance Center....D....612 871-1454
Minneapolis (G-6022)
Wayside House Inc....E....952 926-5626
Minneapolis (G-6027)
Western Mental Health Center....E....507 532-3236
Marshall (G-3335)
Whispering Pines Therapy Ctr....D....218 587-4423
Pine River (G-6822)
Winona Developmental....E....507 452-1798
Winona (G-10147)
Woodland Centers....D....320 235-4613
Willmar (G-10058)
Woodland Centers....C....320 693-7221
Litchfield (G-2993)
Wright Connection Dtnh Inc....E....763 682-2910
Buffalo (G-661)
Zumbro Valley Mental Health....E....507 289-2089
Rochester (G-7299)

SIC

(G-00000) Company's Geographic Section entry number
516
2011 Harris Minnesota
Services Directory
▲=Import ▼=Export
◆=Import/Export

8099 Health & Allied Svcs, NEC

Abbot Northwestern Hospital ..... E 612 863-3150
Minneapolis *(G-3659)*
All Temporaries Caring ..... E 612 378-1474
Minneapolis *(G-3711)*
American National Red Cross ..... C 651 291-6789
Saint Paul *(G-8029)*
American National Red Cross ..... C 651 291-4600
Saint Paul *(G-8030)*
Avada Audiology & Hearing Care ..... E 952 541-1799
Hopkins *(G-2513)*
Biolife Plasma Services LP ..... E 507 344-0300
Mankato *(G-3111)*
Biolife Plasma Services LP ..... E 320 259-6300
Saint Cloud *(G-7459)*
Cannon Valley Clinic ..... E 507 266-2620
Faribault *(G-1996)*
Chronimed Inc ..... B 952 979-3600
Eden Prairie *(G-1625)*
Correctional Medical Services ..... D 651 631-0065
Saint Paul *(G-8254)*
Csl Plasma Inc ..... D 612 331-9180
Minneapolis *(G-4191)*
Csl Plasma Inc ..... E 651 646-2556
Saint Paul *(G-8272)*
Csl Plasma Inc ..... D 218 727-8139
Duluth *(G-1287)*
Health Fitness Corp ..... E 952 831-6830
Bloomington *(G-499)*
Healthcare Options Minnesota ..... E 320 252-5666
Sauk Rapids *(G-9366)*
Human Development Center ..... E 218 728-4491
Duluth *(G-1354)*
Hutchinson Health Care ..... D 320 234-5000
Hutchinson *(G-2700)*
Integra Health Care Inc ..... E 952 985-7290
Lakeville *(G-2911)*
Leptos Biomedical ..... E 763 561-0880
Minneapolis *(G-3516)*
Mayo Clinic ..... B 507 266-4808
Rochester *(G-7171)*
Medevent Inc ..... E 952 445-2342
Prior Lake *(G-6940)*
Medical Messaging Center ..... E 320 255-5640
Saint Cloud *(G-7549)*
Memorial Blood Center ..... C 651 332-7000
Saint Paul *(G-8633)*
Memorial Blood Center ..... E 218 723-8080
Duluth *(G-1389)*
Memorial Blood Center ..... E 218 263-1338
Hibbing *(G-2462)*
Midwest Medical Solutions ..... D 952 838-6700
Minneapolis *(G-5035)*
Minnesota Lions Eye Bank Inc ..... D 612 624-6446
Saint Paul *(G-8696)*
National Marrow Donor Program ..... C 612 627-5800
Minneapolis *(G-5166)*
New Millennium ..... D 763 780-9933
Minneapolis *(G-3555)*
Northern Access Transportation ..... E 218 728-5464
Duluth *(G-1401)*
Nutrition Services Inc ..... C 507 835-5697
Waseca *(G-9884)*
Physicians Examone Inc ..... E 651 731-2949
Saint Paul *(G-9261)*
Rmia ..... E 651 221-4600
Saint Paul *(G-9269)*
Sanford Westbrook Medical Ctr ..... E 507 274-6802
Westbrook *(G-9967)*
Select Transcription Inc ..... D 763 441-3021
Elk River *(G-1892)*
St Jude Medical ..... E 651 523-6900
Saint Paul *(G-8985)*
Tim Orth Memorial Foundation ..... E 320 365-4419
Bird Island *(G-469)*
Transcriptions Inc ..... D 952 831-4480
Eden Prairie *(G-1795)*
United Healthcare of Wyoming ..... D 651 603-8515
Saint Paul *(G-9106)*
Upper Midwest Organ ..... D 651 603-7800
Saint Paul *(G-9114)*
Wm Healthcare Solutions Inc ..... D 763 786-5555
Minneapolis *(G-3642)*

81 LEGAL SERVICES

8111 Legal Svcs

A S K Financial LLP ..... E 651 406-9665
Saint Paul *(G-7685)*
Aafedt, Forde, Gray, & Monson ..... E 612 339-8965
Minneapolis *(G-3656)*
Administrative Office of The ..... D 612 664-5050
Minneapolis *(G-3680)*
Anderson Dove Fretland & Van ..... E 952 545-9000
Minneapolis *(G-3776)*
Anthony Ostlund & Baer ..... E 612 349-6969
Minneapolis *(G-3783)*
Arthur, Chapman, Kettering ..... D 612 339-3500
Minneapolis *(G-3815)*
Attorney's Process Service Ltd ..... C 952 831-7776
Minneapolis *(G-3833)*
Babcock, Neilson, Mannella, La ..... E 763 421-5151
Minneapolis *(G-3413)*
Bankruptcy Solutions Inc ..... E 651 367-2000
Saint Paul *(G-8087)*
Barna Guzy & Steffen Ltd ..... D 763 780-8500
Minneapolis *(G-3415)*
Barnes & Thornburg LLP ..... D 612 333-2111
Minneapolis *(G-3868)*
Bassford Remele ..... D 612 333-3000
Minneapolis *(G-3873)*
Best & Flanagan LLP ..... C 612 339-7121
Minneapolis *(G-3890)*
Borkon, Ramstead, Mariani ..... E 952 546-6000
Minneapolis *(G-3930)*
Bowman & Brooke LLP ..... C 612 339-8682
Minneapolis *(G-3934)*
Brandt Murnane ..... D 651 227-9411
Saint Paul *(G-8121)*
Briggs & Morgan Professional ..... C 651 223-6600
Minneapolis *(G-3947)*
Briggs & Morgan Professional ..... B 612 977-8400
Minneapolis *(G-3946)*
Brown & Carlson ..... E 763 540-1019
Minneapolis *(G-3962)*
Burke Blackwell ..... E 612 343-3200
Minneapolis *(G-3976)*
Carl Crosby Lehmann ..... B 612 632-3000
Minneapolis *(G-4012)*
Casserly Molzahn & Assoc Inc ..... D 952 885-1298
Minneapolis *(G-4025)*
Chestnut & Cammbrone, Prof ..... E 612 339-7300
Minneapolis *(G-4061)*
City of Moorhead ..... D 218 299-5120
Moorhead *(G-6302)*
City of Saint Paul ..... E 651 266-8740
Saint Paul *(G-8212)*
Coldwell Banker Burnet Inc ..... D 952 920-1224
Eden Prairie *(G-1630)*
Collins, Buckley, Sauntry ..... E 651 227-0611
Saint Paul *(G-8225)*
Commercial Auditors Corp ..... E 763 783-9160
Minneapolis *(G-3437)*
County Attorney Office ..... E 218 726-2323
Duluth *(G-1284)*
County of Olmsted ..... E 507 285-8138
Rochester *(G-7089)*
Cousineau McGuire Chartered ..... D 952 546-8400
Minneapolis *(G-4173)*
D C M Services LLC ..... D 612 332-3700
Minneapolis *(G-4212)*
Dicke Billig & Czaja ..... E 612 573-2000
Minneapolis *(G-4254)*
Dorsey & Whitney LLP ..... A 612 340-2600
Minneapolis *(G-4281)*
Dunkley & Bennett ..... E 612 339-1290
Minneapolis *(G-4296)*
Dunlap & Seeger ..... D 507 288-9111
Rochester *(G-7100)*
Emmett J McMahon ..... E 612 349-8728
Minneapolis *(G-4348)*
Erstat & Riemer ..... E 952 854-7638
Minneapolis *(G-4370)*
Evangelical Lutheran Church In ..... C 612 752-4080
Minneapolis *(G-4376)*
Fabyanske, Westra, Hart ..... D 612 338-0115
Minneapolis *(G-4390)*
Fafinski Mark & Johnson ..... E 952 995-9500
Eden Prairie *(G-1661)*
Family Means ..... E 763 780-4986
Minneapolis *(G-4410)*
Felhaber Larson Fenlon & Vogt ..... D 612 339-6321
Minneapolis *(G-4424)*
Felhaber Larson Fenlon & Vogt ..... E 651 222-6321
Saint Paul *(G-8372)*
Fish & Richardson PC ..... C 612 335-5070
Minneapolis *(G-4451)*
Foley & Mansfield LLP ..... D 612 338-8788
Minneapolis *(G-4460)*
Fredrikson & Byron ..... B 612 492-7000
Minneapolis *(G-4484)*
Fryberger, Buchanan, Smith ..... D 218 725-6807
Duluth *(G-1329)*
Fulbright & Jaworski LLP ..... E 612 321-2800
Minneapolis *(G-4490)*
General Electric Capital Corp ..... E 952 897-5600
Minneapolis *(G-4509)*
Goggins & Lavintman ..... E 651 209-1825
Saint Paul *(G-7785)*
Gray Plant Mooty Mooty ..... B 612 632-3000
Minneapolis *(G-4548)*
Greene Espel PLLP ..... E 612 373-0830
Minneapolis *(G-4563)*
Gunhus Grinnell Klinger ..... E 218 236-6462
Moorhead *(G-6317)*
Hamre Schumann Mueller Larson ..... E 612 455-3800
Minneapolis *(G-4592)*
Hanft, Fride, O'Brien ..... E 218 722-4766
Duluth *(G-1346)*
Hansen Dordell Bradt Odlaug, ... D 651 482-8900
Saint Paul *(G-8441)*
Hanson, Lulic & Krall ..... E 612 333-2530
Minneapolis *(G-4596)*
Heacox, Hartman, Mattaini ..... E 651 222-2922
Saint Paul *(G-8446)*
Hellmuth & Johnson PLLC ..... D 952 941-4005
Eden Prairie *(G-1682)*
Henson & Efron ..... D 612 339-2500
Minneapolis *(G-4639)*
Hinshaw & Culbertson LLP ..... D 612 333-3434
Minneapolis *(G-4652)*
Hoglund, Chwialkowski ..... E 651 628-9929
Saint Paul *(G-8491)*
Hubert Melchert Sjodin Pllp ..... E 952 442-5155
Waconia *(G-9786)*
Hutchinson, City of Inc ..... E 320 587-2242
Hutchinson *(G-2703)*
Jardine Logan & O'Brien ..... E 651 290-6500
Lake Elmo *(G-2874)*
Jenson, Beel, Converse ..... E 651 223-4999
Saint Paul *(G-8530)*
Johnson & Condon ..... D 952 831-6544
Minneapolis *(G-4773)*
Johnson Lewis Nilan ..... D 612 338-1838
Minneapolis *(G-4775)*
Jones Stanley & Associates ..... E 507 288-0064
Rochester *(G-7147)*
Kaplan, Strangis & Kaplan ..... E 612 375-1138
Minneapolis *(G-4789)*
Karen B Bjorkman ..... E 612 904-7401
Minneapolis *(G-4791)*
Kelly & Berens ..... E 612 392-7032
Minneapolis *(G-4798)*
Kennedy & Graven Chartered ..... D 612 337-9300
Minneapolis *(G-4801)*
Kinney & Lange ..... E 612 339-1863
Minneapolis *(G-4810)*
Knutson, Flynn, Deans ..... E 651 222-2811
Saint Paul *(G-7819)*
Larkin, Hoffman, Daly ..... C 952 835-3800
Minneapolis *(G-4845)*
Larson King, LLP ..... D 651 312-6500
Saint Paul *(G-8564)*
Law Center Inc ..... E 218 736-5493
Fergus Falls *(G-2086)*
Legal Aid Society of ..... D 612 332-1441
Minneapolis *(G-4855)*
Legal Aid Society of ..... E 612 827-3774
Minneapolis *(G-4856)*
Legal Research Center Inc ..... E 612 332-4950
Minneapolis *(G-4857)*
Legal Service Northwest MN ..... E 218 681-7710
Thief River Falls *(G-9673)*
Legal Services Advocacy Proj 651 222-3749
Saint Paul *(G-8575)*
Leonard, Street & Deinard ..... B 612 335-1500
Minneapolis *(G-4862)*
Lind, Jensen, Sullivan ..... E 612 333-3637
Minneapolis *(G-4888)*
Lindquist & Vennum PLLP ..... C 612 371-3211
Minneapolis *(G-4890)*
Littler Mendelson, PC ..... E 612 630-1000
Minneapolis *(G-4894)*
Lockridge Grindal Nauen LLP ..... D 612 339-6900
Minneapolis *(G-4897)*
Lps Default Solutions Inc ..... D 651 234-3500
Saint Paul *(G-7827)*
Mackall Crounse & Moore PLC ..... D 612 305-1400
Minneapolis *(G-4927)*
Mahoney, Dougherty & Mahoney ..... E 612 339-5863
Minneapolis *(G-4936)*
Mansfield & Tanick ..... D 612 339-4295
Minneapolis *(G-4944)*
Maschka Riedy & Ries ..... E 507 625-6600
Mankato *(G-3168)*
McCollum, Crowley, Moschet ..... D 952 831-4980
Minneapolis *(G-4971)*
McGrann Shea Anderson Carnival ..... E 612 338-2525
Minneapolis *(G-4976)*
Meagher & Geer ..... C 612 338-0661
Minneapolis *(G-4981)*
Meshbesher & Spence Ltd ..... E 612 339-9121
Minneapolis *(G-4996)*
Meshbesher & Spence Ltd ..... E 320 656-0484
Saint Cloud *(G-7551)*
Messerli & Kramer ..... D 763 548-7900
Minneapolis *(G-4997)*
Metro Legal Services Inc ..... D 612 332-0202
Minneapolis *(G-5001)*
Metro Legal Services Inc ..... E 651 291-0008
Saint Paul *(G-8641)*
Michael E Molenda ..... E 952 432-3136
Saint Paul *(G-7839)*
Mid Minnesota Legal Assistance ..... C 612 332-1441
Minneapolis *(G-5021)*
Milavetz Gallop Millavetz ..... E 763 533-1111
Minneapolis *(G-5039)*
Milavetz, Gallop & Milavetz ..... E 612 339-0140
Minneapolis *(G-5040)*
Minnesota Disability Law Ctr ..... E 612 332-1441
Minneapolis *(G-5076)*
Minnesota Legal Services ..... E 320 253-0121
Saint Cloud *(G-7559)*
Minnesota Legal Services 651 228-9105
Saint Paul *(G-8695)*
Monroe Krass ..... D 952 445-5080
Minneapolis *(G-5122)*
Moore, Costello & Hart Pllp ..... E 651 602-2615
Saint Paul *(G-8719)*
Moore, Costello & Hart Pllp ..... E 612 673-0148
Minneapolis *(G-5125)*
More Costello & Hart Pllp ..... E 651 227-7683
Saint Paul *(G-8720)*
Moss & Barnett, A Professional ..... C 612 877-5000
Minneapolis *(G-5135)*
Office of General Council ..... E 612 624-4100
Minneapolis *(G-5266)*
Oppenheimer Wolff Donnelly LLP ..... B 612 607-7000
Minneapolis *(G-5287)*
P Kevin Hickey ..... E 612 376-1620
Minneapolis *(G-5305)*

SIC

Employment codes: A=Over 500 employees, B=251-500
C=101-250, D=51-100, E=25-50

2011 Harris Minnesota
Services Directory

© Harris InfoSource 1-866-281-6415
517

Paige J Donnelly Ltd....E....651 222-2797
Saint Paul *(G-8801)*
Park Nicollet Clinic....D....952 993-9700
Minneapolis *(G-5330)*
Patterson, Thuente, Skaar....D....612 349-5764
Minneapolis *(G-5348)*
Peterson, Fram & Bergman, A....E....651 291-8955
Saint Paul *(G-8821)*
Quinlivan & Hughes....D....320 251-1414
Saint Cloud *(G-7578)*
Rajkowski Hansmeier Ltd....E....320 251-1055
Saint Cloud *(G-7581)*
Ratwik, Roszak, & Maloney....E....612 339-0060
Minneapolis *(G-5468)*
Remele Bassford....D....612 333-3000
Minneapolis *(G-5515)*
Rienhardt & Anderson....E....651 227-9990
Saint Paul *(G-8900)*
Rinke, Noonan, Grote, Smoley....D....320 251-6700
Saint Cloud *(G-7588)*
Robins, Kaplan, Miller....B....612 349-8500
Minneapolis *(G-5555)*
Rust Consulting Inc....C....612 359-2000
Minneapolis *(G-5577)*
Schwebel, Goetz, & Sieben....D....612 333-8361
Minneapolis *(G-5617)*
Severson Sheldon Dougherty....E....952 432-3136
Saint Paul *(G-7901)*
Sieben, Grose, Von Holtum....E....612 333-4500
Minneapolis *(G-5664)*
Siegel, Brill, Greupner Duffy....E....612 339-7131
Minneapolis *(G-5665)*
So MN Regional Service....E....651 222-5863
Saint Paul *(G-8968)*
Stephen M Knutson....E....651 225-0626
Saint Paul *(G-7912)*
Svingen Hagstron Cline Karkela....E....218 739-4696
Fergus Falls *(G-2121)*
Talon Investigation Ltd....E....651 774-6977
Saint Paul *(G-9026)*
Thomsen & Nybeck....E....952 835-7000
Edina *(G-1846)*
Three Rivers Community Action....E....507 732-7391
Zumbrota *(G-10220)*
3M Innovative Properties Co....651 733-8904
Saint Paul *(G-9067)*
Trenti Law Firm Inc....E....218 749-1962
Virginia *(G-9758)*
Votel, Anderson & McEachron....E....651 228-1770
Saint Paul *(G-9133)*
Walling & Berg....E....612 340-1150
Minneapolis *(G-6013)*
Wilkerson & Hegna....E....952 897-1707
Minneapolis *(G-6068)*
Yaeger, Jungbauer & Barczak....D....612 333-6371
Minneapolis *(G-6096)*
Zelle, Hofmann, Voelbel, Mason....D....612 339-2020
Minneapolis *(G-6114)*
Zimmerman Reed PLLP....E....612 341-0400
Minneapolis *(G-6119)*

83 SOCIAL SERVICES

8322 Individual & Family Social Svcs

A Chance To Grow Inc....D....612 789-1236
Minneapolis *(G-3647)*
Accessible Space Inc....E....651 645-7271
Saint Paul *(G-7975)*
Adult Child & Family Services....E....507 344-1721
Mankato *(G-3099)*
Adult Client Training Service....E....320 523-5666
Olivia *(G-6559)*
Adults & Childrens Alliance....E....651 481-9320
Saint Paul *(G-7986)*
African American Family Svcs....E....612 871-7878
Minneapolis *(G-3696)*
African American Family Svcs....E....612 813-0782
Minneapolis *(G-3697)*
Agramson Enterprises Inc....D....763 546-1599
Minneapolis *(G-3700)*
AIN Dah Yung Center....E....651 227-4184
Saint Paul *(G-8001)*
Aitkin County....E....218 927-3744
Aitkin *(G-13)*
Albert Lea Family YMCA....E....507 373-8228
Albert Lea *(G-31)*
Alexandra House Inc....E....763 780-2332
Minneapolis *(G-3388)*
American National Red Cross....E....612 871-7676
Minneapolis *(G-3757)*
American Refugee Committee....E....612 872-7060
Minneapolis *(G-3758)*
Amherst H Wilder Foundation....B....651 280-2000
Saint Paul *(G-8040)*
Amherst H Wilder Foundation....D....651 224-1395
Saint Paul *(G-8043)*
Amherst H Wilder Foundation....D....651 290-8666
Saint Paul *(G-8045)*
Andrew Residence Management....C....612 333-0111
Minneapolis *(G-3779)*
Anna Maries....E....320 253-6900
Saint Cloud *(G-7451)*
Anoka County Community Action....C....763 783-4747
Minneapolis *(G-3404)*
Applewood Pointe Senior Co Op....E....651 636-2161
Saint Paul *(G-8055)*

ARC Greater Twin Cities....D....612 861-9550
Minneapolis *(G-3797)*
ARC Greater Twin Cities....E....952 920-0855
Saint Paul *(G-8057)*
Arcanoka Ramsey & Suburban ARC....D....952 890-3057
Minneapolis *(G-3799)*
Archdiocese of Saint Paul....D....763 425-2210
Minneapolis *(G-3800)*
Arlington House....E....651 771-3040
Saint Paul *(G-8063)*
Associated Clinic of....E....952 925-6033
Minneapolis *(G-3824)*
Associated Clinic of....D....763 503-8560
Minneapolis *(G-3825)*
Autumn Grace Senior Services....E....507 388-3660
Mankato *(G-3108)*
Baker Laura Services Assn....C....507 645-8866
Northfield *(G-6524)*
Barnabas Health Care Services....C....218 829-0901
Brainerd *(G-551)*
Bayport Senior Center....E....651 275-8907
Bayport *(G-346)*
Becker County Human Services....D....218 847-5628
Detroit Lakes *(G-1187)*
Beverly Enterprises - MN....D....507 288-1818
Rochester *(G-7065)*
Bgm-Ceres Environmental Svcs....E....800 218-4424
Minneapolis *(G-3901)*
Bi-County Community Action....E....218 751-4631
Bemidji *(G-382)*
Big Brothers Big Sisters of....D....651 789-2400
Saint Paul *(G-8113)*
Birchwood Care Home Inc....E....612 823-7286
Minneapolis *(G-3906)*
Birthright Inc....E....507 645-7638
Northfield *(G-6525)*
Birthright of Austin Inc....E....507 437-2373
Austin *(G-263)*
Bois Forte Reservation Tribal....E....218 757-3261
Nett Lake *(G-6404)*
Boys & Girls Club of Rochester....E....507 287-2300
Rochester *(G-7067)*
Boys & Girls Clubs of Central....C....320 252-7616
Saint Cloud *(G-7463)*
Boys & Girls Clubs of The....E....218 335-8144
Cass Lake *(G-870)*
Brain Injury Association of MN....E....612 378-2742
Minneapolis *(G-3937)*
Bridge For Youth....D....612 377-8800
Minneapolis *(G-3944)*
Brown County Probation Dept....E....507 233-6628
New Ulm *(G-6444)*
C A P Scott-Carver-Dakota Inc....E....952 496-2125
Shakopee *(G-9425)*
Camp Buckskin Inc....D....952 930-3544
Minneapolis *(G-3996)*
Camp Widji Wagan....E....218 365-2117
Ely *(G-1912)*
Capstone Services LLC....C....651 641-0042
Saint Paul *(G-8155)*
Casa De Esperanza....E....651 646-5553
Saint Paul *(G-8170)*
Catholic Charities of The....E....612 664-8500
Minneapolis *(G-4028)*
Catholic Charities of The....B....320 650-1550
Saint Cloud *(G-7473)*
Catholic Charities of The....E....320 259-8757
Saint Cloud *(G-7475)*
Catholic Charities of The....E....218 739-9325
Fergus Falls *(G-2066)*
Catholic Charities of The....E....507 454-2270
Winona *(G-10086)*
Catholic Charities of The....E....651 222-3001
Saint Paul *(G-8176)*
Catholic Charities of The....C....612 827-6241
Minneapolis *(G-4030)*
Catholic Charities of The Dioc....E....320 240-3337
Saint Cloud *(G-7476)*
Center For Independent Living....B....218 262-6675
Hibbing *(G-2439)*
Central Minnesota Mental....E....763 682-4400
Buffalo *(G-641)*
Central Minnesota Task Force....E....320 252-1603
Saint Cloud *(G-7487)*
Central Minnesota Task Force....E....320 251-7203
Saint Cloud *(G-7486)*
Central Minnesota Task Force....E....320 253-6900
Saint Cloud *(G-7488)*
Central Minnesota Task Force....E....320 252-1603
Saint Cloud *(G-7489)*
Central Territorial of The....E....651 646-2601
Saint Paul *(G-8183)*
Centro Cultural Chicano....E....612 874-1412
Minneapolis *(G-4048)*
Ceres Caribe Ceres Environ....E....800 218-4424
Minneapolis *(G-4051)*
Child Care Resource & Referral....D....507 287-2020
Rochester *(G-7076)*
Children's Home Society....B....651 646-7771
Saint Paul *(G-8196)*
Choice Inc....E....952 446-1475
Saint Bonifacius *(G-7399)*
Church of Our Lady of The Lake....E....952 472-1284
Mound *(G-6384)*
Church of St Bernard....E....651 488-6733
Saint Paul *(G-8200)*
City of Eden Prairie....D....952 949-8470
Eden Prairie *(G-1629)*

City of Menahga....D....218 564-4101
Menahga *(G-3356)*
City of Owatonna....E....507 444-4300
Owatonna *(G-6702)*
City of Waconia....E....952 442-0695
Waconia *(G-9783)*
Clare Housing....E....612 236-9505
Minneapolis *(G-4099)*
Clearwater Suites Inc....E....320 765-8841
Sacred Heart *(G-7398)*
Clyde Johnson....E....218 229-2847
Aurora *(G-256)*
Cokato Charitable Trust....C....320 286-2158
Cokato *(G-1076)*
Common Sense Services For....E....651 552-0288
South Saint Paul *(G-9524)*
Community Action Council Inc....E....952 985-5300
Burnsville *(G-701)*
Community Action of....E....612 348-8858
Minneapolis *(G-4137)*
Community Action Partnership....C....651 645-6445
Saint Paul *(G-8237)*
Community Connection of MN....E....218 525-4126
Duluth *(G-1279)*
Community Involvement Programs....E....952 854-4007
Minneapolis *(G-4144)*
Comunidades Latinas Unidas En....E....651 379-4200
Saint Paul *(G-8244)*
Conect Project....E....763 476-8477
Minneapolis *(G-4152)*
Cornerstone Advocacy Service....E....952 884-0376
Minneapolis *(G-4162)*
County of Anoka....E....763 783-4909
Minneapolis *(G-3445)*
County of Cass....D....218 547-1346
Walker *(G-9849)*
County of Kanabec....E....320 679-6430
Mora *(G-6355)*
County of Meeker....E....320 693-5300
Litchfield *(G-2983)*
County of Mille Lacs....E....763 389-5828
Princeton *(G-6904)*
County of Ramsey....C....651 266-2400
Saint Paul *(G-8260)*
County of Sibley....E....507 237-4000
Gaylord *(G-2199)*
County of Stearns....E....320 202-2100
Saint Cloud *(G-7494)*
County of Washington....B....651 430-6800
Stillwater *(G-9605)*
County of Winona....E....507 457-6410
Winona *(G-10091)*
County of Winona....D....507 457-6200
Winona *(G-10090)*
Courage Center....B....763 588-0811
Minneapolis *(G-4172)*
Dakota County Receiving Center....D....651 437-4209
Hastings *(G-2382)*
Dakota Woodlands Inc....E....651 456-9110
Eagan *(G-1524)*
Darts....C....651 455-1560
Saint Paul *(G-7748)*
Deafblind Services Minnesota....612 362-8454
Minneapolis *(G-4236)*
Department of Corrections MN....D....320 384-7411
Finlayson *(G-2129)*
Diocese of St Cloud....E....320 252-4121
Saint Cloud *(G-7499)*
Divine House Inc....D....320 589-3652
Morris *(G-6372)*
Dodge County Battered Women's....E....507 634-6070
Kasson *(G-2820)*
Domestic Abuse Project Inc....E....612 874-7063
Minneapolis *(G-4271)*
Dovray Community Center....E....507 274-5602
Dovray *(G-1230)*
Duluth Area Family YMCA....E....218 722-4745
Duluth *(G-1297)*
Dungarvin Illinois Inc....D....651 699-6050
Saint Paul *(G-8312)*
Dungarvin Minnesota Inc....B....651 699-6050
Saint Paul *(G-8313)*
Dungarvin New Mexico Inc....D....651 699-6050
Saint Paul *(G-8314)*
East Suburban Resources Inc....E....651 351-0190
Stillwater *(G-9611)*
East Suburban Resources Inc....D....651 464-5137
Stillwater *(G-9612)*
Eden Rs....C....612 287-1600
Minneapolis *(G-4313)*
Elder Network....C....507 285-5272
Rochester *(G-7105)*
Eleah Medical Centre....D....218 685-4461
Elbow Lake *(G-1852)*
Empowerment Services of MN....E....218 724-4014
Duluth *(G-1312)*
Evangelical Lutheran Good....D....651 489-8851
Saint Paul *(G-8348)*
Face To Face Health....E....651 772-5555
Saint Paul *(G-8361)*
Family & Children's Service....E....612 729-0340
Minneapolis *(G-4406)*
Family Child Development Ctr....E....763 545-7271
Minneapolis *(G-4407)*
Family Innovations Inc....D....763 421-5535
Anoka *(G-180)*
Family Innovations Inc....E....651 748-5019
Saint Paul *(G-8367)*

Family Means	E	651 439-4840	Stillwater (G-9616)
Family Means	E	763 780-4986	Minneapolis (G-4410)
Family Partnership	E	612 339-9101	Minneapolis (G-4411)
Family Partnership	E	952 884-7353	Minneapolis (G-4412)
Family Service Center Inc	E	320 564-2211	Granite Falls (G-2315)
Family Violence Network	D	651 770-8544	Minneapolis (G-4413)
Family Violence Network	D	612 825-3333	Minneapolis (G-4414)
Fraser	B	612 861-1688	Minneapolis (G-4478)
Fraser Child & Family Center	A	612 331-9413	Minneapolis (G-4479)
Freeport West Inc	D	612 824-3040	Minneapolis (G-4486)
Genesis Group Homes Inc	D	763 390-0773	Brooklyn Park (G-610)
Glenwood-Lyndale Community Ctr	D	612 342-1500	Minneapolis (G-4530)
Global Volunteers	E	651 407-6100	Saint Paul (G-8415)
Goodwill Industries Inc	C	651 379-5800	Saint Paul (G-8421)
Goodwill Industries Inc	E	952 953-4410	Saint Paul (G-7787)
Goodwill Industries Inc	E	651 439-4207	Stillwater (G-9620)
Goodwill Industries Inc	D	651 603-1544	Saint Paul (G-8422)
Greater Minneapolis Council of	E	612 721-8687	Minneapolis (G-4559)
Greater Minneapolis Crisis	D	763 591-0100	Minneapolis (G-4560)
Greater Minnesota Family Svcs	D	320 214-9692	Willmar (G-10003)
Greater Minnesota Family Svcs	D	320 235-3664	Willmar (G-10004)
Greater Twin Cities United Way	C	612 340-7400	Minneapolis (G-4561)
Grove Chestnut Inc	E	218 749-6846	Virginia (G-9739)
Harriet Tubman Center Inc	E	612 825-3333	Minneapolis (G-4602)
Hastings YMCA	E	651 480-8887	Hastings (G-2390)
Hennepin County	A	612 348-5273	Minneapolis (G-4633)
Hiawatha Valley Mental Health	E	507 454-4341	Winona (G-10102)
Hmong American Partnership	E	651 495-9160	Saint Paul (G-8489)
Home & Community Options Inc	E	507 454-5690	Winona (G-10104)
Homestead At Rochester	E	507 535-2000	Rochester (G-7140)
Hope Common	C	651 917-0917	Saint Paul (G-8494)
Hospice of The Twin Cities Inc	D	763 531-2424	Minneapolis (G-4679)
Hubbard, County of Inc	C	218 732-3329	Park Rapids (G-6755)
Human Services	E	320 634-5750	Glenwood (G-2227)
Human Services Inc In WA	C	651 777-5222	Saint Paul (G-9233)
Human Services of Fairbault	D	507 238-4757	Fairmont (G-1975)
Independent School District	E	651 385-8000	Red Wing (G-6986)
Independent School District	D	651 604-3503	Saint Paul (G-8510)
Independent School District	E	218 236-8172	Moorhead (G-6319)
Indian Health Board of	D	612 721-9800	Minneapolis (G-4696)
Integrity Living Options Inc	D	952 920-9291	Minneapolis (G-4715)
Inter-County Community Council	E	218 796-5144	Oklee (G-6557)
Itasca County Family Young	D	218 327-1161	Grand Rapids (G-2287)
Janine Sahagian	E	507 332-9894	Faribault (G-2014)
Jewish Community Center of	C	952 381-3400	Minneapolis (G-4762)
Jewish Family & Children's Svc	D	952 546-0616	Hopkins (G-2562)
Kcq Inc	E	507 334-4393	Faribault (G-2016)
Keystone Community Services	D	651 645-0349	Saint Paul (G-8548)
Kinderberry Hill	E	763 404-1070	Minneapolis (G-4808)
Knight of Columbus Community	E	952 492-5170	Prior Lake (G-6936)
Lakes & Pines Community Action	E	320 679-1800	Mora (G-6365)
Lakes Homes & Program Devpt	E	218 739-4322	Fergus Falls (G-2085)
Lao Family Community of MN		651 221-0069	Saint Paul (G-8561)
Lee Carlson Center For Mental	E	763 780-3036	Fridley (G-2193)
Lifetrack Resources Inc	D	651 227-8471	Saint Paul (G-8586)
Lifeworks Services Inc	E	763 746-3330	Minneapolis (G-4883)
Lincoln, Lyon, & Murray Human	D	507 532-1239	Marshall (G-3306)
Lrn Associates Management Inc	E	507 836-8955	Slayton (G-9488)
Lutheran Social Service of MN	D	612 871-0221	Minneapolis (G-4912)
Lutheran Social Service of MN	E	320 235-5411	Willmar (G-10020)
Lutheran Social Service of MN	C	218 736-5431	Fergus Falls (G-2089)
Lutheran Social Service Of MN	D	651 642-5990	Saint Paul (G-8598)
Lyngblomsten	B	651 646-2941	Saint Paul (G-8599)
M Dm Rubicon Inc	E	651 731-8621	Saint Paul (G-9245)
Mary T Inc	E	763 754-2505	Minneapolis (G-3530)
Medeligible Services	D	763 585-8400	Minneapolis (G-4983)
Meridian Services Inc	E	320 255-5151	Saint Cloud (G-7550)
Metroplitan Ctr For	D	651 646-8342	Saint Paul (G-8642)
Midway Training Services Inc	D	651 641-0709	Saint Paul (G-8656)
Midwest Mental Health Resource	E	651 647-1900	Saint Paul (G-8659)
Minneapolis Urban League Inc	E	612 302-3100	Minneapolis (G-5065)
Minnesota Aids Project	E	612 341-2060	Minneapolis (G-5066)
Minnesota Autism Center	C	952 767-4200	Minnetonka (G-6196)
Minnesota Department of	C	651 642-0503	Saint Paul (G-8681)
Minnesota Department of Human	A	218 828-2379	Brainerd (G-575)
Minnesota Department of Human	A	651 431-2000	Saint Paul (G-8683)
Minnesota Indian Womens	E	612 728-2000	Minneapolis (G-5078)
Minnesota Valley Action	D	507 345-6822	Mankato (G-3172)
Mothers & Children Program Mac	E	651 484-8241	Saint Paul (G-8724)
Naomi Family Center	E	651 222-7962	Saint Paul (G-8734)
National Multiple Sclerosis	E	612 335-7900	Minneapolis (G-5167)
Neighborhood Counseling Center	E	218 631-1714	Wadena (G-9807)
Neighborhood House	D	651 789-2500	Saint Paul (G-8743)
Neighborhood Involvement	E	612 374-3125	Minneapolis (G-5180)
Nonviolent Peaceforce	E	612 871-0005	Minneapolis (G-5205)
Northeast Residence Inc	B	651 765-0217	Saint Paul (G-8756)
Northern Pines Mental Health		320 632-6647	Little Falls (G-3015)
Northland Chapter American Red	C	218 722-0071	Duluth (G-1405)
Northpoint Health & Wellness	E	612 767-9500	Minneapolis (G-5235)
Northwest Community Action Inc	D	218 528-3258	Badger (G-299)
Northwest Youth & Family Svcs	D	651 486-3808	Saint Paul (G-8770)
Northwood Childrens Home Soc	D	218 724-8815	Duluth (G-1410)
Nothern Cass Bemidji Inc	E	218 759-0052	Bemidji (G-416)
Nutrition Services Inc	C	507 835-5697	Waseca (G-9884)
Nystrom & Associates Ltd	E	651 628-9566	Saint Paul (G-8775)
Oak Ridge Homes of Wadena Inc	E	218 327-1877	Grand Rapids (G-2304)
Oasis of Love Inc	E	612 529-6055	Minneapolis (G-5258)
Olmsted Medical Center	E	507 288-8880	Rochester (G-7196)
Omegon Inc	E	952 541-4738	Hopkins (G-2594)
Options Residential Inc	C	952 564-3030	Burnsville (G-770)
Orono Healthy Youth	E	952 449-8351	Long Lake (G-3029)
Orono Independent School Dist	E	763 479-1530	Maple Plain (G-3280)
Our Place Covenant Enabling	E	218 624-3097	Duluth (G-1416)
Outcomes Inc	E	651 483-9500	Saint Paul (G-8795)
Pacer Center Inc	D	952 838-9000	Minneapolis (G-5309)
Pact For Families	E	320 231-7030	Willmar (G-10034)
Paragon Associates Inc	D	218 722-5009	Duluth (G-1418)
Parkwood Shores Assisted	E	952 924-0400	Minneapolis (G-5339)
Partners In Excellence	E	651 773-5988	Saint Paul (G-8808)
Partnership Resources Inc	E	612 331-2075	Minneapolis (G-5345)
Pathways Psychological Svcs		763 525-8590	Minneapolis (G-5346)
Patrick M Doyle Dr	E	651 454-0114	Saint Paul (G-7865)
People Inc	E	651 227-6321	Saint Paul (G-8817)
Phoenix Alternatives Inc	C	651 426-2484	Saint Paul (G-8825)
Phoenix Residence Inc	C	651 227-7655	Saint Paul (G-7876)
Pine County Health & Human Svc	E	320 245-3020	Sandstone (G-9324)
Pinnacle Services Inc	B	612 977-3100	Minneapolis (G-5382)
Prairie Five Community Action	E	320 269-6578	Montevideo (G-6257)
Prairie Five Community Action	E	320 598-3118	Madison (G-3077)
Professional Association of	E	612 259-1600	Minneapolis (G-5419)
Program In Human Sexuality	E	612 625-1500	Minneapolis (G-5423)
Providers Choice Inc	D	952 944-7010	Hopkins (G-2607)
Quality Care Services Inc	D	320 230-7275	Saint Cloud (G-7577)
R E M Southwest Services C	D	507 223-5633	Canby (G-851)
Ram Woodvale	E	507 433-4924	Austin (G-284)
Rape & Abuse Crisis Center	E	218 643-6110	Breckenridge (G-596)
Regents of The University of	E	612 626-4515	Minneapolis (G-5502)
Relate Counseling Center Inc	E	952 932-7277	Minnetonka (G-6219)
REM Inc	E	218 724-1872	Duluth (G-1434)
REM River Bluffs Inc	E	651 480-4710	Hastings (G-2404)
REM-Ramsey Inc	A	952 925-5067	Minneapolis (G-5514)
Renville County Emergency Food	E	320 523-5339	Olivia (G-6563)
Resources For Child Caring Inc	D	651 641-0305	Saint Paul (G-8893)
Round Lake Senior Citizen Ctr	E	507 945-8477	Round Lake (G-7385)
Sabathani Community Center	D	612 821-2300	Minneapolis (G-5584)
Safe Haven	E	952 846-0608	Burnsville (G-794)
Safe Haven Shelter For Youth	E	952 440-5379	Prior Lake (G-6953)
Saint Peter Counseling Center	D	507 934-9612	Saint Peter (G-9300)
Salvation Army Harbor Light	D	612 338-0113	Minneapolis (G-5598)
SE Rolling Hills LLC	D	952 828-9500	Eden Prairie (G-1771)
Second Harvest Heartland	C	651 484-5117	Saint Paul (G-8941)
Second Harvest Heartland	D	612 209-7980	Minneapolis (G-5624)
Senior Citizens Center of	E	218 494-3750	Felton (G-2063)
Senior Citizens Service Inc	E	507 287-1404	Rochester (G-7251)
Senior Friend Associates Inc	C	218 727-1111	Duluth (G-1447)
Senior Isanti Citizen Com	E	763 444-6100	Isanti (G-2781)
Senior Laurentian Citizen Ctr	D	218 749-3688	Virginia (G-9755)
Shakopee Mdewakanton Sioux Com	D	952 445-8900	Prior Lake (G-6954)
Shelter Care Inc	E	612 823-8483	Minneapolis (G-5653)
Shelter House	E	320 235-0962	Willmar (G-10044)
Someplace Safe	D	320 589-3208	Fergus Falls (G-2120)
South Central Human Relations	D	507 451-2630	Owatonna (G-6737)
South Metro Human Services	D	651 291-1979	Saint Paul (G-8973)
Southern Minnesota Independent	E	507 345-7139	Mankato (G-3200)
Southside Family Nurturing Ctr	E	612 721-2762	Minneapolis (G-5711)
Southwestern Mental Health Ctr	E	507 376-4141	Worthington (G-10195)
St Cloud Hospital	D	320 656-7020	Saint Cloud (G-7601)
St David's Center Child	B	952 939-0396	Hopkins (G-2636)
St James Home of Duluth	C	218 728-7500	Duluth (G-1462)
St Louis, County of Inc	B	218 726-2000	Duluth (G-1464)
St Paul Youth Services	E	651 771-1301	Saint Paul (G-9000)
St Stephen's Human Services	E	612 874-0311	Minneapolis (G-5731)

Employment codes: A=Over 500 employees, B=251-500
C=101-250, D=51-100, E=25-50

2011 Harris Minnesota
Services Directory

© Harris InfoSource 1-866-281-6415

519

Stearns-Benton Employment ....E....320 308-5320
Saint Cloud *(G-7612)*
Steele County Human Services ....D....507 444-7500
Owatonna *(G-6738)*
Stellher Human Services Inc ....E....218 751-5919
Bemidji *(G-428)*
Stepping Stones For Living LLC ....D....218 727-7450
Duluth *(G-1475)*
Stivland Inc ....E....651 436-1153
Afton *(G-11)*
Storefront Group ....E....612 861-1675
Richfield *(G-7038)*
Sustainable Resources Center ....E....612 870-4255
Minneapolis *(G-5776)*
Tamarisk Resources Inc ....E....763 572-1950
Anoka *(G-232)*
Tbi Residential & Community ....D....218 721-3231
Duluth *(G-1480)*
Three Rivers Community Action ....E....507 732-7391
Zumbrota *(G-10220)*
Three Rivers Head Start ....D....507 333-6450
Faribault *(G-2035)*
Traumatic Brain Injury ....D....218 733-1331
Duluth *(G-1486)*
Tri-County Community Action ....E....320 632-3691
Little Falls *(G-3020)*
Tubman ....D....612 871-0118
Minneapolis *(G-5863)*
Tubman Family Alliance ....E....612 825-0000
Minneapolis *(G-5864)*
U S Probation Office ....D....612 664-5400
Minneapolis *(G-5890)*
Udac Inc ....D....218 722-5867
Duluth *(G-1489)*
Union Gospel Mission Assn ....D....651 292-1721
Saint Paul *(G-9102)*
United Support Group ....E....507 437-4110
Austin *(G-292)*
Upper Midwest American Indian ....E....612 522-4436
Minneapolis *(G-5936)*
Vietnamese Social Services of ....E....651 644-1317
Saint Paul *(G-9127)*
Vinland National Center ....E....763 479-3555
Loretto *(G-3054)*
Vision Loss Resources ....E....651 224-7662
Saint Paul *(G-9131)*
Volunteers Of America Inc ....D....763 753-2500
Anoka *(G-237)*
Volunteers of America Inc ....D....952 945-4000
Minneapolis *(G-5984)*
Volunteers of America Inc ....E....952 941-0305
Eden Prairie *(G-1809)*
W I C Program ....E....612 348-6258
Minneapolis *(G-5987)*
Wacosa ....D....320 251-0087
Waite Park *(G-9848)*
Wee Care We Share ....E....320 274-8881
Annandale *(G-144)*
Weiner Memorial Foundation ....B....507 532-9661
Marshall *(G-3332)*
Wildflower Lodge of Chapelwood ....D....763 420-3768
Osseo *(G-6684)*
Women of Nations ....E....651 222-5830
Saint Paul *(G-9163)*
Women's Advocates Inc ....E....651 227-9966
Saint Paul *(G-9164)*
Women's Shelter Inc ....E....507 285-1938
Rochester *(G-7295)*
Womens Life Care Center ....E....651 777-0350
Saint Paul *(G-9165)*
Woodland Centers ....D....320 235-4613
Willmar *(G-10058)*
Y M C A Infant Center ....E....651 646-4557
Saint Paul *(G-9171)*
YMCA ....D....320 222-9622
Willmar *(G-10059)*
YMCA Children's Center ....E....651 777-8103
Saint Paul *(G-9173)*
YMCA of Greater Saint Paul ....E....651 645-6605
Saint Paul *(G-9175)*
YMCA of Greater St Paul ....E....218 365-2117
Ely *(G-1919)*
YMCA of Greater St Paul ....D....651 292-4143
Saint Paul *(G-9178)*
YMCA of Greater St Paul ....D....651 646-4557
Saint Paul *(G-9177)*
YMCA of Greater St Paul ....C....651 483-2671
Saint Paul *(G-9176)*
YMCA of Greater St Paul ....E....651 457-0048
Saint Paul *(G-7953)*
YMCA of Worthington, Minnesota ....E....507 376-6197
Worthington *(G-10199)*
Young Men's Christian Assn ....C....507 387-8255
Mankato *(G-3222)*
Young Men's Chritn Assoc of ....C....763 535-4800
Minneapolis *(G-6101)*
Young Men's Chritn Assoc of ....D....612 827-5401
Minneapolis *(G-6102)*
Young Men's Chritn Assoc of ....E....612 588-9484
Minneapolis *(G-6103)*
Young Men's Chritn Assoc of ....C....952 835-2567
Minneapolis *(G-6104)*
Young Women's Christian Assn ....D....218 722-7425
Duluth *(G-1505)*
Youth Frontiers Inc ....E....952 922-0222
Minneapolis *(G-6107)*
Youthlink ....D....612 252-1200
Minneapolis *(G-6108)*

YWCA of Minneapolis ....D....612 874-7131
Minneapolis *(G-6110)*
YWCA of Minneapolis ....A....612 332-0501
Minneapolis *(G-6111)*

8331 Job Training & Vocational Rehabilitation Svcs

Ability Building Center ....C....507 281-6262
Rochester *(G-7043)*
Accessability Inc ....D....612 331-5958
Minneapolis *(G-3667)*
Adult Training & Habilitation ....E....320 485-4191
Winsted *(G-10155)*
American Indian Oic Inc ....E....612 341-3358
Minneapolis *(G-3753)*
Arrowhead Economic Opportunity ....E....218 742-9187
Virginia *(G-9734)*
Cedar Valley Services Inc ....D....507 451-5897
Owatonna *(G-6698)*
Cedar Valley Services Inc ....E....507 433-2303
Austin *(G-265)*
Cedar Valley Services Inc ....E....507 377-2893
Albert Lea *(G-43)*
Cedar Valley Services Inc ....E....507 373-6064
Albert Lea *(G-42)*
Child Care Choices Inc ....E....320 251-5081
Saint Cloud *(G-7491)*
Chisago Lakes Achievement Ctr ....E....651 257-6709
Chisago City *(G-989)*
Community Involvement Programs ....D....612 362-4400
Minneapolis *(G-4143)*
Connections of Moorhead ....D....218 233-8657
Moorhead *(G-6307)*
County of Anoka ....D....763 783-4800
Minneapolis *(G-3444)*
County of Ramsey ....D....651 770-4499
Saint Paul *(G-8261)*
East Range Developmental ....E....218 744-5130
Eveleth *(G-1930)*
Employment Enterprises Inc ....D....320 632-9251
Little Falls *(G-3002)*
Enterprise North Inc ....E....507 233-8900
New Ulm *(G-6448)*
Epic Enterprise Inc ....E....507 645-6800
Dundas *(G-1511)*
Functional Industries Inc ....D....763 682-4336
Buffalo *(G-645)*
Goodwill Industries Inc ....C....651 379-5800
Saint Paul *(G-8421)*
Goodwill Industries Inc ....E....952 953-4410
Saint Paul *(G-7787)*
Goodwill Industries Inc ....E....651 439-4207
Stillwater *(G-9620)*
Goodwill Industries Inc ....E....651 603-1544
Saint Paul *(G-8422)*
Goodwill Industries Vocational ....D....218 722-6351
Duluth *(G-1338)*
H I R E D ....B....612 529-3342
Minneapolis *(G-4585)*
Homes of Minnesota Educational ....E....763 543-6978
Minneapolis *(G-4670)*
Industries Inc ....E....320 679-2354
Mora *(G-6361)*
Interstate Rehabilitation Ctr ....B....651 388-7108
Red Wing *(G-6987)*
Joint Apprenticeship ....E....218 733-9443
Duluth *(G-1364)*
Kandi-Works Developmental ....E....320 974-8840
Atwater *(G-253)*
Kandi-Works Developmental ....E....320 382-6156
Kandiyohi *(G-2814)*
Le Sueur County Developmental ....E....507 362-8560
Waterville *(G-9896)*
Lifetrack Resources Inc ....E....651 290-0567
Saint Paul *(G-8587)*
Lifetrack Resources Inc ....D....651 227-8471
Saint Paul *(G-8586)*
Mankato Rehabilitation Center ....C....507 386-5600
Mankato *(G-3165)*
Mankato Rehabilitation Center ....D....507 386-5799
Mankato *(G-3164)*
Merrick Inc ....B....612 789-6200
Saint Paul *(G-8639)*
Midway Training Services Inc ....D....651 641-0709
Saint Paul *(G-8656)*
Midwest Special Services Inc ....C....651 778-1000
Saint Paul *(G-8664)*
Midwest Special Services Inc ....E....651 483-3000
Saint Paul *(G-8663)*
Midwest Special Services Inc ....D....763 557-1231
Minneapolis *(G-5037)*
Mille Lacs Cty Area ....E....320 983-2162
Milaca *(G-3380)*
Minneapolis American Indian ....E....612 871-4555
Minneapolis *(G-5050)*
Northeast Minnesota Office of ....E....218 748-2200
Virginia *(G-9748)*
Northern Cass Dac Inc ....E....218 547-1121
Walker *(G-9857)*
Occupational Development Ctr ....E....218 751-6001
Bemidji *(G-417)*
Occupational Development Ctr ....C....218 326-8574
Grand Rapids *(G-2305)*
Occupational Development Ctr ....E....218 463-1123
Roseau *(G-7356)*

Occupational Development Ctr ....D....218 681-4949
Thief River Falls *(G-9677)*
Occupational Development Ctr ....D....218 258-8926
Buhl *(G-668)*
▲ Opportunity Partners Inc ....C....952 938-5511
Hopkins *(G-2595)*
Options Inc ....D....763 263-3684
Big Lake *(G-452)*
Phoenix Alternatives Inc ....C....651 426-2484
Saint Paul *(G-8825)*
Pine Habilitation & Supported ....E....320 245-2246
Sandstone *(G-9325)*
Pinewood Cloquet ....E....218 879-4566
Cloquet *(G-1060)*
Polk County Developmental ....E....218 281-4181
Crookston *(G-1134)*
PPL Industries Inc ....D....612 332-0664
Minneapolis *(G-5399)*
Prairieland Utility ....E....507 625-2404
North Mankato *(G-6513)*
Previsor Inc ....D....612 843-1059
Minneapolis *(G-5407)*
ProAct Inc ....C....651 686-0405
Saint Paul *(G-7884)*
Productive Alternatives Inc ....D....218 998-5630
Fergus Falls *(G-2117)*
Rebuild Resources Inc ....E....651 645-7055
Saint Paul *(G-8880)*
Resource Inc ....D....612 752-8000
Minneapolis *(G-5526)*
Resources For Child Caring Inc ....D....651 641-0305
Saint Paul *(G-8893)*
Rise Inc ....D....763 786-8334
Minneapolis *(G-3585)*
Rise Inc ....E....763 784-0900
Minneapolis *(G-3586)*
Saint Mary's University of MN ....D....612 728-5109
Minneapolis *(G-5591)*
Southwest MN Pic ....E....507 537-6987
Marshall *(G-3329)*
Step Inc ....E....507 238-4341
Fairmont *(G-1982)*
Summit Academy OIC ....D....612 377-0150
Minneapolis *(G-5763)*
Sureservices Inc ....E....763 531-0029
Minneapolis *(G-5772)*
Twin Cities Rise ....E....612 338-0295
Minneapolis *(G-5873)*
Twin Cities Tree Trust ....E....651 644-6237
Saint Paul *(G-9090)*
Vail Place ....E....612 824-8061
Minneapolis *(G-5954)*
Vision Loss Resources Inc ....C....612 871-2222
Minneapolis *(G-5976)*
Vision Loss Resources Inc ....D....612 871-2222
Minneapolis *(G-5977)*
West Central Industries Inc ....D....320 235-5310
Willmar *(G-10054)*
Winona ORC Industries Inc ....B....507 452-1855
Winona *(G-10153)*

8351 Child Day Care Svcs

A Chance To Grow Inc ....D....612 789-1236
Minneapolis *(G-3647)*
Aeoa Headstart ....D....218 749-5856
Virginia *(G-9732)*
Agape 24 Hour Preschool ....E....612 287-9775
Minneapolis *(G-3698)*
Albert Lea Family YMCA ....E....507 373-8228
Albert Lea *(G-31)*
Aldrich Memorial Nursery Sch ....E....507 289-3097
Rochester *(G-7048)*
Anoka Child Care Center ....E....763 427-1897
Anoka *(G-155)*
B'Nai Emet Synagogue Inc ....E....952 927-7309
Minneapolis *(G-3855)*
Barnes Head Start ....E....218 733-2084
Duluth *(G-1246)*
Battle Creek Head Start ....E....651 730-1663
Saint Paul *(G-8090)*
Berean Baptist Church ....E....952 432-7168
Burnsville *(G-686)*
Bluffview Montessori School ....E....507 452-2807
Winona *(G-10083)*
Brainerd School District 181 ....E....218 829-0412
Brainerd *(G-553)*
Bright Horizons Children's ....E....763 571-2375
Minneapolis *(G-3424)*
Building Block Child Care Inc ....E....763 557-1111
Minneapolis *(G-3972)*
C A P Scott-Carver-Dakota Inc ....E....952 496-2125
Shakopee *(G-9425)*
Camp Widji Wagan ....E....218 365-2117
Ely *(G-1912)*
Care Corner ....E....507 386-7444
Mankato *(G-3113)*
Carolyn A Adrianse ....E....507 386-7444
Mankato *(G-3114)*
Catholic Charities of The ....E....612 529-9107
Minneapolis *(G-4029)*
Centennial Independent School ....E....763 792-6000
Circle Pines *(G-1005)*
Centennial Independent School ....E....763 792-6120
Circle Pines *(G-1004)*
Child Care Choices Inc ....E....320 251-5081
Saint Cloud *(G-7491)*

(G-00000) Company's Geographic Section entry number
520

2011 Harris Minnesota
Services Directory

▲=Import ▼=Export
◆=Import/Export

Child Care Resource & Referral D 507 287-2020
Rochester (G-7076)
Children's Center E 507 373-7979
Albert Lea (G-44)
Children's Country Day School E 651 454-4000
Saint Paul (G-7732)
Children's Discovery Learning D 651 653-9871
Saint Paul (G-8192)
Children's Home Society B 651 646-7771
Saint Paul (G-8196)
Children's Home Society E 651 228-7707
Saint Paul (G-8195)
Chrestomathy Inc D 952 974-0339
Eden Prairie (G-1624)
Christian Life Church E 651 463-4545
Farmington (G-2043)
Church of St Matthew D 651 224-9793
Saint Paul (G-8201)
Church of The Nativity of The E 952 881-8160
Minneapolis (G-4074)
Cindy Day Care E 651 688-7678
Saint Paul (G-7733)
CLC Childcare Center E 507 452-5493
Winona (G-10088)
Club Kid of Edina Inc E 952 831-1055
Minneapolis (G-4111)
Community Action Agency E 763 425-7422
Minneapolis (G-4136)
Community Action Partnership E 651 224-4363
Saint Paul (G-8236)
Community Child Care Center E 612 861-4303
Minneapolis (G-4139)
Concordia Creative Learning E 651 793-6624
Saint Paul (G-8246)
Coon Rapids Day Care Center E 763 755-2412
Minneapolis (G-3440)
Crookston Family Service Ctr E 218 281-1343
Crookston (G-1119)
Dakotah Sport & Fitness Center C 952 445-9400
Prior Lake (G-6932)
Discover Magical Moments E 507 289-7463
Rochester (G-7096)
Duluth Area Family YMCA E 218 722-4745
Duluth (G-1297)
E B I Inc E 218 624-3508
Duluth (G-1307)
Early Child Family Education E 507 625-4620
Mankato (G-3123)
Early Childhood Center D 952 556-6400
Chaska (G-963)
Elk River Independent School D 763 241-3480
Elk River (G-1873)
Especially For Children Inc E 952 934-1119
Eden Prairie (G-1658)
Especially For Children Inc E 651 452-0043
Saint Paul (G-7770)
Evergreen Child Care Center E 952 402-0303
Shakopee (G-9439)
Family Child Development Ctr E 763 545-7271
Minneapolis (G-4407)
Golden Heart Child Care Center E 507 625-1454
Mankato (G-3225)
Greenview Alzheimer's E 218 263-3935
Hibbing (G-2447)
Guadalupe Alternative Programs E 651 222-0757
Saint Paul (G-8434)
Hastings YMCA E 651 480-8887
Hastings (G-2390)
Head Start Program Onigum D 218 547-1420
Walker (G-9851)
Hendricks Community Hospital C 507 275-3134
Hendricks (G-2429)
Holy Emmanuel Lutheran Church E 952 888-5116
Minneapolis (G-4662)
Hope Presbyterian Church of 612 866-4055
Minneapolis (G-4674)
Hopkins Early Learning Center E 952 988-5050
Hopkins (G-2554)
House of Hope Presbyterian D 651 227-6311
Saint Paul (G-8497)
Independent School District E 651 385-8000
Red Wing (G-6986)
Independent School District 16 D 763 786-1338
Minneapolis (G-3496)
Independent School District No E 507 444-7900
Owatonna (G-6718)
Inter-County Community Council E 218 796-5144
Oklee (G-6557)
Iron Range Learning & Devpt E 218 741-7441
Virginia (G-9742)
Itasca County Family Young D 218 327-1161
Grand Rapids (G-2287)
Jack & Jill Preschool E 651 604-3810
Saint Paul (G-8527)
Jewish Community Nursery & Day E 651 698-0751
Saint Paul (G-8532)
Khcdii Inc E 952 925-5881
Minneapolis (G-4805)
Kid's Haven of Buffalo Inc D 763 682-3072
Buffalo (G-646)
Kid's Korner Educare Center E 507 451-0312
Owatonna (G-6720)
Kiddie Karousel Day Care Ctr E 218 263-7450
Hibbing (G-2458)
Kids Come 1st Children's Ctr E 507 281-4421
Rochester (G-7152)
Kids Come 1st Corp C 507 281-3284
Rochester (G-7153)
KinderCare Learning Centers E 952 835-4955
Minneapolis (G-4809)
KinderCare Learning Centers E 952 941-5054
Eden Prairie (G-1702)
KinderCare Learning Centers E 651 681-1968
Saint Paul (G-7816)
KinderCare Learning Centers E 651 735-0037
Saint Paul (G-9237)
Kindercare Learning Centers E 952 920-8548
Minnetonka (G-6185)
Kindercare Learning Centers E 651 452-1616
Saint Paul (G-7817)
Kindercare Learning Centers E 952 440-9890
Savage (G-9393)
Kindercare Learning Centers E 651 735-3711
Saint Paul (G-9238)
Kindercare Learning Centers E 952 403-6862
Shakopee (G-9448)
Kindercare Learning Centers E 651 386-6672
Saint Paul (G-9239)
Knowledge Learning Corp E 952 944-3801
Eden Prairie (G-1703)
Knowledge Learning Corp E 952 452-6625
Saint Paul (G-7818)
Knowledge Learning Corp E 763 553-7960
Minneapolis (G-4816)
Knowledge Learning Corp E 651 631-8728
Saint Paul (G-8550)
Knowledge Learning Corp E 507 289-5006
Rochester (G-7156)
Knowledge Learning Corp E 507 529-8455
Rochester (G-7155)
Knowledge Learning Corp E 952 440-2677
Savage (G-9394)
Knowledge Learning Corp E 612 623-4642
Minneapolis (G-4817)
La Creche Early Childhood E 612 377-1786
Minneapolis (G-4829)
La Petite Academy Inc E 651 463-2022
Farmington (G-2053)
Learning For Leadership E 612 789-9598
Minneapolis (G-4852)
Lifetrack Resources Inc D 651 227-8471
Saint Paul (G-8586)
Little Acorns Child Care Inc E 952 475-0828
Long Lake (G-3028)
Little Acorns Day School E 952 475-0828
Wayzata (G-9925)
Lord of Life Lutheran Church E 763 427-1100
Anoka (G-201)
Lutheran Social Service of MN E 218 281-6418
Crookston (G-1127)
Macdonald Montessori Child E 651 227-1039
Saint Paul (G-8604)
Marshall Public School E 507 537-6210
Marshall (G-3311)
Martin County West School Dist E 507 728-8609
Welcome (G-9959)
Maxwell Wsu Children Center D 507 457-5368
Winona (G-10114)
ML Enterprises LLC E 952 401-9051
Excelsior (G-1936)
Mount Olivet Lutheran Church E 612 861-3305
Minneapolis (G-5140)
Mount Zion Hebrew Congregation E 651 698-3881
Saint Paul (G-8726)
New Discoveries Montessori E 320 234-6362
Hutchinson (G-2709)
New Horizon Child Care Inc E 763 574-7450
Minneapolis (G-3553)
New Horizon Child Care Inc E 952 893-1893
Minneapolis (G-5189)
New Horizon Child Care Inc E 952 423-6690
Saint Paul (G-7850)
New Horizon Child Care Inc E 651 481-8069
Saint Paul (G-8749)
New Horizon Child Care Inc E 763 315-3033
Minneapolis (G-5190)
New Horizon Child Care Inc E 952 469-6659
Lakeville (G-2922)
New Horizon Child Care Inc D 763 557-1111
Plymouth (G-6875)
New Horizon Child Care Inc E 763 478-2412
Minneapolis (G-5191)
New Horizon Child Care Inc E 763 757-2604
Minneapolis (G-3554)
New Horizon Enterprises Inc C 763 557-1111
Plymouth (G-6876)
Normandale Evangelical E 952 929-1697
Minneapolis (G-5209)
Northwest Community Action Inc D 218 528-3258
Badger (G-299)
Only For Kids Inc E 763 754-2594
Anoka (G-212)
Opportunity Manor Inc D 320 240-1900
Sartell (G-9339)
Our Savior Lutheran Church E 952 474-5181
Excelsior (G-1952)
Our Savior's Lutheran Church E 763 434-6117
Cedar (G-883)
Parents In Community Action D 612 377-7422
Minneapolis (G-5324)
Parents In Community Action E 612 823-6361
Minneapolis (G-5323)
Parents In Community Action E 612 362-0360
Minneapolis (G-5325)
Peace of Mind Day Care Inc D 651 731-2608
Saint Paul (G-9257)
Pine Haven Care Center Inc D 507 356-8304
Pine Island (G-6817)
Pine Point Public School Dist E 218 573-4100
Ponsford (G-6892)
Pinewood Cloquet E 218 879-4566
Cloquet (G-1060)
Playworks Dakota D 952 445-7529
Prior Lake (G-6948)
Possabilities D 507 281-6116
Rochester (G-7208)
Providence Academy D 763 258-2500
Minneapolis (G-5432)
Reach-Up Inc E 320 253-8110
Saint Cloud (G-7423)
Regents of The University of D 612 627-4014
Minneapolis (G-5493)
Reuben Lindh Family Services D 763 521-3477
Minneapolis (G-5532)
River Hills Early Childhood E 952 895-0413
Burnsville (G-791)
Rocking Horse Ranch E 952 440-1777
Prior Lake (G-6952)
Room For Growing E 651 464-1601
Forest Lake (G-2167)
Room For Growing E 651 257-2441
Chisago City (G-994)
Southside Family Nurturing Ctr E 612 721-2762
Minneapolis (G-5711)
Special School District No 1 D 612 668-1420
Minneapolis (G-5717)
St Andrew Lutheran Church E 952 937-2776
Eden Prairie (G-1781)
St David's Center Child B 952 939-0396
Hopkins (G-2636)
St James Church Inc E 651 293-3945
Saint Paul (G-8984)
St Mary's Medical Center A 218 786-4000
Duluth (G-1474)
St Mary's School E 507 794-6141
Sleepy Eye (G-9502)
St Michaels Lutheran Church E 952 831-5276
Minneapolis (G-5728)
St Paul's Childhood Center E 651 224-4749
Saint Paul (G-9001)
Step By Step Montessori E 763 315-3602
Osseo (G-6667)
Step By Step Montessori School E 763 557-6777
Minneapolis (G-5749)
Step By Step Montessori School E 952 368-4456
Chaska (G-982)
Step By Step Montessori School E 763 498-5437
Loretto (G-3052)
Swan River Montessori Charter E 763 271-7926
Monticello (G-6288)
Tiny Tots & Little Tykes Pre E 651 457-0042
Saint Paul (G-7923)
Tri-County Community Action E 320 632-3691
Little Falls (G-3020)
Under The Rainbow Child Care E 651 388-6433
Red Wing (G-7009)
VA Employee Child Care Center E 612 725-2000
Minneapolis (G-5952)
Wee Pals Child Care Center Inc E 507 451-8355
Owatonna (G-6743)
Westwood Lutheran Church E 952 545-5623
Minneapolis (G-6062)
Wheaton Head Start E 320 563-8191
Wheaton (G-9971)
Y M C A Infant Center E 651 646-4557
Saint Paul (G-9171)
YMCA D 320 222-9622
Willmar (G-10059)
YMCA Children's Center E 651 777-8103
Saint Paul (G-9173)
YMCA of Greater Saint Paul C 651 683-4713
Saint Paul (G-7952)
YMCA of Greater Saint Paul E 651 771-8881
Saint Paul (G-9174)
YMCA of Greater Saint Paul E 651 645-6605
Saint Paul (G-9175)
YMCA of Greater St Paul D 218 365-2117
Ely (G-1919)
YMCA of Greater St Paul D 651 292-4143
Saint Paul (G-9178)
YMCA of Greater St Paul D 651 646-4557
Saint Paul (G-9177)
YMCA of Greater St Paul C 651 483-2671
Saint Paul (G-9176)
YMCA of Greater St Paul C 651 457-0048
Saint Paul (G-7953)
YMCA of Worthington, Minnesota E 507 376-6197
Worthington (G-10199)
Young Men's Chritn Assoc of C 763 535-4800
Minneapolis (G-6101)
Young Men's Chritn Assoc of D 612 827-5401
Minneapolis (G-6102)
Young Men's Chritn Assoc of E 612 588-9484
Minneapolis (G-6103)
Young Men's Chritn Assoc of C 952 835-2567
Minneapolis (G-6104)
Young Women's Christian Assn D 218 722-7425
Duluth (G-1505)
YWCA of Minneapolis A 612 332-0501
Minneapolis (G-6111)

SIC

Employment codes: A=Over 500 employees, B=251-500
C=101-250, D=51-100, E=25-50
2011 Harris Minnesota
Services Directory
© Harris InfoSource 1-866-281-6415
521

8361 Residential Care

A Share Home Inc E 218 631-1853
Wadena (G-9797)
Ability Building Center E 507 895-7161
La Crescent (G-2836)
Accessible Space Inc E 651 645-7271
Saint Paul (G-7976)
Aftenro Society E 218 728-6600
Duluth (G-1233)
Aging Joyfully Inc E 952 941-2510
Eden Prairie (G-1586)
Alternative For Autistic D 763 560-3013
Minneapolis (G-3736)
Alternative For People With D 763 560-5330
Minneapolis (G-3737)
American Baptist Homes of The D 507 373-0188
Albert Lea (G-39)
American Baptist Homes of The E 952 941-3175
Eden Prairie (G-1590)
American Home Health E 612 860-7301
Saint Paul (G-8026)
Arbors At Ridges E 952 898-4005
Burnsville (G-680)
Arrowhead House Foster Care E 218 727-8040
Duluth (G-1241)
Augustana Chapel View Homes B 612 333-1551
Minneapolis (G-3835)
Aveyron Homes Inc C 320 234-6063
Hutchinson (G-2688)
Aveyron Homes Inc C 320 587-6277
Hutchinson (G-2689)
Aviv Health Care Inc C 612 377-4723
Minneapolis (G-3845)
Axis Minnesota Inc D 651 774-5940
Saint Paul (G-8083)
B L E A Inc E 507 895-8111
La Crescent (G-2838)
B L E A Inc E 507 896-3040
Houston (G-2662)
Bell Hill Recovery Center Inc E 218 631-3610
Wadena (G-9798)
Benedictine Health System C 507 534-3191
Plainview (G-6838)
Bethany Covenant Village D 612 781-2691
Minneapolis (G-3893)
Bethel Duluth Society D 218 722-1724
Duluth (G-1251)
Beverly Enterprises - MN C 612 333-0111
Minneapolis (G-3897)
Big Stone Community Homes Inc E 320 839-6139
Ortonville (G-6578)
Boston Health Care Systems Inc C 651 501-2378
Saint Paul (G-8118)
Bridge For Youth D 612 377-8800
Minneapolis (G-3944)
Bridge House E 218 725-7785
Duluth (G-1256)
Cardinal Pointe of Oakdale E 651 578-0650
Saint Paul (G-9192)
Catholic Charities of The C 320 251-8811
Saint Cloud (G-7474)
Cedars of Austin E 507 437-3246
Austin (G-266)
Cenneidigh Inc C 507 334-4347
Faribault (G-1999)
Centennial House of Apple Val E 952 891-2711
Saint Paul (G-7729)
Chandler Place E 612 788-7321
Minneapolis (G-6124)
City of Fertile C 218 945-6194
Fertile (G-2125)
Clark Lake Homes Inc E 218 829-1699
Brainerd (G-558)
Client Community Services Inc E 507 376-6095
Worthington (G-10181)
Cochran Programs D 651 437-4585
Hastings (G-2378)
Colonial Acres Home Inc C 763 544-1555
Golden Valley (G-2239)
Colonial Acres Home Inc C 763 546-6125
Minneapolis (G-4122)
Comforts of Home E 651 287-0265
Saint Paul (G-7735)
Comforts of Home E 651 426-1036
White Bear Lake (G-9974)
Comforts of Home Hugo E 651 653-3282
Hugo (G-2675)
Community Involvement Programs E 320 245-5362
Sandstone (G-9320)
Community Living Inc D 952 443-2048
Victoria (G-9726)
Cornerstone Residence E 218 647-8258
Kelliher (G-2827)
Country Side East Living E 507 446-8334
Owatonna (G-6706)
County of Clay E 218 299-5150
Moorhead (G-6308)
Covenant Home Services LLC E 763 755-9009
Minneapolis (G-3446)
Diversified Lifestyles Inc E 320 235-0270
Willmar (G-10000)
Divine House Inc D 218 847-0574
Detroit Lakes (G-1191)
Dungarvin Illinois Inc D 651 699-6050
Saint Paul (G-8312)
Dungarvin Minnesota Inc B 651 699-6050
Saint Paul (G-8313)
Dungarvin New Mexico Inc D 651 699-6050
Saint Paul (G-8314)
E S I Heritage D 218 865-4135
Gilbert (G-2203)
Ebi Inc E 218 624-3122
Duluth (G-1308)
Ecumen Home Care Inc E 952 888-1010
Minneapolis (G-4312)
Eden Rs C 612 287-1600
Minneapolis (G-4313)
Elm Residence Inc B 507 835-1146
Waseca (G-9877)
Emerald Crest E 952 856-7510
Victoria (G-9728)
Empowerment Services of Rice D 507 333-2583
Faribault (G-2002)
English Roseat Suites Inc E 952 983-0412
Wayzata (G-9916)
Enrich Inc E 651 482-9608
Saint Paul (G-8341)
Evangelical Covenant Church E 763 546-6125
Minneapolis (G-4375)
Evangelical Covenant Church D 612 781-2691
Minneapolis (G-4374)
Family Focus Inc E 612 331-4429
Minneapolis (G-4408)
Foster Four E 320 240-0243
Saint Cloud (G-7414)
Fountain Lake Treatment Center D 507 373-2384
Albert Lea (G-52)
Freeport West Inc D 612 824-3040
Minneapolis (G-4486)
Gables Inc E 507 282-2500
Rochester (G-7122)
Garden House Estates Ltd E 218 628-0271
Duluth (G-1331)
Garkat Inc E 507 835-8227
Waseca (G-9879)
General Pediatric E 612 626-2820
Minneapolis (G-4516)
Golden Oaks Inc E 218 729-5014
Duluth (G-1337)
Grand Meadow Health Care Ctr D 507 754-5212
Grand Meadow (G-2264)
Greenview Alzheimer's E 218 263-3935
Hibbing (G-2447)
Grove Chestnut Inc E 218 749-6846
Virginia (G-9739)
Habilitative Services Inc D 507 532-5366
Marshall (G-3299)
Hammer Residences Inc C 763 473-1261
Wayzata (G-9919)
Harry Meyering Center Inc B 507 388-3551
Mankato (G-3135)
Hawley Retirement Inc E 218 483-3337
Hawley (G-2420)
Hawthorne House Inc E 763 525-1000
Minneapolis (G-4611)
Hazelden Foundation D 612 559-2022
Minneapolis (G-4614)
Healtheast Care System E 651 232-2002
Saint Paul (G-8456)
Heartland Homes Options In Com E 218 732-4572
Park Rapids (G-6752)
Heartland Ranch E 320 843-4815
Benson (G-441)
Heartstone of Minnesota E 651 457-2629
South Saint Paul (G-9529)
Hecla Inc 320 255-9530
Saint Cloud (G-7526)
Hiawatha Valley Mental Health E 507 454-4341
Winona (G-10102)
Hillside Homes E 218 720-5890
Duluth (G-1352)
Home & Community Options Inc E 507 452-9311
Winona (G-10103)
Home For Creative Living Inc D 507 831-5033
Windom (G-10068)
Homestead At Coon Rapids E 763 754-2800
Minneapolis (G-3492)
Homeward Bound Inc D 763 566-7860
Minneapolis (G-4673)
Hope Haven Inc E 507 825-2379
Pipestone (G-6830)
Hope Shilohs Inc E 507 934-2094
Saint Peter (G-9306)
Horizon Health Inc E 218 828-4142
Brainerd (G-569)
Horizon Home Inc D 507 344-3360
Mankato (G-3144)
Howry Residential Services E 651 917-9111
Saint Paul (G-8498)
Industries Inc E 763 689-5434
Cambridge (G-838)
J B Waivered Services E 218 828-4962
Fort Ripley (G-2174)
Jones-Harrison Residence Corp B 612 920-2030
Minneapolis (G-4778)
Karcher Foster Services Inc E 651 674-2031
North Branch (G-6501)
Krushe Residential Services E 218 746-3117
Pillager (G-6810)
Lakeland Hospice & Home Care C 218 998-1400
Fergus Falls (G-2082)
Lakes Homes & Program Devpt D 218 847-5642
Detroit Lakes (G-1203)
Lifetime Resources Inc D 612 804-2252
Minneapolis (G-4881)
Lifeway Services E 218 722-1184
Duluth (G-1382)
Lighthouse Villages D 952 442-1261
Waconia (G-9789)
Linnea Residential Home Inc E 651 257-2211
Chisago City (G-992)
Little Sisters of The Poor of D 651 227-0336
Saint Paul (G-8592)
Lrn Associates Management Inc E 507 836-8955
Slayton (G-9488)
Lutheran Social Service of MN D 651 388-8845
Red Wing (G-6989)
Lyngblomsten B 651 646-2941
Saint Paul (G-8599)
M B W Co C 507 354-3808
New Ulm (G-6459)
Mainstreet Village Retirement E 612 869-6584
Richfield (G-7036)
Maple Leaf Services Inc E 507 765-3848
Preston (G-6899)
Marshall County Group Homes D 218 437-6695
Argyle (G-247)
Martin Luther Manor B 952 888-7751
Minneapolis (G-4960)
Minnesota Department of E 218 226-6300
Silver Bay (G-9483)
Minnesota Indian Primary E 218 879-6731
Sawyer (G-9413)
Minnesota Teen Challenge Inc E 612 373-3366
Minneapolis (G-5095)
Missions Inc Programs D 763 559-1883
Minneapolis (G-5109)
Mount Olivet Lutheran Church E 612 861-3305
Minneapolis (G-5140)
Mount Olivet Rolling Acres Inc B 952 474-5974
Victoria (G-9731)
New Beginnings At Waverly LLC D 763 658-5800
Waverly (G-9904)
New Challenges Inc E 651 681-2044
Saint Paul (G-7849)
New Dawn Inc C 507 425-3278
Fulda (G-2196)
New Life Treatment Center E 507 777-4321
Woodstock (G-10176)
New Perspective of Minnesota E 651 407-9076
Mahtomedi (G-3097)
Norris Square E 651 769-2447
Cottage Grove (G-1106)
North Homes Inc D 218 327-3055
Grand Rapids (G-2298)
Northeast Residence Inc B 651 765-0217
Saint Paul (G-8756)
Northfield Care Center Inc C 507 645-9511
Northfield (G-6536)
Northfield Manor Inc 507 645-9090
Northfield (G-6538)
Northland Counseling Center E 218 327-1105
Grand Rapids (G-2302)
Northwood Childrens Home Soc D 218 724-8815
Duluth (G-1410)
Oak Ridge Homes of Wadena Inc E 218 829-7599
Brainerd (G-579)
Omegon Inc E 952 541-4738
Hopkins (G-2594)
Omnia Family Services E 507 287-2300
Rochester (G-7198)
▲ Opportunity Partners Inc C 952 938-5511
Hopkins (G-2595)
Opportunity Partners Inc E 763 441-0960
Elk River (G-1889)
Paragon Associates Inc D 218 722-5009
Duluth (G-1418)
Parkshore Senior Campus E 952 929-1034
Minneapolis (G-5338)
Parkwood Shores Assisted E 952 924-0400
Minneapolis (G-5339)
People Inc E 651 774-0011
Saint Paul (G-8816)
Phoenix Residence Inc C 651 227-7655
Saint Paul (G-7876)
Pine Manors Inc E 218 732-4337
Nevis (G-6405)
Pine Ridge Homes Inc D 218 879-1257
Cloquet (G-1059)
Pine River Group Home Inc D 218 587-4888
Pine River (G-6820)
Pines E 612 861-3331
Minneapolis (G-5379)
Pinnacle Programs Inc E 507 283-4425
Magnolia (G-3083)
Polk County Developmental E 218 281-4181
Crookston (G-1134)
Port Group Home Office E 218 828-6274
Brainerd (G-581)
Prairie Community Services E 218 739-2045
Fergus Falls (G-2115)
Prairie Community Services E 320 589-2057
Morris (G-6374)
Prairie Lodge E 763 566-1495
Minneapolis (G-5400)
Presbyterian Homes & Services D 651 631-6100
Saint Paul (G-8840)
Presbyterian Homes H & A E 651 631-6659
Saint Paul (G-8841)
Presbyterian Homes of Inver E 651 451-5959
Inver Grove Heights (G-2765)

(G-00000) Company's Geographic Section entry number
522
2011 Harris Minnesota
Services Directory
▲=Import ▼=Export
◆=Import/Export

Progressive Habilitative Svcs ....E.....763 536-8128
Minneapolis (G-5426)
R E M North Star Inc ....E.....218 435-6088
Fosston (G-2179)
Rainbow Residence Inc ....E.....507 451-5327
Owatonna (G-6733)
Rakhma Inc ....D.....612 824-2345
Minneapolis (G-5464)
Range Center Inc ....C.....218 254-3347
Chisholm (G-1000)
Realife Cooperative of Mounds ....D.....763 780-9737
Saint Paul (G-8879)
REM Central Lakes Inc ....E.....320 252-8875
Saint Cloud (G-7586)
REM Greatland Inc ....E.....651 388-7158
Red Wing (G-7001)
REM Inc ....E.....651 647-9243
Saint Paul (G-8888)
REM Inc ....C.....507 287-6824
Rochester (G-7221)
REM Inc ....D.....507 387-3181
Mankato (G-3185)
REM Pillsbury Inc ....D.....612 871-1954
Minneapolis (G-5512)
REM Riverbluff Inc ....E.....507 281-1105
Rochester (G-7222)
REM Southwest Services Inc ....C.....320 235-9174
Willmar (G-10039)
Remwoodvale Inc ....E.....507 634-6073
Kasson (G-2823)
Residential Advantages Inc ....D.....507 831-3804
Lakefield (G-2883)
Residential Services of ....E.....218 728-6823
Duluth (G-1436)
Reverence For Life & Concern ....D.....320 564-4911
Granite Falls (G-2319)
Riesco Inc ....E.....651 771-8235
Saint Paul (G-8901)
Rural Living Environments Inc ....E.....218 827-3495
Babbitt (G-298)
Safe Haven Shelter For Youth ....E.....952 288-2680
Shakopee (G-9472)
Seasons Hospice ....E.....507 285-1930
Rochester (G-7249)
Seek Home Inc ....D.....763 494-0870
Osseo (G-6661)
Semcil Living Inc ....E.....507 285-1815
Rochester (G-7250)
Senior Grace Services ....E.....507 388-3660
Mankato (G-3196)
Senior Southview Living ....E.....651 554-4838
Saint Paul (G-7900)
Sisters of The Good Shepherd ....E.....651 484-0221
Saint Paul (G-8961)
Solstice Corp ....E.....218 729-5014
Duluth (G-1456)
South Metro Human Services ....E.....651 221-9880
Saint Paul (G-8972)
South Metro Human Services ....D.....651 291-1979
Saint Paul (G-8973)
St Anthony Health Center ....B.....612 788-9673
Minneapolis (G-6131)
St Cloud Hospital ....E.....320 259-9149
Sauk Rapids (G-9376)
St James Home of Duluth ....C.....218 728-7500
Duluth (G-1462)
St Williams Nursing Home Inc ....C.....218 338-4671
Parkers Prairie (G-6767)
Stonecrest ....D.....651 264-3200
Saint Paul (G-9278)
Sunrise Senior Living Inc ....D.....952 927-8000
Minneapolis (G-5769)
Sur La Rue Inc ....E.....651 772-4957
Saint Paul (G-9017)
Swift County Homes Inc ....E.....320 843-3509
Benson (G-442)
Tasks Unlimited Inc ....E.....612 871-3320
Minneapolis (G-5792)
Traditions of Owatonna ....D.....507 451-0433
Owatonna (G-6741)
Truman Sr Living Inc ....E.....507 776-2031
Truman (G-9697)
Turning Point Inc ....E.....612 520-4004
Minneapolis (G-5869)
Twin City Christian Homes Inc ....D.....952 944-8982
Eden Prairie (G-1799)
Vinland National Center ....E.....763 479-3555
Loretto (G-3054)
Volunteers Of America Inc ....D.....763 753-2500
Anoka (G-237)
Walker Assisted Living Corp ....E.....952 835-8351
Minneapolis (G-6008)
Walker Methodist Senior Svcs ....A.....612 827-5931
Minneapolis (G-6012)
Wendigo Pines Assisted Ll ....E.....218 326-6900
Grand Rapids (G-2312)
Wesley Residence Inc ....E.....218 628-2307
Duluth (G-1501)
West Central Community Service ....D.....218 643-5952
Breckenridge (G-603)
Whittier Place ....E.....612 872-1926
Minneapolis (G-6066)
Willow Home ....D.....507 426-8277
Fairfax (G-1956)
Willowbrook Co-Op ....E.....507 388-2886
Mankato (G-3219)
Workabilities Inc ....E.....763 541-1844
Minneapolis (G-6085)
Zumbro House Inc ....D.....651 264-1000
Saint Paul (G-9293)

8399 Social Services, NEC

AARP ....D.....952 858-9040
Minneapolis (G-3658)
Alexandra House Inc ....E.....763 780-2332
Minneapolis (G-3388)
Alpha Human Services Inc ....E.....612 872-8218
Minneapolis (G-3732)
American Heart Association Inc ....E.....952 835-3300
Minneapolis (G-3750)
American Indian Community ....D.....612 813-1610
Minneapolis (G-3752)
American Swedish Institute ....E.....612 871-4907
Minneapolis (G-3760)
Amherst H Wilder Foundation ....E.....651 647-9676
Saint Paul (G-8044)
Anoka County Community Action ....E.....763 783-4747
Minneapolis (G-3403)
Arrowhead Economic Opportunity ....D.....218 749-2912
Virginia (G-9735)
Austin Medical Center-Mayo ....A.....507 433-7351
Austin (G-261)
Aveyron Homes Inc ....C.....320 234-6063
Hutchinson (G-2688)
Aveyron Homes Inc ....C.....320 587-6277
Hutchinson (G-2689)
Bethel Duluth Society ....D.....218 722-1724
Duluth (G-1251)
C C R Inc 218 236-6730
Moorhead (G-6301)
Churches United In Ministry ....E.....218 720-6521
Duluth (G-1271)
Chyrsalis of Kandiyohi County ....E.....320 231-1480
Willmar (G-9998)
Citireach International ....E.....952 975-0516
Eden Prairie (G-1628)
Clark Lake Homes Inc ....E.....218 833-1322
Brainerd (G-559)
Communication Service For The ....C.....218 291-1120
Moorhead (G-6305)
Communication Service For The ....E.....651 297-6700
Saint Paul (G-8235)
Community Acton of Minneapolis ....E.....612 335-5837
Minneapolis (G-4138)
Community Drug & Alcohol Svcs ....E.....952 564-3000
Burnsville (G-702)
County of Todd ....D.....320 732-4500
Long Prairie (G-3040)
D A Peterson ....E.....612 782-9860
Minneapolis (G-4211)
East Side Neighborhood Svcs ....D.....612 781-6011
Minneapolis (G-4308)
Elder Network ....C.....507 285-5272
Rochester (G-7105)
Everyday Miracles Inc ....E.....763 323-0012
Anoka (G-179)
Greater Twin Cities United Way ....C.....612 340-7481
Minneapolis (G-4562)
Heartland Community Action ....E.....320 235-0850
Willmar (G-10007)
Hubbard County Developmental ....D.....218 732-3358
Park Rapids (G-6754)
Human Services ....E.....218 935-2568
Mahnomen (G-3087)
Human Services of Fairbault ....D.....507 238-4757
Fairmont (G-1975)
Human Services of Faribault ....E.....507 526-3265
Blue Earth (G-536)
Hutchinson Area Health Care ....A.....320 234-5000
Hutchinson (G-2698)
Initiative Foundation ....E.....320 632-9255
Little Falls (G-3007)
Inter-County Community Council ....E.....218 796-5144
Oklee (G-6557)
International Twins Assoc ....D.....763 571-3022
Minneapolis (G-3501)
Jackson County Developmental ....E.....507 662-6156
Lakefield (G-2882)
Jeremiah Program ....E.....612 692-8711
Minneapolis (G-4759)
Lakes & Pines Community Action ....E.....320 679-1800
Mora (G-6365)
Lakes & Prairies Community ....E.....218 299-7000
Moorhead (G-6324)
Life By Design Inc ....C.....763 757-3263
Minneapolis (G-3518)
Macphail Center For Music ....C.....612 321-0100
Minneapolis (G-4928)
Mahube Community Council Inc ....D.....218 847-1385
Detroit Lakes (G-1209)
Mains'l Services Inc ....E.....763 494-4553
Brooklyn Park (G-615)
Mental Health Resources Inc ....D.....651 659-2900
Saint Paul (G-8634)
Merrick Community Services ....E.....651 771-8821
Saint Paul (G-8638)
Metroplitan Ctr For ....D.....651 646-8342
Saint Paul (G-8642)
Mid-American Baptist Social ....E.....952 443-2024
Victoria (G-9730)
Minneapolis Community Devpt ....C.....612 673-5095
Minneapolis (G-5052)
Minnesota Aids Project ....E.....612 341-2060
Minneapolis (G-5066)
Minnesota Institute of Public ....E.....763 427-5310
Saint Paul (G-8691)
Minnesota Program Development ....D.....218 722-2781
Duluth (G-1395)
Minnesota State Colleges ....E.....218 681-2181
Thief River Falls (G-9675)
Otter Tail County Human Svcs ....D.....218 998-8150
Fergus Falls (G-2106)
P H M Eaglecrest Inc ....D.....651 631-6009
Saint Paul (G-8798)
People Enhancing People ....E.....651 450-5960
Saint Paul (G-8815)
Perspectives Inc ....E.....952 926-2600
Minneapolis (G-5367)
Prairie Island Tribal Council ....D.....651 385-2554
Welch (G-9956)
Productive Alternatives Inc ....E.....218 825-8148
Brainerd (G-583)
Project For Pride In Living ....D.....612 455-5100
Minneapolis (G-5428)
Project For Pride In Living ....D.....612 332-0664
Minneapolis (G-5429)
Saint Paul Foundation Inc ....D.....651 224-5463
Saint Paul (G-8926)
Scholarship America ....C.....952 830-7300
Minneapolis (G-5612)
Scholarship America Inc ....C.....507 931-1682
Saint Peter (G-9313)
Semcac ....E.....507 864-7741
Rushford (G-7392)
Seward CSP ....E.....612 333-0331
Minneapolis (G-5645)
Sigma Tau Omega Inc ....E.....651 644-7200
Inver Grove Heights (G-2769)
Society of Corporate ....E.....952 405-7925
Minneapolis (G-5694)
Southwestern Minnesota ....E.....507 376-4195
Worthington (G-10196)
Stratis Health ....D.....952 854-3306
Minneapolis (G-5759)
Temple of Aaron Sisterhood ....E.....651 698-8874
Saint Paul (G-9036)
Tri-County Action Program Inc ....E.....320 251-1612
Waite Park (G-9845)
Tri-County Action Program Inc ....E.....320 255-0705
Waite Park (G-9846)
Tri-Valley Opportunity Council ....C.....218 281-5832
Crookston (G-1139)
Tri-Valley Opportunity Council ....D.....218 281-5832
Crookston (G-1140)
Tri-Valley Opportunity Council ....E.....218 281-5832
Crookston (G-1141)
Turning Point Foundation ....E.....612 520-4004
Minneapolis (G-5868)
United Way Info & Referral ....E.....651 291-6795
Saint Paul (G-9110)
Vermillion Community College ....D.....218 365-7200
Ely (G-1916)
West Central Minnesota ....D.....218 685-4486
Elbow Lake (G-1855)
White Earth Reservation ....D.....218 983-3387
Ogema (G-6555)

84 MUSEUMS, BOTANICAL, ZOOLOGICAL GARDENS

8412 Museums & Art Galleries

American Swedish Institute ....E.....612 871-4907
Minneapolis (G-3760)
American Wings Air Museum ....E.....763 786-4146
Minneapolis (G-3401)
▲ Art Walker Center ....C.....612 375-7600
Minneapolis (G-3812)
▲ Art Walker Center Inc ....C.....612 375-7600
Minneapolis (G-3813)
Bakken Museum ....E.....612 927-6508
Minneapolis (G-3862)
Commemorative Air Force ....C.....651 455-6942
South Saint Paul (G-9523)
County of Mower ....C.....507 437-9440
Austin (G-268)
Evansville Arts Coalition ....D.....218 948-2787
Evansville (G-1925)
Historical Society of MN ....E.....218 226-6372
Two Harbors (G-9708)
Historical Society of MN ....E.....218 327-4482
Grand Rapids (G-2286)
Historical Society of MN ....E.....651 297-2555
Saint Paul (G-8485)
Ironworld Development Corp ....D.....218 254-7959
Chisholm (G-998)
James Ford Bell Museum of ....E.....612 624-4112
Minneapolis (G-4753)
Lake Superior Railroad Museum ....D.....218 733-7590
Duluth (G-1378)
Mayowood Mansion Tours ....E.....507 282-9447
Rochester (G-7177)
▲ Minneapolis Society of Fine ....C.....612 870-3046
Minneapolis (G-5064)
Minnesota Children's Museum ....D.....651 225-6000
Saint Paul (G-8677)
Regents of The University of ....E.....612 625-9494
Minneapolis (G-5489)
Science Museum of Minnesota ....B.....651 221-9488
Saint Paul (G-8936)

S I C

Employment codes: A=Over 500 employees, B=251-500
C=101-250, D=51-100, E=25-50
2011 Harris Minnesota
Services Directory
© Harris InfoSource 1-866-281-6415
523

8422 Arboreta, Botanical & Zoological Gardens

City of Saint Paul .... E 651 487-8200
Saint Paul (G-8205)
Minnesota Aquarium LLC .... D 952 853-0628
Minneapolis (G-5068)
Zoological Gardens, Minnesota .... C 952 431-9299
Saint Paul (G-7955)

86 MEMBERSHIP ORGANIZATIONS

8611 Business Associations

Aca International .... D 952 926-6547
Minneapolis (G-3663)
Ad Efx of America Inc 952 941-3500
Eden Prairie (G-1583)
American Dairy Association of .... E 651 488-0261
Saint Paul (G-8024)
Better Business Bureau of Minn .... E 651 699-1111
Saint Paul (G-8110)
Brock White Co LLC .... E 651 647-0950
Saint Paul (G-8131)
Central Minnesota Municipal 507 526-2193
Blue Earth (G-531)
City of Blackduck .... E 218 835-4803
Blackduck (G-473)
City of Breckenridge .... E 218 643-1431
Breckenridge (G-593)
Communicating For Agriculture .... E 218 739-3241
Fergus Falls (G-2069)
Communicating For America Inc .... E 218 739-3241
Fergus Falls (G-2070)
East Lake Community Center .... E 218 768-3311
McGregor (G-3339)
Employers Association Inc .... D 763 253-9100
Minneapolis (G-4351)
F R Bigelow Foundation Inc .... D 651 224-5463
Saint Paul (G-8360)
Gemmell Lakes Association .... E 218 897-5318
Mizpah (G-6243)
Hennepin County .... E 612 348-7137
Minneapolis (G-4636)
Idw LLC .... E 952 949-6690
Chanhassen (G-925)
Independent Community Bankers .... D 320 352-6546
Sauk Centre (G-9348)
Industrial Fabrics Association .... D 651 222-2508
Saint Paul (G-8511)
International Association of .... E 763 706-3650
Minneapolis (G-3500)
Kandiyohi County Economic .... E 320 235-7370
Willmar (G-10013)
League of Minnesota Cities .... D 651 281-1200
Saint Paul (G-8573)
Midwest Dairy Association .... D 651 488-0261
Saint Paul (G-8658)
Mike Bishoff .... E 218 697-2800
Hill City (G-2481)
Minnesota Chamber of Commerce .... E 651 292-4650
Saint Paul (G-8675)
Minnesota Chapter of The Natl .... E 952 928-4647
Minneapolis (G-5071)
Minnesota Farmers' Market Assn .... D 320 763-6893
Saint Paul (G-8686)
Minnesota League of Credit .... E 651 288-5170
Saint Paul (G-8694)
Minnesota Liquor Retailers Inc .... E 651 772-0910
Saint Paul (G-8697)
Minnesota Magazine & Pubn .... E 651 290-6281
Saint Paul (G-8698)
Pleasant Valley Township Assn .... E 651 437-5660
Hastings (G-2399)
Professional Association of .... E 612 259-1600
Minneapolis (G-5419)
Riverheights Chamber of .... E 651 451-2266
Inver Grove Heights (G-2766)
Tyler Area Community Club .... D 507 247-3905
Tyler (G-9715)
Western Community Action Inc .... E 507 537-1416
Marshall (G-3334)

8621 Professional Membership Organizations

Aacc International Inc .... D 651 454-7250
Saint Paul (G-7686)
Allina Health System .... E 651 699-1501
Saint Paul (G-8015)
Allina Health System .... A 651 642-2700
Saint Paul (G-8016)
American Academy of Neurology .... D 651 695-1940
Saint Paul (G-8019)
American Phytopathological Soc .... D 651 454-7250
Saint Paul (G-7697)
American Registry of .... E 651 687-0048
Saint Paul (G-7698)
Benedictine Team Health Systs .... E 763 689-1162
Cambridge (G-834)
County of Becker .... E 218 847-2661
Detroit Lakes (G-1190)
Decare Dental LLC .... B 800 371-6561
Saint Paul (G-7750)
Education Minnesota .... D 651 227-9541
Saint Paul (G-8327)
Granite Medical Center .... E 320 564-2511
Granite Falls (G-2316)
Institute For Clinical Systems .... E 952 814-7060
Minneapolis (G-4708)
International Assn For 651 681-8566
Saint Paul (G-7804)
International Association of .... B 612 673-3586
Minneapolis (G-4720)
Lake Superior Medical Society .... E 218 727-3325
Duluth (G-1377)
Lakes Country Service Co-Op .... D 218 739-3273
Fergus Falls (G-2084)
Minnesota Association of Sch .... D 651 645-6272
Saint Paul (G-8673)
Minnesota Bankers Association .... E 952 835-3900
Eden Prairie (G-1725)
Minnesota Hospital Association .... E 651 641-1121
Saint Paul (G-8690)
Minnesota Medical Association .... E 612 378-1875
Minneapolis (G-5084)
Minnesota Nurses' Association .... E 651 646-4807
Saint Paul (G-8700)
Minnesota Society of Certified .... E 952 831-2707
Minneapolis (G-5094)
Potter David MD PHD .... D 612 625-8933
Minneapolis (G-5397)
Veterinary Hospitals Assn .... E 651 451-6669
South Saint Paul (G-9549)

8631 Labor Unions & Similar Organizations

Afscme Building Corp .... E 651 451-7678
South Saint Paul (G-9507)
Boilermakers Local Lodge 650 .... E 651 345-5472
Lake City (G-2851)
Bryant Square Apartments .... E 612 825-4379
Minneapolis (G-3965)
International Association of .... E 651 688-2640
Saint Paul (G-7805)
International Association of .... E 320 251-8732
Saint Cloud (G-7532)
Law Enforcement Labor Services 651 293-4424
Saint Paul (G-8566)
M C C A .... D 651 645-4545
Saint Paul (G-8600)
Minn Health Care Union Local .... E 612 331-4690
Saint Paul (G-8670)
Minnesota Afscme Council 5 .... E 651 455-0773
South Saint Paul (G-9534)
Minnesota State Employees .... E 651 450-4990
South Saint Paul (G-9535)
Mobiliam 952 921-3997
Minneapolis (G-5116)
Operating Engineer No 49 .... E 218 741-8190
Virginia (G-9750)
Pace International Union .... B 320 240-7274
Sartell (G-9340)
Seiu Local 284 .... E 651 256-9102
South Saint Paul (G-9543)
Teamsters Local 2000 .... E 612 379-9157
Minneapolis (G-5803)

8641 Civic, Social & Fraternal Associations

AA Monticello .... E 763 295-5066
Monticello (G-6265)
Acts of St Paul .... E 612 823-4237
Minneapolis (G-3679)
Adults Saving Kids .... D 612 872-0684
Minneapolis (G-3684)
Albert Lea Family YMCA .... E 507 373-8228
Albert Lea (G-31)
American Legion .... E 218 773-1129
East Grand Forks (G-1565)
American Legion 225 Inc .... E 651 464-2600
Forest Lake (G-2156)
American Legion 545 .... E 320 796-5542
Spicer (G-9555)
American Legion Club .... E 763 421-0883
Anoka (G-152)
American Legion Club .... E 320 485-4366
Winsted (G-10156)
American Legion Club .... E 218 927-2965
Aitkin (G-16)
American Legion Club 334 Inc .... E 763 421-6260
Minneapolis (G-3398)
American Legion Minneapolis .... E 612 866-3647
Minneapolis (G-3756)
American Legion Post 212 A .... E 218 732-5238
Park Rapids (G-6747)
American Legion Post 595 .... E 507 895-4595
La Crescent (G-2837)
American Legion Post 627 .... E 218 963-9946
Nisswa (G-6495)
Apple Valley American Legion .... E 952 431-1776
Saint Paul (G-7700)
Boys & Girls Clubs of Central .... C 320 252-7616
Saint Cloud (G-7463)
Camp Widji Wagan .... E 218 365-2117
Ely (G-1912)
Catholic Aid Association .... E 651 490-0170
Saint Paul (G-8174)
Coon Rapids Lions .... E 763 323-1668
Minneapolis (G-3441)
Coon Rapids VFW Post 9625 .... E 763 755-4760
Minneapolis (G-3442)
Corcoran Lions Club .... E 763 420-2555
Hamel (G-2338)
Crookston Firefighter Relief .... E 218 281-4584
Crookston (G-1120)
Cryptic Masons of Minneso .... E 507 437-2851
Austin (G-269)
Delta Kappa Gamma Society .... E 507 451-2523
Owatonna (G-6708)
Duluth Area Family Y M C A .... E 218 372-3188
Sturgeon Lake (G-9657)
Duluth Area Family YMCA .... E 218 722-4745
Duluth (G-1297)
Farmington Eagles Club .... E 651 460-8376
Farmington (G-2050)
Fergus Falls Area Family Young .... D 218 739-4489
Fergus Falls (G-2075)
Firemen's Relief Association .... E 763 593-8080
Minneapolis (G-4436)
1st Avenue Entertainment Group .... E 612 337-6700
Minneapolis (G-4441)
Flying Dutchmen Cycle Club .... D 507 354-2306
New Ulm (G-6449)
Forest Lake VFW Post 4210 Inc .... E 651 464-6827
Forest Lake (G-2162)
Fraternal Order of Eagles Club .... E 507 451-3846
Owatonna (G-6714)
Fraternal Order of Eagles Inc .... E 218 681-2406
Thief River Falls (G-9668)
Fred Babcock Post No 5555 .... E 612 869-5555
Minneapolis (G-4481)
Girl Scouts of Minnesota & WI .... D 651 227-8835
Saint Paul (G-8411)
Glenwood Lions Club .... E 320 634-3263
Glenwood (G-2224)
Golden Valley View Post 7051 .... E 763 545-9996
Minneapolis (G-4537)
Greencastle Condominium Assn .... E 320 587-4040
Hutchinson (G-2697)
Grove Cottage Athletic Assn .... E 651 459-9278
Cottage Grove (G-1102)
Ham Lake American Legion .... E 763 434-7762
Anoka (G-187)
Harrison Community Club .... E 218 624-1510
Duluth (G-1349)
Hastings YMCA .... E 651 480-8887
Hastings (G-2390)
Hill City Lions Club .... E 218 697-8427
Hill City (G-2480)
Hopkins American Legion Post .... E 952 933-1881
Hopkins (G-2553)
Independent School District .... D 952 988-5200
Hopkins (G-2556)
Independent School District .... D 952 806-7000
Minneapolis (G-4695)
Institute For Environmental .... E 763 315-7900
Minneapolis (G-4709)
International Association of .... E 218 338-6129
Parkers Prairie (G-6765)
International Association of .... C 651 439-4659
Stillwater (G-9624)
International Association of .... C 507 283-9127
Luverne (G-3060)
International Association of .... E 952 447-0413
Savage (G-9391)
International Association of .... E 507 454-7643
Winona (G-10105)
International Association of .... E 763 689-3898
Cambridge (G-839)
International Association of .... E 952 975-2985
Chanhassen (G-928)
International Association of .... E 952 933-5972
Hopkins (G-2557)
International Institute of MN .... D 651 647-0191
Saint Paul (G-8516)
Itasca County Family Young .... D 218 327-1161
Grand Rapids (G-2287)
Jewish Community Center of .... C 952 381-3400
Minneapolis (G-4762)
Jewish Community Center of The .... D 651 698-0751
Saint Paul (G-8531)
Kitchi Gammi Club .... D 218 724-8589
Duluth (G-1371)
Kiwanis International Inc .... E 507 275-3748
Hendricks (G-2430)
Kiwanis International Inc .... E 507 859-2635
Walnut Grove (G-9862)
Kiwanis International Inc .... E 320 587-6874
Hutchinson (G-2705)
Knights of Columbus .... E 952 888-1492
Bloomington (G-502)
Knights of Columbus Inc .... D 320 679-4093
Mora (G-6364)
Lanterns Homeowner Association .... E 952 922-4435
Minneapolis (G-4843)
Lincoln Elementry School P T A .... E 320 616-6200
Little Falls (G-3010)
Lions Club of Jasper .... E 507 348-8605
Jasper (G-2804)
Midwest Cleaning & Restoration .... E 763 533-3723
Minneapolis (G-5026)
Minnesota Association of .... E 651 290-7462
Saint Paul (G-8672)
Minnesota Department of .... E 320 231-1729
Willmar (G-10026)
Minnesota Veterans Research .... D 612 467-2895
Minneapolis (G-5100)

National Amtelco Equipment ....E....651 265-7845
Saint Paul *(G-8738)*
National Assoc of Retired ....E....320 245-2629
Sandstone *(G-9323)*
Nature Conservancy ....E....612 331-0700
Minneapolis *(G-5173)*
North Suburban Youth Fndtn ....E....651 697-9865
Saint Paul *(G-8754)*
Northern Star Council, Boy ....D....651 224-1891
Saint Paul *(G-8759)*
Optimist International ....E....952 440-8184
Prior Lake *(G-6947)*
Osseo Maple Grove American ....E....763 425-4858
Osseo *(G-6649)*
Ottertail Lodge 284 ....E....218 863-7913
Pelican Rapids *(G-6781)*
Palmer Lake Post 3915 VFW Inc ....E....763 560-3720
Minneapolis *(G-5315)*
Prior Lake VFW ....E....952 226-6208
Prior Lake *(G-6951)*
Pta Minnesota Congress 28 ....D....763 792-5900
Circle Pines *(G-1020)*
Roseville VFW Post 7555 ....E....651 483-5313
Saint Paul *(G-8913)*
Rudolph Priebe American Legion ....E....763 425-4858
Osseo *(G-6657)*
Saint James Lions Club Inc ....E....507 375-5634
Saint James *(G-7645)*
Saint Paul Foundation Inc ....D....651 224-5463
Saint Paul *(G-8926)*
Scenic Heights Pta ....D....952 401-5400
Hopkins *(G-2627)*
Scottish Rite Temple ....A....651 222-2676
Saint Paul *(G-8938)*
Seventy-Five Hundred York ....D....952 835-1010
Minneapolis *(G-5644)*
Sigma Alpha Epsilon Fraternity ....E....612 331-5986
Minneapolis *(G-5669)*
Society For Preservation ....E....507 452-4425
Winona *(G-10128)*
Space Aliens Grill & Bar ....D....320 259-7670
Waite Park *(G-9840)*
Spring Lake Park Lions Club ....E....763 784-9179
Minneapolis *(G-3606)*
Sprint Lake Park Alliance ....E....763 784-9179
Minneapolis *(G-3607)*
St Cloud Area Family YMCA ....C....320 253-2664
Saint Cloud *(G-7597)*
Swan Lake Association ....E....218 885-3225
Pengilly *(G-6785)*
Sypal Lundgren Post No 7662 ....E....952 460-6888
Farmington *(G-2061)*
Tower Hill Association ....E....763 682-2321
Buffalo *(G-658)*
Tri City Post 513 ....E....651 631-1124
Saint Paul *(G-9081)*
Turning Point Administrative ....E....612 520-4004
Minneapolis *(G-5867)*
University Club of St Paul ....D....651 222-1751
Saint Paul *(G-9112)*
University of Minn Alumni Assn ....E....612 624-2323
Minneapolis *(G-5929)*
Veterans of Foreign Wars ....E....320 587-9929
Hutchinson *(G-2715)*
Veterans of Foreign Wars Inc ....E....507 289-6299
Rochester *(G-7282)*
Veterans of Foreign Wars of ....E....320 963-3405
Maple Lake *(G-3267)*
Veterans of Foreign Wars of ....B....320 252-3617
Sauk Rapids *(G-9379)*
VFW Gallagher-Hanson Post 295 ....E....651 455-1505
South Saint Paul *(G-9550)*
VFW Post 1902 ....E....218 281-1902
Crookston *(G-1142)*
VFW Red River Valley Post 3817 ....E....218 773-2481
East Grand Forks *(G-1579)*
Viking Council of The Boy ....D....763 545-4550
Minneapolis *(G-5971)*
Walker West Music Academy ....E....651 224-2929
Saint Paul *(G-9137)*
Winthrop Honor Guard ....E....507 647-5608
Winthrop *(G-10169)*
Wolf Ridge Environmental ....E....218 353-7414
Finland *(G-2128)*
Woman's Club of Minneapolis ....D....612 870-8001
Minneapolis *(G-6084)*
Y M C A Infant Center ....E....651 646-4557
Saint Paul *(G-9171)*
YMCA ....D....320 222-9622
Willmar *(G-10059)*
YMCA Children's Center ....E....651 777-8103
Saint Paul *(G-9173)*
YMCA of Greater Saint Paul ....C....651 683-4713
Saint Paul *(G-7952)*
YMCA of Greater Saint Paul ....E....612 465-0450
Minneapolis *(G-6100)*
YMCA of Greater Saint Paul ....E....651 771-8881
Saint Paul *(G-9174)*
YMCA of Greater Saint Paul ....E....651 645-6605
Saint Paul *(G-9175)*
YMCA of Greater St Paul ....D....218 365-2117
Ely *(G-1919)*
YMCA of Greater St Paul ....D....651 292-4143
Saint Paul *(G-9178)*
YMCA of Greater St Paul ....D....651 646-4557
Saint Paul *(G-9177)*
YMCA of Greater St Paul ....C....651 483-2671
Saint Paul *(G-9176)*
YMCA of Greater St Paul ....C....651 457-0048
Saint Paul *(G-7953)*
YMCA of Greater St Paul ....C....651 731-9507
Saint Paul *(G-9292)*
YMCA of Worthington, Minnesota ....E....507 376-6197
Worthington *(G-10199)*
Young Men's Christian Assn ....C....507 387-8255
Mankato *(G-3222)*
Young Men's Chritn Assoc of ....D....218 829-4767
Brainerd *(G-590)*
Young Men's Chritn Assoc of ....C....763 535-4800
Minneapolis *(G-6101)*
Young Men's Chritn Assoc of ....D....612 827-5401
Minneapolis *(G-6102)*
Young Men's Chritn Assoc of ....E....612 588-9484
Minneapolis *(G-6103)*
Young Men's Chritn Assoc of ....C....952 835-2567
Minneapolis *(G-6104)*
Young Women's Christian Assn ....C....651 222-3741
Saint Paul *(G-9181)*
Young Women's Christian Assn ....D....218 722-7425
Duluth *(G-1505)*
Youthworks Inc ....E....612 729-5444
Minneapolis *(G-6109)*
YWCA of Minneapolis ....A....612 332-0501
Minneapolis *(G-6111)*
YWCA of Minneapolis ....E....612 863-0970
Minneapolis *(G-6112)*
Zuhrah Temple Trustees Inc ....E....612 871-3555
Minneapolis *(G-6122)*

8651 Political Organizations

Democratic Party of Olmsted ....E....507 536-9785
Rochester *(G-7095)*
Independent Republicans of MN ....E....651 222-0022
Saint Paul *(G-8509)*
Minnesota Network For ....E....952 891-1862
Saint Paul *(G-7843)*

8699 Membership Organizations, NEC

A A A Minneapolis ....D....952 944-9585
Minneapolis *(G-3645)*
AAA Minnesota Iowa ....C....952 707-4222
Burnsville *(G-670)*
Acts of St Paul ....E....612 823-4237
Minneapolis *(G-3679)*
Afs Intercultural Programs ....E....651 647-6337
Saint Paul *(G-7998)*
American Legion ....E....218 773-1129
East Grand Forks *(G-1565)*
Animal Humane Society ....D....763 522-4325
Minneapolis *(G-3780)*
ARC Greater Twin Cities ....E....763 544-0006
Minneapolis *(G-3798)*
Benevolent Protective Order of ....E....507 451-1395
Owatonna *(G-6694)*
Blue Earth Area Mentors ....E....507 526-5219
Blue Earth *(G-530)*
Cedar East Bethel Lions ....D....763 434-8323
Cedar *(G-875)*
Central Territorial of The ....E....651 646-2601
Saint Paul *(G-8183)*
Central Territorial of The ....E....218 722-7934
Duluth *(G-1268)*
Central Territorial of The ....D....507 288-3663
Rochester *(G-7073)*
Central Territorial of The ....C....612 332-5855
Minneapolis *(G-4047)*
Commemorative Air Force ....C....651 455-6942
South Saint Paul *(G-9523)*
Countryside Co-Op ....D....218 675-6865
Hackensack *(G-2332)*
County of St Louis ....D....218 726-2140
Duluth *(G-1285)*
Dairy Farmers of America Inc ....D....218 736-5691
Fergus Falls *(G-2073)*
Duluth Softball Players Assn ....E....218 722-5569
Duluth *(G-1303)*
Evansville Arts Coalition ....D....218 948-2787
Evansville *(G-1925)*
Fisher Education Association ....D....218 891-4905
Fisher *(G-2134)*
Gilman Park & Rec Association ....E....320 387-2941
Foley *(G-2139)*
Glendalough of Austin Inc ....E....507 334-4347
Faribault *(G-2010)*
Global Volunteers ....E....651 407-6100
Saint Paul *(G-8415)*
Historical Society of MN ....C....651 259-3160
Saint Paul *(G-8484)*
Izaak Walton League of America ....E....651 649-1446
Saint Paul *(G-8525)*
Life Time Fitness Inc ....E....612 339-3655
Minneapolis *(G-4879)*
Mesabi Family YMCA ....D....218 749-8020
Virginia *(G-9746)*
Metropolitan Sports Facilities ....E....612 332-0386
Minneapolis *(G-5009)*
Minnesota Twins Baseball Club ....A....612 375-7411
Minneapolis *(G-5099)*
Minnesota Wings Motorcycle ....E....320 632-8427
Little Falls *(G-3014)*
Open Door Health Center ....E....507 388-2120
Mankato *(G-3179)*
Pacer Center Inc ....D....952 838-9000
Minneapolis *(G-5309)*
People Inc ....E....952 736-7802
Burnsville *(G-780)*
▲ **Pheasants Forever Inc** ....E....651 773-2000
Saint Paul *(G-8824)*
Philanthrofund Foundation ....E....612 870-1806
Minneapolis *(G-5374)*
Phoenix Alternatives Vocation ....E....651 747-8740
Saint Paul *(G-8826)*
Rochester Juvenile Hockey ....E....507 280-6345
Rochester *(G-7234)*
Safe Haven Pet Rescue ....E....507 529-4079
Rochester *(G-7245)*
Sahara Sands ....E....763 444-6491
Isanti *(G-2780)*
Sandstone Riders Horse Club ....E....320 245-0370
Sandstone *(G-9327)*
Simpson Housing Services Inc ....E....612 874-8683
Minneapolis *(G-5677)*
Sobriety High Foundation ....E....651 773-8378
Saint Paul *(G-8969)*
St Cloud Area Family YMCA ....C....320 253-2664
Saint Cloud *(G-7597)*
Super Bowl ....E....763 421-7779
Woodbury *(G-10175)*
Tri County Humane Society Inc ....E....320 252-0896
Saint Cloud *(G-7430)*
Upper Sioux Community ....E....320 564-3853
Granite Falls *(G-2322)*

87 ENGINEERING, RESEARCH, MANAGEMENT & RELATED SVCS

8711 Engineering Services

Advanced Research Corp ....E....651 789-9000
White Bear Lake *(G-9973)*
AEC Engineering Inc ....E....612 332-8905
Minneapolis *(G-3690)*
Aecom Technical Services Inc ....E....763 551-1001
Minneapolis *(G-3691)*
Amec Earth & Environmental Inc ....E....612 332-8326
Minneapolis *(G-3743)*
American Consulting Services ....C....651 659-9001
Saint Paul *(G-8023)*
American Engineering Testing ....D....651 659-9001
Saint Paul *(G-8025)*
Analog Technologies, Corp ....E....952 894-9228
Burnsville *(G-677)*
Anderson Engineering of MN LLC ....E....763 383-1084
Minneapolis *(G-3777)*
API Electric Co ....E....218 741-7313
Hibbing *(G-2437)*
Architecture Technology Corp ....E....952 829-5864
Eden Prairie *(G-1595)*
Bakke Kopp Ballou & McFarlin ....E....763 843-0420
Minneapolis *(G-3861)*
Barr Engineering Co ....E....218 262-2262
Hibbing *(G-2438)*
Bdm Consulting Engineers ....E....612 548-3140
Saint Paul *(G-8095)*
Boarman Kroos Vogel Group ....D....612 339-3752
Minneapolis *(G-3921)*
Bolton & Menk Inc ....D....507 625-4171
Mankato *(G-3112)*
Bolton & Menk Inc ....E....320 231-3956
Willmar *(G-9991)*
Braun Intertec Corp ....C....952 995-2000
Minneapolis *(G-3938)*
Braun Intertec Corp ....E....651 487-3245
Saint Paul *(G-8122)*
Canard Aerospace Corp ....E....952 944-7990
Shakopee *(G-9426)*
CC & I Engineering Inc ....E....218 346-3600
Perham *(G-6795)*
Chandler Exhibits Inc ....D....651 389-5900
Afton *(G-8)*
Chevron USA Inc ....E....651 905-5700
Saint Paul *(G-7730)*
Clark Engineering Corp ....E....763 545-9196
Minneapolis *(G-4103)*
Cogent Technologies Inc ....C....952 941-3300
Brooklyn Park *(G-607)*
Colby Yaggy Associates Inc ....D....507 288-6464
Rochester *(G-7084)*
Conestoga-Rovers & Associates ....E....651 639-0913
Saint Paul *(G-8247)*
Consulting Engineers Group Inc 651 463-6263
Farmington *(G-2046)*
Crow Wing County Hwy Dept ....E....218 824-1110
Brainerd *(G-563)*
Cybertrol Engineering LLC ....E....763 559-8660
Minneapolis *(G-4208)*
Dacon Engineering & Service Co ....C....763 544-1686
Minneapolis *(G-4216)*
Dell-Comm Inc ....D....763 783-0035
Saint Paul *(G-8283)*
▲ **Depotstar Inc** ....E....763 506-9990
Anoka *(G-174)*
Distinction In Design Inc ....D....763 550-1138
Minneapolis *(G-4260)*
Dlr Group Kke ....E....612 977-3500
Minneapolis *(G-4266)*

S
I
C

Employment codes: A=Over 500 employees, B=251-500
C=101-250, D=51-100, E=25-50
2011 Harris Minnesota
Services Directory
© Harris InfoSource 1-866-281-6415
525

Dobbs Temporary Services Inc ....E....612 373-2600 — Minneapolis (G-4268)
▲ Donnelly Custom Manufacturing ....C....320 762-2396 — Alexandria (G-95)
Dpra Inc ....E....651 227-6500 — Saint Paul (G-8311)
Duffy Engineering & Associates ....E....320 259-6575 — Saint Cloud (G-7412)
Dunham Associates Inc ....D....612 465-7550 — Minneapolis (G-4294)
E & C Amec Services Inc ....D....612 332-8326 — Minneapolis (G-4299)
EAC Design Inc ....E....952 435-5533 — Burnsville (G-714)
Eagle Tool & Design Inc ....E....763 784-7400 — Minneapolis (G-3460)
Eaton Corp ....E....952 912-1330 — Minnetonka (G-6162)
Efi Global Inc ....E....952 942-9812 — Minneapolis (G-4328)
◆ Electrosonic Inc ....E....952 931-7500 — Minnetonka (G-6165)
Ellerbe Becket Co ....C....612 376-2000 — Minneapolis (G-4341)
EMA Group Inc ....E....651 639-5600 — Saint Paul (G-8335)
EMA Inc ....E....651 639-5600 — Saint Paul (G-8336)
Ema Inc ....651 639-5600 — Saint Paul (G-8337)
Emmons & Oliver Resources ....E....218 732-3323 — Park Rapids (G-6751)
Erdman Automation Corp ....D....763 389-9475 — Princeton (G-6905)
Evergreen Aviation Inc ....D....612 727-1655 — Minneapolis (G-4379)
Excel Engineering Inc ....D....763 571-5008 — Minneapolis (G-3467)
Finley Engineering Co ....E....507 836-8515 — Slayton (G-9487)
Food Systems Design Inc ....E....952 884-4048 — Minneapolis (G-4464)
Fox-1 Resources ....E....651 894-3990 — Saint Paul (G-7776)
▲ Gausman & Moore Associates Inc ....D....651 639-9606 — Saint Paul (G-8403)
Gb Lumina Inc ....E....763 797-9036 — Minneapolis (G-4504)
George Konik Associates Inc ....D....952 835-5550 — Minneapolis (G-4524)
Green Co's Inc ....D....651 644-4389 — Saint Paul (G-8430)
Hallberg Engineering Inc ....E....651 748-1100 — White Bear Lake (G-9975)
Hammel, Green & Abrahamson Inc ....B....612 758-4000 — Minneapolis (G-4591)
Hammel, Green & Abrahamson Inc ....B....507 281-8601 — Rochester (G-7131)
Hansen, Thorp & Pellinen Inc ....E....952 829-0700 — Eden Prairie (G-1676)
HDR Engineering Inc ....C....763 591-5400 — Minneapolis (G-4615)
Heyer Engineering ....E....612 238-3805 — Minneapolis (G-4644)
HNTB Corp ....E....952 920-4668 — Minneapolis (G-4658)
Horty Elving & Associates Inc ....E....612 332-4422 — Minneapolis (G-4676)
Hunt Technologies LLC ....C....218 562-4877 — Pequot Lakes (G-6789)
◆ Hydralift Amclyde Inc ....D....651 293-4646 — Saint Paul (G-8501)
I & S Group Inc ....D....507 387-6651 — Mankato (G-3146)
Ibberson Inc ....952 938-7007 — Hopkins (G-2555)
Industrial Automation Engg ....E....763 450-3800 — Anoka (G-192)
Infinity Precision Systems LLC ....E....952 401-4600 — Chanhassen (G-926)
Innovative Technical Personnel ....E....763 591-9191 — Minneapolis (G-4705)
Inspec Inc ....E....763 546-3434 — Minneapolis (G-4707)
Interpoll Laboratories Inc ....E....763 786-6020 — Circle Pines (G-1012)
Ion Corp ....E....952 936-9490 — Eden Prairie (G-1698)
James R Hill Inc ....E....952 890-6044 — Burnsville (G-738)
James R Hill Inc ....D....763 792-1136 — Minneapolis (G-3505)
Kadrmas, Lee & Jackson Inc ....E....218 287-0300 — Moorhead (G-6321)
Karges-Faulconbridge Inc ....D....651 771-0880 — Saint Paul (G-8540)
Knutson Construction Services ....D....507 280-9788 — Rochester (G-7157)
Krech, Ojard & Associates ....E....218 727-3282 — Duluth (G-1373)
Larson Engineering Inc ....E....651 481-9120 — Saint Paul (G-8563)
Leo A Daly Co ....C....612 338-8741 — Minneapolis (G-4861)
LHB Inc ....C....218 727-8446 — Duluth (G-1381)
Lhb Inc ....E....612 338-2029 — Minneapolis (G-4867)

Liesch Associates Inc ....D....763 489-3100 — Minneapolis (G-4875)
Lkpb Engineers Inc ....E....651 633-1223 — Saint Paul (G-8593)
Logic Product Development Co ....D....612 672-9495 — Minneapolis (G-4900)
Machine & Process Design Inc ....E....763 427-9991 — Anoka (G-202)
McGhie & Betts Inc ....E....507 289-3919 — Rochester (G-7179)
Metropolitan Council, MN ....E....651 772-2585 — Saint Paul (G-8644)
Metropolitan Mechanical Contr ....B....952 941-7010 — Eden Prairie (G-1722)
Meyer, Borgman & Johnson Inc ....E....612 338-0713 — Minneapolis (G-5011)
Mfra Inc ....D....763 476-6010 — Minneapolis (G-5013)
Michaud, Cooley, Erickson ....C....612 339-4941 — Minneapolis (G-5017)
Miller Dunwiddie Architecture ....E....612 337-0000 — Minneapolis (G-5043)
Minnetronix Inc ....C....651 917-4060 — Saint Paul (G-8712)
◆ MTS Systems Corp ....A....952 937-4000 — Eden Prairie (G-1731)
Nol-Tec Systems Inc ....D....651 780-8600 — Circle Pines (G-1018)
Noramco Engineering Corp ....E....218 262-1093 — Hibbing (G-2469)
North Anoka Control Systems ....E....763 444-4747 — Anoka (G-208)
North Point Capital Partners ....D....651 602-0789 — Saint Paul (G-8753)
Northstar Fire Protection Inc ....E....651 456-9111 — Saint Paul (G-7853)
Nova-Tech Engineering LLC ....D....320 231-9660 — Willmar (G-10032)
Oakriver Technology Inc ....E....651 770-8710 — Saint Paul (G-9254)
Office Information Systems Inc ....E....952 884-9199 — Minneapolis (G-5265)
Open Access Technology Intl ....B....763 201-2000 — Minneapolis (G-5283)
Ops America Inc ....E....763 479-1409 — Loretto (G-3051)
Otto Associates Engineers ....E....763 682-4727 — Buffalo (G-655)
Owens Co's Inc ....D....952 854-3800 — Bloomington (G-509)
Palanisami & Associates Inc ....E....763 533-9403 — Minneapolis (G-5314)
Parallel Technologies Inc ....C....952 920-7185 — Minneapolis (G-5322)
Parsons Electric LLC ....C....763 571-8000 — Minneapolis (G-3565)
Passe Engineering Inc ....763 780-4100 — Minneapolis (G-3566)
Power System Engineering Inc ....E....763 755-5122 — Minneapolis (G-3571)
Precision Design Inc ....E....952 933-6550 — Hopkins (G-2604)
QLogic Corp ....C....952 932-4000 — Shakopee (G-9466)
Redprairie Corp ....E....952 656-5400 — Eden Prairie (G-1761)
Rehder & Associates Inc ....D....651 452-5051 — Eagan (G-1547)
Reigstad & Associates Inc ....E....651 292-1123 — Saint Paul (G-8886)
Rlk Inc ....E....952 933-0972 — Hopkins (G-2620)
Roed Ericksen & Associates ....E....651 251-7570 — Saint Paul (G-8911)
Rogers Freels & Associates Inc ....D....952 843-2700 — Eden Prairie (G-1766)
Safegate Airport Systems Inc ....E....763 535-9299 — Minneapolis (G-5589)
Schoell & Madson Inc ....E....763 746-1600 — Minneapolis (G-5610)
Scott County Highway Engineer ....E....952 496-8346 — Jordan (G-2809)
Sebesta Blomberg & Associates ....C....651 634-0775 — Saint Paul (G-8940)
Setter Leach & Lindstrom Inc ....D....612 338-8741 — Minneapolis (G-5639)
Short-Elliott-Hendrickson Inc ....C....651 490-2000 — Saint Paul (G-8954)
Short-Elliott-Hendrickson Inc ....D....800 572-0617 — Saint Cloud (G-7593)
Short-Elliott-Hendrickson Inc ....E....888 722-0547 — Duluth (G-1450)
Short-Elliott-Hendrickson Inc ....E....952 912-2600 — Hopkins (G-2632)
Specsys Inc ....C....320 269-3227 — Montevideo (G-6260)
SRF Consulting Group Inc ....C....763 475-0010 — Minneapolis (G-5725)
Stanley Consultants Inc ....E....952 546-3669 — Minneapolis (G-5739)
Steen Engineering Inc ....E....763 585-6742 — Minneapolis (G-5746)
STS Acquisition Co ....D....763 315-6300 — Osseo (G-6669)
◆ Team Industries Baxter Inc ....E....218 829-1901 — Baxter (G-341)
Team Industries Inc ....C....218 694-3550 — Bagley (G-302)

Teradyne Inc ....E....763 586-0725 — Minneapolis (G-3615)
Terracon Consultants Inc ....E....651 770-1500 — Saint Paul (G-9040)
Third Wave Systems Inc ....E....952 832-5515 — Minneapolis (G-5815)
3M Co ....E....651 733-5000 — Saint Paul (G-9054)
3M Co ....C....651 736-1792 — Saint Paul (G-9056)
Tom Loucks & Associates Inc ....D....763 424-5505 — Osseo (G-6676)
Ulteig Engineers Inc ....D....763 571-2500 — Minneapolis (G-3629)
Ulteig Engineers Inc ....E....218 847-5607 — Detroit Lakes (G-1220)
▼ Uni-Systems LLC ....E....763 536-1407 — Minneapolis (G-5901)
Unified Theory Inc ....651 578-8100 — Saint Paul (G-9286)
URS Group Inc ....E....612 370-0700 — Minneapolis (G-5941)
US Army Corps of Engineers ....A....651 290-5698 — Saint Paul (G-9116)
Vaa LLC ....D....763 559-9100 — Minneapolis (G-5953)
Via Biomedical Inc ....E....763 577-9936 — Osseo (G-6683)
Wenck Associates Inc ....D....763 479-4200 — Maple Plain (G-3281)
Wheeler Consolidated Inc ....E....952 929-6791 — Minneapolis (G-6064)
Widseth, Smith, Nolting ....E....218 281-6522 — Crookston (G-1144)
Widseth, Smith, Nolting ....E....320 762-8149 — Alexandria (G-130)
Widseth, Smith, Nolting ....D....218 829-5117 — Baxter (G-345)
World Architects Inc ....D....651 227-7773 — Saint Paul (G-9168)
Wunderlich-Malec Engineering ....D....952 933-3222 — Hopkins (G-2660)
Zachry Construction Corp ....E....612 215-1300 — Minneapolis (G-6113)

8712 Architectural Services

Architectural Enhancements, LL ....E....320 274-6909 — Annandale (G-137)
Armstrong, Torseth, Skold ....D....763 545-3731 — Minneapolis (G-3810)
Banner & Assoc ....D....507 562-2957 — Pipestone (G-6823)
Bkv Group ....D....612 339-3752 — Minneapolis (G-3909)
Boarman Kroos Vogel Group ....D....612 339-3752 — Minneapolis (G-3921)
Bwbr Architects Inc ....C....651 222-3701 — Saint Paul (G-8144)
Colby Yaggy Associates Inc ....D....507 288-6464 — Rochester (G-7084)
Collaborative Design Group Inc ....E....612 332-3654 — Minneapolis (G-4118)
Cuningham Group Architecture ....C....612 379-3400 — Minneapolis (G-4200)
Damberg Scott Gerzina Wagner ....E....218 727-2626 — Duluth (G-1290)
Dlr Group Kke ....E....612 977-3500 — Minneapolis (G-4266)
Ellerbe Becket Co ....C....612 376-2000 — Minneapolis (G-4341)
Elness Swenson Graham ....D....612 339-5508 — Minneapolis (G-4343)
Hammel, Green & Abrahamson Inc ....B....612 758-4000 — Minneapolis (G-4591)
Hammel, Green & Abrahamson Inc ....B....507 281-8601 — Rochester (G-7131)
HDR Engineering Inc ....C....763 591-5400 — Minneapolis (G-4615)
Hickey Thorstenson Grover Ltd ....E....952 278-8880 — Eden Prairie (G-1684)
Horty Elving & Associates Inc ....E....612 332-4422 — Minneapolis (G-4676)
I & S Group Inc ....D....507 331-1500 — Faribault (G-2011)
Inspec Inc ....E....763 546-3434 — Minneapolis (G-4707)
Leo A Daly Co ....C....612 338-8741 — Minneapolis (G-4861)
LHB Inc ....C....218 727-8446 — Duluth (G-1381)
Lhb Inc ....E....612 338-2029 — Minneapolis (G-4867)
Lunning Wende Bvh Architects ....D....651 221-0915 — Saint Paul (G-8597)
Meyer, Scherer & Rockcastle ....E....612 375-0336 — Minneapolis (G-5012)
Miller Architects & Builders ....E....320 251-4109 — Saint Cloud (G-7555)
Miller Architecture Inc ....E....320 251-4109 — Saint Cloud (G-7556)
Miller Dunwiddie Architecture ....E....612 337-0000 — Minneapolis (G-5043)
Miller Rozeboom Architect Inc ....E....612 332-2110 — Minneapolis (G-5045)
Minnesota Architectural ....D....612 871-5703 — Minneapolis (G-5069)

S I C

(G-00000) Company's Geographic Section entry number
526
2011 Harris Minnesota Services Directory
▲=Import ▼=Export ◆=Import/Export

Opus Architects & Engineers ....C....952 656-4444
Hopkins *(G-2596)*
Perkins + Will Inc ....D....612 851-5000
Minneapolis *(G-5366)*
Pope Associates Inc ....E....651 642-9200
Saint Paul *(G-8831)*
Portfolio Design Services Inc ....E....651 631-1300
Saint Paul *(G-9263)*
Rsp Architects Ltd ....C....612 677-7100
Minneapolis *(G-5571)*
Setter Leach & Lindstrom Inc ....D....612 338-8741
Minneapolis *(G-5639)*
Shea Inc ....E....612 339-2257
Minneapolis *(G-5652)*
Short-Elliott-Hendrickson Inc ....C....651 490-2000
Saint Paul *(G-8954)*
Short-Elliott-Hendrickson Inc ....D....800 572-0617
Saint Cloud *(G-7593)*
T S P Inc ....E....507 288-8155
Rochester *(G-7272)*
T S P One Inc ....E....952 474-3291
Hopkins *(G-2641)*
URS Group Inc ....E....612 370-0700
Minneapolis *(G-5941)*
Vanman Construction Co ....E....763 541-9552
Minneapolis *(G-5958)*
Walsh Bishop Associates Inc ....D....612 338-8799
Minneapolis *(G-6016)*
Wcl Associates Inc ....E....952 541-9969
Minneapolis *(G-6029)*
Weidt Group Inc ....E....952 938-1588
Hopkins *(G-2659)*
Widseth, Smith, Nolting ....E....218 281-6522
Crookston *(G-1144)*
World Architects Inc ....D....651 227-7773
Saint Paul *(G-9168)*

8713 Surveying Services

Aero-Metric Inc ....E....763 420-9606
Osseo *(G-6593)*
Bogart & Peterson & Associates ....E....763 682-9329
Maple Lake *(G-3258)*
Bolton & Menk Inc ....D....507 625-4171
Mankato *(G-3112)*
Bolton & Menk Inc ....E....320 231-3956
Willmar *(G-9991)*
Clark Engineering Corp ....E....763 545-9196
Minneapolis *(G-4103)*
Colby Yaggy Associates Inc ....D....507 288-6464
Rochester *(G-7084)*
Duffy Engineering & Associates ....E....320 259-6575
Saint Cloud *(G-7412)*
Egan, Field, & Nowak Inc ....E....612 466-3300
Minneapolis *(G-4329)*
Emmons & Oliver Resources ....E....218 732-3323
Park Rapids *(G-6751)*
Hansen, Thorp & Pellinen Inc ....E....952 829-0700
Eden Prairie *(G-1676)*
Hennepin County ....E....612 348-3131
Minneapolis *(G-4632)*
Honeywell International Inc ....D....763 954-2712
Plymouth *(G-6864)*
James R Hill Inc ....E....952 890-6044
Burnsville *(G-738)*
McGhie & Betts Inc ....E....507 289-3919
Rochester *(G-7179)*
Otto Associates Engineers ....E....763 682-4727
Buffalo *(G-655)*
Rehder & Associates Inc ....D....651 452-5051
Eagan *(G-1547)*
Schoell & Madson Inc ....E....763 746-1600
Minneapolis *(G-5610)*
SRF Consulting Group Inc ....C....763 475-0010
Minneapolis *(G-5725)*
Sunday Land Surveying ....E....952 881-2455
Minneapolis *(G-5766)*
Sunde Land Surveying LLC ....E....952 881-2455
Minneapolis *(G-5767)*
Tom Loucks & Associates Inc ....D....763 424-5505
Osseo *(G-6676)*
Widseth, Smith, Nolting ....E....218 281-6522
Crookston *(G-1144)*

8721 Accounting, Auditing & Bookkeeping Svcs

Alliance Benefit Group ....D....507 377-9344
Albert Lea *(G-35)*
Anderson Froehling Ltd ....E....952 979-3100
Hopkins *(G-2511)*
Apex Analytix Inc ....E....952 400-2272
Eden Prairie *(G-1593)*
Auditor Wright County ....E....763 682-7578
Buffalo *(G-634)*
Automatic Data Processing Inc ....B....952 814-5800
Minneapolis *(G-3838)*
Baker, Tilly, Virchow Krause ....C....612 876-4500
Minneapolis *(G-3860)*
Baune Dosen & Co LLP ....E....952 473-2002
Minneapolis *(G-3874)*
Bnsf Railway Co ....C....651 298-2121
Saint Paul *(G-8116)*
Boeckermann, Grafstrom & Mayer ....E....952 844-2500
Minneapolis *(G-3922)*
Bottom Line Enhancement Svcs ....C....952 974-9920
Eden Prairie *(G-1609)*
Boulay Heutmaker Zibell & Co ....C....952 893-9320
Eden Prairie *(G-1610)*
Broadston Consulting Services ....E....952 442-9770
Waconia *(G-9779)*
Brunberg Blatt & Co Inc ....E....763 545-2353
Minneapolis *(G-3963)*
Cargill Inc ....E....763 742-5512
Minneapolis *(G-4008)*
Cargill Inc ....E....763 742-7237
Wayzata *(G-9908)*
Carlson Highland Co LLP ....D....218 739-3267
Fergus Falls *(G-2065)*
Carlson, Lundquist & Co Ltd ....E....763 535-8150
Minneapolis *(G-4019)*
Ceridian Corp ....A....952 853-8100
Minneapolis *(G-4052)*
Certes Financial Professionals ....E....952 345-4140
Golden Valley *(G-2238)*
Children's Health Care Inc ....C....651 855-2800
Saint Paul *(G-8194)*
City of Anoka ....E....763 576-2750
Anoka *(G-167)*
Commercial Auditors Corp ....E....763 783-9160
Minneapolis *(G-3437)*
Conner Enterprises Inc ....E....218 998-9376
Fergus Falls *(G-2072)*
Consumer Directions Inc ....A....320 420-3423
Saint Cloud *(G-7409)*
Conway, Deuth & Schmiesing ....E....320 235-3311
Willmar *(G-9999)*
Corporate Commission of The ....E....320 532-8862
Onamia *(G-6569)*
County of Fillmore ....C....507 765-4701
Preston *(G-6896)*
Cummings, Keegan & Co Pllp ....E....952 345-2500
Minneapolis *(G-4199)*
D J Baune & J A Dosen Ptr ....E....952 473-2002
Hopkins *(G-2535)*
Deloitte & Touche LLP ....A....612 397-4772
Minneapolis *(G-4244)*
Diversified Industries Inc ....E....763 513-5951
Minneapolis *(G-4262)*
Ds & B Ltd ....E....612 359-9630
Minneapolis *(G-4287)*
Eide Bailly LLP ....C....952 944-6166
Minneapolis *(G-4332)*
Eide Bailly LLP ....E....507 387-6031
Mankato *(G-3125)*
Eide Bailly LLP ....E....507 387-6031
Madelia *(G-3072)*
Eikill & Schilling Ltd ....E....218 722-4705
Duluth *(G-1311)*
Eikill & Schilling Ltd CPA ....E....218 879-1503
Cloquet *(G-1051)*
Elmo Lake Bank ....E....651 777-8365
Lake Elmo *(G-2870)*
Emergency Physicians Prof ....C....952 835-9880
Minneapolis *(G-4346)*
Ernst & Young LLP ....B....612 343-1000
Minneapolis *(G-4367)*
Ftb Inc ....E....218 326-5960
Grand Rapids *(G-2278)*
Glen Lindseth ....E....218 751-6300
Bemidji *(G-396)*
Grant Thornton LLP ....D....612 332-0001
Minneapolis *(G-4546)*
Health Billing Systems LLC ....D....763 559-3779
Minneapolis *(G-4616)*
Healtheast Care Inc ....A....651 232-2300
Saint Paul *(G-8453)*
Healthline Inc ....E....218 362-6760
Hibbing *(G-2449)*
Herbeck, David J CPA Pfs Chfc ....E....763 546-6211
Minneapolis *(G-4640)*
Hlb Tautges Redpath ....D....651 426-7000
Saint Paul *(G-8488)*
Intermed Consultants Ltd ....E....952 920-2070
Minneapolis *(G-4719)*
Iron Mountain Information MGT ....C....952 888-3852
Minneapolis *(G-4735)*
James A Dosen ....E....952 473-2002
Minneapolis *(G-4752)*
James W Copeland ....E....952 476-7100
Wayzata *(G-9922)*
John A Kanutson ....E....651 641-1099
Saint Paul *(G-8534)*
John A Knutson & Co ....E....651 641-1099
Saint Paul *(G-8535)*
Kern Dewenter Viere Ltd ....E....320 251-7010
Saint Cloud *(G-7541)*
KPMG LLP ....E....612 305-5000
Minneapolis *(G-4820)*
Laron Allen Weishair & Co LLP ....D....507 437-4518
Austin *(G-281)*
Larson Ellen Weisharir Co LLP ....E....320 253-8616
Waite Park *(G-9827)*
Larsonallen LLP ....B....612 376-4500
Minneapolis *(G-4848)*
Larsonallen LLP ....E....218 825-2919
Baxter *(G-335)*
Lephert, Skwira, Shultz & Co ....E....651 265-2051
Saint Paul *(G-8578)*
Lethert, Skwira, Schultz & Co ....E....651 224-5721
Saint Paul *(G-8580)*
Leverz Skira & Shcultz CPA ....E....651 265-2045
Saint Paul *(G-8581)*
Mahoney Ulbrich Christiansen ....E....651 227-6695
Saint Paul *(G-8607)*
Malloy, Karnowski & Co ....E....952 545-0424
Minneapolis *(G-4937)*
McGladrey & Pullen, LLP ....C....952 921-7700
Minneapolis *(G-4974)*
McGladrey & Pullen, LLP ....E....507 288-6476
Rochester *(G-7180)*
McGladrey & Pullen, LLP ....D....218 727-5025
Duluth *(G-1387)*
McGladrey & Pullen, LLP ....D....218 727-6857
Duluth *(G-1388)*
Metropolitan Council, MN ....C....612 373-3333
Saint Paul *(G-8645)*
Meulebroeck Taubert & Co Pllp ....E....507 283-4055
Luverne *(G-3064)*
Minnesota Clerical Inc ....C....763 753-7243
Anoka *(G-205)*
Minnesota Society of Certified ....E....952 831-2707
Minneapolis *(G-5094)*
Moquist Thorvilson Kaufmann ....D....952 854-5700
Minneapolis *(G-5126)*
Myslajek Ltd ....E....612 781-2771
Minneapolis *(G-5153)*
Nathan J Lilleodden CPA ....D....952 476-7107
Wayzata *(G-9931)*
Olsen Thielen Technologies Inc ....C....651 483-4521
Saint Paul *(G-8781)*
Orthopedic Resources Mgt ....E....952 831-5773
Minneapolis *(G-5294)*
Paychex Inc ....D....651 365-5060
Saint Paul *(G-7869)*
Paysource Inc ....D....651 633-9595
Saint Paul *(G-8811)*
Perot Systems Corp ....E....651 999-5600
Saint Paul *(G-8819)*
Pinnacle Financial Group Inc ....D....952 996-0559
Minneapolis *(G-5381)*
Pro Systems Corp ....E....218 847-9277
Detroit Lakes *(G-1214)*
Reese, Winter & Associates Ltd 507 645-4473
Northfield *(G-6541)*
Robert A Kovell ....E....320 253-9505
Saint Cloud *(G-7589)*
Robert Gullick CPA ....E....651 265-2043
Saint Paul *(G-8906)*
RSM McGladrey Business Soln ....C....952 921-7700
Minneapolis *(G-5567)*
RSM McGladrey Business Svcs ....D....952 857-1220
Minneapolis *(G-5568)*
RSM McGladrey Inc ....D....507 288-5363
Rochester *(G-7242)*
RSM McGladrey Inc ....D....218 727-5025
Duluth *(G-1440)*
RSM McGladrey Inc ....C....952 921-7700
Minneapolis *(G-5569)*
RSM McGladrey Inc ....C....612 332-4300
Minneapolis *(G-5570)*
Schechter Dokken Kanter ....D....612 332-5500
Minneapolis *(G-5607)*
Schoeneckers Inc ....A....952 835-4800
Minneapolis *(G-5611)*
Schueller Wenner & Co ....D....320 632-6311
Little Falls *(G-3019)*
Smith Schafer & Associates Ltd ....E....507 288-3277
Rochester *(G-7255)*
State Bank of Faribault ....E....507 332-7401
Faribault *(G-2033)*
Steven N Arendt ....D....952 476-7143
Wayzata *(G-9942)*
Thomas Eling CPA ....E....218 722-4705
Duluth *(G-1484)*
Thomas P Koop CPA ....E....218 825-2903
Baxter *(G-342)*
3M Co ....B....651 733-5562
Saint Paul *(G-9061)*
Timothy V Bergin ....E....218 825-2902
Baxter *(G-343)*
Tk Advisors Ltd ....E....612 373-9000
Minneapolis *(G-5828)*
University of Minnesota ....C....763 782-6400
Minneapolis *(G-5930)*
◆ **Viking Forest Products LLC** ....E....952 941-6512
Eden Prairie *(G-1805)*
Walker, Giroux, Hahne Ltd ....E....218 749-4880
Virginia *(G-9762)*
Wells Fargo Audit Services Inc ....D....612 667-1234
Minneapolis *(G-6038)*
Wells Fargo Bank, National ....E....952 881-7333
Minneapolis *(G-6040)*
Wells Jefferson International ....E....612 338-5400
Minneapolis *(G-6055)*
Wilkerson, Guthmann & Johnson ....E....651 222-1801
Saint Paul *(G-9157)*
Wipfli LLP ....D....952 548-3400
Minneapolis *(G-6079)*
Wipfli LLP ....E....651 636-6468
Saint Paul *(G-9159)*
Wolf Etter & Co ....D....507 642-8882
Madelia *(G-3075)*

8731 Commercial Physical & Biological Research

American Preclinical Services ....E....763 717-7990
Minneapolis *(G-3400)*
Aspen Research Corp ....D....651 264-6000
Saint Paul *(G-8071)*

SIC

Employment codes: A=Over 500 employees, B=251-500
C=101-250, D=51-100, E=25-50
2011 Harris Minnesota
Services Directory
© Harris InfoSource 1-866-281-6415
527

- ▲ Betaseed Inc ..... E 952 445-8090 — Shakopee (G-9421)
- Boreal Energy Inc ..... 651 762-1200 — Vadnais Heights (G-9720)
- Camas Inc ..... E 507 357-4929 — Le Center (G-2949)
- Cargill Inc ..... D 763 441-3330 — Elk River (G-1865)
- Cargill Inc ..... D 952 742-6437 — Wayzata (G-9907)
- Cargill Inc ..... D 763 441-6508 — Elk River (G-1866)
- Dover Fluid Management Inc ..... D 651 388-3565 — Red Wing (G-6978)
- Food Perspectives Inc ..... E 763 553-7787 — Minneapolis (G-4463)
- Geodigm Corp ..... E 952 556-5657 — Chanhassen (G-924)
- Hardwire Tech Inc ..... E 763 783-8111 — Minneapolis (G-3483)
- ▲ Higher Dimension Materials Inc ..... E 651 730-6203 — Saint Paul (G-9228)
- Higher Dimension Research Inc ..... E 651 730-6203 — Saint Paul (G-9229)
- Hysitron Inc ..... D 952 835-6366 — Eden Prairie (G-1689)
- Integra Group Inc ..... E 763 951-7400 — Brooklyn Park (G-611)
- Ion Corp ..... E 952 936-9490 — Eden Prairie (G-1698)
- Lab Holdings Inc ..... 612 607-1700 — Minneapolis (G-4831)
- Leisure Inc ..... E 952 401-8440 — Eden Prairie (G-1707)
- Mednet Solutions Inc ..... D 763 258-2735 — Minnetonka (G-6191)
- Midwest Assistance Program ..... E 952 758-4334 — New Prague (G-6433)
- Minneapolis Medical Research ..... C 612 347-5000 — Minneapolis (G-5057)
- Minnesota Medtec Inc ..... E 763 428-3720 — Osseo (G-6640)
- Minnesota Valley Testing Labs ..... D 507 354-8517 — New Ulm (G-6461)
- Minnetronix Inc ..... C 651 917-4060 — Saint Paul (G-8712)
- Nephrology Analytical Services ..... E 612 337-7345 — Minneapolis (G-5182)
- Pace Analytical Life Sciences ..... E 651 738-2728 — Oakdale (G-6552)
- Pace Analytical Services Inc ..... B 612 607-1700 — Minneapolis (G-5308)
- Pdl Biopharma Inc ..... D 763 255-5000 — Minneapolis (G-5357)
- Prairie Smoke ..... E 507 292-0063 — Rochester (G-7211)
- Prism Research LLC ..... E 651 641-2900 — Saint Paul (G-8849)
- Regents of The University of ..... E 218 245-2200 — Bigfork (G-463)
- Schoell & Madson Inc ..... E 763 746-1600 — Minneapolis (G-5610)
- Segetis Inc ..... E 763 795-7200 — Golden Valley (G-2245)
- Sunopta Food Group LLC ..... 320 763-5977 — Alexandria (G-125)
- Syngenta Seeds Inc ..... D 507 645-5621 — Stanton (G-9582)
- Techne Corp ..... A 612 379-8854 — Minneapolis (G-5804)
- Unisys Corp ..... A 651 635-7777 — Saint Paul (G-9103)
- Vision Processing Technologies ..... E 320 593-1796 — Litchfield (G-2992)
- Yeater Hennings Ruff Architect ..... E 218 233-4422 — Moorhead (G-6348)

8732 Commercial Economic, Sociological & Educational Research

- American Institute of ..... E 651 415-1320 — Saint Paul (G-8027)
- Amherst H Wilder Foundation ..... E 651 647-4600 — Saint Paul (G-8042)
- Anderson, Niebuhr & Associates ..... E 651 486-8712 — Saint Paul (G-8051)
- Badger Acquisition of MN ..... C 763 259-0400 — Minneapolis (G-3857)
- Bette Dickenson Research Inc ..... D 763 420-4385 — Osseo (G-6599)
- C J Olson Market Research ..... E 612 378-5040 — Minneapolis (G-3985)
- Capitol Lien Records & Res ..... E 651 488-0100 — Saint Paul (G-8154)
- Cargill Inc ..... D 763 441-6508 — Elk River (G-1866)
- Compendium Corp ..... D 952 881-1608 — Saint Paul (G-7736)
- Cvrx Inc ..... E 763 416-2840 — Minneapolis (G-4207)
- Data Recognition Corp ..... B 763 268-2000 — Maple Grove (G-3239)
- Educational Cooperative Svc ..... E 612 638-1500 — Minneapolis (G-4327)
- Fieldwork Minneapolis Inc ..... E 952 837-8300 — Minneapolis (G-4430)
- Focus Market Research Inc ..... E 612 869-8181 — Minneapolis (G-4459)
- Food Perspectives Inc ..... E 763 553-7787 — Minneapolis (G-4463)
- Iconoculture Inc ..... E 612 377-0087 — Minneapolis (G-4686)
- Information Specialists Group ..... D 952 941-1600 — Eden Prairie (G-1691)
- Kenexa Corp ..... E 612 332-6383 — Minneapolis (G-4800)
- Leisure Inc ..... E 952 401-8440 — Eden Prairie (G-1707)
- Market Solutions Group Inc ..... D 612 332-1574 — Saint Paul (G-7833)
- Marketline Research Inc ..... E 612 767-2580 — Minneapolis (G-4950)
- Markettools Inc ..... E 952 546-2800 — Minneapolis (G-4951)
- Maxann LLC ..... E 651 484-2677 — Saint Paul (G-8619)
- Meyer Associates Inc ..... C 320 259-4000 — Saint Cloud (G-7552)
- Minnesota Rural Education Assn ..... C 320 762-6574 — Alexandria (G-113)
- Nielsen Co US LLC ..... D 763 593-2000 — Minneapolis (G-5201)
- Orman Guidance Research Inc ..... D 952 831-4911 — Minneapolis (G-5291)
- Power Systems Research Inc ..... E 651 905-8400 — Saint Paul (G-7880)
- Product Deve ..... E 612 676-1474 — Minneapolis (G-5416)
- Quick Test Inc ..... E 952 854-3535 — Minneapolis (G-5451)
- Regents of The University of ..... E 612 624-6328 — Minneapolis (G-5501)
- Research International USA Inc ..... E 952 853-9400 — Minneapolis (G-5521)
- Retail Support Inc ..... E 952 934-1317 — Eden Prairie (G-1763)
- Search Institute ..... E 612 376-8955 — Minneapolis (G-5622)
- Service 800 Inc ..... B 952 475-3747 — Long Lake (G-3032)
- Smith Moreton International ..... E 952 820-4441 — Minneapolis (G-5690)
- Soymor Biodiesel LLC ..... E 507 448-0124 — Albert Lea (G-66)
- TCI Group Inc ..... E 612 823-6214 — Minneapolis (G-5800)
- 3M Co ..... D 651 733-5300 — Saint Paul (G-9047)
- 3M Co ..... C 651 733-3929 — Saint Paul (G-9051)

8733 Noncommercial Research Organizations

- American Lung Association of ..... E 651 227-8014 — Saint Paul (G-8028)
- Celleration Inc ..... E 952 224-8700 — Eden Prairie (G-1618)
- Center For Applied Research ..... E 612 624-0300 — Minneapolis (G-4042)
- Central Regional Pathology Lab ..... E 651 264-1611 — Saint Paul (G-9194)
- Clean Water Action Inc ..... C 612 623-3666 — Minneapolis (G-4105)
- Educational Cooperative Svc ..... E 612 638-1500 — Minneapolis (G-4327)
- Envoy Medical Corp ..... E 651 361-8000 — Saint Paul (G-8343)
- Mednet Solutions Inc ..... D 763 258-2735 — Minnetonka (G-6191)
- Ncs Pearson Inc ..... A 952 681-3000 — Minneapolis (G-5178)
- R Tech Laboratories ..... D 651 481-2207 — Saint Paul (G-8867)
- Regents of The University of ..... C 218 720-4294 — Duluth (G-1433)
- Regents of The University of ..... E 612 625-1551 — Minneapolis (G-5499)
- Rochester Methodist Hospital ..... 507 266-7890 — Rochester (G-7237)
- Spineology Inc ..... E 651 256-8500 — Saint Paul (G-9276)
- Tom Loucks & Associates Inc ..... D 763 424-5505 — Osseo (G-6676)
- University Neurosurgical Assn ..... E 612 624-6666 — Minneapolis (G-5928)

8734 Testing Laboratories

- ▲ Aero Systems Engineering Inc ..... C 651 227-7515 — Saint Paul (G-7993)
- American Consulting Services ..... C 651 659-9001 — Saint Paul (G-8023)
- American Engineering Testing ..... D 651 659-9001 — Saint Paul (G-8025)
- Aspen Research Corp ..... D 651 264-6000 — Saint Paul (G-8071)
- Braun Intertec Corp ..... E 651 487-3245 — Saint Paul (G-8122)
- Cargill Inc ..... D 952 742-6437 — Wayzata (G-9907)
- CIMA LABS Inc ..... D 952 947-8700 — Eden Prairie (G-1627)
- County of Stearns ..... C 320 259-3700 — Saint Cloud (G-7495)
- Diversified Laboratory Testing ..... E 763 785-0484 — Saint Paul (G-8302)
- Environ Electronic Labs ..... E 952 888-7795 — Minneapolis (G-4363)
- Fitzco Inc ..... E 952 471-1185 — Spring Park (G-9563)
- Food Perspectives Inc ..... E 763 553-7787 — Minneapolis (G-4463)
- Interpoll Laboratories Inc ..... E 763 786-6020 — Circle Pines (G-1012)
- Ion Corp ..... E 952 936-9490 — Eden Prairie (G-1698)
- Lab Holdings Inc ..... 612 607-1700 — Minneapolis (G-4831)
- Legend Technical Services Inc ..... E 651 642-1150 — Saint Paul (G-8576)
- Lincoln Lyon Murry & Pipestone ..... E 507 537-6709 — Marshall (G-3305)
- Martin Calibration Inc ..... E 952 882-1528 — Burnsville (G-751)
- MEDTOX Scientific Inc ..... B 651 636-7466 — Saint Paul (G-8632)
- Minnesota Crop Improvement ..... E 612 625-7766 — Saint Paul (G-8680)
- Minnesota Valley Testing Labs ..... D 507 354-8517 — New Ulm (G-6461)
- MSP Corp ..... E 651 287-8100 — Saint Paul (G-8727)
- Northeast Technical Services ..... E 218 741-4290 — Virginia (G-9749)
- Nova Consulting Group Inc ..... E 952 448-9393 — Chaska (G-977)
- Pace Analytical Services Inc ..... B 612 607-1700 — Minneapolis (G-5308)
- Precision Repair & Calibration ..... E 763 784-1704 — Minneapolis (G-3572)
- Prometric Inc ..... D 651 647-1723 — Saint Paul (G-8854)
- R Tech Laboratories ..... D 651 481-2207 — Saint Paul (G-8867)
- Stearns Dairy Herd Improvement ..... E 320 352-2028 — Sauk Centre (G-9353)
- Stork United Corp ..... D 651 645-3601 — Saint Paul (G-9009)
- Ten-E Packaging Services Inc ..... E 651 459-0671 — Newport (G-6489)
- Tuv Sud America Inc ..... E 651 631-2487 — Saint Paul (G-9086)
- Viromed Laboratories Inc ..... E 952 563-3300 — Minnetonka (G-6234)

8741 Management Services

- A T & T Corp ..... B 612 376-5401 — Minneapolis (G-3649)
- Allina Health System ..... A 612 775-5000 — Minneapolis (G-3721)
- American Swedish Institute ..... E 612 871-4907 — Minneapolis (G-3760)
- Atirix Medical Systems Inc ..... E 952 546-2001 — Minnetonka (G-6145)
- Badger Acquisition of MN ..... C 763 259-0400 — Minneapolis (G-3857)
- Bainey Group Inc ..... E 763 557-6911 — Minneapolis (G-3858)
- Best Vendors Management Inc ..... C 763 287-7200 — Minneapolis (G-3892)
- Bethesda Healthy Rehab ..... A 651 232-2000 — Saint Paul (G-8109)
- Bioscrip Pharmacy Inc ..... C 952 979-3600 — Eden Prairie (G-1606)
- Blast Pressure Washing ..... E 507 455-2898 — Owatonna (G-6696)
- Bnsf Railway Co ..... C 651 298-2121 — Saint Paul (G-8116)
- Boldt Co ..... C 218 879-1293 — Cloquet (G-1047)
- Bossardt Corp ..... E 952 837-3346 — Minneapolis (G-3932)
- Bremer Financial Services Inc ..... D 651 227-7621 — Saint Paul (G-8126)
- Bremer Financial Services Inc ..... C 651 734-4040 — Lake Elmo (G-2866)
- Brim Healthcare Inc ..... E 763 546-4801 — Minneapolis (G-3948)
- Central Group Management Co ..... B 320 654-6307 — Saint Cloud (G-7482)
- City of Saint Paul ..... D 651 266-6789 — Saint Paul (G-8208)
- Diversified Pharmaceutical ..... 952 820-7000 — Minneapolis (G-4263)
- Dnk Management Inc ..... D 651 773-8077 — Saint Paul (G-8305)
- Ebenezer Society ..... C 612 879-2262 — Minneapolis (G-4309)
- Ebenezer Society ..... C 612 879-1400 — Minneapolis (G-4310)
- Ebenezer Society ..... D 952 435-8116 — Burnsville (G-716)
- Energy Management Steam ..... E 612 626-7329 — Minneapolis (G-4357)
- Entegris Inc ..... C 952 556-3131 — Chaska (G-965)
- ▲ Expresspoint Technology Svcs ..... C 763 543-6000 — Golden Valley (G-2240)

(G-00000) Company's Geographic Section entry number
528
2011 Harris Minnesota Services Directory
▲=Import ▼=Export ◆=Import/Export

Fairview Health Services ....C....612 672-6800 Minneapolis (G-4393)
Fairview Health Services ....B....651 982-7000 Wyoming (G-10202)
Fairview Health Services ....C....218 262-4881 Hibbing (G-2444)
Fairview Health Services ....C....763 389-1313 Princeton (G-6907)
Fairview Health Services ....B....612 273-3000 Minneapolis (G-4400)
Fairview Health Services ....B....612 672-5500 Minneapolis (G-4399)
Fairview Health Services ....E....651 632-7300 Saint Paul (G-8362)
Fairview Health Services ....E....612 626-2663 Minneapolis (G-4398)
First American Real Estate ....D....800 868-8816 Minneapolis (G-4439)
General Aviation Inc ....E....763 420-6907 Minneapolis (G-4507)
▼ Genmar Holdings Inc ....D....612 339-7900 Minneapolis (G-4521)
Global Capital Management Inc ....D....952 476-7222 Hopkins (G-2545)
Harrington Co ....E....952 928-4666 Minneapolis (G-4603)
Healtheast Care Inc ....A....651 232-2300 Saint Paul (G-8453)
Healtheast Care System ....A....651 232-1000 Saint Paul (G-8454)
Hewitt Associates Inc ....D....612 339-7501 Minneapolis (G-4642)
Historical Society of MN ....E....651 297-2555 Saint Paul (G-8485)
Hormel Financial Services ....E....507 437-5611 Austin (G-274)
Ibberson Inc ....952 938-7007 Hopkins (G-2555)
Inac of VA Inc ....E....218 263-3398 Hibbing (G-2457)
Ingenix Inc ....B....952 833-7100 Eden Prairie (G-1692)
Interstate Co's Inc ....D....952 854-2044 Minneapolis (G-4726)
Jacobs Investors Inc ....E....612 339-9500 Minneapolis (G-4750)
Kinseth Hotel Corp ....C....952 884-8211 Minneapolis (G-4811)
Knutson Construction Services ....D....507 280-9788 Rochester (G-7157)
Kraus-Anderson Construction Co ....E....612 721-7581 Minneapolis (G-4822)
Lakeview Retirement Apartments ....D....218 386-1235 Warroad (G-9871)
Larken Inc ....D....952 830-1300 Minneapolis (G-4844)
Loram Admin LLC ....D....763 478-6014 Hamel (G-2347)
M B W Co ....C....507 354-3808 New Ulm (G-6459)
Macks LLC ....C....507 288-2677 Rochester (G-7164)
Marathon Management Inc ....E....651 259-4093 Saint Paul (G-7831)
Marcus Bloomington LLC ....C....952 893-9500 Bloomington (G-504)
▲ Mayo Foundation For Medical ....A....507 284-2511 Rochester (G-7174)
Mayo Management Services Inc ....C....507 538-5508 Rochester (G-7175)
Minnesota Autism Center ....C....952 767-4200 Minnetonka (G-6196)
Minnesota Dairy Herd ....D....763 682-1091 Buffalo (G-652)
Minnesota Department of Admin ....A....651 296-2600 Saint Paul (G-8682)
Minnesota Hospital ....D....651 641-1121 Saint Paul (G-8689)
Minnesota Surgical Associates ....E....651 776-0724 Saint Paul (G-8708)
Minnesota Vikings Food Svcs ....C....952 835-5250 Saint Paul (G-8709)
Minnetonka Assisted Living Com ....E....952 988-0011 Minnetonka (G-6197)
Minter-Weisman Co ....E....763 545-3700 Minneapolis (G-5104)
Model Cities of St Paul Inc ....651 632-8350 Saint Paul (G-8717)
Motors Management Corp ....E....763 593-5755 Saint Louis Park (G-7668)
Mrg Management Inc ....B....763 537-1460 Minneapolis (G-5144)
Mutual Service Cooperative ....B....651 631-7000 Saint Paul (G-8731)
Nath Minnesota Franchise Group ....E....952 853-1400 Minneapolis (G-5159)
New Dawn Inc ....C....507 425-3278 Fulda (G-2196)
Octagon Financial Group ....E....952 885-2700 Minneapolis (G-5264)
Orthopedic Resources Mgt ....E....952 831-5773 Minneapolis (G-5294)
Otsego Hospitality LLC ....D....763 656-4400 Elk River (G-1903)
Pal Management Inc ....D....952 646-1792 Burnsville (G-774)
▲ Pals Inc ....D....320 235-8860 Willmar (G-10035)
Paragon Strategic Solutions ....C....952 886-8000 Minneapolis (G-5321)
Park Nicollet Health Services ....E....952 993-5495 Minneapolis (G-5335)
Pathway Health Services Inc ....D....651 407-8699 Saint Paul (G-8809)
Pine Ridge Homes Inc ....D....218 879-1257 Cloquet (G-1059)
Powertrack ....E....612 973-3170 Minneapolis (G-5398)
Prime Therapeutics Inc ....C....651 456-1000 Saint Paul (G-7881)
Pro One Management ....E....612 813-0077 Minneapolis (G-5414)
Pro Systems Corp ....E....218 847-9277 Detroit Lakes (G-1214)
Procter & Gamble Distributing ....C....952 942-1857 Eden Prairie (G-1754)
Production Health Associates ....E....507 372-2957 Worthington (G-10191)
REc Inc ....E....952 947-3000 Minneapolis (G-5475)
Recovery One Inc ....C....952 435-7106 Burnsville (G-786)
REM Leadway Inc ....E....952 925-5067 Minneapolis (G-5511)
RMC Project Management Inc ....E....952 846-4484 Minnetonka (G-6220)
Rust Consulting Inc ....C....612 359-2000 Minneapolis (G-5577)
Sanford Health Network ....B....507 223-7272 Canby (G-852)
Sanford Health Network ....D....507 847-2420 Jackson (G-2799)
Sanford Health Network ....C....507 674-2932 Tracy (G-9691)
Sbsb LP ....D....218 628-2700 Duluth (G-1444)
Senior Asset Management Inc ....B....763 544-9934 Minneapolis (G-5636)
Shuett Co's Inc ....763 541-9199 Minneapolis (G-5662)
Sodexo Management Inc ....E....507 333-6772 Faribault (G-2030)
Southwest Casino & Hotel Corp ....E....952 853-9990 Minneapolis (G-5713)
St Francis Health Services of ....A....320 589-2004 Morris (G-6378)
Stahl Construction Co ....E....952 931-9300 Minneapolis (G-5735)
Suburban Radiologic Conslnts ....D....952 837-9700 Minneapolis (G-5762)
Summit Management LLC ....E....651 689-2200 Stillwater (G-9650)
Systems Management & Balancing ....E....651 257-7380 Center City (G-886)
T C Sweatshop Inc ....E....651 646-8418 Saint Paul (G-9023)
Taylor & Katie Inc ....E....320 523-2833 Olivia (G-6565)
Thd At-Home Services Inc ....D....763 542-8826 Minneapolis (G-5812)
Tofte Management Co LLC ....C....218 663-7296 Tofte (G-9684)
Toro Receivables Co ....E....952 888-8801 Minneapolis (G-5833)
Transportation Management Corp ....D....651 642-9292 Saint Paul (G-9076)
Tri-City IV Inc ....D....952 854-7405 Bloomington (G-521)
▼ Unitedhealth Group Inc ....A....952 936-1300 Minnetonka (G-6232)
URS Group Inc ....E....612 370-0700 Minneapolis (G-5941)
US Energy Services Inc ....D....763 543-4600 Minneapolis (G-5947)
Walden Automotive Group Inc ....E....952 512-8800 Minneapolis (G-5995)
XATA Corp ....C....952 707-5600 Eden Prairie (G-1818)
Z M C Hotels Inc ....E....218 723-8433 Duluth (G-1507)
Z M C Hotels Inc ....E....218 727-0461 Duluth (G-1508)

8742 Management Consulting Services

A'Viands LLC ....A....651 631-0940 Saint Paul (G-7969)
Accenture LLP ....C....612 277-0000 Minneapolis (G-3664)
Accord Benefit Resources Inc ....E....763 746-9004 Minneapolis (G-3669)
▼ Advantage Travel & Incentives ....D....952 447-1333 Savage (G-9382)
Aecom Technical Services Inc ....E....763 551-1001 Minneapolis (G-3691)
Affiance Financial LLC ....E....952 253-2564 Hopkins (G-2503)
Aldin Export & Import ....651 483-4184 Saint Paul (G-8007)
All England Enterprises Ltd ....612 332-8011 Minneapolis (G-3708)
All Time Favorites Inc ....E....651 454-1124 Saint Paul (G-7690)
Alquest Inc ....E....763 287-3830 Minneapolis (G-3734)
American Enterprise Investment ....C....612 671-3131 Minneapolis (G-3748)
American-Russian Trade Inc ....D....612 922-1163 Minneapolis (G-3762)
Analog Technologies, Corp ....E....952 894-9228 Burnsville (G-677)
ARAZ Group Inc ....D....952 896-1200 Minneapolis (G-3796)
Archway Marketing Services Inc ....C....763 428-3300 Rogers (G-7316)
Ardel Inc ....E....763 545-1919 Minneapolis (G-3804)
▲ Argenbright Inc ....E....763 477-7600 Rockford (G-7307)
Argenbright Inc ....E....320 693-7314 Litchfield (G-2978)
Argenbright Inc ....C....763 477-7600 Rockford (G-7308)
Associated Anesthesiologists ....C....651 735-0501 Minneapolis (G-3822)
Associated Eye Care Ltd ....E....651 275-3013 Stillwater (G-9599)
Augeo Affinity Marketing Inc ....D....877 781-2586 Saint Paul (G-8078)
Benesyst Inc ....E....612 746-3100 Minneapolis (G-3884)
Bestmark Inc ....C....952 922-2205 Minnetonka (G-6148)
Bjorklund Realty Inc ....D....952 934-0500 Edina (G-1826)
Bonfire Partners LLC ....E....612 455-7400 Minneapolis (G-3926)
Border Foods Inc ....E....763 323-4731 Anoka (G-159)
Bossardt Corp ....E....952 837-3346 Minneapolis (G-3932)
Braun Intertec Corp ....C....952 995-2000 Minneapolis (G-3938)
Braun Intertec Corp ....E....651 487-3245 Saint Paul (G-8122)
Bremer Trust National Assn ....E....320 252-3918 Saint Cloud (G-7466)
Burchfield Group Inc ....E....651 389-5648 Saint Paul (G-7724)
▲ Business Impact Group LLC ....D....952 278-7800 Chanhassen (G-911)
C-ME Marketing Inc ....E....320 587-6565 Hutchinson (G-2690)
▼ Capitol Sales Co Inc ....D....651 688-6830 Saint Paul (G-7727)
Caritas Debt Counseling ....D....320 650-1660 Saint Cloud (G-7471)
Carlson Co's Inc ....B....763 212-5253 Minneapolis (G-4013)
Carlson Hospitality Worldwide ....E....763 540-5035 Minnetonka (G-6153)
Carlson Marketing Worldwide ....E....763 449-3704 Minneapolis (G-4018)
Carlson, Lundquist & Co Ltd ....E....763 535-8150 Minneapolis (G-4019)
Cartika Medical Inc ....E....763 545-5188 Minneapolis (G-4022)
Cassidy Turley Midwest Inc ....D....612 341-4444 Minneapolis (G-4026)
CFC Technology Corp ....E....763 235-5300 Minneapolis (G-4053)
City of Bloomington ....B....952 563-8920 Minneapolis (G-4083)
City of Grand Rapids ....E....218 326-7024 Grand Rapids (G-2274)
Clark & Wamberg LLC ....C....612 339-0919 Minneapolis (G-4102)
Clark Engineering Corp ....E....763 545-9196 Minneapolis (G-4103)
CMI Equipment & Engineering Co ....E....320 864-5894 Glencoe (G-2218)
Coldwell Banker Burnet Inc ....D....952 920-1224 Eden Prairie (G-1630)
Coldwell Banker Burnet Inc ....D....952 474-2525 Excelsior (G-1942)
Colliers Towle Valuation ....612 347-9336 Minneapolis (G-4120)
Construction Coordinators Inc ....E....612 332-2020 Minneapolis (G-4155)
Creatis Inc ....D....612 333-3233 Minneapolis (G-4179)
Creative Marketing Consulting ....E....952 935-9385 Saint Paul (G-8266)
Creative Training Techniques ....E....952 829-1954 Eden Prairie (G-1637)
Customer Elation Inc ....E....320 968-4438 Foley (G-2136)
D L Ryan Co's Ltd ....E....612 204-9790 Minneapolis (G-4214)
D M I LLC ....D....952 841-6200 Minneapolis (G-4215)
Distributed Website Corp ....E....507 453-5164 Winona (G-10093)
Diversified Consulting Assocs ....E....651 436-1330 Stillwater (G-9610)
Donmar Inc ....E....763 631-2233 Princeton (G-6921)
E & C Amec Services Inc ....D....612 332-8326 Minneapolis (G-4299)
▲ E-Group Inc ....E....612 339-4777 Minneapolis (G-4304)
Ecosure ....E....651 293-4320 Saint Paul (G-8321)

Efficio Group Inc ....D....612 805-7288 Osseo *(G-6613)*

Elenas Care Inc ....D....651 482-0549 Saint Paul *(G-8332)*

Eloyalty Corp ....E....952 908-8000 Edina *(G-1830)*

EMA Inc ....E....651 639-5600 Saint Paul *(G-8336)*

Empo Corp ....E....612 285-8707 Minneapolis *(G-4352)*

Energy Resources LLC ....612 889-0447 Saint Louis Park *(G-7660)*

▲ Epredix Holdings Inc ....D....612 843-1059 Minneapolis *(G-4365)*

Ernst & Young LLP ....B....612 343-1000 Minneapolis *(G-4367)*

Ewald Consulting Group Inc ....E....651 290-6260 Saint Paul *(G-8350)*

Faithful & Gould Inc ....E....612 338-3120 Minneapolis *(G-4404)*

Family Health Services of MN ....E....651 772-2077 Saint Paul *(G-8366)*

Family Service Rochester Inc ....D....507 287-2010 Rochester *(G-7110)*

Familymeans Inc ....E....612 874-8164 Stillwater *(G-9617)*

Fintegra Financial Solutions ....763 503-1911 Minneapolis *(G-4435)*

Food Perspectives Inc ....E....763 553-7787 Minneapolis *(G-4463)*

Fredrickson Communications Inc ....E....612 339-7970 Minneapolis *(G-4483)*

Gage Group LLC ....C....763 595-3920 Minneapolis *(G-4495)*

Gardner Financial Services Inc ....E....952 935-4601 Minneapolis *(G-4500)*

Genesis Corp ....A....651 702-3300 Saint Paul *(G-9219)*

Geo-Comm Inc ....D....320 240-0040 Saint Cloud *(G-7517)*

Global Tax Network Minnesota ....E....952 224-2053 Minneapolis *(G-4532)*

Gold Groves ....E....612 884-8383 Minneapolis *(G-4533)*

Gold Points Corp ....D....763 212-1000 Minneapolis *(G-4534)*

Goldleaf Partners ....E....218 824-6119 Brainerd *(G-568)*

Gopher State One Call Inc ....D....651 454-8388 Saint Paul *(G-7788)*

▲ Griffin International Co's Inc ....E....612 344-4700 Minneapolis *(G-4570)*

Gunsbury Alan Quarterdeck ....E....218 963-2482 Nisswa *(G-6492)*

H & J Bliss Enterprises ....E....952 988-9302 Minneapolis *(G-4584)*

Hanley-Wood Custom Publishing ....D....612 338-8300 Minneapolis *(G-4593)*

Hanson McFarland Inc ....D....763 421-9554 Anoka *(G-188)*

Happy Chef Systems Inc ....E....507 345-4571 Mankato *(G-3134)*

Harbinger Partners Inc ....D....651 426-1569 Saint Paul *(G-8442)*

HDR Engineering Inc ....C....763 591-5400 Minneapolis *(G-4615)*

Healing Touch Aquamassage ....E....507 287-6186 Rochester *(G-7135)*

Healthcare Management ....E....651 224-4930 Saint Paul *(G-7797)*

Healthia Consulting Inc ....D....763 923-7900 Minneapolis *(G-4620)*

Healthsense Inc ....E....952 400-7300 Mendota Heights *(G-3364)*

Herbeck, David J CPA Pfs Chfc ....E....763 546-6211 Minneapolis *(G-4640)*

Hire A Host Inc ....D....952 346-8800 Minneapolis *(G-4653)*

Hollstadt & Associates Inc ....D....952 892-3660 Burnsville *(G-732)*

Hormel Foods International ....D....507 437-5611 Austin *(G-277)*

Iconoculture Inc ....E....612 377-0087 Minneapolis *(G-4686)*

Infinity Direct Inc ....E....763 559-1111 Minneapolis *(G-4701)*

Ingenix Inc ....B....952 833-7100 Eden Prairie *(G-1692)*

Insignia Systems Inc ....D....763 392-6200 Minneapolis *(G-4706)*

Interpublic Group of Co's Inc ....D....612 367-5144 Minneapolis *(G-4725)*

J T Mega LLC ....E....952 929-1370 Minneapolis *(G-4749)*

J Thomas & Associates ....218 829-6622 Baxter *(G-331)*

John Ryan Performance Inc ....E....612 924-7700 Minneapolis *(G-4771)*

Kantar Media Intelligences Inc ....E....952 926-5430 Minneapolis *(G-4788)*

Kenexa Corp ....E....612 332-6383 Minneapolis *(G-4800)*

Kersten Management Group Inc ....D....218 543-6977 Pine River *(G-6819)*

Khashi Associates LLC ....E....763 550-0961 Minneapolis *(G-4804)*

Lacek Group ....C....612 359-3700 Minneapolis *(G-4832)*

Larsonallen LLP ....B....612 376-4500 Minneapolis *(G-4848)*

Lawrence Service Co ....E....763 383-5700 Minneapolis *(G-4850)*

Leuthold Asset Allocation Fund ....E....612 332-9141 Minneapolis *(G-4864)*

Life-Science Innovations LLC ....E....320 222-9750 Willmar *(G-10019)*

Lincoln Financial Advisors ....E....952 933-8000 Hopkins *(G-2571)*

Lominger Limited Inc ....E....952 345-3600 Minneapolis *(G-4901)*

Lutheran Brethren Homes Inc ....C....218 736-5441 Fergus Falls *(G-2087)*

M D A Consulting Group Inc ....E....612 332-8182 Minneapolis *(G-4920)*

▲ Magiccom Inc ....E....763 529-2208 Minneapolis *(G-4934)*

Manchester Co's Inc ....E....612 436-2818 Minneapolis *(G-4941)*

Marcus Solutions LLC ....E....952 373-4038 Edina *(G-1836)*

Market Resource Associates Inc ....E....612 334-3056 Minneapolis *(G-4948)*

Marketing Architects Inc ....D....952 449-2500 Minnetonka *(G-6190)*

Marshall-Teichert Group Ltd ....D....952 942-0564 Hopkins *(G-2577)*

Maxfield Research Inc ....612 338-2828 Minneapolis *(G-4967)*

McKinsey & Co Inc ....D....612 371-3100 Minneapolis *(G-4979)*

Medical Learning Inc ....E....651 292-3432 Saint Paul *(G-8630)*

Mercer Inc ....D....612 642-8600 Minneapolis *(G-4989)*

Metrisource Inc ....E....651 686-0097 Saint Paul *(G-7838)*

Metropolitan Financial Mgt ....E....651 631-8000 Saint Paul *(G-8646)*

Michael D Norman & Associates ....E....952 935-0515 Minneapolis *(G-5015)*

Mid-America Business Systems ....E....612 378-3800 Minneapolis *(G-5022)*

Midland Corporate Benefit Svcs ....320 485-3821 Winsted *(G-10163)*

Minnesota Counties Insurance ....E....651 209-6400 Saint Paul *(G-8679)*

Minnesota Pipe Trades Assn ....651 291-8151 Saint Paul *(G-8701)*

Minnesota State Community ....D....218 755-4270 Bemidji *(G-403)*

Miro Management Inc ....E....952 404-8267 Wayzata *(G-9928)*

Modern Climate Inc ....E....612 343-8180 Minneapolis *(G-5117)*

Morris Communications Corp ....D....218 829-4705 Brainerd *(G-576)*

Motivaction LLC ....D....763 412-3000 Minneapolis *(G-5137)*

Motors Management Corp ....E....763 593-5755 Saint Louis Park *(G-7668)*

Narveson Management Inc ....E....218 562-6400 Pequot Lakes *(G-6791)*

1 Micro LLC ....E....952 767-1010 Eden Prairie *(G-1738)*

121 Marketing Services Group ....D....763 428-8123 Rogers *(G-7334)*

Opus National LLC ....C....952 656-4444 Minnetonka *(G-6207)*

Pacific Marketing & Comms ....E....651 967-7135 Minneapolis *(G-5310)*

Par Systems Inc ....B....651 484-7261 Saint Paul *(G-8806)*

Pareo Inc ....E....612 371-0400 Minneapolis *(G-5326)*

Parsons ....E....612 656-7000 Minneapolis *(G-5340)*

Party Music Inc ....E....952 941-3830 Eden Prairie *(G-1744)*

Pathway Health Services Inc ....D....651 407-8699 Saint Paul *(G-8809)*

Peak Performers Network ....E....952 345-3333 Minneapolis *(G-5359)*

Perficient Inc ....D....612 752-1700 Minneapolis *(G-5365)*

Performark Inc ....C....952 946-7300 Minnetonka *(G-6210)*

Police Range ....E....218 751-7641 Bemidji *(G-421)*

Pragmatek Consulting Group Ltd ....D....612 333-3164 Bloomington *(G-511)*

PRC Consulting Inc ....E....952 906-0801 Chanhassen *(G-936)*

Preferredone Administrative ....B....763 847-3525 Minneapolis *(G-5401)*

Presbyterian Homes Management ....E....651 631-6000 Saint Paul *(G-8842)*

Prisma International Inc ....E....612 338-1500 Minneapolis *(G-5412)*

Project Consulting Group Inc ....D....612 330-0123 Minneapolis *(G-5427)*

Protiviti Inc ....E....952 249-2200 Hopkins *(G-2606)*

Radisson Hotels International ....C....763 212-5000 Minnetonka *(G-6218)*

RCM Technologies Inc ....E....952 841-1188 Hopkins *(G-2612)*

Regents of The University of ....C....612 625-4665 Minneapolis *(G-5486)*

Reliability Management Group ....E....952 882-8122 Burnsville *(G-790)*

Retail Support Inc ....E....952 934-1317 Eden Prairie *(G-1763)*

Richard F Tschida ....E....651 426-7958 Saint Paul *(G-8898)*

Right Management Consultants ....E....952 837-0955 Minneapolis *(G-5540)*

Risdall Marketing Group LLC ....D....651 286-6700 New Brighton *(G-6413)*

Rothe Development Inc ....E....612 726-1102 Minneapolis *(G-5561)*

RSM McGladrey Business Soln ....C....952 921-7700 Minneapolis *(G-5567)*

RSM McGladrey Inc ....D....507 288-5363 Rochester *(G-7242)*

RSM McGladrey Inc ....D....218 727-5025 Duluth *(G-1440)*

RSM McGladrey Inc ....C....612 332-4300 Minneapolis *(G-5570)*

Rubenstein Logistics Services ....E....763 542-1121 Golden Valley *(G-2244)*

Sadaka Technology Consultants ....A....952 841-6363 Minneapolis *(G-5586)*

SafeNet Consulting Inc ....D....952 930-3636 Minnetonka *(G-6224)*

SAV Enterprises Inc ....E....763 278-3340 Minneapolis *(G-3596)*

Schoell & Madson Inc ....E....763 746-1600 Minneapolis *(G-5610)*

▲ Schoeneckers Inc ....A....952 835-4800 Edina *(G-1844)*

Schoeneckers Inc ....D....320 453-2600 Eden Valley *(G-1822)*

Seabury Group L L C ....E....612 399-0033 Minneapolis *(G-5621)*

Selftek ....E....612 872-1285 Minneapolis *(G-5635)*

Shea Inc ....E....612 339-2257 Minneapolis *(G-5652)*

Sheffield, Olson & McQueen Inc ....E....651 695-2500 Saint Paul *(G-8951)*

Ske Support Services Inc ....E....651 639-6559 Saint Paul *(G-8962)*

Solutran Inc ....D....763 559-2225 Minneapolis *(G-5697)*

Sopheon Corp ....E....952 851-7555 Minneapolis *(G-5702)*

Southwest Casino & Hotel Corp ....E....952 853-9990 Minneapolis *(G-5713)*

SRF Consulting Group Inc ....C....763 475-0010 Minneapolis *(G-5725)*

Sterling Commerce Inc ....D....952 294-1800 Eden Prairie *(G-1782)*

Superclean Brands LLC ....E....651 365-7500 Eagan *(G-1554)*

Synergetic Solutions Inc ....E....763 331-3300 Minneapolis *(G-3613)*

T-Chek Systems Inc ....D....952 934-3413 Eden Prairie *(G-1790)*

Talent Technical Services Inc ....C....952 417-3600 Minneapolis *(G-5786)*

Target Corp ....B....763 440-2033 Minneapolis *(G-5790)*

◆ Taylor Corp ....C....507 625-2828 North Mankato *(G-6514)*

Taylor Corp ....C....952 888-7945 Minneapolis *(G-5794)*

Tena Co's Inc ....C....651 293-1234 Saint Paul *(G-9037)*

3M Co ....E....651 733-1110 Saint Paul *(G-9048)*

3M Co ....E....651 736-3828 Saint Paul *(G-9063)*

Threewire Inc ....952 852-5556 Eden Prairie *(G-1792)*

▲ Thrivent Financial For ....A....920 734-5721 Minneapolis *(G-5819)*

Total Training Network Inc ....E....952 345-5555 Minneapolis *(G-5837)*

Towers Watson Delaware Inc ....C....952 842-7000 Minneapolis *(G-5839)*

Towers Watson Pennsylvania Inc ....E....952 842-5600 Minneapolis *(G-5840)*

Transway Express Inc ....E....651 686-7000 Northfield *(G-6544)*

Trissential ....D....952 595-7970 Hopkins *(G-2647)*

Trustee Group LLP ....E....952 473-5650 Wayzata *(G-9946)*

Tunheim Partners Inc ....D....952 851-1600 Minneapolis *(G-5865)*

21st Services ....E....612 371-3008 Minneapolis *(G-5871)*

▲ 2020 Promotions LLC ....E....651 451-3850 South Saint Paul *(G-9545)*

▼ Uni-Systems LLC ....E....763 536-1407 Minneapolis *(G-5901)*

Unicom Consulting Inc ....E....952 698-7600 Minneapolis *(G-5902)*

Unisys Corp ....A....651 687-2200 Saint Paul *(G-7935)*

United Check Clearing Corp ....D....763 559-2225 Minneapolis *(G-5908)*

United States Compliance Corp ....E....952 252-3000 Minnetonka *(G-6231)*

SIC

Uponor North America Inc ....E....952 891-2000
Saint Paul *(G-7939)*
VHA Upper Midwest Inc ....E....952 837-4700
Minneapolis *(G-5967)*
Visions Inc ....D....763 425-4251
Brooklyn Park *(G-621)*
Waddell & Reed Inc ....E....651 483-1411
Saint Paul *(G-9135)*
Westwood Professional Services ....C....952 937-5150
Eden Prairie *(G-1815)*
Wiken Promotion & Advertising ....E....952 476-2002
Wayzata *(G-9950)*
Willow Group Inc ....E....952 897-3550
Minneapolis *(G-6072)*
Wilson Learning Corp ....D....952 944-2880
Minneapolis *(G-6075)*
Workman Financial Group Inc ....E....763 746-9420
Minneapolis *(G-6086)*
Zentropy Partners ....E....612 367-5148
Minneapolis *(G-6116)*

8743 Public Relations Svcs

Aca International ....D....952 926-6547
Minneapolis *(G-3663)*
▲ **Beacon Promotions Inc** ....D....507 233-3240
New Ulm *(G-6442)*
Clean Water Action Inc ....C....612 623-3666
Minneapolis *(G-4105)*
D L Ryan Co's Ltd ....E....612 204-9790
Minneapolis *(G-4214)*
Dorf & Stanton Communications ....D....952 832-5000
Minneapolis *(G-4280)*
Franklin Corp ....D....612 455-1700
Minneapolis *(G-4475)*
Gage Group LLC ....C....763 595-3920
Minneapolis *(G-4495)*
Goff & Howard Inc 651 292-8062
Saint Paul *(G-8417)*
Hanley-Wood Custom Publishing ....D....612 338-8300
Minneapolis *(G-4593)*
Lawrence Service Co ....E....763 383-5700
Minneapolis *(G-4850)*
League of Minnesota Cities ....D....651 281-1200
Saint Paul *(G-8573)*
Media Relations Inc ....E....612 798-7200
Burnsville *(G-752)*
Pro Motion Marketing ....E....612 347-1490
Minneapolis *(G-5413)*
Risdall Marketing Group LLC ....D....651 286-6700
New Brighton *(G-6413)*
Swenson Nhb Investor Relations ....E....612 371-0000
Minneapolis *(G-5778)*
3M Co ....C....651 733-1110
Saint Paul *(G-9060)*
Tunheim Partners Inc ....D....952 851-1600
Minneapolis *(G-5865)*
▲ **2020 Promotions LLC** ....E....651 451-3850
South Saint Paul *(G-9545)*
Ultra Creative Inc ....E....612 378-0748
Minneapolis *(G-5896)*

8744 Facilities Support Mgmt Svcs

Bay West Inc ....C....651 291-0456
Saint Paul *(G-8093)*
Bay West-Bem Solutions LLC ....D....651 291-0456
Saint Paul *(G-8094)*
Bem - Bay West Joint Venture ....D....651 291-0456
Saint Paul *(G-8101)*
Corrections Corp of America ....B....320 289-2052
Appleton *(G-245)*
County of Steele ....E....507 444-7410
Owatonna *(G-6707)*
Envirotech Remediation Svcs ....D....763 746-0670
Minneapolis *(G-6125)*
Financial Systems Support ....E....612 625-3493
Minneapolis *(G-4433)*
Guardian Angels of Elk River ....D....763 241-4428
Elk River *(G-1881)*
Lindstrom Environmental Inc ....D....763 545-9740
Plymouth *(G-6870)*
Minnesota Department of ....D....218 751-3196
Bemidji *(G-402)*
Supportive Lifestyles Inc ....E....320 796-5900
Spicer *(G-9559)*

8748 Business Consulting Svcs, NEC

A Chance To Grow Inc ....D....612 789-1236
Minneapolis *(G-3647)*
A D G Inc ....D....651 287-5858
Eagan *(G-1514)*
A G Technologies International ....E....507 444-4157
Owatonna *(G-6687)*
Accenture LLP ....C....612 277-0000
Minneapolis *(G-3664)*
Adapt Inc ....E....952 939-0538
Hopkins *(G-2500)*
Administration Resources Corp ....E....763 421-5510
Minneapolis *(G-3385)*
Aecom Technical Services Inc ....E....763 551-1001
Minneapolis *(G-3691)*
Alliance Benefit Group ....D....507 377-9344
Albert Lea *(G-35)*
Alquest Inc ....E....763 287-3830
Minneapolis *(G-3734)*
Alwaysbethere Inc ....E....612 243-9233
Plymouth *(G-6848)*
Amalfi Consulting LLC 952 893-6732
Minneapolis *(G-3738)*
Analytics Inc ....E....952 404-5700
Chanhassen *(G-908)*
Aquent LLC ....D....952 851-3411
Minneapolis *(G-3794)*
Area Special Education Co-op ....E....218 773-0315
East Grand Forks *(G-1566)*
Arrowhead Regional Development ....E....218 722-5545
Duluth *(G-1242)*
Aston Technologies Inc ....E....952 546-1693
Saint Louis Park *(G-7657)*
Atek Manufacturing LLC ....D....218 829-4719
Brainerd *(G-550)*
Auerbach Pollock Friedlander ....E....952 930-0818
Minneapolis *(G-3834)*
Augeo Communications LLC ....E....651 204-5734
Saint Paul *(G-8079)*
Bahama Consulting Corp ....E....651 994-7900
Inver Grove Heights *(G-2738)*
Baker It Inc ....E....612 822-3664
Minneapolis *(G-3859)*
Braun Intertec Corp ....C....952 995-2000
Minneapolis *(G-3938)*
Braun Intertec Corp ....E....651 487-3245
Saint Paul *(G-8122)*
C P P North America LLC ....C....952 541-5800
Minneapolis *(G-3986)*
Centrol Inc ....E....218 584-5107
Twin Valley *(G-9701)*
Child Care Resource & Referral ....D....507 287-2020
Rochester *(G-7076)*
City of Mahtomedi ....E....651 426-1080
Mahtomedi *(G-3093)*
City of Minneapolis ....E....612 673-2597
Minneapolis *(G-4093)*
Clean Water Action Inc ....C....612 623-3666
Minneapolis *(G-4105)*
▲ **Communications Systems Inc** ....C....952 996-1674
Minnetonka *(G-6156)*
Conestoga-Rovers & Associates ....E....651 639-0913
Saint Paul *(G-8247)*
Connexions Loyalty Travel Soln ....D....952 914-6533
Eden Prairie *(G-1634)*
Dakota County Community Devpt ....C....651 675-4400
Saint Paul *(G-7744)*
Delta Environmental Consints ....D....651 639-9449
Saint Paul *(G-8284)*
Department of Corrections MN ....D....218 376-4411
Togo *(G-9685)*
Digineer Inc ....D....763 210-2300
Minneapolis *(G-4256)*
Dks Systems LLC 952 476-7443
Wayzata *(G-9914)*
Dobbs Temporary Services Inc ....E....612 373-2600
Minneapolis *(G-4268)*
Dover Fluid Management Inc ....D....651 388-3565
Red Wing *(G-6978)*
Dpra Inc ....E....651 227-6500
Saint Paul *(G-8311)*
E & C Amec Services Inc ....D....612 332-8326
Minneapolis *(G-4299)*
Ecm Publishers Inc ....E....320 352-6569
Sauk Centre *(G-9344)*
Ecommerce Network Resource Grp ....E....612 340-1110
Minneapolis *(G-4311)*
Electronics For Imaging Inc ....E....651 365-5255
Saint Paul *(G-7759)*
Elert & Associates Networking ....E....651 430-2772
Stillwater *(G-9614)*
Emmons & Olivier Resources Inc ....E....651 770-8448
Saint Paul *(G-9213)*
Engage Health Inc ....E....651 994-0510
Saint Paul *(G-7762)*
English, Bleeker & Associates ....E....952 230-6500
Saint Louis Park *(G-7661)*
Evergreen Air Services Inc ....E....952 446-8255
Saint Bonifacius *(G-7400)*
Ewing's Assoc ....E....763 258-2733
Minneapolis *(G-4380)*
Experior Assessments LLC ....C....651 646-1170
Saint Paul *(G-8353)*
▲ **Fair Isaac Corp** ....B....612 758-5200
Minneapolis *(G-4392)*
Financial Affairs Consulting ....D....952 443-4188
Chaska *(G-967)*
Fiserv Health Plan ....A....262 879-5565
Minneapolis *(G-4450)*
Foth Production Solutions LLC ....D....651 288-8550
Lake Elmo *(G-2872)*
Fujitsu America Inc ....E....763 595-9600
Minneapolis *(G-4489)*
Geospatial Services ....E....507 457-8723
Winona *(G-10098)*
Haigh Todd & Assoc Inc ....E....952 252-2100
Minneapolis *(G-4587)*
Hanley-Wood Custom Publishing ....D....612 338-8300
Minneapolis *(G-4593)*
▲ **Imago Ltd** ....D....651 690-9724
Saint Paul *(G-8506)*
Independent School District ....E....651 385-8000
Red Wing *(G-6986)*
Industrial Systems Associates ....D....763 574-5208
Minneapolis *(G-3498)*
Institute For Environmental ....E....763 315-7900
Minneapolis *(G-4709)*
Interpoll Laboratories Inc ....E....763 786-6020
Circle Pines *(G-1012)*
Izaak Walton League of America ....E....651 649-1446
Saint Paul *(G-8525)*
J Perzel & Associates ....E....612 455-6060
Minneapolis *(G-4748)*
Ja-Cee Consultants Inc ....E....952 466-4785
Cologne *(G-1092)*
Kandiyohi County Economic ....E....320 235-7370
Willmar *(G-10013)*
Kensington Equity Partners Inc 952 808-1800
Burnsville *(G-741)*
Khashi Associates LLC ....E....763 550-0961
Minneapolis *(G-4804)*
Legend Technical Services Inc ....E....651 642-1150
Saint Paul *(G-8576)*
Little Tigers Den-Educational ....E....763 389-5950
Princeton *(G-6923)*
Lmn Consulting Inc ....E....612 805-7288
Hopkins *(G-2572)*
Loyalton Group Inc ....E....651 480-3126
Hastings *(G-2396)*
Magellan Medical Technology ....C....612 677-0000
Minneapolis *(G-4931)*
Marshall Adult Learning Center ....E....507 537-7046
Marshall *(G-3309)*
Matthew's Family Restaurant ....E....763 784-1499
Circle Pines *(G-1017)*
Mayer Electric Corp ....D....763 537-9357
Minneapolis *(G-4968)*
McGhie & Betts Inc ....E....507 289-3919
Rochester *(G-7179)*
McGladrey & Pullen, LLP ....C....952 921-7700
Minneapolis *(G-4974)*
Milestone Systems Inc ....E....763 404-6200
Minneapolis *(G-5041)*
Minneapolis PTG ....E....612 370-2600
Minneapolis *(G-5059)*
Minnesota Diversified Inds ....E....218 263-3663
Hibbing *(G-2467)*
Minnesota Diversified Inds ....E....218 326-9544
Grand Rapids *(G-2295)*
Mmic Health It ....E....763 201-0300
Minneapolis *(G-5113)*
Nationwide Financial ....E....612 723-6375
Minneapolis *(G-5171)*
Natural Resource Group LLC ....C....612 347-6789
Minneapolis *(G-5172)*
▲ **Ncs Pearson Inc** ....A....952 681-3000
Minneapolis *(G-5177)*
Network Security Professionals ....E....612 465-8880
Minneapolis *(G-5185)*
Norstan Inc ....C....952 352-4000
Hopkins *(G-2590)*
Northeast Technical Services ....E....218 741-4290
Virginia *(G-9749)*
Nova Consulting Group Inc ....E....952 448-9393
Chaska *(G-977)*
Novon Consulting Corp ....E....612 868-7057
Elk River *(G-1858)*
Omni Control Systems Inc ....E....507 454-5293
Winona *(G-10119)*
Onmia Manor ....D....320 982-5405
Onamia *(G-6575)*
Pace Analytical Services Inc ....B....612 607-1700
Minneapolis *(G-5308)*
Pacer Center Inc ....D....952 838-9000
Minneapolis *(G-5309)*
Paisley Consulting Inc ....C....320 286-5870
Cokato *(G-1077)*
Peterson Co's Inc ....D....651 257-6864
Chisago City *(G-993)*
Precision Partners Inc 218 737-0507
Fergus Falls *(G-2116)*
Premier Electrical Corp ....C....763 424-6551
Brooklyn Park *(G-617)*
Prosource Technologies Inc ....E....763 786-1445
Minneapolis *(G-3577)*
Quantum Consulting & Placement ....C....952 820-0160
Saint Paul *(G-8862)*
Questar Assessment Inc ....D....952 997-2700
Saint Paul *(G-7885)*
Radcliffe Systems ....E....952 545-2409
Hopkins *(G-2609)*
Rba Inc ....D....952 404-2676
Wayzata *(G-9938)*
Rockingham Group ....E....763 421-8672
Minneapolis *(G-3591)*
Rothe Development Inc ....E....612 726-1102
Minneapolis *(G-5561)*
Savvysherpa LLC ....E....763 549-3540
Minneapolis *(G-5604)*
Schoeneckers Inc ....D....320 453-2600
Eden Valley *(G-1822)*
Scholarship America ....C....952 830-7300
Minneapolis *(G-5612)*
▲ **Security Products Co** ....E....763 784-6504
Minneapolis *(G-3599)*
Sheffield, Olson & McQueen Inc ....E....651 695-2500
Saint Paul *(G-8951)*
Sick Maihak Inc ....E....952 941-6780
Minneapolis *(G-5663)*
Siham Solutions Inc ....E....651 274-3640
Minneapolis *(G-5672)*
Skylight Corp ....E....651 631-5000
Saint Paul *(G-8964)*
Space150 LLC ....D....612 332-6458
Minneapolis *(G-5714)*

SIC

Employment codes: A=Over 500 employees, B=251-500
C=101-250, D=51-100, E=25-50
2011 Harris Minnesota
Services Directory
© Harris InfoSource 1-866-281-6415
531

Sustainable Resources Center ....E....612 870-4255
   Minneapolis *(G-5776)*
Tom Loucks & Associates Inc ....D....763 424-5505
   Osseo *(G-6676)*
Transcend Communications Inc ....E....763 463-1000
   Minneapolis *(G-5846)*
Travelsmart LLC ....E....952 854-1114
   Bloomington *(G-520)*
Twin City Security Inc ....B....763 784-4160
   Minneapolis *(G-3625)*
United States Compliance Corp ....E....952 252-3000
   Minnetonka *(G-6231)*
Up North Consulting Inc ....E....952 224-8656
   Minneapolis *(G-5932)*
Urban Ventures Leadership ....E....612 822-1628
   Minneapolis *(G-5939)*
V D A Associates ....E....952 937-8833
   Eden Prairie *(G-1802)*
Verifications Inc ....C....763 420-0600
   Osseo *(G-6682)*
▲ Verizon Communications Inc ....C....763 591-0705
   Minneapolis *(G-5965)*
◆ Viking Forest Products LLC ....E....952 941-6512
   Eden Prairie *(G-1805)*
Watson's of Minneapolis Inc ....E....763 560-7727
   Minneapolis *(G-6024)*
Weidt Group Inc ....E....952 938-1588
   Hopkins *(G-2659)*
Widseth, Smith, Nolting ....E....218 281-6522
   Crookston *(G-1144)*

Xmalpha Technologies ....E....651 484-0471
   Saint Paul *(G-9170)*
Xylo Technologies Inc ....D....507 289-9956
   Rochester *(G-7297)*
Youth Frontiers Inc ....E....952 922-0222
   Minneapolis *(G-6107)*

89 SERVICES, NEC

8999 Services Not Elsewhere Classified

A Brighter Christmas ....E....651 808-7495
   Apple Valley *(G-242)*
ABC Co's ....D....877 737-2221
   Faribault *(G-1987)*
▲ ADC Telecommunications Inc ....A....952 938-8080
   Eden Prairie *(G-1584)*
Alden Area Food Shelf ....E....507 377-3683
   Alden *(G-78)*
Bug Co of Minnesota ....E....763 434-0550
   Anoka *(G-160)*
Caspar Inc ....E....507 842-5978
   Brewster *(G-604)*
City of Saint Paul ....E....651 631-0700
   Saint Paul *(G-8209)*
D C C Solutionolutions ....E....320 839-2058
   Ortonville *(G-6581)*
Denco II LLC ....E....320 589-2931
   Morris *(G-6371)*
Fidelity Investments Actuarial ....E....952 831-8595
   Minneapolis *(G-4429)*

Hsi Human Services Inc ....E....651 275-4302
   Stillwater *(G-9622)*
Itasca Consulting Group Inc ....E....612 371-4711
   Minneapolis *(G-4741)*
Milliman Inc ....D....952 897-5300
   Minneapolis *(G-5046)*
Minnesota Department of ....E....218 739-7576
   Fergus Falls *(G-2098)*
Multi Venue Production Inc ....E....952 894-9111
   Saint Paul *(G-7847)*
National Initiatives For ....E....763 229-2753
   Minneapolis *(G-5165)*
Reden & Anders ....E....800 643-7933
   Eden Prairie *(G-1759)*
Riverview Apartments Senior ....B....651 291-1750
   Minneapolis *(G-5546)*
St Louis, County of Inc ....E....218 726-2920
   Duluth *(G-1465)*
St Louis, County of Inc ....E....218 349-8970
   Duluth *(G-1466)*
St Paul Public School ....E....651 436-5243
   Afton *(G-10)*
▲ Tivoli Too Inc ....E....651 698-3335
   Saint Paul *(G-7924)*
Towers Watson Delaware Inc ....C....952 842-7000
   Minneapolis *(G-5839)*
Tricom Communications Inc ....E....651 686-9000
   Saint Paul *(G-7928)*
Xora Inc ....E....651 209-0350
   Saint Paul *(G-7951)*

(G-00000) Company's Geographic Section entry number
532

2011 Harris Minnesota
Services Directory

▲=Import ▼=Export
◆=Import/Export

ALPHABETIC SECTION

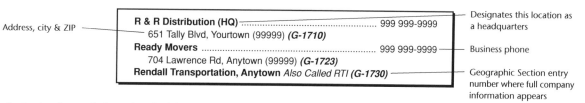

Address, city & ZIP → **R & R Distribution (HQ)** .... 999 999-9999 ← Designates this location as a headquarters
651 Tally Blvd, Yourtown (99999) *(G-1710)*
Ready Movers .... 999 999-9999 ← Business phone
704 Lawrence Rd, Anytown (99999) *(G-1723)*
Rendall Transportation, Anytown *Also Called RTI (G-1730)* ← Geographic Section entry number where full company information appears

See footnotes for symbols and codes identification.

- Companies listed alphabetically.
- Complete physical or mailing address.

'Q' Carriers Inc 952 445-8718
1415 Maras St Shakopee (55379) *(G-9416)*
A & A Electric & Underground 507 634-7453
100 9th St SE Kasson (55944) *(G-2818)*
A & C Farm Service Inc 320 243-3736
412 Bridge St Paynesville (56362) *(G-6768)*
A & C Metals-Sawing Inc 763 786-1048
9170 Davenport St NE Minneapolis (55449) *(G-3382)*
A & H Cartage Inc 651 454-9550
3275 Mike Collins Dr A Saint Paul (55121) *(G-7684)*
A & J Tba Inc 507 233-3000
1201 N Front St New Ulm (56073) *(G-6437)*
A & L Potato Co 218 773-0123
605 4th St NE East Grand Forks (56721) *(G-1564)*
A & R Leasing Inc 218 829-4787
7915 State Highway 210 Baxter (56425) *(G-318)*
A A A Courier Inc 320 259-9292
1 Industrial Blvd Sauk Rapids (56379) *(G-9355)*
A A A Minneapolis 952 944-9585
5400 Auto Club Way Minneapolis (55416) *(G-3645)*
A A Metcalf Moving & Storage 651 484-0211
1255 Highway 36 E Saint Paul (55109) *(G-7967)*
A B E Construction Co 763 542-9070
2525 Nevada Ave N Ste 307 Minneapolis (55427) *(G-3646)*
A B Systems Inc 507 288-9397
209 Woodlake Dr SE Rochester (55904) *(G-7042)*
A Brighter Christmas 651 808-7495
14157 Flagstone Trl Apple Valley (55124) *(G-242)*
A C D, Bloomington *Also Called Advanced Communication Design (G-482)*
A C Equipment, Moorhead *Also Called Aerial Contractors Inc (G-6294)*
A C M C 507 637-2985
1100 E Broadway St Redwood Falls (56283) *(G-7018)*
A Chance To Grow Inc 612 789-1236
1800 2nd St NE Minneapolis (55418) *(G-3647)*
A D B Construction Co Inc 763 424-5550
9240 Cottonwood Ln N Osseo (55369) *(G-6589)*
A D G Inc 651 287-5858
3140 Neil Armstrong Blvd Eagan (55121) *(G-1514)*
A E I Fund Management Inc 800 328-3519
30 7th St E Ste 1300 Saint Paul (55101) *(G-7968)*
A E O A, Virginia *Also Called Arrowhead Economic Opportunity (G-9735)*
A G Edwards & Sons Inc 952 832-1600
8500 Normandale Lake Blvd Bloomington (55437) *(G-480)*
A G O'Brien Plumbing & Heating 218 729-9662
4907 Lightning Dr Hermantown (55811) *(G-2433)*
A G Technologies International 507 444-4157
403 E Broadway St Owatonna (55060) *(G-6687)*
A H Hermel Candy & Tobacco Co (PA) 507 387-5634
23099 Riverfront Dr N Mankato (56001) *(G-3098)*
A I C, Rochester *Also Called Analysts International Corp (G-7055)*
A I M S, Minneapolis *Also Called American Investment Management (G-3754)*
A J Lysne Contracting Corp 507 451-7121
3249 S County Road 45 Owatonna (55060) *(G-6688)*
A J Spanjers Co Inc 763 424-8288
9257 W River Rd Minneapolis (55444) *(G-3648)*
A M P I, Glencoe *Also Called Associated Milk Producers Inc (G-2204)*
A P T, Cokato *Also Called Advanced Process Technologies (G-1074)*
A R I Inc 763 689-1162
1995 E Rum River Dr S Cambridge (55008) *(G-830)*
A S I, Minneapolis *Also Called Applied Statistics Inc (G-3792)*
A S I, Saint Paul *Also Called Accessible Space Inc (G-7975)*
A S K Financial LLP 651 406-9665
2600 Eagan Woods Dr # 400 Saint Paul (55121) *(G-7685)*
A S T Inc 952 888-7340
15900 W 79th St Eden Prairie (55344) *(G-1582)*
A Share Home Inc 218 631-1853
840 Sunnybrook Rd Wadena (56482) *(G-9797)*
A T & T Corp 612 376-5401
901 Marquette Ave Fl 9 Minneapolis (55402) *(G-3649)*
A T S Specialized Inc 320 255-7400
725 Opportunity Dr Saint Cloud (56301) *(G-7445)*
A To Z International Inc 612 729-2328
8933 Lyndale Ave S Minneapolis (55420) *(G-3650)*
A W Kuettel & Sons Inc 218 722-3901
1225 Port Terminal Rd Duluth (55802) *(G-1231)*
A World of Fish Inc 612 866-2026
1516 E 66th St Minneapolis (55423) *(G-3651)*
A'Viands LLC 651 631-0940
1751 County Road B W Ste 300 Saint Paul (55113) *(G-7969)*
A-1 Maintenance Service Corp 952 891-3711
7776 Upper 167th St W Lakeville (55044) *(G-2888)*
A-ABC Appliance & Heating Inc 763 383-8383
4000 Winnetka Ave N # 100 Minneapolis (55427) *(G-3652)*

A-Abco Auto Parts, Minneapolis *Also Called Fridley Auto Parts Inc (G-3472)*
A-Scape Inc 952 496-1178
690 Industrial Cir S Shakopee (55379) *(G-9417)*
A-Veda Corp (HQ) 763 951-4000
4000 Pheasant Ridge Dr NE Minneapolis (55449) *(G-3383)*
A1 Contract Cleaning Inc 763 544-3847
7600 Boone Ave N Ste 71 Minneapolis (55428) *(G-3653)*
AA Monticello 763 295-5066
2025 W River St Monticello (55362) *(G-6265)*
AAA All American Lawn 763 537-5733
21202 Saint Francis Blvd Anoka (55303) *(G-145)*
AAA Auto Salvage Inc 651 423-2432
2871 160th St W Rosemount (55068) *(G-7360)*
AAA Cooper Transportation 651 638-9288
50 14th St NW Saint Paul (55112) *(G-7970)*
AAA Minnesota Iowa (PA) 952 707-4222
600 W Travelers Trl Burnsville (55337) *(G-670)*
AAA Wicks Furnace Duct 651 770-1263
12810 54th Ave N Minneapolis (55442) *(G-3654)*
AAA-American Co 507 894-4156
205 James St Hokah (55941) *(G-2490)*
Aacc International Inc 651 454-7250
3340 Pilot Knob Rd Saint Paul (55121) *(G-7686)*
AAF-Mcquay Inc 763 553-5330
13600 Industrial Park Blvd Minneapolis (55441) *(G-3655)*
Aafedt, Forde, Gray, & Monson 612 339-8965
150 S 5th St Ste 2600 Minneapolis (55402) *(G-3656)*
Aarcee Party & Tent Rental 952 922-7233
5300 W 35th St Minneapolis (55416) *(G-3657)*
AARP 952 858-9040
228 Mrket St Mall Of Amer Minneapolis (55425) *(G-3658)*
Aautomated Pool & Patio, Stillwater *Also Called Minnesota Residential Aquatics (G-9629)*
Abbeycare Inc Home Health Care 651 690-5352
1148 Grand Ave Saint Paul (55105) *(G-7971)*
Abbot Northwestern Hospital 612 863-3150
913 E 26th St Ste 402 Minneapolis (55404) *(G-3659)*
Abbott Arne & Schwindt Inc 218 236-5648
2205 SE Main Ave Moorhead (56560) *(G-6293)*
Abbott Northwestern Hospital, Minneapolis *Also Called Allina Health System (G-3718)*
Abbott Northwestern Hospital 612 863-4000
800 E 28th St Minneapolis (55407) *(G-3660)*
Abbott Paint & Carpet Inc 651 429-3316
2223 4th St Saint Paul (55110) *(G-7972)*
ABC, Excelsior *Also Called Automated Building Components (G-1938)*
ABC Bus Co's Inc (PA) 507 334-1871
1506 30th St NW Faribault (55021) *(G-1985)*
ABC Bus Inc (HQ) 507 334-1871
1506 30th St NW Faribault (55021) *(G-1986)*
ABC Co's 877 737-2221
1506 30th St NW Faribault (55021) *(G-1987)*
ABC Minneapolis LLC 763 428-8777
18270 Territorial Rd Osseo (55369) *(G-6590)*
ABC Seamless, Hastings *Also Called Lifetime Siding & Remodeling (G-2417)*
ABC Seamless, Osseo *Also Called Twin City Exteriors Co Inc (G-6679)*
Abdallah Inc 952 890-4770
3501 County Road 42 W Burnsville (55306) *(G-671)*
ABF Freight System Inc 320 259-5025
2981 Highway 10 SE Saint Cloud (56304) *(G-7432)*
Abfalter Brothers Concrete LLC (PA) 763 635-8088
15546 Cleveland St NW Elk River (55330) *(G-1859)*
Ability Building Center 507 895-7161
62 N 3rd St La Crescent (55947) *(G-2836)*
Ability Building Center (PA) 507 281-6262
1911 14th St NW Rochester (55901) *(G-7043)*
Able One, Saint Paul *Also Called Answer America LLC (G-8053)*
ABM Equipment & Supply Inc (PA) 952 938-5451
333 2nd St NE Hopkins (55343) *(G-2498)*
ABM Equipment & Supply LLC 952 938-5451
333 2nd St NE Hopkins (55343) *(G-2499)*
ABM Janitorial Services - Nthn 612 378-0646
760 Harding St NE Minneapolis (55413) *(G-3661)*
Above All Hardwood Floors LLC 952 440-9663
16861 Welcome Ave SE Prior Lake (55372) *(G-6928)*
Abra Inc (PA) 763 561-7220
6601 Shingle Creek Pkwy Ste 20 Minneapolis (55430) *(G-3662)*
Abraham Technical Services Inc (PA) 763 428-3170
12560 Fletcher Ln Ste 100 Rogers (55374) *(G-7315)*
Abrasive Specialists Inc 763 571-4111
7521 Commerce Ln NE Minneapolis (55432) *(G-3384)*

ALPHABETIC

Abrasives of St Paul Inc 651 636-3955
1000 Labore Industrial Ct Saint Paul (55110) *(G-7973)*

AC Transportation Inc 763 235-2222
11785 Justen Cir Osseo (55369) *(G-6591)*

Aca International (PA) 952 926-6547
4040 W 70th St Minneapolis (55435) *(G-3663)*

Accentra Credit Union 507 433-1829
400 4th Ave NE Austin (55912) *(G-258)*

Accenture LLP 612 277-0000
333 S 7th St Ste 500 Minneapolis (55402) *(G-3664)*

Access Communications Inc 763 545-9998
5005 Cheshire Ln N Ste 1 Minneapolis (55446) *(G-3665)*

Access Health Care Inc 218 326-0004
400B Wittman Dr Grand Rapids (55744) *(G-2267)*

Access Information Systems Inc 952 888-8503
1210 W 96th St Ste A Minneapolis (55431) *(G-3666)*

Accessability Inc 612 331-5958
360 Hoover St NE Minneapolis (55413) *(G-3667)*

Accessible Space, Saint Paul *Also Called Marshall Asi Inc (G-8616)*

Accessible Space Inc 651 690-5216
1085 Montreal Ave Apt 1406 Saint Paul (55116) *(G-7974)*

Accessible Space Inc (PA) 651 645-7271
2550 University Ave W Ste 330N Saint Paul (55114) *(G-7975)*

Accessible Space Inc 651 645-7271
2550 University Ave W 330N Saint Paul (55114) *(G-7976)*

Accessible Space North Inc 651 645-7271
2550 University Ave W 330N Saint Paul (55114) *(G-7977)*

Accessit, Saint Cloud *Also Called Uniquescreen Media Inc (G-7623)*

Acclaim Benefits LLC 763 278-4620
2905 NW Blvd Ste 220 Minneapolis (55441) *(G-3668)*

Accord Benefit Resources Inc 763 746-9004
945 Highway 169 N Minneapolis (55441) *(G-3669)*

Accredo Health Group Inc 651 681-0885
2915 Waters Rd Ste 109 Saint Paul (55121) *(G-7687)*

Accurate Component Sales Inc 651 639-1881
444 2nd St NW Saint Paul (55112) *(G-7978)*

Ace Auto Parts & Salvage Inc 651 224-9479
754 Rice St Saint Paul (55117) *(G-7979)*

Ace Building Maintenance Inc 651 482-1020
5703 Deer Trl W Saint Paul (55126) *(G-7980)*

Ace Communications Group 507 896-3111
207 E Cedar St Houston (55943) *(G-2661)*

Ace Electrical Contractors Inc 763 694-8800
5465 Highway 169 N Minneapolis (55442) *(G-3670)*

Ace Label Systems Inc 763 450-3202
7101 Madison Ave W Golden Valley (55427) *(G-2236)*

Ace Nicollet Rental Place 612 822-3121
3805 Nicollet Ave Minneapolis (55409) *(G-3671)*

Ace Rental Place 218 463-2175
1114 3rd St NE Roseau (56751) *(G-7351)*

Ace Solid Waste Inc 763 427-3110
6601 McKinley St NW Anoka (55303) *(G-146)*

Ace Supply Co Inc 952 929-1618
3825 Edgewood Ave S Minneapolis (55426) *(G-3672)*

ACG Inc 651 488-0574
2400 Pilot Knob Rd Saint Paul (55120) *(G-7688)*

Achieve, Minneapolis *Also Called County of Anoka (G-3445)*

Aci Construction Inc 763 424-9191
11225 90th Ave N Ste 100 Osseo (55369) *(G-6592)*

Acm, Minneapolis *Also Called Advanced Concrete & Masonry (G-3687)*

Acme Comedy Co 612 338-6393
708 N 1st St Ste G31 Minneapolis (55401) *(G-3673)*

Acoustical Innovations, Hamel *Also Called Unicon Inc (G-2359)*

Acoustics Associates Inc 763 544-8901
1250 Zane Ave N Minneapolis (55422) *(G-3674)*

Acp, Minneapolis *Also Called Associated Clinic of (G-3824)*

Acrylic Design Associates Inc 763 559-8392
6050 Nathan Ln N Minneapolis (55442) *(G-3675)*

ACS, Perham *Also Called Arvig Enterprises Inc (G-6793)*

ACS Integrated Doc Inc 651 999-5400
680 Transfer Rd Saint Paul (55114) *(G-7981)*

Act Specialties, Saint Paul *Also Called Asphalt Specialties Co (G-8072)*

Action Mailing Services Inc 763 557-6767
12811 16th Ave N Minneapolis (55441) *(G-3676)*

Action Moving Services Inc 952 894-8888
12400 Washburn Ave S Burnsville (55337) *(G-672)*

Activar Inc 952 835-6850
4450 W 78th Street Cir Minneapolis (55435) *(G-3677)*

Active Software, Minneapolis *Also Called Comsys Information Technology (G-4149)*

Activstyle Inc (HQ) 612 520-9333
3100 Pacific St Minneapolis (55411) *(G-3678)*

Acts of St Paul 612 823-4237
3353 Columbus Ave Minneapolis (55407) *(G-3679)*

Acuo Technologies LLC 952 905-3440
8009 34th Ave S Ste 900 Bloomington (55425) *(G-481)*

Acura Inc 651 967-0607
303 21st St Ste 176 Newport (55055) *(G-6483)*

Ad Efx of America Inc 952 941-3500
6409 City West Pkwy # 206 Eden Prairie (55344) *(G-1583)*

Adair Electric Co 507 289-7696
204 16th St SE Rochester (55904) *(G-7044)*

Adam Services, Minneapolis *Also Called Advance America Services Inc (G-3685)*

Adam's Pest Control Inc 763 478-9810
922 Highway 55 Ste 100 Hamel (55340) *(G-2336)*

Adams Health Care Center, Adams *Also Called City of Adams (G-3)*

Adams Nut & Bolt, Osseo *Also Called Wurth Adams Nut & Bolt Co (G-6685)*

Adapt Inc 952 939-0538
5610 Rowland Rd Ste 160 Hopkins (55343) *(G-2500)*

ADC Telecommunications Inc (PA) 952 938-8080
13625 Technology Dr Eden Prairie (55344) *(G-1584)*

Adevia Spasalon, Forest Lake *Also Called S & S Spa Salon Inc (G-2168)*

Adium Oil Co Inc 320 356-7350
310 Blattner Dr Avon (56310) *(G-293)*

ADM, Mankato *Also Called Archer Daniels Midland Co (G-3106)*

ADM, Minneapolis *Also Called Archer-Daniels-Midland Co (G-3801)*

Admin, Minneapolis *Also Called Riverside Plaza LP (G-5545)*

Administration Resources Corp 763 421-5510
11490 Zeon St NW Ste 200 Minneapolis (55448) *(G-3385)*

Administrative Computing Off, Minneapolis *Also Called Regents of The University of (G-5500)*

Administrative Office of The 612 664-5050
300 S 4th St Minneapolis (55415) *(G-3680)*

Admiral-Merchants Motor 612 332-4819
215 S 11th St Minneapolis (55403) *(G-3681)*

Adobe Systems Inc 651 766-4700
3900 Northwoods Dr Ste 300 Saint Paul (55112) *(G-7982)*

Adolfson & Peterson Inc (PA) 952 544-1561
6701 W 23rd St Minneapolis (55426) *(G-3682)*

Adonai Care Homes Corp 651 227-0574
89 Virginia St Saint Paul (55102) *(G-7983)*

ADP, Minneapolis *Also Called Automatic Data Processing Inc (G-3838)*

Adrian's Resort Inc 218 634-1985
3362 Red Oak Rd NW Baudette (56623) *(G-313)*

ADT, Minneapolis *Also Called Trust Security (G-5860)*

ADT Security Services Inc 651 917-0010
5910 Rice Crk 700 Minneapolis (55432) *(G-3386)*

ADT Security Services Inc 651 917-0000
5910 Rice Creek Pkwy Ste 700 Saint Paul (55126) *(G-7984)*

Aduddell Industries Inc 651 288-2246
69 Empire Dr Saint Paul (55103) *(G-7985)*

Adult & Pediatric Urology 320 259-1411
2351 Connecticut Ave S # 200 Sartell (56377) *(G-9329)*

Adult Child & Family Services 507 344-1721
103 N Broad St Mankato (56001) *(G-3099)*

Adult Client Training Service 320 523-5666
802 E Fairview Ave Olivia (56277) *(G-6559)*

Adult Day Health-Mlk, Saint Paul *Also Called Amherst H Wilder Foundation (G-8045)*

Adult Help & Companion Care 952 377-0411
4584 Cedar Lake Rd S # 5 Minneapolis (55416) *(G-3683)*

Adult Rehabilitatioin Center, Minneapolis *Also Called Central Territorial of The (G-4047)*

Adult Training & Habilitation 320 485-4191
311 Fairlawn Ave W Winsted (55395) *(G-10155)*

Adults & Childrens Alliance 651 481-9320
2885 Country Dr Ste 165 Saint Paul (55117) *(G-7986)*

Adults Saving Kids 612 872-0684
1901 Portland Ave Minneapolis (55404) *(G-3684)*

Advance America Services Inc 952 544-7273
2211 Edgewood Ave S Minneapolis (55426) *(G-3685)*

Advance Equipment Co 651 489-8881
1400 Jackson St Saint Paul (55117) *(G-7987)*

Advance Response Systems, Rogers *Also Called Reinking Enterprises Inc (G-7340)*

Advance Shoring Co 651 489-8881
1400 Jackson St Saint Paul (55117) *(G-7988)*

Advance Specialties Co 651 489-8881
1400 Jackson St Saint Paul (55117) *(G-7989)*

Advance Wall Systems Inc 763 263-8512
16927 231st Ave NW Big Lake (55309) *(G-444)*

Advanced Auto Transport Inc 651 777-7780
2275 McKnight Rd N Ste 4 Saint Paul (55109) *(G-7990)*

Advanced Automotive Industries 651 777-5420
7161 55th St N Saint Paul (55128) *(G-9182)*

Advanced Care Inc 612 721-1957
1415 Park Ave Minneapolis (55404) *(G-3686)*

Advanced Cellular LLC 952 469-4200
20809 Kensington Blvd Lakeville (55044) *(G-2889)*

Advanced Communication Design 952 854-4000
7901 12th Ave S Bloomington (55425) *(G-482)*

Advanced Concrete & Masonry 763 424-9365
9020 Wyoming Ave N Minneapolis (55445) *(G-3687)*

Advanced Duplication Services 763 449-5500
2155 Niagara Ln N Ste 120 Minneapolis (55447) *(G-3688)*

Advanced Imaging Solutions Inc 952 930-1882
6121 Baker Rd Ste 110 Hopkins (55345) *(G-2501)*

Advanced Informatics LLC 612 253-0130
10 2nd St NE Ste 300 Minneapolis (55413) *(G-3689)*

Advanced Masonry Restoration 651 766-8080
2960 Yorkton Blvd Ste A Saint Paul (55117) *(G-7991)*

Advanced Practice Solutions 651 439-8484
8645 Eagle Point Blvd Lake Elmo (55042) *(G-2864)*

Advanced Process Technologies 320 286-5060
150 Swendra Blvd NE Cokato (55321) *(G-1074)*

Advanced Research Corp 651 789-9000
4459 White Bear Pkwy White Bear Lake (55110) *(G-9973)*

Advanced Service Management 763 201-1451
817 Meander Ct Hamel (55340) *(G-2337)*

Advanced Spine Associates 763 577-1877
12225 Champlin Dr Ste 2 Champlin (55316) *(G-887)*

Advancements In Allergy 952 546-6866
12450 Wayzata Blvd # 215 Hopkins (55305) *(G-2502)*

Advanstar Holdings Corp 218 740-7200
131 W 1st St Duluth (55802) *(G-1232)*

Advantage Cabinets Inc 507 455-0833
1040 24th Ave NW Owatonna (55060) *(G-6689)*

Advantage Sales & Marketing, Minneapolis *Also Called Source One Sales & Marketing (G-5704)*

Advantage Travel & Incentives 952 447-1333
7447 Egan Dr Ste 300 Savage (55378) *(G-9382)*

Adventure Zone 952 890-7961
13700 Nicollet Ave Burnsville (55337) *(G-673)*

Advisors Mortgage LLC 763 753-8133
20720 Yellowpine St NW Cedar (55011) *(G-873)*

AEC Engineering Inc (PA) 612 332-8905
400 1st Ave N Ste 400 Minneapolis (55401) *(G-3690)*

Aecom Technical Services Inc 763 551-1001
3033 Campus Dr Ste 290 Minneapolis (55441) *(G-3691)*

AEG Management Twn LLC 612 673-1300
600 1st Ave N Ste SKY Minneapolis (55403) *(G-3692)*

Aegis Fire, Duluth *Also Called First Strike of Duluth Inc (G-1324)*

Aegon USA Inc 952 893-6767
3600 Amercn Blvd W # 200 Minneapolis (55431) *(G-3693)*

Aekill & Schilling Accounting, Duluth *Also Called Thomas Eling CPA (G-1484)*

Aeoa Headstart 218 749-5856
702 S 3rd Ave Virginia (55792) *(G-9732)*

AEP Industries Inc 507 625-3011
2111 3rd Ave Mankato (56001) *(G-3100)*

AEP Industries Inc 507 386-4420
1970 Excel Dr Mankato (56001) *(G-3101)*

Aeration Industries Intl 952 448-6789
4100 Peavey Rd Chaska (55318) *(G-947)*

Aerial Contractors Inc (DH) 218 236-9233
3030 24th Ave S Moorhead (56560) *(G-6294)*

Aeritae Consulting Group Ltd 651 229-0300
380 Jackson St Ste 750 Saint Paul (55101) *(G-7992)*

Aero Systems Engineering Inc (HQ) 651 227-7515
358 Fillmore Ave E Saint Paul (55107) *(G-7993)*

Aero-Metric Inc 763 420-9606
13400 68th Ave N Osseo (55311) *(G-6593)*

Affiance Financial LLC 952 253-2564
10275 Wayzata Blvd # 300 Hopkins (55305) *(G-2503)*

Affiliated Community Medical 320 564-2511
295 10th Ave Granite Falls (56241) *(G-2313)*

Affiliated Community Medical 320 693-3233
520 S Sibley Ave Litchfield (55355) *(G-2977)*

Affiliated Community Medical 507 532-9631
300 S Bruce St Marshall (56258) *(G-3290)*

Affiliated Community Medical 507 637-2985
1100 E Broadway St Redwood Falls (56283) *(G-7019)*

Affiliated Community Medical (PA) 320 231-5000
101 Willmar Ave SW Willmar (56201) *(G-9980)*

Affiliated Emergency 952 942-8272
7717 Flying Cloud Dr Eden Prairie (55344) *(G-1585)*

Affiliated Emergency 763 529-6560
4708 Olson Memorial Hwy Minneapolis (55422) *(G-3694)*

Affiliated Group Inc 507 280-7000
3055 41st St NW Ste 100 Rochester (55901) *(G-7045)*

Affiliated Medical Center 320 843-2030
1805 Wisconsin Ave Benson (56215) *(G-436)*

Affilted Cmnty Med Centers-Mar, Marshall *Also Called Affiliated Community Medical (G-3290)*

Affilted Emrgncy Vtrinary Svcs, Minneapolis *Also Called Affiliated Emergency (G-3694)*

Affinity Plus Credit Union 651 291-3700
2730 Snelling Ave N Saint Paul (55113) *(G-7994)*

Affinity Plus Federal Credit (PA) 651 291-3700
175 W Lafayette Frontage Rd Saint Paul (55107) *(G-7995)*

Affinity Plus Federal Credit 651 291-3700
95 Sherburne Ave Saint Paul (55103) *(G-7996)*

Affinity Plus Federal Credit 651 291-3700
2730 Snelling Ave N Saint Paul (55113) *(G-7997)*

Affliated Pediatric Dentists 952 831-4400
7373 France Ave S Ste 402 Minneapolis (55435) *(G-3695)*

Affordable Professionals Inc 218 682-3351
1048 County 11 NW Hackensack (56452) *(G-2331)*

African American Family Svcs (PA) 612 871-7878
2616 Nicollet Ave Minneapolis (55408) *(G-3696)*

African American Family Svcs 612 813-0782
100 W Franklin Ave Minneapolis (55404) *(G-3697)*

Afs Intercultural Programs 651 647-6337
2356 University Ave W # 424 Saint Paul (55114) *(G-7998)*

Afscme Building Corp 651 451-7678
300 Hardman Ave S Ste 3 South Saint Paul (55075) *(G-9507)*

Aftenro Society 218 728-6600
510 W College St Duluth (55811) *(G-1233)*

Afternro Home, Duluth *Also Called Evangelical Lutheran Good (G-1315)*

Afton Alps Golf Course 651 436-1320
6600 Peller Ave S Hastings (55033) *(G-2411)*

Afton Alps Inc 651 436-5245
6600 Peller Ave S Hastings (55033) *(G-2412)*

Afton St Croix Co 651 436-8883
3291 Saint Croix Trl S Afton (55001) *(G-6)*

AG Electrical Specialists 507 378-2101
202 E Main St Racine (55967) *(G-6966)*

AG Forte LLC 507 847-5110
76645 US Highway 71 Jackson (56143) *(G-2785)*

AG Partners Coop (PA) 651 923-4496
1st And Broadway Goodhue (55027) *(G-2248)*

AG States Agency LLC (HQ) 651 355-6000
5500 Cenex Dr Ste 1 Inver Grove Heights (55077) *(G-2735)*

AG Systems Inc 320 587-4030
1180 Highway 7 E Hutchinson (55350) *(G-2684)*

Agape 24 Hour Preschool 612 287-9775
2304 Emerson Ave N Minneapolis (55411) *(G-3698)*

Ageless Care Options 218 463-3695
702 7th St SW Roseau (56751) *(G-7352)*

Aggregate Industries Inc (DH) 651 683-0600
2915 Waters Rd Ste 105 Saint Paul (55121) *(G-7689)*

Aging Joyfully Inc 952 941-2510
13050 Pioneer Trl Eden Prairie (55347) *(G-1586)*

Aging Services For Communities 507 364-5663
212 1st St S Ste 3 Montgomery (56069) *(G-6263)*

Agmotion Inc (PA) 612 486-3800
730 2nd Ave S Ste 700 Minneapolis (55402) *(G-3699)*

Agnes Saint Baking Co 651 290-7633
644 Olive St Saint Paul (55130) *(G-7999)*

Agralite Electric Cooperative 320 843-4150
320 Highway 12 SE Benson (56215) *(G-437)*

Agramson Enterprises Inc 763 546-1599
9909 S Shore Dr Ste 1000 Minneapolis (55441) *(G-3700)*

Agreliant Genetics LLC 218 631-2954
63585 Highway 10 Wadena (56482) *(G-9796)*

Agri Temps Inc 320 235-5230
1701 2nd Ave SE Willmar (56201) *(G-9981)*

Agri Temps Inc (PA) 320 235-1707
920 Litchfield Ave SW Willmar (56201) *(G-9982)*

Agribank, Fcb 651 282-8800
375 Jackson St Ste A Saint Paul (55101) *(G-8000)*

Agriliance LLC (PA) 651 451-5000
5500 Cenex Dr Inver Grove Heights (55077) *(G-2736)*

Agrimax LLC 218 281-1441
21161 330th Ave SW Fisher (56723) *(G-2133)*

Agstar Financial Services, Aca 507 526-7366
1700 Giant Dr Blue Earth (56013) *(G-528)*

Agstar Financial Services, Aca (PA) 507 387-4174
1921 Premier Dr Mankato (56001) *(G-3102)*

Agstar Financial Services, Aca 507 645-0552
1260 5th St W Northfield (55057) *(G-6523)*

Agstar Financial Services, Aca 320 203-4613
806 3rd St S Waite Park (56387) *(G-9815)*

Agstar Financial Services, Aca 507 376-4144
1791 Diagonal Rd Worthington (56187) *(G-10177)*

Agvantage Software Inc 507 282-6353
107 Woodlake Dr SE Rochester (55904) *(G-7046)*

Ahles & Associates LLC 952 935-8554
1 Hawthorne Rd Hopkins (55343) *(G-2504)*

Ahm Insurance Agency, Minnetonka *Also Called American Hardware Insurance (G-6139)*

Aicota Healthcare Center 218 927-2164
850 2nd St NW Aitkin (56431) *(G-12)*

Aid Electric Corp 763 571-7267
1622 93rd Ln NE Minneapolis (55449) *(G-3387)*

Aimco, Minneapolis *Also Called Loring Towers Apts LP (G-4903)*

AIN Dah Yung Center 651 227-4184
1089 Portland Ave Saint Paul (55104) *(G-8001)*

Air Direct, Minneapolis *Also Called Bemidji Aviation Services Inc (G-3882)*

Air Mechanical Inc (PA) 763 434-7747
16411 Aberdeen St NE Anoka (55304) *(G-147)*

Air Park Dt & H 218 723-4631
4619 Airpark Blvd Duluth (55811) *(G-1234)*

Aircorps LLC 763 550-0707
3700 Annapolis Ln N Ste 175 Plymouth (55447) *(G-6845)*

Aircraft Owner LLC 651 633-1045
121 5th Ave NW Ste 300 Saint Paul (55112) *(G-8002)*

Airgas - North Central Inc 763 712-5100
6191 McKinley St NW Anoka (55303) *(G-148)*

Airport Clinic, Minneapolis *Also Called Park Nicollet Clinic (G-5330)*

Ais, Saint Paul *Also Called Identifix Inc (G-8505)*

Aitkin Agri-Peat Inc 763 441-8387
11555 205th Ave NW Elk River (55330) *(G-1860)*

Aitkin Community Hospital Inc 218 927-2121
200 Bunker Hill Dr Aitkin (56431) *(G-23)*

Aitkin County 218 927-3744
204 1st St NW Aitkin (56431) *(G-13)*

Aitkin County 218 927-3741
1211 Air Park Dr Aitkin (56431) *(G-14)*

Aitkin Health Services 218 927-5545
301 Minnesota Ave S Aitkin (56431) *(G-15)*

Aitkin Iron Works Inc 218 927-2400
301 Bunker Hill Dr Aitkin (56431) *(G-24)*

Aitkin Legion Post, Aitkin *Also Called American Legion Club (G-16)*

AJK Cutters Inc 952 933-7525
8136 Highway 7 Minneapolis (55426) *(G-3701)*

Al Johnson Trucking Inc 612 253-1000
81 Saint Anthony Pkwy Ste 2 Minneapolis (55418) *(G-3702)*

Al Minnerath Inc 320 762-7289
6325 County Road 87 SW Alexandria (56308) *(G-79)*

Al's Cabinets Inc 952 890-3500
14255 W Burnsville Pkwy Burnsville (55306) *(G-674)*

Albany Medical Center, Albany *Also Called Community Health Network (G-26)*

Albers Mechanical Services Inc 651 224-3100
200 Plato Blvd W Ste A Saint Paul (55107) *(G-8003)*

Albers Sheetmetal (PA) 651 224-5428
200 Plato Blvd W Ste A Saint Paul (55107) *(G-8004)*

Albert Lea Bus Co Inc 507 373-1467
1407 Saint John Ave Albert Lea (56007) *(G-30)*

Albert Lea Family YMCA 507 373-8228
2021 W Main St Albert Lea (56007) *(G-31)*

Albert Lea Good Samaritan Ctr, Albert Lea *Also Called Evangelical Lutheran Good (G-50)*

Albert Lea Medical Center-Mayo 507 373-2384
404 W Fountain St Albert Lea (56007) *(G-32)*

Albert Lea Seed House Inc 507 373-3161
1414 W Main St Albert Lea (56007) *(G-33)*

Albert Lee Medical Center Inc 507 377-6393
210 North Ln Albert Lea (56007) *(G-34)*

Albert Lee Medical Center Inc 507 553-3115
55 10th St SE Wells (56097) *(G-9960)*

Albert's Organics Inc 763 780-0101
5230 Quincy St Saint Paul (55112) *(G-8005)*

Albinson Reprographics LLC (PA) 612 374-1120
1401 Glenwood Ave Minneapolis (55405) *(G-3703)*

Albrecht Co's 651 633-4510
1408 County Road C W Saint Paul (55113) *(G-8006)*

Alchemist General Inc (PA) 507 289-3901
1510 Broadway Ave N Rochester (55906) *(G-7047)*

Aldata List Co, Saint Paul *Also Called Harco Marketing Group Inc (G-7795)*

Alden Area Food Shelf 507 377-3683
191 Water St Alden (56009) *(G-78)*

Aldin Export & Import 651 483-4184
1090 Amble Dr Saint Paul (55126) *(G-8007)*

Aldrich Memorial Nursery Sch 507 289-3097
855 Essex Pkwy NW Rochester (55901) *(G-7048)*

Alebra Technologies Inc 651 366-6140
550 Main St Ste 250 Saint Paul (55112) *(G-8008)*

Alentertainment, Saint Paul *Also Called Midwest Sound & Light Inc (G-8662)*

Alex Irrigation Inc 320 852-7595
2750 E Lake Carlos Ln NE Carlos (56319) *(G-866)*

Alexander's Mobility Services, Minneapolis *Also Called Big Ale-Cat (G-3902)*

Alexandra House Inc 763 780-2332
10065 3rd St NE Minneapolis (55434) *(G-3388)*

Alexandria Clinic Properties 320 763-5123
610 30th Ave W Alexandria (56308) *(G-80)*

Alexandria Golf Club 320 762-1093
2300 N Nokomis NE Alexandria (56308) *(G-81)*

Alexandria Pro-Fab Co Inc 320 852-7918
8210 State Highway 29 N Alexandria (56308) *(G-82)*

Alexandria Public Schl Bus Off, Alexandria *Also Called Independent School District (G-105)*

Aliance Health Care Inc 507 252-9737
3224 6th Ave NE Unit A Rochester (55906) *(G-7049)*

Align Health Inc 612 821-7909
1516 W Lake St Ste 300 Minneapolis (55408) *(G-3704)*

**A
L
P
H
A
B
E
T
I
C**

Alignex Inc 952 888-6801
7200 Metro Blvd Minneapolis (55439) *(G-3705)*

Alive Promo Inc 952 960-3677
2401 Edgewood Ave S # 100 Minneapolis (55426) *(G-3706)*

All Agape Construction Co LLC 763 205-1313
14453 Hummingbird Ct NW Anoka (55304) *(G-149)*

All American, Moorhead *Also Called Health Industries Inc (G-6318)*

All American Mortgage Lending 763 560-5815
7420 Unity Ave N Ste 308 Minneapolis (55443) *(G-3707)*

All American Title Co Inc 763 225-8710
9298 Central Ave NE # 102 Minneapolis (55434) *(G-3389)*

All City Elevator Inc 651 646-5600
2340 Capp Rd Saint Paul (55114) *(G-8009)*

All England Enterprises Ltd (PA) 612 332-8011
1110 Nicollet Mall Minneapolis (55403) *(G-3708)*

All Fire Test Co Inc 612 332-3473
915 Washington Ave N Minneapolis (55401) *(G-3709)*

All Furniture Installation, Minneapolis *Also Called 675 Stinson LLC (G-5686)*

All Furniture Installation Inc 763 571-2203
675 Stinson Blvd Ste 100 Minneapolis (55413) *(G-3710)*

All Inc 651 227-6331
185 Plato Blvd W Saint Paul (55107) *(G-8010)*

All Poolside Services Inc 651 483-6600
121 County Road C E Saint Paul (55117) *(G-8011)*

All State Communications Inc 320 203-1511
800 Industrial Dr S Ste 204 Sauk Rapids (56379) *(G-9356)*

All Systems Go 651 628-0000
6031 Culligan Way Hopkins (55345) *(G-2505)*

All Systems Installation Inc 507 281-9466
929 37th Ave NW Rochester (55901) *(G-7050)*

All Temporaries Caring 612 378-1474
3638 Central Ave NE Minneapolis (55418) *(G-3711)*

All Temporaries Inc 320 654-6031
2719 W Division St Ste 11 Saint Cloud (56301) *(G-7446)*

All Time Favorites Inc 651 454-1124
4500 Whitetail Way Saint Paul (55123) *(G-7690)*

All True Clinic Crookston Inc 218 281-9100
400 S Minnesota St Crookston (56716) *(G-1118)*

All-American Co-Op (PA) 507 533-4222
113 4th St SE Stewartville (55976) *(G-9590)*

All-Data Inc 763 571-5719
5400 Main St NE Ste 201 Minneapolis (55421) *(G-3390)*

Allan Mechanical Inc 952 934-3999
7875 Fuller Rd Eden Prairie (55344) *(G-1587)*

Allegiance Financial Group Inc 651 486-5313
2935 Country Dr Ste 102 Saint Paul (55117) *(G-8012)*

Allegis Corp (PA) 763 780-4333
8001 Central Ave NE Minneapolis (55432) *(G-3391)*

Allegra Print & Imaging, Minneapolis *Also Called Minnesota Insty-Prints Inc (G-5079)*

Allen Interactions Inc 651 203-3700
1120 Centre Ste 800 Saint Paul (55120) *(G-7691)*

Allergy & Asthma Clinic 507 474-7830
420 E Sarnia St Ste 1600 Winona (55987) *(G-10079)*

Allergy & Asthma Specialists (PA) 612 338-3333
825 Nicollet Mall Ste 1149 Minneapolis (55402) *(G-3712)*

Allergy & Asthma Specialists 320 654-6565
1350 Lesauk Dr Ste 1149 Sartell (56377) *(G-9330)*

Allete Inc 218 328-5711
1210 NW 3rd St Cohasset (55721) *(G-1070)*

Allete Inc (PA) 218 279-5000
30 W Superior St Duluth (55802) *(G-1235)*

Allete Inc 218 628-3627
4913 W Main St Duluth (55807) *(G-1236)*

Allete Inc 218 722-2641
3217 Persons St Duluth (55811) *(G-1237)*

Allete Inc 320 632-2311
1201 11th St NE Little Falls (56345) *(G-2999)*

Alliance Bank 651 345-3311
105 E Lyon Ave Lake City (55041) *(G-2850)*

Alliance Bank (PA) 507 354-3133
322 N Minnesota St New Ulm (56073) *(G-6438)*

Alliance Benefit Group 507 377-9344
201 E Clark St Albert Lea (56007) *(G-35)*

Alliance Concrete Concepts Inc 507 536-4515
325 Alliance Pl NE Rochester (55906) *(G-7051)*

Alliance Health Care Inc 507 252-9737
3224 6th Ave NE Unit A Rochester (55906) *(G-7052)*

Alliance Health Care Inc (PA) 651 895-8030
2260 Cliff Rd Saint Paul (55122) *(G-7692)*

Alliance Insurance Agency, Minneapolis *Also Called Michael Dam (G-5016)*

Alliancenet Inc 952 934-4104
2230 Timberwood Dr Chanhassen (55317) *(G-907)*

Alliant Precision Fuse Co 763 744-5000
4700 Nathan Ln N Minneapolis (55442) *(G-3713)*

Allianz Life Insurance Co of (PA) 763 765-6500
5701 Golden Hills Dr Minneapolis (55416) *(G-3714)*

Allied Adjusters Inc 612 766-3700
222 S 9th St Ste 1300 Minneapolis (55402) *(G-3715)*

Allied Blacktop Co 763 425-0575
10503 89th Ave N Maple Grove (55369) *(G-3234)*

Allied Interstate Inc (DH) 952 595-2000
12755 Highway 55 Ste 300 Plymouth (55441) *(G-6846)*

Allied National Services, Minneapolis *Also Called Americlean Janitorial Services (G-3763)*

Allied Professionals Inc 952 832-5101
3209 W 76th St Ste 201 Minneapolis (55435) *(G-3716)*

Allied Security LLC 651 604-9414
1611 County Road B W Ste 215 Saint Paul (55113) *(G-8013)*

Allied Systems Ltd 651 458-3005
9450 Ideal Ave S Cottage Grove (55016) *(G-1096)*

Allied Waste Industries Inc 952 941-5174
9813 Flying Cloud Dr Eden Prairie (55347) *(G-1588)*

Allina Health System 763 427-7180
5300 153rd Ave NW Anoka (55303) *(G-150)*

Allina Health System 763 682-1212
303 Catlin St Buffalo (55313) *(G-633)*

Allina Health System 763 689-7700
701 Dellwood St S Cambridge (55008) *(G-831)*

Allina Health System 763 427-9620
11269 Jefferson Hwy N # 1 Champlin (55316) *(G-888)*

Allina Health System 651 458-1884
8611 W Point Douglas Rd S Cottage Grove (55016) *(G-1097)*

Allina Health System 763 236-0414
14181 Business Ctr Dr NW Elk River (55330) *(G-1861)*

Allina Health System 507 334-3921
100 State Ave Faribault (55021) *(G-1988)*

Allina Health System 952 463-7181
21260 Chippendale Ave W Farmington (55024) *(G-2038)*

Allina Health System 651 464-7100
1540 Lake St S Forest Lake (55025) *(G-2155)*

Allina Health System 763 236-5000
550 Osborne Rd NE Fridley (55432) *(G-2189)*

Allina Health System 651 438-1800
1210 1st St W Hastings (55033) *(G-2375)*

Allina Health System 952 936-5600
715 2nd Ave S Hopkins (55343) *(G-2506)*

Allina Health System 320 234-4664
1095 Highway 15 S Hutchinson (55350) *(G-2685)*

Allina Health System 651 450-8000
5565 Blaine Ave Inver Grove Heights (55076) *(G-2737)*

Allina Health System 763 236-0200
7840 Vinewood Ln N Maple Grove (55369) *(G-3235)*

Allina Health System 612 798-8800
407 W 66th St Minneapolis (55423) *(G-3717)*

Allina Health System 612 863-4000
800 E 28th St Minneapolis (55407) *(G-3718)*

Allina Health System 952 851-1000
7920 Old Cedar Ave S Minneapolis (55425) *(G-3719)*

Allina Health System 612 775-8800
2215 Park Ave Minneapolis (55404) *(G-3720)*

Allina Health System (PA) 612 775-5000
2925 Chicago Ave Minneapolis (55407) *(G-3721)*

Allina Health System 952 835-1311
7500 France Ave S Minneapolis (55435) *(G-3722)*

Allina Health System 763 577-7400
2855 Campus Dr Ste 400 Minneapolis (55441) *(G-3723)*

Allina Health System 612 863-3720
920 E 28th St Ste 300 Minneapolis (55407) *(G-3724)*

Allina Health System 763 560-6922
6200 Shingle Creek Pkwy # 480 Minneapolis (55430) *(G-3725)*

Allina Health System 612 863-4466
800 E 28th St Minneapolis (55407) *(G-3726)*

Allina Health System 763 236-9236
3960 Coon Rapids Blvd NW Minneapolis (55433) *(G-3392)*

Allina Health System 763 236-6000
4050 Coon Rapids Blvd NW Minneapolis (55433) *(G-3393)*

Allina Health System 763 780-9155
9055 Springbrook Dr NW Minneapolis (55433) *(G-3394)*

Allina Health System 763 786-6011
500 Osborne Rd NE Ste 200 Minneapolis (55432) *(G-3395)*

Allina Health System 952 992-2500
5601 Smetana Dr Minnetonka (55343) *(G-6138)*

Allina Health System 320 589-1313
400 E 1st St Morris (56267) *(G-6369)*

Allina Health System 507 233-1000
1324 5th St N New Ulm (56073) *(G-6439)*

Allina Health System 507 446-0936
2350 NW 26th St Owatonna (55060) *(G-6690)*

Allina Health System 651 779-2500
1850 Beam Ave Saint Paul (55109) *(G-8014)*

Allina Health System 651 699-1501
2004 Ford Pkwy Saint Paul (55116) *(G-8015)*

Allina Health System 651 642-2700
1021 Bandana Blvd E Saint Paul (55108) *(G-8016)*

Allina Medical Center 651 220-8186
333 Smith Ave N Saint Paul (55102) *(G-8017)*

Allina Medical Clinic West 763 577-7400
2855 Campus Dr Ste 400 Plymouth (55441) *(G-6847)*

Allina Self-Insured 952 992-2500
5601 Smetana Dr Ste LL Hopkins (55343) *(G-2507)*

Allina Specialty Associates 612 863-3753
920 E 28th St Ste 300 Minneapolis (55407) *(G-3727)*

Allregs, Eagan *Also Called Mortgage Resource Center Inc (G-1539)*

Allside Installed Services, Minneapolis *Also Called Alside Builders Service (G-3735)*

Allstate Leasing Corp 651 681-4900
10700 Lyndale Ave S Minneapolis (55420) *(G-3728)*

Allstate Leasing LLC 952 703-3444
10700 Lyndale Ave S Minneapolis (55420) *(G-3729)*

Allstate Sales & Leasing Corp (HQ) 651 455-6500
558 Villuame Ave South Saint Paul (55075) *(G-9508)*

Alltech Engineering Corp 651 452-7893
2515 Pilot Knob Rd Saint Paul (55120) *(G-7693)*

Alltemp Distribution Co 763 571-0215
5400 Main St NE Ste 101A Minneapolis (55421) *(G-3396)*

Ally Financial Inc 800 689-6768
3500 Amercn Blvd W # 300 Minneapolis (55431) *(G-3730)*

Almco Inc 507 377-2102
507 W Front St Albert Lea (56007) *(G-36)*

Almond House 218 825-9255
802 28th St SE Brainerd (56401) *(G-547)*

Aloft Htl Minneapolis 612 455-8400
900 Washington Ave S Minneapolis (55415) *(G-3731)*

Alpha Human Services Inc 612 872-8218
2712 Fremont Ave S Minneapolis (55408) *(G-3732)*

Alpha Tile Co, Minneapolis *Also Called Olympia Tile Inc (G-5274)*

Alpha Video & Audio Inc 952 896-9898
7711 Computer Ave Minneapolis (55435) *(G-3733)*

Alpine Custom Woodworking Inc 320 654-1609
1646 Highway 23 E Saint Cloud (56304) *(G-7406)*

Alquest Inc 763 287-3830
4050 Olson Memorial Hwy Ste 35 Minneapolis (55422) *(G-3734)*

Alside Builders Service 952 888-1339
400 W 86th St Minneapolis (55420) *(G-3735)*

Alter Trading Corp 507 387-6504
804 N Industrial Rd Mankato (56001) *(G-3103)*

Alternative Business Furniture 952 937-7688
6533 Flying Cloud Dr # 800 Eden Prairie (55344) *(G-1589)*
Alternative Continum of Care 507 373-5600
1615 Bridge Ave Apt 261 Albert Lea (56007) *(G-37)*
Alternative For Autistic 763 560-3013
5624 73rd Ave N Minneapolis (55429) *(G-3736)*
Alternative For People With 763 560-5330
5624 73rd Ave N Minneapolis (55429) *(G-3737)*
Alternative Micrographics Inc 320 796-2599
12011 Highway 71 NE Spicer (56288) *(G-9554)*
Alterra Brooklyn Center, Minneapolis *Also Called Prairie Lodge (G-5400)*
Alterra Healthcare Corp 763 755-2800
1005 Paul Pkwy NE Minneapolis (55434) *(G-3397)*
Alterra Healthcare Corp 651 686-5557
1365 Crestridge Ln Saint Paul (55123) *(G-7694)*
Alterra Healthcare Corp 651 482-8111
300 Village Center Dr Saint Paul (55127) *(G-8018)*
Altimate Medical Inc 507 697-6393
262 W First St Morton (56270) *(G-6382)*
Altobella Hair Products Inc 952 707-1900
14301 W Burnsville Pkwy Burnsville (55306) *(G-675)*
Altobelli Hairstyle, Rochester *Also Called Rocco Altobelli Inc (G-7227)*
Altona Hutterian Brethren Inc 507 248-3191
35227 290th St Henderson (56044) *(G-2428)*
Altru Clinic 218 463-1365
711 Delmore Dr Roseau (56751) *(G-7353)*
Alvin E Benike Inc 507 288-6575
2960 Highway 14 W Rochester (55901) *(G-7053)*
Alwaysbethere Inc 612 243-9233
2905 NW Blvd Ste 230 Plymouth (55441) *(G-6848)*
Am & S Trucking Inc 507 629-3224
2901 190th St Tracy (56175) *(G-9689)*
Amalfi Consulting LLC 952 893-6732
3600 Amercn Blvd W # 110 Minneapolis (55431) *(G-3738)*
Amano McGann Inc 612 331-2020
651 Taft St NE Minneapolis (55413) *(G-3739)*
Amb Construction Engineering 763 587-4920
5730 Duluth St Minneapolis (55422) *(G-3740)*
Ambient Consulting LLC 763 582-9000
5500 Wayzata Blvd # 1250 Minneapolis (55416) *(G-3741)*
Ambrion Inc 952 278-1800
1660 Highway 100 S Ste 329 Minneapolis (55416) *(G-3742)*
AMC, Bloomington *Also Called American Multi-Cinema Inc (G-484)*
AMC Entertainment Inc 763 494-0379
12575 Elm Creek Blvd N Maple Grove (55369) *(G-3236)*
Amcom Software Inc (PA) 952 230-5200
10400 Yellow Circle Dr # 100 Hopkins (55343) *(G-2508)*
Amcon Construction Co LLC 651 379-9090
1715 Yankee Doodle Rd Saint Paul (55121) *(G-7695)*
AME Community Service Inc 320 286-6421
615 Mooers Ave SE Cokato (55321) *(G-1075)*
Amec Earth & Environmental Inc 612 332-8326
800 Marquette Ave # 1200 Minneapolis (55402) *(G-3743)*
Ameri-Health, Saint Paul *Also Called American Home Health (G-8026)*
Americ Inn, Red Wing *Also Called Layline Corp (G-6988)*
Americ Inn Lodge & Suites, Moorhead *Also Called PC Hotels LLC (G-6332)*
Americ Inn of Ham Lake 763 755-2100
13440 Highway 65 NE Anoka (55304) *(G-151)*
America Midwest Transportation 507 359-4450
148 Zieske Rd Courtland (56021) *(G-1115)*
America's Racquet & Fitness 320 234-7148
1065 Highway 15 S Hutchinson (55350) *(G-2686)*
America's Racquet & Fitness 320 234-7148
Hwy 15 S Hutchinson (55350) *(G-2687)*
America's Raquette & Fitness 507 345-8833
103 Homestead Rd Mankato (56001) *(G-3104)*
America's Tpa Inc 952 896-1246
7201 W 78th St Minneapolis (55439) *(G-3744)*
American Academy of Neurology 651 695-1940
1080 Montreal Ave Ste 100 Saint Paul (55116) *(G-8019)*
American Accounts & Advisors 651 405-9760
3904 Cedarvale Dr Saint Paul (55122) *(G-7696)*
American Agco Inc (PA) 651 451-1349
7900 97th St S Cottage Grove (55016) *(G-1098)*
American Air Products Inc 651 290-0000
141 S Lafayette Rd W Saint Paul (55107) *(G-8020)*
American Airlines Inc 612 726-5647
Minneapolis St Paul Arprt Saint Paul (55111) *(G-7956)*
American Airlines Inc 612 726-5833
4300 Glumack Dr Ste B27 Saint Paul (55111) *(G-7957)*
American Amusement Arcade, Minneapolis *Also Called Lieberman Co's Inc (G-4874)*
American Bank of St Paul 507 377-7000
217 S Newton Ave Albert Lea (56007) *(G-38)*
American Bank of St Paul (HQ) 651 452-1320
1578 University Ave W Saint Paul (55104) *(G-8021)*
American Bank of St Paul 651 643-8472
1578 University Ave W Saint Paul (55104) *(G-8022)*
American Baptist Homes of The 507 373-0188
617 E 10th St Albert Lea (56007) *(G-39)*
American Baptist Homes of The 507 373-9656
1201 Garfield Ave Albert Lea (56007) *(G-40)*
American Baptist Homes of The (PA) 952 941-3175
14850 Scenic Heights Rd Eden Prairie (55344) *(G-1590)*
American Baptist Homes of The 612 529-7747
512 49th Ave N Minneapolis (55430) *(G-3745)*
American Baptist Homes of The 507 893-3171
211 6th St NW Winnebago (56098) *(G-10075)*
American Bottling Co 651 552-3400
270 Bridgepoint Dr South Saint Paul (55075) *(G-9509)*
American Building Maintenance 612 344-1758
90 S 7th St Ste 5000 Minneapolis (55402) *(G-3746)*
American Business Forms Inc (PA) 320 634-5471
31 E Minnesota Ave Glenwood (56334) *(G-2219)*
American Cellular Corp 218 828-8000
14039 Edgewood Dr Ste 106 Baxter (56425) *(G-319)*
American Cellular Corp 218 727-4700
224 E Central Entrance # 1 Duluth (55811) *(G-1238)*
AMERICAN COLLECTORS ASSOCIATIO, Minneapolis *Also Called Aca International (G-3663)*
American Communications Supply (PA) 507 334-2268
3305 Highway 60 W Faribault (55021) *(G-1989)*
American Consulting Services (PA) 651 659-9001
550 Cleveland Ave N Saint Paul (55114) *(G-8023)*
American Crystal Sugar Co (PA) 218 236-4400
101 3rd St N Moorhead (56560) *(G-6295)*
American Crystal Sugar Co 218 287-3400
2500 11th St N Moorhead (56560) *(G-6296)*
American Dairy Association of 651 488-0261
2015 Rice St Ste 100 Saint Paul (55113) *(G-8024)*
American Dairy Queen Corp (DH) 952 830-0200
7505 Metro Blvd Ste 500 Minneapolis (55439) *(G-3747)*
American Engineering Testing (HQ) 651 659-9001
550 Cleveland Ave N Saint Paul (55114) *(G-8025)*
American Enterprise Investment 612 671-3131
70400 Axp Financial Ctr Minneapolis (55474) *(G-3748)*
American Express Travel 651 731-9396
1811 Weir Dr Ste 340 Saint Paul (55125) *(G-9183)*
American Financial Marketing 763 593-0905
400 Highway 169 S Ste 200 Minneapolis (55426) *(G-3749)*
American Fish & Seafood Inc 952 935-3474
5501 Opportunity Ct Hopkins (55343) *(G-2509)*
American Hardware Insurance 952 939-4510
5605 Green Circle Dr # 100 Minnetonka (55343) *(G-6139)*
American Hearing Systems Inc 763 404-1122
8001 E Bloomington Fwy Bloomington (55420) *(G-483)*
American Heart Association Inc 952 835-3300
4701 W 77th St Minneapolis (55435) *(G-3750)*
American Heritage National (PA) 320 732-6131
24 2nd St S Long Prairie (56347) *(G-3036)*
American Heritage National 320 654-9555
2915 2nd St S Saint Cloud (56301) *(G-7447)*
American Home Health 612 860-7301
2502 Manitou Is Saint Paul (55110) *(G-8026)*
American Hospitality Mgt 507 446-8900
2365 NW 43rd St Owatonna (55060) *(G-6691)*
American Importing Co Inc 612 331-7000
550 Kasota Ave SE Minneapolis (55414) *(G-3751)*
American Indian Community 612 813-1610
1404 E Franklin Ave Minneapolis (55404) *(G-3752)*
American Indian Oic Inc 612 341-3358
1845 E Franklin Ave Minneapolis (55404) *(G-3753)*
American Institute of 651 415-1320
245 6th St E Saint Paul (55101) *(G-8027)*
American Investment Management 763 533-7193
2000 Merrimac Ln N # 200 Minneapolis (55447) *(G-3754)*
American Iron & Steel Co Inc 612 529-9221
2800 Pacific St Minneapolis (55411) *(G-3755)*
American Legion 218 773-1129
1009 Central Ave NW East Grand Forks (56721) *(G-1565)*
American Legion 225 Inc 651 464-2600
355 W Broadway Ave Forest Lake (55025) *(G-2156)*
American Legion 513, Saint Paul *Also Called Tri City Post 513 (G-9081)*
American Legion 545 320 796-5542
155 Lake Ave S Spicer (56288) *(G-9555)*
American Legion Club 218 927-2965
20 1st Ave NE Aitkin (56431) *(G-16)*
American Legion Club 763 421-0883
400 W Main St Anoka (55303) *(G-152)*
American Legion Club 651 460-9909
10 8th St Farmington (55024) *(G-2039)*
American Legion Club 320 485-4366
161 1st St N Winsted (55395) *(G-10156)*
American Legion Club 334 Inc 763 421-6260
11640 Crooked Lk Blvd NW Minneapolis (55433) *(G-3398)*
American Legion Club Apple Vly, Saint Paul *Also Called Apple Valley American Legion (G-7700)*
American Legion Minneapolis 612 866-3647
6501 Portland Ave Minneapolis (55423) *(G-3756)*
American Legion Post 212 A 218 732-5238
900 1st St E Park Rapids (56470) *(G-6747)*
American Legion Post 320, Hopkins *Also Called Hopkins American Legion Post (G-2553)*
American Legion Post 595 507 895-4595
509 N Chestnut St La Crescent (55947) *(G-2837)*
American Legion Post 627 218 963-9946
25807 Main St Nisswa (56468) *(G-6495)*
American Linen Supply, Saint Cloud *Also Called Ameripride Services Inc (G-7448)*
American Lodge & Suite, Belle Plaine *Also Called Orchard Park LLC (G-369)*
American Logistics Services 651 451-1349
7900 97th St S Cottage Grove (55016) *(G-1099)*
American Lung Association of 651 227-8014
490 Concordia Ave Saint Paul (55103) *(G-8028)*
American Manufacturing Inc 763 444-9225
1 Enterprise Ave NE Isanti (55040) *(G-2777)*
American Masonry Restoration 763 502-1400
7701 E River Rd Minneapolis (55432) *(G-3399)*
American Medical Systems Inc (HQ) 952 930-6000
10700 Bren Rd W Minnetonka (55343) *(G-6140)*
American Motel & Suites, Proctor *Also Called Proctor Motel Associates (G-6965)*
American Multi-Cinema Inc 952 851-0073
402 S Avenue Bloomington (55425) *(G-484)*
American National Bank of MN 218 829-1484
7638 Woida Rd Baxter (56425) *(G-320)*
American National Bank of MN (PA) 218 824-7900
1920 S 6th St Brainerd (56401) *(G-548)*
American National Red Cross 612 871-7676
1201 W River Pkwy Minneapolis (55454) *(G-3757)*
American National Red Cross 651 291-6789
176 Robert St S Saint Paul (55107) *(G-8029)*
American National Red Cross 651 291-4600
100 Robert St S Saint Paul (55107) *(G-8030)*
American Paper Recycling Corp 651 644-7806
615 Prior Ave N Saint Paul (55104) *(G-8031)*
American Phytopathological Soc 651 454-7250
3340 Pilot Knob Rd Saint Paul (55121) *(G-7697)*

American Preclinical Services 763 717-7990
8945 Evergreen Blvd NW Minneapolis (55433) *(G-3400)*
American Public Media Group (PA) 651 290-1500
480 Cedar St Saint Paul (55101) *(G-8032)*
American Refugee Committee 612 872-7060
430 Oak Grove St Ste 204 Minneapolis (55403) *(G-3758)*
American Registry of 651 687-0048
1255 Northland Dr Saint Paul (55120) *(G-7698)*
American Reprographics Co LLC 612 722-2303
2001 E 24th St Minneapolis (55404) *(G-3759)*
American Residential Mortgage 763 784-2022
11132 Zealand Ave N Champlin (55316) *(G-889)*
American Residential Mortgage 651 488-1801
235 Roselawn Ave E Ste 12 Saint Paul (55117) *(G-8033)*
American Security & Protection 218 236-5180
1620 26th St S Moorhead (56560) *(G-6297)*
American Security LLC (PA) 651 644-1155
1717 University Ave W Saint Paul (55104) *(G-8034)*
American Swedish Institute 612 871-4907
2600 Park Ave Minneapolis (55407) *(G-3760)*
American Telecare Inc 952 897-0000
15159 Technology Dr Eden Prairie (55344) *(G-1591)*
American Tire Distributors Inc 952 345-0000
5100 W 35th St Minneapolis (55416) *(G-3761)*
American Welding & Gas 320 235-4774
1909 Highway 12 W Willmar (56201) *(G-9983)*
American Wings Air Museum 763 786-4146
2141 Rhode Island Ave Minneapolis (55449) *(G-3401)*
American Wrestling Association 507 281-8842
4739 14th Ave NW Apt 4 Rochester (55901) *(G-7054)*
American-Russian Trade Inc 612 922-1163
2214 W 54th St Minneapolis (55419) *(G-3762)*
Americanna Inn, Saint Cloud *Also Called Foussard Hospitality Inc (G-7415)*
Americare Staffing Service Inc 651 917-1995
2233 University Ave W Ste 301 Saint Paul (55114) *(G-8035)*
Americas Racket & Fitness 507 451-8833
1929 S Cedar Ave Owatonna (55060) *(G-6692)*
Americas Racquet & Fitness Ctr, Hutchinson *Also Called America's Racquet & Fitness (G-2687)*
Americas Racquet & Fitness Ctr, Mankato *Also Called America's Raquette & Fitness (G-3104)*
Americinn, Anoka *Also Called Americ Inn of Ham Lake (G-151)*
AmericInn, Chanhassen *Also Called Northcott Hospitality Intl (G-933)*
AmericInn, Minneapolis *Also Called Shingle Creek Hospitality LLP (G-5655)*
AmericInn, Owatonna *Also Called Owatonna Hospitality Partners (G-6729)*
AmericInn Lodge Suites Wabasha, Wabasha *Also Called Mississippi Eagles LLC (G-9769)*
AmericInn Motel & Suites 952 758-7300
1200 1st St NE New Prague (56071) *(G-6421)*
AmericInn Shakopee 952 445-6775
4100 12th Ave E Shakopee (55379) *(G-9418)*
Americlean Janitorial Services 763 503-0707
6066 Shingle Creek Pkwy Minneapolis (55430) *(G-3763)*
Americom Inc 651 726-2200
308 E Lafayette Rd Saint Paul (55107) *(G-8036)*
Ameripride Services Inc 218 751-5150
300 Paul Bunyan Dr SE Bemidji (56601) *(G-374)*
Ameripride Services Inc 218 263-3611
519 E 19th St Hibbing (55746) *(G-2436)*
Ameripride Services Inc (PA) 952 738-4200
10801 Wayzata Blvd # 100 Hopkins (55305) *(G-2510)*
Ameripride Services Inc 507 345-1039
1290 S Victory Dr Mankato (56001) *(G-3105)*
Ameripride Services Inc 612 331-1600
700 Industrial Blvd NE Minneapolis (55413) *(G-3764)*
Ameripride Services Inc 320 251-2525
6500 Saukview Dr Saint Cloud (56303) *(G-7448)*
Ameriprise 952 835-8180
3800 Amercn Blvd W Ste 200 Minneapolis (55431) *(G-3765)*
Ameriprise Financial 612 671-3131
1246 Axp Financial Center Minneapolis (55474) *(G-3766)*
Ameriprise Financial Inc (HQ) 612 671-3131
1099 Ameriprise Financial Ctr Minneapolis (55474) *(G-3767)*
Ameriprise Financial Services 952 368-3100
1 Oakridge Dr Chaska (55318) *(G-948)*
Ameriprise Financial Services 612 671-7536
1001 S 3rd St Minneapolis (55415) *(G-3768)*
Ameriprise Financial Services 612 671-4343
50032 Axp Financial Ctr Minneapolis (55402) *(G-3769)*
Ameriprise Financial Services 612 671-3131
154 Axp Financial Ctr Minneapolis (55474) *(G-3770)*
Ameriprise Financial Services 651 631-2208
900 Long Lake Rd Ste 300 Saint Paul (55112) *(G-8037)*
Amerisourcebergen Corp 952 903-7600
6810 Shady Oak Rd Eden Prairie (55344) *(G-1592)*
Ames Construction Inc (PA) 952 435-7106
14420 County Road 5 Burnsville (55306) *(G-676)*
AMF Bowling Centers Inc 763 566-6250
6440 James Cir N Minneapolis (55430) *(G-3771)*
AMF Bowling Centers Inc 763 571-3520
6310 Highway 65 NE Minneapolis (55432) *(G-3402)*
AMF Bowling Centers Inc 651 484-6501
61 Little Canada Rd W Saint Paul (55117) *(G-8038)*
AMF Bowling Centers Inc 651 774-8787
1955 English St Saint Paul (55109) *(G-8039)*
Amherst H Wilder Foundation (PA) 651 280-2000
451 Lexington Pkwy N # 1 Saint Paul (55104) *(G-8040)*
Amherst H Wilder Foundation 651 220-1700
514 Humboldt Ave Ofc Saint Paul (55107) *(G-8041)*
Amherst H Wilder Foundation 651 647-4600
1295 Bandana Blvd N Ste 210 Saint Paul (55108) *(G-8042)*
Amherst H Wilder Foundation 651 224-1395
180 Grotto St S Saint Paul (55105) *(G-8043)*
Amherst H Wilder Foundation 651 647-9676
450 Syndicate St N Ste 285 Saint Paul (55104) *(G-8044)*
Amherst H Wilder Foundation 651 290-8666
650 Marshall Ave Saint Paul (55104) *(G-8045)*
AMI, Spicer *Also Called Alternative Micrographics Inc (G-9554)*
AMI Imaging Systems Inc 952 828-0080
7815 Telegraph Rd Bloomington (55438) *(G-485)*

Amoco, Maple Lake *Also Called Roger's Amoco Inc (G-3264)*
Amonea, Minneapolis *Also Called Coloplast Corp (G-4123)*
Amport Foods, Minneapolis *Also Called American Importing Co Inc (G-3751)*
Ampride Convenience Mart, Crookston *Also Called Crookston Fuel Co (G-1121)*
Ampro Services Inc 651 631-5924
2690 Prior Ave N Saint Paul (55113) *(G-8046)*
Amtech Lighting Services Co 651 439-7440
6077 Lake Elmo Ave N Stillwater (55082) *(G-9595)*
Amy Johnson Residence, Saint Paul *Also Called Adonai Care Homes Corp (G-7983)*
Analog Technologies, Corp 952 894-9228
11441 Rupp Dr Burnsville (55337) *(G-677)*
Analysts International Corp 952 897-4500
3601 W 76th St Ste 200 Minneapolis (55435) *(G-3772)*
Analysts International Corp (PA) 952 835-5900
3601 W 76th St Ste 500 Minneapolis (55435) *(G-3773)*
Analysts International Corp 507 280-6663
1530 Greenview Dr SW Rochester (55902) *(G-7055)*
Analytics Inc 952 404-5700
18750 Lake Dr E Chanhassen (55317) *(G-908)*
Analytiks International Inc 612 305-4312
10 S 5th St Ste 720 Minneapolis (55402) *(G-3774)*
Anchor Bank 651 457-1111
66 Thompson Ave E Ste A Saint Paul (55118) *(G-7699)*
Anchor Bank 651 770-2341
2700 7th Ave E Saint Paul (55109) *(G-8047)*
Anchor Bank (PA) 952 473-4606
1055 Wayzata Blvd E Wayzata (55391) *(G-9905)*
Anchor Bank Heritage 651 770-2341
2700 7th Ave E Saint Paul (55109) *(G-8048)*
Anchor Block Co 763 425-9779
8201 Brooklyn Blvd # 55445 Minneapolis (55445) *(G-3775)*
Anchor Block Co 651 777-8321
2300 McKnight Rd N Saint Paul (55109) *(G-8049)*
and Sew On Inc 651 439-9311
10850 62nd St N Stillwater (55082) *(G-9596)*
Anderson Brothers Construction 218 829-1768
11325 E Hwy 210 Brainerd (56401) *(G-549)*
Anderson Bus & Coach Inc 218 334-3171
101 W Juniper Ave Frazee (56544) *(G-2182)*
Anderson Cleaners 651 690-9592
718 Cleveland Ave S Saint Paul (55116) *(G-8050)*
Anderson Diesel Truck Service 952 890-1580
12308 Dupont Ave S Burnsville (55337) *(G-678)*
Anderson Diesel Truck Service (PA) 651 480-7991
3686 140th St E Rosemount (55068) *(G-7361)*
Anderson Dove Fretland & Van 952 545-9000
5881 Cedar Lake Rd S Minneapolis (55416) *(G-3776)*
Anderson Engineering of MN LLC 763 383-1084
13605 1st Ave N Ste 100 Minneapolis (55441) *(G-3777)*
Anderson Florists 320 763-5115
1610 6th Ave E Alexandria (56308) *(G-83)*
Anderson Froehling Ltd 952 979-3100
5720 Green Circle Dr # 101 Hopkins (55343) *(G-2511)*
Anderson Land Survey, Minneapolis *Also Called Passe Engineering Inc (G-3566)*
Anderson McDonald Ltd 952 469-3937
20094 Kenwood Trl Lakeville (55044) *(G-2890)*
Anderson Swenson Associates 612 347-8600
1221 Nicollet Ave Ste 400 Minneapolis (55403) *(G-3778)*
Anderson Trucking Service Inc (PA) 320 255-7400
725 Opportunity Dr Saint Cloud (56301) *(G-7449)*
Anderson's Formal Wear Inc (HQ) 507 285-1884
1945 3rd Ave SE Rochester (55904) *(G-7056)*
Anderson, Autumn L, Saint Paul *Also Called Heacox, Hartman, Mattaini (G-8446)*
Anderson, Niebuhr & Associates 651 486-8712
6 Pine Tree Dr Ste 200 Saint Paul (55112) *(G-8051)*
Anderson-Gilyard (PA) 763 261-5161
12431 Pine St Becker (55308) *(G-354)*
Andover Cinema 763 767-8401
1836 Bunker Lake Blvd NW Anoka (55304) *(G-153)*
Andrew Residence Management 612 333-0111
1215 S 9th St Minneapolis (55404) *(G-3779)*
Andy's Electrical Service Inc 507 378-2101
200 1st St SW Grand Meadow (55936) *(G-2263)*
Andy's Towing Co 320 251-5691
675 Crescent St NE Saint Cloud (56304) *(G-7407)*
Anertec Holdings LLC 507 451-5430
815 Rice Lake St Ste 1 Owatonna (55060) *(G-6693)*
Anesthesia Associates of St 320 258-3090
3701 12th St N Ste 202 Saint Cloud (56303) *(G-7450)*
Angels Care Center, Cannon Falls *Also Called Voans Health Services Corp (G-863)*
Anheuser-Busch Co's Inc 218 326-0571
9 Willow Ln Grand Rapids (55744) *(G-2268)*
Animal Emergency Clinic 651 501-3766
7166 10th St N Ste 1 Saint Paul (55128) *(G-9184)*
Animal Humane Society 763 522-4325
845 Meadow Ln N Minneapolis (55422) *(G-3780)*
Animation Services Inc 612 379-7117
510 1st Ave N Ste 650 Minneapolis (55403) *(G-3781)*
Anixter Inc 952 887-8191
8111 Lyndale Ave S Bloomington (55420) *(G-486)*
Anixter Inc 763 559-2417
6055 Nathan Ln N Ste 14 Minneapolis (55442) *(G-3782)*
Ann Pearson MD 651 426-4844
1055 Centerville Cir Saint Paul (55127) *(G-8052)*
Anna Marie's Alliance, Saint Cloud *Also Called Central Minnesota Task Force (G-7486)*
Anna Marie's Alliance, Saint Cloud *Also Called Central Minnesota Task Force (G-7488)*
Anna Maries 320 253-6900
500 11th Ave N Saint Cloud (56303) *(G-7451)*
Annandale Care Center 320 274-3737
500 Park St E Annandale (55302) *(G-134)*
Annandale Congregate Housing 320 274-3737
500 Park St E Annandale (55302) *(G-135)*
Annandale State Bank Inc 320 274-8216
40 Chestnut St W Annandale (55302) *(G-136)*
Annex Medical Inc 952 942-7576
6018 Blue Circle Dr Minnetonka (55343) *(G-6141)*

ALPHABETIC

www.HarrisInfo.com
538
2011 Harris Minnesota Services Directory
(G-00000) Company's Geographic Section entry number

Anoka Brass Band Assoc Inc 763 427-2790
16021 Sodium St NW Anoka (55303) ***(G-154)***
Anoka Care Center, Anoka *Also Called Evangelical Lutheran Good* ***(G-178)***
Anoka Child Care Center 763 427-1897
3738 7th Ave 4273983 Anoka (55303) ***(G-155)***
Anoka County Community Action 763 783-4747
1201 89th Ave NE Ste 345 Minneapolis (55434) ***(G-3403)***
Anoka County Community Action 763 783-4747
1201 89th Ave NE Ste 345 Minneapolis (55434) ***(G-3404)***
Anoka County Traveler 763 323-5222
2180 108th Ln NE Minneapolis (55449) ***(G-3405)***
Anoka Equine Veterinary Svcs 763 441-3797
16445 70th St NE Elk River (55330) ***(G-1898)***
Anoka Hennepin School District 651 255-7000
1500 Lake St S Ste 100 Forest Lake (55025) ***(G-2157)***
Answer America LLC 651 644-7332
1600 University Ave W Ste 208 Saint Paul (55104) ***(G-8053)***
Answer Arrowhead, Duluth *Also Called Arrowhead Security Systems Inc* ***(G-1243)***
Anthony Ostlund & Baer 612 349-6969
90 S 7th St Ste 3600 Minneapolis (55402) ***(G-3783)***
Antons Inc 320 253-3611
2001 Frontage Rd N Waite Park (56387) ***(G-9816)***
Anytime Fitness LLC 651 438-5000
12181 Margo Ave S Ste 100 Hastings (55033) ***(G-2413)***
AON Benfield 952 886-8000
3600 Amercn Blvd W # 700 Minneapolis (55431) ***(G-3784)***
AON Benfield (HQ) 952 886-8000
3600 American Blvd W Minneapolis (55431) ***(G-3785)***
AON Corp 952 656-8000
8300 Norman Center Dr Ste 1000 Minneapolis (55437) ***(G-3786)***
AON Risk Services Central Inc 952 656-8000
8300 Norman Center Dr # 1000 Minneapolis (55437) ***(G-3787)***
AP Midwest LLC 952 544-1561
6701 W 23rd St Minneapolis (55426) ***(G-3788)***
Apache Animal Medicine 612 781-2734
2503 37th Ave NE Minneapolis (55421) ***(G-6123)***
Apex Analytix Inc 952 400-2272
6520 Edenvale Blvd Ste 110 Eden Prairie (55346) ***(G-1593)***
Apex International Mfg Inc 952 227-3000
134 Columbia Ct Chaska (55318) ***(G-949)***
Apg Cash Drawer LLC 763 571-5000
5250 Industrial Blvd NE Minneapolis (55421) ***(G-3406)***
API Electric Co (HQ) 218 628-3323
4330 W 1st St Ste B Duluth (55807) ***(G-1239)***
API Electric Co 218 741-7313
1711 E 13th St Ste 2 Hibbing (55746) ***(G-2437)***
API Garage Door Co 763 533-3838
5601 Boone Ave N Minneapolis (55428) ***(G-3789)***
API Group Inc (PA) 651 636-4320
1100 Old Highway 8 NW Saint Paul (55112) ***(G-8054)***
API Outsourcing Inc (PA) 651 675-2600
2975 Lone Oak Rd Eagan (55121) ***(G-1515)***
API Outsourcing Inc 218 834-8007
320 7th Ave Two Harbors (55616) ***(G-9704)***
Apollo Dental Center PLC 507 287-8320
3000 43rd St NW Rochester (55901) ***(G-7057)***
Apollo Insurance Agency of St 320 253-1122
28 11th Ave S Saint Cloud (56301) ***(G-7452)***
Apollo Research Center, Saint Paul *Also Called People Inc* ***(G-8817)***
Apothecary Products Inc (PA) 952 890-1940
11750 12th Ave S Burnsville (55337) ***(G-679)***
Appert Foods, Saint Cloud *Also Called Apperts Frozen Foods Inc* ***(G-7434)***
Appert's Inc 320 251-3200
900 Highway 10 SE Saint Cloud (56304) ***(G-7433)***
Apperts Frozen Foods Inc 320 251-3200
809 Highway 10 SE Saint Cloud (56304) ***(G-7434)***
Apple Jack Inc 763 972-6673
4875 37th St SE Delano (55328) ***(G-1181)***
Apple Park Associates, Saint Paul *Also Called Orthogonistic Care Specialist* ***(G-7860)***
Apple Tree Dental 763 784-7570
8960 Springbrook Dr NW # 150 Minneapolis (55433) ***(G-3407)***
Apple Tree Learning Center, Virginia *Also Called Iron Range Learning & Devpt* ***(G-9742)***
Apple Valley American Legion 952 431-1776
14521 Granada Dr Ste 1776 Saint Paul (55124) ***(G-7700)***
Apple Valley Dental Clinic, Saint Paul *Also Called Healthpartners Inc* ***(G-7798)***
Apple Valley Gsrs LLC 952 953-6111
7083 153rd St W Saint Paul (55124) ***(G-7701)***
Apple Valley Medical Clinic 952 432-6161
14655 Galaxie Ave Saint Paul (55124) ***(G-7702)***
Apple Valley Villa Apartments 952 236-2600
14610 Garrett Ave Saint Paul (55124) ***(G-7703)***
Apple Valley, City of Inc 952 953-2323
4851 125th St W Saint Paul (55124) ***(G-7704)***
Appleton Area Health Services 320 289-2422
30 S Behl St Appleton (56208) ***(G-244)***
Appletree Motel Partnership 952 854-9000
3 Appletree Sq Ste 1B Minneapolis (55425) ***(G-3790)***
Applevally Goodwill, Saint Paul *Also Called Goodwill Industries Inc* ***(G-7787)***
Applewood Hills Inc 651 439-7276
11840 60th St N Stillwater (55082) ***(G-9597)***
Applewood Pointe Senior Co Op 651 636-2161
1480 Applewood Ct W # 222 Saint Paul (55113) ***(G-8055)***
Appliance Recycling Centers of (PA) 952 930-9000
7400 Excelsior Blvd Minneapolis (55426) ***(G-3791)***
Appliancesmart, Minneapolis *Also Called Appliance Recycling Centers of* ***(G-3791)***
Applied Business Comms 651 643-6595
213 Old Highway 8 SW New Brighton (55112) ***(G-6406)***
Applied Environmental Services, Minneapolis *Also Called Anderson Engineering of MN LLC* ***(G-3777)***
Applied Power Products Inc 952 985-5100
21005 Heron Way Lakeville (55044) ***(G-2891)***
Applied Power Products Inc 952 985-5100
21005 Heron Way Lakeville (55044) ***(G-2892)***
Applied Power Products Inc (PA) 651 452-2250
1240 Trapp Rd Saint Paul (55121) ***(G-7705)***
Applied Products Inc 952 933-2224
6035 Baker Rd Minnetonka (55345) ***(G-6142)***
Applied Staffing Inc 763 502-1388
7687 Main St NE Fridley (55432) ***(G-2190)***
Applied Statistics Inc (PA) 763 268-0696
2800 Campus Dr Ste 60 Minneapolis (55441) ***(G-3792)***
Appollo Systems Inc 763 493-5821
6250 Sycamore Ln N 500B Osseo (55369) ***(G-6594)***
Apptec Laboratory Services Inc (PA) 651 675-2044
2540 Executive Dr Saint Paul (55120) ***(G-7706)***
Apres Inc 952 942-3399
7625 Cahill Rd Minneapolis (55439) ***(G-3793)***
Apria Healthcare Inc 952 404-1700
131 Cheshire Ln Ste 500 Minnetonka (55305) ***(G-6143)***
Apria Healthcare Inc 651 523-8888
1645 Energy Park Dr # 100 Saint Paul (55108) ***(G-8056)***
APS, Anoka *Also Called Atlas Pet Supply Inc* ***(G-157)***
Aqua Engineering Inc 952 941-1138
6561 City West Pkwy Eden Prairie (55344) ***(G-1594)***
Aquent LLC 952 851-3411
1550 Amrcn Blvd E Ste 750 Minneapolis (55425) ***(G-3794)***
Arabian Horse Times Inc 800 248-4637
299 Johnson Ave SW # 150 Waseca (56093) ***(G-9873)***
Aramark Corp 952 946-1438
6667 W Old Shakopee Rd # 103 Minneapolis (55438) ***(G-3795)***
ARAMARK Uniform & Career 763 586-0020
5330 Industrial Blvd NE Minneapolis (55421) ***(G-3408)***
ARAZ Group Inc 952 896-1200
7201 W 78th St Ste 100 Minneapolis (55439) ***(G-3796)***
Arbors At Ridges 952 898-4005
13810 Community Dr Ste A Burnsville (55337) ***(G-680)***
ARC Greater Twin Cities 612 861-9550
6528 Penn Ave S Minneapolis (55423) ***(G-3797)***
ARC Greater Twin Cities 763 544-0006
2751 Winnetka Ave N Minneapolis (55427) ***(G-3798)***
ARC Greater Twin Cities (PA) 952 920-0855
2446 University Ave W # 110 Saint Paul (55114) ***(G-8057)***
ARC of Anoka & Ramsey Counties, Minneapolis *Also Called Arcanoka Ramsey & Suburban ARC* ***(G-3799)***
Arcanoka Ramsey & Suburban ARC 952 890-3057
4301 Highway 7 Ste 140 Minneapolis (55416) ***(G-3799)***
Arch Capital Services 651 855-7111
30 7th St E Ste 2270 Saint Paul (55101) ***(G-8058)***
Arch Insurance Group Inc 651 855-7100
30 7th St E Ste 2270 Saint Paul (55101) ***(G-8059)***
Archbold Enterprises LLC 651 484-0211
1255 Highway 36 E Saint Paul (55109) ***(G-8060)***
Archdiocese of Saint Paul 763 425-2210
9100 93rd Ave N Minneapolis (55445) ***(G-3800)***
Archer Daniels Midland Co 507 625-7949
2019 3rd Ave Mankato (56001) ***(G-3106)***
Archer-Daniels-Midland Co 612 340-5900
301 4th Ave S Ste 1075 Minneapolis (55415) ***(G-3801)***
Architectural Enhancements, LL 320 274-6909
475 Annandale Blvd Annandale (55302) ***(G-137)***
Architectural Sales of MN 763 533-1595
4550 Quebec Ave N Minneapolis (55428) ***(G-3802)***
Architectural Sheet Metal, Minneapolis *Also Called Les Jones Roofing Inc* ***(G-4863)***
Architectural Testing Inc 651 636-3835
849 Western Ave N Saint Paul (55117) ***(G-8061)***
Architecture Technology Corp (PA) 952 829-5864
9977 Valley View Rd # 300 Eden Prairie (55344) ***(G-1595)***
Archivers, Minnetonka *Also Called Tomsten Inc* ***(G-6228)***
Archives Paper Co Inc 763 533-0612
3401 Nevada Ave N Minneapolis (55427) ***(G-3803)***
Archway Marketing Services, Litchfield *Also Called Argenbright Inc* ***(G-2978)***
Archway Marketing Services Inc (PA) 763 428-3300
19850 S Diamond Lake Rd Rogers (55374) ***(G-7316)***
Ardel Inc 763 545-1919
3650 Annapolis Ln N # 107 Minneapolis (55447) ***(G-3804)***
Arden Hills Dialysis Unit, Saint Paul *Also Called Total Renal Care Inc* ***(G-9072)***
Arden Stephen Salon Inc 952 893-1938
3300 Edinbrgh Way Ste 100 Minneapolis (55435) ***(G-3805)***
Area Mechanical Inc 651 451-9356
3276 Fanum Rd Ste 800 Vadnais Heights (55110) ***(G-9719)***
Area Special Education Co-op 218 773-0315
1505 Central Ave NW East Grand Forks (56721) ***(G-1566)***
Argenbright Inc 320 543-3737
401 13th Ave Howard Lake (55349) ***(G-2665)***
Argenbright Inc 320 693-7314
225 S Gorman Ave Litchfield (55355) ***(G-2978)***
Argenbright Inc (PA) 763 477-7600
7600 69th Ave Rockford (55373) ***(G-7307)***
Argenbright Inc 763 477-7600
7600 69th Ave Rockford (55373) ***(G-7308)***
Argus Homes 651 294-2160
418 County Road D E Saint Paul (55117) ***(G-8062)***
Aria Communications Corp 320 259-5206
717 W Saint Germain St Saint Cloud (56301) ***(G-7453)***
Arizant Healthcare Inc 952 947-1200
10393 W 70th St Eden Prairie (55344) ***(G-1596)***
Arkay Construction Co 763 544-3341
620 Mendelssohn Ave N Ste 156 Minneapolis (55427) ***(G-3806)***
Arkema Inc 507 583-6641
157 Hwy Ave N Blooming Prairie (55917) ***(G-476)***
Arkray Factory USA Inc 952 646-3200
5182 W 76th St Minneapolis (55439) ***(G-3807)***
Arkray USA Inc 952 646-3259
5198 W 76th St Minneapolis (55439) ***(G-3808)***
Arlington Good Samaritan Ctr, Arlington *Also Called Evangelical Lutheran Good* ***(G-249)***
Arlington Home, Fergus Falls *Also Called Prairie Community Services* ***(G-2115)***
Arlington House 651 771-3040
712 Larpenteur Ave E Saint Paul (55117) ***(G-8063)***
Arlington State Bank Inc 507 964-2256
230 W Main St Arlington (55307) ***(G-248)***
Armor Security Inc 612 870-1572
2601 Stevens Ave Minneapolis (55408) ***(G-3809)***

ALPHABETIC

Armstrong, Torseth, Skold ... 763 545-3731
8501 Golden Valley Rd # 300 Minneapolis (55427) *(G-3810)*

Arnage Security Services LLC ... 763 269-8440
12527 Ctrl Ave NE Ste 312 Minneapolis (55434) *(G-3409)*

Arnold's of Mankato Inc (PA) ... 320 398-3800
701 E Hwy 55 Kimball (55353) *(G-2830)*

Arnold's of Willmar Inc ... 320 235-4898
4773 Highway 71 S Willmar (56201) *(G-9984)*

Arnold's Supply & Kleenit Co ... 507 289-2393
835 38th St NW Rochester (55901) *(G-7058)*

Arnolds Elite Crpt Uphl Clean, Rochester *Also Called Arnold's Supply & Kleenit Co (G-7058)*

Arnzen Construction Inc ... 320 836-2284
29033 County Road 17 Freeport (56331) *(G-2187)*

Arran Technologies Inc ... 651 468-0002
1901 Oakcrest Ave Ste 1 Saint Paul (55113) *(G-8064)*

Array Services Group Inc ... 320 534-3401
205 14th Ave E Sartell (56377) *(G-9331)*

Array Services Group Inc ... 320 534-3680
217 N Benton Dr Sauk Rapids (56379) *(G-9357)*

Arrow Electronics Inc ... 952 949-0053
7629 Anagram Dr Eden Prairie (55344) *(G-1597)*

Arrow Sprinkler Inc ... 763 780-2800
1011 Osborne Rd NE Minneapolis (55432) *(G-3410)*

Arrowhead Center Inc ... 218 749-2877
505 S 12th Ave Ste 1 Virginia (55792) *(G-9733)*

Arrowhead Concrete Works Inc ... 218 729-8274
5572 Miller Trunk Hwy Duluth (55811) *(G-1240)*

Arrowhead Economic Opportunity ... 218 742-9187
820 9th St N Ste 240 Virginia (55792) *(G-9734)*

Arrowhead Economic Opportunity (PA) ... 218 749-2912
702 S 3rd Ave Virginia (55792) *(G-9735)*

Arrowhead House Foster Care ... 218 727-8040
218 N 1st Ave W Duluth (55806) *(G-1241)*

Arrowhead Promotion ... 218 327-1165
1105 SE 8th St Grand Rapids (55744) *(G-2269)*

Arrowhead Regional Blood Ctr, Duluth *Also Called Memorial Blood Center (G-1389)*

Arrowhead Regional Development ... 218 722-5545
221 W 1st St Duluth (55802) *(G-1242)*

Arrowhead Security Systems Inc ... 218 722-1234
4901 Woodlawn St Duluth (55804) *(G-1243)*

Arrowhead Tennis Inc ... 218 722-0810
4402 Rice Lake Rd Duluth (55811) *(G-1244)*

Arrowhead Town Hall ... 218 879-6916
9798 Highway 2 Brookston (55711) *(G-624)*

Arrowhead Tree Service Inc ... 218 729-9203
4268 W Calvary Rd Duluth (55803) *(G-1245)*

Arrowwood Rsort Conference Ctr, Alexandria *Also Called Regency Midwest Ventures LP (G-119)*

Art Holdings Corp ... 763 567-2200
6210 Wayzata Blvd Minneapolis (55416) *(G-3811)*

Art Semva Gallery ... 507 281-4920
16 1st St SW Rochester (55902) *(G-7059)*

Art Walker Center ... 612 375-7600
1750 Hennepin Ave Minneapolis (55403) *(G-3812)*

Art Walker Center Inc ... 612 375-7600
725 Vineland Pl Minneapolis (55403) *(G-3813)*

Artco Builders Inc ... 651 486-0761
4434 Harbor Place Dr Saint Paul (55126) *(G-8065)*

Arteka Co's LLC ... 952 934-2000
8810 13th Ave E Shakopee (55379) *(G-9419)*

Artesyn North America Inc ... 952 941-1100
7575 Market Place Dr Eden Prairie (55344) *(G-1598)*

Arthur A Hirman Agency Inc ... 507 285-3111
4001 W River Pkwy NW Rochester (55901) *(G-7060)*

Arthur J Gallagher & Co ... 952 944-8885
7825 Washingtn Ave S Ste 300 Minneapolis (55439) *(G-3814)*

Arthur Shuster Inc ... 651 631-9200
1995 Oakcrest Ave Saint Paul (55113) *(G-8066)*

Arthur, Chapman, Kettering ... 612 339-3500
81 S 9th St Ste 500 Minneapolis (55402) *(G-3815)*

Artic Cold Storage Inc ... 320 253-9979
4139 Roosevelt Rd Saint Cloud (56301) *(G-7454)*

Arvig Enterprises Inc (PA) ... 218 346-5500
160 2nd Ave SW Perham (56573) *(G-6793)*

Arvig Enterprises Inc ... 218 584-5119
204 Main Ave W Twin Valley (56584) *(G-9700)*

As Soon As Possible Inc ... 952 564-2727
3000 France Ave S Minneapolis (55416) *(G-3816)*

ASAP, Minneapolis *Also Called As Soon As Possible Inc (G-3816)*

Aseracare Hospice, Minneapolis *Also Called Hospice Preferred Choice Inc (G-4680)*

Ashford Trs Nickel, LP ... 952 854-2100
3800 American Blvd E Bloomington (55425) *(G-487)*

Ashland Inc ... 612 726-1787
5201 Post Rd Minneapolis (55450) *(G-3817)*

Asi Great Falls Inc ... 651 645-7271
2550 University Ave W 330N Saint Paul (55114) *(G-8067)*

Asi Missoula Inc ... 651 645-7271
2550 University Ave W 330N Saint Paul (55114) *(G-8068)*

ASI-Aero Services, Eden Prairie *Also Called Modern Aero Inc (G-1729)*

Asian Home Care Inc ... 651 999-0268
519 University Ave W # 202 Saint Paul (55103) *(G-8069)*

Asml Us Inc ... 952 876-0713
8054 26th Ave S Bloomington (55425) *(G-488)*

Aspen Medical Group ... 612 728-1800
3024 Snelling Ave Minneapolis (55406) *(G-3818)*

Aspen Medical Group, Saint Paul *Also Called Allina Health System (G-8016)*

Aspen Medical Group ... 651 696-8800
2004 Ford Pkwy Saint Paul (55116) *(G-8070)*

Aspen Research Corp ... 651 264-6000
1700 Buerkle Rd Saint Paul (55110) *(G-8071)*

Aspen Waste Systems Inc (PA) ... 612 884-8000
2951 Weeks Ave SE Minneapolis (55414) *(G-3819)*

Asphalt & Concrete Buy Knox ... 612 781-1112
2828 Anthony Ln S Ste 200 Minneapolis (55418) *(G-3820)*

Asphalt Specialties Co ... 651 484-1696
547 County Road E W Saint Paul (55126) *(G-8072)*

Asphalt Surface Technologies ... 320 363-8500
8348 Ridgewood Rd Saint Joseph (56374) *(G-7650)*

Asplundh Tree Expert Co ... 763 785-2300
4501 103rd Ct Ste 180 Circle Pines (55014) *(G-1002)*

Asset Management Group Inc ... 952 546-3385
5353 Wayzata Blvd Ste 602 Minneapolis (55416) *(G-3821)*

Assisted & Foster Care Svcs, Mankato *Also Called Senior Grace Services (G-3196)*

Associated Anesthesiologists ... 651 735-0501
14700 28th Ave N Ste 20 Minneapolis (55447) *(G-3822)*

Associated Banc-Corp ... 651 385-1600
222 Bush St Red Wing (55066) *(G-6974)*

Associated Bank, Rochester *Also Called First Federal Capital Bank (G-7113)*

Associated Bank Minnesota ... 612 359-4461
800 S 8th St Minneapolis (55440) *(G-3823)*

Associated Clinic of ... 952 925-6033
3100 W Lake St Ste 210 Minneapolis (55416) *(G-3824)*

Associated Clinic of ... 763 503-8560
6200 Shingle Creek Pkwy # 455 Minneapolis (55430) *(G-3825)*

Associated Courier Inc ... 612 623-9999
1122 16th Ave SE Minneapolis (55414) *(G-3826)*

Associated Dentists Ltd ... 651 222-0351
1371 7th St W Saint Paul (55102) *(G-8073)*

Associated Eye Care Ltd (PA) ... 651 439-8500
2950 Curve Crest Blvd W Stillwater (55082) *(G-9598)*

Associated Eye Care Ltd ... 651 275-3013
1719 Tower Dr W Stillwater (55082) *(G-9599)*

Associated Financial Group LLC (DH) ... 952 945-0200
12600 Whitewater Dr # 100 Minnetonka (55343) *(G-6144)*

Associated Material Handling ... 651 688-6175
935 Blue Gentian Rd Saint Paul (55121) *(G-7707)*

Associated Milk Producers Inc ... 320 769-2994
E Hwy 212 Dawson (56232) *(G-1163)*

Associated Milk Producers Inc ... 320 864-5561
330 10th St E Glencoe (55336) *(G-2204)*

Associated Milk Producers Inc (PA) ... 507 354-8295
315 N Broadway St New Ulm (56073) *(G-6440)*

Associated Milk Producers Inc ... 507 233-4600
312 Center St New Ulm (56073) *(G-6441)*

Associated Partnership Ltd ... 952 890-7851
6591 Highway 13 W Savage (55378) *(G-9383)*

Associated Skin Care ... 763 571-4000
7205 University Ave NE Minneapolis (55432) *(G-3411)*

Associates In Womens Health ... 952 806-0011
825 Nicollet Mall Ste 853 Minneapolis (55402) *(G-3827)*

Associates In Womens Health (PA) ... 952 806-0011
6517 Drew Ave S Minneapolis (55435) *(G-3828)*

Associates Plus Inc ... 763 323-8080
3351 Round Lake Blvd NW Ste 1 Anoka (55303) *(G-156)*

Associates Plus Inc ... 763 784-1400
299 Coon Rapids Blvd NW NW201 Minneapolis (55433) *(G-3412)*

Associates Plus Inc (PA) ... 651 484-8800
480 Highway 96 W Ste 200 Saint Paul (55126) *(G-8074)*

Association For The Solidatary ... 952 456-1751
Wright Bldg 2233 Ste 426 Saint Paul (55114) *(G-8075)*

Assocted Eye Physcans Surgeons, Stillwater *Also Called Associated Eye Care Ltd (G-9599)*

Assocted Skin Care Spclists, Minneapolis *Also Called Associated Skin Care (G-3411)*

Assumption Home Inc ... 320 685-3693
715 1st St N Cold Spring (56320) *(G-1082)*

Assurecare ... 763 383-4800
13700 Water Twr Cir Ste D Minneapolis (55441) *(G-3829)*

Assured Decontamination Svcs ... 651 998-0922
860 Mendel Ave N Lake Elmo (55042) *(G-2865)*

ASTECH, Saint Joseph *Also Called Asphalt Surface Technologies (G-7650)*

Astle Ford International Trcks, Minneapolis *Also Called North Star International (G-5219)*

Astleford Equipment Co Inc ... 952 894-9200
12541 Dupont Ave S Burnsville (55337) *(G-681)*

Aston Technologies Inc ... 952 546-1693
7515 Wayzata Blvd Ste 205 Saint Louis Park (55426) *(G-7657)*

At Home Ltd ... 612 673-9594
1622 Park Ave Minneapolis (55404) *(G-3830)*

At Home Services, Minneapolis *Also Called Metro Home Health Care Inc (G-3537)*

Atchison Enterprises Inc (PA) ... 507 376-3175
1307 S Shore Dr Worthington (56187) *(G-10178)*

Atchison Enterprises Inc ... 507 376-5312
965 McMillan St Worthington (56187) *(G-10179)*

Atek Manufacturing LLC ... 218 829-4719
210 10th Ave NE Brainerd (56401) *(G-550)*

ATHC, Winsted *Also Called Adult Training & Habilitation (G-10155)*

Athena Assurance Co ... 651 310-7065
385 Washington St Saint Paul (55102) *(G-8076)*

Athletica, Minneapolis *Also Called Premier Rinks Inc (G-5403)*

ATI Title Co, Hopkins *Also Called RELS Title Services LLC (G-2614)*

ATI Title Co, Saint Paul *Also Called Rels Title Services LLC (G-8887)*

Atirix Medical Systems Inc ... 952 546-2001
10201 Wayzata Blvd # 310 Minnetonka (55305) *(G-6145)*

Atlantis Pools Inc ... 763 560-0103
4321 68th Ave N Minneapolis (55429) *(G-3831)*

Atlantis Technical Services ... 763 657-2500
11230 86th Ave N Osseo (55369) *(G-6595)*

Atlas Cold Storage Midwest ... 507 732-4224
1000 Arctic Ave Zumbrota (55992) *(G-10216)*

Atlas Foundation Co ... 763 428-2261
11730 Brockton Ln N Osseo (55369) *(G-6596)*

Atlas Pet Supply Inc ... 763 753-4818
3347 167th Ln NW Anoka (55304) *(G-157)*

Atm Network Inc ... 952 767-2000
10749 Bren Rd E Minnetonka (55343) *(G-6146)*

Atomic Playpen Inc ... 763 231-3400
701 Xenia Ave S Ste 200 Minneapolis (55416) *(G-3832)*

Atomic Props & Effects Ltd ... 612 331-1335
895 Hale Ave N Saint Paul (55128) *(G-9185)*

Ats Inc ... 320 255-7400
725 Opportunity Dr Saint Cloud (56301) *(G-7455)*

Ats Logistics Services Inc (HQ) ... 320 255-7488
725 Opportunity Dr Saint Cloud (56301) *(G-7456)*

ATT Home Health Care Inc ... 651 646-8771
1543 Como Ave Saint Paul (55108) *(G-8077)*

Attorney's Process Service Ltd 952 831-7776
7800 Glenroy Rd Minneapolis (55439) *(G-3833)*
Atwood Land Co Inc 507 388-9375
209 S 2nd St Ste 200 Mankato (56001) *(G-3107)*
Auburn Manor, Chaska *Also Called Moravian Care Ministries (G-976)*
Auburn West Inc 952 442-2546
594 S Cherry Dr Waconia (55387) *(G-9778)*
Auburn Woods Clubhomes Assn 952 922-5575
7275 Bush Lake Rd Edina (55439) *(G-1825)*
Auction Broadcasting Co, Osseo *Also Called ABC Minneapolis LLC (G-6590)*
Auditor Wright County 763 682-7578
10 2nd St NW Rm 230 Buffalo (55313) *(G-634)*
Auer Steel & Heating Supply Co 763 971-2910
865 Xenium Ln N Plymouth (55441) *(G-6849)*
Auerbach Pollock Friedlander 952 930-0818
6113 Arctic Way Minneapolis (55436) *(G-3834)*
Augeo Affinity Marketing Inc 877 781-2586
2561 Territorial Rd Saint Paul (55114) *(G-8078)*
Augeo Communications LLC 651 204-5734
2561 Territorial Rd Saint Paul (55114) *(G-8079)*
Augusta Electric Inc 320 398-2189
19383 E Shore Dr Kimball (55353) *(G-2831)*
Augustana Chapel View Homes 952 938-2761
615 Minnetonka Mills Rd Hopkins (55343) *(G-2512)*
Augustana Chapel View Homes (HQ) 612 333-1551
1007 E 14th St Minneapolis (55404) *(G-3835)*
Augustana Dassel Lakeside Com 320 275-3308
439 William Ave E Dassel (55325) *(G-1159)*
Augustana Health Care Center 651 437-6176
930 16th St W Hastings (55033) *(G-2376)*
Augustana Health Care Center 952 431-7700
14650 Garrett Ave Saint Paul (55124) *(G-7708)*
Augustana Lutheran Homes Inc 320 693-2430
203 N Armstrong Ave Litchfield (55355) *(G-2979)*
Augustana Regent At Burnsville 952 898-1910
14500 Regent Ln Apt 333 Burnsville (55306) *(G-682)*
Augustine Medical Inc 952 947-1288
10393 W 70th St Eden Prairie (55344) *(G-1599)*
Auriton Solutions, Saint Paul *Also Called Metropolitan Financial Mgt (G-8646)*
Austin Coaches Inc 507 433-5358
103 10th St SE Austin (55912) *(G-259)*
Austin Country Club Inc 507 437-7631
1202 28th St NE Austin (55912) *(G-260)*
Austin Medical Center-Mayo 507 433-7351
1000 1st Dr NW Austin (55912) *(G-261)*
Austin Mutual Insurance Co 800 328-4628
15490 101st Ave N Maple Grove (55369) *(G-3237)*
Austin Utilities 507 433-8886
400 4th St NE Austin (55912) *(G-262)*
Auto Butler Inc (PA) 612 529-3345
4701 Humboldt Ave N Minneapolis (55430) *(G-3836)*
Auto Warehousing Co Inc 651 769-8383
9250 Ideal Ave S Cottage Grove (55016) *(G-1100)*
Auto-Owners Life Insurance Co 651 777-9317
2539 County Road E E Saint Paul (55110) *(G-8080)*
Automated Building Components (PA) 952 474-4374
300 Morse Ave Excelsior (55331) *(G-1938)*
Automated Mailing Corp 612 333-4477
1226 Linden Ave Minneapolis (55403) *(G-3837)*
Automatic Data Processing Inc 952 814-5800
8100 Cedar Ave S 100 Minneapolis (55425) *(G-3838)*
Automation & Process Controls, Saint Paul *Also Called Schneiberg Co (G-8934)*
Automation Fluid Power Inc 763 571-3336
4830 Azelia Ave N Ste 500 Minneapolis (55429) *(G-3839)*
Automotive Cooling Products (PA) 651 731-2414
8934 Springwood Cir Saint Paul (55125) *(G-9186)*
Automotive Procare, Rochester *Also Called Race Automotive of Rochester (G-7216)*
Automotive Restyling Concepts 763 535-2181
2731 Nevada Ave N Minneapolis (55427) *(G-3840)*
Autumn Grace Senior Services 507 388-3660
118 Raven Ct Mankato (56001) *(G-3108)*
Avada Audiology & Hearing Care 952 541-1799
1730 Plymouth Rd Ste 301 Hopkins (55305) *(G-2513)*
Avalon Fortress Security Svcs 763 767-9111
3300 County Road 10 # 512 Minneapolis (55429) *(G-3841)*
Avalon Home Care 763 753-8658
20132 Ulysses St NW Elk River (55330) *(G-1862)*
Avantgard 952 935-3300
601 2nd Ave S Hopkins (55343) *(G-2514)*
Aveda Experience Centres, Minneapolis *Also Called A-Veda Corp (G-3383)*
Avery Weigh-Tronix LLC (HQ) 507 238-4461
1000 Armstrong Dr Fairmont (56031) *(G-1957)*
Aveyron Homes Inc 320 234-6063
360 Lake St SW Hutchinson (55350) *(G-2688)*
Aveyron Homes Inc 320 587-6277
9 Northwoods Ave NE Hutchinson (55350) *(G-2689)*
AVI-Spl Inc 651 287-7000
1427 Energy Park Dr Saint Paul (55108) *(G-8081)*
Aviall Services Inc 651 452-1680
1355 Mendota Heights Rd Mendota Heights (55120) *(G-3360)*
Aviation Charter, Eden Prairie *Also Called Millian Air Executive Aviation (G-1724)*
Aviation Charter Inc 952 943-1519
9960 Flying Cloud Dr Eden Prairie (55347) *(G-1600)*
Avionte LLC 651 556-2121
1270 Eagan Industrial Rd Eagan (55121) *(G-1516)*
Avis Rent A Car System Inc 612 623-3999
2407 University Ave SE Minneapolis (55414) *(G-3842)*
Avis Rent A Car System Inc 651 636-6730
2550 Cleveland Ave N Saint Paul (55113) *(G-8082)*
Avista Solutions International 952 949-0594
2485 Xenium Ln N Minneapolis (55441) *(G-3843)*
Aviv Health Care Inc 952 546-4261
7500 W 22nd St Minneapolis (55426) *(G-3844)*
Aviv Health Care Inc 612 377-4723
275 Penn Ave N Minneapolis (55405) *(G-3845)*
Aviv Health Care Inc 952 546-4261
7500 W 22nd St Minneapolis (55426) *(G-3846)*
Aviv Health Care Inc 763 425-3939
501 2nd St SE Osseo (55369) *(G-6597)*
Avnet Inc 952 346-3000
2740 Amercn Blvd W Ste 150 Bloomington (55431) *(G-489)*
Avnet Inc 763 559-2211
14800 28th Ave N Minneapolis (55447) *(G-3847)*
Avtex Solutions LLC (HQ) 952 831-0888
9401 James Ave S Ste 180 Minneapolis (55431) *(G-3848)*
Aware Integrated Inc 651 662-8000
3535 Blue Cross Rd Saint Paul (55122) *(G-7709)*
Aware Systems Inc 800 783-8919
1660 Highway 100 S # 500 Minneapolis (55416) *(G-3849)*
AWI Manufacturing Inc 320 485-2471
3902 230th St Winsted (55395) *(G-10157)*
Awm Enterprises Inc 651 455-3044
501 Farwell Ave South Saint Paul (55075) *(G-9510)*
Axa Advisors LLC 612 243-3200
2 Meridian Xing Ste 450 Minneapolis (55423) *(G-3850)*
Axdahl Farms Inc 651 439-3134
17120 116th St N Stillwater (55082) *(G-9600)*
Axis Minnesota Inc 651 774-5940
2345 Rice St Ste 112 Saint Paul (55113) *(G-8083)*
Axonom Inc 952 653-0400
10860 Nesbitt Ave S Minneapolis (55437) *(G-3851)*
B & B Sheet Metal & Roofing 763 682-4233
210 Centennial Dr Buffalo (55313) *(G-635)*
B & D Plumbing, Heating & AC 763 497-2290
4145 Mackenzie Ct NE Saint Michael (55376) *(G-7672)*
B & K Windows, Minneapolis *Also Called Asphalt & Concrete Buy Knox (G-3820)*
B H Heselton Co 507 334-3901
680 24th St NW Faribault (55021) *(G-1990)*
B J Transport Inc 651 436-4300
12720 Hudson Rd S Afton (55001) *(G-7)*
B L B Inc 612 825-3737
1600 W Lake St Ste A Minneapolis (55408) *(G-3852)*
B L Dalsin Roofing, Minneapolis *Also Called Bernard L Dalsin Co (G-3888)*
B L E A Inc 507 896-3040
105 W Elm St Houston (55943) *(G-2662)*
B L E A Inc 507 895-8111
1700 Lancer Blvd La Crescent (55947) *(G-2838)*
B Nelson Julius & Son Inc 612 379-3347
962 Central Ave NE Minneapolis (55413) *(G-3853)*
B T & A Construction Co 612 825-6811
3401 Colfax Ave S Ste A Minneapolis (55408) *(G-3854)*
B T I Travel One, Minneapolis *Also Called Travel One Inc (G-5849)*
B&D Associates Inc 651 489-8001
255 Como Ave Saint Paul (55103) *(G-8084)*
B'Nai Emet Synagogue Inc 952 927-7309
3115 Ottawa Ave S Minneapolis (55416) *(G-3855)*
B'S Homecare Inc 763 689-8984
546 21st Ct SE Cambridge (55008) *(G-832)*
Baarts Trucking Inc 507 436-5536
206 Von Holst St Northrop (56075) *(G-6548)*
Babcock, Neilson, Mannella, La 763 421-5151
408 Northdale Blvd NW Minneapolis (55448) *(G-3413)*
Bachman's Inc 952 469-2102
23000 Cedar Ave Farmington (55024) *(G-2040)*
Bachman's Inc 651 463-3288
6877 235th St W Farmington (55024) *(G-2041)*
Bachman's Inc (PA) 612 861-7600
6010 Lyndale Ave S Minneapolis (55419) *(G-3856)*
Bachmans Nursery Wholesale Ctr, Farmington *Also Called Bachman's Inc (G-2041)*
Badger Acquisition of MN 763 259-0400
5534 Lakeland Ave N Minneapolis (55429) *(G-3857)*
Bahama Consulting Corp 651 994-7900
8950 Almquist Way Ste 415 Inver Grove Heights (55077) *(G-2738)*
Bailey Nurseries Inc (PA) 651 459-9744
1325 Bailey Rd Newport (55055) *(G-6484)*
Bailiwick Data Systems Inc 952 556-5502
4260 Norex Dr Chaska (55318) *(G-950)*
Bainey Group Inc 763 557-6911
14700 28th Ave N Ste 30 Minneapolis (55447) *(G-3858)*
Bakemark USA LLC 952 937-9495
14675 Martin Dr Eden Prairie (55344) *(G-1601)*
Baker Colberg & Realty 651 430-7745
2020 Washington Ave S Stillwater (55082) *(G-9601)*
Baker It Inc 612 822-3664
137 W 46th St Minneapolis (55419) *(G-3859)*
Baker Laura Services Assn 507 645-8866
211 Oak St Northfield (55057) *(G-6524)*
Baker National Park Golf Crse, Hamel *Also Called Three Rivers Park District (G-2357)*
Baker, Tilly, Virchow Krause 612 876-4500
225 S 6th St Ste 2300 Minneapolis (55402) *(G-3860)*
Bakke Kopp Ballou & McFarlin 763 843-0420
5930 Brooklyn Blvd Minneapolis (55429) *(G-3861)*
Bakken Museum 612 927-6508
3537 Zenith Ave S Minneapolis (55416) *(G-3862)*
Bakken Securities Inc (PA) 952 926-6561
5000 W 36th St Minneapolis (55416) *(G-3863)*
Bald Eagle Erectors Inc 651 405-9050
3045 Sibley Memorial Hwy # 115 Saint Paul (55121) *(G-7710)*
Baldor Electric Co 763 428-3633
21080 134th Ave N Rogers (55374) *(G-7317)*
Ballantine Inc 763 427-3959
840 McKinley St Anoka (55303) *(G-158)*
Ballet Arts Minnesota Inc 612 340-1071
528 Hennepin Ave Ste 600 Minneapolis (55403) *(G-3864)*
Bally Total Fitness Corp 763 574-8888
7200 University Ave NE Minneapolis (55432) *(G-3414)*
Bally Total Fitness Corp 651 484-4444
71 Minnesota Ave Saint Paul (55117) *(G-8085)*
Balyle Inc 320 253-2910
208 2nd St S Sartell (56377) *(G-9332)*
Ban-Koe Systems Inc 952 888-6688
9100 W Blmgtn Fwy Fwy Ste 195 Minneapolis (55431) *(G-3865)*
Bancnorth Investment Group 320 656-4300
400 1st St S Saint Cloud (56301) *(G-7457)*

ALPHABETIC

Bangasser Co
ALPHABETIC SECTION

Bangasser Co 320 256-5100
422 Elena Ln Saint Joseph (56374) ***(G-7651)***
BANK EASY, Pipestone *Also Called 1st National Bank of Pipestone (G-6827)*
Bank Midwest (PA) 507 235-3327
118 Downtown Plz Fairmont (56031) ***(G-1958)***
Bank Midwest 507 847-3010
509 3rd St Jackson (56143) ***(G-2786)***
Bank Midwest 507 831-1322
245 9th St Windom (56101) ***(G-10065)***
Bank Midwest 507 831-1322
245 9th St Windom (56101) ***(G-10066)***
Bank of Elk River (PA) 763 441-1000
630 Main St NW Elk River (55330) ***(G-1863)***
Bank of Zumbrota 507 732-7555
1440 S Main St Zumbrota (55992) ***(G-10217)***
Bankcherokee 651 227-7071
607 Smith Ave S Saint Paul (55107) ***(G-8086)***
Bankers Life & Casualty Co 952 835-2611
4940 Viking Dr Ste 530 Minneapolis (55435) ***(G-3866)***
Bankruptcy Solutions Inc 651 367-2000
2740 Arthur St Saint Paul (55113) ***(G-8087)***
Banks Brothers Construction 651 644-1723
2402 University Ave W # 204 Saint Paul (55114) ***(G-8088)***
Banner & Assoc 507 562-2957
119 2nd Ave SW Ste 5 Pipestone (56164) ***(G-6823)***
Barbers Hairstyling For Men (HQ) 952 947-7777
7201 Metro Blvd Minneapolis (55439) ***(G-3867)***
Bargen Inc 507 427-2924
606 County Road 1 Mountain Lake (56159) ***(G-6395)***
Barna Guzy & Steffen Ltd 763 780-8500
400 N Town Fincl Plz 200 Minneapolis (55433) ***(G-3415)***
Barnabas Health Care Services 218 829-0901
223 Washington St Brainerd (56401) ***(G-551)***
Barnes & Thornburg LLP 612 333-2111
100 S 5th St Ste 1100 Minneapolis (55402) ***(G-3868)***
Barnes Head Start 218 733-2084
2102 N Blackman Ave Duluth (55811) ***(G-1246)***
Barnesville Good Samaritan Ctr, Barnesville *Also Called Evangelical Lutheran Good (G-305)*
Barnett Chrysler Jeep Kia 651 429-3391
3610 Highway 61 N Saint Paul (55110) ***(G-8089)***
Barole Trucking Inc 651 209-1104
6805 20th Ave Ste 300 Hugo (55038) ***(G-2670)***
Barr Engineering Co 218 262-2262
3128 14th Ave E Hibbing (55746) ***(G-2438)***
Barrett Automatic Products Co 320 528-2512
418 2nd St Barrett (56311) ***(G-307)***
Barrett Care Center Inc 320 528-2527
800 Spruce Ave Barrett (56311) ***(G-308)***
Barrett Moving & Storage Co 952 944-6550
7100 Washington Ave S Eden Prairie (55344) ***(G-1602)***
Barry & Sewall Industrial Sply 612 331-6170
2001 Broadway St NE Minneapolis (55413) ***(G-3869)***
Barton Sand & Gravel Co 763 425-4191
10633 89th Ave N Osseo (55369) ***(G-6598)***
Base Eight Inc 952 941-5888
615 Lakota Ln Chaska (55318) ***(G-951)***
BASF Corp (DH) 763 559-3266
13630 Water Tower Cir Minneapolis (55441) ***(G-3870)***
Basilica of Saint Mary of 612 333-1381
88 N 17th St Minneapolis (55403) ***(G-3871)***
Basset Creek Dental, Minneapolis *Also Called Shari K Bruning DDS (G-5649)*
Bassett Creek Dental 763 546-1301
5851 Duluth St Ste 100 Minneapolis (55422) ***(G-3872)***
Bassford Remele 612 333-3000
33 S 6th St Ste 3800 Minneapolis (55402) ***(G-3873)***
Battered Woman, Saint Cloud *Also Called Central Minnesota Task Force (G-7487)*
Battered Woman, Saint Cloud *Also Called Central Minnesota Task Force (G-7489)*
Battle Creek Head Start 651 730-1663
2181 Suburban Ave Saint Paul (55119) ***(G-8090)***
Battle Lake Good Samaritan Ctr, Battle Lake *Also Called Evangelical Lutheran Good (G-310)*
Battmann Holdings Inc (PA) 651 639-2800
2480 Long Lake Rd Saint Paul (55113) ***(G-8091)***
Bauck Busing Ltd 218 346-4599
43569 Fort Thunder Rd Perham (56573) ***(G-6794)***
Baudora State Forest Nursery 218 652-2385
13885 State 64 Akeley (56433) ***(G-25)***
Bauer Built Inc 651 646-1239
625 Fairview Ave N Saint Paul (55104) ***(G-8092)***
Bauer's Market & Nursery Inc 507 895-4583
221 N 2nd St La Crescent (55947) ***(G-2839)***
Bauerly Dynamics Inc 320 251-9472
4787 Shadowwood Dr NE Sauk Rapids (56379) ***(G-9358)***
Bauernfeind & Goedtel, Faribault *Also Called Gemini 26 Inc (G-2009)*
Baumgartner Trucking Inc 507 895-8490
90 N 1st St La Crescent (55947) ***(G-2840)***
Baune Dosen & Co LLP 952 473-2002
600 Highway 169 S Ste 1750 Minneapolis (55426) ***(G-3874)***
Baxter Service Center, Baxter *Also Called Citi Investor Services Inc (G-324)*
Bay & Bay Transfer Co Inc 651 480-7991
3686 140th St E Rosemount (55068) ***(G-7362)***
Bay Shore Health Center 218 727-8651
1601 Saint Louis Ave Duluth (55802) ***(G-1247)***
Bay West Inc 651 291-0456
5 Empire Dr Saint Paul (55103) ***(G-8093)***
Bay West-Bem Solutions LLC 651 291-0456
5 Empire Dr Saint Paul (55103) ***(G-8094)***
Bayer Built Woodworks Inc 320 254-3651
24614 Highway 71 Belgrade (56312) ***(G-360)***
Bayer Trucking LLC 320 254-3651
24614 Highway 71 Belgrade (56312) ***(G-361)***
Bayport Senior Center 651 275-8907
263 3rd St N Bayport (55003) ***(G-346)***
BBB OF MINNESOTA & NORTH DAK, Saint Paul *Also Called Better Business Bureau of Minn (G-8110)*
Bbdo Worldwide Inc 612 338-8401
150 S 5th St Ste 3500 Minneapolis (55402) ***(G-3875)***
Bbj Inc 651 730-7808
7776 Hudson Rd Saint Paul (55125) ***(G-9187)***
Bcbsm Inc 218 722-3371
21 W Superior St Ste 110 Duluth (55802) ***(G-1248)***
Bcbsm Inc (PA) 651 662-8000
3535 Blue Cross Rd Saint Paul (55122) ***(G-7711)***
Bcbsm Inc 651 662-8951
1305 Corporate Center Dr Saint Paul (55121) ***(G-7712)***
Bcbsm Inc 651 662-8000
1200 Yankee Doodle Rd Saint Paul (55121) ***(G-7713)***
Bcbsm Inc 651 662-8000
3400 Yankee Dr Saint Paul (55121) ***(G-7714)***
Bcbsm Inc 218 748-2700
1301 Chestnut St W Virginia (55792) ***(G-9736)***
Bce Development Corp 612 372-1500
4340 Multifoods Tower Minneapolis (55402) ***(G-3876)***
BCI Coca-Cola Bottling Co of 507 282-2622
1803 14th St NW Rochester (55901) ***(G-7061)***
BCM Construction Inc 507 333-1155
15760 Acorn Trl Faribault (55021) ***(G-1991)***
Bcr Real Estate Services 320 532-4099
9648 385th St Onamia (56359) ***(G-6566)***
Bdm Consulting Engineers 612 548-3140
60 Plato Blvd E Ste 140 Saint Paul (55107) ***(G-8095)***
Beacon Bank 952 474-7309
19765 Highway 7 Excelsior (55331) ***(G-1939)***
Beacon Promotions Inc 507 233-3240
2121 S Bridge St New Ulm (56073) ***(G-6442)***
Beam Central Vacuum Systems, Minneapolis *Also Called J J Vanderson & Co (G-3503)*
Beamkko 651 770-5661
2275 McKnight Rd N Ste 1 Saint Paul (55109) ***(G-8096)***
Bear Creek Care & Rehab 507 288-6514
501 8th Ave SE Rochester (55904) ***(G-7062)***
Bearpath Golf & Country Club 952 975-0123
18100 Bearpath Trl Eden Prairie (55347) ***(G-1603)***
Beaumont Leased Housing Assocs 763 354-5500
2355 Polaris Ln N Ste 100 Plymouth (55447) ***(G-6850)***
Beaumont Leased Housing Assocs 763 354-5500
2355 Polaris Ln N Ste 100 Plymouth (55447) ***(G-6851)***
Beauty Craft Supply & Eqpt 952 935-4420
11110 Bren Rd W Hopkins (55343) ***(G-2515)***
Becker Bros Inc 651 633-8604
825 1st St NW Saint Paul (55112) ***(G-8097)***
Becker County Human Services 218 847-5628
712 Minnesota Ave Detroit Lakes (56501) ***(G-1187)***
Becker County Sheriff Dept, Detroit Lakes *Also Called County of Becker (G-1190)*
Becker HI-Way Frate 507 373-8513
2401 Becker Dr Albert Lea (56007) ***(G-41)***
Becker Meggy Rl Est 507 388-8469
505 Long St Mankato (56001) ***(G-3109)***
Becketwood Cooperative Inc 612 722-4077
4300 W River Pkwy Apt 212 Minneapolis (55406) ***(G-3877)***
Beckhoff Automation LLC 952 890-0000
12150 Nicollet Ave Burnsville (55337) ***(G-683)***
Becklund Personal Care Org 763 546-2030
44005 Quaker Ln Minneapolis (55441) ***(G-3878)***
Behavioral Dimensions Inc 952 814-0207
415 Blake Rd N Ste 240 Hopkins (55343) ***(G-2516)***
Behavioral Health Services Inc 763 689-7887
701 Dellwood St S Cambridge (55008) ***(G-833)***
Behavioral Hlth Care Providers 763 525-9919
1405 Lilac Dr N Ste 151 Minneapolis (55422) ***(G-3879)***
Behaviorl Hlth Svcs Allina CAM, Cambridge *Also Called Behavioral Health Services Inc (G-833)*
Belco Express, Rochester *Also Called Rochester City Delivery Inc (G-7229)*
Belcourt Corp 952 894-0406
3100 W Park Dr Burnsville (55306) ***(G-684)***
Belde Building Maintenance 651 457-6337
450 Southview Blvd South Saint Paul (55075) ***(G-9511)***
Belgrade Commerical Club 320 254-8271
321 Washburn Ave Belgrade (56312) ***(G-362)***
Belgrade Cooperative Assn 320 254-8231
218 Wells St Belgrade (56312) ***(G-363)***
Belgrade Milling Co, Freeport *Also Called M & B Enterprise of Freeport (G-2188)*
Belgrade Nursing Home Inc 320 254-8215
103 School St Belgrade (56312) ***(G-364)***
Bell Ancillary Services Inc 952 893-0865
7650 Edinbrgh Way Ste 100 Minneapolis (55435) ***(G-3880)***
Bell Ancillary Services Inc (PA) 952 591-1880
1000 Shelard Pkwy Ste 500 Minneapolis (55426) ***(G-3881)***
Bell Ancillary Services Inc 952 545-1880
10301 Wayzatta Blve Minnetonka (55305) ***(G-6147)***
Bell Hill Recovery Center Inc 218 631-3610
12213 200th St Wadena (56482) ***(G-9798)***
Bell Industries Inc 651 203-2300
580 Yankee Doodle Rd # 1200 Eagan (55121) ***(G-1517)***
Bell Lumber & Pole Co (PA) 651 633-4334
778 1st St NW Saint Paul (55112) ***(G-8098)***
Bell Telephone Inc 651 298-1332
4444 Centerville Rd Saint Paul (55127) ***(G-8099)***
Belle Plaine Bancorporation 952 873-2296
201 W Main St Belle Plaine (56011) ***(G-366)***
Belle Plaine Cooperative 952 873-4244
820 E Main St Belle Plaine (56011) ***(G-367)***
Beltmann Group Inc (HQ) 651 639-2800
2480 Long Lake Rd Saint Paul (55113) ***(G-8100)***
Beltrami County Health Svcs, Bemidji *Also Called County of Beltrami (G-386)*
Beltrami Electric Co-Op Inc 218 444-2540
4111 Technology Dr NW Bemidji (56601) ***(G-375)***
Beltrami's Tally Inc 218 243-2231
19276 Lake Julia Dr NW Bemidji (56601) ***(G-376)***
Belwin Outdoor Educational Lab, Afton *Also Called St Paul Public School (G-10)*
Bem - Bay West Joint Venture 651 291-0456
5 Empire Dr Saint Paul (55103) ***(G-8101)***
Bemidji Aviation Services Inc (PA) 218 751-1880
4125 Hangar Dr NW Bemidji (56601) ***(G-377)***
Bemidji Aviation Services Inc 612 726-1500
3700 E 70th St Minneapolis (55450) ***(G-3882)***

ALPHABETIC

Bemidji Clinic Merit Care Inc 218 333-5000
1233 34th St NW Bemidji (56601) *(G-378)*
Bemidji Cooperative Assn 218 751-4260
320 3rd St NW Bemidji (56601) *(G-379)*
Bemidji Police Training Center, Bemidji *Also Called Police Range (G-421)*
Bemidji Town & Country Club 218 751-9215
2425 Birchmont Beach Rd NE Bemidji (56601) *(G-380)*
Bemidji Town & Country Club 218 751-4535
2425 Birchmont Dr NE Bemidji (56601) *(G-381)*
Bemis Co Inc 612 788-0100
2705 University Ave NE Minneapolis (55418) *(G-3883)*
Ben Co Electric 507 387-7963
20946 549th Ave Mankato (56001) *(G-3110)*
Ben Franklin Electric Inc 952 888-2210
12401 Washburn Ave S Burnsville (55337) *(G-685)*
Benco Delivery Service Inc 651 486-9999
1144 Larpenteur Ave W # 200 Saint Paul (55113) *(G-8102)*
Benco Electric Cooperative, Mankato *Also Called Ben Co Electric (G-3110)*
Benedict Farms Inc 218 789-7376
7540 50th Ave S Sabin (56580) *(G-7396)*
Benedict Village, Saint Cloud *Also Called St Benedict's Senior Community (G-7441)*
Benedictine Health Center 218 723-6408
935 Kenwood Ave Duluth (55811) *(G-1249)*
Benedictine Health System (PA) 218 786-2370
503 E 3rd St Ste 400 Duluth (55805) *(G-1250)*
Benedictine Health System 218 744-9800
601 Grant Ave Eveleth (55734) *(G-1928)*
Benedictine Health System 507 534-3191
800 2nd Ave NW Plainview (55964) *(G-6838)*
Benedictine Health System 651 388-1234
213 Pioneer Rd Red Wing (55066) *(G-6975)*
Benedictine Health System 952 403-3000
1455 Saint Francis Ave Shakopee (55379) *(G-9420)*
Benedictine Health System 507 457-0280
1455 W Broadway St Ofc Winona (55987) *(G-10080)*
Benedictine Health System 320 485-2151
551 4th St N Ste 101 Winsted (55395) *(G-10158)*
Benedictine Team Health Systs 763 689-1162
1995 E Rum River Dr S Cambridge (55008) *(G-834)*
Benesyst Inc 612 746-3100
800 Washington Ave N # 800 Minneapolis (55401) *(G-3884)*
Benevolent Protective Order of 507 451-1395
126 E Vine St Owatonna (55060) *(G-6694)*
Benham Co's The LLC 651 771-2222
60 Plato Blvd E Ste 300 Saint Paul (55107) *(G-8103)*
Benjamin Bus Inc (PA) 507 645-5720
32611 Northfield Blvd Northfield (55057) *(G-6516)*
Bennett Material Handling Inc 952 933-5544
1009 Hill St Hopkins (55343) *(G-2517)*
Bennett Office Technologies 320 235-6425
312 24th Ave SW Willmar (56201) *(G-9985)*
Bennett Porter III Dvm 612 925-1121
4345 France Ave S Minneapolis (55410) *(G-3885)*
Bentley Instruments Inc 952 448-7600
4004 Peavey Rd Chaska (55318) *(G-952)*
Berbee Information Networks 763 592-5800
7145 Boone Ave N Ste 140 Minneapolis (55428) *(G-3886)*
Berean Baptist Church 952 432-7168
309 County Road 42 E Burnsville (55306) *(G-686)*
Berg Construction Services Inc 651 423-5531
3328 151st St W Rosemount (55068) *(G-7363)*
Berg Drywall LLC 952 448-3130
118 Peavey Cir Chaska (55318) *(G-953)*
Berg Exteriors Inc 763 479-1115
5145 Industrial St # 101 Maple Plain (55359) *(G-3269)*
Bergen's Greenhouses Inc 218 847-2138
801 Willow St W Detroit Lakes (56501) *(G-1188)*
Berger Transfer & Storage Inc (PA) 651 639-2260
2950 Long Lake Rd Saint Paul (55113) *(G-8104)*
Bergerson-Caswell Inc 763 479-3121
5115 Industrial St Maple Plain (55359) *(G-3270)*
Bergin Fruit & Nut Co Inc 651 642-1234
2000 Energy Park Dr Saint Paul (55108) *(G-8105)*
Bergquist Co (PA) 952 835-2322
18930 W 78th St Chanhassen (55317) *(G-909)*
Berkley Risk Administrators Co (HQ) 612 766-3000
222 S 9th St Ste 1300 Minneapolis (55402) *(G-3887)*
Berkley Risk Administrators Co 651 281-1200
145 University Ave W Saint Paul (55103) *(G-8106)*
Berkshire Residence, Osseo *Also Called Aviv Health Care Inc (G-6597)*
Bernard Bus Service Inc (PA) 507 867-3410
103 Division St NW Chatfield (55923) *(G-987)*
Bernard Group Inc 952 934-1900
102 N Jonathan Blvd Chaska (55318) *(G-954)*
Bernard J Mulcahy Co Inc 651 686-8580
2700 Blue Waters Rd Saint Paul (55121) *(G-7715)*
Bernard L Dalsin Co 952 881-7663
8824 Wentworth Ave S Minneapolis (55420) *(G-3888)*
Bernick's Full-Line Vending (PA) 320 656-2131
801 Sundial Dr Waite Park (56387) *(G-9817)*
Bernick's Pepsi Cola of 320 235-1370
2400 19th Ave SW Willmar (56201) *(G-9986)*
Bernick's Sports Unlimited, Waite Park *Also Called Chas A Bernick Inc (G-9819)*
Berry Coffee Co 952 937-8697
14825 Martin Dr Eden Prairie (55344) *(G-1604)*
Bert's Truck Equipment of 218 233-8681
Hwy 75 N Moorhead (56560) *(G-6298)*
Bertelson Brothers Inc 763 546-4371
6645 James Ave N Minneapolis (55430) *(G-3889)*
Berwald Roofing Co Inc (PA) 651 777-7411
2440 Charles St N Ste 1 Saint Paul (55109) *(G-8107)*
Beskau Trucking Inc 651 437-9737
19500 Goodwin Ave Hastings (55033) *(G-2377)*
Best & Flanagan LLP 612 339-7121
225 S 6th St Ste 4000 Minneapolis (55402) *(G-3890)*
Best Access Systems, Saint Paul *Also Called Stanley Security Solutions Inc (G-9004)*
Best Brands Corp (DH) 952 404-7500
111 Cheshire Ln Ste 100 Saint Paul (55121) *(G-7716)*
Best Brands Corp 651 454-5850
1765 Yankee Doodle Rd Saint Paul (55121) *(G-7717)*
Best Care Home Health Inc 612 378-1040
3008 University Ave SE Minneapolis (55414) *(G-3891)*
Best Oil Co (PA) 218 879-4666
30 8th St N Cloquet (55720) *(G-1046)*
Best Source Electronics Corp 763 502-7847
5301 E River Rd Ste 113 Fridley (55421) *(G-2191)*
Best Vendors Management Inc 763 287-7200
4000 Olson Memorial Hwy Minneapolis (55422) *(G-3892)*
Best Western, Duluth *Also Called Diversified Motel Properties (G-1294)*
Best Western, Mankato *Also Called D D D Motel Corp (G-3224)*
Best Western, Rochester *Also Called Midwest of Rochester Inc (G-7185)*
Best Western, Saint Paul *Also Called Kelly Midwest Ventures LP (G-8544)*
Best Western, South Saint Paul *Also Called Drover's Inn & Restaurant Inc (G-9526)*
Best Western Chaska River Inn 952 448-7877
1 River Bend Pl Chaska (55318) *(G-955)*
Best Western Dakota Ridge 651 452-0100
3450 Washington Dr Saint Paul (55122) *(G-7718)*
Best Western Downtown, Minneapolis *Also Called Normandy Inn Inc (G-5210)*
Best Western of Thief River 218 681-7555
1060 Highway 32 S Thief River Falls (56701) *(G-9663)*
Best Western Riverport Inn 507 452-0606
900 Bruski Dr Winona (55987) *(G-10081)*
Best Western South St Paul 651 455-3600
701 Concord St Saint Paul (55107) *(G-8108)*
Best Western Victorian Inn, Hutchinson *Also Called Victoria Inn (G-2716)*
Bester Bros Transfer & Storage 651 451-1018
260 Hardman Ave S South Saint Paul (55075) *(G-9512)*
Bestmark Inc 952 922-2205
5605 Green Circle Dr # 200 Minnetonka (55343) *(G-6148)*
Betaseed Inc (PA) 952 445-8090
1788 Marschall Rd Shakopee (55379) *(G-9421)*
Beth-Fast, Osseo *Also Called E & A Products Inc (G-6611)*
Bethany Covenant Home, Minneapolis *Also Called Evangelical Covenant Church (G-4374)*
Bethany Covenant Village 612 781-2691
2309 Hayes St NE Minneapolis (55418) *(G-3893)*
Bethany Good Samaritan Village, Brainerd *Also Called Evangelical Lutheran Good (G-565)*
Bethany Home, Alexandria *Also Called Ecumen (G-98)*
Bethany Samaritan Inc 507 289-3336
1530 Assisi Dr NW Rochester (55901) *(G-7063)*
Bethany Samaritan Inc 507 289-4031
24 8th St NW Rochester (55901) *(G-7064)*
Bethel Care Center, Saint Paul *Also Called Mission Health Care LLC (G-8716)*
Bethel Duluth Society 218 722-1724
23 Mesaba Ave Duluth (55806) *(G-1251)*
Bethesda 320 235-3924
1012 3rd St SE Willmar (56201) *(G-9987)*
Bethesda 320 235-8364
1604 1st St S Ste 16 Willmar (56201) *(G-9988)*
Bethesda Clinic, Saint Paul *Also Called Regents of The University of (G-8881)*
Bethesda Healthy Rehab 651 232-2000
559 Capitol Blvd Fl 6 Saint Paul (55103) *(G-8109)*
Bethesda Heritage Center 320 235-3924
1012 3rd St SE Willmar (56201) *(G-9989)*
Bette Dickenson Research Inc 763 420-4385
7468 Mariner Dr Osseo (55311) *(G-6599)*
Better Business Bureau of Minn 651 699-1111
2706 Gannon Rd Saint Paul (55116) *(G-8110)*
Bevcomm Inc 507 526-3252
123 W 7th St Blue Earth (56013) *(G-529)*
Bever & Sons Inc 651 426-7733
23950 Lake Blvd N Forest Lake (55025) *(G-2150)*
Beverage Wholesalers 320 759-9009
2720 Latoka Ln SW Alexandria (56308) *(G-84)*
Beverly Enterprises - MN 320 843-2225
2209 Utah Ave Benson (56215) *(G-438)*
Beverly Enterprises - MN 952 474-5488
515 Division St Excelsior (55331) *(G-1940)*
Beverly Enterprises - MN 507 334-3918
1738 Hulett Ave Faribault (55021) *(G-1992)*
Beverly Enterprises - MN 507 557-2211
900 3rd St Franklin (55333) *(G-2180)*
Beverly Enterprises - MN 218 583-2965
907 Marshall Ave Henning (56551) *(G-2431)*
Beverly Enterprises - MN 952 935-3338
725 2nd Ave S Hopkins (55343) *(G-2518)*
Beverly Enterprises - MN 507 895-4445
101 S Hill St La Crescent (55947) *(G-2841)*
Beverly Enterprises - MN 952 935-0333
3201 Virginia Ave S Minneapolis (55426) *(G-3894)*
Beverly Enterprises - MN 612 874-1603
2106 2nd Ave S Minneapolis (55404) *(G-3895)*
Beverly Enterprises - MN 952 881-8676
9200 Nicollet Ave S Minneapolis (55420) *(G-3896)*
Beverly Enterprises - MN 612 333-0111
1215 S 9th St Minneapolis (55404) *(G-3897)*
Beverly Enterprises - MN 218 233-7578
2810 Highway 10 E Moorhead (56560) *(G-6299)*
Beverly Enterprises - MN 320 523-1652
1003 W Maple Ave Olivia (56277) *(G-6560)*
Beverly Enterprises - MN 507 451-6800
201 18th St SW Owatonna (55060) *(G-6695)*
Beverly Enterprises - MN 507 288-1818
2215 Highway 52 N Rochester (55901) *(G-7065)*
Beverly Enterprises - MN 320 358-4765
650 Ramer Ave S Rush City (55069) *(G-7389)*
Beverly Enterprises - MN 507 932-3283
525 Bluff Ave Saint Charles (55972) *(G-7402)*
Beverly Enterprises - MN 651 483-5431
2727 Victoria St N Saint Paul (55113) *(G-8111)*
Beverly Enterprises - MN 651 645-6453
471 Lynnhurst Ave W Saint Paul (55104) *(G-8112)*
Beverly Enterprises - MN 507 836-6135
2957 Redwood Ave Slayton (56172) *(G-9485)*

ALPHABETIC

Beverly Enterprises - MN 651 439-5775
313 Greeley St S Stillwater (55082) *(G-9602)*
Beverly Enterprises - MN 507 342-5166
660 Maple St Wabasso (56293) *(G-9776)*
Beverly Enterprises - MN 952 473-5466
15409 Wayzata Blvd Wayzata (55391) *(G-9906)*
Beverly Outpatient Therapy, Walker *Also Called Woodrest Health Care Center (G-9861)*
Bfg Supply Co LLC 612 781-6068
1500 Jackson St NE Minneapolis (55413) *(G-3898)*
BFI Waste Systems of North 763 259-5570
8661 Rendova St NE Circle Pines (55014) *(G-1003)*
BFI Waste Systems of North 612 522-6558
725 44th Ave N Minneapolis (55412) *(G-3899)*
BFI Waste Systems of North 651 437-8101
2795 117th St E South Saint Paul (55077) *(G-9513)*
Bfs Retail Operations LLC 952 432-9212
7660 150th St W Saint Paul (55124) *(G-7719)*
Bgd Co's Inc 612 338-6804
5323 Lakeland Ave N Ste 100 Minneapolis (55429) *(G-3900)*
Bgm-Ceres Environmental Svcs 800 218-4424
3825 85th Ave N Minneapolis (55443) *(G-3901)*
Bhi Advanced Internet Inc 952 361-5557
7599 Corporate Way Eden Prairie (55344) *(G-1605)*
Bi Consulting Group LLC 651 403-6500
860 Blue Gentian Rd # 290 Saint Paul (55121) *(G-7720)*
Bi-County Community Action 218 751-4631
2529 15th St NW Bemidji (56601) *(G-382)*
Bi-Phase Technologies LLC 651 681-4450
2945 Lone Oak Dr Ste 150 Saint Paul (55121) *(G-7721)*
Biesanz Stone Co 507 454-4336
4600 Goodview Rd Winona (55987) *(G-10082)*
Biff's Billiards Sports Bar 763 784-9446
7777 Highway 65 NE Minneapolis (55432) *(G-3416)*
Biffs Boxes LLC 952 403-1221
8610 Hansen Ave Shakopee (55379) *(G-9422)*
Big Ale-Cat 952 881-4128
335 E 78th St Minneapolis (55420) *(G-3902)*
Big Brothers Big Sisters of 651 789-2400
2550 University Ave W Ste 410N Saint Paul (55114) *(G-8113)*
Big Stone Community Homes Inc 320 839-6139
501 Burdick Ave Ortonville (56278) *(G-6578)*
Bigelow Enterprises, Rochester *Also Called Bigelow, Joel & Sons Entrprs (G-7066)*
Bigelow, Joel & Sons Entrprs 507 529-1161
3428 Lakeridge Pl NW Ste A Rochester (55901) *(G-7066)*
Bigelow-Lennon Construction 507 775-7068
211 1st St SW Byron (55920) *(G-822)*
Bigfork Valley Communities, Bigfork *Also Called Northern Itasca Hospital Dist (G-462)*
Bigos Properties 952 938-6329
6860 Excelsior Blvd Ofc Minneapolis (55426) *(G-3903)*
Bigstone Hutterian Brethren 320 748-7916
75217 Big Stone Colony Rd W Graceville (56240) *(G-2252)*
Bii Di Gain Dash Anwebi Elder 651 291-1750
2410 16th Ave S Minneapolis (55404) *(G-3904)*
Billards Street Cafe, Minneapolis *Also Called University Billiards Inc (G-3630)*
Billie Brown Post, Nisswa *Also Called American Legion Post 627 (G-6495)*
Billington Contracting Inc 218 722-1213
2121 W 3rd St Duluth (55806) *(G-1252)*
Billman Construction Inc 218 729-7570
5010 Miller Trunk Hwy Duluth (55811) *(G-1253)*
Bills Gun Shop, Minneapolis *Also Called Lefty's Shooting & Outdoor (G-4854)*
Bingo Carousel 763 493-2111
7324 Lakeland Ave N Ste A Minneapolis (55428) *(G-3905)*
Bingo Emporium 320 252-3607
2820 1st St S Saint Cloud (56301) *(G-7458)*
Bio-Medical Applications of MN 218 624-7787
4700 Mike Colalillo Dr Duluth (55807) *(G-1254)*
Bio-Medical Applications of MN 763 783-0103
9144 Springbrook Dr NW Minneapolis (55433) *(G-3417)*
Biocleaning Specialists, Lake Elmo *Also Called Assured Decontamination Svcs (G-2865)*
Biolife Plasma Services LP 507 344-0300
35 Teton Ln Mankato (56001) *(G-3111)*
Biolife Plasma Services LP 320 259-6300
2019 Stearns Way Saint Cloud (56303) *(G-7459)*
Biomedix Vascular Solutions 651 762-4010
4215 White Bear Pkwy Saint Paul (55110) *(G-8114)*
Bioscrip Pharmacy Inc 952 979-3600
10050 Crosstown Cir Eden Prairie (55344) *(G-1606)*
Birchwood Care Home Inc 612 823-7286
715 W 31st St Minneapolis (55408) *(G-3906)*
Birchwood Health Care Center 651 464-5600
604 1st St NE Forest Lake (55025) *(G-2158)*
Birchwood Lab Associates LLP 952 937-7900
7900 Fuller Rd Eden Prairie (55344) *(G-1607)*
Birchwood Laboratories Inc 952 937-7900
7900 Fuller Rd Eden Prairie (55344) *(G-1608)*
Bird & Cronin Inc 651 683-1111
1200 Trapp Rd Saint Paul (55121) *(G-7722)*
Birkeland & Associates 952 922-1772
5912 W 35th St Ste C Minneapolis (55416) *(G-3907)*
Birthright Inc 507 645-7638
500 Water St S Ste 103 Northfield (55057) *(G-6525)*
Birthright of Austin Inc 507 437-2373
215 4th Ave NE Ste 2 Austin (55912) *(G-263)*
Bishop Communications Corp (DH) 320 274-8201
9938 State Highway 55 NW Annandale (55302) *(G-138)*
Bituminous Materials LLC 507 334-3901
680 24th St NW Faribault (55021) *(G-1993)*
Bituminous Paving Inc 320 273-2113
43153 County Rd 21 Odessa (56276) *(G-6553)*
Bituminous Roadways Inc (PA) 651 686-7001
1520 Commerce Dr Mendota Heights (55120) *(G-3361)*
Bituminous Roadways Inc 612 721-2451
2825 Cedar Ave S Minneapolis (55407) *(G-3908)*
Bituminous Roadways Inc 952 233-1660
6898 Highway 101 E Shakopee (55379) *(G-9423)*
Bix Produce Co LLC 651 487-8000
1415 L Orient St Saint Paul (55117) *(G-8115)*
Bixby Inc 952 448-6520
10455 Jersey Ave Chaska (55318) *(G-956)*
Bizal Mfg Inc 763 571-4030
7880 Ranchers Rd NE Minneapolis (55432) *(G-3418)*
Bjorklund Realty Inc 952 934-0500
5780 Lincoln Dr Ste 300 Edina (55436) *(G-1826)*
Bjornson SENTINEL-E&L, Maple Grove *Also Called Erickson-Larsen Inc (G-3240)*
Bkv Group 612 339-3752
222 N 2nd St Minneapolis (55401) *(G-3909)*
Black Bear Casino, Carlton *Also Called Fond Du Lac Reservation (G-867)*
Black Bear Casino Resort, Carlton *Also Called Fond Dulac Development Corp (G-868)*
Black Box Corp 763 971-6260
7125 Northland Ter N Ste 400 Minneapolis (55428) *(G-3910)*
Black Jack Express & Repair 507 485-3437
330 6th St Wood Lake (56297) *(G-10170)*
Blackberry Ridge Golf Club LLC 320 257-4653
3125 Clubhouse Rd Sartell (56377) *(G-9333)*
Blackforest Developers LLC 612 872-9200
125 W Broadway Ave # 100 Minneapolis (55411) *(G-3911)*
Blainbrook Entertainment Ctr 763 755-8686
12000 Central Ave NE Minneapolis (55434) *(G-3419)*
Blaine Medical Center, Minneapolis *Also Called Multicare Associates of The (G-3547)*
Blake Drilling Co Inc 763 780-9187
10604 Radisson Rd NE Minneapolis (55449) *(G-3420)*
Blaschko Computers Inc 320 252-0234
3290 33rd St S Saint Cloud (56301) *(G-7460)*
Blast Pressure Washing 507 455-2898
206 W Rose St Owatonna (55060) *(G-6696)*
Blm Technologies Inc 763 559-5100
14755 27th Ave N Ste 100 Minneapolis (55447) *(G-3912)*
Block E Lodging LLC 320 258-2580
404 W Saint Germain St Saint Cloud (56301) *(G-7461)*
Blood Marrow Transplant Clinic, Minneapolis *Also Called Fairview Health Services (G-4398)*
Bloomers Garden Center 218 326-0668
1037 Golf Course Rd Grand Rapids (55744) *(G-2270)*
Bloomington Care Center, Minneapolis *Also Called Beverly Enterprises - MN (G-3896)*
Bloomington Cemetery, Minneapolis *Also Called City of Bloomington (G-4084)*
Bloomington Electric Co 952 888-7905
815 American Blvd E Minneapolis (55420) *(G-3913)*
Bloomington Hospitality LLC 763 367-9200
1700 American Blvd E Minneapolis (55425) *(G-3914)*
Bloomington Hotel Acquisition 952 893-9999
7770 Johnson Ave S Minneapolis (55435) *(G-3915)*
Bloomington Lake Clinic Ltd (PA) 612 721-6511
3017 Bloomington Ave Minneapolis (55407) *(G-3916)*
Bloomington Linoleum & Carpet 952 881-5825
9939 Lyndale Ave S Minneapolis (55420) *(G-3917)*
Bloomington Port Authority, Minneapolis *Also Called City of Bloomington (G-4083)*
Bloomngton Lk Clinic Southtown, Minneapolis *Also Called Bloomington Lake Clinic Ltd (G-3916)*
Blower Balancing & Repair, Minneapolis *Also Called Enviromatic Corp of America (G-4362)*
Blu DOT Design & Manufacturing 612 782-1844
1323 Tyler St NE Minneapolis (55413) *(G-3918)*
Blue Cross, Duluth *Also Called Bcbsm Inc (G-1248)*
Blue Cross, Saint Paul *Also Called Bcbsm Inc (G-7712)*
Blue Cross, Saint Paul *Also Called Bcbsm Inc (G-7714)*
Blue Cross & Blue Shield, Saint Paul *Also Called Bcbsm Inc (G-7711)*
Blue Earth Area Mentors 507 526-5219
216 E 11th St Blue Earth (56013) *(G-530)*
Blue Earth Valley Telephone Co 507 787-2222
191 2nd St SE Wells (56097) *(G-9961)*
Blue Green Vacation Corp 888 456-0412
1701 E 79th St Ste 19 Bloomington (55425) *(G-490)*
Blue Note of Winsted Inc 320 485-9698
320 3rd St S Winsted (55395) *(G-10159)*
Blue Ridge Dental 952 938-4767
11601 Minnetonka Mls D Hopkins (55305) *(G-2519)*
Blue Shield, Virginia *Also Called Bcbsm Inc (G-9736)*
Blue Valley Sod, Winnebago *Also Called Weerts Construction Inc (G-10078)*
Blue Valley Sod Co 218 927-4557
39095 Osprey Ave Aitkin (56431) *(G-17)*
Blue Waters Development Corp 800 242-1988
1521 Superior Shores Dr Two Harbors (55616) *(G-9705)*
Blueberry Pines Golf Club 218 564-4657
39161 US 71 Menahga (56464) *(G-3354)*
Blueberry Pines Golf Club Inc 218 564-4653
39161 US 71 Menahga (56464) *(G-3355)*
BLUEFIN RESORT, Tofte *Also Called Tofte Management Co LLC (G-9684)*
Bluegreen Preview Center, Bloomington *Also Called Blue Green Vacation Corp (G-490)*
Bluffview Montessori School 507 452-2807
1321 Gilmore Ave Winona (55987) *(G-10083)*
BNC National Bank, Minneapolis *Also Called Bnccorp Inc (G-3919)*
Bnccorp Inc 612 305-2200
333 S 7th St Ste 200 Minneapolis (55402) *(G-3919)*
Bnr Excavating Inc 651 438-8692
12175 240th St E Hampton (55031) *(G-2363)*
Bnsf Railway Co 218 727-8194
201 S 19th Ave W Duluth (55806) *(G-1255)*
Bnsf Railway Co 651 298-2121
80 44th Ave NE Minneapolis (55421) *(G-3421)*
Bnsf Railway Co 320 259-3208
1715 Breckenridge Ave Saint Cloud (56303) *(G-7462)*
Bnsf Railway Co 651 298-2121
176 5th St E Fl 1112 Saint Paul (55101) *(G-8116)*
Bnsf Railway Co 651 451-1312
1312 Kassan Dr South Saint Paul (55075) *(G-9514)*
Bnsf Railway Co 218 894-1676
10 Eastside Dr Verndale (56481) *(G-9724)*
Bnsf Railway Co 320 231-5555
400 Pacific Ave SW Willmar (56201) *(G-9990)*
Board of Pensions of The 612 333-7651
800 Marquette Ave # 1050 Minneapolis (55402) *(G-3920)*
Boarman Kroos Vogel Group 612 339-3752
222 N 2nd St Ste 2 Minneapolis (55401) *(G-3921)*
Boarmen Kroos Vogel Group, Minneapolis *Also Called Bkv Group (G-3909)*
Boat House Eatery, Nisswa *Also Called Gunsbury Alan Quarterdeck (G-6492)*
Bob Brink Inc 507 452-1568
165 Steuben St Winona (55987) *(G-10084)*

Bob Dahl 218 874-6321
28248 130th Ave NW Newfolden (56738) *(G-6481)*

Bob Fischer Trucking (PA) 507 263-0384
25445 Northfield Blvd Hampton (55031) *(G-2364)*

Bob Lemieur Sons Chrtr Bus Svc, Little Falls *Also Called Robert Lemieur & Sons Inc (G-3018)*

Bob Pankan & Sons Concrete 763 444-5720
27594 Youngston St NE Isanti (55040) *(G-2778)*

Bobbie Stves Auto Wrld Rchfeld, Minneapolis *Also Called Robert A Williams Enterprises (G-3589)*

Bobby & Steve Auto World, Minneapolis *Also Called Robert A Williams Enterprises (G-5551)*

Bobby & Steve's Auto World, Minneapolis *Also Called Robert A Williams Enterprises (G-5552)*

Boeckermann, Grafstrom & Mayer 952 844-2500
7900 Xerxes Ave S # 1200 Minneapolis (55431) *(G-3922)*

Boedecker Co 952 279-5205
1600 Lake Dr W Chanhassen (55317) *(G-910)*

Boeser Inc 612 378-1803
2901 4th St SE Minneapolis (55414) *(G-3923)*

Bogart & Peterson & Associates 763 682-9329
311 Division St W Maple Lake (55358) *(G-3258)*

Bogarts, Saint Paul *Also Called Rich Mgt Inc (G-7895)*

Boiler Services Inc 763 784-8178
10327 Flanders St NE Minneapolis (55449) *(G-3422)*

Boilermakers Local Lodge 650 651 345-5472
100 W Lyon Ave Lake City (55041) *(G-2851)*

Bois Forte Enterprises 218 753-6400
1430 Bois Forte Rd Tower (55790) *(G-9686)*

Bois Forte Medical Clinic 218 757-3650
13071 Nett Lk Nett Lake (55772) *(G-6403)*

Bois Forte Reservation Tribal 218 757-3261
5344 Lakeshore Dr Nett Lake (55772) *(G-6404)*

Boldt Co 218 879-1293
1001 Tall Pine Ln Cloquet (55720) *(G-1047)*

Bolton & Menk Inc (PA) 507 625-4171
1960 Premier Dr Mankato (56001) *(G-3112)*

Bolton & Menk Inc 320 231-3956
2040 Highway 12 E Willmar (56201) *(G-9991)*

Bolton Development Worldwide 952 886-7211
7760 France Ave S Ste 310 Minneapolis (55435) *(G-3924)*

Bone Adventure Inc 612 920-2201
5045 France Ave S Minneapolis (55410) *(G-3925)*

Bonfe's Plumbing & Heating Svc 651 228-7140
505 Randolph Ave Saint Paul (55102) *(G-8117)*

Bonfire Partners LLC 612 455-7400
100 S 5th St Ste 2000 Minneapolis (55402) *(G-3926)*

Bonner Eye Clinic, Grand Rapids *Also Called John L Bonner Eye Clinic Ltd (G-2288)*

Book Sales Inc 732 225-0530
400 1st Ave N Ste 300 Minneapolis (55401) *(G-3927)*

Bookstore At Fitgers, Duluth *Also Called Fitgers On The Lake LLC (G-1325)*

Boos Dental Lab, Minneapolis *Also Called Sentage Corp (G-5638)*

Bor-Son Building Corp 952 854-8444
2001 Killebrew Dr Ste 400 Minneapolis (55425) *(G-3928)*

Bor-Son Construction Inc 952 854-8444
2001 Killebrew Dr Ste 400 Minneapolis (55425) *(G-3929)*

Border Foods Inc 763 323-4731
13057 Round Lake Blvd Anoka (55304) *(G-159)*

Border State Bank 218 782-2151
133 Main St N Greenbush (56726) *(G-2324)*

Border States Cooperative (PA) 320 695-2575
23 4th St N Browns Valley (56219) *(G-626)*

Border States Electric Supply 320 214-4237
1209 Highway 12 E Willmar (56201) *(G-9992)*

Border States Industries Inc 763 425-5500
9100 Wyoming Ave N Ste 550 Brooklyn Park (55445) *(G-606)*

Boreal Energy Inc (PA) 651 762-1200
1058 Centerville Cir Vadnais Heights (55127) *(G-9720)*

Borkon, Ramstead, Mariani 952 546-6000
5401 Gamble Dr Ste 100 Minneapolis (55416) *(G-3930)*

Born Information Services Inc 763 404-4000
6465 Wayzata Blvd Ste 400 Minneapolis (55426) *(G-3931)*

Boser Construction Inc 320 393-3185
7135 5th Ave NE Sauk Rapids (56379) *(G-9359)*

Boss, Minneapolis *Also Called Box Office Service & Sales Inc (G-3935)*

Bossardt Corp 952 837-3346
8300 Norman Center Dr Ste 770 Minneapolis (55437) *(G-3932)*

Boston Health Care Systems Inc 651 501-2378
1865 Old Hudson Rd Saint Paul (55119) *(G-8118)*

Bottom Line Enhancement Svcs 952 974-9920
6520 Edenvale Blvd # 110 Eden Prairie (55346) *(G-1609)*

Bottomline of NC, Eden Prairie *Also Called Apex Analytix Inc (G-1593)*

Boulay Heutmaker Zibell & Co 952 893-9320
7500 Flying Cloud Dr Eden Prairie (55344) *(G-1610)*

Boulevard Collision Inc 763 595-0006
6901 Laurel Ave Minneapolis (55426) *(G-3933)*

Bowl Rite Inc 651 646-1396
1556 University Ave W Saint Paul (55104) *(G-8119)*

Bowling Bob's 13th Frame Pro 763 755-8686
12000 Central Ave NE Minneapolis (55434) *(G-3423)*

Bowman & Brooke LLP (PA) 612 339-8682
150 S 5th St Ste 3000 Minneapolis (55402) *(G-3934)*

Box Office Service & Sales Inc 952 854-2836
9000 Chicago Ave S Minneapolis (55420) *(G-3935)*

Boy Scouts Amer Viking Council, Minneapolis *Also Called Viking Council of The Boy (G-5971)*

Boyer Building Corp 952 475-2097
3435 County Road 101 Minnetonka (55345) *(G-6149)*

Boys & Girls Club of Rochester 507 287-2300
1026 E Center St Rochester (55904) *(G-7067)*

Boys & Girls Clubs of Central 320 252-7616
345 30th Ave N Saint Cloud (56303) *(G-7463)*

Boys & Girls Clubs of The 218 335-8144
208 Central Ave NW Cass Lake (56633) *(G-870)*

BR Motels Inc 320 253-5530
50 Park Ave S Saint Cloud (56301) *(G-7464)*

Braas Co 952 937-8902
7970 Wallace Rd Eden Prairie (55344) *(G-1611)*

Bracketts Crossing Country CLB, Lakeville *Also Called Northern Gopher Enterprises (G-2923)*

Bradley Distributing Co 651 639-0523
1912 Hastings Ave Newport (55055) *(G-6485)*

Bradshaw Group 651 776-1551
1174 Payne Ave Saint Paul (55130) *(G-8120)*

Bradt Resolutions Services, Saint Paul *Also Called Hansen Dordell Bradt Odlaug, (G-8441)*

Braemar Driving Range 952 826-6786
6364 John Harris Dr Minneapolis (55439) *(G-3936)*

Braemar Golf Course Gar Maint, Minneapolis *Also Called City of Edina (G-4087)*

Brain Injury Association of MN 612 378-2742
34 13th Ave NE Ste B001 Minneapolis (55413) *(G-3937)*

Brainerd Bus Lines Inc 218 829-6955
8342 Industrial Park Rd Baxter (56425) *(G-321)*

Brainerd Daily Dispatch, Brainerd *Also Called Morris Communications Corp (G-576)*

Brainerd Manor, Brainerd *Also Called Carefree Living of America (G-556)*

Brainerd Medical Center 218 828-7100
2024 S 6th St Brainerd (56401) *(G-552)*

Brainerd Rgional Humn Svcs Ctr, Brainerd *Also Called Minnesota Department of Human (G-575)*

Brainerd School Distict 181 218 829-0412
311 10th Ave NE Brainerd (56401) *(G-553)*

Brainerd Service Center, Brainerd *Also Called Citi Investor Services Inc (G-557)*

Brainerd Sports & Marine LLC 218 828-4728
13377 State Highway 25 Brainerd (56401) *(G-554)*

Brandl Anderson Homes Inc 952 898-0231
4555 Erin Dr Ste 120 Saint Paul (55122) *(G-7723)*

Brandl Motor Sports 320 632-2908
14873 113th St Little Falls (56345) *(G-3000)*

Brandt Murnane 651 227-9411
30 7th St E Ste 3200 Saint Paul (55101) *(G-8121)*

Braschler's Bakery Inc 651 388-1589
410 W 3rd St Red Wing (55066) *(G-6976)*

Braun Intertec Corp (PA) 952 995-2000
11001 Hampshire Ave S Minneapolis (55438) *(G-3938)*

Braun Intertec Corp 651 487-3245
1826 Buerkle Rd Saint Paul (55110) *(G-8122)*

Brave New Workshop, Minneapolis *Also Called Into The Mystic Productions (G-4731)*

Break-Thru Home Care 612 659-1505
112 N 3rd St Ste 300 Minneapolis (55401) *(G-3939)*

Breck School 763 381-8100
123 Ottawa Ave N Minneapolis (55422) *(G-3940)*

Breckenridge Public Utilities, Breckenridge *Also Called City of Breckenridge (G-593)*

Brede Inc 612 331-4540
2211 Broadway St NE Minneapolis (55413) *(G-3941)*

Bredemus Hardware Co Inc 651 489-6250
1285 Sylvan St Saint Paul (55117) *(G-8123)*

Brehmer Contracting Inc 952 938-1171
10921 Excelsior Blvd Hopkins (55343) *(G-2520)*

Breitbach Construction Co 320 697-5525
802 1st Ave Elrosa (56325) *(G-1909)*

Bremer Bank 320 763-6622
720 Broadway St Alexandria (56308) *(G-85)*

Bremer Bank (DH) 218 829-8781
321 S 7th St Brainerd (56401) *(G-555)*

Bremer Bank 218 847-9292
115 Holmes St E Detroit Lakes (56501) *(G-1189)*

Bremer Bank 763 389-2020
202 La Grande Ave S Princeton (55371) *(G-6903)*

Bremer Bank (DH) 320 251-3300
1100 W Saint Germain St Saint Cloud (56301) *(G-7465)*

Bremer Bank (DH) 800 908-2265
2100 Bremer Tower 445 Saint Paul (55101) *(G-8124)*

Bremer Bank 320 235-1111
500 Willmar Ave SE Willmar (56201) *(G-9993)*

Bremer Bank National Assn 651 451-6822
633 Concord St N South Saint Paul (55075) *(G-9515)*

Bremer Bank, National Assn 507 537-0222
208 E College Dr Marshall (56258) *(G-3291)*

Bremer Financial Corp 320 589-1026
701 Atlantic Ave Morris (56267) *(G-6370)*

Bremer Financial Corp (HQ) 651 227-7621
445 Minnesota St Ste 2000 Saint Paul (55101) *(G-8125)*

Bremer Financial Services Inc 651 734-4040
8555 Eagle Point Blvd # 110 Lake Elmo (55042) *(G-2866)*

Bremer Financial Services Inc (DH) 651 227-7621
445 Minnesota St Ste 2000 Saint Paul (55101) *(G-8126)*

Bremer Trust National Assn 320 252-3918
4150 2nd St S Ste 180 Saint Cloud (56301) *(G-7466)*

Bremmer Bank 320 763-6622
720 Broadway St Alexandria (56308) *(G-86)*

Bremner Food Group Inc 612 331-5908
824 6th Ave SE Minneapolis (55414) *(G-3942)*

Brennaville Inc 507 467-2512
24461 Heron Rd Preston (55965) *(G-6895)*

Brenntag Great Lakes LLC 651 204-4300
2130 Energy Park Dr Saint Paul (55108) *(G-8127)*

Brenny Specialized Inc 320 363-6996
8505 Ridgewood Rd Saint Joseph (56374) *(G-7652)*

Brickman Group Ltd LLC 952 922-8777
7204 W 27th St Ste 221 Minneapolis (55426) *(G-3943)*

Bridge Const Div North, Virginia *Also Called St Louis County Public Works (G-9756)*

Bridge For Youth 612 377-8800
1111 W 22nd St Minneapolis (55405) *(G-3944)*

Bridge House 218 725-7785
221 N 1st Ave W Duluth (55806) *(G-1256)*

Bridges Medical Services, ADA *Also Called Norman County Ambulance Garage (G-2)*

Bridges Medical Services, Ada *Also Called City of Ada (G-1)*

Bridgewater Bancshares Inc (PA) 952 893-6868
3800 Amercn Blvd W # 100 Minneapolis (55431) *(G-3945)*

Bridgz Marketing Group, Minneapolis *Also Called D M I LLC (G-4215)*

Briggs & Morgan Professional 612 977-8400
80 S 8th St Ste 2200 Minneapolis (55402) *(G-3946)*

Briggs & Morgan Professional (PA) 651 223-6600
2200 S Ids Cntr 80 8th St St Minneapolis (55402) *(G-3947)*

Briggs Hennum Inc 218 634-2168
3502 Four Mile Bay Dr NW Baudette (56623) *(G-314)*

Bright Horizons Children's 763 571-2375
500 Medtronic Pkwy Minneapolis (55432) *(G-3424)*

Bright Star Healthcare, Minneapolis *Also Called Align Health Inc (G-3704)*

ALPHABETIC

Brighter Building Maintenance 651 293-1403
444 Pine St Saint Paul (55101) (G-8128)
Brightkeys Building & Devpt 651 501-6500
707 Commerce Dr Ste 410 Saint Paul (55125) (G-9188)
Brim Healthcare Inc 763 546-4801
10820 38th Pl N Minneapolis (55441) (G-3948)
Brin Glass Co (PA) 612 529-9671
2300 N 2nd St Minneapolis (55411) (G-3949)
Bringgold Wholesale Meats, Minneapolis Also Called Schumacher Wholesale Meats Inc (G-5616)
Brings Co Inc 651 484-2666
600 Lakeview Point Dr Saint Paul (55112) (G-8129)
Brink's Inc 763 486-1730
830 Boone Ave N Ste 2 Minneapolis (55427) (G-3950)
Bristow's Inc 320 253-7878
3653 32nd St SE Saint Cloud (56304) (G-7435)
Brite Signs LLC 763 489-3841
13805 1st Ave N Ste 800 Minneapolis (55441) (G-3951)
Brits, Minneapolis Also Called All England Enterprises Ltd (G-3708)
Bro-Tex Co Inc 651 645-5721
800 Hampden Ave Saint Paul (55114) (G-8130)
Broadband America, Corp 952 941-7900
1772 Steiger Lake Ln Victoria (55386) (G-9725)
Broadston Consulting Services 952 442-9770
400 E 10th St Waconia (55387) (G-9779)
Broadway Apartments, Fergus Falls Also Called Colonial Village Apartments (G-2068)
Broadway Equipment, Minneapolis Also Called Auto Butler Inc (G-3836)
Broadway Medical Center Ltd 320 762-0399
1527 Broadway St Alexandria (56308) (G-87)
Broadway Rental Equipment Co 763 533-1680
6800 W Broadway Ave Minneapolis (55428) (G-3952)
Broadway Resource & Recovery 612 623-8888
2301 N 2nd St Minneapolis (55411) (G-3953)
Brock White Co LLC (HQ) 651 647-0950
2575 Kasota Ave Saint Paul (55108) (G-8131)
Broders' Cucina Italiana, Minneapolis Also Called Molly's Inc (G-5119)
Brook Hall Blaine Brook 763 755-8731
12000 Central Ave NE Minneapolis (55434) (G-3425)
Brook West Family Dentistry 763 561-8901
7950 Mainstreet Ste 205 Osseo (55369) (G-6600)
Brookdale Car Wash Inc 763 561-1123
5500 Brooklyn Blvd Minneapolis (55429) (G-3954)
Brookdale Center, Minneapolis Also Called Lansing Mall LP (G-4842)
Brookdale Honda, Minneapolis Also Called R L Brookdale Motors Inc (G-5459)
Brookdale Integrative Health 763 561-4045
5740 Brooklyn Blvd # 100 Minneapolis (55429) (G-3955)
Brookdale Motor Sales Inc 763 561-8161
4301 68th Ave N Minneapolis (55429) (G-3956)
Brookdale Plastics Inc 763 797-1000
9909 S Shore Dr Ste 3 Plymouth (55441) (G-6852)
Brookfield Commercial 612 372-1500
33 S 6th St Ste 4640 Minneapolis (55402) (G-3957)
Brookfield Development Inc 612 372-1230
555 Nicollet Mall Ste 50 Minneapolis (55402) (G-3958)
Brookfield Properties, Minneapolis Also Called Bce Development Corp (G-3876)
Brooklyn Center Motors LLC 763 535-5200
6121 Brooklyn Blvd Minneapolis (55429) (G-3959)
Brooklyn Park Hospitality LLC 763 566-8855
6900 Lakeland Ave N Minneapolis (55428) (G-3960)
Brookman Motor Sales Inc 651 777-1316
11144 Stillwater Blvd N Lake Elmo (55042) (G-2867)
Brookpark Dental Health Center, Minneapolis Also Called Pdhc Ltd (G-5356)
Brookpark Group 763 424-8525
8525 Edinbrook Xing Ste 101 Minneapolis (55443) (G-3961)
Brooks 507 446-5855
2480 Saint Paul Rd Ofc Owatonna (55060) (G-6697)
Brooks Garden Apts, Minneapolis Also Called Reprise Associates (G-5520)
Brookview Golf Course, Minneapolis Also Called Golden Valley, City of Inc (G-4538)
Brothers Fire Protection Co 763 441-2290
9950 Highway 10 Elk River (55330) (G-1864)
Brown & Bigelow Inc (PA) 651 293-7000
345 Plato Blvd E Saint Paul (55107) (G-8132)
Brown & Carlson 763 540-1019
5411 Circle Down 100 Minneapolis (55416) (G-3962)
Brown County Evaluation Center 507 359-9111
510 N Front St New Ulm (56073) (G-6443)
Brown County Probation Dept 507 233-6628
1 S State St New Ulm (56073) (G-6444)
Brown Tank LLC 651 747-0100
6995 55th St N Saint Paul (55128) (G-9189)
Brown Transportation Inc 218 744-2888
7799 N Airport Dr Eveleth (55734) (G-1929)
Brown-Wilbert Inc (PA) 651 631-1234
2280 Hamline Ave N Saint Paul (55113) (G-8133)
Browning-Ferris Industries Inc 651 641-0009
742 Vandalia St Saint Paul (55114) (G-8134)
Browns Valley Health Center 320 695-2165
114 Jefferson St S Browns Valley (56219) (G-627)
Bruce B Cunningham 651 731-0859
8325 City Centre Dr Saint Paul (55125) (G-9190)
Bruce Johnson 218 284-6555
10 4th St N Moorhead (56560) (G-6300)
Bruce Kreofsky & Sons Inc 507 534-3855
865 Enterprise Dr SW Plainview (55964) (G-6839)
Bruegger's Bagel Bakery 651 486-7135
111 Village Center Dr Saint Paul (55127) (G-8135)
Bruggeman Homes Inc 651 770-2981
3564 Rolling View Dr I Saint Paul (55110) (G-8136)
Brunberg Blatt & Co Inc 763 545-2353
5500 Wayzata Blvd Ste 600 Minneapolis (55416) (G-3963)
Bruns Inc 218 757-3232
4539 Highway 53 Orr (55771) (G-6577)
Brunskill Enterprises 763 477-4546
2992 Gabler Ave SE Buffalo (55313) (G-636)
Brunswick Bowling & Billiards 952 941-0445
12200 Singletree Ln Eden Prairie (55344) (G-1612)
Brush Masters Inc 763 478-3232
12955 Highway 55 Minneapolis (55441) (G-3964)
Brutger Equities Inc 218 727-3110
909 Cottonwood Ave Duluth (55811) (G-1257)
Bryanston Group Inc 651 636-6730
2550 Cleveland Ave N Saint Paul (55113) (G-8137)
Bryant House, Maple Plain Also Called Haven Homes Inc (G-3275)
Bryant Square Apartments 612 825-4379
3115 Aldrich Ave S Minneapolis (55408) (G-3965)
Bryant-Lake Bowl, Minneapolis Also Called B L B Inc (G-3852)
Bryn Mawr Health Care Center, Minneapolis Also Called Aviv Health Care Inc (G-3845)
BT Americas Holdings Ltd 651 746-8739
7007 55th St N Saint Paul (55128) (G-9191)
BT Americas Inc 651 746-8590
2665 Long Lake Rd Ste 300 Saint Paul (55113) (G-8138)
Bub's Brewing Co Inc 507 457-3121
65 E 4th St Winona (55987) (G-10085)
Buca Inc 952 892-7272
14300 Burnhaven Dr Burnsville (55306) (G-687)
Buca Inc 612 288-0138
1204 Harmon Pl Ste C Minneapolis (55403) (G-3966)
Buck Hill Inc (PA) 952 435-7174
15400 Buck Hill Rd Burnsville (55306) (G-688)
Budget Exteriors Inc 952 887-1613
8017 Nicollet Ave S Minneapolis (55420) (G-3967)
Budget Towing Inc of St Paul 651 699-5690
1145 Homer St Saint Paul (55116) (G-8139)
Buena Vista 218 728-3533
320 Pinewood Ln Duluth (55804) (G-1258)
Buena Vista Ski Area, Bemidji Also Called Beltrami's Tally Inc (G-376)
Buerkle Buick Leasing Co 651 484-0231
3350 Highway 61 N Saint Paul (55110) (G-8140)
Buff & Shine Center Inc 952 944-9033
10820 Bush Lake Rd Minneapolis (55438) (G-3968)
Buffalo Clinic 763 682-1313
1700 Highway 25 N Buffalo (55313) (G-637)
Buffalo Drycleaners 763 682-1061
213 1st St S Buffalo (55313) (G-638)
Buffalo Hospital, Buffalo Also Called Allina Health System (G-633)
Buffalo Junction 218 624-9901
2500 Guss Rd Duluth (55810) (G-1259)
Buffalo Lodging 763 682-5660
1002 Highway 55 E Buffalo (55313) (G-639)
Buffalo Wild Wings Inc (PA) 952 593-9943
5500 Wayzata Blvd # 1600 Minneapolis (55416) (G-3969)
Bug Co of Minnesota 763 434-0550
15941 Tippecanoe St NE Anoka (55304) (G-160)
Bug Inc 952 445-1022
441 1st Ave W Shakopee (55379) (G-9424)
Build All Installed Inc 218 692-5115
33106 Industrial Rd Crosslake (56442) (G-1150)
Builders & Remodelers Inc 612 827-5481
3517 Hennepin Ave S Minneapolis (55408) (G-3970)
Builders Inc 952 545-3217
8100 Wayzata Blvd Minneapolis (55426) (G-3971)
Building Block Child Care Inc 763 557-1111
16355 36th Ave N Ste 700 Minneapolis (55446) (G-3972)
Building Fasteners of MN (PA) 612 706-3300
2827 Anthony Ln S Minneapolis (55418) (G-3973)
Building Maintenance Mgt 763 541-4886
1724 Douglas Dr N Ste 100 Minneapolis (55422) (G-3974)
Building Material Supply Inc 763 252-5555
2300 Louisiana Ave N Golden Valley (55427) (G-2237)
Building Resources Inc 612 341-1111
2525 E Franklin Ave # 300 Minneapolis (55406) (G-3975)
Bunker Beach, Anoka Also Called County of Anoka (G-170)
Bunn William Masonry Inc 952 292-2685
219 E Frontage Rd Ste F Waconia (55387) (G-9780)
Bunzl USA Inc 763 571-1011
5301 Industrial Blvd NE Minneapolis (55421) (G-3426)
Burchfield Group Inc 651 389-5648
1295 Northland Dr Ste 350 Saint Paul (55120) (G-7724)
Bureau of Collection Recovery (HQ) 952 934-7777
7575 Corporate Way Eden Prairie (55344) (G-1613)
Bureau of Collection Recovery 320 214-8747
1009 16th St SW Willmar (56201) (G-9994)
Burger King, Saint Paul Also Called Duke & King Acquisition Corp (G-9205)
Burke Blackwell 612 343-3200
431 S 7th St Ste 2500 Minneapolis (55415) (G-3976)
Burkel Turkey Farms Inc 218 334-2833
32913 State Highway 87 Frazee (56544) (G-2183)
Burnet Homeselling Team 651 653-2520
4525 White Bear Pkwy # 2 Saint Paul (55110) (G-8141)
Burnet Realty Inc 651 430-2100
2020 Washington Ave S Stillwater (55082) (G-9603)
Burnet Realty LLC (HQ) 952 844-6400
7550 France Ave S Ste 300 Minneapolis (55435) (G-3977)
Burnet Title LLC 952 844-6200
5151 Edina Industrial Blvd Edina (55439) (G-1827)
Burns Manor Nursing Home, Hutchinson Also Called Hutchinson Health Care (G-2701)
Burnsville Center, Burnsville Also Called Ermc II LP (G-719)
Burnsville Commercial Cleaning 952 469-5423
12330 210th St W Lakeville (55044) (G-2893)
Burnsville Development Ltd 952 435-2100
14201 Nicollet Ave Burnsville (55337) (G-689)
Burnsville Family Physicians 952 435-0303
625 E Nicollet Blvd # 100 Burnsville (55337) (G-690)
Burnsville Hockey Club 952 890-2333
75 Civic Center Pkwy Burnsville (55337) (G-691)
Burnsville Volkswagen Inc 952 892-9400
14700 Buck Hill Rd Burnsville (55306) (G-692)
Burrelle's Information Svcs 612 672-9141
12 S 6th St Ste 1150 Minneapolis (55402) (G-3978)
Bus Garage, East Grand Forks Also Called Independent School District (G-1569)
Bus Garage, Luverne Also Called Luverne Ind School Dist 2184 (G-3061)
Bush Memorial Center, Saint Paul Also Called Amherst H Wilder Foundation (G-8043)
Bushel Boy Farms, Owatonna Also Called Vine Ripe Inc (G-6742)

ALPHABETIC

Business Bank 952 847-1100
11100 Wayzata Blvd # 150 Hopkins (55305) ***(G-2521)***
Business Data Record Services 651 631-8663
201 9th Ave SW Saint Paul (55112) ***(G-8142)***
Business Funding Group LLC 952 697-0202
6400 Flying Cloud Dr Eden Prairie (55344) ***(G-1614)***
Business Impact Group LLC 952 278-7800
2411 Galpin Ct Ste 120 Chanhassen (55317) ***(G-911)***
Business Microvar Inc 651 639-0575
2277 Highway 36 W Ste 300 Saint Paul (55113) ***(G-8143)***
Butler Brothers Enterprises 651 554-9888
10730 Briggs Dr Ste C Inver Grove Heights (55077) ***(G-2739)***
Buttweiler Environmental Inc 320 251-4385
250 Sundial Dr Ste 1 Waite Park (56387) ***(G-9818)***
Buy Best Purchasing LLC 612 291-1000
7601 Penn Ave S Richfield (55423) ***(G-7034)***
Buyonlinenow Inc 507 281-6899
4865 19th St NW Ste 110 Rochester (55901) ***(G-7068)***
Bwbr Architects Inc 651 222-3701
380 Saint Peter St Ste 600 Saint Paul (55102) ***(G-8144)***
Bystrom Precision Industries 952 929-6888
7500 W 27th St Minneapolis (55426) ***(G-3979)***
C & B Operations LLC 507 375-3144
County Rd 57 W Saint James (56081) ***(G-7642)***
C & C Business Solutions 612 875-9488
2409 W 140th St Burnsville (55337) ***(G-693)***
C & D Granite Inc 320 597-2398
767 1st St SE Richmond (56368) ***(G-7040)***
C & G Construction Inc of 218 776-3080
Hwy 5 Lot 4INDUSTRIAL Par Clearbrook (56634) ***(G-1036)***
C & G Holding Co of Clearbrook 218 776-3080
Hwy 5 N Lot 4 Indus Park Clearbrook (56634) ***(G-1037)***
C & R Ross Inc 763 545-7347
2732 Quebec Ave N Minneapolis (55427) ***(G-3980)***
C & S Vending Co Inc 507 334-8414
1919 2nd St NW Faribault (55021) ***(G-1994)***
C A P Scott-Carver-Dakota Inc 952 496-2125
712 Canterbury Rd S Shakopee (55379) ***(G-9425)***
C B C A, Minneapolis *Also Called Loge Group LLC* ***(G-4899)***
C B Richard Ellis Inc 952 278-2106
4400 McRthur Blvd Ste 600 Minneapolis (55439) ***(G-3981)***
C C C I, Melrose *Also Called Commercial Contractors Co of* ***(G-3348)***
C C C T Inc 952 844-0004
5000 W 78th St Minneapolis (55435) ***(G-3982)***
C C R Inc 218 236-6730
725 Center Ave Ste 7 Moorhead (56560) ***(G-6301)***
C C Sharrow Co Inc 651 489-1341
301 County Road E2 W Saint Paul (55112) ***(G-8145)***
C D Haugen Inc 218 751-2738
5049 Scribner Rd NW Bemidji (56601) ***(G-383)***
C E C Entertainment Inc 952 892-7786
1025 Burnsville Ctr Burnsville (55306) ***(G-694)***
C F Haglin & Sons Inc 952 920-6123
3939 W 69th St Minneapolis (55435) ***(G-3983)***
C H I Mnnplis Nat Oprtions Ctr, Minneapolis *Also Called Catholic Health Initiatives* ***(G-4031)***
C H Robinson Worldwide Inc (PA) 952 937-8500
14701 Charlson Rd Eden Prairie (55347) ***(G-1615)***
C H S, South Saint Paul *Also Called CHS Inc* ***(G-9521)***
C H Suites of Chanhassen MN 952 937-2424
591 W 78th St Chanhassen (55317) ***(G-912)***
C J Duffey Paper Co (PA) 612 338-8701
528 Washington Ave N Minneapolis (55401) ***(G-3984)***
C J Olson Market Research 612 378-5040
901 N 3rd St Ste 218 Minneapolis (55401) ***(G-3985)***
C J'S Home Health Care Inc 320 833-2253
114 Church Ave W Buffalo Lake (55314) ***(G-662)***
C L T Floor Coverings Inc 651 451-0069
8731 Alverno Ave Inver Grove Heights (55077) ***(G-2740)***
C M I, Minneapolis *Also Called Construction Midwest Inc* ***(G-4156)***
C M M, Blue Earth *Also Called Central Minnesota Municipal* ***(G-531)***
C N A Financial Corp 952 285-3300
12044 Gantry Ln 1404 Saint Paul (55124) ***(G-7725)***
C O Brown Agency Inc 507 288-7600
2048 Superior Dr NW # 100 Rochester (55901) ***(G-7069)***
C P P North America LLC 952 541-5800
5100 Gamble Dr Ste 600 Minneapolis (55416) ***(G-3986)***
C R C, Austin *Also Called Cooperative Response Center* ***(G-267)***
C R C, Minneapolis *Also Called Commercial Recovery Corp* ***(G-3438)***
C R Fischer & Sons Inc 651 463-7300
3240 220th St W Farmington (55024) ***(G-2042)***
C S Aero-Space Inc 952 884-4725
9270 Bryant Ave S Minneapolis (55420) ***(G-3987)***
C U Mortgage Services Inc 651 631-3111
500 Main St Ste 100 Saint Paul (55112) ***(G-8146)***
C W F Solutions, Little Canada *Also Called Contingent Work Force Soln* ***(G-2995)***
C W Houle Inc 651 484-6077
1300 County Road I W Saint Paul (55126) ***(G-8147)***
C W Logistics LLC 651 209-6814
2985 Commerce Dr Eagan (55121) ***(G-1518)***
C-1 Holdings LLC 651 994-6800
3344 Highway 149 Eagan (55121) ***(G-1519)***
C-ME Marketing Inc 320 587-6565
150 Michigan St SE Hutchinson (55350) ***(G-2690)***
Ca Inc 952 838-1186
7760 France Ave S Ste 500 Minneapolis (55435) ***(G-3988)***
Cabela's Inc 763 493-8600
20200 Rogers Dr Rogers (55374) ***(G-7318)***
Cabinets By Choice Inc 952 924-8958
3300 Gorham Ave Minneapolis (55426) ***(G-3989)***
Cable Connection & Supply Co 507 334-6417
1505 30th St NW Faribault (55021) ***(G-1995)***
Cac Retail Inc 952 944-5600
6436 City West Pkwy Eden Prairie (55344) ***(G-1616)***
Cafe Della Vita, Minneapolis *Also Called Life Time Fitness Inc* ***(G-4878)***
Calabrio Inc 763 592-4600
605 Highway 169 N Ste 800 Minneapolis (55441) ***(G-3990)***
Calco Sprouts Inc 612 724-0276
2751 Minnehaha Ave Minneapolis (55406) ***(G-3991)***
Caledonia Haulers LLC 507 725-9000
420 W Lincoln St Caledonia (55921) ***(G-826)***
Calhoun Beach Club of 612 927-9951
2925 Dean Pkwy Ste 300 Minneapolis (55416) ***(G-3992)***
Calhoun Shores Apartments 612 824-7505
3101 E Calhoun Pkwy # 107 Minneapolis (55408) ***(G-3993)***
California Closet Co, Minneapolis *Also Called C C C T Inc* ***(G-3982)***
Calix Networks Inc 763 268-3300
16305 36th Ave N Ste 300 Minneapolis (55446) ***(G-3994)***
Callista Court, Winona *Also Called Benedictine Health System* ***(G-10080)***
Calmar Group Inc 952 440-8834
17226 Horizon Trl SE Prior Lake (55372) ***(G-6929)***
Camas Inc 507 357-4929
260 W Derrynane St Ste 103 Le Center (56057) ***(G-2949)***
Cambridge Medical Center, Cambridge *Also Called Memorial Hospital Association* ***(G-842)***
Cambridge Medical Center, Cambridge *Also Called Allina Health System* ***(G-831)***
Cambridge Nursing Home Inc 763 689-2323
548 1st Ave W Cambridge (55008) ***(G-835)***
Camco Construction Inc 320 259-1051
3201 Bent Tree Dr Saint Cloud (56301) ***(G-7467)***
Camden Physicians Ltd 612 876-9700
4209 Webber Pkwy Minneapolis (55412) ***(G-3995)***
Camden Physicians Ltd 763 420-5822
12000 Elm Creek Blvd N # 13 Osseo (55369) ***(G-6601)***
Camden Physicians Ltd 763 235-4900
9800 Rockford Rd Ste 100 Plymouth (55442) ***(G-6853)***
Camera Shop of Saint Cloud Inc 320 251-2622
25 7th Ave S Ste 200 Saint Cloud (56301) ***(G-7468)***
Camilia Rose Convalescent Ctr, Minneapolis *Also Called Rose Camilia Co Inc* ***(G-3592)***
Camp Buckskin 218 365-2121
9830 Fredrickson Rd Isabella (55607) ***(G-2776)***
Camp Buckskin Inc 952 930-3544
4124 Quebec Ave N Ste 300 Minneapolis (55427) ***(G-3996)***
Camp Courage, Maple Lake *Also Called Courage Center* ***(G-3259)***
Camp Du Nord, Ely *Also Called Ymc Camp Dunord* ***(G-1918)***
Camp Greenwood Girl Scout 763 684-4243
100 Garrison Ave NE Buffalo (55313) ***(G-640)***
Camp New Hope Inc 218 426-3560
53035 Lake Ave McGregor (55760) ***(G-3338)***
Camp Onamia Inc 320 532-3767
14202 Shakopee Lake Rd Onamia (56359) ***(G-6567)***
Camp Shamineau of The 218 575-2240
2345 Ridge Rd Motley (56466) ***(G-6383)***
Camp Snoopy, Minneapolis *Also Called Moa Entertainment Co LLC* ***(G-5114)***
Camp Widji Wagan 218 365-2117
3788 N Arm Rd Ely (55731) ***(G-1912)***
Camp Wigwagen, Saint Paul *Also Called YMCA of Greater Saint Paul* ***(G-9175)***
Camp Wilderness Bsa Inc 218 732-4674
29984 Journey Trl Park Rapids (56470) ***(G-6748)***
Campbell Mithun Inc (HQ) 612 347-1000
222 S 9th St Ste 2100 Minneapolis (55402) ***(G-3997)***
Campbells Cabins & Trading 218 993-2361
7540 Gold Coast Rd Crane Lake (55725) ***(G-1116)***
Campground Marketing Services 218 562-4204
9252 Breezy Point Dr Pequot Lakes (56472) ***(G-6786)***
Camping World Inc 763 428-7779
21200 Rogers Dr Rogers (55374) ***(G-7319)***
Canadian Border Outfitters Inc 218 365-5847
14635 Canadian Border Rd Ely (55731) ***(G-1911)***
Canadian National, Saint Paul *Also Called Wisconsin Central Ltd* ***(G-9161)***
Canadian Pacific Ltd 612 781-7284
615 30th Ave NE Minneapolis (55418) ***(G-3998)***
Canadian Pacific Railroad 320 634-3307
20 15th St NE Glenwood (56334) ***(G-2220)***
Canadian Pacific Railway, Minneapolis *Also Called SOO Line Railroad Co Inc* ***(G-5701)***
Canadian Pacific Railway, Minneapolis *Also Called Soo Line Corp* ***(G-5700)***
Canal Park Lodge 218 279-6000
250 Canal Park Dr Duluth (55802) ***(G-1260)***
Canal Properties Inc 218 720-3000
310 Canal Park Dr Duluth (55802) ***(G-1261)***
Canam Theatres Moa LLC 952 883-8810
60 E Broadway Bloomington (55425) ***(G-491)***
Canard Aerospace Corp 952 944-7990
250 Fuller St S Ste 201 Shakopee (55379) ***(G-9426)***
Canby Community Hospital Dist 507 223-7277
112 Saint Olaf Ave S Canby (56220) ***(G-848)***
Canby Conerned Citizens 507 223-7061
409 1st St E Canby (56220) ***(G-849)***
Cannon Falls Medical Center 507 263-4221
1116 Mill St W Cannon Falls (55009) ***(G-855)***
Cannon Technologies Inc 763 595-7777
505 Highway 169 N Ste 1200 Minneapolis (55441) ***(G-3999)***
Cannon Valley Clinic 507 266-2620
924 1st St NE Faribault (55021) ***(G-1996)***
Cannon Valley Clinic Mayo 507 333-3300
924 St NE Faribault (55021) ***(G-1997)***
Canteen Vending 651 488-0515
1091 Pierce Butler Rte Saint Paul (55104) ***(G-8148)***
Canterbury Collision, Shakopee *Also Called Shakopee Chevrolet Inc* ***(G-9473)***
Canterbury Park Holding Corp 952 445-7223
1100 Canterbury Rd S Shakopee (55379) ***(G-9427)***
Cap Agency, Shakopee *Also Called C A P Scott-Carver-Dakota Inc* ***(G-9425)***
Cap Real Estate 651 488-5567
954 Minnehaha Ave W Saint Paul (55104) ***(G-8149)***
Capernaum Pediatric Therapy 612 922-2009
7250 France Ave S Ste 305 Edina (55435) ***(G-1828)***
Capernaum Pediatric Therapy 952 938-5348
13924 Lake Street Ext Hopkins (55345) ***(G-2522)***
Capital Beverage Sales Ltd 651 298-0800
6982 Highway 65 NE Minneapolis (55432) ***(G-3427)***
Capital City Travel Inc 651 287-4906
340 Cedar St Ste 1200 Saint Paul (55101) ***(G-8150)***
Capital Express Inc 651 631-3595
601 Campus Dr Ste 12 Saint Paul (55112) ***(G-8151)***
Capital Granite & Marble Inc 320 259-7625
25325 Hwy 23 Saint Cloud (56301) ***(G-7469)***

ALPHABETIC

(PA)=Parent Co (HQ)=Headquarters (DH)=Div Headquarters
2011 Harris Minnesota Services Directory
© Harris InfoSource 1-866-281-6415
547

Capital Maintenance Services 651 773-9777
3065 Spruce St Saint Paul (55117) *(G-8152)*

Capital Wood Products Co 651 225-5613
735 Olive St Saint Paul (55130) *(G-8153)*

Capitol Beverage Sales LP 763 571-4115
6982 Highway 65 NE Minneapolis (55432) *(G-3428)*

Capitol Co's Inc 651 454-4511
1270 Eagan Industrial Rd Ste 1 Saint Paul (55121) *(G-7726)*

Capitol Lien Records & Res (PA) 651 488-0100
1010 Dale St N Saint Paul (55117) *(G-8154)*

Capitol Sales Co Inc 651 688-6830
1245 Trapp Rd Ste 130 Saint Paul (55121) *(G-7727)*

Capstone Services LLC 651 641-0042
1410 Energy Park Dr # 10 Saint Paul (55108) *(G-8155)*

Captionmax Inc 612 341-3566
2438 27th Ave S Minneapolis (55406) *(G-4000)*

Carbide Tool Services Inc 763 421-2210
1020 Lund Blvd Anoka (55303) *(G-161)*

Card Protection Plan, Minneapolis *Also Called C P P North America LLC* *(G-3986)*

Cardenas & Reynolds Entrprs 651 222-7200
391 Pleasant Ave Saint Paul (55102) *(G-8156)*

Cardinal Health 200 Inc 763 323-9666
9000 109th Ave N Champlin (55316) *(G-890)*

Cardinal Health 414 Inc 651 645-9904
1045 Westgate Dr Ste 100 Saint Paul (55114) *(G-8157)*

Cardinal Health Inc 763 398-8321
17400 Medina Rd Minneapolis (55447) *(G-4001)*

Cardinal Health Inc 651 255-1383
1933 County Rd 2 C Saint Paul (55113) *(G-8158)*

Cardinal of Minnesota Ltd 507 281-1077
3008 Wellner Dr NE Rochester (55906) *(G-7070)*

Cardinal Pointe of Oakdale 651 578-0650
1201 Hadley Ave N Saint Paul (55128) *(G-9192)*

Cardiodiagnostics Inc 651 292-0616
225 Smith Ave N Ste 500 Saint Paul (55102) *(G-8159)*

Cardiovascular Consultants Ltd 763 520-2000
3300 Oakdale Ave N Ste 200 Minneapolis (55422) *(G-4002)*

Care 2000 Home Healthcare Svcs 218 736-0246
119 E Lincoln Ave Ste 103 Fergus Falls (56537) *(G-2064)*

Care Corner 507 386-7444
265 Saint Andrews Dr Mankato (56001) *(G-3113)*

Care Institute Inc 651 482-1611
2750 Victoria St N Ofc Saint Paul (55113) *(G-8160)*

Care Network Inc 651 647-5400
2161 University Ave W # 203 Saint Paul (55114) *(G-8161)*

Care Planners Inc 651 645-9887
1919 University Ave W # 114 Saint Paul (55104) *(G-8162)*

Care Plus H H A Inc 763 529-5520
4050 Olson Memorial Hwy Minneapolis (55422) *(G-4003)*

Care Transportation Inc 320 253-7729
2600 7th St N Saint Cloud (56303) *(G-7470)*

Care TV 763 546-1111
8811 Olson Memorial Hwy Minneapolis (55427) *(G-4004)*

Carecall, Sartell *Also Called Array Services Group Inc (G-9331)*

CareCall Inc 320 253-0800
200 14th Ave E Sartell (56377) *(G-9334)*

Carefacts Information Systems 651 636-3890
2140 County Road C W Saint Paul (55113) *(G-8163)*

Carefree Living of America 952 988-0011
2723 Oak St Brainerd (56401) *(G-556)*

Carefree Services Inc 763 479-2600
5541 Industrial Blvd Maple Plain (55359) *(G-3271)*

Carefusion 203 Inc (HQ) 763 398-8300
17400 Medina Rd Ste 100 Minneapolis (55447) *(G-4005)*

Caregivers's Network Inc 952 935-5581
10709 Wayzata Blvd Ste 300 Hopkins (55305) *(G-2523)*

Caremate Home Health Care Inc 651 659-0208
2236 Marshall Ave Saint Paul (55104) *(G-8164)*

Cargill Financial Services (PA) 952 742-7575
12700 Whitewater Dr Hopkins (55343) *(G-2524)*

Cargill Financial Services Int 952 742-7575
405 2nd Ave SE Minneapolis (55414) *(G-4006)*

Cargill Freshwater 952 742-3050
2500 Shadywood Rd Excelsior (55331) *(G-1941)*

Cargill Inc 763 262-1900
20021 176th St NW Big Lake (55309) *(G-445)*

Cargill Inc 218 727-1594
250 Garfield Ave Duluth (55802) *(G-1262)*

Cargill Inc 763 441-3330
10383 165th Ave NW Elk River (55330) *(G-1865)*

Cargill Inc 763 441-6508
10383 165th Ave NW Elk River (55330) *(G-1866)*

Cargill Inc 952 984-8280
12800 Whitewater Dr # 300 Hopkins (55343) *(G-2525)*

Cargill Inc 952 984-3377
9350 Excelsior Blvd Hopkins (55343) *(G-2526)*

Cargill Inc 612 367-3000
7650 Edinbrgh Way Ste 600 Minneapolis (55435) *(G-4007)*

Cargill Inc 763 742-5512
15407 Mc Ginty Rd Minneapolis (55440) *(G-4008)*

Cargill Inc 952 984-3890
12700 Whtwater Dr Fl 2 Minneapolis (55440) *(G-4009)*

Cargill Inc 952 742-4417
15407 McGnty Rd W Ms 20 Minneapolis (55440) *(G-4010)*

Cargill Inc 763 497-2157
12900 Whtwater Dr MS109 109 Ms Minneapolis (55440) *(G-4011)*

Cargill Inc 952 742-7575
12900 Whitewater Dr Minnetonka (55343) *(G-6150)*

Cargill Inc 952 742-6437
2301 Crosby Rd Wayzata (55391) *(G-9907)*

Cargill Inc 763 742-7237
15407 McGinty Rd W Wayzata (55391) *(G-9908)*

Cargill Inc 952 742-7575
156151 McGinty Rd W Wayzata (55391) *(G-9909)*

Cargill Power Markets LLC 952 984-3068
12700 Whitewater Dr Minnetonka (55343) *(G-6151)*

Caribou Highlands, Lutsen *Also Called Townhomes At Lutsen Mountains (G-3058)*

Caring Companions, Saint Paul *Also Called Olafson, Renae (G-8780)*

Caring Hands Home Care Inc 218 732-0088
602 1st St E Park Rapids (56470) *(G-6749)*

Caring Hands Home Care Inc (PA) 218 837-5572
113 Minnesota Ave W Sebeka (56477) *(G-9414)*

Caritas Debt Counseling 320 650-1660
911 18th St N Saint Cloud (56303) *(G-7471)*

Caritas Family Services, Saint Cloud *Also Called Diocese of St Cloud (G-7499)*

Carl Bolander & Sons Co (PA) 651 224-6299
251 Starkey St Ste 1 Saint Paul (55107) *(G-8165)*

Carl Crosby Lehmann 612 632-3000
80 S 8th St Ste 500 Minneapolis (55402) *(G-4012)*

Carl Hanson Drywall Inc 763 753-4112
19580 Camarack St Cedar (55011) *(G-874)*

Carlson & Lyter Distributing 218 829-2978
13394 Dogwood Dr Baxter (56425) *(G-322)*

Carlson & Lyter Distributing (PA) 320 251-7375
1020 Industrial Dr S Sauk Rapids (56379) *(G-9360)*

Carlson Building Maintenance 651 481-9970
1857 Buerkle Rd Saint Paul (55110) *(G-8166)*

Carlson Co's Inc 763 212-5253
1405 Xenium Ln N Minneapolis (55441) *(G-4013)*

Carlson Highland Co LLP 218 739-3267
403 S Union Ave Fergus Falls (56537) *(G-2065)*

Carlson Holdings Inc (PA) 763 212-5000
701 Carlson Pkwy Minnetonka (55305) *(G-6152)*

Carlson Hospitality Worldwide 763 540-5035
701 Carlson Pkwy Minnetonka (55305) *(G-6153)*

Carlson Hotels LP (DH) 763 212-1000
Carlson Parkway 701 Twr St Minneapolis (55459) *(G-4014)*

Carlson Hotels Management Corp 612 339-4900
35 S 7th St Minneapolis (55402) *(G-4015)*

Carlson Hotels Management Corp 763 212-5000
701 Tower Carlson Pike Minneapolis (55459) *(G-4016)*

Carlson Hotels Worldwide Inc 763 212-5000
Carlson Parkway 701 Tower St Minneapolis (55459) *(G-4017)*

Carlson Marketing Worldwide 763 449-3704
12805 Highway 55 Ste 311 Minneapolis (55441) *(G-4018)*

Carlson Real Estate Co, A MN 952 404-5050
301 Carlson Pkwy Ste 100 Minnetonka (55305) *(G-6154)*

Carlson Timber Products Inc 320 245-2920
53778 Fir Ln Sandstone (55072) *(G-9319)*

Carlson Tractor & Equipment Co 651 423-2222
15125 S Robert Trl Rosemount (55068) *(G-7364)*

Carlson Travel Group Inc 651 406-6000
1250 Northland Dr Ste 200 Saint Paul (55120) *(G-7728)*

Carlson, Lundquist & Co Ltd 763 535-8150
7101 Northland Cir N Minneapolis (55428) *(G-4019)*

Carlson-Lavine Inc 651 638-9600
2965 Partridge Rd Saint Paul (55113) *(G-8167)*

Carlton County Fair Assn 218 389-6737
Front St Barnum (55707) *(G-306)*

Carlwood Family Center, Red Wing *Also Called Independent School District (G-6986)*

Carman Berry Farm 218 631-4613
19168 145th Ave Wadena (56482) *(G-9799)*

Carmike Cinemas Inc 763 785-1855
2430 Highway 10 Saint Paul (55112) *(G-8168)*

Carnahan City-Wide Insulation 952 445-1387
1725 3rd Ave W Shakopee (55379) *(G-9428)*

Carnegie, Dale Training, Minneapolis *Also Called Michael D Norman & Associates (G-5015)*

Carolyn A Adrianse 507 386-7444
501 Holly Ln Ste 150 Mankato (56001) *(G-3114)*

Carpe Diem Medical Inc 507 399-0262
2492 Albion Ave Fairmont (56031) *(G-1959)*

Carpenter & Torgerson II LLC 507 536-0040
161 13th Ave SW Rochester (55902) *(G-7071)*

Carpentry Contractors Corp 763 658-4000
1791 Estes Ave SW Waverly (55390) *(G-9902)*

Carpet Factory Outlet Inc 612 988-0400
6363 Highway 7 Minneapolis (55416) *(G-4020)*

Carquest Auto Parts, New Ulm *Also Called Palmer's Auto Supply Inc (G-6472)*

Carrier Commercial 763 231-8300
6325 Sandburg Rd Ste 800 Minneapolis (55427) *(G-4021)*

Carrousel Travel, Minneapolis *Also Called Outdoor Adventure Travel Inc (G-5300)*

Carrs Tree Service Inc 218 367-3355
307 Mn Highway 78 S Ottertail (56571) *(G-6686)*

Cartika Medical Inc 763 545-5188
9909 S Shore Dr Ste 5 Minneapolis (55441) *(G-4022)*

Cartridge Care Inc 612 331-7757
2256 Terminal Rd Saint Paul (55113) *(G-8169)*

Carver County Agricultural Soc 952 442-2333
501 W 3rd St Waconia (55387) *(G-9781)*

Carver Lake Veterinary Center 651 578-3290
2201 Ventura Dr Saint Paul (55125) *(G-9193)*

Carver-Scott Cooperative 952 445-7524
792 Canterbury Rd S Ste 231 Shakopee (55379) *(G-9429)*

Casa De Esperanza 651 646-5553
1821 University Ave W Saint Paul (55104) *(G-8170)*

Cascade Mortgage Inc 612 252-3333
2801 Hennepin Ave Minneapolis (55408) *(G-4023)*

Casey & Groesbeck Construction, Owatonna *Also Called SA Woods Inc (G-6735)*

Cash Pass Network 952 358-7080
181 S River Ridge Cir Burnsville (55337) *(G-695)*

Cash Plus Inc 612 347-6900
222 S 9th St Ste 2100 Minneapolis (55402) *(G-4024)*

Cash Register Sales Inc 651 294-2700
4851 White Bear Pkwy Saint Paul (55110) *(G-8171)*

Cashill Spaulding Properties 651 225-8227
616 Lincoln Ave Apt MGR Saint Paul (55102) *(G-8172)*

Casker Machines, Minneapolis *Also Called Wise Greenwald & Greenwald PC (G-6080)*

Caspar Inc 507 842-5978
36694 190th St Brewster (56119) *(G-604)*

Cass County Child Support Svcs, Walker *Also Called County of Cass (G-9849)*

Casserly Molzahn & Assoc Inc 952 885-1298
8000 Norman Center Dr Ste 1000 Minneapolis (55437) *(G-4025)*

Cassidy Turley Midwest Inc 612 341-4444
200 S 6th St Ste 1400 Minneapolis (55402) *(G-4026)*

Castle Danger LP	218 728-8060
2230 London Rd Ste 100 Duluth (55812) *(G-1263)*	
Castle Realty Inc	320 251-1010
720 8th Ave N Saint Cloud (56303) *(G-7472)*	
Castle Ridge Care Center, Eden Prairie Also Called Twin City Christian Homes Inc *(G-1799)*	
Castrejon Inc	763 450-2055
9201 Isanti St NE Minneapolis (55449) *(G-3429)*	
Catalog Marketing Services (PA)	651 636-6265
6300 Shingle Creek Pkwy Minneapolis (55430) *(G-4027)*	
Catco, Saint Paul Also Called Clutch & Transmission Service *(G-8217)*	
Catco, Saint Paul Also Called Clutch & Transmission Service *(G-8218)*	
Caterpillar, Minneapolis Also Called Ziegler Inc *(G-6117)*	
Caterpillar, Rochester Also Called Ziegler Inc *(G-7298)*	
Caterpillar, Shakopee Also Called Ziegler Inc *(G-9482)*	
Caterpillar Paving Products	763 712-3000
8700 109th Ave N Ste 410 Champlin (55316) *(G-891)*	
Cathedral Hill Homes LP	651 291-1750
268 Dayton Ave Saint Paul (55102) *(G-8173)*	
Catholic Aid Association	651 490-0170
3499 Lexington Ave N # 201 Saint Paul (55126) *(G-8174)*	
Catholic Charities of The (PA)	218 739-9325
4D East Dr Fergus Falls (56537) *(G-2066)*	
Catholic Charities of The (PA)	612 664-8500
1200 2nd Ave S Minneapolis (55403) *(G-4028)*	
Catholic Charities of The	612 529-9107
1000 Plymouth Ave N Minneapolis (55411) *(G-4029)*	
Catholic Charities of The	612 827-6241
1121 E 46th St Minneapolis (55407) *(G-4030)*	
Catholic Charities of The (PA)	320 650-1550
911 18th St N Saint Cloud (56303) *(G-7473)*	
Catholic Charities of The	320 251-8811
1726 7th Ave S Saint Cloud (56301) *(G-7474)*	
Catholic Charities of The	320 259-8757
205 7th Ave N Saint Cloud (56303) *(G-7475)*	
Catholic Charities of The	651 641-1180
1276 University Ave W Saint Paul (55104) *(G-8175)*	
Catholic Charities of The	651 222-3001
215 Old 6th St W Saint Paul (55102) *(G-8176)*	
Catholic Charities of The	507 454-2270
111 Market St Ste 2 Winona (55987) *(G-10086)*	
Catholic Charities of The Dioc	320 240-3337
1730 7th Ave S Saint Cloud (56301) *(G-7476)*	
Catholic Health Initiatives	952 324-9010
7650 Edinbrgh Way Ste 200 Minneapolis (55435) *(G-4031)*	
Catholic Services For The	651 793-2100
200 Earl St Saint Paul (55106) *(G-8177)*	
Catholic Youth Camp	651 636-1645
2131 Fairview Ave N Ste 200 Saint Paul (55113) *(G-8178)*	
Cato Construction Inc	952 736-8134
6707 Highway 13 W Savage (55378) *(G-9384)*	
Catton Wolseth Como & Jacobs	320 253-4778
1500 Northway Dr Saint Cloud (56303) *(G-7477)*	
Causeway & Gull Associates	218 963-3675
8087 Lost Lake Rd Lake Hubert (56468) *(G-2879)*	
CB & L Inc	651 257-8047
11580 Lake Ln Chisago City (55013) *(G-988)*	
CB Richard Ellis Inc	952 924-4600
7760 France Ave S Ste 770 Minneapolis (55435) *(G-4032)*	
Cbc 202 LP	651 291-1750
21001 John Milless Dr Ofc Rogers (55374) *(G-7320)*	
CBS Radio Inc	612 339-1029
625 2nd Ave S Ste 550 Minneapolis (55402) *(G-4033)*	
CC & I Engineering Inc	218 346-3600
150 2nd St SW Perham (56573) *(G-6795)*	
CC Holdings Inc	612 371-8008
712 Ontario Ave W Ste 200 Minneapolis (55403) *(G-4034)*	
CDI Central Florida LLC	952 543-6500
5775 Wayzata Blvd Ste 400 Minneapolis (55416) *(G-4035)*	
CDI Corp	507 282-8773
400 S Broadway Ste 203 Rochester (55904) *(G-7072)*	
CDI Corp	320 251-0609
166 19th St S Ste 100 Sartell (56377) *(G-9335)*	
Ceco Concrete Construction DE	763 434-4637
15924 Lincoln St NE Anoka (55304) *(G-162)*	
Ceda Inc	763 434-4403
15830 Lincoln St NE Anoka (55304) *(G-163)*	
Cedar Crest Estate	320 587-7077
225 Shady Ridge Rd NW Hutchinson (55350) *(G-2691)*	
Cedar East Bethel Lions	763 434-8323
18440 Jackson St NE Cedar (55011) *(G-875)*	
Cedar Fair, LP	952 445-7600
1 Valleyfair Dr Shakopee (55379) *(G-9430)*	
Cedar Lake Electric Inc	507 334-9546
20700 Bagley Ave Faribault (55021) *(G-1998)*	
Cedar Ridge Inc	651 426-8983
320 2nd Ave SE Apt 405 Minneapolis (55414) *(G-4036)*	
Cedar Towing & Auction Inc	612 721-6645
359 Hoover St NE Minneapolis (55413) *(G-4037)*	
Cedar Valley Conservation Club	507 433-4937
Hwy 218 N Austin (55912) *(G-264)*	
Cedar Valley Golf Course Inc	507 457-3241
County Rd 9 Winona (55987) *(G-10087)*	
Cedar Valley Services Inc	507 373-6064
1839 SE Broadway Ave Albert Lea (56007) *(G-42)*	
Cedar Valley Services Inc	507 377-2893
2205 Myers Rd Albert Lea (56007) *(G-43)*	
Cedar Valley Services Inc (PA)	507 433-2303
2111 4th St NW Austin (55912) *(G-265)*	
Cedar Valley Services Inc	507 451-5897
415 N Grove Ave Owatonna (55060) *(G-6698)*	
Cedar-Riverside People's Ctr	612 332-4973
425 20th Ave S Minneapolis (55454) *(G-4038)*	
Cedars of Austin	507 437-3246
700 1st Dr NW Austin (55912) *(G-266)*	
Cedars of Edina Apartments	952 835-3388
7340 Gallagher Dr Ste 1 Minneapolis (55435) *(G-4039)*	
Ceiling Pro Interior Inc	952 947-0007
7456 Washington Ave S Ste A Eden Prairie (55344) *(G-1617)*	

Celebrities Unlimited Inc	651 482-9945
5825 Oxford St N Saint Paul (55126) *(G-8179)*	
Cellco Partnership	763 595-5102
2510 Mendelssohn Ave N Minneapolis (55427) *(G-4040)*	
Celleration Inc	952 224-8700
10250 Valley View Rd # 137 Eden Prairie (55344) *(G-1618)*	
Cellular One, Baxter Also Called American Cellular Corp *(G-319)*	
Cellular One, Duluth Also Called American Cellular Corp *(G-1238)*	
Cemstone Products Co	651 645-0769
2058 Energy Park Dr Saint Paul (55108) *(G-8180)*	
Cemstone Products Co	651 774-7575
1520 Minnehaha Ave E Saint Paul (55106) *(G-8181)*	
Cenaiko Expo Inc	763 755-8111
9697 E River Rd NW Minneapolis (55433) *(G-3430)*	
Cenex, Alexandria Also Called Farmers Union Oil Co of *(G-100)*	
Cenex, Bemidji Also Called Bemidji Cooperative Assn *(G-379)*	
Cenex, Red Lake Falls Also Called Red Lake County Cooperative *(G-6973)*	
Cenex Inc	800 232-3639
5500 Cenex Dr South Saint Paul (55077) *(G-9516)*	
Cenex Nuway Co Op Inc	507 375-4291
620 2nd Ave S Trimont (56176) *(G-9693)*	
Cenex Petro Serve, Moorhead Also Called Farmers Union Oil Co of *(G-6315)*	
Cenneidigh Inc	507 334-4347
402 Heritage Pl Faribault (55021) *(G-1999)*	
Centennial House of Apple Val	952 891-2711
14625 Pennock Ave Apt C1 Saint Paul (55124) *(G-7729)*	
Centennial Independent School	763 792-6120
4707 North Rd Circle Pines (55014) *(G-1004)*	
Centennial Independent School (PA)	763 792-6000
4707 North Rd Circle Pines (55014) *(G-1005)*	
Centennial Lakes Dental Group	952 831-2800
7373 France Ave S Ste 500 Minneapolis (55435) *(G-4041)*	
Centennial Villa Apartments	320 274-3737
660 Park St E Annandale (55302) *(G-139)*	
Center City Housing Corp	218 722-7161
105 1/2 W 1st St Duluth (55802) *(G-1264)*	
Center For Alcohol & Drug	218 723-8444
1402 E Superior St Duluth (55805) *(G-1265)*	
Center For Alcohol & Drug	218 723-8444
1025 London Rd Ste 1 Duluth (55802) *(G-1266)*	
Center For Applied Research	612 624-0300
159 Pillsbury Dr SE # 275 Minneapolis (55455) *(G-4042)*	
Center For Diagnostic Imaging, Saint Louis Park Also Called Minnesota Medical Scanning *(G-7667)*	
Center For Independent Living	218 262-6675
2104 6th Ave E Hibbing (55746) *(G-2439)*	
Center For Pain Management	320 230-7788
166 19th St S Ste 101 Sartell (56377) *(G-9336)*	
Center For Personal Fitness	218 725-5400
402 E 2nd St Duluth (55805) *(G-1267)*	
Center For Rehab & Wellness	507 455-7631
903 S Oak Ave Owatonna (55060) *(G-6699)*	
Center For Sexual Health, Minneapolis Also Called Program In Human Sexuality *(G-5423)*	
Center For Specialty Care, Fairmont Also Called Fairmont Orthopedics & Sports *(G-1965)*	
Center For Urban Rgnal Affairs, Minneapolis Also Called Regents of The University of *(G-5499)*	
Center For Victims of Torture (PA)	612 436-4800
717 E River Pkwy Minneapolis (55455) *(G-4043)*	
Center For Victims of Torture	612 436-4800
2356 University Ave W # 430 Saint Paul (55114) *(G-8182)*	
Center National Bank	320 693-3255
301 N Ramsey Ave Litchfield (55355) *(G-2980)*	
Center On Resid SVC&comm Lvng, Minneapolis Also Called Regents of The University of *(G-5501)*	
Centerpoint, Minneapolis Also Called Motivations For Fitness Inc *(G-5138)*	
Centerpoint Energy Houston	763 757-6200
9320 Evergreen Blvd NW B Minneapolis (55433) *(G-3431)*	
Centerpoint Energy Resources	612 861-8450
501 W 61st St Minneapolis (55419) *(G-4044)*	
Centerpoint Energy Resources	612 372-4720
800 Lasalle Ave Fl 16 Minneapolis (55402) *(G-4045)*	
Centerpoint Energy Resources	651 554-3000
201 Concord Exc N Ste 100 South Saint Paul (55075) *(G-9517)*	
Centex Homes Inc	952 936-7833
12701 Whitewater Dr Ste 300 Minnetonka (55343) *(G-6155)*	
Centracare Clinic	320 732-2131
24 9th St SE Long Prairie (56347) *(G-3037)*	
Centracare Clinic	320 256-4228
525 W Main St Melrose (56352) *(G-3345)*	
Centracare Clinic	320 654-3630
1900 Centracare Cir Saint Cloud (56303) *(G-7478)*	
Centracare Clinic	320 251-1775
1520 Whitney Ct Saint Cloud (56303) *(G-7479)*	
Centracare Clinic (PA)	320 252-5131
1200 6th Ave N Saint Cloud (56303) *(G-7480)*	
Centracare Health Services of	320 732-2131
20 9th St SE Long Prairie (56347) *(G-3038)*	
Centracare Health System	320 256-4231
525 W Main St Melrose (56352) *(G-3346)*	
Centracare Health System	320 251-2700
1406 6th Ave N Saint Cloud (56303) *(G-7481)*	
Centraire Heating & Air Condg	952 941-1044
7402 Washington Ave S Eden Prairie (55344) *(G-1619)*	
Central Allied Enterprises Inc	320 235-5846
605 Lakeland Dr NE Willmar (56201) *(G-9995)*	
Central Bakery, Eden Prairie Also Called Lund Food Holdings Inc *(G-1713)*	
Central Bank	507 498-5589
126 W Main St Spring Grove (55974) *(G-9560)*	
Central Bank (PA)	651 439-3050
2270 Frontage Rd W Stillwater (55082) *(G-9604)*	
Central Boiler Inc	218 782-2575
20502 160th St Greenbush (56726) *(G-2325)*	
Central Car Wash, Minneapolis Also Called Cin-Mar Corp *(G-4075)*	
Central Ctr For Fmly Resources, Fridley Also Called Lee Carlson Center For Mental *(G-2193)*	
Central Florida Lending, Minneapolis Also Called Minnesota Lending Co LLC *(G-5080)*	
Central Group Management Co	320 654-6307
215 Park Ave S Ste 200 Saint Cloud (56301) *(G-7482)*	
Central Health Care Of Le Ctr	507 357-2275
444 N Cordova Ave Le Center (56057) *(G-2950)*	

A L P H A B E T I C

Central Lakes Lodging LLC ... 218 828-0629
7818 Excelsior Rd Baxter (56425) (G-323)

Central Lakes Medical Clinic ... 218 546-8375
318 E Main St Crosby (56441) (G-1145)

Central Mesabi Medical Center, Hibbing *Also Called Range Regional Health Services* (G-2473)

Central Minnesota Diagnostic ... 320 983-6300
150 10th St NW Milaca (56353) (G-3374)

Central Minnesota Emergency ... 320 255-5657
1406 6th Ave N Saint Cloud (56303) (G-7483)

Central Minnesota Erdc Inc ... 320 202-0992
570 1st St SE Saint Cloud (56304) (G-7408)

Central Minnesota Federal (PA) ... 320 256-3669
20 S 4th Ave E Melrose (56352) (G-3347)

Central Minnesota Group Health ... 320 253-5220
1245 15th St N Saint Cloud (56303) (G-7484)

Central Minnesota Jobs ... 763 271-3715
106 Pine St Ste 2 Monticello (55362) (G-6266)

Central Minnesota Mental ... 763 682-4400
308 12th Ave S Ste 1 Buffalo (55313) (G-641)

Central Minnesota Mental (PA) ... 320 252-5010
1321 13th St N Saint Cloud (56303) (G-7485)

Central Minnesota Municipal (PA) ... 507 526-2193
459 S Grove St Blue Earth (56013) (G-531)

Central Minnesota Task Force (PA) ... 320 251-7203
44 28th Ave N Ste E Saint Cloud (56303) (G-7486)

Central Minnesota Task Force ... 320 252-1603
511th Ave N Saint Cloud (56303) (G-7487)

Central Minnesota Task Force ... 320 253-6900
500 11th Ave N Saint Cloud (56303) (G-7488)

Central Minnesota Task Force ... 320 252-1603
511th Ave N Saint Cloud (56303) (G-7489)

Central Motors ... 651 674-7017
5660 392nd St North Branch (55056) (G-6499)

Central Office, Saint Paul *Also Called Metropolitan Council, MN* (G-8645)

Central Parking Inc ... 612 340-9025
81 S 9th St Ste 445 Minneapolis (55402) (G-4046)

Central Pediatrics, Saint Paul *Also Called Daniel P Khoury* (G-9200)

Central Portfolio Control Inc ... 952 944-5440
6640 Shady Oak Rd Ste 300 Eden Prairie (55344) (G-1620)

Central Power Distributors Inc (PA) ... 763 576-0901
3801 Thurston Ave NW Anoka (55303) (G-164)

Central Regional Pathology Lab ... 651 264-1611
1875 Woodwinds Dr Ste 220 Saint Paul (55125) (G-9194)

Central Research Laboratories, Red Wing *Also Called Dover Fluid Management Inc* (G-6978)

Central Roofing Co ... 763 572-0660
4550 Main St NE Minneapolis (55421) (G-3432)

Central Specialties, Alexandria *Also Called Starry Construction Co Inc* (G-123)

Central Specialties Inc ... 320 762-7289
6325 County Road 87 SW Alexandria (56308) (G-88)

Central Territorial of The ... 218 722-7934
215 S 27th Ave W Duluth (55806) (G-1268)

Central Territorial of The ... 612 332-5855
900 N 4th St Minneapolis (55401) (G-4047)

Central Territorial of The ... 507 288-3663
20 1st Ave NE Rochester (55906) (G-7073)

Central Territorial of The ... 651 646-2601
1471 Como Ave Saint Paul (55108) (G-8183)

Central Todd County Care Ctr ... 218 756-3636
406 Highway 71 E Clarissa (56440) (G-1033)

Central Turf Farms ... 651 464-2130
13655 Lake Dr NE Forest Lake (55025) (G-2144)

Central Valley Cooperative (PA) ... 507 451-1230
900 30th Pl NW Owatonna (55060) (G-6700)

Central Wood Products ... 763 753-7374
19801 Highway 65 NE Cedar (55011) (G-876)

Central-Mcgowan Inc ... 320 252-5292
123 Roosevelt Rd Saint Cloud (56301) (G-7490)

Centrax Enterprises Inc ... 612 726-9500
4300 Glumack Dr Saint Paul (55111) (G-7958)

Centre Electric Inc ... 320 352-0160
43543 County Road 17 Sauk Centre (56378) (G-9342)

Centro Cultural Chicano ... 612 874-1412
1915 Chicago Ave Minneapolis (55404) (G-4048)

Centrol Inc ... 218 584-5107
102 Main Ave E Twin Valley (56584) (G-9701)

Centrol Inc Cottonwood, MN ... 507 423-5423
90 W Main Cottonwood (56229) (G-1111)

Century 21 Care Realty ... 763 862-5690
8016 64th Ave N Minneapolis (55428) (G-4049)

Century 21 Jay Blank Realty ... 651 645-5581
1255 Larpenteur Ave E Saint Paul (55109) (G-8184)

Century 21 Luger Realty Inc ... 952 925-3901
4536 France Ave S Minneapolis (55410) (G-4050)

Century Construction Co Inc ... 651 451-1020
820 Concord St N Ste 101 South Saint Paul (55075) (G-9518)

Century Systems Inc ... 651 426-0975
2182 4th St Saint Paul (55110) (G-8185)

Cenveo Inc ... 651 645-0251
2520 Como Ave Saint Paul (55108) (G-8186)

Cerenity Care Ctr On Dlwood Pl, Saint Paul *Also Called Healtheast Care System* (G-8457)

Cerenity Sr Care Center ... 651 232-6000
724 19th Ave N South Saint Paul (55075) (G-9519)

Ceres Caribe Ceres Environ ... 800 218-4424
3825 85th Ave N Minneapolis (55443) (G-4051)

Ceridian Corp (HQ) ... 952 853-8100
3311 E Old Shakopee Rd Minneapolis (55425) (G-4052)

Cernick Enterprises ... 651 552-9005
6710 Cahill Ave Inver Grove Heights (55076) (G-2741)

Certes Financial Professionals ... 952 345-4140
5500 Wayzata Blvd Ste 910 Golden Valley (55416) (G-2238)

Ceva Freight LLC ... 651 675-4000
3169 Dodd Rd Eagan (55121) (G-1520)

CF Industries Inc ... 651 437-6191
5300 Pine Bend Trl Rosemount (55068) (G-7365)

CFC Technology Corp ... 763 235-5300
2600 Fernbrook Ln N # 138 Minneapolis (55447) (G-4053)

CH Robinson International Inc (HQ) ... 952 937-8500
8100 Mitchell Rd Ste 200 Eden Prairie (55344) (G-1621)

CH Robinson International Inc ... 952 937-2914
14800 Charlson Rd Ste 400 Eden Prairie (55347) (G-1622)

Chad Monson Excavating LLC ... 320 995-6703
7600 Highway 71 S Willmar (56201) (G-9996)

Chalich Trucking Inc ... 763 421-1095
8049 146th Ave NW Anoka (55303) (G-165)

Chamber Trill Public Transit ... 320 983-5064
535 8th St NE Milaca (56353) (G-3375)

Chamberlain Oil Co Inc ... 320 843-3434
112 Grace Ave Clontarf (56226) (G-1045)

Champion Auto Store, Lakeville *Also Called Grove Cottage Auto Parts Inc* (G-2942)

Champion Coatings ... 952 707-9000
7385 W 126th St Savage (55378) (G-9385)

Champion Service Corp ... 651 731-9137
6043 Hudson Rd Ste 375 Woodbury (55125) (G-10171)

Champlin Dental Center, Champlin *Also Called Pdhc Ltd* (G-897)

Chandler Exhibits Inc ... 651 389-5900
13523 Hudson Rd S Afton (55001) (G-8)

Chandler Place ... 612 788-7321
3701 Chandler Dr NE Ofc Minneapolis (55421) (G-6124)

Changs Inc ... 763 442-9080
3833 Ewing Ave S Minneapolis (55410) (G-4054)

Chanhassen Theatre LLC ... 952 934-1500
501 W 78th St Chanhassen (55317) (G-913)

Channel 12 ... 763 533-8196
6900 Winnetka Ave N Minneapolis (55428) (G-4055)

Chapel View Care Ctr Aprtments, Hopkins *Also Called Augustana Chapel View Homes* (G-2512)

Chapelwood Community ... 763 493-5910
16500 92nd Ave N Apt 109 Osseo (55311) (G-6602)

Chapin Enterprises Inc ... 320 235-4386
320 Becker Ave SW Willmar (56201) (G-9997)

Chard Tiling & Excavating Inc ... 952 873-6152
26239 State Highway 25 Belle Plaine (56011) (G-372)

Charles R Babst ... 218 722-8377
3617 W Arrowhead Rd Duluth (55811) (G-1269)

Charles Schwab & Co Inc ... 952 835-6784
7400 France Ave S Ste 100 Minneapolis (55435) (G-4056)

Charles Schwab & Co Inc ... 651 222-8600
401 Robert St N Saint Paul (55101) (G-8187)

Charles Schwab & Co Inc ... 952 404-0398
130 Lake St W Wayzata (55391) (G-9910)

Charles Stout ... 651 426-1671
4525 White Bear Pkwy Saint Paul (55110) (G-8188)

Charter Communications ... 888 438-2427
3993 Heritage Pl NW Rochester (55901) (G-7074)

Charter Solutions Inc ... 763 230-6100
3033 Campus Dr Ste 160 Plymouth (55441) (G-6854)

Charterhouse Inc ... 507 266-8572
211 2nd St NW Ofc Rochester (55901) (G-7075)

Charthouse International ... 952 890-1800
221 S River Ridge Cir Burnsville (55337) (G-696)

Chas A Bernick Inc ... 320 252-6441
801 Sundial Dr Waite Park (56387) (G-9819)

Chaska Medical Center (PA) ... 952 448-2050
3000 N Chestnut St Ste 120 Chaska (55318) (G-957)

Chaska Town Course, Chaska *Also Called City of Chaska* (G-959)

Chateau Nursing Home, Minneapolis *Also Called Beverly Enterprises - MN* (G-3895)

Checker Machine Inc ... 763 544-5000
2701 Nevada Ave N Minneapolis (55427) (G-4057)

Checkpoint Security ... 952 227-5353
4250 Norex Dr Waconia (55387) (G-9782)

Checkpoint Security Systems ... 952 942-9431
8180 Upland Cir Chanhassen (55317) (G-914)

Checkpoint Systems Inc ... 952 943-3853
8180 Upland Cir Chanhassen (55317) (G-915)

Checkpoint Systems Inc ... 952 227-5350
4250 Norex Dr Chaska (55318) (G-958)

Chemical Dependency, Stillwater *Also Called Human Services Inc* (G-9623)

Chemical Engineering Dev Assn, Anoka *Also Called Ceda Inc* (G-163)

Chem Vestments Inc ... 952 469-4965
8287 214th St W Lakeville (55044) (G-2894)

Cheney LLC ... 763 559-1980
14025 23rd Ave N Ste A Minneapolis (55447) (G-4058)

Cherished Wings Transportation ... 763 221-8788
2121 S 9th St Apt 315 Minneapolis (55404) (G-4059)

Cherne Co Inc (PA) ... 952 944-4300
9855 W 78th St Ste 400 Eden Prairie (55344) (G-1623)

Cherokee Bancshares Inc (PA) ... 651 227-7071
607 Smith Ave S Saint Paul (55107) (G-8189)

Cherokee Manufacturing Inc (PA) ... 651 451-6568
501 Richmond St E South Saint Paul (55075) (G-9520)

Cherokee State Bank ... 651 290-6112
607 Smith Ave S Saint Paul (55107) (G-8190)

Chesley Truck Sales Inc ... 651 636-3400
370 Quail Rd Saint Paul (55110) (G-9195)

Chester E Groth Music Co ... 952 884-4772
8056 Nicollet Ave S Minneapolis (55420) (G-4060)

Chestnut & Cammbrone, Prof ... 612 339-7300
222 S 9th St Ste 3700 Minneapolis (55402) (G-4061)

Chevrolet, North Branch *Also Called Central Motors* (G-6499)

Chevron USA Inc ... 651 905-5700
2600 Eagan Woods Dr # 300 Saint Paul (55121) (G-7730)

Chevy's, Mankato *Also Called Chevys Inc* (G-3115)

Chevys ... 952 814-9555
2251 Killebrew Dr Minneapolis (55425) (G-4062)

Chevys Inc ... 507 345-1446
119 S Front St Mankato (56001) (G-3115)

Chex Systems Inc ... 651 361-2000
7805 Hudson Rd Ste 100 Saint Paul (55125) (G-9196)

Chez Daniel, Minneapolis *Also Called Tri City Enterprises Inc* (G-5851)

Chianti Grill ... 651 644-2808
1611 Larpenteur Ave W Saint Paul (55113) (G-8191)

Chicago Tube & Iron Co of MN ... 651 454-6800
2940 Eagandale Blvd Saint Paul (55121) (G-7731)

ALPHABETIC

www.HarrisInfo.com
550
2011 Harris Minnesota Services Directory
(G-00000) Company's Geographic Section entry number

Chief's Service Inc 952 881-6404
8610 Harriet Ave S Minneapolis (55420) *(G-4063)*
Chief's Towing Inc 952 888-2201
8610 Harriet Ave S Minneapolis (55420) *(G-4064)*
Child Care Choices Inc 320 251-5081
2901 Clearwater Rd Saint Cloud (56301) *(G-7491)*
Child Care Resource & Referral 507 287-2020
126 Woodlake Dr SE Rochester (55904) *(G-7076)*
Child Dev Ctr Head Start, Saint Paul *Also Called Community Action Partnership (G-8236)*
Children's Beginnings, Rochester *Also Called Knowledge Learning Corp (G-7155)*
Children's Center 507 373-7979
605 James Ave Albert Lea (56007) *(G-44)*
Children's Country Day School 651 454-4000
1588 Victoria Rd S Saint Paul (55118) *(G-7732)*
Children's Discovery Learning (PA) 651 653-9871
3665 Talmage Cir Saint Paul (55110) *(G-8192)*
Children's Health Care Inc 952 930-8600
6050 Clearwater Dr Hopkins (55343) *(G-2527)*
Children's Health Care Inc 952 930-8630
5950 Clearwater Dr # 500 Hopkins (55343) *(G-2528)*
Children's Health Care Inc (PA) 612 813-6100
2525 Chicago Ave Minneapolis (55404) *(G-4065)*
Children's Health Care Inc 651 232-6800
1825 Woodwinds Dr Saint Paul (55125) *(G-9197)*
Children's Health Care Inc 651 220-6000
345 Smith Ave N Saint Paul (55102) *(G-8193)*
Children's Health Care Inc 651 855-2800
2910 Centre Pointe Dr Saint Paul (55113) *(G-8194)*
Children's Home Society 651 228-7707
235 Marshall Ave Saint Paul (55102) *(G-8195)*
Children's Home Society 651 646-7771
1605 Eustis St Saint Paul (55108) *(G-8196)*
Children's Hospital, Minneapolis *Also Called Fairview Health Services (G-4400)*
Children's Mental Health Svcs 218 327-4886
35382 US Highway 2 Grand Rapids (55744) *(G-2271)*
Children's Respiratory 612 863-3226
2530 Chicago Ave Ste 400 Minneapolis (55404) *(G-4066)*
Children's Theatre Co 612 874-0500
2400 3rd Ave S Minneapolis (55404) *(G-4067)*
Children's World, Saint Paul *Also Called Knowledge Learning Corp (G-8550)*
Childrens Home Society Minn, Detroit Lakes *Also Called Becker County Human Services (G-1187)*
Childrens Hsptals Clinics Minn, Hopkins *Also Called Children's Health Care Inc (G-2528)*
Childrens World Learning Ctr, Minneapolis *Also Called Knowledge Learning Corp (G-4817)*
Childrens World Lrng Ctr 246, Saint Paul *Also Called Knowledge Learning Corp (G-7818)*
Childrens World Lrng Ctr 608, Minneapolis *Also Called Knowledge Learning Corp (G-4816)*
Chin Leeann Inc 952 890-9012
1132 Highway 13 E Burnsville (55337) *(G-697)*
Chin Yuen Silver Fox Inn Inc 763 295-4000
1114 Cedar St Monticello (55362) *(G-6267)*
Chippewa County-Montevideo 320 269-8877
824 N 11th St Montevideo (56265) *(G-6244)*
Chisago Lakes Achievement Ctr 651 257-6709
11685 Lake Blvd Chisago City (55013) *(G-989)*
Chisago Lakes Golf Estates Inc 651 257-1484
12975 292nd St Lindstrom (55045) *(G-2968)*
Chisago Lakes Lanes, Chisago City *Also Called CB & L Inc (G-988)*
Chisholm Health Center 218 254-5765
321 6th St NE Ste 1 Chisholm (55719) *(G-995)*
Chisholm-Hibbing Airport 218 262-3451
11038 Highway 37 Ste 12 Hibbing (55746) *(G-2440)*
Choice Communications Inc 651 230-7127
6808 13th Ave S Minneapolis (55423) *(G-4068)*
Choice Connections LLP 507 524-4583
15503 State Highway 22 Mapleton (56065) *(G-3282)*
Choice Inc 952 446-1475
8801 Wildwood Ave Saint Bonifacius (55375) *(G-7399)*
Choice Unlimited Inc 218 724-5869
1829 E Superior St Duluth (55812) *(G-1270)*
Choice Wood Co, Minneapolis *Also Called CNM Inc (G-4115)*
Choices For Children Inc 952 935-3515
1011 1st St S Ste 315 Hopkins (55343) *(G-2529)*
Choices Psychotherapy Ltd 952 544-6806
715 Florida Ave S Ste 307 Minneapolis (55426) *(G-4069)*
Chomonix Golf Course, Circle Pines *Also Called County of Anoka (G-1008)*
Chosen Valley Care Center Inc 507 867-4220
1102 Liberty St SE Chatfield (55923) *(G-986)*
Chrestomathy Inc 952 974-0339
7465 Eden Prairie Rd Eden Prairie (55346) *(G-1624)*
Chris Electronics Distributors 651 631-2647
2023 County Road C2 W Saint Paul (55113) *(G-8197)*
Chris Jensen Nursing Home, Duluth *Also Called St Louis, County of Inc (G-1463)*
Christ's Household of Faith (PA) 651 265-3400
355 Marshall Ave Saint Paul (55102) *(G-8198)*
Christ's Household of Faith 651 602-5600
23 Empire Dr Saint Paul (55103) *(G-8199)*
Christensen Farms & Feedlots (PA) 507 794-5310
23971 County Road 10 Sleepy Eye (56085) *(G-9492)*
Christensen Farms Midwest LLC 507 794-5310
23971 County Road 10 Sleepy Eye (56085) *(G-9493)*
Christensen Group Inc 952 653-1000
11100 Bren Rd W Ste A Hopkins (55343) *(G-2530)*
Christian Grandview Home 763 689-1474
135 Fern St N Cambridge (55008) *(G-836)*
Christian Life Church 651 463-4545
6300 212th St W Farmington (55024) *(G-2043)*
Christians Inc 952 470-2001
1480 Park Rd Chanhassen (55317) *(G-916)*
Christiansen Industrial 218 751-4663
2805 Washington Ave SE Bemidji (56601) *(G-384)*
Christianson Bus Service Inc 218 863-7000
Hwy 59 S Pelican Rapids (56572) *(G-6776)*
Christofersen Meats Co (PA) 612 721-4411
2700 26th Ave S Minneapolis (55406) *(G-4070)*
Christopher & Banks Co 763 551-5000
2400 Xenium Ln N Plymouth (55441) *(G-6855)*
Christopher J Fallert MD 651 731-4300
1099 Helmo Ave N Ste 100 Oakdale (55128) *(G-6549)*
Christopher Maclennan 612 243-3302
2 Merrden Crssngs Ste 450 Minneapolis (55423) *(G-4071)*
Christopherson, John 952 814-7185
8009 34th Ave S Minneapolis (55425) *(G-4072)*
Chromatic Concepts, Co 763 566-1118
2730 Nevada Ave N Minneapolis (55427) *(G-4073)*
Chronimed Inc (HQ) 952 979-3600
10050 Crosstown Cir Eden Prairie (55344) *(G-1625)*
Chrysalis Center, Minneapolis *Also Called Tubman (G-5863)*
CHS Inc 507 238-8900
1833 130th St Fairmont (56031) *(G-1960)*
CHS Inc (PA) 651 355-6000
5500 Cenex Dr Inver Grove Heights (55077) *(G-2742)*
CHS Inc 507 345-2253
2020 S Riverfront Dr Mankato (56001) *(G-3116)*
CHS Inc 651 306-8088
11600 Courthouse Blvd South Saint Paul (55077) *(G-9521)*
Chuck E Cheese's, Burnsville *Also Called C E C Entertainment Inc (G-694)*
Chum, Duluth *Also Called Churches United In Ministry (G-1271)*
Church of Our Lady of The Lake 952 472-1284
2385 Commerce Blvd Mound (55364) *(G-6384)*
Church of St Bernard 651 488-6733
1160 Woodbridge St Saint Paul (55117) *(G-8200)*
Church of St Matthew 651 224-9793
490 Hall Ave Saint Paul (55107) *(G-8201)*
Church of The Nativity of The 952 881-8160
9901 E Bloomington Fwy Minneapolis (55420) *(G-4074)*
Churches United In Ministry 218 720-6521
102 W 2nd St Duluth (55802) *(G-1271)*
Chyrsalis of Kandiyohi County 320 231-1480
1208 9th St SE Willmar (56201) *(G-9998)*
Ciattis Italian Restaurant, Burnsville *Also Called Superior Concepts Inc (G-804)*
Ciber Inc 507 280-9267
2222 18th Ave NW Ste 100 Rochester (55901) *(G-7077)*
Cigna Behavioral Health Inc 952 996-2000
11095 Viking Dr Ste 350 Eden Prairie (55344) *(G-1626)*
CIMA LABS Inc (HQ) 952 947-8700
10000 Valley View Rd Eden Prairie (55344) *(G-1627)*
Cimarron Park, Lake Elmo *Also Called Hometown America LLC (G-2873)*
Cin-Mar Corp 612 781-6924
1814 Central Ave NE Minneapolis (55418) *(G-4075)*
Cindy Day Care 651 688-7678
1996 Chipmunk Ct Saint Paul (55122) *(G-7733)*
Cinedigm Digital Cinema Corp 320 654-6578
4140 Thielman Ln Ste 304 Saint Cloud (56301) *(G-7492)*
Cinema Entertainment Corp 218 729-0334
4351 Stebner Rd Duluth (55811) *(G-1272)*
Cinema Entertainment Corp 218 529-1636
4191 Haines Rd Duluth (55811) *(G-1273)*
Cinemark U S A Inc 507 625-1929
1850 Adams St Ste 15 Mankato (56001) *(G-3117)*
Cineplex Odean Corp 763 591-5921
9900 Shelard Pkwy Minneapolis (55441) *(G-4076)*
Cintas Corp 763 588-2701
2306 Washington Ave N Minneapolis (55411) *(G-4077)*
Cintas Corp No 2 ....763 425-6666
11500 95th Ave N Osseo (55369) *(G-6603)*
Circle of Life Home Care 612 871-2474
1433 E Franklin Ave # 12 Minneapolis (55404) *(G-4078)*
Circle R Ranch Inc 320 547-2176
9 Miles East On Hwy 27 Long Prairie (56347) *(G-3039)*
CIT, Saint Paul *Also Called Computer Integration Techs (G-9198)*
Citgo, Austin *Also Called McK of Austin Ltd (G-282)*
Citi Investor Services Inc 218 825-5000
7651 Universal Dr Baxter (56425) *(G-324)*
Citi Investor Services Inc 218 829-4781
14221 Golf Course Rd Baxter (56425) *(G-325)*
Citi Investor Services Inc 218 825-0552
823 Maple St Brainerd (56401) *(G-557)*
Cities Electric Inc 651 463-3810
3100 225th St W Farmington (55024) *(G-2044)*
Citifinancial Credit Co 763 424-6012
8036 Brooklyn Blvd Minneapolis (55445) *(G-4079)*
Citigroup Derivatives Markets 952 475-5500
130 Cheshire Ln Ste 202 Hopkins (55305) *(G-2531)*
Citigroup Global Markets Inc 612 349-4800
333 S 7th St Ste 2600 Minneapolis (55402) *(G-4080)*
Citigroup Global Markets Inc 651 215-8400
345 Saint Peter St Ste 1800 Saint Paul (55102) *(G-8202)*
Citigroup Inc 952 942-9880
7825 Washington Ave S Minneapolis (55439) *(G-4081)*
Citireach International 952 975-0516
7340 Hunters Run Eden Prairie (55346) *(G-1628)*
Citizens Bancshares of 320 587-2233
102 Main St S Hutchinson (55350) *(G-2692)*
Citizens Bank & Trust Co 320 587-2233
102 Main St S Hutchinson (55350) *(G-2693)*
Citizens Bank Minnesota 507 354-3165
105 N Minnesota St New Ulm (56073) *(G-6445)*
Citizens Independent Bank 952 926-6561
5000 W 36th St Ste 100 Minneapolis (55416) *(G-4082)*
Citizens National Bank Inc 218 732-3393
300 1st St W Park Rapids (56470) *(G-6750)*
Citizens State Bank of 763 675-2265
609 Pacific Ave Waverly (55390) *(G-9903)*
Citizens State Bank of Roseau 218 463-2135
118 Main Ave S Roseau (56751) *(G-7354)*
Citizens Telecommunications Co 952 491-5576
2378 Wilshire Blvd Mound (55364) *(G-6385)*
Citon Computer Corp 218 720-4435
11 E Superior St Ste 240 Duluth (55802) *(G-1274)*
City & County Credit Union 651 225-2700
144 11th St E Saint Paul (55101) *(G-8203)*
City Auto Glass 651 552-1000
116 Concord Exchange S South Saint Paul (55075) *(G-9522)*
City Heights Inc 763 421-3345
2804 5th Ave Anoka (55303) *(G-166)*

City Lights Inc 218 568-4754
30694 Olson St Pequot Lakes (56472) ***(G-6787)***
City Looks Salon International, Minneapolis *Also Called C & R Ross Inc* ***(G-3980)***
City of Ada 218 784-5000
201 9th St W Ste 1 Ada (56510) ***(G-1)***
City of Adams 507 582-3263
810 W Main St Adams (55909) ***(G-3)***
City of Anoka 763 576-2750
2015 1st Ave Anoka (55303) ***(G-167)***
City of Beaver Creek 507 673-2266
311 E 1st Ave Beaver Creek (56116) ***(G-353)***
City of Becker 763 261-4656
14220 Clubhouse Ln Becker (55308) ***(G-355)***
City of Blackduck 218 835-4803
8 Summit Ave E Blackduck (56630) ***(G-473)***
City of Bloomington 952 563-8920
1800 W Old Shakopee Rd Minneapolis (55431) ***(G-4083)***
City of Bloomington 952 563-4925
10340 Lyndale Ave S Minneapolis (55420) ***(G-4084)***
City of Blue Earth 507 526-2715
114 W 14th St Apt 111 Blue Earth (56013) ***(G-532)***
City of Breckenridge 218 643-1431
420 Nebraska Ave Breckenridge (56520) ***(G-593)***
City of Brooklyn Center 763 569-6300
6155 Earle Brown Dr Minneapolis (55430) ***(G-4085)***
City of Chaska 952 443-3748
3000 Town Course Dr Chaska (55318) ***(G-959)***
City of Clarkfield 320 669-7561
805 5th St Clarkfield (56223) ***(G-1034)***
City of Duluth 218 628-2891
9500 Spirit Mountain Pl Duluth (55810) ***(G-1275)***
City of Duluth 218 730-5230
600 Garfield Ave Duluth (55802) ***(G-1276)***
City of Eden Prairie 952 949-8470
16700 Valley View Rd Eden Prairie (55346) ***(G-1629)***
City of Edina 952 832-6792
7499 France Ave S Minneapolis (55435) ***(G-4086)***
City of Edina 952 941-2443
6364 John Harris Dr Minneapolis (55439) ***(G-4087)***
City of Elk River 763 441-2020
13069 Orono Pkwy NW Elk River (55330) ***(G-1867)***
City of Fertile 218 945-6194
300 Garfield Ave SE Fertile (56540) ***(G-2125)***
City of Grand Rapids 218 326-3444
3910 Golf Course Rd Grand Rapids (55744) ***(G-2272)***
City of Grand Rapids 218 326-7604
420 N Pokegama Ave Grand Rapids (55744) ***(G-2273)***
City of Grand Rapids 218 326-7024
500 SE 4th St Grand Rapids (55744) ***(G-2274)***
City of Heron Lake 507 793-2349
941 County Road 9 Heron Lake (56137) ***(G-2435)***
City of Jackson 507 847-2420
1430 North Hwy Jackson (56143) ***(G-2787)***
City of Jackson 507 847-4410
80 W Ashley St Jackson (56143) ***(G-2788)***
City of Lakefield 507 662-6646
403 Colonial Ave Lakefield (56150) ***(G-2881)***
City of Lamberton 507 752-7346
200 9th Ave E Lamberton (56152) ***(G-2945)***
City of Littlefork 218 278-6634
912 Main St Littlefork (56653) ***(G-3022)***
City of Mahtomedi 651 426-1080
600 Stillwater Rd Mahtomedi (55115) ***(G-3093)***
City of Menahga 218 564-4101
427 Main St NE Menahga (56464) ***(G-3356)***
City of Minneapolis 612 370-4900
3800 Bryant Ave S Minneapolis (55409) ***(G-4088)***
City of Minneapolis 612 673-3779
309 2nd Ave S Ste 210 Minneapolis (55401) ***(G-4089)***
City of Minneapolis 612 724-7715
4553 Longfellow Ave Minneapolis (55407) ***(G-4090)***
City of Minneapolis 612 335-6000
1301 2nd Ave S Minneapolis (55403) ***(G-4091)***
City of Minneapolis 612 789-2542
2201 Saint Anthony Blvd Minneapolis (55418) ***(G-4092)***
City of Minneapolis 612 673-2597
350 S 5th St Ste 210 Minneapolis (55415) ***(G-4093)***
City of Minneapolis 612 230-6550
2117 W River Rd Ste 1 Minneapolis (55411) ***(G-4094)***
City of Moorhead 218 299-5120
915 9th Ave N Moorhead (56560) ***(G-6302)***
City of Moorhead 218 299-5422
700 15th Ave N Moorhead (56560) ***(G-6303)***
City of Mora 320 679-1770
461W Maple Ave E Mora (55051) ***(G-6353)***
City of Ortonville 320 839-2502
450 Eastvold Ave Ortonville (56278) ***(G-6579)***
City of Ortonville 320 839-6113
1075 Roy St Ortonville (56278) ***(G-6580)***
City of Owatonna 507 451-2480
208 S Walnut Ave Owatonna (55060) ***(G-6701)***
City of Owatonna 507 444-4300
540 W Hills Cir Owatonna (55060) ***(G-6702)***
City of Owatonna 507 451-2480
208 S Walnut Ave Owatonna (55060) ***(G-6703)***
City of Plainview Ambulance 507 534-3980
110 3rd St SW Plainview (55964) ***(G-6840)***
City of Plymouth 763 509-5262
3650 Plymouth Blvd Minneapolis (55446) ***(G-4095)***
City of Redwood Falls 507 637-4500
100 Fallwood Rd Redwood Falls (56283) ***(G-7020)***
City of Renville 320 329-8381
205 SE Elm St Renville (56284) ***(G-7031)***
City of Richfield 612 861-9385
7000 Nicollet Ave Minneapolis (55423) ***(G-4096)***
City of Rochester 507 280-1657
425 W Silver Lake Dr NE Rochester (55906) ***(G-7078)***
City of Rochester 507 280-1540
4000 E River Rd NE Rochester (55906) ***(G-7079)***
City of Saint Paul 651 266-6400
25 4th St W Ste 400 Saint Paul (55102) ***(G-8204)***
City of Saint Paul 651 487-8200
1250 Kaufman Dr N Saint Paul (55103) ***(G-8205)***
City of Saint Paul 651 489-8871
899 Dale St N Saint Paul (55103) ***(G-8206)***
City of Saint Paul 651 292-6600
873 Dale St N Saint Paul (55103) ***(G-8207)***
City of Saint Paul 651 266-6789
25 4th St W Ste 600 Saint Paul (55102) ***(G-8208)***
City of Saint Paul 651 631-0700
1964 Shryer Ave W Saint Paul (55113) ***(G-8209)***
City of Saint Paul 651 695-3773
1840 Edgcumbe Rd Saint Paul (55116) ***(G-8210)***
City of Saint Paul 651 488-9673
1431 Lexington Pkwy N Saint Paul (55103) ***(G-8211)***
City of Saint Paul 651 266-8740
500 Courthouse 15 Saint Paul (55102) ***(G-8212)***
City of Ulen 218 596-8847
317 1st St NW Ulen (56585) ***(G-9717)***
City of Waconia 952 442-0695
1600 Community Dr Waconia (55387) ***(G-9783)***
City of White Bear Lake 651 429-8566
4701 Highway 61 N Saint Paul (55110) ***(G-8213)***
City of White Bear Lake 651 429-8571
1328 Highway 96 E Saint Paul (55110) ***(G-8214)***
City of Worthington 507 372-2941
1018 6th Ave Worthington (56187) ***(G-10180)***
City Sanitation Service, Sauk Centre *Also Called Gene Bueckers* ***(G-9346)***
City View Electric Inc 651 659-9496
1145 Snelling Ave N Saint Paul (55108) ***(G-8215)***
City-County Federal Credit (PA) 763 549-6000
6160 Summit Dr N Minneapolis (55430) ***(G-4097)***
City-County Federal Credit 763 549-6000
6160 Summit Dr N Minneapolis (55430) ***(G-4098)***
City-Wide Insulation, Shakopee *Also Called Carnahan City-Wide Insulation* ***(G-9428)***
Cityscape Contractors Inc 952 882-0020
12362 River Ridge Blvd Burnsville (55337) ***(G-698)***
Citywide Window Services Inc 763 421-3345
2804 5th Ave Anoka (55303) ***(G-168)***
Ciu 952 469-5520
19107 Inca Ave Lakeville (55044) ***(G-2895)***
Clara City Community Nursing 320 847-2221
1012 Division St N Clara City (56222) ***(G-1026)***
Clare Bridge of Eagan, Saint Paul *Also Called Alterra Healthcare Corp* ***(G-7694)***
Clare Bridge of North Oaks, Saint Paul *Also Called Alterra Healthcare Corp* ***(G-8018)***
Clare Housing 612 236-9505
929 Central Ave NE Minneapolis (55413) ***(G-4099)***
Clarey's Safety Equipment Inc 507 289-6749
3555 9th St NW Ste 200 Rochester (55901) ***(G-7080)***
Clariant Corp 763 535-4511
9101 International Pkwy Minneapolis (55428) ***(G-4100)***
Clarion Hotel, Minneapolis *Also Called Larken Inc* ***(G-4844)***
Clarity Coverdale Fury Adv 612 339-3902
120 S 6th St Ste 1300 Minneapolis (55402) ***(G-4101)***
Clark & Wamberg LLC 612 339-0919
901 Marquette Ave # 2100 Minneapolis (55402) ***(G-4102)***
Clark Engineering Corp 763 545-9196
621 Lilac Dr N Minneapolis (55422) ***(G-4103)***
Clark Lake Homes Inc 218 829-1699
10471 State Highway 25 Brainerd (56401) ***(G-558)***
Clark Lake Homes Inc 218 833-1322
2700 Oak St Brainerd (56401) ***(G-559)***
Clark, Ron Construction, Minneapolis *Also Called REc Inc* ***(G-5475)***
Clarkfield Care Center, Clarkfield *Also Called City of Clarkfield* ***(G-1034)***
Class A Valet Inc 612 677-0071
120 N 4th St Minneapolis (55401) ***(G-4104)***
Class Act Estates Senior 612 229-3881
801 Griffing Park Rd Buffalo (55313) ***(G-642)***
Classic Bowl Inc 763 421-4402
11707 Round Lake Blvd NW Minneapolis (55433) ***(G-3433)***
Classic Cleaning Co, Buffalo *Also Called Brunskill Enterprises* ***(G-636)***
Classic Construction of Cedar 763 434-8870
18542 NE Ulysses St Cedar (55011) ***(G-877)***
Clayhill 2, Saint Paul *Also Called American Air Products Inc* ***(G-8020)***
CLC Childcare Center 507 452-5493
259 W Wabasha St Winona (55987) ***(G-10088)***
Clean Image Mobile Truck Wash 651 484-7776
497 Burgess St Saint Paul (55117) ***(G-8216)***
Clean Response, Saint Paul *Also Called Restoration Contractors Inc* ***(G-8894)***
Clean Water Action Inc 612 623-3666
308 E Hennepin Ave Minneapolis (55414) ***(G-4105)***
Clean-It Group Inc 952 943-1911
10225 Yellow Circle Dr Hopkins (55343) ***(G-2532)***
Cleaning Authority 763 717-9200
1628 County Highway 10 # 15 Minneapolis (55432) ***(G-3434)***
Cleaning Management Group Inc 952 881-8791
8120 Penn Ave S Ste 153 Minneapolis (55431) ***(G-4106)***
Clear Channel Communications 218 727-4500
14 E Central Entrance Duluth (55811) ***(G-1277)***
Clear Channel Communications 952 417-3000
1600 Utica Ave S Ste 400 Minneapolis (55416) ***(G-4107)***
Clear Channel Communications 507 288-3888
1530 Greenview Dr SW Rochester (55902) ***(G-7081)***
Clear Channel Outdoor Inc 612 605-5100
3225 Spring St NE Minneapolis (55413) ***(G-4108)***
Clear Water Cleaners Inc 320 558-6691
9616 140th St NW South Haven (55382) ***(G-9506)***
Clearone Communications Inc 763 550-2300
901 Marquette Ave Ste 250 Minneapolis (55402) ***(G-4109)***
Clearwater County Memorial (PA) 218 694-6501
203 4th St NW Bagley (56621) ***(G-300)***
Clearwater Hospice 218 694-6581
212 Main Ave N Bagley (56621) ***(G-301)***
Clearwater Suites Inc 320 765-8841
16176 810th Ave Sacred Heart (56285) ***(G-7398)***
Clearwater Truck Center Inc 320 558-6565
925 Shorty St Clearwater (55320) ***(G-1042)***

ALPHABETIC

Clements Chevrolet-Cadillac Co 507 289-0491
1000 12th St SW Rochester (55902) *(G-7082)*
Clemons Bus Line Inc 507 833-4438
213 19th Ave NE Waseca (56093) *(G-9874)*
Client Community Services Inc 507 376-6095
1381 Knollwood Dr Worthington (56187) *(G-10181)*
Cliff Viessman Inc 507 625-1435
1930 Lor Ray Dr Mankato (56003) *(G-3223)*
Cliffs Natural Resources Inc 218 262-5917
Highway 5 N Hibbing (55746) *(G-2441)*
Climb Theater Inc 651 453-9275
6415 Carmen Ave Inver Grove Heights (55076) *(G-2743)*
Climb Theatre Inc 651 453-9275
6415 Carmen Ave Inver Grove Heights (55076) *(G-2744)*
Clinic Cab, Osseo *Also Called AC Transportation Inc (G-6591)*
Clinical Dental Research, Minneapolis *Also Called Regents of The University of (G-5496)*
Cloquet Country Club 218 879-8858
400 Country Club Dr Cloquet (55720) *(G-1048)*
Cloquet Transit Co Inc 218 879-3391
1203 Avenue B Cloquet (55720) *(G-1049)*
Clover Super Foods Rt 30 Inc 612 465-8900
2850 Anthony Ln S Minneapolis (55418) *(G-4110)*
Cloverleaf Cold Stor Fairmont, Fairmont *Also Called Fairmont Refrigerated Service (G-1966)*
Cloverleaf Cold Storage Co 507 238-4211
1400 E 8th St Fairmont (56031) *(G-1961)*
Cloverleaf Cold Storage Co 952 469-1221
21755 Cedar Ave Lakeville (55044) *(G-2896)*
Club Kid of Edina Inc 952 831-1055
7541 France Ave S Minneapolis (55435) *(G-4111)*
Club The Campus Inc 612 625-9696
300 Washingtn Ave SE # 401 Minneapolis (55455) *(G-4112)*
Clues, Saint Paul *Also Called Comunidades Latinas Unidas En (G-8244)*
Clusiau Sales & Rental Inc 218 326-9421
815 NW 4th St Grand Rapids (55744) *(G-2275)*
Clutch & Transmission Service (PA) 651 636-4311
2785 Long Lake Rd Saint Paul (55113) *(G-8217)*
Clutch & Transmission Service 651 631-0959
60 Sycamore St W Saint Paul (55117) *(G-8218)*
Clyde Johnson 218 229-2847
327 S 2nd St W Aurora (55705) *(G-256)*
CM Construction Co Inc 952 895-8223
12215 Nicollet Ave Burnsville (55337) *(G-699)*
CMC Enterprises Inc 763 545-3800
9905 13th Ave N Plymouth (55441) *(G-6856)*
Cmgrp Inc 952 832-5588
8400 Norman Ctr Ste 400 Minneapolis (55437) *(G-4113)*
CMI Equipment & Engineering Co 320 864-5894
41663 170th St Glencoe (55336) *(G-2218)*
CMS, Minneapolis *Also Called Catalog Marketing Services (G-4027)*
CNA Insurance, Saint Paul *Also Called C N A Financial Corp (G-7725)*
Cnh America LLC 952 854-1443
2626 E 82nd St Minneapolis (55425) *(G-4114)*
CNM Inc 952 924-0043
3300 Gorham Ave Minneapolis (55426) *(G-4115)*
Cns Managed Health Care Inc 507 289-2411
3249 19th St NW Ste 1 Rochester (55901) *(G-7083)*
Coastal Seafoods, Minneapolis *Also Called Worldwide Fish & Seafood Inc (G-6088)*
Coates Rv Center Inc 651 488-0234
14025 Freeway Dr W Hugo (55038) *(G-2674)*
Coborn Cancer Center 320 229-4907
1900 Centracare Cir # 1500 Saint Cloud (56303) *(G-7493)*
Coborn's Inc 320 679-4003
710 Frankie Ln Mora (55051) *(G-6354)*
Cobra Transportation Services 651 552-1151
301 Eaton St Saint Paul (55107) *(G-8219)*
Coca-Cola, Baxter *Also Called Viking Coca Cola Bottling Co (G-344)*
Coca-Cola, Rochester *Also Called BCI Coca-Cola Bottling Co of (G-7061)*
Coca-Cola Bottling 218 736-5661
832 Industrial Park Blvd Fergus Falls (56537) *(G-2067)*
Coca-Cola Enterprises Inc 218 628-2311
300 S Central Ave Duluth (55807) *(G-1278)*
Coca-Cola Enterprises Inc 218 236-7165
2000 1st Ave N Moorhead (56560) *(G-6304)*
Coca-Cola Enterprises Inc 800 657-4995
2505 Alexander St SW Owatonna (55060) *(G-6704)*
Cochran Programs 651 437-4585
1294 18th St E Bldg 2 Hastings (55033) *(G-2378)*
Code Welding & Mfg Inc 763 792-6632
3151 101st Ave NE Minneapolis (55449) *(G-3435)*
Coffman Mem Union, Minneapolis *Also Called Regents of The University of (G-5486)*
Cogent Technologies Inc (HQ) 952 941-3300
7041 Boone Ave N Brooklyn Park (55428) *(G-607)*
Cokato Charitable Trust 320 286-2158
182 Sunset Ave NW Cokato (55321) *(G-1076)*
Cokem International Ltd 952 358-6000
3880 4th Ave E Shakopee (55379) *(G-9431)*
Colby Yaggy Associates Inc (PA) 507 288-6464
717 3rd Ave SE Ste 101 Rochester (55904) *(G-7084)*
Cold Spring Granite Co Inc (PA) 320 685-3621
17482 Granite West Rd Cold Spring (56320) *(G-1083)*
Cold Spring St Joseph 320 685-3237
111 Red River Ave S Cold Spring (56320) *(G-1084)*
Cold Well Banker At Your Svc 507 285-9115
2510 Superior Dr NW Ste A Rochester (55901) *(G-7085)*
Colder Products Co 651 645-0091
1001 Westgate Dr Saint Paul (55114) *(G-8220)*
Coldwell Banker, Duluth *Also Called Real Services Inc (G-1432)*
Coldwell Banker, Forest Lake *Also Called Gary Thaler (G-2145)*
Coldwell Banker, Minneapolis *Also Called Burnet Realty LLC (G-3977)*
Coldwell Banker, Saint Cloud *Also Called Herges Realty Inc (G-7527)*
Coldwell Banker, Saint Paul *Also Called Charles Stout (G-8188)*
Coldwell Banker Burnet 952 820-4663
1501 W 80th St Minneapolis (55431) *(G-4116)*
Coldwell Banker Burnet Inc (PA) 952 898-5100
190 Cobblestone Ln Burnsville (55337) *(G-700)*
Coldwell Banker Burnet Inc 952 920-1224
7820 Terrey Pine Ct Eden Prairie (55347) *(G-1630)*
Coldwell Banker Burnet Inc 952 474-2525
19400 Highway 7 Excelsior (55331) *(G-1942)*
Coldwell Banker Burnet Inc 651 690-8516
1991 Ford Pkwy Saint Paul (55116) *(G-8221)*
Coldwell Banker Burnet Real 763 754-5400
3495 Northdale Blvd NW # 200 Minneapolis (55448) *(G-3436)*
Coldwell Banker Burnet Realty 763 682-2882
700 Highway 55 E Buffalo (55313) *(G-643)*
Coldwell Banker Burnet Realty 651 227-9144
821 Grand Ave Saint Paul (55105) *(G-8222)*
Coldwell Banker Burnett Real 651 698-2481
1991 Ford Pkwy Saint Paul (55116) *(G-8223)*
Coldwell Banker Vision 763 241-0155
231 Main St NW Ste A Elk River (55330) *(G-1868)*
Cole's Salon 651 454-1390
2131 Cliff Rd Saint Paul (55122) *(G-7734)*
Cole's Salon Management Inc 952 226-5310
8160 W County Road 42 Ste 100 Savage (55378) *(G-9386)*
Colemanbrandworx Worldwide 763 390-1100
18258 Minnetonka Blvd B Wayzata (55391) *(G-9911)*
Colin Co, LP 612 375-9670
800 Lasalle Ave Ste 1750 Minneapolis (55402) *(G-4117)*
Collaborative Design Group Inc 612 332-3654
100 Portland Ave Ste 100 Minneapolis (55401) *(G-4118)*
Colle & McVoy Inc 612 305-6000
400 1st Ave N Ste 700 Minneapolis (55401) *(G-4119)*
College City Beverage Inc 507 645-4106
700 Railway St S Dundas (55019) *(G-1510)*
College Nannies & Tutors, Excelsior *Also Called ML Enterprises LLC (G-1936)*
Colliers Towle Valuation 612 347-9336
200 S 6th St Ste 1400 Minneapolis (55402) *(G-4120)*
Collin Garvey 651 463-4825
22098 Canton Ct Farmington (55024) *(G-2045)*
Collins Electrical Constr 651 224-2833
278 State St Saint Paul (55107) *(G-8224)*
Collins Electrical Systems Inc 763 535-6000
4990 Highway 169 N Minneapolis (55428) *(G-4121)*
Collins, Buckley, Sauntry 651 227-0611
332 Minnesota St Ste W1100 Saint Paul (55101) *(G-8225)*
Collisys, Minneapolis *Also Called Collins Electrical Systems Inc (G-4121)*
Collopy & Saunders Real Estate 952 829-2900
11200 W 78th St Eden Prairie (55344) *(G-1631)*
Colon & Rectal Surgery Assocs 651 312-1500
1055 Westgate Dr Ste 190 Saint Paul (55114) *(G-8226)*
Colonial Acres Home Inc (PA) 763 544-1555
5800 Saint Croix Ave N Golden Valley (55422) *(G-2239)*
Colonial Acres Home Inc 763 546-6125
5825 Saint Croix Ave N Minneapolis (55422) *(G-4122)*
Colonial Lanes Co 507 289-2341
1828 14th St NW Rochester (55901) *(G-7086)*
Colonial Manor Nursing Home, Lakefield *Also Called City of Lakefield (G-2881)*
Colonial Manor of Balaton 507 734-3511
551 US Highway 14 Balaton (56115) *(G-304)*
Colonial Village Apartments 218 739-3795
1234 N Broadway Fergus Falls (56537) *(G-2068)*
Colony At Eden Prairie, Eden Prairie *Also Called SE Rolling Hills LLC (G-1771)*
Colony Court, Waseca *Also Called Garkat Inc (G-9879)*
Coloplast Corp (PA) 612 337-7800
1601 W River Rd Minneapolis (55411) *(G-4123)*
Coloplast Corp 507 345-6200
1940 Commerce Dr North Mankato (56003) *(G-6507)*
Columbia Building Services Inc 612 331-2090
2020 Broadway St NE Minneapolis (55413) *(G-4124)*
Columns Resource Group 612 758-7600
100 Washington Ave S Ste 1200 Minneapolis (55401) *(G-4125)*
Columns Resource of 952 806-9600
3600 Minnesota Dr Ste 300 Minneapolis (55435) *(G-4126)*
Combined Insurance Co of Amer 952 933-2133
11095 Viking Dr Ste 125 Eden Prairie (55344) *(G-1632)*
Comedysportz Twin Cities 612 870-1230
3001 Hennepin Ave E103 Minneapolis (55408) *(G-4127)*
Comfort Care Good Smaritan Ctr, Austin *Also Called Evangelical Lutheran Good (G-270)*
Comfort Home Health Care Group 507 281-2332
2746 Superior Dr NW # 200 Rochester (55901) *(G-7087)*
Comfort Inn, Duluth *Also Called Duluth Lodging Inc (G-1300)*
Comfort Inn, Duluth *Also Called Duluth Lodging Inc (G-1301)*
Comfort Inn, Hopkins *Also Called Sandman Motels LLC (G-2626)*
Comfort Inn, Marshall *Also Called Lyon Lodging LLC (G-3308)*
Comfort Inn, Minneapolis *Also Called Sandman Motel LLC (G-5600)*
Comfort Inn, Minneapolis *Also Called Mplsp Hotel Corp (G-5142)*
Comfort Inn, Owatonna *Also Called Laird LLC (G-6721)*
Comfort Inn, Saint Cloud *Also Called First Class Hospitality Group (G-7510)*
Comfort Inn, Savage *Also Called Somerset Hospitality LLC (G-9407)*
Comfort Inn & Suites 507 289-3344
5708 Bandel Rd NW Rochester (55901) *(G-7088)*
Comfort Services LLC 612 871-2160
2200 Minnehaha Ave Minneapolis (55404) *(G-4128)*
Comforts of Home 651 287-0265
720 Main St Ste 205 Saint Paul (55118) *(G-7735)*
Comforts of Home 651 426-1036
1235 Gun Club Rd White Bear Lake (55110) *(G-9974)*
Comforts of Home Hugo 651 653-3282
5607 150th St N Hugo (55038) *(G-2675)*
Comlink Midwest Inc 763 391-7483
7308 Aspen Ln N Ste 160 Minneapolis (55428) *(G-4129)*
Comm-Works Holdings LLC (HQ) 763 258-5800
1405 Xenium Ln N Ste 120 Minneapolis (55441) *(G-4130)*
Comm-Works LLC 763 258-5800
1405 Xenium Ln N Ste 120 Minneapolis (55441) *(G-4131)*
Commemorative Air Force 651 455-6942
310 Airport Rd South Saint Paul (55075) *(G-9523)*
Commerce Partners LLC 651 292-8777
185 Plato Blvd W Saint Paul (55107) *(G-8227)*
Commercial Auditors Corp 763 783-9160
1635 Coon Rapids Blvd NW Minneapolis (55433) *(G-3437)*

ALPHABETIC C

Commercial Contractors Co of 320 256-7422
631 S Central Ave Melrose (56352) *(G-3348)*
Commercial Drywall Inc 763 862-6020
7040 245th Ave NW Saint Francis (55070) *(G-7639)*
Commercial Furniture Services 952 922-6683
4301 Highway 7 Ste 200 Saint Louis Park (55416) *(G-7658)*
Commercial Insur Underwriters, Lakeville *Also Called Ciu (G-2895)*
Commercial Partners Title LLC 612 337-2470
200 S 6th St Ste 1300 Minneapolis (55402) *(G-4132)*
Commercial Plumbing & Heating 651 464-2988
24428 Greenway Ave Forest Lake (55025) *(G-2151)*
Commercial Products V H Inds 651 224-2831
216 Wabasha St S Saint Paul (55107) *(G-8228)*
Commercial Recovery Corp 763 786-6333
9298 Central Ave NE # 310 Minneapolis (55434) *(G-3438)*
Commercial Roofing Inc 651 483-5298
221 Ryan Dr Saint Paul (55117) *(G-8229)*
Commercial Truck & Trailer Rep 651 639-2260
2275 County Road C2 W Saint Paul (55113) *(G-8230)*
Commodity Specialists Co (PA) 612 330-9120
920 2nd Ave S Ste 850 Minneapolis (55402) *(G-4133)*
Common Sense Building Services 612 379-7106
1300 Godward St NE Ste B1 Minneapolis (55413) *(G-4134)*
Common Sense Services For 651 552-0288
724 19th Ave N Ste 100 South Saint Paul (55075) *(G-9524)*
Commonbond Communities (PA) 651 291-1750
328 Kellogg Blvd W Saint Paul (55102) *(G-8231)*
Commonbond Housing 651 291-1750
328 Kellogg Blvd W Saint Paul (55102) *(G-8232)*
Commonbond Investment Corp 651 291-1750
328 Kellogg Blvd W Saint Paul (55102) *(G-8233)*
Commonsense Mortgage Inc 952 942-8502
8110 Eden Rd Eden Prairie (55344) *(G-1633)*
Commonweal Theatre Co 507 467-2905
208 Parkway Ave N Lanesboro (55949) *(G-2946)*
Commonwealth Land Title Insce 651 227-8571
222 S 9th St Ste 3250 Minneapolis (55402) *(G-4135)*
Communicating For Agriculture 218 739-3241
112 E Lincoln Ave Fergus Falls (56537) *(G-2069)*
Communicating For America Inc 218 739-3241
112 E Lincoln Ave Fergus Falls (56537) *(G-2070)*
Comm Center, Burnsville *Also Called Phoenix Distributing Inc (G-781)*
Communication Mailing Services 651 645-5280
429 Prior Ave N Saint Paul (55104) *(G-8234)*
Communication Service For The 218 291-1120
800 Holiday Dr Ste 260 Moorhead (56560) *(G-6305)*
Communication Service For The 651 297-6700
2055 Rice St Saint Paul (55113) *(G-8235)*
Communications Mid-America, Saint Paul *Also Called Ideacom Mid-America Inc (G-8504)*
Communications Systems Inc (PA) 952 996-1674
10900 Red Circle Dr Minnetonka (55343) *(G-6156)*
Communities of Care Pediatric, Saint Paul *Also Called Elenas Care Inc (G-8332)*
Community Action Agency 763 425-7422
8500 Zane Ave N Minneapolis (55443) *(G-4136)*
Community Action Council Inc 952 985-5300
501 Highway 13 E Ste 102 Burnsville (55337) *(G-701)*
Community Action of 612 348-8858
505 E Grant St Ste 1 Minneapolis (55404) *(G-4137)*
Community Action Partnership 651 224-4363
586 Fuller Ave Saint Paul (55103) *(G-8236)*
Community Action Partnership (PA) 651 645-6445
450 Syndicate St N Ste 5 Saint Paul (55104) *(G-8237)*
Community Acton of Minneapolis 612 335-5837
2104 Park Ave Minneapolis (55404) *(G-4138)*
Community Bank Chaska 952 361-2265
706 N Walnut St Ste 100 Chaska (55318) *(G-960)*
Community Bank Vernon Center 507 625-1551
951 E Madison Ave Mankato (56001) *(G-3118)*
Community Charities of MN 507 386-1934
114 S Riverfront Dr Mankato (56001) *(G-3119)*
Community Child Care Center 612 861-4303
8 W 60th St Minneapolis (55419) *(G-4139)*
Community Connection of MN 218 525-4126
2701 W Superior St # 101 Duluth (55806) *(G-1279)*
Community Dental Care 651 774-2959
828 Hawthorne Ave E Saint Paul (55106) *(G-8238)*
Community Development Inc 763 225-6412
7100 Madison Ave W Minneapolis (55427) *(G-4140)*
Community Drug & Alcohol Svcs 952 564-3000
501 Highway 13 E Ste 108 Burnsville (55337) *(G-702)*
Community Finance Group Inc 763 416-5959
5747 W Broadway Ave Minneapolis (55428) *(G-4141)*
Community Foundation, Saint Paul *Also Called South Metro Human Services (G-8972)*
Community Health Dept, Minneapolis *Also Called Hennepin County (G-4633)*
Community Health Network 320 845-2121
300 3rd Ave Albany (56307) *(G-26)*
Community Home Health Inc 952 440-3955
16670 Franklin Trl SE Ste 120A Prior Lake (55372) *(G-6930)*
Community Housing & Service 952 933-1833
3630 Phillips Pkwy Minneapolis (55426) *(G-4142)*
Community Involvement Programs (PA) 612 362-4400
1600 Broadway St NE Minneapolis (55413) *(G-4143)*
Community Involvement Programs 952 854-4007
1701 E 79th St Ste 16A Minneapolis (55425) *(G-4144)*
Community Involvement Programs 320 245-5362
206 Commercial Ave N Sandstone (55072) *(G-9320)*
Community Living Inc 952 443-2048
1600 Arboretum Blvd Victoria (55386) *(G-9726)*
Community Memorial Home Inc 320 859-2111
410 W Main St Osakis (56360) *(G-6586)*
Community Memorial Hospital 218 879-4641
512 Skyline Blvd Ste 1 Cloquet (55720) *(G-1050)*
Community Memorial Hospital 507 346-7381
800 Memorial Dr Spring Valley (55975) *(G-9568)*
Community National Bank (PA) 507 645-4441
1605 Heritage Dr Northfield (55057) *(G-6526)*

Community of Red River Valley 218 773-2451
1413 Central Ave NW East Grand Forks (56721) *(G-1567)*
Community Services Inc 651 631-6000
2845 Hamline Ave N Saint Paul (55113) *(G-8239)*
Community Support Program, Crookston *Also Called Northwestern Mental Health Ctr (G-1131)*
Community Volunteer Services, Bayport *Also Called Bayport Senior Center (G-346)*
Como Lube & Supplies Inc 218 722-2920
1108 Port Terminal Rd Duluth (55802) *(G-1280)*
Como Ski Center 651 488-9679
1431 Lexington Pkwy N Saint Paul (55103) *(G-8240)*
Compact Offer, Osseo *Also Called Service Lighting Inc (G-6662)*
Companion Housing Program Inc 952 285-5950
475 Cleveland Ave N # 101 Saint Paul (55104) *(G-8241)*
Companioncare Inc 763 533-1919
4124 Quebec Ave N Ste 304 Minneapolis (55427) *(G-4145)*
Companions Home Health Care, Minneapolis *Also Called Companioncare Inc (G-4145)*
Compass Airlines Inc 612 713-6800
7500 Airline Dr Ste 130 Minneapolis (55450) *(G-4146)*
Compass Group USA Inc 651 488-0515
1091 Pierce Butler Rte Saint Paul (55104) *(G-8242)*
Compass Intl RES & Info Svcs, Saint Paul *Also Called Power Systems Research Inc (G-7880)*
Compass Marketing Inc 612 333-5300
251 1st Ave N Fl 2 Minneapolis (55401) *(G-4147)*
Compendium Corp 952 881-1608
2905 W Service Rd Saint Paul (55121) *(G-7736)*
Complete Real Estate Services 651 287-3400
3101 Old Highway 8 # 105 Saint Paul (55113) *(G-8243)*
Complete Title Services LLC 218 828-9611
14275 Golf Course Rd Baxter (56425) *(G-326)*
Computer Friendly, Saint Joseph *Also Called Bangasser Co (G-7651)*
Computer Integration Techs 651 450-0333
2375 Ventura Dr Ste A Saint Paul (55125) *(G-9198)*
Computer Sciences Corp 763 593-1122
5500 Wayzata Blvd # 1100 Minneapolis (55416) *(G-4148)*
Computerland, Willmar *Also Called Bennett Office Technologies (G-9985)*
Comstock Construction Inc, of 218 739-5365
1003 Progress Dr Fergus Falls (56537) *(G-2071)*
Comsys Information Technology 612 630-9100
1201 Harmon Pl Ste 200 Minneapolis (55403) *(G-4149)*
Comunidades Latinas Unidas En 651 379-4200
797 7th St E Saint Paul (55106) *(G-8244)*
Con Spec Corp 651 501-6500
707 Commerce Dr Ste 410 Saint Paul (55125) *(G-9199)*
Con-Way Freight Inc 651 686-2868
3450 Dodd Rd Eagan (55123) *(G-1521)*
Con-Way Freight Inc 763 783-7123
51 81st Ave NE Fridley (55432) *(G-2192)*
Con-Way Freight Inc 507 451-2865
1020 28th Ave NW Owatonna (55060) *(G-6705)*
Con-Way Freight Inc 320 259-0245
301 33rd Ave S Waite Park (56387) *(G-9820)*
Concept Group Inc 651 221-9710
190 5th St E Ste 200 Saint Paul (55101) *(G-8245)*
Concept Landscaping Inc 952 472-4118
3153 Priest Ln Mound (55364) *(G-6386)*
Concept Machine Tool Sales Inc 763 559-1975
15625 Medina Rd Minneapolis (55447) *(G-4150)*
Concierge Enterprises Inc 763 746-8121
7150 Madison Ave W Minneapolis (55427) *(G-4151)*
Concord Inc 952 697-5500
509 2nd Ave S Hopkins (55343) *(G-2533)*
Concordia College 218 299-4321
901 8th St S Moorhead (56562) *(G-6306)*
Concordia Creative Learning 651 793-6624
930 Geranium Ave E Saint Paul (55106) *(G-8246)*
Concordia Language Villages 218 758-3068
40225 Purlieu Rd Dent (56528) *(G-1186)*
Concrete Mobility LLC 952 746-5887
2917 133rd St W Ste 2 Shakopee (55379) *(G-9432)*
Condor Lodge & Beach Resort, Hugo *Also Called Rica Costa Ventures Inc (G-2682)*
Cone Corp 218 245-2313
25929 County Road 59 Bovey (55709) *(G-540)*
Conect Project 763 476-8477
15215 18th Ave N Apt 103 Minneapolis (55447) *(G-4152)*
Conestoga-Rovers & Associates 651 639-0913
1801 Old Highway 8 NW Ste 114 Saint Paul (55112) *(G-8247)*
Connectcare 320 234-5031
710 Park Island Dr SW Hutchinson (55350) *(G-2694)*
Connection, Burnsville *Also Called Data Listing Services LLC (G-709)*
Connections Inc 952 888-5792
1200 E Old Shakopee Rd Minneapolis (55425) *(G-4153)*
Connections of Moorhead 218 233-8657
810 4th Ave S Ste 156 Moorhead (56560) *(G-6307)*
Connectivity Solutions Inc of 763 424-7300
6250 Sycamore Ln N # 500 Osseo (55369) *(G-6604)*
Conner Enterprises Inc 218 998-9376
117 S Mill St Fl 2 Fergus Falls (56537) *(G-2072)*
Connexions Loyalty Travel Soln 952 914-6533
6442 City West Pkwy Eden Prairie (55344) *(G-1634)*
Connexus Energy 763 323-2600
14601 Ramsey Blvd NW Anoka (55303) *(G-169)*
Consan Inc 952 949-0053
7699 Anagram Dr Eden Prairie (55344) *(G-1635)*
Conseco Finance Corp 651 293-3434
1100 Landmark Towers Saint Paul (55102) *(G-8248)*
Conselor Realty, Wayzata *Also Called Counselor Realty Inc (G-9912)*
Consolidated Building Corp 612 759-9313
16935 Gerdine Path W Rosemount (55068) *(G-7366)*
Consolidated Container Co LLC 612 781-0923
109 27th Ave NE Minneapolis (55418) *(G-4154)*
Consolidated Enterprises Inc 651 646-7821
489 Prior Ave N Saint Paul (55104) *(G-8249)*
Consolidated Title & Abstract 218 722-1495
332 W Superior St Ste 100 Duluth (55802) *(G-1281)*
Construction Coordinators Inc 612 332-2020
505 E Grant St Minneapolis (55404) *(G-4155)*
Construction Division, Minneapolis *Also Called M A Mortenson Co (G-4918)*

ALPHABETIC

Construction Labor Force Inc 651 786-0550
448 Lilac St Circle Pines (55014) (G-1006)
Construction Midwest Inc 763 536-8336
3531 Nevada Ave N Ste 100 Minneapolis (55427) (G-4156)
Construction Results Corp 763 559-1100
14170 23rd Ave N Plymouth (55447) (G-6857)
Consultants In Arthritisand 952 832-0246
7250 France Ave S Ste 215 Minneapolis (55435) (G-4157)
Consulting Engineers Group Inc 651 463-6263
21210 Eaton Ave Ste C Farmington (55024) (G-2046)
Consulting Radiologists Ltd (PA) 612 573-2200
1221 Nicollet Ave Ste 600 Minneapolis (55403) (G-4158)
Consulting Radiologists Ltd 952 831-9300
3955 Parklawn Ave Ste 100 Minneapolis (55435) (G-4159)
Consumer Directions Inc 320 420-3423
22 Wilson Ave NE Ste 205 Saint Cloud (56304) (G-7409)
Consumers Cooperative Assn 320 693-2821
1025 E Frontage Rd Litchfield (55355) (G-2981)
Contact Cartage Inc 612 331-4780
1912 Broadway St NE Minneapolis (55413) (G-4160)
Contech Construction Products 952 496-1050
11155 Chaparral Ave Shakopee (55379) (G-9433)
Contemporary Transportation, Minneapolis Also Called Miller Medi Van Inc (G-5044)
Continental Airlines Inc 612 726-5679
4300 Glumack Dr Ste E11 Saint Paul (55111) (G-7959)
Continental Bridge Inc 320 852-7500
8301 State Highway 29 N Alexandria (56308) (G-89)
Contingent Work Force Soln 651 636-5624
2860 Middle St Little Canada (55117) (G-2995)
Continual Feast Companion Care, Minneapolis Also Called Stinson Home Care LLC (G-3609)
Contract Hardware Co Inc 651 780-0010
374 Apollo Dr Circle Pines (55014) (G-1007)
Contract Sod Services Inc 651 457-6037
8140 Courthouse Blvd Inver Grove Heights (55077) (G-2745)
Controlled Air, Farmington Also Called Pro-Temp Inc (G-2058)
Convergent Media, Saint Paul Also Called Collins Electrical Constr (G-8224)
Convergeone Holdings Corp (HQ) 651 796-6411
3344 Highway 149 Eagan (55121) (G-1522)
Converse, Mitchell W, Saint Paul Also Called Jenson, Beel, Converse (G-8530)
Conveyor Belt Service Inc 218 741-5939
400 S 1st Ave Virginia (55792) (G-9737)
Conway, Deuth & Schmiesing 320 235-3311
331 3rd St SW Ste 2 Willmar (56201) (G-9999)
Conzemius Family LP 651 437-2107
13335 Lock Blvd Hastings (55033) (G-2379)
Cook & Koff Enterprises Inc 952 830-0100
7575 France Ave S Minneapolis (55435) (G-4161)
Cook Area Health Services Inc 218 743-3232
135 Pine Tree Dr Bigfork (56628) (G-460)
Cook Area Health Services Inc (PA) 218 666-5941
20 5th St SE Cook (55723) (G-1094)
Cook County North Shore Hosp 218 387-3040
515 5th Ave W Grand Marais (55604) (G-2257)
Cool Air Mechanical Inc 651 489-8821
1441 Rice St Saint Paul (55117) (G-8250)
Coon Rapids Chrysler Inc 763 421-8000
10541 Woodcrest Dr NW Minneapolis (55433) (G-3439)
Coon Rapids Day Care Center 763 755-2412
10506 Hanson Blvd NW Minneapolis (55433) (G-3440)
Coon Rapids Dental, Minneapolis Also Called Healthpartners Inc (G-3487)
Coon Rapids Legion Post 334, Minneapolis Also Called American Legion Club 334 Inc (G-3398)
Coon Rapids Lions 763 323-1668
10800 Xavis St NW Ste 1 Minneapolis (55433) (G-3441)
Coon Rapids VFW Post 9625 ....763 755-4760
1919 Coon Rapids Blvd NW Minneapolis (55433) (G-3442)
Coon Rapids Womens Health Ctr, Minneapolis Also Called Allina Health System (G-3392)
Coop Audubon Elevator Assn 218 439-6111
445 Front St Audubon (56511) (G-254)
Coop FCA (PA) 507 847-4160
105 Jackson St Jackson (56143) (G-2789)
Coop Northern Star 218 246-8660
111 Main Ave W Deer River (56636) (G-1167)
Coop Tricounty 320 748-7187
922 Highway 75 Graceville (56240) (G-2253)
Cooperative Development LLC 218 444-1143
1831 Anne St NW Ste 100 Bemidji (56601) (G-385)
Cooperative Response Center (PA) 507 437-2400
2000 8th St NW Austin (55912) (G-267)
Cooperative Sampo Inc (PA) 218 564-4534
14 Birch Ave SE Menahga (56464) (G-3357)
Coordinated Business Systems 952 894-9460
851 W 128th St Burnsville (55337) (G-703)
Coordinated Business Systems 320 251-1212
624 1st St S Waite Park (56387) (G-9821)
Copeland Buhl, Wayzata Also Called Nathan J Lilleodden CPA (G-9931)
Copeland Buhl & Co, Wayzata Also Called James W Copeland (G-9922)
Copy Service, Minneapolis Also Called Health Care Provider Service (G-4618)
Corcoran Lions Club 763 420-2555
20121 County Road 10 Hamel (55340) (G-2338)
Core Professional Services 218 829-7140
617 Oak St Brainerd (56401) (G-560)
Core Professional Services 320 202-1400
451 E Saint Germain St # 400 Saint Cloud (56304) (G-7410)
Cornerstone Advocacy Service 952 884-0376
1000 E 80th St Minneapolis (55420) (G-4162)
Cornerstone Residence 218 647-8258
280 Main St Kelliher (56650) (G-2827)
Corporate 4 Insurance Agency 952 893-9218
7220 Metro Blvd Minneapolis (55439) (G-4163)
Corporate Commission of The 320 384-7101
777 Lady Luck Dr Hinckley (55037) (G-2483)
Corporate Commission of The (HQ) 320 532-8800
777 Grand Ave Onamia (56359) (G-6568)
Corporate Commission of The 320 532-8862
700 Grand Ave Onamia (56359) (G-6569)
Corporate Express Office Prdts 651 636-2250
1233 County Road E W Saint Paul (55112) (G-8251)
Corporate Graphics Intl 651 494-1740
1170 Grey Fox Rd Saint Paul (55112) (G-8252)
Corporate Image Store, Minneapolis Also Called Mobile Media Inc (G-5115)
Corporate Mechanical Inc 763 533-3070
5114 Hillsboro Ave N Minneapolis (55428) (G-4164)
Corporate Travel Services Inc 651 287-4900
340 Cedar St Ste 1200 Saint Paul (55101) (G-8253)
Correctional Medical Services 651 631-0065
2336 Lexington Ave N Saint Paul (55113) (G-8254)
Corrections Corp of America 320 289-2052
445 S Munsterman St Appleton (56208) (G-245)
CORT Business Services Corp 651 405-0009
1279 Trapp Rd Ste 130 Saint Paul (55121) (G-7737)
Corval Constructors Inc 651 642-0451
1633 Eustis St Saint Paul (55108) (G-8255)
Cosmopolitan & Associates Inc 612 822-3830
711 W Lake St Minneapolis (55408) (G-4165)
Cost Cutters Family Hair Care 612 861-0040
2922 W 66th St Minneapolis (55423) (G-4166)
Costumes & Creatures, Minneapolis Also Called Vee Corp (G-5959)
Cottage Grove Bingo, Cottage Grove Also Called Grove Cottage Athletic Assn (G-1102)
Cottage Grove Ems, Cottage Grove Also Called Grove Cottage Emergency Med (G-1103)
Cottage Grove, City of Inc 651 458-2808
8635 W Point Douglas Rd S Cottage Grove (55016) (G-1101)
Cottonwood Truck Service Inc 651 451-7320
100 Slockman Rd Ste 206 South Saint Paul (55075) (G-9525)
Coughlan Co's Inc (PA) 507 385-8295
151 Good Counsel Dr # 120 Mankato (56001) (G-3120)
Counseling Services of Sthn 507 931-8040
116 S 3rd St Saint Peter (56082) (G-9301)
Counselor Realty Inc 952 921-0911
7250 France Ave S Ste 300 Minneapolis (55435) (G-4167)
Counselor Realty Inc (PA) 763 786-0600
7766 Highway 65 NE Ste 1 Minneapolis (55432) (G-3443)
Counselor Realty Inc 763 420-7080
13601 80th Cir N Ste 300 Osseo (55369) (G-6605)
Counselor Realty Inc 651 779-6000
3580 Linden Ave Saint Paul (55110) (G-8256)
Counselor Realty Inc 952 475-9500
3622 County Road 101 S # 100 Wayzata (55391) (G-9912)
Country Hearth, Minneapolis Also Called Pan-O-Gold Baking Co (G-5316)
Country Hearth, Saint Cloud Also Called Pan-O-Gold Baking Co (G-7421)
Country Hedging Inc 651 355-6500
5500 Cenex Dr Ste 290 Inver Grove Heights (55077) (G-2746)
Country Inn & Suites By 763 241-6990
18894 Dodge St NW Elk River (55330) (G-1869)
Country Inn & Suites By 651 982-9799
1954 W Broadway Ave Forest Lake (55025) (G-2159)
Country Inn & Suites Duluth 218 740-4500
4257 Haines Rd Duluth (55811) (G-1282)
Country Inns & Suites By 763 473-3008
210 Carlson Pkwy N Minneapolis (55447) (G-4168)
Country Inns & Suites By 952 854-5555
2221 Killebrew Dr Minneapolis (55425) (G-4169)
Country Inns & Suites By 763 212-2525
701 Carlson Pkwy Minneapolis (55441) (G-4170)
Country Insurance & Fincl Svcs, Saint Paul Also Called Mutual Service Cooperative (G-8731)
Country Lanes-North Inc 218 722-1741
2327 Mountain Shadow Dr Duluth (55811) (G-1283)
Country Manor, Sartell Also Called Foundation For Healthcare (G-9328)
Country Pride Services Co-op (PA) 507 831-2580
144 9th St Bingham Lake (56118) (G-466)
Country Side East Living 507 446-8334
650 El Dorado St SE Owatonna (55060) (G-6706)
Country Suites By Carlson, Alexandria Also Called Infinity Motel Holdings LLC (G-106)
Country Suites By Carlson, Chanhassen Also Called C H Suites of Chanhassen MN (G-912)
Country Suites By Carlson, Lino Lakes Also Called Lino Lake Lodging LLC (G-2973)
Country Suites By Carlson, Mankato Also Called Sand Co Inc (G-3191)
Country Suites By Carlson, Minneapolis Also Called Travel Suites of Coon Rapids (G-3621)
Country Suites By Carlson, Minneapolis Also Called W B M Holding Co (G-5986)
Country Suites By Carlson, Rochester Also Called Professional Hospitality LLC (G-7212)
Country Suites By Carlson, Saint Cloud Also Called Professional Hospitality LLC (G-7575)
Countryside Co-Op 218 675-6865
Hwy 371 Hackensack (56452) (G-2332)
Countryside Heating & Cooling 763 479-1600
6511 Highway 12 Maple Plain (55359) (G-3272)
Countryvilla Builders, Saint Paul Also Called Brightkeys Building & Devpt (G-9188)
Countrywide Tire & Rubber Inc 763 546-1636
17200 Medina Rd Ste 100 Minneapolis (55447) (G-4171)
County Attorney Office 218 726-2323
100 N 5th Ave W Ste 501 Duluth (55802) (G-1284)
County Library, Jackson Also Called City of Jackson (G-2788)
County News Scottsman, Cambridge Also Called Ecm Publishers Inc (G-837)
County of Anoka 763 767-2871
550 Bunker Lake Blvd NW Anoka (55304) (G-170)
County of Anoka 651 482-8484
646 Sandpiper Dr Circle Pines (55014) (G-1008)
County of Anoka 763 783-4800
1201 89th Ave NE Ste 235 Minneapolis (55434) (G-3444)
County of Anoka 763 783-4909
1201 89th Ave NE Ste 105 Minneapolis (55434) (G-3445)
County of Becker 218 847-2661
925 Lake Ave Detroit Lakes (56501) (G-1190)
County of Beltrami 218 333-8206
616 America Ave NW Bemidji (56601) (G-386)
County of Brown-Nicollet 507 354-4418
1117 Center St New Ulm (56073) (G-6446)
County of Carver 952 466-5200
11360 Highway 212 Ste 2 Cologne (55322) (G-1091)
County of Cass 218 547-1346
400 Michigan Ave W Walker (56484) (G-9849)
County of Clay 218 299-5150
919 8th Ave N Moorhead (56560) (G-6308)

ALPHABETIC

County of Cook 218 387-3265
515 5th Ave W Grand Marais (55604) ***(G-2258)***
County of Dodge 507 374-2578
RR 1 Dodge Center (55927) ***(G-1225)***
County of Douglas 320 762-2400
700 Cedar St Ste 154 Alexandria (56308) ***(G-90)***
County of Douglas 320 762-1511
111 17th Ave E Alexandria (56308) ***(G-91)***
County of Douglas 320 763-6018
725 Elm St Ste 1200 Alexandria (56308) ***(G-92)***
County of Fillmore 507 765-4701
101 Fillmore St Preston (55965) ***(G-6896)***
County of Kanabec 320 679-6430
18 Vine St N Ste 261A Mora (55051) ***(G-6355)***
County of Mahnomen 218 935-2511
414 W Jefferson Ave Mahnomen (56557) ***(G-3084)***
County of Meeker 320 693-3242
612 S Sibley Ave Litchfield (55355) ***(G-2982)***
County of Meeker 320 693-5300
114 N Holcombe Ave Ste 180 Litchfield (55355) ***(G-2983)***
County of Mille Lacs 763 389-5828
304 S Rum River Dr Princeton (55371) ***(G-6904)***
County of Mower (PA) 507 437-9440
201 1st St NE Austin (55912) ***(G-268)***
County of Murray 507 836-6111
2042 Juniper Ave Slayton (56172) ***(G-9486)***
County of Olmsted 507 285-8138
151 4th St SE Rochester (55904) ***(G-7089)***
County of Pennington 218 681-0876
318 Knight Ave N Thief River Falls (56701) ***(G-9664)***
County of Pennington 218 681-1675
123 Baken St Thief River Falls (56701) ***(G-9665)***
County of Ramsey 651 266-3400
50 Kellogg Blvd W Ste 550 Saint Paul (55102) ***(G-8257)***
County of Ramsey 651 777-7486
2000 White Bear Ave N Saint Paul (55109) ***(G-8258)***
County of Ramsey 651 748-2500
2015 Van Dyke St Saint Paul (55109) ***(G-8259)***
County of Ramsey 651 266-2400
90 Plato Blvd W Ste 200 Saint Paul (55107) ***(G-8260)***
County of Ramsey 651 770-4499
2098 11th Ave E Saint Paul (55109) ***(G-8261)***
County of Sibley 507 237-4000
112 5th St S Gaylord (55334) ***(G-2199)***
County of St Louis 218 726-2140
320 W 2nd St Ste 605 Duluth (55802) ***(G-1285)***
County of Stearns 320 202-2100
3333 W Div St Ste 210 Saint Cloud (56301) ***(G-7494)***
County of Stearns 320 259-3700
807 Courthouse Sq Saint Cloud (56303) ***(G-7495)***
County of Steele 507 444-7410
630 Florence Ave Owatonna (55060) ***(G-6707)***
County of Todd 320 732-4500
212 2nd Ave SW Long Prairie (56347) ***(G-3040)***
County of Washington 651 430-6800
14949 62nd St N Stillwater (55082) ***(G-9605)***
County of Washington 651 439-9381
15015 62nd St N Stillwater (55082) ***(G-9606)***
County of Winona 507 457-6400
60 W 3rd St Winona (55987) ***(G-10089)***
County of Winona 507 457-6200
202 W 3rd St Winona (55987) ***(G-10090)***
County of Winona 507 457-6410
60 W 3rd St Winona (55987) ***(G-10091)***
Courage Center 218 266-3658
37569 N Courage Dr Lake George (56458) ***(G-2878)***
Courage Center 320 963-3121
8046 83rd St NW Maple Lake (55358) ***(G-3259)***
Courage Center (PA) 763 588-0811
3915 Golden Valley Rd Minneapolis (55422) ***(G-4172)***
Courage Center 651 439-8283
1460 Curve Crest Blvd W Stillwater (55082) ***(G-9607)***
Courier Systems LLC 651 628-0100
1471 1st Ave NW Saint Paul (55112) ***(G-8262)***
Court House, Preston *Also Called County of Fillmore* ***(G-6896)***
Courtyard, Saint Paul *Also Called CSM Corp of Minnesota* ***(G-8273)***
Courtyard By Marriott 952 942-9100
11391 Viking Dr Eden Prairie (55344) ***(G-1636)***
Courtyard By Marriott, Maple Grove *Also Called Cynw LLC* ***(G-3238)***
Courtyard By Marriott, Moorhead *Also Called Moorhead Hospitality LP* ***(G-6331)***
Courtyard By Marriott 952 452-2000
1352 Northland Dr Saint Paul (55120) ***(G-7738)***
Cousineau McGuire Chartered 952 546-8400
1550 Utica Ave S Ste 600 Minneapolis (55416) ***(G-4173)***
Covanta Energy Group Inc 612 333-7303
505 6th Ave N Minneapolis (55405) ***(G-4174)***
Cove Point Lodge 218 226-3221
Hwy 61 Beaver Bay (55601) ***(G-352)***
Covenant Home Services LLC 763 755-9009
11375 Robinson Dr NW Ste 104 Minneapolis (55433) ***(G-3446)***
Covenant Manor, Minneapolis *Also Called Colonial Acres Home Inc* ***(G-4122)***
Covenant Rtrment Cmmnties Minn, Minneapolis *Also Called Evangelical Covenant Church* ***(G-4375)***
Coyne's & Co Inc 763 425-8666
7400 Boone Ave N Minneapolis (55428) ***(G-4175)***
CP Rail, Saint Paul *Also Called SOO Line Railroad Co Inc* ***(G-8971)***
CP Rail System SOO Line 320 634-3307
20 15th St NE Glenwood (56334) ***(G-2221)***
CP Saddle Brook LLC 952 854-7441
2020 American Blvd E Bloomington (55425) ***(G-492)***
Cragg Railcharger, Minneapolis *Also Called Railway Equipment Co Inc* ***(G-5461)***
Cragun Enterprises Inc 218 825-2800
11000 Craguns Dr Brainerd (56401) ***(G-544)***
Craig G Braun Turf Farms 651 463-2302
2950 232nd St E Hampton (55031) ***(G-2365)***
Craig L Gilbertson MD 218 722-6613
324 W Superior St Ste 302 Duluth (55802) ***(G-1286)***
Craig-Hallum Capital Group LLC 612 334-6300
222 S 9th St Ste 350 Minneapolis (55402) ***(G-4176)***
Cramer Investment Co 612 861-7232
775 Vandalia St Saint Paul (55114) ***(G-8263)***
Crannys 4 Care LLC 218 824-0077
108 S 6th St Ste 3 Brainerd (56401) ***(G-561)***
Crawford & Co 651 631-0055
2387 Rosegate Saint Paul (55113) ***(G-8264)***
Crawford Door Sales Co Twin 651 455-1221
1641 Oakdale Ave Saint Paul (55118) ***(G-7739)***
Crawford-Merz Construction Co 612 874-9011
2316 4th Ave S Minneapolis (55404) ***(G-4177)***
Cre 8 It Inc 612 623-8866
3130 Talmage Ave SE Minneapolis (55414) ***(G-4178)***
Creatis Inc 612 333-3233
227 Colfax Ave N Ste 200 Minneapolis (55405) ***(G-4179)***
Creative Banners, Minneapolis *Also Called Chromatic Concepts, Co* ***(G-4073)***
Creative Business Solutions, Hopkins *Also Called Fishel Information Systems Inc* ***(G-2543)***
Creative Disposal & Packg, Minneapolis *Also Called Great Northern Corp* ***(G-4554)***
Creative Lighting 651 647-0111
1728 Concordia Ave Saint Paul (55104) ***(G-8265)***
Creative Marketing Concepts 320 679-4105
2775 Jade St Mora (55051) ***(G-6356)***
Creative Marketing Consulting 952 935-9385
1600 Gervais Ave Ste 8 Saint Paul (55109) ***(G-8266)***
Creative Promotional Concepts 651 905-9339
1301 Corporate Center Dr # 175 Saint Paul (55121) ***(G-7740)***
Creative Source One, Saint Paul *Also Called Schawk Inc* ***(G-8933)***
Creative Sustainable Solutions 651 602-6644
909 Montreal Cir Saint Paul (55102) ***(G-8267)***
Creative Training Techniques 952 829-1954
14530 Martin Dr Eden Prairie (55344) ***(G-1637)***
Creekridge Capital LLC 952 996-0270
7808 Creekridge Cir # 250 Minneapolis (55439) ***(G-4180)***
Cremation Society Inc 612 825-2435
4343 Nicollet Ave Minneapolis (55409) ***(G-4181)***
Crest Electronics Inc 320 275-3382
195 3rd St Dassel (55325) ***(G-1160)***
Crest Services, Albert Lea *Also Called American Baptist Homes of The* ***(G-39)***
Crest View Corp (PA) 763 782-1611
4444 Reservoir Blvd Minneapolis (55421) ***(G-3447)***
Crest View Corp 763 788-2020
444 Reservois Blvd Minneapolis (55421) ***(G-3448)***
Crestline Hotels & Resorts Inc 651 291-8800
411 Minnesota St Saint Paul (55101) ***(G-8268)***
Crestview Manor Inc 218 948-2219
649 State St NW Evansville (56326) ***(G-1924)***
Crew2 Inc 612 276-1600
2650 Minnehaha Ave Minneapolis (55406) ***(G-4182)***
Cri Securities Inc 612 617-6000
2701 University Ave SE # 100 Minneapolis (55414) ***(G-4183)***
Criminal Investigation Dept 612 673-2941
350 S 5th St Ste 108 Minneapolis (55415) ***(G-4184)***
Critical Care Services Inc 612 638-4900
3010 Broadway St NE Minneapolis (55413) ***(G-4185)***
Croix Oil Co 651 439-5755
1749 Greeley St S Stillwater (55082) ***(G-9608)***
Croixdale Apts 651 275-4800
750 Highway 95 N Bayport (55003) ***(G-347)***
Croixdale Residents, Bayport *Also Called Washington County Association* ***(G-351)***
Cronstrom Furnace & Sheet 952 920-3800
6437 Goodrich Ave Minneapolis (55426) ***(G-4186)***
Crookston Family Service Ctr 218 281-1343
1407 Erskine St Crookston (56716) ***(G-1119)***
Crookston Firefighter Relief 218 281-4584
620 S Main St Crookston (56716) ***(G-1120)***
Crookston Fuel Co 218 281-2157
1020 Highway 75 S Crookston (56716) ***(G-1121)***
Crookston Welding Machine Co 218 281-6911
Hwy 75S Crookston (56716) ***(G-1122)***
Crosby Ironton Transportation 218 546-6156
829 8th St NE Crosby (56441) ***(G-1146)***
Cross Telecom Corp 952 983-3500
10900 Nesbitt Ave S Bloomington (55437) ***(G-493)***
Crosscountry Courier Inc 651 686-5520
1010 Aldrin Dr Saint Paul (55121) ***(G-7741)***
Crossings The, Montevideo *Also Called Montevideo Country Club Inc* ***(G-6254)***
Crossroads At Penn Apartments (PA) 612 866-3628
7620 Penn Ave S Minneapolis (55423) ***(G-4187)***
Crossroads Care Center, Worthington *Also Called Atchison Enterprises Inc* ***(G-10179)***
Crossroads Center Mall, Saint Cloud *Also Called Lansing Mall LP* ***(G-7543)***
Crossroads Medical Centers, Chaska *Also Called Chaska Medical Center* ***(G-957)***
Crossroads South Metro Inc 651 698-8006
2100 Ford Pkwy Ste 201 Saint Paul (55116) ***(G-8269)***
Crossroads Trailer Sales & Svc 507 373-4443
Hwy 65 S Albert Lea (56007) ***(G-45)***
Crosstown Masonry Inc 763 434-6371
1322 159th Ave NE Anoka (55304) ***(G-171)***
Crosstown Used Auto Parts 612 861-3020
218 Pascal St N Saint Paul (55104) ***(G-8270)***
Crow River Country Club 320 587-3070
915 Colorado St NW Hutchinson (55350) ***(G-2695)***
Crow River State Bank (PA) 763 972-3385
710 Babcock Blvd E Delano (55328) ***(G-1182)***
Crow River Technical Inc 763 560-6015
3300 Bass Lake Rd Ste 318 Minneapolis (55429) ***(G-4188)***
Crow Wing Cooperative Power (PA) 218 829-2827
17330 State Highway 371 Brainerd (56401) ***(G-562)***
Crow Wing County Hwy Dept 218 824-1110
16589 County Road 142 Brainerd (56401) ***(G-563)***
Crown Equipment Corp 651 645-8668
860 Vandalia St Saint Paul (55114) ***(G-8271)***
Crown Plastics Inc 763 557-6000
12615 16th Ave N Minneapolis (55441) ***(G-4189)***
Crowne Plaza Northstar Hotel, Minneapolis *Also Called Marcus Hotels Inc* ***(G-4946)***
Cryptic Masons of Minneso 507 437-2851
303A N Main St Austin (55912) ***(G-269)***
Crystal Care Center, Minneapolis *Also Called Voa Care Centers MN* ***(G-5981)***

ALPHABETIC

www.HarrisInfo.com
556
2011 Harris Minnesota
Services Directory
(G-00000) Company's Geographic Section entry number

Crystal Care Home Health Svcs 612 861-4272
6461 Lyndale Ave S Minneapolis (55423) *(G-4190)*

Crystal Distribution Inc 763 391-7790
17560 Tyler St NW Elk River (55330) *(G-1870)*

Crystal Lake Automotive Inc 952 892-3377
16055 Buck Hill Rd Lakeville (55044) *(G-2897)*

Crystal Lake Bus Service Inc 507 243-3282
59780 235th St Madison Lake (56063) *(G-3078)*

Crystal Lake Country Club Inc 952 432-6566
16725 Innsbrook Dr Lakeville (55044) *(G-2898)*

Crystal Marine Inc 952 233-3437
12720 Chestnut Blvd Shakopee (55379) *(G-9434)*

Crystal Valley Coop 507 642-8837
111 S Broadway La Salle (56056) *(G-2846)*

Crysteel Truck Equipment Inc (PA) 507 726-6041
52248 Ember Rd Lake Crystal (56055) *(G-2857)*

Crysteel Truck Equipment Inc 952 469-5678
21470 Grenada Ave Lakeville (55044) *(G-2899)*

CS McCrossan Inc (PA) 763 425-4167
7865 Jefferson Hwy Osseo (55369) *(G-6606)*

CS Solutions Inc 651 603-8288
4660 Slater Rd Ste 200 Eagan (55122) *(G-1523)*

Csi International 952 882-9115
615 E 132nd St Burnsville (55337) *(G-704)*

Csi Sports Properties LLC 320 252-4193
360 Industrial Blvd Sauk Rapids (56379) *(G-9361)*

Csl Plasma Inc 218 727-8139
106 W Superior St Duluth (55802) *(G-1287)*

Csl Plasma Inc 612 331-9180
1026 Washington Ave SE Minneapolis (55414) *(G-4191)*

Csl Plasma Inc 651 646-2556
1054 University Ave W Saint Paul (55104) *(G-8272)*

CSM Corp of Minnesota 952 829-0033
7780 Flying Cloud Dr Eden Prairie (55344) *(G-1638)*

CSM Corp of Minnesota 952 738-7300
5901 Wayzata Blvd Minneapolis (55416) *(G-4192)*

CSM Corp of Minnesota 612 340-1300
425 S 2nd St Minneapolis (55401) *(G-4193)*

CSM Corp of Minnesota 612 375-1700
225 3rd Ave S Minneapolis (55401) *(G-4194)*

CSM Corp of Minnesota 952 593-1918
9960 Wayzata Blvd Minneapolis (55426) *(G-4195)*

CSM Corp of Minnesota 651 746-8000
2905 Centre Pointe Dr Saint Paul (55113) *(G-8273)*

CSM Equities LLC 612 395-7000
500 Washington Ave S # 3000 Minneapolis (55415) *(G-4196)*

CSM Executive Lodging LLC 612 395-7195
500 Washington Ave S 300 Minneapolis (55415) *(G-4197)*

Cssi, Saint Paul *Also Called Creative Sustainable Solutions (G-8267)*

CU Recovery Inc 651 462-4400
26263 Forest Blvd Wyoming (55092) *(G-10201)*

Cub Food Store 5193, Eden Prairie *Also Called Jerry's Enterprises Inc (G-1701)*

Cub Foods Inc 763 755-9802
12595 Central Ave NE Minneapolis (55434) *(G-3449)*

Culbert Realty, Virginia *Also Called Walter W Culbert Jr (G-9763)*

Cullen's Home Center of 320 762-1249
1620 N Nokomis St NE Alexandria (56308) *(G-93)*

Culligan International Co 507 354-2311
918 S German St New Ulm (56073) *(G-6447)*

Culligan Soft Water Service Co 763 535-4545
7165 Boone Ave N Ste 100 Minneapolis (55428) *(G-4198)*

Culligan Soft Water Service Co (PA) 952 933-7200
6030 Culligan Way Minnetonka (55345) *(G-6157)*

Culligan Store Solutions 651 681-9000
1030 Lone Oak Rd Ste 110 Saint Paul (55121) *(G-7742)*

Cummings, Keegan & Co Pllp 952 345-2500
600 Highway 169 S Ste 1625 Minneapolis (55426) *(G-4199)*

Cumulus Media Inc 507 334-0061
601 Central Ave N Faribault (55021) *(G-2000)*

Cumulus Media Inc 507 288-1025
1530 Greenview Dr SW Ste 200 Rochester (55902) *(G-7090)*

Cuneo & Associates, Minneapolis *Also Called Laurence Cuneo & Associates (G-4849)*

Cuningham Group Architecture (PA) 612 379-3400
201 Main St SE Ste 325 Minneapolis (55414) *(G-4200)*

Curb Masters Inc 651 351-9200
500 Poplar St W Stillwater (55082) *(G-9609)*

Curbside Lawn Care 952 403-9012
9084 Windsor Ct Savage (55378) *(G-9387)*

Curry Sales Inc 952 351-4200
5700 Smetana Dr Ste 200 Hopkins (55343) *(G-2534)*

Curtis Oil & Tire 218 729-8241
4995 Miller Trunk Hwy Duluth (55811) *(G-1288)*

Curves For Women, Darwin *Also Called P & D Klitzke Enterprises Inc (G-1158)*

Curves For Women, Fairmont *Also Called Georgie's Fitness Inc (G-1967)*

Cushman & Wakefield Inc 763 450-3600
11095 Viking Dr Ste 240 Eden Prairie (55344) *(G-1639)*

Cushman & Wakefield Inc 612 659-1743
333 S 7th St Ste 320 Minneapolis (55402) *(G-4201)*

Cushman & Wakefield Inc 612 671-7593
1001 S 3rd St Minneapolis (55415) *(G-4202)*

Custom Communications Inc 507 288-5522
1661 Greenview Dr SW Rochester (55902) *(G-7091)*

Custom Door Sales Inc 612 332-0357
5005 Hillsboro Ave N Minneapolis (55428) *(G-4203)*

Custom Drywall Inc 651 488-0533
488 Atwater Cir Saint Paul (55103) *(G-8274)*

Custom Hbc Corp 952 442-8241
888 Industrial Blvd Ste 1 Waconia (55387) *(G-9784)*

Custom Millwork Inc 651 770-2356
2298 2nd St N Saint Paul (55109) *(G-8275)*

Custom One Painting Inc 612 787-1040
2543 Marshall St NE Minneapolis (55418) *(G-4204)*

Custom Plastic Laminates Inc 612 781-8191
1 E 19th St Minneapolis (55403) *(G-4205)*

Custom Remodelers Inc 651 784-2646
474 Apollo Dr Ste 60A Circle Pines (55014) *(G-1009)*

Custom Transfer Inc 320 732-3013
23512 230th St Long Prairie (56347) *(G-3041)*

Custom Tring Svcs Economic Dev, Bemidji *Also Called Minnesota State Community (G-403)*

Customer Elation Inc 320 968-4438
161st Ave S Foley (56329) *(G-2136)*

Customer Traac Inc 218 435-2600
102 Kaiser Ave S Fosston (56542) *(G-2175)*

Customer Traac Inc (PA) 763 553-2989
3030 Harbor Ln N Ste 132 Minneapolis (55447) *(G-4206)*

Customerlink LLC 218 722-2800
1 E 1st St Ste 300 Duluth (55802) *(G-1289)*

Cut Fruit Express Inc 651 438-8834
11585 Courthouse Blvd Inver Grove Heights (55077) *(G-2747)*

Cutting Edge Creations Inc 651 209-8600
920 Apollo Rd Ste 100 Saint Paul (55121) *(G-7743)*

Cuyuna Range Hospital Inc (PA) 218 546-7000
320 E Main St Crosby (56441) *(G-1147)*

Cuyuna Range Hospital Inc 218 546-7000
NE 4th St Crosby (56441) *(G-1148)*

Cvrx Inc 763 416-2840
9201 W Broadway Ave Ste 650 Minneapolis (55445) *(G-4207)*

Cybertrol Engineering LLC 763 559-8660
2950 Xenium Ln N Ste 130 Minneapolis (55441) *(G-4208)*

Cygnia Corp 952 887-9030
10800 Lyndale Ave S # 244 Minneapolis (55420) *(G-4209)*

Cygnus Expositions 952 894-8007
801 Cliff Rd E Ste 201 Burnsville (55337) *(G-705)*

Cynthia Cook Inc 952 854-4975
1701 American Blvd E # 17 Minneapolis (55425) *(G-4210)*

Cynw LLC 763 425-5355
11871 Fountains Way Maple Grove (55369) *(G-3238)*

D & A Truck Line Inc 651 769-1045
700 Broadway Ave Saint Paul Park (55071) *(G-9294)*

D & E Transport Inc 763 878-2880
4141 150th St NW Clearwater (55320) *(G-1043)*

D & G Excavating Inc 507 532-2334
2324 County Road 30 Marshall (56258) *(G-3292)*

D & G Packaging Co 952 890-7525
12039 Riverwood Dr Burnsville (55337) *(G-706)*

D & M Industries Inc 218 287-3100
4205 30th Ave S Moorhead (56560) *(G-6309)*

D & R Star Inc (PA) 507 282-6080
2207 7th St NW Rochester (55901) *(G-7092)*

D & R Vinge, Farmington *Also Called Vinge Tile (G-2062)*

D A C, Milaca *Also Called Mille Lacs Cty Area (G-3380)*

D A Peterson 612 782-9860
2500 Highway 88 Ste 210 Minneapolis (55418) *(G-4211)*

D B Direct Mail 320 485-7827
351 Lewis Ave W Winsted (55395) *(G-10160)*

D C C Solutionolutions 320 839-2058
105 2nd St NW Ortonville (56278) *(G-6581)*

D C International Falls Phrm, International Falls *Also Called Smdc Health System (G-2730)*

D C M Services LLC 612 332-3700
4150 Olson Memorial Hwy Minneapolis (55422) *(G-4212)*

D C Sales Co Inc 612 728-8700
2700 Minnehaha Ave Minneapolis (55406) *(G-4213)*

D D D Motel Corp 507 625-9333
1111 Range St Mankato (56003) *(G-3224)*

D D D Motel Corp 507 345-1234
101 E Main St Mankato (56001) *(G-3121)*

D D P Marketing Inc 952 808-7615
13965 W Preserve Blvd Burnsville (55337) *(G-707)*

D H I Mortgage 952 985-7850
20860 Kenbridge Ct Ste 140 Lakeville (55044) *(G-2900)*

D J Baune & J A Dosen Ptr 952 473-2002
301 Carlson Pkwy Ste 350 Hopkins (55305) *(G-2535)*

D J'S Heating & Air Condg 763 421-5313
9940 Highway 10 Elk River (55330) *(G-1871)*

D L R Excavating Inc 651 437-3128
11545 190th St E Hastings (55033) *(G-2380)*

D L Ricci Corp 651 388-8661
5001 Moundview Dr Red Wing (55066) *(G-6977)*

D L Ryan Co's Ltd 612 204-9790
10 S 5th St Ste 330 Minneapolis (55402) *(G-4214)*

D M & E, Waseca *Also Called Dakota, Minnesota & Eastern (G-9875)*

D M I LLC 952 841-6200
7831 E Bush Lake Rd # 300 Minneapolis (55439) *(G-4215)*

D M S Health Group 763 315-1947
11600 96th Ave N Osseo (55369) *(G-6607)*

D P S, Minneapolis *Also Called Diversified Pharmaceutical (G-4263)*

D Rock Center & Small Engines, Saint Paul *Also Called F M Trucking Inc (G-8359)*

D T I, Winona *Also Called Digital Telecommunications Inc (G-10092)*

D W Jones Trucking Inc 651 227-4854
33 Acker St E Saint Paul (55117) *(G-8276)*

D&R Vending, Rochester *Also Called Richard Hawkins (G-7224)*

D-Rock Center, Saint Paul *Also Called F M Trucking Inc (G-8358)*

D-S Beverages Inc 218 233-1343
201 17th St N Moorhead (56560) *(G-6310)*

Dac Bemidji, Bemidji *Also Called Nothern Cass Bemidji Inc (G-416)*

Dacon Engineering & Service Co 763 544-1686
5101 Olson Memorial Hwy Minneapolis (55422) *(G-4216)*

Daggett Truck Line Inc 218 334-3711
32717 County Road 10 Frazee (56544) *(G-2184)*

Dahl Consulting Inc 651 772-9225
418 County Road D E Saint Paul (55117) *(G-8277)*

Dahl Trucking Inc 507 773-4226
2535 50th St Granada (56039) *(G-2256)*

Dahlgren & Co Inc (PA) 218 281-2985
1220 Sunflower St Crookston (56716) *(G-1123)*

Dahlheimer Distributing Co Inc 763 295-3347
3360 Chelsea Rd W Monticello (55362) *(G-6268)*

Dahlke Trailer Sales Inc 763 783-0077
8170 Hickory St NE Minneapolis (55432) *(G-3450)*

Dain Rauscher Inc 612 371-2711
60 S 6th St Ste 700 Minneapolis (55402) *(G-4217)*

Dairy Farmers of America Inc 218 736-5691
301 S Buse St Fergus Falls (56537) *(G-2073)*

Dairy Farmers Of America Inc 507 732-5124
1313 Northstar Dr Zumbrota (55992) *(G-10218)*

ALPHABETIC

(PA)=Parent Co (HQ)=Headquarters (DH)=Div Headquarters
2011 Harris Minnesota Services Directory
© Harris InfoSource 1-866-281-6415
557

Dairy Quality Control Inst (PA) 763 785-0484
5205 Quincy St Saint Paul (55112) *(G-8278)*

Dairy Queen, Saint Paul *Also Called Theodore F Bolles* *(G-9281)*

Dairyland Peac, Sauk Centre *Also Called Ecm Publishers Inc* *(G-9344)*

Dakota Cook LLC 612 332-1010
1010 Nicollet Mall Minneapolis (55403) *(G-4218)*

Dakota County Abstract & Title 651 437-5600
1250 N Frontage Rd Ste 105 Hastings (55033) *(G-2381)*

Dakota County Community Devpt 651 675-4400
1228 Town Centre Dr Saint Paul (55123) *(G-7744)*

Dakota County Receiving Center 651 437-4209
1294 18th St E Bldg 1 Hastings (55033) *(G-2382)*

Dakota County Transportation 651 423-2101
2800 160th St W Rosemount (55068) *(G-7367)*

Dakota Electric Association (PA) 651 463-6212
4300 220th St W Farmington (55024) *(G-2047)*

Dakota Growers Pasta Co Inc 763 531-5340
7300 36th Ave N Minneapolis (55427) *(G-4219)*

Dakota Highway Department 952 891-7109
14955 Galaxie Ave Ste 55 Saint Paul (55124) *(G-7745)*

Dakota Inn Motel, Redwood Falls *Also Called Lower Sioux Community Council* *(G-7024)*

Dakota Pediatric Clinic 952 997-2572
17504 Dodd Blvd Lakeville (55044) *(G-2901)*

Dakota Rhoads Masonry Inc 651 437-2100
18575 Donnelly Ave Hastings (55033) *(G-2383)*

Dakota Ridge LLC 763 398-1821
3450 Washington Dr Saint Paul (55122) *(G-7746)*

Dakota Sport & Fitness 952 445-9400
2100 Trail Of Dreams Prior Lake (55372) *(G-6931)*

Dakota Supply Group 952 890-3811
12205 Nicollet Ave Burnsville (55337) *(G-708)*

Dakota Supply Group Inc 651 224-5781
475 Minnehaha Ave W Saint Paul (55103) *(G-8279)*

Dakota Turf Inc 651 460-8873
1016 220th St W Farmington (55024) *(G-2048)*

Dakota Unlimited Inc 651 423-3995
15953 Biscayne Ave W Rosemount (55068) *(G-7368)*

Dakota Woodlands Inc 651 456-9110
3430 Wescott Woodlands Eagan (55123) *(G-1524)*

Dakota's Adults Inc 651 688-8808
2031 Victoria Rd S Mendota Heights (55118) *(G-3362)*

Dakota, Minnesota & Eastern 507 835-4185
308 State St S Waseca (56093) *(G-9875)*

Dakotah Sport & Fitness Center 952 445-9400
2100 Trail Of Dreams Prior Lake (55372) *(G-6932)*

Dakt Enterprises Inc 952 474-6683
7472 Washington Ave S Eden Prairie (55344) *(G-1640)*

Dalbec Roofing Inc 952 473-8080
2285 Daniels St Long Lake (55356) *(G-3023)*

Dalco Enterprises Inc 651 604-2966
300 5th Ave NW Saint Paul (55112) *(G-8280)*

Dalco Roofing & Sheet Metal 763 559-0222
15525 32nd Ave N Minneapolis (55447) *(G-4220)*

Dale Tile Co 763 488-1880
8400 89th Ave N Ste 445 Minneapolis (55445) *(G-4221)*

Daley Farm of Lewiston LLP 507 523-3687
18762 Highway 14 Lewiston (55952) *(G-2965)*

Dallas I Hanson Construction 320 839-3455
700 US Highway 75 Ortonville (56278) *(G-6582)*

Dam Lake Sportmens Club 218 927-6263
316 4th St NW Aitkin (56431) *(G-18)*

Damberg Scott Gerzina Wagner 218 727-2626
2 W 1st St Ste 201 Duluth (55802) *(G-1290)*

Dan & Jerry's Greenhouses Inc (PA) 763 271-6594
2121 90th St NE Monticello (55362) *(G-6269)*

Dan Dahlin Inc 763 434-6010
16465 Highway 65 NE Anoka (55304) *(G-172)*

Dan Larson Enterprises Inc 612 331-8550
3101 Spring St NE Minneapolis (55413) *(G-4222)*

Dan Treb Painting & Decorating, Long Lake *Also Called Treb, Dan Painting* *(G-3034)*

Dan-AM Co 507 346-7102
1 Sata Dr Spring Valley (55975) *(G-9569)*

Dana Johnson 651 774-5843
1396 White Bear Ave N A Saint Paul (55106) *(G-8281)*

Dance Art Centre 952 937-2618
7605 Corporate Way Eden Prairie (55344) *(G-1641)*

Danelski Construction Co Inc 218 372-3236
8087 County Highway 61 Willow River (55795) *(G-10060)*

Daniel Building, Saint Cloud *Also Called St Cloud Denovo* *(G-7598)*

Daniel J Olsgaard 218 299-6162
441 Clearview Ct Moorhead (56560) *(G-6311)*

Daniel P Khoury 651 738-0470
7803 Afton Rd Saint Paul (55125) *(G-9200)*

Danny's Construction Co Inc 952 445-4143
1066 3rd Ave W Ste 4 Shakopee (55379) *(G-9435)*

Daran Inc 763 856-4000
12280 255th Ave NW Ste 2 Zimmerman (55398) *(G-10212)*

Darling International Inc 507 526-3296
9000 382nd Ave Blue Earth (56013) *(G-533)*

Darrell B Johnson Disposal Co 218 729-5446
930 Highway 2 Duluth (55810) *(G-1291)*

Dart Transit Co 651 688-2000
800 Lone Oak Rd Saint Paul (55121) *(G-7747)*

Darts 651 455-1560
1645 Marthaler Ln Saint Paul (55118) *(G-7748)*

Dasco Systems Inc 763 574-2275
7787 Ranchers Rd NE Minneapolis (55432) *(G-3451)*

Dascom Systems Group LLC 651 578-1200
2415 Ventura Dr Saint Paul (55125) *(G-9201)*

Dash-Two Advertising, Eden Prairie *Also Called Threewire Inc* *(G-1792)*

Data Listing Services LLC (PA) 952 948-5488
11351 Rupp Dr Ste G Burnsville (55337) *(G-709)*

Data Print Distribution, Edina *Also Called Professional Reproductions Inc* *(G-1841)*

Data Recognition Corp (PA) 763 268-2000
13490 Bass Lake Rd Maple Grove (55311) *(G-3239)*

Data Recognition Corp 763 268-2238
8900 Wyoming Ave N Minneapolis (55445) *(G-4223)*

Data Sales Co Inc (PA) 952 890-8838
3450 W Burnsville Pkwy Burnsville (55337) *(G-710)*

Data Solutions International 952 943-8137
5900 Baker Rd Ste 100 Minnetonka (55345) *(G-6158)*

Data Systems Inc 952 934-4001
6566 Edenvale Blvd Eden Prairie (55346) *(G-1642)*

Datacard Corp (PA) 952 933-1223
11111 Bren Rd W Minnetonka (55343) *(G-6159)*

Datalink Corp (PA) 952 944-3462
8170 Upland Cir Chanhassen (55317) *(G-917)*

Datatrend Technologies Inc 952 931-1203
121 Cheshire Ln Ste 700 Minnetonka (55305) *(G-6160)*

Dave Osborne Construction 763 540-0232
15600 28th Ave N Plymouth (55447) *(G-6858)*

Dave Syverson Inc 507 373-1438
2310 E Main St Albert Lea (56007) *(G-46)*

Dave Syverson Truck Center Inc 507 289-3357
7 County 16 Rd SE Rochester (55904) *(G-7093)*

Dave Taylor Constructon Inc 952 472-1342
5991 Ridgewood Rd Mound (55364) *(G-6387)*

Dave's Floor Sanding 763 784-3000
1451 92nd Ln NE Minneapolis (55449) *(G-3452)*

Davey Tree Expert Co 763 553-9740
2500 Fernbrook Ln N Minneapolis (55447) *(G-4224)*

David Balt Do 507 825-3390
920 4th Ave SW Pipestone (56164) *(G-6824)*

David G McAlphie MD 651 731-0859
8325 City Centre Dr Saint Paul (55125) *(G-9202)*

David Kelloway 952 944-0739
2515 E 26th St Minneapolis (55406) *(G-4225)*

David's Body Shop Inc 612 377-3003
245 Aldrich Ave N Ste 220 Minneapolis (55405) *(G-4226)*

Davida, Minneapolis *Also Called Total Renal Care Inc* *(G-5836)*

Davidson Construction Inc 218 449-4865
65 State St Holt (56738) *(G-2494)*

Davidson Hotel Co 763 566-8000
2200 Freeway Blvd Minneapolis (55430) *(G-4227)*

Davidson Ready Mix Inc 218 449-4865
65 State St Holt (56738) *(G-2495)*

Davies Chapel 612 377-2203
2301 Dupont Ave S Minneapolis (55405) *(G-4228)*

Davies Printing Co 952 473-6924
16507 Holdridge Rd W Wayzata (55391) *(G-9913)*

Davis Dental Lab 952 345-6315
5775 Wayzata Blvd Ste 670 Minneapolis (55416) *(G-4229)*

Davis Drywall Inc 218 444-2532
1100 Industrial Park Dr SE Bemidji (56601) *(G-387)*

Davis Russ Wholesale Inc 218 631-3070
266 4th St NE Wadena (56482) *(G-9800)*

Davis Typewriter Co Inc 507 343-2001
1158 Oxford St Worthington (56187) *(G-10182)*

Davisco Foods International 952 914-0400
11000 W 78th St Ste 210 Eden Prairie (55344) *(G-1643)*

Dawn Food Products Inc 763 428-8826
20195 S Diamond Lake Rd # 200 Rogers (55374) *(G-7321)*

Dawson Area Hospital District 320 769-4323
1282 Walnut St Dawson (56232) *(G-1164)*

Day S P A At Nails Etc 952 830-0100
7575 France Ave S Minneapolis (55435) *(G-4230)*

Day Spa, Minneapolis *Also Called Cook & Koff Enterprises Inc* *(G-4161)*

Daybreak Foods Inc 320 732-2966
609 6th St NE Long Prairie (56347) *(G-3042)*

Dayco Concrete Co Inc 952 556-0278
1850 Lake Dr W Chanhassen (55317) *(G-918)*

Dayport Inc 507 344-3000
209 S 2nd St Ste 408 Mankato (56001) *(G-3122)*

Days Inn, Duluth *Also Called Brutger Equities Inc* *(G-1257)*

Days Inn, Saint Paul *Also Called Em - Ty Corp* *(G-8334)*

Days Inn Roseville, Saint Paul *Also Called Oak Hotels Inc* *(G-8777)*

Days Inn, Eveleth MN, Duluth *Also Called Sbsb LP* *(G-1444)*

Days Inn-St Paul Nw Roseville, Saint Paul *Also Called Bryanston Group Inc* *(G-8137)*

Days Inns & Suites 763 561-8400
6415 James Cir N Minneapolis (55430) *(G-4231)*

Dayton Freight Lines Inc 763 493-5841
10001 89th Ave N Osseo (55369) *(G-6608)*

Dayton Radison Inc 612 672-0060
24 S 8th St Fl 2 Minneapolis (55402) *(G-4232)*

Dayton Residence, Saint Paul *Also Called Boston Health Care Systems Inc* *(G-8118)*

Dayton-Radisson Ramp 612 333-2293
1300 Nicollet Ave Ste 3060 Minneapolis (55403) *(G-4233)*

Dbi Consulting Inc 763 561-4990
6200 Shingle Creek Pkwy # 5 Minneapolis (55430) *(G-4234)*

DCA Title Co 952 432-5600
7373 147th St W Ste 161 Saint Paul (55124) *(G-7749)*

Dcci, Shakopee *Also Called Danny's Construction Co Inc* *(G-9435)*

DCI Environmental Inc 952 894-0012
7217 W 128th St Savage (55378) *(G-9388)*

Dcm Services LLC 763 852-8440
4150 Olson Memorial Hwy # 200 Minneapolis (55422) *(G-4235)*

Deacons Lodge Golf Club, Pequot Lakes *Also Called Sienna Corp* *(G-6792)*

Deafblind Services Minnesota 612 362-8454
1936 Lyndale Ave S Minneapolis (55403) *(G-4236)*

Dealers Choice Auto Clean 763 592-9900
8601 73rd Ave N Minneapolis (55428) *(G-4237)*

Debbie Bolen 218 722-0912
1600 Miller Trunk Hwy Duluth (55811) *(G-1292)*

Debt Management Center, Saint Paul *Also Called VA Departmental Offices* *(G-7966)*

Decare Dental LLC 800 371-6561
3560 Delta Dental Dr Saint Paul (55122) *(G-7750)*

Decc, Duluth *Also Called Duluth Entertainment Conv* *(G-1298)*

Deceased Credit Management LLC 763 852-8400
4150 Olson Memorial Hwy Minneapolis (55422) *(G-4238)*

Deck & Door Co 952 432-1888
6900 151st St W Ste 100 Saint Paul (55124) *(G-7751)*

Deck Images, Hastings *Also Called Stylepointe LLC* *(G-2418)*

Deco Inc (PA) 763 576-9572
11140 Zealand Ave N Champlin (55316) *(G-892)*

Deconstruction Services 888 224-2608
2801 21st Ave S Ste 190 Minneapolis (55407) *(G-4239)*
Decorators Service Co of 763 383-2955
14100 21st Ave N Ste B Plymouth (55447) *(G-6859)*
Dedicated Logistics Inc 763 504-9229
8201 54th Ave N Minneapolis (55428) *(G-4240)*
Dedicated Logistics Inc (PA) 651 631-5918
2900 Granada Ln N Oakdale (55128) *(G-6550)*
Dedina Eye Physicians 952 832-8179
7450 France Ave S Ste 100 Minneapolis (55435) *(G-4241)*
Dee Spee Delivery Service Inc 507 288-0695
4225 Garden Ct SE Rochester (55904) *(G-7094)*
Dee Spee Delivery Service Inc (PA) 320 251-6697
4101 Clearwater Rd Saint Cloud (56301) *(G-7496)*
Deer River Healthcare Center 218 246-2900
1002 Comstock Dr Deer River (56636) *(G-1168)*
Deer River Hired Hands Inc 218 246-8182
309 3rd Ave SE Deer River (56636) *(G-1169)*
Deer River Wild Rice 218 246-2713
E Hwy 2 Deer River (56636) *(G-1170)*
Deer Run Golf Club LLC 952 443-2351
8661 Deer Run Dr Victoria (55386) *(G-9727)*
Deerwood Bancshares Inc (PA) 218 534-3111
21236 Archibald Rd Deerwood (56444) *(G-1175)*
Deerwood Builders Inc 218 534-5408
21279 Archibald Rd Deerwood (56444) *(G-1176)*
Deerwood Plant, Deerwood *Also Called Weyerhaeuser Co (G-1180)*
Definity Health Corp (HQ) 952 277-5500
1600 Utica Ave S Ste 900 Minneapolis (55416) *(G-4242)*
Degidio Inc 651 291-7105
425 7th St W Saint Paul (55102) *(G-8282)*
Degidio's, Saint Paul *Also Called Degidio Inc (G-8282)*
Dehn's Country Manor Inc 763 420-6460
11281 Fernbrook Ln N Osseo (55369) *(G-6609)*
Dehn's Gardens Inc 763 753-2806
16485 Tulip St NW Anoka (55304) *(G-173)*
Delancy Builders Inc 612 354-3724
2210 44th Ave N Minneapolis (55412) *(G-4243)*
Deli Express, Eden Prairie *Also Called E A Sween Deli Express (G-1647)*
Delkor Systems Inc 763 783-0855
8700 Rendova St NE Circle Pines (55014) *(G-1010)*
Dell-Comm Inc (PA) 763 783-0035
4860 Mustang Cir Saint Paul (55112) *(G-8283)*
Dellwood Hills Golf Club 651 426-3218
29 Highway 96 E Saint Paul (55110) *(G-9203)*
Deloitte & Touche LLP 612 397-4772
10824 Johnson Ave S Minneapolis (55437) *(G-4244)*
Deloughery Home LP 507 523-2123
505 E Main St Lewiston (55952) *(G-2966)*
Delta Co's LLC 952 929-5005
4005 W 65th St Ste 208 Minneapolis (55435) *(G-4245)*
Delta Environmental Consints (PA) 651 639-9449
5910 Rice Creek Pkwy # 100 Saint Paul (55126) *(G-8284)*
Delta Industrial Services Inc 763 755-7744
11501 Eagle St NW Minneapolis (55448) *(G-3453)*
Delta Kappa Gamma Society 507 451-2523
909 Truman Ave Owatonna (55060) *(G-6708)*
Delta Protective Services 612 331-1885
1302 2nd St NE Minneapolis (55413) *(G-4246)*
Deluxe Corp (PA) 651 483-7111
3680 Victoria St N Saint Paul (55126) *(G-8285)*
Deluxe Financial Services Inc 651 787-2766
3660 Victoria St N Saint Paul (55126) *(G-8286)*
Delwin Transfer Inc 651 731-0510
7500 Hudson Blvd N Ste 620 Saint Paul (55128) *(G-9204)*
Dem-Con Landfill LLC 952 445-5755
13020 Dem Con Dr Shakopee (55379) *(G-9436)*
Democratic Party of Olmsted 507 536-9785
2002 2nd St SW Rochester (55902) *(G-7095)*
Denali, Minneapolis *Also Called Bonfire Partners LLC (G-3926)*
Denco II LLC 320 589-2931
227 County Road 22 Morris (56267) *(G-6371)*
Denison Mailing Service Inc 952 888-1460
9601 Newton Ave S Ste A Minneapolis (55431) *(G-4247)*
Dennis Co's Inc 651 488-4835
551 Topping St Saint Paul (55103) *(G-8287)*
Dennis Fehn Gravel 763 497-2428
5050 Barthel Indus Dr Albertville (55301) *(G-73)*
Dennis Raedeke Inc 651 465-6365
37350 Wild Mountain Rd Taylors Falls (55084) *(G-9660)*
Denny Kemp Inc 612 676-0300
605 Central Ave SE Minneapolis (55414) *(G-4248)*
Denny's, Saint Paul *Also Called Nath Management Inc (G-8736)*
Densei USA, Saint Paul *Also Called Techscan Corp (G-9035)*
Dental Specialists 952 926-2763
8650 Hudson Blvd N # 105 Lake Elmo (55042) *(G-2868)*
Dentistry At The Center Inc 320 762-5216
2306 S Broadway St Ste 4 Alexandria (56308) *(G-94)*
Dentistry For Children, Minneapolis *Also Called Affliated Pediatric Dentists (G-3695)*
Department of Corrections MN 320 384-7411
61085 State Highway 23 Finlayson (55735) *(G-2129)*
Department of Corrections MN 218 485-5000
1000 Lakeshore Dr Moose Lake (55767) *(G-6349)*
Department of Corrections MN 218 376-4411
62741 County Road 551 Togo (55723) *(G-9685)*
Department of Health Minnesota 218 335-3200
425 7th St NW Cass Lake (56633) *(G-871)*
Department of Public Utilities, Virginia *Also Called Virginia, City of Inc (G-9761)*
Department of Public Works, Saint Paul *Also Called City of White Bear Lake (G-8213)*
Dependable Care Inc 763 438-2811
6001 78th Ave N Ste 201 Brooklyn Park (55443) *(G-608)*
Dependable Home Health Care 651 779-9810
2984 Rice St Saint Paul (55113) *(G-8288)*
Dependable Indoor Air Quality 763 757-5040
2619 Coon Rapids Blvd NW # 100 Minneapolis (55433) *(G-3454)*
Depotstar Inc 763 506-9990
6180 140th Ave NW Anoka (55303) *(G-174)*
Dermatology Department, Minneapolis *Also Called Regents of The University of (G-5498)*
Design Electric Inc 320 252-1658
4807 Heatherwood Rd Saint Cloud (56301) *(G-7497)*
Design Ready Controls Inc 763 565-3000
6704 Bleck Dr Rockford (55373) *(G-7309)*
Design Systems, Minneapolis *Also Called Selftek (G-5635)*
Designed Cabinets Inc 952 469-2700
7965 215th St W Lakeville (55044) *(G-2902)*
Destineer Inc 763 231-8000
13755 1st Ave N Ste 500 Minneapolis (55441) *(G-4249)*
Details Salon & Spa 651 696-8700
757 Cleveland Ave S Ste 4 Saint Paul (55116) *(G-8289)*
Development Resource Group Inc 763 783-7878
7295 Silver Lake Rd Saint Paul (55112) *(G-8290)*
Devicix LLC 952 368-0073
7680 Executive Dr Eden Prairie (55344) *(G-1644)*
Dewar Electric Inc 507 235-6677
724 E Blue Earth Ave Fairmont (56031) *(G-1962)*
Dexterity Dental Arts Inc 651 463-4444
310 Division St Farmington (55024) *(G-2049)*
Dey Appliance Parts of CO 651 490-9191
1401 Willow Lake Blvd Saint Paul (55110) *(G-8291)*
Dey Appliance Parts of North 651 490-9191
1401 Willow Lake Blvd Saint Paul (55110) *(G-8292)*
Dey Distributing 651 490-9191
1401 Willow Lake Blvd Saint Paul (55110) *(G-8293)*
Dey Distributing Inc (PA) 651 490-9191
1401 Willow Lake Blvd Saint Paul (55110) *(G-8294)*
Dey Properties 651 490-9191
1401 Willow Lake Blvd Saint Paul (55110) *(G-8295)*
Dfg Inc 612 343-8936
17 Washington Ave N Minneapolis (55401) *(G-4250)*
DH Blattner & Sons Inc (PA) 320 356-7351
392 County Road 50 Avon (56310) *(G-294)*
Dhm Minneapolis Hotel, LP 763 489-2570
2200 Freeway Blvd Minneapolis (55430) *(G-4251)*
Diamond Drilling & Supply Inc 218 628-3671
2916 W 1st St Duluth (55806) *(G-1293)*
Diamond K Dairy Inc 507 689-2058
19622 County Road 28 Altura (55910) *(G-131)*
Diamond Women's Center 952 927-4045
6545 France Ave S Ste 540 Minneapolis (55435) *(G-4252)*
Diamondrock Minneapolis Tenant 612 376-1000
1001 Marquette Ave Minneapolis (55403) *(G-4253)*
Dick's Sanitation Service Inc 952 469-2239
8984 215th St W Lakeville (55044) *(G-2903)*
Dick's Valley Service Inc 952 891-4431
6781 146th St W Apple Valley (55124) *(G-243)*
Dicke Billig & Czaja 612 573-2000
100 S 5th St Ste 2250 Minneapolis (55402) *(G-4254)*
Dickson Enterprises Inc 218 759-2000
2525 Middle School Rd NW Bemidji (56601) *(G-388)*
Diebold Investments LLC (PA) 952 960-9600
6530 Cortlawn Cir N 300 Minneapolis (55426) *(G-4255)*
Diesel Cast Welding Inc 763 780-5940
2190 107th Ln NE Minneapolis (55449) *(G-3455)*
Dig America Utility Contr (PA) 320 253-3447
25135 22nd Ave Saint Cloud (56301) *(G-7498)*
Diggers Bar & Grill Inc 507 634-7400
401 8th St SE Kasson (55944) *(G-2819)*
Digi-Key Corp 218 681-6674
701 Brooks Ave S Thief River Falls (56701) *(G-9666)*
Digineer Inc 763 210-2300
505 Highway 169 N Ste 750 Minneapolis (55441) *(G-4256)*
Digital Datavoice Corp 651 452-0300
1210 Northland Dr Ste 160 Saint Paul (55120) *(G-7752)*
Digital Images Inc (PA) 651 688-0888
2915 Commers Dr Ste 900 Saint Paul (55121) *(G-7753)*
Digital River Inc (PA) 952 253-1234
9625 W 76th St Ste 150 Eden Prairie (55344) *(G-1645)*
Digital Telecommunications Inc 507 452-2303
111 Riverfront Ste 305 Winona (55987) *(G-10092)*
Digitiliti Inc 651 925-3200
266 7th St E Fl 4 Saint Paul (55101) *(G-8296)*
Dignified Assisted Living Inc 763 428-1981
20600 S Diamond Lake Rd Rogers (55374) *(G-7322)*
Dima Corp 507 373-6969
400 W Front St Albert Lea (56007) *(G-47)*
Dinnaken Properties Inc 612 623-3634
900 Washington Ave SE Apt 216 Minneapolis (55414) *(G-4257)*
Diocese of St Cloud 320 252-4121
305 7th Ave N Ste 100 Saint Cloud (56303) *(G-7499)*
Direct Home Health Care Inc 612 870-8256
1607 Chicago Ave Minneapolis (55404) *(G-4258)*
Direct Mail Mktg Specialists, Minneapolis *Also Called General Marketing Services Inc (G-4511)*
Direct Pub, Inver Grove Heights *Also Called Cernick Enterprises (G-2741)*
Direct Response Insurance 952 556-5600
7930 Century Blvd Chanhassen (55317) *(G-919)*
Direct Source Inc 952 934-8000
8176 Mallory Ct Chanhassen (55317) *(G-920)*
Dirk Miller 651 645-5323
2550 University Ave W Ste 314N Saint Paul (55114) *(G-8297)*
Disable Home Heaklth Care Inc 651 292-8705
1086 Rice St Ste 2 Saint Paul (55117) *(G-8298)*
Discover Magical Moments 507 289-7463
5450 Royal Pl NW Rochester (55901) *(G-7096)*
Discover Mortgage, Minneapolis *Also Called TCS Mortgage Inc (G-5801)*
Discover Property & Casualty 800 878-2660
385 Washington St Saint Paul (55102) *(G-8299)*
Dison's Cleaners & Laundry Inc 507 289-3944
214 Broadway Ave N Rochester (55906) *(G-7097)*
Display Sales Co 952 885-0100
10925 Nesbitt Ave S Minneapolis (55437) *(G-4259)*
Distinction In Design Inc 763 550-1138
14264 23rd Ave N Minneapolis (55447) *(G-4260)*

ALPHABETIC

Distinctive Door Design Inc 763 389-1631
32010 126th St Princeton (55371) *(G-6920)*
Distributed Website Corp 507 453-5164
60 Oakwood Ct Winona (55987) *(G-10093)*
District 196, Rosemount *Also Called Rosemount-Apple Valley & Eagan (G-7374)*
District 7b, Windom *Also Called Minnesota Department of Trans (G-10069)*
District 7e, Mankato *Also Called Minnesota Department of Trans (G-3170)*
District Energy St Paul Inc 651 297-8955
76 Kellogg Blvd W Saint Paul (55102) *(G-8300)*
Diverse Computer Corp 651 766-8138
2353 Rice St Ste 208 Saint Paul (55113) *(G-8301)*
Diversified Adjustment Service 763 783-2301
600 Coon Rapids Blvd NW Minneapolis (55433) *(G-3456)*
Diversified Construction 952 929-7233
4931 W 35th St Ste 100 Saint Louis Park (55416) *(G-7659)*
Diversified Consulting Assocs 651 436-1330
915 Nordic Ct N Stillwater (55082) *(G-9610)*
Diversified Contracting Inc 763 712-8087
13950 Radium St NW # 300 Anoka (55303) *(G-175)*
Diversified Distribution Systs (PA) 612 813-5200
2828 10th Ave S Ste 200 Minneapolis (55407) *(G-4261)*
Diversified Dynamics Corp 763 780-5440
1681 94th Ln NE Minneapolis (55449) *(G-3457)*
Diversified Industries Inc 763 513-5951
6040 Earle Brown Dr # 250 Minneapolis (55430) *(G-4262)*
Diversified Laboratory Testing 763 785-0484
5205 Quincy St Saint Paul (55112) *(G-8302)*
Diversified Lifestyles Inc 320 235-0270
1111 6th St SE Willmar (56201) *(G-10000)*
Diversified Motel Properties 218 728-3601
2400 London Rd Duluth (55812) *(G-1294)*
Diversified Pharmaceutical 952 820-7000
6225 W 78 St Minneapolis (55439) *(G-4263)*
Divine Healthcare Network 651 665-9795
856 University Ave W Saint Paul (55104) *(G-8303)*
Divine House Inc 218 847-0574
26881 County Highway 32 Detroit Lakes (56501) *(G-1191)*
Divine House Inc 320 589-3652
618 Pacific Ave Morris (56267) *(G-6372)*
Divine Providence Community 507 794-3011
700 3rd Ave NW Sleepy Eye (56085) *(G-9494)*
Divine Providence Health Ctr 507 694-1414
312 E George St Ivanhoe (56142) *(G-2784)*
Division of Pulmonary All, Minneapolis *Also Called Regents of The University of (G-5490)*
Division21 Inc 651 917-8805
2402 University Ave W Ste 702 Saint Paul (55114) *(G-8304)*
Djont Jpm Leasing LLC 952 884-4811
2800 American Blvd W Minneapolis (55431) *(G-4264)*
Djont Operations LLC 952 854-1000
7901 34th Ave S Minneapolis (55425) *(G-4265)*
Dkg Management 214 776-1155
12213 17th Ave S Apt B Burnsville (55337) *(G-711)*
Dks Systems LLC 952 476-7443
725 Ferndale Rd N Wayzata (55391) *(G-9914)*
Dl-Dw Holdings LLC 952 942-6818
11905 Technology Dr Eden Prairie (55344) *(G-1646)*
DLM A MN LLP 218 233-0065
3300 8th St S Moorhead (56560) *(G-6312)*
Dlo Excavating & Poured Walls 651 480-8457
12151 120th St S Hastings (55033) *(G-2414)*
Dlr Group Kke 612 977-3500
520 Nicollet Mall Ste 200 Minneapolis (55402) *(G-4266)*
DMC Plumbing & Heating Inc 507 356-4455
301 N Main St Pine Island (55963) *(G-6815)*
DMW Properties Inc 763 432-3401
4317 Flag Ave N Minneapolis (55428) *(G-4267)*
Dmz Trucking Inc 320 252-0313
3635 Quail Rd NE 1 Sauk Rapids (56379) *(G-9362)*
Dnk Management Inc 651 773-8077
3080 Centerville Rd Ste 1 Saint Paul (55117) *(G-8305)*
Dobbs Temporary Services Inc (PA) 612 373-2600
50 S 10th St Ste 500 Minneapolis (55403) *(G-4268)*
Doboszenski & Sons Inc 763 478-6945
9520 County Road 19 Loretto (55357) *(G-3046)*
Doctors Diagnostic Center Ltd 763 550-0707
12805 Highway 55 Ste 111 Minneapolis (55441) *(G-4269)*
Dodge Center Ambulance Svcs 507 374-2600
305 1st St NW Dodge Center (55927) *(G-1226)*
Dodge County Battered Women's 507 634-6070
402 S Mantorville Ave Kasson (55944) *(G-2820)*
Dodge of Burnsville Inc 952 894-9000
12101 Highway 35W S Burnsville (55337) *(G-712)*
Doherty Employment Group Inc 952 832-8383
7625 Parklawn Ave Minneapolis (55435) *(G-4270)*
Doherty Staffing Solutions 952 832-8300
7645 Metro Blvd Ste 1 Edina (55439) *(G-1829)*
Dolce International 952 368-3100
1 Oakridge Dr Chaska (55318) *(G-961)*
Doll Enterprises Inc 651 488-0228
694 County Road B W Saint Paul (55113) *(G-8306)*
Dollars For Scholars, Minneapolis *Also Called Scholarship America (G-5612)*
Dolphin Pools Inc 763 542-9000
3405 Highway 169 N Plymouth (55441) *(G-6860)*
Dolphin Staffing, Minneapolis *Also Called Dfg Inc (G-4250)*
Dom-Ex LLC 218 262-6116
109 Grant St Hibbing (55746) *(G-2442)*
Domaille Ltd 507 287-1170
535 37th St NE Rochester (55906) *(G-7098)*
Domaine Srene Vineyards Winery 763 473-4412
6701 Evenstad Dr N Osseo (55369) *(G-6610)*
DOMESTIC ABUSE INTERVENTION PR, Duluth *Also Called Minnesota Program Development (G-1395)*
Domestic Abuse Project Inc 612 874-7063
204 W Franklin Ave Minneapolis (55404) *(G-4271)*
Dominium Group Inc 763 354-5500
2355 Polaris Ln N Ste 100 Minneapolis (55447) *(G-4272)*
Dominium Management Services 763 560-0244
5805 73rd Ave N Minneapolis (55429) *(G-4273)*
Dominium Management Services (PA) 763 354-5500
2355 Polaris Ln N Ste 100 Minneapolis (55447) *(G-4274)*
Don Cameron & Associates Inc 952 884-0070
396 American Blvd E Minneapolis (55420) *(G-4275)*
Don Stevens Inc 651 452-0872
980 Discovery Rd Eagan (55121) *(G-1525)*
Don Stolz Productions, Excelsior *Also Called Old Log Theater Ltd (G-1951)*
Don's Bus Service Inc 763 497-2585
11108 60th St Albertville (55301) *(G-74)*
Don's Car Washes of Minnesota 763 788-1631
4423 Central Ave NE Minneapolis (55421) *(G-3458)*
Don's Leather Cleaning Inc 612 721-4881
3713 E Lake St Minneapolis (55406) *(G-4276)*
Donahues' Greenhouses Inc 507 334-8404
420 10th St SW Faribault (55021) *(G-2001)*
Donald A Driggs 952 471-9500
2925 Casco Point Rd Wayzata (55391) *(G-9915)*
Donald H Sealock 763 559-7358
4455 Highway 169 N # 100 Minneapolis (55442) *(G-4277)*
Donald Holm Construction Co 218 628-2257
3211 W 3rd St Duluth (55806) *(G-1295)*
Donatelle Properties 651 633-4200
501 County Road E2 Ext Saint Paul (55112) *(G-8307)*
Dondelinger Chevrolet 218 829-4787
7915 State Highway 210 Baxter (56425) *(G-327)*
Dondelinger Chevrolet Cadillac, Baxter *Also Called A & R Leasing Inc (G-318)*
Donlin Co (PA) 320 251-3680
3405 Energy Dr Saint Cloud (56304) *(G-7411)*
Donlyn Manufacture 763 786-1103
1490 94th Ln NE Minneapolis (55449) *(G-3459)*
Donmar Inc 763 631-2233
31337 121st St Princeton (55371) *(G-6921)*
Donnelly Brothers Construction 612 866-1204
5928 Portland Ave Minneapolis (55417) *(G-4278)*
Donnelly Custom Manufacturing 320 762-2396
105 Donovan Dr Alexandria (56308) *(G-95)*
Donnelly Electric Inc 651 487-2877
1126 Rice St Saint Paul (55117) *(G-8308)*
Donner Industries Inc (PA) 651 429-0890
5561 152nd St N Hugo (55038) *(G-2676)*
Doody Mechanical Inc 651 487-1061
1301 L Orient St Ste 1 Saint Paul (55117) *(G-8309)*
Dooley's Petroleum Inc 320 875-2641
304 Main Ave Murdock (56271) *(G-6400)*
Doran Construction Inc 763 421-0553
7803 Glenroy Rd Ste 200 Minneapolis (55439) *(G-4279)*
Dorf & Stanton Communications (HQ) 952 832-5000
8000 Norman Center Dr Ste 400 Minneapolis (55437) *(G-4280)*
Dorsey & Whitney LLP (PA) 612 340-2600
50 S 6th St Ste 1500 Minneapolis (55402) *(G-4281)*
Doubletree Corp 952 542-8600
1500 Park Place Blvd Minneapolis (55416) *(G-4282)*
Doug Bradley Trucking Inc 507 532-9681
1301 W Main St Marshall (56258) *(G-3293)*
Doug Speedling Builders Inc 651 437-3658
1303 Eddy St Hastings (55033) *(G-2384)*
Doug Thorson Sales Co Inc 218 736-2249
105 E Lincoln Ave Fergus Falls (56537) *(G-2074)*
Dougherty & Co LLC 612 376-4000
90 S 7th St Ste 4300 Minneapolis (55402) *(G-4283)*
Dougherty Financial Group LLC (PA) 612 376-4000
90 S 7th St Ste 4300 Minneapolis (55402) *(G-4284)*
Douglas County Hospital, Alexandria *Also Called County of Douglas (G-90)*
Douglas County Hospital, Alexandria *Also Called County of Douglas (G-91)*
Douglas County Public Health, Alexandria *Also Called County of Douglas (G-92)*
Douglas Drive Car Wash Inc 763 533-1581
5301 Douglas Dr N Minneapolis (55429) *(G-4285)*
Dover Fluid Management Inc 651 388-3565
3965 Pepin Ave Red Wing (55066) *(G-6978)*
Dovray Community Center 507 274-5602
Main St Dovray (56125) *(G-1230)*
Downtowner Car Wash 651 222-7045
520 7th St E Saint Paul (55101) *(G-8310)*
Dp Property Acquisition LLC 612 344-1515
322 1st Ave N Minneapolis (55401) *(G-4286)*
Dpra Inc 651 227-6500
332 Minnesota St Saint Paul (55101) *(G-8311)*
Dr Peter Schmitz Inc 218 829-7812
2014 S 6th St Brainerd (56401) *(G-564)*
Dresel Contracting Inc 651 257-9469
24044 July Ave Chisago City (55013) *(G-990)*
Drive 1057, Minneapolis *Also Called Minneapolis Radio LLC (G-5060)*
Drover's Inn & Restaurant Inc 320 252-6034
701 Concord St S South Saint Paul (55075) *(G-9526)*
Drs Acquisitions Inc 320 351-8100
833 Main St S Sauk Centre (56378) *(G-9343)*
Ds & B Ltd 612 359-9630
222 S 9th St Ste 3000 Minneapolis (55402) *(G-4287)*
Dsw Shoe Warehouse Inc 952 876-0991
124 W Market Minneapolis (55425) *(G-4288)*
Dual Temp Inc 763 494-9358
7550 Commerce St Hamel (55340) *(G-2339)*
Duane Kottke Trucking Corp 320 833-5385
211 Hwy 212 E Buffalo Lake (55314) *(G-663)*
Duane Sauke 507 287-7742
4600 18th Ave NW Rochester (55901) *(G-7099)*
Duffy Engineering & Associates 320 259-6575
350 Highway 10 S Ste 101 Saint Cloud (56304) *(G-7412)*
Duininck Inc (PA) 320 978-6011
208 6th St Prinsburg (56281) *(G-6925)*
Duke & King Acquisition Corp (PA) 952 288-2300
12252 Nicollet Ave Burnsville (55337) *(G-713)*
Duke & King Acquisition Corp 651 731-8720
1501 Vly Creek Rd Wier Dr Saint Paul (55125) *(G-9205)*
Duke Co's 612 331-4880
430 Industrial Blvd NE Minneapolis (55413) *(G-4289)*

ALPHABETIC SECTION
Ebert Inc

Duke Financial Group Inc (PA) 612 204-0255
80 S 8th St Ste 2900 Minneapolis (55402) *(G-4290)*
Duke Realty Corp 952 543-2900
1600 Utica Ave S Ste 250 Minneapolis (55416) *(G-4291)*
Duluth 10 Theater 218 722-1573
300 Harbor Dr Duluth (55802) *(G-1296)*
Duluth Area Family Y M C A 218 372-3188
89382 E Frontage Rd Sturgeon Lake (55783) *(G-9657)*
Duluth Area Family YMCA (PA) 218 722-4745
302 W 1st St Duluth (55802) *(G-1297)*
Duluth Clinc- Ely Inc 218 365-7900
300 W Conan St Ely (55731) *(G-1913)*
Duluth Clinic International 218 283-9431
2501 Keenan Dr International Falls (56649) *(G-2719)*
Duluth Clinic of Ely, Ely *Also Called Smdc Health System (G-1915)*
Duluth Clinic West, Duluth *Also Called Smdc Health System (G-1453)*
Duluth Clinic- Deer River, Deer River *Also Called Smdc Health System (G-1173)*
Duluth Detoxification Center, Duluth *Also Called Center For Alcohol & Drug (G-1265)*
Duluth Entertainment Conv 218 722-5573
350 Harbor Dr Duluth (55802) *(G-1298)*
Duluth Graduate Medical Educn 218 529-9105
330 N 8th Ave E Duluth (55805) *(G-1299)*
Duluth Lodging Inc 218 628-1464
3900 W Superior St Duluth (55807) *(G-1300)*
Duluth Lodging Inc (PA) 218 628-1464
3900 W Superior St Duluth (55807) *(G-1301)*
Duluth Missabe & Iron Range 218 723-2016
227 W 1st St Duluth (55802) *(G-1302)*
Duluth Softball Players Assn 218 722-5569
2132 W 3rd St Duluth (55806) *(G-1303)*
Duluth Superior Area 218 724-8567
632 Niagara Ct Duluth (55811) *(G-1304)*
Duluth Superior Erection Inc 218 626-1112
2385 Becks Rd Duluth (55810) *(G-1305)*
Duluth Transit Authority 218 722-7283
2402 W Michigan St Duluth (55806) *(G-1306)*
Dun & Bradstreet Inc 952 841-9961
3600 Amercn Blvd W Fl 6 Bloomington (55431) *(G-494)*
Duncan Co 612 331-1776
425 Hoover St NE Minneapolis (55413) *(G-4292)*
Dundee Nursery & Landscaping (PA) 763 559-4004
16800 Highway 55 Minneapolis (55446) *(G-4293)*
Dungarvin Illinois Inc 651 699-6050
690 Cleveland Ave S Saint Paul (55116) *(G-8312)*
Dungarvin Minnesota Inc 651 699-6050
690 Cleveland Ave S Saint Paul (55116) *(G-8313)*
Dungarvin New Mexico Inc (PA) 651 699-6050
690 Cleveland Ave S Saint Paul (55116) *(G-8314)*
Dunham Associates Inc 612 465-7550
50 S 6th St Ste 1100 Minneapolis (55402) *(G-4294)*
Dunk N Jump 612 788-0404
1500 Jackson St NE # 185 Minneapolis (55413) *(G-4295)*
Dunkley & Bennett 612 339-1290
701 4th Ave S Ste 700 Minneapolis (55415) *(G-4296)*
Dunlap & Seeger 507 288-9111
206 S Broadway Ste 505 Rochester (55904) *(G-7100)*
Dunn Bros Coffee Inc 651 698-0618
1569 Grand Ave Saint Paul (55105) *(G-8315)*
Dunn Enterprises Inc (PA) 612 627-5661
302 Industrial Blvd NE Minneapolis (55413) *(G-4297)*
Duplication Factory LLC 952 448-9912
4275 Norex Dr Chaska (55318) *(G-962)*
Dura-Supreme Inc 320 543-3872
300 Dura Dr Howard Lake (55349) *(G-2666)*
Duracoat Inc 320 587-3135
10 Michigan St NE Hutchinson (55350) *(G-2696)*
Durst Brothers 507 635-5588
56541 245th Ave Mantorville (55955) *(G-3233)*
Dustcoating Inc 952 894-0012
7217 W 128th St Savage (55378) *(G-9389)*
Dvcm ServiceMaster of The 320 763-5551
203 Lake St Alexandria (56308) *(G-96)*
Dymanyk Electric 612 379-4112
1915 Broadway St NE Minneapolis (55413) *(G-4298)*
Dynamax Inc 651 644-8787
2395 Capp Rd Saint Paul (55114) *(G-8316)*
Dynamex Operations East Inc 651 644-8787
2100 Old Highway 8 NW Saint Paul (55112) *(G-8317)*
Dynixa Corp 651 436-8800
16440 7th Street Ln S Lakeland (55043) *(G-2884)*
E & A Products Inc 763 493-3222
11885 Brockton Ln N Osseo (55369) *(G-6611)*
E & C Amec Services Inc 612 332-8326
800 Marquette Ave Ste 1200 Minneapolis (55402) *(G-4299)*
E & H Enterprises of 320 762-8645
2510 S Broadway St Alexandria (56308) *(G-97)*
E A Sween Deli Express (PA) 952 937-9440
16101 W 78th St Eden Prairie (55344) *(G-1647)*
E B I Inc 218 624-3508
3921 W 4th St Duluth (55807) *(G-1307)*
E Frame 952 926-3555
6600 France Ave S Ste 670 Minneapolis (55435) *(G-4300)*
E H Lawrence Co 218 254-5705
6 1st St SE Chisholm (55719) *(G-996)*
E J M Pipe Services Inc 651 786-8041
7807 Lake Dr Circle Pines (55014) *(G-1011)*
E P A Audio Visual Inc 763 477-6931
7910 State Hwy 55 Rockford (55373) *(G-7310)*
E S I Heritage 218 865-4135
5024 Heritage Trl Gilbert (55741) *(G-2203)*
E T C Enterprises Inc 320 240-0567
24707 County Road 75 Saint Cloud (56301) *(G-7500)*
E Tech Inc 612 722-1366
1401 W River Rd Ste D Minneapolis (55411) *(G-4301)*
E W Blanch International Inc 952 886-8000
3600 Amercn Blvd W # 700 Minneapolis (55431) *(G-4302)*
E Weinberg Supply Co Inc 952 920-0888
7434 W 27th St Minneapolis (55426) *(G-4303)*
E Z Air Park Inc 651 454-1302
2804 Lexington Ave S Saint Paul (55121) *(G-7754)*
E-Con-Placer, Saint Paul *Also Called Engineered Concrete Placer of (G-7763)*
E-Group Inc 612 339-4777
901 N 3rd St Ste 195 Minneapolis (55401) *(G-4304)*
EAC Design Inc 952 435-5533
14501 Judicial Rd Ste 10 Burnsville (55306) *(G-714)*
Eagan Cinema 16, Saint Paul *Also Called Regal Cinemas Inc (G-7892)*
Eagan Kindercare, Saint Paul *Also Called Kindercare Learning Centers (G-7817)*
Eagan Lodging Group LLC 651 450-1100
5653 Bishop Ave Inver Grove Heights (55076) *(G-2748)*
Eagan Transport Inc 651 452-6268
3101 Sibley Memorial Hwy Saint Paul (55121) *(G-7755)*
Eagle Construction Co Inc 320 632-5429
515 9th Ave NW Little Falls (56345) *(G-3001)*
Eagle Elevator Corp 651 645-1543
600 Fairview Ave N Saint Paul (55104) *(G-8318)*
Eagle Lake Golf Center 763 694-7695
11000 County Road 10 Minneapolis (55442) *(G-4305)*
Eagle Tool & Design Inc 763 784-7400
7979 Central Ave NE Minneapolis (55432) *(G-3460)*
Eagle Transport Services Inc 507 281-9787
2430 Marion Rd SE Rochester (55904) *(G-7101)*
Eagle's Landing Golf Club Inc 320 632-5721
14825 263rd St Fort Ripley (56449) *(G-2173)*
Eaglecrest, Saint Paul *Also Called P H M Eaglecrest Inc (G-8799)*
Eagles Club, Owatonna *Also Called Fraternal Order of Eagles Club (G-6714)*
Eagles Club Rooms, Thief River Falls *Also Called Fraternal Order of Eagles Inc (G-9668)*
Eagles Hall 218 847-5267
112 Holmes St W Detroit Lakes (56501) *(G-1192)*
Eagles Nest Shelter, Saint Paul *Also Called Women of Nations (G-9163)*
Ear Nose & Throat (PA) 612 871-1144
2211 Park Ave Minneapolis (55404) *(G-4306)*
Ear Nose Throat Specialty Care 763 421-8443
3960 Coon Rapids Blvd NW # 315 Minneapolis (55433) *(G-3461)*
Ear, Nose Throat, Head & Neck 320 252-0233
1528 Northway Dr Saint Cloud (56303) *(G-7501)*
Earle Brown Heritage Center, Minneapolis *Also Called City of Brooklyn Center (G-4085)*
Early Child Family Education 507 625-4620
110 Fulton St Mankato (56001) *(G-3123)*
Early Childhood Center 952 556-6400
110600 Village Rd Chaska (55318) *(G-963)*
Early Childhood Center, Maple Plain *Also Called Orono Independent School Dist (G-3280)*
Early Childhood Development, Circle Pines *Also Called Centennial Independent School (G-1004)*
Early Childhood Family Educatn, Minneapolis *Also Called Independent School District 16 (G-3496)*
Early Intervention Service, Moorhead *Also Called Independent School District (G-6319)*
Earthlink Inc 507 847-2700
924 Highway 71 N Jackson (56143) *(G-2790)*
East Asian Trading Co Inc 763 473-3520
405 Brockton Ln N Minneapolis (55447) *(G-4307)*
East Bay Hotel Corp 218 387-2800
1 Wisconsin St Grand Marais (55604) *(G-2259)*
East Central Energy (PA) 320 396-3351
412 Main Ave N Braham (55006) *(G-541)*
East Central Sanitation, Cambridge *Also Called M & M Sanitation Inc (G-841)*
East Central Veterinary 320 679-4197
2004 Mahogany St Mora (55051) *(G-6357)*
East Lake Community Center 218 768-3311
3666 State Hwy McGregor (55760) *(G-3339)*
East Metro Asc LLC 651 702-7400
8650 Hudson Blvd N # 235 Lake Elmo (55042) *(G-2869)*
East Metro Endoscopy Center 612 870-5482
1997 Sloan Pl Ste 26 Saint Paul (55117) *(G-8319)*
East Metro Family Practice 651 457-2748
2980 Buckley Way Inver Grove Heights (55076) *(G-2749)*
East Metro Family Practice, Saint Paul *Also Called Mark Macdonald Do (G-7832)*
East Metro Family Practice 651 776-2719
911 Maryland Ave E Ste 1 Saint Paul (55106) *(G-8320)*
East Metro Gorman 651 455-2940
234 Wentworth Ave E Saint Paul (55118) *(G-7756)*
East Otter Tail Telephone Co 218 346-5500
150 2nd Ave SW Perham (56573) *(G-6796)*
East Range Developmental 218 744-5130
800 A Ave Eveleth (55734) *(G-1930)*
East Side Neighborhood Svcs 612 781-6011
1700 2nd St NE Minneapolis (55413) *(G-4308)*
East Suburban Resources Inc (PA) 651 351-0190
1754 Washington Ave S Stillwater (55082) *(G-9611)*
East Suburban Resources Inc 651 464-5137
1754 Washington Ave S Stillwater (55082) *(G-9612)*
East View Information Services 952 252-1201
10601 Wayzata Blvd Hopkins (55305) *(G-2536)*
Easter Seal Minnesota, Saint Paul *Also Called Goodwill Industries Inc (G-8421)*
Easton Telephone, Wells *Also Called Blue Earth Valley Telephone Co (G-9961)*
Eastside Beverage, Minneapolis *Also Called JJ Taylor Co's Inc (G-4765)*
Eastside YMCA, Saint Paul *Also Called YMCA of Greater Saint Paul (G-9174)*
Easy Automation Inc 507 728-8214
102 Mill St Welcome (56181) *(G-9958)*
Eaton Corp 952 937-9800
14900 Technology Dr Eden Prairie (55344) *(G-1648)*
Eaton Corp 952 939-5400
5421 Feltl Rd Ste 190 Minnetonka (55343) *(G-6161)*
Eaton Corp 952 912-1330
5421 Feltl Rd Ste 190 Minnetonka (55343) *(G-6162)*
Ebenezer Ridges Inc 952 898-8400
13820 Community Dr Burnsville (55337) *(G-715)*
Ebenezer Society 952 435-8116
13820 Community Dr Burnsville (55337) *(G-716)*
Ebenezer Society 612 879-2262
2545 Portland Ave Minneapolis (55404) *(G-4309)*
Ebenezer Society 612 879-1400
2523 Portland Ave Ste 1 Minneapolis (55404) *(G-4310)*
Ebert Inc 763 498-7844
23350 County Road 10 Loretto (55357) *(G-3047)*

ALPHABETIC

Ebf & Associates LP 952 476-7200
601 Carlson Pkwy Ste 200 Hopkins (55305) *(G-2537)*

Ebi Inc 218 624-3122
625 N 56th Ave W Duluth (55807) *(G-1308)*

Ebureau LLC 320 534-5000
25 6th Ave N Saint Cloud (56303) *(G-7502)*

Eca, Evansville *Also Called Evansville Arts Coalition (G-1925)*

Eckles Telephone Co Inc 507 526-3252
123 W 7th St Blue Earth (56013) *(G-534)*

Eclipse Transportation Inc 651 293-1111
44 Moreland Ave E Saint Paul (55118) *(G-7757)*

Ecm Publishers Inc 763 689-1981
234 Main St S Cambridge (55008) *(G-837)*

ECM Publishers Inc (PA) 763 712-2400
4095 Coon Rapids Blvd NW Minneapolis (55433) *(G-3462)*

Ecm Publishers Inc 320 352-6569
601 Sinclair Lewis Ave Sauk Centre (56378) *(G-9344)*

Ecmc, Saint Paul *Also Called Educational Credit Management (G-9209)*

Ecologic Analytics LLC 952 843-6000
8011 34th Ave S Ste 205 Bloomington (55425) *(G-495)*

Ecommerce Network Resource Grp 612 340-1110
3033 Excelsior Blvd # 307 Minneapolis (55416) *(G-4311)*

Econo Foods, Farmington *Also Called Nash-Finch Co (G-2055)*

Econo Foods, Hutchinson *Also Called Nash-Finch Co (G-2708)*

Econo Foods, Saint Peter *Also Called Nash-Finch Co (G-9309)*

Econofoods, Cannon Falls *Also Called Nash-Finch Co (G-861)*

Econofoods Pharmacy 330, Northfield *Also Called Nash-Finch Co (G-6535)*

Econofoods Quality Care Phrm, Northfield *Also Called Nash-Finch Co (G-6534)*

Economy Garages of Deerwood, Deerwood *Also Called Deerwood Builders Inc (G-1176)*

Economy Inn & Excecutive Ste, Rochester *Also Called Sunstone Hotel Management Inc (G-7268)*

Ecosure 651 293-4320
370 Wabasha St N Saint Paul (55102) *(G-8321)*

Ecowater Systems LLC (DH) 651 739-5330
1890 Woodlane Dr Saint Paul (55125) *(G-9206)*

Ecsi, Saint Paul *Also Called Rhjh Inc (G-8897)*

Ecumen 320 762-1567
1020 Lark St Alexandria (56308) *(G-98)*

Ecumen 651 257-0575
28210 Old Towne Rd Chisago City (55013) *(G-991)*

Ecumen 507 345-4576
718 Mound Ave Ste A Mankato (56001) *(G-3124)*

Ecumen (PA) 651 766-4300
3530 Lexington Ave N Saint Paul (55126) *(G-8322)*

Ecumen 218 834-8374
402 3rd Ave Two Harbors (55616) *(G-9706)*

Ecumen Home Care Inc 952 888-7751
1401 E 100th St Bloomington (55425) *(G-496)*

Ecumen Home Care Inc 218 847-4486
1415 Madison Ave Detroit Lakes (56501) *(G-1193)*

Ecumen Home Care Inc 218 525-1951
4002 London Rd Duluth (55804) *(G-1309)*

Ecumen Home Care Inc 952 888-1010
1301 E 100th St Ofc Minneapolis (55425) *(G-4312)*

Ed Lunn Construction Inc 507 288-4400
6889 10th Ave SW Ste 200 Rochester (55902) *(G-7102)*

Ed Lunn Construction Inc 507 533-6565
901 2nd Ave SW Stewartville (55976) *(G-9591)*

Edcsolutions, Minneapolis *Also Called Electronic Design Co (G-4339)*

Eddie Bauer Inc 651 738-8653
10150 Hudson Rd Ste 106 Saint Paul (55129) *(G-9207)*

Eddy's Lake Mille Lacs Resort 320 532-3657
41334 Shakopee Lake Rd Onamia (56359) *(G-6570)*

Edelweiss Home Health Care 763 315-1050
7014 E Fish Lake Rd Osseo (55311) *(G-6612)*

Eden Fch Prairie LLC 952 952-9000
6330 Point Chase Eden Prairie (55344) *(G-1649)*

Eden Prairie Community Center, Eden Prairie *Also Called City of Eden Prairie (G-1629)*

Eden Prairie Hhp-II LLC 952 942-9000
7740 Flying Cloud Dr Eden Prairie (55344) *(G-1650)*

Eden Rs 612 287-1600
1931 W Broadway Ave # 101 Minneapolis (55411) *(G-4313)*

Edencenter Family Physicians, Eden Prairie *Also Called Fairview Health Services (G-1662)*

Edgar Saldana Dr 218 249-7910
920 E 1st St Ste 201 Duluth (55805) *(G-1310)*

Edgebrook Care Center 507 442-7121
505 Trosky Rd W Edgerton (56128) *(G-1823)*

Edgewater Management LLC 218 751-3603
1019 Paul Bunyan Dr S Bemidji (56601) *(G-389)*

Edgewood Management Inc 651 714-1000
2825 Woodlane Dr Apt 224 Saint Paul (55125) *(G-9208)*

Edina Care Center, Minneapolis *Also Called Volunteers of America Care (G-5983)*

Edina Country Club 952 927-7151
5100 Wooddale Ave Minneapolis (55424) *(G-4314)*

Edina Eye Physicians 952 831-8811
7450 France Ave S Ste 100 Minneapolis (55435) *(G-4315)*

Edina Family Physicians 952 925-2200
5301 Vernon Ave S Minneapolis (55436) *(G-4316)*

Edina Imaging Center, Minneapolis *Also Called Consulting Radiologists Ltd (G-4159)*

Edina Laundry Co 952 927-9991
4500 France Ave S Minneapolis (55410) *(G-4317)*

Edina Park Plaza, Minneapolis *Also Called Partners For Senior (G-5341)*

Edina Pediatrics 952 927-7337
3250 W 66th St Ste 210 Minneapolis (55435) *(G-4318)*

Edina Plastic Surgery Ltd 952 925-1765
6525 France Ave S Ste 300 Minneapolis (55435) *(G-4319)*

Edina Realty 651 450-6876
1519 Central Pkwy Ste 100 Eagan (55121) *(G-1526)*

Edina Realty 952 844-5409
5300 Hyland Pl Minneapolis (55437) *(G-4320)*

Edina Realty Home Services 320 762-8181
815 Broadway St Alexandria (56308) *(G-99)*

Edina Realty Home Services 952 442-1700
2655 W 78th St Chanhassen (55317) *(G-921)*

Edina Realty Home Services 952 944-7107
11800 Singletree Ln # 401 Eden Prairie (55344) *(G-1651)*

Edina Realty Home Services 952 892-7000
17271 Kenyon Ave Ste 102 Lakeville (55044) *(G-2904)*

Edina Realty Home Services 763 559-2894
4425 Highway 169 N Minneapolis (55442) *(G-4321)*

Edina Realty Home Services 612 827-3551
5309 Lyndale Ave S Minneapolis (55419) *(G-4322)*

Edina Realty Home Services 763 545-5000
4800 Olson Memorial Hwy # 100 Minneapolis (55422) *(G-4323)*

Edina Realty Home Services 763 567-7000
3021 Harbor Ln N Minneapolis (55447) *(G-4324)*

Edina Realty Home Services 952 928-5900
6800 France Ave S Ste 600 Minneapolis (55435) *(G-4325)*

Edina Realty Home Services 763 755-1300
3161 Northdale Blvd NW Minneapolis (55433) *(G-3463)*

Edina Realty Home Services 651 636-2299
2407 109th Ave NE Ste 100 Minneapolis (55449) *(G-3464)*

Edina Realty Home Services 763 295-3456
9240 State Highway 25 NE Monticello (55362) *(G-6270)*

Edina Realty Home Services 507 288-7665
1301 Salem Rd SW Ste A Rochester (55902) *(G-7103)*

Edina Realty Home Services 651 770-1775
2966 White Bear Ave N Ste 2 Saint Paul (55109) *(G-8323)*

Edina Realty Home Services 651 481-6711
4570 Churchill St Saint Paul (55126) *(G-8324)*

Edina Realty Home Services 651 426-7172
2137 4th St Saint Paul (55110) *(G-8325)*

Edina Realty Home Services 651 698-2434
735 Cleveland Ave S Ste 1 Saint Paul (55116) *(G-8326)*

Edina Realty Home Services 651 430-3200
14430 60th St N Stillwater (55082) *(G-9613)*

Edina Realty Title 952 928-5181
6800 France Ave S Ste 160 Minneapolis (55435) *(G-4326)*

Edleman Productions, Minneapolis *Also Called New Paradigm Productions Inc (G-5192)*

Edocument Resources LLC 952 607-3505
6101 Baker Rd Ste 207 Minnetonka (55345) *(G-6163)*

Education Minnesota (PA) 651 227-9541
41 Sherburne Ave Saint Paul (55103) *(G-8327)*

Education Minnesota Norma, Gary *Also Called Norman County Education Assoc (G-2198)*

Educational Biometric Tech 507 724-5773
21002 Engen Rd Caledonia (55921) *(G-827)*

Educational Cooperative Svc 612 638-1500
3055 Old Highway 8 # 302 Minneapolis (55418) *(G-4327)*

Educational Credit Management 651 221-0566
1 Imation Pl Saint Paul (55128) *(G-9209)*

Educators Personal Insur Ctr, Saint Paul *Also Called EPIC Holdings Inc (G-7768)*

Edward B Cutter Post 102, Anoka *Also Called American Legion Club (G-152)*

Edwards Oil Co Inc 218 741-9634
820 Hoover Rd N Virginia (55792) *(G-9738)*

Efficio Group Inc 612 805-7288
15966 71st Pl N Osseo (55311) *(G-6613)*

Efi Global Inc 952 942-9812
7667 Cahill Rd Ste 350 Minneapolis (55439) *(G-4328)*

Efunds Corp 651 361-2000
7805 Hudson Rd Ste 100 Saint Paul (55125) *(G-9210)*

Egan Co (PA) 763 544-4131
7625 Boone Ave N Brooklyn Park (55428) *(G-609)*

Egan Co 763 567-0025
15255 23rd Ave N Plymouth (55447) *(G-6861)*

Egan Field & Nowak Surveyors, Minneapolis *Also Called Egan, Field, & Nowak Inc (G-4329)*

Egan Oil Co LLC 763 421-0410
500 Bunker Lake Blvd NW Anoka (55303) *(G-176)*

Egan, Field, & Nowak Inc 612 466-3300
1229 Tyler St NE Ste 100 Minneapolis (55413) *(G-4329)*

Eggleston Medscribe Inc 763 971-5000
3501 Douglas Dr N Minneapolis (55422) *(G-4330)*

Ego Systems Inc 952 200-8246
6500 Excelsior Blvd Fl 3 Minneapolis (55426) *(G-4331)*

Ehlers & Associates Inc 651 697-8500
3060 Centre Pointe Dr Saint Paul (55113) *(G-8328)*

Eich Motor Co 320 251-1737
1933 W Division St Saint Cloud (56301) *(G-7503)*

Eickhoff Enterprises Inc 507 537-0919
615 Kathryn Ave Marshall (56258) *(G-3294)*

Eide Bailly LLP 507 387-6031
8 W Main St Madelia (56062) *(G-3072)*

Eide Bailly LLP 507 387-6031
1911 Excel Dr Mankato (56001) *(G-3125)*

Eide Bailly LLP 952 944-6166
5601 Green Valley Dr Ste 700 Minneapolis (55437) *(G-4332)*

8th Street Garage Inc 612 349-5717
800 Marquette Ave Ste 107 Minneapolis (55402) *(G-4333)*

Eikill & Schilling Ltd 218 722-4705
230 W Superior St Ste 600 Duluth (55802) *(G-1311)*

Eikill & Schilling Ltd CPA 218 879-1503
807 Cloquet Ave Ste 1 Cloquet (55720) *(G-1051)*

Eim, Maple Plain *Also Called Electrical Installation (G-3273)*

Eis Inc 763 493-6800
9210 Wyoming Ave N Ste 215 Minneapolis (55445) *(G-4334)*

El Nuevo Rodeo, Minneapolis *Also Called Midwest Latino Entertainment (G-5030)*

El-Jay Plumbing & Heating Inc 320 251-8330
520 Apollo Ave NE Saint Cloud (56304) *(G-7413)*

Elam Investments 763 544-4264
7759 Medicine Lake Rd Minneapolis (55427) *(G-4335)*

Elander Mechanical Inc 952 445-4692
591 Citation Dr Shakopee (55379) *(G-9437)*

Elastomeric Roofing Systems 763 565-6900
6900 Bleck Dr Rockford (55373) *(G-7300)*

Elca Board of Pension, Minneapolis *Also Called Evangelical Lutheran Church In (G-4376)*

Elcor Realty of Rochester Inc 507 282-3345
3552 W River Pkwy NW Ste C Rochester (55901) *(G-7104)*

Elder Care of Bemidji Inc 218 444-1745
1633 Delton Ave NW Bemidji (56601) *(G-390)*

Elder Meadowland Care Homes 218 586-3740
21368 Gull Lake Loop Rd NE Tenstrike (56683) *(G-9662)*

Elder Network 507 285-5272
1130 1/2 73 NW Ste 205 Rochester (55901) *(G-7105)*

Elder-Jones Inc 952 854-2854
1120 E 80th St Ste 211 Minneapolis (55420) *(G-4336)*

Elderly Care Services LLC 952 882-9300
1600 Cliff Rd E Burnsville (55337) *(G-717)*

ALPHABETIC SECTION
Enn Leasing Co II LLC

Elders' Home Inc 218 385-2005
215 Tousley Ave S New York Mills (56567) *(G-6478)*
Eldon Potthoff 507 695-2784
60771 740th St Dunnell (56127) *(G-1513)*
Eldredge Trading Inc 651 778-8500
1408 Northland Dr Ste 104 Saint Paul (55120) *(G-7758)*
Eleah Medical Center 218 685-4406
930 1st St NE Elbow Lake (56531) *(G-1851)*
Eleah Medical Centre 218 685-4461
930 1st St NE Elbow Lake (56531) *(G-1852)*
Electric Motor Repair Inc 612 588-4693
2010 N 4th St Minneapolis (55411) *(G-4337)*
Electric Resource Contractors 612 522-6511
4024 Washington Ave N Minneapolis (55412) *(G-4338)*
Electrical Installation 763 479-3744
1480 County Road 90 Maple Plain (55359) *(G-3273)*
Electrical Visions Inc 763 425-1153
13501 Balsam Ln N Ste 1 Dayton (55327) *(G-1165)*
Electro-Sensors Inc (PA) 952 930-0100
6111 Blue Circle Dr Minnetonka (55343) *(G-6164)*
Electro-Watchman Inc 651 227-8461
1 Water St W Ste 110 Saint Paul (55107) *(G-8329)*
Electromed Inc 952 758-9299
500 6th Ave NW New Prague (56071) *(G-6426)*
Electronic Check Alliance 952 445-2888
332 Minnesota St Ste W820 Saint Paul (55101) *(G-8330)*
Electronic Communication Systs 651 735-7470
2300 Territorial Rd Saint Paul (55114) *(G-8331)*
Electronic Design Co 612 355-2300
3225 E Hennepin Ave Minneapolis (55413) *(G-4339)*
Electronic Easel, Saint Paul *Also Called Christ's Household of Faith (G-8199)*
Electronics For Imaging Inc 651 365-5255
1340 Corporate Ctr Curv Saint Paul (55121) *(G-7759)*
Electrosonic Inc (PA) 952 931-7500
10320 Bren Rd E Minnetonka (55343) *(G-6165)*
Elenas Care Inc 651 482-0549
500 Highway 96 W Ste 100 Saint Paul (55126) *(G-8332)*
Elert & Associates Networking 651 430-2772
140 3rd St S Stillwater (55082) *(G-9614)*
Elim Care Foundation 952 259-4500
7485 Office Ridge Cir Eden Prairie (55344) *(G-1652)*
Elim Care Inc (PA) 952 259-4500
7485 Office Ridge Cir Eden Prairie (55344) *(G-1653)*
Elim Homes Inc 952 955-2691
409 Jefferson Ave SW Watertown (55388) *(G-9890)*
Elim Nursing Home, Milaca *Also Called Evangelical Free Church of (G-3376)*
Elim Nursing Home, Princeton *Also Called Evangelical Free Church of (G-6906)*
Elite Communications & Constr 651 739-1366
651 Hayward Ave N Saint Paul (55128) *(G-9211)*
Elite Healthcare Staffing Inc 763 315-4488
10650 County Rd 81 Ste 110 Osseo (55369) *(G-6614)*
Elizabeth Charles Corp 952 915-2900
7828 Market Blvd Chanhassen (55317) *(G-922)*
Elizabeth Charles Corp (PA) 952 915-2900
3909 W 49 1/2 St Minneapolis (55424) *(G-4340)*
Elizabeth Charles Corp 952 915-2900
8375 Seasons Pkwy Saint Paul (55125) *(G-9212)*
Elk River Country Club Inc 763 441-4111
20015 Elk Lake Rd NW Elk River (55330) *(G-1872)*
Elk River Independent School 763 241-3480
600 School St NW Elk River (55330) *(G-1873)*
Elk River Municipal Utilities, Elk River *Also Called City of Elk River (G-1867)*
Elk River Nursing Home, Elk River *Also Called Guardian Angels Health Svcs (G-1880)*
Elk River Theatres, Elk River *Also Called Marcus Theatres Corp (G-1883)*
Ellerbe Becket Co (HQ) 612 376-2000
800 Lasalle Ave Ste 400 Minneapolis (55402) *(G-4341)*
Ellermedia Group 612 369-5612
8466 Eastwood Rd Saint Paul (55112) *(G-8333)*
Ellestad & Bogart & Peterson, Maple Lake *Also Called Bogart & Peterson & Associates (G-3258)*
Ellingson Drainage Inc 507 527-2294
56113 State Highway 56 West Concord (55985) *(G-9964)*
Ellingson Plumbing & Heating, Alexandria *Also Called E & H Enterprises of (G-97)*
Elliott Aviation Inc 952 944-1200
13801 Pioneer Trl Ste B Eden Prairie (55347) *(G-1654)*
Elliott Contracting Corp 612 256-0000
901 N 3rd St Ste 330 Minneapolis (55401) *(G-4342)*
Elliott Transport Systems Inc 218 236-9220
4101 32nd Ave S Moorhead (56560) *(G-6313)*
Elm North Inc 507 835-1146
104 22nd Ave NE Waseca (56093) *(G-9876)*
Elm Residence Inc 507 835-1146
204 2nd St Waseca (56093) *(G-9877)*
Elmo Lake Bank 651 777-8365
11465 39th St N Lake Elmo (55042) *(G-2870)*
Elness Swenson Graham 612 339-5508
500 Washington Ave S Ste 1080 Minneapolis (55415) *(G-4343)*
Eloyalty Corp 952 908-8000
7700 France Ave S Ste 325 Edina (55435) *(G-1830)*
Elsie's Restaurant Lounge 612 378-9702
729 Marshall St NE Minneapolis (55413) *(G-4344)*
Elsies Lounge Rest & Bowl Ctr, Minneapolis *Also Called Tuttle Inc (G-5870)*
Elvin Safety LLC 952 829-2950
7300 Washington Ave S Eden Prairie (55344) *(G-1655)*
Em - Ty Corp 651 645-0311
1964 University Ave W Saint Paul (55104) *(G-8334)*
EMA Group Inc (PA) 651 639-5600
1970 Oakcrest Ave Ste 300 Saint Paul (55113) *(G-8335)*
EMA Inc (HQ) 651 639-5600
1970 Oakcrest Ave Ste 300 Saint Paul (55113) *(G-8336)*
Ema Inc 651 639-5600
1970 Oakcrest Ave Ste 300 Saint Paul (55113) *(G-8337)*
Embarq Minnesota Inc 952 556-5679
164 Pioneer Trl Chaska (55318) *(G-964)*
Embassy Suites - Bloomington, Minneapolis *Also Called Djont Jpm Leasing LLC (G-4264)*
Embers America LLC (PA) 651 645-6473
2561 Territorial Rd Saint Paul (55114) *(G-8338)*
EMC Corp 952 828-9005
10400 Viking Dr Ste 400 Eden Prairie (55344) *(G-1656)*
Emerald Crest 952 856-7510
8150 Bavaria Rd Victoria (55386) *(G-9728)*
Emerald Crest of Burnsville 952 736-0766
455 E Travelers Trl Burnsville (55337) *(G-718)*
Emerald Crest of Minnetonka 952 933-9903
13401 Lake Street Ext Hopkins (55305) *(G-2538)*
Emerald Crest of Shakopee 952 233-8811
1855 10th Ave W Shakopee (55379) *(G-9438)*
Emerald Greens Golf Course, Hastings *Also Called Furlong Golf Inc (G-2387)*
Emerald Travel Management Co 507 345-8797
500 S Broad St Mankato (56001) *(G-3126)*
Emerge Community Development 612 529-9267
1101 W Broadway Ave 200 Minneapolis (55411) *(G-4345)*
Emergency Energy Systems 320 354-5380
6925 County Road 40 NE New London (56273) *(G-6414)*
Emergency Physicians Prof 952 835-9880
7301 Ohms Ln Ste 650 Minneapolis (55439) *(G-4346)*
Emergency Social Svc Program, Saint Paul *Also Called United Way Info & Referral (G-9110)*
Emergncy Physcians Prof Associ, Minneapolis *Also Called Emergency Physicians Prof (G-4346)*
Emily Program 952 746-5774
1660 Highway 100 S # 141 Minneapolis (55416) *(G-4347)*
Emily Program, Saint Paul *Also Called Dirk Miller (G-8297)*
Emily's Bakery & Deli Inc 651 437-3338
1212 Vermillion St Hastings (55033) *(G-2385)*
Emma B Howe Family YMCA, Minneapolis *Also Called Young Men's Chritn Assoc of (G-3644)*
Emmanuel Nursing Home, Detroit Lakes *Also Called Ecumen Home Care Inc (G-1193)*
Emmett J McMahon 612 349-8728
800 Lasalle Ave Ste 2800 Minneapolis (55402) *(G-4348)*
Emmons & Oliver Resources 218 732-3323
601 1st St E Park Rapids (56470) *(G-6751)*
Emmons & Olivier Resources Inc 651 770-8448
651 Hale Ave N Saint Paul (55128) *(G-9213)*
Emp Serv L L C 507 825-4211
1300 S Highway 75 Pipestone (56164) *(G-6825)*
Empire Door & Glass Co 612 729-4003
3415 E 27th St Minneapolis (55406) *(G-4349)*
Employer Solutions Group 952 835-1288
7301 Ohms Ln Ste 405 Minneapolis (55439) *(G-4350)*
Employers Association Inc 763 253-9100
9805 45th Ave N Minneapolis (55442) *(G-4351)*
Employers Insurance Co of 651 365-8053
860 Blue Gentian Rd # 355 Saint Paul (55121) *(G-7760)*
Employers Mutual Casualty Co 952 938-4646
6120 Blue Circle Dr Hopkins (55343) *(G-2539)*
Employment Action Center, Minneapolis *Also Called Resource Inc (G-5528)*
Employment Enterprises Inc 320 632-9251
307 9th Ave NW Little Falls (56345) *(G-3002)*
Empo Corp 612 285-8707
3100 W Lake St Ste 100 Minneapolis (55416) *(G-4352)*
Empowerment Services of MN (PA) 218 724-4014
2305 E 3rd St Duluth (55812) *(G-1312)*
Empowerment Services of Rice 507 333-2583
1003 7th St NW Faribault (55021) *(G-2002)*
EMR Innovations, Saint Cloud *Also Called Blaschko Computers Inc (G-7460)*
Enclipse Corp (PA) 612 384-6940
331 2nd Ave S Ste 703 Minneapolis (55401) *(G-4353)*
Enclos Corp (HQ) 651 796-6100
2770 Blue Waters Rd Saint Paul (55121) *(G-7761)*
Encompass Group LLC 651 646-6600
2609 Territorial Rd Saint Paul (55114) *(G-8339)*
Encompass Group LLC 651 646-6600
2609 Territorial Rd Saint Paul (55114) *(G-8340)*
Enderes Tool Co Inc 507 373-2396
924 E 14th St Albert Lea (56007) *(G-48)*
Endres Services Inc 651 438-3113
13420 Court House Blvd Rosemount (55068) *(G-7369)*
Endura Financial Federal (PA) 763 287-4630
820 Lilac Dr N Ste 200 Minneapolis (55422) *(G-4354)*
Enebak Construction Co 507 645-8962
Hwy 3 N Northfield (55057) *(G-6527)*
Energy Center, Minneapolis *Also Called NRG Energy Inc (G-5252)*
Energy Conservation Inc 763 569-0069
1601 67th Ave N Minneapolis (55430) *(G-4355)*
Energy Construction 763 489-7777
7077 Northland Cir N Minneapolis (55428) *(G-4356)*
Energy Economics Inc 507 374-2557
109 South St SE Dodge Center (55927) *(G-1227)*
Energy Management Steam 612 626-7329
3001 Fairmont Ave SE Minneapolis (55414) *(G-4357)*
Energy Resources LLC 612 889-0447
5000 W 36th St Ste 240 Saint Louis Park (55416) *(G-7660)*
Engage Health Inc 651 994-0510
852 Basswood Ln Saint Paul (55123) *(G-7762)*
Engineered Concrete Placer of 651 452-1183
2515 Northland Dr Saint Paul (55120) *(G-7763)*
Engineered Products Co 952 767-8780
5401 Smetana Dr Minnetonka (55343) *(G-6166)*
Engineering America Inc 651 777-4041
647 Hale Ave N Saint Paul (55128) *(G-9214)*
England, Michael D, Saint Paul *Also Called Minnesota Surgical Associates (G-8708)*
English Roseat Suites Inc 952 983-0412
1708 Pondview Ter Wayzata (55391) *(G-9916)*
English, Bleeker & Associates 952 230-6500
435 Ford Rd Ste 165 Saint Louis Park (55426) *(G-7661)*
Englund Graphics Inc 763 536-9100
9100 49th Ave N Minneapolis (55428) *(G-4358)*
Engstrom Excavating Inc 651 437-2782
17162 Red Wing Blvd Hastings (55033) *(G-2386)*
Enhanced Home Systems Inc 952 941-5289
9940 Hamilton Rd Ste B Eden Prairie (55344) *(G-1657)*
Eniva Corp 763 795-8870
1 Eniva Way Anoka (55303) *(G-177)*
Enn Leasing Co II LLC 651 688-0363
3040 Eagandale Pl Saint Paul (55121) *(G-7764)*

ALPHABETIC

Enn Leasing Co II LLC 651 688-0363
3040 Eagandale Pl Saint Paul (55121) *(G-7765)*
Enrich Inc 651 482-9608
3754 Rustic Pl Saint Paul (55126) *(G-8341)*
Entegee Inc 763 383-4343
5620 International Pkwy Minneapolis (55428) *(G-4359)*
Entegee Inc 651 739-7366
6053 Hudson Rd Ste 350 Saint Paul (55125) *(G-9215)*
Entegris Inc 952 556-3131
117 N Jonathan Blvd Chaska (55318) *(G-965)*
Enterprise Leasing Co of MN (DH) 651 905-5000
2775 Blue Waters Rd Saint Paul (55121) *(G-7766)*
Enterprise North Inc 507 233-8900
2100 N Broadway St New Ulm (56073) *(G-6448)*
Entocrinology Clinic 320 229-5000
1900 Centracare Cir # 2500 Saint Cloud (56303) *(G-7504)*
Enventis Telecom Inc 218 720-2686
21 W Superior St Ste 200 Duluth (55802) *(G-1313)*
Enventis Telecom Inc (HQ) 763 577-3900
2950 Xenium Ln N Ste 138 Minneapolis (55441) *(G-4360)*
Envi Waste Management, East Grand Forks *Also Called Mini-Dredge Inc (G-1572)*
Envirobate Inc 612 729-1080
3301 E 26th St Minneapolis (55406) *(G-4361)*
Enviromatic Corp of America 612 861-3330
5936 Pillsbury Ave S Minneapolis (55419) *(G-4362)*
Enviromental Health Lab, Marshall *Also Called Lincoln Lyon Murry & Pipestone (G-3305)*
Environ Electronic Labs (PA) 952 888-7795
9725 Girard Ave S Minneapolis (55431) *(G-4363)*
Environmental Bus Solutions, Minneapolis *Also Called Ktn Acquisition Corp (G-4826)*
Environmental Control Systems 218 863-1766
22 Industrial Park Dr Pelican Rapids (56572) *(G-6777)*
Environmental Learning Center, Ely *Also Called YMCA of Greater St Paul (G-1919)*
Environmental Plant Svcs Inc 651 644-4301
2315 Hampden Ave Saint Paul (55114) *(G-8342)*
Environmental Services Lab, Saint Paul *Also Called Metropolitan Council, MN (G-8643)*
Environmental Systems Research 651 454-0600
880 Blue Gentian Rd # 200 Saint Paul (55121) *(G-7767)*
Environments Inc 952 933-9981
13600 County Road 62 Hopkins (55345) *(G-2540)*
Envirotec, Northfield *Also Called Tom Kelly (G-6543)*
Envirotech Remediation Svcs 763 746-0670
3000 84th Ln NE Minneapolis (55449) *(G-6125)*
Envoy Medical Corp 651 361-8000
5000 Township Pkwy Saint Paul (55110) *(G-8343)*
EPCO, Minnetonka *Also Called Engineered Products Co (G-6166)*
Epic Enterprise Inc 507 645-6800
410 Stafford Rd N Dundas (55019) *(G-1511)*
EPIC Holdings Inc (PA) 952 997-4900
15025 Glazier Ave Ste 100 Saint Paul (55124) *(G-7768)*
Epicor Software Corp 952 417-1400
600 Highway 169 S Minneapolis (55426) *(G-4364)*
Epiphany Assisted Living 763 755-0320
10955 Hanson Blvd NW 221-1 Minneapolis (55433) *(G-3465)*
Episcopal Church Home Of MN 651 646-4061
1879 Feronia Ave Saint Paul (55104) *(G-8344)*
Epredix Holdings Inc (HQ) 612 843-1059
225 S 6th St Ste 400 Minneapolis (55402) *(G-4365)*
Equity Transwestern LLC 612 343-4200
730 2nd Ave S Ste 400 Minneapolis (55402) *(G-4366)*
ER Systems, Rockford *Also Called Elastomeric Roofing Systems (G-7300)*
ERDAC, Eveleth *Also Called East Range Developmental (G-1930)*
Erdman Automation Corp 763 389-9475
1603 14th St S Princeton (55371) *(G-6905)*
Ergotron Inc 651 681-7600
1181 Trapp Rd Ste 100 Saint Paul (55121) *(G-7769)*
Ericksen Roed Johnston Sahlman, Saint Paul *Also Called Roed Ericksen & Associates (G-8911)*
Erickson Engineering, Minneapolis *Also Called Wheeler Consolidated Inc (G-6064)*
Erickson Plumbing Heating 763 783-4545
1471 92nd Ln NE Minneapolis (55449) *(G-3466)*
Erickson Truck Sales & Salvage 507 847-3664
75196 Petersburg Rd Jackson (56143) *(G-2791)*
Erickson-Larsen Inc (PA) 763 535-0055
6425 Sycamore Ct N Maple Grove (55369) *(G-3240)*
Erie L Cliffs L C 218 225-3127
847 County Road NO 666 Hoyt Lakes (55750) *(G-2669)*
Ermc II LP 952 435-8182
1178 Burnsville Ctr Burnsville (55306) *(G-719)*
Ernst & Young LLP 612 343-1000
220 S 6th St Ste 1400 Minneapolis (55402) *(G-4367)*
Erol T Uke MD 952 993-3190
3900 Park Nicollet Blvd Minneapolis (55416) *(G-4368)*
Ers Digital Inc (HQ) 763 694-5900
3005 Ranchview Ln N Minneapolis (55447) *(G-4369)*
Erstat & Riemer 952 854-7638
8009 34th Ave S Ste 200 Minneapolis (55425) *(G-4370)*
Erwin Associates, Duluth *Also Called Z M C Hotels Inc (G-1508)*
ESA P Portfolio Operating 507 536-7444
55 Woodlake Dr SE Rochester (55904) *(G-7106)*
ESA P Portfolio Operating 507 289-7444
2814 43rd St NW Rochester (55901) *(G-7107)*
Esco Industries Inc (PA) 320 259-9470
115 4th St N Waite Park (56387) *(G-9822)*
Esi Holding Corp (PA) 952 853-0924
8009 34th Ave S Ste 1492 Minneapolis (55425) *(G-4371)*
Esi of Minnesota, Duluth *Also Called Empowerment Services of MN (G-1312)*
Especially For Children Inc 952 934-1119
6223 Dell Rd Eden Prairie (55346) *(G-1658)*
Especially For Children Inc 651 452-0043
3370 Coachman Rd Saint Paul (55121) *(G-7770)*
Essentia Health 218 786-8376
502 E 2nd St Duluth (55805) *(G-1314)*
Essilor Laboratories of Amer 763 551-2000
5205 Highway 169 N Ste 5 Minneapolis (55442) *(G-4372)*
Essilor Laboratories of Amer 320 251-8591
6925 Saukview Dr Saint Cloud (56303) *(G-7505)*
Essilor Laboratories of Amer 218 894-3385
605 4th St SW Staples (56479) *(G-9583)*
Estate Jewelry & Coin Inc 952 881-8862
9955 Lyndale Ave S Minneapolis (55420) *(G-4373)*
Estetica 651 228-9327
165 Western Ave N Ste 3 Saint Paul (55102) *(G-8345)*
Etoc Co Inc (PA) 218 963-2906
23611 S Woodward Ave Nisswa (56468) *(G-6496)*
Etoc Co Inc 218 963-2234
23521 Nokomis Ave Nisswa (56468) *(G-6497)*
Eureka Recycling, Minneapolis *Also Called Neighborhood Recycling Corp (G-5181)*
Euro Clean, Plymouth *Also Called Nilfisk-Advance Inc (G-6877)*
Evalumed 651 767-0220
17 Exchange St W Ste 110 Saint Paul (55102) *(G-8346)*
Evangelical Covenant Church 612 781-2691
2309 Hayes St NE Minneapolis (55418) *(G-4374)*
Evangelical Covenant Church 763 546-6125
5800 Saint Croix Ave N Minneapolis (55422) *(G-4375)*
Evangelical Free Church of 320 983-2185
730 2nd St SE Milaca (56353) *(G-3376)*
Evangelical Free Church of 763 389-1171
701 1st St Princeton (55371) *(G-6906)*
Evangelical Lutheran Church In 612 752-4080
800 Marquette Ave Ste 1050 Minneapolis (55402) *(G-4376)*
Evangelical Lutheran Good 507 379-2707
700 County Road 14 Albert Lea (56007) *(G-49)*
Evangelical Lutheran Good 507 373-0683
75507 240th St Albert Lea (56007) *(G-50)*
Evangelical Lutheran Good 763 421-2311
1040 Madison St Anoka (55303) *(G-178)*
Evangelical Lutheran Good 507 964-2251
411 7th Ave NW Arlington (55307) *(G-249)*
Evangelical Lutheran Good 507 437-4526
205 14th St NW Austin (55912) *(G-270)*
Evangelical Lutheran Good 218 354-2254
600 5th Ave SE Barnesville (56514) *(G-305)*
Evangelical Lutheran Good 218 864-5231
105 Glen Haven Dr Battle Lake (56515) *(G-310)*
Evangelical Lutheran Good 218 835-4218
172 Summit Ave W Blackduck (56630) *(G-474)*
Evangelical Lutheran Good 218 829-1407
804 Wright St Brainerd (56401) *(G-565)*
Evangelical Lutheran Good 218 829-1429
100 Buffalo Hills Ln Brainerd (56401) *(G-566)*
Evangelical Lutheran Good 218 776-3157
305 3rd Ave SW Clearbrook (56634) *(G-1038)*
Evangelical Lutheran Good 218 728-6600
510 W College St Duluth (55811) *(G-1315)*
Evangelical Lutheran Good 320 634-4552
515 Franklin St S Glenwood (56334) *(G-2222)*
Evangelical Lutheran Good 320 986-2048
104 6th St S Hoffman (56339) *(G-2489)*
Evangelical Lutheran Good 320 543-3800
413 13th Ave Howard Lake (55349) *(G-2667)*
Evangelical Lutheran Good 218 283-4768
1402 Highway 71 International Falls (56649) *(G-2720)*
Evangelical Lutheran Good 507 847-3100
601 West St Jackson (56143) *(G-2792)*
Evangelical Lutheran Good 507 283-2375
110 S Walnut Ave Luverne (56156) *(G-3059)*
Evangelical Lutheran Good 763 544-4171
8100 Medicine Lake Rd Minneapolis (55427) *(G-4377)*
Evangelical Lutheran Good 612 332-4262
22 27th Ave SE Minneapolis (55414) *(G-4378)*
Evangelical Lutheran Good 507 427-3221
810 3rd Ave Mountain Lake (56159) *(G-6396)*
Evangelical Lutheran Good 507 427-2464
745 Basinger Memorial Dr Mountain Lake (56159) *(G-6397)*
Evangelical Lutheran Good 218 863-2401
119 N Broadway Pelican Rapids (56572) *(G-6778)*
Evangelical Lutheran Good 218 587-4423
518 Jefferson Ave Pine River (56474) *(G-6818)*
Evangelical Lutheran Good 507 825-5428
1311 N Hiawatha Ave Pipestone (56164) *(G-6826)*
Evangelical Lutheran Good 507 637-5711
200 S Dekalb St Redwood Falls (56283) *(G-7021)*
Evangelical Lutheran Good 507 375-3286
1000 2nd St S Saint James (56081) *(G-7643)*
Evangelical Lutheran Good 651 774-9765
550 Roselawn Ave E Saint Paul (55117) *(G-8347)*
Evangelical Lutheran Good 651 489-8851
563 County Road B W Saint Paul (55113) *(G-8348)*
Evangelical Lutheran Good 507 931-9021
830 Sunrise Dr Saint Peter (56082) *(G-9302)*
Evangelical Lutheran Good 651 439-7180
1119 Owens St N Stillwater (55082) *(G-9615)*
Evangelical Lutheran Good 952 442-5111
333 W 5th St Waconia (55387) *(G-9785)*
Evangelical Lutheran Good 507 362-4245
205 1st St N Waterville (56096) *(G-9894)*
Evangelical Lutheran Good 320 764-2300
410 Luella St Watkins (55389) *(G-9897)*
Evangelical Lutheran Good 507 274-6155
149 1st Ave Westbrook (56183) *(G-9966)*
Evangelical Lutheran Good 507 831-1788
705 6th St Windom (56101) *(G-10067)*
Evangelical Lutheran Good 507 647-5391
506 W High St Winthrop (55396) *(G-10167)*
Evansville Arts Coalition 218 948-2787
111 Main St NW Evansville (56326) *(G-1925)*
Evansville Care Campus LLC 218 948-2219
649 State St NW Evansville (56326) *(G-1926)*
Eveleth Hospital Corp 218 744-1950
227 McKinley Ave Eveleth (55734) *(G-1931)*
Evenson Concrete Systems 507 243-3660
23371 610th Ave Madison Lake (56063) *(G-3079)*
Eventide Good Samaritan Center, Mountain Lake *Also Called Evangelical Lutheran Good (G-6396)*
Eventide Home Association Inc 507 427-3221
810 3rd Ave Mountain Lake (56159) *(G-6398)*

ALPHABETIC

ALPHABETIC SECTION
Falls Fabricating

Eventide Senior Living 218 233-7508
1405 7th St S Moorhead (56560) *(G-6314)*
Ever-Green Energy LLC 651 290-2812
345 Saint Peter St # 1350 Saint Paul (55102) *(G-8349)*
Everdry of Minneapolis, Hamel *Also Called Regional Home Services of Minn (G-2355)*
Evergreen Air Services Inc 952 446-8255
4350 Main St Saint Bonifacius (55375) *(G-7400)*
Evergreen Aviation Inc 612 727-1655
7550 22nd Ave S Minneapolis (55450) *(G-4379)*
Evergreen Child Care Center 952 402-0303
712 Canterbury Rd S Shakopee (55379) *(G-9439)*
Evergreen Terrace 218 326-3431
2801 S Highway 169 Grand Rapids (55744) *(G-2276)*
Everyday Miracles Inc 763 323-0012
936 Monroe St Anoka (55303) *(G-179)*
Evolving Solutions Inc 763 516-6500
3989 County Road 116 Hamel (55340) *(G-2340)*
Ewald Consulting Group Inc 651 290-6260
1000 Westgate Dr Ste 252 Saint Paul (55114) *(G-8350)*
Ewing's Assoc 763 258-2733
10700 Highway 55 Ste 220 Minneapolis (55441) *(G-4380)*
Exact Software Erp-Na Inc (HQ) 952 831-7182
7701 York Ave S Ste 350 Minneapolis (55435) *(G-4381)*
Exactec Inc 952 448-7722
1200 Lakeview Dr Chaska (55318) *(G-966)*
Excel Air System Inc 651 779-9725
2075 Prosperity Rd Saint Paul (55109) *(G-8351)*
Excel Building Maintenance Inc 507 288-0913
814 11th St NW Rochester (55901) *(G-7108)*
Excel Engineering Inc 763 571-5008
500 73rd Ave NE Ste 119 Minneapolis (55432) *(G-3467)*
Excel Manufacturing Inc 507 932-4680
778 W 12th St Saint Charles (55972) *(G-7401)*
Excel Marine & Motorsports, Minneapolis *Also Called Perfect Complement Ltd (G-3569)*
Excel Painting Plus Inc 763 557-2821
5550 Dunkirk Ln N Minneapolis (55446) *(G-4382)*
Excelsior Nursing Home, Excelsior *Also Called Beverly Enterprises - MN (G-1940)*
Execu Systems Inc 218 444-1021
1499 Anne St NW Bemidji (56601) *(G-391)*
Executive Services Midwest LLC 952 469-4755
19740 Kenrick Ave Lakeville (55044) *(G-2905)*
Exhibitor Publications Inc 507 289-6556
206 Suth Broadway Ste 745 Rochester (55904) *(G-7109)*
Exhibits Development Group LLC 651 222-1121
75 W Fifth St Landmark Ct Saint Paul (55102) *(G-8352)*
Expedite Drect Mail Fulfilment, Saint Paul *Also Called New ERA Incentives Inc (G-8748)*
Expedited Transportation, Minneapolis *Also Called R A Ventures Inc (G-5455)*
Expeditors International Of WA 651 683-9922
1245 Trapp Rd Ste 100 Saint Paul (55121) *(G-7771)*
Experior Assessments LLC (HQ) 651 646-1170
1260 Energy Ln Saint Paul (55108) *(G-8353)*
Expert Software Inc 952 918-9400
7800 Equitable Dr Ste 200 Eden Prairie (55344) *(G-1659)*
Expresspoint Technology Svcs 763 543-6000
1109 Zane Ave N Golden Valley (55422) *(G-2240)*
Expresss Sweets Customer's, Winona *Also Called Best Western Riverport Inn (G-10081)*
Extended Family Health Care 218 727-0446
1700 Mall Dr Duluth (55811) *(G-1316)*
Extended Family Home Care, Duluth *Also Called Morgan Business Trust (G-1397)*
Extendicare Facilities Inc 651 484-3378
1000 Lovell Ave W Saint Paul (55113) *(G-8354)*
Extendicare Homes Inc 763 588-0771
3130 Grimes Ave N Minneapolis (55422) *(G-4383)*
Extendicare Homes Inc 763 545-0416
7505 Country Club Dr Minneapolis (55427) *(G-4384)*
Extendicare Homes Inc 952 927-9717
4415 W 36 1/2 St Minneapolis (55416) *(G-4385)*
Extendicare Homes Inc 952 927-4949
4415 W 36 1/2 St Minneapolis (55416) *(G-4386)*
Extendicare Homes Inc 952 920-8380
7900 W 28th St Minneapolis (55426) *(G-4387)*
Extendicare Homes Inc 612 861-1691
7727 Portland Ave Richfield (55423) *(G-7035)*
Extendicare Homes Inc 651 633-7875
825 1st Ave NW Saint Paul (55112) *(G-8355)*
Extendicare Homes Inc 651 224-1848
445 Galtier St Saint Paul (55103) *(G-8356)*
Extreme Panel Technologies Inc 507 423-5530
475 E 4th St Cottonwood (56229) *(G-1112)*
Eye Care Associates 612 338-4861
825 Nicollet Mall # 2000 Minneapolis (55402) *(G-4388)*
Eye Department, Minneapolis *Also Called Healthpartners Inc (G-4622)*
Eye Kraft Optical Inc 320 251-0141
8 McLeland Rd Saint Cloud (56303) *(G-7506)*
Eye Surgeons & Physicians 320 253-3637
109 Doctors Park Saint Cloud (56303) *(G-7507)*
F B G Service Corp 651 917-8059
2161 University Ave W # 112 Saint Paul (55114) *(G-8357)*
F B L Financial Services Inc 651 905-2123
3080 Eagandale Pl Saint Paul (55121) *(G-7772)*
F E C, Minneapolis *Also Called Food Engineering Corp (G-4461)*
F M Trucking Inc (PA) 651 639-0446
175 Old Hwy A SW Saint Paul (55112) *(G-8358)*
F M Trucking Inc 651 639-0446
175 Old Highway 8 SW Saint Paul (55112) *(G-8359)*
F R Bigelow Foundation Inc 651 224-5463
55 5th St E Ste 600 Saint Paul (55101) *(G-8360)*
F-M Asphalt Inc 612 798-0245
400 W 61st St Minneapolis (55419) *(G-4389)*
Fabcon Inc (PA) 952 890-4444
6111 Highway 13 W Savage (55378) *(G-9390)*
Fabricated Wood Products Inc 507 451-1019
6150 W Frontage Rd Medford (55049) *(G-3343)*
Fabyanske, Westra, Hart 612 338-0115
800 Lasalle Ave Ste 1900 Minneapolis (55402) *(G-4390)*
Face To Face Health 651 772-5555
1165 Arcade St Saint Paul (55106) *(G-8361)*
Facet Technology Corp 952 944-1839
6517 City West Pkwy Eden Prairie (55344) *(G-1660)*
Factory, Minneapolis *Also Called Anchor Block Co (G-3775)*
Faf Advisors Inc 612 303-3381
800 Nicollet Mall Minneapolis (55402) *(G-4391)*
Fafard Inc 218 476-3022
10108 Hwy 8 Floodwood (55736) *(G-2135)*
Fafinski Mark & Johnson 952 995-9500
775 Paririe Ctr Dr # 400 Eden Prairie (55344) *(G-1661)*
Fagen Inc (PA) 320 564-3324
501 Highway 212 W Granite Falls (56241) *(G-2314)*
Fair Isaac Corp (PA) 612 758-5200
901 Marquette Ave Ste 3200 Minneapolis (55402) *(G-4392)*
Fair Meadow Nursing Home, Fertile *Also Called City of Fertile (G-2125)*
Fair Oaks Lodge Inc 218 631-1391
201 Shady Lane Dr Wadena (56482) *(G-9801)*
Fair's Garden Center, Osseo *Also Called Phasse III of Maple Grove Inc (G-6652)*
Fairfield Inn 218 723-8607
901 Joshua Ave Duluth (55811) *(G-1317)*
Fairhaven Farm 320 236-7685
13835 51st Ave South Haven (55382) *(G-9505)*
Fairmont Community Hospital 507 238-8100
800 Medical Center Dr Fairmont (56031) *(G-1963)*
Fairmont Medical Center Mayo 507 238-4263
800 Clinic Cir Fairmont (56031) *(G-1964)*
Fairmont Orthopedics & Sports 507 238-4949
717 S State St Ste 900 Fairmont (56031) *(G-1965)*
Fairmont Refrigerated Service 507 238-4211
1400 E 8th St Fairmont (56031) *(G-1966)*
Fairveiw University Med Ctr, Minneapolis *Also Called Regents of The University of (G-5495)*
Fairview Clinics 651 688-7860
1440 Duckwood Dr Saint Paul (55122) *(G-7773)*
Fairview Gardens 320 229-2281
1080 35th St NE Sauk Rapids (56379) *(G-9381)*
Fairview Health Line Home Care 218 262-6982
1101 E 37th St Ste 18 Hibbing (55746) *(G-2443)*
Fairview Health Services 952 892-2910
201 E Nicollet Blvd Burnsville (55337) *(G-720)*
Fairview Health Services 952 826-6500
830 Prairie Center Dr Eden Prairie (55344) *(G-1662)*
Fairview Health Services 218 262-4881
750 E 34th St Hibbing (55746) *(G-2444)*
Fairview Health Services 612 672-6800
2020 Minnehaha Ave Minneapolis (55404) *(G-4393)*
Fairview Health Services 612 672-2900
701 25th Ave S Ste 402 Minneapolis (55454) *(G-4394)*
Fairview Health Services 612 721-5044
3809 42nd Ave S Minneapolis (55406) *(G-4395)*
Fairview Health Services (PA) 612 672-6300
2450 Riverside Ave Minneapolis (55454) *(G-4396)*
Fairview Health Services 952 848-5600
6545 France Ave S Ste 150 Minneapolis (55435) *(G-4397)*
Fairview Health Services 612 626-2663
516 Delaware St SE Ste 5B Minneapolis (55455) *(G-4398)*
Fairview Health Services 612 672-5500
323 Stinson Blvd Minneapolis (55413) *(G-4399)*
Fairview Health Services 612 273-3000
500 Harvard St SE Minneapolis (55455) *(G-4400)*
Fairview Health Services 763 389-1313
1407 4th Ave N Princeton (55371) *(G-6907)*
Fairview Health Services 651 632-7300
2577 Territorial Rd Saint Paul (55114) *(G-8362)*
Fairview Health Services 651 632-9835
2200 University Ave W # 110 Saint Paul (55114) *(G-8363)*
Fairview Health Services 612 706-4500
1151 Silver Lake Rd NW Saint Paul (55112) *(G-8364)*
Fairview Health Services 651 982-7000
5200 Fairview Blvd Wyoming (55092) *(G-10202)*
Fairview Health Services 763 856-6900
25945 Gateway Dr Ste 2 Zimmerman (55398) *(G-10213)*
Fairview HomeCare & Hospice (PA) 612 721-2491
2450 26th Ave S Minneapolis (55406) *(G-4401)*
Fairview Homecare & Hospice 763 389-1923
110 6th Ave S Unit LOWER Princeton (55371) *(G-6908)*
Fairview Northland Clinic 763 389-3344
911 Northland Dr Princeton (55371) *(G-6922)*
Fairview Nursing Home, Dodge Center *Also Called County of Dodge (G-1225)*
Fairview Oxboro Clinics Inc 952 885-6100
600 W 98th St Ste 220 Minneapolis (55420) *(G-4402)*
Fairview Pharmacy Services LLC 612 672-5260
711 Kasota Ave SE Minneapolis (55414) *(G-4403)*
Fairview Redwing Health Svcs 651 267-5000
701 Fairview Blvd Red Wing (55066) *(G-6979)*
Fairview Seminary Home Inc 651 385-3434
906 College Ave Red Wing (55066) *(G-6980)*
Fairview University Med Centre, Minneapolis *Also Called University Neurosurgical Assn (G-5928)*
Fairway Collision Center Inc 651 483-4055
125 County Road F E Saint Paul (55127) *(G-8365)*
Faithful & Gould Inc 612 338-3120
900 2nd Ave S Ste 500 Minneapolis (55402) *(G-4404)*
Falcon Ridge Golf Course, Stacy *Also Called Great Northern Golf Co of MN (G-9579)*
Falk Paper & Packaging, Minneapolis *Also Called Martin Falk Paper Co (G-4959)*
Falk's Woodland Pharmacy Inc (PA) 218 728-4242
1 E Calvary Rd Duluth (55803) *(G-1318)*
Falk's Woodland Pharmacy Inc 218 740-2650
221 E 14th St Duluth (55811) *(G-1319)*
Fallon Group Inc (PA) 612 758-2345
901 Marquette Ave # 2400 Minneapolis (55402) *(G-4405)*
Falls Court Dentists 320 632-6621
119 1st St NE Ste 4 Little Falls (56345) *(G-3003)*
Falls Distribution Inc 320 632-3999
16731 Haven Rd Little Falls (56345) *(G-3004)*
Falls Electric Inc 218 681-7299
720 Dawn Ave Thief River Falls (56701) *(G-9667)*
Falls Fabricating 320 632-2322
600 9th Ave NW Little Falls (56345) *(G-3005)*

ALPHABETIC

Falls Memorial Hospital, International Falls *Also Called Lake Rainy Medical Center* ***(G-2726)***
Fame, Minneapolis *Also Called Martin-Williams Inc* ***(G-4962)***
Familias De Esperanza, Saint Paul *Also Called Hope Common* ***(G-8494)***
Family & Children's Service 612 729-0340
4123 E Lake St Minneapolis (55406) ***(G-4406)***
Family Child Development Ctr 763 545-7271
100 Nathan Ln N Minneapolis (55441) ***(G-4407)***
Family Focus Inc 218 740-3146
15 Buchanan St Duluth (55802) ***(G-1320)***
Family Focus Inc 612 331-4429
2800 University Ave SE Ste 204 Minneapolis (55414) ***(G-4408)***
Family Health Medical Clinic, Northfield *Also Called Thomas Oas MD* ***(G-6521)***
Family Health Services of MN 651 457-2748
2980 Buckley Way Inver Grove Heights (55076) ***(G-2750)***
Family Health Services of MN 651 772-2077
2025 Sloan Pl Ste 35 Saint Paul (55117) ***(G-8366)***
Family Home Health Care Inc 612 340-0733
2525 E Franklin Ave # 300 Minneapolis (55406) ***(G-4409)***
Family Innovations Inc 763 421-5535
1833 3rd Ave Anoka (55303) ***(G-180)***
Family Innovations Inc 651 748-5019
2115 County Road D E B100 Saint Paul (55109) ***(G-8367)***
Family Life Mental Health Ctr 763 427-7964
1930 Coon Rapids Blvd NW Minneapolis (55433) ***(G-3468)***
Family Means 763 780-4986
1875 NW Ave S Minneapolis (55401) ***(G-4410)***
Family Means 651 439-4840
1875 Northwestern Ave S Stillwater (55082) ***(G-9616)***
Family Partnership (PA) 612 339-9101
414 S 8th St Minneapolis (55404) ***(G-4411)***
Family Partnership 952 884-7353
1101 E 78th St Ste 318 Minneapolis (55420) ***(G-4412)***
Family Planning Services, New Ulm *Also Called County of Brown-Nicollet* ***(G-6446)***
Family Practice Medical Center 320 235-7232
502 2nd St SW Ste 1 Willmar (56201) ***(G-10001)***
Family Resources Development 651 578-0676
8131 4th St N Saint Paul (55128) ***(G-9216)***
Family Service Center Inc 320 564-2211
930 4th St Ste 4 Granite Falls (56241) ***(G-2315)***
Family Service Rochester Inc 507 287-2010
1110 6th St NW Rochester (55901) ***(G-7110)***
Family Services, Aitkin *Also Called Aitkin County* ***(G-13)***
Family Swim School 952 435-1898
10491 165th St W Lakeville (55044) ***(G-2906)***
Family Tree Landscape Nursery 507 533-8558
1735 Highway 30 SW Stewartville (55976) ***(G-9592)***
Family Violence Network (PA) 651 770-8544
3111 1st Ave S Minneapolis (55408) ***(G-4413)***
Family Violence Network 612 825-3333
3111 1st Ave S Minneapolis (55408) ***(G-4414)***
Familymeans Inc 612 874-8164
1875 Northwestern Ave S Stillwater (55082) ***(G-9617)***
Famous Dave's Of America Inc (PA) 952 294-1300
12701 Whitewater Dr # 200 Minnetonka (55343) ***(G-6167)***
Fantasia LLC 612 338-5811
275 Market St Ste 102 Minneapolis (55405) ***(G-4415)***
Fargo Electronics Inc 952 941-9470
6533 Flying Cloud Dr # 1000 Eden Prairie (55344) ***(G-1663)***
Faribault Bancshares Inc 507 332-7401
428 Central Ave N Faribault (55021) ***(G-2003)***
Faribault Harley Davidson Inc 507 334-5130
2704 Airport Dr Faribault (55021) ***(G-2004)***
Faribault Manor Health Care, Faribault *Also Called Beverly Enterprises - MN* ***(G-1992)***
Faribault Transportation Co 507 334-5121
2615 1st Ave NW Faribault (55021) ***(G-2005)***
Faribo Farm & Home Supply Inc 507 334-3232
80 Western Ave NW Faribault (55021) ***(G-2006)***
Faribo Plumbing & Heating Inc 507 334-6409
513 Central Ave N Faribault (55021) ***(G-2007)***
Farish, Robert W DDS, Hopkins *Also Called Blue Ridge Dental* ***(G-2519)***
Farley's & Sathers Candy Co (PA) 507 945-8181
1 Sather Plz Round Lake (56167) ***(G-7384)***
Farley's & Sathers Candy Co 507 452-3433
1000 W 5th St Winona (55987) ***(G-10094)***
Farm Bureau Financial Service, Saint Paul *Also Called F B L Financial Services Inc* ***(G-7772)***
Farm Country Co-Op 507 356-8313
417 N Main St Pine Island (55963) ***(G-6816)***
Farm Credit Services Minn Vly, Willmar *Also Called Production Credit Association* ***(G-10038)***
Farmers & Merchants State Bank 507 723-4234
101 N Marshall Ave Springfield (56087) ***(G-9571)***
Farmers & Merchants State Bank 507 723-4800
101 N Marshall Ave Springfield (56087) ***(G-9572)***
Farmers Co-Op Oil Co of Clara (PA) 320 847-2318
200 Hwy 7 W Clara City (56222) ***(G-1027)***
Farmers Co-Operative Elevator 507 768-3448
1972 510th St Hanley Falls (56245) ***(G-2368)***
Farmers Co-Operative of Hanska 507 439-6244
103 E 1st St Hanska (56041) ***(G-2370)***
Farmers Co-Operative Oil Co of 507 925-4114
461 Second Ave W Echo (56237) ***(G-1581)***
Farmers State B of Hartland 507 845-2233
601 Broadway St Hartland (56042) ***(G-2374)***
Farmers State Bank of Elkton 507 584-6441
105 Main St Elkton (55933) ***(G-1906)***
Farmers State Bank of Hamel 763 478-6611
145 Hamel Rd Hamel (55340) ***(G-2341)***
Farmers State Bank of West 507 527-2236
181 Main St West Concord (55985) ***(G-9965)***
Farmers Union Oil Co of 320 763-6557
1705 Broadway St Alexandria (56308) ***(G-100)***
Farmers Union Oil Co of 320 269-8856
County Rd 15 73rd Ave SW Montevideo (56265) ***(G-6245)***
Farmers Union Oil Co of 218 233-2497
1321 Center Ave Moorhead (56560) ***(G-6315)***
Farmington Eagles Club 651 460-8376
200 3rd St Farmington (55024) ***(G-2050)***
Farmington Health Service 651 463-7818
3410 213th St W Farmington (55024) ***(G-2051)***
Farnam Street Financial Inc 952 908-0850
5850 Opus Pkwy Ste 240 Hopkins (55343) ***(G-2541)***
Fast Cab Services LLC 952 393-8542
2709 Stevens Ave Apt 3 Minneapolis (55408) ***(G-4416)***
Fast Lane Car Wash 218 444-9130
1702 Paul Bunyan Dr NW Bemidji (56601) ***(G-392)***
Fastenal Co (PA) 507 454-5374
2001 Theurer Blvd Winona (55987) ***(G-10095)***
Fastenal Co Purchasing 507 454-5374
2001 Theurer Blvd Winona (55987) ***(G-10096)***
Father Herman Schmtz Cncl 5078, Mora *Also Called Knights of Columbus Inc* ***(G-6364)***
Father John Deer, Prior Lake *Also Called Knight of Columbus Community* ***(G-6936)***
Fbs Associated Properties Inc 612 333-2086
800 Nicollet Mall Minneapolis (55402) ***(G-4417)***
FCA Construction Co LLC 952 229-7521
2902 Corporate Pl Chanhassen (55317) ***(G-923)***
Fch Minnetonka 952 912-9999
10985 Red Circle Dr Minnetonka (55343) ***(G-6168)***
FDC Services Inc 320 656-8880
720 Anderson Ave Saint Cloud (56303) ***(G-7508)***
Feather, Larson & Synhorst 651 480-0123
12181 Margo Ave S Ste 220 Hastings (55033) ***(G-2415)***
Feda Ridge Inc 651 426-3300
11400 Julianne Ave N Stillwater (55082) ***(G-9618)***
Federal Express Corp 952 884-9212
9219 Grand Ave S Minneapolis (55420) ***(G-4418)***
Federal Express Corp 612 794-3100
7401 24th Ave S Minneapolis (55450) ***(G-4419)***
Federal Express Corp 612 713-8500
2825 Cargo Rd Minneapolis (55450) ***(G-4420)***
Federal Express Corp 651 747-4122
1828 Buerkle Rd Saint Paul (55110) ***(G-8368)***
Federal Reserve Bank of (HQ) 612 204-5000
90 Hennepin Ave Minneapolis (55401) ***(G-4421)***
Federated Coop Inc 320 679-2682
206 Union St S Mora (55051) ***(G-6358)***
Federated Employees Credit 507 455-5430
1929 S Cedar Ave Owatonna (55060) ***(G-6709)***
Federated Mutual Insurance Co 952 831-4300
7700 France Ave S Minneapolis (55435) ***(G-4422)***
Federated Mutual Insurance Co (PA) 507 455-5200
121 E Park Sq Owatonna (55060) ***(G-6710)***
Federated Mutual Insurance Co 507 455-5200
121 E Park Sq Owatonna (55060) ***(G-6711)***
Federated Service Insurance Co 507 455-5200
121 E Park Sq Owatonna (55060) ***(G-6712)***
Fedex, Minneapolis *Also Called Federal Express Corp* ***(G-4418)***
Fedex, Saint Paul *Also Called Federal Express Corp* ***(G-8368)***
Fedex Freight Inc 218 751-9122
3400 Butterfly Dr NW Bemidji (56601) ***(G-393)***
Fedex Freight Inc 507 444-0633
1060 26th Pl NW Owatonna (55060) ***(G-6713)***
Fedex Freight Inc 651 697-9342
2323 Terminal Rd Saint Paul (55113) ***(G-8369)***
Fedex Ground Package System 651 748-8636
7 Long Lake Rd Mahtomedi (55115) ***(G-3094)***
Fedex Office & Print Services 952 892-0200
700 County Road 42 W Burnsville (55337) ***(G-721)***
Fedex Office & Print Services 952 943-4000
7900 Eden Rd Eden Prairie (55344) ***(G-1664)***
Fedex Office & Print Services 952 593-1143
13601 Ridgedale Dr Hopkins (55305) ***(G-2542)***
Fedex Office & Print Services 612 822-7700
1430 W Lake St Minneapolis (55408) ***(G-4423)***
Fedex Office & Print Services 612 578-9000
8300 City Centre Dr Saint Paul (55125) ***(G-9217)***
Fedex Office & Print Services 651 699-9671
58 Snelling Ave S Saint Paul (55105) ***(G-8370)***
Feist Animal Hospital 651 646-7257
1430 Marshall Ave Saint Paul (55104) ***(G-8371)***
Felhaber Larson Fenlon & Vogt (PA) 612 339-6321
220 S 6th St Ste 2200 Minneapolis (55402) ***(G-4424)***
Felhaber Larson Fenlon & Vogt 651 222-6321
444 Cedar St Ste 2100 Saint Paul (55101) ***(G-8372)***
Feltl & Co 952 546-5018
600 Highway 169 S Ste 1960 Minneapolis (55426) ***(G-4425)***
Fenway Development Inc 651 429-8032
3500 Willow Lake Blvd # 100 Saint Paul (55110) ***(G-8373)***
Ferber Inc 320 251-4072
1707 Hillcrest Rd Saint Cloud (56303) ***(G-7509)***
Fergus Falls Area Family Young 218 739-4489
1164 Friberg Ave Fergus Falls (56537) ***(G-2075)***
Fergus Falls Fish & Game Club 320 630-0607
13645 Obrien Ln Dalton (56324) ***(G-1155)***
Fergus Falls Medical Group 218 739-2221
615 S Mill St Ste 4 Fergus Falls (56537) ***(G-2076)***
Fergus Falls Veterans Home, Fergus Falls *Also Called Minnesota Department of* ***(G-2097)***
Fergus FLS Regional Trtmnt Ctr, Fergus Falls *Also Called Minnesota Department of Human* ***(G-2099)***
Ferguson Brothers Excavating 320 762-0622
2050 County Road 82 NW Alexandria (56308) ***(G-101)***
Ferguson Enterprises Inc 218 628-2844
4209 Airpark Blvd Duluth (55811) ***(G-1321)***
Ferguson Enterprises Inc 651 638-5000
2350 County Road C W # 150 Saint Paul (55113) ***(G-8374)***
Festival Events of Minnesota 651 772-9980
1097 Payne Ave Saint Paul (55130) ***(G-8375)***
Ffmc Enterprises, Prior Lake *Also Called Smsc Gaming Enterprise* ***(G-6956)***
Ffusa, Hamel *Also Called First Financial USA Ltd* ***(G-2342)***
Fibercare Inc 612 721-5048
7701 Pillsbury Ave S Minneapolis (55423) ***(G-4426)***
Fidelity Bank 952 831-6600
7600 Parklawn Ave Ste 150 Minneapolis (55435) ***(G-4427)***
Fidelity Bank (PA) 952 831-6600
7600 Parklawn Ave Ste 150 Minneapolis (55435) ***(G-4428)***

ALPHABETIC

ALPHABETIC SECTION
Fiserv Health Inc

Fidelity Building Services Inc 952 854-1447
951 American Blvd E Bloomington (55420) *(G-497)*

Fidelity Investments Actuarial 952 831-8595
7740 France Ave S Minneapolis (55435) *(G-4429)*

Fidelity National Information 651 855-6500
8555 Eagle Point Blvd # 100 Lake Elmo (55042) *(G-2871)*

Fiduciary Counselling Inc 651 228-0935
30 7th St E Ste 2000 Saint Paul (55101) *(G-8376)*

Field Crest Care Center 507 477-3266
318 2nd St NE Hayfield (55940) *(G-2427)*

Field of Dreams, Saint Paul *Also Called Celebrities Unlimited Inc (G-8179)*

Fieldwork Minneapolis Inc 952 837-8300
7650 Edinbrgh Way Ste 700 Minneapolis (55435) *(G-4430)*

Fifty Below Sales & Marketing 218 720-4828
5 W 1st St Ste 302 Duluth (55802) *(G-1322)*

Figgins Transport Ltd 218 326-9477
1407 E Highway 2 Grand Rapids (55744) *(G-2277)*

Fillmore Place, Preston *Also Called Maple Leaf Services Inc (G-6899)*

Filmor Express Inc 507 263-2608
32453 64th Avenue Way Cannon Falls (55009) *(G-856)*

Final Coat Painting Inc 651 789-0790
3185 Terminal Dr Eagan (55121) *(G-1527)*

Finance & Commerce Inc 612 333-4244
730 2nd Ave S Ste 100 Minneapolis (55402) *(G-4431)*

Financial Affairs Consulting 952 443-4188
1212 Adrian Dr Chaska (55318) *(G-967)*

Financial Corp Inc 651 407-5770
4388 Round Lake Rd W Saint Paul (55112) *(G-8377)*

Financial Crimes Services LLC 651 388-2569
406 Main St Ste 200 Red Wing (55066) *(G-6981)*

Financial Information MGT, Eden Prairie *Also Called Telvent Dtn Inc (G-1791)*

Financial Recovery Services (PA) 952 831-4800
4640 W 77th St Ste 300 Minneapolis (55435) *(G-4432)*

Financial Systems Support 612 625-3493
1300 S 2nd St Ste 660 Minneapolis (55454) *(G-4433)*

Fine Associates LLC 612 332-2561
80 S 8th St Ste 1916 Minneapolis (55402) *(G-4434)*

Fine Line Hair Inc 952 457-2620
3902 Silver Lake Rd NE Minneapolis (55421) *(G-6126)*

Finley Engineering Co 507 836-8515
1981 Engebretson Ave Slayton (56172) *(G-9487)*

Fintegra Financial Solutions 763 503-1911
6120 Earle Brown Dr # 550 Minneapolis (55430) *(G-4435)*

Fire-Guard Sprinkler Service, Saint Paul *Also Called Fireguard Sprinkler Service (G-8378)*

Fireguard Sprinkler Service 651 748-9499
575 Minneajaja Ave W Saint Paul (55109) *(G-8378)*

Firemen's Relief Association 763 593-8080
7800 Golden Valley Rd Minneapolis (55427) *(G-4436)*

Firemens Relief Assns 507 532-5141
201 E Saratoga St Marshall (56258) *(G-3295)*

Firenet Systems Inc 763 536-3950
6224 Lakeland Ave N Ste 100 Minneapolis (55428) *(G-4437)*

Firestone, Saint Paul *Also Called Bfs Retail Operations LLC (G-7719)*

Firestone Metal Products LLC (DH) 763 576-9595
1001 Lund Blvd Anoka (55303) *(G-181)*

Firm-A Workout Studio, Minneapolis *Also Called David's Body Shop Inc (G-4226)*

First Aid & Trust (PA) 651 439-5195
950 Highway 95 N Bayport (55003) *(G-348)*

First Alliance Credit Union (PA) 507 288-0330
320 Alliance Pl NE Rochester (55906) *(G-7111)*

First Alliance Credit Union 507 281-7640
501 16th St SE Rochester (55904) *(G-7112)*

First American Bank Valley 218 281-4182
201 N Broadway Ste 1 Crookston (56716) *(G-1124)*

First American National Cml 612 305-2000
801 Nicollet Mall Ste 1900 Minneapolis (55402) *(G-4438)*

First American Real Estate 800 868-8816
7900 Intl Dr Ste 500 Minneapolis (55425) *(G-4439)*

First American Title Insurance 612 337-5900
801 Nicollet Mall # 1900 Minneapolis (55402) *(G-4440)*

1st Avenue Entertainment Group 612 337-6700
650 Hennepin Ave Minneapolis (55403) *(G-4441)*

First Care Medical Services 218 435-1133
900 Hilligoss Blvd SE Fosston (56542) *(G-2176)*

First Choice Home Care Inc 651 225-4255
391 Pleasant Ave Saint Paul (55102) *(G-8379)*

First Class Hospitality Group 320 251-1500
4040 2nd St S Saint Cloud (56301) *(G-7510)*

First Commercial Bank 952 903-0777
8500 Normandale Lake Blvd Minneapolis (55437) *(G-4442)*

First Farmers & Merchants 507 567-2219
106 W Main St Brownsdale (55918) *(G-629)*

First Federal Capital Bank 507 285-2600
206 S Broadway Ste 206 Rochester (55904) *(G-7113)*

First Federal Capital Bank 651 646-8681
176 Snelling Ave N Saint Paul (55104) *(G-8380)*

First Financial USA Ltd 763 231-8120
805 Meander Ct Hamel (55340) *(G-2342)*

First Integrity Bank (PA) 218 894-1522
111 4th St NE Staples (56479) *(G-9584)*

First McLeod Agency Inc 320 864-5581
613 10th St E Glencoe (55336) *(G-2205)*

First Memorial Funeral Chapel 763 560-4694
7835 Brooklyn Blvd Minneapolis (55445) *(G-4443)*

First Minnesota Bank National (PA) 320 864-3161
606 11th St E Ste E Glencoe (55336) *(G-2206)*

First Minnesota Care Inc 612 724-3000
1201 E Lake St Ste 1 Minneapolis (55407) *(G-4444)*

First National Bank 218 254-3371
101 W Lake St Chisholm (55719) *(G-997)*

First National Bank 507 425-2575
109 N St Paul Ave Fulda (56131) *(G-2194)*

First National Bank 507 645-5656
329 Division St S Northfield (55057) *(G-6528)*

First National Bank, Waseca *Also Called 1st National Bank of Waseca (G-9878)*

First National Bank In 218 935-5251
103 N Main St Mahnomen (56557) *(G-3085)*

1st National Bank In Wadena 218 631-1590
25 Bryant Ave SW Wadena (56482) *(G-9802)*

1st National Bank Inc 218 534-3111
21236 Archibald Rd Deerwood (56444) *(G-1177)*

First National Bank of Bemidji 218 751-2430
502 Minnesota Ave NW Bemidji (56601) *(G-394)*

First National Bank of Cold 320 685-8611
301 Main St Cold Spring (56320) *(G-1085)*

First National Bank of Deer 218 246-8221
9 1st St NE Deer River (56636) *(G-1171)*

First National Bank of Milaca 320 983-3101
190 2nd Ave SW Milaca (56353) *(G-3377)*

1st National Bank of Pipestone 507 825-3344
101 2nd St NW Pipestone (56164) *(G-6827)*

1st National Bank of Plainview 507 534-3131
138 W Broadway Ste 1 Plainview (55964) *(G-6841)*

First National Bank of St (HQ) 507 931-4000
226 Nassau St Saint Peter (56082) *(G-9303)*

First National Bank of The N 320 245-5261
510 Main Ave Sandstone (55072) *(G-9321)*

First National Bank of Walker 218 547-1160
600 Minnesota Ave W Walker (56484) *(G-9850)*

1st National Bank of Waseca 507 835-2740
101 State St N Waseca (56093) *(G-9878)*

First National Bank of West St (PA) 651 457-1111
66 Thompson Ave E Saint Paul (55118) *(G-7774)*

1st National Repossessioncom 763 241-5212
950 Highway 10 Ste 4 Elk River (55330) *(G-1874)*

First Protection Corp 952 473-0114
601 Carlson Pkwy Ste 990 Minnetonka (55305) *(G-6169)*

First Realty GMAC 218 751-2511
1425 Paul Bunyan Dr NW Bemidji (56601) *(G-395)*

First Rushmore Bancshares Inc (PA) 507 376-9747
1433 Oxford St Worthington (56187) *(G-10183)*

First Security Bank 218 948-2259
303 Kron St Evansville (56326) *(G-1927)*

First Security Bank - Sleepy (HQ) 507 794-3911
100 Main St E Sleepy Eye (56085) *(G-9495)*

First Solutions (PA) 218 740-2330
525 S Lake Ave Ste 222 Duluth (55802) *(G-1323)*

First Solutions 218 834-7205
1010 4th St Two Harbors (55616) *(G-9707)*

First State Agency of Storden, Storden *Also Called Heartland State Bank (G-9656)*

First State Bank, Okabena *Also Called Hartman Bancshares Inc (G-6556)*

First State Bank & Trust 651 439-5195
950 Highway 95 N Bayport (55003) *(G-349)*

First State Bank of Ashby 218 747-2235
110 Main St Ashby (56309) *(G-251)*

First State Bank of Rosemount 651 423-1121
3025 145th St W Rosemount (55068) *(G-7370)*

First State Bank of Sauk 320 352-5771
423 Main St S Sauk Centre (56378) *(G-9345)*

First State Bank of Wabasha 651 565-3331
111 Main St W Wabasha (55981) *(G-9766)*

First State Bank of Wyoming 651 462-7611
26741 Felton Ave Wyoming (55092) *(G-10203)*

First State Bank South West 507 376-9747
1433 Oxford St Worthington (56187) *(G-10184)*

First State Bank South West (HQ) 507 376-9747
1433 Oxford St Worthington (56187) *(G-10185)*

First State Bk of Red Wing 651 388-4714
3209 S Service Dr Red Wing (55066) *(G-6982)*

First State Tire Disposal Inc 763 434-0578
1500 278th Ln NE Isanti (55040) *(G-2779)*

First Street Credit Corp 612 871-4579
2417 1st Ave S Minneapolis (55404) *(G-4445)*

First Strike of Duluth Inc 218 721-5081
4921 W Pioneer Rd Duluth (55803) *(G-1324)*

First Student Inc 763 421-3199
650 South St Anoka (55303) *(G-182)*

First Student Inc 763 682-5530
1111 Bison Blvd Buffalo (55313) *(G-644)*

First Student Inc 763 421-5785
11911 Champlin Dr Champlin (55316) *(G-893)*

First Student Inc 952 475-0038
505 Tamarack Ave Long Lake (55356) *(G-3024)*

First Student Inc 763 717-9447
2180 108th Ln NE Minneapolis (55449) *(G-3469)*

First Student Inc 612 378-7833
3400 Spring St NE Minneapolis (55413) *(G-4446)*

First Student Inc 763 559-9326
15625 32nd Ave N Minneapolis (55447) *(G-4447)*

First Student Inc 763 389-2342
604 S Old Highway 18 Princeton (55371) *(G-6909)*

First Student Inc 507 289-4541
2021 32nd Ave NW Rochester (55901) *(G-7114)*

First Student Inc 651 628-0046
1717 County Road C W Saint Paul (55113) *(G-8381)*

First Student Inc 651 645-1959
1090 Snelling Ave N Saint Paul (55108) *(G-8382)*

First Student Inc 763 559-8111
3030 Harbor Ln N Ste 124 Saint Paul (55108) *(G-8383)*

First Supply LLC (HQ) 507 287-0202
3815 Highway 14 W Rochester (55901) *(G-7115)*

First Supply LLC 507 287-0202
3815 Highway 14 W Rochester (55901) *(G-7116)*

First Tech Inc 612 374-8000
2640 Hennepin Ave S Minneapolis (55408) *(G-4448)*

1st United Bank 507 334-2201
430 4th St NW Faribault (55021) *(G-2008)*

Firstmark Services LLC 651 265-7600
2101 Wooddale Dr Ste B Saint Paul (55125) *(G-9218)*

Fischer Sand & Aggregate LLP 952 432-7132
14698 Galaxie Ave Saint Paul (55124) *(G-7775)*

Fisco, Eden Prairie *Also Called Elvin Safety LLC (G-1655)*

Fiserv Health Inc 763 549-3359
5500 Wayzata Blvd Minneapolis (55416) *(G-4449)*

ALPHABETIC

Fiserv Health Plan (HQ) 262 879-5565
5500 Wayzata Blvd Ste 500 Minneapolis (55416) ***(G-4450)***
Fish & Richardson PC 612 335-5070
60 S 6th St Ste 3300 Minneapolis (55402) ***(G-4451)***
Fishel Information Systems Inc 952 544-1108
10590 Wayzata Blvd Hopkins (55305) ***(G-2543)***
Fisher Education Association 218 891-4905
313 Park Ave Fisher (56723) ***(G-2134)***
Fisher Paper Box Co 763 425-7444
3901 85th Ave N Minneapolis (55443) ***(G-4452)***
Fit Pro LLC 763 784-4747
12420 Aberdeen St NE Minneapolis (55449) ***(G-3470)***
Fit-Pro II (PA) 763 295-3002
133 Sandberg Rd Monticello (55362) ***(G-6271)***
Fitgers On The Lake LLC 218 727-9077
600 E Superior St Ste 203 Duluth (55802) ***(G-1325)***
Fitness 19 ....952 380-9919
23730 Highway 7 Excelsior (55331) ***(G-1935)***
Fitzco Inc 952 471-1185
4300 Shoreline Dr Spring Park (55384) ***(G-9563)***
Fitzgerald Construction 218 789-7318
9 Osborn Ave N Sabin (56580) ***(G-7397)***
Five County Mental Health Ctr 320 396-3333
521 Broadway Ave N Braham (55006) ***(G-542)***
5 K Enterprises Inc 612 216-6292
124 E Welcome Ave Mankato (56001) ***(G-3127)***
Five Star H Enterprises Inc 612 867-5373
3824 Dunbar Ct Minneapolis (55443) ***(G-4453)***
Flagship Athletic Club Inc 952 941-2000
755 Prairie Center Dr Eden Prairie (55344) ***(G-1665)***
Flagship Bank Minnesota 952 473-1959
445 Lake St E Ste 110 Wayzata (55391) ***(G-9917)***
Flannery Construction Inc 651 225-1105
1375 Saint Anthony Ave Saint Paul (55104) ***(G-8384)***
Flare Heating & Air Condg 763 542-1166
9303 Plymouth Ave N # 104 Minneapolis (55427) ***(G-4454)***
Flatliner Speed Society 507 452-8917
1418 Brookview Dr Winona (55987) ***(G-10097)***
Fleet Wholesale Supply Co Inc 763 424-9668
8400 Lakeland Ave N Minneapolis (55445) ***(G-4455)***
Fleet Wholesale Supply Co Inc 507 281-1130
481 Main St Rochester (55904) ***(G-7117)***
Flint Group LLC (HQ) 763 559-5911
15500 28th Ave N Minneapolis (55447) ***(G-4456)***
Flint Hills Resources, LP 507 532-6331
901 N 7th St Marshall (56258) ***(G-3296)***
Flips Gymnastic Center 651 777-4776
3505 Commerce Blvd Saint Paul (55110) ***(G-8385)***
Floor Store Inc 952 401-0955
2401 Highway 7 Excelsior (55331) ***(G-1943)***
Floyd Lock & Safe Co (PA) 952 881-5625
9036 Grand Ave S Minneapolis (55420) ***(G-4457)***
Floyd Total Security 320 654-9549
777 Anderson Ave Saint Cloud (56303) ***(G-7511)***
Floyd Wild Inc 507 537-0531
2521 County Road 7 Marshall (56258) ***(G-3297)***
Fluid Interiors 612 746-8700
100 N 6th St Ste 100A Minneapolis (55403) ***(G-4458)***
Flying Dutchmen Cycle Club 507 354-2306
2317 N Broadway St New Ulm (56073) ***(G-6449)***
FM 107 W Fmp Real Life 651 642-4107
3415 University Ave W Saint Paul (55114) ***(G-8386)***
FMC Dialysis Svcs Spirit Vly, Duluth *Also Called Bio-Medical Applications of MN **(G-1254)***
FMI Hydraulics Inc 507 296-4551
401 Lone Tree St Porter (56280) ***(G-6893)***
FMMI, Minneapolis *Also Called Food Market Merchandising Inc **(G-4462)***
Fmw Human Svcs Faribault, Blue Earth *Also Called Human Services of Faribault **(G-536)***
FNB Bank of Blue Earth 507 526-3241
306 S Main St Blue Earth (56013) ***(G-535)***
Foam Industries Inc 763 503-9265
8700 109th Ave N Ste 500 Champlin (55316) ***(G-894)***
Focalpoint Inc 952 944-0932
10050 Crosstown Cir # 200 Eden Prairie (55344) ***(G-1666)***
Focus Market Research Inc (PA) 612 869-8181
2 Meridian Xing Ste 160 Minneapolis (55423) ***(G-4459)***
Foley & Mansfield LLP (PA) 612 338-8788
250 Marquette Ave # 1200 Minneapolis (55401) ***(G-4460)***
Foley Dental Clinic (PA) 763 757-3120
11237 Foley Blvd NW Minneapolis (55448) ***(G-3471)***
Foley Health Care Inc 320 968-6201
253 Pine St Foley (56329) ***(G-2137)***
Fond Du Lac Management Inc 218 879-4593
1720 Big Lake Rd Cloquet (55720) ***(G-1052)***
Fond Du Lac Reservation 218 878-2327
1785 Highway 210 Carlton (55718) ***(G-867)***
Fond Du Lac Reservation 218 879-1227
927 Trettel Ln Cloquet (55720) ***(G-1053)***
Fond Dulac Development Corp 218 722-8633
1789 Highway 210 Carlton (55718) ***(G-868)***
Food Engineering Corp 763 559-5200
1210 Dunkirk Ln N Minneapolis (55447) ***(G-4461)***
Food Market Merchandising Inc 952 894-0110
6401 W 106th St Ste 201 Minneapolis (55438) ***(G-4462)***
Food Perspectives Inc 763 553-7787
2880 Vicksburg Ln N Minneapolis (55447) ***(G-4463)***
Food Systems Design Inc 952 884-4048
10640 Lyndale Ave S Ste 1 Minneapolis (55420) ***(G-4464)***
Food-N-Fuel, Walker *Also Called North Stop Inc **(G-9856)***
Foodliner Inc 651 345-2860
415 S 10th St Lake City (55041) ***(G-2852)***
Forbes, John 320 693-3287
60819 US Highway 12 Litchfield (55355) ***(G-2984)***
Forby Contracting Inc 320 384-6061
34363 Swede Aly Hinckley (55037) ***(G-2484)***
Force America Inc (PA) 952 707-1300
501 Cliff Rd E Ste 100 Burnsville (55337) ***(G-722)***
Ford Boyer Trucks Inc 612 378-6000
2425 Broadway St NE Minneapolis (55413) ***(G-4465)***
Ford Lincoln Mercury, Hutchinson *Also Called Jay Malone Motors **(G-2704)***
Ford New Brighten 651 633-9010
1100 Silver Lake Rd NW Saint Paul (55112) ***(G-8387)***
Ford Tenvoorde Inc 320 251-0540
185 Roosevelt Rd Saint Cloud (56301) ***(G-7512)***
Forest Hills Golf Club Inc 651 464-3097
7530 210th St N Forest Lake (55025) ***(G-2160)***
Forest Hills Golf Rv Reso 218 562-7585
9252 Breezy Point Dr Pequot Lakes (56472) ***(G-6788)***
Forest History Center Minn, Grand Rapids *Also Called Historical Society of MN **(G-2286)***
Forest Lake Flyaways 651 464-8648
255 7th Ave NW Forest Lake (55025) ***(G-2161)***
Forest Lake Sanitation Inc 651 464-2321
6320 E Viking Blvd Wyoming (55092) ***(G-10204)***
Forest Lake VFW Post 4210 Inc 651 464-6827
556 12th St SW Forest Lake (55025) ***(G-2162)***
Forest Weekes Products Inc (PA) 651 644-9807
2600 Como Ave Saint Paul (55108) ***(G-8388)***
Forestry Field Station 651 345-3216
1801 S Oak St Lake City (55041) ***(G-2853)***
Forstrom & Torgerson Hnw LLC 763 494-4498
7745 Elm Creek Blvd N Maple Grove (55369) ***(G-3241)***
Forstrom & Torgerson Hs LLC 651 415-1956
1050 Gramsie Rd Saint Paul (55126) ***(G-8389)***
Forstrom & Torgerson LLP 651 482-0402
1000 Gramsie Rd Saint Paul (55126) ***(G-8390)***
Forstrom & Torgerson Ssnw LLC 763 494-8856
7821 Elm Creek Blvd N Maple Grove (55369) ***(G-3242)***
Forsythe Appraisals LLC 651 486-9550
222 Little Canada Rd E Ste 175 Saint Paul (55117) ***(G-8391)***
Fort Snelling National Cmtry, Minneapolis *Also Called National Cemetery Admin **(G-5161)***
FORTUNE BAY RESORT CASINO, Tower *Also Called Bois Forte Enterprises **(G-9686)***
Fortune Transportation Co 507 831-2335
93702 470th Ave Windom (56101) ***(G-10073)***
Foss North America Inc 952 974-9892
8091 Wallace Rd Eden Prairie (55344) ***(G-1667)***
Foss Swim School Inc 952 935-8732
8332 Highway 7 Ste 954 Minneapolis (55426) ***(G-4466)***
Foss Swim School Inc 763 416-8993
9455 Garland Ave Osseo (55311) ***(G-6615)***
Foster Electric Co 507 289-4571
538 6th Ave NW Rochester (55901) ***(G-7118)***
Foster Four 320 240-0243
1708 7th St SE Saint Cloud (56304) ***(G-7414)***
Foster Klima & Co LLC 612 746-2214
920 2nd Ave S Ste 1100 Minneapolis (55402) ***(G-4467)***
Foster Wheeler Twin Cities Inc 612 379-1885
2701 University Ave SE # 105 Minneapolis (55414) ***(G-4468)***
Foth Production Solutions LLC 651 288-8550
8550 Hudson Blvd N Lake Elmo (55042) ***(G-2872)***
Foundation For Healthcare 320 253-1920
520 1st St NE Ste 1 Sartell (56377) ***(G-9328)***
Foundation For Rural Health 218 563-2715
600 Riverside Ave NE McIntosh (56556) ***(G-3341)***
Fountain Centers 507 377-6411
408 W Fountain St Albert Lea (56007) ***(G-51)***
Fountain Lake Treatment Center 507 373-2384
408 W Fountain St Albert Lea (56007) ***(G-52)***
Four Seasons Eye Care, Minneapolis *Also Called Donald H Sealock **(G-4277)***
Four Seasons Services Inc 507 373-9666
636 E 11th St Albert Lea (56007) ***(G-53)***
4 Ster Camps, Prior Lake *Also Called Calmar Group Inc **(G-6929)***
Four TS Inc 320 685-7407
27023 Hidden Cove Rd Cold Spring (56320) ***(G-1086)***
Four51 Inc 952 294-0451
8300 Norman Center Dr Bloomington (55437) ***(G-498)***
Four51 Inc 952 294-0451
7905 Golden Triangle Dr Eden Prairie (55344) ***(G-1668)***
Foussard Hospitality Inc 320 252-8700
520 Highway 10 S Saint Cloud (56304) ***(G-7415)***
Fox Cable Network Services LLC 612 330-2468
90 S 11th St Minneapolis (55403) ***(G-4469)***
Fox Country, Rochester *Also Called Cumulus Media Inc **(G-7090)***
Fox Electrical Co 507 433-7184
500 10th St NE Austin (55912) ***(G-271)***
Fox Television Stations Inc 952 946-1234
11358 Viking Dr Eden Prairie (55344) ***(G-1669)***
Fox-1 Resources 651 894-3990
4155 Old Sibley Memorial Hwy Saint Paul (55122) ***(G-7776)***
Fpd Power Development LLC 612 782-3100
2850 Anthony Ln S Minneapolis (55418) ***(G-4470)***
FPI Paving Contractors Inc 651 484-0385
3230 Rice St Saint Paul (55126) ***(G-8392)***
Fpx LLC 507 388-5000
11 Civic Center Plz # 310 Mankato (56001) ***(G-3128)***
Fpx LLC 866 826-6344
11 Civic Center Plz # 310 Mankato (56001) ***(G-3129)***
Fraboni's Wholesale Distrs 218 263-8991
315 E 13th St Hibbing (55746) ***(G-2445)***
France Avenue Family 952 831-1551
7250 France Ave S Ste 410 Minneapolis (55435) ***(G-4471)***
France Avenue LLC 952 831-0343
3909 Heritage Hills Dr Minneapolis (55437) ***(G-4472)***
Francis A Gross Golf Course, Minneapolis *Also Called City of Minneapolis **(G-4092)***
Franciscan Health Center Inc 218 727-8933
3910 Minnesota Ave Duluth (55802) ***(G-1326)***
Franciscan Health Community (PA) 651 696-8400
1925 Norfolk Ave Saint Paul (55116) ***(G-8393)***
Franciscus Skemp Health Care, Caledonia *Also Called Skemp Walk In Clinic **(G-829)***
Frandsen Bank & Trust 320 968-6293
341 4th Ave N Foley (56329) ***(G-2138)***
Frandsen Bank & Trust (PA) 507 744-2361
116 Central St W Lonsdale (55046) ***(G-3044)***
Franklin Bakery LLC 612 455-3893
1020 E Franklin Ave Minneapolis (55404) ***(G-4473)***

ALPHABETIC

Franklin Co-Op 612 338-4574
2300 E Franklin Ave Ofc Minneapolis (55406) **(G-4474)**
Franklin Corp 612 455-1700
1101 W River Pkwy Ste 400 Minneapolis (55415) **(G-4475)**
Franklin Foods 218 727-6651
1925 W 1st St Duluth (55806) **(G-1327)**
Franklin Healthcare Center, Franklin *Also Called Beverly Enterprises - MN* **(G-2180)**
Franklin Heating Station 507 289-3534
119 3rd St SW Rochester (55902) **(G-7119)**
Frantz Donald R Con Cnstr I, Minneapolis *Also Called Frantz, Donald R Concrete* **(G-4476)**
Frantz, Donald R Concrete 952 929-8568
3501 Xenwood Ave S Minneapolis (55416) **(G-4476)**
Franz Reprographics Inc 763 503-3401
2781 Freeway Blvd Ste 100 Minneapolis (55430) **(G-4477)**
Fraser 612 861-1688
2400 W 64th St Minneapolis (55423) **(G-4478)**
Fraser Child & Family Center 612 331-9413
3333 University Ave SE Minneapolis (55414) **(G-4479)**
Fraser Construction Co 507 288-6583
3725 Enterprise Dr SW Rochester (55902) **(G-7120)**
Fraser-Morris Electric Co Inc 612 332-4328
250 2nd Ave S Ste 109 Minneapolis (55401) **(G-4480)**
Fraternal Order of Eagles Club 507 451-3846
141 E Rose St Owatonna (55060) **(G-6714)**
Fraternal Order of Eagles Inc 218 681-2406
305 Red Lake Blvd Thief River Falls (56701) **(G-9668)**
Fratrans Inc 651 294-3944
587 1st St SW New Brighton (55112) **(G-6407)**
Frattalone Co's Inc 651 484-0448
3205 Spruce St Saint Paul (55117) **(G-8394)**
Frattalone I LLC 651 292-9800
650 Grand Ave Saint Paul (55105) **(G-8395)**
Frattalone Tractor Co Inc 651 484-0448
3205 Spruce St Saint Paul (55117) **(G-8396)**
Fred Babcock Post No 5555 .... 612 869-5555
6715 Lake Shore Dr S Minneapolis (55423) **(G-4481)**
Fred Meyer Jewelers Inc 952 892-6374
1043 Burnsville Ctr Burnsville (55306) **(G-723)**
Fred Vogt & Co 952 929-6767
3260 Gorham Ave Minneapolis (55426) **(G-4482)**
Fredrickson Communications Inc 612 339-7970
119 N 4th St Ste 513 Minneapolis (55401) **(G-4483)**
Fredrikson & Byron 612 492-7000
200 S 6th St Ste 4000 Minneapolis (55402) **(G-4484)**
Freeborn Country Fair Assn 507 373-6965
1031 Bridge Ave Albert Lea (56007) **(G-54)**
Freedom Health Care Inc 952 854-6889
2626 E 82nd St Ste 260 Minneapolis (55425) **(G-4485)**
Freedom Services Inc 952 890-6524
425 W Travelers Trl Burnsville (55337) **(G-724)**
Freeport West Inc 612 824-3040
2219 Oakland Ave Minneapolis (55404) **(G-4486)**
Freerksen Trucking Inc 507 374-6708
67259 210th Ave Dodge Center (55927) **(G-1228)**
Freewheel Bicycle Cooperative 612 339-2219
1812 S 6th St Minneapolis (55454) **(G-4487)**
Freight Office For North West 218 727-8747
4701 Airport Rd Duluth (55811) **(G-1328)**
Freight Plus, Winona *Also Called Ltx Inc* **(G-10112)**
Freightmasters Inc 651 688-6800
3703 Kennebec Dr Saint Paul (55122) **(G-7777)**
Fremont Community Health Svcs 612 588-9411
3300 Fremont Ave N Minneapolis (55412) **(G-4488)**
Frerichs Construction Co 651 787-0687
3600 Labore Rd Ste 8 Saint Paul (55110) **(G-8397)**
Fresh Paint, Saint Paul *Also Called Lawremar Inc* **(G-8568)**
Fresh Seasons Market LLC 952 938-5555
14400 Excelsior Blvd Minnetonka (55345) **(G-6170)**
Fresh Start Enterprises Inc 952 903-0262
7242 Washington Ave S Eden Prairie (55344) **(G-1670)**
Fridley Auto Parts Inc 763 784-8890
7300 Old Central Ave NE Minneapolis (55432) **(G-3472)**
Fridley Medical Center, Minneapolis *Also Called Multicare Associates of The* **(G-3546)**
Fridges Contracting Co LLC 952 469-2121
21980 Kenrick Ave Lakeville (55044) **(G-2907)**
Fridges Drywall Inc 952 461-3288
430 Webster St New Market (55054) **(G-6420)**
Fridges Landscaping Inc 952 469-2996
9380 202nd St W Lakeville (55044) **(G-2908)**
Friendly Chevrolet, Geo Inc 763 786-6100
7501 Highway 65 NE Minneapolis (55432) **(G-3473)**
Frito-Lay Inc 507 446-5888
3401 9th St NW Owatonna (55060) **(G-6715)**
Frito-Lay Inc 507 282-1134
1402 60th Ave NW Rochester (55901) **(G-7121)**
Fritz Co Inc 651 459-9751
1912 Hastings Ave Newport (55055) **(G-6486)**
Frolander Island Resort 218 386-3019
59473 330th St Warroad (56763) **(G-9870)**
Frontier Communications of MN 952 898-6422
1405 W 150th St Burnsville (55306) **(G-725)**
Frontier Construction Co Inc (PA) 218 246-9512
48243 Frontier Ln Deer River (56636) **(G-1172)**
Frontier Enterprises Corp 763 434-6913
18533 Buchanan St NE Cedar (55011) **(G-878)**
Fryberger, Buchanan, Smith (PA) 218 725-6807
302 W Superior St Ste 700 Duluth (55802) **(G-1329)**
Ftb Inc 218 326-5960
1407 E Highway 2 Grand Rapids (55744) **(G-2278)**
Fujitsu America Inc 763 595-9600
605 Highway 169 N Ste 301 Minneapolis (55441) **(G-4489)**
Fujitsu Consulting Information I 952 258-6000
110 Cheshire Ln Ste 300 Minnetonka (55305) **(G-6171)**
Fulbright & Jaworski LLP 612 321-2800
80 S 8th St Ste 2100 Minneapolis (55402) **(G-4490)**
Fulfillment Distribution Ctr 320 656-8880
720 Anderson Ave Saint Cloud (56303) **(G-7513)**

Fulfillment Systems Inc (PA) 763 295-3400
406 E 7th St Monticello (55362) **(G-6272)**
Fulfillment Systems Inc 320 255-0800
4001 Clearwater Rd Saint Cloud (56301) **(G-7514)**
Full Present Inc 763 441-5999
19320 Highway 169 Elk River (55330) **(G-1875)**
Fun Sisters 612 824-9872
5049 Belmont Ave S Minneapolis (55419) **(G-4491)**
Funcity 763 441-8365
9100 Park Ave NE Elk River (55330) **(G-1899)**
Functional Industries, Buffalo *Also Called Wright Connection Dtnh Inc* **(G-661)**
Functional Industries Inc 763 682-4336
1801 N State Hwy 25 Buffalo (55313) **(G-645)**
Furin & Shea Welding & Fabctg 218 262-5271
1432 E 34th St Hibbing (55746) **(G-2446)**
Furlong Golf Inc 651 480-8558
14425 Goodwin Ave Hastings (55033) **(G-2387)**
Fury Motors Inc 651 451-1313
1000 Concord St S South Saint Paul (55075) **(G-9527)**
G & K Services Inc 320 252-9471
1250 Kuhn Dr Saint Cloud (56301) **(G-7515)**
G B & Co Hair & Skin Care 320 253-4832
80 37th Ave S Saint Cloud (56301) **(G-7516)**
G C M Inc 952 882-8500
1211 Cliff Rd E Burnsville (55337) **(G-726)**
G E Young & Co 952 847-2388
11100 Wayzata Blvd # 510 Minnetonka (55305) **(G-6172)**
G G Tucson Inc 218 723-8433
525 S Lake Ave Ste 405 Duluth (55802) **(G-1330)**
G M Clark Co's Inc 763 475-1000
180 Northshore Dr Maple Plain (55359) **(G-3274)**
G P Co's Inc 651 454-6500
1174 Northland Dr Mendota Heights (55120) **(G-3363)**
G R Mechanical Plumbing 763 428-2663
12401 Ironwood Cir Ste 500 Rogers (55374) **(G-7323)**
G&K Services Inc 612 521-4771
2601 49th Ave N Ste 200 Minneapolis (55430) **(G-4492)**
G&K Services Inc 612 333-2225
621 Olson Memorial Hwy Minneapolis (55405) **(G-4493)**
G&K Services Inc (PA) 952 912-5500
5995 Opus Pkwy Ste 500 Minnetonka (55343) **(G-6173)**
G&K Services Inc 507 451-5710
2624 Park Dr Owatonna (55060) **(G-6716)**
G&K Services Inc 651 855-7000
685 Olive St Saint Paul (55130) **(G-8398)**
G&S Staffing Services Inc 320 235-3949
305 7th St SW Ste 4 Willmar (56201) **(G-10002)**
G2 Secure Staff LLC 612 725-6423
4300 Glumack Dr Ste 3225 Saint Paul (55111) **(G-7960)**
G4s Secure Solutions Inc 651 482-1928
2610 University Ave W # 210 Saint Paul (55114) **(G-8399)**
Gables At Arbor Pnte Homeownrs, Saint Paul *Also Called New Concepts Management Group* **(G-8747)**
Gables Inc 507 282-2500
604 5th St SW Rochester (55902) **(G-7122)**
Gabriel Degrood Bendt LLC 612 547-5000
608 2nd Ave S Ste 129 Minneapolis (55402) **(G-4494)**
Gac Development LLC 507 289-5556
225 S Broadway Rochester (55904) **(G-7123)**
Gag Sheet Metal Inc 507 354-3813
125 3rd St N New Ulm (56073) **(G-6450)**
Gage & Gage Inc 952 403-1193
4950 12th Ave E Shakopee (55379) **(G-9440)**
Gage Group LLC (PA) 763 595-3920
10000 Highway 55 Ste 100 Minneapolis (55441) **(G-4495)**
Gagnon & Associates, Eden Prairie *Also Called Redprairie Corp* **(G-1761)**
Gagnon Inc (PA) 651 644-4301
2315 Hampden Ave Saint Paul (55114) **(G-8400)**
Gale's Auto Body Inc 763 786-4110
10600 Highway 65 NE Minneapolis (55434) **(G-3474)**
Galil Medical USA 877 639-2796
4364 Round Lake Rd W Arden Hills (55112) **(G-246)**
Galliard Capital Management 612 667-3210
800 Lasalle Ave Ste 1100 Minneapolis (55402) **(G-4496)**
Galtier Health Center, Saint Paul *Also Called Extendicare Homes Inc* **(G-8356)**
Game Financial Corp 800 363-3321
1550 Utica Ave S Ste 100 Minneapolis (55416) **(G-4497)**
Gamer Packaging Inc 612 788-4444
330 2nd Ave S Ste 895 Minneapolis (55401) **(G-4498)**
Games People Play Inc 507 433-7593
701 18th Ave NW Austin (55912) **(G-272)**
Gander Mountain Co 763 420-9800
8030 Wedgewood Ln N Osseo (55369) **(G-6616)**
Gander Mountain Co 507 252-2033
3470 55th St NW Rochester (55901) **(G-7124)**
Garborg's, Minneapolis *Also Called Garborgs LLC* **(G-4499)**
Garborgs LLC 612 888-5726
2060 W 98th St Minneapolis (55431) **(G-4499)**
Garden Grove LLC 651 699-5300
2177 Youngman Ave Ste 100 Saint Paul (55116) **(G-8401)**
Garden House Estates Ltd 218 628-0271
1 Riverside Dr Duluth (55808) **(G-1331)**
Garden Valley Telephone Co 218 687-2400
201 Ross Ave Erskine (56535) **(G-1920)**
Gardenview Nursing Home, Le Sueur *Also Called Minnesota Valley Memorial Hosp* **(G-2958)**
Gardner Financial Services Inc 952 935-4601
8421 Wayzata Blvd Ste 350 Minneapolis (55426) **(G-4500)**
Garkat Inc 507 835-8227
200 22nd Ave NE Ofc Waseca (56093) **(G-9879)**
Garland's Inc (PA) 612 333-3469
2501 26th Ave S Minneapolis (55406) **(G-4501)**
Garlock French Roofing Corp 612 722-7129
2301 E 25th St Minneapolis (55406) **(G-4502)**
Garlock-East Equipment Co 763 553-1935
2601 Niagara Ln N Minneapolis (55447) **(G-4503)**
Gartner Refrigeration & Mfg 763 559-5880
13205 16th Ave N Plymouth (55441) **(G-6862)**

A
L
P
H
A
B
E
T
I
C

Gartner Refrigeration Co 218 722-4439
2331 W Superior St Duluth (55806) *(G-1332)*
Gartner Studios Inc (PA) 651 351-7700
220 Myrtle St E Stillwater (55082) *(G-9619)*
Gary Halgran 651 917-3634
2200 University Ave W Ste 160 Saint Paul (55114) *(G-8402)*
Gary J Aschenbrenner Trucking 507 233-2539
219 12th St S New Ulm (56073) *(G-6451)*
Gary L Kemp Agency Inc 651 457-3070
60 Marie Ave E Ste 209 Saint Paul (55118) *(G-7778)*
Gary Thaler 651 464-5555
15252 W Freeway Dr NE Forest Lake (55025) *(G-2145)*
Gary Yeager Pro Shop, Hibbing *Also Called Mesaba Country Club (G-2464)*
Gassen Co Inc 952 922-5575
6438 City West Pkwy Eden Prairie (55344) *(G-1671)*
Gateway, Saint Paul *Also Called ACG Inc (G-7688)*
Gateway Building Systems Inc 218 685-4420
33424 US Highway 59 Elbow Lake (56531) *(G-1853)*
Gateway Building Systems Inc 218 236-9336
2200 14th Ave S Moorhead (56560) *(G-6316)*
Gateway Family Health Clinic 218 485-4491
4570 County Hwy 61 Moose Lake (55767) *(G-6350)*
Gaub Inc 320 382-8075
33102 County Road 17 Olivia (56277) *(G-6561)*
Gausman & Moore Associates Inc 651 639-9606
1700 Highway 36 W Ste 700 Saint Paul (55113) *(G-8403)*
Gauthier Industries Inc 507 289-0731
3105 22nd St NW Rochester (55901) *(G-7125)*
Gazda Transportation Mayflower, Minneapolis *Also Called McCollister's Transportation (G-3531)*
Gb Lumina Inc 763 797-9036
6120 Earle Brown Dr # 410 Minneapolis (55430) *(G-4504)*
GE Capital Fleet Services, Eden Prairie *Also Called General Electric Fleet Svcs (G-1674)*
Geek Squad Inc (HQ) 612 343-1028
1213 Washington Ave N Minneapolis (55401) *(G-4505)*
Geek Squad Inc 612 922-9288
3724 W 50th St Minneapolis (55410) *(G-4506)*
Gehling Auction Co Inc 507 765-2131
Hwy 52 No 1/2 Mile Preston (55965) *(G-6897)*
Gelco Information Network Inc (DH) 952 947-1500
10700 Prairie Lakes Dr Eden Prairie (55344) *(G-1672)*
Geldner Construction Inc 507 931-4230
101 Locust St Saint Peter (56082) *(G-9304)*
Gem Lake Hills Inc 651 429-8715
4039 Scheuneman Rd Saint Paul (55110) *(G-8404)*
Gemini 26 Inc 507 334-7951
15760 Acorn Trl Faribault (55021) *(G-2009)*
Gemm Inc 952 591-6730
12411 Wayzata Blvd Minnetonka (55305) *(G-6174)*
Gemmell Lakes Association 218 897-5318
11141 County Road 25 Mizpah (56660) *(G-6243)*
Gene Bueckers 320 352-2876
39864 US Highway 71 Sauk Centre (56378) *(G-9346)*
General Auditing Bureau, Osseo *Also Called Receivables Control Corp (G-6655)*
General Aviation Inc 763 420-6907
7100 Northland Cir N Ste 407 Minneapolis (55428) *(G-4507)*
General Casualty Co of WI 952 941-0980
10400 Viking Dr Ste 300 Eden Prairie (55344) *(G-1673)*
General Cleaning Corp (PA) 218 727-4513
301 W 1st St Ste 511 Duluth (55802) *(G-1333)*
General Cleaning Specialists 218 727-4513
301 W 1st St Ste 511 Duluth (55802) *(G-1334)*
General Dynamics Aviation Svcs 612 638-2000
6925 34th Ave S Minneapolis (55450) *(G-4508)*
General Electric Capital Corp 952 897-5600
8400 Normandale Lake Blvd Minneapolis (55437) *(G-4509)*
General Electric Co 507 368-9222
Hwy 14 W Lake Benton (56149) *(G-2848)*
General Electric Co 612 529-9502
2025 49th Ave N Minneapolis (55430) *(G-4510)*
General Electric Co 218 749-6100
5521 Mineral Ave Mountain Iron (55768) *(G-6392)*
General Electric Fleet Svcs 952 828-1000
3 Capital Dr Eden Prairie (55344) *(G-1674)*
General Marketing Services Inc 952 806-5080
7108 Ohms Ln Minneapolis (55439) *(G-4511)*
General Mills Federal Credit (PA) 763 764-6900
9999 Wayzata Blvd Minnetonka (55305) *(G-6175)*
General Mills Inc 612 721-6811
3600 Dight Ave Minneapolis (55406) *(G-4512)*
General Mills Inc 763 764-3313
301 4th Ave S Ste 680 Minneapolis (55415) *(G-4513)*
General Mills Operations LLC 218 722-7759
200 Garfield Ave Duluth (55802) *(G-1335)*
General Nanosystems Inc 612 331-3690
3014 University Ave SE Minneapolis (55414) *(G-4514)*
General Parts LLC (PA) 952 944-5800
11311 Hampshire Ave S Minneapolis (55438) *(G-4515)*
General Pediatric 612 626-2820
717 Delaware St SE Fl 3 Minneapolis (55414) *(G-4516)*
General Pet Supply Inc 952 890-2300
12155 Nicollet Ave Burnsville (55337) *(G-727)*
General Pump, Mendota Heights *Also Called G P Co's Inc (G-3363)*
General Resource Technology 651 454-4151
2978 Center Ct Saint Paul (55121) *(G-7779)*
General Safety Equipment LLC 651 462-1000
5181 260th St Wyoming (55092) *(G-10205)*
General Security Services Corp (PA) 952 858-5000
9110 Meadowview Rd Minneapolis (55425) *(G-4517)*
General Security Services Corp 320 252-3794
574 And Half E St Germain Saint Cloud (56304) *(G-7416)*
General Sheet Metal Corp 763 544-8747
2330 Louisiana Ave N Minneapolis (55427) *(G-4518)*
General Sprinkler Corp 651 484-5903
1863 Buerkle Rd Saint Paul (55110) *(G-8405)*
Generations Community Support 612 676-1604
2649 Park Ave Minneapolis (55407) *(G-4519)*
Generations Resources For 612 676-1604
2331 University Ave SE Minneapolis (55414) *(G-4520)*
Genereux Fine Wood Products, Monticello *Also Called Tappers Inc (G-6289)*
Genesis Corp 651 702-3300
7650 Currell Blvd Ste 260 Saint Paul (55125) *(G-9219)*
Genesis Group Homes Inc 763 390-0773
4650 Oak Grove Pkwy N Brooklyn Park (55443) *(G-610)*
Genesis Homecare Inc 651 686-5910
13379 Hughes Ct Saint Paul (55124) *(G-7780)*
Geneva Capital LLC 320 762-8400
522 Broadway St Ste 4 Alexandria (56308) *(G-102)*
Genex Cooperative Inc 952 758-2561
412 4th Ave NW New Prague (56071) *(G-6427)*
Genex Farm Systems 952 758-2561
412 4th Ave NW New Prague (56071) *(G-6428)*
Genmar Holdings Inc (HQ) 612 339-7900
2900 80 S 8th St Minneapolis (55402) *(G-4521)*
Genpak LLC 952 881-8673
9611 James Ave S Minneapolis (55431) *(G-4522)*
Genuine Parts Co 952 925-0188
7400 W 27th St Minneapolis (55426) *(G-4523)*
Genz-Ryan Plumbing & Heating 952 882-1144
2200 Highway 13 W Burnsville (55337) *(G-728)*
Geo's Paint & Finish LLC 320 692-2027
26392 State Highway 18 Brainerd (56401) *(G-567)*
Geo-Comm Inc 320 240-0040
601 W Saint Germain St Saint Cloud (56301) *(G-7517)*
Geodigm Corp (PA) 952 556-5657
1630 Lake Dr W Chanhassen (55317) *(G-924)*
George Konik Associates Inc 952 835-5550
7242 Metro Blvd Minneapolis (55439) *(G-4524)*
Georgie's Fitness Inc 507 238-9422
210 Cottonwood Rd Fairmont (56031) *(G-1967)*
Geospatial Services 507 457-8723
360 Vila St Winona (55987) *(G-10098)*
Gephart Electric Co Inc 651 484-4900
3550 Labore Rd Ste 11 Saint Paul (55110) *(G-8406)*
Gephart Electrical Constr 651 484-4900
3550 Labore Rd Ste 11 Saint Paul (55110) *(G-8407)*
Gerald N Evenson Inc 218 863-7101
835 1st St SW Pelican Rapids (56572) *(G-6779)*
Gerten Greenhouses & Garden 651 450-1501
5500 Blaine Ave Inver Grove Heights (55076) *(G-2751)*
Gessell Feed Mill Inc 320 547-2994
302 Degraff Ave Swanville (56382) *(G-9658)*
Ggnsc Minneapolis Bloomington 952 881-8676
9200 Nicollet Ave S Minneapolis (55420) *(G-4525)*
Ggnsc Minneapolis Chateau LLC 612 874-1603
2106 2nd Ave S Minneapolis (55404) *(G-4526)*
Ggnsc St Paul Lake Ridge LLC 651 483-5431
2727 Victoria St N Saint Paul (55113) *(G-8408)*
Ggnsc Wayzata LLC 952 473-5466
15409 Wayzata Blvd Wayzata (55391) *(G-9918)*
Giannetti Properties LLC 651 738-2168
2899 Hudson Rd Saint Paul (55128) *(G-9220)*
Giertsen Co of Minnesota Inc (PA) 763 546-1300
8385 10th Ave N Minneapolis (55427) *(G-4527)*
Gift Connection Minneapolis, Minneapolis *Also Called Coyne's & Co Inc (G-4175)*
Gilbert Mechanical Contractors 952 835-3810
4451 W 76th St Edina (55435) *(G-1831)*
Gillette Children's Specialty 952 936-0977
6060 Clearwater Dr # 100 Hopkins (55343) *(G-2544)*
Gillette Children's Specialty 651 229-3840
183 University Ave E Saint Paul (55101) *(G-8409)*
Gillette Children's Specialty (PA) 651 291-2848
200 University Ave E Saint Paul (55101) *(G-8410)*
Gilman Park & Rec Association 320 387-2941
11765 Highway 25 NE Foley (56329) *(G-2139)*
Girl Scouts of Minnesota & WI 651 227-8835
400 Robert St S Saint Paul (55107) *(G-8411)*
Gittleman Management Corp 952 277-2700
1801 American Blvd E # 21 Minneapolis (55425) *(G-4528)*
Glacial Plains Cooperative 320 843-4820
195 30th Ave NE Benson (56215) *(G-439)*
Glacial Plains Cooperative 320 760-5647
543 Van Norman Ave Murdock (56271) *(G-6401)*
Glacial Ridge Hospital Fndtn (PA) 320 634-4521
10 4th Ave SE Glenwood (56334) *(G-2223)*
Glaciel Plans Coop 320 843-2563
260 20th St NW Benson (56215) *(G-440)*
Glacier International Inc 651 786-9700
1901 Oakcrest Ave Saint Paul (55113) *(G-8412)*
Gladen Construction Inc 218 224-2237
40739 US 71 Laporte (56461) *(G-2948)*
Gladstone Partners 651 455-2940
234 Wentworth Ave E Saint Paul (55118) *(G-7781)*
Gleason Gymnastic School 763 493-2526
9775 85th Ave N Ste 500 Osseo (55369) *(G-6617)*
Gleason Gymnastic School (PA) 651 454-6203
2015 Silver Bell Rd Ste 180 Saint Paul (55122) *(G-7782)*
Glen L Stockman 651 636-1171
2845 Hamline Ave N # 200 Saint Paul (55113) *(G-8413)*
Glen Lindseth 218 751-6300
513 Beltrami Ave NW Bemidji (56601) *(G-396)*
GLEN OAKS CARE CENTER, New London *Also Called Juhl Enterprises Inc (G-6416)*
Glen's Truck Center Inc 763 428-4331
21701 John Deere Ln Rogers (55374) *(G-7324)*
Glencoe Regional Health Svcs 320 864-3121
1805 Hennepin Ave N Glencoe (55336) *(G-2207)*
Glencoe Warehouse, Glencoe *Also Called Young America Holdings Inc (G-2217)*
Glendalough of Austin Inc 507 334-4347
402 Heritage Pl Faribault (55021) *(G-2010)*
Glenmore Foundation 218 281-3123
323 S Minnesota St Crookston (56716) *(G-1125)*
Glenn Lake Elementary School, Hopkins *Also Called Independent School District (G-2556)*
Glenn R Rehbein Excavating Inc 651 674-7937
42285 Iris Ave Harris (55032) *(G-2373)*

ALPHABETIC

Glenn Rehbein Excavating Inc (PA) 763 784-0657
8651 Naples St NE Minneapolis (55449) *(G-3475)*
Glenwood Lions Club 320 634-3263
449 2nd Ave SE Glenwood (56334) *(G-2224)*
Glenwood Village Care Center 320 634-5131
719 2nd St SE Glenwood (56334) *(G-2225)*
Glenwood Yard, Glenwood *Also Called SOO Line Railroad Co Inc (G-2233)*
Glenwood-Inglewood Co 612 374-2253
225 Thomas Ave N Minneapolis (55405) *(G-4529)*
Glenwood-Lyndale Community Ctr 612 342-1500
555 Girard Ter Ste 120 Minneapolis (55405) *(G-4530)*
Glh Seeds Inc 952 445-8090
1788 Marschall Rd Shakopee (55379) *(G-9441)*
Global Anesthesia Business 651 646-3091
1503 Hamline Ave N Saint Paul (55108) *(G-8414)*
Global Capital Management Inc 952 476-7222
601 Carlson Pkwy Ste 200 Hopkins (55305) *(G-2545)*
Global Case Technology Inc 763 553-1313
2 Carlson Pkwy N Ste 225 Minneapolis (55447) *(G-4531)*
Global Communication Services 952 890-3911
2224 E 117th St Burnsville (55337) *(G-729)*
Global Financial Partners Corp 952 544-0640
11100 Cedar Hills Blvd Minnetonka (55305) *(G-6176)*
Global Home 507 282-7471
1032 15th Ave SE Rochester (55904) *(G-7126)*
Global Lending Corp 651 438-7976
1405 Honeysuckle Ln Hastings (55033) *(G-2388)*
Global Markets Inc 612 392-7580
9800 Bren Rd E Ste 450 Minnetonka (55343) *(G-6177)*
Global Medical Instrumentation 763 712-8717
6511 Bunker Lake Blvd NW Anoka (55303) *(G-183)*
Global Specialty Contractors (PA) 651 406-8232
3220 Terminal Dr Saint Paul (55121) *(G-7783)*
Global Tax Network Minnesota 952 224-2053
750 Boone Ave N Ste 102 Minneapolis (55427) *(G-4532)*
Global Ventures I Inc 507 825-5462
319 N Hiawatha Ave Pipestone (56164) *(G-6828)*
Global Volunteers 651 407-6100
375 Little Canada Rd E Saint Paul (55117) *(G-8415)*
Gloria Dei Manor, Litchfield *Also Called Augustana Lutheran Homes Inc (G-2979)*
Gnazzo Technical Services Inc 952 949-1026
16438 S Manor Rd Ste 4 Eden Prairie (55346) *(G-1675)*
Gnw Acquisition Corp 651 325-0060
400 Robert St N Ste 1100 Saint Paul (55101) *(G-8416)*
Go E Bizcom 651 454-0013
1020 Discovery Rd Ste 145 Saint Paul (55121) *(G-7784)*
Godbout's Viking Intallation 218 879-2199
516 Adams St Cloquet (55720) *(G-1054)*
Goff & Howard Inc 651 292-8062
255 Kellogg Blvd E Ste 102 Saint Paul (55101) *(G-8417)*
Goggins & Lavintman 651 209-1825
3140 Neil Armstrong Blvd # 319 Saint Paul (55121) *(G-7785)*
Going Going Gong Inc 651 482-1000
5 S Owasso Blvd E Saint Paul (55117) *(G-8418)*
Gold Country Inc 952 935-9887
4777 Shady Oak Rd S Hopkins (55343) *(G-2546)*
Gold Cross Ambulance Service 218 628-2885
4505 W Michigan St Duluth (55807) *(G-1336)*
Gold Cross Ambulance Service 507 345-7540
1308 Marsh St Mankato (56001) *(G-3130)*
Gold Cross Ambulance Service (PA) 507 255-2230
501 6th Ave NW Rochester (55901) *(G-7127)*
Gold Cross Ambulance Service 320 251-2302
2800 7th St N Saint Cloud (56303) *(G-7518)*
Gold Groves 612 884-8383
761 Kasota Ave SE Minneapolis (55414) *(G-4533)*
Gold Key Realty 952 431-5751
15692 Highview Dr Saint Paul (55124) *(G-7786)*
Gold Points Corp 763 212-1000
1405 Xenium Ln N Minneapolis (55441) *(G-4534)*
Gold'n Plump Marketing Inc 320 251-3570
4150 2nd St S Ste 200 Saint Cloud (56301) *(G-7519)*
Gold's Gym, Monticello *Also Called Fit-Pro II (G-6271)*
Goldberg Bail Bonds 218 847-8122
316 S 4 St Mpls Detroit Lakes (56501) *(G-1194)*
Golden Acres Golf Course Inc 763 428-8244
10705 County Road 116 Rogers (55374) *(G-7325)*
Golden ERA Trading LLC 651 774-4400
1865 Magnolia Ave E # 303 Saint Paul (55119) *(G-8419)*
Golden Heart Child Care Center 507 625-1454
1825 Commerce Dr Mankato (56003) *(G-3225)*
Golden Home Care Plus Inc 507 359-2756
40 Roslyn Rd New Ulm (56073) *(G-6452)*
Golden Lake Pta, Circle Pines *Also Called Pta Minnesota Congress 28 (G-1020)*
Golden Living Care Center, Minneapolis *Also Called Ggnsc Minneapolis Bloomington (G-4525)*
Golden Livingcenter - Chateau, Minneapolis *Also Called Ggnsc Minneapolis Chateau LLC (G-4526)*
Golden Livingcenter - Hopkins, Hopkins *Also Called Beverly Enterprises - MN (G-2518)*
Golden Livingcenter - Lk Ridge, Saint Paul *Also Called Ggnsc St Paul Lake Ridge LLC (G-8408)*
Golden Livingcenter-Wayzata, Wayzata *Also Called Ggnsc Wayzata LLC (G-9918)*
Golden Oaks Inc 218 729-5014
4067 Reinke Rd Duluth (55811) *(G-1337)*
Golden Valley Clinic Inc 952 993-8300
8240 Golden Valley Rd # 200 Minneapolis (55427) *(G-4535)*
Golden Valley Country Club 763 732-4100
7001 Golden Valley Rd Minneapolis (55427) *(G-4536)*
Golden Valley Heating & AC, Minneapolis *Also Called Gv Heating & Air Inc (G-4582)*
Golden Valley View Post 7051 ....763 545-9996
7775 Medicine Lake Rd Minneapolis (55427) *(G-4537)*
Golden Valley, City of Inc 763 593-8000
200 Brookview Pkwy Minneapolis (55426) *(G-4538)*
Golden Vly Rhbltation Care Ctr, Minneapolis *Also Called Extendicare Homes Inc (G-4384)*
Goldencare USA, Minneapolis *Also Called National Independent Brokers (G-5164)*
Goldfinch Estates 507 235-9405
850 Goldfinch St Apt 313 Fairmont (56031) *(G-1968)*
Goldleaf Partners 218 824-6119
605 Laurel St Ste 17 Brainerd (56401) *(G-568)*
Goldsmith, Agio, Helms 612 339-0500
225 S 6th St Fl 46 Minneapolis (55402) *(G-4539)*
Goldwood Kennels Inc 651 429-0648
9500 Dellwood Rd N Saint Paul (55115) *(G-9221)*
Golf Inc 320 251-7804
4498 15th St NE Sauk Rapids (56379) *(G-9363)*
Golf Services Corp 651 777-1436
3200 McKnight Rd N Saint Paul (55110) *(G-8420)*
Gonvick American Legion 218 487-5214
184 Elm St Gonvick (56644) *(G-2247)*
Good Hue County Public Health 651 385-6100
512 W 6th St Red Wing (55066) *(G-6983)*
Good Neighbor Home Health Care 218 829-9238
14387 Edgewood Dr Baxter (56425) *(G-328)*
Good Samaritan Center, Albert Lea *Also Called Evangelical Lutheran Good (G-49)*
Good Samaritan Center, Pelican Rapids *Also Called Evangelical Lutheran Good (G-6778)*
Good Samaritan Ctr Nursing HM, Clearbrook *Also Called Evangelical Lutheran Good (G-1038)*
Good Samaritan Home Care Inc 507 765-2700
608 Winona St NW Preston (55965) *(G-6898)*
Good Samaritan Soc Maplewood, Saint Paul *Also Called Evangelical Lutheran Good (G-8347)*
Good Samaritan Soc Pine River, Pine River *Also Called Evangelical Lutheran Good (G-6818)*
Good Samtin Scty Univ Spec Ctr, Minneapolis *Also Called Evangelical Lutheran Good (G-4378)*
Good Shepherd Cottages, Sauk Rapids *Also Called Shepherd Good Lutheran Home (G-9375)*
Good Smrtan Communities Windom, Windom *Also Called Evangelical Lutheran Good (G-10067)*
Good Smrtan Society-Ambassador, Minneapolis *Also Called Evangelical Lutheran Good (G-4377)*
Good Smrtan Society-Stillwater, Stillwater *Also Called Evangelical Lutheran Good (G-9615)*
Goodcities, Eden Prairie *Also Called Citireach International (G-1628)*
Goodhue County Public Health 651 385-6100
512 W 6th St Red Wing (55066) *(G-6984)*
Goodin Co (PA) 612 588-7811
2700 N 2nd St Minneapolis (55411) *(G-4540)*
Goodin Co 320 259-6086
5205 Foundry Cir Saint Cloud (56303) *(G-7520)*
Goodwill Industries Inc 952 953-4410
7320 153rd St W Saint Paul (55124) *(G-7787)*
Goodwill Industries Inc (PA) 651 379-5800
553 Fairview Ave N Saint Paul (55104) *(G-8421)*
Goodwill Industries Inc 651 603-1544
2505 University Ave W Ste 2 Saint Paul (55114) *(G-8422)*
Goodwill Industries Inc 651 439-4207
5899 Nova Scotia Ave N Stillwater (55082) *(G-9620)*
Goodwill Industries Vocational 218 722-6351
700 Garfield Ave Ste 1 Duluth (55802) *(G-1338)*
Gopher Co Inc 612 331-1555
2701 36th Ave S Minneapolis (55406) *(G-4541)*
Gopher Electronics Co 651 490-4900
222 Little Canada Rd E Saint Paul (55117) *(G-8423)*
Gopher Hills Inc 507 263-2507
26155 Nicolai Ave Cannon Falls (55009) *(G-854)*
Gopher News Co 763 546-5300
9000 10th Ave N Minneapolis (55427) *(G-4542)*
GOPHER SPORT & PLAY WITH A P, Owatonna *Also Called Prophet Corp (G-6730)*
Gopher State One Call, Saint Paul *Also Called One Call Concepts Inc (G-7856)*
Gopher State One Call Inc 651 454-8388
2020 Centre Pointe Blvd Saint Paul (55120) *(G-7788)*
Gopher State Scrap & Metal, Mankato *Also Called Alter Trading Corp (G-3103)*
Gorans Brothers Inc 320 995-6564
14277 15th St SE Blomkest (56216) *(G-475)*
Gordon & Ferguson of Delaware 763 559-8300
830 Decatur Ave N Minneapolis (55427) *(G-4543)*
Gordon Construction Inc 218 935-2191
2222 270th Ave Mahnomen (56557) *(G-3086)*
Gordon Lund 320 275-2006
23682 727th Ave Dassel (55325) *(G-1161)*
Gordy's Glass Inc 651 437-5356
12590 127th St S Ste 1 Hastings (55033) *(G-2416)*
Gordy's Inc 507 847-2074
916 Highway 71 N Jackson (56143) *(G-2793)*
Gordys Food, Jackson *Also Called Gordy's Inc (G-2793)*
Gorham Oien Mechanical Inc 320 679-1612
841 Forest Ave E Mora (55051) *(G-6359)*
Gourmet House, Clearbrook *Also Called Riviana International Inc (G-1040)*
Gov Delivery Inc 866 276-5583
408 Saint Peter St Ste 600 Saint Paul (55102) *(G-8424)*
Governor's Inc 651 778-1045
959 Arcade St Saint Paul (55106) *(G-8425)*
Gowan Construction Inc 701 699-5171
3596 15th St NE Oslo (56744) *(G-6588)*
GPM Inc 218 722-9904
4432 Venture Ave Duluth (55811) *(G-1339)*
Grace Management, Minneapolis *Also Called Senior Asset Management Inc (G-5636)*
Grace Management Inc 763 544-9934
6225 42nd Ave N Minneapolis (55422) *(G-4544)*
Graceville Health Center Inc 320 748-7223
115 W 2 Nd St Graceville (56240) *(G-2254)*
Graceville Missionary 320 748-7223
115 W 2nd St Graceville (56240) *(G-2255)*
Gradstaff Inc 612 339-5332
708 N 1st St Ste 245 Minneapolis (55401) *(G-4545)*
Graffco Inc 651 464-1079
13957 Lake Dr NE Forest Lake (55025) *(G-2146)*
Graham Construction Services 651 687-0648
2995 Lone Oak Cir Ste 1 Saint Paul (55121) *(G-7789)*
Grand Casino Hinckley, Hinckley *Also Called Corporate Commission of The (G-2483)*
Grand Casino Mille Lacs, Onamia *Also Called Corporate Commission of The (G-6568)*
Grand Heritage Properties LLC 651 699-3003
1280 Grand Ave Apt 105 Saint Paul (55105) *(G-8426)*
Grand Itasca Clinic & Hospital 218 326-5000
111 SE 3rd St Grand Rapids (55744) *(G-2279)*
Grand Itasca Clinic & Hospital 218 326-7024
500 SE 4th St Grand Rapids (55744) *(G-2280)*
Grand Marais Hotel Co Inc 218 387-2448
1711 E Highway 61 Grand Marais (55604) *(G-2260)*
Grand Meadow Health Care Ctr 507 754-5212
210 E Ave Grand Meadow (55936) *(G-2264)*
Grand Portage National 218 475-2202
211 Mile Creek Rd Grand Portage (55605) *(G-2266)*

ALPHABETIC

Grand Rapids Development Corp 218 326-8501
2301 S Highway 169 Grand Rapids (55744) ***(G-2281)***
Grand Superior Lodge, Duluth *Also Called Castle Danger LP* ***(G-1263)***
Grand View Lodge, Nisswa *Also Called Etoc Co Inc* ***(G-6496)***
Grand Village 218 326-0543
923 Hale Lake Pointe Grand Rapids (55744) ***(G-2282)***
Grandstay Rsidential Suites Ht, Saint Paul *Also Called Apple Valley Gsrs LLC* ***(G-7701)***
Grandview Good Samaritan, Saint Peter *Also Called Evangelical Lutheran Good* ***(G-9302)***
Grandview Good Samaritan Ctr 507 931-9021
830 Sunrise Dr Saint Peter (56082) ***(G-9305)***
Grandview Manor HRA Office 218 529-6300
222 E 2nd St Duluth (55805) ***(G-1340)***
Granger's Inc 651 429-2524
10909 Radisson Rd NE Minneapolis (55449) ***(G-3476)***
Granite Broadcasting Corp 218 720-9666
246 S Lake Ave Duluth (55802) ***(G-1341)***
Granite Broadcasting Corp 218 720-9642
246 S Lake Ave Duluth (55802) ***(G-1342)***
Granite City Armored Car Inc 320 252-0708
1026 13th Ave N Sauk Rapids (56379) ***(G-9364)***
Granite City Dental Laboratory 320 253-4825
1109 7th St SE Saint Cloud (56304) ***(G-7436)***
Granite City Jobbing Co Inc 320 252-1782
2731 Clearwater Rd Saint Cloud (56301) ***(G-7521)***
Granite City Ready Mix Inc 320 252-4322
2450 Highway 10 S Saint Cloud (56304) ***(G-7437)***
Granite Medical Center 320 564-2511
295 10th Ave Granite Falls (56241) ***(G-2316)***
Grant Thornton LLP 612 332-0001
200 S 6th St Ste 500 Minneapolis (55402) ***(G-4546)***
Graphic Finishing Services Inc 763 767-3026
11490 Xeon St NW Ste 100 Minneapolis (55448) ***(G-3477)***
Grason Co, Minneapolis *Also Called World Wide Publications* ***(G-6087)***
Graves Development Corp 320 252-6034
14 5th Ave S Ste 300 Saint Cloud (56301) ***(G-7522)***
Graves Hospitality Corp 612 677-1100
601 1st Ave N Minneapolis (55403) ***(G-4547)***
Gray Plant Mooty, Minneapolis *Also Called Carl Crosby Lehmann* ***(G-4012)***
Gray Plant Mooty Mooty 612 632-3000
80 S 8th St Ste 500 Minneapolis (55402) ***(G-4548)***
Graybar Electric Co Inc 218 722-6685
2601 W Superior St Duluth (55806) ***(G-1343)***
Graybar Electric Co Inc 763 852-6000
13310 Industrial Park Blvd Minneapolis (55441) ***(G-4549)***
Graybar Electric Co Inc 612 721-3545
2300 E 25th St Minneapolis (55406) ***(G-4550)***
Graybow Communications Group 952 544-5555
1000 Boone Ave N Ste 700 Golden Valley (55427) ***(G-2241)***
Grazzini Brothers & Co 651 452-2700
1175 Eagan Industrial Rd Saint Paul (55121) ***(G-7790)***
Great Clips, Chaska *Also Called Bixby Inc* ***(G-956)***
Great Clips, Minneapolis *Also Called Penco Leasing Corp* ***(G-5362)***
Great Clips, Minneapolis *Also Called AJK Cutters Inc* ***(G-3701)***
Great Clips Inc 952 893-9088
7700 France Ave S Ste 425 Minneapolis (55435) ***(G-4551)***
Great Garage Products Inc (PA) 763 422-4000
1308 113th Ave NE Minneapolis (55434) ***(G-3478)***
Great Harvest Bread Co of MN 612 929-2899
4314 Upton Ave S Minneapolis (55410) ***(G-4552)***
Great Lakes Aquarium, Duluth *Also Called Lake Superior Center* ***(G-1375)***
Great Northern Baking Co LLC 612 331-1043
443 Hoover St NE Minneapolis (55413) ***(G-4553)***
Great Northern Bank 763 497-7777
12725 43rd St NE Ste 100 Saint Michael (55376) ***(G-7673)***
Great Northern Corp 763 493-5521
8600 Wyoming Ave N Minneapolis (55445) ***(G-4554)***
Great Northern Equipment Dstbg 763 428-9405
20195 S Diamond Lake Rd Rogers (55374) ***(G-7326)***
Great Northern Golf Co of MN 651 462-5797
33942 Falcon Ave Stacy (55079) ***(G-9579)***
Great Northern Insurance Co 612 373-7300
100 S 5th St Ste 1800 Minneapolis (55402) ***(G-4555)***
Great Northern Landscapes Inc 763 274-2678
19720 Iguana St NW Elk River (55330) ***(G-1876)***
Great Northern Nursery, Park Rapids *Also Called R D Offutt Co* ***(G-6761)***
Great Northern Resources Inc 952 848-0984
3230 Gorham Ave Ste 1 Minneapolis (55426) ***(G-4556)***
Great Northwest Insurance, Saint Paul *Also Called Gnw Acquisition Corp* ***(G-8416)***
Great River Energy 763 441-3121
17845 Highway 10 Elk River (55330) ***(G-1877)***
Great River Energy (PA) 763 445-5000
12300 Elm Creek Blvd N Maple Grove (55369) ***(G-3243)***
Great River Federal Credit 320 252-3507
4 2nd Ave N Sauk Rapids (56379) ***(G-9365)***
Great River Federal Credit 320 258-5393
206 1st St S Waite Park (56387) ***(G-9823)***
Great River Garden 218 927-2521
43507 US Highway 169 Aitkin (56431) ***(G-19)***
Great River Shakespeare 507 474-7900
79 E 3rd St Winona (55987) ***(G-10099)***
Great Western Recycling Inds 651 224-4877
521 Barge Channel Rd Saint Paul (55107) ***(G-8427)***
Great Western Uron & Metal Co 651 224-4877
521 Barge Channel Rd Saint Paul (55107) ***(G-8428)***
Greatapes Corp 612 872-8284
1523 Nicollet Ave Minneapolis (55403) ***(G-4557)***
Greater Minneapolis Convention 612 767-8000
250 Marquette Ave Ste 1300 Minneapolis (55401) ***(G-4558)***
Greater Minneapolis Council of 612 721-8687
1001 E Lake St Minneapolis (55407) ***(G-4559)***
Greater Minneapolis Crisis 763 591-0100
5400 Glenwood Ave Minneapolis (55422) ***(G-4560)***
Greater Minnesota Credit Union 320 679-8100
112 Lake St S Mora (55051) ***(G-6360)***
Greater Minnesota Family Svcs 320 214-9692
513 5th St SW Willmar (56201) ***(G-10003)***
Greater Minnesota Family Svcs 320 235-3664
3619 15th Ave SW Willmar (56201) ***(G-10004)***
Greater Twin Cities United Way (PA) 612 340-7400
404 S 8th St Ste 100 Minneapolis (55404) ***(G-4561)***
Greater Twin Cities United Way 612 340-7481
404 S 8th St Ste 100 Minneapolis (55404) ***(G-4562)***
Greatstone LLC 651 429-6606
1177 Goose Lake Rd Saint Paul (55110) ***(G-8429)***
Greeley Healthcare Ctr, Stillwater *Also Called Beverly Enterprises - MN* ***(G-9602)***
Green Co's Inc 651 644-4389
2550 University Ave W Ste 400N Saint Paul (55114) ***(G-8430)***
Green Masonry, Glyndon *Also Called Valley Masonry LLC* ***(G-2235)***
Green Mill, Willmar *Also Called Tpi Core Inc* ***(G-10048)***
Green Mill Growers 651 697-1081
2582 Long Lake Rd Saint Paul (55113) ***(G-8431)***
Green Mill Restaurant, Bemidji *Also Called Richard Sigert* ***(G-422)***
Green Pine Acres Nursing Home, Menahga *Also Called City of Menahga* ***(G-3356)***
Green Tree Investment Holdings 651 293-3410
345 Saint Peter St Ste 500 Saint Paul (55102) ***(G-8432)***
Green Tree Servicing LLC (PA) 651 293-4800
345 Saint Peter St Ste 300 Saint Paul (55102) ***(G-8433)***
Green Valley Greenhouse Inc 763 753-1621
6530 Green Valley Rd Anoka (55303) ***(G-184)***
Greenbush Community Nursing Hm, Greenbush *Also Called Lifecare Medical Center* ***(G-2326)***
Greencastle Condominium Assn 320 587-4040
250 Freemont Ave SE # 135 Hutchinson (55350) ***(G-2697)***
Greene Espel PLLP 612 373-0830
200 S 6th St Ste 1200 Minneapolis (55402) ***(G-4563)***
Greenlee Textron Inc 507 238-4357
507 Downtown Plz Fairmont (56031) ***(G-1969)***
Greenview Alzheimer's 218 263-3935
3520 7th Ave E Hibbing (55746) ***(G-2447)***
Greenway Co-Operative Service 507 287-6676
302 Byron Ave N Byron (55920) ***(G-823)***
Greenway Co-Operative Service 507 775-2900
312 Byron Ave N Byron (55920) ***(G-824)***
Greenworks Inc 763 498-7696
8940 Greenfield Rd Loretto (55357) ***(G-3048)***
Greer & Associates Inc 612 338-6171
905 Park Ave Minneapolis (55404) ***(G-4564)***
Greg Gruman 763 546-1177
740 Douglas Dr N Minneapolis (55422) ***(G-4565)***
Greg Haug 218 727-8578
414 Aspen Ln Duluth (55804) ***(G-1344)***
Gregg G Hipple 651 452-3333
1480 Yankee Doodle Rd Saint Paul (55121) ***(G-7791)***
Gregory's Foods Inc 651 454-0277
1301 Trapp Rd Saint Paul (55121) ***(G-7792)***
Greiner Construction Inc 612 338-1696
625 Marquette Ave Ste 840 Minneapolis (55402) ***(G-4566)***
Gresser Co's Inc 651 454-5976
2905 Lexington Ave S Saint Paul (55121) ***(G-7793)***
Greyhound Lines Inc 612 371-3325
950 Hawthorne Ave Minneapolis (55403) ***(G-4567)***
Greystone Masonry Inc 763 413-9633
1548 164th Ln NE Anoka (55304) ***(G-185)***
Griffin & Co Logistics 952 854-2600
7830 12th Ave S Minneapolis (55425) ***(G-4568)***
Griffin Co's 612 338-2828
615 1st Ave NE Ste 500 Minneapolis (55413) ***(G-4569)***
Griffin Housing Services Inc 507 388-6434
117 Capri Dr Mankato (56001) ***(G-3131)***
Griffin International Co's Inc 612 344-4700
100 N 6th St Ste 300C Minneapolis (55403) ***(G-4570)***
Griffin Marketing & Promotions 612 344-4677
100 N 6th St Ste 300C Minneapolis (55403) ***(G-4571)***
Griffin Petroleum Services Inc 763 780-6332
8700 Xylite St NE Minneapolis (55449) ***(G-3479)***
Griffiths Holding Corp 763 559-2288
2727 Niagara Ln N Minneapolis (55447) ***(G-4572)***
Grill Works Inc 507 532-3524
1609 Halbur Rd Marshall (56258) ***(G-3298)***
Grl Investment Co LLC 952 445-6745
100 Fuller St S Ste 200 Shakopee (55379) ***(G-9442)***
Grocery Shopping Network 952 345-3232
10 Bluff Ste 900 Minneapolis (55402) ***(G-4573)***
Grocery Shopping Network Inc 612 746-4232
10 S 5th St Ste 900 Minneapolis (55402) ***(G-4574)***
Groebner Insurance Agency 507 243-3102
513 Main St Madison Lake (56063) ***(G-3082)***
Grossman Chevrolet Co Inc 952 435-8501
1200 W 141st St Burnsville (55337) ***(G-730)***
Groth Music Co, Minneapolis *Also Called Chester E Groth Music Co* ***(G-4060)***
Grounded Air Inc 763 780-1443
7932 Main St NE Minneapolis (55432) ***(G-3480)***
Grove Aquatic Fitness Center 651 450-2480
8055 Barbara Ave Inver Grove Heights (55077) ***(G-2752)***
Grove Chestnut Inc 218 749-6846
1204 Chestnut St W Virginia (55792) ***(G-9739)***
Grove City Lah BNP 320 857-2274
200 South Ave W Grove City (56243) ***(G-2328)***
Grove Cottage Athletic Assn 651 459-9278
7240 E Point Douglas Rd S Cottage Grove (55016) ***(G-1102)***
Grove Cottage Auto Parts Inc 952 469-2801
10186 222nd St E Lakeville (55044) ***(G-2942)***
Grove Cottage Emergency Med 651 458-2865
7516 80th St S Ste 2 Cottage Grove (55016) ***(G-1103)***
Gsr Real Estate Services LLC 612 338-2828
615 1st Ave NE Ste 500 Minneapolis (55413) ***(G-4575)***
Guadalupe Alternative Programs 651 222-0757
381 Robie St E Saint Paul (55107) ***(G-8434)***
Guaranteed Clean Maintenance 651 644-9919
1565 Como Ave Ste 101 Saint Paul (55108) ***(G-8435)***
Guardian, Minneapolis *Also Called Foster Klima & Co LLC* ***(G-4467)***
Guardian Angels By The Lake 763 241-7682
13439 185th Ln NW Ofc Elk River (55330) ***(G-1878)***
Guardian Angels Evan Home Care 763 441-1213
400 Evans Ave NW Elk River (55330) ***(G-1879)***

A
L
P
H
A
B
E
T
I
C

Guardian Angels Health & Rehab 218 263-7583
 1500 3rd Ave E Hibbing (55746) *(G-2448)*
Guardian Angels Health Svcs 763 441-1213
 280 Evans Ave NW Ofc Elk River (55330) *(G-1880)*
Guardian Angels of Elk River 763 241-4428
 280 Evans Ave NW Elk River (55330) *(G-1881)*
Guardian Building Products 612 524-0513
 700 24th Ave SE Minneapolis (55414) *(G-4576)*
Guardian Life Insurance Co of 952 903-2200
 920 2nd Ave S Ste 1100 Minneapolis (55402) *(G-4577)*
Guardian School Bus Co 320 259-8225
 2779 Highway 10 SE Saint Cloud (56304) *(G-7438)*
Guardsmark LLC 952 831-3151
 7230 Metro Blvd Ste 150 Minneapolis (55439) *(G-4578)*
Guest House Inc 507 288-4693
 4800 48th St NE Rochester (55906) *(G-7128)*
Guidant Sales Corp (HQ) 651 582-4000
 4100 Hamline Ave N Saint Paul (55112) *(G-8436)*
Guild Inc 651 291-0067
 130 Wabasha St S Ste 100 Saint Paul (55107) *(G-8437)*
Gulf Northern Inc 952 278-1501
 13911 Ridgedale Dr # 353 Minnetonka (55305) *(G-6178)*
Gull Way Ltd 218 753-1210
 5776 Lake Ave S Tower (55790) *(G-9687)*
Gunflint Lodge Inc 218 388-2294
 143 S Gunflint Lk Grand Marais (55604) *(G-2261)*
Gunhus Grinnell Klinger 218 236-6462
 215 30th St N Moorhead (56560) *(G-6317)*
Gunsbury Alan Quarterdeck 218 963-2482
 9820 Birch Bay Dr SW Nisswa (56468) *(G-6492)*
Gus Chafoulias 507 285-1234
 225 S Broadway Rochester (55904) *(G-7129)*
Gus Post Towing, Saint Paul Also Called Budget Towing Inc of St Paul *(G-8139)*
Gustafson Excavating Inc 651 674-7430
 6610 410th St 230 North Branch (55056) *(G-6500)*
Guthrie Theater Foundation 612 225-6000
 818 S 2nd St Minneapolis (55415) *(G-4579)*
Guy Carpenter & Co LLC 952 920-3300
 3600 Minnesota Dr Ste 400 Minneapolis (55435) *(G-4580)*
Guys Fish Inc 612 339-7720
 301 Royalston Ave Minneapolis (55405) *(G-4581)*
Gv Heating & Air Inc 763 535-2000
 5182 W Broadway Ave Minneapolis (55429) *(G-4582)*
Gwg Holdings LLC 612 746-6119
 220 S 6th St Ste 1200 Minneapolis (55402) *(G-4583)*
GWS Inc 763 551-1700
 550 Clydesdale Trl Hamel (55340) *(G-2343)*
Gyrus Acmi, LP 763 416-3000
 6655 Wedgwood Rd N # 160 Maple Grove (55311) *(G-3244)*
H & G Marketing Inc 763 263-8998
 17217 198th Ave NW Big Lake (55309) *(G-446)*
H & J Bliss Enterprises 952 988-9302
 2811 Aquila Ave S Minneapolis (55426) *(G-4584)*
H & R Block, Rochester Also Called H&R Block Inc *(G-7130)*
H & R Const Co 218 589-8707
 13349 County Highway 35 Dalton (56324) *(G-1156)*
H Brooks & Co 651 635-0126
 600 Lakeview Point Dr New Brighton (55112) *(G-6408)*
H C C Life Insurance Co 877 843-5743
 11100 Wayzata Blvd # 350 Hopkins (55305) *(G-2547)*
H Enterprises International 320 453-2626
 480 Park Ave E Eden Valley (55329) *(G-1821)*
H G A, Minneapolis Also Called Hammel, Green & Abrahamson Inc *(G-4591)*
H I R E D 612 529-3342
 1200 Plymouth Ave N Ste 2 Minneapolis (55411) *(G-4585)*
H J K S Inc 952 935-3427
 8200 Minnetonka Blvd Minneapolis (55426) *(G-4586)*
H T Klatzky & Associates Inc 218 728-3651
 1511 E Superior St Duluth (55812) *(G-1345)*
H&R Block Inc 507 345-1040
 111 Star St Ste 105 Mankato (56001) *(G-3132)*
H&R Block Inc 507 280-8406
 3120 Wellner Dr NE Ste 1 Rochester (55906) *(G-7130)*
Habilitative Services Inc 507 625-6047
 1400 E Madison Ave # 206 Mankato (56001) *(G-3133)*
Habilitative Services Inc 507 532-5366
 109 S 5th St Ste 250 Marshall (56258) *(G-3299)*
Hader Farms 507 824-2327
 41905 Highway 57 Blvd Wanamingo (55983) *(G-9863)*
Hader Farms Inc 507 824-2543
 40890 Highway 57 Blvd Zumbrota (55992) *(G-10219)*
Hage Concrete Works 651 690-4243
 2030 Saint Clair Ave Saint Paul (55105) *(G-8438)*
Haigh Todd & Assoc Inc 952 252-2100
 600 Highway 169 S Ste 655 Minneapolis (55426) *(G-4587)*
Hair District 952 836-0816
 3925 W 50th St Ste 104 Minneapolis (55424) *(G-4588)*
Hajoca Corp 763 315-0100
 6601A Parkway Cir Minneapolis (55430) *(G-4589)*
Haldeman-Homme Inc 612 331-4880
 430 Industrial Blvd NE Minneapolis (55413) *(G-4590)*
Halderman Homme, Minneapolis Also Called Duke Co's *(G-4289)*
Haley Comfort Systems Inc 507 534-2901
 445 W Broadway Plainview (55964) *(G-6842)*
Hallberg Engineering Inc 651 748-1100
 1750 Commerce Ct White Bear Lake (55110) *(G-9975)*
Hallett Cottages 218 546-6265
 350 4th St NE Crosby (56441) *(G-1149)*
Halverson Concrete Inc 763 434-0318
 1345 157th Ave NE Ste C Anoka (55304) *(G-186)*
Ham Lake American Legion 763 434-7762
 14750 Palm St NW Anoka (55304) *(G-187)*
Ham Lake Lanes, Anoka Also Called Dan Dahlin Inc *(G-172)*
Hamernick Paint Co 651 489-7007
 1321 Rice St Saint Paul (55117) *(G-8439)*
Hammel, Green & Abrahamson Inc (PA) 612 758-4000
 701 Washington Ave N Minneapolis (55401) *(G-4591)*
Hammel, Green & Abrahamson Inc 507 281-8601
 202 1st Ave SW Ste 200 Rochester (55902) *(G-7131)*

Hammer Residences Inc 763 473-1261
 1909 Wayzata Blvd Wayzata (55391) *(G-9919)*
Hammerlund Construction Inc 218 326-1881
 3201 W US Highway 2 Grand Rapids (55744) *(G-2283)*
Hampton Inn, Bemidji Also Called Edgewater Management LLC *(G-389)*
Hampton Inn, Duluth Also Called Canal Properties Inc *(G-1261)*
Hampton Inn, Hopkins Also Called W2005 New Century Hotel *(G-2656)*
Hampton Inn, Maple Grove Also Called Forstrom & Torgerson Hnw LLC *(G-3241)*
Hampton Inn, Rochester Also Called Raymond Management Co Inc *(G-7217)*
Hampton Inn & Suites Roger's, Rogers Also Called Zenith Rogers LLC *(G-7348)*
Hampton Inn North St Paul Mpls, Saint Paul Also Called Forstrom & Torgerson LLP *(G-8390)*
Hamre Schumann Mueller Larson 612 455-3800
 225 S 6th St Ste 2650 Minneapolis (55402) *(G-4592)*
Hance Distributing Inc 952 935-6429
 1 Loring Rd Hopkins (55305) *(G-2548)*
Hanco Corp 651 456-5600
 3650 Dodd Rd Saint Paul (55123) *(G-7794)*
Hancor Inc 507 238-4791
 1001 Timberlake Rd Fairmont (56031) *(G-1970)*
Handi Medical Supply Inc 651 644-9770
 2505 University Ave W # 1 Saint Paul (55114) *(G-8440)*
Hanft Fride A Prof Assn, Duluth Also Called Hanft, Fride, O'Brien *(G-1346)*
Hanft, Fride, O'Brien 218 722-4766
 130 W Superior St Ste 1000 Duluth (55802) *(G-1346)*
Hank's Specialties Inc 651 633-5020
 2050 Old Highway 8 NW New Brighton (55112) *(G-6409)*
Hanley-Wood Custom Publishing 612 338-8300
 430 1st Ave N Ste 550 Minneapolis (55401) *(G-4593)*
Hannay's Inc 612 781-7411
 1708 Central Ave NE Minneapolis (55413) *(G-4594)*
Hannon Security Services Inc 952 881-5865
 9036 Grand Ave S Minneapolis (55420) *(G-4595)*
Hanover Accessories LLC 763 509-6100
 3500 Holly Ln N Ste 10 Plymouth (55447) *(G-6863)*
Hans Hagen Homes Inc 763 586-7200
 941 Hillwind Rd NE Ste 300 Minneapolis (55432) *(G-3481)*
Hansen Dordell Bradt Odlaug, ... 651 482-8900
 3900 Northwoods Dr Ste 250 Saint Paul (55112) *(G-8441)*
Hansen, Thorp & Pellinen Inc 952 829-0700
 7510 Market Place Dr # 101 Eden Prairie (55344) *(G-1676)*
Hanson Communications Inc (PA) 320 235-2260
 1700 Technology Dr NE Willmar (56201) *(G-10005)*
Hanson Electric Of Bemidji Inc 218 751-5833
 3125 Bemidji Ave N Bemidji (56601) *(G-397)*
Hanson McFarland Inc 763 421-9554
 2501 4th Ave Anoka (55303) *(G-188)*
Hanson's Plumbing & Heating 218 342-2422
 99 Railway Ave Vergas (56587) *(G-9722)*
Hanson, Lulic & Krall 612 333-2530
 608 2nd Ave S Minneapolis (55402) *(G-4596)*
Happy Chef Systems Inc (PA) 507 345-4571
 500 S Front St Ste 103 Mankato (56001) *(G-3134)*
Harbinger Partners Inc 651 426-1569
 855 Village Center Dr # 356 Saint Paul (55127) *(G-8442)*
Harbor City Masonry Inc 218 628-3686
 310 S Central Ave Duluth (55807) *(G-1347)*
Harbor City Oil Co 218 624-3633
 3020 W Superior St Duluth (55806) *(G-1348)*
Harbor Shelter, Afton Also Called Stivland Inc *(G-11)*
Harco Marketing Group Inc 952 432-6900
 7000 151st St W Saint Paul (55124) *(G-7795)*
Harco Moving & Storage Inc 763 571-6227
 11365 Xeon St NW Minneapolis (55448) *(G-3482)*
Hardcore Computer Inc 507 285-0101
 2717 Hwy 14 W Ste D Rochester (55901) *(G-7132)*
Hardrives Inc 218 744-2913
 2372 N Yoki Rd Forbes (55738) *(G-2143)*
Hardrives Inc 651 436-8444
 15001 Hudson Blvd Lakeland (55043) *(G-2885)*
Hardwire Tech Inc 763 783-8111
 7930 University Ave NE Minneapolis (55432) *(G-3483)*
Hardwood Golf Resort 320 692-4325
 18517 Captive Lake Rd Garrison (56450) *(G-2197)*
Harkraft Inc 763 546-9161
 3101 Louisiana Ave N Minneapolis (55427) *(G-4597)*
Harleysville Insurance Co 952 829-4000
 7900 W 78th St Ste 400 Minneapolis (55439) *(G-4598)*
Harmon Inc (HQ) 952 944-5700
 11095 Viking Dr Ste 450 Eden Prairie (55344) *(G-1677)*
Harmony Community Healthcare 507 886-6544
 815 Main Ave S Harmony (55939) *(G-2371)*
Harmony Holdings Inc 952 925-8840
 15500 Wayzata Blvd # 604221 Wayzata (55391) *(G-9920)*
Harmony Homes Inc 763 434-3439
 1120 Winter St NE Minneapolis (55413) *(G-4599)*
Harmony House, Pierz Also Called Horizon Health Inc *(G-6804)*
Harmony House West, Brainerd Also Called Horizon Health Inc *(G-569)*
Harmony Nursing Homes Inc 651 488-6658
 135 Geranium Ave E Saint Paul (55117) *(G-8443)*
Harold Chevrolet Inc 952 884-3333
 1601 Southtown Dr Minneapolis (55431) *(G-4600)*
Harold Pitman M Co 612 781-8988
 2650 2nd St NE Minneapolis (55418) *(G-4601)*
Harriet Tubman Center Inc 612 825-3333
 3111 1st Ave S Minneapolis (55408) *(G-4602)*
Harrington Co 952 928-4666
 4248 Park Glen Rd Minneapolis (55416) *(G-4603)*
Harris Communications Inc 952 906-1180
 15155 Technology Dr Eden Prairie (55344) *(G-1678)*
Harris Contracting Co 507 282-8128
 1400 7th St NW Rochester (55901) *(G-7133)*
Harris Contracting Co (PA) 651 602-6500
 909 Montreal Cir Saint Paul (55102) *(G-8444)*
Harrison Community Club 218 624-1510
 3002 W 3rd St Duluth (55806) *(G-1349)*
Harrison Dental Studio Inc 651 457-6600
 5 Wentworth Ave E Saint Paul (55118) *(G-7796)*

Harriston-Mayo LLC 218 773-1234
Business Hwy 2 East Grand Forks (56721) ***(G-1568)***
Harry Meyering Center Inc 507 388-3551
109 Homestead Rd Ste OFC Mankato (56001) ***(G-3135)***
Harsco Corp 507 235-7127
415 N Main St Fairmont (56031) ***(G-1971)***
Hartel's Dbj Disposal Co's LLC 218 729-5446
930 Highway 2 Proctor (55810) ***(G-6963)***
Hartfiel Co (PA) 952 974-2500
8117 Wallace Rd Eden Prairie (55344) ***(G-1679)***
Hartford Life Inc 952 893-9236
3800 Amercn Blvd W # 675 Minneapolis (55431) ***(G-4604)***
Hartford Life Inc 877 952-9222
6820 Wedgwood Rd N Osseo (55311) ***(G-6618)***
Hartford Life Inc 651 738-4516
500 Bielenberg Dr Saint Paul (55125) ***(G-9222)***
Hartman Bancshares Inc 507 853-4421
117 S Minnesota Ave Okabena (56161) ***(G-6556)***
Hartman Co's Inc 952 443-2958
8011 Bavaria Rd Victoria (55386) ***(G-9729)***
Harty Mechanical Inc 507 437-8201
1600 1st Ave NE Austin (55912) ***(G-273)***
Hartz Truck Line Inc 218 681-3295
124 State Ave S Thief River Falls (56701) ***(G-9669)***
Harvest Facility Holdings LP 651 779-9255
3666 E County Line N # 126 Saint Paul (55110) ***(G-9223)***
Harvey-Winchell Co 952 881-7964
1801 E 79th St Ste 9 Minneapolis (55425) ***(G-4605)***
Hasslen Construction Co Inc 320 839-2529
45 1st St SE Ortonville (56278) ***(G-6583)***
Hastings Country Club Inc 651 437-4612
2015 Westview Dr Hastings (55033) ***(G-2389)***
Hastings YMCA 651 480-8887
1175 Nininger Rd Hastings (55033) ***(G-2390)***
Haubenschild Farm Dairy Inc 763 389-2867
7201 349th Ave NW Princeton (55371) ***(G-6902)***
Haug Implement Co (PA) 320 235-8115
3711 Highway 12 E Willmar (56201) ***(G-10006)***
Haugen Masonry Contractors, Moorhead *Also Called Vincent Haugen **(G-6346)***
Haugen Trucking, Bemidji *Also Called C D Haugen Inc **(G-383)***
Haugen, John A Associates 952 927-6561
3250 W 66th St Ste 200 Minneapolis (55435) ***(G-4606)***
Haugen, John A Associates (PA) 612 333-2503
801 Nicollet Mall Ste 400 Minneapolis (55402) ***(G-4607)***
Haunted LLC 507 388-7966
156 Country Club Dr Mankato (56001) ***(G-3136)***
Havco Inc 320 746-2781
17578 400th St Avon (56310) ***(G-295)***
Haven Chemical Health System 651 734-9633
2042 Wooddale Dr Ste 220 Saint Paul (55125) ***(G-9224)***
Haven Homes Inc 763 479-1993
1520 Wyman Ave Maple Plain (55359) ***(G-3275)***
Haven Homes Of Maple Plain 763 479-1993
1520 Wyman Ave Maple Plain (55359) ***(G-3276)***
Havenwood Care Center, Bemidji *Also Called Elder Care of Bemidji Inc **(G-390)***
Hawk & Sons Inc 507 285-0508
5937 15th St NW Rochester (55901) ***(G-7134)***
Hawk Construction Inc 218 327-0069
1833 W US Highway 2 A Grand Rapids (55744) ***(G-2284)***
Hawkeye Foodservice Distbn 507 238-4721
1500 Winnebago Ave Fairmont (56031) ***(G-1972)***
Hawkins Chevrolet-Cadillac Inc 507 238-4786
1304 E Blue Earth Ave Fairmont (56031) ***(G-1973)***
Hawkins Inc (PA) 612 331-6910
3100 E Hennepin Ave Minneapolis (55413) ***(G-4608)***
Hawkins Pharmaceutical Group 612 617-8600
3000 E Hennepin Ave Minneapolis (55413) ***(G-4609)***
Hawkins Water Treatment Group 612 331-6910
3100 E Hennepin Ave Minneapolis (55413) ***(G-4610)***
Hawley Golf & Country Club Inc 218 483-4808
Hwy 10 Hawley (56549) ***(G-2419)***
Hawley Retirement Inc 218 483-3337
923 5th St Hawley (56549) ***(G-2420)***
Hawthorn Suites, Minneapolis *Also Called Shaner Hotel Group LP **(G-5648)***
Hawthorne House Inc 763 525-1000
6931 Country Club Dr Minneapolis (55427) ***(G-4611)***
Hayden-Murphy Equipment Co 952 884-2301
9301 E Bloomington Fwy Minneapolis (55420) ***(G-4612)***
Hayes Residence Inc 651 690-1032
1620 Randolph Ave Saint Paul (55105) ***(G-8445)***
Hayfield Lanes, Hayfield *Also Called Spare Times Lanes & Lounge **(G-2426)***
Hays Group Inc (PA) 612 333-3323
80 S 8th St Ste 700 Minneapolis (55402) ***(G-4613)***
Hayworth Partners LP 952 476-7200
601 Carlson Pkwy Ste 200 Hopkins (55305) ***(G-2549)***
Hazel Park, Saint Paul *Also Called Saint Paul Regional Water Svcs **(G-8928)***
Hazelden Foundation 612 559-2022
11505 36th Ave N Minneapolis (55441) ***(G-4614)***
Haztran Inc 218 327-1116
18884 Sherrys Arm Rd Grand Rapids (55744) ***(G-2285)***
Hd Supply Waterworks Ltd 952 937-9666
15800 W 79th St Eden Prairie (55344) ***(G-1680)***
HDR Engineering Inc 763 591-5400
701 Xenia Ave S Ste 600 Minneapolis (55416) ***(G-4615)***
Heacox, Hartman, Mattaini 651 222-2922
408 Saint Peter St Ste 550 Saint Paul (55102) ***(G-8446)***
Head Start Program Onigum 218 547-1420
8825 Onigum Rd NW Walker (56484) ***(G-9851)***
Headerson Limousine, Saint Paul *Also Called Twin City Limousine **(G-9093)***
Headstart, Crookston *Also Called Tri-Valley Opportunity Council **(G-1140)***
Headstart, Saint Paul *Also Called Community Action Partnership **(G-8237)***
Heafner Tires & Products 510, Minneapolis *Also Called American Tire Distributors Inc **(G-3761)***
Healing Touch Aquamassage 507 287-6186
20 2nd Ave SW Ste B5 Rochester (55902) ***(G-7135)***
Health & Human Services, Gaylord *Also Called County of Sibley **(G-2199)***
Health Activation Management 763 398-8888
2000 Plymouth Rd Ste 245 Hopkins (55305) ***(G-2550)***
Health Billing Systems LLC 763 559-3779
14700 28th Ave N Ste 20 Minneapolis (55447) ***(G-4616)***
Health Care Center 612 724-5495
3720 23rd Ave S Minneapolis (55407) ***(G-4617)***
Health Care Provider Service 952 831-8114
7800 Glenroy Rd Minneapolis (55439) ***(G-4618)***
Health Care Services Inc 651 777-7435
2375 Skillman Ave E Saint Paul (55109) ***(G-8447)***
Health East, Saint Paul *Also Called Olson M D, Peter J **(G-8783)***
Health East Care Center White 651 232-1818
1891 Florence St Saint Paul (55110) ***(G-8448)***
Health East Medical Laboratory 651 232-3500
45 10th St W Saint Paul (55102) ***(G-8449)***
Health East Residence, Saint Paul *Also Called Amherst H Wilder Foundation **(G-8041)***
Health East Woodbury Clinic, Saint Paul *Also Called Pediatricians For Health **(G-9258)***
Health Fitness Corp (HQ) 952 831-6830
1650 W 82nd St Ste 1100 Bloomington (55431) ***(G-499)***
Health Industries Inc 218 233-1516
3501 US Highway 75 S Moorhead (56560) ***(G-6318)***
Health Internal Medicine, Saint Paul *Also Called Minnesota Internal Medicine **(G-8692)***
Health Orientated Pool 507 452-1646
1897 W 4th St Winona (55987) ***(G-10100)***
Health Partners Organization, Minneapolis *Also Called Hospice Of The Lakes **(G-4678)***
Health Reach, Albert Lea *Also Called Mayo Clinic Rochester **(G-61)***
Health Rhbltation New Brighton, Saint Paul *Also Called Extendicare Homes Inc **(G-8355)***
Health System Minnesota, Minneapolis *Also Called Park Nicollet Health Services **(G-5335)***
Health Systems Cooperative 651 774-8620
55 5th St E Ste 960 Saint Paul (55101) ***(G-8450)***
Healthcare & Wellness Fndtn 218 643-0410
2400 St Francis Dr Breckenridge (56520) ***(G-594)***
Healthcare Management 651 224-4930
2854 Highway 55 Ste 130 Saint Paul (55121) ***(G-7797)***
Healthcare Options Inc 763 545-3042
2738 Winnetka Ave N Minneapolis (55427) ***(G-4619)***
Healthcare Options Minnesota 320 252-5666
1000 S Benton Dr Unit 405 Sauk Rapids (56379) ***(G-9366)***
Healtheast 651 232-3008
69 Exchange St W Unit 3AB Saint Paul (55102) ***(G-8451)***
Healtheast 651 232-1717
481 Front Ave Saint Paul (55117) ***(G-8452)***
Healtheast Care Inc 651 232-2300
559 Capitol Blvd Saint Paul (55103) ***(G-8453)***
Healtheast Care System (PA) 651 232-1000
1700 University Ave W # 5 Saint Paul (55104) ***(G-8454)***
Healtheast Care System 651 232-3222
69 Exchange St W Saint Paul (55102) ***(G-8455)***
Healtheast Care System 651 232-2002
1690 University Ave W Ste 450 Saint Paul (55104) ***(G-8456)***
Healtheast Care System 651 776-4107
753 7th St E Saint Paul (55106) ***(G-8457)***
Healtheast Care System 651 232-1700
799 Reaney Ave Saint Paul (55106) ***(G-8458)***
Healtheast Clinics Infoline 651 426-4844
1010 Highway 96 E Saint Paul (55127) ***(G-8459)***
Healtheast Co's Inc 651 232-4000
1925 Woodwinds Dr Saint Paul (55125) ***(G-9225)***
Healtheast Diversified Svcs 651 489-8061
980 Rice St Saint Paul (55117) ***(G-8460)***
Healtheast Diversified Svcs (DH) 651 232-2300
559 Capitol Blvd Saint Paul (55103) ***(G-8461)***
Healtheast Home Care Inc 651 232-2800
1700 University Ave W Saint Paul (55104) ***(G-8462)***
Healtheast Maplewood Out 651 232-7780
1655 Beam Ave Ste B Saint Paul (55109) ***(G-8463)***
Healtheast Medical Research 651 489-8061
1006 Rice St Saint Paul (55117) ***(G-8464)***
Healtheast St John's Hospital 651 232-7000
1575 Beam Ave Saint Paul (55109) ***(G-8465)***
Healthez, Minneapolis *Also Called America's Tpa Inc **(G-3744)***
Healthia Consulting Inc 763 923-7900
701 Xenia Ave S Ste 170 Minneapolis (55416) ***(G-4620)***
Healthland Inc (PA) 320 634-5331
625 S Lake Shore Dr Glenwood (56334) ***(G-2226)***
Healthline Inc (HQ) 218 362-6760
750 E 34th St Hibbing (55746) ***(G-2449)***
Healthline Inc 218 262-6981
1101 E 37th St Ste 18 Hibbing (55746) ***(G-2450)***
HealthPartners Central MN 320 253-5220
1245 15th St N Saint Cloud (56303) ***(G-7523)***
HealthPartners Inc (PA) 952 883-6000
8170 33rd Ave S Bloomington (55425) ***(G-500)***
Healthpartners Inc 952 944-0432
9700 W 76th St Ste A Eden Prairie (55344) ***(G-1681)***
HealthPartners Inc 952 546-2500
14001 Ridgedale Dr Ste 32 Hopkins (55305) ***(G-2551)***
Healthpartners Inc 651 552-2600
5625 Cenex Dr Inver Grove Heights (55077) ***(G-2753)***
Healthpartners Inc 763 754-0041
11475 Robinson Dr NW Minneapolis (55433) ***(G-3484)***
Healthpartners Inc 763 780-1292
1415 81st Ave NE Minneapolis (55432) ***(G-3485)***
Healthpartners Inc 763 754-0041
2003 Northdale Blvd NW Minneapolis (55433) ***(G-3486)***
Healthpartners Inc 763 754-4600
11475 Robinson Dr NW Minneapolis (55433) ***(G-3487)***
Healthpartners Inc 612 371-1600
2220 Riverside Ave Minneapolis (55454) ***(G-4621)***
Healthpartners Inc 952 593-8777
5100 Gamble Dr Ste 100 Minneapolis (55416) ***(G-4622)***
Healthpartners Inc 612 623-4002
3105 E 80th St Minneapolis (55425) ***(G-4623)***
Healthpartners Inc 651 702-5300
8450 Seasons Pkwy Saint Paul (55125) ***(G-9226)***
Healthpartners Inc 651 702-5871
8325 Seasons Pkwy Ste 103 Saint Paul (55125) ***(G-9227)***

ALPHABETIC

www.HarrisInfo.com
574
2011 Harris Minnesota Services Directory
(G-00000) Company's Geographic Section entry number

Healthpartners Inc 952 431-8500
15290 Pennock Ln Saint Paul (55124) ***(G-7798)***
Healthpartners Inc 651 653-2100
1430 Highway 96 E Saint Paul (55110) ***(G-8466)***
Healthpartners Inc 651 293-8100
205 Wabasha St S Saint Paul (55107) ***(G-8467)***
Healthpartners Inc 651 227-3757
205 Wabasha St S Saint Paul (55107) ***(G-8468)***
Healthpartners Inc 651 779-1500
2165 White Bear Ave N Saint Paul (55109) ***(G-8469)***
Healthpartners Inc 651 254-3500
2635 University Ave W Ste 160 Saint Paul (55114) ***(G-8470)***
Healthpartners Inc 651 770-8828
2165 White Bear Ave N Saint Paul (55109) ***(G-8471)***
Healthpartners Inc 651 999-4740
451 Dunlap St N Saint Paul (55104) ***(G-8472)***
Healthpartners Inc 651 772-9757
860 Arcade St Saint Paul (55106) ***(G-8473)***
Healthpartners Inc 651 641-6200
2500 Como Ave Saint Paul (55108) ***(G-8474)***
Healthpartners Inc 651 552-1720
5625 Cenex Dr South Saint Paul (55077) ***(G-9528)***
Healthprtners Rvrside Partners, Minneapolis *Also Called Healthpartners Inc* ***(G-4621)***
Healthprtners Wodbury Eye Dntl, Saint Paul *Also Called Healthpartners Inc* ***(G-9227)***
Healthsense Inc 952 400-7300
1191 Northland Dr Ste 100 Mendota Heights (55120) ***(G-3364)***
HealthSouth Corp 952 921-0100
3209 W 76th St Ste 202 Minneapolis (55435) ***(G-4624)***
HealthSouth Corp 320 251-8385
1526 Northway Dr Saint Cloud (56303) ***(G-7524)***
Healthworks Home Medical 507 238-9200
820 Winnebago Ave Ste 2 Fairmont (56031) ***(G-1974)***
Healthworks Home Medical Inc 507 344-8500
606 N Riverfront Dr Mankato (56001) ***(G-3137)***
Healthy Kids, Saint Paul *Also Called YMCA of Greater St Paul* ***(G-7953)***
Healthztoz, Golden Valley *Also Called Medical Network Inc* ***(G-2243)***
Hearth & Home Technologies Inc (HQ) 952 985-6000
7571 215th St W Lakeville (55044) ***(G-2909)***
Heartland America, Chaska *Also Called Import Specialties Inc* ***(G-969)***
Heartland Auto Glass 952 697-0765
6975 Washingtn Ave S # 225 Minneapolis (55439) ***(G-4625)***
Heartland Community Action 320 235-0850
409 19th Ave SW Willmar (56201) ***(G-10007)***
Heartland Express, Mahnomen *Also Called Mahnomen County Heartland* ***(G-3088)***
Heartland Family Practice Inc 320 251-2042
1520 Whitney Ct Ste 100 Saint Cloud (56303) ***(G-7525)***
Heartland Homes Options In Com 218 732-4572
609 7th St W Park Rapids (56470) ***(G-6752)***
Heartland Hospice Services Inc 320 654-1136
605 Franklin Ave NE Saint Cloud (56304) ***(G-7417)***
Heartland Hospice Services Inc 651 633-6522
2250 County Road C W Saint Paul (55113) ***(G-8475)***
Heartland Information Services 612 371-9255
527 Marquette Ave Ste 900 Minneapolis (55402) ***(G-4626)***
Heartland Orthopedic 320 762-1144
1500 Irving St Alexandria (56308) ***(G-103)***
Heartland Ranch 320 843-4815
185 Highway 9 NE Benson (56215) ***(G-441)***
Heartland Services LLC 763 477-3000
6800 Electric Dr Rockford (55373) ***(G-7301)***
Heartland State Bank 507 445-3417
311 America St Storden (56174) ***(G-9656)***
Heartman Agency Inc 507 288-3834
1635 Greenview Dr SW Rochester (55902) ***(G-7136)***
Heartstone of Minnesota 651 457-2629
222 Grand Ave W Ste 200 South Saint Paul (55075) ***(G-9529)***
Heat & Frost Insulators Asbes 218 724-3223
2002 London Rd Ste 210 Duluth (55812) ***(G-1350)***
Heatilator, Lakeville *Also Called Hearth & Home Technologies Inc* ***(G-2909)***
Heating & Cooling Two Inc 763 428-3677
18550 County Road 81 Osseo (55369) ***(G-6619)***
Hecla Inc (PA) 320 255-9530
600 25th Ave S Ste 105 Saint Cloud (56301) ***(G-7526)***
Hector Communications Corp (PA) 218 346-5500
27 N Minnesota St New Ulm (56073) ***(G-6453)***
Hedberg Aggregates Inc (PA) 763 545-4400
1205 Nathan Ln N Minneapolis (55441) ***(G-4627)***
Heelside Inc 612 508-0887
305 Oakwood Dr Anoka (55303) ***(G-189)***
Hegman Machine Tool Inc 763 424-5622
8718 Monticello Ln N Osseo (55369) ***(G-6620)***
Heidelberg USA Inc 952 831-6501
7400 Metro Blvd Ste 222 Minneapolis (55439) ***(G-4628)***
Heikes Enterprises Inc 651 437-3847
19595 Lillehei Ave Hastings (55033) ***(G-2391)***
Heim Drywall Inc 507 932-5448
19485 County Road 39 Saint Charles (55972) ***(G-7403)***
Helen Andresen 218 659-4491
64037 County Road 149 Squaw Lake (56681) ***(G-9577)***
Helgeson Enterprises Inc 651 762-9700
4461 White Bear Pkwy Saint Paul (55110) ***(G-8476)***
Heller Drywall Ltd 952 496-2525
1480 3rd Ave W Shakopee (55379) ***(G-9443)***
Hellmuth & Johnson PLLC 952 941-4005
10400 Viking Dr Ste 500 Eden Prairie (55344) ***(G-1682)***
Help Systems LLC 952 933-0609
6533 Flying Cloud Dr # 200 Eden Prairie (55344) ***(G-1683)***
Hempel Properties Inc 612 355-2600
527 Marquette Ave Ste 500 Minneapolis (55402) ***(G-4629)***
Hendricks Community Hospital 507 275-3134
503 E Lincoln St Hendricks (56136) ***(G-2429)***
Hengel Landfill & Service Corp 218 746-3198
12883 Upper Sylvan Rd SW Pillager (56473) ***(G-6809)***
Hennepin Broadway Series 612 373-5665
800 Lasalle Ave ATE120 Minneapolis (55402) ***(G-4630)***
Hennepin County 612 348-9260
417 N 5th St Ste 320 Minneapolis (55401) ***(G-4631)***
Hennepin County 612 348-3131
300 S 6th St Rm A-703 Minneapolis (55487) ***(G-4632)***
Hennepin County 612 348-5273
525 Portland Ave Minneapolis (55415) ***(G-4633)***
Hennepin County 612 348-3050
300 S 6th St Minneapolis (55487) ***(G-4634)***
Hennepin County 612 596-0071
1145 Shenandoah Ln N Minneapolis (55447) ***(G-4635)***
Hennepin County 612 348-7137
3000 N 2nd St Ste C Minneapolis (55411) ***(G-4636)***
Hennepin Faculty Associates 612 347-5110
914 S 8th St Ste 700 Minneapolis (55404) ***(G-4637)***
Hennepin Healthcare System Inc 612 873-3000
701 Park Ave Minneapolis (55415) ***(G-4638)***
Hennepin Parks, Plymouth *Also Called Three Rivers Park District* ***(G-6887)***
Henning Health Care Center, Henning *Also Called Beverly Enterprises - MN* ***(G-2431)***
Henry Courts II, Saint Paul *Also Called Accessible Space Inc* ***(G-7976)***
Henry's Foods Inc 320 763-3194
104 McKay Ave N Alexandria (56308) ***(G-104)***
Henson & Efron 612 339-2500
220 S 6th St Ste 1800 Minneapolis (55402) ***(G-4639)***
Heppners Woodbury Auto Wash, Saint Paul *Also Called Bbj Inc* ***(G-9187)***
Herbeck, David J CPA Pfs Chfc 763 546-6211
7500 Olson Memorial Hwy Minneapolis (55427) ***(G-4640)***
Herc-U-Lift Inc (PA) 763 479-2501
5655 Highway 12 Maple Plain (55359) ***(G-3277)***
Herges Realty Inc 320 253-1366
25 11th Ave N Saint Cloud (56303) ***(G-7527)***
Heritage Bank 320 235-5720
310 1st St S Willmar (56201) ***(G-10008)***
Heritage Estates 651 735-1776
2040 Wilson Ave Apt 7 Saint Paul (55119) ***(G-8477)***
Heritage Links, Lakeville *Also Called Zweber LLC* ***(G-2944)***
Heritage Living Center, Park Rapids *Also Called Hubbard, County of Inc* ***(G-6755)***
Heritage Millwork Inc 763 323-7501
6190 McKinley St NW Anoka (55303) ***(G-190)***
Heritage of Edina Inc 952 920-9145
3434 Heritage Dr Office Minneapolis (55435) ***(G-4641)***
Heritage Park Estates 320 240-7939
3600 W Saint Germain St # 268 Saint Cloud (56301) ***(G-7528)***
Hermal Wholesale & Vending, Mankato *Also Called Hermel Coffee Service* ***(G-3138)***
Herman Manufacturing Co 507 553-5256
295 3rd St NE Wells (56097) ***(G-9962)***
Hermantown Clinic 218 786-3540
4855 W Arrowhead Rd Duluth (55811) ***(G-1351)***
Hermel Coffee Service 507 387-5634
23099 Riverfront Dr N Mankato (56001) ***(G-3138)***
Hermes Floral Co Inc 651 646-6344
1790 Larpenteur Ave W Saint Paul (55113) ***(G-8478)***
Heron Lake Bioenergy LLC 507 793-0077
91246 390th Ave Heron Lake (56137) ***(G-2434)***
Herregan Distributors Inc 651 452-7200
3695 Kennebec Dr Saint Paul (55122) ***(G-7799)***
Herzog Roofing Inc 218 847-1121
30183 State Highway 34 Detroit Lakes (56501) ***(G-1195)***
Heselton Construction, Faribault *Also Called B H Heselton Co* ***(G-1990)***
Hetricks Construction Inc 507 645-8629
1909 Lincoln St S Northfield (55057) ***(G-6529)***
Hewitt Associates Inc 612 339-7501
45 S 7th St Ste 2100 Minneapolis (55402) ***(G-4642)***
Hey City Theater Co 612 333-9202
824 Hennepin Ave Minneapolis (55403) ***(G-4643)***
Heyer Engineering 612 238-3805
123 N 3rd St Ste 600 Minneapolis (55401) ***(G-4644)***
Heymann Construction Co 507 354-3174
210 3rd South St New Ulm (56073) ***(G-6454)***
Hgib LLC 952 831-1012
5140 American Blvd W Bloomington (55437) ***(G-501)***
Hhh Metrodome, Minneapolis *Also Called Metropolitan Sports Facilities* ***(G-5008)***
Hi-Park Care Center, Red Wing *Also Called Benedictine Health System* ***(G-6975)***
HI-Tech Express Inc 763 537-1690
1743 County Road C W Saint Paul (55113) ***(G-8479)***
Hi-Tech Floors Inc 952 895-1602
12701 Sheridan Ave # 101 Burnsville (55337) ***(G-731)***
Hiawatha Aviation of Rochester 507 282-1717
7300 Brataas Dr SW Ste 2 Rochester (55902) ***(G-7137)***
Hiawatha Broadband Comms 507 932-3942
1242 Whitewater Ave Saint Charles (55972) ***(G-7404)***
Hiawatha Broadband Comms 507 474-4000
58 Johnson St Winona (55987) ***(G-10101)***
Hiawatha Golf Course, Minneapolis *Also Called City of Minneapolis* ***(G-4090)***
Hiawatha Manor Inc 507 825-5697
107 5th Ave NE Pipestone (56164) ***(G-6829)***
Hiawatha Transport, Winona *Also Called Lawrence Transportation* ***(G-10111)***
Hiawatha Valley Mental Health 651 565-2234
611 Broadway Ave Ste 100 Wabasha (55981) ***(G-9767)***
Hiawatha Valley Mental Health (PA) 507 454-4341
166 Main St Winona (55987) ***(G-10102)***
Hiawathal Home Care 651 388-2223
4920 Moundview Dr Ste 2 Red Wing (55066) ***(G-6985)***
Hibbing Park Hotel, Hibbing *Also Called Improvement LP* ***(G-2456)***
Hibbing Public Utilities Commn 218 262-7700
1902 6th Ave E Hibbing (55746) ***(G-2451)***
Hibbing Taconite Co 218 262-5950
County Hwy 5 N Hibbing (55746) ***(G-2452)***
Hibbing, City of Inc 218 263-5264
1425 E 23rd St Ste 2 Hibbing (55746) ***(G-2453)***
Hibtac Mining, Hibbing *Also Called Cliffs Natural Resources Inc* ***(G-2441)***
Hickey Thorstenson Grover Ltd 952 278-8880
9300 Hennepin Town Rd Eden Prairie (55347) ***(G-1684)***
Hickory Tech Information Soln (HQ) 507 625-1691
221 E Hickory St Mankato (56001) ***(G-3139)***
Hickory Tech Information Soln 507 625-1691
215 E Hickory St Mankato (56001) ***(G-3140)***
HickoryTech Corp (PA) 507 386-3636
221 E Hickory St Mankato (56001) ***(G-3141)***

ALPHABETIC

Hicks Bill & Co Ltd 763 476-6200
15155 23rd Ave N Minneapolis (55447) ***(G-4645)***
Hicks Concrete Construction 763 420-7755
7545 Commerce St Hamel (55340) ***(G-2344)***
Hicks Trucking Co of 320 693-3292
104 N Gorman Ave Litchfield (55355) ***(G-2985)***
Hicks Trucking Inc 320 693-3292
102 N Gorman Ave Litchfield (55355) ***(G-2986)***
Hidden Greens Inc 651 437-3085
14176 210th St E Hastings (55033) ***(G-2392)***
Hidden Haven Country Club, Cedar *Also Called Jala Contracting Co* ***(G-880)***
Hidden Haven Golf Course Inc 763 434-6867
20520 Polk St NE Cedar (55011) ***(G-879)***
Hie LLC 651 681-9266
1950 Rahncliff Ct Eagan (55122) ***(G-1528)***
High Plains Cooperative 507 534-3111
300 W Broadway Plainview (55964) ***(G-6843)***
High Pointe Surgery Center, Lake Elmo *Also Called East Metro Asc LLC* ***(G-2869)***
High Wire Networks Inc 952 934-9080
7162 Shady Oak Rd Eden Prairie (55344) ***(G-1685)***
High-Tech Institute Inc 763 560-9700
5100 Gamble Dr Ste 200 Minneapolis (55416) ***(G-4646)***
Higher Dimension Materials Inc (PA) 651 730-6203
570 Hale Ave N Saint Paul (55128) ***(G-9228)***
Higher Dimension Research Inc 651 730-6203
570 Hale Ave N Saint Paul (55128) ***(G-9229)***
Highjump Software Inc (PA) 952 947-4088
6455 City West Pkwy Eden Prairie (55344) ***(G-1686)***
Highland Chateau Inc 651 698-0793
2319 7th St W Saint Paul (55116) ***(G-8480)***
Highland Chateau Suites LLC 651 698-0793
2319 7th St W Saint Paul (55116) ***(G-8481)***
Highland Management Group Inc 952 925-1020
5290 Villa Way Minneapolis (55436) ***(G-4647)***
Highland Manor Inc 507 359-2026
1314 8th St N New Ulm (56073) ***(G-6455)***
Highland Manufacturing Co LLC 507 376-9460
1660 Rowe Ave Worthington (56187) ***(G-10186)***
Highland Nursery Inc 651 698-1708
1742 7th St W Saint Paul (55116) ***(G-8482)***
Highway Department, Aitkin *Also Called Aitkin County* ***(G-14)***
Highway Services, Rogers *Also Called Penhall Co* ***(G-7337)***
Hill City Lions Club 218 697-8427
66641 345th Pl Hill City (55748) ***(G-2480)***
Hill-Rom Inc 651 490-1468
1020 County Road F W Saint Paul (55126) ***(G-8483)***
Hillco Real Estate Holdings 320 532-3237
205 Lindquist St Onamia (56359) ***(G-6571)***
Hillcrest Development, Lllp (PA) 612 371-0123
2424 Kennedy St NE Minneapolis (55413) ***(G-4648)***
Hillcrest Health Care Center, Mankato *Also Called Thro Co* ***(G-3203)***
Hillcrest Nursing Home 218 253-2157
311 Broadway Ave NE Red Lake Falls (56750) ***(G-6971)***
Hillcrest Rehab Hlth Care Ctr, Wayzata *Also Called Beverly Enterprises - MN* ***(G-9906)***
Hilligoss Chevrolet Inc 218 263-7578
1502 E Howard St Hibbing (55746) ***(G-2454)***
Hillside Cemetery Association 612 781-3391
2600 19th Ave NE Minneapolis (55418) ***(G-4649)***
Hillside Homes 218 720-5890
408 N 8th Ave E Duluth (55805) ***(G-1352)***
Hillton Grdn Inn Eden Prairie, Eden Prairie *Also Called Shady Oak Hospitality LP* ***(G-1776)***
Hilltop Good Samaritan Center, Watkins *Also Called Evangelical Lutheran Good* ***(G-9897)***
Hilltop Trailer Sales Inc 763 571-9103
7810 University Ave NE Minneapolis (55432) ***(G-3488)***
Hilton, Minneapolis *Also Called Davidson Hotel Co* ***(G-4227)***
Hilton, Minneapolis *Also Called Meristar Investment Partners L* ***(G-4991)***
Hilton, Osseo *Also Called North Central Management Inc* ***(G-6642)***
Hilton, Saint Paul *Also Called Forstrom & Torgerson Hs LLC* ***(G-8389)***
Hilton Garden Inn 651 686-4605
1975 Rahncliff Ct Eagan (55122) ***(G-1529)***
Hilton Garden Inn - St Paul 651 735-4100
420 Inwood Ave N Saint Paul (55128) ***(G-9230)***
Hilton Garden Inn Maple Grove, Maple Grove *Also Called Maple Grove Lodging Investors* ***(G-3249)***
Hilton Grdn Inn Rchster Dwntwn, Rochester *Also Called Gus Chafoulias* ***(G-7129)***
Hilton Hotels Corp 612 376-1000
1001 Marquette Ave Minneapolis (55403) ***(G-4650)***
Hilton Hotels Corp 952 884-4811
2800 W 80th St Minneapolis (55431) ***(G-4651)***
Hilton Minneapolis Bloomington, Bloomington *Also Called Marcus Bloomington LLC* ***(G-504)***
Hilton Minneapolis St Paul, Bloomington *Also Called Ashford Trs Nickel, LP* ***(G-487)***
HiMec Inc (PA) 507 281-4000
1400 7th St NW Rochester (55901) ***(G-7138)***
Hinshaw & Culbertson LLP 612 333-3434
333 S 7th St Ste 2000 Minneapolis (55402) ***(G-4652)***
Hinw LLC 763 425-3800
11801 Fountains Way Maple Grove (55369) ***(G-3245)***
Hinw LLC 763 425-3800
103 15th Ave NW Ste 200 Willmar (56201) ***(G-10009)***
Hire A Host Inc 952 346-8800
10800 Lyndale Ave S # 210 Minneapolis (55420) ***(G-4653)***
Hire Thinking Inc 612 339-0535
1750 80 South 8th St Minneapolis (55402) ***(G-4654)***
Hirman Insurors, Rochester *Also Called Arthur A Hirman Agency Inc* ***(G-7060)***
Hirshfield's Inc (PA) 612 377-3910
725 2nd Ave N Minneapolis (55405) ***(G-4655)***
Historic Afton House Inn, Afton *Also Called Afton St Croix Co* ***(G-6)***
Historic Aviation, Saint Paul *Also Called Sky Media LLC* ***(G-8963)***
Historic Calumet Inn, Pipestone *Also Called National Lodging Co's Inc* ***(G-6832)***
Historical Society of MN 218 327-4482
2609 County Road 76 Grand Rapids (55744) ***(G-2286)***
Historical Society of MN (PA) 651 259-3160
345 Kellogg Blvd W Saint Paul (55102) ***(G-8484)***
Historical Society of MN 651 297-2555
240 Summit Ave Saint Paul (55102) ***(G-8485)***
Historical Society of MN 218 226-6372
3713 Split Rock Lighthouse Rd Two Harbors (55616) ***(G-9708)***
History Theatre Inc 651 292-4323
30 10th St E Saint Paul (55101) ***(G-8486)***
Hiway Federal Credit Union 651 291-1515
111 Empire Dr Saint Paul (55103) ***(G-8487)***
Hlb Tautges Redpath 651 426-7000
4810 White Bear Pkwy Saint Paul (55110) ***(G-8488)***
Hlthptnrs Coon Rapids Dntl CL, Minneapolis *Also Called Healthpartners Inc* ***(G-3484)***
Hmn Mortgage Services Inc 952 914-7440
7101 Northland Cir N Ste 200 Minneapolis (55428) ***(G-4656)***
Hmong American Partnership 651 495-9160
1075 Arcade St Saint Paul (55106) ***(G-8489)***
Hmong Home Health 651 488-1680
933 White Bear Ave N 1 Saint Paul (55106) ***(G-8490)***
Hnp Managment 763 475-1872
18105 31st Ave N Minneapolis (55447) ***(G-4657)***
HNTB Corp 952 920-4668
7900 Intrntl Dr Ste 600 Minneapolis (55425) ***(G-4658)***
Hockenbergs 612 331-1300
701 Kasota Ave SE Minneapolis (55414) ***(G-4659)***
Hoffman Care Center, Hoffman *Also Called Evangelical Lutheran Good* ***(G-2489)***
Hoffman Construction Co 507 794-5230
24214 220th St Sleepy Eye (56085) ***(G-9496)***
Hoffman Controls Inc 218 732-8374
2506 Albert Ave S Park Rapids (56470) ***(G-6753)***
Hoffman House, Morris *Also Called Prairie Community Services* ***(G-6374)***
Hoglund Bus Co Inc 763 295-5119
116 Oakwood Dr E Monticello (55362) ***(G-6273)***
Hoglund Transportation Inc 763 295-3604
119 Oakwood Dr E Monticello (55362) ***(G-6274)***
Hoglund, Chwialkowski 651 628-9929
1611 County Road B W # 102 Saint Paul (55113) ***(G-8491)***
Hohensteins Inc 651 735-4978
2330 Ventura Dr Saint Paul (55125) ***(G-9231)***
Hohenwald Properties 651 735-1333
711 Hale Ave N Saint Paul (55128) ***(G-9232)***
Holden Farms Inc 507 663-0003
12346 Hall Ave Northfield (55057) ***(G-6530)***
Holiday, New Prague *Also Called Witt Dohm Properties Inc* ***(G-6425)***
Holiday Diversified Services 952 830-8700
4567 W 80th St Minneapolis (55437) ***(G-4660)***
Holiday Inn, Alexandria *Also Called Lakeland Lodging LP* ***(G-110)***
Holiday Inn, Austin *Also Called Tpi Core Inc* ***(G-291)***
Holiday Inn, Brainerd *Also Called Lakeside Hospitality LLP* ***(G-572)***
Holiday Inn, Detroit Lakes *Also Called Madison Properties Inc* ***(G-1208)***
Holiday Inn, Duluth *Also Called Lyric Block Development Corp* ***(G-1386)***
Holiday Inn, Fairmont *Also Called Torgerson Properties LP* ***(G-1983)***
Holiday Inn, International Falls *Also Called International Management Co* ***(G-2724)***
Holiday Inn, Mankato *Also Called D D D Motel Corp* ***(G-3121)***
Holiday Inn, Maple Grove *Also Called Hinw LLC* ***(G-3245)***
Holiday Inn, Minneapolis *Also Called Kinseth Hotel Corp* ***(G-4811)***
Holiday Inn, Minneapolis *Also Called Seven Corners Hotel Partners* ***(G-5641)***
Holiday Inn, Minneapolis *Also Called Seven Corners Hotel Partners* ***(G-5642)***
Holiday Inn, Minnetonka *Also Called Fch Minnetonka* ***(G-6168)***
Holiday Inn, New Ulm *Also Called Torgerson Hospitality LLC* ***(G-6477)***
Holiday Inn, Owatonna *Also Called American Hospitality Mgt* ***(G-6691)***
Holiday Inn, Rochester *Also Called Sonor Hotel Corp* ***(G-7257)***
Holiday Inn, Saint Paul *Also Called Tcbh Inc* ***(G-7918)***
Holiday Inn, Shakopee *Also Called Mirumi Inc* ***(G-9458)***
Holiday Inn, Vadnais Heights *Also Called Wks Vadnais Heights LLC* ***(G-9721)***
Holiday Inn, Winona *Also Called Rivers Hotel Co Inc* ***(G-10121)***
Holiday Inn Alexandria, Alexandria *Also Called Madison Properties Inc* ***(G-112)***
Holiday Inn Arbor Lakes, Willmar *Also Called Hinw LLC* ***(G-10009)***
Holiday Inn Burnsville, Burnsville *Also Called Burnsville Development Ltd* ***(G-689)***
Holiday Inn Express & Suites 651 275-1401
2000 Washington Ave S Stillwater (55082) ***(G-9621)***
Holiday Inn Saint Paul Dwntwn, Saint Paul *Also Called 175 Fort LLC* ***(G-8787)***
Holiday Inn Saint Paul East, Saint Paul *Also Called Nb Saint Paul Inc* ***(G-8742)***
Holiday Inn Select Intl, Minneapolis *Also Called Appletree Motel Partnership* ***(G-3790)***
Holiday Inn St Paul East, Saint Paul *Also Called MB St Paul Inc* ***(G-8620)***
Holiday Inn Sunspree Resort 218 365-6565
400 N Pioneer Rd Ely (55731) ***(G-1914)***
Holland Lodging Inc 218 847-6997
935 N Shore Dr Detroit Lakes (56501) ***(G-1196)***
Hollandale Marketing Assn 507 889-3181
26722 825th Ave Hollandale (56045) ***(G-2492)***
Hollenback & Nelson Inc 763 862-7525
1206 114th Ln NW Minneapolis (55448) ***(G-3489)***
Hollstadt & Associates Inc 952 892-3660
200 E Travelers Trl # 210 Burnsville (55337) ***(G-732)***
Holly Properties 507 388-6265
309 Holly Ln Mankato (56001) ***(G-3142)***
Holmes Center Inc 218 844-4221
826 Summit Ave Detroit Lakes (56501) ***(G-1197)***
Holmes Hooper Inc 763 545-5641
4825 Olson Memorial Hwy Minneapolis (55422) ***(G-4661)***
Holmquist Lumber Co 320 857-2031
201 Pacific Ave Grove City (56243) ***(G-2329)***
Holtkoetter International Inc 651 552-8776
155 Hardman Ave S South Saint Paul (55075) ***(G-9530)***
Holy Emmanuel Lutheran Church 952 888-5116
201 E 104th St Minneapolis (55420) ***(G-4662)***
HOLY FAMILY RESIDENCE, Saint Paul *Also Called Little Sisters of The Poor of* ***(G-8592)***
Holy Land Brand Inc 612 781-2627
2513 Central Ave NE Minneapolis (55418) ***(G-4663)***
Hom Furniture Inc 952 884-8800
7800 Dupont Ave S Minneapolis (55420) ***(G-4664)***
Hom Furniture Inc 651 634-6600
2480 Cleveland Ave N Saint Paul (55113) ***(G-8492)***
Homark Co Inc 218 253-2777
100 3rd St SW Red Lake Falls (56750) ***(G-6972)***
Home & Community Options Inc 507 452-9311
66 E 3rd St Ste 101 Winona (55987) ***(G-10103)***
Home & Community Options Inc 507 454-5690
721 Main St Winona (55987) ***(G-10104)***

Home & Community Service, Crookston *Also Called Lutheran Social Service of MN* ***(G-1127)***
Home Care & Hospice, Crookston *Also Called Riverview Healthcare Assn* ***(G-1136)***
Home Care & PCA Services LLC 763 566-5063
6500 Brooklyn Blvd # 205 Minneapolis (55429) ***(G-4665)***
Home Care Solutions 952 924-0677
3390 Annapolis Ln N Ste A Minneapolis (55447) ***(G-4666)***
Home Depot USA Inc 218 829-0341
7207 Foley Rd Baxter (56425) ***(G-329)***
Home Depot USA Inc 651 452-2323
3220 Denmark Ave Eagan (55121) ***(G-1530)***
Home Depot USA Inc 763 422-1200
3550 124th Ave NW Minneapolis (55433) ***(G-3490)***
Home Depot USA Inc 763 717-0316
4550 Pheasant Ridge Dr NE Minneapolis (55449) ***(G-3491)***
Home Depot USA Inc 763 509-9590
1705 Annapolis Ln N Minneapolis (55441) ***(G-4667)***
Home Depot USA Inc 952 432-7171
15101 Flagstaff Ave Saint Paul (55124) ***(G-7800)***
Home Depot USA Inc 952 496-3076
1701 County Road 18 Shakopee (55379) ***(G-9444)***
Home Depot USA Inc 320 235-1975
300 28th Ave SE Willmar (56201) ***(G-10010)***
Home Energy Center, Minneapolis *Also Called Thomas M Meyer Enterprises Inc* ***(G-5818)***
Home Federal Savings Bank (HQ) 507 535-1200
1016 Civic Center Dr NW # 1 Rochester (55901) ***(G-7139)***
Home For Creative Living Inc 507 831-5033
108 9th St Windom (56101) ***(G-10068)***
Home Free Inc 952 814-7400
8100 26th Ave S Ste 125 Minneapolis (55425) ***(G-4668)***
Home Furniture, Minneapolis *Also Called Hom Furniture Inc* ***(G-4664)***
Home Health Inc 218 262-5887
101 E Howard St Hibbing (55746) ***(G-2455)***
Home Instead Senior Care, Brainerd *Also Called Crannys 4 Care LLC* ***(G-561)***
Home Instead Senior Care, Burnsville *Also Called Elderly Care Services LLC* ***(G-717)***
Home Instead Senior Care 651 747-8722
2580 White Bear Ave N # 104 Saint Paul (55109) ***(G-8493)***
Home Link Mortgage, Hopkins *Also Called Homelink Mortgage Corp* ***(G-2552)***
Home Medical, Willmar *Also Called Rice Home Medical LLC* ***(G-10040)***
Home Savings of America 320 632-5461
35 E Broadway Little Falls (56345) ***(G-3006)***
Home Smart Realty & Logo Dsgn 763 421-0481
4401 158th Ave NW Anoka (55304) ***(G-191)***
Home Town Federal Credit Union 507 451-3798
2400 W Bridge St Owatonna (55060) ***(G-6717)***
Homecare Specialists, Hibbing *Also Called Home Health Inc* ***(G-2455)***
Homecomings Financial Network 952 854-5432
7801 Metro Pkwy Ste 100 Minneapolis (55425) ***(G-4669)***
Homecrest Outdoor Living LLC 218 631-1000
1250 Homecrest Ave SE Wadena (56482) ***(G-9803)***
Homefront 320 269-2930
224 N 19th St Montevideo (56265) ***(G-6246)***
Homelink Mortgage Corp 952 935-1986
14550 Excelsior Blvd # 205 Hopkins (55345) ***(G-2552)***
Homes of Minnesota Educational 763 543-6978
3001 Metro Dr Ste 300 Minneapolis (55425) ***(G-4670)***
Homeservices Lending LLC (PA) 952 928-5300
333 S 7th St Fl 27 Minneapolis (55402) ***(G-4671)***
Homeservices Lending LLC 763 494-8138
13603 80th Cir N Fl 1 Osseo (55369) ***(G-6621)***
Homeservices of America Inc (DH) 888 485-0018
333 S 7th St Ste 2700 Minneapolis (55402) ***(G-4672)***
Homestead At Coon Rapids 763 754-2800
1770 113th Ln NW Minneapolis (55433) ***(G-3492)***
Homestead At Rochester 507 535-2000
1900 Ballington Blvd NW Rochester (55901) ***(G-7140)***
Hometime Video Publishing Inc 952 448-3812
4355 Peavey Rd Ste 300 Chaska (55318) ***(G-968)***
Hometown America LLC 651 436-2790
901 Lake Elmo Ave N Lake Elmo (55042) ***(G-2873)***
Hometown Community Bank 320 795-2533
101 W Main St Cyrus (56323) ***(G-1154)***
Homeward Bound Inc 763 566-7860
7839 Brooklyn Blvd Minneapolis (55445) ***(G-4673)***
Homewatch Home Care 507 388-5589
209 S 2nd St Ste 307 Mankato (56001) ***(G-3143)***
Homewood Suites, New Brighton *Also Called Hsnb LLC* ***(G-6410)***
Homewood Suites, Saint Louis Park *Also Called Hsslp LLC* ***(G-7662)***
Honda Electric Inc 763 498-8433
5075 Nielsen Cir Loretto (55357) ***(G-3049)***
Honeywell International Inc 763 493-6400
7550 Meridian Cir N # 100 Osseo (55369) ***(G-6622)***
Honeywell International Inc 763 954-2712
12001 Highway 55 Plymouth (55441) ***(G-6864)***
Hope Common 651 917-0917
550 Vandalia St Ste 1 Saint Paul (55114) ***(G-8494)***
Hope Haven Inc 507 825-2379
913 3rd Ave SW Pipestone (56164) ***(G-6830)***
Hope Presbyterian Church of 612 866-4055
7132 Portland Ave Minneapolis (55423) ***(G-4674)***
Hope Shilohs Inc 507 934-2094
1746 Riggs Rd Saint Peter (56082) ***(G-9306)***
Hopkins American Legion Post 952 933-1881
10 12th Ave S Hopkins (55343) ***(G-2553)***
Hopkins Cinema Six, Hopkins *Also Called Mann Theaters Inc* ***(G-2574)***
Hopkins Early Learning Center 952 988-5050
125 Monroe Ave S Hopkins (55343) ***(G-2554)***
Horizon Agency Inc 952 944-2929
6500 City West Pkwy # 100 Eden Prairie (55344) ***(G-1687)***
Horizon Health Inc 218 828-4142
218 SW 9th St Brainerd (56401) ***(G-569)***
Horizon Health Inc 320 468-2811
301 1st Ave SE Pierz (56364) ***(G-6804)***
Horizon Home Inc 507 344-3360
306 Byron St Mankato (56001) ***(G-3144)***
Horizon Milling LLC 507 388-1680
200 N Riverfront Dr Mankato (56001) ***(G-3145)***
Horizon Roofing Inc 320 252-1608
2010 County Road 137 Waite Park (56387) ***(G-9824)***
Horizontal Integration, Minnetonka *Also Called Global Markets Inc* ***(G-6177)***
Hormel Financial Services 507 437-5611
1 Hormel Pl Austin (55912) ***(G-274)***
Hormel Foods Corp (PA) 507 437-5611
1 Hormel Pl Austin (55912) ***(G-275)***
Hormel Foods Corporate Svcs (HQ) 507 437-5611
1 Hormel Pl Austin (55912) ***(G-276)***
Hormel Foods Corporate Svcs 952 931-9030
6500 City West Pkwy Ste 102 Eden Prairie (55344) ***(G-1688)***
Hormel Foods International 507 437-5611
1 Hormel Pl Austin (55912) ***(G-277)***
Hornig Properties Inc 612 874-4400
1000 W 22nd St Minneapolis (55405) ***(G-4675)***
Horst Salons, Minneapolis *Also Called Juut Midwest Inc* ***(G-4783)***
Horty Elving & Associates Inc 612 332-4422
505 E Grant St Ste 3 Minneapolis (55404) ***(G-4676)***
Horwitz Inc 763 533-1900
4401 Quebec Ave N Minneapolis (55428) ***(G-4677)***
Hose Conveyors Inc 651 456-0200
2725 Highway 55 Saint Paul (55121) ***(G-7801)***
Hospice of Healtheast Inc 651 232-3312
69 Exchange St W Saint Paul (55102) ***(G-8495)***
Hospice Of The Lakes 952 883-6877
8170 33rd Ave S Minneapolis (55425) ***(G-4678)***
Hospice of The Twin Cities Inc 763 531-2424
10405 6th Ave N Ste 250 Minneapolis (55441) ***(G-4679)***
Hospice Preferred Choice Inc 952 943-0009
5001 Amrcn Blvd W Ste 655 Minneapolis (55437) ***(G-4680)***
Hospital Pathology Associates 651 483-2033
2345 Rice St Ste 160 Saint Paul (55113) ***(G-8496)***
Hospitality Investors LLC 218 729-5616
4257 Haines Rd Duluth (55811) ***(G-1353)***
Hospitality Services Corp 763 323-3141
6540 Sioux Trl Rockford (55373) ***(G-7302)***
Hospitex Lintex, Saint Paul *Also Called Encompass Group LLC* ***(G-8340)***
Hot Dish Advertising LLC 612 341-3100
800 Washington Ave N A Minneapolis (55401) ***(G-4681)***
Hotel Ivy, Minneapolis *Also Called Rhm Receiver 3211 Co LLC* ***(G-5536)***
Hotel Ivy 612 746-4600
201 S 11th St Unit 400 Minneapolis (55403) ***(G-4682)***
Hotel Minneapolis, Minneapolis *Also Called Thm Master Te LLC* ***(G-5816)***
Hotel Sofitel, Minneapolis *Also Called 78th Street Leaseco LLC* ***(G-5643)***
Hough Inc 218 847-7391
18262 Old Pit Rd Detroit Lakes (56501) ***(G-1198)***
Hough Inc of Detroit Lakes 218 847-7391
18262 Old Pit Rd Detroit Lakes (56501) ***(G-1199)***
House of Hope Presbyterian 651 227-6311
797 Summit Ave Saint Paul (55105) ***(G-8497)***
Houston County Group Home, Houston *Also Called B L E A Inc* ***(G-2662)***
Houston Leased Housing Assocs 763 354-5500
2355 Polaris Ln N Ste 100 Plymouth (55447) ***(G-6865)***
Howard Lake Care Center, Howard Lake *Also Called Evangelical Lutheran Good* ***(G-2667)***
Howry Residential Services 651 917-9111
475 Cleveland Ave N Saint Paul (55104) ***(G-8498)***
Hsbc Card Services Inc 952 358-4000
10900 Wayzata Blvd Fl 1 Minnetonka (55305) ***(G-6179)***
Hsi Human Services Inc 651 275-4302
5650 Memorial Ave N Stillwater (55082) ***(G-9622)***
Hsml, Minneapolis *Also Called Hamre Schumann Mueller Larson* ***(G-4592)***
Hsnb LLC 651 631-8002
1815 Old Highway 8 NW New Brighton (55112) ***(G-6410)***
Hsslp LLC 952 544-0495
5305 Wayzata Blvd Saint Louis Park (55416) ***(G-7662)***
Htg Architects, Eden Prairie *Also Called Hickey Thorstenson Grover Ltd* ***(G-1684)***
Hubbard Broadcasting Inc 651 646-5555
3415 University Ave W Saint Paul (55114) ***(G-8499)***
Hubbard County Developmental 218 732-3358
109 Pleasant Ave S Park Rapids (56470) ***(G-6754)***
Hubbard, County of Inc 218 732-3329
619 6th St W Park Rapids (56470) ***(G-6755)***
Huber Bros Building Maintence 952 224-7000
12040 Riverwood Cir Burnsville (55337) ***(G-733)***
Hubert Melchert Sjodin Pllp 952 442-5155
121 W Main St Ste 200 Waconia (55387) ***(G-9786)***
Hudalla Associates Inc 218 346-2734
47500 County Highway 51 Perham (56573) ***(G-6797)***
Huddle's South Shore Resort 218 836-2420
1696 Whipholt Beach Rd NW Walker (56484) ***(G-9852)***
Huisken Meat Co of Sauk Rapids 320 259-0305
245 Industrial Blvd Sauk Rapids (56379) ***(G-9367)***
Hull Co 763 262-4855
19672 172nd St NW Big Lake (55309) ***(G-447)***
Human Development Center (PA) 218 728-4491
1401 E 1st St Duluth (55805) ***(G-1354)***
Human Development Center 218 728-5192
1401 E 1st St Duluth (55805) ***(G-1355)***
Human Resourses Div, Saint Paul *Also Called Minnesota Department of Admin* ***(G-8682)***
Human Service Conference Fund, Duluth *Also Called County of St Louis* ***(G-1285)***
Human Services 320 634-5750
211 Minnesota Ave E Ste 200 Glenwood (56334) ***(G-2227)***
Human Services 218 935-2568
311 S Main St Mahnomen (56557) ***(G-3087)***
Human Services, Marshall *Also Called Lincoln, Lyon, & Murray Human* ***(G-3306)***
Human Services Inc 651 430-2720
375 Orleans St E Stillwater (55082) ***(G-9623)***
Human Services Inc In WA (PA) 651 777-5222
7066 Stillwater Blvd N Saint Paul (55128) ***(G-9233)***
Human Services of Fairbault 507 238-4757
115 W 1st St Fairmont (56031) ***(G-1975)***
Human Services of Faribault 507 526-3265
412 N Nicollet St Blue Earth (56013) ***(G-536)***
Hunt Electric Corp 507 281-3226
6301 Bandel Rd NW Ste 201 Rochester (55901) ***(G-7141)***
Hunt Electric Corp (PA) 651 646-2911
2300 Territorial Rd Ste 1 Saint Paul (55114) ***(G-8500)***

ALPHABETIC

Hunt Technologies LLC 218 562-4877
6436 County Road 11 Pequot Lakes (56472) ***(G-6789)***
Hunts Bus, Anoka *Also Called First Student Inc* ***(G-182)***
Hunts Hillcrest Drug & Gift, Rochester *Also Called Alchemist General Inc* ***(G-7047)***
Hutchinson Area Health Care 320 234-5000
1095 Highway 15 S Hutchinson (55350) ***(G-2698)***
Hutchinson Auto Center 320 587-4748
1165 Highway 22 S Hutchinson (55350) ***(G-2699)***
Hutchinson Community Hospital, Hutchinson *Also Called Allina Health System* ***(G-2685)***
Hutchinson Health Care 320 234-5000
1095 Highway 15 S Hutchinson (55350) ***(G-2700)***
Hutchinson Health Care 320 234-4906
135 N High Dr NE Hutchinson (55350) ***(G-2701)***
Hutchinson Police Dept, Hutchinson *Also Called Hutchinson, City of Inc* ***(G-2703)***
Hutchinson Telephone Co 320 587-2323
235 Franklin St SW Hutchinson (55350) ***(G-2702)***
Hutchinson, City of Inc 320 587-2242
10 Franklin St SW Hutchinson (55350) ***(G-2703)***
Hutchinsonk Auto Center, Hutchinson *Also Called Hutchinson Auto Center* ***(G-2699)***
Hvh Auto Parts Inc 763 784-1711
10506 Central Ave NE Minneapolis (55434) ***(G-3493)***
Hy-TEC Construction of 218 829-8529
11360 Business 371 Brainerd (56401) ***(G-570)***
Hyatt Corp 612 370-1234
1300 Nicollet Ave Ste H Minneapolis (55403) ***(G-4683)***
Hyatt Pl Mnnpolis Eden Prairie, Eden Prairie *Also Called Select Hotels Group LLC* ***(G-1774)***
Hyatt Place Minneapolis, Minneapolis *Also Called W2007 Equity Inns Realty LLC* ***(G-5991)***
Hydralift Amclyde Inc (HQ) 651 293-4646
240 Plato Blvd E Saint Paul (55107) ***(G-8501)***
Hydraulic Headquarters Inc 763 478-6220
295 Highway 55 Hamel (55340) ***(G-2345)***
Hydraulic Specialty Co Inc 763 571-3072
1131 72nd Ave NE Minneapolis (55432) ***(G-3494)***
Hyland Care, Grand Rapids *Also Called Life's Companion PCA Inc* ***(G-2291)***
Hyperion Solutions Corp 952 837-2680
8400 Nrmndl Lk Blvd # 920 Minneapolis (55437) ***(G-4684)***
Hysitron Inc 952 835-6366
10025 Valley View Rd # 190 Eden Prairie (55344) ***(G-1689)***
I & S Group Inc 507 331-1500
1415 Town Square Ln Faribault (55021) ***(G-2011)***
I & S Group Inc 507 387-6651
1409 N Riverfront Dr Mankato (56001) ***(G-3146)***
I B Industries Inc 507 567-2701
27199 State Highway 56 Brownsdale (55918) ***(G-630)***
I C A N Inc 507 835-9140
100 State St N Ste 1 Waseca (56093) ***(G-9880)***
I C B A, Sauk Centre *Also Called Independent Community Bankers* ***(G-9348)***
I C O, Duluth *Also Called Inter City Oil Co Inc* ***(G-1358)***
I C System Inc 651 486-0118
1170 Grey Fox Rd Saint Paul (55112) ***(G-8502)***
I D D D Inc 507 334-3333
2519 Lyndale Ave N Faribault (55021) ***(G-2012)***
I D D D Inc 320 352-5241
1420 Main St S Sauk Centre (56378) ***(G-9347)***
I E A, Minneapolis *Also Called Institute For Environmental* ***(G-4709)***
I-State Truck Center 651 455-9775
11152 Courthouse Blvd Inver Grove Heights (55077) ***(G-2754)***
I-State Truck Center 651 636-3400
8950 Eldorado St NE Minneapolis (55449) ***(G-3495)***
I-State Truck Center (HQ) 952 854-5511
2601 American Blvd E Minneapolis (55425) ***(G-4685)***
IAI, Saint Paul *Also Called International Assn For* ***(G-7804)***
Iam Air Trnspt Dst Lodge 143, Saint Paul *Also Called International Association of* ***(G-7805)***
Iamaw Dist Lodge 165, Saint Cloud *Also Called International Association of* ***(G-7532)***
Ibberson Inc (PA) 952 938-7007
828 5th St S Hopkins (55343) ***(G-2555)***
Ibt Consolidated Inc 218 285-5290
101 2nd St International Falls (56649) ***(G-2721)***
Icentera Inc 952 898-0888
14551 Judicial Rd Ste 121 Burnsville (55306) ***(G-734)***
Icon Services Corp 651 695-8778
1043 Grand Ave Ste 312 Saint Paul (55105) ***(G-8503)***
Iconoculture Inc 612 377-0087
244 1st Ave N Ste 200 Minneapolis (55401) ***(G-4686)***
ID Wholesaler, Chanhassen *Also Called Idw LLC* ***(G-925)***
Idea Drilling LLC 218 741-9287
1997 N 9th Ave Virginia (55792) ***(G-9740)***
Idea Inc 218 741-9287
115 S 14th Ave Virginia (55792) ***(G-9741)***
Ideacom Mid-America Inc 651 292-0102
30 Water St W Saint Paul (55107) ***(G-8504)***
Identifix Inc 651 633-8007
2714 Patton Rd Saint Paul (55113) ***(G-8505)***
IDI Distributors, Chanhassen *Also Called Insulation Distributors Inc* ***(G-927)***
Idw LLC 952 949-6690
18640 Lake Dr E Chanhassen (55317) ***(G-925)***
IFP Inc 507 334-2730
2125 Airport Dr Faribault (55021) ***(G-2013)***
IG Inc 612 338-7581
212 2nd Ave N Minneapolis (55401) ***(G-4687)***
IKON Office Solutions Inc 320 251-4566
400 Great Oak Dr Saint Cloud (56387) ***(G-7529)***
Ilbnc 612 879-2521
3001 Metro Dr Ste 330 Minneapolis (55425) ***(G-4688)***
Ilm Professional Services Inc 952 960-2220
4445 W 77th St Ste 140 Edina (55435) ***(G-1832)***
Image Sea Co's Inc 952 882-0884
11900 Portland Ave Burnsville (55337) ***(G-735)***
Image Shoppe Inc 952 949-1313
995 Prairie Center Dr Eden Prairie (55344) ***(G-1690)***
Imagetrend Inc 952 469-1589
20855 Kensington Blvd Lakeville (55044) ***(G-2910)***
Imaginet LLC 612 752-5500
1300 Nicollet Ave # 5005 Minneapolis (55403) ***(G-4689)***
Imaging Alliance Group LLC 612 588-9944
2601 Minnehaha Ave Minneapolis (55406) ***(G-4690)***
Imago Ltd 651 690-9724
1190 James Ave Saint Paul (55105) ***(G-8506)***

Imation Enterprises Corp 651 704-4000
1 Imation Way Oakdale (55128) ***(G-6551)***
Immanuel St Joseph Mayo Health 507 625-4031
1025 Marsh St Mankato (56001) ***(G-3147)***
Immanuel-St Joseph's Hospital (HQ) 507 625-4031
1025 Marsh St Mankato (56001) ***(G-3148)***
Immanuel-St Joseph's Hospital 507 385-4700
1015 Marsh St Mankato (56001) ***(G-3149)***
Immedia Inc 612 524-3400
3311 Broadway St NE Ste A Minneapolis (55413) ***(G-4691)***
Impact, Minneapolis *Also Called Donlyn Manufacture* ***(G-3459)***
Impact Innovations Inc (PA) 320 847-1210
223 1st Ave SE Clara City (56222) ***(G-1028)***
Impact Mailing Of Minnesota 612 521-6245
4600 Lyndale Ave N Minneapolis (55412) ***(G-4692)***
Impact Physical Medicine 651 641-0688
1600 University Ave W # 10 Saint Paul (55104) ***(G-8507)***
Imperial Bottle Co, Saint Paul *Also Called Culligan Store Solutions* ***(G-7742)***
Imperial Developers Inc 651 454-3330
1771 Yankee Doodle Rd Saint Paul (55121) ***(G-7802)***
Imperial Leasing Inc 651 454-3330
1771 Yankee Doodle Rd Saint Paul (55121) ***(G-7803)***
Import Specialties Inc 952 361-3640
8085 Century Blvd Chaska (55318) ***(G-969)***
Improvement LP 218 262-3481
1402 E Howard St Hibbing (55746) ***(G-2456)***
In Fisherman Inc 218 829-1648
7819 Highland Scenic Rd Baxter (56425) ***(G-330)***
In Home Personal Care Inc 763 546-1000
8441 Wayzata Blvd Ste 130 Minneapolis (55426) ***(G-4693)***
Inac of VA Inc 218 263-3398
1114 E 23rd St Hibbing (55746) ***(G-2457)***
Incline Station Bowling Center, Duluth *Also Called Kegler's Inc* ***(G-1369)***
Incresing Self Sfficiency Fund, Minneapolis *Also Called Greater Twin Cities United Way* ***(G-4562)***
Indelco Plastics Corp 952 925-5075
6530 Cambridge St Minneapolis (55426) ***(G-4694)***
Independence Plus Inc 218 281-3506
27885 170th Ave SW Crookston (56716) ***(G-1126)***
Independent Community Bankers 320 352-6546
518 Lincoln Rd Sauk Centre (56378) ***(G-9348)***
Independent Delivery Services 651 487-1050
440 Minnehaha Ave W Saint Paul (55103) ***(G-8508)***
Independent Packing Services 763 425-7155
11253 91st Ave N Osseo (55369) ***(G-6623)***
Independent Republicans of MN 651 222-0022
525 Park St Ste 250 Saint Paul (55103) ***(G-8509)***
Independent School District 320 762-2148
617 18th Ave E Alexandria (56308) ***(G-105)***
Independent School District 218 723-4119
916 E 3rd St Duluth (55805) ***(G-1356)***
Independent School District 218 773-0476
1319 6th Ave NW East Grand Forks (56721) ***(G-1569)***
Independent School District 952 988-5200
4801 Woodridge Rd Hopkins (55345) ***(G-2556)***
Independent School District 952 806-7000
9501 Toledo Ave S Minneapolis (55437) ***(G-4695)***
Independent School District 218 236-8172
2410 14th St S Moorhead (56560) ***(G-6319)***
Independent School District 651 385-8000
269 E 5th St Red Wing (55066) ***(G-6986)***
Independent School District 320 252-8770
115 13th Ave S Saint Cloud (56301) ***(G-7530)***
Independent School District 651 604-3503
1910 County Road B W Saint Paul (55113) ***(G-8510)***
Independent School District 16 ....763 786-1338
8000 Highway 65 NE Minneapolis (55432) ***(G-3496)***
Independent School District No 507 444-7900
122 E McKinley St Owatonna (55060) ***(G-6718)***
Indian Health Board of 612 721-9800
1315 E 24th St Ste 1 Minneapolis (55404) ***(G-4696)***
Indian Health Service 218 983-6317
40520 County Highway 34 Ogema (56569) ***(G-6554)***
Indian Health Service 320 532-4163
43500 Migizi Dr Onamia (56359) ***(G-6572)***
Indian Health Service 218 679-3316
24760 Hospital Dr Redlake (56671) ***(G-7015)***
Indoff Inc 952 472-1295
6343 Bay Ridge Rd Minnetrista (55364) ***(G-6242)***
Indulge Salon & Tanning LLP 507 345-3400
1713 Commerce Dr Mankato (56003) ***(G-3226)***
Industrial Automation Engg 763 450-3800
14022 Lincoln St NE Anoka (55304) ***(G-192)***
Industrial Commercial Farm 218 377-4485
4161 County Road 97 International Falls (56649) ***(G-2722)***
Industrial Door Co Inc (PA) 763 786-4730
360 Coon Rapids Blvd NW Minneapolis (55433) ***(G-3497)***
Industrial Electric Co 612 331-1268
660 Taft St NE Minneapolis (55413) ***(G-4697)***
Industrial Fabrics Association 651 222-2508
1801 County Road B W Saint Paul (55113) ***(G-8511)***
Industrial Help Inc 612 871-5650
2110 Lyndale Ave S Minneapolis (55405) ***(G-4698)***
Industrial Pntg Specialists, Hugo *Also Called Maciej Paint Corp* ***(G-2679)***
Industrial Supply Co Inc (PA) 763 559-0033
12905 Highway 55 Minneapolis (55441) ***(G-4699)***
Industrial Systems Associates 763 574-5208
1400 73rd Ave NE Minneapolis (55432) ***(G-3498)***
Industrial Tool Inc 763 533-7244
9210 52nd Ave N Minneapolis (55428) ***(G-4700)***
Industrial Welders 218 628-1011
3902 Oneota St Duluth (55807) ***(G-1357)***
Industries Inc 763 689-5434
601 Cleveland St S Cambridge (55008) ***(G-838)***
Industries Inc (PA) 320 679-2354
500 Walnut St S Mora (55051) ***(G-6361)***
INFECTION CONTROL & SAFETY SYS, Lakeville *Also Called Unimed-Midwest Inc* ***(G-2938)***

ALPHABETIC

Infinite Campus Inc 651 631-0000
4321 109th Ave NE Minneapolis (55449) *(G-3499)*

Infiniti Marketing Inc 612 789-2025
5400 Shoreline Dr Mound (55364) *(G-6388)*

Infinity Direct Inc 763 559-1111
13220 County Road 6 # 200 Minneapolis (55441) *(G-4701)*

Infinity Marketing Group Minn, Saint Paul *Also Called Electronic Check Alliance (G-8330)*

Infinity Motel Holdings LLC 320 763-9900
5304 Highway 29 S Alexandria (56308) *(G-106)*

Infinity Pdts Design Engrg Ctr, Mound *Also Called Infiniti Marketing Inc (G-6388)*

Infinity Precision Systems LLC 952 401-4600
7850 Park Dr Chanhassen (55317) *(G-926)*

Infloor Heating System, Hamel *Also Called Maxxon Corp (G-2350)*

Infopet Identification Systems, Burnsville *Also Called Vantro Systems LLC (G-817)*

Information Builders Inc 651 602-9100
444 Cedar St Ste 2000 Saint Paul (55101) *(G-8512)*

Information Management Svcs, Minneapolis *Also Called Fairview Health Services (G-4399)*

Information Security Tech 651 287-0823
2550 University Ave W 155S Saint Paul (55114) *(G-8513)*

Information Services, Saint Paul *Also Called County of Ramsey (G-8257)*

Information Specialists Group 952 941-1600
9905 Hamilton Rd Frnt Eden Prairie (55344) *(G-1691)*

Information Systems Sciences 507 754-4405
100 N School St Elkton (55933) *(G-1907)*

Infosecure Technology Inc 202 898-5790
655 Windemere Curv Plymouth (55441) *(G-6866)*

Infosoft Group 952 806-0631
7760 France Ave S Edina (55435) *(G-1833)*

Infrastructure Technologies 763 428-6488
21040 Commerce Blvd Ste 1 Rogers (55374) *(G-7327)*

Infratech, Rogers *Also Called Infrastructure Technologies (G-7327)*

Ing Bank Fsb 320 229-4200
600 W Saint Germain St Ste 200 Saint Cloud (56301) *(G-7531)*

Ing Financial Partners Inc 612 372-5507
111 Washington Ave S Minneapolis (55401) *(G-4702)*

Ing North America Insurance 612 342-7878
20 Washington Ave S Minneapolis (55401) *(G-4703)*

Ing Reinsurance, Minneapolis *Also Called Reinsurance Group of America (G-5506)*

Ingenix Inc (HQ) 952 833-7100
12125 Technology Dr Eden Prairie (55344) *(G-1692)*

Ingram Excavating Inc 952 934-0917
18900 Pioneer Trl Eden Prairie (55347) *(G-1693)*

Ingstad Broadcasting Inc 218 681-4900
Hwy 32 N Thief River Falls (56701) *(G-9670)*

Initiative Foundation 320 632-9255
405 1st St SE Little Falls (56345) *(G-3007)*

Inn Hampton & Suites 763 746-7999
563 Apollo Dr Lino Lakes (55014) *(G-2972)*

Inn On Lake Superior, Duluth *Also Called Z M C Hotels Inc (G-1506)*

Inner State Protection Inc 651 771-1501
13911 Ridgedale Dr Ste 353 Minnetonka (55305) *(G-6180)*

Innovance Inc 507 373-5152
507 W Front St Albert Lea (56007) *(G-55)*

Innovative Building Concepts 952 885-0262
849 W 80th St Minneapolis (55420) *(G-4704)*

Innovative Computer Systems 952 934-5665
6321 Bury Dr Ste 1 Eden Prairie (55346) *(G-1694)*

Innovative Living Inc 218 624-7005
319 7th St Proctor (55810) *(G-6964)*

Innovative Office Solutions 952 808-9900
151 Cliff Rd E Ste 40 Burnsville (55337) *(G-736)*

Innovative Packaging 763 488-9708
11010 93rd Ave N Ste B Maple Grove (55369) *(G-3246)*

Innovative Surfaces Inc 651 437-1004
515 Spiral Blvd Hastings (55033) *(G-2393)*

Innovative Technical Personnel 763 591-9191
4050 Olson Memorial Hwy Minneapolis (55422) *(G-4705)*

Innovis Health LLC 218 844-2300
125 Frazee St E Detroit Lakes (56501) *(G-1200)*

Innovis Health LLC 218 732-2800
705 Pleasant Ave S Park Rapids (56470) *(G-6756)*

Innsbruck Healthcare Center 651 633-1686
1101 Black Oak Dr New Brighton (55112) *(G-6411)*

Inntech Personnel, Minneapolis *Also Called Innovative Technical Personnel (G-4705)*

Inside Edge Commercial 651 389-3900
2700 Blue Waters Rd Eagan (55121) *(G-1531)*

Insignia Systems Inc 763 392-6200
8799 Brooklyn Blvd Minneapolis (55445) *(G-4706)*

Inspec Inc 763 546-3434
5801 Duluth St Ste 212 Minneapolis (55422) *(G-4707)*

Installed Building Products 763 441-2313
5861 Queens Ave NE Elk River (55330) *(G-1900)*

Instant Passport Photos, Saint Paul *Also Called International Institute of MN (G-8516)*

Instant Web Inc 320 616-5100
1910 Haven Rd Little Falls (56345) *(G-3008)*

INSTITUTE FOR BLACK CHEMICAL A, Minneapolis *Also Called African American Family Svcs (G-3696)*

Institute For Clinical Systems 952 814-7060
8009 34th Ave S Minneapolis (55425) *(G-4708)*

Institute For Corp & Indus, Minneapolis *Also Called Saint Mary's University of MN (G-5591)*

Institute For Environmental 763 315-7900
9201 W Broadway Ave Ste 600 Minneapolis (55445) *(G-4709)*

Institute For Low Back & Neck, Minneapolis *Also Called Ilbnc (G-4688)*

Institute of Production 612 375-1900
312 Washington Ave N Minneapolis (55401) *(G-4710)*

Instrument & Valve Services Co 800 654-7768
12001 Technology Dr Eden Prairie (55344) *(G-1695)*

Instymeds Corp (PA) 952 653-2525
6501 City West Pkwy Eden Prairie (55344) *(G-1696)*

Insulation Distributors Inc (PA) 952 937-2000
8303 Audubon Rd Chanhassen (55317) *(G-927)*

Insulation Midwest, Minneapolis *Also Called U S Insulation Inc (G-3627)*

Insurance Paramedical Services 952 226-2213
4785 Dakota St SE Prior Lake (55372) *(G-6933)*

Insurance Service Agency, Duluth *Also Called Otis-Magie Insurance Agency (G-1415)*

Integra Group Inc 763 951-7400
7100 Northland Cir N # 205 Brooklyn Park (55428) *(G-611)*

Integra Health Care Inc 952 985-7290
20726 Ibex Ave Lakeville (55044) *(G-2911)*

Integra Telecom Holdings Inc 952 226-7000
4690 Colorado St SE Prior Lake (55372) *(G-6934)*

Integra Telecom Inc 763 745-8000
511 11th Ave S Minneapolis (55415) *(G-4711)*

Integra Telecom of Minnesota 952 746-7100
6160 Golden Hills Dr Golden Valley (55416) *(G-2242)*

Integral 7 Inc 612 436-0701
100 S 5th St Ste 1725 Minneapolis (55402) *(G-4712)*

Integrated Hlth Care Strategy, Minneapolis *Also Called Clark & Wamberg LLC (G-4102)*

Integrated Medical Rehab 952 837-8991
7250 France Ave S Ste 111 Minneapolis (55435) *(G-4713)*

Integris Group Inc 651 490-0000
450 Oak Grove Pkwy Saint Paul (55127) *(G-8514)*

Integrity Home Health Co 612 827-1479
2100 Plymouth Ave N Minneapolis (55411) *(G-4714)*

Integrity Living Options Inc 952 920-9291
4210 W 44th St Minneapolis (55424) *(G-4715)*

Inteleserve Inc 800 390-4851
419 S Minnesota Ave Saint Peter (56082) *(G-9307)*

Inter City Oil Co Inc 218 728-3641
1923 South St Duluth (55812) *(G-1358)*

Inter Savings Bank Fsb 952 920-6700
3400 W 66th St Ste 100 Edina (55435) *(G-1834)*

Inter-County Community Council 218 796-5144
207 Main St Oklee (56742) *(G-6557)*

Inter-Tax Inc 952 512-9000
13911 Ridgedale Dr # 100 Minnetonka (55305) *(G-6181)*

Interbank Fsb, Edina *Also Called Inter Savings Bank Fsb (G-1834)*

Intercim LLC 651 289-5700
1915 Plaza Dr Ste 100 Eagan (55122) *(G-1532)*

Interclad, Plymouth *Also Called Egan Co (G-6861)*

Intercounty Nursing Service, Thief River Falls *Also Called County of Pennington (G-9664)*

Intereum Inc 763 417-3300
845 Berkshire Ln N Minneapolis (55441) *(G-4716)*

Interfaith Care Center Inc 218 384-4258
811 3rd St Carlton (55718) *(G-869)*

Interim Healthcare Of Lake 218 722-0053
227 W 1st St Ste 400 Duluth (55802) *(G-1359)*

Interim Services, Saint Paul *Also Called Gary Halgran (G-8402)*

Interlachen Cntry CLB Golf Sp, Minneapolis *Also Called Olson, Jock Interlachen (G-5273)*

Interlachen Country Club 952 929-1661
6200 Interlachen Blvd Minneapolis (55436) *(G-4717)*

Interline Brands Inc 651 644-7075
1930 Energy Park Dr Saint Paul (55108) *(G-8515)*

Interlog USA Inc (PA) 612 789-3456
2818A Anthony Ln S Minneapolis (55418) *(G-4718)*

Intermed Consultants Ltd 952 920-2070
6363 France Ave S Ste 400 Minneapolis (55435) *(G-4719)*

International Assn For 651 681-8566
2535 Pilot Knob Rd # 117 Saint Paul (55120) *(G-7804)*

International Association of 763 689-3898
31122 Polk St NE Cambridge (55008) *(G-839)*

International Association of 952 975-2985
7406 Frontier Trl Chanhassen (55317) *(G-928)*

International Association of 952 933-5972
16209 Minnetonka Blvd Hopkins (55345) *(G-2557)*

International Association of 507 283-9127
419 W Brown St Luverne (56156) *(G-3060)*

International Association of 763 706-3650
555 Mill St NE Minneapolis (55421) *(G-3500)*

International Association of 612 673-3586
30 S 7th St Minneapolis (55402) *(G-4720)*

International Association of 218 338-6129
10653 State Highway 29 Parkers Prairie (56361) *(G-6765)*

International Association of 320 251-8732
1903 4th St N Ste 101 Saint Cloud (56303) *(G-7532)*

International Association of 651 688-2640
2510 Lexington Ave S Saint Paul (55120) *(G-7805)*

International Association of 952 447-0413
6917 Connelly Cir Savage (55378) *(G-9391)*

International Association of 651 439-4659
2397 Driftwood Ln Stillwater (55082) *(G-9624)*

International Association of 507 454-7643
24094 Spillway Ln Winona (55987) *(G-10105)*

International Dairy Queen Inc (HQ) 952 830-0200
7505 Metro Blvd Ste 500 Minneapolis (55439) *(G-4721)*

International Diabetes Center 952 993-3393
3800 Park Nicollet Blvd 6F Minneapolis (55416) *(G-4722)*

International Falls, City of 218 283-3500
600 4th St International Falls (56649) *(G-2723)*

International Institute of MN 651 647-0191
1694 Como Ave Saint Paul (55108) *(G-8516)*

International Management Co 218 283-4451
1500 Highway 71 International Falls (56649) *(G-2724)*

International Packaging Inc 763 315-6200
8921 Wyoming Ave N Minneapolis (55445) *(G-4723)*

International Paper Co 507 433-3467
1900 8th St NE Austin (55912) *(G-278)*

International Paper Co 612 781-6611
345 Industrial Blvd NE Minneapolis (55413) *(G-4724)*

International Paper Co 651 426-0345
1699 9th St Saint Paul (55110) *(G-8517)*

International Quality Homecare 507 451-6262
606 Hoffman Dr Owatonna (55060) *(G-6719)*

International Quality Homecare 507 252-8117
3261 19th St NW Rochester (55901) *(G-7142)*

International Seal Co Inc (DH) 952 894-8400
1087 Park Pl Shakopee (55379) *(G-9445)*

International Twins Assoc 763 571-3022
6898 Channel Rd NE Minneapolis (55432) *(G-3501)*

Internet Broadcasting Systems 651 365-4000
355 Randolph Ave Saint Paul (55102) *(G-8518)*

Interplastic Corp (PA) 651 481-6860
1225 Willow Lake Blvd Saint Paul (55110) *(G-8519)*

A L P H A B E T I C

Interplastic Corp 651 481-6860
1219 Willow Lake Blvd Saint Paul (55110) (G-8520)
Interplx Inc 952 403-7180
1157 Valley Park Dr # 115 Shakopee (55379) (G-9446)
Interpoll Laboratories Inc 763 786-6020
4500 Ball Rd NE Circle Pines (55014) (G-1012)
Interpretation & Trans 651 292-9701
778 University Ave W Saint Paul (55104) (G-8521)
Interpublic Group of Co's Inc 612 367-5144
222 S 9th St Ste 2825 Minneapolis (55402) (G-4725)
Interscope Records Inc 952 828-6060
7500 Office Ridge Cir Ste 325 Eden Prairie (55344) (G-1697)
Interstate Brands Corp 952 935-3034
8090 Excelsior Blvd 103 Hopkins (55343) (G-2558)
Interstate Brands Corp 651 484-6020
2404 Rice St Saint Paul (55113) (G-8522)
Interstate Co's Inc (PA) 952 854-2044
2601 American Blvd E Minneapolis (55425) (G-4726)
Interstate Hotels & Resorts 952 854-5558
814 American Blvd E Minneapolis (55420) (G-4727)
Interstate Hotels & Resorts 952 854-2100
3800 American Blvd E Minneapolis (55425) (G-4728)
Interstate Meat Service Inc 507 377-2228
2309 Myers Rd Albert Lea (56007) (G-56)
Interstate Motor Trucks Inc 507 373-0653
1900 Sorenson Rd Albert Lea (56007) (G-57)
Interstate Power & Light Co 507 373-2371
100 N Broadway Ave Albert Lea (56007) (G-58)
Interstate Power Systems 952 854-5511
2501 American Blvd E Minneapolis (55425) (G-4729)
Interstate Power Systems Inc 952 854-5511
8950 Eldorado St NE Minneapolis (55449) (G-3502)
Interstate Power Systems Inc (HQ) 952 854-2044
2601 American Blvd E Minneapolis (55425) (G-4730)
Interstate Rehabilitation Ctr 651 388-7108
204 Mississippi Ave Red Wing (55066) (G-6987)
Interstate Removal Co 651 765-0765
6671 Lake Blvd Forest Lake (55025) (G-2152)
Interstate Service of Fergus 218 739-3284
I94 County Rd 1 Fergus Falls (56537) (G-2077)
Intertech Inc 651 994-8558
1020 Discovery Rd Ste 145 Saint Paul (55121) (G-7806)
Into The Mystic Productions 612 332-6620
2605 Hennepin Ave Minneapolis (55408) (G-4731)
Intouch Inc 651 255-7700
2 Pine Tree Dr Ste 307 Saint Paul (55112) (G-8523)
Intran Media LLC 952 646-0036
294 Grove Ln E Ste 400 Wayzata (55391) (G-9921)
Intrepid Home Health Care Inc 952 285-7300
6600 France Ave S Ste 510 Minneapolis (55435) (G-4732)
Intrepid of Golden Valley Inc 952 513-5400
5353 Wayzata Blvd Ste 300 Saint Louis Park (55416) (G-7663)
Intrepid of Texas Inc (DH) 952 285-7300
6600 France Ave S Ste 510 Minneapolis (55435) (G-4733)
Intuitive Technology Group LLC 952 854-1663
2001 Killebrew Dr Ste 305 Minneapolis (55425) (G-4734)
Inver Grove Heights Clinic, Inver Grove Heights *Also Called Healthpartners Inc* (G-2753)
Inver Grove Toyota, Inver Grove Heights *Also Called Midwest Motors LLC* (G-2763)
Ion Corp 952 936-9490
7500 Equitable Dr Eden Prairie (55344) (G-1698)
Ipcs, Minneapolis *Also Called Nternational Projects* (G-5254)
Irish Genealogical Society 763 574-1436
1185 Concord St N Ste 218 South Saint Paul (55075) (G-9531)
Iron Mountain Inc 651 452-0169
950 Apollo Rd Saint Paul (55121) (G-7807)
Iron Mountain Information MGT 952 888-3852
9715 James Ave S Minneapolis (55431) (G-4735)
Iron Mountain Information Mgt 651 452-6515
950 Apollo Dock 29 Saint Paul (55121) (G-7808)
Iron Range Learning & Devpt 218 741-7441
409 1st St N Virginia (55792) (G-9742)
Iron Range Rehabilitation Ctr 218 741-2147
901 9th St N Ste 100 Virginia (55792) (G-9743)
Ironwood Electronics Inc 952 229-8200
11351 Rupp Dr Ste 400 Burnsville (55337) (G-737)
Ironworld Development Corp 218 254-7959
1005 Discovery Dr Chisholm (55719) (G-998)
Isaac Fair Corp 651 482-8593
4295 Lexington Ave N Saint Paul (55126) (G-8524)
Isanti Snior Citizen Cmnty Ctr, Isanti *Also Called Senior Isanti Citizen Com* (G-2781)
Isensee Bus Service 320 732-2795
24496 US 71 Long Prairie (56347) (G-3043)
Isgn Fulfillment Services Inc 952 512-7400
5401 Gamble Dr Ste 300 Minneapolis (55416) (G-4736)
Isj Clinic - Northridge, North Mankato *Also Called Mayo Clinic Rochester* (G-6510)
Isj Regional Women's Imaging 507 304-7770
101 Martin Luther King Dr Mankato (56001) (G-3150)
Island Freight Brokerage LLC 507 288-5758
3270 19th St NW Ste 108 Rochester (55901) (G-7143)
Isle View Apartments 320 676-8624
205 N 1st St Fl 1 Isle (56342) (G-2783)
Isle West Associates, LLP 612 331-1800
601 Marquette Ave Ste 100 Minneapolis (55402) (G-4737)
ISS Facility Services Inc 763 559-6679
4222 Park Glen Rd Minneapolis (55416) (G-4738)
Istate Truck Center 651 455-9775
11152 Courthouse Blvd Inver Grove Heights (55077) (G-2755)
Istate Truck Inc (PA) 952 854-2044
2601 American Blvd E Minneapolis (55425) (G-4739)
It's About Time Theater 507 280-8956
618 23rd St NE Rochester (55906) (G-7144)
Italian American Club of 612 781-0625
2223 Central Ave NE Minneapolis (55418) (G-4740)
Itasca Consulting Group Inc (PA) 612 371-4711
111 3rd Ave S Ste 450 Minneapolis (55401) (G-4741)
Itasca County Family Young 218 327-1161
400 River Rd Grand Rapids (55744) (G-2287)
Itasca-Mantrap Co-Op Electric 218 732-3377
16930 County 6 Park Rapids (56470) (G-6757)
Ivo Appliance Inc 650 286-1300
7825 Washingtn Ave S # 500 Minneapolis (55439) (G-4742)
Iyanka Dakota Coaches Inc 507 644-3380
39411 County Highway 24 Morton (56270) (G-6381)
Izaak Walton League of America 651 649-1446
1619 Dayton Ave Ste 202 Saint Paul (55104) (G-8525)
Izatys Group LLC 320 532-3101
40005 85th Ave Onamia (56359) (G-6573)
J & B Group Inc (PA) 763 497-3913
13200 43rd St NE Saint Michael (55376) (G-7674)
J & D Construction Inc 320 269-2101
1100 Hwy 212WEST Montevideo (56265) (G-6247)
J & D Drywall Inc 952 461-4078
11111 Deuce Rd Elko (55020) (G-1905)
J & J Distributing Co 651 221-0560
653 Rice St Saint Paul (55103) (G-8526)
J & J Packing Inc 763 263-2296
19292 County Rd 43 S Big Lake (55309) (G-448)
J & K Marina 218 847-7291
121 W Lake Dr Detroit Lakes (56501) (G-1201)
J & L Hennum Inc 218 634-1342
3244 Bur Oak Rd NW Baudette (56623) (G-315)
J & L Nursing Care Inc 507 529-0018
3705 Enterprise Dr SW Rochester (55902) (G-7145)
J & L Schwieters Construction 651 762-1110
13925 Fenway Blvd N Hugo (55038) (G-2677)
J & R Schugel Trucking Inc (PA) 507 359-2037
2026 N Broadway St New Ulm (56073) (G-6456)
J A Swenson & Assoc Inc 952 469-3585
20141 Icenic Trl Lakeville (55044) (G-2912)
J B Distributing Co Inc 952 934-7354
14760 Martin Dr Eden Prairie (55344) (G-1699)
J B Hunt Transport Inc 612 362-9419
722 Kasota Cir SE Minneapolis (55414) (G-4743)
J B Waivered Services 218 828-4962
867 Lawson Rd Fort Ripley (56449) (G-2174)
J Benson Construction 952 920-0717
3230 Gorham Ave Ste 1 Minneapolis (55426) (G-4744)
J C Christensen & Associates 320 534-3629
200 14th Ave E Sartell (56377) (G-9337)
J C Penney Co Inc 952 920-8557
6601 France Ave Fl 3 Minneapolis (55435) (G-4745)
J C Penny Beauty Salon 507 625-5630
1850 Adams St Ste 2 Mankato (56001) (G-3151)
J C Trux Inc 218 927-4450
40538 Diamond Lake Rd Aitkin (56431) (G-20)
J D Fingerman Enterprises Inc 612 861-1697
2901 W 66th St Minneapolis (55423) (G-4746)
J D L Technologies Inc (HQ) 952 946-1810
10900 Red Circle Dr Hopkins (55343) (G-2559)
J E Dunn Construction Co 952 830-9000
9855 W 78th St Ste 270 Eden Prairie (55344) (G-1700)
J Eiden Construction Inc 651 450-5978
1696 63rd St E Inver Grove Heights (55077) (G-2756)
J H Larson Electrical Co (PA) 763 545-1717
10200 51st Ave N Ste B Plymouth (55442) (G-6867)
J J Vanderson & Co 651 641-1376
1214 98th Ave NE Minneapolis (55434) (G-3503)
J K F Warehouse 507 354-5528
1823 S Valley St New Ulm (56073) (G-6457)
J L Buchanan Inc 612 334-1710
50 S 10th St Ste 440 Minneapolis (55403) (G-4747)
J L Industries, Minneapolis *Also Called Activar Inc* (G-3677)
J M Oil Co 320 251-2082
3341 Southway Dr Saint Cloud (56301) (G-7533)
J Maas Co 218 631-3498
224 Jefferson St S Wadena (56482) (G-9804)
J Perzel & Associates 612 455-6060
4829 Minnetonka Blvd # 201 Minneapolis (55416) (G-4748)
J R & R Partnership 507 532-9566
911 Michigan Rd Marshall (56258) (G-3300)
J T Electric Service Inc 320 845-4789
111 County Road 10 Albany (56307) (G-27)
J T Mega LLC 952 929-1370
4020 Minnetonka Blvd # 302 Minneapolis (55416) (G-4749)
J Thomas & Associates 218 829-6622
5244 Ashdale Ln Baxter (56425) (G-331)
J&M Co 218 998-4062
1220 N Tower Rd Fergus Falls (56537) (G-2078)
J-Berd Mechanical Contractors 320 656-0847
3308 Southway Dr Saint Cloud (56301) (G-7534)
J-I-T Services Inc 763 545-6991
10550 Wayzata Blvd Hopkins (55305) (G-2560)
J-M Manufacturing Co Inc 507 893-3121
743 Main St S Winnebago (56098) (G-10076)
Ja-Cee Consultants Inc 952 466-4785
8570 Maple View Dr Cologne (55322) (G-1092)
Jack & Jill Preschool 651 604-3810
1910 County Road B W Saint Paul (55113) (G-8527)
Jack's House 218 824-5225
300 Highway 25 S Brainerd (56401) (G-571)
Jackson City Ambulance 507 847-5306
309 Sheridan St Jackson (56143) (G-2794)
Jackson Cottonwood Community 507 847-2366
407 5th St Rm 209 Jackson (56143) (G-2795)
Jackson County Developmental 507 662-6156
304 2nd Ave N Lakefield (56150) (G-2882)
Jackson Good Samaritan Center, Jackson *Also Called Evangelical Lutheran Good* (G-2792)
Jackson Landscape Supply Inc 952 435-6927
7870 218th St W Lakeville (55044) (G-2913)
Jackson Medical Center, Jackson *Also Called Sanford Health Network* (G-2799)
Jackson Municipal Clinic 507 847-2200
1430 North Hwy Jackson (56143) (G-2796)
Jackson Spah Dental Studio Inc 763 785-2435
1150 Osborne Rd NE Minneapolis (55432) (G-3504)

ALPHABETIC

Jackson Street Associates LLC ... 651 228-9456
180 5th St E Ste 160 Saint Paul (55101) *(G-8528)*
Jacobs Investors Inc ... 612 339-9500
80 S 8th St Ste 2900 Minneapolis (55402) *(G-4750)*
Jacobs Trading LLC ... 763 843-2066
8090 Excelsior Blvd Hopkins (55343) *(G-2561)*
Jade Catering Inc ... 763 767-3336
13545 Martin St NW Anoka (55304) *(G-193)*
Jaeckle Minnesota ... 612 676-0388
504 Malcolm Ave SE Ste 100 Minneapolis (55414) *(G-4751)*
Jala Contracting Co ... 763 434-4626
20520 Polk St NE Cedar (55011) *(G-880)*
Jam Hops Gymnastics Factory ... 763 413-0647
14216 Lincoln St NE Anoka (55304) *(G-194)*
James A Dosen ... 952 473-2002
600 Highway 169 S Ste 1750 Minneapolis (55426) *(G-4752)*
James Ford Bell Museum of ... 612 624-4112
10 Church St SE Minneapolis (55455) *(G-4753)*
James J Hill House, Saint Paul *Also Called Historical Society of MN (G-8485)*
James M Smith MD ... 320 253-7257
3701 12th St N Ste 100 Saint Cloud (56303) *(G-7535)*
James R Hill Inc ... 952 890-6044
2500 County Road 42 W # 120 Burnsville (55337) *(G-738)*
James R Hill Inc ... 763 792-1136
1523 94th Ln NE Ste B Minneapolis (55449) *(G-3505)*
James Steele Construction Co ... 651 488-6755
1410 Sylvan St Saint Paul (55117) *(G-8529)*
James W Copeland ... 952 476-7100
800 Wayzata Blvd E # 300 Wayzata (55391) *(G-9922)*
Janesville Nursing Home Inc ... 507 231-5113
102 E North St Janesville (56048) *(G-2802)*
Janine Sahagian ... 507 332-9894
310 11th Ave NE Faribault (55021) *(G-2014)*
Japs-Olson Co (PA) ... 952 932-9393
7500 Excelsior Blvd Minneapolis (55426) *(G-4754)*
Jardine Logan & O'Brien ... 651 290-6500
8519 Eagle Point Blvd # 100 Lake Elmo (55042) *(G-2874)*
JAS Apartments Inc ... 612 872-4444
1 E 19th St Ste 100 Minneapolis (55403) *(G-4755)*
Javaology Enterprises LLC ... 952 943-3990
114215 Hundertmark Rd Chaska (55318) *(G-970)*
Jay Bros Inc ... 651 464-6400
9218 Lake Dr NE Forest Lake (55025) *(G-2147)*
Jay Malone Motors ... 320 587-4748
1165 Highway 7 W Hutchinson (55350) *(G-2704)*
Jazz Arts Group Fargomoorhead ... 218 236-0421
2700 12th Ave S Moorhead (56560) *(G-6320)*
JC Custom Welding Inc ... 218 444-9353
489 Amos Way NW Bemidji (56601) *(G-398)*
JC Penney Corp Inc ... 218 727-8111
1600 Miller Trunk Hwy # 3 Duluth (55811) *(G-1360)*
JC Penney Corp Inc ... 507 625-1606
1850 Adams St Ste 2 Mankato (56001) *(G-3152)*
JD Driver Ltd (PA) ... 507 437-6050
61441 170th St Ste 3 Rose Creek (55970) *(G-7350)*
Jde Studios Inc ... 612 825-4076
3224 Nicollet Ave Minneapolis (55408) *(G-4756)*
Jeff's, Bobby & Steves ... 763 788-1113
3701 Central Ave NE Minneapolis (55421) *(G-3506)*
Jefferson Capital Systems LLC ... 866 417-2561
16 McLeland Rd Saint Cloud (56303) *(G-7536)*
Jefferson Partners LP ... 612 359-3400
2100 E 26th St Minneapolis (55404) *(G-4757)*
Jefferson-Pilot, Minneapolis *Also Called Lincoln Life & Annunity Co of (G-4887)*
Jeffrey Slocum & Associates ... 612 338-7020
43 Main St SE Ste 300 Minneapolis (55414) *(G-4758)*
JEM Technical Marketing Co Inc ... 952 473-5012
2250 Daniels St Long Lake (55356) *(G-3025)*
Jennie-O Turkey Store Inc ... 320 974-8891
501 Pleasant Ave W Atwater (56209) *(G-252)*
Jennie-O Turkey Store Inc ... 507 334-0087
25475 Cabot Ave Faribault (55021) *(G-2015)*
Jennie-O Turkey Store Inc ... 218 736-6931
428 E Wash Ave Fergus Falls (56537) *(G-2079)*
Jennie-O Turkey Store Inc ... 218 583-2204
375 Fredrick Ln Henning (56551) *(G-2432)*
Jennie-O Turkey Store Inc ... 320 243-3764
409 E Hwy 55 Paynesville (56362) *(G-6769)*
Jennie-O Turkey Store Inc (HQ) ... 320 235-2622
2505 Willmar Ave SW Willmar (56201) *(G-10011)*
Jennifer's Restaurant, Belle Plaine *Also Called Morris-Walker Ltd (G-368)*
Jensen's Supper Club ... 651 688-7969
3840 Sibley Memorial Hwy Saint Paul (55122) *(G-7809)*
Jenson, Beel, Converse ... 651 223-4999
1700 Highway 36 W Ste 110 Saint Paul (55113) *(G-8530)*
Jeremiah Program ... 612 692-8711
1510 Laurel Ave Ste 100 Minneapolis (55403) *(G-4759)*
Jeremiah Saint Paul LP ... 612 259-3001
1510 Laurel Ave Ste 100 Minneapolis (55403) *(G-4760)*
Jerky Snack Brands Inc ... 507 388-1661
1829 1st Ave Mankato (56001) *(G-3153)*
Jerry Dutler's Bowl, Mankato *Also Called Twin Town Bowl Inc (G-3210)*
Jerry's Enterprises Inc ... 952 941-9050
8015 Den Rd Ste 2 Eden Prairie (55344) *(G-1701)*
Jerry's Enterprises Inc ... 952 929-4601
5033 Vernon Ave S Minneapolis (55436) *(G-4761)*
Jerry's Farm Market ... 320 968-7001
991 115th Ave NE Foley (56329) *(G-2140)*
Jerry's Floor Store, Excelsior *Also Called Floor Store Inc (G-1943)*
Jet Edge, Saint Michael *Also Called Tc American Monorail Inc (G-7683)*
Jetways, Minneapolis *Also Called General Aviation Inc (G-4507)*
Jewelry Repair Centers Inc ... 763 370-2511
12031 Ilex St NW Minneapolis (55448) *(G-3507)*
Jewish Community Center of ... 952 381-3400
4330 Cedar Lake Rd S Minneapolis (55416) *(G-4762)*
Jewish Community Center of The ... 651 698-0751
1375 Saint Paul Ave Saint Paul (55116) *(G-8531)*
Jewish Community Nursery & Day ... 651 698-0751
1375 Saint Paul Ave Saint Paul (55116) *(G-8532)*
Jewish Family & Children's Svc (PA) ... 952 546-0616
13100 Wayzata Blvd # 300 Hopkins (55305) *(G-2562)*
Jill H Rusterholz ... 952 806-0011
825 Nicollet Mall Minneapolis (55402) *(G-4763)*
Jim Bern Co ... 952 854-4141
8162 Bloomington Ave Minneapolis (55425) *(G-4764)*
Jim Conway ... 507 287-7717
4600 18th Ave NW Rochester (55901) *(G-7146)*
Jim Hill & Associates, Burnsville *Also Called James R Hill Inc (G-738)*
Jimmy's Conference & Catering ... 651 482-1233
3565 Labore Rd Saint Paul (55110) *(G-8533)*
Jirik Sod Farm Inc ... 651 460-6555
20245 Blaine Ave Farmington (55024) *(G-2052)*
JJ Taylor Co's Inc ... 651 482-1133
701 Industrial Blvd NE Minneapolis (55413) *(G-4765)*
Jlm Landscape LLC ... 952 941-9818
7141 Amundson Ave Minneapolis (55439) *(G-4766)*
Jmc Impact, Clara City *Also Called Midwest - Cbk Inc (G-1029)*
Jmdl Inc ... 952 873-2636
20652 255th Ave Belle Plaine (56011) *(G-373)*
JME Of Monticello Inc (PA) ... 763 295-3122
1401 Fallon Ave NE Monticello (55362) *(G-6275)*
JMS Equities Inc ... 952 949-3630
5250 W 74th St Ste 1 Minneapolis (55439) *(G-4767)*
Jnr Adjustment Co ... 763 519-2710
7001 E Fish Lake Rd # 200 Osseo (55311) *(G-6624)*
Job Training Center Anoka Cnty, Minneapolis *Also Called County of Anoka (G-3444)*
John A Dalsin & Son Inc ... 612 729-9334
2830 20th Ave S Minneapolis (55407) *(G-4768)*
John A Haugen - Edina, Minneapolis *Also Called Haugen, John A Associates (G-4607)*
John A Kanutson ... 651 641-1099
1781 Prior Ave N Saint Paul (55113) *(G-8534)*
John A Knutson & Co ... 651 641-1099
1781 Prior Ave N Saint Paul (55113) *(G-8535)*
John B Collins Associates Inc ... 952 820-1000
8500 Normandale Ste 2400 Minneapolis (55437) *(G-4769)*
John Henry Foster Minnesota ... 651 452-8452
3103 Mike Collins Dr Saint Paul (55121) *(G-7810)*
John L Bonner Eye Clinic Ltd ... 218 326-3433
1542 Golf Course Rd Ste 201 Grand Rapids (55744) *(G-2288)*
John Pulsifer Construction Inc ... 320 354-2602
9338 187th Ave NE New London (56273) *(G-6415)*
John Robert Powers Inc ... 952 854-8577
7900 Intrntl Dr Ste 100 Minneapolis (55425) *(G-4770)*
John Ryan Co Inc ... 612 924-7700
11100 Wayzata Blvd # 350 Minnetonka (55305) *(G-6182)*
John Ryan Performance Inc ... 612 924-7700
700 S 3rd St Ste 300W Minneapolis (55415) *(G-4771)*
John Schmitz MD ... 320 255-5777
1406 6th Ave N Saint Cloud (56303) *(G-7537)*
John T Beecher MD ... 952 925-2200
5301 Vernon Ave S Minneapolis (55436) *(G-4772)*
John's Auto Parts, Minneapolis *Also Called Hvh Auto Parts Inc (G-3493)*
Johnson & Condon ... 952 831-6544
7401 Metro Blvd Ste 600 Minneapolis (55439) *(G-4773)*
Johnson Anderson & Associates ... 952 496-6699
5010 Valley Ind Blvd S Shakopee (55379) *(G-9447)*
Johnson Assoc Consulting Group, Saint Paul *Also Called Dana Johnson (G-8281)*
Johnson Brothers Liquor Co ... 651 649-5800
1999 Shepard Rd Saint Paul (55116) *(G-8536)*
Johnson Brothers Liquor Co ... 651 649-5800
1999 Shepard Rd Saint Paul (55116) *(G-8537)*
Johnson Carl E Mechanical, Milaca *Also Called Johnson, Carl E Plumbing (G-3378)*
Johnson Co Inc, R M ... 320 398-6080
211 Willow Creek Rd Kimball (55353) *(G-2832)*
Johnson Controls Holding Co ... 763 566-7650
3605 Burnbrook Ln N Minneapolis (55447) *(G-4774)*
Johnson Controls Inc ... 763 566-7650
2605 Fernbrook Ln N Plymouth (55447) *(G-6868)*
Johnson Controls Inc ... 763 566-7650
2605 Fernbrook Ln N Plymouth (55447) *(G-6869)*
Johnson Controls Interiors LLC ... 218 727-8996
4627 Airpark Blvd Duluth (55811) *(G-1361)*
Johnson Lewis Nilan ... 612 338-1838
120 S 6th St Minneapolis (55402) *(G-4775)*
Johnson Memorial Health Svcs, Dawson *Also Called Dawson Area Hospital District (G-1164)*
Johnson Outdoors Inc ... 507 345-4623
1531 E Madison Ave Mankato (56001) *(G-3154)*
Johnson Plastics, Minneapolis *Also Called Signcaster Corp (G-5671)*
Johnson's Carpet Tile ... 218 628-2249
5611 Grand Ave Duluth (55807) *(G-1362)*
Johnson's Riverside Boarding ... 218 681-1278
16117 160th St NE Thief River Falls (56701) *(G-9671)*
Johnson, Carl E Plumbing ... 320 983-2171
12724 160th St Milaca (56353) *(G-3378)*
Johnson-Williams Auto Livery, Minneapolis *Also Called Dunn Enterprises Inc (G-4297)*
Johnson-Wilson Constructors ... 218 628-0202
4431 W Michigan St Duluth (55807) *(G-1363)*
Johnstone Supply, Minneapolis *Also Called Triple J Enterprises Inc (G-5858)*
Johnstone Supply, Minneapolis *Also Called Triple J Enterprises Inc (G-5859)*
Joint Apprenticeship ... 218 733-9443
4402 Airpark Blvd Duluth (55811) *(G-1364)*
Jomar Investments Inc ... 651 686-6100
3275 Dodd Rd Saint Paul (55121) *(G-7811)*
Jon Bowar MD ... 320 255-5777
1406 6th Ave N Saint Cloud (56303) *(G-7538)*
Jon English Salon ... 612 824-2474
1439 W Lake St Minneapolis (55408) *(G-4776)*
Jon S Nielsen MD ... 763 257-4400
3366 Oakdale Ave N Ste 150 Minneapolis (55422) *(G-4777)*
Jones Dw Management ... 218 547-3307
609 8th St W Park Rapids (56470) *(G-6758)*
Jones Stanley & Associates ... 507 288-0064
2746 Superior Dr NW Ste 300 Rochester (55901) *(G-7147)*

Jones-Harrison Residence Corp 612 920-2030
3700 Cedar Lake Ave Minneapolis (55416) ***(G-4778)***
Jordan Ray Sons 763 434-1644
1901 Klondike Dr NE Cedar (55011) ***(G-881)***
Jordan Realty Inc 612 827-3844
400 E Lake St Ste 3 Minneapolis (55408) ***(G-4779)***
Jordan Transformer LLC 952 492-2720
1000 Syndicate St Jordan (55352) ***(G-2805)***
Joseph Co Inc 507 437-3284
2003 14th St NE Ste 106 Austin (55912) ***(G-279)***
Joseph T Ryerson & Son Inc 763 544-4401
1605 Highway 169 N Minneapolis (55441) ***(G-4780)***
Joshco Construction Inc 952 361-8000
1107 Hazeltine Blvd # 200 Chaska (55318) ***(G-971)***
Josuda Inc 763 263-0313
575 Humboldt Dr Big Lake (55309) ***(G-449)***
Jourdain Prpch Extndd Cr Fclty, Redlake *Also Called Red Lake Band of Chippewa* ***(G-7016)***
Journey Home Halfway House, Sauk Rapids *Also Called St Cloud Hospital* ***(G-9376)***
Joy US Cares 320 983-5708
7219 140th St Milaca (56353) ***(G-3379)***
Jpg & Associates Inc 651 779-1072
8991 Highway 5 Lake Elmo (55042) ***(G-2875)***
Jra Financial Advisors 763 315-8000
7373 Kirkwood Ct N # 300 Osseo (55369) ***(G-6625)***
Jubilee Enterprises Inc 507 532-2332
403 Donita Ave Marshall (56258) ***(G-3301)***
Juhl Brokerage Inc 763 519-0120
12700 Industrial Park Blvd Ste Minneapolis (55441) ***(G-4781)***
Juhl Enterprises Inc 320 354-2231
100 Glenoaks Dr New London (56273) ***(G-6416)***
Julie's Helping Hands 320 833-6082
114 Church Ave W Buffalo Lake (55314) ***(G-664)***
JUST FOR KIX PRECISION DANCE, Baxter *Also Called Mini Kix Inc* ***(G-336)***
Justice Brothers, Eden Prairie *Also Called J B Distributing Co Inc* ***(G-1699)***
Justin Paul Inc 218 727-0034
26 E Superior St Ste 203 Duluth (55802) ***(G-1365)***
Justman Freight Lines Inc 651 423-1024
4855 S Robert Trl Saint Paul (55123) ***(G-7812)***
Justman Trucking Inc 651 423-1020
4855 S Robert Trl Saint Paul (55123) ***(G-7813)***
Juut Midwest Inc (HQ) 612 676-2250
201 Main St SE Ste 324 Minneapolis (55414) ***(G-4782)***
Juut Midwest Inc 612 332-3512
651 Nicollet Mall Ste 247 Minneapolis (55402) ***(G-4783)***
Juut Midwest Inc 651 222-4121
857 Grand Ave Ste 3 Saint Paul (55105) ***(G-8538)***
Juut Midwest Inc 651 639-0576
2480 Fairview Ave N Saint Paul (55113) ***(G-8539)***
Jwa Mankato, Mankato *Also Called Johnson Outdoors Inc* ***(G-3154)***
K & K METAL RECYCLING, Minneapolis *Also Called Kirschbaum-Krupp Metal* ***(G-4812)***
K & S Heating & Air Condg 507 282-4328
4205 Hwy 14 W Rochester (55901) ***(G-7148)***
K & S Millwrights Inc 320 833-2228
217 E Hall Ave Buffalo Lake (55314) ***(G-665)***
K 2 International Inc 651 209-8770
2782 Eagandale Blvd Saint Paul (55121) ***(G-7814)***
K A G E Inc 507 452-2867
752 Bluffview Cir Winona (55987) ***(G-10106)***
K A R E TV Channel 11, Minneapolis *Also Called Multimedia Holdings* ***(G-5148)***
K A Witt Construction Inc 952 758-2108
1530 W 280th St New Prague (56071) ***(G-6429)***
K B I, Chaska *Also Called Klein Financial Inc* ***(G-972)***
K B R F Radio, Fergus Falls *Also Called Result Radio Inc* ***(G-2118)***
K G M Contractors Inc 218 666-5698
9211 Hwy 53 N Angora (55703) ***(G-133)***
K J Country 965 ....218 736-7596
728 Western Ave Fergus Falls (56537) ***(G-2080)***
K L L Z F M 218 444-1500
502 Beltrami Ave NW Bemidji (56601) ***(G-399)***
K M L Design Studio LLC 651 731-6672
731 Bielenberg Dr Ste 105 Woodbury (55125) ***(G-10172)***
K M S Management Inc 952 593-9930
5801 Cedar Lake Rd S A Minneapolis (55416) ***(G-4784)***
K M S P Fox 9, Eden Prairie *Also Called Fox Television Stations Inc* ***(G-1669)***
K N Air Domestic 651 688-7650
980 Lone Oak Rd Saint Paul (55121) ***(G-7815)***
K N O W 911 F M, Saint Paul *Also Called Minnesota Public Radio* ***(G-8703)***
K N R Communication Services 763 478-2058
7180 Northland Cir N Ste 138 Brooklyn Park (55428) ***(G-612)***
K O P P Funds 952 841-0480
7701 France Ave S Ste 500 Minneapolis (55435) ***(G-4785)***
K R C H Web Radio Stations 507 288-3888
1530 Greenview Dr SW # 200 Rochester (55902) ***(G-7149)***
K R Wagner Inc 218 283-3700
300 Van Lynn Rd International Falls (56649) ***(G-2725)***
K S U M-AM, Fairmont *Also Called Woodward Broadcasting Inc* ***(G-1984)***
K T I Inc 612 378-9731
10301 Wayzata Blvd Ste 100 Minnetonka (55305) ***(G-6183)***
K&G Enterprises Inc 763 263-7997
20033 176th St NW Big Lake (55309) ***(G-450)***
K-M Building Co of Minneapolis 612 977-9060
801 2nd Ave N Ste 1 Minneapolis (55405) ***(G-4786)***
K-Tel International Inc 763 559-5566
7600 Wayzata Blvd Ste 2B Minneapolis (55426) ***(G-4787)***
K-Way Express Inc 320 485-2325
323 Main Ave W Winsted (55395) ***(G-10161)***
Kaal TV, Austin *Also Called Midwest Kaal Corp* ***(G-283)***
Kadrmas, Lee & Jackson Inc 218 287-0300
1505 30th Ave S Ste A Moorhead (56560) ***(G-6321)***
Kahler Hotel, Rochester *Also Called Sunstone Hotel Properties Inc* ***(G-7269)***
Kaleidoscope Health System, Minneapolis *Also Called Orthopedic Resources Mgt* ***(G-5294)***
Kaliski, Cathy Cmt, Mankato *Also Called J C Penny Beauty Salon* ***(G-3151)***
Kalk-Young Inc 218 864-5265
505 N Lake Ave Battle Lake (56515) ***(G-311)***
Kalway Construction Co Inc 651 746-0179
14160 Basalt St NW Anoka (55303) ***(G-195)***
Kamish Excavating Inc 651 457-3600
1301 Concord St S South Saint Paul (55075) ***(G-9532)***
Kanabec County Hospital 320 679-1212
301 Highway 65 S Mora (55051) ***(G-6362)***
Kandi Entertainment Center Inc 320 235-3800
500 19th Ave SE Willmar (56201) ***(G-10012)***
Kandi-Works Developmental (PA) 320 974-8840
111 5th St Atwater (56209) ***(G-253)***
Kandi-Works Developmental 320 382-6156
537 Pacific Ave Kandiyohi (56251) ***(G-2814)***
Kandihyohi Cnty Rrl Dvl Financ, Willmar *Also Called Kandiyohi County Economic* ***(G-10013)***
Kandiyohi County Economic 320 235-7370
333 Litchfield Ave SW # 100 Willmar (56201) ***(G-10013)***
Kandiyohi Power Cooperative 320 796-1155
8605 47th St NE Spicer (56288) ***(G-9556)***
Kandiyohi Power Cooperative 320 235-4155
1311 Highway 71 NE Willmar (56201) ***(G-10014)***
Kane Transport Inc 507 532-2788
2328 State Highway 19 Marshall (56258) ***(G-3302)***
Kane Transport Inc 320 352-5800
40925 403rd Ave Newfolden (56738) ***(G-6482)***
Kane Transport Inc (PA) 320 352-2762
40925 403rd St Sauk Centre (56378) ***(G-9349)***
Kantar Media Intelligences Inc 952 926-5430
6750 France Ave S Ste 365 Minneapolis (55435) ***(G-4788)***
Kaplan, Strangis & Kaplan 612 375-1138
90 S 7th St Ste 5500 Minneapolis (55402) ***(G-4789)***
Karcher Foster Services Inc 651 674-2031
6551 Main St North Branch (55056) ***(G-6501)***
Kardia Health Systems Inc 763 432-8420
5500 Wayzata Blvd Ste 215 Minneapolis (55416) ***(G-4790)***
Karen B Bjorkman 612 904-7401
2000 Midwest Plz Bldg W Minneapolis (55402) ***(G-4791)***
Karges-Faulconbridge Inc 651 771-0880
670 County Road B W Saint Paul (55113) ***(G-8540)***
Karian Peterson Power Line 320 269-6769
4437 Highway 212 Montevideo (56265) ***(G-6262)***
Karlstad Heathcare Center, Karlstad *Also Called Tealwood Care Centers Inc* ***(G-2815)***
Kasa Capital LLC 612 524-5460
800 Nicollet Mall # 1180 Minneapolis (55402) ***(G-4792)***
Kaska Inc 320 632-9281
920 4th St SE Little Falls (56345) ***(G-3009)***
Kasson & Mantorville Telephone 507 634-2511
18 2nd Ave NW Kasson (55944) ***(G-2821)***
Kasson-Mayo Fmly Prctice Clnic, Kasson *Also Called Mayo Clinic Rochester* ***(G-2822)***
Kate Anne Hunter 651 578-3290
2201 Ventura Dr Saint Paul (55125) ***(G-9234)***
Kath Management Co 651 484-3325
3096 Rice St Saint Paul (55113) ***(G-8541)***
Kato Distributing Inc (PA) 507 289-7456
3731 Enterprise Dr SW Rochester (55902) ***(G-7150)***
Kato Radiator, Mankato *Also Called Westman Freightliner Inc* ***(G-3217)***
Kato Tool, Willmar *Also Called Northern States Supply Inc* ***(G-10031)***
Katun Corp (HQ) 952 941-9505
10951 Bush Lake Rd # 100 Minneapolis (55438) ***(G-4793)***
Kaufman Container Co Inc 612 331-8880
1227 E Hennepin Ave Minneapolis (55414) ***(G-4794)***
Kavanaugh's, Brainerd *Also Called Kavco Inc* ***(G-545)***
Kavco Inc 218 829-5226
1685 Kavanaugh Dr Brainerd (56401) ***(G-545)***
KAWE TV, CHANNEL 9, Bemidji *Also Called Northern Minnesota Public* ***(G-413)***
Kbhp-Fm, Bemidji *Also Called Paul Bunyan Broadcasting Co* ***(G-418)***
Kbjr Inc 218 727-8484
246 S Lake Ave Duluth (55802) ***(G-1366)***
Kbjr Television, Duluth *Also Called Granite Broadcasting Corp* ***(G-1342)***
Kbjr-TV, Duluth *Also Called Kbjr Inc* ***(G-1366)***
Kbmx Mix 108 Studio 218 740-2649
14 E Central Entrance Duluth (55811) ***(G-1367)***
Kcq Inc 507 334-4393
402 Heritage Pl Faribault (55021) ***(G-2016)***
Kdhl Radio, Faribault *Also Called Cumulus Media Inc* ***(G-2000)***
KDLH News Channel 218 733-0303
246 S Lake Ave Duluth (55802) ***(G-1368)***
Keane Inc 952 915-6393
6700 France Ave S Ste 300 Minneapolis (55435) ***(G-4795)***
Keebler Co 651 484-0833
1275 Willow Lake Blvd Saint Paul (55110) ***(G-8542)***
Keenan & Sveiven Inc 952 475-1229
15119 Minnetonka Blvd A Minnetonka (55345) ***(G-6184)***
Keep In Touch of Burnsville 952 953-3313
1100 County Road 42 E # 104 Burnsville (55337) ***(G-739)***
Kegler's Inc 218 722-0671
601 W Superior St Duluth (55802) ***(G-1369)***
Kehne Electric Corp 651 645-5781
2330 Wycliff St Saint Paul (55114) ***(G-8543)***
Keinath Leasing Co 952 944-8000
12800 Hwy 13 S Ste 500 Savage (55378) ***(G-9392)***
Keith Carlson Trucking Inc 651 923-4822
19179 385th St Goodhue (55027) ***(G-2249)***
Kelbro Co 612 824-9803
2900 5th Ave S Minneapolis (55408) ***(G-4796)***
Kelleher Construction Corp 952 890-6772
11531 Rupp Dr Burnsville (55337) ***(G-740)***
Keller Williams Premier Realty 507 424-4422
2765 Commerce Dr NW Rochester (55901) ***(G-7151)***
Keller Williams Realty Inc 952 746-9696
10515 165th St W Ste A Lakeville (55044) ***(G-2914)***
Kellington Construction Inc 763 416-3200
2301 N 2nd St Minneapolis (55411) ***(G-4797)***
Kelloway Digital, Minneapolis *Also Called David Kelloway* ***(G-4225)***
Kelly & Berens 612 392-7032
80 S 8th St Ste 3720 Minneapolis (55402) ***(G-4798)***
Kelly Midwest Ventures LP 320 253-0606
100 4th Ave S Saint Cloud (56301) ***(G-7539)***
Kelly Midwest Ventures LP 651 227-8711
161 Saint Anthony Ave A Saint Paul (55103) ***(G-8544)***

ALPHABETIC

Kempf Paper Corp 612 781-9225
3145 Columbia Ave NE Minneapolis (55418) *(G-4799)*
Kendeco Supply Co 320 253-1020
1202 Sun Ridge Dr Saint Cloud (56301) *(G-7540)*
Kendell Doors & Hardware Inc 651 905-0144
2425 Entp Dr Ste 100 Mendota Heights (55120) *(G-3365)*
Kendell Doors & Hardware Inc (PA) 507 454-1723
222 E 2nd St Winona (55987) *(G-10107)*
Kendrick Electric, Saint Paul *Also Called MJM Investments Inc (G-7844)*
Kenexa Corp 612 332-6383
901 Marquette Ave # 1900 Minneapolis (55402) *(G-4800)*
Kennedy & Graven Chartered 612 337-9300
200 S 6th St Ste 470 Minneapolis (55402) *(G-4801)*
Kennedy Brissman 651 646-7933
1930 Energy Park Dr Ste 2 Saint Paul (55108) *(G-8545)*
Kensington Equity Partners Inc 952 808-1800
11974 Portland Ave Burnsville (55337) *(G-741)*
Kenwood Retirement Community, Minneapolis *Also Called Partners For Senior (G-5342)*
Kenyon Sunset Home 507 789-6134
127 Gunderson Blvd Kenyon (55946) *(G-2828)*
Keomed Inc 952 933-3940
11515 K Tel Dr Hopkins (55343) *(G-2563)*
Kern Dewenter Viere Ltd (PA) 320 251-7010
220 Park Ave S Saint Cloud (56301) *(G-7541)*
Kerry Logistics Inc 763 717-1400
9124 Isanti St NE Minneapolis (55449) *(G-3508)*
Kersten Management Group Inc 218 543-6977
10602 Wabigoniss Shrs Pine River (56474) *(G-6819)*
Kevin Switzer 320 231-8888
502 2nd St SW Willmar (56201) *(G-10015)*
Key Medical Supply Inc 651 792-3860
5910 Rice Creek Pkwy # 1000 Saint Paul (55126) *(G-8546)*
Key Sales Group Inc 952 979-1531
11011 Smetana Rd Hopkins (55343) *(G-2564)*
Key-Land Homes 952 440-9400
4719 Park Nicollet Ave SE Prior Lake (55372) *(G-6935)*
Keyc TV Channel 12, Mankato *Also Called United Communications Corp (G-3232)*
Keyc-TV, North Mankato *Also Called United Communications Corp (G-6515)*
Keys Well Drilling Co Inc 651 646-7871
1156 Homer St Saint Paul (55116) *(G-8547)*
Keystone Automotive Industries 763 788-3039
3900 Jackson St NE # 100 Minneapolis (55421) *(G-3509)*
Keystone Automotive Industries (DH) 612 789-1919
3615 Marshall St NE Minneapolis (55418) *(G-4802)*
Keystone Bluffs 218 727-2800
2528 Trinity Rd Duluth (55811) *(G-1370)*
Keystone Community Services 651 645-0349
2000 Saint Anthony Ave Saint Paul (55104) *(G-8548)*
Kforce Inc 952 835-5100
7650 Edinbrgh Way Ste 650 Minneapolis (55435) *(G-4803)*
Kgp Logistics Inc (HQ) 507 334-2268
3305 Highway 60 W Faribault (55021) *(G-2017)*
Kgp Telecommunications Inc (PA) 507 334-2268
3305 Highway 60 W Faribault (55021) *(G-2018)*
Khashi Associates LLC 763 550-0961
3020 Harbor Ln N Ste 110 Minneapolis (55447) *(G-4804)*
Khc Construction Inc 507 532-6768
703 Ontario Rd Marshall (56258) *(G-3303)*
Khcdii Inc 952 925-5881
3950 W 70th St Minneapolis (55435) *(G-4805)*
Kia of St Cloud, Waite Park *Also Called Saint Cloud Auto Center LLC (G-9835)*
Kibble Equipment Inc (PA) 320 269-6466
Hwy 7 E Montevideo (56265) *(G-6248)*
Kibble Equipment Inc 507 644-3571
Hwy 19 & 71 E Redwood Falls (56283) *(G-7022)*
Kid's Haven of Buffalo Inc 763 682-3072
302 12th Ave S Buffalo (55313) *(G-646)*
Kid's Korner Educare Center 507 451-0312
600 Florence Ave Owatonna (55060) *(G-6720)*
Kiddie Karousel Day Care Ctr 218 263-7450
3920 13th Ave E Ste 5 Hibbing (55746) *(G-2458)*
Kidney Specialists of MN 763 561-5349
6200 Shingle Creek Pkwy Ste 30 Minneapolis (55430) *(G-4806)*
Kids Come 1st Children's Ctr 507 281-4421
3615 15th Ave NW Rochester (55901) *(G-7152)*
Kids Come 1st Corp 507 281-3284
1818 Greenview Pl SW Rochester (55902) *(G-7153)*
Kielmeyer Construction Inc 507 334-6088
86 Main St Nerstrand (55053) *(G-6402)*
Killmer Electric Co Inc 763 425-2525
5141 Lakeland Ave N Minneapolis (55429) *(G-4807)*
Kiltie Corp 651 770-3166
6348 Highway 36 Blvd N Ste 1 Saint Paul (55128) *(G-9235)*
Kim Kunwook 651 578-7627
2820 White Eagle Dr Saint Paul (55129) *(G-9236)*
Kimball Golf Club Inc 320 398-2285
11823 County Rd 150 Kimball (55353) *(G-2833)*
Kimball Railcar Repair, Kimball *Also Called Johnson Co Inc, R M (G-2832)*
Kimmy Clean LLC 952 758-4238
26881 Naylor Ave New Prague (56071) *(G-6430)*
Kinderberry Hill 763 404-1070
185 Cheshire Ln N Minneapolis (55441) *(G-4808)*
Kinderberry Hill Child Dev, Minneapolis *Also Called Khcdii Inc (G-4805)*
KinderCare Learning Centers 952 941-5054
12760 Anderson Lakes Pkwy Eden Prairie (55344) *(G-1702)*
KinderCare Learning Centers 952 835-4955
8950 France Ave S Minneapolis (55431) *(G-4809)*
Kindercare Learning Centers 952 920-8548
17701 Excelsior Blvd Minnetonka (55345) *(G-6185)*
KinderCare Learning Centers 651 735-0037
8425 City Centre Dr Saint Paul (55125) *(G-9237)*
Kindercare Learning Centers 651 735-3711
7380 10th St N Saint Paul (55128) *(G-9238)*
Kindercare Learning Centers 651 386-6672
8425 City Centre Dr Saint Paul (55125) *(G-9239)*
KinderCare Learning Centers 651 681-1968
3620 Krestwood Ln Saint Paul (55123) *(G-7816)*
Kindercare Learning Centers 651 452-1616
1865 Plaza Dr Saint Paul (55122) *(G-7817)*
Kindercare Learning Centers 952 440-9890
5710 Loftus Dr Savage (55378) *(G-9393)*
Kindercare Learning Centers 952 403-6862
1308 Greenwood Ct Shakopee (55379) *(G-9448)*
King Shipping Inc 763 428-5464
11011 Holly Ln N Maple Grove (55369) *(G-3247)*
King Solutions Inc (PA) 763 428-5464
11011 Holly Ln N Osseo (55369) *(G-6626)*
Kingsway Transportation System 507 288-9375
4515 Highway 63 N Rochester (55906) *(G-7154)*
Kinney & Lange 612 339-1863
312 S 3rd St Ste 120 Minneapolis (55415) *(G-4810)*
Kinseth Hotel Corp 952 884-8211
1201 W 94th St Minneapolis (55431) *(G-4811)*
Kinship Youth Mentoring 763 631-5967
604 3rd St S Apt 151 Princeton (55371) *(G-6910)*
Kirschbaum-Krupp Metal 612 521-9212
1728 N 2nd St Minneapolis (55411) *(G-4812)*
Kit Fucile 952 435-3030
190 Cobblestone Ln Burnsville (55337) *(G-742)*
Kitchi Gammi Club 218 724-8589
831 E Superior St Duluth (55802) *(G-1371)*
Kittson Memorial Hospital Assn 218 843-3612
1010 S Birch Ave Hallock (56728) *(G-2333)*
Kittson Memorial Hospital Assn 218 843-3612
1010 S Birch Ave Hallock (56728) *(G-2334)*
Kiwanis International Inc 507 275-3748
306 S Oak St Hendricks (56136) *(G-2430)*
Kiwanis International Inc 320 587-6874
645 Waller Dr NE Hutchinson (55350) *(G-2705)*
Kiwanis International Inc 507 859-2635
810 Clark St Walnut Grove (56180) *(G-9862)*
Kiwikai Imports Inc 763 550-9545
17300 Medina Rd Ste 100 Minneapolis (55447) *(G-4813)*
Kj & E Properties 218 727-8811
4845 Miller Trunk Hwy Duluth (55811) *(G-1372)*
Kj International Resources Ltd 612 288-9494
800 Washington Ave N Minneapolis (55401) *(G-4814)*
Kkaq AM 1460 .....218 681-4900
1433 N Main St Thief River Falls (56701) *(G-9672)*
Kkdq, Thief River Falls *Also Called Ingstad Broadcasting Inc (G-9670)*
Kldj-FM, Duluth *Also Called Clear Channel Communications (G-1277)*
Klein Bank 952 467-2313
800 Faxon Rd Young America (55397) *(G-10209)*
Klein Financial Inc 952 448-2924
1550 Audubon Rd Chaska (55318) *(G-972)*
Kleinbank 763 682-1142
910 Commercial Dr Buffalo (55313) *(G-647)*
Kleinbank 952 442-4471
53 W Main St Waconia (55387) *(G-9787)*
Kleinman Realty Co 763 572-9400
5301 E River Rd Ste 101 Minneapolis (55421) *(G-3510)*
Klick & Associate Inc 763 420-3296
17003 Weaver Lake Dr Osseo (55311) *(G-6627)*
Kline Oil Co, Braham *Also Called Mille Lacs Oil Co (G-543)*
Kline Volvo Inc (PA) 651 379-4300
3040 Highway 61 Saint Paul (55109) *(G-8549)*
Klingelhutz Co's Inc 952 448-6776
2970 Chaska Blvd Chaska (55318) *(G-973)*
Kliz FM Powerloon 107 5 .....218 822-4440
13225 Dogwood Dr Baxter (56425) *(G-332)*
Km Telecom, Kasson *Also Called Kasson & Mantorville Telephone (G-2821)*
Kmart Corp 952 445-2936
901 Canterbury Rd S Shakopee (55379) *(G-9449)*
Kmwb, Saint Paul *Also Called Sinclair Broadcasting Group (G-8960)*
Knife Lake Concrete Inc 320 679-4141
2026 Rowland Rd Mora (55051) *(G-6363)*
Knife River Corp - North 218 829-4726
7925 Industrial Park Rd Baxter (56425) *(G-333)*
Knife River Corp - North (DH) 320 251-9472
4787 Shadowwood Dr NE Sauk Rapids (56379) *(G-9368)*
Knife River Midwest LLC 507 498-3377
601 E Main St Spring Grove (55974) *(G-9561)*
Knight Financial Products LLC 952 249-5500
130 Cheshire Ln Ste 102 Hopkins (55305) *(G-2565)*
Knight of Columbus Community 952 492-5170
20135 Lake Ridge Dr Prior Lake (55372) *(G-6936)*
Knights of Columbus 952 888-1492
1114 79th St W Bloomington (55420) *(G-502)*
Knights of Columbus Inc 320 679-4093
26204 Nelsons Rd Mora (55051) *(G-6364)*
Knock Inc 612 333-6511
1315 Glenwood Ave Minneapolis (55405) *(G-4815)*
Knollwood Boys Group Home, Grand Rapids *Also Called North Homes Inc (G-2298)*
Knollwood Place Apartments, Minneapolis *Also Called Community Housing & Service (G-4142)*
Knopp Valley Apartments, Winona *Also Called Sauer Memorial Home (G-10125)*
Knowledge Computers Inc 952 249-9940
2360 Daniels St Long Lake (55356) *(G-3026)*
Knowledge Learning Corp 952 944-3801
8825 Aztec Dr Eden Prairie (55347) *(G-1703)*
Knowledge Learning Corp 763 553-7960
3050 Fernbrook Ln N Minneapolis (55447) *(G-4816)*
Knowledge Learning Corp 612 623-4642
525 Huron Blvd SE Minneapolis (55414) *(G-4817)*
Knowledge Learning Corp 507 529-8455
3089 25th St NW Rochester (55901) *(G-7155)*
Knowledge Learning Corp 507 289-5006
2801 Superior Dr NW Rochester (55901) *(G-7156)*
Knowledge Learning Corp 952 452-6625
4194 Pilot Knob Rd Saint Paul (55122) *(G-7818)*
Knowledge Learning Corp 651 631-8728
4545 Hamline Ave N Saint Paul (55112) *(G-8550)*
Knowledge Learning Corp 952 440-2677
14014 Hwy 13 S Savage (55378) *(G-9394)*

Knute Nelson (PA) 320 763-6653
420 12th Ave E Alexandria (56308) *(G-107)*
Knutson Construction Services 507 280-9788
5985 Bandel Rd NW Rochester (55901) *(G-7157)*
Knutson, Flynn, Deans 651 222-2811
1155 Centre Pte Dr Ste 10 Saint Paul (55120) *(G-7819)*
Knw Group LLC 952 593-0265
4350 Baker Rd Ste 250 Hopkins (55343) *(G-2566)*
Kober & Sons Nursery, Madelia *Also Called Richard Koberski (G-3074)*
Koch Industries Inc 218 564-4495
10632 110th St Menahga (56464) *(G-3358)*
Koch Logistics, Saint Paul *Also Called Stan Koch & Sons Trucking Inc (G-9003)*
Koch NationaLease, Minneapolis *Also Called Stan Koch & Sons Trucking Inc (G-5736)*
KOEHLER & DRAMM WHOLESALE FLOR, Minneapolis *Also Called Ls Acquisitions Inc (G-4907)*
Kohner Realty Co Inc 507 454-5093
4980 W 6th St Winona (55987) *(G-10108)*
Kolstad Co Inc 763 792-1033
8501 Naples St NE Minneapolis (55449) *(G-3511)*
Kone Inc 952 688-6827
815 Northwest Pkwy # 120 Eagan (55121) *(G-1533)*
Konica Minolta Business Soln 952 820-8385
7300 Metro Blvd Ste 250 Minneapolis (55439) *(G-4818)*
Konica Minolta Business Soln 763 531-1721
5500 Lakeland Ave N Minneapolis (55429) *(G-4819)*
Koronis Hills Golf Club 320 243-4111
29757 State Hwy 23 W Paynesville (56362) *(G-6770)*
Korsmo Inc 507 285-1109
2411 7th St NW Rochester (55901) *(G-7158)*
Kottke Trucking Inc 320 833-5385
211 Hwy 212 E Buffalo Lake (55314) *(G-666)*
Kowsary Turf Inc 763 862-4646
22968 142nd St NW Elk River (55330) *(G-1882)*
Kozlowski Insurance Agency 507 825-3366
401 8th Ave SE Pipestone (56164) *(G-6831)*
KPMG LLP 612 305-5000
4200 Wells Fargo Ctr Minneapolis (55402) *(G-4820)*
Kraft Foods Global Inc 612 331-4311
749 Stinson Blvd Minneapolis (55413) *(G-4821)*
Kraft Foods Global Inc 507 359-2511
2525 S Bridge St New Ulm (56073) *(G-6458)*
Kraus Anderson Insurance, Burnsville *Also Called Osborne Properties LP (G-772)*
Kraus-Anderson Construction Co 218 759-0596
206 Beltrami Ave NW Bemidji (56601) *(G-400)*
Kraus-Anderson Construction Co 763 786-7711
8625 Rendova St NE Circle Pines (55014) *(G-1013)*
Kraus-Anderson Construction Co 612 721-7581
2500 Minnehaha Ave Minneapolis (55404) *(G-4822)*
Kraus-Anderson Inc (PA) 612 332-7281
523 S 8th St Minneapolis (55404) *(G-4823)*
Kraus-Anderson Insurance Agcy, Burnsville *Also Called Osborne Properties LP (G-771)*
Kraus-Anderson Realty Co 952 881-8166
4210 W Old Shakopee Rd Minneapolis (55437) *(G-4824)*
Krech, Ojard & Associates 218 727-3282
227 W 1st St Ste 200 Duluth (55802) *(G-1373)*
Kreger Farms Inc 320 983-5060
40412 Tiger St NW Milaca (56353) *(G-3373)*
Kristico Inc 507 625-2900
3801 3rd Ave Mankato (56001) *(G-3155)*
Krl Exterior Inc 612 296-0222
15501 Kings Ct Burnsville (55306) *(G-743)*
Kroll Ontrack Inc (HQ) 952 937-1107
9023 Columbine Rd Eden Prairie (55347) *(G-1704)*
Kronick Industries Inc 612 331-8080
3101 E Hennepin Ave Minneapolis (55413) *(G-4825)*
Kruse Family Enterprises LLC 507 345-5926
125 Kingswood Rd Mankato (56001) *(G-3156)*
Krushe Residential Services 218 746-3117
12760 W Sylvan Dr SW Pillager (56473) *(G-6810)*
KSA Real Estate Services Inc 651 290-0507
740 Linwood Ave Saint Paul (55105) *(G-8551)*
Kstp FM LLC 651 642-4242
3415 University Ave W Saint Paul (55114) *(G-8552)*
Kstp TV, Saint Paul *Also Called Hubbard Broadcasting Inc (G-8499)*
Ktcz FM, Minneapolis *Also Called Clear Channel Communications (G-4107)*
Ktm Paving Inc 218 628-7025
5513 Highway 2 Duluth (55810) *(G-1374)*
Ktn Acquisition Corp 952 941-9505
10951 Bush Lake Rd # 100 Minneapolis (55438) *(G-4826)*
Kttc Television Inc 507 288-4444
6301 Bandel Rd NW Ste A Rochester (55901) *(G-7159)*
Kuechle Underground Inc 320 398-8888
10998 State Hwy 55 Kimball (55353) *(G-2834)*
Kuehne + Nagel Inc 651 688-6645
980 Lone Oak Rd Ste 128 Saint Paul (55121) *(G-7820)*
Kuepers Construction Inc 888 829-0707
14643 Edgewood Dr Ste 115 Baxter (56425) *(G-334)*
Kunz Oil Co 952 352-8600
7900 Excelsior Blvd Hopkins (55343) *(G-2567)*
Kurt Manufacturing Co Inc 763 572-4592
9445 E River Rd NW Minneapolis (55433) *(G-3512)*
Kusske Mechanical Inc 651 437-8404
2651 Industrial Ct Hastings (55033) *(G-2394)*
Kutzke Oil Co Inc 320 629-2075
9865 Pine Shores Dr Pine City (55063) *(G-6812)*
Kwik Kargo Inc Trucking 320 743-2021
230 State St Clear Lake (55319) *(G-1035)*
Kwlm-AM, Willmar *Also Called Lakeland Broadcasting Co Inc (G-10016)*
Kzpk FM, Saint Cloud *Also Called Radio City Marketing Group Inc (G-7580)*
L & K Landscaping Inc 763 497-4700
3333 Iffert Ave NE Saint Michael (55376) *(G-7675)*
L & M Investment Inc 218 346-2798
323 4th St SW Perham (56573) *(G-6798)*
L & M Supply Inc 218 751-3237
2740 Paul Bunyan Dr NW Bemidji (56601) *(G-401)*
L & M Supply Inc (PA) 218 326-9451
1200 E US Highway 169 Grand Rapids (55744) *(G-2289)*
L & M Supply Inc 218 732-4465
1415 1st St E Park Rapids (56470) *(G-6759)*
L & R Suburban Landscaping Inc 952 935-0389
11421 47th St W Minnetonka (55343) *(G-6186)*
L & S Construction 507 648-3382
12226 Knox Ave Sanborn (56083) *(G-9318)*
L & S Electric Inc 763 780-3234
9300 Evergreen Blvd NW Minneapolis (55433) *(G-3513)*
L A Fitness International LLC 952 392-4400
1801 County Road 42 W Burnsville (55306) *(G-744)*
L C S Coaches Inc 218 879-3391
1203 Avenue B Cloquet (55720) *(G-1055)*
L D Properties, Worthington *Also Called Larry Davis (G-10187)*
L H Bolduc Co Inc 763 427-4330
649 Garfield St W Anoka (55303) *(G-196)*
L H Hendrickson & Co Inc 952 896-3456
3600 W 80th St Ste 200 Minneapolis (55431) *(G-4827)*
L Jireh Inc 218 387-2688
20 Naniboujou Trl Grand Marais (55604) *(G-2262)*
L L Brustad & Associates Inc 952 842-1142
3309 Casco Cir Wayzata (55391) *(G-9923)*
L L Hage Seamless Gutters Inc 507 433-1158
1700 8th St SE Austin (55912) *(G-280)*
L S Black Constructors Inc 651 774-8445
1959 Sloan Pl Ste 140 Saint Paul (55117) *(G-8553)*
L S Starrett Co 320 251-7171
1101 Prosper Dr Waite Park (56387) *(G-9825)*
L T T Inc 952 929-4556
9013 Penn Ave S Minneapolis (55431) *(G-4828)*
L&M Fleet Supply True Value 218 847-1171
1100 Highway 59 S Detroit Lakes (56501) *(G-1202)*
L&W Supply Corp 952 890-0828
12450 Beard Ave S Burnsville (55337) *(G-745)*
La Calhene Inc 320 358-4713
1325 S Field Ave Rush City (55069) *(G-7390)*
La Creche Early Childhood 612 377-1786
1800 Olson Memorial Hwy Minneapolis (55411) *(G-4829)*
La Crescent Healthcare Center, La Crescent *Also Called Beverly Enterprises - MN (G-2841)*
La Grande' Salon Ltd 651 464-4371
56 E Broadway Ave Ste 106 Forest Lake (55025) *(G-2163)*
La Petite Academy Inc 651 463-2022
90 Locust St Farmington (55024) *(G-2053)*
Labor Services Co 952 884-0765
55 W 78th St Minneapolis (55420) *(G-4830)*
Lab Holdings Inc (PA) 612 607-1700
7901 Xerxes Ave S Ste 201 Minneapolis (55431) *(G-4831)*
Lac Enterprises Inc 651 482-0205
1175 Highway 36 E Saint Paul (55109) *(G-8554)*
Lac Qui Parle Clinic, Madison *Also Called Madison Lutheran Home (G-3076)*
Lacek Group 612 359-3700
900 2nd Ave S Ste 1800 Minneapolis (55402) *(G-4832)*
Lacek Group Inc 612 359-3700
900 2nd Ave S Minneapolis (55402) *(G-4833)*
Ladue Construction Inc 218 846-9865
2354 340th St Waubun (56589) *(G-9900)*
Lady Wellness Management Inc 320 253-3371
136 Division St Waite Park (56387) *(G-9826)*
Lafayette Club 952 471-8493
2800 Northview Rd Minnetonka Beach (55361) *(G-6241)*
Lafayette Litho Inc 651 665-5617
285 Florida St Saint Paul (55107) *(G-8555)*
Laird LLC 507 444-0818
2345 NW 43rd St Owatonna (55060) *(G-6721)*
Lake Area Bank (HQ) 651 257-1117
12790 N 1st Ave Lindstrom (55045) *(G-2969)*
Lake Area Bank 651 653-9619
1400 Highway 96 E Ste 1 Saint Paul (55110) *(G-8556)*
Lake Area Mortgage 651 257-1114
1400 Highway 96 E Ste 1 Saint Paul (55110) *(G-8557)*
Lake Bank National Association (PA) 218 834-2111
613 1st Ave Two Harbors (55616) *(G-9709)*
Lake Carlos Villas 320 846-1784
3954 County Road 42 NE Alexandria (56308) *(G-108)*
Lake Center Industries Trans 507 457-3750
5676 Industrial Park Rd Winona (55987) *(G-10109)*
Lake City Medical Center-Mayo 651 345-3321
500 W Grant St Lake City (55041) *(G-2849)*
Lake Community Bank 952 473-7347
1964 W Wayzata Blvd Long Lake (55356) *(G-3027)*
Lake Country Builders Ltd 952 474-7121
339 2nd St Excelsior (55331) *(G-1944)*
Lake Country Logistics LLC 218 233-2686
4225 30th Ave S Moorhead (56560) *(G-6322)*
Lake Country Power 218 741-8137
8535 Park Ridge Dr Mountain Iron (55768) *(G-6393)*
Lake Country Sales, Waterville *Also Called Lcs Precision Molding Inc (G-9895)*
Lake County Ambulance 218 834-7110
421 20th Ave Two Harbors (55616) *(G-9710)*
Lake Crystal Area Recreation 507 726-6730
621 W Nathan St Lake Crystal (56055) *(G-2858)*
Lake Crystal Coaches, Madison Lake *Also Called Crystal Lake Bus Service Inc (G-3078)*
Lake Crystal Fire Department 507 726-2440
181 S Hunt St Lake Crystal (56055) *(G-2859)*
Lake Elmo Chrysler, Lake Elmo *Also Called Brookman Motor Sales Inc (G-2867)*
Lake Haven Manor, Cambridge *Also Called A R I Inc (G-830)*
Lake Minnetonka Care Center, Excelsior *Also Called Minnetonka Health Care Center (G-1950)*
Lake Minnetonka Orthodontics 952 938-1443
11601 Minnetonka Mills Rd Hopkins (55305) *(G-2568)*
Lake Minnetonka Sailing School 952 404-1645
3645 Laurel Dr Wayzata (55391) *(G-9924)*
Lake of Woods Ambulance 218 634-2100
111 1st St SW Baudette (56623) *(G-316)*
Lake Rainy Medical Center 218 283-4481
1400 Highway 71 International Falls (56649) *(G-2726)*
Lake Region Co-Op Oil Assn 763 682-1431
512 7th St NE Buffalo (55313) *(G-648)*
Lake Region Electric Co-op 218 863-1171
1401 S Brdwy Pelican Rapids (56572) *(G-6780)*

ALPHABETIC SECTION

Larsonallen LLP

Lake Region Healthcare Corp 218 736-8000
712 S Cascade St Fergus Falls (56537) *(G-2081)*
Lake Ridge Care Center of 763 682-1434
310 Lake Blvd S Buffalo (55313) *(G-649)*
Lake Shore Inn Nursing Home 507 835-2800
108 8th St NW Waseca (56093) *(G-9881)*
Lake State Federal Credit (PA) 218 485-4444
301 Elm Ave Moose Lake (55767) *(G-6351)*
Lake State Federal Credit 320 245-5251
406 N Commercial Sandstone (55072) *(G-9322)*
Lake States Lumber Inc 218 927-2125
995 Pacific St NW Aitkin (56431) *(G-21)*
Lake States Lumber Inc 763 425-0204
9110 83rd Ave N Ste 100 Brooklyn Park (55445) *(G-613)*
Lake States Tree Service Inc 218 326-5872
25172 Commercial Dr Grand Rapids (55744) *(G-2290)*
Lake Superior Center 218 740-3474
353 Harbor Dr Duluth (55802) *(G-1375)*
Lake Superior Dental 218 728-6445
1225 E 1st St Duluth (55805) *(G-1376)*
Lake Superior Medical Society 218 727-3325
324 W Superior St Ste 910 Duluth (55802) *(G-1377)*
Lake Superior Railroad Museum 218 733-7590
506 W Michigan St Ste 19 Duluth (55802) *(G-1378)*
Lake Superior Software Inc 952 941-1000
6423 City West Pkwy Eden Prairie (55344) *(G-1705)*
Lake Wobegon Brass Band, Anoka *Also Called Anoka Brass Band Assoc Inc (G-154)*
Lake Wood Home, Spicer *Also Called Prairie Community Services (G-9558)*
Lakedale Telephone Co 320 274-8201
9938 State Highway 55 NW Annandale (55302) *(G-140)*
Lakehead Constructors Inc 218 328-5429
856 NW 3rd St Cohasset (55721) *(G-1071)*
Lakehead Electric, Hibbing *Also Called API Electric Co (G-2437)*
Lakehead Electric Co, Duluth *Also Called API Electric Co (G-1239)*
Lakehead Trucking Inc 218 721-3521
6035 Lavaque Rd Duluth (55803) *(G-1379)*
Lakeland Broadcasting Co Inc 320 235-1340
1340 N 7th St Willmar (56201) *(G-10016)*
Lakeland Distribution Services 320 762-8385
225 7th Ave E Alexandria (56308) *(G-109)*
Lakeland Florist Supply Inc 952 944-5160
7035 Washington Ave S Minneapolis (55439) *(G-4834)*
Lakeland Hospice & Home Care 218 998-1400
1505 Pebble Lake Rd # 400 Fergus Falls (56537) *(G-2082)*
Lakeland Lodging LP 218 829-8730
5637 Hwy 9 S Alexandria (56308) *(G-110)*
Lakeland Mental Health Center (PA) 218 736-6987
21081 County Highway 1 Fergus Falls (56537) *(G-2083)*
Lakeland Mental Health Center 218 233-7524
1010 32nd Ave S Moorhead (56560) *(G-6323)*
Lakes & Pines Community Action 320 679-1800
1700 Maple Ave E Mora (55051) *(G-6365)*
Lakes & Prairies Community 218 299-7000
715 11th St N Ste 402 Moorhead (56560) *(G-6324)*
Lakes 10, Duluth *Also Called Cinema Entertainment Corp (G-1272)*
Lakes Area Realty Inc 612 874-1916
1428 W 28th St Minneapolis (55408) *(G-4835)*
Lakes Country Service Co-Op 218 739-3273
1001 E Mount Faith Ave Fergus Falls (56537) *(G-2084)*
Lakes Homes & Program Devpt (PA) 218 847-5642
847 Highway 10 E Detroit Lakes (56501) *(G-1203)*
Lakes Homes & Program Devpt 218 739-4322
1381 Lenore Way Fergus Falls (56537) *(G-2085)*
Lakes Medi-Van Inc 218 847-1729
16777 Longview Dr Detroit Lakes (56501) *(G-1204)*
Lakes Radio, Fergus Falls *Also Called K J Country 965 (G-2080)*
Lakes Region EMS Inc 651 277-4911
39840 Grand Ave North Branch (55056) *(G-6502)*
Lakes State Bank 218 568-4473
31113 Front St Pequot Lakes (56472) *(G-6790)*
Lakeshirts Inc 218 847-2171
750 Randolph Rd Detroit Lakes (56501) *(G-1205)*
Lakeshore Lutheran Home, Duluth *Also Called Ecumen Home Care Inc (G-1309)*
Lakeside Hospitality LLP 218 847-2121
2215 S 6th St Brainerd (56401) *(G-572)*
Lakeside House Painters Inc 952 942-9709
8800 Highway 7 Ste 224 Minneapolis (55426) *(G-4836)*
Lakeside Medical Center Inc 320 629-2542
129 6th Ave SE Pine City (55063) *(G-6813)*
Lakeview Care Center, Burnsville *Also Called Northwest Investors Inc (G-768)*
Lakeview Clinic (PA) 952 442-4461
424 W Highway 5 Waconia (55387) *(G-9788)*
Lakeview Clinic 952 955-1921
309 Jefferson Ave SW Watertown (55388) *(G-9891)*
Lakeview Good Samaritan Center, Glenwood *Also Called Evangelical Lutheran Good (G-2222)*
Lakeview Industries Inc 952 368-3500
1225 Lakeview Dr Chaska (55318) *(G-974)*
Lakeview Medical Clinic 320 352-6591
433 Elm St N Sauk Centre (56378) *(G-9350)*
Lakeview Memorial Hospital 651 439-5330
927 Churchill St W Stillwater (55082) *(G-9625)*
Lakeview Methodist Health Care 507 235-6606
610 Summit Dr Ofc OFC Fairmont (56031) *(G-1976)*
Lakeview Nursing Home, Heron Lake *Also Called City of Heron Lake (G-2435)*
Lakeview Ranch Inc 320 275-4027
69531 213th St Darwin (55324) *(G-1157)*
Lakeview Retirement Apartments 218 386-1235
611 Lake St NE Warroad (56763) *(G-9871)*
Lakeville Motor Express Inc 651 636-8900
500 County Road D W Saint Paul (55112) *(G-8558)*
LAKEVILLE SANITARY, Lakeville *Also Called Dick's Sanitation Service Inc (G-2903)*
Lakewalk Surgery Center Inc 218 728-0650
1420 London Rd Ste 100 Duluth (55805) *(G-1380)*
Lakewood Cemetery Association 612 822-2171
3600 Hennepin Ave Minneapolis (55408) *(G-4837)*
Lakewood Health Center 218 634-2120
600 Main Ave S Baudette (56623) *(G-317)*
Lakewood Health System 218 894-1515
49725 County 83 Staples (56479) *(G-9586)*
Lambsoft & Lamb & Co 612 813-3727
2429 Nicollet Ave Minneapolis (55404) *(G-4838)*
Lametti & Sons Inc 651 426-1380
16028 Forest Blvd N Hugo (55038) *(G-2678)*
Lamettry Collision Inc 952 898-1636
14601 Burnhaven Dr Burnsville (55306) *(G-746)*
Lamettry Collision Inc 651 766-9770
2923 Maplewood Dr Saint Paul (55109) *(G-8559)*
Lamettry's Collision, Burnsville *Also Called Lamettry Collision Inc (G-746)*
Lancer House, La Crescent *Also Called B L E A Inc (G-2838)*
Lancet Software Development 952 230-7360
11980 Portland Ave Burnsville (55337) *(G-747)*
Land & Cabins LLC 320 384-6488
24226 Lone Pine Rd Hinckley (55037) *(G-2485)*
Land O'Lakes Inc 320 543-2566
917 6th St Howard Lake (55349) *(G-2668)*
Land O'Lakes Inc 218 233-8609
2103 5th Ave N Moorhead (56560) *(G-6325)*
Land O'Lakes Purina Feed LLC 218 847-3176
1110 13th Ave SE Detroit Lakes (56501) *(G-1206)*
Land O'Lakes Purina Feed LLC 651 681-5917
11620 Courthouse Blvd A Inver Grove Heights (55077) *(G-2757)*
Land O'Lakes Purina Feed LLC 651 437-7762
3763 117th St E Inver Grove Heights (55077) *(G-2758)*
Land O'Lakes Purina Feed LLC 320 235-6000
22nd St SW Willmar (56201) *(G-10017)*
Land Title Inc 651 638-1900
1900 Silver Lake Rd NW Ste 200 Saint Paul (55112) *(G-8560)*
Landfall Terrace Inc 651 739-8284
50 Aspen Way Saint Paul (55128) *(G-9240)*
LANDMARK CENTER, Saint Paul *Also Called Minnesota Landmarks Inc (G-8693)*
Landmark Community Bank 763 444-7787
14150 Saint Francis Blvd # 1 Anoka (55303) *(G-197)*
Landmark Financial Group Inc 763 572-8626
11490 Hanson Blvd NW Ste 2 Minneapolis (55433) *(G-3514)*
Landscape Brands Inc 507 452-1112
1101 E Sanborn St Winona (55987) *(G-10110)*
Landscape Renovations Inc 651 769-0010
12515 40th St S Afton (55001) *(G-9)*
Landstyle Design & Constr 763 479-1200
110 Railway St W Loretto (55357) *(G-3050)*
Landwehr Construction Inc 320 252-1494
846 33rd St S Saint Cloud (56301) *(G-7542)*
Lane Memory 612 721-6211
2520 26th Ave S Minneapolis (55406) *(G-4839)*
Lanesboro Sales Commission Inc 507 467-2192
402 Coffee St Lanesboro (55949) *(G-2947)*
Laney's Mechanical Inc 218 847-1309
1034 Highway 59 S Unit 3 Detroit Lakes (56501) *(G-1207)*
Lang Builders Inc 763 780-9090
620 Civic Heights Dr Ste 100 Circle Pines (55014) *(G-1014)*
Lang-Nelson Associates Inc 763 533-9389
7000 62nd Ave N Ofc Minneapolis (55428) *(G-4840)*
Lang-Nelson Associates Inc (PA) 952 920-0400
4601 Excelsior Blvd # 650 Minneapolis (55416) *(G-4841)*
Langer Construction Co Inc 651 457-5993
54 Moreland Ave E Saint Paul (55118) *(G-7821)*
Lanners Brothers Construction 507 532-5457
2653 County Road 7 Marshall (56258) *(G-3304)*
Lanovation, Minneapolis *Also Called New Boundary Technologies Inc (G-5186)*
Lansing Mall LP 763 566-3373
1108 Brookdale Ctr Minneapolis (55430) *(G-4842)*
Lansing Mall LP 320 252-2856
4101 W Division St Saint Cloud (56301) *(G-7543)*
Lanterns Homeowner Association 952 922-4435
4075 W 51st St Minneapolis (55424) *(G-4843)*
Lao Family Community of MN 651 221-0069
320 University Ave W Saint Paul (55103) *(G-8561)*
Lapp Tannehill Inc 952 881-6700
8675 Eagle Creek Pkwy Savage (55378) *(G-9395)*
Larken Inc 952 830-1300
5151 American Blvd W Minneapolis (55437) *(G-4844)*
Larkin Industries Inc 651 645-6000
2020 Energy Park Dr Saint Paul (55108) *(G-8562)*
Larkin, Hoffman, Daly 952 835-3800
7900 Xerxes Ave S Ste 1500 Minneapolis (55431) *(G-4845)*
Laron Allen Weishair & Co LLP 507 437-4518
109 N Main St Austin (55912) *(G-281)*
Larry A Larson 320 235-1294
5479 15th St SE Willmar (56201) *(G-10018)*
Larry Davis 507 372-7774
1158 Oxford St Worthington (56187) *(G-10187)*
Larry Schefus Trucking Inc 507 644-5588
Hwy 71 S Redwood Falls (56283) *(G-7023)*
Larsen Design Office Inc 952 835-2271
7101 York Ave S Ste 120 Minneapolis (55435) *(G-4846)*
Larson Allen, Austin *Also Called Laron Allen Weishair & Co LLP (G-281)*
Larson Contracting Inc 507 373-6645
508 W Main St Albert Lea (56007) *(G-59)*
Larson Custom Cabinets, Hutchinson *Also Called Richard Larson Builders Inc (G-2711)*
Larson Ellen Weisharir Co LLP 320 253-8616
818 2nd St S Ste 320 Waite Park (56387) *(G-9827)*
Larson Engineering Inc (PA) 651 481-9120
3524 Labore Rd Saint Paul (55110) *(G-8563)*
Larson King, LLP 651 312-6500
30 7th St E Ste 2800 Saint Paul (55101) *(G-8564)*
Larson Plumbing Inc 763 427-7680
3095 162nd Ln NW Ste 100 Anoka (55304) *(G-198)*
Larson Transfer & Storage Co 952 884-0765
55 W 78th St Minneapolis (55420) *(G-4847)*
Larson Utilities Inc (PA) 507 557-2275
318 2nd Ave E Franklin (55333) *(G-2181)*
Larson's Home Improvement 507 288-7111
6910 38th Ave SE Rochester (55904) *(G-7160)*
Larsonallen LLP 218 825-2919
581 Edgewood Dr N Baxter (56425) *(G-335)*

ALPHABETIC

Larsonallen LLP 218 692-5750
35258 County Road 3 Crosslake (56442) *(G-1151)*
Larsonallen LLP (PA) 612 376-4500
220 S 6th St Ste 300 Minneapolis (55402) *(G-4848)*
Laser Printing Technologies 952 888-7375
2500 Lexington Ave S Mendota Heights (55120) *(G-3366)*
LasX Industries Inc 651 407-0011
4817 White Bear Pkwy Saint Paul (55110) *(G-8565)*
Lathrop Paint, Minneapolis *Also Called Hirshfield's Inc (G-4655)*
Latour Construction Inc 320 963-5993
2134 County Rd Ste 8NW Maple Lake (55358) *(G-3260)*
Laurence Cuneo & Associates 952 707-1212
1401 American Blvd E # 6 Minneapolis (55425) *(G-4849)*
Laurent Builders Inc 952 445-6745
100 Fuller St S Ste 200 Shakopee (55379) *(G-9450)*
Laurentian Leasing Inc 218 741-6000
501 9th St N Virginia (55792) *(G-9744)*
Lavine Place, Elk River *Also Called Opportunity Partners Inc (G-1889)*
Law Center Inc 218 736-5493
110 N Mill St Fergus Falls (56537) *(G-2086)*
Law Enforcement Labor Services 651 293-4424
327 York Ave Saint Paul (55130) *(G-8566)*
Law Office, Fergus Falls *Also Called Svingen Hagstron Cline Karkela (G-2121)*
Lawn King Inc 763 420-2909
7555 County Road 116 Hamel (55340) *(G-2346)*
Lawn Professionals & Treasures 651 482-1431
948 Lydia Dr W Saint Paul (55113) *(G-8567)*
Lawn Ranger Inc 952 937-6076
6368 Carlson Dr Eden Prairie (55346) *(G-1706)*
Lawremar Inc 651 429-4475
2372 Leibel St Saint Paul (55110) *(G-8568)*
Lawrence Service Co 763 383-5700
3500 Holly Ln N Ste 10 Minneapolis (55447) *(G-4850)*
Lawrence Transportation 507 454-3911
6830 Martina Rd Winona (55987) *(G-10111)*
Lawson Software Americas Inc (HQ) 651 767-7000
380 Saint Peter St Ste 323 Saint Paul (55102) *(G-8569)*
Lawson Software Inc (PA) 651 767-7000
380 Saint Peter St # 323 Saint Paul (55102) *(G-8570)*
Layline Corp 651 385-9060
1819 Old West Main St Red Wing (55066) *(G-6988)*
Lbp Mechanical Inc 612 333-1515
315 Royalston Ave Minneapolis (55405) *(G-4851)*
Lcomuity National Bank 651 483-4656
845 County Road E E Saint Paul (55127) *(G-8571)*
Lcs Precision Molding Inc 507 362-8685
119 2nd St S Waterville (56096) *(G-9895)*
Le Center Volunteer Ambulance 507 357-4844
175 S Cordova Ave Le Center (56057) *(G-2951)*
Le Clair Insurance Services 651 739-2010
6701 Upper Afton Rd Saint Paul (55125) *(G-9241)*
Le Febvre & Sons Inc 952 432-8228
6055 150th St W Saint Paul (55124) *(G-7822)*
Le Jeune Investment Inc 651 483-2681
2780 Highway 61 Saint Paul (55109) *(G-8572)*
Le Sueur Country Club 507 665-8839
36195 311th Ave Le Sueur (56058) *(G-2956)*
Le Sueur County Developmental 507 362-8560
519 Paquin St W Waterville (56096) *(G-9896)*
Le Sueur, City of Inc 507 665-3325
821 Ferry St Le Sueur (56058) *(G-2957)*
Lea Albert Electric Co 507 373-6650
1410 Olsen Dr Albert Lea (56007) *(G-60)*
League of Minnesota Cities 651 281-1200
145 University Ave W Saint Paul (55103) *(G-8573)*
Learning For Leadership 612 789-9598
3300 5th St NE Minneapolis (55418) *(G-4852)*
Lecy Construction 952 944-9499
15012 Highway 7 Hopkins (55345) *(G-2569)*
Lee Carlson Center For Mental 763 780-3036
7954 University Ave NE Fridley (55432) *(G-2193)*
Lee F Murphy Inc 651 644-7200
2515 Wabash Ave Ste 300 Saint Paul (55114) *(G-8574)*
Lee Hydra-Mac Sales 218 574-2237
11880 360th St SW Fertile (56540) *(G-2126)*
Lee's Ceramic Contracting Inc 612 720-1653
10980 180th St E Hastings (55033) *(G-2395)*
Lee's Construction Inc 320 762-0325
615 Nokomis St Ste 200 Alexandria (56308) *(G-111)*
Lee's Pro Shop Inc 320 629-7568
625 Henriette Rd NW Pine City (55063) *(G-6814)*
Leech Lake Distributors Inc 218 547-1505
522 Minnesota Ave NW Walker (56484) *(G-9853)*
Leech Lake Palace & Casino 218 335-7000
6280 Upper Cass Frontage Rd Cass Lake (56633) *(G-872)*
Leech Lake Reservation 218 547-2744
6800 Y Frontage Rd NW Walker (56484) *(G-9854)*
Leeds Precision Instruments 763 546-8575
800 Boone Ave N Minneapolis (55427) *(G-4853)*
Lefty's Shooting & Outdoor 763 533-9594
4080 W Broadway Ave # 109 Minneapolis (55422) *(G-4854)*
Legacy Courses At Cragun, Brainerd *Also Called Cragun Enterprises Inc (G-544)*
Legacy Golf Corp 507 332-0777
1515 Shumway Ave Faribault (55021) *(G-2019)*
Legal Aid Society of (PA) 612 332-1441
430 1st Ave N Ste 300 Minneapolis (55401) *(G-4855)*
Legal Aid Society of 612 827-3774
2929 4th Ave S Ste 201 Minneapolis (55408) *(G-4856)*
Legal Research Center Inc 612 332-4950
310 4th Ave S Ste 1100 Minneapolis (55415) *(G-4857)*
Legal Service Northwest MN 218 681-7710
220 Pennington Ave B Thief River Falls (56701) *(G-9673)*
Legal Services Advocacy Proj (PA) 651 222-3749
46 4th St E Ste 726 Saint Paul (55101) *(G-8575)*
Legend Technical Services Inc 651 642-1150
88 Empire Dr Saint Paul (55103) *(G-8576)*

Legends Club LLC 952 226-4777
8670 Credit River Blvd Prior Lake (55372) *(G-6937)*
Legion Pavilion Co Inc 952 758-4603
300 Lexington Ave S New Prague (56071) *(G-6422)*
Legislative Solutions, Saint Paul *Also Called Xmalpha Technologies (G-9170)*
Lehman's Garage Inc (PA) 952 888-8700
171 American Blvd W Minneapolis (55420) *(G-4858)*
Lehman's Garage Inc 651 454-1120
1979 Seneca Rd Saint Paul (55122) *(G-7823)*
Lehman's Garage Inc 952 888-8700
8533 Highway 101 W Savage (55378) *(G-9396)*
Lehman's Garage Minneapolis 612 827-5431
5431 Lyndale Ave S Minneapolis (55419) *(G-4859)*
Leighton Enterprises Inc (PA) 320 251-1450
619 W Saint Germain St # 1 Saint Cloud (56301) *(G-7544)*
Leinvestors Inc 952 854-1114
7800 Metro Pkwy Ste 300 Bloomington (55425) *(G-503)*
Leisure Hills Care Center, Grand Rapids *Also Called Mission Healthcare LLC (G-2296)*
Leisure Hills Health, Grand Rapids *Also Called Evergreen Terrace (G-2276)*
Leisure Inc 952 401-8440
6811 Flying Cloud Dr Eden Prairie (55344) *(G-1707)*
Lemaster Restoration Inc 952 707-1256
14261 W Burnsville Pkwy Burnsville (55306) *(G-748)*
Lemke Dental Laboratory Inc 651 482-9911
1420 E County Road D Ct A Saint Paul (55109) *(G-8577)*
Lemna Corp (PA) 612 253-2000
2445 Park Ave Minneapolis (55404) *(G-4860)*
Lenci Enterprises Inc 218 741-3482
1021 S 2nd Ave Virginia (55792) *(G-9745)*
Leneave Financial Group 952 542-0777
301 Carlson Pkwy Ste 300 Hopkins (55305) *(G-2570)*
Lenox, Eden Prairie *Also Called Ovp Inc (G-1740)*
Lenox Group Inc 952 943-4100
6436 City West Pkwy Eden Prairie (55344) *(G-1708)*
Lenzen Chevrolet Buick Inc 952 448-2850
2860 Chaska Blvd Chaska (55318) *(G-975)*
Leo A Daly Co 612 338-8741
730 2nd Ave S Ste 1100 Minneapolis (55402) *(G-4861)*
Leonard V Ackerman DDS 763 757-7540
11441 Osage St NW Minneapolis (55433) *(G-3515)*
Leonard, Street & Deinard 612 335-1500
150 S 5th St Ste 2300 Minneapolis (55402) *(G-4862)*
Leone Enterprises Inc 763 427-9657
2040 N Ferry St Anoka (55303) *(G-199)*
Leone's Building Services, Anoka *Also Called Leone Enterprises Inc (G-199)*
Lephert, Skwira, Shultz & Co 651 265-2051
170 7th Pl E Ste 100 Saint Paul (55101) *(G-8578)*
Leptos Biomedical 763 561-0880
452 Northco Dr Ste 100 Minneapolis (55432) *(G-3516)*
Les Bolstold U MN Golf Course, Saint Paul *Also Called Regents of The University of (G-8882)*
Les Jones Roofing Inc 952 881-2241
941 W 80th St Minneapolis (55420) *(G-4863)*
Leslie E Fishman Inc 651 227-7806
233 Smith Ave N Saint Paul (55102) *(G-8579)*
Lessors Inc 651 789-9270
1056 Gemini Rd Saint Paul (55121) *(G-7824)*
Lester Buildings LLC 320 395-2531
1111 2nd Ave S Lester Prairie (55354) *(G-2963)*
Lester Park Golf Course, Duluth *Also Called Paul Schintz Inc (G-1419)*
Lethert, Skwira, Schultz & Co 651 224-5721
170 7th Pl E Ste 100 Saint Paul (55101) *(G-8580)*
Leuthold Asset Allocation Fund 612 332-9141
33 S 6th St Ste 4600 Minneapolis (55402) *(G-4864)*
Level Brand Inc 612 338-8000
724 N 1st St Ste 500 Minneapolis (55401) *(G-4865)*
Leverz Skira & Shcultz CPA 651 265-2045
170 7th Pl E Ste 100 Saint Paul (55101) *(G-8581)*
Lewiston Auto Co Inc 507 523-2164
US Hwy 14 At Rice St Lewiston (55952) *(G-2967)*
Lewiston Villa Nursing Home, Lewiston *Also Called Deloughery Home LP (G-2966)*
Lex A Nerenberg MD 763 520-2980
2805 Campus Dr Ste 345 Minneapolis (55441) *(G-4866)*
Lexion Medical LLC 651 635-0000
5000 Township Pkwy Saint Paul (55110) *(G-8582)*
LHB Inc (PA) 218 727-8446
21 W Superior St Ste 500 Duluth (55802) *(G-1381)*
Lhb Inc 612 338-2029
250 3rd Ave N Ste 450 Minneapolis (55401) *(G-4867)*
Lho Bloomington One Lessee LLC 952 835-7800
7800 Normandale Blvd Minneapolis (55439) *(G-4868)*
Liberty Display Group Inc 763 785-1593
10087 Goodhue St NE Minneapolis (55449) *(G-3517)*
Liberty Diversified Industries (PA) 763 536-6600
5600 Highway 169 N Minneapolis (55428) *(G-4869)*
Liberty Lanes Inc 218 773-3477
1500 5th Ave NE East Grand Forks (56721) *(G-1570)*
Liberty Mutual Insurance Co 763 546-7550
701 Xenia Ave S Ste 400 Minneapolis (55416) *(G-4870)*
Liberty Paper Inc 763 261-6100
13500 Liberty Ln Becker (55308) *(G-356)*
Liberty Property Trust 952 947-1100
10400 Viking Dr Ste 130 Eden Prairie (55344) *(G-1709)*
Liberty Savings Bank Fsb 320 252-2841
111 7th Ave S Ste 101 Saint Cloud (56301) *(G-7545)*
Libor Management LLC 763 561-0900
2550 Freeway Blvd Minneapolis (55430) *(G-4871)*
Libra Inc 612 522-2600
3310 N 2nd St Minneapolis (55412) *(G-4872)*
Lieberman Co's Inc (PA) 952 887-5299
9549 Penn Ave S Ste 100 Minneapolis (55431) *(G-4873)*
Lieberman Co's Inc 952 887-5200
2100 W 96th St Minneapolis (55431) *(G-4874)*
Liesch Associates Inc (PA) 763 489-3100
13400 15th Ave N Ste A Minneapolis (55441) *(G-4875)*
Life By Design Inc 763 757-3263
7866 University Ave NE Minneapolis (55432) *(G-3518)*

LIFE LINK III, Minneapolis *Also Called Critical Care Services Inc (G-4185)*
Life Safety Systems Inc 763 560-2048
3700 74th Ave N Minneapolis (55443) *(G-4876)*
Life Style Inc 507 451-8524
311 N Cedar Ave Owatonna (55060) *(G-6722)*
Life Time Fitness Inc 763 576-3000
11989 Champlin Dr Champlin (55316) *(G-895)*
Life Time Fitness Inc (PA) 952 947-0000
2902 Corporate Pl Chanhassen (55317) *(G-929)*
Life Time Fitness Inc 763 257-1067
2100 Northdale Blvd NW Minneapolis (55433) *(G-3519)*
Life Time Fitness Inc 952 835-2222
5250 W 84th St Minneapolis (55437) *(G-4877)*
Life Time Fitness Inc 612 752-9589
615 2nd Ave S Minneapolis (55402) *(G-4878)*
Life Time Fitness Inc 612 339-3655
615 2nd Ave S Minneapolis (55402) *(G-4879)*
Life Time Fitness Inc 763 509-0909
3600 Plymouth Blvd Minneapolis (55446) *(G-4880)*
Life Time Fitness Inc 651 730-6000
675 Commons Dr Saint Paul (55125) *(G-9242)*
Life Time Fitness Inc 651 633-4444
2480 Fairview Ave N Saint Paul (55113) *(G-8583)*
Life Time Fitness Inc 651 698-5000
2145 Ford Pkwy Bsmt 1 Saint Paul (55116) *(G-8584)*
Life Time Fitness Inc 651 426-1308
4800 White Bear Pkwy Saint Paul (55110) *(G-8585)*
Life's Companion PCA Inc 218 326-1179
111 NW 11th St Grand Rapids (55744) *(G-2291)*
Life-Science Innovations LLC 320 222-9750
1800 Technology Dr NE Willmar (56201) *(G-10019)*
Lifecare Medical Center 218 782-2131
152 5th St S Greenbush (56726) *(G-2326)*
Lifecare Medical Center (PA) 218 463-4305
715 Delmore Dr Roseau (56751) *(G-7355)*
Lifes Companion PCA Inc 763 786-3439
10307 University Ave NE Minneapolis (55434) *(G-3520)*
Lifespan of Minnesota Inc 651 681-0616
3920 Sibley Memorial Hwy Eagan (55122) *(G-1534)*
Lifetech Corp 612 369-5050
8940 Yucca Ln N Osseo (55369) *(G-6628)*
Lifetime Fitness, Chanhassen *Also Called Life Time Fitness Inc (G-929)*
Lifetime Fitness, Minneapolis *Also Called Life Time Fitness Inc (G-4880)*
Lifetime Resources Inc 612 804-2252
9600 Thomas Ave N Minneapolis (55444) *(G-4881)*
Lifetime Siding & Remodeling 651 458-0844
11825 Point Douglas Dr S Hastings (55033) *(G-2417)*
Lifetouch National School (HQ) 952 826-4000
11000 Viking Dr Ste 300 Eden Prairie (55344) *(G-1710)*
Lifetouch National School 952 826-4500
7800 Picture Dr Minneapolis (55439) *(G-4882)*
Lifetouch Portrait Studios Inc (HQ) 952 826-5000
11000 Viking Dr Ste 200 Eden Prairie (55344) *(G-1711)*
Lifetrack Resources Inc (PA) 651 227-8471
709 University Ave W Saint Paul (55104) *(G-8586)*
Lifetrack Resources Inc 651 290-0567
341 Chester St Saint Paul (55107) *(G-8587)*
Lifeway Services 218 722-1184
4897 Miller Trunk Hwy # 200 Duluth (55811) *(G-1382)*
Lifeworks Services Inc 763 746-3330
7040 Lakeland Ave N Ste 108 Minneapolis (55428) *(G-4883)*
Lighthouse On Homestead Inc 218 525-4525
5730 Homestead Rd Duluth (55804) *(G-1383)*
Lighthouse Villages 952 442-1261
500 S Cherry St Apt 207 Waconia (55387) *(G-9789)*
Lighthouse1 LLC 952 852-7099
9800 Bren Rd E Ste 250 Minneapolis (55437) *(G-4884)*
Lights On Broadway Inc 763 533-3366
6900 W Broadway Ave Minneapolis (55428) *(G-4885)*
Lights On Inc 612 331-6620
61 Bedford St SE Minneapolis (55414) *(G-4886)*
Lincoln Elementary School, Elk River *Also Called Elk River Independent School (G-1873)*
Lincoln Elementry School P T A 320 616-6200
300 6th St SW Little Falls (56345) *(G-3010)*
Lincoln Financial Advisors 952 933-8000
5850 Opus Pkwy Ste 200 Hopkins (55343) *(G-2571)*
Lincoln Life & Annunity Co of 612 373-7460
200 S 6th St Ste 1000 Minneapolis (55402) *(G-4887)*
Lincoln Lyon Murry & Pipestone 507 537-6709
607 W Main St Marshall (56258) *(G-3305)*
Lincoln, Lyon, & Murray Human 507 532-1239
607 W Main St Marshall (56258) *(G-3306)*
Lind Jensen & Sullivan, Minneapolis *Also Called Lind, Jensen, Sullivan (G-4888)*
Lind, Jensen, Sullivan 612 333-3637
150 S 5th St Ste 1700 Minneapolis (55402) *(G-4888)*
Linda Kay Properties, Brainerd *Also Called Almond House (G-547)*
Linda Waterman 507 287-7741
4600 18th Ave NW Rochester (55901) *(G-7161)*
Lindenberg & Associates - Twin 612 375-0234
105 S 5th St Ste 1850 Minneapolis (55402) *(G-4889)*
Linder's Greenhouses Inc 651 488-1927
270 Larpenteur Ave W Saint Paul (55113) *(G-8588)*
Linder's Greenhouses Inc (PA) 651 488-6717
275 Wheelock Pkwy W Saint Paul (55117) *(G-8589)*
Lindhaus USA Inc 952 707-1131
2500 County Road 42 W # 12 Burnsville (55337) *(G-749)*
Lindquist & Vennum PLLP (PA) 612 371-3211
80 S 8th St Ste 4200 Minneapolis (55402) *(G-4890)*
Lindstrom Cleaning & Constr 763 544-8761
9621 10th Ave N Minneapolis (55441) *(G-4891)*
Lindstrom Environmental Inc 763 545-9740
9621 10th Ave N Plymouth (55441) *(G-6870)*
Lindstrom Metric LLC (PA) 763 780-4200
2950 100th Ct NE Minneapolis (55449) *(G-3521)*
Link Lakedale Inc 320 274-7777
9938 State Highway 55 NW Annandale (55302) *(G-141)*
Links At Northfork LLP 763 241-0506
9333 Alpine Dr NW Anoka (55303) *(G-200)*
Links On The Mississippi Inc 651 768-7611
10351 Grey Cloud Trl S Cottage Grove (55016) *(G-1104)*
Linn Building Maintenance Inc 651 778-1322
1899 Rice St Saint Paul (55113) *(G-8590)*
Linnea Residential Home Inc 651 257-2211
28770 Old Towne Rd Chisago City (55013) *(G-992)*
Lino Lake Lodging LLC 763 746-9500
725 Town Center Pkwy Lino Lakes (55014) *(G-2973)*
Linstrom, Samuelson, & Hardten 612 813-3600
710 E 24th St Ste 106 Minneapolis (55404) *(G-4892)*
Lintex Corp 651 646-6600
2609 Territorial Rd Saint Paul (55114) *(G-8591)*
Lions Club of Jasper 507 348-8605
221 Wall St E Jasper (56144) *(G-2804)*
Lipe Brothers Construction Inc 218 525-3364
5116 Jean Duluth Rd Duluth (55803) *(G-1384)*
Lipham, William J MD, Minneapolis *Also Called Linstrom, Samuelson, & Hardten (G-4892)*
Liquors Plus Inc 651 501-1199
9887 Norma Ln Saint Paul (55125) *(G-9243)*
Lismore Hutterian Brethern 320 325-5485
80391 330th St Clinton (56225) *(G-1044)*
Litchfield Golf Club 320 693-6059
405 W Pleasure Dr Litchfield (55355) *(G-2987)*
Litho Tech Custom Cover, Minneapolis *Also Called Taylor Corp (G-5794)*
Litin Paper Co Inc 612 333-4331
3003 Pacific St Minneapolis (55411) *(G-4893)*
Little & Co, Minneapolis *Also Called M Little & Co Inc (G-4922)*
Little Acorns Child Care Inc 952 475-0828
1865 W Wayzata Blvd # 110 Long Lake (55356) *(G-3028)*
Little Acorns Day School 952 475-0828
1865 Wayzata Blvd Wayzata (55391) *(G-9925)*
Little Elk Youth Ranch Inc 320 594-2750
31500 291st Ave Browerville (56438) *(G-625)*
Little Falls Golf Association 320 616-5520
1 Edgewater Dr Little Falls (56345) *(G-3011)*
Little Moran Hunting Club 218 894-3852
44357 Red Oak Rd Staples (56479) *(G-9585)*
Little Sisters of The Poor of 651 227-0336
330 Exchange St S Saint Paul (55102) *(G-8592)*
Little Six Casino 952 445-6000
2354 Sioux Trl NW Prior Lake (55372) *(G-6938)*
Little Store, Cloquet *Also Called Best Oil Co (G-1046)*
Little Tigers Den-Educational 763 389-5950
31426 125th St NW Princeton (55371) *(G-6923)*
Little Yukon Greenhouse Inc 218 692-3536
36318 County Road 66 Crosslake (56442) *(G-1152)*
Littlefork Medical Center, Littlefork *Also Called City of Littlefork (G-3022)*
Littler Mendelson, PC 612 630-1000
1300 Ids Center 80 S 8 St Minneapolis (55402) *(G-4894)*
Live Nation Worldwide Inc 612 673-8308
600 1st Ave N Minneapolis (55403) *(G-4895)*
Living Benefits Financial Svcs 952 903-9800
10505 Wayzata Blvd Ste 1000 Minnetonka (55305) *(G-6187)*
Living Services Foundation 507 872-5300
700 N Monroe St Minneota (56264) *(G-6134)*
Living Services Foundation 320 485-2151
551 4th St N Winsted (55395) *(G-10162)*
Ljk Co's Inc 952 944-5462
10225 Yellow Circle Dr Ste 200 Minnetonka (55343) *(G-6188)*
Lkpb Engineers Inc 651 633-1223
1935 County Road B2 W Ste 300 Saint Paul (55113) *(G-8593)*
Lloyd Management Inc 507 625-5573
135 W Lind St Mankato (56001) *(G-3157)*
Lloyd Truss Systems 507 387-4250
1880 Commerce Dr North Mankato (56003) *(G-6508)*
Lloyds Construction Services 952 746-5832
7207 W 128th St Savage (55378) *(G-9397)*
Lmn Consulting Inc 612 805-7288
1600 Hopkins Xrd Hopkins (55305) *(G-2572)*
Loan & Thrift Co of Rochester, Rochester *Also Called Minnesota First Credit (G-7187)*
Local 2000 Airline Attendants, Minneapolis *Also Called Teamsters Local 2000 (G-5803)*
Local 7-274, Sartell *Also Called Pace International Union (G-9340)*
Local Government Information 763 543-2600
5750 Duluth St Minneapolis (55422) *(G-4896)*
Local Motion, Eden Prairie *Also Called Dakt Enterprises Inc (G-1640)*
Locher Bros Inc (PA) 507 326-5471
18098 365th Ave Green Isle (55338) *(G-2323)*
Locher Bros Inc 507 625-4198
1119 Center St Mankato (56003) *(G-3227)*
Lockridge Grindal Nauen LLP 612 339-6900
100 Washington Ave S # 2200 Minneapolis (55401) *(G-4897)*
Lodermeiers 651 923-4441
103 N 3rd St Goodhue (55027) *(G-2250)*
Lodge At Brainerd Lake 218 822-5634
6967 Lake Forest Rd Brainerd (56401) *(G-573)*
Lodge At Giants Ridge 218 865-7170
6373 Wynne Creek Dr Biwabik (55708) *(G-470)*
Lodge At Sugar Lake Inc 218 327-1462
37584 Otis Ln Cohasset (55721) *(G-1072)*
Lodge At White Bear, Saint Paul *Also Called Harvest Facility Holdings LP (G-9223)*
Lodgex Airline Solutions Div, Minnetonka *Also Called Ljk Co's Inc (G-6188)*
Lofton Label Inc 651 457-8118
6290 Claude Way Inver Grove Heights (55076) *(G-2759)*
Log House Foods Inc 763 546-8395
700 Berkshire Ln N Minneapolis (55441) *(G-4898)*
Loge Group LLC 952 829-3500
10900 Hampshire Ave S Minneapolis (55438) *(G-4899)*
Loger Builders, Cedar *Also Called Frontier Enterprises Corp (G-878)*
Logic Product Development Co 612 672-9495
411 Washington Ave N # 400 Minneapolis (55401) *(G-4900)*
Logis, Minneapolis *Also Called Local Government Information (G-4896)*
Logistics International LLC 952 697-4800
1150 Gateway Dr W Shakopee (55379) *(G-9451)*
Logos Productions Inc 651 451-9945
6160 Carmen Ave Inver Grove Heights (55076) *(G-2760)*

ALPHABETIC

Lominger Limited Inc 952 345-3600
5051 Highway 7 Ste 100 Minneapolis (55416) ***(G-4901)***
London Road Car Wash Inc 218 728-4201
1530 London Rd Duluth (55812) ***(G-1385)***
Lonesome Pine Restaurant 218 678-2874
13726 Katrine Dr Deerwood (56444) ***(G-1178)***
Long Haul Trucking Inc 763 497-3727
6600 Jansen Ave NE Albertville (55301) ***(G-75)***
Long Term Care Associates Inc 320 679-1411
110 7th St N Mora (55051) ***(G-6366)***
Long Term Care Group Inc (PA) 952 516-6829
11000 Prairie Lakes Dr Eden Prairie (55344) ***(G-1712)***
Long Term Care Group Inc 651 501-4000
7805 Hudson Rd Ste 180 Saint Paul (55125) ***(G-9244)***
Lonsdale Packaging 507 744-2376
629 Industrial Dr SE Lonsdale (55046) ***(G-3045)***
Loomis Armored Us Inc 651 645-4511
735 Raymond Ave Saint Paul (55114) ***(G-8594)***
Loons & Ladys Slippers, Red Wing *Also Called Pottery Red Wings* ***(G-6995)***
Loop Parking Co 612 333-2293
1300 Nicollet Ave # 3060 Minneapolis (55403) ***(G-4902)***
Loram Admin LLC 763 478-6014
3900 Arrowhead Dr Hamel (55340) ***(G-2347)***
Loram Rail Services LLC 763 478-6014
3900 Arrowhead Dr Hamel (55340) ***(G-2348)***
Lord Fletcher's Old Lake Lodge, Spring Park *Also Called Restaurants No Limit Inc* ***(G-9564)***
Lord of Life Lutheran Church 763 427-1100
14501 Nowthen Blvd NW Anoka (55303) ***(G-201)***
Lorentz Etc Inc 507 263-3618
705 Cannon Ind Blvd W Cannon Falls (55009) ***(G-857)***
Lorenz Bus Service Inc 763 784-7196
8600 Xylite St NE Minneapolis (55449) ***(G-3522)***
Loring Towers Apts LP 612 871-7202
15 E Grant St Apt 717 Minneapolis (55403) ***(G-4903)***
Lost Spur Country Club, Saint Paul *Also Called Spur Inc* ***(G-7911)***
Loucks & Associates, Osseo *Also Called Tom Loucks & Associates Inc* ***(G-6676)***
Louis Industries Inc 320 243-3696
222 Industrial Loop W Paynesville (56362) ***(G-6771)***
Lovegreen Industrial Services 651 890-1166
2280 Sibley Ct Saint Paul (55122) ***(G-7825)***
Lovingcare Nursing Services 651 848-0061
501 Dale St N Ste 205 Saint Paul (55103) ***(G-8595)***
Lowe's Home Centers Inc 763 691-6040
2324 3rd Ave NE Cambridge (55008) ***(G-840)***
Lowe's Home Centers Inc 218 262-7460
12025 Highway 169 W Hibbing (55746) ***(G-2459)***
Lowe's Home Centers Inc 507 385-3560
2015 Bassett Dr Mankato (56001) ***(G-3158)***
Lowe's Home Centers Inc 763 367-1120
11651 Ulysses St NE Minneapolis (55434) ***(G-3523)***
Lowe's Home Centers Inc 763 367-1340
2700 Main St NW Minneapolis (55448) ***(G-3524)***
Lowe's Home Centers Inc 763 367-9000
3205 Vicksburg Ln N Minneapolis (55447) ***(G-4904)***
Lowe's Home Centers Inc 763 488-2001
11201 Fountains Dr Osseo (55369) ***(G-6629)***
Lowe's Home Centers Inc 507 446-4900
1280 21st Ave NW Owatonna (55060) ***(G-6723)***
Lowe's Home Centers Inc 507 328-8920
4550 Maine Ave SE Rochester (55904) ***(G-7162)***
Lowe's Home Centers Inc 763 428-5970
13800 Rogers Dr Rogers (55374) ***(G-7328)***
Lowe's Home Centers Inc 763 367-4139
1795 Robert St S Saint Paul (55118) ***(G-7826)***
Lowe's Home Centers Inc 952 367-9000
4270 Dean Lakes Blvd Shakopee (55379) ***(G-9452)***
Lowe's Home Centers Inc 651 275-9910
5888 Nova Scotia Ave N Stillwater (55082) ***(G-9626)***
Lowell Inn, Stillwater *Also Called Simper Lowell LLC* ***(G-9639)***
Lowell's Paint Plus, Minneapolis *Also Called Zitco Inc* ***(G-6121)***
Lower Saint Croix Valley Fire 651 436-7033
1520 Saint Croix Trl S Lakeland (55043) ***(G-2886)***
Lower Sioux Community Council 507 637-5933
410 W Park Rd Redwood Falls (56283) ***(G-7024)***
Lowry Manufacturing Co 320 283-5450
317 Cherry St Lowry (56349) ***(G-3055)***
Loyalton Group Inc 651 480-3126
1620 S Frontage Rd # 200 Hastings (55033) ***(G-2396)***
Loyear Cleaning & Restoration 952 831-0777
415 W 60th St Minneapolis (55419) ***(G-4905)***
Lpl LLC 952 345-8240
5207 W 73rd St Edina (55439) ***(G-1835)***
Lps Default Solutions Inc 651 234-3500
1270 Northland Dr Ste 200 Saint Paul (55120) ***(G-7827)***
Lq Management LLC 952 881-7311
7815 Nicollet Ave S Minneapolis (55420) ***(G-4906)***
Lrn Associates Management Inc 507 836-8955
2220 27th St Slayton (56172) ***(G-9488)***
Ls Acquisitions Inc 612 331-4141
2407 E Hennepin Ave Minneapolis (55413) ***(G-4907)***
Lsa LLC 763 744-0246
5015 Cheshire Pkwy N Plymouth (55446) ***(G-6871)***
LSS Data Systems, Eden Prairie *Also Called Lake Superior Software Inc* ***(G-1705)***
Ltf Club Operations Co Inc 952 229-7427
2902 Corporate Pl Chanhassen (55317) ***(G-930)***
Ltx Inc (PA) 507 282-6715
1515 Industrial Dr NW Rochester (55901) ***(G-7163)***
Ltx Inc 507 452-4738
6830 Martina Rd Winona (55987) ***(G-10112)***
Lube-Tech, Minneapolis *Also Called Lubrication Technologies Inc* ***(G-4908)***
Lubrication Technologies Inc (PA) 763 545-0707
900 Mendelssohn Ave N Minneapolis (55427) ***(G-4908)***
Lubrication Technologies Inc 651 636-7990
2420 County Road C W Saint Paul (55113) ***(G-8596)***
Luma Corp 952 995-6500
5200 12th Ave E Shakopee (55379) ***(G-9453)***
Lumber Baron's Hotel Resta, Stillwater *Also Called St Croix Preservation Co Inc* ***(G-9644)***
Lumber Mart Inc (PA) 218 773-1151
1910 Business Hwy 2 East Grand Forks (56721) ***(G-1571)***
Lumber One, Avon Inc 320 356-7342
101 2nd St NW Avon (56310) ***(G-296)***
Lumber One, Cold Spring Inc 320 685-3631
700 3rd St S Cold Spring (56320) ***(G-1087)***
Lumina Engineering, Minneapolis *Also Called Gb Lumina Inc* ***(G-4504)***
Lund Food Holdings Inc 952 915-4888
7752 Mitchell Rd Eden Prairie (55344) ***(G-1713)***
Lund Poured Walls, Dassel *Also Called Gordon Lund* ***(G-1161)***
Lund-Martin Construction Inc 612 782-2250
3023 Randolph St NE Minneapolis (55418) ***(G-4909)***
Lunda Construction Co 651 437-9666
15601 Clayton Ave E Rosemount (55068) ***(G-7371)***
Lundell Enterprises LLC 952 261-7617
1838 Westchester Ln Shakopee (55379) ***(G-9454)***
Lunning Wende Bvh Architects 651 221-0915
275 4th St E Ste 620 Saint Paul (55101) ***(G-8597)***
Luoma Egg Ranch Inc 320 233-6122
35705 State Highway 18 Finlayson (55735) ***(G-2130)***
Lupient Oldsmobile Co Inc 763 546-2222
7100 Wayzata Blvd Minneapolis (55426) ***(G-4910)***
Luther Brookdale, Minneapolis *Also Called Brooklyn Center Motors LLC* ***(G-3959)***
Luther Dell Bible Camp, Remer *Also Called Lutheran Bible Camp* ***(G-7030)***
Luther Haven 320 269-6517
1109 E Highway 7 Montevideo (56265) ***(G-6249)***
Lutheran Bible Camp 218 566-2329
2760 S Boy Lake Dr NE Remer (56672) ***(G-7030)***
Lutheran Brethren Homes Inc 218 736-5441
824 S Sheridan St Fergus Falls (56537) ***(G-2087)***
Lutheran Brethren Retirement 218 736-5441
824 S Sheridan St Fergus Falls (56537) ***(G-2088)***
Lutheran Brotherhood Research 612 340-7000
625 4th Ave S Minneapolis (55415) ***(G-4911)***
Lutheran Care Center Inc 320 632-9211
1200 1st Ave NE Little Falls (56345) ***(G-3012)***
Lutheran Memorial Home 218 456-2105
133 4th Ave E Halstad (56548) ***(G-2335)***
Lutheran Memorial Home (PA) 218 584-5181
208 Oppegard Ave NW Twin Valley (56584) ***(G-9702)***
Lutheran Memorial Home 218 584-5181
205 3rd St NW Apt 302 Twin Valley (56584) ***(G-9703)***
Lutheran Retirement Home of 507 776-2031
400 N 4th Ave E Truman (56088) ***(G-9695)***
Lutheran Social Service of MN 218 281-6418
1601 Summerfield Dr Crookston (56716) ***(G-1127)***
Lutheran Social Service of MN 218 736-5431
731 Western Ave Fergus Falls (56537) ***(G-2089)***
Lutheran Social Service of MN 612 871-0221
2414 Park Ave Minneapolis (55404) ***(G-4912)***
Lutheran Social Service of MN 651 388-8845
5225 Highway 61 W Red Wing (55066) ***(G-6989)***
Lutheran Social Service Of MN (PA) 651 642-5990
2485 Como Ave Saint Paul (55108) ***(G-8598)***
Lutheran Social Service of MN 320 235-5411
1601 Highway 12 E Ste 6 Willmar (56201) ***(G-10020)***
Lutheran Trust 218 998-4058
1421 Terrace Dr Fergus Falls (56537) ***(G-2090)***
Luthern Brothern School Inc 218 739-3375
815 W Vernon Ave Fergus Falls (56537) ***(G-2091)***
Lutsen Resort Co 218 663-7212
5700 W Hwy 61 Lutsen (55612) ***(G-3056)***
Luverne Ind School Dist 2184 ....507 283-8197
428 W Dodge St Luverne (56156) ***(G-3061)***
Luverne Medical Center, Luverne *Also Called Sioux Valley Physician* ***(G-3069)***
Luverne Residential Advantage 507 283-4088
107 S Blue Mound Ave Luverne (56156) ***(G-3062)***
Luverne Veterans Home, Luverne *Also Called Minnesota Department of* ***(G-3065)***
Luverne, City of Inc 507 449-5036
802 N Blue Mound Ave Luverne (56156) ***(G-3063)***
Lyman Lumber Co 952 470-4800
18900 W 78th St Chanhassen (55317) ***(G-931)***
Lyman Lumber Co (PA) 952 470-3600
300 Morse Ave Excelsior (55331) ***(G-1945)***
Lyndale Plant Service, Edina *Also Called Lpl LLC* ***(G-1835)***
Lynde Greenhouse & Nursery Inc 763 420-4400
9293 Pineview Ln N Osseo (55369) ***(G-6630)***
Lyngblomsten 651 646-2941
1415 Almond Ave Saint Paul (55108) ***(G-8599)***
Lynnhurst, Saint Paul *Also Called Beverly Enterprises - MN* ***(G-8112)***
Lyon Financial Services Inc 507 532-7763
1310 Madrid St Ste 100 Marshall (56258) ***(G-3307)***
Lyon Lodging LLC 507 532-3070
1511 E College Dr Marshall (56258) ***(G-3308)***
Lyric Block Development Corp 218 722-1202
200 W 1st St Duluth (55802) ***(G-1386)***
M & B Enterprise of Freeport (PA) 320 836-2145
446 Industrial Dr Freeport (56331) ***(G-2188)***
M & C Hotel Interests Inc 612 332-6000
1313 Nicollet Ave Minneapolis (55403) ***(G-4913)***
M & I Marshall & Ilsley Bank 952 544-3100
5775 Wayzata Blvd Minneapolis (55416) ***(G-4914)***
M & I Marshall & Ilsley Bank 612 904-8000
651 Nicollet Mall Minneapolis (55402) ***(G-4915)***
M & L Industries Inc 763 428-4220
23001 Industrial Blvd Rogers (55374) ***(G-7329)***
M & M Bus Service Inc 320 274-8313
10606 Hemlock St NW Annandale (55302) ***(G-142)***
M & M Sanitation Inc 320 358-4078
33368 Xylite St NE Cambridge (55008) ***(G-841)***
M & N Equipment Services Inc 612 379-4147
620 Malcolm Ave SE Minneapolis (55414) ***(G-4916)***
M & P Utilities Inc 320 963-2400
500 County Road 37 Maple Lake (55358) ***(G-3261)***
M & S Drywall Supply, Burnsville *Also Called L&W Supply Corp* ***(G-745)***

www.HarrisInfo.com
588
2011 Harris Minnesota Services Directory
(G-00000) Company's Geographic Section entry number

M A Mortenson Co (PA) 763 522-2100
700 Meadow Ln N Minneapolis (55422) *(G-4917)*
M A Mortenson Co 763 522-2100
700 Meadow Ln N Minneapolis (55422) *(G-4918)*
M A Peterson Designbuild Inc 952 925-9455
6161 Wooddale Ave Ste 200 Minneapolis (55424) *(G-4919)*
M B W Co 507 354-3808
1200 S Broadway St New Ulm (56073) *(G-6459)*
M C C A 651 645-4545
2550 University Ave W Ste 350S Saint Paul (55114) *(G-8600)*
M C U Intermodal Inc 651 222-2224
380 E Lafayette Frontage Rd Saint Paul (55107) *(G-8601)*
M D & W Railway, International Falls *Also Called Minnesota Dakota & Western (G-2727)*
M D A Consulting Group Inc 612 332-8182
150 S 5th St Ste 3300 Minneapolis (55402) *(G-4920)*
M D I, Marshall *Also Called Material Distributors Inc (G-3312)*
M D I Government Services 218 326-9544
825 Lily Ln Grand Rapids (55744) *(G-2292)*
M D I Government Services 218 263-3663
1937 4th Ave E Hibbing (55746) *(G-2460)*
M D I Government Services (PA) 651 999-8200
1700 Wynne Ave Saint Paul (55108) *(G-8602)*
M Dm Rubicon Inc 651 731-8621
6053 Hudson Rd Ste 175 Saint Paul (55125) *(G-9245)*
M Heath, Paul MD 320 253-7257
3701 12th St N Ste 100 Saint Cloud (56303) *(G-7546)*
M L T Inc (DH) 952 474-2540
4660 76th Ave N Minneapolis (55443) *(G-4921)*
M Little & Co Inc 612 375-0077
920 2nd Ave S Ste 1400 Minneapolis (55402) *(G-4922)*
M M Miller Brothers Excavating 763 420-9170
20150 75th Ave N Ste A Hamel (55340) *(G-2349)*
M P Johnson Construction Inc 612 339-3733
50 S 6th St Ste 950 Minneapolis (55402) *(G-4923)*
M P Systems Inc 651 484-9632
53 S Owasso Blvd W Saint Paul (55117) *(G-8603)*
M R I, Minneapolis *Also Called Minneapolis Refuse Inc (G-5063)*
M S I Services 763 572-0500
7825 Washingtn Ave S # 210 Minneapolis (55439) *(G-4924)*
M V R Home Care Inc 651 994-9583
3435 Washington Dr # 104 Saint Paul (55122) *(G-7828)*
Maax US Corp 763 424-3335
9224 73rd Ave N Brooklyn Park (55428) *(G-614)*
Maax US Corp (PA) 763 424-3335
9224 73rd Ave N Minneapolis (55428) *(G-4925)*
Mac Enterprises Inc 612 789-9392
1535 4th St NE Minneapolis (55413) *(G-4926)*
Mac Management Inc (PA) 952 938-8048
5929 Baker Rd Ste 420 Minnetonka (55345) *(G-6189)*
Mac's Inc (PA) 218 233-4600
5970 50th Ave S Moorhead (56560) *(G-6326)*
MacDermid ColorSpan Inc 952 944-9457
11311 K Tel Dr Hopkins (55343) *(G-2573)*
Macdonald Montessori Child 651 227-1039
175 Western Ave S Saint Paul (55102) *(G-8604)*
Machine & Process Design Inc 763 427-9991
820 McKinley St Anoka (55303) *(G-202)*
Machine Tool Supply Corp 651 452-4400
3150 Mike Collins Dr Saint Paul (55121) *(G-7829)*
Machinewell Inc 218 294-6101
115 W State St Grygla (56727) *(G-2330)*
Maciej Paint Corp 651 407-8000
5858 152nd St N Hugo (55038) *(G-2679)*
Mackall Crounse & Moore PLC 612 305-1400
901 Marquette Ave # 1400 Minneapolis (55402) *(G-4927)*
Mackin Book Co 952 895-9540
3505 County Road 42 W Burnsville (55306) *(G-750)*
Macks LLC 507 288-2677
401 6th St SW Rochester (55902) *(G-7164)*
Macphail Center For Music 612 321-0100
501 S 2nd St Minneapolis (55401) *(G-4928)*
Macqueen Equipment Inc 651 645-5726
595 Aldine St Saint Paul (55104) *(G-8605)*
Macro Group Inc 612 332-7880
100 Portland Ave Ste 250 Minneapolis (55401) *(G-4929)*
Macy's Retail Holdings Inc 612 343-0868
81 S 9th St Ste 350 Minneapolis (55402) *(G-4930)*
Macy's Retail Holdings Inc 507 280-5400
901 Apache Mall Rochester (55902) *(G-7165)*
Madden Brothers Inc 218 829-2811
11266 Pine Beach Peninsula Rd Brainerd (56401) *(G-546)*
Madden's On Gull Lake, Brainerd *Also Called Madden Brothers Inc (G-546)*
Madelia Community Hospital Inc 507 642-3255
121 Drew Ave SE Madelia (56062) *(G-3073)*
Madison Lutheran Home 320 598-7536
900 2nd Ave Madison (56256) *(G-3076)*
Madison Properties Inc 320 763-2498
5637 Highway 29 S Alexandria (56308) *(G-112)*
Madison Properties Inc 218 847-2121
1155 Highway 10 E Detroit Lakes (56501) *(G-1208)*
Madonna Meadows of Rochester 507 252-5400
3035 Salem Meadows Dr SW Rochester (55902) *(G-7166)*
Madonna Towers of Rochester 507 288-3911
4001 19th Ave NW Apt 607 Rochester (55901) *(G-7167)*
Maertens-Brenny Construction 763 786-4779
8251 Mn St NE Ste 105 Minneapolis (55432) *(G-3525)*
Magellan Medical Technology 612 677-0000
120 S 6th St Ste 2150 Minneapolis (55402) *(G-4931)*
Magenic Technologies Inc (PA) 763 398-4800
4150 Olson Memorial Hwy Minneapolis (55422) *(G-4932)*
Magic Media Inc 507 288-1866
1734 15th St NW Rochester (55901) *(G-7168)*
Magical History Tour 612 331-7171
125 Main St SE Minneapolis (55414) *(G-4933)*
Magiccom Inc 763 529-2208
925 Boone Ave N Minneapolis (55427) *(G-4934)*
Magnetic Products & Services 763 424-2700
7500 Boone Ave N Ste 104 Minneapolis (55428) *(G-4935)*
Magnum Co LLC 651 255-3000
14475 Quiram Dr Ste 1 Rogers (55374) *(G-7349)*
Magnum Electric Inc 218 236-8753
1810 23rd St S Moorhead (56560) *(G-6327)*
Magnum Ltl Inc 763 795-9534
3686 Flowerfield Rd Circle Pines (55014) *(G-1015)*
Magnuson Huisinga & Sons Inc (PA) 320 599-4474
2020 5th St SW Willmar (56201) *(G-10021)*
Maguire Agency Inc 651 638-9100
1935 County Road B2 W Ste 241 Saint Paul (55113) *(G-8606)*
Mahnomen County Heartland 218 935-2560
311 S Main St Fl 6 Mahnomen (56557) *(G-3088)*
Mahnomen County Sheriff's 218 935-2255
311 N Main St Mahnomen (56557) *(G-3089)*
Mahoney Ulbrich Christiansen 651 227-6695
30 Plato Blvd E Saint Paul (55107) *(G-8607)*
Mahoney, Dougherty & Mahoney 612 339-5863
801 Park Ave Minneapolis (55404) *(G-4936)*
Mahube Community Council Inc 218 847-1385
1125 W River Rd Detroit Lakes (56501) *(G-1209)*
Maid Brigade, Saint Paul *Also Called Minnesota Housekeeping Svcs (G-7842)*
Maiers Transport & Warehousing 320 251-6882
640 54th Ave N Ste B Saint Cloud (56303) *(G-7547)*
Maiers Transport & Warehousing 320 251-6882
5 McLeland Rd Ste A Saint Cloud (56303) *(G-7548)*
Mail Handling Inc 952 975-5000
7550 Corporate Way Eden Prairie (55344) *(G-1714)*
Mail-Well, Saint Paul *Also Called Cenveo Inc (G-8186)*
Mailand Management Corp 651 451-9034
149 Thompson Ave E Ste 210 Saint Paul (55118) *(G-7830)*
Mailers of Minnesota, Minneapolis *Also Called Mercury Mailers Of Minnesota (G-4990)*
Main Street Bank (PA) 651 451-2133
835 Southview Blvd South Saint Paul (55075) *(G-9533)*
Mains'l Services Inc 763 494-4553
7000 78th Ave N Brooklyn Park (55445) *(G-615)*
Mainstreet Village Retirement 612 869-6584
7601 Lyndale Ave S Richfield (55423) *(G-7036)*
Maintenance Building 320 384-7084
300 Lady Luck Dr Hinckley (55037) *(G-2486)*
Maintenance Dept, Duluth *Also Called Independent School District (G-1356)*
Maintenance Professionals Inc 651 774-2334
843 7th St E Saint Paul (55106) *(G-8608)*
Maintenance Team 952 942-5000
10250 Valley View Rd # 133 Eden Prairie (55344) *(G-1715)*
Mairs & Power Balanced Fund 651 222-8478
332 Minnesota St Ste W1520 Saint Paul (55101) *(G-8609)*
Major Mechanical Inc 763 424-6680
11201 86th Ave N Osseo (55369) *(G-6631)*
Makemusic Inc 952 937-9611
7615 Golden Triangle Dr Eden Prairie (55344) *(G-1716)*
Mala Strana Health Care Center 952 758-2511
1001 Columbus Ave N New Prague (56071) *(G-6431)*
Mala Strana Nursing Home, New Prague *Also Called Thro Co (G-6435)*
Malark Logistics Inc 763 428-3564
9100 85th Ave N Ste 200 Brooklyn Park (55445) *(G-616)*
Malark Motor 763 428-4880
17700 113th St N Osseo (55369) *(G-6632)*
Malco Products Inc 320 274-8246
14080 State Highway 55 NW Annandale (55302) *(G-143)*
Mall of America, Bloomington *Also Called Moac Mall Holdings LLC (G-507)*
Malloy, Karnowski & Co 952 545-0424
5353 Wayzata Blvd Ste 410 Minneapolis (55416) *(G-4937)*
Malmborgs Inc 763 535-4695
5120 Lilac Dr N Minneapolis (55429) *(G-4938)*
Malone Golf Inc 952 492-2644
21775 Ridges Dr Jordan (55352) *(G-2806)*
Malton Electric Co 763 571-7758
7580 Commerce Ln NE Minneapolis (55432) *(G-3526)*
Maly Co's LLC 612 788-9688
2050 E Center Cir Ste 200 Minneapolis (55441) *(G-4939)*
Mammoth-Webco Inc 952 361-2711
13200 Pioneer Trl Ste 150 Eden Prairie (55347) *(G-1717)*
Managed Services Inc 952 925-4111
6500 Oxford St Minneapolis (55426) *(G-4940)*
Manchester Co's Inc 612 436-2818
80 S 8th St Ste 4700 Minneapolis (55402) *(G-4941)*
Manders Diesel Repair Inc 952 469-1800
11250 215th St W Lakeville (55044) *(G-2915)*
Manhattan Group LLC 612 337-9600
430 1st Ave N Ste 500 Minneapolis (55401) *(G-4942)*
Manheim Auctions Inc 763 425-7653
8001 Jefferson Hwy Osseo (55369) *(G-6633)*
Manion Lumber & Truss Inc 218 746-3200
220 River St N Pillager (56473) *(G-6811)*
MANITOU RIDGE GOLF CLUB, Saint Paul *Also Called Golf Services Corp (G-8420)*
Mankato Airport 507 625-2511
3030 Airport Rd N Mankato (56001) *(G-3159)*
Mankato Auto Mall Owners Inc 507 387-7877
2009 Roe Crest Dr Mankato (56003) *(G-3228)*
Mankato Clinic Ltd 507 625-5027
1575 Lookout Dr Mankato (56003) *(G-3229)*
Mankato Clinic Ltd (PA) 507 625-1811
1230 E Main St Mankato (56001) *(G-3160)*
Mankato Fairfield Inn 507 386-1220
141 Apache Pl Mankato (56001) *(G-3161)*
Mankato Golf Club Inc 507 387-5676
Hwy 22 N Mankato (56001) *(G-3162)*
Mankato House Health, Mankato *Also Called Thro Co (G-3204)*
Mankato Lodging LLC 507 388-8555
1900 Premier Dr Mankato (56001) *(G-3163)*
Mankato Lutheran Homes Inc 507 345-4576
3530 Lexington Ave N Saint Paul (55126) *(G-8610)*
Mankato Mack Sales, Mankato *Also Called Nuss Truck Group Inc (G-3178)*
Mankato Rehabilitation Center 507 386-5799
1611 Monks Ave Mankato (56001) *(G-3164)*
Mankato Rehabilitation Center (PA) 507 386-5600
15 Map Dr Mankato (56001) *(G-3165)*

Mankato Surgical Center LLC 507 388-6000
1411 Premier Dr Mankato (56001) *(G-3166)*
Mankato Symphony Orchestra 507 625-8880
223 S St 2 Mankato (56001) *(G-3167)*
Manley Toyota, Willmar Also Called Mills Pontiac, Buick *(G-10024)*
Mann Theaters Inc 952 931-3191
1118 Mainstreet Hopkins (55343) *(G-2574)*
Mannanah Snow Blazers 320 693-6658
62384 310th St Litchfield (55355) *(G-2988)*
Manning Transfer Inc 763 784-4022
2775 101st Ave NE Minneapolis (55449) *(G-3527)*
Manor Concrete Construction 763 497-5420
4370 Naber Ave NE Saint Michael (55376) *(G-7676)*
Manor Electric Inc 763 479-4170
5350 Pioneer Creek Dr # 3 Maple Plain (55359) *(G-3278)*
Manpower Inc 952 831-3338
7831 Glenroy Rd Ste 400 Minneapolis (55439) *(G-4943)*
Mansfield & Tanick 612 339-4295
220 S 6th St Ste 1700 Minneapolis (55402) *(G-4944)*
Manske Bus Service Inc 507 243-3282
59780 235th St Madison Lake (56063) *(G-3080)*
Maple Grove Ambulatory Surgery 763 981-3234
9855 Hospital Dr Ste 175 Maple Grove (55369) *(G-3248)*
Maple Grove Lodging Investors 763 509-9500
6350 Vinewood Ln N Maple Grove (55311) *(G-3249)*
Maple Grove Urgent Care 763 420-5279
12000 Elm Creek Blvd N # 1 Osseo (55369) *(G-6634)*
Maple Hills LP 651 291-1750
521 Maple St Red Wing (55066) *(G-6990)*
Maple Hills LP 651 291-1750
328 Kellogg Blvd W Saint Paul (55102) *(G-8611)*
Maple Island Inc 507 824-2224
25 Main St 57 Wanamingo (55983) *(G-9864)*
Maple Lawn Nursing Home 507 425-2571
400 Th St NE Fulda (56131) *(G-2195)*
Maple Leaf Services Inc 507 765-3848
110 Fillmore Pl SE Preston (55965) *(G-6899)*
Maple Valley Golf & Country 507 932-5444
1920 Gladiola Dr Saint Charles (55972) *(G-7405)*
Maplewood Bowl Inc 651 774-8787
1955 English St Saint Paul (55109) *(G-8612)*
Maplewood Clinic, Saint Paul Also Called Healthpartners Inc *(G-8469)*
Maplewood Dental Associates, Saint Paul Also Called Scott W Kajer DDS *(G-8937)*
Maplewood Dental Associates 651 770-3831
1736 Cope Ave E Ste 3 Saint Paul (55109) *(G-8613)*
Maplewood Dental Clinic, Saint Paul Also Called Healthpartners Inc *(G-8471)*
Maplewood Imports, Saint Paul Also Called Le Jeune Investment Inc *(G-8572)*
Maplewood Motors Inc 651 482-1322
2873 Highway 61 Saint Paul (55109) *(G-8614)*
Maplewood Oakdale School Dist 651 714-9251
740 Greenway Ave N Saint Paul (55128) *(G-9246)*
Maplewood Surgery Center, Saint Paul Also Called Healtheast Maplewood Out *(G-8463)*
Mar's Carpet Sales, Minneapolis Also Called Ziem's Carpet Workroom Inc *(G-6118)*
Marathon Group Inc 952 929-1990
3356 Gorham Ave Minneapolis (55426) *(G-4945)*
Marathon Management Inc 651 259-4093
2303 Waters Dr Saint Paul (55120) *(G-7831)*
Marathon Petroleum Co LP 651 459-9771
301 St Saint Paul Park (55071) *(G-9295)*
Marathon Petroleum Co LP 651 459-9771
459 3rd St Saint Paul Park (55071) *(G-9296)*
Marco Investments LLC 763 795-8145
9280 Lake Dr Circle Pines (55014) *(G-1016)*
Marcus Bloomington LLC 952 893-9500
3900 American Blvd W Bloomington (55437) *(G-504)*
Marcus Construction Co Inc 320 978-6616
7360 195th Ave SW Prinsburg (56281) *(G-6926)*
Marcus Hotels Inc 612 338-2288
618 2nd Ave S Minneapolis (55402) *(G-4946)*
Marcus Solutions LLC 952 373-4038
6101 Zenith Ave S Edina (55410) *(G-1836)*
Marcus Theatres Corp 763 441-1234
570 Frport Elk River Mall Elk River (55330) *(G-1883)*
Marcy Construction Co 952 525-9700
2246 Edgewood Ave S Minneapolis (55426) *(G-4947)*
Marian Center of St Paul, Saint Paul Also Called Catholic Services For The *(G-8177)*
Marina Associates, Minneapolis Also Called Stephen Scott Management Inc *(G-5751)*
Marix Technologies Inc 952 582-9100
12450 Wayzata Blvd # 121 Hopkins (55305) *(G-2575)*
Mark Doman 320 203-9004
621 17th St N Sartell (56377) *(G-9338)*
Mark Macdonald Do 651 455-2940
234 Wentworth Ave E Saint Paul (55118) *(G-7832)*
Mark Sand & Gravel Co 218 736-7523
525 Kennedy Park Rd Fergus Falls (56537) *(G-2092)*
Market Resource Associates Inc 612 334-3056
15 S 5th St Ste 800 Minneapolis (55402) *(G-4948)*
Market Solutions Group Inc 612 332-1574
3356 Sherman Ct Ste 104 Saint Paul (55121) *(G-7833)*
Marketing Architects Inc 952 449-2500
110 Cheshire Ln Ste 200 Minnetonka (55305) *(G-6190)*
Marketing Bridge LLC 763 504-4610
10000 Highway 55 Minneapolis (55441) *(G-4949)*
Marketing Concepts of MN 320 796-6245
130 Lake Ave N Spicer (56288) *(G-9557)*
Marketing Focus Inc 952 939-9880
10601 Red Circle Dr Hopkins (55343) *(G-2576)*
Marketline Research Inc 612 767-2580
1313 5th St SE Ste 309 Minneapolis (55414) *(G-4950)*
Markettools Inc 952 546-2800
6465 Wayzata Blvd Ste 170 Minneapolis (55426) *(G-4951)*
Markhurd, Osseo Also Called Aero-Metric Inc *(G-6593)*
Marquette Bank Monticello 763 271-2700
407 Pine St Ste 200 Monticello (55362) *(G-6276)*
Marquette Financial Co's (PA) 612 661-3880
60 S 6th St Ste 3800 Minneapolis (55402) *(G-4952)*
Marquette Hotel 612 333-4545
710 Marquette Ave Minneapolis (55402) *(G-4953)*

Marquette Transportation 952 703-7474
1600 W 82nd St Ste 150 Minneapolis (55431) *(G-4954)*
Marriott, Bloomington Also Called CP Saddle Brook LLC *(G-492)*
Marriott 952 893-9300
3400 Edinborough Way Minneapolis (55435) *(G-4955)*
Marriott 763 577-1600
2750 Annapolis Cir N Plymouth (55441) *(G-6872)*
Marriott Execustay, Minneapolis Also Called CSM Executive Lodging LLC *(G-4197)*
Mars, W P & R S Co Inc 952 884-9388
215 E 78th St Minneapolis (55420) *(G-4956)*
Marschall Bus Service Inc 952 463-8689
21044 Chippendale Ct Farmington (55024) *(G-2054)*
Marsden Holding LLC (PA) 651 641-1717
1717 University Ave W Saint Paul (55104) *(G-8615)*
MARSH, Minnetonka Also Called Ruth Stricker's Fitness Unltd *(G-6222)*
Marsh Heating & Air Condg 763 536-0667
6248 Lakeland Ave N # 110 Minneapolis (55428) *(G-4957)*
Marsh USA Inc 612 692-7848
333 S 7th St Ste 1600 Minneapolis (55402) *(G-4958)*
Marshall Adult Learning Center 507 537-7046
607 W Main St Marshall (56258) *(G-3309)*
Marshall Asi Inc 651 645-7271
2550 University Ave W 330N Saint Paul (55114) *(G-8616)*
Marshall County Group Homes 218 437-6695
603 Cedar Ave Argyle (56713) *(G-247)*
Marshall Golf Club 507 532-2278
800 Country Club Dr 23 Marshall (56258) *(G-3310)*
Marshall Public School 507 537-6210
1420 E College Dr Marshall (56258) *(G-3311)*
Marshall-Teichert Group Ltd 952 942-0564
10901 Red Circle Dr # 315 Hopkins (55343) *(G-2577)*
Marson Contractors Inc 320 255-5506
3636 Quail Rd NE Sauk Rapids (56379) *(G-9369)*
Martin Calibration Inc 952 882-1528
11965 12th Ave S Ste 100 Burnsville (55337) *(G-751)*
Martin County West School Dist 507 728-8609
308 4th St Welcome (56181) *(G-9959)*
Martin Falk Paper Co 612 332-8626
618 N 3rd St Minneapolis (55401) *(G-4959)*
Martin Kruger Post 407, Winsted Also Called American Legion Club *(G-10156)*
Martin Luther Manor, Bloomington Also Called Ecumen Home Care Inc *(G-496)*
Martin Luther Manor 952 888-7751
1401 E 100th St Minneapolis (55425) *(G-4960)*
Martin Marietta Materials Inc 320 251-7141
1450 Division St Waite Park (56387) *(G-9828)*
Martin-Brower Co L L C 763 571-6311
51 52nd Way NE Minneapolis (55421) *(G-3528)*
Martin-Williams Inc (HQ) 612 340-0800
60 S 6th St Ste 2800 Minneapolis (55402) *(G-4961)*
Martin-Williams Inc 612 746-3263
120 S 6th St Ste 200 Minneapolis (55402) *(G-4962)*
Marudas Graphics Inc 651 697-7820
20 Yorkton Ct Saint Paul (55117) *(G-8617)*
Mary Jane Brown Good Samaritan, Luverne Also Called Evangelical Lutheran Good *(G-3059)*
Mary T Associates Inc 763 754-6706
1555 118th Ln NW Ste 1 Minneapolis (55448) *(G-3529)*
Mary T Inc 763 754-2505
1555 118th Ln NW Ste 1 Minneapolis (55448) *(G-3530)*
Marynole Genetics & Energy 612 275-2518
580 Simon Ave W Dassel (55325) *(G-1162)*
MASA, Saint Paul Also Called Minnesota Association of Sch *(G-8673)*
Maschka Riedy & Ries 507 625-6600
201 N Broad St Ste 200 Mankato (56001) *(G-3168)*
Master Collision Group LLC (PA) 763 509-0900
2980 Empire Ln N Minneapolis (55447) *(G-4963)*
Master Collision Group LLC 612 827-4697
224 W Lake St Ste A Minneapolis (55408) *(G-4964)*
Master Electric Co Inc 952 890-3555
8555 W 123rd St Savage (55378) *(G-9398)*
Master Mechanical Inc 651 905-1600
1027 Gemini Rd Ste A Saint Paul (55121) *(G-7834)*
Master Technology Group Inc 952 960-1212
8555 W 123rd St Savage (55378) *(G-9399)*
Master's Miracle Inc 763 493-3200
9060 Zachary Ln N Ste 104 Osseo (55369) *(G-6635)*
Masterpiece Studios Inc (DH) 507 388-8788
2080 Lookout Dr North Mankato (56003) *(G-6509)*
Masterworks Of Minneapolis 612 333-8210
1121 S 7th St Minneapolis (55415) *(G-4965)*
Matagorda Ht & Conference Ctr, Saint Paul Also Called Stockman Hotel Corp *(G-9007)*
Mate Precision Tooling Inc 763 421-0230
1295 Lund Blvd Anoka (55303) *(G-203)*
Material Distributors Inc 507 532-4463
211 N 11th St Marshall (56258) *(G-3312)*
Materials Management Co, Minneapolis Also Called Garland's Inc *(G-4501)*
Mathiowetz Enterprises Inc 507 794-6953
30676 County Road 24 Sleepy Eye (56085) *(G-9497)*
Mathy Construction Co 507 288-7447
4105 E River Rd NE Rochester (55906) *(G-7169)*
Mathy Construction Co 507 932-3200
24206 Highway 43 Winona (55987) *(G-10113)*
Mathy Trucking Inc 507 777-4395
1585 State Highway 30 Edgerton (56128) *(G-1824)*
Matrix Adhesives Inc 952 912-2452
6035 Baker Rd Hopkins (55345) *(G-2578)*
Matrix Communications Inc (PA) 763 475-5500
171 Cheshire Ln N Ste 700 Minneapolis (55441) *(G-4966)*
Mats Inc (PA) 651 406-8300
940 Aldrin Dr Ste 100 Eagan (55121) *(G-1535)*
Matthew's Family Restaurant 763 784-1499
2 Pine Dr Circle Pines (55014) *(G-1017)*
Mavo Systems Inc 763 788-7713
4330 Centerville Rd Saint Paul (55127) *(G-8618)*
Max Gray Construction Inc 218 262-6622
2501 5th Ave W Hibbing (55746) *(G-2461)*

2011 Harris Minnesota
Services Directory
(G-00000) Company's Geographic Section entry number

Max Johnson Trucking Inc 507 357-6313
240 W Derrynane St Le Center (56057) *(G-2952)*
Maxann LLC 651 484-2677
3212 Rice St Saint Paul (55126) *(G-8619)*
Maxfield Research Inc 612 338-2828
615 1st Ave NE Ste 500 Minneapolis (55413) *(G-4967)*
Maxwell Wsu Children Center 507 457-5368
1010 E 7th St Winona (55987) *(G-10114)*
Maxxon Corp 763 478-6000
920 Hamel Rd Hamel (55340) *(G-2350)*
Mayer Electric Corp 763 537-9357
7224 Winnetka Ave N Minneapolis (55428) *(G-4968)*
Mayfield, Saint Paul *Also Called Presbyterian Homes H & A (G-8841)*
Mayflower Distributing Co Inc 651 452-4892
1155 Medallion Dr Saint Paul (55120) *(G-7835)*
Mayo Clinic 507 284-9077
200 1st St SW Ste W15A Rochester (55905) *(G-7170)*
Mayo Clinic 507 266-4808
200 1st St SW Rochester (55905) *(G-7171)*
Mayo Clinic 507 931-2110
622 Sunrise Dr Saint Peter (56082) *(G-9308)*
Mayo Clinic 507 723-4231
602 N Jackson Ave Springfield (56087) *(G-9573)*
Mayo Clinic 651 565-4571
1202 Grant Blvd W Wabasha (55981) *(G-9768)*
Mayo Clinic Employees Credit 507 535-1460
130 23rd Ave SW Rochester (55902) *(G-7172)*
Mayo Clinic Rochester 507 377-5900
1705 SE Broadway Ave Albert Lea (56007) *(G-61)*
Mayo Clinic Rochester 507 634-4744
411 W Main St Kasson (55944) *(G-2822)*
Mayo Clinic Rochester 507 387-8231
1695 Lor Ray Dr North Mankato (56003) *(G-6510)*
Mayo Clinic Rochester 507 284-5135
10 3rd Ave NW Fl 3 Rochester (55901) *(G-7173)*
Mayo Foundation For Medical 507 284-2511
200 1st St SW Rochester (55905) *(G-7174)*
Mayo Management Services Inc 507 538-5508
4001 41st St NW Rochester (55901) *(G-7175)*
Mayo Midair 507 255-2808
1216 2nd St SW Rochester (55902) *(G-7176)*
Mayowood Mansion Tours 507 282-9447
1195 W Circle Dr Rochester (55902) *(G-7177)*
Maytag Coin-Op Washers 651 688-7000
2430 Enterprise Dr Saint Paul (55120) *(G-7836)*
MB St Paul Inc 651 731-2220
2201 Burns Ave Saint Paul (55119) *(G-8620)*
MBA, Saint Paul *Also Called Minnesota Benefit Association (G-9249)*
Mc Be Co 507 289-1666
1814 15th St NW Rochester (55901) *(G-7178)*
Mc Donough Truck Line Inc 507 334-9374
3115 Industrial Dr Faribault (55021) *(G-2020)*
Mc Guire Mechanical Services 952 469-4988
20830 Holt Ave Lakeville (55044) *(G-2916)*
Mc Kimm Milk Transit Inc 320 587-3167
1145 Adams St SE Hutchinson (55350) *(G-2706)*
Mc Knight Foundation 612 333-4220
710 S 2nd St Ste 400 Minneapolis (55401) *(G-4969)*
Mc Phillips Bros Roofing Co 651 770-2062
2590 Centennial Dr Saint Paul (55109) *(G-8621)*
Mc Quillan Brothers Plumbing 651 292-0124
688 Hague Ave Saint Paul (55104) *(G-8622)*
MCC Group Inc 952 941-0552
10125 Crosstown Cir # 100 Eden Prairie (55344) *(G-1718)*
McC Inc 763 477-4774
7900 69th Ave Rockford (55373) *(G-7311)*
McCallum Transfer Inc 651 633-1612
3501 Marshall St NE Minneapolis (55418) *(G-4970)*
McCaren Design Inc 651 646-4764
760 Vandalia St Ste 100 Saint Paul (55114) *(G-8623)*
McCarron Pump Station, Saint Paul *Also Called Saint Paul Regional Water Svcs (G-8929)*
McCollister's Transportation 763 502-2120
223 Osborne Rd NE Minneapolis (55432) *(G-3531)*
McCollum, Crowley, Moschet 952 831-4980
7900 Xerxes Ave S Ste 700 Minneapolis (55431) *(G-4971)*
McCombs Frank Roos Associates, Minneapolis *Also Called Mfra Inc (G-5013)*
McCrady Janitorial Inc 952 758-3097
25664 Willow Ln New Prague (56071) *(G-6432)*
McData Services Corp 763 268-6000
6000 Nathan Ln N Ste 200 Minneapolis (55442) *(G-4972)*
McDonald Homes Inc 651 455-5142
6015 Cahill Ave Ste 100 Inver Grove Heights (55076) *(G-2761)*
McDonald Rentals Inc 218 879-9060
1208 Highway 33 S Cloquet (55720) *(G-1056)*
McDonald, A Mod, Lakeville *Also Called Anderson McDonald Ltd (G-2890)*
McDowall Co 320 251-8640
1431 Prosper Dr Waite Park (56387) *(G-9829)*
McG Energy Solutions LLC 612 376-7757
901 Marquette Ave # 1000 Minneapolis (55402) *(G-4973)*
McGann Associates, Minneapolis *Also Called Amano McGann Inc (G-3739)*
McGhie & Betts Inc 507 289-3919
1648 3rd Ave SE Rochester (55904) *(G-7179)*
McGladrey & Pullen, LLP 218 727-5025
227 W 1st St Ste 700 Duluth (55802) *(G-1387)*
McGladrey & Pullen, LLP 218 727-6857
700 Missabe Building Duluth (55802) *(G-1388)*
McGladrey & Pullen, LLP (PA) 952 921-7700
3600 Amercn Blvd W # 300 Minneapolis (55431) *(G-4974)*
McGladrey & Pullen, LLP 507 288-6476
310 S Broadway Ste 300 Rochester (55904) *(G-7180)*
McGough Construction Co Inc (PA) 651 633-5050
2737 Fairview Ave N Saint Paul (55113) *(G-8624)*
McGovern & Fisher Insurance 952 996-8818
8200 Highwood Dr Minneapolis (55438) *(G-4975)*
McGrann Shea Anderson Carnival 612 338-2525
800 Nicollet Mall Ste 2600 Minneapolis (55402) *(G-4976)*
MCI Paint & Drywall Inc (PA) 952 985-7778
21400 Hamburg Ave Lakeville (55044) *(G-2917)*
McIl, Saint Paul *Also Called Metroplitan Ctr For (G-8642)*
McIntosh Manor Nursing Home, McIntosh *Also Called Foundation For Rural Health (G-3341)*
McK of Austin Ltd 507 437-6702
1509 10th Pl NE Austin (55912) *(G-282)*
McKesson Corp 651 484-4811
3230 Spruce St Little Canada (55117) *(G-2996)*
McKesson Information Solutions 651 697-5900
2700 Snelling Ave N Ste 400 Saint Paul (55113) *(G-8625)*
McKesson Medical-Surgical 763 424-7201
8790 Valley Forge Ln N Osseo (55369) *(G-6636)*
McKesson Medical-Surgical Inc 952 881-8040
316 W 86th St Minneapolis (55420) *(G-4977)*
McKesson Medical-Surgical MN 763 595-6000
8121 10th Ave N Minneapolis (55427) *(G-4978)*
McKinley Group Inc 952 476-2107
601 Carlson Pkwy Ste 630 Hopkins (55305) *(G-2579)*
McKinsey & Co Inc 612 371-3100
80 S 8th St Ste 3800 Minneapolis (55402) *(G-4979)*
McLane Minnesota Inc 507 664-3000
1111 5th St W Northfield (55057) *(G-6531)*
McLeod Cooperative Power Assn 320 864-3148
1231 Ford Ave N Glencoe (55336) *(G-2208)*
McLeodusa Inc 800 593-1177
2996 Centre Pointe Dr Saint Paul (55113) *(G-8626)*
McNeilus Steel Inc (PA) 507 374-6336
702 2nd Ave S Dodge Center (55927) *(G-1229)*
MCP Foods Inc 507 233-7406
100 N Valley St New Ulm (56073) *(G-6460)*
McPherson Insulation Inc 320 259-5735
810 Mayhew Lake Rd NE Saint Cloud (56304) *(G-7418)*
Mdi LP 38 ....651 646-7848
1600 University Ave W # 212 Saint Paul (55104) *(G-8627)*
MDU Resources Group Inc 218 736-6935
105 W Lincoln Ave Fergus Falls (56537) *(G-2093)*
Mead Metals Inc 651 484-1400
555 Cardigan Rd Saint Paul (55126) *(G-8628)*
Meadow Lakes Golf Club LLC 507 285-1190
70 45th Ave SW Rochester (55902) *(G-7181)*
Meadow Lane Health Care Center, Benson *Also Called Beverly Enterprises - MN (G-438)*
Meadow Star Dairy, LLP 320 392-5609
26406 470th Ave Morris (56267) *(G-6373)*
Meadow Woods, Minneapolis *Also Called Ecumen Home Care Inc (G-4312)*
Meadow Woods, Minneapolis *Also Called Martin Luther Manor (G-4960)*
Meadowbrook Manor Apartments, Minneapolis *Also Called Bigos Properties (G-3903)*
Meadowbrook Women's Clinic 612 376-7708
825 S 8th St Ste 1018 Minneapolis (55404) *(G-4980)*
Meagher & Geer 612 338-0661
33 S 6th St Ste 4400 Minneapolis (55402) *(G-4981)*
Means Telcom, Chokio *Also Called Onvoy Inc (G-1001)*
Meca Sportswear Inc (PA) 651 638-3888
3499 Lexington Ave N # 205 Saint Paul (55126) *(G-8629)*
Mechanical Contractors 952 440-9751
5218 Candy Cove Trl SE Prior Lake (55372) *(G-6939)*
Mechanical Energy Systems Inc 320 253-4859
629 Lincoln Ave NE Saint Cloud (56304) *(G-7419)*
Mechanical Systems Inc 507 645-5675
800 Weaver Ln Ste A Dundas (55019) *(G-1512)*
Medafor Inc 763 571-6300
2700 Freeway Blvd Ste 800 Minneapolis (55430) *(G-4982)*
Medeligible Services 763 585-8400
6160 Summit Dr N Ste 400 Minneapolis (55430) *(G-4983)*
Medevent Inc 952 445-2342
14195 Badger Cir Prior Lake (55372) *(G-6940)*
Media Productions Inc 612 379-4678
710 S 2nd St Fl 7 Minneapolis (55401) *(G-4984)*
Media Relations Inc 612 798-7200
350 W Burnsville Pkwy # 350 Burnsville (55337) *(G-752)*
Media Service, Saint Cloud *Also Called Independent School District (G-7530)*
Mediacom Inc 952 440-9650
14162 Commerce Ave NE Ste 100 Prior Lake (55372) *(G-6941)*
Mediacom LLC 507 835-5975
1504 2nd St SE Waseca (56093) *(G-9882)*
Medical Advanced Pain 763 537-6000
2104 Northdale Blvd NW # 220 Minneapolis (55433) *(G-3532)*
Medical Care For Seniors, Saint Paul *Also Called Healtheast Care System (G-8456)*
Medical Center 320 632-6611
811 2nd St SE Ste A Little Falls (56345) *(G-3013)*
Medical Evaluations Inc (PA) 952 229-8500
5100 Gamble Dr Ste 540 Saint Louis Park (55416) *(G-7664)*
Medical Learning Inc 651 292-3432
287 6th St E Ste 400 Saint Paul (55101) *(G-8630)*
Medical Messaging Center 320 255-5640
1406 6th Ave N Saint Cloud (56303) *(G-7549)*
Medical Network Inc 763 595-3208
6300 Olson Memorial Hwy Golden Valley (55427) *(G-2243)*
Medical Records Inc 952 831-6778
7800 Glenroy Rd Minneapolis (55439) *(G-4985)*
Medical Scanning Consultants 952 513-6841
5775 Wayzata Blvd Ste 190 Saint Louis Park (55416) *(G-7665)*
Medina Electric Inc 763 478-6828
22510 Highway 55 Hamel (55340) *(G-2351)*
Medina Inn 763 478-6661
500 Highway 55 Hamel (55340) *(G-2352)*
Mednet Solutions Inc 763 258-2735
601 Carlson Pkwy Ste 605 Minnetonka (55305) *(G-6191)*
Meds 1 Ambulance Service Inc 218 326-0020
1328 NW 5th St Grand Rapids (55744) *(G-2293)*
Medstat Systems Inc 763 586-8146
5155 E River Rd Ste 418 Minneapolis (55421) *(G-3533)*
Medtox Laboratories Inc 651 636-7466
402 County Road D W # 402 Saint Paul (55112) *(G-8631)*
MEDTOX Scientific Inc (PA) 651 636-7466
402 County Road D W Saint Paul (55112) *(G-8632)*
Medtronic USA Inc (HQ) 763 514-4000
710 Medtronic Pkwy Minneapolis (55432) *(G-3534)*
Medtronic World Headquarters 763 574-4000
710 Medtronic Pkwy Minneapolis (55432) *(G-3535)*

ALPHABETIC

Meeker County Memorial Hosp, Litchfield *Also Called County of Meeker* **(G-2982)**
Meeker Social Services, Litchfield *Also Called County of Meeker* **(G-2983)**
Melrose Diversicom Telephone 320 256-8288
320 E Main St Melrose (56352) **(G-3349)**
Melrose Metalworks Inc 320 256-4170
313 N 8th Ave W Melrose (56352) **(G-3350)**
Melrose-Albany-Upsula 320 256-4252
222 County Road 173 Melrose (56352) **(G-3351)**
Melyx Corp 763 428-6000
21830 Industrial Blvd Rogers (55374) **(G-7330)**
Members Cooperative Credit 218 879-3304
101 14th St Cloquet (55720) **(G-1057)**
Memorial Blood Center 218 723-8080
5115 Burning Tree Rd # 300 Duluth (55811) **(G-1389)**
Memorial Blood Center 218 263-1338
750 E 34th St Hibbing (55746) **(G-2462)**
Memorial Blood Center (PA) 651 332-7000
737 Pelham Blvd Saint Paul (55114) **(G-8633)**
Memorial Hospital Association 763 689-7700
701 Dellwood St S Cambridge (55008) **(G-842)**
Memsi, Minneapolis *Also Called Siemens Hearing Inc* **(G-5666)**
Menard Inc 763 684-0830
1415 County Road 134 Buffalo (55313) **(G-650)**
Menard Inc 218 722-0078
4809 Miller Trunk Hwy Duluth (55811) **(G-1390)**
Menard Inc 952 941-4400
12600 Plaza Dr Eden Prairie (55344) **(G-1719)**
Menasha Packaging Co LLC 952 469-4451
8085 220th St W Lakeville (55044) **(G-2918)**
Menasha Packaging Co LLC 763 424-6606
7301 Northland Dr N Minneapolis (55428) **(G-4986)**
Mencept Epileptic Clinic 952 525-2400
5775 Wayzata Blvd Ste 200 Minneapolis (55416) **(G-4987)**
Mendakota Country Club Inc 651 454-2822
2075 Mendakota Dr Saint Paul (55120) **(G-7837)**
Mendota Insurance Co (HQ) 800 422-0792
2805 Dodd Rd Ste 300 Eagan (55121) **(G-1536)**
Menstar Technologies Inc 218 326-5566
4201 E US Highway 169 Grand Rapids (55744) **(G-2294)**
Mental Health Resources Inc 612 337-4021
2105 Minnehaha Ave Minneapolis (55404) **(G-4988)**
Mental Health Resources Inc (PA) 651 659-2900
1821 University Ave W N464A Saint Paul (55104) **(G-8634)**
Mentor Network, Minneapolis *Also Called REM Williams* **(G-5513)**
Mercer Inc 612 642-8600
333 S 7th St Ste 1600 Minneapolis (55402) **(G-4989)**
Merchants Bank, National Assn (HQ) 507 457-1100
102 E 3rd St Winona (55987) **(G-10115)**
Merchants National Bank of 507 457-1100
102 E 3rd St Winona (55987) **(G-10116)**
Mercury Mailers Of Minnesota 763 544-1881
2500 La Ave N Ste C Minneapolis (55427) **(G-4990)**
Mercy Hospital, Minneapolis *Also Called Allina Health System* **(G-3393)**
Mercy Hospital Health Care Ctr 218 485-4481
710 S Kenwood Ave Moose Lake (55767) **(G-6352)**
Meridian Behavioral Health LLC 612 326-7600
550 Main St Ste 230 New Brighton (55112) **(G-6412)**
Meridian Manor, Minneapolis *Also Called Wayzata Partners LP* **(G-6028)**
Meridian Manor, Wayzata *Also Called Wayzata Partners LP* **(G-9949)**
Meridian Services Inc 320 255-5151
44 28th Ave N Ste D Saint Cloud (56303) **(G-7550)**
Meristar Investment Partners L 952 854-2100
3800 E 80th St Minneapolis (55425) **(G-4991)**
Merit Contracting Inc 507 281-4317
4615 Highway 63 N Rochester (55906) **(G-7182)**
Merit Dental Lab Inc 651 644-4042
1630 University Ave W # 102 Saint Paul (55104) **(G-8635)**
Meritcare Health System 218 846-2000
1245 Washington Ave Detroit Lakes (56501) **(G-1210)**
Meritex Enterprises Inc (PA) 651 855-9700
24 University Ave NE Minneapolis (55413) **(G-4992)**
Meritide Inc 651 255-7300
2670 Patton Rd Saint Paul (55113) **(G-8636)**
Mermaid Inc 763 784-7350
2200 Highway 10 Saint Paul (55112) **(G-8637)**
Merrick Community Services 651 771-8821
1526 6th St E Saint Paul (55106) **(G-8638)**
Merrick Inc 612 789-6200
3210 Labore Rd Saint Paul (55110) **(G-8639)**
Merrill Lynch, Pierce, Fenner 218 726-3140
130 W Superior St Ste 800 Duluth (55802) **(G-1391)**
Merrill Lynch, Pierce, Fenner 952 820-1900
8300 Norman Center Dr # 1250 Minneapolis (55437) **(G-4993)**
Merrill Lynch, Pierce, Fenner 612 349-7801
225 S 6th St Ste 4400 Minneapolis (55402) **(G-4994)**
Merrill Lynch, Pierce, Fenner 651 298-1700
30 7th St E Ste 3400 Saint Paul (55101) **(G-8640)**
Merrill Lynch, Pierce, Fenner 651 275-8040
219 Main St N Ste 4 Stillwater (55082) **(G-9627)**
Merrill Lynch, Pierce, Fenner 952 476-5600
308 Walker Ave S Fl 2 Wayzata (55391) **(G-9926)**
Merry Maids, Saint Paul *Also Called Beamkko* **(G-8096)**
Merry Maids, Saint Paul *Also Called ServiceMaster Inc* **(G-8946)**
Merwin Home Medical 763 535-5335
4082 Lakeland Ave N Minneapolis (55422) **(G-4995)**
Mesaba Airlines 651 367-5000
E Gentian Rd Eagan (55121) **(G-1537)**
Mesaba Aviation Inc (HQ) 651 367-5000
1000 Blue Gentian Rd # 200 Eagan (55121) **(G-1538)**
Mesaba Clinic 218 263-9426
3605 Mayfair Ave Ste 2 Hibbing (55746) **(G-2463)**
Mesaba Country Club 218 262-2851
First Ave At 51st St T S Hibbing (55746) **(G-2464)**
Mesaba Country Club 218 262-2851
415 E 51st St Hibbing (55746) **(G-2465)**
Mesabi Family YMCA 218 749-8020
8367 Unity Dr Virginia (55792) **(G-9746)**
Meshbesher & Spence Ltd (PA) 612 339-9121
1616 Park Ave Minneapolis (55404) **(G-4996)**
Meshbesher & Spence Ltd 320 656-0484
1015 W Saint Germain St Ste 51 Saint Cloud (56301) **(G-7551)**
Messerli & Kramer 763 548-7900
3405 Annapolis Ln N Minneapolis (55447) **(G-4997)**
Mestad's Wedding World, Rochester *Also Called Weber & Barlow Stores Inc* **(G-7286)**
Met Con Kato Inc 507 332-2266
15760 Acorn Trl Faribault (55021) **(G-2021)**
Met-Con Construction Inc (PA) 507 332-2266
15760 Acorn Trl Faribault (55021) **(G-2022)**
Met-Con Metro Inc 952 884-6250
10640 Lyndale Ave S Ste 4 Minneapolis (55420) **(G-4998)**
Metcalf Moving & Storage Co, Saint Paul *Also Called Archbold Enterprises LLC* **(G-8060)**
Metes & Bounds Management Co 612 861-8526
6640 Lyndale Ave S # 100 Minneapolis (55423) **(G-4999)**
Methodist Hospital 952 993-5000
6500 Excelsior Blvd Saint Louis Park (55426) **(G-7666)**
Metris Co's Inc 952 358-4000
10900 Wayzata Blvd Fl 5 Hopkins (55305) **(G-2580)**
Metrisource Inc 651 686-0097
3140 Neil Armstrong Blvd # 323 Saint Paul (55121) **(G-7838)**
Metro - Sales Inc 612 861-4000
1640 E 78th St Minneapolis (55423) **(G-5000)**
Metro Air Inc 952 447-8124
16980 Welcome Ave SE Prior Lake (55372) **(G-6942)**
Metro Commercial Maintainence, Minneapolis *Also Called Mac Enterprises Inc* **(G-4926)**
Metro Communication Services 651 702-3100
7250 Hudson Blvd N Ste 160 Saint Paul (55128) **(G-9247)**
Metro Construction, Saint Paul *Also Called Metropolitan Council, MN* **(G-8644)**
Metro Dental Care 952 435-8525
14344 Burnhaven Dr Burnsville (55306) **(G-753)**
Metro East Region, Saint Paul *Also Called Northern States Power Co* **(G-8761)**
METRO ECSU, Minneapolis *Also Called Educational Cooperative Svc* **(G-4327)**
Metro Fire Protection Inc 651 784-0417
8145 Lake Dr Lino Lakes (55014) **(G-2974)**
Metro Framing Inc 763 785-1482
1550 91st Ave NE Ste 110 Minneapolis (55449) **(G-3536)**
Metro Hardwoods, Osseo *Also Called Midwest Hardwood Corp* **(G-6638)**
Metro Home Health Care Inc 763 323-2099
3931 Coon Rapids Blvd NW # 101 Minneapolis (55433) **(G-3537)**
Metro Home Insulation Inc 763 441-2313
5861 Queens Ave NE Elk River (55330) **(G-1901)**
Metro Home Services Network 612 827-0643
19925 Butternut St NW Cedar (55011) **(G-882)**
Metro Legal Services Inc (PA) 612 332-0202
330 2nd Ave S Ste 150 Minneapolis (55401) **(G-5001)**
Metro Legal Services Inc 651 291-0008
332 Minnesota St Ste N105 Saint Paul (55101) **(G-8641)**
Metro Packaging Corp 763 586-0808
7000 Highway 65 NE Ste 1A Minneapolis (55432) **(G-3538)**
Metro Parkway Assoc 952 854-4244
7800 Metro Pkwy Ste 200 Minneapolis (55425) **(G-5002)**
Metro Paving Inc 763 428-4121
14350 Northdale Blvd Rogers (55374) **(G-7331)**
Metro Produce Distributors Inc 612 722-5575
2700 E 28th St Ste B Minneapolis (55406) **(G-5003)**
Metro Siding Inc 763 557-1808
2750 Niagara Ln N Plymouth (55447) **(G-6873)**
Metro Systems Furniture Inc 952 933-5050
1101 W River Pkwy Ste 100 Minneapolis (55415) **(G-5004)**
Metro Transit Garage, Minneapolis *Also Called Minnesota Department of Trans* **(G-5074)**
Metro Urology, Saint Paul *Also Called Metropolitan Urologic* **(G-8649)**
Metrodentalcare, Minneapolis *Also Called Metropolitan Dental Associates* **(G-5006)**
Metrodentallcare, PLC 612 861-9123
6601 Lyndale Ave S Minneapolis (55423) **(G-5005)**
Metroplitan Ctr For 651 646-8342
1600 University Ave W Ste 16 Saint Paul (55104) **(G-8642)**
Metroplitan Pediatric Dental 763 786-4260
500 Osborne Rd NE Ste 345 Minneapolis (55432) **(G-3539)**
Metropolis Salon Spa 952 473-8664
18166 Minnetonka Blvd Wayzata (55391) **(G-9927)**
Metropolitan Cardiology 763 427-9980
4040 Coon Rapids Blvd NW 12 Minneapolis (55433) **(G-3540)**
Metropolitan Corp 952 944-2438
12475 Plaza Dr Eden Prairie (55344) **(G-1720)**
Metropolitan Corp 952 943-9000
12790 Plaza Dr Eden Prairie (55344) **(G-1721)**
Metropolitan Council, MN 651 602-8393
2400 Childs Rd Saint Paul (55106) **(G-8643)**
Metropolitan Council, MN 651 772-2585
2500 Childs Rd Saint Paul (55106) **(G-8644)**
Metropolitan Council, MN 612 373-3333
390 Robert St N Saint Paul (55101) **(G-8645)**
Metropolitan Dental Associates (HQ) 612 866-0054
7400 Lyndale Ave S Minneapolis (55423) **(G-5006)**
Metropolitan Financial Mgt 651 631-8000
1700 Highway 36 W Ste 301 Saint Paul (55113) **(G-8646)**
Metropolitan Gravel Co Inc 651 458-0170
37 21st St Newport (55055) **(G-6487)**
Metropolitan Hand Surgery 651 223-5406
310 Smith Ave N Ste 370 Saint Paul (55102) **(G-8647)**
Metropolitan Mechanical Contr 952 941-7010
7450 Flying Cloud Dr Eden Prairie (55344) **(G-1722)**
Metropolitan Obstetrics & Gyn 651 770-1385
1655 Beam Ave Ste 206 Saint Paul (55109) **(G-8648)**
Metropolitan Pediatric 952 435-2450
303 E Nicollet Blvd Ste 260 Burnsville (55337) **(G-754)**
Metropolitan Pediatric 952 445-6700
1515 Saint Francis Ave # 230 Shakopee (55379) **(G-9455)**
Metropolitan Productions Inc 612 333-1025
1201 Harmon Pl Ste 300 Minneapolis (55403) **(G-5007)**
Metropolitan School & Charter 218 724-1707
3941 E Calvary Rd Duluth (55803) **(G-1392)**
Metropolitan Sports Facilities 612 332-0386
900 S 5th St Ste A Minneapolis (55415) **(G-5008)**
Metropolitan Sports Facilities 612 332-0386
900 S 5th St Minneapolis (55415) **(G-5009)**

Metropolitan Transit Commn 612 341-4287
560 6th Ave N Minneapolis (55411) *(G-5010)*
Metropolitan Transportation 763 571-1541
8960 Evergreen Blvd NW Minneapolis (55433) *(G-3541)*
Metropolitan Urologic 651 999-7034
2550 University Ave W Ste 240N Saint Paul (55114) *(G-8649)*
Metropolitan Ymca-Northwest, Minneapolis *Also Called Young Men's Chrltn Assoc of (G-6101)*
Meulebroeck Taubert & Co Pllp 507 283-4055
109 S Freeman Ave Luverne (56156) *(G-3064)*
Meyer Associates Inc 320 259-4000
14 7th Ave N Saint Cloud (56303) *(G-7552)*
Meyer Contracting Inc 763 391-5959
11010 93rd Ave N Ste A Maple Grove (55369) *(G-3250)*
Meyer, Borgman & Johnson Inc 612 338-0713
12 S 6th St Ste 810 Minneapolis (55402) *(G-5011)*
Meyer, Scherer & Rockcastle 612 375-0336
710 S 2nd St Ste 800 Minneapolis (55401) *(G-5012)*
Mfra Inc 763 476-6010
14800 28th Ave N Ste 140 Minneapolis (55447) *(G-5013)*
MG Kraus Construction LLC 952 895-5300
1504 E 122nd St Burnsville (55337) *(G-755)*
MG Waldbaum Co 952 258-4000
301 Carlson Pkwy Ste 400 Minnetonka (55305) *(G-6192)*
MGM Home Care Inc 612 338-3636
325 Cedar Ave S Ste 5 Minneapolis (55454) *(G-5014)*
Mgmt Five Inc 651 451-2201
4725 S Robert Trl Inver Grove Heights (55077) *(G-2762)*
Mhc Machining & Fabricating, Glenwood *Also Called Tc American Monorail Inc (G-2234)*
Mhc Material Handling 320 634-4593
17835 211th Ave Glenwood (56334) *(G-2228)*
Mhc Software Inc 952 882-0884
11900 Portland Ave Burnsville (55337) *(G-756)*
Mic Services LLC 651 379-9590
1722 Terrace Dr Saint Paul (55113) *(G-8650)*
Michael C Magnuson 952 435-0303
625 E Nicollet Blvd # 100 Burnsville (55337) *(G-757)*
Michael D Norman & Associates 952 935-0515
4938 Lincoln Dr Minneapolis (55436) *(G-5015)*
Michael Dam 952 831-1928
5241 Viking Dr Minneapolis (55435) *(G-5016)*
Michael E Molenda 952 432-3136
7300 147th St W Ste 600 Saint Paul (55124) *(G-7839)*
Michael Erpelding 651 647-1000
2550 University Ave W Ste 455S Saint Paul (55114) *(G-8651)*
Michael Foods Group Inc (DH) 952 258-4000
301 Carlson Pkwy Ste 400 Minnetonka (55305) *(G-6193)*
Michael Foods Inc 507 237-2429
3400 Tower St Gaylord (55334) *(G-2200)*
Michael Foods Inc 507 665-8851
34187 County Road 20 Le Sueur (56058) *(G-2962)*
Michael J Morris 320 231-8888
502 2nd St SW Willmar (56201) *(G-10022)*
Michael Nelson Masonry Inc 952 496-0217
4620 Manitou Rd Excelsior (55331) *(G-1946)*
Michael's Restaurant 320 252-7100
510 Highway 10 S Saint Cloud (56304) *(G-7420)*
Michaels' Lighting Inc 507 454-5560
2 Kansas St Winona (55987) *(G-10117)*
Michaud, Cooley, Erickson 612 339-4941
333 S 7th St Ste 1200 Minneapolis (55402) *(G-5017)*
Michel Amish Tours, Preston *Also Called Brennaville Inc (G-6895)*
Mickelson Farms 218 346-3876
14870 County Highway 43 Frazee (56544) *(G-2185)*
Micro Electronics Inc 952 285-4040
3710 Highway 100 S Minneapolis (55416) *(G-5018)*
Microsoft Corp 952 832-8000
8300 Norman Center Dr # 950 Minneapolis (55437) *(G-5019)*
Mics Construction, Saint Paul *Also Called Mic Services LLC (G-8650)*
Mid American Financial Group 952 258-5000
301 Carlson Pkwy Ste 300 Minnetonka (55305) *(G-6194)*
Mid American Transportation 612 726-9162
7700 24th Ave S Minneapolis (55450) *(G-5020)*
Mid Coutry Bank 952 931-2200
14617 Highway 7 Hopkins (55345) *(G-2581)*
Mid Minnesota Federal Credit 218 829-0371
200 S 6th St Brainerd (56401) *(G-574)*
MID MINNESOTA LEAGAL ASSISTANC, Minneapolis *Also Called Legal Aid Society of (G-4855)*
Mid Minnesota Legal, Minneapolis *Also Called Legal Aid Society of (G-4856)*
Mid Minnesota Legal Assistance 612 332-1441
430 1st Ave N Ste 300 Minneapolis (55401) *(G-5021)*
Mid Northern Electric Inc 651 452-3996
1299 Eagan Industrial Rd # 101 Saint Paul (55121) *(G-7840)*
Mid-America Business Systems 612 378-3800
2500 Broadway St NE # 100 Minneapolis (55413) *(G-5022)*
Mid-America Cedar Inc 763 425-0125
10285 89th Ave N Osseo (55369) *(G-6637)*
Mid-America Festivals Corp 952 445-7361
1244 Canterbury Rd S # 306 Shakopee (55379) *(G-9456)*
Mid-American Baptist Social 952 443-2024
7600 Victoria Dr Victoria (55386) *(G-9730)*
Mid-Central Federal Saings 218 631-1414
520 Jefferson St S Wadena (56482) *(G-9805)*
Mid-Continent Engineering Inc 612 781-0260
405 35th Ave NE Ste 1 Minneapolis (55418) *(G-5023)*
Mid-State Auto Auction Inc 218 385-3777
100 Bach Ave New York Mills (56567) *(G-6479)*
Mid-State Reclamation Inc 952 985-5555
21955 Grenada Ave Lakeville (55044) *(G-2919)*
Mid-State Telephone Co 320 354-7805
7902 Chapin Dr NE New London (56273) *(G-6417)*
Mid-States Distributing Co Inc 651 698-8831
548 Snelling Ave S Saint Paul (55116) *(G-8652)*
Midcontinent Media Inc (PA) 952 844-2600
3600 Minnesota Dr Ste 700 Minneapolis (55435) *(G-5024)*
Midcountry Bank Inc 320 234-4500
201 Main St S Hutchinson (55350) *(G-2707)*
Midcountry Bank Inc (PA) 952 997-5608
14617 Highway 7 Minnetonka (55345) *(G-6195)*
Midcountry Mortgage Corp 651 766-7000
1001 Labore Industrial Ct Saint Paul (55110) *(G-8653)*
Midland Corporate Benefit Svcs 320 485-3821
131 6th St N Winsted (55395) *(G-10163)*
Midland Hills Country Club 651 631-0440
2001 Fulham St Saint Paul (55113) *(G-8654)*
Midland Nursery Inc 763 478-6122
3536 State Highway 55 SE Buffalo (55313) *(G-651)*
Midland Paper Co 612 623-2400
1860 Elm St SE Minneapolis (55414) *(G-5025)*
Midsota Plastic 320 253-7257
3701 12th St N Ste 100 Saint Cloud (56303) *(G-7553)*
Midsota Regional Hand Center 320 253-7257
3701 12th St N Ste 100 Saint Cloud (56303) *(G-7554)*
Midstates Retreading & Whsle 507 288-7752
6233 Bandel Rd NW Rochester (55901) *(G-7183)*
Midwave Corp 952 279-5600
10050 Crosstown Cir Ste 500 Eden Prairie (55344) *(G-1723)*
Midway Care Center Inc 218 435-1272
114 2nd St NE Fosston (56542) *(G-2177)*
Midway Family YMCA, Saint Paul *Also Called YMCA of Greater St Paul (G-9177)*
Midway Industrial Supply Co 763 780-3000
4759 Old Highway 8 Saint Paul (55112) *(G-8655)*
Midway Pro Bowl, Saint Paul *Also Called Bowl Rite Inc (G-8119)*
Midway Training Services Inc 651 641-0709
1246 Unver Ave W 239 Saint Paul (55104) *(G-8656)*
Midway University LLC 651 292-9844
1625 Energy Park Dr Ste 100 Saint Paul (55108) *(G-8657)*
Midwest - Cbk Inc 507 263-4261
32057 64th Ave Cannon Falls (55009) *(G-858)*
Midwest - Cbk Inc 320 847-1210
223 1st Ave SE Clara City (56222) *(G-1029)*
Midwest Asphalt Corp (HQ) 952 937-8033
5929 Baker Rd Ste 420 Hopkins (55345) *(G-2582)*
Midwest Assistance Program 952 758-4334
212 Lady Slipper Ave NE New Prague (56071) *(G-6433)*
Midwest Bank (PA) 218 847-4771
613 Highway 10 E Detroit Lakes (56501) *(G-1211)*
Midwest Cleaning & Restoration 763 533-3723
6020 Ensign Ave N Minneapolis (55428) *(G-5026)*
Midwest Communication Inc 218 749-3000
807 W 37th St Hibbing (55746) *(G-2466)*
Midwest Craft Distributors Inc 952 252-7043
2745 Kelly Ave Excelsior (55331) *(G-1947)*
Midwest Dairy Association 651 488-0261
2015 Rice St Ste 100 Saint Paul (55113) *(G-8658)*
Midwest Data Inc 320 235-8880
3735 County Road 5 SW Willmar (56201) *(G-10023)*
Midwest Diesel Service Inc 763 780-8533
8284 W 35W Service Dr NE Minneapolis (55449) *(G-6127)*
Midwest Driver Corp 952 884-0765
55 W 78th St Minneapolis (55420) *(G-5027)*
Midwest Family Mutual Insce 952 545-6000
10601 Wayzata Blvd Hopkins (55305) *(G-2583)*
Midwest Family Mutual Insce 763 951-7000
3033 Campus Dr Ste E195 Minneapolis (55441) *(G-5028)*
Midwest Financial Processing 507 647-2856
204 N Carver St Winthrop (55396) *(G-10168)*
Midwest Fixture Group Inc 763 712-9637
900 McKinley St Anoka (55303) *(G-204)*
Midwest Hardwood Corp (PA) 763 425-8700
9540 83rd Ave N Osseo (55369) *(G-6638)*
Midwest Heritage Inn of 952 858-8475
2401 American Blvd E Bloomington (55425) *(G-505)*
Midwest Home Health Care Inc 612 343-3265
801 Park Ave Minneapolis (55404) *(G-5029)*
Midwest Internal Medicine 763 236-9428
3960 Coon Rapids Blvd NW # 100 Minneapolis (55433) *(G-3542)*
Midwest Kaal Corp 507 437-6666
1701 10th Pl NE Austin (55912) *(G-283)*
Midwest Landscapes Inc 763 241-1320
6221 Oakwood Ave NE Elk River (55330) *(G-1902)*
Midwest Latino Entertainment 612 728-0101
2709 E Lake St Minneapolis (55406) *(G-5030)*
Midwest Maintenance & Mech 763 544-2700
710 Penns Ave S Ste B Minneapolis (55426) *(G-5031)*
Midwest Mechanical Solutions 952 525-2003
5831 Cedar Lake Rd S Minneapolis (55416) *(G-5032)*
Midwest Medical Equipment 218 722-3420
4418 Haines Rd Ste 1200 Duluth (55811) *(G-1393)*
Midwest Medical Insurance (PA) 952 838-6700
7650 Edinbrgh Way Ste 400 Minneapolis (55435) *(G-5033)*
Midwest Medical Insurance Co 952 838-6700
7650 Edinbrgh Way Ste 400 Minneapolis (55435) *(G-5034)*
Midwest Medical Management LLC 651 430-3892
1950 Curve Crest Blvd W Ste 10 Stillwater (55082) *(G-9628)*
Midwest Medical Services Inc 763 717-7676
8400 Coral Sea St NE S Mounds View (55112) *(G-6389)*
Midwest Medical Solutions 952 838-6700
7650 Edinbrgh Way Ste 400 Minneapolis (55435) *(G-5035)*
Midwest Mental Health Resource 651 647-1900
2550 University Ave W 435S Saint Paul (55114) *(G-8659)*
Midwest Motor & Equipment Inc 952 955-1962
601 Lewis Ave N Watertown (55388) *(G-9892)*
Midwest Motor Express Inc 763 784-0650
2169 Mustang Dr Mounds View (55112) *(G-6390)*
Midwest Motor Express Inc 763 784-0650
2169 Mustang Dr Saint Paul (55112) *(G-8660)*
Midwest Motors LLC 651 455-6000
1037 Highway 110 Inver Grove Heights (55077) *(G-2763)*
Midwest MRI, Saint Paul *Also Called St Paul Radiology (G-8999)*
Midwest of Rochester Inc (PA) 507 289-8866
1517 16th St SW Rochester (55902) *(G-7184)*
Midwest of Rochester Inc 507 289-8866
1517 16th St SW Rochester (55902) *(G-7185)*
Midwest Patrol Div, Saint Cloud *Also Called General Security Services Corp (G-7416)*

ALPHABETIC

Midwest Protection Agency Inc 763 421-2966
3797 Larabee Ave NE Saint Michael (55376) *(G-7677)*
Midwest Recreational 507 263-9234
6352 320th Street Way # 200 Cannon Falls (55009) *(G-859)*
Midwest Restaurant Group 507 444-0303
4455 W Frontage Rd Owatonna (55060) *(G-6724)*
Midwest Rubber Service & Sply 763 559-2551
14307 28th Pl N Minneapolis (55447) *(G-5036)*
Midwest Sign & Screen Printing (PA) 651 489-9999
45 Maryland Ave E Saint Paul (55117) *(G-8661)*
Midwest Sound & Light Inc 651 644-4111
970 Raymond Ave Ste G70 Saint Paul (55114) *(G-8662)*
Midwest Special Services Inc 763 557-1231
7600 Boone Ave N Ste 86 Minneapolis (55428) *(G-5037)*
Midwest Special Services Inc 651 483-3000
1045 Tomlyn Ave Saint Paul (55126) *(G-8663)*
Midwest Special Services Inc (PA) 651 778-1000
900 Ocean St Saint Paul (55106) *(G-8664)*
Midwest Specialized Trans 507 288-5649
4515 Highway 63 N Rochester (55906) *(G-7186)*
Midwest Spine Institute LLC 651 430-3800
675 E Nicollet Blvd # 245 Burnsville (55337) *(G-758)*
Midwest Stone Management, A MN 651 633-9414
1885 County Road C W Saint Paul (55113) *(G-8665)*
Midwest Surgery Center 651 642-9199
2080 Woodwinds Dr Ste 200 Saint Paul (55125) *(G-9248)*
Midwest Urologic Stone Unit LP 651 633-9414
1885 County Road C W Saint Paul (55113) *(G-8666)*
Midwest Veterinary Specialty 763 754-5000
11850 Aberdeen St NE Minneapolis (55449) *(G-3543)*
Midwest Veterinary Supply Inc (PA) 952 894-4350
11965 Larc Ind Blvd Burnsville (55337) *(G-759)*
Midwest Wireless Comms 507 385-2396
2000 Technology Dr Mankato (56001) *(G-3169)*
Mielke Electric Works Inc 218 727-7411
2606 W Michigan St Duluth (55806) *(G-1394)*
Mies Equipment Inc 320 764-5310
720 State Highway 55 Watkins (55389) *(G-9898)*
Mikara Corp 763 541-1000
3109 Louisiana Ave N Minneapolis (55427) *(G-5038)*
Mike Bishoff 218 697-2800
65742 U S Hwy 169 Hill City (55748) *(G-2481)*
Mike Hall Chevrolet Inc 651 484-4671
3191 Fanum Rd Saint Paul (55110) *(G-8667)*
Mike Wingard 763 441-8247
19671 Hudson Cir NW Elk River (55330) *(G-1884)*
Mikroprecision Division, Minneapolis *Also Called Newport Corp (G-5195)*
Milavetz Gallop Millavetz 763 533-1111
6500 France Ave S Minneapolis (55435) *(G-5039)*
Milavetz, Gallop & Milavetz 612 339-0140
6500 France Ave S Minneapolis (55435) *(G-5040)*
Milestone Systems Inc 763 404-6200
8401 Golden Valley Rd # 300 Minneapolis (55427) *(G-5041)*
Milk Specialties Co 507 427-3222
2204 3rd Ave Mountain Lake (56159) *(G-6399)*
Mill City Electric Inc 612 724-4900
2710 E 33rd St Minneapolis (55406) *(G-5042)*
Mill City Kennel 763 755-3595
11247 Foley Blvd NW Minneapolis (55448) *(G-3544)*
Mill End Textiles, Eden Prairie *Also Called Stone Fabrics Inc (G-1783)*
Mill Street Residence Inc 218 739-2900
802 S Mill St Ofc Fergus Falls (56537) *(G-2094)*
Mille Lacs Cty Area 320 983-2162
1st St E Milaca (56353) *(G-3380)*
Mille Lacs Electric Co-op 218 927-2191
36559 US Highway 169 Aitkin (56431) *(G-22)*
Mille Lacs Fairgrounds, Princeton *Also Called Princeton Speedway (G-6915)*
Mille Lacs Health System 320 532-3154
200 Elm St N Onamia (56359) *(G-6574)*
Mille Lacs Oil Co 320 396-2693
209 N Main St Braham (55006) *(G-543)*
Millennium Credit Consultants 651 306-9344
33 Wentworth Ave E # 220 Saint Paul (55118) *(G-7841)*
Millennium Hotel Minneapolis, Minneapolis *Also Called Trimark Hotel Corp (G-5856)*
Miller Architects & Builders 320 251-4109
3335 W Saint Germain St Saint Cloud (56301) *(G-7555)*
Miller Architecture Inc 320 251-4109
3335 W Saint Germain St Saint Cloud (56301) *(G-7556)*
Miller Brands of Mankato, Mankato *Also Called Locher Bros Inc (G-3227)*
Miller Bros Excavating, Hamel *Also Called M M Miller Brothers Excavating (G-2349)*
Miller Dunwiddie Architecture 612 337-0000
123 N 3rd St Ste 104 Minneapolis (55401) *(G-5043)*
Miller Enterprises Inc (PA) 320 251-8900
2930 2nd St S Saint Cloud (56301) *(G-7557)*
Miller Manufacturing Co Inc 320 864-4039
1400 13th St W Glencoe (55336) *(G-2209)*
Miller Manufacturing Co Inc 320 864-4189
1450 13th St W Glencoe (55336) *(G-2210)*
Miller Medi Van Inc 612 332-2888
904 19th Ave S Minneapolis (55404) *(G-5044)*
Miller Pontiac-Buick-Gmc Inc 320 251-1363
2930 2nd St S Saint Cloud (56301) *(G-7558)*
Miller Rozeboom Architect Inc 612 332-2110
244 1st Ave N Minneapolis (55401) *(G-5045)*
Miller Sellner Equipment Inc 507 831-1106
495 2nd Ave Bingham Lake (56118) *(G-467)*
Miller Sellner Implement Inc (PA) 507 794-2131
22024 State Highway 4 Sleepy Eye (56085) *(G-9498)*
Miller Wally Heiser & Co, Saint Cloud *Also Called Robert A Kovell (G-7589)*
Millers Architects & Bldrs, Saint Cloud *Also Called Miller Architecture Inc (G-7556)*
Millers Roofing 218 263-4406
7283 Highway 53 Canyon (55717) *(G-865)*
Millers Roofing & Siding Co 218 751-4337
7393 Randall Rd Cotton (55724) *(G-1110)*
Millian Air Executive Aviation 952 943-1519
9960 Flying Cloud Dr Eden Prairie (55347) *(G-1724)*
Milliman Inc 952 897-5300
8500 Normandale Lake Blvd 18 Minneapolis (55437) *(G-5046)*
Millionzillion Software Inc 952 932-9048
3306 Decatur Ln Minneapolis (55426) *(G-5047)*
Mills Fleet Farm, Minneapolis *Also Called Fleet Wholesale Supply Co Inc (G-4455)*
Mills Pontiac, Buick (HQ) 320 231-1160
2000 1st St S Willmar (56201) *(G-10024)*
Mills Pontiac, Buick 320 231-1160
2000 1st St S Willmar (56201) *(G-10025)*
Milwaukee Insulation Co I 651 659-2211
2400 Wycliff St Saint Paul (55114) *(G-8668)*
Mimlic Sales Corp, Saint Paul *Also Called Secruian Financial Services (G-8942)*
Min-No-Aya-win Clinic Pharmacy, Cloquet *Also Called Fond Du Lac Reservation (G-1053)*
Mincep Epilepsy Care 952 525-2400
5775 Wayzata Blvd Ste 200 Minneapolis (55416) *(G-5048)*
Mindot, Baxter *Also Called Minnesota Department of Trans (G-337)*
Minesota State Patrol, Marshall *Also Called Minnesota Department of Public (G-3314)*
Mini-Dredge Inc 218 773-3331
1006 6th Ave SE East Grand Forks (56721) *(G-1572)*
Mini Kix Inc 218 829-7107
7842 College Rd Baxter (56425) *(G-336)*
Minikahda Club 952 926-4167
3205 Excelsior Blvd Minneapolis (55416) *(G-5049)*
Minn Health 651 739-5050
2716 Upper Afton Rd E Saint Paul (55119) *(G-8669)*
Minn Health Care Union Local 612 331-4690
345 Randolph Ave Ste 100 Saint Paul (55102) *(G-8670)*
Minn Star Bank (PA) 507 726-2137
202 N Main St Lake Crystal (56055) *(G-2860)*
Minn-Dak Asphalt Inc 218 281-6840
423 W Zea St Thief River Falls (56701) *(G-9674)*
Minn-Dakota Coaches, Fergus Falls *Also Called Ottertail Coaches Inc (G-2112)*
Minn-Dakota Coaches Inc 218 739-3393
1116 N Tower Rd Fergus Falls (56537) *(G-2095)*
Minn-Kota AG Products Inc (PA) 218 643-8464
90 8th St N Breckenridge (56520) *(G-595)*
Minn-Tex Express Inc 320 277-3562
432 State Highway 25 Pierz (56364) *(G-6805)*
Minnco Credit Union 763 689-1071
235 1st Ave W Cambridge (55008) *(G-843)*
Minne Ha Ha Lanes, Minneapolis *Also Called Reese Brooks Hospitality Inds (G-3581)*
Minneapolis American Indian 612 871-4555
1530 E Franklin Ave Minneapolis (55404) *(G-5050)*
Minneapolis Auto Auction, Osseo *Also Called Manheim Auctions Inc (G-6633)*
Minneapolis Cardiology Assoc, Minneapolis *Also Called Allina Specialty Associates (G-3727)*
Minneapolis Clinic of (PA) 763 588-0661
4225 Golden Valley Rd Minneapolis (55422) *(G-5051)*
Minneapolis Community Devpt 612 673-5095
105 5th Ave S Ste 200 Minneapolis (55401) *(G-5052)*
Minneapolis Electrical Jatc 763 497-0072
13100 Frankfort Pkwy NE Saint Michael (55376) *(G-7678)*
Minneapolis Floral Co 612 377-8080
2420 Hennepin Ave Minneapolis (55405) *(G-5053)*
Minneapolis Foundation 612 672-3878
800 Ids Ctr 80 S 8th St Minneapolis (55402) *(G-5054)*
Minneapolis Glass Co 763 559-0635
14600 28th Ave N Plymouth (55447) *(G-6874)*
Minneapolis Golf Club 952 544-4471
2001 Flag Ave S Minneapolis (55426) *(G-5055)*
Minneapolis Grain Exchange 612 321-7101
400 S 4th St Ste 130 Minneapolis (55415) *(G-5056)*
Minneapolis Jewish Federation 952 593-2600
13100 Wayzata Blvd Ste 200 Hopkins (55305) *(G-2584)*
Minneapolis Lifetime Athc CLB, Minneapolis *Also Called Life Time Fitness Inc (G-4879)*
Minneapolis Medical Research 612 347-5000
914 S 8th St Ste 600 Minneapolis (55404) *(G-5057)*
Minneapolis Oxygen Co 612 588-8855
3842 Washington Ave N Minneapolis (55412) *(G-5058)*
Minneapolis Park Police, Minneapolis *Also Called City of Minneapolis (G-4094)*
Minneapolis Plumbing & Heating, Saint Paul *Also Called St Paul Plumbing & Heating Co (G-8996)*
Minneapolis Prof Nursing Svc, Minneapolis *Also Called Minnesota Professional Nursing (G-5090)*
Minneapolis PTG 612 370-2600
60 S 6th St Ste 2450 Minneapolis (55402) *(G-5059)*
Minneapolis Radio LLC 612 617-4000
2000 Elm St SE Minneapolis (55414) *(G-5060)*
Minneapolis Radiology Assocs 763 398-6600
3366 Oakdale Ave N Ste 604 Minneapolis (55422) *(G-5061)*
Minneapolis Radiology Assocs 763 559-2171
2800 Campus Dr Ste 10 Minneapolis (55441) *(G-5062)*
Minneapolis Refuse Inc 612 529-4788
1609 49th Ave N Minneapolis (55430) *(G-5063)*
Minneapolis Rental, Minneapolis *Also Called Cintas Corp (G-4077)*
Minneapolis Society of Fine 612 870-3046
2400 3rd Ave S Minneapolis (55404) *(G-5064)*
Minneapolis Urban League Inc (PA) 612 302-3100
2100 Plymouth Ave N Minneapolis (55411) *(G-5065)*
Minneapolis Veterans Home, Minneapolis *Also Called Minnesota Department of (G-5073)*
Minnegasco, Minneapolis *Also Called Centerpoint Energy Resources (G-4044)*
Minnegasco, South Saint Paul *Also Called Centerpoint Energy Resources (G-9517)*
Minnehaha Bowling Center Inc 651 488-7208
955 Seminary Ave Saint Paul (55104) *(G-8671)*
Minneota Manor Health Care Ctr 507 872-5300
700 N Monroe St Minneota (56264) *(G-6135)*
Minnerath Construction Inc 320 685-3162
500 3rd Ave S Cold Spring (56320) *(G-1088)*
Minnesota Abstract & Title, Saint Paul *Also Called Capitol Lien Records & Res (G-8154)*
Minnesota Afscme Council 5 ....651 455-0773
300 Hardman Ave S South Saint Paul (55075) *(G-9534)*
Minnesota Aids Project 612 341-2060
1400 Park Ave Minneapolis (55404) *(G-5066)*
Minnesota Air Inc 952 918-8000
6901 W Old Shakopee Rd Minneapolis (55438) *(G-5067)*
Minnesota Aquarium LLC 952 853-0628
120 E Broadway Minneapolis (55425) *(G-5068)*
Minnesota Architectural 612 871-5703
400 Clifton Ave Minneapolis (55403) *(G-5069)*

ALPHABETIC

Minnesota Association of 651 290-7462
1000 Westgate Dr Ste 252 Saint Paul (55114) ***(G-8672)***
Minnesota Association of Sch 651 645-6272
1884 Como Ave Saint Paul (55108) ***(G-8673)***
Minnesota Autism Center 952 767-4200
5710 Baker Rd Minnetonka (55345) ***(G-6196)***
Minnesota Bankers Association 952 835-3900
9521 W 78th St Eden Prairie (55344) ***(G-1725)***
Minnesota Benefit Association 651 739-4550
6701 Upper Afton Rd Saint Paul (55125) ***(G-9249)***
Minnesota Blueprint, Minneapolis *Also Called American Reprographics Co LLC* ***(G-3759)***
Minnesota Brd of Med Prac 651 642-0538
2700 University Ave W # 106 Saint Paul (55114) ***(G-8674)***
Minnesota Care Staffing Inc 612 216-1938
3638 Central Ave NE Minneapolis (55418) ***(G-5070)***
Minnesota Chamber of Commerce 651 292-4650
400 Robert St N Ste 1500 Saint Paul (55101) ***(G-8675)***
Minnesota Chapter of The Natl 952 928-4647
4248 Park Glen Rd Minneapolis (55416) ***(G-5071)***
Minnesota Chemical Co 651 646-7521
2285 Hampden Ave Saint Paul (55114) ***(G-8676)***
Minnesota Children's Museum 651 225-6000
10 7th St W Saint Paul (55102) ***(G-8677)***
Minnesota City Bus Service Inc 507 454-5871
32 Wenonah Rd Minnesota City (55959) ***(G-6136)***
Minnesota Clerical Inc 763 753-7243
17230 Uplander St NW Anoka (55304) ***(G-205)***
Minnesota Clipping Service, Minneapolis *Also Called Burrelle's Information Svcs* ***(G-3978)***
Minnesota Commercial Railway (PA) 651 646-2010
508 Cleveland Ave N Saint Paul (55114) ***(G-8678)***
Minnesota Community Foundation, Saint Paul *Also Called Saint Paul Foundation Inc* ***(G-8926)***
Minnesota Comprehensive E, Minneapolis *Also Called Mincep Epilepsy Care* ***(G-5048)***
Minnesota Conway Fire & Safety, Minneapolis *Also Called William LLC* ***(G-6069)***
Minnesota Conway Fire & Safety 952 345-3473
314 W 86th St Minneapolis (55420) ***(G-5072)***
Minnesota Correction Facility, Moose Lake *Also Called Department of Corrections MN* ***(G-6349)***
Minnesota Counties Insurance 651 209-6400
100 Empire Dr Ste 100 Saint Paul (55103) ***(G-8679)***
Minnesota Crop Improvement 612 625-7766
1900 Hendon Ave Saint Paul (55108) ***(G-8680)***
Minnesota Dairy Herd 763 682-1091
307 Brighton Ave S Buffalo (55313) ***(G-652)***
Minnesota Dakota & Western 218 285-5690
101 2nd St International Falls (56649) ***(G-2727)***
Minnesota Dakota Generating Co 218 739-8200
215 S Cascade St Fergus Falls (56537) ***(G-2096)***
Minnesota Dehydrated 218 435-1997
915 Omland Ave N Fosston (56542) ***(G-2178)***
Minnesota Department of 218 751-3196
1231 5th St NE Bemidji (56601) ***(G-402)***
Minnesota Department of 218 736-0400
1821 N Park St Fergus Falls (56537) ***(G-2097)***
Minnesota Department of 218 739-7576
1509 N 1st Ave Fergus Falls (56537) ***(G-2098)***
Minnesota Department of 320 384-6591
30065 Saint Croix Park Rd Hinckley (55037) ***(G-2487)***
Minnesota Department of 507 283-1100
1300 N Kniss Ave Luverne (56156) ***(G-3065)***
Minnesota Department of 507 537-6236
607 W Main St Fl 3 Marshall (56258) ***(G-3313)***
Minnesota Department of 612 721-0600
5101 Minnehaha Ave Minneapolis (55417) ***(G-5073)***
Minnesota Department of 651 642-0503
2200 University Ave W Ste 240 Saint Paul (55114) ***(G-8681)***
Minnesota Department of 612 713-2196
642 Hercules Ave Saint Paul (55111) ***(G-7961)***
Minnesota Department of 218 226-6300
45 Banks Blvd Silver Bay (55614) ***(G-9483)***
Minnesota Department of 218 753-2245
1379 Stuntz Bay Rd Soudan (55782) ***(G-9504)***
Minnesota Department of 218 425-7793
16945 State Highway 89 Wannaska (56761) ***(G-9868)***
Minnesota Department of 320 231-1729
1808 Civic Center Dr Willmar (56201) ***(G-10026)***
Minnesota Department of Admin 651 296-2600
50 Sherburne Ave Ste 114 Saint Paul (55155) ***(G-8682)***
Minnesota Department of Human 218 828-2379
1777 Highway 18 E Brainerd (56401) ***(G-575)***
Minnesota Department of Human 218 739-7200
1400 N Union Ave Fergus Falls (56537) ***(G-2099)***
Minnesota Department of Human 651 431-2000
444 Lafayette Rd N Saint Paul (55155) ***(G-8683)***
Minnesota Department of Human 507 931-7137
2100 Sheppard Dr Saint Peter (56082) ***(G-9299)***
Minnesota Department of Public 507 537-3664
1800 E College Dr Marshall (56258) ***(G-3314)***
Minnesota Department of Trans 218 828-2678
7694 Industrial Park Rd Baxter (56425) ***(G-337)***
Minnesota Department of Trans 507 389-6351
501 S Victory Dr Mankato (56001) ***(G-3170)***
Minnesota Department of Trans 612 349-7332
570 6th Ave N Minneapolis (55411) ***(G-5074)***
Minnesota Department of Trans 651 582-1364
3485 Hadley Ave N Saint Paul (55128) ***(G-9250)***
Minnesota Department of Trans 507 831-1200
180 County Road 26 Windom (56101) ***(G-10069)***
Minnesota Diagnostic Ctr 612 879-1528
910 E 26th St Ste LL10 Minneapolis (55404) ***(G-5075)***
Minnesota Disability Law Ctr 612 332-1441
430 1st Ave N Ste 300 Minneapolis (55401) ***(G-5076)***
Minnesota Diversified Inds 218 326-9544
825 Lily Ln Grand Rapids (55744) ***(G-2295)***
Minnesota Diversified Inds 218 263-3663
1937 4th Ave E Hibbing (55746) ***(G-2467)***
Minnesota Diversified Inds 218 263-3663
1937 4th Ave E Hibbing (55746) ***(G-2468)***
Minnesota Diversified Inds (PA) 651 999-8200
1700 Wynne Ave Saint Paul (55108) ***(G-8684)***
Minnesota Ear Head & Neck Clin 612 339-2836
701 25th Ave S Ste 200 Minneapolis (55454) ***(G-5077)***
Minnesota Electric Technology 507 893-3181
352 Main St S Winnebago (56098) ***(G-10077)***
Minnesota Elevator Inc 507 245-3060
19336 607th Ave Mankato (56001) ***(G-3171)***
Minnesota Energy Resources 651 322-8902
2665 145th St W Rosemount (55068) ***(G-7372)***
Minnesota Epilepsy Group 651 241-5305
225 Smith Ave N Ste 201 Saint Paul (55102) ***(G-8685)***
Minnesota Exteriors Inc 763 493-5500
8600 Jefferson Hwy Osseo (55369) ***(G-6639)***
Minnesota Farmers' Market Assn 320 763-6893
625 Robert St N Saint Paul (55155) ***(G-8686)***
Minnesota Field Office, Minneapolis *Also Called Nature Conservancy* ***(G-5173)***
Minnesota First Credit 507 289-0411
1932 Viking Dr NW Rochester (55901) ***(G-7187)***
Minnesota Flexible Corp (PA) 651 645-7522
803 Transfer Rd Ste 1 Saint Paul (55114) ***(G-8687)***
Minnesota Gastroenterology PA 612 871-1145
2550 University Ave W Ste 423S Saint Paul (55114) ***(G-8688)***
Minnesota Heart Clinic Inc 952 836-3700
6405 France Ave S Ste 200 Edina (55435) ***(G-1837)***
Minnesota Horse & Hunt Club 952 447-2272
2920 220th St E Ste 1 Prior Lake (55372) ***(G-6943)***
Minnesota Hospital 651 641-1121
2250 University Ave W Saint Paul (55114) ***(G-8689)***
Minnesota Hospital Association 651 641-1121
2550 University Ave W Ste 350S Saint Paul (55114) ***(G-8690)***
Minnesota Housekeeping Svcs 651 686-0900
2535 Pilot Knob Rd # 118 Saint Paul (55120) ***(G-7842)***
Minnesota Indian Primary 218 879-6731
1150 Mission Rd Sawyer (55780) ***(G-9413)***
Minnesota Indian Womens 612 728-2000
2300 15th Ave S Minneapolis (55404) ***(G-5078)***
Minnesota Institute of Public 763 427-5310
2720 Highway 10 NE Saint Paul (55112) ***(G-8691)***
Minnesota Insty-Prints Inc 612 332-8669
618 2nd Ave S Ste B50 Minneapolis (55402) ***(G-5079)***
Minnesota Insurance Brokers, Saint Paul *Also Called Gary L Kemp Agency Inc* ***(G-7778)***
Minnesota Internal Medicine 651 232-4800
1690 University Ave W Ste 570 Saint Paul (55104) ***(G-8692)***
Minnesota Landmarks Inc 651 292-3233
75 5th St W Ste 404 Saint Paul (55102) ***(G-8693)***
Minnesota League of Credit 651 288-5170
555 Wabasha St N Ste 250 Saint Paul (55102) ***(G-8694)***
Minnesota Legal Services 320 253-0121
830 W Saint Germain St Saint Cloud (56301) ***(G-7559)***
Minnesota Legal Services (PA) 651 228-9105
2324 University Ave W Ste 101B Saint Paul (55114) ***(G-8695)***
Minnesota Lending Co LLC 952 960-9600
6465 Wayzata Blvd Ste 300 Minneapolis (55426) ***(G-5080)***
Minnesota Limited Inc 763 428-4444
18640 200th St Big Lake (55309) ***(G-451)***
Minnesota Lions Eye Bank Inc 612 624-6446
1000 Westgate Dr Ste 260 Saint Paul (55114) ***(G-8696)***
Minnesota Liquor Retailers Inc 651 772-0910
1983 Sloan Pl Ste 15 Saint Paul (55117) ***(G-8697)***
Minnesota Magazine & Pubn 651 290-6281
1821 University Ave W S256 Saint Paul (55104) ***(G-8698)***
Minnesota Masonic Charities 952 948-6004
11501 Masonic Home Dr Minneapolis (55437) ***(G-5081)***
Minnesota Masonic Home 952 948-7000
11501 Masonic Home Dr # 102 Minneapolis (55437) ***(G-5082)***
Minnesota Masonic Home North 763 592-3000
5430 Boone Ave N Minneapolis (55428) ***(G-5083)***
Minnesota Medical Association 612 378-1875
1300 Godward St NE # 2500 Minneapolis (55413) ***(G-5084)***
Minnesota Medical Scanning (PA) 952 541-1840
5775 Wayzata Blvd Ste 190 Saint Louis Park (55416) ***(G-7667)***
Minnesota Medtec Inc 763 428-3720
11760 Justen Cir Ste B Osseo (55369) ***(G-6640)***
Minnesota Monitoring Inc 763 253-5401
2300 Nevada Ave N Ste 100 Minneapolis (55427) ***(G-5085)***
Minnesota Motor Bus Inc 507 238-4454
820 Winnebago Ave Ste 3 Fairmont (56031) ***(G-1977)***
Minnesota Mutual Co's Inc 651 665-3500
400 Robert St N Ste A Saint Paul (55101) ***(G-8699)***
Minnesota Network For 952 891-1862
13440 Gunflint Ct Saint Paul (55124) ***(G-7843)***
Minnesota News Service Inc 952 703-0075
7836 2nd Ave S Minneapolis (55420) ***(G-5086)***
Minnesota Northern Railroad 218 281-4704
28997 255th Ave SW Crookston (56716) ***(G-1128)***
Minnesota Nurses' Association 651 646-4807
1625 Energy Park Dr # 200 Saint Paul (55108) ***(G-8700)***
Minnesota Odd Fellows Home (PA) 507 645-6611
815 Forest Ave Northfield (55057) ***(G-6532)***
Minnesota Odd Fellows Home 507 645-6611
815 Forest Ave Northfield (55057) ***(G-6533)***
Minnesota Opera 612 333-2700
620 N 1st St Minneapolis (55401) ***(G-5087)***
Minnesota Orchestral Assn (PA) 612 371-5600
1111 Nicollet Mall Minneapolis (55403) ***(G-5088)***
Minnesota Orchestral Assn 612 371-5600
1111 Nicollet Mall Minneapolis (55403) ***(G-5089)***
Minnesota Pipe Trades Assn 651 291-8151
411 Main St Ste 309 Saint Paul (55102) ***(G-8701)***
Minnesota Pipestone 952 294-5100
250 Lake Dr E Chanhassen (55317) ***(G-932)***
Minnesota Power Co, Duluth *Also Called Upper Minnesota Properties Inc* ***(G-1494)***
Minnesota Prairie Line Inc 320 864-7200
2925 12th St E Glencoe (55336) ***(G-2211)***
Minnesota Professional Nursing 612 627-9524
2021 E Hennepin Ave # 408 Minneapolis (55413) ***(G-5090)***
Minnesota Program Development 218 722-2781
202 E Superior St Duluth (55802) ***(G-1395)***

ALPHABETIC

Minnesota Prophy Power Inc 952 898-1594
17799 Kenwood Trl Lakeville (55044) *(G-2920)*
Minnesota Public Radio (HQ) 651 290-1500
480 Cedar St Saint Paul (55101) *(G-8702)*
Minnesota Public Radio 651 290-1500
45 7th St E Bldg 100 Saint Paul (55101) *(G-8703)*
Minnesota Radiation Oncology 612 863-4060
800 E 28th St Minneapolis (55407) *(G-5091)*
Minnesota Real State Service 952 928-4640
4248 Park Glen Rd Minneapolis (55416) *(G-5092)*
Minnesota Relay, Moorhead *Also Called Communication Service For The (G-6305)*
Minnesota Renaissance Festival, Shakopee *Also Called Mid-America Festivals Corp (G-9456)*
Minnesota Residential Aquatics 651 439-8467
263 Pineridge Ln Stillwater (55082) *(G-9629)*
MINNESOTA RIVER VALLEY JUVENIL, New Ulm *Also Called Brown County Evaluation Center (G-6443)*
Minnesota Rural Education Assn 320 762-6574
700 Cedar St Ste 208 Alexandria (56308) *(G-113)*
Minnesota Rural Health Co-op 507 423-5300
190 E 4th St Cottonwood (56229) *(G-1113)*
Minnesota Salt Service 651 774-6237
2500 Walnut St Ste 100 Saint Paul (55113) *(G-8704)*
Minnesota Select Sires Co-Op 320 259-6680
6601 Gregory Park Rd S Saint Cloud (56301) *(G-7560)*
Minnesota Shredding LLC 763 493-3007
8400 89th Ave N Ste 430 Minneapolis (55445) *(G-5093)*
Minnesota Society of Certified 952 831-2707
1650 W 82nd St Ste 600 Minneapolis (55431) *(G-5094)*
Minnesota Soybean Processors 507 842-6677
121 Zeh Ave Brewster (56119) *(G-605)*
Minnesota State Agricultural 651 288-4400
1265 Snelling Ave N Saint Paul (55108) *(G-8705)*
Minnesota State Bar Assn 651 227-8266
2550 University Ave W 160S Saint Paul (55114) *(G-8706)*
Minnesota State Colleges 218 681-2181
1101 Highway 1 E Thief River Falls (56701) *(G-9675)*
Minnesota State Community 218 755-4270
905 Grant Ave SE Bemidji (56601) *(G-403)*
Minnesota State Employees 651 450-4990
300 Hardman Ave S Ste 3 South Saint Paul (55075) *(G-9535)*
Minnesota Street Associates 651 225-3666
332 Minnesota St Ste W120 Saint Paul (55101) *(G-8707)*
Minnesota Structures Inc 952 401-3820
21930 Minnetonka Blvd Excelsior (55331) *(G-1948)*
Minnesota Supply Co 952 828-7300
6470 Flying Cloud Dr Eden Prairie (55344) *(G-1726)*
Minnesota Surgical Associates 651 776-0724
1973 Sloan Pl Ste 225 Saint Paul (55117) *(G-8708)*
Minnesota Teen Challenge Inc 612 373-3366
1619 Portland Ave Minneapolis (55404) *(G-5095)*
Minnesota Tile Supply, Minneapolis *Also Called Dale Tile Co (G-4221)*
Minnesota Timberwolves 612 673-1600
600 1st Ave N Minneapolis (55403) *(G-5096)*
Minnesota Tobacco Document 612 378-5707
980 E Hennepin Ave Minneapolis (55414) *(G-5097)*
Minnesota Twins Baseball Club (PA) 612 659-3400
1 Twins Way Minneapolis (55403) *(G-5098)*
Minnesota Twins Baseball Club 612 375-7411
34 Kirby Puckett Pl Minneapolis (55415) *(G-5099)*
Minnesota Valley Action 507 345-6822
464 Raintree Rd Mankato (56001) *(G-3172)*
Minnesota Valley Cooperative 320 269-2163
501 S 1st St Montevideo (56265) *(G-6250)*
Minnesota Valley Country Club 612 884-2409
6300 Auto Club Rd Bloomington (55438) *(G-506)*
Minnesota Valley Electric 952 492-2313
125 Minnesota Valley Dr Jordan (55352) *(G-2807)*
Minnesota Valley Irrigation 218 631-9271
12317 150th St Wadena (56482) *(G-9806)*
Minnesota Valley Memorial Hosp 507 665-3375
621 S 4th St Le Sueur (56058) *(G-2958)*
Minnesota Valley Mill Work, Prior Lake *Also Called Key-Land Homes (G-6935)*
Minnesota Valley Millwork Inc 952 440-9404
17021 Fish Point Rd SE Prior Lake (55372) *(G-6944)*
Minnesota Valley Testing Labs 507 354-8517
1126 N Front St New Ulm (56073) *(G-6461)*
Minnesota Valley Transport Inc 507 354-3276
301 Water St New Ulm (56073) *(G-6462)*
Minnesota Veterans Research 612 467-2895
1 Veterans Dr Minneapolis (55417) *(G-5100)*
Minnesota Vikings Food Svcs (HQ) 952 835-5250
2830 Fairview Ave N Saint Paul (55113) *(G-8709)*
Minnesota Vikings Football (PA) 952 828-6500
9520 Viking Dr Eden Prairie (55344) *(G-1727)*
Minnesota Vikings Football LLC 952 828-6500
9520 Viking Dr Eden Prairie (55344) *(G-1728)*
Minnesota Vinyl & Aluminum 952 403-0805
12820 Emery Way Shakopee (55379) *(G-9457)*
Minnesota Visiting Nurse Agcy 612 617-4600
3433 Broadway St NE Ste 300 Minneapolis (55413) *(G-5101)*
Minnesota Water Well Assn 651 290-6270
1000 Westgate Dr Ste 252 Saint Paul (55114) *(G-8710)*
Minnesota Wild Hockey Club LP 651 602-6000
317 Washington St Saint Paul (55102) *(G-8711)*
Minnesota Wings Motorcycle 320 632-8427
205 3rd Ave NW Little Falls (56345) *(G-3014)*
Minnetonka Assisted Living Com 952 988-0011
14505 Minnetonka Dr Minnetonka (55345) *(G-6197)*
Minnetonka Country Club 952 474-5222
24575 Smithtown Rd Excelsior (55331) *(G-1949)*
Minnetonka Health Care Center 952 474-4474
20395 Summerville Rd Excelsior (55331) *(G-1950)*
Minnetonka Minnesota Hotel L P 952 593-0000
12201 Ridgedale Dr Minnetonka (55305) *(G-6198)*
Minnetonka Moccasin Co Inc (PA) 612 331-8493
1113 E Hennepin Ave Minneapolis (55414) *(G-5102)*
Minnetonka Transportation Inc 952 935-1990
5801 Baker Rd Minnetonka (55345) *(G-6199)*
Minnetronix Inc 651 917-4060
1635 Energy Park Dr Saint Paul (55108) *(G-8712)*
Minnewaska District Hospital, Starbuck *Also Called Western Pope County Hospital (G-9589)*
Minnhealth Family Physicians, Saint Paul *Also Called Bruce B Cunningham (G-9190)*
Minnhealth Family Physicians 651 487-2831
1050 Larpenteur Ave W # 2 Saint Paul (55113) *(G-8713)*
Minnhealth Family Physicians 651 426-6402
4786 Banning Ave White Bear Lake (55110) *(G-9976)*
Minnhouse 651 426-6402
4786 Banning Ave Saint Paul (55110) *(G-8714)*
Minnowa Construction Inc 507 886-6162
850 Wickett Dr NW Harmony (55939) *(G-2372)*
Minnpar LLC 612 379-0606
900 6th Ave SE Ste 13 Minneapolis (55414) *(G-5103)*
Minnstar Bank 507 726-2137
202 N Main St Lake Crystal (56055) *(G-2861)*
Minnwest Bank Central 320 269-6565
107 N 1st St Montevideo (56265) *(G-6251)*
Minnwest Bank Luverne 507 283-2366
116 E Main St Luverne (56156) *(G-3066)*
Minnwest Bank M V 507 637-5731
300 S Washington St Redwood Falls (56283) *(G-7025)*
Minnwest Bank South 507 836-6141
2565 King Ave Slayton (56172) *(G-9489)*
Minter-Weisman Co 763 545-3700
1035 Nathan Ln N Ste A Minneapolis (55441) *(G-5104)*
Minter-Weisman Co (DH) 763 545-3706
1035 Nathan Ln N Minneapolis (55441) *(G-5105)*
Minuteclinic LLC 612 659-7111
920 2nd Ave S Ste 400 Minneapolis (55402) *(G-5106)*
Minvalco Inc (PA) 952 920-0131
3340 Gorham Ave Minneapolis (55426) *(G-5107)*
Miramar Inc 763 559-2527
3205 Harbor Ln N Ofc OFC Minneapolis (55447) *(G-5108)*
Miratec Systems Inc 651 222-8440
640 Olive St Saint Paul (55130) *(G-8715)*
Miro Management Inc 952 404-8267
1001 Twelve Oaks Ctr Ste D Wayzata (55391) *(G-9928)*
Mirumi Inc 952 445-9779
511 Marschall Rd Shakopee (55379) *(G-9458)*
Mission Health Care LLC 651 224-2368
420 Marshall Ave Saint Paul (55102) *(G-8716)*
Mission Healthcare LLC 218 326-3431
2801 Pokegama Ave S Grand Rapids (55744) *(G-2296)*
Missions Inc Programs 763 559-1883
3409 E Medicine Lake Blvd Minneapolis (55441) *(G-5109)*
Mississippi Dunes Golf Links, Cottage Grove *Also Called Links On The Mississippi Inc (G-1104)*
Mississippi Eagles LLC 651 565-5366
150 Commerce St Wabasha (55981) *(G-9769)*
Mississippi Transport Inc 651 439-5773
2930 Quant Ave N Stillwater (55082) *(G-9630)*
Mississippi Valley Fruit LLC 507 876-2891
28085 County Road 25 Elgin (55932) *(G-1856)*
Mississippi Welders Supply Co (PA) 507 454-5231
5150 W 6th St Winona (55987) *(G-10118)*
Mister Car Wash 952 931-9412
8650 Highway 7 Minneapolis (55426) *(G-5110)*
Mitel Technologies Inc 952 930-4400
5929 Baker Rd Ste 410 Minnetonka (55345) *(G-6200)*
Miwrc, Minneapolis *Also Called Minnesota Indian Womens (G-5078)*
MJM Investments Inc 952 432-5036
14540 Pennock Ave Saint Paul (55124) *(G-7844)*
Mjsk Investment Securities 763 542-3700
5500 Wayzata Blvd Ste 190 Minneapolis (55416) *(G-5111)*
ML Enterprises LLC 952 401-9051
23570 Highway 7 Excelsior (55331) *(G-1936)*
Mlaskoch Excavating Inc 218 372-4067
8060 Park Dr Willow River (55795) *(G-10061)*
Mlaskoch Utility Construction 218 372-3977
3006 County Road 43 Willow River (55795) *(G-10062)*
MLS Online 763 427-0539
11144 Commerce Ln N Champlin (55316) *(G-896)*
Mmic 952 838-6700
7650 Edinbrgh Way Ste 400 Minneapolis (55435) *(G-5112)*
Mmic Health It 763 201-0300
7650 Edinbrgh Way Ste 400 Minneapolis (55435) *(G-5113)*
Mmk International Marine Svcs 507 263-0975
101 State St W Ste 2 Cannon Falls (55009) *(G-860)*
MN Airlines LLC 651 681-3900
1300 Mendota Heights Rd Mendota Heights (55120) *(G-3367)*
MN Crop Improvement Assn, Saint Paul *Also Called Minnesota Crop Improvement (G-8680)*
MN Vinyl & Aluminum Systems, Shakopee *Also Called Minnesota Vinyl & Aluminum (G-9457)*
Mna, Saint Paul *Also Called Minnesota Nurses' Association (G-8700)*
Mnpact, Saint Paul *Also Called Minnesota Network For (G-7843)*
Mo-Tech Corp 651 770-1515
2920 Granada Ave N Saint Paul (55128) *(G-9251)*
Moa Entertainment Co LLC 952 883-8810
5000 Center Ct Minneapolis (55425) *(G-5114)*
Moac Mall Holdings LLC 952 883-8810
60 E Broadway Bloomington (55425) *(G-507)*
Mobile Media Inc 952 884-6201
9425 Syndicate Ave Minneapolis (55420) *(G-5115)*
Mobiliam 952 921-3997
8400 Normandale Lake Blvd Minneapolis (55437) *(G-5116)*
Mocco Enterprises Inc 507 537-1421
901 Michigan Rd Marshall (56258) *(G-3315)*
Model Cities of St Paul Inc (PA) 651 632-8350
839 University Ave W Saint Paul (55104) *(G-8717)*
Modern Aero Inc 952 941-2595
14801 Pioneer Trl Eden Prairie (55347) *(G-1729)*
Modern Climate Inc 612 343-8180
800 Hennepin Ave Fl 8 Minneapolis (55403) *(G-5117)*
Modern Heating & Air Condg 612 781-3358
2318 1st St NE Minneapolis (55418) *(G-5118)*
Mohagen Hansen Architectural 952 426-7400
1000 Twelve Oaks Ste 200 Wayzata (55391) *(G-9929)*

ALPHABETIC

www.HarrisInfo.com
596
2011 Harris Minnesota Services Directory
(G-00000) Company's Geographic Section entry number

Mohawk Industries Inc 651 405-8300
2359 Waters Dr Saint Paul (55120) *(G-7845)*
Mohawk Moving & Storage Inc 763 717-3705
8271 W 35W Service Dr NE Minneapolis (55449) *(G-6128)*
Mohawk United 651 481-0000
8271 W 35W Service Dr NE Minneapolis (55449) *(G-6129)*
Moisture Control Services, Burnsville *Also Called Munters Corp (G-761)*
Molly's Inc 612 925-3113
2308 W 50th St Minneapolis (55410) *(G-5119)*
Monaco Air Duluth LLC 218 727-2911
4535 Airport Approach Rd Duluth (55811) *(G-1396)*
Monarch Heights, Ortonville *Also Called Big Stone Community Homes Inc (G-6578)*
Money Gram Payment Systems Inc (HQ) 952 591-3000
1550 Utica Ave S Ste 100 Minneapolis (55416) *(G-5120)*
Moneygram Payment Systems Inc 763 549-7100
6601 Shingle Creek Pkwy Ste 14 Minneapolis (55430) *(G-5121)*
Monitor Tire Disposal Inc 320 548-3496
130 Maine St Saint Martin (56376) *(G-7671)*
Monroe Krass 952 445-5080
8000 Norman Center Dr Ste 1000 Minneapolis (55437) *(G-5122)*
Monsanto Co 507 524-3475
310 Main St E Mapleton (56065) *(G-3283)*
Monson Corp 320 995-6703
7600 Highway 71 S Willmar (56201) *(G-10027)*
Montage Inc (PA) 651 633-1955
3050 Centre Pte Dr Ste 50 Saint Paul (55113) *(G-8718)*
Montavon Motors Inc 218 326-0551
1510 S Pokegama Ave Grand Rapids (55744) *(G-2297)*
Montevideo Clinic 320 269-6435
908 N 11th St Montevideo (56265) *(G-6252)*
Montevideo Country Club Inc 320 269-8600
Hwy 212W Montevideo (56265) *(G-6253)*
Montevideo Country Club Inc 320 269-6828
W Hwy 212 Montevideo (56265) *(G-6254)*
Montevideo Hospital Home Care 320 367-2877
1100 Warrings Ave Apt 129 Clara City (56222) *(G-1030)*
Montgomery Golf & Recreation 507 364-5602
900 Rogers Dr Montgomery (56069) *(G-6264)*
Monticello Country Club Inc 763 295-3323
1209 Golf Course Rd Monticello (55362) *(G-6277)*
Monticello-Big Lake Community 763 295-2945
1013 Hart Blvd Monticello (55362) *(G-6278)*
Montincello Ford-Mercury Inc 763 295-2056
500 Ford Rd Minneapolis (55426) *(G-5123)*
Montreal I, Saint Paul *Also Called Accessible Space Inc (G-7974)*
Moondance Enterprises 651 464-1875
356 2nd Ave NW Forest Lake (55025) *(G-2164)*
Moore Wallace North America 952 844-2000
7400 Metro Blvd Ste 300 Minneapolis (55439) *(G-5124)*
Moore, Costello & Hart Pllp 612 673-0148
900 2nd Ave S Ste 1500 Minneapolis (55402) *(G-5125)*
Moore, Costello & Hart Pllp (PA) 651 602-2615
55 5th St E Ste 1400 Saint Paul (55101) *(G-8719)*
Moorehead Youth Hockey Assn 218 233-5021
707 SE Main Ave Moorhead (56560) *(G-6328)*
Moorhead Country Club Inc 218 236-0100
2101 N River Dr Moorhead (56560) *(G-6329)*
Moorhead Electric Inc (DH) 218 284-1963
3030 24th Ave S Moorhead (56560) *(G-6330)*
Moorhead Health Care Center, Moorhead *Also Called Beverly Enterprises - MN (G-6299)*
Moorhead Hospitality LP 218 284-1000
1080 28th Ave S Moorhead (56560) *(G-6331)*
Moorhead Police Department, Moorhead *Also Called City of Moorhead (G-6302)*
Moquist Thorvilson Kaufmann 952 854-5700
7650 Edinbrgh Way Ste 225 Minneapolis (55435) *(G-5126)*
Mora Village Garage, Mora *Also Called City of Mora (G-6353)*
Moravian Care Ministries 952 448-9303
501 Oak St N Chaska (55318) *(G-976)*
Morcon Construction Co Inc 763 546-6066
5905 Golden Valley Rd # 231 Minneapolis (55422) *(G-5127)*
More Costello & Hart Pllp 651 227-7683
55 5th St E Ste 1400 Saint Paul (55101) *(G-8720)*
Morgan Business Trust 218 348-1359
6016 N Pike Lake Rd Duluth (55811) *(G-1397)*
Morgan Stanley 763 475-4100
701 Lake St E Wayzata (55391) *(G-9930)*
Morgan Stanley & Co Inc 952 921-1900
8300 Norman Center Dr Ste 1150 Minneapolis (55437) *(G-5128)*
Morgan Stanley & Co Inc 612 340-6700
225 S 6th St Ste 5100 Minneapolis (55402) *(G-5129)*
Morgan Tire & Auto Inc 218 828-8552
14370 Dellwood Dr 100 Baxter (56425) *(G-338)*
Morgan Tire & Auto Inc 507 388-6461
1661 E Madison Ave Mankato (56001) *(G-3173)*
Morgan Tire & Auto Inc 612 861-2278
500 W 78th St Minneapolis (55423) *(G-5130)*
Morgan Tire & Auto Inc 651 452-4091
3595 Krestwood Ln Saint Paul (55123) *(G-7846)*
Morgan Tire & Auto LLC 763 682-4979
1002 3rd St S Buffalo (55313) *(G-653)*
Morgan Tire & Auto LLC 651 458-1812
7199 E Point Douglas Rd S Cottage Grove (55016) *(G-1105)*
Morgan Tire & Auto LLC 952 944-0458
8453 Joiner Way Eden Prairie (55344) *(G-1730)*
Morgan Tire & Auto LLC 507 532-9686
1100 E Main St Marshall (56258) *(G-3316)*
Morgan Tire & Auto LLC 763 571-4392
5126 Central Ave NE Minneapolis (55421) *(G-3545)*
Morgan Tire & Auto LLC 763 525-1583
3520 Winnetka Ave N Minneapolis (55427) *(G-5131)*
Morgan Tire & Auto LLC 651 789-4361
3805 Silver Lake Rd NE Minneapolis (55421) *(G-6130)*
Morgan Tire & Auto LLC 507 354-4972
1807 S Broadway St New Ulm (56073) *(G-6463)*
Morgan Tire & Auto LLC 651 388-3266
828 Main St Red Wing (55066) *(G-6991)*
Morgan Tire & Auto LLC 651 690-5007
2185 Ford Pkwy Saint Paul (55116) *(G-8721)*
Morgan Tire & Auto LLC 320 235-1073
1801 1st St S Willmar (56201) *(G-10028)*
Morning Star Healthcare Svcs 651 209-2950
2147 University Ave W # 206 Saint Paul (55114) *(G-8722)*
Morning Star Home Health 507 373-0201
1008 Dunham St Albert Lea (56007) *(G-62)*
Morrell Transfer Inc 763 441-2011
10752 171st Ave NW Elk River (55330) *(G-1885)*
Morries New Buffalo Chrysler 763 682-1800
705 Highway 55 E Buffalo (55313) *(G-654)*
Morris Communications Corp 218 829-4705
506 James St Brainerd (56401) *(G-576)*
Morris-Walker Ltd 952 873-4334
351 Enterprise Dr E Belle Plaine (56011) *(G-368)*
Mort's Transportation Inc 320 269-7340
5010 10th Ave SW Montevideo (56265) *(G-6255)*
Mortgage & Investment Conslnts 651 483-0200
2489 Rice St Ste 202 Saint Paul (55113) *(G-8723)*
Mortgage Assurance 507 388-8140
220 E Main St Ste 4 Mankato (56001) *(G-3174)*
Mortgage Centers, Duluth *Also Called Western National Bank (G-1503)*
Mortgage Resource Center Inc 651 683-9705
2975 Lone Oak Dr Ste 140 Eagan (55121) *(G-1539)*
Mortgages Unlimited 763 633-0576
13737 210th Ave NW Elk River (55330) *(G-1886)*
Mortgages Unlimited Inc 763 416-2600
7365 Kirkwood Ct N Ste 300 Maple Grove (55369) *(G-3251)*
Morton's of Chicago Inc 612 673-9700
555 Nicollet Mall Minneapolis (55402) *(G-5132)*
Mosaic Co (HQ) 763 577-2700
3033 Campus Dr Ste E490 Minneapolis (55441) *(G-5133)*
Mosaic Global Holdings Inc (DH) 763 577-2700
3033 Campus Dr Ste E490 Minneapolis (55441) *(G-5134)*
Moss & Barnett, A Professional 612 877-5000
90 S 7th St Ste 4800 Minneapolis (55402) *(G-5135)*
Mothers & Children Program Mac 651 484-8241
1140 Gervais Ave Saint Paul (55109) *(G-8724)*
Motion International Inc 952 746-5630
3800 Amrcn Blvd W Ste 425 Minneapolis (55431) *(G-5136)*
Motion Tech Automation Inc 651 730-9010
7166 4th St N Saint Paul (55128) *(G-9252)*
Motivaction LLC 763 412-3000
16355 36th Ave N Ste 100 Minneapolis (55446) *(G-5137)*
Motivations For Fitness Inc 612 617-9090
1313 5th St SE Ste 336 Minneapolis (55414) *(G-5138)*
Motorola Inc 952 895-7800
2900 County Road 42 W # 120 Burnsville (55337) *(G-760)*
Motors Management Corp (PA) 763 593-5755
3701 Alabama Ave S Saint Louis Park (55416) *(G-7668)*
Moundsview Banquet 763 717-4041
5394 Edgewood Dr Saint Paul (55112) *(G-8725)*
Mount Olivet Careview Home 612 827-5677
5517 Lyndale Ave S Minneapolis (55419) *(G-5139)*
Mount Olivet Lutheran Church 612 861-3305
5601 Lyndale Ave S Minneapolis (55419) *(G-5140)*
Mount Olivet Rolling Acres Inc 952 474-5974
7200 Rolling Acres Rd Victoria (55386) *(G-9731)*
Mount Yale Portfolio Advisors, Minneapolis *Also Called Mt Yale Capital Group LLC (G-5146)*
Mount Yale Portfolio Advisors 952 897-5390
8000 Norman Center Dr Ste 630 Minneapolis (55437) *(G-5141)*
Mount Zion Hebrew Congregation 651 698-3881
1300 Summit Ave Saint Paul (55105) *(G-8726)*
Mountain Lk Good Samaritan Vlg, Mountain Lake *Also Called Evangelical Lutheran Good (G-6397)*
Movies At Burnsville II, Burnsville *Also Called Regal Cinemas Inc (G-788)*
MOWER COUNTY HISTORICAL SOCIET, Austin *Also Called County of Mower (G-268)*
Mp Nexlevel LLC 320 963-2400
500 County Road 37 Maple Lake (55358) *(G-3262)*
Mp Technologies LLC 320 963-2499
501 County Road 37 Maple Lake (55358) *(G-3263)*
Mpls Hotel Management Ltd 507 281-8000
150 S Broadway Rochester (55904) *(G-7188)*
Mpls Radiology Assoc Clinic, Minneapolis *Also Called Minneapolis Radiology Assocs (G-5061)*
Mplsp Hotel Corp 952 854-3400
1321 E 78th St Minneapolis (55425) *(G-5142)*
MPS Group Properties Inc 507 533-8330
101 10th St NW Stewartville (55976) *(G-9593)*
MQ Software Inc 952 345-8720
1660 Highway 100 S # 400 Minneapolis (55416) *(G-5143)*
MR Paving & Excavating Inc 507 354-4171
1000 N Front St New Ulm (56073) *(G-6464)*
Mrci Worksource, Mankato *Also Called Mankato Rehabilitation Center (G-3165)*
Mrg Management Inc 763 537-1460
8601 73rd Ave N Ste 21 Minneapolis (55428) *(G-5144)*
MSFC, Minneapolis *Also Called Metropolitan Sports Facilities (G-5009)*
MSP Corp 651 287-8100
5910 Rice Creek Pkwy # 300 Saint Paul (55126) *(G-8727)*
MSP Real Estate Inc 952 351-4540
7201 Walker St Ste 20 Minneapolis (55426) *(G-5145)*
Mt Royal Medical Center, Duluth *Also Called St Luke's Hospital of Duluth (G-1468)*
Mt Yale Capital Group LLC 952 897-5390
8000 Norman Center Dr # 630 Minneapolis (55437) *(G-5146)*
Mtec Electric Inc 763 537-1570
3707 50th Ave N Minneapolis (55429) *(G-5147)*
MTS Systems Corp (PA) 952 937-4000
14000 Technology Dr Eden Prairie (55344) *(G-1731)*
Mulcahy Inc 651 770-5250
3050 Echo Lake Ave Ste 300 Mahtomedi (55115) *(G-3095)*
Muller Boat Co 651 465-6315
37350 Wild Mountain Rd Taylors Falls (55084) *(G-9661)*
Multi Clean, Minneapolis *Also Called Paquette Maintenance Inc (G-5318)*
Multi Venue Production Inc 952 894-9111
3625 Ashbury Rd Saint Paul (55122) *(G-7847)*
Multi-County AG LLC 507 223-5634
1204 Saint Olaf Ave N Canby (56220) *(G-850)*
Multi-Services Inc 952 944-4000
7595 Anagram Dr Eden Prairie (55344) *(G-1732)*

ALPHABETIC

Multicare Associates of The (PA) ...763 785-4500
7675 Madison St NE Minneapolis (55432) *(G-3546)*
Multicare Associates of The ...763 785-4250
11855 Ulymnes St NE 100 Minneapolis (55434) *(G-3547)*
Multicare Associates of The ...763 785-4300
1835 County Road C W Ste 20 Saint Paul (55113) *(G-8728)*
Multiconcepts, Minneapolis *Also Called DMW Properties Inc (G-4267)*
Multihousing Credit Control, Eden Prairie *Also Called MCC Group Inc (G-1718)*
Multimedia Holdings ...763 546-1111
8811 Olson Memorial Hwy Minneapolis (55427) *(G-5148)*
Municipal Parking Inc ...612 673-9644
1030 2nd Ave S Minneapolis (55403) *(G-5149)*
Municipal Parking Inc ...612 339-2003
516 2nd Ave N Minneapolis (55403) *(G-5150)*
Munters Corp ...952 831-9418
1800 Cliff Rd E Ste 8 Burnsville (55337) *(G-761)*
Murlowski Construction Co Inc ...651 786-1300
2200 Old Highway 8 NW Saint Paul (55112) *(G-8729)*
Murphy Automotive Inc ...952 432-2454
7358 160th St W Rosemount (55068) *(G-7373)*
Murphy Bros Designers ...763 780-3262
1613 93rd Ln NE Minneapolis (55449) *(G-3548)*
Murphy Warehouse Co ...612 623-1226
4700 Main St NE Minneapolis (55421) *(G-3549)*
Murphy Warehouse Co (PA) ...612 623-1200
701 24th Ave SE Minneapolis (55414) *(G-5151)*
Murray Williamson ...218 751-8481
1815 Paul Bunyan Dr NW Bemidji (56601) *(G-404)*
Murray's Co Inc ...612 333-2507
24 S 6th St Minneapolis (55402) *(G-5152)*
Muska Electric Co ...651 636-5820
1985 Oakcrest Ave Saint Paul (55113) *(G-8730)*
Mutual Service Cooperative ...651 631-7000
2 Pine Tree Dr Saint Paul (55112) *(G-8731)*
Muzak LLC ...763 424-5533
6901 E Fish Lake Rd Ste 132 Osseo (55369) *(G-6641)*
Mvna, Minneapolis *Also Called Minnesota Visiting Nurse Agcy (G-5101)*
Mvri, Minneapolis *Also Called Minnesota Veterans Research (G-5100)*
MVTL Labs, New Ulm *Also Called Minnesota Valley Testing Labs (G-6461)*
Mycull Fixtures Inc ...763 389-4400
1005 16th Ave S Princeton (55371) *(G-6911)*
Myseeks Inc ...651 967-4150
356 9th Ave Ste 304 Saint Paul Park (55071) *(G-9297)*
Myslajek Ltd ...612 781-2771
648 Lowry Ave NE Minneapolis (55418) *(G-5153)*
Mystic Lake Casino, Prior Lake *Also Called Smsc Gaming Enterprise (G-6955)*
N A E O, Saint Paul *Also Called National Amtelco Equipment (G-8738)*
N A H Inc ...507 462-3331
10091 Hwy 22 N Minnesota Lake (56068) *(G-6137)*
N A Trading & Technology Inc ...952 888-7654
9216 Grand Ave S Minneapolis (55420) *(G-5154)*
N Bruce Christense ...952 653-1000
11100 Bren Rd W Hopkins (55343) *(G-2585)*
N C Holdings (PA) ...952 933-7060
10395 Yellow Circle Dr Hopkins (55343) *(G-2586)*
N F P Transportation, Sauk Centre *Also Called Robert Chapin (G-9352)*
N P D Inc ...218 720-3324
1202 Maple Grove Rd Duluth (55811) *(G-1398)*
N P L, Grand Rapids *Also Called Npl Construction Co (G-2303)*
N'Compass Solutions Inc ...612 379-2100
718 Washington Ave N # 401 Minneapolis (55401) *(G-5155)*
NA Corp (PA) ...651 636-9654
2230 Albert St N Saint Paul (55113) *(G-8732)*
Nabisco, Minneapolis *Also Called Kraft Foods Global Inc (G-4821)*
Nadeau Excavating Inc ...651 438-8628
12175 240th St E Hampton (55031) *(G-2366)*
Naeve Parkview Home, Wells *Also Called Albert Lee Medical Center Inc (G-9960)*
Naiop Minnesota Chapter, Minneapolis *Also Called Minnesota Chapter of The Natl (G-5071)*
Nalco Chemical Co ...763 559-3209
5000 Cheshire Ln N Ste 2 Minneapolis (55446) *(G-5156)*
Nalco Distributing Inc ...651 636-8124
1000 Labore Industrial Ct Saint Paul (55110) *(G-8733)*
Naniboujou Lodge & Rest, Grand Marais *Also Called L Jireh Inc (G-2262)*
Naomi Family Center ...651 222-7962
77 9th St E Saint Paul (55101) *(G-8734)*
NAPA Auto Parts, Minneapolis *Also Called Genuine Parts Co (G-4523)*
NAPA Auto Parts, Saint Cloud *Also Called Tri-County Parts Supply Inc (G-7620)*
NAPA CROOKSTON WELDING, Crookston *Also Called Crookston Welding Machine Co (G-1122)*
Napco International LLC (PA) ...952 931-2400
11055 Excelsior Blvd Hopkins (55343) *(G-2587)*
Nardini Fire Equipment Co Inc ...651 483-6631
405 County Road E W Saint Paul (55126) *(G-8735)*
Narveson Management Inc ...218 562-6400
6810 County Road 11 Pequot Lakes (56472) *(G-6791)*
Nash Frame Design Inc ...612 338-9041
10 S 13th St Minneapolis (55403) *(G-5157)*
Nash-Finch Co ...507 263-3643
425 Main St W Cannon Falls (55009) *(G-861)*
Nash-Finch Co (PA) ...952 832-0534
7600 France Ave S Ste 200 Edina (55435) *(G-1838)*
Nash-Finch Co ...651 463-3404
115 Elm St Ste A Farmington (55024) *(G-2055)*
Nash-Finch Co ...218 739-5272
1205 W Lincoln Ave Fergus Falls (56537) *(G-2100)*
Nash-Finch Co ...320 587-8233
205 Washington Ave E Hutchinson (55350) *(G-2708)*
Nash-Finch Co ...507 645-9514
601 Division St S Northfield (55057) *(G-6534)*
Nash-Finch Co ...507 645-4489
603 Division St S Northfield (55057) *(G-6535)*
Nash-Finch Co ...651 388-2869
615 Main St Red Wing (55066) *(G-6992)*
Nash-Finch Co ...320 251-3961
360 Hoffman Ct Saint Cloud (56303) *(G-7561)*
Nash-Finch Co ...507 931-5541
612 S Minnesota Ave Saint Peter (56082) *(G-9309)*

Nath Co, Minneapolis *Also Called Prime Investments Inc (G-5409)*
Nath Management Inc ...651 739-2377
255 Century Ave N Saint Paul (55119) *(G-8736)*
Nath Midwest Lodging LLC ...952 853-1400
900 E 79th St Ste 300 Minneapolis (55420) *(G-5158)*
Nath Midwest Lodging LLC ...952 853-1423
2540 Cleveland Ave N Saint Paul (55113) *(G-8737)*
Nath Minnesota Franchise Group (PA) ...952 853-1400
900 E 79th St Ste 300 Minneapolis (55420) *(G-5159)*
Nathan J Lilleodden CPA ...952 476-7107
800 Wayzata Blvd E # 300 Wayzata (55391) *(G-9931)*
National Amtelco Equipment ...651 265-7845
1000 Westgate Dr Ste 252 Saint Paul (55114) *(G-8738)*
National Arbitration Forum Inc ...952 516-6400
6465 Wayzata Blvd Ste 500 Minneapolis (55426) *(G-5160)*
National Assoc of Retired ...320 245-2629
222 Court Ave S Sandstone (55072) *(G-9323)*
National Automatic Sprinkler ...763 784-8902
10351 Jamestown St NE Minneapolis (55449) *(G-3550)*
National Business Systems Inc (PA) ...651 688-0202
2919 W Service Rd Eagan (55121) *(G-1540)*
National Camera Exchange Inc ...952 898-4888
14380 Burnhaven Dr Burnsville (55306) *(G-762)*
National Camera Exchange Inc ...651 636-0693
2401 Fairview Ave N # 10 Saint Paul (55113) *(G-8739)*
National Car Rental System Inc ...218 283-8486
County Rd 108 International Falls (56649) *(G-2728)*
National Cemetery Admin ...612 726-1127
7601 34th Ave S Minneapolis (55450) *(G-5161)*
National Communications Svcs ...763 576-9977
1100 Lund Blvd Anoka (55303) *(G-206)*
National Dairy Council, Saint Paul *Also Called American Dairy Association of (G-8024)*
National Dentex Corp ...507 625-5079
121 E Main St Ste 308 Mankato (56001) *(G-3175)*
National Dentex Corp ...763 566-0210
6500 Shingle Creek Pkwy Minneapolis (55430) *(G-5162)*
National Engineering Resources ...763 561-7610
7100 Northland Cir N Ste 301 Minneapolis (55428) *(G-5163)*
National Floor Maintenance Inc ...303 771-0509
1670 Robert St S 292 Saint Paul (55118) *(G-7848)*
National Independent Brokers ...763 525-1111
10700 County Road 15 # 450 Minneapolis (55441) *(G-5164)*
National Initiatives For ...763 229-2753
6125 Virginia Ave N Minneapolis (55428) *(G-5165)*
National Lodging Co's Inc ...507 825-5871
104 W Main St Pipestone (56164) *(G-6832)*
National Marrow Donor Program ...612 627-5800
3001 Broadway St NE Ste 500 Minneapolis (55413) *(G-5166)*
National Multiple Sclerosis ...612 335-7900
200 12th Ave S Minneapolis (55415) *(G-5167)*
National Oilwell Varco Inc ...651 293-4699
240 Plato Blvd E Saint Paul (55107) *(G-8740)*
National Parts & Abrasive's, Chanhassen *Also Called Total Automotive Inc (G-944)*
National Recoveries Inc ...763 754-1931
14735 Highway 65 NE # 100 Anoka (55304) *(G-207)*
National Retirement Plan Inc ...651 789-1037
2600 Eagan Woods Dr # 450 Eagan (55121) *(G-1541)*
National Salon Resources Div, Minneapolis *Also Called Mikara Corp (G-5038)*
National Service, Eden Prairie *Also Called Volunteers of America Inc (G-1809)*
National Service Co of Iowa ...507 372-2276
1016 Oxford St Worthington (56187) *(G-10188)*
National Sports Center Fndtn ...763 785-5600
1700 105th Ave NE Minneapolis (55449) *(G-3551)*
National Tack North Inc ...651 464-7733
7995 200th St N Forest Lake (55025) *(G-2165)*
National Theatre For Children ...612 617-4903
2733 Park Ave Minneapolis (55407) *(G-5168)*
National Truck Underwriting ...952 893-1234
5001 Amrcn Blvd W Ste 801 Minneapolis (55437) *(G-5169)*
Nations Title Agency ...952 545-2808
6465 Wayzata Blvd Ste 710 Minneapolis (55426) *(G-5170)*
Nationwide Financial ...612 723-6375
4046 Bryant Ave N Minneapolis (55412) *(G-5171)*
Nativity Mary Catholic School, Minneapolis *Also Called Church of The Nativity of The (G-4074)*
Natural Resource Group LLC ...612 347-6789
1000 Ids Ctr 80 S 8th St Minneapolis (55402) *(G-5172)*
Natural Resources RES Inst, Duluth *Also Called Regents of The University of (G-1433)*
Nature Conservancy ...612 331-0700
1101 W River Pkwy Ste 200 Minneapolis (55415) *(G-5173)*
Natures Garden World Inc ...218 739-9641
1335 Highway 210 E Fergus Falls (56537) *(G-2101)*
Natus Corp ...651 487-3211
1381 Rice St Saint Paul (55117) *(G-8741)*
Navarre Corp (PA) ...763 535-8333
7400 49th Ave N Minneapolis (55428) *(G-5174)*
Navigant International Rocky ...612 375-2884
700 Nicollet Mall Ste 550 Minneapolis (55402) *(G-5175)*
Navitaire Inc ...612 317-7000
333 S 7th St Ste 500 Minneapolis (55402) *(G-5176)*
Naylor Electrical Construction ...218 751-2620
1430 Paul Bunyan Dr NW Bemidji (56601) *(G-405)*
Naylor Heating & Refrigeration ...218 444-4328
1430 Paul Bunyan Dr NW Bemidji (56601) *(G-406)*
Naylor's, Bemidji *Also Called Naylor Electrical Construction (G-405)*
Nb Saint Paul Inc ...651 731-2220
2201 Burns Ave Saint Paul (55119) *(G-8742)*
Ncs Pearson Inc (DH) ...952 681-3000
5601 Green Valley Dr # 220 Minneapolis (55437) *(G-5177)*
Ncs Pearson Inc ...952 681-3000
5601 Green Valley Dr # 220 Minneapolis (55437) *(G-5178)*
Ndn Mulcahy LLC ...651 747-4201
3050 Echo Lake Ave Mahtomedi (55115) *(G-3096)*
Ne-la-Shing Clinic, Onamia *Also Called Indian Health Service (G-6572)*
Nedeau Inc ...651 438-8628
12175 240th St E Hampton (55031) *(G-2367)*
Nedegaard Construction Co Inc ...763 757-2926
1521 94th Ln NE Minneapolis (55449) *(G-3552)*

Nedmac Inc 763 537-8435
5410 International Pkwy Minneapolis (55428) *(G-5179)*
Nei Bottling Inc 218 751-3847
730 Industrial Park Dr SE Bemidji (56601) *(G-407)*
Neighborhood Counseling Center 218 631-1714
11 2nd St SW Ste 1 Wadena (56482) *(G-9807)*
Neighborhood House 651 789-2500
179 Robie St E Saint Paul (55107) *(G-8743)*
Neighborhood Involvement 612 374-3125
2431 Hennepin Ave S Minneapolis (55405) *(G-5180)*
Neighborhood Recycling Corp 651 222-7678
2828 Kennedy St NE Minneapolis (55413) *(G-5181)*
Nelnet Inc 651 265-7600
180 5th St E Ste 1350 Saint Paul (55101) *(G-8744)*
Nels Nelson & Sons Inc 218 879-4561
1000 Tall Pine Ln Cloquet (55720) *(G-1058)*
Nelson Chrysler Dodge GMC Inc 218 739-2283
2228 College Way Fergus Falls (56537) *(G-2102)*
Nelson Co's 507 289-6789
2829 43rd St NW Rochester (55901) *(G-7189)*
Nelson Leasing Inc (PA) 320 235-2770
2700 Highway 12 E Willmar (56201) *(G-10029)*
Nelson Nursery Inc 763 856-2441
25834 Main St Zimmerman (55398) *(G-10214)*
Nelson, Bruce Plumbing 651 738-9354
1272 Point Douglas Rd S Saint Paul (55119) *(G-8745)*
Nemadji Research Corp 320 838-3838
100 Birch St Bruno (55712) *(G-631)*
Nephrology Analytical Services 612 337-7345
914 S 8th St Minneapolis (55404) *(G-5182)*
Ner, Minneapolis *Also Called National Engineering Resources (G-5163)*
Netaspx Minnesota, Minneapolis *Also Called Network Computing Services Inc (G-5183)*
Netspi, Minneapolis *Also Called Network Security Professionals (G-5185)*
Network Computing Services Inc 612 337-0200
1200 Washington Ave S Minneapolis (55415) *(G-5183)*
Network Design Inc 763 475-5500
171 Cheshire Ln N Ste 700 Minneapolis (55441) *(G-5184)*
Network Instruments LLC 952 358-3800
10701 Red Circle Dr Minnetonka (55343) *(G-6201)*
Network of Contractors Inc 763 639-1440
15861 Dolomite St NW Ramsey (55303) *(G-6968)*
Network Security Professionals 612 465-8880
800 Washington Ave N Minneapolis (55401) *(G-5185)*
Neufeldt Industrial Services 651 388-4347
2568 Eagle Ridge Dr Red Wing (55066) *(G-6993)*
Neurological Associates of St 651 221-9051
1650 Beam Ave Ste 200 Saint Paul (55109) *(G-8746)*
New Beginnings At Waverly LLC 763 658-5800
109 N Shore Dr Waverly (55390) *(G-9904)*
New Boundary Technologies Inc 612 379-3805
1300 Godward St NE # 3100 Minneapolis (55413) *(G-5186)*
New Brighton Care Center, Saint Paul *Also Called North Cities Health Care Inc (G-8751)*
New Challenges Inc 651 681-2044
3513 Widgeon Way Saint Paul (55123) *(G-7849)*
New Concepts Management Group 952 922-2500
5707 Excelsior Blvd Minneapolis (55416) *(G-5187)*
New Concepts Management Group 952 922-2500
3065 Centre Pointe Dr Saint Paul (55113) *(G-8747)*
New Dawn Inc 507 425-3278
101 S Baltimore Ave Fulda (56131) *(G-2196)*
New Discoveries Montessori 320 234-6362
1000 5th Ave SE Hutchinson (55350) *(G-2709)*
New England Financial, Hopkins *Also Called Leneave Financial Group (G-2570)*
New England Financial, Minnetonka *Also Called Mid American Financial Group (G-6194)*
New ERA Incentives Inc 651 486-0252
3770 Dunlap St N Saint Paul (55112) *(G-8748)*
New Fashion Pork Inc 507 847-4610
164 Industrial Park Jackson (56143) *(G-2797)*
New French Bakery Inc 612 728-0193
2609 26th Ave S Minneapolis (55406) *(G-5188)*
New Hall Animal Hospital, Minneapolis *Also Called Randall J Herman (G-5466)*
New Homes Realty Inc 952 469-6003
20638 Hartford Way Lakeville (55044) *(G-2921)*
New Horizon Child Care Inc 952 469-6659
9085 203rd St W Lakeville (55044) *(G-2922)*
New Horizon Child Care Inc 763 574-7450
999 Moore Lake Dr E Minneapolis (55432) *(G-3553)*
New Horizon Child Care Inc 763 757-2604
2381 108th Ln NE Minneapolis (55449) *(G-3554)*
New Horizon Child Care Inc 952 893-1893
4201 Minnesota Dr Minneapolis (55435) *(G-5189)*
New Horizon Child Care Inc 763 315-3033
8547 Edinburgh Center Dr Minneapolis (55443) *(G-5190)*
New Horizon Child Care Inc 763 478-2412
4345 Peony Ln N Minneapolis (55446) *(G-5191)*
New Horizon Child Care Inc (HQ) 763 557-1111
16355 36th Ave N Ste 700 Plymouth (55446) *(G-6875)*
New Horizon Child Care Inc 952 423-6690
14088 141st St W Saint Paul (55124) *(G-7850)*
New Horizon Child Care Inc 651 481-8069
2360 Lexington Ave N Saint Paul (55113) *(G-8749)*
New Horizon Enterprises Inc (PA) 763 557-1111
16355 36th Ave N Ste 700 Plymouth (55446) *(G-6876)*
New Life Farms LLP 218 346-7587
47947 140th St Frazee (56544) *(G-2186)*
New Life Farms, Lllp 218 346-4959
105 Jake St Perham (56573) *(G-6799)*
New Life Multi-Family Mgt 952 831-0866
7455 France Ave S 381 Edina (55435) *(G-1839)*
New Life Treatment Center 507 777-4321
130 Dakota St S Woodstock (56186) *(G-10176)*
New Midwest Co LLC 320 329-3363
209 N Main St Renville (56284) *(G-7032)*
New Millennium 763 780-9933
7931 6th St NE Minneapolis (55432) *(G-3555)*
New Paradigm Productions Inc 612 321-9091
800 Washington Ave N # 506 Minneapolis (55401) *(G-5192)*
New Perspective of Minnesota 651 407-9076
113 East Ave Mahtomedi (55115) *(G-3097)*
New Prague Golf Club Inc 952 758-5326
400 Lexington Ave S New Prague (56071) *(G-6423)*
New Richland Care Center 507 465-3292
312 1st St NE New Richland (56072) *(G-6436)*
New Streams International Inc 651 777-8020
1686 Village Trl E Unit 4 Maplewood (55109) *(G-3286)*
New Ulm Bus Lines Inc 507 354-4711
1400 S Minnesota St New Ulm (56073) *(G-6465)*
New Ulm Country Club 507 354-8896
1 Golf Dr New Ulm (56073) *(G-6466)*
New Ulm Dental Clinic 507 354-3321
127 N Broadway St New Ulm (56073) *(G-6467)*
New Ulm Telecom Inc (PA) 507 354-4111
27 N Minnesota St New Ulm (56073) *(G-6468)*
New Ulm Turnverein Inc 507 354-4916
102 S State St New Ulm (56073) *(G-6469)*
New Ulm, City of Inc 507 359-8264
310 1st St N New Ulm (56073) *(G-6470)*
New Unbank Co LLC 952 544-5155
10550 Wayzata Blvd Ste C Hopkins (55305) *(G-2588)*
New York Life Insurance Co 952 897-5000
3600 Minnesota Dr Ste 100 Minneapolis (55435) *(G-5193)*
New York Mint Ltd 952 949-6588
5577 W 78th St Minneapolis (55439) *(G-5194)*
Newport Corp 763 593-0722
5480 Nathan Ln N Ste 122 Minneapolis (55442) *(G-5195)*
News Dept, Duluth *Also Called Granite Broadcasting Corp (G-1341)*
Newtown Solutions Inc 952 440-4400
8608 Eagle Creek Pkwy Savage (55378) *(G-9400)*
Nexpro Personnel Services Inc 952 224-9855
5353 Gamble Dr Ste 112 Minneapolis (55416) *(G-5196)*
Next Level Electronics Inc 320 363-7716
30593 Pearl Dr Ste 1A Saint Joseph (56374) *(G-7653)*
Nextel Communications Inc 952 703-7600
7700 France Ave S Ste 400 Minneapolis (55435) *(G-5197)*
Nextmedia Outdoor Inc 763 489-3841
13805 1st Ave N Ste 800 Minneapolis (55441) *(G-5198)*
Nibi, Mankato *Also Called Hickory Tech Information Soln (G-3139)*
Nico Properties 612 822-2185
2929 1st Ave S Minneapolis (55408) *(G-5199)*
Nicollet County Bank of Saint 507 931-3310
220 S 3rd St Saint Peter (56082) *(G-9310)*
Nicollet Island Inn, Minneapolis *Also Called Isle West Associates, LLP (G-4737)*
Niecc Inc 763 536-8300
7025 Northland Dr N Minneapolis (55428) *(G-5200)*
Nielsen Co US LLC 763 593-2000
600 Highway 169 S Ste 400 Minneapolis (55426) *(G-5201)*
Nightingale Home Health Care 763 545-3131
8085 Wayzata Blvd Ste 105 Minneapolis (55426) *(G-5202)*
Nightowl Document Management 612 337-0448
724 N 1st St Ste 500 Minneapolis (55401) *(G-5203)*
Nile Health Care Center, Minneapolis *Also Called Health Care Center (G-4617)*
Niles - Wiese Construction Co 507 446-0825
112 S Mn St Medford (55049) *(G-3344)*
Nilfisk-Advance Inc (PA) 763 745-3500
14600 21st Ave N Plymouth (55447) *(G-6877)*
9900 Properties 952 881-5825
9939 Lyndale Ave S Minneapolis (55420) *(G-5204)*
19th Ave Grill & Lounge, Willmar *Also Called Kandi Entertainment Center Inc (G-10012)*
Nintey Four Services Inc 763 295-3604
119 Oakwood Dr E Monticello (55362) *(G-6279)*
Nisswa Marine Inc 218 963-2292
24238 Smiley Rd Nisswa (56468) *(G-6498)*
No Name 218 547-3334
Hwy 371 Walker (56484) *(G-9855)*
Noah Insurance Group 651 430-0085
5795 Morning Dove Ave N # 101 Stillwater (55082) *(G-9631)*
Nobel Welding & Manufacturing 651 426-1511
7075 21st Ave Hugo (55038) *(G-2671)*
Noble Welding, Hugo *Also Called Nobel Welding & Manufacturing (G-2671)*
Nobles Rock Public Health 507 372-8256
315 10th St Worthington (56187) *(G-10189)*
Nodland Construction Co 320 763-5159
322 Fairgrounds Rd Alexandria (56308) *(G-114)*
Nokomis Cleaners & Launderers, Eden Prairie *Also Called Pilgrim Cleaners & Launderers (G-1747)*
Nol-Tec Systems Inc 651 780-8600
425 Apollo Dr Circle Pines (55014) *(G-1018)*
Nonviolent Peaceforce 612 871-0005
425 Oak Grove St Minneapolis (55403) *(G-5205)*
Nor-Son Inc 218 828-1722
7900 Hastings Rd Baxter (56425) *(G-339)*
Nor-Tech, Burnsville *Also Called Northern Computer Technologies (G-763)*
Noramco Engineering Corp 218 262-1093
2729 13th Ave E Hibbing (55746) *(G-2469)*
Noran Neurological Clinic 763 786-8406
500 Osborne Rd NE Ste 365 Minneapolis (55432) *(G-3556)*
Noran Neurological Clinic (PA) 612 879-1000
2828 Chicago Ave Minneapolis (55407) *(G-5206)*
Norcostco Inc 763 544-0601
825 Rhode Island Ave S Minneapolis (55426) *(G-5207)*
Nordaas Retail, Minnesota Lake *Also Called N A H Inc (G-6137)*
Nordic Insulation Inc 763 784-7893
1550 93rd Ln NE Minneapolis (55449) *(G-3557)*
Nordquist Sign Co 612 823-7291
312 W Lake St Minneapolis (55408) *(G-5208)*
Norex Inc 952 447-8898
5505 Cottonwood Ln SE Prior Lake (55372) *(G-6945)*
Norman County Ambulance Garage 218 784-5000
201 9th St W Ste 1 ADA (56510) *(G-2)*
Norman County Education Assoc 218 356-8773
3536 260th Ave Gary (56545) *(G-2198)*
Normandale Evangelical 952 929-1697
6100 Normandale Rd Minneapolis (55436) *(G-5209)*
Normandale Hills Elem School, Minneapolis *Also Called Independent School District (G-4695)*
Normandale Tennis Club, Minneapolis *Also Called Starmark Northwest Management (G-5743)*

ALPHABETIC

Normandy Inn Inc 612 370-1400
405 S 8th St Minneapolis (55404) *(G-5210)*

Normark Corp (HQ) 952 933-7060
10395 Yellow Circle Dr Hopkins (55343) *(G-2589)*

Norris Dispenser, Minneapolis *Also Called Silver King Refrigeration Inc (G-5674)*

Norris Square 651 769-2447
8200 Hadley Ave S Ofc OFC Cottage Grove (55016) *(G-1106)*

Norseman Motors Inc 218 847-4415
425 E Hwy 10 Detroit Lakes (56501) *(G-1212)*

Norseman Motors Inc 218 847-1639
425 Frazee St E Detroit Lakes (56501) *(G-1213)*

Norsemen Inc 507 835-5060
32960 State Highway 13 Waseca (56093) *(G-9883)*

Norstan Communications Inc (DH) 952 352-4300
5101 Shady Oak Rd S Minnetonka (55343) *(G-6202)*

Norstan Inc (HQ) 952 352-4000
5101 Shady Oak Rd S Hopkins (55343) *(G-2590)*

Nortech Systems Inc (PA) 952 345-2244
1120 Wayzata Blvd E 201 Wayzata (55391) *(G-9932)*

Nortel Networks Inc 952 897-1150
8000 Norman Center Dr Ste 650 Minneapolis (55437) *(G-5211)*

North Ambulance, Minneapolis *Also Called Oakdale Health Enterprises Inc (G-5256)*

North Ambulance Faribault 507 334-6031
1226 Willow St Faribault (55021) *(G-2023)*

North American Abrasives, Saint Paul *Also Called Nalco Distributing Inc (G-8733)*

North American Affinity Clubs 952 936-9333
12301 Whitewater Dr Minnetonka (55343) *(G-6203)*

North American Banking Co 651 636-9654
2230 Albert St N Saint Paul (55113) *(G-8750)*

North American Communications (DH) 651 994-6800
3344 Highway 149 Eagan (55121) *(G-1542)*

North American Communications 952 942-7200
10525 Hampshire Ave S Minneapolis (55438) *(G-5212)*

North American Composites Co (HQ) 651 481-6860
300 Apollo Dr Circle Pines (55014) *(G-1019)*

North American Framing Inc 763 784-4855
8411 Center Dr NE Minneapolis (55432) *(G-3558)*

North American Membership Grp (HQ) 952 936-9333
12301 Whitewater Dr Hopkins (55343) *(G-2591)*

North American Membership Grp 952 988-7451
5555 12th Ave E Ste 170 Shakopee (55379) *(G-9459)*

North American State Bank (PA) 320 254-8271
321 Washburn Ave Belgrade (56312) *(G-365)*

North American State Bank 320 697-5533
201 Main St Elrosa (56325) *(G-1910)*

North American Systems Intl 952 374-6700
2901 E 78th St Minneapolis (55425) *(G-5213)*

North Anoka Control Systems 763 444-4747
13828 Lincoln St NE Anoka (55304) *(G-208)*

North Beverage LLC 507 282-5462
2222 32nd Ave NW Rochester (55901) *(G-7190)*

North Central Co's Inc 952 449-0885
601 Carlson Pkwy Ste 400 Minnetonka (55305) *(G-6204)*

North Central Container of New 507 359-3136
209 3rd South St New Ulm (56073) *(G-6471)*

North Central Management Inc 763 509-9500
6350 Vinewood Ln N Osseo (55311) *(G-6642)*

North Central Service Inc 218 776-3855
227 1st Ave SW Clearbrook (56634) *(G-1039)*

North Cities Health Care Inc 651 633-7200
805 6th Ave NW Saint Paul (55112) *(G-8751)*

North Coast Partners LLP 952 947-3000
7500 W 78th St Minneapolis (55439) *(G-5214)*

North Country Business Prdts (PA) 218 751-4140
1112 Railroad St SE Bemidji (56601) *(G-408)*

North Country Business Prdts 800 937-4140
9905 45th Ave N Ste 200 Plymouth (55442) *(G-6878)*

North Country Concrete Inc 763 576-8602
7040 143rd Ave NW Anoka (55303) *(G-209)*

North Country Hospital 218 751-0220
1000 Anne St NW Bemidji (56601) *(G-409)*

North Country Hospital (PA) 218 751-5430
1300 Anne St NW Bemidji (56601) *(G-410)*

North Country Hospital 218 333-5665
3525 Pine Ridge Ave NW Bemidji (56601) *(G-411)*

North Country Regional Hosp 218 751-5430
1300 Anne St NW Bemidji (56601) *(G-412)*

North Crest Gymnastics & Dance 320 251-3416
1009 Industrial Dr S Sauk Rapids (56379) *(G-9370)*

North Dakota Pigs Co-Op 218 685-6888
26955 Oak Point Rd Elbow Lake (56531) *(G-1854)*

North Homes Inc 218 327-3055
1880 River Rd Grand Rapids (55744) *(G-2298)*

North Mamorial Ambulatory, Maple Grove *Also Called Maple Grove Ambulatory Surgery (G-3248)*

North Mankato Med Fmly Clinic, Mankato *Also Called Mankato Clinic Ltd (G-3229)*

North Memorial Ambulance 651 464-6738
246 11th Ave SE Ste B Forest Lake (55025) *(G-2166)*

North Memorial Ambulance Svcs 763 389-2082
4187 Highway 169 Princeton (55371) *(G-6912)*

North Memorial Clinic 763 520-5551
4080 W Broadway Ave Ste 200 Minneapolis (55422) *(G-5215)*

North Memorial Health Care 320 763-6160
708 Nokomis St Alexandria (56308) *(G-115)*

North Memorial Health Care 218 829-8767
210 NW 5th St Brainerd (56401) *(G-577)*

North Memorial Health Care 763 520-3900
3500 France Ave N Ste 101 Minneapolis (55422) *(G-5216)*

North Memorial Health Care (PA) 763 520-5200
3300 Oakdale Ave N Minneapolis (55422) *(G-5217)*

North Memorial Health Care 763 420-7002
12000 Elm Creek Blvd N Osseo (55369) *(G-6643)*

North Memorial Health Care 507 637-5055
614 S Mill St Redwood Falls (56283) *(G-7026)*

North Memorial Imaging Center 763 398-4400
9855 Hospital Dr Ste 150 Osseo (55369) *(G-6644)*

North Metro Harness Initiative 651 925-4600
15201 Zurich St NE Forest Lake (55025) *(G-2148)*

North Metro Landscaping Inc 763 497-4898
11050 Lamont Ave NE Hanover (55341) *(G-2369)*

North Oaks Golf Club Inc 651 484-6311
54 E Oaks Rd Saint Paul (55127) *(G-8752)*

North Pine Aggregate Inc 651 464-6802
14551 Lake Dr NE Forest Lake (55025) *(G-2149)*

North Point 507 344-0059
2135 Lor Ray Dr Apt 218 North Mankato (56003) *(G-6511)*

North Point Capital Partners 651 602-0789
2299 Territorial Rd Saint Paul (55114) *(G-8753)*

North Ridge Care Center, Minneapolis *Also Called Minnesota Masonic Home North (G-5083)*

North Ridge Community Credit 218 741-1222
921 17th St S Virginia (55792) *(G-9747)*

North Second Street Steel Sply 612 522-6626
2212 N 2nd St Minneapolis (55411) *(G-5218)*

North Shore Bank of Commerce 218 722-4784
131 W Superior St Duluth (55802) *(G-1399)*

North Shore Financial Corp (PA) 218 722-4784
131 W Superior St Duluth (55802) *(G-1400)*

North Shore Hosp & Care Ctr, Grand Marais *Also Called Cook County North Shore Hosp (G-2257)*

North Shore Hospital, Grand Marais *Also Called County of Cook (G-2258)*

NORTH ST PAUL TRANSITIONAL CAR, Saint Paul *Also Called Health Care Services Inc (G-8447)*

North Star Auto Auction 952 445-5544
4908 Valley Ind Blvd N Shakopee (55379) *(G-9460)*

North Star Bumper, Minneapolis *Also Called Keystone Automotive Industries (G-3509)*

North Star Camp 218 829-6631
1214 Eagleview Dr NE Brainerd (56401) *(G-578)*

North Star General Insurance 507 423-6262
269 Barstad Rd S Cottonwood (56229) *(G-1114)*

North Star International (HQ) 612 378-1660
3000 Broadway St NE Minneapolis (55413) *(G-5219)*

North Star International Inc 651 379-5030
1060 Lone Oak Rd Ste 112 Saint Paul (55121) *(G-7851)*

North Star Nursing Inc 218 573-2238
22119 480th Ave Osage (56570) *(G-6585)*

North Star Rail Intermodal LLC (PA) 952 831-4011
7400 Metro Blvd Ste 300 Minneapolis (55439) *(G-5220)*

North Star Resource Group (HQ) 612 617-6000
2701 University Ave SE Ste 100 Minneapolis (55414) *(G-5221)*

North Star Title Inc 952 512-7400
5401 Gamble Dr Ste 300 Minneapolis (55416) *(G-5222)*

North Star World Trade Svcs 651 379-5030
1060 Lone Oak Rd Ste 112 Saint Paul (55121) *(G-7852)*

North Stop Inc 218 547-1859
Hwy 34SOUTH Walker (56484) *(G-9856)*

North Suburban Dialysis Center, Minneapolis *Also Called Bio-Medical Applications of MN (G-3417)*

North Suburban Youth Fndtn 651 697-9865
1970 Oakcrest Ave Ste 118 Saint Paul (55113) *(G-8754)*

North Valley Health Center, Warren *Also Called Warren Community Hospital Inc (G-9869)*

North Way Dental, Saint Cloud *Also Called Catton Wolseth Como & Jacobs (G-7477)*

North Way Investment Co 651 646-7901
2227 University Ave W Saint Paul (55114) *(G-8755)*

North West Eye Clinic 763 383-4140
8401 Golden Valley Rd # 330 Minneapolis (55427) *(G-5223)*

North Western Research 218 327-4615
1861 E US Highway 169 Grand Rapids (55744) *(G-2299)*

Northcott Hospitality Intl 952 934-3888
570 Pond Promenade Chanhassen (55317) *(G-933)*

Northcott Hospitality Intl 952 294-5000
250 Lake Dr E Chanhassen (55317) *(G-934)*

Northeast Bank 612 379-8811
77 Broadway St NE Minneapolis (55413) *(G-5224)*

Northeast Family YMCA, Saint Paul *Also Called YMCA Children's Center (G-9173)*

Northeast Minnesota Office of 218 748-2200
820 9th St N Ste 250 Virginia (55792) *(G-9748)*

Northeast Residence Inc 651 765-0217
410 Little Canada Rd E Saint Paul (55117) *(G-8756)*

Northeast Securities Corp (PA) 612 379-8811
77 Broadway St NE Minneapolis (55413) *(G-5225)*

Northeast Technical Services 218 741-4290
315 Chestnut St Virginia (55792) *(G-9749)*

Northern Access Transportation 218 728-5464
3133 Truck Center Dr Duluth (55806) *(G-1401)*

Northern Air Corp 651 490-9868
1001 Labore Industrial Ct B Saint Paul (55110) *(G-8757)*

Northern Alternative Energy 612 370-1061
15600 Wayzta Blvd Ste 209 Wayzata (55391) *(G-9933)*

Northern Belt & Conveyor Inc 218 744-9950
2700 Elliots Lake Rd Eveleth (55734) *(G-1932)*

Northern Business Products Inc 218 726-0167
2326 W Superior St Duluth (55806) *(G-1402)*

Northern Capital Commercial 952 996-8818
8200 Highwood Dr Minneapolis (55438) *(G-5226)*

Northern Cass Dac Inc 218 547-1121
8059 County Rd 12 Walker (56484) *(G-9857)*

Northern Communities Credit 218 279-3200
3311 W Arrowhead Rd Duluth (55811) *(G-1403)*

Northern Computer Technologies (PA) 952 808-1000
901 Cliff Rd E Burnsville (55337) *(G-763)*

Northern Counties Secretarial 763 427-0166
6139 157th Ln NW Anoka (55303) *(G-210)*

Northern Dewatering Inc 763 428-2616
14405 Northdale Blvd Rogers (55374) *(G-7332)*

Northern Factory Sales Inc 320 235-2288
2701 4th Ave SW Willmar (56201) *(G-10030)*

Northern Gopher Enterprises 952 435-7600
17976 Judicial Rd Lakeville (55044) *(G-2923)*

Northern Grain Design & Constr 320 367-2881
8015 Highway 7 SE Clara City (56222) *(G-1031)*

Northern Industrial Erectors 218 326-8466
2500 Glenwood Dr Grand Rapids (55744) *(G-2300)*

Northern Industrial Insulation 218 624-0574
3757 Midway Rd Duluth (55810) *(G-1404)*

Northern Itasca Hospital Dist (PA) 218 743-3177
258 Pinetree Dr Bigfork (56628) ***(G-461)***
Northern Itasca Hospital Dist 218 743-3177
258 Pine Tree Dr Bigfork (56628) ***(G-462)***
Northern Lghts Assisted Living, Ulen *Also Called City of Ulen* ***(G-9717)***
Northern Light Pediatrics 651 484-3942
3585 Lexington Ave N # 350 Saint Paul (55126) ***(G-8758)***
Northern Lights Broadcasting 952 842-7200
5300 Edina Ind Blvd Edina (55439) ***(G-1840)***
Northern Lights Casino, Walker *Also Called Leech Lake Reservation* ***(G-9854)***
Northern Lights Mortgage Co 612 435-3500
501 Washington Ave S # 300 Minneapolis (55415) ***(G-5227)***
Northern Minnesota Public 218 751-3407
1500 Birchmont Dr NE Bemidji (56601) ***(G-413)***
Northern Natural Gas Co 952 887-1700
1600 W 82nd St Ste 210 Minneapolis (55431) ***(G-5228)***
Northern Oil & Gas Inc 952 476-9800
315 Manitoba Ave Ste 200 Wayzata (55391) ***(G-9934)***
Northern Oral & Faxillofacial, Duluth *Also Called Charles R Babst* ***(G-1269)***
Northern Orthopedics, Brainerd *Also Called Dr Peter Schmitz Inc* ***(G-564)***
Northern Pines Mental Health 320 632-6647
1906 5th Ave SE Little Falls (56345) ***(G-3015)***
Northern Plains Railroad, Duluth *Also Called Greg Haug* ***(G-1344)***
Northern Pnes Good Smritan Ctr, Blackduck *Also Called Evangelical Lutheran Good* ***(G-474)***
Northern Sales & Consulting 651 429-5757
6800 Otter Lake Rd Lino Lakes (55038) ***(G-2975)***
Northern Star Co 612 339-8981
3171 5th St SE Minneapolis (55414) ***(G-5229)***
Northern Star Council, Boy (PA) 651 224-1891
393 Marshall Ave Saint Paul (55102) ***(G-8759)***
Northern Star Therapy Ltd Inc 320 240-6955
251 County Road 120 Ste A Saint Cloud (56303) ***(G-7562)***
Northern States Power Co 651 731-5701
1103 King Plant Rd Bayport (55003) ***(G-350)***
Northern States Power Co 763 261-4100
13999 Industrial Blvd Becker (55308) ***(G-357)***
Northern States Power Co 763 441-3800
10700 165th Ave NW Elk River (55330) ***(G-1887)***
Northern States Power Co 507 387-9629
210 E Lime St Mankato (56001) ***(G-3176)***
Northern States Power Co 763 295-5151
2807 W County Road 75 Bldg 1 Monticello (55362) ***(G-6280)***
Northern States Power Co 763 295-4141
2100 W River St Monticello (55362) ***(G-6281)***
Northern States Power Co 763 493-1500
8701 Monticello Ln N Osseo (55369) ***(G-6645)***
Northern States Power Co 320 255-8601
3515 3rd St N Saint Cloud (56303) ***(G-7563)***
Northern States Power Co 651 639-4470
3115 Centre Pointe Dr Saint Paul (55113) ***(G-8760)***
Northern States Power Co 612 330-5674
825 Rice St Saint Paul (55117) ***(G-8761)***
Northern States Power Co 612 330-6349
1717 Wakonade Dr E Welch (55089) ***(G-9954)***
Northern States Supply Inc 320 235-0555
600 Industrial Dr SW Willmar (56201) ***(G-10031)***
Northern Tool & Equipment Co 952 894-0326
12205 River Ridge Blvd Burnsville (55337) ***(G-764)***
Northern Valley Animal Clinic 507 282-0867
3309 Alberta Dr NE Rochester (55906) ***(G-7191)***
Northern Wholesale Supply Inc 651 429-1515
6800 Otter Lake Rd Ste 2 Hugo (55038) ***(G-2672)***
Northern X-Ray Co (PA) 612 870-1561
2118 4th Ave S Minneapolis (55404) ***(G-5230)***
Northfield Care Center Inc 507 645-9511
900 Cannon Valley Dr W Northfield (55057) ***(G-6536)***
Northfield Construction Co Inc 507 645-8975
1600 Riverview Ln Northfield (55057) ***(G-6537)***
Northfield Hospital & Skilled 507 646-1000
2000 North Ave Northfield (55057) ***(G-6517)***
Northfield Insurance Co 651 688-4100
385 Washington St Saint Paul (55102) ***(G-8762)***
Northfield Lines Inc 507 645-5267
32611 Northfield Blvd Northfield (55057) ***(G-6518)***
Northfield Manor Inc 507 645-9090
901 Cannon Valley Dr W # 120 Northfield (55057) ***(G-6538)***
Northland Capital Financial 320 252-2122
333 33rd Ave S Ste 100 Saint Cloud (56301) ***(G-7564)***
Northland Chapter American Red 218 722-0071
2524 Maple Grove Rd Duluth (55811) ***(G-1405)***
Northland Concrete & Masonry 952 890-1650
12026 Riverwood Dr Burnsville (55337) ***(G-765)***
Northland Constructors of 218 722-8170
4843 Rice Lake Rd Duluth (55803) ***(G-1406)***
Northland Counseling Center (PA) 218 326-1274
215 SE 2nd Ave Grand Rapids (55744) ***(G-2301)***
Northland Counseling Center 218 327-1105
1215 SE 7th Ave Grand Rapids (55744) ***(G-2302)***
Northland Country Club Inc 218 525-1941
3901 E Superior St Duluth (55804) ***(G-1407)***
Northland Dealer Finance Inc 651 773-4973
3564 Rolling View Dr Saint Paul (55110) ***(G-8763)***
Northland Fishing Tackle Inc 218 286-5441
3441 County Rd 20 Ranier (56668) ***(G-6969)***
Northland Group Inc 952 831-4005
7831 Glenroy Rd Ste 350 Minneapolis (55439) ***(G-5231)***
Northland Hardwood Lumber Co 218 751-0550
4445 Cardinal Rd Bemidji (56601) ***(G-414)***
Northland Inn, Minneapolis *Also Called Niecc Inc* ***(G-5200)***
Northland Inn of Crookston 218 281-5210
2200 University Ave Crookston (56716) ***(G-1129)***
Northland Insurance Co (HQ) 651 688-4100
385 Washington St Saint Paul (55102) ***(G-8764)***
Northland Mechanical Contr 763 544-5100
9001 Science Center Dr Minneapolis (55428) ***(G-5232)***
Northland Mortgage Corp 507 388-8600
79 Navaho Ave Ste 14 Mankato (56001) ***(G-3177)***
Northland Ob Gyn Associates 218 722-5629
1000 E 1st St Ste LL Duluth (55805) ***(G-1408)***
Northland Painting 651 645-9791
15260 15th St N Stillwater (55082) ***(G-9632)***
Northland Power Washing 320 763-6593
2401 Basswood Ln Alexandria (56308) ***(G-116)***
Northland Transportation 952 885-0580
7210 154th St W Prior Lake (55372) ***(G-6946)***
Northland Transportation Inc 952 922-6876
11990 Riverwood Dr Burnsville (55337) ***(G-766)***
Northmarq Capital LLC (HQ) 952 356-0100
3500 Amercn Blvd W # 500 Minneapolis (55431) ***(G-5233)***
Northmarq Real Estate Services 952 831-1000
3500 Amercn Blvd W # 200 Minneapolis (55431) ***(G-5234)***
Northome Health Care Inc 218 897-5235
Main St Northome (56661) ***(G-6547)***
Northpark Dental 763 786-1560
9120 Baltimore St NE Minneapolis (55449) ***(G-3559)***
Northpoint Health & Wellness 612 767-9500
1315 Penn Ave N Minneapolis (55411) ***(G-5235)***
Northridge Nursing Home, Ortonville *Also Called City of Ortonville* ***(G-6580)***
Northrup Memorial Auditorium, Minneapolis *Also Called Regents of The University of* ***(G-5497)***
Northshore Mining Co 218 226-4125
10 Outer Dr Silver Bay (55614) ***(G-9484)***
Northshore Resources Inc 612 375-0315
212 3rd Ave N Ste 356 Minneapolis (55401) ***(G-5236)***
Northside Child Dev Center, Minneapolis *Also Called Catholic Charities of The* ***(G-4029)***
Northside Construction Inc 651 426-2632
15627 Forest Blvd N Hugo (55038) ***(G-2680)***
Northside Service Center 612 370-4902
1126 44th Ave N Minneapolis (55412) ***(G-5237)***
Northstar Access 763 691-0885
210 Main St S Cambridge (55008) ***(G-844)***
Northstar Arabian Breeders Inc 507 947-3541
20827 489th Ave Lake Crystal (56055) ***(G-2862)***
Northstar Capital Markets Svcs 651 290-8781
444 Cedar St Ste 800 Saint Paul (55101) ***(G-8765)***
Northstar Ethanol LLC 507 726-2645
19200 499th Ave Lake Crystal (56055) ***(G-2863)***
Northstar Fire Protection Inc (PA) 651 456-9111
875 Blue Gentian Rd # 12 Saint Paul (55121) ***(G-7853)***
Northstar Forest Materials, Saint Paul *Also Called Forest Weekes Products Inc* ***(G-8388)***
Northstar Genetics Ltd 507 824-2878
104 Main St Wanamingo (55983) ***(G-9865)***
Northstar Imaging Inc 763 463-5650
19875 S Diamond Lk Rd Ste 10 Rogers (55374) ***(G-7333)***
Northview Bank (HQ) 320 233-7575
2203 Finland Ave Finlayson (55735) ***(G-2131)***
Northview Bank (PA) 320 233-7575
2203 Finland Ave Finlayson (55735) ***(G-2132)***
Northwest Aircraft Inc 612 726-2331
2700 Lone Oak Pkwy Saint Paul (55121) ***(G-7854)***
Northwest Airlines Corp (HQ) 612 726-2111
2700 Lone Oak Pkwy Eagan (55121) ***(G-1543)***
Northwest Airlines Inc 218 254-7575
601 Iron Dr Chisholm (55719) ***(G-999)***
Northwest Airlines Inc 218 727-8791
4701 Grinden Dr Ste 2 Duluth (55811) ***(G-1409)***
Northwest Airlines Inc (HQ) 612 726-2111
7500 Airline Dr Minneapolis (55450) ***(G-5238)***
Northwest Airlines Inc 612 726-8000
7500 Airline Dr Ste 6550C Minneapolis (55450) ***(G-5239)***
Northwest Airlines Inc 612 727-9209
7200 34th Ave S Minneapolis (55450) ***(G-5240)***
Northwest Airlines Inc 507 282-9425
Rochester Municipal Arprt Rochester (55902) ***(G-7192)***
Northwest Airlines Inc 612 726-3896
1500 Towerview Rd Saint Paul (55121) ***(G-7855)***
Northwest Anesthesia 612 871-7639
2828 Chicago Ave Ste 300 Minneapolis (55407) ***(G-5241)***
Northwest Area Foundation 651 224-9635
60 Plato Blvd E Ste 400 Saint Paul (55107) ***(G-8766)***
Northwest Asphalt Inc 952 445-1003
1451 Stagecoach Rd Shakopee (55379) ***(G-9461)***
Northwest Bituminous Inc 952 890-3005
12400 Beard Ave S Burnsville (55337) ***(G-767)***
Northwest Community Action Inc 218 528-3258
312 N Main St Badger (56714) ***(G-299)***
Northwest Dairy Forwarding Co 763 434-6654
1305 159th Ave NE Anoka (55304) ***(G-211)***
Northwest Dental Group of 507 282-1271
1615 14th St NW Rochester (55901) ***(G-7193)***
Northwest Family Physicians 763 476-6776
1495 County Road 101 N # 1 Minneapolis (55447) ***(G-5242)***
Northwest Health Care Inc 320 251-9120
1717 University Dr SE Saint Cloud (56304) ***(G-7439)***
Northwest Investors Inc 952 894-7795
1905 E 123rd St Burnsville (55337) ***(G-768)***
Northwest Medical Center 218 681-4240
120 Labree Ave S Ste A Thief River Falls (56701) ***(G-9676)***
Northwest Orthopedic Surgeons 763 520-7870
3366 Oakdale Ave N Ste 103 Minneapolis (55422) ***(G-5243)***
Northwest Region, Saint Cloud *Also Called Northern States Power Co* ***(G-7563)***
Northwest Respiratory Services 651 603-8720
716 Prior Ave N Ste 1 Saint Paul (55104) ***(G-8767)***
Northwest Sheet Metal Co of St 651 310-0102
110 Sycamore St W Saint Paul (55117) ***(G-8768)***
Northwest Suburbs Community 763 533-8196
6900 Winnetka Ave N Minneapolis (55428) ***(G-5244)***
Northwest Title & Escrow Inc 651 490-9056
4255 White Bear Pkwy Saint Paul (55110) ***(G-8769)***
Northwest YMCA, Saint Paul *Also Called YMCA of Greater St Paul* ***(G-9176)***
Northwest Youth & Family Svcs 651 486-3808
3490 Lexington Ave N Saint Paul (55126) ***(G-8770)***
Northwestern Bank 218 287-2311
4 Main St N Dilworth (56529) ***(G-1223)***

ALPHABETIC

Northwestern Casket Co Inc 612 789-4356
4300 Quebec Ave N Ste 100 Minneapolis (55428) *(G-5245)*
Northwestern Fruit Co 651 224-4373
616 Pine St Saint Paul (55130) *(G-8771)*
Northwestern Manor, Fergus Falls *Also Called Lutheran Brethren Retirement (G-2088)*
Northwestern Marble & Granite 952 941-8601
7705 Bush Lake Rd Minneapolis (55439) *(G-5246)*
Northwestern Mental Health Ctr (PA) 218 281-3940
603 Bruce St Crookston (56716) *(G-1130)*
Northwestern Mental Health Ctr 218 281-3940
603 Bruce St Crookston (56716) *(G-1131)*
Northwestern Minn Juvenile Ctr, Bemidji *Also Called Minnesota Department of (G-402)*
Northwestern Mutl Fincl Netwrk, Saint Paul *Also Called Michael Erpelding (G-8651)*
Northwestern Mutual Life 651 456-9446
1191 Northland Dr Mendota Heights (55120) *(G-3368)*
Northwood Childrens Home Soc 218 724-8815
714 W College St Duluth (55811) *(G-1410)*
Nortrax Equipment Co SE 218 759-1996
3419 Washington Ave SE Bemidji (56601) *(G-415)*
Norwest Bank Minnesota North 612 667-1234
6 Street & Marquette Ave Minneapolis (55479) *(G-5247)*
Norwest Equity Capital LLC 612 215-1600
80 S 8th St Ste 3600 Minneapolis (55402) *(G-5248)*
Norwest Venture Capital Mgt (HQ) 612 215-1600
80 S 8th St Ste 3600 Minneapolis (55402) *(G-5249)*
Nothern Cass Bemidji Inc 218 759-0052
735 Mahnomen Dr SE Bemidji (56601) *(G-416)*
Nott Co (PA) 651 415-3400
4480 Round Lake Rd W Saint Paul (55112) *(G-8772)*
Nova Consulting Group Inc 952 448-9393
1107 Hazeltine Blvd # 400 Chaska (55318) *(G-977)*
Nova-Tech Engineering LLC 320 231-9660
1705 Engineering Ave Willmar (56201) *(G-10032)*
Novaspect Inc 952 934-5100
7565 Corporate Way Eden Prairie (55344) *(G-1733)*
Novologix 952 826-2500
10400 Viking Dr Ste 200 Eden Prairie (55344) *(G-1734)*
Novon Consulting Corp 612 868-7057
21453 Nowthen Blvd NW Elk River (55330) *(G-1858)*
Novus Franchising Inc 952 944-8000
12800 Hwy 13 S Ste 500 Savage (55378) *(G-9401)*
Novus Inc 952 944-8152
12800 Hwy 13 S Ste 500 Savage (55378) *(G-9402)*
Novus Marketing Inc 612 252-1618
931 Nicollet Mall Minneapolis (55402) *(G-5250)*
Novus Media Inc 612 758-8625
2 Carlson Pkwy N Ste 400 Minneapolis (55447) *(G-5251)*
Now Care Medical Centers Inc 651 635-0054
1955 County Road B2 W # 10 Saint Paul (55113) *(G-8773)*
Now Micro Inc 651 633-9072
1645 Energy Park Dr # 200 Saint Paul (55108) *(G-8774)*
Nowdocs International Inc 888 669-3627
1985 Lookout Dr North Mankato (56003) *(G-6512)*
Nowthen Nursery, Elk River *Also Called Great Northern Landscapes Inc (G-1876)*
Npl Construction Co 218 327-9467
21880 US Highway 169 Grand Rapids (55744) *(G-2303)*
NRG Energy Inc 612 349-6087
816 4th Ave S Minneapolis (55404) *(G-5252)*
NRG Energy Plus Relocation 952 512-5500
600 Highway 169 S Ste 500 Minneapolis (55426) *(G-5253)*
Nsl Holdings Inc 952 943-8474
1157 Valley Park Dr # 130 Shakopee (55379) *(G-9462)*
Nternational Projects 952 541-4888
600 Highway 169 S Ste 1595 Minneapolis (55426) *(G-5254)*
Nu-Con Equipment, Chanhassen *Also Called Boedecker Co (G-910)*
Nu-Look Exteriors Inc 952 882-8787
3801 W 145th St Burnsville (55306) *(G-769)*
Nurses That Care 218 724-2800
1901 South St Ste 3 Duluth (55812) *(G-1411)*
Nursing Enterprise, Willmar *Also Called Spectrum Community Health Inc (G-10045)*
Nuss Truck Group Inc 507 345-6225
53976 Two O Eight Ln Mankato (56001) *(G-3178)*
Nutri-Dyn Midwest Inc 763 479-3444
5414 Highway 12 Maple Plain (55359) *(G-3279)*
Nutrition Dynamics Gmp, Maple Plain *Also Called Nutri-Dyn Midwest Inc (G-3279)*
Nutrition Services Inc 507 835-5697
812 4th Ave NE Waseca (56093) *(G-9884)*
Nuvo Network Management 952 933-4600
5400 Opportunity Ct Ste 140 Hopkins (55343) *(G-2592)*
NXC Imaging, Minneapolis *Also Called Northern X-Ray Co (G-5230)*
Nyberg & Assoc PA Inc 763 441-9181
303 Main St NW Elk River (55330) *(G-1888)*
Nyco Inc 651 457-4069
10730 Briggs Dr Ste B Inver Grove Heights (55077) *(G-2764)*
Nystrom & Associates Ltd 651 628-9566
1900 Silver Lake Rd NW # 110 Saint Paul (55112) *(G-8775)*
O & S Cattle Co 651 455-1102
100 Stockyards Rd Ste 106 South Saint Paul (55075) *(G-9536)*
O D C, Bemidji *Also Called Occupational Development Ctr (G-417)*
O D C, Thief River Falls *Also Called Occupational Development Ctr (G-9677)*
O K Corral Inc 952 492-6700
20201 Johnson Memorial Dr Jordan (55352) *(G-2808)*
O'Malley Construction Inc 507 357-6330
35799 241st Ave Le Center (56057) *(G-2953)*
O'Neil Associates Inc 651 738-2694
801 Crestview Dr S Saint Paul (55119) *(G-8776)*
Oak Dale Healtheast 651 326-5300
1099 Helmo Ave N Ste 100 Saint Paul (55128) *(G-9253)*
Oak Glen LLC 651 439-6981
1599 McKusick Rd N Stillwater (55082) *(G-9633)*
Oak Hill Golf Club Inc 320 259-8969
8852 Indian Rd NW Rice (56367) *(G-7033)*
Oak Hotels Inc 651 636-6730
2550 Cleveland Ave N Saint Paul (55113) *(G-8777)*
Oak Inn Family Restaurant Inc 651 674-9977
Jct I 35 And Hwy 95 North Branch (55056) *(G-6503)*
Oak Inn Restaurant, North Branch *Also Called 3R North Inc (G-6506)*
Oak Meadows, Saint Paul *Also Called Family Resources Development (G-9216)*
Oak Park Place Assisted Living, Albert Lea *Also Called Alternative Continum of Care (G-37)*
Oak Ridge Conference Center, Chaska *Also Called Dolce International (G-961)*
Oak Ridge Country Club 952 935-7721
700 Oak Ridge Rd Hopkins (55305) *(G-2593)*
Oak Ridge Homes of Wadena Inc (PA) 218 829-7599
1021 Industrial Pk Rd SW Brainerd (56401) *(G-579)*
Oak Ridge Homes of Wadena Inc 218 327-1877
706 Allen Dr Grand Rapids (55744) *(G-2304)*
Oakdale Country Club Inc 320 833-5518
55106 County Road 38 Buffalo Lake (55314) *(G-667)*
Oakdale Ear Nose & Throat Clin 763 520-7840
3366 Oakdale Ave N Ste 150 Minneapolis (55422) *(G-5255)*
Oakdale Health Enterprises Inc 763 520-5357
4501 68th Ave N Minneapolis (55429) *(G-5256)*
Oakdale Kindercare, Saint Paul *Also Called Kindercare Learning Centers (G-9238)*
Oakdale Obstetrics & Gynecolog 763 520-2999
2855 Campus Dr Ste 600 Minneapolis (55441) *(G-5257)*
Oakdale-Granada Lakes LP 651 291-1750
328 Kellogg Blvd W Saint Paul (55102) *(G-8778)*
Oakland Park Nursing Home, Thief River Falls *Also Called County of Pennington (G-9665)*
Oaklawn Health Care Ctr, Mankato *Also Called Thro Co (G-3205)*
Oakridge Homes, Brainerd *Also Called Oak Ridge Homes of Wadena Inc (G-579)*
Oakriver Technology Inc 651 770-8710
640 Hayward Ave N Saint Paul (55128) *(G-9254)*
Oaks Country Club Inc 507 477-3233
Country Club Rd Hayfield (55940) *(G-2424)*
Oakwood Builders Inc 952 941-9730
12901 Pioneer Trl Eden Prairie (55347) *(G-1735)*
Oasis of Love Inc 612 529-6055
2304 Emerson Ave N Minneapolis (55411) *(G-5258)*
Object Partners Inc 612 746-1580
100 N 6th St Ste 302A Minneapolis (55403) *(G-5259)*
ObjectFX Corp 612 312-2002
10 2nd St NE Ste 400 Minneapolis (55413) *(G-5260)*
Obstetrics & Gyn 952 920-2200
6545 France Ave S Ste 600 Minneapolis (55435) *(G-5261)*
Obstetrics & Gynecology 952 920-2200
6545 France Ave S Ste 600 Minneapolis (55435) *(G-5262)*
Obstetrics, Gynecology 952 920-2730
6405 France Ave S Ste W400 Minneapolis (55435) *(G-5263)*
Occupational Development Ctr 218 751-6001
1260 Industrial Park Dr SE Bemidji (56601) *(G-417)*
Occupational Development Ctr 218 258-8926
100 S Industrial Park Rd Buhl (55713) *(G-668)*
Occupational Development Ctr 218 326-8574
401 SE 11th St Grand Rapids (55744) *(G-2305)*
Occupational Development Ctr 218 463-1123
1194 Center St W Roseau (56751) *(G-7356)*
Occupational Development Ctr (PA) 218 681-4949
1520 Highway 32 S Thief River Falls (56701) *(G-9677)*
Occupro Inc 320 839-4090
820 Roy St Ortonville (56278) *(G-6584)*
Octagon Financial Group 952 885-2700
1650 W 82nd St Ste 850 Minneapolis (55431) *(G-5264)*
Octopus Car Wash, Minneapolis *Also Called Douglas Drive Car Wash Inc (G-4285)*
Odyssey Development Inc 218 728-8060
2230 London Rd 100 Duluth (55812) *(G-1412)*
Office Depot Inc 952 525-1919
1005 Plymouth Rd AD Minnetonka (55305) *(G-6205)*
Office Information Systems Inc 952 884-9199
10800 Lyndale Ave S Minneapolis (55420) *(G-5265)*
Office of Financial Services, Saint Paul *Also Called City of Saint Paul (G-8208)*
Office of General Council 612 624-4100
200 Oak St SE Ste 360 Minneapolis (55455) *(G-5266)*
OfficeMax North America Inc 218 287-3755
1411 Center Ave W Dilworth (56529) *(G-1224)*
OfficeMax North America Inc 651 686-6606
1271 Promenade Pl Eagan (55121) *(G-1544)*
OfficeMax North America Inc 763 391-6629
8085 Brooklyn Blvd Minneapolis (55445) *(G-5267)*
Officeteam, Saint Paul *Also Called Robert Half International Inc (G-8907)*
Oil-Air Products LLC 763 478-8744
295 Highway 55 Hamel (55340) *(G-2353)*
Okay Construction Co Inc 763 633-8729
9774 18th St Princeton (55371) *(G-6913)*
Oki Systems Limited 651 645-8668
860 Vandalia St Saint Paul (55114) *(G-8779)*
Olafson, Renae 651 452-6825
2324 University Ave W # 102 Saint Paul (55114) *(G-8780)*
Old Log Theater Ltd 952 474-5951
5175 Meadville St Excelsior (55331) *(G-1951)*
Old Republic National Title (DH) 612 371-1111
400 2nd Ave S Minneapolis (55401) *(G-5268)*
Olivia Healthcare Center, Olivia *Also Called Beverly Enterprises - MN (G-6560)*
Olmsted Medical Center 507 529-6600
1650 4th St SE Rochester (55904) *(G-7194)*
Olmsted Medical Center (PA) 507 288-3443
210 9th St SE Rochester (55904) *(G-7195)*
Olmsted Medical Center 507 288-8880
3611 Salem Rd SW Rochester (55902) *(G-7196)*
Olmsted National Bank Inc 507 280-0028
120 Elton Hills Dr NW Rochester (55901) *(G-7197)*
Olr America Inc 612 436-4970
1200 Washington Ave S # 280 Minneapolis (55415) *(G-5269)*
Olsen Fire Protection Inc 612 331-3111
321 Wilson St NE Minneapolis (55413) *(G-5270)*
Olsen Thielen Technologies Inc 651 483-4521
2675 Long Lake Rd Saint Paul (55113) *(G-8781)*
Olson & Johnson Body Shop Inc 507 537-1669
Hwy 59 N Marshall (56258) *(G-3317)*
Olson & Johnson International 507 532-5718
503 N Highway 59 Marshall (56258) *(G-3318)*
Olson + Co Inc 612 215-9800
1625 Hennepin Ave Minneapolis (55403) *(G-5271)*
Olson Coffee Roasters Inc 651 645-1729
2325 Endicott St Ste 207W Saint Paul (55114) *(G-8782)*

ALPHABETIC

www.HarrisInfo.com
602
2011 Harris Minnesota Services Directory
(G-00000) Company's Geographic Section entry number

Olson General Contractors Inc 763 535-1481
9201 49th Ave N Minneapolis (55428) *(G-5272)*
Olson M D, Peter J 651 326-9020
980 Rice St Saint Paul (55117) *(G-8783)*
Olson Oil Co Inc 218 736-2786
1425 W Lincoln Ave Fergus Falls (56537) *(G-2103)*
Olson, Jock Interlachen 952 924-7424
6200 Interlachen Blvd Minneapolis (55436) *(G-5273)*
Olympia Tile Inc (PA) 763 545-5455
701 Berkshire Ln N Minneapolis (55441) *(G-5274)*
Olympic Hills Corp 952 941-6262
10625 Mount Curve Rd Eden Prairie (55347) *(G-1736)*
Olympic Steel Minneapolis Inc 763 544-7100
13100 15th Ave N Minneapolis (55441) *(G-5275)*
Omegon Inc 952 541-4738
2000 Hopkins Xrd Hopkins (55305) *(G-2594)*
Omicron Associates 952 345-5240
14850 Scenic Heights Rd Eden Prairie (55344) *(G-1737)*
Omni Control Systems Inc 507 454-5293
370 W 2nd St Ste 100 Winona (55987) *(G-10119)*
Omni Workspace Co 612 627-1600
1300 Washington Ave N # 200 Minneapolis (55411) *(G-5276)*
Omni Workspace Co (HQ) 612 627-1600
1300 Washington Ave N Ste 100 Minneapolis (55411) *(G-5277)*
Omnia Family Services 507 287-2300
1635 Greenview Dr SW Rochester (55902) *(G-7198)*
Omnicare Pharmacy & Supply (HQ) 763 259-0188
5534 Lakeland Ave N Minneapolis (55429) *(G-5278)*
On Assignment Staffing Svcs 651 647-1160
2550 University Ave W Ste 315N Saint Paul (55114) *(G-8784)*
On Movin Inc 763 784-7111
1493 94th Ln NE Minneapolis (55449) *(G-3560)*
On Time Lawn & Snow Services 763 786-0652
8794 Dunkirk Ct NE Minneapolis (55449) *(G-3561)*
On-Site Sanitation Inc 651 429-3781
95 Woodlyn Ave Ste 1 Saint Paul (55117) *(G-8785)*
Oncologic Consultants 952 928-2900
6363 France Ave S Ste 300 Minneapolis (55435) *(G-5279)*
Oncologic Consultants (PA) 651 602-5335
2550 University Ave W Ste 110N Saint Paul (55114) *(G-8786)*
One Call Concepts, Saint Paul *Also Called Gopher State One Call Inc (G-7788)*
One Call Concepts Inc 651 454-0002
2020 Centre Pointe Blvd Saint Paul (55120) *(G-7856)*
1 Micro LLC 952 767-1010
15153 Technology Dr Ste A Eden Prairie (55344) *(G-1738)*
One Way Building Services Inc 952 942-0412
6811 Washington Ave S Minneapolis (55439) *(G-5280)*
121 Marketing Services Group 763 428-8123
12999 Wilfred Ln N Rogers (55374) *(G-7334)*
133rd Medical Squadron, Saint Paul *Also Called Minnesota Department of (G-7961)*
175 Fort LLC 651 225-1515
175 7th St W Saint Paul (55102) *(G-8787)*
180 Degrees Inc 612 813-5010
300 Clifton Ave Minneapolis (55403) *(G-5281)*
Oneida Realty Co Inc 218 722-0816
306 W Superior St Ste 1605 Duluth (55802) *(G-1413)*
Oneka Ridge LLC 651 429-2390
5610 120th St N Saint Paul (55110) *(G-9255)*
Online Freight Services Inc 651 468-6868
2275 Waters Dr Saint Paul (55120) *(G-7857)*
Only For Kids Inc 763 754-2594
13654 Thrush St NW Anoka (55304) *(G-212)*
Onmia Manor 320 982-5405
100 Elm St S Apt 125 Onamia (56359) *(G-6575)*
Ontrack Data Recovery Inc 952 937-1107
9023 Columbine Rd Eden Prairie (55347) *(G-1739)*
Onvoy Inc 320 324-7530
206 Main St Chokio (56221) *(G-1001)*
Onvoy Inc (HQ) 952 230-4100
300 Highway 169 S Ste 700 Minneapolis (55426) *(G-5282)*
Open Access Technology Intl 763 201-2000
2300 Berkshire Ln N Ste F Minneapolis (55441) *(G-5283)*
Open Arms Christian Pre-School, Minneapolis *Also Called Holy Emmanuel Lutheran Church (G-4662)*
Open Cities Health Center 651 290-9200
409 Dunlap St N Saint Paul (55104) *(G-8788)*
Open Door Health Center 507 388-2120
309 Holly Ln Mankato (56001) *(G-3179)*
Open Systems Holdings Corp (PA) 952 403-5700
4301 Dean Lakes Blvd Shakopee (55379) *(G-9463)*
Open Systems Inc 952 403-5700
4301 Dean Lakes Blvd Shakopee (55379) *(G-9464)*
Open Systems International Inc 763 551-0559
3600 Holly Ln N Ste 40 Minneapolis (55447) *(G-5284)*
Open-C Solutions Inc 952 842-3200
7300 Metro Blvd Ste 645 Minneapolis (55439) *(G-5285)*
Operating Engineer No 49 ....218 741-8190
8381 Enterprise Dr NE Virginia (55792) *(G-9750)*
Ophthalmology 952 925-3150
3100 W 70th St Minneapolis (55435) *(G-5286)*
Oppenheimer Wolff Donnelly LLP 612 607-7000
45 S 7th St Ste 3300 Minneapolis (55402) *(G-5287)*
Opportunity Manor, Saint Cloud *Also Called Foster Four (G-7414)*
Opportunity Manor Inc 320 240-1900
1908 Kruchten Ct S Sartell (56377) *(G-9339)*
Opportunity Partners Inc 763 441-0960
11754191 One Half Ave NW Elk River (55330) *(G-1889)*
Opportunity Partners Inc (PA) 952 938-5511
5500 Opportunity Ct Hopkins (55343) *(G-2595)*
Ops America Inc 763 479-1409
689 N Medina St Ste 150 Loretto (55357) *(G-3051)*
Opthalmology Department, Minneapolis *Also Called Regents of The University of (G-5503)*
Optimist International 952 440-8184
4627 Parkwood Dr SE Prior Lake (55372) *(G-6947)*
Option Care, Sauk Rapids *Also Called Healthcare Options Minnesota (G-9366)*
Option Care Inc 651 635-9272
2750 Arthur St Saint Paul (55113) *(G-8789)*
Options Family & Behavior Svcs, Burnsville *Also Called Community Drug & Alcohol Svcs (G-702)*
Options Inc 763 263-3684
16820 197th Ave NW Big Lake (55309) *(G-452)*
Options Residential Inc 952 564-3030
2709 Highland Dr Burnsville (55337) *(G-770)*
Opus Architects & Engineers 952 656-4444
10350 Bren Rd W Hopkins (55343) *(G-2596)*
Opus Corp (PA) 952 656-4444
10350 Bren Rd W Hopkins (55343) *(G-2597)*
Opus Design Build LLC 952 656-4444
10350 Bren Rd W Minnetonka (55343) *(G-6206)*
Opus National LLC (HQ) 952 656-4444
10350 Bren Rd W Minnetonka (55343) *(G-6207)*
Opus Northwest Construction 952 656-4444
10350 Bren Rd W Hopkins (55343) *(G-2598)*
Opus Properties Inc 952 656-4444
9900 Bren Rd E Hopkins (55343) *(G-2599)*
Oracle Systems Corp 612 587-5000
950 Nicollet Mall Minneapolis (55403) *(G-5288)*
Oral & Max Facial Specialist 763 494-8825
13998 Maple Knoll Way LL101 Osseo (55369) *(G-6646)*
Oral & Maxillofacial Surgical 952 835-5003
7373 France Ave S Ste 602 Minneapolis (55435) *(G-5289)*
ORBIT Systems Inc 651 767-3322
860 Blue Gentian Rd Ste 2 Saint Paul (55121) *(G-7858)*
Orchard Park LLC 952 873-6017
510 S Elm St Belle Plaine (56011) *(G-369)*
Ordway Center For The 651 282-3000
345 Washington St Ste 775 Saint Paul (55102) *(G-8790)*
Orient Products Services, Loretto *Also Called Ops America Inc (G-3051)*
Orion Communication Services 763 694-7540
15395 31st Ave N Ste 1 Minneapolis (55447) *(G-5290)*
Orion Consulting, Minneapolis *Also Called SSIT North America Inc (G-5726)*
Orman Guidance Research Inc 952 831-4911
5001 W 80th St Ste 715 Minneapolis (55437) *(G-5291)*
Orono Healthy Youth 952 449-8351
705 N Old Crystal Bay Rd Long Lake (55356) *(G-3029)*
Orono Independent School Dist 763 479-1530
5050 Independence St Maple Plain (55359) *(G-3280)*
Orsten Turkeys Inc 320 235-5751
8481 15th St NW Willmar (56201) *(G-10033)*
Orthodonic Care Specialist 651 490-6732
3930 Northwoods Dr Saint Paul (55112) *(G-8791)*
Orthodontics Care Specialist 952 432-2682
14605 Glazier Ave Ste 200 Saint Paul (55124) *(G-7859)*
Orthogonistic Care Specialist 952 432-4941
14605 Glazier Ave Saint Paul (55124) *(G-7860)*
Orthopaedic Consultants 952 832-0076
7373 France Ave S Ste 312 Minneapolis (55435) *(G-5292)*
Orthopaedic Fracture Clinic, Mankato *Also Called Orthopedic & Fracture Clinic (G-3180)*
Orthopedic & Fracture Clinic 507 386-6600
1431 Premier Dr Mankato (56001) *(G-3180)*
Orthopedic Associates of 218 722-5513
1000 E 1st St Ste 404 Duluth (55805) *(G-1414)*
Orthopedic Medicine & Surgery 952 920-0970
3250 W 66th St Ste 100 Minneapolis (55435) *(G-5293)*
Orthopedic Partners (PA) 763 786-9543
8290 University Ave NE # 200 Minneapolis (55432) *(G-3562)*
Orthopedic Resources Mgt 952 831-5773
7801 E Bush Lake Rd # 320 Minneapolis (55439) *(G-5294)*
Orthopedic Sports Inc 651 439-8540
1700 Tower Dr W Stillwater (55082) *(G-9634)*
Orthopedic Surgeons Ltd 952 927-7565
6363 France Ave S Ste 404 Minneapolis (55435) *(G-5295)*
Ortonville Area Health Svcs, Ortonville *Also Called City of Ortonville (G-6579)*
Osberg Psola Scamp Kivo Larson, Eden Prairie *Also Called Parkway Dental (G-1743)*
OSBORNE CONSTRUCTION, Plymouth *Also Called Dave Osborne Construction (G-6858)*
Osborne Properties LP 952 881-8166
4210 W Old Shakopee Rd Bloomington (55437) *(G-508)*
Osborne Properties LP 952 890-0414
420 Gateway Blvd Burnsville (55337) *(G-771)*
Osborne Properties LP (PA) 952 707-8200
420 Gateway Blvd Burnsville (55337) *(G-772)*
Osborne Properties LP 952 881-8166
523 S 8th St Minneapolis (55404) *(G-5296)*
Oshkosh, McNeilus Financia 507 775-3310
1067 4th St NE Byron (55920) *(G-825)*
OSI Physical Therapy, Stillwater *Also Called Orthopedic Sports Inc (G-9634)*
Osland Janitorial Supply Inc 952 894-4815
1401 Cliff Rd E Burnsville (55337) *(G-773)*
Ossel Brooklyn Bus Co Inc 952 891-1031
14800 Everest Ave Saint Paul (55124) *(G-7861)*
Osseo Brooklyn School Bus Co 763 425-2542
11800 95th Ave N Osseo (55369) *(G-6647)*
Osseo Gardens Assisted Living 763 315-4869
525 2nd St SE Ofc Osseo (55369) *(G-6648)*
Osseo Maple Grove American 763 425-4858
260 4th Ave SE Osseo (55369) *(G-6649)*
Otis-Magie Insurance Agency 218 722-7753
227 W 1st St Ste 900 Duluth (55802) *(G-1415)*
Otpt, Fergus Falls *Also Called Otter Tail Power Co (G-2110)*
Otsego Hospitality LLC 763 656-4400
9200 Quaday Ave NE Elk River (55330) *(G-1903)*
Otter Tail Corp 218 739-8100
1012 Water Plant Rd Fergus Falls (56537) *(G-2104)*
Otter Tail Corp (PA) 866 410-8780
215 S Cascade St Fergus Falls (56537) *(G-2105)*
Otter Tail County Human Svcs 218 998-8150
530 W Fir Ave Fergus Falls (56537) *(G-2106)*
Otter Tail Energy Services Co 218 739-8888
224 E Washington Ave Fergus Falls (56537) *(G-2107)*
Otter Tail Nursing Home 218 495-2993
28930 County Highway 145 Battle Lake (56515) *(G-312)*
Otter Tail Power Co 218 281-3632
410 College Ave Crookston (56716) *(G-1132)*

ALPHABETIC

Otter Tail Power Co 218 736-6947
216 S Cascade St Fergus Falls (56537) ***(G-2108)***
Otter Tail Power Co (HQ) 866 410-8780
215 S Cascade St Fergus Falls (56537) ***(G-2109)***
Otter Tail Power Co 218 739-8200
215 S Cascade St Fergus Falls (56537) ***(G-2110)***
Otter Tail Telcom LLC 218 998-2000
230 W Lincoln Ave Fergus Falls (56537) ***(G-2111)***
Otteraial Area Medical, Wadena *Also Called Tri-County Hospital Inc* ***(G-9813)***
Ottertail Coaches Inc (PA) 218 739-3393
1116 N Tower Rd Fergus Falls (56537) ***(G-2112)***
Ottertail Lodge 284 ....218 863-7913
13 W Mill St Pelican Rapids (56572) ***(G-6781)***
Otto Associates Engineers 763 682-4727
9 Division St W Buffalo (55313) ***(G-655)***
Otto Bock Healthcare LP (PA) 763 553-9464
2 Carlson Pkwy N Ste 100 Minneapolis (55447) ***(G-5297)***
Otto Bock Healthcare North (PA) 763 553-9464
2 Carlson Pkwy N Ste 100 Minneapolis (55447) ***(G-5298)***
Otto Bock US Polyurethane Foam 763 553-9464
2 Carlson Pkwy N Ste 100 Minneapolis (55447) ***(G-5299)***
Otto Bremer Foundation (PA) 651 227-8036
445 Minnesota St Ste 2250 Saint Paul (55101) ***(G-8792)***
Otto Packaging Midwest LLC 651 488-0474
391 Topping St Saint Paul (55117) ***(G-8793)***
Our Circle of Friends 507 334-4346
211 Minnesota Pl Faribault (55021) ***(G-2024)***
Our Lady of Good Counsel Home 651 646-2797
2076 Saint Anthony Ave Saint Paul (55104) ***(G-8794)***
Our Lady of Lk Elementary Schl, Mound *Also Called Church of Our Lady of The Lake* ***(G-6384)***
Our Place Covenant Enabling 218 624-3097
322 N 60th Ave W Duluth (55807) ***(G-1416)***
Our Savior Lutheran Church 952 474-5181
23290 Highway 7 Excelsior (55331) ***(G-1952)***
Our Savior's Lutheran Church 763 434-6117
19001 Jackson St NE Cedar (55011) ***(G-883)***
Outcomes Inc 651 483-9500
3508 Rice St Ste 1 Saint Paul (55126) ***(G-8795)***
Outdoor Adventure Travel Inc 612 866-2503
6625 Lyndale Ave S 104 Minneapolis (55423) ***(G-5300)***
Outdoor Environments Inc 952 496-1000
12488 Xenwood Ave Savage (55378) ***(G-9403)***
Outdoor Images Inc 651 480-2000
2551 Glendale Rd Hastings (55033) ***(G-2397)***
OUTREACH & ADVOCACY PROGRAM, Minneapolis *Also Called Minneapolis Urban League Inc* ***(G-5065)***
Outsource Administrators Inc 952 944-5462
10225 Yellow Circle Dr # 2 Minnetonka (55343) ***(G-6208)***
Outsourceone Inc 612 436-2740
730 2nd Ave S Ste 530 Minneapolis (55402) ***(G-5301)***
Outsourceone Inc 612 338-7940
730 2nd Ave S Ste 530 Minneapolis (55402) ***(G-5302)***
Oval Cleaning Service Inc 612 605-3166
1516 W Lake St Ste 200 Minneapolis (55408) ***(G-5303)***
Ovations Inc (HQ) 952 936-1300
9900 Bren Rd E Ste 300W Hopkins (55343) ***(G-2600)***
Ovp Inc 952 944-5600
6436 City West Pkwy Eden Prairie (55344) ***(G-1740)***
Owatonna Bus Co Inc 507 451-5262
1145 Park Dr Owatonna (55060) ***(G-6725)***
Owatonna Chapter, Owatonna *Also Called Delta Kappa Gamma Society* ***(G-6708)***
Owatonna Clinic — Mayo Health 507 451-1120
134 Southview St Owatonna (55060) ***(G-6726)***
Owatonna Community Education, Owatonna *Also Called Independent School District No* ***(G-6718)***
Owatonna Country Club Inc 507 451-6120
1991 Lemond Rd Owatonna (55060) ***(G-6727)***
Owatonna Fairlanes Corp 507 451-2524
333 18th St SE Owatonna (55060) ***(G-6728)***
Owatonna Health Care Center, Owatonna *Also Called Beverly Enterprises - MN* ***(G-6695)***
Owatonna Home Care & Hospice, Owatonna *Also Called Allina Health System* ***(G-6690)***
Owatonna Hospitality Partners 507 455-1142
245 Florence Ave Owatonna (55060) ***(G-6729)***
Owatonna Public Util, Owatonna *Also Called City of Owatonna* ***(G-6701)***
Owatonna Public Utilities, Owatonna *Also Called City of Owatonna* ***(G-6703)***
Owatonna Senior Place, Owatonna *Also Called City of Owatonna* ***(G-6702)***
Owens & Minor Inc 763 785-9100
2151 County Road H2 Saint Paul (55112) ***(G-8796)***
Owens Co's Inc 952 854-3800
930 E 80th St Bloomington (55420) ***(G-509)***
Oxygen Service Co Inc 651 644-7273
1111 Pierce Butler Rte Saint Paul (55104) ***(G-8797)***
P & D Klitzke Enterprises Inc 320 275-3555
68306 215th St Darwin (55324) ***(G-1158)***
P & L Automotive Inc 952 941-0888
7449 Cahill Rd Ste 120 Minneapolis (55439) ***(G-5304)***
P D Management, LLP 612 281-1464
7551 240th St E Lakeville (55044) ***(G-2943)***
P Fund, Minneapolis *Also Called Philanthrofund Foundation* ***(G-5374)***
P H M Eaglecrest Inc 651 628-3000
2945 Lincoln Dr Ofc Saint Paul (55113) ***(G-8799)***
P H M Eaglecrest Inc (PA) 651 631-6009
3220 Lake Johanna Blvd Saint Paul (55112) ***(G-8798)***
P H Selly & Co Inc 507 334-3251
805 3rd Ave SW Faribault (55021) ***(G-2025)***
P Kevin Hickey 612 376-1620
33 S 6th St Minneapolis (55402) ***(G-5305)***
P O S Business Systems Inc 763 559-1341
9905 45th Ave N Ste 200 Minneapolis (55442) ***(G-5306)***
P P L, Minneapolis *Also Called Project For Pride In Living* ***(G-5428)***
P P S, Saint Paul *Also Called Performance Pool & Spa Inc* ***(G-9259)***
P R K Inc 612 341-3300
225 S 11th St Minneapolis (55403) ***(G-5307)***
P S Rudie & Associates Ltd 218 722-6613
324 W Superior St Ste 302 Duluth (55802) ***(G-1417)***
P T O S I, Minneapolis *Also Called Physical Therapy Orthopedic* ***(G-5377)***
Paape Distributing Co 507 345-8057
307 McKinzie St S Mankato (56001) ***(G-3181)***
Pace Analytical Life Sciences 651 738-2728
1281 Helmo Ave N Oakdale (55128) ***(G-6552)***
Pace Analytical Services Inc (HQ) 612 607-1700
1700 Elm St SE Ste 200 Minneapolis (55414) ***(G-5308)***
Pace Deis Corp 651 702-2900
403 Hayward Ave N Saint Paul (55128) ***(G-9256)***
Pace Electronics Inc 507 288-1853
3582 Technology Dr NW Rochester (55901) ***(G-7199)***
Pace International Union 320 240-7274
100 E Sartell St Sartell (56377) ***(G-9340)***
Pace Pediatrics, Saint Paul *Also Called Pediatric & Adolescent Care of* ***(G-8812)***
Pacer Center Inc 952 838-9000
8161 Normandale Blvd Minneapolis (55437) ***(G-5309)***
Pacific Marketing & Comms 651 967-7135
123 N 3rd St Minneapolis (55401) ***(G-5310)***
Pacific Mutual Door Co 651 631-2211
2655 Fairview Ave N Saint Paul (55113) ***(G-8800)***
Packaging Automation Corp 651 456-0003
2725 Highway 55 Saint Paul (55121) ***(G-7862)***
Packaging Corp of America 763 521-3611
4300 Highway 55 Minneapolis (55422) ***(G-5311)***
Packaging First, Saint Paul *Also Called Lifetrack Resources Inc* ***(G-8587)***
Packaging Systems Automation 763 473-1032
2200 Niagara Ln N Minneapolis (55447) ***(G-5312)***
Pact For Families 320 231-7030
2200 23rd St NE Willmar (56201) ***(G-10034)***
PADILLA SPEAR BEARDSLEY, Minneapolis *Also Called Franklin Corp* ***(G-4475)***
Pah-Dt Minneapolis Suites 612 332-6800
1101 Lasalle Ave Minneapolis (55403) ***(G-5313)***
Paige J Donnelly Ltd 651 222-2797
325 Cedar St Ste 900 Saint Paul (55101) ***(G-8801)***
Painting By Nakasone Inc 651 646-6999
1535 Marshall Ave Saint Paul (55104) ***(G-8802)***
Painting Perfection Ltd 651 762-9011
1971 Gateway Blvd Saint Paul (55112) ***(G-8803)***
Paisley Consulting Inc 320 286-5870
400 Cokato St E Cokato (55321) ***(G-1077)***
Pakor Inc (PA) 763 559-8484
6450 Wedgwood Rd N # 110 Osseo (55311) ***(G-6650)***
Pal Management Inc 952 646-1792
181 S River Ridge Cir Burnsville (55337) ***(G-774)***
Palace Bingo & Casino, Cass Lake *Also Called Leech Lake Palace & Casino* ***(G-872)***
Palanisami & Associates Inc 763 533-9403
5661 International Pkwy Minneapolis (55428) ***(G-5314)***
Palco Marketing Inc 763 559-5539
8575 Monticello Ln N Osseo (55369) ***(G-6651)***
Palen Kimball LLC 651 646-2800
550 Vandalia St Ste 4 Saint Paul (55114) ***(G-8804)***
Palmer Bus Service 320 528-2670
302 Hawkins Ave Barrett (56311) ***(G-309)***
Palmer Bus Service 320 847-3109
22 Division St S Clara City (56222) ***(G-1032)***
Palmer Bus Service Inc 320 634-3272
17631 210th Ave Glenwood (56334) ***(G-2229)***
Palmer Bus Service Inc 507 477-3014
35 E Main St Hayfield (55940) ***(G-2425)***
Palmer Bus Service of Bold MN 507 386-0210
115 S 1st St Olivia (56277) ***(G-6562)***
Palmer Bus Service of Mankato 507 386-0210
1770 Howard Dr Mankato (56003) ***(G-3230)***
Palmer Bus Service of N 320 632-1555
17043 Haven Rd Little Falls (56345) ***(G-3016)***
Palmer Bus Service of St 507 931-1811
43336 371st Ave Saint Peter (56082) ***(G-9311)***
Palmer Bus Services 952 445-1166
730 3rd Ave W Shakopee (55379) ***(G-9465)***
Palmer Charter Service Inc 320 632-1555
17043 Haven Rd Little Falls (56345) ***(G-3017)***
Palmer Lake Post 3915 VFW Inc 763 560-3720
2817 Brookdale Dr Minneapolis (55444) ***(G-5315)***
Palmer Soderberg Inc 507 288-4213
3730 40th Ave NW Rochester (55901) ***(G-7200)***
Palmer West Construction Co 763 428-1867
14595 James Rd Rogers (55374) ***(G-7335)***
Palmer's Auto Supply Inc 507 354-3154
426 S Minnesota St New Ulm (56073) ***(G-6472)***
Palmino Bistro, Minneapolis *Also Called Restaurants Unlimited Inc* ***(G-5530)***
Pals Inc (PA) 320 235-8860
3735 1st Ave W Willmar (56201) ***(G-10035)***
Pals Inc 320 235-8860
3735 County Road 5 SW Willmar (56201) ***(G-10036)***
Pan-O-Gold Baking Co 763 559-1515
3200 Ranchview Ln N Minneapolis (55447) ***(G-5316)***
Pan-O-Gold Baking Co (PA) 320 251-9361
444 E Saint Germain St Saint Cloud (56304) ***(G-7421)***
Paper Depot Inc 612 333-0512
221 Border Ave Minneapolis (55405) ***(G-5317)***
Paquette Maintenance Inc 952 888-1801
2224 W 94th St Minneapolis (55431) ***(G-5318)***
Par Nuclear Holding Co Inc (DH) 651 278-0007
899 Highway 96 W Saint Paul (55126) ***(G-8805)***
Par Piping & Fabrication LLC 320 564-2173
114 Winter Dr Granite Falls (56241) ***(G-2317)***
Par Systems Inc (HQ) 651 484-7261
707 County Road E W Saint Paul (55126) ***(G-8806)***
Paradigm Publishing Inc 651 290-2800
875 Montreal Way Saint Paul (55102) ***(G-8807)***
Paradis Mail Service Inc 218 698-4613
Hwy 92 Brooks (56715) ***(G-622)***
Paradis Mail Service Inc 218 698-4613
812 Highway 92 W Brooks (56715) ***(G-623)***
Paradise Car Wash 952 888-5388
9201 Lyndale Ave S Minneapolis (55420) ***(G-5319)***
Paradysz Matera Co Inc 952 544-5121
505 Highway 169 N Fl 8 Minneapolis (55441) ***(G-5320)***

ALPHABETIC

Paragon Associates Inc 218 722-5009
4629 Airpark Blvd Duluth (55811) *(G-1418)*
Paragon Moving & Storage Inc 952 936-9122
401 11th Ave N Hopkins (55343) *(G-2601)*
Paragon Store Fixtures Inc 763 263-0660
20020 176th St NW Big Lake (55309) *(G-453)*
Paragon Strategic Solutions 952 886-8000
5600 W 83rd St 8200 Minneapolis (55437) *(G-5321)*
Parallel Technologies Inc 952 920-7185
4242 Park Glen Rd Minneapolis (55416) *(G-5322)*
Paramount, Minneapolis Also Called Master Collision Group LLC *(G-4964)*
Paramount Theater 320 259-5463
913 W Saint Germain St Saint Cloud (56301) *(G-7565)*
Parent & Community Action, Minneapolis Also Called Community Action Agency *(G-4136)*
Parents In Community Action 612 823-6361
4225 3rd Ave S Minneapolis (55409) *(G-5323)*
Parents In Community Action (PA) 612 377-7422
700 Humboldt Ave N Minneapolis (55411) *(G-5324)*
Parents In Community Action 612 362-0360
96 Saint Marys Ave SE Minneapolis (55414) *(G-5325)*
Pareo Inc 612 371-0400
120 S 6th St Ste 2550 Minneapolis (55402) *(G-5326)*
Park & Recreation, Minneapolis Also Called City of Minneapolis *(G-4088)*
Park & Recreation Department, Saint Paul Also Called County of Ramsey *(G-8259)*
Park 'n Fly Inc 952 854-0606
3750 American Blvd E Minneapolis (55425) *(G-5327)*
Park Ballroom, New Prague Also Called Legion Pavilion Co Inc *(G-6422)*
Park Brooklyn Housing Assocs 763 354-5500
2355 Polaris Ln N Ste 100 Minneapolis (55447) *(G-5328)*
Park Construction Co 763 786-9800
500 73rd Ave NE Ste 123 Minneapolis (55432) *(G-3563)*
Park Dental, Hopkins Also Called Pdhc Ltd *(G-2602)*
Park Dental, Minneapolis Also Called PDHC Ltd *(G-5355)*
Park Dental Blaine 763 755-1330
12904 Central Ave NE Minneapolis (55434) *(G-3564)*
Park Dental Eden Prairie 952 949-2536
18315 Cascade Dr Ste 120 Eden Prairie (55347) *(G-1741)*
Park Gooseberry Motel Cabins 218 834-3751
2778 Highway 61 Two Harbors (55616) *(G-9711)*
Park N' Go of Minnesota LP 952 854-3386
7901 International Dr Minneapolis (55425) *(G-5329)*
Park Nicollet Clinic 952 993-8700
14000 Fairview Dr Burnsville (55337) *(G-775)*
Park Nicollet Clinic 952 993-7400
8455 Flying Cloud Dr Ste 205 Eden Prairie (55344) *(G-1742)*
Park Nicollet Clinic 952 993-9700
7550 34th Ave S Minneapolis (55450) *(G-5330)*
Park Nicollet Clinic 952 993-8900
3007 Harbor Ln N Minneapolis (55447) *(G-5331)*
Park Nicollet Clinic (HQ) 952 993-3123
3800 Park Nicollet Blvd Minneapolis (55416) *(G-5332)*
Park Nicollet Clinic 952 993-4001
1885 Plaza Dr Saint Paul (55122) *(G-7863)*
Park Nicollet Health Services 952 993-5353
6500 Excelsior Blvd Minneapolis (55426) *(G-5333)*
Park Nicollet Health Services 952 993-8000
2001 Blaisdell Ave Minneapolis (55404) *(G-5334)*
Park Nicollet Health Services 952 993-5495
6701 Country Club Dr Minneapolis (55427) *(G-5335)*
Park Nicollet Health Services (PA) 952 993-9900
3800 Park Nicollet Blvd Minneapolis (55416) *(G-5336)*
Park Nrsing An Convasclent Ctr, Minneapolis Also Called Extendicare Homes Inc *(G-4386)*
Park Nursing & Covalescent Ctr, Minneapolis Also Called Extendicare Homes Inc *(G-4385)*
Park Rapids-Walker Clinic, Park Rapids Also Called Innovis Health LLC *(G-6756)*
Park Region Cooperative 218 863-2811
120 S Broadway Pelican Rapids (56572) *(G-6782)*
Park Region Mutual Telephone 218 826-6161
100 Main St N Underwood (56586) *(G-9718)*
Park Systems Inc 612 822-3180
2727 E 26th St Minneapolis (55406) *(G-5337)*
Park Tavern Bowl & Entrmt Ctr, Minneapolis Also Called Philip's Investment Co *(G-5375)*
Park View Care Center Inc 763 682-1131
200 Park Ln Buffalo (55313) *(G-656)*
Park Waite Manufacturing Inc 320 251-8616
430 7th Ave N Waite Park (56387) *(G-9830)*
Parker Oaks, Winnebago Also Called American Baptist Homes of The *(G-10075)*
Parker-Hannifin Corp 952 469-5000
21337 Hemlock Ave Lakeville (55044) *(G-2924)*
Parkers Prairrie Lions Club, Parkers Prairie Also Called International Association of *(G-6765)*
Parking Ramp, Minneapolis Also Called Dayton Radison Inc *(G-4232)*
Parks & Recreation Dept, Saint Paul Also Called City of Saint Paul *(G-8205)*
Parks & Recreation Dept, Saint Paul Also Called City of Saint Paul *(G-8211)*
Parks & Recreation Dept, Saint Paul Also Called City of Saint Paul *(G-8210)*
Parkshore Place, Minneapolis Also Called Silvercross Properties *(G-5675)*
Parkshore Senior Campus 952 929-1034
3663 Park Center Blvd Ste A Minneapolis (55416) *(G-5338)*
Parkview Ford - Mercury Inc 320 269-5565
2207 E Highway 7 Montevideo (56265) *(G-6256)*
Parkview Golf Associates LLC 651 452-5098
1310 Cliff Rd Saint Paul (55123) *(G-7864)*
Parkview Manor Inc 507 967-2482
308 W Sherman Ave Ellsworth (56129) *(G-1908)*
Parkview Motel, Saint Paul Also Called Glen L Stockman *(G-8413)*
Parkway Dental 952 937-2137
16518 W 78th St Eden Prairie (55346) *(G-1743)*
Parkwood 18 Theatres 320 251-1188
1533 Frontage Rd N Waite Park (56387) *(G-9831)*
Parkwood Shores Assisted 952 924-0400
3633 Park Center Blvd Minneapolis (55416) *(G-5339)*
Parmly Senior Housing & Svcs, Chisago City Also Called Ecumen *(G-991)*
Parsons 612 656-7000
60 S 6th St Ste 2450 Minneapolis (55402) *(G-5340)*
Parsons Electric LLC (PA) 763 571-8000
5960 Main St NE Minneapolis (55432) *(G-3565)*
Partners For Senior 952 831-4084
3330 Edinbrgh Way Ste 100 Minneapolis (55435) *(G-5341)*

Partners For Senior 612 374-8100
825 Summit Ave Ofc Minneapolis (55403) *(G-5342)*
Partners In Excellence 651 773-5988
2344 Helen St N Saint Paul (55109) *(G-8808)*
Partners In Excellence Inc 952 746-5350
14301 Ewing Ave S Burnsville (55306) *(G-776)*
Partners In Pediatrics Ltd 763 425-1211
8500 Edinbrook Pkwy Minneapolis (55443) *(G-5343)*
Partners Pediatric 612 827-4055
3145 Hennepin Ave Minneapolis (55408) *(G-5344)*
Partnership Resources Inc 612 331-2075
950 E Hennepin Ave Minneapolis (55414) *(G-5345)*
Party Music Inc 952 941-3830
9825 Valley View Rd Eden Prairie (55344) *(G-1744)*
Paschke Properties 763 428-7711
4611 Palmgren Ln NE Rogers (55374) *(G-7336)*
Passe Engineering Inc 763 780-4100
1611 County Highway 10 # 2 Minneapolis (55432) *(G-3566)*
Pat S Electric 507 483-2857
320 Delaware Ave Adrian (56110) *(G-4)*
Path, Minneapolis Also Called Professional Association of *(G-5419)*
Pathfinder Village St Croix 320 384-7726
200 Pathfinder Vlg Hinckley (55037) *(G-2488)*
Pathway Health Services Inc 651 407-8699
2025 4th St Saint Paul (55110) *(G-8809)*
Pathways Psychological Svcs 763 525-8590
7575 Golden Valley Rd # 230 Minneapolis (55427) *(G-5346)*
Patrick M Doyle Dr 651 454-0114
3450 Oleary Ln Saint Paul (55123) *(G-7865)*
Patrick Plunkett, Saint Paul Also Called Moore, Costello & Hart Pllp *(G-8719)*
Patriot Bank Minnesota (PA) 651 462-8854
26727 Faxton St Wyoming (55092) *(G-10206)*
Patriot Builders Inc 763 434-1702
17162 Lincoln St NE 100 Anoka (55304) *(G-213)*
Patriot Holding Corp (PA) 612 338-5912
90 S 7th St Ste 3700 Minneapolis (55402) *(G-5347)*
Pattern Stations Inc 763 441-6833
10990 95th St NE Monticello (55362) *(G-6282)*
Patterson Co's Inc 651 688-9265
2930 Waters Rd Ste 160 Eagan (55121) *(G-1545)*
Patterson Co's Inc (PA) 651 686-1600
1031 Mendota Heights Rd Saint Paul (55120) *(G-7866)*
Patterson Dental Supply Inc 651 688-6054
2930 Waters Rd Ste 100 Saint Paul (55121) *(G-7867)*
Patterson Dental Supply Inc (HQ) 651 686-1600
1031 Mendota Heights Rd Saint Paul (55120) *(G-7868)*
Patterson, Thuente, Skaar 612 349-5764
80 S 8th St Ste 4800 Minneapolis (55402) *(G-5348)*
Patzig Testing Laboratories 651 659-7554
662 Cromwell Ave Saint Paul (55114) *(G-8810)*
Paul A Schmitt Music Co 763 566-4560
2400 Freeway Blvd Minneapolis (55430) *(G-5349)*
Paul Bunyan Broadcasting Co 218 444-1011
502 Beltrami Ave NW Bemidji (56601) *(G-418)*
Paul Bunyan Community Theater 218 751-7270
314 Beltrami Ave NW Bemidji (56601) *(G-419)*
Paul Bunyan Rural Telephone 218 444-1234
1831 Anne St NW Ste 100 Bemidji (56601) *(G-420)*
Paul Johnston 800 862-7919
200 Ameriprise Financial Ctr Minneapolis (55474) *(G-5350)*
Paul Larson Ob-Gyn Clinic 952 927-4021
6525 France Ave S Ste 100 Minneapolis (55435) *(G-5351)*
Paul Lesieur 612 788-5584
635 Lowry Ave NE Minneapolis (55418) *(G-5352)*
Paul Minneapolis-St (PA) 612 726-8100
6040 28th Ave S Minneapolis (55450) *(G-5353)*
Paul Minneapolis-St 612 726-5107
4300 Glumack Dr Ste 3060 Saint Paul (55111) *(G-7962)*
Paul Newport-St Cold Storage 651 459-5555
2233 Maxwell Ave Newport (55055) *(G-6488)*
Paul Schintz Inc 218 525-0828
1860 Lester River Rd Duluth (55804) *(G-1419)*
Paustis & Sons, Minneapolis Also Called Kiwikai Imports Inc *(G-4813)*
Pavilion Surgery Center LLC 218 279-6200
920 E 1st St Ste 101 Duluth (55805) *(G-1420)*
Paychex Inc 651 365-5060
1210 Northland Dr Ste 100 Saint Paul (55120) *(G-7869)*
Payday America LLC 952 646-1793
181 S River Ridge Cir Burnsville (55337) *(G-777)*
Paynesville Farmers Union 320 243-3751
419 E Hoffman St Paynesville (56362) *(G-6772)*
Paynesville Motor & Transfer 320 243-4455
314 Minnie St Paynesville (56362) *(G-6773)*
Payroll Controls Systems, Minneapolis Also Called Diversified Industries Inc *(G-4262)*
Paysource Inc 651 633-9595
2258 Sioux Blvd Saint Paul (55112) *(G-8811)*
Pazaaz Hair & Nail Design, Minneapolis Also Called Elam Investments *(G-4335)*
PC Hotels LLC 218 233-6171
600 30th Ave S Moorhead (56560) *(G-6332)*
PC Productions Inc 651 451-6222
1625 Robert St S Saint Paul (55118) *(G-7870)*
PC Solutions Inc 763 852-1600
5155 E River Rd Ste 409 Minneapolis (55421) *(G-3567)*
PCA RC Programs, Winona Also Called Home & Community Options Inc *(G-10103)*
PCiRoads LLC 763 497-6100
14123 42nd St NE Saint Michael (55376) *(G-7679)*
Pciroads, Corp 763 497-6100
14123 42nd St NE Saint Michael (55376) *(G-7680)*
PCL Construction Services Inc 952 882-9600
12200 Nicollet Ave Burnsville (55337) *(G-778)*
PCL Construction Services Inc 952 882-9600
12200 Nicollet Ave Burnsville (55337) *(G-779)*
Pcr Computer Services 763 557-6824
5361 Dallas Ln N Minneapolis (55446) *(G-5354)*
Pdhc Ltd 763 421-5206
11269 Jefferson Hwy N Champlin (55316) *(G-897)*

A L P H A B E T I C

Pdhc Ltd 952 949-2536
18315 Cascade Dr Eden Prairie (55347) ***(G-1745)***
Pdhc Ltd 952 545-8603
13911 Ridgedale Dr Ste 395 Hopkins (55305) ***(G-2602)***
PDHC Ltd (HQ) 612 338-4546
6415 Brooklyn Blvd Minneapolis (55429) ***(G-5355)***
Pdhc Ltd 763 535-2960
6437 Brooklyn Blvd Minneapolis (55429) ***(G-5356)***
Pdl Biopharma Inc 763 255-5000
9450 Winnetka Ave N Minneapolis (55445) ***(G-5357)***
Peace of Mind Day Care Inc 651 731-2608
9025 Tamarack Rd Saint Paul (55125) ***(G-9257)***
Peace Transportation Inc 952 595-9030
7500 Wayzata Blvd Minneapolis (55426) ***(G-5358)***
Peak Performers Network 952 345-3333
7831 E Bush Lake Rd # 200 Minneapolis (55439) ***(G-5359)***
Pearson Mechanical Services 651 275-1100
13497 Fenway Blvd Cir N 1 Hugo (55038) ***(G-2681)***
Pearson Vue, Minneapolis *Also Called Ncs Pearson Inc* ***(G-5178)***
Pebble Creek Country Club, Becker *Also Called City of Becker* ***(G-355)***
Peck Construction Inc 763 421-2201
13900 Sunfish Lake Blvd NW Anoka (55303) ***(G-214)***
Pederson Team 218 692-5253
35548 County Rd 66 Crosslake (56442) ***(G-1153)***
Pediatric & Adolescent Care of 651 770-2124
3615 Grand Ave Saint Paul (55110) ***(G-8812)***
Pediatric & Adolescent Care of (PA) 651 451-8050
1547 Livingston Ave Saint Paul (55118) ***(G-7871)***
Pediatric & Young Adult Med 651 227-7806
233 Grand Ave Saint Paul (55102) ***(G-8813)***
Pediatric Young Adult Medicine, Saint Paul *Also Called Leslie E Fishman Inc* ***(G-8579)***
Pediatricians For Health 651 232-6700
1875 Woodwinds Dr WL200 Saint Paul (55125) ***(G-9258)***
Pelican Bay Foods, Orr *Also Called Bruns Inc* ***(G-6577)***
Pelican Rapids Good Samaritan 218 863-2401
119 N Broadway Pelican Rapids (56572) ***(G-6783)***
Pella Products Inc (PA) 763 745-1400
15300 25th Ave N Ste 100 Minneapolis (55447) ***(G-5360)***
Pella Windows & Doors Twin 763 745-1400
15300 25th Ave N Ste 100 Minneapolis (55447) ***(G-5361)***
Penco Leasing Corp 612 927-4748
5011 France Ave S Minneapolis (55410) ***(G-5362)***
Pengo Corp 320 286-5581
13369 60th St SW Cokato (55321) ***(G-1078)***
Penhall Co 763 542-9999
850 Mendelssohn Ave N Minneapolis (55427) ***(G-5363)***
Penhall Co 763 428-2244
14045 Northdale Blvd Rogers (55374) ***(G-7337)***
Penn-Co Construction Inc 651 687-0648
2995 Lone Oak Cir Ste 5 Saint Paul (55121) ***(G-7872)***
Penske Truck Leasing Co, LP 651 631-3399
2460 County Road C W Saint Paul (55113) ***(G-8814)***
Penske Truck Leasing Co, LP 651 454-0000
965 Aldrin Dr Saint Paul (55121) ***(G-7873)***
People Enhancing People 651 450-5960
1600 University Ave W # 301 Saint Paul (55104) ***(G-8815)***
People Inc 952 736-7802
904 McAndrews Rd W Burnsville (55337) ***(G-780)***
People Inc (PA) 651 774-0011
317 York Ave Saint Paul (55130) ***(G-8816)***
People Inc 651 227-6321
313 Dale St N Apt 337 Saint Paul (55103) ***(G-8817)***
People's Express Inc 218 631-2909
15578 Shady Acres Dr Wadena (56482) ***(G-9808)***
PeopleNet Communications Corp 952 908-6200
4400 Baker Rd Minnetonka (55343) ***(G-6209)***
Peoples Bank of Commerce 763 689-1212
234 1st Ave E Cambridge (55008) ***(G-845)***
Peoples Cmnty Care Residence, Saint Paul *Also Called Axis Minnesota Inc* ***(G-8083)***
Peoples Cooperative Services 507 288-4004
3935 Highway 14 E Rochester (55904) ***(G-7201)***
Peoples National Bank of Mora 320 679-3100
45 Union St N Mora (55051) ***(G-6367)***
Peoples State Bank of Madison (PA) 507 257-3544
405 Parkway Ave Eagle Lake (56024) ***(G-1563)***
Pepsi Cola Bottling Co 507 825-4207
1809 Forman Dr Pipestone (56164) ***(G-6833)***
Pepsi Cola Bottling Co of 218 628-0276
4301 W Michigan St Duluth (55807) ***(G-1421)***
Pepsi Cola Bottling Co of 507 288-3772
1307 Valleyhigh Dr NW Rochester (55901) ***(G-7202)***
Pepsi-Cola Metropolitan Btlng 218 829-4196
2024 SE 13th St Brainerd (56401) ***(G-580)***
Pepsi-Cola Metropolitan Btlng 218 326-1271
1154 E US Highway 169 Grand Rapids (55744) ***(G-2306)***
Pepsico, Bemidji *Also Called Nei Bottling Inc* ***(G-407)***
Pepsico, Duluth *Also Called Pepsi Cola Bottling Co of* ***(G-1421)***
Pepsico, Rochester *Also Called Pepsi Cola Bottling Co of* ***(G-7202)***
Pepsico, Willmar *Also Called Bernick's Pepsi Cola of* ***(G-9986)***
Pequaywan Area Trail Blazers 218 848-2510
8926 W Branch Rd Duluth (55803) ***(G-1422)***
Percy Nelson Enterprises Inc 651 209-6360
7616 Currell Blvd Ste 200 Woodbury (55125) ***(G-10173)***
Peregrine Capital Management 612 343-7600
800 Lasalle Ave Ste 1850 Minneapolis (55402) ***(G-5364)***
Perennial Management LLC 651 644-9600
1360 Energy Park Dr # 300 Saint Paul (55108) ***(G-8818)***
Perfect 10 Car Wash Inc 651 227-9274
999 Highway 10 NE Minneapolis (55432) ***(G-3568)***
Perfect Complement Ltd 763 421-8360
3050 Coon Rapids Blvd NW Minneapolis (55433) ***(G-3569)***
Perfect Pickle 651 779-6129
22570 Elston Ct Forest Lake (55025) ***(G-2153)***
Perfered Pickle, Forest Lake *Also Called Perfect Pickle* ***(G-2153)***
Perficient Inc 612 752-1700
100 N 6th St Ste 935C Minneapolis (55403) ***(G-5365)***
Performance Pool & Spa Inc 651 731-3440
1890 Wooddale Dr Ste 800 Saint Paul (55125) ***(G-9259)***
Performance Seed, Waite Park *Also Called Esco Industries Inc* ***(G-9822)***
Performark Inc 952 946-7300
10400 Yellow Circle Dr # 101 Minnetonka (55343) ***(G-6210)***
Perham Hospital District 218 346-4500
665 3rd St SW Bldg 2 Perham (56573) ***(G-6800)***
Perham Lakeside Golf Club Inc 218 346-6070
2727 450th St Perham (56573) ***(G-6801)***
Perkins + Will Inc 612 851-5000
84 S 10th St Ste 200 Minneapolis (55403) ***(G-5366)***
Perkins Family Restaurant, Austin *Also Called Torgerson Properties LP* ***(G-290)***
Perkins Family Restaurant, Chanhassen *Also Called Northcott Hospitality Intl* ***(G-934)***
Perkins Lumber Co Inc 320 235-9420
1010 Benson Ave SW Willmar (56201) ***(G-10037)***
Perkins Motor Transport Inc 651 463-4600
1800 Riverview Dr Northfield (55057) ***(G-6539)***
Perlman Rocque Co Fridley, Minneapolis *Also Called Martin-Brower Co L L C* ***(G-3528)***
Permasteelisa North America 651 905-1515
2060 Centre Pointe Blvd Ste 10 Saint Paul (55120) ***(G-7874)***
Perot Systems Corp 651 999-5600
2550 University Ave W # 143 Saint Paul (55114) ***(G-8819)***
Perpetual Motion Children's 651 459-5837
257 Rivertown Dr Saint Paul (55125) ***(G-9260)***
Perspectives Inc 952 926-2600
3381 Gorham Ave Ste 101 Minneapolis (55426) ***(G-5367)***
Pet Co 952 541-1981
13691 Ridgedale Dr Minnetonka (55305) ***(G-6211)***
Petco Animal Supplies Stores 763 420-5236
7625 Jolly Ln Minneapolis (55428) ***(G-5368)***
Petco Animal Supplies Stores 320 253-1004
35 Waite Ave N Waite Park (56387) ***(G-9832)***
Peter's Body Shop Inc 320 252-2993
205 Osseo Ave N Saint Cloud (56303) ***(G-7566)***
Peters Sunset Beach Inc 320 634-4501
20000 S Lake Shore Dr Glenwood (56334) ***(G-2230)***
Petersen Home Care Services 763 557-1126
12800 Industrial Park Blvd 2 Minneapolis (55441) ***(G-5369)***
Peterson Biddick Co 218 631-2954
63585 W Hwy 10 Crookston (56716) ***(G-1133)***
Peterson Bros Roofing & Constr 651 488-5630
481 Burgess St Saint Paul (55117) ***(G-8820)***
Peterson Bus Princeton 763 631-5315
604 S County Road 18 Princeton (55371) ***(G-6914)***
Peterson Bus Service Inc 320 354-2414
302 Oak St S New London (56273) ***(G-6418)***
Peterson Co's Inc 651 257-6864
8326 Wyoming Trl Chisago City (55013) ***(G-993)***
Peterson Group Management Corp 952 835-9232
7340 Gallagher Dr Minneapolis (55435) ***(G-5370)***
Peterson Sheet Metal, Bemidji *Also Called Shannon-Peterson Inc* ***(G-427)***
Peterson Stolberg, Minneapolis *Also Called Hillside Cemetery Association* ***(G-4649)***
Peterson Turkey Hatchery Inc 507 263-2352
31659 County 24 Blvd Cannon Falls (55009) ***(G-862)***
Peterson's North Branch Mill (PA) 651 674-4425
39015 Branch Ave North Branch (55056) ***(G-6504)***
Peterson, Fram & Bergman, A 651 291-8955
55 5th St E Ste 800 Saint Paul (55101) ***(G-8821)***
Petraflex, Minneapolis *Also Called Petratech Inc* ***(G-5371)***
Petratech Inc 952 897-0475
4444 W 78th St Minneapolis (55435) ***(G-5371)***
Petsmart Inc 952 941-4660
11200 Prairie Lakes Dr Ste A Eden Prairie (55344) ***(G-1746)***
Petsmart Inc 612 798-3665
1100 W 78th St Ste B Minneapolis (55423) ***(G-5372)***
Petsmart Inc 320 251-4365
320 2nd St S Saint Cloud (56301) ***(G-7567)***
Petsmart Inc 320 251-4459
320 2nd St S Ste 1 Waite Park (56387) ***(G-9833)***
Petsmart Inc 800 702-9779
8460 Tamarack Vlg Woodbury (55125) ***(G-10174)***
Petters Aviation LLC (PA) 952 936-5000
4400 Baker Rd Minnetonka (55343) ***(G-6212)***
Pezhekee Lounge Inc 320 634-4502
20000 S Lake Shore Dr Glenwood (56334) ***(G-2231)***
Pga Tour Inc 763 795-0800
11444 Tournament Players Pkwy Minneapolis (55449) ***(G-3570)***
Pgi Fulfillment Inc 952 933-5745
11354 K Tel Dr Minnetonka (55343) ***(G-6213)***
Pgw Auto Glass LLC 952 888-0413
316 W 86th St Minneapolis (55420) ***(G-5373)***
Phalen Village Apartments 651 771-5625
1511 Westminster St # 201 Saint Paul (55130) ***(G-8822)***
Pharmaceutical Specialties Inc 507 288-8500
1620 Industrial Dr NW Rochester (55901) ***(G-7203)***
Phase I Rice-Marion 763 540-8600
195 Edmund Ave Ofc Saint Paul (55103) ***(G-8823)***
Phasse III of Maple Grove Inc 763 425-4212
9340 Fair Way Osseo (55369) ***(G-6652)***
Pheasant Acres Run Golf Club, Rogers *Also Called Golden Acres Golf Course Inc* ***(G-7325)***
Pheasants Forever Inc (PA) 651 773-2000
1783 Buerkle Cir Saint Paul (55110) ***(G-8824)***
Philanthrofund Foundation 612 870-1806
1409 Willow St Ste 210 Minneapolis (55403) ***(G-5374)***
Philip's Investment Co 952 929-6810
3401 Louisiana Ave S Minneapolis (55426) ***(G-5375)***
Phillippi Equipment Co (PA) 651 406-4900
2875 Highway 55 Saint Paul (55121) ***(G-7875)***
Phillips Eye Institute, Minneapolis *Also Called Allina Health System* ***(G-3720)***
Phillips Recycling Systems LLC 320 251-5980
119 6th Ave NE Saint Cloud (56304) ***(G-7422)***
Phillips Wine & Spirits, Saint Paul *Also Called Johnson Brothers Liquor Co* ***(G-8536)***
Phoenix Alternatives Inc 651 426-2484
4453 White Bear Pkwy Saint Paul (55110) ***(G-8825)***
Phoenix Alternatives Vocation 651 747-8740
1754 Commerce Ct Saint Paul (55110) ***(G-8826)***

ALPHABETIC

Phoenix Distributing Inc 952 882-9949
451 Cliff Rd E Ste 108 Burnsville (55337) *(G-781)*
Phoenix Residence Inc (PA) 651 227-7655
330 Marie Ave E Saint Paul (55118) *(G-7876)*
Physical Distribution Services (PA) 952 884-0765
55 W 78th St Minneapolis (55420) *(G-5376)*
Physical Therapy Orthopedic 612 872-2700
2800 Chicago Ave Ste 200 Minneapolis (55407) *(G-5377)*
Physicans Neck & Back Clinic (PA) 651 639-9150
3050 Centre Pointe Dr Saint Paul (55113) *(G-8827)*
Physician Sales & Service, Rogers *Also Called PSS World Medical Inc (G-7338)*
Physicians Examone Inc 651 731-2949
436 Hayward Ave N Saint Paul (55128) *(G-9261)*
Pica, Minneapolis *Also Called Parents In Community Action (G-5325)*
Pica Headstart, Minneapolis *Also Called Parents In Community Action (G-5324)*
Picture Perfect Cleaning 612 865-4522
18990 Embry Ave Farmington (55024) *(G-2056)*
Piedmont Heights Dental Assocs 218 722-0823
2860 Piedmont Ave Duluth (55811) *(G-1423)*
Pieper Electric, Saint Paul *Also Called M P Systems Inc (G-8603)*
Piepho Moving & Storage Inc 507 289-4515
4121 Hwy 14 W Rochester (55901) *(G-7204)*
Piepho Moving & Storage Inc 507 289-4515
4121 Hwy 14 W Rochester (55901) *(G-7205)*
Pierz Villa Inc 320 468-6405
119 Faust St Pierz (56364) *(G-6806)*
Pilgrim Cleaners & Launderers 952 937-9391
16382 Wagner Way Eden Prairie (55344) *(G-1747)*
Pillsbury Co LLC 952 903-5262
7500 Flying Cloud Dr Ste 670 Eden Prairie (55344) *(G-1748)*
Pillsbury Co LLC 612 330-4003
2025 Pillsbury Ave Minneapolis (55404) *(G-5378)*
Pine Bend Paving Inc 651 437-2333
16500 Fischer Ave Hastings (55033) *(G-2398)*
Pine County Health & Human Svc 320 245-3020
130 Oriole St E Ste 1 Sandstone (55072) *(G-9324)*
Pine Habilitation & Supported (PA) 320 245-2246
106 Main St Sandstone (55072) *(G-9325)*
Pine Haven Care Center Inc 507 356-8304
210 3rd St NW Pine Island (55963) *(G-6817)*
Pine Manors Inc 218 732-4337
22195 State 34 Nevis (56467) *(G-6405)*
Pine Point Public School Dist 218 573-4100
27075 County Road 124 Ponsford (56575) *(G-6892)*
Pine Point Wood Products Inc 763 428-4301
19380 County Rd 81 Osseo (55369) *(G-6653)*
Pine Ridge Homes Inc 218 879-1257
1509 14th St Cloquet (55720) *(G-1059)*
Pine River Capital Management 612 238-3300
601 Carlson Pkwy Ste 330 Minnetonka (55305) *(G-6214)*
Pine River Group Home Inc 218 587-4888
103 5th St Pine River (56474) *(G-6820)*
Pinehurst Development Inc 952 469-3202
23111 Cedar Ave Farmington (55024) *(G-2057)*
Pines 612 861-3331
400 W 67th St Minneapolis (55423) *(G-5379)*
Pines, Nisswa *Also Called Etoc Co Inc (G-6497)*
Pineview Park Bmx 320 230-7820
6655 Saukview Dr Saint Cloud (56303) *(G-7568)*
Pinewood Cloquet 218 879-4566
915 18th St Cloquet (55720) *(G-1060)*
Piney Ridge Lodge Inc 218 587-2296
37400 Piney Ridge Rd Pine River (56474) *(G-6821)*
Pinnacle Credit Services 952 939-8100
7900 Highway 7 Minneapolis (55426) *(G-5380)*
Pinnacle Financial Group Inc (PA) 952 996-0559
7825 Washingtn Ave S # 410 Minneapolis (55439) *(G-5381)*
Pinnacle Financial Group Inc 763 295-0113
108 Thomas Cir Monticello (55362) *(G-6283)*
Pinnacle Programs Inc 507 283-4425
401 W Luverne St Magnolia (56158) *(G-3083)*
Pinnacle Services Inc 612 977-3100
724 Central Ave SE Minneapolis (55414) *(G-5382)*
Pinnacle Technologies Inc 651 735-3239
680 Hale Ave N Ste 120 Saint Paul (55128) *(G-9262)*
Pioneer Bank 507 524-3630
301 Main St E Mapleton (56065) *(G-3284)*
Pioneer Home Inc 218 739-7701
1006 S Sheridan St Fergus Falls (56537) *(G-2113)*
Pioneer Industries Inc (PA) 612 374-2280
155 Irving Ave N Minneapolis (55405) *(G-5383)*
Pioneer Memorial Care Center 218 687-2365
23028 347th St SE Erskine (56535) *(G-1921)*
Pioneer National Bank (PA) 218 624-3676
331 N Central Ave Duluth (55807) *(G-1424)*
Pioneer National Bank 218 728-1172
120 Mount Royal Shopping Cir Duluth (55803) *(G-1425)*
Pioneer National Bank 507 375-3201
123 Armstrong Blvd S Saint James (56081) *(G-7644)*
Pioneer Peat Inc 701 746-4300
Hwy 2 E East Grand Forks (56721) *(G-1573)*
Pioneer Power Inc 651 488-5561
570 Hatch Ave Saint Paul (55117) *(G-8828)*
Pioneer Press Inc 651 222-8298
220 Fillmore Ave E Saint Paul (55107) *(G-8829)*
Pioneer Senior Cottages 218 998-9678
1307 S Mabelle Ave Fergus Falls (56537) *(G-2114)*
Pipeline Supply Inc 952 935-0445
620 16th Ave S Hopkins (55343) *(G-2603)*
Piper Breast Center, Minneapolis *Also Called Abbot Northwestern Hospital (G-3659)*
Piper Jaffray Co's (PA) 612 303-6000
800 Nicollet Mall Ste 800 Minneapolis (55402) *(G-5384)*
Piper Jaffray Co's 952 476-3939
681 Lake St E Ste 354 Wayzata (55391) *(G-9935)*
Pipestone Adult Sls, Pipestone *Also Called Hope Haven Inc (G-6830)*
Pipestone County Medical Ctr 507 825-5811
916 4th Ave SW Pipestone (56164) *(G-6834)*
Pipestone Good Samaritan Vlg, Pipestone *Also Called Evangelical Lutheran Good (G-6826)*
Pipestone Livestock Auction 507 825-3306
E Hwy 30 One Fourth Mile Pipestone (56164) *(G-6835)*
Pipestone Medical Group Inc 507 825-5700
920 4th Ave SW Pipestone (56164) *(G-6836)*
Pipestone Veterinary Clinic 507 825-4211
1300 S Highway 75 Pipestone (56164) *(G-6837)*
Pitman Co, Minneapolis *Also Called Harold Pitman M Co (G-4601)*
Pitney Bowes Inc 952 983-1600
7905 Golden Triangle Dr Eden Prairie (55344) *(G-1749)*
Pitney Bowes Inc 952 885-7287
10800 Lyndale Ave S Fl 3 Minneapolis (55420) *(G-5385)*
Pixel Farm Inc 612 339-7644
251 1st Ave N Ste 600 Minneapolis (55401) *(G-5386)*
Pl Enterprises Inc 612 588-9000
1500 Washington Ave N Minneapolis (55411) *(G-5387)*
Plaas Inc 651 388-8881
1427 Old West Main St Red Wing (55066) *(G-6994)*
Plains Construction & Devpt 218 284-0424
3101 S Frontage Rd # 101 Moorhead (56560) *(G-6333)*
Plainview Ambulance, Plainview *Also Called City of Plainview Ambulance (G-6840)*
Plaisted Co's Inc 763 441-1100
11555 205th Ave NW Elk River (55330) *(G-1890)*
Planned Investments Inc 952 920-3890
5900 Schaefer Rd Minneapolis (55436) *(G-5388)*
Planned Parenthood of MN 651 698-2401
1965 Ford Pkwy Saint Paul (55116) *(G-8830)*
Plastic Products Co Inc 651 257-3143
30625 Olinda Trl Lindstrom (55045) *(G-2970)*
Plastic Promotions Inc 651 686-0660
1286 Trapp Rd Saint Paul (55121) *(G-7877)*
Plastics International Inc 952 934-2303
7600 Anagram Dr Eden Prairie (55344) *(G-1750)*
Platinum Staffing LLC 763 560-8430
7710 Brooklyn Blvd # 106 Minneapolis (55443) *(G-5389)*
Plato Learning Inc 952 832-1000
10801 Nesbitt Ave S Bloomington (55437) *(G-510)*
Plato Woodwork Inc 320 238-2193
200 3rd St SW Plato (55370) *(G-6844)*
Playworks Dakota 952 445-7529
2200 Trail Of Dreams Prior Lake (55372) *(G-6948)*
Plaza Park State Bank Inc 320 252-4200
131 6th Ave S Ste 100 Waite Park (56387) *(G-9834)*
Pleasant Lake Landscaping, Cedar *Also Called Metro Home Services Network (G-882)*
Pleasant Manor Inc 507 334-3558
27 Brand Ave Faribault (55021) *(G-2026)*
Pleasant Valley Township Assn 651 437-5660
1357 Jefferson St Hastings (55033) *(G-2399)*
Pleasntview Good Samaritan Ctr, Saint James *Also Called Evangelical Lutheran Good (G-7643)*
Pleasureland Inc (PA) 320 251-7588
25064 Augusta Dr Saint Cloud (56302) *(G-7569)*
Plekkenpol Builders Inc 952 888-2225
401 E 78th St Minneapolis (55420) *(G-5390)*
Plus Relocation Services Inc (PA) 952 512-5500
600 Highway 169 S Ste 500 Minneapolis (55426) *(G-5391)*
Plymouth Heights Pet Hospital 763 544-4141
9200 49th Ave N Minneapolis (55428) *(G-5392)*
Plymouth Ice Center, Minneapolis *Also Called City of Plymouth (G-4095)*
Plymouth Industries Inc (HQ) 763 553-1935
2601 Niagara Ln N Minneapolis (55447) *(G-5393)*
Plymouth Senior Housing 651 631-6300
16205 36th Ave N Plymouth (55446) *(G-6879)*
Pokegama Golf Course, Grand Rapids *Also Called City of Grand Rapids (G-2272)*
Polaroid Consumer Electronics (PA) 952 936-5000
4400 Baker Rd Ste 900 Minnetonka (55343) *(G-6215)*
Polaroid Holdings LLC (PA) 952 934-9918
4350 Baker Rd Minnetonka (55343) *(G-6216)*
Police Department, Saint Paul *Also Called Paul Minneapolis-St (G-7962)*
Police Range 218 751-7641
329 Rako St SW Bemidji (56601) *(G-421)*
Polinsky Rehabilitation Center 218 786-5360
530 E 2nd St Duluth (55805) *(G-1426)*
Polk County Developmental 218 281-4181
515 5th Ave S Crookston (56716) *(G-1134)*
Polk County Highway Shop 218 945-6952
355 Garfield Ave SE Fertile (56540) *(G-2127)*
Polka Dot Dairy Inc 651 438-2793
110 17th St E Hastings (55033) *(G-2400)*
Pollution Control Agency, MN 218 723-4660
525 S Lake Ave Ste 400A Duluth (55802) *(G-1427)*
Pollution Control Agency, MN 507 285-7343
18 Woodlake Dr SE Rochester (55904) *(G-7206)*
Polman Transfer Inc 218 631-1753
63254 Hwy 10W Wadena (56482) *(G-9809)*
Polyphase Electric Co (PA) 218 723-1413
2515 W Superior St Duluth (55806) *(G-1428)*
Pompeii Painting Inc 507 288-8494
29 9th Ave NE Rochester (55906) *(G-7207)*
Ponds Golf Course LLC 763 753-1100
2881 229th Ave NW Saint Francis (55070) *(G-7636)*
Pool & Yacht Club 651 455-3900
1600 Lilydale Rd Saint Paul (55118) *(G-7878)*
Poolside, Saint Paul *Also Called All Poolside Services Inc (G-8011)*
Pope Associates Inc 651 642-9200
1255 Energy Park Dr Saint Paul (55108) *(G-8831)*
Pope Douglas Solid Waste Mgt 320 763-9340
2115 Jefferson St Alexandria (56308) *(G-117)*
Popp Telcom Inc 763 546-9707
620 Mendelssohn Ave N Ste 101 Minneapolis (55427) *(G-5394)*
Popular Front Studio Inc 612 362-0900
555 1st Ave NE Minneapolis (55413) *(G-5395)*
Port Group Home Office 218 828-6274
115 N 1st St Brainerd (56401) *(G-581)*
Port of Call, Lake City *Also Called Rothgarn Enterprise Inc (G-2854)*

ALPHABETIC

PORT REHABILITATION CENTER, Duluth *Also Called Bethel Duluth Society* ***(G-1251)***
Portamedic 881, Minneapolis *Also Called Holmes Hooper Inc* ***(G-4661)***
Portfolio Design Services Inc 651 631-1300
752 Stillwater Rd Saint Paul (55115) ***(G-9263)***
Positive Body Dynamics Inc 952 920-9514
4815 Minnetonka Blvd Minneapolis (55416) ***(G-5396)***
Positive Realty & Investment 218 829-1777
514 S 6th St Brainerd (56401) ***(G-582)***
Possabilities 507 281-6116
1808 3rd Ave SE Ste 5 Rochester (55904) ***(G-7208)***
Possabilities of Southern MN 507 287-7100
1808 3rd Ave SE Rochester (55904) ***(G-7209)***
Post 513, Saint Paul *Also Called Tri City American Legion* ***(G-9080)***
Post 7664, Maple Lake *Also Called Veterans of Foreign Wars of* ***(G-3267)***
Post 906, Hutchinson *Also Called Veterans of Foreign Wars* ***(G-2715)***
Postal Credit Union, Saint Paul *Also Called St Paul Postal Employees* ***(G-8997)***
Potlatch Corp 218 751-6144
50518 County 45 Bemidji (56601) ***(G-435)***
Potter David MD PHD 612 625-8933
420 Delaware St SE Minneapolis (55455) ***(G-5397)***
Pottery Red Wings 651 388-3562
1920 Old West Main St Red Wing (55066) ***(G-6995)***
Pouchtec Industries LLC 320 968-4868
347 Sheridan Rd SE Foley (56329) ***(G-2141)***
Powel Inc 651 251-3005
930 Blue Gentian Rd Ste 1 Saint Paul (55121) ***(G-7879)***
Power Mation Division Inc (PA) 651 605-3300
1310 Energy Ln Saint Paul (55108) ***(G-8832)***
Power System Engineering Inc 763 755-5122
10710 Town Square Dr NE Minneapolis (55449) ***(G-3571)***
Power Systems LLC 952 361-6800
8325 Commerce Dr Chanhassen (55317) ***(G-935)***
Power Systems Research Inc 651 905-8400
1365 Corporate Center Curv Saint Paul (55121) ***(G-7880)***
Powertrack 612 973-3170
200 S 6th St Fl 27 Minneapolis (55402) ***(G-5398)***
PPL Industries Inc 612 332-0664
1179 15th Ave SE Minneapolis (55414) ***(G-5399)***
Ppt Vision Inc 952 942-5747
12988 Valley View Rd Eden Prairie (55344) ***(G-1751)***
Pragmatek Consulting Group Ltd 612 333-3164
8500 Normandale Lake Blvd Bloomington (55437) ***(G-511)***
Prairie Arts Continuum 507 831-4862
183 1/2 10th St Windom (56101) ***(G-10070)***
Prairie Community Services 218 739-2045
1505 S Arlington St Fergus Falls (56537) ***(G-2115)***
Prairie Community Services 320 589-2057
605 W 6th St Morris (56267) ***(G-6374)***
Prairie Community Services 320 796-6999
256 Lake Ave N Spicer (56288) ***(G-9558)***
Prairie Dance Alliance 507 532-3195
408 N 5th St Marshall (56258) ***(G-3319)***
Prairie Electric Co Inc 952 949-0074
6595 Edenvale Blvd # 120 Eden Prairie (55346) ***(G-1752)***
Prairie Five Community Action 320 598-3118
422 5th Ave Ste 307 Madison (56256) ***(G-3077)***
Prairie Five Community Action (PA) 320 269-6578
7th St & Washington Ave S Montevideo (56265) ***(G-6257)***
Prairie Island Indian Com (PA) 651 388-0083
5636 Sturgeon Lake Rd Welch (55089) ***(G-9955)***
Prairie Island Nuclear Generat, Welch *Also Called Northern States Power Co* ***(G-9954)***
Prairie Island Tribal Council 651 385-2554
5636 Sturgeon Lake Rd Welch (55089) ***(G-9956)***
Prairie Lake Optimist, Prior Lake *Also Called Optimist International* ***(G-6947)***
Prairie Lakes Youth Program, Willmar *Also Called Minnesota Department of* ***(G-10026)***
Prairie Lodge 763 566-1495
6011 Earle Brown Dr Minneapolis (55430) ***(G-5400)***
Prairie Manor Nursing Home 507 583-4434
220 3rd St NW Blooming Prairie (55917) ***(G-477)***
Prairie Medical 320 589-4008
24 E 7th St Morris (56267) ***(G-6375)***
Prairie Pride Cooperative (PA) 507 532-9686
1100 E Main St Marshall (56258) ***(G-3320)***
Prairie Restorations Inc 763 389-4342
31922 128th St NW Princeton (55371) ***(G-6924)***
Prairie River Home Care Inc 507 345-8591
227 E Main St Ste 200 Mankato (56001) ***(G-3182)***
Prairie River Home Care Inc 507 532-2264
1411 E College Dr Ste 103 Marshall (56258) ***(G-3321)***
Prairie River Home Care Inc 507 252-9844
1907 2nd St SW Rochester (55902) ***(G-7210)***
Prairie Smoke 507 292-0063
3011 Nelson Ct SE Rochester (55904) ***(G-7211)***
Prairie Technologies Inc of MN 763 255-3200
5600 Queens Ave NE # 400 Elk River (55330) ***(G-1904)***
Prairie View, Slayton *Also Called Lrn Associates Management Inc* ***(G-9488)***
Prairie's Edge Casino Resort 320 564-2121
5616 Prairies Edge Ln Granite Falls (56241) ***(G-2318)***
Prairieland Utility 507 625-2404
1990 Lookout Dr North Mankato (56003) ***(G-6513)***
Prarie View Healthcare Center 507 629-3331
250 5th St E Tracy (56175) ***(G-9690)***
Pratt Construction Inc 651 765-0572
3500 Willow Lake Blvd # 100 Saint Paul (55110) ***(G-8833)***
Pratt Construction Inc 651 429-8032
3500 Willow Lake Blvd Saint Paul (55110) ***(G-8834)***
Pratt Homes, Saint Paul *Also Called Fenway Development Inc* ***(G-8373)***
Pratt Nedegaard 651 429-8032
3500 Willow Lake Blvd # 100 Saint Paul (55110) ***(G-8835)***
Praxair Inc 651 633-6781
2455 Rosegate Saint Paul (55113) ***(G-8836)***
PRC Consulting Inc 952 906-0801
600 W 78th St Ste 230 Chanhassen (55317) ***(G-936)***
Precision Design Inc 952 933-6550
10501 Wayzata Blvd # 101 Hopkins (55305) ***(G-2604)***
Precision Nutrition Inc 507 372-4723
727 Oxford St Worthington (56187) ***(G-10190)***
Precision Optics, Saint Cloud *Also Called Essilor Laboratories of Amer* ***(G-7505)***
Precision Partners Inc 218 737-0507
421 N Broadway Fergus Falls (56537) ***(G-2116)***
Precision Repair & Calibration 763 784-1704
9150 Isanti St NE Minneapolis (55449) ***(G-3572)***
Precision Turf & Chemical Inc 763 477-5885
7728 Commerce Cir Rockford (55373) ***(G-7303)***
Preferred Credit Inc 320 202-7000
3051 2nd St S Ste 200 Saint Cloud (56301) ***(G-7570)***
Preferredone Administrative 763 847-3525
6105 Golden Hills Dr Minneapolis (55416) ***(G-5401)***
Prefinishing Specialists Inc 320 356-2217
314 Blattner Dr Avon (56310) ***(G-297)***
Premier Bank Inc 651 777-7700
2866 White Bear Ave N Saint Paul (55109) ***(G-8837)***
Premier Co's Inc 218 348-1991
7511 Grand Ave Duluth (55807) ***(G-1429)***
Premier Electrical Corp 763 424-6551
4401 85th Ave N Brooklyn Park (55443) ***(G-617)***
Premier Irrigation Inc 651 480-8857
1031 Zweber Ln Hastings (55033) ***(G-2401)***
Premier Limousine, Minneapolis *Also Called Taylor Limousines Inc* ***(G-5795)***
Premier Resorts Ltd 952 253-2500
7760 France Ave S # 1100 Minneapolis (55435) ***(G-5402)***
Premier Rinks Inc 763 249-7417
15300 25th Ave N Ste 600 Minneapolis (55447) ***(G-5403)***
Premier Technologies Inc 952 475-2317
1 Premier Dr Long Lake (55356) ***(G-3030)***
Premier Tile Inc 651 483-1576
3440 Victoria St N Saint Paul (55126) ***(G-8838)***
Premiere Theatres 218 879-7985
904 Highway 33 S Cloquet (55720) ***(G-1061)***
Premium Tools, Albert Lea *Also Called Enderes Tool Co Inc* ***(G-48)***
Prep Preschool Program, Brainerd *Also Called Brainerd School Distict 181* ***(G-553)***
Presbyterian Home Farm Stead 763 712-7000
13733 Quay St NW Ofc Anoka (55304) ***(G-215)***
Presbyterian Homes & Services 952 948-3000
9889 Penn Ave S Minneapolis (55431) ***(G-5404)***
Presbyterian Homes & Services 651 631-6200
1910 County Road D W Saint Paul (55112) ***(G-8839)***
Presbyterian Homes & Services (PA) 651 631-6100
2845 Hamline Ave N # 200 Saint Paul (55113) ***(G-8840)***
Presbyterian Homes & Svcs, Saint Paul *Also Called Stonecrest* ***(G-9278)***
Presbyterian Homes H & A 651 631-6659
2850 Market Place Dr Saint Paul (55117) ***(G-8841)***
Presbyterian Homes Management 651 631-6000
3220 Lake Johanna Blvd Saint Paul (55112) ***(G-8842)***
Presbyterian Homes of Arden 651 631-6000
3220 Lake Johanna Blvd Saint Paul (55112) ***(G-8843)***
Presbyterian Homes of Inver 651 451-5959
6307 Burnham Cir Ofc Inver Grove Heights (55076) ***(G-2765)***
Presbyterian Homes, Housing 651 631-6100
2845 Hamline Ave N # 200 Saint Paul (55113) ***(G-8844)***
Presbyterian Nursing Homes Inc 952 888-9461
9889 Penn Ave S Minneapolis (55431) ***(G-5405)***
Prescription Landscape Inc 651 488-8965
1311 Sylvan St Saint Paul (55117) ***(G-8845)***
Prescription Optical 303 343-0427
311 S 72nd Ave Saint Cloud (56301) ***(G-7571)***
Prestige Drywall Inc 763 506-0030
800 Industry Ave Anoka (55303) ***(G-216)***
Preston Kelly 612 843-4000
222 1st Ave NE Minneapolis (55413) ***(G-5406)***
Prestwick Golf Club Inc 651 459-0288
9372 Bailey Rd Saint Paul (55129) ***(G-9264)***
Previsor Inc 612 843-1059
650 3rd Ave S Ste 1300 Minneapolis (55402) ***(G-5407)***
Prewire Specialists Inc 651 452-9192
401 4th St E Saint Paul (55101) ***(G-8846)***
Pride Institute Inc 952 934-7554
14400 Martin Dr Eden Prairie (55344) ***(G-1753)***
Pride N'Living Home Care Inc 763 572-2390
7691 Central Ave NE Ste 102 Minneapolis (55432) ***(G-3573)***
Prima Laserdyne Inc 763 433-3700
8600 109th Ave N Ste 400 Champlin (55316) ***(G-898)***
Primary Care Center 612 624-9499
420 Delaware St SE Minneapolis (55455) ***(G-5408)***
Prime Country Bank 320 584-5522
412 N Highway 10 Royalton (56373) ***(G-7386)***
Prime Investments Inc (PA) 952 853-1680
900 American Blvd E # 300 Minneapolis (55420) ***(G-5409)***
Prime Mortgage Corp 952 544-3181
11100 Wayzata Blvd Ste 200 Minnetonka (55305) ***(G-6217)***
Prime Ridge Pet Care 763 427-2220
7245 Highway 10 NW Anoka (55303) ***(G-217)***
Prime Therapeutics Inc 651 456-1000
1305 Corporate Center Dr Saint Paul (55121) ***(G-7881)***
Prime West Central County 320 763-4135
2209 Jefferson St Ste 101 Alexandria (56308) ***(G-118)***
Primerica Financial Services 952 895-1091
900 W 128th St Ste 110A Burnsville (55337) ***(G-782)***
Primerica Financial Services 763 546-8627
400 Highway 169 S Ste 170 Minneapolis (55426) ***(G-5410)***
Primerica Financial Services 651 290-9822
332 Minnesota St Ste E840 Saint Paul (55101) ***(G-8847)***
Primerica Financial Services 651 688-9088
3410 Federal Dr Ste 110 Saint Paul (55122) ***(G-7882)***
Primestaff Inc 651 697-2120
3434 Lexington Ave N # 400 Saint Paul (55126) ***(G-8848)***
Primevest Financial Services (HQ) 320 656-4300
400 1st St S Ste 300 Saint Cloud (56301) ***(G-7572)***
Princeton Speedway 763 389-3135
1400 3rd St N Princeton (55371) ***(G-6915)***
Principal Life Insurance Co 952 277-4300
11100 Wayzata Blvd # 211 Hopkins (55305) ***(G-2605)***
Principal Life Insurance Co 651 227-7717
7300 Hudson Blvd N # 245 Saint Paul (55128) ***(G-9265)***

Prinsburg Farmers Co-Op 320 978-8040
401 Railroad Ave Prinsburg (56281) *(G-6927)*
Prior Lake Bus Association 952 440-1166
16245 Northwood Rd NW Prior Lake (55372) *(G-6949)*
Prior Lake State Bank Inc 952 447-2101
16677 Duluth Ave SE # 100 Prior Lake (55372) *(G-6950)*
Prior Lake VFW 952 226-6208
16306 Main Ave SE Prior Lake (55372) *(G-6951)*
Priority Courier Experts, Saint Paul *Also Called Timberland Transportation Inc (G-9068)*
Prism Commercial & Industrial 763 420-4080
7523 Commerce St Hamel (55340) *(G-2354)*
Prism Mortgage Inc 952 546-6272
6465 Wayzata Blvd Ste 304 Minneapolis (55426) *(G-5411)*
Prism Research LLC 651 641-2900
1000 Westgate Dr Ste 149 Saint Paul (55114) *(G-8849)*
Prisma International Inc 612 338-1500
204 N 1st St Minneapolis (55401) *(G-5412)*
Private Industry Council 507 537-6236
607 W Main St Fl 3 Marshall (56258) *(G-3322)*
Pro Courier Inc 763 571-8811
8375 Sunset Rd NE Minneapolis (55432) *(G-3574)*
Pro Motion Marketing 612 347-1490
222 S 9th St 2210 Minneapolis (55402) *(G-5413)*
Pro One Management 612 813-0077
2400 Blaisdell Ave Minneapolis (55404) *(G-5414)*
Pro Staff, Minneapolis *Also Called Dobbs Temporary Services Inc (G-4268)*
Pro Stop Truck Service Inc 651 452-8137
1066 Gemini Rd Ste B Saint Paul (55121) *(G-7883)*
Pro Systems Corp (PA) 218 847-9277
1271 Highway 10 W Detroit Lakes (56501) *(G-1214)*
Pro-Clean, Rockford *Also Called Hospitality Services Corp (G-7302)*
Pro-Maintenance Service, Alexandria *Also Called Rick L Schoenrock (G-120)*
Pro-TEC Design Inc 763 553-1477
5005 Cheshire Ln N Ste 3 Plymouth (55446) *(G-6880)*
Pro-Temp Inc 651 460-6022
21210 Eaton Ave Ste A Farmington (55024) *(G-2058)*
Pro-Wall Inc 763 477-5172
7990 69th Ave Rockford (55373) *(G-7312)*
ProAct Inc 651 686-0405
3195 Neil Armstrong Blvd Saint Paul (55121) *(G-7884)*
Probe Technical Services, Eagan *Also Called A D G Inc (G-1514)*
Probuild Co LLC 952 469-2116
9130 202nd St W Lakeville (55044) *(G-2925)*
Probuild Co LLC 952 469-3466
11356 215th St W Lakeville (55044) *(G-2926)*
Probuild Co LLC 320 251-0861
2915 Roosevelt Rd Saint Cloud (56301) *(G-7573)*
Probuild Co LLC 218 631-2607
1000 Jefferson St N Wadena (56482) *(G-9810)*
Probuilt America Inc 651 770-5570
2211 11th Ave E Ste 130 Saint Paul (55109) *(G-8850)*
Procon Co's Inc 952 258-6300
3100 W Lake St Ste 100 Minneapolis (55416) *(G-5415)*
Procter & Gamble Distributing 952 942-1857
7500 Flying Cloud Dr Eden Prairie (55344) *(G-1754)*
Proctor Motel Associates (PA) 218 624-1026
185 Highway 2 Proctor (55810) *(G-6965)*
Product Deve 612 676-1474
333 Washington Ave N Minneapolis (55401) *(G-5416)*
Product Safety Resources Inc 651 917-6100
1295 Bandana Blvd N # 335 Saint Paul (55108) *(G-8851)*
Production Credit Association 320 235-1771
3881 Abbott Dr Willmar (56201) *(G-10038)*
Production Health Associates 507 372-2957
727 Oxford St Worthington (56187) *(G-10191)*
Productive Alternatives Inc 218 825-8148
213 NW 4th St Brainerd (56401) *(G-583)*
Productive Alternatives Inc (PA) 218 998-5630
1205 N Tower Rd Fergus Falls (56537) *(G-2117)*
Productivity Inc 763 476-8600
15150 25th Ave N Minneapolis (55447) *(G-5417)*
Productivity Quality Inc 763 249-8130
15150 25th Ave N Ste 200 Minneapolis (55447) *(G-5418)*
Products Division, Minneapolis *Also Called Kurt Manufacturing Co Inc (G-3512)*
Proex Photo 651 699-4394
2130 Ford Pkwy Saint Paul (55116) *(G-8852)*
Proex Photo Systems Inc 952 941-5232
574 Paririe Ctr Dr # 100 Eden Prairie (55344) *(G-1755)*
Proex Photo Systems Inc (PA) 952 893-1915
12680 Riverdale Blvd NW Minneapolis (55448) *(G-3575)*
Professional Alternatives L L 952 404-2600
15600 Wayzata Blvd Ste 300 Wayzata (55391) *(G-9936)*
Professional Association of (PA) 612 259-1600
2021 E Hennepin Ave # 100 Minneapolis (55413) *(G-5419)*
Professional Gallery Inc 320 252-8446
24795 County Road 75 Saint Cloud (56301) *(G-7574)*
Professional Hospitality LLC 507 287-6758
77 Woodlake Dr SE Rochester (55904) *(G-7212)*
Professional Hospitality LLC 320 259-8999
235 Park Ave S Saint Cloud (56301) *(G-7575)*
Professional Insur Providers, Glencoe *Also Called First McLeod Agency Inc (G-2205)*
Professional Litho-Art Co Inc 612 338-0400
807 13th Ave S Minneapolis (55404) *(G-5420)*
Professional Physical Therapy 952 935-0333
3201 Virginia Ave S Minneapolis (55426) *(G-5421)*
Professional Radiology Svcs 763 560-0010
6300 Shingle Creek Pkwy Ste 33 Minneapolis (55430) *(G-5422)*
Professional Reproductions Inc 952 946-1200
7415 Cahill Rd Edina (55439) *(G-1841)*
Profinium Financial Inc 507 235-5538
105 Lake Ave Fairmont (56031) *(G-1978)*
Profinium Financial Inc (HQ) 507 776-2311
414 N 5th Ave E Truman (56088) *(G-9696)*
Proform Thermal Systems Inc 763 572-2200
10401 Jamestown St NE Minneapolis (55449) *(G-3576)*
Program In Human Sexuality 612 625-1500
1300 S 2nd St Ste 180 Minneapolis (55454) *(G-5423)*
Programming Alternative of NM, Hopkins *Also Called RCM Technologies Inc (G-2612)*
Programming Solutions Inc 763 424-8154
9000 Telford Xing Minneapolis (55443) *(G-5424)*
Progress Valley Inc 612 869-3223
308 E 78th St Minneapolis (55423) *(G-5425)*
Progressive Concrete & Masonry 651 489-2200
345 Atwater St Ste 1 Saint Paul (55117) *(G-8853)*
Progressive Habilitative Svcs 763 536-8128
4900 Highway 169 N Minneapolis (55428) *(G-5426)*
Progressive Interiors Inc 612 718-1868
10450 Knight Ave Waconia (55387) *(G-9790)*
Progressive Rail Inc 952 985-7245
21778 Highview Ave Lakeville (55044) *(G-2927)*
Project Consulting Group Inc 612 330-0123
510 1st Ave N Ste 400 Minneapolis (55403) *(G-5427)*
Project For Pride In Living (PA) 612 455-5100
1035 E Franklin Ave Minneapolis (55404) *(G-5428)*
Project For Pride In Living 612 332-0664
1179 15th Ave SE Minneapolis (55414) *(G-5429)*
PROJECT TURNABOUT, Granite Falls *Also Called Reverence For Life & Concern (G-2319)*
Prometric Inc 651 647-1723
1260 Energy Ln Saint Paul (55108) *(G-8854)*
Promises + Inc 763 497-3727
6600 Jansen Ave NE Albertville (55301) *(G-76)*
Promotion Management Center 651 462-1213
31205 Falcon Ave Stacy (55079) *(G-9580)*
Property Solutions & Services 612 746-0400
708 N 1st St Ste 241 Minneapolis (55401) *(G-5430)*
Prophet Corp (PA) 507 451-7470
2525 Lemond St Owatonna (55060) *(G-6730)*
Prophet Corp 952 841-0021
2525 Lemond St Owatonna (55060) *(G-6731)*
Prophet Corp 800 533-0446
2525 Lemond St Owatonna (55060) *(G-6732)*
Prophy Power, Lakeville *Also Called Minnesota Prophy Power Inc (G-2920)*
Prosar, Saint Paul *Also Called Product Safety Resources Inc (G-8851)*
Prosource Billing, Sauk Rapids *Also Called Array Services Group Inc (G-9357)*
Prosource Technologies Inc 763 786-1445
9219 E River Rd NW Minneapolis (55433) *(G-3577)*
Protiviti Inc 952 249-2200
601 Carlson Pkwy Ste 1120 Hopkins (55305) *(G-2606)*
Protouch Painting Inc 651 457-5628
139 Concord Exchange S South Saint Paul (55075) *(G-9537)*
Provation Medical Inc 612 313-1500
800 Washington Ave N Ste 400 Minneapolis (55401) *(G-5431)*
Providence Academy 763 258-2500
15100 Schmidt Lake Rd Minneapolis (55446) *(G-5432)*
Providence Place 612 724-5495
3720 23rd Ave S Minneapolis (55407) *(G-5433)*
Provident Mortgage Corp of MN 612 285-6275
3100 W Lake St Ste 100 Minneapolis (55416) *(G-5434)*
Provider Call Center, Saint Paul *Also Called Minnesota Department of Human (G-8683)*
Providers Choice Inc 952 944-7010
10901 Red Circle Dr Ste 100 Hopkins (55343) *(G-2607)*
Prudencial Sundial Realty Inc 763 571-9200
961 Hillwind Rd NE Minneapolis (55432) *(G-3578)*
Prudential Insurance Co of 612 349-1000
3701 Wayzata Blvd Minneapolis (55416) *(G-5435)*
Prudential Insurance Co of 763 553-6056
9220 Bass Lake Rd Lowr Minneapolis (55428) *(G-5436)*
Prudential Insurance Co of 507 281-4200
140 Elton Hills Ln NW Rochester (55901) *(G-7213)*
Prudential Pladson Realty Inc 320 253-9074
2680 W Saint Germain St Saint Cloud (56301) *(G-7576)*
Prudential Truscott Realtors 218 726-1255
1820 Maple Grove Rd Duluth (55811) *(G-1430)*
Pse, Minneapolis *Also Called Power System Engineering Inc (G-3571)*
PSS World Medical Inc 763 428-2388
12999 Wilfred Ln N # 250 Rogers (55374) *(G-7338)*
Psychiatric Clinic of Mankato 507 387-3195
1400 E Madison Ave Ste 352 Mankato (56001) *(G-3183)*
Pta Minnesota Congress, Little Falls *Also Called Lincoln Elementry School P T A (G-3010)*
Pta Minnesota Congress 28 ....763 792-5900
1 School Rd Circle Pines (55014) *(G-1020)*
Public Employees Retirement 651 296-7460
60 Empire Dr Ste 200 Saint Paul (55103) *(G-8855)*
Public Health Dept, Saint Paul *Also Called County of Ramsey (G-8260)*
Public Health Solutions I 763 754-7427
12770 Raven St NW Minneapolis (55448) *(G-3579)*
Public Indian Hospital, Cass Lake *Also Called Department of Health Minnesota (G-871)*
Public Markets Inc 763 546-3139
2701 Brunswick Ave N Minneapolis (55422) *(G-5437)*
Public Radio International Inc 612 330-9266
401 2nd Ave N Ste 500 Minneapolis (55401) *(G-5438)*
Public Safety Council 763 550-9200
13120 County Road 6 # 100 Minneapolis (55441) *(G-5439)*
Public Utilities, Grand Rapids *Also Called City of Grand Rapids (G-2273)*
Public Works Department, Cologne *Also Called County of Carver (G-1091)*
Public Works Dept, Saint Paul *Also Called City of Saint Paul (G-8206)*
Public Works Highway Maint 218 742-9800
7823 Highway 135 Virginia (55792) *(G-9751)*
Publishing Business Systems 651 639-0662
2611 Hamline Ave N Ste 100 Saint Paul (55113) *(G-8856)*
Pugleasa Co Inc 651 636-6442
1253 Connelly Ave Saint Paul (55112) *(G-8857)*
Pulmonary Health Realty Assocs 651 224-5895
255 Smith Ave N Ste 300 Saint Paul (55102) *(G-8858)*
Pulte Homes 763 241-9001
7020 Quaday Ave Elk River (55330) *(G-1891)*
Pulte Homes of Minnesota LLC 651 452-5200
815 Northwest Pkwy # 140 Eagan (55121) *(G-1546)*
Pump & Meter Service Inc 952 933-4800
11303 Excelsior Blvd Hopkins (55343) *(G-2608)*
Purchasing Dept, Minneapolis *Also Called Uhc - Edina (G-5894)*
Putting All Cmmnities Together, Willmar *Also Called Pact For Families (G-10034)*
Q B F, Minneapolis *Also Called Quality Business Forms of (G-5441)*

ALPHABETIC

Q3 Contracting Inc 651 224-2424
3066 Spruce St Saint Paul (55117) *(G-8859)*
QLogic Corp 952 932-4000
4601 Dean Lakes Blvd Shakopee (55379) *(G-9466)*
Qrs Diagnostic LLC 763 559-8492
14755 27th Ave N Ste 150 Minneapolis (55447) *(G-5440)*
Qsc of Northfield Inc 507 366-7149
450 Armstrong Rd Northfield (55057) *(G-6540)*
Quality Building Maintenance 507 289-0603
2002 14th St NW Rochester (55901) *(G-7214)*
Quality Business Forms of (PA) 763 559-4330
5097 Nathan Ln N Minneapolis (55442) *(G-5441)*
Quality Car Wash Ops Ltd Inc 952 473-4535
1405 Wayzata Blvd E Wayzata (55391) *(G-9937)*
Quality Care Services Inc 320 230-7275
3333 W Div St Ste 213 Saint Cloud (56301) *(G-7577)*
Quality Drywall Inc 763 424-5774
8620 Monticello Ln N # 100 Osseo (55369) *(G-6654)*
Quality Drywall Midwest Inc 763 424-5774
8620 Monticello Ln N # 100 Maple Grove (55369) *(G-3252)*
Quality Forklift Sales & Svc 952 445-6607
587 Citation Dr Shakopee (55379) *(G-9467)*
Quality Inn, Minneapolis *Also Called Nath Midwest Lodging LLC (G-5158)*
Quality Inn, Winona *Also Called Winona Inn LP (G-10150)*
Quality Insulation Inc 952 929-6889
3509 Raleigh Ave Minneapolis (55416) *(G-5442)*
Quality Life Styles Inc 952 445-4155
1340 3rd Ave W Shakopee (55379) *(G-9468)*
Quality Living Home Health 507 454-6800
164 E 4th St Ste 4 Winona (55987) *(G-10120)*
Quality Mechanical, Rochester *Also Called Harris Contracting Co (G-7133)*
Quality Metals Inc 651 645-5875
2575 Doswell Ave Saint Paul (55108) *(G-8860)*
Quality Refrigeration Inc 612 861-7350
6237 Penn Ave S Ste 1 Minneapolis (55423) *(G-5443)*
Quality Resource Group Inc (PA) 763 478-8636
12795 16th Ave N Plymouth (55441) *(G-6881)*
Quality Underground Services 651 224-0413
3066 Spruce St Saint Paul (55117) *(G-8861)*
Quality Wine & Spirits Co 952 854-8600
7900 Chicago Ave S Minneapolis (55420) *(G-5444)*
Quantum Co's Inc 952 943-4357
10525 Hampshire Ave S # 100 Minneapolis (55438) *(G-5445)*
Quantum Consulting & Placement 952 820-0160
3000 Centre Pointe Dr Saint Paul (55113) *(G-8862)*
Quantum Retail Technology Inc 612 486-3491
36 S 9th St Minneapolis (55402) *(G-5446)*
Quarry At Giants Ridge 218 865-3092
5832 Giants Ridge Rd Biwabik (55708) *(G-471)*
Quarterdeck At Pleasant Acres 218 963-2482
9820 Birch Bay Dr SW Nisswa (56468) *(G-6493)*
Quarterdeck Resort & Rest 218 963-7537
9820 Birch Bay Dr SW Nisswa (56468) *(G-6494)*
Queen City Federal Savings 218 741-2040
501 Chestnut St Virginia (55792) *(G-9752)*
Queen of Peace Hospital 952 758-4431
301 2nd St NE New Prague (56071) *(G-6434)*
Quello Clinic 952 985-8100
7373 France Ave S Ste 202 Minneapolis (55435) *(G-5447)*
Quest Diagnostics Clinical 651 635-1500
600 County Road D W Ste 11 Saint Paul (55112) *(G-8863)*
Quest Engineering Inc (PA) 952 546-4441
2300 Edgewood Ave S Minneapolis (55426) *(G-5448)*
Quest Management Associates 612 379-3800
1313 5th St SE Ste 100 Minneapolis (55414) *(G-5449)*
Quest Software Inc 952 229-3500
10340 Viking Dr Ste 100 Eden Prairie (55344) *(G-1756)*
Questar Assessment Inc 952 997-2700
5550 Upper 147th St W Saint Paul (55124) *(G-7885)*
Questar Capital Corp 888 446-5872
5701 Golden Hills Dr Minneapolis (55416) *(G-5450)*
Questar Data Systems Inc 651 688-0089
2905 W Service Rd Saint Paul (55121) *(G-7886)*
Quick Service Battery Co Inc 651 645-0485
1156 Robert St S Saint Paul (55118) *(G-7887)*
Quick Test Inc 952 854-3535
300 E Broadway Minneapolis (55425) *(G-5451)*
Quicksilver Express Courier (PA) 651 484-1111
203 Little Canada Rd E Saint Paul (55117) *(G-8864)*
Quicksilver Express Courier of 651 484-1111
203 Little Canada Rd E Saint Paul (55117) *(G-8865)*
Quincy Newspapers Inc 507 895-9969
3705 County Road 25 La Crescent (55947) *(G-2842)*
Quinlan Care Home, Saint Paul *Also Called Cardenas & Reynolds Entrprs (G-8156)*
Quinlivan & Hughes 320 251-1414
400 1st St S Ste 600 Saint Cloud (56301) *(G-7578)*
Quixotic Distribution, Plymouth *Also Called CMC Enterprises Inc (G-6856)*
Qwest Corp 612 663-2073
150 S 5th St Ste 3300 Minneapolis (55402) *(G-5452)*
Qwest Corp 612 381-5202
2800 Wayzata Blvd Ste 42 Minneapolis (55405) *(G-5453)*
R & D Batteries Inc 952 890-0629
3300 Corporate Center Dr Burnsville (55306) *(G-783)*
R & E Enterprises of Mankato 507 388-3364
55173 State Highway 68 Mankato (56001) *(G-3184)*
R & G Construction Co 507 537-1473
2694 County Road 6 Marshall (56258) *(G-3323)*
R & O Elevator Co Inc 612 588-7844
1801 W River Rd Minneapolis (55411) *(G-5454)*
R & R Ready Mix Inc 218 943-4601
13947 State Highway 29 N Miltona (56354) *(G-3381)*
R & R Transportation Inc 218 439-6144
500 N Main St Audubon (56511) *(G-255)*
R & S Heating & Air Condg 952 894-0376
12600 Creek View Ave Savage (55378) *(G-9404)*
R A Ventures Inc 612 721-9155
2500 E 25th St Ste 2 Minneapolis (55406) *(G-5455)*
R B C Capital Market (PA) 612 371-2711
60 S 6th St Minneapolis (55402) *(G-5456)*
R D Offutt Co 218 732-1461
15357 US 71 Park Rapids (56470) *(G-6760)*
R D Offutt Co 218 732-4163
11385 State Hwy 34 Park Rapids (56470) *(G-6761)*
R E I, Minneapolis *Also Called Recreational Equipment Inc (G-5476)*
R E M North Star Inc 218 435-6088
323 Mark Ave N Fosston (56542) *(G-2179)*
R E M Southwest Services C 507 223-5633
110 Saint Olaf Ave N Canby (56220) *(G-851)*
R E Purvis & Associates Inc 952 829-5532
6667 W Old Shakopee Rd Ste 107 Minneapolis (55438) *(G-5457)*
R J Ahmann Co 952 947-9761
7555 Market Place Dr Eden Prairie (55344) *(G-1757)*
R J M Construction Inc 952 837-8600
7003 W Lake St Ste 400 Minneapolis (55426) *(G-5458)*
R J M Enterprises of Minnesota 763 323-8389
6650 143rd Ave NW Anoka (55303) *(G-218)*
R J Mechanical Inc 320 679-0602
510 Highway 65 S Mora (55051) *(G-6368)*
R J Ryan Construction Inc 651 681-0200
1100 Mendota Heights Rd Mendota Heights (55120) *(G-3369)*
R J Tool Crib LLC 320 253-1020
1202 Sun Ridge Dr Saint Cloud (56301) *(G-7579)*
R J Zavoral & Sons Inc 218 773-0586
18297 County Highway 72 SW East Grand Forks (56721) *(G-1574)*
R J Zavoral Ed's Construction 218 773-0586
18297 County Highway 72 SW East Grand Forks (56721) *(G-1575)*
R L Bodeker & Sons Inc (PA) 651 452-0377
3330 Mike Collins Dr Saint Paul (55121) *(G-7888)*
R L Brookdale Motors Inc 763 561-8111
6801 Brooklyn Blvd Minneapolis (55429) *(G-5459)*
R M G, Hopkins *Also Called Residential Mortgage Group Inc (G-2616)*
R M L S Minnesota 651 251-5458
2550 University Ave W 259S Saint Paul (55114) *(G-8866)*
R Pope Douglas Solid Waste MGT, Alexandria *Also Called Pope Douglas Solid Waste Mgt (G-117)*
R Tech Laboratories 651 481-2207
1150 County Road F W Saint Paul (55112) *(G-8867)*
R Z Solutions, Minneapolis *Also Called Rubenstein & Ziff Inc (G-5574)*
R&S Transport Inc 507 289-5080
1725 Highway 14 E Rochester (55904) *(G-7215)*
Race Automotive of Rochester 507 282-5200
457 16th Ave NW Rochester (55901) *(G-7216)*
Rachel Contracting LLC 763 424-9955
4125 Napier Ct NE Saint Michael (55376) *(G-7681)*
Radcliffe Systems 952 545-2409
11900 Wayzata Blvd # 209 Hopkins (55305) *(G-2609)*
Radio City Marketing Group Inc 320 253-6500
619 W Saint Germain St Saint Cloud (56301) *(G-7580)*
Radio Talking Book, Saint Paul *Also Called Minnesota Department of (G-8681)*
Radison Hotel 651 636-4567
2540 Cleveland Ave N Saint Paul (55113) *(G-8868)*
Radisson Hotel Bloomington, Bloomington *Also Called Wsi - Rwp LLC (G-527)*
Radisson Hotels International 763 212-5000
701 Carlson Pkwy Minnetonka (55305) *(G-6218)*
Radisson Hotels International 651 291-8800
411 Minnesota St Saint Paul (55101) *(G-8869)*
Radisson Ht Duluth Harborview, Duluth *Also Called Tb Duluth LLC (G-1479)*
Radisson Inn, Minneapolis *Also Called Regency Plymouth Hotel (G-5485)*
Radisson Inn, Minneapolis *Also Called Carlson Hotels Management Corp (G-4016)*
Radisson Inn, Saint Cloud *Also Called St Cloud Suite Hotel Inc (G-7606)*
Radisson Univ Ht - Minneapolis, Minneapolis *Also Called University Inn Associates, A (G-5924)*
Rag Minneapolis Stock Co 612 333-6576
113 27th Ave NE Ste I Minneapolis (55418) *(G-5460)*
RAGSTOCK STORES, Minneapolis *Also Called Rag Minneapolis Stock Co (G-5460)*
Railway Equipment Co Inc 763 537-3702
15400 Medina Rd Minneapolis (55447) *(G-5461)*
Railworks Track Systems Inc 952 469-4907
8485 210th St W Lakeville (55044) *(G-2928)*
Rain & Hail Insurance Service 763 473-2421
2 Carlson Pkwy N Ste 255 Minneapolis (55447) *(G-5462)*
Rainbow Inc 763 535-4041
7324 36th Ave N Minneapolis (55427) *(G-5463)*
Rainbow Residence Inc 507 451-5327
285 Cedardale Dr SE Owatonna (55060) *(G-6733)*
Rainy Lake Houseboats Inc 218 286-5391
2031 Town Road 488 International Falls (56649) *(G-2729)*
Raiper Clinic 218 879-1271
417 Skyline Blvd Cloquet (55720) *(G-1062)*
Raiter Clinic Ltd 218 879-1271
417 Skyline Blvd Cloquet (55720) *(G-1063)*
Rajkowski Hansmeier Ltd 320 251-1055
11 7th Ave N Ste 3 Saint Cloud (56303) *(G-7581)*
Rakhma Inc 612 824-2345
4953 Aldrich Ave S Minneapolis (55419) *(G-5464)*
Ram Buildings Inc 320 485-2844
592 Industrial Blvd Winsted (55395) *(G-10164)*
Ram Construction Services of 651 765-1950
3065 Spruce St Ste 104 Little Canada (55117) *(G-2997)*
Ram Mutual Insurance Co Inc 218 879-3321
16 E Highway 61 Esko (55733) *(G-1922)*
Ram Woodvale 507 433-4924
301 N Main St Austin (55912) *(G-284)*
Ramada Hotel & Conference Ctr, Rochester *Also Called Midwest of Rochester Inc (G-7184)*
Ramada Inn, Minneapolis *Also Called River Valley Hospitality LLC (G-5544)*
Ramada Inn, Saint Paul *Also Called Radison Hotel (G-8868)*
Ramada Mall of America, Bloomington *Also Called Sanford Hospitality LLC (G-512)*
Ramada Minneapo, Minneapolis *Also Called Brooklyn Park Hospitality LLC (G-3960)*
Rambow Inc 320 354-2570
1000 Rambow Pkwy New London (56273) *(G-6419)*
Ramler Trucking Inc 320 845-4500
400 13th St Albany (56307) *(G-28)*
Ramsey County Care Center, Saint Paul *Also Called County of Ramsey (G-8258)*
Ramsey Excavating Co 612 529-0077
4060 Washington Ave N Minneapolis (55412) *(G-5465)*
Ramstead, John H, Minneapolis *Also Called Borkon, Ramstead, Mariani (G-3930)*

Randall J Herman 763 559-3111
13015 38th Pl N Minneapolis (55441) *(G-5466)*
Randall, Omlie, Haas 952 835-5003
7373 France Ave S Ste 602 Minneapolis (55435) *(G-5467)*
Randt Recycling Technologies 763 417-1370
60571 US Highway 12 Litchfield (55355) *(G-2989)*
Randy Kramer Excavating Inc 320 764-6871
67962 State Highway 55 Watkins (55389) *(G-9899)*
Range Center Inc (PA) 218 254-3347
1001 8th Ave NW Chisholm (55719) *(G-1000)*
Range Co Operatives Inc 218 741-7393
102 Hoover Rd S Virginia (55792) *(G-9753)*
Range Cornice & Roofing Co 218 263-8812
510 W 41st St Hibbing (55746) *(G-2470)*
Range Cornice & Roofing Co Inc 218 262-4581
510 W 41st St Hibbing (55746) *(G-2471)*
Range Mental Health Center Inc 218 263-9237
3203 3rd Ave W Hibbing (55746) *(G-2472)*
Range Mental Health Center Inc (PA) 218 749-2881
624 13th St S Virginia (55792) *(G-9754)*
Range Regional Health Services (PA) 218 262-4881
750 E 34th St Hibbing (55746) *(G-2473)*
Ranger-Chevrolet-Cadillac, Hibbing *Also Called Hilligoss Chevrolet Inc (G-2454)*
Rangerland Dental Group Inc 218 534-3141
21343 Archival Rd Deerwood (56444) *(G-1179)*
Rape & Abuse Crisis Center 218 643-6110
317 8th St S Breckenridge (56520) *(G-596)*
Rape & Sexual Abuse Center, Minneapolis *Also Called Neighborhood Involvement (G-5180)*
Rapid Packaging Inc 763 404-8900
8700 109th Ave N Ste 300 Champlin (55316) *(G-899)*
Raske Building Systems Inc 320 877-7221
240 Milkyway St N Cosmos (56228) *(G-1095)*
Ratner Steel Supply Co 651 631-8515
2500 County Road B W 1A Saint Paul (55113) *(G-8870)*
Ratwik, Roszak, & Maloney 612 339-0060
730 2nd Ave S Ste 300 Minneapolis (55402) *(G-5468)*
Raveill Trucking Inc 218 768-2701
20982 State Highway 210 McGregor (55760) *(G-3340)*
Ray Drachenberg 507 644-2108
29668 US Highway 71 Redwood Falls (56283) *(G-7027)*
Ray N Welter Heating Co 612 825-6867
4637 Chicago Ave Minneapolis (55407) *(G-5469)*
Ray Riihiluoma Inc 218 879-3317
1415 Highway 33 S Cloquet (55720) *(G-1064)*
Rayco Construction Inc 612 788-0077
211 Saint Anthony Pkwy Minneapolis (55418) *(G-5470)*
Raymond Auto Body Inc 651 488-0588
1075 Pierce Butler Rte Saint Paul (55104) *(G-8871)*
Raymond Management Co Inc 507 287-9050
1755 S Broadway Rochester (55904) *(G-7217)*
Rba Inc 952 404-2676
100 Lake St W Wayzata (55391) *(G-9938)*
Rbc Global Asset Management 612 376-7000
100 S 5th St Ste 2300 Minneapolis (55402) *(G-5471)*
Rbc Tile & Stone, Minneapolis *Also Called Rollin B Child Inc (G-5558)*
Rbc Wealth Management (PA) 612 371-7750
60 S 6th St Ste 700 Minneapolis (55402) *(G-5472)*
Rbc Wealth Management 651 228-6900
400 Robert St N Ste 1400 Saint Paul (55101) *(G-8872)*
Rbc Wealth Managment 218 724-2100
1420 London Rd Ste 201 Duluth (55805) *(G-1431)*
Rbc Wealth Managment 763 476-3700
601 Carlson Pkwy Ste 500 Hopkins (55305) *(G-2610)*
Rbc Wealth Managment 952 838-7000
7650 Edinbrgh Way Ste 800 Minneapolis (55435) *(G-5473)*
Rbc Wealth Managment 651 766-4920
520 Highway 96 W Ste 100 Saint Paul (55126) *(G-8873)*
Rbm Services Inc 952 361-0897
1107 Hazeltine Blvd Ste 120 Chaska (55318) *(G-978)*
RC Erickson & Associates Inc 651 452-6758
2915 Waters Rd Ste 112 Saint Paul (55121) *(G-7889)*
Rcb Holding Co 651 631-1040
1501 County Road C W Saint Paul (55113) *(G-8874)*
Rcc Liquidating Corp 763 546-3771
13185 Ridgedale Dr Hopkins (55305) *(G-2611)*
Rcc Liquidating Corp 507 281-0313
710 Apache Mall Rochester (55902) *(G-7218)*
Rcc Liquidating Corp 651 699-0988
2130 Ford Pkwy Saint Paul (55116) *(G-8875)*
Rck Inc 320 693-7422
27744 Csah 34 Litchfield (55355) *(G-2990)*
RCM Technologies Inc 952 841-1188
11100 Wayzata Blvd Ste 530 Hopkins (55305) *(G-2612)*
Rdlp Financial Corp 952 857-1479
3600 Minnesota Dr Minneapolis (55435) *(G-5474)*
Rdo Agriculture Equipment Co 218 643-2601
905 Buffalo Ave Breckenridge (56520) *(G-597)*
RDO Construction Equipment Co 952 890-8880
12500 Dupont Ave S Burnsville (55337) *(G-784)*
Rdo Construction Equipment Co 218 282-8440
2900 SE Main Ave Moorhead (56560) *(G-6334)*
Rdo Equipment Co 218 483-3353
920 Odonnel St Hawley (56549) *(G-2421)*
Rdo Material Handling Co 651 905-7025
2985 Lone Oak Cir Saint Paul (55121) *(G-7890)*
Re Max, Eden Prairie *Also Called Collopy & Saunders Real Estate (G-1631)*
Re Max, Minneapolis *Also Called Associates Plus Inc (G-3412)*
Re Max, Rochester *Also Called Linda Waterman (G-7161)*
Re Max, Saint Paul *Also Called Crossroads South Metro Inc (G-8269)*
RE Max Advisors 952 898-1112
1500 McAndrews Rd W Ste 200 Burnsville (55337) *(G-785)*
Re Max Associates Plus, Anoka *Also Called Associates Plus Inc (G-156)*
Re Max Associates Plus, Saint Paul *Also Called Associates Plus Inc (G-8074)*
RE MAX of Rochester 507 287-7735
4600 18th Ave NW Rochester (55901) *(G-7219)*
RE Max Real Estate Properties 763 755-1100
11905 Highway 65 NE Minneapolis (55434) *(G-3580)*

Reach-Up Inc 320 253-8110
1250 Johnson Rd Saint Cloud (56304) *(G-7423)*
Reading Bus Line Inc 507 926-5404
19771 McCall Ave Reading (56165) *(G-6970)*
Ready Bus Line Co Inc 507 895-2349
1369 County Road 6 La Crescent (55947) *(G-2843)*
Real Estate Equites Inc 651 227-6925
345 Saint Peter St Ste 16 Saint Paul (55102) *(G-8876)*
Real Estate Equities Inc (PA) 651 227-6925
345 Saint Peter St Ste 1600 Saint Paul (55102) *(G-8877)*
Real Estate Masters Inc 651 484-4818
312 County Road D E Saint Paul (55117) *(G-8878)*
Real Services Inc 218 728-5161
1732 London Rd Duluth (55812) *(G-1432)*
Realife Cooperative of Mounds 763 780-9737
7735 Silver Lake Rd Saint Paul (55112) *(G-8879)*
Rebs Supply Inc 952 942-5457
9911 Valley View Rd Eden Prairie (55344) *(G-1758)*
Rebuild Resources Inc 651 645-7055
602 Prior Ave N Saint Paul (55104) *(G-8880)*
REc Inc 952 947-3000
7500 W 78th St Minneapolis (55439) *(G-5475)*
Receivables Control Corp 763 315-9600
7373 Kirkwood Ct N # 200 Osseo (55369) *(G-6655)*
Receivables Management Soln 651 457-1130
260 E Wentworth Ave Saint Paul (55118) *(G-7891)*
Recovery One Inc 952 435-7106
14420 County Road 5 Burnsville (55306) *(G-786)*
Recovery Resource Center, Minneapolis *Also Called Resource Inc (G-5526)*
Recreational Equipment Inc 952 884-4315
750 79th St W Minneapolis (55420) *(G-5476)*
Red Cross, Saint Paul *Also Called American National Red Cross (G-8030)*
Red Lake Band of Chippewa 218 679-3400
24856 Hospital Dr Redlake (56671) *(G-7016)*
Red Lake Chemical Health 218 679-3995
Hwy 1 & Main St Redlake (56671) *(G-7017)*
Red Lake County Cooperative 218 253-2149
702 12th St Red Lake Falls (56750) *(G-6973)*
Red Light Rescue, Hopkins *Also Called Ahles & Associates LLC (G-2504)*
Red Line Medical Supply, Osseo *Also Called McKesson Medical-Surgical (G-6636)*
Red River Basin Commission 218 291-0422
119 5th St S Ste 209 Moorhead (56560) *(G-6335)*
Red River Electric Inc 218 236-0502
2323 16th Ave S Ste 105 Moorhead (56560) *(G-6336)*
Red River Implement Co Inc 218 643-2601
905 Buffalo Ave Breckenridge (56520) *(G-598)*
Red River Trails Inc 218 236-0300
4838 Highway 75 S Moorhead (56560) *(G-6337)*
Red River Valley & Western 218 643-4994
501 Minnesota Ave Breckenridge (56520) *(G-599)*
Red Rock Fire Inc 651 765-0765
6671 Lake Blvd Forest Lake (55025) *(G-2154)*
Red Roof Inns Inc 952 890-1420
12920 Aldrich Ave S Burnsville (55337) *(G-787)*
Red Roof Inns Inc 651 738-7160
1806 Wooddale Dr Saint Paul (55125) *(G-9266)*
Red Rooster Auto Stores LLC (HQ) 763 533-4321
5140 W Broadway Ave Minneapolis (55429) *(G-5477)*
Red Wing Brass Band Inc 651 388-2656
365 Oak Hill Dr Red Wing (55066) *(G-6996)*
Red Wing Healthcare LLC 651 388-2843
1412 W 4th St Red Wing (55066) *(G-6997)*
Red Wing Hotel Corp 651 388-2846
406 Main St Ste A Red Wing (55066) *(G-6998)*
Red Wing Young Men's Christian 651 388-4724
434 Main St Red Wing (55066) *(G-6999)*
Red's Auto Inc 320 468-6478
104 Main St S Pierz (56364) *(G-6807)*
Redbrick Health Corp 612 659-3000
920 2nd Ave S Ste 1000 Minneapolis (55402) *(G-5478)*
Redeemer Residence Inc 612 827-2555
625 W 31st St Minneapolis (55408) *(G-5479)*
Reden & Anders 800 643-7933
12125 Technology Dr Eden Prairie (55344) *(G-1759)*
Redpharm Drug 952 653-2525
6501 City West Pkwy Eden Prairie (55344) *(G-1760)*
Redprairie Corp 952 656-5400
6385 Old Shady Oak Rd # 180 Eden Prairie (55344) *(G-1761)*
Redwood Area Hospital, Redwood Falls *Also Called City of Redwood Falls (G-7020)*
Redwood Long Distance Co 507 644-3844
731 Main St Wabasso (56293) *(G-9777)*
Reed Elsevier Inc 651 385-1895
491 Highway 19 Blvd # 102 Red Wing (55066) *(G-7000)*
Reed's Sporting Goods, Walker *Also Called Leech Lake Distributors Inc (G-9853)*
ReEntry House Inc 612 869-2411
5812 Lyndale Ave S Minneapolis (55419) *(G-5480)*
Reese Brooks Hospitality Inds 763 767-0754
1737 122nd Ln NW Minneapolis (55448) *(G-3581)*
Reese, Winter & Associates Ltd 507 645-4473
112 5th St W Northfield (55057) *(G-6541)*
Reeves Park Inc 952 930-0290
5050 Lincoln Dr Ste 470 Minneapolis (55436) *(G-5481)*
Referral Mortgage Inc 952 933-4400
7505 Metro Blvd Ste 400 Minneapolis (55439) *(G-5482)*
Refuge Golf Club 763 753-7770
1323 Coon Rapids Blvd NW Minneapolis (55433) *(G-3582)*
Regal Cinemas Inc 952 435-8080
14300 Buck Hill Rd Burnsville (55306) *(G-788)*
Regal Cinemas Inc 651 452-8329
2055 Cliff Rd Saint Paul (55122) *(G-7892)*
Regal Contractors Inc 320 253-1161
2133 Julep Rd Saint Cloud (56301) *(G-7582)*
Regal Minneapolis Hotel, Minneapolis *Also Called M & C Hotel Interests Inc (G-4913)*
Regency Athletic Club & Spa 612 343-3131
1300 Nicollet Ave Ste 6000 Minneapolis (55403) *(G-5483)*
Regency Hospital Co LLC 763 588-2750
1300 Hidden Lakes Pkwy Minneapolis (55422) *(G-5484)*

ALPHABETIC

Regency Midwest Ventures LP 320 762-1124
2100 Arrowwood Ln NW Alexandria (56308) *(G-119)*
Regency Plymouth Hotel 763 559-6600
3131 Campus Dr Minneapolis (55441) *(G-5485)*
Regency Point Apartment Homes, Minneapolis *Also Called Miramar Inc (G-5108)*
Regent Broadcasting of St 320 251-4422
640 Lincoln Ave SE Saint Cloud (56304) *(G-7424)*
Regents of The University of 218 245-2200
1 Gayley Ave Bigfork (56628) *(G-463)*
Regents of The University of 218 281-8376
131 Kiehle Bldg Crookston (56716) *(G-1135)*
Regents of The University of 218 720-4294
5013 Miller Trunk Hwy Duluth (55811) *(G-1433)*
Regents of The University of 612 625-4665
300 Washington Ave S Minneapolis (55415) *(G-5486)*
Regents of The University of 612 625-3500
300 Washington Ave SE Minneapolis (55455) *(G-5487)*
Regents of The University of 612 625-1612
410 Church St SE Minneapolis (55455) *(G-5488)*
Regents of The University of 612 625-9494
333 E River Pkwy 200 Minneapolis (55455) *(G-5489)*
Regents of The University of 612 624-0999
Mmc 276 420 Del St SE 276 Mmc Minneapolis (55455) *(G-5490)*
Regents of The University of 612 627-4564
606 24th Ave S Ste 500 Minneapolis (55454) *(G-5491)*
Regents of The University of 612 626-7275
511 Washington Ave SE Minneapolis (55455) *(G-5492)*
Regents of The University of 612 627-4014
1600 Rollins Ave SE Minneapolis (55455) *(G-5493)*
Regents of The University of 612 625-2874
717 Delaware St SE Ste 1 Minneapolis (55414) *(G-5494)*
Regents of The University of 612 624-9499
420 Delaware St SE Minneapolis (55455) *(G-5495)*
Regents of The University of 612 626-5722
515 Delaware St SE Rm 1 Minneapolis (55455) *(G-5496)*
Regents of The University of 612 624-2345
84 Church St SE Minneapolis (55455) *(G-5497)*
Regents of The University of 612 625-8625
516 Delaware St SE Minneapolis (55455) *(G-5498)*
Regents of The University of 612 625-1551
330 Hubert Humphrey Ctr Minneapolis (55455) *(G-5499)*
Regents of The University of 612 624-8865
1300 S 2nd St Ste 300 Minneapolis (55454) *(G-5500)*
Regents of The University of 612 624-6328
150 Pillsbury Dr SE 204 Minneapolis (55455) *(G-5501)*
Regents of The University of 612 626-4515
2221 University Ave SE Ste 111 Minneapolis (55414) *(G-5502)*
Regents of The University of 612 625-4400
516 Delaware St SE Fl 9 Minneapolis (55455) *(G-5503)*
Regents of The University of 651 227-6551
580 Rice St Ste 1 Saint Paul (55103) *(G-8881)*
Regents of The University of 612 627-4000
2275 Larpenteur Ave W Saint Paul (55113) *(G-8882)*
Regents of The University of 952 997-4177
15650 Cedar Ave Ste 1 Saint Paul (55124) *(G-7893)*
Regina Medical Center (PA) 651 480-4100
1175 Nininger Rd Hastings (55033) *(G-2402)*
Regina Medical Center 651 480-4200
1285 Nininger Rd Ste 1 Hastings (55033) *(G-2403)*
Region Communications 320 252-5852
640 Lincoln Ave SE Saint Cloud (56304) *(G-7425)*
Regional Diagnostics Radiology 320 255-5619
1406 6th Ave N Saint Cloud (56303) *(G-7583)*
Regional Elite, Duluth *Also Called Freight Office For North West (G-1328)*
Regional Home Services of Minn 763 416-5607
20170 75th Ave N Hamel (55340) *(G-2355)*
Regions Hospital Alcohol 651 254-4804
445 Etna St Ste 55 Saint Paul (55106) *(G-8883)*
Regions Hospital Foundation 651 254-3456
640 Jackson St Saint Paul (55101) *(G-8884)*
Regis Corp 952 435-5545
915 County Road 42 W Burnsville (55306) *(G-789)*
Regis Corp (PA) 952 947-7777
7201 Metro Blvd Minneapolis (55439) *(G-5504)*
Regis Corp 952 851-9999
134 W Market Minneapolis (55425) *(G-5505)*
Regis Corp 320 253-5353
41st & W Division St Saint Cloud (56301) *(G-7584)*
Regis Corp 651 636-9966
139 Rosedale Ctr Saint Paul (55113) *(G-8885)*
Registered Abstractors Inc 763 427-3012
2115 3rd Ave Anoka (55303) *(G-219)*
Rehbein Transit Inc 651 484-1809
6298 Hodgson Rd Circle Pines (55014) *(G-1021)*
Rehder & Associates Inc 651 452-5051
3440 Federal Dr Ste 110 Eagan (55122) *(G-1547)*
Reichel Foods Inc 507 289-7264
3706 Enterprise Dr SW Rochester (55902) *(G-7220)*
Reichert Bus Lines, Baxter *Also Called Brainerd Bus Lines Inc (G-321)*
Reichert Enterprises Inc (PA) 218 829-6955
8342 Industrial Park Rd Brainerd (56425) *(G-584)*
Reigstad & Associates Inc 651 292-1123
192 9th St W Ste 200 Saint Paul (55102) *(G-8886)*
Reiner Contracting Inc 320 587-9886
21541 Highway 7 W Hutchinson (55350) *(G-2710)*
Reinhart Foodservice LLC 507 537-1451
702 Fairview St Marshall (56258) *(G-3324)*
Reinhart Foodservice LLC 763 428-6500
13400 Commerce Blvd Rogers (55374) *(G-7339)*
Reinking Enterprises Inc 763 428-1430
13175 George Weber Dr Rogers (55374) *(G-7340)*
Reinsurance Group of America 612 372-5432
20 Washington Ave S Minneapolis (55401) *(G-5506)*
Relate Counseling Center Inc 952 932-7277
15320 Minnetonka Blvd # 200 Minnetonka (55345) *(G-6219)*
Reliability Management Group 952 882-8122
151 W Burnsville Pkwy # 224 Burnsville (55337) *(G-790)*
Reliable Medical Supply Inc 763 255-3800
9401 Winnetka Ave N Brooklyn Park (55445) *(G-618)*
Reliakor Services Inc (PA) 952 403-1440
8600 Hansen Ave Shakopee (55379) *(G-9469)*
Reliastar Life Insurance Co (HQ) 612 372-5432
20 Washington Ave S Minneapolis (55401) *(G-5507)*
RELS LLC 952 933-8804
5700 Smetana Dr Ste 400 Hopkins (55343) *(G-2613)*
RELS Title Services LLC (PA) 952 933-8804
5700 Smetana Dr Ste 400 Hopkins (55343) *(G-2614)*
Rels Title Services LLC 651 647-4855
2550 University Ave W Ste 135N Saint Paul (55114) *(G-8887)*
REM & Tyler Inc 507 247-5568
303 Highland Ct Tyler (56178) *(G-9712)*
REM Canby Inc 952 925-5067
6921 York Ave S Minneapolis (55435) *(G-5508)*
REM Central Lakes Inc 507 238-4751
107 Dorothy St Fairmont (56031) *(G-1979)*
REM Central Lakes Inc 320 253-8134
1775 Roosevelt Rd Saint Cloud (56301) *(G-7585)*
REM Central Lakes Inc 320 252-8875
1506 33rd Ave N Saint Cloud (56303) *(G-7586)*
REM Greatland Inc 651 388-7158
2606 Malmquist Ave Red Wing (55066) *(G-7001)*
REM Health Inc 952 926-9808
6800 France Ave S Ste 500 Minneapolis (55435) *(G-5509)*
REM Hennepin Inc 952 925-5067
6600 France Ave S Ste 500 Minneapolis (55435) *(G-5510)*
REM Inc 218 724-1872
1831 E Superior St Duluth (55812) *(G-1434)*
REM Inc 507 387-3181
210 Thomas Dr Mankato (56001) *(G-3185)*
REM Inc 507 287-6824
1905 3rd Ave SE Ste B Rochester (55904) *(G-7221)*
REM Inc (PA) 651 647-9243
2266 2nd St N Saint Paul (55109) *(G-8888)*
REM Leadway Inc 952 925-5067
6921 York Ave S Minneapolis (55435) *(G-5511)*
REM Pillsbury Inc 612 871-1954
2311 Pillsbury Ave Minneapolis (55404) *(G-5512)*
REM River Bluffs Inc 651 480-4710
919 Vermillion St Ste 110 Hastings (55033) *(G-2404)*
REM Riverbluff Inc 507 281-1105
2509 55th St NW Rochester (55901) *(G-7222)*
REM Southwest Services Inc 320 235-9174
903 Highway 71 NE Willmar (56201) *(G-10039)*
REM Williams 952 925-3292
5100 William Ave Minneapolis (55436) *(G-5513)*
REM Woodvale Inc 507 451-1296
592 Adams Ave NW Ofc Owatonna (55060) *(G-6734)*
Rem-Fairmont, Fairmont *Also Called REM Central Lakes Inc (G-1979)*
REM-Ramsey Inc 952 925-5067
6921 York Ave S Minneapolis (55435) *(G-5514)*
Remax Northern Properties 218 263-8877
4325 9th Ave W Hibbing (55746) *(G-2474)*
Remax Realty Source 320 251-2200
405 33rd Ave N Saint Cloud (56303) *(G-7587)*
Remele Bassford 612 333-3000
33 S 6th St Ste 3800 Minneapolis (55402) *(G-5515)*
Remmele Engineering Inc 763 263-3650
17465 198th Ave NW Big Lake (55309) *(G-454)*
Remodeler's Choice Inc 612 767-7000
13605 1st Ave N Ste 200 Minneapolis (55441) *(G-5516)*
Remwoodvale Inc 507 634-6073
1406 5th St NW Kasson (55944) *(G-2823)*
Renaissance-Depot, Minneapolis *Also Called CSM Corp of Minnesota (G-4194)*
Renew Resources Inc 763 533-9200
5121 Winnetka Ave N # 150 Minneapolis (55428) *(G-5517)*
Renew Services Inc 651 699-3504
1410 Energy Park Dr Ste 6 Saint Paul (55108) *(G-8889)*
Renneberg Hardwoods Inc (PA) 218 564-4912
11773 State Highway 87 Menahga (56464) *(G-3359)*
Renodis Holdings Inc 651 556-1203
476 Robert St N Saint Paul (55101) *(G-8890)*
Renovation Systems Inc 763 550-9600
2735 Cheshire Ln N # 100 Minneapolis (55447) *(G-5518)*
Renovo Software Inc 952 931-0790
5666 Lincoln Dr Ste 206 Minneapolis (55436) *(G-5519)*
Renstrom Dental Studio Inc 651 407-0491
4225 White Bear Pkwy Ste 1240 Saint Paul (55110) *(G-8891)*
Rent A Ford Car 320 352-6561
203 10th St S Sauk Centre (56378) *(G-9351)*
Rental Research Services Inc 952 935-5700
11300 Minnetonka Mills Rd C Hopkins (55305) *(G-2615)*
Renvilla Nursing Home, Renville *Also Called City of Renville (G-7031)*
Renville County Emergency Food 320 523-5339
902 W Depue Ave Olivia (56277) *(G-6563)*
Renville County Hospice Inc 320 523-1261
611 E Fairview Ave Ste A Olivia (56277) *(G-6564)*
Replenex 952 941-9150
9815 W 74th St Eden Prairie (55344) *(G-1762)*
Reprise Associates 763 566-5416
5550 69th Ave N Minneapolis (55429) *(G-5520)*
Reproductive Medicine 651 221-4620
2101 Woodwinds Dr Ste 100 Saint Paul (55125) *(G-9267)*
Reproductive Medicine Center, Minneapolis *Also Called Regents of The University of (G-5491)*
Republic Bancshares Inc (PA) 218 722-3445
306 W Superior St Ste 100 Duluth (55802) *(G-1435)*
Research International USA Inc 952 853-9400
8040 Old Cedar Ave S # 1 Minneapolis (55425) *(G-5521)*
Research Lab, Bigfork *Also Called Regents of The University of (G-463)*
Reser's Fine Foods Inc 651 646-1298
2550 Wabash Ave Ste 2 Saint Paul (55114) *(G-8892)*
Reshare Corp 952 908-0818
5051 Highway 7 Ste 260 Minneapolis (55416) *(G-5522)*
Reshetar Systems Inc 763 421-1152
730 Bunker Lake Blvd NW Anoka (55303) *(G-220)*

www.HarrisInfo.com
612
2011 Harris Minnesota
Services Directory
(G-00000) Company's Geographic Section entry number

Residence Inn 612 677-1000
45 S 8th St Minneapolis (55402) *(G-5523)*
Residence Inn By Marriott, Eden Prairie *Also Called CSM Corp of Minnesota (G-1638)*
Residence Inn By Marriott, Minneapolis *Also Called CSM Corp of Minnesota (G-4193)*
Residence Inn By Marriott, Plymouth *Also Called Marriott (G-6872)*
Residence Inn Mrt MN Arpt Egon, Saint Paul *Also Called Enn Leasing Co II LLC (G-7764)*
Residential Advantages Inc 507 831-3804
220 Milwaukee St Ste 2 Lakefield (56150) *(G-2883)*
Residential Funding Co LLC 952 857-8700
1 Meridian Xing Ste 100 Minneapolis (55423) *(G-5524)*
Residential Funding Securities 952 857-7000
1 Meridian Xing Ste 100 Minneapolis (55423) *(G-5525)*
Residential Mortgage Group Inc 952 593-1169
11100 Wayzata Blvd # 570 Hopkins (55305) *(G-2616)*
Residential Services of 218 728-6823
707 W Arrowhead Rd Duluth (55811) *(G-1436)*
Resource Group Inc 952 974-9225
7935 Stone Creek Dr # 110 Chanhassen (55317) *(G-937)*
Resource Inc (PA) 612 752-8000
1900 Chicago Ave Minneapolis (55404) *(G-5526)*
Resource Inc 612 752-8200
1825 Chicago Ave Minneapolis (55404) *(G-5527)*
Resource Inc 952 925-9195
6715 Minnetonka Blvd # 212 Minneapolis (55426) *(G-5528)*
Resources For Child Caring Inc 651 641-0305
10 Yorkton Ct Saint Paul (55117) *(G-8893)*
Resources For You Inc 320 864-5871
1218 Greeley Ave N Glencoe (55336) *(G-2212)*
Response Delivery Inc 952 941-6813
8657 Pine Hill Rd Minneapolis (55438) *(G-5529)*
Response Fire Protection Inc 763 717-4740
8201 Central Ave NE Ste J Minneapolis (55432) *(G-3583)*
Restaurant Technologies Inc 651 796-1600
3711 Kennebec Dr Ste 100 Saint Paul (55122) *(G-7894)*
Restaurants No Limit Inc 952 471-8513
3746 Sunset Dr Spring Park (55384) *(G-9564)*
Restaurants Unlimited Inc 612 339-3800
825 Hennepin Ave Ste 825 Minneapolis (55402) *(G-5530)*
Restoration Contractors Inc 651 646-3408
480 Prior Ave N Saint Paul (55104) *(G-8894)*
Restoration Professionals Inc 651 379-1990
505 Minnehaha Ave W Saint Paul (55103) *(G-8895)*
Result Radio Inc 218 736-7596
728 Western Ave Fergus Falls (56537) *(G-2118)*
Retail Construction Services 651 704-9000
11343 39th St N Lake Elmo (55042) *(G-2876)*
Retail Data Systems of NM, Eden Prairie *Also Called Data Systems Inc (G-1642)*
Retail Employees Credit Union 952 930-0700
3670 Aquila Ave S Minneapolis (55426) *(G-5531)*
Retail Inventory Services Ltd 651 631-9081
2400 County Road D W Ste 100 Saint Paul (55112) *(G-8896)*
Retail Support Inc 952 934-1317
6459 Pinnacle Dr Eden Prairie (55346) *(G-1763)*
Retailer Services Corp 763 421-6868
3750 Thurston Ave Anoka (55303) *(G-221)*
Retka Enterprises Inc 218 829-4076
7611 College Rd Ste 105 Baxter (56425) *(G-340)*
Return Inc 763 295-4659
9560 Kalenda Ave NE Monticello (55362) *(G-6284)*
Reuben Lindh Family Services 763 521-3477
1501 Xerxes Ave N Minneapolis (55411) *(G-5532)*
Reuse Center, Minneapolis *Also Called Deconstruction Services (G-4239)*
Rev Solutions Inc 952 746-6005
10400 Viking Dr Eden Prairie (55344) *(G-1764)*
Revamp Salon & Spa 612 341-0404
2910 Hennepin Ave Minneapolis (55408) *(G-5533)*
Reverence For Life & Concern 320 564-4911
660 18th St Granite Falls (56241) *(G-2319)*
Reviva Inc (PA) 763 535-8900
5130 Main St NE Minneapolis (55421) *(G-3584)*
Rex Granite Co 320 252-2060
414 Lincoln Ave NE Saint Cloud (56304) *(G-7426)*
Rfg Distributing Inc 763 540-0335
7301 32nd Ave N Minneapolis (55427) *(G-5534)*
Rgis LLC 952 858-8319
2626 E 82nd St Minneapolis (55425) *(G-5535)*
Rgis LLC 507 281-7665
1530 Greenview Dr SW S20 Rochester (55902) *(G-7223)*
Rhjh Inc 651 735-7470
2300 Territorial Rd Saint Paul (55114) *(G-8897)*
Rhm Receiver 3211 Co LLC 612 746-4600
201 S 11th St Minneapolis (55403) *(G-5536)*
Rica Costa Ventures Inc 651 426-9262
13845 Forest Blvd N Hugo (55038) *(G-2682)*
Rice County District One Hosp 507 334-6451
200 State Ave Faribault (55021) *(G-2027)*
Rice Home Medical LLC 320 235-8434
1033 19th Ave SW Willmar (56201) *(G-10040)*
Rice Lake Lumber Inc 218 727-3213
4728 Rice Lake Rd Duluth (55803) *(G-1437)*
Rice Memorial Hospital (HQ) 320 235-4543
301 Becker Ave SW Willmar (56201) *(G-10041)*
Rice Memorial Hospital 320 231-7077
2200 23rd St NE Willmar (56201) *(G-10042)*
Rice Memorial Hospital 320 231-4175
311 3rd St SW Willmar (56201) *(G-10043)*
Rice Street Clinic, Saint Paul *Also Called Healtheast Medical Research (G-8464)*
Rice Street Clinic, Saint Paul *Also Called Healtheast Diversified Svcs (G-8460)*
Rice Wild Electric Cooperative 218 935-2517
502 N Main St Mahnomen (56557) *(G-3090)*
Rich Mgt Inc 952 432-1515
14917 Garrett Ave Saint Paul (55124) *(G-7895)*
Rich Prairie Livestock 320 468-2514
96 Hwy 27 W Pierz (56364) *(G-6808)*
Rich Schmitz Dvm 507 233-2520
401 20th St S New Ulm (56073) *(G-6473)*
Rich-Spring Golf Club Inc 320 685-8810
17467 Fairway Cir Cold Spring (56320) *(G-1089)*
Richard F Tschida 651 426-7958
5350 Highway 61 N Saint Paul (55110) *(G-8898)*
Richard Hawkins 507 282-6080
2207 7th St NW Rochester (55901) *(G-7224)*
Richard Koberski 507 642-8380
80505 Elm Creek Rd Madelia (56062) *(G-3074)*
Richard Larson Builders Inc 320 587-5555
640 Adams St SE Hutchinson (55350) *(G-2711)*
Richard R Rodenborn 763 533-5155
4722 Perry Ave N Minneapolis (55429) *(G-5537)*
Richard Sankovitz 507 835-4836
101 Clear Lake Dr Waseca (56093) *(G-9885)*
Richard Scales Advertising 651 641-0226
2303 Wycliff St Ste 1E Saint Paul (55114) *(G-8899)*
Richard Sigert 218 444-1875
1025 Paul Bunyan Dr S Bemidji (56601) *(G-422)*
Richards Transportation Svc 218 233-3404
2139 100th Ave N Moorhead (56560) *(G-6338)*
Richfield Bloomington Credit (PA) 612 798-7100
345 E 77th St Richfield (55423) *(G-7037)*
Richfield Bus Co 952 881-1111
9237 Grand Ave S Minneapolis (55420) *(G-5538)*
Richfield Youth Employment Svc, Minneapolis *Also Called City of Richfield (G-4096)*
Richie Eye Clinic 507 332-9900
1575 20th St NW Ste 101 Faribault (55021) *(G-2028)*
Richmond Bus Service Inc 320 597-2055
718 Main St E Richmond (56368) *(G-7041)*
Richtone Painting, Eden Prairie *Also Called Fresh Start Enterprises Inc (G-1670)*
Rick Electric Inc 218 233-6194
3010 24th Ave S Moorhead (56560) *(G-6339)*
Rick Gentling 507 287-7714
4600 18th Ave NW Rochester (55901) *(G-7225)*
Rick L Schoenrock 320 763-7144
1208 Lakeside Dr Alexandria (56308) *(G-120)*
Rick Pavek Construction 507 663-0804
32971 Northfield Blvd Northfield (55057) *(G-6519)*
Rick S Shand 651 770-8710
6400 Hayward Ave Saint Paul (55128) *(G-9268)*
Ricoh Americas Corp 866 856-3000
10905 Valley View Rd Eden Prairie (55344) *(G-1765)*
Ricoh Americas Corp 651 294-2600
1110 Cntr Pointe Cur 10 Mendota Heights (55120) *(G-3370)*
Ricsons Inc 612 617-9480
333 Harrison St NE Minneapolis (55413) *(G-5539)*
Ridgedale Electric Inc 952 473-2714
500 Brimhall Ave Long Lake (55356) *(G-3031)*
Ridges At Sand Creek, Jordan *Also Called Malone Golf Inc (G-2806)*
Ridgeview Country Club Inc 218 728-5128
700 W Redwing St Duluth (55803) *(G-1438)*
Ridgeview Home Support Service 952 442-6032
501 S Maple St Ste 1 Waconia (55387) *(G-9791)*
Ridgeview Medical Center 952 442-2191
500 S Maple St Waconia (55387) *(G-9792)*
Ridgeview Medical Clinic 952 471-2585
4695 Shoreline Dr Spring Park (55384) *(G-9565)*
Ridgeview Place LP 320 251-5228
1009 10th Ave NE Ofc Sauk Rapids (56379) *(G-9371)*
Ridgewood, Worthington *Also Called Client Community Services Inc (G-10181)*
Rienhardt & Anderson 651 227-9990
332 Minnesota St Ste E1250 Saint Paul (55101) *(G-8900)*
Ries Electric Co 651 451-2238
777 Concord St N South Saint Paul (55075) *(G-9538)*
Riesco Inc 651 771-8235
1885 University Ave W # 1 Saint Paul (55104) *(G-8901)*
Rigels Inc 218 233-6104
609 Main Ave Moorhead (56560) *(G-6340)*
Right Management Consultants 952 837-0955
3600 Minnesota Dr Ste 850 Minneapolis (55435) *(G-5540)*
Right Staff Inc 952 546-1100
12450 Wayzata Blvd Hopkins (55305) *(G-2617)*
Rihm Motor Co 651 646-7833
2108 University Ave W Saint Paul (55114) *(G-8902)*
Riley Bros Construction Inc 320 589-2500
46369 208th St Morris (56267) *(G-6376)*
Rinke, Noonan, Grote, Smoley 320 251-6700
1015 W Saint Germain St Ste 30 Saint Cloud (56301) *(G-7588)*
Risdall Marketing Group LLC 651 286-6700
550 Main St New Brighton (55112) *(G-6413)*
Rise Inc (PA) 763 786-8334
8406 Sunset Rd NE Minneapolis (55432) *(G-3585)*
Rise Inc 763 784-0900
1156 114th Ln NW Minneapolis (55448) *(G-3586)*
Rison Homes Administrative 507 332-0547
16 5th St NE Ste 1 Faribault (55021) *(G-2029)*
Rita Ambourn Hair Designers 651 698-5537
464 Snelling Ave S Saint Paul (55105) *(G-8903)*
Ritalka Inc (PA) 320 269-3227
121 N 1st St Ste 201 Montevideo (56265) *(G-6258)*
Ritchie Engineering Co Inc 952 943-1300
10950 Hampshire Ave S Minneapolis (55438) *(G-5541)*
Rite-Way Waterproofing, Circle Pines *Also Called Construction Labor Force Inc (G-1006)*
Rivard Contracting Inc 763 753-7888
19801 Highway 65 NE Cedar (55011) *(G-884)*
River Boat Bingo 507 388-6086
145 Good Counsel Dr Mankato (56001) *(G-3186)*
River City Lanes 763 295-3390
101 Chelsea Rd Monticello (55362) *(G-6285)*
River City Mortgage 952 915-5300
6700 France Ave S Ste 230 Minneapolis (55435) *(G-5542)*
River City Mortgage Corp (PA) 651 406-5000
1895 Plaza Dr Ste 250 Saint Paul (55122) *(G-7896)*
River Hills Early Childhood 952 895-0413
11100 River Hills Dr Burnsville (55337) *(G-791)*
River of Goods Inc 651 917-5335
2475 Doswell Ave Ste B Saint Paul (55108) *(G-8904)*
River Services Inc 612 588-8141
3750 Washington Ave N Minneapolis (55412) *(G-5543)*

ALPHABETIC

River Valley Home Care ALPHABETIC SECTION

River Valley Home Care 651 460-4201
916 8th St Farmington (55024) ***(G-2059)***
River Valley Hospitality LLC 952 854-1771
2300 American Blvd E Minneapolis (55425) ***(G-5544)***
River Valley Lawnscape Inc 651 388-7000
3399 S Service Dr Red Wing (55066) ***(G-7002)***
River Valley Truck Centers Inc (PA) 507 345-1129
2120 3rd Ave Mankato (56001) ***(G-3187)***
River's End Holdings LLC (PA) 952 912-2543
415 11th Ave S Hopkins (55343) ***(G-2618)***
Riverbank MN 651 408-9203
26777 Fallbrook Ave Wyoming (55092) ***(G-10207)***
Riverbend Auto Sales Inc 507 345-8967
222 E Madison Ave Mankato (56001) ***(G-3188)***
Riverheights Chamber of 651 451-2266
5782 Blackshire Path Inver Grove Heights (55076) ***(G-2766)***
Rivers End Trading Co 952 912-2500
415 11th Ave S Hopkins (55343) ***(G-2619)***
Rivers Hotel Co Inc (PA) 507 457-0977
356 E Sarnia St Ste 2 Winona (55987) ***(G-10121)***
Riverside Auto Wash Inc 763 571-2700
6520 E River Rd Minneapolis (55432) ***(G-3587)***
Riverside Lodging 651 388-0491
232 Withers Harbor Dr Red Wing (55066) ***(G-7003)***
Riverside Plaza LP 612 338-8925
1600 S 6th St Minneapolis (55454) ***(G-5545)***
Riverstar Inc 507 452-5109
1705 Wilkie Dr Winona (55987) ***(G-10122)***
Riverton Community Housing, Minneapolis *Also Called Franklin Co-Op **(G-4474)***
Riverview Apartments Senior 651 291-1750
5100 E 54th St Minneapolis (55417) ***(G-5546)***
Riverview Dairy Inc 320 392-5609
26402 470th Ave Morris (56267) ***(G-6377)***
Riverview Healthcare Assn 218 281-9478
323 S Minnesota St Crookston (56716) ***(G-1136)***
Riverview Manor Inc 507 824-2091
400 Hillcrest Ave Wanamingo (55983) ***(G-9866)***
Riverview Packaging Inc 651 415-1121
35 E Pleasant Lake Rd Saint Paul (55127) ***(G-8905)***
Riverway Clinic 763 712-6000
1833 2nd Ave Anoka (55303) ***(G-222)***
Riverwood Bank 218 751-5120
214 5th St NW Bemidji (56601) ***(G-423)***
Riverwood Inn & Conference Ctr, Monticello *Also Called Pattern Stations Inc **(G-6282)***
Rivett Group LLC 952 888-8800
7800 2nd Ave S Minneapolis (55420) ***(G-5547)***
Riviana International Inc 218 776-3118
301 Tower St NW Clearbrook (56634) ***(G-1040)***
Rjf Agencies Inc 763 746-8000
7225 Northland Dr N Ste 300 Minneapolis (55428) ***(G-5548)***
Rjs Software Systems Inc 952 736-5800
2970 Judicial Rd Ste 100 Burnsville (55337) ***(G-792)***
Rlj Bloomington Hotel LLC 952 854-0900
2261 Killebrew Dr Minneapolis (55425) ***(G-5549)***
Rlk Inc 952 933-0972
6110 Blue Circle Dr Ste 100 Hopkins (55343) ***(G-2620)***
RMC Project Management Inc 952 846-4484
10953 Bren Rd E Minnetonka (55343) ***(G-6220)***
Rmia 651 221-4600
2101 Woodwinds Dr Ste 100 Saint Paul (55125) ***(G-9269)***
RMR Services LLC 763 786-7323
9272 Isanti St NE Minneapolis (55449) ***(G-3588)***
RMS, Saint Paul *Also Called Receivables Management Soln **(G-7891)***
Road Equipment, Saint Paul *Also Called Jomar Investments Inc **(G-7811)***
Road Machinery & Supplies Co (PA) 952 895-9595
5633 Highway 13 W Savage (55378) ***(G-9405)***
Robbinsdale Clinic PA Inc 763 533-2534
3819 W Broadway Ave Minneapolis (55422) ***(G-5550)***
Robbinsdale Rhbltiton Care Ctr, Minneapolis *Also Called Extendicare Homes Inc **(G-4383)***
Robert A Kovell 320 253-9505
4170 Thielman Ln Ste 101 Saint Cloud (56301) ***(G-7589)***
Robert A Schneider Agency Inc 952 938-0655
5620 Smetana Dr Ste 225 Hopkins (55343) ***(G-2621)***
Robert A Williams Enterprises (PA) 763 788-1113
3701 Central Ave NE Minneapolis (55421) ***(G-3589)***
Robert A Williams Enterprises 612 333-8900
1221 Washington Ave S Minneapolis (55415) ***(G-5551)***
Robert A Williams Enterprises 952 831-6250
7920 France Ave S Minneapolis (55435) ***(G-5552)***
Robert Aby MD 507 372-1840
508 10th St Worthington (56187) ***(G-10192)***
Robert B Diasio 507 284-3977
200 1st St SW GONDA19 Rochester (55905) ***(G-7226)***
Robert C Meisterling MD 651 439-8807
1701 Curve Crest Blvd W Stillwater (55082) ***(G-9635)***
Robert Chapin 320 351-8901
39465 415th St Ste A Sauk Centre (56378) ***(G-9352)***
Robert Fitzsimmons & Sons LLP 507 524-4511
503 Silver St E Mapleton (56065) ***(G-3285)***
Robert Gullick CPA 651 265-2043
170 7th Pl E Ste 100 Saint Paul (55101) ***(G-8906)***
Robert Half International Inc 612 339-9001
800 Nicollet Mall Ste 2700 Minneapolis (55402) ***(G-5553)***
Robert Half International Inc 952 831-5970
8500 Normandale Lake Blvd Minneapolis (55437) ***(G-5554)***
Robert Half International Inc 651 293-8033
444 Cedar St Ste 1150 Saint Paul (55101) ***(G-8907)***
Robert Lemieur & Sons Inc 320 632-9141
14827 Pine Ave Little Falls (56345) ***(G-3018)***
Robins, Kaplan, Miller (PA) 612 349-8500
800 Lasalle Ave Ste 2800 Minneapolis (55402) ***(G-5555)***
Rocco Altobelli Inc (PA) 952 707-1900
14301 W Burnsville Pkwy Burnsville (55306) ***(G-793)***
Rocco Altobelli Inc 952 920-5006
3260 Galleria Minneapolis (55435) ***(G-5556)***
Rocco Altobelli Inc 507 288-8582
400 S Broadway Ste 204 Rochester (55904) ***(G-7227)***
Rocco Altobelli Inc 651 690-5491
665 Snelling Ave S Saint Paul (55116) ***(G-8908)***
Rocco Altobelli Inc 651 730-7077
8390 Tamarack Vlg Ste 515 Saint Paul (55125) ***(G-9270)***
Rochester Athletic Club Inc 507 282-6000
3100 19th St NW Rochester (55901) ***(G-7228)***
Rochester City Delivery Inc 507 289-2774
3101 40th Ave NW Rochester (55901) ***(G-7229)***
Rochester City Line Co 507 288-4353
1825 N Broadway Rochester (55906) ***(G-7230)***
Rochester Fitness Inc 507 282-4445
1112 7th St NW Rochester (55901) ***(G-7231)***
Rochester Golf & Country Club 507 282-2708
3100 Country Club Rd SW Rochester (55902) ***(G-7232)***
Rochester Health & Rehab West 507 288-1818
2215 Hwy 52 N Rochester (55901) ***(G-7233)***
Rochester Juvenile Hockey 507 280-6345
2625 Hwy 14 W Ste AB Rochester (55901) ***(G-7234)***
Rochester Meats Inc (PA) 507 289-0701
1825 7th St NW Rochester (55901) ***(G-7235)***
Rochester Methodist Hospital 507 255-5123
1216 2nd St SW Rochester (55902) ***(G-7236)***
Rochester Methodist Hospital 507 266-7890
201 W Center St Rochester (55902) ***(G-7237)***
Rochester Office, Rochester *Also Called Pollution Control Agency, MN **(G-7206)***
Rochester Parking Ramps 507 282-0558
14 2nd St SE Rochester (55904) ***(G-7238)***
Rochester Plumbing & Heating 507 289-1613
2840 Wilser Rd NW Rochester (55901) ***(G-7239)***
Rochester Sand & Gravel Div, Rochester *Also Called Mathy Construction Co **(G-7169)***
Rochester Service Co Inc 507 281-5333
2510 Schuster Ln NW Rochester (55901) ***(G-7240)***
Rochester Transfer & Storage, Rochester *Also Called Piepho Moving & Storage Inc **(G-7204)***
Rochester Transfer & Storage, Rochester *Also Called Piepho Moving & Storage Inc **(G-7205)***
Rochford Supply, Minneapolis *Also Called Pl Enterprises Inc **(G-5387)***
Rock 'n Water 218 439-6400
22931 185th St Detroit Lakes (56501) ***(G-1215)***
Rock Bottom of Minneapolis Inc (HQ) 612 332-2739
800 Lasalle Ave Ste 125 Minneapolis (55402) ***(G-5557)***
Rock Cnty Cmnty Swimming Pool, Luverne *Also Called Luverne, City of Inc **(G-3063)***
Rock Creek Motor Stop, Pine City *Also Called Kutzke Oil Co Inc **(G-6812)***
Rock Electric Corp 763 792-9664
9701 6th St NE Minneapolis (55434) ***(G-3590)***
Rock Island Co 651 228-0935
30 7th St E Ste 2000 Saint Paul (55101) ***(G-8909)***
Rock-Tenn Co 651 641-4874
2250 Wabash Ave Saint Paul (55114) ***(G-8910)***
Rockblock Cellers, Osseo *Also Called Domaine Srene Vineyards Winery **(G-6610)***
Rockford Bus Garage Inc 763 477-6100
7700 County Road 50 Rockford (55373) ***(G-7304)***
Rocking Horse Ranch 952 440-1777
14859 Louisiana Ave S Prior Lake (55372) ***(G-6952)***
Rockingham Group 763 421-8672
11412 Ivywood St NW Minneapolis (55433) ***(G-3591)***
Rockwood Retaining Walls Inc 507 529-2871
325 Alliance Pl NE Rochester (55906) ***(G-7241)***
Rodeway Inn, Duluth *Also Called G G Tucson Inc **(G-1330)***
Roed Ericksen & Associates 651 251-7570
2550 University Ave W Ste 201S Saint Paul (55114) ***(G-8911)***
Roger Illies Realtor 320 685-8119
15637 241st St Cold Spring (56320) ***(G-1090)***
Roger's Amoco Inc 320 963-6555
300 State Hwy 55 NW Maple Lake (55358) ***(G-3264)***
Rogers Freels & Associates Inc 952 843-2700
11495 Valley View Rd Eden Prairie (55344) ***(G-1766)***
Rogers Hospitality LLC 763 428-3000
20930 135th Ave N Rogers (55374) ***(G-7341)***
Roghard Financial LLC 952 351-8300
7505 Metro Blvd Ste 300 Edina (55439) ***(G-1842)***
Rohlfing of Brainerd Inc 218 829-0303
923 Wright St Brainerd (56401) ***(G-585)***
Rohn Industries Inc-St Paul 651 647-1300
862 Hersey St Saint Paul (55114) ***(G-8912)***
Roisum Elite Rosium Foods 952 227-3199
1400 Lake Dr W Chanhassen (55317) ***(G-938)***
Roller Garden, Minneapolis *Also Called Xenophon Corp **(G-6092)***
Rollie's Sales & Service Inc 320 859-4811
Hwy 27 W Ste 13790 Osakis (56360) ***(G-6587)***
Rollin B Child Inc 763 559-5531
1820 Berkshire Ln N Minneapolis (55441) ***(G-5558)***
Ron Boelter Window & Siding 507 243-4354
48636 Orchard Rd Madison Lake (56063) ***(G-3081)***
Ron's Cabinets Inc 320 252-7667
380 Industrial Blvd Sauk Rapids (56379) ***(G-9372)***
Roof Tech Inc 651 351-7302
14520 61st Street Ct N Stillwater (55082) ***(G-9636)***
Room For Growing 651 257-2441
11125 Lake Blvd Chisago City (55013) ***(G-994)***
Room For Growing 651 464-1601
268 12th St SW Forest Lake (55025) ***(G-2167)***
Root River Hardwoods Inc 507 765-2284
1300 Highway 52 N Preston (55965) ***(G-6900)***
Root River Valley Transfer Inc 507 388-7670
1120 Center St Mankato (56003) ***(G-3231)***
Rorke Data Inc 952 829-0300
7626 Golden Triangle Dr Eden Prairie (55344) ***(G-1767)***
Rose Arbor 763 493-5910
16500 92nd Ave N Apt 109 Osseo (55311) ***(G-6656)***
Rose Camilia Co Inc 763 755-8400
11800 Xeon Blvd NW Minneapolis (55448) ***(G-3592)***
Rose Floral & Greenhouse Inc 651 439-3765
14298 60th St N Stillwater (55082) ***(G-9637)***
Rose of Sharon Manor, Saint Paul *Also Called Extendicare Facilities Inc **(G-8354)***
Roseau Diesel Service Inc 218 463-1711
112 2nd St SW Roseau (56751) ***(G-7357)***
Roseau Electric Cooperative 218 463-1543
1107 3rd St NE Roseau (56751) ***(G-7358)***

ALPHABETIC

www.HarrisInfo.com
614
2011 Harris Minnesota Services Directory
(G-00000) Company's Geographic Section entry number

Roseau Occupational Dev Ctr, Roseau *Also Called Occupational Development Ctr* ***(G-7356)***
Rosedale Medical Center, Saint Paul *Also Called Multicare Associates of The* ***(G-8728)***
Rosemount Aerospace Inc 651 681-8900
1256 Trapp Rd Eagan (55121) ***(G-1548)***
Rosemount Inc (DH) 952 949-7000
8200 Market Blvd Chanhassen (55317) ***(G-939)***
Rosemount-Apple Valley & Eagan 651 423-7700
14445 Diamond Path W Rosemount (55068) ***(G-7374)***
Rosen's Diversified Inc (HQ) 507 238-4201
1120 Lake Ave Fairmont (56031) ***(G-1980)***
Rosenbauer Motors LLC 651 462-1000
5181 260th St Wyoming (55092) ***(G-10208)***
Rosenquist Construction Inc 612 724-1356
2541 24th Ave S Minneapolis (55406) ***(G-5559)***
Roseville VFW Post 7555 ....651 483-5313
1145 Woodhill Dr Saint Paul (55113) ***(G-8913)***
Rosewood Construction, Saint Paul *Also Called Portfolio Design Services Inc* ***(G-9263)***
Rosewood Estate, Saint Paul *Also Called Care Institute Inc* ***(G-8160)***
Ross Capital Pmc Inc 612 929-9222
2710 W Lake St Minneapolis (55416) ***(G-5560)***
Ross Nesbit Agencies Inc 952 941-9418
7500 Flying Cloud Dr Eden Prairie (55344) ***(G-1768)***
Rothe Development Inc 612 726-1102
760 Military Hwy Minneapolis (55450) ***(G-5561)***
Rothgarn Enterprise Inc 651 345-2324
104 N Washington St Lake City (55041) ***(G-2854)***
Rothsay Truck Stop & Cafe 218 867-2233
544 Center St N Rothsay (56579) ***(G-7383)***
Roto-Rooter Services Co 651 738-8355
7041 6th St N Saint Paul (55128) ***(G-9271)***
Rottlund Co Inc (PA) 651 638-0500
3065 Centre Pointe Dr Saint Paul (55113) ***(G-8914)***
Round Lake Senior Citizen Ctr 507 945-8477
206 Main St Round Lake (56167) ***(G-7385)***
Roundbank 507 835-4220
200 2nd St NE Waseca (56093) ***(G-9886)***
Rouse Mechanical Inc 952 933-5300
7320 Oxford St Minneapolis (55426) ***(G-5562)***
Roxbury Capital Management LLC 952 230-6140
6001 Shady Oak Rd S Minnetonka (55343) ***(G-6221)***
Royal Financial LLC 763 746-9480
4111 Central Ave NE # 201 Minneapolis (55421) ***(G-3593)***
Royal Foods Inc 952 936-0336
8098 Excelsior Blvd Hopkins (55343) ***(G-2622)***
Royal Home Health Care 763 504-4559
5637 Brooklyn Blvd Ste 300 Minneapolis (55429) ***(G-5563)***
Royal Medical Center 218 249-8800
1400 Woodland Ave Duluth (55803) ***(G-1439)***
Royal Oaks Car Wash, Saint Paul *Also Called S J C Inc* ***(G-8919)***
Royal Palms Senior Residence, Chaska *Also Called Joshco Construction Inc* ***(G-971)***
Royal Tire Inc (PA) 320 258-7070
3955 Roosevelt Rd Saint Cloud (56301) ***(G-7590)***
Royale Resources Inc 218 346-3000
154 1st Ave S Perham (56573) ***(G-6802)***
Royalton Bancshares Inc (PA) 320 584-5522
412 N Highway 10 Royalton (56373) ***(G-7387)***
Royce Place, Minneapolis *Also Called Crest View Corp* ***(G-3448)***
Rp Schroeder Construction Inc 763 856-2230
26657 146th St NW Zimmerman (55398) ***(G-10215)***
RSC Equipment Rental Inc 763 509-2400
3200 Harbor Ln N Ste 100 Minneapolis (55447) ***(G-5564)***
RSC Equipment Rental Inc 763 557-1234
2340 Fernbrook Ln N Minneapolis (55447) ***(G-5565)***
RSC Equipment Rental Inc 763 509-2423
3200 Harbor Ln N Minneapolis (55447) ***(G-5566)***
RSI Hartley, Duluth *Also Called Residential Services of* ***(G-1436)***
RSM McGladrey Business Soln (HQ) 952 921-7700
3600 American Blvd W Minneapolis (55431) ***(G-5567)***
RSM McGladrey Business Svcs 952 857-1220
7601 France Ave S Ste 600 Minneapolis (55435) ***(G-5568)***
RSM McGladrey Inc 218 727-5025
227 W 1st St Ste 700 Duluth (55802) ***(G-1440)***
RSM McGladrey Inc (DH) 952 921-7700
3600 American Blvd W Fl 3 Minneapolis (55431) ***(G-5569)***
RSM McGladrey Inc 612 332-4300
801 Nicollet Mall # 1300 Minneapolis (55402) ***(G-5570)***
RSM McGladrey Inc 507 288-5363
310 S Broadway Ste 300 Rochester (55904) ***(G-7242)***
Rsp Architects Ltd 612 677-7100
1220 Marshall St NE Minneapolis (55413) ***(G-5571)***
Rti Services Inc (PA) 952 475-0242
800 Berkshire Ln N Plymouth (55441) ***(G-6882)***
Rtl Construction Inc 952 934-4695
4000 Valley Ind Blvd S Shakopee (55379) ***(G-9470)***
Rtw Inc 952 893-0403
8500 Normandale Lake Blvd Minneapolis (55437) ***(G-5572)***
Rubber Specialties Inc 952 888-9225
8117 Pleasant Ave S Minneapolis (55420) ***(G-5573)***
Rubble Stone Co Inc 952 938-2599
6001 Culligan Way Hopkins (55345) ***(G-2623)***
Rubenstein & Ziff Inc 952 854-1460
1055 E 79th St Minneapolis (55420) ***(G-5574)***
Rubenstein Logistics Services 763 542-1121
6960 Madison Ave W Ste 7 Golden Valley (55427) ***(G-2244)***
Rud Construction Inc 952 652-2886
4275 Bagley Ave Webster (55088) ***(G-9953)***
Rudisill Advertising 651 636-0345
501 Main St N Ste 402 Stillwater (55082) ***(G-9638)***
Rudolph Priebe American Legion 763 425-4858
260 4th Ave SE Osseo (55369) ***(G-6657)***
Rudy Hopkins Luther's Motors 952 938-1717
250 5th Ave S Hopkins (55343) ***(G-2624)***
Rug & Carpet Caretakers 507 388-5384
101 Country Club Dr Mankato (56001) ***(G-3189)***
Ruhr Development, Buffalo *Also Called Buffalo Lodging* ***(G-639)***
Rule One Trasportation 952 703-7318
5501 W Old Shakopee Rd Minneapolis (55437) ***(G-5575)***
Runestone Electric Association 320 763-6641
Lake Mary Township Alexandria (56308) ***(G-121)***
Running Aces Harness Park, Forest Lake *Also Called North Metro Harness Initiative* ***(G-2148)***
Rupp Construction Co Inc 507 836-8555
Highway 59 N Slayton (56172) ***(G-9490)***
Rural Cellular Corp (DH) 320 762-2000
3905 Dakota St Alexandria (56308) ***(G-122)***
Rural Community Insurance Agcy (DH) 763 427-0290
3501 Thurston Ave Anoka (55303) ***(G-223)***
Rural Computer Consultants Inc 320 365-4027
104 Main St Bird Island (55310) ***(G-468)***
Rural Living Environments Inc 218 827-3495
20 Balsam Cir Babbitt (55706) ***(G-298)***
Rural Minnesota Cep Inc 218 755-4458
616 America Ave NW # 220 Bemidji (56601) ***(G-424)***
Rusciano-Hyland Inc 612 871-4434
6314 Cambridge St Minneapolis (55416) ***(G-5576)***
Rush Creek Golf Club Limited 763 494-8844
7801 Troy Ln N Osseo (55311) ***(G-6658)***
RUSHFORD HALL-ITALIAN AMERICAN, Minneapolis *Also Called Italian American Club of* ***(G-4740)***
Russel Metals Williams Bahcall 651 688-8138
3250 Spruce St Little Canada (55117) ***(G-2998)***
Russnick Contractors Inc 763 420-3737
20170 75th Ave N Hamel (55340) ***(G-2356)***
Rust Consulting Inc (DH) 612 359-2000
625 Marquette Ave Ste 880 Minneapolis (55402) ***(G-5577)***
Rustic Inn Gifts, Two Harbors *Also Called Park Gooseberry Motel Cabins* ***(G-9711)***
Rute Agency 612 240-1795
9716 Zilla St NW Minneapolis (55433) ***(G-3594)***
Ruth Stricker's Fitness Unltd 952 935-2202
15000 Minnetonka Blvd Minnetonka (55345) ***(G-6222)***
Ruth's Hospitality Group Inc 612 672-9000
920 2nd Ave S Ste 100 Minneapolis (55402) ***(G-5578)***
Ruttger's Birchmont Lodge Inc 218 751-4131
530 Birchmont Beach Rd NE Bemidji (56601) ***(G-425)***
Ruttger's Sugar Lake Lodge, Cohasset *Also Called Lodge At Sugar Lake Inc* ***(G-1072)***
Rvi Inc (PA) 320 269-3227
121 N 1st St Ste 201 Montevideo (56265) ***(G-6259)***
Ryan Co's US Inc (PA) 612 492-4000
50 S 10th St Ste 300 Minneapolis (55403) ***(G-5579)***
Ryan Contracting Co 952 894-3200
8700 13th Ave E Shakopee (55379) ***(G-9471)***
Ryan Partnership, Minneapolis *Also Called D L Ryan Co's Ltd* ***(G-4214)***
Ryder Truck Rental Inc 763 545-9417
835 Decatur Ave N Minneapolis (55427) ***(G-5580)***
Ryder Truck Rental Inc 651 636-6906
2580 Long Lake Rd Saint Paul (55113) ***(G-8915)***
Ryder Truck Rental Inc 651 631-1755
1901 Lake Valentine Rd Saint Paul (55112) ***(G-8916)***
Ryerson Tull Coil Processing, Minneapolis *Also Called Joseph T Ryerson & Son Inc* ***(G-4780)***
Ryland Group Inc 952 949-0013
7600 Executive Dr Eden Prairie (55344) ***(G-1769)***
Ryland Group Inc 952 229-6000
7599 Anagram Dr Edina (55439) ***(G-1843)***
Ryt-Way Industries LLC 952 469-1417
21850 Grenada Ave Lakeville (55044) ***(G-2929)***
S & D Cleaning 651 558-7336
2371 Linwood Ave E Maplewood (55119) ***(G-3287)***
S & L Team Cleaning 612 558-4502
1821 University Ave W S321 Saint Paul (55104) ***(G-8917)***
S & S Moving & Storage Inc 507 289-0779
6101 Bandel Rd NW Rochester (55901) ***(G-7243)***
S & S Sales Inc 763 476-9599
1866 Berkshire Ln N Minneapolis (55441) ***(G-5581)***
S & S Spa Salon Inc 651 464-6612
280 12th St SW Ste 1 Forest Lake (55025) ***(G-2168)***
S & S Tree & Horticultural 651 451-8907
405 Hardman Ave S South Saint Paul (55075) ***(G-9539)***
S & S Tree Specialists Inc 612 872-3901
405 Hardman Ave S South Saint Paul (55075) ***(G-9540)***
S & T Office Products Inc 651 483-4411
1000 Kristen Ct Saint Paul (55110) ***(G-8918)***
S D Q Ltd 952 929-5263
4737 County Road 101 # 250 Minnetonka (55345) ***(G-6223)***
S E H, Hopkins *Also Called Short-Elliott-Hendrickson Inc* ***(G-2632)***
S E H, Saint Paul *Also Called Short-Elliott-Hendrickson Inc* ***(G-8954)***
S E Rental 507 765-3805
Junction Highway 52 16 E Preston (55965) ***(G-6901)***
S J C Inc 651 483-1752
4595 Hodgson Rd Saint Paul (55126) ***(G-8919)***
S J Louis Construction Inc (PA) 320 253-9291
1351 Broadway St W Rockville (56369) ***(G-7314)***
S KB Environmental 507 433-8131
251 Starkey St Austin (55912) ***(G-285)***
S M D C St Mary's Duluth Clin 218 786-4020
407 E 3rd St Duluth (55805) ***(G-1441)***
S M D Sel-Mor, Minneapolis *Also Called Sel-Mor Distributing Co* ***(G-5629)***
S O A P Medical Transcription, Minneapolis *Also Called Soap Transcription Services* ***(G-5693)***
S P Richards Co 651 484-8459
2416 Maplewood Dr Saint Paul (55109) ***(G-8920)***
S P S Co's Inc 507 387-5691
1201 N Riverfront Dr Mankato (56001) ***(G-3190)***
S P S Co's Inc (PA) 952 929-1377
6363 Highway 7 Minneapolis (55416) ***(G-5582)***
S P S S Inc 507 287-2800
4115 Hwy 52 N Ste 300 Rochester (55901) ***(G-7244)***
S R Weidema Inc 763 428-9110
17600 113th Ave N Osseo (55369) ***(G-6659)***
S T C Aviation Inc 320 253-1500
1544 45th Ave SE Saint Cloud (56304) ***(G-7440)***
S-R-F-t-c Brokers, Golden Valley *Also Called Rubenstein Logistics Services* ***(G-2244)***
SA Group Properties Inc 612 303-7833
800 Nicollet Mall Minneapolis (55402) ***(G-5583)***

ALPHABETIC

SA Woods Inc
ALPHABETIC SECTION

SA Woods Inc 507 451-7084
1414 S Oak Ave Ste 6 Owatonna (55060) ***(G-6735)***
Sabathani Community Center 612 821-2300
310 E 38th St Ste 200 Minneapolis (55409) ***(G-5584)***
Saber Dental, Minneapolis *Also Called National Dentex Corp* ***(G-5162)***
Sabre Plumbing, Heating & Air 763 473-2267
3062 Ranchview Ln N Minneapolis (55447) ***(G-5585)***
Sacred Heart Care Center 507 433-1808
1200 12th St SW Austin (55912) ***(G-286)***
Sadaka Technology Consultants 952 841-6363
7701 France Ave S 203 Minneapolis (55435) ***(G-5586)***
Safari Airport Taxi Service 763 424-9070
6808 Candlewood Cir Minneapolis (55445) ***(G-5587)***
Safari Island Community Center, Waconia *Also Called City of Waconia* ***(G-9783)***
Safco Products Co (HQ) 763 536-6700
9300 Research Center Rd W Minneapolis (55428) ***(G-5588)***
SAFE, Hopkins *Also Called Security American Financial* ***(G-2628)***
Safe Air Repair Inc 507 373-7129
401 Airport Rd Albert Lea (56007) ***(G-63)***
Safe Haven 952 846-0608
13212 Irving Ave S Burnsville (55337) ***(G-794)***
Safe Haven Pet Rescue 507 529-4079
1001 1/2 1st Ave SE Rochester (55904) ***(G-7245)***
Safe Haven Shelter For Youth 952 440-5379
14544 Glendale Ave SE Prior Lake (55372) ***(G-6953)***
Safe Haven Shelter For Youth 952 288-2680
13780 McKenna Rd NW Ofc Shakopee (55379) ***(G-9472)***
Safe Step Inc 952 229-8282
12400 Princeton Ave Ste C Savage (55378) ***(G-9406)***
Safe-Way Bus Co (PA) 651 451-1375
6030 Carmen Ave Inver Grove Heights (55076) ***(G-2767)***
Safegate Airport Systems Inc 763 535-9299
7101 Northland Cir N Ste 203 Minneapolis (55428) ***(G-5589)***
SafeNet Consulting Inc 952 930-3636
5810 Baker Rd Ste 100 Minnetonka (55345) ***(G-6224)***
Safety Awareness Inc 763 550-9200
13120 County Road 6 # 100 Minneapolis (55441) ***(G-5590)***
Safety Signs Inc 952 469-6700
19784 Kenrick Ave Ste C Lakeville (55044) ***(G-2930)***
Safety-Kleen Systems Inc 952 469-8356
21750 Cedar Ave Lakeville (55044) ***(G-2931)***
Safeway Hydraulics Inc 952 466-6220
4040 Norex Dr Chaska (55318) ***(G-979)***
Safezone LLC 612 716-0856
275 4th St E Ste 110 Saint Paul (55101) ***(G-8921)***
Saginaw Contracting Inc Wgcc 218 348-6000
815 County Road 75 Saint Joseph (56374) ***(G-7654)***
Sagitec Solutions LLC 612 235-4122
2233 Hamline Ave N # 420 Saint Paul (55113) ***(G-8922)***
Sahara Sands 763 444-6491
465 265th Ave NE Isanti (55040) ***(G-2780)***
Saint Anne of Winona 507 454-3621
1347 W Broadway St Winona (55987) ***(G-10123)***
Saint Anthony Health Center, Minneapolis *Also Called St Anthony Health Center* ***(G-6131)***
Saint Benedict's Senior Com 763 295-4051
1301 E 7th St Ofc Monticello (55362) ***(G-6286)***
Saint Cloud Auto Center LLC 320 259-4542
903 2nd St S Waite Park (56387) ***(G-9835)***
SAINT CLOUD AVIATION, Saint Cloud *Also Called S T C Aviation Inc* ***(G-7440)***
Saint Cloud Care Free Living, Saint Cloud *Also Called Spectrum Community Health Inc* ***(G-7428)***
Saint Club Medical Group, Saint Cloud *Also Called Tl Wyne* ***(G-7617)***
Saint Croix Girl's Camp, Finlayson *Also Called Department of Corrections MN* ***(G-2129)***
Saint Elizabeth's Hospital (PA) 651 565-4531
1200 Grant Blvd W Wabasha (55981) ***(G-9770)***
Saint Elizabeth's Hospital of 651 565-4581
626 Shields Ave Wabasha (55981) ***(G-9771)***
Saint James Lions Club Inc 507 375-5634
116 Sunset Dr Saint James (56081) ***(G-7645)***
Saint Luke's Outpatient Mental 218 249-7000
220 N 6th Ave E Duluth (55805) ***(G-1442)***
Saint Luke's Plastic Surgery, Duluth *Also Called Edgar Saldana Dr* ***(G-1310)***
Saint Lukes Cardiology Assocs 218 249-3057
1001 E Superior St # 201 Duluth (55802) ***(G-1443)***
Saint Lukes Microlab, Duluth *Also Called St Luke's Hospital of Duluth* ***(G-1471)***
Saint Martin Commercial Club 320 548-3208
27392 Sauk Landing Rd Paynesville (56362) ***(G-6774)***
Saint Mary's University of MN 612 728-5109
2500 Park Ave Minneapolis (55404) ***(G-5591)***
Saint Marys Hospital of 507 255-5123
1216 2nd St SW Rochester (55902) ***(G-7246)***
Saint Marys Parish Credit Un, Sleepy Eye *Also Called Southpoint Federal Credit* ***(G-9501)***
Saint McHael Veterinary Clinic, Saint Michael *Also Called St Michael Veterinary Clinic* ***(G-7682)***
Saint Olaf Retirement 612 522-6561
2912 Fremont Ave N Minneapolis (55411) ***(G-5592)***
Saint Patrick's Guild Inc 651 690-1506
1554 Randolph Ave Saint Paul (55105) ***(G-8923)***
Saint Paul Burlington LP 651 228-9456
180 5th St E Ste 160 Saint Paul (55101) ***(G-8924)***
Saint Paul Chamber Orchestra 651 292-3241
408 Saint Peter St Fl 3 Saint Paul (55102) ***(G-8925)***
Saint Paul Foundation Inc 651 224-5463
55 5th St E Ste 600 Saint Paul (55101) ***(G-8926)***
Saint Paul Lung Clinic 651 726-6200
225 Smith Ave N Ste 300 Saint Paul (55102) ***(G-8927)***
Saint Paul Regional Water Svcs 651 776-6960
1585 Maryland Ave E Saint Paul (55106) ***(G-8928)***
Saint Paul Regional Water Svcs 651 266-1635
1900 Rice St Saint Paul (55113) ***(G-8929)***
Saint Paul Rivercentre Conv 651 265-4800
175 Kellogg Blvd W # 501 Saint Paul (55102) ***(G-8930)***
Saint Peter Agency Inc (PA) 507 931-3310
220 S 3rd St Saint Peter (56082) ***(G-9312)***
Saint Peter Counseling Center 507 934-9612
1711 Sheppard Dr Saint Peter (56082) ***(G-9300)***
Saint Vncent De Paul Cthlic Ch, Minneapolis *Also Called Archdiocese of Saint Paul* ***(G-3800)***
Saint William's Living Center 218 338-4671
212 W Soo St Parkers Prairie (56361) ***(G-6766)***

Sajjadi, Hamed MD, Minneapolis *Also Called Minnesota Ear Head & Neck Clin* ***(G-5077)***
Sakada 952 938-9400
15306 Highway 7 Ste 100 Hopkins (55345) ***(G-2625)***
Salad Makers Inc 218 236-4959
1820 1st Ave N Moorhead (56560) ***(G-6341)***
Salo Project LLC 612 230-7256
20 S 13th St Minneapolis (55403) ***(G-5593)***
Salo Search LLC 612 230-7256
20 S 13th St Minneapolis (55403) ***(G-5594)***
Salon, Saint Paul *Also Called Rocco Altobelli Inc* ***(G-9270)***
Salon 2000 & Day Spa 952 942-8444
574 Paririe Ctr Dr Ste 155 Eden Prairie (55344) ***(G-1770)***
Salon 4862 Inc 612 298-8310
4710 Humboldt Ave N Minneapolis (55430) ***(G-5595)***
Salon Intrigue 952 922-0588
3070 Excelsior Blvd Ste 203 Minneapolis (55416) ***(G-5596)***
Salon Sabell Inc 612 866-3679
1609 W Lake St Minneapolis (55408) ***(G-5597)***
Salonek Concrete & Constr 507 723-4218
12 W Lincoln St Springfield (56087) ***(G-9574)***
Salvation Army Booth, Saint Paul *Also Called Central Territorial of The* ***(G-8183)***
Salvation Army Harbor Light 612 338-0113
1010 Currie Ave Minneapolis (55403) ***(G-5598)***
Samaritan Bethany HM On Eighth, Rochester *Also Called Bethany Samaritan Inc* ***(G-7064)***
Samaritan Wholesale Tire Co 612 729-8000
5100 W 35th St Minneapolis (55416) ***(G-5599)***
Sanctuary Salonspa, Eden Prairie *Also Called Image Shoppe Inc* ***(G-1690)***
Sand Co Inc 507 388-8555
1900 Premier Dr Mankato (56001) ***(G-3191)***
Sand Co's Inc 320 202-3100
366 10th Ave S Waite Park (56387) ***(G-9836)***
Sandman Motel LLC 763 559-1222
3000 Harbor Ln N Minneapolis (55447) ***(G-5600)***
Sandman Motels LLC 952 932-9987
6110 Blue Circle Dr Ste 237 Hopkins (55343) ***(G-2626)***
Sandra Hamer 651 254-0116
1870 50th St E Ste 9 Inver Grove Heights (55077) ***(G-2768)***
Sandstone Area Nursing Home 320 245-2212
109 Court Ave S Sandstone (55072) ***(G-9326)***
Sandstone Riders Horse Club 320 245-0370
52803 County Rd 61 Sandstone (55072) ***(G-9327)***
Sandstrom's Inc 218 326-0567
2057 E Highway 2 Grand Rapids (55744) ***(G-2307)***
Sanford Health 507 847-2420
1430 North Hwy Jackson (56143) ***(G-2798)***
Sanford Health 507 283-2321
1600 N Kniss Ave Luverne (56156) ***(G-3067)***
Sanford Health Network 507 223-7272
112 Saint Olaf Ave S Canby (56220) ***(G-852)***
Sanford Health Network 507 847-2420
1430 North Hwy Jackson (56143) ***(G-2799)***
Sanford Health Network 507 283-2321
1600 N Kniss Ave Luverne (56156) ***(G-3068)***
Sanford Health Network 507 674-2932
251 5th St E Tracy (56175) ***(G-9691)***
Sanford Hospitality LLC 952 854-3411
2300 American Blvd E Bloomington (55425) ***(G-512)***
Sanford Westbrook Medical Ctr 507 274-6802
920 Bell Ave Westbrook (56183) ***(G-9967)***
Sanofi Pasteur Inc 952 893-8080
3601 Minnesota Dr Minneapolis (55435) ***(G-5601)***
Sapphire Technologies, LP 612 332-8700
100 N 6th St Ste 405B Minneapolis (55403) ***(G-5602)***
SAR Inc 507 373-7129
401 Airport Rd Albert Lea (56007) ***(G-64)***
Sara Lee Bakery Group Inc 651 688-9275
3255 Neil Armstrong Blvd Saint Paul (55121) ***(G-7897)***
Sara Lee Corp 763 572-2506
350 73rd Ave NE Ste 15 Minneapolis (55432) ***(G-3595)***
Sargent's Landscape Nursery 507 289-0022
7955 18th Ave NW Rochester (55901) ***(G-7247)***
Sargent's Nursery Inc 651 388-3847
3352 N Service Dr Red Wing (55066) ***(G-7004)***
Sartell Group Inc 612 548-3101
310 4th Ave S Ste 800 Minneapolis (55415) ***(G-5603)***
Sasker Manufacturing Inc 320 532-4268
34769 US Highway 169 Onamia (56359) ***(G-6576)***
Sauer Memorial Home (PA) 507 454-5540
1635 W Service Dr Winona (55987) ***(G-10124)***
Sauer Memorial Home 507 454-5540
1635 W Service Dr Winona (55987) ***(G-10125)***
Saunatec Inc (PA) 320 286-5584
575 Cokato St E Cokato (55321) ***(G-1079)***
SAV Enterprises Inc 763 278-3340
11325 Xeon St NW Minneapolis (55448) ***(G-3596)***
Sav Logistics Inc 763 489-4213
11325 Xeon St NW Minneapolis (55448) ***(G-3597)***
Savage Kindercare, Savage *Also Called Kindercare Learning Centers* ***(G-9393)***
Savvysherpa LLC 763 549-3540
6200 Shingle Creek Pkwy Minneapolis (55430) ***(G-5604)***
Sawatdee Inc (PA) 612 338-6451
607 Washington Ave S Minneapolis (55415) ***(G-5605)***
Sawhorse Designer's & Builders 952 475-4477
239 Lake St E Wayzata (55391) ***(G-9939)***
Sawhose Inc 763 533-0352
4740 42nd Ave N Minneapolis (55422) ***(G-5606)***
Sawmill Inn, Grand Rapids *Also Called Grand Rapids Development Corp* ***(G-2281)***
Saxon, Mike Inver Grove Ford, Inver Grove Heights *Also Called Mgmt Five Inc* ***(G-2762)***
Saxons, Saint Paul *Also Called Suburban Auto Body Inc* ***(G-9011)***
SBC Datacomm Inc 763 315-5343
833 3rd St SW Ste 1 Saint Paul (55112) ***(G-8931)***
Sbetc, Saint Cloud *Also Called Stearns-Benton Employment* ***(G-7612)***
SBS Transportation Inc 651 256-1555
1700 Wynne Ave Saint Paul (55108) ***(G-8932)***
Sbsb LP 218 628-2700
5713 Grand Ave Ste B Duluth (55807) ***(G-1444)***

www.HarrisInfo.com
616
2011 Harris Minnesota
Services Directory
(G-00000) Company's Geographic Section entry number

ALPHABETIC

Sbse LLC 651 994-7810
4675 Rahncliff Rd Eagan (55122) *(G-1549)*
Scantron Corp (HQ) 651 683-6000
1313 Lone Oak Rd Eagan (55121) *(G-1550)*
Scenic Heights Pta 952 401-5400
5650 Scenic Heights Dr Hopkins (55345) *(G-2627)*
Scenic Rivers Health Services, Bigfork *Also Called Cook Area Health Services Inc (G-460)*
Scenic Sign Corp 320 252-9400
828 5th St S Sauk Rapids (56379) *(G-9373)*
Schaap Sanitation Inc 507 376-9218
27008 US Highway 59 Worthington (56187) *(G-10193)*
Schadegg Mechanical Inc 651 292-9933
225 Bridgepoint Dr South Saint Paul (55075) *(G-9541)*
Schadegg Properties LLC 651 292-9933
225 Bridgepoint Dr South Saint Paul (55075) *(G-9542)*
Schak Trucking Inc 507 247-5204
201 E Highway 14 Tyler (56178) *(G-9713)*
Schanfield, Paul M MD, Saint Paul *Also Called Neurological Associates of St (G-8746)*
Schawk Inc 651 636-0611
2269 County Road C W Saint Paul (55113) *(G-8933)*
Schechter Dokken Kanter 612 332-5500
100 Washington Ave S Ste 1600 Minneapolis (55401) *(G-5607)*
Scheid Electric Inc 507 388-9305
53936 208th Ln Mankato (56001) *(G-3192)*
Schenker Inc 651 367-2500
3191 Mike Collins Dr Eagan (55121) *(G-1551)*
Scherer & Sons Trucking Inc 320 363-8846
1007 E Minnesota St Saint Joseph (56374) *(G-7655)*
Scherer Bros Lumber Co (PA) 612 379-9633
9401 73rd Ave N Ste 400 Minneapolis (55428) *(G-5608)*
Schmid & Son Packaging Inc 651 452-0588
7699 95th St S Cottage Grove (55016) *(G-1107)*
Schmidt's Meat Market Inc 507 232-3438
319 Pine St Nicollet (56074) *(G-6491)*
Schmit Towing Inc 763 253-1568
92 43rd Ave NE Minneapolis (55421) *(G-3598)*
Schneiberg Co (PA) 651 489-7489
1259 Gervais Ave Ste 100 Saint Paul (55109) *(G-8934)*
Schneider Electric USA Inc 763 543-5500
9220 Bass Lake Rd Ste 230 Minneapolis (55428) *(G-5609)*
Schneiderman Furniture Inc 952 435-3399
17630 Juniper Path Lakeville (55044) *(G-2932)*
Schoell & Madson Inc 763 746-1600
14800 28th Ave N Ste 140 Minneapolis (55447) *(G-5610)*
Schoeneckers Inc 320 453-2600
479 Meeker Ave E Eden Valley (55329) *(G-1822)*
Schoeneckers Inc (PA) 952 835-4800
7630 Bush Lake Rd Edina (55439) *(G-1844)*
Schoeneckers Inc 952 835-4800
7760 Bush Lake Rd Minneapolis (55439) *(G-5611)*
Scholarship America 952 830-7300
1550 Amrcn Blvd E Ste 155 Minneapolis (55425) *(G-5612)*
Scholarship America Inc 507 931-1682
1 Scholarship Way Saint Peter (56082) *(G-9313)*
Scholastic Book Fairs Inc 763 391-0930
9201 Wyoming Ave N Ste 102 Minneapolis (55445) *(G-5613)*
Schott Distributing Co Inc 507 289-3555
6735 Highway 14 E Rochester (55904) *(G-7248)*
Schroeder Moving Systems Inc 763 694-6070
2405 Annapolis Ln N # 270 Minneapolis (55441) *(G-5614)*
Schueller Wenner & Co 320 632-6311
109 E Broadway Little Falls (56345) *(G-3019)*
Schum Drywall Co Inc 952 881-3350
815 W 106th St Minneapolis (55420) *(G-5615)*
Schumacher Wholesale Meats Inc 763 546-3291
1114 Zane Ave N Minneapolis (55422) *(G-5616)*
Schwab-Vollhaber-Lubratt Inc 651 481-8000
4600 Churchill St Ste 1 Saint Paul (55126) *(G-8935)*
Schwalbach Hardware Inc 507 831-2523
193 9th St Windom (56101) *(G-10071)*
Schwan Food Co (PA) 507 532-3274
115 W College Dr Marshall (56258) *(G-3325)*
Schwan's Consumer Brands North (HQ) 952 832-4300
8500 Normandale Lake Blvd Bloomington (55437) *(G-513)*
Schwan's Global Food Service 507 532-3274
115 W College Dr Marshall (56258) *(G-3326)*
Schwan's Home Service Inc 218 879-5470
5 Jay Cooke Rd Esko (55733) *(G-1923)*
Schwan's Home Service Inc 507 451-8538
2795 Park Dr Owatonna (55060) *(G-6736)*
Schwan's Technology Group Inc (HQ) 651 388-1821
5140 Moundview Dr Red Wing (55066) *(G-7005)*
Schwan's Technology Group Inc 651 681-4450
2945 Lone Oak Dr Ste 150 Saint Paul (55121) *(G-7898)*
Schwartz Bros Inc 507 794-5779
32296 190th St Sleepy Eye (56085) *(G-9499)*
Schwartzman Co Inc 763 421-1187
2905 N Ferry St Anoka (55303) *(G-224)*
Schwebel, Goetz, & Sieben 612 333-8361
80 S 8th St Ste 5120 Minneapolis (55402) *(G-5617)*
Schwegman, Lundberg & Woessner 612 373-6900
121 S 8th St Ste 1600 Minneapolis (55402) *(G-5618)*
Schwickert Co 507 387-3101
330 Poplar St Mankato (56001) *(G-3193)*
Schwickert Inc 507 387-3106
221 Minnesota St Mankato (56001) *(G-3194)*
Schwickert's, Mankato *Also Called Schwickert Co (G-3193)*
Schwickert's of Rochester Inc (HQ) 507 387-3106
221 Minnesota St Mankato (56001) *(G-3195)*
Schwieters Chevrolet of 320 634-4507
110 Franklin St N Glenwood (56334) *(G-2232)*
Schwieters' Co's Inc 651 407-1618
13925 Fenway Blvd N Hugo (55038) *(G-2673)*
SCI Services of Minneapolis, Eden Prairie *Also Called Shelard Group Inc (G-1777)*
Scicom Data Services Ltd 952 933-4200
10101 Bren Rd E Minnetonka (55343) *(G-6225)*

Science Museum of Minnesota 651 221-9488
120 Kellogg Blvd W Saint Paul (55102) *(G-8936)*
Scimed Inc 763 494-1700
1 Scimed Pl Osseo (55311) *(G-6660)*
Scott A Polzin DDS 218 728-6445
1225 E 1st St Duluth (55805) *(G-1445)*
Scott County Highway Engineer 952 496-8346
600 Country Trl E Jordan (55352) *(G-2809)*
Scott R McGarvey MD 952 832-0076
7373 France Ave S Ste 312 Minneapolis (55435) *(G-5619)*
Scott W Kajer DDS 651 770-3831
1736 Cope Ave E Ste 3 Saint Paul (55109) *(G-8937)*
Scottish Rite Temple 651 222-2676
200 Plato Blvd E Saint Paul (55107) *(G-8938)*
Scotts Salon Svc Minneapolis, Minneapolis *Also Called Verde Lawn Care LLC (G-5963)*
Scoular Co 612 335-8700
400 S 4th St Minneapolis (55415) *(G-5620)*
Scout Information Services Inc 651 686-4646
2980 Commers Dr Ste 400 Saint Paul (55121) *(G-7899)*
Scs Dialaride 952 474-7441
4140 Shoreline Dr Spring Park (55384) *(G-9566)*
SE Rolling Hills LLC 952 828-9500
431 Paririe Ctr Dr # 114 Eden Prairie (55344) *(G-1771)*
Seabury Group L L C 612 399-0033
730 2nd Ave S Ste 730 Minneapolis (55402) *(G-5621)*
Seaco Inc 952 470-7400
20540 Summerville Rd Excelsior (55331) *(G-1953)*
Seal Guard Systems Inc 612 787-0700
18300 Norell Ave N Marine On Saint Croix (55047) *(G-3289)*
Search America, A Part of 763 416-1007
6450 Wedgwood Rd N # 100 Maple Grove (55311) *(G-3253)*
Search Institute 612 376-8955
615 1st Ave NE Ste 125 Minneapolis (55413) *(G-5622)*
Sears Logistics Services Inc 612 379-5600
2700 Winter St NE Ste 8 Minneapolis (55413) *(G-5623)*
Sears Product Services, Waite Park *Also Called Sears, Roebuck & Co (G-9837)*
Sears, Roebuck & Co 952 435-2380
14250 Buck Hill Rd Burnsville (55306) *(G-795)*
Sears, Roebuck & Co 952 944-4911
8301 Flying Cloud Dr Eden Prairie (55344) *(G-1772)*
Sears, Roebuck & Co 651 291-4397
425 Rice St Saint Paul (55103) *(G-8939)*
Sears, Roebuck & Co 800 882-5351
41 Division St Waite Park (56387) *(G-9837)*
Seasonal Specialties LLC 952 942-6555
11455 Valley View Rd Eden Prairie (55344) *(G-1773)*
Seasons Hospice 507 285-1930
5650 Weatherhill Rd SW Rochester (55902) *(G-7249)*
Seaver Co 507 665-3321
200 Minnesota Ave Le Sueur (56058) *(G-2959)*
Sebesta Blomberg & Associates (PA) 651 634-0775
2381 Rosegate Saint Paul (55113) *(G-8940)*
Sebrite Agency Inc 952 563-1234
5421 Feltl Rd Ste 140 Minnetonka (55343) *(G-6226)*
Secoa Inc 763 506-8800
8650 109th Ave N Champlin (55316) *(G-900)*
Second Data Enterprises Inc 612 326-6833
3601 Minnesota Dr Ste 800 Edina (55435) *(G-1845)*
Second Harvest Heartland 612 209-7980
3100 California St NE Minneapolis (55418) *(G-5624)*
Second Harvest Heartland 651 484-5117
1140 Gervais Ave Saint Paul (55109) *(G-8941)*
Secruian Financial Services 651 223-4252
400 Robert St N Saint Paul (55101) *(G-8942)*
Secure Computing Corp 651 628-2700
2340 Energy Park Dr Saint Paul (55108) *(G-8943)*
Securian Financial Network Inc (PA) 651 665-3500
400 Robert St N Ste A Saint Paul (55101) *(G-8944)*
Securian Financial Services 651 665-4244
401 Robert St N Saint Paul (55101) *(G-8945)*
Securitas Security Services 218 727-7870
394 S Lake Ave Ste 300 Duluth (55802) *(G-1446)*
Security American Financial (PA) 952 544-2121
10901 Red Circle Dr Fl 4 Hopkins (55343) *(G-2628)*
Security Auto Loans Inc 763 559-5892
4900 Highway 169 N # 205 Minneapolis (55428) *(G-5625)*
Security Auto Loans Inc 763 559-5892
12800 Industrial Blvd Plymouth (55441) *(G-6883)*
Security Bank & Trust Co Inc 320 864-3171
735 11th St E Glencoe (55336) *(G-2213)*
Security Bank Minnesota 507 373-1481
437 Bridge Ave Albert Lea (56007) *(G-65)*
Security Bank USA 218 751-1510
1025 Paul Bunyan Dr NW Bemidji (56601) *(G-426)*
Security Bankshares Co Inc (PA) 320 864-3171
735 11th St E Glencoe (55336) *(G-2214)*
Security Life Insurance Co of 952 544-2121
10901 Red Circle Dr # 400 Hopkins (55343) *(G-2629)*
Security Products Co 763 784-6504
4005 Pheasant Ridge Dr NE Minneapolis (55449) *(G-3599)*
Security Response Services Inc 952 346-8922
9036 Grand Ave S Minneapolis (55420) *(G-5626)*
Security State Bank of Kenyon 507 789-6123
602 2nd St Kenyon (55946) *(G-2829)*
Seeds 2000 Inc 218 643-2410
115 3rd St N Breckenridge (56520) *(G-600)*
Seek Home Inc 763 494-0870
100 Central Ave Ste 3 Osseo (55369) *(G-6661)*
Seelye Plastics Inc 952 881-2658
9700 Newton Ave S # 9702 Minneapolis (55431) *(G-5627)*
Segetis Inc 763 795-7200
680 Mendelssohn Ave N Golden Valley (55427) *(G-2245)*
Seh, Duluth *Also Called Short-Elliott-Hendrickson Inc (G-1450)*
Seh Architectural Svcs Group, Saint Cloud *Also Called Short-Elliott-Hendrickson Inc (G-7593)*
Seh Technology Solutions Inc 612 758-6728
100 N 6th St Ste 710C Minneapolis (55403) *(G-5628)*
SEITZ STAINLESS, Avon *Also Called Havco Inc (G-295)*
Seiu Local 113, Saint Paul *Also Called Minn Health Care Union Local (G-8670)*

ALPHABETIC

Seiu Local 284 ....651 256-9102
450 Southview Blvd Ste 101 South Saint Paul (55075) *(G-9543)*
Sel-Mor Distributing Co 952 929-0888
6520 W Lake St Minneapolis (55426) *(G-5629)*
Sela Investments Ltd, LLP 952 925-3878
4915 W 35th St Ste 201 Minneapolis (55416) *(G-5630)*
Sela Roofing & Remodeling Inc (PA) 612 823-8046
4100 Excelsior Blvd Minneapolis (55416) *(G-5631)*
Sela Roofing & Remodeling Inc 763 592-5420
3400 48th Ave N Minneapolis (55429) *(G-5632)*
Select Communications Inc 763 744-0900
12975 16th Ave N Ste 100 Minneapolis (55441) *(G-5633)*
Select Hotels Group LLC 952 944-9700
11369 Viking Dr Eden Prairie (55344) *(G-1774)*
Select Inn of Bloomington LP 952 835-7400
7851 Normandale Blvd Minneapolis (55435) *(G-5634)*
Select Surfaces, Saint Paul *Also Called Premier Tile Inc (G-8838)*
Select Transcription Inc 763 441-3021
11040 183rd Cir NW Ste C Elk River (55330) *(G-1892)*
Selftek 612 872-1285
2722 Irving Ave S Minneapolis (55408) *(G-5635)*
Sellin Brothers Inc 218 483-3522
1204 Hobart St Hawley (56549) *(G-2422)*
Semcac 507 864-7741
204 N Elm St Rushford (55971) *(G-7392)*
Semcil Living Inc 507 285-1815
2720 Broadway Ave N Rochester (55906) *(G-7250)*
Semva Gallery, Rochester *Also Called Art Semva Gallery (G-7059)*
Senior Asset Management Inc 763 544-9934
6225 42nd Ave N Minneapolis (55422) *(G-5636)*
Senior Citizens Center of 218 494-3750
Main St Felton (56536) *(G-2063)*
Senior Citizens Service Inc 507 287-1404
121 Broadway Ave N Rochester (55906) *(G-7251)*
Senior Epoch Living Inc 952 473-3330
500 Carlson Pkwy Hopkins (55305) *(G-2630)*
Senior Friend 218 878-0990
116 Avenue C Cloquet (55720) *(G-1065)*
Senior Friend Associates Inc 218 727-1111
301 W 1st St Ste 309 Duluth (55802) *(G-1447)*
Senior Grace Services 507 388-3660
118 Raven Ct Mankato (56001) *(G-3196)*
Senior Health & Home Care Inc 952 920-9399
6332 Millers Ln Minneapolis (55424) *(G-5637)*
Senior Home Living MN LLC 952 935-0789
175 Jackson Ave N Ste 429 Hopkins (55343) *(G-2631)*
Senior Hutchinson Care Svcs 320 234-4751
1555 Sherwood St SE Hutchinson (55350) *(G-2712)*
Senior Isanti Citizen Com 763 444-6100
121 Norelius St Isanti (55040) *(G-2781)*
Senior Laurentian Citizen Ctr 218 749-3688
RR Box 2374 Virginia (55792) *(G-9755)*
Senior Living Center, Winsted *Also Called Benedictine Health System (G-10158)*
Senior Management Inc 507 725-3351
425 N Badger St Caledonia (55921) *(G-828)*
Senior McIntosh Living 218 563-3043
175 N Broadway McIntosh (56556) *(G-3342)*
Senior Outreach Program, Minneapolis *Also Called Anoka County Community Action (G-3404)*
Senior Southview Living 651 554-4838
1984 Oakdale Ave Ofc Saint Paul (55118) *(G-7900)*
Seniors Caring Companions Inc 651 770-2288
3070 Chisholm Ct N Maplewood (55109) *(G-3288)*
Seniors' Choice At Home, Minneapolis *Also Called Agramson Enterprises Inc (G-3700)*
Sentage Corp 612 529-9655
801 12th Ave N Minneapolis (55411) *(G-5638)*
Sentencing To Service, Minneapolis *Also Called Hennepin County (G-4636)*
Sentry Systems Alarms, Saint Paul *Also Called Century Systems Inc (G-8185)*
Sentry Systems Inc 651 426-4627
2182 4th St White Bear Lake (55110) *(G-9977)*
Service 800 Inc 952 475-3747
2190 W Wayzata Blvd Long Lake (55356) *(G-3032)*
Service Lighting Inc 763 571-3001
11621 95th Ave N Osseo (55369) *(G-6662)*
Servicemaster, International Falls *Also Called Woodfam Inc (G-2734)*
ServiceMaster, Minneapolis *Also Called Rusciano-Hyland Inc (G-5576)*
ServiceMaster Inc 651 552-4979
1350 Highway 96 E Saint Paul (55110) *(G-8946)*
Servicemaster Inc 612 794-4100
4300 Glumack Dr 79 Saint Paul (55111) *(G-7963)*
ServiceMaster of Lakes Area, Alexandria *Also Called Dvcm ServiceMaster of The (G-96)*
Servicemaster of St Cloud Inc 320 252-4622
501 17th Ave N Saint Cloud (56303) *(G-7591)*
ServiceMaster Osseo, Osseo *Also Called Specialty Contracting Services (G-6666)*
ServiceMaster Total Cleaning 952 873-6070
501 17th Ave N Saint Cloud (56303) *(G-7592)*
Services To Handicapped, Saint Cloud *Also Called Catholic Charities of The (G-7475)*
Servisair USA Inc 612 726-5533
5398 Northwest Dr Saint Paul (55111) *(G-7964)*
Servsair Globeground, Saint Paul *Also Called Servisair USA Inc (G-7964)*
Seton Services, Saint Paul *Also Called Catholic Charities of The (G-8175)*
Setter Leach & Lindstrom Inc 612 338-8741
730 2nd Ave S Ste 1100 Minneapolis (55402) *(G-5639)*
Seve Enterprises Inc 612 605-6230
100 S 5th St Fl 19 Minneapolis (55402) *(G-5640)*
Seven Corners Hotel Partners (PA) 612 333-4646
1500 Washington Ave S Minneapolis (55454) *(G-5641)*
Seven Corners Hotel Partners 612 333-4646
1500 Washington Ave S Minneapolis (55454) *(G-5642)*
7 West Secretarial Answering 952 936-4000
7525 Mitchell Rd Ste 315 Eden Prairie (55344) *(G-1775)*
702 COMMUNICATIONS, Moorhead *Also Called Val-Ed Joint Venture, LLP (G-6345)*
78th Street Leaseco LLC 952 835-1900
5601 W 78th St Minneapolis (55439) *(G-5643)*
Seventy-Five Hundred York 952 835-1010
7500 York Ave S Minneapolis (55435) *(G-5644)*
Severson Oil Co 507 452-4743
508 Louisa St Winona (55987) *(G-10126)*
Severson Sheldon Dougherty 952 432-3136
7300 147th St W Ste 600 Saint Paul (55124) *(G-7901)*
Severson Transport Inc 507 454-5090
508 Louisa St Winona (55987) *(G-10127)*
Seward CSP 612 333-0331
2105 Minnehaha Ave Minneapolis (55404) *(G-5645)*
Sexton Partners 651 457-9255
250 Lothenbach Ave Saint Paul (55118) *(G-7902)*
SFM Mutual Insurance Co (PA) 952 838-4200
3500 Amercn Blvd W # 700 Bloomington (55431) *(G-514)*
Sfn Group Inc 952 469-7583
21340 Hamburg Ave Lakeville (55044) *(G-2933)*
Sfn Group Inc 952 543-3300
5601 Green Valley Dr # 200 Minneapolis (55437) *(G-5646)*
Sfn Group Inc 651 501-5037
585 Hale Ave N Saint Paul (55128) *(G-9272)*
Sfn Group Inc 952 467-1770
717 Faxon Rd Young America (55397) *(G-10210)*
Sgo Roofing & Construction LLC 952 469-8560
21017 Heron Way Ste 101 Lakeville (55044) *(G-2934)*
Shaddric & Le Beau Housing 763 784-9824
7365 Central Ave NE Minneapolis (55432) *(G-3600)*
Shade Tree, Big Lake *Also Called Josuda Inc (G-449)*
Shade Warren Co 612 331-5939
600 Hoover St NE Minneapolis (55413) *(G-5647)*
Shadowbrooke Golf Course Inc 320 395-4251
3192 Highway 7 Lester Prairie (55354) *(G-2964)*
Shady Lane Nursing Home 218 631-1391
201 Shady Lane Dr Wadena (56482) *(G-9811)*
Shady Oak Hospitality LP 952 995-9000
6330 Point Chase Eden Prairie (55344) *(G-1776)*
Shady Oaks Nursery 507 835-5033
400 15th Ave SE Waseca (56093) *(G-9887)*
Shafer Contracting Co Inc 651 257-5019
30405 Regal Ave Shafer (55074) *(G-9415)*
Shakopee Chevrolet Inc 952 445-4148
1220 1st Ave E Shakopee (55379) *(G-9473)*
Shakopee Friendship Manor, Shakopee *Also Called Quality Life Styles Inc (G-9468)*
Shakopee Mdewakanton Sioux Com (PA) 952 445-8900
2330 Sioux Trl NW Prior Lake (55372) *(G-6954)*
Shakopee Public Utilities 952 233-1505
255 Sarazin St Shakopee (55379) *(G-9474)*
Shakopee Valley Kindercare, Shakopee *Also Called Kindercare Learning Centers (G-9448)*
Shamineau Ministris, Motley *Also Called Camp Shamineau of The (G-6383)*
Shamrock Enterprises LLC 507 288-9494
6415 Bandel Rd NW Rochester (55901) *(G-7252)*
Shaner Hotel Group LP 952 893-9300
3400 Edinborough Way Minneapolis (55435) *(G-5648)*
Shannon-Peterson Inc 218 751-4502
3728 Bemidji Ave N Bemidji (56601) *(G-427)*
Shari K Bruning DDS 763 546-1301
5851 Duluth St Ste 100 Minneapolis (55422) *(G-5649)*
Shark Industries Ltd 763 565-1900
6700 Bleck Dr Rockford (55373) *(G-7313)*
Shavlik Technologies Corp 651 426-6624
2665 Long Lake Rd Ste 400 Saint Paul (55113) *(G-8947)*
Shavlik Technologies LLC 651 426-6624
2665 Long Lake Rd Ste 400 Saint Paul (55113) *(G-8948)*
Shaw - Lundquist Associates 651 454-0670
2757 W Service Rd Saint Paul (55121) *(G-7903)*
Shaw Acquisition Corp 612 378-1520
645 Johnson St NE Minneapolis (55413) *(G-5650)*
Shaw Lumber Co (PA) 651 488-2525
645 Johnson St NE Minneapolis (55413) *(G-5651)*
Shaw Trucking Inc 763 434-3300
15850 Lincoln St NE Anoka (55304) *(G-225)*
Shea Inc 612 339-2257
100 N 6th St Ste 650C Minneapolis (55403) *(G-5652)*
Sheehy Construction Co 651 488-6691
360 Larpenteur Ave W Saint Paul (55113) *(G-8949)*
Sheet Metal Worker Federal 651 770-2385
1691 Cope Ave E Saint Paul (55109) *(G-8950)*
Sheffield, Olson & McQueen Inc 651 695-2500
2145 Ford Pkwy Ste 200 Saint Paul (55116) *(G-8951)*
Shel Don Group Inc 218 727-2817
124 E Superior St Duluth (55802) *(G-1448)*
Shelard Group Inc 952 941-7493
6385 Old Shady Oak Rd # 230 Eden Prairie (55344) *(G-1777)*
Shelter Care Inc 612 823-8483
3103 Columbus Ave Minneapolis (55407) *(G-5653)*
Shelter House 320 235-0962
804 Willmar Ave SE Willmar (56201) *(G-10044)*
Shelter Products Inc 507 354-4176
810 N Front St New Ulm (56073) *(G-6474)*
Shepherd Good Lutheran Home 507 864-7714
800 Home St Rushford (55971) *(G-7393)*
Shepherd Good Lutheran Home (PA) 320 252-6525
1115 4th Ave N Sauk Rapids (56379) *(G-9374)*
Shepherd Good Lutheran Home 320 258-8665
307 11th St N Sauk Rapids (56379) *(G-9375)*
Sheraton Blmngton Ht Mnnplis S, Minneapolis *Also Called Lho Bloomington One Lessee LLC (G-4868)*
Sheraton Duluth 218 733-5660
301 E Superior St Duluth (55802) *(G-1449)*
Sheraton Minneapolis West, Minnetonka *Also Called Minnetonka Minnesota Hotel L P (G-6198)*
Sheraton St Paul-Woodbury 651 209-3280
676 Bielenberg Dr Saint Paul (55125) *(G-9273)*
Sherburne County Rural 763 262-4100
440 Eagle Lake Rd N Big Lake (55309) *(G-455)*
Sherburne State Bank 763 261-4200
12500 Sherburne Ave Becker (55308) *(G-358)*
Sherburne Tele Systems Inc (DH) 763 262-4100
440 Eagle Lake Rd N Big Lake (55309) *(G-456)*
Sheridan Sheet Metal Co 763 537-3686
4108 Quebec Ave N Minneapolis (55427) *(G-5654)*
Shine-Way Janitorial Service 507 388-7439
22800 Lime Valley Rd Mankato (56001) *(G-3197)*

www.HarrisInfo.com
618
2011 Harris Minnesota Services Directory
(G-00000) Company's Geographic Section entry number

Shingle Creek Elementary, Minneapolis *Also Called Special School District No 1 (G-5717)*
Shingle Creek Hospitality LLP 763 566-7500
2050 Freeway Blvd Minneapolis (55430) **(G-5655)**
Shingle Creek Option, Minneapolis *Also Called Alternative For Autistic (G-3736)*
Shock City Cellular 952 233-5281
205 Lewis St S Shakopee (55379) **(G-9475)**
Sholom Community Alliance (PA) 952 935-6311
3620 Phillips Pkwy Minneapolis (55426) **(G-5656)**
Sholom Community Alliance 952 939-1601
3630 Phillips Pkwy Minneapolis (55426) **(G-5657)**
Sholom Community Alliance 952 908-1776
3610 Phillips Pkwy Minneapolis (55426) **(G-5658)**
Sholom Home East Inc 651 646-6311
740 K Ave Saint Paul (55102) **(G-8952)**
Sholom Home West Inc 952 935-6311
3620 Phillips Pkwy Minneapolis (55426) **(G-5659)**
Sholom St Paul Senior Housing 651 328-2022
760 Perlman St Saint Paul (55102) **(G-8953)**
Shooters Billiard Club & Pro 952 894-1100
1934 Highway 13 E Burnsville (55337) **(G-796)**
Shooting Star Casino, Mahnomen *Also Called White Earth Band of Chippewa (G-3091)*
Shopjimmycom LLC 952 881-6492
9701 Penn Ave S Ste 105 Bloomington (55431) **(G-515)**
Shopko Stores Operating Co LLC 507 437-7785
1209 18th Ave NW Austin (55912) **(G-287)**
Shopko Stores Operating Co LLC 507 532-3266
1200 E Southview Dr Marshall (56258) **(G-3327)**
Shopko Stores Operating Co LLC 507 281-0656
3708 Highway 63 N Rochester (55906) **(G-7253)**
Shoreline Restaurant & Lanes, Battle Lake *Also Called Kalk-Young Inc (G-311)*
Short Stop Service Station, Sauk Rapids *Also Called Bauerly Dynamics Inc (G-9358)*
Short-Elliott-Hendrickson Inc 888 722-0547
418 W Superior St Ste 200 Duluth (55802) **(G-1450)**
Short-Elliott-Hendrickson Inc 952 912-2600
10901 Red Circle Dr # 200 Hopkins (55343) **(G-2632)**
Short-Elliott-Hendrickson Inc 800 572-0617
1200 25th Ave S Saint Cloud (56301) **(G-7593)**
Short-Elliott-Hendrickson Inc (PA) 651 490-2000
3535 Vadnais Center Dr # 200 Saint Paul (55110) **(G-8954)**
Shorty's Heavy Duty Wrecker 763 784-1411
1257 Osborne Rd NE Minneapolis (55432) **(G-3601)**
Shoulder & Sports Medicine 612 879-6623
8100 W 78th St Ste 230 Minneapolis (55439) **(G-5660)**
Showcase, Rochester *Also Called S P S S Inc (G-7244)*
Showplace 16 Kerasotes Theatre 763 757-6233
10051 Woodcrest Dr NW Minneapolis (55433) **(G-3602)**
Shred-It, Minneapolis *Also Called Minnesota Shredding LLC (G-5093)*
Shriners Hospitals For 612 596-6100
2025 E River Pkwy Minneapolis (55414) **(G-5661)**
Shubat Transportation Co 218 262-1042
618 W 41st St Hibbing (55746) **(G-2475)**
Shuett Co's Inc 763 541-9199
620 Mendelssohn Ave N # 107 Minneapolis (55427) **(G-5662)**
Sibley Aggregates, Div, Belle Plaine *Also Called Chard Tiling & Excavating Inc (G-372)*
Sibley Medical Center 507 964-2271
601 W Chandler St Arlington (55307) **(G-250)**
Sick Maihak Inc 952 941-6780
6900 W 110th St Minneapolis (55438) **(G-5663)**
Siding, Osseo *Also Called Top Notch Siding Co (G-6677)*
Sieben, Grose, Von Holtum 612 333-4500
800 Marquette Ave Ste 900 Minneapolis (55402) **(G-5664)**
Siegel, Brill, Greupner Duffy 612 339-7131
100 Washington Ave S Ste 1300 Minneapolis (55401) **(G-5665)**
Siemens Hearing Inc 763 268-4500
5010 Cheshire Ln N Ste 1 Minneapolis (55446) **(G-5666)**
Siemens Industry Inc 651 631-8533
2350 County Road C W Ste 100 Saint Paul (55113) **(G-8955)**
Siemens Product Lifecycle Mgt 651 482-4219
4233 Lexington Ave N Saint Paul (55126) **(G-8956)**
Siemens Water Technologies 651 766-2722
1239 Willow Lake Blvd Saint Paul (55110) **(G-8957)**
Sienna Corp 218 562-6262
9348 Arnold Palmer Dr Pequot Lakes (56472) **(G-6792)**
Sierra Bravo Corp 952 948-1211
9555 James Ave S Ste 245 Bloomington (55431) **(G-516)**
Sierra Corp of Shoreview 763 783-9616
17149 Lincoln St NE # 100 Anoka (55304) **(G-226)**
Siewert Construction Co Inc 651 437-1728
925 Highway 55 Ste 203 Hastings (55033) **(G-2405)**
Sifco Industries Inc 763 544-3511
2430 Winnetka Ave N Minneapolis (55427) **(G-5667)**
Sightpath Medical Inc 952 881-2500
5775 W Old Shakopee Rd Minneapolis (55437) **(G-5668)**
Sigma Alpha Epsilon Fraternity 612 331-5986
1815 University Ave SE Minneapolis (55414) **(G-5669)**
Sigma Tau Omega Inc 651 644-7200
8345 Delaney Cir Inver Grove Heights (55076) **(G-2769)**
Sign-Zone Inc 763 746-1350
6400 Bunker Lake Blvd NW Anoka (55303) **(G-227)**
Signal Financial Corp 651 905-3100
1395 Commerce Dr Ste A Saint Paul (55120) **(G-7904)**
Signature Bank 952 936-7800
9800 Bren Rd E Ste 200 Hopkins (55343) **(G-2633)**
Signature Flight Support Corp 612 726-5700
3800 E 70th St Minneapolis (55450) **(G-5670)**
Signature Flight Support Corp 651 224-1100
515 Eaton St Saint Paul (55107) **(G-8958)**
Signature Healthcare Inc 507 288-6514
501 8th Ave SE Rochester (55904) **(G-7254)**
Signature Stucco Concepts Inc 763 241-4110
17258 Ulysses St NW Elk River (55330) **(G-1893)**
Signature Title Co 952 942-5155
11010 Prairie Lakes Dr Eden Prairie (55344) **(G-1778)**
Signcaster Corp 952 888-9507
9240 Grand Ave S Ste A Minneapolis (55420) **(G-5671)**
Signsearch Inc 952 960-4470
1548 Cliff Rd E Burnsville (55337) **(G-797)**
Siham Solutions Inc 651 274-3640
1421 Park Ave Ste 202 Minneapolis (55404) **(G-5672)**
Silent Knight Security Systems 952 881-0038
9057 Lyndale Ave S Minneapolis (55420) **(G-5673)**
Silliker Inc 952 932-2800
11585 K Tel Dr Hopkins (55343) **(G-2634)**
Silver Bay Veterans Home, Silver Bay *Also Called Minnesota Department of (G-9483)*
Silver King Refrigeration Inc 763 559-1141
13430 County Road 6 Minneapolis (55441) **(G-5674)**
Silver Lake Clinic At Shorevw 651 481-0818
4625 Churchill St Ste 110 Saint Paul (55126) **(G-8959)**
Silvercross Properties 952 925-6231
3663 Park Center Blvd A Minneapolis (55416) **(G-5675)**
Simmons Engineering, Minneapolis *Also Called E & C Amec Services Inc (G-4299)*
Simonson Venture Inc (PA) 763 416-7823
3507 Round Lake Blvd NW S Anoka (55303) **(G-228)**
Simonson Venture Inc 763 494-4863
13744 83rd Way N Osseo (55369) **(G-6663)**
Simonson's, Osseo *Also Called Simonson Venture Inc (G-6663)*
Simonson's Salon & Day Spa, Anoka *Also Called Simonson Venture Inc (G-228)*
Simper Lowell LLC 651 439-1100
102 2nd St N Stillwater (55082) **(G-9639)**
Simplexgrinnell LP 763 367-5000
5400 Nathan Ln N Ste 100 Minneapolis (55442) **(G-5676)**
Simplexgrinnell LP 320 253-8883
605 Franklin Ave NE Saint Cloud (56304) **(G-7427)**
Simplexgrinnell LP 320 253-8883
820 Sundial Dr Waite Park (56387) **(G-9838)**
Simpson Housing Services Inc 612 874-8683
2100 Pillsbury Ave S Minneapolis (55404) **(G-5677)**
Simtek Corp 952 831-7472
4550 W 77th St Ste 125 Minneapolis (55435) **(G-5678)**
Sinclair Broadcasting Group 651 646-2300
1640 Como Ave Saint Paul (55108) **(G-8960)**
Single-Ply Systems Inc 651 688-7554
909 Apollo Rd Saint Paul (55121) **(G-7905)**
Sioux Valley Canby Campus 507 223-7221
112 Saint Olaf Ave S Canby (56220) **(G-853)**
Sioux Valley Hospital, New Ulm *Also Called Allina Health System (G-6439)*
Sioux Valley Physician 507 283-4476
300 E Brown St Luverne (56156) **(G-3069)**
Sirius Computer Solutions Inc 952 470-6144
856 Kimberly Ln Chanhassen (55317) **(G-940)**
SIS Enterprises Inc 763 789-0956
6707 Shingle Creek Pkwy # 300 Minneapolis (55430) **(G-5679)**
Sister Knny Rhabilitation Inst, Minneapolis *Also Called Allina Health System (G-3726)*
Sisters of The Good Shepherd 651 484-0221
5100 Hodgson Rd Saint Paul (55126) **(G-8961)**
Sisu Medical Solutions LLC 218 529-7900
5 W 1st St Ste 200 Duluth (55802) **(G-1451)**
Sit Fixed Income Advisors II 612 332-3223
80 S 8th St Ste 3300 Minneapolis (55402) **(G-5680)**
Sit Investment Associates Inc (PA) 612 332-3223
80 S 8th St Ste 3300 Minneapolis (55402) **(G-5681)**
Sit Mutual Funds Inc 612 332-3223
3300 Ids Ctr Minneapolis (55402) **(G-5682)**
Site R47, South Saint Paul *Also Called BFI Waste Systems of North (G-9513)*
Site U71, Circle Pines *Also Called BFI Waste Systems of North (G-1003)*
Siwek Lumber & Millwork Inc 952 492-6666
350 Valley View Dr Jordan (55352) **(G-2810)**
Six Continents Hotels Inc 952 831-8000
5401 Green Valley Dr Minneapolis (55437) **(G-5683)**
Six Hundred Washington 612 331-9041
610 Washington Ave SE Minneapolis (55414) **(G-5684)**
614 Co 612 333-6128
81 S 9th St Ste 220 Minneapolis (55402) **(G-5685)**
675 Stinson LLC 612 238-3200
675 Stinson Blvd Ste 100 Minneapolis (55413) **(G-5686)**
Sjf Material Handling Inc 320 485-2824
211 Baker Ave W Winsted (55395) **(G-10165)**
Skamp Corp 952 937-8990
17270 Tilia Rdg Eden Prairie (55347) **(G-1779)**
Skarnes Inc 763 231-3600
2100 Niagara Ln N Minneapolis (55447) **(G-5687)**
Ske Support Services Inc 651 639-6559
100 9th Ave SW Saint Paul (55112) **(G-8962)**
Skemp Walk In Clinic 507 724-3353
701 N Sprague St Caledonia (55921) **(G-829)**
Skip's Home Center, Duluth *Also Called Rice Lake Lumber Inc (G-1437)*
Sky Blue Leasing Inc 320 692-2027
26392 State Highway 18 Brainerd (56401) **(G-586)**
Sky Media LLC 651 635-0100
121 5th Ave NW Ste 300 Saint Paul (55112) **(G-8963)**
Skybridge Marketing Group, Rockford *Also Called Argenbright Inc (G-7308)*
Skycom Inc 952 361-4248
9555 James Ave S Ste 215 Minneapolis (55431) **(G-5688)**
Skylight Corp 651 631-5000
3003 Snelling Ave N Saint Paul (55113) **(G-8964)**
Skyline Bowling Lanes Inc 218 727-8555
4894 Miller Trunk Hwy Duluth (55811) **(G-1452)**
Skyline Displays Midwest Inc 952 895-6000
11901 Portland Ave Ste A Burnsville (55337) **(G-798)**
Skyline Fire Protection Inc 763 425-4441
10900 73rd Ave N Ste 108 Osseo (55369) **(G-6664)**
Skyvision Inc 218 739-5231
1010 Frontier Dr Fergus Falls (56537) **(G-2119)**
Skyway YMCA, Saint Paul *Also Called YMCA of Greater St Paul (G-9178)*
Slayton Manor Care Center, Slayton *Also Called Beverly Enterprises - MN (G-9485)*
Sleep Inn, Rogers *Also Called Rogers Hospitality LLC (G-7341)*
Sleepy Eye Area Home Health 507 794-3594
1100 1st Ave S Sleepy Eye (56085) **(G-9500)**
Sleepy Eye Care Center, Sleepy Eye *Also Called Volunteers of America Care (G-9503)*
Sletta-Strom Memorial Hall, Fergus Falls *Also Called Luthern Brothern School Inc (G-2091)*
Slumberland Inc 952 888-6204
7801 Xerxes Ave S Minneapolis (55431) **(G-5689)**
Slumberland Inc 320 251-1024
2121 Frontage Rd N Waite Park (56387) **(G-9839)**

ALPHABETIC

SMA Elevator Construction Inc 763 295-4367
113 Chelsea Rd Monticello (55362) (G-6287)
Small Change Diaper Service 507 895-8625
62 N 3rd St La Crescent (55947) (G-2844)
Small Treasures Pre School, Welcome Also Called Martin County West School Dist (G-9959)
Smart Data Solutions Inc 651 690-3140
1120 Centre Pointe Dr 100 Saint Paul (55120) (G-7906)
Smart Legal Asstt, Minneapolis Also Called Minnesota Tobacco Document (G-5097)
Smarte Carte Inc (HQ) 651 429-3614
4455 White Bear Pkwy Saint Paul (55110) (G-8965)
Smdc, Duluth Also Called St Mary's Duluth Clinic Health (G-1473)
Smdc, Duluth Also Called Hermantown Clinic (G-1351)
Smdc Health System 218 246-8275
1025 10th Ave NE Deer River (56636) (G-1173)
Smdc Health System 218 786-3500
4212 Grand Ave Duluth (55807) (G-1453)
Smdc Health System (PA) 218 786-8364
400 E 3rd St Duluth (55805) (G-1454)
Smdc Health System 218 365-3151
300 W Conan St Ely (55731) (G-1915)
Smdc Health System 218 285-6222
2501 Keenan Dr International Falls (56649) (G-2730)
Smdc Medical Center 218 727-8762
502 E 2nd St Duluth (55805) (G-1455)
Smead Manufacturing Co Inc (PA) 651 437-4111
600 Smead Blvd Hastings (55033) (G-2406)
SMI & Hydraulics Inc 507 296-4551
401 Lone Tree St Porter (56280) (G-6894)
Smidt Sheet Metal Co Inc 507 378-4080
107 Highway 63 S Racine (55967) (G-6967)
Smile Center, Deerwood Also Called Rangerland Dental Group Inc (G-1179)
Smith Metal Products, Lindstrom Also Called Plastic Products Co Inc (G-2970)
Smith Micro Technologies Inc 651 482-8718
3435 Labore Rd Saint Paul (55110) (G-8966)
Smith Moreton International 952 820-4441
8400 Normandale Lake Blvd Minneapolis (55437) (G-5690)
Smith Schafer & Associates Ltd 507 288-3277
220 S Broadway Ste 102 Rochester (55904) (G-7255)
Smith Trucking Inc 507 376-5080
1451 Joosten Rd Worthington (56187) (G-10194)
Smith's Mill Implement Inc 507 234-5191
63065 206th St Janesville (56048) (G-2803)
Smith's Winter Products 763 493-3332
10960 County Road 81 Osseo (55369) (G-6665)
Smith, David O MD, Minneapolis Also Called Suburban Plastic Surgery (G-5761)
Smiths Medical Asd Inc 651 628-7030
3350 Granada Ave N Ste 100 Saint Paul (55128) (G-9274)
Smmpa, Rochester Also Called Southern Minnesota Municipal (G-7259)
Smsc, Prior Lake Also Called Dakota Sport & Fitness (G-6931)
Smsc Gaming Enterprise (HQ) 952 445-6000
2400 Mystic Lake Blvd Prior Lake (55372) (G-6955)
Smsc Gaming Enterprise 952 445-8982
2354 Sioux Trl NW Prior Lake (55372) (G-6956)
Smurfit-Stone Container 507 288-2305
4165 Hwy 14 W Rochester (55901) (G-7256)
Smurfit-Stone Container Corp 612 789-2485
50 37th Ave NE Minneapolis (55421) (G-5691)
Smurfit-Stone Container Corp 320 252-3660
655 41st Ave N Saint Cloud (56303) (G-7594)
Smw Federal Credit Union, Saint Paul Also Called Sheet Metal Worker Federal (G-8950)
Smyth Co's Inc (HQ) 651 646-4544
1085 Snelling Ave N Saint Paul (55108) (G-8967)
SNG Construction Inc 763 795-8496
8383 Sunset Rd NE Minneapolis (55432) (G-3603)
Snips of Eden Prairie Inc 952 941-1495
5147 W 98th St Minneapolis (55437) (G-5692)
Snyder's Drug Stores Inc 763 427-8111
12455 Champlin Dr Champlin (55316) (G-901)
Snyder's Drug Stores Inc 507 345-1002
602 S Front St Mankato (56001) (G-3198)
So MN Regional Service 651 222-5863
166 4th St E Ste 200 Saint Paul (55101) (G-8968)
Soap Transcription Services 612 706-1588
2855 Anthony Ln S Ste 110 Minneapolis (55418) (G-5693)
Sobriety High Foundation 651 773-8378
2233 University Ave W # 357 Saint Paul (55114) (G-8969)
Soccer Blast Minnesota 952 895-1962
3601 W 145th St Burnsville (55306) (G-799)
Social Adjsment Prog For SE As, Saint Paul Also Called Amherst H Wilder Foundation (G-8044)
Society For Preservation 507 452-4425
163 E Howard St Winona (55987) (G-10128)
Society of Corporate 952 405-7925
6500 Barrie Rd Ste 250 Minneapolis (55435) (G-5694)
Socon Construction Inc 763 754-4027
11306 Ibis St NW Minneapolis (55433) (G-3604)
Soderberg Inc (HQ) 651 291-1400
230 Eva St Saint Paul (55107) (G-8970)
Sodexo Management Inc 507 333-6772
925 Parshall St Faribault (55021) (G-2030)
Soft Touch Car Care of St 320 253-4204
3104 W Division St Ste 1 Saint Cloud (56301) (G-7595)
Softbrands Inc (PA) 612 851-1500
800 Lasalle Ave Ste 2100 Minneapolis (55402) (G-5695)
Softbrands Manufacturing Inc 612 851-1500
800 Lasalle Ave Ste 2100 Minneapolis (55402) (G-5696)
Solbrekk Inc 763 404-4712
1000 Boone Ave N Ste 650 Golden Valley (55427) (G-2246)
Solid Logic Computer Solutions 952 949-0140
14867 Boulder Pointe Rd Eden Prairie (55347) (G-1780)
Solid Waste & Recycling, Minneapolis Also Called City of Minneapolis (G-4089)
Solimar Wellness Spa 651 686-6686
1121 Town Centre Dr # 105 Saint Paul (55123) (G-7907)
Solstice Corp 218 729-5014
5072 Jennifer Cir Duluth (55811) (G-1456)
Solutia Consulting Inc 651 351-0123
1241 Amundson Cir Stillwater (55082) (G-9640)
Solutran, Minneapolis Also Called United Check Clearing Corp (G-5908)
Solutran Inc 763 559-2225
3600 Holly Ln N Ste 60 Minneapolis (55447) (G-5697)
Someplace Safe 320 589-3208
1005 Pebble Lake Rd # 108 Fergus Falls (56537) (G-2120)
Somerset Hospitality LLC 952 894-6124
4601 Highway 13 W Savage (55378) (G-9407)
Son Sheim Music School, Minneapolis Also Called Sondance Studio (G-3605)
Son-D-Farms Inc 507 483-2245
25751 State Highway 91 Adrian (56110) (G-5)
Sondance Studio 763 784-2920
8301 Sunset Rd NE Ste 6 Minneapolis (55432) (G-3605)
Sonny Peterson Trucking Inc 320 547-2489
Hwy 28 N Swanville (56382) (G-9659)
Sonor Hotel Corp 507 288-1844
1630 S Broadway Rochester (55904) (G-7257)
Sons of Norway 612 827-3611
1455 W Lake St Fl 2 Minneapolis (55408) (G-5698)
Sons of Norway Foundation 612 827-3611
1455 W Lake St Fl 2 Minneapolis (55408) (G-5699)
Soo Line Corp (PA) 612 337-5333
501 Marquette Ave # 1700 Minneapolis (55402) (G-5700)
SOO Line Railroad Co Inc 320 634-3012
20 15th St NE Glenwood (56334) (G-2233)
SOO Line Railroad Co Inc (HQ) 800 766-4357
501 Marquette Ave # 1500 Minneapolis (55402) (G-5701)
SOO Line Railroad Co Inc 651 646-6044
1000 Shop Rd Saint Paul (55106) (G-8971)
Sopheon Corp (PA) 952 851-7555
3050 Metro Dr Ste 200 Minneapolis (55425) (G-5702)
Sorensen & Sorensen Painting 507 289-5368
2515 50th Ave SE Rochester (55904) (G-7258)
SOS Janitorial Inc 763 560-9611
6741 Edgewood Ave N Minneapolis (55428) (G-5703)
Soudan Undgrd Mine State Pk, Soudan Also Called Minnesota Department of (G-9504)
Source Fluid Power Inc 952 448-4440
331 Lake Hazeltine Dr Chaska (55318) (G-980)
Source One Sales & Marketing 952 829-0833
6300 W Old Shakopee Rd Minneapolis (55438) (G-5704)
South Bend Township Fire Dept 507 345-4863
306 McKinzie St S Mankato (56001) (G-3199)
South Cedar Greenhouses, Farmington Also Called Pinehurst Development Inc (G-2057)
South Central Grain & Energy 507 426-8263
64908 State Hwy 4 Fairfax (55332) (G-1955)
South Central Human Relations 507 451-2630
610 Florence Ave Owatonna (55060) (G-6737)
South Central Surgical Center 507 235-3939
717 S State St Ste 1000 Fairmont (56031) (G-1981)
South Lake Pediatrics (PA) 952 401-8300
17705 Hutchins Dr Ste 101 Hopkins (55345) (G-2635)
South Metro Human Services 651 221-9880
796 Capitol Hts Saint Paul (55103) (G-8972)
South Metro Human Services (PA) 651 291-1979
400 Sibley St Ste 500 Saint Paul (55101) (G-8973)
South Shore Care Center, Worthington Also Called Atchison Enterprises Inc (G-10178)
South Side Electric Inc 952 888-5500
9201 E Bloomington Fwy Ste X Bloomington (55420) (G-517)
Southdale Dental Associates 952 896-1111
7373 France Ave S Ste 600 Minneapolis (55435) (G-5705)
Southdale Family Practice 952 927-4235
7428 W Shore Dr Minneapolis (55435) (G-5706)
Southdale Ob Gyn Consultants 952 435-9505
305 E Ncltte Blvd Ste 393 Burnsville (55337) (G-800)
Southdale Obstetric 952 920-7001
3625 W 65th St Ste 100 Minneapolis (55435) (G-5707)
Southdale Pediatrics Assocs 952 898-5900
14050 Nicollet Ave Ste 204 Burnsville (55337) (G-801)
Southdale Pediatrics Assocs (PA) 952 831-4454
3955 Parklawn Ave Ste 120 Minneapolis (55435) (G-5708)
Southdale YMCA, Minneapolis Also Called Young Men's Chritn Assoc of (G-6104)
Southeast Area YMCA, Saint Paul Also Called YMCA of Greater St Paul (G-9292)
Southeast Asian Health Svcs 651 222-2889
421 Dale St N Ste B Saint Paul (55103) (G-8974)
Southern Hospitality Inc 952 831-9595
5120 American Blvd W Minneapolis (55437) (G-5709)
Southern Lighting Inc 952 890-8977
12550 W Frontage Rd Burnsville (55337) (G-802)
Southern Minnesota Independent 507 345-7139
709 S Front St Ste 7 Mankato (56001) (G-3200)
Southern Minnesota Municipal 507 285-0478
500 1st Ave SW Rochester (55902) (G-7259)
Southern Minnesota Oral 507 625-9330
1990 Premier Dr Mankato (56001) (G-3201)
Southern Minnesota Wing, South Saint Paul Also Called Commemorative Air Force (G-9523)
Southhill Dental 651 439-9400
2850 Curve Crest Blvd W # 200 Stillwater (55082) (G-9641)
Southpark Lanes & Lounge, Owatonna Also Called Owatonna Fairlanes Corp (G-6728)
Southpoint Federal Credit 877 794-6712
920 Main St E Sleepy Eye (56085) (G-9501)
Southside Community Health 612 822-3186
4730 Chicago Ave Ste 1 Minneapolis (55407) (G-5710)
Southside Family Nurturing Ctr 612 721-2762
2448 18th Ave S Minneapolis (55404) (G-5711)
Southtown Freeway Toyota Inc 952 888-5581
1750 W 80th St Minneapolis (55431) (G-5712)
Southview Acres Health Care 651 451-1821
2000 Oakdale Ave Saint Paul (55118) (G-7908)
Southview Country Club 651 451-6856
239 Mendota Rd E Saint Paul (55118) (G-7909)
Southwest Casino & Hotel Corp (HQ) 952 853-9990
2001 Killebrew Dr Ste 350 Minneapolis (55425) (G-5713)
Southwest Coaches Inc 507 532-4043
2660 State Highway 23 Marshall (56258) (G-3328)
Southwest MN Pic 507 537-6987
607 W Main St Marshall (56258) (G-3329)
Southwest YMCA Child Care, Saint Paul Also Called YMCA of Greater Saint Paul (G-7952)

ALPHABETIC

Southwestern Mental Health Ctr (PA) 507 283-9511
216 E Luverne St Luverne (56156) ***(G-3070)***
Southwestern Mental Health Ctr 507 376-4141
1024 7th Ave Worthington (56187) ***(G-10195)***
Southwestern Minnesota 507 376-4195
1106 3rd Ave Worthington (56187) ***(G-10196)***
Southwestern Minnesota Radio 507 452-4000
752 Bluffview Cir Winona (55987) ***(G-10129)***
Southwind Estates, Saint Paul *Also Called Asi Great Falls Inc* ***(G-8067)***
Sovran Inc 651 686-0515
2915 Commers Dr Ste 100 Eagan (55121) ***(G-1552)***
Sowles Co (PA) 651 287-9700
3045 Highway 13 Ste 100 Saint Paul (55121) ***(G-7910)***
Soymor Biodiesel LLC 507 448-0124
15200 780th Ave Albert Lea (56007) ***(G-66)***
Sp Hotels LLC 651 291-8800
411 Minnesota St Saint Paul (55101) ***(G-8975)***
Space Aliens Grill & Bar 320 259-7670
700 2nd St S Waite Park (56387) ***(G-9840)***
Space150 LLC 612 332-6458
212 3rd Ave N Ste 150 Minneapolis (55401) ***(G-5714)***
Spalon Montage, Minneapolis *Also Called Elizabeth Charles Corp* ***(G-4340)***
Spalon Montage Chanhassen, Chanhassen *Also Called Elizabeth Charles Corp* ***(G-922)***
Spalon Montage Woodbury, Saint Paul *Also Called Elizabeth Charles Corp* ***(G-9212)***
Spanier Bus Service Inc 320 251-3313
1310 Sun Ridge Dr Saint Cloud (56301) ***(G-7596)***
Spanlink Communications Inc 763 971-2000
605 Highway 169 N Ste 900 Minneapolis (55441) ***(G-5715)***
Spare Times Lanes & Lounge 507 477-3492
18 2nd St NE Hayfield (55940) ***(G-2426)***
Spartan Commercial Group, Saint Paul *Also Called Hohenwald Properties* ***(G-9232)***
Spartan Promotional Group Inc 651 735-1333
711 Hale Ave N Saint Paul (55128) ***(G-9275)***
Spc Communications Inc 952 912-2800
5775 W Old Shakopee Rd Ste 160 Minneapolis (55437) ***(G-5716)***
Speak Easy Restaurant 218 844-1326
1100 N Shore Dr Detroit Lakes (56501) ***(G-1216)***
Special School District No 1 .....612 668-1420
5034 Oliver Ave N Minneapolis (55430) ***(G-5717)***
Special Waste Disposal Inc, Minneapolis *Also Called Stericycle Specialty Waste* ***(G-3608)***
Specialized Care Services, Hopkins *Also Called Unitedhealth Group Inc* ***(G-2651)***
Specialty Contracting Services 763 424-4100
9702 85th Ave N Osseo (55369) ***(G-6666)***
Specialty Systems Engineering, Montevideo *Also Called Specsys Inc* ***(G-6260)***
Specsys Inc 320 269-3227
121 N 1st St Ste 201 Montevideo (56265) ***(G-6260)***
Spectro Alloys Corp 651 437-2815
13220 Doyle Path E Rosemount (55068) ***(G-7375)***
Spectrum Community Health 507 332-7471
211 1st Ave NW Ste 4 Faribault (55021) ***(G-2031)***
Spectrum Community Health Inc 218 326-4202
412 N Pokegama Ave Ste 1 Grand Rapids (55744) ***(G-2308)***
Spectrum Community Health Inc 507 282-8052
1831 24th St NW Ste B Rochester (55901) ***(G-7260)***
Spectrum Community Health Inc 320 252-9640
1225 E Division St Saint Cloud (56304) ***(G-7428)***
Spectrum Community Health Inc 320 235-5684
1415 1st St S Ste 1C Willmar (56201) ***(G-10045)***
Spectrum Community Mental Hlth, Minneapolis *Also Called Resource Inc* ***(G-5527)***
Spectrum Electronics & Distrg, Baxter *Also Called J Thomas & Associates* ***(G-331)***
Spectrum Lanes Bowling Alley 763 553-0333
3050 Quinwood Ln N Minneapolis (55441) ***(G-5718)***
Spectrum Property Management 952 853-0036
7800 Metro Pkwy Ste 112 Minneapolis (55425) ***(G-5719)***
Spectrum Solutions Inc (PA) 952 835-8338
7801 E Bush Lake Rd # 210 Minneapolis (55439) ***(G-5720)***
Spectrum Solutions Inc 651 634-1800
2920 Centre Pointe Dr Saint Paul (55113) ***(G-8976)***
Speedway Superamerica LLC 651 774-7270
390 Maryland Ave E Saint Paul (55130) ***(G-8977)***
SPI Group Inc 218 283-9397
1919 Main Ave International Falls (56649) ***(G-2731)***
Spineology Inc 651 256-8500
7800 3rd St N Ste 600 Saint Paul (55128) ***(G-9276)***
Spire Federal Credit Union 651 215-3500
2025 Larpenteur Ave W Saint Paul (55113) ***(G-8978)***
Spirit Mountain Travel Lodge 218 628-3691
5910 Fremont St Duluth (55807) ***(G-1457)***
Spl Integrated Solutions, Saint Paul *Also Called AVI-Spl Inc* ***(G-8081)***
Splatball Inc 612 378-0385
2412 University Ave SE # 2 Minneapolis (55414) ***(G-5721)***
Split Rock Lighthouse, Two Harbors *Also Called Historical Society of MN* ***(G-9708)***
Sports & Orthopaedic 952 946-9777
8100 W 78th St Ste 225 Minneapolis (55439) ***(G-5722)***
Sportsman's Lodge, Baudette *Also Called J & L Hennum Inc* ***(G-315)***
Spray Control Systems Inc 507 583-2112
500 Minimizer Way Blooming Prairie (55917) ***(G-478)***
Spriggs Plumbing & Heating Inc 651 224-5616
124 Eva St Saint Paul (55107) ***(G-8979)***
Spring Hill Golf Club 952 473-1500
725 Spring Hill Rd Wayzata (55391) ***(G-9940)***
Spring Hill Golf Club 952 473-1500
725 County Road 6 Wayzata (55391) ***(G-9941)***
Spring Lake Park Dental Ctr, Minneapolis *Also Called Healthpartners Inc* ***(G-3485)***
Spring Lake Park Lions Club 763 784-9179
8433 Center Dr NE Minneapolis (55432) ***(G-3606)***
Spring Prairie Hutterian 218 498-0222
6189 170th St N Hawley (56549) ***(G-2423)***
Spring Valley Area Ambulance 507 346-7414
201 S Broadway St Spring Valley (55975) ***(G-9570)***
Spring Valley Health Mart, Rochester *Also Called Mc Be Co* ***(G-7178)***
Springfield Medical Center 507 723-6201
625 N Jackson Ave Springfield (56087) ***(G-9575)***
Springhill Suites, Minneapolis *Also Called CSM Corp of Minnesota* ***(G-4192)***
Sprint, Minneapolis *Also Called Choice Communications Inc* ***(G-4068)***
Sprint Communications Co LP 507 454-8386
166 W 3rd St Winona (55987) ***(G-10130)***
Sprint Lake Park Alliance 763 784-9179
8433 Center Dr NE Minneapolis (55432) ***(G-3607)***
Sprint Spectrum LP 507 358-4727
4400 W Frontage Rd NW Rochester (55901) ***(G-7261)***
Spruce Co 952 888-1639
9311 Bryant Ave S Minneapolis (55420) ***(G-5723)***
SPS Commerce Inc 612 435-9400
333 S 7th St Ste 1000 Minneapolis (55402) ***(G-5724)***
Spss Inc 507 287-2835
4151 Hwy 52 N Ste 300 Rochester (55901) ***(G-7262)***
Spur Inc 651 454-2330
2750 Sibley Memorial Hwy Saint Paul (55121) ***(G-7911)***
Sr Mechanical Inc 952 933-6933
7320 Oxford St Ste 200 Saint Louis Park (55426) ***(G-7669)***
SRF Consulting Group Inc 763 475-0010
1 Carlson Pkwy N Ste 150 Minneapolis (55447) ***(G-5725)***
Ssab Enterprises LLC 651 631-9031
2500 County Road B W Saint Paul (55113) ***(G-8980)***
Ssb LLC 952 831-7900
5150 American Blvd W Bloomington (55437) ***(G-518)***
SSIT North America Inc 952 857-1600
3900 80th Ave N Ste 1420 Minneapolis (55443) ***(G-5726)***
St Andrew Lutheran Church 952 937-2776
13600 Technology Dr Eden Prairie (55344) ***(G-1781)***
St Ann's Home 218 727-8831
330 E 3rd St Apt 532 Duluth (55805) ***(G-1458)***
St Anthony Health Center 612 788-9673
3700 Foss Rd Minneapolis (55421) ***(G-6131)***
St Anthony Park Home Inc 651 646-7486
2237 Commonwealth Ave Saint Paul (55108) ***(G-8981)***
St Benedict's Senior Community 320 252-0010
1810 Minnesota Blvd # 228 Saint Cloud (56304) ***(G-7441)***
St Bernard Grade School, Saint Paul *Also Called Church of St Bernard* ***(G-8200)***
St Charles Golf Course, Saint Charles *Also Called Maple Valley Golf & Country* ***(G-7405)***
St Cloud Area Family YMCA 320 253-2664
1530 Northway Dr Saint Cloud (56303) ***(G-7597)***
St Cloud Children's Home, Fergus Falls *Also Called Catholic Charities of The* ***(G-2066)***
ST CLOUD CHILDREN'S HOME, Saint Cloud *Also Called Catholic Charities of The* ***(G-7473)***
St Cloud Children's Home Sch, Saint Cloud *Also Called Catholic Charities of The* ***(G-7474)***
St Cloud Denovo 320 251-1055
11 7th Ave N Ste 3 Saint Cloud (56303) ***(G-7598)***
St Cloud Ear, Nose, Throat 320 252-0233
1528 Northway Dr Saint Cloud (56303) ***(G-7599)***
St Cloud Federal Employees 320 252-2634
3030 1st St S Saint Cloud (56301) ***(G-7600)***
St Cloud Hospital, Saint Cloud *Also Called Entocrinology Clinic* ***(G-7504)***
St Cloud Hospital 320 656-7020
1406 6th Ave N Saint Cloud (56303) ***(G-7601)***
St Cloud Hospital (HQ) 320 251-2700
1406 6th Ave N Saint Cloud (56303) ***(G-7602)***
St Cloud Hospital 320 251-2700
48 29th Ave N Ste 15 Saint Cloud (56303) ***(G-7603)***
St Cloud Hospital 320 259-9149
1485 10th Ave NE Sauk Rapids (56379) ***(G-9376)***
St Cloud Medical Group (PA) 320 202-8949
251 County Road 120 Saint Cloud (56303) ***(G-7604)***
St Cloud Refrigeration Inc 320 251-6861
604 Lincoln Ave NE Saint Cloud (56304) ***(G-7429)***
St Cloud Subaru 320 258-0163
4110 W Division St Saint Cloud (56301) ***(G-7605)***
St Cloud Suite Hotel Inc 320 654-1661
404 W Saint Germain St Saint Cloud (56301) ***(G-7606)***
St Cloud Surgical Center 320 251-8385
1526 Northway Dr Saint Cloud (56303) ***(G-7607)***
St Cloud Truck Sales Inc 320 251-0931
701 15th Ave SE Saint Cloud (56304) ***(G-7442)***
ST Cotter Turbine Services Inc 763 263-5611
16804 170th St SE Big Lake (55309) ***(G-457)***
St Croix Boat & Packet Inc 651 430-1234
301 2nd St S Stillwater (55082) ***(G-9642)***
St Croix Orthopaedics 651 439-8807
1991 Northwestern Ave S Stillwater (55082) ***(G-9643)***
St Croix Preservation Co Inc 651 439-6000
101 Water St S Stillwater (55082) ***(G-9644)***
St Croix State Park, Hinckley *Also Called Minnesota Department of* ***(G-2487)***
St Croix Valley Hardwoods Inc 651 407-2800
4250 Otter Lake Rd Saint Paul (55110) ***(G-8982)***
St Croix Valley Hardwoods Inc (PA) 651 407-2800
4250 Otter Lake Rd Saint Paul (55110) ***(G-8983)***
St David's Center Child 952 939-0396
3395 Plymouth Rd Hopkins (55305) ***(G-2636)***
St Francis Health Services of 218 727-8801
3111 Church Pl Duluth (55811) ***(G-1459)***
St Francis Health Services of (PA) 320 589-2004
801 Nevada Ave Ste 100 Morris (56267) ***(G-6378)***
St Francis Medical Center 218 643-3000
2400 St Francis Dr Breckenridge (56520) ***(G-601)***
St Francis Regional Med Ctr, Shakopee *Also Called Benedictine Health System* ***(G-9420)***
St Francis Regional Medical 952 403-3000
1455 Saint Francis Ave Shakopee (55379) ***(G-9476)***
St Francis Youth Hockey Assn 763 913-7395
4826 232nd Ave NW Saint Francis (55070) ***(G-7637)***
St Gabriel's Hospital, Little Falls *Also Called Unity Family Health Care* ***(G-3021)***
St Germain's Cabinet Inc 218 624-1234
5741 Old Highway 61 Duluth (55810) ***(G-1460)***
St Germain's Glass Inc 218 628-0221
212 N 40th Ave W Duluth (55807) ***(G-1461)***
St Gertrude's Health Center 952 233-4400
1850 Sarazin St Ofc OFC Shakopee (55379) ***(G-9477)***
St Hilaire Seed Co Inc 218 964-5407
415 Hwy 32 S Saint Hilaire (56754) ***(G-7640)***
St Hilaire Supply Co 218 964-5222
211 Bdway Way Saint Hilaire (56754) ***(G-7641)***
St Isidore Help Center, Plainview *Also Called Benedictine Health System* ***(G-6838)***

(PA)=Parent Co (HQ)=Headquarters (DH)=Div Headquarters
2011 Harris Minnesota Services Directory
© Harris InfoSource 1-866-281-6415
621

A L P H A B E T I C

St James Bus Service Inc 507 375-4181
910 Weston Ave Saint James (56081) ***(G-7646)***
St James Church Inc 651 293-3945
749 Juno Ave Saint Paul (55102) ***(G-8984)***
St James Home of Duluth 218 728-7500
4321 Allendale Ave Duluth (55803) ***(G-1462)***
St James Medical Center-Mayo 507 375-3261
1101 Moulton And Parsons Dr Saint James (56081) ***(G-7647)***
St John Lutheran Home Inc 507 723-3200
201 S County Road 5 Springfield (56087) ***(G-9576)***
St Johns Lutheran Home 507 373-8226
901 Luther Pl Albert Lea (56007) ***(G-67)***
St Joseph Equipment Inc 952 445-5400
6340 Highway 101 E Shakopee (55379) ***(G-9478)***
St Joseph's Area Health Svcs 218 732-3311
600 Pleasant Ave S Park Rapids (56470) ***(G-6762)***
St Joseph's Home For Children, Minneapolis *Also Called Catholic Charities of The* ***(G-4030)***
St Joseph's Medical Center 218 829-2861
523 N 3rd St Brainerd (56401) ***(G-587)***
St Jude Medical 651 523-6900
1410 Energy Park Dr Saint Paul (55108) ***(G-8985)***
St Jude Medical SC Inc 651 483-2000
1 Lillehei Plz Saint Paul (55117) ***(G-8986)***
St Louis County Public Works 218 742-9804
7823 Highway 135 Virginia (55792) ***(G-9756)***
St Louis Park Plaza, Minneapolis *Also Called Beverly Enterprises - MN* ***(G-3894)***
St Louis Park Plaza Nursing HM, Minneapolis *Also Called Professional Physical Therapy* ***(G-5421)***
St Louis Park Transportation 952 591-1538
2211 Edgewood Ave S Minneapolis (55426) ***(G-5727)***
St Louis, County of Inc 218 720-1500
2501 Rice Lake Rd Duluth (55811) ***(G-1463)***
St Louis, County of Inc 218 726-2000
320 W 2nd St Ste 505 Duluth (55802) ***(G-1464)***
St Louis, County of Inc 218 726-2920
4848 Lackland St Duluth (55811) ***(G-1465)***
St Louis, County of Inc 218 349-8970
5735 Old Miller Trunk Hwy Duluth (55811) ***(G-1466)***
St Lucas Care Center 507 332-5100
500 1st St SE Faribault (55021) ***(G-2032)***
St Luke's Clinics 218 249-5555
915 E 1st St Duluth (55805) ***(G-1467)***
St Luke's Hospital of Duluth 218 249-8800
1400 Woodland Ave Duluth (55803) ***(G-1468)***
St Luke's Hospital of Duluth (PA) 218 726-5555
915 E 1st St Duluth (55805) ***(G-1469)***
St Luke's Hospital of Duluth 218 249-4600
4884 Miller Trunk Hwy Duluth (55811) ***(G-1470)***
St Luke's Hospital of Duluth 218 249-5564
915 E 1st St Fl 2 Duluth (55805) ***(G-1471)***
St Luke's Hospital of Duluth 218 362-7100
1120 E 34th St Hibbing (55746) ***(G-2476)***
St Luke's Internal Medicine 218 249-7960
1001 E Superior St # 101 Duluth (55802) ***(G-1472)***
St Luke's Lutheran Care Center 507 526-2184
1219 S Ramsey St Blue Earth (56013) ***(G-537)***
St Maries Gopher News, Minneapolis *Also Called Gopher News Co* ***(G-4542)***
St Mark's Lutheran Home Inc 507 437-4594
400 15th Ave SW Austin (55912) ***(G-288)***
St Mary's Care Center, Winsted *Also Called Living Services Foundation* ***(G-10162)***
St Mary's Duluth Clinic Health (DH) 218 786-4000
400 E 3rd St Duluth (55805) ***(G-1473)***
St Mary's Home, Saint Paul *Also Called Franciscan Health Community* ***(G-8393)***
St Mary's Medical Center (DH) 218 786-4000
407 E 3rd St Duluth (55805) ***(G-1474)***
St Mary's Regional Health Ctr (DH) 218 847-5611
1027 Washington Ave Detroit Lakes (56501) ***(G-1217)***
St Mary's Regional Health Ctr 218 847-5611
1040 Lincoln Ave Detroit Lakes (56501) ***(G-1218)***
St Mary's School 507 794-6141
104 Saint Marys St NW Sleepy Eye (56085) ***(G-9502)***
St Matthews Pre-School, Saint Paul *Also Called Church of St Matthew* ***(G-8201)***
St Michael Veterinary Clinic 763 497-2424
312 Central Ave E Saint Michael (55376) ***(G-7682)***
St Michael's Health & Rehab 218 748-7800
1201 8th St S Virginia (55792) ***(G-9757)***
St Michaels Lutheran Church 952 831-5276
9201 Normandale Blvd Minneapolis (55437) ***(G-5728)***
St Olaf Retirement Center Inc 612 522-6561
2912 Fremont Ave N Minneapolis (55411) ***(G-5729)***
St Paul Cardiology 651 232-4320
17 Exchange St W Ste 750 Saint Paul (55102) ***(G-8987)***
St Paul Clinic, Saint Paul *Also Called Healthpartners Inc* ***(G-8467)***
St Paul Customer Service Ctr, Saint Paul *Also Called Weyerhaeuser Co* ***(G-9152)***
St Paul Eye Clinic 651 641-0457
393 Dunlap St N Ste 861 Saint Paul (55104) ***(G-8988)***
St Paul Fire & Marine Insce 952 893-5602
3600 W 80th St Minneapolis (55431) ***(G-5730)***
St Paul Fire & Marine Insce 651 310-5000
408 Saint Peter St Ste 300 Saint Paul (55102) ***(G-8989)***
St Paul Fire & Marine Insce (HQ) 651 221-7911
385 Washington St Saint Paul (55102) ***(G-8990)***
St Paul Guardian Insurance Co 651 221-7911
385 Washington St Saint Paul (55102) ***(G-8991)***
St Paul Harley Davidson Inc 651 738-2168
2899 Hudson Rd Saint Paul (55128) ***(G-9277)***
St Paul Heart Clinic (PA) 651 292-0616
225 Smith Ave N Ste 500 Saint Paul (55102) ***(G-8992)***
St Paul Heart Clinic 651 779-9449
1600 Saint Johns Blvd Ste 200 Saint Paul (55109) ***(G-8993)***
St Paul Hotel, Saint Paul *Also Called 3608 Park Street LLC* ***(G-9043)***
St Paul Linoleum & Carpet Co 651 686-7770
2956 Center Ct Eagan (55121) ***(G-1553)***
St Paul Mercury Insurance Co 651 221-7911
385 Washington St Saint Paul (55102) ***(G-8994)***
St Paul Offc, Saint Paul *Also Called Catholic Charities of The* ***(G-8176)***
St Paul Plumbers Joint 651 846-1389
235 Marshall Ave Saint Paul (55102) ***(G-8995)***
St Paul Plumbing & Heating Co 651 228-9200
640 Grand Ave Saint Paul (55105) ***(G-8996)***
St Paul Postal Employees 651 770-7000
2401 McKnight Rd N Saint Paul (55109) ***(G-8997)***
St Paul Public School 651 436-5243
1553 Stagecoach Trl S Afton (55001) ***(G-10)***
St Paul Radiology (PA) 651 292-2000
166 4th St E Ste 100 Saint Paul (55101) ***(G-8998)***
St Paul Radiology 651 297-6504
250 Thompson St Saint Paul (55102) ***(G-8999)***
St Paul Youth Services 651 771-1301
2100 Wilson Ave Saint Paul (55119) ***(G-9000)***
St Paul's Childhood Center 651 224-4749
900 Summit Ave Saint Paul (55105) ***(G-9001)***
St Pauls Saints Baseball Club 651 644-6659
1771 Energy Park Dr Saint Paul (55108) ***(G-9002)***
St Peter, City of Inc 507 931-7354
1900 Sunrise Dr Saint Peter (56082) ***(G-9314)***
St Raphels Hlth Rhbltation Ctr, Eveleth *Also Called Benedictine Health System* ***(G-1928)***
St Stephen's Human Services 612 874-0311
2211 Clinton Ave Minneapolis (55404) ***(G-5731)***
St Teresa Campus Schools 507 453-5555
360 Vila St Ste A Winona (55987) ***(G-10131)***
St Therese Apartments Inc 763 531-5400
8008 Bass Lake Rd Minneapolis (55428) ***(G-5732)***
St Therese Home Inc 763 537-4503
8000 Bass Lake Rd Minneapolis (55428) ***(G-5733)***
St Therese South West Inc 952 933-3333
1011 Feltl Ct Apt 905 Hopkins (55343) ***(G-2637)***
St Williams Nursing Home Inc 218 338-4671
212 W Soo St Parkers Prairie (56361) ***(G-6767)***
Stacy's Nursery Inc 320 235-6010
2305 Highway 12 E Willmar (56201) ***(G-10046)***
Stagecoach Express Inc 651 437-8138
7965 190th St E Hastings (55033) ***(G-2407)***
Staging Concepts Inc 763 533-2094
7008 Northland Dr N # 150 Minneapolis (55428) ***(G-5734)***
Stahl Construction Co 952 931-9300
5755 Wayzata Blvd Minneapolis (55416) ***(G-5735)***
Stahlke Bus Service Inc 763 972-3991
5280 County Line Rd SE Delano (55328) ***(G-1183)***
Stallion Door & Millwork, Saint Cloud *Also Called Trimpac Inc* ***(G-7621)***
Stan Koch & Sons Trucking Inc (PA) 763 302-5400
4200 Dahlberg Dr Ste 100 Minneapolis (55422) ***(G-5736)***
Stan Koch & Sons Trucking Inc 651 999-8500
2230 Energy Park Dr Saint Paul (55108) ***(G-9003)***
Standard Parking Corp 612 371-0938
50 S 6th St Ste 1320 Minneapolis (55402) ***(G-5737)***
Standard Water Control Systems 763 537-4849
5337 Lakeland Ave N Minneapolis (55429) ***(G-5738)***
Stanford Medical Ctr Jackson, Jackson *Also Called City of Jackson* ***(G-2787)***
Stanley Consultants Inc 952 546-3669
5775 Wayzata Blvd Ste 300 Minneapolis (55416) ***(G-5739)***
Stanley Security Solutions Inc 952 894-3830
537 Phalen Blvd Saint Paul (55130) ***(G-9004)***
Stanley Steamer Carpet Clg, Eden Prairie *Also Called A S T Inc* ***(G-1582)***
Star Limousine Service 507 281-0969
420 1st Ave NW Ste A Rochester (55901) ***(G-7263)***
Star Tribune Media Co LLC 612 673-7100
800 N 1st St Minneapolis (55401) ***(G-5740)***
Starchtech Inc (PA) 763 545-5400
720 Florida Ave S Minneapolis (55426) ***(G-5741)***
Stardust Lanes, Minneapolis *Also Called Lane Memory* ***(G-4839)***
Starmark Northwest Management 612 673-1200
600 1st Ave N Ste SKY Minneapolis (55403) ***(G-5742)***
Starmark Northwest Management 952 944-2434
6701 W 78th St Minneapolis (55439) ***(G-5743)***
Starry Construction Co Inc 320 762-7289
6325 County Road 87 SW Alexandria (56308) ***(G-123)***
Startech Computing Inc 651 385-0607
1755 Old West Main St Red Wing (55066) ***(G-7006)***
Starwood Hotels & Resorts 612 331-1900
1330 Industrial Blvd NE Minneapolis (55413) ***(G-5744)***
Starwood Hotels & Resorts 612 215-3720
821 Marquette Ave Minneapolis (55402) ***(G-5745)***
State Bank & Trust 218 233-3107
1333 8th St S Moorhead (56560) ***(G-6342)***
State Bank of Belle Plaine 952 873-2296
201 W Main St Belle Plaine (56011) ***(G-370)***
State Bank of Cokato 320 286-2146
101 3rd St SE Cokato (55321) ***(G-1080)***
State Bank of Delano 763 972-2935
1300 Babcock Blvd E Delano (55328) ***(G-1184)***
State Bank of Faribault 507 332-7401
428 Central Ave N Faribault (55021) ***(G-2033)***
State Bank of New Prague 952 758-4491
1101 1st St SE New Prague (56071) ***(G-6424)***
State Bank of Park Rapids 218 732-3366
200 1st St E Park Rapids (56470) ***(G-6763)***
State Bank of Tower Inc 218 753-6100
415 Main St Tower (55790) ***(G-9688)***
State Farm Mutual Automobile 952 895-3900
12281 Nicollet Ave Burnsville (55337) ***(G-803)***
State Mechanical Inc 651 463-8220
5050 220th St W Farmington (55024) ***(G-2060)***
Staybridge Suites, Bloomington *Also Called Ssb LLC* ***(G-518)***
Staybridge Suites, Eagan *Also Called Sbse LLC* ***(G-1549)***
Staybridge Suites, Maple Grove *Also Called Forstrom & Torgerson Ssnw LLC* ***(G-3242)***
Stealth Muffler Co, Tower *Also Called Gull Way Ltd* ***(G-9687)***
Stearns Aggregate, Watkins *Also Called Randy Kramer Excavating Inc* ***(G-9899)***
Stearns Bank National Assn (HQ) 320 253-6607
4191 2nd St S Saint Cloud (56301) ***(G-7608)***
Stearns Cooperative Electric 320 256-4241
900 E Kraft Dr Melrose (56352) ***(G-3352)***

ALPHABETIC

www.HarrisInfo.com
622
2011 Harris Minnesota Services Directory
(G-00000) Company's Geographic Section entry number

Stearns County National Assn 320 845-2149
500 13th St Albany (56307) *(G-29)*
Stearns County National Assn (HQ) 320 253-6607
4191 2nd St S Saint Cloud (56301) *(G-7609)*
Stearns County National Assn 320 253-6607
4140 Thielman Ln Ste 101 Saint Cloud (56301) *(G-7610)*
Stearns County Sheriff Dept, Saint Cloud *Also Called County of Stearns (G-7495)*
Stearns Dairy Herd Improvement 320 352-2028
825 12th St S Sauk Centre (56378) *(G-9353)*
Stearns Financial Services Inc (PA) 320 253-6607
4191 2nd St S Saint Cloud (56301) *(G-7611)*
Stearns Veterinary Outlet 320 256-3303
222 County Road 173 Melrose (56352) *(G-3353)*
Stearns-Benton Employment 320 308-5320
1542 Northway Dr Saint Cloud (56303) *(G-7612)*
Stearns-Bntn Emplymnt Train, Saint Cloud *Also Called County of Stearns (G-7494)*
Steele County Human Services 507 444-7500
630 Florence Ave Owatonna (55060) *(G-6738)*
Steele Dention Center, Owatonna *Also Called County of Steele (G-6707)*
Steele-Waseca Cooperative Elec 507 451-7340
2411 W Bridge St Owatonna (55060) *(G-6739)*
Steen Engineering Inc 763 585-6742
5430 Douglas Dr N Minneapolis (55429) *(G-5746)*
Steenberg Watrud Construction 651 457-2291
10967 Clark Rd Inver Grove Heights (55077) *(G-2770)*
Stein Industries Inc (HQ) 763 504-3500
7153 Northland Dr N Minneapolis (55428) *(G-5747)*
Steinbrecher Painting Inc 763 389-3887
1408 7th St N Princeton (55371) *(G-6916)*
Steine Cold Storage Inc 763 416-4681
2355 Polaris Ln N Ste 130 Minneapolis (55447) *(G-5748)*
Steinkraus Plumbing Inc 952 361-0128
112 E 5th St Ste 101 Chaska (55318) *(G-981)*
Stellar Contractors Inc 952 469-0900
21900 Kenrick Ave Lakeville (55044) *(G-2935)*
Stellher Human Services Inc 218 751-5919
514 Beltrami Ave NW Bemidji (56601) *(G-428)*
Stemm Transfer & Storage Inc 320 251-4080
2300 6th St N Saint Cloud (56303) *(G-7613)*
Stencil Cutting & Supply Co (PA) 800 783-4633
310 Cannon River Ave N Red Wing (55066) *(G-7007)*
Step By Step Montessori 763 315-3602
11601 73rd Ave N Osseo (55369) *(G-6667)*
Step By Step Montessori School 952 368-4456
1485 White Oak Dr Chaska (55318) *(G-982)*
Step By Step Montessori School 763 498-5437
23610 County Road 10 Loretto (55357) *(G-3052)*
Step By Step Montessori School (PA) 763 557-6777
4355 Highway 169 N Minneapolis (55442) *(G-5749)*
Step Inc 507 238-4341
411 S State St Fairmont (56031) *(G-1982)*
Stephen Donnelly Co 952 884-1848
5200 W 74th St Minneapolis (55439) *(G-5750)*
Stephen J Russell 507 284-8384
200 1st St SW Rochester (55905) *(G-7264)*
Stephen M Knutson 651 225-0626
1155 Centre Pte Dr Ste 10 Saint Paul (55120) *(G-7912)*
Stephen Scott Management Inc 763 540-8600
5402 Parkdale Dr Ste 200 Minneapolis (55416) *(G-5751)*
Stepping Stones For Living LLC 218 727-7450
5270 Miller Trunk Hwy Duluth (55811) *(G-1475)*
Stericycle Inc 651 641-0009
742 Vandalia St Saint Paul (55114) *(G-9005)*
Stericycle Specialty Waste 612 285-9865
2850 100th Ct NE Minneapolis (55449) *(G-3608)*
Sterilmed Inc (PA) 763 488-3400
11400 73rd Ave N Ste 100 Osseo (55369) *(G-6668)*
Sterling Bancorporation Inc (PA) 507 433-7325
1419 1st Ave SW Austin (55912) *(G-289)*
Sterling Commerce Inc 952 294-1800
7800 Equitable Dr Ste 200 Eden Prairie (55344) *(G-1782)*
Sterling House of Blaine, Minneapolis *Also Called Alterra Healthcare Corp (G-3397)*
Sterling Park Health Care Ctr 320 252-9595
142 1st St N Waite Park (56387) *(G-9841)*
Sterling State Bank 507 282-1845
102 S Broadway Ste 225 Rochester (55904) *(G-7265)*
Sterling Systems Inc 952 697-1060
2265 W Wayzata Blvd Long Lake (55356) *(G-3033)*
Steve Yaggy Specialized Truck 507 282-1715
6978 10th Ave SW Rochester (55902) *(G-7266)*
Steve's Elk River Nursery Inc 763 441-3090
15101 Highway 10 Elk River (55330) *(G-1894)*
Steven Cabinets Inc 612 378-1812
2211 E Hennepin Ave Minneapolis (55413) *(G-5752)*
Steven Fabrics Co 612 781-6671
600 Hoover St NE Minneapolis (55413) *(G-5753)*
Steven N Arendt 952 476-7143
800 Wayzata Blvd E Wayzata (55391) *(G-9942)*
Steven Scott Management Inc 952 540-8600
5402 Parkdale Dr Ste 200 Minneapolis (55416) *(G-5754)*
Stevens Community Medical Ctr, Morris *Also Called Allina Health System (G-6369)*
Stevens Community Medical Ctr 320 589-1313
400 E 1st St Morris (56267) *(G-6379)*
Stevens Foster' Financial 952 843-4200
7901 Xerxes Ave S Ste 325 Minneapolis (55431) *(G-5755)*
Stewart T Chris, Minneapolis *Also Called Dunkley & Bennett (G-4296)*
Stewart Title of Minnesota (DH) 763 422-1116
1700 W 82nd St Ste 100 Minneapolis (55431) *(G-5756)*
Stewartville Bowl, Stewartville *Also Called MPS Group Properties Inc (G-9593)*
Stewartville Nursing Home Inc 507 533-4288
120 4th St NE Stewartville (55976) *(G-9594)*
STI, Waseca *Also Called Norsemen Inc (G-9883)*
Stier Transport Services Inc 952 873-2362
406 S Meridian St Belle Plaine (56011) *(G-371)*
Stifel, Nicolaus & Co Inc 763 542-3700
5500 Wayzata Blvd # 1400 Minneapolis (55416) *(G-5757)*
Stillwater Country Club Inc 651 439-7979
1421 4th St N Stillwater (55082) *(G-9645)*
Stillwater Fitness Club Inc 651 430-1584
110 Greeley St S Stillwater (55082) *(G-9646)*
Stillwater Lions Clubs, Stillwater *Also Called International Association of (G-9624)*
Stillwater Medical Clinic 651 439-1234
1500 Curve Crest Blvd W Stillwater (55082) *(G-9647)*
Stillwater Medical Group 651 439-1234
1500 Curve Crest Blvd W Stillwater (55082) *(G-9648)*
Stinson Home Care LLC 763 755-4801
1425 Coon Rapids Blvd NW # 202 Minneapolis (55433) *(G-3609)*
Stivland Inc 651 436-1153
15234 50th St S Afton (55001) *(G-11)*
Stock Yards Meat Packing Co 651 450-6000
280 Grand Ave E South Saint Paul (55075) *(G-9544)*
Stockbridge Insurance Co (PA) 651 631-7000
2 Pine Tree Dr Saint Paul (55112) *(G-9006)*
Stocker Excavating Inc 952 890-4241
12336 Boone Ave Savage (55378) *(G-9408)*
Stockman Hotel Corp 651 636-1171
4730 White Bear Pkwy Saint Paul (55110) *(G-9007)*
Stockman Transfer Inc 320 864-2381
10636 Cameo Cir Glencoe (55336) *(G-2215)*
Stockmen's Truck Stop, South Saint Paul *Also Called Awm Enterprises Inc (G-9510)*
Stockness Construction Inc 651 484-1286
13427 Fenway Blvd Cir N 1 Hugo (55038) *(G-2683)*
Stoltz Dry Cleaners Inc 651 698-0120
1580 Grand Ave Saint Paul (55105) *(G-9008)*
Stone Fabrics Inc (PA) 952 941-2303
6900 Shady Oak Rd Eden Prairie (55344) *(G-1783)*
Stone Gate Foods, Shakopee *Also Called Trudeau Holdings LLC (G-9481)*
Stone Mountain Crpt Fctry Outl, Minneapolis *Also Called Carpet Factory Outlet Inc (G-4020)*
Stone Source Inc 763 540-9000
15831 Highway 55 Ste B Plymouth (55447) *(G-6884)*
Stone Systems & Services Inc 651 683-9672
2425 Waters Dr Saint Paul (55120) *(G-7913)*
Stonecrest 651 264-3200
8725 Promenade Ln Saint Paul (55125) *(G-9278)*
Stoneridge Management Co, Rochester *Also Called Macks LLC (G-7164)*
Storefront Group 612 861-1675
6425 Nicollet Ave Ste 210 Richfield (55423) *(G-7038)*
Stork Twin City Testing, Saint Paul *Also Called Patzig Testing Laboratories (G-8810)*
Stork United Corp 651 645-3601
662 Cromwell Ave Saint Paul (55114) *(G-9009)*
Stpaul Health Partner Clinic, Saint Paul *Also Called Healthpartners Inc (G-8468)*
Strack Construction Co Inc 320 251-5933
1139 Franklin Ave Ste 2 Sauk Rapids (56379) *(G-9377)*
Strategic Equipment Inc 320 252-2977
100 Roosevelt Rd Saint Cloud (56301) *(G-7614)*
Strategic Technologies Inc 763 559-1959
9905 45th Ave N Ste 220 Minneapolis (55442) *(G-5758)*
Stratis Health 952 854-3306
2901 Metro Dr Ste 400 Minneapolis (55425) *(G-5759)*
Streamfeeder LLC 763 502-0000
103 Osborne Rd NE Minneapolis (55432) *(G-3610)*
Street Maintenance Department, Saint Paul *Also Called City of Saint Paul (G-8207)*
Streeter & Associates Inc 952 449-9448
18312 Minnetonka Blvd Wayzata (55391) *(G-9943)*
Stresstech Inc (PA) 651 388-7117
1007 Tile Dr Red Wing (55066) *(G-7008)*
Stretar Masonry & Concrete Inc 218 624-4824
5719 Roosevelt St Duluth (55807) *(G-1476)*
Stringer Business Systems Inc 651 994-7700
960 Blue Gentian Rd Saint Paul (55121) *(G-7914)*
Strongform Inc 218 462-2607
208 Baker St N Deer Creek (56527) *(G-1166)*
Structural Restoration Inc 612 825-8614
811 E 54th St Minneapolis (55417) *(G-5760)*
Structural Wood Corp 651 426-8111
4000 Labore Rd Saint Paul (55110) *(G-9010)*
STS Acquisition Co 763 315-6300
10900 73rd Ave N Ste 150 Osseo (55369) *(G-6669)*
STS Operating Inc 320 564-3057
113 Winter Dr Granite Falls (56241) *(G-2320)*
STS Operating Inc 952 563-1700
12800 Hwy 13 S Ste 100 Savage (55378) *(G-9409)*
Student Assurance Services Inc 651 439-7098
333 Main St N Ste 300 Stillwater (55082) *(G-9649)*
Student Experience Inc 218 728-8009
120 Mount Royal Shopping Cir Duluth (55803) *(G-1477)*
Styer Transportation Co 952 469-4491
7870 215th St W Lakeville (55044) *(G-2936)*
Stylepointe LLC 651 437-5356
12590 127th St S Ste 4 Hastings (55033) *(G-2418)*
Suburban Auto Body Inc 651 983-4438
1100 Silver Lake Rd NW Saint Paul (55112) *(G-9011)*
Suburban Plastic Surgery 952 922-0895
6545 France Ave S Ste 505 Minneapolis (55435) *(G-5761)*
Suburban Radiologic Conslnts 763 792-1900
8990 Springbrook Dr NW Ste 140 Minneapolis (55433) *(G-3611)*
Suburban Radiologic Conslnts 763 786-9460
8990 Springbrook Dr NW Ste 125 Minneapolis (55433) *(G-3612)*
Suburban Radiologic Conslnts (PA) 952 837-9700
4801 W 81st St Ste 108 Minneapolis (55437) *(G-5762)*
Sudhko Inc 952 595-8500
13911 Ridgedale Dr Ste 300 Hopkins (55305) *(G-2638)*
Sue Chapman Dvm 507 233-2520
401 20th St S New Ulm (56073) *(G-6475)*
Sugar Lake Supported Living 320 963-7571
6523 117th St NW Maple Lake (55358) *(G-3265)*
Sulco Cleaning Service 952 937-8777
6408 Kurtz Ln Eden Prairie (55346) *(G-1784)*
Summer On The Farm, Saint Paul *Also Called Children's Country Day School (G-7732)*
Summit Academy OIC 612 377-0150
935 Olson Memorial Hwy Minneapolis (55405) *(G-5763)*
Summit Employment Inc 651 501-0531
3894 Homestead Dr Saint Paul (55125) *(G-9279)*

ALPHABETIC

Summit Fire Protection Co (PA) 651 251-1880
575 Minnehaha Ave W Saint Paul (55103) *(G-9012)*

Summit Holdings Corp (PA) 952 445-8718
1415 Maras St Shakopee (55379) *(G-9479)*

Summit Landmark Orthopedics 651 842-5200
17 Exchange St W Ste 307 Saint Paul (55102) *(G-9013)*

Summit Management LLC 651 689-2200
122 Water St S Stillwater (55082) *(G-9650)*

Summit Mortgage Corp (PA) 763 390-7200
13355 10th Ave N Ste 100 Minneapolis (55441) *(G-5764)*

Sun Bear Spa & Tan Inc 651 426-5884
2207 3rd St Saint Paul (55110) *(G-9014)*

Sun Country Airlines, Mendota Heights *Also Called MN Airlines LLC* *(G-3367)*

Sunbelt Business Brokers, Saint Paul *Also Called Maxann LLC* *(G-8619)*

Sundance Golf & Bowl Inc 763 420-4700
15240 113th Ave N Osseo (55369) *(G-6670)*

Sundance Staffing Minnesota 763 559-7700
12805 Highway 55 Ste 106 Minneapolis (55441) *(G-5765)*

Sunday Land Surveying 952 881-2455
9001 E Bloomington Fwy # 118 Minneapolis (55420) *(G-5766)*

Sunde Land Surveying LLC 952 881-2455
9001 E Bloomington Fwy # 118 Minneapolis (55420) *(G-5767)*

Sunfish Express Inc 763 433-8383
6401 Highway 10 NW Anoka (55303) *(G-229)*

Sungard Financial Systems LLC 952 935-3300
601 2nd Ave S Hopkins (55343) *(G-2639)*

Sunglass Display, Le Sueur *Also Called Seaver Co* *(G-2959)*

Sunnyside Care Center 218 238-5944
16561 US Highway 10 Lake Park (56554) *(G-2880)*

Sunopta, Minnetonka *Also Called Sunrich Inc* *(G-6227)*

Sunopta Aseptic Inc 320 763-9822
3915 Minnesota St Alexandria (56308) *(G-124)*

Sunopta Food Group LLC (PA) 320 763-5977
3915 Minnesota St Alexandria (56308) *(G-125)*

Sunopta Sunflower, Breckenridge *Also Called Sunrich LLC* *(G-602)*

Sunrich Inc 507 451-3316
3824 SW 93rd St Hope (56046) *(G-2496)*

Sunrich Inc 952 939-3949
5850 Opus Pkwy Ste 150 Minnetonka (55343) *(G-6227)*

Sunrich LLC 218 643-8467
227 6th St N Breckenridge (56520) *(G-602)*

Sunrich LLC (HQ) 507 451-4724
3824 SW 93rd St Hope (56046) *(G-2497)*

Sunrise A G Repair 320 584-0010
4859 State Highway 25 Royalton (56373) *(G-7388)*

Sunrise AG Cooperative (PA) 320 468-6433
9361 Creamery Dr Buckman (56317) *(G-632)*

Sunrise Cottage of Mankato 507 345-8787
300 Bunting Ln Mankato (56001) *(G-3202)*

Sunrise Estates Mobile Home 651 462-4047
5335 Stacy Trl Stacy (55079) *(G-9581)*

Sunrise Hair STYling&tanning 651 777-2344
2043 County Road E E Saint Paul (55110) *(G-9015)*

Sunrise Health Services 651 462-9331
22350 Sunrise Rd NE Stacy (55079) *(G-9578)*

Sunrise Manor, Tyler *Also Called Tyler Healthcare Center Inc* *(G-9716)*

Sunrise Manor Nursing Home 507 247-5839
208 Highland Ct Tyler (56178) *(G-9714)*

Sunrise Nursing Home, Two Harbors *Also Called Ecumen* *(G-9706)*

Sunrise Painting 763 557-0100
12975 16th Ave N Ste 400 Minneapolis (55441) *(G-5768)*

Sunrise Senior Living Inc 763 682-5489
201 1st St NE Ofc OFC Buffalo (55313) *(G-657)*

Sunrise Senior Living Inc 952 927-8000
7128 France Ave S Minneapolis (55435) *(G-5769)*

Sunshine Readers Inc 763 433-2534
11156 Zealand Ave N Champlin (55316) *(G-902)*

Sunsource Fauver, Granite Falls *Also Called STS Operating Inc* *(G-2320)*

Sunsource Fauver, Savage *Also Called STS Operating Inc* *(G-9409)*

Sunstone Hotel Management Inc 507 252-7500
225 Woodlake Dr SE Rochester (55904) *(G-7267)*

Sunstone Hotel Management Inc 507 289-8646
9 3rd Ave NW Rochester (55901) *(G-7268)*

Sunstone Hotel Properties Inc 507 282-2581
20 2nd Ave SW Ste G13 Rochester (55902) *(G-7269)*

Super 8 Motel, Bemidji *Also Called Murray Williamson* *(G-404)*

Super 8 Motel, Grand Marais *Also Called Grand Marais Hotel Co Inc* *(G-2260)*

Super 8 Motel, Minneapolis *Also Called Turnery Properties LP* *(G-5866)*

Super 8 Motel, Red Wing *Also Called Riverside Lodging* *(G-7003)*

Super 8 Motel, Saint Cloud *Also Called BR Motels Inc* *(G-7464)*

Super Bowl 763 421-7779
6720 Riverdale Dr Woodbury (55125) *(G-10175)*

Superclean Brands LLC 651 365-7500
1380 Corporate Center Curv Eagan (55121) *(G-1554)*

Supercuts Inc (HQ) 952 947-7777
7201 Metro Blvd Minneapolis (55439) *(G-5770)*

Superior Brokerage Services 651 256-1555
1700 Wynne Ave Saint Paul (55108) *(G-9016)*

Superior Concepts Inc 952 892-7555
14296 Plymouth Ave Burnsville (55337) *(G-804)*

Superior Construction Services 763 424-9434
9702 85th Ave N Osseo (55369) *(G-6671)*

Superior Fire Protection Inc 763 263-1929
11560 185th Ave SE Big Lake (55309) *(G-458)*

Superior Ford Inc 763 559-9111
9700 56th Ave N Minneapolis (55442) *(G-5771)*

Superior Glass Duluth 218 722-7400
4911 Matterhorn Dr Duluth (55811) *(G-1478)*

Superior Health Community Care, Two Harbors *Also Called First Solutions* *(G-9707)*

Superior Masonry & Concrete 651 786-0884
19960 Saint Francis Blvd Anoka (55303) *(G-230)*

Superior Mechanical Systems 507 289-5126
1244 60th Ave NW Ste C Rochester (55901) *(G-7270)*

Superior National At Lutsen 218 663-7865
5731 W Hwy 61 Lutsen (55612) *(G-3057)*

Superior Water Conditioning 507 289-0229
1244 60th Ave NW Rochester (55901) *(G-7271)*

Superl Inc 763 571-7464
7301 Apollo Ct Lino Lakes (55014) *(G-2976)*

Supershuttle Minnesota Inc 612 827-7777
4500 Glumack Dr Ste 1300 Saint Paul (55111) *(G-7965)*

Supervalu Equipment Services 952 828-4000
11840 Valley View Rd Eden Prairie (55344) *(G-1785)*

Supervalu Inc 952 906-6260
19011 Lake Dr E Chanhassen (55317) *(G-941)*

Supervalu Inc 952 906-6600
18791 Lake Dr E Chanhassen (55317) *(G-942)*

Supervalu Inc 952 238-3400
300 2nd Ave S Eden Prairie (55343) *(G-1786)*

SUPERVALU Inc (PA) 952 828-4000
11840 Valley View Rd Eden Prairie (55344) *(G-1787)*

Supervalu Inc 952 947-3700
7075 Flying Cloud Dr Eden Prairie (55344) *(G-1788)*

Supervalu Inc 952 380-9900
23800 Highway 7 Excelsior (55331) *(G-1937)*

SUPERVALU Inc 952 932-4300
101 Jefferson Ave S Hopkins (55343) *(G-2640)*

Supervalu Transportation Inc 952 828-4000
11840 Valley View Rd Eden Prairie (55344) *(G-1789)*

Supportive Lifestyles Inc 320 796-5900
5465 132nd Ave NE Spicer (56288) *(G-9559)*

Supreme Building Maintenance 763 972-8425
4735 37th St SE Delano (55328) *(G-1185)*

Sur La Rue Inc 651 772-4957
1174 Breen St Saint Paul (55106) *(G-9017)*

Sureservices Inc 763 531-0029
7317 39th Ave N Minneapolis (55427) *(G-5772)*

Sureway Transportation Co, Saint Cloud *Also Called Ats Logistics Services Inc* *(G-7456)*

Surfacequest Inc 952 361-9431
7760 France Ave S # 1400 Minneapolis (55435) *(G-5773)*

Surgical Care Affiliates LLC 952 832-9360
7373 France Ave S Ste 404 Minneapolis (55435) *(G-5774)*

Surgical Consultants Prof (PA) 952 832-0805
4570 W 77th St Ste 235 Minneapolis (55435) *(G-5775)*

Surveyors Office, Minneapolis *Also Called Hennepin County* *(G-4632)*

Sushi Avenue Inc 651 294-7000
895 Blue Gentian Rd Ste 6 Eagan (55121) *(G-1555)*

Sustainable Resources Center 612 870-4255
1081 10th Ave SE Minneapolis (55414) *(G-5776)*

Suzanne's Cuisine 651 726-2535
1046 Portland Ave Saint Paul (55104) *(G-9018)*

Svingen Hagstron Cline Karkela 218 739-4696
309 S Mill St Ste 105 Fergus Falls (56537) *(G-2121)*

Swampsiders Snowmobile Club 218 245-3222
29730 County Road 52 Bigfork (56628) *(G-464)*

Swan Lake Association 218 885-3225
29215 Kaleva Beach Rd Pengilly (55775) *(G-6785)*

Swan River Montessori Charter 763 271-7926
500 Maple St Monticello (55362) *(G-6288)*

Swanson Meats Inc 612 721-4411
2700 26th Ave S Minneapolis (55406) *(G-5777)*

Swanson's Repair Rental Center 218 847-7487
1145 13th Ave SE Detroit Lakes (56501) *(G-1219)*

Swanson-Flosystems Co 763 383-4700
151 Cheshire Ln N Ste 700 Plymouth (55441) *(G-6885)*

Sweatshop Inc 651 646-8418
167 Snelling Ave N Saint Paul (55104) *(G-9019)*

Swedberg Wood Products Inc 320 762-0738
1420 County Road 82 NW Alexandria (56308) *(G-126)*

Sweeney Brothers Tractor Co 952 894-9595
12540 Dupont Ave S Burnsville (55337) *(G-805)*

Swenke Co Inc 507 634-7778
103 1/2 W Main St Kasson (55944) *(G-2824)*

Swenke Properties Inc 507 634-7778
101 W Main St Kasson (55944) *(G-2825)*

Swenson Anderson Fincl Group, Minneapolis *Also Called Anderson Swenson Associates* *(G-3778)*

Swenson Motor Co 320 235-3434
1301 Highway 12 E Willmar (56201) *(G-10047)*

Swenson Nhb Investor Relations 612 371-0000
150 S 5th St Ste 1300 Minneapolis (55402) *(G-5778)*

Swift County Homes Inc 320 843-3509
1650 Stone Ave Benson (56215) *(G-442)*

Swift County-Benson Hospital 320 843-4232
1815 Wisconsin Ave Benson (56215) *(G-443)*

Swift Transportation Corp 651 480-7850
11380 Courthouse Blvd Inver Grove Heights (55077) *(G-2771)*

Swimming Pool, Blue Earth *Also Called City of Blue Earth* *(G-532)*

Sylva Corp Inc 763 389-2748
900 Airport Rd Princeton (55371) *(G-6917)*

Symantec Corp 651 746-7000
2815 Cleveland Ave N Saint Paul (55113) *(G-9020)*

Synera Solutions 952 403-9911
1674 Sage Ln Shakopee (55379) *(G-9480)*

Synergetic Solutions Inc 763 331-3300
3890 Pheasant Ridge Dr NE Minneapolis (55449) *(G-3613)*

Synergistic Software Soln 612 367-7300
2 Meridian Xing Ste 310 Minneapolis (55423) *(G-5779)*

Synergy Advantage Group Inc 320 695-2000
201 W Broadway Browns Valley (56219) *(G-628)*

Syngenta Seeds Inc 507 674-3320
11307 US Highway 169 Amboy (56010) *(G-132)*

Syngenta Seeds Inc 320 286-5511
4915 Reardon Ave SW Cokato (55321) *(G-1081)*

Syngenta Seeds Inc 507 645-5621
317 330th St Stanton (55018) *(G-9582)*

Synico Staffing Inc 612 926-6000
3033 Excelsior Blvd Minneapolis (55416) *(G-5780)*

Sypal Lundgren Post No 7662 952 460-6888
421 3rd St Farmington (55024) *(G-2061)*

Sysco Asian Foods Inc 651 558-2400
1300 L Orient St Saint Paul (55117) *(G-9021)*

System Design Advantage LLC 952 703-3500
9655 Penn Ave S Minneapolis (55431) *(G-5781)*

Systemarmed Usacom Inc ... 877 900-0238
5716 Nicollet Ave Minneapolis (55419) *(G-5782)*

Systems Management & Balancing ... 651 257-7380
332 Summit Ave Center City (55012) *(G-886)*

Syverson, Dave Volkswagen, Albert Lea *Also Called Dave Syverson Inc (G-46)*

T & J Concrete & Masonry Inc ... 763 413-0988
9100 Baltimore St NE # 105 Minneapolis (55449) *(G-3614)*

T & L Credit Union Sauk Rapids, Sauk Rapids *Also Called Great River Federal Credit (G-9365)*

T C B X Inc ... 651 644-5547
1912 Broadway St NE Minneapolis (55413) *(G-5783)*

T C Field & Co ... 651 227-8405
530 Robert St N Saint Paul (55101) *(G-9022)*

T C Sweatshop Inc ... 651 646-8418
167 Snelling Ave N Saint Paul (55104) *(G-9023)*

T D & I Cable Maintenance Inc ... 651 436-3383
1378 Quinlan Ave S Lakeland (55043) *(G-2887)*

T Distribution Inc (PA) ... 651 636-6367
1880 Oakcrest Ave Saint Paul (55113) *(G-9024)*

T George & Associates ... 651 647-0900
411 Lexington Pkwy N Ste G Saint Paul (55104) *(G-9025)*

T I E S, Saint Paul *Also Called Technology & Information (G-9033)*

T L C Co's, Minneapolis *Also Called Transport Leasing Contract Inc (G-5848)*

T M B Consulting Inc ... 952 249-1223
18305 Minnetonka Blvd Wayzata (55391) *(G-9944)*

T R W, Winona *Also Called Lake Center Industries Trans (G-10109)*

T Ray Construction Co Inc ... 763 757-6859
13535 Johnson St NE Anoka (55304) *(G-231)*

T S P Inc ... 507 288-8155
1500 Highway 52 N Rochester (55901) *(G-7272)*

T S P One Inc ... 952 474-3291
18707 Excelsior Blvd Hopkins (55345) *(G-2641)*

T W Enterprises Ltd ... 320 654-0551
2789 Clearwater Rd Saint Cloud (56301) *(G-7615)*

T-Chek Systems Inc ... 952 934-3413
14800 Charlson Rd Ste 100 Eden Prairie (55347) *(G-1790)*

Taco Bell, Anoka *Also Called Border Foods Inc (G-159)*

Tactile Systems Technology Inc ... 952 224-4060
1331 Tyler St NE Ste 200 Minneapolis (55413) *(G-5784)*

Tailwind Voice & Data Inc ... 763 577-4000
15350 25th Ave N Ste 114 Minneapolis (55447) *(G-5785)*

TAJ Technologies Inc ... 651 405-7412
1168 Northland Dr Mendota Heights (55120) *(G-3371)*

Talberg Lawn & Landscape Inc ... 763 428-3550
11770 Justen Cir Osseo (55369) *(G-6672)*

Talent Technical Services Inc ... 952 417-3600
5353 Wayzata Blvd Ste 200 Minneapolis (55416) *(G-5786)*

Talisman Brookdale LLC ... 763 566-3373
1108 Brookdale Ctr Minneapolis (55430) *(G-5787)*

Talon Investigation Ltd ... 651 774-6977
1538 White Bear Ave N Ste 206 Saint Paul (55106) *(G-9026)*

Talus Group Inc ... 952 544-2526
19675 Near Mountain Blvd Excelsior (55331) *(G-1954)*

Tamarack Village Shopping Cent ... 651 702-6311
8278 Tamarack Vlg Ste 311 Saint Paul (55125) *(G-9280)*

Tamarisk Resources Inc ... 763 572-1950
1657 161st Ave NW Anoka (55304) *(G-232)*

Tandem Printing Inc ... 651 289-2970
2970 Lexington Ave S Eagan (55121) *(G-1556)*

Tandem Products Inc ... 507 583-7222
520 Industrial Dr Blooming Prairie (55917) *(G-479)*

Tandem Products Inc (PA) ... 612 721-2911
3444 Dight Ave Minneapolis (55406) *(G-5788)*

Tanners Brook Golf Club LLP ... 651 464-2300
5810 190th St N Forest Lake (55025) *(G-2169)*

Tapemark Charity Pro AM ... 651 455-1611
150 Marie Ave E Saint Paul (55118) *(G-7915)*

Tapemark Co ... 651 455-1611
1685 Marthaler Ln Saint Paul (55118) *(G-7916)*

Tappe Construction Co ... 651 994-0200
915 Blue Gentian Rd Ste 13 Saint Paul (55121) *(G-7917)*

Tappers Inc ... 763 295-4222
212 Chelsea Rd Monticello (55362) *(G-6289)*

Target Brands Inc ... 612 304-6073
33 S 6th St Minneapolis (55402) *(G-5789)*

Target Center, Minneapolis *Also Called AEG Management Twn LLC (G-3692)*

Target Corp ... 763 440-2033
7000 Target Pkwy N Minneapolis (55445) *(G-5790)*

Target Corp ... 612 304-6073
33 S 6th St Ste CC1 Minneapolis (55402) *(G-5791)*

Target Corp ... 320 253-4740
4201 W Division St Ste 71 Saint Cloud (56301) *(G-7616)*

Tartan Arena, Saint Paul *Also Called Maplewood Oakdale School Dist (G-9246)*

Tartan Park Recreation Center, Lake Elmo *Also Called 3 M Club of St Paul Inc (G-2877)*

TAS Adventures Inc ... 507 833-8164
905 9th Ave SE Waseca (56093) *(G-9888)*

Tasks Unlimited Inc (PA) ... 612 871-3320
2419 Nicollet Ave Minneapolis (55404) *(G-5792)*

Taste of Minnesota, Saint Paul *Also Called Festival Events of Minnesota (G-8375)*

Tavis Metal & Fabrication Corp ... 763 428-8483
14240 James Rd Rogers (55374) *(G-7342)*

Tax-Sheltered Compensation Inc ... 952 806-4300
7300 Metro Blvd Ste 450 Minneapolis (55439) *(G-5793)*

Taylor & Katie Inc ... 320 523-2833
2425 W Lincoln Ave Olivia (56277) *(G-6565)*

Taylor Corp ... 952 888-7945
1600 W 92nd St Minneapolis (55431) *(G-5794)*

Taylor Corp (PA) ... 507 625-2828
1725 Roe Crest Dr North Mankato (56003) *(G-6514)*

Taylor Limousines Inc ... 612 722-4467
4225 Hiawatha Ave Minneapolis (55406) *(G-5795)*

Taylor Made Construction of MN ... 952 440-8510
6648 Rustic Rd SE Prior Lake (55372) *(G-6957)*

Taylor Truck Line Inc ... 507 645-4531
31485 Northfield Blvd Northfield (55057) *(G-6520)*

Taylors Falls Boats & Canoes, Taylors Falls *Also Called Muller Boat Co (G-9661)*

Tb Duluth LLC ... 218 727-8981
505 W Superior St Duluth (55802) *(G-1479)*

Tbi Residential & Community ... 218 721-3231
1615 Piedmont Ave Duluth (55811) *(G-1480)*

Tbs Office Automations, Saint Paul *Also Called Technifax Business Systems Inc (G-7919)*

Tc American Monorail Inc ... 320 634-4531
17835 211th Ave Glenwood (56334) *(G-2234)*

Tc American Monorail Inc ... 763 497-8700
12070 43rd St NE Saint Michael (55376) *(G-7683)*

Tcbh Inc ... 651 454-3434
2700 Pilot Knob Rd Saint Paul (55121) *(G-7918)*

TCF Equipment Finance Inc ... 952 934-4404
11100 Wayzata Blvd # 801 Hopkins (55305) *(G-2642)*

TCF Equipment Finance Inc (DH) ... 952 656-5080
801 Marquette Ave Minneapolis (55402) *(G-5796)*

TCF Financial Corp (PA) ... 952 745-2760
200 Lake St E Wayzata (55391) *(G-9945)*

TCF National Bank ... 763 546-5637
1801 Plymouth Rd Hopkins (55305) *(G-2643)*

TCF National Bank ... 612 379-8597
1501 University Ave SE Minneapolis (55414) *(G-5797)*

TCF National Bank ... 952 888-8375
7800 Penn Ave S Minneapolis (55431) *(G-5798)*

TCF National Bank (HQ) ... 612 661-6500
801 Marquette Ave Minneapolis (55402) *(G-5799)*

TCF National Bank ... 651 291-4095
405 Robert St N Ste 220 Saint Paul (55101) *(G-9027)*

TCF National Bank ... 651 735-6510
1988 Suburban Ave Saint Paul (55119) *(G-9028)*

TCF National Bank ... 651 770-2273
2989 White Bear Ave N Saint Paul (55109) *(G-9029)*

TCI Business Capital Inc ... 952 656-3400
12270 Nicollet Ave Burnsville (55337) *(G-806)*

TCI Group Inc ... 612 823-6214
4301 Lyndale Ave S Minneapolis (55409) *(G-5800)*

TCS Mortgage Inc ... 612 767-5002
2801 Wayzata Blvd Ste 101 Minneapolis (55405) *(G-5801)*

TDS Telecommunications, New London *Also Called Mid-State Telephone Co (G-6417)*

Teaching Temps Inc ... 763 797-9000
4050 Olson Memorial Hwy Minneapolis (55422) *(G-5802)*

Tealwood Care Centers, Northome *Also Called Northome Health Care Inc (G-6547)*

Tealwood Care Centers Inc ... 218 436-2161
304 Washington Ave W Karlstad (56732) *(G-2815)*

Tealwood Care Centers Inc ... 320 252-9595
142 1st St N Waite Park (56387) *(G-9842)*

Team Industries Baxter Inc ... 218 829-1901
13143 Cypress Dr Baxter (56425) *(G-341)*

Team Industries Inc (PA) ... 218 694-3550
105 Park Ave NW Bagley (56621) *(G-302)*

Team Informatics Inc (PA) ... 651 222-8326
3900 Northwoods Dr Ste 350 Saint Paul (55112) *(G-9030)*

Team Tires Plus, Bemidji *Also Called Dickson Enterprises Inc (G-388)*

Team Tires Plus, Buffalo *Also Called Morgan Tire & Auto LLC (G-653)*

Team Tires Plus, Circle Pines *Also Called Marco Investments LLC (G-1016)*

Team Tires Plus, Eden Prairie *Also Called Morgan Tire & Auto LLC (G-1730)*

Team Tires Plus, Mankato *Also Called Morgan Tire & Auto Inc (G-3173)*

Team Tires Plus, Marshall *Also Called Morgan Tire & Auto LLC (G-3316)*

Team Tires Plus, Minneapolis *Also Called Morgan Tire & Auto LLC (G-6130)*

Team Tires Plus, Minneapolis *Also Called Morgan Tire & Auto Inc (G-5130)*

Team Tires Plus, Minneapolis *Also Called Morgan Tire & Auto LLC (G-3545)*

Team Tires Plus, Minneapolis *Also Called Morgan Tire & Auto LLC (G-5131)*

Team Tires Plus, Red Wing *Also Called Morgan Tire & Auto LLC (G-6991)*

Team Tires Plus, Saint Paul *Also Called Morgan Tire & Auto LLC (G-8721)*

Team Tires Plus, Saint Paul *Also Called Morgan Tire & Auto Inc (G-7846)*

Team Tires Plus, Willmar *Also Called Morgan Tire & Auto LLC (G-10028)*

Team USA Mortgage LLC ... 651 848-0484
546 Rice St Ste 200 Saint Paul (55103) *(G-9031)*

Teamsters Local 2000 ... 612 379-9157
3001 University Ave SE # 510 Minneapolis (55414) *(G-5803)*

Tech-Pro Inc ... 651 634-1400
3000 Centre Pointe Dr Saint Paul (55113) *(G-9032)*

Techbarncom Inc ... 651 275-8300
270 Main St N Ste 300 Stillwater (55082) *(G-9651)*

Techne Corp (PA) ... 612 379-8854
614 McKinley Pl NE Minneapolis (55413) *(G-5804)*

Technical Resources, Chanhassen *Also Called Resource Group Inc (G-937)*

Technifax Business Systems Inc ... 651 905-7090
1385 Mendota Heights Rd # 100 Saint Paul (55120) *(G-7919)*

Technology & Information ... 651 999-6001
1667 Snelling Ave N Saint Paul (55108) *(G-9033)*

Tech Central Inc ... 952 837-8000
3300 Edinbrgh Way Ste 204 Minneapolis (55435) *(G-5805)*

Tech Investments Inc ... 218 733-0214
4502 Airpark Blvd Duluth (55811) *(G-1481)*

Tech Restoration Services Inc ... 651 292-9638
192 9th St W Ste 200 Saint Paul (55102) *(G-9034)*

Techpower Inc ... 952 831-7444
9340 James Ave S Minneapolis (55431) *(G-5806)*

Techscan Corp ... 651 636-3030
85 2nd Ave SE Ste G Saint Paul (55112) *(G-9035)*

Tekstar Cablevision, Twin Valley *Also Called Arvig Enterprises Inc (G-9700)*

Teksystems Inc ... 952 886-4800
7505 Metro Blvd Ste 450 Minneapolis (55439) *(G-5807)*

Telcom Construction Inc ... 320 558-9485
2218 200th St E Clearwater (55320) *(G-1041)*

Tele Resources Inc ... 218 724-2026
1203 London Rd Duluth (55802) *(G-1482)*

Tele Resources Inc (PA) ... 218 724-2026
1203 London Rd Duluth (55802) *(G-1483)*

Teleconcepts Inc ... 763 566-5360
7111 W Broadway Ave Ste 203 Minneapolis (55428) *(G-5808)*

Telemarketing Results Inc ... 763 519-0874
3131 Fernbrook Ln N Ste 2 Minneapolis (55447) *(G-5809)*

Telepak Industries Inc ... 507 332-0012
1505 30th St NW Faribault (55021) *(G-2034)*

Telin Transportation Group LLC ... 763 262-3328
14990 Industry Ave SE Becker (55308) *(G-359)*

Telvent Dtn Inc 952 941-6628
11000 W 78th St Ste 250 Eden Prairie (55344) ***(G-1791)***
Tembua Inc 952 435-8178
17870 Irons Ct Lakeville (55044) ***(G-2937)***
Temp-Air Inc (PA) 952 707-5203
3700 W Preserve Blvd Burnsville (55337) ***(G-807)***
Temple of Aaron Sisterhood 651 698-8874
616 Mississippi River Blvd S Saint Paul (55116) ***(G-9036)***
Tempworks Software Inc 651 452-0366
3140 Neil Armstrong Blvd # 205 Saint Paul (55121) ***(G-7920)***
Ten Brook Pork LLP 952 440-5737
15439 Wood Duck Trl NW Prior Lake (55372) ***(G-6958)***
Ten Dollar Trophy LLC 952 912-9972
810 1st St S 115 Hopkins (55343) ***(G-2644)***
Ten Thousand Things Theatre 612 724-4494
3153 36th Ave S Minneapolis (55406) ***(G-5810)***
Ten-E Packaging Services Inc 651 459-0671
1666 County Road 74 Newport (55055) ***(G-6489)***
Tena Co's Inc 651 293-1234
251 W Lafayette Frontage Rd Saint Paul (55107) ***(G-9037)***
Tenacious Holdings Inc 651 642-9889
1021 Bandana Blvd E Saint Paul (55108) ***(G-9038)***
Tenet Painting 952 914-9550
7435 Washington Ave S Minneapolis (55439) ***(G-5811)***
Tennis & Life Camps Inc 507 931-1614
800 W College Ave Saint Peter (56082) ***(G-9315)***
Tennis Sanitation LLC 651 459-1887
720 4th St Saint Paul Park (55071) ***(G-9298)***
Tenson Construction Inc 218 743-3874
39036 County Road 225 Bigfork (56628) ***(G-465)***
Teradyne Inc 763 586-0725
5301 E River Rd Ste 106 Minneapolis (55421) ***(G-3615)***
Terminal Transport Inc 651 407-6200
2982 Cleveland Ave N Saint Paul (55113) ***(G-9039)***
Terrace Hts As Living Apartmnt, Osakis *Also Called Community Memorial Home Inc* ***(G-6586)***
Terracon Consultants Inc 651 770-1500
3535 Hoffman Rd E Saint Paul (55110) ***(G-9040)***
Tes Construction Inc 763 783-2496
17149 Lincoln St NE # 600 Anoka (55304) ***(G-233)***
Testquest Inc 952 936-7887
18976 Lake Dr E Chanhassen (55317) ***(G-943)***
Texa-Tonka Lanes, Minneapolis *Also Called H J K S Inc* ***(G-4586)***
Texas Terrace Care Center, Minneapolis *Also Called Extendicare Homes Inc* ***(G-4387)***
Textile Care Services, Rochester *Also Called Sunstone Hotel Management Inc* ***(G-7267)***
Tfx Medical Wire Products Inc 763 559-6414
3750 Annapolis Ln N Ste 160 Plymouth (55447) ***(G-6886)***
Tgp Inc 218 694-2378
421 6th St NE Ofc Bagley (56621) ***(G-303)***
Thane Hawkins Polar Chevrolet 651 429-7791
1801 County Road F E White Bear Lake (55110) ***(G-9978)***
Thd At-Home Services Inc 763 542-8826
656 Mendelssohn Ave N Minneapolis (55427) ***(G-5812)***
Theatres At Mall of America, Bloomington *Also Called Canam Theatres Moa LLC* ***(G-491)***
Thein Well Co 763 271-4200
102 Dundas Rd Monticello (55362) ***(G-6290)***
Theisen Vending Inc 612 827-5588
2335 Nevada Ave N Minneapolis (55427) ***(G-5813)***
Themescapes Inc 651 778-1784
794 15th St SW Forest Lake (55025) ***(G-2170)***
Theodore F Bolles 651 731-9436
7249 Courtly Rd Saint Paul (55125) ***(G-9281)***
Therapy Network Inc 507 454-6724
1635 W Service Dr Winona (55987) ***(G-10132)***
Thermo King Sales & Service 651 633-2820
1951 Old Highway 8 NW Saint Paul (55112) ***(G-9041)***
Thermo Leasing Corp 763 421-2505
8390 Highway 10 NW Anoka (55303) ***(G-234)***
Thermoskin 651 674-8302
6459 Ash St North Branch (55056) ***(G-6505)***
Thief River Golf Club 218 681-2955
Hwy 32 N Thief River Falls (56701) ***(G-9678)***
Thielen Bus Lines Inc 507 637-3600
220 W 11th St Redwood Falls (56283) ***(G-7028)***
Thielen Motors, Park Rapids *Also Called U Save Lease & Rental Inc* ***(G-6764)***
Thier Feedlots Inc 507 478-4137
23225 County Highway 35 Rushmore (56168) ***(G-7395)***
Think Equity Partners LLC 612 677-5757
80 S 8th St Ste 1200 Minneapolis (55402) ***(G-5814)***
Think Mutual Bank (PA) 507 288-3425
5200 Members Pkwy NW Rochester (55901) ***(G-7273)***
Third Wave Systems Inc 952 832-5515
7900 W 78th St Ste 300 Minneapolis (55439) ***(G-5815)***
Thistledew Camp, Togo *Also Called Department of Corrections MN* ***(G-9685)***
Thm Master Te LLC 612 340-2000
215 S 4th St Minneapolis (55401) ***(G-5816)***
Thoele Dental Laboratories Inc 320 252-2070
540 Progress Rd Waite Park (56387) ***(G-9843)***
Thomas Charles Salon II Inc 952 925-4277
4008 Minnetonka Blvd Minneapolis (55416) ***(G-5817)***
Thomas Eling CPA 218 722-4705
230 W Superior St Ste 600 Duluth (55802) ***(G-1484)***
Thomas Furlong 651 437-2518
14690 Furlong Cir Hastings (55033) ***(G-2408)***
Thomas Grace Construction Inc 651 342-1298
1912 Greeley St S Stillwater (55082) ***(G-9652)***
Thomas Koll 763 323-9797
6230 McKinley St NW Ste C2 Anoka (55303) ***(G-235)***
Thomas M Meyer Enterprises Inc 763 476-1990
2415 Annapolis Ln N # 170 Minneapolis (55441) ***(G-5818)***
Thomas Oas MD 507 646-1494
2000 North Ave Northfield (55057) ***(G-6521)***
Thomas P Koop CPA 218 825-2903
14275 Golf Course Rd # 300 Baxter (56425) ***(G-342)***
Thompson Lightning Protection 651 455-7661
901 Sibley Memorial Hwy Saint Paul (55118) ***(G-7921)***
Thompson Motors of Wykoff Inc 507 352-2435
125 Gold St S Wykoff (55990) ***(G-10200)***
Thompson Plumbing Co Inc 952 933-7717
15001 Minnetonka Industrial Rd Hopkins (55345) ***(G-2645)***
Thomsen & Nybeck 952 835-7000
3300 Edinbrgh Way Ste 600 Edina (55435) ***(G-1846)***
Thomson Reuters LLC 651 846-2000
30 7th St E Ste 2900 Saint Paul (55101) ***(G-9042)***
Thor Construction Inc 763 571-2580
5400 Main St NE Ste 203 Minneapolis (55421) ***(G-3616)***
Thorco Inc 320 564-3086
1801 County Rd 38 Granite Falls (56241) ***(G-2321)***
Thorn Crest South, Albert Lea *Also Called American Baptist Homes of The* ***(G-40)***
Thorpe Distributing Co 763 463-2000
20240 S Diamond Lake Rd Rogers (55374) ***(G-7343)***
Thorstad Construction Co Inc 320 367-2159
467 Spicer Ave Maynard (56260) ***(G-3337)***
3 Br's Inc 507 645-8600
517 Loomis Ct Northfield (55057) ***(G-6542)***
Three Links Care Center, Northfield *Also Called Minnesota Odd Fellows Home* ***(G-6532)***
3 M Club of St Paul Inc 651 733-3466
11455 20th St N Lake Elmo (55042) ***(G-2877)***
Three Rivers Community Action 507 732-7391
1414 Northstar Dr Zumbrota (55992) ***(G-10220)***
Three Rivers Head Start 507 333-6450
201 Lyndale Ave S Ste 201 Faribault (55021) ***(G-2035)***
Three Rivers Park District 763 694-7670
2935 Parkview Dr Hamel (55340) ***(G-2357)***
Three Rivers Park District 763 694-7894
12400 James Tim Pkwy Osseo (55369) ***(G-6673)***
Three Rivers Park District (PA) 763 559-9000
3000 Xenium Ln N Plymouth (55441) ***(G-6887)***
3-D CNC Inc 320 587-5923
1055 5th Ave SE Hutchinson (55350) ***(G-2713)***
300 Financial Inc 507 424-4799
2768 Superior Dr NW Rochester (55901) ***(G-7274)***
3608 Park Street LLC (DH) 651 221-7911
385 Washington St Saint Paul (55102) ***(G-9043)***
3M Co 507 354-8271
1700 N Minn St Bldg 1 New Ulm (56073) ***(G-6476)***
3M Co 651 733-2147
3M Center Bldg 223SW08 Saint Paul (55144) ***(G-9044)***
3M Co 651 778-5302
690 Bayfield St Saint Paul (55107) ***(G-9045)***
3M Co 651 736-3490
3 M Ctr Bldg 2756SW01 Saint Paul (55144) ***(G-9046)***
3M Co 651 733-5300
3M Center Bldg 223 Saint Paul (55144) ***(G-9047)***
3M Co 651 733-1110
3M Center Bldg 2755E01 Saint Paul (55144) ***(G-9048)***
3M Co 651 733-8432
3 M Ctr Bldg 2233N05 Saint Paul (55144) ***(G-9049)***
3M Co 651 733-2008
3M Center Saint Paul (55144) ***(G-9050)***
3M Co 651 733-3929
3M Center Bldg 2253S05 Saint Paul (55144) ***(G-9051)***
3M Co 651 736-9682
3M Center Saint Paul (55144) ***(G-9052)***
3M Co 651 733-4740
3M Center Bldg 2232N21 Saint Paul (55144) ***(G-9053)***
3M Co 651 733-5000
3M Center Bldg 2232N26 Saint Paul (55144) ***(G-9054)***
3M Co 651 733-1941
3M Center Bldg 223 Saint Paul (55144) ***(G-9055)***
3M Co 651 736-1792
3M Center Bldg 2900402 Saint Paul (55144) ***(G-9056)***
3M Co 651 736-2326
3M Center Bldg 223 Saint Paul (55144) ***(G-9057)***
3M Co 651 733-5623
3M Center Saint Paul (55144) ***(G-9058)***
3M Co 651 733-6678
3M Center Bldg 2208E05 Saint Paul (55144) ***(G-9059)***
3M Co 651 733-1110
3M Center Bldg 2255S08 Saint Paul (55144) ***(G-9060)***
3M Co 651 733-5562
3M Center Bldg 216 Saint Paul (55144) ***(G-9061)***
3M Co 651 733-3154
1024 Hazel St N Bldg 424 Saint Paul (55119) ***(G-9062)***
3M Co 651 736-3828
3 M Ctr Bldg 2234NE13 Saint Paul (55144) ***(G-9063)***
3M Co 651 733-5094
-07 Bldg 216-2N Saint Paul (55106) ***(G-9064)***
3M Co 651 733-0963
3 M Ctr Bldg 2254512 Saint Paul (55144) ***(G-9065)***
3M Co 651 733-6611
3M Center Bldg 5492N18 Saint Paul (55144) ***(G-9066)***
3M Innovative Properties Co 651 733-8904
3M Center Bldg 2254N14 Saint Paul (55144) ***(G-9067)***
3R North Inc 651 674-9977
1234 Main St North Branch (55056) ***(G-6506)***
3Wire Group Inc (DH) 763 488-3000
101 Broadway St W Ste 300 Osseo (55369) ***(G-6674)***
3Wire Group Inc 763 488-3000
201 Broadway St W Osseo (55369) ***(G-6675)***
Threewire Inc 952 852-5556
10250 Valley View Rd # 145 Eden Prairie (55344) ***(G-1792)***
Thrivent Financial For 952 894-6772
350 W Burnsville Pkwy Burnsville (55337) ***(G-808)***
Thrivent Financial For (PA) 920 734-5721
625 4th Ave S Ste 100 Minneapolis (55415) ***(G-5819)***
Thrivent Life Insurance Co 612 340-7000
625 4th Ave S Ste 100 Minneapolis (55415) ***(G-5820)***
Thro Co 507 387-3491
714 Southbend Ave Mankato (56001) ***(G-3203)***
Thro Co 507 345-4631
700 James Ave Mankato (56001) ***(G-3204)***
Thro Co 507 388-2913
201 Oaklawn Ave Mankato (56001) ***(G-3205)***
Thro Co 952 758-2511
1001 Columbus Ave N New Prague (56071) ***(G-6435)***

Thull Construction 320 987-3432
120 2nd Ave S Greenwald (56335) *(G-2327)*
Thunderbird Aviation Inc 952 941-1212
14091 Pioneer Trl Eden Prairie (55347) *(G-1793)*
Thunderbird Lodge Inc 218 286-3151
2170 County Road 139 International Falls (56649) *(G-2732)*
Thygeson Construction Co 218 681-1924
17913 US Highway 59 NE Thief River Falls (56701) *(G-9679)*
Tianna Country Club Inc 218 547-1712
7470 State 34 NW Walker (56484) *(G-9858)*
Ticen's Pro Care, Burnsville *Also Called TPC Landscape Inc (G-809)*
Tidy Clean LLC 507 344-1742
500 Patterson Ave Ste 200 Mankato (56001) *(G-3206)*
Tidy Disposal, Belle Plaine *Also Called Jmdl Inc (G-373)*
Tidy Service of Minnesota Inc 612 332-5461
4301 Blenheim Cir Hopkins (55345) *(G-2646)*
Tierney Brothers Inc 612 331-5500
3300 University Ave SE Minneapolis (55414) *(G-5821)*
Tiffany & Co 952 922-0066
3624 Galleria Minneapolis (55435) *(G-5822)*
Tile By Design Inc 763 551-5900
1720 Annapolis Ln N Minneapolis (55441) *(G-5823)*
Tile Shop Inc (PA) 763 541-1444
14000 Carlson Pkwy Minneapolis (55441) *(G-5824)*
Tile Shop LLC 763 541-1444
14000 Carlson Pkwy Minneapolis (55441) *(G-5825)*
Tile Super Store & More, Rochester *Also Called Korsmo Inc (G-7158)*
Tiller Corp (PA) 763 425-4191
7200 Hemlock Ln N Ste 200 Maple Grove (55369) *(G-3254)*
Tilton Equipment Co (PA) 763 783-7030
30405 Neal Ave Apt 1 Lindstrom (55045) *(G-2971)*
Tim Flanigan Trucking 218 385-3034
409 Heidi Pkwy New York Mills (56567) *(G-6480)*
Tim Orth Memorial Foundation 320 365-4419
80850 400th St Bird Island (55310) *(G-469)*
Timber Creek Golf Course Inc 952 955-3600
9750 County Road 24 Watertown (55388) *(G-9893)*
Timber Roots LLC 507 452-2361
125 W 5th St Winona (55987) *(G-10133)*
Timberland Group Inc 952 924-9070
2635 Louisiana Ave S Minneapolis (55426) *(G-5826)*
Timberland Partners Management 952 893-1216
8000 Norman Center Dr # 830 Minneapolis (55437) *(G-5827)*
Timberland Transportation Inc 651 748-4477
3545 Hoffman Rd E Saint Paul (55110) *(G-9068)*
Timberlodge Steak House, Owatonna *Also Called Midwest Restaurant Group (G-6724)*
Time Communications, Saint Paul *Also Called Bell Telephone Inc (G-8099)*
Timothy J Hernandez MD 651 455-2940
234 Wentworth Ave E Saint Paul (55118) *(G-7922)*
Timothy V Bergin 218 825-2902
581 Edgewood Dr N Baxter (56425) *(G-343)*
Tiny Tots & Little Tykes Pre 651 457-0042
1200 Oakdale Ave Saint Paul (55118) *(G-7923)*
Tire Associates Warehouse Inc 507 625-2975
305 Lundin Blvd Mankato (56001) *(G-3207)*
Tires To Fuel LLC 218 624-5009
226 N Central Ave Duluth (55807) *(G-1485)*
Tisco, Saint Paul *Also Called Woods Equipment Co (G-9166)*
Titan Machinery Inc 218 281-4668
500 Ingersoll Ave Crookston (56716) *(G-1137)*
Titan Machinery Inc 218 681-1423
17108 US Highway 59 NE Thief River Falls (56701) *(G-9680)*
Tivoli Too Inc 651 698-3335
2444 Enterprise Dr Ste A Saint Paul (55120) *(G-7924)*
Tk Advisors Ltd 612 373-9000
920 2nd Ave S Ste 1550 Minneapolis (55402) *(G-5828)*
Tl Nexlevel Co's LLC (PA) 320 963-2400
500 County Road 37 Maple Lake (55358) *(G-3266)*
Tl Wyne 320 240-2180
1301 W Saint Germain St Saint Cloud (56301) *(G-7617)*
TLC Cleaning Specialists 218 263-4778
2512 1st Ave Hibbing (55746) *(G-2477)*
TLC Electronics 651 488-2933
18 Long Lake Rd Saint Paul (55115) *(G-9282)*
TLC Home Health Care Inc 218 326-3555
32809 S Shoal Lake Rd Grand Rapids (55744) *(G-2309)*
TLC Nursing Services of 651 647-0017
1255 Larpenteur Ave E Saint Paul (55109) *(G-9069)*
TMC Enterprises Inc 952 943-9077
9979 Valley View Rd Ste 200 Eden Prairie (55344) *(G-1794)*
TMI Coatings Inc 651 452-6100
3291 Terminal Dr Saint Paul (55121) *(G-7925)*
Tms Construction Inc 952 226-6300
5990 Meadowlark Ln Prior Lake (55372) *(G-6959)*
Todd County Social Services, Long Prairie *Also Called County of Todd (G-3040)*
Todd Wadena Electric Co-op 218 631-3120
550 Ash Ave NE Wadena (56482) *(G-9812)*
Tofte Management Co LLC 218 663-7296
7198 W Highway 61 Tofte (55615) *(G-9684)*
Toll Co 763 551-5355
3005 Niagara Ln N Ste 1 Minneapolis (55447) *(G-5829)*
Tom Johnson 651 645-3000
1045 Westgate Dr Ste 100 Saint Paul (55114) *(G-9070)*
Tom Kelly 507 645-7464
204 7th St W Northfield (55057) *(G-6543)*
Tom Loucks & Associates Inc 763 424-5505
7200 Hemlock Ln N Ste 300 Osseo (55369) *(G-6676)*
Tomsten Inc (PA) 952 516-3300
5900 Clearwater Dr # 500 Minnetonka (55343) *(G-6228)*
Tonna Mechanical Inc 507 288-1908
2411 7th St NW Rochester (55901) *(G-7275)*
Top Notch Siding Co 612 269-7923
8532 Jefferson Hwy Osseo (55369) *(G-6677)*
Top Notch Treecare 763 253-8733
5505 Highway 169 N # 200 Minneapolis (55442) *(G-5830)*
Top Secret Hair Salon 651 500-9233
3925 3rd St NE Minneapolis (55421) *(G-3617)*
Top Star Group, Minneapolis *Also Called East Asian Trading Co Inc (G-4307)*
Top-All Roofing Inc 651 291-7663
291 Eva St Saint Paul (55107) *(G-9071)*
Topline Federal Credit Union 763 391-9494
9353 Jefferson Hwy Maple Grove (55369) *(G-3255)*
Torgerson Hospitality LLC 507 359-2941
2101 S Broadway St New Ulm (56073) *(G-6477)*
Torgerson Properties LP 507 433-6720
701 17th Ave NW Austin (55912) *(G-290)*
Torgerson Properties LP 507 238-4771
1200 Torgerson Dr Fairmont (56031) *(G-1983)*
Toro Co (PA) 952 888-8801
8111 Lyndale Ave S Bloomington (55420) *(G-519)*
Toro Credit Co 952 888-8801
8111 Lyndale Ave S Minneapolis (55420) *(G-5831)*
Toro LLC 952 888-8801
8111 Lyndale Ave S Minneapolis (55420) *(G-5832)*
Toro Receivables Co 952 888-8801
8111 Lyndale Ave S Minneapolis (55420) *(G-5833)*
Torrini Plastering Co Inc 612 332-3933
1967 Timber Wolf Trl S Saint Paul (55122) *(G-7926)*
Toshiba Business Solutions, Saint Paul *Also Called Stringer Business Systems Inc (G-7914)*
Total Automotive Inc 952 448-7750
2431 Galpin Ct Ste 110 Chanhassen (55317) *(G-944)*
Total Card Inc 507 449-6401
1 Roundwind Rd Luverne (56156) *(G-3071)*
Total Comfort, Minneapolis *Also Called A-ABC Appliance & Heating Inc (G-3652)*
Total Concrete Services 763 786-8477
2699 Rodeo Dr NE Minneapolis (55449) *(G-3618)*
Total Quality Maintenance 763 377-6530
1 Westwood Dr N Minneapolis (55422) *(G-5834)*
Total Renal Care Inc 612 347-5972
825 S 8th St Ste 400 Minneapolis (55404) *(G-5835)*
Total Renal Care Inc 612 873-6089
825 S 8th St Ste 400 Minneapolis (55404) *(G-5836)*
Total Renal Care Inc 651 483-3159
3900 Northwoods Dr Ste 110 Saint Paul (55112) *(G-9072)*
Total Rental, Shakopee *Also Called Bug Inc (G-9424)*
Total Tool Supply Inc 651 646-4055
315 Pierce St N Ste A Saint Paul (55104) *(G-9073)*
Total Training Network Inc 952 345-5555
7831 E Bush Lake Rd # 200 Minneapolis (55439) *(G-5837)*
Total Transportation Corp 651 770-5668
3565 Hoffman Rd E Saint Paul (55110) *(G-9074)*
Tourco's Firstline Tours Inc 763 780-2985
1313 Osborne Rd NE Minneapolis (55432) *(G-3619)*
Tournament Club of Iowa LLC 952 252-4474
6800 France Ave S Ste 178 Minneapolis (55435) *(G-5838)*
Tournament Players Club, Minneapolis *Also Called Pga Tour Inc (G-3570)*
Tow Distributing Corp 507 388-2931
3100 3rd Ave Mankato (56001) *(G-3208)*
Tower Asphalt, Lakeland *Also Called Hardrives Inc (G-2885)*
Tower Hill Association 763 682-2321
110 1st Ave NE Buffalo (55313) *(G-658)*
Towers Watson Delaware Inc 952 842-7000
8400 Normandale Lake Blvd Minneapolis (55437) *(G-5839)*
Towers Watson Pennsylvania Inc 952 842-5600
7650 Edinbrgh Way Ste 500 Minneapolis (55435) *(G-5840)*
Town & Country Bus Co Inc 763 786-2510
9015 Radisson Rd NE Minneapolis (55449) *(G-3620)*
Town & Country Caterers Inc 763 559-4461
3155 Empire Ln N Plymouth (55447) *(G-6888)*
Town & Country Club of St 651 646-7121
300 Mississippi River Blvd N Saint Paul (55104) *(G-9075)*
Town & Country Fence Inc 763 425-5050
8511 Xylon Ave N Minneapolis (55445) *(G-5841)*
Townhomes At Lutsen Mountains 218 663-7241
371 Ski Hill Rd Lutsen (55612) *(G-3058)*
Toyota City Inc 763 566-0060
7325 Brooklyn Blvd Minneapolis (55443) *(G-5842)*
Toyota-Lift of Minnesota Inc 763 425-9066
8601 Xylon Ct Brooklyn Park (55445) *(G-619)*
TPC Landscape Inc 952 898-7600
14284 Newton Ave S Burnsville (55306) *(G-809)*
Tpg Credit Management, LP 612 851-3000
4600 Wells Fargo Ctr Minneapolis (55402) *(G-5843)*
Tpi Core Inc 507 433-1000
1701 4th St NW Austin (55912) *(G-291)*
Tpi Core Inc 320 231-2301
2100 Highway 12 E Willmar (56201) *(G-10048)*
Tracy Area Medical Services, Tracy *Also Called Sanford Health Network (G-9691)*
Tracy Healthcare Center Inc 507 629-3331
250 5th St E Tracy (56175) *(G-9692)*
Tradition Capital Bank 952 806-6600
7601 France Ave S Ste 140 Edina (55435) *(G-1847)*
Tradition Development 952 920-5100
6800 France Ave S Ste 178 Minneapolis (55435) *(G-5844)*
Tradition Mortgage LLC 952 920-5100
6800 France Ave S Ste 178 Minneapolis (55435) *(G-5845)*
Traditions of Minnesota LLC 507 455-0700
195 24th Pl NW Owatonna (55060) *(G-6740)*
Traditions of Owatonna 507 451-0433
150 24th Pl NW Owatonna (55060) *(G-6741)*
Trail Dodge Inc 651 455-2201
4665 S Robert Trl Inver Grove Heights (55077) *(G-2772)*
Trailers Plus, Hill City *Also Called Mike Bishoff (G-2481)*
Trammell Crow Co 952 936-3671
9900 Bren Rd E Minnetonka (55343) *(G-6229)*
Trans Group, Shakopee *Also Called Logistics International LLC (G-9451)*
Trans-Alarm Inc (PA) 952 894-1700
500 E Travelers Trl # 600 Burnsville (55337) *(G-810)*
Transcend Communications Inc 763 463-1000
2101 Kennedy St NE Minneapolis (55413) *(G-5846)*
Transcriptions Inc 952 831-4480
6500 City West Pkwy # 310 Eden Prairie (55344) *(G-1795)*
Transformation House Inc 763 427-7155
1410 S Ferry St Anoka (55303) *(G-236)*

ALPHABETIC

Transit Team Inc 612 332-3323
1154 N 5th St Minneapolis (55411) **(G-5847)**
Transit TEC Ltd 320 253-5940
23823 67th Ave Saint Cloud (56301) **(G-7618)**
Transport Corp Of America Inc (HQ) 651 686-2500
1715 Yankee Doodle Rd Eagan (55121) **(G-1557)**
Transport Designs Inc 952 894-8242
3451 W Burnsville Pkwy Burnsville (55337) **(G-811)**
Transport Leasing Contract Inc (PA) 763 585-7000
6160 Summit Dr N Ste 500 Minneapolis (55430) **(G-5848)**
Transportation Management Corp 651 642-9292
1907 Charles Ave Saint Paul (55104) **(G-9076)**
Transunion LLC 651 639-0007
2780 Snelling Ave N Ste 309 Saint Paul (55113) **(G-9077)**
Transway Express Inc 651 686-7000
812 Water St S Northfield (55057) **(G-6544)**
Transystems LLC 218 281-7514
Hwy 25 S B Crookston (56716) **(G-1138)**
Transystems LLC 218 773-8813
43994 Business Highway 2 East Grand Forks (56721) **(G-1576)**
Transystems LLC 218 233-8121
2486 11th St N Moorhead (56560) **(G-6343)**
Trapper's Landing Lodge 218 836-2500
1812 Merit Rd NW Walker (56484) **(G-9859)**
Traumatic Brain Injury 218 733-1331
1731 W Superior St Duluth (55806) **(G-1486)**
Travel Leaders 952 941-8900
6409 City West Pkwy # 104 Eden Prairie (55344) **(G-1796)**
Travel Leaders Group LLC (PA) 952 914-6500
6442 City West Pkwy Eden Prairie (55344) **(G-1797)**
Travel One Inc 952 854-2551
8009 34th Ave S Ste 1500 Minneapolis (55425) **(G-5849)**
Travel Suites of Coon Rapids 763 780-3797
155 Coon Rapids Blvd NW Minneapolis (55433) **(G-3621)**
Travelnet Solutions Inc 651 757-4905
9900 Hemingway Ave S Cottage Grove (55016) **(G-1108)**
Travelodge & Suite 218 233-5333
3027 S Frontage Rd Moorhead (56560) **(G-6344)**
Travelodge Tower 651 735-2333
1870 Old Hudson Rd Saint Paul (55119) **(G-9078)**
Travelsmart LLC 952 854-1114
7800 Metro Pkwy Ste 300 Bloomington (55425) **(G-520)**
Traverse Care Center 320 563-8124
303 7th St S Wheaton (56296) **(G-9969)**
Traxler Construction Inc 507 357-2235
625 Commerce Dr Le Center (56057) **(G-2954)**
Tre Hus Builders, Minneapolis *Also Called Trehus Builders Inc* **(G-5850)**
Treasure Island Casino & Bingo 651 388-6300
5734 Sturgeon Lake Rd Welch (55089) **(G-9957)**
Treb, Dan Painting 952 476-8163
488 Tamarack Ave Long Lake (55356) **(G-3034)**
Tree of Life LLC 612 752-6300
601 Campus Dr Ste 11 Saint Paul (55112) **(G-9079)**
Trehus Builders Inc 612 729-2992
3017 4th Ave S Minneapolis (55408) **(G-5850)**
Trenti Law Firm Inc 218 749-1962
1000 Lincoln Bldg Virginia (55792) **(G-9758)**
Trentroy Corp 952 445-3820
18440 Langford Ave Jordan (55352) **(G-2811)**
Tri, Minneapolis *Also Called Telemarketing Results Inc* **(G-5809)**
Tri Cap Tri County Action 320 255-0769
2341 County Road 137 Waite Park (56387) **(G-9844)**
Tri City American Legion 651 631-1124
400 Old Highway 8 NW Saint Paul (55112) **(G-9080)**
Tri City Enterprises Inc 952 888-4447
2800 American Blvd W Minneapolis (55431) **(G-5851)**
Tri City Post 513 ....651 631-1124
400 Old Highway 8 NW Saint Paul (55112) **(G-9081)**
Tri County Ambulance Service 218 436-2230
Karlstad Memorial Hosp Karlstad (56732) **(G-2816)**
Tri County Humane Society Inc 320 252-0896
735 8th St NE Saint Cloud (56304) **(G-7430)**
Tri State Machinery Co 952 224-1500
13400 Bryant Ave S Burnsville (55337) **(G-812)**
Tri-City IV Inc 952 854-7405
8030 Cedar Ave S Ste 120 Bloomington (55425) **(G-521)**
Tri-County Abstract & Title 320 253-2096
122 12th Ave N Saint Cloud (56303) **(G-7619)**
Tri-County Action Program Inc (PA) 320 251-1612
1210 23rd Ave S Waite Park (56387) **(G-9845)**
Tri-County Action Program Inc 320 255-0705
2341 County Road 137 Waite Park (56387) **(G-9846)**
Tri-County Community Action (PA) 320 632-3691
501 Lemieur St Little Falls (56345) **(G-3020)**
Tri-County Electric Co-op 507 864-7783
31110 Cooperative Way Rushford (55971) **(G-7394)**
Tri-County Hospital Inc 218 631-3510
415 Jefferson St N Wadena (56482) **(G-9813)**
Tri-County Parts Supply Inc 320 253-5050
46 33rd Ave N Saint Cloud (56303) **(G-7620)**
Tri-State Drilling Inc 763 553-1234
16940 Highway 55 Minneapolis (55446) **(G-5852)**
Tri-Valley Opportunity Council (PA) 218 281-5832
102 N Broadway Crookston (56716) **(G-1139)**
Tri-Valley Opportunity Council 218 281-5832
102 N Broadway Crookston (56716) **(G-1140)**
Tri-Valley Opportunity Council 218 281-5832
102 N Broadway Crookston (56716) **(G-1141)**
Tria Orthopaedic Center Asc 952 831-8742
8100 Northland Dr Minneapolis (55431) **(G-5853)**
Triadvantage Credit Services 651 255-2047
1160 Centre Pointe Dr Ste 1 Saint Paul (55120) **(G-7927)**
Triangle Services Inc 651 294-0020
1611 County Road B W # 320 Saint Paul (55113) **(G-9082)**
Triangle Warehouse Inc 651 633-8912
3501 Marshall St NE Minneapolis (55418) **(G-5854)**
Trico Tcwind Inc 320 693-6200
111 E 10th St Litchfield (55355) **(G-2991)**
Tricom Communications Inc 651 686-9000
2401 Pilot Knob Rd Ste 126 Saint Paul (55120) **(G-7928)**
Tricord Systems Inc 763 557-9005
2905 NW Blvd Ste 20 Minneapolis (55441) **(G-5855)**
Tricounty Implement, Saint James *Also Called C & B Operations LLC* **(G-7642)**
Triggers Restaurant, Prior Lake *Also Called Minnesota Horse & Hunt Club* **(G-6943)**
Trimark Hotel Corp 612 305-9763
1313 Nicollet Ave Minneapolis (55403) **(G-5856)**
Trimark Industrial, Virginia *Also Called Edwards Oil Co Inc* **(G-9738)**
Trimark Sportswear Group, Hopkins *Also Called River's End Holdings LLC* **(G-2618)**
TriMin Systems Inc 651 636-7667
2277 Highway 36 W 101E Saint Paul (55113) **(G-9083)**
Trimline 763 540-9737
705 Pennsylvania Ave S Minneapolis (55426) **(G-5857)**
Trimont Health Care Center 507 639-2381
303 Broadway St S Trimont (56176) **(G-9694)**
Trimpac Inc 320 650-0420
6380 Saukview Dr Saint Cloud (56303) **(G-7621)**
Trimpac Inc (PA) 320 202-3200
1030 Stearns Dr Sauk Rapids (56379) **(G-9378)**
Triple Crown Gaming Inc 320 251-5373
2769 Clearwater Rd Saint Cloud (56301) **(G-7622)**
Triple D Construction 218 465-4249
Csah 5 Oklee (56742) **(G-6558)**
Triple J Enterprises Inc (PA) 952 853-9898
2680 E 81st St Minneapolis (55425) **(G-5858)**
Triple J Enterprises Inc 952 853-9898
2680 E 81st St Minneapolis (55425) **(G-5859)**
Trissential 952 595-7970
301 Carlson Pkwy Ste 303 Hopkins (55305) **(G-2647)**
Triton Tire & Battery LLC 651 239-1200
1300 Corporate Ctr Curv Saint Paul (55121) **(G-7929)**
Trobec's Bus Service Inc 320 251-1202
413 County Road 2 S Saint Stephen (56375) **(G-9317)**
Trout Enterprises Inc of Nthn 218 246-8165
Hwy 2 E Deer River (56636) **(G-1174)**
Tru Green-Chemlawn, Burnsville *Also Called Trugreen Ltd Ptn* **(G-814)**
Tru Green-Chemlawn, Hopkins *Also Called Trugreen LP* **(G-2648)**
Tru Green-Chemlawn, Rochester *Also Called Trugreen LP* **(G-7276)**
Tru Green-Chemlawn, Saint Paul *Also Called Trugreen Ltd Ptn* **(G-9085)**
Tru-Stone Technologies, Waite Park *Also Called L S Starrett Co* **(G-9825)**
Truck Crane Service-Illinois 651 406-4949
2875 Highway 55 Saint Paul (55121) **(G-7930)**
Truck Utilities Inc (PA) 651 484-3305
2370 English St Saint Paul (55109) **(G-9084)**
Truckers Inn, Sauk Centre *Also Called I D D D Inc* **(G-9347)**
Truckers Inn Truck Stop, Faribault *Also Called I D D D Inc* **(G-2012)**
Trudeau Holdings LLC (PA) 952 882-8295
25 Cliff Rd W Ste 115 Burnsville (55337) **(G-813)**
Trudeau Holdings LLC 952 445-1350
4218 Valley Ind Blvd S Shakopee (55379) **(G-9481)**
Trudell Trailers of Minnesota 763 497-7084
9600 71st St NE Albertville (55301) **(G-77)**
True Value Co 507 625-6021
2415 3rd Ave Mankato (56001) **(G-3209)**
True Value Hardware, Faribault *Also Called Faribo Farm & Home Supply Inc* **(G-2006)**
Trueblue Inc 218 624-6222
4402 Grand Ave Duluth (55807) **(G-1487)**
Trugreen Landcare LLC 651 994-9855
3259 Terminal Dr Ste 100 Saint Paul (55121) **(G-7931)**
Trugreen LP 952 933-7360
6010 Culligan Way Hopkins (55345) **(G-2648)**
Trugreen LP 612 493-5035
11755 95th Ave N Osseo (55369) **(G-6678)**
Trugreen LP 507 289-8798
6636 10th Ave SW Rochester (55902) **(G-7276)**
Trugreen Ltd Ptn 952 895-3400
14360 Ewing Ave S Burnsville (55306) **(G-814)**
Trugreen Ltd Ptn 651 407-3400
4240 Centerville Rd Saint Paul (55127) **(G-9085)**
Truman Sr Living Inc 507 776-2031
400 N 4th Ave E Truman (56088) **(G-9697)**
Truseal America LLC 952 895-9197
4980 Dodd Rd Eagan (55123) **(G-1558)**
Trust Mortgage, Bemidji *Also Called Trustcorp Mortgage Co* **(G-429)**
Trust Security 952 914-9300
5100 Edina Industrial Blvd Minneapolis (55439) **(G-5860)**
Trustar Federal Credit Union 218 283-2000
601 4th St International Falls (56649) **(G-2733)**
Trustcorp Mortgage Co 218 444-5626
1499 Anne St NW Bemidji (56601) **(G-429)**
Trustee Group LLP 952 473-5650
3610 County Road 101 S Wayzata (55391) **(G-9946)**
Trustone Financial Federal (PA) 763 544-1517
14601 27th Ave N Ste 104 Minneapolis (55447) **(G-5861)**
Trustone Financial Federal 763 544-1517
6681 Country Club Dr Minneapolis (55427) **(G-5862)**
Tubman 612 871-0118
4432 Chicago Ave Ste 1 Minneapolis (55407) **(G-5863)**
Tubman Family Alliance 612 825-0000
3111 1st Ave S Minneapolis (55408) **(G-5864)**
Tuesday Networking Inc 952 942-7378
9196 Neill Lake Rd Eden Prairie (55347) **(G-1798)**
Tuff Memorial Homes Inc 507 962-3275
505 E 4th St Hills (56138) **(G-2482)**
Tunheim Partners Inc 952 851-1600
8009 34th Ave S Ste 1100 Minneapolis (55425) **(G-5865)**
Turkey Valley Farms LLC 507 337-3100
112 S 6th St Marshall (56258) **(G-3330)**
Turner Club, New Ulm *Also Called New Ulm Turnverein Inc* **(G-6469)**
Turner Excavating Co 952 890-1645
12520 Nevada Ave Savage (55378) **(G-9410)**
Turnery Properties LP 763 546-6277
6300 Wayzata Blvd Minneapolis (55416) **(G-5866)**
Turning Point Administrative 612 520-4004
1500 Golden Valley Rd Minneapolis (55411) **(G-5867)**

ALPHABETIC SECTION
Uni-Systems LLC

Turning Point Foundation 612 520-4004
1500 Golden Valley Rd Minneapolis (55411) *(G-5868)*
Turning Point Inc 612 520-4004
1500 Golden Valley Rd Minneapolis (55411) *(G-5869)*
Tuttle Inc 612 378-9701
729 Marshall St NE Minneapolis (55413) *(G-5870)*
Tuttle's Bowling Bar & Grill 952 938-4090
107 Shady Oak Rd S Hopkins (55343) *(G-2649)*
Tuv Sud America Inc 651 631-2487
1775 Old Highway 8 NW Ste 104 Saint Paul (55112) *(G-9086)*
TW Telecom Inc 952 351-2300
5480 Feltl Rd Hopkins (55343) *(G-2650)*
Tweeten-Lutheran Health Care 507 498-3211
125 5th Ave SE Spring Grove (55974) *(G-9562)*
21st Century Bank 763 479-1901
699 N Medina St Loretto (55357) *(G-3053)*
21st Century Bank (HQ) 763 767-2178
9380 Central Ave NE # 120 Minneapolis (55434) *(G-3622)*
21st Century Bank (PA) 763 767-2178
9380 Central Ave NE # 120 Minneapolis (55434) *(G-3623)*
21st Services 612 371-3008
200 S 6th St Ste 350 Minneapolis (55402) *(G-5871)*
21st Services LLC 612 371-3008
200 S 6th St Ste 350 Minneapolis (55402) *(G-5872)*
Twenty One Centry Farm System, New Prague *Also Called Genex Farm Systems* *(G-6428)*
Twig Bakery & Cafe, Duluth *Also Called Tech Investments Inc* *(G-1481)*
Twin Cities & Western Railroad (PA) 320 864-7200
2925 12th St E Glencoe (55336) *(G-2216)*
Twin Cities Div, Saint Paul *Also Called Albert's Organics Inc* *(G-8005)*
Twin Cities Mack Volvo Trucks 651 633-4810
2195 County Road C2 W Saint Paul (55113) *(G-9087)*
Twin Cities Public Television 651 222-1717
172 4th St E Saint Paul (55101) *(G-9088)*
Twin Cities Rise 612 338-0295
800 Washington Ave N Minneapolis (55401) *(G-5873)*
Twin Cities Spine Surgeons Ltd 612 775-6200
913 E 26th St Ste 600 Minneapolis (55404) *(G-5874)*
Twin Cities Transport 651 642-1446
1396 Concordia Ave Saint Paul (55104) *(G-9089)*
Twin Cities Transport (PA) 651 770-0816
274 N1 Geneva Ave Saint Paul (55128) *(G-9283)*
Twin Cities Tree Trust 651 644-6237
2350 Wycliff St Ste 200 Saint Paul (55114) *(G-9090)*
Twin City Acoustics Inc 763 535-6697
2655 Cheshire Ln N # 100 Minneapolis (55447) *(G-5875)*
Twin City Agency Inc 952 924-6900
4500 Park Glen Rd Ste 400 Minneapolis (55416) *(G-5876)*
Twin City Auto Body Collision 952 884-9878
419 W 90th St Minneapolis (55420) *(G-5877)*
Twin City Christian Homes Inc 952 944-8982
625 Prairie Center Dr Eden Prairie (55344) *(G-1799)*
Twin City Concrete Products Co 651 489-8095
1351 Trout Brook Cir Saint Paul (55117) *(G-9091)*
Twin City Container Inc (PA) 651 480-3786
990 Spiral Blvd Hastings (55033) *(G-2409)*
Twin City Cremation Supply, Minneapolis *Also Called Cremation Society Inc* *(G-4181)*
Twin City Custom Railings & GL 763 780-7314
1582 93rd Ln NE Minneapolis (55449) *(G-3624)*
Twin City Exteriors Co Inc 763 425-4737
9060 Zachary Ln N Ste 108 Osseo (55369) *(G-6679)*
Twin City Fan Co's Ltd (PA) 763 551-7600
5959 Trenton Ln N Minneapolis (55442) *(G-5878)*
Twin City Florist Supply Inc 612 377-7849
2308 Humboldt Ave S Minneapolis (55405) *(G-5879)*
Twin City Glass Contractors 651 746-0650
520 Atwater Cir Saint Paul (55103) *(G-9092)*
Twin City Group Inc (PA) 952 924-6900
4500 Park Glen Rd # 400 Minneapolis (55416) *(G-5880)*
Twin City Hardware Co 763 535-4660
5650 International Pkwy Minneapolis (55428) *(G-5881)*
Twin City Hardware Co (PA) 651 735-2200
723 Hadley Ave N Saint Paul (55128) *(G-9284)*
Twin City Hose Inc 763 428-5100
20615 Commerce Blvd Rogers (55374) *(G-7344)*
Twin City Limousine 651 222-8553
584 Stryker Ave Fl 13 Saint Paul (55107) *(G-9093)*
Twin City Optical, Minneapolis *Also Called Essilor Laboratories of Amer* *(G-4372)*
Twin City Oral & Maxillofacial 651 437-3262
925 Highway 55 Ste 202 Hastings (55033) *(G-2410)*
Twin City Poultry Co 763 592-6500
4630 Quebec Ave N Uppr Minneapolis (55428) *(G-5882)*
Twin City Produce Supplies Inc 612 378-1055
744 Kasota Cir SE Minneapolis (55414) *(G-5883)*
Twin City Red Cross, Minneapolis *Also Called American National Red Cross* *(G-3757)*
Twin City Risk Group Inc 952 924-6900
4500 Park Glen Rd Ste 400 Minneapolis (55416) *(G-5884)*
Twin City Security Inc 763 784-4160
519 Coon Rapids Blvd NW Minneapolis (55433) *(G-3625)*
Twin City Tile & Marble Co Inc 651 602-5800
900 Montreal Way Saint Paul (55102) *(G-9094)*
Twin City Twisters Inc 763 421-3046
9001 123rd Ave N Champlin (55316) *(G-903)*
Twin City West 76 Auto Truck 763 428-2277
13400 Rogers Dr Rogers (55374) *(G-7345)*
Twin Courier Corp 763 576-1133
11029 Woodhaven Ct N Champlin (55316) *(G-904)*
Twin Express Inc 763 428-4969
21840 Industrial Ct # 100 Rogers (55374) *(G-7346)*
Twin Town Bowl Inc 507 387-3439
1247 Range St Mankato (56001) *(G-3210)*
Twin Town Treatment Center LLC (PA) 651 645-3661
1706 University Ave W Saint Paul (55104) *(G-9095)*
Twinco Romax LLC (PA) 763 478-2360
4635 Willow Dr Hamel (55340) *(G-2358)*
Two Men & Truck 651 645-1279
670 Commerce Dr Ste 240 Saint Paul (55125) *(G-9285)*
Two Rivers Enterprises Inc 320 746-3156
490 River St W Holdingford (56340) *(G-2491)*
Two Rivers Inc 715 262-5292
14345 Conley Ave Rosemount (55068) *(G-7376)*
2020 Promotions LLC 651 451-3850
135 Grand Ave E South Saint Paul (55075) *(G-9545)*
Twv LP 651 291-1750
12861 Ctrl Ave NE Apt 103 Minneapolis (55434) *(G-3626)*
Twv LP 651 291-1750
422 Concord St Saint Paul (55107) *(G-9096)*
Tyco Electronics Corp 651 565-2601
1313 Grant Blvd W Wabasha (55981) *(G-9772)*
Tyler Area Community Club 507 247-3905
151 N Tyker St Tyler (56178) *(G-9715)*
Tyler Healthcare Center Inc 507 247-5521
240 Willow St Tyler (56178) *(G-9716)*
Tympany LLC 866 316-3606
5000 Township Pkwy Saint Paul (55110) *(G-9097)*
Tyson Fresh Meats Inc 507 776-2828
2241 State Highway 15 Truman (56088) *(G-9698)*
U About Inc 612 866-4884
6702 Penn Ave S Richfield (55423) *(G-7039)*
U M D Facilities Management 218 726-8262
1049 University Dr Rm 241 Duluth (55812) *(G-1488)*
U of M Parking & Trnsp Svcs, Minneapolis *Also Called Regents of The University of* *(G-5492)*
U S Bancorp (PA) 651 466-3000
800 Nicollet Mall Ste 800 Minneapolis (55402) *(G-5885)*
U S Bank Home Mortgage (HQ) 952 851-5494
1550 Amrcn Blvd E Ste 880 Bloomington (55425) *(G-522)*
U S Bank National Association 612 728-8300
2800 E Lake St Minneapolis (55406) *(G-5886)*
U S Bank National Association 952 925-7333
4100 W 50th St Ste 1 Minneapolis (55424) *(G-5887)*
U S Bank National Association 651 426-8266
4700 Clark Ave Saint Paul (55110) *(G-9098)*
U S Commodities L L C 612 486-3800
730 2nd Ave S Ste 700 Minneapolis (55402) *(G-5888)*
U S Distilled Products, Princeton *Also Called United States Distilled Prdts* *(G-6918)*
U S Filter Recovery Services 651 638-1300
2430 Rose Pl Saint Paul (55113) *(G-9099)*
U S Filter Waterpro 952 893-9130
4570 W 77th St Ste 300 Minneapolis (55435) *(G-5889)*
U S Insulation Inc 763 785-1726
2201 108th Ln NE Minneapolis (55449) *(G-3627)*
U S Internet Corp 651 222-4638
12450 Wayzata Blvd Ste 121 Minnetonka (55305) *(G-6230)*
U S Probation Office 612 664-5400
300 S 4th St Ste 406 Minneapolis (55415) *(G-5890)*
U S Steel, Mountain Iron *Also Called United States Steel Corp* *(G-6394)*
U S Warehouse Supply Inc 651 405-3500
2861 Eagandale Blvd Saint Paul (55121) *(G-7932)*
U Save Auto Auto Rental, Monticello *Also Called Nintey Four Services Inc* *(G-6279)*
U Save Lease & Rental Inc 218 732-3347
E Highway 34 Park Rapids (56470) *(G-6764)*
U-Haul Co of Minnesota (DH) 763 780-9746
9890 Central Ave NE Minneapolis (55434) *(G-3628)*
Uafp, Minneapolis *Also Called University Affiliated Family* *(G-5923)*
UBS Financial Services Inc 952 921-7900
8500 Nrmndl Lk Blvd Ste 210 Minneapolis (55437) *(G-5891)*
UBS Financial Services Inc 651 298-1616
444 Cedar St Ste 2200 Saint Paul (55101) *(G-9100)*
Ucare Minnesota 612 676-6500
500 Stinson Blvd Minneapolis (55413) *(G-5892)*
Udac Inc 218 722-5867
500 E 10th St Duluth (55805) *(G-1489)*
Udell Dental Laboratory Inc 952 926-9266
3361 Gorham Ave Minneapolis (55426) *(G-5893)*
Uhc - Edina 763 519-1335
5901 Lincoln Dr Minneapolis (55436) *(G-5894)*
Uhl Co Inc 763 425-7226
9065 Zachary Ln N Osseo (55369) *(G-6680)*
Uhs, Minneapolis *Also Called Universal Hospital Services* *(G-5919)*
Uline Inc 651 688-3495
985 Aldrin Dr Saint Paul (55121) *(G-7933)*
Uline Inc 651 688-3495
985 Aldrin Dr Saint Paul (55121) *(G-7934)*
Ulland Brothers Inc 507 373-1960
2400 Myers Rd Albert Lea (56007) *(G-68)*
Ulland Brothers Inc 218 262-3406
505 W 37th St Hibbing (55746) *(G-2478)*
Uls of New England LLC (PA) 651 227-9855
55 5th St E Ste 960 Saint Paul (55101) *(G-9101)*
Ulteig Engineers Inc 218 847-5607
1041 Hawk St Detroit Lakes (56501) *(G-1220)*
Ulteig Engineers Inc 763 571-2500
5201 E River Rd Ste 308 Minneapolis (55421) *(G-3629)*
Ultima Bank Minnesota (PA) 218 938-4144
Main St Winger (56592) *(G-10074)*
Ultimate Acquisition Partners 952 830-0010
7435 France Ave S Minneapolis (55435) *(G-5895)*
Ultra Creative Inc 612 378-0748
43 Main St SE Ste 430 Minneapolis (55414) *(G-5896)*
Ulysses Telemedia Networks Inc 763 225-5000
1300 Godward St NE # 3100 Minneapolis (55413) *(G-5897)*
Um Electric Utlts Shop 612 625-8081
319 15th Ave SE Ste 300 Minneapolis (55455) *(G-5898)*
Umi Co Inc 612 331-2566
2950 Weeks Ave SE Minneapolis (55414) *(G-5899)*
Umyc, Spring Park *Also Called Upper Minnetonka Yacht Club* *(G-9567)*
Under The Rainbow Child Care 651 388-6433
555 Technology Dr Red Wing (55066) *(G-7009)*
UNI-Select USA Inc 952 352-8603
7900 Excelsior Blvd Eden Prairie (55343) *(G-1800)*
UNI-Select USA Inc 763 566-1285
6001 78th Ave N Minneapolis (55443) *(G-5900)*
Uni-Systems LLC 763 536-1407
4600 Lake Road Ave Minneapolis (55422) *(G-5901)*

ALPHABETIC

Unicom Consulting Inc 952 698-7600
7400 Metro Blvd Ste 400 Minneapolis (55439) ***(G-5902)***
Unicon Inc 763 424-7892
7610 Commerce St Hamel (55340) ***(G-2359)***
Unified Theory Inc 651 578-8100
1811 Weir Dr Ste 365 Saint Paul (55125) ***(G-9286)***
Unimax Systems Corp 612 341-0946
430 1st Ave N Ste 790 Minneapolis (55401) ***(G-5903)***
Unimed-Midwest Inc 952 469-9400
21875 Grenada Ave Lakeville (55044) ***(G-2938)***
Unimin Corp 507 665-3386
39770 Ottawa Rd Le Sueur (56058) ***(G-2960)***
Union Bank & Trust Co 612 379-3222
312 Central Ave SE Minneapolis (55414) ***(G-5904)***
Union Gospel Mission Assn 651 292-1721
435 University Ave E Saint Paul (55130) ***(G-9102)***
Union Pacific Railroad Co 507 452-4337
50 Harvester Ave Winona (55987) ***(G-10134)***
Union Pacific Railroad Co Inc 651 552-3925
301 Hardman Ave N South Saint Paul (55075) ***(G-9546)***
Union Security Insurance Co 952 920-8990
6600 France Ave S Ste 314 Minneapolis (55435) ***(G-5905)***
Unipatch, Wabasha *Also Called Tyco Electronics Corp* ***(G-9772)***
Unipower Industrial Corp 952 884-2933
1216 W 96th St Minneapolis (55431) ***(G-5906)***
Uniprise Inc 763 765-0852
12755 Highway 55 Ste 100 Plymouth (55441) ***(G-6889)***
Uniquescreen, Saint Cloud *Also Called Cinedigm Digital Cinema Corp* ***(G-7492)***
Uniquescreen Media Inc 320 654-6578
4140 Thielman Ln Ste 304 Saint Cloud (56301) ***(G-7623)***
Unishippers of Minnesota, Moorhead *Also Called Lake Country Logistics LLC* ***(G-6322)***
Unison Insurance 952 345-2305
3173 Shady Cove Pt NW # 10901 Prior Lake (55372) ***(G-6960)***
Unisource Worldwide Inc 763 488-7200
9001 Wyoming Ave N Brooklyn Park (55445) ***(G-620)***
Unisys Corp 651 635-7777
2470 Highcrest Rd Saint Paul (55113) ***(G-9103)***
Unisys Corp 651 687-2200
3199 Pilot Knob Rd Saint Paul (55121) ***(G-7935)***
United Building Centers, Lakeville *Also Called Probuild Co LLC* ***(G-2925)***
United Building Centers, Saint Cloud *Also Called Probuild Co LLC* ***(G-7573)***
United Building Centers, Wadena *Also Called Probuild Co LLC* ***(G-9810)***
United Business Mail Inc 612 782-2044
405 35th Ave NE Ste 2 Minneapolis (55418) ***(G-5907)***
United Check Clearing Corp 763 559-2225
3600 Holly Ln N Ste 60 Minneapolis (55447) ***(G-5908)***
United Clinic of Faribault 507 526-7388
435 S Grove St Ste 1 Blue Earth (56013) ***(G-538)***
United Communications Corp 507 625-7905
1570 Lookout Dr Mankato (56003) ***(G-3232)***
United Communications Corp 507 625-7905
1570 Lookout Dr North Mankato (56003) ***(G-6515)***
United Community Bank 218 346-5700
155 2nd Ave SW Perham (56573) ***(G-6803)***
United Entertainment Corp 320 203-1003
2700 1st St N Ste 200 Saint Cloud (56303) ***(G-7624)***
United Family Practice Health 651 241-1000
1026 7th St W Saint Paul (55102) ***(G-9104)***
United Farmers Co Op 507 237-2281
120 High Ave Gaylord (55334) ***(G-2201)***
United Farmers Cooperative 507 228-8224
840 Pioneer Ave Lafayette (56054) ***(G-2847)***
United Fcs (PA) 320 235-1771
3881 Abbott Dr Willmar (56201) ***(G-10049)***
United Glass Inc 651 633-2529
1480 County Road C W Saint Paul (55113) ***(G-9105)***
United Hardware Distributing (PA) 763 559-1800
5005 Nathan Ln N Minneapolis (55442) ***(G-5909)***
United Healthcare, Minnetonka *Also Called Unitedhealth Group Inc* ***(G-6232)***
United Healthcare of Wyoming 218 279-5642
4316 Rice Lake Rd Duluth (55811) ***(G-1490)***
United Healthcare of Wyoming 952 992-5450
5901 Lincoln Dr Edina (55436) ***(G-1848)***
United Healthcare of Wyoming 651 603-8515
2550 University Ave W Ste 401S Saint Paul (55114) ***(G-9106)***
United Homecare Inc 952 898-9780
15001 Willa Ct Burnsville (55306) ***(G-815)***
United Hospital, Saint Paul *Also Called Allina Medical Center* ***(G-8017)***
United Hospital District (PA) 507 526-3273
515 S Moore St Blue Earth (56013) ***(G-539)***
United Hospital District 218 894-8610
49725 County 83 Staples (56479) ***(G-9587)***
United Linen Services Inc 651 227-9855
55 5th St E Ste 960 Saint Paul (55101) ***(G-9107)***
United Noodles Inc 612 721-6677
2015 E 24th St Minneapolis (55404) ***(G-5910)***
United Operations Inc of 763 551-0202
5025 Cheshire Ln N Ste 1 Minneapolis (55446) ***(G-5911)***
United Parcel Service Inc 507 373-4392
707 E 12th St Albert Lea (56007) ***(G-69)***
United Parcel Service Inc 320 762-2746
Hwy 27 E Alexandria (56308) ***(G-127)***
United Parcel Service Inc 218 829-6240
1009 Madison St Brainerd (56401) ***(G-588)***
United Parcel Service Inc 218 847-4439
1045 13th Ave SE Detroit Lakes (56501) ***(G-1221)***
United Parcel Service Inc 218 722-0150
111 Port Terminal Rd Duluth (55802) ***(G-1491)***
United Parcel Service Inc 800 742-5877
3312 Broadway St NE Minneapolis (55413) ***(G-5912)***
United Parcel Service Inc 651 388-6555
880 Bench St Red Wing (55066) ***(G-7010)***
United Parcel Service Inc 507 281-0468
1616 Opportunity Rd NW Rochester (55901) ***(G-7277)***
United Parcel Service Inc 507 375-4666
423 14th St S Saint James (56081) ***(G-7648)***
United Parcel Service Inc 651 367-8200
3025 Lunar Ln Saint Paul (55121) ***(G-7936)***
United Parcel Service Inc 320 235-6615
2200 Trott Ave SW Willmar (56201) ***(G-10050)***
United Parcel Service Inc 507 454-2307
1157 E Broadway St Winona (55987) ***(G-10135)***
United Parcel Service of New 218 751-9109
945 Industrial Park Dr SE Bemidji (56601) ***(G-430)***
United Parcel Service of New 507 334-7924
1820 6th St NW Faribault (55021) ***(G-2036)***
United Parcel Service of New 218 739-4910
1515 N 1st Ave Fergus Falls (56537) ***(G-2122)***
United Parcel Service of New 218 326-8520
425 SE 11th St Grand Rapids (55744) ***(G-2310)***
United Parcel Service of New 320 253-4100
3057 Highway 10 SE Saint Cloud (56304) ***(G-7443)***
United Parcel Service of New 507 836-6671
1930 Engebretson Ave Slayton (56172) ***(G-9491)***
United Piping Inc 218 727-7676
4510 Airport Rd Duluth (55811) ***(G-1492)***
United Products Corp of Amer 763 545-1273
9800 13th Ave N Minneapolis (55441) ***(G-5913)***
United Products Corp of Amer (PA) 651 227-8735
200 Sycamore St W Saint Paul (55117) ***(G-9108)***
United Properties Investment 952 893-8272
1650 W 82nd St Ste 1500 Bloomington (55431) ***(G-523)***
United Property Investment LLC (PA) 952 831-1000
3500 Amercn Blvd W # 200 Minneapolis (55431) ***(G-5914)***
United Residential Mortgage 952 820-0272
7301 Ohms Ln Ste 195 Minneapolis (55439) ***(G-5915)***
United Services, Minneapolis *Also Called Safari Airport Taxi Service* ***(G-5587)***
United States Compliance Corp 952 252-3000
4350 Baker Rd Ste 100 Minnetonka (55343) ***(G-6231)***
United States Distilled Prdts 763 389-4903
1607 12th St S Princeton (55371) ***(G-6918)***
United States Mechanical Inc 763 780-9030
3527 88th Ave NE Circle Pines (55014) ***(G-1022)***
United States Postal Service 651 293-3172
314 Eva St Saint Paul (55107) ***(G-9109)***
United States Steel Corp 218 778-8700
1 Old Mine Rd Keewatin (55753) ***(G-2826)***
United States Steel Corp 218 749-7200
County Rd 102 Mountain Iron (55768) ***(G-6394)***
United Stationers Supply Co 651 681-1720
1720 Alexander Rd Saint Paul (55121) ***(G-7937)***
United Sugars Corp 952 896-0131
7803 Glenroy Rd Ste 300 Minneapolis (55439) ***(G-5916)***
United Support Group 507 437-4110
1013 4th Ave NE Austin (55912) ***(G-292)***
United Taconite LLC 218 744-7800
1200 County Hwy 16 Eveleth (55734) ***(G-1933)***
United Water New Rochelle Inc 952 820-1666
701 4th Ave S Ste 1200 Minneapolis (55415) ***(G-5917)***
United Way Info & Referral 651 291-6795
176 Robert St S Saint Paul (55107) ***(G-9110)***
Unitedhealth Group Inc 952 936-1300
9900 Bren Rd E Ste 300W Hopkins (55343) ***(G-2651)***
Unitedhealth Group Inc (PA) 952 936-1300
9900 Bren Rd E Minnetonka (55343) ***(G-6232)***
Unity Bank East 320 358-3600
1180 W 4th St Rush City (55069) ***(G-7391)***
Unity Bank North 952 465-3000
7101 Washington Ave S Edina (55439) ***(G-1849)***
Unity Family Health Care 320 632-5441
815 2nd St SE Little Falls (56345) ***(G-3021)***
Unity Healthcare 612 285-8743
2221 W 55th St Minneapolis (55419) ***(G-5918)***
Unity Hospital, Fridley *Also Called Allina Health System* ***(G-2189)***
Univ of Minnesota Clinical, Minneapolis *Also Called Regents of The University of* ***(G-5494)***
Univar USA Inc 651 774-9400
845 Terrace Ct Saint Paul (55130) ***(G-9111)***
Universal Cooperatives Inc (HQ) 651 239-1000
1300 Corporate Center Curv Saint Paul (55121) ***(G-7938)***
Universal Hospital Services 612 721-3374
2020 E 28th St Ste 103 Minneapolis (55407) ***(G-5919)***
Universal Hospital Services (PA) 952 893-3200
7700 France Ave S Ste 275 Minneapolis (55435) ***(G-5920)***
Universal Marketing 218 722-1698
1917 W Superior St Duluth (55806) ***(G-1493)***
Universal Painting & Drywall 763 315-0095
7308 Aspen Ln N Ste 156 Minneapolis (55428) ***(G-5921)***
Universal Power Marketing LLC 320 202-0243
3333 W Div St Ste 218 Saint Cloud (56301) ***(G-7625)***
Universal Title & Financial (PA) 952 829-0899
7777 Washington Ave S Minneapolis (55439) ***(G-5922)***
University Affiliated Family 612 333-0770
2615 E Franklin Ave Minneapolis (55406) ***(G-5923)***
University Billiards Inc 763 574-1399
7178 University Ave NE Minneapolis (55432) ***(G-3630)***
University Club of St Paul 651 222-1751
420 Summit Ave Saint Paul (55102) ***(G-9112)***
University Display Co, Saint Paul *Also Called Consolidated Enterprises Inc* ***(G-8249)***
University Inn Associates, A 612 379-8888
615 Washington Ave SE Ste A Minneapolis (55414) ***(G-5924)***
University Inn Property LLC 612 379-8888
615 Washington Ave SE Minneapolis (55414) ***(G-5925)***
University Language Center Inc 612 379-3823
1313 5th St SE Ste 201 Minneapolis (55414) ***(G-5926)***
University Mental Health 612 626-8100
1300 S 2nd St Ste 180 Minneapolis (55454) ***(G-5927)***
University National Bank 651 265-5600
200 University Ave W # 100 Saint Paul (55103) ***(G-9113)***
University Neurosurgical Assn 612 624-6666
420 Delaware St SE Ste 1 Minneapolis (55455) ***(G-5928)***
University of Minn Alumni Assn 612 624-2323
200 Oak St SE Ste 200 Minneapolis (55455) ***(G-5929)***
University of Minnesota 763 782-6400
720 Washingtn Ave SE # 200 Minneapolis (55414) ***(G-5930)***

ALPHABETIC

University Womens Health ... 612 625-6991
420 Delaware St SE Rm 520 Minneapolis (55455) *(G-5931)*
Up North Consulting Inc ... 952 224-8656
9100 W Bloomington Fwy Minneapolis (55431) *(G-5932)*
Upfront Productions Inc ... 612 623-4433
761 Kasota Ave SE Minneapolis (55414) *(G-5933)*
Upi Property Management Group ... 612 870-8500
800 W Franklin Ave Minneapolis (55405) *(G-5934)*
Uplink Staffing ... 763 781-8888
5901 Brooklyn Blvd # 206 Minneapolis (55429) *(G-5935)*
Uponor Inc ... 952 891-2000
21900 Dodd Blvd Lakeville (55044) *(G-2939)*
Uponor North America Inc (PA) ... 952 891-2000
5925 148th St W Saint Paul (55124) *(G-7939)*
Upper Lakes Foods Inc (PA) ... 218 879-1265
801 Industry Ave Cloquet (55720) *(G-1066)*
Upper Midwest American Indian ... 612 522-4436
1035 W Broadway Ave Minneapolis (55411) *(G-5936)*
Upper Midwest Organ ... 651 603-7800
2550 University Ave W Ste 315S Saint Paul (55114) *(G-9114)*
Upper Minnesota Properties Inc ... 218 722-2641
30 W Superior St Duluth (55802) *(G-1494)*
Upper Minnetonka Yacht Club ... 952 471-8783
4165 Shoreline Dr Ste 10 Spring Park (55384) *(G-9567)*
Upper Mississippi Mental ... 218 751-3280
722 15th St NW Bemidji (56601) *(G-431)*
Upper River Services LLC ... 651 292-9293
40 State St Saint Paul (55107) *(G-9115)*
Upper Sioux Community ... 320 564-3853
2511 565th St Granite Falls (56241) *(G-2322)*
UPS, Albert Lea *Also Called United Parcel Service Inc (G-69)*
UPS, Alexandria *Also Called United Parcel Service Inc (G-127)*
UPS, Bemidji *Also Called United Parcel Service of New (G-430)*
UPS, Brainerd *Also Called United Parcel Service Inc (G-588)*
UPS, Detroit Lakes *Also Called United Parcel Service Inc (G-1221)*
UPS, Duluth *Also Called United Parcel Service Inc (G-1491)*
UPS, Faribault *Also Called United Parcel Service of New (G-2036)*
UPS, Fergus Falls *Also Called United Parcel Service of New (G-2122)*
UPS, Grand Rapids *Also Called United Parcel Service of New (G-2310)*
UPS, Red Wing *Also Called United Parcel Service Inc (G-7010)*
UPS, Rochester *Also Called United Parcel Service Inc (G-7277)*
UPS, Saint Cloud *Also Called United Parcel Service of New (G-7443)*
UPS, Saint James *Also Called United Parcel Service Inc (G-7648)*
UPS, Slayton *Also Called United Parcel Service of New (G-9491)*
UPS, Willmar *Also Called United Parcel Service Inc (G-10050)*
UPS, Winona *Also Called United Parcel Service Inc (G-10135)*
UPS Ground Freight Inc ... 763 780-9800
8600 Rendova St NE Circle Pines (55014) *(G-1023)*
UPS Supply Chain Solutions Inc ... 612 726-1680
7550 22nd Ave S Minneapolis (55450) *(G-5937)*
Upsher-Smith Laboratories Inc ... 763 315-2000
6701 Evenstad Dr N Osseo (55369) *(G-6681)*
Uptown Cafe, Wadena *Also Called J Maas Co (G-9804)*
Uptown Classic Properties, Minneapolis *Also Called Upi Property Management Group (G-5934)*
Uptown Psychic Studio ... 612 374-9906
2617 Hennepin Ave Minneapolis (55408) *(G-5938)*
Urban Ventures Leadership ... 612 822-1628
3041 4th Ave S Minneapolis (55408) *(G-5939)*
Urologix Inc ... 763 475-1400
14405 21st Ave N Ste 110 Minneapolis (55447) *(G-5940)*
URS Group Inc ... 612 370-0700
100 S 5th St Ste 1500 Minneapolis (55402) *(G-5941)*
US Army Corps of Engineers ... 651 290-5698
190 5th St E Ste 401 Saint Paul (55101) *(G-9116)*
US Asian Home Care ... 763 533-7750
4124 Quebec Ave N Ste 305 Minneapolis (55427) *(G-5942)*
US Bancorp Information Svcs ... 800 925-4324
200 S 6th St Minneapolis (55402) *(G-5943)*
US Bancorp Information Svcs (HQ) ... 651 466-3000
332 Minnesota St Ste A Saint Paul (55101) *(G-9117)*
US Bancorp Legal Department ... 612 303-7879
2100 US Bancorp Ctr Minneapolis (55402) *(G-5944)*
US Bank, Bloomington *Also Called U S Bank Home Mortgage (G-522)*
US Bank, Wayzata *Also Called Piper Jaffray Co's (G-9935)*
US Bank National Association ... 218 878-7878
715 Cloquet Ave Cloquet (55720) *(G-1067)*
US Bank National Association ... 763 536-5328
4000 W Broadway Ave Minneapolis (55422) *(G-5945)*
US Bank National Association ... 612 303-3021
800 Nicollet Mall Fl 4 Minneapolis (55402) *(G-5946)*
US Bank National Association ... 651 229-6123
1071 Grand Ave Saint Paul (55105) *(G-9118)*
US Bank National Association ... 952 997-9600
15025 Garrett Ave Ste 100 Saint Paul (55124) *(G-7940)*
US Bank Trust National Assn ... 800 934-6802
180 5th St E Ste 200 Saint Paul (55101) *(G-9119)*
US District Crt Mnnapolis Bldg, Minneapolis *Also Called Administrative Office of The (G-3680)*
US Energy Services Inc ... 763 543-4600
605 Highway 169 N Ste 1200 Minneapolis (55441) *(G-5947)*
US Family Net, Minneapolis *Also Called Xpandable Technology Inc (G-6095)*
US Foodservice Inc ... 651 454-6580
2864 Eagandale Blvd Eagan (55121) *(G-1559)*
US Foodservice Inc ... 763 559-9494
9605 54th Ave N Minneapolis (55442) *(G-5948)*
US Foodservice Inc ... 651 634-4380
708 Cleveland Ave SW Saint Paul (55112) *(G-9120)*
US Foodservice Inc ... 651 450-6000
280 Grand Ave E South Saint Paul (55075) *(G-9547)*
US Oncology Inc ... 612 863-8585
800 E 28th St Ste 405 Minneapolis (55407) *(G-5949)*
US Post Office, Saint Paul *Also Called United States Postal Service (G-9109)*
US Steel Kwtino Taconite Plant, Keewatin *Also Called United States Steel Corp (G-2826)*
US Union Tool Inc ... 651 552-0440
953 Concord St S South Saint Paul (55075) *(G-9548)*
US Venture Inc ... 763 591-5827
1105 Xenium Ln N Ste 200 Minneapolis (55441) *(G-5950)*
USA Mobility Wireless Inc ... 952 996-0400
11437 Valley View Rd Eden Prairie (55344) *(G-1801)*
USF Holland Inc ... 507 847-2625
172 Industrial Park Jackson (56143) *(G-2800)*
USFreightways, Jackson *Also Called USF Holland Inc (G-2800)*
USG Interiors Inc ... 218 878-4000
35 Arch St Cloquet (55720) *(G-1068)*
USG Interiors Inc ... 952 853-1233
2950 Metro Dr Ste 116 Minneapolis (55425) *(G-5951)*
USP Hotel Services LLC ... 651 578-2563
970 Helena Ave N Saint Paul (55128) *(G-9287)*
UTC Fire & Security America ... 651 777-2690
1275 Red Fox Rd Saint Paul (55112) *(G-9121)*
Uti, Saint Paul *Also Called Unified Theory Inc (G-9286)*
Utili-Trax Contracting ... 763 323-2800
9774 18th St Princeton (55371) *(G-6919)*
Utility Bill Inquiries, Anoka *Also Called City of Anoka (G-167)*
V Care Home Health Inc ... 651 793-7635
1049 Payne Ave Saint Paul (55130) *(G-9122)*
V D A Associates ... 952 937-8833
17406 ADA Ct Eden Prairie (55347) *(G-1802)*
V S I, Burnsville *Also Called Vac System Industries of MN (G-816)*
V-TEK Inc (PA) ... 507 387-2039
751 Summit Ave Mankato (56001) *(G-3211)*
VA Departmental Offices ... 612 970-5700
1 Federal Dr Rm 156 Saint Paul (55111) *(G-7966)*
VA Employee Child Care Center ... 612 725-2000
1 Veterans Dr Minneapolis (55417) *(G-5952)*
Vaa LLC ... 763 559-9100
2955 Xenium Ln N Ste 10 Minneapolis (55441) *(G-5953)*
Vac System Industries of MN ... 952 808-1616
1800 Cliff Rd E Ste 11 Burnsville (55337) *(G-816)*
Vacava Inc ... 507 252-9076
3131 Superior Dr NW Ste B Rochester (55901) *(G-7278)*
Vail Place ... 612 824-8061
1412 W 36th St Minneapolis (55408) *(G-5954)*
Val-Ed Joint Venture, LLP ... 218 284-5702
702 Main Ave Moorhead (56560) *(G-6345)*
Valere LLC ... 763 390-9286
1988 Oak Knoll Dr White Bear Lake (55110) *(G-9979)*
Valley Craft Inc ... 651 345-3386
2001 S Highway 61 Lake City (55041) *(G-2855)*
Valley Creek Mall, Saint Paul *Also Called Wellington Management Inc (G-9144)*
Valley Dental Arts Inc ... 651 439-2855
1745 Northwestern Ave S Stillwater (55082) *(G-9653)*
Valley Dental Group ... 763 544-2213
7501 Golden Valley Rd Minneapolis (55427) *(G-5955)*
Valley Golf Association ... 218 773-1207
1800 21st St NW East Grand Forks (56721) *(G-1577)*
Valley High Golf Club ... 507 896-3239
9203 Mound Prairie Dr Houston (55943) *(G-2663)*
Valley Home Society ... 218 681-3286
523 Arnold Ave S Thief River Falls (56701) *(G-9681)*
Valley Hospital, Minneapolis *Also Called Regency Hospital Co LLC (G-5484)*
Valley Masonry LLC ... 218 498-2244
205 Foundation Ave Glyndon (56547) *(G-2235)*
Valley National Gases Inc ... 651 628-4848
305 2nd St NW Ste 125 Saint Paul (55112) *(G-9123)*
Valley National Gases WV LLC ... 320 235-3430
1501 Highway 12 E Willmar (56201) *(G-10051)*
Valley News Co ... 507 345-4819
1305 Stadium Rd Mankato (56001) *(G-3212)*
Valley Plumbing Co Inc ... 952 492-2121
860 Quaker Ave Jordan (55352) *(G-2812)*
Valley Sales Inc ... 952 314-8560
1320 Mill Ln Waconia (55387) *(G-9793)*
Valley Sales of Hutchinson Inc ... 320 587-2240
525 Highway 7 E Hutchinson (55350) *(G-2714)*
Valley Security Service Inc ... 507 454-2233
110 Gould St Ste 100 Winona (55987) *(G-10136)*
Valley Transportation ... 507 754-5558
73137 State Highway 16 Grand Meadow (55936) *(G-2265)*
Valley Truck Parts & Service ... 218 773-3486
1717 Central Ave NW East Grand Forks (56721) *(G-1578)*
Valley View Nursing Home of ... 507 896-3125
510 E Cedar St Houston (55943) *(G-2664)*
Valleyfair Amusement Park, Shakopee *Also Called Cedar Fair, LP (G-9430)*
Valleyview Manor Nursing Home, Lamberton *Also Called City of Lamberton (G-2945)*
Valleywood Golf Course, Saint Paul *Also Called Apple Valley, City of Inc (G-7704)*
Value Gardens Supply ... 952 884-6477
9100 W Bloomington Fwy Minneapolis (55431) *(G-5956)*
Value Realty Inc ... 952 898-0230
4555 Erin Dr Ste 120 Saint Paul (55122) *(G-7941)*
Value Village Thrift Store, Minneapolis *Also Called ARC Greater Twin Cities (G-3798)*
Valvoline Instant Oil Change, Granite Falls *Also Called Thorco Inc (G-2321)*
Van Minneapolis & Warehouse Co ... 651 636-6000
3780 Macalaster Dr NE Minneapolis (55421) *(G-6132)*
Vanco Services LLC ... 952 983-8660
6499 City West Pkwy Eden Prairie (55344) *(G-1803)*
Vanman Co's Architects ... 763 541-9552
669 Winnetka Ave N Ste 210 Minneapolis (55427) *(G-5957)*
Vanman Construction Co ... 763 541-9552
669 Winnetka Ave N # 210 Minneapolis (55427) *(G-5958)*
Vantro Systems LLC ... 952 890-2080
11401 Rupp Dr Burnsville (55337) *(G-817)*
Vasa Lutheran Home, Red Wing *Also Called Lutheran Social Service of MN (G-6989)*
VCA Animal Hospitals Inc ... 952 884-3228
8830 Lyndale Ave S Bloomington (55420) *(G-524)*
Vee Corp ... 612 333-2223
504 Malcolm Ave SE Ste 200 Minneapolis (55414) *(G-5959)*
Veit & Co Inc ... 763 428-2242
14000 Veit Pl Rogers (55374) *(G-7347)*
Veit Container Corp ... 507 281-3867
5920 15th St NW Rochester (55901) *(G-7279)*
Velocity Express Mid-West Inc ... 612 492-2400
6521 James Ave N Minneapolis (55430) *(G-5960)*
Velocity Express Northeast Inc ... 612 492-2400
6521 James Ave N Minneapolis (55430) *(G-5961)*
Vendor Management Services, Minneapolis *Also Called First American Real Estate (G-4439)*

Venture Bank (PA) ... 952 830-9999
5601 Green Valley Dr # 120 Minneapolis (55437) ***(G-5962)***
Venture Bank ... 651 289-2222
2640 Eagan Woods Dr # 100 Saint Paul (55121) ***(G-7942)***
Veolia Environmental Services ... 651 774-0916
309 Como Ave Saint Paul (55103) ***(G-9124)***
Veolia Es Solid Waste Midwest ... 507 281-5850
4245 Highway 14 E Rochester (55904) ***(G-7280)***
Veolia Es Solid Waste Midwest ... 651 459-3029
309 Como Ave Saint Paul (55103) ***(G-9125)***
Veolia Es Solid Waste of Pa ... 320 251-8919
2355 12th St SE Saint Cloud (56304) ***(G-7444)***
Verde Lawn Care LLC ... 763 550-9400
15675 Medina Rd Minneapolis (55447) ***(G-5963)***
Vericenter Minnesota Inc ... 952 918-2000
1125 Energy Park Dr Ste 100 Saint Paul (55108) ***(G-9126)***
Verifications Inc (PA) ... 763 420-0600
6900 Wedgwood Rd N # 120 Osseo (55311) ***(G-6682)***
Verified Credentials Inc ... 952 985-2335
20890 Kenbridge Ct Ste 2 Lakeville (55044) ***(G-2940)***
Verisae Inc ... 612 455-2305
100 N 6th St Ste 710A Minneapolis (55403) ***(G-5964)***
Verizon, Minneapolis *Also Called Cellco Partnership* ***(G-4040)***
Verizon Business Network Svcs ... 612 607-1116
7383 County Road 140 Cologne (55322) ***(G-1093)***
Verizon Communications Inc ... 763 591-0705
5500 Wayzata Blvd Ste 400 Minneapolis (55416) ***(G-5965)***
Verizon Wireless Inc ... 320 241-5433
126 Division St Waite Park (56387) ***(G-9847)***
Vermillion Community College ... 218 365-7200
1900 E Camp St Ely (55731) ***(G-1916)***
Vermillion State Bank ... 651 437-4433
107 Main St E Vermillion (55085) ***(G-9723)***
Vern Cooper & Associates Inc ... 507 319-4139
2883 Viola Heights Dr NE Rochester (55906) ***(G-7281)***
Versa-Lok Retaining Wall Sys, Saint Paul *Also Called Kiltie Corp* ***(G-9235)***
Vertical Limit Construction ... 507 824-1222
811 3rd Ave Wanamingo (55983) ***(G-9867)***
Vet Mart Inc ... 763 546-4452
5669 Duluth St Minneapolis (55422) ***(G-5966)***
Veterans of Foreign Wars, Crookston *Also Called VFW Post 1902* ***(G-1142)***
Veterans of Foreign Wars, Forest Lake *Also Called Forest Lake VFW Post 4210 Inc* ***(G-2162)***
Veterans of Foreign Wars ... 320 587-9929
247 1st Ave SE Hutchinson (55350) ***(G-2715)***
Veterans of Foreign Wars, South Saint Paul *Also Called VFW Gallagher-Hanson Post 295* ***(G-9550)***
Veterans of Foreign Wars Inc ... 507 289-6299
16 6th St SW Rochester (55902) ***(G-7282)***
Veterans of Foreign Wars of ... 320 963-3405
66 Maple Ave N Maple Lake (55358) ***(G-3267)***
Veterans of Foreign Wars of ... 320 252-3617
901 N Benton Dr Sauk Rapids (56379) ***(G-9379)***
Veterinary Hospitals Assn ... 651 451-6669
370 Bridgepoint Dr South Saint Paul (55075) ***(G-9549)***
Veterinary Medical Center Prof ... 507 372-2957
600 Oxford St Worthington (56187) ***(G-10197)***
VFW Gallagher-Hanson Post 295 ... 651 455-1505
111 Concord Exchange St S South Saint Paul (55075) ***(G-9550)***
VFW POST #5555, Minneapolis *Also Called Fred Babcock Post No 5555* ***(G-4481)***
VFW Post 1902 ... 218 281-1902
121 N Main St Crookston (56716) ***(G-1142)***
VFW Red River Valley Post 3817 ... 218 773-2481
312 Demers Ave East Grand Forks (56721) ***(G-1579)***
VHA Upper Midwest Inc ... 952 837-4700
7601 France Ave S Ste 500 Minneapolis (55435) ***(G-5967)***
Via Biomedical Inc ... 763 577-9936
6655 Wedgwood Rd N # 150 Osseo (55311) ***(G-6683)***
Vibes Technologies Inc ... 763 971-6260
7125 Nrthlnd Trl N Ste 40 Minneapolis (55428) ***(G-5968)***
Vibrant Technologies Inc ... 952 653-1700
6031 Culligan Way Minnetonka (55345) ***(G-6233)***
Vic's Heavy Haul Trucking ... 651 423-7401
3000 145th St E Rosemount (55068) ***(G-7377)***
Victor Lundeen Co (PA) ... 218 736-5433
126 W Lincoln Ave Fergus Falls (56537) ***(G-2123)***
Victoria Inn ... 320 587-6030
1000 Highway 7 W Hutchinson (55350) ***(G-2716)***
Victory Corps Flags Floats ... 763 561-5600
2730 Nevada Ave N Minneapolis (55427) ***(G-5969)***
Victory Home Care Inc ... 763 566-3318
7420 Unity Ave N Ste 209 Minneapolis (55443) ***(G-5970)***
Videotronix Inc ... 952 894-5343
401 W Travelers Trl Burnsville (55337) ***(G-818)***
Vietnamese Social Services of ... 651 644-1317
1159 University Ave W Ste 100 Saint Paul (55104) ***(G-9127)***
Viewcrest Health Center, Duluth *Also Called St Francis Health Services of* ***(G-1459)***
Vigen Construction Inc ... 218 773-1159
42247 180th St SW East Grand Forks (56721) ***(G-1580)***
Viking Auto Salvage Inc ... 651 460-6166
26548 Chippendale Ave Northfield (55057) ***(G-6522)***
Viking Automatic Sprinkler Co ... 218 628-2150
4425 Venture Ave Duluth (55811) ***(G-1495)***
Viking Automatic Sprinkler Co ... 218 733-0962
4425 Venture Ave Duluth (55811) ***(G-1496)***
Viking Automatic Sprinkler Co ... 507 289-8270
4420 19th St NW Rochester (55901) ***(G-7283)***
Viking Automatic Sprinkler Co (HQ) ... 651 558-3300
301 York Ave Saint Paul (55130) ***(G-9128)***
Viking Coca Cola Bottling Co ... 218 829-2204
7842 Industrial Park Rd Baxter (56425) ***(G-344)***
Viking Collection Service Inc ... 952 944-7575
7500 Office Ridge Cir # 100 Eden Prairie (55344) ***(G-1804)***
Viking Council of The Boy ... 763 545-4550
5300 Glenwood Ave Minneapolis (55422) ***(G-5971)***
Viking Drywall Inc ... 952 888-6442
8601 2nd Ave S Minneapolis (55420) ***(G-5972)***
Viking Electric Supply Inc ... 952 890-8420
4531 W 1st St Duluth (55807) ***(G-1497)***
Viking Electric Supply Inc (HQ) ... 612 627-1300
451 Industrial Blvd NE # 2 Minneapolis (55413) ***(G-5973)***
Viking Explosives & Supply Inc ... 218 263-8845
4469 Highway 5 Hibbing (55746) ***(G-2479)***
Viking Forest Products LLC ... 952 941-6512
7615 Smetana Ln Ste 140 Eden Prairie (55344) ***(G-1805)***
Viking Materials Inc ... 612 617-5800
3225 Como Ave SE Minneapolis (55414) ***(G-5974)***
Viking Meadows Inc ... 763 434-4205
1788 Viking Blvd NE Cedar (55011) ***(G-885)***
Viking Savings Association ... 320 762-0236
1311 Broadway St Ste 1 Alexandria (56308) ***(G-128)***
Viking Vending, Minneapolis *Also Called Lieberman Co's Inc* ***(G-4873)***
Vilana Financial Inc ... 763 416-5959
5747 W Broadway Ave Minneapolis (55428) ***(G-5975)***
Villa ... 218 865-4155
6266 Giants Ridge Rd Biwabik (55708) ***(G-472)***
Villa Health Care Center, Mora *Also Called Long Term Care Associates Inc* ***(G-6366)***
Villa St Vincent Inc ... 218 281-3424
516 Walsh St Ofc Crookston (56716) ***(G-1143)***
Village Bank (PA) ... 763 753-3007
3350 Bridge St NW Saint Francis (55070) ***(G-7638)***
Village Chevrolet Co - Wayzata ... 952 473-5444
16200 Wayzata Blvd Wayzata (55391) ***(G-9947)***
Village Green Golf Course, Moorhead *Also Called City of Moorhead* ***(G-6303)***
Village Green Lawn Maintenance ... 651 488-2733
520 Front Ave Saint Paul (55117) ***(G-9129)***
Village Health Care Inc ... 952 361-8000
1107 Hazeltine Blvd # 200 Chaska (55318) ***(G-983)***
Villsaat The Giants Ridge, Biwabik *Also Called Villa* ***(G-472)***
Vincent Haugen ... 218 233-3776
1702 30th Ave S Moorhead (56560) ***(G-6346)***
Vinco Inc ... 651 982-4642
18995 Forest Blvd N Forest Lake (55025) ***(G-2171)***
Vine Ripe Inc ... 507 451-5692
215 32nd Ave SW Owatonna (55060) ***(G-6742)***
Vinge Tile ... 952 431-1000
21205 Eaton Ave Ste 1 Farmington (55024) ***(G-2062)***
Vinland National Center ... 763 479-3555
3675 Ihduhapi Rd Loretto (55357) ***(G-3054)***
Vintage Inc ... 651 487-6878
1419 Arona St Saint Paul (55108) ***(G-9130)***
Virginia Coop Credit Union Inc ... 218 741-5644
307 1st St N Ste 1 Virginia (55792) ***(G-9759)***
Virginia Regional Medical Ctr, Virginia *Also Called Virginia, City of Inc* ***(G-9760)***
Virginia Workforce Center, Virginia *Also Called Arrowhead Economic Opportunity* ***(G-9734)***
Virginia, City of Inc ... 218 741-3340
901 9th St N Virginia (55792) ***(G-9760)***
Virginia, City of Inc ... 218 748-7540
620 2nd St S Virginia (55792) ***(G-9761)***
Viromed Laboratories Inc ... 952 563-3300
6101 Blue Circle Dr Minnetonka (55343) ***(G-6234)***
Virtelligence Inc ... 952 746-9220
6216 Baker Rd Ste 100 Eden Prairie (55346) ***(G-1806)***
Virteva LLC ... 952 843-1200
5775 Wayzata Blvd Ste 900 Saint Louis Park (55416) ***(G-7670)***
Virtual Radiologic Corp ... 952 595-1100
11995 Singletree Ln # 500 Eden Prairie (55344) ***(G-1807)***
Vision Financial & Home Mtge ... 952 224-3370
509 2nd Ave S Hopkins (55343) ***(G-2652)***
Vision Loss Resources ... 651 224-7662
216 Wabasha St S Saint Paul (55107) ***(G-9131)***
Vision Loss Resources Inc (PA) ... 612 871-2222
1936 Lyndale Ave S Minneapolis (55403) ***(G-5976)***
Vision Loss Resources Inc ... 612 871-2222
1936 Lyndale Ave S Minneapolis (55403) ***(G-5977)***
Vision of Elk River Inc ... 763 441-4420
12508 Elk Lake Rd NW Elk River (55330) ***(G-1895)***
Vision Processing Technologies ... 320 593-1796
125 E Commercial St Litchfield (55355) ***(G-2992)***
Vision Purchasing, Saint Cloud *Also Called E T C Enterprises Inc* ***(G-7500)***
Vision Solutions Inc ... 507 252-3440
3535 40th Ave NW Ste 200 Rochester (55901) ***(G-7284)***
Vision Woodworking Inc ... 763 571-5767
7890 Hickory St NE Minneapolis (55432) ***(G-3631)***
Visions Inc ... 763 425-4251
8801 Wyoming Ave N Brooklyn Park (55445) ***(G-621)***
Visionshare Inc ... 612 460-4301
2829 University Ave SE # 800 Minneapolis (55414) ***(G-5978)***
Visiting Angels, Hopkins *Also Called Senior Home Living MN LLC* ***(G-2631)***
Vista Villa Inc ... 218 644-3331
1197 N Hwy 73 Cromwell (55726) ***(G-1117)***
Vistar Corp ... 800 333-3056
8555 Revere Ln N Ste 100 Maple Grove (55369) ***(G-3256)***
Visual Impact Signs Inc ... 763 783-9411
8732 W 35W Svc Dr NE Minneapolis (55449) ***(G-3632)***
Visual Packaging Corp ... 952 938-1575
11121 Excelsior Blvd Hopkins (55343) ***(G-2653)***
Vital Images Inc ... 952 487-9500
5850 Opus Pkwy Ste 300 Minnetonka (55343) ***(G-6235)***
Vital Link Three Lnks Care Ctr, Northfield *Also Called Minnesota Odd Fellows Home* ***(G-6533)***
Vitatron Inc ... 763 574-4000
7000 Central Ave NE Minneapolis (55432) ***(G-3633)***
Vitran Express Inc ... 763 913-3450
2160 Mustang Dr Mounds View (55112) ***(G-6391)***
Vitran Express Inc ... 320 485-2101
1300 County Road 1 Winsted (55395) ***(G-10154)***
Vitran Express Inc ... 320 485-2333
1300 6th St S Winsted (55395) ***(G-10166)***
Vitreal Retinal Surgery ... 952 929-1131
7760 France Ave S Ste 310 Minneapolis (55435) ***(G-5979)***
Vitreorentinal Surgery ... 952 929-1131
7760 France Ave S Ste 310 Minneapolis (55435) ***(G-5980)***
Voa Anoka Care Center Inc ... 952 941-0305
7530 Market Place Dr Eden Prairie (55344) ***(G-1808)***
Voa Care Centers MN ... 763 535-6260
3245 Vera Cruz Ave N Minneapolis (55422) ***(G-5981)***

Voans Health Services Corp 507 263-4658
300 Dow St N Cannon Falls (55009) *(G-863)*
Voice & Data Networks Inc 952 946-7999
6981 Washington Ave S Minneapolis (55439) *(G-5982)*
Voigt's Bus Service Inc 320 252-1807
24243 County Road 7 Saint Cloud (56301) *(G-7626)*
Voigt's Motorcoach Travel Inc 320 253-0510
24243 County Road 7 Saint Cloud (56301) *(G-7627)*
Voigt's of Waconia 952 442-2818
308 S Birch St Waconia (55387) *(G-9794)*
Volk Transfer Inc 507 388-1683
104 Lundin Blvd Mankato (56001) *(G-3213)*
Volunteers of America Care 952 925-8500
6200 Xerxes Ave S Minneapolis (55423) *(G-5983)*
Volunteers of America Care 507 794-7995
1105 3rd Ave SW Sleepy Eye (56085) *(G-9503)*
Volunteers Of America Inc 763 753-2500
22426 Saint Francis Blvd Anoka (55303) *(G-237)*
Volunteers of America Inc 952 941-0305
7530 Market Place Dr Eden Prairie (55344) *(G-1809)*
Volunteers of America Inc 952 945-4000
7625 Metro Blvd Ste 200 Minneapolis (55439) *(G-5984)*
Volunteers of America National (PA) 952 941-0305
7530 Market Place Dr Eden Prairie (55344) *(G-1810)*
Vomela Specialty Co (PA) 651 228-2200
274 Fillmore Ave E Saint Paul (55107) *(G-9132)*
Von Ruden Manufacturing Inc 763 682-3122
1008 1st St NE Buffalo (55313) *(G-659)*
Voson Plumbing Inc 952 938-3143
1515 5th St S Ste A Hopkins (55343) *(G-2654)*
Voss Plumbing & Heating of 320 243-3644
316 E Hoffman St Paynesville (56362) *(G-6775)*
Votel, Anderson & McEachron 651 228-1770
444 Cedar St Ste 1250 Saint Paul (55101) *(G-9133)*
Voyager Aluminum Inc 320 834-4940
803 Central Ave N Brandon (56315) *(G-591)*
Voyager Bank (PA) 952 345-7600
775 Prairie Center Dr Ste 100 Eden Prairie (55344) *(G-1811)*
Voyageur Bus Co, Duluth *Also Called Metropolitan School & Charter (G-1392)*
Voyageur Co's Inc 612 376-7000
100 S 5th St Ste 2300 Minneapolis (55402) *(G-5985)*
VSI Construction Inc 763 493-3000
11751 Troy Ln N Maple Grove (55369) *(G-3257)*
Vti Security Integrators, Burnsville *Also Called Videotronix Inc (G-818)*
Vukelich Oil Co 320 253-6546
3267 Roosevelt Rd Saint Cloud (56301) *(G-7628)*
W B M Holding Co (PA) 952 831-9595
5120 American Blvd W Minneapolis (55437) *(G-5986)*
W E Nelson Stucco Co 763 377-3631
768 Rice St Saint Paul (55117) *(G-9134)*
W Gohman Construction Co 320 363-7781
815 County Road 75 Saint Joseph (56374) *(G-7656)*
W I C Program 612 348-6258
330 S 12th St Ste 4710 Minneapolis (55404) *(G-5987)*
W L Hall Co 952 937-8400
530 15th Ave S Hopkins (55343) *(G-2655)*
W M M R, Minneapolis *Also Called Regents of The University of (G-5487)*
W W Grainger Inc 612 486-3300
2505 Kennedy St NE Minneapolis (55413) *(G-5988)*
W W Grainger Inc 763 531-0300
2450 Annapolis Ln N Minneapolis (55441) *(G-5989)*
W Zintl Construction Inc 651 439-7973
5670 Memorial Ave N Ste 1 Stillwater (55082) *(G-9654)*
W2005 Fargo Hotels Realty, LP 952 854-1687
1601 American Blvd E Bloomington (55425) *(G-525)*
W2005 New Century Hotel 763 541-1094
10420 Wayzata Blvd Hopkins (55305) *(G-2656)*
W2005 New Century Hotel 952 835-6643
4201 American Blvd W Minneapolis (55437) *(G-5990)*
W2007 Equity Inns Realty LLC 952 854-0700
7800 International Dr Minneapolis (55425) *(G-5991)*
W3i Holdings LLC 320 257-7500
1900 Medical Arts Ave S Sartell (56377) *(G-9341)*
Wabasha City Ambulance Svc 651 565-2633
129 Hiawatha Dr E Wabasha (55981) *(G-9773)*
Wabasha Clinic Mayo Health 651 565-4571
1202 Grant Blvd W Wabasha (55981) *(G-9774)*
Wabasha Community Clinic, Wabasha *Also Called Mayo Clinic (G-9768)*
Wabasha County Highway 651 565-3366
821 Hiawatha Dr W Wabasha (55981) *(G-9775)*
Wabasso Healthcare Center, Wabasso *Also Called Beverly Enterprises - MN (G-9776)*
Wacker Stucco, Big Lake *Also Called K&G Enterprises Inc (G-450)*
Waconia Good Samaritan Center, Waconia *Also Called Evangelical Lutheran Good (G-9785)*
Wacosa 320 251-0087
320 Sundial Dr Waite Park (56387) *(G-9848)*
Waddell & Reed Inc 952 884-1503
3601 Minnesota Dr Ste 550 Minneapolis (55435) *(G-5992)*
Waddell & Reed Inc 651 483-1411
6 Pine Tree Dr Ste 380 Saint Paul (55112) *(G-9135)*
Wadena Medical Center Ltd 218 631-1360
4 Deerwood Ave NW Wadena (56482) *(G-9814)*
Wagamon Brothers Inc 763 789-7227
3719 3rd St NE Minneapolis (55421) *(G-3634)*
Wagers Business Systems Inc 651 644-3830
960 Blue Gentian Rd Saint Paul (55121) *(G-7943)*
Wagner Greenhouses Inc 612 922-1262
6024 Penn Ave S Minneapolis (55419) *(G-5993)*
Wagner Sod Co Inc 651 457-6037
8150 Courthouse Blvd Inver Grove Heights (55077) *(G-2773)*
Wagner Trucking Inc 320 524-2250
15380 Long Lake Rd NW Brandon (56315) *(G-592)*
Wagner's, Minneapolis *Also Called Wagner Greenhouses Inc (G-5993)*
Wair Products Inc 952 881-9449
11201 Hampshire Ave S B Minneapolis (55438) *(G-5994)*
Wakefield Pork Inc 507 237-5581
410 Main Ave E Gaylord (55334) *(G-2202)*
Wal-Mart Stores Inc 320 587-1020
1300 Trunk Ave Hwy 15 S Hutchinson (55350) *(G-2717)*
Wala Group, Saint Paul *Also Called American Institute of (G-8027)*
Walbon & Co Inc (PA) 651 437-2011
4230 Pine Bend Trl Ste A Rosemount (55068) *(G-7378)*
Walbon Co Trucking Svcs 651 437-2011
4230 Pine Bend Trl Ste A Rosemount (55068) *(G-7379)*
Walbon Transport Inc 651 437-2011
4230 Pine Bend Trl Ste A Rosemount (55068) *(G-7380)*
Walden Automotive Group Inc (PA) 952 512-8800
500 Ford Rd Minneapolis (55426) *(G-5995)*
Walden Leasing Inc 952 512-8924
500 Ford Rd Minneapolis (55426) *(G-5996)*
Waldorf-Nevens Dry Cleaners 952 914-9755
7079 Amundson Ave Minneapolis (55439) *(G-5997)*
Walgreen Co 763 576-0388
1911 S Ferry St Anoka (55303) *(G-238)*
Walgreen Co 952 882-7998
2200 Highway 13 E Burnsville (55337) *(G-819)*
Walgreen Co 763 427-6389
11401 Marketplace Dr N Champlin (55316) *(G-905)*
Walgreen Co 952 448-1180
3110 Chaska Blvd Chaska (55318) *(G-984)*
Walgreen Co 763 783-7005
9273 Lake Dr Circle Pines (55014) *(G-1024)*
Walgreen Co 952 941-8666
10180 Hennepin Town Rd Eden Prairie (55347) *(G-1812)*
Walgreen Co 952 938-1168
540 Blake Rd N Hopkins (55343) *(G-2657)*
Walgreen Co 763 755-1259
10686 University Ave NW Minneapolis (55448) *(G-3635)*
Walgreen Co 763 586-0730
6525 University Ave NE Minneapolis (55432) *(G-3636)*
Walgreen Co 763 545-6466
4200 Winnetka Ave N Minneapolis (55428) *(G-5998)*
Walgreen Co 612 722-4249
4547 Hiawatha Ave Minneapolis (55406) *(G-5999)*
Walgreen Co 763 553-9731
4005 Vinewood Ln N Minneapolis (55442) *(G-6000)*
Walgreen Co 612 827-8902
200 W Lake St Minneapolis (55408) *(G-6001)*
Walgreen Co 952 920-3561
6975 York Ave S Minneapolis (55435) *(G-6002)*
Walgreen Co 612 822-9712
4323 Chicago Ave Minneapolis (55407) *(G-6003)*
Walgreen Co 952 884-8246
9800 Lyndale Ave S Minneapolis (55420) *(G-6004)*
Walgreen Co 763 566-8350
7700 Brooklyn Blvd Minneapolis (55443) *(G-6005)*
Walgreen Co 612 861-7276
12 W 66th St Minneapolis (55423) *(G-6006)*
Walgreen Co 763 585-9946
6390 Brooklyn Blvd Minneapolis (55429) *(G-6007)*
Walgreen Co 320 251-9433
2505 W Division St Saint Cloud (56301) *(G-7629)*
Walgreen Co 320 253-6601
10 S Benton Dr Sauk Rapids (56379) *(G-9380)*
Walgreen Co 952 226-1283
8100 W County Road 42 Savage (55378) *(G-9411)*
Walgreens, Anoka *Also Called Walgreen Co (G-238)*
Walgreens, Burnsville *Also Called Walgreen Co (G-819)*
Walgreens, Champlin *Also Called Walgreen Co (G-905)*
Walgreens, Chaska *Also Called Walgreen Co (G-984)*
Walgreens, Circle Pines *Also Called Walgreen Co (G-1024)*
Walgreens, Eden Prairie *Also Called Walgreen Co (G-1812)*
Walgreens, Hopkins *Also Called Walgreen Co (G-2657)*
Walgreens, Minneapolis *Also Called Walgreen Co (G-6006)*
Walgreens, Minneapolis *Also Called Walgreen Co (G-6001)*
Walgreens, Minneapolis *Also Called Walgreen Co (G-3635)*
Walgreens, Minneapolis *Also Called Walgreen Co (G-6005)*
Walgreens, Minneapolis *Also Called Walgreen Co (G-6003)*
Walgreens, Minneapolis *Also Called Walgreen Co (G-5999)*
Walgreens, Minneapolis *Also Called Walgreen Co (G-6000)*
Walgreens, Minneapolis *Also Called Walgreen Co (G-6004)*
Walgreens, Minneapolis *Also Called Walgreen Co (G-6002)*
Walgreens, Minneapolis *Also Called Walgreen Co (G-5998)*
Walgreens, Minneapolis *Also Called Walgreen Co (G-3636)*
Walgreens, Minneapolis *Also Called Walgreen Co (G-6007)*
Walgreens, Saint Cloud *Also Called Walgreen Co (G-7629)*
Walgreens, Sauk Rapids *Also Called Walgreen Co (G-9380)*
Walgreens, Savage *Also Called Walgreen Co (G-9411)*
Walker Ambulance Service 218 547-5500
205 Minnesota Ave W Walker (56484) *(G-9860)*
Walker Art Center Shop, Minneapolis *Also Called Art Walker Center (G-3812)*
Walker Assisted Living Corp 952 835-8351
7400 York Ave S Minneapolis (55435) *(G-6008)*
Walker Care Corp I 612 827-8390
6130 Lyndale Ave S Minneapolis (55419) *(G-6009)*
Walker Methodist Health Center 612 827-8517
3737 Bryant Ave S Minneapolis (55409) *(G-6010)*
Walker Methodist Inc 612 827-5931
3737 Bryant Ave S Minneapolis (55409) *(G-6011)*
Walker Methodist Senior Svcs (PA) 612 827-5931
3737 Bryant Ave S Minneapolis (55409) *(G-6012)*
Walker Plaza 763 422-1226
131 Monroe St Ofc Anoka (55303) *(G-239)*
Walker Roofing Co 651 251-0910
2274 Capp Rd Saint Paul (55114) *(G-9136)*
Walker West Music Academy 651 224-2929
777 Selby Ave Saint Paul (55104) *(G-9137)*
Walker, Giroux, Hahne Ltd 218 749-4880
225 1st St N Ste 2400 Virginia (55792) *(G-9762)*
Wallace Marx & Associates, Minneapolis *Also Called Kantar Media Intelligences Inc (G-4788)*
Walling & Berg 612 340-1150
121 S 8th St Ste 1100 Minneapolis (55402) *(G-6013)*
Wally Mc Carthys Oldsmobile 651 636-6060
2325 Prior Ave N Saint Paul (55113) *(G-9138)*

ALPHABETIC

Wally McCarthy's Cadillac 651 636-6060
2325 Prior Ave N Saint Paul (55113) *(G-9139)*

Walman Optical Co (PA) 612 520-6000
801 12th Ave N Ste 2 Minneapolis (55411) *(G-6014)*

Walser Collision & Glass Inc 952 884-8884
9001 Grand Ave S Minneapolis (55420) *(G-6015)*

Walsh Bishop Associates Inc 612 338-8799
900 2nd Ave S Ste 300 Minneapolis (55402) *(G-6016)*

Walsh Title & Real Estate Svcs 952 835-3320
4820 W 77th St Ste 220 Minneapolis (55435) *(G-6017)*

Walstad Tile & Stone Co 763 519-1444
3700 Annapolis Ln N # 115 Minneapolis (55447) *(G-6018)*

Walter Pontiac Buick GMC Inc 952 888-9800
4601 American Blvd W Minneapolis (55437) *(G-6019)*

Walter W Culbert Jr 218 741-8026
601 S 5th Ave Virginia (55792) *(G-9763)*

Walter's Recycling & Refuse 763 780-8464
2830 101st Ave NE Minneapolis (55449) *(G-3637)*

Walters Trucking Inc 320 352-2207
411 Lincoln Loop Sauk Centre (56378) *(G-9354)*

Wand Corp 952 361-6200
7593 Corporate Way Eden Prairie (55344) *(G-1813)*

Wannaska Forestry Office, Wannaska *Also Called Minnesota Department of (G-9868)*

Wapasha Construction Co Inc 507 454-2707
927 E King St Winona (55987) *(G-10137)*

Wapicada Golf Course, Sauk Rapids *Also Called Golf Inc (G-9363)*

Ware Tad & Co Inc 612 338-2311
716 N 1st St Ste 336 Minneapolis (55401) *(G-6020)*

Warecorp 952 938-5448
3611 Farmington Rd Hopkins (55305) *(G-2658)*

Warehouse Depot LLC 612 728-5238
1860 E 28th St Minneapolis (55407) *(G-6021)*

Warners' Stellian Co Inc 651 222-0011
550 Atwater Cir Saint Paul (55103) *(G-9140)*

Warnert Racing Inc 320 251-2882
1203 33rd St S Saint Cloud (56301) *(G-7630)*

Warren Community Hospital Inc 218 745-4211
109 S Minnesota St Ste 4 Warren (56762) *(G-9869)*

Warroad Care Center Inc 218 386-1235
611 Lake St NE Warroad (56763) *(G-9872)*

Waseca Medical Center — Mayo 507 835-1210
501 State St N Waseca (56093) *(G-9889)*

Washburn Child Guidance Center 612 871-1454
2430 Nicollet Ave Minneapolis (55404) *(G-6022)*

Washington County Association 651 439-4946
334 7th Ave N Bayport (55003) *(G-351)*

Washington County Sheriffs Off, Stillwater *Also Called County of Washington (G-9606)*

Washington Inventory Service 763 784-2055
7978 University Ave NE Minneapolis (55432) *(G-3638)*

Washington Post Co 651 523-1094
1295 Bandana Blvd N Saint Paul (55108) *(G-9141)*

Waste Management of Minnesota 507 826-3610
Junction County Rd 22 25 Albert Lea (56007) *(G-70)*

Waste Management of Minnesota 952 736-2428
1601 Highway 13 E Ste 100 Burnsville (55337) *(G-820)*

Waste Management of North MN (PA) 218 624-7838
3101 W Superior St Duluth (55806) *(G-1498)*

Waste Management of Wisconsin 507 665-3096
739 Beaver Ave Le Sueur (56058) *(G-2961)*

Waste Management of Wisconsin 952 890-1100
10050 Naples St NE Minneapolis (55449) *(G-3639)*

Waste Management of Wisconsin 952 890-1100
12448 Pennsylvania Ave Savage (55378) *(G-9412)*

WATCHGUARD, Minneapolis *Also Called Eden Rs (G-4313)*

Water Medical Group (PA) 651 439-1234
1500 Curve Crest Blvd W Stillwater (55082) *(G-9655)*

Water Reclamation Plant 507 281-6190
301 37th St NW Rochester (55901) *(G-7285)*

Waterford In Park Apartments, Minneapolis *Also Called Lang-Nelson Associates Inc (G-4840)*

Waterfront Plaza Hotel Co LLC 218 727-4663
325 S Lake Ave Duluth (55802) *(G-1499)*

Waterproofing By Experts Inc 651 786-5042
448 Lilac St Circle Pines (55014) *(G-1025)*

Watkins Inc (HQ) 507 457-3300
150 Liberty St Winona (55987) *(G-10138)*

Watkins Inc 507 457-6136
730 W 3rd St Winona (55987) *(G-10139)*

Watonwan Farm Service Inc (PA) 507 776-2831
233 W Ciro St Truman (56088) *(G-9699)*

Watson Centers Inc (PA) 612 920-5034
3100 W Lake St Ste 420 Minneapolis (55416) *(G-6023)*

Watson Co Inc 763 689-3722
1555 320th Ln NE Cambridge (55008) *(G-846)*

Watson's of Minneapolis Inc 763 560-7727
7007 Lakeland Ave N Minneapolis (55428) *(G-6024)*

Watson-Forsberg Co 952 544-7761
6465 Wayzata Blvd Ste 110 Minneapolis (55426) *(G-6025)*

Wausau Insurance Co's, Saint Paul *Also Called Employers Insurance Co of (G-7760)*

Wausau Supply Co 952 469-2500
21700 Highview Ave Lakeville (55044) *(G-2941)*

Waymore Transportation Inc 763 786-9076
8201 Hickory St NE Minneapolis (55432) *(G-3640)*

Waymouth Farms Inc 763 533-5300
5300 Boone Ave N Minneapolis (55428) *(G-6026)*

Wayne Baumgart Distributors 952 447-2750
16677 Duluth Ave SE # 207 Prior Lake (55372) *(G-6961)*

Wayne Transports Inc (PA) 651 437-6422
14345 Conley Ave Rosemount (55068) *(G-7381)*

Wayne Transports Inc 218 749-6050
1917 S 15th Ave Virginia (55792) *(G-9764)*

Wayside House Inc 952 926-5626
3705 Park Center Blvd Minneapolis (55416) *(G-6027)*

Waytek Inc 952 949-0765
2440 Galpin Ct Chanhassen (55317) *(G-945)*

Wayzata Country Club Inc 952 473-8846
200 Wayzata Blvd W Wayzata (55391) *(G-9948)*

Wayzata Partners LP (PA) 952 920-5338
4601 Excelsior Blvd # 301 Minneapolis (55416) *(G-6028)*

Wayzata Partners LP 763 473-3200
163 Wayzata Blvd W Ofc Wayzata (55391) *(G-9949)*

Wb Enterprises of America Inc 507 324-5050
11384 790th Ave Le Roy (55951) *(G-2955)*

Wcl Associates Inc 952 541-9969
4931 W 35th St Ste 200 Minneapolis (55416) *(G-6029)*

Wdse Channel 8, Duluth *Also Called Duluth Superior Area (G-1304)*

We Do-Care Inc 612 866-7800
1300 E 66th St Uppr Minneapolis (55423) *(G-6030)*

Wealth Enhancement Group LLC 763 417-1428
505 Highway 169 N Ste 900 Plymouth (55441) *(G-6890)*

Web Construction Co Inc 507 387-1667
200 Saint Andrews Dr # 300 Mankato (56001) *(G-3214)*

Webb Business Promotions Inc 651 322-8200
15197 Boulder Ave Rosemount (55068) *(G-7382)*

Weber & Barlow Stores Inc 507 289-2444
1171 6th St NW Rochester (55901) *(G-7286)*

Weber & Judd Co (PA) 507 289-6047
1814 15th St NW Rochester (55901) *(G-7287)*

Weber Electric Inc 651 490-1333
577 Shoreview Park Rd Saint Paul (55126) *(G-9142)*

Webmd Health Corp 763 512-2600
605 Highway 169 N Fl 10 Minneapolis (55441) *(G-6031)*

Webster Dental Laboratory Inc 651 779-9160
1380 Frost Ave Saint Paul (55109) *(G-9143)*

Wedding Chapel Inc 763 533-4228
7201 Bass Lake Rd Minneapolis (55428) *(G-6032)*

Wee Care We Share 320 274-8881
8222 132nd St NW Annandale (55302) *(G-144)*

Wee Pals Child Care Center Inc 507 451-8355
560 Dunnell Dr Owatonna (55060) *(G-6743)*

Weeres Pontoon 320 251-3551
1045 33rd St S Saint Cloud (56301) *(G-7631)*

Weerts Construction Inc 507 893-3313
524 Main St S Winnebago (56098) *(G-10078)*

Weidner Plumbing & Heating Co 320 252-3000
29 Wilson Ave NE Saint Cloud (56304) *(G-7431)*

Weidt Group Inc 952 938-1588
5800 Baker Rd Ste 100 Hopkins (55345) *(G-2659)*

Weinberg Apartments, Saint Paul *Also Called Sholom St Paul Senior Housing (G-8953)*

Weinberg Supply & Equipment Co, Minneapolis *Also Called E Weinberg Supply Co Inc (G-4303)*

Weiner Memorial Foundation 507 537-7070
1104 E College Dr Marshall (56258) *(G-3331)*

Weiner Memorial Foundation (PA) 507 532-9661
300 N Bruce St Apt 1 Marshall (56258) *(G-3332)*

Weis Builders Inc (PA) 612 243-5000
7645 Lyndale Ave S # 300 Minneapolis (55423) *(G-6033)*

Weis Builders Inc 507 288-2041
2227 7th St NW Rochester (55901) *(G-7288)*

Welander Quist, Minneapolis *Also Called Davies Chapel (G-4228)*

Welcome Home Management, North Mankato *Also Called North Point (G-6511)*

Welders Supply Co Inc 320 235-3430
1501 Highway 12 E Willmar (56201) *(G-10052)*

Welle Construction Inc 763 427-5830
6361 Sunfish Lake Ct NW Ste 40 Anoka (55303) *(G-240)*

Wellington Management Inc 651 292-9844
1625 Energy Park Dr # 100 Saint Paul (55108) *(G-9144)*

Wellington Window Co (PA) 952 933-2737
3938 Meadowbrook Rd Minneapolis (55426) *(G-6034)*

Wells Capital Management Inc (HQ) 612 667-4230
90 S 7th St Ste 5000 Minneapolis (55402) *(G-6035)*

Wells Fargo, Faribault *Also Called Wf National Bank South Central (G-2037)*

Wells Fargo, Monticello *Also Called Marquette Bank Monticello (G-6276)*

Wells Fargo Advisors LLC 612 332-1212
80 S 8th St Ste 3400 Minneapolis (55402) *(G-6036)*

Wells Fargo Advisors LLC 952 835-3111
8500 Normandale Lake Blvd Minneapolis (55437) *(G-6037)*

Wells Fargo Audit Services Inc 612 667-1234
1200 Norwest Center Minneapolis (55479) *(G-6038)*

Wells Fargo Bank 320 762-2181
304 Maple St Alexandria (56308) *(G-129)*

Wells Fargo Bank 651 464-3334
208 Lake St S Forest Lake (55025) *(G-2172)*

Wells Fargo Bank 651 388-6751
401 Plum St Red Wing (55066) *(G-7011)*

Wells Fargo Bank 651 205-8839
1815 N Saint Paul Rd Saint Paul (55109) *(G-9145)*

Wells Fargo Bank 218 681-1930
208 Main Ave N Thief River Falls (56701) *(G-9682)*

Wells Fargo Bank, National 507 373-1423
122 E Main St Albert Lea (56007) *(G-71)*

Wells Fargo Bank, National 952 890-1424
350 W Burnsville Pkwy Ste 100 Burnsville (55337) *(G-821)*

Wells Fargo Bank, National 218 847-1361
211 Holmes St W Detroit Lakes (56501) *(G-1222)*

Wells Fargo Bank, National 218 726-9325
1339 W Arrowhead Rd Duluth (55811) *(G-1500)*

Wells Fargo Bank, National 218 326-8521
220 NW 1st Ave Ste 210 Grand Rapids (55744) *(G-2311)*

Wells Fargo Bank, National 320 587-2122
135 Main St N Hutchinson (55350) *(G-2718)*

Wells Fargo Bank, National 507 387-9254
1600 E Madison Ave # 100 Mankato (56001) *(G-3215)*

Wells Fargo Bank, National 507 625-1872
206 E Hickory St Mankato (56001) *(G-3216)*

Wells Fargo Bank, National 507 532-4405
400 W Main St Marshall (56258) *(G-3333)*

Wells Fargo Bank, National 612 316-3965
12120 Aberdeen St NE Minneapolis (55449) *(G-3641)*

Wells Fargo Bank, National 612 667-2753
1455 W Lake St Fl 1 Minneapolis (55408) *(G-6039)*

Wells Fargo Bank, National 952 881-7333
7901 Xerxes Ave S Ste 108 Minneapolis (55431) *(G-6040)*

Wells Fargo Bank, National 612 667-1234
625 Marquette Ave Fl 16 Minneapolis (55402) *(G-6041)*

ALPHABETIC

Wells Fargo Bank, National 612 667-8710
733 Marquette Ave Minneapolis (55402) *(G-6042)*
Wells Fargo Bank, National 763 295-2290
407 Pine St Ste 200 Monticello (55362) *(G-6291)*
Wells Fargo Bank, National 507 663-7300
700 Water St S Northfield (55057) *(G-6545)*
Wells Fargo Bank, National 507 451-5670
101 N Cedar Ave Owatonna (55060) *(G-6744)*
Wells Fargo Bank, National 651 385-2328
4th & Plum Red Wing (55066) *(G-7012)*
Wells Fargo Bank, National 507 285-2990
940 37th St NW Rochester (55901) *(G-7289)*
Wells Fargo Bank, National 507 285-2800
21 1st St SW Ste 611 Rochester (55902) *(G-7290)*
Wells Fargo Bank, National 507 285-3015
3360 55th St NW Rochester (55901) *(G-7291)*
Wells Fargo Bank, National 320 259-3100
400 1st St S Ste 100 Saint Cloud (56301) *(G-7632)*
Wells Fargo Bank, National 651 205-7583
430 Wabasha St N Saint Paul (55101) *(G-9146)*
Wells Fargo Bank, National 952 953-3991
14325 Cedar Ave Saint Paul (55124) *(G-7944)*
Wells Fargo Bank, National 651 450-4054
161 Concord Exchange N South Saint Paul (55075) *(G-9551)*
Wells Fargo Bank, National 218 749-5920
401 Chestnut St Virginia (55792) *(G-9765)*
Wells Fargo Business Credit (DH) 612 673-8500
109 S 7th St Ste 400 Minneapolis (55402) *(G-6043)*
Wells Fargo Equipment Finance (DH) 612 667-9876
733 Marquette Ave Ste 700 Minneapolis (55402) *(G-6044)*
Wells Fargo Financial (DH) 952 920-9270
3101 W 69th St 204 Minneapolis (55435) *(G-6045)*
Wells Fargo Financial Indiana 952 920-9270
3101 W 69th St Ste 204 Minneapolis (55435) *(G-6046)*
Wells Fargo Funding Inc 800 328-5074
2701 Wells Fargo Way Fl 5 Minneapolis (55467) *(G-6047)*
Wells Fargo Home Mortgage Inc 952 939-9066
600 Highway 169 S Ste 1950 Minneapolis (55426) *(G-6048)*
Wells Fargo Insurance Inc 952 921-3601
600 W Market Minneapolis (55425) *(G-6049)*
Wells Fargo Insurance Inc (HQ) 612 667-5600
600 Highway 169 S Fl 12 Minneapolis (55426) *(G-6050)*
Wells Fargo Insurance Services 952 830-3000
4300 Market Pointe Dr # 600 Minneapolis (55435) *(G-6051)*
Wells Fargo Minnesota West 218 736-7391
216 S Court St Fergus Falls (56537) *(G-2124)*
Wells Fargo Minnesota West (HQ) 218 233-6183
730 Center Ave Lbby LBBY Moorhead (56560) *(G-6347)*
Wells Fargo Minnesota West 218 681-1930
110 3rd St E Thief River Falls (56701) *(G-9683)*
Wells Fargo Properties Inc (HQ) 612 667-8690
Wells Fargo Ctr # 6 Minneapolis (55402) *(G-6052)*
Wells Fargo Services Inc (HQ) 612 667-1234
255 2nd Ave S Minneapolis (55401) *(G-6053)*
Wells Fargo Services Inc 612 667-1234
255 2nd Ave S Minneapolis (55401) *(G-6054)*
Wells Federal Bank Fsb 507 553-3151
53 1st St SW Wells (56097) *(G-9963)*
Wells Jefferson International 612 338-5400
3600 Minnesota Dr Ste 850 Minneapolis (55435) *(G-6055)*
Wells Lanes Inc 651 455-3220
365 Concord Exchange N South Saint Paul (55075) *(G-9552)*
Wells Technology Inc (PA) 218 751-5117
4885 Windsor Ct NW Bemidji (56601) *(G-432)*
Wells Technology Inc 218 751-1412
5015 Windsor Ct NW Bemidji (56601) *(G-433)*
Wellstead of Rogers, Rogers *Also Called Dignified Assisted Living Inc (G-7322)*
Welsh Co's LLC 952 897-7700
4350 Baker Rd Ste 400 Minnetonka (55343) *(G-6236)*
Wenck Associates Inc 763 479-4200
1800 Pioneer Creek Ctr Maple Plain (55359) *(G-3281)*
Wendigo Pines Assisted Ll 218 326-6900
20371 Wendigo Park Rd Grand Rapids (55744) *(G-2312)*
Wensman Seed Co, Wadena *Also Called Agreliant Genetics LLC (G-9796)*
Wenzel Plumbing & Heating Inc 651 452-1565
1710 Alexander Rd Saint Paul (55121) *(G-7945)*
Werner Electric Ventures LLC (PA) 651 769-6841
7450 95th St S Cottage Grove (55016) *(G-1109)*
Wes Hanson Builders Inc 218 765-4122
13645 N Horseshoe Lake Rd Merrifield (56465) *(G-3372)*
Wesco Distribution Inc 651 582-3945
601 Lakeview Point Dr Saint Paul (55112) *(G-9147)*
Wescott Agri-Products Inc 507 876-2891
28085 County Road 25 Elgin (55932) *(G-1857)*
Wesley Residence Inc 218 628-2307
5601 Grand Ave Duluth (55807) *(G-1501)*
West Bank School of Music 612 333-6651
1813 S 6th St Minneapolis (55454) *(G-6056)*
West Central Chemicals 507 444-0275
3925 N County Road 45 Owatonna (55060) *(G-6745)*
West Central Community Service 218 643-5952
732 5th St S Breckenridge (56520) *(G-603)*
West Central Inc 320 235-8518
2700 Trott Ave SW Willmar (56201) *(G-10053)*
West Central Industries Inc (PA) 320 235-5310
1300 22nd St SW Willmar (56201) *(G-10054)*
West Central Internal Medicine, Morris *Also Called Prairie Medical (G-6375)*
West Central Irrigation Inc 320 239-2230
810 Industrial Dr Starbuck (56381) *(G-9588)*
West Central Minnesota 218 685-4486
411 Industrial Park Blvd Elbow Lake (56531) *(G-1855)*
West Central Reg Juv Center, Moorhead *Also Called County of Clay (G-6308)*
West Central Steel Inc 320 235-4070
110 19th St NW Willmar (56201) *(G-10055)*
West Central Turkeys LLC 218 863-1491
704 N Broadway Pelican Rapids (56572) *(G-6784)*
West Plains Dairy LLC 651 258-4666
11755 County 1 Blvd Goodhue (55027) *(G-2251)*
West Publishing Corp (HQ) 651 687-8000
610 Opperman Dr Saint Paul (55123) *(G-7946)*
West Publishing Corp 651 687-7000
610 Opperman Dr Saint Paul (55123) *(G-7947)*
West Side Community Health 651 222-1816
153 Cesar Chavez St Saint Paul (55107) *(G-9148)*
West Side Lanes, Saint Paul *Also Called PC Productions Inc (G-7870)*
West St Paul Office, Saint Paul *Also Called Anchor Bank (G-7699)*
West Wind Village 320 589-1133
1001 Scotts Ave Morris (56267) *(G-6380)*
Westaff Inc 218 463-4418
301 5th Ave SW Roseau (56751) *(G-7359)*
Westbrook Health Center 507 274-6121
920 Bell Ave Westbrook (56183) *(G-9968)*
Westco Systems Inc 763 559-7046
4655 Juneau Ln N Minneapolis (55446) *(G-6057)*
Western Bank (HQ) 651 290-8100
663 University Ave W Saint Paul (55104) *(G-9149)*
Western Bank (PA) 651 290-8100
663 University Ave W Saint Paul (55104) *(G-9150)*
Western Bank Edina 952 857-1707
4700 W 77th St Ste 160 Minneapolis (55435) *(G-6058)*
Western Co-Op Transport Assn 320 269-5531
4501 72nd St SW Montevideo (56265) *(G-6261)*
Western Community Action Inc (PA) 507 537-1416
1400 S Saratoga St Marshall (56258) *(G-3334)*
Western Consolidated Co-op (PA) 320 394-2171
101 Rand St Holloway (56249) *(G-2493)*
Western Delivery Inc 651 665-0702
5605 Wentworth Ave Minneapolis (55419) *(G-6059)*
Western Eastern Ob Gyn Limited 952 556-0071
3000 Hundertmark Rd Ste 9 Chaska (55318) *(G-985)*
Western Lake Superior Sanitary 218 722-3336
2626 Courtland St Duluth (55806) *(G-1502)*
Western Mental Health Center 507 532-3236
1212 E College Dr Marshall (56258) *(G-3335)*
Western National Bank 218 723-5152
201 N Central Duluth (55807) *(G-1503)*
Western National Mutual Insce (PA) 952 835-5350
5350 W 78th St Minneapolis (55439) *(G-6060)*
Western Ob Gyne Ltd 952 442-2137
560 S Maple St Ste 130 Waconia (55387) *(G-9795)*
Western Pope County Hospital 320 239-2201
610 W 6th St Starbuck (56381) *(G-9589)*
Western Steel Erection Inc 952 473-4344
485 Stubbs Bay Rd Long Lake (55356) *(G-3035)*
Western Walls Inc 507 282-4624
604 11th Ave NW Ste 100 Rochester (55901) *(G-7292)*
Western Waterproofing Co Inc 612 781-7100
111 Lowry Ave NE Minneapolis (55418) *(G-6061)*
Westfield Golf Club Inc 507 452-8700
1460 W 5th St Winona (55987) *(G-10140)*
Westhealth Inc 763 577-7000
2855 Campus Dr Ste 465 Plymouth (55441) *(G-6891)*
Westlund Dental Studio Inc 952 942-9464
7535 Office Ridge Cir Eden Prairie (55344) *(G-1814)*
Westlund's, South Saint Paul *Also Called Stock Yards Meat Packing Co (G-9544)*
Westman Freightliner Inc (PA) 507 625-4118
2200 4th Ave Mankato (56001) *(G-3217)*
Westner National Bank Inc 218 723-5100
202 W Superior St Ste 100 Duluth (55802) *(G-1504)*
Westside Equipment Installers 763 478-9572
902 Highway 55 Hamel (55340) *(G-2360)*
Westside Wholesale Tire Inc 763 420-2100
19925 75th Ave N Hamel (55340) *(G-2361)*
Westway Exteriors Inc 651 251-0910
2274 Capp Rd Saint Paul (55114) *(G-9151)*
Westwood Health Care Center, Minneapolis *Also Called Aviv Health Care Inc (G-3844)*
Westwood Health Care Center, Minneapolis *Also Called Aviv Health Care Inc (G-3846)*
Westwood Lutheran Church 952 545-5623
9001 Cedar Lake Rd S Minneapolis (55426) *(G-6062)*
Westwood Professional Services 952 937-5150
7699 Anagram Dr Eden Prairie (55344) *(G-1815)*
Westwood Sports Inc 952 881-2222
9601 Garfield Ave S Minneapolis (55420) *(G-6063)*
Weyerhaeuser Co 218 546-8114
County Rd 102 Deerwood (56444) *(G-1180)*
Weyerhaeuser Co 651 645-0811
700 Emerald St Saint Paul (55114) *(G-9152)*
Wf National Bank South Central 507 334-5546
104 5th St NW Faribault (55021) *(G-2037)*
Wheaton Community Hospital 320 563-8226
401 12th St N Wheaton (56296) *(G-9970)*
Wheaton Head Start 320 563-8191
710 4th Ave N Wheaton (56296) *(G-9971)*
Wheaton Liquor 320 563-4155
920 Broadway Wheaton (56296) *(G-9972)*
Wheeler Consolidated Inc 952 929-6791
9330 James Ave S Minneapolis (55431) *(G-6064)*
Wheeler Hardware Co 651 645-4501
2645 Fairview Ave N Saint Paul (55113) *(G-9153)*
Wherley Moving, Duluth *Also Called Kj & E Properties (G-1372)*
Whirl-Air-Flow Corp 763 262-1200
20055 177th St NW Big Lake (55309) *(G-459)*
Whispering Pines Therapy Ctr 218 587-4423
518 Jefferson Ave Pine River (56474) *(G-6822)*
White Bear Animal Hospital 651 777-1393
1909 County Road E E Saint Paul (55110) *(G-9154)*
White Bear Dodge Inc 651 482-6100
3430 Highway 61 N Saint Paul (55110) *(G-9155)*
White Bear Lake Clinic, Saint Paul *Also Called Healthpartners Inc (G-8466)*
White Bear Lake Sports Center, Saint Paul *Also Called City of White Bear Lake (G-8214)*
White Bear Racquet & Swim LP 651 426-1308
4800 White Bear Pkwy Saint Paul (55110) *(G-9156)*

ALPHABETIC

(PA)=Parent Co (HQ)=Headquarters (DH)=Div Headquarters

White Bear Raquet & Swim, Saint Paul *Also Called Life Time Fitness Inc* ***(G-8585)***
White Community Hospital Corp 218 229-2211
5211 Highway 110 Aurora (55705) ***(G-257)***
White Earth Band of Chippewa 218 935-2711
777 SE Casino Rd Mahnomen (56557) ***(G-3091)***
White Earth Health Center, Ogema *Also Called Indian Health Service* ***(G-6554)***
White Earth Housing Authority 218 473-4663
3303 US Highway 59 Waubun (56589) ***(G-9901)***
White Earth Reservation 218 983-3387
35525 County Highway 34 Ogema (56569) ***(G-6555)***
White House Custom Colour Inc 651 646-8263
2840 Lone Oak Pkwy Eagan (55121) ***(G-1560)***
White Rock Bank (HQ) 507 263-3030
31377 County 24 Blvd Cannon Falls (55009) ***(G-864)***
White Rock Coffee Roasters, Saint Paul *Also Called Olson Coffee Roasters Inc* ***(G-8782)***
Whitebox Advisors LLC 612 253-6025
3033 Excelsior Blvd Ste 300 Minneapolis (55416) ***(G-6065)***
Whitehouse Health Care Center, Saint Paul *Also Called Evangelical Lutheran Good* ***(G-8348)***
Whitewater Health Care Center, Saint Charles *Also Called Beverly Enterprises - MN* ***(G-7402)***
Whiting, Jim Nursery & Garden 507 289-3741
3430 19th St NW Rochester (55901) ***(G-7293)***
Whittier Place 612 872-1926
2405 1st Ave S Minneapolis (55404) ***(G-6066)***
Wholesale Produce Supply LLC 612 378-2025
752 Kasota Cir SE Minneapolis (55414) ***(G-6067)***
Widseth, Smith, Nolting 320 762-8149
610 Fillmore St Alexandria (56308) ***(G-130)***
Widseth, Smith, Nolting 218 829-5117
7804 Industrial Park Rd Baxter (56425) ***(G-345)***
Widseth, Smith, Nolting (PA) 218 281-6522
216 S Main St Ste 1 Crookston (56716) ***(G-1144)***
Wieser Brothers General Contr 507 895-8903
200 Twilite St La Crescent (55947) ***(G-2845)***
Wigwam Resort, Baudette *Also Called Briggs Hennum Inc* ***(G-314)***
Wiha Tools, Monticello *Also Called Willi Hahn Corp* ***(G-6292)***
Wiken Promotion & Advertising 952 476-2002
681 Lake St E Ste 262 Wayzata (55391) ***(G-9950)***
Wikstrom Telephone Co Inc 218 436-2121
212 Main St S Karlstad (56732) ***(G-2817)***
Wilcon Construction Inc 507 345-6653
232 Quail Path Mankato (56001) ***(G-3218)***
Wilcon Construction Inc 507 375-5464
1512 7th Ave S Saint James (56081) ***(G-7649)***
Wilcox Paper LLC 763 404-8400
111000 Jefferson Hwy N Champlin (55316) ***(G-906)***
Wild Golf Club 952 445-3500
3151 Wilds Ridge Ct NW Prior Lake (55372) ***(G-6962)***
Wild Marsh Golf Club LLC 763 682-4476
1710 Montrose Blvd Buffalo (55313) ***(G-660)***
Wild Mountain, Taylors Falls *Also Called Dennis Raedeke Inc* ***(G-9660)***
Wild Wings LLC (HQ) 651 345-5355
2101 S Highway 61 Lake City (55041) ***(G-2856)***
Wilder Research Center, Saint Paul *Also Called Amherst H Wilder Foundation* ***(G-8042)***
Wildflower Lodge of Chapelwood 763 420-3768
9251 Black Oaks Ln N Osseo (55311) ***(G-6684)***
Wilds, Prior Lake *Also Called Wild Golf Club* ***(G-6962)***
Wilds of San Prairie 507 931-4375
700 Knight St Apt 221 Saint Peter (56082) ***(G-9316)***
Wilkerson & Hegna 952 897-1707
7300 Metro Blvd Ste 300 Minneapolis (55439) ***(G-6068)***
Wilkerson, Guthmann & Johnson 651 222-1801
55 5th St E Ste 1300 Saint Paul (55101) ***(G-9157)***
Wille Transport Inc 218 999-0900
521 W Highway 2 Cohasset (55721) ***(G-1073)***
Willet Hauser Architectural 507 457-3500
1685 Wilkie Dr Winona (55987) ***(G-10141)***
Willi Hahn Corp 763 295-0666
1348 Dundas Cir Monticello (55362) ***(G-6292)***
William LLC 952 345-3461
314 W 86th St Minneapolis (55420) ***(G-6069)***
Williams Funeral Home Inc 320 252-2522
1900 Veterans Dr Saint Cloud (56303) ***(G-7633)***
Williams Steel & Hardware Co (PA) 612 588-9800
416 35th Ave NE Ste 1 Minneapolis (55418) ***(G-6070)***
Willing Partners Inc 952 652-2500
6900 Canby Trl Northfield (55057) ***(G-6546)***
Willinger's Golf Club, Northfield *Also Called Willing Partners Inc* ***(G-6546)***
Willis of Minnesota Inc 763 302-7100
1600 Utica Ave S Ste 600 Minneapolis (55416) ***(G-6071)***
Willmar Municpl Utilities Comm, Willmar *Also Called Willmar, City of Inc* ***(G-10056)***
Willmar Poultry Farms Inc 320 968-6211
411 Pine St Foley (56329) ***(G-2142)***
Willmar Readymix, Willmar *Also Called Central Allied Enterprises Inc* ***(G-9995)***
Willmar, City of Inc 320 235-4422
700 Litchfield Ave SW Willmar (56201) ***(G-10056)***
Willow Creek Concrete Products 320 398-5415
12626 County Road 150 Kimball (55353) ***(G-2835)***
Willow Creek Golf Course of 507 285-0305
1700 48th St SW Rochester (55902) ***(G-7294)***
Willow Group Inc 952 897-3550
8201 Norman Center Dr # 210 Minneapolis (55437) ***(G-6072)***
Willow Home 507 426-8277
1001 1st St SE Fairfax (55332) ***(G-1956)***
Willowbrook Co-Op 507 388-2886
700 Agency Trl Mankato (56001) ***(G-3219)***
Willows 763 533-1883
6232 65th Ave N Apt 117 Minneapolis (55429) ***(G-6073)***
Wilmer Medical Center, Granite Falls *Also Called Granite Medical Center* ***(G-2316)***
Wilmont Farmers Elevator Co 507 926-5131
101 N 4th Ave Wilmont (56185) ***(G-10064)***
Wilpro Inc 320 235-8850
3735 County Road 5 SW Willmar (56201) ***(G-10057)***
Wilson - McShane Corp 952 854-0795
3001 Metro Dr Ste 500 Minneapolis (55425) ***(G-6074)***
Wilson Learning Corp 952 944-2880
8000 W 78th St Ste 200 Minneapolis (55439) ***(G-6075)***
Wilson Lines of Minnesota Inc 651 459-8193
155 21st St Newport (55055) ***(G-6490)***
Wilson Oil Co Inc 651 388-5783
2355 W Main St Red Wing (55066) ***(G-7013)***
Wilson's Nursery Inc 952 445-3630
9150 Great Plains Blvd Chanhassen (55317) ***(G-946)***
Winco Landscape Inc 651 455-3070
1848 50th St E Ste 102 Inver Grove Heights (55077) ***(G-2774)***
Wincom Systems Inc 952 828-4000
11840 Valley View Rd Eden Prairie (55344) ***(G-1816)***
Windom, City of Inc 507 831-2400
2150 Hospital Dr Windom (56101) ***(G-10072)***
Window Concepts of Minnesota 651 905-0105
990 Lone Oak Rd Ste 114 Saint Paul (55121) ***(G-7948)***
Window World, Saint Paul *Also Called Probuilt America Inc* ***(G-8850)***
Wine Merchants, Saint Paul *Also Called Johnson Brothers Liquor Co* ***(G-8537)***
Winfield Solutions LLC (HQ) 651 481-2222
1080 County Road F W Saint Paul (55126) ***(G-9158)***
Wingard Farms 763 263-2635
457 196th Dr NW Elk River (55330) ***(G-1896)***
Wingate Inn Oakdale, Saint Paul *Also Called USP Hotel Services LLC* ***(G-9287)***
Wingfoot Commercial Tire Systs 507 454-5181
5110 Service Dr Winona (55987) ***(G-10142)***
Wings Financial Credit Union 612 726-2073
8101 34th Ave S Ste 100 Bloomington (55425) ***(G-526)***
Wings Financial Credit Union (PA) 952 997-8000
14985 Glazier Ave Ste 100 Saint Paul (55124) ***(G-7949)***
Winkley Co, Minneapolis *Also Called Greg Gruman* ***(G-4565)***
Winmark Capital Corp 763 520-8500
605 Highway 169 N Ste 400 Minneapolis (55441) ***(G-6076)***
Winmark Corp (PA) 763 520-8500
605 Highway 169 N Ste 400 Minneapolis (55441) ***(G-6077)***
Winona Agency Inc 507 452-3366
174 Center St Winona (55987) ***(G-10143)***
Winona Area Barber Shoppers, Winona *Also Called Society For Preservation* ***(G-10128)***
Winona Clinic Ltd 507 454-3680
859 Mankato Ave Winona (55987) ***(G-10144)***
Winona Community Memorial Hosp (PA) 507 454-3650
855 Mankato Ave Winona (55987) ***(G-10145)***
Winona Country Club 507 454-3767
22852 County Road 17 Winona (55987) ***(G-10146)***
Winona County Dept Humn Svc, Winona *Also Called County of Winona* ***(G-10090)***
Winona Developmental 507 452-1798
1721 W Service Dr Winona (55987) ***(G-10147)***
Winona Health 507 457-4468
175 E Wabasha St Winona (55987) ***(G-10148)***
Winona Heating & Ventilating 507 452-2064
374 E 2nd St Winona (55987) ***(G-10149)***
Winona Inn LP 507 454-4390
956 Mankato Ave Winona (55987) ***(G-10150)***
Winona Lighting Inc 507 454-5113
3760 W 4th St Winona (55987) ***(G-10151)***
Winona National Holding Co Inc 507 454-4320
204 Main St Winona (55987) ***(G-10152)***
Winona ORC Industries Inc 507 452-1855
1053 E Mark St Winona (55987) ***(G-10153)***
Winona Radio, Winona *Also Called Southwestern Minnesota Radio* ***(G-10129)***
Winroc Corp (PA) 651 777-8222
5262 Glenbrook Ave N Saint Paul (55128) ***(G-9288)***
Winsted Corp 952 944-9050
10901 Hampshire Ave S Ste A Minneapolis (55438) ***(G-6078)***
Winston Courts, Saint Paul *Also Called Accessible Space North Inc* ***(G-7977)***
Winter Truck Line Inc 218 935-2236
1485 230th St Mahnomen (56557) ***(G-3092)***
Wintergreen Dogsled Lodge Inc 218 365-6602
205 E Sheridan St Ely (55731) ***(G-1917)***
Winthrop Honor Guard 507 647-5608
27076 541st Ave Winthrop (55396) ***(G-10169)***
Winthrop Resources Corp 952 936-0226
11100 Wayzata Blvd Ste 800 Minnetonka (55305) ***(G-6237)***
Wipaire Inc 651 451-1205
1700 Henry Ave South Saint Paul (55075) ***(G-9553)***
Wipfli LLP 952 548-3400
7601 France Ave S Ste 400 Minneapolis (55435) ***(G-6079)***
Wipfli LLP 651 636-6468
4000 Lexington Ave N # 201 Saint Paul (55126) ***(G-9159)***
Wipple Hieghts School, Faribault *Also Called Janine Sahagian* ***(G-2014)***
Wireless Ronin Technologies 952 564-3500
5929 Baker Rd Ste 475 Minnetonka (55345) ***(G-6238)***
Wirth Business Credit, Minneapolis *Also Called Winmark Capital Corp* ***(G-6076)***
Wirtz Beverage Minnesota Beer 651 646-6063
475 Prior Ave N Saint Paul (55104) ***(G-9160)***
Wisconsin Central Ltd 651 633-8771
669 1st St NW Saint Paul (55112) ***(G-9161)***
Wisconsin Public Service Corp 218 879-1571
910 Cloquet Ave Cloquet (55720) ***(G-1069)***
Wise Essentials Inc 651 699-4468
716 Mount Curve Blvd Saint Paul (55116) ***(G-9162)***
Wise Greenwald & Greenwald PC 763 535-0501
4800 Lilac Dr N Minneapolis (55429) ***(G-6080)***
Witt Dohm Properties Inc 952 758-5252
102 County Road 37 New Prague (56071) ***(G-6425)***
Wks Vadnais Heights LLC 651 484-2400
1100 County Road E E Vadnais Heights (55110) ***(G-9721)***
Wkt Properties LLC 763 525-4000
9201 International Pkwy Minneapolis (55428) ***(G-6081)***
WLOL, Rochester *Also Called Clear Channel Communications* ***(G-7081)***
Wm Healthcare Solutions Inc 763 786-5555
961 73rd Ave NE Minneapolis (55432) ***(G-3642)***
Wmhs Minnesota Wisconsin, Minneapolis *Also Called Wm Healthcare Solutions Inc* ***(G-3642)***
Wolcyn Tree Farms 763 689-3346
4542 Highway 95 NW Cambridge (55008) ***(G-847)***
Wolf Etter & Co 507 642-8882
8 W Main St Madelia (56062) ***(G-3075)***
Wolf Motors Co Inc 952 492-2340
600 2nd St W Jordan (55352) ***(G-2813)***

Wolf Ridge Environmental ... 218 353-7414
6282 Cranberry Rd Finland (55603) *(G-2128)*
Wolf Springs Ranches ... 952 942-5566
7321 Washington Ave S Minneapolis (55439) *(G-6082)*
Wolfnet Technologies LLC ... 612 342-0088
211 N 1st St Ste 455 Minneapolis (55401) *(G-6083)*
Wolters Kluwer Financial Svcs (DH) ... 320 251-3060
6815 Saukview Dr Saint Cloud (56303) *(G-7634)*
Woman's Club of Minneapolis ... 612 870-8001
410 Oak Grove St Minneapolis (55403) *(G-6084)*
Women of Nations ... 651 222-5830
73 Leech St Saint Paul (55102) *(G-9163)*
Women's Advocates Inc ... 651 227-9966
588 Grand Ave Saint Paul (55102) *(G-9164)*
Women's Shelter Inc ... 507 285-1938
823 W Center St Rochester (55902) *(G-7295)*
Womens Life Care Center ... 651 777-0350
2870 Middle St Saint Paul (55117) *(G-9165)*
Womens Shelter, Kasson *Also Called Dodge County Battered Women's (G-2820)*
Wonder & Hostess, Saint Paul *Also Called Interstate Brands Corp (G-8522)*
Wonderbread Hostess Cake Bky, Hopkins *Also Called Interstate Brands Corp (G-2558)*
Wood Dale Nursing Home, Redwood Falls *Also Called Wood-Dale Home Inc (G-7029)*
Wood Products Unlimited Inc ... 218 829-4353
15909 Inglewood Dr Brainerd (56401) *(G-589)*
Wood-Dale Home Inc ... 507 637-3587
600 Sunrise Blvd Redwood Falls (56283) *(G-7029)*
Woodbury Clinic, Saint Paul *Also Called Healthpartners Inc (G-9226)*
Woodbury Estates, Saint Paul *Also Called Edgewood Management Inc (G-9208)*
Woodbury Financial Services (HQ) ... 651 738-4000
500 Bielenberg Dr Saint Paul (55125) *(G-9289)*
Wooddale Recreation Center, Saint Paul *Also Called Xenophon Corp (G-9291)*
Woodfam Inc ... 218 283-4775
611 11th St International Falls (56649) *(G-2734)*
Woodgroup Field Services Inc ... 763 785-0650
8010 Ranchers Rd NE Minneapolis (55432) *(G-3643)*
Woodhill Country Club ... 952 473-7333
200 Woodhill Rd Wayzata (55391) *(G-9951)*
Woodlake Park, Rochester *Also Called A B Systems Inc (G-7042)*
Woodland Centers ... 320 693-7221
114 N Holcombe Ave # 230 Litchfield (55355) *(G-2993)*
Woodland Centers (PA) ... 320 235-4613
1125 6th St SE Willmar (56201) *(G-10058)*
Woodland Good Samaritan Vlg, Brainerd *Also Called Evangelical Lutheran Good (G-566)*
Woodland Heights Health Care ... 651 451-1881
2060 Upper 55th St E Inver Grove Heights (55077) *(G-2775)*
Woodland Hills, Duluth *Also Called St James Home of Duluth (G-1462)*
Woodline Manufacturing Inc (PA) ... 218 744-5966
4097 Highway 53 Eveleth (55734) *(G-1934)*
Woodrest Health Care Center ... 218 547-1855
209 Birchwood Ave Walker (56484) *(G-9861)*
Woodruff Co ... 507 285-2500
1524 3rd Ave SE Rochester (55904) *(G-7296)*
Woods Equipment Co ... 651 455-6681
2340 County Road C W Ste 120 Saint Paul (55113) *(G-9166)*
Woodward Broadcasting Inc ... 507 235-5595
1371 W Lair Rd Fairmont (56031) *(G-1984)*
Woodwinds Health Campus, Saint Paul *Also Called Healtheast Co's Inc (G-9225)*
Woodwinds Health Campus ... 651 232-0100
1925 Woodwinds Dr Saint Paul (55125) *(G-9290)*
Woody's Rebar Co ... 651 592-5038
3580 Centerville Rd Saint Paul (55127) *(G-9167)*
Woolleys Restaurant, Bloomington *Also Called Tri-City IV Inc (G-521)*
Work Connection Inc ... 320 693-8871
201 S Sibley Ave Ste 1 Litchfield (55355) *(G-2994)*
Workabilities Inc ... 763 541-1844
7400 Laurel Ave Minneapolis (55426) *(G-6085)*
Workforce Center, Bemidji *Also Called Rural Minnesota Cep Inc (G-424)*
Workforce Solutions, Saint Paul *Also Called County of Ramsey (G-8261)*
Workman Financial Group Inc ... 763 746-9420
3370 Annapolis Ln N Ste B Minneapolis (55447) *(G-6086)*
World Architects Inc ... 651 227-7773
305 Saint Peter St Saint Paul (55102) *(G-9168)*
World Class Wines Inc ... 952 941-8795
7666 Washington Ave S Eden Prairie (55344) *(G-1817)*
World Data Products Inc ... 952 476-9000
121 Cheshire Ln Ste 100 Minnetonka (55305) *(G-6239)*
World Distribution Services ... 651 686-9252
3470 Washington Dr Ste 211 Saint Paul (55122) *(G-7950)*
World Wide Publications ... 612 333-0940
1303 Hennepin Ave Minneapolis (55403) *(G-6087)*
Worldwide Fish & Seafood Inc ... 612 724-5911
2330 Minnehaha Ave Minneapolis (55404) *(G-6088)*
Wornson-Polzin Dental Labs, Mankato *Also Called National Dentex Corp (G-3175)*
Worthington Area YMCA, Worthington *Also Called YMCA of Worthington, Minnesota (G-10199)*
Worthington Regional Hospital, Worthington *Also Called City of Worthington (G-10180)*
Worthington Tractor Parts Inc ... 507 372-2911
27170 US Highway 59 Worthington (56187) *(G-10198)*
Worthngton Small Animal Clinic, Worthington *Also Called Veterinary Medical Center Prof (G-10197)*
Wovenhearts of Apple Valley, Saint Paul *Also Called Centennial House of Apple Val (G-7729)*
Wrecker Services Inc ... 612 330-0013
200 E Lyndale Ave N Ste 1 Minneapolis (55405) *(G-6089)*
Wren Corp (PA) ... 651 636-8900
2975 Partridge Rd Saint Paul (55113) *(G-9169)*
Wrico Stamping of Minnesota, Minneapolis *Also Called Griffiths Holding Corp (G-4572)*
Wright Aero Inc ... 320 963-5094
Municipal Airport Maple Lake (55358) *(G-3268)*
Wright Connection Dtnh Inc ... 763 682-2910
1803 Hwy 25 N Buffalo (55313) *(G-661)*
Wright Tree Service Inc ... 507 625-6950
230 Lundin Blvd Mankato (56001) *(G-3220)*
Wright's General Construction ... 218 372-3329
8098 County Highway 61 Willow River (55795) *(G-10063)*
Wright-Hennepin Cooperative (PA) ... 763 477-3000
6800 Electric Dr Rockford (55373) *(G-7305)*
Wright-Hennepin Security Corp ... 763 477-3000
6800 Electric Dr Rockford (55373) *(G-7306)*
Wsi - Rwp LLC ... 901 821-4117
1700 American Blvd E Bloomington (55425) *(G-527)*
Wunderlich-Malec Engineering (PA) ... 952 933-3222
5501 Feltl Rd Hopkins (55343) *(G-2660)*
Wuollet Bakery Inc ... 763 473-8621
771 Lake St E Wayzata (55391) *(G-9952)*
Wurth Adams Nut & Bolt Co (HQ) ... 763 493-0877
10100 85th Ave N Osseo (55369) *(G-6685)*
Ww Constructors Inc ... 763 420-4177
20095 75th Ave N Hamel (55340) *(G-2362)*
Wwtc ... 651 289-4404
2110 Cliff Rd Eagan (55122) *(G-1561)*
Wxow-TV, La Crescent *Also Called Quincy Newspapers Inc (G-2842)*
Wyde Corp ... 651 882-2400
4660 Slater Rd Ste 222 Eagan (55122) *(G-1562)*
Wynco, Mankato *Also Called Kruse Family Enterprises LLC (G-3156)*
Wyndham International Inc ... 952 831-3131
4460 W 78th Street Cir Minneapolis (55435) *(G-6090)*
X Tex, Sartell *Also Called Mark Doman (G-9338)*
Xact Duplicating, Minneapolis *Also Called Xcellence Inc (G-6091)*
XATA Corp (PA) ... 952 707-5600
965 Prairie Center Dr Eden Prairie (55344) *(G-1818)*
XCEL Energy, Bayport *Also Called Northern States Power Co (G-350)*
XCEL Energy, Becker *Also Called Northern States Power Co (G-357)*
XCEL Energy, Elk River *Also Called Northern States Power Co (G-1887)*
XCEL Energy, Monticello *Also Called Northern States Power Co (G-6281)*
XCEL Energy, Monticello *Also Called Northern States Power Co (G-6280)*
XCEL Energy, Osseo *Also Called Northern States Power Co (G-6645)*
XCEL Energy, Saint Paul *Also Called Northern States Power Co (G-8760)*
XCEL Energy Inc ... 651 385-5604
801 E 5th St Red Wing (55066) *(G-7014)*
Xcellence Inc ... 612 305-1330
400 2nd Ave S Ste 1000 Minneapolis (55401) *(G-6091)*
Xenophon Corp (PA) ... 952 929-5518
5622 W Lake St Minneapolis (55416) *(G-6092)*
Xenophon Corp ... 651 735-6214
2122 Wooddale Dr Saint Paul (55125) *(G-9291)*
Xerox Corp ... 952 921-1300
3500 Amercn Blvd W # 400 Minneapolis (55431) *(G-6093)*
Xerxes Computer Corp (PA) ... 952 936-9280
5735 W Old Shakopee Rd Ste 100 Minneapolis (55437) *(G-6094)*
Xiotech Corp ... 952 983-3000
6455 Flying Cloud Dr Eden Prairie (55344) *(G-1819)*
Xmalpha Technologies ... 651 484-0471
935 Arbogast St Saint Paul (55126) *(G-9170)*
Xora Inc ... 651 209-0350
2770 Blue Waters Rd Saint Paul (55121) *(G-7951)*
Xpandable Technology Inc ... 763 521-0401
4050 Olson Memorial Hwy # 100 Minneapolis (55422) *(G-6095)*
Xylo Technologies Inc ... 507 289-9956
2434 Superior Dr NW Ste 104 Rochester (55901) *(G-7297)*
Y M C A, Albert Lea *Also Called Albert Lea Family YMCA (G-31)*
Y M C A, Grand Rapids *Also Called Itasca County Family Young (G-2287)*
Y M C A, Minneapolis *Also Called Young Men's Chritn Assoc of (G-6103)*
Y M C A, Virginia *Also Called Mesabi Family YMCA (G-9746)*
Y M C A Infant Center ... 651 646-4557
1761 University Ave W Saint Paul (55104) *(G-9171)*
Y W C A of Saint Paul, Saint Paul *Also Called Young Women's Christian Assn (G-9181)*
Y'S World of Learning, Brainerd *Also Called Young Men's Chritn Assoc of (G-590)*
Yada Systems Inc ... 651 631-3237
2717 Lincoln Dr Saint Paul (55113) *(G-9172)*
Yaeger Bus Service Inc ... 507 345-5470
56548 Doc Jones Rd Mankato (56001) *(G-3221)*
Yaeger, Jungbauer & Barczak ... 612 333-6371
745 Kasota Ave SE Minneapolis (55414) *(G-6096)*
Yaggy Trucking, Rochester *Also Called Steve Yaggy Specialized Truck (G-7266)*
Yale Materials Handling - MN ... 763 434-3832
15735 Central Ave NE Anoka (55304) *(G-241)*
Yale Mechanical Inc ... 952 884-1661
9649 Girard Ave S Minneapolis (55431) *(G-6097)*
Yale Mechanical LLC ... 952 884-1661
9649 Girard Ave S Minneapolis (55431) *(G-6098)*
Yamamoto Moss Mackenzie ... 612 375-0180
252 1st Ave N Minneapolis (55401) *(G-6099)*
Yarosh, James A, Minneapolis *Also Called Siegel, Brill, Greupner Duffy (G-5665)*
Yeater Hennings Ruff Architect ... 218 233-4422
420 Main Ave Moorhead (56560) *(G-6348)*
Yerigan Construction Co ... 763 444-5353
27741 University Ave NE Isanti (55040) *(G-2782)*
Ymc Camp Dunord ... 218 365-3681
3606 N Arm Rd Ely (55731) *(G-1918)*
YMCA, Ely *Also Called Camp Widji Wagan (G-1912)*
YMCA, Fergus Falls *Also Called Fergus Falls Area Family Young (G-2075)*
YMCA, Minneapolis *Also Called Young Men's Chritn Assoc of (G-6102)*
YMCA ... 320 222-9622
1000 Lakeland Dr SE Willmar (56201) *(G-10059)*
YMCA Camp Miller, Sturgeon Lake *Also Called Duluth Area Family Y M C A (G-9657)*
YMCA Children's Center ... 651 777-8103
2100 Orchard Ln Saint Paul (55110) *(G-9173)*
YMCA of Greater Saint Paul (PA) ... 612 465-0450
2125 E Hennepin Ave Ste 100 Minneapolis (55413) *(G-6100)*
YMCA of Greater Saint Paul ... 651 771-8881
875 Arcade St Saint Paul (55106) *(G-9174)*
YMCA of Greater Saint Paul ... 651 645-6605
2 E Hennepin Ste 150 Saint Paul (55108) *(G-9175)*
YMCA of Greater Saint Paul ... 651 683-4713
550 Opperman Dr Saint Paul (55123) *(G-7952)*
YMCA of Greater St Paul ... 218 365-2117
3788 N Arm Rd Ely (55731) *(G-1919)*
YMCA of Greater St Paul ... 651 483-2671
3760 Lexington Ave N Saint Paul (55126) *(G-9176)*
YMCA of Greater St Paul ... 651 646-4557
1761 University Ave W Saint Paul (55104) *(G-9177)*

ALPHABETIC

YMCA of Greater St Paul	651 292-4143	
194 6th St E Saint Paul (55101) *(G-9178)*		
YMCA of Greater St Paul	651 731-9507	
2175 Radio Dr Saint Paul (55125) *(G-9292)*		
YMCA of Greater St Paul	651 457-0048	
150 Thompson Ave E Saint Paul (55118) *(G-7953)*		
YMCA of Worthington, Minnesota	507 376-6197	
1501 Collegeway Worthington (56187) *(G-10199)*		
Yocum Oil Co Inc	651 739-9141	
2719 Stillwater Rd E Saint Paul (55119) *(G-9179)*		
Yorkdale Townhomes Inc	651 291-1750	
328 Kellogg Blvd W Saint Paul (55102) *(G-9180)*		
Young & Davis Drywall Inc	218 751-6048	
170 Anne St NW Bemidji (56601) *(G-434)*		
Young America Corp (PA)	800 533-4529	
717 Faxon Rd Young America (55397) *(G-10211)*		
Young America Holdings Inc	320 864-6125	
1207 Cardinal Ave N Glencoe (55336) *(G-2217)*		
Young Men's Christian Assn	507 387-8255	
1401 S Riverfront Dr Mankato (56001) *(G-3222)*		
Young Men's Chrtn Assoc of	218 829-4767	
602 Oak St Brainerd (56401) *(G-590)*		
Young Men's Chrtn Assoc of	763 785-7882	
8950 Springbrook Dr NW Minneapolis (55433) *(G-3644)*		
Young Men's Chrtn Assoc of	763 535-4800	
7601 42nd Ave N Minneapolis (55427) *(G-6101)*		
Young Men's Chrtn Assoc of	612 827-5401	
3335 Blaisdell Ave Minneapolis (55408) *(G-6102)*		
Young Men's Chrtn Assoc of	612 588-9484	
1711 W Broadway Ave Minneapolis (55411) *(G-6103)*		
Young Men's Chrtn Assoc of	952 835-2567	
7355 York Ave S Minneapolis (55435) *(G-6104)*		
Young Women's Christian Assn	218 722-7425	
32 E 1st St Ste 202 Duluth (55802) *(G-1505)*		
Young Women's Christian Assn	651 222-3741	
375 Selby Ave Saint Paul (55102) *(G-9181)*		
Young, Quinlan Assoc LLP	612 337-5109	
81 S 9th St Ste 210 Minneapolis (55402) *(G-6105)*		
Youngblood Lumber Co	612 789-3521	
1335 Central Ave NE Minneapolis (55413) *(G-6106)*		
Youth Frontiers Inc	952 922-0222	
6009 Excelsior Blvd Minneapolis (55416) *(G-6107)*		
Youthlink	612 252-1200	
41 N 12th St Minneapolis (55403) *(G-6108)*		
Youthworks Inc	612 729-5444	
3530 E 28th St Minneapolis (55406) *(G-6109)*		
Yrc Inc	651 452-0338	
2950 Lone Oak Cir Saint Paul (55121) *(G-7954)*		
YWCA of Minneapolis	612 874-7131	
2808 Hennepin Ave Minneapolis (55408) *(G-6110)*		
YWCA of Minneapolis (PA)	612 332-0501	
1130 Nicollet Ave Minneapolis (55403) *(G-6111)*		
YWCA of Minneapolis	612 863-0970	
800 E 28th St Ste 15103 Minneapolis (55407) *(G-6112)*		
Z M C Hotels Inc	218 726-1111	
350 Canal Park Dr Duluth (55802) *(G-1506)*		
Z M C Hotels Inc (PA)	218 723-8433	
525 S Lake Ave Ste 405 Duluth (55802) *(G-1507)*		
Z M C Hotels Inc	218 727-0461	
525 S Lake Ave Ste 405 Duluth (55802) *(G-1508)*		
Zachry Construction Corp	612 215-1300	
222 S 9th St Ste 1500 Minneapolis (55402) *(G-6113)*		
Zahl Petroleum Maintenance Co, Minneapolis *Also Called Dan Larson Enterprises Inc* *(G-4222)*		
Zanby LLC	952 938-5448	
3611 Farmington Rd Minnetonka (55305) *(G-6240)*		

Zelle, Hofmann, Voelbel, Mason (PA)	612 339-2020	
500 Washington Ave S Minneapolis (55415) *(G-6114)*		
Zeman Construction Co	612 521-4300	
8900 10th Ave N Minneapolis (55427) *(G-6115)*		
Zenith Rogers LLC	763 425-0044	
13550 Commerce Blvd Rogers (55374) *(G-7348)*		
Zentropy Partners	612 367-5148	
222 S 9th St Ste 2955 Minneapolis (55402) *(G-6116)*		
Zep Inc	763 792-2050	
8490 Coral Sea St NE Minneapolis (55449) *(G-6133)*		
Zero Variance, Fergus Falls *Also Called Conner Enterprises Inc* *(G-2072)*		
Ziegler AG Equipment	507 847-7600	
191 Industrial Park Jackson (56143) *(G-2801)*		
Ziegler Inc	218 258-3232	
10081 Hwy 169 Buhl (55713) *(G-669)*		
Ziegler Inc	218 722-6628	
210 Garfield Ave Duluth (55802) *(G-1509)*		
Ziegler Inc	507 532-4403	
1200 N Highway 59 Marshall (56258) *(G-3336)*		
Ziegler Inc (PA)	952 888-4121	
901 W 94th St Minneapolis (55420) *(G-6117)*		
Ziegler Inc	507 285-1775	
6340 Highway 63 S Rochester (55904) *(G-7298)*		
Ziegler Inc	320 253-2234	
2225 255th St Saint Cloud (56301) *(G-7635)*		
Ziegler Inc	952 445-4292	
8050 Highway 101 E Shakopee (55379) *(G-9482)*		
Ziem's Carpet Workroom Inc	952 884-0058	
9201 Penn Ave S Ste 28 Minneapolis (55431) *(G-6118)*		
Zimmerman Reed PLLP	612 341-0400	
651 Nicollet Mall Ste 501 Minneapolis (55402) *(G-6119)*		
Zina's Inc	952 929-0093	
5101 Vernon Ave S Ste 2B Minneapolis (55436) *(G-6120)*		
Zinpro Animal Nutrition Inc	952 944-2736	
10400 Viking Dr Ste 240 Eden Prairie (55344) *(G-1820)*		
Zintl W, Stillwater *Also Called W Zintl Construction Inc* *(G-9654)*		
Zitco Inc	952 392-6060	
5251 W 74th St Minneapolis (55439) *(G-6121)*		
Zoological Gardens, Minnesota	952 431-9299	
13000 Zoo Blvd Saint Paul (55124) *(G-7955)*		
Zuhrah Temple Trustees Inc	612 871-3555	
2540 Park Ave Minneapolis (55404) *(G-6122)*		
Zumbro House Inc	651 264-1000	
1103 Weir Dr Ste 100 Saint Paul (55125) *(G-9293)*		
Zumbro River Brand Inc	507 377-9776	
1215 Hershey St Albert Lea (56007) *(G-72)*		
Zumbro River Brand Inc (PA)	507 446-9097	
138 W Front St Owatonna (55060) *(G-6746)*		
Zumbro Valley Mental Health	507 289-2089	
343 Woodlake Dr SE Rochester (55904) *(G-7299)*		
Zumbrota Area Ambulance Assn	507 732-7845	
1450 Jefferson Dr Zumbrota (55992) *(G-10221)*		
Zumbrota Ford Sales LLC	507 732-5127	
1660 S Main St Zumbrota (55992) *(G-10222)*		
Zumbrota Nursing Home	507 732-8400	
433 Mill St Zumbrota (55992) *(G-10223)*		
Zumbrota Veterinary Clinic, PA	507 732-7301	
1412 Northstar Dr Zumbrota (55992) *(G-10224)*		
Zurich North American Insce	952 229-3600	
3600 Minnesota Dr Ste 200 Edina (55435) *(G-1850)*		
Zweber LLC	952 440-4653	
8075 Lucerne Blvd Lakeville (55044) *(G-2944)*		
Zylstra Harley Davidson Inc	763 241-2000	
19600 Evans St NW Elk River (55330) *(G-1897)*		

ALPHABETIC

2011 Harris Minnesota
Services Directory

(G-00000) Company's Geographic Section entry number

SERVICES INDEX

• Service categories are listed in alphabetical order.

A

ABORTION CLINIC
ACCIDENT & HEALTH INSURANCE CARRIERS
ACCIDENT & HEALTH INSURANCE: Fraternal Organizations
ACCOMMODATION LOCATING SVCS
ACCOUNTING MACHINES WHOLESALERS
ACCOUNTING SVCS, NEC
ACCOUNTING SVCS: Certified Public
ACCOUNTING, AUDITING & BOOKKEEPING
ACOUSTICAL TILE CLEANING SVCS
ADDRESSING SVCS
ADOPTION SVCS
ADULT DAYCARE CENTERS
ADVERTISING & DISTRIBUTING SVCS: Shopping News
ADVERTISING AGENCIES
ADVERTISING AGENCIES: Consultants
ADVERTISING MATERIAL DISTRIBUTION
ADVERTISING REPRESENTATIVES: Electronic Media
ADVERTISING REPRESENTATIVES: Magazine
ADVERTISING REPRESENTATIVES: Radio
ADVERTISING SPECIALTIES, WHOLESALE
ADVERTISING SVCS: Billboards
ADVERTISING SVCS: Direct Mail
ADVERTISING SVCS: Display
ADVERTISING SVCS: Outdoor
ADVERTISING SVCS: Poster, Exc Outdoor
ADVERTISING SVCS: Sample Distribution
ADVERTISING, PROMOTIONAL & TRADE SHOW SVCS
ADVOCACY GROUP
AEROBIC DANCE & EXERCISE CLASSES
AGENTS, BROKERS & BUREAUS: Personal Service
AGENTS: Theatrical Talent
AGRICULTURAL CREDIT INSTITUTIONS
AGRICULTURAL LOAN COMPANIES
AGRICULTURAL MACHINERY & EQPT REPAIR
AGRICULTURAL MACHINERY & EQPT: Wholesalers
AID TO FAMILIES WITH DEPENDENT CHILDREN OR AFDC
AIR CONDITIONING & VENTILATION EQPT & SPLYS: Wholesales
AIR CONDITIONING EQPT, WHOLE HOUSE: Wholesalers
AIR CONDITIONING REPAIR SVCS
AIR DUCT CLEANING SVCS
AIR POLLUTION MEASURING SVCS
AIR-CONDITIONING SPLY SVCS
AIRCRAFT & HEAVY EQPT REPAIR SVCS
AIRCRAFT EQPT & SPLYS WHOLESALERS
AIRCRAFT FUELING SVCS
AIRCRAFT MAINTENANCE & REPAIR SVCS
AIRCRAFT PARTS WHOLESALERS
AIRCRAFT SERVICING & REPAIRING
AIRPORT
AIRPORTS, FLYING FIELDS & SVCS
ALCOHOL TREATMENT CLINIC, OUTPATIENT
ALCOHOLISM COUNSELING, NONTREATMENT
AMBULANCE SVCS
AMBULANCE SVCS: Air
AMBULATORY SURGICAL CENTERS
AMMUNITION, EXC SPORTING, WHOLESALE
AMUSEMENT & REC SVCS: Attractions, Concessions & Rides
AMUSEMENT & REC SVCS: Baseball Club, Exc Pro & Semi-Pro
AMUSEMENT & REC SVCS: Skating Instruction, Ice Or Roller
AMUSEMENT & RECREATION SVCS: Agricultural Fair
AMUSEMENT & RECREATION SVCS: Amusement Ride
AMUSEMENT & RECREATION SVCS: Arcades
AMUSEMENT & RECREATION SVCS: Art Gallery, Commercial

AMUSEMENT & RECREATION SVCS: Bowling League Or Team
AMUSEMENT & RECREATION SVCS: Card & Game Svcs
AMUSEMENT & RECREATION SVCS: Concession Operator
AMUSEMENT & RECREATION SVCS: Curling Rinks
AMUSEMENT & RECREATION SVCS: Exhibition Operation
AMUSEMENT & RECREATION SVCS: Fair, NEC
AMUSEMENT & RECREATION SVCS: Festival Operation
AMUSEMENT & RECREATION SVCS: Fishing Boat Operations, Party
AMUSEMENT & RECREATION SVCS: Fortune Tellers
AMUSEMENT & RECREATION SVCS: Gambling & Lottery Svcs
AMUSEMENT & RECREATION SVCS: Gambling, Coin Machines
AMUSEMENT & RECREATION SVCS: Game Parlor
AMUSEMENT & RECREATION SVCS: Golf Club, Membership
AMUSEMENT & RECREATION SVCS: Golf Professionals
AMUSEMENT & RECREATION SVCS: Golf Svcs & Professionals
AMUSEMENT & RECREATION SVCS: Hunting Club, Membership
AMUSEMENT & RECREATION SVCS: Ice Skating Rink
AMUSEMENT & RECREATION SVCS: Massage Instruction
AMUSEMENT & RECREATION SVCS: Outdoor Field Clubs
AMUSEMENT & RECREATION SVCS: Outfitters, Recreation
AMUSEMENT & RECREATION SVCS: Racquetball Club, Membership
AMUSEMENT & RECREATION SVCS: Recreation Center
AMUSEMENT & RECREATION SVCS: Recreation SVCS
AMUSEMENT & RECREATION SVCS: Sailing Instruction
AMUSEMENT & RECREATION SVCS: School, Hockey Instruction
AMUSEMENT & RECREATION SVCS: Shooting Range
AMUSEMENT & RECREATION SVCS: Skating Rink Operation
AMUSEMENT & RECREATION SVCS: Ski Instruction
AMUSEMENT & RECREATION SVCS: Ski Rental Concession
AMUSEMENT & RECREATION SVCS: Swimming Club, Membership
AMUSEMENT & RECREATION SVCS: Swimming Pool, Non-Membership
AMUSEMENT & RECREATION SVCS: Tennis & Professionals
AMUSEMENT & RECREATION SVCS: Tennis Club, Membership
AMUSEMENT & RECREATION SVCS: Tennis Courts, Non-Member
AMUSEMENT & RECREATION SVCS: Tennis Professional
AMUSEMENT & RECREATION SVCS: Theme Park
AMUSEMENT & RECREATION SVCS: Tour & Guide
AMUSEMENT & RECREATION SVCS: Tourist Attraction, Commercial
AMUSEMENT & RECREATION SVCS: Video Game Arcades
AMUSEMENT & RECREATION SVCS: Waterslide Operation
AMUSEMENT ARCADES
AMUSEMENT PARKS
AMUSEMENT/REC SVCS: Aerial Tramway/Ski Lift, Amusemnt/Scenic
AMUSEMENT/REC SVCS: Ticket Sales, Sporting Events, Contract
ANIMAL FEED: Wholesalers
ANIMAL GROOMING SVCS
ANIMAL HOSPITAL SVCS, LIVESTOCK
ANIMAL HOSPITALS

ANIMAL PRODUCTION, NEC
ANIMAL SPECIALTY SVCS, EXC VETERINARY
ANTIPOVERTY BOARD
APARTMENT LOCATING SVCS
APPLICATIONS SOFTWARE PROGRAMMING
APPRAISAL SVCS, EXC REAL ESTATE
AQUARIUMS & ZOOLOGICAL GARDENS
ARBITRATION & CONCILIATION SVCS
ARBORIST SVCS
ARCHEOLOGICAL EXPEDITIONS
ARCHITECT'S SUPPLIES WHOLESALERS
ARCHITECTURAL SVCS
ARCHITECTURAL SVCS: Engineering
ARMATURE REPAIRING & REWINDING SVC
ARMORED CAR SVCS
ART DESIGN SVCS
ART GALLERY, NONCOMMERCIAL
ART GOODS & SPLYS WHOLESALERS
ART GOODS, WHOLESALE
ARTIFICIAL INSEMINATION SVCS, ANIMAL SPECIALTIES
ARTISTS' MATERIALS, WHOLESALE
ARTS OR SCIENCES CENTER
ASSOCIATION FOR THE HANDICAPPED
ASSOCIATIONS: Alumni
ASSOCIATIONS: Business
ASSOCIATIONS: Fraternal
ASSOCIATIONS: Homeowners
ASSOCIATIONS: Manufacturers'
ASSOCIATIONS: Parent Teacher
ASSOCIATIONS: Real Estate Management
ASSOCIATIONS: Scientists'
ASSOCIATIONS: Trade
ATHLETIC CLUB & GYMNASIUMS, MEMBERSHIP
ATHLETIC ORGANIZATION
AUCTION SVCS: Livestock
AUCTION SVCS: Motor Vehicle
AUCTION, APPRAISAL & EXCHANGE SVCS
AUCTIONEERS: Fee Basis
AUDIO & VIDEO TAPES WHOLESALERS
AUDIO-VISUAL PROGRAM PRODUCTION SVCS
AUDITING SVCS
AUTHORS' AGENTS & BROKERS
AUTO SPLYS & PARTS, NEW, WHSLE: Exhaust Sys, Mufflers, Etc
AUTOMATED TELLER MACHINE NETWORK
AUTOMATED TELLER MACHINE OR ATM REPAIR SVCS
AUTOMATIC TELLER MACHINES: Wholesalers
AUTOMOBILE FINANCE LEASING
AUTOMOBILES & OTHER MOTOR VEHICLES WHOLESALERS
AUTOMOBILES: Wholesalers
AUTOMOTIVE & TRUCK GENERAL REPAIR SVC
AUTOMOTIVE BATTERIES WHOLESALERS
AUTOMOTIVE BODY SHOP
AUTOMOTIVE BODY, PAINT & INTERIOR REPAIR & MAINTENANCE SVC
AUTOMOTIVE BRAKE REPAIR SHOPS
AUTOMOTIVE COLLISION SHOPS
AUTOMOTIVE EXTERIOR REPAIR SVCS
AUTOMOTIVE GLASS REPLACEMENT SHOPS
AUTOMOTIVE PAINT SHOP
AUTOMOTIVE RADIO REPAIR SVCS
AUTOMOTIVE REPAIR SHOPS: Diesel Engine Repair
AUTOMOTIVE REPAIR SHOPS: Engine Repair
AUTOMOTIVE REPAIR SHOPS: Engine Repair, Exc Diesel
AUTOMOTIVE REPAIR SHOPS: Machine Shop
AUTOMOTIVE REPAIR SHOPS: Powertrain Components Repair Svcs
AUTOMOTIVE REPAIR SHOPS: Rebuilding & Retreading Tires
AUTOMOTIVE REPAIR SHOPS: Sound System Svc & Installation
AUTOMOTIVE REPAIR SHOPS: Tire Recapping
AUTOMOTIVE REPAIR SHOPS: Trailer Repair

AUTOMOTIVE REPAIR SHOPS: Truck Engine Repair, Exc Indl
AUTOMOTIVE REPAIR SHOPS: Turbocharger & Blower Repair
AUTOMOTIVE REPAIR SHOPS: Wheel Alignment
AUTOMOTIVE REPAIR SVC
AUTOMOTIVE RUSTPROOFING & UNDERCOATING SHOPS
AUTOMOTIVE SPLYS & PARTS, NEW, WHOL: Auto Servicing Eqpt
AUTOMOTIVE SPLYS & PARTS, NEW, WHOL: Auto Svc Station Eqpt
AUTOMOTIVE SPLYS & PARTS, NEW, WHOLESALE: Clutches
AUTOMOTIVE SPLYS & PARTS, NEW, WHOLESALE: Engines/Eng Parts
AUTOMOTIVE SPLYS & PARTS, NEW, WHOLESALE: Filters, Air & Oil
AUTOMOTIVE SPLYS & PARTS, NEW, WHOLESALE: Heaters
AUTOMOTIVE SPLYS & PARTS, NEW, WHOLESALE: Radiators
AUTOMOTIVE SPLYS & PARTS, NEW, WHOLESALE: Splys
AUTOMOTIVE SPLYS & PARTS, NEW, WHOLESALE: Tools & Eqpt
AUTOMOTIVE SPLYS & PARTS, NEW, WHOLESALE: Trailer Parts
AUTOMOTIVE SPLYS & PARTS, USED, WHOLESALE
AUTOMOTIVE SPLYS & PARTS, USED, WHOLESALE: Dry Cell Batt
AUTOMOTIVE SPLYS & PARTS, WHOLESALE, NEC
AUTOMOTIVE SPLYS, USED, WHOLESALE & RETAIL
AUTOMOTIVE SPLYS/PARTS, NEW, WHOL: Body Rpr/Paint Shop Splys
AUTOMOTIVE SVCS
AUTOMOTIVE SVCS, EXC REPAIR & CARWASHES: Customizing
AUTOMOTIVE SVCS, EXC REPAIR & CARWASHES: Glass Tinting
AUTOMOTIVE SVCS, EXC REPAIR & CARWASHES: Lubrication
AUTOMOTIVE SVCS, EXC REPAIR & CARWASHES: Maintenance
AUTOMOTIVE SVCS, EXC REPAIR & CARWASHES: Trailer Maintenance
AUTOMOTIVE SVCS, EXC REPAIR: Carwash, Automatic
AUTOMOTIVE SVCS, EXC REPAIR: Carwash, Self-Service
AUTOMOTIVE SVCS, EXC REPAIR: Truck Wash
AUTOMOTIVE SVCS, EXC REPAIR: Washing & Polishing
AUTOMOTIVE TOWING & WRECKING SVC
AUTOMOTIVE TOWING SVCS
AUTOMOTIVE TRANSMISSION REPAIR SVC

B

BAIL BONDING SVCS
BAKERY PRDTS: Wholesalers
BALLOONS: Novelty & Toy
BANKRUPTCY REFEREE
BANKS: Commercial, NEC
BANKS: Mortgage & Loan
BANKS: National Commercial
BANKS: Other Activities, NEC
BANKS: State Commercial
BANQUET HALL FACILITIES
BARBER SHOPS
BATTERIES, EXC AUTOMOTIVE: Wholesalers
BEAUTY SALONS
BEEF CATTLE FEEDLOTS
BEEF CATTLE RANCHING & FARMING
BEER & ALE WHOLESALERS
BEER & ALE, WHOLESALE: Beer & Other Fermented Malt Liquors
BEVERAGES, WINE & DISTILLED ALCOHOLIC, WHOLESALE: Liquor
BEVERAGES, WINE & DISTILLED ALCOHOLIC, WHOLESALE: Wine
BEVERAGES, WINE WHOLESALE : Wine Coolers

S V C   I N D E X

S V C

I N D E X

S
V
C

I
N
D
E
X

FIRE, MARINE & CASUALTY INSURANCE: Stock
FIREARMS & AMMUNITION, EXC SPORTING, WHOLESALE
FISH & SEAFOOD WHOLESALERS
FISH, PACKAGED FROZEN: Wholesalers
FISHING CAMPS
FIXED BASE OPERATOR
FLOOR COVERINGS WHOLESALERS
FLOOR TRADERS: Security
FLOOR WAXING SVCS
FLORISTS' SPLYS, WHOLESALE
FLOWERS & FLORISTS' SPLYS WHOLESALERS
FLOWERS & NURSERY STOCK, WHOLESALE
FLOWERS, FRESH, WHOLESALE
FOAMS & RUBBER, WHOLESALE
FOOD PRDTS, CONFECTIONERY, WHOLESALE: Candy
FOOD PRDTS, CONFECTIONERY, WHOLESALE: Nuts, Salted/Roasted
FOOD PRDTS, CONFECTIONERY, WHOLESALE: Potato Chips
FOOD PRDTS, CONFECTIONERY, WHOLESALE: Snack Foods
FOOD PRDTS, CONFECTIONERY, WHOLESALE: Toppings, Fountain
FOOD PRDTS, DAIRY, WHOLESALE: Frozen Dairy Desserts
FOOD PRDTS, DAIRY, WHOLESALE: Milk & Cream, Fluid
FOOD PRDTS, FISH & SEAFOOD, WHOLESALE: Fresh
FOOD PRDTS, FISH & SEAFOOD, WHOLESALE: Seafood
FOOD PRDTS, FROZEN, WHOLESALE: Fish, Meat & Poultry
FOOD PRDTS, FRUITS & VEGETABLES, FRESH, WHOLESALE
FOOD PRDTS, FRUITS & VEGETABLES, FRESH, WHOLESALE: Fruits
FOOD PRDTS, FRUITS & VEGETABLES, FRESH, WHOLESALE: Potatoes
FOOD PRDTS, FRUITS & VEGETABLES, FRESH, WHOLESALE: Vegetable
FOOD PRDTS, MEAT & MEAT PRDTS, WHOLESALE: Cured Or Smoked
FOOD PRDTS, MEAT & MEAT PRDTS, WHOLESALE: Fresh
FOOD PRDTS, POULTRY, WHOLESALE: Eggs, Clean, Pack/Grade
FOOD PRDTS, WHOLESALE: Beans, Field
FOOD PRDTS, WHOLESALE: Beverages, Exc Coffee & Tea
FOOD PRDTS, WHOLESALE: Breading Mixes
FOOD PRDTS, WHOLESALE: Coffee & Tea
FOOD PRDTS, WHOLESALE: Coffee, Green Or Roasted
FOOD PRDTS, WHOLESALE: Cooking Oils
FOOD PRDTS, WHOLESALE: Corn
FOOD PRDTS, WHOLESALE: Crackers, Cookies & Bakery Prdts
FOOD PRDTS, WHOLESALE: Dog Food
FOOD PRDTS, WHOLESALE: Dried or Canned Foods
FOOD PRDTS, WHOLESALE: Flavorings & Fragrances
FOOD PRDTS, WHOLESALE: Flour
FOOD PRDTS, WHOLESALE: Grain Elevators
FOOD PRDTS, WHOLESALE: Grains
FOOD PRDTS, WHOLESALE: Juices
FOOD PRDTS, WHOLESALE: Molasses, Indl
FOOD PRDTS, WHOLESALE: Natural & Organic
FOOD PRDTS, WHOLESALE: Oats
FOOD PRDTS, WHOLESALE: Pasta & Rice
FOOD PRDTS, WHOLESALE: Rice, Unpolished
FOOD PRDTS, WHOLESALE: Salt, Edible
FOOD PRDTS, WHOLESALE: Soybeans
FOOD PRDTS, WHOLESALE: Specialty
FOOD PRDTS, WHOLESALE: Sugar, Refined
FOOD PRDTS, WHOLESALE: Water, Distilled
FOOD PRDTS, WHOLESALE: Water, Mineral Or Spring, Bottled
FOOD PRDTS, WHOLESALE: Wheat
FOOTWEAR, WHOLESALE: Boots
FOOTWEAR, WHOLESALE: Shoes
FOREIGN CURRENCY EXCHANGE
FORESTRY SVCS
FORMAL WRITING SVCS
FRAMES & FRAMING WHOLESALE
FRANCHISES, SELLING OR LICENSING
FREIGHT CAR LOADING & UNLOADING SVCS
FREIGHT CONSOLIDATION SVCS

FREIGHT FORWARDING ARRANGEMENTS
FREIGHT FORWARDING ARRANGEMENTS: Domestic
FREIGHT FORWARDING ARRANGEMENTS: Foreign
FREIGHT HANDLING SVCS: Air
FREIGHT TRANSPORTATION ARRANGEMENTS
FRUIT, FARM-DRIED, PACKING SVCS
FRUITS & VEGETABLES WHOLESALERS: Fresh
FUND RAISING ORGANIZATION, NON-FEE BASIS
FUNDRAISING SVCS
FUNDS: Pension, Health & Welfare
FUNERAL DIRECTOR
FUNERAL HOME
FUNERAL HOMES & SVCS
FURNITURE WHOLESALERS
FURNITURE, HOUSEHOLD: Wholesalers
FURNITURE, MATTRESSES: Wholesalers
FURNITURE, OFFICE: Wholesalers
FURNITURE, WHOLESALE: Beds & Bedding
FURNITURE, WHOLESALE: Chairs

G

GAMBLING, NEC
GARDEN PLANNING SVCS
GARDEN PLANTING SVCS
GARDEN SVCS
GARMENT: Pressing & cleaners' agents
GAS & OTHER COMBINED SVCS
GAS PRODUCTION & DISTRIBUTION
GASOLINE WHOLESALERS
GENEALOGICAL INVESTIGATION SVCS
GENERAL COUNSELING SVCS
GENERAL MERCHANDISE, NONDURABLE, WHOLESALE
GENERATOR REPAIR SVCS
GERIATRIC RESIDENTIAL CARE FACILITY
GERIATRIC SOCIAL SVCS
GIFT WRAPPING SVCS
GIFTS & NOVELTIES: Wholesalers
GIRLS CAMPS
GLASS, AUTOMOTIVE: Wholesalers
GOLF COURSES: Public
GOLF DRIVING RANGES
GRADING SVCS
GRAIN & FIELD BEANS WHOLESALERS
GRANITE: Crushed & Broken
GRANTMAKING FOUNDATIONS
GRAPHIC ARTS & RELATED DESIGN SVCS
GRAPHIC LAYOUT SVCS: Printed Circuitry
GRAVEL MINING
GREASES, ANIMAL OR VEGETABLE, WHOLESALE
GRINDING SVC: Precision, Commercial Or Indl
GROCERIES WHOLESALERS, NEC
GROCERIES, GENERAL LINE WHOLESALERS
GROUP DAY CARE CENTER
GROUP FOSTER HOME
GROUP HOSPITALIZATION PLANS
GUARD PROTECTIVE SVCS
GUARD SVCS
GUN SVCS
GYMNASTICS INSTRUCTION

H

HAIR REPLACEMENT & WEAVING SVCS
HAIRDRESSERS
HALFWAY GROUP HOME, PERSONS WITH SOCIAL OR PERSONAL PROBLEMS
HALFWAY HOME FOR DELINQUENTS & OFFENDERS
HAND TOOLS, NEC: Wholesalers
HARDWARE WHOLESALERS
HARDWARE, WHOLESALE: Bolts
HARDWARE, WHOLESALE: Bolts, Nuts & Screws
HARDWARE, WHOLESALE: Builders', NEC
HARDWARE, WHOLESALE: Chains
HARDWARE, WHOLESALE: Nuts
HARDWARE, WHOLESALE: Power Tools & Access
HARDWARE, WHOLESALE: Rivets
HARDWARE, WHOLESALE: Screws
HAT CLEANING & BLOCKING SHOP
HATCHERIES: Poultry
HEAD START CENTER, EXC IN CONJUNCTION WITH SCHOOL
HEALTH & ALLIED SERVICES, NEC
HEALTH & WELFARE COUNCIL
HEALTH CLUBS

HEALTH INSURANCE CARRIERS
HEALTH MAINTENANCE ORGANIZATION: Insurance Only
HEALTH PRACTITIONERS' OFFICES, NEC
HEALTH SCREENING SVCS
HEALTH SYSTEMS AGENCY
HEARING AID REPAIR SVCS
HEARING TESTING SVCS
HEATING & AIR CONDITIONING EQPT & SPLYS WHOLESALERS
HELP SUPPLY SERVICES
HELPING HAND SVCS, INCLUDING BIG BROTHER, ETC
HIGHWAY & STREET MAINTENANCE SVCS
HOG FEEDLOT
HOGS WHOLESALERS
HOLDING COMPANIES: Banks
HOLDING COMPANIES: Investment, Exc Banks
HOLDING COMPANIES: Personal, Exc Banks
HOLDING COMPANIES: Public Utility
HOME ENTERTAINMENT REPAIR SVCS
HOME FOR THE EMOTIONALLY DISTURBED
HOME FOR THE MENTALLY HANDICAPPED
HOME FOR THE MENTALLY RETARDED
HOME FOR THE MENTALLY RETARDED, EXC SKILLED OR INTERMEDIATE
HOME FOR THE PHYSICALLY HANDICAPPED
HOME FURNISHINGS WHOLESALERS
HOME HEALTH CARE SVCS
HOME IMPROVEMENT & RENOVATION CONTRACTOR AGENCY
HOMEBUILDERS & OTHER OPERATIVE BUILDERS
HOMEFURNISHINGS & SPLYS, WHOLESALE: Decorative
HOMEFURNISHINGS, WHOL: Resilient Floor Coverings, Tile/Sheet
HOMEFURNISHINGS, WHOLESALE: Blinds, Venetian
HOMEFURNISHINGS, WHOLESALE: Carpets
HOMEFURNISHINGS, WHOLESALE: Curtains
HOMEFURNISHINGS, WHOLESALE: Draperies
HOMEFURNISHINGS, WHOLESALE: Fireplace Eqpt & Access
HOMEFURNISHINGS, WHOLESALE: Grills, Barbecue
HOMEFURNISHINGS, WHOLESALE: Kitchenware
HOMEFURNISHINGS, WHOLESALE: Linens, Table
HOMEFURNISHINGS, WHOLESALE: Mirrors/Pictures, Framed/Unframd
HOMEFURNISHINGS, WHOLESALE: Sheets, Textile
HOMEMAKERS' SVCS
HOMES FOR THE ELDERLY
HORSE & OTHER EQUINE BREEDING & PRODUCTION
HOSPITAL BEDS WHOLESALERS
HOSPITAL EQPT REPAIR SVCS
HOSPITALS: AMA Approved Residency
HOSPITALS: Children's
HOSPITALS: Chronic Disease
HOSPITALS: Medical & Surgical
HOSPITALS: Medical School Affiliation
HOSPITALS: Mental Retardation
HOSPITALS: Mental, Exc For The Mentally Retarded
HOSPITALS: Orthopedic
HOSPITALS: Psychiatric
HOSPITALS: Rehabilitation, Alcoholism
HOSPITALS: Rehabilitation, Drug Addiction
HOSPITALS: Specialty, NEC
HOSPITALS: Substance Abuse
HOSTELS
HOTEL: Franchised
HOTEL: Seasonal
HOTEL: YMCA/YMHA
HOTELS & MOTELS
HOUSEHOLD APPLIANCE PARTS: Wholesalers
HOUSEHOLD APPLIANCE REPAIR SVCS
HOUSEKEEPING & MAID SVCS
HOUSES: Rooming & Boarding
HOUSING AUTHORITY OPERATOR
HUMANE SOCIETIES
HUNTING PRESERVES
HYDRAULIC EQPT REPAIR SVC

I

IGNEOUS ROCK: Crushed & Broken
INDEMNITY PLANS HEALTH INSURANCE, EXC MEDICAL SVCS

INDL & PERSONAL SVC PAPER WHOLESALERS
INDL & PERSONAL SVC PAPER, WHOL: Bags, Paper/Disp Plastic
INDL & PERSONAL SVC PAPER, WHOL: Boxes, Corrugtd/Solid Fiber
INDL & PERSONAL SVC PAPER, WHOL: Boxes, Paperbrd/Plastic
INDL & PERSONAL SVC PAPER, WHOL: Container, Paper/Plastic
INDL & PERSONAL SVC PAPER, WHOL: Dishes, Disp, Plastic/Paper
INDL & PERSONAL SVC PAPER, WHOL: Paper, Wrap/Coarse/Prdts
INDL & PERSONAL SVC PAPER, WHOLESALE: Disposable
INDL & PERSONAL SVC PAPER, WHOLESALE: Press Sensitive Tape
INDL & PERSONAL SVC PAPER, WHOLESALE: Shipping Splys
INDL EQPT SVCS
INDL GASES WHOLESALERS
INDL HELP SVCS
INDL MACHINERY & EQPT WHOLESALERS
INDL MACHINERY REPAIR & MAINTENANCE
INDL SALTS WHOLESALERS
INDL SPLYS WHOLESALERS
INDL SPLYS, WHOL: Fasteners, Incl Nuts, Bolts, Screws, Etc
INDL SPLYS, WHOLESALE: Abrasives
INDL SPLYS, WHOLESALE: Abrasives & Adhesives
INDL SPLYS, WHOLESALE: Adhesives, Tape & Plasters
INDL SPLYS, WHOLESALE: Bearings
INDL SPLYS, WHOLESALE: Bins & Containers, Storage
INDL SPLYS, WHOLESALE: Bottler Splys
INDL SPLYS, WHOLESALE: Brushes, Indl
INDL SPLYS, WHOLESALE: Clean Room Splys
INDL SPLYS, WHOLESALE: Electric Tools
INDL SPLYS, WHOLESALE: Fasteners & Fastening Eqpt
INDL SPLYS, WHOLESALE: Fittings
INDL SPLYS, WHOLESALE: Gas Eqpt, Parts & Splys
INDL SPLYS, WHOLESALE: Gaskets
INDL SPLYS, WHOLESALE: Glass Bottles
INDL SPLYS, WHOLESALE: Hose, Belting & Packing
INDL SPLYS, WHOLESALE: Mill Splys
INDL SPLYS, WHOLESALE: Plastic Bottles
INDL SPLYS, WHOLESALE: Power Transmission, Eqpt & Apparatus
INDL SPLYS, WHOLESALE: Rope, Cord & Thread
INDL SPLYS, WHOLESALE: Rubber Goods, Mechanical
INDL SPLYS, WHOLESALE: Seals
INDL SPLYS, WHOLESALE: Signmaker Eqpt & Splys
INDL SPLYS, WHOLESALE: Tools
INDL SPLYS, WHOLESALE: Tools, NEC
INDL SPLYS, WHOLESALE: Valves & Fittings
INDL TRUCK REPAIR SVCS
INFORMATION BUREAU SVCS
INFORMATION RETRIEVAL SERVICES
INFORMATION SVCS: Consumer
INNS
INSPECTION & TESTING SVCS
INSULATION MATERIALS WHOLESALERS
INSURANCE AGENCIES & BROKERS
INSURANCE AGENTS, NEC
INSURANCE BROKERS, NEC
INSURANCE CARRIERS: Automobile
INSURANCE CARRIERS: Dental
INSURANCE CARRIERS: Direct Accident & Health
INSURANCE CARRIERS: Hospital & Medical
INSURANCE CARRIERS: Life
INSURANCE CARRIERS: Property & Casualty
INSURANCE CARRIERS: Title
INSURANCE CARRIERS: Worker's Compensation
INSURANCE CLAIM ADJUSTERS, NOT EMPLOYED BY INSURANCE COMPANY
INSURANCE CLAIM PROCESSING, EXC MEDICAL
INSURANCE EDUCATION SVCS
INSURANCE INFORMATION & CONSULTING SVCS
INSURANCE INFORMATION BUREAUS
INSURANCE INSPECTION & INVESTIGATIONS SVCS

INSURANCE RATEMAKING ORGANIZATIONS
INSURANCE RESEARCH SVCS
INSURANCE: Agents, Brokers & Service
INTERIOR DECORATING SVCS
INTERIOR DESIGN SVCS, NEC
INTERIOR DESIGNING SVCS
INTERMEDIATE CARE FACILITY
INVENTORY COMPUTING SVCS
INVENTORY STOCKING SVCS
INVESTMENT ADVISORY SVCS
INVESTMENT BANKERS
INVESTMENT CERTIFICATE SALES
INVESTMENT COUNSELORS
INVESTMENT FIRM: General Brokerage
INVESTMENT FUNDS: Open-Ended
INVESTMENT OFFICES: Management, Closed-End
INVESTMENT OFFICES: Mutual Fund Sales, On Own Account
INVESTORS, NEC
INVESTORS: Real Estate, Exc Property Operators
IRON ORE MINING
IRRIGATION EQPT WHOLESALERS

J

JANITORIAL & CUSTODIAL SVCS
JANITORIAL EQPT & SPLYS WHOLESALERS
JEWELRY & PRECIOUS STONES WHOLESALERS
JEWELRY REPAIR SVCS
JEWELRY, WHOLESALE
JOB COUNSELING
JOB TRAINING & VOCATIONAL REHABILITATION SVCS
JOB TRAINING SVCS
JUVENILE CORRECTIONAL FACILITIES

K

KIDNEY DIALYSIS CENTERS
KITCHEN CABINETS WHOLESALERS

L

LABELING SVC: Bottles, Cans, Cartons, Etc
LABOR UNION
LABORATORIES, TESTING: Food
LABORATORIES, TESTING: Forensic
LABORATORIES, TESTING: Hazardous Waste
LABORATORIES, TESTING: Pollution
LABORATORIES, TESTING: Product Testing, Safety/Performance
LABORATORIES, TESTING: Seed
LABORATORIES, TESTING: Soil Analysis
LABORATORIES, TESTING: Water
LABORATORIES: Biological
LABORATORIES: Biotechnology
LABORATORIES: Blood Analysis
LABORATORIES: Commercial Nonphysical Research
LABORATORIES: Dental
LABORATORIES: Dental & Medical X-Ray
LABORATORIES: Dental, Artificial Teeth Production
LABORATORIES: Dental, Crown & Bridge Production
LABORATORIES: Dental, Denture Production
LABORATORIES: Electronic Research
LABORATORIES: Environmental Research
LABORATORIES: Medical
LABORATORIES: Medical Bacteriological
LABORATORIES: Medical Pathology
LABORATORIES: Noncommercial Research
LABORATORIES: Physical Research, Commercial
LABORATORIES: Testing
LABORATORIES: Urinalysis
LABORATORY EQPT, EXC MEDICAL: Wholesalers
LAMINATING SVCS
LAND SUBDIVIDERS & DEVELOPERS: Commercial
LAND SUBDIVIDERS & DEVELOPERS: Residential
LAND SUBDIVISION & DEVELOPMENT
LANDSCAPE ARCHITECTURAL SVCS
LANDSCAPE CONSULTING & PLANNING
LANDSCAPE PLANNING SVCS
LANDSCAPE SVCS
LANDSCAPING SVC
LAUNDRIES, EXC POWER & COIN-OPERATED
LAUNDRY & DRYCLEANING SVCS, EXC COIN-OPERATED: Pickup

LAUNDRY & GARMENT SVCS, NEC: Diapers
LAUNDRY & GARMENT SVCS, NEC: Fur Cleaning, Repairing/Storage
LAUNDRY & GARMENT SVCS: Tailor Shop, Exc Custom/Merchant
LAUNDRY SVC: Indl Clothing
LAUNDRY SVC: Mat & Rug Sply
LAUNDRY SVC: Treated Eqpt Sply, Mats, Rugs, Mops, Etc
LAUNDRY SVC: Wiping Towel Sply
LAUNDRY SVCS: Indl
LAWN CARE SVCS
LAWN MOWER REPAIR SHOP
LAWN SVCS
LEASING & RENTAL SVCS: Computer Hardware, Exc Finance
LEASING & RENTAL SVCS: Computer Peripheral Eqpt
LEASING & RENTAL SVCS: Cranes & Aerial Lift Eqpt
LEASING & RENTAL: Automobile With Driver
LEASING & RENTAL: Computers & Eqpt
LEASING & RENTAL: Construction & Mining Eqpt
LEASING & RENTAL: Medical Machinery & Eqpt
LEASING & RENTAL: Mobile Home Sites
LEASING & RENTAL: Office Machines & Eqpt
LEASING & RENTAL: Other Real Estate Property
LEASING & RENTAL: Trucks, Without Drivers
LEASING & RENTAL: Utility Trailers & RV's
LEASING: Laundry Eqpt
LEASING: Passenger Car
LEASING: Residential Buildings
LEASING: Truck, Without Drivers
LEATHER GOODS, CLEANING & REPAIR SVCS
LEGAL & TAX SVCS
LEGAL AID SVCS
LEGAL OFFICES & SVCS
LEGAL PROCESS SERVERS
LEGAL SVCS: Bankruptcy Law
LEGAL SVCS: Corporate, Partnership & Business Law
LEGAL SVCS: Criminal Law
LEGAL SVCS: Environmental Law
LEGAL SVCS: General Practice Attorney or Lawyer
LEGAL SVCS: General Practice Law Office
LEGAL SVCS: Immigration & Naturalization Law
LEGAL SVCS: Labor & Employment Law
LEGAL SVCS: Patent, Trademark & Copyright Law
LEGAL SVCS: Real Estate Law
LEGAL SVCS: Specialized Law Offices, Attorney
LEGITIMATE LIVE THEATER PRODUCERS
LESSORS: Landholding Office
LIABILITY INSURANCE
LIFE INSURANCE AGENTS
LIFE INSURANCE CARRIERS
LIFE INSURANCE: Fraternal Organizations
LIFE INSURANCE: Mutual Association
LIFEGUARD SVC
LIGHTING FIXTURES WHOLESALERS
LIGHTING MAINTENANCE SVC
LIMESTONE: Crushed & Broken
LIMOUSINE SVCS
LINEN SPLY SVC
LINEN SPLY SVC: Apron
LINEN SPLY SVC: Towel
LINEN SPLY SVC: Uniform
LIQUEFIED PETROLEUM GAS WHOLESALERS
LIQUIDATORS
LIVESTOCK BREEDING & PRODUCTION
LIVESTOCK WHOLESALERS, NEC
LOAN CORRESPONDENTS
LOBBYING SVCS
LOCKS & LOCK SETS, WHOLESALE
LOCKSMITHS
LOGS, HEWN TIES, POSTS & POLES, WHOLESALE
LUBRICATING OIL & GREASE WHOLESALERS
LUMBER, PLYWOOD & MILLWORK WHOLESALERS

M

MACHINERY & EQPT FINANCE LEASING
MACHINERY & EQPT, AGRICULTURAL, WHOL: Farm Eqpt Parts/Splys
MACHINERY & EQPT, AGRICULTURAL, WHOL: Grain Elev Eqpt/Splys

MACHINERY & EQPT, AGRICULTURAL, WHOL: Poultry/Livestock Eqpt
MACHINERY & EQPT, AGRICULTURAL, WHOLESALE: Agricultural, NEC
MACHINERY & EQPT, AGRICULTURAL, WHOLESALE: Dairy
MACHINERY & EQPT, AGRICULTURAL, WHOLESALE: Farm Implements
MACHINERY & EQPT, AGRICULTURAL, WHOLESALE: Garden, NEC
MACHINERY & EQPT, AGRICULTURAL, WHOLESALE: Landscaping Eqpt
MACHINERY & EQPT, AGRICULTURAL, WHOLESALE: Lawn
MACHINERY & EQPT, AGRICULTURAL, WHOLESALE: Lawn & Garden
MACHINERY & EQPT, AGRICULTURAL, WHOLESALE: Livestock Eqpt
MACHINERY & EQPT, AGRICULTURAL, WHOLESALE: Poultry Eqpt
MACHINERY & EQPT, INDL, WHOL: Controlling Instruments/Access
MACHINERY & EQPT, INDL, WHOL: Environ Pollution Cntrl, Air
MACHINERY & EQPT, INDL, WHOL: Environ Pollution Cntrl, Water
MACHINERY & EQPT, INDL, WHOLESALE: Chainsaws
MACHINERY & EQPT, INDL, WHOLESALE: Conveyor Systems
MACHINERY & EQPT, INDL, WHOLESALE: Engines & Parts, Diesel
MACHINERY & EQPT, INDL, WHOLESALE: Engines, Gasoline
MACHINERY & EQPT, INDL, WHOLESALE: Engs & Parts, Air-Cooled
MACHINERY & EQPT, INDL, WHOLESALE: Engs/Transportation Eqpt
MACHINERY & EQPT, INDL, WHOLESALE: Food Manufacturing
MACHINERY & EQPT, INDL, WHOLESALE: Food Product Manufacturng
MACHINERY & EQPT, INDL, WHOLESALE: Hoists
MACHINERY & EQPT, INDL, WHOLESALE: Hydraulic Systems
MACHINERY & EQPT, INDL, WHOLESALE: Indl Machine Parts
MACHINERY & EQPT, INDL, WHOLESALE: Instruments & Cntrl Eqpt
MACHINERY & EQPT, INDL, WHOLESALE: Lift Trucks & Parts
MACHINERY & EQPT, INDL, WHOLESALE: Machine Tools & Access
MACHINERY & EQPT, INDL, WHOLESALE: Measure/Test, Electric
MACHINERY & EQPT, INDL, WHOLESALE: Metal Refining
MACHINERY & EQPT, INDL, WHOLESALE: Milk Prdts Manufacturing
MACHINERY & EQPT, INDL, WHOLESALE: Packaging
MACHINERY & EQPT, INDL, WHOLESALE: Paint Spray
MACHINERY & EQPT, INDL, WHOLESALE: Plastic Prdts Machinery
MACHINERY & EQPT, INDL, WHOLESALE: Pneumatic Tools
MACHINERY & EQPT, INDL, WHOLESALE: Power Plant Machinery
MACHINERY & EQPT, INDL, WHOLESALE: Processing & Packaging
MACHINERY & EQPT, INDL, WHOLESALE: Recycling
MACHINERY & EQPT, INDL, WHOLESALE: Safety Eqpt
MACHINERY & EQPT, INDL, WHOLESALE: Water Pumps
MACHINERY & EQPT, WHOLESALE: Concrete Processing
MACHINERY & EQPT, WHOLESALE: Construction, Cranes
MACHINERY & EQPT, WHOLESALE: Construction, General
MACHINERY & EQPT, WHOLESALE: Construction, Tractors
MACHINERY & EQPT, WHOLESALE: Contractors Materials
MACHINERY & EQPT, WHOLESALE: Front End Loaders
MACHINERY & EQPT, WHOLESALE: Logging
MACHINERY & EQPT, WHOLESALE: Masonry
MACHINERY & EQPT, WHOLESALE: Road Construction & Maintenance
MAGAZINES, WHOLESALE
MAILING LIST: Brokers
MAILING LIST: Management
MAILING MACHINES WHOLESALERS
MAILING SVCS, NEC

MANAGEMENT CONSULTING SVCS: Administrative
MANAGEMENT CONSULTING SVCS: Automation & Robotics
MANAGEMENT CONSULTING SVCS: Banking & Finance
MANAGEMENT CONSULTING SVCS: Business
MANAGEMENT CONSULTING SVCS: Business Planning & Organizing
MANAGEMENT CONSULTING SVCS: Compensation & Benefits Planning
MANAGEMENT CONSULTING SVCS: Construction Project
MANAGEMENT CONSULTING SVCS: Corporate Objectives & Policies
MANAGEMENT CONSULTING SVCS: Corporation Organizing
MANAGEMENT CONSULTING SVCS: Food & Beverage
MANAGEMENT CONSULTING SVCS: Foreign Trade
MANAGEMENT CONSULTING SVCS: General
MANAGEMENT CONSULTING SVCS: Hospital & Health
MANAGEMENT CONSULTING SVCS: Incentive Or Award Program
MANAGEMENT CONSULTING SVCS: Industrial
MANAGEMENT CONSULTING SVCS: Industrial Hygiene
MANAGEMENT CONSULTING SVCS: Industry Specialist
MANAGEMENT CONSULTING SVCS: Information Systems
MANAGEMENT CONSULTING SVCS: Labor & Union Relations
MANAGEMENT CONSULTING SVCS: Manufacturing
MANAGEMENT CONSULTING SVCS: Merchandising
MANAGEMENT CONSULTING SVCS: New Products & Svcs
MANAGEMENT CONSULTING SVCS: Planning
MANAGEMENT CONSULTING SVCS: Programmed Instruction
MANAGEMENT CONSULTING SVCS: Public Utilities
MANAGEMENT CONSULTING SVCS: Quality Assurance
MANAGEMENT CONSULTING SVCS: Real Estate
MANAGEMENT CONSULTING SVCS: Restaurant & Food
MANAGEMENT CONSULTING SVCS: School, College & University
MANAGEMENT CONSULTING SVCS: Site Location
MANAGEMENT CONSULTING SVCS: Training & Development
MANAGEMENT CONSULTING SVCS: Transportation
MANAGEMENT SERVICES
MANAGEMENT SVCS, FACILITIES SUPPORT: Environ Remediation
MANAGEMENT SVCS, FACILITIES SUPPORT: Jails, Privately Ops
MANAGEMENT SVCS: Administrative
MANAGEMENT SVCS: Business
MANAGEMENT SVCS: Construction
MANAGEMENT SVCS: Financial, Business
MANAGEMENT SVCS: Hospital
MANAGEMENT SVCS: Hotel Or Motel
MANAGEMENT SVCS: Nursing & Personal Care Facility
MANAGEMENT SVCS: Personnel
MANAGEMENT SVCS: Restaurant
MANPOWER POOLS
MAPMAKING SVCS
MARINAS
MARINE CARGO HANDLING SVCS: Docks, Piers & Terminals
MARINE CARGO HANDLING SVCS: Marine Terminal
MARINE CARGO HANDLING SVCS: Waterfront Terminal Operations
MARTIAL ARTS INSTRUCTION
MASSAGE PARLOR & STEAM BATH SVCS
MASSAGE PARLORS
MATERIALS HANDLING EQPT WHOLESALERS
MEAL DELIVERY PROGRAMS
MEAT & MEAT PRDTS WHOLESALERS
MEATS, PACKAGED FROZEN: Wholesalers
MED, DENTAL & HOSPITAL EQPT, WHOL: Incontinent Prdts/Splys

MEDIA BUYING AGENCIES
MEDICAL & HOSPITAL EQPT WHOLESALERS
MEDICAL CENTERS
MEDICAL EQPT REPAIR SVCS, NON-ELECTRIC
MEDICAL FIELD ASSOCIATION
MEDICAL HELP SVCS
MEDICAL INSURANCE CLAIM PROCESSING: Contract Or Fee Basis
MEDICAL RESCUE SQUAD
MEDICAL SVCS ORGANIZATION
MEDICAL X-RAY MACHINES & TUBES WHOLESALERS
MEDICAL, DENTAL & HOSP EQPT, WHOLESALE: X-ray Film & Splys
MEDICAL, DENTAL & HOSPITAL EQPT, WHOL: Dentists' Prof Splys
MEDICAL, DENTAL & HOSPITAL EQPT, WHOL: Hospital Eqpt & Splys
MEDICAL, DENTAL & HOSPITAL EQPT, WHOL: Hosptl Eqpt/Furniture
MEDICAL, DENTAL & HOSPITAL EQPT, WHOL: Physician Eqpt/Splys
MEDICAL, DENTAL & HOSPITAL EQPT, WHOL: Surgical Eqpt & Splys
MEDICAL, DENTAL & HOSPITAL EQPT, WHOLESALE: Artificial Limbs
MEDICAL, DENTAL & HOSPITAL EQPT, WHOLESALE: Diagnostic, Med
MEDICAL, DENTAL & HOSPITAL EQPT, WHOLESALE: Hearing Aids
MEDICAL, DENTAL & HOSPITAL EQPT, WHOLESALE: Med Eqpt & Splys
MEDICAL, DENTAL & HOSPITAL EQPT, WHOLESALE: Orthopedic
MEDICAL, DENTAL/HOSPITAL EQPT, WHOL: Tech Aids, Handicapped
MEDICAL, DENTAL/HOSPITAL EQPT, WHOL: Veterinarian Eqpt/Sply
MEMBER ORGS, CIVIC, SOCIAL & FRATERNAL: Bars & Restaurants
MEMBERSHIP HOTELS
MEMBERSHIP ORGANIZATIONS, BUS: Banker's Org, Advisory Svcs
MEMBERSHIP ORGANIZATIONS, BUSINESS: Better Business Bureau
MEMBERSHIP ORGANIZATIONS, BUSINESS: Community Affairs & Svcs
MEMBERSHIP ORGANIZATIONS, BUSINESS: Growers' Association
MEMBERSHIP ORGANIZATIONS, BUSINESS: Public Utility Assoc
MEMBERSHIP ORGANIZATIONS, CIVIC, SOCIAL/FRAT: Boy Scout Org
MEMBERSHIP ORGANIZATIONS, CIVIC, SOCIAL/FRAT: Rec Assoc
MEMBERSHIP ORGANIZATIONS, CIVIC, SOCIAL/FRAT: Social Assoc
MEMBERSHIP ORGANIZATIONS, CIVIC, SOCIAL/FRAT: Youth Orgs
MEMBERSHIP ORGANIZATIONS, LABOR UNIONS & SIMILAR: Trade
MEMBERSHIP ORGANIZATIONS, NEC: Art Council
MEMBERSHIP ORGANIZATIONS, NEC: Automobile Owner Association
MEMBERSHIP ORGANIZATIONS, NEC: Bowling club
MEMBERSHIP ORGANIZATIONS, NEC: Charitable
MEMBERSHIP ORGANIZATIONS, NEC: Food Co-Operative
MEMBERSHIP ORGANIZATIONS, NEC: Historical Club
MEMBERSHIP ORGANIZATIONS, NEC: Personal Interest
MEMBERSHIP ORGANIZATIONS, PROF: Education/Teacher Assoc
MEMBERSHIP ORGANIZATIONS, PROFESSIONAL: Health Association
MEMBERSHIP ORGANIZATIONS, PROFESSIONAL: Nursing Association
MEMBERSHIP ORGANIZATIONS: Reading Rooms/Other Cultural Orgs
MEMBERSHIP ORGS, CIVIC, SOCIAL & FRAT: Comm Member Club
MEMBERSHIP ORGS, CIVIC, SOCIAL & FRAT: Dwelling-Related
MEMBERSHIP ORGS, CIVIC, SOCIAL & FRAT: Girl Scout
MEMBERSHIP ORGS, CIVIC, SOCIAL & FRATERNAL: Citizens Union
MEMBERSHIP ORGS, CIVIC, SOCIAL & FRATERNAL: Civic Assoc
MEMBERSHIP ORGS, CIVIC, SOCIAL & FRATERNAL: Condo Assoc
MEMBERSHIP ORGS, CIVIC, SOCIAL & FRATERNAL: Protection

MEMBERSHIP ORGS, CIVIC, SOCIAL & FRATERNAL: Singing Society
MEMBERSHIP ORGS, CIVIC, SOCIAL/FRAT: Business Persons Club
MEMBERSHIP SPORTS & RECREATION CLUBS
MEN'S & BOYS' CLOTHING WHOLESALERS, NEC
MEN'S & BOYS' SPORTSWEAR WHOLESALERS
MENTAL HEALTH CLINIC, OUTPATIENT
MENTAL HEALTH PRACTITIONERS' OFFICES
METAL CUTTING SVCS
METAL SERVICE CENTERS & OFFICES
METAL SLITTING & SHEARING
METALS SVC CENTERS & WHOL: Structural Shapes, Iron Or Steel
METALS SVC CENTERS & WHOLESALERS: Bale Ties, Wire
METALS SVC CENTERS & WHOLESALERS: Cable, Wire
METALS SVC CENTERS & WHOLESALERS: Concrete Reinforcing Bars
METALS SVC CENTERS & WHOLESALERS: Copper
METALS SVC CENTERS & WHOLESALERS: Flat Prdts, Iron Or Steel
METALS SVC CENTERS & WHOLESALERS: Iron & Steel Prdt, Ferrous
METALS SVC CENTERS & WHOLESALERS: Nonferrous Sheets, Etc
METALS SVC CENTERS & WHOLESALERS: Pipe & Tubing, Steel
METALS SVC CENTERS & WHOLESALERS: Reinforcement Mesh, Wire
METALS SVC CENTERS & WHOLESALERS: Rods, Metal
METALS SVC CENTERS & WHOLESALERS: Sheets, Metal
METALS SVC CENTERS & WHOLESALERS: Steel
METALS SVC CENTERS & WHOLESALERS: Tubing, Metal
METALS SVC CNTRS & WHOL: Metal Wires, Ties, Cables/Screening
METALS SVC CTRS & WHOLESALERS: Aluminum Bars, Rods, Etc
METALWORKING MACHINERY WHOLESALERS
METER READERS: Remote
MICROFILM EQPT WHOLESALERS
MICROFILM SVCS
MILK PRODUCTION
MILK, FLUID: Wholesalers
MILKING MACHINERY & EQPT WHOLESALERS
MIMEOGRAPHING SVCS
MINIATURE GOLF COURSES
MINING EXPLORATION & DEVELOPMENT SVCS
MINING MACHINERY & EQPT WHOLESALERS
MISC FINAN INVEST ACTIVITY: Mutual Fund, Ind Salesperson
MODELING SVCS
MONEY ORDER ISSUANCE SVCS
MONTESSORI CHILD DEVELOPMENT CENTER
MORTGAGE BANKERS
MORTGAGE COMPANIES: Urban
MOSS GATHERING
MOTEL
MOTEL: Franchised
MOTION PICTURE & VIDEO PRODUCTION SVCS
MOTION PICTURE & VIDEO PRODUCTION SVCS: Commercials, TV
MOTION PICTURE & VIDEO PRODUCTION SVCS: Educational
MOTION PICTURE & VIDEO PRODUCTION SVCS: Educational, TV
MOTION PICTURE & VIDEO PRODUCTION SVCS: Training
MOTION PICTURE DISTRIBUTION, EXCLUSIVE OF PRODUCTION
MOTION PICTURE PRODUCTION ALLIED SVCS
MOTOR REBUILDING SVCS, EXC AUTOMOTIVE
MOTOR VEHICLE SPLYS & PARTS WHOLESALERS: New
MOTOR VEHICLE SPLYS & PARTS WHOLESALERS: Used
MOTOR VEHICLES, WHOLESALE: Ambulances
MOTOR VEHICLES, WHOLESALE: Snowmobiles

MOTOR VEHICLES, WHOLESALE: Trailers, Truck, New & Used
MOTOR VEHICLES, WHOLESALE: Truck tractors
MOTOR VEHICLES, WHOLESALE: Trucks, Noncommercial
MOTOR VEHICLES, WHOLESALE: Trucks, commercial
MOTOR VEHICLES, WHOLESALE: Vans, Noncommercial
MOTORCYCLE REPAIR SHOPS
MOTORCYCLES: Wholesalers
MOVIE THEATERS, EXC DRIVE-IN
MOVING SVC & STORAGE: Local
MOVING SVC: Local
MOVING SVC: Long-Distance
MULTI-SVCS CENTER
MUSEUMS
MUSEUMS & ART GALLERIES
MUSIC BROADCASTING SVCS
MUSIC DISTRIBUTION SYSTEM SVCS
MUSIC RECORDING PRODUCER
MUSICAL INSTRUMENT REPAIR
MUTUAL ACCIDENT ASSOCIATIONS
MUTUAL FUND MANAGEMENT

N

NAIL SALONS
NATURAL ETHANE PRODUCTION
NATURAL GAS DISTRIBUTION TO CONSUMERS
NATURAL GAS PRODUCTION
NATURAL GAS STORAGE SVCS
NATURAL RESOURCE PRESERVATION SVCS
NEIGHBORHOOD CENTER
NEIGHBORHOOD DEVELOPMENT GROUP
NEWSPAPERS, WHOLESALE
NONMETALLIC MINERALS: Support Activities, Exc Fuels
NOVELTIES, PAPER, WHOLESALE
NURSERY SCHOOLS
NURSERY STOCK, WHOLESALE
NURSING & PERSONAL CARE FACILITIES, NEC
NURSING CARE FACILITIES: Skilled
NURSING HOME, EXC SKILLED & INTERMEDIATE CARE FACILITY
NUTRITION SVCS

O

OFC/CLINIC OF MED DRS: Special, Phys Or Surgeon, Eye Or ENT
OFC/CLINIC OF MED DRS: Specl, Phys Or Surgeon, Occup & Indl
OFCS & CLINICS, MEDICAL DRS: Specl, Physician Or Surgn, ENT
OFFENDER REHABILITATION AGENCY
OFFENDER SELF-HELP AGENCY
OFFICE CLEANING OR CHARRING SVCS
OFFICE EQPT WHOLESALERS
OFFICE EQPT, WHOLESALE: Blueprinting
OFFICE EQPT, WHOLESALE: Dictating Machines
OFFICE EQPT, WHOLESALE: Duplicating Machines
OFFICE EQPT, WHOLESALE: Photocopy Machines
OFFICE EQPT, WHOLESALE: Typewriters
OFFICE FURNITURE REPAIR & MAINTENANCE SVCS
OFFICE MANAGEMENT SVCS
OFFICE SPLYS, NEC, WHOLESALE
OFFICES & CLINICS DOCTORS OF MED: Intrnl Med Practitioners
OFFICES & CLINICS DRS OF MED: Psychiatrists/Psychoanalysts
OFFICES & CLINICS HLTH PRACTITNRS: Psychiatric Social Wrkr
OFFICES & CLINICS OF DENTISTS: Dental Clinic
OFFICES & CLINICS OF DENTISTS: Dental Clinics & Offices
OFFICES & CLINICS OF DENTISTS: Dental Surgeon
OFFICES & CLINICS OF DENTISTS: Dentists' Office
OFFICES & CLINICS OF DENTISTS: Endodontist
OFFICES & CLINICS OF DENTISTS: Group & Corporate Practice
OFFICES & CLINICS OF DENTISTS: Oral Pathologist
OFFICES & CLINICS OF DENTISTS: Periodontist

OFFICES & CLINICS OF DENTISTS: Specialist, Maxillofacial
OFFICES & CLINICS OF DENTISTS: Specialist, Practitioners
OFFICES & CLINICS OF DOCTORS OF MEDICINE: Allergist
OFFICES & CLINICS OF DOCTORS OF MEDICINE: Anesthesiologist
OFFICES & CLINICS OF DOCTORS OF MEDICINE: Dermatologist
OFFICES & CLINICS OF DOCTORS OF MEDICINE: Dispensary
OFFICES & CLINICS OF DOCTORS OF MEDICINE: Endocrinologist
OFFICES & CLINICS OF DOCTORS OF MEDICINE: Gastronomist
OFFICES & CLINICS OF DOCTORS OF MEDICINE: Group Health Assoc
OFFICES & CLINICS OF DOCTORS OF MEDICINE: Gynecologist
OFFICES & CLINICS OF DOCTORS OF MEDICINE: Hematologist
OFFICES & CLINICS OF DOCTORS OF MEDICINE: Med Insurance Plan
OFFICES & CLINICS OF DOCTORS OF MEDICINE: Nephrologist
OFFICES & CLINICS OF DOCTORS OF MEDICINE: Neurologist
OFFICES & CLINICS OF DOCTORS OF MEDICINE: Neurosurgeon
OFFICES & CLINICS OF DOCTORS OF MEDICINE: Obstetrician
OFFICES & CLINICS OF DOCTORS OF MEDICINE: Oncologist
OFFICES & CLINICS OF DOCTORS OF MEDICINE: Ophthalmologist
OFFICES & CLINICS OF DOCTORS OF MEDICINE: Pathologist
OFFICES & CLINICS OF DOCTORS OF MEDICINE: Pediatrician
OFFICES & CLINICS OF DOCTORS OF MEDICINE: Psychiatric Clinic
OFFICES & CLINICS OF DOCTORS OF MEDICINE: Psychiatrist
OFFICES & CLINICS OF DOCTORS OF MEDICINE: Radiologist
OFFICES & CLINICS OF DOCTORS OF MEDICINE: Surgeon
OFFICES & CLINICS OF DOCTORS OF MEDICINE: Surgeon, Plastic
OFFICES & CLINICS OF DOCTORS OF MEDICINE: Urologist
OFFICES & CLINICS OF DOCTORS, MEDICINE: Gen & Fam Practice
OFFICES & CLINICS OF DRS OF MED: Cardiologist & Vascular
OFFICES & CLINICS OF DRS OF MED: Clinic, Op by Physicians
OFFICES & CLINICS OF DRS OF MED: Health Maint Org Or HMO
OFFICES & CLINICS OF DRS OF MED: Physician/Surgeon, Int Med
OFFICES & CLINICS OF DRS OF MED: Physician/Surgeon, Phy Med
OFFICES & CLINICS OF DRS OF MED: Specialist/Phy, Fertility
OFFICES & CLINICS OF DRS OF MEDICINE: Diabetes
OFFICES & CLINICS OF DRS OF MEDICINE: Med Clinic, Pri Care
OFFICES & CLINICS OF DRS OF MEDICINE: Physician, Orthopedic
OFFICES & CLINICS OF DRS OF MEDICINE: Physician, Thoracic
OFFICES & CLINICS OF DRS OF MEDICINE: Pulmonary
OFFICES & CLINICS OF DRS OF MEDICINE: Rheumatology
OFFICES & CLINICS OF DRS, MED: Specialized Practitioners
OFFICES & CLINICS OF HEALTH PRACTITIONERS: Occu Therapist
OFFICES & CLINICS OF HEALTH PRACTITIONERS: Physical Therapy
OFFICES & CLINICS OF HEALTH PRACTITIONERS: Physiotherapist
OFFICES & CLINICS OF HEALTH PRACTITIONERS: Psychotherapist
OFFICES & CLINICS OF HEALTH PRACTITIONERS: Speech Pathology
OFFICES & CLINICS OF HEALTH PRACTITIONERS: Speech Specialist
OFFICES & CLINICS OF HEALTH PRACTRS: Clinical Psychologist
OFFICES & CLINICS OF HLTH PRACTITIONERS: Reg/Practical Nurse
OIL FIELD SVCS, NEC
OILS, ANIMAL OR VEGETABLE, WHOLESALE

SERVICES INDEX

OLD AGE ASSISTANCE
ON-LINE DATABASE INFORMATION
  RETRIEVAL SVCS
OPEN PIT COPPER ORE MINING
OPEN PIT GOLD MINING
OPEN PIT IRON MINING, NEC
OPEN PIT TACONITE MINING
OPERA COMPANIES
OPERATIVE BUILDERS: Townhouse
OPERATOR: Apartment Buildings
OPERATOR: Nonresidential Buildings
OPHTHALMIC GOODS WHOLESALERS
OPTICAL SCANNING SVCS
OPTOMETRIC EQPT & SPLYS
  WHOLESALERS
OPTOMETRISTS' OFFICES
ORCHESTRAS & BANDS
ORGAN BANK
ORGANIZATIONS & UNIONS: Labor
ORGANIZATIONS, NEC
ORGANIZATIONS: Civic & Social
ORGANIZATIONS: Economic Research,
  Noncommercial
ORGANIZATIONS: Educational Research
  Agency
ORGANIZATIONS: Medical Research
ORGANIZATIONS: Political
ORGANIZATIONS: Professional
ORGANIZATIONS: Research Institute
ORGANIZATIONS: Scientific Research Agency
ORGANIZATIONS: Veterans' Membership
ORNAMENTAL NURSERY PRODUCTS
ORNAMENTAL SHRUB & TREE SVC
ORTHODONTIST
OUTREACH PROGRAM
OXYGEN TENT SVCS

P

PACKAGE DESIGN SVCS
PACKAGED FROZEN FOODS
  WHOLESALERS, NEC
PACKAGING & LABELING SVCS
PACKAGING MATERIALS, WHOLESALE
PACKING & CRATING SVC
PACKING SVCS: Shipping
PAGING SVCS
PAINT BRUSHES, ROLLERS & SPRAYERS
  WHOLESALERS
PAINTS, VARNISHES & SPLYS
  WHOLESALERS
PAINTS, VARNISHES & SPLYS,
  WHOLESALE: Paints
PAINTS, VARNISHES & SPLYS,
  WHOLESALE: Varnishes
PALLET REPAIR SVCS
PAPER NAPKINS WHOLESALERS
PAPER, WHOLESALE: Fine
PAPER, WHOLESALE: Printing
PAPER, WHOLESALE: Writing
PARADE FLOATS: Decorating Svcs
PARKING GARAGE
PARKING LOTS
PARKING LOTS & GARAGES
PARKING STRUCTURE
PARTY & SPECIAL EVENT PLANNING SVCS
PARTY FAVORS, BALLOONS, HATS, ETC,
  WHOLESALE
PASSENGER AIRLINE SVCS
PATENT BUYING, LICENSING & LEASING
PATENT OWNERS & LESSORS
PAYROLL SVCS
PEAT GRINDING SVCS
PEAT MINING SVCS
PENSION & RETIREMENT PLAN
  CONSULTANTS
PENSION FUNDS
PENSIONS
PERFORMING ARTS CENTER PRODUCTION
  SVCS
PERIODICALS, WHOLESALE
PERSONAL APPEARANCE SVCS
PERSONAL CARE FACILITY
PERSONAL CARE HOME, WITH HEALTH
  CARE
PERSONAL CREDIT INSTITUTIONS:
  Auto/Consumer Finance Co's
PERSONAL CREDIT INSTITUTIONS:
  Consumer Finance Companies
PERSONAL CREDIT INSTITUTIONS:
  Financing, Autos, Furniture
PERSONAL CREDIT INSTITUTIONS: Install
  Sales Finance
PERSONAL DOCUMENT & INFORMATION
  SVCS
PERSONAL INVESTIGATION SVCS

PERSONAL ITEM CARE & STORAGE SVCS
PERSONAL SVCS
PEST CONTROL IN STRUCTURES SVCS
PESTICIDES WHOLESALERS
PET FOOD WHOLESALERS
PET SPLYS WHOLESALERS
PETROLEUM & PETROLEUM PRDTS, WHOL
  Svc Station Splys, Petro
PETROLEUM & PETROLEUM PRDTS,
  WHOLESALE Diesel Fuel
PETROLEUM & PETROLEUM PRDTS,
  WHOLESALE Engine Fuels & Oils
PETROLEUM & PETROLEUM PRDTS,
  WHOLESALE Fuel Oil
PETROLEUM & PETROLEUM PRDTS,
  WHOLESALE Gases
PETROLEUM & PETROLEUM PRDTS,
  WHOLESALE Petroleum Terminals
PETROLEUM & PETROLEUM PRDTS,
  WHOLESALE: Bulk Stations
PETROLEUM BULK STATIONS &
  TERMINALS
PETROLEUM PRDTS WHOLESALERS
PETS & PET SPLYS, WHOLESALE
PHARMACEUTICALS, DRUG
  PROPRIETARIES & SUNDRIES
  WHOLESALERS
PHOSPHATE ROCK MINING
PHOTOCOPY MACHINE REPAIR SVCS
PHOTOCOPY SPLYS WHOLESALERS
PHOTOCOPYING & DUPLICATING SVCS
PHOTOFINISHING LABORATORIES
PHOTOGRAPHIC EQPT & CAMERAS,
  WHOLESALE
PHOTOGRAPHIC EQPT & SPLYS
  WHOLESALERS
PHOTOGRAPHIC EQPT & SPLYS,
  WHOLESALE: Developing Apparatus
PHOTOGRAPHIC EQPT & SPLYS,
  WHOLESALE: Motion Picture
PHOTOGRAPHIC EQPT & SPLYS,
  WHOLESALE: Processing
PHOTOGRAPHIC SVCS
PHOTOGRAPHY SVCS: Commercial
PHOTOGRAPHY SVCS: Portrait Studios
PHOTOGRAPHY SVCS: School
PHOTOGRAPHY SVCS: Still Or Video
PHOTOGRAPHY: Aerial
PHYSICAL EXAMINATION & TESTING SVCS
PHYSICAL EXAMINATION SVCS,
  INSURANCE
PHYSICAL FITNESS CENTERS
PHYSICAL FITNESS CLUBS WITH TRAINING
  EQPT
PHYSICIANS' OFFICES & CLINICS: Medical
PHYSICIANS' OFFICES & CLINICS: Medical
  doctors
PHYSICIANS' OFFICES & CLINICS:
  Osteopathic
PICTURE FRAMING SVCS, CUSTOM
PIECE GOODS & NOTIONS WHOLESALERS
PIECE GOODS, NOTIONS & DRY GOODS,
  WHOL: Textiles, Woven
PIECE GOODS, NOTIONS & DRY GOODS,
  WHOLESALE: Fabrics, Knit
PIECE GOODS, NOTIONS & OTHER DRY
  GOODS, WHOL: Flags/Banners
PIECE GOODS, NOTIONS/DRY GOODS,
  WHOL: Drapery Mtrl, Woven
PIECE GOODS, NOTIONS/DRY GOODS,
  WHOL: Linen Piece, Woven
PIECE GOODS, NOTIONS/DRY GOODS,
  WHOL: Sewing Splys/Notions
PIPELINE TERMINAL FACILITIES:
  Independent
PIPELINES: Crude Petroleum
PIPELINES: Natural Gas
PIPELINES: Refined Petroleum
PLANT CARE SVCS
PLANTING, PRUNING & TRIMMING SVCS
PLANTS, POTTED, WHOLESALE
PLASMAPHEROUS CENTER
PLASTICS MATERIALS, BASIC FORMS &
  SHAPES WHOLESALERS
PLAYS, ROAD & STOCK COMPANIES
PLUMBING & HEATING EQPT & SPLY,
  WHOLESALE: Hydronic Htg Eqpt
PLUMBING & HEATING EQPT & SPLYS
  WHOLESALERS
PLUMBING & HEATING EQPT & SPLYS,
  WHOL: Pipe/Fitting, Plastic
PLUMBING & HEATING EQPT & SPLYS,
  WHOL: Plumbing Fitting/Sply
PLUMBING & HEATING EQPT & SPLYS,
  WHOL: Plumbng/Heatng Valves
PLUMBING & HEATING EQPT & SPLYS,
  WHOL: Water Purif Eqpt

PLUMBING & HEATING EQPT & SPLYS,
  WHOLESALE: Brass/Fittings
PLUMBING & HEATING EQPT, WHOLESALE:
  Water Heaters/Purif
PLUMBING & HEATING EQPT/SPLYS,
  WHOL: Boilers, Hot Water Htg
PLUMBING/HEATING EQPT/SPLYS, WHOL:
  Radiators/Parts, Exc Elec
POSTERS, WHOLESALE
POSTHARVEST CROP ACTIVITIES
POTASH MINING
POTATO CURING SVCS
POTATOES, MACHINE HARVESTING SVCS
POULTRY & POULTRY PRDTS
  WHOLESALERS
POULTRY, PACKAGED FROZEN:
  Wholesalers
POWER HAND TOOLS WHOLESALERS
POWER TOOL REPAIR SVCS
PRECIOUS METALS WHOLESALERS
PRECISION INSTRUMENT REPAIR SVCS
PRERECORDED TAPES & CASSETTES
  WHOLESALERS
PRESCHOOL CENTERS
PRESS CLIPPING SVC
PRINTERS' SVCS: Folding, Collating, Etc
PRINTING & WRITING PAPER
  WHOLESALERS
PRINTING INKS WHOLESALERS
PRINTING MACHINERY, EQPT & SPLYS:
  Wholesalers
PRIVATE INVESTIGATOR SVCS
PROBATION OFFICE
PROFESSIONAL EQPT & SPLYS,
  WHOLESALE: Analytical Instruments
PROFESSIONAL EQPT & SPLYS,
  WHOLESALE: Engineers', NEC
PROFESSIONAL EQPT & SPLYS,
  WHOLESALE: Optical Goods
PROFESSIONAL EQPT & SPLYS,
  WHOLESALE: Scientific & Engineerg
PROFESSIONAL EQPT & SPLYS,
  WHOLESALE: Theatrical
PROFESSIONAL INSTRUMENT REPAIR
  SVCS
PROFESSIONAL STANDARDS REVIEW
  BOARDS
PROMOTERS OF SHOWS & EXHIBITIONS
PROMOTION SVCS
PROPERTY & CASUALTY INSURANCE
  AGENTS
PROPERTY DAMAGE INSURANCE
PRUNING SVCS, ORNAMENTAL TREE
PUBLIC RELATIONS & PUBLICITY SVCS
PUBLIC RELATIONS SVCS
PUBLIC WELFARE CENTER
PUMPS & PUMPING EQPT REPAIR SVCS
PUMPS & PUMPING EQPT WHOLESALERS
PURCHASING SVCS

R

RACETRACKS
RACETRACKS: Horse
RADIO & TELEVISION REPAIR
RADIO BROADCASTING STATIONS
RADIO REPAIR & INSTALLATION SVCS
RAILROAD CAR REPAIR SVCS
RAILROAD CARGO LOADING & UNLOADING
  SVCS
RAILROAD EQPT & SPLYS WHOLESALERS
RAILROAD FREIGHT AGENCY
RAILROAD MAINTENANCE & REPAIR SVCS
RAILROAD SWITCHING & TERMINAL SVCS
RAILROADS: Long Haul
REAL ESTATE AGENCIES & BROKERS
REAL ESTATE AGENCIES: Commercial
REAL ESTATE AGENCIES: Leasing & Rentals
REAL ESTATE AGENCIES: Multiple Listing
  Svc
REAL ESTATE AGENCIES: Rental
REAL ESTATE AGENCIES: Residential
REAL ESTATE AGENCIES: Selling
REAL ESTATE AGENTS & MANAGERS
REAL ESTATE APPRAISERS
REAL ESTATE INVESTMENT TRUSTS
REAL ESTATE MANAGERS: Condominium
REAL ESTATE MANAGERS: Cooperative
  Apartment
REAL ESTATE OPERATORS, EXC DEVEL:
  Theater Bldg, Owner & Op
REAL ESTATE OPERATORS, EXC
  DEVELOPERS: Apartment Hotel
REAL ESTATE OPERATORS, EXC
  DEVELOPERS: Auditorium & Hall
REAL ESTATE OPERATORS, EXC
  DEVELOPERS: Commercial/Indl Bldg

REAL ESTATE OPERATORS, EXC
  DEVELOPERS: Property, Retail
REAL ESTATE OPERATORS, EXC
  DEVELOPERS: Retirement Hotel
REAL ESTATE OPERATORS, EXC
  DEVELOPERS: Shopping Ctr, Commnty
RECIPROCAL INTERINSURANCE
  EXCHANGES: Fire, Marine & Casualty
RECIPROCAL INTERINSURANCE
  EXCHANGES: Surety & Fidelity
RECREATIONAL & SPORTING CAMPS
RECREATIONAL CAMPS
RECREATIONAL SPORTING EQPT REPAIR
  SVCS
RECREATIONAL VEHICLE PARKS
RECREATIONAL VEHICLE PARKS &
  CAMPGROUNDS
RECREATIONAL VEHICLE REPAIR SVCS
RECREATIONAL VEHICLE REPAIRS
RECYCLABLE SCRAP & WASTE MATERIALS
  WHOLESALERS
REFERRAL SVCS, PERSONAL & SOCIAL
  PROBLEMS
REFRIGERATION EQPT & SPLYS
  WHOLESALERS
REFRIGERATION EQPT & SPLYS, WHOL:
  Refrig Units, Motor Veh
REFRIGERATION EQPT & SPLYS,
  WHOLESALE: Beverage Dispensers
REFRIGERATION EQPT & SPLYS,
  WHOLESALE: Commercial Eqpt
REFRIGERATION EQPT & SPLYS,
  WHOLESALE: Ice Making Machines
REFRIGERATION REPAIR SVCS
REFRIGERATION SVC & REPAIR
REFUGEE SVCS
REFUSE SYSTEMS
REGIONAL PLANNING ORGANIZATION
REHABILITATION CENTER, OUTPATIENT
  TREATMENT
REHABILITATION CTR, RESIDENTIAL WITH
  HEALTH CARE INCIDENTAL
REHABILITATION SVCS
REINSURANCE CARRIERS: Accident &
  Health
REINSURANCE CARRIERS: Life
REINSURANCE CARRIERS: Surety
RELIGIOUS SPLYS WHOLESALERS
RELOCATION SVCS
REMOTE DATABASE INFORMATION
  RETRIEVAL SVCS
REMOVAL SVCS, BUSH & TREE
RENT-A-CAR SVCS
RENTAL & OPERATION SVCS: Go-Cart
  Raceway
RENTAL CENTERS: Furniture
RENTAL CENTERS: General
RENTAL CENTERS: Party & Banquet Eqpt &
  Splys
RENTAL CENTERS: Tools
RENTAL SVCS: Aircraft
RENTAL SVCS: Audio-Visual Eqpt & Sply
RENTAL SVCS: Business Machine &
  Electronic Eqpt
RENTAL SVCS: Clothing
RENTAL SVCS: Costume
RENTAL SVCS: Eqpt, Motion Picture
RENTAL SVCS: Eqpt, Theatrical
RENTAL SVCS: Home Appliance, Furniture &
  Entertainment
RENTAL SVCS: Home Cleaning &
  Maintenance Eqpt
RENTAL SVCS: Houseboat
RENTAL SVCS: Invalid Splys
RENTAL SVCS: Lawn & Garden Eqpt
RENTAL SVCS: Live Plant
RENTAL SVCS: Locker, Exc Cold Storage
RENTAL SVCS: Musical Instrument
RENTAL SVCS: Pleasure Boat
RENTAL SVCS: Recreational Vehicle
RENTAL SVCS: Sporting Goods, NEC
RENTAL SVCS: Stores & Yards Eqpt
RENTAL SVCS: Tent & Tarpaulin
RENTAL SVCS: Trailer
RENTAL SVCS: Travel, Camping Or
  Recreational Trailer
RENTAL SVCS: Truck, Without Drivers
RENTAL SVCS: Tuxedo
RENTAL SVCS: Vending Machine
RENTAL SVCS: Work Zone Traffic Eqpt,
  Flags, Cones, Etc
RENTAL: Passenger Car
RENTAL: Portable Toilet
RENTAL: Trucks, With Drivers
RENTAL: Video Tape & Disc

S V C   I N D E X

www.HarrisInfo.com
646

2011 Harris Minnesota
Services Directory

REPERTORY, ROAD OR STOCK COMPANIES, THEATRICAL
REPOSSESSION SVCS
REPRODUCTION SVCS: Video Tape Or Disk
RESEARCH, DEV & TESTING SVCS, COMM: Chem Lab, Exc Testing
RESEARCH, DEVELOPMENT & TEST SVCS, COMM: Cmptr Hardware Dev
RESEARCH, DEVELOPMENT & TEST SVCS, COMM: Research, Exc Lab
RESEARCH, DEVELOPMENT & TESTING SVCS, COMM: Agricultural
RESEARCH, DEVELOPMENT & TESTING SVCS, COMM: Natural Resource
RESEARCH, DEVELOPMENT & TESTING SVCS, COMM: Research Lab
RESEARCH, DEVELOPMENT & TESTING SVCS, COMM: Sociological
RESEARCH, DEVELOPMENT & TESTING SVCS, COMMERCIAL: Business
RESEARCH, DEVELOPMENT & TESTING SVCS, COMMERCIAL: Economic
RESEARCH, DEVELOPMENT & TESTING SVCS, COMMERCIAL: Education
RESEARCH, DEVELOPMENT & TESTING SVCS, COMMERCIAL: Energy
RESEARCH, DEVELOPMENT & TESTING SVCS, COMMERCIAL: Food
RESEARCH, DEVELOPMENT & TESTING SVCS, COMMERCIAL: Medical
RESEARCH, DEVELOPMENT & TESTING SVCS, COMMERCIAL: Physical
RESEARCH, DVLPMT & TESTING SVCS, COMM: Merger, Acq & Reorg
RESEARCH, DVLPT & TEST SVCS, COMM: Mkt Analysis or Research
RESEARCH, DVLPT & TESTING SVCS, COMM: Mkt, Bus & Economic
RESEARCH, DVLPT & TESTING SVCS, COMM: Survey, Mktg
RESIDENCE CLUB: Organization
RESIDENTIAL CARE FOR CHILDREN
RESIDENTIAL CARE FOR THE HANDICAPPED
RESIDENTIAL MENTAL HEALTH & SUBSTANCE ABUSE FACILITIES
RESIDENTIAL MENTALLY HANDICAPPED FACILITIES
RESIDENTIAL REMODELERS
RESORT HOTEL: Franchised
RESORT HOTELS
REST HOME, WITH HEALTH CARE INCIDENTAL
RETIREMENT COMMUNITIES WITH NURSING
ROAD CONSTRUCTION EQUIPMENT WHOLESALERS
ROOFING, SIDING & SHEET METAL WORK
ROOMING & BOARDING HOUSES: Furnished Room Rental
ROOMING & BOARDING HOUSES: Lodging House, Exc Organization
RUBBER PRDTS REPAIR SVCS

S

SAFETY EQPT & SPLYS WHOLESALERS
SAFETY INSPECTION SVCS
SALES PROMOTION SVCS
SAND & GRAVEL
SAND MINING
SAND: Silica
SANITARY SVCS: Garbage Collecting, Destroying & Processing
SANITARY SVCS: Hazardous Waste, Collection & Disposal
SANITARY SVCS: Incinerator, Operation Of
SANITARY SVCS: Refuse Collection & Disposal Svcs
SANITARY SVCS: Road, Airport & Parking Lot Sweeping
SANITARY SVCS: Rubbish Collection & Disposal
SANITARY SVCS: Sanitary Landfill, Operation Of
SANITARY SVCS: Sewage Treatment Facility
SANITARY SVCS: Waste Materials, Recycling
SAVINGS & LOAN ASSOCIATIONS, NOT FEDERALLY CHARTERED
SAVINGS INSTITUTIONS: Federally Chartered
SCAFFOLDING WHOLESALERS
SCHOOL BUS SVC
SCHOOL SPLYS, EXC BOOKS: Wholesalers
SCIENTIFIC INSTRUMENTS WHOLESALERS
SCRAP & WASTE MATERIALS, WHOLESALE: Ferrous Metal

SCRAP & WASTE MATERIALS, WHOLESALE: Junk & Scrap
SCRAP & WASTE MATERIALS, WHOLESALE: Metal
SCRAP & WASTE MATERIALS, WHOLESALE: Nonferrous Metals Scrap
SCRAP & WASTE MATERIALS, WHOLESALE: Paper
SCRAP & WASTE MATERIALS, WHOLESALE: Rags
SCRAP & WASTE MATERIALS, WHOLESALE: Textile
SEARCH & RESCUE SVCS
SECRETARIAL & COURT REPORTING
SECRETARIAL SVCS
SECURE STORAGE SVC: Document
SECURITIES DEALING
SECURITY & COMMODITY EXCHANGES: Futures, Contract
SECURITY DISTRIBUTORS
SECURITY GUARD SVCS
SECURITY PROTECTIVE DEVICES MAINTENANCE & MONITORING SVCS
SECURITY SYSTEMS SERVICES
SECURITY UNDERWRITERS
SEEDING SVCS, LAWN
SEEDS & BULBS WHOLESALERS
SELF-HELP GROUP HOME
SELF-HELP ORGANIZATION, NEC
SERVICES, NEC
SEWAGE FACILITIES
SEWER CLEANING & RODDING SVC
SEWING CONTRACTORS
SEWING MACHINE REPAIR SHOP
SHELTERED WORKSHOPS
SHIPPING AGENTS
SHOES & BOOTS WHOLESALERS
SHOPPING CENTERS & MALLS
SIGN LETTERING & PAINTING SVCS
SIGN PAINTING & LETTERING SHOP
SIGNS, EXC ELECTRIC, WHOLESALE
SILK SCREEN DESIGN SVCS
SKATING RINKS: Roller
SKI LODGE
SKILL TRAINING CENTER
SLAUGHTERING, CUSTOM, LIVESTOCK SVCS
SMALL BUSINESS INVESTMENT COMPANIES
SNOW PLOWING SVCS
SNOWMOBILE REPAIR SVCS
SOCIAL CHANGE ASSOCIATION
SOCIAL CLUBS
SOCIAL SERVICES INFORMATION EXCHANGE
SOCIAL SERVICES, NEC
SOCIAL SVCS CENTER
SOCIAL SVCS, HANDICAPPED
SOCIAL SVCS: Individual & Family
SODDING CONTRACTOR
SOFT DRINKS WHOLESALERS
SOFTWARE PUBLISHERS: Application
SOFTWARE PUBLISHERS: Business & Professional
SOFTWARE PUBLISHERS: Education
SOFTWARE PUBLISHERS: NEC
SOFTWARE PUBLISHERS: Operating Systems
SOFTWARE PUBLISHERS: Publisher's
SOIL CHEMICAL TREATMENT SVCS
SOIL PREPARATION SVCS
SOIL PREPARATION, PLANTING & CULTIVATING SVCS
SPAS
SPECIAL EVENTS DECORATION SVCS
SPECIALIZED LEGAL SVCS
SPECIALTY OUTPATIENT CLINICS, NEC
SPECULATIVE BUILDERS: Single-Family Housing
SPORTING & REC GOODS, WHOLESALE: Boats, Canoes, Etc/Eqpt
SPORTING & RECREATIONAL GOODS & SPLYS WHOLESALERS
SPORTING & RECREATIONAL GOODS, WHOLESALE: Athletic Goods
SPORTING & RECREATIONAL GOODS, WHOLESALE: Boat Access & Part
SPORTING & RECREATIONAL GOODS, WHOLESALE: Exercise
SPORTING & RECREATIONAL GOODS, WHOLESALE: Fishing
SPORTING & RECREATIONAL GOODS, WHOLESALE: Fishing Tackle
SPORTING & RECREATIONAL GOODS, WHOLESALE: Gymnasium

SPORTING & RECREATIONAL GOODS, WHOLESALE: Hunting
SPORTING & RECREATIONAL GOODS, WHOLESALE: Motorboats
SPORTING & RECREATIONAL GOODS, WHOLESALE: Outboard Motors
SPORTING & RECREATIONAL GOODS, WHOLESALE: Spa
SPORTS CLUBS, MANAGERS & PROMOTERS
SPORTS TEAMS & CLUBS
SPORTS TEAMS & CLUBS: Baseball
SPORTS TEAMS & CLUBS: Basketball
SPORTS TEAMS & CLUBS: Football
SPORTS TEAMS & CLUBS: Soccer
SPRAYING SVCS, ORNAMENTAL TREE
STAFFING, EMPLOYMENT PLACEMENT
STATE CREDIT UNIONS, NOT FEDERALLY CHARTERED
STATE SAVINGS BANKS, NOT FEDERALLY CHARTERED
STATION OPERATION SVCS
STATIONARY & OFFICE SPLYS, WHOL: Computer/Photocopying Splys
STATIONARY & OFFICE SPLYS, WHOLESALE: Data Processing Splys
STATIONARY & OFFICE SPLYS, WHOLESALE: Manifold Business Form
STATIONARY & OFFICE SPLYS, WHOLESALE: Photo Albums/Scrapbook
STATIONARY & OFFICE SPLYS, WHOLESALE: Stationers, Commercial
STATIONARY & OFFICE SPLYS, WHOLESALE: Stationery
STATIONERY & OFFICE SPLYS WHOLESALERS
STEAM HEATING SYSTEMS SPLY SVCS
STEAM SPLY SYSTEMS SVCS INCLUDING GEOTHERMAL
STENOGRAPHIC SVCS
STEVEDORING SVCS
STITCHING SVCS: Custom
STONE: Dimension, NEC
STORE FIXTURES, EXC REFRIGERATED: Wholesalers
STUDIOS: Sculptor's
SUBSCRIPTION FULFILLMENT SVCS: Magazine, Newspaper, Etc
SUBSTANCE ABUSE CLINICS, OUTPATIENT
SUMMER CAMPS, EXC DAY & SPORTS INSTRUCTIONAL
SUNGLASSES, WHOLESALE
SURGERY SVCS, ORNAMENTAL TREE
SURVEYING & MAPPING: Land Parcels
SURVEYING SVCS: Photogrammetric Engineering
SVC ESTABLISHMENT EQPT & SPLYS WHOLESALERS
SVC ESTABLISHMENT EQPT, WHOL: Cleaning & Maint Eqpt & Splys
SVC ESTABLISHMENT EQPT, WHOLESALE : Barber Shop Eqpt & Splys
SVC ESTABLISHMENT EQPT, WHOLESALE: Beauty Parlor Eqpt & Sply
SVC ESTABLISHMENT EQPT, WHOLESALE: Firefighting Eqpt
SVC ESTABLISHMENT EQPT, WHOLESALE: Floor Machinery, Maint
SVC ESTABLISHMENT EQPT, WHOLESALE: Laundry Eqpt & Splys
SVC ESTABLISHMENT EQPT, WHOLESALE: Moving Eqpt & Splys
SVC ESTABLISHMENT EQPT, WHOLESALE: Restaurant Splys
SVC ESTABLISHMENT EQPT, WHOLESALE: Vacuum Cleaning Systems
SVC ESTABLISHMENT EQPT, WHOLESALE: Vending Machines & Splys
SWIMMING INSTRUCTION
SWIMMING POOL & HOT TUB CLEANING & MAINTENANCE SVCS
SYMPHONY ORCHESTRA
SYSTEMS ENGINEERING: Computer Related
SYSTEMS INTEGRATION SVCS
SYSTEMS INTEGRATION SVCS: Local Area Network
SYSTEMS SOFTWARE DEVELOPMENT SVCS

T

TABULATING SVCS
TANK REPAIR SVCS
TANNING SALON EQPT & SPLYS, WHOLESALE
TANNING SALONS
TAPE SLITTING SVCS
TAX RETURN PREPARATION SVCS

TAXI CABS
TELECOMMUNICATION EQPT REPAIR SVCS, EXC TELEPHONES
TELECOMMUNICATIONS CARRIERS & SVCS: Wired
TELECOMMUNICATIONS CARRIERS & SVCS: Wireless
TELECONFERENCING SVCS
TELEMARKETING BUREAUS
TELEPHONE ANSWERING SVCS
TELEPHONE EQPT INSTALLATION
TELEPHONE SET REPAIR SVCS
TELEPHONE SOLICITATION SVCS
TELEPHONE SVCS
TELEVISION BROADCASTING STATIONS
TELEVISION FILM PRODUCTION SVCS
TEMPORARY HELP SVCS
TEMPORARY RELIEF SVCS
TEN PIN CENTERS
TEXTILE BAGS WHOLESALERS
THEATER COMPANIES
THEATRICAL PRODUCERS & SVCS
THEATRICAL PRODUCTION SVCS
TIMBER TRACT OPERATIONS
TIRE & TUBE REPAIR MATERIALS, WHOLESALE
TIRE RECAPPING & RETREADING
TIRES & TUBES WHOLESALERS
TIRES & TUBES, WHOLESALE: Automotive
TIRES & TUBES, WHOLESALE: Truck
TITLE & TRUST COMPANIES
TITLE ABSTRACT & SETTLEMENT OFFICES
TITLE INSURANCE AGENTS
TITLE INSURANCE: Guarantee Of Titles
TITLE INSURANCE: Real Estate
TITLE SEARCH COMPANIES
TOBACCO & PRDTS, WHOLESALE: Cigarettes
TOBACCO & TOBACCO PRDTS WHOLESALERS
TOILETRIES, WHOLESALE: Cosmetics, Perfumes & Hair Prdts
TOILETRIES, WHOLESALE: Hair Preparations
TOILETRIES, WHOLESALE: Toilet Preparations
TOILETRIES, WHOLESALE: Toilet Soap
TOILETRIES, WHOLESALE: Toiletries
TOLL BRIDGE OPERATIONS
TOOL REPAIR SVCS
TOUR OPERATORS
TOURIST AGENCY: Transportation, Lodging & Car Rental
TOURIST INFORMATION BUREAU
TOURIST LODGINGS
TOYS & HOBBY GOODS & SPLYS, WHOLESALE: Arts/Crafts Eqpt/Sply
TOYS & HOBBY GOODS & SPLYS, WHOLESALE: Bingo Games & Splys
TOYS & HOBBY GOODS & SPLYS, WHOLESALE: Toys & Games
TOYS & HOBBY GOODS & SPLYS, WHOLESALE: Toys, NEC
TOYS & HOBBY GOODS & SPLYS, WHOLESALE: Video Games
TOYS, HOBBY GOODS & SPLYS WHOLESALERS
TRACTOR REPAIR SVCS
TRADE SHOW ARRANGEMENT SVCS
TRANSLATION & INTERPRETATION SVCS
TRANSPORTATION AGENTS & BROKERS
TRANSPORTATION ARRANGEMENT SVCS, PASSENGER: Airline Ticket
TRANSPORTATION ARRANGEMENT SVCS, PASSENGER: Carpool/Vanpool
TRANSPORTATION ARRANGEMENT SVCS, PASSENGER: Tours, Conducted
TRANSPORTATION ARRANGEMNT SVCS, PASS: Travel Tour Pkgs, Whol
TRANSPORTATION BROKERS: Truck
TRANSPORTATION EPQT & SPLYS, WHOL: Aircraft Engs/Eng Parts
TRANSPORTATION EPQT & SPLYS, WHOLESALE: Acft/Space Vehicle
TRANSPORTATION EPQT & SPLYS, WHOLESALE: Marine Crafts/Splys
TRANSPORTATION EQPT & SPLYS WHOLESALERS, NEC
TRANSPORTATION SVCS, AIR, SCHEDULED: Helicopter Carriers
TRANSPORTATION SVCS, NEC
TRANSPORTATION SVCS, WATER: Bays & Sounds-Ocean, Freight
TRANSPORTATION SVCS: Airport
TRANSPORTATION SVCS: Bus Line Operations
TRANSPORTATION SVCS: Bus Line, Intercity

SERVICES SECTION

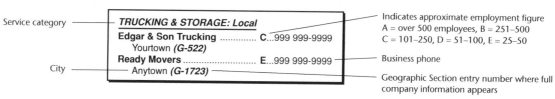
ABORTION CLINIC

Meadowbrook Women's Clinic ....E... 612 376-7708
Minneapolis *(G-4980)*

Robbinsdale Clinic PA Inc ....E... 763 533-2534
Minneapolis *(G-5550)*

ACCIDENT & HEALTH INSURANCE CARRIERS

St Paul Fire & Marine Insce ....A... 651 221-7911
Saint Paul *(G-8990)*

ACCIDENT & HEALTH INSURANCE: Fraternal Organizations

Thrivent Financial For ....A... 920 734-5721
Minneapolis *(G-5819)*

ACCOMMODATION LOCATING SVCS

American Legion Club ....E... 763 421-0883
Anoka *(G-152)*

Brook Hall Blaine Brook ....E... 763 755-8731
Minneapolis *(G-3425)*

City of Minneapolis ....C... 612 335-6000
Minneapolis *(G-4091)*

Italian American Club of ....D... 612 781-0625
Minneapolis *(G-4740)*

Paynesville Motor & Transfer ....E... 320 243-4455
Paynesville *(G-6773)*

Tri City Post 513 ....E... 651 631-1124
Saint Paul *(G-9081)*

ACCOUNTING MACHINES WHOLESALERS

Cash Register Sales Inc ....D... 651 294-2700
Saint Paul *(G-8171)*

ACCOUNTING SVCS, NEC

Children's Health Care Inc ....C... 651 855-2800
Saint Paul *(G-8194)*

Corporate Commission of The ....E... 320 532-8862
Onamia *(G-6569)*

Ds & B Ltd...E... 612 359-9630
Minneapolis *(G-4287)*

Eikill & Schilling Ltd ....E... 218 722-4705
Duluth *(G-1311)*

Grant Thornton LLP.............................D... 612 332-0001
Minneapolis *(G-4546)*

Kern Dewenter Viere Ltd ....E... 320 251-7010
Saint Cloud *(G-7541)*

Laron Allen Weishair & Co LLP ....D... 507 437-4518
Austin *(G-281)*

Reese, Winter & Associates Ltd 507 645-4473
Northfield *(G-6541)*

ACCOUNTING SVCS: Certified Public

Anderson Froehling Ltd ....E... 952 979-3100
Hopkins *(G-2511)*

Baker, Tilly, Virchow Krause..................C... 612 876-4500
Minneapolis *(G-3860)*

Baune Dosen & Co LLP ....E... 952 473-2002
Minneapolis *(G-3874)*

Boeckermann, Grafstrom & Mayer......E... 952 844-2500
Minneapolis *(G-3922)*

Boulay Heutmaker Zibell & Co..............C... 952 893-9320
Eden Prairie *(G-1610)*

Brunberg Blatt & Co Inc ....E... 763 545-2353
Minneapolis *(G-3963)*

Carlson, Lundquist & Co Ltd ....E... 763 535-8150
Minneapolis *(G-4019)*

Conway, Deuth & Schmiesing ....E... 320 235-3311
Willmar *(G-9999)*

Cummings, Keegan & Co Pllp ....E... 952 345-2500
Minneapolis *(G-4199)*

D J Baune & J A Dosen Ptr ....E... 952 473-2002
Hopkins *(G-2535)*

Eide Bailly LLP ....C... 952 944-6166
Minneapolis *(G-4332)*

Eide Bailly LLP ....E... 507 387-6031
Mankato *(G-3125)*

Eide Bailly LLP ....E... 507 387-6031
Madelia *(G-3072)*

Eikill & Schilling Ltd ....E... 218 722-4705
Duluth *(G-1311)*

Eikill & Schilling Ltd CPA ....E... 218 879-1503
Cloquet *(G-1051)*

Ernst & Young LLP ....B... 612 343-1000
Minneapolis *(G-4367)*

Glen Lindseth ....E... 218 751-6300
Bemidji *(G-396)*

Herbeck, David J CPA Pfs Chfc ....E... 763 546-6211
Minneapolis *(G-4640)*

James A Dosen ....E... 952 473-2002
Minneapolis *(G-4752)*

James W Copeland ....E... 952 476-7100
Wayzata *(G-9922)*

John A Kanutson ....E... 651 641-1099
Saint Paul *(G-8534)*

John A Knutson & Co...........................E... 651 641-1099
Saint Paul *(G-8535)*

Kern Dewenter Viere Ltd ....E... 320 251-7010
Saint Cloud *(G-7541)*

KPMG LLP ....E... 612 305-5000
Minneapolis *(G-4820)*

Laron Allen Weishair & Co LLP ....D... 507 437-4518
Austin *(G-281)*

Larson Ellen Weisharir Co LLP ....E... 320 253-8616
Waite Park *(G-9827)*

Larsonallen LLP ....B... 612 376-4500
Minneapolis *(G-4848)*

Lephert, Skwira, Shultz & Co ....E... 651 265-2051
Saint Paul *(G-8578)*

Lethert, Skwira, Schultz & Co ....E... 651 224-5721
Saint Paul *(G-8580)*

Leverz Skira & Shcultz CPA ....E... 651 265-2045
Saint Paul *(G-8581)*

Mahoney Ulbrich Christiansen ....E... 651 227-6695
Saint Paul *(G-8607)*

Malloy, Karnowski & Co ....E... 952 545-0424
Minneapolis *(G-4937)*

McGladrey & Pullen, LLP ....E... 507 288-6476
Rochester *(G-7180)*

McGladrey & Pullen, LLP ....D... 218 727-5025
Duluth *(G-1387)*

McGladrey & Pullen, LLP ....D... 218 727-6857
Duluth *(G-1388)*

Meulebroeck Taubert & Co Pllp...........E... 507 283-4055
Luverne *(G-3064)*

Moquist Thorvilson Kaufmann ....D... 952 854-5700
Minneapolis *(G-5126)*

Myslajek Ltd ....E... 612 781-2771
Minneapolis *(G-5153)*

Nathan J Lilleodden CPA ....D... 952 476-7107
Wayzata *(G-9931)*

Olsen Thielen Technologies Inc ....C... 651 483-4521
Saint Paul *(G-8781)*

Robert A Kovell ....E... 320 253-9505
Saint Cloud *(G-7589)*

Robert Gullick CPA ....E... 651 265-2043
Saint Paul *(G-8906)*

RSM McGladrey Business Svcs ....D... 952 857-1220
Minneapolis *(G-5568)*

Schechter Dokken Kanter ....D... 612 332-5500
Minneapolis *(G-5607)*

Schueller Wenner & Co ....D... 320 632-6311
Little Falls *(G-3019)*

Smith Schafer & Associates Ltd ....E... 507 288-3277
Rochester *(G-7255)*

Thomas Eling CPA ....E... 218 722-4705
Duluth *(G-1484)*

Thomas P Koop CPA............................E... 218 825-2903
Baxter *(G-342)*

Tk Advisors Ltd ....E... 612 373-9000
Minneapolis *(G-5828)*

Wilkerson, Guthmann & Johnson........E... 651 222-1801
Saint Paul *(G-9157)*

Wipfli LLP..D... 952 548-3400
Minneapolis *(G-6079)*

Wipfli LLP ....E... 651 636-6468
Saint Paul *(G-9159)*

ACCOUNTING, AUDITING & BOOKEEPING

Automatic Data Processing Inc...........B... 952 814-5800
Minneapolis *(G-3838)*

Bnsf Railway Co ....C... 651 298-2121
Saint Paul *(G-8116)*

Carlson Highland Co LLP ....D... 218 739-3267
Fergus Falls *(G-2065)*

Certes Financial Professionals ....E... 952 345-4140
Golden Valley *(G-2238)*

Commercial Auditors Corp ....E... 763 783-9160
Minneapolis *(G-3437)*

Deloitte & Touche LLP ....A... 612 397-4772
Minneapolis *(G-4244)*

Elmo Lake Bank....................................E... 651 777-8365
Lake Elmo *(G-2870)*

Emergency Physicians Prof ....C... 952 835-9880
Minneapolis *(G-4346)*

Healtheast Care Inc ....A... 651 232-2300
Saint Paul *(G-8453)*

Hlb Tautges Redpath............................D... 651 426-7000
Saint Paul *(G-8488)*

Iron Mountain Information MGT ....C... 952 888-3852
Minneapolis *(G-4735)*

Larsonallen LLP ....E... 218 825-2919
Baxter *(G-335)*

Metropolitan Council, MN ....C... 612 373-3333
Saint Paul *(G-8645)*

Minnesota Society of Certified ....E... 952 831-2707
Minneapolis *(G-5094)*

Pro Systems Corp ....E... 218 847-9277
Detroit Lakes *(G-1214)*

RSM McGladrey Business Soln ....C... 952 921-7700
Minneapolis *(G-5567)*

RSM McGladrey Inc ....D... 507 288-5363
Rochester *(G-7242)*

RSM McGladrey Inc ....D... 218 727-5025
Duluth *(G-1440)*

RSM McGladrey Inc ....C... 952 921-7700
Minneapolis *(G-5569)*

RSM McGladrey Inc ....C... 612 332-4300
Minneapolis *(G-5570)*

State Bank of Faribault ....E... 507 332-7401
Faribault *(G-2033)*

Steven N Arendt....................................E... 952 476-7143
Wayzata *(G-9942)*

3M Co ....B... 651 733-5562
Saint Paul *(G-9061)*

Timothy V Bergin..................................E... 218 825-2902
Baxter *(G-343)*

University of Minnesota ....C... 763 782-6400
Minneapolis *(G-5930)*

Walker, Giroux, Hahne Ltd....................E... 218 749-4880
Virginia *(G-9762)*

Wells Jefferson International ....E... 612 338-5400
Minneapolis *(G-6055)*

Wolf Etter & Co ....D... 507 642-8882
Madelia *(G-3075)*

Employment codes: A=Over 500 employees, B=251-500,
C=101-250, D=51-100, E=25-50

2011 Harris Minnesota
Services Directory

© Harris InfoSource 1-866-281-6415
649

S E R V I C E S

ACOUSTICAL TILE CLEANING SVCS

Ceiling Pro Interior Inc ....E... 952 947-0007
Eden Prairie *(G-1617)*

ADDRESSING SVCS

Japs-Olson Co..........................A... 952 932-9393
Minneapolis *(G-4754)*

ADOPTION SVCS

Becker County Human Services..........D... 218 847-5628
Detroit Lakes *(G-1187)*

Diocese of St Cloud......................E... 320 252-4121
Saint Cloud *(G-7499)*

ADULT DAYCARE CENTERS

Birchwood Care Home Inc ....E... 612 823-7286
Minneapolis *(G-3906)*

Choice Inc..................................E... 952 446-1475
Saint Bonifacius *(G-7399)*

City of Menahga ....D... 218 564-4101
Menahga *(G-3356)*

Clyde Johnson ....E... 218 229-2847
Aurora *(G-256)*

Evangelical Lutheran Good ....D... 651 489-8851
Saint Paul *(G-8348)*

Genesis Group Homes Inc ....D... 763 390-0773
Brooklyn Park *(G-610)*

Grove Chestnut Inc ....E... 218 749-6846
Virginia *(G-9739)*

Hennepin County ....A... 612 348-5273
Minneapolis *(G-4633)*

Hubbard, County of Inc ....C... 218 732-3329
Park Rapids *(G-6755)*

Options Residential Inc ....C... 952 564-3030
Burnsville *(G-770)*

Wildflower Lodge of Chapelwood ....D... 763 420-3768
Osseo *(G-6684)*

ADVERTISING & DISTRIBUTING SVCS: Shopping News

ECM Publishers Inc ....E... 763 712-2400
Minneapolis *(G-3462)*

Independent Delivery Services.............D... 651 487-1050
Saint Paul *(G-8508)*

ADVERTISING AGENCIES

Bbdo Worldwide Inc ....E... 612 338-8401
Minneapolis *(G-3875)*

Campbell Mithun Inc........................B... 612 347-1000
Minneapolis *(G-3997)*

Clarity Coverdale Fury Adv ....E... 612 339-3902
Minneapolis *(G-4101)*

Cmgrp Inc ....C... 952 832-5588
Minneapolis *(G-4113)*

Colle & McVoy Inc ....C... 612 305-6000
Minneapolis *(G-4119)*

Compass Marketing Inc.....................D... 612 333-5300
Minneapolis *(G-4147)*

Concept Group Inc ....E... 651 221-9710
Saint Paul *(G-8245)*

Fallon Group Inc ....C... 612 758-2345
Minneapolis *(G-4405)*

Gabriel Degrood Bendt LLC..................E... 612 547-5000
Minneapolis *(G-4494)*

H T Klatzky & Associates Inc ....E... 218 728-3651
Duluth *(G-1345)*

Hot Dish Advertising LLC ....E... 612 341-3100
Minneapolis *(G-4681)*

Intran Media LLC.............................E... 952 646-0036
Wayzata *(G-9921)*

J T Mega LLC..................................E... 952 929-1370
Minneapolis *(G-4749)*

Laurence Cuneo & Associates ....D... 952 707-1212
Minneapolis *(G-4849)*

Level Brand Inc ....E... 612 338-8000
Minneapolis *(G-4865)*

Martin-Williams Inc ....C... 612 340-0800
Minneapolis *(G-4961)*

Mobile Media Inc ....E... 952 884-6201
Minneapolis *(G-5115)*

Modern Climate Inc ....E... 612 343-8180
Minneapolis *(G-5117)*

Olson + Co Inc...............................C... 612 215-9800
Minneapolis *(G-5271)*

Popular Front Studio Inc ....E... 612 362-0900
Minneapolis *(G-5395)*

Richard Scales Advertising ....D... 651 641-0226
Saint Paul *(G-8899)*

Risdall Marketing Group LLC ....D... 651 286-6700
New Brighton *(G-6413)*

Rudisill Advertising ....E... 651 636-0345
Stillwater *(G-9638)*

Uniquescreen Media Inc ....C... 320 654-6578
Saint Cloud *(G-7623)*

Verified Credentials Inc ....D... 952 985-2335
Lakeville *(G-2940)*

Wally Mc Carthys Oldsmobile...............D... 651 636-6060
Saint Paul *(G-9138)*

Ware Tad & Co Inc ....E... 612 338-2311
Minneapolis *(G-6020)*

ADVERTISING AGENCIES: Consultants

Creative Marketing Consulting ....E... 952 935-9385
Saint Paul *(G-8266)*

Lacek Group Inc ....E... 612 359-3700
Minneapolis *(G-4833)*

Martin-Williams Inc ....E... 612 746-3263
Minneapolis *(G-4962)*

Preston Kelly ....E... 612 843-4000
Minneapolis *(G-5406)*

Wiken Promotion & Advertising ....E... 952 476-2002
Wayzata *(G-9950)*

ADVERTISING MATERIAL DISTRIBUTION

ECM Publishers Inc ....E... 763 712-2400
Minneapolis *(G-3462)*

Gage Group LLC ....C... 763 595-3920
Minneapolis *(G-4495)*

K-Tel International Inc 763 559-5566
Minneapolis *(G-4787)*

Lakeland Distribution Services ....E... 320 762-8385
Alexandria *(G-109)*

ADVERTISING REPRESENTATIVES: Electronic Media

Brite Signs LLC ....D... 763 489-3841
Minneapolis *(G-3951)*

ADVERTISING REPRESENTATIVES: Magazine

Public Safety Council ....E... 763 550-9200
Minneapolis *(G-5439)*

ADVERTISING REPRESENTATIVES: Radio

K J Country 965...............................E... 218 736-7596
Fergus Falls *(G-2080)*

Kbmx Mix 108 Studio ....E... 218 740-2649
Duluth *(G-1367)*

Result Radio Inc...............................E... 218 736-7596
Fergus Falls *(G-2118)*

ADVERTISING SPECIALTIES, WHOLESALE

Albinson Reprographics LLC ....E... 612 374-1120
Minneapolis *(G-3703)*

American Business Forms Inc ....C... 320 634-5471
Glenwood *(G-2219)*

Brown & Bigelow Inc ....C... 651 293-7000
Saint Paul *(G-8132)*

E-Group Inc ....E... 612 339-4777
Minneapolis *(G-4304)*

GWS Inc ....E... 763 551-1700
Hamel *(G-2343)*

Marudas Graphics Inc ....E... 651 697-7820
Saint Paul *(G-8617)*

Meca Sportswear Inc ....E... 651 638-3888
Saint Paul *(G-8629)*

Professional Gallery Inc ....D... 320 252-8446
Saint Cloud *(G-7574)*

Quality Business Forms of ....E... 763 559-4330
Minneapolis *(G-5441)*

Quality Resource Group Inc ....E... 763 478-8636
Plymouth *(G-6881)*

Rambow Inc ....E... 320 354-2570
New London *(G-6419)*

Spartan Promotional Group Inc ....D... 651 735-1333
Saint Paul *(G-9275)*

Tandem Printing Inc ....E... 651 289-2970
Eagan *(G-1556)*

2020 Promotions LLC ....E... 651 451-3850
South Saint Paul *(G-9545)*

Webb Business Promotions Inc ....D... 651 322-8200
Rosemount *(G-7382)*

ADVERTISING SVCS: Billboards

Magic Media Inc ....E... 507 288-1866
Rochester *(G-7168)*

ADVERTISING SVCS: Direct Mail

Action Mailing Services Inc ....D... 763 557-6767
Minneapolis *(G-3676)*

Advanstar Holdings Corp 218 740-7200
Duluth *(G-1232)*

Argenbright Inc ....C... 320 543-3737
Howard Lake *(G-2665)*

Arrowhead Promotion ....B... 218 327-1165
Grand Rapids *(G-2269)*

Communication Mailing Services ....E... 651 645-5280
Saint Paul *(G-8234)*

D B Direct Mail ....E... 320 485-7827
Winsted *(G-10160)*

General Marketing Services Inc ....D... 952 806-5080
Minneapolis *(G-4511)*

I C System Inc ....C... 651 486-0118
Saint Paul *(G-8502)*

Impact Mailing Of Minnesota...............D... 612 521-6245
Minneapolis *(G-4692)*

Infinity Direct Inc ....E... 763 559-1111
Minneapolis *(G-4701)*

Instant Web Inc...............................A... 320 616-5100
Little Falls *(G-3008)*

Kandi-Works Developmental...............E... 320 382-6156
Kandiyohi *(G-2814)*

New ERA Incentives Inc ....E... 651 486-0252
Saint Paul *(G-8748)*

North American Membership Grp ....D... 952 988-7451
Shakopee *(G-9459)*

Novus Marketing Inc ....E... 612 252-1618
Minneapolis *(G-5250)*

Pgi Fulfillment Inc............................D... 952 933-5745
Minnetonka *(G-6213)*

Professional Reproductions Inc ....E... 952 946-1200
Edina *(G-1841)*

ADVERTISING SVCS: Display

Alive Promo Inc ....E... 952 960-3677
Minneapolis *(G-3706)*

Cinedigm Digital Cinema Corp.............C... 320 654-6578
Saint Cloud *(G-7492)*

John Ryan Co Inc ....E... 612 924-7700
Minnetonka *(G-6182)*

Lawrence Service Co ....E... 763 383-5700
Minneapolis *(G-4850)*

ADVERTISING SVCS: Outdoor

Clear Channel Outdoor Inc ....D... 612 605-5100
Minneapolis *(G-4108)*

ADVERTISING SVCS: Poster, Exc Outdoor

Nextmedia Outdoor Inc ....E... 763 489-3841
Minneapolis *(G-5198)*

ADVERTISING SVCS: Sample Distribution

Independent Delivery Services ....D... 651 487-1050
Saint Paul *(G-8508)*

ADVERTISING, PROMOTIONAL & TRADE SHOW SVCS

Dolce International ....E... 952 368-3100
Chaska *(G-961)*

Exhibitor Publications Inc ....E... 507 289-6556
Rochester *(G-7109)*

Greater Minneapolis Convention ....C... 612 767-8000
Minneapolis *(G-4558)*

Insignia Systems Inc ....D... 763 392-6200
Minneapolis *(G-4706)*

Liberty Display Group Inc...................E... 763 785-1593
Minneapolis *(G-3517)*

Lifetech Corp ....D... 612 369-5050
Osseo *(G-6628)*

Skyline Displays Midwest Inc ....E... 952 895-6000
Burnsville *(G-798)*

Young America Corp.........................B... 800 533-4529
Young America *(G-10211)*

ADVOCACY GROUP

Communication Service For The ....E... 651 297-6700
Saint Paul *(G-8235)*

Community Drug & Alcohol Svcs ....E... 952 564-3000
Burnsville *(G-702)*

AEROBIC DANCE & EXERCISE CLASSES

David's Body Shop Inc.......................D... 612 377-3003
Minneapolis *(G-4226)*

AGENTS, BROKERS & BUREAUS: Personal Service

Bystrom Precision Industries...............E... 952 929-6888
Minneapolis *(G-3979)*

Counseling Services of Sthn ....E... 507 931-8040
Saint Peter *(G-9301)*

S
E
R
V
I
C
E
S

D L Ricci Corp ....D... 651 388-8661
Red Wing *(G-6977)*

Dakota Growers Pasta Co Inc............C... 763 531-5340
Minneapolis *(G-4219)*

E Frame ....D... 952 926-3555
Minneapolis *(G-4300)*

Global Ventures I Inc ....D... 507 825-5462
Pipestone *(G-6828)*

Minneapolis Electrical Jatc ....E... 763 497-0072
Saint Michael *(G-7678)*

Northern Tool & Equipment Co ....E... 952 894-0326
Burnsville *(G-764)*

Rochester Service Co Inc ....E... 507 281-5333
Rochester *(G-7240)*

Rosemount-Apple Valley & Eagan ....A... 651 423-7700
Rosemount *(G-7374)*

Stork United Corp ....D... 651 645-3601
Saint Paul *(G-9009)*

Sunfish Express Inc ....E... 763 433-8383
Anoka *(G-229)*

AGENTS: Theatrical Talent

Midwest Latino Entertainment..............E... 612 728-0101
Minneapolis *(G-5030)*

AGRICULTURAL CREDIT INSTITUTIONS

Agstar Financial Services, Aca.............E... 507 526-7366
Blue Earth *(G-528)*

U S Bancorp ....B... 651 466-3000
Minneapolis *(G-5885)*

AGRICULTURAL LOAN COMPANIES

Agstar Financial Services, Aca.............E... 507 645-0552
Northfield *(G-6523)*

AGRICULTURAL MACHINERY & EQPT REPAIR

F M Trucking Inc ....E... 651 639-0446
Saint Paul *(G-8358)*

K & S Millwrights Inc ....E... 320 833-2228
Buffalo Lake *(G-665)*

AGRICULTURAL MACHINERY & EQPT: Wholesalers

A & C Farm Service Inc ....E... 320 243-3736
Paynesville *(G-6768)*

Agriliance LLC.....................................C... 651 451-5000
Inver Grove Heights *(G-2736)*

Arnold's of Mankato Inc ....E... 320 398-3800
Kimball *(G-2830)*

Arnold's of Willmar Inc ....E... 320 235-4898
Willmar *(G-9984)*

Arnzen Construction Inc ....E... 320 836-2284
Freeport *(G-2187)*

Avery Weigh-Tronix LLC ....A... 507 238-4461
Fairmont *(G-1957)*

Bruce Kreofsky & Sons Inc.................D... 507 534-3855
Plainview *(G-6839)*

Gateway Building Systems Inc.............E... 218 685-4420
Elbow Lake *(G-1853)*

Gehling Auction Co Inc ....E... 507 765-2131
Preston *(G-6897)*

Haug Implement Co ....E... 320 235-8115
Willmar *(G-10006)*

Precision Turf & Chemical Inc 763 477-5885
Rockford *(G-7303)*

Rdo Agriculture Equipment Co ....E... 218 643-2601
Breckenridge *(G-597)*

Red River Implement Co Inc ....E... 218 643-2601
Breckenridge *(G-598)*

AID TO FAMILIES WITH DEPENDENT CHILDREN OR AFDC

American Refugee Committee...............E... 612 872-7060
Minneapolis *(G-3758)*

Janine Sahagian..................................E... 507 332-9894
Faribault *(G-2014)*

AIR CONDITIONING & VENTILATION EQPT & SPLYS: Wholesales

Ace Supply Co Inc ....E... 952 929-1618
Minneapolis *(G-3672)*

Boeser Inc...E... 612 378-1803
Minneapolis *(G-3923)*

Don Stevens Inc ....E... 651 452-0872
Eagan *(G-1525)*

S P S Co's Inc.....................................C... 952 929-1377
Minneapolis *(G-5582)*

Schwab-Vollhaber-Lubratt Inc ....D... 651 481-8000
Saint Paul *(G-8935)*

Triple J Enterprises Inc ....E... 952 853-9898
Minneapolis *(G-5858)*

Triple J Enterprises Inc ....E... 952 853-9898
Minneapolis *(G-5859)*

AIR CONDITIONING EQPT, WHOLE HOUSE: Wholesalers

D C Sales Co Inc ....E... 612 728-8700
Minneapolis *(G-4213)*

Goodin Co ....C... 612 588-7811
Minneapolis *(G-4540)*

Johnson Controls Inc ....D... 763 566-7650
Plymouth *(G-6869)*

Uhl Co Inc ....D... 763 425-7226
Osseo *(G-6680)*

AIR CONDITIONING REPAIR SVCS

Dependable Indoor Air Quality ....E... 763 757-5040
Minneapolis *(G-3454)*

McDowall Co..D... 320 251-8640
Waite Park *(G-9829)*

AIR DUCT CLEANING SVCS

Marsh Heating & Air Condg ....E... 763 536-0667
Minneapolis *(G-4957)*

Vac System Industries of MN................E... 952 808-1616
Burnsville *(G-816)*

AIR POLLUTION MEASURING SVCS

Interpoll Laboratories Inc ....E... 763 786-6020
Circle Pines *(G-1012)*

AIR-CONDITIONING SPLY SVCS

Franklin Heating Station.......................E... 507 289-3534
Rochester *(G-7119)*

Interstate Co's Inc ....D... 952 854-2044
Minneapolis *(G-4726)*

AIRCRAFT & HEAVY EQPT REPAIR SVCS

General Dynamics Aviation Svcs ....D... 612 638-2000
Minneapolis *(G-4508)*

General Safety Equipment LLC ....D... 651 462-1000
Wyoming *(G-10205)*

Monaco Air Duluth LLC ....E... 218 727-2911
Duluth *(G-1396)*

Rosemount Aerospace Inc....................C... 651 681-8900
Eagan *(G-1548)*

Sifco Industries Inc ....D... 763 544-3511
Minneapolis *(G-5667)*

Wipaire Inc..D... 651 451-1205
South Saint Paul *(G-9553)*

AIRCRAFT EQPT & SPLYS WHOLESALERS

Aviall Services Inc ....E... 651 452-1680
Mendota Heights *(G-3360)*

Canard Aerospace Corp ....E... 952 944-7990
Shakopee *(G-9426)*

Safe Air Repair Inc ....D... 507 373-7129
Albert Lea *(G-63)*

Sky Media LLC ....E... 651 635-0100
Saint Paul *(G-8963)*

AIRCRAFT FUELING SVCS

Aviation Charter Inc ....D... 952 943-1519
Eden Prairie *(G-1600)*

Monaco Air Duluth LLC ....E... 218 727-2911
Duluth *(G-1396)*

AIRCRAFT MAINTENANCE & REPAIR SVCS

Bemidji Aviation Services Inc...............E... 218 751-1880
Bemidji *(G-377)*

Petters Aviation LLC............................ 952 936-5000
Minnetonka *(G-6212)*

Signature Flight Support Corp ....B... 612 726-5700
Minneapolis *(G-5670)*

AIRCRAFT PARTS WHOLESALERS

Modern Aero Inc..................................D... 952 941-2595
Eden Prairie *(G-1729)*

Northwest Aircraft Inc ....E... 612 726-2331
Saint Paul *(G-7854)*

Thunderbird Aviation Inc ....E... 952 941-1212
Eden Prairie *(G-1793)*

AIRCRAFT SERVICING & REPAIRING

Aviation Charter Inc ....E... 952 943-1519
Eden Prairie *(G-1600)*

Elliott Aviation Inc...............................D... 952 944-1200
Eden Prairie *(G-1654)*

Modern Aero Inc ....D... 952 941-2595
Eden Prairie *(G-1729)*

Thunderbird Aviation Inc ....E... 952 941-1212
Eden Prairie *(G-1793)*

Wright Aero Inc....................................E... 320 963-5094
Maple Lake *(G-3268)*

AIRPORT

Mankato Airport ....E... 507 625-2511
Mankato *(G-3159)*

Millian Air Executive Aviation ....E... 952 943-1519
Eden Prairie *(G-1724)*

Paul Minneapolis-St ....D... 612 726-5107
Saint Paul *(G-7962)*

Paul Minneapolis-St ....D... 612 726-8100
Minneapolis *(G-5353)*

Safari Airport Taxi Service....................D... 763 424-9070
Minneapolis *(G-5587)*

AIRPORTS, FLYING FIELDS & SVCS

Hiawatha Aviation of Rochester...........E... 507 282-1717
Rochester *(G-7137)*

Safe Air Repair Inc..............................D... 507 373-7129
Albert Lea *(G-63)*

Servisair USA Inc.................................C... 612 726-5533
Saint Paul *(G-7964)*

Signature Flight Support Corp ....E... 651 224-1100
Saint Paul *(G-8958)*

United Parcel Service Inc.....................E... 651 367-8200
Saint Paul *(G-7936)*

ALCOHOL TREATMENT CLINIC, OUTPATIENT

AA Monticello......................................E... 763 295-5066
Monticello *(G-6265)*

Arrowhead Center Inc ....E... 218 749-2877
Virginia *(G-9733)*

Guest House Inc ....E... 507 288-4693
Rochester *(G-7128)*

Hazelden Foundation ....D... 612 559-2022
Minneapolis *(G-4614)*

Northwestern Mental Health Ctr...........D... 218 281-3940
Crookston *(G-1130)*

Range Mental Health Center Inc...........E... 218 749-2881
Virginia *(G-9754)*

Regions Hospital Alcohol ....E... 651 254-4804
Saint Paul *(G-8883)*

Skemp Walk In Clinic ....E... 507 724-3353
Caledonia *(G-829)*

Southwestern Mental Health Ctr 507 283-9511
Luverne *(G-3070)*

ALCOHOLISM COUNSELING, NONTREATMENT

Dakota County Receiving Center.........D... 651 437-4209
Hastings *(G-2382)*

AMBULANCE SVCS

City of Plainview Ambulance.................E... 507 534-3980
Plainview *(G-6840)*

County of Washington ....B... 651 439-9381
Stillwater *(G-9606)*

Critical Care Services Inc ....C... 612 638-4900
Minneapolis *(G-4185)*

Dodge Center Ambulance Svcs ....E... 507 374-2600
Dodge Center *(G-1226)*

Gold Cross Ambulance Service ....D... 320 251-2302
Saint Cloud *(G-7518)*

Gold Cross Ambulance Service ....D... 218 628-2885
Duluth *(G-1336)*

Gold Cross Ambulance Service ....D... 507 255-2230
Rochester *(G-7127)*

Gold Cross Ambulance Service ....E... 507 345-7540
Mankato *(G-3130)*

Healtheast ....C... 651 232-1717
Saint Paul *(G-8452)*

International Falls, City of....................E... 218 283-3500
International Falls *(G-2723)*

Jackson City Ambulance ....E... 507 847-5306
Jackson *(G-2794)*

Kittson Memorial Hospital Assn ....C... 218 843-3612
Hallock *(G-2333)*

Lake County Ambulance.......................E... 218 834-7110
Two Harbors *(G-9710)*

Lake of Woods Ambulance....................E... 218 634-2100
Baudette *(G-316)*

Lakes Region EMS Inc ....E... 651 277-4911
North Branch *(G-6502)*

Le Center Volunteer Ambulance............E... 507 357-4844
Le Center *(G-2951)*

Mayo Midair ....E... 507 255-2808
Rochester *(G-7176)*

Employment codes: A=Over 500 employees, B=251-500,
C=101-250, D=51-100, E=25-50

2011 Harris Minnesota
Services Directory

© Harris InfoSource 1-866-281-6415

651

SERVICES

Meds 1 Ambulance Service Inc ....E... 218 326-0020
Grand Rapids *(G-2293)*
Monticello-Big Lake Community ....B... 763 295-2945
Monticello *(G-6278)*
Norman County Ambulance Garage ....C... 218 784-5000
ADA *(G-2)*
North Ambulance Faribault ....E... 507 334-6031
Faribault *(G-2023)*
North Memorial Ambulance ....E... 651 464-6738
Forest Lake *(G-2166)*
North Memorial Ambulance Svcs ....D... 763 389-2082
Princeton *(G-6912)*
North Memorial Health Care ....E... 320 763-6160
Alexandria *(G-115)*
North Memorial Health Care ....D... 218 829-8767
Brainerd *(G-577)*
North Memorial Health Care ....E... 507 637-5055
Redwood Falls *(G-7026)*
Northland Transportation ....E... 952 885-0580
Prior Lake *(G-6946)*
Oakdale Health Enterprises Inc ....E... 763 520-5357
Minneapolis *(G-5256)*
Spring Valley Area Ambulance ....E... 507 346-7414
Spring Valley *(G-9570)*
St Peter, City of Inc ....C... 507 931-7354
Saint Peter *(G-9314)*
Tri County Ambulance Service ....E... 218 436-2230
Karlstad *(G-2816)*
Wabasha City Ambulance Svc ....E... 651 565-2633
Wabasha *(G-9773)*
Walker Ambulance Service ....E... 218 547-5500
Walker *(G-9860)*
Zumbrota Area Ambulance Assn ....E... 507 732-7845
Zumbrota *(G-10221)*

AMBULANCE SVCS: Air

Critical Care Services Inc ....C... 612 638-4900
Minneapolis *(G-4185)*
Mayo Midair ....E... 507 255-2808
Rochester *(G-7176)*

AMBULATORY SURGICAL CENTERS

Bemidji Clinic Merit Care Inc ....D... 218 333-5000
Bemidji *(G-378)*
Children's Health Care Inc ....E... 952 930-8600
Hopkins *(G-2527)*
East Metro Asc LLC ....D... 651 702-7400
Lake Elmo *(G-2869)*
Lakewalk Surgery Center Inc ....E... 218 728-0650
Duluth *(G-1380)*
Midwest Surgery Center ....E... 651 642-9199
Saint Paul *(G-9248)*

AMMUNITION, EXC SPORTING, WHOLESALE

Stencil Cutting & Supply Co ....D... 800 783-4633
Red Wing *(G-7007)*

AMUSEMENT & REC SVCS: Attractions, Concessions & Rides

Moa Entertainment Co LLC ....A... 952 883-8810
Minneapolis *(G-5114)*
Pineview Park Bmx ....E... 320 230-7820
Saint Cloud *(G-7568)*
Playworks Dakota ....D... 952 445-7529
Prior Lake *(G-6948)*
Smsc Gaming Enterprise ....A... 952 445-8982
Prior Lake *(G-6956)*

AMUSEMENT & REC SVCS: Baseball Club, Exc Pro & Semi-Pro

Minnesota Twins Baseball Club ....A... 612 375-7411
Minneapolis *(G-5099)*
Saint Martin Commercial Club ....E... 320 548-3208
Paynesville *(G-6774)*

AMUSEMENT & REC SVCS: Skating Instruction, Ice Or Roller

Dakota Sport & Fitness ....C... 952 445-9400
Prior Lake *(G-6931)*
Dakotah Sport & Fitness Center ....C... 952 445-9400
Prior Lake *(G-6932)*
Maplewood Oakdale School Dist ....E... 651 714-9251
Saint Paul *(G-9246)*

AMUSEMENT & RECREATION SVCS: Agricultural Fair

Minnesota State Agricultural ....D... 651 288-4400
Saint Paul *(G-8705)*

AMUSEMENT & RECREATION SVCS: Amusement Ride

Dennis Raedeke Inc ....D... 651 465-6365
Taylors Falls *(G-9660)*

AMUSEMENT & RECREATION SVCS: Arcades

Lieberman Co's Inc ....E... 952 887-5200
Minneapolis *(G-4874)*

AMUSEMENT & RECREATION SVCS: Art Gallery, Commercial

Art Semva Gallery ....D... 507 281-4920
Rochester *(G-7059)*
Pottery Red Wings ....E... 651 388-3562
Red Wing *(G-6995)*

AMUSEMENT & RECREATION SVCS: Bowling League Or Team

H J K S Inc ....E... 952 935-3427
Minneapolis *(G-4586)*

AMUSEMENT & RECREATION SVCS: Card & Game Svcs

Awm Enterprises Inc ....E... 651 455-3044
South Saint Paul *(G-9510)*
Canterbury Park Holding Corp ....E... 952 445-7223
Shakopee *(G-9427)*

AMUSEMENT & RECREATION SVCS: Concession Operator

Colin Co, LP ....E... 612 375-9670
Minneapolis *(G-4117)*
Paul Schintz Inc ....E... 218 525-0828
Duluth *(G-1419)*

AMUSEMENT & RECREATION SVCS: Curling Rinks

Recreational Equipment Inc ....C... 952 884-4315
Minneapolis *(G-5476)*

AMUSEMENT & RECREATION SVCS: Exhibition Operation

Exhibits Development Group LLC ....E... 651 222-1121
Saint Paul *(G-8352)*

AMUSEMENT & RECREATION SVCS: Fair, NEC

Carlton County Fair Assn ....E... 218 389-6737
Barnum *(G-306)*
Carver County Agricultural Soc ....E... 952 442-2333
Waconia *(G-9781)*
Freeborn Country Fair Assn ....E... 507 373-6965
Albert Lea *(G-54)*

AMUSEMENT & RECREATION SVCS: Festival Operation

Festival Events of Minnesota ....D... 651 772-9980
Saint Paul *(G-8375)*
Mid-America Festivals Corp ....E... 952 445-7361
Shakopee *(G-9456)*

AMUSEMENT & RECREATION SVCS: Fishing Boat Operations, Party

Gage Group LLC ....C... 763 595-3920
Minneapolis *(G-4495)*

AMUSEMENT & RECREATION SVCS: Fortune Tellers

Uptown Psychic Studio ....E... 612 374-9906
Minneapolis *(G-5938)*

AMUSEMENT & RECREATION SVCS: Gambling & Lottery Svcs

Community Charities of MN ....E... 507 386-1934
Mankato *(G-3119)*

AMUSEMENT & RECREATION SVCS: Gambling, Coin Machines

Corporate Commission of The ....A... 320 532-8800
Onamia *(G-6568)*
Corporate Commission of The ....A... 320 384-7101
Hinckley *(G-2483)*

AMUSEMENT & RECREATION SVCS: Game Parlor

Treasure Island Casino & Bingo ....A... 651 388-6300
Welch *(G-9957)*

AMUSEMENT & RECREATION SVCS: Golf Club, Membership

Bearpath Golf & Country Club ....D... 952 975-0123
Eden Prairie *(G-1603)*
Blueberry Pines Golf Club Inc ....E... 218 564-4653
Menahga *(G-3355)*
Chisago Lakes Golf Estates Inc ....E... 651 257-1484
Lindstrom *(G-2968)*
Cloquet Country Club ....E... 218 879-8858
Cloquet *(G-1048)*
Crow River Country Club ....E... 320 587-3070
Hutchinson *(G-2695)*
Dellwood Hills Golf Club ....D... 651 426-3218
Saint Paul *(G-9203)*
Edina Country Club ....C... 952 927-7151
Minneapolis *(G-4314)*
Elk River Country Club Inc ....E... 763 441-4111
Elk River *(G-1872)*
Forest Hills Golf Club Inc ....D... 651 464-3097
Forest Lake *(G-2160)*
Golf Inc ....E... 320 251-7804
Sauk Rapids *(G-9363)*
Hastings Country Club Inc ....D... 651 437-4612
Hastings *(G-2389)*
Koronis Hills Golf Club ....E... 320 243-4111
Paynesville *(G-6770)*
Lafayette Club ....C... 952 471-8493
Minnetonka Beach *(G-6241)*
Le Sueur Country Club ....E... 507 665-8809
Le Sueur *(G-2956)*
Legends Club LLC ....D... 952 226-4777
Prior Lake *(G-6937)*
Litchfield Golf Club ....E... 320 693-6059
Litchfield *(G-2987)*
Mankato Golf Club Inc ....E... 507 387-5676
Mankato *(G-3162)*
Marshall Golf Club ....E... 507 532-2278
Marshall *(G-3310)*
Mendakota Country Club Inc ....C... 651 454-2822
Saint Paul *(G-7837)*
Mesaba Country Club ....E... 218 262-2851
Hibbing *(G-2465)*
Minneapolis Golf Club ....E... 952 544-4471
Minneapolis *(G-5055)*
Minnetonka Country Club ....E... 952 474-5222
Excelsior *(G-1949)*
Montevideo Country Club Inc ....E... 320 269-8600
Montevideo *(G-6253)*
Montgomery Golf & Recreation ....E... 507 364-5602
Montgomery *(G-6264)*
Monticello Country Club Inc ....E... 763 295-3323
Monticello *(G-6277)*
Moorhead Country Club Inc ....E... 218 236-0100
Moorhead *(G-6329)*
New Ulm Country Club ....E... 507 354-8896
New Ulm *(G-6466)*
North Oaks Golf Club Inc ....E... 651 484-6311
Saint Paul *(G-8752)*
Northern Gopher Enterprises ....C... 952 435-7600
Lakeville *(G-2923)*
Oak Ridge Country Club ....C... 952 935-7721
Hopkins *(G-2593)*
Oaks Country Club Inc ....E... 507 477-3233
Hayfield *(G-2424)*
Olympic Hills Corp ....E... 952 941-6262
Eden Prairie *(G-1736)*
Owatonna Country Club Inc ....D... 507 451-6120
Owatonna *(G-6727)*
Perham Lakeside Golf Club Inc ....E... 218 346-6070
Perham *(G-6801)*
Pga Tour Inc ....D... 763 795-0800
Minneapolis *(G-3570)*
Rich-Spring Golf Club Inc ....E... 320 685-8810
Cold Spring *(G-1089)*
Ridgeview Country Club Inc ....E... 218 728-5128
Duluth *(G-1438)*
Southview Country Club ....D... 651 451-6856
Saint Paul *(G-7909)*
Spring Hill Golf Club ....E... 952 473-1500
Wayzata *(G-9941)*
Thief River Golf Club ....E... 218 681-2955
Thief River Falls *(G-9678)*
Tianna Country Club Inc ....E... 218 547-1712
Walker *(G-9858)*
Valley Golf Association ....E... 218 773-1207
East Grand Forks *(G-1577)*
Valley High Golf Club ....E... 507 896-3239
Houston *(G-2663)*

Westfield Golf Club Inc..........................E... 507 452-8700
Winona *(G-10140)*

Woodhill Country Club ....D... 952 473-7333
Wayzata *(G-9951)*

AMUSEMENT & RECREATION SVCS: Golf Professionals

Madden Brothers Inc ....E... 218 829-2811
Brainerd *(G-546)*

Mesaba Country Club ....E... 218 262-2851
Hibbing *(G-2464)*

Winona Country Club ....E... 507 454-3767
Winona *(G-10146)*

AMUSEMENT & RECREATION SVCS: Golf Svcs & Professionals

City of Chaska ....E... 952 443-3748
Chaska *(G-959)*

Great Northern Golf Co of MN ....E... 651 462-5797
Stacy *(G-9579)*

Hardwood Golf Resort............................E... 320 692-4325
Garrison *(G-2197)*

Meadow Lakes Golf Club LLC ....E... 507 285-1190
Rochester *(G-7181)*

AMUSEMENT & RECREATION SVCS: Hunting Club, Membership

North American Membership Grp ....D... 952 988-7451
Shakopee *(G-9459)*

North American Membership Grp ....B... 952 936-9333
Hopkins *(G-2591)*

AMUSEMENT & RECREATION SVCS: Ice Skating Rink

Breck School ....C... 763 381-8100
Minneapolis *(G-3940)*

City of Plymouth ....E... 763 509-5262
Minneapolis *(G-4095)*

Eddy's Lake Mille Lacs Resort ....E... 320 532-3657
Onamia *(G-6570)*

Recreational Equipment Inc.................C... 952 884-4315
Minneapolis *(G-5476)*

AMUSEMENT & RECREATION SVCS: Massage Instruction

High-Tech Institute Inc ....D... 763 560-9700
Minneapolis *(G-4646)*

Motivations For Fitness Inc ....E... 612 617-9090
Minneapolis *(G-5138)*

AMUSEMENT & RECREATION SVCS: Outdoor Field Clubs

Pequaywan Area Trail Blazers ....E... 218 848-2510
Duluth *(G-1422)*

AMUSEMENT & RECREATION SVCS: Outfitters, Recreation

Canadian Border Outfitters Inc.............E... 218 365-5847
Ely *(G-1911)*

Wintergreen Dogsled Lodge Inc...........E... 218 365-6602
Ely *(G-1917)*

AMUSEMENT & RECREATION SVCS: Racquetball Club, Membership

America's Raquette & Fitness ....E... 507 345-8833
Mankato *(G-3104)*

Crow River Country Club ....E... 320 587-3070
Hutchinson *(G-2695)*

Fergus Falls Area Family Young ....D... 218 739-4489
Fergus Falls *(G-2075)*

Starmark Northwest Management.......E... 612 673-1200
Minneapolis *(G-5742)*

AMUSEMENT & RECREATION SVCS: Recreation Center

City of Saint Paul ....E... 651 266-6400
Saint Paul *(G-8204)*

Courage Center ....E... 320 963-3121
Maple Lake *(G-3259)*

Lake Crystal Area Recreation ....E... 507 726-6730
Lake Crystal *(G-2858)*

Lake Superior Center............................E... 218 740-3474
Duluth *(G-1375)*

Le Sueur, City of Inc ....E... 507 665-3325
Le Sueur *(G-2957)*

Mesabi Family YMCA............................D... 218 749-8020
Virginia *(G-9746)*

Recreational Equipment Inc.................C... 952 884-4315
Minneapolis *(G-5476)*

Red Wing Young Men's Christian ....C... 651 388-4724
Red Wing *(G-6999)*

Young Men's Christian Assn ....C... 507 387-8255
Mankato *(G-3222)*

AMUSEMENT & RECREATION SVCS: Recreation SVCS

Adventure Zone....................................E... 952 890-7961
Burnsville *(G-673)*

City of Minneapolis ....D... 612 230-6550
Minneapolis *(G-4094)*

Eddy's Lake Mille Lacs Resort ....E... 320 532-3657
Onamia *(G-6570)*

Three Rivers Park District ....C... 763 559-9000
Plymouth *(G-6887)*

AMUSEMENT & RECREATION SVCS: Sailing Instruction

Lake Minnetonka Sailing School ....E... 952 404-1645
Wayzata *(G-9924)*

AMUSEMENT & RECREATION SVCS: School, Hockey Instruction

Moorehead Youth Hockey Assn ....E... 218 233-5021
Moorehead *(G-6328)*

AMUSEMENT & RECREATION SVCS: Shooting Range

Renew Resources Inc ....E... 763 533-9200
Minneapolis *(G-5517)*

AMUSEMENT & RECREATION SVCS: Skating Rink Operation

City of White Bear Lake ....E... 651 429-8571
Saint Paul *(G-8214)*

AMUSEMENT & RECREATION SVCS: Ski Instruction

Afton Alps Inc......................................A... 651 436-5245
Hastings *(G-2412)*

Buck Hill Inc 952 435-7174
Burnsville *(G-688)*

AMUSEMENT & RECREATION SVCS: Ski Rental Concession

Buck Hill Inc 952 435-7174
Burnsville *(G-688)*

AMUSEMENT & RECREATION SVCS: Swimming Club, Membership

Fergus Falls Area Family Young ....D... 218 739-4489
Fergus Falls *(G-2075)*

Le Sueur Country Club ....E... 507 665-8839
Le Sueur *(G-2956)*

Owatonna Country Club Inc.................D... 507 451-6120
Owatonna *(G-6727)*

Woodhill Country Club ....D... 952 473-7333
Wayzata *(G-9951)*

AMUSEMENT & RECREATION SVCS: Swimming Pool, Non-Membership

City of Saint Paul ....E... 651 695-3773
Saint Paul *(G-8210)*

Luverne, City of Inc..............................E... 507 449-5036
Luverne *(G-3063)*

AMUSEMENT & RECREATION SVCS: Tennis & Professionals

St Teresa Campus Schools...................E... 507 453-5555
Winona *(G-10131)*

Tennis & Life Camps Inc ....E... 507 931-1614
Saint Peter *(G-9315)*

Xenophon Corp ....E... 952 929-5518
Minneapolis *(G-6092)*

Xenophon Corp ....E... 651 735-6214
Saint Paul *(G-9291)*

AMUSEMENT & RECREATION SVCS: Tennis Club, Membership

America's Raquette & Fitness ....E... 507 345-8833
Mankato *(G-3104)*

Arrowhead Tennis Inc ....E... 218 722-0810
Duluth *(G-1244)*

Flagship Athletic Club Inc....................B... 952 941-2000
Eden Prairie *(G-1665)*

Le Sueur Country Club ....E... 507 665-8839
Le Sueur *(G-2956)*

Life Time Fitness Inc ....C... 651 426-1308
Saint Paul *(G-8585)*

Minnetonka Country Club ....E... 952 474-5222
Excelsior *(G-1949)*

Olympic Hills Corp ....E... 952 941-6262
Eden Prairie *(G-1736)*

Owatonna Country Club Inc ....D... 507 451-6120
Owatonna *(G-6727)*

Ridgeview Country Club Inc..................E... 218 728-5128
Duluth *(G-1438)*

Starmark Northwest Management ......D... 952 944-2434
Minneapolis *(G-5743)*

White Bear Racquet & Swim LP ....C... 651 426-1308
Saint Paul *(G-9156)*

Woodhill Country Club..........................D... 952 473-7333
Wayzata *(G-9951)*

AMUSEMENT & RECREATION SVCS: Tennis Courts, Non-Member

City of Duluth......................................B... 218 628-2891
Duluth *(G-1275)*

Madden Brothers Inc............................E... 218 829-2811
Brainerd *(G-546)*

AMUSEMENT & RECREATION SVCS: Tennis Professional

Golden Valley Country Club ....D... 763 732-4100
Minneapolis *(G-4536)*

AMUSEMENT & RECREATION SVCS: Theme Park

County of Anoka...................................D... 763 767-2871
Anoka *(G-170)*

Moa Entertainment Co LLC ....A... 952 883-8810
Minneapolis *(G-5114)*

AMUSEMENT & RECREATION SVCS: Tour & Guide

Haunted LLC ....E... 507 388-7966
Mankato *(G-3136)*

Magical History Tour ....E... 612 331-7171
Minneapolis *(G-4933)*

AMUSEMENT & RECREATION SVCS: Tourist Attraction, Commercial

Minnesota Department of ....E... 218 753-2245
Soudan *(G-9504)*

AMUSEMENT & RECREATION SVCS: Video Game Arcades

B L B Inc ....D... 612 825-3737
Minneapolis *(G-3852)*

AMUSEMENT & RECREATION SVCS: Waterslide Operation

Dennis Raedeke Inc..............................D... 651 465-6365
Taylors Falls *(G-9660)*

AMUSEMENT ARCADES

D & R Star Inc......................................D... 507 282-6080
Rochester *(G-7092)*

Prairie's Edge Casino Resort ....B... 320 564-2121
Granite Falls *(G-2318)*

Theisen Vending Inc.............................D... 612 827-5588
Minneapolis *(G-5813)*

AMUSEMENT PARKS

Cedar Fair, LP ....D... 952 445-7600
Shakopee *(G-9430)*

City of Minneapolis...............................C... 612 370-4900
Minneapolis *(G-4088)*

Grand Portage National ....E... 218 475-2202
Grand Portage *(G-2266)*

AMUSEMENT/REC SVCS: Aerial Tramway/Ski Lift, Amusemnt/Scenic

Dennis Raedeke Inc..............................D... 651 465-6365
Taylors Falls *(G-9660)*

AMUSEMENT/REC SVCS: Ticket Sales, Sporting Events, Contract

Basilica of Saint Mary of ....E... 612 333-1381
Minneapolis *(G-3871)*

Box Office Service & Sales Inc.............D... 952 854-2836
Minneapolis *(G-3935)*

Minnesota Twins Baseball Club...........A... 612 375-7411
Minneapolis *(G-5099)*

Employment codes: A=Over 500 employees, B=251-500,
C=101-250, D=51-100, E=25-50

2011 Harris Minnesota
Services Directory

© Harris InfoSource 1-866-281-6415

653

SERVICES

ANIMAL FEED: Wholesalers

Archer Daniels Midland Co ....D... 507 625-7949
Mankato *(G-3106)*

Cargill Inc ....D... 763 497-2157
Minneapolis *(G-4011)*

Cargill Inc ....C... 952 742-7575
Minnetonka *(G-6150)*

Commodity Specialists Co ....E... 612 330-9120
Minneapolis *(G-4133)*

Cooperative Sampo Inc ....D... 218 564-4534
Menahga *(G-3357)*

Kristico Inc ....E... 507 625-2900
Mankato *(G-3155)*

Land O'Lakes Inc ....E... 320 543-2566
Howard Lake *(G-2668)*

Michael Foods Inc ....C... 507 665-8851
Le Sueur *(G-2962)*

Pals Inc ....D... 320 235-8860
Willmar *(G-10035)*

Precision Nutrition Inc ....E... 507 372-4723
Worthington *(G-10190)*

Zinpro Animal Nutrition Inc ....E... 952 944-2736
Eden Prairie *(G-1820)*

ANIMAL GROOMING SVCS

Bone Adventure Inc ....E... 612 920-2201
Minneapolis *(G-3925)*

Penco Leasing Corp ....E... 612 927-4748
Minneapolis *(G-5362)*

Pet Co ....E... 952 541-1981
Minnetonka *(G-6211)*

Petco Animal Supplies Stores ....E... 320 253-1004
Waite Park *(G-9832)*

Petco Animal Supplies Stores ....E... 763 420-5236
Minneapolis *(G-5368)*

Petsmart Inc ....E... 320 251-4459
Waite Park *(G-9833)*

Petsmart Inc ....D... 952 941-4660
Eden Prairie *(G-1746)*

ANIMAL HOSPITAL SVCS, LIVESTOCK

Northern Valley Animal Clinic 507 282-0867
Rochester *(G-7191)*

St Michael Veterinary Clinic ....E... 763 497-2424
Saint Michael *(G-7682)*

ANIMAL HOSPITALS

Affiliated Emergency ....E... 763 529-6560
Minneapolis *(G-3694)*

Affiliated Emergency ....E... 952 942-8272
Eden Prairie *(G-1585)*

Animal Emergency Clinic ....E... 651 501-3766
Saint Paul *(G-9184)*

Apache Animal Medicine ....E... 612 781-2734
Minneapolis *(G-6123)*

Bennett Porter III Dvm ....E... 612 925-1121
Minneapolis *(G-3885)*

Kate Anne Hunter ....E... 651 578-3290
Saint Paul *(G-9234)*

Melrose-Albany-Upsula ....E... 320 256-4252
Melrose *(G-3351)*

Northern Valley Animal Clinic 507 282-0867
Rochester *(G-7191)*

Plymouth Heights Pet Hospital ....E... 763 544-4141
Minneapolis *(G-5392)*

Prime Ridge Pet Care ....E... 763 427-2220
Anoka *(G-217)*

Rich Schmitz Dvm ....E... 507 233-2520
New Ulm *(G-6473)*

St Michael Veterinary Clinic ....E... 763 497-2424
Saint Michael *(G-7682)*

Sue Chapman Dvm ....E... 507 233-2520
New Ulm *(G-6475)*

White Bear Animal Hospital 651 777-1393
Saint Paul *(G-9154)*

ANIMAL PRODUCTION, NEC

Wolf Springs Ranches ....E... 952 942-5566
Minneapolis *(G-6082)*

ANIMAL SPECIALTY SVCS, EXC VETERINARY

Animal Humane Society ....D... 763 522-4325
Minneapolis *(G-3780)*

Circle R Ranch Inc ....E... 320 547-2176
Long Prairie *(G-3039)*

Petsmart Inc ....E... 612 798-3665
Minneapolis *(G-5372)*

Petsmart Inc ....E... 320 251-4365
Saint Cloud *(G-7567)*

Petsmart Inc ....E... 800 702-9779
Woodbury *(G-10174)*

ANTIPOVERTY BOARD

Aveyron Homes Inc ....C... 320 234-6063
Hutchinson *(G-2688)*

Aveyron Homes Inc ....C... 320 587-6277
Hutchinson *(G-2689)*

APARTMENT LOCATING SVCS

Heritage Park Estates ....E... 320 240-7939
Saint Cloud *(G-7528)*

Jde Studios Inc ....E... 612 825-4076
Minneapolis *(G-4756)*

APPLICATIONS SOFTWARE PROGRAMMING

Comsys Information Technology ....C... 612 630-9100
Minneapolis *(G-4149)*

Dahl Consulting Inc ....A... 651 772-9225
Saint Paul *(G-8277)*

Fargo Electronics Inc ....C... 952 941-9470
Eden Prairie *(G-1663)*

Fpx LLC ....E... 866 826-6344
Mankato *(G-3129)*

Fujitsu Consulting Information ....B... 952 258-6000
Minnetonka *(G-6171)*

Sadaka Technology Consultants ....A... 952 841-6363
Minneapolis *(G-5586)*

SSIT North America Inc ....C... 952 857-1600
Minneapolis *(G-5726)*

Vericenter Minnesota Inc ....E... 952 918-2000
Saint Paul *(G-9126)*

APPRAISAL SVCS, EXC REAL ESTATE

Retail Inventory Services Ltd ....D... 651 631-9081
Saint Paul *(G-8896)*

AQUARIUMS & ZOOLOGICAL GARDENS

Minnesota Aquarium LLC ....D... 952 853-0628
Minneapolis *(G-5068)*

ARBITRATION & CONCILIATION SVCS

Midwest Recreational ....D... 507 263-9234
Cannon Falls *(G-859)*

National Arbitration Forum Inc ....C... 952 516-6400
Minneapolis *(G-5160)*

ARBORIST SVCS

S & S Tree & Horticultural ....E... 651 451-8907
South Saint Paul *(G-9539)*

ARCHEOLOGICAL EXPEDITIONS

Tom Loucks & Associates Inc ....D... 763 424-5505
Osseo *(G-6676)*

ARCHITECT'S SUPPLIES WHOLESALERS

Albinson Reprographics LLC ....E... 612 374-1120
Minneapolis *(G-3703)*

Ers Digital Inc ....D... 763 694-5900
Minneapolis *(G-4369)*

ARCHITECTURAL SVCS

Architectural Enhancements, LL ....E... 320 274-6909
Annandale *(G-137)*

Boarman Kroos Vogel Group ....D... 612 339-3752
Minneapolis *(G-3921)*

Bwbr Architects Inc ....C... 651 222-3701
Saint Paul *(G-8144)*

Cuningham Group Architecture ....C... 612 379-3400
Minneapolis *(G-4200)*

Damberg Scott Gerzina Wagner ....E... 218 727-2626
Duluth *(G-1290)*

Elness Swenson Graham ....D... 612 339-5508
Minneapolis *(G-4343)*

Hammel, Green & Abrahamson Inc ....B... 612 758-4000
Minneapolis *(G-4591)*

Hammel, Green & Abrahamson Inc ....B... 507 281-8601
Rochester *(G-7131)*

HDR Engineering Inc ....C... 763 591-5400
Minneapolis *(G-4615)*

Hickey Thorstenson Grover Ltd ....E... 952 278-8880
Eden Prairie *(G-1684)*

Horty Elving & Associates Inc ....E... 612 332-4422
Minneapolis *(G-4676)*

Inspec Inc ....E... 763 546-3434
Minneapolis *(G-4707)*

Leo A Daly Co ....C... 612 338-8741
Minneapolis *(G-4861)*

LHB Inc ....C... 218 727-8446
Duluth *(G-1381)*

Lhb Inc ....E... 612 338-2029
Minneapolis *(G-4867)*

Lunning Wende Bvh Architects ....D... 651 221-0915
Saint Paul *(G-8597)*

Meyer, Scherer & Rockcastle ....E... 612 375-0336
Minneapolis *(G-5012)*

Miller Architects & Builders ....E... 320 251-4109
Saint Cloud *(G-7555)*

Miller Architecture Inc ....E... 320 251-4109
Saint Cloud *(G-7556)*

Miller Dunwiddie Architecture ....E... 612 337-0000
Minneapolis *(G-5043)*

Miller Rozeboom Architect Inc ....E... 612 332-2110
Minneapolis *(G-5045)*

Minnesota Architectural ....D... 612 871-5703
Minneapolis *(G-5069)*

Perkins + Will Inc ....D... 612 851-5000
Minneapolis *(G-5366)*

Pope Associates Inc ....E... 651 642-9200
Saint Paul *(G-8831)*

Portfolio Design Services Inc ....E... 651 631-1300
Saint Paul *(G-9263)*

Setter Leach & Lindstrom Inc ....D... 612 338-8741
Minneapolis *(G-5639)*

Shea Inc ....E... 612 339-2257
Minneapolis *(G-5652)*

Short-Elliott-Hendrickson Inc ....D... 800 572-0617
Saint Cloud *(G-7593)*

T S P One Inc ....E... 952 474-3291
Hopkins *(G-2641)*

Vanman Construction Co ....E... 763 541-9552
Minneapolis *(G-5958)*

Walsh Bishop Associates Inc ....D... 612 338-8799
Minneapolis *(G-6016)*

Wcl Associates Inc ....E... 952 541-9969
Minneapolis *(G-6029)*

Weidt Group Inc ....E... 952 938-1588
Hopkins *(G-2659)*

World Architects Inc ....D... 651 227-7773
Saint Paul *(G-9168)*

ARCHITECTURAL SVCS: Engineering

Armstrong, Torseth, Skold ....D... 763 545-3731
Minneapolis *(G-3810)*

Banner & Assoc ....D... 507 562-2957
Pipestone *(G-6823)*

Bkv Group ....D... 612 339-3752
Minneapolis *(G-3909)*

Colby Yaggy Associates Inc ....D... 507 288-6464
Rochester *(G-7084)*

Collaborative Design Group Inc ....E... 612 332-3654
Minneapolis *(G-4118)*

Dlr Group Kke ....E... 612 977-3500
Minneapolis *(G-4266)*

Ellerbe Becket Co ....C... 612 376-2000
Minneapolis *(G-4341)*

I & S Group Inc ....D... 507 331-1500
Faribault *(G-2011)*

Opus Architects & Engineers ....C... 952 656-4444
Hopkins *(G-2596)*

Rsp Architects Ltd ....C... 612 677-7100
Minneapolis *(G-5571)*

Short-Elliott-Hendrickson Inc ....C... 651 490-2000
Saint Paul *(G-8954)*

T S P Inc ....E... 507 288-8155
Rochester *(G-7272)*

URS Group Inc ....E... 612 370-0700
Minneapolis *(G-5941)*

Widseth, Smith, Nolting ....E... 218 281-6522
Crookston *(G-1144)*

ARMATURE REPAIRING & REWINDING SVC

General Electric Co ....E... 612 529-9502
Minneapolis *(G-4510)*

General Electric Co ....E... 218 749-6100
Mountain Iron *(G-6392)*

ARMORED CAR SVCS

American Security & Protection ....D... 218 236-5180
Moorhead *(G-6297)*

American Security LLC ....A... 651 644-1155
Saint Paul *(G-8034)*

Brink's Inc ....D... 763 486-1730
Minneapolis *(G-3950)*

Granite City Armored Car Inc ....E... 320 252-0708
Sauk Rapids *(G-9364)*

Loomis Armored Us Inc ....E... 651 645-4511
Saint Paul *(G-8594)*

ART DESIGN SVCS

Media Relations Inc ....E... 612 798-7200
Burnsville *(G-752)*

SERVICES

ART GALLERY, NONCOMMERCIAL

Minneapolis Society of Fine..............C... 612 870-3046
Minneapolis *(G-5064)*

ART GOODS & SPLYS WHOLESALERS

Miratec Systems Inc ....E... 651 222-8440
Saint Paul *(G-8715)*

ART GOODS, WHOLESALE

Art Holdings Corp ....E... 763 567-2200
Minneapolis *(G-3811)*
East Asian Trading Co Inc ....B... 763 473-3520
Minneapolis *(G-4307)*
Nsl Holdings Inc.............................E... 952 943-8474
Shakopee *(G-9462)*
Sky Media LLC ....E... 651 635-0100
Saint Paul *(G-8963)*

ARTIFICIAL INSEMINATION SVCS, ANIMAL SPECIALTIES

Minnesota Select Sires Co-Op.............E... 320 259-6680
Saint Cloud *(G-7560)*

ARTISTS' MATERIALS, WHOLESALE

Art Holdings Corp ....E... 763 567-2200
Minneapolis *(G-3811)*

ARTS OR SCIENCES CENTER

Evansville Arts Coalition ....D... 218 948-2787
Evansville *(G-1925)*

ASSOCIATION FOR THE HANDICAPPED

Center For Independent Living............B... 218 262-6675
Hibbing *(G-2439)*
Courage Center..............................B... 763 588-0811
Minneapolis *(G-4172)*
Partners In Excellence......................E... 651 773-5988
Saint Paul *(G-8808)*

ASSOCIATIONS: Alumni

National Assoc of Retired ....E... 320 245-2629
Sandstone *(G-9323)*
University of Minn Alumni Assn...........E... 612 624-2323
Minneapolis *(G-5929)*

ASSOCIATIONS: Business

Ad Efx of America Inc........................E... 952 941-3500
Eden Prairie *(G-1583)*
American Dairy Association of............E... 651 488-0261
Saint Paul *(G-8024)*
Brock White Co LLC ....E... 651 647-0950
Saint Paul *(G-8131)*
City of Blackduck............................E... 218 835-4803
Blackduck *(G-473)*
City of Breckenridge.........................E... 218 643-1431
Breckenridge *(G-593)*
Communicating For Agriculture............E... 218 739-3241
Fergus Falls *(G-2069)*
Employers Association Inc ....D... 763 253-9100
Minneapolis *(G-4351)*
Idw LLC ....E... 952 949-6690
Chanhassen *(G-925)*
Kandiyohi County Economic ....E... 320 235-7370
Willmar *(G-10013)*
League of Minnesota Cities ....D... 651 281-1200
Saint Paul *(G-8573)*
Midwest Dairy Association ....D... 651 488-0261
Saint Paul *(G-8658)*
Minnesota League of Credit.................E... 651 288-5170
Saint Paul *(G-8694)*
Minnesota Liquor Retailers Inc............E... 651 772-0910
Saint Paul *(G-8697)*
Minnesota Magazine & Pubn ....E... 651 290-6281
Saint Paul *(G-8698)*
Pleasant Valley Township Assn ....E... 651 437-5660
Hastings *(G-2399)*
Professional Association of..................E... 612 259-1600
Minneapolis *(G-5419)*
Tyler Area Community Club..................D... 507 247-3905
Tyler *(G-9715)*

ASSOCIATIONS: Fraternal

American Legion 225 Inc....................E... 651 464-2600
Forest Lake *(G-2156)*
American Legion 545.........................E... 320 796-5542
Spicer *(G-9555)*
Apple Valley American Legion ....E... 952 431-1776
Saint Paul *(G-7700)*
Catholic Aid Association......................E... 651 490-0170
Saint Paul *(G-8174)*

Cryptic Masons of Minneso ....E... 507 437-2851
Austin *(G-269)*
Fraternal Order of Eagles Inc..............E... 218 681-2406
Thief River Falls *(G-9668)*
Hopkins American Legion Post............E... 952 933-1881
Hopkins *(G-2553)*
Knights of Columbus Inc ....D... 320 679-4093
Mora *(G-6364)*
Ottertail Lodge 284 ....E... 218 863-7913
Pelican Rapids *(G-6781)*
Rudolph Priebe American Legion ....E... 763 425-4858
Osseo *(G-6657)*
Scottish Rite Temple ....A... 651 222-2676
Saint Paul *(G-8938)*
Sigma Alpha Epsilon Fraternity............E... 612 331-5986
Minneapolis *(G-5669)*
YWCA of Minneapolis.........................E... 612 863-0970
Minneapolis *(G-6112)*
Zuhrah Temple Trustees Inc ....E... 612 871-3555
Minneapolis *(G-6122)*

ASSOCIATIONS: Homeowners

Tower Hill Association ....E... 763 682-2321
Buffalo *(G-658)*

ASSOCIATIONS: Manufacturers'

Mike Bishoff..................................E... 218 697-2800
Hill City *(G-2481)*

ASSOCIATIONS: Parent Teacher

Independent School District ....D... 952 806-7000
Minneapolis *(G-4695)*
Lincoln Elementry School P T A...........E... 320 616-6200
Little Falls *(G-3010)*
Pta Minnesota Congress 28 ....D... 763 792-5900
Circle Pines *(G-1020)*
Scenic Heights Pta............................D... 952 401-5400
Hopkins *(G-2627)*

ASSOCIATIONS: Real Estate Management

Accessible Space Inc ....E... 651 645-7271
Saint Paul *(G-7975)*
Asset Management Group Inc ....D... 952 546-3385
Minneapolis *(G-3821)*
Atwood Land Co Inc ....E... 507 388-9375
Mankato *(G-3107)*
Campground Marketing Services.........D... 218 562-4204
Pequot Lakes *(G-6786)*
Carlson Hotels Management Corp ....C... 763 212-5000
Minneapolis *(G-4016)*
Cashill Spaulding Properties ....E... 651 225-8227
Saint Paul *(G-8172)*
Commonbond Housing ....E... 651 291-1750
Saint Paul *(G-8232)*
Dominium Management Services.........C... 763 354-5500
Minneapolis *(G-4274)*
France Avenue LLC ....C... 952 831-0343
Minneapolis *(G-4472)*
Gsr Real Estate Services LLC..............D... 612 338-2828
Minneapolis *(G-4575)*
K M S Management Inc ....C... 952 593-9930
Minneapolis *(G-4784)*
Kleinman Realty Co ....D... 763 572-9400
Minneapolis *(G-3510)*
Kraus-Anderson Realty Co ....E... 952 881-8166
Minneapolis *(G-4824)*
Lang-Nelson Associates Inc ....E... 952 920-0400
Minneapolis *(G-4841)*
Life Style Inc..................................D... 507 451-8524
Owatonna *(G-6722)*
Meritex Enterprises Inc ....E... 651 855-9700
Minneapolis *(G-4992)*
Metes & Bounds Management Co ....E... 612 861-8526
Minneapolis *(G-4999)*
Minnesota Street Associates ....D... 651 225-3666
Saint Paul *(G-8707)*
Opus Corp ....C... 952 656-4444
Hopkins *(G-2597)*
Perennial Management LLC...................E... 651 644-9600
Saint Paul *(G-8818)*
Peterson Group Management Corp .....E... 952 835-9232
Minneapolis *(G-5370)*
Planned Investments Inc......................E... 952 920-3890
Minneapolis *(G-5388)*
Radisson Hotels International ....C... 763 212-5000
Minnetonka *(G-6218)*
Real Estate Equities Inc ....D... 651 227-6925
Saint Paul *(G-8877)*
Shelard Group Inc.............................E... 952 941-7493
Eden Prairie *(G-1777)*
614 Co ....E... 612 333-6128
Minneapolis *(G-5685)*
Steven Scott Management Inc ....E... 952 540-8600
Minneapolis *(G-5754)*

Watson Centers Inc ....D... 612 920-5034
Minneapolis *(G-6023)*

ASSOCIATIONS: Scientists'

American Phytopathological Soc ....D... 651 454-7250
Saint Paul *(G-7697)*
International Assn For ....E... 651 681-8566
Saint Paul *(G-7804)*

ASSOCIATIONS: Trade

Aca International ....D... 952 926-6547
Minneapolis *(G-3663)*
Industrial Fabrics Association ....D... 651 222-2508
Saint Paul *(G-8511)*
International Association of ....E... 763 706-3650
Minneapolis *(G-3500)*
Minnesota Chapter of The Natl............E... 952 928-4647
Minneapolis *(G-5071)*

ATHLETIC CLUB & GYMNASIUMS, MEMBERSHIP

Fit-Pro II ....E... 763 295-3002
Monticello *(G-6271)*
Health Industries Inc ....E... 218 233-1516
Moorhead *(G-6318)*
Regency Athletic Club & Spa ....E... 612 343-3131
Minneapolis *(G-5483)*
University Club of St Paul....................D... 651 222-1751
Saint Paul *(G-9112)*

ATHLETIC ORGANIZATION

Duluth Softball Players Assn ....E... 218 722-5569
Duluth *(G-1303)*
Life Time Fitness Inc ....E... 612 339-3655
Minneapolis *(G-4879)*
Mesabi Family YMCA ....D... 218 749-8020
Virginia *(G-9746)*
Minnesota Twins Baseball Club..........A... 612 375-7411
Minneapolis *(G-5099)*
Rochester Juvenile Hockey ....E... 507 280-6345
Rochester *(G-7234)*

AUCTION SVCS: Livestock

Lanesboro Sales Commission Inc ....E... 507 467-2192
Lanesboro *(G-2947)*

AUCTION SVCS: Motor Vehicle

ABC Minneapolis LLC ....C... 763 428-8777
Osseo *(G-6590)*
Mid-State Auto Auction Inc..................C... 218 385-3777
New York Mills *(G-6479)*
North Star Auto Auction ....C... 952 445-5544
Shakopee *(G-9460)*

AUCTION, APPRAISAL & EXCHANGE SVCS

Birkeland & Associates.......................E... 952 922-1772
Minneapolis *(G-3907)*

AUCTIONEERS: Fee Basis

Gehling Auction Co Inc.......................E... 507 765-2131
Preston *(G-6897)*

AUDIO & VIDEO TAPES WHOLESALERS

Gopher News Co...............................D... 763 546-5300
Minneapolis *(G-4542)*

AUDIO-VISUAL PROGRAM PRODUCTION SVCS

Electrosonic Inc...............................E... 952 931-7500
Minnetonka *(G-6165)*
Greatapes Corp................................E... 612 872-8284
Minneapolis *(G-4557)*
Hometime Video Publishing Inc...........E... 952 448-3812
Chaska *(G-968)*
Media Productions Inc ....E... 612 379-4678
Minneapolis *(G-4984)*

AUDITING SVCS

Apex Analytix Inc.............................E... 952 400-2272
Eden Prairie *(G-1593)*
Auditor Wright County ....E... 763 682-7578
Buffalo *(G-634)*
Bottom Line Enhancement Svcs...........C... 952 974-9920
Eden Prairie *(G-1609)*
Conner Enterprises Inc ....E... 218 998-9376
Fergus Falls *(G-2072)*
County of Fillmore............................C... 507 765-4701
Preston *(G-6896)*
Ernst & Young LLP.............................B... 612 343-1000
Minneapolis *(G-4367)*

McGladrey & Pullen, LLP ....C... 952 921-7700
Minneapolis (G-4974)

Wells Fargo Audit Services Inc ....D... 612 667-1234
Minneapolis (G-6038)

AUTHORS' AGENTS & BROKERS

Saint Paul Rivercentre Conv ....D... 651 265-4800
Saint Paul (G-8930)

AUTO SPLYS & PARTS, NEW, WHSLE:
Exhaust Sys, Mufflers, Etc

Forbes, John ....E... 320 693-3287
Litchfield (G-2984)

AUTOMATED TELLER MACHINE NETWORK

Security Products Co ....E... 763 784-6504
Minneapolis (G-3599)

AUTOMATED TELLER MACHINE OR ATM
REPAIR SVCS

Expresspoint Technology Svcs..........C... 763 543-6000
Golden Valley (G-2240)

AUTOMATIC TELLER MACHINES:
Wholesalers

Atm Network Inc..................................E... 952 767-2000
Minnetonka (G-6146)

AUTOMOBILE FINANCE LEASING

Ally Financial Inc...............................E... 800 689-6768
Minneapolis (G-3730)

Citigroup Inc ....C... 952 942-9880
Minneapolis (G-4081)

U Save Lease & Rental Inc ....E... 218 732-3347
Park Rapids (G-6764)

AUTOMOBILES & OTHER MOTOR VEHICLES
WHOLESALERS

ABC Bus Inc ....D... 507 334-1871
Faribault (G-1986)

Brooklyn Center Motors LLC ....D... 763 535-5200
Minneapolis (G-3959)

Central Motors...................................E... 651 674-7017
North Branch (G-6499)

Hoglund Bus Co Inc ....E... 763 295-5119
Monticello (G-6273)

Manheim Auctions Inc ....B... 763 425-7653
Osseo (G-6633)

Riverbend Auto Sales Inc....................E... 507 345-8967
Mankato (G-3188)

AUTOMOBILES: Wholesalers

Midwest Motors LLC............................D... 651 455-6000
Inver Grove Heights (G-2763)

Security Auto Loans Inc......................E... 763 559-5892
Plymouth (G-6883)

St Cloud Subaru.................................E... 320 258-0163
Saint Cloud (G-7605)

Walden Leasing Inc ....E... 952 512-8924
Minneapolis (G-5996)

AUTOMOTIVE & TRUCK GENERAL REPAIR
SVC

A & R Leasing Inc ....D... 218 829-4787
Baxter (G-318)

Barnett Chrysler Jeep Kia ....D... 651 429-3391
Saint Paul (G-8089)

Bfs Retail Operations LLC ....E... 952 432-9212
Saint Paul (G-7719)

Bi-Phase Technologies LLC ....E... 651 681-4450
Saint Paul (G-7721)

Brookdale Motor Sales Inc ....C... 763 561-8161
Minneapolis (G-3956)

Brookman Motor Sales Inc ....E... 651 777-1316
Lake Elmo (G-2867)

Bruns Inc ....E... 218 757-3232
Orr (G-6577)

Burnsville Volkswagen Inc..................D... 952 892-9400
Burnsville (G-692)

Cedar Towing & Auction Inc ....E... 612 721-6645
Minneapolis (G-4037)

City of Mora ....E... 320 679-1770
Mora (G-6353)

Clearwater Truck Center Inc ....E... 320 558-6565
Clearwater (G-1042)

Coates Rv Center Inc ....E... 651 488-0234
Hugo (G-2674)

Commercial Truck & Trailer Rep ....E... 651 639-2260
Saint Paul (G-8230)

Coon Rapids Chrysler Inc ....C... 763 421-8000
Minneapolis (G-3439)

Dick's Valley Service Inc ....E... 952 891-4431
Apple Valley (G-243)

Dondelinger Chevrolet ....D... 218 829-4787
Baxter (G-327)

Farmers Union Oil Co of......................E... 218 233-2497
Moorhead (G-6315)

Forbes, John ....E... 320 693-3287
Litchfield (G-2984)

Ford Boyer Trucks Inc ....D... 612 378-6000
Minneapolis (G-4465)

Ford New Brighten ....D... 651 633-9010
Saint Paul (G-8387)

Friendly Chevrolet, Geo Inc ....C... 763 786-6100
Minneapolis (G-3473)

Granger's Inc ....E... 651 429-2524
Minneapolis (G-3476)

Harold Chevrolet Inc ....C... 952 884-3333
Minneapolis (G-4600)

Hawkins Chevrolet-Cadillac Inc...........E... 507 238-4786
Fairmont (G-1973)

Hilligoss Chevrolet Inc ....E... 218 263-7578
Hibbing (G-2454)

Independent School District ....E... 218 773-0476
East Grand Forks (G-1569)

Jeff's, Bobby & Steves ....E... 763 788-1113
Minneapolis (G-3506)

Kline Volvo Inc ....D... 651 379-4300
Saint Paul (G-8549)

Le Jeune Investment Inc ....E... 651 483-2681
Saint Paul (G-8572)

Lehman's Garage Inc ....D... 952 888-8700
Minneapolis (G-4858)

Lehman's Garage Inc ....E... 651 454-1120
Saint Paul (G-7823)

Lehman's Garage Minneapolis ....E... 612 827-5431
Minneapolis (G-4859)

Lewiston Auto Co Inc ....E... 507 523-2164
Lewiston (G-2967)

Lupient Oldsmobile Co Inc ....C... 763 546-2222
Minneapolis (G-4910)

McK of Austin Ltd ....D... 507 437-6702
Austin (G-282)

Metropolitan Corp ....E... 952 944-2438
Eden Prairie (G-1720)

Metropolitan Corp ....E... 952 943-9000
Eden Prairie (G-1721)

Morries New Buffalo Chrysler...............E... 763 682-1800
Buffalo (G-654)

Nelson Chrysler Dodge GMC Inc...........E... 218 739-2283
Fergus Falls (G-2102)

Norseman Motors Inc ....E... 218 847-4415
Detroit Lakes (G-1212)

Norseman Motors Inc ....E... 218 847-1639
Detroit Lakes (G-1213)

Nuss Truck Group Inc ....E... 507 345-6225
Mankato (G-3178)

Olson & Johnson Body Shop Inc ....E... 507 537-1669
Marshall (G-3317)

Parkview Ford - Mercury Inc ....E... 320 269-5565
Montevideo (G-6256)

R L Brookdale Motors Inc ....D... 763 561-8111
Minneapolis (G-5459)

Red's Auto Inc ....E... 320 468-6478
Pierz (G-6807)

Richards Transportation Svc ....E... 218 233-3404
Moorhead (G-6338)

Robert A Williams Enterprises ....E... 952 831-6250
Minneapolis (G-5552)

Rockford Bus Garage Inc ....E... 763 477-6100
Rockford (G-7304)

Roger's Amoco Inc ....E... 320 963-6555
Maple Lake (G-3264)

Rudy Hopkins Luther's Motors.............C... 952 938-1717
Hopkins (G-2624)

Southtown Freeway Toyota Inc ....E... 952 888-5581
Minneapolis (G-5712)

Superior Ford Inc ....C... 763 559-9111
Minneapolis (G-5771)

Swenson Motor Co ....E... 320 235-3434
Willmar (G-10047)

Toyota City Inc ....D... 763 566-0060
Minneapolis (G-5842)

Twin City West 76 Auto Truck ....D... 763 428-2277
Rogers (G-7345)

United States Postal Service ....D... 651 293-3172
Saint Paul (G-9109)

Valley Sales Inc ....E... 952 314-8560
Waconia (G-9793)

Valley Sales of Hutchinson Inc.............E... 320 587-2240
Hutchinson (G-2714)

Village Chevrolet Co - Wayzata ....C... 952 473-5444
Wayzata (G-9947)

Wagamon Brothers Inc ....E... 763 789-7227
Minneapolis (G-3634)

Wally McCarthy's Cadillac ....D... 651 636-6060
Saint Paul (G-9139)

Walter Pontiac Buick GMC Inc ....D... 952 888-9800
Minneapolis (G-6019)

AUTOMOTIVE BATTERIES WHOLESALERS

Universal Cooperatives Inc ....D... 651 239-1000
Saint Paul (G-7938)

AUTOMOTIVE BODY SHOP

Abra Inc ....D... 763 561-7220
Minneapolis (G-3662)

Crystal Lake Automotive Inc ....E... 952 892-3377
Lakeville (G-2897)

Domaille Ltd ....D... 507 287-1170
Rochester (G-7098)

Fairway Collision Center Inc ....E... 651 483-4055
Saint Paul (G-8365)

Ford Boyer Trucks Inc ....D... 612 378-6000
Minneapolis (G-4465)

Fury Motors Inc..................................E... 651 451-1313
South Saint Paul (G-9527)

Gale's Auto Body Inc ....E... 763 786-4110
Minneapolis (G-3474)

Granger's Inc ....E... 651 429-2524
Minneapolis (G-3476)

Harold Chevrolet Inc ....C... 952 884-3333
Minneapolis (G-4600)

Jay Malone Motors ....E... 320 587-4748
Hutchinson (G-2704)

Lehman's Garage Inc ....D... 952 888-8700
Minneapolis (G-4858)

Lenzen Chevrolet Buick Inc..................E... 952 448-2850
Chaska (G-975)

Master Collision Group LLC ....E... 763 509-0900
Minneapolis (G-4963)

Mgmt Five Inc....................................D... 651 451-2201
Inver Grove Heights (G-2762)

Nelson Chrysler Dodge GMC Inc ....E... 218 739-2283
Fergus Falls (G-2102)

Olson & Johnson Body Shop Inc..........E... 507 537-1669
Marshall (G-3317)

Peter's Body Shop Inc ....E... 320 252-2993
Saint Paul (G-7566)

Raymond Auto Body Inc ....E... 651 488-0588
Saint Paul (G-8871)

Rudy Hopkins Luther's Motors ....C... 952 938-1717
Hopkins (G-2624)

Shakopee Chevrolet Inc......................E... 952 445-4148
Shakopee (G-9473)

Suburban Auto Body Inc ....E... 651 983-4438
Saint Paul (G-9011)

Swenson Motor Co ....E... 320 235-3434
Willmar (G-10047)

Thane Hawkins Polar Chevrolet...........C... 651 429-7791
White Bear Lake (G-9978)

Twin City Auto Body Collision 952 884-9878
Minneapolis (G-5877)

Wolf Motors Co Inc.............................E... 952 492-2340
Jordan (G-2813)

AUTOMOTIVE BODY, PAINT & INTERIOR
REPAIR & MAINTENANCE SVC

A & R Leasing Inc ....D... 218 829-4787
Baxter (G-318)

Ford New Brighten ....D... 651 633-9010
Saint Paul (G-8387)

Friendly Chevrolet, Geo Inc.................C... 763 786-6100
Minneapolis (G-3473)

Lamettry Collision Inc ....E... 952 898-1636
Burnsville (G-746)

Lehman's Garage Inc ....E... 952 888-8700
Savage (G-9396)

Lehman's Garage Minneapolis.............E... 612 827-5431
Minneapolis (G-4859)

Master Collision Group LLC ....E... 612 827-4697
Minneapolis (G-4964)

Metropolitan Corp...............................C... 952 944-2438
Eden Prairie (G-1720)

Wally McCarthy's Cadillac ....D... 651 636-6060
Saint Paul (G-9139)

AUTOMOTIVE BRAKE REPAIR SHOPS

Morgan Tire & Auto Inc ....E... 612 861-2278
Minneapolis (G-5130)

AUTOMOTIVE COLLISION SHOPS

Boulevard Collision Inc.......................E... 763 595-0006
Minneapolis (G-3933)

Mike Hall Chevrolet Inc ....E... 651 484-4671
Saint Paul (G-8667)

(G-00000) Company's Geographic Section entry number

SERVICES

Walser Collision & Glass Inc 952 884-8884
Minneapolis (G-6015)

AUTOMOTIVE EXTERIOR REPAIR SVCS

Hutchinson Auto Center..........................E... 320 587-4748
Hutchinson (G-2699)
Lamettry Collision Inc ....E... 651 766-9770
Saint Paul (G-8559)
Miller Pontiac-Buick-Gmc Inc ....D... 320 251-1363
Saint Cloud (G-7558)

AUTOMOTIVE GLASS REPLACEMENT SHOPS

Heartland Auto Glass ....E... 952 697-0765
Minneapolis (G-4625)
Novus Inc...E... 952 944-8152
Savage (G-9402)
Pgw Auto Glass LLC............................E... 952 888-0413
Minneapolis (G-5373)

AUTOMOTIVE PAINT SHOP

Boulevard Collision Inc ....E... 763 595-0006
Minneapolis (G-3933)
Fairway Collision Center Inc.................E... 651 483-4055
Saint Paul (G-8365)
Lamettry Collision Inc ....E... 651 766-9770
Saint Paul (G-8559)
Master Collision Group LLC ....E... 763 509-0900
Minneapolis (G-4963)
Suburban Auto Body Inc ....E... 651 983-4438
Saint Paul (G-9011)

AUTOMOTIVE RADIO REPAIR SVCS

Phoenix Distributing Inc.......................E... 952 882-9949
Burnsville (G-781)
Ultimate Acquisition Partners...............E... 952 830-0010
Minneapolis (G-5895)

AUTOMOTIVE REPAIR SHOPS: Diesel Engine Repair

Interstate Co's Inc ....D... 952 854-2044
Minneapolis (G-4726)
Pro Stop Truck Service Inc ....D... 651 452-8137
Saint Paul (G-7883)

AUTOMOTIVE REPAIR SHOPS: Engine Repair

Hutchinson Auto Center........................E... 320 587-4748
Hutchinson (G-2699)
Wolf Motors Co Inc ....E... 952 492-2340
Jordan (G-2813)

AUTOMOTIVE REPAIR SHOPS: Engine Repair, Exc Diesel

Crystal Lake Automotive Inc.................E... 952 892-3377
Lakeville (G-2897)
Dodge of Burnsville Inc.........................E... 952 894-9000
Burnsville (G-712)
Maplewood Motors Inc ....D... 651 482-1322
Saint Paul (G-8614)

AUTOMOTIVE REPAIR SHOPS: Machine Shop

Genuine Parts Co.................................D... 952 925-0188
Minneapolis (G-4523)
Red Rooster Auto Stores LLC ....D... 763 533-4321
Minneapolis (G-5477)

AUTOMOTIVE REPAIR SHOPS: Powertrain Components Repair Svcs

Twin City Custom Railings & GL ....E... 763 780-7314
Minneapolis (G-3624)

AUTOMOTIVE REPAIR SHOPS: Rebuilding & Retreading Tires

First State Tire Disposal Inc.................E... 763 434-0578
Isanti (G-2779)
Midstates Retreading & Whsle ....E... 507 288-7752
Rochester (G-7183)
Royal Tire Inc ....D... 320 258-7070
Saint Cloud (G-7590)

AUTOMOTIVE REPAIR SHOPS: Sound System Svc & Installation

Automotive Restyling Concepts...........D... 763 535-2181
Minneapolis (G-3840)

AUTOMOTIVE REPAIR SHOPS: Tire Recapping

Tire Associates Warehouse Inc ....E... 507 625-2975
Mankato (G-3207)

AUTOMOTIVE REPAIR SHOPS: Trailer Repair

Crossroads Trailer Sales & Svc............E... 507 373-4443
Albert Lea (G-45)
Dahlke Trailer Sales Inc........................E... 763 783-0077
Minneapolis (G-3450)
Roseau Diesel Service Inc 218 463-1711
Roseau (G-7357)
Smith's Winter Products ....E... 763 493-3332
Osseo (G-6665)

AUTOMOTIVE REPAIR SHOPS: Truck Engine Repair, Exc Indl

Allstate Sales & Leasing Corp ....D... 651 455-6500
South Saint Paul (G-9508)
Astleford Equipment Co Inc...................E... 952 894-9200
Burnsville (G-681)
Black Jack Express & Repair.................E... 507 485-3437
Wood Lake (G-10170)
Kolstad Co Inc.....................................D... 763 792-1033
Minneapolis (G-3511)
Manders Diesel Repair Inc ....E... 952 469-1800
Lakeville (G-2915)
North Star International ....D... 612 378-1660
Minneapolis (G-5219)
River Valley Truck Centers Inc ....D... 507 345-1129
Mankato (G-3187)
Roseau Diesel Service Inc 218 463-1711
Roseau (G-7357)
Twin Cities Mack Volvo Trucks ....D... 651 633-4810
Saint Paul (G-9087)
Valley Truck Parts & Service ....E... 218 773-3486
East Grand Forks (G-1578)
Westman Freightliner Inc ....E... 507 625-4118
Mankato (G-3217)

AUTOMOTIVE REPAIR SHOPS: Turbocharger & Blower Repair

Istate Truck Inc.. 952 854-2044
Minneapolis (G-4739)

AUTOMOTIVE REPAIR SHOPS: Wheel Alignment

Jay Malone Motors................................E... 320 587-4748
Hutchinson (G-2704)

AUTOMOTIVE REPAIR SVC

Montincello Ford-Mercury Inc................C... 763 295-2056
Minneapolis (G-5123)
Murphy Automotive Inc ....E... 952 432-2454
Rosemount (G-7373)
Race Automotive of Rochester..............E... 507 282-5200
Rochester (G-7216)
Schwieters Chevrolet of ....E... 320 634-4507
Glenwood (G-2232)
Smith's Winter Products ....E... 763 493-3332
Osseo (G-6665)
Spring Prairie Hutterian.........................C... 218 498-0222
Hawley (G-2423)
Zumbrota Ford Sales LLC ....E... 507 732-5127
Zumbrota (G-10222)

AUTOMOTIVE RUSTPROOFING & UNDERCOATING SHOPS

P & L Automotive Inc ....E... 952 941-0888
Minneapolis (G-5304)

AUTOMOTIVE SPLYS & PARTS, NEW, WHOL: Auto Servicing Eqpt

U S Warehouse Supply Inc ....D... 651 405-3500
Saint Paul (G-7932)

AUTOMOTIVE SPLYS & PARTS, NEW, WHOL: Auto Svc Station Eqpt

Graffco Inc ....E... 651 464-1079
Forest Lake (G-2146)

AUTOMOTIVE SPLYS & PARTS, NEW, WHOLESALE: Clutches

Clutch & Transmission Service ....E... 651 636-4311
Saint Paul (G-8217)
Clutch & Transmission Service ....D... 651 631-0959
Saint Paul (G-8218)

AUTOMOTIVE SPLYS & PARTS, NEW, WHOLESALE: Engines/Eng Parts

Reviva Inc..D... 763 535-8900
Minneapolis (G-3584)

AUTOMOTIVE SPLYS & PARTS, NEW, WHOLESALE: Filters, Air & Oil

Universal Cooperatives Inc ....D... 651 239-1000
Saint Paul (G-7938)

AUTOMOTIVE SPLYS & PARTS, NEW, WHOLESALE: Heaters

Northern Factory Sales Inc...................E... 320 235-2288
Willmar (G-10030)

AUTOMOTIVE SPLYS & PARTS, NEW, WHOLESALE: Radiators

Automotive Cooling Products ....E... 651 731-2414
Saint Paul (G-9186)
Northern Factory Sales Inc...................E... 320 235-2288
Willmar (G-10030)

AUTOMOTIVE SPLYS & PARTS, NEW, WHOLESALE: Splys

A & J Tba Inc... 507 233-3000
New Ulm (G-6437)
CMC Enterprises Inc ....E... 763 545-3800
Plymouth (G-6856)
Quick Service Battery Co Inc ....E... 651 645-0485
Saint Paul (G-7887)

AUTOMOTIVE SPLYS & PARTS, NEW, WHOLESALE: Tools & Eqpt

Northern Factory Sales Inc...................E... 320 235-2288
Willmar (G-10030)

AUTOMOTIVE SPLYS & PARTS, NEW, WHOLESALE: Trailer Parts

Dahlke Trailer Sales Inc ....E... 763 783-0077
Minneapolis (G-3450)
Smith's Winter Products ....E... 763 493-3332
Osseo (G-6665)
Trudell Trailers of Minnesota ....E... 763 497-7084
Albertville (G-77)

AUTOMOTIVE SPLYS & PARTS, USED, WHOLESALE

AAA Auto Salvage Inc ....E... 651 423-2432
Rosemount (G-7360)
Ace Auto Parts & Salvage Inc ....E... 651 224-9479
Saint Paul (G-7979)
Crosstown Used Auto Parts ....E... 612 861-3020
Saint Paul (G-8270)
Fridley Auto Parts Inc ....D... 763 784-8890
Minneapolis (G-3472)
Glen's Truck Center Inc ....E... 763 428-4331
Rogers (G-7324)
Hvh Auto Parts Inc ....C... 763 784-1711
Minneapolis (G-3493)

AUTOMOTIVE SPLYS & PARTS, USED, WHOLESALE: Dry Cell Batt

Triton Tire & Battery LLC ....E... 651 239-1200
Saint Paul (G-7929)

AUTOMOTIVE SPLYS & PARTS, WHOLESALE, NEC

Automotive Cooling Products ....E... 651 731-2414
Saint Paul (G-9186)
Como Lube & Supplies Inc ....E... 218 722-2920
Duluth (G-1280)
Crookston Welding Machine Co ....E... 218 281-6911
Crookston (G-1122)
Genuine Parts Co.................................D... 952 925-0188
Minneapolis (G-4523)
Grossman Chevrolet Co Inc ....C... 952 435-8501
Burnsville (G-730)
Grove Cottage Auto Parts Inc 952 469-2801
Lakeville (G-2942)
Hance Distributing Inc ....E... 952 935-6429
Hopkins (G-2548)
J B Distributing Co Inc..........................E... 952 934-7354
Eden Prairie (G-1699)
Kath Management Co ....D... 651 484-3325
Saint Paul (G-8541)
Keystone Automotive Industries ....D... 612 789-1919
Minneapolis (G-4802)

Employment codes: A=Over 500 employees, B=251-500,
C=101-250, D=51-100, E=25-50

2011 Harris Minnesota
Services Directory

© Harris InfoSource 1-866-281-6415
657

S E R V I C E S

Kolstad Co Inc	D	763 792-1033
Minneapolis (G-3511)		
L & M Supply Inc		218 751-3237
Bemidji (G-401)		
L & M Supply Inc	E	218 732-4465
Park Rapids (G-6759)		
Mid-States Distributing Co Inc	E	651 698-8831
Saint Paul (G-8652)		
Mills Pontiac, Buick	E	320 231-1160
Willmar (G-10024)		
Mills Pontiac, Buick	E	320 231-1160
Willmar (G-10025)		
Minter-Weisman Co	B	763 545-3706
Minneapolis (G-5105)		
Northern Factory Sales Inc	E	320 235-2288
Willmar (G-10030)		
P & L Automotive Inc	E	952 941-0888
Minneapolis (G-5304)		
Palmer's Auto Supply Inc	E	507 354-3154
New Ulm (G-6472)		
Red Rooster Auto Stores LLC	D	763 533-4321
Minneapolis (G-5477)		
Total Automotive Inc	E	952 448-7750
Chanhassen (G-944)		
Tri-County Parts Supply Inc	E	320 253-5050
Saint Cloud (G-7620)		
Twinco Romax LLC	E	763 478-2360
Hamel (G-2358)		
U S Warehouse Supply Inc	D	651 405-3500
Saint Paul (G-7932)		
UNI-Select USA Inc	E	952 352-8603
Eden Prairie (G-1800)		
UNI-Select USA Inc	E	763 566-1285
Minneapolis (G-5900)		
Universal Cooperatives Inc	E	651 239-1000
Saint Paul (G-7938)		
US Venture Inc	D	763 591-5827
Minneapolis (G-5950)		
Viking Auto Salvage Inc	E	651 460-6166
Northfield (G-6522)		
Von Ruden Manufacturing Inc	D	763 682-3122
Buffalo (G-659)		
Zitco Inc	D	952 392-6060
Minneapolis (G-6121)		

AUTOMOTIVE SPLYS, USED, WHOLESALE & RETAIL

Erickson Truck Sales & Salvage	E	507 847-3664
Jackson (G-2791)		

AUTOMOTIVE SPLYS/PARTS, NEW, WHOL: Body Rpr/Paint Shop Splys

Innovance Inc	E	507 373-5152
Albert Lea (G-55)		
Zitco Inc	D	952 392-6060
Minneapolis (G-6121)		

AUTOMOTIVE SVCS

Brandl Motor Sports	E	320 632-2908
Little Falls (G-3000)		

AUTOMOTIVE SVCS, EXC REPAIR & CARWASHES: Customizing

P & L Automotive Inc	E	952 941-0888
Minneapolis (G-5304)		

AUTOMOTIVE SVCS, EXC REPAIR & CARWASHES: Glass Tinting

P & L Automotive Inc	E	952 941-0888
Minneapolis (G-5304)		

AUTOMOTIVE SVCS, EXC REPAIR & CARWASHES: Lubrication

McDonald Rentals Inc	E	218 879-9060
Cloquet (G-1056)		

AUTOMOTIVE SVCS, EXC REPAIR & CARWASHES: Maintenance

Identifix Inc	D	651 633-8007
Saint Paul (G-8505)		
Saint Cloud Auto Center LLC	E	320 259-4542
Waite Park (G-9835)		
Thorco Inc	E	320 564-3086
Granite Falls (G-2321)		

AUTOMOTIVE SVCS, EXC REPAIR & CARWASHES: Trailer Maintenance

Black Jack Express & Repair	E	507 485-3437
Wood Lake (G-10170)		

AUTOMOTIVE SVCS, EXC REPAIR: Carwash, Automatic

Don's Car Washes of Minnesota	E	763 788-1631
Minneapolis (G-3458)		
Douglas Drive Car Wash Inc	E	763 533-1581
Minneapolis (G-4285)		
Mankato Auto Mall Owners Inc	E	507 387-7877
Mankato (G-3228)		
Quality Car Wash Ops Ltd Inc	E	952 473-4535
Wayzata (G-9937)		

AUTOMOTIVE SVCS, EXC REPAIR: Carwash, Self-Service

Riverside Auto Wash Inc	E	763 571-2700
Minneapolis (G-3587)		

AUTOMOTIVE SVCS, EXC REPAIR: Truck Wash

Clean Image Mobile Truck Wash	E	651 484-7776
Saint Paul (G-8216)		
Riverside Auto Wash Inc	E	763 571-2700
Minneapolis (G-3587)		

AUTOMOTIVE SVCS, EXC REPAIR: Washing & Polishing

Bbj Inc	E	651 730-7808
Saint Paul (G-9187)		
Buff & Shine Center Inc	E	952 944-9033
Minneapolis (G-3968)		
Cin-Mar Corp	E	612 781-6924
Minneapolis (G-4075)		
Douglas Drive Car Wash Inc	E	763 533-1581
Minneapolis (G-4285)		
Mister Car Wash	E	952 931-9412
Minneapolis (G-5110)		
Norseman Motors Inc	E	218 847-4415
Detroit Lakes (G-1212)		
Witt Dohm Properties Inc	E	952 758-5252
New Prague (G-6425)		

AUTOMOTIVE TOWING & WRECKING SVC

Chief's Service Inc	E	952 881-6404
Minneapolis (G-4063)		

AUTOMOTIVE TOWING SVCS

Andy's Towing Co	E	320 251-5691
Saint Cloud (G-7407)		
Budget Towing Inc of St Paul	E	651 699-5690
Saint Paul (G-8139)		
Cedar Towing & Auction Inc	E	612 721-6645
Minneapolis (G-4037)		
Chief's Towing Inc	E	952 888-2201
Minneapolis (G-4064)		
Robert A Williams Enterprises	E	952 831-6250
Minneapolis (G-5552)		
Schmit Towing Inc	E	763 253-1568
Minneapolis (G-3598)		
Shorty's Heavy Duty Wrecker	E	763 784-1411
Minneapolis (G-3601)		
Twin Cities Transport	E	651 770-0816
Saint Paul (G-9283)		
Twin Cities Transport	E	651 642-1446
Saint Paul (G-9089)		
Wrecker Services Inc	E	612 330-0013
Minneapolis (G-6089)		

AUTOMOTIVE TRANSMISSION REPAIR SVC

Mankato Auto Mall Owners Inc	E	507 387-7877
Mankato (G-3228)		
Norseman Motors Inc	E	218 847-4415
Detroit Lakes (G-1212)		

BAIL BONDING SVCS

Goldberg Bail Bonds	D	218 847-8122
Detroit Lakes (G-1194)		

BAKERY PRDTS: Wholesalers

American Importing Co Inc	D	612 331-7000
Minneapolis (G-3751)		
Bakemark USA LLC	E	952 937-9495
Eden Prairie (G-1601)		
Best Brands Corp	C	952 404-7500
Saint Paul (G-7716)		
Bruegger's Bagel Bakery	E	651 486-7135
Saint Paul (G-8135)		
Emily's Bakery & Deli Inc	E	651 437-3338
Hastings (G-2385)		
Franklin Bakery LLC	C	612 455-3893
Minneapolis (G-4473)		

Great Harvest Bread Co of MN	E	612 929-2899
Minneapolis (G-4552)		
Gregory's Foods Inc	E	651 454-0277
Saint Paul (G-7792)		
Holy Land Brand Inc	C	612 781-2627
Minneapolis (G-4663)		
Interstate Brands Corp	E	651 484-6020
Saint Paul (G-8522)		
Interstate Brands Corp	D	952 935-3034
Hopkins (G-2558)		
Log House Foods Inc	E	763 546-8395
Minneapolis (G-4898)		
Lund Food Holdings Inc	D	952 915-4888
Eden Prairie (G-1713)		
New French Bakery Inc	C	612 728-0193
Minneapolis (G-5188)		
Pan-O-Gold Baking Co	C	320 251-9361
Saint Cloud (G-7421)		
Pillsbury Co LLC	E	952 903-5262
Eden Prairie (G-1748)		
Pillsbury Co LLC	D	612 330-4003
Minneapolis (G-5378)		
Tech Investments Inc	E	218 733-0214
Duluth (G-1481)		

BALLOONS: Novelty & Toy

Aarcee Party & Tent Rental	E	952 922-7233
Minneapolis (G-3657)		

BANKRUPTCY REFEREE

Bankruptcy Solutions Inc	E	651 367-2000
Saint Paul (G-8087)		
Family Means	E	763 780-4986
Minneapolis (G-4410)		
Lps Default Solutions Inc	D	651 234-3500
Saint Paul (G-7827)		

BANKS: Commercial, NEC

Bremer Bank	E	320 763-6622
Alexandria (G-85)		
Cherokee State Bank	E	651 290-6112
Saint Paul (G-8190)		
Citizens Bank Minnesota	E	507 354-3165
New Ulm (G-6445)		
Citizens State Bank of	E	763 675-2265
Waverly (G-9903)		
Community Bank Chaska	E	952 361-2265
Chaska (G-960)		
Fidelity Bank	D	952 831-6600
Minneapolis (G-4428)		
Frandsen Bank & Trust	E	320 968-6293
Foley (G-2138)		
Lake Area Bank	E	651 653-9619
Saint Paul (G-8556)		
Landmark Community Bank	E	763 444-7787
Anoka (G-197)		
Minnwest Bank Central	E	320 269-6565
Montevideo (G-6251)		
Peoples Bank of Commerce	E	763 689-1212
Cambridge (G-845)		
Richard Sankovitz	E	507 835-4836
Waseca (G-9885)		
Wells Fargo Bank, National	E	763 295-2290
Monticello (G-6291)		
Wells Fargo Bank, National	E	218 726-9325
Duluth (G-1500)		

BANKS: Mortgage & Loan

Advisors Mortgage LLC	E	763 753-8133
Cedar (G-873)		
Affinity Plus Credit Union	E	651 291-3700
Saint Paul (G-7994)		
Agribank, Fcb	B	651 282-8800
Saint Paul (G-8000)		
American Residential Mortgage	E	763 784-2022
Champlin (G-889)		
American Residential Mortgage	D	651 488-1801
Saint Paul (G-8033)		
Bell Ancillary Services Inc	E	952 893-0865
Minneapolis (G-3880)		
Bremer Bank	E	800 908-2265
Saint Paul (G-8124)		
Cherokee State Bank	E	651 290-6112
Saint Paul (G-8190)		
D H I Mortgage	E	952 985-7850
Lakeville (G-2900)		
Home Savings of America	E	320 632-5461
Little Falls (G-3006)		
Homeservices Lending LLC	D	952 928-5300
Minneapolis (G-4671)		
Homeservices Lending LLC	E	763 494-8138
Osseo (G-6621)		
Lake Area Mortgage	D	651 257-1114
Saint Paul (G-8557)		

SERVICES SECTION BANKS

Lyman Lumber Co ....B... 952 470-3600
Excelsior (G-1945)
Mortgage Assurance ....E... 507 388-8140
Mankato (G-3174)
Mortgages Unlimited ....E... 763 633-0576
Elk River (G-1886)
Mortgages Unlimited Inc ....D... 763 416-2600
Maple Grove (G-3251)
Nations Title Agency ....E... 952 545-2808
Minneapolis (G-5170)
Northland Mortgage Corp ....E... 507 388-8600
Mankato (G-3177)
Residential Funding Co LLC ....B... 952 857-8700
Minneapolis (G-5524)
Residential Funding Securities ....B... 952 857-7000
Minneapolis (G-5525)
State Bank of Belle Plaine ....E... 952 873-2296
Belle Plaine (G-370)
Team USA Mortgage LLC ....D... 651 848-0484
Saint Paul (G-9031)
Trustcorp Mortgage Co ....E... 218 444-5626
Bemidji (G-429)
Wells Fargo Bank, National ....E... 320 587-2122
Hutchinson (G-2718)
Wells Fargo Bank, National ....E... 952 890-1424
Burnsville (G-821)
Wells Fargo Home Mortgage Inc ....E... 952 939-9066
Minneapolis (G-6048)
Western National Bank ....E... 218 723-5152
Duluth (G-1503)
Westner National Bank Inc ....E... 218 723-5100
Duluth (G-1504)

BANKS: National Commercial

Alliance Bank ....E... 507 354-3133
New Ulm (G-6438)
American Bank of St Paul ....C... 651 643-8472
Saint Paul (G-8022)
American Heritage National ....E... 320 732-6131
Long Prairie (G-3036)
American Heritage National ....E... 320 654-9555
Saint Cloud (G-7447)
Anchor Bank Heritage ....E... 651 770-2341
Saint Paul (G-8048)
Associated Banc-Corp ....E... 651 385-1600
Red Wing (G-6974)
Bank Midwest ....E... 507 847-3010
Jackson (G-2786)
Bank Midwest ....E... 507 235-3327
Fairmont (G-1958)
Bank Midwest ....E... 507 831-1322
Windom (G-10066)
Bremer Bank ....D... 320 251-3300
Saint Cloud (G-7465)
Bremer Bank ....E... 320 235-1111
Willmar (G-9993)
Bremer Bank National Assn ....D... 651 451-6822
South Saint Paul (G-9515)
Center National Bank ....E... 320 693-3255
Litchfield (G-2980)
Citizens National Bank Inc ....E... 218 732-3393
Park Rapids (G-6750)
Farmers State B of Hartland 507 845-2233
Hartland (G-2374)
First American Bank Valley ....E... 218 281-4182
Crookston (G-1124)
First Minnesota Bank National 320 864-3161
Glencoe (G-2206)
First National Bank ....E... 507 645-5656
Northfield (G-6528)
First National Bank ....E... 218 254-3371
Chisholm (G-997)
First National Bank In ....E... 218 935-5251
Mahnomen (G-3085)
1st National Bank In Wadena ....E... 218 631-1590
Wadena (G-9802)
1st National Bank Inc ....E... 218 534-3111
Deerwood (G-1177)
First National Bank of Bemidji ....D... 218 751-2430
Bemidji (G-394)
First National Bank of Deer 218 246-8221
Deer River (G-1171)
First National Bank of Milaca ....E... 320 983-3101
Milaca (G-3377)
1st National Bank of Pipestone ....E... 507 825-3344
Pipestone (G-6827)
1st National Bank of Plainview ....E... 507 534-3131
Plainview (G-6841)
First National Bank of The N ....E... 320 245-5261
Sandstone (G-9321)
First National Bank of Walker ....E... 218 547-1160
Walker (G-9850)
1st National Bank of Waseca ....E... 507 835-2740
Waseca (G-9878)
First National Bank of West St ....E... 651 457-1111
Saint Paul (G-7774)
Marquette Bank Monticello ....E... 763 271-2700
Monticello (G-6276)
Merchants Bank, National Assn ....C... 507 457-1100
Winona (G-10115)
Merchants National Bank of ....C... 507 457-1100
Winona (G-10116)
Midcountry Bank Inc ....E... 320 234-4500
Hutchinson (G-2707)
Minnstar Bank ....E... 507 726-2137
Lake Crystal (G-2861)
Minnwest Bank Central ....E... 320 269-6565
Montevideo (G-6251)
Minnwest Bank Luverne ....E... 507 283-2366
Luverne (G-3066)
Minnwest Bank South ....E... 507 836-6141
Slayton (G-9489)
Norwest Bank Minnesota North ....C... 612 667-1234
Minneapolis (G-5247)
Olmsted National Bank Inc 507 280-0028
Rochester (G-7197)
Patriot Bank Minnesota 651 462-8854
Wyoming (G-10206)
Peoples National Bank of Mora ....E... 320 679-3100
Mora (G-6367)
Pioneer National Bank ....E... 218 624-3676
Duluth (G-1424)
Pioneer National Bank ....E... 218 728-1172
Duluth (G-1425)
Profinium Financial Inc ....D... 507 235-5538
Fairmont (G-1978)
Riverwood Bank ....E... 218 751-5120
Bemidji (G-423)
Security Bank & Trust Co Inc ....E... 320 864-3171
Glencoe (G-2213)
Signal Financial Corp ....E... 651 905-3100
Saint Paul (G-7904)
State Bank & Trust ....D... 218 233-3107
Moorhead (G-6342)
Stearns Bank National Assn 320 253-6607
Saint Cloud (G-7608)
Stearns County National Assn ....E... 320 253-6607
Saint Cloud (G-7609)
Stearns County National Assn ....E... 320 253-6607
Saint Cloud (G-7610)
TCF Financial Corp ....A... 952 745-2760
Wayzata (G-9945)
TCF National Bank ....D... 612 661-6500
Minneapolis (G-5799)
U S Bancorp ....B... 651 466-3000
Minneapolis (G-5885)
U S Bank National Association ....E... 612 728-8300
Minneapolis (G-5886)
U S Bank National Association ....E... 952 925-7333
Minneapolis (G-5887)
U S Bank National Association ....E... 651 426-8266
Saint Paul (G-9098)
Unity Bank North ....D... 952 465-3000
Edina (G-1849)
US Bancorp Information Svcs ....E... 800 925-4324
Minneapolis (G-5943)
US Bancorp Legal Department ....D... 612 303-7879
Minneapolis (G-5944)
US Bank National Association ....E... 651 229-6123
Saint Paul (G-9118)
US Bank National Association ....E... 763 536-5328
Minneapolis (G-5945)
US Bank National Association ....E... 952 997-9600
Saint Paul (G-7940)
US Bank National Association ....E... 218 878-7878
Cloquet (G-1067)
US Bank National Association ....D... 612 303-3021
Minneapolis (G-5946)
Venture Bank ....E... 952 830-9999
Minneapolis (G-5962)
Venture Bank ....E... 651 289-2222
Saint Paul (G-7942)
Wells Fargo Bank ....E... 651 388-6751
Red Wing (G-7011)
Wells Fargo Bank ....E... 320 762-2181
Alexandria (G-129)
Wells Fargo Bank ....E... 218 681-1930
Thief River Falls (G-9682)
Wells Fargo Bank, National ....E... 218 326-8521
Grand Rapids (G-2311)
Wells Fargo Bank, National ....E... 507 373-1423
Albert Lea (G-71)
Wells Fargo Bank, National ....E... 218 749-5920
Virginia (G-9765)
Wells Fargo Bank, National ....E... 507 285-2800
Rochester (G-7290)
Wells Fargo Bank, National ....E... 507 285-2990
Rochester (G-7289)
Wells Fargo Bank, National ....E... 507 387-9254
Mankato (G-3215)
Wells Fargo Bank, National ....E... 612 316-3965
Minneapolis (G-3641)
Wells Fargo Bank, National ....E... 507 663-7300
Northfield (G-6545)
Wells Fargo Bank, National ....E... 507 451-5670
Owatonna (G-6744)
Wells Fargo Bank, National ....E... 507 532-4405
Marshall (G-3333)
Wells Fargo Bank, National ....E... 320 259-3100
Saint Cloud (G-7632)
Wells Fargo Bank, National ....D... 507 625-1872
Mankato (G-3216)
Wells Fargo Bank, National ....E... 952 953-3991
Saint Paul (G-7944)
Wells Fargo Bank, National ....E... 218 847-1361
Detroit Lakes (G-1222)
Wells Fargo Bank, National ....E... 612 667-8710
Minneapolis (G-6042)
Wells Fargo Business Credit ....D... 612 673-8500
Minneapolis (G-6043)
Wells Fargo Financial ....C... 952 920-9270
Minneapolis (G-6045)
Wells Fargo Minnesota West ....E... 218 736-7391
Fergus Falls (G-2124)
Wells Fargo Minnesota West ....E... 218 681-1930
Thief River Falls (G-9683)
Wells Fargo Minnesota West ....D... 218 233-6183
Moorhead (G-6347)
Wf National Bank South Central ....E... 507 334-5546
Faribault (G-2037)

BANKS: Other Activities, NEC

Unity Bank East 320 358-3600
Rush City (G-7391)
Western Bank Edina ....D... 952 857-1707
Minneapolis (G-6058)

BANKS: State Commercial

Alliance Bank ....E... 507 354-3133
New Ulm (G-6438)
Alliance Bank ....E... 651 345-3311
Lake City (G-2850)
American Bank of St Paul ....D... 651 452-1320
Saint Paul (G-8021)
American Bank of St Paul ....E... 507 377-7000
Albert Lea (G-38)
Annandale State Bank Inc ....E... 320 274-8216
Annandale (G-136)
Arlington State Bank Inc ....E... 507 964-2256
Arlington (G-248)
Associated Bank Minnesota ....E... 612 359-4461
Minneapolis (G-3823)
Bank Midwest ....E... 507 831-1322
Windom (G-10065)
Bank of Zumbrota ....E... 507 732-7555
Zumbrota (G-10217)
Bankcherokee ....E... 651 227-7071
Saint Paul (G-8086)
Beacon Bank ....E... 952 474-7309
Excelsior (G-1939)
Bnccorp Inc ....E... 612 305-2200
Minneapolis (G-3919)
Border State Bank ....E... 218 782-2151
Greenbush (G-2324)
Bremer Bank ....E... 800 908-2265
Saint Paul (G-8124)
Bremer Bank ....E... 218 847-9292
Detroit Lakes (G-1189)
Bremer Bank ....E... 763 389-2020
Princeton (G-6903)
Bremer Bank ....E... 320 235-1111
Willmar (G-9993)
Bremer Financial Corp ....D... 651 227-7621
Saint Paul (G-8125)
Bremmer Bank ....D... 320 763-6622
Alexandria (G-86)
Business Bank ....E... 952 847-1100
Hopkins (G-2521)
Central Bank ....E... 651 439-3050
Stillwater (G-9604)
Central Bank ....E... 507 498-5589
Spring Grove (G-9560)
Cherokee Bancshares Inc ....D... 651 227-7071
Saint Paul (G-8189)
Citizens Bank & Trust Co ....E... 320 587-2233
Hutchinson (G-2693)
Citizens Bank Minnesota ....E... 507 354-3165
New Ulm (G-6445)
Citizens Independent Bank ....E... 952 926-6561
Minneapolis (G-4082)
Citizens State Bank of ....E... 763 675-2265
Waverly (G-9903)
Citizens State Bank of Roseau ....E... 218 463-2135
Roseau (G-7354)

SERVICES

Employment codes: A=Over 500 employees, B=251-500, C=101-250, D=51-100, E=25-50
2011 Harris Minnesota Services Directory
© Harris InfoSource 1-866-281-6415
659

Community Bank Vernon Center..........E... 507 625-1551
Mankato (G-3118)

Community of Red River Valley...........D... 218 773-2451
East Grand Forks (G-1567)

Crow River State Bank ....E... 763 972-3385
Delano (G-1182)

Elmo Lake Bank....................................E... 651 777-8365
Lake Elmo (G-2870)

Faribault Bancshares Inc ....D... 507 332-7401
Faribault (G-2003)

Farmers & Merchants State Bank........E... 507 723-4234
Springfield (G-9571)

Farmers & Merchants State Bank........... 507 723-4800
Springfield (G-9572)

Farmers State Bank of Elkton 507 584-6441
Elkton (G-1906)

Farmers State Bank of Hamel ....E... 763 478-6611
Hamel (G-2341)

Farmers State Bank of West ....E... 507 527-2236
West Concord (G-9965)

Fidelity Bank..E... 952 831-6600
Minneapolis (G-4427)

First Aid & Trust ....E... 651 439-5195
Bayport (G-348)

First Commercial Bank 952 903-0777
Minneapolis (G-4442)

First Farmers & Merchants 507 567-2219
Brownsdale (G-629)

First National Bank 507 425-2575
Fulda (G-2194)

First Security Bank 218 948-2259
Evansville (G-1927)

First Security Bank - Sleepy ....E... 507 794-3911
Sleepy Eye (G-9495)

First State Bank & Trust ....D... 651 439-5195
Bayport (G-349)

First State Bank of Ashby 218 747-2235
Ashby (G-251)

First State Bank of Sauk ....E... 320 352-5771
Sauk Centre (G-9345)

First State Bank of Wabasha ....E... 651 565-3331
Wabasha (G-9766)

First State Bank of Wyoming ....E... 651 462-7611
Wyoming (G-10203)

First State Bank South West ....E... 507 376-9747
Worthington (G-10184)

First State Bank South West 507 376-9747
Worthington (G-10185)

First State Bk of Red Wing 651 388-4714
Red Wing (G-6982)

Flagship Bank Minnesota..................... 952 473-1959
Wayzata (G-9917)

FNB Bank of Blue Earth ....E... 507 526-3241
Blue Earth (G-535)

Frandsen Bank & Trust ....E... 507 744-2361
Lonsdale (G-3044)

Frandsen Bank & Trust ....E... 320 968-6293
Foley (G-2138)

Great Northern Bank............................E... 763 497-7777
Saint Michael (G-7673)

Hartman Bancshares Inc 507 853-4421
Okabena (G-6556)

Heartland State Bank............................ 507 445-3417
Storden (G-9656)

Heritage Bank......................................E... 320 235-5720
Willmar (G-10008)

Hometown Community Bank 320 795-2533
Cyrus (G-1154)

Klein Bank ....E... 952 467-2313
Young America (G-10209)

Lake Area Bank 651 257-1117
Lindstrom (G-2969)

Lake Bank National Association ....E... 218 834-2111
Two Harbors (G-9709)

Lake Community Bank ....E... 952 473-7347
Long Lake (G-3027)

Lakes State Bank 218 568-4473
Pequot Lakes (G-6790)

M & I Marshall & Ilsley Bank ....E... 952 544-3100
Minneapolis (G-4914)

M & I Marshall & Ilsley Bank ....D... 612 904-8000
Minneapolis (G-4915)

Marquette Financial Co's ....E... 612 661-3880
Minneapolis (G-4952)

Midwest Bank ....E... 218 847-4771
Detroit Lakes (G-1211)

Minnwest Bank Luverne.......................E... 507 283-2366
Luverne (G-3066)

Minnwest Bank M V ....E... 507 637-5731
Redwood Falls (G-7025)

Nicollet County Bank of Saint.............E... 507 931-3310
Saint Peter (G-9310)

North American Banking Co ....E... 651 636-9654
Saint Paul (G-8750)

North American State Bank ....E... 320 254-8271
Belgrade (G-365)

North American State Bank ....E... 320 697-5533
Elrosa (G-1910)

North Shore Bank of Commerce ....D... 218 722-4784
Duluth (G-1399)

North Shore Financial Corp ....D... 218 722-4784
Duluth (G-1400)

Northeast Bank....................................D... 612 379-8811
Minneapolis (G-5224)

Northeast Securities Corp.................... 612 379-8811
Minneapolis (G-5225)

Northview Bank....................................E... 320 233-7575
Finlayson (G-2131)

Northview Bank.................................... 320 233-7575
Finlayson (G-2132)

Northwestern Bank ....D... 218 287-2311
Dilworth (G-1223)

Otto Bremer Foundation ....C... 651 227-8036
Saint Paul (G-8792)

Peoples Bank of Commerce ....E... 763 689-1212
Cambridge (G-845)

Peoples State Bank of Madison............ 507 257-3544
Eagle Lake (G-1563)

Pioneer Bank 507 524-3630
Mapleton (G-3284)

Pioneer National Bank 507 375-3201
Saint James (G-7644)

Premier Bank Inc.................................D... 651 777-7700
Saint Paul (G-8837)

Prime Country Bank 320 584-5522
Royalton (G-7386)

Prior Lake State Bank Inc ....E... 952 447-2101
Prior Lake (G-6950)

Profinium Financial Inc ....E... 507 776-2311
Truman (G-9696)

Republic Bancshares Inc ....E... 218 722-3445
Duluth (G-1435)

Roundbank ....E... 507 835-4220
Waseca (G-9886)

Security Bank & Trust Co Inc ....E... 320 864-3171
Glencoe (G-2213)

Security Bank Minnesota ....E... 507 373-1481
Albert Lea (G-65)

Security Bank USA ....E... 218 751-1510
Bemidji (G-426)

Security Bankshares Co Inc ....E... 320 864-3171
Glencoe (G-2214)

Security State Bank of Kenyon............E... 507 789-6123
Kenyon (G-2829)

Sherburne State Bank ....E... 763 261-4200
Becker (G-358)

Signature Bank.................................... 952 936-7800
Hopkins (G-2633)

State Bank of Belle Plaine ....E... 952 873-2296
Belle Plaine (G-370)

State Bank of Cokato 320 286-2146
Cokato (G-1080)

State Bank of Delano ....E... 763 972-2935
Delano (G-1184)

State Bank of Faribault ....E... 507 332-7401
Faribault (G-2033)

State Bank of New Prague ....D... 952 758-4491
New Prague (G-6424)

State Bank of Park Rapids ....E... 218 732-3366
Park Rapids (G-6763)

State Bank of Tower Inc 218 753-6100
Tower (G-9688)

Stearns County National Assn ....D... 320 845-2149
Albany (G-29)

Sterling State Bank ....E... 507 282-1845
Rochester (G-7265)

Tradition Capital Bank 952 806-6600
Edina (G-1847)

21st Century Bank ....E... 763 479-1901
Loretto (G-3053)

21st Century Bank ....E... 763 767-2178
Minneapolis (G-3622)

21st Century Bank ....E... 763 767-2178
Minneapolis (G-3623)

U S Bancorp ....B... 651 466-3000
Minneapolis (G-5885)

Ultima Bank Minnesota 218 938-4144
Winger (G-10074)

Union Bank & Trust Co ....E... 612 379-3222
Minneapolis (G-5904)

United Community Bank ....E... 218 346-5700
Perham (G-6803)

Vermillion State Bank ....E... 651 437-4433
Vermillion (G-9723)

Village Bank ....E... 763 753-3007
Saint Francis (G-7638)

Wells Fargo Bank ....E... 651 205-8839
Saint Paul (G-9145)

Wells Fargo Bank ....E... 651 464-3334
Forest Lake (G-2172)

Western Bank ....E... 651 290-8100
Saint Paul (G-9149)

White Rock Bank ....C... 507 263-3030
Cannon Falls (G-864)

BANQUET HALL FACILITIES

American Hospitality Mgt ....E... 507 446-8900
Owatonna (G-6691)

American Legion Club ....E... 651 460-9909
Farmington (G-2039)

American Legion Club ....E... 763 421-0883
Anoka (G-152)

Appletree Motel Partnership................C... 952 854-9000
Minneapolis (G-3790)

Best Western South St Paul ....E... 651 455-3600
Saint Paul (G-8108)

Brook Hall Blaine Brook ....E... 763 755-8731
Minneapolis (G-3425)

Bub's Brewing Co Inc ....E... 507 457-3121
Winona (G-10085)

Buca Inc...D... 612 288-0138
Minneapolis (G-3966)

Buca Inc...D... 952 892-7272
Burnsville (G-687)

Chanhassen Theatre LLC ....C... 952 934-1500
Chanhassen (G-913)

Chevys..D... 952 814-9555
Minneapolis (G-4062)

Chevys Inc..E... 507 345-1446
Mankato (G-3115)

Chianti Grill ....E... 651 644-2808
Saint Paul (G-8191)

City of Brooklyn Center ....E... 763 569-6300
Minneapolis (G-4085)

City of Minneapolis ....C... 612 335-6000
Minneapolis (G-4091)

Diggers Bar & Grill Inc ....D... 507 634-7400
Kasson (G-2819)

8th Street Garage Inc ....E... 612 349-5717
Minneapolis (G-4333)

Hidden Haven Golf Course Inc.............E... 763 434-6867
Cedar (G-879)

Hyatt Corp ....B... 612 370-1234
Minneapolis (G-4683)

J Maas Co ....E... 218 631-3498
Wadena (G-9804)

Jade Catering Inc................................E... 763 767-3336
Anoka (G-193)

Jala Contracting Co.............................E... 763 434-4626
Cedar (G-880)

Jensen's Supper Club..........................E... 651 688-7969
Saint Paul (G-7809)

Jimmy's Conference & Catering ....E... 651 482-1233
Saint Paul (G-8533)

Knight of Columbus Community ....E... 952 492-5170
Prior Lake (G-6936)

Links On The Mississippi Inc ....E... 651 768-7611
Cottage Grove (G-1104)

Madison Properties Inc ....D... 218 847-2121
Detroit Lakes (G-1208)

Marshall Golf Club ....E... 507 532-2278
Marshall (G-3310)

Meadow Lakes Golf Club LLC ....E... 507 285-1190
Rochester (G-7181)

Mermaid Inc..C... 763 784-7350
Saint Paul (G-8637)

Michael's Restaurant ....E... 320 252-7100
Saint Cloud (G-7420)

Midwest of Rochester Inc ....D... 507 289-8866
Rochester (G-7184)

Midwest Restaurant Group ....D... 507 444-0303
Owatonna (G-6724)

Morton's of Chicago Inc.......................E... 612 673-9700
Minneapolis (G-5132)

Moundsview Banquet............................E... 763 717-4041
Saint Paul (G-8725)

Niecc Inc...C... 763 536-8300
Minneapolis (G-5200)

Normandy Inn Inc ....E... 612 370-1400
Minneapolis (G-5210)

North Central Management Inc ....E... 763 509-9500
Osseo (G-6642)

O K Corral Inc ....D... 952 492-6700
Jordan (G-2808)

Oak Glen LLC......................................D... 651 439-6981
Stillwater (G-9633)

Oak Inn Family Restaurant Inc.............E... 651 674-9977
North Branch (G-6503)

Restaurants No Limit Inc ....D... 952 471-8513
Spring Park (G-9564)

Restaurants Unlimited Inc ....E... 612 339-3800
Minneapolis (G-5530)

Rock Bottom of Minneapolis Inc...........D... 612 332-2739
Minneapolis (G-5557)

Ruth's Hospitality Group Inc ....D... 612 672-9000
Minneapolis (G-5578)

SERVICES

Sawatdee Inc ....E... 612 338-6451
Minneapolis *(G-5605)*

Speak Easy Restaurant ....E... 218 844-1326
Detroit Lakes *(G-1216)*

Spectrum Lanes Bowling Alley ....C... 763 553-0333
Minneapolis *(G-5718)*

St Cloud Suite Hotel Inc ....D... 320 654-1661
Saint Cloud *(G-7606)*

St Croix Preservation Co Inc ....E... 651 439-6000
Stillwater *(G-9644)*

Starwood Hotels & Resorts...........C... 612 331-1900
Minneapolis *(G-5744)*

Superior Concepts Inc...........D... 952 892-7555
Burnsville *(G-804)*

Suzanne's Cuisine ....E... 651 726-2535
Saint Paul *(G-9018)*

Tri City American Legion ....E... 651 631-1124
Saint Paul *(G-9080)*

Tri City Enterprises Inc ....E... 952 888-4447
Minneapolis *(G-5851)*

Tri City Post 513 ....E... 651 631-1124
Saint Paul *(G-9081)*

Trimark Hotel Corp ....C... 612 305-9763
Minneapolis *(G-5856)*

VFW Gallagher-Hanson Post 295 ....E... 651 455-1505
South Saint Paul *(G-9550)*

Victoria Inn ....D... 320 587-6030
Hutchinson *(G-2716)*

Vintage Inc ....E... 651 487-6878
Saint Paul *(G-9130)*

Wild Golf Club ....C... 952 445-3500
Prior Lake *(G-6962)*

BARBER SHOPS

Sunrise Hair STYling&tanning ....E... 651 777-2344
Saint Paul *(G-9015)*

BATTERIES, EXC AUTOMOTIVE: Wholesalers

Yale Materials Handling - MN ....D... 763 434-3832
Anoka *(G-241)*

BEAUTY SALONS

Arden Stephen Salon Inc ....E... 952 893-1938
Minneapolis *(G-3805)*

Elam Investments ....E... 763 544-4264
Minneapolis *(G-4335)*

Estetica ....E... 651 228-9327
Saint Paul *(G-8345)*

Fine Line Hair Inc ....E... 952 457-2620
Minneapolis *(G-6126)*

Flagship Athletic Club Inc ....B... 952 941-2000
Eden Prairie *(G-1665)*

G B & Co Hair & Skin Care ....E... 320 253-4832
Saint Cloud *(G-7516)*

Indulge Salon & Tanning LLP ....E... 507 345-3400
Mankato *(G-3226)*

J C Penney Co Inc ....E... 952 920-8557
Minneapolis *(G-4745)*

JC Penney Corp Inc ....C... 218 727-8111
Duluth *(G-1360)*

JC Penney Corp Inc ....D... 507 625-1606
Mankato *(G-3152)*

Jon English Salon ....E... 612 824-2474
Minneapolis *(G-4776)*

Justin Paul Inc ....E... 218 727-0034
Duluth *(G-1365)*

Juut Midwest Inc ....E... 612 332-3512
Minneapolis *(G-4783)*

Juut Midwest Inc ....E... 651 639-0576
Saint Paul *(G-8539)*

La Grande' Salon Ltd ....E... 651 464-4371
Forest Lake *(G-2163)*

Metropolis Salon Spa ....E... 952 473-8664
Wayzata *(G-9927)*

Pharmaceutical Specialties Inc ....E... 507 288-8500
Rochester *(G-7203)*

Regents of The University of ....E... 612 624-8865
Minneapolis *(G-5500)*

Regis Corp...........E... 320 253-5353
Saint Cloud *(G-7584)*

Regis Corp...........E... 952 435-5545
Burnsville *(G-789)*

Regis Corp...........E... 952 851-9999
Minneapolis *(G-5505)*

Regis Corp...........E... 651 636-9966
Saint Paul *(G-8885)*

Revamp Salon & Spa ....E... 612 341-0404
Minneapolis *(G-5533)*

Richard R Rodenborn ....E... 763 533-5155
Minneapolis *(G-5537)*

Rocco Altobelli Inc...........C... 952 707-1900
Burnsville *(G-793)*

Rocco Altobelli Inc...........E... 507 288-8582
Rochester *(G-7227)*

Rocco Altobelli Inc...........E... 651 690-5491
Saint Paul *(G-8908)*

Rocco Altobelli Inc...........E... 651 730-7077
Saint Paul *(G-9270)*

Rocco Altobelli Inc...........D... 952 920-5006
Minneapolis *(G-5556)*

Sakada ....E... 952 938-9400
Hopkins *(G-2625)*

Salon 2000 & Day Spa ....E... 952 942-8444
Eden Prairie *(G-1770)*

Salon Intrigue ....E... 952 922-0588
Minneapolis *(G-5596)*

Sunrise Hair STYling&tanning ....E... 651 777-2344
Saint Paul *(G-9015)*

Thomas Charles Salon II Inc ....E... 952 925-4277
Minneapolis *(G-5817)*

Zina's Inc ....E... 952 929-0093
Minneapolis *(G-6120)*

BEEF CATTLE FEEDLOTS

Helen Andresen...........E... 218 659-4491
Squaw Lake *(G-9577)*

Thier Feedlots Inc ....E... 507 478-4137
Rushmore *(G-7395)*

BEEF CATTLE RANCHING & FARMING

Lismore Hutterian Brethern ....D... 320 325-5485
Clinton *(G-1044)*

BEER & ALE WHOLESALERS

Beverage Wholesalers...........D... 320 759-9009
Alexandria *(G-84)*

Capital Beverage Sales Ltd ....E... 651 298-0800
Minneapolis *(G-3427)*

Carlson & Lyter Distributing ....E... 218 829-2978
Baxter *(G-322)*

Dahlheimer Distributing Co Inc ....E... 763 295-3347
Monticello *(G-6268)*

Kiwikai Imports Inc ....E... 763 550-9545
Minneapolis *(G-4813)*

Rohlfing of Brainerd Inc ....E... 218 829-0303
Brainerd *(G-585)*

BEER & ALE, WHOLESALE: Beer & Other Fermented Malt Liquors

Capitol Beverage Sales LP...........D... 763 571-4115
Minneapolis *(G-3428)*

Carlson & Lyter Distributing ....D... 320 251-7375
Sauk Rapids *(G-9360)*

Chas A Bernick Inc ....D... 320 252-6441
Waite Park *(G-9819)*

College City Beverage Inc ....D... 507 645-4106
Dundas *(G-1510)*

D-S Beverages Inc ....E... 218 233-1343
Moorhead *(G-6310)*

Hohensteins Inc...........E... 651 735-4978
Saint Paul *(G-9231)*

JJ Taylor Co's Inc ....C... 651 482-1133
Minneapolis *(G-4765)*

Locher Bros Inc...........E... 507 625-4198
Mankato *(G-3227)*

Locher Bros Inc...........E... 507 326-5471
Green Isle *(G-2323)*

North Beverage LLC ....E... 507 282-5462
Rochester *(G-7190)*

Quality Wine & Spirits Co...........D... 952 854-8600
Minneapolis *(G-5444)*

Schott Distributing Co Inc...........E... 507 289-3555
Rochester *(G-7248)*

Thorpe Distributing Co ....D... 763 463-2000
Rogers *(G-7343)*

Tow Distributing Corp ....E... 507 388-2931
Mankato *(G-3208)*

Wirtz Beverage Minnesota Beer ....C... 651 646-6063
Saint Paul *(G-9160)*

BEVERAGES, WINE & DISTILLED ALCOHOLIC, WHOLESALE: Liquor

Consolidated Enterprises Inc ....C... 651 646-7821
Saint Paul *(G-8249)*

Quality Wine & Spirits Co...........D... 952 854-8600
Minneapolis *(G-5444)*

BEVERAGES, WINE & DISTILLED ALCOHOLIC, WHOLESALE: Wine

Johnson Brothers Liquor Co ....C... 651 649-5800
Saint Paul *(G-8537)*

Kiwikai Imports Inc ....E... 763 550-9545
Minneapolis *(G-4813)*

Quality Wine & Spirits Co...........D... 952 854-8600
Minneapolis *(G-5444)*

World Class Wines Inc ....E... 952 941-8795
Eden Prairie *(G-1817)*

BEVERAGES, WINE WHOLESALE : Wine Coolers

Liquors Plus Inc...........E... 651 501-1199
Saint Paul *(G-9243)*

Quality Wine & Spirits Co ....D... 952 854-8600
Minneapolis *(G-5444)*

BEVERAGES, WINE/DISTILLED ALCOHOLIC, WHOL: Bttlg Wine/Liquor

United States Distilled Prdts ....C... 763 389-4903
Princeton *(G-6918)*

BIBLE CAMPS

Camp Shamineau of The...........E... 218 575-2240
Motley *(G-6383)*

Lutheran Bible Camp ....E... 218 566-2329
Remer *(G-7030)*

BICYCLE REPAIR SHOP

Freewheel Bicycle Cooperative...........E... 612 339-2219
Minneapolis *(G-4487)*

BILLIARD & POOL PARLORS

Biff's Billiards Sports Bar ....E... 763 784-9446
Minneapolis *(G-3416)*

Shooters Billiard Club & Pro ....E... 952 894-1100
Burnsville *(G-796)*

University Billiards Inc...........E... 763 574-1399
Minneapolis *(G-3630)*

BILLIARD EQPT & SPLYS WHOLESALERS

Watson's of Minneapolis Inc ....E... 763 560-7727
Minneapolis *(G-6024)*

BILLING & BOOKKEEPING SVCS

Broadston Consulting Services ....E... 952 442-9770
Waconia *(G-9779)*

Cargill Inc ....E... 763 742-5512
Minneapolis *(G-4008)*

Cargill Inc ....E... 763 742-7237
Wayzata *(G-9908)*

City of Anoka ....E... 763 576-2750
Anoka *(G-167)*

Health Billing Systems LLC ....D... 763 559-3779
Minneapolis *(G-4616)*

Healthline Inc ....E... 218 362-6760
Hibbing *(G-2449)*

Intermed Consultants Ltd ....E... 952 920-2070
Minneapolis *(G-4719)*

Orthopedic Resources Mgt...........E... 952 831-5773
Minneapolis *(G-5294)*

Perot Systems Corp ....E... 651 999-5600
Saint Paul *(G-8819)*

Pinnacle Financial Group Inc ....D... 952 996-0559
Minneapolis *(G-5381)*

Schoeneckers Inc...........A... 952 835-4800
Minneapolis *(G-5611)*

Viking Forest Products LLC ....E... 952 941-6512
Eden Prairie *(G-1805)*

Wells Fargo Bank, National ....E... 952 881-7333
Minneapolis *(G-6040)*

BINGO HALL

Bingo Carousel...........D... 763 493-2111
Minneapolis *(G-3905)*

Bingo Emporium ....D... 320 252-3607
Saint Cloud *(G-7458)*

Prairie Island Indian Com ....C... 651 388-0083
Welch *(G-9955)*

River Boat Bingo ....E... 507 388-6086
Mankato *(G-3186)*

Smsc Gaming Enterprise ....A... 952 445-6000
Prior Lake *(G-6955)*

Treasure Island Casino & Bingo ....A... 651 388-6300
Welch *(G-9957)*

BLOOD BANK

Abbot Northwestern Hospital...........E... 612 863-3150
Minneapolis *(G-3659)*

American National Red Cross ....C... 651 291-4600
Saint Paul *(G-8030)*

Csl Plasma Inc ....E... 651 646-2556
Saint Paul *(G-8272)*

Csl Plasma Inc ....D... 218 727-8139
Duluth *(G-1287)*

Memorial Blood Center ....C... 651 332-7000
Saint Paul *(G-8633)*

Employment codes: A=Over 500 employees, B=251-500,
C=101-250, D=51-100, E=25-50

2011 Harris Minnesota
Services Directory

© Harris InfoSource 1-866-281-6415

661

Memorial Blood Center......................E... 218 723-8080
Duluth (G-1389)

Memorial Blood Center......................E... 218 263-1338
Hibbing (G-2462)

BLOOD RELATED HEALTH SVCS

American National Red Cross ....C... 651 291-6789
Saint Paul (G-8029)

BLUEPRINTING SVCS

Albinson Reprographics LLC ....E... 612 374-1120
Minneapolis (G-3703)

American Reprographics Co LLC ....D... 612 722-2303
Minneapolis (G-3759)

Ers Digital Inc ....D... 763 694-5900
Minneapolis (G-4369)

Franz Reprographics Inc ....E... 763 503-3401
Minneapolis (G-4477)

Shel Don Group Inc ....E... 218 727-2817
Duluth (G-1448)

BOARDING SVCS, KENNELS

Goldwood Kennels Inc ....E... 651 429-0648
Saint Paul (G-9221)

Mill City Kennel ....E... 763 755-3595
Minneapolis (G-3544)

Minnesota Horse & Hunt Club ....D... 952 447-2272
Prior Lake (G-6943)

Northern Valley Animal Clinic..................... 507 282-0867
Rochester (G-7191)

BOAT REPAIR SVCS

Brainerd Sports & Marine LLC.................. 218 828-4728
Brainerd (G-554)

Perfect Complement Ltd ....E... 763 421-8360
Minneapolis (G-3569)

BOAT YARD: Boat yards, storage & incidental repair

Nisswa Marine Inc................................E... 218 963-2292
Nisswa (G-6498)

BOILER & HEATING REPAIR SVCS

Albers Mechanical Services Inc ....E... 651 224-3100
Saint Paul (G-8003)

API Group Inc ....E... 651 636-4320
Saint Paul (G-8054)

BOILER REPAIR SHOP

Boiler Services Inc..............................E... 763 784-8178
Minneapolis (G-3422)

Harris Contracting Co...........................E... 507 282-8128
Rochester (G-7133)

BOOKS, PERIODICALS & NEWSPAPERS WHOLESALERS

East View Information Services..........E... 952 252-1201
Hopkins (G-2536)

BOOKS, WHOLESALE

Book Sales Inc ....D... 732 225-0530
Minneapolis (G-3927)

East View Information Services..........E... 952 252-1201
Hopkins (G-2536)

Gopher News Co ....D... 763 546-5300
Minneapolis (G-4542)

Mackin Book Co ....B... 952 895-9540
Burnsville (G-750)

Scholastic Book Fairs Inc ....D... 763 391-0930
Minneapolis (G-5613)

Sky Media LLC ....E... 651 635-0100
Saint Paul (G-8963)

Valley News Co ....D... 507 345-4819
Mankato (G-3212)

World Wide Publications.....................E... 612 333-0940
Minneapolis (G-6087)

BOULDER: Crushed & Broken

DH Blattner & Sons Inc........................D... 320 356-7351
Avon (G-294)

BOWLING CENTERS

AMF Bowling Centers Inc.....................E... 651 484-6501
Saint Paul (G-8038)

AMF Bowling Centers Inc.....................E... 763 571-3520
Minneapolis (G-3402)

AMF Bowling Centers Inc.....................E... 651 774-8787
Saint Paul (G-8039)

B L B Inc ....D... 612 825-3737
Minneapolis (G-3852)

Bowl Rite Inc ....E... 651 646-1396
Saint Paul (G-8119)

Bowling Bob's 13th Frame Pro ....D... 763 755-8686
Minneapolis (G-3423)

Brunswick Bowling & Billiards ....E... 952 941-0445
Eden Prairie (G-1612)

CB & L Inc ....E... 651 257-8047
Chisago City (G-988)

Cernick Enterprises ....D... 651 552-9005
Inver Grove Heights (G-2741)

Church of St Bernard...........................E... 651 488-6733
Saint Paul (G-8200)

Classic Bowl Inc ....E... 763 421-4402
Minneapolis (G-3433)

Colonial Lanes Co ....E... 507 289-2341
Rochester (G-7086)

Country Lanes-North Inc ....E... 218 722-1741
Duluth (G-1283)

Dan Dahlin Inc ....E... 763 434-6010
Anoka (G-172)

Elsie's Restaurant Lounge ....E... 612 378-9702
Minneapolis (G-4344)

Jack's House ....E... 218 824-5225
Brainerd (G-571)

Kalk-Young Inc ....E... 218 864-5265
Battle Lake (G-311)

Kandi Entertainment Center Inc ....D... 320 235-3800
Willmar (G-10012)

Kegler's Inc..E... 218 722-0671
Duluth (G-1369)

Minnehaha Bowling Center Inc............E... 651 488-7208
Saint Paul (G-8671)

Reese Brooks Hospitality Inds ....E... 763 767-0754
Minneapolis (G-3581)

River City Lanes.................................E... 763 295-3390
Monticello (G-6285)

Skyline Bowling Lanes Inc ....E... 218 727-8555
Duluth (G-1452)

Spare Times Lanes & Lounge ....E... 507 477-3492
Hayfield (G-2426)

Spectrum Lanes Bowling Alley ....C... 763 553-0333
Minneapolis (G-5718)

Sundance Golf & Bowl Inc ....E... 763 420-4700
Osseo (G-6670)

Tuttle Inc ....E... 612 378-9701
Minneapolis (G-5870)

Tuttle's Bowling Bar & Grill ....E... 952 938-4090
Hopkins (G-2649)

Wells Lanes Inc ....E... 651 455-3220
South Saint Paul (G-9552)

BOXING & WRESTLING ARENA

Premier Rinks Inc................................E... 763 249-7417
Minneapolis (G-5403)

BOYS' CAMPS

Circle R Ranch Inc ....E... 320 547-2176
Long Prairie (G-3039)

Etoc Co Inc ....D... 218 963-2906
Nisswa (G-6496)

Little Elk Youth Ranch Inc....................E... 320 594-2750
Browerville (G-625)

BOYS' TOWNS

North Homes Inc ....D... 218 327-3055
Grand Rapids (G-2298)

St James Home of Duluth ....C... 218 728-7500
Duluth (G-1462)

BRACING & SURGERY SVCS

Top Notch Treecare ....E... 763 253-8733
Minneapolis (G-5830)

BRACING SVCS, ORNAMENTAL TREE

S & S Tree & Horticultural ....E... 651 451-8907
South Saint Paul (G-9539)

BRICK, STONE & RELATED PRDTS WHOLESALERS

Advance Specialties Co ....E... 651 489-8881
Saint Paul (G-7989)

Brock White Co LLC ....E... 651 647-0950
Saint Paul (G-8131)

Hedberg Aggregates Inc ....D... 763 545-4400
Minneapolis (G-4627)

L&W Supply Corp ....E... 952 890-0828
Burnsville (G-745)

BROADCASTING STATIONS, RADIO: Country Music

Kkaq AM 1460 ....E... 218 681-4900
Thief River Falls (G-9672)

BROADCASTING STATIONS, RADIO: Rock Music

Minneapolis Radio LLC ....D... 612 617-4000
Minneapolis (G-5060)

BROADCASTING STATIONS, TELEVISION: Translator Station

Care TV ....C... 763 546-1111
Minneapolis (G-4004)

BROKERS & DEALERS: Mortgages, Buying & Selling

Cascade Mortgage Inc ....E... 612 252-3333
Minneapolis (G-4023)

Community Finance Group Inc ....E... 763 416-5959
Minneapolis (G-4141)

BROKERS & DEALERS: Securities

Cargill Financial Services ....C... 952 742-7575
Hopkins (G-2524)

Cargill Financial Services Int...............A... 952 742-7575
Minneapolis (G-4006)

Charles Schwab & Co Inc ....D... 952 835-6784
Minneapolis (G-4056)

Charles Schwab & Co Inc ....E... 952 404-0398
Wayzata (G-9910)

Citigroup Derivatives Markets ....D... 952 475-5500
Hopkins (G-2531)

Citigroup Global Markets Inc................E... 651 215-8400
Saint Paul (G-8202)

Craig-Hallum Capital Group LLC ....D... 612 334-6300
Minneapolis (G-4176)

F B L Financial Services Inc ....E... 651 905-2123
Saint Paul (G-7772)

Feltl & Co..E... 952 546-5018
Minneapolis (G-4425)

Fintegra Financial Solutions 763 503-1911
Minneapolis (G-4435)

Knight Financial Products LLC ....D... 952 249-5500
Hopkins (G-2565)

Merrill Lynch, Pierce, Fenner ....D... 651 298-1700
Saint Paul (G-8640)

Merrill Lynch, Pierce, Fenner ....E... 218 726-3140
Duluth (G-1391)

Merrill Lynch, Pierce, Fenner ....E... 952 820-1900
Minneapolis (G-4993)

Merrill Lynch, Pierce, Fenner ....E... 612 349-7801
Minneapolis (G-4994)

Merrill Lynch, Pierce, Fenner ....E... 651 275-8040
Stillwater (G-9627)

Mid Coutry Bank ....C... 952 931-2200
Hopkins (G-2581)

Morgan Stanley ....E... 763 475-4100
Wayzata (G-9930)

Questar Capital Corp ....E... 888 446-5872
Minneapolis (G-5450)

Rbc Wealth Managment ....E... 651 766-4920
Saint Paul (G-8873)

RSM McGladrey Business Soln ....C... 952 921-7700
Minneapolis (G-5567)

Thrivent Financial For ....A... 920 734-5721
Minneapolis (G-5819)

Thrivent Financial For ....E... 952 894-6772
Burnsville (G-808)

Wells Fargo Advisors LLC ....E... 952 835-3111
Minneapolis (G-6037)

Wells Fargo Advisors LLC ....E... 612 332-1212
Minneapolis (G-6036)

BROKERS & DEALERS: Security

Anderson Swenson Associates ....E... 612 347-8600
Minneapolis (G-3778)

Cri Securities Inc ....C... 612 617-6000
Minneapolis (G-4183)

Gardner Financial Services Inc ....E... 952 935-4601
Minneapolis (G-4500)

Piper Jaffray Co's ....A... 612 303-6000
Minneapolis (G-5384)

Rbc Wealth Managment ....E... 763 476-3700
Hopkins (G-2610)

Stifel, Nicolaus & Co Inc ....E... 763 542-3700
Minneapolis (G-5757)

Voyageur Co's Inc ....D... 612 376-7000
Minneapolis (G-5985)

Wells Fargo Bank, National ....E... 507 373-1423
Albert Lea (G-71)

S
E
R
V
I
C
E
S

Wells Fargo Bank, National..................E... 651 385-2328
Red Wing (G-7012)

Wells Fargo Bank, National..................E... 651 205-7583
Saint Paul (G-9146)

BROKERS & DEALERS: Stock

A G Edwards & Sons Inc....................D... 952 832-1600
Bloomington (G-480)

Citigroup Global Markets Inc................E... 612 349-4800
Minneapolis (G-4080)

Dougherty & Co LLC............................C... 612 376-4000
Minneapolis (G-4283)

Morgan Stanley & Co Inc....................D... 952 921-1900
Minneapolis (G-5128)

BROKERS' SVCS

A G Edwards & Sons Inc....................D... 952 832-1600
Bloomington (G-480)

BROKERS, MARINE TRANSPORTATION

Advanced Service Management..........E... 763 201-1451
Hamel (G-2337)

K 2 International Inc................................ 651 209-8770
Saint Paul (G-7814)

Rubenstein Logistics Services............E... 763 542-1121
Golden Valley (G-2244)

Volk Transfer Inc.................................E... 507 388-1683
Mankato (G-3213)

BROKERS: Automotive

Gull Way Ltd.......................................E... 218 753-1210
Tower (G-9687)

BROKERS: Commodity Futures

Archer-Daniels-Midland Co...................E... 612 340-5900
Minneapolis (G-3801)

Country Hedging Inc.............................E... 651 355-6500
Inver Grove Heights (G-2746)

BROKERS: Contract Basis

Wilpro Inc..D... 320 235-8850
Willmar (G-10057)

BROKERS: Food

Belgrade Cooperative Assn...............E... 320 254-8231
Belgrade (G-363)

Best Brands Corp................................B... 651 454-5850
Saint Paul (G-7717)

Fraboni's Wholesale Distrs.................E... 218 263-8991
Hibbing (G-2445)

Juhl Brokerage Inc..............................E... 763 519-0120
Minneapolis (G-4781)

Key Sales Group Inc............................E... 952 979-1531
Hopkins (G-2564)

Roisum Elite Rosium Foods.................E... 952 227-3199
Chanhassen (G-938)

Source One Sales & Marketing............C... 952 829-0833
Minneapolis (G-5704)

US Foodservice Inc.............................B... 651 454-6580
Eagan (G-1559)

BROKERS: Loan

Complete Real Estate Services............E... 651 287-3400
Saint Paul (G-8243)

Dougherty Financial Group LLC............C... 612 376-4000
Minneapolis (G-4284)

First Integrity Bank.............................E... 218 894-1522
Staples (G-9584)

1st National Bank of Pipestone............E... 507 825-3344
Pipestone (G-6827)

Great Northern Bank............................E... 763 497-7777
Saint Michael (G-7673)

Lake Community Bank.........................E... 952 473-7347
Long Lake (G-3027)

Landmark Community Bank..................E... 763 444-7787
Anoka (G-197)

Minnesota League of Credit.................E... 651 288-5170
Saint Paul (G-8694)

Minnwest Bank Central........................E... 320 269-6565
Montevideo (G-6251)

North American Banking Co..................E... 651 636-9654
Saint Paul (G-8750)

Northstar Capital Markets Svcs............E... 651 290-8781
Saint Paul (G-8765)

Northwestern Bank..............................D... 218 287-2311
Dilworth (G-1223)

Roundbank...E... 507 835-4220
Waseca (G-9886)

Security Bank USA..............................E... 218 751-1510
Bemidji (G-426)

St Cloud Federal Employees................D... 320 252-2634
Saint Cloud (G-7600)

Sterling State Bank..............................E... 507 282-1845
Rochester (G-7265)

Wells Fargo Home Mortgage Inc..........E... 952 939-9066
Minneapolis (G-6048)

Winona National Holding Co Inc..........D... 507 454-4320
Winona (G-10152)

BROKERS: Mortgage, Arranging For Loans

All American Mortgage Lending...........E... 763 560-5815
Minneapolis (G-3707)

American Investment Management......E... 763 533-7193
Minneapolis (G-3754)

C U Mortgage Services Inc..................D... 651 631-3111
Saint Paul (G-8146)

Commonsense Mortgage Inc................E... 952 942-8502
Eden Prairie (G-1633)

Global Lending Corp...........................E... 651 438-7976
Hastings (G-2388)

Hmn Mortgage Services Inc................E... 952 914-7440
Minneapolis (G-4656)

Landmark Financial Group Inc.............E... 763 572-8626
Minneapolis (G-3514)

Midcountry Mortgage Corp..................D... 651 766-7000
Saint Paul (G-8653)

Minnesota Lending Co LLC...................D... 952 960-9600
Minneapolis (G-5080)

Mortgage & Investment ConsInts........E... 651 483-0200
Saint Paul (G-8723)

Northern Lights Mortgage Co............... 612 435-3500
Minneapolis (G-5227)

Prism Mortgage Inc............................E... 952 546-6272
Minneapolis (G-5411)

Provident Mortgage Corp of MN..........E... 612 285-6275
Minneapolis (G-5434)

Referral Mortgage Inc.........................E... 952 933-4400
Minneapolis (G-5482)

Residential Mortgage Group Inc..........E... 952 593-1169
Hopkins (G-2616)

River City Mortgage............................D... 952 915-5300
Minneapolis (G-5542)

Royal Financial LLC............................E... 763 746-9480
Minneapolis (G-5593)

Summit Mortgage Corp........................E... 763 390-7200
Minneapolis (G-5764)

Tradition Mortgage LLC.......................E... 952 920-5100
Minneapolis (G-5845)

United Residential Mortgage................E... 952 820-0272
Minneapolis (G-5915)

BROKERS: Printing

Davies Printing Co..............................E... 952 473-6924
Wayzata (G-9913)

Image Sea Co's Inc.............................D... 952 882-0884
Burnsville (G-735)

BROKERS: Security

Ameriprise Financial Inc.....................A... 612 671-3131
Minneapolis (G-3767)

Charles Schwab & Co Inc.....................D... 651 222-8600
Saint Paul (G-8187)

Dain Rauscher Inc..............................A... 612 371-2711
Minneapolis (G-4217)

Dougherty & Co LLC............................C... 612 376-4000
Minneapolis (G-4283)

Ing Financial Partners Inc...................D... 612 372-5507
Minneapolis (G-4702)

Merrill Lynch, Pierce, Fenner..............E... 952 476-5600
Wayzata (G-9926)

Piper Jaffray Co's...............................A... 612 303-6000
Minneapolis (G-5384)

Primevest Financial Services...............B... 320 656-4300
Saint Cloud (G-7572)

Rbc Wealth Management......................E... 651 228-6900
Saint Paul (G-8872)

Rbc Wealth Management......................A... 612 371-7750
Minneapolis (G-5472)

Rbc Wealth Managmt............................D... 952 838-7000
Minneapolis (G-5473)

Rbc Wealth Managmt...........................E... 218 724-2100
Duluth (G-1431)

Secruian Financial Services................ 651 223-4252
Saint Paul (G-8942)

BUILDING & OFFICE CLEANING SVCS

Ace Building Maintenance Inc.............E... 651 482-1020
Saint Paul (G-7980)

Burnsville Commercial Cleaning..........E... 952 469-5423
Lakeville (G-2893)

Fidelity Building Services Inc..............B... 952 854-1447
Bloomington (G-497)

SOS Janitorial Inc..............................E... 763 560-9611
Minneapolis (G-5703)

BUILDING CLEANING & MAINTENANCE SVCS

A1 Contract Cleaning Inc.....................E... 763 544-3847
Minneapolis (G-3653)

Assured Decontamination Svcs...........D... 651 998-0922
Lake Elmo (G-2865)

Building Material Supply Inc................E... 763 252-5555
Golden Valley (G-2237)

Capital Maintenance Services.............D... 651 773-9777
Saint Paul (G-8152)

Ceda Inc...E... 763 434-4403
Anoka (G-163)

Clean-It Group Inc..............................C... 952 943-1911
Hopkins (G-2532)

Clear Water Cleaners Inc.....................D... 320 558-6691
South Haven (G-9506)

Columbia Building Services Inc............E... 612 331-2090
Minneapolis (G-4124)

Deer River Hired Hands Inc.................E... 218 246-8182
Deer River (G-1169)

Dvcm ServiceMaster of The.................E... 320 763-5551
Alexandria (G-96)

Epic Enterprise Inc.............................E... 507 645-6800
Dundas (G-1511)

Five Star H Enterprises Inc.................D... 612 867-5373
Minneapolis (G-4453)

Hospitality Services Corp....................C... 763 323-3141
Rockford (G-7302)

Independent School District.................E... 218 723-4119
Duluth (G-1356)

Mac Enterprises Inc............................E... 612 789-9392
Minneapolis (G-4926)

Maintenance Professionals Inc............E... 651 774-2334
Saint Paul (G-8608)

Melrose Diversicom Telephone............E... 320 256-8288
Melrose (G-3349)

Minnesota Housekeeping Svcs............E... 651 686-0900
Saint Paul (G-7842)

Qsc of Northfield Inc...........................E... 507 366-7149
Northfield (G-6540)

Quality Building Maintenance..............D... 507 289-0603
Rochester (G-7214)

Rick L Schoenrock..............................E... 320 763-7144
Alexandria (G-120)

Rusciano-Hyland Inc...........................E... 612 871-4434
Minneapolis (G-5576)

S & D Cleaning....................................E... 651 558-7336
Maplewood (G-3287)

Servicemaster of St Cloud Inc..............C... 320 252-4622
Saint Cloud (G-7591)

ServiceMaster Total Cleaning..............C... 952 873-6070
Saint Cloud (G-7592)

Specialty Contracting Services............C... 763 424-4100
Osseo (G-6666)

Sulco Cleaning Service.......................E... 952 937-8777
Eden Prairie (G-1784)

Supreme Building Maintenance............E... 763 972-8425
Delano (G-1185)

TLC Cleaning Specialists.....................E... 218 263-4778
Hibbing (G-2477)

Triangle Services Inc..........................C... 651 294-0020
Saint Paul (G-9082)

U M D Facilities Management................E... 218 726-8262
Duluth (G-1488)

Woodfam Inc.......................................E... 218 283-4775
International Falls (G-2734)

BUILDING CLEANING SVCS

Belde Building Maintenance................D... 651 457-6337
South Saint Paul (G-9511)

Brunskill Enterprises..........................E... 763 477-4546
Buffalo (G-636)

Carlson Building Maintenance.............B... 651 481-9970
Saint Paul (G-8166)

Ceda Inc...E... 763 434-4403
Anoka (G-163)

Christians Inc.....................................E... 952 470-2001
Chanhassen (G-916)

General Cleaning Corp........................D... 218 727-4513
Duluth (G-1333)

Huber Bros Building Maintence............E... 952 224-7000
Burnsville (G-733)

L T T Inc...E... 952 929-4556
Minneapolis (G-4828)

Managed Services Inc.........................C... 952 925-4111
Minneapolis (G-4940)

McCrady Janitorial Inc........................E... 952 758-3097
New Prague (G-6432)

Servicemaster of St Cloud Inc..............C... 320 252-4622
Saint Cloud (G-7591)

Employment codes: A=Over 500 employees, B=251-500,
C=101-250, D=51-100, E=25-50

2011 Harris Minnesota
Services Directory

© Harris InfoSource 1-866-281-6415

663

BUILDING EXTERIOR CLEANING SVCS

Renew Services Inc ....E... 651 699-3504
Saint Paul *(G-8889)*

BUILDING INSPECTION SVCS

AAA-American Co ....E... 507 894-4156
Hokah *(G-2490)*

BUILDING ITEM REPAIR SVCS, MISCELLANEOUS

Atlas Foundation Co ....E... 763 428-2261
Osseo *(G-6596)*
United Operations Inc of ....E... 763 551-0202
Minneapolis *(G-5911)*

BUILDING MAINTENANCE SVCS, EXC REPAIRS

General Cleaning Corp ....D... 218 727-4513
Duluth *(G-1333)*
Maintenance Team ....E... 952 942-5000
Eden Prairie *(G-1715)*
Tidy Service of Minnesota Inc ....E... 612 332-5461
Hopkins *(G-2646)*

BUMPER SHOP: Automotive Repair

Lewiston Auto Co Inc ....E... 507 523-2164
Lewiston *(G-2967)*

BURGLAR ALARM MAINTENANCE & MONITORING SVCS

ADT Security Services Inc ....C... 651 917-0000
Saint Paul *(G-7984)*
ADT Security Services Inc ....E... 651 917-0010
Minneapolis *(G-3386)*
Arrowhead Security Systems Inc ....E... 218 722-1234
Duluth *(G-1243)*
Checkpoint Security Systems ....C... 952 942-9431
Chanhassen *(G-914)*
Checkpoint Systems Inc ....E... 952 227-5350
Chaska *(G-958)*
Checkpoint Systems Inc ....C... 952 943-3853
Chanhassen *(G-915)*
Electro-Watchman Inc ....E... 651 227-8461
Saint Paul *(G-8329)*
Pro-TEC Design Inc ....E... 763 553-1477
Plymouth *(G-6880)*
Security Response Services Inc...........E... 952 346-8922
Minneapolis *(G-5626)*
Trans-Alarm Inc..D... 952 894-1700
Burnsville *(G-810)*

BUS CHARTER SVC: Local

Albert Lea Bus Co Inc............................E... 507 373-1467
Albert Lea *(G-30)*
Austin Coaches Inc.................................E... 507 433-5358
Austin *(G-259)*
Jefferson Partners LP ....C... 612 359-3400
Minneapolis *(G-4757)*
Lorenz Bus Service Inc ....D... 763 784-7196
Minneapolis *(G-3522)*
Manske Bus Service Inc ....E... 507 243-3282
Madison Lake *(G-3080)*
Minnesota City Bus Service Inc...........E... 507 454-5871
Minnesota City *(G-6136)*
Minnetonka Transportation Inc ....D... 952 935-1990
Minnetonka *(G-6199)*
Osseo Brooklyn School Bus Co ....C... 763 425-2542
Osseo *(G-6647)*
Palmer Charter Service Inc ....E... 320 632-1555
Little Falls *(G-3017)*
Reading Bus Line Inc ....E... 507 926-5404
Reading *(G-6970)*
Ready Bus Line Co Inc ....D... 507 895-2349
La Crescent *(G-2843)*
Reichert Enterprises Inc........................C... 218 829-6955
Brainerd *(G-584)*
Southwest Coaches Inc..........................D... 507 532-4043
Marshall *(G-3328)*
Trobec's Bus Service Inc ....D... 320 251-1202
Saint Stephen *(G-9317)*

BUS CHARTER SVC: Long-Distance

Brainerd Bus Lines Inc ....D... 218 829-6955
Baxter *(G-321)*
Crystal Lake Bus Service Inc ....E... 507 243-3282
Madison Lake *(G-3078)*
Faribault Transportation Co...................E... 507 334-5121
Faribault *(G-2005)*
First Student Inc.....................................C... 763 559-8111
Saint Paul *(G-8383)*

Jefferson Partners LP............................C... 612 359-3400
Minneapolis *(G-4757)*
L C S Coaches Inc..................................E... 218 879-3391
Cloquet *(G-1055)*
Marschall Bus Service Inc.....................D... 952 463-8689
Farmington *(G-2054)*
Metropolitan School & Charter ....C... 218 724-1707
Duluth *(G-1392)*
Minn-Dakota Coaches Inc ....E... 218 739-3393
Fergus Falls *(G-2095)*
New Ulm Bus Lines Inc ....E... 507 354-4711
New Ulm *(G-6465)*
Northfield Lines Inc ....E... 507 645-5267
Northfield *(G-6518)*
Ossel Brooklyn Bus Co Inc ....E... 952 891-1031
Saint Paul *(G-7861)*
Ottertail Coaches Inc ....D... 218 739-3393
Fergus Falls *(G-2112)*
Owatonna Bus Co Inc ....D... 507 451-5262
Owatonna *(G-6725)*
Palmer Bus Service Inc ....E... 320 634-3272
Glenwood *(G-2229)*
Palmer Bus Service of Mankato ....E... 507 386-0210
Mankato *(G-3230)*
Palmer Bus Service of N ....E... 320 632-1555
Little Falls *(G-3016)*
Palmer Charter Service Inc ....E... 320 632-1555
Little Falls *(G-3017)*
Peterson Bus Service Inc ....D... 320 354-2414
New London *(G-6418)*
Ready Bus Line Co Inc ....D... 507 895-2349
La Crescent *(G-2843)*
Red River Trails Inc ....E... 218 236-0300
Moorhead *(G-6337)*
Richards Transportation Svc ....E... 218 233-3404
Moorhead *(G-6338)*
Richfield Bus Co ....D... 952 881-1111
Minneapolis *(G-5538)*
Rochester City Line Co ....E... 507 288-4353
Rochester *(G-7230)*
Shubat Transportation Co ....E... 218 262-1042
Hibbing *(G-2475)*
Southwest Coaches Inc..........................D... 507 532-4043
Marshall *(G-3328)*
Thielen Bus Lines Inc ....E... 507 637-3600
Redwood Falls *(G-7028)*
Town & Country Bus Co Inc ....D... 763 786-2510
Minneapolis *(G-3620)*
Trobec's Bus Service Inc ....D... 320 251-1202
Saint Stephen *(G-9317)*
Voigt's Bus Service Inc ....D... 320 252-1807
Saint Cloud *(G-7626)*
Voigt's Motorcoach Travel Inc ....C... 320 253-0510
Saint Cloud *(G-7627)*
Voigt's of Waconia ....E... 952 442-2818
Waconia *(G-9794)*

BUS TERMINALS & SVC FACILITIES

Minnesota Department of Trans ....A... 612 349-7332
Minneapolis *(G-5074)*

BUSES: Wholesalers

ABC Bus Co's Inc ....D... 507 334-1871
Faribault *(G-1985)*
Hoglund Bus Co Inc................................E... 763 295-5119
Monticello *(G-6273)*

BUSINESS ACTIVITIES: Non-Commercial Site

Canby Conerned Citizens ....E... 507 223-7061
Canby *(G-849)*
Celebrities Unlimited Inc 651 482-9945
Saint Paul *(G-8179)*
City of Beaver Creek...............................E... 507 673-2266
Beaver Creek *(G-353)*
Greatstone LLC ....E... 651 429-6606
Saint Paul *(G-8429)*
Kinship Youth Mentoring ....D... 763 631-5967
Princeton *(G-6910)*
Lighthouse On Homestead Inc ....E... 218 525-4525
Duluth *(G-1463)*
Mahnomen County Sheriff's ....E... 218 935-2255
Mahnomen *(G-3089)*
Prairie Arts Continuum ....E... 507 831-4862
Windom *(G-10070)*
Schwieters' Co's Inc ....D... 651 407-1618
Hugo *(G-2673)*
Zanby LLC ....E... 952 938-5448
Minnetonka *(G-6240)*

BUSINESS FORMS WHOLESALERS

American Business Forms Inc ....D... 320 634-5471
Glenwood *(G-2219)*
Corporate Graphics Intl..........................C... 651 494-1740
Saint Paul *(G-8252)*

Marudas Graphics Inc ....E... 651 697-7820
Saint Paul *(G-8617)*
Moore Wallace North America...............E... 952 844-2000
Minneapolis *(G-5124)*
Quality Business Forms of ....E... 763 559-4330
Minneapolis *(G-5441)*

BUSINESS MACHINE REPAIR, ELECTRIC

Bennett Office Technologies ....E... 320 235-6425
Willmar *(G-9985)*
Davis Typewriter Co Inc ....E... 507 343-2001
Worthington *(G-10182)*
North Country Business Prdts ....D... 218 751-4140
Bemidji *(G-408)*
North Country Business Prdts ....E... 800 937-4140
Plymouth *(G-6878)*
Smith Micro Technologies Inc...............C... 651 482-8718
Saint Paul *(G-8966)*
System Design Advantage LLC ....E... 952 703-3500
Minneapolis *(G-5781)*

BUSINESS SUPPORT SVCS

Alliant Precision Fuse Co ....D... 763 744-5000
Minneapolis *(G-3713)*
America's Tpa Inc ....E... 952 896-1246
Minneapolis *(G-3744)*
Castle Danger LP ....D... 218 728-8060
Duluth *(G-1263)*
Commercial Products V H Inds..............E... 651 224-2831
Saint Paul *(G-8228)*
Cosmopolitan & Associates Inc ....A... 612 822-3830
Minneapolis *(G-4165)*
Ellermedia Group....................................E... 612 369-5612
Saint Paul *(G-8333)*
Lake Crystal Fire Department................E... 507 726-2440
Lake Crystal *(G-2859)*
Midwest Protection Agency Inc ....E... 763 421-2966
Saint Michael *(G-7677)*
National Retirement Plan Inc ....D... 651 789-1037
Eagan *(G-1541)*
Ndn Mulcahy LLC ....E... 651 747-4201
Mahtomedi *(G-3096)*
Pattern Stations Inc ....D... 763 441-6833
Monticello *(G-6282)*
Rule One Trasportation...........................E... 952 703-7318
Minneapolis *(G-5575)*
Safezone LLC ....D... 612 716-0856
Saint Paul *(G-8921)*

BUTCHER SVCS: Processing Only, Does Not Sell Meat

West Central Turkeys LLC ....A... 218 863-1491
Pelican Rapids *(G-6784)*

BUTTER WHOLESALERS

Franklin Foods...D... 218 727-6651
Duluth *(G-1327)*
Michael Foods Group Inc........................C... 952 258-4000
Minnetonka *(G-6193)*

CABLE & OTHER PAY TELEVISION DISTRIBUTION

Arvig Enterprises Inc ....E... 218 584-5119
Twin Valley *(G-9700)*
Captionmax Inc..E... 612 341-3566
Minneapolis *(G-4000)*
Charter Communications ....D... 888 438-2427
Rochester *(G-7074)*
Fox Cable Network Services LLC ....D... 612 330-2468
Minneapolis *(G-4469)*
Mediacom Inc ....E... 952 440-9650
Prior Lake *(G-6941)*

CABLE TELEVISION

Arvig Enterprises Inc ....C... 218 346-5500
Perham *(G-6793)*
Hector Communications Corp................D... 218 346-5500
New Ulm *(G-6453)*
Hiawatha Broadband Comms.................D... 507 474-4000
Winona *(G-10101)*
Kasson & Mantorville Telephone ....E... 507 634-2511
Kasson *(G-2821)*
Mediacom LLC ....E... 507 835-5975
Waseca *(G-9882)*
Midcontinent Media Inc ....C... 952 844-2600
Minneapolis *(G-5024)*
Prewire Specialists Inc...........................C... 651 452-9192
Saint Paul *(G-8846)*

2011 Harris Minnesota
Services Directory

(G-00000) Company's Geographic Section entry number

CALENDARS, WHOLESALE
J L Buchanan Inc 612 334-1710
Minneapolis *(G-4747)*

CALIBRATING SVCS, NEC
Martin Calibration Inc ....E... 952 882-1528
Burnsville *(G-751)*

Precision Repair & Calibration ....E... 763 784-1704
Minneapolis *(G-3572)*

CAMERA REPAIR SHOP
H & J Bliss Enterprises ....E... 952 988-9302
Minneapolis *(G-4584)*

CAMPGROUNDS
Brennaville Inc ....E... 507 467-2512
Preston *(G-6895)*

Buffalo Junction ....E... 218 624-9901
Duluth *(G-1259)*

CAR WASH EQPT & SPLYS WHOLESALERS
Zep Inc ....D... 763 792-2050
Minneapolis *(G-6133)*

CAR WASHES
Brookdale Car Wash Inc..............E... 763 561-1123
Minneapolis *(G-3954)*

Dealers Choice Auto Clean ....E... 763 592-9900
Minneapolis *(G-4237)*

Downtowner Car Wash..................E... 651 222-7045
Saint Paul *(G-8310)*

Fast Lane Car Wash......................E... 218 444-9130
Bemidji *(G-392)*

London Road Car Wash Inc ....E... 218 728-4201
Duluth *(G-1385)*

Northland Power Washing ....E... 320 763-6593
Alexandria *(G-116)*

Paradise Car Wash ....E... 952 888-5388
Minneapolis *(G-5319)*

Perfect 10 Car Wash Inc ....E... 651 227-9274
Minneapolis *(G-3568)*

S J C Inc..E... 651 483-1752
Saint Paul *(G-8919)*

Soft Touch Car Care of St ....E... 320 253-4204
Saint Cloud *(G-7595)*

Wally Mc Carthys Oldsmobile..............D... 651 636-6060
Saint Paul *(G-9138)*

CARNIVAL SPLYS, WHOLESALE
Dunk N Jump..................................D... 612 788-0404
Minneapolis *(G-4295)*

CARPET & RUG CLEANING PLANTS
Lindstrom Cleaning & Constr ....E... 763 544-8761
Minneapolis *(G-4891)*

CARPET & UPHOLSTERY CLEANING SVCS
Loyear Cleaning & Restoration ....E... 952 831-0777
Minneapolis *(G-4905)*

Restoration Contractors Inc ....E... 651 646-3408
Saint Paul *(G-8894)*

Restoration Professionals Inc ....D... 651 379-1990
Saint Paul *(G-8895)*

Rick L Schoenrock........................E... 320 763-7144
Alexandria *(G-120)*

Rug & Carpet Caretakers ....E... 507 388-5384
Mankato *(G-3189)*

Servicemaster of St Cloud Inc ....C... 320 252-4622
Saint Cloud *(G-7591)*

Shine-Way Janitorial Service..............D... 507 388-7439
Mankato *(G-3197)*

CARPET & UPHOLSTERY CLEANING SVCS: Carpet/Furniture, On Loc
A S T Inc..E... 952 888-7340
Eden Prairie *(G-1582)*

Christians Inc ....E... 952 470-2001
Chanhassen *(G-916)*

Fibercare Inc..................................E... 612 721-5048
Minneapolis *(G-4426)*

Quantum Co's Inc ....E... 952 943-4357
Minneapolis *(G-5445)*

CARPET & UPHOLSTERY CLEANING SVCS: On Customer Premises
Jubilee Enterprises Inc................E... 507 532-2332
Marshall *(G-3301)*

CASH GRAIN CROPS PREPARATION SVCS
Cargill Freshwater........................E... 952 742-3050
Excelsior *(G-1941)*

Farmers Co-Operative Elevator ....D... 507 768-3448
Hanley Falls *(G-2368)*

CASH REGISTERS WHOLESALERS
Cash Register Sales Inc ....D... 651 294-2700
Saint Paul *(G-8171)*

Data Systems Inc ....E... 952 934-4001
Eden Prairie *(G-1642)*

P O S Business Systems Inc ....E... 763 559-1341
Minneapolis *(G-5306)*

Wand Corp......................................C... 952 361-6200
Eden Prairie *(G-1813)*

CASINO HOTELS & MOTELS
Fond Du Lac Reservation......................A... 218 878-2327
Carlton *(G-867)*

Leech Lake Palace & Casino ....A... 218 335-7000
Cass Lake *(G-872)*

Leech Lake Reservation ....A... 218 547-2744
Walker *(G-9854)*

Madison Properties Inc ....D... 320 763-2498
Alexandria *(G-112)*

Prairie Island Indian Com ....C... 651 388-0083
Welch *(G-9955)*

Smsc Gaming Enterprise ....A... 952 445-6000
Prior Lake *(G-6955)*

Smsc Gaming Enterprise ....A... 952 445-8982
Prior Lake *(G-6956)*

CASKETS WHOLESALERS
Northwestern Casket Co Inc ....E... 612 789-4356
Minneapolis *(G-5245)*

CATTLE WHOLESALERS
Rich Prairie Livestock ....E... 320 468-2514
Pierz *(G-6808)*

CEMETERIES
City of Bloomington..........................C... 952 563-4925
Minneapolis *(G-4084)*

National Cemetery Admin ....D... 612 726-1127
Minneapolis *(G-5161)*

CEMETERIES: Real Estate Operation
Hillside Cemetery Association ....E... 612 781-3391
Minneapolis *(G-4649)*

Lakewood Cemetery Association........E... 612 822-2171
Minneapolis *(G-4837)*

CERAMIC FLOOR & WALL TILE WHOLESALERS
Olympia Tile Inc ....E... 763 545-5455
Minneapolis *(G-5274)*

Pro-Wall Inc..................................E... 763 477-5172
Rockford *(G-7312)*

Rollin B Child Inc ....E... 763 559-5531
Minneapolis *(G-5558)*

Rubble Stone Co Inc......................E... 952 938-2599
Hopkins *(G-2623)*

CERTIFICATE ISSUING: Face Amount
Ameriprise Financial Inc ....A... 612 671-3131
Minneapolis *(G-3767)*

CERTIFICATE ISSUING: Face Amount Installment
Ameriprise Financial Inc ....A... 612 671-3131
Minneapolis *(G-3767)*

CHAMBERS OF COMMERCE
Minnesota Chamber of Commerce......E... 651 292-4650
Saint Paul *(G-8675)*

Riverheights Chamber of ....E... 651 451-2266
Inver Grove Heights *(G-2766)*

CHARGE ACCOUNT SVCS
Deluxe Corp ....B... 651 483-7111
Saint Paul *(G-8285)*

CHARTER FLYING SVC
Aviation Charter Inc........................D... 952 943-1519
Eden Prairie *(G-1600)*

CHAUFFEUR SVCS
Transit TEC Ltd..............................D... 320 253-5940
Saint Cloud *(G-7618)*

CHECK CASHING SVCS
Game Financial Corp........................C... 800 363-3321
Minneapolis *(G-4497)*

United Check Clearing Corp ....D... 763 559-2225
Minneapolis *(G-5908)*

CHECK VALIDATION SVCS
Deluxe Corp ....B... 651 483-7111
Saint Paul *(G-8285)*

Electronic Check Alliance..................E... 952 445-2888
Saint Paul *(G-8330)*

CHEESE WHOLESALERS
Michael Foods Group Inc..................C... 952 258-4000
Minnetonka *(G-6193)*

CHEMICAL CLEANING SVCS
Ceda Inc ....E... 763 434-4403
Anoka *(G-163)*

CHEMICALS & ALLIED PRDTS WHOLESALERS, NEC
Brenntag Great Lakes LLC ....E... 651 204-4300
Saint Paul *(G-8127)*

Hawkins Inc....................................C... 612 331-6910
Minneapolis *(G-4608)*

Lubrication Technologies Inc..............D... 763 545-0707
Minneapolis *(G-4908)*

Nalco Chemical Co..........................E... 763 559-3209
Minneapolis *(G-5156)*

Praxair Inc ....E... 651 633-6781
Saint Paul *(G-8836)*

3M Co..E... 651 733-5623
Saint Paul *(G-9058)*

3M Co..E... 651 736-2326
Saint Paul *(G-9057)*

Univar USA Inc..............................E... 651 774-9400
Saint Paul *(G-9111)*

CHEMICALS & ALLIED PRDTS, WHOL: Chemicals, Swimming Pool/Spa
Hawkins Inc....................................C... 612 331-6910
Minneapolis *(G-4608)*

CHEMICALS & ALLIED PRDTS, WHOL: Food Additives/Preservatives
Arkema Inc ....E... 507 583-6641
Blooming Prairie *(G-476)*

MCP Foods Inc................................D... 507 233-7406
New Ulm *(G-6460)*

CHEMICALS & ALLIED PRDTS, WHOL: Gases, Compressed/Liquefied
Minneapolis Oxygen Co..................E... 612 588-8855
Minneapolis *(G-5058)*

Toll Co ....E... 763 551-5355
Minneapolis *(G-5829)*

CHEMICALS & ALLIED PRDTS, WHOLESALE: Adhesives
3M Co..B... 651 733-6678
Saint Paul *(G-9059)*

CHEMICALS & ALLIED PRDTS, WHOLESALE: Alkalines & Chlorine
Ashland Inc ....E... 612 726-1787
Minneapolis *(G-3817)*

CHEMICALS & ALLIED PRDTS, WHOLESALE: Anti-Freeze Compounds
Lubrication Technologies Inc..............D... 651 636-7990
Saint Paul *(G-8596)*

Universal Cooperatives Inc ....D... 651 239-1000
Saint Paul *(G-7938)*

US Venture Inc..............................D... 763 591-5827
Minneapolis *(G-5950)*

CHEMICALS & ALLIED PRDTS, WHOLESALE: Chemical Additives
Universal Cooperatives Inc ....D... 651 239-1000
Saint Paul *(G-7938)*

Employment codes: A=Over 500 employees, B=251-500,
C=101-250, D=51-100, E=25-50

2011 Harris Minnesota
Services Directory

© Harris InfoSource 1-866-281-6415
665

SERVICES

CHEMICALS & ALLIED PRDTS, WHOLESALE: Chemicals, Indl

Hawkins Inc ....C... 612 331-6910
Minneapolis (G-4608)
Lubrication Technologies Inc ....D... 651 636-7990
Saint Paul (G-8596)

CHEMICALS & ALLIED PRDTS, WHOLESALE: Chemicals, Indl & Heavy

Zep Inc ....D... 763 792-2050
Minneapolis (G-6133)

CHEMICALS & ALLIED PRDTS, WHOLESALE: Compressed Gas

Airgas - North Central Inc ....E... 763 712-5100
Anoka (G-148)
Oxygen Service Co Inc ....D... 651 644-7273
Saint Paul (G-8797)

CHEMICALS & ALLIED PRDTS, WHOLESALE: Concrete Additives

General Resource Technology ....E... 651 454-4151
Saint Paul (G-7779)

CHEMICALS & ALLIED PRDTS, WHOLESALE: Indl Gases

Valley National Gases Inc ....E... 651 628-4848
Saint Paul (G-9123)

CHEMICALS & ALLIED PRDTS, WHOLESALE: Oxygen

American Welding & Gas ....E... 320 235-4774
Willmar (G-9983)
Healthline Inc ....E... 218 262-6981
Hibbing (G-2450)
Oxygen Service Co Inc ....D... 651 644-7273
Saint Paul (G-8797)

CHEMICALS & ALLIED PRDTS, WHOLESALE: Plastics Film

Martin Falk Paper Co ....E... 612 332-8626
Minneapolis (G-4959)

CHEMICALS & ALLIED PRDTS, WHOLESALE: Plastics Materials, NEC

Genpak LLC ....C... 952 881-8673
Minneapolis (G-4522)
North American Composites Co..........C... 651 481-6860
Circle Pines (G-1019)

CHEMICALS & ALLIED PRDTS, WHOLESALE: Plastics Prdts, NEC

AEP Industries Inc ....D... 507 625-3011
Mankato (G-3100)
AEP Industries Inc ....D... 507 386-4420
Mankato (G-3101)
Indelco Plastics Corp ....E... 952 925-5075
Minneapolis (G-4694)
J-M Manufacturing Co Inc ....D... 507 893-3121
Winnebago (G-10076)
Plastic Promotions Inc ....E... 651 686-0660
Saint Paul (G-7877)
Spray Control Systems Inc ....E... 507 583-2112
Blooming Prairie (G-478)

CHEMICALS & ALLIED PRDTS, WHOLESALE: Plastics Sheets & Rods

Acrylic Design Associates Inc ....D... 763 559-8392
Minneapolis (G-3675)
Crown Plastics Inc ....E... 763 557-6000
Minneapolis (G-4189)
Indelco Plastics Corp ....E... 952 925-5075
Minneapolis (G-4694)
Plastics International Inc ....E... 952 934-2303
Eden Prairie (G-1750)
Tandem Products Inc ....E... 612 721-2911
Minneapolis (G-5788)

CHEMICALS & ALLIED PRDTS, WHOLESALE: Polyurethane Prdts

BASF Corp ....E... 763 559-3266
Minneapolis (G-3870)
Otto Bock US Polyurethane Foam ......E... 763 553-9464
Minneapolis (G-5299)

CHEMICALS & ALLIED PRDTS, WHOLESALE: Resin, Synthetic Rubber

BASF Corp ....E... 763 559-3266
Minneapolis (G-3870)

CHEMICALS & ALLIED PRDTS, WHOLESALE: Sanitation Preparations

Kennedy Brissman ....E... 651 646-7933
Saint Paul (G-8545)

CHEMICALS & ALLIED PRDTS, WHOLESALE: Sealants

Auto Butler Inc ....E... 612 529-3345
Minneapolis (G-3836)

CHEMICALS & ALLIED PRDTS, WHOLESALE: Spec Clean/Sanitation

Kennedy Brissman ....E... 651 646-7933
Saint Paul (G-8545)

CHEMICALS & ALLIED PRDTS, WHOLESALE: Surface Active Agents

Auto Butler Inc ....E... 612 529-3345
Minneapolis (G-3836)
Surfacequest Inc 952 361-9431
Minneapolis (G-5773)

CHEMICALS & ALLIED PRDTS, WHOLESALE: Syn Resin, Rub/Plastic

Clariant Corp ....D... 763 535-4511
Minneapolis (G-4100)
Interplastic Corp ....E... 651 481-6860
Saint Paul (G-8519)
Interplastic Corp ....E... 651 481-6860
Saint Paul (G-8520)

CHEMICALS, AGRICULTURE: Wholesalers

Belgrade Cooperative Assn ....E... 320 254-8231
Belgrade (G-363)
Bemidji Cooperative Assn ....E... 218 751-4260
Bemidji (G-379)
Coop FCA ....E... 507 847-4160
Jackson (G-2789)
Country Pride Services Co-op ....E... 507 831-2580
Bingham Lake (G-466)
Crystal Valley Coop ....E... 507 642-8837
La Salle (G-2846)
Farmers Co-Operative of Hanska ....E... 507 439-6244
Hanska (G-2370)
Farmers Co-Operative Oil Co of ....E... 507 925-4114
Echo (G-1581)
Farmers Union Oil Co of........................E... 320 269-8856
Montevideo (G-6245)
Hollandale Marketing Assn ....E... 507 889-3181
Hollandale (G-2492)
Minn-Kota AG Products Inc ....E... 218 643-8464
Breckenridge (G-595)
Multi-County AG LLC..............................E... 507 223-5634
Canby (G-850)
Peterson's North Branch Mill................E... 651 674-4425
North Branch (G-6504)
Precision Turf & Chemical Inc ....E... 763 477-5885
Rockford (G-7303)
Rosen's Diversified Inc ....E... 507 238-4201
Fairmont (G-1980)
Sunrich Inc ....D... 507 451-3316
Hope (G-2496)
Sunrise AG Cooperative.........................E... 320 468-6433
Buckman (G-632)
United Farmers Co Op ....E... 507 237-2281
Gaylord (G-2201)
Watonwan Farm Service Inc ....E... 507 776-2831
Truman (G-9699)
West Central Inc ....E... 320 235-8518
Willmar (G-10053)
Western Consolidated Co-op.................E... 320 394-2171
Holloway (G-2493)
Wilmont Farmers Elevator Co...............E... 507 926-5131
Wilmont (G-10064)

CHILD & YOUTH SVCS, NEC

A Chance To Grow Inc............................D... 612 789-1236
Minneapolis (G-3647)
AIN Dah Yung Center...............................E... 651 227-4184
Saint Paul (G-8001)
County of Cass ....D... 218 547-1346
Walker (G-9849)
Face To Face Health ....E... 651 772-5555
Saint Paul (G-8361)

Family Child Development Ctr ....E... 763 545-7271
Minneapolis (G-4407)
Greater Minneapolis Crisis ....D... 763 591-0100
Minneapolis (G-4560)
Hope Common ....C... 651 917-0917
Saint Paul (G-8494)
Ram Woodvale ....E... 507 433-4924
Austin (G-284)
Safe Haven ....E... 952 846-0608
Burnsville (G-794)
St Paul Youth Services ....E... 651 771-1301
Saint Paul (G-9000)
Stellher Human Services Inc ....E... 218 751-5919
Bemidji (G-428)
Stivland Inc ....E... 651 436-1153
Afton (G-11)
Tri-County Community Action ....E... 320 632-3691
Little Falls (G-3020)

CHILD DAY CARE SVCS

A Chance To Grow Inc............................D... 612 789-1236
Minneapolis (G-3647)
Albert Lea Family YMCA ....E... 507 373-8228
Albert Lea (G-31)
Anoka Child Care Center ....E... 763 427-1897
Anoka (G-155)
Berean Baptist Church............................952 432-7168
Burnsville (G-686)
Bright Horizons Children's ....E... 763 571-2375
Minneapolis (G-3424)
Camp Widji Wagan ....E... 218 365-2117
Ely (G-1912)
Care Corner...E... 507 386-7444
Mankato (G-3113)
Carolyn A Adrianse ....E... 507 386-7444
Mankato (G-3114)
Child Care Choices Inc ....E... 320 251-5081
Saint Cloud (G-7491)
Child Care Resource & Referral ....D... 507 287-2020
Rochester (G-7076)
Children's Center ....E... 507 373-7979
Albert Lea (G-44)
Children's Home Society ....B... 651 646-7771
Saint Paul (G-8196)
Children's Home Society ....E... 651 228-7707
Saint Paul (G-8195)
Christian Life Church ....E... 651 463-4545
Farmington (G-2043)
Church of St Matthew..............................E... 651 224-9793
Saint Paul (G-8201)
Church of The Nativity of The ....E... 952 881-8160
Minneapolis (G-4074)
Cindy Day Care ....E... 651 688-7678
Saint Paul (G-7733)
CLC Childcare Center ....E... 507 452-5493
Winona (G-10088)
Club Kid of Edina Inc ....E... 952 831-1055
Minneapolis (G-4111)
Community Action Partnership............E... 651 224-4363
Saint Paul (G-8236)
Community Child Care Center ....E... 612 861-4303
Minneapolis (G-4139)
Concordia Creative Learning ....E... 651 793-6624
Saint Paul (G-8246)
Coon Rapids Day Care Center ....E... 763 755-2412
Minneapolis (G-3440)
Crookston Family Service Ctr ....E... 218 281-1343
Crookston (G-1119)
Dakotah Sport & Fitness Center ....C... 952 445-9400
Prior Lake (G-6932)
Discover Magical Moments ....E... 507 289-7463
Rochester (G-7096)
Duluth Area Family YMCA ....E... 218 722-4745
Duluth (G-1297)
E B I Inc ....E... 218 624-3508
Duluth (G-1307)
Elk River Independent School..............D... 763 241-3480
Elk River (G-1873)
Especially For Children Inc ....E... 651 452-0043
Saint Paul (G-7770)
Evergreen Child Care Center ....E... 952 402-0303
Shakopee (G-9439)
Family Child Development Ctr ....E... 763 545-7271
Minneapolis (G-4407)
Golden Heart Child Care Center...........E... 507 625-1454
Mankato (G-3225)
Greenview Alzheimer's ....E... 218 263-3935
Hibbing (G-2447)
Guadalupe Alternative Programs.........E... 651 222-0757
Saint Paul (G-8434)
Hastings YMCA...E... 651 480-8887
Hastings (G-2390)
Head Start Program Onigum ....D... 218 547-1420
Walker (G-9851)

www.HarrisInfo.com
666
2011 Harris Minnesota
Services Directory
(G-00000) Company's Geographic Section entry number

S
E
R
V
I
C
E
S

Hendricks Community Hospital............C... 507 275-3134
Hendricks **(G-2429)**

Hope Presbyterian Church of 612 866-4055
Minneapolis **(G-4674)**

Hopkins Early Learning Center ....E... 952 988-5050
Hopkins **(G-2554)**

House of Hope Presbyterian.................D... 651 227-6311
Saint Paul **(G-8497)**

Independent School District 16 ....D... 763 786-1338
Minneapolis **(G-3496)**

Iron Range Learning & Devpt ....E... 218 741-7441
Virginia **(G-9742)**

Itasca County Family Young..................D... 218 327-1161
Grand Rapids **(G-2287)**

Jack & Jill Preschool ....E... 651 604-3810
Saint Paul **(G-8527)**

Jewish Community Nursery & Day ......E... 651 698-0751
Saint Paul **(G-8532)**

Kid's Haven of Buffalo Inc ....D... 763 682-3072
Buffalo **(G-646)**

Kid's Korner Educare Center...............E... 507 451-0312
Owatonna **(G-6720)**

Kiddie Karousel Day Care Ctr ....E... 218 263-7450
Hibbing **(G-2458)**

Kids Come 1st Children's Ctr ....E... 507 281-4421
Rochester **(G-7152)**

KinderCare Learning Centers ....E... 952 941-5054
Eden Prairie **(G-1702)**

KinderCare Learning Centers ....E... 651 681-1968
Saint Paul **(G-7816)**

KinderCare Learning Centers ....E... 651 735-0037
Saint Paul **(G-9237)**

Kindercare Learning Centers ....E... 952 920-8548
Minnetonka **(G-6185)**

Kindercare Learning Centers ....E... 651 452-1616
Saint Paul **(G-7817)**

Kindercare Learning Centers...............E... 952 440-9890
Savage **(G-9393)**

Kindercare Learning Centers...............E... 651 735-3711
Saint Paul **(G-9238)**

Knowledge Learning Corp ....E... 952 452-6625
Saint Paul **(G-7818)**

Knowledge Learning Corp ....E... 763 553-7960
Minneapolis **(G-4816)**

Knowledge Learning Corp ....E... 651 631-8728
Saint Paul **(G-8550)**

Knowledge Learning Corp ....E... 507 289-5006
Rochester **(G-7156)**

Knowledge Learning Corp ....E... 507 529-8455
Rochester **(G-7155)**

Knowledge Learning Corp ....E... 952 440-2677
Savage **(G-9394)**

Knowledge Learning Corp ....E... 612 623-4642
Minneapolis **(G-4817)**

La Petite Academy Inc ....E... 651 463-2022
Farmington **(G-2053)**

Learning For Leadership ....E... 612 789-9598
Minneapolis **(G-4852)**

Lifetrack Resources Inc ....D... 651 227-8471
Saint Paul **(G-8586)**

Little Acorns Child Care Inc ....E... 952 475-0828
Long Lake **(G-3028)**

Little Acorns Day School ....E... 952 475-0828
Wayzata **(G-9925)**

Lord of Life Lutheran Church ....E... 763 427-1100
Anoka **(G-201)**

Lutheran Social Service of MN ....E... 218 281-6418
Crookston **(G-1127)**

Marshall Public School..........................E... 507 537-6210
Marshall **(G-3311)**

Martin County West School Dist ....E... 507 728-8609
Welcome **(G-9959)**

Maxwell Wsu Children Center...............D... 507 457-5368
Winona **(G-10114)**

ML Enterprises LLC ....E... 952 401-9051
Excelsior **(G-1936)**

Mount Olivet Lutheran Church ....E... 612 861-3305
Minneapolis **(G-5140)**

New Horizon Child Care Inc ....E... 763 574-7450
Minneapolis **(G-3553)**

New Horizon Child Care Inc ....E... 952 893-1893
Minneapolis **(G-5189)**

New Horizon Child Care Inc ....E... 952 423-6690
Saint Paul **(G-7850)**

New Horizon Child Care Inc ....E... 651 481-8069
Saint Paul **(G-8749)**

New Horizon Child Care Inc ....E... 763 315-3033
Minneapolis **(G-5190)**

New Horizon Child Care Inc ....E... 763 757-2604
Minneapolis **(G-3554)**

New Horizon Enterprises Inc ....C... 763 557-1111
Plymouth **(G-6876)**

Northwest Community Action Inc ....D... 218 528-3258
Badger **(G-299)**

Only For Kids Inc ....E... 763 754-2594
Anoka **(G-212)**

Opportunity Manor Inc ....D... 320 240-1900
Sartell **(G-9339)**

Our Savior Lutheran Church...................E... 952 474-5181
Excelsior **(G-1952)**

Parents In Community Action...............E... 612 362-0360
Minneapolis **(G-5325)**

Peace of Mind Day Care Inc ....D... 651 731-2608
Saint Paul **(G-9257)**

Pine Haven Care Center Inc ....D... 507 356-8304
Pine Island **(G-6817)**

Pinewood Cloquet....................................E... 218 879-4566
Cloquet **(G-1060)**

Playworks Dakota ....D... 952 445-7529
Prior Lake **(G-6948)**

Possabilities ....D... 507 281-6116
Rochester **(G-7208)**

Providence Academy................................D... 763 258-2500
Minneapolis **(G-5432)**

Regents of The University of ....D... 612 627-4014
Minneapolis **(G-5493)**

River Hills Early Childhood...................E... 952 895-0413
Burnsville **(G-791)**

Rocking Horse Ranch ....E... 952 440-1777
Prior Lake **(G-6952)**

Room For Growing ....E... 651 257-2441
Chisago City **(G-994)**

Southside Family Nurturing Ctr...........E... 612 721-2762
Minneapolis **(G-5711)**

Special School District No 1 ....D... 612 668-1420
Minneapolis **(G-5717)**

St Andrew Lutheran Church ....E... 952 937-2776
Eden Prairie **(G-1781)**

St James Church Inc ....E... 651 293-3945
Saint Paul **(G-8984)**

St Mary's School ....E... 507 794-6141
Sleepy Eye **(G-9502)**

St Paul's Childhood Center...................E... 651 224-4749
Saint Paul **(G-9001)**

Tiny Tots & Little Tykes Pre ....E... 651 457-0042
Saint Paul **(G-7923)**

Under The Rainbow Child Care ....E... 651 388-6433
Red Wing **(G-7009)**

VA Employee Child Care Center...........E... 612 725-2000
Minneapolis **(G-5952)**

Wee Pals Child Care Center Inc ....E... 507 451-8355
Owatonna **(G-6743)**

Y M C A Infant Center ....E... 651 646-4557
Saint Paul **(G-9171)**

YMCA ....D... 320 222-9622
Willmar **(G-10059)**

YMCA Children's Center ....E... 651 777-8103
Saint Paul **(G-9173)**

YMCA of Greater Saint Paul...................C... 651 683-4713
Saint Paul **(G-7952)**

YMCA of Greater Saint Paul ....E... 651 771-8881
Saint Paul **(G-9174)**

YMCA of Greater Saint Paul ....E... 651 645-6605
Saint Paul **(G-9175)**

YMCA of Greater St Paul ....D... 218 365-2117
Ely **(G-1919)**

YMCA of Greater St Paul ....D... 651 292-4143
Saint Paul **(G-9178)**

YMCA of Greater St Paul ....D... 651 646-4557
Saint Paul **(G-9177)**

YMCA of Greater St Paul ....C... 651 483-2671
Saint Paul **(G-9176)**

YMCA of Greater St Paul ....C... 651 457-0048
Saint Paul **(G-7953)**

YMCA of Worthington, Minnesota.........E... 507 376-6197
Worthington **(G-10199)**

Young Men's Chrtn Assoc of................C... 763 535-4800
Minneapolis **(G-6101)**

Young Men's Chrtn Assoc of................D... 612 827-5401
Minneapolis **(G-6102)**

Young Men's Chrtn Assoc of................E... 612 588-9484
Minneapolis **(G-6103)**

Young Men's Chrtn Assoc of................C... 952 835-2567
Minneapolis **(G-6104)**

Young Women's Christian Assn ....D... 218 722-7425
Duluth **(G-1505)**

YWCA of Minneapolis.............................A... 612 332-0501
Minneapolis **(G-6111)**

CHILD GUIDANCE SVCS

Glenwood-Lyndale Community Ctr......D... 612 342-1500
Minneapolis **(G-4530)**

Independent School District ....E... 218 236-8172
Moorhead **(G-6319)**

CHILDBIRTH PREPARATION CLINIC

Rmia ....E... 651 221-4600
Saint Paul **(G-9269)**

CHILDREN'S AID SOCIETY

Adults & Childrens Alliance ....E... 651 481-9320
Saint Paul **(G-7986)**

Professional Association of ....E... 612 259-1600
Minneapolis **(G-5419)**

CHILDREN'S HOME

Lutheran Social Service of MN............D... 651 388-8845
Red Wing **(G-6989)**

Mount Olivet Rolling Acres Inc ....B... 952 474-5974
Victoria **(G-9731)**

St James Home of Duluth ....C... 218 728-7500
Duluth **(G-1462)**

CHIROPRACTORS' OFFICES

Brookdale Integrative Health ....E... 763 561-4045
Minneapolis **(G-3955)**

P H Selly & Co Inc ....E... 507 334-3251
Faribault **(G-2025)**

CHRISTMAS NOVELTIES, WHOLESALE

Display Sales Co.....................................E... 952 885-0100
Minneapolis **(G-4259)**

J L Buchanan Inc 612 334-1710
Minneapolis **(G-4747)**

Seasonal Specialties LLC ....E... 952 942-6555
Eden Prairie **(G-1773)**

CIRCUIT BOARD REPAIR SVCS

US Union Tool Inc...................................E... 651 552-0440
South Saint Paul **(G-9548)**

CLAIMS ADJUSTING SVCS

Crawford & Co ....E... 651 631-0055
Saint Paul **(G-8264)**

G E Young & Co.......................................E... 952 847-2388
Minnetonka **(G-6172)**

CLEANING SVCS

AAA Wicks Furnace Duct ....D... 651 770-1263
Minneapolis **(G-3654)**

General Cleaning Specialists ....D... 218 727-4513
Duluth **(G-1334)**

CLEANING SVCS: Industrial Or Commercial

Christians Inc...E... 952 470-2001
Chanhassen **(G-916)**

Cleaning Authority ....E... 763 717-9200
Minneapolis **(G-3434)**

Cleaning Management Group Inc ....E... 952 881-8791
Minneapolis **(G-4106)**

Four TS Inc...E... 320 685-7407
Cold Spring **(G-1086)**

Guaranteed Clean Maintenance ....D... 651 644-9919
Saint Paul **(G-8435)**

Retka Enterprises Inc............................D... 218 829-4076
Baxter **(G-340)**

S & L Team Cleaning ....E... 612 558-4502
Saint Paul **(G-8917)**

Tidy Clean LLC ....D... 507 344-1742
Mankato **(G-3206)**

CLEARINGHOUSE ASSOCIATIONS: Bank Or Check

Solutran Inc..D... 763 559-2225
Minneapolis **(G-5697)**

CLOTHING & ACCESS, WOMEN, CHILDREN & INFANT, WHOL: Access

Christopher & Banks Co ....D... 763 551-5000
Plymouth **(G-6855)**

Hanover Accessories LLC ....D... 763 509-6100
Plymouth **(G-6863)**

CLOTHING & ACCESS, WOMEN, CHILDREN & INFANTS, WHOL: Purses

Fun Sisters ....E... 612 824-9872
Minneapolis **(G-4491)**

CLOTHING & ACCESS, WOMEN, CHILDREN/INFANT, WHOL: Caps/Gowns

River's End Holdings LLC 952 912-2543
Hopkins **(G-2618)**

Rivers End Trading Co............................D... 952 912-2500
Hopkins **(G-2619)**

Employment codes: A=Over 500 employees, B=251-500,
C=101-250, D=51-100, E=25-50

2011 Harris Minnesota
Services Directory

© Harris InfoSource 1-866-281-6415

S E R V I C E S

CLOTHING & ACCESS, WOMEN, CHILDREN/INFANT, WHOL: Outerwear

River's End Holdings LLC 952 912-2543
Hopkins (G-2618)

Rivers End Trading Co ....D... 952 912-2500
Hopkins (G-2619)

CLOTHING & FURNISHINGS, MEN & BOY, WHOLESALE: Suits/Trousers

Anderson's Formal Wear Inc ....E... 507 285-1884
Rochester (G-7056)

CLOTHING & FURNISHINGS, MEN'S & BOYS', WHOLESALE: Caps

Rivers End Trading Co ....D... 952 912-2500
Hopkins (G-2619)

CLOTHING & FURNISHINGS, MEN'S & BOYS', WHOLESALE: Outerwear

Rivers End Trading Co ....D... 952 912-2500
Hopkins (G-2619)

CLOTHING & FURNISHINGS, MEN'S & BOYS', WHOLESALE: Shirts

River's End Holdings LLC 952 912-2543
Hopkins (G-2618)

Rivers End Trading Co ....D... 952 912-2500
Hopkins (G-2619)

CLOTHING & FURNISHINGS, MEN/BOY, WHOL: Hats, Scarves/Gloves

River's End Holdings LLC 952 912-2543
Hopkins (G-2618)

CLOTHING & FURNISHINGS, MENS & BOYS, WHOL: Sportswear/Work

Eldredge Trading Inc 651 778-8500
Saint Paul (G-7758)

COAL MINING: Anthracite

Allete Inc ....C... 218 279-5000
Duluth (G-1235)

COAL MINING: Bituminous, Auger

Pengo Corp...................................E... 320 286-5581
Cokato (G-1078)

COAL, MINERALS & ORES, WHOLESALE: Coal

Great Western Recycling Inds ....E... 651 224-4877
Saint Paul (G-8427)

COFFEE SVCS

Aramark Corp ....E... 952 946-1438
Minneapolis (G-3795)

COIN OPERATED LAUNDRIES & DRYCLEANERS

Awm Enterprises Inc ....E... 651 455-3044
South Saint Paul (G-9510)

COIN-OPERATED EQUIPMENT WHOLESALERS

Silver King Refrigeration Inc................C... 763 559-1141
Minneapolis (G-5674)

COIN-OPERATED SVC MACH OP: Scale, Shoeshine, & Locker

Smarte Carte Inc ....D... 651 429-3614
Saint Paul (G-8965)

COINS, WHOLESALE

New York Mint Ltd...............................E... 952 949-6588
Minneapolis (G-5194)

COLLECTION AGENCIES

Array Services Group Inc....................C... 320 534-3401
Sartell (G-9331)

Array Services Group Inc....................C... 320 534-3680
Sauk Rapids (G-9357)

Central Portfolio Control Inc................E... 952 944-5440
Eden Prairie (G-1620)

Dcm Services LLC ....C... 763 852-8440
Minneapolis (G-4235)

Financial Recovery Services ....D... 952 831-4800
Minneapolis (G-4432)

Millennium Credit Consultants 651 306-9344
Saint Paul (G-7841)

National Recoveries Inc ....E... 763 754-1931
Anoka (G-207)

Pinnacle Financial Group Inc ....D... 952 996-0559
Minneapolis (G-5381)

Pinnacle Financial Group Inc..............D... 763 295-0113
Monticello (G-6283)

Receivables Management Soln ....C... 651 457-1130
Saint Paul (G-7891)

VA Departmental Offices ....D... 612 970-5700
Saint Paul (G-7966)

COLLECTION AGENCY, EXC REAL ESTATE

Affiliated Group Inc ....D... 507 280-7000
Rochester (G-7045)

Allied Interstate Inc ....B... 952 595-2000
Plymouth (G-6846)

American Accounts & Advisors ....E... 651 405-9760
Saint Paul (G-7696)

Bureau of Collection Recovery ....E... 952 934-7777
Eden Prairie (G-1613)

Bureau of Collection Recovery............E... 320 214-8747
Willmar (G-9994)

Chex Systems Inc ....B... 651 361-2000
Saint Paul (G-9196)

Commercial Recovery Corp ....E... 763 786-6333
Minneapolis (G-3438)

CU Recovery Inc ....E... 651 462-4400
Wyoming (G-10201)

Deceased Credit Management LLC 763 852-8400
Minneapolis (G-4238)

Diversified Adjustment Service ....C... 763 783-2301
Minneapolis (G-3456)

Homecomings Financial Network ....C... 952 854-5432
Minneapolis (G-4669)

J C Christensen & Associates ....D... 320 534-3629
Sartell (G-9337)

Jefferson Capital Systems LLC ....C... 866 417-2561
Saint Cloud (G-7536)

Jnr Adjustment Co ....C... 763 519-2710
Osseo (G-6624)

MCC Group Inc ....E... 952 941-0552
Eden Prairie (G-1718)

Northland Group Inc ....D... 952 831-4005
Minneapolis (G-5231)

Receivables Control Corp ....D... 763 315-9600
Osseo (G-6655)

Triadvantage Credit Services ....B... 651 255-2047
Saint Paul (G-7927)

Viking Collection Service Inc................B... 952 944-7575
Eden Prairie (G-1804)

COLOR SEPARATION: Photographic & Movie Film

Professional Litho-Art Co Inc ....D... 612 338-0400
Minneapolis (G-5420)

COMBINATION UTILITIES, NEC

Energy Management Steam ....E... 612 626-7329
Minneapolis (G-4357)

Ever-Green Energy LLC ....D... 651 290-2812
Saint Paul (G-8349)

New Ulm, City of Inc ....D... 507 359-8264
New Ulm (G-6470)

Willmar, City of Inc............................D... 320 235-4422
Willmar (G-10056)

COMMERCIAL & INDL SHELVING WHOLESALERS

Safco Products Co ....C... 763 536-6700
Minneapolis (G-5588)

COMMERCIAL & OFFICE BUILDINGS RENOVATION & REPAIR

A J Spanjers Co Inc ....E... 763 424-8288
Minneapolis (G-3648)

Alvin E Benike Inc...............................C... 507 288-6575
Rochester (G-7053)

Amb Construction Engineering ....E... 763 587-4920
Minneapolis (G-3740)

Arkay Construction Co ....E... 763 544-3341
Minneapolis (G-3806)

Banks Brothers Construction ....E... 651 644-1723
Saint Paul (G-8088)

Brehmer Contracting Inc ....E... 952 938-1171
Hopkins (G-2520)

C F Haglin & Sons Inc.........................D... 952 920-6123
Minneapolis (G-3983)

Carlson-Lavine Inc ....E... 651 638-9600
Saint Paul (G-8167)

Century Construction Co Inc...............E... 651 451-1020
South Saint Paul (G-9518)

Christians Inc ....E... 952 470-2001
Chanhassen (G-916)

Con Spec Corp ....E... 651 501-6500
Saint Paul (G-9199)

Diversified Construction ....E... 952 929-7233
Saint Louis Park (G-7659)

Donald Holm Construction Co ....E... 218 628-2257
Duluth (G-1295)

Elder-Jones Inc..................................E... 952 854-2854
Minneapolis (G-4336)

Flannery Construction Inc ....E... 651 225-1105
Saint Paul (G-8384)

Haztran Inc ....E... 218 327-1116
Grand Rapids (G-2285)

Heymann Construction Co ....D... 507 354-3174
New Ulm (G-6454)

Hy-TEC Construction of ....E... 218 829-8529
Brainerd (G-570)

J E Dunn Construction Co ....C... 952 830-9000
Eden Prairie (G-1700)

James Steele Construction Co.............E... 651 488-6755
Saint Paul (G-8529)

L S Black Constructors Inc..................D... 651 774-8445
Saint Paul (G-8553)

Lawremar Inc ....E... 651 429-4475
Saint Paul (G-8568)

Lee's Construction Inc ....D... 320 762-0325
Alexandria (G-111)

Lindstrom Cleaning & Constr...............E... 763 544-8761
Minneapolis (G-4891)

Murphy Bros Designers ....E... 763 780-3262
Minneapolis (G-3548)

Nor-Son Inc ....C... 218 828-1722
Baxter (G-339)

Oakwood Builders Inc.........................E... 952 941-9730
Eden Prairie (G-1735)

Olson General Contractors Inc ....E... 763 535-1481
Minneapolis (G-5272)

One Way Building Services Inc ....E... 952 942-0412
Minneapolis (G-5280)

Ray Riihiluoma Inc ....E... 218 879-3317
Cloquet (G-1064)

Retail Construction Services................C... 651 704-9000
Lake Elmo (G-2876)

Shaw - Lundquist Associates...............D... 651 454-0670
Saint Paul (G-7903)

Socon Construction Inc ....E... 763 754-4027
Minneapolis (G-3604)

Strack Construction Co Inc ....E... 320 251-5933
Sauk Rapids (G-9377)

Structural Restoration Inc ....E... 612 825-8614
Minneapolis (G-5760)

VSI Construction Inc ....E... 763 493-3000
Maple Grove (G-3257)

Watson-Forsberg Co ....E... 952 544-7761
Minneapolis (G-6025)

Wilcon Construction Inc ....E... 507 375-5464
Saint James (G-7649)

COMMERCIAL ART & GRAPHIC DESIGN SVCS

Christ's Household of Faith...................E... 651 602-5600
Saint Paul (G-8199)

Cinedigm Digital Cinema Corp ....C... 320 654-6578
Saint Cloud (G-7492)

Corporate Graphics Intl ....C... 651 494-1740
Saint Paul (G-8252)

Immedia Inc.......................................C... 612 524-3400
Minneapolis (G-4691)

Knock Inc ....E... 612 333-6511
Minneapolis (G-4815)

Larsen Design Office Inc ....E... 952 835-2271
Minneapolis (G-4846)

Signsearch Inc ....E... 952 960-4470
Burnsville (G-797)

Target Brands Inc ....E... 612 304-6073
Minneapolis (G-5789)

Upfront Productions Inc ....E... 612 623-4433
Minneapolis (G-5933)

Visions Inc...D... 763 425-4251
Brooklyn Park (G-621)

COMMERCIAL CONTAINERS WHOLESALERS

Consolidated Container Co LLC ....D... 612 781-0923
Minneapolis (G-4154)

Kaufman Container Co Inc ....D... 612 331-8880
Minneapolis (G-4794)

S
E
R
V
I
C
E
S

COMMERCIAL CREDIT REPORTING BUREAU

Dun & Bradstreet Inc ....E... 952 841-9961
Bloomington *(G-494)*

RELS LLC ....A... 952 933-8804
Hopkins *(G-2613)*

COMMERCIAL EQPT WHOLESALERS, NEC

Amano McGann Inc ....E... 612 331-2020
Minneapolis *(G-3739)*

C & S Vending Co Inc ....D... 507 334-8414
Faribault *(G-1994)*

Direct Source Inc ....D... 952 934-8000
Chanhassen *(G-920)*

Silver King Refrigeration Inc ....C... 763 559-1141
Minneapolis *(G-5674)*

Skyline Displays Midwest Inc ....E... 952 895-6000
Burnsville *(G-798)*

Supervalu Equipment Services ....E... 952 828-4000
Eden Prairie *(G-1785)*

Upper Lakes Foods Inc ....C... 218 879-1265
Cloquet *(G-1066)*

COMMERCIAL EQPT, WHOLESALE: Bakery Eqpt & Splys

Bakemark USA LLC ....E... 952 937-9495
Eden Prairie *(G-1601)*

Dawn Food Products Inc ....E... 763 428-8826
Rogers *(G-7321)*

Hockenbergs ....E... 612 331-1300
Minneapolis *(G-4659)*

Kristico Inc ....E... 507 625-2900
Mankato *(G-3155)*

COMMERCIAL EQPT, WHOLESALE: Coffee Brewing Eqpt & Splys

Aramark Corp ....E... 952 946-1438
Minneapolis *(G-3795)*

COMMERCIAL EQPT, WHOLESALE: Comm Cooking & Food Svc Eqpt

Clover Super Foods Rt 30 Inc ....E... 612 465-8900
Minneapolis *(G-4110)*

Don Stevens Inc ....E... 651 452-0872
Eagan *(G-1525)*

5 K Enterprises Inc ....E... 612 216-6292
Mankato *(G-3127)*

Hockenbergs ....E... 612 331-1300
Minneapolis *(G-4659)*

Martin Falk Paper Co ....E... 612 332-8626
Minneapolis *(G-4959)*

US Foodservice Inc ....C... 763 559-9494
Minneapolis *(G-5948)*

Zumbro River Brand Inc ....E... 507 377-9776
Albert Lea *(G-72)*

COMMERCIAL EQPT, WHOLESALE: Restaurant, NEC

Hockenbergs ....E... 612 331-1300
Minneapolis *(G-4659)*

Kelbro Co ....E... 612 824-9803
Minneapolis *(G-4796)*

Strategic Equipment Inc ....D... 320 252-2977
Saint Cloud *(G-7614)*

COMMERCIAL EQPT, WHOLESALE: Scales, Exc Laboratory

Data Systems Inc ....E... 952 934-4001
Eden Prairie *(G-1642)*

COMMERCIAL EQPT, WHOLESALE: Store Fixtures & Display Eqpt

Mycull Fixtures Inc ....E... 763 389-4400
Princeton *(G-6911)*

Paragon Store Fixtures Inc ....E... 763 263-0660
Big Lake *(G-453)*

Safco Products Co ....C... 763 536-6700
Minneapolis *(G-5588)*

Stein Industries Inc ....C... 763 504-3500
Minneapolis *(G-5747)*

COMMERCIAL EQPT, WHOLESALE: Vending Machines, Coin-Operated

Canteen Vending ....E... 651 488-0515
Saint Paul *(G-8148)*

Compass Group USA Inc ....E... 651 488-0515
Saint Paul *(G-8242)*

Richard Hawkins ....E... 507 282-6080
Rochester *(G-7224)*

Theisen Vending Inc ....D... 612 827-5588
Minneapolis *(G-5813)*

COMMERCIAL PHOTOGRAPHIC STUDIO

Ware Tad & Co Inc ....E... 612 338-2311
Minneapolis *(G-6020)*

COMMODITY CONTRACTS BROKERS, DEALERS

Cargill Inc ....C... 952 984-3890
Minneapolis *(G-4009)*

Dougherty Financial Group LLC ....C... 612 376-4000
Minneapolis *(G-4284)*

COMMON SAND MINING

Dennis Fehn Gravel ....E... 763 497-2428
Albertville *(G-73)*

COMMUNICATIONS EQPT REPAIR & MAINTENANCE

Comm-Works Holdings LLC ....D... 763 258-5800
Minneapolis *(G-4130)*

COMMUNICATIONS EQPT WHOLESALERS

C-1 Holdings LLC ....D... 651 994-6800
Eagan *(G-1519)*

Capitol Sales Co Inc ....D... 651 688-6830
Saint Paul *(G-7727)*

Clearone Communications Inc ....E... 763 550-2300
Minneapolis *(G-4109)*

Crest Electronics Inc ....D... 320 275-3382
Dassel *(G-1160)*

Cross Telecom Corp ....D... 952 983-3500
Bloomington *(G-493)*

Napco International LLC ....E... 952 931-2400
Hopkins *(G-2587)*

North American Communications ......E... 952 942-7200
Minneapolis *(G-5212)*

SBC Datacomm Inc ....E... 763 315-5343
Saint Paul *(G-8931)*

Voice & Data Networks Inc ....E... 952 946-7999
Minneapolis *(G-5982)*

COMMUNICATIONS SVCS

ADC Telecommunications Inc ....A... 952 938-8080
Eden Prairie *(G-1584)*

D C C Solutionolutions ....E... 320 839-2058
Ortonville *(G-6581)*

St Louis, County of Inc ....E... 218 726-2920
Duluth *(G-1465)*

Tricom Communications Inc ....E... 651 686-9000
Saint Paul *(G-7928)*

Xora Inc ....E... 651 209-0350
Saint Paul *(G-7951)*

COMMUNICATIONS SVCS: Cellular

American Cellular Corp ....D... 218 727-4700
Duluth *(G-1238)*

American Cellular Corp ....E... 218 828-8000
Baxter *(G-319)*

Cellco Partnership ....E... 763 595-5102
Minneapolis *(G-4040)*

Hutchinson Telephone Co ....D... 320 587-2323
Hutchinson *(G-2702)*

Midwest Wireless Comms ....B... 507 385-2396
Mankato *(G-3169)*

Motorola Inc ....C... 952 895-7800
Burnsville *(G-760)*

Rural Cellular Corp ....C... 320 762-2000
Alexandria *(G-122)*

SBC Datacomm Inc ....E... 763 315-5343
Saint Paul *(G-8931)*

Shock City Cellular ....E... 952 233-5281
Shakopee *(G-9475)*

Sprint Spectrum LP ....E... 507 358-4727
Rochester *(G-7261)*

Verizon Wireless Inc ....D... 320 241-5433
Waite Park *(G-9847)*

COMMUNICATIONS SVCS: Data

Access Communications Inc ....E... 763 545-9998
Minneapolis *(G-3665)*

Animation Services Inc ....E... 612 379-7117
Minneapolis *(G-3781)*

Hiawatha Broadband Comms ....D... 507 474-4000
Winona *(G-10101)*

Spectrum Solutions Inc ....E... 952 835-8338
Minneapolis *(G-5720)*

Thomas Koll ....E... 763 323-9797
Anoka *(G-235)*

COMMUNICATIONS SVCS: Facsimile Transmission

Fedex Office & Print Services ....E... 651 699-9671
Saint Paul *(G-8370)*

Fedex Office & Print Services ....E... 952 892-0200
Burnsville *(G-721)*

Hutchinson Telephone Co ....D... 320 587-2323
Hutchinson *(G-2702)*

COMMUNICATIONS SVCS: Internet Connectivity Svcs

HickoryTech Corp ....B... 507 386-3636
Mankato *(G-3141)*

Link Lakedale Inc ....E... 320 274-7777
Annandale *(G-141)*

Marketing Bridge LLC ....E... 763 504-4610
Minneapolis *(G-4949)*

New Ulm Telecom Inc ....D... 507 354-4111
New Ulm *(G-6468)*

Xpandable Technology Inc ....E... 763 521-0401
Minneapolis *(G-6095)*

COMMUNICATIONS SVCS: Internet Host Svcs

Lefty's Shooting & Outdoor 763 533-9594
Minneapolis *(G-4854)*

Skyvision Inc ....E... 218 739-5231
Fergus Falls *(G-2119)*

Xpandable Technology Inc ....E... 763 521-0401
Minneapolis *(G-6095)*

COMMUNICATIONS SVCS: Online Svc Providers

Earthlink Inc ....E... 507 847-2700
Jackson *(G-2790)*

Four51 Inc ....E... 952 294-0451
Eden Prairie *(G-1668)*

Hector Communications Corp ....D... 218 346-5500
New Ulm *(G-6453)*

Hiawatha Broadband Comms ....D... 507 474-4000
Winona *(G-10101)*

Hiawatha Broadband Comms ....D... 507 932-3942
Saint Charles *(G-7404)*

Integra Telecom of Minnesota ....D... 952 746-7100
Golden Valley *(G-2242)*

Popular Front Studio Inc ....E... 612 362-0900
Minneapolis *(G-5395)*

Shavlik Technologies LLC ....D... 651 426-6624
Saint Paul *(G-8948)*

U S Internet Corp ....E... 651 222-4638
Minnetonka *(G-6230)*

W3i Holdings LLC ....D... 320 257-7500
Sartell *(G-9341)*

COMMUNICATIONS SVCS: Proprietary Online Svcs Networks

Enventis Telecom Inc ....D... 763 577-3900
Minneapolis *(G-4360)*

Lefty's Shooting & Outdoor 763 533-9594
Minneapolis *(G-4854)*

COMMUNICATIONS SVCS: Signal Enhancement Network Svcs

Dascom Systems Group LLC ....E... 651 578-1200
Saint Paul *(G-9201)*

Weber Electric Inc ....D... 651 490-1333
Saint Paul *(G-9142)*

COMMUNICATIONS SVCS: Telephone Or Video

New Ulm Telecom Inc ....D... 507 354-4111
New Ulm *(G-6468)*

Renodis Holdings Inc ....E... 651 556-1203
Saint Paul *(G-8890)*

COMMUNICATIONS SVCS: Telephone, Data

Select Communications Inc ....E... 763 744-0900
Minneapolis *(G-5633)*

COMMUNICATIONS SVCS: Telephone, Local

Bishop Communications Corp ....D... 320 274-8201
Annandale *(G-138)*

East Otter Tail Telephone Co ....C... 218 346-5500
Perham *(G-6796)*

Eckles Telephone Co Inc ....E... 507 526-3252
Blue Earth *(G-534)*

Garden Valley Telephone Co ....D... 218 687-2400
Erskine *(G-1920)*

Employment codes: A=Over 500 employees, B=251-500,
C=101-250, D=51-100, E=25-50

2011 Harris Minnesota
Services Directory

© Harris InfoSource 1-866-281-6415

669

SERVICES

Hector Communications Corp ....D... 218 346-5500
New Ulm *(G-6453)*

HickoryTech Corp ....B... 507 386-3636
Mankato *(G-3141)*

Hutchinson Telephone Co ....D... 320 587-2323
Hutchinson *(G-2702)*

Link Lakedale Inc ....E... 320 274-7777
Annandale *(G-141)*

New Ulm Telecom Inc ....D... 507 354-4111
New Ulm *(G-6468)*

Park Region Mutual Telephone ....E... 218 826-6161
Underwood *(G-9718)*

Paul Bunyan Rural Telephone ....D... 218 444-1234
Bemidji *(G-420)*

Qwest Corp ....B... 612 381-5202
Minneapolis *(G-5453)*

Sherburne County Rural ....E... 763 262-4100
Big Lake *(G-455)*

Sherburne Tele Systems Inc ....E... 763 262-4100
Big Lake *(G-456)*

Val-Ed Joint Venture, LLP ....E... 218 284-5702
Moorhead *(G-6345)*

Wikstrom Telephone Co Inc...............D... 218 436-2121
Karlstad *(G-2817)*

COMMUNICATIONS SVCS: Telephone, Local & Long Distance

Integra Telecom Inc ....C... 763 745-8000
Minneapolis *(G-4711)*

Kasson & Mantorville Telephone ....E... 507 634-2511
Kasson *(G-2821)*

Lakedale Telephone Co........................D... 320 274-8201
Annandale *(G-140)*

SBC Datacomm Inc ....E... 763 315-5343
Saint Paul *(G-8931)*

COMMUNICATIONS SVCS: Telephone, Long Distance

Digital Telecommunications Inc ....E... 507 452-2303
Winona *(G-10092)*

Link Lakedale Inc ....E... 320 274-7777
Annandale *(G-141)*

Midcontinent Media Inc ....C... 952 844-2600
Minneapolis *(G-5024)*

Popp Telcom Inc ....D... 763 546-9707
Minneapolis *(G-5394)*

Sprint Communications Co LP ....C... 507 454-8386
Winona *(G-10130)*

Verizon Communications Inc...............C... 763 591-0705
Minneapolis *(G-5965)*

COMMUNITY ACTION AGENCY

Arrowhead Economic Opportunity ......D... 218 749-2912
Virginia *(G-9735)*

Bethel Duluth Society ....D... 218 722-1724
Duluth *(G-1251)*

Heartland Community Action ....E... 320 235-0850
Willmar *(G-10007)*

Lakes & Pines Community Action........E... 320 679-1800
Mora *(G-6365)*

Lakes & Prairies Community ....E... 218 299-7000
Moorhead *(G-6324)*

Mahube Community Council Inc ....D... 218 847-1385
Detroit Lakes *(G-1209)*

Minnesota Program Development........D... 218 722-2781
Duluth *(G-1395)*

Semcac ....E... 507 864-7741
Rushford *(G-7392)*

Southwestern Minnesota ....E... 507 376-4195
Worthington *(G-10196)*

Tri-County Action Program Inc.............E... 320 251-1612
Waite Park *(G-9845)*

Tri-County Action Program Inc.............E... 320 255-0705
Waite Park *(G-9846)*

Tri-Valley Opportunity Council ....C... 218 281-5832
Crookston *(G-1139)*

Tri-Valley Opportunity Council ....D... 218 281-5832
Crookston *(G-1140)*

Tri-Valley Opportunity Council ....E... 218 281-5832
Crookston *(G-1141)*

West Central Minnesota ....D... 218 685-4486
Elbow Lake *(G-1855)*

COMMUNITY CENTER

Church of St Bernard............................E... 651 488-6733
Saint Paul *(G-8200)*

City of Eden Prairie..............................D... 952 949-8470
Eden Prairie *(G-1629)*

City of Waconia ....E... 952 442-0695
Waconia *(G-9783)*

Community Action Council Inc.............E... 952 985-5300
Burnsville *(G-701)*

Dovray Community Center....................E... 507 274-5602
Dovray *(G-1230)*

Fraser ....B... 612 861-1688
Minneapolis *(G-4478)*

Independent School District ....D... 651 604-3503
Saint Paul *(G-8510)*

Jewish Community Center of ....C... 952 381-3400
Minneapolis *(G-4762)*

Knight of Columbus Community ....E... 952 492-5170
Prior Lake *(G-6936)*

Orono Independent School Dist ....E... 763 479-1530
Maple Plain *(G-3280)*

Upper Midwest American Indian ....E... 612 522-4436
Minneapolis *(G-5936)*

COMMUNITY CENTERS: Adult

Bayport Senior Center ....E... 651 275-8907
Bayport *(G-346)*

City of Owatonna ....E... 507 444-4300
Owatonna *(G-6702)*

Clare Housing ....E... 612 236-9505
Minneapolis *(G-4099)*

Darts ....C... 651 455-1560
Saint Paul *(G-7748)*

Homestead At Rochester ....E... 507 535-2000
Rochester *(G-7140)*

SE Rolling Hills LLC ....D... 952 828-9500
Eden Prairie *(G-1771)*

Senior Citizens Center of ....E... 218 494-3750
Felton *(G-2063)*

Senior Citizens Service Inc ....E... 507 287-1404
Rochester *(G-7251)*

Senior Laurentian Citizen Ctr ....D... 218 749-3688
Virginia *(G-9755)*

Weiner Memorial Foundation...............B... 507 532-9661
Marshall *(G-3332)*

COMMUNITY CENTERS: Youth

Boys & Girls Clubs of The....................E... 218 335-8144
Cass Lake *(G-870)*

Department of Corrections MN ....D... 320 384-7411
Finlayson *(G-2129)*

Youth Frontiers Inc ....E... 952 922-0222
Minneapolis *(G-6107)*

Youthlink...D... 612 252-1200
Minneapolis *(G-6108)*

YWCA of Minneapolis ....E... 612 874-7131
Minneapolis *(G-6110)*

COMMUNITY DEVELOPMENT GROUPS

Communication Service For The ....C... 218 291-1120
Moorhead *(G-6305)*

East Side Neighborhood Svcs ....D... 612 781-6011
Minneapolis *(G-4308)*

Everyday Miracles Inc ....E... 763 323-0012
Anoka *(G-179)*

Hubbard County Developmental ....D... 218 732-3358
Park Rapids *(G-6754)*

Initiative Foundation ....E... 320 632-9255
Little Falls *(G-3007)*

Life By Design Inc ....C... 763 757-3263
Minneapolis *(G-3518)*

Merrick Community Services................E... 651 771-8821
Saint Paul *(G-8638)*

Minneapolis Community Devpt ....C... 612 673-5095
Minneapolis *(G-5052)*

Productive Alternatives Inc..................E... 218 825-8148
Brainerd *(G-583)*

Sigma Tau Omega Inc ....E... 651 644-7200
Inver Grove Heights *(G-2769)*

COMMUNITY SVCS EMPLOYMENT TRAINING PROGRAM

Arrowhead Economic Opportunity ......E... 218 742-9187
Virginia *(G-9734)*

Chisago Lakes Achievement Ctr ....E... 651 257-6709
Chisago City *(G-989)*

Joint Apprenticeship ....E... 218 733-9443
Duluth *(G-1364)*

Minneapolis American Indian ....E... 612 871-4555
Minneapolis *(G-5050)*

Resource Inc ....D... 612 752-8000
Minneapolis *(G-5526)*

Southwest MN Pic ....E... 507 537-6987
Marshall *(G-3329)*

Sureservices Inc ....E... 763 531-0029
Minneapolis *(G-5772)*

COMMUNITY THEATER PRODUCTION SVCS

Hennepin Broadway Series...................D... 612 373-5665
Minneapolis *(G-4630)*

Paul Bunyan Community Theater ....E... 218 751-7270
Bemidji *(G-419)*

COMPACT DISCS OR CD'S, WHOLESALE

K-Tel International Inc 763 559-5566
Minneapolis *(G-4787)*

COMPRESSORS: Wholesalers

John Henry Foster Minnesota ....D... 651 452-8452
Saint Paul *(G-7810)*

COMPUTER & DATA PROCESSING EQPT REPAIR & MAINTENANCE

All Systems Go ....E... 651 628-0000
Hopkins *(G-2505)*

Solbrekk Inc ....E... 763 404-4712
Golden Valley *(G-2246)*

Sovran Inc ....E... 651 686-0515
Eagan *(G-1552)*

World Data Products Inc ....D... 952 476-9000
Minnetonka *(G-6239)*

COMPUTER & OFFICE MACHINE MAINTENANCE & REPAIR

Blm Technologies Inc ....E... 763 559-5100
Minneapolis *(G-3912)*

Citon Computer Corp ....E... 218 720-4435
Duluth *(G-1274)*

Expresspoint Technology Svcs ....C... 763 543-6000
Golden Valley *(G-2240)*

National Communications Svcs ....E... 763 576-9977
Anoka *(G-206)*

Nortech Systems Inc ....C... 952 345-2244
Wayzata *(G-9932)*

PC Solutions Inc ....E... 763 852-1600
Minneapolis *(G-3567)*

Pcr Computer Services ....E... 763 557-6824
Minneapolis *(G-5354)*

System Design Advantage LLC ....E... 952 703-3500
Minneapolis *(G-5781)*

COMPUTER CALCULATING SVCS

Hickory Tech Information Soln ....D... 507 625-1691
Mankato *(G-3139)*

Hickory Tech Information Soln ....D... 507 625-1691
Mankato *(G-3140)*

Questar Data Systems Inc ....C... 651 688-0089
Saint Paul *(G-7886)*

COMPUTER FACILITIES MANAGEMENT SVCS

I B Industries Inc.................................D... 507 567-2701
Brownsdale *(G-630)*

Local Government Information ....E... 763 543-2600
Minneapolis *(G-4896)*

Unisys Corp ....A... 651 687-2200
Saint Paul *(G-7935)*

COMPUTER GRAPHICS SVCS

Arrowhead Promotion...........................B... 218 327-1165
Grand Rapids *(G-2269)*

Atomic Playpen Inc ....E... 763 231-3400
Minneapolis *(G-3832)*

Go E Bizcom ....E... 651 454-0013
Saint Paul *(G-7784)*

Gov Delivery Inc ....D... 866 276-5583
Saint Paul *(G-8424)*

Imaginet LLC ....D... 612 752-5500
Minneapolis *(G-4689)*

Popular Front Studio Inc......................E... 612 362-0900
Minneapolis *(G-5395)*

Rev Solutions Inc ....E... 952 746-6005
Eden Prairie *(G-1764)*

Shea Inc..E... 612 339-2257
Minneapolis *(G-5652)*

Xpandable Technology Inc ....E... 763 521-0401
Minneapolis *(G-6095)*

COMPUTER PERIPHERAL EQPT, WHOLESALE

Consan Inc ....D... 952 949-0053
Eden Prairie *(G-1635)*

Expresspoint Technology Svcs ....C... 763 543-6000
Golden Valley *(G-2240)*

Micro Electronics Inc ....D... 952 285-4040
Minneapolis *(G-5018)*

Midwave Corp ....C... 952 279-5600
Eden Prairie *(G-1723)*

Rorke Data Inc ....D... 952 829-0300
Eden Prairie *(G-1767)*

Sirius Computer Solutions Inc ....D... 952 470-6144
Chanhassen *(G-940)*

(G-00000) Company's Geographic Section entry number

COMPUTER PROGRAMMING SVCS

API Outsourcing Inc ....E... 218 834-8007
Two Harbors *(G-9704)*
Aquent LLC ....D... 952 851-3411
Minneapolis *(G-3794)*
Architecture Technology Corp ....E... 952 829-5864
Eden Prairie *(G-1595)*
Citi Investor Services Inc ....E... 218 825-0552
Brainerd *(G-557)*
Computer Sciences Corp ....E... 763 593-1122
Minneapolis *(G-4148)*
Dayport Inc ....E... 507 344-3000
Mankato *(G-3122)*
Development Resource Group Inc ....D... 763 783-7878
Saint Paul *(G-8290)*
Distributed Website Corp ....E... 507 453-5164
Winona *(G-10093)*
Diverse Computer Corp ....E... 651 766-8138
Saint Paul *(G-8301)*
Global Communication Services ....E... 952 890-3911
Burnsville *(G-729)*
Grocery Shopping Network ....E... 952 345-3232
Minneapolis *(G-4573)*
Innovative Computer Systems ....E... 952 934-5665
Eden Prairie *(G-1694)*
Lake Superior Software Inc ....C... 952 941-1000
Eden Prairie *(G-1705)*
Lawson Software Americas Inc ....A... 651 767-7000
Saint Paul *(G-8569)*
Lawson Software Inc ....A... 651 767-7000
Saint Paul *(G-8570)*
Lindenberg & Associates - Twin ....E... 612 375-0234
Minneapolis *(G-4889)*
Local Government Information ....E... 763 543-2600
Minneapolis *(G-4896)*
Macro Group Inc ....E... 612 332-7880
Minneapolis *(G-4929)*
Magenic Technologies Inc ....C... 763 398-4800
Minneapolis *(G-4932)*
Media Relations Inc ....E... 612 798-7200
Burnsville *(G-752)*
Olsen Thielen Technologies Inc ....C... 651 483-4521
Saint Paul *(G-8781)*
Powel Inc ....E... 651 251-3005
Saint Paul *(G-7879)*
Procon Co's Inc ....E... 952 258-6300
Minneapolis *(G-5415)*
Programming Solutions Inc ....E... 763 424-8154
Minneapolis *(G-5424)*
Quest Software Inc ....E... 952 229-3500
Eden Prairie *(G-1756)*
Rural Computer Consultants Inc ....E... 320 365-4027
Bird Island *(G-468)*
Secure Computing Corp ....C... 651 628-2700
Saint Paul *(G-8943)*
Smart Data Solutions Inc ....E... 651 690-3140
Saint Paul *(G-7906)*
Solid Logic Computer Solutions ....E... 952 949-0140
Eden Prairie *(G-1780)*
Sterling Commerce Inc ....D... 952 294-1800
Eden Prairie *(G-1782)*
Thomson Reuters LLC ....E... 651 846-2000
Saint Paul *(G-9042)*
3-D CNC Inc ....E... 320 587-5923
Hutchinson *(G-2713)*
Unisys Corp ....A... 651 635-7777
Saint Paul *(G-9103)*
Virtelligence Inc ....C... 952 746-9220
Eden Prairie *(G-1806)*
Virteva LLC ....E... 952 843-1200
Saint Louis Park *(G-7670)*
Wand Corp ....C... 952 361-6200
Eden Prairie *(G-1813)*
Warecorp ....D... 952 938-5448
Hopkins *(G-2658)*

COMPUTER PROGRAMMING SVCS: Custom

Ahles & Associates LLC ....E... 952 935-8554
Hopkins *(G-2504)*
Analysts International Corp ....C... 952 835-5900
Minneapolis *(G-3773)*
Analysts International Corp ....E... 507 280-6663
Rochester *(G-7055)*
Born Information Services Inc ....D... 763 404-4000
Minneapolis *(G-3931)*
Fujitsu Consulting Information ....B... 952 258-6000
Minnetonka *(G-6171)*
Sudhko Inc ....E... 952 595-8500
Hopkins *(G-2638)*

COMPUTER RELATED MAINTENANCE SVCS

Advanced Duplication Services ....C... 763 449-5500
Minneapolis *(G-3688)*
Blm Technologies Inc ....E... 763 559-5100
Minneapolis *(G-3912)*
Dobbs Temporary Services Inc ....E... 612 373-2600
Minneapolis *(G-4268)*
English, Bleeker & Associates ....E... 952 230-6500
Saint Louis Park *(G-7661)*
Expresspoint Technology Svcs ....C... 763 543-6000
Golden Valley *(G-2240)*
Ncs Pearson Inc ....A... 952 681-3000
Minneapolis *(G-5177)*
Tom Kelly ....E... 507 645-7464
Northfield *(G-6543)*

COMPUTER RELATED SVCS, NEC

Infosecure Technology Inc ....E... 202 898-5790
Plymouth *(G-6866)*
Lambsoft & Lamb & Co ....E... 612 813-3727
Minneapolis *(G-4838)*

COMPUTER SERVICE BUREAU

Catalog Marketing Services ....C... 651 636-6265
Minneapolis *(G-4027)*
Isaac Fair Corp ....B... 651 482-8593
Saint Paul *(G-8524)*
Mortgage Resource Center Inc ....E... 651 683-9705
Eagan *(G-1539)*

COMPUTER SOFTWARE DEVELOPMENT

Acuo Technologies LLC ....E... 952 905-3440
Bloomington *(G-481)*
Advanced Informatics LLC ....E... 612 253-0130
Minneapolis *(G-3689)*
Amano McGann Inc ....E... 612 331-2020
Minneapolis *(G-3739)*
Arran Technologies Inc ....E... 651 468-0002
Saint Paul *(G-8064)*
Avantgard ....E... 952 935-3300
Hopkins *(G-2514)*
Avionte LLC ....E... 651 556-2121
Eagan *(G-1516)*
Axonom Inc ....E... 952 653-0400
Minneapolis *(G-3851)*
Bi Consulting Group LLC ....D... 651 403-6500
Saint Paul *(G-7720)*
Biomedix Vascular Solutions ....E... 651 762-4010
Saint Paul *(G-8114)*
Comsys Information Technology ....C... 612 630-9100
Minneapolis *(G-4149)*
Csi International ....E... 952 882-9115
Burnsville *(G-704)*
Exact Software Erp-Na Inc ....D... 952 831-7182
Minneapolis *(G-4381)*
Fujitsu Consulting Information ....B... 952 258-6000
Minnetonka *(G-6171)*
Global Case Technology Inc ....E... 763 553-1313
Minneapolis *(G-4531)*
Grocery Shopping Network Inc ....E... 612 746-4232
Minneapolis *(G-4574)*
Icentera Inc ....E... 952 898-0888
Burnsville *(G-734)*
Imagetrend Inc ....C... 952 469-1589
Lakeville *(G-2910)*
Infinite Campus Inc ....C... 651 631-0000
Minneapolis *(G-3499)*
Ingenix Inc ....B... 952 833-7100
Eden Prairie *(G-1692)*
Lancet Software Development ....E... 952 230-7360
Burnsville *(G-747)*
Lighthouse1 LLC ....C... 952 852-7099
Minneapolis *(G-4884)*
Marix Technologies Inc ....E... 952 582-9100
Hopkins *(G-2575)*
McG Energy Solutions LLC ....E... 612 376-7757
Minneapolis *(G-4973)*
Meritide Inc ....E... 651 255-7300
Saint Paul *(G-8636)*
Millionzillion Software Inc ....E... 952 932-9048
Minneapolis *(G-5047)*
Mortgage Resource Center Inc ....E... 651 683-9705
Eagan *(G-1539)*
Myseeks Inc ....E... 651 967-4150
Saint Paul Park *(G-9297)*
New Boundary Technologies Inc ....E... 612 379-3805
Minneapolis *(G-5186)*
Nternational Projects ....D... 952 541-4888
Minneapolis *(G-5254)*
Open Access Technology Intl ....B... 763 201-2000
Minneapolis *(G-5283)*
Open Systems International Inc ....D... 763 551-0559
Minneapolis *(G-5284)*
Provation Medical Inc ....C... 612 313-1500
Minneapolis *(G-5431)*
Publishing Business Systems ....D... 651 639-0662
Saint Paul *(G-8856)*
Quantum Retail Technology Inc ....E... 612 486-3491
Minneapolis *(G-5446)*
Reshare Corp ....E... 952 908-0818
Minneapolis *(G-5522)*
Sadaka Technology Consultants ....A... 952 841-6363
Minneapolis *(G-5586)*
Sagitec Solutions LLC ....D... 612 235-4122
Saint Paul *(G-8922)*
Scout Information Services Inc ....E... 651 686-4646
Saint Paul *(G-7899)*
Sierra Bravo Corp ....C... 952 948-1211
Bloomington *(G-516)*
Spss Inc ....C... 507 287-2835
Rochester *(G-7262)*
Strategic Technologies Inc ....E... 763 559-1959
Minneapolis *(G-5758)*
Team Informatics Inc ....E... 651 222-8326
Saint Paul *(G-9030)*
Towers Watson Delaware Inc ....C... 952 842-7000
Minneapolis *(G-5839)*
Unimax Systems Corp ....E... 612 341-0946
Minneapolis *(G-5903)*
Verisae Inc ....E... 612 455-2305
Minneapolis *(G-5964)*
Weidt Group Inc ....E... 952 938-1588
Hopkins *(G-2659)*

COMPUTER SOFTWARE DEVELOPMENT & APPLICATIONS

Aware Systems Inc ....E... 800 783-8919
Minneapolis *(G-3849)*
Christopherson, John ....D... 952 814-7185
Minneapolis *(G-4072)*
Grocery Shopping Network Inc ....E... 612 746-4232
Minneapolis *(G-4574)*
Integral 7 Inc ....E... 612 436-0701
Minneapolis *(G-4712)*
Mhc Software Inc ....D... 952 882-0884
Burnsville *(G-756)*
Open-C Solutions Inc ....D... 952 842-3200
Minneapolis *(G-5285)*
Rjs Software Systems Inc ....E... 952 736-5800
Burnsville *(G-792)*
Sadaka Technology Consultants ....A... 952 841-6363
Minneapolis *(G-5586)*
Softbrands Inc ....D... 612 851-1500
Minneapolis *(G-5695)*
Softbrands Manufacturing Inc ....C... 612 851-1500
Minneapolis *(G-5696)*
Spanlink Communications Inc ....D... 763 971-2000
Minneapolis *(G-5715)*
Technology & Information ....D... 651 999-6001
Saint Paul *(G-9033)*
Vacava Inc ....E... 507 252-9076
Rochester *(G-7278)*
Vision Solutions Inc ....E... 507 252-3440
Rochester *(G-7284)*
Visions Inc ....D... 763 425-4251
Brooklyn Park *(G-621)*

COMPUTER SOFTWARE SYSTEMS ANALYSIS & DESIGN: Custom

Alebra Technologies Inc ....E... 651 366-6140
Saint Paul *(G-8008)*
Allen Interactions Inc ....E... 651 203-3700
Saint Paul *(G-7691)*
Ambient Consulting LLC ....C... 763 582-9000
Minneapolis *(G-3741)*
Analysts International Corp ....C... 952 835-5900
Minneapolis *(G-3773)*
Analytiks International Inc ....E... 612 305-4312
Minneapolis *(G-3774)*
Blaschko Computers Inc ....E... 320 252-0234
Saint Cloud *(G-7460)*
Ciber Inc ....D... 507 280-9267
Rochester *(G-7077)*
Comsys Information Technology ....C... 612 630-9100
Minneapolis *(G-4149)*
Fujitsu America Inc ....E... 763 595-9600
Minneapolis *(G-4489)*
Intertech Inc ....E... 651 994-8558
Saint Paul *(G-7806)*
Northshore Resources Inc ....E... 612 375-0315
Minneapolis *(G-5236)*
Pareo Inc ....E... 612 371-0400
Minneapolis *(G-5326)*
Sadaka Technology Consultants ....A... 952 841-6363
Minneapolis *(G-5586)*
SafeNet Consulting Inc ....D... 952 930-3636
Minnetonka *(G-6224)*
Shavlik Technologies LLC ....D... 651 426-6624
Saint Paul *(G-8948)*
T M B Consulting Inc ....D... 952 249-1223
Wayzata *(G-9944)*

SERVICES

Employment codes: A=Over 500 employees, B=251-500, C=101-250, D=51-100, E=25-50
2011 Harris Minnesota Services Directory
© Harris InfoSource 1-866-281-6415
671

Talent Technical Services Inc..............C... 952 417-3600
Minneapolis (G-5786)

Tech-Pro Inc ....B... 651 634-1400
Saint Paul (G-9032)

Testquest Inc ....E... 952 936-7887
Chanhassen (G-943)

Towers Watson Delaware Inc ....C... 952 842-7000
Minneapolis (G-5839)

COMPUTER SOFTWARE WRITERS

API Outsourcing Inc ....E... 651 675-2600
Eagan (G-1515)

COMPUTER SOFTWARE WRITERS:
Freelance

Network Instruments LLC ....E... 952 358-3800
Minnetonka (G-6201)

COMPUTER SYSTEM SELLING SVCS

Nuvo Network Management.................D... 952 933-4600
Hopkins (G-2592)

Pcr Computer Services ....E... 763 557-6824
Minneapolis (G-5354)

COMPUTER SYSTEMS ANALYSIS & DESIGN

Information Builders Inc.......................E... 651 602-9100
Saint Paul (G-8512)

Itasca Consulting Group Inc ....E... 612 371-4711
Minneapolis (G-4741)

Sartell Group Inc ....D... 612 548-3101
Minneapolis (G-5603)

Visions Inc ....D... 763 425-4251
Brooklyn Park (G-621)

COMPUTER TIME-SHARING

Network Computing Services Inc.........E... 612 337-0200
Minneapolis (G-5183)

COMPUTER-AIDED DESIGN SYSTEMS SVCS

Anertec Holdings LLC ....E... 507 451-5430
Owatonna (G-6693)

COMPUTER-AIDED ENGINEERING SYSTEMS
SVCS

Applied Statistics Inc...........................D... 763 268-0696
Minneapolis (G-3792)

COMPUTER-AIDED SYSTEM SVCS

Applied Statistics Inc...........................D... 763 268-0696
Minneapolis (G-3792)

COMPUTERS, NEC, WHOLESALE

Agvantage Software Inc ....E... 507 282-6353
Rochester (G-7046)

Evolving Solutions Inc ....E... 763 516-6500
Hamel (G-2340)

Healthland Inc ....C... 320 634-5331
Glenwood (G-2226)

Hickory Tech Information Soln ....D... 507 625-1691
Mankato (G-3139)

Hickory Tech Information Soln ....D... 507 625-1691
Mankato (G-3140)

PC Solutions Inc ....E... 763 852-1600
Minneapolis (G-3567)

Regents of The University of ....E... 218 281-8376
Crookston (G-1135)

Rural Computer Consultants Inc ....E... 320 365-4027
Bird Island (G-468)

Smith Micro Technologies Inc ....C... 651 482-8718
Saint Paul (G-8966)

TriMin Systems Inc ....E... 651 636-7667
Saint Paul (G-9083)

COMPUTERS, PERIPH & SOFTWARE,
WHLSE: Personal & Home Entrtn

Micro Electronics Inc...........................D... 952 285-4040
Minneapolis (G-5018)

Midwest Data Inc ....E... 320 235-8880
Willmar (G-10023)

System Design Advantage LLC ....E... 952 703-3500
Minneapolis (G-5781)

COMPUTERS, PERIPHERALS & SOFTWARE
WHOLESALERS

Beckhoff Automation LLC.....................E... 952 890-0000
Burnsville (G-683)

Bennett Office Technologies ....E... 320 235-6425
Willmar (G-9985)

Blm Technologies Inc ....E... 763 559-5100
Minneapolis (G-3912)

Cartridge Care Inc ....E... 612 331-7757
Saint Paul (G-8169)

Data Sales Co Inc ....D... 952 890-8838
Burnsville (G-710)

Expresspoint Technology Svcs............C... 763 543-6000
Golden Valley (G-2240)

First Tech Inc.......................................D... 612 374-8000
Minneapolis (G-4448)

G C M Inc ....E... 952 882-8500
Burnsville (G-726)

General Nanosystems Inc ....E... 612 331-3690
Minneapolis (G-4514)

Information Security Tech ....E... 651 287-0823
Saint Paul (G-8513)

J D L Technologies Inc ....E... 952 946-1810
Hopkins (G-2559)

Knowledge Computers Inc ....E... 952 249-9940
Long Lake (G-3026)

MacDermid ColorSpan Inc ....C... 952 944-9457
Hopkins (G-2573)

North American Systems Intl ....D... 952 374-6700
Minneapolis (G-5213)

Northern Computer Technologies ....E... 952 808-1000
Burnsville (G-763)

Now Micro Inc.......................................E... 651 633-9072
Saint Paul (G-8774)

Oracle Systems Corp ....B... 612 587-5000
Minneapolis (G-5288)

PC Solutions Inc ....E... 763 852-1600
Minneapolis (G-3567)

Power Mation Division Inc ....D... 651 605-3300
Saint Paul (G-8832)

3M Co ....C... 651 733-2147
Saint Paul (G-9044)

World Data Products Inc ....D... 952 476-9000
Minnetonka (G-6239)

Xerxes Computer Corp ....E... 952 936-9280
Minneapolis (G-6094)

Yada Systems Inc ....E... 651 631-3237
Saint Paul (G-9172)

COMPUTERS, PERIPHERALS & SOFTWARE,
WHOLESALE: Software

American Institute of ....E... 651 415-1320
Saint Paul (G-8027)

Avionte LLC ....E... 651 556-2121
Eagan (G-1516)

Calabrio Inc ....D... 763 592-4600
Minneapolis (G-3990)

Cokem International Ltd ....D... 952 358-6000
Shakopee (G-9431)

Direct Source Inc ....D... 952 934-8000
Chanhassen (G-920)

Edocument Resources LLC ....E... 952 607-3505
Minnetonka (G-6163)

Environmental Systems Research ....D... 651 454-0600
Saint Paul (G-7767)

Facet Technology Corp ....E... 952 944-1839
Eden Prairie (G-1660)

General Nanosystems Inc ....E... 612 331-3690
Minneapolis (G-4514)

Higher Dimension Research Inc...........E... 651 730-6203
Saint Paul (G-9229)

Magnetic Products & Services ....E... 763 424-2700
Minneapolis (G-4935)

Midwest Data Inc ....E... 320 235-8880
Willmar (G-10023)

Navarre Corp ....C... 763 535-8333
Minneapolis (G-5174)

Rubenstein & Ziff Inc ....E... 952 854-1460
Minneapolis (G-5574)

Smith Micro Technologies Inc ....C... 651 482-8718
Saint Paul (G-8966)

Telvent Dtn Inc ....E... 952 941-6628
Eden Prairie (G-1791)

TriMin Systems Inc ....E... 651 636-7667
Saint Paul (G-9083)

CONCRETE BUILDING PRDTS
WHOLESALERS

Brock White Co LLC ....E... 651 647-0950
Saint Paul (G-8131)

Maxxon Corp ....E... 763 478-6000
Hamel (G-2350)

CONDOMINIUM TIME SHARE EXCHANGE
SVCS

Lake Carlos Villas ....E... 320 846-1784
Alexandria (G-108)

CONFECTIONERY PRDTS WHOLESALERS

Abdallah Inc ....D... 952 890-4770
Burnsville (G-671)

Farley's & Sathers Candy Co ....B... 507 945-8181
Round Lake (G-7384)

Farley's & Sathers Candy Co ....C... 507 452-3433
Winona (G-10094)

Fritz Co Inc ....D... 651 459-9751
Newport (G-6486)

Granite City Jobbing Co Inc ....E... 320 252-1782
Saint Cloud (G-7521)

Henry's Foods Inc ....C... 320 763-3194
Alexandria (G-104)

Vistar Corp ....E... 800 333-3056
Maple Grove (G-3256)

Watson Co Inc......................................E... 763 689-3722
Cambridge (G-846)

Waymouth Farms Inc ....C... 763 533-5300
Minneapolis (G-6026)

CONSTRUCTION & MINING MACHINERY
WHOLESALERS

ABM Equipment & Supply Inc ....E... 952 938-5451
Hopkins (G-2498)

ABM Equipment & Supply LLC ....E... 952 938-5451
Hopkins (G-2499)

Ballantine Inc ....E... 763 427-3959
Anoka (G-158)

Contech Construction Products ....E... 952 496-1050
Shakopee (G-9433)

Dom-Ex LLC ....E... 218 262-6116
Hibbing (G-2442)

Penhall Co ....E... 763 542-9999
Minneapolis (G-5363)

Rdo Equipment Co ....E... 218 483-3353
Hawley (G-2421)

RSC Equipment Rental Inc ....E... 763 557-1234
Minneapolis (G-5565)

Ziegler Inc..D... 218 258-3232
Buhl (G-669)

Ziegler Inc..A... 952 888-4121
Minneapolis (G-6117)

Ziegler Inc..D... 952 445-4292
Shakopee (G-9482)

Ziegler Inc..E... 218 722-6628
Duluth (G-1509)

Ziegler Inc..E... 507 285-1775
Rochester (G-7298)

CONSTRUCTION EQPT REPAIR SVCS

Aerial Contractors Inc ....E... 218 236-9233
Moorhead (G-6294)

Hayden-Murphy Equipment Co ....E... 952 884-2301
Minneapolis (G-4612)

RSC Equipment Rental Inc ....E... 763 557-1234
Minneapolis (G-5565)

Ulland Brothers Inc ....E... 218 262-3406
Hibbing (G-2478)

CONSTRUCTION MATERIALS
WHOLESALERS

Trimline ....E... 763 540-9737
Minneapolis (G-5857)

CONSTRUCTION MATERIALS, WHOL:
Concrete/Cinder Bldg Prdts

Brock White Co LLC ....E... 651 647-0950
Saint Paul (G-8131)

CONSTRUCTION MATERIALS, WHOLESALE:
Aggregate

Hedberg Aggregates Inc ....D... 763 545-4400
Minneapolis (G-4627)

CONSTRUCTION MATERIALS, WHOLESALE:
Air Ducts, Sheet Metal

United Products Corp of Amer.............E... 763 545-1273
Minneapolis (G-5913)

CONSTRUCTION MATERIALS, WHOLESALE:
Architectural Metalwork

Stylepointe LLC ....E... 651 437-5356
Hastings (G-2418)

CONSTRUCTION MATERIALS, WHOLESALE:
Building Stone

Tile By Design Inc.................................E... 763 551-5900
Minneapolis (G-5823)

CONSTRUCTION MATERIALS, WHOLESALE:
Building Stone, Granite

Capital Granite & Marble Inc ....E... 320 259-7625
Saint Cloud *(G-7469)*

Dale Tile Co ....E... 763 488-1880
Minneapolis *(G-4221)*

Rubble Stone Co Inc ....E... 952 938-2599
Hopkins *(G-2623)*

CONSTRUCTION MATERIALS, WHOLESALE:
Building Stone, Marble

Capital Granite & Marble Inc ....E... 320 259-7625
Saint Cloud *(G-7469)*

Dale Tile Co ....E... 763 488-1880
Minneapolis *(G-4221)*

Rubble Stone Co Inc ....E... 952 938-2599
Hopkins *(G-2623)*

Tile Shop LLC ....E... 763 541-1444
Minneapolis *(G-5825)*

CONSTRUCTION MATERIALS, WHOLESALE:
Building, Exterior

Arrowhead Concrete Works Inc ....E... 218 729-8274
Duluth *(G-1240)*

Donlin Co ....E... 320 251-3680
Saint Cloud *(G-7411)*

Lowe's Home Centers Inc ....C... 763 367-1340
Minneapolis *(G-3524)*

Lowe's Home Centers Inc ....C... 507 446-4900
Owatonna *(G-6723)*

Lowe's Home Centers Inc ....C... 763 367-9000
Minneapolis *(G-4904)*

Lowe's Home Centers Inc ....C... 952 367-9000
Shakopee *(G-9452)*

Lowe's Home Centers Inc ....C... 763 428-5970
Rogers *(G-7328)*

Lowe's Home Centers Inc ....C... 763 488-2001
Osseo *(G-6629)*

Lowe's Home Centers Inc ....C... 218 262-7460
Hibbing *(G-2459)*

Lowe's Home Centers Inc ....C... 651 275-9910
Stillwater *(G-9626)*

Lowe's Home Centers Inc ....C... 507 328-8920
Rochester *(G-7162)*

Lowe's Home Centers Inc ....C... 507 385-3560
Mankato *(G-3158)*

Lowe's Home Centers Inc ....C... 763 367-4139
Saint Paul *(G-7826)*

Lowe's Home Centers Inc ....C... 763 367-1120
Minneapolis *(G-3523)*

Lowe's Home Centers Inc ....C... 763 691-6040
Cambridge *(G-840)*

Material Distributors Inc ....E... 507 532-4463
Marshall *(G-3312)*

Timber Roots LLC ....C... 507 452-2361
Winona *(G-10133)*

CONSTRUCTION MATERIALS, WHOLESALE:
Building, Interior

Arrowhead Concrete Works Inc ....E... 218 729-8274
Duluth *(G-1240)*

Christ's Household of Faith ....D... 651 265-3400
Saint Paul *(G-8198)*

Donlin Co ....E... 320 251-3680
Saint Cloud *(G-7411)*

Jaeckle Minnesota ....D... 612 676-0388
Minneapolis *(G-4751)*

Lowe's Home Centers Inc ....C... 763 367-1340
Minneapolis *(G-3524)*

Lowe's Home Centers Inc ....C... 507 446-4900
Owatonna *(G-6723)*

Lowe's Home Centers Inc ....C... 763 367-9000
Minneapolis *(G-4904)*

Lowe's Home Centers Inc ....C... 952 367-9000
Shakopee *(G-9452)*

Lowe's Home Centers Inc ....C... 763 428-5970
Rogers *(G-7328)*

Lowe's Home Centers Inc ....C... 763 488-2001
Osseo *(G-6629)*

Lowe's Home Centers Inc ....C... 218 262-7460
Hibbing *(G-2459)*

Lowe's Home Centers Inc ....C... 651 275-9910
Stillwater *(G-9626)*

Lowe's Home Centers Inc ....C... 507 328-8920
Rochester *(G-7162)*

Lowe's Home Centers Inc ....C... 507 385-3560
Mankato *(G-3158)*

Lowe's Home Centers Inc ....C... 763 367-4139
Saint Paul *(G-7826)*

Lowe's Home Centers Inc ....C... 763 367-1120
Minneapolis *(G-3523)*

Lowe's Home Centers Inc ....C... 763 691-6040
Cambridge *(G-840)*

Material Distributors Inc ....E... 507 532-4463
Marshall *(G-3312)*

CONSTRUCTION MATERIALS, WHOLESALE:
Ceiling Systems & Prdts

Architectural Sales of MN ....D... 763 533-1595
Minneapolis *(G-3802)*

St Paul Linoleum & Carpet Co ....D... 651 686-7770
Eagan *(G-1553)*

CONSTRUCTION MATERIALS, WHOLESALE:
Cement

Winroc Corp ....D... 651 777-8222
Saint Paul *(G-9288)*

CONSTRUCTION MATERIALS, WHOLESALE:
Concrete Mixtures

Twin City Concrete Products Co ....E... 651 489-8095
Saint Paul *(G-9091)*

CONSTRUCTION MATERIALS, WHOLESALE:
Door Frames

Contract Hardware Co Inc ....E... 651 780-0010
Circle Pines *(G-1007)*

D & M Industries Inc ....E... 218 287-3100
Moorhead *(G-6309)*

Kendell Doors & Hardware Inc ....E... 507 454-1723
Winona *(G-10107)*

Kendell Doors & Hardware Inc ....D... 651 905-0144
Mendota Heights *(G-3365)*

Twin City Hardware Co ....E... 651 735-2200
Saint Paul *(G-9284)*

Twin City Hardware Co ....E... 763 535-4660
Minneapolis *(G-5881)*

Wheeler Hardware Co ....E... 651 645-4501
Saint Paul *(G-9153)*

CONSTRUCTION MATERIALS, WHOLESALE:
Doors, Garage

Crawford Door Sales Co Twin ....E... 651 455-1221
Saint Paul *(G-7739)*

Custom Door Sales Inc ....D... 612 332-0357
Minneapolis *(G-4203)*

CONSTRUCTION MATERIALS, WHOLESALE:
Doors, NEC

Crawford Door Sales Co Twin ....E... 651 455-1221
Saint Paul *(G-7739)*

D & M Industries Inc ....E... 218 287-3100
Moorhead *(G-6309)*

Probuild Co LLC ....D... 952 469-3466
Lakeville *(G-2926)*

Twin City Hardware Co ....E... 651 735-2200
Saint Paul *(G-9284)*

W L Hall Co ....E... 952 937-8400
Hopkins *(G-2655)*

CONSTRUCTION MATERIALS, WHOLESALE:
Doors, Sash & Trim, Metal

API Garage Door Co ....E... 763 533-3838
Minneapolis *(G-3789)*

Contract Hardware Co Inc ....E... 651 780-0010
Circle Pines *(G-1007)*

Kendell Doors & Hardware Inc ....E... 507 454-1723
Winona *(G-10107)*

Kendell Doors & Hardware Inc ....D... 651 905-0144
Mendota Heights *(G-3365)*

Twin City Hardware Co ....E... 651 735-2200
Saint Paul *(G-9284)*

Wheeler Hardware Co ....E... 651 645-4501
Saint Paul *(G-9153)*

CONSTRUCTION MATERIALS, WHOLESALE:
Drywall Materials

Winroc Corp ....D... 651 777-8222
Saint Paul *(G-9288)*

CONSTRUCTION MATERIALS, WHOLESALE:
Glass

Brin Glass Co ....C... 612 529-9671
Minneapolis *(G-3949)*

Harmon Inc ....E... 952 944-5700
Eden Prairie *(G-1677)*

St Germain's Glass Inc ....E... 218 628-0221
Duluth *(G-1461)*

CONSTRUCTION MATERIALS, WHOLESALE:
Gravel

Cemstone Products Co ....E... 651 645-0769
Saint Paul *(G-8180)*

Mac Management Inc ....E... 952 938-8048
Minnetonka *(G-6189)*

Midwest Asphalt Corp ....E... 952 937-8033
Hopkins *(G-2582)*

Randy Kramer Excavating Inc ....E... 320 764-6871
Watkins *(G-9899)*

CONSTRUCTION MATERIALS, WHOLESALE:
Insulation, Thermal

Shelter Products Inc ....E... 507 354-4176
New Ulm *(G-6474)*

Wausau Supply Co ....D... 952 469-2500
Lakeville *(G-2941)*

CONSTRUCTION MATERIALS, WHOLESALE:
Limestone

Mac Management Inc ....E... 952 938-8048
Minnetonka *(G-6189)*

Midwest Asphalt Corp ....E... 952 937-8033
Hopkins *(G-2582)*

CONSTRUCTION MATERIALS, WHOLESALE:
Masons' Materials

Brock White Co LLC ....E... 651 647-0950
Saint Paul *(G-8131)*

CONSTRUCTION MATERIALS, WHOLESALE:
Millwork

Bayer Built Woodworks Inc ....C... 320 254-3651
Belgrade *(G-360)*

Custom Millwork Inc ....E... 651 770-2356
Saint Paul *(G-8275)*

Donlin Co ....E... 320 251-3680
Saint Cloud *(G-7411)*

Minnesota Valley Millwork Inc ....E... 952 440-9404
Prior Lake *(G-6944)*

Pacific Mutual Door Co ....E... 651 631-2211
Saint Paul *(G-8800)*

Shelter Products Inc ....E... 507 354-4176
New Ulm *(G-6474)*

Trimpac Inc ....D... 320 202-3200
Sauk Rapids *(G-9378)*

Twin City Hardware Co ....E... 651 735-2200
Saint Paul *(G-9284)*

CONSTRUCTION MATERIALS, WHOLESALE:
Molding, All Materials

Harkraft Inc ....E... 763 546-9161
Minneapolis *(G-4597)*

Midwest Hardwood Corp ....D... 763 425-8700
Osseo *(G-6638)*

Mo-Tech Corp ....E... 651 770-1515
Saint Paul *(G-9251)*

Plastic Products Co Inc ....E... 651 257-3143
Lindstrom *(G-2970)*

CONSTRUCTION MATERIALS, WHOLESALE:
Particleboard

Midwest Hardwood Corp ....D... 763 425-8700
Osseo *(G-6638)*

St Croix Valley Hardwoods Inc ....D... 651 407-2800
Saint Paul *(G-8983)*

St Croix Valley Hardwoods Inc ....E... 651 407-2800
Saint Paul *(G-8982)*

Youngblood Lumber Co ....E... 612 789-3521
Minneapolis *(G-6106)*

CONSTRUCTION MATERIALS, WHOLESALE:
Plywood

Material Distributors Inc ....E... 507 532-4463
Marshall *(G-3312)*

Midwest Hardwood Corp ....D... 763 425-8700
Osseo *(G-6638)*

Pine Point Wood Products Inc ....E... 763 428-4301
Osseo *(G-6653)*

Shelter Products Inc ....E... 507 354-4176
New Ulm *(G-6474)*

St Croix Valley Hardwoods Inc ....D... 651 407-2800
Saint Paul *(G-8983)*

Youngblood Lumber Co ....E... 612 789-3521
Minneapolis *(G-6106)*

**S
E
R
V
I
C
E
S**

Employment codes: A=Over 500 employees, B=251-500,
C=101-250, D=51-100, E=25-50

2011 Harris Minnesota
Services Directory

© Harris InfoSource 1-866-281-6415

673

CONSTRUCTION MATERIALS, WHOLESALE: Prefabricated Structures

Menard Inc ....C... 763 684-0830
Buffalo (G-650)

CONSTRUCTION MATERIALS, WHOLESALE: Roof, Asphalt/Sheet Metal

Garlock-East Equipment Co ....E... 763 553-1935
Minneapolis (G-4503)
Shelter Products Inc ....E... 507 354-4176
New Ulm (G-6474)

CONSTRUCTION MATERIALS, WHOLESALE: Roofing & Siding Material

Structural Wood Corp.....................E... 651 426-8111
Saint Paul (G-9010)
United Products Corp of Amer ....D... 651 227-8735
Saint Paul (G-9108)
United Products Corp of Amer ....E... 763 545-1273
Minneapolis (G-5913)

CONSTRUCTION MATERIALS, WHOLESALE: Sand

Cemstone Products Co ....E... 651 645-0769
Saint Paul (G-8180)
Mac Management Inc ....E... 952 938-8048
Minnetonka (G-6189)
Midwest Asphalt Corp ....E... 952 937-8033
Hopkins (G-2582)

CONSTRUCTION MATERIALS, WHOLESALE: Sewer Pipe, Clay

Hancor Inc ....E... 507 238-4791
Fairmont (G-1970)

CONSTRUCTION MATERIALS, WHOLESALE: Siding, Exc Wood

Minnesota Exteriors Inc ....C... 763 493-5500
Osseo (G-6639)
Shelter Products Inc ....E... 507 354-4176
New Ulm (G-6474)
Wausau Supply Co ....D... 952 469-2500
Lakeville (G-2941)

CONSTRUCTION MATERIALS, WHOLESALE: Stucco

Hedberg Aggregates Inc ....D... 763 545-4400
Minneapolis (G-4627)
K&G Enterprises Inc ....E... 763 263-7997
Big Lake (G-450)
Winroc Corp ....D... 651 777-8222
Saint Paul (G-9288)

CONSTRUCTION MATERIALS, WHOLESALE: Tile, Clay/Other Ceramic

Dale Tile Co ....E... 763 488-1880
Minneapolis (G-4221)
Olympia Tile Inc ....E... 763 545-5455
Minneapolis (G-5274)
Tile By Design Inc ....E... 763 551-5900
Minneapolis (G-5823)

CONSTRUCTION MATERIALS, WHOLESALE: Wallboard

Winroc Corp ....D... 651 777-8222
Saint Paul (G-9288)

CONSTRUCTION MATERIALS, WHOLESALE: Window Frames

Contract Hardware Co Inc ....E... 651 780-0010
Circle Pines (G-1007)
D & M Industries Inc ....E... 218 287-3100
Moorhead (G-6309)

CONSTRUCTION MATERIALS, WHOLESALE: Windows

Alside Builders Service ....E... 952 888-1339
Minneapolis (G-3735)
D & M Industries Inc ....E... 218 287-3100
Moorhead (G-6309)
Maly Co's LLC ....E... 612 788-9688
Minneapolis (G-4939)
Minnesota Exteriors Inc ....C... 763 493-5500
Osseo (G-6639)
Probuild Co LLC ....D... 952 469-3466
Lakeville (G-2926)

Trimpac Inc ....D... 320 202-3200
Sauk Rapids (G-9378)
United Products Corp of Amer ....D... 651 227-8735
Saint Paul (G-9108)
W L Hall Co ....E... 952 937-8400
Hopkins (G-2655)

CONSTRUCTION MATL, WHOLESALE: Structural Assy, Prefab, Wood

Extreme Panel Technologies Inc ....E... 507 423-5530
Cottonwood (G-1112)

CONSTRUCTION MATLS, WHOL: Composite Board Prdts, Woodboard

Lumber Mart Inc ....E... 218 773-1151
East Grand Forks (G-1571)

CONSTRUCTION MATLS, WHOL: Lumber, Rough, Dressed/Finished

Lake States Lumber Inc...................E... 218 927-2125
Aitkin (G-21)
Lyman Lumber Co ....B... 952 470-3600
Excelsior (G-1945)
Lyman Lumber Co ....D... 952 470-4800
Chanhassen (G-931)
Material Distributors Inc ....E... 507 532-4463
Marshall (G-3312)
Mid-America Cedar Inc ....E... 763 425-0125
Osseo (G-6637)
Midwest Hardwood Corp ....D... 763 425-8700
Osseo (G-6638)
Pine Point Wood Products Inc ....E... 763 428-4301
Osseo (G-6653)
Renneberg Hardwoods Inc ....D... 218 564-4912
Menahga (G-3359)
Shaw Acquisition Corp....................D... 612 378-1520
Minneapolis (G-5650)
Shelter Products Inc ....E... 507 354-4176
New Ulm (G-6474)
St Croix Valley Hardwoods Inc ....E... 651 407-2800
Saint Paul (G-8982)
Structural Wood Corp.......................E... 651 426-8111
Saint Paul (G-9010)
Viking Forest Products LLC.............E... 952 941-6512
Eden Prairie (G-1805)
Wheeler Consolidated Inc ....E... 952 929-6791
Minneapolis (G-6064)
Woodline Manufacturing Inc ....D... 218 744-5966
Eveleth (G-1934)
Youngblood Lumber Co ....E... 612 789-3521
Minneapolis (G-6106)

CONSTRUCTION MTRLS, WHOL: Exterior Flat Glass, Plate/Window

Minneapolis Glass Co......................D... 763 559-0635
Plymouth (G-6874)

CONSTRUCTION MTRLS, WHOL: Interior Flat Glass, Plate/Window

Minneapolis Glass Co......................D... 763 559-0635
Plymouth (G-6874)

CONSTRUCTION SITE PREPARATION SVCS

Doboszenski & Sons Inc ....E... 763 478-6945
Loretto (G-3046)
Rivard Contracting Inc ....E... 763 753-7888
Cedar (G-884)
Veit & Co Inc ....C... 763 428-2242
Rogers (G-7347)

CONSTRUCTION: Agricultural Building

Ebert Inc ....E... 763 498-7844
Loretto (G-3047)
Siwek Lumber & Millwork Inc ....E... 952 492-6666
Jordan (G-2810)

CONSTRUCTION: Airport Runway

Ames Construction Inc....................B... 952 435-7106
Burnsville (G-676)

CONSTRUCTION: Apartment Building

Builders Inc ....E... 952 545-3217
Minneapolis (G-3971)
Kraus-Anderson Inc ....E... 612 332-7281
Minneapolis (G-4823)
Kuepers Construction Inc ....E... 888 829-0707
Baxter (G-334)
Lumber One, Cold Spring Inc ....E... 320 685-3631
Cold Spring (G-1087)

Siewert Construction Co Inc ....E... 651 437-1728
Hastings (G-2405)
Weis Builders Inc............................C... 612 243-5000
Minneapolis (G-6033)

CONSTRUCTION: Athletic & Recreation Facilities

Premier Electrical Corp...................C... 763 424-6551
Brooklyn Park (G-617)

CONSTRUCTION: Bank

Vanman Construction Co ....E... 763 541-9552
Minneapolis (G-5958)

CONSTRUCTION: Bridge

CS McCrossan Inc ....C... 763 425-4167
Osseo (G-6606)
DH Blattner & Sons Inc ....D... 320 356-7351
Avon (G-294)
Graham Construction Services ....D... 651 687-0648
Saint Paul (G-7789)
Lunda Construction Co ....C... 651 437-9666
Rosemount (G-7371)
Minnowa Construction Inc ....D... 507 886-6162
Harmony (G-2372)
Park Construction Co ....D... 763 786-9800
Minneapolis (G-3563)
Structural Restoration Inc ....E... 612 825-8614
Minneapolis (G-5760)
Swenke Co Inc ....E... 507 634-7778
Kasson (G-2824)

CONSTRUCTION: Cable Television Line

Comlink Midwest Inc ....E... 763 391-7483
Minneapolis (G-4129)
T D & I Cable Maintenance Inc ....E... 651 436-3383
Lakeland (G-2887)

CONSTRUCTION: Chemical Facility

Cherne Co Inc ....D... 952 944-4300
Eden Prairie (G-1623)

CONSTRUCTION: Commercial & Institutional Building

All Agape Construction Co LLC ....E... 763 205-1313
Anoka (G-149)
Amcon Construction Co LLC ....E... 651 379-9090
Saint Paul (G-7695)
Bainey Group Inc.............................E... 763 557-6911
Minneapolis (G-3858)
Bor-Son Construction Inc ....B... 952 854-8444
Minneapolis (G-3929)
Breitbach Construction Co ....D... 320 697-5525
Elrosa (G-1909)
Donlyn Manufacture ....E... 763 786-1103
Minneapolis (G-3459)
Ellerbe Becket Inc ....C... 612 376-2000
Minneapolis (G-4341)
Food Engineering Corp....................C... 763 559-5200
Minneapolis (G-4461)
Gateway Building Systems Inc ....E... 218 685-4420
Elbow Lake (G-1853)
JD Driver Ltd ....E... 507 437-6050
Rose Creek (G-7350)
Joseph Co Inc ....E... 507 437-3284
Austin (G-279)
Knutson Construction Services ....D... 507 280-9788
Rochester (G-7157)
Kraus-Anderson Construction Co ......D... 763 786-7711
Circle Pines (G-1013)
Kraus-Anderson Construction Co ......E... 218 759-0596
Bemidji (G-400)
Lester Buildings LLC ....C... 320 395-2531
Lester Prairie (G-2963)
M A Mortenson Co...........................A... 763 522-2100
Minneapolis (G-4918)
McGough Construction Co Inc.........A... 651 633-5050
Saint Paul (G-8624)
Meyer Contracting Inc.....................E... 763 391-5959
Maple Grove (G-3250)
Minnesota Department of Trans.........D... 507 831-1200
Windom (G-10069)
Northfield Construction Co Inc ....E... 507 645-8975
Northfield (G-6537)
Opus Design Build LLC ....D... 952 656-4444
Minnetonka (G-6206)
PCL Construction Services Inc ....E... 952 882-9600
Burnsville (G-778)
Perkins Lumber Co Inc ....E... 320 235-9420
Willmar (G-10037)
Pump & Meter Service Inc ....E... 952 933-4800
Hopkins (G-2608)

Raske Building Systems Inc ....E... 320 877-7221
Cosmos *(G-1095)*

Saginaw Contracting Inc Wgcc ....E... 218 348-6000
Saint Joseph *(G-7654)*

Salonek Concrete & Constr ....E... 507 723-4218
Springfield *(G-9574)*

Stellar Contractors Inc ....C... 952 469-0900
Lakeville *(G-2935)*

Trout Enterprises Inc of Nthn ....E... 218 246-8165
Deer River *(G-1174)*

Vinco Inc ....D... 651 982-4642
Forest Lake *(G-2171)*

Weis Builders Inc ....E... 507 288-2041
Rochester *(G-7288)*

CONSTRUCTION: Commercial & Office Building, New

A B Systems Inc.................................E... 507 288-9397
Rochester *(G-7042)*

A J Lysne Contracting Corp ....D... 507 451-7121
Owatonna *(G-6688)*

Adolfson & Peterson Inc ....C... 952 544-1561
Minneapolis *(G-3682)*

Alvin E Benike Inc ....C... 507 288-6575
Rochester *(G-7053)*

Arkay Construction Co ....E... 763 544-3341
Minneapolis *(G-3806)*

Berg Construction Services Inc ....E... 651 423-5531
Rosemount *(G-7363)*

Bigelow, Joel & Sons Entrprs ....E... 507 529-1161
Rochester *(G-7066)*

Billman Construction Inc ....E... 218 729-7570
Duluth *(G-1253)*

Bor-Son Building Corp ....C... 952 854-8444
Minneapolis *(G-3928)*

Bruce Kreofsky & Sons Inc ....D... 507 534-3855
Plainview *(G-6839)*

Builders Inc ....E... 952 545-3217
Minneapolis *(G-3971)*

C F Haglin & Sons Inc ....D... 952 920-6123
Minneapolis *(G-3983)*

Carlson-Lavine Inc ....E... 651 638-9600
Saint Paul *(G-8167)*

Con Spec Corp ....E... 651 501-6500
Saint Paul *(G-9199)*

Donald Holm Construction Co ....E... 218 628-2257
Duluth *(G-1295)*

Eagle Construction Co Inc ....E... 320 632-5429
Little Falls *(G-3001)*

Ed Lunn Construction Inc ....E... 507 288-4400
Rochester *(G-7102)*

Flannery Construction Inc ....E... 651 225-1105
Saint Paul *(G-8384)*

Frerichs Construction Co....................E... 651 787-0687
Saint Paul *(G-8397)*

Graham Construction Services ....D... 651 687-0648
Saint Paul *(G-7789)*

Heymann Construction Co..................D... 507 354-3174
New Ulm *(G-6454)*

Hy-TEC Construction of ....E... 218 829-8529
Brainerd *(G-570)*

J E Dunn Construction Co ....C... 952 830-9000
Eden Prairie *(G-1700)*

James Steele Construction Co ....E... 651 488-6755
Saint Paul *(G-8529)*

Johnson-Wilson Constructors ....D... 218 628-0202
Duluth *(G-1363)*

K A Witt Construction Inc ....E... 952 758-2108
New Prague *(G-6429)*

K-M Building Co of Minneapolis.........E... 612 977-9060
Minneapolis *(G-4786)*

Kraus-Anderson Inc ....E... 612 332-7281
Minneapolis *(G-4823)*

Kuepers Construction Inc ....E... 888 829-0707
Baxter *(G-334)*

L S Black Constructors Inc ....D... 651 774-8445
Saint Paul *(G-8553)*

Lanners Brothers Construction..................507 532-5457
Marshall *(G-3304)*

Lee's Construction Inc ....D... 320 762-0325
Alexandria *(G-111)*

Lenci Enterprises Inc........................E... 218 741-3482
Virginia *(G-9745)*

Lodermeiers ....D... 651 923-4441
Goodhue *(G-2250)*

Lund-Martin Construction Inc...........E... 612 782-2250
Minneapolis *(G-4909)*

M A Mortenson Co ....B... 763 522-2100
Minneapolis *(G-4917)*

Marcus Construction Co Inc ....E... 320 978-6616
Prinsburg *(G-6926)*

McDonald Homes Inc.........................E... 651 455-5142
Inver Grove Heights *(G-2761)*

Murlowski Construction Co Inc ....E... 651 786-1300
Saint Paul *(G-8729)*

Nor-Son Inc..C... 218 828-1722
Baxter *(G-339)*

Olson General Contractors Inc..........E... 763 535-1481
Minneapolis *(G-5272)*

Opus Northwest Construction.............C... 952 656-4444
Hopkins *(G-2598)*

PCL Construction Services Inc ....D... 952 882-9600
Burnsville *(G-779)*

Prestige Drywall Inc ....E... 763 506-0030
Anoka *(G-216)*

R J Ryan Construction Inc ....E... 651 681-0200
Mendota Heights *(G-3369)*

Reiner Contracting Inc ....E... 320 587-9886
Hutchinson *(G-2710)*

Reshetar Systems Inc........................E... 763 421-1152
Anoka *(G-220)*

Retail Construction Services ....C... 651 704-9000
Lake Elmo *(G-2876)*

Ryan Co's US Inc ....B... 612 492-4000
Minneapolis *(G-5579)*

Sand Co's Inc ....E... 320 202-3100
Waite Park *(G-9836)*

Shaw - Lundquist Associates ....D... 651 454-0670
Saint Paul *(G-7903)*

Sheehy Construction Co ....D... 651 488-6691
Saint Paul *(G-8949)*

Socon Construction Inc ....E... 763 754-4027
Minneapolis *(G-3604)*

Strack Construction Co Inc................E... 320 251-5933
Sauk Rapids *(G-9377)*

Thorstad Construction Co Inc ....E... 320 367-2159
Maynard *(G-3337)*

Wapasha Construction Co Inc ....E... 507 454-2707
Winona *(G-10137)*

Watson-Forsberg Co ....E... 952 544-7761
Minneapolis *(G-6025)*

Web Construction Co Inc ....E... 507 387-1667
Mankato *(G-3214)*

Weis Builders Inc ....C... 612 243-5000
Minneapolis *(G-6033)*

Wilcon Construction Inc.....................E... 507 375-5464
Saint James *(G-7649)*

Zeman Construction Co ....E... 612 521-4300
Minneapolis *(G-6115)*

CONSTRUCTION: Condominium

Brightkeys Building & Devpt ....E... 651 501-6500
Saint Paul *(G-9188)*

Siewert Construction Co Inc...............E... 651 437-1728
Hastings *(G-2405)*

CONSTRUCTION: Curb

C R Fischer & Sons Inc ....E... 651 463-7300
Farmington *(G-2042)*

Cone Corp...E... 218 245-2313
Bovey *(G-540)*

Curb Masters Inc ....E... 651 351-9200
Stillwater *(G-9609)*

Halverson Concrete Inc......................E... 763 434-0318
Anoka *(G-186)*

Ryan Contracting Co ....C... 952 894-3200
Shakopee *(G-9471)*

CONSTRUCTION: Dam

DH Blattner & Sons Inc......................D... 320 356-7351
Avon *(G-294)*

Park Construction Co ....D... 763 786-9800
Minneapolis *(G-3563)*

CONSTRUCTION: Dams, Waterways, Docks & Other Marine

Global Specialty Contractors...................651 406-8232
Saint Paul *(G-7783)*

Nels Nelson & Sons Inc.....................C... 218 879-4561
Cloquet *(G-1058)*

Park Construction Co ....D... 763 786-9800
Minneapolis *(G-3563)*

CONSTRUCTION: Drainage System

Chard Tiling & Excavating Inc ....D... 952 873-6152
Belle Plaine *(G-372)*

Traxler Construction Inc ....E... 507 357-2235
Le Center *(G-2954)*

Tri-State Drilling Inc...........................D... 763 553-1234
Minneapolis *(G-5852)*

CONSTRUCTION: Electric Power Line

Aerial Contractors Inc ....E... 218 236-9233
Moorhead *(G-6294)*

Dig America Utility Contr ....E... 320 253-3447
Saint Cloud *(G-7498)*

Karian Peterson Power Line ....E... 320 269-6769
Montevideo *(G-6262)*

Okay Construction Co Inc ....E... 763 633-8729
Princeton *(G-6913)*

CONSTRUCTION: Elevated Highway

Dakota Highway Department...............E... 952 891-7109
Saint Paul *(G-7745)*

Swenke Properties Inc ....E... 507 634-7778
Kasson *(G-2825)*

CONSTRUCTION: Farm Building

Bruce Kreofsky & Sons Inc ....D... 507 534-3855
Plainview *(G-6839)*

Gateway Building Systems Inc ....E... 218 685-4420
Elbow Lake *(G-1853)*

Lanners Brothers Construction 507 532-5457
Marshall *(G-3304)*

Lodermeiers.......................................D... 651 923-4441
Goodhue *(G-2250)*

Thorstad Construction Co Inc.............E... 320 367-2159
Maynard *(G-3337)*

CONSTRUCTION: Food Prdts Manufacturing or Packing Plant

Boldt Co...C... 218 879-1293
Cloquet *(G-1047)*

Fagen Inc ....D... 320 564-3324
Granite Falls *(G-2314)*

Ibberson Inc 952 938-7007
Hopkins *(G-2555)*

CONSTRUCTION: Golf Course

Duininck Inc ....C... 320 978-6011
Prinsburg *(G-6925)*

Ellingson Drainage Inc ....D... 507 527-2294
West Concord *(G-9964)*

Hartman Co's Inc...............................E... 952 443-2958
Victoria *(G-9729)*

Veit & Co Inc ....C... 763 428-2242
Rogers *(G-7347)*

CONSTRUCTION: Grain Elevator

J & D Construction Inc.......................E... 320 269-2101
Montevideo *(G-6247)*

SMA Elevator Construction Inc...........E... 763 295-4367
Monticello *(G-6287)*

Structural Restoration Inc ....E... 612 825-8614
Minneapolis *(G-5760)*

Vigen Construction Inc.......................E... 218 773-1159
East Grand Forks *(G-1580)*

CONSTRUCTION: Guardrails, Highway

Global Specialty Contractors 651 406-8232
Saint Paul *(G-7783)*

H & R Const Co..................................E... 218 589-8707
Dalton *(G-1156)*

CONSTRUCTION: Heavy Highway & Street

B H Heselton Co ....D... 507 334-3901
Faribault *(G-1990)*

Bituminous Roadways Inc...................E... 612 721-2451
Minneapolis *(G-3908)*

Christiansen Industrial ....E... 218 751-4663
Bemidji *(G-384)*

Dresel Contracting Inc ....E... 651 257-9469
Chisago City *(G-990)*

Dustcoating Inc..................................E... 952 894-0012
Savage *(G-9389)*

Imperial Developers Inc ....D... 651 454-3330
Saint Paul *(G-7802)*

Lunda Construction Co.......................C... 651 437-9666
Rosemount *(G-7371)*

Mark Sand & Gravel Co ....D... 218 736-7523
Fergus Falls *(G-2092)*

Mathiowetz Enterprises Inc ....C... 507 794-6953
Sleepy Eye *(G-9497)*

Minnesota Department of Trans...........D... 507 389-6351
Mankato *(G-3170)*

Minnesota Department of Trans...........A... 651 582-1364
Saint Paul *(G-9250)*

Northland Constructors of...................E... 218 722-8170
Duluth *(G-1406)*

Pciroads, Corp ....D... 763 497-6100
Saint Michael *(G-7680)*

Penhall Co ....D... 763 428-2244
Rogers *(G-7337)*

R J Zavoral & Sons Inc.......................E... 218 773-0586
East Grand Forks *(G-1574)*

Rupp Construction Co Inc ....E... 507 836-8555
Slayton *(G-9490)*

Sellin Brothers Inc.............................E... 218 483-3522
Hawley *(G-2422)*

Tenson Construction Inc ....E... 218 743-3874
Bigfork *(G-465)*

Employment codes: A=Over 500 employees, B=251-500,
C=101-250, D=51-100, E=25-50

2011 Harris Minnesota
Services Directory

© Harris InfoSource 1-866-281-6415
675

SERVICES

CONSTRUCTION: Hospital

Alvin E Benike Inc ....C... 507 288-6575
Rochester *(G-7053)*

Meyer Contracting Inc ....E... 763 391-5959
Maple Grove *(G-3250)*

PCL Construction Services Inc ....D... 952 882-9600
Burnsville *(G-779)*

Ryan Co's US Inc ....B... 612 492-4000
Minneapolis *(G-5579)*

CONSTRUCTION: Hotel, Motel & Multi-family Housing

Klingelhutz Co's Inc ....D... 952 448-6776
Chaska *(G-973)*

CONSTRUCTION: Indl Building & Warehouse

Amcon Construction Co LLC ....E... 651 379-9090
Saint Paul *(G-7695)*

Boldt Co ....C... 218 879-1293
Cloquet *(G-1047)*

Bolton Development Worldwide ....E... 952 886-7211
Minneapolis *(G-3924)*

Bor-Son Building Corp ....C... 952 854-8444
Minneapolis *(G-3928)*

Breitbach Construction Co ....D... 320 697-5525
Elrosa *(G-1909)*

C F Haglin & Sons Inc ....D... 952 920-6123
Minneapolis *(G-3983)*

CM Construction Co Inc ....E... 952 895-8223
Burnsville *(G-699)*

Dallas I Hanson Construction ....E... 320 839-3455
Ortonville *(G-6582)*

Fagen Inc ....D... 320 564-3324
Granite Falls *(G-2314)*

Global Specialty Contractors 651 406-8232
Saint Paul *(G-7783)*

Hawk Construction Inc ....E... 218 327-0069
Grand Rapids *(G-2284)*

Heymann Construction Co ....D... 507 354-3174
New Ulm *(G-6454)*

Hy-TEC Construction of ....E... 218 829-8529
Brainerd *(G-570)*

Ibberson Inc 952 938-7007
Hopkins *(G-2555)*

Joseph Co Inc ....E... 507 437-3284
Austin *(G-279)*

Kellington Construction Inc ....D... 763 416-3200
Minneapolis *(G-4797)*

Knutson Construction Services ....D... 507 280-9788
Rochester *(G-7157)*

Maertens-Brenny Construction ....E... 763 786-4779
Minneapolis *(G-3525)*

Marcy Construction Co ....D... 952 525-9700
Minneapolis *(G-4947)*

McC Inc ....C... 763 477-4774
Rockford *(G-7311)*

Met-Con Construction Inc 507 332-2266
Faribault *(G-2022)*

Murlowski Construction Co Inc ....E... 651 786-1300
Saint Paul *(G-8729)*

Permasteelisa North America ....E... 651 905-1515
Saint Paul *(G-7874)*

Proform Thermal Systems Inc ....E... 763 572-2200
Minneapolis *(G-3576)*

Ray Riihiluoma Inc ....E... 218 879-3317
Cloquet *(G-1064)*

Riverstar Inc ....E... 507 452-5109
Winona *(G-10122)*

SA Woods Inc 507 451-7084
Owatonna *(G-6735)*

Strack Construction Co Inc ....E... 320 251-5933
Sauk Rapids *(G-9377)*

Vinco Inc ....D... 651 982-4642
Forest Lake *(G-2171)*

Ww Constructors Inc ....E... 763 420-4177
Hamel *(G-2362)*

Zeman Construction Co ....E... 612 521-4300
Minneapolis *(G-6115)*

CONSTRUCTION: Indl Buildings, New, NEC

Alltech Engineering Corp ....D... 651 452-7893
Saint Paul *(G-7693)*

Arkay Construction Co ....E... 763 544-3341
Minneapolis *(G-3806)*

C F Haglin & Sons Inc ....D... 952 920-6123
Minneapolis *(G-3983)*

Comstock Construction Inc, of ....E... 218 739-5365
Fergus Falls *(G-2071)*

Graham Construction Services ....D... 651 687-0648
Saint Paul *(G-7789)*

Kraus-Anderson Inc ....E... 612 332-7281
Minneapolis *(G-4823)*

L S Black Constructors Inc ....D... 651 774-8445
Saint Paul *(G-8553)*

Lund-Martin Construction Inc ....E... 612 782-2250
Minneapolis *(G-4909)*

Max Gray Construction Inc ....E... 218 262-6622
Hibbing *(G-2461)*

McGough Construction Co Inc ....A... 651 633-5050
Saint Paul *(G-8624)*

Nor-Son Inc ....C... 218 828-1722
Baxter *(G-339)*

Olson General Contractors Inc ....E... 763 535-1481
Minneapolis *(G-5272)*

Opus Northwest Construction ....C... 952 656-4444
Hopkins *(G-2598)*

Penn-Co Construction Inc ....E... 651 687-0648
Saint Paul *(G-7872)*

R J Ryan Construction Inc ....E... 651 681-0200
Mendota Heights *(G-3369)*

Ray Riihiluoma Inc ....E... 218 879-3317
Cloquet *(G-1064)*

Ryan Co's US Inc ....B... 612 492-4000
Minneapolis *(G-5579)*

Shaw - Lundquist Associates ....D... 651 454-0670
Saint Paul *(G-7903)*

W Gohman Construction Co ....E... 320 363-7781
Saint Joseph *(G-7656)*

Weis Builders Inc ....C... 612 243-5000
Minneapolis *(G-6033)*

CONSTRUCTION: Indl Plant

M A Mortenson Co ....B... 763 522-2100
Minneapolis *(G-4917)*

CONSTRUCTION: Institutional Building

Adolfson & Peterson Inc ....C... 952 544-1561
Minneapolis *(G-3682)*

C F Haglin & Sons Inc ....D... 952 920-6123
Minneapolis *(G-3983)*

M A Mortenson Co ....B... 763 522-2100
Minneapolis *(G-4917)*

Shaw - Lundquist Associates ....D... 651 454-0670
Saint Paul *(G-7903)*

CONSTRUCTION: Irrigation System

Aqua Engineering Inc ....E... 952 941-1138
Eden Prairie *(G-1594)*

Premier Irrigation Inc ....E... 651 480-8857
Hastings *(G-2401)*

CONSTRUCTION: Land Preparation

Park Construction Co ....D... 763 786-9800
Minneapolis *(G-3563)*

CONSTRUCTION: Multi-Family Housing

Bruggeman Homes Inc ....E... 651 770-2981
Saint Paul *(G-8136)*

Lumber One, Avon Inc ....D... 320 356-7342
Avon *(G-296)*

Schwieters' Co's Inc ....E... 651 407-1618
Hugo *(G-2673)*

CONSTRUCTION: Multi-family Dwellings, New

Con Spec Corp ....E... 651 501-6500
Saint Paul *(G-9199)*

Fabricated Wood Products Inc ....E... 507 451-1019
Medford *(G-3343)*

Johnson-Wilson Constructors ....D... 218 628-0202
Duluth *(G-1363)*

Keystone Bluffs ....E... 218 727-2800
Duluth *(G-1370)*

Lipe Brothers Construction Inc ....E... 218 525-3364
Duluth *(G-1384)*

Sand Co's Inc ....E... 320 202-3100
Waite Park *(G-9836)*

CONSTRUCTION: Oil & Gas Pipeline Construction

Minnesota Limited Inc ....D... 763 428-4444
Big Lake *(G-451)*

Npl Construction Co ....E... 218 327-9467
Grand Rapids *(G-2303)*

CONSTRUCTION: Paper & Pulp Mill

Boldt Co ....C... 218 879-1293
Cloquet *(G-1047)*

Fagen Inc ....D... 320 564-3324
Granite Falls *(G-2314)*

CONSTRUCTION: Parking Lot

Asphalt Specialties Co 651 484-1696
Saint Paul *(G-8072)*

CONSTRUCTION: Pier

Tri-State Drilling Inc ....D... 763 553-1234
Minneapolis *(G-5852)*

CONSTRUCTION: Pipeline, NEC

A W Kuettel & Sons Inc ....D... 218 722-3901
Duluth *(G-1231)*

C & G Construction Inc of ....D... 218 776-3080
Clearbrook *(G-1036)*

CONSTRUCTION: Power & Communication Transmission Tower

M & P Utilities Inc ....C... 320 963-2400
Maple Lake *(G-3261)*

Vertical Limit Construction ....D... 507 824-1222
Wanamingo *(G-9867)*

CONSTRUCTION: Power Plant

Cherne Co Inc ....D... 952 944-4300
Eden Prairie *(G-1623)*

M A Mortenson Co ....B... 763 522-2100
Minneapolis *(G-4917)*

Park Construction Co ....D... 763 786-9800
Minneapolis *(G-3563)*

CONSTRUCTION: Railroad & Subway

Railworks Track Systems Inc ....D... 952 469-4907
Lakeville *(G-2928)*

CONSTRUCTION: Religious Building

Breitbach Construction Co ....D... 320 697-5525
Elrosa *(G-1909)*

McGough Construction Co Inc ....A... 651 633-5050
Saint Paul *(G-8624)*

Vanman Construction Co ....E... 763 541-9552
Minneapolis *(G-5958)*

CONSTRUCTION: Residential, Nec

Advance Wall Systems Inc ....E... 763 263-8512
Big Lake *(G-444)*

Bor-Son Construction Inc ....B... 952 854-8444
Minneapolis *(G-3929)*

Build All Installed Inc ....E... 218 692-5115
Crosslake *(G-1150)*

Ebert Inc ....E... 763 498-7844
Loretto *(G-3047)*

Klingelhutz Co's Inc ....D... 952 448-6776
Chaska *(G-973)*

Patriot Builders Inc ....E... 763 434-1702
Anoka *(G-213)*

Pratt Construction Inc ....E... 651 765-0572
Saint Paul *(G-8833)*

Restoration Professionals Inc ....E... 651 379-1990
Saint Paul *(G-8895)*

Wes Hanson Builders Inc ....E... 218 765-4122
Merrifield *(G-3372)*

CONSTRUCTION: Restaurant

Retail Construction Services ....C... 651 704-9000
Lake Elmo *(G-2876)*

CONSTRUCTION: Retaining Wall

Concept Landscaping Inc ....E... 952 472-4118
Mound *(G-6386)*

Metro Home Services Network ....E... 612 827-0643
Cedar *(G-882)*

Rockwood Retaining Walls Inc ....E... 507 529-2871
Rochester *(G-7241)*

Willow Creek Concrete Products ....E... 320 398-5415
Kimball *(G-2835)*

CONSTRUCTION: Roads, Gravel or Dirt

DCI Environmental Inc ....E... 952 894-0012
Savage *(G-9388)*

CONSTRUCTION: Roads, Highways & Sidewalks, Concrete

C R Fischer & Sons Inc ....E... 651 463-7300
Farmington *(G-2042)*

Cone Corp ....E... 218 245-2313
Bovey *(G-540)*

County of Carver ....D... 952 466-5200
Cologne *(G-1091)*

Davidson Ready Mix Inc ....E... 218 449-4865
Holt *(G-2495)*

Khc Construction Inc............................E... 507 532-6768
Marshall *(G-3303)*

CONSTRUCTION: School Building

Adolfson & Peterson Inc ....C... 952 544-1561
Minneapolis *(G-3682)*

Breitbach Construction Co ....D... 320 697-5525
Elrosa *(G-1909)*

McGough Construction Co Inc ....A... 651 633-5050
Saint Paul *(G-8624)*

PCL Construction Services Inc ....D... 952 882-9600
Burnsville *(G-779)*

CONSTRUCTION: Sewer Line

B H Heselton Co.................................D... 507 334-3901
Faribault *(G-1990)*

C W Houle Inc.....................................D... 651 484-6077
Saint Paul *(G-8147)*

Fraser Construction Co.........................E... 507 288-6583
Rochester *(G-7120)*

Friedges Landscaping Inc....................E... 952 469-2996
Lakeville *(G-2908)*

Gaub Inc..E... 320 382-8075
Olivia *(G-6561)*

Hibbing, City of Inc ....E... 218 263-5264
Hibbing *(G-2453)*

Lametti & Sons Inc...............................E... 651 426-1380
Hugo *(G-2678)*

Latour Construction Inc ....E... 320 963-5993
Maple Lake *(G-3260)*

Nels Nelson & Sons Inc ....C... 218 879-4561
Cloquet *(G-1058)*

Nodland Construction Co ....D... 320 763-5159
Alexandria *(G-114)*

Northland Constructors of ....E... 218 722-8170
Duluth *(G-1406)*

Ryan Contracting Co ....C... 952 894-3200
Shakopee *(G-9471)*

Swenke Co Inc.....................................E... 507 634-7778
Kasson *(G-2824)*

TI Nexlevel Co's LLC ....C... 320 963-2400
Maple Lake *(G-3266)*

CONSTRUCTION: Shopping Center & Mall

Elder-Jones Inc ....E... 952 854-2854
Minneapolis *(G-4336)*

Retail Construction Services ....C... 651 704-9000
Lake Elmo *(G-2876)*

Ryan Co's US Inc ....B... 612 492-4000
Minneapolis *(G-5579)*

CONSTRUCTION: Sidewalk

C R Fischer & Sons Inc ....E... 651 463-7300
Farmington *(G-2042)*

CONSTRUCTION: Silo, Agricultural

Gateway Building Systems Inc.............E... 218 685-4420
Elbow Lake *(G-1853)*

CONSTRUCTION: Single-Family Housing

Argus Homes..E... 651 294-2160
Saint Paul *(G-8062)*

Arnzen Construction Inc ....E... 320 836-2284
Freeport *(G-2187)*

Baker Colberg & Realty ....E... 651 430-7745
Stillwater *(G-9601)*

Bigelow-Lennon Construction...............E... 507 775-7068
Byron *(G-822)*

Brandl Anderson Homes Inc.................E... 952 898-0231
Saint Paul *(G-7723)*

Budget Exteriors Inc.............................E... 952 887-1613
Minneapolis *(G-3967)*

Comstock Construction Inc, of.............E... 218 739-5365
Fergus Falls *(G-2071)*

Deck & Door Co....................................E... 952 432-1888
Saint Paul *(G-7751)*

Doug Speedling Builders Inc ....D... 651 437-3658
Hastings *(G-2384)*

Elite Communications & Constr ....E... 651 739-1366
Saint Paul *(G-9211)*

Energy Construction ....E... 763 489-7777
Minneapolis *(G-4356)*

Evenson Concrete Systems...................E... 507 243-3660
Madison Lake *(G-3079)*

Excel Building Maintenance Inc............E... 507 288-0913
Rochester *(G-7108)*

FCA Construction Co LLC......................C... 952 229-7521
Chanhassen *(G-923)*

Food Engineering Corp ....C... 763 559-5200
Minneapolis *(G-4461)*

Frontier Enterprises Corp ....E... 763 434-6913
Cedar *(G-878)*

Greystone Masonry Inc ....E... 763 413-9633
Anoka *(G-185)*

Hans Hagen Homes Inc ....E... 763 586-7200
Minneapolis *(G-3481)*

Highland Manufacturing Co LLC ....C... 507 376-9460
Worthington *(G-10186)*

Hnp Managment ....E... 763 475-1872
Minneapolis *(G-4657)*

Homark Co Inc.....................................D... 218 253-2777
Red Lake Falls *(G-6972)*

Lakehead Constructors Inc...................E... 218 328-5429
Cohasset *(G-1071)*

Lemaster Restoration Inc ....E... 952 707-1256
Burnsville *(G-748)*

Mic Services LLC ....E... 651 379-9590
Saint Paul *(G-8650)*

N A H Inc...E... 507 462-3331
Minnesota Lake *(G-6137)*

Northfield Construction Co Inc..............E... 507 645-8975
Northfield *(G-6537)*

O'Neil Associates Inc ....E... 651 738-2694
Saint Paul *(G-8776)*

Paschke Properties ....E... 763 428-7711
Rogers *(G-7336)*

Pulte Homes of Minnesota LLC ....D... 651 452-5200
Eagan *(G-1546)*

Rottlund Co Inc ....D... 651 638-0500
Saint Paul *(G-8914)*

Rtl Construction Inc..............................D... 952 934-4695
Shakopee *(G-9470)*

Socon Construction Inc ....E... 763 754-4027
Minneapolis *(G-3604)*

St Louis County Public Works..............E... 218 742-9804
Virginia *(G-9756)*

Superior Construction Services ....E... 763 424-9434
Osseo *(G-6671)*

Swanson's Repair Rental Center...........E... 218 847-7487
Detroit Lakes *(G-1219)*

Tes Construction Inc ....E... 763 783-2496
Anoka *(G-233)*

Tri Cap Tri County Action ....E... 320 255-0769
Waite Park *(G-9844)*

Wb Enterprises of America Inc.............E... 507 324-5050
Le Roy *(G-2955)*

Wilcon Construction Inc........................E... 507 345-6653
Mankato *(G-3218)*

CONSTRUCTION: Single-family Housing, New

Berg Construction Services Inc ....E... 651 423-5531
Rosemount *(G-7363)*

Bigelow, Joel & Sons Entrprs ....E... 507 529-1161
Rochester *(G-7066)*

Billman Construction Inc ....E... 218 729-7570
Duluth *(G-1253)*

Boyer Building Corp ....E... 952 475-2097
Minnetonka *(G-6149)*

Bruggeman Homes Inc ....E... 651 770-2981
Saint Paul *(G-8136)*

Centex Homes Inc................................E... 952 936-7833
Minnetonka *(G-6155)*

Deerwood Builders Inc ....E... 218 534-5408
Deerwood *(G-1176)*

Delancy Builders Inc............................D... 612 354-3724
Minneapolis *(G-4243)*

Fabricated Wood Products Inc..............E... 507 451-1019
Medford *(G-3343)*

Flannery Construction Inc ....E... 651 225-1105
Saint Paul *(G-8384)*

Grl Investment Co LLC ....E... 952 445-6745
Shakopee *(G-9442)*

Holmquist Lumber Co 320 857-2031
Grove City *(G-2329)*

K A Witt Construction Inc ....E... 952 758-2108
New Prague *(G-6429)*

Key-Land Homes...................................E... 952 440-9400
Prior Lake *(G-6935)*

Kuepers Construction Inc ....E... 888 829-0707
Baxter *(G-334)*

Lang Builders Inc.................................E... 763 780-9090
Circle Pines *(G-1014)*

Laurent Builders Inc ....E... 952 445-6745
Shakopee *(G-9450)*

Lecy Construction ....E... 952 944-9499
Hopkins *(G-2569)*

Lumber One, Avon Inc..........................D... 320 356-7342
Avon *(G-296)*

Lumber One, Cold Spring Inc ....E... 320 685-3631
Cold Spring *(G-1087)*

McDonald Homes Inc............................E... 651 455-5142
Inver Grove Heights *(G-2761)*

Minnesota Structures Inc ....E... 952 401-3820
Excelsior *(G-1948)*

Murphy Bros Designers ....E... 763 780-3262
Minneapolis *(G-3548)*

Nedegaard Construction Co Inc............E... 763 757-2926
Minneapolis *(G-3552)*

Nor-Son Inc ....C... 218 828-1722
Baxter *(G-339)*

Pratt Construction Inc...........................E... 651 429-8032
Saint Paul *(G-8834)*

Richard Larson Builders Inc..................E... 320 587-5555
Hutchinson *(G-2711)*

Ryland Group Inc..................................C... 952 949-0013
Eden Prairie *(G-1769)*

Siewert Construction Co Inc 651 437-1728
Hastings *(G-2405)*

Stonecrest ....D... 651 264-3200
Saint Paul *(G-9278)*

Streeter & Associates Inc ....E... 952 449-9448
Wayzata *(G-9943)*

Weis Builders Inc.................................E... 507 288-2041
Rochester *(G-7288)*

Yerigan Construction Co ....E... 763 444-5353
Isanti *(G-2782)*

CONSTRUCTION: Single-family Housing, Prefabricated

Hawk & Sons Inc..................................E... 507 285-0508
Rochester *(G-7134)*

CONSTRUCTION: Stadium

Zeman Construction Co.........................E... 612 521-4300
Minneapolis *(G-6115)*

CONSTRUCTION: Steel Buildings

Continental Bridge Inc ....D... 320 852-7500
Alexandria *(G-89)*

Met-Con Metro Inc ....E... 952 884-6250
Minneapolis *(G-4998)*

CONSTRUCTION: Street Sign Installation & Mntnce

Global Specialty Contractors 651 406-8232
Saint Paul *(G-7783)*

H & R Const Co ....E... 218 589-8707
Dalton *(G-1156)*

CONSTRUCTION: Street Surfacing & Paving

Aci Construction Inc ....E... 763 424-9191
Osseo *(G-6592)*

Allied Blacktop Co................................D... 763 425-0575
Maple Grove *(G-3234)*

Bituminous Roadways Inc.....................E... 651 686-7001
Mendota Heights *(G-3361)*

Bituminous Roadways Inc.....................E... 952 233-1660
Shakopee *(G-9423)*

C R Fischer & Sons Inc ....E... 651 463-7300
Farmington *(G-2042)*

Caterpillar Paving Products ....E... 763 712-3000
Champlin *(G-891)*

Knife River Midwest LLC ....D... 507 498-3377
Spring Grove *(G-9561)*

Ktm Paving Inc.....................................E... 218 628-7025
Duluth *(G-1374)*

Metro Paving Inc..................................E... 763 428-4121
Rogers *(G-7331)*

Minn-Dak Asphalt Inc...........................E... 218 281-6840
Thief River Falls *(G-9674)*

CONSTRUCTION: Swimming Pools

All Poolside Services Inc ....E... 651 483-6600
Saint Paul *(G-8011)*

Atlantis Pools Inc ....E... 763 560-0103
Minneapolis *(G-3831)*

Dolphin Pools Inc ....E... 763 542-9000
Plymouth *(G-6860)*

Minnesota Residential Aquatics 651 439-8467
Stillwater *(G-9629)*

Performance Pool & Spa Inc ....E... 651 731-3440
Saint Paul *(G-9259)*

Watson's of Minneapolis Inc ....E... 763 560-7727
Minneapolis *(G-6024)*

CONSTRUCTION: Telephone & Communication Line

Connectivity Solutions Inc of ....D... 763 424-7300
Osseo *(G-6604)*

Danelski Construction Co Inc ....E... 218 372-3236
Willow River *(G-10060)*

Dig America Utility Contr ....E... 320 253-3447
Saint Cloud *(G-7498)*

Geldner Construction Inc ....E... 507 931-4230
Saint Peter *(G-9304)*

Employment codes: A=Over 500 employees, B=251-500,
C=101-250, D=51-100, E=25-50

2011 Harris Minnesota
Services Directory

© Harris InfoSource 1-866-281-6415

677

CONSTRUCTION: Townhouse

Bauerly Dynamics Inc..................E... 320 251-9472
Sauk Rapids *(G-9358)*

Berg Construction Services Inc ....E... 651 423-5531
Rosemount *(G-7363)*

Grl Investment Co LLC ....E... 952 445-6745
Shakopee *(G-9442)*

Lang Builders Inc.....................E... 763 780-9090
Circle Pines *(G-1014)*

Laurent Builders Inc ....E... 952 445-6745
Shakopee *(G-9450)*

Pratt Construction Inc ....E... 651 429-8032
Saint Paul *(G-8834)*

Siewert Construction Co Inc 651 437-1728
Hastings *(G-2405)*

CONSTRUCTION: Transmitting Tower, Telecommunication

Global Specialty Contractors.................651 406-8232
Saint Paul *(G-7783)*

CONSTRUCTION: Utility Line

City Lights Inc........................D... 218 568-4754
Pequot Lakes *(G-6787)*

Energy Economics Inc ....D... 507 374-2557
Dodge Center *(G-1227)*

M P Systems Inc......................E... 651 484-9632
Saint Paul *(G-8603)*

Telcom Construction Inc ....D... 320 558-9485
Clearwater *(G-1041)*

TI Nexlevel Co's LLC ....C... 320 963-2400
Maple Lake *(G-3266)*

United Piping Inc.....................E... 218 727-7676
Duluth *(G-1492)*

Utili-Trax Contracting ....C... 763 323-2800
Princeton *(G-6919)*

CONSTRUCTION: Warehouse

Malark Logistics Inc..................D... 763 428-3564
Brooklyn Park *(G-616)*

Proform Thermal Systems Inc ....E... 763 572-2200
Minneapolis *(G-3576)*

CONSTRUCTION: Waste Disposal Plant

Cherne Co Inc........................D... 952 944-4300
Eden Prairie *(G-1623)*

CONSTRUCTION: Waste Water & Sewage Treatment Plant

A B E Construction Co ....E... 763 542-9070
Minneapolis *(G-3646)*

DH Blattner & Sons Inc..............D... 320 356-7351
Avon *(G-294)*

M A Mortenson Co ....B... 763 522-2100
Minneapolis *(G-4917)*

CONSTRUCTION: Water & Sewer Line

Abbott Arne & Schwindt Inc ....E... 218 236-5648
Moorhead *(G-6293)*

BCM Construction Inc ....E... 507 333-1155
Faribault *(G-1991)*

Bnr Excavating Inc ....E... 651 438-8692
Hampton *(G-2363)*

Duluth Superior Erection Inc ....E... 218 626-1112
Duluth *(G-1305)*

Hammerlund Construction Inc ....E... 218 326-1881
Grand Rapids *(G-2283)*

Imperial Developers Inc................D... 651 454-3330
Saint Paul *(G-7802)*

Infrastructure Technologies ....E... 763 428-6488
Rogers *(G-7327)*

Kuechle Underground Inc ....E... 320 398-8888
Kimball *(G-2834)*

M & P Utilities Inc ....C... 320 963-2400
Maple Lake *(G-3261)*

Metropolitan Council, MN ....D... 651 602-8393
Saint Paul *(G-8643)*

Mp Nexlevel LLC ....C... 320 963-2400
Maple Lake *(G-3262)*

Randy Kramer Excavating Inc ....E... 320 764-6871
Watkins *(G-9899)*

S J Louis Construction Inc ....C... 320 253-9291
Rockville *(G-7314)*

Sellin Brothers Inc ....E... 218 483-3522
Hawley *(G-2422)*

Voson Plumbing Inc ....E... 952 938-3143
Hopkins *(G-2654)*

CONSTRUCTION: Water Main

B H Heselton Co ....D... 507 334-3901
Faribault *(G-1990)*

C W Houle Inc.........................D... 651 484-6077
Saint Paul *(G-8147)*

Friedges Landscaping Inc...............E... 952 469-2996
Lakeville *(G-2908)*

Gaub Inc..............................E... 320 382-8075
Olivia *(G-6561)*

Lametti & Sons Inc....................E... 651 426-1380
Hugo *(G-2678)*

Nels Nelson & Sons Inc ....C... 218 879-4561
Cloquet *(G-1058)*

Nodland Construction Co ....D... 320 763-5159
Alexandria *(G-114)*

Ryan Contracting Co ....C... 952 894-3200
Shakopee *(G-9471)*

CONSTRUCTION: Waterway

DH Blattner & Sons Inc..............D... 320 356-7351
Avon *(G-294)*

Ellingson Drainage Inc ....D... 507 527-2294
West Concord *(G-9964)*

CONSULTING SVC: Actuarial

Fidelity Investments Actuarial ....E... 952 831-8595
Minneapolis *(G-4429)*

Milliman Inc ....D... 952 897-5300
Minneapolis *(G-5046)*

Reden & Anders ....E... 800 643-7933
Eden Prairie *(G-1759)*

Towers Watson Delaware Inc ....C... 952 842-7000
Minneapolis *(G-5839)*

CONSULTING SVC: Business, NEC

A Chance To Grow Inc..................D... 612 789-1236
Minneapolis *(G-3647)*

A D G Inc.............................D... 651 287-5858
Eagan *(G-1514)*

Accenture LLP........................C... 612 277-0000
Minneapolis *(G-3664)*

Adapt Inc.............................E... 952 939-0538
Hopkins *(G-2500)*

Alquest Inc...........................E... 763 287-3830
Minneapolis *(G-3734)*

Amalfi Consulting LLC 952 893-6732
Minneapolis *(G-3738)*

Analytics Inc..........................E... 952 404-5700
Chanhassen *(G-908)*

Aquent LLC ....D... 952 851-3411
Minneapolis *(G-3794)*

Area Special Education Co-op.............E... 218 773-0315
East Grand Forks *(G-1566)*

Aston Technologies Inc ....E... 952 546-1693
Saint Louis Park *(G-7657)*

Auerbach Pollock Friedlander ....E... 952 930-0818
(G-3834)

Bahama Consulting Corp................E... 651 994-7900
Inver Grove Heights *(G-2738)*

Baker It Inc...........................E... 612 822-3664
Minneapolis *(G-3859)*

C P P North America LLC ....C... 952 541-5800
Minneapolis *(G-3986)*

Child Care Resource & Referral ....D... 507 287-2020
Rochester *(G-7076)*

City of Mahtomedi.....................E... 651 426-1080
Mahtomedi *(G-3093)*

Connexions Loyalty Travel Soln ....D... 952 914-6533
Eden Prairie *(G-1634)*

Department of Corrections MN ....D... 218 376-4411
Togo *(G-9685)*

Digineer Inc ....D... 763 210-2300
Minneapolis *(G-4256)*

Dks Systems LLC......................952 476-7443
Wayzata *(G-9914)*

Dover Fluid Management Inc ....D... 651 388-3565
Red Wing *(G-6978)*

Ecommerce Network Resource Grp.....E... 612 340-1110
Minneapolis *(G-4311)*

Electronics For Imaging Inc...............E... 651 365-5255
Saint Paul *(G-7759)*

Engage Health Inc ....E... 651 994-0510
Minneapolis *(G-7762)*

English, Bleeker & Associates ....E... 952 230-6500
Saint Louis Park *(G-7661)*

Fair Isaac Corp ....B... 612 758-5200
Minneapolis *(G-4392)*

Financial Affairs Consulting ....D... 952 443-4188
Chaska *(G-967)*

Foth Production Solutions LLC ....D... 651 288-8550
Lake Elmo *(G-2872)*

Fujitsu America Inc....................E... 763 595-9600
Minneapolis *(G-4489)*

Geospatial Services ....E... 507 457-8723
Winona *(G-10098)*

Imago Ltd ....D... 651 690-9724
Saint Paul *(G-8506)*

Independent School District ....E... 651 385-8000
Red Wing *(G-6986)*

Industrial Systems Associates...........D... 763 574-5208
Minneapolis *(G-3498)*

J Perzel & Associates ....E... 612 455-6060
Minneapolis *(G-4748)*

Ja-Cee Consultants Inc..................E... 952 466-4785
Cologne *(G-1092)*

Kensington Equity Partners Inc 952 808-1800
Burnsville *(G-741)*

Lmn Consulting Inc ....E... 612 805-7288
Hopkins *(G-2572)*

Magellan Medical Technology ....C... 612 677-0000
Minneapolis *(G-4931)*

Matthew's Family Restaurant ....E... 763 784-1499
Circle Pines *(G-1017)*

McGladrey & Pullen, LLP ....C... 952 921-7700
Minneapolis *(G-4974)*

Minneapolis PTG ....E... 612 370-2600
Minneapolis *(G-5059)*

Minnesota Diversified Inds ....E... 218 326-9544
Grand Rapids *(G-2295)*

Mmic Health It ....E... 763 201-0300
Minneapolis *(G-5113)*

Nationwide Financial ....E... 612 723-6375
Minneapolis *(G-5171)*

Network Security Professionals...........E... 612 465-8880
Minneapolis *(G-5185)*

Nova Consulting Group Inc ....E... 952 448-9393
Chaska *(G-977)*

Omni Control Systems Inc................E... 507 454-5293
Winona *(G-10119)*

Pace Analytical Services Inc ....B... 612 607-1700
Minneapolis *(G-5308)*

Pacer Center Inc ....D... 952 838-9000
Minneapolis *(G-5309)*

Paisley Consulting Inc ....C... 320 286-5870
Cokato *(G-1077)*

Peterson Co's Inc ....D... 651 257-6864
Chisago City *(G-993)*

Questar Assessment Inc.................D... 952 997-2700
Saint Paul *(G-7885)*

Rba Inc ....D... 952 404-2676
Wayzata *(G-9938)*

Rockingham Group ....E... 763 421-8672
Minneapolis *(G-3591)*

Savvysherpa LLC ....E... 763 549-3540
Minneapolis *(G-5604)*

Schoeneckers Inc ....D... 320 453-2600
Eden Valley *(G-1822)*

Security Products Co ....E... 763 784-6501
Minneapolis *(G-3599)*

Siham Solutions Inc ....E... 651 274-3640
Minneapolis *(G-5672)*

Travelsmart LLC ....E... 952 854-1114
Bloomington *(G-520)*

Twin City Security Inc ....B... 763 784-4160
Minneapolis *(G-3625)*

Up North Consulting Inc ....E... 952 224-8656
Minneapolis *(G-5932)*

V D A Associates ....E... 952 937-8833
Eden Prairie *(G-1802)*

Verifications Inc......................C... 763 420-0600
Osseo *(G-6682)*

Verizon Communications Inc ....C... 763 591-0705
Minneapolis *(G-5965)*

Viking Forest Products LLC ....E... 952 941-6512
Eden Prairie *(G-1805)*

Watson's of Minneapolis Inc ....E... 763 560-7727
Minneapolis *(G-6024)*

Xmalpha Technologies ....E... 651 484-0471
Saint Paul *(G-9170)*

CONSULTING SVC: Computer

Acura Inc.............................E... 651 967-0607
Newport *(G-6483)*

Aeritae Consulting Group Ltd ....E... 651 229-0300
Saint Paul *(G-7992)*

Analysts International Corp...............C... 952 835-5900
Minneapolis *(G-3773)*

Analysts International Corp...............C... 952 897-4500
Minneapolis *(G-3772)*

Arran Technologies Inc..................E... 651 468-0002
Saint Paul *(G-8064)*

As Soon As Possible Inc ....D... 952 564-2727
Minneapolis *(G-3816)*

Bailiwick Data Systems Inc ....D... 952 556-5502
Chaska *(G-950)*

Bangasser Co 320 256-5100
Saint Joseph *(G-7651)*

Business Microvar Inc ....E... 651 639-0575
Saint Paul *(G-8143)*

Charter Solutions Inc ....D... 763 230-6100
Plymouth *(G-6854)*

SERVICES

Concord Inc ....D... 952 697-5500
Hopkins *(G-2533)*

CS Solutions Inc ....E... 651 603-8288
Eagan *(G-1523)*

Dbi Consulting Inc ....D... 763 561-4990
Minneapolis *(G-4234)*

Digital River Inc ....B... 952 253-1234
Eden Prairie *(G-1645)*

Dks Systems LLC 952 476-7443
Wayzata *(G-9914)*

Edocument Resources LLC ....E... 952 607-3505
Minnetonka *(G-6163)*

Enclipse Corp ....E... 612 384-6940
Minneapolis *(G-4353)*

Facet Technology Corp ....E... 952 944-1839
Eden Prairie *(G-1660)*

Fishel Information Systems Inc ....E... 952 544-1108
Hopkins *(G-2543)*

Geek Squad Inc ....E... 612 343-1028
Minneapolis *(G-4505)*

Geek Squad Inc ....D... 612 922-9288
Minneapolis *(G-4506)*

Genesis Corp ....A... 651 702-3300
Saint Paul *(G-9219)*

Gnazzo Technical Services Inc ....E... 952 949-1026
Eden Prairie *(G-1675)*

Harbinger Partners Inc ....D... 651 426-1569
Saint Paul *(G-8442)*

Ilm Professional Services Inc ....E... 952 960-2220
Edina *(G-1832)*

Intuitive Technology Group LLC ....E... 952 854-1663
Minneapolis *(G-4734)*

J D L Technologies Inc ....E... 952 946-1810
Hopkins *(G-2559)*

Kardia Health Systems Inc ....E... 763 432-8420
Minneapolis *(G-4790)*

Laser Printing Technologies ....D... 952 888-7375
Mendota Heights *(G-3366)*

Midwave Corp ....C... 952 279-5600
Eden Prairie *(G-1723)*

Milestone Systems Inc ....E... 763 404-6200
Minneapolis *(G-5041)*

Motion International Inc ....D... 952 746-5630
Minneapolis *(G-5136)*

MQ Software Inc ....D... 952 345-8720
Minneapolis *(G-5143)*

Norex Inc ....E... 952 447-8898
Prior Lake *(G-6945)*

Norstan Inc ....C... 952 352-4000
Hopkins *(G-2590)*

North Point Capital Partners ....D... 651 602-0789
Saint Paul *(G-8753)*

Northshore Resources Inc ....E... 612 375-0315
Minneapolis *(G-5236)*

Nternational Projects ....D... 952 541-4888
Minneapolis *(G-5254)*

Object Partners Inc ....E... 612 746-1580
Minneapolis *(G-5259)*

ORBIT Systems Inc ....D... 651 767-3322
Saint Paul *(G-7858)*

Quantum Retail Technology Inc ....E... 612 486-3491
Minneapolis *(G-5446)*

RCM Technologies Inc ....E... 952 841-1188
Hopkins *(G-2612)*

Rubenstein & Ziff Inc ....E... 952 854-1460
Minneapolis *(G-5574)*

Sadaka Technology Consultants ....A... 952 841-6363
Minneapolis *(G-5586)*

Seh Technology Solutions Inc ....E... 612 758-6728
Minneapolis *(G-5628)*

Shavlik Technologies LLC ....D... 651 426-6624
Saint Paul *(G-8948)*

Skamp Corp ....E... 952 937-8990
Eden Prairie *(G-1779)*

Solid Logic Computer Solutions ....E... 952 949-0140
Eden Prairie *(G-1780)*

TAJ Technologies Inc ....D... 651 405-7412
Mendota Heights *(G-3371)*

Tech-Pro Inc ....B... 651 634-1400
Saint Paul *(G-9032)*

Teksystems Inc ....E... 952 886-4800
Minneapolis *(G-5807)*

Tuesday Networking Inc ....E... 952 942-7378
Eden Prairie *(G-1798)*

Valere LLC ....E... 763 390-9286
White Bear Lake *(G-9979)*

Virtelligence Inc ....C... 952 746-9220
Eden Prairie *(G-1806)*

Virteva LLC ....E... 952 843-1200
Saint Louis Park *(G-7670)*

Visionshare Inc ....E... 612 460-4301
Minneapolis *(G-5978)*

Wolfnet Technologies LLC ....E... 612 342-0088
Minneapolis *(G-6083)*

CONSULTING SVC: Data Processing

Ciber Inc ....D... 507 280-9267
Rochester *(G-7077)*

Keane Inc ....B... 952 915-6393
Minneapolis *(G-4795)*

Macro Group Inc ....E... 612 332-7880
Minneapolis *(G-4929)*

Nemadji Research Corp ....E... 320 838-3838
Bruno *(G-631)*

Search America, A Part of ....E... 763 416-1007
Maple Grove *(G-3253)*

Solutia Consulting Inc ....E... 651 351-0123
Stillwater *(G-9640)*

Talus Group Inc ....E... 952 544-2526
Excelsior *(G-1954)*

TriMin Systems Inc ....E... 651 636-7667
Saint Paul *(G-9083)*

CONSULTING SVC: Educational

Experior Assessments LLC ....C... 651 646-1170
Saint Paul *(G-8353)*

Little Tigers Den-Educational ....E... 763 389-5950
Princeton *(G-6923)*

Marshall Adult Learning Center ....E... 507 537-7046
Marshall *(G-3309)*

Scholarship America ....C... 952 830-7300
Minneapolis *(G-5612)*

Youth Frontiers Inc ....E... 952 922-0222
Minneapolis *(G-6107)*

CONSULTING SVC: Engineering

Advanced Research Corp ....E... 651 789-9000
White Bear Lake *(G-9973)*

Amec Earth & Environmental Inc ....E... 612 332-8326
Minneapolis *(G-3743)*

Bdm Consulting Engineers ....E... 612 548-3140
Saint Paul *(G-8095)*

Bolton & Menk Inc ....D... 507 625-4171
Mankato *(G-3112)*

CC & I Engineering Inc ....E... 218 346-3600
Perham *(G-6795)*

Conestoga-Rovers & Associates ....E... 651 639-0913
Saint Paul *(G-8247)*

Consulting Engineers Group Inc 651 463-6263
Farmington *(G-2046)*

Dpra Inc ....E... 651 227-6500
Saint Paul *(G-8311)*

Dunham Associates Inc ....D... 612 465-7550
Minneapolis *(G-4294)*

EMA Group Inc ....E... 651 639-5600
Saint Paul *(G-8335)*

EMA Inc ....E... 651 639-5600
Saint Paul *(G-8336)*

Ema Inc 651 639-5600
Saint Paul *(G-8337)*

Excel Engineering Inc ....D... 763 571-5008
Minneapolis *(G-3467)*

Finley Engineering Co ....E... 507 836-8515
Slayton *(G-9487)*

Food Systems Design Inc ....E... 952 884-4048
Minneapolis *(G-4464)*

Fox-1 Resources ....E... 651 894-3990
Saint Paul *(G-7776)*

George Konik Associates Inc ....D... 952 835-5550
Minneapolis *(G-4524)*

Hammel, Green & Abrahamson Inc ....B... 507 281-8601
Rochester *(G-7131)*

Hansen, Thorp & Pellinen Inc ....E... 952 829-0700
Eden Prairie *(G-1676)*

HNTB Corp ....E... 952 920-4668
Minneapolis *(G-4658)*

I & S Group Inc ....D... 507 387-6651
Mankato *(G-3146)*

Innovative Technical Personnel ....E... 763 591-9191
Minneapolis *(G-4705)*

Interpoll Laboratories Inc ....E... 763 786-6020
Circle Pines *(G-1012)*

Karges-Faulconbridge Inc ....D... 651 771-0880
Saint Paul *(G-8540)*

Krech, Ojard & Associates ....E... 218 727-3282
Duluth *(G-1373)*

Larson Engineering Inc ....E... 651 481-9120
Saint Paul *(G-8563)*

Leo A Daly Co ....C... 612 338-8741
Minneapolis *(G-4861)*

LHB Inc ....C... 218 727-8446
Duluth *(G-1381)*

Lkpb Engineers Inc ....E... 651 633-1223
Saint Paul *(G-8593)*

Meyer, Borgman & Johnson Inc ....E... 612 338-0713
Minneapolis *(G-5011)*

Michaud, Cooley, Erickson ....C... 612 339-4941
Minneapolis *(G-5017)*

Office Information Systems Inc ....E... 952 884-9199
Minneapolis *(G-5265)*

Parallel Technologies Inc ....C... 952 920-7185
Minneapolis *(G-5322)*

Power System Engineering Inc ....E... 763 755-5122
Minneapolis *(G-3571)*

Precision Design Inc ....E... 952 933-6550
Hopkins *(G-2604)*

Redprairie Corp ....E... 952 656-5400
Eden Prairie *(G-1761)*

Schoell & Madson Inc ....E... 763 746-1600
Minneapolis *(G-5610)*

Short-Elliott-Hendrickson Inc ....C... 651 490-2000
Saint Paul *(G-8954)*

Short-Elliott-Hendrickson Inc ....E... 952 912-2600
Hopkins *(G-2632)*

SRF Consulting Group Inc ....C... 763 475-0010
Minneapolis *(G-5725)*

Stanley Consultants Inc ....E... 952 546-3669
Minneapolis *(G-5739)*

Steen Engineering Inc ....E... 763 585-6742
Minneapolis *(G-5746)*

STS Acquisition Co ....D... 763 315-6300
Osseo *(G-6669)*

Ulteig Engineers Inc ....E... 218 847-5607
Detroit Lakes *(G-1220)*

URS Group Inc ....E... 612 370-0700
Minneapolis *(G-5941)*

Wunderlich-Malec Engineering ....D... 952 933-3222
Hopkins *(G-2660)*

CONSULTING SVC: Executive Placement & Search

Ambrion Inc ....E... 952 278-1800
Minneapolis *(G-3742)*

Dana Johnson ....E... 651 774-5843
Saint Paul *(G-8281)*

McKinley Group Inc ....E... 952 476-2107
Hopkins *(G-2579)*

Office Information Systems Inc ....E... 952 884-9199
Minneapolis *(G-5265)*

Professional Alternatives L L ....E... 952 404-2600
Wayzata *(G-9936)*

CONSULTING SVC: Financial Management

Aldin Export & Import 651 483-4184
Saint Paul *(G-8007)*

American Enterprise Investment ....C... 612 671-3131
Minneapolis *(G-3748)*

Bremer Trust National Assn ....E... 320 252-3918
Saint Cloud *(G-7466)*

Gardner Financial Services Inc ....E... 952 935-4601
Minneapolis *(G-4500)*

Global Tax Network Minnesota ....E... 952 224-2053
Minneapolis *(G-4532)*

Goldleaf Partners ....E... 218 824-6119
Brainerd *(G-568)*

Herbeck, David J CPA Pfs Chfc ....E... 763 546-6211
Minneapolis *(G-4640)*

Lincoln Financial Advisors ....E... 952 933-8000
Hopkins *(G-2571)*

Solutran Inc ....D... 763 559-2225
Minneapolis *(G-5697)*

21st Services ....E... 612 371-3008
Minneapolis *(G-5871)*

United Check Clearing Corp ....D... 763 559-2225
Minneapolis *(G-5908)*

Waddell & Reed Inc ....E... 651 483-1411
Saint Paul *(G-9135)*

Workman Financial Group Inc ....E... 763 746-9420
Minneapolis *(G-6086)*

CONSULTING SVC: Human Resource

Empo Corp ....E... 612 285-8707
Minneapolis *(G-4352)*

Lominger Limited Inc ....E... 952 345-3600
Minneapolis *(G-4901)*

Metrisource Inc ....E... 651 686-0097
Saint Paul *(G-7838)*

Target Corp ....B... 763 440-2033
Minneapolis *(G-5790)*

Towers Watson Delaware Inc ....C... 952 842-7000
Minneapolis *(G-5839)*

CONSULTING SVC: Management

Accenture LLP ....C... 612 277-0000
Minneapolis *(G-3664)*

Affiance Financial LLC ....E... 952 253-2564
Hopkins *(G-2503)*

Alquest Inc ....E... 763 287-3830
Minneapolis *(G-3734)*

ARAZ Group Inc ....D... 952 896-1200
Minneapolis *(G-3796)*

Employment codes: A=Over 500 employees, B=251-500, C=101-250, D=51-100, E=25-50
2011 Harris Minnesota Services Directory
© Harris InfoSource 1-866-281-6415
679

Argenbright Inc ....E... 320 693-7314 Litchfield (G-2978)	Perficient Inc ....D... 612 752-1700 Minneapolis (G-5365)	Gold Points Corp ....D... 763 212-1000 Minneapolis (G-4534)
Border Foods Inc ....E... 763 323-4731 Anoka (G-159)	Pragmatek Consulting Group Ltd ....D... 612 333-3164 Bloomington (G-511)	Hanley-Wood Custom Publishing.......D... 612 338-8300 Minneapolis (G-4593)
Carlson Hospitality Worldwide ....E... 763 540-5035 Minnetonka (G-6153)	PRC Consulting Inc ....E... 952 906-0801 Chanhassen (G-936)	Iconoculture Inc ....E... 612 377-0087 Minneapolis (G-4686)
Carlson, Lundquist & Co Ltd ....E... 763 535-8150 Minneapolis (G-4019)	Presbyterian Homes Management ......E... 651 631-6000 Saint Paul (G-8842)	Interpublic Group of Co's Inc ....D... 612 367-5144 Minneapolis (G-4725)
Clark & Wamberg LLC ....C... 612 339-0919 Minneapolis (G-4102)	Project Consulting Group Inc ....D... 612 330-0123 Minneapolis (G-5427)	John Ryan Performance Inc ....E... 612 924-7700 Minneapolis (G-4771)
Clark Engineering Corp ....E... 763 545-9196 Minneapolis (G-4103)	Protiviti Inc ....E... 952 249-2200 Hopkins (G-2606)	Kantar Media Intelligences Inc ....E... 952 926-5430 Minneapolis (G-4788)
Creatis Inc ....D... 612 333-3233 Minneapolis (G-4179)	RCM Technologies Inc ....E... 952 841-1188 Hopkins (G-2612)	Marketing Architects Inc ....D... 952 449-2500 Minnetonka (G-6190)
Creative Marketing Consulting ....E... 952 935-9385 Saint Paul (G-8266)	Reliability Management Group ....E... 952 882-8122 Burnsville (G-790)	Modern Climate Inc ....E... 612 343-8180 Minneapolis (G-5117)
Distributed Website Corp ....E... 507 453-5164 Winona (G-10093)	Right Management Consultants ....E... 952 837-0955 Minneapolis (G-5540)	1 Micro LLC ....E... 952 767-1010 Eden Prairie (G-1738)
Efficio Group Inc ....D... 612 805-7288 Osseo (G-6613)	Rothe Development Inc ....E... 612 726-1102 Minneapolis (G-5561)	121 Marketing Services Group ....D... 763 428-8123 Rogers (G-7334)
Eloyalty Corp ....E... 952 908-8000 Edina (G-1830)	RSM McGladrey Business Soln ....C... 952 921-7700 Minneapolis (G-5567)	Opus National LLC ....C... 952 656-4444 Minnetonka (G-6207)
EMA Inc ....E... 651 639-5600 Saint Paul (G-8336)	RSM McGladrey Inc ....D... 507 288-5363 Rochester (G-7242)	Pacific Marketing & Comms ....E... 651 967-7135 Minneapolis (G-5310)
Energy Resources LLC .... 612 889-0447 Saint Louis Park (G-7660)	RSM McGladrey Inc ....E... 218 727-5025 Duluth (G-1440)	Party Music Inc ....E... 952 941-3830 Eden Prairie (G-1744)
Epredix Holdings Inc ....D... 612 843-1059 Minneapolis (G-4365)	RSM McGladrey Inc ....C... 612 332-4300 Minneapolis (G-5570)	Radisson Hotels International ....C... 763 212-5000 Minnetonka (G-6218)
Ewald Consulting Group Inc ....E... 651 290-6260 Saint Paul (G-8350)	Schoell & Madson Inc ....E... 763 746-1600 Minneapolis (G-5610)	Risdall Marketing Group LLC ....D... 651 286-6700 New Brighton (G-6413)
Family Service Rochester Inc ....D... 507 287-2010 Rochester (G-7110)	Schoeneckers Inc ....D... 320 453-2600 Eden Valley (G-1822)	Selftek ....E... 612 872-1285 Minneapolis (G-5635)
Familymeans Inc ....E... 612 874-8164 Stillwater (G-9617)	Sopheon Corp ....E... 952 851-7555 Minneapolis (G-5702)	Superclean Brands LLC ....E... 651 365-7500 Eagan (G-1554)
Fintegra Financial Solutions .... 763 503-1911 Minneapolis (G-4435)	SRF Consulting Group Inc ....C... 763 475-0010 Minneapolis (G-5725)	3M Co ....E... 651 736-3828 Saint Paul (G-9063)
Fredrickson Communications Inc ....E... 612 339-7970 Minneapolis (G-4483)	Sterling Commerce Inc ....D... 952 294-1800 Eden Prairie (G-1782)	Threewire Inc .... 952 852-5556 Eden Prairie (G-1792)
Genesis Corp ....A... 651 702-3300 Saint Paul (G-9219)	Superclean Brands LLC ....E... 651 365-7500 Eagan (G-1554)	2020 Promotions LLC ....E... 651 451-3850 South Saint Paul (G-9545)
Griffin International Co's Inc ....E... 612 344-4700 Minneapolis (G-4570)	T-Chek Systems Inc ....D... 952 934-3413 Eden Prairie (G-1790)	Unisys Corp ....A... 651 687-2200 Saint Paul (G-7935)
Harbinger Partners Inc ....D... 651 426-1569 Saint Paul (G-8442)	Taylor Corp ....C... 507 625-2828 North Mankato (G-6514)	Visions Inc ....D... 763 425-4251 Brooklyn Park (G-621)
HDR Engineering Inc ....C... 763 591-5400 Minneapolis (G-4615)	Taylor Corp ....C... 952 888-7945 Minneapolis (G-5794)	Wiken Promotion & Advertising.........E... 952 476-2002 Wayzata (G-9950)
Healing Touch Aquamassage ....E... 507 287-6186 Rochester (G-7135)	3M Co ....E... 651 733-1110 Saint Paul (G-9048)	**CONSULTING SVC: Online Technology**
Healthcare Management..................E... 651 224-4930 Saint Paul (G-7797)	Thrivent Financial For ....A... 920 734-5721 Minneapolis (G-5819)	As Soon As Possible Inc ....D... 952 564-2727 Minneapolis (G-3816)
Hollstadt & Associates Inc ....D... 952 892-3660 Burnsville (G-732)	Tunheim Partners Inc ....E... 952 851-1600 Minneapolis (G-5865)	Ego Systems Inc ....D... 952 200-8246 Minneapolis (G-4331)
Ingenix Inc ....B... 952 833-7100 Eden Prairie (G-1692)	Unicom Consulting Inc ....E... 952 698-7600 Minneapolis (G-5902)	Global Markets Inc ....E... 612 392-7580 Minnetonka (G-6177)
J T Mega LLC ....E... 952 929-1370 Minneapolis (G-4749)	Uponor North America Inc ....E... 952 891-2000 Saint Paul (G-7939)	Legal Research Center Inc ....E... 612 332-4950 Minneapolis (G-4857)
Kenexa Corp ....E... 612 332-6383 Minneapolis (G-4800)	Westwood Professional Services........C... 952 937-5150 Eden Prairie (G-1815)	Olr America Inc ....E... 612 436-4970 Minneapolis (G-5269)
Kersten Management Group Inc ....D... 218 543-6977 Pine River (G-6819)	Willow Group Inc..........................E... 952 897-3550 Minneapolis (G-6072)	Sadaka Technology Consultants ....A... 952 841-6363 Minneapolis (G-5586)
Khashi Associates LLC ....E... 763 550-0961 Minneapolis (G-4804)	Zentropy Partners ....E... 612 367-5148 Minneapolis (G-6116)	Ulysses Telemedia Networks Inc .....D... 763 225-5000 Minneapolis (G-5897)
Lacek Group ....C... 612 359-3700 Minneapolis (G-4832)	**CONSULTING SVC: Marketing Management**	Visionshare Inc ....E... 612 460-4301 Minneapolis (G-5978)
Leuthold Asset Allocation Fund ....E... 612 332-9141 Minneapolis (G-4864)	Aldin Export & Import .... 651 483-4184 Saint Paul (G-8007)	**CONSULTING SVC: Productivity Improvement**
M D A Consulting Group Inc ....E... 612 332-8182 Minneapolis (G-4920)	Archway Marketing Services Inc ....C... 763 428-3300 Rogers (G-7316)	Marshall-Teichert Group Ltd ....D... 952 942-0564 Hopkins (G-2577)
Manchester Co's Inc ....E... 612 436-2818 Minneapolis (G-4941)	Argenbright Inc ....E... 763 477-7600 Rockford (G-7307)	**CONSULTING SVC: Sales Management**
Market Resource Associates Inc ......E... 612 334-3056 Minneapolis (G-4948)	Argenbright Inc ....E... 763 477-7600 Rockford (G-7308)	Gunsbury Alan Quarterdeck.............E... 218 963-2482 Nisswa (G-6492)
McKinsey & Co Inc ....D... 612 371-3100 Minneapolis (G-4979)	Augeo Affinity Marketing Inc ....D... 877 781-2586 Saint Paul (G-8078)	Larsonallen LLP ....B... 612 376-4500 Minneapolis (G-4848)
Mercer Inc ....D... 612 642-8600 Minneapolis (G-4989)	Bestmark Inc ....C... 952 922-2205 Minnetonka (G-6148)	Performark Inc ....C... 952 946-7300 Minnetonka (G-6210)
Metropolitan Financial Mgt ....E... 651 631-8000 Saint Paul (G-8646)	Bonfire Partners LLC ....E... 612 455-7400 Minneapolis (G-3926)	**CONSULTING SVC: Telecommunications**
Michael D Norman & Associates ....E... 952 935-0515 Minneapolis (G-5015)	Business Impact Group LLC.............D... 952 278-7800 Chanhassen (G-911)	Alwaysbethere Inc ....E... 612 243-9233 Plymouth (G-6848)
Mid-America Business Systems ....E... 612 378-3800 Minneapolis (G-5022)	C-ME Marketing Inc ....E... 320 587-6565 Hutchinson (G-2690)	Atek Manufacturing LLC ....D... 218 829-4719 Brainerd (G-550)
Minnesota State Community ....D... 218 755-4270 Bemidji (G-403)	Carlson Co's Inc ....B... 763 212-5253 Minneapolis (G-4013)	Augeo Communications LLC ....E... 651 204-5734 Saint Paul (G-8079)
Miro Management Inc ....E... 952 404-8267 Wayzata (G-9928)	Carlson Marketing Worldwide ....E... 763 449-3704 Minneapolis (G-4018)	Communications Systems Inc ....C... 952 996-1674 Minnetonka (G-6156)
Morris Communications Corp ....D... 218 829-4705 Brainerd (G-576)	Customer Elation Inc ....E... 320 968-4438 Foley (G-2136)	Elert & Associates Networking ....E... 651 430-2772 Stillwater (G-9614)
Motors Management Corp................E... 763 593-5755 Saint Louis Park (G-7668)	D L Ryan Co's Ltd ....E... 612 204-9790 Minneapolis (G-4214)	Haigh Todd & Assoc Inc ....E... 952 252-2100 Minneapolis (G-4587)
Narveson Management Inc ....E... 218 562-6400 Pequot Lakes (G-6791)	Gage Group LLC ....C... 763 595-3920 Minneapolis (G-4495)	Norstan Inc ....C... 952 352-4000 Hopkins (G-2590)
Pareo Inc ....E... 612 371-0400 Minneapolis (G-5326)	Gold Groves ....E... 612 884-8383 Minneapolis (G-4533)	
Parsons ....E... 612 656-7000 Minneapolis (G-5340)		

Transcend Communications Inc ....E... 763 463-1000
Minneapolis *(G-5846)*

CONSULTING SVCS, BUSINESS: Agricultural

A G Technologies International...........E... 507 444-4157
Owatonna *(G-6687)*
Centrol Inc ....E... 218 584-5107
Twin Valley *(G-9701)*
Precision Partners Inc 218 737-0507
Fergus Falls *(G-2116)*

CONSULTING SVCS, BUSINESS: Communications

Milestone Systems Inc ....E... 763 404-6200
Minneapolis *(G-5041)*
Rothe Development Inc ....E... 612 726-1102
Minneapolis *(G-5561)*
Skylight Corp...E... 651 631-5000
Saint Paul *(G-8964)*
Space150 LLC ....D... 612 332-6458
Minneapolis *(G-5714)*

CONSULTING SVCS, BUSINESS: Economic

Arrowhead Regional Development ......E... 218 722-5545
Duluth *(G-1242)*
Dpra Inc ....E... 651 227-6500
Saint Paul *(G-8311)*
Kandiyohi County Economic ....E... 320 235-7370
Willmar *(G-10013)*

CONSULTING SVCS, BUSINESS: Employee Programs Administration

Administration Resources Corp...........E... 763 421-5510
Minneapolis *(G-3385)*
Alliance Benefit Group ....D... 507 377-9344
Albert Lea *(G-35)*
Ewing's Assoc....................................E... 763 258-2733
Minneapolis *(G-4380)*
Fiserv Health Plan ....A... 262 879-5565
Minneapolis *(G-4450)*
Minnesota Diversified Inds ....E... 218 263-3663
Hibbing *(G-2467)*
Sheffield, Olson & McQueen Inc...........E... 651 695-2500
Saint Paul *(G-8951)*

CONSULTING SVCS, BUSINESS: Energy Conservation

Braun Intertec Corp ....C... 952 995-2000
Minneapolis *(G-3938)*
Braun Intertec Corp ....E... 651 487-3245
Saint Paul *(G-8122)*
Loyalton Group Inc ....E... 651 480-3126
Hastings *(G-2396)*
Mayer Electric Corp ....D... 763 537-9357
Minneapolis *(G-4968)*
Sustainable Resources Center ....E... 612 870-4255
Minneapolis *(G-5776)*
Weidt Group Inc ....E... 952 938-1588
Hopkins *(G-2659)*

CONSULTING SVCS, BUSINESS: Environmental

Aecom Technical Services Inc ....E... 763 551-1001
Minneapolis *(G-3691)*
Clean Water Action Inc..........................C... 612 623-3666
Minneapolis *(G-4105)*
Conestoga-Rovers & Associates ....E... 651 639-0913
Saint Paul *(G-8247)*
Delta Environmental ConsInts............D... 651 639-9449
Saint Paul *(G-8284)*
E & C Amec Services Inc....................D... 612 332-8326
Minneapolis *(G-4299)*
Emmons & Olivier Resources Inc ....E... 651 770-8448
Saint Paul *(G-9213)*
Evergreen Air Services Inc ....E... 952 446-8255
Saint Bonifacius *(G-7400)*
Institute For Environmental ....E... 763 315-7900
Minneapolis *(G-4709)*
Interpoll Laboratories Inc.....................E... 763 786-6020
Circle Pines *(G-1012)*
Izaak Walton League of America ....E... 651 649-1446
Saint Paul *(G-8525)*
Khashi Associates LLC ....E... 763 550-0961
Minneapolis *(G-4804)*
Legend Technical Services Inc............E... 651 642-1150
Saint Paul *(G-8576)*
McGhie & Betts Inc ....E... 507 289-3919
Rochester *(G-7179)*
Natural Resource Group LLC ....C... 612 347-6789
Minneapolis *(G-5172)*
Northeast Technical Services................E... 218 741-4290
Virginia *(G-9749)*

Prosource Technologies Inc................E... 763 786-1445
Minneapolis *(G-3577)*
Sick Maihak Inc ....E... 952 941-6780
Minneapolis *(G-5663)*
United States Compliance Corp ....E... 952 252-3000
Minnetonka *(G-6231)*
Widseth, Smith, Nolting........................E... 218 281-6522
Crookston *(G-1144)*

CONSULTING SVCS, BUSINESS: Lighting

Premier Electrical Corp ....C... 763 424-6551
Brooklyn Park *(G-617)*

CONSULTING SVCS, BUSINESS: Publishing

Ecm Publishers Inc ....E... 320 352-6569
Sauk Centre *(G-9344)*
Hanley-Wood Custom Publishing ....D... 612 338-8300
Minneapolis *(G-4593)*

CONSULTING SVCS, BUSINESS: Sys Engnrg, Exc Computer/Prof

Dobbs Temporary Services Inc ....E... 612 373-2600
Minneapolis *(G-4268)*
Novon Consulting Corp..........................E... 612 868-7057
Elk River *(G-1858)*
Quantum Consulting & Placement......C... 952 820-0160
Saint Paul *(G-8862)*
Xylo Technologies Inc ....D... 507 289-9956
Rochester *(G-7297)*

CONSULTING SVCS, BUSINESS: Systems Analysis & Engineering

Radcliffe Systems ....E... 952 545-2409
Hopkins *(G-2609)*

CONSULTING SVCS, BUSINESS: Testing, Educational Or Personnel

Ncs Pearson Inc ....A... 952 681-3000
Minneapolis *(G-5177)*

CONSULTING SVCS, BUSINESS: Urban Planning & Consulting

City of Minneapolis ....E... 612 673-2597
Minneapolis *(G-4093)*
Dakota County Community Devpt........C... 651 675-4400
Saint Paul *(G-7744)*
Onmia Manor...D... 320 982-5405
Onamia *(G-6575)*
Tom Loucks & Associates Inc ....D... 763 424-5505
Osseo *(G-6676)*
Urban Ventures Leadership ....E... 612 822-1628
Minneapolis *(G-5939)*

CONSUMER BUYING SVCS

Financial Crimes Services LLC ....E... 651 388-2569
Red Wing *(G-6981)*

CONSUMER CREDIT REPORTING BUREAU

Affiliated Group Inc...............................D... 507 280-7000
Rochester *(G-7045)*
Rental Research Services Inc...............E... 952 935-5700
Hopkins *(G-2615)*
Transunion LLC ....E... 651 639-0007
Saint Paul *(G-9077)*

CONTRACTOR: Dredging

Mini-Dredge Inc 218 773-3331
East Grand Forks *(G-1572)*

CONTRACTOR: Framing

Ed Lunn Construction Inc ....E... 507 533-6565
Stewartville *(G-9591)*
Metro Framing Inc..................................E... 763 785-1482
Minneapolis *(G-3536)*
North American Framing Inc.................E... 763 784-4855
Minneapolis *(G-3558)*
Sierra Corp of Shoreview ....E... 763 783-9616
Anoka *(G-226)*
Tappe Construction Co ....B... 651 994-0200
Saint Paul *(G-7917)*
Welle Construction Inc ....E... 763 427-5830
Anoka *(G-240)*

CONTRACTORS: Excavation & Grading, Building Construction

BCM Construction Inc ....E... 507 333-1155
Faribault *(G-1991)*
Billington Contracting Inc ....E... 218 722-1213
Duluth *(G-1252)*

Carl Bolander & Sons Co.....................D... 651 224-6299
Saint Paul *(G-8165)*
Davidson Construction Inc....................E... 218 449-4865
Holt *(G-2494)*
Doboszenski & Sons Inc.......................E... 763 478-6945
Loretto *(G-3046)*
Fraser Construction Co ....E... 507 288-6583
Rochester *(G-7120)*
Frontier Construction Co Inc................E... 218 246-9512
Deer River *(G-1172)*
Glenn Rehbein Excavating Inc ....C... 763 784-0657
Minneapolis *(G-3475)*
Hammerlund Construction Inc ....E... 218 326-1881
Grand Rapids *(G-2283)*
Imperial Developers Inc ....D... 651 454-3330
Saint Paul *(G-7802)*
L & S Construction ....E... 507 648-3382
Sanborn *(G-9318)*
Niles - Wiese Construction Co ....E... 507 446-0825
Medford *(G-3344)*
North Pine Aggregate Inc ....D... 651 464-6802
Forest Lake *(G-2149)*
Thygeson Construction Co ....E... 218 681-1924
Thief River Falls *(G-9679)*
Triple D Construction ....E... 218 465-4249
Oklee *(G-6558)*
Trout Enterprises Inc of Nthn ....E... 218 246-8165
Deer River *(G-1174)*
Turner Excavating Co ....E... 952 890-1645
Savage *(G-9410)*
Western Walls Inc..................................E... 507 282-4624
Rochester *(G-7292)*

CONTRACTORS: Access Control System Eqpt

Electro-Watchman Inc............................E... 651 227-8461
Saint Paul *(G-8329)*
Trans-Alarm Inc ....D... 952 894-1700
Burnsville *(G-810)*

CONTRACTORS: Access Flooring System Installation

Renovation Systems Inc ....E... 763 550-9600
Minneapolis *(G-5518)*

CONTRACTORS: Acoustical & Ceiling Work

Acoustics Associates Inc ....C... 763 544-8901
Minneapolis *(G-3674)*
Architectural Sales of MN ....D... 763 533-1595
Minneapolis *(G-3802)*
Ceiling Pro Interior Inc ....E... 952 947-0007
Eden Prairie *(G-1617)*
Twin City Acoustics Inc ....D... 763 535-6697
Minneapolis *(G-5875)*

CONTRACTORS: Acoustical & Insulation Work

Build All Installed Inc ....E... 218 692-5115
Crosslake *(G-1150)*

CONTRACTORS: Asbestos Removal & Encapsulation

Ceiling Pro Interior Inc ....E... 952 947-0007
Eden Prairie *(G-1617)*
Dennis Co's Inc......................................E... 651 488-4835
Saint Paul *(G-8287)*
Envirobate Inc ....C... 612 729-1080
Minneapolis *(G-4361)*
Heat & Frost Insulators Asbes ....D... 218 724-3223
Duluth *(G-1350)*
Mavo Systems Inc ....C... 763 788-7713
Saint Paul *(G-8618)*
Sterling Systems Inc ....E... 952 697-1060
Long Lake *(G-3033)*

CONTRACTORS: Asphalt

Bituminous Roadways Inc.....................E... 952 233-1660
Shakopee *(G-9423)*
Fitzgerald Construction ....E... 218 789-7318
Sabin *(G-7397)*
Flint Hills Resources, LP ....E... 507 532-6331
Marshall *(G-3296)*
FPI Paving Contractors Inc...................E... 651 484-0385
Saint Paul *(G-8392)*
Metro Paving Inc....................................E... 763 428-4121
Rogers *(G-7331)*
Minn-Dak Asphalt Inc ....E... 218 281-6840
Thief River Falls *(G-9674)*
Northland Constructors of....................E... 218 722-8170
Duluth *(G-1406)*
Northwest Asphalt Inc...........................E... 952 445-1003
Shakopee *(G-9461)*

Employment codes: A=Over 500 employees, B=251-500,
C=101-250, D=51-100, E=25-50

2011 Harris Minnesota
Services Directory

© Harris InfoSource 1-866-281-6415
681

Q3 Contracting Inc ....B... 651 224-2424
Saint Paul *(G-8859)*

Shamrock Enterprises LLC ....E... 507 288-9494
Rochester *(G-7252)*

Truseal America LLC ....E... 952 895-9197
Eagan *(G-1558)*

CONTRACTORS: Bathtub Refinishing

Safe Step Inc ....E... 952 229-8282
Savage *(G-9406)*

CONTRACTORS: Blasting, Exc Building Demolition

DH Blattner & Sons Inc ....D... 320 356-7351
Avon *(G-294)*

CONTRACTORS: Boiler & Furnace

Palen Kimball LLC ....E... 651 646-2800
Saint Paul *(G-8804)*

CONTRACTORS: Boiler Maintenance Contractor

Albers Sheetmetal ....D... 651 224-5428
Saint Paul *(G-8004)*

API Group Inc ....E... 651 636-4320
Saint Paul *(G-8054)*

Boiler Services Inc ....E... 763 784-8178
Minneapolis *(G-3422)*

Gagnon Inc ....E... 651 644-4301
Saint Paul *(G-8400)*

CONTRACTORS: Boiler Setting

Boiler Services Inc ....E... 763 784-8178
Minneapolis *(G-3422)*

Gagnon Inc ....E... 651 644-4301
Saint Paul *(G-8400)*

CONTRACTORS: Boring, Building Construction

Blake Drilling Co Inc ....E... 763 780-9187
Minneapolis *(G-3420)*

CONTRACTORS: Bricklaying

Steenberg Watrud Construction ....E... 651 457-2291
Inver Grove Heights *(G-2770)*

Winco Landscape Inc ....E... 651 455-3070
Inver Grove Heights *(G-2774)*

CONTRACTORS: Building Eqpt & Machinery Installation

Neufeldt Industrial Services ....E... 651 388-4347
Red Wing *(G-6993)*

Pump & Meter Service Inc ....E... 952 933-4800
Hopkins *(G-2608)*

CONTRACTORS: Building Fireproofing

Mulcahy Inc ....C... 651 770-5250
Mahtomedi *(G-3095)*

CONTRACTORS: Building Sign Installation & Mntnce

Amtech Lighting Services Co ....E... 651 439-7440
Stillwater *(G-9595)*

Nordquist Sign Co ....E... 612 823-7291
Minneapolis *(G-5208)*

Safety Signs Inc ....E... 952 469-6700
Lakeville *(G-2930)*

CONTRACTORS: Building Site Preparation

Meyer Contracting Inc ....E... 763 391-5959
Maple Grove *(G-3250)*

Rick Pavek Construction ....E... 507 663-0804
Northfield *(G-6519)*

CONTRACTORS: Cable Laying

A & A Electric & Underground ....E... 507 634-7453
Kasson *(G-2818)*

T Ray Construction Co Inc ....D... 763 757-6859
Anoka *(G-231)*

Wright's General Construction ....E... 218 372-3329
Willow River *(G-10063)*

CONTRACTORS: Cable TV Installation

Castrejon Inc ....E... 763 450-2055
Minneapolis *(G-3429)*

CONTRACTORS: Caisson Drilling

Atlas Foundation Co ....E... 763 428-2261
Osseo *(G-6596)*

CONTRACTORS: Carpentry Work

API Garage Door Co ....E... 763 533-3838
Minneapolis *(G-3789)*

Carpentry Contractors Corp ....D... 763 658-4000
Waverly *(G-9902)*

Consolidated Building Corp ....C... 612 759-9313
Rosemount *(G-7366)*

J & L Schwieters Construction ....C... 651 762-1110
Hugo *(G-2677)*

J Eiden Construction Inc ....E... 651 450-5978
Inver Grove Heights *(G-2756)*

Kendell Doors & Hardware Inc ....E... 507 454-1723
Winona *(G-10107)*

L L Hage Seamless Gutters Inc ....E... 507 433-1158
Austin *(G-280)*

Les Jones Roofing Inc ....E... 952 881-2241
Minneapolis *(G-4863)*

Northside Construction Inc ....E... 651 426-2632
Hugo *(G-2680)*

Paul Lesieur ....E... 612 788-5584
Minneapolis *(G-5352)*

Wellington Window Co ....D... 952 933-2737
Minneapolis *(G-6034)*

CONTRACTORS: Carpentry, Cabinet & Finish Work

Al's Cabinets Inc ....D... 952 890-3500
Burnsville *(G-674)*

Designed Cabinets Inc ....D... 952 469-2700
Lakeville *(G-2902)*

Dura-Supreme Inc ....A... 320 543-3872
Howard Lake *(G-2666)*

Plato Woodwork Inc ....C... 320 238-2193
Plato *(G-6844)*

Richard Larson Builders Inc ....E... 320 587-5555
Hutchinson *(G-2711)*

Ron's Cabinets Inc ....E... 320 252-7667
Sauk Rapids *(G-9372)*

CONTRACTORS: Carpentry, Cabinet Building & Installation

Advantage Cabinets Inc ....E... 507 455-0833
Owatonna *(G-6689)*

Alpine Custom Woodworking Inc ....E... 320 654-1609
Saint Cloud *(G-7406)*

Cabinets By Choice Inc ....D... 952 924-8958
Minneapolis *(G-3989)*

Swedberg Wood Products Inc ....E... 320 762-0738
Alexandria *(G-126)*

Wood Products Unlimited Inc ....E... 218 829-4353
Brainerd *(G-589)*

CONTRACTORS: Carpentry, Finish & Trim Work

Doug Speedling Builders Inc ....D... 651 437-3658
Hastings *(G-2384)*

North American Framing Inc ....E... 763 784-4855
Minneapolis *(G-3558)*

Russnick Contractors Inc ....E... 763 420-3737
Hamel *(G-2356)*

Tappe Construction Co ....B... 651 994-0200
Saint Paul *(G-7917)*

Taylor Made Construction of MN ....E... 952 440-8510
Prior Lake *(G-6957)*

CONTRACTORS: Carpet Laying

Architectural Sales of MN ....D... 763 533-1595
Minneapolis *(G-3802)*

C L T Floor Coverings Inc ....E... 651 451-0069
Inver Grove Heights *(G-2740)*

Lee's Ceramic Contracting Inc ....D... 612 720-1653
Hastings *(G-2395)*

Ziem's Carpet Workroom Inc ....E... 952 884-0058
Minneapolis *(G-6118)*

CONTRACTORS: Closed Circuit Television Installation

Checkpoint Security Systems ....C... 952 942-9431
Chanhassen *(G-914)*

Checkpoint Systems Inc ....E... 952 227-5350
Chaska *(G-958)*

Checkpoint Systems Inc ....C... 952 943-3853
Chanhassen *(G-915)*

Electro-Watchman Inc ....E... 651 227-8461
Saint Paul *(G-8329)*

Electronic Design Co ....E... 612 355-2300
Minneapolis *(G-4339)*

Trans-Alarm Inc ....D... 952 894-1700
Burnsville *(G-810)*

CONTRACTORS: Closet Organizers, Installation & Design

C C C T Inc ....E... 952 844-0004
Minneapolis *(G-3982)*

CONTRACTORS: Coating, Caulking & Weather, Water & Fire

Bargen Inc 507 427-2924
Mountain Lake *(G-6395)*

Petratech Inc ....E... 952 897-0475
Minneapolis *(G-5371)*

Restoration Professionals Inc ....D... 651 379-1990
Saint Paul *(G-8895)*

TMI Coatings Inc ....D... 651 452-6100
Saint Paul *(G-7925)*

CONTRACTORS: Commercial & Office Building

AP Midwest LLC ....C... 952 544-1561
Minneapolis *(G-3788)*

Arnzen Construction Inc ....E... 320 836-2284
Freeport *(G-2187)*

Boser Construction Inc ....E... 320 393-3185
Sauk Rapids *(G-9359)*

Construction Results Corp ....E... 763 559-1100
Plymouth *(G-6857)*

Corval Constructors Inc ....C... 651 642-0451
Saint Paul *(G-8255)*

Dallas I Hanson Construction ....E... 320 839-3455
Ortonville *(G-6582)*

Doran Construction Inc ....E... 763 421-0553
Minneapolis *(G-4279)*

Ebert Inc ....E... 763 498-7844
Loretto *(G-3047)*

Elder-Jones Inc ....E... 952 854-2854
Minneapolis *(G-4336)*

G M Clark Co's Inc ....E... 763 475-1000
Maple Plain *(G-3274)*

Gordon Construction Inc ....E... 218 935-2191
Mahnomen *(G-3086)*

Hasslen Construction Co Inc ....E... 320 839-2529
Ortonville *(G-6583)*

Kalway Construction Co Inc ....E... 651 746-0179
Anoka *(G-195)*

Kellington Construction Inc ....D... 763 416-3200
Minneapolis *(G-4797)*

Langer Construction Co Inc ....D... 651 457-5993
Saint Paul *(G-7821)*

Larson Contracting Inc ....D... 507 373-6645
Albert Lea *(G-59)*

M P Johnson Construction Inc ....E... 612 339-3733
Minneapolis *(G-4923)*

Maertens-Brenny Construction ....E... 763 786-4779
Minneapolis *(G-3525)*

Magnum Co LLC ....E... 651 255-3000
Rogers *(G-7349)*

Max Gray Construction Inc ....E... 218 262-6622
Hibbing *(G-2461)*

Met Con Kato Inc ....C... 507 332-2266
Faribault *(G-2021)*

Met-Con Construction Inc 507 332-2266
Faribault *(G-2022)*

Monson Corp ....D... 320 995-6703
Willmar *(G-10027)*

Morcon Construction Co Inc ....D... 763 546-6066
Minneapolis *(G-5127)*

Network of Contractors Inc ....E... 763 639-1440
Ramsey *(G-6968)*

Penn-Co Construction Inc ....E... 651 687-0648
Saint Paul *(G-7872)*

Plains Construction & Devpt ....C... 218 284-0424
Moorhead *(G-6333)*

R J M Construction Inc ....E... 952 837-8600
Minneapolis *(G-5458)*

Raske Building Systems Inc ....E... 320 877-7221
Cosmos *(G-1095)*

Ray Riihiluoma Inc ....E... 218 879-3317
Cloquet *(G-1064)*

SA Woods Inc 507 451-7084
Owatonna *(G-6735)*

Stahl Construction Co ....E... 952 931-9300
Minneapolis *(G-5735)*

Thor Construction Inc ....D... 763 571-2580
Minneapolis *(G-3616)*

W Gohman Construction Co ....E... 320 363-7781
Saint Joseph *(G-7656)*

S
E
R
V
I
C
E
S

CONTRACTORS: Communications Svcs

All State Communications Inc ....E... 320 203-1511
Sauk Rapids *(G-9356)*

Appollo Systems Inc ....E... 763 493-5821
Osseo *(G-6594)*

Avtex Solutions LLC ....E... 952 831-0888
Minneapolis *(G-3848)*

Custom Communications Inc ....D... 507 288-5522
Rochester *(G-7091)*

Master Electric Co Inc ....D... 952 890-3555
Savage *(G-230)*

Metro Communication Services ....D... 651 702-3100
Saint Paul *(G-9247)*

Network Design Inc ....E... 763 475-5500
Minneapolis *(G-5184)*

Parallel Technologies Inc ....C... 952 920-7185
Minneapolis *(G-5322)*

CONTRACTORS: Computer Installation

All Systems Installation Inc ....D... 507 281-9466
Rochester *(G-7050)*

Fishel Information Systems Inc ....E... 952 544-1108
Hopkins *(G-2543)*

Parallel Technologies Inc ....C... 952 920-7185
Minneapolis *(G-5322)*

CONTRACTORS: Computerized Controls Installation

Rhjh Inc ....E... 651 735-7470
Saint Paul *(G-8897)*

CONTRACTORS: Concrete

Aduddell Industries Inc ....E... 651 288-2246
Saint Paul *(G-7985)*

Al Minnerath Inc ....C... 320 762-7289
Alexandria *(G-79)*

Anderson Brothers Construction ....C... 218 829-1768
Brainerd *(G-549)*

Asphalt & Concrete Buy Knox ....E... 612 781-1112
Minneapolis *(G-3820)*

Bituminous Roadways Inc ....E... 612 721-2451
Minneapolis *(G-3908)*

Bob Pankan & Sons Concrete ....E... 763 444-5720
Isanti *(G-2778)*

Camco Construction Inc ....E... 320 259-1051
Saint Cloud *(G-7467)*

Collin Garvey ....E... 651 463-4825
Farmington *(G-2045)*

Concrete Mobility LLC ....E... 952 746-5887
Shakopee *(G-9432)*

Crosstown Masonry Inc ....E... 763 434-6371
Anoka *(G-171)*

Dallas I Hanson Construction ....E... 320 839-3455
Ortonville *(G-6582)*

Dayco Concrete Co Inc ....D... 952 556-0278
Chanhassen *(G-918)*

DH Blattner & Sons Inc ....D... 320 356-7351
Avon *(G-294)*

Duluth Superior Erection Inc ....E... 218 626-1112
Duluth *(G-1305)*

Duracoat Inc ....E... 320 587-3135
Hutchinson *(G-2696)*

Evenson Concrete Systems ....E... 507 243-3660
Madison Lake *(G-3079)*

Fabcon Inc ....C... 952 890-4444
Savage *(G-9390)*

Ferber Inc ....E... 320 251-4072
Saint Cloud *(G-7509)*

Frantz, Donald R Concrete ....E... 952 929-8568
Minneapolis *(G-4476)*

Gordon Lund ....E... 320 275-2006
Dassel *(G-1161)*

Gresser Co's Inc ....C... 651 454-5976
Saint Paul *(G-7793)*

Hage Concrete Works ....E... 651 690-4243
Saint Paul *(G-8438)*

Harbor City Masonry Inc ....D... 218 628-3686
Duluth *(G-1347)*

Hicks Concrete Construction ....E... 763 420-7755
Hamel *(G-2344)*

Hollenback & Nelson Inc ....E... 763 862-7525
Minneapolis *(G-3489)*

Kelleher Construction Corp ....E... 952 890-6772
Burnsville *(G-740)*

Knife Lake Concrete Inc ....E... 320 679-4141
Mora *(G-6363)*

Manor Concrete Construction ....C... 763 497-5420
Saint Michael *(G-7676)*

Met-Con Metro Inc ....E... 952 884-6250
Minneapolis *(G-4998)*

Northland Concrete & Masonry ....D... 952 890-1650
Burnsville *(G-765)*

Peck Construction Inc ....D... 763 421-2201
Anoka *(G-214)*

Progressive Concrete & Masonry ....E... 651 489-2200
Saint Paul *(G-8853)*

Ryan Contracting Co ....C... 952 894-3200
Shakopee *(G-9471)*

Salonek Concrete & Constr ....E... 507 723-4218
Springfield *(G-9574)*

Stockness Construction Inc ....E... 651 484-1286
Hugo *(G-2683)*

Superior Masonry & Concrete ....E... 651 786-0884
Anoka *(G-230)*

T & J Concrete & Masonry Inc ....D... 763 413-0988
Minneapolis *(G-3614)*

Themescapes Inc ....E... 651 778-1784
Forest Lake *(G-2170)*

Total Concrete Services ....E... 763 786-8477
Minneapolis *(G-3618)*

Web Construction Co Inc ....E... 507 387-1667
Mankato *(G-3214)*

Winco Landscape Inc ....E... 651 455-3070
Inver Grove Heights *(G-2774)*

CONTRACTORS: Concrete Block Masonry Laying

Steenberg Watrud Construction ....E... 651 457-2291
Inver Grove Heights *(G-2770)*

CONTRACTORS: Concrete Pumping

Engineered Concrete Placer of ....E... 651 452-1183
Saint Paul *(G-7763)*

CONTRACTORS: Concrete Reinforcement Placing

Sowles Co ....C... 651 287-9700
Saint Paul *(G-7910)*

Western Steel Erection Inc ....E... 952 473-4344
Long Lake *(G-3035)*

CONTRACTORS: Concrete Repair

A D B Construction Co Inc ....E... 763 424-5550
Osseo *(G-6589)*

Q3 Contracting Inc ....B... 651 224-2424
Saint Paul *(G-8859)*

CONTRACTORS: Construction Caulking

A J Spanjers Co Inc ....E... 763 424-8288
Minneapolis *(G-3648)*

Merit Contracting Inc ....D... 507 281-4317
Rochester *(G-7182)*

CONTRACTORS: Construction Site Cleanup

Arch Insurance Group Inc ....E... 651 855-7100
Saint Paul *(G-8059)*

Lloyds Construction Services ....E... 952 746-5832
Savage *(G-9397)*

CONTRACTORS: Construction Site Metal Structure Coating

TMI Coatings Inc ....D... 651 452-6100
Saint Paul *(G-7925)*

CONTRACTORS: Core Drilling & Cutting

Idea Drilling LLC ....D... 218 741-9287
Virginia *(G-9740)*

Idea Inc ....E... 218 741-9287
Virginia *(G-9741)*

CONTRACTORS: Countertop Installation

Bloomington Linoleum & Carpet ....E... 952 881-5825
Minneapolis *(G-3917)*

Capital Granite & Marble Inc ....E... 320 259-7625
Saint Cloud *(G-7469)*

Custom Plastic Laminates Inc ....E... 612 781-8191
Minneapolis *(G-4205)*

St Germain's Cabinet Inc ....E... 218 624-1234
Duluth *(G-1460)*

Stone Source Inc 763 540-9000
Plymouth *(G-6884)*

Stone Systems & Services Inc ....D... 651 683-9672
Saint Paul *(G-7913)*

CONTRACTORS: Curb & Sidewalk

North Country Concrete Inc ....D... 763 576-8602
Anoka *(G-209)*

O'Malley Construction Inc ....E... 507 357-6330
Le Center *(G-2953)*

CONTRACTORS: Decontamination Svcs

Dustcoating Inc ....E... 952 894-0012
Savage *(G-9389)*

CONTRACTORS: Demolition, Building & Other Structures

Carl Bolander & Sons Co ....D... 651 224-6299
Saint Paul *(G-8165)*

Deconstruction Services ....E... 888 224-2608
Minneapolis *(G-4239)*

Landwehr Construction Inc ....E... 320 252-1494
Saint Cloud *(G-7542)*

Veit & Co Inc ....C... 763 428-2242
Rogers *(G-7347)*

CONTRACTORS: Dewatering

Blake Drilling Co Inc ....E... 763 780-9187
Minneapolis *(G-3420)*

Northern Dewatering Inc ....D... 763 428-2616
Rogers *(G-7332)*

Tri-State Drilling Inc ....D... 763 553-1234
Minneapolis *(G-5852)*

CONTRACTORS: Drapery Track Installation

Secoa Inc ....D... 763 506-8800
Champlin *(G-900)*

CONTRACTORS: Driveway

Asphalt Specialties Co 651 484-1696
Saint Paul *(G-8072)*

Halverson Concrete Inc ....E... 763 434-0318
Anoka *(G-186)*

CONTRACTORS: Driveway, Parking Lot & Blacktop

Asphalt Specialties Co 651 484-1696
Saint Paul *(G-8072)*

Northwest Asphalt Inc ....E... 952 445-1003
Shakopee *(G-9461)*

Pine Bend Paving Inc ....E... 651 437-2333
Hastings *(G-2398)*

CONTRACTORS: Drywall

Berg Drywall LLC ....C... 952 448-3130
Chaska *(G-953)*

Boser Construction Inc ....E... 320 393-3185
Sauk Rapids *(G-9359)*

Brush Masters Inc ....C... 763 478-3232
Minneapolis *(G-3964)*

Carl Hanson Drywall Inc ....E... 763 753-4112
Cedar *(G-874)*

Commercial Drywall Inc ....E... 763 862-6020
Saint Francis *(G-7639)*

Custom Drywall Inc ....C... 651 488-0533
Saint Paul *(G-8274)*

Davis Drywall Inc ....E... 218 444-2532
Bemidji *(G-387)*

Friedges Drywall Inc ....E... 952 461-3288
New Market *(G-6420)*

Heim Drywall Inc ....E... 507 932-5448
Saint Charles *(G-7403)*

Heller Drywall Ltd ....E... 952 496-2525
Shakopee *(G-9443)*

J & D Drywall Inc ....E... 952 461-4078
Elko *(G-1905)*

JD Driver Ltd ....E... 507 437-6050
Rose Creek *(G-7350)*

Ladue Construction Inc ....E... 218 846-9865
Waubun *(G-9900)*

MCI Paint & Drywall Inc ....E... 952 985-7778
Lakeville *(G-2917)*

Mulcahy Inc ....C... 651 770-5250
Mahtomedi *(G-3095)*

N P D Inc ....E... 218 720-3324
Duluth *(G-1398)*

Palmer Soderberg Inc ....E... 507 288-4213
Rochester *(G-7200)*

Quality Drywall Inc ....E... 763 424-5774
Osseo *(G-6654)*

Russnick Contractors Inc ....E... 763 420-3737
Hamel *(G-2356)*

Schum Drywall Co Inc ....E... 952 881-3350
Minneapolis *(G-5615)*

Universal Painting & Drywall ....E... 763 315-0095
Minneapolis *(G-5921)*

Viking Drywall Inc ....E... 952 888-6442
Minneapolis *(G-5972)*

W Zintl Construction Inc ....C... 651 439-7973
Stillwater *(G-9654)*

Young & Davis Drywall Inc ....E... 218 751-6048
Bemidji *(G-434)*

CONTRACTORS: Drywall, Plastering & Insulation

Architectural Sales of MN ....D... 763 533-1595
Minneapolis *(G-3802)*
Installed Building Products ....D... 763 441-2313
Elk River *(G-1900)*
Marathon Group Inc ....D... 952 929-1990
Minneapolis *(G-4945)*
McPherson Insulation Inc ....E... 320 259-5735
Saint Cloud *(G-7418)*
MG Kraus Construction LLC ....E... 952 895-5300
Burnsville *(G-755)*
Prestige Drywall Inc ....E... 763 506-0030
Anoka *(G-216)*
Quality Drywall Midwest Inc ....E... 763 424-5774
Maple Grove *(G-3252)*

CONTRACTORS: Earthmoving

Carl Bolander & Sons Co ....D... 651 224-6299
Saint Paul *(G-8165)*
Doboszenski & Sons Inc ....E... 763 478-6945
Loretto *(G-3046)*
Fraser Construction Co ....E... 507 288-6583
Rochester *(G-7120)*
Tri-State Drilling Inc ....D... 763 553-1234
Minneapolis *(G-5852)*
Turner Excavating Co ....D... 952 890-1645
Savage *(G-9410)*

CONTRACTORS: Electric Power Systems

General Electric Co ....E... 612 529-9502
Minneapolis *(G-4510)*
Gephart Electrical Constr ....E... 651 484-4900
Saint Paul *(G-8407)*

CONTRACTORS: Electrical

A & A Electric & Underground ....E... 507 634-7453
Kasson *(G-2818)*
Adair Electric Co ....D... 507 289-7696
Rochester *(G-7044)*
Aid Electric Corp ....E... 763 571-7267
Minneapolis *(G-3387)*
Applied Business Comms ....D... 651 643-6595
New Brighton *(G-6406)*
Calix Networks Inc ....D... 763 268-3300
Minneapolis *(G-3994)*
Cedar Lake Electric Inc ....E... 507 334-9546
Faribault *(G-1998)*
Centre Electric Inc ....E... 320 352-0160
Sauk Centre *(G-9342)*
Cities Electric Inc ....D... 651 463-3810
Farmington *(G-2044)*
City View Electric Inc ....D... 651 659-9496
Saint Paul *(G-8215)*
Donnelly Electric Inc ....E... 651 487-2877
Saint Paul *(G-8308)*
Electrical Visions Inc ....E... 763 425-1153
Dayton *(G-1165)*
Erickson Plumbing Heating ....E... 763 783-4545
Minneapolis *(G-3466)*
Fagen Inc ....D... 320 564-3324
Granite Falls *(G-2314)*
Falls Electric Inc ....E... 218 681-7299
Thief River Falls *(G-9667)*
Foster Electric Co ....E... 507 289-4571
Rochester *(G-7118)*
Gephart Electric Co Inc ....C... 651 484-4900
Saint Paul *(G-8406)*
Hoffman Controls Inc ....E... 218 732-8374
Park Rapids *(G-6753)*
Honda Electric Inc ....E... 763 498-8433
Loretto *(G-3049)*
Industrial Commercial Farm 218 377-4485
International Falls *(G-2722)*
Industrial Electric Co ....D... 612 331-1268
Minneapolis *(G-4697)*
Kehne Electric Corp ....E... 651 645-5781
Saint Paul *(G-8543)*
Killmer Electric Co Inc ....D... 763 425-2525
Minneapolis *(G-4807)*
Lea Albert Electric Co ....E... 507 373-6650
Albert Lea *(G-60)*
Magnum Electric Inc ....E... 218 236-8753
Moorhead *(G-6327)*
Mayer Electric Corp ....D... 763 537-9357
Minneapolis *(G-4968)*
Mill City Electric Inc ....E... 612 724-4900
Minneapolis *(G-5042)*
Mtec Electric Inc ....E... 763 537-1570
Minneapolis *(G-5147)*
Naylor Electrical Construction ....E... 218 751-2620
Bemidji *(G-405)*

Parsons Electric LLC ....C... 763 571-8000
Minneapolis *(G-3565)*
Pat S Electric ....E... 507 483-2857
Adrian *(G-4)*
Polyphase Electric Co ....D... 218 723-1413
Duluth *(G-1428)*
Red River Electric Inc ....E... 218 236-0502
Moorhead *(G-6336)*
Rick Electric Inc ....E... 218 233-6194
Moorhead *(G-6339)*
Ridgedale Electric Inc ....E... 952 473-2714
Long Lake *(G-3031)*
Rock Electric Corp ....E... 763 792-9664
Minneapolis *(G-3590)*
Thompson Lightning Protection ....E... 651 455-7661
Saint Paul *(G-7921)*
Um Electric Utlts Shop ....E... 612 625-8081
Minneapolis *(G-5898)*
Woody's Rebar Co ....E... 651 592-5038
Saint Paul *(G-9167)*

CONTRACTORS: Electronic Controls Installation

General Electric Co ....E... 612 529-9502
Minneapolis *(G-4510)*
RMR Services LLC ....D... 763 786-7323
Minneapolis *(G-3588)*
Uhl Co Inc ....D... 763 425-7226
Osseo *(G-6680)*

CONTRACTORS: Elevator Front Installation, Metal

Stencil Cutting & Supply Co ....D... 800 783-4633
Red Wing *(G-7007)*

CONTRACTORS: Energy Management Control

Prairie Technologies Inc of MN ....E... 763 255-3200
Elk River *(G-1904)*

CONTRACTORS: Environmental Controls Installation

Johnson Controls Inc ....D... 763 566-7650
Plymouth *(G-6868)*
Rhjh Inc ....E... 651 735-7470
Saint Paul *(G-8897)*

CONTRACTORS: Epoxy Application

Diversified Contracting Inc ....E... 763 712-8087
Anoka *(G-175)*

CONTRACTORS: Erection & Dismantling, Poured Concrete Forms

Ceco Concrete Construction DE ....D... 763 434-4637
Anoka *(G-162)*

CONTRACTORS: Excavating

Ames Construction Inc ....B... 952 435-7106
Burnsville *(G-676)*
Bnr Excavating Inc ....E... 651 438-8692
Hampton *(G-2363)*
Chad Monson Excavating LLC ....D... 320 995-6703
Willmar *(G-9996)*
Chard Tiling & Excavating Inc ....D... 952 873-6152
Belle Plaine *(G-372)*
Christiansen Industrial ....E... 218 751-4663
Bemidji *(G-384)*
Columbia Building Services Inc ....E... 612 331-2090
Minneapolis *(G-4124)*
D & G Excavating Inc ....E... 507 532-2334
Marshall *(G-3292)*
D L R Excavating Inc ....D... 651 437-3128
Hastings *(G-2380)*
Dennis Fehn Gravel ....E... 763 497-2428
Albertville *(G-73)*
Dlo Excavating & Poured Walls ....E... 651 480-8457
Hastings *(G-2414)*
Engstrom Excavating Inc ....E... 651 437-2782
Hastings *(G-2386)*
Ferguson Brothers Excavating ....E... 320 762-0622
Alexandria *(G-101)*
Frattalone Co's Inc ....C... 651 484-0448
Saint Paul *(G-8394)*
Friedges Landscaping Inc ....E... 952 469-2996
Lakeville *(G-2908)*
Geldner Construction Inc ....E... 507 931-4230
Saint Peter *(G-9304)*
Gordon Construction Inc ....E... 218 935-2191
Mahnomen *(G-3086)*
Gustafson Excavating Inc ....E... 651 674-7430
North Branch *(G-6500)*

Hartman Co's Inc ....E... 952 443-2958
Victoria *(G-9729)*
Hoffman Construction Co ....E... 507 794-5230
Sleepy Eye *(G-9496)*
Ingram Excavating Inc ....D... 952 934-0917
Eden Prairie *(G-1693)*
Jay Bros Inc ....E... 651 464-6400
Forest Lake *(G-2147)*
K A Witt Construction Inc ....E... 952 758-2108
New Prague *(G-6429)*
Kamish Excavating Inc ....E... 651 457-3600
South Saint Paul *(G-9532)*
Lakehead Trucking Inc ....E... 218 721-3521
Duluth *(G-1379)*
Landwehr Construction Inc ....E... 320 252-1494
Saint Cloud *(G-7542)*
M M Miller Brothers Excavating ....E... 763 420-9170
Hamel *(G-2349)*
MR Paving & Excavating Inc ....D... 507 354-4171
New Ulm *(G-6464)*
Nadeau Excavating Inc ....E... 651 438-8628
Hampton *(G-2366)*
Nedeau Inc ....E... 651 438-8628
Hampton *(G-2367)*
R & G Construction Co ....E... 507 537-1473
Marshall *(G-3323)*
R J Zavoral Ed's Construction ....D... 218 773-0586
East Grand Forks *(G-1575)*
Rachel Contracting LLC ....E... 763 424-9955
Saint Michael *(G-7681)*
Ramsey Excavating Co ....E... 612 529-0077
Minneapolis *(G-5465)*
Randy Kramer Excavating Inc ....E... 320 764-6871
Watkins *(G-9899)*
Stocker Excavating Inc ....E... 952 890-4241
Savage *(G-9408)*
Tms Construction Inc ....E... 952 226-6300
Prior Lake *(G-6959)*
Trentroy Corp ....D... 952 445-3820
Jordan *(G-2811)*

CONTRACTORS: Exterior Concrete Stucco

Berg Exteriors Inc ....E... 763 479-1115
Maple Plain *(G-3269)*
W E Nelson Stucco Co ....E... 763 377-3631
Saint Paul *(G-9134)*
Young & Davis Drywall Inc ....E... 218 751-6048
Bemidji *(G-434)*

CONTRACTORS: Exterior Painting

Brush Masters Inc ....C... 763 478-3232
Minneapolis *(G-3964)*
Cityscape Contractors Inc ....D... 952 882-0020
Burnsville *(G-698)*
Custom One Painting Inc ....E... 612 787-1040
Minneapolis *(G-4204)*
Lawremar Inc ....E... 651 429-4475
Saint Paul *(G-8568)*

CONTRACTORS: Fence Construction

Dakota Unlimited Inc ....E... 651 423-3995
Rosemount *(G-7368)*
H & R Const Co ....E... 218 589-8707
Dalton *(G-1156)*
Town & Country Fence Inc ....E... 763 425-5050
Minneapolis *(G-5841)*
Twin City Custom Railings & GL ....E... 763 780-7314
Minneapolis *(G-3624)*

CONTRACTORS: Fiber Optic Cable Installation

Master Electric Co Inc ....D... 952 890-3555
Savage *(G-9398)*
North Central Service Inc ....C... 218 776-3855
Clearbrook *(G-1039)*
Orion Communication Services ....E... 763 694-7540
Minneapolis *(G-5290)*

CONTRACTORS: Fire Detection & Burglar Alarm Systems

Appollo Systems Inc ....E... 763 493-5821
Osseo *(G-6594)*
Checkpoint Security Systems ....C... 952 942-9431
Chanhassen *(G-914)*
Checkpoint Systems Inc ....E... 952 227-5350
Chaska *(G-958)*
Checkpoint Systems Inc ....C... 952 943-3853
Chanhassen *(G-915)*
Custom Communications Inc ....D... 507 288-5522
Rochester *(G-7091)*
Electro-Watchman Inc ....E... 651 227-8461
Saint Paul *(G-8329)*

2011 Harris Minnesota
Services Directory

(G-00000) Company's Geographic Section entry number

Firenet Systems Inc ....E... 763 536-3950
Minneapolis (G-4437)

Life Safety Systems Inc ....E... 763 560-2048
Minneapolis (G-4876)

Northstar Fire Protection Inc ....E... 651 456-9111
Saint Paul (G-7853)

Silent Knight Security Systems ....E... 952 881-0038
Minneapolis (G-5673)

Simplexgrinnell LP...............................E... 320 253-8883
Saint Cloud (G-7427)

Simplexgrinnell LP...............................C... 763 367-5000
Minneapolis (G-5676)

Superior Fire Protection Inc ....E... 763 263-1929
Big Lake (G-458)

Trans-Alarm Inc....................................D... 952 894-1700
Burnsville (G-810)

Wright-Hennepin Security Corp ....C... 763 477-3000
Rockford (G-7306)

CONTRACTORS: Fire Sprinkler System Installation Svcs

Arrow Sprinkler Inc...............................E... 763 780-2800
Minneapolis (G-3410)

Brothers Fire Protection Co ....D... 763 441-2290
Elk River (G-1864)

Corval Constructors Inc ....C... 651 642-0451
Saint Paul (G-8255)

General Sprinkler Corp..........................E... 651 484-5903
Saint Paul (G-8405)

Gilbert Mechanical Contractors...........C... 952 835-3810
Edina (G-1831)

Metro Fire Protection Inc.....................E... 651 784-0417
Lino Lakes (G-2974)

National Automatic Sprinkler...............E... 763 784-8902
Minneapolis (G-3550)

Olsen Fire Protection Inc ....E... 612 331-3111
Minneapolis (G-5270)

Response Fire Protection Inc ....E... 763 717-4740
Minneapolis (G-3583)

Simplexgrinnell LP...............................E... 320 253-8883
Saint Cloud (G-7427)

Simplexgrinnell LP...............................C... 763 367-5000
Minneapolis (G-5676)

Skyline Fire Protection Inc ....E... 763 425-4441
Osseo (G-6664)

Summit Fire Protection Co ....C... 651 251-1880
Saint Paul (G-9012)

Superior Fire Protection Inc.................E... 763 263-1929
Big Lake (G-458)

Viking Automatic Sprinkler Co ....E... 651 558-3300
Saint Paul (G-9128)

Viking Automatic Sprinkler Co ....E... 218 628-2150
Duluth (G-1495)

Viking Automatic Sprinkler Co ....E... 507 289-8270
Rochester (G-7283)

CONTRACTORS: Floor Laying & Other Floor Work

Above All Hardwood Floors LLC ....E... 952 440-9663
Prior Lake (G-6928)

Architectural Sales of MN ....D... 763 533-1595
Minneapolis (G-3802)

Becker Bros Inc.....................................D... 651 633-8604
Saint Paul (G-8097)

C L T Floor Coverings Inc ....E... 651 451-0069
Inver Grove Heights (G-2740)

Crew2 Inc ....D... 612 276-1600
Minneapolis (G-4182)

Dave's Floor Sanding ....D... 763 784-3400
Minneapolis (G-3452)

Johnson's Carpet Tile ....E... 218 628-2249
Duluth (G-1362)

National Floor Maintenance Inc............D... 303 771-0509
Saint Paul (G-7848)

St Paul Linoleum & Carpet Co ....D... 651 686-7770
Eagan (G-1553)

CONTRACTORS: Flooring

Acoustics Associates Inc.......................C... 763 544-8901
Minneapolis (G-3674)

Commercial Contractors Co of ....E... 320 256-7422
Melrose (G-3348)

Hi-Tech Floors Inc.................................E... 952 895-1602
Burnsville (G-731)

Inside Edge Commercial ....E... 651 389-3900
Eagan (G-1531)

CONTRACTORS: Foundation & Footing

Strongform Inc ....E... 218 462-2607
Deer Creek (G-1166)

CONTRACTORS: Foundation Building

Steenberg Watrud Construction...........E... 651 457-2291
Inver Grove Heights (G-2770)

CONTRACTORS: Garage Doors

Crawford Door Sales Co Twin ....E... 651 455-1221
Saint Paul (G-7739)

Deerwood Builders Inc ....E... 218 534-5408
Deerwood (G-1176)

Great Garage Products Inc ....E... 763 422-4000
Minneapolis (G-3478)

Industrial Door Co Inc ....E... 763 786-4730
Minneapolis (G-3497)

Lipe Brothers Construction Inc ....E... 218 525-3364
Duluth (G-1384)

CONTRACTORS: Gasoline Pump Installation

Dan Larson Enterprises Inc ....E... 612 331-8550
Minneapolis (G-4222)

Rollie's Sales & Service Inc ....E... 320 859-4811
Osakis (G-6587)

CONTRACTORS: General Electric

Ace Electrical Contractors Inc..............D... 763 694-8800
Minneapolis (G-3670)

Adair Electric Co ....D... 507 289-7696
Rochester (G-7044)

API Electric Co ....D... 218 628-3323
Duluth (G-1239)

Augusta Electric Inc ....E... 320 398-2189
Kimball (G-2831)

Ben Franklin Electric Inc ....D... 952 888-2210
Burnsville (G-685)

Bloomington Electric Co ....E... 952 888-7905
Minneapolis (G-3913)

Chapin Enterprises Inc..........................C... 320 235-4386
Willmar (G-9997)

Collins Electrical Constr ....C... 651 224-2833
Saint Paul (G-8224)

Collins Electrical Systems Inc ....D... 763 535-6000
Minneapolis (G-4121)

Design Electric Inc ....D... 320 252-1658
Saint Cloud (G-7497)

Dewar Electric Inc ....E... 507 235-6677
Fairmont (G-1962)

Dymanyk Electric ....E... 612 379-4112
Minneapolis (G-4298)

Egan Co ....C... 763 544-4131
Brooklyn Park (G-609)

Electric Resource Contractors ....C... 612 522-6511
Minneapolis (G-4338)

Electrical Installation ....E... 763 479-3744
Maple Plain (G-3273)

Electronic Communication Systs ....D... 651 735-7470
Saint Paul (G-8331)

Elliott Contracting Corp ....E... 612 256-0000
Minneapolis (G-4342)

Fox Electrical Co ....E... 507 433-7184
Austin (G-271)

Fraser-Morris Electric Co Inc ....E... 612 332-4328
Minneapolis (G-4480)

Gilbert Mechanical Contractors...........C... 952 835-3810
Edina (G-1831)

Hanson Electric Of Bemidji Inc............E... 218 751-5833
Bemidji (G-397)

Hunt Electric Corp ....B... 651 646-2911
Saint Paul (G-8500)

Hunt Electric Corp ....E... 507 281-3226
Rochester (G-7141)

J T Electric Service Inc ....E... 320 845-4789
Albany (G-27)

JC Custom Welding Inc ....E... 218 444-9353
Bemidji (G-398)

Manor Electric Inc ....E... 763 479-4170
Maple Plain (G-3278)

Marsh Heating & Air Condg ....E... 763 536-0667
Minneapolis (G-4957)

Medina Electric Inc ....C... 763 478-6828
Hamel (G-2351)

Mid Northern Electric Inc ....E... 651 452-3996
Saint Paul (G-7840)

MJM Investments Inc.............................E... 952 432-5036
Saint Paul (G-7844)

Moorhead Electric Inc...........................E... 218 284-1963
Moorhead (G-6330)

Muska Electric Co ....E... 651 636-5820
Saint Paul (G-8730)

One Way Building Services Inc ....E... 952 942-0412
Minneapolis (G-5280)

Otter Tail Corp.. 866 410-8780
Fergus Falls (G-2105)

Prairie Electric Co Inc ....E... 952 949-0074
Eden Prairie (G-1752)

Premier Electrical Corp.........................C... 763 424-6551
Brooklyn Park (G-617)

Ries Electric Co ....E... 651 451-2238
South Saint Paul (G-9538)

Scheid Electric Inc................................E... 507 388-9305
Mankato (G-8903)

South Side Electric Inc ....D... 952 888-5500
Bloomington (G-517)

Weber Electric Inc ....D... 651 490-1333
Saint Paul (G-9142)

CONTRACTORS: Glass Tinting, Architectural & Automotive

Automotive Restyling Concepts ....D... 763 535-2181
Minneapolis (G-3840)

CONTRACTORS: Glass, Glazing & Tinting

ACG Inc ....D... 651 488-0574
Saint Paul (G-7688)

Brin Glass Co...C... 612 529-9671
Minneapolis (G-3949)

Egan Co 763 567-0025
Plymouth (G-6861)

Empire Door & Glass Co ....E... 612 729-4003
Minneapolis (G-4349)

Enclos Corp ....D... 651 796-6100
Saint Paul (G-7761)

Minneapolis Glass Co ....D... 763 559-0635
Plymouth (G-6874)

Mulcahy Inc ....C... 651 770-5250
Mahtomedi (G-3095)

St Germain's Glass Inc ....E... 218 628-0221
Duluth (G-1461)

Superior Glass Duluth............................E... 218 722-7400
Duluth (G-1478)

Twin City Glass Contractors ....E... 651 746-0650
Saint Paul (G-9092)

United Glass Inc ....E... 651 633-2529
Saint Paul (G-9105)

Willet Hauser Architectural...................E... 507 457-3500
Winona (G-10141)

CONTRACTORS: Gutters & Downspouts

L L Hage Seamless Gutters Inc............E... 507 433-1158
Austin (G-280)

Larson's Home Improvement ....E... 507 288-7111
Rochester (G-7160)

Metro Siding Inc....................................E... 763 557-1808
Plymouth (G-6873)

Probuild Co LLC ....D... 320 251-0861
Saint Cloud (G-7573)

CONTRACTORS: Heating & Air Conditioning

A W Kuettel & Sons Inc.........................D... 218 722-3901
Duluth (G-1231)

A-ABC Appliance & Heating Inc ....E... 763 383-8383
Minneapolis (G-3652)

AAF-Mcquay Inc ....B... 763 553-5330
Minneapolis (G-3655)

Area Mechanical Inc ....E... 651 451-9356
Vadnais Heights (G-9719)

Commercial Plumbing & Heating...........D... 651 464-2988
Forest Lake (G-2151)

Countryside Heating & Cooling ....E... 763 479-1600
Maple Plain (G-3272)

County of Douglas.................................D... 320 763-6018
Alexandria (G-92)

Cronstrom Furnace & Sheet..................E... 952 920-3800
Minneapolis (G-4186)

D J'S Heating & Air Condg ....E... 763 421-5313
Elk River (G-1871)

Dependable Indoor Air Quality ....E... 763 757-5040
Minneapolis (G-3454)

Diversified Contracting Inc....................E... 763 712-8087
Anoka (G-175)

El-Jay Plumbing & Heating Inc..............D... 320 251-8330
Saint Cloud (G-7413)

Erickson Plumbing Heating ....E... 763 783-4545
Minneapolis (G-3466)

Faribo Plumbing & Heating Inc ....E... 507 334-6409
Faribault (G-2007)

Flare Heating & Air Condg.....................E... 763 542-1166
Minneapolis (G-4454)

Gag Sheet Metal Inc ....E... 507 354-3813
New Ulm (G-6450)

Gartner Refrigeration Co ....E... 218 722-4439
Duluth (G-1332)

General Sheet Metal Corp......................C... 763 544-8747
Minneapolis (G-4518)

Goodin Co ....E... 320 259-6086
Saint Cloud (G-7520)

Gv Heating & Air Inc ....E... 763 535-2000
Minneapolis (G-4582)

Employment codes: A=Over 500 employees, B=251-500,
C=101-250, D=51-100, E=25-50

2011 Harris Minnesota
Services Directory

© Harris InfoSource 1-866-281-6415

685

SERVICES

Harris Contracting Co................E... 507 282-8128
Rochester (G-7133)

HiMec Inc................C... 507 281-4000
Rochester (G-7138)

Horwitz Inc................C... 763 533-1900
Minneapolis (G-4677)

Laney's Mechanical Inc................E... 218 847-1309
Detroit Lakes (G-1207)

Major Mechanical Inc................D... 763 424-6680
Osseo (G-6631)

Managed Services Inc................C... 952 925-4111
Minneapolis (G-4940)

Marsh Heating & Air Condg................E... 763 536-0667
Minneapolis (G-4957)

McDowall Co................D... 320 251-8640
Waite Park (G-9829)

Mechanical Energy Systems Inc................E... 320 253-4859
Saint Cloud (G-7419)

Nelson, Bruce Plumbing................E... 651 738-9354
Saint Paul (G-8745)

Northland Mechanical Contr................C... 763 544-5100
Minneapolis (G-5232)

Owens Co's Inc................D... 952 854-3800
Bloomington (G-509)

Paape Distributing Co................E... 507 345-8057
Mankato (G-3181)

Quality Refrigeration Inc................E... 612 861-7350
Minneapolis (G-5443)

R & S Heating & Air Condg................E... 952 894-0376
Savage (G-9404)

R J Mechanical Inc................E... 320 679-0602
Mora (G-6368)

Rochester Plumbing & Heating................D... 507 289-1613
Rochester (G-7239)

Rouse Mechanical Inc................E... 952 933-5300
Minneapolis (G-5562)

Sabre Plumbing, Heating & Air................D... 763 473-2267
Minneapolis (G-5585)

SPI Group Inc................D... 218 283-9397
International Falls (G-2731)

Spriggs Plumbing & Heating Inc................E... 651 224-5616
Saint Paul (G-8979)

St Cloud Refrigeration Inc................C... 320 251-6861
Saint Cloud (G-7429)

Superior Mechanical Systems................E... 507 289-5126
Rochester (G-7270)

Superior Water Conditioning................E... 507 289-0229
Rochester (G-7271)

Voss Plumbing & Heating of................E... 320 243-3644
Paynesville (G-6775)

Weidner Plumbing & Heating Co................D... 320 252-3000
Saint Cloud (G-7431)

CONTRACTORS: Heating Systems Repair & Maintenance Svc

Albers Sheetmetal................D... 651 224-5428
Saint Paul (G-8004)

Diversified Contracting Inc................E... 763 712-8087
Anoka (G-175)

Fibercare Inc................E... 612 721-5048
Minneapolis (G-4426)

Gagnon Inc................E... 651 644-4301
Saint Paul (G-8400)

Harbor City Oil Co................E... 218 624-3633
Duluth (G-1348)

CONTRACTORS: Highway & Street Construction, General

Al Minnerath Inc................C... 320 762-7289
Alexandria (G-79)

Anderson Brothers Construction................C... 218 829-1768
Brainerd (G-549)

Central Allied Enterprises Inc................D... 320 235-5846
Willmar (G-9995)

Central Specialties Inc................D... 320 762-7289
Alexandria (G-88)

City of White Bear Lake................E... 651 429-8566
Saint Paul (G-8213)

DH Blattner & Sons Inc................D... 320 356-7351
Avon (G-294)

Duininck Inc................C... 320 978-6011
Prinsburg (G-6925)

Duluth Superior Erection Inc................E... 218 626-1112
Duluth (G-1305)

Enebak Construction Co................E... 507 645-8962
Northfield (G-6527)

Knife River Midwest LLC................D... 507 498-3377
Spring Grove (G-9561)

Minnerath Construction Inc................ 320 685-3162
Cold Spring (G-1088)

Riley Bros Construction Inc................E... 320 589-2500
Morris (G-6376)

Rud Construction Inc................E... 952 652-2886
Webster (G-9953)

Shafer Contracting Co Inc................E... 651 257-5019
Shafer (G-9415)

Ulland Brothers Inc................E... 507 373-1960
Albert Lea (G-68)

Ulland Brothers Inc................E... 218 262-3406
Hibbing (G-2478)

Wieser Brothers General Contr................D... 507 895-8903
La Crescent (G-2845)

CONTRACTORS: Highway & Street Paving

Allied Blacktop Co................D... 763 425-0575
Maple Grove (G-3234)

Ames Construction Inc................B... 952 435-7106
Burnsville (G-676)

Bituminous Materials LLC................D... 507 334-3901
Faribault (G-1993)

Bituminous Paving Inc................C... 320 273-2113
Odessa (G-6553)

CS McCrossan Inc................C... 763 425-4167
Osseo (G-6606)

Hardrives Inc................E... 218 744-2913
Forbes (G-2143)

Hardrives Inc................D... 651 436-8444
Lakeland (G-2885)

Interstate Removal Co................E... 651 765-0765
Forest Lake (G-2152)

Knife River Corp - North................B... 320 251-9472
Sauk Rapids (G-9368)

Knife River Corp - North................E... 218 829-4726
Baxter (G-333)

Mac Management Inc................E... 952 938-8048
Minnetonka (G-6189)

Mathy Construction Co................D... 507 288-7447
Rochester (G-7169)

Midwest Asphalt Corp................E... 952 937-8033
Hopkins (G-2582)

PCiRoads LLC................E... 763 497-6100
Saint Michael (G-7679)

Pine Bend Paving Inc................E... 651 437-2333
Hastings (G-2398)

Riley Bros Construction Inc................E... 320 589-2500
Morris (G-6376)

Starry Construction Co Inc................E... 320 762-7289
Alexandria (G-123)

CONTRACTORS: Highway & Street Resurfacing

Allied Blacktop Co................D... 763 425-0575
Maple Grove (G-3234)

Asphalt Surface Technologies................D... 320 363-8500
Saint Joseph (G-7650)

Mac Management Inc................E... 952 938-8048
Minnetonka (G-6189)

Midwest Asphalt Corp................E... 952 937-8033
Hopkins (G-2582)

MR Paving & Excavating Inc................D... 507 354-4171
New Ulm (G-6464)

Northwest Bituminous Inc................E... 952 890-3005
Burnsville (G-767)

CONTRACTORS: Home & Office Intrs Finish, Furnish/Remodel

Innovative Surfaces Inc................E... 651 437-1004
Hastings (G-2393)

Marathon Group Inc................D... 952 929-1990
Minneapolis (G-4945)

VSI Construction Inc................E... 763 493-3000
Maple Grove (G-3257)

CONTRACTORS: Hydraulic Eqpt Installation & Svcs

Westside Equipment Installers................E... 763 478-9572
Hamel (G-2360)

CONTRACTORS: Indl Building Renovation, Remodeling & Repair

Alltech Engineering Corp................D... 651 452-7893
Saint Paul (G-7693)

Arkay Construction Co................E... 763 544-3341
Minneapolis (G-3806)

Crawford-Merz Construction Co................E... 612 874-9011
Minneapolis (G-4177)

Donnelly Brothers Construction................E... 612 866-1204
Minneapolis (G-4278)

Greiner Construction Inc................E... 612 338-1696
Minneapolis (G-4566)

L S Black Constructors Inc................D... 651 774-8445
Saint Paul (G-8553)

Nor-Son Inc................C... 218 828-1722
Baxter (G-339)

Oakwood Builders Inc................E... 952 941-9730
Eden Prairie (G-1735)

Olson General Contractors Inc................E... 763 535-1481
Minneapolis (G-5272)

Shaw - Lundquist Associates................D... 651 454-0670
Saint Paul (G-7903)

Strack Construction Co Inc................E... 320 251-5933
Sauk Rapids (G-9377)

Zeman Construction Co................E... 612 521-4300
Minneapolis (G-6115)

CONTRACTORS: Insulation Installation, Building

API Group Inc................E... 651 636-4320
Saint Paul (G-8054)

Carnahan City-Wide Insulation................D... 952 445-1387
Shakopee (G-9428)

Cullen's Home Center of................D... 320 762-1249
Alexandria (G-93)

Dual Temp Inc................E... 763 494-9358
Hamel (G-2339)

Metro Home Insulation Inc................E... 763 441-2313
Elk River (G-1901)

Milwaukee Insulation Co I................E... 651 659-2211
Saint Paul (G-8668)

Nordic Insulation Inc................E... 763 784-7893
Minneapolis (G-3557)

Northern Industrial Insulation................E... 218 624-0574
Duluth (G-1404)

Nyco Inc................D... 651 457-4069
Inver Grove Heights (G-2764)

Quality Insulation Inc................E... 952 929-6889
Minneapolis (G-5442)

Superl Inc................E... 763 571-7464
Lino Lakes (G-2976)

U S Insulation Inc................E... 763 785-1726
Minneapolis (G-3627)

CONTRACTORS: Lighting Syst

Winco Landscape Inc................E... 651 455-3070
Inver Grove Heights (G-2774)

CONTRACTORS: Machinery Installation

Godbout's Viking Intallation................E... 218 879-2199
Cloquet (G-1054)

Lovegreen Industrial Services................D... 651 890-1166
Saint Paul (G-7825)

Northern Industrial Erectors................D... 218 326-8466
Grand Rapids (G-2300)

CONTRACTORS: Maintenance, Parking Facility Eqpt

Minnesota Department of................E... 320 384-6591
Hinckley (G-2487)

Northside Service Center................E... 612 370-4902
Minneapolis (G-5237)

CONTRACTORS: Marble Installation, Interior

Northwestern Marble & Granite................E... 952 941-8601
Minneapolis (G-5246)

Walstad Tile & Stone Co................E... 763 519-1444
Minneapolis (G-6018)

CONTRACTORS: Masonry & Stonework

Abfalter Brothers Concrete LLC................E... 763 635-8088
Elk River (G-1859)

Advanced Concrete & Masonry................E... 763 424-9365
Minneapolis (G-3687)

American Masonry Restoration................E... 763 502-1400
Minneapolis (G-3399)

B&D Associates Inc................E... 651 489-8001
Saint Paul (G-8084)

Bob Pankan & Sons Concrete................E... 763 444-5720
Isanti (G-2778)

Bunn William Masonry Inc................E... 952 292-2685
Waconia (G-9780)

C & D Granite Inc................E... 320 597-2398
Richmond (G-7040)

Camco Construction Inc................E... 320 259-1051
Saint Cloud (G-7467)

Classic Construction of Cedar................E... 763 434-8870
Cedar (G-877)

Cold Spring Granite Co Inc................A... 320 685-3621
Cold Spring (G-1083)

Commercial Contractors Co of................E... 320 256-7422
Melrose (G-3348)

Coughlan Co's Inc................C... 507 385-8295
Mankato (G-3120)

Crosstown Masonry Inc................E... 763 434-6371
Anoka (G-171)

Dakota Rhoads Masonry Inc................E... 651 437-2100
Hastings (G-2383)

Dayco Concrete Co Inc................D... 952 556-0278
Chanhassen (G-918)

Frantz, Donald R Concrete ....E... 952 929-8568
Minneapolis *(G-4476)*

Greatstone LLC ....E... 651 429-6606
Saint Paul *(G-8429)*

Gresser Co's Inc ....C... 651 454-5976
Saint Paul *(G-7793)*

Greystone Masonry Inc ....E... 763 413-9633
Anoka *(G-185)*

Harbor City Masonry Inc ....D... 218 628-3686
Duluth *(G-1347)*

Hicks Concrete Construction ....E... 763 420-7755
Hamel *(G-2344)*

Hollenback & Nelson Inc ....E... 763 862-7525
Minneapolis *(G-3489)*

Knife Lake Concrete Inc ....E... 320 679-4141
Mora *(G-6363)*

Manor Concrete Construction ....C... 763 497-5420
Saint Michael *(G-7676)*

Michael Nelson Masonry Inc ....E... 952 496-0217
Excelsior *(G-1946)*

Northland Concrete & Masonry ....D... 952 890-1650
Burnsville *(G-765)*

Northwestern Marble & Granite ....E... 952 941-8601
Minneapolis *(G-5246)*

Peck Construction Inc ....D... 763 421-2201
Anoka *(G-214)*

Progressive Concrete & Masonry ....E... 651 489-2200
Saint Paul *(G-8853)*

Stretar Masonry & Concrete Inc ....E... 218 624-4824
Duluth *(G-1476)*

Superior Masonry & Concrete ....E... 651 786-0884
Anoka *(G-230)*

Valley Masonry LLC ....D... 218 498-2244
Glyndon *(G-2235)*

Vincent Haugen ....E... 218 233-3776
Moorhead *(G-6346)*

Yerigan Construction Co ....E... 763 444-5353
Isanti *(G-2782)*

CONTRACTORS: Mechanical

Albers Sheetmetal ....D... 651 224-5428
Saint Paul *(G-8004)*

Boiler Services Inc ....E... 763 784-8178
Minneapolis *(G-3422)*

Cool Air Mechanical Inc ....D... 651 489-8821
Saint Paul *(G-8250)*

Corporate Mechanical Inc ....D... 763 533-3070
Minneapolis *(G-4164)*

Corval Constructors Inc ....C... 651 642-0451
Saint Paul *(G-8255)*

Doody Mechanical Inc ....E... 651 487-1061
Saint Paul *(G-8309)*

Fagen Inc ....D... 320 564-3324
Granite Falls *(G-2314)*

Gilbert Mechanical Contractors ....C... 952 835-3810
Edina *(G-1831)*

Harris Contracting Co ....D... 651 602-6500
Saint Paul *(G-8444)*

Horwitz Inc ....C... 763 533-1900
Minneapolis *(G-4677)*

J-Berd Mechanical Contractors ....D... 320 656-0847
Saint Cloud *(G-7534)*

Lbp Mechanical Inc ....E... 612 333-1515
Minneapolis *(G-4851)*

Master Mechanical Inc ....C... 651 905-1600
Saint Paul *(G-7834)*

Metropolitan Mechanical Contr ....B... 952 941-7010
Eden Prairie *(G-1722)*

Pearson Mechanical Services ....E... 651 275-1100
Hugo *(G-2681)*

Pioneer Power Inc ....D... 651 488-5561
Saint Paul *(G-8828)*

Plaas Inc ....C... 651 388-8881
Red Wing *(G-6994)*

Schadegg Mechanical Inc ....D... 651 292-9933
South Saint Paul *(G-9541)*

Schwickert Inc ....D... 507 387-3106
Mankato *(G-3194)*

Ww Constructors Inc ....E... 763 420-4177
Hamel *(G-2362)*

Yale Mechanical Inc ....C... 952 884-1661
Minneapolis *(G-6097)*

CONTRACTORS: Millwrights

A J Lysne Contracting Corp ....D... 507 451-7121
Owatonna *(G-6688)*

Alltech Engineering Corp ....D... 651 452-7893
Saint Paul *(G-7693)*

Corval Constructors Inc ....C... 651 642-0451
Saint Paul *(G-8255)*

J & D Construction Inc ....E... 320 269-2101
Montevideo *(G-6247)*

K & S Millwrights Inc ....E... 320 833-2228
Buffalo Lake *(G-665)*

CONTRACTORS: Multi-Family Home Remodeling

Con Spec Corp ....E... 651 501-6500
Saint Paul *(G-9199)*

Lemaster Restoration Inc ....E... 952 707-1256
Burnsville *(G-748)*

CONTRACTORS: Nonresidential Building Design & Construction

Mohagen Hansen Architectural ....E... 952 426-7400
Wayzata *(G-9929)*

Opus Corp ....C... 952 656-4444
Hopkins *(G-2597)*

CONTRACTORS: Nuclear Power Refueling

Par Nuclear Holding Co Inc 651 278-0007
Saint Paul *(G-8805)*

CONTRACTORS: Office Furniture Installation

All Furniture Installation Inc ....E... 763 571-2203
Minneapolis *(G-3710)*

Marathon Group Inc ....D... 952 929-1990
Minneapolis *(G-4945)*

CONTRACTORS: On-Site Welding

AWI Manufacturing Inc ....E... 320 485-2471
Winsted *(G-10157)*

Code Welding & Mfg Inc ....E... 763 792-6632
Minneapolis *(G-3435)*

Kusske Mechanical Inc ....E... 651 437-8404
Hastings *(G-2394)*

Lsa LLC ....E... 763 744-0246
Plymouth *(G-6871)*

Park Waite Manufacturing Inc ....C... 320 251-8616
Waite Park *(G-9830)*

Tavis Metal & Fabrication Corp ....E... 763 428-8483
Rogers *(G-7342)*

CONTRACTORS: Painting & Wall Covering

Changs Inc ....E... 763 442-9080
Minneapolis *(G-4054)*

Excel Painting Plus Inc ....E... 763 557-2821
Minneapolis *(G-4382)*

Hamernick Paint Co ....D... 651 489-7007
Saint Paul *(G-8439)*

MCI Paint & Drywall Inc ....E... 952 985-7778
Lakeville *(G-2917)*

Northland Painting ....E... 651 645-9791
Stillwater *(G-9632)*

Painting Perfection Ltd ....E... 651 762-9011
Saint Paul *(G-8803)*

Protouch Painting Inc ....E... 651 457-5628
South Saint Paul *(G-9537)*

Regal Contractors Inc ....E... 320 253-1161
Saint Cloud *(G-7582)*

Tenet Painting ....D... 952 914-9550
Minneapolis *(G-5811)*

Torrini Plastering Co Inc ....E... 612 332-3933
Saint Paul *(G-7926)*

Treb, Dan Painting ....E... 952 476-8163
Long Lake *(G-3034)*

Universal Painting & Drywall ....E... 763 315-0095
Minneapolis *(G-5921)*

CONTRACTORS: Painting, Commercial

Maciej Paint Corp ....E... 651 407-8000
Hugo *(G-2679)*

Painting By Nakasone Inc ....E... 651 646-6999
Saint Paul *(G-8802)*

Prefinishing Specialists Inc ....E... 320 356-2217
Avon *(G-297)*

Prism Commercial & Industrial ....E... 763 420-4080
Hamel *(G-2354)*

Rainbow Inc ....C... 763 535-4041
Minneapolis *(G-5463)*

Sunrise Painting ....E... 763 557-0100
Minneapolis *(G-5768)*

CONTRACTORS: Painting, Commercial, Exterior

B Nelson Julius & Son Inc ....E... 612 379-3347
Minneapolis *(G-3853)*

Final Coat Painting Inc ....D... 651 789-0790
Eagan *(G-1527)*

Fresh Start Enterprises Inc ....E... 952 903-0262
Eden Prairie *(G-1670)*

Lawremar Inc ....E... 651 429-4475
Saint Paul *(G-8568)*

Pompeii Painting Inc ....D... 507 288-8494
Rochester *(G-7207)*

Steinbrecher Painting Inc ....E... 763 389-3887
Princeton *(G-6916)*

CONTRACTORS: Painting, Commercial, Interior

B Nelson Julius & Son Inc ....E... 612 379-3347
Minneapolis *(G-3853)*

Geo's Paint & Finish LLC ....E... 320 692-2027
Brainerd *(G-567)*

Lawremar Inc ....E... 651 429-4475
Saint Paul *(G-8568)*

Pompeii Painting Inc ....D... 507 288-8494
Rochester *(G-7207)*

Steinbrecher Painting Inc ....E... 763 389-3887
Princeton *(G-6916)*

CONTRACTORS: Painting, Indl

Prism Commercial & Industrial ....E... 763 420-4080
Hamel *(G-2354)*

Rainbow Inc ....C... 763 535-4041
Minneapolis *(G-5463)*

CONTRACTORS: Painting, Residential

Champion Coatings ....E... 952 707-9000
Savage *(G-9385)*

Decorators Service Co of ....E... 763 383-2955
Plymouth *(G-6859)*

Lakeside House Painters Inc ....D... 952 942-9709
Minneapolis *(G-4836)*

Painting By Nakasone Inc ....E... 651 646-6999
Saint Paul *(G-8802)*

Prefinishing Specialists Inc ....E... 320 356-2217
Avon *(G-297)*

Sorensen & Sorensen Painting ....E... 507 289-5368
Rochester *(G-7258)*

CONTRACTORS: Painting, Residential, Interior

Brush Masters Inc ....C... 763 478-3232
Minneapolis *(G-3964)*

Cityscape Contractors Inc ....D... 952 882-0020
Burnsville *(G-698)*

Geo's Paint & Finish LLC ....E... 320 692-2027
Brainerd *(G-567)*

Lawremar Inc ....E... 651 429-4475
Saint Paul *(G-8568)*

CONTRACTORS: Parking Lot Maintenance

Bargen Inc 507 427-2924
Mountain Lake *(G-6395)*

Bituminous Roadways Inc ....E... 612 721-2451
Minneapolis *(G-3908)*

Bituminous Roadways Inc ....E... 952 233-1660
Shakopee *(G-9423)*

Reliakor Services Inc ....E... 952 403-1440
Shakopee *(G-9469)*

Tech Restoration Services Inc ....E... 651 292-9638
Saint Paul *(G-9034)*

CONTRACTORS: Patio & Deck Construction & Repair

Boyer Building Corp ....E... 952 475-2097
Minnetonka *(G-6149)*

Jlm Landscape LLC ....E... 952 941-9818
Minneapolis *(G-4766)*

Ron Boelter Window & Siding ....E... 507 243-4354
Madison Lake *(G-3081)*

CONTRACTORS: Pavement Marking

Safety Signs Inc ....E... 952 469-6700
Lakeville *(G-2930)*

CONTRACTORS: Pile Driving

Atlas Foundation Co ....E... 763 428-2261
Osseo *(G-6596)*

Carl Bolander & Sons Co ....D... 651 224-6299
Saint Paul *(G-8165)*

L H Bolduc Co Inc ....D... 763 427-4330
Anoka *(G-196)*

CONTRACTORS: Pipe & Boiler Insulating

API Group Inc ....E... 651 636-4320
Saint Paul *(G-8054)*

CS McCrossan Inc ....C... 763 425-4167
Osseo *(G-6606)*

Energy Conservation Inc ....E... 763 569-0069
Minneapolis *(G-4355)*

Kusske Mechanical Inc ....E... 651 437-8404
Hastings *(G-2394)*

Employment codes: A=Over 500 employees, B=251-500,
C=101-250, D=51-100, E=25-50

2011 Harris Minnesota
Services Directory

© Harris InfoSource 1-866-281-6415

687

SERVICES

CONTRACTORS: Plaster & Drywall Work

Regal Contractors Inc ....E... 320 253-1161
Saint Cloud *(G-7582)*

CONTRACTORS: Plastering, Plain or Ornamental

Donnelly Brothers Construction ....E... 612 866-1204
Minneapolis *(G-4278)*

Mulcahy Inc ....C... 651 770-5250
Mahtomedi *(G-3095)*

Stephen Donnelly Co ....D... 952 884-1848
Minneapolis *(G-5750)*

W Zintl Construction Inc ....C... 651 439-7973
Stillwater *(G-9654)*

CONTRACTORS: Plumbing

A G O'Brien Plumbing & Heating ....E... 218 729-9662
Hermantown *(G-2433)*

A W Kuettel & Sons Inc ....D... 218 722-3901
Duluth *(G-1231)*

Area Mechanical Inc ....E... 651 451-9356
Vadnais Heights *(G-9719)*

Bonfe's Plumbing & Heating Svc ....E... 651 228-7140
Saint Paul *(G-8117)*

Commercial Plumbing & Heating ....D... 651 464-2988
Forest Lake *(G-2151)*

Corval Constructors Inc ....C... 651 642-0451
Saint Paul *(G-8255)*

DMC Plumbing & Heating Inc ....E... 507 356-4455
Pine Island *(G-6815)*

E & H Enterprises of ....D... 320 762-8645
Alexandria *(G-97)*

Egan Co ....C... 763 544-4131
Brooklyn Park *(G-609)*

El-Jay Plumbing & Heating Inc ....D... 320 251-8330
Saint Cloud *(G-7413)*

Elander Mechanical Inc ....E... 952 445-4692
Shakopee *(G-9437)*

Faribo Plumbing & Heating Inc ....E... 507 334-6409
Faribault *(G-2007)*

Genz-Ryan Plumbing & Heating ....C... 952 882-1144
Burnsville *(G-728)*

Gilbert Mechanical Contractors ....C... 952 835-3810
Edina *(G-1831)*

Gorham Oien Mechanical Inc ....D... 320 679-1612
Mora *(G-6359)*

Hanson's Plumbing & Heating ....E... 218 342-2422
Vergas *(G-9722)*

Harris Contracting Co ....D... 651 602-6500
Saint Paul *(G-8444)*

Harris Contracting Co ....E... 507 282-8128
Rochester *(G-7133)*

Harty Mechanical Inc ....E... 507 437-8201
Austin *(G-273)*

HiMec Inc ....C... 507 281-4000
Rochester *(G-7138)*

Horwitz Inc ....C... 763 533-1900
Minneapolis *(G-4677)*

Johnson, Carl E Plumbing ....E... 320 983-2171
Milaca *(G-3378)*

Laney's Mechanical Inc ....E... 218 847-1309
Detroit Lakes *(G-1207)*

Larson Plumbing Inc ....E... 763 427-7680
Anoka *(G-198)*

Major Mechanical Inc ....D... 763 424-6680
Osseo *(G-6631)*

Mc Guire Mechanical Services ....E... 952 469-4988
Lakeville *(G-2916)*

Mc Quillan Brothers Plumbing ....E... 651 292-0124
Saint Paul *(G-8622)*

Metropolitan Mechanical Contr ....B... 952 941-7010
Eden Prairie *(G-1722)*

Nelson, Bruce Plumbing ....E... 651 738-9354
Saint Paul *(G-8745)*

Northland Mechanical Contr ....C... 763 544-5100
Minneapolis *(G-5232)*

R J Mechanical Inc ....E... 320 679-0602
Mora *(G-6368)*

Rochester Plumbing & Heating ....D... 507 289-1613
Rochester *(G-7239)*

Schwalbach Hardware Inc ....E... 507 831-2523
Windom *(G-10071)*

SPI Group Inc ....D... 218 283-9397
International Falls *(G-2731)*

Spriggs Plumbing & Heating Inc ....E... 651 224-5616
Saint Paul *(G-8979)*

St Paul Plumbers Joint ....E... 651 846-1389
Saint Paul *(G-8995)*

St Paul Plumbing & Heating Co ....E... 651 228-9200
Saint Paul *(G-8996)*

State Mechanical Inc ....E... 651 463-8220
Farmington *(G-2060)*

Steinkraus Plumbing Inc ....E... 952 361-0128
Chaska *(G-981)*

Superior Water Conditioning ....E... 507 289-0229
Rochester *(G-7271)*

Thompson Plumbing Co Inc ....E... 952 933-7717
Hopkins *(G-2645)*

Valley Plumbing Co Inc ....C... 952 492-2121
Jordan *(G-2812)*

Voson Plumbing Inc ....E... 952 938-3143
Hopkins *(G-2654)*

Voss Plumbing & Heating of ....E... 320 243-3644
Paynesville *(G-6775)*

Weidner Plumbing & Heating Co ....D... 320 252-3000
Saint Cloud *(G-7431)*

Wenzel Plumbing & Heating Inc ....D... 651 452-1565
Saint Paul *(G-7945)*

CONTRACTORS: Plumbing, Heating & Air Conditioning

Advance Wall Systems Inc ....E... 763 263-8512
Big Lake *(G-444)*

B & D Plumbing, Heating & AC ....E... 763 497-2290
Saint Michael *(G-7672)*

Creative Sustainable Solutions ....D... 651 602-6644
Saint Paul *(G-8267)*

Curbside Lawn Care ....C... 952 403-9012
Savage *(G-9387)*

Environmental Plant Svcs Inc ....E... 651 644-4301
Saint Paul *(G-8342)*

G R Mechanical Plumbing ....E... 763 428-2663
Rogers *(G-7323)*

Johnson Controls Inc ....D... 763 566-7650
Plymouth *(G-6868)*

Mechanical Contractors ....E... 952 440-9751
Prior Lake *(G-6939)*

Midwest Maintenance & Mech ....E... 763 544-2700
Minneapolis *(G-5031)*

Sr Mechanical Inc ....D... 952 933-6933
Saint Louis Park *(G-7669)*

United States Mechanical Inc ....E... 763 780-9030
Circle Pines *(G-1022)*

Wright-Hennepin Security Corp ....C... 763 477-3000
Rockford *(G-7306)*

CONTRACTORS: Post Disaster Renovations

Dvcm ServiceMaster of The ....E... 320 763-5551
Alexandria *(G-96)*

Great Northern Resources Inc ....E... 952 848-0984
Minneapolis *(G-4556)*

Lemaster Restoration Inc ....E... 952 707-1256
Burnsville *(G-748)*

Quantum Co's Inc ....E... 952 943-4357
Minneapolis *(G-5445)*

Rusciano-Hyland Inc ....E... 612 871-4434
Minneapolis *(G-5576)*

CONTRACTORS: Prefabricated Window & Door Installation

Harmony Homes Inc ....E... 763 434-3439
Minneapolis *(G-4599)*

Metro Siding Inc ....E... 763 557-1808
Plymouth *(G-6873)*

Seal Guard Systems Inc ....E... 612 787-0700
Marine On Saint Croix *(G-3289)*

Window Concepts of Minnesota ....E... 651 905-0105
Saint Paul *(G-7948)*

CONTRACTORS: Process Piping

Horwitz Inc ....C... 763 533-1900
Minneapolis *(G-4677)*

Johnson, Carl E Plumbing ....E... 320 983-2171
Milaca *(G-3378)*

Kusske Mechanical Inc ....E... 651 437-8404
Hastings *(G-2394)*

Spriggs Plumbing & Heating Inc ....E... 651 224-5616
Saint Paul *(G-8979)*

CONTRACTORS: Prop, Set Or Scenery Construction, Theatrical

Atomic Props & Effects Ltd ....E... 612 331-1335
Saint Paul *(G-9185)*

Secoa Inc ....D... 763 506-8800
Champlin *(G-900)*

CONTRACTORS: Protective Lining Install, Underground Sewage

Friedges Contracting Co LLC ....E... 952 469-2121
Lakeville *(G-2907)*

CONTRACTORS: Refrigeration

Carrier Commercial ....E... 763 231-8300
Minneapolis *(G-4021)*

Gartner Refrigeration & Mfg ....D... 763 559-5880
Plymouth *(G-6862)*

Laney's Mechanical Inc ....E... 218 847-1309
Detroit Lakes *(G-1207)*

Marsh Heating & Air Condg ....E... 763 536-0667
Minneapolis *(G-4957)*

Northern Air Corp ....C... 651 490-9868
Saint Paul *(G-8757)*

Quality Refrigeration Inc ....E... 612 861-7350
Minneapolis *(G-5443)*

St Cloud Refrigeration Inc ....E... 320 251-6861
Saint Cloud *(G-7429)*

Steine Cold Storage Inc ....E... 763 416-4681
Minneapolis *(G-5748)*

CONTRACTORS: Rigging, Theatrical

Secoa Inc ....D... 763 506-8800
Champlin *(G-900)*

CONTRACTORS: Roof Repair

Cato Construction Inc ....E... 952 736-8134
Savage *(G-9384)*

E H Lawrence Co ....E... 218 254-5705
Chisholm *(G-996)*

CONTRACTORS: Roofing

A W Kuettel & Sons Inc ....D... 218 722-3901
Duluth *(G-1231)*

Bernard L Dalsin Co ....E... 952 881-7663
Minneapolis *(G-3888)*

Berwald Roofing Co Inc ....C... 651 777-7411
Saint Paul *(G-8107)*

Central Roofing Co ....E... 763 572-0660
Minneapolis *(G-3432)*

Commercial Roofing Inc ....E... 651 483-5298
Saint Paul *(G-8229)*

Dalbec Roofing Inc ....E... 952 473-8080
Long Lake *(G-3023)*

Dalco Roofing & Sheet Metal ....D... 763 559-0222
Minneapolis *(G-4220)*

Gag Sheet Metal Inc ....E... 507 354-3813
New Ulm *(G-6450)*

Garlock French Roofing Corp ....E... 612 722-7129
Minneapolis *(G-4502)*

Gemini 26 Inc ....E... 507 334-7951
Faribault *(G-2009)*

Herzog Roofing Inc ....E... 218 847-1121
Detroit Lakes *(G-1195)*

Horizon Roofing Inc ....E... 320 252-1608
Waite Park *(G-9824)*

Innovative Building Concepts ....E... 952 885-0262
Minneapolis *(G-4704)*

Les Jones Roofing Inc ....E... 952 881-2241
Minneapolis *(G-4863)*

Mc Phillips Bros Roofing Co ....E... 651 770-2062
Saint Paul *(G-8621)*

McDowall Co ....D... 320 251-8640
Waite Park *(G-9829)*

Merit Contracting Inc ....D... 507 281-4317
Rochester *(G-7182)*

Millers Roofing ....E... 218 263-4406
Canyon *(G-865)*

Millers Roofing & Siding Co ....E... 218 751-4337
Cotton *(G-1110)*

Palmer West Construction Co ....D... 763 428-1867
Rogers *(G-7335)*

Peterson Bros Roofing & Constr ....E... 651 488-5630
Saint Paul *(G-8820)*

Range Cornice & Roofing Co ....E... 218 263-8812
Hibbing *(G-2470)*

Range Cornice & Roofing Co Inc ....E... 218 262-4581
Hibbing *(G-2471)*

Schwickert Co ....D... 507 387-3101
Mankato *(G-3193)*

Schwickert Inc ....D... 507 387-3106
Mankato *(G-3194)*

Schwickert's of Rochester Inc ....E... 507 387-3106
Mankato *(G-3195)*

Sela Roofing & Remodeling Inc ....E... 612 823-8046
Minneapolis *(G-5631)*

Sela Roofing & Remodeling Inc ....E... 763 592-5420
Minneapolis *(G-5632)*

Sgo Roofing & Construction LLC ....E... 952 469-8560
Lakeville *(G-2934)*

Single-Ply Systems Inc ....D... 651 688-7554
Saint Paul *(G-7905)*

Top-All Roofing Inc ....E... 651 291-7663
Saint Paul *(G-9071)*

Walker Roofing Co ....E... 651 251-0910
Saint Paul *(G-9136)*

SERVICES

Winona Heating & Ventilating..............C... 507 452-2064
Winona *(G-10149)*

CONTRACTORS: Roofing & Gutter Work

Bargen Inc 507 427-2924
Mountain Lake *(G-6395)*

Installed Building Products ....D... 763 441-2313
Elk River *(G-1900)*

Walker Roofing Co...............................E... 651 251-0910
Saint Paul *(G-9136)*

Westway Exteriors Inc.........................E... 651 251-0910
Saint Paul *(G-9151)*

CONTRACTORS: Safety & Security Eqpt

Egan Co ....C... 763 544-4131
Brooklyn Park *(G-609)*

Life Safety Systems Inc.......................E... 763 560-2048
Minneapolis *(G-4876)*

Minnesota Conway Fire & Safety ....E... 952 345-3473
Minneapolis *(G-5072)*

Security Products Co ....E... 763 784-6504
Minneapolis *(G-3599)*

Trans-Alarm Inc..................................D... 952 894-1700
Burnsville *(G-810)*

CONTRACTORS: Sandblasting Svc, Building Exteriors

Maciej Paint Corp ....E... 651 407-8000
Hugo *(G-2679)*

CONTRACTORS: Sheet Metal Work, NEC

Bernard L Dalsin Co ....E... 952 881-7663
Minneapolis *(G-3888)*

Berwald Roofing Co Inc ....C... 651 777-7411
Saint Paul *(G-8107)*

Central Roofing Co ....E... 763 572-0660
Minneapolis *(G-3432)*

Corval Constructors Inc ....C... 651 642-0451
Saint Paul *(G-8255)*

Dalbec Roofing Inc ....E... 952 473-8080
Long Lake *(G-3023)*

Dalco Roofing & Sheet Metal ....D... 763 559-0222
Minneapolis *(G-4220)*

Donlyn Manufacture ....E... 763 786-1103
Minneapolis *(G-3459)*

Excel Air System Inc ....D... 651 779-9725
Saint Paul *(G-8351)*

Garlock French Roofing Corp...............E... 612 722-7129
Minneapolis *(G-4502)*

Gemini 26 Inc......................................E... 507 334-7951
Faribault *(G-2009)*

Les Jones Roofing Inc..........................E... 952 881-2241
Minneapolis *(G-4863)*

Sheridan Sheet Metal Co ....E... 763 537-3686
Minneapolis *(G-5654)*

CONTRACTORS: Sheet metal Work, Architectural

McDowall Co.......................................D... 320 251-8640
Waite Park *(G-9829)*

Nu-Look Exteriors Inc...........................E... 952 882-8787
Burnsville *(G-769)*

Top-All Roofing Inc ....E... 651 291-7663
Saint Paul *(G-9071)*

CONTRACTORS: Ship Boiler & Tank Cleaning & Repair

M & N Equipment Services Inc ....E... 612 379-4147
Minneapolis *(G-4916)*

CONTRACTORS: Sidewalk

Cone Corp..E... 218 245-2313
Bovey *(G-540)*

Dallas I Hanson Construction................E... 320 839-3455
Ortonville *(G-6582)*

Halverson Concrete Inc ....E... 763 434-0318
Anoka *(G-186)*

CONTRACTORS: Siding

Artco Builders Inc ....E... 651 486-0761
Saint Paul *(G-8065)*

Builders & Remodelers Inc ....E... 612 827-5481
Minneapolis *(G-3970)*

Cullen's Home Center of ....D... 320 762-1249
Alexandria *(G-93)*

Garlock French Roofing Corp...............E... 612 722-7129
Minneapolis *(G-4502)*

Larson's Home Improvement ....E... 507 288-7111
Rochester *(G-7160)*

Lifetime Siding & Remodeling ....E... 651 458-0844
Hastings *(G-2417)*

Metro Siding Inc ....E... 763 557-1808
Plymouth *(G-6873)*

Minnesota Exteriors Inc ....E... 763 493-5500
Osseo *(G-6639)*

Ron Boelter Window & Siding ....E... 507 243-4354
Madison Lake *(G-3081)*

Sela Roofing & Remodeling Inc............E... 763 592-5420
Minneapolis *(G-5632)*

SNG Construction Inc..........................D... 763 795-8496
Minneapolis *(G-3603)*

Westway Exteriors Inc.........................E... 651 251-0910
Saint Paul *(G-9151)*

CONTRACTORS: Single-Family Home Fire Damage Repair

Giertsen Co of Minnesota Inc ....E... 763 546-1300
Minneapolis *(G-4527)*

J Benson Construction ....E... 952 920-0717
Minneapolis *(G-4744)*

Lindstrom Cleaning & Constr ....E... 763 544-8761
Minneapolis *(G-4891)*

Quantum Co's Inc ....E... 952 943-4357
Minneapolis *(G-5445)*

Superior Construction Services ....E... 763 424-9434
Osseo *(G-6671)*

CONTRACTORS: Single-family Home General Remodeling

Christ's Household of Faith ....D... 651 265-3400
Saint Paul *(G-8198)*

Custom Remodelers Inc ....C... 651 784-2646
Circle Pines *(G-1009)*

Dave Taylor Constructon Inc ....E... 952 472-1342
Mound *(G-6387)*

Diversified Construction ....E... 952 929-7233
Saint Louis Park *(G-7659)*

Holmquist Lumber Co 320 857-2031
Grove City *(G-2329)*

J Benson Construction ....E... 952 920-0717
Minneapolis *(G-4744)*

Lake Country Builders Ltd ....E... 952 474-7121
Excelsior *(G-1944)*

Lang Builders Inc ....E... 763 780-9090
Circle Pines *(G-1014)*

Larson's Home Improvement ....E... 507 288-7111
Rochester *(G-7160)*

M A Peterson Designbuild Inc ....D... 952 925-9455
Minneapolis *(G-4919)*

Murphy Bros Designers ....E... 763 780-3262
Minneapolis *(G-3548)*

Plekkenpol Builders Inc ....E... 952 888-2225
Minneapolis *(G-5390)*

Pratt Construction Inc ....E... 651 429-8032
Saint Paul *(G-8834)*

Probuilt America Inc 651 770-5570
Saint Paul *(G-8850)*

Sawhorse Designer's & Builders..........E... 952 475-4477
Wayzata *(G-9939)*

Sela Roofing & Remodeling Inc............D... 612 823-8046
Minneapolis *(G-5631)*

Sela Roofing & Remodeling Inc............E... 763 592-5420
Minneapolis *(G-5632)*

Steven Cabinets Inc.............................E... 612 378-1812
Minneapolis *(G-5752)*

Streeter & Associates Inc.....................E... 952 449-9448
Wayzata *(G-9943)*

Trehus Builders Inc ....E... 612 729-2992
Minneapolis *(G-5850)*

Yerigan Construction Co.......................E... 763 444-5353
Isanti *(G-2782)*

CONTRACTORS: Skylight Installation

Seal Guard Systems Inc ....E... 612 787-0700
Marine On Saint Croix *(G-3289)*

CONTRACTORS: Sound Eqpt Installation

Electronic Design Co ....E... 612 355-2300
Minneapolis *(G-4339)*

Enhanced Home Systems Inc................E... 952 941-5289
Eden Prairie *(G-1657)*

Muzak LLC ....E... 763 424-5533
Osseo *(G-6641)*

CONTRACTORS: Spa & Hot Tub Construction & Installation

All Poolside Services Inc ....E... 651 483-6600
Saint Paul *(G-8011)*

Dolphin Pools Inc................................E... 763 542-9000
Plymouth *(G-6860)*

Minnesota Residential Aquatics 651 439-8467
Stillwater *(G-9629)*

Performance Pool & Spa Inc.................E... 651 731-3440
Saint Paul *(G-9259)*

Ron Boelter Window & Siding ....E... 507 243-4354
Madison Lake *(G-3081)*

CONTRACTORS: Specialized Public Building

Alvin E Benike Inc ....C... 507 288-6575
Rochester *(G-7053)*

Boldt Co..C... 218 879-1293
Cloquet *(G-1047)*

Capital Wood Products Co ....E... 651 225-5613
Saint Paul *(G-8153)*

Joshco Construction Inc ....D... 952 361-8000
Chaska *(G-971)*

PCL Construction Services Inc ....D... 952 882-9600
Burnsville *(G-779)*

Ram Buildings Inc ....E... 320 485-2844
Winsted *(G-10164)*

Stahl Construction Co..........................E... 952 931-9300
Minneapolis *(G-5735)*

CONTRACTORS: Sprinkler System

Fireguard Sprinkler Service..................E... 651 748-9499
Saint Paul *(G-8378)*

Simplexgrinnell LP ....C... 320 253-8883
Waite Park *(G-9838)*

Viking Automatic Sprinkler Co..............E... 218 733-0962
Duluth *(G-1496)*

CONTRACTORS: Storage Tank Erection, Metal

Brown Tank LLC...................................D... 651 747-0100
Saint Paul *(G-9189)*

Engineering America Inc ....E... 651 777-4041
Saint Paul *(G-9214)*

CONTRACTORS: Store Fixture Installation

Dave Osborne Construction ....B... 763 540-0232
Plymouth *(G-6858)*

Thomas Grace Construction Inc ....E... 651 342-1298
Stillwater *(G-9652)*

CONTRACTORS: Store Front Construction

Division21 Inc ....E... 651 917-8805
Saint Paul *(G-8304)*

CONTRACTORS: Structural Iron Work, Structural

Hawk & Sons Inc..................................E... 507 285-0508
Rochester *(G-7134)*

Sowles Co ....C... 651 287-9700
Saint Paul *(G-7910)*

Western Steel Erection Inc ....E... 952 473-4344
Long Lake *(G-3035)*

CONTRACTORS: Structural Steel Erection

Advanced Process Technologies ....D... 320 286-5060
Cokato *(G-1074)*

Bald Eagle Erectors Inc ....E... 651 405-9050
Saint Paul *(G-7710)*

Danny's Construction Co Inc ....C... 952 445-4143
Shakopee *(G-9435)*

John Pulsifer Construction Inc ....E... 320 354-2602
New London *(G-6415)*

Northern Industrial Erectors................D... 218 326-8466
Grand Rapids *(G-2300)*

Strongform Inc.....................................E... 218 462-2607
Deer Creek *(G-1166)*

Web Construction Co Inc......................E... 507 387-1667
Mankato *(G-3214)*

Ww Constructors Inc............................E... 763 420-4177
Hamel *(G-2362)*

CONTRACTORS: Stucco, Gunite & Grouting

Alliance Concrete Concepts Inc............E... 507 536-4515
Rochester *(G-7051)*

Donnelly Brothers Construction ....E... 612 866-1204
Minneapolis *(G-4278)*

CONTRACTORS: Stucco, Interior

Signature Stucco Concepts Inc ....E... 763 241-4110
Elk River *(G-1893)*

W E Nelson Stucco Co ....E... 763 377-3631
Saint Paul *(G-9134)*

Young & Davis Drywall Inc ....E... 218 751-6048
Bemidji *(G-434)*

CONTRACTORS: Svc Station Eqpt

Dan Larson Enterprises Inc..................E... 612 331-8550
Minneapolis *(G-4222)*

Griffin Petroleum Services Inc ....E... 763 780-6332
Minneapolis *(G-3479)*

Employment codes: A=Over 500 employees, B=251-500,
C=101-250, D=51-100, E=25-50

2011 Harris Minnesota
Services Directory

© Harris InfoSource 1-866-281-6415

689

CONTRACTORS: Svc Station Eqpt Installation, Maint & Repair

Dan Larson Enterprises Inc ....E... 612 331-8550
Minneapolis *(G-4222)*

Griffin Petroleum Services Inc..........E... 763 780-6332
Minneapolis *(G-3479)*

Pump & Meter Service Inc ....E... 952 933-4800
Hopkins *(G-2608)*

Westside Equipment Installers ....E... 763 478-9572
Hamel *(G-2360)*

CONTRACTORS: Terrazzo Work

Grazzini Brothers & Co..........C... 651 452-2700
Saint Paul *(G-7790)*

CONTRACTORS: Tile Installation, Ceramic

Grazzini Brothers & Co..........C... 651 452-2700
Saint Paul *(G-7790)*

Northwestern Marble & Granite ....E... 952 941-8601
Minneapolis *(G-5246)*

Olympia Tile Inc ....E... 763 545-5455
Minneapolis *(G-5274)*

Palmer Soderberg Inc..........E... 507 288-4213
Rochester *(G-7200)*

Tile Shop LLC ....E... 763 541-1444
Minneapolis *(G-5825)*

Vinge Tile ....E... 952 431-1000
Farmington *(G-2062)*

Walstad Tile & Stone Co..........E... 763 519-1444
Minneapolis *(G-6018)*

CONTRACTORS: Tile, Marble, Terrazzo & Mosaic

Korsmo Inc ....D... 507 285-1109
Rochester *(G-7158)*

Premier Tile Inc ....E... 651 483-1576
Saint Paul *(G-8838)*

Twin City Tile & Marble Co Inc..........D... 651 602-5800
Saint Paul *(G-9094)*

Walstad Tile & Stone Co..........E... 763 519-1444
Minneapolis *(G-6018)*

CONTRACTORS: Trenching

D & G Excavating Inc ....E... 507 532-2334
Marshall *(G-3292)*

CONTRACTORS: Tuck Pointing & Restoration

Advanced Masonry Restoration ....E... 651 766-8080
Saint Paul *(G-7991)*

CONTRACTORS: Underground Utilities

Castrejon Inc ....E... 763 450-2055
Minneapolis *(G-3429)*

Cooperative Development LLC..........D... 218 444-1143
Bemidji *(G-385)*

Dell-Comm Inc ....D... 763 783-0035
Saint Paul *(G-8283)*

Dig America Utility Contr ....E... 320 253-3447
Saint Cloud *(G-7498)*

E J M Pipe Services Inc ....E... 651 786-8041
Circle Pines *(G-1011)*

Mlaskoch Excavating Inc ....D... 218 372-4067
Willow River *(G-10061)*

Mlaskoch Utility Construction ....E... 218 372-3977
Willow River *(G-10062)*

Quality Underground Services ....D... 651 224-0413
Saint Paul *(G-8861)*

Rp Schroeder Construction Inc ....E... 763 856-2230
Zimmerman *(G-10215)*

S R Weidema Inc ....D... 763 428-9110
Osseo *(G-6659)*

State Mechanical Inc..........E... 651 463-8220
Farmington *(G-2060)*

CONTRACTORS: Ventilation & Duct Work

Air Mechanical Inc ....C... 763 434-7747
Anoka *(G-147)*

Aircorps LLC ....E... 763 550-0707
Plymouth *(G-6845)*

Albers Sheetmetal..........D... 651 224-5428
Saint Paul *(G-8004)*

Allan Mechanical Inc..........E... 952 934-3999
Eden Prairie *(G-1587)*

General Sheet Metal Corp ....C... 763 544-8747
Minneapolis *(G-4518)*

Maintenance Team ....E... 952 942-5000
Eden Prairie *(G-1715)*

Marsh Heating & Air Condg ....E... 763 536-0667
Minneapolis *(G-4957)*

Mc Quillan Brothers Plumbing ....E... 651 292-0124
Saint Paul *(G-8622)*

McDowall Co..........D... 320 251-8640
Waite Park *(G-9829)*

Modern Heating & Air Condg ....E... 612 781-3358
Minneapolis *(G-5118)*

Northern Air Corp ....C... 651 490-9868
Saint Paul *(G-8757)*

Northwest Sheet Metal Co of St..........D... 651 310-0102
Saint Paul *(G-8768)*

Quality Refrigeration Inc ....E... 612 861-7350
Minneapolis *(G-5443)*

Shannon-Peterson Inc..........E... 218 751-4502
Bemidji *(G-427)*

St Cloud Refrigeration Inc ....C... 320 251-6861
Saint Cloud *(G-7429)*

Tonna Mechanical Inc..........E... 507 288-1908
Rochester *(G-7275)*

Weidner Plumbing & Heating Co ....D... 320 252-3000
Saint Cloud *(G-7431)*

Winona Heating & Ventilating ....C... 507 452-2064
Winona *(G-10149)*

CONTRACTORS: Vinyl Flooring Installation, Tile & Sheet

C L T Floor Coverings Inc ....E... 651 451-0069
Inver Grove Heights *(G-2740)*

CONTRACTORS: Voice, Data & Video Wiring

AVI-Spl Inc ....E... 651 287-7000
Saint Paul *(G-8081)*

Broadband America, Corp ....E... 952 941-7900
Victoria *(G-9725)*

Electronic Design Co ....E... 612 355-2300
Minneapolis *(G-4339)*

Master Technology Group Inc ....E... 952 960-1212
Savage *(G-9399)*

CONTRACTORS: Wall Covering

Decorators Service Co of ....E... 763 383-2955
Plymouth *(G-6859)*

Sunrise Painting..........E... 763 557-0100
Minneapolis *(G-5768)*

CONTRACTORS: Wall Covering, Commercial

Painting By Nakasone Inc ....E... 651 646-6999
Saint Paul *(G-8802)*

Steinbrecher Painting Inc..........E... 763 389-3887
Princeton *(G-6916)*

CONTRACTORS: Wall Covering, Residential

Painting By Nakasone Inc ....E... 651 646-6999
Saint Paul *(G-8802)*

CONTRACTORS: Warm Air Heating & Air Conditioning

A G O'Brien Plumbing & Heating ....E... 218 729-9662
Hermantown *(G-2433)*

Air Mechanical Inc ....C... 763 434-7747
Anoka *(G-147)*

Aircorps LLC ....E... 763 550-0707
Plymouth *(G-6845)*

Allan Mechanical Inc..........E... 952 934-3999
Eden Prairie *(G-1587)*

Centraire Heating & Air Condg ....E... 952 941-1044
Eden Prairie *(G-1619)*

Corval Constructors Inc ....C... 651 642-0451
Saint Paul *(G-8255)*

DMC Plumbing & Heating Inc ....E... 507 356-4455
Pine Island *(G-6815)*

E & H Enterprises of ....D... 320 762-8645
Alexandria *(G-97)*

Egan Co ....C... 763 544-4131
Brooklyn Park *(G-609)*

Flare Heating & Air Condg ....E... 763 542-1166
Minneapolis *(G-4454)*

Fred Vogt & Co ....D... 952 929-6767
Minneapolis *(G-4482)*

Gemini 26 Inc ....E... 507 334-7951
Faribault *(G-2009)*

General Sheet Metal Corp ....C... 763 544-8747
Minneapolis *(G-4518)*

Genz-Ryan Plumbing & Heating ....C... 952 882-1144
Burnsville *(G-728)*

Gilbert Mechanical Contractors..........C... 952 835-3810
Edina *(G-1831)*

Gorham Oien Mechanical Inc..........D... 320 679-1612
Mora *(G-6359)*

Haley Comfort Systems Inc ....E... 507 534-2901
Plainview *(G-6842)*

Hanson's Plumbing & Heating..........E... 218 342-2422
Vergas *(G-9722)*

Harty Mechanical Inc ....E... 507 437-8201
Austin *(G-273)*

Heating & Cooling Two Inc ....D... 763 428-3677
Osseo *(G-6619)*

K & S Heating & Air Condg..........D... 507 282-4328
Rochester *(G-7148)*

Magnuson Huisinga & Sons Inc 320 599-4474
Willmar *(G-10021)*

Maintenance Team ....E... 952 942-5000
Eden Prairie *(G-1715)*

Mc Guire Mechanical Services ....E... 952 469-4988
Lakeville *(G-2916)*

Mc Quillan Brothers Plumbing ....E... 651 292-0124
Saint Paul *(G-8622)*

Metro Air Inc ....E... 952 447-8124
Prior Lake *(G-6942)*

Metropolitan Mechanical Contr ....B... 952 941-7010
Eden Prairie *(G-1722)*

Modern Heating & Air Condg ....E... 612 781-3358
Minneapolis *(G-5118)*

Northern Air Corp ....C... 651 490-9868
Saint Paul *(G-8757)*

Northwest Sheet Metal Co of St ....D... 651 310-0102
Saint Paul *(G-8768)*

Paape Distributing Co ....E... 507 345-8057
Mankato *(G-3181)*

Pro-Temp Inc..........E... 651 460-6022
Farmington *(G-2058)*

Range Cornice & Roofing Co Inc ....E... 218 262-4581
Hibbing *(G-2471)*

Ray N Welter Heating Co ....E... 612 825-6867
Minneapolis *(G-5469)*

Schwalbach Hardware Inc ....E... 507 831-2523
Windom *(G-10071)*

Schwickert Co ....D... 507 387-3101
Mankato *(G-3193)*

Shannon-Peterson Inc..........E... 218 751-4502
Bemidji *(G-427)*

St Paul Plumbing & Heating Co ....E... 651 228-9200
Saint Paul *(G-8996)*

Thomas M Meyer Enterprises Inc ....E... 763 476-1990
Minneapolis *(G-5818)*

Tonna Mechanical Inc..........E... 507 288-1908
Rochester *(G-7275)*

Wenzel Plumbing & Heating Inc..........D... 651 452-1565
Saint Paul *(G-7945)*

Winona Heating & Ventilating ....C... 507 452-2064
Winona *(G-10149)*

Yale Mechanical LLC ....C... 952 884-1661
Minneapolis *(G-6098)*

CONTRACTORS: Water Well Drilling

Bergerson-Caswell Inc ....E... 763 479-3121
Maple Plain *(G-3270)*

Keys Well Drilling Co Inc ....E... 651 646-7871
Saint Paul *(G-8547)*

Minnesota Water Well Assn..........E... 651 290-6270
Saint Paul *(G-8710)*

Thein Well Co ....E... 763 271-4200
Monticello *(G-6290)*

CONTRACTORS: Water Well Servicing

Bergerson-Caswell Inc ....E... 763 479-3121
Maple Plain *(G-3270)*

CONTRACTORS: Waterproofing

Construction Labor Force Inc ....E... 651 786-0550
Circle Pines *(G-1006)*

E H Lawrence Co ....E... 218 254-5705
Chisholm *(G-996)*

Ram Construction Services of ....E... 651 765-1950
Little Canada *(G-2997)*

Rayco Construction Inc ....E... 612 788-0077
Minneapolis *(G-5470)*

Regional Home Services of Minn ....E... 763 416-5607
Hamel *(G-2355)*

Standard Water Control Systems ....E... 763 537-4849
Minneapolis *(G-5738)*

Waterproofing By Experts Inc ....E... 651 786-5042
Circle Pines *(G-1025)*

Western Waterproofing Co Inc ....E... 612 781-7100
Minneapolis *(G-6061)*

CONTRACTORS: Weather Stripping

Sustainable Resources Center ....E... 612 870-4255
Minneapolis *(G-5776)*

CONTRACTORS: Window Treatment Installation

Larson's Home Improvement ....E... 507 288-7111
Rochester *(G-7160)*

Maciej Paint Corp ....E... 651 407-8000
Hugo *(G-2679)*

CONTRACTORS: Windows & Doors

Builders & Remodelers Inc ....E... 612 827-5481
Minneapolis *(G-3970)*

Hetricks Construction Inc ....E... 507 645-8629
Northfield *(G-6529)*

Ron Boelter Window & Siding ....E... 507 243-4354
Madison Lake *(G-3081)*

CONTRACTORS: Wood Floor Installation & Refinishing

C L T Floor Coverings Inc ....E... 651 451-0069
Inver Grove Heights *(G-2740)*

Dave's Floor Sanding ....D... 763 784-3000
Minneapolis *(G-3452)*

CONTRACTORS: Wrecking & Demolition

Century Construction Co Inc ....E... 651 451-1020
South Saint Paul *(G-9518)*

Frattalone Co's Inc..............................C... 651 484-0448
Saint Paul *(G-8394)*

Hengel Landfill & Service Corp ....E... 218 746-3198
Pillager *(G-6809)*

Lloyds Construction Services ....E... 952 746-5832
Savage *(G-9397)*

Rachel Contracting LLC ....E... 763 424-9955
Saint Michael *(G-7681)*

CONVALESCENT HOME

Bear Creek Care & Rehab ....C... 507 288-6514
Rochester *(G-7062)*

Evangelical Free Church of..................C... 320 983-2185
Milaca *(G-3376)*

Haven Homes Inc ....D... 763 479-1993
Maple Plain *(G-3275)*

Haven Homes Of Maple Plain ....D... 763 479-1993
Maple Plain *(G-3276)*

Mission Health Care LLC......................C... 651 224-2368
Saint Paul *(G-8716)*

R E M North Star Inc ....E... 218 435-6088
Fosston *(G-2179)*

Rainbow Residence Inc.......................E... 507 451-5327
Owatonna *(G-6733)*

REM Riverbluff Inc ....E... 507 281-1105
Rochester *(G-7222)*

Sunrise Manor Nursing Home ....D... 507 247-5839
Tyler *(G-9714)*

CONVALESCENT HOMES

American Baptist Homes of The..........E... 507 373-9656
Albert Lea *(G-40)*

American Baptist Homes of The..........E... 952 941-3175
Eden Prairie *(G-1590)*

Augustana Chapel View Homes ....B... 612 333-1551
Minneapolis *(G-3835)*

Augustana Lutheran Homes Inc..........E... 320 693-2430
Litchfield *(G-2979)*

Aviv Health Care Inc ....C... 952 546-4261
Minneapolis *(G-3846)*

Bay Shore Health Center ....C... 218 727-8651
Duluth *(G-1247)*

Benedictine Health System ....D... 651 388-1234
Red Wing *(G-6975)*

Bethesda Heritage Center ....D... 320 235-3924
Willmar *(G-9989)*

Beverly Enterprises - MN ....E... 507 557-2211
Franklin *(G-2180)*

Beverly Enterprises - MN ....E... 952 881-8676
Minneapolis *(G-3896)*

Beverly Enterprises - MN ....D... 218 583-2965
Henning *(G-2431)*

Beverly Enterprises - MN ....D... 320 843-2225
Benson *(G-438)*

Beverly Enterprises - MN ....D... 218 233-7578
Moorhead *(G-6299)*

Beverly Enterprises - MN ....E... 507 451-6800
Owatonna *(G-6695)*

Beverly Enterprises - MN ....D... 651 645-6453
Saint Paul *(G-8112)*

Beverly Enterprises - MN ....D... 507 342-5166
Wabasso *(G-9776)*

Chisholm Health Center ....C... 218 254-5765
Chisholm *(G-995)*

City of Menahga ....D... 218 564-4101
Menahga *(G-3356)*

Cook County North Shore Hosp...........C... 218 387-3040
Grand Marais *(G-2257)*

Crest View Corp ....C... 763 782-1611
Minneapolis *(G-3447)*

Crestview Manor Inc ....D... 218 948-2219
Evansville *(G-1924)*

Delougherry Home LP..........................D... 507 523-2123
Lewiston *(G-2966)*

Evangelical Lutheran Good ....D... 507 437-4526
Austin *(G-270)*

Evangelical Lutheran Good ....D... 320 764-2300
Watkins *(G-9897)*

Evangelical Lutheran Good ....D... 218 864-5231
Battle Lake *(G-310)*

Evangelical Lutheran Good ....D... 507 283-2375
Luverne *(G-3059)*

Evangelical Lutheran Good ....D... 218 776-3157
Clearbrook *(G-1038)*

Evangelical Lutheran Good ....C... 507 831-1788
Windom *(G-10067)*

Evangelical Lutheran Good ....C... 507 637-5711
Redwood Falls *(G-7021)*

Evangelical Lutheran Good ....D... 507 274-6155
Westbrook *(G-9966)*

Evangelical Lutheran Good ....E... 218 728-6600
Duluth *(G-1315)*

Evangelical Lutheran Good ....D... 218 829-1429
Brainerd *(G-566)*

Evangelical Lutheran Good ....C... 507 379-2707
Albert Lea *(G-490)*

First Care Medical Services ....E... 218 435-1133
Fosston *(G-2176)*

Foundation For Rural Health ....D... 218 563-2715
McIntosh *(G-3341)*

Guardian Angels Health Svcs...............C... 763 441-1213
Elk River *(G-1880)*

Haven Homes Of Maple Plain ....D... 763 479-1993
Maple Plain *(G-3276)*

Highland Chateau Inc ....C... 651 698-0793
Saint Paul *(G-8480)*

Innsbruck Healthcare Center ....D... 651 633-1686
New Brighton *(G-6411)*

Lutheran Memorial Home ....C... 218 584-5181
Twin Valley *(G-9702)*

Lutheran Memorial Home ....C... 218 584-5181
Twin Valley *(G-9703)*

Mankato Lutheran Homes Inc.............C... 507 345-4576
Saint Paul *(G-8610)*

Maple Lawn Nursing Home ....C... 507 425-2571
Fulda *(G-2195)*

Minnesota Masonic Home ....A... 952 948-7000
Minneapolis *(G-5082)*

Pine Haven Care Center Inc ....D... 507 356-8304
Pine Island *(G-6817)*

Pipestone County Medical Ctr ....C... 507 825-5811
Pipestone *(G-6834)*

Signature Healthcare Inc.....................C... 507 288-6514
Rochester *(G-7254)*

St Anthony Health Center ....B... 612 788-9673
Minneapolis *(G-6131)*

St John Lutheran Home Inc ....B... 507 723-3200
Springfield *(G-9576)*

St Lucas Care Center...........................C... 507 332-5100
Faribault *(G-2032)*

St Therese Home Inc ....A... 763 537-4503
Minneapolis *(G-5733)*

Stewartville Nursing Home Inc.............C... 507 533-4288
Stewartville *(G-9594)*

Tealwood Care Centers Inc..................D... 218 436-2161
Karlstad *(G-2815)*

Volunteers of America Care ....C... 952 925-8500
Minneapolis *(G-5983)*

Walker Care Corp I..............................C... 612 827-8390
Minneapolis *(G-6009)*

Walker Methodist Health Center...........C... 612 827-8517
Minneapolis *(G-6010)*

CONVENTION & TRADE SHOW SVCS

All Time Favorites Inc ....E... 651 454-1124
Saint Paul *(G-7690)*

Ardel Inc ....E... 763 545-1919
Minneapolis *(G-3804)*

Brede Inc...C... 612 331-4540
Minneapolis *(G-3941)*

City of Brooklyn Center........................E... 763 569-6300
Minneapolis *(G-4085)*

Duluth Entertainment Conv ....A... 218 722-5573
Duluth *(G-1298)*

Niecc Inc ....C... 763 536-8300
Minneapolis *(G-5200)*

Normandy Inn Inc................................E... 612 370-1400
Minneapolis *(G-5210)*

Playworks Dakota ....D... 952 445-7529
Prior Lake *(G-6948)*

COOLED AIR SPLY SVCS

Franklin Heating Station.......................E... 507 289-3534
Rochester *(G-7119)*

COPY MACHINES WHOLESALERS

Imaging Alliance Group LLC.................D... 612 588-9944
Minneapolis *(G-4690)*

COPYRIGHT BUYING & LICENSING

Schwegman, Lundberg & Woessner ...D... 612 373-6900
Minneapolis *(G-5618)*

CORRECTIONAL FACILITY OPERATIONS

Corrections Corp of America ....B... 320 289-2052
Appleton *(G-245)*

Minnesota Department of ....D... 218 751-3196
Bemidji *(G-402)*

COSMETICS WHOLESALERS

Barbers Hairstyling For Men ....D... 952 947-7777
Minneapolis *(G-3867)*

COSMETOLOGIST

Elizabeth Charles Corp ....C... 952 915-2900
Minneapolis *(G-4340)*

Elizabeth Charles Corp ....D... 952 915-2900
Saint Paul *(G-9212)*

Elizabeth Charles Corp ....D... 952 915-2900
Chanhassen *(G-922)*

COSMETOLOGY & PERSONAL HYGIENE SALONS

Juut Midwest Inc.................................E... 612 676-2250
Minneapolis *(G-4782)*

Juut Midwest Inc.................................D... 651 222-4121
Saint Paul *(G-8538)*

Simonson Venture Inc..........................E... 763 416-7823
Anoka *(G-228)*

Simonson Venture Inc..........................E... 763 494-4863
Osseo *(G-6663)*

COSMETOLOGY SCHOOL

A-Veda Corp..B... 763 951-4000
Minneapolis *(G-3383)*

COUNCIL FOR SOCIAL AGENCY

Amherst H Wilder Foundation..............E... 651 647-9676
Saint Paul *(G-8044)*

D A Peterson ....E... 612 782-9860
Minneapolis *(G-4211)*

COUNTRY CLUBS

Alexandria Golf Club ....E... 320 762-1093
Alexandria *(G-81)*

Austin Country Club Inc ....D... 507 437-7631
Austin *(G-260)*

Bearpath Golf & Country Club ....D... 952 975-0123
Eden Prairie *(G-1603)*

Bemidji Town & Country Club..............D... 218 751-9215
Bemidji *(G-380)*

Crow River Country Club......................E... 320 587-3070
Hutchinson *(G-2695)*

Hastings Country Club Inc ....D... 651 437-4612
Hastings *(G-2389)*

Interlachen Country Club......................C... 952 929-1661
Minneapolis *(G-4717)*

Le Sueur Country Club ....E... 507 665-8839
Le Sueur *(G-2956)*

Midland Hills Country Club...................D... 651 631-0440
Saint Paul *(G-8654)*

Minikahda Club....................................D... 952 926-4167
Minneapolis *(G-5049)*

Minnesota Valley Country Club............D... 612 884-2409
Bloomington *(G-506)*

Minnetonka Country Club.....................E... 952 474-5222
Excelsior *(G-1949)*

Northland Country Club Inc..................E... 218 525-1941
Duluth *(G-1407)*

Oak Glen LLC......................................D... 651 439-6981
Stillwater *(G-9633)*

Oak Ridge Country Club ....C... 952 935-7721
Hopkins *(G-2593)*

Oaks Country Club Inc.........................E... 507 477-3233
Hayfield *(G-2424)*

Olson, Jock Interlachen ....C... 952 924-7424
Minneapolis *(G-5273)*

Ridgeview Country Club Inc.................E... 218 728-5128
Duluth *(G-1438)*

Rochester Golf & Country Club ....E... 507 282-2708
Rochester *(G-7232)*

Stillwater Country Club Inc...................E... 651 439-7979
Stillwater *(G-9645)*

Tianna Country Club Inc ....E... 218 547-1712
Walker *(G-9858)*

Town & Country Club of St...................D... 651 646-7121
Saint Paul *(G-9075)*

Wayzata Country Club Inc ....D... 952 473-8846
Wayzata *(G-9948)*

SERVICES (vertical tab)

Employment codes: A=Over 500 employees, B=251-500,
C=101-250, D=51-100, E=25-50

2011 Harris Minnesota
Services Directory

© Harris InfoSource 1-866-281-6415
691

Woodhill Country Club ....D... 952 473-7333
Wayzata   (G-9951)

COUPON REDEMPTION SVCS

Young America Corp ....B... 800 533-4529
Young America   (G-10211)

COURIER OR MESSENGER SVCS

Benco Delivery Service Inc ....E... 651 486-9999
Saint Paul   (G-8102)
Capital Express Inc ....E... 651 631-3595
Saint Paul   (G-8151)
Courier Systems LLC ....D... 651 628-0100
Saint Paul   (G-8262)
R A Ventures Inc ....C... 612 721-9155
Minneapolis   (G-5455)
Timberland Transportation Inc ....E... 651 748-4477
Saint Paul   (G-9068)

COURIER SVCS, AIR: Letter Delivery, Private

Federal Express Corp ....D... 952 884-9212
Minneapolis   (G-4418)

COURIER SVCS, AIR: Package Delivery, Private

Federal Express Corp ....D... 952 884-9212
Minneapolis   (G-4418)

COURIER SVCS, AIR: Parcel Delivery, Private

Federal Express Corp ....D... 952 884-9212
Minneapolis   (G-4418)

COURIER SVCS: Air

Bemidji Aviation Services Inc ....E... 612 726-1500
Minneapolis   (G-3882)
Greyhound Lines Inc ....D... 612 371-3325
Minneapolis   (G-4567)
Northwest Airlines Inc ....A... 612 726-2111
Minneapolis   (G-5238)
Northwest Airlines Inc ....E... 218 727-8791
Duluth   (G-1409)
United Parcel Service Inc ....C... 218 722-0150
Duluth   (G-1491)
Velocity Express Northeast Inc ....C... 612 492-2400
Minneapolis   (G-5961)

COURIER SVCS: Ground

Associated Courier Inc ....E... 612 623-9999
Minneapolis   (G-3826)
Centrax Enterprises Inc ....D... 612 726-9500
Saint Paul   (G-7958)
Dynamex Operations East Inc ....D... 651 644-8787
Saint Paul   (G-8317)
Fedex Ground Package System ....B... 651 748-8636
Mahtomedi   (G-3094)
Pro Courier Inc ....E... 763 571-8811
Minneapolis   (G-3574)
Quicksilver Express Courier of ....B... 651 484-1111
Saint Paul   (G-8865)
R A Ventures Inc ....C... 612 721-9155
Minneapolis   (G-5455)
Response Delivery Inc ....D... 952 941-6813
Minneapolis   (G-5529)
Twin Courier Corp ....C... 763 576-1133
Champlin   (G-904)
United Parcel Service Inc ....E... 651 388-6555
Red Wing   (G-7010)
Velocity Express Mid-West Inc ....E... 612 492-2400
Minneapolis   (G-5960)
Velocity Express Northeast Inc ....C... 612 492-2400
Minneapolis   (G-5961)

COURIER SVCS: Package By Vehicle

Dynamax Inc ....C... 651 644-8787
Saint Paul   (G-8316)
United Parcel Service Inc ....E... 507 375-4666
Saint James   (G-7648)
United Parcel Service Inc ....E... 320 235-6615
Willmar   (G-10050)
United Parcel Service Inc ....A... 800 742-5877
Minneapolis   (G-5912)
United Parcel Service of New ....E... 218 751-9109
Bemidji   (G-430)
United Parcel Service of New ....E... 218 739-4910
Fergus Falls   (G-2122)
United Parcel Service of New ....E... 507 334-7924
Faribault   (G-2036)
United Parcel Service of New ....E... 218 326-8520
Grand Rapids   (G-2310)

COURIER SVCS: Parcel By Vehicle

United Parcel Service Inc ....C... 218 722-0150
Duluth   (G-1491)
United Parcel Service Inc ....E... 507 373-4392
Albert Lea   (G-69)
United Parcel Service Inc ....E... 218 847-4439
Detroit Lakes   (G-1221)
United Parcel Service Inc ....E... 507 375-4666
Saint James   (G-7648)
United Parcel Service Inc ....E... 320 762-2746
Alexandria   (G-127)
United Parcel Service Inc ....D... 218 829-6240
Brainerd   (G-588)
United Parcel Service Inc ....D... 507 281-0468
Rochester   (G-7277)
United Parcel Service Inc ....E... 507 454-2307
Winona   (G-10135)
United Parcel Service Inc ....A... 800 742-5877
Minneapolis   (G-5912)
United Parcel Service of New ....C... 320 253-4100
Saint Cloud   (G-7443)
United Parcel Service of New ....E... 507 836-6671
Slayton   (G-9491)

COURT REPORTING SVCS

Metro Legal Services Inc ....D... 612 332-0202
Minneapolis   (G-5001)

CRACKED CASTING REPAIR SVCS

Diesel Cast Welding Inc ....E... 763 780-5940
Minneapolis   (G-3455)

CRANE & AERIAL LIFT SVCS

Kraus-Anderson Construction Co........E... 218 759-0596
Bemidji   (G-400)
S K B Environmental ....E... 507 433-8131
Austin   (G-285)
Salonek Concrete & Constr ....E... 507 723-4218
Springfield   (G-9574)
Truck Crane Service-Illinois.................E... 651 406-4949
Saint Paul   (G-7930)
Western Steel Erection Inc..................E... 952 473-4344
Long Lake   (G-3035)

CRATING SVCS: Shipping

Independent Packing Services ....E... 763 425-7155
Osseo   (G-6623)

CREATIVE SVCS: Advertisers, Exc Writers

Alpha Video & Audio Inc ....D... 952 896-9898
Minneapolis   (G-3733)
Intouch Inc ....D... 651 255-7700
Saint Paul   (G-8523)
John Ryan Performance Inc ....E... 612 924-7700
Minneapolis   (G-4771)
Larsen Design Office Inc......................E... 952 835-2271
Minneapolis   (G-4846)

CREDIT AGENCIES: Federal & Federally Sponsored

Agstar Financial Services, Aca............C... 507 387-4174
Mankato   (G-3102)
Educational Credit Management ....C... 651 221-0566
Saint Paul   (G-9209)
Lcomuity National Bank ....E... 651 483-4656
Saint Paul   (G-8571)
United Fcs...E... 320 235-1771
Willmar   (G-10049)

CREDIT AGENCIES: Federal Land Banks

Agribank, Fcb ....B... 651 282-8800
Saint Paul   (G-8000)
Agstar Financial Services, Aca.............E... 507 526-7366
Blue Earth   (G-528)

CREDIT AGENCIES: Government National Mortgage Association

City of Jackson ....E... 507 847-4410
Jackson   (G-2788)

CREDIT AGENCIES: National Consumer Cooperative Bank

Cenex Nuway Co Op Inc......................D... 507 375-4291
Trimont   (G-9693)

CREDIT BUREAUS

Chex Systems Inc ....B... 651 361-2000
Saint Paul   (G-9196)

Tena Co's Inc ....C... 651 293-1234
Saint Paul   (G-9037)

CREDIT CARD PROCESSING SVCS

Total Card Inc....................................C... 507 449-6401
Luverne   (G-3071)

CREDIT CARD SVCS

Datacard Corp ....A... 952 933-1223
Minnetonka   (G-6159)
First Financial USA Ltd ....D... 763 231-8120
Hamel   (G-2342)
Pinnacle Credit Services......................E... 952 939-8100
Minneapolis   (G-5380)

CREDIT INST, SHORT-TERM BUSINESS: Accts Receiv & Coml Paper

TCI Business Capital Inc......................D... 952 656-3400
Burnsville   (G-806)

CREDIT INSTITUTIONS, SHORT-TERM BUS: Wrkg Capital Finance

Business Funding Group LLC..............E... 952 697-0202
Eden Prairie   (G-1614)

CREDIT INSTITUTIONS, SHORT-TERM BUSINESS: Commercial Paper

Aircraft Owner LLC.............................E... 651 633-1045
Saint Paul   (G-8002)

CREDIT INSTITUTIONS, SHORT-TERM BUSINESS: Factoring Svcs

Marquette Transportation ....E... 952 703-7474
Minneapolis   (G-4954)
Security Auto Loans Inc ....E... 763 559-5892
Minneapolis   (G-5625)

CREDIT INSTITUTIONS, SHORT-TERM BUSINESS: Mercantile Finance

Toro Co...A... 952 888-8801
Bloomington   (G-519)

CREDIT INSTITUTIONS: Personal

American Building Maintenance ....E... 612 344-1758
Minneapolis   (G-3746)
Citifinancial Credit Co ....E... 763 424-6012
Minneapolis   (G-4079)
Firstmark Services LLC ....D... 651 265-7600
Saint Paul   (G-9218)
General Electric Capital Corp...............E... 952 897-5600
Minneapolis   (G-4509)
Marquette Financial Co's ....E... 612 661-3880
Minneapolis   (G-4952)
Metris Co's Inc...................................A... 952 358-4000
Hopkins   (G-2580)
Minnesota First Credit.........................507 289-0411
Rochester   (G-7187)
Minnwest Bank South ....E... 507 836-6141
Slayton   (G-9489)
Mortgages Unlimited ....E... 763 633-0576
Elk River   (G-1886)
Nelnet Inc ....C... 651 265-7600
Saint Paul   (G-8744)
Northland Dealer Finance Inc..............E... 651 773-4973
Saint Paul   (G-8763)
Wells Fargo Business Credit................D... 612 673-8500
Minneapolis   (G-6043)

CREDIT INSTITUTIONS: Short-Term Business

Citifinancial Credit Co ....E... 763 424-6012
Minneapolis   (G-4079)
Winmark Corp ....C... 763 520-8500
Minneapolis   (G-6077)

CREDIT INVESTIGATION SVCS

MCC Group Inc ....E... 952 941-0552
Eden Prairie   (G-1718)

CREDIT UNIONS: Federally Chartered

American Hardware Insurance.............D... 952 939-4510
Minnetonka   (G-6139)
Anoka Hennepin School District..........E... 651 255-7000
Forest Lake   (G-2157)
City-County Federal Credit ....C... 763 549-6000
Minneapolis   (G-4097)
City-County Federal Credit ....D... 763 549-6000
Minneapolis   (G-4098)
First Alliance Credit Union ....E... 507 288-0330
Rochester   (G-7111)

General Mills Federal Credit ....D... 763 764-6900
  Minnetonka *(G-6175)*
Great River Federal Credit ....E... 320 252-3507
  Sauk Rapids *(G-9365)*
Great River Federal Credit ....D... 320 258-5393
  Waite Park *(G-9823)*
Hiway Federal Credit Union ....C... 651 291-1515
  Saint Paul *(G-8487)*
Home Town Federal Credit Union ....E... 507 451-3798
  Owatonna *(G-6717)*
Lake State Federal Credit....................D... 218 485-4444
  Moose Lake *(G-6351)*
Lake State Federal Credit....................D... 320 245-5251
  Sandstone *(G-9322)*
Mid Minnesota Federal Credit..............E... 218 829-0371
  Brainerd *(G-574)*
North Ridge Community Credit ....E... 218 741-1222
  Virginia *(G-9747)*
Spire Federal Credit Union ....D... 651 215-3500
  Saint Paul *(G-8978)*
St Cloud Federal Employees ....D... 320 252-2634
  Saint Cloud *(G-7600)*
Think Mutual Bank ....C... 507 288-3425
  Rochester *(G-7273)*
Trustar Federal Credit Union ....E... 218 283-2000
  International Falls *(G-2733)*
Trustone Financial Federal ....D... 763 544-1517
  Minneapolis *(G-5861)*
Trustone Financial Federal ....D... 763 544-1517
  Minneapolis *(G-5862)*
Wings Financial Credit Union ....E... 612 726-2073
  Bloomington *(G-526)*
Wings Financial Credit Union ....C... 952 997-8000
  Saint Paul *(G-7949)*

CREDIT UNIONS: State Chartered

Accentra Credit Union ....E... 507 433-1829
  Austin *(G-258)*
Affinity Plus Federal Credit ....E... 651 291-3700
  Saint Paul *(G-7996)*
Affinity Plus Federal Credit ....E... 651 291-3700
  Saint Paul *(G-7997)*
Central Minnesota Federal ....E... 320 256-3669
  Melrose *(G-3347)*
City & County Credit Union....................E... 651 225-2700
  Saint Paul *(G-8203)*
Endura Financial Federal ....E... 763 287-4630
  Minneapolis *(G-4354)*
Federated Employees Credit 507 455-5430
  Owatonna *(G-6709)*
First Alliance Credit Union......................507 281-7640
  Rochester *(G-7112)*
Mayo Clinic Employees Credit..............E... 507 535-1460
  Rochester *(G-7172)*
Minnco Credit Union.............................D... 763 689-1071
  Cambridge *(G-843)*
Northern Communities Credit....................218 279-3200
  Duluth *(G-1403)*
Retail Employees Credit Union..............E... 952 930-0700
  Minneapolis *(G-5531)*
Richfield Bloomington Credit ....E... 612 798-7100
  Richfield *(G-7037)*
Sheet Metal Worker Federal ....E... 651 770-2385
  Saint Paul *(G-8950)*
Southpoint Federal Credit....................E... 877 794-6712
  Sleepy Eye *(G-9501)*
Topline Federal Credit Union................D... 763 391-9494
  Maple Grove *(G-3255)*

CRISIS CENTER

Harriet Tubman Center Inc....................E... 612 825-3333
  Minneapolis *(G-4602)*
Rape & Abuse Crisis Center ....E... 218 643-6110
  Breckenridge *(G-596)*
Women of Nations ....E... 651 222-5830
  Saint Paul *(G-9163)*
Women's Advocates Inc.......................E... 651 227-9966
  Saint Paul *(G-9164)*

CRISIS INTERVENTION CENTERS

Central Territorial of The ....E... 651 646-2601
  Saint Paul *(G-8183)*
Cornerstone Advocacy Service...........E... 952 884-0376
  Minneapolis *(G-4162)*
Dodge County Battered Women's........E... 507 634-6070
  Kasson *(G-2820)*
Domestic Abuse Project Inc ....E... 612 874-7063
  Minneapolis *(G-4271)*
Tubman Family Alliance........................E... 612 825-0000
  Minneapolis *(G-5864)*

CROP DUSTING

Agrimax LLC.. 218 281-1441
  Fisher *(G-2133)*

CRUDE PETROLEUM & NATURAL GAS PRODUCTION

I D D D Inc ....E... 507 334-3333
  Faribault *(G-2012)*
Northern Oil & Gas Inc ....E... 952 476-9800
  Wayzata *(G-9934)*

CRUDE PETROLEUM PRODUCTION

Cenex Inc ....A... 800 232-3639
  South Saint Paul *(G-9516)*
CHS Inc ....A... 651 355-6000
  Inver Grove Heights *(G-2742)*
Mosaic Co ....C... 763 577-2700
  Minneapolis *(G-5133)*
Speedway Superamerica LLC..............E... 651 774-7270
  Saint Paul *(G-8977)*

CUSTOMHOUSE BROKERS

Griffin & Co Logistics ....E... 952 854-2600
  Minneapolis *(G-4568)*
North Star World Trade Svcs ....E... 651 379-5030
  Saint Paul *(G-7852)*
UPS Supply Chain Solutions Inc ....E... 612 726-1680
  Minneapolis *(G-5937)*

CUSTOMS CLEARANCE OF FREIGHT

Freightmasters Inc ....C... 651 688-6800
  Saint Paul *(G-7777)*

DAIRY PRDTS WHOLESALERS: Fresh

Associated Milk Producers Inc............E... 507 233-4600
  New Ulm *(G-6441)*
Associated Milk Producers Inc............E... 320 864-5561
  Glencoe *(G-2204)*
Bix Produce Co LLC ....C... 651 487-8000
  Saint Paul *(G-8115)*
Dairy Farmers of America Inc ....D... 218 736-5691
  Fergus Falls *(G-2073)*
Davisco Foods International ....E... 952 914-0400
  Eden Prairie *(G-1643)*
Franklin Foods ....D... 218 727-6651
  Duluth *(G-1327)*
Land O'Lakes Inc ....E... 218 233-8609
  Moorhead *(G-6325)*
Polka Dot Dairy Inc ....E... 651 438-2793
  Hastings *(G-2400)*
Stock Yards Meat Packing Co ....C... 651 450-6000
  South Saint Paul *(G-9544)*
SUPERVALU Inc..................................A... 952 828-4000
  Eden Prairie *(G-1787)*
Supervalu Inc ....C... 952 906-6260
  Chanhassen *(G-941)*

DAMAGED MERCHANDISE SALVAGING, SVCS ONLY

Return Inc ....E... 763 295-4659
  Monticello *(G-6284)*
Rti Services Inc ....E... 952 475-0242
  Plymouth *(G-6882)*

DANCE HALL OR BALLROOM OPERATION

Blue Note of Winsted Inc.....................E... 320 485-9698
  Winsted *(G-10159)*
Legion Pavilion Co Inc ....E... 952 758-4603
  New Prague *(G-6422)*

DANCE INSTRUCTOR

Sondance Studio..................................E... 763 784-2920
  Minneapolis *(G-3605)*

DANCE INSTRUCTOR & SCHOOL SVCS

Ballet Arts Minnesota Inc ....E... 612 340-1071
  Minneapolis *(G-3864)*

DANCE STUDIOS, SCHOOLS & HALLS

Dance Art Centre..................................E... 952 937-2618
  Eden Prairie *(G-1641)*
North Crest Gymnastics & Dance ....E... 320 251-3416
  Sauk Rapids *(G-9370)*
Prairie Dance Alliance ....E... 507 532-3195
  Marshall *(G-3319)*

DATA ENTRY SVCS

Helgeson Enterprises Inc ....D... 651 762-9700
  Saint Paul *(G-8476)*
National Business Systems Inc............D... 651 688-0202
  Eagan *(G-1540)*

DATA PROCESSING & PREPARATION SVCS

Abraham Technical Services Inc ....E... 763 428-3170
  Rogers *(G-7315)*
Ambient Consulting LLC ....C... 763 582-9000
  Minneapolis *(G-3741)*
Aquent LLC ....D... 952 851-3411
  Minneapolis *(G-3794)*
Automatic Data Processing Inc............B... 952 814-5800
  Minneapolis *(G-3838)*
Computer Sciences Corp.....................E... 763 593-1122
  Minneapolis *(G-4148)*
County of Ramsey ....D... 651 266-3400
  Saint Paul *(G-8257)*
Data Solutions International.................E... 952 943-8137
  Minnetonka *(G-6158)*
Digitiliti Inc ....E... 651 925-3200
  Saint Paul *(G-8296)*
Ebureau LLC ....E... 320 534-5000
  Saint Cloud *(G-7502)*
Efunds Corp ....A... 651 361-2000
  Saint Paul *(G-9210)*
Fairview Health Services ....C... 612 672-6800
  Minneapolis *(G-4393)*
Fidelity National Information ....D... 651 855-6500
  Lake Elmo *(G-2871)*
Fifty Below Sales & Marketing ....C... 218 720-4828
  Duluth *(G-1322)*
Klein Financial Inc ....D... 952 448-2924
  Chaska *(G-972)*
Kroll Ontrack Inc..................................C... 952 937-1107
  Eden Prairie *(G-1704)*
Mark Doman ....E... 320 203-9004
  Sartell *(G-9338)*
RSM McGladrey Inc ....D... 507 288-5363
  Rochester *(G-7242)*
Second Data Enterprises Inc ....D... 612 326-6833
  Edina *(G-1845)*
Siemens Water Technologies...............C... 651 766-2722
  Saint Paul *(G-8957)*
SPS Commerce Inc..............................D... 612 435-9400
  Minneapolis *(G-5724)*
Webmd Health Corp ....E... 763 512-2600
  Minneapolis *(G-6031)*

DATA PROCESSING SVCS

Adapt Inc ....E... 952 939-0538
  Hopkins *(G-2500)*
Automatic Data Processing Inc............B... 952 814-5800
  Minneapolis *(G-3838)*
Bremer Financial Services Inc ....D... 651 227-7621
  Saint Paul *(G-8126)*
Bremer Financial Services Inc ....C... 651 734-4040
  Lake Elmo *(G-2866)*
Comsys Information Technology.........C... 612 630-9100
  Minneapolis *(G-4149)*
Hickory Tech Information Soln ....D... 507 625-1691
  Mankato *(G-3139)*
Hickory Tech Information Soln ....D... 507 625-1691
  Mankato *(G-3140)*
Impact Mailing Of Minnesota ....D... 612 521-6245
  Minneapolis *(G-4692)*
Mail Handling Inc ....C... 952 975-5000
  Eden Prairie *(G-1714)*
Midwest Data Inc ....D... 320 235-8880
  Willmar *(G-10023)*
National Business Systems Inc ....D... 651 688-0202
  Eagan *(G-1540)*
Questar Data Systems Inc ....C... 651 688-0089
  Saint Paul *(G-7886)*
R B C Capital Market............................A... 612 371-2711
  Minneapolis *(G-5456)*
Reed Elsevier Inc.................................E... 651 385-1895
  Red Wing *(G-7000)*
Scicom Data Services Ltd....................C... 952 933-4200
  Minnetonka *(G-6225)*
Sungard Financial Systems LLC..........B... 952 935-3300
  Hopkins *(G-2639)*
Wells Fargo Services Inc ....A... 612 667-1234
  Minneapolis *(G-6053)*
Wells Fargo Services Inc ....A... 612 667-1234
  Minneapolis *(G-6054)*

DATABASE INFORMATION RETRIEVAL SVCS

Finance & Commerce Inc.....................E... 612 333-4244
  Minneapolis *(G-4431)*
Ingenix Inc ....B... 952 833-7100
  Eden Prairie *(G-1692)*
West Publishing Corp ....A... 651 687-8000
  Saint Paul *(G-7946)*

S
E
R
V
I
C
E
S

Employment codes: A=Over 500 employees, B=251-500,
C=101-250, D=51-100, E=25-50

2011 Harris Minnesota
Services Directory

© Harris InfoSource 1-866-281-6415
693

DELIVERY SVCS, BY VEHICLE

A A A Courier Inc ....E... 320 259-9292
Sauk Rapids *(G-9355)*

Centrax Enterprises Inc........................D... 612 726-9500
Saint Paul *(G-7958)*

Crosscountry Courier Inc ....D... 651 686-5520
Saint Paul *(G-7741)*

Dee Spee Delivery Service Inc.............B... 320 251-6697
Saint Cloud *(G-7496)*

Freightmasters Inc ....C... 651 688-6800
Saint Paul *(G-7777)*

Greyhound Lines Inc ....D... 612 371-3325
Minneapolis *(G-4567)*

Independent Delivery Services ....D... 651 487-1050
Saint Paul *(G-8508)*

Quicksilver Express Courier ....B... 651 484-1111
Saint Paul *(G-8864)*

Quicksilver Express Courier of ....B... 651 484-1111
Saint Paul *(G-8865)*

R A Ventures Inc ....C... 612 721-9155
Minneapolis *(G-5455)*

Ricsons Inc ....E... 612 617-9480
Minneapolis *(G-5539)*

Rochester City Delivery Inc ....E... 507 289-2774
Rochester *(G-7229)*

Schwan's Home Service Inc ....E... 507 451-8538
Owatonna *(G-6736)*

Western Delivery Inc.............................E... 651 665-0702
Minneapolis *(G-6059)*

DENTAL EQPT & SPLYS WHOLESALERS

Patterson Co's Inc ....C... 651 686-1600
Saint Paul *(G-7866)*

Patterson Dental Supply Inc ....E... 651 688-6054
Saint Paul *(G-7867)*

Patterson Dental Supply Inc ....B... 651 686-1600
Saint Paul *(G-7868)*

Unimed-Midwest Inc ....E... 952 469-9400
Lakeville *(G-2938)*

DENTAL HYGIENISTS' OFFICES

Allied Professionals Inc ....B... 952 832-5101
Minneapolis *(G-3716)*

Cook Area Health Services Inc ....E... 218 666-5941
Cook *(G-1094)*

DENTAL INSTRUMENT REPAIR SVCS

Minnesota Prophy Power Inc ....D... 952 898-1594
Lakeville *(G-2920)*

Patterson Co's Inc ....C... 651 686-1600
Saint Paul *(G-7866)*

DENTISTS' OFFICES & CLINICS

Apollo Dental Center PLC ....E... 507 287-8320
Rochester *(G-7057)*

Blue Ridge Dental ....E... 952 938-4767
Hopkins *(G-2519)*

Charles R Babst ....E... 218 722-8377
Duluth *(G-1269)*

Dentistry At The Center Inc ....E... 320 762-5216
Alexandria *(G-94)*

Foley Dental Clinic ....E... 763 757-3120
Minneapolis *(G-3471)*

Gregg G Hipple ....E... 651 452-3333
Saint Paul *(G-7791)*

Healthpartners Inc ....E... 763 754-0041
Minneapolis *(G-3484)*

Metroplitan Pediatric Dental ....E... 763 786-4260
Minneapolis *(G-3539)*

Oral & Max Facial Specialist ....E... 763 494-8825
Osseo *(G-6646)*

Park Dental Eden Prairie ....E... 952 949-2536
Eden Prairie *(G-1741)*

Pdhc Ltd ....E... 952 949-2536
Eden Prairie *(G-1745)*

Pdhc Ltd ....E... 952 545-8603
Hopkins *(G-2602)*

Pdhc Ltd ....E... 763 421-5206
Champlin *(G-897)*

Piedmont Heights Dental Assocs........E... 218 722-0823
Duluth *(G-1423)*

Regents of The University of ....E... 612 626-5722
Minneapolis *(G-5496)*

Scott A Polzin DDS ....E... 218 728-6445
Duluth *(G-1445)*

Scott W Kajer DDS ....E... 651 770-3831
Saint Paul *(G-8937)*

3M Co ....C... 651 736-3490
Saint Paul *(G-9046)*

Udell Dental Laboratory Inc ....E... 952 926-9266
Minneapolis *(G-5893)*

Valley Dental Arts Inc ....D... 651 439-2855
Stillwater *(G-9653)*

Westlund Dental Studio Inc ....E... 952 942-9464
Eden Prairie *(G-1814)*

DEPOSIT INSURANCE

Bremer Financial Corp ....E... 320 589-1026
Morris *(G-6370)*

DESIGN SVCS, NEC

Colemanbrandworx Worldwide ....E... 763 390-1100
Wayzata *(G-9911)*

Devicix LLC ....E... 952 368-0073
Eden Prairie *(G-1644)*

DESIGN SVCS: Commercial & Indl

Apg Cash Drawer LLC ....D... 763 571-5000
Minneapolis *(G-3406)*

E & C Amec Services Inc ....D... 612 332-8326
Minneapolis *(G-4299)*

Food Systems Design Inc ....E... 952 884-4048
Minneapolis *(G-4464)*

Hickey Thorstenson Grover Ltd ....E... 952 278-8880
Eden Prairie *(G-1684)*

Leisure Inc ....E... 952 401-8440
Eden Prairie *(G-1707)*

DESIGN SVCS: Computer Integrated Systems

Advanced Communication Design.......E... 952 854-4000
Bloomington *(G-482)*

Architecture Technology Corp ....E... 952 829-5864
Eden Prairie *(G-1595)*

Avista Solutions International ....E... 952 949-0594
Minneapolis *(G-3843)*

Blaschko Computers Inc ....E... 320 252-0234
Saint Cloud *(G-7460)*

Citon Computer Corp ....E... 218 720-4435
Duluth *(G-1274)*

Computer Integration Techs ....D... 651 450-0333
Saint Paul *(G-9198)*

Datalink Corp..D... 952 944-3462
Chanhassen *(G-917)*

Datatrend Technologies Inc ....E... 952 931-1203
Minnetonka *(G-6160)*

Digital River Inc.....................................B... 952 253-1234
Eden Prairie *(G-1645)*

Dynixa Corp ....B... 651 436-8800
Lakeland *(G-2884)*

Ergotron Inc..C... 651 681-7600
Saint Paul *(G-7769)*

High Wire Networks Inc ....E... 952 934-9080
Eden Prairie *(G-1685)*

Highjump Software Inc ....D... 952 947-4088
Eden Prairie *(G-1686)*

Intercim LLC ....E... 651 289-5700
Eagan *(G-1532)*

Ivo Appliance Inc ....D... 650 286-1300
Minneapolis *(G-4742)*

McData Services Corp ....B... 763 268-6000
Minneapolis *(G-4972)*

Navitaire Inc..C... 612 317-7000
Minneapolis *(G-5176)*

Network Design Inc ....E... 763 475-5500
Minneapolis *(G-5184)*

Nternational Projects ....D... 952 541-4888
Minneapolis *(G-5254)*

ORBIT Systems Inc ....D... 651 767-3322
Saint Paul *(G-7858)*

Schwan's Technology Group Inc ....D... 651 388-1821
Red Wing *(G-7005)*

Sovran Inc ....E... 651 686-0515
Eagan *(G-1552)*

Startech Computing Inc ....E... 651 385-0607
Red Wing *(G-7006)*

Virtelligence Inc ....C... 952 746-9220
Eden Prairie *(G-1806)*

Wireless Ronin Technologies ....E... 952 564-3500
Minnetonka *(G-6238)*

DETECTIVE & ARMORED CAR SERVICES

G2 Secure Staff LLC ....C... 612 725-6423
Saint Paul *(G-7960)*

DETECTIVE SVCS

T George & Associates...........................E... 651 647-0900
Saint Paul *(G-9025)*

DETOXIFICATION CENTERS, OUTPATIENT

Central Minnesota Mental ....D... 320 252-5010
Saint Cloud *(G-7485)*

Range Mental Health Center Inc ....E... 218 749-2881
Virginia *(G-9754)*

DIAMONDS, GEMS, WHOLESALE

Estate Jewelry & Coin Inc ....E... 952 881-8862
Minneapolis *(G-4373)*

DIETICIANS' OFFICES

Rochester Fitness Inc ....E... 507 282-4445
Rochester *(G-7231)*

DISASTER SVCS

American National Red Cross ....E... 612 871-7676
Minneapolis *(G-3757)*

Bgm-Ceres Environmental Svcs ....E... 800 218-4424
Minneapolis *(G-3901)*

Ceres Caribe Ceres Environ ....E... 800 218-4424
Minneapolis *(G-4051)*

DISC JOCKEYS

Creative Promotional Concepts ....D... 651 905-9339
Saint Paul *(G-7740)*

Party Music Inc ....E... 952 941-3830
Eden Prairie *(G-1744)*

DISPLAY LETTERING SVCS

Creative Marketing Concepts ....E... 320 679-4105
Mora *(G-6356)*

DISPOSABLE PLASTIC UTENSILS WHOLESALERS

International Dairy Queen Inc...............B... 952 830-0200
Minneapolis *(G-4721)*

DOCK OPERATION SVCS, INCL BLDGS, FACILITIES, OPERS & MAINT

Nisswa Marine Inc ....E... 218 963-2292
Nisswa *(G-6498)*

DOCUMENT DESTRUCTION SVC

Archives Paper Co Inc ....E... 763 533-0612
Minneapolis *(G-3803)*

Iron Mountain Information Mgt..............E... 651 452-6515
Saint Paul *(G-7808)*

Minnesota Shredding LLC ....E... 763 493-3007
Minneapolis *(G-5093)*

Rohn Industries Inc-St Paul...................E... 651 647-1300
Saint Paul *(G-8912)*

DOCUMENT STORAGE SVCS

All-Data Inc ....E... 763 571-5719
Minneapolis *(G-3390)*

Healtheast Care System........................A... 651 232-1000
Saint Paul *(G-8454)*

Kj International Resources Ltd ....E... 612 288-9494
Minneapolis *(G-4814)*

DOMESTIC HELP SVCS

Rusciano-Hyland Inc ....E... 612 871-4434
Minneapolis *(G-5576)*

Sureservices Inc ....E... 763 531-0029
Minneapolis *(G-5772)*

DOMICILIARY CARE FACILITY

Family Home Health Care Inc ....C... 612 340-0733
Minneapolis *(G-4409)*

Mission Healthcare LLC ....C... 218 326-3431
Grand Rapids *(G-2296)*

DOOR & WINDOW REPAIR SVCS

API Garage Door Co ....E... 763 533-3838
Minneapolis *(G-3789)*

DOORS & WINDOWS WHOLESALERS: All Materials

Donlin Co...E... 320 251-3680
Saint Cloud *(G-7411)*

Erdman Automation Corp.......................D... 763 389-9475
Princeton *(G-6905)*

Gordy's Glass Inc ....E... 651 437-5356
Hastings *(G-2416)*

Kendell Doors & Hardware Inc ....E... 507 454-1723
Winona *(G-10107)*

Kendell Doors & Hardware Inc ....D... 651 905-0144
Mendota Heights *(G-3365)*

Minnesota Valley Millwork Inc ....E... 952 440-9404
Prior Lake *(G-6944)*

Pella Products Inc ....E... 763 745-1400
Minneapolis *(G-5360)*

S E R V I C E S

Pella Windows & Doors Twin ....D... 763 745-1400
Minneapolis (G-5361)
Shelter Products Inc ....E... 507 354-4176
New Ulm (G-6474)
Trimpac Inc ....E... 320 650-0420
Saint Cloud (G-7621)
W L Hall Co ....E... 952 937-8400
Hopkins (G-2655)

DRAFTING SPLYS WHOLESALERS

Franz Reprographics Inc ....E... 763 503-3401
Minneapolis (G-4477)

DRAFTING SVCS

George Konik Associates Inc ....D... 952 835-5550
Minneapolis (G-4524)

DRIED FRUITS WHOLESALERS

American Importing Co Inc ....D... 612 331-7000
Minneapolis (G-3751)

DRUG ABUSE COUNSELOR, NONTREATMENT

African American Family Svcs ....E... 612 871-7878
Minneapolis (G-3696)
African American Family Svcs ....E... 612 813-0782
Minneapolis (G-3697)

DRUG CLINIC, OUTPATIENT

Beverly Enterprises - MN ....D... 507 342-5166
Wabasso (G-9776)
Center For Alcohol & Drug ....D... 218 723-8444
Duluth (G-1266)
Dakota County Receiving Center ....D... 651 437-4209
Hastings (G-2382)
Healtheast Care System ....E... 651 232-3222
Saint Paul (G-8455)
Human Services Inc ....E... 651 430-2720
Stillwater (G-9623)
Northland Counseling Center ....E... 218 327-1105
Grand Rapids (G-2302)
Northwestern Mental Health Ctr ....D... 218 281-3940
Crookston (G-1130)
Progress Valley Inc ....E... 612 869-3223
Minneapolis (G-5425)
Southwestern Mental Health Ctr 507 283-9511
Luverne (G-3070)
St Cloud Hospital ....E... 320 259-9149
Sauk Rapids (G-9376)

DRUGS & DRUG PROPRIETARIES, WHOL: Biologicals/Allied Prdts

Kruse Family Enterprises LLC ....E... 507 345-5926
Mankato (G-3156)

DRUGS & DRUG PROPRIETARIES, WHOLESALE

Sanofi Pasteur Inc ....E... 952 893-8080
Minneapolis (G-5601)

DRUGS & DRUG PROPRIETARIES, WHOLESALE: Animal Medicines

Eniva Corp ....E... 763 795-8870
Anoka (G-177)
Kruse Family Enterprises LLC ....E... 507 345-5926
Mankato (G-3156)
Midwest Veterinary Supply Inc ....E... 952 894-4350
Burnsville (G-759)
Universal Cooperatives Inc ....D... 651 239-1000
Saint Paul (G-7938)

DRUGS & DRUG PROPRIETARIES, WHOLESALE: Druggists' Sundries

Walgreen Co ....E... 952 938-1168
Hopkins (G-2657)

DRUGS & DRUG PROPRIETARIES, WHOLESALE: Medicinals/Botanicals

Omnicare Pharmacy & Supply ....C... 763 259-0188
Minneapolis (G-5278)

DRUGS & DRUG PROPRIETARIES, WHOLESALE: Pharmaceuticals

Accredo Health Group Inc ....E... 651 681-0885
Saint Paul (G-7687)
Apothecary Products Inc ....C... 952 890-1940
Burnsville (G-679)

Badger Acquisition of MN ....C... 763 259-0400
Minneapolis (G-3857)
Cardinal Health 414 Inc ....E... 651 645-9904
Saint Paul (G-8157)
Fresh Seasons Market LLC ....D... 952 938-5555
Minnetonka (G-6170)
Hawkins Pharmaceutical Group ....E... 612 617-8600
Minneapolis (G-4609)
Instymeds Corp ....E... 952 653-2525
Eden Prairie (G-1696)
Kruse Family Enterprises LLC ....E... 507 345-5926
Mankato (G-3156)
Nash-Finch Co ....D... 507 645-4489
Northfield (G-6535)
Omnicare Pharmacy & Supply ....C... 763 259-0188
Minneapolis (G-5278)

DRUGS & DRUG PROPRIETARIES, WHOLESALE: Vitamins & Minerals

Nutri-Dyn Midwest Inc ....E... 763 479-3444
Maple Plain (G-3279)

DRUM & BUGLE CORPS

Mini Kix Inc ....C... 218 829-7107
Baxter (G-336)

DRYCLEANING & LAUNDRY SVCS: Commercial & Family

Dison's Cleaners & Laundry Inc ....E... 507 289-3944
Rochester (G-7097)
Edina Laundry Co ....E... 952 927-9991
Minneapolis (G-4317)
Sunstone Hotel Management Inc ....E... 507 252-7500
Rochester (G-7267)
Uls of New England LLC ....D... 651 227-9855
Saint Paul (G-9101)
United Linen Services Inc ....B... 651 227-9855
Saint Paul (G-9107)
Waldorf-Nevens Dry Cleaners ....D... 952 914-9755
Minneapolis (G-5997)

DRYCLEANING EQPT & SPLYS WHOLESALERS

Minnesota Chemical Co ....E... 651 646-7521
Saint Paul (G-8676)

DRYCLEANING PLANTS

Dison's Cleaners & Laundry Inc ....E... 507 289-3944
Rochester (G-7097)
Edina Laundry Co ....E... 952 927-9991
Minneapolis (G-4317)
G & K Services Inc ....C... 320 252-9471
Saint Cloud (G-7515)
Pilgrim Cleaners & Launderers ....E... 952 937-9391
Eden Prairie (G-1747)
Stoltz Dry Cleaners Inc ....E... 651 698-0120
Saint Paul (G-9008)
Sunstone Hotel Management Inc ....E... 507 252-7500
Rochester (G-7267)
Waldorf-Nevens Dry Cleaners ....D... 952 914-9755
Minneapolis (G-5997)

DRYCLEANING SVC: Collecting & Distributing Agency

Buffalo Drycleaners ....E... 763 682-1061
Buffalo (G-638)

DRYCLEANING SVC: Drapery & Curtain

Anderson Cleaners ....E... 651 690-9592
Saint Paul (G-8050)

DURABLE GOODS WHOLESALERS, NEC

Berg Exteriors Inc ....E... 763 479-1115
Maple Plain (G-3269)
Frattalone I LLC ....E... 651 292-9800
Saint Paul (G-8395)

EARTH SCIENCE SVCS

Itasca Consulting Group Inc ....E... 612 371-4711
Minneapolis (G-4741)

EGG WHOLESALERS

Michael Foods Group Inc ....C... 952 258-4000
Minnetonka (G-6193)
New Midwest Co LLC ....B... 320 329-3363
Renville (G-7032)

ELECTRIC & OTHER SERVICES COMBINED

Austin Utilities ....D... 507 433-8886
Austin (G-262)
City of Rochester ....C... 507 280-1540
Rochester (G-7079)
City of Rochester ....E... 507 280-1657
Rochester (G-7078)
Cottage Grove, City of Inc ....E... 651 458-2808
Cottage Grove (G-1101)
Emergency Energy Systems ....E... 320 354-5380
New London (G-6414)
Hibbing Public Utilities Commn ....D... 218 262-7700
Hibbing (G-2451)
NRG Energy Inc ....E... 612 349-6087
Minneapolis (G-5252)
Shakopee Public Utilities ....E... 952 233-1505
Shakopee (G-9474)

ELECTRIC MOTOR REPAIR SVCS

Electric Motor Repair Inc ....E... 612 588-4693
Minneapolis (G-4337)
Malton Electric Co ....E... 763 571-7758
Minneapolis (G-3526)
Mielke Electric Works Inc ....E... 218 727-7411
Duluth (G-1394)
Spring Prairie Hutterian ....C... 218 498-0222
Hawley (G-2423)
Trico Tcwind Inc ....E... 320 693-6200
Litchfield (G-2991)

ELECTRIC POWER DISTRIBUTION TO CONSUMERS

Agralite Electric Cooperative ....E... 320 843-4150
Benson (G-437)
Allete Inc ....C... 218 279-5000
Duluth (G-1235)
Connexus Energy ....C... 763 323-2600
Anoka (G-169)
Crow Wing Cooperative Power ....D... 218 829-2827
Brainerd (G-562)
Dakota Electric Association ....C... 651 463-6212
Farmington (G-2047)
East Central Energy ....C... 320 396-3351
Braham (G-541)
Itasca-Mantrap Co-Op Electric ....E... 218 732-3377
Park Rapids (G-6757)
Kandiyohi Power Cooperative ....E... 320 235-4155
Willmar (G-10014)
Lake Region Electric Co-op ....D... 218 863-1171
Pelican Rapids (G-6780)
McLeod Cooperative Power Assn ....E... 320 864-3148
Glencoe (G-2208)
Mille Lacs Electric Co-op ....D... 218 927-2191
Aitkin (G-22)
Minnesota Valley Cooperative ....E... 320 269-2163
Montevideo (G-6250)
Minnesota Valley Electric ....D... 952 492-2313
Jordan (G-2807)
Otter Tail Power Co ....C... 866 410-8780
Fergus Falls (G-2109)
Otter Tail Power Co ....B... 218 739-8200
Fergus Falls (G-2110)
Peoples Cooperative Services ....E... 507 288-4004
Rochester (G-7201)
Rice Wild Electric Cooperative ....E... 218 935-2517
Mahnomen (G-3090)
Roseau Electric Cooperative ....E... 218 463-1543
Roseau (G-7358)
Runestone Electric Association ....E... 320 763-6641
Alexandria (G-121)
Southern Minnesota Municipal ....E... 507 285-0478
Rochester (G-7259)
Stearns Cooperative Electric ....D... 320 256-4241
Melrose (G-3352)
Steele-Waseca Cooperative Elec ....E... 507 451-7340
Owatonna (G-6739)
Telepak Industries Inc ....E... 507 332-0012
Faribault (G-2034)
Todd Wadena Electric Co-op ....E... 218 631-3120
Wadena (G-9812)
Tri-County Electric Co-op ....D... 507 864-7783
Rushford (G-7394)
Virginia, City of Inc ....D... 218 748-7540
Virginia (G-9761)
Wright-Hennepin Cooperative ....D... 763 477-3000
Rockford (G-7305)

ELECTRIC SERVICES

Allete Inc ....C... 218 279-5000
Duluth (G-1235)
Allete Inc ....D... 320 632-2311
Little Falls (G-2999)

Employment codes: A=Over 500 employees, B=251-500,
C=101-250, D=51-100, E=25-50

2011 Harris Minnesota
Services Directory

© Harris InfoSource 1-866-281-6415
695

S E R V I C E S

Allete Inc ....E... 218 628-3627
Duluth *(G-1236)*

Allete Inc ....E... 218 722-2641
Duluth *(G-1237)*

Beltrami Electric Co-Op Inc ....D... 218 444-2540
Bemidji *(G-375)*

Ben Co Electric ....E... 507 387-7963
Mankato *(G-3110)*

City of Elk River ....E... 763 441-2020
Elk River *(G-1867)*

City of Grand Rapids ....D... 218 326-7604
Grand Rapids *(G-2273)*

City of Owatonna ....D... 507 451-2480
Owatonna *(G-6701)*

City of Rochester ....C... 507 280-1540
Rochester *(G-7079)*

General Electric Co ....E... 507 368-9222
Lake Benton *(G-2848)*

Interstate Power & Light Co ....D... 507 373-2371
Albert Lea *(G-58)*

Kandiyohi Power Cooperative ....E... 320 796-1155
Spicer *(G-9556)*

Lake Country Power ....E... 218 741-8137
Mountain Iron *(G-6393)*

Mp Technologies LLC........................E... 320 963-2499
Maple Lake *(G-3263)*

Northern States Power Co ....E... 763 295-5151
Monticello *(G-6280)*

Northern States Power Co ....B... 763 261-4100
Becker *(G-357)*

Northern States Power Co ....E... 763 295-4141
Monticello *(G-6281)*

Northern States Power Co ....C... 320 255-8601
Saint Cloud *(G-7563)*

Northern States Power Co ....E... 612 330-6349
Welch *(G-9954)*

Northern States Power Co ....C... 507 387-9629
Mankato *(G-3176)*

Northern States Power Co ....D... 763 493-1500
Osseo *(G-6645)*

Otter Tail Corp ....E... 218 739-8100
Fergus Falls *(G-2104)*

Otter Tail Corp 866 410-8780
Fergus Falls *(G-2105)*

Otter Tail Power Co............................C... 866 410-8780
Fergus Falls *(G-2109)*

Otter Tail Power Co............................B... 218 739-8200
Fergus Falls *(G-2110)*

Willmar, City of Inc............................D... 320 235-4422
Willmar *(G-10056)*

Wisconsin Public Service Corp ....E... 218 879-1571
Cloquet *(G-1069)*

Wright-Hennepin Security Corp ....C... 763 477-3000
Rockford *(G-7306)*

XCEL Energy Inc ....E... 651 385-5604
Red Wing *(G-7014)*

ELECTRIC SVCS, NEC Power Broker

Central Minnesota Municipal 507 526-2193
Blue Earth *(G-531)*

ELECTRIC SVCS, NEC Power Transmission

Great River Energy ....B... 763 445-5000
Maple Grove *(G-3243)*

Great River Energy ....C... 763 441-3121
Elk River *(G-1877)*

Minnesota Valley Cooperative ....E... 320 269-2163
Montevideo *(G-6250)*

Northern States Power Co ....D... 763 441-3800
Elk River *(G-1887)*

Northern States Power Co ....B... 612 330-5674
Saint Paul *(G-8761)*

Northern States Power Co ....C... 651 639-4470
Saint Paul *(G-8760)*

Northern States Power Co ....D... 651 731-5701
Bayport *(G-350)*

Otter Tail Power Co............................C... 866 410-8780
Fergus Falls *(G-2109)*

Otter Tail Power Co............................B... 218 739-8200
Fergus Falls *(G-2110)*

Steele-Waseca Cooperative Elec......E... 507 451-7340
Owatonna *(G-6739)*

ELECTRIC SVCS, NEC: Power Generation

Allete Inc ....B... 218 328-5711
Cohasset *(G-1070)*

Centerpoint Energy Resources ....E... 612 372-4720
Minneapolis *(G-4045)*

FMI Hydraulics Inc ....E... 507 296-4551
Porter *(G-6893)*

Fpd Power Development LLC ....C... 612 782-3100
Minneapolis *(G-4470)*

Great River Energy ....B... 763 445-5000
Maple Grove *(G-3243)*

Great River Energy ....C... 763 441-3121
Elk River *(G-1877)*

Interstate Power & Light Co ....D... 507 373-2371
Albert Lea *(G-58)*

Northern Alternative Energy ....E... 612 370-1061
Wayzata *(G-375)*

Otter Tail Power Co............................C... 866 410-8780
Fergus Falls *(G-2109)*

Otter Tail Power Co............................E... 218 281-3632
Crookston *(G-1132)*

Otter Tail Power Co............................B... 218 736-6947
Fergus Falls *(G-2108)*

Otter Tail Power Co............................B... 218 739-8200
Fergus Falls *(G-2110)*

Southern Minnesota Municipal ....E... 507 285-0478
Rochester *(G-7259)*

ELECTRICAL APPARATUS & EQPT WHOLESALERS

Anixter Inc ....E... 952 887-8191
Bloomington *(G-486)*

Border States Industries Inc ....D... 763 425-5500
Brooklyn Park *(G-606)*

Checkpoint Systems Inc ....E... 952 227-5350
Chaska *(G-958)*

Dakota Supply Group ....D... 952 890-3811
Burnsville *(G-708)*

Dakota Supply Group Inc ....E... 651 224-5781
Saint Paul *(G-8279)*

Eaton Corp ....E... 952 939-5400
Minnetonka *(G-6161)*

Engineered Products Co ....D... 952 767-8780
Minnetonka *(G-6166)*

Graybar Electric Co Inc ....D... 763 852-6000
Minneapolis *(G-4549)*

Griffin Marketing & Promotions...........D... 612 344-4677
Minneapolis *(G-4571)*

Honeywell International Inc ....C... 763 493-6400
Osseo *(G-6622)*

Interstate Power Systems ....D... 952 854-5511
Minneapolis *(G-4729)*

Interstate Power Systems Inc ....D... 952 854-5511
Minneapolis *(G-3502)*

J H Larson Electrical Co......................E... 763 545-1717
Plymouth *(G-6867)*

Lapp Tannehill Inc ....E... 952 881-6700
Savage *(G-9395)*

Luma Corp ....E... 952 995-6500
Shakopee *(G-9453)*

Michaels' Lighting Inc ....E... 507 454-5560
Winona *(G-10117)*

Schneider Electric USA Inc ....E... 763 543-5500
Minneapolis *(G-5609)*

Service Lighting Inc ....E... 763 571-3001
Osseo *(G-6662)*

3M Co ....C... 651 733-3154
Saint Paul *(G-9062)*

3M Co ....D... 651 733-6611
Saint Paul *(G-9066)*

Trico Tcwind Inc.................................E... 320 693-6200
Litchfield *(G-2991)*

Viking Electric Supply Inc ....C... 612 627-1300
Minneapolis *(G-5973)*

Werner Electric Ventures LLC ....C... 651 769-6841
Cottage Grove *(G-1109)*

Wesco Distribution Inc ....D... 651 582-3945
Saint Paul *(G-9147)*

Winona Lighting Inc............................E... 507 454-5113
Winona *(G-10151)*

Yale Materials Handling - MN ....D... 763 434-3832
Anoka *(G-241)*

ELECTRICAL APPLIANCES, TELEVISIONS & RADIOS WHOLESALERS

Curry Sales Inc..................................E... 952 351-4200
Hopkins *(G-2534)*

Lowe's Home Centers Inc ....C... 763 367-1340
Minneapolis *(G-3524)*

Lowe's Home Centers Inc ....C... 507 446-4900
Owatonna *(G-6723)*

Lowe's Home Centers Inc ....C... 763 367-9000
Minneapolis *(G-4904)*

Lowe's Home Centers Inc ....C... 952 367-9000
Shakopee *(G-9452)*

Lowe's Home Centers Inc ....C... 763 428-5970
Rogers *(G-7328)*

Lowe's Home Centers Inc ....C... 763 488-2001
Osseo *(G-6629)*

Lowe's Home Centers Inc ....C... 218 262-7460
Hibbing *(G-2459)*

Lowe's Home Centers Inc ....C... 651 275-9910
Stillwater *(G-9626)*

Lowe's Home Centers Inc ....C... 507 328-8920
Rochester *(G-7162)*

Lowe's Home Centers Inc ....C... 507 385-3560
Mankato *(G-3158)*

Lowe's Home Centers Inc ....C... 763 367-4139
Saint Paul *(G-7826)*

Lowe's Home Centers Inc ....C... 763 367-1120
Minneapolis *(G-3523)*

Lowe's Home Centers Inc ....C... 763 691-6040
Cambridge *(G-840)*

ELECTRICAL CONSTRUCTION MATERIALS WHOLESALERS

Cable Connection & Supply Co...........E... 507 334-6417
Faribault *(G-1995)*

Dakota Supply Group Inc ....E... 651 224-5781
Saint Paul *(G-8279)*

ELECTRICAL EQPT REPAIR & MAINTENANCE

Andy's Electrical Service Inc...............E... 507 378-2101
Grand Meadow *(G-2263)*

F M Trucking Inc ....E... 651 639-0446
Saint Paul *(G-8359)*

Stresstech Inc ....E... 651 388-7117
Red Wing *(G-7008)*

ELECTRICAL EQPT REPAIR SVCS

General Electric Co ....E... 218 749-6100
Mountain Iron *(G-6392)*

Party Music Inc ....E... 952 941-3830
Eden Prairie *(G-1744)*

ELECTRICAL EQPT REPAIR SVCS: High Voltage

Jordan Transformer LLC ....D... 952 492-2720
Jordan *(G-2805)*

ST Cotter Turbine Services Inc ....C... 763 263-5611
Big Lake *(G-457)*

ELECTRICAL GOODS, WHOLESALE: Air Conditioning Appliances

Midwest Mechanical Solutions.............E... 952 525-2003
Minneapolis *(G-5032)*

ELECTRICAL GOODS, WHOLESALE: Alarms & Signaling Eqpt

Sentry Systems Inc ....E... 651 426-4627
White Bear Lake *(G-9977)*

ELECTRICAL GOODS, WHOLESALE: Batteries, Storage, Indl

R & D Batteries Inc ....E... 952 890-0629
Burnsville *(G-783)*

Unipower Industrial Corp.....................E... 952 884-2933
Minneapolis *(G-5906)*

ELECTRICAL GOODS, WHOLESALE: Burglar Alarm Systems

Arrowhead Security Systems Inc.........E... 218 722-1234
Duluth *(G-1243)*

Century Systems Inc ....E... 651 426-0975
Saint Paul *(G-8185)*

Wright-Hennepin Security Corp ....C... 763 477-3000
Rockford *(G-7306)*

ELECTRICAL GOODS, WHOLESALE: Electrical Appliances, Major

All Inc...D... 651 227-6331
Saint Paul *(G-8010)*

ELECTRICAL GOODS, WHOLESALE: Electrical Entertainment Eqpt

Capitol Sales Co Inc ....D... 651 688-6830
Saint Paul *(G-7727)*

Motivaction LLC.................................D... 763 412-3000
Minneapolis *(G-5137)*

Performark Inc ....C... 952 946-7300
Minnetonka *(G-6210)*

ELECTRICAL GOODS, WHOLESALE: Electronic Parts

Arrow Electronics Inc.........................E... 952 949-0053
Eden Prairie *(G-1597)*

Automation Fluid Power Inc ....E... 763 571-3336
Minneapolis *(G-3839)*

Bergquist Inc ....C... 952 835-2322
Chanhassen *(G-909)*

C S Aero-Space Inc ....E... 952 884-4725
Minneapolis *(G-3987)*

Chris Electronics Distributors ....E... 651 631-2647
Saint Paul **(G-8197)**

Delta Industrial Services Inc ....D... 763 755-7744
Minneapolis **(G-3453)**

Digi-Key Corp ....A... 218 681-6674
Thief River Falls **(G-9666)**

North Point Capital Partners ....D... 651 602-0789
Saint Paul **(G-8753)**

Pace Electronics Inc ....E... 507 288-1853
Rochester **(G-7199)**

Shopjimmycom LLC ....E... 952 881-6492
Bloomington **(G-515)**

TLC Electronics ....D... 651 488-2933
Saint Paul **(G-9282)**

Waytek Inc ....E... 952 949-0765
Chanhassen **(G-945)**

ELECTRICAL GOODS, WHOLESALE: Facsimile Or Fax Eqpt

Advanced Imaging Solutions Inc ....E... 952 930-1882
Hopkins **(G-2501)**

IKON Office Solutions Inc ....E... 320 251-4566
Saint Cloud **(G-7529)**

Metro - Sales Inc ....C... 612 861-4000
Minneapolis **(G-5000)**

Ricoh Americas Corp ....D... 651 294-2600
Mendota Heights **(G-3370)**

Sel-Mor Distributing Co ....E... 952 929-0888
Minneapolis **(G-5629)**

ELECTRICAL GOODS, WHOLESALE: Fans, Household

Lights On Broadway Inc ....E... 763 533-3366
Minneapolis **(G-4885)**

ELECTRICAL GOODS, WHOLESALE: Fire Alarm Systems

Arrowhead Security Systems Inc ....E... 218 722-1234
Duluth **(G-1243)**

Ban-Koe Systems Inc ....D... 952 888-6688
Minneapolis **(G-3865)**

ELECTRICAL GOODS, WHOLESALE: Flashlights

Fastenal Co ....B... 507 454-5374
Winona **(G-10095)**

ELECTRICAL GOODS, WHOLESALE: Generators

Great Northern Equipment Dstbg ....E... 763 428-9405
Rogers **(G-7326)**

ELECTRICAL GOODS, WHOLESALE: Household Appliances, NEC

Warners' Stellian Co Inc ....D... 651 222-0011
Saint Paul **(G-9140)**

ELECTRICAL GOODS, WHOLESALE: Insulators

Eis Inc ....E... 763 493-6800
Minneapolis **(G-4334)**

Lapp Tannehill Inc ....E... 952 881-6700
Savage **(G-9395)**

ELECTRICAL GOODS, WHOLESALE: Lighting Fixtures, Comm & Indl

Luma Corp ....E... 952 995-6500
Shakopee **(G-9453)**

Secoa Inc ....D... 763 506-8800
Champlin **(G-900)**

ELECTRICAL GOODS, WHOLESALE: Lighting Fixtures, Residential

Holtkoetter International Inc ....E... 651 552-8776
South Saint Paul **(G-9530)**

ELECTRICAL GOODS, WHOLESALE: Lugs & Connectors

Cable Connection & Supply Co ....E... 507 334-6417
Faribault **(G-1995)**

ELECTRICAL GOODS, WHOLESALE: Mobile telephone Eqpt

Nextel Communications Inc ....D... 952 703-7600
Minneapolis **(G-5197)**

SBC Datacomm Inc ....E... 763 315-5343
Saint Paul **(G-8931)**

ELECTRICAL GOODS, WHOLESALE: Motor Ctrls, Starters & Relays

Electric Motor Repair Inc ....E... 612 588-4693
Minneapolis **(G-4337)**

L & S Electric Inc ....E... 763 780-3234
Minneapolis **(G-3513)**

Motion Tech Automation Inc ....E... 651 730-9010
Saint Paul **(G-9252)**

ELECTRICAL GOODS, WHOLESALE: Motors

AG Electrical Specialists ....E... 507 378-2101
Racine **(G-6966)**

Baldor Electric Co ....D... 763 428-3633
Rogers **(G-7317)**

Electric Motor Repair Inc ....E... 612 588-4693
Minneapolis **(G-4337)**

L & S Electric Inc ....E... 763 780-3234
Minneapolis **(G-3513)**

Malton Electric Co ....E... 763 571-7758
Minneapolis **(G-3526)**

Mielke Electric Works Inc ....E... 218 727-7411
Duluth **(G-1394)**

Minnesota Electric Technology ....E... 507 893-3181
Winnebago **(G-10077)**

Viking Electric Supply Inc ....E... 952 890-8420
Duluth **(G-1497)**

ELECTRICAL GOODS, WHOLESALE: Panelboards

Activar Inc ....E... 952 835-6850
Minneapolis **(G-3677)**

ELECTRICAL GOODS, WHOLESALE: Public Address Eqpt

Ban-Koe Systems Inc ....D... 952 888-6688
Minneapolis **(G-3865)**

Electronic Design Co ....E... 612 355-2300
Minneapolis **(G-4339)**

ELECTRICAL GOODS, WHOLESALE: Radio & TV Or TV Eqpt & Parts

Pixel Farm Inc ....E... 612 339-7644
Minneapolis **(G-5386)**

ELECTRICAL GOODS, WHOLESALE: Radio Parts & Access, NEC

Napco International LLC ....E... 952 931-2400
Hopkins **(G-2587)**

ELECTRICAL GOODS, WHOLESALE: Security Control Eqpt & Systems

J J Vanderson & Co ....E... 651 641-1376
Minneapolis **(G-3503)**

Napco International LLC ....E... 952 931-2400
Hopkins **(G-2587)**

Pro-TEC Design Inc ....E... 763 553-1477
Plymouth **(G-6880)**

Westco Systems Inc ....E... 763 559-7046
Minneapolis **(G-6057)**

ELECTRICAL GOODS, WHOLESALE: Sound Eqpt

Graybow Communications Group ....E... 952 544-5555
Golden Valley **(G-2241)**

Muzak LLC ....E... 763 424-5533
Osseo **(G-6641)**

ELECTRICAL GOODS, WHOLESALE: Switches, Exc Electronic, NEC

Stein Industries Inc ....C... 763 504-3500
Minneapolis **(G-5747)**

ELECTRICAL GOODS, WHOLESALE: Telephone & Telegraphic Eqpt

Comm-Works Holdings LLC ....D... 763 258-5800
Minneapolis **(G-4130)**

Cross Telecom Corp ....D... 952 983-3500
Bloomington **(G-493)**

Kgp Logistics Inc ....A... 507 334-2268
Faribault **(G-2017)**

North American Communications ....E... 952 942-7200
Minneapolis **(G-5212)**

ELECTRICAL GOODS, WHOLESALE: Telephone Eqpt

Avtex Solutions LLC ....E... 952 831-0888
Minneapolis **(G-3848)**

Kgp Telecommunications Inc ....D... 507 334-2268
Faribault **(G-2018)**

Norstan Communications Inc ....C... 952 352-4300
Minnetonka **(G-6202)**

Popp Telcom Inc ....D... 763 546-9707
Minneapolis **(G-5394)**

SBC Datacomm Inc ....E... 763 315-5343
Saint Paul **(G-8931)**

Sel-Mor Distributing Co ....E... 952 929-0888
Minneapolis **(G-5629)**

Spectrum Solutions Inc ....E... 651 634-1800
Saint Paul **(G-8976)**

Unicon Inc ....D... 763 424-7892
Hamel **(G-2359)**

ELECTRICAL GOODS, WHOLESALE: Vacuum Cleaners, Household

Lindhaus USA Inc ....E... 952 707-1131
Burnsville **(G-749)**

ELECTRICAL GOODS, WHOLESALE: Video Eqpt

Alpha Video & Audio Inc ....D... 952 896-9898
Minneapolis **(G-3733)**

BT Americas Inc ....D... 651 746-8590
Saint Paul **(G-8138)**

Graybow Communications Group ....E... 952 544-5555
Golden Valley **(G-2241)**

ELECTRICAL GOODS, WHOLESALE: Wire & Cable

Anixter Inc ....E... 763 559-2417
Minneapolis **(G-3782)**

Anixter Inc ....E... 952 887-8191
Bloomington **(G-486)**

Cable Connection & Supply Co ....E... 507 334-6417
Faribault **(G-1995)**

Menstar Technologies Inc ....D... 218 326-5566
Grand Rapids **(G-2294)**

Viking Electric Supply Inc ....C... 612 627-1300
Minneapolis **(G-5973)**

Viking Electric Supply Inc ....E... 952 890-8420
Duluth **(G-1497)**

ELECTRICAL GOODS, WHOLESALE: Wire & Cable, Ctrl & Sig

Anixter Inc ....E... 952 887-8191
Bloomington **(G-486)**

ELECTRICAL GOODS, WHOLESALE: Wire & Cable, Electronic

Lapp Tannehill Inc ....E... 952 881-6700
Savage **(G-9395)**

ELECTRICAL HOUSEHOLD APPLIANCE REPAIR

Sears, Roebuck & Co ....D... 952 944-4911
Eden Prairie **(G-1772)**

ELECTRICAL SPLYS

Border States Electric Supply ....C... 320 214-4237
Willmar **(G-9992)**

Dakota Supply Group Inc ....E... 651 224-5781
Saint Paul **(G-8279)**

Graybar Electric Co Inc ....C... 612 721-3545
Minneapolis **(G-4550)**

Graybar Electric Co Inc ....E... 218 722-6685
Duluth **(G-1343)**

Lapp Tannehill Inc ....E... 952 881-6700
Savage **(G-9395)**

Midwest Sign & Screen Printing ....D... 651 489-9999
Saint Paul **(G-8661)**

Next Level Electronics Inc ....E... 320 363-7716
Saint Joseph **(G-7653)**

3M Co ....A... 507 354-8271
New Ulm **(G-6476)**

ELECTROLYSIS & EPILATORY SVCS

Rita Ambourn Hair Designers ....E... 651 698-5537
Saint Paul **(G-8903)**

ELECTROMEDICAL EQPT WHOLESALERS

Tyco Electronics Corp ....C... 651 565-2601
Wabasha **(G-9772)**

ELECTRONIC EQPT REPAIR SVCS

Artesyn North America Inc ....C... 952 941-1100
Eden Prairie **(G-1598)**

Employment codes: A=Over 500 employees, B=251-500,
C=101-250, D=51-100, E=25-50

2011 Harris Minnesota
Services Directory

© Harris InfoSource 1-866-281-6415
697

Rvi Inc ....E... 320 269-3227
Montevideo **(G-6259)**

ELECTRONIC FUNDS TRANSFER NETWORK, INCLUDING SWITCHING

Money Gram Payment Systems Inc .....A... 952 591-3000
Minneapolis **(G-5120)**

T-Chek Systems Inc..............................D... 952 934-3413
Eden Prairie **(G-1790)**

Vanco Services LLC ....E... 952 983-8660
Eden Prairie **(G-1803)**

ELECTRONIC PARTS & EQPT WHOLESALERS

Aldin Export & Import.................................. 651 483-4184
Saint Paul **(G-8007)**

American Communications Supply 507 334-2268
Faribault **(G-1989)**

Asml Us Inc ....E... 952 876-0713
Bloomington **(G-488)**

Avnet Inc ....E... 763 559-2211
Minneapolis **(G-3847)**

Avnet Inc ....E... 952 346-3000
Bloomington **(G-489)**

Bell Telephone Inc ....D... 651 298-1332
Saint Paul **(G-8099)**

Bergquist Co ....C... 952 835-2322
Chanhassen **(G-909)**

Best Source Electronics Corp ....E... 763 502-7847
Fridley **(G-2191)**

Black Box Corp ....D... 763 971-6260
Minneapolis **(G-3910)**

BT Americas Inc ....D... 651 746-8590
Saint Paul **(G-8138)**

Buy Best Purchasing LLC ....A... 612 291-1000
Richfield **(G-7034)**

Cash Register Sales Inc ....D... 651 294-2700
Saint Paul **(G-8171)**

Delta Industrial Services Inc ....D... 763 755-7744
Minneapolis **(G-3453)**

Gopher Electronics Co ....E... 651 490-4900
Saint Paul **(G-8423)**

Graybar Electric Co Inc ....E... 218 722-6685
Duluth **(G-1343)**

Integra Telecom Inc ....C... 763 745-8000
Minneapolis **(G-4711)**

Ironwood Electronics Inc ....E... 952 229-8200
Burnsville **(G-737)**

Matrix Communications Inc ....E... 763 475-5500
Minneapolis **(G-4966)**

Mitel Technologies Inc ....E... 952 930-4400
Minnetonka **(G-6200)**

Power Mation Division Inc ....D... 651 605-3300
Saint Paul **(G-8832)**

Pro-TEC Design Inc ....E... 763 553-1477
Plymouth **(G-6880)**

Schneider Electric USA Inc ....E... 763 543-5500
Minneapolis **(G-5609)**

Techscan Corp 651 636-3030
Saint Paul **(G-9035)**

3M Co ....C... 651 733-2147
Saint Paul **(G-9044)**

UTC Fire & Security America ....D... 651 777-2690
Saint Paul **(G-9121)**

Wesco Distribution Inc ....D... 651 582-3945
Saint Paul **(G-9147)**

ELEVATOR: Grain, Storage Only

General Mills Inc ....D... 612 721-6811
Minneapolis **(G-4512)**

General Mills Operations LLC...............E... 218 722-7759
Duluth **(G-1335)**

Northern Grain Design & Constr ....E... 320 367-2881
Clara City **(G-1031)**

ELEVATORS WHOLESALERS

Premier Technologies Inc ....D... 952 475-2317
Long Lake **(G-3030)**

ELEVATORS, INSPECTION, SVC & REPAIR

All City Elevator Inc ....E... 651 646-5600
Saint Paul **(G-8009)**

Eagle Elevator Corp ....E... 651 645-1543
Saint Paul **(G-8318)**

Kone Inc ....D... 952 688-6827
Eagan **(G-1533)**

Minnesota Elevator Inc ....C... 507 245-3060
Mankato **(G-3171)**

R & O Elevator Co Inc ....D... 612 588-7844
Minneapolis **(G-5454)**

ELEVATORS: Installation & Conversion

Minnesota Elevator Inc ....C... 507 245-3060
Mankato **(G-3171)**

R & O Elevator Co Inc ....D... 612 588-7844
Minneapolis **(G-5454)**

EMBROIDERY ADVERTISING SVCS

Games People Play Inc ....E... 507 433-7593
Austin **(G-272)**

EMERGENCY & RELIEF SVCS

Birthright Inc ....E... 507 645-7638
Northfield **(G-6525)**

County of Meeker 320 693-5300
Litchfield **(G-2983)**

Family Violence Network ....D... 651 770-8544
Minneapolis **(G-4413)**

Family Violence Network ....D... 612 825-3333
Minneapolis **(G-4414)**

Someplace Safe ....D... 320 589-3208
Fergus Falls **(G-2120)**

EMERGENCY SHELTERS

Anna Maries ....E... 320 253-6900
Saint Cloud **(G-7451)**

Arlington House ....E... 651 771-3040
Saint Paul **(G-8063)**

Central Minnesota Task Force ....E... 320 252-1603
Saint Cloud **(G-7487)**

Central Minnesota Task Force ....E... 320 251-7203
Saint Cloud **(G-7486)**

Central Minnesota Task Force ....E... 320 253-6900
Saint Cloud **(G-7488)**

Central Minnesota Task Force ....E... 320 252-1603
Saint Cloud **(G-7489)**

Dakota Woodlands Inc ....E... 651 456-9110
Eagan **(G-1524)**

Shelter Care Inc ....E... 612 823-8483
Minneapolis **(G-5653)**

Shelter House ....E... 320 235-0962
Willmar **(G-10044)**

Union Gospel Mission Assn ....D... 651 292-1721
Saint Paul **(G-9102)**

EMPLOYEE LEASING SVCS

Emp Serv L L C ....E... 507 825-4211
Pipestone **(G-6825)**

Empo Corp ....E... 612 285-8707
Minneapolis **(G-4352)**

Executive Services Midwest LLC ....E... 952 469-4755
Lakeville **(G-2905)**

Royale Resources Inc..........................D... 218 346-3000
Perham **(G-6802)**

EMPLOYMENT AGENCY SVCS

Advanced Practice Solutions ....E... 651 439-8484
Lake Elmo **(G-2864)**

Agri Temps Inc ....D... 320 235-1707
Willmar **(G-9982)**

Alliancenet Inc ....E... 952 934-4104
Chanhassen **(G-907)**

Allied Professionals Inc ....B... 952 832-5101
Minneapolis **(G-3716)**

Americare Staffing Service Inc ....D... 651 917-1995
Saint Paul **(G-8035)**

Applied Staffing Inc ....E... 763 502-1388
Fridley **(G-2190)**

Aquent LLC ....D... 952 851-3411
Minneapolis **(G-3794)**

Central Minnesota Jobs ....D... 763 271-3715
Monticello **(G-6266)**

Choice Unlimited Inc ....D... 218 724-5869
Duluth **(G-1270)**

City of Richfield ....E... 612 861-9385
Minneapolis **(G-4096)**

Consumer Directions Inc ....A... 320 420-3423
Saint Cloud **(G-7409)**

Crow River Technical Inc ....E... 763 560-6015
Minneapolis **(G-4188)**

Delta Co's LLC ....E... 952 929-5005
Minneapolis **(G-4245)**

Dobbs Temporary Services Inc ....E... 612 373-2600
Minneapolis **(G-4268)**

Doherty Employment Group Inc............E... 952 832-8383
Minneapolis **(G-4270)**

East Suburban Resources Inc ....E... 651 351-0190
Stillwater **(G-9611)**

Emerge Community Development ....E... 612 529-9267
Minneapolis **(G-4345)**

Employer Solutions Group ....D... 952 835-1288
Minneapolis **(G-4350)**

Infosoft Group ....D... 952 806-0631
Edina **(G-1833)**

Jpg & Associates Inc ....E... 651 779-1072
Lake Elmo **(G-2875)**

Kforce Inc ....E... 952 835-5100
Minneapolis **(G-4803)**

Labor Services Co ....B... 952 884-0765
Minneapolis **(G-4830)**

Lifetrack Resources Inc ....D... 651 227-8471
Saint Paul **(G-8586)**

Minnesota Department of ....E... 507 537-6236
Marshall **(G-3313)**

Minnesota Professional Nursing...........D... 612 627-9524
Minneapolis **(G-5090)**

National Engineering Resources ....D... 763 561-7610
Minneapolis **(G-5163)**

National Service Co of Iowa ....D... 507 372-2276
Worthington **(G-10188)**

Newtown Solutions Inc ....E... 952 440-4400
Savage **(G-9400)**

Nexpro Personnel Services Inc ....D... 952 224-9855
Minneapolis **(G-5196)**

Platinum Staffing LLC ....D... 763 560-8430
Minneapolis **(G-5389)**

PPL Industries Inc ....D... 612 332-0664
Minneapolis **(G-5399)**

Precision Design Inc ....E... 952 933-6550
Hopkins **(G-2604)**

Primestaff Inc ....C... 651 697-2120
Saint Paul **(G-8848)**

Private Industry Council ....E... 507 537-6236
Marshall **(G-3322)**

Programming Solutions Inc ....E... 763 424-8154
Minneapolis **(G-5424)**

Resource Group Inc ....E... 952 974-9225
Chanhassen **(G-937)**

Resource Inc ....E... 952 925-9195
Minneapolis **(G-5528)**

Resources For You Inc ....D... 320 864-5871
Glencoe **(G-2212)**

Rural Minnesota Cep Inc......................E... 218 755-4458
Bemidji **(G-424)**

Salo Project LLC..................................D... 612 230-7256
Minneapolis **(G-5593)**

Salo Search LLC..................................E... 612 230-7256
Minneapolis **(G-5594)**

Sfn Group Inc ....B... 952 467-1770
Young America **(G-10210)**

Tech Central Inc..................................C... 952 837-8000
Minneapolis **(G-5805)**

Tempworks Software Inc ....D... 651 452-0366
Saint Paul **(G-7920)**

Valere LLC...E... 763 390-9286
White Bear Lake **(G-9979)**

Westaff Inc ....C... 218 463-4418
Roseau **(G-7359)**

Wilson Learning Corp ....E... 952 944-2880
Minneapolis **(G-6075)**

Work Connection Inc............................D... 320 693-8871
Litchfield **(G-2994)**

EMPLOYMENT SVCS: Labor Contractors

Contingent Work Force Soln ....C... 651 636-5624
Little Canada **(G-2995)**

EMPLOYMENT SVCS: Nurses' Registry

Advanced Care Inc ....D... 612 721-1957
Minneapolis **(G-3686)**

Aliance Health Care Inc ....D... 507 252-9737
Rochester **(G-7049)**

All Temporaries Inc ....E... 320 654-6031
Saint Cloud **(G-7446)**

Caremate Home Health Care Inc ....C... 651 659-0208
Saint Paul **(G-8164)**

Comfort Home Health Care Group.......C... 507 281-2332
Rochester **(G-7087)**

County of Beltrami ....D... 218 333-8206
Bemidji **(G-386)**

Fairview Health Line Home Care ....D... 218 262-6982
Hibbing **(G-2443)**

International Quality Homecare ....E... 507 451-6262
Owatonna **(G-6719)**

North Memorial Health Care ....D... 763 520-3900
Minneapolis **(G-5216)**

REM Health Inc ....E... 952 926-9808
Minneapolis **(G-5509)**

Spectrum Community Health Inc ....E... 218 326-4202
Grand Rapids **(G-2308)**

EMPLOYMENT SVCS: Registries

Vantro Systems LLC ....E... 952 890-2080
Burnsville **(G-817)**

S E R V I C E S

EMPLOYMENT SVCS: Teachers' Registry

Norman County Education Assoc ....E... 218 356-8773
Gary *(G-2198)*

ENGINEERING HELP SVCS

Tech Central Inc ....C... 952 837-8000
Minneapolis *(G-5805)*

ENGINEERING SVCS

Aecom Technical Services Inc ....E... 763 551-1001
Minneapolis *(G-3691)*
Amec Earth & Environmental Inc ....E... 612 332-8326
Minneapolis *(G-3743)*
American Consulting Services ....C... 651 659-9001
Saint Paul *(G-8023)*
American Engineering Testing ....D... 651 659-9001
Saint Paul *(G-8025)*
Architecture Technology Corp ....E... 952 829-5864
Eden Prairie *(G-1595)*
Barr Engineering Co ....E... 218 262-2262
Hibbing *(G-2438)*
Braun Intertec Corp ....E... 651 487-3245
Saint Paul *(G-8122)*
Cogent Technologies Inc ....C... 952 941-3300
Brooklyn Park *(G-607)*
Colby Yaggy Associates Inc ....D... 507 288-6464
Rochester *(G-7084)*
Crow Wing County Hwy Dept ....E... 218 824-1110
Brainerd *(G-563)*
Cybertrol Engineering LLC ....E... 763 559-8660
Minneapolis *(G-4208)*
Dacon Engineering & Service Co ....C... 763 544-1686
Minneapolis *(G-4216)*
Dell-Comm Inc ....D... 763 783-0035
Saint Paul *(G-8283)*
Dobbs Temporary Services Inc ....E... 612 373-2600
Minneapolis *(G-4268)*
Donnelly Custom Manufacturing ....C... 320 762-2396
Alexandria *(G-95)*
E & C Amec Services Inc ....D... 612 332-8326
Minneapolis *(G-4299)*
Eaton Corp ....E... 952 912-1330
Minnetonka *(G-6162)*
Efi Global Inc ....E... 952 942-9812
Minneapolis *(G-4328)*
Electrosonic Inc ....E... 952 931-7500
Minnetonka *(G-6165)*
Gb Lumina Inc ....E... 763 797-9036
Minneapolis *(G-4504)*
Green Co's Inc ....D... 651 644-4389
Saint Paul *(G-8430)*
Hammel, Green & Abrahamson Inc ....B... 612 758-4000
Minneapolis *(G-4591)*
HDR Engineering Inc ....C... 763 591-5400
Minneapolis *(G-4615)*
Heyer Engineering ....E... 612 238-3805
Minneapolis *(G-4644)*
Ibberson Inc 952 938-7007
Hopkins *(G-2555)*
Industrial Automation Engg ....E... 763 450-3800
Anoka *(G-192)*
Infinity Precision Systems LLC ....E... 952 401-4600
Chanhassen *(G-926)*
Inspec Inc ....E... 763 546-3434
Minneapolis *(G-4707)*
Ion Corp ....E... 952 936-9490
Eden Prairie *(G-1698)*
James R Hill Inc ....E... 952 890-6044
Burnsville *(G-738)*
James R Hill Inc ....D... 763 792-1136
Minneapolis *(G-3505)*
Lhb Inc ....E... 612 338-2029
Minneapolis *(G-4867)*
Logic Product Development Co ....D... 612 672-9495
Minneapolis *(G-4900)*
McGhie & Betts Inc ....E... 507 289-3919
Rochester *(G-7179)*
Metropolitan Council, MN ....E... 651 772-2585
Saint Paul *(G-8644)*
Metropolitan Mechanical Contr ....B... 952 941-7010
Eden Prairie *(G-1722)*
Miller Dunwiddie Architecture ....E... 612 337-0000
Minneapolis *(G-5043)*
Minnetronix Inc ....C... 651 917-4060
Saint Paul *(G-8712)*
MTS Systems Corp ....A... 952 937-4000
Eden Prairie *(G-1731)*
Noramco Engineering Corp ....E... 218 262-1093
Hibbing *(G-2469)*
North Anoka Control Systems ....E... 763 444-4747
Anoka *(G-208)*
Nova-Tech Engineering LLC ....D... 320 231-9660
Willmar *(G-10032)*
Ops America Inc ....E... 763 479-1409
Loretto *(G-3051)*
QLogic Corp ....C... 952 932-4000
Shakopee *(G-9466)*
Roed Ericksen & Associates ....E... 651 251-7570
Saint Paul *(G-8911)*
Safegate Airport Systems Inc ....E... 763 535-9299
Minneapolis *(G-5589)*
Scott County Highway Engineer ....E... 952 496-8346
Jordan *(G-2809)*
Sebesta Blomberg & Associates ....C... 651 634-0775
Saint Paul *(G-8940)*
Setter Leach & Lindstrom Inc ....D... 612 338-8741
Minneapolis *(G-5639)*
Short-Elliott-Hendrickson Inc ....D... 800 572-0617
Saint Cloud *(G-7593)*
Specsys Inc ....C... 320 269-3227
Montevideo *(G-6260)*
SRF Consulting Group Inc ....C... 763 475-0010
Minneapolis *(G-5725)*
Team Industries Baxter Inc ....E... 218 829-1901
Baxter *(G-341)*
Team Industries Inc ....C... 218 694-3550
Bagley *(G-302)*
Teradyne Inc ....E... 763 586-0725
Minneapolis *(G-3615)*
Terracon Consultants Inc ....E... 651 770-1500
Saint Paul *(G-9040)*
Third Wave Systems Inc ....E... 952 832-5515
Minneapolis *(G-5815)*
3M Co ....E... 651 733-5000
Saint Paul *(G-9054)*
3M Co ....C... 651 736-1792
Saint Paul *(G-9056)*
Uni-Systems LLC ....E... 763 536-1407
Minneapolis *(G-5901)*
Unified Theory Inc 651 578-8100
Saint Paul *(G-9286)*
URS Group Inc ....E... 612 370-0700
Minneapolis *(G-5941)*
US Army Corps of Engineers ....A... 651 290-5698
Saint Paul *(G-9116)*
Vaa LLC ....D... 763 559-9100
Minneapolis *(G-5953)*
Wenck Associates Inc ....D... 763 479-4200
Maple Plain *(G-3281)*
Widseth, Smith, Nolting ....E... 320 762-8149
Alexandria *(G-130)*
Widseth, Smith, Nolting ....D... 218 829-5117
Baxter *(G-345)*
Zachry Construction Corp ....E... 612 215-1300
Minneapolis *(G-6113)*

ENGINEERING SVCS: Aviation Or Aeronautical

Canard Aerospace Corp ....E... 952 944-7990
Shakopee *(G-9426)*
Evergreen Aviation Inc ....D... 612 727-1655
Minneapolis *(G-4379)*

ENGINEERING SVCS: Building Construction

Ellerbe Becket Co ....C... 612 376-2000
Minneapolis *(G-4341)*
Horty Elving & Associates Inc ....E... 612 332-4422
Minneapolis *(G-4676)*
Ibberson Inc 952 938-7007
Hopkins *(G-2555)*
Knutson Construction Services ....D... 507 280-9788
Rochester *(G-7157)*
Krech, Ojard & Associates ....E... 218 727-3282
Duluth *(G-1373)*
Widseth, Smith, Nolting ....E... 218 281-6522
Crookston *(G-1144)*

ENGINEERING SVCS: Civil

Anderson Engineering of MN LLC ....E... 763 383-1084
Minneapolis *(G-3777)*
Bakke Kopp Ballou & McFarlin ....E... 763 843-0420
Minneapolis *(G-3861)*
Bolton & Menk Inc ....D... 507 625-4171
Mankato *(G-3112)*
Bolton & Menk Inc ....E... 320 231-3956
Willmar *(G-9991)*
Clark Engineering Corp ....E... 763 545-9196
Minneapolis *(G-4103)*
Colby Yaggy Associates Inc ....D... 507 288-6464
Rochester *(G-7084)*
Emmons & Oliver Resources ....E... 218 732-3323
Park Rapids *(G-6751)*
Kadrmas, Lee & Jackson Inc ....E... 218 287-0300
Moorhead *(G-6321)*
Krech, Ojard & Associates ....E... 218 727-3282
Duluth *(G-1373)*
Liesch Associates Inc ....D... 763 489-3100
Minneapolis *(G-4875)*
Mfra Inc ....D... 763 476-6010
Minneapolis *(G-5013)*
Otto Associates Engineers ....E... 763 682-4727
Buffalo *(G-655)*
Passe Engineering Inc 763 780-4100
Minneapolis *(G-3566)*
Rehder & Associates Inc ....D... 651 452-5051
Eagan *(G-1547)*
Rlk Inc ....E... 952 933-0972
Hopkins *(G-2620)*
Short-Elliott-Hendrickson Inc ....C... 651 490-2000
Saint Paul *(G-8954)*
SRF Consulting Group Inc ....C... 763 475-0010
Minneapolis *(G-5725)*
Tom Loucks & Associates Inc ....D... 763 424-5505
Osseo *(G-6676)*

ENGINEERING SVCS: Designing, Ship, Boat, Machine & Product

Chandler Exhibits Inc ....D... 651 389-5900
Afton *(G-8)*
Dell-Comm Inc ....D... 763 783-0035
Saint Paul *(G-8283)*
Hunt Technologies LLC ....C... 218 562-4877
Pequot Lakes *(G-6789)*
Hydralift Amclyde Inc ....D... 651 293-4646
Saint Paul *(G-8501)*
Nol-Tec Systems Inc ....D... 651 780-8600
Circle Pines *(G-1018)*
Ulteig Engineers Inc ....D... 763 571-2500
Minneapolis *(G-3629)*

ENGINEERING SVCS: Electrical Or Electronic

Analog Technologies, Corp ....E... 952 894-9228
Burnsville *(G-677)*
API Electric Co ....E... 218 741-7313
Hibbing *(G-2437)*
Bakke Kopp Ballou & McFarlin ....E... 763 843-0420
Minneapolis *(G-3861)*
Boarman Kroos Vogel Group ....D... 612 339-3752
Minneapolis *(G-3921)*
Depotstar Inc ....E... 763 506-9990
Anoka *(G-174)*
Distinction In Design Inc ....D... 763 550-1138
Minneapolis *(G-4260)*
Dlr Group Kke ....E... 612 977-3500
Minneapolis *(G-4266)*
Gausman & Moore Associates Inc ....D... 651 639-9606
Saint Paul *(G-8403)*
Lkpb Engineers Inc ....E... 651 633-1223
Saint Paul *(G-8593)*
North Point Capital Partners ....D... 651 602-0789
Saint Paul *(G-8753)*
Open Access Technology Intl ....B... 763 201-2000
Minneapolis *(G-5283)*
Parsons Electric LLC ....C... 763 571-8000
Minneapolis *(G-3565)*
World Architects Inc ....D... 651 227-7773
Saint Paul *(G-9168)*

ENGINEERING SVCS: Energy conservation

Chevron USA Inc ....E... 651 905-5700
Saint Paul *(G-7730)*

ENGINEERING SVCS: Fire Protection

Northstar Fire Protection Inc ....E... 651 456-9111
Saint Paul *(G-7853)*

ENGINEERING SVCS: Heating & Ventilation

Owens Co's Inc ....D... 952 854-3800
Bloomington *(G-509)*

ENGINEERING SVCS: Industrial

Oakriver Technology Inc ....E... 651 770-8710
Saint Paul *(G-9254)*

ENGINEERING SVCS: Mechanical

Bakke Kopp Ballou & McFarlin ....E... 763 843-0420
Minneapolis *(G-3861)*
Boarman Kroos Vogel Group ....D... 612 339-3752
Minneapolis *(G-3921)*
Distinction In Design Inc ....D... 763 550-1138
Minneapolis *(G-4260)*
EAC Design Inc ....E... 952 435-5533
Burnsville *(G-714)*
Eagle Tool & Design Inc ....E... 763 784-7400
Minneapolis *(G-3460)*
Erdman Automation Corp ....D... 763 389-9475
Princeton *(G-6905)*

Employment codes: A=Over 500 employees, B=251-500, C=101-250, D=51-100, E=25-50
2011 Harris Minnesota Services Directory
© Harris InfoSource 1-866-281-6415
699

Gausman & Moore Associates Inc ......D... 651 639-9606
Saint Paul *(G-8403)*

Hallberg Engineering Inc ....E... 651 748-1100
White Bear Lake *(G-9975)*

Lkpb Engineers Inc ....E... 651 633-1223
Saint Paul *(G-8593)*

Machine & Process Design Inc ....E... 763 427-9991
Anoka *(G-202)*

Rogers Freels & Associates Inc ......D... 952 843-2700
Eden Prairie *(G-1766)*

Via Biomedical Inc ....E... 763 577-9936
Osseo *(G-6683)*

World Architects Inc ....D... 651 227-7773
Saint Paul *(G-9168)*

ENGINEERING SVCS: Pollution Control

Liesch Associates Inc ....D... 763 489-3100
Minneapolis *(G-4875)*

ENGINEERING SVCS: Professional

AEC Engineering Inc ....E... 612 332-8905
Minneapolis *(G-3690)*

Braun Intertec Corp ....C... 952 995-2000
Minneapolis *(G-3938)*

Wheeler Consolidated Inc ....E... 952 929-6791
Minneapolis *(G-6064)*

ENGINEERING SVCS: Sanitary

Short-Elliott-Hendrickson Inc ......C... 651 490-2000
Saint Paul *(G-8954)*

Short-Elliott-Hendrickson Inc ......E... 888 722-0547
Duluth *(G-1450)*

ENGINEERING SVCS: Structural

Bakke Kopp Ballou & McFarlin ....E... 763 843-0420
Minneapolis *(G-3861)*

Boarman Kroos Vogel Group ....D... 612 339-3752
Minneapolis *(G-3921)*

Clark Engineering Corp ....E... 763 545-9196
Minneapolis *(G-4103)*

Duffy Engineering & Associates ....E... 320 259-6575
Saint Cloud *(G-7412)*

Krech, Ojard & Associates ....E... 218 727-3282
Duluth *(G-1373)*

Larson Engineering Inc ....E... 651 481-9120
Saint Paul *(G-8563)*

Meyer, Borgman & Johnson Inc ....E... 612 338-0713
Minneapolis *(G-5011)*

Palanisami & Associates Inc ....E... 763 533-9403
Minneapolis *(G-5314)*

Reigstad & Associates Inc ....E... 651 292-1123
Saint Paul *(G-8886)*

ENTERTAINERS & ENTERTAINMENT GROUPS

Dunk N Jump ....D... 612 788-0404
Minneapolis *(G-4295)*

Mankato Symphony Orchestra ....D... 507 625-8880
Mankato *(G-3167)*

Rinke, Noonan, Grote, Smoley ....D... 320 251-6700
Saint Cloud *(G-7588)*

ENTERTAINMENT PROMOTION SVCS

Creative Promotional Concepts ....D... 651 905-9339
Saint Paul *(G-7740)*

Dakota Cook LLC ....D... 612 332-1010
Minneapolis *(G-4218)*

Live Nation Worldwide Inc ....E... 612 673-8308
Minneapolis *(G-4895)*

ENTERTAINMENT SVCS

Acme Comedy Co ....E... 612 338-6393
Minneapolis *(G-3673)*

Midwest Sound & Light Inc ....E... 651 644-4111
Saint Paul *(G-8662)*

Party Music Inc ....E... 952 941-3830
Eden Prairie *(G-1744)*

ENVELOPES WHOLESALERS

Cenveo Inc ....E... 651 645-0251
Saint Paul *(G-8186)*

Johnson Anderson & Associates ....D... 952 496-6699
Shakopee *(G-9447)*

EQUIPMENT & VEHICLE FINANCE LEASING COMPANIES

Allegiance Financial Group Inc 651 486-5313
Saint Paul *(G-8012)*

Glacier International Inc 651 786-9700
Saint Paul *(G-8412)*

Lyon Financial Services Inc ....C... 507 532-7763
Marshall *(G-3307)*

Schwan Food Co ....A... 507 532-3274
Marshall *(G-3325)*

U S Bancorp ....B... 651 466-3000
Minneapolis *(G-5885)*

EQUIPMENT: Rental & Leasing, NEC

Ace Nicollet Rental Place ....E... 612 822-3121
Minneapolis *(G-3671)*

Advance Shoring Co ....E... 651 489-8881
Saint Paul *(G-7988)*

Bug Inc ....E... 952 445-1022
Shakopee *(G-9424)*

Creekridge Capital LLC ....E... 952 996-0270
Minneapolis *(G-4180)*

Farnam Street Financial Inc ....E... 952 908-0850
Hopkins *(G-2541)*

Geneva Capital LLC ....E... 320 762-8400
Alexandria *(G-102)*

Glenwood-Inglewood Co ....D... 612 374-2253
Minneapolis *(G-4529)*

Imperial Leasing Inc ....E... 651 454-3330
Saint Paul *(G-7803)*

Information Systems Sciences ....E... 507 754-4405
Elkton *(G-1907)*

Keinath Leasing Co ....E... 952 944-8000
Savage *(G-9392)*

Lpl LLC ....E... 952 345-8240
Edina *(G-1835)*

Minnesota Supply Co ....D... 952 828-7300
Eden Prairie *(G-1726)*

Norcostco Inc ....E... 763 544-0601
Minneapolis *(G-5207)*

Northern Dewatering Inc ....D... 763 428-2616
Rogers *(G-7332)*

Northland Capital Financial ....E... 320 252-2122
Saint Cloud *(G-7564)*

Novus Inc ....E... 952 944-8152
Savage *(G-9402)*

RSC Equipment Rental Inc ....E... 763 557-1234
Minneapolis *(G-5565)*

Sky Blue Leasing Inc ....E... 320 692-2027
Brainerd *(G-586)*

Stearns County National Assn ....E... 320 253-6607
Saint Cloud *(G-7609)*

Temp-Air Inc ....D... 952 707-5203
Burnsville *(G-807)*

Vanman Co's Architects ....E... 763 541-9552
Minneapolis *(G-5957)*

Winmark Capital Corp ....D... 763 520-8500
Minneapolis *(G-6076)*

Winmark Corp ....C... 763 520-8500
Minneapolis *(G-6077)*

ESCORT SVCS

Dependable Care Inc ....E... 763 438-2811
Brooklyn Park *(G-608)*

EXCURSION BOATS

Muller Boat Co ....E... 651 465-6315
Taylors Falls *(G-9661)*

St Croix Boat & Packet Inc ....D... 651 430-1234
Stillwater *(G-9642)*

EXERCISE FACILITY

L A Fitness International LLC ....E... 952 392-4400
Burnsville *(G-744)*

EXERCISE SALON

Georgie's Fitness Inc ....E... 507 238-9422
Fairmont *(G-1967)*

P & D Klitzke Enterprises Inc ....E... 320 275-3555
Darwin *(G-1158)*

EXHAUST HOOD OR FAN CLEANING SVCS

Enviromatic Corp of America ....D... 612 861-3330
Minneapolis *(G-4362)*

EXHIBITORS, ITINERANT, MOTION PICTURE

Carmike Cinemas Inc ....D... 763 785-1855
Saint Paul *(G-8168)*

EXPLOSIVES, EXC AMMO & FIREWORKS WHOLESALERS

Viking Explosives & Supply Inc ....E... 218 263-8845
Hibbing *(G-2479)*

EXTENDED CARE FACILITY

Alterra Healthcare Corp ....E... 651 482-8111
Saint Paul *(G-8018)*

Alterra Healthcare Corp ....E... 651 686-5557
Saint Paul *(G-7694)*

Benedictine Health System ....D... 651 388-1234
Red Wing *(G-6975)*

Bethany Samaritan Inc ....C... 507 289-4031
Rochester *(G-7064)*

Cerenity Sr Care Center ....C... 651 232-6000
South Saint Paul *(G-9519)*

Christian Grandview Home ....C... 763 689-1474
Cambridge *(G-836)*

Evangelical Lutheran Good ....C... 218 587-4423
Pine River *(G-6818)*

Franciscan Health Community ....C... 651 696-8400
Saint Paul *(G-8393)*

Kenyon Sunset Home ....D... 507 789-6134
Kenyon *(G-2828)*

Lake Ridge Care Center of ....C... 763 682-1434
Buffalo *(G-649)*

Lakewood Health System ....B... 218 894-1515
Staples *(G-9586)*

Lifecare Medical Center ....E... 218 782-2131
Greenbush *(G-2326)*

North Country Hospital ....A... 218 751-5430
Bemidji *(G-410)*

Presbyterian Homes & Services ....B... 651 631-6200
Saint Paul *(G-8839)*

Sandstone Area Nursing Home ....C... 320 245-2212
Sandstone *(G-9326)*

Traverse Care Center ....D... 320 563-8124
Wheaton *(G-9969)*

Volunteers of America National ....E... 952 941-0305
Eden Prairie *(G-1810)*

Warroad Care Center Inc ....D... 218 386-1235
Warroad *(G-9872)*

EXTERMINATING & FUMIGATING SVCS

Adam's Pest Control Inc ....E... 763 478-9810
Hamel *(G-2336)*

EYE BANKS

Minnesota Lions Eye Bank Inc ....D... 612 624-6446
Saint Paul *(G-8696)*

FACIAL SALONS

Coloplast Corp ....D... 507 345-6200
North Mankato *(G-6507)*

Elizabeth Charles Corp ....C... 952 915-2900
Minneapolis *(G-4340)*

Elizabeth Charles Corp ....D... 952 915-2900
Saint Paul *(G-9212)*

Elizabeth Charles Corp ....E... 952 915-2900
Chanhassen *(G-922)*

FACILITIES SUPPORT SVCS

Bay West Inc ....C... 651 291-0456
Saint Paul *(G-8093)*

Bay West-Bem Solutions LLC ....D... 651 291-0456
Saint Paul *(G-8094)*

Bem - Bay West Joint Venture ....D... 651 291-0456
Saint Paul *(G-8101)*

Financial Systems Support ....E... 612 625-3493
Minneapolis *(G-4433)*

Guardian Angels of Elk River ....D... 763 241-4428
Elk River *(G-1881)*

Supportive Lifestyles Inc ....E... 320 796-5900
Spicer *(G-9559)*

FACILITIES: Inspection & fixed

Ibt Consolidated Inc ....E... 218 285-5290
International Falls *(G-2721)*

Vitran Express Inc ....E... 320 485-2333
Winsted *(G-10166)*

FACILITY RENTAL & PARTY PLANNING SVCS

Lho Bloomington One Lessee LLC ......C... 952 835-7800
Minneapolis *(G-4868)*

Town & Country Caterers Inc ....D... 763 559-4461
Plymouth *(G-6888)*

Zuhrah Temple Trustees Inc ....E... 612 871-3555
Minneapolis *(G-6122)*

FAMILY COUNSELING SVCS

Family Innovations Inc ....E... 651 748-5019
Saint Paul *(G-8367)*

Family Means ....E... 763 780-4986
Minneapolis *(G-4410)*

Greater Minnesota Family Svcs ....D... 320 214-9692
Willmar *(G-10003)*

Jewish Family & Children's Svc ....D... 952 546-0616
Hopkins *(G-2562)*

(G-00000) Company's Geographic Section entry number

FAMILY OR MARRIAGE COUNSELING

Catholic Charities of The ....B... 320 650-1550
Saint Cloud *(G-7473)*

Pathways Psychological Svcs 763 525-8590
Minneapolis *(G-5346)*

Storefront Group ....E... 612 861-1675
Richfield *(G-7038)*

FAMILY PLANNING CENTERS

County of Brown-Nicollet ....E... 507 354-4418
New Ulm *(G-6446)*

Planned Parenthood of MN ....E... 651 698-2401
Saint Paul *(G-8830)*

FAMILY PLANNING CLINIC

Fairview Health Services ....E... 612 721-5044
Minneapolis *(G-4395)*

FAMILY SVCS AGENCY

Aitkin County ....E... 218 927-3744
Aitkin *(G-13)*

Glenwood-Lyndale Community Ctr ......D... 612 342-1500
Minneapolis *(G-4530)*

Goodwill Industries Inc ....C... 651 379-5800
Saint Paul *(G-8421)*

Goodwill Industries Inc ....E... 952 953-4410
Saint Paul *(G-7787)*

Goodwill Industries Inc ....E... 651 439-4207
Stillwater *(G-9620)*

Goodwill Industries Inc ....D... 651 603-1544
Saint Paul *(G-8422)*

Harriet Tubman Center Inc ....E... 612 825-3333
Minneapolis *(G-4602)*

Human Services ....E... 320 634-5750
Glenwood *(G-2227)*

Minnesota Department of Human ....A... 651 431-2000
Saint Paul *(G-8683)*

FARM & GARDEN MACHINERY WHOLESALERS

C & B Operations LLC ....E... 507 375-3144
Saint James *(G-7642)*

Cnh America LLC ....E... 952 854-1443
Minneapolis *(G-4114)*

Frattalone Tractor Co Inc ....C... 651 484-0448
Saint Paul *(G-8396)*

Interstate Service of Fergus ....E... 218 739-3284
Fergus Falls *(G-2077)*

Lee Hydra-Mac Sales ....E... 218 574-2237
Fertile *(G-2126)*

Power Systems LLC ....E... 952 361-6800
Chanhassen *(G-935)*

Rdo Equipment Co ....E... 218 483-3353
Hawley *(G-2421)*

Tilton Equipment Co ....D... 763 783-7030
Lindstrom *(G-2971)*

Worthington Tractor Parts Inc ....E... 507 372-2911
Worthington *(G-10198)*

Ziegler AG Equipment ....E... 507 847-7600
Jackson *(G-2801)*

FARM MACHINERY REPAIR SVCS

Kibble Equipment Inc ....D... 320 269-6466
Montevideo *(G-6248)*

FARM MANAGEMENT SVCS

Centrol Inc ....E... 218 584-5107
Twin Valley *(G-9701)*

Centrol Inc Cottonwood, MN ....E... 507 423-5423
Cottonwood *(G-1111)*

Larry A Larson ....E... 320 235-1294
Willmar *(G-10018)*

FARM MORTGAGE COMPANIES

Agstar Financial Services, Aca ....E... 507 376-4144
Worthington *(G-10177)*

Production Credit Association ....D... 320 235-1771
Willmar *(G-10038)*

FARM PRDTS, RAW MATERIALS, WHOLESALE: Cotton Merchants

Starchtech Inc ....E... 763 545-5400
Minneapolis *(G-5741)*

FARM PRDTS, RAW MATERIALS, WHOLESALE: Furs

North Central Co's Inc ....E... 952 449-0885
Minnetonka *(G-6204)*

FARM PRDTS, RAW MATERIALS, WHOLESALE: Hides

Darling International Inc ....D... 507 526-3296
Blue Earth *(G-533)*

North Central Co's Inc ....E... 952 449-0885
Minnetonka *(G-6204)*

FARM PRDTS, RAW MATERIALS, WHOLESALE: Hops

North Central Co's Inc ....E... 952 449-0885
Minnetonka *(G-6204)*

FARM PRDTS, RAW MATERIALS, WHOLESALE: Sugar

United Sugars Corp ....E... 952 896-0131
Minneapolis *(G-5916)*

FARM SPLYS WHOLESALERS

Agreliant Genetics LLC ....E... 218 631-2954
Wadena *(G-9796)*

Albert Lea Seed House Inc ....E... 507 373-3161
Albert Lea *(G-33)*

American Agco Inc ....D... 651 451-1349
Cottage Grove *(G-1098)*

Belle Plaine Cooperative ....E... 952 873-4244
Belle Plaine *(G-367)*

Border States Cooperative ....E... 320 695-2575
Browns Valley *(G-626)*

Coop FCA ....E... 507 847-4160
Jackson *(G-2789)*

F M Trucking Inc ....E... 651 639-0446
Saint Paul *(G-8358)*

Faribo Farm & Home Supply Inc ....E... 507 334-3232
Faribault *(G-2006)*

Farm Country Co-Op ....E... 507 356-8313
Pine Island *(G-6816)*

Farmers Co-Operative Oil Co of ....E... 507 925-4114
Echo *(G-1581)*

Farmers Union Oil Co of ....E... 320 763-6557
Alexandria *(G-100)*

Federated Coop Inc ....E... 320 679-2682
Mora *(G-6358)*

Fleet Wholesale Supply Co Inc ....D... 507 281-1130
Rochester *(G-7117)*

Fleet Wholesale Supply Co Inc ....C... 763 424-9668
Minneapolis *(G-4455)*

Glh Seeds Inc 952 445-8090
Shakopee *(G-9441)*

High Plains Cooperative ....D... 507 534-3111
Plainview *(G-6843)*

Jirik Sod Farm Inc ....E... 651 460-6555
Farmington *(G-2052)*

Land O'Lakes Purina Feed LLC ....E... 651 681-5917
Inver Grove Heights *(G-2757)*

Mid-States Distributing Co Inc ....E... 651 698-8831
Saint Paul *(G-8652)*

Peterson's North Branch Mill ....E... 651 674-4425
North Branch *(G-6504)*

Syngenta Seeds Inc ....E... 320 286-5511
Cokato *(G-1081)*

U S Commodities L L C ....D... 612 486-3800
Minneapolis *(G-5888)*

Universal Cooperatives Inc ....D... 651 239-1000
Saint Paul *(G-7938)*

West Central Chemicals ....E... 507 444-0275
Owatonna *(G-6745)*

FARM SPLYS, WHOLESALE: Equestrian Eqpt

National Tack North Inc ....E... 651 464-7733
Forest Lake *(G-2165)*

FARM SPLYS, WHOLESALE: Feed

American Agco Inc ....D... 651 451-1349
Cottage Grove *(G-1098)*

Belle Plaine Cooperative ....E... 952 873-4244
Belle Plaine *(G-367)*

Bemidji Cooperative Assn ....E... 218 751-4260
Bemidji *(G-379)*

Bremner Food Group Inc ....E... 612 331-5908
Minneapolis *(G-3942)*

Coop FCA ....E... 507 847-4160
Jackson *(G-2789)*

Crystal Valley Coop ....E... 507 642-8837
La Salle *(G-2846)*

Farm Country Co-Op ....E... 507 356-8313
Pine Island *(G-6816)*

Farmers Co-Operative of Hanska ....E... 507 439-6244
Hanska *(G-2370)*

Federated Coop Inc ....E... 320 679-2682
Mora *(G-6358)*

Gessell Feed Mill Inc ....E... 320 547-2994
Swanville *(G-9658)*

Kruse Family Enterprises LLC ....E... 507 345-5926
Mankato *(G-3156)*

Land O'Lakes Purina Feed LLC ....E... 320 235-6000
Willmar *(G-10017)*

Land O'Lakes Purina Feed LLC ....E... 218 847-3176
Detroit Lakes *(G-1206)*

Land O'Lakes Purina Feed LLC ....E... 651 437-7762
Inver Grove Heights *(G-2758)*

MG Waldbaum Co ....D... 952 258-4000
Minnetonka *(G-6192)*

Minn-Kota AG Products Inc ....E... 218 643-8464
Breckenridge *(G-595)*

Peterson Biddick Co ....E... 218 631-2954
Crookston *(G-1133)*

Peterson's North Branch Mill ....E... 651 674-4425
North Branch *(G-6504)*

Sunrich Inc ....D... 507 451-3316
Hope *(G-2496)*

Sunrise AG Cooperative ....E... 320 468-6433
Buckman *(G-632)*

United Farmers Co Op ....E... 507 237-2281
Gaylord *(G-2201)*

Watonwan Farm Service Inc ....E... 507 776-2831
Truman *(G-9699)*

Western Consolidated Co-op ....E... 320 394-2171
Holloway *(G-2493)*

Wilmont Farmers Elevator Co ....E... 507 926-5131
Wilmont *(G-10064)*

FARM SPLYS, WHOLESALE: Garden Splys

American Agco Inc ....D... 651 451-1349
Cottage Grove *(G-1098)*

Bfg Supply Co LLC ....D... 612 781-6068
Minneapolis *(G-3898)*

FARM SPLYS, WHOLESALE: Insecticides

Kruse Family Enterprises LLC ....E... 507 345-5926
Mankato *(G-3156)*

FARM SPLYS, WHOLESALE: Seed, Grass

Esco Industries Inc ....E... 320 259-9470
Waite Park *(G-9822)*

FARM SPLYS, WHOLESALE: Seeds, Field, Garden & Flower

Albert Lea Seed House Inc ....E... 507 373-3161
Albert Lea *(G-33)*

American Crystal Sugar Co ....C... 218 236-4400
Moorhead *(G-6295)*

Belle Plaine Cooperative ....E... 952 873-4244
Belle Plaine *(G-367)*

Bemidji Cooperative Assn ....E... 218 751-4260
Bemidji *(G-379)*

Betaseed Inc ....E... 952 445-8090
Shakopee *(G-9421)*

Coop Audubon Elevator Assn 218 439-6111
Audubon *(G-254)*

Coop FCA ....E... 507 847-4160
Jackson *(G-2789)*

Crystal Valley Coop ....E... 507 642-8837
La Salle *(G-2846)*

Farm Country Co-Op ....E... 507 356-8313
Pine Island *(G-6816)*

Farmers Co-Operative of Hanska ....E... 507 439-6244
Hanska *(G-2370)*

Farmers Union Oil Co of ....E... 320 269-8856
Montevideo *(G-6245)*

Monsanto Co ....E... 507 524-3475
Mapleton *(G-3283)*

Multi-County AG LLC ....E... 507 223-5634
Canby *(G-850)*

Seeds 2000 Inc ....E... 218 643-2410
Breckenridge *(G-600)*

St Hilaire Seed Co Inc ....E... 218 964-5407
Saint Hilaire *(G-7640)*

Sunrich Inc ....D... 507 451-3316
Hope *(G-2496)*

Sunrich LLC ....D... 218 643-8467
Breckenridge *(G-602)*

United Farmers Co Op ....E... 507 237-2281
Gaylord *(G-2201)*

Watonwan Farm Service Inc ....E... 507 776-2831
Truman *(G-9699)*

Western Consolidated Co-op ....E... 320 394-2171
Holloway *(G-2493)*

Wilmont Farmers Elevator Co ....E... 507 926-5131
Wilmont *(G-10064)*

Employment codes: A=Over 500 employees, B=251-500,
C=101-250, D=51-100, E=25-50

2011 Harris Minnesota
Services Directory

© Harris InfoSource 1-866-281-6415
701

SERVICES

FARM SPLYS, WHOLESALE: Soil, Potting & Planting

Aitkin Agri-Peat Inc ....E... 763 441-8387
Elk River *(G-1860)*

FARMING: Alfalfa

Salad Makers Inc ....E... 218 236-4959
Moorhead *(G-6341)*

FARMING: Animal Specialty, General

Robert Fitzsimmons & Sons LLP ....E... 507 524-4511
Mapleton *(G-3285)*

FARMING: Apple

Morris-Walker Ltd ....C... 952 873-4334
Belle Plaine *(G-368)*
Wescott Agri-Products Inc ....E... 507 876-2891
Elgin *(G-1857)*

FARMING: Bean Sprouts, Grown Under Cover

Calco Sprouts Inc ....E... 612 724-0276
Minneapolis *(G-3991)*
Salad Makers Inc ....E... 218 236-4959
Moorhead *(G-6341)*

FARMING: Bedding Plants

Nelson Nursery Inc ....D... 763 856-2441
Zimmerman *(G-10214)*

FARMING: Chicken Eggs

Luoma Egg Ranch Inc ....E... 320 233-6122
Finlayson *(G-2130)*
Michael Foods Group Inc ....C... 952 258-4000
Minnetonka *(G-6193)*
Michael Foods Inc ....C... 507 665-8851
Le Sueur *(G-2962)*

FARMING: Corn

Bigstone Hutterian Brethren ....E... 320 748-7916
Graceville *(G-2252)*
Eldon Potthoff ....E... 507 695-2784
Dunnell *(G-1513)*
Gorans Brothers Inc ....E... 320 995-6564
Blomkest *(G-475)*
Hader Farms Inc ....E... 507 824-2543
Zumbrota *(G-10219)*
Kreger Farms Inc ....E... 320 983-5060
Milaca *(G-3373)*

FARMING: Crops, NEC

Altona Hutterian Brethren Inc ....E... 507 248-3191
Henderson *(G-2428)*
Benedict Farms Inc ....E... 218 789-7376
Sabin *(G-7396)*
Carman Berry Farm ....E... 218 631-4613
Wadena *(G-9799)*
Durst Brothers ....E... 507 635-5588
Mantorville *(G-3233)*
Fairhaven Farm ....E... 320 236-7685
South Haven *(G-9505)*
Lismore Hutterian Brethern ....D... 320 325-5485
Clinton *(G-1044)*
Son-D-Farms Inc ....E... 507 483-2245
Adrian *(G-5)*
Spring Prairie Hutterian ....C... 218 498-0222
Hawley *(G-2423)*

FARMING: Dairy

Daley Farm of Lewiston LLP ....E... 507 523-3687
Lewiston *(G-2965)*
Diamond K Dairy Inc ....E... 507 689-2058
Altura *(G-131)*
Durst Brothers ....E... 507 635-5588
Mantorville *(G-3233)*
Haubenschild Farm Dairy Inc ....E... 763 389-2867
Princeton *(G-6902)*
Meadow Star Dairy, LLP ....E... 320 392-5609
Morris *(G-6373)*
Rck Inc ....E... 320 693-7422
Litchfield *(G-2990)*
Riverview Dairy Inc ....E... 320 392-5609
Morris *(G-6377)*

FARMING: Flowers, Grown In Field Nurseries

Sargent's Landscape Nursery ....E... 507 289-0022
Rochester *(G-7247)*
Sargent's Nursery Inc ....E... 651 388-3847
Red Wing *(G-7004)*

FARMING: Flowers, Grown Under Cover

Anderson Florists ....E... 320 763-5115
Alexandria *(G-83)*

FARMING: Grain, NEC

Bigstone Hutterian Brethren ....E... 320 748-7916
Graceville *(G-2252)*
Daniel J Olsgaard ....E... 218 299-6162
Moorhead *(G-6311)*

FARMING: Herb, Open Field

Dehn's Gardens Inc ....E... 763 753-2806
Anoka *(G-173)*

FARMING: Hog & Pig

Altona Hutterian Brethren Inc ....E... 507 248-3191
Henderson *(G-2428)*
Choice Connections LLP ....E... 507 524-4583
Mapleton *(G-3282)*
Christensen Farms Midwest LLC ....D... 507 794-5310
Sleepy Eye *(G-9493)*
Eldon Potthoff ....E... 507 695-2784
Dunnell *(G-1513)*
Holden Farms Inc ....D... 507 663-0003
Northfield *(G-6530)*
New Fashion Pork Inc ....C... 507 847-4610
Jackson *(G-2797)*
North Dakota Pigs Co-Op ....E... 218 685-6888
Elbow Lake *(G-1854)*
Schwartz Bros Inc ....E... 507 794-5779
Sleepy Eye *(G-9499)*
Son-D-Farms Inc ....E... 507 483-2245
Adrian *(G-5)*
Ten Brook Pork LLP ....E... 952 440-5737
Prior Lake *(G-6958)*
Wakefield Pork Inc ....D... 507 237-5581
Gaylord *(G-2202)*

FARMING: Hydroponic Crops

Vine Ripe Inc ....D... 507 451-5692
Owatonna *(G-6742)*

FARMING: Livestock, General

Spring Prairie Hutterian ....C... 218 498-0222
Hawley *(G-2423)*

FARMING: Noncitrus Fruit, NEC

Apple Jack Inc ....E... 763 972-6673
Delano *(G-1181)*

FARMING: Nursery Stock Production

Baudora State Forest Nursery ....D... 218 652-2385
Akeley *(G-25)*
Dan & Jerry's Greenhouses Inc ....D... 763 271-6594
Monticello *(G-6269)*
Great River Garden ....E... 218 927-2521
Aitkin *(G-19)*
Lynde Greenhouse & Nursery Inc ....E... 763 420-4400
Osseo *(G-6630)*
Nelson Nursery Inc ....D... 763 856-2441
Zimmerman *(G-10214)*
Prairie Restorations Inc ....E... 763 389-4342
Princeton *(G-6924)*
Richard Koberski 507 642-8380
Madelia *(G-3074)*
Sargent's Landscape Nursery ....E... 507 289-0022
Rochester *(G-7247)*
Sargent's Nursery Inc ....E... 651 388-3847
Red Wing *(G-7004)*
Wilson's Nursery Inc ....E... 952 445-3630
Chanhassen *(G-946)*
Wolcyn Tree Farms ....E... 763 689-3346
Cambridge *(G-847)*

FARMING: Plants, Potted

Donahues' Greenhouses Inc ....E... 507 334-8404
Faribault *(G-2001)*
Lynde Greenhouse & Nursery Inc ....E... 763 420-4400
Osseo *(G-6630)*

FARMING: Plants, foliage & shrubberies

Wilson's Nursery Inc ....E... 952 445-3630
Chanhassen *(G-946)*

FARMING: Potato

R D Offutt Co ....E... 218 732-1461
Park Rapids *(G-6760)*

FARMING: Pumpkin

Axdahl Farms Inc ....E... 651 439-3134
Stillwater *(G-9600)*

FARMING: Rice

Riviana International Inc ....D... 218 776-3118
Clearbrook *(G-1040)*

FARMING: Seeds, Vegetable

Betaseed Inc ....E... 952 445-8090
Shakopee *(G-9421)*

FARMING: Shrubberies, Grown In Field Nurseries

Nelson Nursery Inc ....D... 763 856-2441
Zimmerman *(G-10214)*
Wilson's Nursery Inc ....E... 952 445-3630
Chanhassen *(G-946)*

FARMING: Shrubberies, Grown Under Cover

Lynde Greenhouse & Nursery Inc ....E... 763 420-4400
Osseo *(G-6630)*

FARMING: Sod

Blue Valley Sod Co ....E... 218 927-4557
Aitkin *(G-17)*
Central Turf Farms ....E... 651 464-2130
Forest Lake *(G-2144)*
Contract Sod Services Inc ....E... 651 457-6037
Inver Grove Heights *(G-2745)*
Glenn R Rehbein Excavating Inc ....E... 651 674-7937
Harris *(G-2373)*
Glenn Rehbein Excavating Inc ....C... 763 784-0657
Minneapolis *(G-3475)*
Kowsary Turf Inc ....E... 763 862-4646
Elk River *(G-1882)*
Wagner Sod Co Inc ....E... 651 457-6037
Inver Grove Heights *(G-2773)*

FARMING: Soybean

Eldon Potthoff ....E... 507 695-2784
Dunnell *(G-1513)*
Gorans Brothers Inc ....E... 320 995-6564
Blomkest *(G-475)*
Hader Farms ....E... 507 824-2327
Wanamingo *(G-9863)*
Hader Farms Inc ....E... 507 824-2543
Zumbrota *(G-10219)*
Kreger Farms Inc ....E... 320 983-5060
Milaca *(G-3373)*
Larry A Larson ....E... 320 235-1294
Willmar *(G-10018)*

FARMING: Tomatoes, Grown Under Cover

Vine Ripe Inc ....D... 507 451-5692
Owatonna *(G-6742)*

FARMING: Turkey Egg

Orsten Turkeys Inc ....E... 320 235-5751
Willmar *(G-10033)*

FARMING: Turkeys

AG Forte LLC ....E... 507 847-5110
Jackson *(G-2785)*
Burkel Turkey Farms Inc ....E... 218 334-2833
Frazee *(G-2183)*
Gorans Brothers Inc ....E... 320 995-6564
Blomkest *(G-475)*
Holden Farms Inc ....D... 507 663-0003
Northfield *(G-6530)*
Hormel Foods Corp ....A... 507 437-5611
Austin *(G-275)*
Jennie-O Turkey Store Inc ....C... 320 235-2622
Willmar *(G-10011)*
Jennie-O Turkey Store Inc ....E... 320 974-8891
Atwater *(G-252)*
Jennie-O Turkey Store Inc ....E... 507 334-0087
Faribault *(G-2015)*
Jennie-O Turkey Store Inc ....E... 218 583-2204
Henning *(G-2432)*
Jennie-O Turkey Store Inc ....C... 320 243-3764
Paynesville *(G-6769)*
New Life Farms LLP ....D... 218 346-7587
Frazee *(G-2186)*
New Life Farms, Lllp ....D... 218 346-4959
Perham *(G-6799)*
Pals Inc ....D... 320 235-8860
Willmar *(G-10035)*
Prinsburg Farmers Co-Op ....E... 320 978-8040
Prinsburg *(G-6927)*

Turkey Valley Farms LLC ....B... 507 337-3100
Marshall *(G-3330)*

FARMING: Turkeys & Turkey Eggs

Jennie-O Turkey Store Inc ....E... 218 736-6931
Fergus Falls *(G-2079)*

Mickelson Farms......................................E... 218 346-3876
Frazee *(G-2185)*

FARMING: Wheat

Bob Dahl ....E... 218 874-6321
Newfolden *(G-6481)*

FASTENERS WHOLESALERS

Accurate Component Sales Inc ....E... 651 639-1881
Saint Paul *(G-7978)*

Lindstrom Metric LLC ....D... 763 780-4200
Minneapolis *(G-3521)*

Wurth Adams Nut & Bolt Co ....D... 763 493-0877
Osseo *(G-6685)*

FEDERAL SAVINGS & LOAN ASSOCIATIONS

1st United Bank....................................E... 507 334-2201
Faribault *(G-2008)*

Home Savings of America.....................E... 320 632-5461
Little Falls *(G-3006)*

Mid-Central Federal Saings...................E... 218 631-1414
Wadena *(G-9805)*

Queen City Federal Savings 218 741-2040
Virginia *(G-9752)*

TCF National Bank ....E... 651 770-2273
Saint Paul *(G-9029)*

TCF National Bank ....E... 612 379-8597
Minneapolis *(G-5797)*

TCF National Bank ....E... 651 735-6510
Saint Paul *(G-9028)*

TCF National Bank ....E... 952 888-8375
Minneapolis *(G-5798)*

TCF National Bank ....E... 651 291-4095
Saint Paul *(G-9027)*

Viking Savings Association ....E... 320 762-0236
Alexandria *(G-128)*

FEDERAL SAVINGS BANKS

Home Federal Savings Bank.................E... 507 535-1200
Rochester *(G-7139)*

Inter Savings Bank Fsb ....E... 952 920-6700
Edina *(G-1834)*

Liberty Savings Bank Fsb ....E... 320 252-2841
Saint Cloud *(G-7545)*

TCF Equipment Finance Inc..................C... 952 656-5080
Minneapolis *(G-5796)*

TCF National Bank ....E... 763 546-5637
Hopkins *(G-2643)*

Voyager Bank ....E... 952 345-7600
Eden Prairie *(G-1811)*

Wells Federal Bank Fsb ....E... 507 553-3151
Wells *(G-9963)*

FERTILIZER, AGRICULTURAL: Wholesalers

AG Partners Coop ....E... 651 923-4496
Goodhue *(G-2248)*

Belgrade Cooperative Assn ....E... 320 254-8231
Belgrade *(G-363)*

Belle Plaine Cooperative ....E... 952 873-4244
Belle Plaine *(G-367)*

Bemidji Cooperative Assn ....E... 218 751-4260
Bemidji *(G-379)*

Cargill Inc...D... 763 441-6508
Elk River *(G-1866)*

Central Valley Cooperative 507 451-1230
Owatonna *(G-6700)*

Country Pride Services Co-op ....E... 507 831-2580
Bingham Lake *(G-466)*

Crystal Valley Coop ....E... 507 642-8837
La Salle *(G-2846)*

Farmers Co-Op Oil Co of Clara 320 847-2318
Clara City *(G-1027)*

Farmers Co-Operative of Hanska ....E... 507 439-6244
Hanska *(G-2370)*

Farmers Co-Operative Oil Co of ....E... 507 925-4114
Echo *(G-1581)*

Farmers Union Oil Co of........................E... 320 269-8856
Montevideo *(G-6245)*

Federated Coop Inc ....E... 320 679-2682
Mora *(G-6358)*

Glacial Plains Cooperative ....D... 320 843-4820
Benson *(G-439)*

Greenway Co-Operative Service ....E... 507 775-2900
Byron *(G-7242)*

Hollandale Marketing Assn ....E... 507 889-3181
Hollandale *(G-2492)*

Minn-Kota AG Products Inc ....E... 218 643-8464
Breckenridge *(G-595)*

Multi-County AG LLC ....E... 507 223-5634
Canby *(G-850)*

Peterson's North Branch Mill................E... 651 674-4425
North Branch *(G-6504)*

Precision Turf & Chemical Inc 763 477-5885
Rockford *(G-7303)*

Red Lake County Cooperative ....E... 218 253-2149
Red Lake Falls *(G-6973)*

Sunrich Inc ....D... 507 451-3316
Hope *(G-2496)*

United Farmers Co Op ....E... 507 237-2281
Gaylord *(G-2201)*

Watonwan Farm Service Inc ....E... 507 776-2831
Truman *(G-9699)*

West Central Inc...................................E... 320 235-8518
Willmar *(G-10053)*

Western Consolidated Co-op ....E... 320 394-2171
Holloway *(G-2493)*

Wilmont Farmers Elevator Co...............E... 507 926-5131
Wilmont *(G-10064)*

FIDELITY RESPONSIBILITY INSURANCE

St Paul Fire & Marine Insce ....A... 651 221-7911
Saint Paul *(G-8990)*

FILM DEVELOPING & PRINTING SVCS

Camera Shop of Saint Cloud Inc ....E... 320 251-2622
Saint Cloud *(G-7468)*

FILM PROCESSING & FINISHING LABORATORY

Falk's Woodland Pharmacy Inc ....E... 218 728-4242
Duluth *(G-1318)*

Falk's Woodland Pharmacy Inc ....E... 218 740-2650
Duluth *(G-1319)*

National Camera Exchange Inc ....E... 651 636-0693
Saint Paul *(G-8739)*

Rcc Liquidating Corp............................E... 507 281-0313
Rochester *(G-7218)*

Rcc Liquidating Corp............................E... 651 699-0988
Saint Paul *(G-8875)*

Rcc Liquidating Corp............................E... 763 546-3771
Hopkins *(G-2611)*

FILM STRIP, SLIDE & STILL FILM PRODUCTION SVCS

Greer & Associates Inc.........................E... 612 338-6171
Minneapolis *(G-4564)*

FINANCIAL INVESTMENT ACTIVITIES, NEC: Financial Reporting

Christopher Maclennan ....E... 612 243-3302
Minneapolis *(G-4071)*

FINANCIAL INVESTMENT ACTIVITIES, NEC: Stock Transfer Agents

Wells Fargo Bank, National...................C... 651 450-4054
South Saint Paul *(G-9551)*

FINANCIAL INVESTMENT ADVICE

Ameriprise ....E... 952 835-8180
Minneapolis *(G-3765)*

Ameriprise Financial Inc ....A... 612 671-3131
Minneapolis *(G-3767)*

Ameriprise Financial Services ....C... 612 671-7536
Minneapolis *(G-3768)*

Ameriprise Financial Services ....C... 612 671-4343
Minneapolis *(G-3769)*

Bancnorth Investment Group ....E... 320 656-4300
Saint Cloud *(G-7457)*

Deluxe Financial Services Inc...............D... 651 787-2766
Saint Paul *(G-8286)*

Ebf & Associates LP ....E... 952 476-7200
Hopkins *(G-2537)*

Knight Financial Products LLC ....D... 952 249-5500
Hopkins *(G-2565)*

Midwest Financial Processing..............E... 507 647-2856
Winthrop *(G-10168)*

Oshkosh, McNeilus Financia ....E... 507 775-3310
Byron *(G-825)*

Primerica Financial Services ....D... 952 895-1091
Burnsville *(G-782)*

Roxbury Capital Management LLC ....E... 952 230-6140
Minnetonka *(G-6221)*

RSM McGladrey Inc ....D... 507 288-5363
Rochester *(G-7274)*

300 Financial Inc ....E... 507 424-4799
Rochester *(G-7274)*

Vilana Financial Inc ....E... 763 416-5959
Minneapolis *(G-5975)*

FINANCIAL SVCS

Acclaim Benefits LLC...........................D... 763 278-4620
Minneapolis *(G-3668)*

Agstar Financial Services, Aca ....E... 320 203-4613
Waite Park *(G-9815)*

Cash Pass Network ....E... 952 358-7080
Burnsville *(G-695)*

Columns Resource of ....E... 952 806-9600
Minneapolis *(G-4126)*

Deluxe Corp ....B... 651 483-7111
Saint Paul *(G-8285)*

Evangelical Lutheran Church In............C... 612 752-4080
Minneapolis *(G-4376)*

Fair Isaac Corp.....................................B... 612 758-5200
Minneapolis *(G-4392)*

Financial Systems Support ....E... 612 625-3493
Minneapolis *(G-4433)*

First Street Credit Corp ....E... 612 871-4579
Minneapolis *(G-4445)*

Gelco Information Network Inc ....C... 952 947-1500
Eden Prairie *(G-1672)*

Green Tree Investment Holdings ....D... 651 293-3410
Saint Paul *(G-8432)*

Gwg Holdings LLC ....E... 612 746-6119
Minneapolis *(G-4583)*

Homelink Mortgage Corp......................E... 952 935-1986
Hopkins *(G-2552)*

Hsbc Card Services Inc.........................C... 952 358-4000
Minnetonka *(G-6179)*

Living Benefits Financial Svcs ....E... 952 903-9800
Minnetonka *(G-6187)*

Money Gram Payment Systems Inc.....A... 952 591-3000
Minneapolis *(G-5120)*

Primerica Financial Services ....E... 763 546-8627
Minneapolis *(G-5410)*

Primerica Financial Services ....D... 651 688-9088
Saint Paul *(G-7882)*

Rbc Global Asset Management ....D... 612 376-7000
Minneapolis *(G-5471)*

Rdlp Financial Corp..............................E... 952 857-1479
Minneapolis *(G-5474)*

Redbrick Health Corp ....D... 612 659-3000
Minneapolis *(G-5478)*

Roghard Financial LLC ....C... 952 351-8300
Edina *(G-1842)*

RSM McGladrey Business Svcs............D... 952 857-1220
Minneapolis *(G-5568)*

Washington Post Co ....E... 651 523-1094
Saint Paul *(G-9141)*

Wealth Enhancement Group LLC ....D... 763 417-1428
Plymouth *(G-6890)*

Wolters Kluwer Financial Svcs ....A... 320 251-3060
Saint Cloud *(G-7634)*

FIRE ALARM MAINTENANCE & MONITORING SVCS

Arrowhead Security Systems Inc.........E... 218 722-1234
Duluth *(G-1243)*

Checkpoint Security Systems ....C... 952 942-9431
Chanhassen *(G-914)*

Checkpoint Systems Inc ....E... 952 227-5350
Chaska *(G-958)*

Checkpoint Systems Inc ....C... 952 943-3853
Chanhassen *(G-915)*

Electro-Watchman Inc...........................E... 651 227-8461
Saint Paul *(G-8329)*

Pro-TEC Design Inc ....E... 763 553-1477
Plymouth *(G-6880)*

Rhjh Inc ....E... 651 735-7470
Saint Paul *(G-8897)*

FIRE CONTROL EQPT REPAIR SVCS, MILITARY

Nardini Fire Equipment Co Inc ....D... 651 483-6631
Saint Paul *(G-8735)*

FIRE EXTINGUISHER SVC

All Fire Test Co Inc ....E... 612 332-3473
Minneapolis *(G-3709)*

William LLC..E... 952 345-3461
Minneapolis *(G-6069)*

FIRE EXTINGUISHERS, WHOLESALE

AAA-American Co ....E... 507 894-4156
Hokah *(G-2490)*

Activar Inc..E... 952 835-6850
Minneapolis *(G-3677)*

Minnesota Conway Fire & Safety ....E... 952 345-3473
Minneapolis *(G-5072)*

Employment codes: A=Over 500 employees, B=251-500,
C=101-250, D=51-100, E=25-50

2011 Harris Minnesota
Services Directory

© Harris InfoSource 1-866-281-6415
703

S E R V I C E S

FIRE FIGHTING SVCS, FOREST

Nardini Fire Equipment Co Inc ....D... 651 483-6631
Saint Paul (G-8735)

FIRE FIGHTING SVCS, FOREST

First Strike of Duluth Inc ....E... 218 721-5081
Duluth (G-1324)

FIRE PROTECTION SVCS: Contracted

A G O'Brien Plumbing & Heating ....E... 218 729-9662
Hermantown (G-2433)
Lower Saint Croix Valley Fire ....E... 651 436-7033
Lakeland (G-2886)
Red Rock Fire Inc..................................E... 651 765-0765
Forest Lake (G-2154)
South Bend Township Fire Dept ....E... 507 345-4863
Mankato (G-3199)

FIRE, MARINE & CASUALTY INSURANCE CARRIERS

Discover Property & Casualty 800 878-2660
Saint Paul (G-8299)
First Protection Corp ....E... 952 473-0114
Minnetonka (G-6169)
Harleysville Insurance Co ....D... 952 829-4000
Minneapolis (G-4598)
Midwest Family Mutual Insce ....D... 952 545-6000
Hopkins (G-2583)
St Paul Fire & Marine Insce ....C... 952 893-5602
Minneapolis (G-5730)
St Paul Guardian Insurance Co ....A... 651 221-7911
Saint Paul (G-8991)
St Paul Mercury Insurance Co 651 221-7911
Saint Paul (G-8994)

FIRE, MARINE & CASUALTY INSURANCE: Assessment Associations

Rtw Inc ....D... 952 893-0403
Minneapolis (G-5572)

FIRE, MARINE & CASUALTY INSURANCE: Mutual

Employers Insurance Co of ....D... 651 365-8053
Saint Paul (G-7760)
Federated Mutual Insurance Co ....C... 507 455-5200
Owatonna (G-6710)
Ram Mutual Insurance Co Inc...............D... 218 879-3321
Esko (G-1922)
Western National Mutual Insce ....B... 952 835-5350
Minneapolis (G-6060)

FIRE, MARINE & CASUALTY INSURANCE: Stock

Employers Mutual Casualty Co ....E... 952 938-4646
Hopkins (G-2539)

FIREARMS & AMMUNITION, EXC SPORTING, WHOLESALE

Lefty's Shooting & Outdoor 763 533-9594
Minneapolis (G-4854)
Minnpar LLC ....D... 612 379-0606
Minneapolis (G-5103)

FISH & SEAFOOD WHOLESALERS

American Fish & Seafood Inc ....D... 952 935-3474
Hopkins (G-2509)
Chin Leeann Inc ....E... 952 890-9012
Burnsville (G-697)
Guys Fish Inc ....E... 612 339-7720
Minneapolis (G-4581)

FISH, PACKAGED FROZEN: Wholesalers

American Fish & Seafood Inc ....D... 952 935-3474
Hopkins (G-2509)
Apperts Frozen Foods Inc.....................D... 320 251-3200
Saint Cloud (G-7434)

FISHING CAMPS

Peters Sunset Beach Inc ....E... 320 634-4501
Glenwood (G-2230)

FIXED BASE OPERATOR

Bemidji Aviation Services Inc...............E... 218 751-1880
Bemidji (G-377)
Hiawatha Aviation of Rochester ....E... 507 282-1717
Rochester (G-7137)
S T C Aviation Inc ....E... 320 253-1500
Saint Cloud (G-7440)

FLOOR COVERINGS WHOLESALERS

C L T Floor Coverings Inc ....E... 651 451-0069
Inver Grove Heights (G-2740)
Carpet Factory Outlet Inc 612 988-0400
Minneapolis (G-4020)
Floor Store Inc ....E... 952 401-0955
Excelsior (G-1943)
Grill Works Inc.....................................E... 507 532-3524
Marshall (G-3298)
Hank's Specialties Inc ....E... 651 633-5020
New Brighton (G-6409)
Herregan Distributors Inc.....................E... 651 452-7200
Saint Paul (G-7799)
Mohawk Industries Inc ....E... 651 405-8300
Saint Paul (G-7845)
Olympia Tile Inc ....E... 763 545-5455
Minneapolis (G-5274)

FLOOR TRADERS: Security

Piper Jaffray Co's ....E... 952 476-3939
Wayzata (G-9935)

FLOOR WAXING SVCS

Carlson Building Maintenance ....B... 651 481-9970
Saint Paul (G-8166)
Paquette Maintenance Inc....................D... 952 888-1801
Minneapolis (G-5318)

FLORISTS' SPLYS, WHOLESALE

Hermes Floral Co Inc ....D... 651 646-6344
Saint Paul (G-8478)
Lakeland Florist Supply Inc ....E... 952 944-5160
Minneapolis (G-4834)
Ls Acquisitions Inc ....D... 612 331-4141
Minneapolis (G-4907)
Twin City Florist Supply Inc ....E... 612 377-7849
Minneapolis (G-5879)

FLOWERS & FLORISTS' SPLYS WHOLESALERS

Cherokee Manufacturing Inc.................E... 651 451-6568
South Saint Paul (G-9520)
Value Gardens Supply ....E... 952 884-6477
Minneapolis (G-5956)

FLOWERS & NURSERY STOCK, WHOLESALE

Bailey Nurseries Inc............................E... 651 459-9744
Newport (G-6484)
Bergen's Greenhouses Inc ....E... 218 847-2138
Detroit Lakes (G-1188)
Ls Acquisitions Inc ....D... 612 331-4141
Minneapolis (G-4907)

FLOWERS, FRESH, WHOLESALE

Donahues' Greenhouses Inc ....E... 507 334-8404
Faribault (G-2001)
Hermes Floral Co Inc ....D... 651 646-6344
Saint Paul (G-8478)
Minneapolis Floral Co ....E... 612 377-8080
Minneapolis (G-5053)
Twin City Florist Supply Inc ....E... 612 377-7849
Minneapolis (G-5879)

FOAMS & RUBBER, WHOLESALE

Belcourt Corp ....E... 952 894-0406
Burnsville (G-684)
Foam Industries Inc ....E... 763 503-9265
Champlin (G-894)

FOOD PRDTS, CONFECTIONERY, WHOLESALE: Candy

A H Hermel Candy & Tobacco Co ....D... 507 387-5634
Mankato (G-3098)
American Importing Co Inc ....D... 612 331-7000
Minneapolis (G-3751)
Bernick's Full-Line Vending..................E... 320 656-2131
Waite Park (G-9817)
Debbie Bolen ....E... 218 722-0912
Duluth (G-1292)
Fritz Co Inc ....D... 651 459-9751
Newport (G-6486)
Harvey-Winchell Co ....E... 952 881-7964
Minneapolis (G-4605)
International Dairy Queen Inc ....B... 952 830-0200
Minneapolis (G-4721)
Minter-Weisman Co ....B... 763 545-3706
Minneapolis (G-5105)

FOOD PRDTS, CONFECTIONERY, WHOLESALE: Nuts, Salted/Roasted

Sandstrom's Inc...................................D... 218 326-0567
Grand Rapids (G-2307)

American Importing Co Inc...................D... 612 331-7000
Minneapolis (G-3751)
Bergin Fruit & Nut Co Inc ....D... 651 642-1234
Saint Paul (G-8105)
International Dairy Queen Inc ....B... 952 830-0200
Minneapolis (G-4721)

FOOD PRDTS, CONFECTIONERY, WHOLESALE: Potato Chips

Frito-Lay Inc ....E... 507 282-1134
Rochester (G-7121)

FOOD PRDTS, CONFECTIONERY, WHOLESALE: Snack Foods

American Importing Co Inc...................D... 612 331-7000
Minneapolis (G-3751)
Bradley Distributing Co ....E... 651 639-0523
Newport (G-6485)
Frito-Lay Inc ....B... 507 446-5888
Owatonna (G-6715)
Jerky Snack Brands Inc ....E... 507 388-1661
Mankato (G-3153)
Kraft Foods Global Inc ....E... 612 331-4311
Minneapolis (G-4821)
Schott Distributing Co Inc ....E... 507 289-3555
Rochester (G-7248)

FOOD PRDTS, CONFECTIONERY, WHOLESALE: Toppings, Fountain

International Dairy Queen Inc ....B... 952 830-0200
Minneapolis (G-4721)

FOOD PRDTS, DAIRY, WHOLESALE: Frozen Dairy Desserts

Schwan's Global Food Service ....C... 507 532-3274
Marshall (G-3326)

FOOD PRDTS, DAIRY, WHOLESALE: Milk & Cream, Fluid

Associated Milk Producers Inc ....D... 320 769-2994
Dawson (G-1163)
Sunrise AG Cooperative ....E... 320 468-6433
Buckman (G-632)

FOOD PRDTS, FISH & SEAFOOD, WHOLESALE: Fresh

Worldwide Fish & Seafood Inc ....E... 612 724-5911
Minneapolis (G-6088)

FOOD PRDTS, FISH & SEAFOOD, WHOLESALE: Seafood

Stock Yards Meat Packing Co ....C... 651 450-6000
South Saint Paul (G-9544)
Sushi Avenue Inc ....D... 651 294-7000
Eagan (G-1555)
Worldwide Fish & Seafood Inc ....E... 612 724-5911
Minneapolis (G-6088)

FOOD PRDTS, FROZEN, WHOLESALE: Fish, Meat & Poultry

Appert's Inc...C... 320 251-3200
Saint Cloud (G-7433)
Royal Foods Inc...................................E... 952 936-0336
Hopkins (G-2622)

FOOD PRDTS, FRUITS & VEGETABLES, FRESH, WHOLESALE

Davis Russ Wholesale Inc ....D... 218 631-3070
Wadena (G-9800)
H Brooks & Co ....D... 651 635-0126
New Brighton (G-6408)
Nash-Finch Co ....B... 952 832-0534
Edina (G-1838)
Northwestern Fruit Co...........................E... 651 224-4373
Saint Paul (G-8771)
Twin City Produce Supplies Inc ....E... 612 378-1055
Minneapolis (G-5883)

FOOD PRDTS, FRUITS & VEGETABLES, FRESH, WHOLESALE: Fruits

Bergin Fruit & Nut Co Inc.....................D... 651 642-1234
Saint Paul (G-8105)

Bix Produce Co LLC ....C... 651 487-8000
Saint Paul **(G-8115)**
SUPERVALU Inc ....A... 952 828-4000
Eden Prairie **(G-1787)**
Supervalu Inc ....C... 952 906-6260
Chanhassen **(G-941)**
Wescott Agri-Products Inc ....E... 507 876-2891
Elgin **(G-1857)**
Wholesale Produce Supply LLC ....C... 612 378-2025
Minneapolis **(G-6067)**

FOOD PRDTS, FRUITS & VEGETABLES, FRESH, WHOLESALE: Potatoes

A & L Potato Co....................................E... 218 773-0123
East Grand Forks **(G-1564)**
Hull Co ....E... 763 262-4855
Big Lake **(G-447)**
Michael Foods Group Inc ....C... 952 258-4000
Minnetonka **(G-6193)**
Wingard Farms ....E... 763 263-2635
Elk River **(G-1896)**

FOOD PRDTS, FRUITS & VEGETABLES, FRESH, WHOLESALE: Vegetable

Bergin Fruit & Nut Co Inc ....D... 651 642-1234
Saint Paul **(G-8105)**
Bix Produce Co LLC ....C... 651 487-8000
Saint Paul **(G-8115)**
Brings Co Inc ....E... 651 484-2666
Saint Paul **(G-8129)**
Davis Russ Wholesale Inc ....D... 218 631-3070
Wadena **(G-9800)**
H Brooks & Co......................................D... 651 635-0126
New Brighton **(G-6408)**
Hollandale Marketing Assn ....E... 507 889-3181
Hollandale **(G-2492)**
Hull Co ....E... 763 262-4855
Big Lake **(G-447)**
Nash-Finch Co......................................B... 952 832-0534
Edina **(G-1838)**
Northwestern Fruit Co ....E... 651 224-4373
Saint Paul **(G-8771)**
Salad Makers Inc ....E... 218 236-4959
Moorhead **(G-6341)**
SUPERVALU Inc ....A... 952 828-4000
Eden Prairie **(G-1787)**
Supervalu Inc ....C... 952 906-6260
Chanhassen **(G-1787)**
Twin City Produce Supplies Inc ....E... 612 378-1055
Minneapolis **(G-5883)**
Wescott Agri-Products Inc ....E... 507 876-2891
Elgin **(G-1857)**
Wholesale Produce Supply LLC ....C... 612 378-2025
Minneapolis **(G-6067)**

FOOD PRDTS, MEAT & MEAT PRDTS, WHOLESALE: Cured Or Smoked

Interstate Meat Service Inc..................E... 507 377-2228
Albert Lea **(G-56)**
Nash-Finch Co......................................B... 952 832-0534
Edina **(G-1838)**

FOOD PRDTS, MEAT & MEAT PRDTS, WHOLESALE: Fresh

Christofersen Meats Co........................ 612 721-4411
Minneapolis **(G-4070)**
International Dairy Queen Inc ....B... 952 830-0200
Minneapolis **(G-4721)**
Interstate Meat Service Inc..................E... 507 377-2228
Albert Lea **(G-56)**
Nash-Finch Co......................................B... 952 832-0534
Edina **(G-1838)**
Royal Foods Inc ....E... 952 936-0336
Hopkins **(G-2622)**
Upper Lakes Foods Inc ....C... 218 879-1265
Cloquet **(G-1066)**

FOOD PRDTS, POULTRY, WHOLESALE: Eggs, Clean, Pack/Grade

Daybreak Foods Inc..............................D... 320 732-2966
Long Prairie **(G-3042)**
Michael Foods Group Inc ....C... 952 258-4000
Minnetonka **(G-6193)**

FOOD PRDTS, WHOLESALE: Beans, Field

St Hilaire Seed Co Inc..........................E... 218 964-5407
Saint Hilaire **(G-7640)**

FOOD PRDTS, WHOLESALE: Beverages, Exc Coffee & Tea

Berry Coffee Co....................................E... 952 937-8697
Eden Prairie **(G-1604)**
Hohensteins Inc ....E... 651 735-4978
Saint Paul **(G-9231)**
United States Distilled Prdts..................C... 763 389-4903
Princeton **(G-6918)**
Viking Coca Cola Bottling Co ....E... 218 829-2204
Baxter **(G-344)**
Wirtz Beverage Minnesota Beer ....C... 651 646-6063
Saint Paul **(G-9160)**

FOOD PRDTS, WHOLESALE: Breading Mixes

Don Stevens Inc ....E... 651 452-0872
Eagan **(G-1525)**

FOOD PRDTS, WHOLESALE: Coffee & Tea

Sara Lee Corp.......................................D... 763 572-2506
Minneapolis **(G-3595)**

FOOD PRDTS, WHOLESALE: Coffee, Green Or Roasted

Berry Coffee Co....................................E... 952 937-8697
Eden Prairie **(G-1604)**
Bradley Distributing Co ....E... 651 639-0523
Newport **(G-6485)**
Dunn Bros Coffee Inc ....E... 651 698-0618
Saint Paul **(G-8315)**
Javaology Enterprises LLC...................D... 952 943-3990
Chaska **(G-970)**
Olson Coffee Roasters Inc ....E... 651 645-1729
Saint Paul **(G-8782)**
Procter & Gamble Distributing ....C... 952 942-1857
Eden Prairie **(G-1754)**

FOOD PRDTS, WHOLESALE: Cooking Oils

Restaurant Technologies Inc................D... 651 796-1600
Saint Paul **(G-7894)**

FOOD PRDTS, WHOLESALE: Corn

All-American Co-Op...............................E... 507 533-4222
Stewartville **(G-9590)**
Cargill Inc ....A... 952 742-7575
Wayzata **(G-9909)**
CHS Inc ....A... 651 355-6000
Inver Grove Heights **(G-2742)**
Coop FCA ....E... 507 847-4160
Jackson **(G-2789)**
Wilmont Farmers Elevator Co...............E... 507 926-5131
Wilmont **(G-10064)**

FOOD PRDTS, WHOLESALE: Crackers, Cookies & Bakery Prdts

Braschler's Bakery Inc ....E... 651 388-1589
Red Wing **(G-6976)**

FOOD PRDTS, WHOLESALE: Dog Food

Waymouth Farms Inc.............................C... 763 533-5300
Minneapolis **(G-6026)**

FOOD PRDTS, WHOLESALE: Dried or Canned Foods

5 K Enterprises Inc ....E... 612 216-6292
Mankato **(G-3127)**
Minnesota Dehydrated ....D... 218 435-1997
Fosston **(G-2178)**
US Foodservice Inc..............................C... 651 634-4380
Saint Paul **(G-9120)**

FOOD PRDTS, WHOLESALE: Flavorings & Fragrances

Sunopta Food Group LLC 320 763-5977
Alexandria **(G-125)**

FOOD PRDTS, WHOLESALE: Flour

Horizon Milling LLC ....E... 507 388-1680
Mankato **(G-3145)**

FOOD PRDTS, WHOLESALE: Grain Elevators

AG Partners Coop.................................E... 651 923-4496
Goodhue **(G-2248)**
Coop FCA ....E... 507 847-4160
Jackson **(G-2789)**
Farm Country Co-Op ....E... 507 356-8313
Pine Island **(G-6816)**
Glaciel Plans Coop ....E... 320 843-2563
Benson **(G-440)**

FOOD PRDTS, WHOLESALE: Grains (continued)

Greenway Co-Operative Service ....E... 507 775-2900
Byron **(G-824)**
Greenway Co-Operative Service ....E... 507 287-6676
Byron **(G-823)**
Minn-Kota AG Products Inc...................E... 218 643-8464
Breckenridge **(G-595)**
Western Consolidated Co-op ....E... 320 394-2171
Holloway **(G-2493)**

FOOD PRDTS, WHOLESALE: Grains

Agmotion Inc..E... 612 486-3800
Minneapolis **(G-3699)**
All-American Co-Op ....E... 507 533-4222
Stewartville **(G-9590)**
Bremner Food Group Inc ....E... 612 331-5908
Minneapolis **(G-3942)**
Cargill Inc ....C... 952 742-4417
Minneapolis **(G-4010)**
Crystal Valley Coop..............................E... 507 642-8837
La Salle **(G-2846)**
Farmers Co-Operative of Hanska.........E... 507 439-6244
Hanska **(G-2370)**
General Mills Inc ....E... 763 764-3313
Minneapolis **(G-4513)**
M & B Enterprise of Freeport................ 320 836-2145
Freeport **(G-2188)**
MG Waldbaum Co ....D... 952 258-4000
Minnetonka **(G-6192)**
Sunrich Inc ....D... 507 451-3316
Hope **(G-2496)**
Sunrich LLC ....D... 507 451-4724
Hope **(G-2497)**
United Farmers Cooperative ....E... 507 228-8224
Lafayette **(G-2847)**
Wagner Trucking Inc 320 524-2250
Brandon **(G-592)**
Watonwan Farm Service Inc ....E... 507 776-2831
Truman **(G-9699)**
Wilmont Farmers Elevator Co ....E... 507 926-5131
Wilmont **(G-10064)**

FOOD PRDTS, WHOLESALE: Juices

Johnson Brothers Liquor Co.................C... 651 649-5800
Saint Paul **(G-8537)**
Johnson Brothers Liquor Co.................B... 651 649-5800
Saint Paul **(G-8536)**
Nei Bottling Inc ....E... 218 751-3847
Bemidji **(G-407)**
Wirtz Beverage Minnesota Beer...........C... 651 646-6063
Saint Paul **(G-9160)**

FOOD PRDTS, WHOLESALE: Molasses, Indl

American Crystal Sugar Co ....B... 218 287-3400
Moorhead **(G-6296)**

FOOD PRDTS, WHOLESALE: Natural & Organic

Albert's Organics Inc ....C... 763 780-0101
Saint Paul **(G-8005)**
Sunrich Inc ....B... 952 939-3949
Minnetonka **(G-6227)**

FOOD PRDTS, WHOLESALE: Oats

All-American Co-Op ....E... 507 533-4222
Stewartville **(G-9590)**
Coop FCA ....E... 507 847-4160
Jackson **(G-2789)**
Wilmont Farmers Elevator Co ....E... 507 926-5131
Wilmont **(G-10064)**

FOOD PRDTS, WHOLESALE: Pasta & Rice

Dakota Growers Pasta Co Inc ....C... 763 531-5340
Minneapolis **(G-4219)**

FOOD PRDTS, WHOLESALE: Rice, Unpolished

Anheuser-Busch Co's Inc......................E... 218 326-0571
Grand Rapids **(G-2268)**

FOOD PRDTS, WHOLESALE: Salt, Edible

Cargill Inc ....D... 952 984-8280
Hopkins **(G-2525)**

FOOD PRDTS, WHOLESALE: Soybeans

All-American Co-Op ....E... 507 533-4222
Stewartville **(G-9590)**
Cargill Inc ....A... 952 742-7575
Wayzata **(G-9909)**
CHS Inc..A... 651 355-6000
Inver Grove Heights **(G-2742)**

Employment codes: A=Over 500 employees, B=251-500,
C=101-250, D=51-100, E=25-50

2011 Harris Minnesota
Services Directory

© Harris InfoSource 1-866-281-6415
705

Coop FCA ....E... 507 847-4160
Jackson *(G-2789)*

Minnesota Soybean Processors..........D... 507 842-6677
Brewster *(G-605)*

Northstar Genetics Ltd 507 824-2878
Wanamingo *(G-9865)*

Ray Drachenberg ....E... 507 644-2108
Redwood Falls *(G-7027)*

Wilmont Farmers Elevator Co.............E... 507 926-5131
Wilmont *(G-10064)*

FOOD PRDTS, WHOLESALE: Specialty

Bernick's Full-Line Vending...............E... 320 656-2131
Waite Park *(G-9817)*

Perfect Pickle ....E... 651 779-6129
Forest Lake *(G-2153)*

Royal Foods Inc ....E... 952 936-0336
Hopkins *(G-2622)*

United Noodles Inc ....E... 612 721-6677
Minneapolis *(G-5910)*

FOOD PRDTS, WHOLESALE: Sugar, Refined

American Crystal Sugar Co ....B... 218 287-3400
Moorhead *(G-6296)*

FOOD PRDTS, WHOLESALE: Water, Distilled

Culligan Store Solutions ....D... 651 681-9000
Saint Paul *(G-7742)*

Glenwood-Inglewood Co ....D... 612 374-2253
Minneapolis *(G-4529)*

FOOD PRDTS, WHOLESALE: Water, Mineral Or Spring, Bottled

Bradley Distributing Co ....E... 651 639-0523
Newport *(G-6485)*

Culligan Soft Water Service Co ....E... 763 535-4545
Minneapolis *(G-4198)*

Nei Bottling Inc................................E... 218 751-3847
Bemidji *(G-407)*

Quality Wine & Spirits Co...................D... 952 854-8600
Minneapolis *(G-5444)*

FOOD PRDTS, WHOLESALE: Wheat

Cargill Inc.......................................A... 952 742-7575
Wayzata *(G-9909)*

CHS Inc ....A... 651 355-6000
Inver Grove Heights *(G-2742)*

FOOTWEAR, WHOLESALE: Boots

Dsw Shoe Warehouse Inc ....E... 952 876-0991
Minneapolis *(G-4288)*

FOOTWEAR, WHOLESALE: Shoes

Golden ERA Trading LLC ....D... 651 774-4400
Saint Paul *(G-8419)*

FOREIGN CURRENCY EXCHANGE

New Unbank Co LLC.............................D... 952 544-5155
Hopkins *(G-2588)*

FORESTRY SVCS

Forestry Field Station ....E... 651 345-3216
Lake City *(G-2853)*

Minnesota Department of......................E... 218 425-7793
Wannaska *(G-9868)*

FORMAL WRITING SVCS

Jpg & Associates Inc.........................E... 651 779-1072
Lake Elmo *(G-2875)*

FRAMES & FRAMING WHOLESALE

T Distribution Inc ....E... 651 636-6367
Saint Paul *(G-9024)*

FRANCHISES, SELLING OR LICENSING

Abra Inc..D... 763 561-7220
Minneapolis *(G-3662)*

American Dairy Queen Corp ....B... 952 830-0200
Minneapolis *(G-3747)*

Barbers Hairstyling For Men ....D... 952 947-7777
Minneapolis *(G-3867)*

Buffalo Wild Wings Inc ....D... 952 593-9943
Minneapolis *(G-3969)*

Carlson Hotels LP ....C... 763 212-1000
Minneapolis *(G-4014)*

Carlson Hotels Management Corp ....C... 763 212-5000
Minneapolis *(G-4016)*

Carlson Hotels Worldwide Inc ....E... 763 212-5000
Minneapolis *(G-4017)*

Country Inns & Suites By ....E... 763 212-2525
Minneapolis *(G-4170)*

Duke & King Acquisition Corp..............A... 952 288-2300
Burnsville *(G-713)*

Duke & King Acquisition Corp..............E... 651 731-8720
Saint Paul *(G-9205)*

Embers America LLC ....E... 651 645-6473
Saint Paul *(G-8338)*

Famous Dave's Of America Inc ....E... 952 294-1300
Minnetonka *(G-6167)*

Holiday Diversified Services ....B... 952 830-8700
Minneapolis *(G-4660)*

International Dairy Queen Inc ....B... 952 830-0200
Minneapolis *(G-4721)*

International Quality Homecare ....D... 507 252-8117
Rochester *(G-7142)*

Novus Franchising Inc ....E... 952 944-8000
Savage *(G-9401)*

Radisson Hotels International ....C... 763 212-5000
Minnetonka *(G-6218)*

Winmark Corp ....C... 763 520-8500
Minneapolis *(G-6077)*

FREIGHT CAR LOADING & UNLOADING SVCS

Duluth Missabe & Iron Range ....A... 218 723-2016
Duluth *(G-1302)*

FREIGHT CONSOLIDATION SVCS

King Solutions Inc ....D... 763 428-5464
Osseo *(G-6626)*

FREIGHT FORWARDING ARRANGEMENTS

C H Robinson Worldwide Inc ....A... 952 937-8500
Eden Prairie *(G-1615)*

Ceva Freight LLC ....D... 651 675-4000
Eagan *(G-1520)*

CH Robinson International Inc ....D... 952 937-2914
Eden Prairie *(G-1622)*

K N Air Domestic...............................E... 651 688-7650
Saint Paul *(G-7815)*

K T I Inc ....E... 612 378-9731
Minnetonka *(G-6183)*

King Shipping Inc ....E... 763 428-5464
Maple Grove *(G-3247)*

King Solutions Inc ....D... 763 428-5464
Osseo *(G-6626)*

Kuehne + Nagel Inc............................E... 651 688-6645
Saint Paul *(G-7820)*

M & N Equipment Services Inc ....E... 612 379-4147
Minneapolis *(G-4916)*

Schenker Inc.....................................D... 651 367-2500
Eagan *(G-1551)*

FREIGHT FORWARDING ARRANGEMENTS: Domestic

Don Cameron & Associates Inc............E... 952 884-0070
Minneapolis *(G-4275)*

Griffin & Co Logistics ....E... 952 854-2600
Minneapolis *(G-4568)*

FREIGHT FORWARDING ARRANGEMENTS: Foreign

A & H Cartage Inc..............................E... 651 454-9550
Saint Paul *(G-7684)*

CH Robinson International Inc ....E... 952 937-8500
Eden Prairie *(G-1621)*

Don Cameron & Associates Inc............E... 952 884-0070
Minneapolis *(G-4275)*

Expeditors International Of WA............D... 651 683-9922
Saint Paul *(G-7771)*

Griffin & Co Logistics ....E... 952 854-2600
Minneapolis *(G-4568)*

Superior Brokerage Services................E... 651 256-1555
Saint Paul *(G-9016)*

UPS Supply Chain Solutions Inc ....E... 612 726-1680
Minneapolis *(G-5937)*

FREIGHT HANDLING SVCS: Air

Freight Office For North West...............E... 218 727-8747
Duluth *(G-1328)*

North Star International Inc..................E... 651 379-5030
Saint Paul *(G-7851)*

FREIGHT TRANSPORTATION ARRANGEMENTS

Ats Logistics Services Inc ....D... 320 255-7488
Saint Cloud *(G-7456)*

Canadian Pacific Ltd...........................E... 612 781-7284
Minneapolis *(G-3998)*

Cobra Transportation Services ....E... 651 552-1151
Saint Paul *(G-8219)*

Contact Cartage Inc...........................E... 612 331-4780
Minneapolis *(G-4160)*

Dayton Freight Lines Inc ....E... 763 493-5841
Osseo *(G-6608)*

Lake Country Logistics LLC ....E... 218 233-2686
Moorhead *(G-6322)*

Lawrence Transportation.......................D... 507 454-3911
Winona *(G-10111)*

Logistics International LLC ....D... 952 697-4800
Shakopee *(G-9451)*

M C U Intermodal Inc ....E... 651 222-2224
Saint Paul *(G-8601)*

Mid American Transportation.................D... 612 726-9162
Minneapolis *(G-5020)*

Morrell Transfer Inc ....E... 763 441-2011
Elk River *(G-1885)*

Stan Koch & Sons Trucking Inc ....A... 763 302-5400
Minneapolis *(G-5736)*

Stan Koch & Sons Trucking Inc ....E... 651 999-8500
Saint Paul *(G-9003)*

FRUIT, FARM-DRIED, PACKING SVCS

Mississippi Valley Fruit LLC ....E... 507 876-2891
Elgin *(G-1856)*

FRUITS & VEGETABLES WHOLESALERS: Fresh

Apperts Frozen Foods Inc ....D... 320 251-3200
Saint Cloud *(G-7434)*

Cre 8 It Inc ....D... 612 623-8866
Minneapolis *(G-4178)*

Cut Fruit Express Inc ....D... 651 438-8834
Inver Grove Heights *(G-2747)*

J & J Distributing Co ....C... 651 221-0560
Saint Paul *(G-8526)*

Jerry's Farm Market ....A... 320 968-7001
Foley *(G-2140)*

Metro Produce Distributors Inc............E... 612 722-5575
Minneapolis *(G-5003)*

Northern Star Co................................C... 612 339-8981
Minneapolis *(G-5229)*

Stock Yards Meat Packing Co ....C... 651 450-6000
South Saint Paul *(G-9544)*

FUND RAISING ORGANIZATION, NON-FEE BASIS

American Indian Community.................D... 612 813-1610
Minneapolis *(G-3752)*

Aveyron Homes Inc ....C... 320 234-6063
Hutchinson *(G-2688)*

Aveyron Homes Inc ....C... 320 587-6277
Hutchinson *(G-2689)*

Macphail Center For Music ....C... 612 321-0100
Minneapolis *(G-4928)*

Saint Paul Foundation Inc ....D... 651 224-5463
Saint Paul *(G-8926)*

Scholarship America...........................E... 952 830-7300
Minneapolis *(G-5612)*

Scholarship America Inc......................C... 507 931-1682
Saint Peter *(G-9313)*

Temple of Aaron Sisterhood ....E... 651 698-8874
Saint Paul *(G-9036)*

Vermillion Community College ....D... 218 365-7200
Ely *(G-1916)*

FUNDRAISING SVCS

Glenmore Foundation ....E... 218 281-3123
Crookston *(G-1125)*

Minneapolis Jewish Federation ....E... 952 593-2600
Hopkins *(G-2584)*

Northwest Area Foundation ....E... 651 224-9635
Saint Paul *(G-8766)*

Safety Awareness Inc..........................D... 763 550-9200
Minneapolis *(G-5590)*

FUNDS: Pension, Health & Welfare

Alliance Benefit Group.........................D... 507 377-9344
Albert Lea *(G-35)*

Clark & Wamberg LLC.........................C... 612 339-0919
Minneapolis *(G-4102)*

Federated Mutual Insurance Co ....C... 507 455-5200
Owatonna *(G-6710)*

Sheffield, Olson & McQueen Inc ....E... 651 695-2500
Saint Paul *(G-8951)*

FUNERAL DIRECTOR

Hillside Cemetery Association ....E... 612 781-3391
Minneapolis *(G-4649)*

SERVICES

FUNERAL HOME

Bradshaw Group ....E... 651 776-1551
Saint Paul *(G-8120)*

Range Co Operatives Inc 218 741-7393
Virginia *(G-9753)*

Williams Funeral Home Inc 320 252-2522
Saint Cloud *(G-7633)*

FUNERAL HOMES & SVCS

Brown-Wilbert Inc ....E... 651 631-1234
Saint Paul *(G-8133)*

Cremation Society Inc 612 825-2435
Minneapolis *(G-4181)*

Davies Chapel ....E... 612 377-2203
Minneapolis *(G-4228)*

First Memorial Funeral Chapel ....E... 763 560-4694
Minneapolis *(G-4443)*

FURNITURE WHOLESALERS

Blu DOT Design & Manufacturing ....E... 612 782-1844
Minneapolis *(G-3918)*

Buyonlinenow Inc ....E... 507 281-6899
Rochester *(G-7068)*

Fluid Interiors ....E... 612 746-8700
Minneapolis *(G-4458)*

Haldeman-Homme Inc ....C... 612 331-4880
Minneapolis *(G-4590)*

Jacobs Trading LLC ....E... 763 843-2066
Hopkins *(G-2561)*

River of Goods Inc ....D... 651 917-5335
Saint Paul *(G-8904)*

Winsted Corp ....E... 952 944-9050
Minneapolis *(G-6078)*

FURNITURE, HOUSEHOLD: Wholesalers

E T C Enterprises Inc ....E... 320 240-0567
Saint Cloud *(G-7500)*

Wayne Baumgart Distributors 952 447-2750
Prior Lake *(G-6961)*

FURNITURE, MATTRESSES: Wholesalers

Encompass Group LLC ....D... 651 646-6600
Saint Paul *(G-8339)*

Encompass Group LLC ....C... 651 646-6600
Saint Paul *(G-8340)*

Lintex Corp ....C... 651 646-6600
Saint Paul *(G-8591)*

FURNITURE, OFFICE: Wholesalers

Alternative Business Furniture ....D... 952 937-7688
Eden Prairie *(G-1589)*

Bennett Office Technologies ....E... 320 235-6425
Willmar *(G-9985)*

Bertelson Brothers Inc ....E... 763 546-4371
Minneapolis *(G-3889)*

Corporate Express Office Prdts ....C... 651 636-2250
Saint Paul *(G-8251)*

Ecm Publishers Inc ....E... 763 689-1981
Cambridge *(G-837)*

Innovative Office Solutions ....D... 952 808-9900
Burnsville *(G-736)*

Intereum Inc ....C... 763 417-3300
Minneapolis *(G-4716)*

Macy's Retail Holdings Inc ....D... 612 343-0868
Minneapolis *(G-4930)*

Metro Systems Furniture Inc ....E... 952 933-5050
Minneapolis *(G-5004)*

North Country Business Prdts ....D... 218 751-4140
Bemidji *(G-408)*

North Country Business Prdts ....E... 800 937-4140
Plymouth *(G-6878)*

Northern Business Products Inc ....E... 218 726-0167
Duluth *(G-1402)*

S & T Office Products Inc ....C... 651 483-4411
Saint Paul *(G-8918)*

S P Richards Co ....E... 651 484-8459
Saint Paul *(G-8920)*

FURNITURE, WHOLESALE: Beds & Bedding

E T C Enterprises Inc ....E... 320 240-0567
Saint Cloud *(G-7500)*

FURNITURE, WHOLESALE: Chairs

Bgd Co's Inc ....E... 612 338-6804
Minneapolis *(G-3900)*

GAMBLING, NEC

Bois Forte Enterprises ....B... 218 753-6400
Tower *(G-9686)*

Climb Theater Inc ....D... 651 453-9275
Inver Grove Heights *(G-2743)*

Fond Du Lac Management Inc ....D... 218 879-4593
Cloquet *(G-1052)*

Leech Lake Reservation ....A... 218 547-2744
Walker *(G-9854)*

Little Six Casino ....B... 952 445-6000
Prior Lake *(G-6938)*

Shakopee Mdewakanton Sioux Com ...D... 952 445-8900
Prior Lake *(G-6954)*

Smsc Gaming Enterprise ....A... 952 445-6000
Prior Lake *(G-6955)*

Triple Crown Gaming Inc ....E... 320 251-5373
Saint Cloud *(G-7622)*

White Earth Band of Chippewa ....A... 218 935-2711
Mahnomen *(G-3091)*

GARDEN PLANNING SVCS

Jlm Landscape LLC ....E... 952 941-9818
Minneapolis *(G-4766)*

GARDEN PLANTING SVCS

Highland Nursery Inc ....E... 651 698-1708
Saint Paul *(G-8482)*

GARDEN SVCS

Garden Grove LLC ....E... 651 699-5300
Saint Paul *(G-8401)*

GARMENT: Pressing & cleaners' agents

Antons Inc ....E... 320 253-3611
Waite Park *(G-9816)*

GAS & OTHER COMBINED SVCS

Centerpoint Energy Resources ....E... 651 554-3000
South Saint Paul *(G-9517)*

City of Owatonna ....D... 507 451-2480
Owatonna *(G-6703)*

Otter Tail Energy Services Co ....A... 218 739-8888
Fergus Falls *(G-2107)*

GAS PRODUCTION & DISTRIBUTION

Hearth & Home Technologies Inc ....C... 952 985-6000
Lakeville *(G-2909)*

GASOLINE WHOLESALERS

Croix Oil Co ....E... 651 439-5755
Stillwater *(G-9608)*

Curtis Oil & Tire ....E... 218 729-8241
Duluth *(G-1288)*

Egan Oil Co LLC ....E... 763 421-0410
Anoka *(G-176)*

Inter City Oil Co Inc ....E... 218 728-3641
Duluth *(G-1358)*

Lubrication Technologies Inc ....D... 651 636-7990
Saint Paul *(G-8596)*

Wilson Oil Co Inc 651 388-5783
Red Wing *(G-7013)*

Yocum Oil Co Inc ....C... 651 739-9141
Saint Paul *(G-9179)*

GENEALOGICAL INVESTIGATION SVCS

Irish Genealogical Society ....E... 763 574-1436
South Saint Paul *(G-9531)*

GENERAL COUNSELING SVCS

Adult Child & Family Services ....E... 507 344-1721
Mankato *(G-3099)*

Associated Clinic of ....E... 952 925-6033
Minneapolis *(G-3824)*

Associated Clinic of ....D... 763 503-8560
Minneapolis *(G-3825)*

C A P Scott-Carver-Dakota Inc ....E... 952 496-2125
Shakopee *(G-9425)*

Camp Buckskin Inc ....D... 952 930-3544
Minneapolis *(G-3996)*

Casa De Esperanza ....E... 651 646-5553
Saint Paul *(G-8170)*

Catholic Charities of The ....E... 507 454-2270
Winona *(G-10086)*

Centro Cultural Chicano ....E... 612 874-1412
Minneapolis *(G-4048)*

Child Care Resource & Referral ....D... 507 287-2020
Rochester *(G-7076)*

Community Connection of MN ....E... 218 525-4126
Duluth *(G-1279)*

Comunidades Latinas Unidas En ....E... 651 379-4200
Saint Paul *(G-8244)*

Domestic Abuse Project Inc ....E... 612 874-7063
Minneapolis *(G-4271)*

East Suburban Resources Inc ....E... 651 351-0190
Stillwater *(G-9611)*

Face To Face Health ....E... 651 772-5555
Saint Paul *(G-8361)*

Family Innovations Inc ....D... 763 421-5535
Anoka *(G-180)*

Greater Minnesota Family Svcs ....D... 320 235-3664
Willmar *(G-10004)*

Hiawatha Valley Mental Health ....E... 507 454-4341
Winona *(G-10102)*

Metroplitan Ctr For ....D... 651 646-8342
Saint Paul *(G-8642)*

Midwest Mental Health Resource ....E... 651 647-1900
Saint Paul *(G-8659)*

Neighborhood Counseling Center ....E... 218 631-1714
Wadena *(G-9807)*

Northern Pines Mental Health 320 632-6647
Little Falls *(G-3015)*

Nystrom & Associates Ltd ....E... 651 628-9566
Saint Paul *(G-8775)*

Patrick M Doyle Dr ....E... 651 454-0114
Saint Paul *(G-7865)*

Program In Human Sexuality ....E... 612 625-1500
Minneapolis *(G-5423)*

Relate Counseling Center Inc ....E... 952 932-7277
Minnetonka *(G-6219)*

South Central Human Relations ....D... 507 451-2630
Owatonna *(G-6737)*

Southwestern Mental Health Ctr ....E... 507 376-4141
Worthington *(G-10195)*

Storefront Group ....E... 612 861-1675
Richfield *(G-7038)*

GENERAL MERCHANDISE, NONDURABLE, WHOLESALE

Food Market Merchandising Inc ....E... 952 894-0110
Minneapolis *(G-4462)*

Libra Inc ....E... 612 522-2600
Minneapolis *(G-4872)*

New Streams International Inc 651 777-8020
Maplewood *(G-5995)*

Polaroid Consumer Electronics ....D... 952 936-5000
Minnetonka *(G-6215)*

Polaroid Holdings LLC 952 934-9918
Minnetonka *(G-6216)*

2020 Promotions LLC ....E... 651 451-3850
South Saint Paul *(G-9545)*

GENERATOR REPAIR SVCS

Woodgroup Field Services Inc ....D... 763 785-0650
Minneapolis *(G-3643)*

GERIATRIC RESIDENTIAL CARE FACILITY

Cardinal Pointe of Oakdale ....E... 651 578-0650
Saint Paul *(G-9192)*

Colonial Acres Home Inc ....C... 763 544-1555
Golden Valley *(G-2239)*

Cornerstone Residence ....E... 218 647-8258
Kelliher *(G-2827)*

Healtheast Care System ....E... 651 232-2002
Saint Paul *(G-8456)*

Jones-Harrison Residence Corp ....B... 612 920-2030
Minneapolis *(G-4778)*

Krushe Residential Services ....E... 218 746-3117
Pillager *(G-6810)*

Lighthouse Villages ....D... 952 442-1261
Waconia *(G-9789)*

Norris Square ....E... 651 769-2447
Cottage Grove *(G-1106)*

Parkshore Senior Campus ....E... 952 929-1034
Minneapolis *(G-5338)*

Seasons Hospice ....E... 507 285-1930
Rochester *(G-7249)*

Solstice Corp ....E... 218 729-5014
Duluth *(G-1456)*

Stonecrest ....D... 651 264-3200
Saint Paul *(G-9278)*

Walker Methodist Senior Svcs ....A... 612 827-5931
Minneapolis *(G-6012)*

GERIATRIC SOCIAL SVCS

Autumn Grace Senior Services ....E... 507 388-3660
Mankato *(G-3108)*

Cokato Charitable Trust 320 286-2158
Cokato *(G-1076)*

Round Lake Senior Citizen Ctr ....E... 507 945-8477
Round Lake *(G-7385)*

Senior Citizens Service Inc ....E... 507 287-1404
Rochester *(G-7251)*

Senior Friend Associates Inc ....C... 218 727-1111
Duluth *(G-1447)*

Senior Isanti Citizen Com ....E... 763 444-6100
Isanti *(G-2781)*

SERVICES

GIFT WRAPPING SVCS

Impact Innovations Inc ....D... 320 847-1210
Clara City *(G-1028)*

GIFTS & NOVELTIES: Wholesalers

Cac Retail Inc ....D... 952 944-5600
Eden Prairie *(G-1616)*
Coyne's & Co Inc ....D... 763 425-8666
Minneapolis *(G-4175)*
Curry Sales Inc ....E... 952 351-4200
Hopkins *(G-2534)*
Doug Thorson Sales Co Inc ....E... 218 736-2249
Fergus Falls *(G-2074)*
Garborgs LLC ....E... 612 888-5726
Minneapolis *(G-4499)*
Lenox Group Inc ....C... 952 943-4100
Eden Prairie *(G-1708)*
Midwest - Cbk Inc ....E... 320 847-1210
Clara City *(G-1029)*
Midwest - Cbk Inc ....D... 507 263-4261
Cannon Falls *(G-858)*
Nsl Holdings Inc ....E... 952 943-8474
Shakopee *(G-9462)*
Ovp Inc ....C... 952 944-5600
Eden Prairie *(G-1740)*
Seasonal Specialties LLC ....E... 952 942-6555
Eden Prairie *(G-1773)*

GIRLS CAMPS

Camp Greenwood Girl Scout ....E... 763 684-4243
Buffalo *(G-640)*
Circle R Ranch Inc ....E... 320 547-2176
Long Prairie *(G-3039)*
Etoc Co Inc ....D... 218 963-2906
Nisswa *(G-6496)*
Little Elk Youth Ranch Inc ....E... 320 594-2750
Browerville *(G-625)*

GLASS, AUTOMOTIVE: Wholesalers

Pgw Auto Glass LLC ....E... 952 888-0413
Minneapolis *(G-5373)*

GOLF COURSES: Public

Afton Alps Golf Course ....E... 651 436-1320
Hastings *(G-2411)*
Apple Valley, City of Inc ....E... 952 953-2323
Saint Paul *(G-7704)*
Applewood Hills Inc ....E... 651 439-7276
Stillwater *(G-9597)*
Bemidji Town & Country Club ....D... 218 751-9215
Bemidji *(G-380)*
Blackberry Ridge Golf Club LLC ....E... 320 257-4653
Sartell *(G-9333)*
Blueberry Pines Golf Club ....E... 218 564-4657
Menahga *(G-3354)*
Cedar Valley Golf Course Inc ....E... 507 457-3241
Winona *(G-10087)*
City of Becker ....E... 763 261-4656
Becker *(G-355)*
City of Chaska ....E... 952 443-3748
Chaska *(G-959)*
City of Edina ....E... 952 941-2443
Minneapolis *(G-4087)*
City of Grand Rapids ....D... 218 326-3444
Grand Rapids *(G-2272)*
City of Minneapolis ....E... 612 724-7715
Minneapolis *(G-4090)*
City of Minneapolis ....E... 612 789-2542
Minneapolis *(G-4092)*
City of Moorhead ....D... 218 299-5422
Moorhead *(G-6303)*
City of Saint Paul ....E... 651 488-9673
Saint Paul *(G-8211)*
Como Ski Center ....E... 651 488-9679
Saint Paul *(G-8240)*
County of Anoka ....E... 651 482-8484
Circle Pines *(G-1008)*
Cragun Enterprises Inc ....E... 218 825-2800
Brainerd *(G-544)*
Crystal Lake Country Club Inc ....E... 952 432-6566
Lakeville *(G-2898)*
Deer Run Golf Club LLC ....E... 952 443-2351
Victoria *(G-9727)*
Eagle Lake Golf Center ....E... 763 694-7695
Minneapolis *(G-4305)*
Eagle's Landing Golf Club Inc ....D... 320 632-5721
Fort Ripley *(G-2173)*
Etoc Co Inc ....D... 218 963-2906
Nisswa *(G-6496)*
Fond Du Lac Reservation ....A... 218 878-2327
Carlton *(G-867)*
Forest Hills Golf Rv Reso ....E... 218 562-7585
Pequot Lakes *(G-6788)*
Furlong Golf Inc ....E... 651 480-8558
Hastings *(G-2387)*
Gem Lake Hills Inc ....E... 651 429-8715
Saint Paul *(G-8404)*
Golden Acres Golf Course Inc ....E... 763 428-8244
Rogers *(G-7325)*
Golden Valley, City of Inc ....D... 763 593-8000
Minneapolis *(G-4538)*
Golf Services Corp ....D... 651 777-1436
Saint Paul *(G-8420)*
Gopher Hills Inc ....E... 507 263-2507
Cannon Falls *(G-854)*
Grl Investment Co LLC ....E... 952 445-6745
Shakopee *(G-9442)*
Hawley Golf & Country Club Inc ....E... 218 483-4808
Hawley *(G-2419)*
Hidden Greens Inc ....E... 651 437-3085
Hastings *(G-2392)*
Hidden Haven Golf Course Inc ....E... 763 434-6867
Cedar *(G-879)*
Izatys Group LLC ....E... 320 532-3101
Onamia *(G-6573)*
Jala Contracting Co ....E... 763 434-4626
Cedar *(G-880)*
Kimball Golf Club Inc ....E... 320 398-2285
Kimball *(G-2833)*
Legacy Golf Corp ....E... 507 332-0777
Faribault *(G-2019)*
Links At Northfork LLP ....E... 763 241-0506
Anoka *(G-200)*
Links On The Mississippi Inc ....E... 651 768-7611
Cottage Grove *(G-1104)*
Little Falls Golf Association ....E... 320 616-5520
Little Falls *(G-3011)*
Madden Brothers Inc ....E... 218 829-2811
Brainerd *(G-546)*
Malone Golf Inc ....D... 952 492-2644
Jordan *(G-2806)*
Meadow Lakes Golf Club LLC ....E... 507 285-1190
Rochester *(G-7181)*
Mendakota Country Club Inc ....C... 651 454-2822
Saint Paul *(G-7837)*
New Prague Golf Club Inc ....E... 952 758-5326
New Prague *(G-6423)*
Oak Hill Golf Club Inc ....E... 320 259-8969
Rice *(G-7033)*
Oakdale Country Club Inc ....E... 320 833-5518
Buffalo Lake *(G-667)*
Oneka Ridge LLC ....D... 651 429-2390
Saint Paul *(G-9255)*
Parkview Golf Associates LLC ....E... 651 452-5098
Saint Paul *(G-7864)*
Perham Lakeside Golf Club Inc ....E... 218 346-6070
Perham *(G-6801)*
Ponds Golf Course LLC ....E... 763 753-1100
Saint Francis *(G-7636)*
Prestwick Golf Club Inc ....E... 651 459-0288
Saint Paul *(G-9264)*
Quarry At Giants Ridge ....E... 218 865-3092
Biwabik *(G-471)*
Refuge Golf Club ....E... 763 753-7770
Minneapolis *(G-3582)*
Regents of The University of ....E... 612 627-4000
Saint Paul *(G-8882)*
Rush Creek Golf Club Limited ....C... 763 494-8844
Osseo *(G-6658)*
Shadowbrooke Golf Course Inc ....E... 320 395-4251
Lester Prairie *(G-2964)*
Sienna Corp ....E... 218 562-6262
Pequot Lakes *(G-6792)*
Spur Inc ....E... 651 454-2330
Saint Paul *(G-7911)*
Sundance Golf & Bowl Inc ....E... 763 420-4700
Osseo *(G-6670)*
Superior National At Lutsen ....E... 218 663-7865
Lutsen *(G-3057)*
Tanners Brook Golf Club LLP ....D... 651 464-2300
Forest Lake *(G-2169)*
Three Rivers Park District ....D... 763 694-7670
Hamel *(G-2357)*
Timber Creek Golf Course Inc ....E... 952 955-3600
Watertown *(G-9893)*
Viking Meadows Inc ....E... 763 434-4205
Cedar *(G-885)*
Wild Golf Club ....C... 952 445-3500
Prior Lake *(G-6962)*
Wild Marsh Golf Club LLC ....E... 763 682-4476
Buffalo *(G-660)*
Willing Partners Inc ....E... 952 652-2500
Northfield *(G-6546)*
Willow Creek Golf Course of ....E... 507 285-0305
Rochester *(G-7294)*

GOLF DRIVING RANGES

Bemidji Town & Country Club ....D... 218 751-9215
Bemidji *(G-380)*
Braemar Driving Range ....E... 952 826-6786
Minneapolis *(G-3936)*
Cedar Valley Golf Course Inc ....E... 507 457-3241
Winona *(G-10087)*
County of Ramsey ....D... 651 748-2500
Saint Paul *(G-8259)*
Oak Hill Golf Club Inc ....E... 320 259-8969
Rice *(G-7033)*
Three Rivers Park District ....D... 763 694-7670
Hamel *(G-2357)*

GRADING SVCS

B H Heselton Co ....D... 507 334-3901
Faribault *(G-1990)*
Bnr Excavating Inc ....E... 651 438-8692
Hampton *(G-2363)*
C W Houle Inc ....D... 651 484-6077
Saint Paul *(G-8147)*
Christiansen Industrial ....E... 218 751-4663
Bemidji *(G-384)*
D L R Excavating Inc ....D... 651 437-3128
Hastings *(G-2380)*
Enebak Construction Co ....E... 507 645-8962
Northfield *(G-6527)*
Gladen Construction Inc ....D... 218 224-2237
Laporte *(G-2948)*
Gowan Construction Inc ....E... 701 699-5171
Oslo *(G-6588)*
Imperial Developers Inc ....D... 651 454-3330
Saint Paul *(G-7802)*
K G M Contractors Inc ....E... 218 666-5698
Angora *(G-133)*
Nels Nelson & Sons Inc ....C... 218 879-4561
Cloquet *(G-1058)*
Park Construction Co ....D... 763 786-9800
Minneapolis *(G-3563)*
R & G Construction Co ....E... 507 537-1473
Marshall *(G-3323)*
Ryan Contracting Co ....C... 952 894-3200
Shakopee *(G-9471)*
Veit & Co Inc ....C... 763 428-2242
Rogers *(G-7347)*

GRAIN & FIELD BEANS WHOLESALERS

Cargill Inc ....A... 952 742-7575
Wayzata *(G-9909)*
CHS Inc ....A... 651 355-6000
Inver Grove Heights *(G-2742)*
CHS Inc ....C... 507 345-2253
Mankato *(G-3116)*
Coop Audubon Elevator Assn 218 439-6111
Audubon *(G-254)*
Glacial Plains Cooperative ....D... 320 760-5647
Murdock *(G-6401)*
Peterson's North Branch Mill ....E... 651 674-4425
North Branch *(G-6504)*
Scoular Co ....D... 612 335-8700
Minneapolis *(G-5620)*
South Central Grain & Energy ....D... 507 426-8263
Fairfax *(G-1955)*

GRANITE: Crushed & Broken

Martin Marietta Materials Inc ....E... 320 251-7141
Waite Park *(G-9828)*

GRANTMAKING FOUNDATIONS

Faf Advisors Inc 612 303-3381
Minneapolis *(G-4391)*
Otto Bremer Foundation ....C... 651 227-8036
Saint Paul *(G-8792)*

GRAPHIC ARTS & RELATED DESIGN SVCS

Alpha Video & Audio Inc ....D... 952 896-9898
Minneapolis *(G-3733)*
Data Recognition Corp ....E... 763 268-2238
Minneapolis *(G-4223)*
Greer & Associates Inc ....E... 612 338-6171
Minneapolis *(G-4564)*
Independent School District ....E... 320 252-8770
Saint Cloud *(G-7530)*
Lafayette Litho Inc ....E... 651 665-5617
Saint Paul *(G-8555)*
Larsen Design Office Inc ....E... 952 835-2271
Minneapolis *(G-4846)*
Logos Productions Inc ....E... 651 451-9945
Inver Grove Heights *(G-2760)*
M Little & Co Inc ....E... 612 375-0077
Minneapolis *(G-4922)*

Marketing Concepts of MN..............C... 320 796-6245
Spicer *(G-9557)*
Pace Deis Corp...........................E... 651 702-2900
Saint Paul *(G-9256)*
Vomela Specialty Co....................C... 651 228-2200
Saint Paul *(G-9132)*
Ware Tad & Co Inc ....E... 612 338-2311
Minneapolis *(G-6020)*

GRAPHIC LAYOUT SVCS: Printed Circuitry

Visual Impact Signs Inc ....E... 763 783-9411
Minneapolis *(G-3632)*

GRAVEL MINING

Dennis Fehn Gravel ....E... 763 497-2428
Albertville *(G-73)*
F-M Asphalt Inc ....D... 612 798-0245
Minneapolis *(G-4389)*
Fitzgerald Construction ....E... 218 789-7318
Sabin *(G-7397)*
Kielmeyer Construction Inc ....E... 507 334-6088
Nerstrand *(G-6402)*
Knife River Corp - North ....B... 320 251-9472
Sauk Rapids *(G-9368)*
Rupp Construction Co Inc ....D... 507 836-8555
Slayton *(G-9490)*

GREASES, ANIMAL OR VEGETABLE, WHOLESALE

North Central Co's Inc................E... 952 449-0885
Minnetonka *(G-6204)*

GRINDING SVC: Precision, Commercial Or Indl

Carbide Tool Services Inc ....E... 763 421-2210
Anoka *(G-161)*
Checker Machine Inc ....E... 763 544-5000
Minneapolis *(G-4057)*

GROCERIES WHOLESALERS, NEC

Agnes Saint Baking Co ....E... 651 290-7633
Saint Paul *(G-7999)*
American Bottling Co ....C... 651 552-3400
South Saint Paul *(G-9509)*
Coca-Cola Bottling.....................C... 218 736-5661
Fergus Falls *(G-2067)*
Cub Foods Inc ....B... 763 755-9802
Minneapolis *(G-3449)*
Deer River Wild Rice ....D... 218 246-2713
Deer River *(G-1170)*
Gordy's Inc ....E... 507 847-2074
Jackson *(G-2793)*
Great Northern Baking Co LLC......E... 612 331-1043
Minneapolis *(G-4553)*
Minter-Weisman Co ....B... 763 545-3706
Minneapolis *(G-5105)*
Molly's Inc................................D... 612 925-3113
Minneapolis *(G-5119)*
Pepsi Cola Bottling Co of ....C... 507 288-3772
Rochester *(G-7202)*
Pepsi Cola Bottling Co of ....E... 218 628-0276
Duluth *(G-1421)*
Pepsi-Cola Metropolitan Btlng......E... 218 326-1271
Grand Rapids *(G-2306)*
Reser's Fine Foods Inc ....E... 651 646-1298
Saint Paul *(G-8892)*
Sara Lee Bakery Group Inc ....D... 651 688-9275
Saint Paul *(G-7897)*
SUPERVALU Inc.........................C... 952 932-4300
Hopkins *(G-2640)*
Sysco Asian Foods Inc ....E... 651 558-2400
Saint Paul *(G-9021)*
Tree of Life LLC.........................C... 612 752-6300
Saint Paul *(G-9079)*
US Foodservice Inc ....C... 763 559-9494
Minneapolis *(G-5948)*
US Foodservice Inc ....C... 651 450-6000
South Saint Paul *(G-9547)*
Wuollet Bakery Inc.....................E... 763 473-8621
Wayzata *(G-9952)*

GROCERIES, GENERAL LINE WHOLESALERS

Appert's Inc ....C... 320 251-3200
Saint Cloud *(G-7433)*
Apperts Frozen Foods Inc............D... 320 251-3200
Saint Cloud *(G-7434)*
Bradley Distributing Co ....E... 651 639-0523
Newport *(G-6485)*
Curry Sales Inc..........................E... 952 351-4200
Hopkins *(G-2534)*

Fritz Co Inc ....D... 651 459-9751
Newport *(G-6486)*
Hawkeye Foodservice Distbn ....E... 507 238-4721
Fairmont *(G-1972)*
Henry's Foods Inc ....C... 320 763-3194
Alexandria *(G-104)*
Jerry's Enterprises Inc ....C... 952 941-9050
Eden Prairie *(G-1701)*
Martin-Brower Co L L C ....C... 763 571-6311
Minneapolis *(G-3528)*
McLane Minnesota Inc ....B... 507 664-3000
Northfield *(G-6531)*
Nash-Finch Co ....B... 952 832-0534
Edina *(G-1838)*
Nash-Finch Co ....D... 507 931-5541
Saint Peter *(G-9309)*
Nash-Finch Co ....E... 651 388-2869
Red Wing *(G-6992)*
Nash-Finch Co ....C... 218 739-5272
Fergus Falls *(G-2100)*
Nash-Finch Co ....D... 651 463-3404
Farmington *(G-2055)*
Nash-Finch Co ....D... 507 645-9514
Northfield *(G-6534)*
Nash-Finch Co ....C... 320 251-3961
Saint Cloud *(G-7561)*
Nash-Finch Co ....E... 320 587-8233
Hutchinson *(G-2708)*
Nash-Finch Co ....D... 507 263-3643
Cannon Falls *(G-861)*
Reinhart Foodservice LLC ....C... 507 537-1451
Marshall *(G-3324)*
Reinhart Foodservice LLC ....B... 763 428-6500
Rogers *(G-7339)*
SUPERVALU Inc.........................A... 952 828-4000
Eden Prairie *(G-1787)*
SUPERVALU Inc.........................C... 952 932-4300
Hopkins *(G-2640)*
Supervalu Inc ....C... 952 906-6260
Chanhassen *(G-941)*
Supervalu Inc ....C... 952 380-9900
Excelsior *(G-1937)*
Supervalu Inc ....C... 952 906-6600
Chanhassen *(G-942)*
Supervalu Inc ....C... 952 947-3700
Eden Prairie *(G-1788)*
Twin City Poultry Co ....E... 763 592-6500
Minneapolis *(G-5882)*
Upper Lakes Foods Inc ....C... 218 879-1265
Cloquet *(G-1066)*
US Foodservice Inc ....C... 763 559-9494
Minneapolis *(G-5948)*
Watson Co Inc ....E... 763 689-3722
Cambridge *(G-846)*
Wincom Systems Inc ....B... 952 828-4000
Eden Prairie *(G-1816)*

GROUP DAY CARE CENTER

Children's Country Day School ....E... 651 454-4000
Saint Paul *(G-7732)*
Children's Discovery Learning ....D... 651 653-9871
Saint Paul *(G-8192)*
Especially For Children Inc............E... 952 934-1119
Eden Prairie *(G-1658)*
Khcdii Inc ....E... 952 925-5881
Minneapolis *(G-4805)*
Kids Come 1st Corp....................C... 507 281-3284
Rochester *(G-7153)*
KinderCare Learning Centers ....E... 952 835-4955
Minneapolis *(G-4809)*
Kindercare Learning Centers.........E... 952 403-6862
Shakopee *(G-9448)*
Kindercare Learning Centers.........E... 651 386-6672
Saint Paul *(G-9239)*
La Creche Early Childhood ....E... 612 377-1786
Minneapolis *(G-4829)*
Room For Growing ....E... 651 464-1601
Forest Lake *(G-2167)*
St David's Center Child ....B... 952 939-0396
Hopkins *(G-2636)*
St Mary's Medical Center ....A... 218 786-4000
Duluth *(G-1474)*
Step By Step Montessori School........E... 763 557-6777
Minneapolis *(G-5749)*

GROUP FOSTER HOME

Divine House Inc ....D... 218 847-0574
Detroit Lakes *(G-1191)*
E S I Heritage............................D... 218 865-4135
Gilbert *(G-2203)*
Enrich Inc.................................E... 651 482-9608
Saint Paul *(G-8341)*
Family Focus Inc ....E... 612 331-4429
Minneapolis *(G-4408)*

Foster Four................................E... 320 240-0243
Saint Cloud *(G-7414)*
Heartland Ranch ....E... 320 843-4815
Benson *(G-441)*
Howry Residential Services...........E... 651 917-9111
Saint Paul *(G-8498)*
J B Waivered Services ....E... 218 828-4962
Fort Ripley *(G-2174)*
Karcher Foster Services Inc ....E... 651 674-2031
North Branch *(G-6501)*
Lifetime Resources Inc ....D... 612 804-2252
Minneapolis *(G-4881)*
North Homes Inc ....D... 218 327-3055
Grand Rapids *(G-2298)*
Port Group Home Office ....E... 218 828-6274
Brainerd *(G-581)*
Riesco Inc.................................E... 651 771-8235
Saint Paul *(G-8901)*
Senior Grace Services ....E... 507 388-3660
Mankato *(G-3196)*
Zumbro House Inc ....D... 651 264-1000
Saint Paul *(G-9293)*

GROUP HOSPITALIZATION PLANS

Fiserv Health Plan ....A... 262 879-5565
Minneapolis *(G-4450)*
Reliastar Life Insurance Co ....A... 612 372-5432
Minneapolis *(G-5507)*

GUARD PROTECTIVE SVCS

American Security LLC ....A... 651 644-1155
Saint Paul *(G-8034)*
Deco Inc....................................A... 763 576-9572
Champlin *(G-892)*
General Security Services Corp........D... 320 252-3794
Saint Cloud *(G-7416)*
Minnesota Department of Public........E... 507 537-3664
Marshall *(G-3314)*

GUARD SVCS

Checkpoint Security ....E... 952 227-5353
Waconia *(G-9782)*
Valley Security Service Inc ....C... 507 454-2233
Winona *(G-10136)*

GUN SVCS

Gander Mountain Co ....E... 507 252-2033
Rochester *(G-7124)*

GYMNASTICS INSTRUCTION

Flips Gymnastic Center ....E... 651 777-4776
Saint Paul *(G-8385)*
Forest Lake Flyaways ....E... 651 464-8648
Forest Lake *(G-2161)*
Gleason Gymnastic School ....E... 651 454-6203
Saint Paul *(G-7782)*
Gleason Gymnastic School ....E... 763 493-2526
Osseo *(G-6617)*
Jam Hops Gymnastics Factory ....E... 763 413-0647
Anoka *(G-194)*
New Ulm Turnverein Inc...............E... 507 354-4916
New Ulm *(G-6469)*
Perpetual Motion Children's ....E... 651 459-5837
Saint Paul *(G-9260)*
Twin City Twisters Inc..................E... 763 421-3046
Champlin *(G-903)*

HAIR REPLACEMENT & WEAVING SVCS

Regis Corp ....A... 952 947-7777
Minneapolis *(G-5504)*

HAIRDRESSERS

Doll Enterprises Inc ....E... 651 488-0228
Saint Paul *(G-8306)*
Hair District ....E... 952 836-0816
Minneapolis *(G-4588)*
Salon Sabell Inc ....E... 612 866-3679
Minneapolis *(G-5597)*

HALFWAY GROUP HOME, PERSONS WITH SOCIAL OR PERSONAL PROBLEMS

Alternative For People With...........D... 763 560-5330
Minneapolis *(G-3737)*
Cochran Programs ....D... 651 437-4585
Hastings *(G-2378)*
Industries Inc ....E... 763 689-5434
Cambridge *(G-838)*
Omnia Family Services ....E... 507 287-2300
Rochester *(G-7198)*

S E R V I C E S

Employment codes: A=Over 500 employees, B=251-500,
C=101-250, D=51-100, E=25-50

2011 Harris Minnesota
Services Directory

© Harris InfoSource 1-866-281-6415
709

HALFWAY HOME FOR DELINQUENTS & OFFENDERS

Cochran Programs ....D... 651 437-4585
Hastings *(G-2378)*

Eden Rs ....C... 612 287-1600
Minneapolis *(G-4313)*

Omnia Family Services ....E... 507 287-2300
Rochester *(G-7198)*

HAND TOOLS, NEC: Wholesalers

Cable Connection & Supply Co ....E... 507 334-6417
Faribault *(G-1995)*

Enderes Tool Co Inc ....E... 507 373-2396
Albert Lea *(G-48)*

Willi Hahn Corp ....E... 763 295-0666
Monticello *(G-6292)*

HARDWARE WHOLESALERS

Allegis Corp ....E... 763 780-4333
Minneapolis *(G-3391)*

C C Sharrow Co Inc ....E... 651 489-1341
Saint Paul *(G-8145)*

Curry Sales Inc ....E... 952 351-4200
Hopkins *(G-2534)*

D & M Industries Inc ....E... 218 287-3100
Moorhead *(G-6309)*

E & A Products Inc ....E... 763 493-3222
Osseo *(G-6611)*

Frattalone I LLC ....E... 651 292-9800
Saint Paul *(G-8395)*

Harkraft Inc ....E... 763 546-9161
Minneapolis *(G-4597)*

Import Specialties Inc ....C... 952 361-3640
Chaska *(G-969)*

Kendell Doors & Hardware Inc ....E... 507 454-1723
Winona *(G-10107)*

Kendell Doors & Hardware Inc ....D... 651 905-0144
Mendota Heights *(G-3365)*

L&M Fleet Supply True Value ....E... 218 847-1171
Detroit Lakes *(G-1202)*

Lcs Precision Molding Inc ....E... 507 362-8685
Waterville *(G-9895)*

Mac's Inc ....E... 218 233-4600
Moorhead *(G-6326)*

Malco Products Inc ....C... 320 274-8246
Annandale *(G-143)*

Mid-States Distributing Co Inc ....E... 651 698-8831
Saint Paul *(G-8652)*

Park Systems Inc ....E... 612 822-3180
Minneapolis *(G-5337)*

S & S Sales Inc 763 476-9599
Minneapolis *(G-5581)*

Stanley Security Solutions Inc ....E... 952 894-3830
Saint Paul *(G-9004)*

Tappers Inc ....D... 763 295-4222
Monticello *(G-6289)*

Titan Machinery Inc ....E... 218 681-1423
Thief River Falls *(G-9680)*

True Value Co ....C... 507 625-6021
Mankato *(G-3209)*

Twin City Hardware Co ....E... 651 735-2200
Saint Paul *(G-9284)*

Twin City Hardware Co ....E... 763 535-4660
Minneapolis *(G-5881)*

United Hardware Distributing ....C... 763 559-1800
Minneapolis *(G-5909)*

HARDWARE, WHOLESALE: Bolts

Accurate Component Sales Inc ....E... 651 639-1881
Saint Paul *(G-7978)*

C S Aero-Space Inc ....E... 952 884-4725
Minneapolis *(G-3987)*

E & A Products Inc ....E... 763 493-3222
Osseo *(G-6611)*

Wurth Adams Nut & Bolt Co ....D... 763 493-0877
Osseo *(G-6685)*

HARDWARE, WHOLESALE: Bolts, Nuts & Screws

Building Fasteners of MN ....D... 612 706-3300
Minneapolis *(G-3973)*

Fastenal Co ....B... 507 454-5374
Winona *(G-10095)*

Import Specialties Inc ....C... 952 361-3640
Chaska *(G-969)*

HARDWARE, WHOLESALE: Builders', NEC

Bredemus Hardware Co Inc ....E... 651 489-6250
Saint Paul *(G-8123)*

Building Fasteners of MN ....D... 612 706-3300
Minneapolis *(G-3973)*

Contract Hardware Co Inc ....E... 651 780-0010
Circle Pines *(G-1007)*

Holmquist Lumber Co 320 857-2031
Grove City *(G-2329)*

Jaeckle Minnesota ....D... 612 676-0388
Minneapolis *(G-4751)*

Trimpac Inc ....D... 320 202-3200
Sauk Rapids *(G-9378)*

Twin City Hardware Co ....E... 651 735-2200
Saint Paul *(G-9284)*

Wheeler Hardware Co ....E... 651 645-4501
Saint Paul *(G-9153)*

HARDWARE, WHOLESALE: Chains

Fastenal Co ....B... 507 454-5374
Winona *(G-10095)*

HARDWARE, WHOLESALE: Nuts

Accurate Component Sales Inc ....E... 651 639-1881
Saint Paul *(G-7978)*

C S Aero-Space Inc ....E... 952 884-4725
Minneapolis *(G-3987)*

E & A Products Inc ....E... 763 493-3222
Osseo *(G-6611)*

Wurth Adams Nut & Bolt Co ....D... 763 493-0877
Osseo *(G-6685)*

HARDWARE, WHOLESALE: Power Tools & Access

Fastenal Co ....B... 507 454-5374
Winona *(G-10095)*

Import Specialties Inc ....C... 952 361-3640
Chaska *(G-969)*

HARDWARE, WHOLESALE: Rivets

C S Aero-Space Inc ....E... 952 884-4725
Minneapolis *(G-3987)*

Wurth Adams Nut & Bolt Co ....D... 763 493-0877
Osseo *(G-6685)*

HARDWARE, WHOLESALE: Screws

C S Aero-Space Inc ....E... 952 884-4725
Minneapolis *(G-3987)*

E & A Products Inc ....E... 763 493-3222
Osseo *(G-6611)*

HAT CLEANING & BLOCKING SHOP

Don's Leather Cleaning Inc ....E... 612 721-4881
Minneapolis *(G-4276)*

HATCHERIES: Poultry

Pals Inc ....D... 320 235-8860
Willmar *(G-10035)*

Peterson Turkey Hatchery Inc ....E... 507 263-2352
Cannon Falls *(G-862)*

Willmar Poultry Farms Inc ....E... 320 968-6211
Foley *(G-2142)*

HEAD START CENTER, EXC IN CONJUNCTION WITH SCHOOL

Aeoa Headstart ....D... 218 749-5856
Virginia *(G-9732)*

Barnes Head Start ....E... 218 733-2084
Duluth *(G-1246)*

Battle Creek Head Start ....E... 651 730-1663
Saint Paul *(G-8090)*

C A P Scott-Carver-Dakota Inc ....E... 952 496-2125
Shakopee *(G-9425)*

Crookston Family Service Ctr ....E... 218 281-1343
Crookston *(G-1119)*

Inter-County Community Council ....E... 218 796-5144
Oklee *(G-6557)*

Parents In Community Action ....D... 612 377-7422
Minneapolis *(G-5324)*

Parents In Community Action ....E... 612 823-6361
Minneapolis *(G-5323)*

Tri-County Community Action ....E... 320 632-3691
Little Falls *(G-3020)*

Wheaton Head Start ....E... 320 563-8191
Wheaton *(G-9971)*

HEALTH & ALLIED SERVICES, NEC

All Temporaries Caring ....E... 612 378-1474
Minneapolis *(G-3711)*

Cannon Valley Clinic ....E... 507 266-2620
Faribault *(G-1996)*

Hutchinson Health Care ....D... 320 234-5000
Hutchinson *(G-2700)*

Integra Health Care Inc ....E... 952 985-7290
Lakeville *(G-2911)*

Leptos Biomedical ....E... 763 561-0880
Minneapolis *(G-3516)*

Medevent Inc ....E... 952 445-2342
Prior Lake *(G-6940)*

New Millennium ....D... 763 780-9933
Minneapolis *(G-3555)*

Sanford Westbrook Medical Ctr ....E... 507 274-6802
Westbrook *(G-9967)*

St Jude Medical ....E... 651 523-6900
Saint Paul *(G-8985)*

Wm Healthcare Solutions Inc ....D... 763 786-5555
Minneapolis *(G-3642)*

HEALTH & WELFARE COUNCIL

Human Services of Fairbault ....D... 507 238-4757
Fairmont *(G-1975)*

Human Services of Faribault ....E... 507 526-3265
Blue Earth *(G-536)*

Minnesota Aids Project ....E... 612 341-2060
Minneapolis *(G-5066)*

People Enhancing People ....E... 651 450-5960
Saint Paul *(G-8815)*

Perspectives Inc ....E... 952 926-2600
Minneapolis *(G-5367)*

HEALTH CLUBS

America's Racquet & Fitness ....E... 320 234-7148
Hutchinson *(G-2686)*

Bally Total Fitness Corp ....E... 763 574-8888
Minneapolis *(G-3414)*

Bally Total Fitness Corp ....E... 651 484-4444
Saint Paul *(G-8085)*

City of White Bear Lake ....E... 651 429-8571
Saint Paul *(G-8214)*

Dakota Sport & Fitness ....C... 952 445-9400
Prior Lake *(G-6931)*

Life Time Fitness Inc ....A... 952 947-0000
Chanhassen *(G-929)*

Life Time Fitness Inc ....D... 612 752-9589
Minneapolis *(G-4878)*

Life Time Fitness Inc ....C... 763 576-3000
Champlin *(G-895)*

Life Time Fitness Inc ....C... 651 426-1308
Saint Paul *(G-8585)*

Moondance Enterprises ....E... 651 464-1875
Forest Lake *(G-2164)*

North Crest Gymnastics & Dance ....E... 320 251-3416
Sauk Rapids *(G-9370)*

Rochester Fitness Inc ....E... 507 282-4445
Rochester *(G-7231)*

Ruth Stricker's Fitness Unltd ....C... 952 935-2202
Minnetonka *(G-6222)*

Stillwater Fitness Club Inc ....E... 651 430-1584
Stillwater *(G-9646)*

Sweatshop Inc ....E... 651 646-8418
Saint Paul *(G-9019)*

White Bear Racquet & Swim LP ....C... 651 426-1308
Saint Paul *(G-9156)*

YWCA of Minneapolis ....D... 612 874-7131
Minneapolis *(G-6110)*

HEALTH INSURANCE CARRIERS

Bcbsm Inc ....E... 218 722-3371
Duluth *(G-1248)*

Bcbsm Inc ....B... 651 662-8000
Saint Paul *(G-7713)*

Long Term Care Group Inc ....C... 651 501-4000
Saint Paul *(G-9244)*

Reliastar Life Insurance Co ....A... 612 372-5432
Minneapolis *(G-5507)*

Security American Financial ....E... 952 544-2121
Hopkins *(G-2628)*

Security Life Insurance Co of ....D... 952 544-2121
Hopkins *(G-2629)*

HEALTH MAINTENANCE ORGANIZATION: Insurance Only

HealthPartners Inc ....A... 952 883-6000
Bloomington *(G-500)*

Healthpartners Inc ....B... 612 623-4002
Minneapolis *(G-4623)*

Ucare Minnesota ....B... 612 676-6500
Minneapolis *(G-5892)*

United Healthcare of Wyoming ....A... 952 992-5450
Edina *(G-1848)*

Unitedhealth Group Inc ....A... 952 936-1300
Minnetonka *(G-6232)*

HEALTH PRACTITIONERS' OFFICES, NEC

Advanced Spine Associates ....E... 763 577-1877
Champlin *(G-887)*

Aspen Medical Group ....E... 651 696-8800
Saint Paul *(G-8070)*

(G-00000) Company's Geographic Section entry number

SERVICES

Center For Rehab & Wellness...............E... 507 455-7631
Owatonna *(G-6699)*

Coborn Cancer Center..........................E... 320 229-4907
Saint Cloud *(G-7493)*

Entocrinology Clinic ....E... 320 229-5000
Saint Cloud *(G-7504)*

Healtheast Clinics Infoline ....E... 651 426-4844
Saint Paul *(G-8459)*

J C Penny Beauty Salon ....E... 507 625-5630
Mankato *(G-3151)*

Jill H Rusterholz..................................E... 952 806-0011
Minneapolis *(G-4763)*

Kevin Switzer......................................E... 320 231-8888
Willmar *(G-10015)*

Metropolitan Obstetrics & Gyn ....E... 651 770-1385
Saint Paul *(G-8648)*

Michael J Morris..................................E... 320 231-8888
Willmar *(G-10022)*

Midsota Regional Hand Center.............E... 320 253-7257
Saint Cloud *(G-7554)*

Minnhouse ....E... 651 426-6402
Saint Paul *(G-8714)*

Tom Johnson ....E... 651 645-3000
Saint Paul *(G-9070)*

Vitreorentinal Surgery ....E... 952 929-1131
Minneapolis *(G-5980)*

HEALTH SCREENING SVCS

Health Fitness Corp ....E... 952 831-6830
Bloomington *(G-499)*

HEALTH SYSTEMS AGENCY

AARP...D... 952 858-9040
Minneapolis *(G-3658)*

American Heart Association Inc ....E... 952 835-3300
Minneapolis *(G-3750)*

Austin Medical Center-Mayo ....A... 507 433-7351
Austin *(G-261)*

Mains'l Services Inc ....E... 763 494-4553
Brooklyn Park *(G-615)*

Mental Health Resources Inc ....D... 651 659-2900
Saint Paul *(G-8634)*

Minnesota Institute of Public ....E... 763 427-5310
Saint Paul *(G-8691)*

Stratis Health ....D... 952 854-3306
Minneapolis *(G-5759)*

HEARING AID REPAIR SVCS

Siemens Hearing Inc............................B... 763 268-4500
Minneapolis *(G-5666)*

HEARING TESTING SVCS

Avada Audiology & Hearing Care.........E... 952 541-1799
Hopkins *(G-2513)*

HEATING & AIR CONDITIONING EQPT & SPLYS WHOLESALERS

Auer Steel & Heating Supply Co...........E... 763 971-2910
Plymouth *(G-6849)*

Automotive Cooling Products ....E... 651 731-2414
Saint Paul *(G-9186)*

Cramer Investment Co..........................D... 612 861-7232
Saint Paul *(G-8263)*

First Supply LLC ....D... 507 287-0202
Rochester *(G-7115)*

First Supply LLC ....E... 507 287-0202
Rochester *(G-7116)*

Johnson Controls Interiors LLC ....E... 218 727-8996
Duluth *(G-1361)*

Minnesota Air Inc ....D... 952 918-8000
Minneapolis *(G-5067)*

Paape Distributing Co ....E... 507 345-8057
Mankato *(G-3181)*

HELP SUPPLY SERVICES

Advanced Auto Transport Inc...............C... 651 777-7780
Saint Paul *(G-7990)*

Agri Temps Inc ....E... 320 235-5230
Willmar *(G-9981)*

Association For The Solidarity ....C... 952 456-1751
Saint Paul *(G-8075)*

Atlantis Technical Services ....E... 763 657-2500
Osseo *(G-6595)*

Doherty Employment Group Inc...........E... 952 832-8383
Minneapolis *(G-4270)*

Elite Healthcare Staffing Inc ....C... 763 315-4488
Osseo *(G-6614)*

Healthcare Options Inc ....C... 763 545-3042
Minneapolis *(G-4619)*

Hire Thinking Inc.................................E... 612 339-0535
Minneapolis *(G-4654)*

Minnesota Professional Nursing ....D... 612 627-9524
Minneapolis *(G-5090)*

Minnesota Prophy Power Inc ....D... 952 898-1594
Lakeville *(G-2920)*

Montage Inc ....E... 651 633-1955
Saint Paul *(G-8718)*

Right Staff Inc.....................................E... 952 546-1100
Hopkins *(G-2617)*

Robert Half International Inc................D... 612 339-9001
Minneapolis *(G-5553)*

Robert Half International Inc................E... 952 831-5970
Minneapolis *(G-5554)*

Robert Half International Inc................E... 651 293-8033
Saint Paul *(G-8907)*

Summit Employment Inc ....D... 651 501-0531
Saint Paul *(G-9279)*

Sundance Staffing Minnesota ....D... 763 559-7700
Minneapolis *(G-5765)*

Trueblue Inc...C... 218 624-6222
Duluth *(G-1487)*

Uplink Staffing....................................E... 763 781-8888
Minneapolis *(G-5935)*

HELPING HAND SVCS, INCLUDING BIG BROTHER, ETC

Big Brothers Big Sisters of ....D... 651 789-2400
Saint Paul *(G-8113)*

HIGHWAY & STREET MAINTENANCE SVCS

Aitkin County.......................................E... 218 927-3741
Aitkin *(G-14)*

City of Saint Paul ....D... 651 489-8871
Saint Paul *(G-8206)*

City of Saint Paul ....D... 651 292-6600
Saint Paul *(G-8207)*

Dakota County Transportation ....E... 651 423-2101
Rosemount *(G-7367)*

Enebak Construction Co ....E... 507 645-8962
Northfield *(G-6527)*

Forby Contracting Inc..........................E... 320 384-6061
Hinckley *(G-2484)*

Polk County Highway Shop ....E... 218 945-6952
Fertile *(G-2127)*

Public Works Highway Maint ....D... 218 742-9800
Virginia *(G-9751)*

Tenson Construction Inc.......................E... 218 743-3874
Bigfork *(G-465)*

Wabasha County Highway ....E... 651 565-3366
Wabasha *(G-9775)*

HOG FEEDLOT

Christensen Farms & Feedlots ....C... 507 794-5310
Sleepy Eye *(G-9492)*

HOGS WHOLESALERS

Tyson Fresh Meats Inc ....E... 507 776-2828
Truman *(G-9698)*

HOLDING COMPANIES: Banks

Bakken Securities Inc...........................E... 952 926-6561
Minneapolis *(G-3863)*

Belle Plaine Bancorporation ....E... 952 873-2296
Belle Plaine *(G-366)*

Bridgewater Bancshares Inc.................E... 952 893-6868
Minneapolis *(G-3945)*

Deerwood Bancshares Inc ....D... 218 534-3111
Deerwood *(G-1175)*

Duke Financial Group Inc.....................E... 612 204-0255
Minneapolis *(G-4290)*

Great Northern Bank.............................E... 763 497-7777
Saint Michael *(G-7673)*

Marquette Financial Co's ....E... 612 661-3880
Minneapolis *(G-4952)*

Minn Star Bank ....E... 507 726-2137
Lake Crystal *(G-2860)*

NA Corp ....D... 651 636-9654
Saint Paul *(G-8732)*

Rcb Holding Co ....E... 651 631-1040
Saint Paul *(G-8874)*

Riverwood Bank...................................E... 218 751-5120
Bemidji *(G-423)*

Royalton Bancshares Inc ....E... 320 584-5522
Royalton *(G-7387)*

Saint Peter Agency Inc ....E... 507 931-3310
Saint Peter *(G-9312)*

Stearns Financial Services Inc ....C... 320 253-6607
Saint Cloud *(G-7611)*

Sterling Bancorporation Inc.................E... 507 433-7325
Austin *(G-289)*

Western Bank Edina ....D... 952 857-1707
Minneapolis *(G-6058)*

Winona National Holding Co Inc ....D... 507 454-4320
Winona *(G-10152)*

HOLDING COMPANIES: Investment, Exc Banks

C & G Holding Co of Clearbrook ....D... 218 776-3080
Clearbrook *(G-1037)*

Diebold Investments LLC ....E... 952 960-9600
Minneapolis *(G-4255)*

Eldredge Trading Inc ....E... 651 778-8500
Saint Paul *(G-7758)*

Hayworth Partners LP ....E... 952 476-7200
Hopkins *(G-2549)*

J & B Group Inc ....B... 763 497-3913
Saint Michael *(G-7674)*

King Solutions Inc ....E... 763 428-5464
Osseo *(G-6626)*

Maax US Corp ....D... 763 424-3335
Minneapolis *(G-4925)*

Michael Foods Group Inc.....................C... 952 258-4000
Minnetonka *(G-6193)*

Midwest Medical Insurance ....D... 952 838-6700
Minneapolis *(G-5033)*

Mt Yale Capital Group LLC ....E... 952 897-5390
Minneapolis *(G-5146)*

Ritalka Inc...E... 320 269-3227
Montevideo *(G-6258)*

Yamamoto Moss Mackenzie ....E... 612 375-0180
Minneapolis *(G-6099)*

HOLDING COMPANIES: Personal, Exc Banks

Esi Holding Corp ....D... 952 853-0924
Minneapolis *(G-4371)*

Johnson Controls Holding Co..............E... 763 566-7650
Minneapolis *(G-4774)*

Murray's Co Inc...................................D... 612 333-2507
Minneapolis *(G-5152)*

Rosenbauer Motors LLC ....D... 651 462-1000
Wyoming *(G-10208)*

Summit Holdings Corp.........................E... 952 445-8718
Shakopee *(G-9479)*

HOLDING COMPANIES: Public Utility

Integris Group Inc................................D... 651 490-0000
Saint Paul *(G-8514)*

HOME ENTERTAINMENT REPAIR SVCS

Ultimate Acquisition Partners ....E... 952 830-0010
Minneapolis *(G-5895)*

HOME FOR THE EMOTIONALLY DISTURBED

Heartstone of Minnesota......................E... 651 457-2629
South Saint Paul *(G-9529)*

St James Home of Duluth ....C... 218 728-7500
Duluth *(G-1462)*

HOME FOR THE MENTALLY HANDICAPPED

American Baptist Homes of The ....D... 507 373-0188
Albert Lea *(G-39)*

Aveyron Homes Inc ....C... 320 234-6063
Hutchinson *(G-2688)*

Aveyron Homes Inc ....C... 320 587-6277
Hutchinson *(G-2689)*

Big Stone Community Homes Inc.........E... 320 839-6139
Ortonville *(G-6578)*

Boston Health Care Systems Inc ....C... 651 501-2378
Saint Paul *(G-8118)*

Clark Lake Homes Inc ....E... 218 829-1699
Brainerd *(G-558)*

Habilitative Services Inc ....D... 507 532-5366
Marshall *(G-3299)*

Hammer Residences Inc ....C... 763 473-1261
Wayzata *(G-9919)*

Heartland Homes Options In Com ......E... 218 732-4572
Park Rapids *(G-6752)*

Hecla Inc.. 320 255-9530
Saint Cloud *(G-7526)*

Hiawatha Valley Mental Health ....E... 507 454-4341
Winona *(G-10102)*

Hope Haven Inc....................................E... 507 825-2379
Pipestone *(G-6830)*

Horizon Home Inc ....D... 507 344-3360
Mankato *(G-3144)*

Lakes Homes & Program Devpt ....D... 218 847-5642
Detroit Lakes *(G-1203)*

Linnea Residential Home Inc................E... 651 257-2211
Chisago City *(G-992)*

People Inc..E... 651 774-0011
Saint Paul *(G-8816)*

Phoenix Residence Inc ....E... 651 227-7655
Saint Paul *(G-7876)*

Prairie Community Services..................E... 320 589-2057
Morris *(G-6374)*

REM Greatland Inc...............................E... 651 388-7158
Red Wing *(G-7001)*

Employment codes: A=Over 500 employees, B=251-500,
C=101-250, D=51-100, E=25-50

2011 Harris Minnesota
Services Directory

© Harris InfoSource 1-866-281-6415

711

REM Southwest Services Inc ....C... 320 235-9174
Willmar (G-10039)

Remwoodvale Inc............................E... 507 634-6073
Kasson (G-2823)

South Metro Human Services ....E... 651 221-9880
Saint Paul (G-8972)

South Metro Human Services ....D... 651 291-1979
Saint Paul (G-8973)

Sur La Rue Inc ....E... 651 772-4957
Saint Paul (G-9017)

HOME FOR THE MENTALLY RETARDED

A Share Home Inc ....E... 218 631-1853
Wadena (G-9797)

Alternative For Autistic ....D... 763 560-3013
Minneapolis (G-3736)

Aveyron Homes Inc ....C... 320 234-6063
Hutchinson (G-2688)

Aveyron Homes Inc ....C... 320 587-6277
Hutchinson (G-2689)

Cenneidigh Inc ....C... 507 334-4347
Faribault (G-1999)

Ebi Inc ....E... 218 624-3122
Duluth (G-1308)

Home For Creative Living Inc ....D... 507 831-5033
Windom (G-10068)

M B W Co ....C... 507 354-3808
New Ulm (G-6459)

Marshall County Group Homes ....D... 218 437-6695
Argyle (G-247)

Mount Olivet Rolling Acres Inc...........B... 952 474-5974
Victoria (G-9731)

New Dawn Inc ....C... 507 425-3278
Fulda (G-2196)

Pine Ridge Homes Inc ....D... 218 879-1257
Cloquet (G-1059)

Rainbow Residence Inc ....E... 507 451-5327
Owatonna (G-6733)

Range Center Inc ....C... 218 254-3347
Chisholm (G-1000)

REM Central Lakes Inc ....E... 320 252-8875
Saint Cloud (G-7586)

REM Inc ....E... 651 647-9243
Saint Paul (G-8888)

REM Inc ....D... 507 387-3181
Mankato (G-3185)

Residential Advantages Inc ....D... 507 831-3804
Lakefield (G-2883)

Swift County Homes Inc ....E... 320 843-3509
Benson (G-442)

HOME FOR THE MENTALLY RETARDED, EXC SKILLED OR INTERMEDIATE

B L E A Inc ....E... 507 896-3040
Houston (G-2662)

Catholic Charities of The..................C... 612 827-6241
Minneapolis (G-4030)

Community Living Inc ....D... 952 443-2048
Victoria (G-9726)

Companion Housing Program Inc.......C... 952 285-5950
Saint Paul (G-8241)

Connections Inc ....D... 952 888-5792
Minneapolis (G-4153)

Griffin Housing Services Inc..............E... 507 388-6434
Mankato (G-3131)

Hiawatha Manor Inc ....E... 507 825-5697
Pipestone (G-6829)

Janesville Nursing Home Inc ....D... 507 231-5113
Janesville (G-2802)

REM & Tyler Inc...............................E... 507 247-5568
Tyler (G-9712)

REM Woodvale Inc...........................E... 507 451-1296
Owatonna (G-6734)

Riverview Manor Inc ....E... 507 824-2091
Wanamingo (G-9866)

Rose Camilia Co Inc ....C... 763 755-8400
Minneapolis (G-3592)

HOME FOR THE PHYSICALLY HANDICAPPED

Ability Building Center ....E... 507 895-7161
La Crescent (G-2836)

Accessible Space Inc ....E... 651 645-7271
Saint Paul (G-7976)

B L E A Inc.....................................E... 507 895-8111
La Crescent (G-2838)

Big Stone Community Homes Inc.......E... 320 839-6139
Ortonville (G-6578)

Hammer Residences Inc ....C... 763 473-1261
Wayzata (G-9919)

Maple Leaf Services Inc ....E... 507 765-3848
Preston (G-6899)

People Inc ....E... 651 774-0011
Saint Paul (G-8816)

Phoenix Residence Inc ....C... 651 227-7655
Saint Paul (G-7876)

Pine River Group Home Inc ....D... 218 587-4888
Pine River (G-6820)

HOME FURNISHINGS WHOLESALERS

Compass Marketing Inc.....................D... 612 333-5300
Minneapolis (G-4147)

Homecrest Outdoor Living LLC...........D... 218 631-1000
Wadena (G-9803)

Impact Innovations Inc ....D... 320 847-1210
Clara City (G-1028)

Jacobs Trading LLC ....E... 763 843-2066
Hopkins (G-2561)

Wild Wings LLC................................D... 651 345-5355
Lake City (G-2856)

HOME HEALTH CARE SVCS

A Chance To Grow Inc......................D... 612 789-1236
Minneapolis (G-3647)

Abbeycare Inc Home Health Care ......B... 651 690-5352
Saint Paul (G-7971)

Access Health Care Inc ....D... 218 326-0004
Grand Rapids (G-2267)

Adult Help & Companion Care............E... 952 377-0411
Minneapolis (G-3683)

Advanced Care Inc...........................D... 612 721-1957
Minneapolis (G-3686)

Affordable Professionals Inc ....C... 218 682-3351
Hackensack (G-2331)

Ageless Care Options.......................E... 218 463-3695
Roseau (G-7352)

Albert Lee Medical Center Inc...........C... 507 377-6393
Albert Lea (G-34)

Aliance Health Care Inc ....D... 507 252-9737
Rochester (G-7049)

All Temporaries Inc ....E... 320 654-6031
Saint Cloud (G-7446)

Alliance Health Care Inc ....A... 651 895-8030
Saint Paul (G-7692)

Alliance Health Care Inc ....E... 507 252-9737
Rochester (G-7052)

Allina Health System ....C... 651 779-2500
Saint Paul (G-8014)

Allina Health System ....E... 507 446-0936
Owatonna (G-6690)

Asian Home Care Inc ....E... 651 999-0268
Saint Paul (G-8069)

At Home Ltd....................................D... 612 673-9594
Minneapolis (G-3830)

ATT Home Health Care Inc................E... 651 646-8771
Saint Paul (G-8077)

Avalon Home Care ....D... 763 753-8658
Elk River (G-1862)

B'S Homecare Inc ....E... 763 689-8984
Cambridge (G-832)

Badger Acquisition of MN ....C... 763 259-0400
Minneapolis (G-3857)

Barnabas Health Care Services ....C... 218 829-0901
Brainerd (G-551)

Best Care Home Health Inc ....C... 612 378-1040
Minneapolis (G-3891)

Break-Thru Home Care ....E... 612 659-1505
Minneapolis (G-3939)

C J'S Home Health Care Inc ....E... 320 833-2253
Buffalo Lake (G-662)

Cardinal of Minnesota Ltd ....C... 507 281-1077
Rochester (G-7070)

Care 2000 Home Healthcare Svcs ......E... 218 736-0246
Fergus Falls (G-2064)

Care Plus H H A Inc 763 529-5520
Minneapolis (G-4003)

Caregivers's Network Inc ....E... 952 935-5581
Hopkins (G-2523)

Caremate Home Health Care Inc ....C... 651 659-0208
Saint Paul (G-8164)

Caring Hands Home Care Inc ....E... 218 837-5572
Sebeka (G-9414)

Caring Hands Home Care Inc ....D... 218 732-0088
Park Rapids (G-6749)

Choices For Children Inc ....D... 952 935-3515
Hopkins (G-2529)

Circle of Life Home Care ....B... 612 871-2474
Minneapolis (G-4078)

Clearwater Hospice ....E... 218 694-6581
Bagley (G-301)

Cns Managed Health Care Inc ....D... 507 289-2411
Rochester (G-7083)

Cokato Charitable Trust ....C... 320 286-2158
Cokato (G-1076)

Comfort Home Health Care Group .....C... 507 281-2332
Rochester (G-7087)

Comfort Services LLC ....E... 612 871-2160
Minneapolis (G-4128)

Community Home Health Inc..............E... 952 440-3955
Prior Lake (G-6930)

Companioncare Inc ....E... 763 533-1919
Minneapolis (G-4145)

Connectcare ....E... 320 234-5031
Hutchinson (G-2694)

County of Cook ....C... 218 387-3265
Grand Marais (G-2258)

County of Winona ....E... 507 457-6400
Winona (G-10089)

Covenant Home Services LLC ....E... 763 755-9009
Minneapolis (G-3446)

Crannys 4 Care LLC ....D... 218 824-0077
Brainerd (G-561)

Crest View Corp...............................C... 763 782-1611
Minneapolis (G-3447)

Crystal Care Home Health Svcs ....B... 612 861-4272
Minneapolis (G-4190)

Dependable Home Health Care ....E... 651 779-9810
Saint Paul (G-8288)

Direct Home Health Care Inc ....E... 612 870-8256
Minneapolis (G-4258)

Divine Healthcare Network ....D... 651 665-9795
Saint Paul (G-8303)

Edelweiss Home Health Care ....E... 763 315-1050
Osseo (G-6612)

Elderly Care Services LLC ....D... 952 882-9300
Burnsville (G-717)

Elenas Care Inc...............................D... 651 482-0549
Saint Paul (G-8332)

Evangelical Lutheran Good ....C... 218 829-1429
Brainerd (G-566)

Eventide Senior Living......................B... 218 233-7508
Moorhead (G-6314)

Extended Family Health Care ....E... 218 727-0446
Duluth (G-1316)

Fairview Health Line Home Care.........D... 218 262-6982
Hibbing (G-2443)

Fairview Health Services ....E... 651 982-7000
Wyoming (G-10202)

Fairview HomeCare & Hospice............B... 612 721-2491
Minneapolis (G-4401)

Fairview Homecare & Hospice ....E... 763 389-1923
Princeton (G-6908)

First Care Medical Services ....C... 218 435-1133
Fosston (G-2176)

First Choice Home Care Inc...............E... 651 225-4255
Saint Paul (G-8379)

First Minnesota Care Inc ....D... 612 724-3000
Minneapolis (G-4444)

Foundation For Healthcare ....B... 320 253-1920
Sartell (G-9328)

Freedom Health Care Inc ....D... 952 854-6889
Minneapolis (G-4485)

Galil Medical USA ....D... 877 639-2796
Arden Hills (G-246)

Genesis Homecare Inc ....D... 651 686-5910
Saint Paul (G-7780)

Global Home ....E... 507 282-7471
Rochester (G-7126)

Golden Home Care Plus Inc ....B... 507 359-2756
New Ulm (G-6452)

Good Hue County Public Health ....D... 651 385-6100
Red Wing (G-6983)

Good Neighbor Home Health Care .....C... 218 829-9238
Baxter (G-328)

Good Samaritan Home Care Inc.........D... 507 765-2700
Preston (G-6898)

Goodhue County Public Health...........D... 651 385-6100
Red Wing (G-6984)

Grove City Lah BNP ....D... 320 857-2274
Grove City (G-2328)

Guardian Angels Evan Home Care ......C... 763 441-1213
Elk River (G-1879)

Guardian Angels Health Svcs ....C... 763 441-1213
Elk River (G-1880)

Harry Meyering Center Inc ....B... 507 388-3551
Mankato (G-3135)

Healtheast ....D... 651 232-3008
Saint Paul (G-8451)

Healtheast Diversified Svcs...............651 232-2300
Saint Paul (G-8461)

Healtheast Home Care Inc ....B... 651 232-2800
Saint Paul (G-8462)

Healthline Inc ....E... 218 362-6760
Hibbing (G-2449)

Healthline Inc ....E... 218 262-6981
Hibbing (G-2450)

Healthworks Home Medical ....D... 507 238-9200
Fairmont (G-1974)

Healthworks Home Medical Inc ....E... 507 344-8500
Mankato (G-3137)

Heartland Hospice Services Inc ....C... 651 633-6522
Saint Paul (G-8475)

2011 Harris Minnesota
Services Directory

(G-00000) Company's Geographic Section entry number

SERVICES

Heartland Hospice Services Inc ....D... 320 654-1136
Saint Cloud *(G-7417)*

Hiawathal Home Care ....D... 651 388-2223
Red Wing *(G-6985)*

Hmong Home Health..............................E... 651 488-1680
Saint Paul *(G-8490)*

Home Care Solutions..............................D... 952 924-0677
Minneapolis *(G-4666)*

Home Health Inc.....................................C... 218 262-5887
Hibbing *(G-2455)*

Home Instead Senior Care ....C... 651 747-8722
Saint Paul *(G-8493)*

Homewatch Home Care ....E... 507 388-5589
Mankato *(G-3143)*

Hospice of Healtheast Inc ....D... 651 232-3312
Saint Paul *(G-8495)*

Hospice of The Twin Cities Inc ....D... 763 531-2424
Minneapolis *(G-4679)*

Hospice Preferred Choice Inc ....E... 952 943-0009
Minneapolis *(G-4680)*

I C A N Inc ....D... 507 835-9140
Waseca *(G-9880)*

Immanuel St Joseph Mayo Health........A... 507 625-4031
Mankato *(G-3147)*

In Home Personal Care Inc ....C... 763 546-1000
Minneapolis *(G-4693)*

Independence Plus Inc ....C... 218 281-3506
Crookston *(G-1126)*

Integra Health Care Inc ....E... 952 985-7290
Lakeville *(G-2911)*

Integrity Home Health Co ....E... 612 827-1479
Minneapolis *(G-4714)*

International Quality Homecare..........E... 507 451-6262
Owatonna *(G-6719)*

International Quality Homecare..........D... 507 252-8117
Rochester *(G-7142)*

Intrepid Home Health Care Inc.............E... 952 285-7300
Minneapolis *(G-4732)*

Intrepid of Golden Valley Inc ....D... 952 513-5400
Saint Louis Park *(G-7663)*

Intrepid of Texas Inc ....E... 952 285-7300
Minneapolis *(G-4733)*

Jones Stanley & Associates ....E... 507 288-0064
Rochester *(G-7147)*

Joy US Cares ....E... 320 983-5708
Milaca *(G-3379)*

Julie's Helping Hands............................C... 320 833-6082
Buffalo Lake *(G-664)*

Kittson Memorial Hospital Assn..........C... 218 843-3612
Hallock *(G-2333)*

Lakeland Hospice & Home Care..........C... 218 998-1400
Fergus Falls *(G-2082)*

Life By Design Inc ....C... 763 757-3263
Minneapolis *(G-3518)*

Life's Companion PCA Inc ....D... 218 326-1179
Grand Rapids *(G-2291)*

Lifes Companion PCA Inc ....C... 763 786-3439
Minneapolis *(G-3520)*

Lyngblomsten ....B... 651 646-2941
Saint Paul *(G-8599)*

M V R Home Care Inc ....E... 651 994-9583
Saint Paul *(G-7828)*

Mary T Associates Inc ....E... 763 754-6706
Minneapolis *(G-3529)*

Metro Home Health Care Inc ....C... 763 323-2099
Minneapolis *(G-3537)*

MGM Home Care Inc ....E... 612 338-3636
Minneapolis *(G-5014)*

Midwest Home Health Care Inc............B... 612 343-3265
Minneapolis *(G-5029)*

Minnesota Autism Center......................C... 952 767-4200
Minnetonka *(G-6196)*

Minuteclinic LLC ....E... 612 659-7111
Minneapolis *(G-5106)*

Montevideo Hospital Home Care..........E... 320 367-2877
Clara City *(G-1030)*

Morgan Business Trust ....E... 218 348-1359
Duluth *(G-1397)*

Morning Star Home Health ....E... 507 373-0201
Albert Lea *(G-62)*

Nightingale Home Health Care ....E... 763 545-3131
Minneapolis *(G-5202)*

Nobles Rock Public Health ....E... 507 372-8256
Worthington *(G-10189)*

North Country Hospital ....E... 218 333-5665
Bemidji *(G-411)*

North Memorial Health Care..................D... 763 520-3900
Minneapolis *(G-5216)*

Nurses That Care ....E... 218 724-2800
Duluth *(G-1411)*

Olafson, Renae ....E... 651 452-6825
Saint Paul *(G-8780)*

Option Care Inc ....C... 651 635-9272
Saint Paul *(G-8789)*

Our Circle of Friends ....E... 507 334-4346
Faribault *(G-2024)*

Percy Nelson Enterprises Inc ....E... 651 209-6360
Woodbury *(G-10173)*

Petersen Home Care Services ....E... 763 557-1126
Minneapolis *(G-5369)*

Prairie River Home Care Inc..................D... 507 345-8591
Mankato *(G-3182)*

Prairie River Home Care Inc..................C... 507 252-9844
Rochester *(G-7210)*

Prairie River Home Care Inc..................D... 507 532-2264
Marshall *(G-3321)*

Pride N'Living Home Care Inc..............E... 763 572-2390
Minneapolis *(G-3573)*

Public Health Solutions I ....E... 763 754-7427
Minneapolis *(G-3579)*

Quality Living Home Health ....E... 507 454-6800
Winona *(G-10120)*

REM Health Inc ....E... 952 926-9808
Minneapolis *(G-5509)*

Rice Memorial Hospital ....E... 320 231-7077
Willmar *(G-10042)*

River Valley Home Care........................C... 651 460-4201
Farmington *(G-2059)*

Riverview Healthcare Assn ....E... 218 281-9478
Crookston *(G-1136)*

Rose Arbor ....D... 763 493-5910
Osseo *(G-6656)*

Royal Home Health Care ....E... 763 504-4559
Minneapolis *(G-5563)*

Sacred Heart Care Center ....C... 507 433-1808
Austin *(G-286)*

Saint Elizabeth's Hospital ....C... 651 565-4531
Wabasha *(G-9770)*

Senior Friend..E... 218 878-0990
Cloquet *(G-1065)*

Senior Friend Associates Inc................C... 218 727-1111
Duluth *(G-1447)*

Senior Health & Home Care Inc ....E... 952 920-9399
Minneapolis *(G-5637)*

Senior Home Living MN LLC................D... 952 935-0789
Hopkins *(G-2631)*

Sleepy Eye Area Home Health 507 794-3594
Sleepy Eye *(G-9500)*

Southeast Asian Health Svcs ....C... 651 222-2889
Saint Paul *(G-8974)*

Spectrum Community Health................E... 507 332-7471
Faribault *(G-2031)*

Spectrum Community Health Inc ....E... 507 282-8052
Rochester *(G-7260)*

Spectrum Community Health Inc ....E... 320 235-5684
Willmar *(G-10045)*

Spectrum Community Health Inc ....E... 218 326-4202
Grand Rapids *(G-2308)*

Spectrum Community Health Inc ....E... 320 252-9640
Saint Cloud *(G-7428)*

St Cloud Hospital ....C... 320 251-2700
Saint Cloud *(G-7603)*

St Mary's Medical Center ....A... 218 786-4000
Duluth *(G-1474)*

Stinson Home Care LLC ....E... 763 755-4801
Minneapolis *(G-3609)*

Student Experience Inc ....E... 218 728-8009
Duluth *(G-1477)*

Sugar Lake Supported Living ....E... 320 963-7571
Maple Lake *(G-3265)*

Sunrise Health Services ....D... 651 462-9331
Stacy *(G-9578)*

Tgp Inc ....E... 218 694-2378
Bagley *(G-303)*

TLC Home Health Care Inc ....E... 218 326-3555
Grand Rapids *(G-2309)*

TLC Nursing Services of ....D... 651 647-0017
Saint Paul *(G-9069)*

Transformation House Inc ....E... 763 427-7155
Anoka *(G-236)*

U About Inc ....C... 612 866-4884
Richfield *(G-7039)*

United Homecare Inc ....E... 952 898-9780
Burnsville *(G-815)*

Unity Healthcare....................................E... 612 285-8743
Minneapolis *(G-5918)*

US Asian Home Care ....E... 763 533-7750
Minneapolis *(G-5942)*

Victory Home Care Inc..........................E... 763 566-3318
Minneapolis *(G-5970)*

Village Health Care Inc 952 361-8000
Chaska *(G-983)*

Walker Methodist Inc ....B... 612 827-5931
Minneapolis *(G-6011)*

Warren Community Hospital Inc ....D... 218 745-4211
Warren *(G-9869)*

We Do-Care Inc ....C... 612 866-7800
Minneapolis *(G-6030)*

Weiner Memorial Foundation................B... 507 532-9661
Marshall *(G-3332)*

Weiner Memorial Foundation ....E... 507 537-7070
Marshall *(G-3331)*

West Wind Village..................................C... 320 589-1133
Morris *(G-6380)*

HOME IMPROVEMENT & RENOVATION CONTRACTOR AGENCY

Maly Co's LLC..E... 612 788-9688
Minneapolis *(G-4939)*

HOMEBUILDERS & OTHER OPERATIVE BUILDERS

Rottlund Co Inc......................................D... 651 638-0500
Saint Paul *(G-8914)*

Ryland Group Inc ....D... 952 229-6000
Edina *(G-1843)*

HOMEFURNISHINGS & SPLYS, WHOLESALE: Decorative

T Distribution Inc ....E... 651 636-6367
Saint Paul *(G-9024)*

HOMEFURNISHINGS, WHOL: Resilient Floor Coverings, Tile/Sheet

Herregan Distributors Inc ....D... 651 452-7200
Saint Paul *(G-7799)*

Stone Source Inc 763 540-9000
Plymouth *(G-6884)*

Tile Shop Inc ....E... 763 541-1444
Minneapolis *(G-5824)*

HOMEFURNISHINGS, WHOLESALE: Blinds, Venetian

Steven Fabrics Co ....C... 612 781-6671
Minneapolis *(G-5753)*

HOMEFURNISHINGS, WHOLESALE: Carpets

Cheney LLC..E... 763 559-1980
Minneapolis *(G-4058)*

Encompass Group LLC..........................D... 651 646-6600
Saint Paul *(G-8339)*

Encompass Group LLC..........................C... 651 646-6600
Saint Paul *(G-8340)*

Herregan Distributors Inc ....D... 651 452-7200
Saint Paul *(G-7799)*

Lintex Corp..C... 651 646-6600
Saint Paul *(G-8591)*

HOMEFURNISHINGS, WHOLESALE: Curtains

Encompass Group LLC..........................D... 651 646-6600
Saint Paul *(G-8339)*

Encompass Group LLC..........................C... 651 646-6600
Saint Paul *(G-8340)*

Lintex Corp..C... 651 646-6600
Saint Paul *(G-8591)*

HOMEFURNISHINGS, WHOLESALE: Draperies

Shade Warren Co....................................D... 612 331-5939
Minneapolis *(G-5647)*

HOMEFURNISHINGS, WHOLESALE: Fireplace Eqpt & Access

Hajoca Corp ....E... 763 315-0100
Minneapolis *(G-4589)*

HOMEFURNISHINGS, WHOLESALE: Grills, Barbecue

Hom Furniture Inc..................................D... 952 884-8800
Minneapolis *(G-4664)*

Hom Furniture Inc..................................E... 651 634-6600
Saint Paul *(G-8492)*

HOMEFURNISHINGS, WHOLESALE: Kitchenware

Lenox Group Inc ....C... 952 943-4100
Eden Prairie *(G-1708)*

HOMEFURNISHINGS, WHOLESALE: Linens, Table

Encompass Group LLC..........................D... 651 646-6600
Saint Paul *(G-8339)*

Encompass Group LLC..........................C... 651 646-6600
Saint Paul *(G-8340)*

Lintex Corp..C... 651 646-6600
Saint Paul *(G-8591)*

S
E
R
V
I
C
E
S

Employment codes: A=Over 500 employees, B=251-500,
C=101-250, D=51-100, E=25-50

2011 Harris Minnesota
Services Directory

© Harris InfoSource 1-866-281-6415
713

HOMEFURNISHINGS, WHOLESALE: Mirrors/Pictures, Framed/Unframd

Gordy's Glass Inc ....E... 651 437-5356
Hastings (G-2416)

HOMEFURNISHINGS, WHOLESALE: Sheets, Textile

Encompass Group LLC ....D... 651 646-6600
Saint Paul (G-8339)
Encompass Group LLC ....C... 651 646-6600
Saint Paul (G-8340)
Lintex Corp ....C... 651 646-6600
Saint Paul (G-8591)

HOMEMAKERS' SVCS

Agramson Enterprises Inc ....D... 763 546-1599
Minneapolis (G-3700)

HOMES FOR THE ELDERLY

Aftenro Society ....E... 218 728-6600
Duluth (G-1233)
Benedictine Health System ....C... 507 534-3191
Plainview (G-6838)
Cedars of Austin ....E... 507 437-3246
Austin (G-266)
City of Fertile ....C... 218 945-6194
Fertile (G-2125)
Comforts of Home ....E... 651 287-0265
Saint Paul (G-7735)
Comforts of Home ....E... 651 426-1036
White Bear Lake (G-9974)
Country Side East Living ....E... 507 446-8334
Owatonna (G-6706)
Emerald Crest ....E... 952 856-7510
Victoria (G-9728)
Garkat Inc ....E... 507 835-8227
Waseca (G-9879)
Golden Oaks Inc ....E... 218 729-5014
Duluth (G-1337)
Hope Shilohs Inc ....E... 507 934-2094
Saint Peter (G-9306)
Northfield Manor Inc ....E... 507 645-9090
Northfield (G-6538)
Prairie Lodge ....E... 763 566-1495
Minneapolis (G-5400)
Presbyterian Homes & Services ...D... 651 631-6100
Saint Paul (G-8840)
Rural Living Environments Inc ......E... 218 827-3495
Babbitt (G-298)
Seek Home Inc ....D... 763 494-0870
Osseo (G-6661)
Semcil Living Inc ....E... 507 285-1815
Rochester (G-7250)
Senior Southview Living ....E... 651 554-4838
Saint Paul (G-7900)
St Anthony Health Center ....B... 612 788-9673
Minneapolis (G-6131)
St James Home of Duluth ....C... 218 728-7500
Duluth (G-1462)
Truman Sr Living Inc ....E... 507 776-2031
Truman (G-9697)
Walker Assisted Living Corp ....E... 952 835-8351
Minneapolis (G-6008)

HORSE & OTHER EQUINE BREEDING & PRODUCTION

Northstar Arabian Breeders Inc.....E... 507 947-3541
Lake Crystal (G-2862)

HOSPITAL BEDS WHOLESALERS

Slumberland Inc ....E... 320 251-1024
Waite Park (G-9839)
Slumberland Inc ....D... 952 888-6204
Minneapolis (G-5689)

HOSPITAL EQPT REPAIR SVCS

Sterilmed Inc ....B... 763 488-3400
Osseo (G-6668)

HOSPITALS: AMA Approved Residency

Rochester Methodist Hospital ....A... 507 255-5123
Rochester (G-7236)
St Luke's Hospital of Duluth ....A... 218 726-5555
Duluth (G-1469)

HOSPITALS: Children's

Children's Health Care Inc ....A... 612 813-6100
Minneapolis (G-4065)

Gillette Children's Specialty ....B... 651 291-2848
Saint Paul (G-8410)
Shriners Hospitals For ....C... 612 596-6100
Minneapolis (G-5661)

HOSPITALS: Chronic Disease

Children's Health Care Inc ....A... 651 220-6000
Saint Paul (G-8193)

HOSPITALS: Medical & Surgical

Abbott Northwestern Hospital 612 863-4000
Minneapolis (G-3660)
Aitkin Community Hospital Inc ....B... 218 927-2121
Aitkin (G-23)
Albert Lea Medical Center-Mayo .....A... 507 373-2384
Albert Lea (G-32)
Allina Health System ....A... 612 775-5000
Minneapolis (G-3721)
Allina Health System ....A... 763 236-6000
Minneapolis (G-3393)
Allina Health System ....A... 612 863-4000
Minneapolis (G-3718)
Allina Health System ....E... 952 992-2500
Minnetonka (G-6138)
Allina Health System ....A... 763 236-5000
Fridley (G-2189)
Allina Health System ....B... 763 682-1212
Buffalo (G-633)
Allina Health System ....B... 507 233-1000
New Ulm (G-6439)
Appleton Area Health Services ......C... 320 289-2422
Appleton (G-244)
Bethesda Healthy Rehab ....B... 651 232-2000
Saint Paul (G-8109)
Canby Community Hospital Dist ....C... 507 223-7277
Canby (G-848)
Cannon Falls Medical Center ....C... 507 263-4221
Cannon Falls (G-855)
Catholic Health Initiatives ....B... 952 324-9010
Minneapolis (G-4031)
Centracare Health Services of 320 732-2131
Long Prairie (G-3038)
Centracare Health System ....A... 320 256-4231
Melrose (G-3346)
Centracare Health System ....D... 320 251-2700
Saint Cloud (G-7481)
Central Minnesota Group Health ......A... 320 253-5220
Saint Cloud (G-7484)
Chippewa County-Montevideo ....C... 320 269-8877
Montevideo (G-6244)
City of Ada ....C... 218 784-5000
Ada (G-1)
City of Jackson ....D... 507 847-2420
Jackson (G-2787)
City of Ortonville ....C... 320 839-2502
Ortonville (G-6579)
City of Redwood Falls ....C... 507 637-4500
Redwood Falls (G-7020)
City of Worthington ....A... 507 372-2941
Worthington (G-10180)
Clearwater County Memorial ....C... 218 694-6501
Bagley (G-300)
Community Health Network ....C... 320 845-2121
Albany (G-26)
Community Memorial Hospital ....B... 218 879-4641
Cloquet (G-1050)
Cook County North Shore Hosp ....C... 218 387-3040
Grand Marais (G-2257)
County of Douglas ....A... 320 762-1511
Alexandria (G-91)
County of Mahnomen ....D... 218 935-2511
Mahnomen (G-3084)
County of Meeker ....C... 320 693-3242
Litchfield (G-2982)
County of Murray ....C... 507 836-6111
Slayton (G-9486)
Cuyuna Range Hospital Inc ....B... 218 546-7000
Crosby (G-1147)
Dawson Area Hospital District........C... 320 769-4323
Dawson (G-1164)
Deer River Healthcare Center ....C... 218 246-2900
Deer River (G-1168)
Divine Providence Health Ctr ....C... 507 694-1414
Ivanhoe (G-2784)
Essentia Health 218 786-8376
Duluth (G-1314)
Fairmont Community Hospital.........A... 507 238-8100
Fairmont (G-1963)
Fairview Health Services ....A... 612 672-6300
Minneapolis (G-4396)
Fairview Health Services ....C... 612 672-6800
Minneapolis (G-4393)
Fairview Health Services ....B... 651 982-7000
Wyoming (G-10202)

Fairview Health Services ....E... 952 848-5600
Minneapolis (G-4397)
Fairview Health Services ....B... 952 892-2910
Burnsville (G-720)
Fairview Health Services ....C... 218 262-4881
Hibbing (G-2444)
Fairview Health Services ....E... 651 632-7300
Saint Paul (G-8362)
Fairview Redwing Health Svcs ....A... 651 267-5000
Red Wing (G-6979)
First Care Medical Services ....C... 218 435-1133
Fosston (G-2176)
Glacial Ridge Hospital Fndtn..........C... 320 634-4521
Glenwood (G-2223)
Graceville Health Center Inc ....C... 320 748-7223
Graceville (G-2254)
Graceville Missionary ....D... 320 748-7223
Graceville (G-2255)
Grand Itasca Clinic & Hospital ....B... 218 326-7024
Grand Rapids (G-2280)
Harmony Community Healthcare......D... 507 886-6544
Harmony (G-2371)
Healthcare & Wellness Fndtn ....D... 218 643-0410
Breckenridge (G-594)
Healtheast Care System................A... 651 232-1000
Saint Paul (G-8454)
Healtheast Co's Inc ....B... 651 232-4000
Saint Paul (G-9225)
Healtheast Diversified Svcs 651 232-2300
Saint Paul (G-8461)
Healtheast Maplewood Out............E... 651 232-7780
Saint Paul (G-8463)
Healtheast St John's Hospital ....A... 651 232-7000
Saint Paul (G-8465)
HealthSouth Corp ....E... 952 921-0100
Minneapolis (G-4624)
HealthSouth Corp ....C... 320 251-8385
Saint Cloud (G-7524)
Hendricks Community Hospital ....C... 507 275-3134
Hendricks (G-2429)
Hennepin Healthcare System Inc......A... 612 873-3000
Minneapolis (G-4638)
Hospice Of The Lakes ....D... 952 883-6877
Minneapolis (G-4678)
Hutchinson Area Health Care..........A... 320 234-5000
Hutchinson (G-2698)
Immanuel-St Joseph's Hospital ....A... 507 625-4031
Mankato (G-3148)
Indian Health Service ....C... 218 679-3316
Redlake (G-7015)
Kanabec County Hospital ....B... 320 679-1212
Mora (G-6362)
Kittson Memorial Hospital Assn ....C... 218 843-3612
Hallock (G-2333)
Kittson Memorial Hospital Assn ....C... 218 843-3612
Hallock (G-2334)
Lake Rainy Medical Center ....C... 218 283-4481
International Falls (G-2726)
Lake Region Healthcare Corp ....A... 218 736-8000
Fergus Falls (G-2081)
Lakeside Medical Center Inc ....C... 320 629-2542
Pine City (G-6813)
Lakeview Memorial Hospital............B... 651 439-5330
Stillwater (G-9625)
Lakewood Health Center...............C... 218 634-2120
Baudette (G-317)
Lakewood Health System ....B... 218 894-1515
Staples (G-9586)
Lifecare Medical Center ....C... 218 463-4305
Roseau (G-7355)
Lincoln Lyon Murry & Pipestone ....E... 507 537-6709
Marshall (G-3305)
Madelia Community Hospital Inc ....D... 507 642-5016
Madelia (G-3073)
Mankato Surgical Center LLC ....E... 507 388-6000
Mankato (G-3166)
Maple Grove Ambulatory Surgery ......E... 763 981-3234
Maple Grove (G-3248)
Mayo Midair...............................E... 507 255-2808
Rochester (G-7176)
Memorial Hospital Association ....A... 763 689-7700
Cambridge (G-842)
Mercy Hospital Health Care Ctr.......B... 218 485-4481
Moose Lake (G-6352)
Meridian Behavioral Health LLC 612 326-7600
New Brighton (G-6412)
Methodist Hospital ....A... 952 993-5000
Saint Louis Park (G-7666)
Mille Lacs Health System..............B... 320 532-3154
Onamia (G-6574)
Minnesota Department of ....D... 612 713-2196
Saint Paul (G-7961)
Minnesota Department of Human ....B... 218 739-7200
Fergus Falls (G-2099)
Minnesota Valley Memorial Hosp........C... 507 665-3375
Le Sueur (G-2958)

Monticello-Big Lake Community ....B... 763 295-2945
  Monticello *(G-6278)*
North Country Hospital ....A... 218 751-5430
  Bemidji *(G-410)*
North Country Regional Hosp ....B... 218 751-5430
  Bemidji *(G-412)*
North Memorial Health Care..................A... 763 520-5200
  Minneapolis *(G-5217)*
Northern Itasca Hospital Dist...............C... 218 743-3177
  Bigfork *(G-461)*
Northfield Hospital & Skilled................B... 507 646-1000
  Northfield *(G-6517)*
Northwest Medical Center ....B... 218 681-4240
  Thief River Falls *(G-9676)*
Olmsted Medical Center ....B... 507 288-3443
  Rochester *(G-7195)*
Olmsted Medical Center ....A... 507 529-6600
  Rochester *(G-7194)*
Park Nicollet Health Services ....C... 952 993-5353
  Minneapolis *(G-5333)*
Perham Hospital District ....B... 218 346-4500
  Perham *(G-6800)*
Pipestone County Medical Ctr ....C... 507 825-5811
  Pipestone *(G-6834)*
Queen of Peace Hospital......................B... 952 758-4431
  New Prague *(G-6434)*
Range Regional Health Services ....A... 218 262-4881
  Hibbing *(G-2473)*
Regina Medical Center ....A... 651 480-4100
  Hastings *(G-2402)*
Regions Hospital Foundation ....A... 651 254-3456
  Saint Paul *(G-8884)*
Renville County Hospice Inc................D... 320 523-1261
  Olivia *(G-6564)*
Rice County District One Hosp.............B... 507 334-6451
  Faribault *(G-2027)*
Rice Memorial Hospital ....C... 320 235-4543
  Willmar *(G-10041)*
Ridgeview Medical Center.....................A... 952 442-2191
  Waconia *(G-9792)*
Robert B Diasio ....D... 507 284-3977
  Rochester *(G-7226)*
Rochester Methodist Hospital 507 266-7890
  Rochester *(G-7237)*
S M D C St Mary's Duluth Clin ....A... 218 786-4020
  Duluth *(G-1441)*
Saint Elizabeth's Hospital ....C... 651 565-4531
  Wabasha *(G-9770)*
Saint Marys Hospital of ....A... 507 255-5123
  Rochester *(G-7246)*
Sanford Health ....C... 507 283-2321
  Luverne *(G-3067)*
Sanford Health ....E... 507 847-2420
  Jackson *(G-2798)*
Sanford Health Network ....C... 507 283-2321
  Luverne *(G-3068)*
Sibley Medical Center..........................C... 507 964-2271
  Arlington *(G-250)*
Sioux Valley Canby Campus..................C... 507 223-7221
  Canby *(G-853)*
Smdc Medical Center ....A... 218 727-8762
  Duluth *(G-1455)*
Springfield Medical Center....................D... 507 723-6201
  Springfield *(G-9575)*
St Cloud Hospital ....B... 320 251-2700
  Saint Cloud *(G-7602)*
St Francis Medical Center ....B... 218 643-3000
  Breckenridge *(G-601)*
St Francis Regional Medical ....A... 952 403-3000
  Shakopee *(G-9476)*
St Joseph's Area Health Svcs...............B... 218 732-3311
  Park Rapids *(G-6762)*
St Joseph's Medical Center ....A... 218 829-2861
  Brainerd *(G-587)*
St Mary's Duluth Clinic Health ....A... 218 786-4000
  Duluth *(G-1473)*
St Mary's Medical Center ....A... 218 786-4000
  Duluth *(G-1474)*
St Mary's Regional Health Ctr...............C... 218 847-5611
  Detroit Lakes *(G-1217)*
St Peter, City of Inc ....C... 507 931-7354
  Saint Peter *(G-9314)*
Stevens Community Medical Ctr ....C... 320 589-1313
  Morris *(G-6379)*
Swift County-Benson Hospital ....D... 320 843-4232
  Benson *(G-443)*
Tri-County Hospital Inc ....B... 218 631-3510
  Wadena *(G-9813)*
Tweeten-Lutheran Health Care ....C... 507 498-3211
  Spring Grove *(G-9562)*
Tyler Healthcare Center Inc ....C... 507 247-5521
  Tyler *(G-9716)*
United Hospital District ....C... 507 526-3273
  Blue Earth *(G-539)*
United Hospital District ....D... 218 894-8610
  Staples *(G-9587)*

Unity Family Health Care......................A... 320 632-5441
  Little Falls *(G-3021)*
Virginia, City of Inc ....A... 218 741-3340
  Virginia *(G-9760)*
Warren Community Hospital Inc ....D... 218 745-4211
  Warren *(G-9869)*
Waseca Medical Center — Mayo ....C... 507 835-1210
  Waseca *(G-9889)*
Weiner Memorial Foundation................B... 507 532-9661
  Marshall *(G-3332)*
Westbrook Health Center ....E... 507 274-6121
  Westbrook *(G-9968)*
Western Pope County Hospital ....D... 320 239-2201
  Starbuck *(G-9589)*
Wheaton Community Hospital ....D... 320 563-8226
  Wheaton *(G-9970)*
White Community Hospital Corp ....C... 218 229-2211
  Aurora *(G-257)*
Windom, City of Inc ....D... 507 831-2400
  Windom *(G-10072)*
Winona Community Memorial Hosp ....A... 507 454-3650
  Winona *(G-10145)*

HOSPITALS: Medical School Affiliation

Cuyuna Range Hospital Inc ....B... 218 546-7000
  Crosby *(G-1147)*
Regents of The University of ....D... 612 625-2874
  Minneapolis *(G-5494)*

HOSPITALS: Mental Retardation

American Baptist Homes of The..........E... 952 941-3175
  Eden Prairie *(G-1590)*
Benedictine Health System ....D... 651 388-1234
  Red Wing *(G-6975)*

HOSPITALS: Mental, Exc For The Mentally Retarded

County of Douglas ....E... 320 762-2400
  Alexandria *(G-90)*
Minnesota Department of Human.........B... 507 931-7137
  Saint Peter *(G-9299)*
Northwestern Mental Health Ctr ....D... 218 281-3940
  Crookston *(G-1131)*
Range Mental Health Center Inc ....E... 218 749-2881
  Virginia *(G-9754)*
Relate Counseling Center Inc ....E... 952 932-7277
  Minnetonka *(G-6219)*
REM Inc ....C... 507 287-6824
  Rochester *(G-7221)*
Southwestern Mental Health Ctr................507 283-9511
  Luverne *(G-3070)*

HOSPITALS: Orthopedic

Tria Orthopaedic Center Asc ....D... 952 831-8742
  Minneapolis *(G-5853)*

HOSPITALS: Psychiatric

Albert Lea Medical Center-Mayo ....A... 507 373-2384
  Albert Lea *(G-32)*
Cedar Ridge Inc.................................D... 651 426-8983
  Minneapolis *(G-4036)*

HOSPITALS: Rehabilitation, Alcoholism

AA Monticello ....E... 763 295-5066
  Monticello *(G-6265)*
Bell Hill Recovery Center Inc ....E... 218 631-3610
  Wadena *(G-9798)*
Brown County Evaluation Center..........E... 507 359-9111
  New Ulm *(G-6443)*
Guest House Inc.................................E... 507 288-4693
  Rochester *(G-7128)*
Healtheast Care System ....E... 651 232-3222
  Saint Paul *(G-8455)*
Human Services Inc ....E... 651 430-2720
  Stillwater *(G-9623)*
Minnesota Department of Human.........B... 218 739-7200
  Fergus Falls *(G-2099)*
Northland Counseling Center ....E... 218 327-1105
  Grand Rapids *(G-2302)*
Progress Valley Inc ....E... 612 869-3223
  Minneapolis *(G-5425)*
Relate Counseling Center Inc ....E... 952 932-7277
  Minnetonka *(G-6219)*
Skemp Walk In Clinic ....E... 507 724-3353
  Caledonia *(G-829)*
Southwestern Mental Health Ctr...........E... 507 376-4141
  Worthington *(G-10195)*

HOSPITALS: Rehabilitation, Drug Addiction

Hazelden Foundation...........................D... 612 559-2022
  Minneapolis *(G-4614)*

HOSPITALS: Specialty, NEC

Bethesda Healthy Rehab ....A... 651 232-2000
  Saint Paul *(G-8109)*
Beverly Enterprises - MN ....D... 507 932-3283
  Saint Charles *(G-7402)*
Beverly Enterprises - MN ....C... 651 483-5431
  Saint Paul *(G-8111)*
County of Mahnomen ....D... 218 935-2511
  Mahnomen *(G-3084)*
County of Murray ....C... 507 836-6111
  Slayton *(G-9486)*
Evangelical Lutheran Good ....D... 218 776-3157
  Clearbrook *(G-1038)*
Fountain Centers ....E... 507 377-6411
  Albert Lea *(G-51)*
Lifecare Medical Center ....D... 218 782-2131
  Greenbush *(G-2326)*
Red Wing Healthcare LLC.....................C... 651 388-2843
  Red Wing *(G-6997)*
Unitedhealth Group Inc........................A... 952 936-1300
  Hopkins *(G-2651)*
Westbrook Health Center.....................E... 507 274-6121
  Westbrook *(G-9968)*
Woodwinds Health Campus ....A... 651 232-0100
  Saint Paul *(G-9290)*

HOSPITALS: Substance Abuse

Albert Lea Medical Center-Mayo ....A... 507 373-2384
  Albert Lea *(G-32)*
Cedar Ridge Inc ....D... 651 426-8983
  Minneapolis *(G-4036)*
Northland Counseling Center...............E... 218 326-1274
  Grand Rapids *(G-2301)*
Twin Town Treatment Center LLC ....E... 651 645-3661
  Saint Paul *(G-9095)*
Wayside House Inc ....E... 952 926-5626
  Minneapolis *(G-6027)*

HOSTELS

Sp Hotels LLC....................................E... 651 291-8800
  Saint Paul *(G-8975)*

HOTEL: Franchised

Carlson Hotels LP...............................C... 763 212-1000
  Minneapolis *(G-4014)*
Carlson Hotels Worldwide Inc ....E... 763 212-5000
  Minneapolis *(G-4017)*
DI-Dw Holdings LLC ....E... 952 942-6818
  Eden Prairie *(G-1646)*
ESA P Portfolio Operating ....E... 507 289-7444
  Rochester *(G-7107)*
ESA P Portfolio Operating ....E... 507 536-7444
  Rochester *(G-7106)*
Lho Bloomington One Lessee LLC......C... 952 835-7800
  Minneapolis *(G-4868)*

HOTEL: Seasonal

L Jireh Inc...E... 218 387-2688
  Grand Marais *(G-2262)*

HOTEL: YMCA/YMHA

Young Men's Chrtn Assoc of ....C... 763 785-7882
  Minneapolis *(G-3644)*

HOTELS & MOTELS

Aloft Htl Minneapolis...........................D... 612 455-8400
  Minneapolis *(G-3731)*
AmericInn Shakopee ....D... 952 445-6775
  Shakopee *(G-9418)*
Ameriprise Financial Services ....E... 952 368-3100
  Chaska *(G-948)*
Apple Valley Gsrs LLC ....E... 952 953-6111
  Saint Paul *(G-7701)*
Ashford Trs Nickel, LP ....D... 952 854-2100
  Bloomington *(G-487)*
Best Western South St Paul ....E... 651 455-3600
  Saint Paul *(G-8108)*
Bloomington Hotel Acquisition ....E... 952 893-9999
  Minneapolis *(G-3915)*
Blue Waters Development Corp...........D... 800 242-1988
  Two Harbors *(G-9705)*
Buffalo Lodging ....E... 763 682-5660
  Buffalo *(G-639)*
CSM Equities LLC...............................D... 612 395-7000
  Minneapolis *(G-4196)*
Dakota Ridge LLC...............................E... 763 398-1821
  Saint Paul *(G-7746)*
Days Inns & Suites ....D... 763 561-8400
  Minneapolis *(G-4231)*
Diamondrock Minneapolis Tenant ....D... 612 376-1000
  Minneapolis *(G-4253)*

S E R V I C E S

Djont Jpm Leasing LLC ....D... 952 884-4811
Minneapolis *(G-4264)*

East Bay Hotel Corp ....E... 218 387-2800
Grand Marais *(G-2259)*

Eden Prairie Hhp-II LLC ....E... 952 942-9000
Eden Prairie *(G-1650)*

Fitgers On The Lake LLC ....C... 218 727-9077
Duluth *(G-1325)*

Foussard Hospitality Inc ....E... 320 252-8700
Saint Cloud *(G-7415)*

Graves Development Corp ....E... 320 252-6034
Saint Cloud *(G-7522)*

Gus Chafoulias ....D... 507 285-1234
Rochester *(G-7129)*

Hilton Hotels Corp ....D... 952 884-4811
Minneapolis *(G-4651)*

Hotel Ivy ....D... 612 746-4600
Minneapolis *(G-4682)*

Lundell Enterprises LLC ....D... 952 261-7617
Shakopee *(G-9454)*

Maple Grove Lodging Investors ....E... 763 509-9500
Maple Grove *(G-3249)*

Marquette Hotel ....B... 612 333-4545
Minneapolis *(G-4953)*

Meristar Investment Partners L ....D... 952 854-2100
Minneapolis *(G-4991)*

Mermaid Inc ....C... 763 784-7350
Saint Paul *(G-8637)*

Nath Midwest Lodging LLC ....D... 952 853-1423
Saint Paul *(G-8737)*

PC Hotels LLC ....D... 218 233-6171
Moorhead *(G-6332)*

Red Wing Hotel Corp ....C... 651 388-2846
Red Wing *(G-6998)*

Rhm Receiver 3211 Co LLC ....D... 612 746-4600
Minneapolis *(G-5536)*

Sanford Hospitality LLC 952 854-3411
Bloomington *(G-512)*

Select Hotels Group LLC ....E... 952 944-9700
Eden Prairie *(G-1774)*

Select Inn of Bloomington LP ....E... 952 835-7400
Minneapolis *(G-5634)*

78th Street Leaseco LLC ....B... 952 835-1900
Minneapolis *(G-5643)*

Sheraton St Paul-Woodbury ....D... 651 209-3280
Saint Paul *(G-9273)*

Simper Lowell LLC ....E... 651 439-1100
Stillwater *(G-9639)*

Ssb LLC ....E... 952 831-7900
Bloomington *(G-518)*

St Croix Preservation Co Inc ....E... 651 439-6000
Stillwater *(G-9644)*

Stockman Hotel Corp ....E... 651 636-1171
Saint Paul *(G-9007)*

3608 Park Street LLC 651 221-7911
Saint Paul *(G-9043)*

Treasure Island Casino & Bingo.........A... 651 388-6300
Welch *(G-9957)*

Trimark Hotel Corp ....C... 612 305-9763
Minneapolis *(G-5856)*

University Inn Property LLC ....C... 612 379-8888
Minneapolis *(G-5925)*

Z M C Hotels Inc ....E... 218 726-1111
Duluth *(G-1506)*

HOUSEHOLD APPLIANCE PARTS:
Wholesalers

AAF-Mcquay Inc........................B... 763 553-5330
Minneapolis *(G-3655)*

Dependable Indoor Air Quality ....E... 763 757-5040
Minneapolis *(G-3454)*

Dey Appliance Parts of CO ....D... 651 490-9191
Saint Paul *(G-8291)*

Dey Appliance Parts of North 651 490-9191
Saint Paul *(G-8292)*

Dey Distributing ....E... 651 490-9191
Saint Paul *(G-8293)*

Dey Distributing Inc ....E... 651 490-9191
Saint Paul *(G-8294)*

Dey Properties ....D... 651 490-9191
Saint Paul *(G-8295)*

Goodin Co...............................E... 320 259-6086
Saint Cloud *(G-7520)*

Hajoca Corp ....E... 763 315-0100
Minneapolis *(G-4589)*

Park Systems Inc ....E... 612 822-3180
Minneapolis *(G-5337)*

HOUSEHOLD APPLIANCE REPAIR SVCS

Rigels Inc ....E... 218 233-6104
Moorhead *(G-6340)*

Sears, Roebuck & Co..................D... 800 882-5351
Waite Park *(G-9837)*

HOUSEKEEPING & MAID SVCS

Beamkko ....E... 651 770-5661
Saint Paul *(G-8096)*

S & L Team Cleaning ....E... 612 558-4502
Saint Paul *(G-8917)*

ServiceMaster Inc ....E... 651 552-4979
Saint Paul *(G-8946)*

Servicemaster of St Cloud Inc ....C... 320 252-4622
Saint Cloud *(G-7591)*

Synera Solutions ....D... 952 403-9911
Shakopee *(G-9480)*

HOUSES: Rooming & Boarding

Brooklyn Park Hospitality LLC ....D... 763 566-8855
Minneapolis *(G-3960)*

CSM Executive Lodging LLC 612 395-7195
Minneapolis *(G-4197)*

Ecumen Home Care Inc ....E... 952 888-1010
Minneapolis *(G-4312)*

HOUSING AUTHORITY OPERATOR

Center City Housing Corp ....E... 218 722-7161
Duluth *(G-1264)*

Jeremiah Saint Paul LP ....E... 612 259-3001
Minneapolis *(G-4760)*

White Earth Housing Authority..........E... 218 473-4663
Waubun *(G-9901)*

HUMANE SOCIETIES

Animal Humane Society ....D... 763 522-4325
Minneapolis *(G-3780)*

Pheasants Forever Inc ....E... 651 773-2000
Saint Paul *(G-8824)*

Safe Haven Pet Rescue ....E... 507 529-4079
Rochester *(G-7245)*

Tri County Humane Society Inc ....E... 320 252-0896
Saint Cloud *(G-7430)*

HUNTING PRESERVES

Minnesota Horse & Hunt Club ....D... 952 447-2272
Prior Lake *(G-6943)*

HYDRAULIC EQPT REPAIR SVC

Clutch & Transmission Service ....E... 651 636-4311
Saint Paul *(G-8217)*

Clutch & Transmission Service ....D... 651 631-0959
Saint Paul *(G-8218)*

Electric Motor Repair Inc ....E... 612 588-4693
Minneapolis *(G-4337)*

Griffin Petroleum Services Inc..........E... 763 780-6332
Minneapolis *(G-3479)*

Hydraulic Specialty Co Inc ....E... 763 571-3072
Minneapolis *(G-3494)*

SMI & Hydraulics Inc ....E... 507 296-4551
Porter *(G-6894)*

IGNEOUS ROCK: Crushed & Broken

Mathy Construction Co ....E... 507 932-3200
Winona *(G-10113)*

INDEMNITY PLANS HEALTH INSURANCE, EXC MEDICAL SVCS

First Solutions ....D... 218 740-2330
Duluth *(G-1323)*

INDL & PERSONAL SVC PAPER WHOLESALERS

Bunzl USA Inc ....E... 763 571-1011
Minneapolis *(G-3426)*

C J Duffey Paper Co ....D... 612 338-8701
Minneapolis *(G-3984)*

Dalco Enterprises Inc ....D... 651 604-2966
Saint Paul *(G-8280)*

Great Northern Corp ....C... 763 493-5521
Minneapolis *(G-4554)*

Henry's Foods Inc ....C... 320 763-3194
Alexandria *(G-104)*

Kennedy Brissman ....E... 651 646-7933
Saint Paul *(G-8545)*

Martin Falk Paper Co ....E... 612 332-8626
Minneapolis *(G-4959)*

Mayflower Distributing Co Inc ....C... 651 452-4892
Saint Paul *(G-7835)*

Procter & Gamble Distributing ....C... 952 942-1857
Eden Prairie *(G-1754)*

Rohlfing of Brainerd Inc ....E... 218 829-0303
Brainerd *(G-585)*

3M Co ....E... 651 733-8432
Saint Paul *(G-9049)*

3M Co ....E... 651 733-4740
Saint Paul *(G-9053)*

Unisource Worldwide Inc ....B... 763 488-7200
Brooklyn Park *(G-620)*

Watson Co Inc ....E... 763 689-3722
Cambridge *(G-846)*

INDL & PERSONAL SVC PAPER, WHOL:
Bags, Paper/Disp Plastic

Fisher Paper Box Co ....E... 763 425-7444
Minneapolis *(G-4452)*

Gage & Gage Inc ....E... 952 403-1193
Shakopee *(G-9440)*

INDL & PERSONAL SVC PAPER, WHOL:
Boxes, Corrugtd/Solid Fiber

International Paper Co ....C... 507 433-3467
Austin *(G-278)*

Menasha Packaging Co LLC ....C... 952 469-4451
Lakeville *(G-2918)*

Menasha Packaging Co LLC ....C... 763 424-6606
Minneapolis *(G-4986)*

Packaging Corp of America.............D... 763 521-3611
Minneapolis *(G-5311)*

Rock-Tenn Co ....A... 651 641-4874
Saint Paul *(G-8910)*

Smurfit-Stone Container ....E... 507 288-2305
Rochester *(G-7256)*

Smurfit-Stone Container Corp ....C... 612 789-2485
Minneapolis *(G-5691)*

Smurfit-Stone Container Corp ....C... 320 252-3660
Saint Cloud *(G-7594)*

INDL & PERSONAL SVC PAPER, WHOL:
Boxes, Paperbrd/Plastic

Gage & Gage Inc ....E... 952 403-1193
Shakopee *(G-9440)*

INDL & PERSONAL SVC PAPER, WHOL:
Container, Paper/Plastic

Rohn Industries Inc-St Paul...............E... 651 647-1300
Saint Paul *(G-8912)*

INDL & PERSONAL SVC PAPER, WHOL:
Dishes, Disp, Plastic/Paper

International Dairy Queen Inc............B... 952 830-0200
Minneapolis *(G-4721)*

INDL & PERSONAL SVC PAPER, WHOL:
Paper, Wrap/Coarse/Prdts

Gage & Gage Inc ....E... 952 403-1193
Shakopee *(G-9440)*

Litin Paper Co Inc ....E... 612 333-4331
Minneapolis *(G-4893)*

Rohn Industries Inc-St Paul...............E... 651 647-1300
Saint Paul *(G-8912)*

INDL & PERSONAL SVC PAPER, WHOLESALE: Disposable

Berry Coffee Co ....E... 952 937-8697
Eden Prairie *(G-1604)*

INDL & PERSONAL SVC PAPER, WHOLESALE: Press Sensitive Tape

V-TEK Inc..............................D... 507 387-2039
Mankato *(G-3211)*

INDL & PERSONAL SVC PAPER, WHOLESALE: Shipping Splys

Great Northern Corp ....C... 763 493-5521
Minneapolis *(G-4554)*

Rapid Packaging Inc ....E... 763 404-8900
Champlin *(G-899)*

Uline Inc ....D... 651 688-3495
Saint Paul *(G-7933)*

Uline Inc ....C... 651 688-3495
Saint Paul *(G-7934)*

INDL EQPT SVCS

General Parts LLC ....E... 952 944-5800
Minneapolis *(G-4515)*

Instrument & Valve Services Co ....E... 800 654-7768
Eden Prairie *(G-1695)*

Northern Belt & Conveyor Inc ....E... 218 744-9950
Eveleth *(G-1932)*

Quality Forklift Sales & Svc..............E... 952 445-6607
Shakopee *(G-9467)*

INDL GASES WHOLESALERS

American Welding & Gas ....E... 320 235-4774
Willmar (G-9983)

INDL HELP SVCS

SAR Inc ....E... 507 373-7129
Albert Lea (G-64)

INDL MACHINERY & EQPT WHOLESALERS

Ace Label Systems Inc ....E... 763 450-3202
Golden Valley (G-2236)

Aeration Industries Intl ....E... 952 448-6789
Chaska (G-947)

Aldin Export & Import...............................651 483-4184
Saint Paul (G-8007)

Applied Products Inc ....E... 952 933-2224
Minnetonka (G-6142)

Associated Material Handling................E... 651 688-6175
Saint Paul (G-7707)

Barrett Automatic Products Co ....E... 320 528-2512
Barrett (G-307)

Barry & Sewall Industrial Sply ....E... 612 331-6170
Minneapolis (G-3869)

Benham Co's The LLC ....E... 651 771-2222
Saint Paul (G-8103)

Braas Co ....D... 952 937-8902
Eden Prairie (G-1611)

Cartridge Care Inc ....E... 612 331-7757
Saint Paul (G-8169)

Colder Products Co ....C... 651 645-0091
Saint Paul (G-8220)

Concept Machine Tool Sales Inc ....E... 763 559-1975
Minneapolis (G-4150)

Conveyor Belt Service Inc....................E... 218 741-5939
Virginia (G-9737)

Crown Equipment Corp ....E... 651 645-8668
Saint Paul (G-8271)

Dan Larson Enterprises Inc ....E... 612 331-8550
Minneapolis (G-4222)

Easy Automation Inc ....E... 507 728-8214
Welcome (G-9958)

Edwards Oil Co Inc ....E... 218 741-9634
Virginia (G-9738)

Engineering America Inc......................E... 651 777-4041
Saint Paul (G-9214)

Glacier International Inc 651 786-9700
Saint Paul (G-8412)

Haldeman-Homme Inc ....C... 612 331-4880
Minneapolis (G-4590)

Hartfiel Co ....D... 952 974-2500
Eden Prairie (G-1679)

Hydraulic Headquarters Inc ....E... 763 478-6220
Hamel (G-2345)

I-State Truck Center..............................E... 651 455-9775
Inver Grove Heights (G-2754)

I-State Truck Center..............................E... 952 854-5511
Minneapolis (G-4685)

I-State Truck Center..............................D... 651 636-3400
Minneapolis (G-3495)

Industrial Tool Inc ....E... 763 533-7244
Minneapolis (G-4700)

JEM Technical Marketing Co Inc ....D... 952 473-5012
Long Lake (G-3025)

John Henry Foster Minnesota ....D... 651 452-8452
Saint Paul (G-7810)

Macqueen Equipment Inc......................E... 651 645-5726
Saint Paul (G-8605)

Marketing Focus Inc ....E... 952 939-9880
Hopkins (G-2576)

Mate Precision Tooling Inc ....B... 763 421-0230
Anoka (G-203)

Mechanical Systems Inc........................E... 507 645-5675
Dundas (G-1512)

Minnesota Supply Co ....D... 952 828-7300
Eden Prairie (G-1726)

National Oilwell Varco Inc ....D... 651 293-4699
Saint Paul (G-8740)

Oki Systems Limited.............................D... 651 645-8668
Saint Paul (G-8779)

Packaging Automation Corp..................E... 651 456-0003
Saint Paul (G-7862)

Parker-Hannifin Corp ....E... 952 469-5000
Lakeville (G-2924)

Power Mation Division Inc ....D... 651 605-3300
Saint Paul (G-8832)

Ppt Vision Inc ....C... 952 942-5747
Eden Prairie (G-1751)

Pugleasa Co Inc ....E... 651 636-6442
Saint Paul (G-8857)

Quest Engineering Inc..........................E... 952 546-4441
Minneapolis (G-5448)

Rdo Equipment Co................................E... 218 483-3353
Hawley (G-2421)

Rollie's Sales & Service Inc ....E... 320 859-4811
Osakis (G-6587)

Rosemount Inc ....A... 952 949-7000
Chanhassen (G-939)

Rubber Specialties Inc ....E... 952 888-9225
Minneapolis (G-5573)

Source Fluid Power Inc ....E... 952 448-4440
Chaska (G-980)

Tapemark Co ....C... 651 455-1611
Saint Paul (G-7916)

Tc American Monorail Inc ....D... 763 497-8700
Saint Michael (G-7683)

Tc American Monorail Inc ....E... 320 634-4531
Glenwood (G-2234)

Toyota-Lift of Minnesota Inc ....D... 763 425-9066
Brooklyn Park (G-619)

Twin City Fan Co's Ltd ....C... 763 551-7600
Minneapolis (G-5878)

Valley Craft Inc ....C... 651 345-3386
Lake City (G-2855)

Valley National Gases Inc ....E... 651 628-4848
Saint Paul (G-9123)

Westside Equipment Installers ....E... 763 478-9572
Hamel (G-2360)

INDL MACHINERY REPAIR & MAINTENANCE

Bentley Instruments Inc ....E... 952 448-7600
Chaska (G-952)

Conveyor Belt Service Inc....................E... 218 741-5939
Virginia (G-9737)

General Electric Co ....E... 612 529-9502
Minneapolis (G-4510)

General Electric Co ....E... 218 749-6100
Mountain Iron (G-6392)

LasX Industries Inc ....E... 651 407-0011
Saint Paul (G-8565)

Minnesota Chemical Co ....E... 651 646-7521
Saint Paul (G-8676)

Minnesota Supply Co ....D... 952 828-7300
Eden Prairie (G-1726)

Smyth Co's Inc ....E... 651 646-4544
Saint Paul (G-8967)

Sweeney Brothers Tractor Co ....E... 952 894-9595
Burnsville (G-805)

Twin City Container Inc ....E... 651 480-3786
Hastings (G-2409)

Yale Materials Handling - MN.................D... 763 434-3832
Anoka (G-241)

INDL SALTS WHOLESALERS

Minnesota Salt Service ....E... 651 774-6237
Saint Paul (G-8704)

INDL SPLYS WHOLESALERS

Applied Power Products Inc ....E... 952 985-5100
Lakeville (G-2891)

Applied Power Products Inc ....D... 651 452-2250
Saint Paul (G-7705)

Applied Power Products Inc ....D... 952 985-5100
Lakeville (G-2892)

Barry & Sewall Industrial Sply ....E... 612 331-6170
Minneapolis (G-3869)

Central-Mcgowan Inc............................E... 320 252-5292
Saint Cloud (G-7490)

Duncan Co...E... 612 331-1776
Minneapolis (G-4292)

Ferguson Enterprises Inc......................D... 651 638-5000
Saint Paul (G-8374)

Hajoca Corp ....E... 763 315-0100
Minneapolis (G-4589)

Hose Conveyors Inc ....E... 651 456-0200
Saint Paul (G-7801)

Kendeco Supply Co ....E... 320 253-1020
Saint Cloud (G-7540)

MacDermid ColorSpan Inc ....C... 952 944-9457
Hopkins (G-2573)

Machine Tool Supply Corp....................E... 651 452-4400
Saint Paul (G-7829)

North Central Container of New ....E... 507 359-3136
New Ulm (G-6471)

Northern States Supply Inc ....E... 320 235-0555
Willmar (G-10031)

Nott Co ....C... 651 415-3400
Saint Paul (G-8772)

Power Mation Division Inc ....D... 651 605-3300
Saint Paul (G-8832)

R J Tool Crib LLC..................................E... 320 253-1020
Saint Cloud (G-7579)

Replenex...D... 952 941-9150
Eden Prairie (G-1762)

Safeway Hydraulics Inc ....E... 952 466-6220
Chaska (G-979)

STS Operating Inc ....D... 952 563-1700
Savage (G-9409)

Swanson-Flosystems Co ....E... 763 383-4700
Plymouth (G-6885)

W W Grainger Inc..................................E... 763 531-0300
Minneapolis (G-5989)

W W Grainger Inc..................................E... 612 486-3300
Minneapolis (G-5988)

Wesco Distribution Inc..........................D... 651 582-3945
Saint Paul (G-9147)

INDL SPLYS, WHOL: Fasteners, Incl Nuts, Bolts, Screws, Etc

Building Fasteners of MN ....D... 612 706-3300
Minneapolis (G-3973)

Fastenal Co Purchasing.........................E... 507 454-5374
Winona (G-10096)

Northern States Supply Inc ....E... 320 235-0555
Willmar (G-10031)

Wells Technology Inc............................E... 218 751-5117
Bemidji (G-432)

Wells Technology Inc............................E... 218 751-1412
Bemidji (G-433)

Williams Steel & Hardware Co..............D... 612 588-9800
Minneapolis (G-6070)

INDL SPLYS, WHOLESALE: Abrasives

Abrasives of St Paul Inc........................D... 651 636-3955
Saint Paul (G-7973)

Duncan Co...E... 612 331-1776
Minneapolis (G-4292)

Kendeco Supply Co ....E... 320 253-1020
Saint Cloud (G-7540)

Nalco Distributing Inc ....D... 651 636-8124
Saint Paul (G-8733)

Shark Industries Ltd ....E... 763 565-1900
Rockford (G-7313)

3M Co ....E... 651 733-2008
Saint Paul (G-9050)

INDL SPLYS, WHOLESALE: Abrasives & Adhesives

Fastenal Co ....B... 507 454-5374
Winona (G-10095)

INDL SPLYS, WHOLESALE: Adhesives, Tape & Plasters

Applied Products Inc.............................E... 952 933-2224
Minnetonka (G-6142)

Matrix Adhesives Inc.............................E... 952 912-2452
Hopkins (G-2578)

INDL SPLYS, WHOLESALE: Bearings

Industrial Supply Co Inc ....E... 763 559-0033
Minneapolis (G-4699)

International Seal Co Inc........................D... 952 894-8400
Shakopee (G-9445)

INDL SPLYS, WHOLESALE: Bins & Containers, Storage

Gamer Packaging Inc ....E... 612 788-4444
Minneapolis (G-4498)

INDL SPLYS, WHOLESALE: Bottler Splys

Cone Corp ....E... 218 245-2313
Bovey (G-540)

Gamer Packaging Inc ....E... 612 788-4444
Minneapolis (G-4498)

INDL SPLYS, WHOLESALE: Brushes, Indl

Duncan Co...E... 612 331-1776
Minneapolis (G-4292)

INDL SPLYS, WHOLESALE: Clean Room Splys

G&K Services Inc..................................C... 612 333-2225
Minneapolis (G-4493)

INDL SPLYS, WHOLESALE: Electric Tools

Diamond Drilling & Supply Inc 218 628-3671
Duluth (G-1293)

INDL SPLYS, WHOLESALE: Fasteners & Fastening Eqpt

Fastenal Co ....B... 507 454-5374
Winona (G-10095)

INDL SPLYS, WHOLESALE: Fittings

Quest Engineering Inc..........................E... 952 546-4441
Minneapolis (G-5448)

S
E
R
V
I
C
E
S

INDL SPLYS, WHOLESALE: Gas Eqpt, Parts & Splys

Central-Mcgowan Inc ....E... 320 252-5292
Saint Cloud *(G-7490)*

INDL SPLYS, WHOLESALE: Gaskets

Belcourt Corp ....E... 952 894-0406
Burnsville *(G-684)*

INDL SPLYS, WHOLESALE: Glass Bottles

Gamer Packaging Inc ....E... 612 788-4444
Minneapolis *(G-4498)*
Kaufman Container Co Inc ....D... 612 331-8880
Minneapolis *(G-4794)*

INDL SPLYS, WHOLESALE: Hose, Belting & Packing

Applied Power Products Inc ....D... 651 452-2250
Saint Paul *(G-7705)*
Applied Power Products Inc ....D... 952 985-5100
Lakeville *(G-2892)*
Hose Conveyors Inc ....E... 651 456-0200
Saint Paul *(G-7801)*
Midwest Rubber Service & Sply ....E... 763 559-2551
Minneapolis *(G-5036)*
Minnesota Flexible Corp ....E... 651 645-7522
Saint Paul *(G-8687)*
Ritchie Engineering Co Inc ....C... 952 943-1300
Minneapolis *(G-5541)*
Twin City Hose Inc ....E... 763 428-5100
Rogers *(G-7344)*

INDL SPLYS, WHOLESALE: Mill Splys

Williams Steel & Hardware Co ....D... 612 588-9800
Minneapolis *(G-6070)*

INDL SPLYS, WHOLESALE: Plastic Bottles

Gamer Packaging Inc ....E... 612 788-4444
Minneapolis *(G-4498)*
Kaufman Container Co Inc ....D... 612 331-8880
Minneapolis *(G-4794)*

INDL SPLYS, WHOLESALE: Power Transmission, Eqpt & Apparatus

Applied Power Products Inc ....D... 651 452-2250
Saint Paul *(G-7705)*
Applied Power Products Inc ....D... 952 985-5100
Lakeville *(G-2892)*
Industrial Supply Co Inc ....E... 763 559-0033
Minneapolis *(G-4699)*
Power Mation Division Inc ....D... 651 605-3300
Saint Paul *(G-8832)*

INDL SPLYS, WHOLESALE: Rope, Cord & Thread

Fastenal Co..B... 507 454-5374
Winona *(G-10095)*

INDL SPLYS, WHOLESALE: Rubber Goods, Mechanical

Ritchie Engineering Co Inc ....C... 952 943-1300
Minneapolis *(G-5541)*

INDL SPLYS, WHOLESALE: Seals

International Seal Co Inc ....D... 952 894-8400
Shakopee *(G-9445)*
R E Purvis & Associates Inc ....E... 952 829-5532
Minneapolis *(G-5457)*

INDL SPLYS, WHOLESALE: Signmaker Eqpt & Splys

Signcaster Corp ....E... 952 888-9507
Minneapolis *(G-5671)*

INDL SPLYS, WHOLESALE: Tools

Abrasive Specialists Inc ....E... 763 571-4111
Minneapolis *(G-3384)*
Carbide Tool Services Inc ....E... 763 421-2210
Anoka *(G-161)*
Fastenal Co..B... 507 454-5374
Winona *(G-10095)*

INDL SPLYS, WHOLESALE: Tools, NEC

Fastenal Co Purchasing ....E... 507 454-5374
Winona *(G-10096)*
Northern States Supply Inc ....E... 320 235-0555
Willmar *(G-10031)*

INDL SPLYS, WHOLESALE: Valves & Fittings

Chicago Tube & Iron Co of MN ....D... 651 454-6800
Saint Paul *(G-7731)*
Duncan Co ....E... 612 331-1776
Minneapolis *(G-4292)*
JEM Technical Marketing Co Inc ....D... 952 473-5012
Long Lake *(G-3025)*
Swanson-Flosystems Co ....E... 763 383-4700
Plymouth *(G-6885)*
Wair Products Inc ....E... 952 881-9449
Minneapolis *(G-5994)*

INDL TRUCK REPAIR SVCS

Chesley Truck Sales Inc ....C... 651 636-3400
Saint Paul *(G-9195)*
Crysteel Truck Equipment Inc ....E... 952 469-5678
Lakeville *(G-2899)*

INFORMATION BUREAU SVCS

City of Saint Paul ....E... 651 631-0700
Saint Paul *(G-8209)*

INFORMATION RETRIEVAL SERVICES

C & C Business Solutions.....................D... 612 875-9488
Burnsville *(G-693)*
Diversified Pharmaceutical 952 820-7000
Minneapolis *(G-4263)*
Heartland Information Services ....E... 612 371-9255
Minneapolis *(G-4626)*
Hiawatha Broadband Comms ....D... 507 474-4000
Winona *(G-10101)*
Hickory Tech Information Soln ....D... 507 625-1691
Mankato *(G-3139)*
Hickory Tech Information Soln ....D... 507 625-1691
Mankato *(G-3140)*
Internet Broadcasting Systems ....C... 651 365-4000
Saint Paul *(G-8518)*
Medical Records Inc ....D... 952 831-6778
Minneapolis *(G-4985)*
One Call Concepts Inc...........................D... 651 454-0002
Saint Paul *(G-7856)*
Quick Test Inc ....E... 952 854-3535
Minneapolis *(G-5451)*
Schwan's Technology Group Inc ....D... 651 388-1821
Red Wing *(G-7005)*
Schwan's Technology Group Inc ....E... 651 681-4450
Saint Paul *(G-7898)*
Sopheon Corp ....E... 952 851-7555
Minneapolis *(G-5702)*
Techbarncom Inc ....E... 651 275-8300
Stillwater *(G-9651)*
Val-Ed Joint Venture, LLP ....E... 218 284-5702
Moorhead *(G-6345)*
West Publishing Corp............................E... 651 687-7000
Saint Paul *(G-7947)*

INFORMATION SVCS: Consumer

Minnesota State Bar Assn.....................E... 651 227-8266
Saint Paul *(G-8706)*

INNS

Afton St Croix Co ....E... 651 436-8883
Afton *(G-6)*
Comfort Inn & Suites ....D... 507 289-3344
Rochester *(G-7088)*
Inn Hampton & Suites ....D... 763 746-7999
Lino Lakes *(G-2972)*
Medina Inn ....D... 763 478-6661
Hamel *(G-2352)*
Niecc Inc ....C... 763 536-8300
Minneapolis *(G-5200)*
3R North Inc..E... 651 674-9977
North Branch *(G-6506)*

INSPECTION & TESTING SVCS

Access Information Systems Inc...........C... 952 888-8503
Minneapolis *(G-3666)*
Inspec Inc ....E... 763 546-3434
Minneapolis *(G-4707)*
Interpoll Laboratories Inc......................E... 763 786-6020
Circle Pines *(G-1012)*
Patzig Testing Laboratories ....D... 651 659-7554
Saint Paul *(G-8810)*

INSULATION MATERIALS WHOLESALERS

Insulation Distributors Inc ....E... 952 937-2000
Chanhassen *(G-927)*

INSURANCE AGENCIES & BROKERS

AG States Agency LLC ....E... 651 355-6000
Inver Grove Heights *(G-2735)*
Berkley Risk Administrators Co...........E... 651 281-1200
Saint Paul *(G-8106)*
Berkley Risk Administrators Co...........A... 612 766-3000
Minneapolis *(G-3887)*
Cedar Valley Conservation Club ....B... 507 433-4937
Austin *(G-264)*
Erickson-Larsen Inc ....E... 763 535-0055
Maple Grove *(G-3240)*
First McLeod Agency Inc 320 864-5581
Glencoe *(G-2205)*
Hays Group Inc.....................................C... 612 333-3323
Minneapolis *(G-4613)*
Knw Group LLC ....E... 952 593-0265
Hopkins *(G-2566)*
L L Brustad & Associates Inc 952 842-1142
Wayzata *(G-9923)*
Leneave Financial Group ....E... 952 542-0777
Hopkins *(G-2570)*
Long Term Care Group Inc ....B... 952 516-6829
Eden Prairie *(G-1712)*
Ross Nesbit Agencies Inc.....................E... 952 941-9418
Eden Prairie *(G-1768)*
Sandra Hamer ....E... 651 254-0116
Inver Grove Heights *(G-2768)*
Sebrite Agency Inc ....E... 952 563-1234
Minnetonka *(G-6226)*
State Farm Mutual Automobile..............E... 952 895-3900
Burnsville *(G-803)*
Twin City Risk Group Inc ....E... 952 924-6900
Minneapolis *(G-5884)*
Wells Fargo Insurance Services ....C... 952 830-3000
Minneapolis *(G-6051)*

INSURANCE AGENTS, NEC

Anderson Swenson Associates ....E... 612 347-8600
Minneapolis *(G-3778)*
C O Brown Agency Inc...........................E... 507 288-7600
Rochester *(G-7069)*
Christensen Group Inc ....D... 952 653-1000
Hopkins *(G-2530)*
Columns Resource Group ....D... 612 758-7600
Minneapolis *(G-4125)*
Combined Insurance Co of Amer...........D... 952 933-2133
Eden Prairie *(G-1632)*
Corporate 4 Insurance Agency ....D... 952 893-9218
Minneapolis *(G-4163)*
D D P Marketing Inc..............................D... 952 808-7615
Burnsville *(G-707)*
First State Bank South West 507 376-9747
Worthington *(G-10185)*
Heartman Agency Inc............................E... 507 288-3834
Rochester *(G-7136)*
Kozlowski Insurance Agency 507 825-3366
Pipestone *(G-6831)*
Mid American Financial Group...............D... 952 258-5000
Minnetonka *(G-6194)*
National Independent Brokers ....D... 763 525-1111
Minneapolis *(G-5164)*
National Truck Underwriting ....E... 952 893-1234
Minneapolis *(G-5169)*
Osborne Properties LP ....D... 952 890-0414
Burnsville *(G-771)*
Osborne Properties LP ....D... 952 707-8200
Burnsville *(G-772)*
Prime West Central County ....D... 320 763-4135
Alexandria *(G-118)*
Principal Life Insurance Co ....E... 651 227-7717
Saint Paul *(G-9265)*
State Bank of Tower Inc 218 753-6100
Tower *(G-9688)*
T C Field & Co ....E... 651 227-8405
Saint Paul *(G-9022)*
Twin City Group Inc............................... 952 924-6900
Minneapolis *(G-5880)*
Vern Cooper & Associates Inc ....E... 507 319-4139
Rochester *(G-7281)*
Waddell & Reed Inc ....E... 952 884-1503
Minneapolis *(G-5992)*
Western Bank ....E... 651 290-8100
Saint Paul *(G-9150)*
Winona Agency Inc ....E... 507 452-3366
Winona *(G-10143)*
Workman Financial Group Inc...............E... 763 746-9420
Minneapolis *(G-6086)*

INSURANCE BROKERS, NEC

AON Corp ....C... 952 656-8000
Minneapolis *(G-3786)*
AON Risk Services Central Inc...............C... 952 656-8000
Minneapolis *(G-3787)*

(G-00000) Company's Geographic Section entry number

S E R V I C E S

Ciu ....E... 952 469-5520
Lakeville (G-2895)

Clark & Wamberg LLC ....C... 612 339-0919
Minneapolis (G-4102)

H C C Life Insurance Co ....E... 877 843-5743
Hopkins (G-2547)

Lee F Murphy Inc ....E... 651 644-7200
Saint Paul (G-8574)

Minnesota Benefit Association.........E... 651 739-4550
Saint Paul (G-9249)

Robert A Schneider Agency Inc ....E... 952 938-0655
Hopkins (G-2621)

U S Bancorp ....B... 651 466-3000
Minneapolis (G-5885)

US Bancorp Information Svcs ....A... 651 466-3000
Saint Paul (G-9117)

Workman Financial Group Inc ....E... 763 746-9420
Minneapolis (G-6086)

INSURANCE CARRIERS: Automobile

EPIC Holdings Inc ....E... 952 997-4900
Saint Paul (G-7768)

St Paul Fire & Marine Insce ....A... 651 221-7911
Saint Paul (G-8990)

St Paul Mercury Insurance Co 651 221-7911
Saint Paul (G-8994)

INSURANCE CARRIERS: Dental

Decare Dental LLC ....B... 800 371-6561
Saint Paul (G-7750)

Fiserv Health Plan ....A... 262 879-5565
Minneapolis (G-4450)

INSURANCE CARRIERS: Direct Accident & Health

Allina Self-Insured ....D... 952 992-2500
Hopkins (G-2507)

Bcbsm Inc.......................................A... 651 662-8000
Saint Paul (G-7711)

Federated Mutual Insurance Co ....D... 952 831-4300
Minneapolis (G-4422)

Hartford Life Inc ....D... 651 738-4516
Saint Paul (G-9222)

League of Minnesota Cities ....D... 651 281-1200
Saint Paul (G-8573)

Medical Network Inc ....E... 763 595-3208
Golden Valley (G-2243)

Rute Agency ....E... 612 240-1795
Minneapolis (G-3594)

Union Security Insurance Co ....D... 952 920-8990
Minneapolis (G-5905)

Unitedhealth Group Inc ....A... 952 936-1300
Minnetonka (G-6232)

INSURANCE CARRIERS: Hospital & Medical

ARAZ Group Inc.............................D... 952 896-1200
Minneapolis (G-3796)

Assurecare....................................D... 763 383-4800
Minneapolis (G-3829)

Aware Integrated Inc.......................A... 651 662-8000
Saint Paul (G-7709)

Bcbsm Inc......................................A... 651 662-8000
Saint Paul (G-7711)

Bcbsm Inc......................................A... 651 662-8951
Saint Paul (G-7712)

Bcbsm Inc......................................C... 651 662-8000
Saint Paul (G-7714)

Cigna Behavioral Health Inc ....B... 952 996-2000
Eden Prairie (G-1626)

Department of Health Minnesota.........D... 218 335-3200
Cass Lake (G-871)

Healthpartners Inc ....D... 952 944-0432
Eden Prairie (G-1681)

Long Term Care Group Inc ....C... 651 501-4000
Saint Paul (G-9244)

Outsourceone Inc ....E... 612 436-2740
Minneapolis (G-5301)

Ovations Inc ....A... 952 936-1300
Hopkins (G-2600)

Regency Hospital Co LLC................C... 763 588-2750
Minneapolis (G-5484)

Uniprise Inc ....A... 763 765-0852
Plymouth (G-6889)

INSURANCE CARRIERS: Life

Aegon USA Inc ....C... 952 893-6767
Minneapolis (G-3693)

Allianz Life Insurance Co of.............A... 763 765-6500
Minneapolis (G-3714)

Auto-Owners Life Insurance Co ....D... 651 777-9317
Saint Paul (G-8080)

Federated Mutual Insurance Co ....D... 952 831-4300
Minneapolis (G-4422)

Financial Corp Inc..........................E... 651 407-5770
Saint Paul (G-8377)

General Casualty Co of WI ....D... 952 941-0980
Eden Prairie (G-1673)

Gnw Acquisition Corp ....D... 651 325-0060
Saint Paul (G-8416)

Guardian Life Insurance Co of..........D... 952 903-2200
Minneapolis (G-4577)

Hartford Life Inc ....D... 952 893-9236
Minneapolis (G-4604)

Hartford Life Inc ....A... 877 952-9222
Osseo (G-6618)

Ing North America Insurance...............D... 612 342-7878
Minneapolis (G-4703)

McGovern & Fisher Insurance ....D... 952 996-8818
Minneapolis (G-4975)

Midwest Family Mutual Insce...........D... 763 951-7000
Minneapolis (G-5028)

Principal Life Insurance Co..................E... 952 277-4300
Hopkins (G-2605)

Prudential Insurance Co of ....A... 612 349-1000
Minneapolis (G-5435)

Prudential Insurance Co of ....E... 507 281-4200
Rochester (G-7213)

Securian Financial Network Inc..........D... 651 665-3500
Saint Paul (G-8944)

Security American Financial...............E... 952 544-2121
Hopkins (G-2628)

Security Life Insurance Co of ....D... 952 544-2121
Hopkins (G-2629)

INSURANCE CARRIERS: Property & Casualty

AAA Minnesota Iowa ....C... 952 707-4222
Burnsville (G-670)

Austin Mutual Insurance Co ....D... 800 328-4628
Maple Grove (G-3237)

Discover Property & Casualty 800 878-2660
Saint Paul (G-8299)

Federated Mutual Insurance Co ....D... 952 831-4300
Minneapolis (G-4422)

Federated Service Insurance Co ....C... 507 455-5200
Owatonna (G-6712)

General Casualty Co of WI ....D... 952 941-0980
Eden Prairie (G-1673)

Great Northern Insurance Co...............D... 612 373-7300
Minneapolis (G-4555)

Liberty Mutual Insurance Co..............C... 763 546-7550
Minneapolis (G-4870)

St Paul Fire & Marine Insce ....A... 651 221-7911
Saint Paul (G-8990)

Wells Fargo Insurance Inc ....D... 952 921-3601
Minneapolis (G-6049)

INSURANCE CARRIERS: Title

All American Title Co Inc.....................E... 763 225-8710
Minneapolis (G-3389)

Burnet Realty LLC............................B... 952 844-6400
Minneapolis (G-3977)

Commercial Partners Title LLC ....E... 612 337-2470
Minneapolis (G-4132)

Complete Title Services LLC ....E... 218 828-9611
Baxter (G-326)

First American National Cml................E... 612 305-2000
Minneapolis (G-4438)

Isgn Fulfillment Services Inc ....D... 952 512-7400
Minneapolis (G-4736)

Land Title Inc..................................D... 651 638-1900
Saint Paul (G-8560)

Registered Abstractors Inc ....E... 763 427-3012
Anoka (G-219)

RELS Title Services LLC ....D... 952 933-8804
Hopkins (G-2614)

Stewart Title of Minnesota ....E... 763 422-1116
Minneapolis (G-5756)

Tri-County Abstract & Title ....E... 320 253-2096
Saint Cloud (G-7619)

Walsh Title & Real Estate Svcs.............E... 952 835-3320
Minneapolis (G-6017)

INSURANCE CARRIERS: Worker's Compensation

Ram Mutual Insurance Co Inc.............D... 218 879-3321
Esko (G-1922)

Rtw Inc ....D... 952 893-0403
Minneapolis (G-5572)

SFM Mutual Insurance Co ....C... 952 838-4200
Bloomington (G-514)

St Paul Fire & Marine Insce ....A... 651 221-7911
Saint Paul (G-8990)

INSURANCE CLAIM ADJUSTERS, NOT EMPLOYED BY INSURANCE COMPANY

Prudential Insurance Co of...................E... 763 553-6056
Minneapolis (G-5436)

INSURANCE CLAIM PROCESSING, EXC MEDICAL

Allied Adjusters Inc ....E... 612 766-3700
Minneapolis (G-3715)

INSURANCE EDUCATION SVCS

Student Assurance Services Inc..........E... 651 439-7098
Stillwater (G-9649)

INSURANCE INFORMATION & CONSULTING SVCS

American Financial Marketing..............D... 763 593-0905
Minneapolis (G-3749)

Direct Response Insurance ....D... 952 556-5600
Chanhassen (G-919)

Midland Corporate Benefit Svcs 320 485-3821
Winsted (G-10163)

INSURANCE INFORMATION BUREAUS

Holmes Hooper Inc ....D... 763 545-5641
Minneapolis (G-4661)

INSURANCE INSPECTION & INVESTIGATIONS SVCS

Icon Services Corp ....E... 651 695-8778
Saint Paul (G-8503)

INSURANCE RATEMAKING ORGANIZATIONS

Milliman Inc ....D... 952 897-5300
Minneapolis (G-5046)

INSURANCE RESEARCH SVCS

North Western Research......................E... 218 327-4615
Grand Rapids (G-2299)

INSURANCE: Agents, Brokers & Service

American Hardware Insurance.............D... 952 939-4510
Minnetonka (G-6139)

Ameriprise Financial Services ....C... 612 671-3131
Minneapolis (G-3770)

Apollo Insurance Agency of St ....E... 320 253-1122
Saint Cloud (G-7452)

ARAZ Group Inc...............................D... 952 896-1200
Minneapolis (G-3796)

Arthur A Hirman Agency Inc ....E... 507 285-3111
Rochester (G-7060)

Arthur J Gallagher & Co.....................E... 952 944-8885
Minneapolis (G-3814)

Associated Financial Group LLC ....D... 952 945-0200
Minnetonka (G-6144)

Bankers Life & Casualty Co................E... 952 835-2611
Minneapolis (G-3866)

Bcbsm Inc......................................C... 218 748-2700
Virginia (G-9736)

C N A Financial Corp.........................D... 952 285-3300
Saint Paul (G-7725)

Citizens Bancshares of ....E... 320 587-2233
Hutchinson (G-2692)

Evalumed.......................................E... 651 767-0220
Saint Paul (G-8346)

Federated Mutual Insurance Co ....D... 952 831-4300
Minneapolis (G-4422)

Gary L Kemp Agency Inc 651 457-3070
Saint Paul (G-7778)

Groebner Insurance Agency 507 243-3102
Madison Lake (G-3082)

Horizon Agency Inc ....E... 952 944-2929
Eden Prairie (G-1687)

Insurance Paramedical Services.............D... 952 226-2213
Prior Lake (G-6933)

Lake Bank National Association ....E... 218 834-2111
Two Harbors (G-9709)

Le Clair Insurance Services..................E... 651 739-2010
Saint Paul (G-9241)

Lincoln Life & Annuity Co of ....D... 612 373-7460
Minneapolis (G-4887)

Maguire Agency Inc..........................E... 651 638-9100
Saint Paul (G-8606)

Marsh USA Inc ....C... 612 692-7848
Minneapolis (G-4958)

Michael Dam...................................E... 952 831-1928
Minneapolis (G-5016)

Michael Erpelding.............................E... 651 647-1000
Saint Paul (G-8651)

Employment codes: A=Over 500 employees, B=251-500,
C=101-250, D=51-100, E=25-50

2011 Harris Minnesota
Services Directory

© Harris InfoSource 1-866-281-6415
719

SERVICES

Minnesota Chamber of Commerce.......E... 651 292-4650
Saint Paul *(G-8675)*
Mmic.......C... 952 838-6700
Minneapolis *(G-5112)*
Mmk International Marine Svcs.......E... 507 263-0975
Cannon Falls *(G-860)*
N Bruce Christense.......D... 952 653-1000
Hopkins *(G-2585)*
Noah Insurance Group.......E... 651 430-0085
Stillwater *(G-9631)*
North Star General Insurance.......D... 507 423-6262
Cottonwood *(G-1114)*
North Star Resource Group.......C... 612 617-6000
Minneapolis *(G-5221)*
Northern Capital Commercial.......D... 952 996-8818
Minneapolis *(G-5226)*
Northwestern Mutual Life.......E... 651 456-9446
Mendota Heights *(G-3368)*
Otis-Magie Insurance Agency.......E... 218 722-7753
Duluth *(G-1415)*
Outsourceone Inc.......E... 612 436-2740
Minneapolis *(G-5301)*
Outsourceone Inc.......E... 612 338-7940
Minneapolis *(G-5302)*
Prime Therapeutics Inc.......C... 651 456-1000
Saint Paul *(G-7881)*
Primerica Financial Services.......D... 952 895-1091
Burnsville *(G-782)*
R J Ahmann Co.......D... 952 947-9761
Eden Prairie *(G-1757)*
Ram Mutual Insurance Co Inc.......D... 218 879-3321
Esko *(G-1922)*
Rural Community Insurance Agcy.......C... 763 427-0290
Anoka *(G-223)*
Securian Financial Services.......C... 651 665-4244
Saint Paul *(G-8945)*
Sheffield, Olson & McQueen Inc.......E... 651 695-2500
Saint Paul *(G-8951)*
Stockbridge Insurance Co.......A... 651 631-7000
Saint Paul *(G-9006)*
Thrivent Financial For.......A... 920 734-5721
Minneapolis *(G-5819)*
Thrivent Financial For.......E... 952 894-6772
Burnsville *(G-808)*
Thrivent Life Insurance Co.......C... 612 340-7000
Minneapolis *(G-5820)*
Twin City Agency Inc.......E... 952 924-6900
Minneapolis *(G-5876)*
Unitedhealth Group Inc.......A... 952 936-1300
Minnetonka *(G-6232)*
Wells Fargo Insurance Inc.......E... 612 667-5600
Minneapolis *(G-6050)*
Western Bank.......E... 651 290-8100
Saint Paul *(G-9149)*
Willis of Minnesota Inc.......D... 763 302-7100
Minneapolis *(G-6071)*
Zurich North American Insce.......D... 952 229-3600
Edina *(G-1850)*

INTERIOR DECORATING SVCS

Bwbr Architects Inc.......C... 651 222-3701
Saint Paul *(G-8144)*
Natus Corp.......D... 651 487-3211
Saint Paul *(G-8741)*

INTERIOR DESIGN SVCS, NEC

Arthur Shuster Inc.......E... 651 631-9200
Saint Paul *(G-8066)*
Boarman Kroos Vogel Group.......D... 612 339-3752
Minneapolis *(G-3921)*
Bwbr Architects Inc.......C... 651 222-3701
Saint Paul *(G-8144)*
Elness Swenson Graham.......D... 612 339-5508
Minneapolis *(G-4343)*
K M L Design Studio LLC.......E... 651 731-6672
Woodbury *(G-10172)*
Lhb Inc.......E... 612 338-2029
Minneapolis *(G-4867)*
McCaren Design Inc.......E... 651 646-4764
Saint Paul *(G-8623)*
Meyer, Scherer & Rockcastle.......E... 612 375-0336
Minneapolis *(G-5012)*
Schneiderman Furniture Inc.......E... 952 435-3399
Lakeville *(G-2932)*
Walsh Bishop Associates Inc.......D... 612 338-8799
Minneapolis *(G-6016)*

INTERIOR DESIGNING SVCS

Environments Inc.......E... 952 933-9981
Hopkins *(G-2540)*
Progressive Interiors Inc.......E... 612 718-1868
Waconia *(G-9790)*
World Architects Inc.......D... 651 227-7773
Saint Paul *(G-9168)*

INTERMEDIATE CARE FACILITY

Almond House.......E... 218 825-9255
Brainerd *(G-547)*
American Baptist Homes of The.......D... 507 893-3171
Winnebago *(G-10075)*
Amherst H Wilder Foundation.......C... 651 220-1700
Saint Paul *(G-8041)*
Arbors At Ridges.......E... 952 898-4005
Burnsville *(G-680)*
Aviv Health Care Inc.......C... 763 425-3939
Osseo *(G-6597)*
Barrett Care Center Inc.......D... 320 528-2527
Barrett *(G-308)*
Belgrade Nursing Home Inc.......D... 320 254-8215
Belgrade *(G-364)*
Bethany Covenant Village.......D... 612 781-2691
Minneapolis *(G-3893)*
Big Stone Community Homes Inc.......E... 320 839-6139
Ortonville *(G-6578)*
Cardinal of Minnesota Ltd.......C... 507 281-1077
Rochester *(G-7070)*
Catholic Services For The.......C... 651 793-2100
Saint Paul *(G-8177)*
Cedar Crest Estate.......E... 320 587-7077
Hutchinson *(G-2691)*
Cenneidigh Inc.......C... 507 334-4347
Faribault *(G-1999)*
Chandler Place.......E... 612 788-7321
Minneapolis *(G-6124)*
Charterhouse Inc.......C... 507 266-8572
Rochester *(G-7075)*
Christian Grandview Home.......C... 763 689-1474
Cambridge *(G-836)*
City of Lakefield.......D... 507 662-6646
Lakefield *(G-2881)*
City of Renville.......D... 320 329-8381
Renville *(G-7031)*
Community Involvement Programs.......E... 320 245-5362
Sandstone *(G-9320)*
Community Memorial Home Inc.......D... 320 859-2111
Osakis *(G-6586)*
County of Pennington.......D... 218 681-1675
Thief River Falls *(G-9665)*
Crest View Corp.......C... 763 782-1611
Minneapolis *(G-3447)*
Dakota's Adults Inc.......E... 651 688-8808
Mendota Heights *(G-3362)*
Ecumen.......C... 507 345-4576
Mankato *(G-3124)*
Edgewood Management Inc.......E... 651 714-1000
Saint Paul *(G-9208)*
Elders' Home Inc.......D... 218 385-2005
New York Mills *(G-6478)*
Elm Residence Inc.......B... 507 835-1146
Waseca *(G-9877)*
Emerald Crest of Burnsville.......E... 952 736-0766
Burnsville *(G-718)*
Emerald Crest of Minnetonka.......C... 952 933-9903
Hopkins *(G-2538)*
Epiphany Assisted Living.......E... 763 755-0320
Minneapolis *(G-3465)*
Episcopal Church Home Of MN.......C... 651 646-4061
Saint Paul *(G-8344)*
Evangelical Lutheran Good.......C... 651 439-7180
Stillwater *(G-9615)*
Eventide Senior Living.......B... 218 233-7508
Moorhead *(G-6314)*
Franciscan Health Center Inc.......D... 218 727-8933
Duluth *(G-1326)*
Goldfinch Estates.......E... 507 235-9405
Fairmont *(G-1968)*
Guardian Angels By The Lake.......E... 763 241-7682
Elk River *(G-1878)*
Hallett Cottages.......E... 218 546-6265
Crosby *(G-1149)*
Hawley Retirement Inc.......E... 218 483-3337
Hawley *(G-2420)*
Hayes Residence Inc.......E... 651 690-1032
Saint Paul *(G-8445)*
Hillcrest Nursing Home.......D... 218 253-2157
Red Lake Falls *(G-6971)*
Home For Creative Living Inc.......D... 507 831-5033
Windom *(G-10068)*
Homefront.......E... 320 269-2930
Montevideo *(G-6246)*
Innovative Living Inc.......E... 218 624-7005
Proctor *(G-6964)*
Lifecare Medical Center.......D... 218 782-2131
Greenbush *(G-2326)*
Lifecare Medical Center.......C... 218 463-4305
Roseau *(G-7355)*
Linnea Residential Home Inc.......E... 651 257-2211
Chisago City *(G-992)*
Little Sisters of The Poor of.......D... 651 227-0336
Saint Paul *(G-8592)*
Lutheran Memorial Home.......D... 218 456-2105
Halstad *(G-2335)*
Luverne Residential Advantage.......D... 507 283-4088
Luverne *(G-3062)*
Madonna Meadows of Rochester....... 507 252-5400
Rochester *(G-7166)*
Marshall County Group Homes.......D... 218 437-6695
Argyle *(G-247)*
Martin Luther Manor.......B... 952 888-7751
Minneapolis *(G-4960)*
Minnesota Department of.......C... 507 283-1100
Luverne *(G-3065)*
Minnesota Masonic Charities....... 952 948-6004
Minneapolis *(G-5081)*
Minnetonka Health Care Center.......E... 952 474-4474
Excelsior *(G-1950)*
North Cities Health Care Inc.......D... 651 633-7200
Saint Paul *(G-8751)*
Northfield Care Center Inc.......C... 507 645-9511
Northfield *(G-6536)*
Now Care Medical Centers Inc.......E... 651 635-0054
Saint Paul *(G-8773)*
Phoenix Residence Inc.......C... 651 227-7655
Saint Paul *(G-7876)*
Pine Ridge Homes Inc.......D... 218 879-1257
Cloquet *(G-1059)*
Pines.......E... 612 861-3331
Minneapolis *(G-5379)*
Prairie Community Services.......E... 320 589-2057
Morris *(G-6374)*
Prairie Community Services.......E... 320 796-6999
Spicer *(G-9558)*
Presbyterian Homes & Services.......B... 952 948-3000
Minneapolis *(G-5404)*
Presbyterian Homes of Inver.......E... 651 451-5959
Inver Grove Heights *(G-2765)*
Presbyterian Homes, Housing.......A... 651 631-6100
Saint Paul *(G-8844)*
Presbyterian Nursing Homes Inc.......B... 952 888-9461
Minneapolis *(G-5405)*
Rainbow Residence Inc.......E... 507 451-5327
Owatonna *(G-6733)*
REM Canby Inc.......E... 952 925-5067
Minneapolis *(G-5508)*
REM Central Lakes Inc.......D... 320 253-8134
Saint Cloud *(G-7585)*
REM Inc.......E... 651 647-9243
Saint Paul *(G-8888)*
REM Inc.......D... 507 387-3181
Mankato *(G-3185)*
Residential Advantages Inc.......D... 507 831-3804
Lakefield *(G-2883)*
Reverence For Life & Concern.......D... 320 564-4911
Granite Falls *(G-2319)*
Rison Homes Administrative.......E... 507 332-0547
Faribault *(G-2029)*
Riverview Manor Inc.......E... 507 824-2091
Wanamingo *(G-9866)*
Saint Benedict's Senior Com....... 763 295-4051
Monticello *(G-6286)*
Shady Lane Nursing Home.......C... 218 631-1391
Wadena *(G-9811)*
Signature Healthcare Inc.......C... 507 288-6514
Rochester *(G-7254)*
St Benedict's Senior Community.......A... 320 252-0010
Saint Cloud *(G-7441)*
St Williams Nursing Home Inc.......C... 218 338-4671
Parkers Prairie *(G-6767)*
Sunrise Senior Living Inc.......D... 952 927-8000
Minneapolis *(G-5769)*
Swift County Homes Inc.......E... 320 843-3509
Benson *(G-442)*
Traverse Care Center.......D... 320 563-8124
Wheaton *(G-9969)*
Twin City Christian Homes Inc.......D... 952 944-8982
Eden Prairie *(G-1799)*
Villa St Vincent Inc.......C... 218 281-3424
Crookston *(G-1143)*
Vista Villa Inc.......E... 218 644-3331
Cromwell *(G-1117)*
Volunteers of America National.......E... 952 941-0305
Eden Prairie *(G-1810)*
Warroad Care Center Inc.......D... 218 386-1235
Warroad *(G-9872)*
Washington County Association.......D... 651 439-4946
Bayport *(G-351)*

INVENTORY COMPUTING SVCS

1 Micro LLC.......E... 952 767-1010
Eden Prairie *(G-1738)*
Retail Inventory Services Ltd.......D... 651 631-9081
Saint Paul *(G-8896)*

Rgis LLC ....D... 507 281-7665
Rochester (G-7223)

Rgis LLC ....C... 952 858-8319
Minneapolis (G-5535)

Washington Inventory Service ....E... 763 784-2055
Minneapolis (G-3638)

INVENTORY STOCKING SVCS

Jacobs Trading LLC ....E... 763 843-2066
Hopkins (G-2561)

INVESTMENT ADVISORY SVCS

Alliance Benefit Group ....D... 507 377-9344
Albert Lea (G-35)

Ameriprise Financial Inc ....A... 612 671-3131
Minneapolis (G-3767)

Ameriprise Financial Services ....E... 952 368-3100
Chaska (G-948)

Ameriprise Financial Services ....D... 651 631-2208
Saint Paul (G-8037)

Ameriprise Financial Services ....C... 612 671-7536
Minneapolis (G-3768)

Ameriprise Financial Services ....C... 612 671-4343
Minneapolis (G-3769)

Ameriprise Financial Services ....C... 612 671-3131
Minneapolis (G-3770)

Dougherty Financial Group LLC ....C... 612 376-4000
Minneapolis (G-4284)

Ehlers & Associates Inc ....E... 651 697-8500
Saint Paul (G-8328)

Fiduciary Counselling Inc ....E... 651 228-0935
Saint Paul (G-8376)

Foster Klima & Co LLC ....D... 612 746-2214
Minneapolis (G-4467)

Island Freight Brokerage LLC ....E... 507 288-5758
Rochester (G-7143)

Jeffrey Slocum & Associates ....D... 612 338-7020
Minneapolis (G-4758)

Jra Financial Advisors.......................E... 763 315-8000
Osseo (G-6625)

Peregrine Capital Management ....E... 612 343-7600
Minneapolis (G-5364)

Prime Investments Inc ....E... 952 853-1680
Minneapolis (G-5409)

Rock Island Co ....E... 651 228-0935
Saint Paul (G-8909)

Sit Investment Associates Inc ....D... 612 332-3223
Minneapolis (G-5681)

Voyageur Co's Inc............................D... 612 376-7000
Minneapolis (G-5985)

Wells Capital Management Inc 612 667-4230
Minneapolis (G-6035)

Wells Fargo Bank, National ....E... 507 285-3015
Rochester (G-7291)

INVESTMENT BANKERS

Dain Rauscher Inc...........................A... 612 371-2711
Minneapolis (G-4217)

Dougherty Financial Group LLC ....C... 612 376-4000
Minneapolis (G-4284)

Goldsmith, Agio, Helms ....D... 612 339-0500
Minneapolis (G-4539)

Piper Jaffray Co's ....A... 612 303-6000
Minneapolis (G-5384)

Rbc Wealth Management ....E... 651 228-6900
Saint Paul (G-8872)

Rbc Wealth Management ....A... 612 371-7750
Minneapolis (G-5472)

Rbc Wealth Managment ....E... 763 476-3700
Hopkins (G-2610)

Think Equity Partners LLC ....C... 612 677-5757
Minneapolis (G-5814)

INVESTMENT CERTIFICATE SALES

Lutheran Brotherhood Research..........E... 612 340-7000
Minneapolis (G-4911)

INVESTMENT COUNSELORS

Sit Fixed Income Advisors II ....D... 612 332-3223
Minneapolis (G-5680)

INVESTMENT FIRM: General Brokerage

Morgan Stanley & Co Inc...................D... 612 340-6700
Minneapolis (G-5129)

UBS Financial Services Inc ....E... 952 921-7900
Minneapolis (G-5891)

UBS Financial Services Inc ....D... 651 298-1616
Saint Paul (G-9100)

Waddell & Reed Inc.........................E... 651 483-1411
Saint Paul (G-9135)

Workman Financial Group Inc ....E... 763 746-9420
Minneapolis (G-6086)

INVESTMENT FUNDS: Open-Ended

Ameriprise Financial.......................D... 612 671-3131
Minneapolis (G-3766)

Galliard Capital Management ....E... 612 667-3210
Minneapolis (G-4496)

Knight Financial Products LLC ....D... 952 249-5500
Hopkins (G-2565)

Mairs & Power Balanced Fund ....E... 651 222-8478
Saint Paul (G-8609)

Mount Yale Portfolio Advisors.........E... 952 897-5390
Minneapolis (G-5141)

Paul Johnston ....E... 800 862-7919
Minneapolis (G-5350)

Pine River Capital Management ....D... 612 238-3300
Minnetonka (G-6214)

Sit Mutual Funds Inc.......................D... 612 332-3223
Minneapolis (G-5682)

Woodbury Financial Services ....C... 651 738-4000
Saint Paul (G-9289)

INVESTMENT OFFICES: Management, Closed-End

Tpg Credit Management, LP ....E... 612 851-3000
Minneapolis (G-5843)

INVESTMENT OFFICES: Mutual Fund Sales, On Own Account

Ameriprise Financial Inc ....A... 612 671-3131
Minneapolis (G-3767)

Woodbury Financial Services ....C... 651 738-4000
Saint Paul (G-9289)

INVESTORS, NEC

Elim Care Foundation ....E... 952 259-4500
Eden Prairie (G-1652)

Kasa Capital LLC ....E... 612 524-5460
Minneapolis (G-4792)

L & M Investment Inc ....D... 218 346-2798
Perham (G-6798)

Minnesota Vikings Football ....C... 952 828-6500
Eden Prairie (G-1727)

Reshare Corp ....E... 952 908-0818
Minneapolis (G-5522)

Rock Island Co ....E... 651 228-0935
Saint Paul (G-8909)

Ross Capital Pmc Inc ....E... 612 929-9222
Minneapolis (G-5560)

Whitebox Advisors LLC ....E... 612 253-6025
Minneapolis (G-6065)

INVESTORS: Real Estate, Exc Property Operators

Midway University LLC.....................E... 651 292-9844
Saint Paul (G-8657)

Northmarq Real Estate Services ....E... 952 831-1000
Minneapolis (G-5234)

IRON ORE MINING

Cliffs Natural Resources Inc ....A... 218 262-5917
Hibbing (G-2441)

Erie L Cliffs L C ....E... 218 225-3127
Hoyt Lakes (G-2669)

Northshore Mining Co ....C... 218 226-4125
Silver Bay (G-9484)

United States Steel Corp ....D... 218 778-8700
Keewatin (G-2826)

IRRIGATION EQPT WHOLESALERS

Albrecht Co's...............................E... 651 633-4510
Saint Paul (G-8006)

Alex Irrigation Inc...........................E... 320 852-7595
Carlos (G-866)

Minnesota Valley Irrigation ....E... 218 631-9271
Wadena (G-9806)

JANITORIAL & CUSTODIAL SVCS

A-1 Maintenance Service Corp ....E... 952 891-3711
Lakeville (G-2888)

ABM Janitorial Services - Nthn............E... 612 378-0646
Minneapolis (G-3661)

Americlean Janitorial Services............A... 763 503-0707
Minneapolis (G-3763)

Arnold's Supply & Kleenit Co ....C... 507 289-2393
Rochester (G-7058)

Brighter Building Maintenance ....E... 651 293-1403
Saint Paul (G-8128)

Building Maintenance Mgt ....E... 763 541-4886
Minneapolis (G-3974)

Building Resources Inc ....C... 612 341-1111
Minneapolis (G-3975)

Buttweiler Environmental Inc ....C... 320 251-4385
Waite Park (G-9818)

Ceda Inc.....................................E... 763 434-4403
Anoka (G-163)

Champion Service Corp....................E... 651 731-9137
Woodbury (G-10171)

F B G Service Corp ....D... 651 917-8059
Saint Paul (G-8357)

General Cleaning Corp....................D... 218 727-4513
Duluth (G-1333)

Hanson McFarland Inc ....D... 763 421-9554
Anoka (G-188)

ISS Facility Services Inc ....E... 763 559-6679
Minneapolis (G-4738)

Jubilee Enterprises Inc ....E... 507 532-2332
Marshall (G-3301)

Kim Kunwook..............................E... 651 578-7627
Saint Paul (G-9236)

Kimmy Clean LLC..........................E... 952 758-4238
New Prague (G-6430)

Leone Enterprises Inc ....C... 763 427-9657
Anoka (G-199)

Linn Building Maintenance Inc...........D... 651 778-1322
Saint Paul (G-8590)

Marsden Holding LLC ....A... 651 641-1717
Saint Paul (G-8615)

Multi-Services Inc ....D... 952 944-4000
Eden Prairie (G-1732)

Osland Janitorial Supply Inc ....E... 952 894-4815
Burnsville (G-773)

Oval Cleaning Service Inc...................E... 612 605-3166
Minneapolis (G-5303)

Picture Perfect Cleaning ....E... 612 865-4522
Farmington (G-2056)

Rbm Services Inc...........................D... 952 361-0897
Chaska (G-978)

S D Q Ltd ....C... 952 929-5263
Minnetonka (G-6223)

Shine-Way Janitorial Service ....D... 507 388-7439
Mankato (G-3197)

Tidy Service of Minnesota Inc ....E... 612 332-5461
Hopkins (G-2646)

Total Quality Maintenance ....D... 763 377-6530
Minneapolis (G-5834)

JANITORIAL EQPT & SPLYS WHOLESALERS

A-1 Maintenance Service Corp.............E... 952 891-3711
Lakeville (G-2888)

Common Sense Building Services ......D... 612 379-7106
Minneapolis (G-4134)

Dalco Enterprises Inc........................E... 651 604-2966
Saint Paul (G-8280)

Osland Janitorial Supply Inc ....E... 952 894-4815
Burnsville (G-773)

Paquette Maintenance Inc ....D... 952 888-1801
Minneapolis (G-5318)

Strategic Equipment Inc ....D... 320 252-2977
Saint Cloud (G-7614)

JEWELRY & PRECIOUS STONES WHOLESALERS

Fred Meyer Jewelers Inc ....E... 952 892-6374
Burnsville (G-723)

JEWELRY REPAIR SVCS

Jewelry Repair Centers Inc...................E... 763 370-2511
Minneapolis (G-3507)

JEWELRY, WHOLESALE

Hanover Accessories LLC ....D... 763 509-6100
Plymouth (G-6863)

Reeves Park Inc ....E... 952 930-0290
Minneapolis (G-5481)

Tiffany & Co ....E... 952 922-0066
Minneapolis (G-5822)

JOB COUNSELING

H I R E D ....D... 612 529-3342
Minneapolis (G-4585)

Rebuild Resources Inc.........................E... 651 645-7055
Saint Paul (G-8880)

JOB TRAINING & VOCATIONAL REHABILITATION SVCS

Adult Training & Habilitation ....E... 320 485-4191
Winsted (G-10155)

American Indian Oic Inc.....................E... 612 341-3358
Minneapolis (G-3753)

County of Anoka ....D... 763 783-4800
Minneapolis (G-3444)

County of Ramsey ....D... 651 770-4499
Saint Paul (G-8261)

East Range Developmental ....E... 218 744-5130
   Eveleth *(G-1930)*

Enterprise North Inc ....E... 507 233-8900
   New Ulm *(G-6448)*

Epic Enterprise Inc ....E... 507 645-6800
   Dundas *(G-1511)*

H I R E D ....D... 612 529-3342
   Minneapolis *(G-4585)*

Interstate Rehabilitation Ctr ....B... 651 388-7108
   Red Wing *(G-6987)*

Kandi-Works Developmental ....E... 320 974-8840
   Atwater *(G-253)*

Le Sueur County Developmental ....E... 507 362-8560
   Waterville *(G-9896)*

Lifetrack Resources Inc ....E... 651 290-0567
   Saint Paul *(G-8587)*

Mankato Rehabilitation Center ....C... 507 386-5600
   Mankato *(G-3165)*

Mankato Rehabilitation Center ....D... 507 386-5799
   Mankato *(G-3164)*

Northeast Minnesota Office of ....E... 218 748-2200
   Virginia *(G-9748)*

Opportunity Partners Inc ....C... 952 938-5511
   Hopkins *(G-2595)*

Phoenix Alternatives Inc ....C... 651 426-2484
   Saint Paul *(G-8825)*

Polk County Developmental ....E... 218 281-4181
   Crookston *(G-1134)*

PPL Industries Inc ....D... 612 332-0664
   Minneapolis *(G-5399)*

Previsor Inc ....D... 612 843-1059
   Minneapolis *(G-5407)*

ProAct Inc ....C... 651 686-0405
   Saint Paul *(G-7884)*

Resource Inc ....D... 612 752-8000
   Minneapolis *(G-5526)*

Resources For Child Caring Inc ....D... 651 641-0305
   Saint Paul *(G-8893)*

Saint Mary's University of MN ....D... 612 728-5109
   Minneapolis *(G-5591)*

Twin Cities Tree Trust ....E... 651 644-6237
   Saint Paul *(G-9090)*

Vision Loss Resources Inc ....D... 612 871-2222
   Minneapolis *(G-5977)*

JOB TRAINING SVCS

Goodwill Industries Inc ....C... 651 379-5800
   Saint Paul *(G-8421)*

Goodwill Industries Inc ....E... 952 953-4410
   Saint Paul *(G-7787)*

Goodwill Industries Inc ....E... 651 439-4207
   Stillwater *(G-9620)*

Goodwill Industries Inc ....D... 651 603-1544
   Saint Paul *(G-8422)*

H I R E D ....D... 612 529-3342
   Minneapolis *(G-4585)*

Midway Training Services Inc ....D... 651 641-0709
   Saint Paul *(G-8656)*

Midwest Special Services Inc ....C... 651 778-1000
   Saint Paul *(G-8664)*

Midwest Special Services Inc ....E... 651 483-3000
   Saint Paul *(G-8663)*

Midwest Special Services Inc ....D... 763 557-1231
   Minneapolis *(G-5037)*

Opportunity Partners Inc ....C... 952 938-5511
   Hopkins *(G-2595)*

Pine Habilitation & Supported ....E... 320 245-2246
   Sandstone *(G-9325)*

West Central Industries Inc ....D... 320 235-5310
   Willmar *(G-10054)*

JUVENILE CORRECTIONAL FACILITIES

County of Clay ....E... 218 299-5150
   Moorhead *(G-6308)*

Northwood Childrens Home Soc ....D... 218 724-8815
   Duluth *(G-1410)*

Pinnacle Programs Inc ....E... 507 283-4425
   Magnolia *(G-3083)*

KIDNEY DIALYSIS CENTERS

Bio-Medical Applications of MN ....E... 218 624-7787
   Duluth *(G-1254)*

Bio-Medical Applications of MN ....E... 763 783-0103
   Minneapolis *(G-3417)*

Total Renal Care Inc ....E... 612 347-5972
   Minneapolis *(G-5835)*

Total Renal Care Inc ....E... 651 483-3159
   Saint Paul *(G-9072)*

KITCHEN CABINETS WHOLESALERS

Automated Building Components ....E... 952 474-4374
   Excelsior *(G-1938)*

Distinctive Door Design Inc ....E... 763 389-1631
   Princeton *(G-6920)*

Ron's Cabinets Inc ....E... 320 252-7667
   Sauk Rapids *(G-9372)*

LABELING SVC: Bottles, Cans, Cartons, Etc

Masterworks Of Minneapolis Inc ....E... 612 333-8210
   Minneapolis *(G-4965)*

Ryt-Way Industries LLC ....A... 952 469-1417
   Lakeville *(G-2929)*

LABOR UNION

International Association of ....E... 651 688-2640
   Saint Paul *(G-7805)*

International Association of ....E... 320 251-8732
   Saint Cloud *(G-7532)*

Law Enforcement Labor Services 651 293-4424
   Saint Paul *(G-8566)*

Minn Health Care Union Local ....E... 612 331-4690
   Saint Paul *(G-8670)*

Minnesota State Employees ....E... 651 450-4990
   South Saint Paul *(G-9535)*

Pace International Union ....B... 320 240-7274
   Sartell *(G-9340)*

Teamsters Local 2000 ....E... 612 379-9157
   Minneapolis *(G-5803)*

LABORATORIES, TESTING: Food

Cargill Inc ....D... 952 742-6437
   Wayzata *(G-9907)*

Food Perspectives Inc ....E... 763 553-7787
   Minneapolis *(G-4463)*

Minnesota Valley Testing Labs ....D... 507 354-8517
   New Ulm *(G-6461)*

LABORATORIES, TESTING: Forensic

Fitzco Inc ....E... 952 471-1185
   Spring Park *(G-9563)*

MEDTOX Scientific Inc ....B... 651 636-7466
   Saint Paul *(G-8632)*

LABORATORIES, TESTING: Hazardous Waste

Lab Holdings Inc 612 607-1700
   Minneapolis *(G-4831)*

Nova Consulting Group Inc ....E... 952 448-9393
   Chaska *(G-977)*

Pace Analytical Services Inc ....B... 612 607-1700
   Minneapolis *(G-5308)*

LABORATORIES, TESTING: Pollution

American Consulting Services ....C... 651 659-9001
   Saint Paul *(G-8023)*

American Engineering Testing ....D... 651 659-9001
   Saint Paul *(G-8025)*

Interpoll Laboratories Inc ....E... 763 786-6020
   Circle Pines *(G-1012)*

MSP Corp ....E... 651 287-8100
   Saint Paul *(G-8727)*

LABORATORIES, TESTING: Product Testing, Safety/Performance

Environ Electronic Labs ....E... 952 888-7795
   Minneapolis *(G-4363)*

LABORATORIES, TESTING: Seed

Minnesota Crop Improvement ....E... 612 625-7766
   Saint Paul *(G-8680)*

LABORATORIES, TESTING: Soil Analysis

American Consulting Services ....C... 651 659-9001
   Saint Paul *(G-8023)*

American Engineering Testing ....D... 651 659-9001
   Saint Paul *(G-8025)*

Interpoll Laboratories Inc ....E... 763 786-6020
   Circle Pines *(G-1012)*

Lab Holdings Inc 612 607-1700
   Minneapolis *(G-4831)*

Northeast Technical Services ....E... 218 741-4290
   Virginia *(G-9749)*

Pace Analytical Services Inc ....B... 612 607-1700
   Minneapolis *(G-5308)*

LABORATORIES, TESTING: Water

American Consulting Services ....C... 651 659-9001
   Saint Paul *(G-8023)*

American Engineering Testing ....D... 651 659-9001
   Saint Paul *(G-8025)*

County of Stearns ....C... 320 259-3700
   Saint Cloud *(G-7495)*

Interpoll Laboratories Inc ....E... 763 786-6020
   Circle Pines *(G-1012)*

Lab Holdings Inc 612 607-1700
   Minneapolis *(G-4831)*

Lincoln Lyon Murry & Pipestone ....E... 507 537-6709
   Marshall *(G-3305)*

Pace Analytical Services Inc ....B... 612 607-1700
   Minneapolis *(G-5308)*

LABORATORIES: Biological

Marynole Genetics & Energy ....D... 612 275-2518
   Dassel *(G-1162)*

Medtox Laboratories Inc ....B... 651 636-7466
   Saint Paul *(G-8631)*

Silliker Inc ....E... 952 932-2800
   Hopkins *(G-2634)*

LABORATORIES: Biotechnology

Higher Dimension Research Inc ....E... 651 730-6203
   Saint Paul *(G-9229)*

LABORATORIES: Blood Analysis

American National Red Cross ....C... 651 291-4600
   Saint Paul *(G-8030)*

LABORATORIES: Commercial Nonphysical Research

Cargill Inc ....D... 763 441-6508
   Elk River *(G-1866)*

Compendium Corp ....D... 952 881-1608
   Saint Paul *(G-7736)*

Educational Cooperative Svc ....E... 612 638-1500
   Minneapolis *(G-4327)*

Product Deve ....E... 612 676-1474
   Minneapolis *(G-5416)*

Research International USA Inc ....E... 952 853-9400
   Minneapolis *(G-5521)*

Smith Moreton International ....E... 952 820-4441
   Minneapolis *(G-5690)*

Soymor Biodiesel LLC ....E... 507 448-0124
   Albert Lea *(G-66)*

3M Co ....D... 651 733-5300
   Saint Paul *(G-9047)*

LABORATORIES: Dental

Davis Dental Lab ....E... 952 345-6315
   Minneapolis *(G-4229)*

Dexterity Dental Arts Inc ....E... 651 463-4444
   Farmington *(G-2049)*

Granite City Dental Laboratory ....E... 320 253-4825
   Saint Cloud *(G-7436)*

Harrison Dental Studio Inc ....E... 651 457-6600
   Saint Paul *(G-7796)*

Lemke Dental Laboratory Inc ....E... 651 482-9911
   Saint Paul *(G-8577)*

Merit Dental Lab Inc ....E... 651 644-4042
   Saint Paul *(G-8635)*

National Dentex Corp ....E... 763 566-0210
   Minneapolis *(G-5162)*

National Dentex Corp ....E... 507 625-5079
   Mankato *(G-3175)*

Renstrom Dental Studio Inc ....E... 651 407-0491
   Saint Paul *(G-8891)*

Sentage Corp ....E... 612 529-9655
   Minneapolis *(G-5638)*

Udell Dental Laboratory Inc ....E... 952 926-9266
   Minneapolis *(G-5893)*

Valley Dental Arts Inc ....D... 651 439-2855
   Stillwater *(G-9653)*

Webster Dental Laboratory Inc ....E... 651 779-9160
   Saint Paul *(G-9143)*

Westlund Dental Studio Inc ....E... 952 942-9464
   Eden Prairie *(G-1814)*

LABORATORIES: Dental & Medical X-Ray

CDI Central Florida LLC ....D... 952 543-6500
   Minneapolis *(G-4035)*

Isj Regional Women's Imaging ....D... 507 304-7770
   Mankato *(G-3150)*

St Paul Radiology ....D... 651 297-6504
   Saint Paul *(G-8999)*

LABORATORIES: Dental, Artificial Teeth Production

Thoele Dental Laboratories Inc ....E... 320 252-2070
   Waite Park *(G-9843)*

LABORATORIES: Dental, Crown & Bridge Production

Granite City Dental Laboratory ....E... 320 253-4825
   Saint Cloud *(G-7436)*

Jackson Spah Dental Studio Inc ....E... 763 785-2435
   Minneapolis *(G-3504)*

(G-00000) Company's Geographic Section entry number

S E R V I C E S

LABORATORIES: Dental, Denture Production

Granite City Dental Laboratory ....E... 320 253-4825
Saint Cloud (G-7436)

Thoele Dental Laboratories Inc ....E... 320 252-2070
Waite Park (G-9843)

LABORATORIES: Electronic Research

Minnetronix Inc ....C... 651 917-4060
Saint Paul (G-8712)

LABORATORIES: Environmental Research

Midwest Assistance Program ....E... 952 758-4334
New Prague (G-6433)

Schoell & Madson Inc ....E... 763 746-1600
Minneapolis (G-5610)

LABORATORIES: Medical

Allina Medical Center.............................E... 651 220-8186
Saint Paul (G-8017)

Consultants In Arthritisand...................E... 952 832-0246
Minneapolis (G-4157)

Health East Medical Laboratory ....D... 651 232-3500
Saint Paul (G-8449)

MEDTOX Scientific Inc ....B... 651 636-7466
Saint Paul (G-8632)

Minnesota Medical Scanning.................C... 952 541-1840
Saint Louis Park (G-7667)

Quest Diagnostics Clinical...................C... 651 635-1500
Saint Paul (G-8863)

Rochester Methodist Hospital 507 266-7890
Rochester (G-7237)

St Luke's Hospital of Duluth ....E... 218 249-5564
Duluth (G-1471)

Tuv Sud America Inc ....E... 651 631-2487
Saint Paul (G-9086)

Viromed Laboratories Inc......................E... 952 563-3300
Minnetonka (G-6234)

LABORATORIES: Medical Bacteriological

Medtox Laboratories Inc ....B... 651 636-7466
Saint Paul (G-8631)

LABORATORIES: Medical Pathology

Central Regional Pathology Lab...........E... 651 264-1611
Saint Paul (G-9194)

LABORATORIES: Noncommercial Research

Clean Water Action Inc ....C... 612 623-3666
Minneapolis (G-4105)

Regents of The University of ....C... 218 720-4294
Duluth (G-1433)

LABORATORIES: Physical Research, Commercial

Aspen Research Corp ....D... 651 264-6000
Saint Paul (G-8071)

Camas Inc...E... 507 357-4929
Le Center (G-2949)

Cargill Inc..D... 952 742-6437
Wayzata (G-9907)

Dover Fluid Management Inc ....D... 651 388-3565
Red Wing (G-6978)

Hardwire Tech Inc ....E... 763 783-8111
Minneapolis (G-3483)

Higher Dimension Materials Inc ....E... 651 730-6203
Saint Paul (G-9228)

Hysitron Inc ....D... 952 835-6366
Eden Prairie (G-1689)

Integra Group Inc ....E... 763 951-7400
Brooklyn Park (G-611)

Ion Corp ....E... 952 936-9490
Eden Prairie (G-1698)

Lab Holdings Inc 612 607-1700
Minneapolis (G-4831)

Leisure Inc..E... 952 401-8440
Eden Prairie (G-1707)

Minnesota Medtec Inc............................E... 763 428-3720
Osseo (G-6640)

Minnesota Valley Testing Labs.............D... 507 354-8517
New Ulm (G-6461)

Pace Analytical Services Inc................B... 612 607-1700
Minneapolis (G-5308)

Pdl Biopharma Inc ....D... 763 255-5000
Minneapolis (G-5357)

Techne Corp ....A... 612 379-8854
Minneapolis (G-5804)

Yeater Hennings Ruff Architect...........E... 218 233-4422
Moorhead (G-6348)

LABORATORIES: Testing

Aero Systems Engineering Inc ....C... 651 227-7515
Saint Paul (G-7993)

Apptec Laboratory Services Inc ....C... 651 675-2044
Saint Paul (G-7706)

Architectural Testing Inc.......................E... 651 636-3835
Saint Paul (G-8061)

Aspen Research Corp ....D... 651 264-6000
Saint Paul (G-8071)

Braun Intertec Corp ....E... 651 487-3245
Saint Paul (G-8122)

Central Minnesota Diagnostic ....E... 320 983-6300
Milaca (G-3374)

CIMA LABS Inc.......................................D... 952 947-8700
Eden Prairie (G-1627)

Dairy Quality Control Inst......................E... 763 785-0484
Saint Paul (G-8278)

Diversified Laboratory Testing ....E... 763 785-0484
Saint Paul (G-8302)

Ion Corp ....E... 952 936-9490
Eden Prairie (G-1698)

Legend Technical Services Inc.............E... 651 642-1150
Saint Paul (G-8576)

Medtox Laboratories Inc ....B... 651 636-7466
Saint Paul (G-8631)

MEDTOX Scientific Inc ....B... 651 636-7466
Saint Paul (G-8632)

Minnesota Valley Testing Labs.............D... 507 354-8517
New Ulm (G-6461)

On Assignment Staffing Svcs...............D... 651 647-1160
Saint Paul (G-8784)

Prometric Inc...D... 651 647-1723
Saint Paul (G-8854)

R Tech Laboratories ....D... 651 481-2207
Saint Paul (G-8867)

Stearns Dairy Herd Improvement ....E... 320 352-2028
Sauk Centre (G-9353)

Stork United Corp ....D... 651 645-3601
Saint Paul (G-9009)

Ten-E Packaging Services Inc ....E... 651 459-0671
Newport (G-6489)

Tuv Sud America Inc ....E... 651 631-2487
Saint Paul (G-9086)

Viromed Laboratories Inc......................E... 952 563-3300
Minnetonka (G-6234)

LABORATORIES: Urinalysis

Medtox Laboratories Inc ....B... 651 636-7466
Saint Paul (G-8631)

LABORATORY EQPT, EXC MEDICAL: Wholesalers

La Calhene Inc...E... 320 358-4713
Rush City (G-7390)

LAMINATING SVCS

Fedex Office & Print Services ....E... 952 892-0200
Burnsville (G-721)

Sign-Zone Inc ....C... 763 746-1350
Anoka (G-227)

Smyth Co's Inc ....E... 651 646-4544
Saint Paul (G-8967)

LAND SUBDIVIDERS & DEVELOPERS: Commercial

A B Systems Inc......................................E... 507 288-9397
Rochester (G-7042)

Allete Inc ....C... 218 279-5000
Duluth (G-1235)

Carlson Hotels Management Corp ....C... 763 212-5000
Minneapolis (G-4016)

MSP Real Estate Inc..............................C... 952 351-4540
Minneapolis (G-5145)

Odyssey Development Inc ....E... 218 728-8060
Duluth (G-1412)

Opus Corp ....C... 952 656-4444
Hopkins (G-2597)

Opus Northwest Construction ....C... 952 656-4444
Hopkins (G-2598)

Radisson Hotels International ....C... 763 212-5000
Minnetonka (G-6218)

Ryan Co's US Inc ....B... 612 492-4000
Minneapolis (G-5759)

Watson Centers Inc ....D... 612 920-5034
Minneapolis (G-6023)

Wells Fargo Properties Inc...................E... 612 667-8690
Minneapolis (G-6052)

LAND SUBDIVIDERS & DEVELOPERS: Residential

Allete Inc...C... 218 279-5000
Duluth (G-1235)

Commonbond Communities ....D... 651 291-1750
Saint Paul (G-8231)

Keystone Bluffs ....E... 218 727-2800
Duluth (G-1370)

LAND SUBDIVISION & DEVELOPMENT

Allete Inc...C... 218 279-5000
Duluth (G-1235)

Bce Development Corp ....E... 612 372-1500
Minneapolis (G-3876)

Beaumont Leased Housing Assocs ....D... 763 354-5500
Plymouth (G-6851)

Beaumont Leased Housing Assocs ....D... 763 354-5500
Plymouth (G-6850)

Blackforest Developers LLC.................E... 612 872-9200
Minneapolis (G-3911)

Brookpark Group.....................................E... 763 424-8525
Minneapolis (G-3961)

Dominium Group Inc ....D... 763 354-5500
Minneapolis (G-4272)

E T C Enterprises Inc ....E... 320 240-0567
Saint Cloud (G-7500)

Fbs Associated Properties Inc 612 333-2086
Minneapolis (G-4417)

Fenway Development Inc.......................D... 651 429-8032
Saint Paul (G-8373)

Fine Associates LLC ....E... 612 332-2561
Minneapolis (G-4434)

Houston Leased Housing Assocs ....D... 763 354-5500
Plymouth (G-6865)

Liberty Property Trust............................E... 952 947-1100
Eden Prairie (G-1709)

Mdi LP 38 ....E... 651 646-7848
Saint Paul (G-8627)

Opus National LLC ....C... 952 656-4444
Minnetonka (G-6207)

Partners For Senior ....E... 612 374-8100
Minneapolis (G-5342)

Pratt Nedegaard.....................................D... 651 429-8032
Saint Paul (G-8835)

Tradition Development............................E... 952 920-5100
Minneapolis (G-5844)

Western Walls Inc ....E... 507 282-4624
Rochester (G-7292)

LANDSCAPE ARCHITECTURAL SVCS

Carrs Tree Service Inc...........................E... 218 367-3355
Ottertail (G-6686)

Keenan & Sveiven Inc ....E... 952 475-1229
Minnetonka (G-6184)

Lhb Inc...E... 612 338-2029
Minneapolis (G-4867)

Whiting, Jim Nursery & Garden 507 289-3741
Rochester (G-7293)

LANDSCAPE CONSULTING & PLANNING

Hough Inc of Detroit Lakes...................E... 218 847-7391
Detroit Lakes (G-1199)

LANDSCAPE PLANNING SVCS

A-Scape Inc...E... 952 496-1178
Shakopee (G-9417)

Outdoor Environments Inc ....E... 952 496-1000
Savage (G-9403)

Phasse III of Maple Grove Inc..............E... 763 425-4212
Osseo (G-6652)

Schoell & Madson Inc ....E... 763 746-1600
Minneapolis (G-5610)

Stacy's Nursery Inc ....E... 320 235-6010
Willmar (G-10046)

LANDSCAPE SVCS

AAA All American Lawn..........................E... 763 537-5733
Anoka (G-145)

Brickman Group Ltd LLC ....E... 952 922-8777
Minneapolis (G-3943)

Butler Brothers Enterprises..................E... 651 554-9888
Inver Grove Heights (G-2739)

Carefree Services Inc ....E... 763 479-2600
Maple Plain (G-3271)

Concept Landscaping Inc ....E... 952 472-4118
Mound (G-6386)

Concierge Enterprises Inc ....E... 763 746-8121
Minneapolis (G-4151)

Dundee Nursery & Landscaping ....E... 763 559-4004
Minneapolis (G-4293)

Employment codes: A=Over 500 employees, B=251-500,
C=101-250, D=51-100, E=25-50

2011 Harris Minnesota
Services Directory

© Harris InfoSource 1-866-281-6415
723

LANDSCAPE SVCS (continued)

Family Tree Landscape Nursery.............E... 507 533-8558
Stewartville (G-9592)

Jackson Landscape Supply Inc...............E... 952 435-6927
Lakeville (G-2913)

Jordan Ray Sons.....................................E... 763 434-1644
Cedar (G-881)

Landscape Brands Inc ....E... 507 452-1112
Winona (G-10110)

Lawn Ranger Inc ....D... 952 937-6076
Eden Prairie (G-1706)

Metro Home Services Network ....E... 612 827-0643
Cedar (G-882)

Schoell & Madson Inc ....E... 763 746-1600
Minneapolis (G-5610)

Trugreen Landcare LLC...........................D... 651 994-9855
Saint Paul (G-7931)

LANDSCAPING SVC

Alex Irrigation Inc...................................E... 320 852-7595
Carlos (G-866)

Arrowhead Tree Service Inc....................E... 218 729-9203
Duluth (G-1245)

Bauer's Market & Nursery Inc.................E... 507 895-4583
La Crescent (G-2839)

Bever & Sons Inc ....E... 651 426-7733
Forest Lake (G-2150)

Bloomers Garden Center ....E... 218 326-0668
Grand Rapids (G-2270)

Concept Landscaping Inc ....E... 952 472-4118
Mound (G-6386)

Curbside Lawn Care ....D... 952 403-9012
Savage (G-9387)

Dakota Turf Inc..E... 651 460-8873
Farmington (G-2048)

Fairview Gardens ....E... 320 229-2281
Sauk Rapids (G-9381)

Friedges Landscaping Inc.......................E... 952 469-2996
Lakeville (G-2908)

Great Northern Landscapes Inc ....E... 763 274-2678
Elk River (G-1876)

Greenworks Inc ....E... 763 498-7696
Loretto (G-3048)

Hartman Co's Inc ....E... 952 443-2958
Victoria (G-9729)

Hough Inc ....E... 218 847-7391
Detroit Lakes (G-1198)

Jim Landscape LLC ....E... 952 941-9818
Minneapolis (G-4766)

Keenan & Sveiven Inc.............................E... 952 475-1229
Minnetonka (G-6184)

Kowsary Turf Inc ....E... 763 862-4646
Elk River (G-1882)

L & K Landscaping Inc ....E... 763 497-4700
Saint Michael (G-7675)

L & R Suburban Landscaping Inc ....E... 952 935-0389
Minnetonka (G-6186)

Lac Enterprises Inc ....E... 651 482-0205
Saint Paul (G-8554)

Landscape Renovations Inc ....E... 651 769-0010
Afton (G-9)

Landstyle Design & Constr ....E... 763 479-1200
Loretto (G-3050)

Lawn King Inc..E... 763 420-2909
Hamel (G-2346)

Linder's Greenhouses Inc ....E... 651 488-1927
Saint Paul (G-8588)

Little Yukon Greenhouse Inc ....D... 218 692-3536
Crosslake (G-1152)

Metro Home Services Network ....E... 612 827-0643
Cedar (G-882)

Midland Nursery Inc................................E... 763 478-6122
Buffalo (G-651)

Midwest Landscapes Inc.........................E... 763 241-1320
Elk River (G-1902)

Natures Garden World Inc.......................E... 218 739-9641
Fergus Falls (G-2101)

North Metro Landscaping Inc ....E... 763 497-4898
Hanover (G-2369)

Outdoor Images Inc ....E... 651 480-2000
Hastings (G-2397)

Prescription Landscape Inc ....E... 651 488-8965
Saint Paul (G-8845)

River Valley Lawnscape Inc ....E... 651 388-7000
Red Wing (G-7002)

Sargent's Landscape Nursery ....E... 507 289-0022
Rochester (G-7247)

Steve's Elk River Nursery Inc ....E... 763 441-3090
Elk River (G-1894)

Talberg Lawn & Landscape Inc ....D... 763 428-3550
Osseo (G-6672)

TPC Landscape Inc ....E... 952 898-7600
Burnsville (G-809)

Village Green Lawn Maintenance ....E... 651 488-2733
Saint Paul (G-9129)

Wagner Sod Co Inc ....E... 651 457-6037
Inver Grove Heights (G-2773)

Whiting, Jim Nursery & Garden...............507 289-3741
Rochester (G-7293)

Willow Creek Concrete Products ....E... 320 398-5415
Kimball (G-2835)

Winco Landscape Inc ....E... 651 455-3070
Inver Grove Heights (G-2774)

LAUNDRIES, EXC POWER & COIN-OPERATED

Health Systems Cooperative ....D... 651 774-8620
Saint Paul (G-8450)

LAUNDRY & DRYCLEANING SVCS, EXC COIN-OPERATED: Pickup

J D Fingerman Enterprises Inc ....E... 612 861-1697
Minneapolis (G-4746)

LAUNDRY & GARMENT SVCS, NEC: Diapers

Small Change Diaper Service ....E... 507 895-8625
La Crescent (G-2844)

LAUNDRY & GARMENT SVCS, NEC: Fur Cleaning, Repairing/Storage

Don's Leather Cleaning Inc....................E... 612 721-4881
Minneapolis (G-4276)

LAUNDRY & GARMENT SVCS: Tailor Shop, Exc Custom/Merchant

Stoltz Dry Cleaners Inc ....E... 651 698-0120
Saint Paul (G-9008)

LAUNDRY SVC: Indl Clothing

G & K Services Inc ....C... 320 252-9471
Saint Cloud (G-7515)

G&K Services Inc ....C... 612 333-2225
Minneapolis (G-4493)

LAUNDRY SVC: Mat & Rug Sply

G&K Services Inc ....C... 952 912-5500
Minnetonka (G-6173)

G&K Services Inc ....C... 651 855-7000
Saint Paul (G-8398)

LAUNDRY SVC: Treated Eqpt Sply, Mats, Rugs, Mops, Etc

G&K Services Inc ....C... 952 912-5500
Minnetonka (G-6173)

G&K Services Inc ....C... 651 855-7000
Saint Paul (G-8398)

LAUNDRY SVC: Wiping Towel Sply

G&K Services Inc ....C... 952 912-5500
Minnetonka (G-6173)

G&K Services Inc ....C... 651 855-7000
Saint Paul (G-8398)

LAUNDRY SVCS: Indl

Ameripride Services Inc ....D... 952 738-4200
Hopkins (G-2510)

Ameripride Services Inc ....D... 218 263-3611
Hibbing (G-2436)

Ameripride Services Inc ....D... 507 345-1039
Mankato (G-3105)

Ameripride Services Inc ....B... 612 331-1600
Minneapolis (G-3764)

ARAMARK Uniform & Career...................C... 763 586-0020
Minneapolis (G-3408)

Cintas Corp No 2 ....C... 763 425-6666
Osseo (G-6603)

United Linen Services Inc ....B... 651 227-9855
Saint Paul (G-9107)

LAWN CARE SVCS

A-Scape Inc ....E... 952 496-1178
Shakopee (G-9417)

Natures Garden World Inc.......................E... 218 739-9641
Fergus Falls (G-2101)

On Time Lawn & Snow Services ....E... 763 786-0652
Minneapolis (G-3561)

Outdoor Environments Inc ....E... 952 496-1000
Savage (G-9403)

Trugreen LP ....E... 507 289-8798
Rochester (G-7276)

Trugreen LP ....E... 612 493-5035
Osseo (G-6678)

Trugreen LP ....D... 952 933-7360
Hopkins (G-2648)

Trugreen Ltd Ptn.....................................D... 651 407-3400
Saint Paul (G-9085)

Verde Lawn Care LLC ....E... 763 550-9400
Minneapolis (G-5963)

LAWN MOWER REPAIR SHOP

Hance Distributing Inc ....E... 952 935-6429
Hopkins (G-2548)

Jerry's Enterprises Inc............................E... 952 929-4601
Minneapolis (G-4761)

LAWN SVCS

Arteka Co's LLC.......................................C... 952 934-2000
Shakopee (G-9419)

Davey Tree Expert Co ....E... 763 553-9740
Minneapolis (G-4224)

Trugreen Ltd Ptn.....................................E... 952 895-3400
Burnsville (G-814)

LEASING & RENTAL SVCS: Computer Hardware, Exc Finance

Data Sales Co Inc ....D... 952 890-8838
Burnsville (G-710)

LEASING & RENTAL SVCS: Computer Peripheral Eqpt

Data Sales Co Inc ....D... 952 890-8838
Burnsville (G-710)

Vibrant Technologies Inc ....E... 952 653-1700
Minnetonka (G-6233)

LEASING & RENTAL SVCS: Cranes & Aerial Lift Eqpt

Advance Equipment Co ....E... 651 489-8881
Saint Paul (G-7987)

Sowles Co ....C... 651 287-9700
Saint Paul (G-7910)

Truck Crane Service-Illinois ....E... 651 406-4949
Saint Paul (G-7930)

Truck Utilities Inc....................................D... 651 484-3305
Saint Paul (G-9084)

LEASING & RENTAL: Automobile With Driver

U Save Lease & Rental Inc......................E... 218 732-3347
Park Rapids (G-6764)

LEASING & RENTAL: Computers & Eqpt

Xerxes Computer Corp ....E... 952 936-9280
Minneapolis (G-6094)

LEASING & RENTAL: Construction & Mining Eqpt

Advance Equipment Co ....E... 651 489-8881
Saint Paul (G-7987)

Broadway Rental Equipment Co ....E... 763 533-1680
Minneapolis (G-3952)

K R Wagner Inc ....E... 218 283-3700
International Falls (G-2725)

Penhall Co ....E... 763 542-9999
Minneapolis (G-5363)

Phillippi Equipment Co ....E... 651 406-4900
Saint Paul (G-7875)

RSC Equipment Rental Inc ....E... 763 509-2423
Minneapolis (G-5566)

RSC Equipment Rental Inc ....E... 763 509-2400
Minneapolis (G-5564)

Tri State Machinery Co............................E... 952 224-1500
Burnsville (G-812)

Ziegler Inc...E... 320 253-2234
Saint Cloud (G-7635)

LEASING & RENTAL: Medical Machinery & Eqpt

Northwest Respiratory Services ....D... 651 603-8720
Saint Paul (G-8767)

Rice Home Medical LLC ....E... 320 235-8404
Willmar (G-10040)

Sightpath Medical Inc.............................C... 952 881-2500
Minneapolis (G-5668)

Universal Hospital Services ....D... 952 893-3200
Minneapolis (G-5920)

LEASING & RENTAL: Mobile Home Sites

Hometown America LLC ....E... 651 436-2790
Lake Elmo (G-2873)

Landfall Terrace Inc................................E... 651 739-8284
Saint Paul (G-9240)

Sunrise Estates Mobile Home ....E... 651 462-4047
Stacy (G-9581)

S
E
R
V
I
C
E
S

LEASING & RENTAL: Office Machines & Eqpt

Lyon Financial Services Inc ....C... 507 532-7763
Marshall *(G-3307)*

Metro - Sales Inc ....C... 612 861-4000
Minneapolis *(G-5000)*

Ricoh Americas Corp ....D... 651 294-2600
Mendota Heights *(G-3370)*

LEASING & RENTAL: Other Real Estate Property

Coop Tricounty ....E... 320 748-7187
Graceville *(G-2253)*

Employers Mutual Casualty Co ....E... 952 938-4646
Hopkins *(G-2539)*

Theodore F Bolles ....D... 651 731-9436
Saint Paul *(G-9281)*

Thomas Furlong ....E... 651 437-2518
Hastings *(G-2408)*

Upper Minnesota Properties Inc ....E... 218 722-2641
Duluth *(G-1494)*

Wagers Business Systems Inc ....D... 651 644-3830
Saint Paul *(G-7943)*

LEASING & RENTAL: Trucks, Without Drivers

Brookdale Motor Sales Inc ....C... 763 561-8161
Minneapolis *(G-3956)*

Penske Truck Leasing Co, LP ....E... 651 631-3399
Saint Paul *(G-8814)*

R L Brookdale Motors Inc ....D... 763 561-8111
Minneapolis *(G-5459)*

Robert A Williams Enterprises ....D... 612 333-8900
Minneapolis *(G-5551)*

RSC Equipment Rental Inc ....E... 763 509-2400
Minneapolis *(G-5564)*

Superior Ford Inc ....C... 763 559-9111
Minneapolis *(G-5771)*

U-Haul Co of Minnesota ....D... 763 780-9746
Minneapolis *(G-3628)*

Wally McCarthy's Cadillac ....D... 651 636-6060
Saint Paul *(G-9139)*

Zumbrota Ford Sales LLC ....E... 507 732-5127
Zumbrota *(G-10222)*

LEASING & RENTAL: Utility Trailers & RV's

Brookman Motor Sales Inc ....E... 651 777-1316
Lake Elmo *(G-2867)*

Penske Truck Leasing Co, LP ....E... 651 454-0000
Saint Paul *(G-7873)*

LEASING: Laundry Eqpt

Maytag Coin-Op Washers ....E... 651 688-7000
Saint Paul *(G-7836)*

LEASING: Passenger Car

A & R Leasing Inc ....D... 218 829-4787
Baxter *(G-318)*

Associated Partnership Ltd ....C... 952 890-7851
Savage *(G-9383)*

Barnett Chrysler Jeep Kia ....D... 651 429-3391
Saint Paul *(G-8089)*

Brookdale Motor Sales Inc ....C... 763 561-8161
Minneapolis *(G-3956)*

Buerkle Buick Leasing Co ....C... 651 484-0231
Saint Paul *(G-8140)*

Clements Chevrolet-Cadillac Co ....C... 507 289-0491
Rochester *(G-7082)*

Coon Rapids Chrysler Inc ....C... 763 421-8000
Minneapolis *(G-3439)*

Duke Co's ....D... 612 331-4880
Minneapolis *(G-4289)*

Eich Motor Co ....E... 320 251-1737
Saint Cloud *(G-7503)*

Ford New Brighten ....D... 651 633-9010
Saint Paul *(G-8387)*

Ford Tenvoorde Inc ....D... 320 251-0540
Saint Cloud *(G-7512)*

Friendly Chevrolet, Geo Inc ....C... 763 786-6100
Minneapolis *(G-3473)*

Interstate Motor Trucks Inc ....E... 507 373-0653
Albert Lea *(G-57)*

Laurentian Leasing Inc ....E... 218 741-6000
Virginia *(G-9744)*

Miller Enterprises Inc ....C... 320 251-8900
Saint Cloud *(G-7557)*

Montavon Motors Inc ....E... 218 326-0551
Grand Rapids *(G-2297)*

R L Brookdale Motors Inc ....D... 763 561-8111
Minneapolis *(G-5459)*

Superior Ford Inc ....C... 763 559-9111
Minneapolis *(G-5771)*

Trail Dodge Inc ....D... 651 455-2201
Inver Grove Heights *(G-2772)*

Walden Leasing Inc ....E... 952 512-8924
Minneapolis *(G-5996)*

Wally McCarthy's Cadillac ....D... 651 636-6060
Saint Paul *(G-9139)*

White Bear Dodge Inc ....D... 651 482-6100
Saint Paul *(G-9155)*

Yamamoto Moss Mackenzie ....E... 612 375-0180
Minneapolis *(G-6099)*

Zumbrota Ford Sales LLC ....E... 507 732-5127
Zumbrota *(G-10222)*

LEASING: Residential Buildings

Brookfield Commercial ....C... 612 372-1500
Minneapolis *(G-3957)*

Hornig Properties Inc ....E... 612 874-4400
Minneapolis *(G-4675)*

Jim Bern Co ....E... 952 854-4141
Minneapolis *(G-4764)*

LEASING: Truck, Without Drivers

Allstate Leasing Corp ....E... 651 681-4900
Minneapolis *(G-3728)*

Allstate Leasing LLC ....E... 952 703-3444
Minneapolis *(G-3729)*

Buerkle Buick Leasing Co ....C... 651 484-0231
Saint Paul *(G-8140)*

Coop Tricounty ....E... 320 748-7187
Graceville *(G-2253)*

Dave Syverson Inc ....D... 507 373-1438
Albert Lea *(G-46)*

First Student Inc ....D... 763 559-9326
Minneapolis *(G-4447)*

Nelson Leasing Inc ....E... 320 235-2770
Willmar *(G-10029)*

LEATHER GOODS, CLEANING & REPAIR SVCS

Don's Leather Cleaning Inc ....E... 612 721-4881
Minneapolis *(G-4276)*

LEGAL & TAX SVCS

Aca International ....D... 952 926-6547
Minneapolis *(G-3663)*

Metro Legal Services Inc ....E... 612 332-0202
Minneapolis *(G-5001)*

LEGAL AID SVCS

Jardine Logan & O'Brien ....E... 651 290-6500
Lake Elmo *(G-2874)*

Metro Legal Services Inc ....D... 612 332-0202
Minneapolis *(G-5001)*

Metro Legal Services Inc ....E... 651 291-0008
Saint Paul *(G-8641)*

So MN Regional Service ....E... 651 222-5863
Saint Paul *(G-8968)*

LEGAL OFFICES & SVCS

Attorney's Process Service Ltd ....C... 952 831-7776
Minneapolis *(G-3833)*

Barnes & Thornburg LLP ....D... 612 333-2111
Minneapolis *(G-3868)*

Briggs & Morgan Professional ....B... 612 977-8400
Minneapolis *(G-3946)*

Burke Blackwell ....E... 612 343-3200
Minneapolis *(G-3976)*

Casserly Molzahn & Assoc Inc ....D... 952 885-1298
Minneapolis *(G-4025)*

City of Moorhead ....D... 218 299-5120
Moorhead *(G-6302)*

Coldwell Banker Burnet Inc ....D... 952 920-1224
Eden Prairie *(G-1630)*

Commercial Auditors Corp ....E... 763 783-9160
Minneapolis *(G-3437)*

County of Olmsted ....E... 507 285-8138
Rochester *(G-7089)*

Dorsey & Whitney LLP ....A... 612 340-2600
Minneapolis *(G-4281)*

Emmett J McMahon ....E... 612 349-8728
Minneapolis *(G-4348)*

Evangelical Lutheran Church In ....C... 612 752-4080
Minneapolis *(G-4376)*

Felhaber Larson Fenlon & Vogt ....E... 651 222-6321
Saint Paul *(G-8372)*

Fish & Richardson PC ....E... 612 335-5070
Minneapolis *(G-4451)*

Fryberger, Buchanan, Smith ....D... 218 725-6807
Duluth *(G-1329)*

General Electric Capital Corp ....E... 952 897-5600
Minneapolis *(G-4509)*

Hutchinson, City of Inc ....E... 320 587-2242
Hutchinson *(G-2703)*

LEGAL SVCS (continued)

Jenson, Beel, Converse ....E... 651 223-4999
Saint Paul *(G-8530)*

Johnson Lewis Nilan ....D... 612 338-1838
Minneapolis *(G-4775)*

Jones Stanley & Associates ....E... 507 288-0064
Rochester *(G-7147)*

Karen B Bjorkman ....E... 612 904-7401
Minneapolis *(G-4791)*

Larkin, Hoffman, Daly ....C... 952 835-3800
Minneapolis *(G-4845)*

Legal Aid Society of ....D... 612 332-1441
Minneapolis *(G-4855)*

Legal Aid Society of ....E... 612 827-3774
Minneapolis *(G-4856)*

Legal Research Center Inc ....E... 612 332-4950
Minneapolis *(G-4857)*

Legal Service Northwest MN ....E... 218 681-7710
Thief River Falls *(G-9673)*

Littler Mendelson, PC ....E... 612 630-1000
Minneapolis *(G-4894)*

Messerli & Kramer ....D... 763 548-7900
Minneapolis *(G-4997)*

Milavetz Gallop Millavetz ....E... 763 533-1111
Minneapolis *(G-5039)*

Minnesota Legal Services ....E... 320 253-0121
Saint Cloud *(G-7559)*

Minnesota Legal Services ....E... 651 228-9105
Saint Paul *(G-8695)*

Moss & Barnett, A Professional ....C... 612 877-5000
Minneapolis *(G-5135)*

Remele Bassford ....D... 612 333-3000
Minneapolis *(G-5515)*

Rienhardt & Anderson ....E... 651 227-9990
Saint Paul *(G-8900)*

Robins, Kaplan, Miller ....B... 612 349-8500
Minneapolis *(G-5555)*

Rust Consulting Inc ....C... 612 359-2000
Minneapolis *(G-5577)*

Svingen Hagstron Cline Karkela ....E... 218 739-4696
Fergus Falls *(G-2121)*

Talon Investigation Ltd ....E... 651 774-6977
Saint Paul *(G-9026)*

Three Rivers Community Action ....E... 507 732-7391
Zumbrota *(G-10220)*

3M Innovative Properties Co ....E... 651 733-8904
(G-9067)

LEGAL PROCESS SERVERS

Attorney's Process Service Ltd ....C... 952 831-7776
Minneapolis *(G-3833)*

Metro Legal Services Inc ....E... 651 291-0008
Saint Paul *(G-8641)*

LEGAL SVCS: Bankruptcy Law

Hoglund, Chwialkowski ....E... 651 628-9929
Saint Paul *(G-8491)*

LEGAL SVCS: Corporate, Partnership & Business Law

Knutson, Flynn, Deans ....E... 651 222-2811
Saint Paul *(G-7819)*

More Costello & Hart Pllp ....E... 651 227-7683
Saint Paul *(G-8720)*

LEGAL SVCS: Criminal Law

Administrative Office of The ....D... 612 664-5050
Minneapolis *(G-3680)*

Meshbesher & Spence Ltd ....E... 612 339-9121
Minneapolis *(G-4996)*

LEGAL SVCS: Environmental Law

Bowman & Brooke LLP ....C... 612 339-8682
Minneapolis *(G-3934)*

LEGAL SVCS: General Practice Attorney or Lawyer

Aafedt, Forde, Gray, & Monson ....E... 612 339-8965
Minneapolis *(G-3656)*

Anderson Dove Fretland & Van ....E... 952 545-9000
Minneapolis *(G-3776)*

Anthony Ostlund & Baer ....E... 612 349-6969
Minneapolis *(G-3783)*

Babcock, Neilson, Mannella, La ....E... 763 421-5151
Minneapolis *(G-3413)*

Borkon, Ramstead, Mariani ....E... 952 546-6000
Minneapolis *(G-3930)*

Briggs & Morgan Professional ....C... 651 223-6600
Minneapolis *(G-3947)*

Brown & Carlson ....E... 763 540-1019
Minneapolis *(G-3962)*

Chestnut & Cammbrone, Prof ....E... 612 339-7300
Minneapolis *(G-4061)*

Employment codes: A=Over 500 employees, B=251-500,
C=101-250, D=51-100, E=25-50

2011 Harris Minnesota
Services Directory

© Harris InfoSource 1-866-281-6415
725

SERVICES

City of Saint Paul ....E... 651 266-8740
Saint Paul *(G-8212)*

Collins, Buckley, Sauntry ....E... 651 227-0611
Saint Paul *(G-8225)*

County Attorney Office.........................E... 218 726-2323
Duluth *(G-1284)*

D C M Services LLC ....D... 612 332-3700
Minneapolis *(G-4212)*

Dunkley & Bennett ....E... 612 339-1290
Minneapolis *(G-4296)*

Dunlap & Seeger ....D... 507 288-9111
Rochester *(G-7100)*

Fafinski Mark & Johnson ....E... 952 995-9500
Eden Prairie *(G-1661)*

Felhaber Larson Fenlon & Vogt............D... 612 339-6321
Minneapolis *(G-4424)*

Foley & Mansfield LLP ....D... 612 338-8788
Minneapolis *(G-4460)*

Fulbright & Jaworski LLP ....E... 612 321-2800
Minneapolis *(G-4490)*

Goggins & Lavintman............................E... 651 209-1825
Saint Paul *(G-7785)*

Hanft, Fride, O'Brien ....E... 218 722-4766
Duluth *(G-1346)*

Hanson, Lulic & Krall ....E... 612 333-2530
Minneapolis *(G-4596)*

Hellmuth & Johnson PLLC....................D... 952 941-4005
Eden Prairie *(G-1682)*

Johnson & Condon ....D... 952 831-6544
Minneapolis *(G-4773)*

Kennedy & Graven Chartered ....D... 612 337-9300
Minneapolis *(G-4801)*

Kinney & Lange ....E... 612 339-1863
Minneapolis *(G-4810)*

Law Center Inc ....E... 218 736-5493
Fergus Falls *(G-2086)*

Legal Services Advocacy Proj...................... 651 222-3749
Saint Paul *(G-8575)*

Lind, Jensen, Sullivan ....E... 612 333-3637
Minneapolis *(G-4888)*

Maschka Riedy & Ries ....E... 507 625-6600
Mankato *(G-3168)*

Michael E Molenda ....E... 952 432-3136
Saint Paul *(G-7839)*

Milavetz, Gallop & Milavetz ....E... 612 339-0140
Minneapolis *(G-5040)*

Minnesota Disability Law Ctr ....E... 612 332-1441
Minneapolis *(G-5076)*

Monroe Krass ....D... 952 445-5080
Minneapolis *(G-5122)*

Office of General Council ....E... 612 624-4100
Minneapolis *(G-5266)*

Oppenheimer Wolff Donnelly LLP ....B... 612 607-7000
Minneapolis *(G-5287)*

Paige J Donnelly Ltd............................E... 651 222-2797
Saint Paul *(G-8801)*

Ratwik, Roszak, & Maloney ....E... 612 339-0060
Minneapolis *(G-5468)*

Schwebel, Goetz, & Sieben ....D... 612 333-8361
Minneapolis *(G-5617)*

Sieben, Grose, Von Holtum ....E... 612 333-4500
Minneapolis *(G-5664)*

Siegel, Brill, Greupner Duffy ....E... 612 339-7131
Minneapolis *(G-5665)*

Stephen M Knutson ....E... 651 225-0626
Saint Paul *(G-7912)*

Trenti Law Firm Inc ....E... 218 749-1962
Virginia *(G-9758)*

Votel, Anderson & McEachron ....E... 651 228-1770
Saint Paul *(G-9133)*

Wilkerson & Hegna ....E... 952 897-1707
Minneapolis *(G-6068)*

LEGAL SVCS: General Practice Law Office

Arthur, Chapman, Kettering ....D... 612 339-3500
Minneapolis *(G-3815)*

Barna Guzy & Steffen Ltd.....................D... 763 780-8500
Minneapolis *(G-3415)*

Bassford Remele ....D... 612 333-3000
Minneapolis *(G-3873)*

Best & Flanagan LLP ....C... 612 339-7121
Minneapolis *(G-3890)*

Brandt Murnane ....D... 651 227-9411
Saint Paul *(G-8121)*

Cousineau McGuire Chartered ....D... 952 546-8400
Minneapolis *(G-4173)*

Fabyanske, Westra, Hart ....D... 612 338-0115
Minneapolis *(G-4390)*

Felhaber Larson Fenlon & Vogt............D... 612 339-6321
Minneapolis *(G-4424)*

Fredrikson & Byron ....B... 612 492-7000
Minneapolis *(G-4484)*

Gray Plant Mooty Mooty ....B... 612 632-3000
Minneapolis *(G-4548)*

Greene Espel PLLP ....E... 612 373-0830
Minneapolis *(G-4563)*

Gunhus Grinnell Klinger ....E... 218 236-6462
Moorhead *(G-6317)*

Hansen Dordell Bradt Odlaug,..............D... 651 482-8900
Saint Paul *(G-8441)*

Henson & Efron ....D... 612 339-2500
Minneapolis *(G-4639)*

Hinshaw & Culbertson LLP ....E... 612 333-3434
Minneapolis *(G-4652)*

Hubert Melchert Sjodin Pllp ....E... 952 442-5155
Waconia *(G-9786)*

Kaplan, Strangis & Kaplan ....E... 612 375-1138
Minneapolis *(G-4789)*

Kelly & Berens ....E... 612 392-7032
Minneapolis *(G-4798)*

Knutson, Flynn, Deans ....E... 651 222-2811
Saint Paul *(G-7819)*

Larson King, LLP ....D... 651 312-6500
Saint Paul *(G-8564)*

Leonard, Street & Deinard ....B... 612 335-1500
Minneapolis *(G-4862)*

Lindquist & Vennum PLLP ....C... 612 371-3211
Minneapolis *(G-4890)*

Lockridge Grindal Nauen LLP ....D... 612 339-6900
Minneapolis *(G-4897)*

Mackall Crounse & Moore PLC ....D... 612 305-1400
Minneapolis *(G-4927)*

Mahoney, Dougherty & Mahoney..........E... 612 339-5863
Minneapolis *(G-4936)*

Mansfield & Tanick ....D... 612 339-4295
Minneapolis *(G-4944)*

McCollum, Crowley, Moschet ....D... 952 831-4980
Minneapolis *(G-4971)*

McGrann Shea Anderson Carnival ....E... 612 338-2525
Minneapolis *(G-4976)*

Meagher & Geer ....C... 612 338-0661
Minneapolis *(G-4981)*

Moore, Costello & Hart Pllp..................E... 651 602-2615
Saint Paul *(G-8719)*

Moore, Costello & Hart Pllp..................E... 612 673-0148
Minneapolis *(G-5125)*

P Kevin Hickey ....E... 612 376-1620
Minneapolis *(G-5305)*

Patterson, Thuente, Skaar....................D... 612 349-5764
Minneapolis *(G-5348)*

Peterson, Fram & Bergman, A ....E... 651 291-8955
Saint Paul *(G-8821)*

Quinlivan & Hughes ....D... 320 251-1414
Saint Cloud *(G-7578)*

Rajkowski Hansmeier Ltd ....E... 320 251-1055
Saint Cloud *(G-7581)*

Severson Sheldon Dougherty...............E... 952 432-3136
Saint Paul *(G-7901)*

Thomsen & Nybeck ....E... 952 835-7000
Edina *(G-1846)*

Walling & Berg ....E... 612 340-1150
Minneapolis *(G-6013)*

Zelle, Hofmann, Voelbel, Mason ....D... 612 339-2020
Minneapolis *(G-6114)*

Zimmerman Reed PLLP..........................E... 612 341-0400
Minneapolis *(G-6119)*

LEGAL SVCS: Immigration & Naturalization Law

Park Nicollet Clinic ....D... 952 993-9700
Minneapolis *(G-5330)*

LEGAL SVCS: Labor & Employment Law

Bowman & Brooke LLP ....C... 612 339-8682
Minneapolis *(G-3934)*

Erstat & Riemer ....E... 952 854-7638
Minneapolis *(G-4370)*

LEGAL SVCS: Patent, Trademark & Copyright Law

Dicke Billig & Czaja.............................E... 612 573-2000
Minneapolis *(G-4254)*

Patterson, Thuente, Skaar....................D... 612 349-5764
Minneapolis *(G-5348)*

LEGAL SVCS: Real Estate Law

Hamre Schumann Mueller Larson........E... 612 455-3800
Minneapolis *(G-4592)*

LEGAL SVCS: Specialized Law Offices, Attorney

A S K Financial LLP ....E... 651 406-9665
Saint Paul *(G-7685)*

Bowman & Brooke LLP ....C... 612 339-8682
Minneapolis *(G-3934)*

Heacox, Hartman, Mattaini ....E... 651 222-2922
Saint Paul *(G-8446)*

Kelly & Berens ....E... 612 392-7032
Minneapolis *(G-4798)*

Meshbesher & Spence Ltd....................E... 612 339-9121
Minneapolis *(G-4996)*

Meshbesher & Spence Ltd....................E... 320 656-0484
Saint Cloud *(G-7551)*

Mid Minnesota Legal Assistance ....C... 612 332-1441
Minneapolis *(G-5021)*

Rinke, Noonan, Grote, Smoley ....D... 320 251-6700
Saint Cloud *(G-7588)*

Yaeger, Jungbauer & Barczak ....D... 612 333-6371
Minneapolis *(G-6096)*

LEGITIMATE LIVE THEATER PRODUCERS

Chanhassen Theatre LLC ....C... 952 934-1500
Chanhassen *(G-913)*

Hey City Theater Co ....D... 612 333-9202
Minneapolis *(G-4643)*

Into The Mystic Productions ....E... 612 332-6620
Minneapolis *(G-4731)*

It's About Time Theater........................E... 507 280-8956
Rochester *(G-7144)*

National Theatre For Children ....D... 612 617-4903
Minneapolis *(G-5168)*

Paramount Theater ....E... 320 259-5463
Saint Cloud *(G-7565)*

LESSORS: Landholding Office

Kohner Realty Co Inc ....E... 507 454-5093
Winona *(G-10108)*

Robert A Williams Enterprises ....E... 763 788-1113
Minneapolis *(G-3589)*

LIABILITY INSURANCE

Arch Capital Services...........................E... 651 855-7111
Saint Paul *(G-8058)*

Midwest Medical Insurance Co ....D... 952 838-6700
Minneapolis *(G-5034)*

St Paul Fire & Marine Insce ....B... 651 310-5000
Saint Paul *(G-8989)*

St Paul Fire & Marine Insce ....A... 651 221-7911
Saint Paul *(G-8990)*

LIFE INSURANCE AGENTS

Catholic Aid Association ....E... 651 490-0170
Saint Paul *(G-8174)*

John B Collins Associates Inc ....C... 952 820-1000
Minneapolis *(G-4769)*

Lincoln Financial Advisors ....E... 952 933-8000
Hopkins *(G-2571)*

T C Field & Co......................................E... 651 227-8405
Saint Paul *(G-9022)*

Twin City Risk Group Inc ....E... 952 924-6900
Minneapolis *(G-5884)*

Unison Insurance ....E... 952 345-2305
Prior Lake *(G-6960)*

Wells Fargo Insurance Services ....C... 952 830-3000
Minneapolis *(G-6051)*

LIFE INSURANCE CARRIERS

Employers Mutual Casualty Co............E... 952 938-4646
Hopkins *(G-2539)*

Federated Mutual Insurance Co ....C... 507 455-5200
Owatonna *(G-6710)*

Federated Mutual Insurance Co ....A... 507 455-5200
Owatonna *(G-6711)*

Minnesota Mutual Co's Inc ....A... 651 665-3500
Saint Paul *(G-8699)*

New York Life Insurance Co ....E... 952 897-5000
Minneapolis *(G-5193)*

Primerica Financial Services................D... 651 290-9822
Saint Paul *(G-8847)*

Reliastar Life Insurance Co ....A... 612 372-5432
Minneapolis *(G-5507)*

LIFE INSURANCE: Fraternal Organizations

Sons of Norway ....E... 612 827-3611
Minneapolis *(G-5698)*

Sons of Norway Foundation ....E... 612 827-3611
Minneapolis *(G-5699)*

Thrivent Financial For ....A... 920 734-5721
Minneapolis *(G-5819)*

LIFE INSURANCE: Mutual Association

Rain & Hail Insurance Service..............E... 763 473-2421
Minneapolis *(G-5462)*

LIFEGUARD SVC

Dkg Management...................................E... 214 776-1155
Burnsville *(G-711)*

2011 Harris Minnesota
Services Directory

(G-00000) Company's Geographic Section entry number

LIGHTING FIXTURES WHOLESALERS

Creative Lighting.....................................E... 651 647-0111
Saint Paul (G-8265)

Lights On Broadway Inc ....E... 763 533-3366
Minneapolis (G-4885)

Southern Lighting Inc ....E... 952 890-8977
Burnsville (G-802)

LIGHTING MAINTENANCE SVC

Amtech Lighting Services Co ....E... 651 439-7440
Stillwater (G-9595)

Ermc II LP ....E... 952 435-8182
Burnsville (G-719)

LIMESTONE: Crushed & Broken

Northland Constructors of ....E... 218 722-8170
Duluth (G-1406)

LIMOUSINE SVCS

Dunn Enterprises Inc ....C... 612 627-5661
Minneapolis (G-4297)

Eclipse Transportation Inc.....................E... 651 293-1111
Saint Paul (G-7757)

Star Limousine Service ....E... 507 281-0969
Rochester (G-7263)

Taylor Limousines Inc ....C... 612 722-4467
Minneapolis (G-5795)

Total Transportation Corp.....................E... 651 770-5668
Saint Paul (G-9074)

Twin City Limousine ....C... 651 222-8553
Saint Paul (G-9093)

LINEN SPLY SVC

Ameripride Services Inc ....D... 952 738-4200
Hopkins (G-2510)

Ameripride Services Inc ....D... 320 251-2525
Saint Cloud (G-7448)

Ameripride Services Inc ....D... 507 345-1039
Mankato (G-3105)

Ameripride Services Inc ....E... 218 751-5150
Bemidji (G-374)

Ameripride Services Inc ....B... 612 331-1600
Minneapolis (G-3764)

Buffalo Drycleaners ....E... 763 682-1061
Buffalo (G-638)

Spruce Co ....E... 952 888-1639
Minneapolis (G-5723)

LINEN SPLY SVC: Apron

G&K Services Inc ....C... 952 912-5500
Minnetonka (G-6173)

G&K Services Inc ....C... 651 855-7000
Saint Paul (G-8398)

LINEN SPLY SVC: Towel

G&K Services Inc ....C... 952 912-5500
Minnetonka (G-6173)

G&K Services Inc ....C... 651 855-7000
Saint Paul (G-8398)

Spruce Co ....E... 952 888-1639
Minneapolis (G-5723)

LINEN SPLY SVC: Uniform

ARAMARK Uniform & Career.............C... 763 586-0020
Minneapolis (G-3408)

Cintas Corp ....E... 763 588-2701
Minneapolis (G-4077)

Cintas Corp No 2 ....C... 763 425-6666
Osseo (G-6603)

G & K Services Inc ....C... 320 252-9471
Saint Cloud (G-7515)

G&K Services Inc ....C... 612 521-4771
Minneapolis (G-4492)

G&K Services Inc ....C... 612 333-2225
Minneapolis (G-4493)

G&K Services Inc ....E... 507 451-5710
Owatonna (G-6716)

LIQUEFIED PETROLEUM GAS WHOLESALERS

Wilson Oil Co Inc 651 388-5783
Red Wing (G-7013)

LIQUIDATORS

1st National Repossessioncom............E... 763 241-5212
Elk River (G-1874)

LIVESTOCK BREEDING & PRODUCTION

Minnesota Select Sires Co-Op ....E... 320 259-6680
Saint Cloud (G-7560)

LIVESTOCK WHOLESALERS, NEC

Northstar Ethanol LLC ....E... 507 726-2645
Lake Crystal (G-2863)

O & S Cattle Co ....E... 651 455-1102
South Saint Paul (G-9536)

Pipestone Livestock Auction ....E... 507 825-3306
Pipestone (G-6835)

LOAN CORRESPONDENTS

Green Tree Servicing LLC ....E... 651 293-4800
Saint Paul (G-8433)

LOBBYING SVCS

Clean Water Action Inc ....C... 612 623-3666
Minneapolis (G-4105)

League of Minnesota Cities ....D... 651 281-1200
Saint Paul (G-8573)

LOCKS & LOCK SETS, WHOLESALE

Stanley Security Solutions Inc ....E... 952 894-3830
Saint Paul (G-9004)

Twin City Hardware Co ....E... 763 535-4660
Minneapolis (G-5881)

LOCKSMITHS

Armor Security Inc ....E... 612 870-1572
Minneapolis (G-3809)

LOGS, HEWN TIES, POSTS & POLES, WHOLESALE

Bell Lumber & Pole Co ....E... 651 633-4334
Saint Paul (G-8098)

LUBRICATING OIL & GREASE WHOLESALERS

Best Oil Co ....E... 218 879-4666
Cloquet (G-1046)

Egan Oil Co LLC ....E... 763 421-0410
Anoka (G-176)

Lubrication Technologies Inc ....D... 763 545-0707
Minneapolis (G-4908)

Lubrication Technologies Inc ....D... 651 636-7990
Saint Paul (G-8596)

Yocum Oil Co Inc ....C... 651 739-9141
Saint Paul (G-9179)

LUMBER, PLYWOOD & MILLWORK WHOLESALERS

Bruce Kreofsky & Sons Inc ....D... 507 534-3855
Plainview (G-6839)

Construction Midwest Inc ....E... 763 536-8336
Minneapolis (G-4156)

Contract Hardware Co Inc ....E... 651 780-0010
Circle Pines (G-1007)

Forest Weekes Products Inc.................D... 651 644-9807
Saint Paul (G-8388)

Heritage Millwork Inc ....E... 763 323-7501
Anoka (G-190)

Lake States Lumber Inc ....E... 763 425-0204
Brooklyn Park (G-613)

Manion Lumber & Truss Inc.................E... 218 746-3200
Pillager (G-6811)

Menard Inc ....C... 218 722-0078
Duluth (G-1390)

Menard Inc ....C... 952 941-4400
Eden Prairie (G-1719)

Minnesota Vinyl & Aluminum ....E... 952 403-0805
Shakopee (G-9457)

N A H Inc ....E... 507 462-3331
Minnesota Lake (G-6137)

Northland Hardwood Lumber Co ....E... 218 751-0550
Bemidji (G-414)

Pine Point Wood Products Inc..............E... 763 428-4301
Osseo (G-6653)

Probuild Co LLC.................................D... 218 631-2607
Wadena (G-9810)

Probuild Co LLC.................................D... 320 251-0861
Saint Cloud (G-7573)

Probuild Co LLC.................................E... 952 469-2116
Lakeville (G-2925)

Remodeler's Choice Inc ....E... 612 767-7000
Minneapolis (G-5516)

Rice Lake Lumber Inc..........................E... 218 727-3213
Duluth (G-1437)

Root River Hardwoods Inc...................E... 507 765-2284
Preston (G-6900)

Scherer Bros Lumber Co ....E... 612 379-9633
Minneapolis (G-5608)

Shaw Lumber Co ....C... 651 488-2525
Minneapolis (G-5651)

Twin City Custom Railings & GL.........E... 763 780-7314
Minneapolis (G-3624)

USG Interiors Inc ....E... 952 853-1233
Minneapolis (G-5951)

USG Interiors Inc ....B... 218 878-4000
Cloquet (G-1068)

Weyerhaeuser Co ....E... 651 645-0811
Saint Paul (G-9152)

Weyerhaeuser Co ....C... 218 546-8114
Deerwood (G-1180)

Youngblood Lumber Co ....E... 612 789-3521
Minneapolis (G-6106)

MACHINERY & EQPT FINANCE LEASING

Geneva Capital LLC ....E... 320 762-8400
Alexandria (G-102)

Toro Credit Co ....E... 952 888-8801
Minneapolis (G-5831)

Wells Fargo Equipment Finance ....C... 612 667-9876
Minneapolis (G-6044)

MACHINERY & EQPT, AGRICULTURAL, WHOL: Farm Eqpt Parts/Splys

Kibble Equipment Inc ....D... 320 269-6466
Montevideo (G-6248)

Mies Equipment Inc ....E... 320 764-5310
Watkins (G-9898)

RDO Construction Equipment Co........D... 952 890-8880
Burnsville (G-784)

Smith's Mill Implement Inc ....E... 507 234-5191
Janesville (G-2803)

Woods Equipment Co ....D... 651 455-6681
Saint Paul (G-9166)

MACHINERY & EQPT, AGRICULTURAL, WHOL: Grain Elev Eqpt/Splys

Thorstad Construction Co Inc ....E... 320 367-2159
Maynard (G-3337)

MACHINERY & EQPT, AGRICULTURAL, WHOL: Poultry/Livestock Eqpt

Pals Inc ....E... 320 235-8860
Willmar (G-10036)

MACHINERY & EQPT, AGRICULTURAL, WHOLESALE: Agricultural, NEC

AG Systems Inc ....E... 320 587-4030
Hutchinson (G-2684)

MACHINERY & EQPT, AGRICULTURAL, WHOLESALE: Dairy

Genex Farm Systems 952 758-2561
New Prague (G-6428)

Stearns Veterinary Outlet ....E... 320 256-3303
Melrose (G-3353)

MACHINERY & EQPT, AGRICULTURAL, WHOLESALE: Farm Implements

Kibble Equipment Inc ....D... 320 269-6466
Montevideo (G-6248)

Kibble Equipment Inc ....E... 507 644-3571
Redwood Falls (G-7022)

Lodermeiers ....D... 651 923-4441
Goodhue (G-2250)

Mies Equipment Inc ....E... 320 764-5310
Watkins (G-9898)

Miller Sellner Equipment Inc ....E... 507 831-1106
Bingham Lake (G-467)

Miller Sellner Implement Inc ....E... 507 794-2131
Sleepy Eye (G-9498)

Titan Machinery Inc ....E... 218 281-4668
Crookston (G-1137)

Titan Machinery Inc ....E... 218 681-1423
Thief River Falls (G-9680)

MACHINERY & EQPT, AGRICULTURAL, WHOLESALE: Garden, NEC

Hance Distributing Inc ....E... 952 935-6429
Hopkins (G-2548)

S & S Sales Inc...................................763 476-9599
Minneapolis (G-5581)

Employment codes: A=Over 500 employees, B=251-500,
C=101-250, D=51-100, E=25-50

2011 Harris Minnesota
Services Directory

© Harris InfoSource 1-866-281-6415
727

S E R V I C E S

MACHINERY & EQPT, AGRICULTURAL, WHOLESALE: Landscaping Eqpt

Hedberg Aggregates Inc ....D... 763 545-4400
Minneapolis (G-4627)

Pinehurst Development Inc..................E... 952 469-3202
Farmington (G-2057)

Sylva Corp Inc ....E... 763 389-2748
Princeton (G-6917)

MACHINERY & EQPT, AGRICULTURAL, WHOLESALE: Lawn

Hance Distributing Inc ....E... 952 935-6429
Hopkins (G-2548)

S & S Sales Inc 763 476-9599
Minneapolis (G-5581)

MACHINERY & EQPT, AGRICULTURAL, WHOLESALE: Lawn & Garden

Haug Implement Co ....E... 320 235-8115
Willmar (G-10006)

Toro LLC ....A... 952 888-8801
Minneapolis (G-5832)

MACHINERY & EQPT, AGRICULTURAL, WHOLESALE: Livestock Eqpt

Pals Inc ....D... 320 235-8860
Willmar (G-10035)

Tandem Products Inc ....D... 507 583-7222
Blooming Prairie (G-479)

MACHINERY & EQPT, AGRICULTURAL, WHOLESALE: Poultry Eqpt

Miller Manufacturing Co Inc ....D... 320 864-4039
Glencoe (G-2209)

Pals Inc ....D... 320 235-8860
Willmar (G-10035)

MACHINERY & EQPT, INDL, WHOL: Controlling Instruments/Access

Applied Products Inc ....E... 952 933-2224
Minnetonka (G-6142)

Environmental Control Systems ....E... 218 863-1766
Pelican Rapids (G-6777)

Novaspect Inc.......................................E... 952 934-5100
Eden Prairie (G-1733)

Siemens Industry Inc ....D... 651 631-8533
Saint Paul (G-8955)

Swanson-Flosystems Co ....E... 763 383-4700
Plymouth (G-6885)

MACHINERY & EQPT, INDL, WHOL: Environ Pollution Cntrl, Air

Boedecker Co.......................................E... 952 279-5205
Chanhassen (G-910)

Design Ready Controls Inc ....D... 763 565-3000
Rockford (G-7309)

MACHINERY & EQPT, INDL, WHOL: Environ Pollution Cntrl, Water

Boedecker Co.......................................E... 952 279-5205
Chanhassen (G-910)

Design Ready Controls Inc ....D... 763 565-3000
Rockford (G-7309)

MACHINERY & EQPT, INDL, WHOLESALE: Chainsaws

Tilton Equipment Co ....D... 763 783-7030
Lindstrom (G-2971)

MACHINERY & EQPT, INDL, WHOLESALE: Conveyor Systems

Boedecker Co.......................................E... 952 279-5205
Chanhassen (G-910)

MACHINERY & EQPT, INDL, WHOLESALE: Engines & Parts, Diesel

Ziegler Inc ....A... 952 888-4121
Minneapolis (G-6117)

MACHINERY & EQPT, INDL, WHOLESALE: Engines, Gasoline

Great Northern Equipment Dstbg.......E... 763 428-9405
Rogers (G-7326)

Jerry's Enterprises Inc ....E... 952 929-4601
Minneapolis (G-4761)

MACHINERY & EQPT, INDL, WHOLESALE: Engs & Parts, Air-Cooled

Central Power Distributors Inc ....E... 763 576-0901
Anoka (G-164)

MACHINERY & EQPT, INDL, WHOLESALE: Engs/Transportation Eqpt

Interstate Power Systems ....D... 952 854-5511
Minneapolis (G-4729)

Interstate Power Systems Inc ....D... 952 854-5511
Minneapolis (G-3502)

MACHINERY & EQPT, INDL, WHOLESALE: Food Manufacturing

5 K Enterprises Inc ....E... 612 216-6292
Mankato (G-3127)

MACHINERY & EQPT, INDL, WHOLESALE: Food Product Manufacturng

Aldin Export & Import...............................651 483-4184
Saint Paul (G-8007)

MACHINERY & EQPT, INDL, WHOLESALE: Hoists

Crysteel Truck Equipment Inc ....E... 507 726-6041
Lake Crystal (G-2857)

MACHINERY & EQPT, INDL, WHOLESALE: Hydraulic Systems

Applied Products Inc ....E... 952 933-2224
Minnetonka (G-6142)

Eaton Corp...B... 952 937-9800
Eden Prairie (G-1648)

Force America Inc ....E... 952 707-1300
Burnsville (G-722)

Greenlee Textron Inc ....D... 507 238-4357
Fairmont (G-1969)

Hartfiel Co ....D... 952 974-2500
Eden Prairie (G-1679)

Hydraulic Specialty Co Inc ....E... 763 571-3072
Minneapolis (G-3494)

Oil-Air Products LLC ....E... 763 478-8744
Hamel (G-2353)

SMI & Hydraulics Inc ....E... 507 296-4551
Porter (G-6894)

STS Operating Inc ....D... 952 563-1700
Savage (G-9409)

STS Operating Inc ....E... 320 564-3057
Granite Falls (G-2320)

MACHINERY & EQPT, INDL, WHOLESALE: Indl Machine Parts

Harriston-Mayo LLC.............................E... 218 773-1234
East Grand Forks (G-1568)

MACHINERY & EQPT, INDL, WHOLESALE: Instruments & Cntrl Eqpt

Palen Kimball LLC ....E... 651 646-2800
Saint Paul (G-8804)

Productivity Quality Inc........................E... 763 249-8130
Minneapolis (G-5418)

Schneiberg Co... 651 489-7489
Saint Paul (G-8934)

Swanson-Flosystems Co ....E... 763 383-4700
Plymouth (G-6885)

MACHINERY & EQPT, INDL, WHOLESALE: Lift Trucks & Parts

Bennett Material Handling Inc ....E... 952 933-5544
Hopkins (G-2517)

Herc-U-Lift Inc ....D... 763 479-2501
Maple Plain (G-3277)

Yale Materials Handling - MN ....D... 763 434-3832
Anoka (G-241)

MACHINERY & EQPT, INDL, WHOLESALE: Machine Tools & Access

Hegman Machine Tool Inc....................E... 763 424-5622
Osseo (G-6620)

Machine Tool Supply Corp....................E... 651 452-4400
Saint Paul (G-7829)

Productivity Inc ....D... 763 476-8600
Minneapolis (G-5417)

MACHINERY & EQPT, INDL, WHOLESALE: Measure/Test, Electric

Cable Connection & Supply Co............E... 507 334-6417
Faribault (G-1995)

Cannon Technologies Inc......................E... 763 595-7777
Minneapolis (G-3999)

Northstar Imaging Inc ....E... 763 463-5650
Rogers (G-7333)

MACHINERY & EQPT, INDL, WHOLESALE: Metal Refining

Melrose Metalworks Inc ....E... 320 256-4170
Melrose (G-3350)

MACHINERY & EQPT, INDL, WHOLESALE: Milk Prdts Manufacturing

Aldin Export & Import...............................651 483-4184
Saint Paul (G-8007)

MACHINERY & EQPT, INDL, WHOLESALE: Packaging

Delkor Systems Inc ....D... 763 783-0855
Circle Pines (G-1010)

J A Swenson & Assoc Inc.....................E... 952 469-3585
Lakeville (G-2912)

Packaging Systems Automation ....E... 763 473-1032
Minneapolis (G-5312)

Rapid Packaging Inc ....E... 763 404-8900
Champlin (G-899)

MACHINERY & EQPT, INDL, WHOLESALE: Paint Spray

Midway Industrial Supply Co................E... 763 780-3000
Saint Paul (G-8655)

MACHINERY & EQPT, INDL, WHOLESALE: Plastic Prdts Machinery

BASF Corp ....E... 763 559-3266
Minneapolis (G-3870)

Midway Industrial Supply Co................E... 763 780-3000
Saint Paul (G-8655)

MACHINERY & EQPT, INDL, WHOLESALE: Pneumatic Tools

American Air Products Inc ....E... 651 290-0000
Saint Paul (G-8020)

Applied Products Inc............................E... 952 933-2224
Minnetonka (G-6142)

Automation Fluid Power Inc ....E... 763 571-3336
Minneapolis (G-3839)

John Henry Foster Minnesota ....D... 651 452-8452
Saint Paul (G-7810)

Mars, W P & R S Co Inc........................E... 952 884-9388
Minneapolis (G-4956)

MACHINERY & EQPT, INDL, WHOLESALE: Power Plant Machinery

Hartfiel Co ....D... 952 974-2500
Eden Prairie (G-1679)

MACHINERY & EQPT, INDL, WHOLESALE: Processing & Packaging

Gateway Building Systems Inc ....E... 218 236-9336
Moorhead (G-6316)

Smyth Co's Inc......................................E... 651 646-4544
Saint Paul (G-8967)

Vac System Industries of MN ....E... 952 808-1616
Burnsville (G-816)

MACHINERY & EQPT, INDL, WHOLESALE: Recycling

Excel Manufacturing Inc ....E... 507 932-4680
Saint Charles (G-7401)

MACHINERY & EQPT, INDL, WHOLESALE: Safety Eqpt

Midway Industrial Supply Co................E... 763 780-3000
Saint Paul (G-8655)

Safety Signs Inc...................................E... 952 469-6700
Lakeville (G-2930)

MACHINERY & EQPT, INDL, WHOLESALE: Water Pumps

G P Co's Inc ....D... 651 454-6500
Mendota Heights (G-3363)

2011 Harris Minnesota
Services Directory

(G-00000) Company's Geographic Section entry number

MACHINERY & EQPT, WHOLESALE: Concrete Processing

Engineered Concrete Placer of.............E... 651 452-1183
Saint Paul *(G-7763)*

MACHINERY & EQPT, WHOLESALE: Construction, Cranes

Advance Equipment Co........................E... 651 489-8881
Saint Paul *(G-7987)*
Hawk & Sons Inc ....E... 507 285-0508
Rochester *(G-7134)*

MACHINERY & EQPT, WHOLESALE: Construction, General

Advance Equipment Co........................E... 651 489-8881
Saint Paul *(G-7987)*
Advance Shoring Co............................E... 651 489-8881
Saint Paul *(G-7988)*
Carlson Tractor & Equipment Co ....E... 651 423-2222
Rosemount *(G-7364)*
Hayden-Murphy Equipment Co ....E... 952 884-2301
Minneapolis *(G-4612)*
Phillippi Equipment Co.........................E... 651 406-4900
Saint Paul *(G-7875)*
Pinnacle Technologies Inc ....E... 651 735-3239
Saint Paul *(G-9262)*
Plymouth Industries Inc ....D... 763 553-1935
Minneapolis *(G-5393)*
RDO Construction Equipment Co ....D... 952 890-8880
Burnsville *(G-784)*
Road Machinery & Supplies Co............D... 952 895-9595
Savage *(G-9405)*
St Joseph Equipment Inc ....E... 952 445-5400
Shakopee *(G-9478)*
Sweeney Brothers Tractor Co ....E... 952 894-9595
Burnsville *(G-805)*
Tri State Machinery Co ....E... 952 224-1500
Burnsville *(G-812)*

MACHINERY & EQPT, WHOLESALE: Construction, Tractors

Ziegler Inc ....A... 952 888-4121
Minneapolis *(G-6117)*

MACHINERY & EQPT, WHOLESALE: Contractors Materials

Nortrax Equipment Co SE ....E... 218 759-1996
Bemidji *(G-415)*
Rdo Construction Equipment Co ....E... 218 282-8440
Moorhead *(G-6334)*

MACHINERY & EQPT, WHOLESALE: Front End Loaders

Ziegler Inc ....A... 952 888-4121
Minneapolis *(G-6117)*

MACHINERY & EQPT, WHOLESALE: Logging

Road Machinery & Supplies Co............D... 952 895-9595
Savage *(G-9405)*

MACHINERY & EQPT, WHOLESALE: Masonry

Advance Specialties Co ....E... 651 489-8881
Saint Paul *(G-7989)*

MACHINERY & EQPT, WHOLESALE: Road Construction & Maintenance

Macqueen Equipment Inc......................E... 651 645-5726
Saint Paul *(G-8605)*
Ziegler Inc ....E... 507 532-4403
Marshall *(G-3336)*

MAGAZINES, WHOLESALE

Arabian Horse Times Inc ....E... 800 248-4637
Waseca *(G-9873)*
Gopher News Co ....D... 763 546-5300
Minneapolis *(G-4542)*
Valley News Co ....D... 507 345-4819
Mankato *(G-3212)*

MAILING LIST: Brokers

Paradysz Matera Co Inc.......................D... 952 544-5121
Minneapolis *(G-5320)*

MAILING LIST: Management

Gage Group LLC ....C... 763 595-3920
Minneapolis *(G-4495)*

Novus Marketing Inc ....E... 612 252-1618
Minneapolis *(G-5250)*

MAILING MACHINES WHOLESALERS

Streamfeeder LLC ....D... 763 502-0000
Minneapolis *(G-3610)*

MAILING SVCS, NEC

Air Park Dt & H ....E... 218 723-4631
Duluth *(G-1234)*
Aria Communications Corp ....C... 320 259-5206
Saint Cloud *(G-7453)*
Automated Mailing Corp ....D... 612 333-4477
Minneapolis *(G-3837)*
Capitol Co's Inc ....D... 651 454-4511
Saint Paul *(G-7726)*
Denison Mailing Service Inc ....E... 952 888-1460
Minneapolis *(G-4247)*
Fulfillment Systems Inc ....D... 763 295-3400
Monticello *(G-6272)*
Fulfillment Systems Inc ....D... 320 255-0800
Saint Cloud *(G-7514)*
Gage Group LLC ....C... 763 595-3920
Minneapolis *(G-4495)*
Harco Marketing Group Inc...................... 952 432-6900
Saint Paul *(G-7795)*
Japs-Olson Co.....................................A... 952 932-9393
Minneapolis *(G-4754)*
Mail Handling Inc ....C... 952 975-5000
Eden Prairie *(G-1714)*
Mercury Mailers Of Minnesota ....E... 763 544-1881
Minneapolis *(G-4990)*
Promotion Management Center............D... 651 462-1213
Stacy *(G-9580)*
Rebs Supply Inc ....E... 952 942-5457
Eden Prairie *(G-1758)*
Reinking Enterprises Inc ....D... 763 428-1430
Rogers *(G-7340)*
Scicom Data Services Ltd ....C... 952 933-4200
Minnetonka *(G-6225)*
United Business Mail Inc......................D... 612 782-2044
Minneapolis *(G-5907)*
World Distribution Services ....D... 651 686-9252
Saint Paul *(G-7950)*

MANAGEMENT CONSULTING SVCS: Administrative

Benesyst Inc ....E... 612 746-3100
Minneapolis *(G-3884)*
Family Health Services of MN ....E... 651 772-2077
Saint Paul *(G-8366)*
Life-Science Innovations LLC...............E... 320 222-9750
Willmar *(G-10019)*
Marshall-Teichert Group Ltd ....D... 952 942-0564
Hopkins *(G-2577)*

MANAGEMENT CONSULTING SVCS: Automation & Robotics

E & C Amec Services Inc......................D... 612 332-8326
Minneapolis *(G-4299)*
Par Systems Inc ....B... 651 484-7261
Saint Paul *(G-8806)*

MANAGEMENT CONSULTING SVCS: Banking & Finance

Caritas Debt Counseling ....D... 320 650-1660
Saint Cloud *(G-7471)*
CFC Technology Corp ....E... 763 235-5300
Minneapolis *(G-4053)*

MANAGEMENT CONSULTING SVCS: Business

Aldin Export & Import..................................... 651 483-4184
Saint Paul *(G-8007)*
Elenas Care Inc ....D... 651 482-0549
Saint Paul *(G-8332)*
Ernst & Young LLP ....B... 612 343-1000
Minneapolis *(G-4367)*
J Thomas & Associates............................... 218 829-6622
Baxter *(G-331)*
Marcus Solutions LLC ....E... 952 373-4038
Edina *(G-1836)*
Preferredone Administrative.................B... 763 847-3525
Minneapolis *(G-5401)*
Southwest Casino & Hotel Corp...........E... 952 853-9990
Minneapolis *(G-5713)*
Trissential ....D... 952 595-7970
Hopkins *(G-2647)*

MANAGEMENT CONSULTING SVCS: Business Planning & Organizing

Ardel Inc ....E... 763 545-1919
Minneapolis *(G-3804)*
Associated Eye Care Ltd ....E... 651 275-3013
Stillwater *(G-9599)*
H & J Bliss Enterprises ....E... 952 988-9302
Minneapolis *(G-4584)*
Hire A Host Inc....................................D... 952 346-8800
Minneapolis *(G-4653)*
Retail Support Inc ....E... 952 934-1317
Eden Prairie *(G-1763)*

MANAGEMENT CONSULTING SVCS: Compensation & Benefits Planning

Accord Benefit Resources Inc ....E... 763 746-9004
Minneapolis *(G-3669)*
Burchfield Group Inc............................E... 651 389-5648
Saint Paul *(G-7724)*
Midland Corporate Benefit Svcs 320 485-3821
Winsted *(G-10163)*
Minnesota Counties Insurance ....E... 651 209-6400
Saint Paul *(G-8679)*
Sheffield, Olson & McQueen Inc ....E... 651 695-2500
(G-8951)
Synergetic Solutions Inc......................E... 763 331-3300
Minneapolis *(G-3613)*
Towers Watson Delaware Inc ....C... 952 842-7000
Minneapolis *(G-5839)*

MANAGEMENT CONSULTING SVCS: Construction Project

Bossardt Corp......................................E... 952 837-3346
Minneapolis *(G-3932)*
Construction Coordinators Inc ....E... 612 332-2020
Minneapolis *(G-4155)*
Shea Inc ....E... 612 339-2257
Minneapolis *(G-5652)*
Uni-Systems LLC.................................E... 763 536-1407
Minneapolis *(G-5901)*

MANAGEMENT CONSULTING SVCS: Corporate Objectives & Policies

Larsonallen LLP...................................B... 612 376-4500
Minneapolis *(G-4848)*
Marshall-Teichert Group Ltd ....D... 952 942-0564
Hopkins *(G-2577)*

MANAGEMENT CONSULTING SVCS: Corporation Organizing

Metrisource Inc ....E... 651 686-0097
Saint Paul *(G-7838)*

MANAGEMENT CONSULTING SVCS: Food & Beverage

Food Perspectives Inc ....E... 763 553-7787
Minneapolis *(G-4463)*
Happy Chef Systems Inc.......................E... 507 345-4571
Mankato *(G-3134)*
Hormel Foods International...................D... 507 437-5611
Austin *(G-277)*

MANAGEMENT CONSULTING SVCS: Foreign Trade

American-Russian Trade Inc ....D... 612 922-1163
Minneapolis *(G-3762)*
Prisma International Inc ....E... 612 338-1500
Minneapolis *(G-5412)*

MANAGEMENT CONSULTING SVCS: General

Sadaka Technology Consultants ....A... 952 841-6363
Minneapolis *(G-5586)*
Seabury Group L L C ....E... 612 399-0033
Minneapolis *(G-5621)*
Ske Support Services Inc ....E... 651 639-6559
Saint Paul *(G-8962)*
Talent Technical Services Inc ....C... 952 417-3600
Minneapolis *(G-5786)*

MANAGEMENT CONSULTING SVCS: Hospital & Health

Associated Anesthesiologists ....C... 651 735-0501
Minneapolis *(G-3822)*
Diversified Consulting Assocs..............E... 651 436-1330
Stillwater *(G-9610)*
Lutheran Brethren Homes Inc ....C... 218 736-5441
Fergus Falls *(G-2087)*

Employment codes: A=Over 500 employees, B=251-500,
C=101-250, D=51-100, E=25-50

2011 Harris Minnesota
Services Directory

© Harris InfoSource 1-866-281-6415
729

SERVICES

Medical Learning Inc ....E... 651 292-3432
Saint Paul *(G-8630)*

Pathway Health Services Inc ....D... 651 407-8699
Saint Paul *(G-8809)*

Towers Watson Pennsylvania Inc ....E... 952 842-5600
Minneapolis *(G-5840)*

VHA Upper Midwest Inc ....E... 952 837-4700
Minneapolis *(G-5967)*

MANAGEMENT CONSULTING SVCS: Incentive Or Award Program

Advantage Travel & Incentives ....D... 952 447-1333
Savage *(G-9382)*

Capitol Sales Co Inc ....E... 651 688-6830
Saint Paul *(G-7727)*

E-Group Inc ....E... 612 339-4777
Minneapolis *(G-4304)*

Motivaction LLC ....D... 763 412-3000
Minneapolis *(G-5137)*

Performark Inc ....C... 952 946-7300
Minnetonka *(G-6210)*

Schoeneckers Inc ....A... 952 835-4800
Edina *(G-1844)*

2020 Promotions LLC ....E... 651 451-3850
South Saint Paul *(G-9545)*

MANAGEMENT CONSULTING SVCS: Industrial

Analog Technologies, Corp ....E... 952 894-9228
Burnsville *(G-677)*

United States Compliance Corp ....E... 952 252-3000
Minnetonka *(G-6231)*

MANAGEMENT CONSULTING SVCS: Industrial Hygiene

Aecom Technical Services Inc ....E... 763 551-1001
Minneapolis *(G-3691)*

Braun Intertec Corp ....C... 952 995-2000
Minneapolis *(G-3938)*

Braun Intertec Corp ....E... 651 487-3245
Saint Paul *(G-8122)*

MANAGEMENT CONSULTING SVCS: Industry Specialist

Bossardt Corp ....E... 952 837-3346
Minneapolis *(G-3932)*

Cartika Medical Inc ....E... 763 545-5188
Minneapolis *(G-4022)*

CMI Equipment & Engineering Co ......E... 320 864-5894
Glencoe *(G-2218)*

Geo-Comm Inc ....D... 320 240-0040
Saint Cloud *(G-7517)*

Hanson McFarland Inc ....D... 763 421-9554
Anoka *(G-188)*

MANAGEMENT CONSULTING SVCS: Information Systems

Ernst & Young LLP ....B... 612 343-1000
Minneapolis *(G-4367)*

SafeNet Consulting Inc ....D... 952 930-3636
Minnetonka *(G-6224)*

Towers Watson Pennsylvania Inc ....E... 952 842-5600
Minneapolis *(G-5840)*

MANAGEMENT CONSULTING SVCS: Labor & Union Relations

Minnesota Pipe Trades Assn 651 291-8151
Saint Paul *(G-8701)*

MANAGEMENT CONSULTING SVCS: Manufacturing

Richard F Tschida ....E... 651 426-7958
Saint Paul *(G-8898)*

MANAGEMENT CONSULTING SVCS: Merchandising

Infinity Direct Inc ....E... 763 559-1111
Minneapolis *(G-4701)*

Insignia Systems Inc ....D... 763 392-6200
Minneapolis *(G-4706)*

Lawrence Service Co ....E... 763 383-5700
Minneapolis *(G-4850)*

Magiccom Inc ....E... 763 529-2208
Minneapolis *(G-4934)*

MANAGEMENT CONSULTING SVCS: New Products & Svcs

D M I LLC ....D... 952 841-6200
Minneapolis *(G-4215)*

Healthia Consulting Inc ....D... 763 923-7900
Minneapolis *(G-4620)*

Healthsense Inc ....E... 952 400-7300
Mendota Heights *(G-3364)*

MANAGEMENT CONSULTING SVCS: Planning

All Time Favorites Inc ....E... 651 454-1124
Saint Paul *(G-7690)*

City of Bloomington ....B... 952 563-8920
Minneapolis *(G-4083)*

Larsonallen LLP ....B... 612 376-4500
Minneapolis *(G-4848)*

MANAGEMENT CONSULTING SVCS: Programmed Instruction

Wilson Learning Corp ....D... 952 944-2880
Minneapolis *(G-6075)*

MANAGEMENT CONSULTING SVCS: Public Utilities

City of Grand Rapids ....E... 218 326-7024
Grand Rapids *(G-2274)*

MANAGEMENT CONSULTING SVCS: Quality Assurance

Ecosure ....E... 651 293-4320
Saint Paul *(G-8321)*

Faithful & Gould Inc ....E... 612 338-3120
Minneapolis *(G-4404)*

Marshall-Teichert Group Ltd ....D... 952 942-0564
Hopkins *(G-2577)*

MANAGEMENT CONSULTING SVCS: Real Estate

All England Enterprises Ltd 612 332-8011
Minneapolis *(G-3708)*

Bjorklund Realty Inc ....D... 952 934-0500
Edina *(G-1826)*

Cassidy Turley Midwest Inc ....D... 612 341-4444
Minneapolis *(G-4026)*

Coldwell Banker Burnet Inc ....D... 952 920-1224
Eden Prairie *(G-1630)*

Coldwell Banker Burnet Inc ....D... 952 474-2525
Excelsior *(G-1942)*

Colliers Towle Valuation 612 347-9336
Minneapolis *(G-4120)*

Maxfield Research Inc 612 338-2828
Minneapolis *(G-4967)*

Tena Co's Inc ....C... 651 293-1234
Saint Paul *(G-9037)*

Trustee Group LLP ....E... 952 473-5650
Wayzata *(G-9946)*

MANAGEMENT CONSULTING SVCS: Restaurant & Food

A'Viands LLC ....A... 651 631-0940
Saint Paul *(G-7969)*

Bestmark Inc ....C... 952 922-2205
Minnetonka *(G-6148)*

Donmar Inc ....E... 763 631-2233
Princeton *(G-6921)*

MANAGEMENT CONSULTING SVCS: School, College & University

Regents of The University of ....C... 612 625-4665
Minneapolis *(G-5486)*

MANAGEMENT CONSULTING SVCS: Site Location

Gopher State One Call Inc ....D... 651 454-8388
Saint Paul *(G-7788)*

MANAGEMENT CONSULTING SVCS: Training & Development

Creative Training Techniques ....E... 952 829-1954
Eden Prairie *(G-1637)*

Peak Performers Network ....E... 952 345-3333
Minneapolis *(G-5359)*

Police Range ....E... 218 751-7641
Bemidji *(G-421)*

Radisson Hotels International ....C... 763 212-5000
Minnetonka *(G-6218)*

Schoeneckers Inc ....A... 952 835-4800
Edina *(G-1844)*

Total Training Network Inc ....E... 952 345-5555
Minneapolis *(G-5837)*

MANAGEMENT CONSULTING SVCS: Transportation

Rubenstein Logistics Services ....E... 763 542-1121
Golden Valley *(G-2244)*

SAV Enterprises Inc ....E... 763 278-3340
Minneapolis *(G-3596)*

Transway Express Inc ....E... 651 686-7000
Northfield *(G-6544)*

MANAGEMENT SERVICES

A T & T Corp ....B... 612 376-5401
Minneapolis *(G-3649)*

Best Vendors Management Inc ....C... 763 287-7200
Minneapolis *(G-3892)*

Bioscrip Pharmacy Inc ....C... 952 979-3600
Eden Prairie *(G-1606)*

Bnsf Railway Co ....C... 651 298-2121
Saint Paul *(G-8116)*

Bremer Financial Services Inc ....D... 651 227-7621
Saint Paul *(G-8126)*

Bremer Financial Services Inc ....C... 651 734-4040
Lake Elmo *(G-2866)*

Central Group Management Co ....B... 320 654-6307
Saint Cloud *(G-7482)*

City of Saint Paul ....D... 651 266-6789
Saint Paul *(G-8208)*

Diversified Pharmaceutical 952 820-7000
Minneapolis *(G-4263)*

Dnk Management Inc ....C... 651 773-8077
Saint Paul *(G-8305)*

Ebenezer Society ....C... 612 879-2262
Minneapolis *(G-4309)*

Ebenezer Society ....C... 612 879-1400
Minneapolis *(G-4310)*

Ebenezer Society ....D... 952 435-8116
Burnsville *(G-716)*

Energy Management Steam ....E... 612 626-7329
Minneapolis *(G-4357)*

Entegris Inc ....C... 952 556-3131
Chaska *(G-965)*

Expresspoint Technology Svcs ....C... 763 543-6000
Golden Valley *(G-2240)*

General Aviation Inc ....E... 763 420-6907
Minneapolis *(G-4507)*

Genmar Holdings Inc ....D... 612 339-7900
Minneapolis *(G-4521)*

Global Capital Management Inc ....D... 952 476-7222
Hopkins *(G-2545)*

Hewitt Associates Inc ....D... 612 339-7501
Minneapolis *(G-4642)*

Interstate Co's Inc ....D... 952 854-2044
Minneapolis *(G-4726)*

Jacobs Investors Inc ....E... 612 339-9500
Minneapolis *(G-4750)*

M B W Co ....C... 507 354-3808
New Ulm *(G-6459)*

Macks LLC ....C... 507 288-2677
Rochester *(G-7164)*

Marathon Management Inc ....E... 651 259-4093
Saint Paul *(G-7831)*

Mayo Management Services Inc ....C... 507 538-5508
Rochester *(G-7175)*

Minnesota Autism Center ....E... 952 767-4200
Minnetonka *(G-6196)*

Minnesota Dairy Herd ....D... 763 682-1091
Buffalo *(G-652)*

Minnesota Surgical Associates ....E... 651 776-0724
Saint Paul *(G-8708)*

Minnetonka Assisted Living Com ....E... 952 988-0011
Minnetonka *(G-6197)*

Motors Management Corp ....E... 763 593-5755
Saint Louis Park *(G-7668)*

Nath Minnesota Franchise Group ....E... 952 853-1400
Minneapolis *(G-5159)*

New Dawn Inc ....C... 507 425-3278
Fulda *(G-2196)*

Pal Management Inc ....D... 952 646-1792
Burnsville *(G-774)*

Pals Inc ....D... 320 235-8860
Willmar *(G-10035)*

Paragon Strategic Solutions ....C... 952 886-8000
Minneapolis *(G-5321)*

Pathway Health Services Inc ....D... 651 407-8699
Saint Paul *(G-8809)*

Pine Ridge Homes Inc ....D... 218 879-1257
Cloquet *(G-1059)*

Prime Therapeutics Inc ....C... 651 456-1000
Saint Paul *(G-7881)*

Procter & Gamble Distributing ....C... 952 942-1857
Eden Prairie *(G-1754)*

RMC Project Management Inc ....E... 952 846-4484
Minnetonka *(G-6220)*

SERVICES

Senior Asset Management Inc.............B... 763 544-9934
Minneapolis *(G-5636)*

Shuett Co's Inc.. 763 541-9199
Minneapolis *(G-5662)*

Sodexo Management Inc.....................E... 507 333-6772
Faribault *(G-2030)*

Suburban Radiologic ConsInts...........D... 952 837-9700
Minneapolis *(G-5762)*

Summit Management LLC.....................E... 651 689-2200
Stillwater *(G-9650)*

Systems Management & Balancing.....E... 651 257-7380
Center City *(G-886)*

Transportation Management Corp.......D... 651 642-9292
Saint Paul *(G-9076)*

US Energy Services Inc.......................D... 763 543-4600
Minneapolis *(G-5947)*

XATA Corp...C... 952 707-5600
Eden Prairie *(G-1818)*

MANAGEMENT SVCS, FACILITIES SUPPORT: Environ Remediation

Bay West Inc...C... 651 291-0456
Saint Paul *(G-8093)*

Envirotech Remediation Svcs.............D... 763 746-0670
Minneapolis *(G-6125)*

Lindstrom Environmental Inc..............D... 763 545-9740
Plymouth *(G-6870)*

MANAGEMENT SVCS, FACILITIES SUPPORT: Jails, Privately Ops

County of Steele...................................E... 507 444-7410
Owatonna *(G-6707)*

MANAGEMENT SVCS: Administrative

Interstate Co's Inc..............................D... 952 854-2044
Minneapolis *(G-4726)*

Minter-Weisman Co..............................E... 763 545-3700
Minneapolis *(G-5104)*

Model Cities of St Paul Inc....................... 651 632-8350
Saint Paul *(G-8717)*

Mutual Service Cooperative..................B... 651 631-7000
Saint Paul *(G-8731)*

Orthopedic Resources Mgt..................E... 952 831-5773
Minneapolis *(G-5294)*

REM Leadway Inc..................................E... 952 925-5067
Minneapolis *(G-5511)*

Rust Consulting Inc.............................C... 612 359-2000
Minneapolis *(G-5577)*

MANAGEMENT SVCS: Business

First American Real Estate..................D... 800 868-8816
Minneapolis *(G-4439)*

Harrington Co.......................................E... 952 928-4666
Minneapolis *(G-4603)*

Ingenix Inc..B... 952 833-7100
Eden Prairie *(G-1692)*

Kraus-Anderson Construction Co........E... 612 721-7581
Minneapolis *(G-4822)*

Pro One Management.............................E... 612 813-0077
Minneapolis *(G-5414)*

Southwest Casino & Hotel Corp...........E... 952 853-9990
Minneapolis *(G-5713)*

T C Sweatshop Inc................................E... 651 646-8418
Saint Paul *(G-9023)*

Toro Receivables Co.............................E... 952 888-8801
Minneapolis *(G-5833)*

Unitedhealth Group Inc........................A... 952 936-1300
Minnetonka *(G-6232)*

Walden Automotive Group Inc.............E... 952 512-8800
Minneapolis *(G-5995)*

MANAGEMENT SVCS: Construction

American Swedish Institute..................E... 612 871-4907
Minneapolis *(G-3760)*

Bainey Group Inc...................................E... 763 557-6911
Minneapolis *(G-3858)*

Boldt Co...C... 218 879-1293
Cloquet *(G-1047)*

Bossardt Corp.......................................E... 952 837-3346
Minneapolis *(G-3932)*

Historical Society of MN......................E... 651 297-2555
Saint Paul *(G-8485)*

Ibberson Inc.. 952 938-7007
Hopkins *(G-2555)*

Knutson Construction Services...........D... 507 280-9788
Rochester *(G-7157)*

REc Inc..E... 952 947-3000
Minneapolis *(G-5475)*

Recovery One Inc.................................C... 952 435-7106
Burnsville *(G-786)*

Stahl Construction Co..........................E... 952 931-9300
Minneapolis *(G-5735)*

Thd At-Home Services Inc....................D... 763 542-8826
Minneapolis *(G-5812)*

URS Group Inc......................................E... 612 370-0700
Minneapolis *(G-5941)*

MANAGEMENT SVCS: Financial, Business

Hormel Financial Services....................E... 507 437-5611
Austin *(G-274)*

Octagon Financial Group......................E... 952 885-2700
Minneapolis *(G-5264)*

Powertrack..E... 612 973-3170
Minneapolis *(G-5398)*

MANAGEMENT SVCS: Hospital

Allina Health System............................A... 612 775-5000
Minneapolis *(G-3721)*

Atirix Medical Systems Inc....................E... 952 546-2001
Minnetonka *(G-6145)*

Bethesda Healthy Rehab......................A... 651 232-2000
Saint Paul *(G-8109)*

Brim Healthcare Inc..............................E... 763 546-4801
Minneapolis *(G-3948)*

Fairview Health Services......................C... 612 672-6800
Minneapolis *(G-4393)*

Fairview Health Services......................B... 651 982-7000
Wyoming *(G-10202)*

Fairview Health Services......................C... 218 262-4881
Hibbing *(G-2444)*

Fairview Health Services......................C... 763 389-1313
Princeton *(G-6907)*

Fairview Health Services......................B... 612 273-3000
Minneapolis *(G-4400)*

Fairview Health Services......................B... 612 672-5500
Minneapolis *(G-4399)*

Fairview Health Services......................E... 651 632-7300
Saint Paul *(G-8362)*

Fairview Health Services......................E... 612 626-2663
Minneapolis *(G-4398)*

Healtheast Care Inc..............................A... 651 232-2300
Saint Paul *(G-8453)*

Healtheast Care System.......................A... 651 232-1000
Saint Paul *(G-8454)*

Mayo Foundation For Medical.............A... 507 284-2511
Rochester *(G-7174)*

Minnesota Hospital...............................D... 651 641-1121
Saint Paul *(G-8689)*

Park Nicollet Health Services...............E... 952 993-5495
Minneapolis *(G-5335)*

Production Health Associates..............E... 507 372-2957
Worthington *(G-10191)*

Sanford Health Network.......................B... 507 223-7272
Canby *(G-852)*

Sanford Health Network.......................D... 507 847-2420
Jackson *(G-2799)*

Sanford Health Network.......................C... 507 674-2932
Tracy *(G-9691)*

St Francis Health Services of...............A... 320 589-2004
Morris *(G-6378)*

MANAGEMENT SVCS: Hotel Or Motel

Central Group Management Co............B... 320 654-6307
Saint Cloud *(G-7482)*

Kinseth Hotel Corp...............................C... 952 884-8211
Minneapolis *(G-4811)*

Larken Inc...D... 952 830-1300
Minneapolis *(G-4844)*

Marcus Bloomington LLC.....................C... 952 893-9500
Bloomington *(G-504)*

Otsego Hospitality LLC.........................D... 763 656-4400
Elk River *(G-1903)*

Sbsb LP...D... 218 628-2700
Duluth *(G-1444)*

Tofte Management Co LLC....................C... 218 663-7296
Tofte *(G-9684)*

Tri-City IV Inc..D... 952 854-7405
Bloomington *(G-521)*

Z M C Hotels Inc...................................A... 218 723-8433
Duluth *(G-1507)*

Z M C Hotels Inc...................................E... 218 727-0461
Duluth *(G-1508)*

MANAGEMENT SVCS: Nursing & Personal Care Facility

Atirix Medical Systems Inc....................E... 952 546-2001
Minnetonka *(G-6145)*

Badger Acquisition of MN.....................C... 763 259-0400
Minneapolis *(G-3857)*

Bethesda Healthy Rehab......................A... 651 232-2000
Saint Paul *(G-8109)*

Fairview Health Services......................B... 612 273-3000
Minneapolis *(G-4400)*

Lakeview Retirement Apartments........D... 218 386-1235
Warroad *(G-9871)*

Minnesota Hospital...............................D... 651 641-1121
Saint Paul *(G-8689)*

Production Health Associates..............E... 507 372-2957
Worthington *(G-10191)*

St Francis Health Services of...............A... 320 589-2004
Morris *(G-6378)*

MANAGEMENT SVCS: Personnel

Minnesota Department of Admin.........A... 651 296-2600
Saint Paul *(G-8682)*

MANAGEMENT SVCS: Restaurant

Blast Pressure Washing.......................E... 507 455-2898
Owatonna *(G-6696)*

Inac of VA Inc.......................................E... 218 263-3398
Hibbing *(G-2457)*

Minnesota Vikings Food Svcs..............C... 952 835-5250
Saint Paul *(G-8709)*

Mrg Management Inc............................B... 763 537-1460
Minneapolis *(G-5144)*

Taylor & Katie Inc.................................E... 320 523-2833
Olivia *(G-6565)*

Tri-City IV Inc..D... 952 854-7405
Bloomington *(G-521)*

MANPOWER POOLS

Manpower Inc..E... 952 831-3338
Minneapolis *(G-4943)*

MAPMAKING SVCS

Aero-Metric Inc....................................E... 763 420-9606
Osseo *(G-6593)*

MARINAS

Gunflint Lodge Inc................................E... 218 388-2294
Grand Marais *(G-2261)*

J & K Marina...E... 218 847-7291
Detroit Lakes *(G-1201)*

Rainy Lake Houseboats Inc..................E... 218 286-5391
International Falls *(G-2729)*

MARINE CARGO HANDLING SVCS: Docks, Piers & Terminals

Upper River Services LLC.....................E... 651 292-9293
Saint Paul *(G-9115)*

MARINE CARGO HANDLING SVCS: Marine Terminal

River Services Inc.................................E... 612 588-8141
Minneapolis *(G-5543)*

MARINE CARGO HANDLING SVCS: Waterfront Terminal Operations

Great Western Recycling Inds..............E... 651 224-4877
Saint Paul *(G-8427)*

MARTIAL ARTS INSTRUCTION

North Crest Gymnastics & Dance........E... 320 251-3416
Sauk Rapids *(G-9370)*

MASSAGE PARLOR & STEAM BATH SVCS

Simonson Venture Inc...........................E... 763 494-4863
Osseo *(G-6663)*

MASSAGE PARLORS

Keep In Touch of Burnsville.................E... 952 953-3313
Burnsville *(G-739)*

Positive Body Dynamics Inc.................E... 952 920-9514
Minneapolis *(G-5396)*

MATERIALS HANDLING EQPT WHOLESALERS

Bennett Material Handling Inc..............E... 952 933-5544
Hopkins *(G-2517)*

E Tech Inc...D... 612 722-1366
Minneapolis *(G-4301)*

Garland's Inc..E... 612 333-3469
Minneapolis *(G-4501)*

Herc-U-Lift Inc......................................D... 763 479-2501
Maple Plain *(G-3277)*

Indoff Inc..B... 952 472-1295
Minnetrista *(G-6242)*

Mhc Material Handling.........................E... 320 634-4593
Glenwood *(G-2228)*

Minnesota Supply Co...........................D... 952 828-7300
Eden Prairie *(G-1726)*

Nott Co..C... 651 415-3400
Saint Paul *(G-8772)*

Employment codes: A=Over 500 employees, B=251-500,
C=101-250, D=51-100, E=25-50

2011 Harris Minnesota
Services Directory

© Harris InfoSource 1-866-281-6415
731

S E R V I C E S

Rdo Construction Equipment Co ....E... 218 282-8440
Moorhead (G-6334)

Rdo Material Handling Co ....E... 651 905-7025
Saint Paul (G-7890)

Sjf Material Handling Inc ....D... 320 485-2824
Winsted (G-10165)

Skarnes Inc ....E... 763 231-3600
Minneapolis (G-5687)

MEAL DELIVERY PROGRAMS

Catholic Charities of The......................B... 320 650-1550
Saint Cloud (G-7473)

Community Action Partnership ....C... 651 645-6445
Saint Paul (G-8237)

Volunteers of America Inc.....................D... 952 945-4000
Minneapolis (G-5984)

MEAT & MEAT PRDTS WHOLESALERS

Cargill Inc...E... 763 262-1900
Big Lake (G-445)

Hormel Foods Corporate Svcs ....E... 952 931-9030
Eden Prairie (G-1688)

Hormel Foods Corporate Svcs ....D... 507 437-5611
Austin (G-276)

Hormel Foods International ....D... 507 437-5611
Austin (G-277)

Huisken Meat Co of Sauk Rapids ....D... 320 259-0305
Sauk Rapids (G-9367)

Rochester Meats Inc ....C... 507 289-0701
Rochester (G-7235)

Schumacher Wholesale Meats Inc ....E... 763 546-3291
Minneapolis (G-5616)

Stock Yards Meat Packing Co ....C... 651 450-6000
South Saint Paul (G-9544)

SUPERVALU Inc....................................A... 952 828-4000
Eden Prairie (G-1787)

Supervalu Inc ....C... 952 906-6260
Chanhassen (G-941)

Swanson Meats Inc...............................D... 612 721-4411
Minneapolis (G-5777)

Trudeau Holdings LLC ....C... 952 882-8295
Burnsville (G-813)

Trudeau Holdings LLC ....D... 952 445-1350
Shakopee (G-9481)

MEATS, PACKAGED FROZEN: Wholesalers

Apperts Frozen Foods Inc ....D... 320 251-3200
Saint Cloud (G-7434)

Trudeau Holdings LLC ....C... 952 882-8295
Burnsville (G-813)

Trudeau Holdings LLC ....D... 952 445-1350
Shakopee (G-9481)

MED, DENTAL & HOSPITAL EQPT, WHOL: Incontinent Prdts/Splys

Activstyle Inc..D... 612 520-9333
Minneapolis (G-3678)

MEDIA BUYING AGENCIES

Cash Plus Inc ....E... 612 347-6900
Minneapolis (G-4024)

Marketing Architects Inc ....D... 952 449-2500
Minnetonka (G-6190)

Novus Media Inc....................................C... 612 758-8625
Minneapolis (G-5251)

MEDICAL & HOSPITAL EQPT WHOLESALERS

Annex Medical Inc.................................E... 952 942-7576
Minnetonka (G-6141)

Arizant Healthcare Inc ....C... 952 947-1200
Eden Prairie (G-1596)

Augustine Medical Inc ....D... 952 947-1288
Eden Prairie (G-1599)

Badger Acquisition of MN ....C... 763 259-0400
Minneapolis (G-3857)

Cardinal Health 200 Inc ....D... 763 323-9666
Champlin (G-890)

Carefusion 203 Inc ....D... 763 398-8300
Minneapolis (G-4005)

Carpe Diem Medical Inc........................E... 507 399-0262
Fairmont (G-1959)

Coloplast Corp ....B... 612 337-7800
Minneapolis (G-4123)

Global Medical Instrumentation ....E... 763 712-8717
Anoka (G-183)

Guidant Sales Corp...............................D... 651 582-4000
Saint Paul (G-8436)

Gyrus Acmi, LP ....D... 763 416-3000
Maple Grove (G-3244)

Healthworks Home Medical ....D... 507 238-9200
Fairmont (G-1974)

Medtronic USA Inc.................................A... 763 514-4000
Minneapolis (G-3534)

Medtronic World Headquarters ....A... 763 574-4000
Minneapolis (G-3535)

Minneapolis Oxygen Co ....E... 612 588-8855
Minneapolis (G-5058)

Otter Tail Corp 866 410-8780
Fergus Falls (G-2105)

Patterson Co's Inc ....D... 651 688-9265
Eagan (G-1545)

Rice Home Medical LLC ....E... 320 235-8434
Willmar (G-10040)

Scimed Inc..C... 763 494-1700
Osseo (G-6660)

Tactile Systems Technology Inc ....D... 952 224-4060
Minneapolis (G-5784)

Tfx Medical Wire Products Inc..............D... 763 559-6414
Plymouth (G-6886)

3M Co ....D... 651 733-0963
Saint Paul (G-9065)

Tympany LLC ....E... 866 316-3606
Saint Paul (G-9097)

MEDICAL CENTERS

Allina Health System ....A... 612 775-5000
Minneapolis (G-3721)

Allina Health System ....E... 763 427-9620
Champlin (G-888)

Allina Health System ....B... 612 798-8800
Minneapolis (G-3717)

Allina Health System ....E... 952 835-1311
Minneapolis (G-3722)

Allina Health System ....E... 763 786-6011
Minneapolis (G-3395)

Allina Health System ....E... 763 577-7400
Minneapolis (G-3723)

Allina Health System ....A... 612 863-4466
Minneapolis (G-3726)

Appleton Area Health Services.............C... 320 289-2422
Appleton (G-244)

Center For Pain Management ....E... 320 230-7788
Sartell (G-9336)

Centracare Clinic ....B... 320 252-5131
Saint Cloud (G-7480)

Centracare Clinic ....E... 320 251-1775
Saint Cloud (G-7479)

City of Littlefork ....D... 218 278-6634
Littlefork (G-3022)

County of Douglas ....D... 320 763-6018
Alexandria (G-92)

Glacial Ridge Hospital Fndtn ....C... 320 634-4521
Glenwood (G-2223)

Glencoe Regional Health Svcs ....B... 320 864-3121
Glencoe (G-2207)

HealthPartners Inc ....E... 952 546-2500
Hopkins (G-2551)

Healthpartners Inc ....E... 651 999-4740
Saint Paul (G-8472)

Hennepin Faculty Associates ....A... 612 347-5110
Minneapolis (G-4637)

Medical Scanning Consultants ....E... 952 513-6841
Saint Louis Park (G-7665)

Multicare Associates of The ....C... 763 785-4500
Minneapolis (G-3546)

Multicare Associates of The ....D... 763 785-4250
Minneapolis (G-3547)

Multicare Associates of The ....E... 763 785-4300
Saint Paul (G-8728)

North Memorial Health Care..................A... 763 520-5200
Minneapolis (G-5217)

Orthogonistic Care Specialist...............D... 952 432-4941
Saint Paul (G-7860)

Pride Institute Inc.................................E... 952 934-7554
Eden Prairie (G-1753)

Rochester Methodist Hospital 507 266-7890
Rochester (G-7237)

Smdc Health System ....E... 218 365-3151
Ely (G-1915)

Stillwater Medical Group ....C... 651 439-1234
Stillwater (G-9648)

Virginia, City of Inc ....A... 218 741-3340
Virginia (G-9760)

Warren Community Hospital Inc ....D... 218 745-4211
Warren (G-9869)

MEDICAL EQPT REPAIR SVCS, NON-ELECTRIC

Handi Medical Supply Inc......................D... 651 644-9770
Saint Paul (G-8440)

MEDICAL FIELD ASSOCIATION

Allina Health System ....E... 651 699-1501
Saint Paul (G-8015)

Allina Health System ....A... 651 642-2700
Saint Paul (G-8016)

American Academy of Neurology ....D... 651 695-1940
Saint Paul (G-8019)

Granite Medical Center ....E... 320 564-2511
Granite Falls (G-2316)

Institute For Clinical Systems ....E... 952 814-7060
Minneapolis (G-4708)

Minnesota Medical Association ....E... 612 378-1875
Minneapolis (G-5084)

Veterinary Hospitals Assn ....E... 651 451-6669
South Saint Paul (G-9549)

MEDICAL HELP SVCS

Accessible Space Inc............................E... 651 645-7271
Saint Paul (G-7975)

Accessible Space Inc............................E... 651 690-5216
Saint Paul (G-7974)

American Telecare Inc ....E... 952 897-0000
Eden Prairie (G-1591)

Health Orientated Pool ....E... 507 452-1646
Winona (G-10100)

Minnesota Care Staffing Inc ....C... 612 216-1938
Minneapolis (G-5070)

People's Express Inc.............................E... 218 631-2909
Wadena (G-9808)

Pride Institute Inc.................................E... 952 934-7554
Eden Prairie (G-1753)

MEDICAL INSURANCE CLAIM PROCESSING: Contract Or Fee Basis

Diversified Pharmaceutical................... 952 820-7000
Minneapolis (G-4263)

Freedom Services Inc ....E... 952 890-6524
Burnsville (G-724)

Loge Group LLC ....C... 952 829-3500
Minneapolis (G-4899)

Novologix ....E... 952 826-2500
Eden Prairie (G-1734)

Smart Data Solutions Inc ....E... 651 690-3140
Saint Paul (G-7906)

MEDICAL RESCUE SQUAD

Northern Access Transportation ....E... 218 728-5464
Duluth (G-1401)

MEDICAL SVCS ORGANIZATION

Chronimed Inc ....B... 952 979-3600
Eden Prairie (G-1625)

Human Development Center ....E... 218 728-4491
Duluth (G-1354)

Mayo Clinic ....B... 507 266-4808
Rochester (G-7171)

Medical Messaging Center ....E... 320 255-5640
Saint Cloud (G-7549)

National Marrow Donor Program ....C... 612 627-5800
Minneapolis (G-5166)

Select Transcription Inc ....D... 763 441-3021
Elk River (G-1892)

Tim Orth Memorial Foundation ....E... 320 365-4419
Bird Island (G-469)

Transcriptions Inc ....D... 952 831-4480
Eden Prairie (G-1795)

United Healthcare of Wyoming ....D... 651 603-8515
Saint Paul (G-9106)

MEDICAL X-RAY MACHINES & TUBES WHOLESALERS

Northern X-Ray Co ....E... 612 870-1561
Minneapolis (G-5230)

Patterson Co's Inc ....C... 651 686-1600
Saint Paul (G-7866)

Patterson Dental Supply Inc..................E... 651 688-6054
Saint Paul (G-7867)

MEDICAL, DENTAL & HOSP EQPT, WHOLESALE: X-ray Film & Splys

Northern X-Ray Co ....E... 612 870-1561
Minneapolis (G-5230)

Patterson Co's Inc ....C... 651 686-1600
Saint Paul (G-7866)

Patterson Dental Supply Inc..................E... 651 688-6054
Saint Paul (G-7867)

MEDICAL, DENTAL & HOSPITAL EQPT, WHOL: Dentists' Prof Splys

Patterson Co's Inc ....C... 651 686-1600
Saint Paul (G-7866)

Patterson Dental Supply Inc..................E... 651 688-6054
Saint Paul (G-7867)

MEDICAL, DENTAL & HOSPITAL EQPT, WHOL: Hospital Eqpt & Splys

Hill-Rom Inc ....D... 651 490-1468
Saint Paul (G-8483)

PSS World Medical Inc ....E... 763 428-2388
Rogers (G-7338)

Universal Hospital Services ....D... 612 721-3374
Minneapolis (G-5919)

MEDICAL, DENTAL & HOSPITAL EQPT, WHOL: Hosptl Eqpt/Furniture

Apria Healthcare Inc ....E... 651 523-8888
Saint Paul (G-8056)

Apria Healthcare Inc ....C... 952 404-1700
Minnetonka (G-6143)

D M S Health Group ....E... 763 315-1947
Osseo (G-6607)

MEDICAL, DENTAL & HOSPITAL EQPT, WHOL: Physician Eqpt/Splys

PSS World Medical Inc ....E... 763 428-2388
Rogers (G-7338)

MEDICAL, DENTAL & HOSPITAL EQPT, WHOL: Surgical Eqpt & Splys

McKesson Medical-Surgical Inc ....E... 952 881-8040
Minneapolis (G-4977)

PSS World Medical Inc ....E... 763 428-2388
Rogers (G-7338)

Sightpath Medical Inc ....C... 952 881-2500
Minneapolis (G-5668)

MEDICAL, DENTAL & HOSPITAL EQPT, WHOLESALE: Artificial Limbs

Otto Bock Healthcare LP ....C... 763 553-9464
Minneapolis (G-5297)

MEDICAL, DENTAL & HOSPITAL EQPT, WHOLESALE: Diagnostic, Med

Arkray Factory USA Inc ....D... 952 646-3200
Minneapolis (G-3807)

Arkray USA Inc ....D... 952 646-3259
Minneapolis (G-3808)

Guidant Sales Corp ....D... 651 582-4000
Saint Paul (G-8436)

PSS World Medical Inc ....E... 763 428-2388
Rogers (G-7338)

MEDICAL, DENTAL & HOSPITAL EQPT, WHOLESALE: Hearing Aids

American Hearing Systems Inc ....C... 763 404-1122
Bloomington (G-483)

MEDICAL, DENTAL & HOSPITAL EQPT, WHOLESALE: Med Eqpt & Splys

Alchemist General Inc ....D... 507 289-3901
Rochester (G-7047)

Altimate Medical Inc ....E... 507 697-6393
Morton (G-6382)

Guidant Sales Corp ....D... 651 582-4000
Saint Paul (G-8436)

Healthline Inc ....E... 218 262-6981
Hibbing (G-2450)

Keomed Inc ....E... 952 933-3940
Hopkins (G-2563)

Key Medical Supply Inc ....E... 651 792-3860
Saint Paul (G-8546)

McKesson Medical-Surgical ....E... 763 424-7201
Osseo (G-6636)

McKesson Medical-Surgical MN ....B... 763 595-6000
Minneapolis (G-4978)

Medafor Inc ....E... 763 571-6300
Minneapolis (G-4982)

Merwin Home Medical ....D... 763 535-5335
Minneapolis (G-4995)

Midwest Medical Equipment ....E... 218 722-3420
Duluth (G-1393)

Midwest Medical Management LLC ......E... 651 430-3892
Stillwater (G-9628)

Midwest Medical Services Inc ....D... 763 717-7676
Mounds View (G-6389)

Owens & Minor Inc ....D... 763 785-9100
Saint Paul (G-8796)

Qrs Diagnostic LLC ....E... 763 559-8492
Minneapolis (G-5440)

Reliable Medical Supply Inc ....D... 763 255-3800
Brooklyn Park (G-618)

St Jude Medical SC Inc ....B... 651 483-2000
Saint Paul (G-8986)

Thermoskin..E... 651 674-8302
North Branch (G-6505)

Unimed-Midwest Inc ....E... 952 469-9400
Lakeville (G-2938)

Universal Hospital Services ....D... 952 893-3200
Minneapolis (G-5920)

Urologix Inc ....D... 763 475-1400
Minneapolis (G-5940)

Vitatron Inc ....E... 763 574-4000
Minneapolis (G-3633)

Weiner Memorial Foundation..................E... 507 537-7070
Marshall (G-3331)

MEDICAL, DENTAL & HOSPITAL EQPT, WHOLESALE: Orthopedic

Bird & Cronin Inc ....D... 651 683-1111
Saint Paul (G-7722)

Otto Bock Healthcare North ....D... 763 553-9464
Minneapolis (G-5298)

MEDICAL, DENTAL/HOSPITAL EQPT, WHOL: Tech Aids, Handicapped

Harris Communications Inc ....E... 952 906-1180
Eden Prairie (G-1678)

MEDICAL, DENTAL/HOSPITAL EQPT, WHOL: Veterinarian Eqpt/Sply

Cold Spring St Joseph ....E... 320 685-3237
Cold Spring (G-1084)

General Pet Supply Inc ....E... 952 890-2300
Burnsville (G-727)

Kruse Family Enterprises LLC ....E... 507 345-5926
Mankato (G-3156)

Midwest Veterinary Supply Inc ....E... 952 894-4350
Burnsville (G-759)

Stearns Veterinary Outlet ....E... 320 256-3303
Melrose (G-3353)

Veterinary Hospitals Assn ....E... 651 451-6669
South Saint Paul (G-9549)

MEMBER ORGS, CIVIC, SOCIAL & FRATERNAL: Bars & Restaurants

American Legion 545 ....E... 320 796-5542
Spicer (G-9555)

1st Avenue Entertainment Group ....E... 612 337-6700
Minneapolis (G-4441)

Fraternal Order of Eagles Club ....E... 507 451-3846
Owatonna (G-6714)

Palmer Lake Post 3915 VFW Inc ....E... 763 560-3720
Minneapolis (G-5315)

Rudolph Priebe American Legion ....E... 763 425-4858
Osseo (G-6657)

Space Aliens Grill & Bar ....D... 320 259-7670
Waite Park (G-9840)

MEMBERSHIP HOTELS

Interstate Hotels & Resorts ....C... 952 854-2100
Minneapolis (G-4728)

MEMBERSHIP ORGANIZATIONS, BUS: Banker's Org, Advisory Svcs

Independent Community Bankers........D... 320 352-6546
Sauk Centre (G-9348)

MEMBERSHIP ORGANIZATIONS, BUSINESS: Better Business Bureau

Better Business Bureau of Minn ....E... 651 699-1111
Saint Paul (G-8110)

MEMBERSHIP ORGANIZATIONS, BUSINESS: Community Affairs & Svcs

East Lake Community Center ....E... 218 768-3311
McGregor (G-3339)

F R Bigelow Foundation Inc..................D... 651 224-5463
Saint Paul (G-8360)

Gemmell Lakes Association ....E... 218 897-5318
Mizpah (G-6243)

Hennepin County ....E... 612 348-7137
Minneapolis (G-4636)

Western Community Action Inc............E... 507 537-1416
Marshall (G-3334)

MEMBERSHIP ORGANIZATIONS, BUSINESS: Growers' Association

Communicating For America Inc..........E... 218 739-3241
Fergus Falls (G-2070)

Minnesota Farmers' Market Assn........D... 320 763-6893
Saint Paul (G-8686)

MEMBERSHIP ORGANIZATIONS, BUSINESS: Public Utility Assoc

Central Minnesota Municipal 507 526-2193
Blue Earth (G-531)

MEMBERSHIP ORGANIZATIONS, CIVIC, SOCIAL/FRAT: Boy Scout Org

Northern Star Council, Boy ....D... 651 224-1891
Saint Paul (G-8759)

Viking Council of The Boy ....D... 763 545-4550
Minneapolis (G-5971)

MEMBERSHIP ORGANIZATIONS, CIVIC, SOCIAL/FRAT: Rec Assoc

Flying Dutchmen Cycle Club ....D... 507 354-2306
New Ulm (G-6449)

Young Men's Chritn Assoc of ....D... 218 829-4767
Brainerd (G-590)

Young Women's Christian Assn ....C... 651 222-3741
Saint Paul (G-9181)

MEMBERSHIP ORGANIZATIONS, CIVIC, SOCIAL/FRAT: Social Assoc

Optimist International ....E... 952 440-8184
Prior Lake (G-6947)

MEMBERSHIP ORGANIZATIONS, CIVIC, SOCIAL/FRAT: Youth Orgs

Acts of St Paul ....E... 612 823-4237
Minneapolis (G-3679)

Adults Saving Kids ....D... 612 872-0684
Minneapolis (G-3684)

Albert Lea Family YMCA........................E... 507 373-8228
Albert Lea (G-31)

Boys & Girls Clubs of Central ....C... 320 252-7616
Saint Cloud (G-7463)

Camp Widji Wagan ....E... 218 365-2117
Ely (G-1912)

Duluth Area Family Y M C A ....E... 218 372-3188
Sturgeon Lake (G-9657)

Duluth Area Family YMCA......................E... 218 722-4745
Duluth (G-1297)

Fergus Falls Area Family Young.........D... 218 739-4489
Fergus Falls (G-2075)

Hastings YMCA ....E... 651 480-8887
Hastings (G-2390)

Itasca County Family Young ....D... 218 327-1161
Grand Rapids (G-2287)

Minnesota Department of ....E... 320 231-1729
Willmar (G-10026)

North Suburban Youth Fndtn ....E... 651 697-9865
Saint Paul (G-8754)

St Cloud Area Family YMCA ....C... 320 253-2664
Saint Cloud (G-7597)

Y M C A Infant Center.............................E... 651 646-4557
Saint Paul (G-9171)

YMCA...D... 320 222-9622
Willmar (G-10059)

YMCA Children's Center ....E... 651 777-8103
Saint Paul (G-9173)

YMCA of Greater Saint Paul ....C... 651 683-4713
Saint Paul (G-7952)

YMCA of Greater Saint Paul ....E... 612 465-0450
Minneapolis (G-6100)

YMCA of Greater Saint Paul ....E... 651 771-8881
Saint Paul (G-9174)

YMCA of Greater Saint Paul ....E... 651 645-6605
Saint Paul (G-9175)

YMCA of Greater St Paul........................D... 218 365-2117
Ely (G-1919)

YMCA of Greater St Paul........................D... 651 292-4143
Saint Paul (G-9178)

YMCA of Greater St Paul........................E... 651 646-4557
Saint Paul (G-9177)

YMCA of Greater St Paul........................C... 651 483-2671
Saint Paul (G-9176)

YMCA of Greater St Paul........................E... 651 457-0048
Saint Paul (G-7953)

YMCA of Greater St Paul........................E... 651 731-9507
Saint Paul (G-9292)

YMCA of Worthington, Minnesota ....E... 507 376-6197
Worthington (G-10199)

Young Men's Chritn Assoc of ....D... 218 829-4767
Brainerd (G-590)

Young Men's Chritn Assoc of ....C... 763 535-4800
Minneapolis (G-6101)

Young Men's Chritn Assoc of ....D... 612 827-5401
Minneapolis (G-6102)

Young Men's Chritn Assoc of 612 588-9484
Minneapolis (G-6103)

S
E
R
V
I
C
E
S

Employment codes: A=Over 500 employees, B=251-500,
C=101-250, D=51-100, E=25-50

2011 Harris Minnesota
Services Directory

© Harris InfoSource 1-866-281-6415
733

Young Men's Chrtn Assoc of ....C... 952 835-2567
Minneapolis *(G-6104)*

Young Women's Christian Assn ....C... 651 222-3741
Saint Paul *(G-9181)*

Young Women's Christian Assn ....D... 218 722-7425
Duluth *(G-1505)*

Youthworks Inc ....E... 612 729-5444
Minneapolis *(G-6109)*

YWCA of Minneapolis ....A... 612 332-0501
Minneapolis *(G-6111)*

MEMBERSHIP ORGANIZATIONS, LABOR UNIONS & SIMILAR: Trade

M C C A ....D... 651 645-4545
Saint Paul *(G-8600)*

MEMBERSHIP ORGANIZATIONS, NEC: Art Council

Evansville Arts Coalition ....D... 218 948-2787
Evansville *(G-1925)*

MEMBERSHIP ORGANIZATIONS, NEC: Automobile Owner Association

A A A Minneapolis ....D... 952 944-9585
Minneapolis *(G-3645)*

AAA Minnesota Iowa ....C... 952 707-4222
Burnsville *(G-670)*

MEMBERSHIP ORGANIZATIONS, NEC: Bowling club

Super Bowl ....E... 763 421-7779
Woodbury *(G-10175)*

MEMBERSHIP ORGANIZATIONS, NEC: Charitable

Acts of St Paul ....E... 612 823-4237
Minneapolis *(G-3679)*

American Legion ....E... 218 773-1129
East Grand Forks *(G-1565)*

ARC Greater Twin Cities ....E... 763 544-0006
Minneapolis *(G-3798)*

Blue Earth Area Mentors ....E... 507 526-5219
Blue Earth *(G-530)*

Cedar East Bethel Lions ....D... 763 434-8323
Cedar *(G-875)*

Central Territorial of The ....E... 651 646-2601
Saint Paul *(G-8183)*

Central Territorial of The ....E... 218 722-7934
Duluth *(G-1268)*

Central Territorial of The ....D... 507 288-3663
Rochester *(G-7073)*

Central Territorial of The ....C... 612 332-5855
Minneapolis *(G-4047)*

Gilman Park & Rec Association ....E... 320 387-2941
Foley *(G-2139)*

Glendalough of Austin Inc ....E... 507 334-4347
Faribault *(G-2010)*

Izaak Walton League of America ....E... 651 649-1446
Saint Paul *(G-8525)*

Metropolitan Sports Facilities ....E... 612 332-0386
Minneapolis *(G-5009)*

Open Door Health Center ....E... 507 388-2120
Mankato *(G-3179)*

Pacer Center Inc ....D... 952 838-9000
Minneapolis *(G-5309)*

People Inc ....E... 952 736-7802
Burnsville *(G-780)*

Philanthrofund Foundation ....E... 612 870-1806
Minneapolis *(G-5374)*

Simpson Housing Services Inc ....E... 612 874-8683
Minneapolis *(G-5677)*

Sobriety High Foundation ....E... 651 773-8378
Saint Paul *(G-8969)*

St Cloud Area Family YMCA ....C... 320 253-2664
Saint Cloud *(G-7597)*

Upper Sioux Community ....E... 320 564-3853
Granite Falls *(G-2322)*

MEMBERSHIP ORGANIZATIONS, NEC: Food Co-Operative

Countryside Co-Op ....D... 218 675-6865
Hackensack *(G-2332)*

Dairy Farmers of America Inc ....D... 218 736-5691
Fergus Falls *(G-2073)*

MEMBERSHIP ORGANIZATIONS, NEC: Historical Club

Commemorative Air Force ....C... 651 455-6942
South Saint Paul *(G-9523)*

Historical Society of MN ....C... 651 259-3160
Saint Paul *(G-8484)*

MEMBERSHIP ORGANIZATIONS, NEC: Personal Interest

Benevolent Protective Order of ....E... 507 451-1395
Owatonna *(G-6694)*

Fisher Education Association ....D... 218 891-4905
Fisher *(G-2134)*

Global Volunteers ....E... 651 407-6100
Saint Paul *(G-8415)*

Minnesota Wings Motorcycle ....E... 320 632-8427
Little Falls *(G-3014)*

Sahara Sands ....E... 763 444-6491
Isanti *(G-2780)*

Sandstone Riders Horse Club ....E... 320 245-0370
Sandstone *(G-9327)*

MEMBERSHIP ORGANIZATIONS, PROF: Education/Teacher Assoc

Education Minnesota ....D... 651 227-9541
Saint Paul *(G-8327)*

Minnesota Association of Sch ....D... 651 645-6272
Saint Paul *(G-8673)*

MEMBERSHIP ORGANIZATIONS, PROFESSIONAL: Health Association

Benedictine Team Health Systs ....E... 763 689-1162
Cambridge *(G-834)*

Lake Superior Medical Society ....E... 218 727-3325
Duluth *(G-1377)*

MEMBERSHIP ORGANIZATIONS, PROFESSIONAL: Nursing Association

Minnesota Nurses' Association ....E... 651 646-4807
Saint Paul *(G-8700)*

MEMBERSHIP ORGANIZATIONS: Reading Rooms/Other Cultural Orgs

Afs Intercultural Programs ....E... 651 647-6337
Saint Paul *(G-7998)*

Evansville Arts Coalition ....D... 218 948-2787
Evansville *(G-1925)*

MEMBERSHIP ORGS, CIVIC, SOCIAL & FRAT: Comm Member Club

Harrison Community Club ....E... 218 624-1510
Duluth *(G-1349)*

Jewish Community Center of The ....D... 651 698-0751
Saint Paul *(G-8531)*

Saint Paul Foundation Inc ....D... 651 224-5463
Saint Paul *(G-8926)*

MEMBERSHIP ORGS, CIVIC, SOCIAL & FRAT: Dwelling-Related

Seventy-Five Hundred York ....D... 952 835-1010
Minneapolis *(G-5644)*

MEMBERSHIP ORGS, CIVIC, SOCIAL & FRAT: Girl Scout

Girl Scouts of Minnesota & WI ....D... 651 227-8835
Saint Paul *(G-8411)*

MEMBERSHIP ORGS, CIVIC, SOCIAL & FRATERNAL: Citizens Union

Swan Lake Association ....E... 218 885-3225
Pengilly *(G-6785)*

MEMBERSHIP ORGS, CIVIC, SOCIAL & FRATERNAL: Civic Assoc

Coon Rapids Lions ....E... 763 323-1668
Minneapolis *(G-3441)*

Glenwood Lions Club ....E... 320 634-3263
Glenwood *(G-2224)*

Hill City Lions Club ....E... 218 697-8427
Hill City *(G-2480)*

International Association of ....E... 218 338-6129
Parkers Prairie *(G-6765)*

International Association of ....C... 651 439-4659
Stillwater *(G-9624)*

International Association of ....C... 507 283-9127
Luverne *(G-3060)*

International Association of ....E... 952 447-0413
Savage *(G-9391)*

International Association of ....E... 507 454-7643
Winona *(G-10105)*

International Association of ....E... 763 689-3898
Cambridge *(G-839)*

International Association of ....E... 952 975-2985
Chanhassen *(G-928)*

International Association of ....E... 952 933-5972
Hopkins *(G-2557)*

Kiwanis International Inc ....E... 507 275-3748
Hendricks *(G-2430)*

Kiwanis International Inc ....E... 507 859-2635
Walnut Grove *(G-9862)*

Kiwanis International Inc ....E... 320 587-6874
Hutchinson *(G-2705)*

Lions Club of Jasper ....E... 507 348-8605
Jasper *(G-2804)*

Saint James Lions Club Inc ....E... 507 375-5634
Saint James *(G-7645)*

Spring Lake Park Lions Club ....E... 763 784-9179
Minneapolis *(G-3606)*

MEMBERSHIP ORGS, CIVIC, SOCIAL & FRATERNAL: Condo Assoc

Greencastle Condominium Assn ....E... 320 587-4040
Hutchinson *(G-2697)*

Lanterns Homeowner Association ....E... 952 922-4435
Minneapolis *(G-4843)*

MEMBERSHIP ORGS, CIVIC, SOCIAL & FRATERNAL: Protection

Institute For Environmental ....E... 763 315-7900
Minneapolis *(G-4709)*

Nature Conservancy ....E... 612 331-0700
Minneapolis *(G-5173)*

MEMBERSHIP ORGS, CIVIC, SOCIAL & FRATERNAL: Singing Society

Society For Preservation ....E... 507 452-4425
Winona *(G-10128)*

MEMBERSHIP ORGS, CIVIC, SOCIAL/FRAT: Business Persons Club

Minnesota Department of ....E... 320 231-1729
Willmar *(G-10026)*

MEMBERSHIP SPORTS & RECREATION CLUBS

America's Raquette & Fitness ....E... 507 345-8833
Mankato *(G-3104)*

Anytime Fitness LLC ....D... 651 438-5000
Hastings *(G-2413)*

Auburn Woods Clubhomes Assn ....D... 952 922-5575
Edina *(G-1825)*

Bemidji Town & Country Club ....E... 218 751-4535
Bemidji *(G-381)*

Burnsville Hockey Club ....E... 952 890-2333
Burnsville *(G-691)*

Calhoun Beach Club of ....D... 612 927-9951
Minneapolis *(G-3992)*

City of Blue Earth ....E... 507 526-2715
Blue Earth *(G-532)*

Club The Campus Inc ....E... 612 625-9696
Minneapolis *(G-4112)*

Coon Rapids VFW Post 9625 ....E... 763 755-4760
Minneapolis *(G-3442)*

Dakotah Sport & Fitness Center ....C... 952 445-9400
Prior Lake *(G-6932)*

Eagles Hall ....E... 218 847-5267
Detroit Lakes *(G-1192)*

Flagship Athletic Club Inc ....B... 952 941-2000
Eden Prairie *(G-1665)*

Gonvick American Legion ....C... 218 487-5214
Gonvick *(G-2247)*

Hidden Haven Golf Course Inc ....E... 763 434-6867
Cedar *(G-879)*

Kraus-Anderson Construction Co ....E... 218 759-0596
Bemidji *(G-400)*

Leech Lake Reservation ....A... 218 547-2744
Walker *(G-9854)*

Little Moran Hunting Club ....E... 218 894-3852
Staples *(G-9585)*

Madden Brothers Inc ....E... 218 829-2811
Brainerd *(G-546)*

Mannahah Snow Blazers ....C... 320 693-6658
Litchfield *(G-2988)*

Maple Valley Golf & Country ....E... 507 932-5444
Saint Charles *(G-7405)*

Montevideo Country Club Inc ....E... 320 269-6828
Montevideo *(G-6254)*

North American Affinity Clubs ....B... 952 936-9333
Minnetonka *(G-6203)*

North American Membership Grp ....D... 952 988-7451
Shakopee *(G-9459)*

North American Membership Grp ....B... 952 936-9333
Hopkins *(G-2591)*

Parkview Golf Associates LLC ....E... 651 452-5098
　Saint Paul (G-7864)
Pezhekee Lounge Inc ....E... 320 634-4502
　Glenwood (G-2231)
Pool & Yacht Club..............................E... 651 455-3900
　Saint Paul (G-7878)
Rochester Athletic Club Inc ....B... 507 282-6000
　Rochester (G-7228)
Spring Hill Golf Club ....D... 952 473-1500
　Wayzata (G-9940)
St Francis Youth Hockey Assn..........C... 763 913-7395
　Saint Francis (G-7637)
Swampsiders Snowmobile Club..........C... 218 245-3222
　Bigfork (G-464)
3 M Club of St Paul Inc ....D... 651 733-3466
　Lake Elmo (G-2877)
Tournament Club of Iowa LLC ....E... 952 252-4474
　Minneapolis (G-5838)
Upper Minnetonka Yacht Club............D... 952 471-8783
　Spring Park (G-9567)
Wild Marsh Golf Club LLC...................E... 763 682-4476
　Buffalo (G-660)
Young Men's Chritn Assoc of..............C... 763 785-7882
　Minneapolis (G-3644)

MEN'S & BOYS' CLOTHING WHOLESALERS, NEC

Gordon & Ferguson of Delaware ....E... 763 559-8300
　Minneapolis (G-4543)
Mid-States Distributing Co Inc.............E... 651 698-8831
　Saint Paul (G-8652)

MEN'S & BOYS' SPORTSWEAR WHOLESALERS

River's End Holdings LLC 952 912-2543
　Hopkins (G-2618)
Rivers End Trading Co ....D... 952 912-2500
　Hopkins (G-2619)

MENTAL HEALTH CLINIC, OUTPATIENT

Allina Health System ....B... 320 589-1313
　Morris (G-6369)
Allina Health System ....E... 320 234-4664
　Hutchinson (G-2685)
Behavioral Dimensions Inc ....E... 952 814-0207
　Hopkins (G-2516)
Behavioral Health Services Inc............E... 763 689-7887
　Cambridge (G-833)
Center For Independent Living............B... 218 262-6675
　Hibbing (G-2439)
Central Minnesota Mental ....E... 763 682-4400
　Buffalo (G-641)
Central Minnesota Mental ....D... 320 252-5010
　Saint Cloud (G-7485)
Children's Mental Health Svcs..............E... 218 327-4886
　Grand Rapids (G-2271)
Core Professional Services ....E... 218 829-7140
　Brainerd (G-560)
Face To Face Health ....E... 651 772-5555
　Saint Paul (G-8361)
Five County Mental Health Ctr..............E... 320 396-3333
　Braham (G-542)
Hecla Inc 320 255-9530
　Saint Cloud (G-7526)
Hiawatha Valley Mental Health ....E... 507 454-4341
　Winona (G-10102)
Hiawatha Valley Mental Health ....D... 651 565-2234
　Wabasha (G-9767)
Human Development Center.................D... 218 728-5192
　Duluth (G-1355)
Indian Health Board of..........................D... 612 721-9800
　Minneapolis (G-4696)
Lakeland Mental Health Center...........D... 218 736-6987
　Fergus Falls (G-2083)
Lakeland Mental Health Center...........D... 218 233-7524
　Moorhead (G-6323)
Lifespan of Minnesota Inc....................D... 651 681-0616
　Eagan (G-1534)
Meridian Behavioral Health LLC............612 326-7600
　New Brighton (G-6412)
Minnesota Department of Human........B... 218 739-7200
　Fergus Falls (G-2099)
Monticello-Big Lake Community ....B... 763 295-2945
　Monticello (G-6278)
Neighborhood Counseling Center ....E... 218 631-1714
　Wadena (G-9807)
Northland Counseling Center ....E... 218 326-1274
　Grand Rapids (G-2301)
Northwestern Mental Health Ctr ....D... 218 281-3940
　Crookston (G-1130)
Nystrom & Associates Ltd ....E... 651 628-9566
　Saint Paul (G-8775)

Omegon Inc ....E... 952 541-4738
　Hopkins (G-2594)
Partners In Excellence Inc ....D... 952 746-5350
　Burnsville (G-776)
Relate Counseling Center Inc ....E... 952 932-7277
　Minnetonka (G-6219)
Resource Inc ....E... 612 752-8200
　Minneapolis (G-5527)
Southwestern Mental Health Ctr..........E... 507 376-4141
　Worthington (G-10195)
Southwestern Mental Health Ctr 507 283-9511
　Luverne (G-3070)
St Mary's Duluth Clinic Health ....A... 218 786-4000
　Duluth (G-1473)
Stevens Community Medical Ctr ....C... 320 589-1313
　Morris (G-6379)
Storefront Group ....E... 612 861-1675
　Richfield (G-7038)
Upper Mississippi Mental ....D... 218 751-3280
　Bemidji (G-431)
Vail Place 612 824-8061
　Minneapolis (G-5954)
Western Mental Health Center ....E... 507 532-3236
　Marshall (G-3335)
Woodland Centers ....C... 320 693-7221
　Litchfield (G-2993)
Zumbro Valley Mental Health ....E... 507 289-2089
　Rochester (G-7299)

MENTAL HEALTH PRACTITIONERS' OFFICES

M D A Consulting Group Inc ....E... 612 332-8182
　Minneapolis (G-4920)
Woodland Centers ....D... 320 235-4613
　Willmar (G-10058)

METAL CUTTING SVCS

A & C Metals-Sawing Inc ....E... 763 786-1048
　Minneapolis (G-3382)

METAL SERVICE CENTERS & OFFICES

A & C Metals-Sawing Inc ....E... 763 786-1048
　Minneapolis (G-3382)
C C Sharrow Co Inc ....E... 651 489-1341
　Saint Paul (G-8145)
Firestone Metal Products LLC ....C... 763 576-9595
　Anoka (G-181)
Great Western Recycling Inds ....E... 651 224-4877
　Saint Paul (G-8427)
Quality Metals Inc ....E... 651 645-5875
　Saint Paul (G-8860)
Russel Metals Williams Bahcall..............E... 651 688-8138
　Little Canada (G-2998)
West Central Steel Inc ....C... 320 235-4070
　Willmar (G-10055)

METAL SLITTING & SHEARING

R L Bodeker & Sons Inc ....D... 651 452-0377
　Saint Paul (G-7888)
Ratner Steel Supply Co ....E... 651 631-8515
　Saint Paul (G-8870)

METALS SVC CENTERS & WHOL: Structural Shapes, Iron Or Steel

McNeilus Steel Inc ....C... 507 374-6336
　Dodge Center (G-1229)

METALS SVC CENTERS & WHOLESALERS: Bale Ties, Wire

Excel Manufacturing Inc.........................E... 507 932-4680
　Saint Charles (G-7401)

METALS SVC CENTERS & WHOLESALERS: Cable, Wire

C S Aero-Space Inc ....E... 952 884-4725
　Minneapolis (G-3987)

METALS SVC CENTERS & WHOLESALERS: Concrete Reinforcing Bars

McNeilus Steel Inc ....C... 507 374-6336
　Dodge Center (G-1229)

METALS SVC CENTERS & WHOLESALERS: Copper

Mead Metals Inc ....E... 651 484-1400
　Saint Paul (G-8628)

METALS SVC CENTERS & WHOLESALERS: Flat Prdts, Iron Or Steel

Mead Metals Inc......................................E... 651 484-1400
　Saint Paul (G-8628)

METALS SVC CENTERS & WHOLESALERS: Iron & Steel Prdt, Ferrous

Joseph T Ryerson & Son Inc.................C... 763 544-4401
　Minneapolis (G-4780)

METALS SVC CENTERS & WHOLESALERS: Nonferrous Sheets, Etc

Kronick Industries Inc............................E... 612 331-8080
　Minneapolis (G-4825)

METALS SVC CENTERS & WHOLESALERS: Pipe & Tubing, Steel

Chicago Tube & Iron Co of MN.............D... 651 454-6800
　Saint Paul (G-7731)
Goodin Co ....E... 320 259-6086
　Saint Cloud (G-7520)
Hajoca Corp ....E... 763 315-0100
　Minneapolis (G-4589)
Hd Supply Waterworks Ltd ....E... 952 937-9666
　Eden Prairie (G-1680)
Mead Metals Inc......................................E... 651 484-1400
　Saint Paul (G-8628)

METALS SVC CENTERS & WHOLESALERS: Reinforcement Mesh, Wire

McNeilus Steel Inc ....C... 507 374-6336
　Dodge Center (G-1229)

METALS SVC CENTERS & WHOLESALERS: Rods, Metal

Louis Industries Inc................................E... 320 243-3696
　Paynesville (G-6771)

METALS SVC CENTERS & WHOLESALERS: Sheets, Metal

Louis Industries Inc................................E... 320 243-3696
　Paynesville (G-6771)
Mead Metals Inc......................................E... 651 484-1400
　Saint Paul (G-8628)

METALS SVC CENTERS & WHOLESALERS: Steel

Cargill Inc ....C... 612 367-3000
　Minneapolis (G-4007)
Cargill Inc ....E... 952 984-3377
　Hopkins (G-2526)
North Second Street Steel Sply............E... 612 522-6626
　Minneapolis (G-5218)
Olympic Steel Minneapolis Inc..............D... 763 544-7100
　Minneapolis (G-5275)
Ratner Steel Supply Co ....E... 651 631-8515
　Saint Paul (G-8870)
Ssab Enterprises LLC ....E... 651 631-9031
　Saint Paul (G-8980)
Two Rivers Enterprises Inc ....E... 320 746-3156
　Holdingford (G-2491)
Viking Materials Inc................................D... 612 617-5800
　Minneapolis (G-5974)

METALS SVC CENTERS & WHOLESALERS: Tubing, Metal

Chicago Tube & Iron Co of MN.............D... 651 454-6800
　Saint Paul (G-7731)
Louis Industries Inc................................E... 320 243-3696
　Paynesville (G-6771)

METALS SVC CNTRS & WHOL: Metal Wires, Ties, Cables/Screening

Donner Industries Inc.............................E... 651 429-0890
　Hugo (G-2676)

METALS SVC CTRS & WHOLESALERS: Aluminum Bars, Rods, Etc

Joseph T Ryerson & Son Inc.................C... 763 544-4401
　Minneapolis (G-4780)
Spectro Alloys Corp ....C... 651 437-2815
　Rosemount (G-7375)
Voyager Aluminum Inc............................E... 320 834-4940
　Brandon (G-591)

Employment codes: A=Over 500 employees, B=251-500,
C=101-250, D=51-100, E=25-50

2011 Harris Minnesota
Services Directory

© Harris InfoSource 1-866-281-6415
735

METALWORKING MACHINERY WHOLESALERS

Almco Inc ....E... 507 377-2102
Albert Lea *(G-36)*

Prima Laserdyne Inc ....E... 763 433-3700
Champlin *(G-898)*

METER READERS: Remote

RMR Services LLC ....D... 763 786-7323
Minneapolis *(G-3588)*

MICROFILM EQPT WHOLESALERS

AMI Imaging Systems Inc ....E... 952 828-0080
Bloomington *(G-485)*

National Business Systems Inc ....D... 651 688-0202
Eagan *(G-1540)*

MICROFILM SVCS

ACS Integrated Doc Inc ....E... 651 999-5400
Saint Paul *(G-7981)*

Alternative Micrographics Inc ....E... 320 796-2599
Spicer *(G-9554)*

National Business Systems Inc ....D... 651 688-0202
Eagan *(G-1540)*

MILK PRODUCTION

Maple Island Inc ....E... 507 824-2224
Wanamingo *(G-9864)*

MILK, FLUID: Wholesalers

Associated Milk Producers Inc ....D... 507 354-8295
New Ulm *(G-6440)*

Milk Specialties Co ....D... 507 427-3222
Mountain Lake *(G-6399)*

Sunrise A G Repair ....E... 320 584-0010
Royalton *(G-7388)*

West Plains Dairy LLC ....E... 651 258-4666
Goodhue *(G-2251)*

MILKING MACHINERY & EQPT WHOLESALERS

Dairy Farmers Of America Inc ....E... 507 732-5124
Zumbrota *(G-10218)*

MIMEOGRAPHING SVCS

American Reprographics Co LLC ....D... 612 722-2303
Minneapolis *(G-3759)*

MINIATURE GOLF COURSES

City of Edina ....E... 952 832-6792
Minneapolis *(G-4086)*

Funcity ....E... 763 441-8365
Elk River *(G-1899)*

Maintenance Building ....E... 320 384-7084
Hinckley *(G-2486)*

Owatonna Fairlanes Corp ....E... 507 451-2524
Owatonna *(G-6728)*

Rock 'n Water ....E... 218 439-6400
Detroit Lakes *(G-1215)*

MINING EXPLORATION & DEVELOPMENT SVCS

DH Blattner & Sons Inc ....D... 320 356-7351
Avon *(G-294)*

MINING MACHINERY & EQPT WHOLESALERS

Road Machinery & Supplies Co ....D... 952 895-9595
Savage *(G-9405)*

MISC FINAN INVEST ACTIVITY: Mutual Fund, Ind Salesperson

Ameriprise Financial Inc ....A... 612 671-3131
Minneapolis *(G-3767)*

K O P P Funds ....E... 952 841-0480
Minneapolis *(G-4785)*

Lutheran Brotherhood Research ....E... 612 340-7000
Minneapolis *(G-4911)*

MODELING SVCS

John Robert Powers Inc ....E... 952 854-8577
Minneapolis *(G-4770)*

MONEY ORDER ISSUANCE SVCS

Money Gram Payment Systems Inc ....A... 952 591-3000
Minneapolis *(G-5120)*

Moneygram Payment Systems Inc ......D... 763 549-7100
Minneapolis *(G-5121)*

MONTESSORI CHILD DEVELOPMENT CENTER

Bluffview Montessori School ....E... 507 452-2807
Winona *(G-10083)*

Catholic Charities of The ....E... 612 529-9107
Minneapolis *(G-4029)*

Chrestomathy Inc ....D... 952 974-0339
Eden Prairie *(G-1624)*

Macdonald Montessori Child ....E... 651 227-1039
Saint Paul *(G-8604)*

New Discoveries Montessori ....E... 320 234-6362
Hutchinson *(G-2709)*

Step By Step Montessori ....E... 763 315-3602
Osseo *(G-6667)*

Step By Step Montessori School ......E... 763 557-6777
Minneapolis *(G-5749)*

Step By Step Montessori School ......E... 952 368-4456
Chaska *(G-982)*

Step By Step Montessori School ......E... 763 498-5437
Loretto *(G-3052)*

Swan River Montessori Charter ....E... 763 271-7926
Monticello *(G-6288)*

MORTGAGE BANKERS

Bell Ancillary Services Inc ....E... 952 591-1880
Minneapolis *(G-3881)*

Bell Ancillary Services Inc ....D... 952 545-1880
Minnetonka *(G-6147)*

Midcountry Mortgage Corp ....D... 651 766-7000
Saint Paul *(G-8653)*

Northmarq Capital LLC ....D... 952 356-0100
Minneapolis *(G-5233)*

River City Mortgage Corp ....E... 651 406-5000
Saint Paul *(G-7896)*

Ryland Group Inc ....D... 952 229-6000
Edina *(G-1843)*

TCS Mortgage Inc ....E... 612 767-5002
Minneapolis *(G-5801)*

U S Bancorp ....B... 651 466-3000
Minneapolis *(G-5885)*

U S Bank Home Mortgage 952 851-5494
Bloomington *(G-522)*

Vision Financial & Home Mtge ....E... 952 224-3370
Hopkins *(G-2652)*

Wells Fargo Bank, National ....A... 612 667-1234
Minneapolis *(G-6041)*

Wells Fargo Funding Inc ....C... 800 328-5074
Minneapolis *(G-6047)*

MORTGAGE COMPANIES: Urban

Prime Mortgage Corp ....E... 952 544-3181
Minnetonka *(G-6217)*

MOSS GATHERING

Fafard Inc ....E... 218 476-3022
Floodwood *(G-2135)*

MOTEL

Buena Vista ....E... 218 728-3533
Duluth *(G-1258)*

Canadian Border Outfitters Inc ......E... 218 365-5847
Ely *(G-1911)*

Concordia College ....A... 218 299-4321
Moorhead *(G-6306)*

Cove Point Lodge ....E... 218 226-3221
Beaver Bay *(G-352)*

Glen L Stockman ....E... 651 636-1171
Saint Paul *(G-8413)*

Grand Rapids Development Corp ....D... 218 326-8501
Grand Rapids *(G-2281)*

J & L Hennum Inc ....D... 218 634-1342
Baudette *(G-315)*

Lodge At Giants Ridge ....D... 218 865-7170
Biwabik *(G-470)*

Lower Sioux Community Council ....E... 507 637-5933
Redwood Falls *(G-7024)*

Lutsen Resort Co ....E... 218 663-7212
Lutsen *(G-3056)*

Mississippi Eagles LLC ....E... 651 565-5366
Wabasha *(G-9769)*

Northland Inn of Crookston ....D... 218 281-5210
Crookston *(G-1129)*

Orchard Park LLC ....E... 952 873-6017
Belle Plaine *(G-369)*

Proctor Motel Associates ....E... 218 624-1026
Proctor *(G-6965)*

Richard Sigert ....D... 218 444-1875
Bemidji *(G-422)*

Rivett Group LLC ....E... 952 888-8800
Minneapolis *(G-5547)*

Spirit Mountain Travel Lodge ....E... 218 628-3691
Duluth *(G-1457)*

MOTEL: Franchised

Lq Management LLC ....E... 952 881-7311
Minneapolis *(G-4906)*

No Name ....E... 218 547-3334
Walker *(G-9855)*

Sbse LLC ....E... 651 994-7810
Eagan *(G-1549)*

MOTION PICTURE & VIDEO PRODUCTION SVCS

Distributed Website Corp ....E... 507 453-5164
Winona *(G-10093)*

Nowdocs International Inc ....D... 888 669-3627
North Mankato *(G-6512)*

Paradigm Publishing Inc ....E... 651 290-2800
Saint Paul *(G-8807)*

Rick S Shand ....E... 651 770-8710
Saint Paul *(G-9268)*

MOTION PICTURE & VIDEO PRODUCTION SVCS: Commercials, TV

Harmony Holdings Inc ....D... 952 925-8840
Wayzata *(G-9920)*

MOTION PICTURE & VIDEO PRODUCTION SVCS: Educational

Charthouse International ....E... 952 890-1800
Burnsville *(G-696)*

MOTION PICTURE & VIDEO PRODUCTION SVCS: Educational, TV

In Fisherman Inc ....E... 218 829-1648
Baxter *(G-330)*

MOTION PICTURE & VIDEO PRODUCTION SVCS: Training

Charthouse International ....E... 952 890-1800
Burnsville *(G-696)*

MOTION PICTURE DISTRIBUTION, EXCLUSIVE OF PRODUCTION

Quest Management Associates ....E... 612 379-3800
Minneapolis *(G-5449)*

MOTION PICTURE PRODUCTION ALLIED SVCS

Duplication Factory LLC ....D... 952 448-9912
Chaska *(G-962)*

MOTOR REBUILDING SVCS, EXC AUTOMOTIVE

Electric Motor Repair Inc ....E... 612 588-4693
Minneapolis *(G-4337)*

MOTOR VEHICLE SPLYS & PARTS WHOLESALERS: New

ABM Equipment & Supply Inc 952 938-5451
Hopkins *(G-2498)*

ABM Equipment & Supply LLC ....E... 952 938-5451
Hopkins *(G-2499)*

Advanced Automotive Industries ......E... 651 777-5420
Saint Paul *(G-9182)*

Allstate Sales & Leasing Corp ....D... 651 455-6500
South Saint Paul *(G-9508)*

Automotive Restyling Concepts ....D... 763 535-2181
Minneapolis *(G-3840)*

Bell Industries Inc ....C... 651 203-2300
Eagan *(G-1517)*

Best Oil Co ....E... 218 879-4666
Cloquet *(G-1046)*

Hoglund Bus Co Inc ....E... 763 295-5119
Monticello *(G-6273)*

Hvh Auto Parts Inc ....C... 763 784-1711
Minneapolis *(G-3493)*

Infiniti Marketing Inc ....E... 612 789-2025
Mound *(G-6388)*

Kato Distributing Inc ....D... 507 289-7456
Rochester *(G-7150)*

Keystone Automotive Industries ......E... 763 788-3039
Minneapolis *(G-3509)*

Kunz Oil Co ....D... 952 352-8600
Hopkins *(G-2567)*

L & M Supply Inc ....C... 218 326-9451
Grand Rapids *(G-2289)*

(G-00000) Company's Geographic Section entry number

SERVICES

Lakeview Industries Inc........................E... 952 368-3500
Chaska *(G-974)*

Northern Wholesale Supply Inc..........D... 651 429-1515
Hugo *(G-2672)*

Smith's Winter Products ....E... 763 493-3332
Osseo *(G-6665)*

3M Co ....D... 651 733-5300
Saint Paul *(G-9047)*

Toyota City Inc ....D... 763 566-0060
Minneapolis *(G-5842)*

MOTOR VEHICLE SPLYS & PARTS WHOLESALERS: Used

Viking Auto Salvage Inc ....E... 651 460-6166
Northfield *(G-6522)*

MOTOR VEHICLES, WHOLESALE: Ambulances

Nintey Four Services Inc ....E... 763 295-3604
Monticello *(G-6279)*

MOTOR VEHICLES, WHOLESALE: Snowmobiles

Northern Wholesale Supply Inc............D... 651 429-1515
Hugo *(G-2672)*

MOTOR VEHICLES, WHOLESALE: Trailers, Truck, New & Used

ABM Equipment & Supply Inc 952 938-5451
Hopkins *(G-2498)*

ABM Equipment & Supply LLC.............E... 952 938-5451
Hopkins *(G-2499)*

Allstate Sales & Leasing Corp ....D... 651 455-6500
South Saint Paul *(G-9508)*

Crossroads Trailer Sales & Svc...........E... 507 373-4443
Albert Lea *(G-45)*

Dahlke Trailer Sales Inc......................E... 763 783-0077
Minneapolis *(G-3450)*

River Valley Truck Centers Inc ....D... 507 345-1129
Mankato *(G-3187)*

St Cloud Truck Sales Inc ....D... 320 251-0931
Saint Cloud *(G-7442)*

Trudell Trailers of Minnesota...............E... 763 497-7084
Albertville *(G-77)*

Westman Freightliner Inc ....E... 507 625-4118
Mankato *(G-3217)*

MOTOR VEHICLES, WHOLESALE: Truck tractors

Astleford Equipment Co Inc.................E... 952 894-9200
Burnsville *(G-681)*

Istate Truck Inc... 952 854-2044
Minneapolis *(G-4739)*

Rihm Motor Co ....D... 651 646-7833
Saint Paul *(G-8902)*

St Cloud Truck Sales Inc ....D... 320 251-0931
Saint Cloud *(G-7442)*

Titan Machinery Inc ....E... 218 281-4668
Crookston *(G-1137)*

MOTOR VEHICLES, WHOLESALE: Trucks, Noncommercial

River Valley Truck Centers Inc ....D... 507 345-1129
Mankato *(G-3187)*

MOTOR VEHICLES, WHOLESALE: Trucks, commercial

Allstate Sales & Leasing Corp ....D... 651 455-6500
South Saint Paul *(G-9508)*

Astleford Equipment Co Inc.................E... 952 894-9200
Burnsville *(G-681)*

Chesley Truck Sales Inc.......................C... 651 636-3400
Saint Paul *(G-9195)*

Glen's Truck Center Inc.......................E... 763 428-4331
Rogers *(G-7324)*

Manders Diesel Repair Inc ....E... 952 469-1800
Lakeville *(G-2915)*

Midwest Diesel Service Inc ....E... 763 780-8533
Minneapolis *(G-6127)*

Nelson Leasing Inc ....E... 320 235-2770
Willmar *(G-10029)*

North Star International ....D... 612 378-1660
Minneapolis *(G-5219)*

Nuss Truck Group Inc ....E... 507 345-6225
Mankato *(G-3178)*

Olson & Johnson International..............E... 507 532-5718
Marshall *(G-3318)*

River Valley Truck Centers Inc ....D... 507 345-1129
Mankato *(G-3187)*

St Cloud Truck Sales Inc ....D... 320 251-0931
Saint Cloud *(G-7442)*

Thompson Motors of Wykoff Inc ....E... 507 352-2435
Wykoff *(G-10200)*

Westman Freightliner Inc ....E... 507 625-4118
Mankato *(G-3217)*

MOTOR VEHICLES, WHOLESALE: Vans, Noncommercial

Associated Partnership Ltd ....C... 952 890-7851
Savage *(G-9383)*

MOTORCYCLE REPAIR SHOPS

Faribault Harley Davidson Inc ....E... 507 334-5130
Faribault *(G-2004)*

St Paul Harley Davidson Inc ....D... 651 738-2168
Saint Paul *(G-9277)*

Zylstra Harley Davidson Inc.................E... 763 241-2000
Elk River *(G-1897)*

MOTORCYCLES: Wholesalers

Gull Way Ltd.......................................E... 218 753-1210
Tower *(G-9687)*

MOVIE THEATERS, EXC DRIVE-IN

AMC Entertainment Inc ....E... 763 494-0379
Maple Grove *(G-3236)*

American Multi-Cinema Inc ....E... 952 851-0073
Bloomington *(G-484)*

Andover Cinema ....E... 763 767-8401
Anoka *(G-153)*

Canam Theatres Moa LLC ....E... 952 883-8810
Bloomington *(G-491)*

Cinema Entertainment Corp ....E... 218 729-0334
Duluth *(G-1272)*

Cinema Entertainment Corp ....E... 218 529-1636
Duluth *(G-1273)*

Cinemark U S A Inc ....E... 507 625-1929
Mankato *(G-3117)*

Cineplex Odean Corp ....E... 763 591-5921
Minneapolis *(G-4076)*

Climb Theater Inc................................D... 651 453-9275
Inver Grove Heights *(G-2743)*

Mann Theaters Inc ....E... 952 931-3191
Hopkins *(G-2574)*

Marcus Theatres Corp ....E... 763 441-1234
Elk River *(G-1883)*

Parkwood 18 Theatres ....E... 320 251-1188
Waite Park *(G-9831)*

Premiere Theatres...............................E... 218 879-7985
Cloquet *(G-1061)*

Regal Cinemas Inc ....E... 651 452-8329
Saint Paul *(G-7892)*

Regal Cinemas Inc ....E... 952 435-8080
Burnsville *(G-788)*

Regents of The University of ....E... 612 624-2345
Minneapolis *(G-5497)*

Showplace 16 Kerasotes Theatre.........D... 763 757-6233
Minneapolis *(G-3602)*

Ten Thousand Things Theatre..............E... 612 724-4494
Minneapolis *(G-5810)*

MOVING SVC & STORAGE: Local

Action Moving Services Inc ....D... 952 894-8888
Burnsville *(G-672)*

Battmann Holdings Inc.........................D... 651 639-2800
Saint Paul *(G-8091)*

Beltmann Group Inc.............................D... 651 639-2800
Saint Paul *(G-8100)*

Bester Bros Transfer & Storage ....E... 651 451-1018
South Saint Paul *(G-9512)*

Dakt Enterprises Inc ....C... 952 474-6683
Eden Prairie *(G-1640)*

Paragon Moving & Storage Inc ....E... 952 936-9122
Hopkins *(G-2601)*

S & S Moving & Storage Inc.................E... 507 289-0779
Rochester *(G-7243)*

Van Minneapolis & Warehouse Co........D... 651 636-6000
Minneapolis *(G-6132)*

MOVING SVC: Local

Big Ale-Cat..E... 952 881-4128
Minneapolis *(G-3902)*

Harco Moving & Storage Inc ....E... 763 571-6227
Minneapolis *(G-3482)*

McCollister's Transportation ....E... 763 502-2120
Minneapolis *(G-3531)*

Mohawk United ....E... 651 481-0000
Minneapolis *(G-6129)*

Schroeder Moving Systems Inc............E... 763 694-6070
Minneapolis *(G-5614)*

MOVING SVC: Long-Distance

A A Metcalf Moving & Storage ....C... 651 484-0211
Saint Paul *(G-7967)*

Action Moving Services Inc.................D... 952 894-8888
Burnsville *(G-672)*

Archbold Enterprises LLC ....E... 651 484-0211
Saint Paul *(G-8060)*

Barrett Moving & Storage Co ....D... 952 944-6550
Eden Prairie *(G-1602)*

Battmann Holdings Inc.........................D... 651 639-2800
Saint Paul *(G-8091)*

Beltmann Group Inc.............................D... 651 639-2800
Saint Paul *(G-8100)*

Berger Transfer & Storage Inc ....D... 651 639-2260
Saint Paul *(G-8104)*

Mohawk Moving & Storage Inc.............D... 763 717-3705
Minneapolis *(G-6128)*

Paragon Moving & Storage Inc ....E... 952 936-9122
Hopkins *(G-2601)*

S & S Moving & Storage Inc ....E... 507 289-0779
Rochester *(G-7243)*

Van Minneapolis & Warehouse Co ......D... 651 636-6000
Minneapolis *(G-6132)*

MULTI-SVCS CENTER

Amherst H Wilder Foundation..............B... 651 280-2000
Saint Paul *(G-8040)*

Amherst H Wilder Foundation..............D... 651 224-1395
Saint Paul *(G-8043)*

Amherst H Wilder Foundation..............E... 651 290-8666
Saint Paul *(G-8045)*

Church of Our Lady of The Lake..........E... 952 472-1284
Mound *(G-6384)*

Community Action Council Inc ....E... 952 985-5300
Burnsville *(G-701)*

Glenwood-Lyndale Community Ctr .....D... 612 342-1500
Minneapolis *(G-4530)*

Neighborhood Involvement ....E... 612 374-3125
Minneapolis *(G-5180)*

Volunteers of America Inc ....E... 952 941-0305
Eden Prairie *(G-1809)*

MUSEUMS

American Wings Air Museum...............E... 763 786-4146
Minneapolis *(G-3401)*

Bakken Museum ....E... 612 927-6508
Minneapolis *(G-3862)*

Commemorative Air Force...................C... 651 455-6942
South Saint Paul *(G-9523)*

County of Mower ....C... 507 437-9440
Austin *(G-268)*

Historical Society of MN ....E... 218 226-6372
Two Harbors *(G-9708)*

Historical Society of MN ....E... 218 327-4482
Grand Rapids *(G-2286)*

Historical Society of MN ....E... 651 297-2555
Saint Paul *(G-8485)*

Ironworld Development Corp ....D... 218 254-7959
Chisholm *(G-998)*

James Ford Bell Museum of.................E... 612 624-4112
Minneapolis *(G-4753)*

Lake Superior Railroad Museum...........D... 218 733-7590
Duluth *(G-1378)*

Mayowood Mansion Tours ....E... 507 282-9447
Rochester *(G-7177)*

Minnesota Children's Museum.............D... 651 225-6000
Saint Paul *(G-8677)*

Regents of The University of................E... 612 625-9494
Minneapolis *(G-5489)*

Science Museum of Minnesota ....B... 651 221-9488
Saint Paul *(G-8936)*

MUSEUMS & ART GALLERIES

American Swedish Institute.................E... 612 871-4907
Minneapolis *(G-3760)*

Art Walker Center ....C... 612 375-7600
Minneapolis *(G-3812)*

Art Walker Center Inc ....E... 612 375-7600
Minneapolis *(G-3813)*

MUSIC BROADCASTING SVCS

Captionmax Inc..................................E... 612 341-3566
Minneapolis *(G-4000)*

CC Holdings Inc..................................E... 612 371-8008
Minneapolis *(G-4034)*

Institute of Production ....D... 612 375-1900
Minneapolis *(G-4710)*

Muzak LLC..E... 763 424-5533
Osseo *(G-6641)*

Public Radio International Inc ....D... 612 330-9266
Minneapolis *(G-5438)*

Employment codes: A=Over 500 employees, B=251-500,
C=101-250, D=51-100, E=25-50

2011 Harris Minnesota
Services Directory

© Harris InfoSource 1-866-281-6415
737

MUSIC DISTRIBUTION SYSTEM SVCS

Custom Communications Inc ....D... 507 288-5522
Rochester *(G-7091)*

MUSIC RECORDING PRODUCER

Interscope Records Inc ....E... 952 828-6060
Eden Prairie *(G-1697)*

MUSICAL INSTRUMENT REPAIR

Paul A Schmitt Music Co......................E... 763 566-4560
Minneapolis *(G-5349)*

MUTUAL ACCIDENT ASSOCIATIONS

Federated Mutual Insurance Co ....C... 507 455-5200
Owatonna *(G-6710)*

MUTUAL FUND MANAGEMENT

Ameriprise Financial Inc ....A... 612 671-3131
Minneapolis *(G-3767)*
Rbc Wealth Management ....A... 612 371-7750
Minneapolis *(G-5472)*
Voyageur Co's Inc................................D... 612 376-7000
Minneapolis *(G-5985)*

NAIL SALONS

Day S P A At Nails Etc ....E... 952 830-0100
Minneapolis *(G-4230)*
Image Shoppe Inc ....E... 952 949-1313
Eden Prairie *(G-1690)*
Salon Sabell Inc ....E... 612 866-3679
Minneapolis *(G-5597)*
Snips of Eden Prairie Inc......................E... 952 941-1495
Minneapolis *(G-5692)*

NATURAL ETHANE PRODUCTION

Heron Lake Bioenergy LLC ....E... 507 793-0077
Heron Lake *(G-2434)*

NATURAL GAS DISTRIBUTION TO CONSUMERS

Allete Inc ....C... 218 279-5000
Duluth *(G-1235)*
Cargill Power Markets LLC ....E... 952 984-3068
Minnetonka *(G-6151)*
Centerpoint Energy Houston ....E... 763 757-6200
Minneapolis *(G-3431)*
Centerpoint Energy Resources ....D... 612 861-8450
Minneapolis *(G-4044)*
City of Owatonna ....D... 507 451-2480
Owatonna *(G-6701)*
MDU Resources Group Inc ....E... 218 736-6935
Fergus Falls *(G-2093)*
Minnesota Energy Resources................C... 651 322-8902
Rosemount *(G-7372)*
Northern States Power Co ....C... 320 255-8601
Saint Cloud *(G-7563)*
Virginia, City of Inc ....D... 218 748-7540
Virginia *(G-9761)*

NATURAL GAS PRODUCTION

Cenex Inc ....A... 800 232-3639
South Saint Paul *(G-9516)*
CHS Inc ....A... 651 355-6000
Inver Grove Heights *(G-2742)*

NATURAL GAS STORAGE SVCS

Cenex Inc ....A... 800 232-3639
South Saint Paul *(G-9516)*

NATURAL RESOURCE PRESERVATION SVCS

Minnesota Department of ....E... 218 739-7576
Fergus Falls *(G-2098)*
St Paul Public School 651 436-5243
Afton *(G-10)*

NEIGHBORHOOD CENTER

Neighborhood House ....D... 651 789-2500
Saint Paul *(G-8743)*

NEIGHBORHOOD DEVELOPMENT GROUP

Project For Pride In Living ....D... 612 455-5100
Minneapolis *(G-5428)*
Project For Pride In Living ....D... 612 332-0664
Minneapolis *(G-5429)*

NEWSPAPERS, WHOLESALE

Lakeland Distribution Services ....E... 320 762-8385
Alexandria *(G-109)*
Minnesota News Service Inc ....D... 952 703-0075
Minneapolis *(G-5086)*
3 Br's Inc..E... 507 645-8600
Northfield *(G-6542)*

NONMETALLIC MINERALS: Support Activities, Exc Fuels

Mosaic Co ....C... 763 577-2700
Minneapolis *(G-5133)*

NOVELTIES, PAPER, WHOLESALE

Berry Coffee Co..................................E... 952 937-8697
Eden Prairie *(G-1604)*
5 K Enterprises Inc ....E... 612 216-6292
Mankato *(G-3127)*

NURSERY SCHOOLS

Aldrich Memorial Nursery Sch..............E... 507 289-3097
Rochester *(G-7048)*
Building Block Child Care Inc...............763 557-1111
Minneapolis *(G-3972)*
Normandale Evangelical ....E... 952 929-1697
Minneapolis *(G-5209)*
Westwood Lutheran Church ....E... 952 545-5623
Minneapolis *(G-6062)*

NURSERY STOCK, WHOLESALE

Bachman's Inc.....................................C... 612 861-7600
Minneapolis *(G-3856)*
Bachman's Inc.....................................E... 651 463-3288
Farmington *(G-2041)*
Gerten Greenhouses & Garden ....B... 651 450-1501
Inver Grove Heights *(G-2751)*
Great River Garden ....E... 218 927-2521
Aitkin *(G-19)*
Little Yukon Greenhouse Inc ....D... 218 692-3536
Crosslake *(G-1152)*
Midland Nursery Inc.............................E... 763 478-6122
Buffalo *(G-651)*
R D Offutt Co ....E... 218 732-4163
Park Rapids *(G-6761)*

NURSING & PERSONAL CARE FACILITIES, NEC

Cherished Wings Transportation ....E... 763 221-8788
Minneapolis *(G-4059)*
Class Act Estates Senior......................D... 612 229-3881
Buffalo *(G-642)*
Luverne Residential Advantage ....D... 507 283-4088
Luverne *(G-3062)*
Plymouth Senior Housing ....D... 651 631-6300
Plymouth *(G-6879)*
Semcil Living Inc..................................E... 507 285-1815
Rochester *(G-7250)*
Senior Management Inc.........................D... 507 725-3351
Caledonia *(G-828)*
V Care Home Health Inc ....D... 651 793-7635
Saint Paul *(G-9122)*

NURSING CARE FACILITIES: Skilled

A R I Inc...E... 763 689-1162
Cambridge *(G-830)*
Aicota Healthcare Center ....C... 218 927-2164
Aitkin *(G-12)*
Albert Lea Medical Center-Mayo ....A... 507 373-2384
Albert Lea *(G-32)*
Alternative Continum of Care ....D... 507 373-5600
Albert Lea *(G-37)*
American Baptist Homes of The............D... 507 893-3171
Winnebago *(G-10075)*
Amherst H Wilder Foundation ....C... 651 220-1700
Saint Paul *(G-8041)*
Annandale Care Center ....C... 320 274-3737
Annandale *(G-134)*
Appleton Area Health Services..............C... 320 289-2422
Appleton *(G-244)*
Assumption Home Inc ....C... 320 685-3693
Cold Spring *(G-1082)*
Atchison Enterprises Inc.......................D... 507 376-3175
Worthington *(G-10178)*
Auburn West Inc ....E... 952 442-2546
Waconia *(G-9778)*
Augustana Chapel View Homes ....C... 952 938-2761
Hopkins *(G-2512)*
Augustana Dassel Lakeside Com ....D... 320 275-3308
Dassel *(G-1159)*

Augustana Health Care Center............C... 651 437-6176
Hastings *(G-2376)*
Augustana Health Care Center............B... 952 431-7700
Saint Paul *(G-7708)*
Aviv Health Care Inc.............................C... 612 377-4723
Minneapolis *(G-3845)*
Aviv Health Care Inc.............................C... 952 546-4261
Minneapolis *(G-3844)*
Barrett Care Center Inc ....D... 320 528-2527
Barrett *(G-308)*
Behavioral Hlth Care Providers............E... 763 525-9919
Minneapolis *(G-3879)*
Belgrade Nursing Home Inc ....D... 320 254-8215
Belgrade *(G-364)*
Benedictine Health Center....................C... 218 723-6408
Duluth *(G-1249)*
Benedictine Health System ....D... 320 485-2151
Winsted *(G-10158)*
Benedictine Health System ....E... 507 457-0280
Winona *(G-10080)*
Bethany Samaritan Inc..........................C... 507 289-3336
Rochester *(G-7063)*
Bethesda ....C... 320 235-3924
Willmar *(G-9987)*
Bethesda ....E... 320 235-8364
Willmar *(G-9988)*
Beverly Enterprises - MN ....D... 507 932-3283
Saint Charles *(G-7402)*
Beverly Enterprises - MN ....E... 507 557-2211
Franklin *(G-2180)*
Beverly Enterprises - MN ....D... 507 334-3918
Faribault *(G-1992)*
Beverly Enterprises - MN ....E... 952 881-8676
Minneapolis *(G-3896)*
Beverly Enterprises - MN ....C... 651 483-5431
Saint Paul *(G-8111)*
Beverly Enterprises - MN ....D... 651 439-5775
Stillwater *(G-9602)*
Beverly Enterprises - MN ....D... 320 523-1652
Olivia *(G-6560)*
Beverly Enterprises - MN ....D... 218 583-2965
Henning *(G-2431)*
Beverly Enterprises - MN ....B... 952 935-0333
Minneapolis *(G-3894)*
Beverly Enterprises - MN ....C... 612 874-1603
Minneapolis *(G-3895)*
Beverly Enterprises - MN ....D... 320 843-2225
Benson *(G-438)*
Beverly Enterprises - MN ....C... 952 474-5488
Excelsior *(G-1940)*
Beverly Enterprises - MN ....C... 952 935-3338
Hopkins *(G-2518)*
Beverly Enterprises - MN ....D... 507 895-4445
La Crescent *(G-2841)*
Beverly Enterprises - MN ....D... 507 836-6135
Slayton *(G-9485)*
Beverly Enterprises - MN ....C... 651 645-6453
Saint Paul *(G-8112)*
Beverly Enterprises - MN ....E... 320 358-4765
Rush City *(G-7389)*
Beverly Enterprises - MN ....D... 507 342-5166
Wabasso *(G-9776)*
Beverly Enterprises - MN ....C... 612 333-0111
Minneapolis *(G-3897)*
Beverly Enterprises - MN ....B... 952 473-5466
Wayzata *(G-9906)*
Birchwood Health Care Center..............C... 651 464-5600
Forest Lake *(G-2158)*
Browns Valley Health Center................D... 320 695-2165
Browns Valley *(G-627)*
Cambridge Nursing Home Inc ....C... 763 689-2323
Cambridge *(G-835)*
Catholic Services For The ....C... 651 793-2100
Saint Paul *(G-8177)*
Central Health Care Of Le Ctr...............D... 507 357-2275
Le Center *(G-2950)*
Central Todd County Care Ctr...............C... 218 756-3636
Clarissa *(G-1033)*
Charterhouse Inc ....C... 507 266-8572
Rochester *(G-7075)*
Chosen Valley Care Center Inc ....C... 507 867-4220
Chatfield *(G-986)*
City of Adams ....D... 507 582-3263
Adams *(G-3)*
City of Clarkfield ....C... 320 669-7561
Clarkfield *(G-1034)*
City of Fertile ....C... 218 945-6194
Fertile *(G-2125)*
City of Heron Lake...............................D... 507 793-2349
Heron Lake *(G-2435)*
City of Lakefield ....D... 507 662-6646
Lakefield *(G-2881)*
City of Lamberton ....E... 507 752-7346
Lamberton *(G-2945)*

S
E
R
V
I
C
E
S

Name	Location	Code	Phone
City of Ortonville	Ortonville (G-6580)	D	320 839-6113
City of Renville	Renville (G-7031)	D	320 329-8381
Clara City Community Nursing	Clara City (G-1026)	D	320 847-2221
Clearwater County Memorial	Bagley (G-300)	C	218 694-6501
Cokato Charitable Trust	Cokato (G-1076)	C	320 286-2158
Colonial Acres Home Inc	Golden Valley (G-2239)	C	763 544-1555
Colonial Acres Home Inc	Minneapolis (G-4122)	C	763 546-6125
Colonial Manor of Balaton	Balaton (G-304)	D	507 734-3511
Community Memorial Home Inc	Osakis (G-6586)	D	320 859-2111
Community Memorial Hospital	Spring Valley (G-9568)	C	507 346-7381
Community Services Inc	Saint Paul (G-8239)	D	651 631-6000
County of Dodge	Dodge Center (G-1225)	D	507 374-2578
County of Mahnomen	Mahnomen (G-3084)	D	218 935-2511
County of Pennington	Thief River Falls (G-9665)	D	218 681-1675
County of Ramsey	Saint Paul (G-8258)	C	651 777-7486
Cuyuna Range Hospital Inc	Crosby (G-1147)	B	218 546-7000
Dawson Area Hospital District	Dawson (G-1164)	C	320 769-4323
Deer River Healthcare Center	Deer River (G-1168)	C	218 246-2900
Dignified Assisted Living Inc	Rogers (G-7322)	D	763 428-1981
Divine Providence Community	Sleepy Eye (G-9494)	D	507 794-3011
Divine Providence Health Ctr	Ivanhoe (G-2784)	C	507 694-1414
Ebenezer Ridges Inc	Burnsville (G-715)	C	952 898-8400
Ebenezer Society	Minneapolis (G-4309)	C	612 879-2262
Ebenezer Society	Minneapolis (G-4310)	C	612 879-1400
Ebenezer Society	Burnsville (G-716)	D	952 435-8116
Ecumen	Mankato (G-3124)	C	507 345-4576
Ecumen	Alexandria (G-98)	C	320 762-1567
Ecumen	Saint Paul (G-8322)	D	651 766-4300
Ecumen	Chisago City (G-991)	C	651 257-0575
Ecumen	Two Harbors (G-9706)	D	218 834-8374
Ecumen Home Care Inc	Bloomington (G-496)	B	952 888-7751
Ecumen Home Care Inc	Detroit Lakes (G-1193)	C	218 847-4486
Ecumen Home Care Inc	Duluth (G-1309)	C	218 525-1951
Edgebrook Care Center	Edgerton (G-1823)	D	507 442-7121
Elder Care of Bemidji Inc	Bemidji (G-390)	C	218 444-1745
Elder Meadowland Care Homes	Tenstrike (G-9662)	E	218 586-3740
Elders' Home Inc	New York Mills (G-6478)	D	218 385-2005
Elim Care Inc	Eden Prairie (G-1653)	E	952 259-4500
Elim Homes Inc	Watertown (G-9890)	D	952 955-2691
Episcopal Church Home Of MN	Saint Paul (G-8344)	C	651 646-4061
Evangelical Covenant Church	Minneapolis (G-4374)	D	612 781-2691
Evangelical Free Church of	Princeton (G-6906)	C	763 389-1171
Evangelical Free Church of	Milaca (G-3376)	C	320 983-2185
Evangelical Lutheran Good	Waconia (G-9785)	C	952 442-5111
Evangelical Lutheran Good	Jackson (G-2792)	C	507 847-3100
Evangelical Lutheran Good	Howard Lake (G-2667)	D	320 543-3800
Evangelical Lutheran Good	Pelican Rapids (G-6778)	D	218 863-2401
Evangelical Lutheran Good	Stillwater (G-9615)	C	651 439-7180
Evangelical Lutheran Good	Arlington (G-249)	D	507 964-2251
Evangelical Lutheran Good	Saint James (G-7643)	C	507 375-3286
Evangelical Lutheran Good	Blackduck (G-474)	D	218 835-4218
Evangelical Lutheran Good	Saint Paul (G-8347)	C	651 774-9765
Evangelical Lutheran Good	Winthrop (G-10167)	D	507 647-5391
Evangelical Lutheran Good	Waterville (G-9894)	C	507 362-4245
Evangelical Lutheran Good	Hoffman (G-2489)	D	320 986-2048
Evangelical Lutheran Good	Brainerd (G-565)	B	218 829-1407
Evangelical Lutheran Good	Mountain Lake (G-6397)	C	507 427-2464
Evangelical Lutheran Good	Minneapolis (G-4377)	C	763 544-4171
Evangelical Lutheran Good	Pipestone (G-6826)	C	507 825-5428
Evangelical Lutheran Good	Glenwood (G-2222)	D	320 634-4552
Evangelical Lutheran Good	International Falls (G-2720)	D	218 283-4768
Evangelical Lutheran Good	Saint Peter (G-9302)	D	507 931-9021
Evangelical Lutheran Good	Albert Lea (G-50)	B	507 373-0683
Evangelical Lutheran Good	Anoka (G-178)	C	763 421-2311
Evansville Care Campus LLC	Evansville (G-1926)	E	218 948-2219
Eveleth Hospital Corp	Eveleth (G-1931)	E	218 744-1950
Eventide Senior Living	Moorhead (G-6314)	B	218 233-7508
Evergreen Terrace	Grand Rapids (G-2276)	C	218 326-3431
Extendicare Facilities Inc	Saint Paul (G-8354)	C	651 484-3378
Extendicare Homes Inc	Saint Paul (G-8356)	C	651 224-1848
Extendicare Homes Inc	Saint Paul (G-8355)	C	651 633-7875
Extendicare Homes Inc	Minneapolis (G-4383)	B	763 588-0771
Extendicare Homes Inc	Richfield (G-7035)	D	612 861-1691
Extendicare Homes Inc	Minneapolis (G-4384)	B	763 545-0416
Extendicare Homes Inc	Minneapolis (G-4386)	C	952 927-4949
Extendicare Homes Inc	Minneapolis (G-4387)	C	952 920-8380
Extendicare Homes Inc	Minneapolis (G-4385)	C	952 927-9717
Fair Oaks Lodge Inc	Wadena (G-9801)	C	218 631-1391
Fairmont Community Hospital	Fairmont (G-1963)	A	507 238-8100
Fairview Health Services	Wyoming (G-10202)	B	651 982-7000
Fairview Seminary Home Inc	Red Wing (G-6980)	C	651 385-3434
Farmington Health Service	Farmington (G-2051)	E	651 463-7818
Field Crest Care Center	Hayfield (G-2427)	C	507 477-3266
First Solutions	Two Harbors (G-9707)	E	218 834-7205
Foley Health Care Inc	Foley (G-2137)	D	320 968-6201
Foundation For Healthcare	Sartell (G-9328)	B	320 253-1920
Franciscan Health Center Inc	Duluth (G-1326)	D	218 727-8933
Ggnsc Minneapolis Bloomington	Minneapolis (G-4525)	D	952 881-8676
Ggnsc Minneapolis Chateau LLC	Minneapolis (G-4526)	D	612 874-1603
Ggnsc St Paul Lake Ridge LLC	Saint Paul (G-8408)	D	651 483-5431
Ggnsc Wayzata LLC	Wayzata (G-9918)	D	952 473-5466
Glenwood Village Care Center	Glenwood (G-2225)	C	320 634-5131
Goldfinch Estates	Fairmont (G-1968)	E	507 235-9405
Grand Village	Grand Rapids (G-2282)	C	218 326-0543
Grandview Good Samaritan Ctr	Saint Peter (G-9305)	D	507 931-9021
Guardian Angels Health & Rehab	Hibbing (G-2448)	C	218 263-7583
Harmony Community Healthcare	Harmony (G-2371)	D	507 886-6544
Harmony Nursing Homes Inc	Saint Paul (G-8443)	D	651 488-6658
Haven Homes Inc	Maple Plain (G-3275)	D	763 479-1993
Health Care Center	Minneapolis (G-4617)	C	612 724-5495
Health Care Services Inc	Saint Paul (G-8447)	D	651 777-7435
Health East Care Center White	Saint Paul (G-8448)	C	651 232-1818
Hendricks Community Hospital	Hendricks (G-2429)	C	507 275-3134
Heritage of Edina Inc	Minneapolis (G-4641)	C	952 920-9145
Highland Manor Inc	New Ulm (G-6455)	C	507 359-2026
Hillcrest Nursing Home	Red Lake Falls (G-6971)	D	218 253-2157
Hospice of Healtheast Inc	Saint Paul (G-8495)	C	651 232-3312
Hubbard, County of Inc	Park Rapids (G-6755)	C	218 732-3329
Hutchinson Health Care	Hutchinson (G-2701)	C	320 234-4906
Interfaith Care Center Inc	Carlton (G-869)	C	218 384-4258
J & L Nursing Care Inc	Rochester (G-7145)	E	507 529-0018
Jackson Cottonwood Community	Jackson (G-2795)	E	507 847-2366
Janesville Nursing Home Inc	Janesville (G-2802)	D	507 231-5113
Jones-Harrison Residence Corp	Minneapolis (G-4778)	B	612 920-2030
Joshco Construction Inc	Chaska (G-971)	D	952 361-8000
Knute Nelson	Alexandria (G-107)	B	320 763-6653
Lake Shore Inn Nursing Home	Waseca (G-9881)	C	507 835-2800
Lakeland Hospice & Home Care	Fergus Falls (G-2082)	C	218 998-1400
Lakeside Medical Center Inc	Pine City (G-6813)	C	320 629-2542
Lakeview Methodist Health Care	Fairmont (G-1976)	C	507 235-6606
Lakewood Health Center	Baudette (G-317)	C	218 634-2120
Lifecare Medical Center	Roseau (G-7355)	C	218 463-4305
Little Sisters of The Poor of	Saint Paul (G-8592)	D	651 227-0336
Living Services Foundation	Winsted (G-10162)	D	320 485-2151
Living Services Foundation	Minneota (G-6134)	C	507 872-5300
Long Term Care Associates Inc	Mora (G-6366)	D	320 679-1411
Lovingcare Nursing Services	Saint Paul (G-8595)	E	651 848-0061
Luther Haven	Montevideo (G-6249)	C	320 269-6517
Lutheran Brethren Retirement	Fergus Falls (G-2088)	C	218 736-5441
Lutheran Care Center Inc	Little Falls (G-3012)	D	320 632-9211
Lutheran Memorial Home	Halstad (G-2335)	D	218 456-2105
Lutheran Retirement Home of	Truman (G-9695)	C	507 776-2031
Lyngblomsten	Saint Paul (G-8599)	B	651 646-2941
Madison Lutheran Home	Madison (G-3076)	B	320 598-7536
Martin Luther Manor	Minneapolis (G-4960)	B	952 888-7751
Mercy Hospital Health Care Ctr	Moose Lake (G-6352)	B	218 485-4481
Midway Care Center Inc	Fosston (G-2177)	E	218 435-1272
Mille Lacs Health System	Onamia (G-6574)	B	320 532-3154
Minneota Manor Health Care Ctr	Minneota (G-6135)	C	507 872-5300
Minnesota Department of	Luverne (G-3065)	C	507 283-1100
Minnesota Department of	Minneapolis (G-5073)	E	612 721-0600

Employment codes: A=Over 500 employees, B=251-500,
C=101-250, D=51-100, E=25-50

2011 Harris Minnesota
Services Directory

© Harris InfoSource 1-866-281-6415
739

Minnesota Department of ....E... 218 736-0400
Fergus Falls *(G-2097)*

Minnesota Masonic Home North ....A... 763 592-3000
Minneapolis *(G-5083)*

Minnesota Odd Fellows Home ....C... 507 645-6611
Northfield *(G-6532)*

Minnesota Odd Fellows Home ....C... 507 645-6611
Northfield *(G-6533)*

Minnesota Valley Memorial Hosp ....C... 507 665-3375
Le Sueur *(G-2958)*

Mission Healthcare LLC ....C... 218 326-3431
Grand Rapids *(G-2296)*

Monticello-Big Lake Community ....B... 763 295-2945
Monticello *(G-6278)*

Moravian Care Ministries ....C... 952 448-9303
Chaska *(G-976)*

Mount Olivet Careview Home ....B... 612 827-5677
Minneapolis *(G-5139)*

New Richland Care Center ....C... 507 465-3292
New Richland *(G-6436)*

North Cities Health Care Inc ....D... 651 633-7200
Saint Paul *(G-8751)*

North Country Hospital ....C... 218 751-0220
Bemidji *(G-409)*

North Memorial Health Care ....D... 763 520-3900
Minneapolis *(G-5216)*

North Star Nursing Inc ....E... 218 573-2238
Osage *(G-6585)*

Northern Itasca Hospital Dist ....C... 218 743-3177
Bigfork *(G-461)*

Northfield Care Center Inc ....C... 507 645-9511
Northfield *(G-6536)*

Northome Health Care Inc ....D... 218 897-5235
Northome *(G-6547)*

Northwest Health Care Inc ....C... 320 251-9120
Saint Cloud *(G-7439)*

Northwest Investors Inc ....E... 952 894-7795
Burnsville *(G-768)*

Osseo Gardens Assisted Living ....E... 763 315-4869
Osseo *(G-6648)*

Otter Tail Nursing Home ....D... 218 495-2993
Battle Lake *(G-312)*

Our Lady of Good Counsel Home ....E... 651 646-2797
Saint Paul *(G-8794)*

Park View Care Center Inc ....C... 763 682-1131
Buffalo *(G-656)*

Parkview Manor Inc ....D... 507 967-2482
Ellsworth *(G-1908)*

Perham Hospital District ....B... 218 346-4500
Perham *(G-6800)*

Pines ....E... 612 861-3331
Minneapolis *(G-5379)*

Pioneer Home Inc................................C... 218 739-7701
Fergus Falls *(G-2113)*

Pioneer Memorial Care Center.............D... 218 687-2365
Erskine *(G-1921)*

Pleasant Manor Inc ....D... 507 334-3558
Faribault *(G-2026)*

Prairie Manor Nursing Home ....C... 507 583-4434
Blooming Prairie *(G-477)*

Prarie View Healthcare Center ....D... 507 629-3331
Tracy *(G-9690)*

Presbyterian Home Farm Stead...........E... 763 712-7000
Anoka *(G-215)*

Presbyterian Homes & Services...........B... 952 948-3000
Minneapolis *(G-5404)*

Presbyterian Homes of Arden ....A... 651 631-6000
Saint Paul *(G-8843)*

Presbyterian Homes, Housing..............A... 651 631-6100
Saint Paul *(G-8844)*

Presbyterian Nursing Homes Inc ....B... 952 888-9461
Minneapolis *(G-5405)*

Quality Life Styles Inc........................D... 952 445-4155
Shakopee *(G-9468)*

Red Lake Band of Chippewa................D... 218 679-3400
Redlake *(G-7016)*

Red Wing Healthcare LLC ....C... 651 388-2843
Red Wing *(G-6997)*

Redeemer Residence Inc ....C... 612 827-2555
Minneapolis *(G-5479)*

Regina Medical Center ....A... 651 480-4100
Hastings *(G-2402)*

Ridgeview Home Support Service.........E... 952 442-6032
Waconia *(G-9791)*

Rochester Health & Rehab West ....D... 507 288-1818
Rochester *(G-7233)*

Sacred Heart Care Center ....C... 507 433-1808
Austin *(G-286)*

Saint Anne of Winona ....C... 507 454-3621
Winona *(G-10123)*

Saint Elizabeth's Hospital ....C... 651 565-4531
Wabasha *(G-9770)*

Saint Elizabeth's Hospital of ....C... 651 565-4581
Wabasha *(G-9771)*

Saint Olaf Retirement ....C... 612 522-6561
Minneapolis *(G-5592)*

Sauer Memorial Home ....C... 507 454-5540
Winona *(G-10124)*

Senior Epoch Living Inc ....E... 952 473-3330
Hopkins *(G-2630)*

Senior Hutchinson Care Svcs...............D... 320 234-4751
Hutchinson *(G-2712)*

Senior McIntosh Living ....D... 218 563-3043
McIntosh *(G-3342)*

Shady Lane Nursing Home ....C... 218 631-1391
Wadena *(G-9811)*

Shepherd Good Lutheran Home............C... 320 252-6525
Sauk Rapids *(G-9374)*

Shepherd Good Lutheran Home............C... 507 864-7714
Rushford *(G-7393)*

Shepherd Good Lutheran Home............E... 320 258-8665
Sauk Rapids *(G-9375)*

Sholom Community Alliance ....B... 952 935-6311
Minneapolis *(G-5656)*

Sholom Home East Inc ....A... 651 646-6311
Saint Paul *(G-8952)*

Sholom Home West Inc ....C... 952 935-6311
Minneapolis *(G-5659)*

Sioux Valley Canby Campus.................C... 507 223-7221
Canby *(G-853)*

Southview Acres Health Care ....B... 651 451-1821
Saint Paul *(G-7908)*

St Anthony Park Home Inc ....C... 651 646-7486
Saint Paul *(G-8981)*

St Benedict's Senior Community ....A... 320 252-0010
Saint Cloud *(G-7441)*

St Francis Health Services of ....C... 218 727-8801
Duluth *(G-1459)*

St Francis Medical Center ....B... 218 643-3000
Breckenridge *(G-601)*

St Gertrude's Health Center ....D... 952 233-4400
Shakopee *(G-9477)*

St Johns Lutheran Home ....B... 507 373-8226
Albert Lea *(G-67)*

St Louis, County of Inc ....B... 218 720-1500
Duluth *(G-1463)*

St Luke's Lutheran Care Center ....C... 507 526-2184
Blue Earth *(G-537)*

St Mark's Lutheran Home Inc ....C... 507 437-4594
Austin *(G-288)*

St Mary's Regional Health Ctr..............C... 218 847-5611
Detroit Lakes *(G-1217)*

St Mary's Regional Health Ctr..............C... 218 847-5611
Detroit Lakes *(G-1218)*

St Michael's Health & Rehab ....D... 218 748-7800
Virginia *(G-9757)*

St Olaf Retirement Center Inc ....C... 612 522-6561
Minneapolis *(G-5729)*

St Peter, City of Inc ....C... 507 931-7354
Saint Peter *(G-9314)*

St Williams Nursing Home Inc ....C... 218 338-4671
Parkers Prairie *(G-6767)*

Sterling Park Health Care Ctr...............A... 320 252-9595
Waite Park *(G-9841)*

Sunnyside Care Center ....D... 218 238-5944
Lake Park *(G-2880)*

Sunrise Cottage of Mankato ....E... 507 345-8787
Mankato *(G-3202)*

Sunrise Senior Living Inc ....E... 763 682-5489
Buffalo *(G-657)*

Tealwood Care Centers Inc ....D... 320 252-9595
Waite Park *(G-9842)*

Thro Co ....C... 507 387-3491
Mankato *(G-3203)*

Thro Co ....C... 507 345-4631
Mankato *(G-3204)*

Thro Co ....C... 952 758-2511
New Prague *(G-6435)*

Thro Co ....D... 507 388-2913
Mankato *(G-3205)*

Tracy Healthcare Center Inc ....D... 507 629-3331
Tracy *(G-9692)*

Traverse Care Center..........................D... 320 563-8124
Wheaton *(G-9969)*

Tuff Memorial Homes Inc ....D... 507 962-3275
Hills *(G-2482)*

Tweeten-Lutheran Health Care ....C... 507 498-3211
Spring Grove *(G-9562)*

Twin City Christian Homes Inc ....D... 952 944-8982
Eden Prairie *(G-1799)*

Tyler Healthcare Center Inc ....C... 507 247-5521
Tyler *(G-9716)*

Valley View Nursing Home of ....D... 507 896-3125
Houston *(G-2664)*

Villa St Vincent Inc ....C... 218 281-3424
Crookston *(G-1143)*

Voa Anoka Care Center Inc ....D... 952 941-0305
Eden Prairie *(G-1808)*

Voa Care Centers MN ....D... 763 535-6260
Minneapolis *(G-5981)*

Voans Health Services Corp.................D... 507 263-4658
Cannon Falls *(G-863)*

Volunteers of America Care ....C... 507 794-7995
Sleepy Eye *(G-9503)*

Weiner Memorial Foundation ....B... 507 532-9661
Marshall *(G-3332)*

West Wind Village................................C... 320 589-1133
Morris *(G-6380)*

White Community Hospital Corp ....C... 218 229-2211
Aurora *(G-257)*

Winona Community Memorial Hosp .....A... 507 454-3650
Winona *(G-10145)*

Winona Health...................................E... 507 457-4468
Winona *(G-10148)*

Wood-Dale Home Inc..........................D... 507 637-3587
Redwood Falls *(G-7029)*

Woodland Heights Health Care ....C... 651 451-1881
Inver Grove Heights *(G-2775)*

Woodrest Health Care Center...............D... 218 547-1855
Walker *(G-9861)*

Zumbrota Nursing Home ....D... 507 732-8400
Zumbrota *(G-10223)*

NURSING HOME, EXC SKILLED & INTERMEDIATE CARE FACILITY

Aitkin Health Services..........................D... 218 927-5545
Aitkin *(G-15)*

Albert Lee Medical Center Inc ....D... 507 553-3115
Wells *(G-9960)*

American Baptist Homes of The ....D... 612 529-7747
Minneapolis *(G-3745)*

Atchison Enterprises Inc ....D... 507 376-5312
Worthington *(G-10179)*

Augustana Health Care Center.............C... 651 437-6176
Hastings *(G-2376)*

Aviv Health Care Inc...........................C... 763 425-3939
Osseo *(G-6597)*

Cardenas & Reynolds Entrprs..............D... 651 222-7200
Saint Paul *(G-8156)*

City of Clarkfield................................C... 320 669-7561
Clarkfield *(G-1034)*

City of Ortonville................................D... 320 839-6113
Ortonville *(G-6580)*

City of Ulen..D... 218 596-8847
Ulen *(G-9717)*

Cuyuna Range Hospital Inc ....C... 218 546-7000
Crosby *(G-1148)*

Elder Care of Bemidji Inc ....C... 218 444-1745
Bemidji *(G-390)*

Elders' Home Inc................................D... 218 385-2005
New York Mills *(G-6478)*

Elim Homes Inc..................................D... 952 955-2691
Watertown *(G-9890)*

Evangelical Free Church of ....C... 763 389-1171
Princeton *(G-6906)*

Evangelical Lutheran Good ....C... 507 847-3100
Jackson *(G-2792)*

Evangelical Lutheran Good ....D... 320 543-3800
Howard Lake *(G-2667)*

Evangelical Lutheran Good ....B... 612 332-4262
Minneapolis *(G-4378)*

Evangelical Lutheran Good ....D... 507 964-2251
Arlington *(G-249)*

Evangelical Lutheran Good ....C... 507 375-3286
Saint James *(G-7643)*

Evangelical Lutheran Good ....D... 218 354-2254
Barnesville *(G-305)*

Evangelical Lutheran Good ....D... 507 274-6155
Westbrook *(G-9966)*

Evangelical Lutheran Good ....E... 507 427-3221
Mountain Lake *(G-6396)*

Evangelical Lutheran Good ....B... 218 829-1407
Brainerd *(G-565)*

Evangelical Lutheran Good ....C... 507 427-2464
Mountain Lake *(G-6397)*

Evangelical Lutheran Good ....C... 507 825-5428
Pipestone *(G-6826)*

Eventide Home Association Inc ....E... 507 427-3221
Mountain Lake *(G-6398)*

Eventide Senior Living ....B... 218 233-7508
Moorhead *(G-6314)*

Extendicare Homes Inc ....C... 952 927-4949
Minneapolis *(G-4386)*

Grand Village ....C... 218 326-0543
Grand Rapids *(G-2282)*

Healtheast Care System......................C... 651 776-4107
Saint Paul *(G-8457)*

Highland Chateau Suites LLC ....D... 651 698-0793
Saint Paul *(G-8481)*

Juhl Enterprises Inc ....C... 320 354-2231
New London *(G-6416)*

Kaska Inc..D... 320 632-9281
Little Falls *(G-3009)*

(G-00000) Company's Geographic Section entry number

Kittson Memorial Hospital Assn ....C... 218 843-3612
Hallock (G-2333)

Lake Shore Inn Nursing Home..............C... 507 835-2800
Waseca (G-9881)

Lutheran Brethren Retirement ....C... 218 736-5441
Fergus Falls (G-2088)

Lutheran Memorial Home ....D... 218 456-2105
Halstad (G-2335)

Madonna Towers of Rochester...........C... 507 288-3911
Rochester (G-7167)

Mala Strana Health Care Center ....C... 952 758-2511
New Prague (G-6431)

Mission Health Care LLC ....C... 651 224-2368
Saint Paul (G-8716)

North Country Hospital ....C... 218 751-0220
Bemidji (G-409)

Northern Itasca Hospital Dist..............D... 218 743-3177
Bigfork (G-462)

Pelican Rapids Good Samaritan ....D... 218 863-2401
Pelican Rapids (G-6783)

Pierz Villa Inc ....E... 320 468-6405
Pierz (G-6806)

Pioneer Senior Cottages ....E... 218 998-9678
Fergus Falls (G-2114)

Regina Medical Center ....A... 651 480-4100
Hastings (G-2402)

Ridgeview Place LP ....E... 320 251-5228
Sauk Rapids (G-9371)

Saint William's Living Center...............D... 218 338-4671
Parkers Prairie (G-6766)

Senior Epoch Living Inc ....E... 952 473-3330
Hopkins (G-2630)

Thro Co ....C... 952 758-2511
New Prague (G-6435)

Thro Co ....D... 507 388-2913
Mankato (G-3205)

Traditions of Minnesota LLC ....E... 507 455-0700
Owatonna (G-6740)

NUTRITION SVCS

Healthcare Options Minnesota ....E... 320 252-5666
Sauk Rapids (G-9366)

Nutrition Services Inc ....C... 507 835-5697
Waseca (G-9884)

OFC/CLINIC OF MED DRS: Special, Phys Or Surgeon, Eye Or ENT

Ear Nose & Throat..............................E... 612 871-1144
Minneapolis (G-4306)

Eye Surgeons & Physicians.................E... 320 253-3637
Saint Cloud (G-7507)

Healthpartners Inc ....B... 952 593-8777
Minneapolis (G-4622)

OFC/CLINIC OF MED DRS: Specl, Phys Or Surgeon, Occup & Indl

Colon & Rectal Surgery Assocs ....E... 651 312-1500
Saint Paul (G-8226)

Health Activation Management............D... 763 398-8888
Hopkins (G-2550)

Holmes Hooper Inc ....D... 763 545-5641
Minneapolis (G-4661)

North Memorial Clinic..........................E... 763 520-5551
Minneapolis (G-5215)

OFCS & CLINICS, MEDICAL DRS: Specl, Physician Or Surgn, ENT

Ear Nose Throat Specialty Care ....D... 763 421-8443
Minneapolis (G-3461)

Minnesota Ear Head & Neck Clin.........E... 612 339-2836
Minneapolis (G-5077)

Oakdale Ear Nose & Throat Clin ....E... 763 520-7840
Minneapolis (G-5255)

St Cloud Ear, Nose, Throat ....E... 320 252-0233
Saint Cloud (G-7599)

OFFENDER REHABILITATION AGENCY

Eden Rs...C... 612 287-1600
Minneapolis (G-4313)

OFFENDER SELF-HELP AGENCY

Minnesota Department of Human........A... 651 431-2000
Saint Paul (G-8683)

OFFICE CLEANING OR CHARRING SVCS

General Cleaning Corp ....D... 218 727-4513
Duluth (G-1333)

Paquette Maintenance Inc...................D... 952 888-1801
Minneapolis (G-5318)

OFFICE EQPT WHOLESALERS

AMI Imaging Systems Inc.....................E... 952 828-0080
Bloomington (G-485)

Ban-Koe Systems Inc ....D... 952 888-6688
Minneapolis (G-3865)

Bennett Office Technologies ....E... 320 235-6425
Willmar (G-9985)

Coordinated Business Systems ....D... 952 894-9460
Burnsville (G-703)

Davis Typewriter Co Inc ....E... 507 343-2001
Worthington (G-10182)

IKON Office Solutions Inc ....E... 320 251-4566
Saint Cloud (G-7529)

Konica Minolta Business Soln..............E... 763 531-1721
Minneapolis (G-4819)

Laser Printing Technologies.................D... 952 888-7375
Mendota Heights (G-3366)

Metro - Sales Inc ....C... 612 861-4000
Minneapolis (G-5000)

North Country Business Prdts...............D... 218 751-4140
Bemidji (G-408)

North Country Business Prdts...............E... 800 937-4140
Plymouth (G-6878)

S P Richards Co ....E... 651 484-8459
Saint Paul (G-8920)

Smith Micro Technologies Inc ....C... 651 482-8718
Saint Paul (G-8966)

Stringer Business Systems Inc ....D... 651 994-7700
Saint Paul (G-7914)

Technifax Business Systems Inc ....E... 651 905-7090
Saint Paul (G-7919)

OFFICE EQPT, WHOLESALE: Blueprinting

Coordinated Business Systems ....D... 320 251-1212
Waite Park (G-9821)

Franz Reprographics Inc......................E... 763 503-3401
Minneapolis (G-4477)

OFFICE EQPT, WHOLESALE: Dictating Machines

Ricoh Americas Corp ....E... 866 856-3000
Eden Prairie (G-1765)

OFFICE EQPT, WHOLESALE: Duplicating Machines

Konica Minolta Business Soln..............D... 952 820-8385
Minneapolis (G-4818)

Metro - Sales Inc ....C... 612 861-4000
Minneapolis (G-5000)

OFFICE EQPT, WHOLESALE: Photocopy Machines

Advanced Imaging Solutions Inc ....E... 952 930-1882
Hopkins (G-2501)

Ecm Publishers Inc.............................E... 763 689-1981
Cambridge (G-837)

N A Trading & Technology Inc..............E... 952 888-7654
Minneapolis (G-5154)

Ricoh Americas Corp ....D... 651 294-2600
Mendota Heights (G-3370)

Sel-Mor Distributing Co ....E... 952 929-0888
Minneapolis (G-5629)

OFFICE EQPT, WHOLESALE: Typewriters

Metro - Sales Inc ....C... 612 861-4000
Minneapolis (G-5000)

OFFICE FURNITURE REPAIR & MAINTENANCE SVCS

Commercial Furniture Services............E... 952 922-6683
Saint Louis Park (G-7658)

Omni Workspace Co............................C... 612 627-1600
Minneapolis (G-5277)

Omni Workspace Co............................E... 612 627-1600
Minneapolis (G-5276)

OFFICE MANAGEMENT SVCS

Loram Admin LLC ....D... 763 478-6014
Hamel (G-2347)

Pro Systems Corp...............................E... 218 847-9277
Detroit Lakes (G-1214)

OFFICE SPLYS, NEC, WHOLESALE

Bertelson Brothers Inc ....E... 763 546-4371
Minneapolis (G-3889)

Buyonlinenow Inc ....E... 507 281-6899
Rochester (G-7068)

Corporate Express Office Prdts ....C... 651 636-2250
Saint Paul (G-8251)

Diversified Distribution Systs ....C... 612 813-5200
Minneapolis (G-4261)

Innovative Office Solutions ....D... 952 808-9900
Burnsville (G-736)

Ktn Acquisition Corp...........................E... 952 941-9505
Burnsville (G-4826)

OfficeMax North America Inc ....E... 218 287-3755
Dilworth (G-1224)

OfficeMax North America Inc ....E... 651 686-6606
Eagan (G-1544)

Ricoh Americas Corp ....D... 651 294-2600
Mendota Heights (G-3370)

S & T Office Products Inc ....C... 651 483-4411
Saint Paul (G-8918)

Safco Products Co ....C... 763 536-6700
Minneapolis (G-5588)

Victor Lundeen Co..............................E... 218 736-5433
Fergus Falls (G-2123)

OFFICES & CLINICS DOCTORS OF MED: Intrnl Med Practitioners

Aspen Medical Group..........................E... 612 728-1800
Minneapolis (G-3818)

Fairview Oxboro Clinics Inc ....B... 952 885-6100
Minneapolis (G-4402)

Regents of The University of................E... 612 627-4564
Minneapolis (G-5491)

Ridgeview Medical Clinic ....E... 952 471-2585
Spring Park (G-9565)

Total Renal Care Inc ....D... 612 873-6089
Minneapolis (G-5836)

Westhealth Inc ....C... 763 577-7000
Plymouth (G-6891)

OFFICES & CLINICS DRS OF MED: Psychiatrists/Psychoanalysts

Center For Victims of Torture...............D... 612 436-4800
Minneapolis (G-4043)

OFFICES & CLINICS HLTH PRACTITNRS: Psychiatric Social Wrkr

Family Focus Inc ....E... 218 740-3146
Duluth (G-1320)

OFFICES & CLINICS OF DENTISTS: Dental Clinic

Healthpartners Inc ....E... 651 227-3757
Saint Paul (G-8468)

Healthpartners Inc ....E... 651 770-8828
Saint Paul (G-8471)

Healthpartners Inc ....E... 651 702-5871
Saint Paul (G-9227)

Healthpartners Inc ....B... 952 431-8500
Saint Paul (G-7798)

Healthpartners Inc ....D... 763 754-4600
Minneapolis (G-3487)

Indian Health Board of ....D... 612 721-9800
Minneapolis (G-4696)

Northpark Dental 763 786-1560
Minneapolis (G-3559)

Park Dental Blaine ....D... 763 755-1330
Minneapolis (G-3564)

PDHC Ltd ....E... 612 338-4546
Minneapolis (G-5355)

Shari K Bruning DDS............................E... 763 546-1301
Minneapolis (G-5649)

Valley Dental Group ....D... 763 544-2213
Minneapolis (G-5955)

West Side Community Health...............D... 651 222-1816
Saint Paul (G-9148)

OFFICES & CLINICS OF DENTISTS: Dental Clinics & Offices

Metrodentallcare, PLC.........................E... 612 861-9123
Minneapolis (G-5005)

Pdhc Ltd ....D... 763 535-2960
Minneapolis (G-5356)

OFFICES & CLINICS OF DENTISTS: Dental Surgeon

Oral & Maxillofacial Surgical ....E... 952 835-5003
Minneapolis (G-5289)

Twin City Oral & Maxillofacial ....E... 651 437-3262
Hastings (G-2410)

OFFICES & CLINICS OF DENTISTS: Dentists' Office

Affliated Pediatric Dentists...................E... 952 831-4400
Minneapolis (G-3695)

Employment codes: A=Over 500 employees, B=251-500,
C=101-250, D=51-100, E=25-50

2011 Harris Minnesota
Services Directory

© Harris InfoSource 1-866-281-6415
741

Associated Dentists Ltd ....E... 651 222-0351
Saint Paul *(G-8073)*

Bassett Creek Dental ....E... 763 546-1301
Minneapolis *(G-3872)*

Brook West Family Dentistry ....E... 763 561-8901
Osseo *(G-6600)*

Centennial Lakes Dental Group............E... 952 831-2800
Minneapolis *(G-4041)*

Community Dental Care ....E... 651 774-2959
Saint Paul *(G-8238)*

Cook Area Health Services Inc ....E... 218 666-5941
Cook *(G-1094)*

Falls Court Dentists ....E... 320 632-6621
Little Falls *(G-3003)*

Healthpartners Inc ....E... 763 780-1292
Minneapolis *(G-3485)*

Lake Superior Dental ....E... 218 728-6445
Duluth *(G-1376)*

Maplewood Dental Associates ....E... 651 770-3831
Saint Paul *(G-8613)*

Metro Dental Care ....E... 952 435-8525
Burnsville *(G-753)*

Metropolitan Dental Associates ....D... 612 866-0054
Minneapolis *(G-5006)*

New Ulm Dental Clinic ....E... 507 354-3321
New Ulm *(G-6467)*

Northwest Dental Group of ....E... 507 282-1271
Rochester *(G-7193)*

Nyberg & Assoc PA Inc ....E... 763 441-9181
Elk River *(G-1888)*

Parkway Dental ....E... 952 937-2137
Eden Prairie *(G-1743)*

Rangerland Dental Group Inc ....E... 218 534-3141
Deerwood *(G-1179)*

Southdale Dental Associates.................E... 952 896-1111
Minneapolis *(G-5705)*

Southern Minnesota Oral ....E... 507 625-9330
Mankato *(G-3201)*

Southhill Dental.......................................E... 651 439-9400
Stillwater *(G-9641)*

OFFICES & CLINICS OF DENTISTS: Endodontist

Northpark Dental.....................................763 786-1560
Minneapolis *(G-3559)*

OFFICES & CLINICS OF DENTISTS: Group & Corporate Practice

Catton Wolseth Como & Jacobs ....E... 320 253-4778
Saint Cloud *(G-7477)*

OFFICES & CLINICS OF DENTISTS: Oral Pathologist

Northpark Dental.....................................763 786-1560
Minneapolis *(G-3559)*

OFFICES & CLINICS OF DENTISTS: Periodontist

Dental Specialists ....E... 952 926-2763
Lake Elmo *(G-2868)*

Northpark Dental.....................................763 786-1560
Minneapolis *(G-3559)*

OFFICES & CLINICS OF DENTISTS: Specialist, Maxillofacial

Oral & Maxillofacial Surgical..................E... 952 835-5003
Minneapolis *(G-5289)*

OFFICES & CLINICS OF DENTISTS: Specialist, Practitioners

Apple Tree Dental ....E... 763 784-7570
Minneapolis *(G-3407)*

OFFICES & CLINICS OF DOCTORS OF MEDICINE: Allergist

Allergy & Asthma Clinic ....E... 507 474-7830
Winona *(G-10079)*

Allergy & Asthma Specialists ....E... 612 338-3333
Minneapolis *(G-3712)*

Southdale Pediatrics Assocs................D... 952 831-4454
Minneapolis *(G-5708)*

OFFICES & CLINICS OF DOCTORS OF MEDICINE: Anesthesiologist

Anesthesia Associates of St.................E... 320 258-3090
Saint Cloud *(G-7450)*

Northwest Anesthesia ....D... 612 871-7639
Minneapolis *(G-5241)*

OFFICES & CLINICS OF DOCTORS OF MEDICINE: Dermatologist

Associated Skin Care ....E... 763 571-4000
Minneapolis *(G-3411)*

OFFICES & CLINICS OF DOCTORS OF MEDICINE: Dispensary

Regents of The University of ....C... 612 625-1612
Minneapolis *(G-5488)*

OFFICES & CLINICS OF DOCTORS OF MEDICINE: Endocrinologist

Southdale Pediatrics Assocs................D... 952 831-4454
Minneapolis *(G-5708)*

OFFICES & CLINICS OF DOCTORS OF MEDICINE: Gastronomist

East Metro Endoscopy Center ....E... 612 870-5482
Saint Paul *(G-8319)*

Minnesota Gastroenterology PA ....D... 612 871-1145
Saint Paul *(G-8688)*

OFFICES & CLINICS OF DOCTORS OF MEDICINE: Group Health Assoc

Allina Self-Insured ....D... 952 992-2500
Hopkins *(G-2507)*

OFFICES & CLINICS OF DOCTORS OF MEDICINE: Gynecologist

Associates In Womens Health ....E... 952 806-0011
Minneapolis *(G-3827)*

Associates In Womens Health ....E... 952 806-0011
Minneapolis *(G-3828)*

Fairview Health Services ....E... 612 672-2900
Minneapolis *(G-4394)*

Haugen, John A Associates....................E... 952 927-6561
Minneapolis *(G-4606)*

Haugen, John A Associates.....................612 333-2503
Minneapolis *(G-4607)*

Northland Ob Gyn Associates ....E... 218 722-5629
Duluth *(G-1408)*

Obstetrics & Gyn......................................952 920-2200
Minneapolis *(G-5261)*

Paul Larson Ob-Gyn Clinic ....D... 952 927-4021
Minneapolis *(G-5351)*

Southdale Obstetric...............................E... 952 920-7001
Minneapolis *(G-5707)*

Western Eastern Ob Gyn Limited.........E... 952 556-0071
Chaska *(G-985)*

Western Ob Gyne Ltd ....E... 952 442-2137
Waconia *(G-9795)*

OFFICES & CLINICS OF DOCTORS OF MEDICINE: Hematologist

Oncologic Consultants...........................E... 651 602-5335
Saint Paul *(G-8786)*

Oncologic Consultants...........................E... 952 928-2900
Minneapolis *(G-5279)*

OFFICES & CLINICS OF DOCTORS OF MEDICINE: Med Insurance Plan

Definity Health Corp ....C... 952 277-5500
Minneapolis *(G-4242)*

OFFICES & CLINICS OF DOCTORS OF MEDICINE: Nephrologist

Kidney Specialists of MN ....E... 763 561-5349
Minneapolis *(G-4806)*

Nephrology Analytical Services ....E... 612 337-7345
Minneapolis *(G-5182)*

OFFICES & CLINICS OF DOCTORS OF MEDICINE: Neurologist

Minneapolis Clinic of ....C... 763 588-0661
Minneapolis *(G-5051)*

Minnesota Epilepsy Group......................E... 651 241-5305
Saint Paul *(G-8685)*

Neurological Associates of St ....E... 651 221-9051
Saint Paul *(G-8746)*

Noran Neurological Clinic ....D... 612 879-1000
Minneapolis *(G-5206)*

Noran Neurological Clinic ....E... 763 786-8406
Minneapolis *(G-3556)*

OFFICES & CLINICS OF DOCTORS OF MEDICINE: Neurosurgeon

Adult & Pediatric Urology ....E... 320 259-1411
Sartell *(G-9329)*

OFFICES & CLINICS OF DOCTORS OF MEDICINE: Obstetrician

Allina Health System ....E... 763 786-6011
Minneapolis *(G-3395)*

Associates In Womens Health ....E... 952 806-0011
Minneapolis *(G-3827)*

Associates In Womens Health ....E... 952 806-0011
Minneapolis *(G-3828)*

Haugen, John A Associates ....E... 952 927-6561
Minneapolis *(G-4606)*

Haugen, John A Associates 612 333-2503
Minneapolis *(G-4607)*

Mayo Clinic Rochester ....D... 507 284-5135
Rochester *(G-7173)*

Obstetrics & Gyn 952 920-2200
Minneapolis *(G-5261)*

Obstetrics & Gynecology........................E... 952 920-2200
Minneapolis *(G-5262)*

Paul Larson Ob-Gyn Clinic ....D... 952 927-4021
Minneapolis *(G-5351)*

Southdale Ob Gyn Consultants ....E... 952 435-9505
Burnsville *(G-800)*

Southdale Obstetric................................E... 952 920-7001
Minneapolis *(G-5707)*

University Womens Health ....E... 612 625-6991
Minneapolis *(G-5931)*

Western Ob Gyne Ltd..............................E... 952 442-2137
Waconia *(G-9795)*

OFFICES & CLINICS OF DOCTORS OF MEDICINE: Oncologist

Minnesota Internal Medicine ....E... 651 232-4800
Saint Paul *(G-8692)*

Oncologic Consultants ....E... 651 602-5335
Saint Paul *(G-8786)*

Oncologic Consultants ....E... 952 928-2900
Minneapolis *(G-5279)*

OFFICES & CLINICS OF DOCTORS OF MEDICINE: Ophthalmologist

Allina Health System ....C... 612 775-8800
Minneapolis *(G-3720)*

Associated Eye Care Ltd ....E... 651 439-8500
Stillwater *(G-9598)*

Dedina Eye Physicians ....D... 952 832-8179
Minneapolis *(G-4241)*

Edina Eye Physicians.............................E... 952 831-8811
Minneapolis *(G-4315)*

Eye Care Associates ....E... 612 338-4861
Minneapolis *(G-4388)*

John L Bonner Eye Clinic Ltd ....E... 218 326-3433
Grand Rapids *(G-2288)*

Ophthalmology...E... 952 925-3150
Minneapolis *(G-5286)*

St Paul Eye Clinic ....E... 651 641-0457
Saint Paul *(G-8988)*

OFFICES & CLINICS OF DOCTORS OF MEDICINE: Pathologist

Hospital Pathology Associates ....E... 651 483-2033
Saint Paul *(G-8496)*

OFFICES & CLINICS OF DOCTORS OF MEDICINE: Pediatrician

Children's Respiratory ....E... 612 863-3226
Minneapolis *(G-4066)*

Dakota Pediatric Clinic...........................E... 952 997-2572
Lakeville *(G-2901)*

Daniel P Khoury......................................D... 651 738-0470
Saint Paul *(G-9200)*

Edina Pediatrics.......................................E... 952 927-7337
Minneapolis *(G-4318)*

Healthpartners Inc ....B... 651 641-6200
Saint Paul *(G-8474)*

Metropolitan Pediatric.............................E... 952 435-2450
Burnsville *(G-754)*

Metropolitan Pediatric.............................D... 952 445-6700
Shakopee *(G-9455)*

Northern Light Pediatrics ....E... 651 484-3942
Saint Paul *(G-8758)*

Partners In Pediatrics Ltd ....E... 763 425-1211
Minneapolis *(G-5343)*

Partners Pediatric....................................612 827-4055
Minneapolis *(G-5344)*

Pediatric & Adolescent Care of ....E... 651 770-2124
Saint Paul *(G-8812)*

Pediatric & Adolescent Care of ....E... 651 451-8050
Saint Paul *(G-7871)*

Pediatric & Young Adult Med................E... 651 227-7806
Saint Paul *(G-8813)*

Pediatricians For Health ....E... 651 232-6700
Saint Paul *(G-9258)*

Ridgeview Medical Clinic ....E... 952 471-2585
Spring Park *(G-9565)*

South Lake Pediatrics ....E... 952 401-8300
Hopkins *(G-2635)*

Southdale Pediatrics Assocs................D... 952 831-4454
Minneapolis *(G-5708)*

Southdale Pediatrics Assocs................E... 952 898-5900
Burnsville *(G-801)*

OFFICES & CLINICS OF DOCTORS OF MEDICINE: Psychiatric Clinic

Northern Pines Mental Health 320 632-6647
Little Falls *(G-3015)*

Psychiatric Clinic of Mankato ....E... 507 387-3195
Mankato *(G-3183)*

OFFICES & CLINICS OF DOCTORS OF MEDICINE: Psychiatrist

Associated Clinic of.............................D... 763 503-8560
Minneapolis *(G-3825)*

OFFICES & CLINICS OF DOCTORS OF MEDICINE: Radiologist

CDI Corp ....E... 320 251-0609
Sartell *(G-9335)*

Consulting Radiologists Ltd ....C... 612 573-2200
Minneapolis *(G-4158)*

Consulting Radiologists Ltd ....D... 952 831-9300
Minneapolis *(G-4159)*

Minneapolis Radiology Assocs..............E... 763 398-6600
Minneapolis *(G-5061)*

Minneapolis Radiology Assocs..............D... 763 559-2171
Minneapolis *(G-5062)*

Minnesota Radiation Oncology ....E... 612 863-4060
Minneapolis *(G-5091)*

North Memorial Imaging Center ....E... 763 398-4400
Osseo *(G-6644)*

Regional Diagnostics Radiology ....E... 320 255-5619
Saint Cloud *(G-7583)*

St Paul Radiology ....D... 651 292-2000
Saint Paul *(G-8998)*

Suburban Radiologic ConsInts ....D... 952 837-9700
Minneapolis *(G-5762)*

Suburban Radiologic ConsInts ....E... 763 792-1900
Minneapolis *(G-3611)*

Suburban Radiologic ConsInts ....E... 763 786-9460
Minneapolis *(G-3612)*

Virtual Radiologic Corp ....C... 952 595-1100
Eden Prairie *(G-1807)*

OFFICES & CLINICS OF DOCTORS OF MEDICINE: Surgeon

Associated Eye Care Ltd ....E... 651 439-8500
Stillwater *(G-9598)*

Edgar Saldana Dr ....E... 218 249-7910
Duluth *(G-1310)*

Edina Pediatrics ....E... 952 927-7337
Minneapolis *(G-4318)*

Fairmont Medical Center Mayo ....A... 507 238-4263
Fairmont *(G-1964)*

Metropolitan Hand Surgery ....E... 651 223-5406
Saint Paul *(G-8647)*

Minnesota Heart Clinic Inc...................D... 952 836-3700
Edina *(G-1837)*

Minnesota Surgical Associates ....E... 651 776-0724
Saint Paul *(G-8708)*

Northwest Orthopedic Surgeons............D... 763 520-7870
Minneapolis *(G-5243)*

Orthopaedic Consultants ....E... 952 832-0076
Minneapolis *(G-5292)*

Orthopedic Associates of ....E... 218 722-5513
Duluth *(G-1414)*

Orthopedic Medicine & Surgery ....E... 952 920-0970
Minneapolis *(G-5293)*

Pavilion Surgery Center LLC ....E... 218 279-6200
Duluth *(G-1420)*

Southdale Family Practice ....E... 952 927-4235
Minneapolis *(G-5706)*

Sports & Orthopaedic............................E... 952 946-9777
Minneapolis *(G-5722)*

Surgical Care Affiliates LLC.................E... 952 832-9360
Minneapolis *(G-5774)*

Surgical Consultants Prof.....................E... 952 832-0805
Minneapolis *(G-5775)*

Twin Cities Spine Surgeons Ltd ....D... 612 775-6200
Minneapolis *(G-5874)*

OFFICES & CLINICS OF DOCTORS OF MEDICINE: Surgeon, Plastic

Edina Plastic Surgery Ltd ....E... 952 925-1765
Minneapolis *(G-4319)*

James M Smith MD ....D... 320 253-7257
Saint Cloud *(G-7535)*

Midsota Plastic....................................E... 320 253-7257
Saint Cloud *(G-7553)*

Olmsted Medical Center ....A... 507 529-6600
Rochester *(G-7194)*

Suburban Plastic Surgery ....D... 952 922-0895
Minneapolis *(G-5761)*

OFFICES & CLINICS OF DOCTORS OF MEDICINE: Urologist

Metropolitan Urologic ....E... 651 999-7034
Saint Paul *(G-8649)*

Midwest Stone Management, A MN......E... 651 633-9414
Saint Paul *(G-8665)*

OFFICES & CLINICS OF DOCTORS, MEDICINE: Gen & Fam Practice

Affiliated Community Medical..............B... 320 693-3233
Litchfield *(G-2977)*

Affiliated Medical Center ....E... 320 843-2030
Benson *(G-436)*

Altru Clinic ....D... 218 463-1365
Roseau *(G-7353)*

Ann Pearson MD ....E... 651 426-4844
Saint Paul *(G-8052)*

Buffalo Clinic ....D... 763 682-1313
Buffalo *(G-637)*

Centracare Clinic ....E... 320 732-2131
Long Prairie *(G-3037)*

Cook Area Health Services Inc ....E... 218 743-3232
Bigfork *(G-460)*

David G McAlphie MD ....E... 651 731-0859
Saint Paul *(G-9202)*

Duluth Clinic International ....D... 218 283-9431
International Falls *(G-2719)*

Duluth Graduate Medical Educn............E... 218 529-9105
Duluth *(G-1299)*

Edina Family Physicians ....E... 952 925-2200
Minneapolis *(G-4316)*

Fairmont Medical Center Mayo.............A... 507 238-4263
Fairmont *(G-1964)*

Family Health Services of MN ....E... 651 457-2748
Inver Grove Heights *(G-2750)*

Family Practice Medical Center ....E... 320 235-7232
Willmar *(G-10001)*

France Avenue Family ....E... 952 831-1551
Minneapolis *(G-4471)*

Golden Valley Clinic Inc ....E... 952 993-8300
Minneapolis *(G-4535)*

Healthpartners Inc ....D... 651 772-9757
Saint Paul *(G-8473)*

Heartland Family Practice Inc..............D... 320 251-2042
Saint Cloud *(G-7525)*

Lakeview Medical Clinic ....E... 320 352-6591
Sauk Centre *(G-9350)*

Mayo Clinic Rochester ....E... 507 387-8231
North Mankato *(G-6510)*

Minnesota Brd of Med Prac...................E... 651 642-0538
Saint Paul *(G-8674)*

Minnhealth Family Physicians ....E... 651 487-2831
Saint Paul *(G-8713)*

Montevideo Clinic ....E... 320 269-6435
Montevideo *(G-6252)*

Northwest Family Physicians ....E... 763 476-6776
Minneapolis *(G-5242)*

P S Rudie & Associates Ltd ....E... 218 722-6613
Duluth *(G-1417)*

Park Nicollet Clinic ....D... 952 993-4001
Saint Paul *(G-7863)*

Raiper Clinic ....D... 218 879-1271
Cloquet *(G-1062)*

Regina Medical Center ....E... 651 480-4200
Hastings *(G-2403)*

Silver Lake Clinic At Shorevw ....E... 651 481-0818
Saint Paul *(G-8959)*

Smdc Health System ....E... 218 246-8275
Deer River *(G-1173)*

Southdale Family Practice ....E... 952 927-4235
Minneapolis *(G-5706)*

United Family Practice Health ....D... 651 241-1000
Saint Paul *(G-9104)*

Wabasha Clinic Mayo Health ....E... 651 565-4571
Wabasha *(G-9774)*

Wadena Medical Center Ltd ....E... 218 631-1360
Wadena *(G-9814)*

West Side Community Health..............D... 651 222-1816
Saint Paul *(G-9148)*

OFFICES & CLINICS OF DRS OF MED: Cardiologist & Vascular

Allina Health System ....C... 612 863-3720
Minneapolis *(G-3724)*

Cardiodiagnostics Inc ....C... 651 292-0616
Saint Paul *(G-8159)*

Cardiovascular Consultants Ltd ....D... 763 520-2000
Minneapolis *(G-4002)*

Metropolitan Cardiology ....C... 763 427-9980
Minneapolis *(G-3540)*

Minnesota Heart Clinic Inc...................D... 952 836-3700
Edina *(G-1837)*

Saint Lukes Cardiology Assocs.........E... 218 249-3057
Duluth *(G-1443)*

St Paul Cardiology...............................E... 651 232-4320
Saint Paul *(G-8987)*

St Paul Heart Clinic ....C... 651 292-0616
Saint Paul *(G-8992)*

St Paul Heart Clinic ....B... 651 779-9449
Saint Paul *(G-8993)*

OFFICES & CLINICS OF DRS OF MED: Clinic, Op by Physicians

A C M C ....E... 507 637-2985
Redwood Falls *(G-7018)*

Advancements In Allergy......................E... 952 546-6866
Hopkins *(G-2502)*

Affiliated Community Medical ....B... 320 231-5000
Willmar *(G-9980)*

Albert Lea Medical Center-Mayo ....A... 507 373-2384
Albert Lea *(G-32)*

Albert Lee Medical Center Inc ....D... 507 553-3115
Wells *(G-9960)*

Alexandria Clinic Properties.................C... 320 763-5123
Alexandria *(G-80)*

All True Clinic Crookston Inc ....D... 218 281-9100
Crookston *(G-1118)*

Allina Health System ....D... 651 458-1884
Cottage Grove *(G-1097)*

Allina Health System ....E... 763 427-7180
Anoka *(G-150)*

Allina Health System ....D... 763 236-9236
Minneapolis *(G-3392)*

Allina Health System ....E... 651 464-7100
Forest Lake *(G-2155)*

Allina Health System ....E... 952 851-1000
Minneapolis *(G-3719)*

Allina Health System ....E... 763 780-9155
Minneapolis *(G-3394)*

Allina Health System ....C... 651 438-1800
Hastings *(G-2375)*

Allina Health System ....E... 763 236-0414
Elk River *(G-1861)*

Allina Health System ....D... 507 334-3921
Faribault *(G-1988)*

Allina Health System ....E... 763 236-0200
Maple Grove *(G-3235)*

Allina Health System ....A... 763 689-7700
Cambridge *(G-831)*

Allina Health System ....E... 952 463-7181
Farmington *(G-2038)*

Allina Health System ....E... 763 560-6922
Minneapolis *(G-3725)*

Allina Medical Clinic West ....D... 763 577-7400
Plymouth *(G-6847)*

Apple Valley Medical Clinic ....C... 952 432-6161
Saint Paul *(G-7702)*

Bois Forte Medical Clinic.....................E... 218 757-3650
Nett Lake *(G-6403)*

Brainerd Medical Center ....D... 218 828-7100
Brainerd *(G-552)*

Burnsville Family Physicians ....E... 952 435-0303
Burnsville *(G-690)*

Camden Physicians Ltd ....E... 763 420-5822
Osseo *(G-6601)*

Camden Physicians Ltd ....D... 763 235-4900
Plymouth *(G-6853)*

Cannon Valley Clinic Mayo...................D... 507 333-3300
Faribault *(G-1997)*

Catholic Charities of The ....E... 651 641-1180
Saint Paul *(G-8175)*

Cedar-Riverside People's Ctr ....E... 612 332-4973
Minneapolis *(G-4038)*

Centracare Clinic ....C... 320 654-3630
Saint Cloud *(G-7478)*

Centracare Clinic ....E... 320 256-4228
Melrose *(G-3345)*

Central Lakes Medical Clinic ....D... 218 546-8375
Crosby *(G-1145)*

Chaska Medical Center ....E... 952 448-2050
Chaska *(G-957)*

Employment codes: A=Over 500 employees, B=251-500,
C=101-250, D=51-100, E=25-50

2011 Harris Minnesota
Services Directory

© Harris InfoSource 1-866-281-6415
743

SERVICES

Department of Corrections MN ....B... 218 485-5000
Moose Lake *(G-6349)*

East Metro Family Practice ....E... 651 776-2719
Saint Paul *(G-8320)*

Emergency Physicians Prof ....C... 952 835-9880
Minneapolis *(G-4346)*

Fairview Clinics ....E... 651 688-7860
Saint Paul *(G-7773)*

Fairview Health Services ....E... 952 826-6500
Eden Prairie *(G-1662)*

Fairview Health Services ....E... 763 856-6900
Zimmerman *(G-10213)*

Fairview Northland Clinic ....D... 763 389-3344
Princeton *(G-6922)*

Fergus Falls Medical Group ....C... 218 739-2221
Fergus Falls *(G-2076)*

Fond Du Lac Reservation ....C... 218 879-1227
Cloquet *(G-1053)*

Fremont Community Health Svcs ....E... 612 588-9411
Minneapolis *(G-4488)*

Grand Itasca Clinic & Hospital ....C... 218 326-5000
Grand Rapids *(G-2279)*

Healtheast Diversified Svcs ....E... 651 489-8061
Saint Paul *(G-8460)*

Healtheast Diversified Svcs ....E... 651 232-2300
Saint Paul *(G-8461)*

Healtheast Maplewood Out ....E... 651 232-7780
Saint Paul *(G-8463)*

Healtheast Medical Research ....E... 651 489-8061
Saint Paul *(G-8464)*

Indian Health Board of ....D... 612 721-9800
Minneapolis *(G-4696)*

Innovis Health LLC ....C... 218 844-2300
Detroit Lakes *(G-1200)*

Jackson Municipal Clinic ....E... 507 847-2200
Jackson *(G-2796)*

Lakeview Clinic ....E... 952 955-1921
Watertown *(G-9891)*

Mankato Clinic Ltd ....B... 507 625-1811
Mankato *(G-3160)*

Maple Grove Urgent Care ....E... 763 420-5279
Osseo *(G-6634)*

Mayo Clinic ....E... 507 931-2110
Saint Peter *(G-9308)*

Mayo Clinic ....E... 651 565-4571
Wabasha *(G-9768)*

Mayo Clinic Rochester ....E... 507 634-4744
Kasson *(G-2822)*

Meritcare Health System ....E... 218 846-2000
Detroit Lakes *(G-1210)*

Mesaba Clinic ....C... 218 263-9426
Hibbing *(G-2463)*

Minnesota Valley Memorial Hosp ....C... 507 665-3375
Le Sueur *(G-2958)*

Noran Neurological Clinic ....E... 763 786-8406
Minneapolis *(G-3556)*

Open Cities Health Center ....D... 651 290-9200
Saint Paul *(G-8788)*

Orthopedic & Fracture Clinic ....D... 507 386-6600
Mankato *(G-3180)*

Owatonna Clinic — Mayo Health ....B... 507 451-1120
Owatonna *(G-6726)*

Park Nicollet Clinic ....A... 952 993-3123
Minneapolis *(G-5332)*

Park Nicollet Health Services ....C... 952 993-8000
Minneapolis *(G-5334)*

Riverway Clinic ....C... 763 712-6000
Anoka *(G-222)*

Robbinsdale Clinic PA Inc ....E... 763 533-2534
Minneapolis *(G-5550)*

Sioux Valley Canby Campus ....C... 507 223-7221
Canby *(G-853)*

Sioux Valley Physician ....E... 507 283-4476
Luverne *(G-3069)*

Skemp Walk In Clinic ....E... 507 724-3353
Caledonia *(G-829)*

Smdc Health System ....A... 218 786-8364
Duluth *(G-1454)*

Smdc Health System ....E... 218 786-3500
Duluth *(G-1453)*

Smdc Health System ....D... 218 285-6222
International Falls *(G-2730)*

Southside Community Health ....E... 612 822-3186
Minneapolis *(G-5710)*

St Cloud Medical Group ....C... 320 202-8949
Saint Cloud *(G-7604)*

St Luke's Hospital of Duluth ....E... 218 249-4600
Duluth *(G-1470)*

Stillwater Medical Clinic ....C... 651 439-1234
Stillwater *(G-9647)*

Water Medical Group ....C... 651 439-1234
Stillwater *(G-9655)*

OFFICES & CLINICS OF DRS OF MED: Health Maint Org Or HMO

Fiserv Health Inc ....E... 763 549-3359
Minneapolis *(G-4449)*

HealthPartners Central MN ....C... 320 253-5220
Saint Cloud *(G-7523)*

Healthpartners Inc ....B... 612 371-1600
Minneapolis *(G-4621)*

Healthpartners Inc ....C... 651 653-2100
Saint Paul *(G-8466)*

Healthpartners Inc ....C... 651 293-8100
Saint Paul *(G-8467)*

Healthpartners Inc ....E... 651 254-3500
Saint Paul *(G-8470)*

Minnesota Rural Health Co-op ....D... 507 423-5300
Cottonwood *(G-1113)*

Preferredone Administrative ....B... 763 847-3525
Minneapolis *(G-5401)*

United Healthcare of Wyoming ....A... 218 279-5642
Duluth *(G-1490)*

OFFICES & CLINICS OF DRS OF MED: Physician/Surgeon, Int Med

Doctors Diagnostic Center Ltd ....E... 763 550-0707
Minneapolis *(G-4269)*

Fairmont Medical Center Mayo ....A... 507 238-4263
Fairmont *(G-1964)*

Minnesota Internal Medicine ....E... 651 232-4800
Saint Paul *(G-8692)*

Prairie Medical ....E... 320 589-4008
Morris *(G-6375)*

OFFICES & CLINICS OF DRS OF MED: Physician/Surgeon, Phy Med

Allina Specialty Associates ....E... 612 863-3753
Minneapolis *(G-3727)*

Gillette Children's Specialty ....E... 651 229-3840
Saint Paul *(G-8409)*

Leslie E Fishman Inc ....E... 651 227-7806
Saint Paul *(G-8579)*

Minnhealth Family Physicians ....E... 651 426-6402
White Bear Lake *(G-9976)*

Olson M D, Peter J ....E... 651 326-9020
Saint Paul *(G-8783)*

Physicans Neck & Back Clinic ....E... 651 639-9150
Saint Paul *(G-8827)*

Saint Paul Lung Clinic ....D... 651 726-6200
Saint Paul *(G-8927)*

OFFICES & CLINICS OF DRS OF MED: Specialist/Phy, Fertility

Reproductive Medicine ....E... 651 221-4620
Saint Paul *(G-9267)*

OFFICES & CLINICS OF DRS OF MEDICINE: Diabetes

International Diabetes Center ....C... 952 993-3393
Minneapolis *(G-4722)*

OFFICES & CLINICS OF DRS OF MEDICINE: Med Clinic, Pri Care

Fairview Health Services ....E... 952 848-5600
Minneapolis *(G-4397)*

Lakeview Clinic ....C... 952 442-4461
Waconia *(G-9788)*

Mankato Clinic Ltd ....E... 507 625-5027
Mankato *(G-3229)*

Primary Care Center ....E... 612 624-9499
Minneapolis *(G-5408)*

Stevens Community Medical Ctr ....C... 320 589-1313
Morris *(G-6379)*

University of Minnesota ....C... 763 782-6400
Minneapolis *(G-5930)*

OFFICES & CLINICS OF DRS OF MEDICINE: Physician, Orthopedic

Fairmont Orthopedics & Sports ....D... 507 238-4949
Fairmont *(G-1965)*

Midwest Spine Institute LLC ....E... 651 430-3800
Burnsville *(G-758)*

Northwest Orthopedic Surgeons ....D... 763 520-7870
Minneapolis *(G-5243)*

Orthopedic & Fracture Clinic ....D... 507 386-6600
Mankato *(G-3180)*

Orthopedic Associates of ....E... 218 722-5513
Duluth *(G-1414)*

Orthopedic Medicine & Surgery ....E... 952 920-0970
Minneapolis *(G-5293)*

Orthopedic Partners ....E... 763 786-9543
Minneapolis *(G-3562)*

Orthopedic Sports Inc ....D... 651 439-8540
Stillwater *(G-9634)*

Orthopedic Surgeons Ltd ....E... 952 927-7565
Minneapolis *(G-5295)*

South Central Surgical Center ....E... 507 235-3939
Fairmont *(G-1981)*

St Croix Orthopaedics ....D... 651 439-8807
Stillwater *(G-9643)*

Summit Landmark Orthopedics ....C... 651 842-5200
Saint Paul *(G-9013)*

OFFICES & CLINICS OF DRS OF MEDICINE: Physician, Thoracic

Fairmont Orthopedics & Sports ....D... 507 238-4949
Fairmont *(G-1965)*

OFFICES & CLINICS OF DRS OF MEDICINE: Pulmonary

Children's Respiratory ....E... 612 863-3226
Minneapolis *(G-4066)*

Pulmonary Health Realty Assocs ....E... 651 224-5895
Saint Paul *(G-8858)*

OFFICES & CLINICS OF DRS OF MEDICINE: Rheumatology

Minnesota Internal Medicine ....E... 651 232-4800
Saint Paul *(G-8692)*

OFFICES & CLINICS OF DRS, MED: Specialized Practitioners

Allergy & Asthma Specialists ....E... 320 654-6565
Sartell *(G-9330)*

Center For Victims of Torture ....D... 612 436-4800
Minneapolis *(G-4043)*

Medical Advanced Pain ....D... 763 537-6000
Minneapolis *(G-3532)*

Oakdale Obstetrics & Gynecolog ....D... 763 520-2999
Minneapolis *(G-5257)*

OFFICES & CLINICS OF HEALTH PRACTITIONERS: Occu Therapist

Jones Stanley & Associates ....E... 507 288-0064
Rochester *(G-7147)*

Occupro Inc ....E... 320 839-4090
Ortonville *(G-6584)*

Park Nicollet Clinic ....D... 952 993-9700
Minneapolis *(G-5330)*

OFFICES & CLINICS OF HEALTH PRACTITIONERS: Physical Therapy

Allina Health System ....E... 763 427-7180
Anoka *(G-150)*

Brookdale Integrative Health ....E... 763 561-4045
Minneapolis *(G-3955)*

Capernaum Pediatric Therapy ....E... 952 938-5348
Hopkins *(G-2522)*

Evangelical Lutheran Good ....D... 320 634-4552
Glenwood *(G-2222)*

Impact Physical Medicine ....E... 651 641-0688
Saint Paul *(G-8507)*

Medical Advanced Pain ....D... 763 537-6000
Minneapolis *(G-3532)*

Metropolitan Hand Surgery ....E... 651 223-5406
Saint Paul *(G-8647)*

Northern Star Therapy Ltd Inc ....E... 320 240-6955
Saint Cloud *(G-7562)*

Physical Therapy Orthopedic ....E... 612 872-2700
Minneapolis *(G-5377)*

Physicans Neck & Back Clinic ....E... 651 639-9150
Saint Paul *(G-8827)*

Rice Memorial Hospital ....E... 320 231-4175
Willmar *(G-10043)*

OFFICES & CLINICS OF HEALTH PRACTITIONERS: Physiotherapist

Professional Physical Therapy ....E... 952 935-0333
Minneapolis *(G-5421)*

OFFICES & CLINICS OF HEALTH PRACTITIONERS: Psychotherapist

Choices Psychotherapy Ltd ....E... 952 544-6806
Minneapolis *(G-4069)*

Generations Community Support ....D... 612 676-1604
Minneapolis *(G-4519)*

Generations Resources For ....E... 612 676-1604
Minneapolis *(G-4520)*

SERVICES

OFFICES & CLINICS OF HEALTH PRACTITIONERS: Speech Pathology

North Memorial Health Care..................A... 763 420-7002
Osseo *(G-6643)*

OFFICES & CLINICS OF HEALTH PRACTITIONERS: Speech Specialist

County of Douglas ....A... 320 762-1511
Alexandria *(G-91)*

OFFICES & CLINICS OF HEALTH PRACTRS: Clinical Psychologist

Associated Clinic of........................E... 952 925-6033
Minneapolis *(G-3824)*
Center For Independent Living............B... 218 262-6675
Hibbing *(G-2439)*
Core Professional Services ....E... 320 202-1400
Saint Cloud *(G-7410)*
Dirk Miller.....................................E... 651 645-5323
Saint Paul *(G-8297)*
Pathways Psychological Svcs 763 525-8590
Minneapolis *(G-5346)*
Patrick M Doyle Dr ....E... 651 454-0114
Saint Paul *(G-7865)*
Program In Human Sexuality ....E... 612 625-1500
Minneapolis *(G-5423)*
Range Mental Health Center Inc ....E... 218 263-9237
Hibbing *(G-2472)*
University Mental Health ....E... 612 626-8100
Minneapolis *(G-5927)*

OFFICES & CLINICS OF HLTH PRACTITIONERS: Reg/Practical Nurse

County of Pennington ....E... 218 681-0876
Thief River Falls *(G-9664)*
Global Anesthesia Business.................E... 651 646-3091
Saint Paul *(G-8414)*

OIL FIELD SVCS, NEC

CHS Inc ....E... 507 238-8900
Fairmont *(G-1960)*

OILS, ANIMAL OR VEGETABLE, WHOLESALE

North Central Co's Inc ....E... 952 449-0885
Minnetonka *(G-6204)*

OLD AGE ASSISTANCE

C A P Scott-Carver-Dakota Inc ....E... 952 496-2125
Shakopee *(G-9425)*
Catholic Charities of The......................E... 651 222-3001
Saint Paul *(G-8176)*
Clearwater Suites Inc........................E... 320 765-8841
Sacred Heart *(G-7398)*
Parkwood Shores Assisted....................E... 952 924-0400
Minneapolis *(G-5339)*

ON-LINE DATABASE INFORMATION RETRIEVAL SVCS

Epredix Holdings Inc ....D... 612 843-1059
Minneapolis *(G-4365)*
Exhibitor Publications Inc....................E... 507 289-6556
Rochester *(G-7109)*
U S Internet Corp ....E... 651 222-4638
Minnetonka *(G-6230)*

OPEN PIT COPPER ORE MINING

Ames Construction Inc...................B... 952 435-7106
Burnsville *(G-676)*

OPEN PIT GOLD MINING

Ames Construction Inc...................B... 952 435-7106
Burnsville *(G-676)*

OPEN PIT IRON MINING, NEC

United States Steel Corp ....C... 218 749-7200
Mountain Iron *(G-6394)*

OPEN PIT TACONITE MINING

Hibbing Taconite Co ....A... 218 262-5950
Hibbing *(G-2452)*
United Taconite LLC ....B... 218 744-7800
Eveleth *(G-1933)*

OPERA COMPANIES

Minnesota Opera..........................C... 612 333-2700
Minneapolis *(G-5087)*

OPERATIVE BUILDERS: Townhouse

Auburn Woods Clubhomes Assn ....D... 952 922-5575
Edina *(G-1825)*

OPERATOR: Apartment Buildings

Accessible Space North Inc ....D... 651 645-7271
Saint Paul *(G-7977)*
Amherst H Wilder Foundation ....C... 651 220-1700
Saint Paul *(G-8041)*
Annandale Congregate Housing ....D... 320 274-3737
Annandale *(G-135)*
Apple Valley Villa Apartments ....E... 952 236-2600
Saint Paul *(G-7703)*
Asi Great Falls Inc............................E... 651 645-7271
Saint Paul *(G-8067)*
Asi Missoula Inc..............................E... 651 645-7271
Saint Paul *(G-8068)*
B T & A Construction Co ....D... 612 825-6811
Minneapolis *(G-3854)*
Big Stone Community Homes Inc ....E... 320 839-6139
Ortonville *(G-6578)*
Bigos Properties ....E... 952 938-6329
Minneapolis *(G-3903)*
Bii Di Gain Dash Anwebi Elder ....D... 651 291-1750
Minneapolis *(G-3904)*
Brookfield Commercial.......................C... 612 372-1500
Minneapolis *(G-3957)*
Calhoun Shores Apartments ....E... 612 824-7505
Minneapolis *(G-3993)*
Cashill Spaulding Properties.................E... 651 225-8227
Saint Paul *(G-8172)*
Cathedral Hill Homes LP ....D... 651 291-1750
Saint Paul *(G-8173)*
Cbc 202 LP....................................D... 651 291-1750
Rogers *(G-7320)*
Cedars of Edina Apartments..................E... 952 835-3388
Minneapolis *(G-4039)*
Centennial Villa Apartments ....E... 320 274-3737
Annandale *(G-139)*
Chapelwood Community ....E... 763 493-5910
Osseo *(G-6602)*
Colonial Village Apartments ....E... 218 739-3795
Fergus Falls *(G-2068)*
Community Housing & Service ....E... 952 933-1833
Minneapolis *(G-4142)*
Community Memorial Home Inc ....D... 320 859-2111
Osakis *(G-6586)*
Crest View Corp ....D... 763 788-2020
Minneapolis *(G-3448)*
Croixdale Apts................................D... 651 275-4800
Bayport *(G-347)*
Crossroads At Penn Apartments ....E... 612 866-3628
Minneapolis *(G-4187)*
Dominium Management Services..........E... 763 560-0244
Minneapolis *(G-4273)*
Family Resources Development...........E... 651 578-0676
Saint Paul *(G-9216)*
Fine Associates LLC..........................E... 612 332-2561
Minneapolis *(G-4434)*
Foundation For Healthcare ....B... 320 253-1920
Sartell *(G-9328)*
France Avenue LLC ....C... 952 831-0343
Minneapolis *(G-4472)*
Franklin Co-Op ....E... 612 338-4574
Minneapolis *(G-4474)*
Governor's Inc................................E... 651 778-1045
Saint Paul *(G-8425)*
Grand Heritage Properties LLC ....D... 651 699-3003
Saint Paul *(G-8426)*
Grandview Manor HRA Office.............D... 218 529-6300
Duluth *(G-1340)*
Griffin Co's ....E... 612 338-2828
Minneapolis *(G-4569)*
Guardian Angels Health Svcs..............C... 763 441-1213
Elk River *(G-1880)*
Gunflint Lodge Inc ....E... 218 388-2294
Grand Marais *(G-2261)*
Harvest Facility Holdings LP ....E... 651 779-9255
Saint Paul *(G-9223)*
Heritage Estates..............................E... 651 735-1776
Saint Paul *(G-8477)*
Heritage Park Estates ....E... 320 240-7939
Saint Cloud *(G-7528)*
Highland Management Group Inc........E... 952 925-1020
Minneapolis *(G-4647)*
Isle View Apartments ....E... 320 676-8624
Isle *(G-2783)*
JAS Apartments Inc ....E... 612 872-4444
Minneapolis *(G-4755)*

Lang-Nelson Associates Inc................E... 763 533-9389
Minneapolis *(G-4840)*
Lloyd Management Inc ....D... 507 625-5573
Mankato *(G-3157)*
Loring Towers Apts LP ....D... 612 871-7202
Minneapolis *(G-4903)*
Mailand Management Corp 651 451-9034
Saint Paul *(G-7830)*
Maple Hills LP ....D... 651 291-1750
Saint Paul *(G-8611)*
Maple Hills LP ....D... 651 291-1750
Red Wing *(G-6990)*
Marshall Asi Inc ....E... 651 645-7271
Saint Paul *(G-8616)*
Mill Street Residence Inc ....E... 218 739-2900
Fergus Falls *(G-2094)*
Miramar Inc....................................E... 763 559-2527
Minneapolis *(G-5108)*
Model Cities of St Paul Inc 651 632-8350
Saint Paul *(G-8717)*
North Point ....E... 507 344-0059
North Mankato *(G-6511)*
Northern Itasca Hospital Dist ....C... 218 743-3177
Bigfork *(G-461)*
Oakdale-Granada Lakes LP ....D... 651 291-1750
Saint Paul *(G-8778)*
Park Brooklyn Housing Assocs ....D... 763 354-5500
Minneapolis *(G-5328)*
Partners For Senior ....E... 952 831-4084
Minneapolis *(G-5341)*
Phalen Village Apartments ....D... 651 771-5625
Saint Paul *(G-8822)*
Phase I Rice-Marion ....E... 763 540-8600
Saint Paul *(G-8823)*
Public Markets Inc ....E... 763 546-3139
Minneapolis *(G-5437)*
Real Estate Equites Inc ....E... 651 227-6925
Saint Paul *(G-8876)*
Reprise Associates ....E... 763 566-5416
Minneapolis *(G-5520)*
Richard Sigert................................D... 218 444-1875
Bemidji *(G-422)*
Riverside Plaza LP ....E... 612 338-8925
Minneapolis *(G-5545)*
Rose Arbor....................................E... 763 493-5910
Osseo *(G-6656)*
Sauer Memorial Home.........................E... 507 454-5540
Winona *(G-10125)*
Sholom St Paul Senior Housing............D... 651 328-2022
Saint Paul *(G-8953)*
Siewert Construction Co Inc 651 437-1728
Hastings *(G-2405)*
Silvercross Properties ....E... 952 925-6231
Minneapolis *(G-5675)*
St Therese Apartments Inc ....D... 763 531-5400
Minneapolis *(G-5732)*
St Therese South West Inc ....E... 952 933-3333
Hopkins *(G-2637)*
Stephen Scott Management Inc ....E... 763 540-8600
Minneapolis *(G-5751)*
Steven Scott Management Inc............E... 952 540-8600
Minneapolis *(G-5754)*
Stewartville Nursing Home Inc............C... 507 533-4288
Stewartville *(G-9594)*
Twv LP ....D... 651 291-1750
Minneapolis *(G-3626)*
Twv LP ....D... 651 291-1750
Saint Paul *(G-9096)*
United Properties Investment...........E... 952 893-8272
Bloomington *(G-523)*
Walker Plaza...................................E... 763 422-1226
Anoka *(G-239)*
Warroad Care Center Inc ....D... 218 386-1235
Warroad *(G-9872)*
Wayzata Partners LP ....D... 952 920-5338
Minneapolis *(G-6028)*
Wayzata Partners LP ....E... 763 473-3200
Wayzata *(G-9949)*
Willows ....E... 763 533-1883
Minneapolis *(G-6073)*
Yorkdale Townhomes Inc ....D... 651 291-1750
Saint Paul *(G-9180)*

OPERATOR: Nonresidential Buildings

American Investment Management .....E... 763 533-7193
Minneapolis *(G-3754)*
Birchwood Lab Associates LLP...........D... 952 937-7900
Eden Prairie *(G-1607)*
Brookfield Commercial.......................C... 612 372-1500
Minneapolis *(G-3957)*
Cap Real Estate ....E... 651 488-5567
Saint Paul *(G-8149)*
City of Minneapolis.............................C... 612 335-6000
Minneapolis *(G-4091)*

Employment codes: A=Over 500 employees, B=251-500,
C=101-250, D=51-100, E=25-50

2011 Harris Minnesota
Services Directory

© Harris InfoSource 1-866-281-6415
745

SERVICES

Diversified Motel Properties ....C... 218 728-3601
Duluth *(G-1294)*

DMW Properties Inc ....D... 763 432-3401
Minneapolis *(G-4267)*

Duluth Entertainment Conv ....A... 218 722-5573
Duluth *(G-1298)*

Gac Development LLC ....E... 507 289-5556
Rochester *(G-7123)*

Giannetti Properties LLC ....C... 651 738-2168
Saint Paul *(G-9220)*

Greg Gruman ....E... 763 546-1177
Minneapolis *(G-4565)*

Healtheast Diversified Svcs 651 232-2300
Saint Paul *(G-8461)*

Highland Management Group Inc ....E... 952 925-1020
Minneapolis *(G-4647)*

Hohenwald Properties ....D... 651 735-1333
Saint Paul *(G-9232)*

Holly Properties ....D... 507 388-6265
Mankato *(G-3142)*

Metro Parkway Assoc ....E... 952 854-4244
Minneapolis *(G-5002)*

Minnehaha Bowling Center Inc ....E... 651 488-7208
Saint Paul *(G-8671)*

Minnesota State Agricultural ....D... 651 288-4400
Saint Paul *(G-8705)*

Mocco Enterprises Inc ....E... 507 537-1421
Marshall *(G-3315)*

Model Cities of St Paul Inc 651 632-8350
Saint Paul *(G-8717)*

180 Degrees Inc ....E... 612 813-5010
Minneapolis *(G-5281)*

Osborne Properties LP ....D... 952 707-8200
Burnsville *(G-772)*

Osborne Properties LP ....E... 952 881-8166
Minneapolis *(G-5296)*

Osborne Properties LP ....E... 952 881-8166
Bloomington *(G-508)*

Pattern Stations Inc ....D... 763 441-6833
Monticello *(G-6282)*

Penco Leasing Corp ....E... 612 927-4748
Minneapolis *(G-5362)*

Playworks Dakota ....D... 952 445-7529
Prior Lake *(G-6948)*

Ryan Co's US Inc ....B... 612 492-4000
Minneapolis *(G-5579)*

SA Group Properties Inc ....D... 612 303-7833
Minneapolis *(G-5583)*

Saint Paul Burlington LP ....C... 651 228-9456
Saint Paul *(G-8924)*

Sexton Partners ....C... 651 457-9255
Saint Paul *(G-7902)*

Shaddric & Le Beau Housing ....E... 763 784-9824
Minneapolis *(G-3600)*

Six Hundred Washington ....D... 612 331-9041
Minneapolis *(G-5684)*

Structural Wood Corp ....E... 651 426-8111
Saint Paul *(G-9010)*

Talisman Brookdale LLC ....E... 763 566-3373
Minneapolis *(G-5787)*

Timberland Partners Management ....D... 952 893-1216
Minneapolis *(G-5827)*

Tofte Management Co LLC ....C... 218 663-7296
Tofte *(G-9684)*

Trimark Hotel Corp ....C... 612 305-9763
Minneapolis *(G-5856)*

Weeres Pontoon ....D... 320 251-3551
Saint Cloud *(G-7631)*

Wise Greenwald & Greenwald PC ....D... 763 535-0501
Minneapolis *(G-6080)*

Wkt Properties LLC ....E... 763 525-4000
Minneapolis *(G-6081)*

OPHTHALMIC GOODS WHOLESALERS

Soderberg Inc ....C... 651 291-1400
Saint Paul *(G-8970)*

OPTICAL SCANNING SVCS

AMI Imaging Systems Inc ....E... 952 828-0080
Bloomington *(G-485)*

Data Recognition Corp ....E... 763 268-2238
Minneapolis *(G-4223)*

Ncs Pearson Inc ....A... 952 681-3000
Minneapolis *(G-5177)*

Nowdocs International Inc ....D... 888 669-3627
North Mankato *(G-6512)*

Questar Data Systems Inc ....C... 651 688-0089
Saint Paul *(G-7886)*

OPTOMETRIC EQPT & SPLYS WHOLESALERS

Essilor Laboratories of Amer ....B... 763 551-2000
Minneapolis *(G-4372)*

Soderberg Inc ....C... 651 291-1400
Saint Paul *(G-8970)*

Walman Optical Co ....C... 612 520-6000
Minneapolis *(G-6014)*

OPTOMETRISTS' OFFICES

Centracare Clinic ....E... 320 256-4228
Melrose *(G-3345)*

Donald H Sealock ....D... 763 559-7358
Minneapolis *(G-4277)*

Linstrom, Samuelson, & Hardten ....E... 612 813-3600
Minneapolis *(G-4892)*

North West Eye Clinic ....C... 763 383-4140
Minneapolis *(G-5223)*

Richie Eye Clinic ....E... 507 332-9900
Faribault *(G-2028)*

Shopko Stores Operating Co LLC ....C... 507 532-3266
Marshall *(G-3327)*

Shopko Stores Operating Co LLC ....C... 507 437-7785
Austin *(G-287)*

Vitreal Retinal Surgery ....E... 952 929-1131
Minneapolis *(G-5979)*

ORCHESTRAS & BANDS

Anoka Brass Band Assoc Inc ....E... 763 427-2790
Anoka *(G-154)*

Red Wing Brass Band Inc ....E... 651 388-2656
Red Wing *(G-6996)*

Saint Paul Chamber Orchestra ....D... 651 292-3241
Saint Paul *(G-8925)*

ORGAN BANK

Upper Midwest Organ ....D... 651 603-7800
Saint Paul *(G-9114)*

ORGANIZATIONS & UNIONS: Labor

Afscme Building Corp ....E... 651 451-7678
South Saint Paul *(G-9507)*

Boilermakers Local Lodge 650 ....E... 651 345-5472
Lake City *(G-2851)*

Bryant Square Apartments ....E... 612 825-4379
Minneapolis *(G-3965)*

Minnesota Afscme Council 5 ....E... 651 455-0773
South Saint Paul *(G-9534)*

Mobiliam 952 921-3997
Minneapolis *(G-5116)*

Operating Engineer No 49 ....E... 218 741-8190
Virginia *(G-9750)*

Seiu Local 284 ....E... 651 256-9102
South Saint Paul *(G-9543)*

ORGANIZATIONS, NEC

County of St Louis ....D... 218 726-2140
Duluth *(G-1285)*

Phoenix Alternatives Vocation ....E... 651 747-8740
Saint Paul *(G-8826)*

ORGANIZATIONS: Civic & Social

American Legion Club ....E... 763 421-0883
Anoka *(G-152)*

American Legion Club ....E... 320 485-4366
Winsted *(G-10156)*

American Legion Club ....E... 218 927-2965
Aitkin *(G-16)*

Corcoran Lions Club ....E... 763 420-2555
Hamel *(G-2338)*

Crookston Firefighter Relief ....E... 218 281-4584
Crookston *(G-1120)*

Delta Kappa Gamma Society ....E... 507 451-2523
Owatonna *(G-6708)*

Farmington Eagles Club ....E... 651 460-8376
Farmington *(G-2050)*

Firemen's Relief Association ....E... 763 593-8080
Minneapolis *(G-4436)*

Grove Cottage Athletic Assn ....E... 651 459-9278
Cottage Grove *(G-1102)*

Independent School District ....D... 952 988-5200
Hopkins *(G-2556)*

International Institute of MN ....D... 651 647-0191
Saint Paul *(G-8516)*

Jewish Community Center of ....C... 952 381-3400
Minneapolis *(G-4762)*

Knights of Columbus ....E... 952 888-1492
Bloomington *(G-502)*

National Amtelco Equipment ....E... 651 265-7845
Saint Paul *(G-8738)*

Sprint Lake Park Alliance ....E... 763 784-9179
Minneapolis *(G-3607)*

Turning Point Administrative ....E... 612 520-4004
Minneapolis *(G-5867)*

Walker West Music Academy ....E... 651 224-2929
Saint Paul *(G-9137)*

Wolf Ridge Environmental ....E... 218 353-7414
Finland *(G-2128)*

Young Men's Christian Assn ....C... 507 387-8255
Mankato *(G-3222)*

YWCA of Minneapolis ....E... 612 863-0970
Minneapolis *(G-6112)*

ORGANIZATIONS: Economic Research, Noncommercial

Regents of The University of ....E... 612 625-1551
Minneapolis *(G-5499)*

ORGANIZATIONS: Educational Research Agency

American Lung Association of ....E... 651 227-8014
Saint Paul *(G-8028)*

Center For Applied Research ....E... 612 624-0300
Minneapolis *(G-4042)*

Educational Cooperative Svc ....E... 612 638-1500
Minneapolis *(G-4327)*

Ncs Pearson Inc ....A... 952 681-3000
Minneapolis *(G-5178)*

Regents of The University of ....E... 612 625-1551
Minneapolis *(G-5499)*

ORGANIZATIONS: Medical Research

Celleration Inc ....E... 952 224-8700
Eden Prairie *(G-1618)*

Central Regional Pathology Lab ....E... 651 264-1611
Saint Paul *(G-9194)*

Envoy Medical Corp ....E... 651 361-8000
Saint Paul *(G-8343)*

Mednet Solutions Inc ....D... 763 258-2735
Minnetonka *(G-6191)*

Rochester Methodist Hospital 507 266-7890
Rochester *(G-7237)*

Spineology Inc ....E... 651 256-8500
Saint Paul *(G-9276)*

ORGANIZATIONS: Political

Democratic Party of Olmsted ....E... 507 536-9785
Rochester *(G-7095)*

Independent Republicans of MN ....E... 651 222-0022
Saint Paul *(G-8509)*

Minnesota Network For ....E... 952 891-1862
Saint Paul *(G-7843)*

ORGANIZATIONS: Professional

Aacc International Inc ....D... 651 454-7250
Saint Paul *(G-7686)*

American Registry of ....E... 651 687-0048
Saint Paul *(G-7698)*

County of Becker ....E... 218 847-2661
Detroit Lakes *(G-1190)*

Decare Dental LLC ....B... 800 371-6561
Saint Paul *(G-7750)*

International Association of ....B... 612 673-3586
Minneapolis *(G-4720)*

Lakes Country Service Co-Op ....D... 218 739-3273
Fergus Falls *(G-2084)*

Minnesota Association of Sch ....D... 651 645-6272
Saint Paul *(G-8673)*

Minnesota Bankers Association ....E... 952 835-3900
Eden Prairie *(G-1725)*

Minnesota Hospital Association ....E... 651 641-1121
Saint Paul *(G-8690)*

Minnesota Society of Certified ....E... 952 831-2707
Minneapolis *(G-5094)*

ORGANIZATIONS: Research Institute

Envoy Medical Corp ....E... 651 361-8000
Saint Paul *(G-8343)*

University Neurosurgical Assn ....E... 612 624-6666
Minneapolis *(G-5928)*

ORGANIZATIONS: Scientific Research Agency

R Tech Laboratories ....D... 651 481-2207
Saint Paul *(G-8867)*

ORGANIZATIONS: Veterans' Membership

American Legion ....E... 218 773-1129
East Grand Forks *(G-1565)*

American Legion Club 334 Inc ....E... 763 421-6260
Minneapolis *(G-3398)*

American Legion Minneapolis ....E... 612 866-3647
Minneapolis *(G-3756)*

American Legion Post 212 A ....E... 218 732-5238
Park Rapids *(G-6747)*

American Legion Post 595 ....E... 507 895-4595
La Crescent *(G-2837)*

American Legion Post 627 ....E... 218 963-9946
Nisswa *(G-6495)*
Coon Rapids VFW Post 9625 ....E... 763 755-4760
Minneapolis *(G-3442)*
Forest Lake VFW Post 4210 Inc ....E... 651 464-6827
Forest Lake *(G-2162)*
Fred Babcock Post No 5555 ....E... 612 869-5555
Minneapolis *(G-4481)*
Golden Valley View Post 7051 ....E... 763 545-9996
Minneapolis *(G-4537)*
Ham Lake American Legion ....E... 763 434-7762
Anoka *(G-187)*
Minnesota Veterans Research ....D... 612 467-2895
Minneapolis *(G-5100)*
Osseo Maple Grove American ....E... 763 425-4858
Osseo *(G-6649)*
Palmer Lake Post 3915 VFW Inc ....E... 763 560-3720
Minneapolis *(G-5315)*
Prior Lake VFW ....E... 952 226-6208
Prior Lake *(G-6951)*
Roseville VFW Post 7555 ....E... 651 483-5313
Saint Paul *(G-8913)*
Sypal Lundgren Post No 7662 ....E... 952 460-6888
Farmington *(G-2061)*
Tri City Post 513 ....E... 651 631-1124
Saint Paul *(G-9081)*
Veterans of Foreign Wars ....E... 320 587-9929
Hutchinson *(G-2715)*
Veterans of Foreign Wars Inc ....E... 507 289-6299
Rochester *(G-7282)*
Veterans of Foreign Wars of ....E... 320 963-3405
Maple Lake *(G-3267)*
Veterans of Foreign Wars of ....B... 320 252-3617
Sauk Rapids *(G-9379)*
VFW Gallagher-Hanson Post 295 ....E... 651 455-1505
South Saint Paul *(G-9550)*
VFW Post 1902 ....E... 218 281-1902
Crookston *(G-1142)*
VFW Red River Valley Post 3817 ....E... 218 773-2481
East Grand Forks *(G-1579)*
Winthrop Honor Guard ....E... 507 647-5608
Winthrop *(G-10169)*

ORNAMENTAL NURSERY PRODUCTS

Bachman's Inc..............................C... 612 861-7600
Minneapolis *(G-3856)*
Bachman's Inc..............................E... 952 469-2102
Farmington *(G-2040)*
Donahues' Greenhouses Inc ....E... 507 334-8404
Faribault *(G-2001)*
Green Mill Growers ....D... 651 697-1081
Saint Paul *(G-8431)*
Linder's Greenhouses Inc ....C... 651 488-6717
Saint Paul *(G-8589)*
Pinehurst Development Inc.................E... 952 469-3202
Farmington *(G-2057)*
Rose Floral & Greenhouse Inc.............E... 651 439-3765
Stillwater *(G-9637)*
Shady Oaks Nursery ....E... 507 835-5033
Waseca *(G-9887)*
Syngenta Seeds Inc ....E... 507 674-3320
Amboy *(G-132)*
Wagner Greenhouses Inc ....E... 612 922-1262
Minneapolis *(G-5993)*
Wright Tree Service Inc ....C... 507 625-6950
Mankato *(G-3220)*

ORNAMENTAL SHRUB & TREE SVC

Asplundh Tree Expert Co ....C... 763 785-2300
Circle Pines *(G-1002)*
City of Minneapolis ....C... 612 370-4900
Minneapolis *(G-4088)*
Dakota Turf Inc ....E... 651 460-8873
Farmington *(G-2048)*
Davey Tree Expert Co ....E... 763 553-9740
Minneapolis *(G-4224)*
Top Notch Treecare ....E... 763 253-8733
Minneapolis *(G-5830)*
Wright Tree Service Inc ....C... 507 625-6950
Mankato *(G-3220)*

ORTHODONTIST

Lake Minnetonka Orthodontics ....E... 952 938-1443
Hopkins *(G-2568)*
Lake Superior Dental ....E... 218 728-6445
Duluth *(G-1376)*
Leonard V Ackerman DDS ....E... 763 757-7540
Minneapolis *(G-3515)*
Orthodonic Care Specialist.................D... 651 490-6732
Saint Paul *(G-8791)*
Orthodontics Care Specialist...............E... 952 432-2682
Saint Paul *(G-7859)*

OUTREACH PROGRAM

Accessible Space Inc ....E... 651 645-7271
Saint Paul *(G-7975)*
Indian Health Board of.......................D... 612 721-9800
Minneapolis *(G-4696)*
Orono Healthy Youth ....E... 952 449-8351
Long Lake *(G-3029)*
Regents of The University of ....E... 612 626-4515
Minneapolis *(G-5502)*

OXYGEN TENT SVCS

Barnabas Health Care Services............C... 218 829-0901
Brainerd *(G-551)*

PACKAGE DESIGN SVCS

International Paper Co........................C... 507 433-3467
Austin *(G-278)*

PACKAGED FROZEN FOODS
WHOLESALERS, NEC

A H Hermel Candy & Tobacco Co ....D... 507 387-5634
Mankato *(G-3098)*
Appert's Inc...................................C... 320 251-3200
Saint Cloud *(G-7433)*
Apperts Frozen Foods Inc...................D... 320 251-3200
Saint Cloud *(G-7434)*
E A Sween Deli Express ....C... 952 937-9440
Eden Prairie *(G-1647)*
5 K Enterprises Inc ....E... 612 216-6292
Mankato *(G-3127)*
Hawkeye Foodservice Distbn ....E... 507 238-4721
Fairmont *(G-1972)*
Martin-Brower Co L L C ....C... 763 571-6311
Minneapolis *(G-3528)*
Nash-Finch Co ....B... 952 832-0534
Edina *(G-1838)*
Schwan's Consumer Brands North......C... 952 832-4300
Bloomington *(G-513)*
Schwan's Global Food Service............C... 507 532-3274
Marshall *(G-3326)*
Schwan's Home Service Inc ....E... 218 879-5470
Esko *(G-1923)*
SUPERVALU Inc.............................A... 952 828-4000
Eden Prairie *(G-1787)*
Supervalu Inc ....C... 952 906-6260
Chanhassen *(G-941)*
Trudeau Holdings LLC ....C... 952 882-8295
Burnsville *(G-813)*
Trudeau Holdings LLC ....D... 952 445-1350
Shakopee *(G-9481)*
Twin City Poultry Co ....E... 763 592-6500
Minneapolis *(G-5882)*
Upper Lakes Foods Inc ....C... 218 879-1265
Cloquet *(G-1066)*

PACKAGING & LABELING SVCS

Abraham Technical Services Inc ....E... 763 428-3170
Rogers *(G-7315)*
Birchwood Laboratories Inc ....D... 952 937-7900
Eden Prairie *(G-1608)*
Brookdale Plastics Inc.......................D... 763 797-1000
Plymouth *(G-6852)*
D & G Packaging Co ....E... 952 890-7525
Burnsville *(G-706)*
FDC Services Inc.............................C... 320 656-8880
Saint Cloud *(G-7508)*
Federal Express Corp ....B... 612 794-3100
Minneapolis *(G-4419)*
Hennepin County ....E... 612 596-0071
Minneapolis *(G-4635)*
International Packaging Inc ....D... 763 315-6200
Minneapolis *(G-4723)*
International Paper Co........................C... 651 426-0345
Saint Paul *(G-8517)*
Interstate Rehabilitation Ctr.................B... 651 388-7108
Red Wing *(G-6987)*
Lifetrack Resources Inc ....E... 651 290-0567
Saint Paul *(G-8587)*
Lonsdale Packaging ....D... 507 744-2376
Lonsdale *(G-3045)*
M D I Government Services ....E... 218 326-9544
Grand Rapids *(G-2292)*
M D I Government Services ....C... 218 263-3663
Hibbing *(G-2460)*
M D I Government Services ....B... 651 999-8200
Saint Paul *(G-8602)*
Minnesota Diversified Inds ....E... 651 999-8200
Saint Paul *(G-8684)*
Minnesota Diversified Inds ....C... 218 263-3663
Hibbing *(G-2468)*
Pouchtec Industries LLC....................D... 320 968-4868
Foley *(G-2141)*

ProAct Inc.....................................C.:. 651 686-0405
Saint Paul *(G-7884)*
R J M Enterprises of Minnesota ....C... 763 323-8389
Anoka *(G-218)*
Ryt-Way Industries LLC ....A... 952 469-1417
Lakeville *(G-2929)*
Schmid & Son Packaging Inc ....D... 651 452-0588
Cottage Grove *(G-1107)*
Swanson-Flosystems Co ....E... 763 383-4700
Plymouth *(G-6885)*
Timberland Group Inc ....E... 952 924-9070
Minneapolis *(G-5826)*

PACKAGING MATERIALS, WHOLESALE

Bemis Co Inc..................................E... 612 788-0100
Minneapolis *(G-3883)*
Delkor Systems Inc ....D... 763 783-0855
Circle Pines *(G-1010)*

PACKING & CRATING SVC

Business Impact Group LLC ....D... 952 278-7800
Chanhassen *(G-911)*
Innovative Packaging ....E... 763 488-9708
Maple Grove *(G-3246)*
Riverview Packaging Inc.....................E... 651 415-1121
Saint Paul *(G-8905)*
Visual Packaging Corp.......................E... 952 938-1575
Hopkins *(G-2653)*

PACKING SVCS: Shipping

Independent Packing Services.............E... 763 425-7155
Osseo *(G-6623)*
Sunopta Aseptic Inc ....D... 320 763-9822
Alexandria *(G-124)*

PAGING SVCS

Hutchinson Telephone Co ....D... 320 587-2323
Hutchinson *(G-2702)*
Rural Cellular Corp ....C... 320 762-2000
Alexandria *(G-122)*
SBC Datacomm Inc ....E... 763 315-5343
Saint Paul *(G-8931)*

PAINT BRUSHES, ROLLERS & SPRAYERS
WHOLESALERS

Hirshfield's Inc................................D... 612 377-3910
Minneapolis *(G-4655)*

PAINTS, VARNISHES & SPLYS
WHOLESALERS

Abbott Paint & Carpet Inc ....E... 651 429-3316
Saint Paul *(G-7972)*
Fastenal Co ....B... 507 454-5374
Winona *(G-10095)*

PAINTS, VARNISHES & SPLYS,
WHOLESALE: Paints

Fastenal Co ....B... 507 454-5374
Winona *(G-10095)*
Hirshfield's Inc................................D... 612 377-3910
Minneapolis *(G-4655)*

PAINTS, VARNISHES & SPLYS,
WHOLESALE: Varnishes

Hirshfield's Inc................................D... 612 377-3910
Minneapolis *(G-4655)*

PALLET REPAIR SVCS

Otto Packaging Midwest LLC ....E... 651 488-0474
Saint Paul *(G-8793)*

PAPER NAPKINS WHOLESALERS

International Dairy Queen Inc...............B... 952 830-0200
Minneapolis *(G-4721)*

PAPER, WHOLESALE: Fine

C J Duffey Paper Co.........................D... 612 338-8701
Minneapolis *(G-3984)*
Midland Paper Co ....E... 612 623-2400
Minneapolis *(G-5025)*

PAPER, WHOLESALE: Printing

Kempf Paper Corp............................D... 612 781-9225
Minneapolis *(G-4799)*
Wilcox Paper LLC ....E... 763 404-8400
Champlin *(G-906)*

Employment codes: A=Over 500 employees, B=251-500,
C=101-250, D=51-100, E=25-50

2011 Harris Minnesota
Services Directory

© Harris InfoSource 1-866-281-6415
747

SERVICES

PAPER, WHOLESALE: Writing

Wilcox Paper LLC ....E... 763 404-8400
Champlin *(G-906)*

PARADE FLOATS: Decorating Svcs

Victory Corps Flags Floats ....D... 763 561-5600
Minneapolis *(G-5969)*

PARKING GARAGE

Loop Parking Co 612 333-2293
Minneapolis *(G-4902)*
Municipal Parking Inc ....E... 612 339-2003
Minneapolis *(G-5150)*
Oneida Realty Co Inc ....D... 218 722-0816
Duluth *(G-1413)*
Park N' Go of Minnesota LP ....D... 952 854-3386
Minneapolis *(G-5329)*
Rochester Parking Ramps ....E... 507 282-0558
Rochester *(G-7238)*

PARKING LOTS

E Z Air Park Inc ....E... 651 454-1302
Saint Paul *(G-7754)*
Loop Parking Co 612 333-2293
Minneapolis *(G-4902)*
Park 'n Fly Inc ....D... 952 854-0606
Minneapolis *(G-5327)*
Standard Parking Corp ....C... 612 371-0938
Minneapolis *(G-5737)*

PARKING LOTS & GARAGES

Central Parking Inc ....E... 612 340-9025
Minneapolis *(G-4046)*
City of Mora ....E... 320 679-1770
Mora *(G-6353)*
Dayton Radison Inc ....E... 612 672-0060
Minneapolis *(G-4232)*
Municipal Parking Inc ....E... 612 673-9644
Minneapolis *(G-5149)*
Regents of The University of ....E... 612 626-7275
Minneapolis *(G-5492)*
Young, Quinlan Assoc LLP ....E... 612 337-5109
Minneapolis *(G-6105)*

PARKING STRUCTURE

Dayton-Radisson Ramp ....D... 612 333-2293
Minneapolis *(G-4233)*

PARTY & SPECIAL EVENT PLANNING SVCS

Aarcee Party & Tent Rental ....E... 952 922-7233
Minneapolis *(G-3657)*
C E C Entertainment Inc ....E... 952 892-7786
Burnsville *(G-694)*
Playworks Dakota ....D... 952 445-7529
Prior Lake *(G-6948)*

PARTY FAVORS, BALLOONS, HATS, ETC, WHOLESALE

Mayflower Distributing Co Inc ....C... 651 452-4892
Saint Paul *(G-7835)*

PASSENGER AIRLINE SVCS

American Airlines Inc ....C... 612 726-5833
Saint Paul *(G-7957)*
American Airlines Inc ....D... 612 726-5647
Saint Paul *(G-7956)*
Continental Airlines Inc ....D... 612 726-5679
Saint Paul *(G-7959)*
MN Airlines LLC ....A... 651 681-3900
Mendota Heights *(G-3367)*
Northwest Airlines Corp ....A... 612 726-2111
Eagan *(G-1543)*
Northwest Airlines Inc ....A... 612 726-2111
Minneapolis *(G-5238)*
Northwest Airlines Inc ....E... 507 282-9425
Rochester *(G-7192)*
Northwest Airlines Inc ....A... 218 254-7575
Chisholm *(G-999)*
Northwest Airlines Inc ....E... 612 726-8000
Minneapolis *(G-5239)*
Northwest Airlines Inc ....C... 612 727-9209
Minneapolis *(G-5240)*
Servicemaster Inc ....D... 612 794-4100
Saint Paul *(G-7963)*

PATENT BUYING, LICENSING & LEASING

Kiltie Corp ....E... 651 770-3166
Saint Paul *(G-9235)*

PATENT OWNERS & LESSORS

Carlson Holdings Inc ....A... 763 212-5000
Minnetonka *(G-6152)*

PAYROLL SVCS

Alliance Benefit Group ....D... 507 377-9344
Albert Lea *(G-35)*
Ceridian Corp ....A... 952 853-8100
Minneapolis *(G-4052)*
Children's Health Care Inc ....C... 651 855-2800
Saint Paul *(G-8194)*
Consumer Directions Inc ....A... 320 420-3423
Saint Cloud *(G-7409)*
Diversified Industries Inc ....E... 763 513-5951
Minneapolis *(G-4262)*
Ftb Inc ....E... 218 326-5960
Grand Rapids *(G-2278)*
Minnesota Clerical Inc ....C... 763 753-7243
Anoka *(G-205)*
Paychex Inc ....E... 651 365-5060
Saint Paul *(G-7869)*
Paysource Inc ....D... 651 633-9595
Saint Paul *(G-8811)*
Wells Fargo Bank, National ....E... 952 881-7333
Minneapolis *(G-6040)*

PEAT GRINDING SVCS

Pioneer Peat Inc 701 746-4300
East Grand Forks *(G-1573)*

PEAT MINING SVCS

Pioneer Peat Inc 701 746-4300
East Grand Forks *(G-1573)*

PENSION & RETIREMENT PLAN CONSULTANTS

Citi Investor Services Inc ....B... 218 825-5000
Baxter *(G-324)*
Citi Investor Services Inc ....B... 218 829-4781
Baxter *(G-325)*
Citi Investor Services Inc ....E... 218 825-0552
Brainerd *(G-557)*
Foster Klima & Co LLC ....D... 612 746-2214
Minneapolis *(G-4467)*
L H Hendrickson & Co Inc ....E... 952 896-3456
Minneapolis *(G-4827)*
Tax-Sheltered Compensation Inc ....E... 952 806-4300
Minneapolis *(G-5793)*
Towers Watson Pennsylvania Inc ....E... 952 842-5600
Minneapolis *(G-5840)*

PENSION FUNDS

Firemens Relief Assns ....E... 507 532-5141
Marshall *(G-3295)*
Public Employees Retirement ....D... 651 296-7460
Saint Paul *(G-8855)*

PENSIONS

Board of Pensions of The ....C... 612 333-7651
Minneapolis *(G-3920)*

PERFORMING ARTS CENTER PRODUCTION SVCS

Holmes Center Inc ....D... 218 844-4221
Detroit Lakes *(G-1197)*
Jazz Arts Group Fargomoorhead ....E... 218 236-0421
Moorhead *(G-6320)*
Minnesota Landmarks Inc ....E... 651 292-3233
Saint Paul *(G-8693)*
Ordway Center For The 651 282-3000
Saint Paul *(G-8790)*
West Bank School of Music ....E... 612 333-6651
Minneapolis *(G-6056)*

PERIODICALS, WHOLESALE

Minnesota News Service Inc ....D... 952 703-0075
Minneapolis *(G-5086)*
Valley News Co ....D... 507 345-4819
Mankato *(G-3212)*

PERSONAL APPEARANCE SVCS

D M S Health Group ....E... 763 315-1947
Osseo *(G-6607)*
Life Time Fitness Inc ....D... 612 752-9589
Minneapolis *(G-4878)*
Life Time Fitness Inc ....E... 952 835-2222
Minneapolis *(G-4877)*
Life Time Fitness Inc ....C... 763 576-3000
Champlin *(G-895)*

Life Time Fitness Inc ....C... 763 509-0909
Minneapolis *(G-4880)*
Life Time Fitness Inc ....C... 763 257-1067
Minneapolis *(G-3519)*

PERSONAL CARE FACILITY

Augustana Chapel View Homes ....B... 612 333-1551
Minneapolis *(G-3835)*
Benedictine Health System ....D... 651 388-1234
Red Wing *(G-6975)*
Graceville Health Center Inc ....C... 320 748-7223
Graceville *(G-2254)*
Innsbruck Healthcare Center ....D... 651 633-1686
New Brighton *(G-6411)*
Kenyon Sunset Home ....D... 507 789-6134
Kenyon *(G-2828)*
Minnesota Masonic Home ....A... 952 948-7000
Minneapolis *(G-5082)*
Providence Place ....C... 612 724-5495
Minneapolis *(G-5433)*
Rose Camilia Co Inc ....C... 763 755-8400
Minneapolis *(G-3592)*

PERSONAL CARE HOME, WITH HEALTH CARE

Becklund Personal Care Org ....E... 763 546-2030
Minneapolis *(G-3878)*
Benedictine Health System ....D... 218 786-2370
Duluth *(G-1250)*
Benedictine Health System ....A... 952 403-3000
Shakopee *(G-9420)*
Care Institute Inc ....E... 651 482-1611
Saint Paul *(G-8160)*
City of Adams ....D... 507 582-3263
Adams *(G-3)*
City of Fertile......................................C... 218 945-6194
Fertile *(G-2125)*
Disable Home Heaklth Care Inc ....C... 651 292-8705
Saint Paul *(G-8298)*
Emerald Crest of Shakopee..................E... 952 233-8811
Shakopee *(G-9438)*
Glenwood Village Care Center ....C... 320 634-5131
Glenwood *(G-2225)*
Home Care & PCA Services LLC............D... 763 566-5063
Minneapolis *(G-4665)*
Home Free Inc ....C... 952 814-7400
Minneapolis *(G-4668)*
Horizon Health Inc ....E... 320 468-2811
Pierz *(G-6804)*
Lake Ridge Care Center of...................C... 763 682-1434
Buffalo *(G-649)*
Lakeview Ranch Inc ....E... 320 275-4027
Darwin *(G-1157)*
Lyngblomsten ....B... 651 646-2941
Saint Paul *(G-8599)*
Martin Luther Manor ....B... 952 888-7751
Minneapolis *(G-4960)*
Morning Star Healthcare Svcs..............E... 651 209-2950
Saint Paul *(G-8722)*
Rakhma Inc ....D... 612 824-2345
Minneapolis *(G-5464)*
REM Williams ....E... 952 925-3292
Minneapolis *(G-5513)*
Seniors Caring Companions Inc ....E... 651 770-2288
Maplewood *(G-3288)*
Sholom Community Alliance..................E... 952 908-1776
Minneapolis *(G-5658)*
Thro Co...C... 507 345-4631
Mankato *(G-3204)*
Washington County Association ....D... 651 439-4946
Bayport *(G-351)*
Wilds of San Prairie ....E... 507 931-4375
Saint Peter *(G-9316)*

PERSONAL CREDIT INSTITUTIONS: Auto/Consumer Finance Co's

Conseco Finance Corp ....C... 651 293-3434
Saint Paul *(G-8248)*

PERSONAL CREDIT INSTITUTIONS: Consumer Finance Companies

Conseco Finance Corp ....C... 651 293-3434
Saint Paul *(G-8248)*
Hsbc Card Services Inc ....C... 952 358-4000
Minnetonka *(G-6179)*
Payday America LLC ....E... 952 646-1793
Burnsville *(G-777)*
Wells Fargo Financial Indiana ....E... 952 920-9270
Minneapolis *(G-6046)*

SERVICES

PERSONAL CREDIT INSTITUTIONS: Financing, Autos, Furniture

Citigroup Inc ....C... 952 942-9880
Minneapolis *(G-4081)*

Conseco Finance Corp ....C... 651 293-3434
Saint Paul *(G-8248)*

PERSONAL CREDIT INSTITUTIONS: Install Sales Finance

Preferred Credit Inc ....C... 320 202-7000
Saint Cloud *(G-7570)*

PERSONAL DOCUMENT & INFORMATION SVCS

Minnesota Tobacco Document ....E... 612 378-5707
Minneapolis *(G-5097)*

PERSONAL INVESTIGATION SVCS

Icon Services Corp ....E... 651 695-8778
Saint Paul *(G-8503)*

PERSONAL ITEM CARE & STORAGE SVCS

Apex International Mfg Inc ....C... 952 227-3000
Chaska *(G-949)*

PERSONAL SVCS

Bug Co of Minnesota ....E... 763 434-0550
Anoka *(G-160)*

PEST CONTROL IN STRUCTURES SVCS

Adam's Pest Control Inc ....E... 763 478-9810
Hamel *(G-2336)*

PESTICIDES WHOLESALERS

Kruse Family Enterprises LLC..............E... 507 345-5926
Mankato *(G-3156)*

PET FOOD WHOLESALERS

American Agco Inc ....D... 651 451-1349
Cottage Grove *(G-1098)*

American Logistics Services ....D... 651 451-1349
Cottage Grove *(G-1099)*

Rfg Distributing Inc............................D... 763 540-0335
Minneapolis *(G-5534)*

PET SPLYS WHOLESALERS

Atlas Pet Supply Inc ....E... 763 753-4818
Anoka *(G-157)*

General Pet Supply Inc ....E... 952 890-2300
Burnsville *(G-727)*

Miller Manufacturing Co Inc ....D... 320 864-4189
Glencoe *(G-2210)*

PETROLEUM & PETROLEUM PRDTS, WHOL Svc Station Splys, Petro

Dan Larson Enterprises Inc ....E... 612 331-8550
Minneapolis *(G-4222)*

Graffco Inc ....E... 651 464-1079
Forest Lake *(G-2146)*

PETROLEUM & PETROLEUM PRDTS, WHOLESALE Diesel Fuel

Croix Oil Co ....E... 651 439-5755
Stillwater *(G-9608)*

Lubrication Technologies Inc ....D... 651 636-7990
Saint Paul *(G-8596)*

PETROLEUM & PETROLEUM PRDTS, WHOLESALE Engine Fuels & Oils

Como Lube & Supplies Inc ....E... 218 722-2920
Duluth *(G-1280)*

PETROLEUM & PETROLEUM PRDTS, WHOLESALE Fuel Oil

Croix Oil Co ....E... 651 439-5755
Stillwater *(G-9608)*

Egan Oil Co LLC...............................E... 763 421-0410
Anoka *(G-176)*

Kath Management Co ....D... 651 484-3325
Saint Paul *(G-8541)*

Lubrication Technologies Inc ....D... 651 636-7990
Saint Paul *(G-8596)*

Yocum Oil Co Inc ....C... 651 739-9141
Saint Paul *(G-9179)*

PETROLEUM & PETROLEUM PRDTS, WHOLESALE Gases

Valley National Gases WV LLC ....E... 320 235-3430
Willmar *(G-10051)*

PETROLEUM & PETROLEUM PRDTS, WHOLESALE Petroleum Terminals

J M Oil Co ....E... 320 251-2082
Saint Cloud *(G-7533)*

PETROLEUM & PETROLEUM PRDTS, WHOLESALE: Bulk Stations

Anderson-Gilyard...............................E... 763 261-5161
Becker *(G-354)*

Belgrade Cooperative Assn ....E... 320 254-8231
Belgrade *(G-363)*

Central Valley Cooperative ....E... 507 451-1230
Owatonna *(G-6700)*

Consumers Cooperative Assn..............E... 320 693-2821
Litchfield *(G-2981)*

Coop FCA ....E... 507 847-4160
Jackson *(G-2789)*

Country Pride Services Co-op ....E... 507 831-2580
Bingham Lake *(G-466)*

Crystal Valley Coop ....E... 507 642-8837
La Salle *(G-2846)*

Dooley's Petroleum Inc ....D... 320 875-2641
Murdock *(G-6400)*

Edwards Oil Co Inc ....E... 218 741-9634
Virginia *(G-9738)*

Egan Oil Co LLC...............................E... 763 421-0410
Anoka *(G-176)*

Farmers Co-Operative of Hanska ....E... 507 439-6244
Hanska *(G-2370)*

Farmers Co-Operative Oil Co of ....E... 507 925-4114
Echo *(G-1581)*

Farmers Union Oil Co of ....E... 320 269-8856
Montevideo *(G-6245)*

High Plains Cooperative......................D... 507 534-3111
Plainview *(G-6843)*

J M Oil Co ....E... 320 251-2082
Saint Cloud *(G-7533)*

Kutzke Oil Co Inc ....E... 320 629-2075
Pine City *(G-6812)*

Lake Region Co-Op Oil Assn ....E... 763 682-1431
Buffalo *(G-648)*

Mille Lacs Oil Co ....E... 320 396-2693
Braham *(G-543)*

Multi-County AG LLC........................E... 507 223-5634
Canby *(G-850)*

Paynesville Farmers Union ....E... 320 243-3751
Paynesville *(G-6772)*

Prairie Pride Cooperative ....E... 507 532-9686
Marshall *(G-3320)*

Wilson Oil Co Inc 651 388-5783
Red Wing *(G-7013)*

PETROLEUM BULK STATIONS & TERMINALS

Best Oil Co..E... 218 879-4666
Cloquet *(G-1046)*

Coop Northern Star..............................D... 218 246-8660
Deer River *(G-1167)*

Farmers Co-Op Oil Co of Clara 320 847-2318
Clara City *(G-1027)*

Greenway Co-Operative Service ....E... 507 775-2900
Byron *(G-824)*

Park Region Cooperative 218 863-2811
Pelican Rapids *(G-6782)*

Rothsay Truck Stop & Cafe...................E... 218 867-2233
Rothsay *(G-7383)*

United Farmers Co Op ....E... 507 237-2281
Gaylord *(G-2201)*

PETROLEUM PRDTS WHOLESALERS

Adium Oil Co Inc ....E... 320 356-7350
Avon *(G-293)*

Belle Plaine Cooperative ....E... 952 873-4244
Belle Plaine *(G-367)*

Bemidji Cooperative Assn ....E... 218 751-4260
Bemidji *(G-379)*

Border States Cooperative...................E... 320 695-2575
Browns Valley *(G-626)*

Chamberlain Oil Co Inc ....E... 320 843-3434
Clontarf *(G-1045)*

Cooperative Sampo Inc ....D... 218 564-4534
Menahga *(G-3357)*

Crookston Fuel Co.............................E... 218 281-2157
Crookston *(G-1121)*

Farmers Union Oil Co of.....................E... 218 233-2497
Moorhead *(G-6315)*

Federated Coop Inc ....E... 320 679-2682
Mora *(G-6358)*

Kath Management Co ....D... 651 484-3325
Saint Paul *(G-8541)*

Kunz Oil Co ....D... 952 352-8600
Hopkins *(G-2567)*

Marathon Petroleum Co LP ....B... 651 459-9771
Saint Paul Park *(G-9296)*

Marathon Petroleum Co LP ....B... 651 459-9771
Saint Paul Park *(G-9295)*

North Stop Inc ....E... 218 547-1859
Walker *(G-9856)*

Olson Oil Co Inc................................E... 218 736-2786
Fergus Falls *(G-2103)*

Severson Oil Co.................................E... 507 452-4743
Winona *(G-10126)*

US Venture Inc ....D... 763 591-5827
Minneapolis *(G-5950)*

Vukelich Oil Co 320 253-6546
Saint Cloud *(G-7628)*

Watonwan Farm Service Inc................E... 507 776-2831
Truman *(G-9699)*

PETS & PET SPLYS, WHOLESALE

Town & Country Fence Inc ....E... 763 425-5050
Minneapolis *(G-5841)*

PHARMACEUTICALS, DRUG PROPRIETARIES & SUNDRIES WHOLESALERS

Amerisourcebergen Corp ....B... 952 903-7600
Eden Prairie *(G-1592)*

Cardinal Health Inc ....C... 763 398-8321
Minneapolis *(G-4001)*

Cardinal Health Inc ....D... 651 255-1383
Saint Paul *(G-8158)*

Curry Sales Inc ....E... 952 351-4200
Hopkins *(G-2534)*

Fairview Health Services ....E... 651 632-9835
Saint Paul *(G-8363)*

Fairview Pharmacy Services LLC ....B... 612 672-5260
Minneapolis *(G-4403)*

McKesson Corp ....D... 651 484-4811
Little Canada *(G-2996)*

Procter & Gamble Distributing ....C... 952 942-1857
Eden Prairie *(G-1754)*

Redpharm Drug ....E... 952 653-2525
Eden Prairie *(G-1760)*

Watkins Inc ....C... 507 457-3300
Winona *(G-10138)*

PHOSPHATE ROCK MINING

Mosaic Co...C... 763 577-2700
Minneapolis *(G-5133)*

Mosaic Global Holdings Inc..................E... 763 577-2700
Minneapolis *(G-5134)*

PHOTOCOPY MACHINE REPAIR SVCS

Sel-Mor Distributing Co ....E... 952 929-0888
Minneapolis *(G-5629)*

PHOTOCOPY SPLYS WHOLESALERS

Katun Corp.......................................B... 952 941-9505
Minneapolis *(G-4793)*

Ricoh Americas Corp ....D... 651 294-2600
Mendota Heights *(G-3370)*

PHOTOCOPYING & DUPLICATING SVCS

Albinson Reprographics LLC................E... 612 374-1120
Minneapolis *(G-3703)*

American Reprographics Co LLC ....D... 612 722-2303
Minneapolis *(G-3759)*

Bernard Group Inc.............................D... 952 934-1900
Chaska *(G-954)*

Englund Graphics Inc ....E... 763 536-9100
Minneapolis *(G-4358)*

Fedex Office & Print Services ....E... 651 699-9671
Saint Paul *(G-8370)*

Fedex Office & Print Services ....C... 952 593-1143
Hopkins *(G-2542)*

Fedex Office & Print Services ....E... 952 892-0200
Burnsville *(G-721)*

Fedex Office & Print Services ....E... 612 822-7700
Minneapolis *(G-4423)*

Fedex Office & Print Services ....E... 612 578-9000
Saint Paul *(G-9217)*

Fedex Office & Print Services ....E... 952 943-4000
Eden Prairie *(G-1664)*

Health Care Provider Service ....E... 952 831-8114
Minneapolis *(G-4618)*

Minnesota Insty-Prints Inc...................E... 612 332-8669
Minneapolis *(G-5079)*

Employment codes: A=Over 500 employees, B=251-500,
C=101-250, D=51-100, E=25-50

2011 Harris Minnesota
Services Directory

© Harris InfoSource 1-866-281-6415
749

SERVICES

National Business Systems Inc............D... 651 688-0202
Eagan *(G-1540)*

Nightowl Document Management ......D... 612 337-0448
Minneapolis *(G-5203)*

Professional Reproductions Inc..........E... 952 946-1200
Edina *(G-1841)*

Simtek Corp..................................E... 952 831-7472
Minneapolis *(G-5678)*

Xcellence Inc.................................E... 612 305-1330
Minneapolis *(G-6091)*

Xerox Corp...................................C... 952 921-1300
Minneapolis *(G-6093)*

PHOTOFINISHING LABORATORIES

Mc Be Co......................................507 289-1666
Rochester *(G-7178)*

National Camera Exchange Inc ....E... 952 898-4888
Burnsville *(G-762)*

Proex Photo...................................E... 651 699-4394
Saint Paul *(G-8852)*

Proex Photo Systems Inc..................E... 952 893-1915
Minneapolis *(G-3575)*

Proex Photo Systems Inc..................E... 952 941-5232
Eden Prairie *(G-1755)*

Shopko Stores Operating Co LLC ....C... 507 281-0656
Rochester *(G-7253)*

Snyder's Drug Stores Inc..................E... 763 427-8111
Champlin *(G-901)*

Snyder's Drug Stores Inc..................E... 507 345-1002
Mankato *(G-3198)*

Walgreen Co ....E... 320 251-9433
Saint Cloud *(G-7629)*

Walgreen Co ....E... 952 448-1180
Chaska *(G-984)*

Walgreen Co ....E... 763 427-6389
Champlin *(G-905)*

Walgreen Co ....E... 612 822-9712
Minneapolis *(G-6003)*

Walgreen Co ....E... 952 226-1283
Savage *(G-9411)*

Walgreen Co ....E... 763 566-8350
Minneapolis *(G-6005)*

Walgreen Co ....E... 952 938-1168
Hopkins *(G-2657)*

Walgreen Co ....E... 612 861-7276
Minneapolis *(G-6006)*

Walgreen Co ....E... 612 827-8902
Minneapolis *(G-6001)*

Walgreen Co ....E... 763 755-1259
Minneapolis *(G-3635)*

Walgreen Co ....E... 320 253-6601
Sauk Rapids *(G-9380)*

Walgreen Co ....E... 763 576-0388
Anoka *(G-238)*

Walgreen Co ....E... 763 545-6466
Minneapolis *(G-5998)*

Walgreen Co ....E... 763 783-7005
Circle Pines *(G-1024)*

Walgreen Co ....D... 612 722-4249
Minneapolis *(G-5999)*

Walgreen Co ....E... 763 553-9731
Minneapolis *(G-6000)*

Walgreen Co ....D... 952 884-8246
Minneapolis *(G-6004)*

Walgreen Co ....E... 952 920-3561
Minneapolis *(G-6002)*

Walgreen Co ....E... 952 882-7998
Burnsville *(G-819)*

Walgreen Co ....E... 763 586-0730
Minneapolis *(G-3636)*

Walgreen Co ....E... 952 941-8666
Eden Prairie *(G-1812)*

Walgreen Co ....E... 763 585-9946
Minneapolis *(G-6007)*

Weber & Judd Co ....E... 507 289-6047
Rochester *(G-7287)*

White House Custom Colour Inc ....C... 651 646-8263
Eagan *(G-1560)*

PHOTOGRAPHIC EQPT & CAMERAS, WHOLESALE

H & J Bliss Enterprises ....E... 952 988-9302
Minneapolis *(G-4584)*

PHOTOGRAPHIC EQPT & SPLYS WHOLESALERS

Pakor Inc......................................E... 763 559-8484
Osseo *(G-6650)*

PHOTOGRAPHIC EQPT & SPLYS, WHOLESALE: Developing Apparatus

3M Co ....D... 651 733-1941
Saint Paul *(G-9055)*

PHOTOGRAPHIC EQPT & SPLYS, WHOLESALE: Motion Picture

Tierney Brothers Inc ....D... 612 331-5500
Minneapolis *(G-5821)*

PHOTOGRAPHIC EQPT & SPLYS, WHOLESALE: Processing

Pakor Inc......................................E... 763 559-8484
Osseo *(G-6650)*

PHOTOGRAPHIC SVCS

Camera Shop of Saint Cloud Inc ....E... 320 251-2622
Saint Cloud *(G-7468)*

Tomsten Inc ....E... 952 516-3300
Minnetonka *(G-6228)*

PHOTOGRAPHY SVCS: Commercial

David Kelloway ....E... 952 944-0739
Minneapolis *(G-4225)*

Greer & Associates Inc ....E... 612 338-6171
Minneapolis *(G-4564)*

PHOTOGRAPHY SVCS: Portrait Studios

In Fisherman Inc ....E... 218 829-1648
Baxter *(G-330)*

JC Penney Corp Inc.........................C... 218 727-8111
Duluth *(G-1360)*

Proex Photo Systems Inc..................E... 952 893-1915
Minneapolis *(G-3575)*

PHOTOGRAPHY SVCS: School

Lifetouch National School.................C... 952 826-4500
Minneapolis *(G-4882)*

Lifetouch National School.................B... 952 826-4000
Eden Prairie *(G-1710)*

PHOTOGRAPHY SVCS: Still Or Video

H & J Bliss Enterprises ....E... 952 988-9302
Minneapolis *(G-4584)*

Lifetouch Portrait Studios Inc.............D... 952 826-5000
Eden Prairie *(G-1711)*

PHOTOGRAPHY: Aerial

Aero-Metric Inc ....E... 763 420-9606
Osseo *(G-6593)*

PHYSICAL EXAMINATION & TESTING SVCS

Correctional Medical Services ....D... 651 631-0065
Saint Paul *(G-8254)*

Physicians Examone Inc ....E... 651 731-2949
Saint Paul *(G-9261)*

PHYSICAL EXAMINATION SVCS, INSURANCE

Midwest Medical Solutions ....D... 952 838-6700
Minneapolis *(G-5035)*

PHYSICAL FITNESS CENTERS

Albert Lea Family YMCA ....E... 507 373-8228
Albert Lea *(G-31)*

America's Racquet & Fitness ....E... 320 234-7148
Hutchinson *(G-2687)*

Americas Racket & Fitness ....E... 507 451-8833
Owatonna *(G-6692)*

Anytime Fitness LLC ....D... 651 438-5000
Hastings *(G-2413)*

Bemidji Town & Country Club ....D... 218 751-9215
Bemidji *(G-380)*

C H Suites of Chanhassen MN...........E... 952 937-2424
Chanhassen *(G-912)*

Camp Widji Wagan...........................E... 218 365-2117
Ely *(G-1912)*

Center For Personal Fitness ....E... 218 725-5400
Duluth *(G-1267)*

D D D Motel Corp ....D... 507 625-9333
Mankato *(G-3224)*

Dakotah Sport & Fitness Center ....C... 952 445-9400
Prior Lake *(G-6932)*

Duluth Area Family YMCA.................E... 218 722-4745
Duluth *(G-1297)*

Fit Pro LLC ....D... 763 784-4747
Minneapolis *(G-3470)*

Fitness 19 ....E... 952 380-9919
Excelsior *(G-1935)*

Flagship Athletic Club Inc ....B... 952 941-2000
Eden Prairie *(G-1665)*

Grove Aquatic Fitness Center ....B... 651 450-2480
Inver Grove Heights *(G-2752)*

Hastings YMCA ....E... 651 480-8887
Hastings *(G-2390)*

Health Fitness Corp.........................E... 952 831-6830
Bloomington *(G-499)*

Holmes Center Inc ....D... 218 844-4221
Detroit Lakes *(G-1197)*

Improvement LP ....D... 218 262-3481
Hibbing *(G-2456)*

Itasca County Family Young ....D... 218 327-1161
Grand Rapids *(G-2287)*

Life Time Fitness Inc ....E... 952 835-2222
Minneapolis *(G-4877)*

Life Time Fitness Inc ....D... 651 698-5000
Saint Paul *(G-8584)*

Life Time Fitness Inc ....C... 651 730-6000
Saint Paul *(G-9242)*

Life Time Fitness Inc ....E... 651 633-4444
Saint Paul *(G-8583)*

Life Time Fitness Inc ....C... 763 509-0909
Minneapolis *(G-4880)*

Life Time Fitness Inc ....C... 763 257-1067
Minneapolis *(G-3519)*

Ltf Club Operations Co Inc ....D... 952 229-7427
Chanhassen *(G-930)*

Pga Tour Inc ....D... 763 795-0800
Minneapolis *(G-3570)*

Raymond Management Co Inc ....E... 507 287-9050
Rochester *(G-7217)*

Red Wing Young Men's Christian ......C... 651 388-4724
Red Wing *(G-6999)*

Rochester Athletic Club Inc...............B... 507 282-6000
Rochester *(G-7228)*

Sandman Motel LLC ....E... 763 559-1222
Minneapolis *(G-5600)*

St Cloud Suite Hotel Inc ....D... 320 654-1661
Saint Cloud *(G-7606)*

Starmark Northwest Management ......D... 952 944-2434
Minneapolis *(G-5743)*

Starmark Northwest Management ......E... 612 673-1200
Minneapolis *(G-5742)*

Upper Minnetonka Yacht Club ....D... 952 471-8783
Spring Park *(G-9567)*

Weiner Memorial Foundation ....B... 507 532-9661
Marshall *(G-3332)*

Y M C A Infant Center......................E... 651 646-4557
Saint Paul *(G-9171)*

YMCA...D... 320 222-9622
Willmar *(G-10059)*

YMCA Children's Center ....E... 651 777-8103
Saint Paul *(G-9173)*

YMCA of Greater Saint Paul ....E... 651 645-6605
Saint Paul *(G-9175)*

YMCA of Greater St Paul ....D... 218 365-2117
Ely *(G-1919)*

YMCA of Greater St Paul ....D... 651 292-4143
Saint Paul *(G-9178)*

YMCA of Greater St Paul ....D... 651 646-4557
Saint Paul *(G-9177)*

YMCA of Greater St Paul ....C... 651 483-2671
Saint Paul *(G-9176)*

YMCA of Greater St Paul ....C... 651 457-0048
Saint Paul *(G-7953)*

YMCA of Worthington, Minnesota ......E... 507 376-6197
Worthington *(G-10199)*

Young Men's Chrtn Assoc of ....C... 763 785-7882
Minneapolis *(G-3644)*

Young Men's Chrtn Assoc of ....C... 763 535-4800
Minneapolis *(G-6101)*

Young Men's Chrtn Assoc of ....D... 612 827-5401
Minneapolis *(G-6102)*

Young Men's Chrtn Assoc of ....E... 612 588-9484
Minneapolis *(G-6103)*

Young Men's Chrtn Assoc of ....C... 952 835-2567
Minneapolis *(G-6104)*

Young Women's Christian Assn ....D... 218 722-7425
Duluth *(G-1505)*

YWCA of Minneapolis ....A... 612 332-0501
Minneapolis *(G-6111)*

PHYSICAL FITNESS CLUBS WITH TRAINING EQPT

Lady Wellness Management Inc ....E... 320 253-3371
Waite Park *(G-9826)*

PHYSICIANS' OFFICES & CLINICS: Medical

Children's Health Care Inc.................C... 651 232-6800
Saint Paul *(G-9197)*

Donald H Sealock ....D... 763 559-7358
Minneapolis *(G-4277)*

Dr Peter Schmitz Inc ....E... 218 829-7812
Brainerd *(G-564)*

Erol T Uke MD ....E... 952 993-3190
Minneapolis *(G-4368)*

Fairmont Orthopedics & Sports ....D... 507 238-4949
Fairmont *(G-1965)*

Family Practice Medical Center ....E... 320 235-7232
Willmar (G-10001)

Hermantown Clinic ....E... 218 786-3540
Duluth (G-1351)

Ilbnc...E... 612 879-2521
Minneapolis (G-4688)

Northland Ob Gyn Associates ....E... 218 722-5629
Duluth (G-1408)

Obstetrics, Gynecology....................E... 952 920-2730
Minneapolis (G-5263)

Pipestone Medical Group Inc.............E... 507 825-5700
Pipestone (G-6836)

Quello Clinic ....D... 952 985-8100
Minneapolis (G-5447)

Raiter Clinic Ltd ....E... 218 879-1271
Cloquet (G-1063)

Sioux Valley Canby Campus................C... 507 223-7221
Canby (G-853)

Thomas Oas MD ....E... 507 646-1494
Northfield (G-6521)

United Clinic of Faribault ....E... 507 526-7388
Blue Earth (G-538)

PHYSICIANS' OFFICES & CLINICS: Medical doctors

Affiliated Community Medical...............D... 507 532-9631
Marshall (G-3290)

Affiliated Community Medical...............E... 320 564-2511
Granite Falls (G-2313)

Affiliated Community Medical...............E... 507 637-2985
Redwood Falls (G-7019)

Align Health Inc..............................D... 612 821-7909
Minneapolis (G-3704)

Allina Health System ....A... 612 863-4000
Minneapolis (G-3718)

Allina Health System ....E... 952 936-5600
Hopkins (G-2506)

Allina Health System ....E... 651 450-8000
Inver Grove Heights (G-2737)

American Medical Systems Inc ....B... 952 930-6000
Minnetonka (G-6140)

Anderson McDonald Ltd ....E... 952 469-3937
Lakeville (G-2890)

Asian Home Care Inc ....E... 651 999-0268
Saint Paul (G-8069)

Bloomington Lake Clinic Ltd ....E... 612 721-6511
Minneapolis (G-3916)

Broadway Medical Center Ltd.............C... 320 762-0399
Alexandria (G-87)

Camden Physicians Ltd ....E... 612 876-9700
Minneapolis (G-3995)

Center For Victims of Torture ....D... 612 436-4800
Saint Paul (G-8182)

Central Minnesota Emergency ....E... 320 255-5657
Saint Cloud (G-7483)

Children's Respiratory ....E... 612 863-3226
Minneapolis (G-4066)

Christopher J Fallert MD ....E... 651 731-4300
Oakdale (G-6549)

City of Redwood Falls ....C... 507 637-4500
Redwood Falls (G-7020)

Cook Area Health Services Inc ....E... 218 666-5941
Cook (G-1094)

Craig L Gilbertson MD ....E... 218 722-6613
Duluth (G-1286)

Dawson Area Hospital District............C... 320 769-4323
Dawson (G-1164)

Diamond Women's Center ....E... 952 927-4045
Minneapolis (G-4252)

Duluth Clinc- Ely Inc ....E... 218 365-7900
Ely (G-1913)

Ear, Nose Throat, Head & Neck ....E... 320 252-0233
Saint Cloud (G-7501)

East Metro Family Practice ....E... 651 457-2748
Inver Grove Heights (G-2749)

East Metro Gorman ....E... 651 455-2940
Saint Paul (G-7756)

Electromed Inc ....E... 952 758-9299
New Prague (G-6426)

Fairmont Medical Center Mayo............A... 507 238-4263
Fairmont (G-1964)

Fairview Health Services....................E... 612 706-4500
Saint Paul (G-8364)

Family Life Mental Health Ctr.............E... 763 427-7964
Minneapolis (G-3468)

Gateway Family Health Clinic ....D... 218 485-4491
Moose Lake (G-6350)

Glencoe Regional Health Svcs ....B... 320 864-3121
Glencoe (G-2207)

Grand Itasca Clinic & Hospital............B... 218 326-7024
Grand Rapids (G-2280)

Healtheast Care System ....C... 651 232-1700
Saint Paul (G-8458)

HealthPartners Inc ....A... 952 883-6000
Bloomington (G-500)

Healthpartners Inc ....D... 651 702-5300
Saint Paul (G-9226)

Healthpartners Inc ....D... 651 552-1720
South Saint Paul (G-9528)

Healthpartners Inc ....B... 651 779-1500
Saint Paul (G-8469)

Healthpartners Inc ....B... 763 754-0041
Minneapolis (G-3486)

Heartland Orthopedic ....E... 320 762-1144
Alexandria (G-103)

Indian Health Service ....D... 320 532-4163
Onamia (G-6572)

Innovis Health LLC ....D... 218 732-2800
Park Rapids (G-6756)

John Schmitz MD ....E... 320 255-5777
Saint Cloud (G-7537)

John T Beecher MD ....E... 952 925-2200
Minneapolis (G-4772)

Jon Bowar MD ....E... 320 255-5777
Saint Cloud (G-7538)

Jon S Nielsen MD.............................E... 763 257-4400
Minneapolis (G-4777)

Lake City Medical Center-Mayo ....B... 651 345-3321
Lake City (G-2849)

Lex A Nerenberg MD ....E... 763 520-2980
Saint Paul (G-4866)

Lexion Medical LLC ....E... 651 635-0000
Saint Paul (G-8582)

M Heath, Paul MD ....E... 320 253-7257
Saint Cloud (G-7546)

Mark Macdonald Do ....E... 651 455-2940
Saint Paul (G-7832)

Mayo Clinic ....D... 507 723-4231
Springfield (G-9573)

Mayo Clinic ....E... 507 284-9077
Rochester (G-7170)

Mayo Clinic Rochester ....E... 507 377-5900
Albert Lea (G-61)

Meadowbrook Women's Clinic ....E... 612 376-7708
Minneapolis (G-4980)

Medical Center ....D... 320 632-6611
Little Falls (G-3013)

Medical Evaluations Inc ....E... 952 229-8500
Saint Louis Park (G-7664)

Mencept Epileptic Clinic ....E... 952 525-2400
Minneapolis (G-4987)

Metropolitan Obstetrics & Gyn ....E... 651 770-1385
Saint Paul (G-8648)

Michael C Magnuson ....E... 952 435-0303
Burnsville (G-757)

Midwest Internal Medicine ....E... 763 236-9428
Minneapolis (G-3542)

Mille Lacs Health System ....B... 320 532-3154
Onamia (G-6574)

Mincep Epilepsy Care ....E... 952 525-2400
Minneapolis (G-5048)

Minn Health.....................................E... 651 739-5050
Saint Paul (G-8669)

Minnesota Diagnostic Ctr...................E... 612 879-1528
Minneapolis (G-5075)

Montevideo Clinic ....E... 320 269-6435
Montevideo (G-6252)

Oak Dale Healtheast ....E... 651 326-5300
Saint Paul (G-9253)

Open Door Health Center ....E... 507 388-2120
Mankato (G-3179)

Park Nicollet Clinic ....E... 952 993-7400
Eden Prairie (G-1742)

Park Nicollet Clinic ....E... 952 993-8900
Minneapolis (G-5331)

Park Nicollet Clinic ....B... 952 993-8700
Burnsville (G-775)

Park Nicollet Health Services ....C... 952 993-9900
Minneapolis (G-5336)

Prairie Medical.................................E... 320 589-4008
Morris (G-6375)

Randall, Omlie, Haas ....E... 952 835-5003
Minneapolis (G-5467)

Range Mental Health Center Inc ....E... 218 263-9237
Hibbing (G-2472)

Regents of The University of ....E... 952 997-4177
Saint Paul (G-7893)

Regents of The University of ....E... 651 227-6551
Saint Paul (G-8881)

Regents of The University of ....E... 612 624-0999
Minneapolis (G-5490)

Regents of The University of ....D... 612 625-4400
Minneapolis (G-5503)

Regents of The University of ....E... 612 625-8625
Minneapolis (G-5498)

Regina Medical Center ....A... 651 480-4100
Hastings (G-2402)

Ridgeview Medical Clinic ....E... 952 471-2585
Spring Park (G-9565)

Robert Aby MD.................................D... 507 372-1840
Worthington (G-10192)

Robert C Meisterling MD ....D... 651 439-8807
Stillwater (G-9635)

Royal Medical Center ....E... 218 249-8800
Duluth (G-1439)

Saint Luke's Outpatient Mental ....E... 218 249-7000
Duluth (G-1442)

Sanford Health Network......................B... 507 223-7272
Canby (G-852)

Sanford Health Network......................D... 507 847-2420
Jackson (G-2799)

Sanford Health Network......................C... 507 674-2932
Tracy (G-9691)

Scott R McGarvey MD ....E... 952 832-0076
Minneapolis (G-5619)

Shoulder & Sports Medicine.................E... 612 879-6623
Minneapolis (G-5660)

Springfield Medical Center ....D... 507 723-6201
Springfield (G-9575)

St Cloud Surgical Center ....C... 320 251-8385
Saint Cloud (G-7607)

St James Medical Center-Mayo ....D... 507 375-3261
Saint James (G-7647)

St Luke's Clinics..............................D... 218 249-5555
Duluth (G-1467)

St Luke's Hospital of Duluth ....A... 218 726-5555
Duluth (G-1469)

St Luke's Hospital of Duluth ....E... 218 249-8800
Duluth (G-1468)

St Luke's Hospital of Duluth ....E... 218 362-7100
Hibbing (G-2476)

St Luke's Internal Medicine ....E... 218 249-7960
Duluth (G-1472)

St Mary's Duluth Clinic Health ....A... 218 786-4000
Duluth (G-1473)

Stephen J Russell.............................D... 507 284-8384
Rochester (G-7264)

Stillwater Fitness Club Inc ....E... 651 430-1584
Stillwater (G-9646)

Stratis Health ....D... 952 854-3306
Minneapolis (G-5759)

Timothy J Hernandez MD.....................E... 651 455-2940
Saint Paul (G-7922)

Tl Wyne...E... 320 240-2180
Saint Cloud (G-7617)

Trimont Health Care Center ....D... 507 639-2381
Trimont (G-9694)

University Affiliated Family ....E... 612 333-0770
Minneapolis (G-5923)

University Neurosurgical Assn ....E... 612 624-6666
Minneapolis (G-5928)

University of Minnesota ....C... 763 782-6400
Minneapolis (G-5930)

Upsher-Smith Laboratories Inc ....D... 763 315-2000
Osseo (G-6681)

US Oncology Inc...............................E... 612 863-8585
Minneapolis (G-5949)

Wal-Mart Stores Inc ....B... 320 587-1020
Hutchinson (G-2717)

Winona Clinic Ltd ....C... 507 454-3680
Winona (G-10144)

PHYSICIANS' OFFICES & CLINICS: Osteopathic

Bruce B Cunningham ....E... 651 731-0859
Saint Paul (G-9190)

David Balt Do ....E... 507 825-3390
Pipestone (G-6824)

Eleah Medical Center ....E... 218 685-4406
Elbow Lake (G-1851)

Family Health Services of MN ....E... 651 457-2748
Inver Grove Heights (G-2750)

Lakeview Medical Clinic ....E... 320 352-6591
Sauk Centre (G-9350)

Thomas Oas MD ....E... 507 646-1494
Northfield (G-6521)

PICTURE FRAMING SVCS, CUSTOM

Nash Frame Design Inc.......................E... 612 338-9041
Minneapolis (G-5157)

PIECE GOODS & NOTIONS WHOLESALERS

Dasco Systems Inc............................E... 763 574-2275
Minneapolis (G-3451)

PIECE GOODS, NOTIONS & DRY GOODS, WHOL: Textiles, Woven

Encompass Group LLC........................D... 651 646-6600
Saint Paul (G-8339)

Encompass Group LLC........................C... 651 646-6600
Saint Paul (G-8340)

Employment codes: A=Over 500 employees, B=251-500,
C=101-250, D=51-100, E=25-50

2011 Harris Minnesota
Services Directory

© Harris InfoSource 1-866-281-6415
751

S E R V I C E S

Lintex Corp ....C... 651 646-6600
Saint Paul *(G-8591)*

Rubenstein & Ziff Inc ....E... 952 854-1460
Minneapolis *(G-5574)*

Stone Fabrics Inc ....E... 952 941-2303
Eden Prairie *(G-1783)*

PIECE GOODS, NOTIONS & DRY GOODS, WHOLESALE: Fabrics, Knit

Stone Fabrics Inc ....E... 952 941-2303
Eden Prairie *(G-1783)*

PIECE GOODS, NOTIONS & OTHER DRY GOODS, WHOL: Flags/Banners

Chromatic Concepts, Co ....D... 763 566-1118
Minneapolis *(G-4073)*

Display Sales Co ....E... 952 885-0100
Minneapolis *(G-4259)*

PIECE GOODS, NOTIONS/DRY GOODS, WHOL: Drapery Mtrl, Woven

Steven Fabrics Co ....C... 612 781-6671
Minneapolis *(G-5753)*

PIECE GOODS, NOTIONS/DRY GOODS, WHOL: Linen Piece, Woven

Encompass Group LLC ....D... 651 646-6600
Saint Paul *(G-8339)*

Encompass Group LLC ....C... 651 646-6600
Saint Paul *(G-8340)*

Lintex Corp ....C... 651 646-6600
Saint Paul *(G-8591)*

PIECE GOODS, NOTIONS/DRY GOODS, WHOL: Sewing Splys/Notions

Rubenstein & Ziff Inc ....E... 952 854-1460
Minneapolis *(G-5574)*

PIPELINE TERMINAL FACILITIES: Independent

Cenex Inc ....A... 800 232-3639
South Saint Paul *(G-9516)*

PIPELINES: Crude Petroleum

Koch Industries Inc........................D... 218 564-4495
Menahga *(G-3358)*

PIPELINES: Natural Gas

Cenex Inc ....A... 800 232-3639
South Saint Paul *(G-9516)*

Northern Natural Gas Co ....E... 952 887-1700
Minneapolis *(G-5228)*

PIPELINES: Refined Petroleum

Cenex Inc ....A... 800 232-3639
South Saint Paul *(G-9516)*

PLANT CARE SVCS

McCaren Design Inc.......................E... 651 646-4764
Saint Paul *(G-8623)*

PLANTING, PRUNING & TRIMMING SVCS

Maiers Transport & Warehousing ....E... 320 251-6882
Saint Cloud *(G-7547)*

Top Notch Treecare ....E... 763 253-8733
Minneapolis *(G-5830)*

PLANTS, POTTED, WHOLESALE

Donahues' Greenhouses Inc ....E... 507 334-8404
Faribault *(G-2001)*

Green Valley Greenhouse Inc ....D... 763 753-1621
Anoka *(G-184)*

Hermes Floral Co Inc......................D... 651 646-6344
Saint Paul *(G-8478)*

Malmborgs Inc ....E... 763 535-4695
Minneapolis *(G-4938)*

Minneapolis Floral Co......................E... 612 377-8080
Minneapolis *(G-5053)*

Pinehurst Development Inc ....E... 952 469-3202
Farmington *(G-2057)*

Twin City Florist Supply Inc...............E... 612 377-7849
Minneapolis *(G-5879)*

PLASMAPHEROUS CENTER

Biolife Plasma Services LP ....E... 507 344-0300
Mankato *(G-3111)*

Biolife Plasma Services LP ....E... 320 259-6300
Saint Cloud *(G-7459)*

Csl Plasma Inc..............................D... 612 331-9180
Minneapolis *(G-4191)*

PLASTICS MATERIALS, BASIC FORMS & SHAPES WHOLESALERS

Infiniti Marketing Inc ....E... 612 789-2025
Mound *(G-6388)*

Minnesota Flexible Corp ....E... 651 645-7522
Saint Paul *(G-8687)*

Youngblood Lumber Co ....E... 612 789-3521
Minneapolis *(G-6106)*

PLAYS, ROAD & STOCK COMPANIES

Children's Theatre Co......................C... 612 874-0500
Minneapolis *(G-4067)*

Old Log Theater Ltd ....E... 952 474-5951
Excelsior *(G-1951)*

PLUMBING & HEATING EQPT & SPLY, WHOLESALE: Hydronic Htg Eqpt

D C Sales Co Inc ....E... 612 728-8700
Minneapolis *(G-4213)*

Northern Wholesale Supply Inc ....D... 651 429-1515
Hugo *(G-2672)*

Park Systems Inc ....E... 612 822-3180
Minneapolis *(G-5337)*

Pipeline Supply Inc ....D... 952 935-0445
Hopkins *(G-2603)*

PLUMBING & HEATING EQPT & SPLYS WHOLESALERS

AAA-American Co ....E... 507 894-4156
Hokah *(G-2490)*

Bernard J Mulcahy Co Inc ....E... 651 686-8580
Saint Paul *(G-7715)*

Central Boiler Inc ....C... 218 782-2575
Greenbush *(G-2325)*

D J'S Heating & Air Condg ....E... 763 421-5313
Elk River *(G-1871)*

Ferguson Enterprises Inc ....E... 218 628-2844
Duluth *(G-1321)*

First Supply LLC ....D... 507 287-0202
Rochester *(G-7115)*

First Supply LLC ....E... 507 287-0202
Rochester *(G-7116)*

Goodin Co...................................E... 320 259-6086
Saint Cloud *(G-7520)*

Marketing Focus Inc ....E... 952 939-9880
Hopkins *(G-2576)*

Maxxon Corp ....E... 763 478-6000
Hamel *(G-2350)*

Minnesota Air Inc ....D... 952 918-8000
Minneapolis *(G-5067)*

Minvalco Inc ....E... 952 920-0131
Minneapolis *(G-5107)*

Park Systems Inc ....E... 612 822-3180
Minneapolis *(G-5337)*

S P S Co's Inc ....C... 952 929-1377
Minneapolis *(G-5582)*

S P S Co's Inc ....E... 507 387-5691
Mankato *(G-3190)*

St Hilaire Supply Co ....E... 218 964-5222
Saint Hilaire *(G-7641)*

U S Filter Waterpro ....E... 952 893-9130
Minneapolis *(G-5889)*

Woodruff Co ....E... 507 285-2500
Rochester *(G-7296)*

PLUMBING & HEATING EQPT & SPLYS, WHOL: Pipe/Fitting, Plastic

Goodin Co...................................C... 612 588-7811
Minneapolis *(G-4540)*

Seelye Plastics Inc ....D... 952 881-2658
Minneapolis *(G-5627)*

PLUMBING & HEATING EQPT & SPLYS, WHOL: Plumbing Fitting/Sply

D C Sales Co Inc ....E... 612 728-8700
Minneapolis *(G-4213)*

Fantasia LLC 612 338-5811
Minneapolis *(G-4415)*

First Supply LLC ....E... 507 287-0202
Rochester *(G-7116)*

Hajoca Corp ....E... 763 315-0100
Minneapolis *(G-4589)*

Pipeline Supply Inc ....D... 952 935-0445
Hopkins *(G-2603)*

Seelye Plastics Inc ....D... 952 881-2658
Minneapolis *(G-5627)*

PLUMBING & HEATING EQPT & SPLYS, WHOL: Plumbng/Heatng Valves

First Supply LLC ....E... 507 287-0202
Rochester *(G-7116)*

PLUMBING & HEATING EQPT & SPLYS, WHOL: Water Purif Eqpt

Ecowater Systems LLC ....B... 651 739-5330
Saint Paul *(G-9206)*

Hawkins Inc ....C... 612 331-6910
Minneapolis *(G-4608)*

Hawkins Water Treatment Group........D... 612 331-6910
Minneapolis *(G-4610)*

Lemna Corp ....E... 612 253-2000
Minneapolis *(G-4860)*

PLUMBING & HEATING EQPT & SPLYS, WHOLESALE: Brass/Fittings

First Supply LLC ....E... 507 287-0202
Rochester *(G-7116)*

PLUMBING & HEATING EQPT, WHOLESALE: Water Heaters/Purif

Northern Sales & Consulting..............D... 651 429-5757
Lino Lakes *(G-2975)*

PLUMBING & HEATING EQPT/SPLYS, WHOL: Boilers, Hot Water Htg

Goodin Co...................................C... 612 588-7811
Minneapolis *(G-4540)*

PLUMBING/HEATING EQPT/SPLYS, WHOL: Radiators/Parts, Exc Elec

Goodin Co...................................C... 612 588-7811
Minneapolis *(G-4540)*

POSTERS, WHOLESALE

Scholastic Book Fairs Inc..................D... 763 391-0930
Minneapolis *(G-5613)*

POSTHARVEST CROP ACTIVITIES

Dahlgren & Co Inc ....C... 218 281-2985
Crookston *(G-1123)*

Deer River Wild Rice ....D... 218 246-2713
Deer River *(G-1170)*

Reichel Foods Inc ....C... 507 289-7264
Rochester *(G-7220)*

Sunrich LLC ....D... 218 643-8467
Breckenridge *(G-602)*

Syngenta Seeds Inc ....E... 507 674-3320
Amboy *(G-132)*

POTASH MINING

Mosaic Global Holdings Inc...............E... 763 577-2700
Minneapolis *(G-5134)*

POTATO CURING SVCS

Hull Co ....E... 763 262-4855
Big Lake *(G-447)*

POTATOES, MACHINE HARVESTING SVCS

Mike Wingard ....E... 763 441-8247
Elk River *(G-1884)*

POULTRY & POULTRY PRDTS WHOLESALERS

American Fish & Seafood Inc ....D... 952 935-3474
Hopkins *(G-2509)*

Gold'n Plump Marketing Inc ....D... 320 251-3570
Saint Cloud *(G-7519)*

Michael Foods Inc ....E... 507 237-2429
Gaylord *(G-2200)*

New Midwest Co LLC ....B... 320 329-3363
Renville *(G-7032)*

POULTRY, PACKAGED FROZEN: Wholesalers

American Fish & Seafood Inc ....D... 952 935-3474
Hopkins *(G-2509)*

Trudeau Holdings LLC ....C... 952 882-8295
Burnsville *(G-813)*

Trudeau Holdings LLC ....D... 952 445-1350
Shakopee *(G-9481)*

SERVICES

POWER HAND TOOLS WHOLESALERS

Import Specialties Inc..........................C... 952 361-3640
Chaska *(G-969)*

POWER TOOL REPAIR SVCS

Total Tool Supply Inc..........................D... 651 646-4055
Saint Paul *(G-9073)*

PRECIOUS METALS WHOLESALERS

Estate Jewelry & Coin Inc ....E... 952 881-8862
Minneapolis *(G-4373)*

PRECISION INSTRUMENT REPAIR SVCS

Precision Repair & Calibration ....E... 763 784-1704
Minneapolis *(G-3572)*

PRERECORDED TAPES & CASSETTES WHOLESALERS

Sky Media LLC ....E... 651 635-0100
Saint Paul *(G-8963)*

PRESCHOOL CENTERS

Agape 24 Hour Preschool ....E... 612 287-9775
Minneapolis *(G-3698)*
B'Nai Emet Synagogue Inc ....E... 952 927-7309
Minneapolis *(G-3855)*
Brainerd School District 181 ....E... 218 829-0412
Brainerd *(G-553)*
Centennial Independent School ....E... 763 792-6000
Circle Pines *(G-1005)*
Centennial Independent School ....E... 763 792-6120
Circle Pines *(G-1004)*
Children's Country Day School ....E... 651 454-4000
Saint Paul *(G-7732)*
Community Action Agency ....E... 763 425-7422
Minneapolis *(G-4136)*
Early Child Family Education ....E... 507 625-4620
Mankato *(G-3123)*
Early Childhood Center ....D... 952 556-6400
Chaska *(G-963)*
Holy Emmanuel Lutheran Church ....E... 952 888-5116
Minneapolis *(G-4662)*
Hope Presbyterian Church of 612 866-4055
Minneapolis *(G-4674)*
Independent School District ....E... 651 385-8000
Red Wing *(G-6986)*
Independent School District No ....E... 507 444-7900
Owatonna *(G-6718)*
Kid's Haven of Buffalo Inc ....D... 763 682-3072
Buffalo *(G-646)*
KinderCare Learning Centers ....E... 952 835-4955
Minneapolis *(G-4809)*
Knowledge Learning Corp ....E... 952 944-3801
Eden Prairie *(G-1703)*
Mount Zion Hebrew Congregation .....E... 651 698-3881
Saint Paul *(G-8726)*
New Horizon Child Care Inc ....E... 952 469-6659
Lakeville *(G-2922)*
New Horizon Child Care Inc ....D... 763 557-1111
Plymouth *(G-6875)*
New Horizon Child Care Inc ....E... 763 478-2412
Minneapolis *(G-5191)*
Our Savior's Lutheran Church..............E... 763 434-6117
Cedar *(G-883)*
Pine Point Public School Dist..............E... 218 573-4100
Ponsford *(G-6892)*
Reach-Up Inc ....E... 320 253-8110
Saint Cloud *(G-7423)*
Reuben Lindh Family Services ....D... 763 521-3477
Minneapolis *(G-5532)*
St David's Center Child ....B... 952 939-0396
Hopkins *(G-2636)*
St Michaels Lutheran Church ....E... 952 831-5276
Minneapolis *(G-5728)*
Step By Step Montessori School..........E... 763 557-6777
Minneapolis *(G-5749)*

PRESS CLIPPING SVC

Burrelle's Information Svcs ....E... 612 672-9141
Minneapolis *(G-3978)*

PRINTERS' SVCS: Folding, Collating, Etc

Graphic Finishing Services Inc ....E... 763 767-3026
Minneapolis *(G-3477)*
J&M Co..E... 218 998-4062
Fergus Falls *(G-2078)*
Larkin Industries Inc...........................E... 651 645-6000
Saint Paul *(G-8562)*

PRINTING & WRITING PAPER WHOLESALERS

Henry's Foods Inc ....C... 320 763-3194
Alexandria *(G-104)*
International Paper Co.........................C... 612 781-6611
Minneapolis *(G-4724)*
Litin Paper Co Inc ....E... 612 333-4331
Minneapolis *(G-4893)*
Unisource Worldwide Inc ....B... 763 488-7200
Brooklyn Park *(G-620)*

PRINTING INKS WHOLESALERS

Flint Group LLC..................................D... 763 559-5911
Minneapolis *(G-4456)*

PRINTING MACHINERY, EQPT & SPLYS: Wholesalers

Harold Pitman M Co ....E... 612 781-8988
Minneapolis *(G-4601)*
Heidelberg USA Inc ....E... 952 831-6501
Minneapolis *(G-4628)*
Lofton Label Inc ....D... 651 457-8118
Inver Grove Heights *(G-2759)*
Midwest Sign & Screen Printing..........D... 651 489-9999
Saint Paul *(G-8661)*

PRIVATE INVESTIGATOR SVCS

Criminal Investigation Dept ....E... 612 673-2941
Minneapolis *(G-4184)*

PROBATION OFFICE

Eden Rs...C... 612 287-1600
Minneapolis *(G-4313)*
U S Probation Office ....D... 612 664-5400
Minneapolis *(G-5890)*

PROFESSIONAL EQPT & SPLYS, WHOLESALE: Analytical Instruments

Foss North America Inc.......................E... 952 974-9892
Eden Prairie *(G-1667)*

PROFESSIONAL EQPT & SPLYS, WHOLESALE: Engineers', NEC

GPM Inc..E... 218 722-9904
Duluth *(G-1339)*
Tierney Brothers Inc ....D... 612 331-5500
Minneapolis *(G-5821)*

PROFESSIONAL EQPT & SPLYS, WHOLESALE: Optical Goods

Essilor Laboratories of Amer...............C... 320 251-8591
Saint Cloud *(G-7505)*
Essilor Laboratories of Amer...............E... 218 894-3385
Staples *(G-9583)*
Eye Kraft Optical Inc..........................D... 320 251-0141
Saint Cloud *(G-7506)*
Newport Corp ....D... 763 593-0722
Minneapolis *(G-5195)*
Prescription Optical............................E... 303 343-0427
Saint Cloud *(G-7571)*

PROFESSIONAL EQPT & SPLYS, WHOLESALE: Scientific & Engineerg

Base Eight Inc 952 941-5888
Chaska *(G-951)*
Leeds Precision Instruments ....D... 763 546-8575
Minneapolis *(G-4853)*

PROFESSIONAL EQPT & SPLYS, WHOLESALE: Theatrical

Norcostco Inc ....E... 763 544-0601
Minneapolis *(G-5207)*

PROFESSIONAL INSTRUMENT REPAIR SVCS

City Auto Glass ....E... 651 552-1000
South Saint Paul *(G-9522)*

PROFESSIONAL STANDARDS REVIEW BOARDS

Potter David MD PHD...........................D... 612 625-8933
Minneapolis *(G-5397)*

PROMOTERS OF SHOWS & EXHIBITIONS

Carlson Holdings Inc ....A... 763 212-5000
Minnetonka *(G-6152)*

Gold Country Inc ....E... 952 935-9887
Hopkins *(G-2546)*

PROMOTION SVCS

Beacon Promotions Inc ....D... 507 233-3240
New Ulm *(G-6442)*
Gage Group LLC ....C... 763 595-3920
Minneapolis *(G-4495)*
Pro Motion Marketing..........................E... 612 347-1490
Minneapolis *(G-5413)*
3M Co..C... 651 733-1110
Saint Paul *(G-9060)*

PROPERTY & CASUALTY INSURANCE AGENTS

EPIC Holdings Inc ....E... 952 997-4900
Saint Paul *(G-7768)*
McGovern & Fisher Insurance..............D... 952 996-8818
Minneapolis *(G-4975)*
Rjf Agencies Inc..................................C... 763 746-8000
Minneapolis *(G-5548)*
T C Field & Co ....E... 651 227-8405
Saint Paul *(G-9022)*
Wells Fargo Insurance Services ....C... 952 830-3000
Minneapolis *(G-6051)*

PROPERTY DAMAGE INSURANCE

Athena Assurance Co ....E... 651 310-7065
Saint Paul *(G-8076)*
Discover Property & Casualty 800 878-2660
Saint Paul *(G-8299)*
Harleysville Insurance Co....................D... 952 829-4000
Minneapolis *(G-4598)*
Mendota Insurance Co 800 422-0792
Eagan *(G-1536)*
Northfield Insurance Co.......................E... 651 688-4100
Saint Paul *(G-8762)*
Northland Insurance Co.......................B... 651 688-4100
Saint Paul *(G-8764)*
Ram Mutual Insurance Co Inc ....D... 218 879-3321
Esko *(G-1922)*
St Paul Fire & Marine Insce ....B... 651 310-5000
Saint Paul *(G-8989)*
St Paul Guardian Insurance Co...........A... 651 221-7911
Saint Paul *(G-8991)*
St Paul Mercury Insurance Co..................651 221-7911
Saint Paul *(G-8994)*
Western National Mutual Insce ....B... 952 835-5350
Minneapolis *(G-6060)*

PRUNING SVCS, ORNAMENTAL TREE

Arrowhead Tree Service Inc ....E... 218 729-9203
Duluth *(G-1245)*

PUBLIC RELATIONS & PUBLICITY SVCS

Aca International ....D... 952 926-6547
Minneapolis *(G-3663)*
Hanley-Wood Custom Publishing.........D... 612 338-8300
Minneapolis *(G-4593)*
Media Relations Inc ....E... 612 798-7200
Burnsville *(G-752)*

PUBLIC RELATIONS SVCS

Dorf & Stanton Communications ....D... 952 832-5000
Minneapolis *(G-4280)*
Franklin Corp ....D... 612 455-1700
Minneapolis *(G-4475)*
Goff & Howard Inc 651 292-8062
Saint Paul *(G-8417)*
Risdall Marketing Group LLC ....D... 651 286-6700
New Brighton *(G-6413)*
Swenson Nhb Investor Relations..........E... 612 371-0000
Minneapolis *(G-5778)*
Tunheim Partners Inc...........................D... 952 851-1600
Minneapolis *(G-5865)*

PUBLIC WELFARE CENTER

County of Sibley ....E... 507 237-4000
Gaylord *(G-2199)*
Pine County Health & Human Svc ....E... 320 245-3020
Sandstone *(G-9324)*

PUMPS & PUMPING EQPT REPAIR SVCS

Electric Motor Repair Inc ....E... 612 588-4693
Minneapolis *(G-4337)*
Northern Dewatering Inc......................D... 763 428-2616
Rogers *(G-7332)*

PUMPS & PUMPING EQPT WHOLESALERS

Diversified Dynamics Corp..................D... 763 780-5440
Minneapolis *(G-3457)*

S
E
R
V
I
C
E
S

Employment codes: A=Over 500 employees, B=251-500,
C=101-250, D=51-100, E=25-50

2011 Harris Minnesota
Services Directory

© Harris InfoSource 1-866-281-6415
753

First Supply LLC ....E... 507 287-0202
Rochester (G-7116)
Indelco Plastics Corp ....E... 952 925-5075
Minneapolis (G-4694)
Midway Industrial Supply Co ....E... 763 780-3000
Saint Paul (G-8655)

PURCHASING SVCS

Central Minnesota Erdc Inc ....E... 320 202-0992
Saint Cloud (G-7408)
Expresspoint Technology Svcs ....C... 763 543-6000
Golden Valley (G-2240)
Kurt Manufacturing Co Inc ....E... 763 572-4592
Minneapolis (G-3512)
N'Compass Solutions Inc ....E... 612 379-2100
Minneapolis (G-5155)
Radisson Hotels International ....C... 763 212-5000
Minnetonka (G-6218)
Uhc - Edina ....E... 763 519-1335
Minneapolis (G-5894)

RACETRACKS

Canterbury Park Holding Corp ....E... 952 445-7223
Shakopee (G-9427)
Flatliner Speed Society ....E... 507 452-8917
Winona (G-10097)
Princeton Speedway ....E... 763 389-3135
Princeton (G-6915)
Warnert Racing Inc ....E... 320 251-2882
Saint Cloud (G-7630)

RACETRACKS: Horse

North Metro Harness Initiative ....B... 651 925-4600
Forest Lake (G-2148)

RADIO & TELEVISION REPAIR

Nextel Communications Inc ....D... 952 703-7600
Minneapolis (G-5197)

RADIO BROADCASTING STATIONS

American Public Media Group ....B... 651 290-1500
Saint Paul (G-8032)
CBS Radio Inc ....E... 612 339-1029
Minneapolis (G-4033)
Clear Channel Communications ....C... 952 417-3000
Minneapolis (G-4107)
Clear Channel Communications ....E... 507 288-3888
Rochester (G-7081)
Clear Channel Communications ....E... 218 727-4500
Duluth (G-1277)
Cumulus Media Inc ....E... 507 334-0061
Faribault (G-2000)
FM 107 W Fmp Real Life ....D... 651 642-4107
Saint Paul (G-8386)
Ingstad Broadcasting Inc ....E... 218 681-4900
Thief River Falls (G-9670)
K A G E Inc ....E... 507 452-2867
Winona (G-10106)
K L L Z F M ....E... 218 444-1500
Bemidji (G-399)
K R C H Web Radio Stations ....E... 507 288-3888
Rochester (G-7149)
Kliz FM Powerloon 107 5 ....E... 218 822-4440
Baxter (G-332)
Kstp FM LLC ....E... 651 642-4242
Saint Paul (G-8552)
Lakeland Broadcasting Co Inc ....E... 320 235-1340
Willmar (G-10016)
Leighton Enterprises Inc ....E... 320 251-1450
Saint Cloud (G-7544)
Midcontinent Media Inc ....C... 952 844-2600
Minneapolis (G-5024)
Midwest Communication Inc ....E... 218 749-3000
Hibbing (G-2466)
Minnesota Public Radio ....D... 651 290-1500
Saint Paul (G-8703)
Minnesota Public Radio ....B... 651 290-1500
Saint Paul (G-8702)
Northern Lights Broadcasting ....E... 952 842-7200
Edina (G-1840)
Paul Bunyan Broadcasting Co ....E... 218 444-1011
Bemidji (G-418)
Radio City Marketing Group Inc ....D... 320 253-6500
Saint Cloud (G-7580)
Regent Broadcasting of St ....E... 320 251-4422
Saint Cloud (G-7424)
Regents of The University of ....D... 612 625-3500
Minneapolis (G-5487)
Region Communications ....E... 320 252-5852
Saint Cloud (G-7425)
Result Radio Inc ....E... 218 736-7596
Fergus Falls (G-2118)
Southwestern Minnesota Radio ....E... 507 452-4000
Winona (G-10129)
Woodward Broadcasting Inc ....E... 507 235-5595
Fairmont (G-1984)
Wwtc ....E... 651 289-4404
Eagan (G-1561)

RADIO REPAIR & INSTALLATION SVCS

Phoenix Distributing Inc ....E... 952 882-9949
Burnsville (G-781)

RAILROAD CAR REPAIR SVCS

Johnson Co Inc, R M ....E... 320 398-6080
Kimball (G-2832)

RAILROAD CARGO LOADING & UNLOADING SVCS

America Midwest Transportation ....E... 507 359-4450
Courtland (G-1115)
Kraft Foods Global Inc ....E... 507 359-2511
New Ulm (G-6458)
North Star Rail Intermodal LLC 952 831-4011
Minneapolis (G-5220)
Progressive Rail Inc ....E... 952 985-7245
Lakeville (G-2927)

RAILROAD EQPT & SPLYS WHOLESALERS

Harsco Corp ....E... 507 235-7127
Fairmont (G-1971)
Railway Equipment Co Inc ....E... 763 537-3702
Minneapolis (G-5461)

RAILROAD FREIGHT AGENCY

Bnsf Railway Co ....C... 320 231-5555
Willmar (G-9990)
Cobra Transportation Services ....E... 651 552-1151
Saint Paul (G-8219)
Fratrans Inc ....E... 651 294-3944
New Brighton (G-6407)

RAILROAD MAINTENANCE & REPAIR SVCS

Loram Rail Services LLC ....B... 763 478-6014
Hamel (G-2348)

RAILROAD SWITCHING & TERMINAL SVCS

Ibt Consolidated Inc ....E... 218 285-5290
International Falls (G-2721)
Minnesota Dakota & Western ....E... 218 285-5690
International Falls (G-2727)
Minnesota Prairie Line Inc ....E... 320 864-7200
Glencoe (G-2211)
Twin Cities & Western Railroad ....E... 320 864-7200
Glencoe (G-2216)
Union Pacific Railroad Co ....B... 507 452-4337
Winona (G-10134)
Wisconsin Central Ltd ....E... 651 633-8771
Saint Paul (G-9161)

RAILROADS: Long Haul

Bnsf Railway Co ....D... 218 894-1676
Verndale (G-9724)
Bnsf Railway Co ....C... 651 298-2121
Saint Paul (G-8116)
Bnsf Railway Co ....C... 651 451-1312
South Saint Paul (G-9514)
Bnsf Railway Co ....C... 651 298-2121
Minneapolis (G-3421)
Canadian Pacific Railroad ....E... 320 634-3307
Glenwood (G-2220)
CP Rail System SOO Line ....E... 320 634-3307
Glenwood (G-2221)
Dakota, Minnesota & Eastern ....D... 507 835-4185
Waseca (G-9875)
Greg Haug ....E... 218 727-8578
Duluth (G-1344)
Hennepin County ....E... 612 348-9260
Minneapolis (G-4631)
Minnesota Dakota & Western ....E... 218 285-5690
International Falls (G-2727)
Minnesota Northern Railroad ....E... 218 281-4704
Crookston (G-1128)
Red River Valley & Western ....E... 218 643-4994
Breckenridge (G-599)
Soo Line Corp ....D... 612 337-5333
Minneapolis (G-5700)
SOO Line Railroad Co Inc ....A... 651 646-6044
Saint Paul (G-8971)
SOO Line Railroad Co Inc ....E... 320 634-3012
Glenwood (G-2233)
SOO Line Railroad Co Inc ....B... 800 766-4357
Minneapolis (G-5701)
Twin Cities & Western Railroad ....E... 320 864-7200
Glencoe (G-2216)
Union Pacific Railroad Co ....B... 507 452-4337
Winona (G-10134)
Union Pacific Railroad Co Inc ....C... 651 552-3925
South Saint Paul (G-9546)

REAL ESTATE AGENCIES & BROKERS

Bcr Real Estate Services ....E... 320 532-4099
Onamia (G-6566)
Becker Meggy Rl Est ....E... 507 388-8469
Mankato (G-3109)
Burnet Realty LLC ....B... 952 844-6400
Minneapolis (G-3977)
Cassidy Turley Midwest Inc ....D... 612 341-4444
Minneapolis (G-4026)
CB Richard Ellis Inc ....D... 952 924-4600
Minneapolis (G-4032)
Century 21 Care Realty ....E... 763 862-5690
Minneapolis (G-4049)
Coldwell Banker Burnett Real ....D... 651 698-2481
Saint Paul (G-8223)
Collopy & Saunders Real Estate 952 829-2900
Eden Prairie (G-1631)
Counselor Realty Inc ....D... 763 786-0600
Minneapolis (G-3443)
Cushman & Wakefield Inc ....E... 612 671-7593
Minneapolis (G-4202)
Edina Realty Home Services ....D... 763 755-1300
Minneapolis (G-3463)
Edina Realty Home Services ....E... 612 827-3551
Minneapolis (G-4322)
Edina Realty Home Services ....D... 763 295-3456
Monticello (G-6270)
Edina Realty Home Services ....D... 952 928-5900
Minneapolis (G-4325)
Edina Realty Home Services ....D... 651 770-1775
Saint Paul (G-8323)
Edina Realty Home Services ....E... 763 545-5000
Minneapolis (G-4323)
Edina Realty Home Services ....D... 651 430-3200
Stillwater (G-9613)
Edina Realty Home Services ....E... 651 636-2299
Minneapolis (G-3464)
Edina Realty Home Services ....D... 763 559-2894
Minneapolis (G-4321)
Edina Realty Home Services ....D... 507 288-7665
Rochester (G-7103)
Edina Realty Home Services ....D... 952 892-7000
Lakeville (G-2904)
Edina Realty Home Services ....D... 651 426-7172
Saint Paul (G-8325)
Edina Realty Home Services ....E... 320 762-8181
Alexandria (G-99)
Edina Realty Home Services ....D... 651 698-2434
Saint Paul (G-8326)
Edina Realty Home Services ....D... 952 442-1700
Chanhassen (G-921)
Edina Realty Home Services ....D... 952 944-7107
Eden Prairie (G-1651)
Execu Systems Inc ....E... 218 444-1021
Bemidji (G-391)
First Realty GMAC ....E... 218 751-2511
Bemidji (G-395)
Genex Cooperative Inc ....E... 952 758-2561
New Prague (G-6427)
Gold Key Realty ....E... 952 431-5751
Saint Paul (G-7786)
Hennepin County ....D... 612 348-3050
Minneapolis (G-4634)
Homeservices of America Inc ....E... 888 485-0018
Minneapolis (G-4672)
Jordan Realty Inc ....E... 612 827-3844
Minneapolis (G-4779)
Kit Fucile ....D... 952 435-3030
Burnsville (G-742)
Positive Realty & Investment ....E... 218 829-1777
Brainerd (G-582)
Real Estate Masters Inc ....C... 651 484-4818
Saint Paul (G-8878)
Roger Illies Realtor ....E... 320 685-8119
Cold Spring (G-1090)
Upi Property Management Group ....D... 612 870-8500
Minneapolis (G-5934)
Zweber LLC ....E... 952 440-4653
Lakeville (G-2944)

REAL ESTATE AGENCIES: Commercial

Cassidy Turley Midwest Inc ....D... 612 341-4444
Minneapolis (G-4026)
Colliers Towle Valuation 612 347-9336
Minneapolis (G-4120)
Equity Transwestern LLC ....E... 612 343-4200
Minneapolis (G-4366)

Gassen Co Inc ....E... 952 922-5575
Eden Prairie *(G-1671)*

Hempel Properties Inc ....E... 612 355-2600
Minneapolis *(G-4629)*

Jackson Street Associates LLC ....E... 651 228-9456
Saint Paul *(G-8528)*

Property Solutions & Services ....E... 612 746-0400
Minneapolis *(G-5430)*

Timberland Partners Management ......D... 952 893-1216
Minnetonka *(G-5827)*

Trammell Crow Co ....D... 952 936-3671
Minnetonka *(G-6229)*

United Water New Rochelle Inc ....E... 952 820-1666
Minneapolis *(G-5917)*

Welsh Co's LLC ....C... 952 897-7700
Minnetonka *(G-6236)*

Young, Quinlan Assoc LLP ....E... 612 337-5109
Minneapolis *(G-6105)*

REAL ESTATE AGENCIES: Leasing & Rentals

Atlas Pet Supply Inc ....E... 763 753-4818
Anoka *(G-157)*

Carlson Real Estate Co, A MN ....E... 952 404-5050
Minnetonka *(G-6154)*

Kraus-Anderson Realty Co ....E... 952 881-8166
Minneapolis *(G-4824)*

REAL ESTATE AGENCIES: Multiple Listing Svc

R M L S Minnesota ....E... 651 251-5458
Saint Paul *(G-8866)*

United Property Investment LLC ....C... 952 831-1000
Minneapolis *(G-5914)*

REAL ESTATE AGENCIES: Rental

Izatys Group LLC ....E... 320 532-3101
Onamia *(G-6573)*

New Life Multi-Family Mgt ....C... 952 831-0866
Edina *(G-1839)*

REAL ESTATE AGENCIES: Residential

Associates Plus Inc ....E... 651 484-8800
Saint Paul *(G-8074)*

Associates Plus Inc ....D... 763 784-1400
Minneapolis *(G-3412)*

Century 21 Jay Blank Realty ....E... 651 645-5581
Saint Paul *(G-8184)*

Charles Stout.....................................E... 651 426-1671
Saint Paul *(G-8188)*

Cold Well Banker At Your Svc ....E... 507 285-9115
Rochester *(G-7085)*

Coldwell Banker Burnet Inc ....D... 952 898-5100
Burnsville *(G-700)*

Coldwell Banker Burnet Inc ....E... 651 690-8516
Saint Paul *(G-8221)*

Coldwell Banker Burnet Real ....D... 763 754-5400
Minneapolis *(G-3436)*

Crossroads South Metro Inc ....E... 651 698-8006
Saint Paul *(G-8269)*

Gary Thaler ....E... 651 464-5555
Forest Lake *(G-2145)*

Herges Realty Inc ....E... 320 253-1366
Saint Cloud *(G-7527)*

Keller Williams Realty Inc ....E... 952 746-9696
Lakeville *(G-2914)*

Linda Waterman ....D... 507 287-7741
Rochester *(G-7161)*

Minnesota Dakota Generating Co 218 739-8200
Fergus Falls *(G-2096)*

MLS Online ....D... 763 427-0539
Champlin *(G-896)*

Property Solutions & Services ....E... 612 746-0400
Minneapolis *(G-5430)*

Prudential Pladson Realty Inc ....E... 320 253-9074
Saint Cloud *(G-7576)*

RE Max Advisors................................E... 952 898-1112
Burnsville *(G-785)*

RE MAX of Rochester ....E... 507 287-7735
Rochester *(G-7219)*

RE Max Real Estate Properties ....D... 763 755-1100
Minneapolis *(G-3580)*

Real Services Inc ....E... 218 728-5161
Duluth *(G-1432)*

Value Realty Inc ....E... 952 898-0230
Saint Paul *(G-7941)*

REAL ESTATE AGENCIES: Selling

Campground Marketing Services.........D... 218 562-4204
Pequot Lakes *(G-6786)*

Prudencial Sundial Realty Inc..............E... 763 571-9200
Minneapolis *(G-3578)*

REAL ESTATE AGENTS & MANAGERS

A E I Fund Management Inc ....E... 800 328-3519
Saint Paul *(G-7968)*

American Investment Management......E... 763 533-7193
Minneapolis *(G-3754)*

Associates Plus Inc ....C... 763 323-8080
Anoka *(G-156)*

Bce Development Corp ....E... 612 372-1500
Minneapolis *(G-3876)*

Belgrade Commerical Club ....E... 320 254-8271
Belgrade *(G-362)*

Brandl Anderson Homes Inc...............E... 952 898-0231
Saint Paul *(G-7723)*

Brookfield Development Inc ....E... 612 372-1230
Minneapolis *(G-3958)*

Brookpark Group ....E... 763 424-8525
Minneapolis *(G-3961)*

Bruce Johnson..................................E... 218 284-6555
Moorhead *(G-6300)*

Burnet Homeselling Team..................D... 651 653-2520
Saint Paul *(G-8141)*

Burnet Realty Inc ....E... 651 430-2100
Stillwater *(G-9603)*

C B Richard Ellis Inc ....B... 952 278-2106
Minneapolis *(G-3981)*

Castle Realty Inc ....E... 320 251-1010
Saint Cloud *(G-7472)*

Century 21 Luger Realty Inc ....E... 952 925-3901
Minneapolis *(G-4050)*

Coldwell Banker Burnet ....E... 952 820-4663
Minneapolis *(G-4116)*

Coldwell Banker Burnet Inc ....D... 952 920-1224
Eden Prairie *(G-1630)*

Coldwell Banker Burnet Inc ....D... 952 474-2525
Excelsior *(G-1942)*

Coldwell Banker Burnet Realty ....D... 651 227-9144
Saint Paul *(G-8222)*

Coldwell Banker Burnet Realty............E... 763 682-2882
Buffalo *(G-643)*

Coldwell Banker Vision ....D... 763 241-0155
Elk River *(G-1868)*

Commonbond Investment Corp ....D... 651 291-1750
Saint Paul *(G-8233)*

Community Development Inc ....E... 763 225-6412
Minneapolis *(G-4140)*

Community Finance Group Inc.............E... 763 416-5959
Minneapolis *(G-4141)*

Counselor Realty Inc ....C... 763 420-7080
Osseo *(G-6605)*

Counselor Realty Inc ....D... 952 475-9500
Wayzata *(G-9912)*

Counselor Realty Inc ....E... 952 921-0911
Minneapolis *(G-4167)*

Counselor Realty Inc ....E... 651 779-6000
Saint Paul *(G-8256)*

Cushman & Wakefield Inc ....D... 612 659-1743
Minneapolis *(G-4201)*

Cushman & Wakefield Inc ....E... 763 450-3600
Eden Prairie *(G-1639)*

Dakota County Abstract & Title ....E... 651 437-5600
Hastings *(G-2381)*

Dinnaken Properties Inc.....................E... 612 623-3634
Minneapolis *(G-4257)*

Donald A Driggs.................................E... 952 471-9500
Wayzata *(G-9915)*

Duane Sauke ....E... 507 287-7742
Rochester *(G-7099)*

Edina Realty ....D... 952 844-5409
Minneapolis *(G-4320)*

Edina Realty ....D... 651 450-6876
Eagan *(G-1526)*

Edina Realty Home Services...............E... 763 567-7000
Minneapolis *(G-4324)*

Edina Realty Home Services...............D... 651 481-6711
Saint Paul *(G-8324)*

Elcor Realty of Rochester Inc ....E... 507 282-3345
Rochester *(G-7104)*

Equity Transwestern LLC....................E... 612 343-4200
Minneapolis *(G-4366)*

Fbs Associated Properties Inc 612 333-2086
Minneapolis *(G-4417)*

Hillco Real Estate Holdings ....E... 320 532-3237
Onamia *(G-6571)*

Home Smart Realty & Logo Dsgn........E... 763 421-0481
Anoka *(G-191)*

Hometown America LLC ....E... 651 436-2790
Lake Elmo *(G-2873)*

Jim Conway.......................................E... 507 287-7717
Rochester *(G-7146)*

JMS Equities Inc ....E... 952 949-3630
Minneapolis *(G-4767)*

Jones Dw Management ....E... 218 547-3307
Park Rapids *(G-6758)*

Keller Williams Premier Realty............D... 507 424-4422
Rochester *(G-7151)*

KSA Real Estate Services Inc..............E... 651 290-0507
Saint Paul *(G-8551)*

Lakes Area Realty Inc 612 874-1916
Minneapolis *(G-4835)*

Land Title Inc ....D... 651 638-1900
Saint Paul *(G-8560)*

Leinvestors Inc ....E... 952 854-1114
Bloomington *(G-503)*

Minnesota Real State Service..............E... 952 928-4640
Minneapolis *(G-5092)*

Nelson Co's.......................................E... 507 289-6789
Rochester *(G-7189)*

New Concepts Management Group .....E... 952 922-2500
Saint Paul *(G-8747)*

New Homes Realty Inc ....E... 952 469-6003
Lakeville *(G-2921)*

Nuvo Network Management ....D... 952 933-4600
Hopkins *(G-2592)*

Oneida Realty Co Inc..........................D... 218 722-0816
Duluth *(G-1413)*

P D Management, LLP ....E... 612 281-1464
Lakeville *(G-2943)*

P H M Eaglecrest Inc ....E... 651 628-3000
Saint Paul *(G-8799)*

Pederson Team ....E... 218 692-5253
Crosslake *(G-1153)*

Pine Ridge Homes Inc ....D... 218 879-1257
Cloquet *(G-1059)*

Prudential Truscott Realtors ....E... 218 726-1255
Duluth *(G-1430)*

Quest Management Associates ....E... 612 379-3800
Minneapolis *(G-5449)*

Remax Northern Properties.................E... 218 263-8877
Hibbing *(G-2474)*

Remax Realty Source ....E... 320 251-2200
Saint Cloud *(G-7587)*

Rick Gentling ....E... 507 287-7714
Rochester *(G-7225)*

Sela Investments Ltd, LLP...................E... 952 925-3878
Minneapolis *(G-5630)*

Spectrum Property Management ....E... 952 853-0036
Minneapolis *(G-5719)*

Walsh Title & Real Estate Svcs ....E... 952 835-3320
Minneapolis *(G-6017)*

White Earth Housing Authority ....E... 218 473-4663
Waubun *(G-9901)*

REAL ESTATE APPRAISERS

AAA-American Co ....E... 507 894-4156
Hokah *(G-2490)*

Access Information Systems Inc ....C... 952 888-8503
Minneapolis *(G-3666)*

Bcr Real Estate Services ....E... 320 532-4099
Onamia *(G-6566)*

Forsythe Appraisals LLC ....D... 651 486-9550
Saint Paul *(G-8391)*

Isgn Fulfillment Services Inc ....D... 952 512-7400
Minneapolis *(G-4736)*

RELS LLC ....A... 952 933-8804
Hopkins *(G-2613)*

Walter W Culbert Jr ....E... 218 741-8026
Virginia *(G-9763)*

REAL ESTATE INVESTMENT TRUSTS

Global Financial Partners Corp............E... 952 544-0640
Minnetonka *(G-6176)*

Hospitality Investors LLC ....B... 218 729-5616
Duluth *(G-1353)*

Opus Properties Inc ....D... 952 656-4444
Hopkins *(G-2599)*

REAL ESTATE MANAGERS: Condominium

Gassen Co Inc...................................E... 952 922-5575
Eden Prairie *(G-1671)*

Gittleman Management Corp................E... 952 277-2700
Minneapolis *(G-4528)*

Greencastle Condominium Assn ....E... 320 587-4040
Hutchinson *(G-2697)*

New Concepts Management Group .....E... 952 922-2500
Minneapolis *(G-5187)*

Tower Hill Association ....E... 763 682-2321
Buffalo *(G-658)*

REAL ESTATE MANAGERS: Cooperative Apartment

Becketwood Cooperative Inc ....E... 612 722-4077
Minneapolis *(G-3877)*

Gassen Co Inc...................................E... 952 922-5575
Eden Prairie *(G-1671)*

Employment codes: A=Over 500 employees, B=251-500,
C=101-250, D=51-100, E=25-50

2011 Harris Minnesota
Services Directory

© Harris InfoSource 1-866-281-6415

755

REAL ESTATE OPERATORS, EXC DEVEL:
Theater Bldg, Owner & Op

Duluth 10 Theater.....................E... 218 722-1573
Duluth *(G-1296)*

Quest Management Associates............E... 612 379-3800
Minneapolis *(G-5449)*

REAL ESTATE OPERATORS, EXC DEVELOPERS: Apartment Hotel

Commerce Partners LLC.....................D... 651 292-8777
Saint Paul *(G-8227)*

Grace Management Inc......................A... 763 544-9934
Minneapolis *(G-4544)*

Larry Davis...............................E... 507 372-7774
Worthington *(G-10187)*

Rbc Wealth Management.....................A... 612 371-7750
Minneapolis *(G-5472)*

REAL ESTATE OPERATORS, EXC DEVELOPERS: Auditorium & Hall

Arrowhead Town Hall.....................E... 218 879-6916
Brookston *(G-624)*

Blainbrook Entertainment Ctr............D... 763 755-8686
Minneapolis *(G-3419)*

Italian American Club of.................D... 612 781-0625
Minneapolis *(G-4740)*

Luthern Brothern School Inc.............D... 218 739-3375
Fergus Falls *(G-2091)*

Metropolitan Sports Facilities..........D... 612 332-0386
Minneapolis *(G-5008)*

Tri City American Legion.................E... 651 631-1124
Saint Paul *(G-9080)*

REAL ESTATE OPERATORS, EXC DEVELOPERS: Commercial/Indl Bldg

A E I Fund Management Inc................E... 800 328-3519
Saint Paul *(G-7968)*

Chem Vestments Inc.......................E... 952 469-4965
Lakeville *(G-2894)*

Colliers Towle Valuation................... 612 347-9336
Minneapolis *(G-4120)*

Commerce Partners LLC.....................D... 651 292-8777
Saint Paul *(G-8227)*

DLM A MN LLP..............................E... 218 233-0065
Moorhead *(G-6312)*

Donatelle Properties......................C... 651 633-4200
Saint Paul *(G-8307)*

Dp Property Acquisition LLC..............E... 612 344-1515
Minneapolis *(G-4286)*

Duke Co's.................................D... 612 331-4880
Minneapolis *(G-4289)*

Duke Realty Corp..........................D... 952 543-2900
Minneapolis *(G-4291)*

E Weinberg Supply Co Inc.................E... 952 920-0888
Minneapolis *(G-4303)*

Gladstone Partners.......................E... 651 455-2940
Saint Paul *(G-7781)*

Grace Management Inc......................A... 763 544-9934
Minneapolis *(G-4544)*

Happy Chef Systems Inc...................E... 507 345-4571
Mankato *(G-3134)*

Hillcrest Development, LIlp..............E... 612 371-0123
Minneapolis *(G-4648)*

IFP Inc...................................D... 507 334-2730
Faribault *(G-2013)*

J R & R Partnership......................D... 507 532-9566
Marshall *(G-3300)*

Kraus-Anderson Inc.......................E... 612 332-7281
Minneapolis *(G-4823)*

Maiers Transport & Warehousing..........E... 320 251-6882
Saint Cloud *(G-7547)*

Meritex Enterprises Inc..................E... 651 855-9700
Minneapolis *(G-4992)*

Nico Properties..........................D... 612 822-2185
Minneapolis *(G-5199)*

9900 Properties..........................E... 952 881-5825
Minneapolis *(G-5204)*

Oneida Realty Co Inc.....................D... 218 722-0816
Duluth *(G-1413)*

Public Markets Inc.......................E... 763 546-3139
Minneapolis *(G-5437)*

Rbc Wealth Management.....................A... 612 371-7750
Minneapolis *(G-5472)*

Real Estate Equites Inc.................E... 651 227-6925
Saint Paul *(G-8876)*

Schadegg Properties LLC..................D... 651 292-9933
South Saint Paul *(G-9542)*

Shelard Group Inc........................E... 952 941-7493
Eden Prairie *(G-1777)*

Siewert Construction Co Inc.............. 651 437-1728
Hastings *(G-2405)*

614 Co....................................E... 612 333-6128
Minneapolis *(G-5685)*

St Cloud Denovo...........................D... 320 251-1055
Saint Cloud *(G-7598)*

Western Bank.............................E... 651 290-8100
Saint Paul *(G-9150)*

REAL ESTATE OPERATORS, EXC DEVELOPERS: Property, Retail

North Coast Partners LLP.................E... 952 947-3000
Minneapolis *(G-5214)*

North Way Investment Co..................E... 651 646-7901
Saint Paul *(G-8755)*

Red Wing Hotel Corp......................C... 651 388-2846
Red Wing *(G-6998)*

REAL ESTATE OPERATORS, EXC DEVELOPERS: Retirement Hotel

Augustana Chapel View Homes............B... 612 333-1551
Minneapolis *(G-3835)*

Augustana Chapel View Homes............C... 952 938-2761
Hopkins *(G-2512)*

Augustana Dassel Lakeside Com..........D... 320 275-3308
Dassel *(G-1159)*

Augustana Regent At Burnsville..........D... 952 898-1910
Burnsville *(G-682)*

Carefree Living of America...............E... 952 988-0011
Brainerd *(G-556)*

Charterhouse Inc.........................C... 507 266-8572
Rochester *(G-7075)*

Chosen Valley Care Center Inc............C... 507 867-4220
Chatfield *(G-986)*

Edgebrook Care Center.....................E... 507 442-7121
Edgerton *(G-1823)*

Grace Management Inc......................A... 763 544-9934
Minneapolis *(G-4544)*

Joshco Construction Inc..................D... 952 361-8000
Chaska *(G-971)*

Minnesota Masonic Home North...........A... 763 592-3000
Minneapolis *(G-5083)*

Pioneer Home Inc.........................C... 218 739-7701
Fergus Falls *(G-2113)*

Presbyterian Homes of Arden.............A... 651 631-6000
Saint Paul *(G-8843)*

Presbyterian Homes, Housing.............A... 651 631-6100
Saint Paul *(G-8844)*

Shepherd Good Lutheran Home...........C... 320 252-6525
Sauk Rapids *(G-9374)*

Shepherd Good Lutheran Home...........E... 320 258-8665
Sauk Rapids *(G-9375)*

Sholom Community Alliance...............E... 952 939-1601
Minneapolis *(G-5657)*

Tuff Memorial Homes Inc..................D... 507 962-3275
Hills *(G-2482)*

REAL ESTATE OPERATORS, EXC DEVELOPERS: Shopping Ctr, Commnty

Wellington Management Inc................E... 651 292-9844
Saint Paul *(G-9144)*

RECIPROCAL INTERINSURANCE EXCHANGES: Fire, Marine & Casualty

Ram Mutual Insurance Co Inc..............D... 218 879-3321
Esko *(G-1922)*

St Paul Fire & Marine Insce..............A... 651 221-7911
Saint Paul *(G-8990)*

RECIPROCAL INTERINSURANCE EXCHANGES: Surety & Fidelity

St Paul Fire & Marine Insce..............A... 651 221-7911
Saint Paul *(G-8990)*

RECREATIONAL & SPORTING CAMPS

Camp Buckskin............................D... 218 365-2121
Isabella *(G-2776)*

Camp New Hope Inc........................E... 218 426-3560
McGregor *(G-3338)*

Camp Onamia Inc..........................E... 320 532-3767
Onamia *(G-6567)*

Camp Wilderness Bsa Inc..................D... 218 732-4674
Park Rapids *(G-6748)*

Concordia Language Villages..............E... 218 758-3068
Dent *(G-1186)*

Duluth Area Family Y M C A...............E... 218 372-3188
Sturgeon Lake *(G-9657)*

North Star Camp..........................E... 218 829-6631
Brainerd *(G-578)*

Ymc Camp Dunord.........................E... 218 365-3681
Ely *(G-1918)*

RECREATIONAL CAMPS

Courage Center...........................D... 218 266-3658
Lake George *(G-2878)*

RECREATIONAL SPORTING EQPT REPAIR SVCS

Gander Mountain Co.......................E... 763 420-9800
Osseo *(G-6616)*

RECREATIONAL VEHICLE PARKS

Pathfinder Village St Croix..............E... 320 384-7726
Hinckley *(G-2488)*

RECREATIONAL VEHICLE PARKS & CAMPGROUNDS

Corporate Commission of The............A... 320 384-7101
Hinckley *(G-2483)*

Sunrise Estates Mobile Home.............E... 651 462-4047
Stacy *(G-9581)*

Three Rivers Park District................D... 763 694-7894
Osseo *(G-6673)*

RECREATIONAL VEHICLE REPAIR SVCS

Bristow's Inc............................E... 320 253-7878
Saint Cloud *(G-7435)*

RECREATIONAL VEHICLE REPAIRS

Camping World Inc........................E... 763 428-7779
Rogers *(G-7319)*

Pleasureland Inc.........................D... 320 251-7588
Saint Cloud *(G-7569)*

St Cloud Truck Sales Inc.................D... 320 251-0931
Saint Cloud *(G-7442)*

Thermo Leasing Corp......................E... 763 421-2505
Anoka *(G-234)*

RECYCLABLE SCRAP & WASTE MATERIALS WHOLESALERS

Phillips Recycling Systems LLC..........D... 320 251-5980
Saint Cloud *(G-7422)*

REFERRAL SVCS, PERSONAL & SOCIAL PROBLEMS

Capstone Services LLC....................C... 651 641-0042
Saint Paul *(G-8155)*

REFRIGERATION EQPT & SPLYS WHOLESALERS

Don Stevens Inc..........................E... 651 452-0872
Eagan *(G-1525)*

First Supply LLC.........................E... 507 287-0202
Rochester *(G-7116)*

REFRIGERATION EQPT & SPLYS, WHOL: Refrig Units, Motor Veh

Crossroads Trailer Sales & Svc...........E... 507 373-4443
Albert Lea *(G-45)*

Thermo King Sales & Service.............E... 651 633-2820
Saint Paul *(G-9041)*

REFRIGERATION EQPT & SPLYS, WHOLESALE: Beverage Dispensers

3Wire Group Inc..........................D... 763 488-3000
Osseo *(G-6674)*

REFRIGERATION EQPT & SPLYS, WHOLESALE: Commercial Eqpt

First Supply LLC.........................E... 507 287-0202
Rochester *(G-7116)*

REFRIGERATION EQPT & SPLYS, WHOLESALE: Ice Making Machines

Carrier Commercial.......................E... 763 231-8300
Minneapolis *(G-4021)*

REFRIGERATION REPAIR SVCS

Quality Refrigeration Inc................E... 612 861-7350
Minneapolis *(G-5443)*

Thermo King Sales & Service.............E... 651 633-2820
Saint Paul *(G-9041)*

REFRIGERATION SVC & REPAIR

Egan Co...................................C... 763 544-4131
Brooklyn Park *(G-609)*

Naylor Heating & Refrigeration.............E... 218 444-4328
Bemidji *(G-406)*

Palen Kimball LLC ....E... 651 646-2800
Saint Paul *(G-8804)*

REFUGEE SVCS

Catholic Charities of The...................B... 320 650-1550
Saint Cloud *(G-7473)*

REFUSE SYSTEMS

Employment Enterprises Inc ....D... 320 632-9251
Little Falls *(G-3002)*

Mid-State Reclamation Inc ....E... 952 985-5555
Lakeville *(G-2919)*

Minneapolis Refuse Inc ....E... 612 529-4788
Minneapolis *(G-5063)*

Monitor Tire Disposal Inc 320 548-3496
Saint Martin *(G-7671)*

New Ulm, City of Inc ....D... 507 359-8264
New Ulm *(G-6470)*

Pioneer Industries Inc ....D... 612 374-2280
Minneapolis *(G-5383)*

Pollution Control Agency, MN ....E... 507 285-7343
Rochester *(G-7206)*

Pollution Control Agency, MN ....D... 218 723-4660
Duluth *(G-1427)*

Randt Recycling Technologies............E... 763 417-1370
Litchfield *(G-2989)*

Safety-Kleen Systems Inc ....E... 952 469-8356
Lakeville *(G-2931)*

Stericycle Inc..E... 651 641-0009
Saint Paul *(G-9005)*

Waste Management of Minnesota ....E... 507 826-3610
Albert Lea *(G-70)*

Waste Management of Minnesota ....E... 952 736-2428
Burnsville *(G-820)*

REGIONAL PLANNING ORGANIZATION

Mid-American Baptist Social ....E... 952 443-2024
Victoria *(G-9730)*

REHABILITATION CENTER, OUTPATIENT TREATMENT

American Baptist Homes of The..........D... 507 373-0188
Albert Lea *(G-39)*

Benedictine Health System..................C... 218 744-9800
Eveleth *(G-1928)*

Capernaum Pediatric Therapy ....E... 952 938-5348
Hopkins *(G-2522)*

Capernaum Pediatric Therapy ....E... 612 922-2009
Edina *(G-1828)*

Children's Health Care Inc ....E... 952 930-8630
Hopkins *(G-2528)*

Chrestomathy Inc...................................D... 952 974-0339
Eden Prairie *(G-1624)*

Cokato Charitable Trust ....C... 320 286-2158
Cokato *(G-1076)*

County of Douglas ....A... 320 762-1511
Alexandria *(G-91)*

County of Mille Lacs ....E... 763 389-5828
Princeton *(G-6904)*

Courage Center ....C... 651 439-8283
Stillwater *(G-9607)*

Courage Center ....E... 320 963-3121
Maple Lake *(G-3259)*

Extendicare Homes Inc ....B... 763 588-0771
Minneapolis *(G-4383)*

Extendicare Homes Inc ....D... 612 861-1691
Richfield *(G-7035)*

Extendicare Homes Inc ....B... 763 545-0416
Minneapolis *(G-4384)*

Extendicare Homes Inc ....C... 952 920-8380
Minneapolis *(G-4387)*

Fairview Clinics.....................................E... 651 688-7860
Saint Paul *(G-7773)*

Gillette Children's Specialty ....E... 952 936-0977
Hopkins *(G-2544)*

Guardian Angels Health & Rehab........C... 218 263-7583
Hibbing *(G-2448)*

Habilitative Services Inc ....C... 507 625-6047
Mankato *(G-3133)*

Haven Chemical Health System ....E... 651 734-9633
Saint Paul *(G-9224)*

Iron Range Rehabilitation Ctr ....E... 218 741-2147
Virginia *(G-9743)*

Jones Stanley & Associates ....E... 507 288-0064
Rochester *(G-7147)*

Lifetrack Resources Inc ....D... 651 227-8471
Saint Paul *(G-8586)*

Mayo Clinic Rochester ....E... 507 377-5900
Albert Lea *(G-61)*

Midsota Regional Hand Center............E... 320 253-7257
Saint Cloud *(G-7554)*

Northern Star Therapy Ltd Inc ....E... 320 240-6955
Saint Cloud *(G-7562)*

Occupational Development Ctr ....C... 218 326-8574
Grand Rapids *(G-2305)*

Physicans Neck & Back Clinic..............E... 651 639-9150
Saint Paul *(G-8827)*

Polinsky Rehabilitation Center ....C... 218 786-5360
Duluth *(G-1426)*

Possabilies of Southern MN ....D... 507 287-7100
Rochester *(G-7209)*

ReEntry House Inc ....E... 612 869-2411
Minneapolis *(G-5480)*

Rice Memorial Hospital ....E... 320 231-4175
Willmar *(G-10043)*

Therapy Network Inc.............................E... 507 454-6724
Winona *(G-10132)*

Whispering Pines Therapy Ctr.............D... 218 587-4423
Pine River *(G-6822)*

Wright Connection Dtnh Inc ....E... 763 682-2910
Buffalo *(G-661)*

REHABILITATION CTR, RESIDENTIAL WITH HEALTH CARE INCIDENTAL

Bell Hill Recovery Center Inc ....E... 218 631-3610
Wadena *(G-9798)*

Bethel Duluth Society ....D... 218 722-1724
Duluth *(G-1251)*

Gables Inc..E... 507 282-2500
Rochester *(G-7122)*

Grand Meadow Health Care Ctr ....D... 507 754-5212
Grand Meadow *(G-2264)*

Hazelden Foundation..............................D... 612 559-2022
Minneapolis *(G-4614)*

Martin Luther Manor ....B... 952 888-7751
Minneapolis *(G-4960)*

Minnesota Indian Primary ....E... 218 879-6731
Sawyer *(G-9413)*

Minnesota Teen Challenge Inc ....E... 612 373-3366
Minneapolis *(G-5095)*

Missions Inc Programs..........................D... 763 559-1883
Minneapolis *(G-5109)*

New Beginnings At Waverly LLC ....D... 763 658-5800
Waverly *(G-9904)*

New Life Treatment Center ....E... 507 777-4321
Woodstock *(G-10176)*

People Inc ....E... 651 774-0011
Saint Paul *(G-8816)*

Pine Manors Inc ....E... 218 732-4337
Nevis *(G-6405)*

Polk County Developmental ....E... 218 281-4181
Crookston *(G-1134)*

Reverence For Life & Concern ....D... 320 564-4911
Granite Falls *(G-2319)*

Sisters of The Good Shepherd ....E... 651 484-0221
Saint Paul *(G-8961)*

Turning Point Inc ....E... 612 520-4004
Minneapolis *(G-5869)*

Vinland National Center ....E... 763 479-3555
Loretto *(G-3054)*

Workabilities Inc ....E... 763 541-1844
Minneapolis *(G-6085)*

REHABILITATION SVCS

Beverly Enterprises - MN ....D... 507 288-1818
Rochester *(G-7065)*

County of Anoka ....E... 763 783-4909
Minneapolis *(G-3445)*

Eden Rs ....C... 612 287-1600
Minneapolis *(G-4313)*

Kcq Inc ....E... 507 334-4393
Faribault *(G-2016)*

Nothern Cass Bemidji Inc ....E... 218 759-0052
Bemidji *(G-416)*

Southern Minnesota Independent ....E... 507 345-7139
Mankato *(G-3200)*

REINSURANCE CARRIERS: Accident & Health

AON Benfield..B... 952 886-8000
Minneapolis *(G-3784)*

AON Benfield..E... 952 886-8000
Minneapolis *(G-3785)*

E W Blanch International Inc ....D... 952 886-8000
Minneapolis *(G-4302)*

Employers Mutual Casualty Co ....E... 952 938-4646
Hopkins *(G-2539)*

Reinsurance Group of America ....D... 612 372-5432
Minneapolis *(G-5506)*

Reliastar Life Insurance Co...................A... 612 372-5432
Minneapolis *(G-5507)*

St Paul Fire & Marine Insce...................A... 651 221-7911
Saint Paul *(G-8990)*

REINSURANCE CARRIERS: Life

Guy Carpenter & Co LLC ....C... 952 920-3300
Minneapolis *(G-4580)*

Reliastar Life Insurance Co ....A... 612 372-5432
Minneapolis *(G-5507)*

21st Services LLC...................................D... 612 371-3008
Minneapolis *(G-5872)*

REINSURANCE CARRIERS: Surety

Axa Advisors LLC...................................D... 612 243-3200
Minneapolis *(G-3850)*

St Paul Fire & Marine Insce ....A... 651 221-7911
Saint Paul *(G-8990)*

RELIGIOUS SPLYS WHOLESALERS

Saint Patrick's Guild Inc ....E... 651 690-1506
Saint Paul *(G-8923)*

RELOCATION SVCS

NRG Energy Plus Relocation ....D... 952 512-5500
Minneapolis *(G-5253)*

Plus Relocation Services Inc................D... 952 512-5500
Minneapolis *(G-5391)*

REMOTE DATABASE INFORMATION RETRIEVAL SVCS

Ontrack Data Recovery Inc...................A... 952 937-1107
Eden Prairie *(G-1739)*

REMOVAL SVCS, BUSH & TREE

Arrowhead Tree Service Inc ....E... 218 729-9203
Duluth *(G-1245)*

S & S Tree & Horticultural.....................E... 651 451-8907
South Saint Paul *(G-9539)*

S & S Tree Specialists Inc.....................E... 612 872-3901
South Saint Paul *(G-9540)*

RENT-A-CAR SVCS

Avis Rent A Car System Inc ....E... 612 623-3999
Minneapolis *(G-3842)*

Avis Rent A Car System Inc ....E... 651 636-6730
Saint Paul *(G-8082)*

Chisholm-Hibbing Airport......................E... 218 262-3451
Hibbing *(G-2440)*

Enterprise Leasing Co of MN ....E... 651 905-5000
Saint Paul *(G-7766)*

General Electric Fleet Svcs ....B... 952 828-1000
Eden Prairie *(G-1674)*

Metropolitan Corp..................................D... 952 943-9000
Eden Prairie *(G-1721)*

National Car Rental System Inc ....E... 218 283-8486
International Falls *(G-2728)*

Nintey Four Services Inc.......................E... 763 295-3604
Monticello *(G-6279)*

U Save Lease & Rental Inc....................E... 218 732-3347
Park Rapids *(G-6764)*

Valley Sales Inc.....................................E... 952 314-8560
Waconia *(G-9793)*

RENTAL & OPERATION SVCS: Go-Cart Raceway

Dennis Raedeke Inc...............................D... 651 465-6365
Taylors Falls *(G-9660)*

RENTAL CENTERS: Furniture

CORT Business Services Corp ....E... 651 405-0009
Saint Paul *(G-7737)*

RENTAL CENTERS: General

A To Z International Inc.........................E... 612 729-2328
Minneapolis *(G-3650)*

Buerkle Buick Leasing Co ....C... 651 484-0231
Saint Paul *(G-8140)*

RENTAL CENTERS: Party & Banquet Eqpt & Splys

Aarcee Party & Tent Rental ....E... 952 922-7233
Minneapolis *(G-3657)*

Apres Inc ....E... 952 942-3399
Minneapolis *(G-3793)*

Broadway Rental Equipment Co ....E... 763 533-1680
Minneapolis *(G-3952)*

RENTAL CENTERS: Tools

Home Depot USA Inc..............................C... 218 829-0341
Baxter *(G-329)*

Home Depot USA Inc..............................C... 763 422-1200
Minneapolis *(G-3490)*

Employment codes: A=Over 500 employees, B=251-500,
C=101-250, D=51-100, E=25-50

2011 Harris Minnesota
Services Directory

© Harris InfoSource 1-866-281-6415

757

SERVICES

Home Depot USA Inc ....C... 763 509-9590
Minneapolis *(G-4667)*
Home Depot USA Inc ....C... 651 452-2323
Eagan *(G-1530)*
Home Depot USA Inc ....C... 763 717-0316
Minneapolis *(G-3491)*
Home Depot USA Inc ....C... 952 432-7171
Saint Paul *(G-7800)*
Home Depot USA Inc ....C... 320 235-1975
Willmar *(G-10010)*
Home Depot USA Inc ....C... 952 496-3076
Shakopee *(G-9444)*
IFP Inc ....D... 507 334-2730
Faribault *(G-2013)*
Total Tool Supply Inc...........................D... 651 646-4055
Saint Paul *(G-9073)*

RENTAL SVCS: Aircraft

Bemidji Aviation Services Inc...............E... 612 726-1500
Minneapolis *(G-3882)*
Elliott Aviation Inc ....D... 952 944-1200
Eden Prairie *(G-1654)*
Modern Aero Inc ....D... 952 941-2595
Eden Prairie *(G-1729)*
Monaco Air Duluth LLC ....E... 218 727-2911
Duluth *(G-1396)*
Northwest Aircraft Inc ....E... 612 726-2331
Saint Paul *(G-7854)*
Thunderbird Aviation Inc ....E... 952 941-1212
Eden Prairie *(G-1793)*

RENTAL SVCS: Audio-Visual Eqpt & Sply

Alpha Video & Audio Inc ....D... 952 896-9898
Minneapolis *(G-3733)*
Electrosonic Inc ....E... 952 931-7500
Minnetonka *(G-6165)*

RENTAL SVCS: Business Machine & Electronic Eqpt

Duke Co's ....D... 612 331-4880
Minneapolis *(G-4289)*
Pitney Bowes Inc ....D... 952 885-7287
Minneapolis *(G-5385)*
Pitney Bowes Inc ....E... 952 983-1600
Eden Prairie *(G-1749)*

RENTAL SVCS: Clothing

Norcostco Inc ....E... 763 544-0601
Minneapolis *(G-5207)*
Weber & Barlow Stores Inc ....E... 507 289-2444
Rochester *(G-7286)*

RENTAL SVCS: Costume

Norcostco Inc ....E... 763 544-0601
Minneapolis *(G-5207)*
Vee Corp ....E... 612 333-2223
Minneapolis *(G-5959)*

RENTAL SVCS: Eqpt, Motion Picture

Lights On Inc 612 331-6620
Minneapolis *(G-4886)*

RENTAL SVCS: Eqpt, Theatrical

Staging Concepts Inc ....E... 763 533-2094
Minneapolis *(G-5734)*

RENTAL SVCS: Home Appliance, Furniture & Entertainment

McDonald Rentals Inc..........................E... 218 879-9060
Cloquet *(G-1056)*

RENTAL SVCS: Home Cleaning & Maintenance Eqpt

Broadway Rental Equipment Co ....E... 763 533-1680
Minneapolis *(G-3952)*

RENTAL SVCS: Houseboat

Rainy Lake Houseboats Inc ....E... 218 286-5391
International Falls *(G-2729)*

RENTAL SVCS: Invalid Splys

Apria Healthcare Inc ....C... 952 404-1700
Minnetonka *(G-6143)*
Universal Hospital Services..................D... 612 721-3374
Minneapolis *(G-5919)*

RENTAL SVCS: Lawn & Garden Eqpt

U-Haul Co of Minnesota ....D... 763 780-9746
Minneapolis *(G-3628)*

RENTAL SVCS: Live Plant

Bachman's Inc....................................C... 612 861-7600
Minneapolis *(G-3856)*

RENTAL SVCS: Locker, Exc Cold Storage

Smarte Carte Inc ....D... 651 429-3614
Saint Paul *(G-8965)*

RENTAL SVCS: Musical Instrument

Chester E Groth Music Co ....E... 952 884-4772
Minneapolis *(G-4060)*

RENTAL SVCS: Pleasure Boat

Briggs Hennum Inc ....E... 218 634-2168
Baudette *(G-314)*
Eddy's Lake Mille Lacs Resort ....E... 320 532-3657
Onamia *(G-6570)*
Muller Boat Co....................................E... 651 465-6315
Taylors Falls *(G-9661)*

RENTAL SVCS: Recreational Vehicle

Thermo Leasing Corp ....E... 763 421-2505
Anoka *(G-234)*

RENTAL SVCS: Sporting Goods, NEC

Cabela's Inc ....C... 763 493-8600
Rogers *(G-7318)*
Splatball Inc ....E... 612 378-0385
Minneapolis *(G-5721)*

RENTAL SVCS: Stores & Yards Eqpt

S E Rental ....E... 507 765-3805
Preston *(G-6901)*

RENTAL SVCS: Tent & Tarpaulin

Broadway Rental Equipment Co ....E... 763 533-1680
Minneapolis *(G-3952)*

RENTAL SVCS: Trailer

Dahlke Trailer Sales Inc........................E... 763 783-0077
Minneapolis *(G-3450)*
U-Haul Co of Minnesota ....D... 763 780-9746
Minneapolis *(G-3628)*

RENTAL SVCS: Travel, Camping Or Recreational Trailer

Hilltop Trailer Sales Inc ....E... 763 571-9103
Minneapolis *(G-3488)*

RENTAL SVCS: Truck, Without Drivers

Penske Truck Leasing Co, LP...............E... 651 454-0000
Saint Paul *(G-7873)*
R & R Transportation Inc......................D... 218 439-6144
Audubon *(G-255)*
RSC Equipment Rental Inc....................E... 763 509-2423
Minneapolis *(G-5566)*
Ryder Truck Rental Inc ....C... 763 545-9417
Minneapolis *(G-5580)*
Ryder Truck Rental Inc ....E... 651 636-6906
Saint Paul *(G-8915)*
Ryder Truck Rental Inc ....E... 651 631-1755
Saint Paul *(G-8916)*

RENTAL SVCS: Tuxedo

Anderson's Formal Wear Inc ....E... 507 285-1884
Rochester *(G-7056)*
Norcostco Inc ....E... 763 544-0601
Minneapolis *(G-5207)*
Wedding Chapel Inc............................E... 763 533-4228
Minneapolis *(G-6032)*

RENTAL SVCS: Vending Machine

A H Hermel Candy & Tobacco Co ....D... 507 387-5634
Mankato *(G-3098)*
Safety Signs Inc ....E... 952 469-6700
Lakeville *(G-2930)*

RENTAL SVCS: Work Zone Traffic Eqpt, Flags, Cones, Etc

McDonald Rentals Inc..........................E... 218 879-9060
Cloquet *(G-1056)*
Safety Signs Inc ....E... 952 469-6700
Lakeville *(G-2930)*

RENTAL: Passenger Car

Brookman Motor Sales Inc....................E... 651 777-1316
Lake Elmo *(G-2867)*
Clusiau Sales & Rental Inc....................E... 218 326-9421
Grand Rapids *(G-2275)*

Miller Enterprises Inc ....C... 320 251-8900
Saint Cloud *(G-7557)*
Montavon Motors Inc ....E... 218 326-0551
Grand Rapids *(G-2297)*
Rent A Ford Car ....E... 320 352-6561
Sauk Centre *(G-9351)*
Ryder Truck Rental Inc ....E... 651 636-6906
Saint Paul *(G-8915)*

RENTAL: Portable Toilet

Biffs Boxes LLC..................................E... 952 403-1221
Shakopee *(G-9422)*
On-Site Sanitation Inc ....E... 651 429-3781
Saint Paul *(G-8785)*

RENTAL: Trucks, With Drivers

Duane Kottke Trucking Corp.................E... 320 833-5385
Buffalo Lake *(G-663)*

RENTAL: Video Tape & Disc

Coborn's Inc......................................C... 320 679-4003
Mora *(G-6354)*
McDonald Rentals Inc ....E... 218 879-9060
Cloquet *(G-1056)*
United Entertainment Corp...................B... 320 203-1003
Saint Cloud *(G-7624)*

REPERTORY, ROAD OR STOCK COMPANIES, THEATRICAL

Old Log Theater Ltd ....E... 952 474-5951
Excelsior *(G-1951)*

REPOSSESSION SVCS

Broadway Resource & Recovery ....E... 612 623-8888
Minneapolis *(G-3953)*
1st National Repossessioncom ....E... 763 241-5212
Elk River *(G-1874)*

REPRODUCTION SVCS: Video Tape Or Disk

Metropolitan Productions Inc...............D... 612 333-1025
Minneapolis *(G-5007)*

RESEARCH, DEV & TESTING SVCS, COMM: Chem Lab, Exc Testing

Higher Dimension Research Inc ....E... 651 730-6203
Saint Paul *(G-9229)*
Segetis Inc..E... 763 795-7200
Golden Valley *(G-2245)*

RESEARCH, DEVELOPMENT & TEST SVCS, COMM: Cmptr Hardware Dev

Geodigm Corp ....E... 952 556-5657
Chanhassen *(G-924)*
Unisys Corp ....A... 651 635-7777
Saint Paul *(G-9103)*

RESEARCH, DEVELOPMENT & TEST SVCS, COMM: Research, Exc Lab

Amherst H Wilder Foundation...............E... 651 647-4600
Saint Paul *(G-8042)*
Anderson, Niebuhr & Associates.........E... 651 486-8712
Saint Paul *(G-8051)*
Capitol Lien Records & Res ....E... 651 488-0100
Saint Paul *(G-8154)*
Orman Guidance Research Inc ....D... 952 831-4911
Minneapolis *(G-5291)*

RESEARCH, DEVELOPMENT & TESTING SVCS, COMM: Agricultural

Betaseed Inc ....E... 952 445-8090
Shakopee *(G-9421)*
Cargill Inc ....D... 763 441-3330
Elk River *(G-1865)*
Cargill Inc ....D... 763 441-6508
Elk River *(G-1866)*
Segetis Inc..E... 763 795-7200
Golden Valley *(G-2245)*
Syngenta Seeds Inc............................D... 507 645-5621
Stanton *(G-9582)*

RESEARCH, DEVELOPMENT & TESTING SVCS, COMM: Natural Resource

Prairie Smoke......................................E... 507 292-0063
Rochester *(G-7211)*

S
E
R
V
I
C
E
S

RESEARCH, DEVELOPMENT & TESTING SVCS, COMM: Research Lab

Pace Analytical Life Sciences...............E... 651 738-2728
Oakdale *(G-6552)*

RESEARCH, DEVELOPMENT & TESTING SVCS, COMM: Sociological

Search Institute ....E... 612 376-8955
Minneapolis *(G-5622)*

RESEARCH, DEVELOPMENT & TESTING SVCS, COMMERCIAL: Business

Badger Acquisition of MN ....C... 763 259-0400
Minneapolis *(G-3857)*
Cvrx Inc..E... 763 416-2840
Minneapolis *(G-4207)*

RESEARCH, DEVELOPMENT & TESTING SVCS, COMMERCIAL: Economic

American Institute of ....E... 651 415-1320
Saint Paul *(G-8027)*

RESEARCH, DEVELOPMENT & TESTING SVCS, COMMERCIAL: Education

Data Recognition Corp ....B... 763 268-2000
Maple Grove *(G-3239)*
Minnesota Rural Education Assn........C... 320 762-6574
Alexandria *(G-113)*
Regents of The University of ....E... 612 624-6328
Minneapolis *(G-5501)*

RESEARCH, DEVELOPMENT & TESTING SVCS, COMMERCIAL: Energy

Boreal Energy Inc 651 762-1200
Vadnais Heights *(G-9720)*

RESEARCH, DEVELOPMENT & TESTING SVCS, COMMERCIAL: Food

Food Perspectives Inc ....E... 763 553-7787
Minneapolis *(G-4463)*
Higher Dimension Research Inc...........E... 651 730-6203
Saint Paul *(G-9229)*
Sunopta Food Group LLC 320 763-5977
Alexandria *(G-125)*

RESEARCH, DEVELOPMENT & TESTING SVCS, COMMERCIAL: Medical

American Preclinical Services..............E... 763 717-7990
Minneapolis *(G-3400)*
Mednet Solutions Inc ....D... 763 258-2735
Minnetonka *(G-6191)*
Minneapolis Medical Research ....C... 612 347-5000
Minneapolis *(G-5057)*
Nephrology Analytical Services ....E... 612 337-7345
Minneapolis *(G-5182)*
Prism Research LLC ....E... 651 641-2900
Saint Paul *(G-8849)*

RESEARCH, DEVELOPMENT & TESTING SVCS, COMMERCIAL: Physical

Regents of The University of ....E... 218 245-2200
Bigfork *(G-463)*
Vision Processing Technologies..........E... 320 593-1796
Litchfield *(G-2992)*

RESEARCH, DVLPMT & TESTING SVCS, COMM: Merger, Acq & Reorg

Maxann LLC...E... 651 484-2677
Saint Paul *(G-8619)*

RESEARCH, DVLPT & TEST SVCS, COMM: Mkt Analysis or Research

Anderson, Niebuhr & Associates ....E... 651 486-8712
Saint Paul *(G-8051)*
Bette Dickenson Research Inc ....D... 763 420-4385
Osseo *(G-6599)*
C J Olson Market Research ....E... 612 378-5040
Minneapolis *(G-3985)*
Fieldwork Minneapolis Inc ....E... 952 837-8300
Minneapolis *(G-4430)*
Focus Market Research Inc ....E... 612 869-8181
Minneapolis *(G-4459)*
Food Perspectives Inc ....E... 763 553-7787
Minneapolis *(G-4463)*
Iconoculture Inc ....E... 612 377-0087
Minneapolis *(G-4686)*

Leisure Inc..E... 952 401-8440
Eden Prairie *(G-1707)*
Market Solutions Group Inc ....D... 612 332-1574
Saint Paul *(G-7833)*
Marketline Research Inc ....E... 612 767-2580
Minneapolis *(G-4950)*
Markettools Inc......................................E... 952 546-2800
Minneapolis *(G-4951)*
Nielsen Co US LLC ....D... 763 593-2000
Minneapolis *(G-5201)*
Orman Guidance Research Inc..............D... 952 831-4911
Minneapolis *(G-5291)*
Power Systems Research Inc ....E... 651 905-8400
Saint Paul *(G-7880)*
Quick Test Inc ....E... 952 854-3535
Minneapolis *(G-5451)*
Retail Support Inc ....E... 952 934-1317
Eden Prairie *(G-1763)*
Service 800 Inc ....B... 952 475-3747
Long Lake *(G-3032)*
TCI Group Inc ....E... 612 823-6214
Minneapolis *(G-5800)*
3M Co ....C... 651 733-3929
Saint Paul *(G-9051)*

RESEARCH, DVLPT & TESTING SVCS, COMM: Mkt, Bus & Economic

Information Specialists Group...............D... 952 941-1600
Eden Prairie *(G-1691)*
Kenexa Corp ....E... 612 332-6383
Minneapolis *(G-4800)*

RESEARCH, DVLPT & TESTING SVCS, COMM: Survey, Mktg

Anderson, Niebuhr & Associates ....E... 651 486-8712
Saint Paul *(G-8051)*
Meyer Associates Inc ....C... 320 259-4000
Saint Cloud *(G-7552)*
Retail Support Inc ....E... 952 934-1317
Eden Prairie *(G-1763)*

RESIDENCE CLUB: Organization

T C Sweatshop Inc ....E... 651 646-8418
Saint Paul *(G-9023)*

RESIDENTIAL CARE FOR CHILDREN

Bridge For Youth.....................................D... 612 377-8800
Minneapolis *(G-3944)*
General Pediatric ....E... 612 626-2820
Minneapolis *(G-4516)*
Krushe Residential Services.................E... 218 746-3117
Pillager *(G-6810)*
Northwood Childrens Home Soc ....D... 218 724-8815
Duluth *(G-1410)*

RESIDENTIAL CARE FOR THE HANDICAPPED

Client Community Services Inc ....E... 507 376-6095
Worthington *(G-10181)*
Hammer Residences Inc ....C... 763 473-1261
Wayzata *(G-9919)*
Paragon Associates Inc ....D... 218 722-5009
Duluth *(G-1418)*
REM Pillsbury Inc...................................D... 612 871-1954
Minneapolis *(G-5512)*
Residential Services of.........................E... 218 728-6823
Duluth *(G-1436)*
Tasks Unlimited Inc ....E... 612 871-3320
Minneapolis *(G-5792)*

RESIDENTIAL MENTAL HEALTH & SUBSTANCE ABUSE FACILITIES

Aging Joyfully Inc ....E... 952 941-2510
Eden Prairie *(G-1586)*
American Home Health...........................E... 612 860-7301
Saint Paul *(G-8026)*
Arbors At Ridges ....E... 952 898-4005
Burnsville *(G-680)*
Arrowhead House Foster Care ....E... 218 727-8040
Duluth *(G-1241)*
Augustana Chapel View Homes ....B... 612 333-1551
Minneapolis *(G-3835)*
Aviv Health Care Inc ....C... 612 377-4723
Minneapolis *(G-3845)*
Axis Minnesota Inc ....D... 651 774-5940
Saint Paul *(G-8083)*
B L E A Inc ....E... 507 896-3040
Houston *(G-2662)*
Bethany Covenant Village.....................D... 612 781-2691
Minneapolis *(G-3893)*

Beverly Enterprises - MN ....C... 612 333-0111
Minneapolis *(G-3897)*
Bridge House ....E... 218 725-7785
Duluth *(G-1256)*
Catholic Charities of The ....C... 320 251-8811
Saint Cloud *(G-7474)*
Centennial House of Apple Val ....E... 952 891-2711
Saint Paul *(G-7729)*
Chandler Place..E... 612 788-7321
Minneapolis *(G-6124)*
Colonial Acres Home Inc ....C... 763 546-6125
Minneapolis *(G-4122)*
Comforts of Home Hugo ....E... 651 653-3282
Hugo *(G-2675)*
Community Involvement Programs .....E... 320 245-5362
Sandstone *(G-9320)*
Community Living Inc ....D... 952 443-2048
Victoria *(G-9726)*
Covenant Home Services LLC ....E... 763 755-9009
Minneapolis *(G-3446)*
Diversified Lifestyles Inc ....E... 320 235-0270
Willmar *(G-10000)*
Dungarvin Illinois Inc ....D... 651 699-6050
Saint Paul *(G-8312)*
Dungarvin Minnesota Inc......................B... 651 699-6050
Saint Paul *(G-8313)*
Dungarvin New Mexico Inc ....D... 651 699-6050
Saint Paul *(G-8314)*
Ecumen Home Care Inc ....E... 952 888-1010
Minneapolis *(G-4312)*
Elm Residence Inc.................................B... 507 835-1146
Waseca *(G-9877)*
Empowerment Services of Rice ....D... 507 333-2583
Faribault *(G-2002)*
English Roseat Suites Inc......................E... 952 983-0412
Wayzata *(G-9916)*
Freeport West Inc ....D... 612 824-3040
Minneapolis *(G-4486)*
Garden House Estates Ltd.....................E... 218 628-0271
Duluth *(G-1331)*
Greenview Alzheimer's ....E... 218 263-3935
Hibbing *(G-2447)*
Grove Chestnut Inc ....E... 218 749-6846
Virginia *(G-9739)*
Harry Meyering Center Inc....................B... 507 388-3551
Mankato *(G-3135)*
Hawley Retirement Inc ....E... 218 483-3337
Hawley *(G-2420)*
Hawthorne House Inc.............................E... 763 525-1000
Minneapolis *(G-4611)*
Home & Community Options Inc ....E... 507 452-9311
Winona *(G-10103)*
Homestead At Coon Rapids ....E... 763 754-2800
Minneapolis *(G-3492)*
Homeward Bound Inc.............................D... 763 566-7860
Minneapolis *(G-4673)*
Horizon Health Inc ....E... 218 828-4142
Brainerd *(G-569)*
Lakeland Hospice & Home Care ....C... 218 998-1400
Fergus Falls *(G-2082)*
Lifeway Services....................................E... 218 722-1184
Duluth *(G-1382)*
Little Sisters of The Poor of...................D... 651 227-0336
Saint Paul *(G-8592)*
Lrn Associates Management Inc...........E... 507 836-8955
Slayton *(G-9488)*
Lyngblomsten ....B... 651 646-2941
Saint Paul *(G-8599)*
Mainstreet Village Retirement ....E... 612 869-6584
Richfield *(G-7036)*
Minnesota Department of ....E... 218 226-6300
Silver Bay *(G-9483)*
Mount Olivet Lutheran Church.............E... 612 861-3305
Minneapolis *(G-5140)*
Northeast Residence Inc.......................B... 651 765-0217
Saint Paul *(G-8756)*
Northfield Care Center Inc ....C... 507 645-9511
Northfield *(G-6536)*
Northland Counseling Center...............E... 218 327-1105
Grand Rapids *(G-2302)*
Oak Ridge Homes of Wadena Inc ....E... 218 829-7599
Brainerd *(G-579)*
Omegon Inc...E... 952 541-4738
Hopkins *(G-2594)*
Opportunity Partners Inc ....C... 952 938-5511
Hopkins *(G-2595)*
Opportunity Partners Inc ....E... 763 441-0960
Elk River *(G-1889)*
Parkwood Shores Assisted ....E... 952 924-0400
Minneapolis *(G-5339)*
Pines ....E... 612 861-3331
Minneapolis *(G-5379)*
Prairie Community Services...................E... 218 739-2045
Fergus Falls *(G-2115)*

Employment codes: A=Over 500 employees, B=251-500,
C=101-250, D=51-100, E=25-50

2011 Harris Minnesota
Services Directory

© Harris InfoSource 1-866-281-6415
759

SERVICES

Presbyterian Homes H & A ....E... 651 631-6659
Saint Paul (G-8841)

Presbyterian Homes of Inver ....E... 651 451-5959
Inver Grove Heights (G-2765)

Progressive Habilitative Svcs ....E... 763 536-8128
Minneapolis (G-5426)

Rakhma Inc ....D... 612 824-2345
Minneapolis (G-5464)

Realife Cooperative of Mounds ....D... 763 780-9737
Saint Paul (G-8879)

REM Inc ....C... 507 287-6824
Rochester (G-7221)

REM Riverbluff Inc ....E... 507 281-1105
Rochester (G-7222)

St Cloud Hospital ....E... 320 259-9149
Sauk Rapids (G-9376)

St Williams Nursing Home Inc ....C... 218 338-4671
Parkers Prairie (G-6767)

Sunrise Senior Living Inc ....D... 952 927-8000
Minneapolis (G-5769)

Traditions of Owatonna ....D... 507 451-0433
Owatonna (G-6741)

Twin City Christian Homes Inc ....D... 952 944-8982
Eden Prairie (G-1799)

Volunteers Of America Inc ....D... 763 753-2500
Anoka (G-237)

Wendigo Pines Assisted LI ....E... 218 326-6900
Grand Rapids (G-2312)

Wesley Residence Inc ....E... 218 628-2307
Duluth (G-1501)

West Central Community Service ....D... 218 643-5952
Breckenridge (G-603)

Whittier Place ....E... 612 872-1926
Minneapolis (G-6066)

Willowbrook Co-Op ....E... 507 388-2886
Mankato (G-3219)

RESIDENTIAL MENTALLY HANDICAPPED FACILITIES

Adonai Care Homes Corp ....E... 651 227-0574
Saint Paul (G-7983)

AME Community Service Inc 320 286-6421
Cokato (G-1075)

American Baptist Homes of The...............E... 952 941-3175
Eden Prairie (G-1590)

Benedictine Health System ....D... 651 388-1234
Red Wing (G-6975)

Care Planners Inc ....D... 651 645-9887
Saint Paul (G-8162)

Elm North Inc ....E... 507 835-1146
Waseca (G-9876)

Harry Meyering Center Inc ....B... 507 388-3551
Mankato (G-3135)

Johnson's Riverside Boarding 218 681-1278
Thief River Falls (G-9671)

REM Central Lakes Inc ....E... 507 238-4751
Fairmont (G-1979)

REM Hennepin Inc ....D... 952 925-5067
Minneapolis (G-5510)

REM Woodvale Inc ....E... 507 451-1296
Owatonna (G-6734)

RESIDENTIAL REMODELERS

Christians Inc ....E... 952 470-2001
Chanhassen (G-916)

CNM Inc ....D... 952 924-0043
Minneapolis (G-4115)

Krl Exterior Inc ....D... 612 296-0222
Burnsville (G-743)

Lipe Brothers Construction Inc ....E... 218 525-3364
Duluth (G-1384)

Sawhose Inc ....E... 763 533-0352
Minneapolis (G-5606)

Seal Guard Systems Inc ....E... 612 787-0700
Marine On Saint Croix (G-3289)

Twin City Exteriors Co Inc ....D... 763 425-4737
Osseo (G-6679)

RESORT HOTEL: Franchised

Carlson Hotels LP ....C... 763 212-1000
Minneapolis (G-4014)

RESORT HOTELS

Adrian's Resort Inc ....D... 218 634-1985
Baudette (G-313)

Afton Alps Inc ....A... 651 436-5245
Hastings (G-2412)

Campbells Cabins & Trading ....E... 218 993-2361
Crane Lake (G-1116)

Causeway & Gull Associates ....E... 218 963-3675
Lake Hubert (G-2879)

Eddy's Lake Mille Lacs Resort ....E... 320 532-3657
Onamia (G-6570)

Etoc Co Inc ....D... 218 963-2906
Nisswa (G-6496)

Etoc Co Inc ....E... 218 963-2234
Nisswa (G-6497)

Fond Dulac Development Corp ....D... 218 722-8633
Carlton (G-868)

Gunflint Lodge Inc ....E... 218 388-2294
Grand Marais (G-2261)

Huddle's South Shore Resort ....E... 218 836-2420
Walker (G-9852)

Izatys Group LLC ....E... 320 532-3101
Onamia (G-6573)

Kavco Inc 218 829-5226
Brainerd (G-545)

Lodge At Sugar Lake Inc ....E... 218 327-1462
Cohasset (G-1072)

Lonesome Pine Restaurant ....E... 218 678-2874
Deerwood (G-1178)

Madden Brothers Inc ....E... 218 829-2811
Brainerd (G-546)

Piney Ridge Lodge Inc ....E... 218 587-2296
Pine River (G-6821)

Premier Resorts Ltd ....C... 952 253-2500
Minneapolis (G-5402)

Quarterdeck At Pleasant Acres ....E... 218 963-2482
Nisswa (G-6493)

Rica Costa Ventures Inc ....E... 651 426-9262
Hugo (G-2682)

Sheraton Duluth ....D... 218 733-5660
Duluth (G-1449)

Thunderbird Lodge Inc ....D... 218 286-3151
International Falls (G-2732)

Townhomes At Lutsen Mountains 218 663-7241
Lutsen (G-3058)

Trapper's Landing Lodge ....E... 218 836-2500
Walker (G-9859)

Villa ....E... 218 865-4155
Biwabik (G-472)

REST HOME, WITH HEALTH CARE INCIDENTAL

American Baptist Homes of The...............E... 952 941-3175
Eden Prairie (G-1590)

Evangelical Covenant Church ....E... 763 546-6125
Minneapolis (G-4375)

Evangelical Covenant Church ....D... 612 781-2691
Minneapolis (G-4374)

New Perspective of Minnesota ....E... 651 407-9076
Mahtomedi (G-3097)

RESTAURANT EQPT REPAIR SVCS

Enviromatic Corp of America ....D... 612 861-3330
Minneapolis (G-4362)

Kelbro Co ....E... 612 824-9803
Minneapolis (G-4796)

RETIREMENT COMMUNITIES WITH NURSING

Alterra Healthcare Corp ....E... 763 755-2800
Minneapolis (G-3397)

Brooks ....E... 507 446-5855
Owatonna (G-6697)

Heritage of Edina Inc ....C... 952 920-9145
Minneapolis (G-4641)

Lutheran Memorial Home ....C... 218 584-5181
Twin Valley (G-9702)

Rochester Health & Rehab West ....D... 507 288-1818
Rochester (G-7233)

St Ann's Home ....D... 218 727-8831
Duluth (G-1458)

Valley Home Society ....D... 218 681-3286
Thief River Falls (G-9681)

ROAD CONSTRUCTION EQUIPMENT WHOLESALERS

Garlock-East Equipment Co ....E... 763 553-1935
Minneapolis (G-4503)

RDO Construction Equipment Co ....D... 952 890-8880
Burnsville (G-784)

Road Machinery & Supplies Co ....D... 952 895-9595
Savage (G-9405)

ROOFING, SIDING & SHEET METAL WORK

A W Kuettel & Sons Inc ....D... 218 722-3901
Duluth (G-1231)

B & B Sheet Metal & Roofing ....E... 763 682-4233
Buffalo (G-635)

Elastomeric Roofing Systems ....E... 763 565-6900
Rockford (G-7300)

Gopher Co Inc ....E... 612 331-1555
Minneapolis (G-4541)

John A Dalsin & Son Inc ....C... 612 729-9334
Minneapolis (G-4768)

Metro Siding Inc ....E... 763 557-1808
Plymouth (G-6873)

Roof Tech Inc ....E... 651 351-7302
Stillwater (G-9636)

Rosenquist Construction Inc ....E... 612 724-1356
Minneapolis (G-5559)

Smidt Sheet Metal Co Inc ....E... 507 378-4080
Racine (G-6967)

Top Notch Siding Co ....E... 612 269-7923
Osseo (G-6677)

Window Concepts of Minnesota ....E... 651 905-0105
Saint Paul (G-7948)

ROOMING & BOARDING HOUSES: Furnished Room Rental

Ace Rental Place ....E... 218 463-2175
Roseau (G-7351)

ROOMING & BOARDING HOUSES: Lodging House, Exc Organization

Minnesota Pipestone ....D... 952 294-5100
Chanhassen (G-932)

RUBBER PRDTS REPAIR SVCS

Cutting Edge Creations Inc ....D... 651 209-8600
Saint Paul (G-7743)

SAFETY EQPT & SPLYS WHOLESALERS

Dan-AM Co ....E... 507 346-7102
Spring Valley (G-9569)

Elvin Safety LLC ....E... 952 829-2950
Eden Prairie (G-1655)

Nardini Fire Equipment Co Inc ....D... 651 483-6631
Saint Paul (G-8735)

Tenacious Holdings Inc ....C... 651 642-9889
Saint Paul (G-9038)

3M Co ....C... 651 736-9682
Saint Paul (G-9052)

SAFETY INSPECTION SVCS

Product Safety Resources Inc ....E... 651 917-6100
Saint Paul (G-8851)

SALES PROMOTION SVCS

D L Ryan Co's Ltd ....E... 612 204-9790
Minneapolis (G-4214)

Lawrence Service Co ....E... 763 383-5700
Minneapolis (G-4850)

2020 Promotions LLC ....E... 651 451-3850
South Saint Paul (G-9545)

Ultra Creative Inc ....E... 612 378-0748
Minneapolis (G-5896)

SAND & GRAVEL

Aggregate Industries Inc ....D... 651 683-0600
Saint Paul (G-7689)

Anchor Block Co ....D... 763 425-9779
Minneapolis (G-3775)

Anchor Block Co ....D... 651 777-8321
Saint Paul (G-8049)

Barton Sand & Gravel Co ....E... 763 425-4191
Osseo (G-6598)

Cemstone Products Co ....E... 651 774-7575
Saint Paul (G-8181)

Fischer Sand & Aggregate LLP ....E... 952 432-7132
Saint Paul (G-7775)

Granite City Ready Mix Inc ....E... 320 252-4322
Saint Cloud (G-7437)

Kielmeyer Construction Inc ....E... 507 334-6088
Nerstrand (G-6402)

R & R Ready Mix Inc ....E... 218 943-4601
Miltona (G-3381)

Tiller Corp ....D... 763 425-4191
Maple Grove (G-3254)

SAND MINING

Fitzgerald Construction ....E... 218 789-7318
Sabin (G-7397)

Kielmeyer Construction Inc ....E... 507 334-6088
Nerstrand (G-6402)

Thull Construction ....E... 320 987-3432
Greenwald (G-2327)

SAND: Silica

Unimin Corp ....D... 507 665-3386
Le Sueur (G-2960)

SANITARY SVCS: Garbage Collecting, Destroying & Processing

Darrell B Johnson Disposal Co ....E... 218 729-5446
Duluth *(G-1291)*

Dick's Sanitation Service Inc ....D... 952 469-2239
Lakeville *(G-2903)*

Gene Bueckers...E... 320 352-2876
Sauk Centre *(G-9346)*

Palmer Bus Services ....E... 952 445-1166
Shakopee *(G-9465)*

Reliakor Services Inc ....E... 952 403-1440
Shakopee *(G-9469)*

Schaap Sanitation Inc...........................E... 507 376-9218
Worthington *(G-10193)*

Tennis Sanitation LLC...........................E... 651 459-1887
Saint Paul Park *(G-9298)*

Veolia Es Solid Waste Midwest ....D... 507 281-5850
Rochester *(G-7280)*

Waste Management of Wisconsin ....C... 952 890-1100
Minneapolis *(G-3639)*

SANITARY SVCS: Hazardous Waste, Collection & Disposal

Pope Douglas Solid Waste Mgt ....E... 320 763-9340
Alexandria *(G-117)*

U S Filter Recovery Services ....E... 651 638-1300
Saint Paul *(G-9099)*

Veit Container Corp ....E... 507 281-3867
Rochester *(G-7279)*

SANITARY SVCS: Incinerator, Operation Of

Minnesota Dakota Generating Co 218 739-8200
Fergus Falls *(G-2096)*

Pope Douglas Solid Waste Mgt ....E... 320 763-9340
Alexandria *(G-117)*

SANITARY SVCS: Refuse Collection & Disposal Svcs

BFI Waste Systems of North ....E... 612 522-6558
Minneapolis *(G-3899)*

BFI Waste Systems of North ....C... 763 259-5570
Circle Pines *(G-1003)*

Browning-Ferris Industries Inc.............E... 651 641-0009
Saint Paul *(G-8134)*

Forest Lake Sanitation Inc ....E... 651 464-2321
Wyoming *(G-10204)*

Hartel's Dbj Disposal Co's LLC ....E... 218 729-5446
Proctor *(G-6963)*

JME Of Monticello Inc............................E... 763 295-3122
Monticello *(G-6275)*

Stericycle Specialty Waste...................E... 612 285-9865
Minneapolis *(G-3608)*

Veolia Es Solid Waste Midwest ....E... 651 459-3029
Saint Paul *(G-9125)*

Waste Management of North MN ....D... 218 624-7838
Duluth *(G-1498)*

SANITARY SVCS: Road, Airport & Parking Lot Sweeping

Carefree Services Inc ....E... 763 479-2600
Maple Plain *(G-3271)*

SANITARY SVCS: Rubbish Collection & Disposal

Allied Waste Industries Inc ....D... 952 941-5174
Eden Prairie *(G-1588)*

Aspen Waste Systems Inc ....E... 612 884-8000
Minneapolis *(G-3819)*

M & M Sanitation Inc..............................E... 320 358-4078
Cambridge *(G-841)*

Veolia Environmental Services.............E... 651 774-0916
Saint Paul *(G-9124)*

Veolia Es Solid Waste Midwest ....D... 507 281-5850
Rochester *(G-7280)*

Veolia Es Solid Waste of Pa ....E... 320 251-8919
Saint Cloud *(G-7444)*

Walter's Recycling & Refuse ....E... 763 780-8464
Minneapolis *(G-3637)*

SANITARY SVCS: Sanitary Landfill, Operation Of

S KB Environmental ....E... 507 433-8131
Austin *(G-285)*

Veit & Co Inc...C... 763 428-2242
Rogers *(G-7347)*

SANITARY SVCS: Sewage Treatment Facility

Water Reclamation Plant.......................E... 507 281-6190
Rochester *(G-7285)*

SANITARY SVCS: Waste Materials, Recycling

American Paper Recycling Corp ....E... 651 644-7806
Saint Paul *(G-8031)*

Appliance Recycling Centers of ....E... 952 930-9000
Minneapolis *(G-3791)*

BFI Waste Systems of North ....E... 651 437-8101
South Saint Paul *(G-9513)*

City of Minneapolis ....E... 612 673-3779
Minneapolis *(G-4089)*

Covanta Energy Group Inc.....................E... 612 333-7303
Minneapolis *(G-4174)*

Deer River Hired Hands Inc...................E... 218 246-8182
Deer River *(G-1169)*

Dem-Con Landfill LLC ....E... 952 445-5755
Shakopee *(G-9436)*

Dick's Sanitation Service Inc ....D... 952 469-2239
Lakeville *(G-2903)*

Endres Services Inc ....D... 651 438-3113
Rosemount *(G-7369)*

Goodwill Industries Inc ....C... 651 379-5800
Saint Paul *(G-8421)*

Goodwill Industries Inc ....E... 952 953-4410
Saint Paul *(G-7787)*

Goodwill Industries Inc ....E... 651 439-4207
Stillwater *(G-9620)*

Jmdl Inc ....E... 952 873-2636
Belle Plaine *(G-373)*

Liberty Paper Inc ....D... 763 261-6100
Becker *(G-356)*

M & M Sanitation Inc..............................E... 320 358-4078
Cambridge *(G-841)*

Minnesota Shredding LLC ....E... 763 493-3007
Minneapolis *(G-5093)*

Neighborhood Recycling Corp ....E... 651 222-7678
Minneapolis *(G-5181)*

Pope Douglas Solid Waste Mgt ....E... 320 763-9340
Alexandria *(G-117)*

Rock-Tenn Co..A... 651 641-4874
Saint Paul *(G-8910)*

Schaap Sanitation Inc...........................E... 507 376-9218
Worthington *(G-10193)*

Schwartzman Co Inc...............................E... 763 421-1187
Anoka *(G-224)*

Tires To Fuel LLC 218 624-5009
Duluth *(G-1485)*

Veolia Es Solid Waste Midwest ....D... 507 281-5850
Rochester *(G-7280)*

Waste Management of North MN ....D... 218 624-7838
Duluth *(G-1498)*

SAVINGS & LOAN ASSOCIATIONS, NOT FEDERALLY CHARTERED

1st United Bank ....E... 507 334-2201
Faribault *(G-2008)*

SAVINGS INSTITUTIONS: Federally Chartered

Bremer Bank..E... 218 847-9292
Detroit Lakes *(G-1189)*

Federal Reserve Bank of ....A... 612 204-5000
Minneapolis *(G-4421)*

First Federal Capital Bank.....................D... 507 285-2600
Rochester *(G-7113)*

First Federal Capital Bank.....................D... 651 646-8681
Saint Paul *(G-8380)*

Ing Bank Fsb ....B... 320 229-4200
Saint Cloud *(G-7531)*

Midcountry Bank Inc...............................952 997-5608
Minnetonka *(G-6195)*

TCF Equipment Finance Inc...................E... 952 934-4404
Hopkins *(G-2642)*

Winthrop Resources Corp ....D... 952 936-0226
Minnetonka *(G-6237)*

SCAFFOLDING WHOLESALERS

Advance Shoring Co................................E... 651 489-8881
Saint Paul *(G-7988)*

SCHOOL BUS SVC

Advance America Services Inc ....E... 952 544-7273
Minneapolis *(G-3685)*

Albert Lea Bus Co Inc............................E... 507 373-1467
Albert Lea *(G-30)*

Anderson Bus & Coach Inc....................D... 218 334-3171
Frazee *(G-2182)*

Benjamin Bus Inc....................................E... 507 645-5720
Northfield *(G-6516)*

Bernard Bus Service Inc ....E... 507 867-3410
Chatfield *(G-987)*

Brown Transportation Inc ....E... 218 744-2888
Eveleth *(G-1929)*

Christianson Bus Service Inc ....E... 218 863-7000
Pelican Rapids *(G-6776)*

Clemons Bus Line Inc ....E... 507 833-4438
Waseca *(G-9874)*

Cloquet Transit Co Inc ....E... 218 879-3391
Cloquet *(G-1049)*

Don's Bus Service Inc ....E... 763 497-2585
Albertville *(G-74)*

Faribault Transportation Co ....E... 507 334-5121
Faribault *(G-2005)*

First Student Inc ....C... 507 289-4541
Rochester *(G-7114)*

First Student Inc ....E... 763 389-2342
Princeton *(G-6909)*

First Student Inc ....D... 763 421-5785
Champlin *(G-893)*

First Student Inc ....D... 763 682-5530
Buffalo *(G-644)*

First Student Inc ....E... 763 717-9447
Minneapolis *(G-3469)*

First Student Inc ....E... 651 645-1959
Saint Paul *(G-8382)*

First Student Inc ....C... 763 559-8111
Saint Paul *(G-8383)*

First Student Inc ....C... 763 421-3199
Anoka *(G-182)*

First Student Inc ....E... 952 475-0038
Long Lake *(G-3024)*

Guardian School Bus Co ....E... 320 259-8225
Saint Cloud *(G-7438)*

Hoglund Transportation Inc ....E... 763 295-3604
Monticello *(G-6274)*

Independent School District...................D... 320 762-2148
Alexandria *(G-105)*

Isensee Bus Service ....E... 320 732-2795
Long Prairie *(G-3043)*

Luverne Ind School Dist 2184 ....E... 507 283-8197
Luverne *(G-3061)*

M & M Bus Service Inc ....E... 320 274-8313
Annandale *(G-142)*

Manske Bus Service Inc.........................E... 507 243-3282
Madison Lake *(G-3080)*

Metropolitan School & Charter..............C... 218 724-1707
Duluth *(G-1392)*

Midwest Motor & Equipment Inc ....E... 952 955-1962
Watertown *(G-9892)*

Minnesota City Bus Service Inc ....E... 507 454-5871
Minnesota City *(G-6136)*

Minnesota Motor Bus Inc........................E... 507 238-4454
Fairmont *(G-1977)*

Minnetonka Transportation Inc ....D... 952 935-1990
Minnetonka *(G-6199)*

New Ulm Bus Lines Inc ....E... 507 354-4711
New Ulm *(G-6465)*

Ossel Brooklyn Bus Co Inc ....D... 952 891-1031
Saint Paul *(G-7861)*

Osseo Brooklyn School Bus Co ....C... 763 425-2542
Osseo *(G-6647)*

Ottertail Coaches Inc..............................D... 218 739-3393
Fergus Falls *(G-2112)*

Owatonna Bus Co Inc ....D... 507 451-5262
Owatonna *(G-6725)*

Palmer Bus Service ....E... 320 847-3109
Clara City *(G-1032)*

Palmer Bus Service ....E... 320 528-2670
Barrett *(G-309)*

Palmer Bus Service Inc ....E... 507 477-3014
Hayfield *(G-2425)*

Palmer Bus Service of St ....E... 507 931-1811
Saint Peter *(G-9311)*

Palmer Bus Services ....E... 952 445-1166
Shakopee *(G-9465)*

Palmer Charter Service Inc....................E... 320 632-1555
Little Falls *(G-3017)*

Peterson Bus Princeton.........................D... 763 631-5315
Princeton *(G-6914)*

Peterson Bus Service Inc ....E... 320 354-2414
New London *(G-6418)*

Prior Lake Bus Association....................D... 952 440-1166
Prior Lake *(G-6949)*

Ready Bus Line Co Inc............................D... 507 895-2349
La Crescent *(G-2843)*

Red River Trails Inc ....E... 218 236-0300
Moorhead *(G-6337)*

Rehbein Transit Inc ....C... 651 484-1809
Circle Pines *(G-1021)*

Reichert Enterprises Inc ....C... 218 829-6955
Brainerd *(G-584)*

Richmond Bus Service Inc ....E... 320 597-2055
Richmond *(G-7041)*

Safe-Way Bus Co....................................D... 651 451-1375
Inver Grove Heights *(G-2767)*

Shubat Transportation Co ....E... 218 262-1042
Hibbing *(G-2475)*

Southwest Coaches Inc ....D... 507 532-4043
Marshall *(G-3328)*

Employment codes: A=Over 500 employees, B=251-500,
C=101-250, D=51-100, E=25-50

2011 Harris Minnesota
Services Directory

© Harris InfoSource 1-866-281-6415
761

SERVICES

SCHOOL BUS SVC

Spanier Bus Service Inc ....E... 320 251-3313
Saint Cloud *(G-7596)*

St James Bus Service Inc ....E... 507 375-4181
Saint James *(G-7646)*

Stahlke Bus Service Inc ....E... 763 972-3991
Delano *(G-1183)*

Stier Transport Services Inc ....E... 952 873-2362
Belle Plaine *(G-371)*

Thielen Bus Lines Inc ....E... 507 637-3600
Redwood Falls *(G-7028)*

Town & Country Bus Co Inc ....D... 763 786-2510
Minneapolis *(G-3620)*

Trobec's Bus Service Inc ....D... 320 251-1202
Saint Stephen *(G-9317)*

Vision of Elk River Inc ....C... 763 441-4420
Elk River *(G-1895)*

Yaeger Bus Service Inc ....E... 507 345-5470
Mankato *(G-3221)*

SCHOOL SPLYS, EXC BOOKS: *Wholesalers*

Central Minnesota Erdc Inc...................E... 320 202-0992
Saint Cloud *(G-7408)*

Corporate Express Office Prdts ....C... 651 636-2250
Saint Paul *(G-8251)*

SCIENTIFIC INSTRUMENTS WHOLESALERS

Hysitron Inc ....D... 952 835-6366
Eden Prairie *(G-1689)*

Omicron Associates ....C... 952 345-5240
Eden Prairie *(G-1737)*

SCRAP & WASTE MATERIALS, WHOLESALE: *Ferrous Metal*

American Iron & Steel Co Inc.................E... 612 529-9221
Minneapolis *(G-3755)*

SCRAP & WASTE MATERIALS, WHOLESALE: *Junk & Scrap*

Crosstown Used Auto Parts ....E... 612 861-3020
Saint Paul *(G-8270)*

Fridley Auto Parts Inc ....D... 763 784-8890
Minneapolis *(G-3472)*

SCRAP & WASTE MATERIALS, WHOLESALE: *Metal*

Alter Trading Corp ....E... 507 387-6504
Mankato *(G-3103)*

Great Western Uron & Metal Co ....E... 651 224-4877
Saint Paul *(G-8428)*

Kirschbaum-Krupp Metal ....E... 612 521-9212
Minneapolis *(G-4812)*

Schwartzman Co Inc ....E... 763 421-1187
Anoka *(G-224)*

SCRAP & WASTE MATERIALS, WHOLESALE: *Nonferrous Metals Scrap*

American Iron & Steel Co Inc.................E... 612 529-9221
Minneapolis *(G-3755)*

SCRAP & WASTE MATERIALS, WHOLESALE: *Paper*

Minnesota Shredding LLC ....E... 763 493-3007
Minneapolis *(G-5093)*

Pioneer Industries Inc ....D... 612 374-2280
Minneapolis *(G-5383)*

Rock-Tenn Co ....A... 651 641-4874
Saint Paul *(G-8910)*

SCRAP & WASTE MATERIALS, WHOLESALE: *Rags*

Rag Minneapolis Stock Co....................D... 612 333-6576
Minneapolis *(G-5460)*

SCRAP & WASTE MATERIALS, WHOLESALE: *Textile*

Pioneer Industries Inc ....D... 612 374-2280
Minneapolis *(G-5383)*

SEARCH & RESCUE SVCS

St Louis, County of Inc ....E... 218 349-8970
Duluth *(G-1466)*

SECRETARIAL & COURT REPORTING

Fedex Office & Print Services...............C... 952 593-1143
Hopkins *(G-2542)*

Schawk Inc ....E... 651 636-0611
Saint Paul *(G-8933)*

SECRETARIAL SVCS

Eggleston Medscribe Inc......................E... 763 971-5000
Minneapolis *(G-4330)*

Minnesota Clerical Inc ....C... 763 753-7243
Anoka *(G-205)*

Northern Counties Secretarial ....D... 763 427-0166
Anoka *(G-210)*

7 West Secretarial Answering...............E... 952 936-4000
Eden Prairie *(G-1775)*

Soap Transcription Services ....E... 612 706-1588
Minneapolis *(G-5693)*

SECURE STORAGE SVC: *Document*

Business Data Record Services............E... 651 631-8663
Saint Paul *(G-8142)*

Granite City Armored Car Inc ....E... 320 252-0708
Sauk Rapids *(G-9364)*

Iron Mountain Information MGT ....C... 952 888-3852
Minneapolis *(G-4735)*

Xiotech Corp...E... 952 983-3000
Eden Prairie *(G-1819)*

SECURITIES DEALING

Ameriprise Financial Inc ....A... 612 671-3131
Minneapolis *(G-3767)*

Dain Rauscher Inc.................................A... 612 371-2711
Minneapolis *(G-4217)*

Mid American Financial Group ....D... 952 258-5000
Minnetonka *(G-6194)*

Mjsk Investment Securities ....E... 763 542-3700
Minneapolis *(G-5111)*

Piper Jaffray Co's ....A... 612 303-6000
Minneapolis *(G-5384)*

Rbc Wealth Management ....A... 612 371-7750
Minneapolis *(G-5472)*

SECURITY & COMMODITY EXCHANGES: *Futures, Contract*

Minneapolis Grain Exchange.................E... 612 321-7101
Minneapolis *(G-5056)*

SECURITY DISTRIBUTORS

Ameriprise Financial Inc ....A... 612 671-3131
Minneapolis *(G-3767)*

SECURITY GUARD SVCS

Allied Security LLC ....D... 651 604-9414
Saint Paul *(G-8013)*

Arnage Security Services LLC...............D... 763 269-8440
Minneapolis *(G-3409)*

Avalon Fortress Security Svcs ....C... 763 767-9111
Minneapolis *(G-3841)*

Deco Inc ....A... 763 576-9572
Champlin *(G-892)*

Delta Protective Services ....E... 612 331-1885
Minneapolis *(G-4246)*

G4s Secure Solutions Inc.....................B... 651 482-1928
Saint Paul *(G-8399)*

General Security Services Corp ....D... 952 858-5000
Minneapolis *(G-4517)*

Guardsmark LLC...................................D... 952 831-3151
Minneapolis *(G-4578)*

Gulf Northern Inc ....E... 952 278-1501
Minnetonka *(G-6178)*

Hannon Security Services Inc ....B... 952 881-5865
Minneapolis *(G-4595)*

Heartland Information Services.............E... 612 371-9255
Minneapolis *(G-4626)*

Inner State Protection Inc ....E... 651 771-1501
Minnetonka *(G-6180)*

Securitas Security Services ....C... 218 727-7870
Duluth *(G-1446)*

Talon Investigation Ltd..........................E... 651 774-6977
Saint Paul *(G-9026)*

Twin City Security Inc ....B... 763 784-4160
Minneapolis *(G-3625)*

SECURITY PROTECTIVE DEVICES MAINTENANCE & MONITORING SVCS

Checkpoint Security Systems ....C... 952 942-9431
Chanhassen *(G-914)*

Checkpoint Systems Inc ....E... 952 227-5350
Chaska *(G-958)*

Checkpoint Systems Inc ....C... 952 943-3853
Chanhassen *(G-915)*

SECURITY SYSTEMS SERVICES

AAF-Mcquay Inc....................................B... 763 553-5330
Minneapolis *(G-3655)*

Century Systems Inc ....E... 651 426-0975
Saint Paul *(G-8185)*

Floyd Lock & Safe Co............................E... 952 881-5625
Minneapolis *(G-4457)*

Floyd Total Security ....E... 320 654-9549
Saint Cloud *(G-7511)*

Parsons Electric LLC ....C... 763 571-8000
Minneapolis *(G-3565)*

Sentry Systems Inc ....E... 651 426-4627
White Bear Lake *(G-9977)*

Silent Knight Security Systems ....E... 952 881-0038
Minneapolis *(G-5673)*

Simplexgrinnell LP ....E... 320 253-8883
Saint Cloud *(G-7427)*

Systemarmed Usacom Inc ....A... 877 900-0238
Minneapolis *(G-5782)*

Trust Security ....E... 952 914-9300
Minneapolis *(G-5860)*

Videotronix Inc.....................................D... 952 894-5343
Burnsville *(G-818)*

Westco Systems Inc ....E... 763 559-7046
Minneapolis *(G-6057)*

Wright-Hennepin Security Corp ....C... 763 477-3000
Rockford *(G-7306)*

SECURITY UNDERWRITERS

Dain Rauscher Inc ....A... 612 371-2711
Minneapolis *(G-4217)*

Rbc Wealth Management ....A... 612 371-7750
Minneapolis *(G-5472)*

SEEDING SVCS, LAWN

Alex Irrigation Inc ....E... 320 852-7595
Carlos *(G-866)*

Q3 Contracting Inc ....B... 651 224-2424
Saint Paul *(G-8859)*

Weerts Construction Inc ....E... 507 893-3313
Winnebago *(G-10078)*

SEEDS & BULBS WHOLESALERS

Farm Country Co-Op ....E... 507 356-8313
Pine Island *(G-6816)*

SELF-HELP GROUP HOME

Fountain Lake Treatment Center ....D... 507 373-2384
Albert Lea *(G-52)*

Hillside Homes......................................E... 218 720-5890
Duluth *(G-1352)*

New Challenges Inc ....E... 651 681-2044
Saint Paul *(G-7849)*

R E M North Star Inc ....E... 218 435-6088
Fosston *(G-2179)*

Safe Haven Shelter For Youth ....E... 952 288-2680
Shakopee *(G-9472)*

Willow Home ....D... 507 426-8277
Fairfax *(G-1956)*

SELF-HELP ORGANIZATION, NEC

Conect Project ....E... 763 476-8477
Minneapolis *(G-4152)*

Dodge County Battered Women's ....E... 507 634-6070
Kasson *(G-2820)*

Glenwood-Lyndale Community Ctr ....D... 612 342-1500
Minneapolis *(G-4530)*

Medeligible Services ....D... 763 585-8400
Minneapolis *(G-4983)*

SERVICES, NEC

A Brighter Christmas ....E... 651 808-7495
Apple Valley *(G-242)*

ABC Co's ....D... 877 737-2221
Faribault *(G-1987)*

Alden Area Food Shelf ....E... 507 377-3683
Alden *(G-78)*

Caspar Inc ....E... 507 842-5978
Brewster *(G-604)*

Denco II LLC..E... 320 589-2931
Morris *(G-6371)*

Hsi Human Services Inc........................E... 651 275-4302
Stillwater *(G-9622)*

Multi Venue Production Inc ....E... 952 894-9111
Saint Paul *(G-7847)*

National Initiatives For ....E... 763 229-2753
Minneapolis *(G-5165)*

Riverview Apartments Senior ....B... 651 291-1750
Minneapolis *(G-5546)*

SEWAGE FACILITIES

New Ulm, City of Inc ....D... 507 359-8264
New Ulm *(G-6470)*

Western Lake Superior Sanitary ....D... 218 722-3336
Duluth *(G-1502)*

SEWER CLEANING & RODDING SVC

Infrastructure Technologies ....E... 763 428-6488
Rogers *(G-7327)*

Roto-Rooter Services Co ....E... 651 738-8355
Saint Paul *(G-9271)*

SEWING CONTRACTORS

Accessability Inc...............................D... 612 331-5958
Minneapolis *(G-3667)*

Imago Ltd ....D... 651 690-9724
Saint Paul *(G-8506)*

SIS Enterprises Inc ....C... 763 789-0956
Minneapolis *(G-5679)*

SEWING MACHINE REPAIR SHOP

and Sew On Inc 651 439-9311
Stillwater *(G-9596)*

SHELTERED WORKSHOPS

Ability Building Center ....C... 507 281-6262
Rochester *(G-7043)*

Cedar Valley Services Inc ....D... 507 451-5897
Owatonna *(G-6698)*

Cedar Valley Services Inc ....E... 507 377-2893
Albert Lea *(G-43)*

Child Care Choices Inc ....E... 320 251-5081
Saint Cloud *(G-7491)*

Connections of Moorhead...................D... 218 233-8657
Moorhead *(G-6307)*

Employment Enterprises Inc ....D... 320 632-9251
Little Falls *(G-3002)*

Opportunity Partners Inc...................C... 952 938-5511
Hopkins *(G-2595)*

Pine Habilitation & Supported ....E... 320 245-2246
Sandstone *(G-9325)*

Vail Place 612 824-8061
Minneapolis *(G-5954)*

Vision Loss Resources Inc ....C... 612 871-2222
Minneapolis *(G-5976)*

SHIPPING AGENTS

Sears Logistics Services Inc ....E... 612 379-5600
Minneapolis *(G-5623)*

SHOES & BOOTS WHOLESALERS

Minnetonka Moccasin Co Inc...............D... 612 331-8493
Minneapolis *(G-5102)*

SHOPPING CENTERS & MALLS

Brookfield Development Inc ....E... 612 372-1230
Minneapolis *(G-3958)*

Carver-Scott Cooperative...................E... 952 445-7524
Shakopee *(G-9429)*

Fitgers On The Lake LLC ....C... 218 727-9077
Duluth *(G-1325)*

Lansing Mall LP................................E... 763 566-3373
Minneapolis *(G-4842)*

Lansing Mall LP................................D... 320 252-2856
Saint Cloud *(G-7543)*

Moac Mall Holdings LLC ....A... 952 883-8810
Bloomington *(G-507)*

Tamarack Village Shopping Cent ....E... 651 702-6311
Saint Paul *(G-9280)*

SIGN LETTERING & PAINTING SVCS

Argenbright Inc ....C... 320 543-3737
Howard Lake *(G-2665)*

SIGN PAINTING & LETTERING SHOP

Scenic Sign Corp ....E... 320 252-9400
Sauk Rapids *(G-9373)*

SIGNS, EXC ELECTRIC, WHOLESALE

Skyline Displays Midwest Inc ....E... 952 895-6000
Burnsville *(G-798)*

SILK SCREEN DESIGN SVCS

Lakeshirts Inc..................................B... 218 847-2171
Detroit Lakes *(G-1205)*

SKATING RINKS: Roller

Xenophon Corp ....E... 952 929-5518
Minneapolis *(G-6092)*

Xenophon Corp ....E... 651 735-6214
Saint Paul *(G-9291)*

SKI LODGE

Afton Alps Inc..................................A... 651 436-5245
Hastings *(G-2412)*

Beltrami's Tally Inc ....E... 218 243-2231
Bemidji *(G-376)*

Buck Hill Inc 952 435-7174
Burnsville *(G-688)*

City of Duluth ....B... 218 628-2891
Duluth *(G-1275)*

Quarterdeck Resort & Rest ....D... 218 963-7537
Nisswa *(G-6494)*

SKILL TRAINING CENTER

Accessability Inc..............................D... 612 331-5958
Minneapolis *(G-3667)*

Homes of Minnesota Educational ....E... 763 543-6978
Minneapolis *(G-4670)*

Industries Inc...................................E... 320 679-2354
Mora *(G-6361)*

Mille Lacs Cty Area ....E... 320 983-2162
Milaca *(G-3380)*

Pinewood Cloquet.............................E... 218 879-4566
Cloquet *(G-1060)*

Prairieland Utility ....E... 507 625-2404
North Mankato *(G-6513)*

Step Inc ....E... 507 238-4341
Fairmont *(G-1982)*

Twin Cities Rise ....E... 612 338-0295
Minneapolis *(G-5873)*

SLAUGHTERING, CUSTOM, LIVESTOCK SVCS

Lorentz Etc Inc ....D... 507 263-3618
Cannon Falls *(G-857)*

Schmidt's Meat Market Inc ....E... 507 232-3438
Nicollet *(G-6491)*

SMALL BUSINESS INVESTMENT COMPANIES

Wells Fargo Bank, National...................E... 612 667-2753
Minneapolis *(G-6039)*

SNOW PLOWING SVCS

A-Scape Inc ....E... 952 496-1178
Shakopee *(G-9417)*

AAA All American Lawn ....E... 763 537-5733
Anoka *(G-145)*

Asphalt Surface Technologies ....D... 320 363-8500
Saint Joseph *(G-7650)*

Carefree Services Inc ....E... 763 479-2600
Maple Plain *(G-3271)*

Ferguson Brothers Excavating...............E... 320 762-0622
Alexandria *(G-101)*

Heikes Enterprises Inc ....E... 651 437-3847
Hastings *(G-2391)*

Lawn Professionals & Treasures ....E... 651 482-1431
Saint Paul *(G-8567)*

Outdoor Environments Inc...................E... 952 496-1000
Savage *(G-9403)*

Premier Co's Inc...............................E... 218 348-1991
Duluth *(G-1429)*

Reliakor Services Inc ....E... 952 403-1440
Shakopee *(G-9469)*

Wagner Sod Co Inc ....E... 651 457-6037
Inver Grove Heights *(G-2773)*

SNOWMOBILE REPAIR SVCS

Smith's Winter Products ....E... 763 493-3332
Osseo *(G-6665)*

SOCIAL CHANGE ASSOCIATION

Alexandra House Inc ....E... 763 780-2332
Minneapolis *(G-3388)*

Alpha Human Services Inc...................E... 612 872-8218
Minneapolis *(G-3732)*

American Swedish Institute ....E... 612 871-4907
Minneapolis *(G-3760)*

Anoka County Community Action........E... 763 783-4747
Minneapolis *(G-3403)*

C C R Inc 218 236-6730
Moorhead *(G-6301)*

Clark Lake Homes Inc........................E... 218 833-1322
Brainerd *(G-559)*

Elder Network...................................C... 507 285-5272
Rochester *(G-7105)*

Greater Twin Cities United Way...........C... 612 340-7481
Minneapolis *(G-4562)*

Hutchinson Area Health Care ....A... 320 234-5000
Hutchinson *(G-2698)*

SOCIAL SVCS CENTER (continued)

Inter-County Community Council ....E... 218 796-5144
Oklee *(G-6557)*

International Twins Assoc ....D... 763 571-3022
Minneapolis *(G-3501)*

Jackson County Developmental ....E... 507 662-6156
Lakefield *(G-2882)*

Jeremiah Program ....E... 612 692-8711
Minneapolis *(G-4759)*

Minnesota Institute of Public...............E... 763 427-5310
Saint Paul *(G-8691)*

Minnesota State Colleges ....E... 218 681-2181
Thief River Falls *(G-9675)*

P H M Eaglecrest Inc ....D... 651 631-6009
Saint Paul *(G-8798)*

Prairie Island Tribal Council ....D... 651 385-2554
Welch *(G-9956)*

Turning Point Foundation...................E... 612 520-4004
Minneapolis *(G-5868)*

SOCIAL CLUBS

AA Monticello...................................E... 763 295-5066
Monticello *(G-6265)*

Kitchi Gammi Club ....D... 218 724-8589
Duluth *(G-1371)*

Midwest Cleaning & Restoration...........E... 763 533-3723
Minneapolis *(G-5026)*

Minnesota Association of ....E... 651 290-7462
Saint Paul *(G-8672)*

University Club of St Paul...................D... 651 222-1751
Saint Paul *(G-9112)*

Woman's Club of Minneapolis ....D... 612 870-8001
Minneapolis *(G-6084)*

YMCA of Greater Saint Paul ....C... 651 683-4713
Saint Paul *(G-7952)*

YMCA of Greater Saint Paul ....E... 612 465-0450
Minneapolis *(G-6100)*

YMCA of Greater Saint Paul ....E... 651 771-8881
Saint Paul *(G-9174)*

YMCA of Greater St Paul.....................C... 651 731-9507
Saint Paul *(G-9292)*

SOCIAL SERVICES INFORMATION EXCHANGE

Churches United In Ministry ....E... 218 720-6521
Duluth *(G-1271)*

County of Todd ....D... 320 732-4500
Long Prairie *(G-3040)*

Human Services.................................E... 218 935-2568
Mahnomen *(G-3087)*

Metropolitan Ctr For ....D... 651 646-8342
Saint Paul *(G-8642)*

SOCIAL SERVICES, NEC

Chyrsalis of Kandiyohi County...........E... 320 231-1480
Willmar *(G-9998)*

Citireach International ....E... 952 975-0516
Eden Prairie *(G-1628)*

Community Acton of Minneapolis ....E... 612 335-5837
Minneapolis *(G-4138)*

Otter Tail County Human Svcs...............D... 218 998-8150
Fergus Falls *(G-2106)*

Seward CSP ....E... 612 333-0331
Minneapolis *(G-5645)*

Society of Corporate ....E... 952 405-7925
Minneapolis *(G-5694)*

White Earth Reservation ....D... 218 983-3387
Ogema *(G-6555)*

SOCIAL SVCS CENTER

Anoka County Community Action ....C... 763 783-4747
Minneapolis *(G-3404)*

ARC Greater Twin Cities ....D... 612 861-9550
Minneapolis *(G-3797)*

ARC Greater Twin Cities ....E... 952 920-0855
Saint Paul *(G-8057)*

Bi-County Community Action ....E... 218 751-4631
Bemidji *(G-382)*

Catholic Charities of The ....E... 612 664-8500
Minneapolis *(G-4028)*

Children's Home Society ....B... 651 646-7771
Saint Paul *(G-8196)*

Community Action Council Inc ....E... 952 985-5300
Burnsville *(G-701)*

Community Action of ....E... 612 348-8858
Minneapolis *(G-4137)*

Community Action Partnership...........C... 651 645-6445
Saint Paul *(G-8237)*

Freeport West Inc ....D... 612 824-3040
Minneapolis *(G-4486)*

Greater Minneapolis Council of ....E... 612 721-8687
Minneapolis *(G-4559)*

Human Services Inc In WA ....C... 651 777-5222
Saint Paul *(G-9233)*

Employment codes: A=Over 500 employees, B=251-500,
C=101-250, D=51-100, E=25-50

2011 Harris Minnesota
Services Directory

© Harris InfoSource 1-866-281-6415
763

SERVICES

Lutheran Social Service of MN ....E... 320 235-5411
Willmar (G-10020)

Minnesota Aids Project ....E... 612 341-2060
Minneapolis (G-5066)

Nonviolent Peaceforce ....E... 612 871-0005
Minneapolis (G-5205)

Northwest Community Action Inc ....D... 218 528-3258
Badger (G-299)

Quality Care Services Inc....................D... 320 230-7275
Saint Cloud (G-7577)

Sabathani Community Center................D... 612 821-2300
Minneapolis (G-5584)

St Louis, County of Inc.......................B... 218 726-2000
Duluth (G-1464)

Tubman...D... 612 871-0118
Minneapolis (G-5863)

Vietnamese Social Services of ....E... 651 644-1317
Saint Paul (G-9127)

Youthlink..E... 612 252-1200
Minneapolis (G-6108)

SOCIAL SVCS, HANDICAPPED

Baker Laura Services Assn..................C... 507 645-8866
Northfield (G-6524)

Community Involvement Programs .....E... 952 854-4007
Minneapolis (G-4144)

Empowerment Services of MN ....E... 218 724-4014
Duluth (G-1312)

Lakes Homes & Program Devpt ....E... 218 739-4322
Fergus Falls (G-2085)

Lifeworks Services Inc ....E... 763 746-3330
Minneapolis (G-4883)

Minnesota Department of ....C... 651 642-0503
Saint Paul (G-8681)

Oak Ridge Homes of Wadena Inc........E... 218 327-1877
Grand Rapids (G-2304)

Partnership Resources Inc ....E... 612 331-2075
Minneapolis (G-5345)

REM-Ramsey Inc................................A... 952 925-5067
Minneapolis (G-5514)

Udac Inc ....D... 218 722-5867
Duluth (G-1489)

Wacosa ....D... 320 251-0087
Waite Park (G-9848)

SOCIAL SVCS: Individual & Family

Adult Client Training Service ....E... 320 523-5666
Olivia (G-6559)

AIN Dah Yung Center...........................E... 651 227-4184
Saint Paul (G-8001)

Albert Lea Family YMCA ....E... 507 373-8228
Albert Lea (G-31)

Alexandra House Inc ....E... 763 780-2332
Minneapolis (G-3388)

Andrew Residence Management..........C... 612 333-0111
Minneapolis (G-3779)

Applewood Pointe Senior Co Op..........E... 651 636-2161
Saint Paul (G-8055)

Arcanoka Ramsey & Suburban ARC....D... 952 890-3057
Minneapolis (G-3799)

Archdiocese of Saint Paul....................D... 763 425-2210
Minneapolis (G-3800)

Barnabas Health Care Services...........C... 218 829-0901
Brainerd (G-551)

Birthright of Austin Inc.......................E... 507 437-2373
Austin (G-263)

Bois Forte Reservation Tribal ....E... 218 757-3261
Nett Lake (G-6404)

Boys & Girls Club of Rochester ....E... 507 287-2300
Rochester (G-7067)

Boys & Girls Clubs of Central..............C... 320 252-7616
Saint Cloud (G-7463)

Brain Injury Association of MN............E... 612 378-2742
Minneapolis (G-3937)

Bridge For Youth................................D... 612 377-8800
Minneapolis (G-3944)

Brown County Probation Dept..............E... 507 233-6628
New Ulm (G-6444)

Camp Widji Wagan..............................E... 218 365-2117
Ely (G-1912)

Catholic Charities of The.....................E... 320 259-8757
Saint Cloud (G-7475)

Catholic Charities of The.....................E... 218 739-9325
Fergus Falls (G-2066)

Catholic Charities of The.....................C... 612 827-6241
Minneapolis (G-4030)

Catholic Charities of The Dioc.............E... 320 240-3337
Saint Cloud (G-7476)

Central Minnesota Mental ....E... 763 682-4400
Buffalo (G-641)

Common Sense Services For ....E... 651 552-0288
South Saint Paul (G-9524)

Community Action Partnership ....C... 651 645-6445
Saint Paul (G-8237)

County of Kanabec ....E... 320 679-6430
Mora (G-6355)

County of Mille Lacs ....E... 763 389-5828
Princeton (G-6904)

County of Ramsey ....C... 651 266-2400
Saint Paul (G-8260)

County of Stearns ....E... 320 202-2100
Saint Cloud (G-7494)

County of Washington........................B... 651 430-6800
Stillwater (G-9605)

County of Winona ....E... 507 457-6410
Winona (G-10091)

County of Winona ....E... 507 457-6200
Winona (G-10090)

Deafblind Services Minnesota 612 362-8454
Minneapolis (G-4236)

Divine House Inc ....D... 320 589-3652
Morris (G-6372)

Duluth Area Family YMCA....................E... 218 722-4745
Duluth (G-1297)

Dungarvin Illinois Inc.........................D... 651 699-6050
Saint Paul (G-8312)

Dungarvin Minnesota Inc ....B... 651 699-6050
Saint Paul (G-8313)

Dungarvin New Mexico Inc ....E... 651 699-6050
Saint Paul (G-8314)

East Suburban Resources Inc ....D... 651 464-5137
Stillwater (G-9612)

Elder Network....................................C... 507 285-5272
Rochester (G-7105)

Eleah Medical Centre..........................D... 218 685-4461
Elbow Lake (G-1852)

Family & Children's Service.................E... 612 729-0340
Minneapolis (G-4406)

Family Means ....E... 651 439-4840
Stillwater (G-9616)

Family Partnership..............................E... 612 339-9101
Minneapolis (G-4411)

Family Partnership..............................E... 952 884-7353
Minneapolis (G-4412)

Family Service Center Inc ....E... 320 564-2211
Granite Falls (G-2315)

Fraser Child & Family Center...............A... 612 331-9413
Minneapolis (G-4479)

Global Volunteers ....E... 651 407-6100
Saint Paul (G-8415)

Greater Twin Cities United Way...........C... 612 340-7400
Minneapolis (G-4561)

Hastings YMCA....................................E... 651 480-8887
Hastings (G-2390)

Hmong American Partnership ....E... 651 495-9160
Saint Paul (G-8489)

Home & Community Options Inc..........E... 507 454-5690
Winona (G-10104)

Hospice of The Twin Cities Inc ....D... 763 531-2424
Minneapolis (G-4679)

Human Services of Fairbault ....D... 507 238-4757
Fairmont (G-1975)

Independent School District ....E... 651 385-8000
Red Wing (G-6986)

Integrity Living Options Inc ....E... 952 920-9291
Minneapolis (G-4715)

Inter-County Community Council.........E... 218 796-5144
Oklee (G-6557)

Itasca County Family Young................D... 218 327-1161
Grand Rapids (G-2287)

Jewish Family & Children's Svc ....D... 952 546-0616
Hopkins (G-2562)

Keystone Community Services ....D... 651 645-0349
Saint Paul (G-8548)

Kinderberry Hill ....E... 763 404-1070
Minneapolis (G-4808)

Lakes & Pines Community Action........E... 320 679-1800
Mora (G-6365)

Lao Family Community of MN 651 221-0069
Saint Paul (G-8561)

Lee Carlson Center For Mental............E... 763 780-3036
Fridley (G-2193)

Lifetrack Resources Inc ....D... 651 227-8471
Saint Paul (G-8586)

Lincoln, Lyon, & Murray Human ....D... 507 532-1239
Marshall (G-3306)

Lrn Associates Management Inc ....E... 507 836-8955
Slayton (G-9488)

Lutheran Social Service of MN ....D... 612 871-0221
Minneapolis (G-4912)

Lutheran Social Service of MN ....C... 218 736-5431
Fergus Falls (G-2089)

Lutheran Social Service Of MN............D... 651 642-5990
Saint Paul (G-8598)

Lyngblomsten.....................................B... 651 646-2941
Saint Paul (G-8599)

M Dm Rubicon Inc..............................E... 651 731-8621
Saint Paul (G-9245)

Mary T Inc ....E... 763 754-2505
Minneapolis (G-3530)

Meridian Services Inc..........................E... 320 255-5151
Saint Cloud (G-7550)

Midway Training Services Inc ....D... 651 641-0709
Saint Paul (G-8656)

Minneapolis Urban League Inc............E... 612 302-3100
Minneapolis (G-5065)

Minnesota Autism Center ....C... 952 767-4200
Minnetonka (G-6196)

Minnesota Department of Human ....A... 218 828-2379
Brainerd (G-575)

Minnesota Indian Womens ....E... 612 728-2000
Minneapolis (G-5078)

Minnesota Valley Action ....D... 507 345-6822
Mankato (G-3172)

Mothers & Children Program Mac........E... 651 484-8241
Saint Paul (G-8724)

Naomi Family Center...........................E... 651 222-7962
Saint Paul (G-8734)

National Multiple Sclerosis ....E... 612 335-7900
Minneapolis (G-5167)

Northeast Residence Inc......................B... 651 765-0217
Saint Paul (G-8756)

Northland Chapter American Red........D... 218 722-0071
Duluth (G-1405)

Northpoint Health & Wellness ....E... 612 767-9500
Minneapolis (G-5235)

Northwest Youth & Family Svcs ....D... 651 486-3808
Saint Paul (G-8770)

Northwood Childrens Home Soc ....D... 218 724-8815
Duluth (G-1410)

Nutrition Services Inc..........................C... 507 835-5697
Waseca (G-9884)

Oasis of Love Inc................................E... 612 529-6055
Minneapolis (G-5258)

Olmsted Medical Center.......................E... 507 288-8880
Rochester (G-7196)

Omegon Inc.......................................E... 952 541-4738
Hopkins (G-2594)

Our Place Covenant Enabling ....E... 218 624-3097
Duluth (G-1416)

Outcomes Inc.....................................E... 651 483-9500
Saint Paul (G-8795)

Pacer Center Inc ....D... 952 838-9000
Minneapolis (G-5309)

Pact For Families................................E... 320 231-7030
Willmar (G-10034)

Paragon Associates Inc ....D... 218 722-5009
Duluth (G-1418)

People Inc..E... 651 227-6321
Saint Paul (G-8817)

Phoenix Alternatives Inc......................C... 651 426-2484
Saint Paul (G-8825)

Phoenix Residence Inc ....C... 651 227-7655
Saint Paul (G-7876)

Pinnacle Services Inc..........................B... 612 977-3100
Minneapolis (G-5382)

Prairie Five Community Action ....E... 320 269-6578
Montevideo (G-6257)

Prairie Five Community Action ....E... 320 598-3118
Madison (G-3077)

Providers Choice Inc...........................D... 952 944-7010
Hopkins (G-2607)

R E M Southwest Services C ....D... 507 223-5633
Canby (G-851)

REM Inc...E... 218 724-1872
Duluth (G-1434)

REM River Bluffs Inc...........................E... 651 480-4710
Hastings (G-2404)

Renville County Emergency Food ....E... 320 523-5339
Olivia (G-6563)

Resources For Child Caring Inc............D... 651 641-0305
Saint Paul (G-8893)

Safe Haven Shelter For Youth ....E... 952 440-5379
Prior Lake (G-6953)

Saint Peter Counseling Center.............E... 507 934-9612
Saint Peter (G-9300)

Salvation Army Harbor Light ....D... 612 338-0113
Minneapolis (G-5598)

Second Harvest Heartland....................C... 651 484-5117
Saint Paul (G-8941)

Second Harvest Heartland....................D... 612 209-7980
Minneapolis (G-5624)

Shakopee Mdewakanton Sioux Com ...D... 952 445-8900
Prior Lake (G-6954)

South Metro Human Services...............D... 651 291-1979
Saint Paul (G-8973)

Southside Family Nurturing Ctr ....E... 612 721-2762
Minneapolis (G-5711)

St Cloud Hospital................................D... 320 656-7020
Saint Cloud (G-7593)

St David's Center Child.......................B... 952 939-0396
Hopkins (G-2636)

St James Home of Duluth ....C... 218 728-7500
Duluth (G-1462)

SERVICES

St Stephen's Human Services ....E... 612 874-0311
Minneapolis *(G-5731)*

Stearns-Benton Employment................E... 320 308-5320
Saint Cloud *(G-7612)*

Steele County Human Services ....D... 507 444-7500
Owatonna *(G-6738)*

Stepping Stones For Living LLC ....D... 218 727-7450
Duluth *(G-1475)*

Sustainable Resources Center ....E... 612 870-4255
Minneapolis *(G-5776)*

Tamarisk Resources Inc......................E... 763 572-1950
Anoka *(G-232)*

Tbi Residential & Community ....D... 218 721-3231
Duluth *(G-1480)*

Three Rivers Community Action ....E... 507 732-7391
Zumbrota *(G-10220)*

Three Rivers Head Start ....D... 507 333-6450
Faribault *(G-2035)*

Traumatic Brain Injury ....D... 218 733-1331
Duluth *(G-1486)*

Tri-County Community Action ....E... 320 632-3691
Little Falls *(G-3020)*

United Support Group ....E... 507 437-4110
Austin *(G-292)*

Vinland National Center ....E... 763 479-3555
Loretto *(G-3054)*

Vision Loss Resources ....E... 651 224-7662
Saint Paul *(G-9131)*

Volunteers Of America Inc ....D... 763 753-2500
Anoka *(G-237)*

W I C Program ....E... 612 348-6258
Minneapolis *(G-5987)*

Wee Care We Share ....E... 320 274-8881
Annandale *(G-144)*

Women's Shelter Inc............................E... 507 285-1938
Rochester *(G-7295)*

Womens Life Care Center ....E... 651 777-0350
Saint Paul *(G-9165)*

Woodland Centers ....D... 320 235-4613
Willmar *(G-10058)*

Y M C A Infant Center ....E... 651 646-4557
Saint Paul *(G-9171)*

YMCA ....D... 320 222-9622
Willmar *(G-10059)*

YMCA Children's Center ....E... 651 777-8103
Saint Paul *(G-9173)*

YMCA of Greater Saint Paul.................E... 651 645-6605
Saint Paul *(G-9175)*

YMCA of Greater St Paul ....D... 218 365-2117
Ely *(G-1919)*

YMCA of Greater St Paul ....D... 651 292-4143
Saint Paul *(G-9178)*

YMCA of Greater St Paul ....D... 651 646-4557
Saint Paul *(G-9177)*

YMCA of Greater St Paul ....C... 651 483-2671
Saint Paul *(G-9176)*

YMCA of Greater St Paul ....C... 651 457-0048
Saint Paul *(G-7953)*

YMCA of Worthington, Minnesota ....E... 507 376-6197
Worthington *(G-10199)*

Young Men's Christian Assn ....C... 507 387-8255
Mankato *(G-3222)*

Young Men's Chritn Assoc of...............C... 763 535-4800
Minneapolis *(G-6101)*

Young Men's Chritn Assoc of...............D... 612 827-5401
Minneapolis *(G-6102)*

Young Men's Chritn Assoc of...............E... 612 588-9484
Minneapolis *(G-6103)*

Young Men's Chritn Assoc of...............C... 952 835-2567
Minneapolis *(G-6104)*

Young Women's Christian Assn ....D... 218 722-7425
Duluth *(G-1505)*

YWCA of Minneapolis...........................A... 612 332-0501
Minneapolis *(G-6111)*

SODDING CONTRACTOR

Craig G Braun Turf Farms....................D... 651 463-2302
Hampton *(G-2365)*

Jirik Sod Farm Inc ....E... 651 460-6555
Farmington *(G-2052)*

Q3 Contracting Inc ....B... 651 224-2424
Saint Paul *(G-8859)*

Weerts Construction Inc ....E... 507 893-3313
Winnebago *(G-10078)*

SOFT DRINKS WHOLESALERS

BCI Coca-Cola Bottling Co of ....E... 507 282-2622
Rochester *(G-7061)*

Bernick's Full-Line Vending..................E... 320 656-2131
Waite Park *(G-9817)*

Bernick's Pepsi Cola of ....E... 320 235-1370
Willmar *(G-9986)*

Coca-Cola Enterprises Inc ....E... 800 657-4995
Owatonna *(G-6704)*

Coca-Cola Enterprises Inc ....E... 218 628-2311
Duluth *(G-1278)*

Coca-Cola Enterprises Inc ....D... 218 236-7165
Moorhead *(G-6304)*

Nei Bottling Inc...................................E... 218 751-3847
Bemidji *(G-407)*

Pepsi Cola Bottling Co ....E... 507 825-4207
Pipestone *(G-6833)*

Pepsi-Cola Metropolitan Btlng.............E... 218 829-4196
Brainerd *(G-580)*

Rohlfing of Brainerd Inc ....E... 218 829-0303
Brainerd *(G-585)*

Wirtz Beverage Minnesota Beer ....C... 651 646-6063
Saint Paul *(G-9160)*

SOFTWARE PUBLISHERS: Application

Amcom Software Inc ....D... 952 230-5200
Hopkins *(G-2508)*

Ca Inc ....C... 952 838-1186
Minneapolis *(G-3988)*

Ecologic Analytics LLC ....E... 952 843-6000
Bloomington *(G-495)*

Innovative Computer Systems ....E... 952 934-5665
Eden Prairie *(G-1694)*

Kroll Ontrack Inc ....C... 952 937-1107
Eden Prairie *(G-1704)*

Lawson Software Americas Inc ....A... 651 767-7000
Saint Paul *(G-8569)*

Lawson Software Inc ....A... 651 767-7000
Saint Paul *(G-8570)*

Melyx Corp ....E... 763 428-6000
Rogers *(G-7330)*

Ncs Pearson Inc ....A... 952 681-3000
Minneapolis *(G-5177)*

Open Systems Holdings Corp ....E... 952 403-5700
Shakopee *(G-9463)*

SOFTWARE PUBLISHERS: Business & Professional

Agvantage Software Inc ....E... 507 282-6353
Rochester *(G-7046)*

Ca Inc ....C... 952 838-1186
Minneapolis *(G-3988)*

Corporate Travel Services Inc ....D... 651 287-4900
Saint Paul *(G-8253)*

Ecologic Analytics LLC ....E... 952 843-6000
Bloomington *(G-495)*

Educational Biometric Tech..................E... 507 724-5773
Caledonia *(G-827)*

Fair Isaac Corp ....B... 612 758-5200
Minneapolis *(G-4392)*

Four51 Inc ....E... 952 294-0451
Bloomington *(G-498)*

Fpx LLC ....D... 507 388-5000
Mankato *(G-3128)*

Interplx Inc ....E... 952 403-7180
Shakopee *(G-9446)*

Open Systems Holdings Corp ....E... 952 403-5700
Shakopee *(G-9463)*

Open Systems Inc ....D... 952 403-5700
Shakopee *(G-9464)*

Paisley Consulting Inc..........................C... 320 286-5870
Cokato *(G-1077)*

Patterson Co's Inc ....C... 651 686-1600
Saint Paul *(G-7866)*

Smead Manufacturing Co Inc ....B... 651 437-4111
Hastings *(G-2406)*

Sungard Financial Systems LLC ....B... 952 935-3300
Hopkins *(G-2639)*

Symantec Corp....................................B... 651 746-7000
Saint Paul *(G-9020)*

XATA Corp...C... 952 707-5600
Eden Prairie *(G-1818)*

SOFTWARE PUBLISHERS: Education

Plato Learning Inc...............................C... 952 832-1000
Bloomington *(G-510)*

Scantron Corp ....C... 651 683-6000
Eagan *(G-1550)*

SOFTWARE PUBLISHERS: NEC

Adobe Systems Inc ....E... 651 766-4700
Saint Paul *(G-7982)*

Alignex Inc...E... 952 888-6801
Minneapolis *(G-3705)*

Architecture Technology Corp ....E... 952 829-5864
Eden Prairie *(G-1595)*

Carefacts Information Systems ....E... 651 636-3890
Saint Paul *(G-8163)*

Cygnia Corp...E... 952 887-9030
Minneapolis *(G-4209)*

Digital River Inc...................................B... 952 253-1234
Eden Prairie *(G-1645)*

Easy Automation Inc ....E... 507 728-8214
Welcome *(G-9958)*

Electro-Sensors Inc.............................E... 952 930-0100
Minnetonka *(G-6164)*

EMC Corp ....C... 952 828-9005
Eden Prairie *(G-1656)*

Epicor Software Corp ....C... 952 417-1400
Minneapolis *(G-4364)*

Fishel Information Systems Inc ....E... 952 544-1108
Hopkins *(G-2543)*

Fpx LLC ....E... 866 826-6344
Mankato *(G-3129)*

George Konik Associates Inc ....D... 952 835-5550
Minneapolis *(G-4524)*

Hyperion Solutions Corp ....E... 952 837-2680
Minneapolis *(G-4684)*

Innovative Computer Systems ....E... 952 934-5665
Eden Prairie *(G-1694)*

Makemusic Inc ....D... 952 937-9611
Eden Prairie *(G-1716)*

Microsoft Corp.....................................D... 952 832-8000
Minneapolis *(G-5019)*

MQ Software Inc ....D... 952 345-8720
Minneapolis *(G-5143)*

Network Instruments LLC ....E... 952 358-3800
Minnetonka *(G-6201)*

Nternational Projects ....D... 952 541-4888
Minneapolis *(G-5254)*

ObjectFX Corp ....E... 612 312-2002
Minneapolis *(G-5260)*

Oracle Systems Corp ....B... 612 587-5000
Minneapolis *(G-5288)*

Quest Software Inc ....E... 952 229-3500
Eden Prairie *(G-1756)*

RC Erickson & Associates Inc ....E... 651 452-6758
Saint Paul *(G-7889)*

Rural Computer Consultants Inc ....E... 320 365-4027
Bird Island *(G-468)*

S P S S Inc..D... 507 287-2800
Rochester *(G-7244)*

Scantron Corp.....................................C... 651 683-6000
Eagan *(G-1550)*

Shavlik Technologies Corp ....D... 651 426-6624
Saint Paul *(G-8947)*

Siemens Product Lifecycle Mgt ....D... 651 482-4219
Saint Paul *(G-8956)*

Sopheon Corp......................................E... 952 851-7555
Minneapolis *(G-5702)*

Startech Computing Inc ....E... 651 385-0607
Red Wing *(G-7006)*

Synergistic Software Soln ....E... 612 367-7300
Minneapolis *(G-5779)*

Tempworks Software Inc ....D... 651 452-0366
Saint Paul *(G-7920)*

Testquest Inc ....D... 952 936-7887
Chanhassen *(G-943)*

TMC Enterprises Inc.............................E... 952 943-9077
Eden Prairie *(G-1794)*

TriMin Systems Inc ....E... 651 636-7667
Saint Paul *(G-9083)*

Virtelligence Inc ....C... 952 746-9220
Eden Prairie *(G-1806)*

Vital Images Inc ....C... 952 487-9500
Minnetonka *(G-6235)*

SOFTWARE PUBLISHERS: Operating Systems

Business Microvar Inc ....E... 651 639-0575
Saint Paul *(G-8143)*

Sisu Medical Solutions LLC ....D... 218 529-7900
Duluth *(G-1451)*

SOFTWARE PUBLISHERS: Publisher's

Expert Software Inc ....E... 952 918-9400
Eden Prairie *(G-1659)*

SOIL CHEMICAL TREATMENT SVCS

Fountain Centers ....E... 507 377-6411
Albert Lea *(G-51)*

SOIL PREPARATION SVCS

Plaisted Co's Inc..................................E... 763 441-1100
Elk River *(G-1890)*

SOIL PREPARATION, PLANTING & CULTIVATING SVCS

Winfield Solutions LLC ....C... 651 481-2222
Saint Paul *(G-9158)*

SPAS

Cook & Koff Enterprises Inc.................E... 952 830-0100
Minneapolis *(G-4161)*

Employment codes: A=Over 500 employees, B=251-500, C=101-250, D=51-100, E=25-50

2011 Harris Minnesota
Services Directory

© Harris InfoSource 1-866-281-6415

765

S E R V I C E S

Elizabeth Charles Corp ....C... 952 915-2900
Minneapolis (G-4340)

Elizabeth Charles Corp ....D... 952 915-2900
Saint Paul (G-9212)

Elizabeth Charles Corp ....D... 952 915-2900
Chanhassen (G-922)

Full Present Inc ....E... 763 441-5999
Elk River (G-1875)

Gemm Inc ....E... 952 591-6730
Minnetonka (G-6174)

Maax US Corp ....D... 763 424-3335
Brooklyn Park (G-614)

S & S Spa Salon Inc ....E... 651 464-6612
Forest Lake (G-2168)

Seve Enterprises Inc ....E... 612 605-6230
Minneapolis (G-5640)

Solimar Wellness Spa ....E... 651 686-6686
Saint Paul (G-7907)

Sun Bear Spa & Tan Inc ....E... 651 426-5884
Saint Paul (G-9014)

SPECIAL EVENTS DECORATION SVCS

All Time Favorites Inc ....E... 651 454-1124
Saint Paul (G-7690)

SPECIALIZED LEGAL SVCS

Carl Crosby Lehmann ....B... 612 632-3000
Minneapolis (G-4012)

SPECIALTY OUTPATIENT CLINICS, NEC

A Chance To Grow Inc ....D... 612 789-1236
Minneapolis (G-3647)

Allina Health System ....C... 651 464-7100
Forest Lake (G-2155)

Catholic Charities of The ....C... 612 827-6241
Minneapolis (G-4030)

Center For Alcohol & Drug ....E... 218 723-8444
Duluth (G-1265)

County of Mahnomen ....D... 218 935-2511
Mahnomen (G-3084)

County of Ramsey ....C... 651 266-2400
Saint Paul (G-8260)

Emily Program ....E... 952 746-5774
Minneapolis (G-4347)

Feda Ridge Inc ....E... 651 426-3300
Stillwater (G-9618)

Guild Inc ....E... 651 291-0067
Saint Paul (G-8437)

Healtheast Maplewood Out ....E... 651 232-7780
Saint Paul (G-8463)

Healthpartners Inc ....D... 651 552-2600
Inver Grove Heights (G-2753)

Immanuel-St Joseph's Hospital ....D... 507 385-4700
Mankato (G-3149)

Indian Health Service ....D... 218 983-6317
Ogema (G-6554)

Integrated Medical Rehab ....E... 952 837-8991
Minneapolis (G-4713)

Mental Health Resources Inc ....E... 612 337-4021
Minneapolis (G-4988)

Midwest Urologic Stone Unit LP ....E... 651 633-9414
Saint Paul (G-8666)

Regents of The University of ....A... 612 624-9499
Minneapolis (G-5495)

St Cloud Surgical Center ....C... 320 251-8385
Saint Cloud (G-7607)

Stevens Community Medical Ctr ....C... 320 589-1313
Morris (G-6379)

Washburn Child Guidance Center ....D... 612 871-1454
Minneapolis (G-6022)

Wayside House Inc ....E... 952 926-5626
Minneapolis (G-6027)

Winona Developmental ....E... 507 452-1798
Winona (G-10147)

Woodland Centers ....D... 320 235-4613
Willmar (G-10058)

SPECULATIVE BUILDERS: Single-Family Housing

Lecy Construction ....E... 952 944-9499
Hopkins (G-2569)

Pulte Homes ....D... 763 241-9001
Elk River (G-1891)

SPORTING & REC GOODS, WHOLESALE: Boats, Canoes, Etc/Eqpt

Crystal Marine Inc ....E... 952 233-3437
Shakopee (G-9434)

Northern Wholesale Supply Inc ....D... 651 429-1515
Hugo (G-2672)

SPORTING & RECREATIONAL GOODS & SPLYS WHOLESALERS

Bell Industries Inc ....C... 651 203-2300
Eagan (G-1517)

H & G Marketing Inc ....E... 763 263-8998
Big Lake (G-446)

Heelside Inc ....E... 612 508-0887
Anoka (G-189)

Johnson Outdoors Inc ....C... 507 345-4623
Mankato (G-3154)

Leech Lake Distributors Inc ....E... 218 547-1505
Walker (G-9853)

Mid-States Distributing Co Inc ....E... 651 698-8831
Saint Paul (G-8652)

Motivaction LLC ....D... 763 412-3000
Minneapolis (G-5137)

N C Holdings ....E... 952 933-7060
Hopkins (G-2586)

New York Mint Ltd ....E... 952 949-6588
Minneapolis (G-5194)

Normark Corp ....D... 952 933-7060
Hopkins (G-2589)

Palco Marketing Inc ....E... 763 559-5539
Osseo (G-6651)

S & S Sales Inc ....E... 763 476-9599
Minneapolis (G-5581)

Westwood Sports Inc ....D... 952 881-2222
Minneapolis (G-6063)

SPORTING & RECREATIONAL GOODS, WHOLESALE: Athletic Goods

Prophet Corp ....D... 507 451-7470
Owatonna (G-6730)

Prophet Corp ....D... 952 841-0021
Owatonna (G-6731)

SPORTING & RECREATIONAL GOODS, WHOLESALE: Boat Access & Part

Csi Sports Properties LLC ....C... 320 252-4193
Sauk Rapids (G-9361)

Josuda Inc ....E... 763 263-0313
Big Lake (G-449)

SPORTING & RECREATIONAL GOODS, WHOLESALE: Exercise

Prophet Corp ....D... 507 451-7470
Owatonna (G-6730)

Prophet Corp ....D... 952 841-0021
Owatonna (G-6731)

Prophet Corp ....C... 800 533-0446
Owatonna (G-6732)

SPORTING & RECREATIONAL GOODS, WHOLESALE: Fishing

Leech Lake Distributors Inc ....E... 218 547-1505
Walker (G-9853)

SPORTING & RECREATIONAL GOODS, WHOLESALE: Fishing Tackle

Csi Sports Properties LLC ....C... 320 252-4193
Sauk Rapids (G-9361)

N C Holdings ....E... 952 933-7060
Hopkins (G-2586)

Normark Corp ....D... 952 933-7060
Hopkins (G-2589)

Northland Fishing Tackle Inc ....D... 218 286-5441
Ranier (G-6969)

SPORTING & RECREATIONAL GOODS, WHOLESALE: Gymnasium

Prophet Corp ....D... 507 451-7470
Owatonna (G-6730)

Prophet Corp ....D... 952 841-0021
Owatonna (G-6731)

SPORTING & RECREATIONAL GOODS, WHOLESALE: Hunting

Csi Sports Properties LLC ....C... 320 252-4193
Sauk Rapids (G-9361)

Hicks Bill & Co Ltd ....D... 763 476-6200
Minneapolis (G-4645)

Hudalla Associates Inc ....E... 218 346-2734
Perham (G-6797)

Leech Lake Distributors Inc ....E... 218 547-1505
Walker (G-9853)

N C Holdings ....E... 952 933-7060
Hopkins (G-2586)

Normark Corp ....D... 952 933-7060
Hopkins (G-2589)

SPORTING & RECREATIONAL GOODS, WHOLESALE: Motorboats

Hannay's Inc ....E... 612 781-7411
Minneapolis (G-4594)

SPORTING & RECREATIONAL GOODS, WHOLESALE: Outboard Motors

Hannay's Inc ....E... 612 781-7411
Minneapolis (G-4594)

SPORTING & RECREATIONAL GOODS, WHOLESALE: Spa

Saunatec Inc ....D... 320 286-5584
Cokato (G-1079)

SPORTS CLUBS, MANAGERS & PROMOTERS

AEG Management Twn LLC ....A... 612 673-1300
Minneapolis (G-3692)

American Wrestling Association ....E... 507 281-8842
Rochester (G-7054)

Dam Lake Sportmens Club ....E... 218 927-6263
Aitkin (G-18)

Minnesota Wild Hockey Club LP ....D... 651 602-6000
Saint Paul (G-8711)

Tapemark Charity Pro AM ....B... 651 455-1611
Saint Paul (G-7915)

SPORTS TEAMS & CLUBS

National Sports Center Fndtn ....E... 763 785-5600
Minneapolis (G-3551)

SPORTS TEAMS & CLUBS: Baseball

Minnesota Twins Baseball Club ....D... 612 659-3400
Minneapolis (G-5098)

Minnesota Twins Baseball Club ....A... 612 375-7411
Minneapolis (G-5099)

St Pauls Saints Baseball Club ....C... 651 644-6659
Saint Paul (G-9002)

SPORTS TEAMS & CLUBS: Basketball

Minnesota Timberwolves ....C... 612 673-1600
Minneapolis (G-5096)

SPORTS TEAMS & CLUBS: Football

Minnesota Vikings Football ....C... 952 828-6500
Eden Prairie (G-1727)

Minnesota Vikings Football LLC 952 828-6500
Eden Prairie (G-1728)

SPORTS TEAMS & CLUBS: Soccer

Soccer Blast Minnesota ....E... 952 895-1962
Burnsville (G-799)

SPRAYING SVCS, ORNAMENTAL TREE

Arrowhead Tree Service Inc ....E... 218 729-9203
Duluth (G-1245)

S & S Tree Specialists Inc ....E... 612 872-3901
South Saint Paul (G-9540)

STAFFING, EMPLOYMENT PLACEMENT

Innovative Technical Personnel ....E... 763 591-9191
Minneapolis (G-4705)

Sapphire Technologies, LP ....D... 612 332-8700
Minneapolis (G-5602)

Talus Group Inc ....E... 952 544-2526
Excelsior (G-1954)

STATE CREDIT UNIONS, NOT FEDERALLY CHARTERED

Affinity Plus Federal Credit ....E... 651 291-3700
Saint Paul (G-7995)

Greater Minnesota Credit Union ....E... 320 679-8100
Mora (G-6360)

Members Cooperative Credit ....D... 218 879-3304
Cloquet (G-1057)

St Paul Postal Employees ....E... 651 770-7000
Saint Paul (G-8997)

Virginia Coop Credit Union Inc ....E... 218 741-5644
Virginia (G-9759)

STATE SAVINGS BANKS, NOT FEDERALLY CHARTERED

American National Bank of MN ....E... 218 824-7900
Brainerd (G-548)

American National Bank of MN ....D... 218 829-1484
Baxter (G-320)

(G-00000) Company's Geographic Section entry number

Bremer Bank.........................D... 218 829-8781
Brainerd *(G-555)*

Citizens Bank & Trust Co ....E... 320 587-2233
Hutchinson *(G-2693)*

Community National Bank ....E... 507 645-4441
Northfield *(G-6526)*

First Integrity Bank ....E... 218 894-1522
Staples *(G-9584)*

First State Bank of Rosemount ....E... 651 423-1121
Rosemount *(G-7370)*

Main Street Bank.................................E... 651 451-2133
South Saint Paul *(G-9533)*

Riverbank MN ....D... 651 408-9203
Wyoming *(G-10207)*

Security State Bank of Kenyon.............E... 507 789-6123
Kenyon *(G-2829)*

STATION OPERATION SVCS

Awm Enterprises Inc ....E... 651 455-3044
South Saint Paul *(G-9510)*

STATIONARY & OFFICE SPLYS, WHOL: Computer/Photocopying Splys

Metro - Sales Inc ....C... 612 861-4000
Minneapolis *(G-5000)*

STATIONARY & OFFICE SPLYS, WHOLESALE: Data Processing Splys

Imation Enterprises Corp ....A... 651 704-4000
Oakdale *(G-6551)*

STATIONARY & OFFICE SPLYS, WHOLESALE: Manifold Business Form

Quality Business Forms of ....E... 763 559-4330
Minneapolis *(G-5441)*

STATIONARY & OFFICE SPLYS, WHOLESALE: Photo Albums/Scrapbook

Tomsten Inc ....E... 952 516-3300
Minnetonka *(G-6228)*

STATIONARY & OFFICE SPLYS, WHOLESALE: Stationers, Commercial

Quality Business Forms of ....E... 763 559-4330
Minneapolis *(G-5441)*

S & T Office Products Inc.....................C... 651 483-4411
Saint Paul *(G-8918)*

STATIONARY & OFFICE SPLYS, WHOLESALE: Stationery

Masterpiece Studios Inc ....C... 507 388-8788
North Mankato *(G-6509)*

STATIONARY & OFFICE SPLYS WHOLESALERS

Corporate Express Office Prdts ....C... 651 636-2250
Saint Paul *(G-8251)*

Curry Sales Inc....................................E... 952 351-4200
Hopkins *(G-2534)*

Gartner Studios Inc..............................E... 651 351-7700
Stillwater *(G-9619)*

Help Systems LLC ....E... 952 933-0609
Eden Prairie *(G-1683)*

J L Buchanan Inc ....E... 612 334-1710
Minneapolis *(G-4747)*

Liberty Diversified Industries ....D... 763 536-6600
Minneapolis *(G-4869)*

Litin Paper Co Inc ....E... 612 333-4331
Minneapolis *(G-4893)*

Metro - Sales Inc ....C... 612 861-4000
Minneapolis *(G-5000)*

North Country Business Prdts ....D... 218 751-4140
Bemidji *(G-408)*

North Country Business Prdts ....E... 800 937-4140
Plymouth *(G-6878)*

Northern Business Products Inc ....E... 218 726-0167
Duluth *(G-1402)*

Office Depot Inc ....E... 952 525-1919
Minnetonka *(G-6205)*

OfficeMax North America Inc................E... 763 391-6629
Minneapolis *(G-5267)*

Paper Depot Inc...................................E... 612 333-0512
Minneapolis *(G-5317)*

Patterson Co's Inc ....C... 651 686-1600
Saint Paul *(G-7866)*

Quality Business Forms of ....E... 763 559-4330
Minneapolis *(G-5441)*

S P Richards Co ....E... 651 484-8459
Saint Paul *(G-8920)*

3M Co ....D... 651 733-5094
Saint Paul *(G-9064)*

Unisource Worldwide Inc ....B... 763 488-7200
Brooklyn Park *(G-620)*

United Stationers Supply Co ....C... 651 681-1720
Saint Paul *(G-7937)*

STEAM HEATING SYSTEMS SPLY SVCS

Foster Wheeler Twin Cities Inc.............E... 612 379-1885
Minneapolis *(G-4468)*

Franklin Heating Station.......................E... 507 289-3534
Rochester *(G-7119)*

STEAM SPLY SYSTEMS SVCS INCLUDING GEOTHERMAL

Franklin Heating Station.......................E... 507 289-3534
Rochester *(G-7119)*

STENOGRAPHIC SVCS

Eggleston Medscribe Inc......................E... 763 971-5000
Minneapolis *(G-4330)*

STEVEDORING SVCS

Cargill Inc...D... 218 727-1594
Duluth *(G-1262)*

STITCHING SVCS: Custom

Lee's Pro Shop Inc..............................E... 320 629-7568
Pine City *(G-6814)*

STONE: Dimension, NEC

L S Starrett Co....................................E... 320 251-7171
Waite Park *(G-9825)*

Rex Granite Co ....E... 320 252-2060
Saint Cloud *(G-7426)*

STORE FIXTURES, EXC REFRIGERATED: Wholesalers

Exactec Inc ....E... 952 448-7722
Chaska *(G-966)*

Midwest Fixture Group Inc ....E... 763 712-9637
Anoka *(G-204)*

Retailer Services Corp.........................E... 763 421-6868
Anoka *(G-221)*

Vision Woodworking Inc ....E... 763 571-5767
Minneapolis *(G-3631)*

STUDIOS: Sculptor's

Tivoli Too Inc.......................................E... 651 698-3335
Saint Paul *(G-7924)*

SUBSCRIPTION FULFILLMENT SVCS: Magazine, Newspaper, Etc

Impact Mailing Of Minnesota ....D... 612 521-6245
Minneapolis *(G-4692)*

3 Br's Inc..E... 507 645-8600
Northfield *(G-6542)*

SUBSTANCE ABUSE CLINICS, OUTPATIENT

Minnesota Monitoring Inc ....E... 763 253-5401
Minneapolis *(G-5085)*

Northland Counseling Center ....E... 218 326-1274
Grand Rapids *(G-2301)*

Omegon Inc ....E... 952 541-4738
Hopkins *(G-2594)*

Red Lake Chemical Health ....D... 218 679-3995
Redlake *(G-7017)*

Stevens Community Medical Ctr ....C... 320 589-1313
Morris *(G-6379)*

SUMMER CAMPS, EXC DAY & SPORTS INSTRUCTIONAL

Calmar Group Inc ....D... 952 440-8834
Prior Lake *(G-6929)*

Catholic Youth Camp............................E... 651 636-1645
Saint Paul *(G-8178)*

Circle R Ranch Inc ....E... 320 547-2176
Long Prairie *(G-3039)*

SUNGLASSES, WHOLESALE

Seaver Co ....D... 507 665-3321
Le Sueur *(G-2959)*

SURGERY SVCS, ORNAMENTAL TREE

S & S Tree & Horticultural ....E... 651 451-8907
South Saint Paul *(G-9539)*

SURVEYING & MAPPING: Land Parcels

Bogart & Peterson & Associates ....E... 763 682-9329
Maple Lake *(G-3258)*

Bolton & Menk Inc ....D... 507 625-4171
Mankato *(G-3112)*

Bolton & Menk Inc ....E... 320 231-3956
Willmar *(G-9991)*

Clark Engineering Corp ....E... 763 545-9196
Minneapolis *(G-4103)*

Colby Yaggy Associates Inc ....D... 507 288-6464
Rochester *(G-7084)*

Duffy Engineering & Associates ....E... 320 259-6575
Saint Cloud *(G-7412)*

Egan, Field, & Nowak Inc ....E... 612 466-3300
Minneapolis *(G-4329)*

Hansen, Thorp & Pellinen Inc ....E... 952 829-0700
Eden Prairie *(G-1676)*

Hennepin County ....E... 612 348-3131
Minneapolis *(G-4632)*

Honeywell International Inc ....D... 763 954-2712
Plymouth *(G-6864)*

James R Hill Inc ....E... 952 890-6044
Burnsville *(G-738)*

McGhie & Betts Inc ....E... 507 289-3919
Rochester *(G-7179)*

Otto Associates Engineers ....E... 763 682-4727
Buffalo *(G-655)*

Rehder & Associates Inc ....D... 651 452-5051
Eagan *(G-1547)*

Schoell & Madson Inc ....E... 763 746-1600
Minneapolis *(G-5610)*

SRF Consulting Group Inc....................C... 763 475-0010
Minneapolis *(G-5725)*

Sunday Land Surveying........................E... 952 881-2455
Minneapolis *(G-5766)*

Sunde Land Surveying LLC...................E... 952 881-2455
Minneapolis *(G-5767)*

Tom Loucks & Associates Inc...............D... 763 424-5505
Osseo *(G-6676)*

Widseth, Smith, Nolting ....E... 218 281-6522
Crookston *(G-1144)*

SURVEYING SVCS: Photogrammetric Engineering

Aero-Metric Inc ....E... 763 420-9606
Osseo *(G-6593)*

Emmons & Oliver Resources ....E... 218 732-3323
Park Rapids *(G-6751)*

SVC ESTABLISHMENT EQPT & SPLYS WHOLESALERS

E Weinberg Supply Co Inc....................E... 952 920-0888
Minneapolis *(G-4303)*

Guardian Building Products ....E... 612 524-0513
Minneapolis *(G-4576)*

Nilfisk-Advance Inc ....A... 763 745-3500
Plymouth *(G-6877)*

PI Enterprises Inc ....E... 612 588-9000
Minneapolis *(G-5387)*

Pump & Meter Service Inc ....E... 952 933-4800
Hopkins *(G-2608)*

TAS Adventures Inc ....E... 507 833-8164
Waseca *(G-9888)*

3Wire Group Inc...................................E... 763 488-3000
Osseo *(G-6675)*

Zumbro River Brand Inc........................E... 507 446-9097
Owatonna *(G-6746)*

SVC ESTABLISHMENT EQPT, WHOL: Cleaning & Maint Eqpt & Splys

Bro-Tex Co Inc.....................................D... 651 645-5721
Saint Paul *(G-8130)*

C J Duffey Paper Co ....D... 612 338-8701
Minneapolis *(G-3984)*

Ceiling Pro Interior Inc ....E... 952 947-0007
Eden Prairie *(G-1617)*

G P Co's Inc ....D... 651 454-6500
Mendota Heights *(G-3363)*

Kennedy Brissman ....E... 651 646-7933
Saint Paul *(G-8545)*

Osland Janitorial Supply Inc ....E... 952 894-4815
Burnsville *(G-773)*

SVC ESTABLISHMENT EQPT, WHOLESALE : Barber Shop Eqpt & Splys

Barbers Hairstyling For Men ....D... 952 947-7777
Minneapolis *(G-3867)*

Beauty Craft Supply & Eqpt..................E... 952 935-4420
Hopkins *(G-2515)*

Mikara Corp...E... 763 541-1000
Minneapolis *(G-5038)*

Employment codes: A=Over 500 employees, B=251-500,
C=101-250, D=51-100, E=25-50

2011 Harris Minnesota
Services Directory

© Harris InfoSource 1-866-281-6415

767

S E R V I C E S

SVC ESTABLISHMENT EQPT, WHOLESALE: Beauty Parlor Eqpt & Sply

Altobella Hair Products Inc ....E... 952 707-1900
Burnsville *(G-675)*

Barbers Hairstyling For Men ....D... 952 947-7777
Minneapolis *(G-3867)*

Beauty Craft Supply & Eqpt ....E... 952 935-4420
Hopkins *(G-2515)*

Mikara Corp ....E... 763 541-1000
Minneapolis *(G-5038)*

SVC ESTABLISHMENT EQPT, WHOLESALE: Firefighting Eqpt

Activar Inc ....E... 952 835-6850
Minneapolis *(G-3677)*

Clarey's Safety Equipment Inc ....E... 507 289-6749
Rochester *(G-7080)*

Simplexgrinnell LP ....C... 763 367-5000
Minneapolis *(G-5676)*

SVC ESTABLISHMENT EQPT, WHOLESALE: Floor Machinery, Maint

Dalco Enterprises Inc ....D... 651 604-2966
Saint Paul *(G-8280)*

SVC ESTABLISHMENT EQPT, WHOLESALE: Laundry Eqpt & Splys

Minnesota Chemical Co ....E... 651 646-7521
Saint Paul *(G-8676)*

SVC ESTABLISHMENT EQPT, WHOLESALE: Moving Eqpt & Splys

Pugleasa Co Inc ....E... 651 636-6442
Saint Paul *(G-8857)*

675 Stinson LLC ....D... 612 238-3200
Minneapolis *(G-5686)*

SVC ESTABLISHMENT EQPT, WHOLESALE: Restaurant Splys

Strategic Equipment Inc ....D... 320 252-2977
Saint Cloud *(G-7614)*

SVC ESTABLISHMENT EQPT, WHOLESALE: Vacuum Cleaning Systems

J J Vanderson & Co ....E... 651 641-1376
Minneapolis *(G-3503)*

SVC ESTABLISHMENT EQPT, WHOLESALE: Vending Machines & Splys

Four Seasons Services Inc ....E... 507 373-9666
Albert Lea *(G-53)*

Lieberman Co's Inc ....D... 952 887-5299
Minneapolis *(G-4873)*

SWIMMING INSTRUCTION

Family Swim School ....E... 952 435-1898
Lakeville *(G-2906)*

Foss Swim School Inc ....E... 763 416-8993
Osseo *(G-6615)*

Foss Swim School Inc ....E... 952 935-8732
Minneapolis *(G-4466)*

SWIMMING POOL & HOT TUB CLEANING & MAINTENANCE SVCS

All Poolside Services Inc ....E... 651 483-6600
Saint Paul *(G-8011)*

Atlantis Pools Inc ....E... 763 560-0103
Minneapolis *(G-3831)*

L & R Suburban Landscaping Inc ....E... 952 935-0389
Minnetonka *(G-6186)*

Minnesota Residential Aquatics 651 439-8467
Stillwater *(G-9629)*

Performance Pool & Spa Inc ....E... 651 731-3440
Saint Paul *(G-9259)*

SYMPHONY ORCHESTRA

Minnesota Orchestral Assn ....E... 612 371-5600
Minneapolis *(G-5088)*

Minnesota Orchestral Assn ....E... 612 371-5600
Minneapolis *(G-5089)*

SYSTEMS ENGINEERING: Computer Related

PeopleNet Communications Corp ....C... 952 908-6200
Minnetonka *(G-6209)*

SYSTEMS INTEGRATION SVCS

Americom Inc ....E... 651 726-2200
Saint Paul *(G-8036)*

Berbee Information Networks ....D... 763 592-5800
Minneapolis *(G-3886)*

Digital Images Inc ....E... 651 688-0888
Saint Paul *(G-7753)*

Evolving Solutions Inc ....E... 763 516-6500
Hamel *(G-2340)*

N'Compass Solutions Inc ....E... 612 379-2100
Minneapolis *(G-5155)*

Parallel Technologies Inc ....E... 952 920-7185
Minneapolis *(G-5322)*

Sovran Inc ....E... 651 686-0515
Eagan *(G-1552)*

Spc Communications Inc ....E... 952 912-2800
Minneapolis *(G-5716)*

TAJ Technologies Inc ....E... 651 405-7412
Mendota Heights *(G-3371)*

Unisys Corp ....A... 651 687-2200
Saint Paul *(G-7935)*

SYSTEMS INTEGRATION SVCS: Local Area Network

Comm-Works Holdings LLC ....D... 763 258-5800
Minneapolis *(G-4130)*

Computer Integration Techs ....D... 651 450-0333
Saint Paul *(G-9198)*

Nortel Networks Inc ....E... 952 897-1150
Minneapolis *(G-5211)*

SafeNet Consulting Inc ....D... 952 930-3636
Minnetonka *(G-6224)*

Tricord Systems Inc ....E... 763 557-9005
Minneapolis *(G-5855)*

SYSTEMS SOFTWARE DEVELOPMENT SVCS

Gb Lumina Inc ....E... 763 797-9036
Minneapolis *(G-4504)*

Hardcore Computer Inc ....E... 507 285-0101
Rochester *(G-7132)*

McKesson Information Solutions ....C... 651 697-5900
Saint Paul *(G-8625)*

Renovo Software Inc ....E... 952 931-0790
Minneapolis *(G-5519)*

Sadaka Technology Consultants ....A... 952 841-6363
Minneapolis *(G-5586)*

TAJ Technologies Inc ....D... 651 405-7412
Mendota Heights *(G-3371)*

Wyde Corp ....D... 651 882-2400
Eagan *(G-1562)*

TABULATING SVCS

Ncs Pearson Inc ....A... 952 681-3000
Minneapolis *(G-5177)*

Questar Data Systems Inc ....C... 651 688-0089
Saint Paul *(G-7886)*

TANK REPAIR SVCS

Havco Inc ....E... 320 746-2781
Avon *(G-295)*

TANNING SALON EQPT & SPLYS, WHOLESALE

T W Enterprises Ltd ....D... 320 654-0551
Saint Cloud *(G-7615)*

TANNING SALONS

Dakotah Sport & Fitness Center ....C... 952 445-9400
Prior Lake *(G-6932)*

Elam Investments ....E... 763 544-4264
Minneapolis *(G-4335)*

S & S Spa Salon Inc ....E... 651 464-6612
Forest Lake *(G-2168)*

TAPE SLITTING SVCS

V-TEK Inc ....D... 507 387-2039
Mankato *(G-3211)*

TAX RETURN PREPARATION SVCS

Global Tax Network Minnesota ....E... 952 224-2053
Minneapolis *(G-4532)*

H&R Block Inc ....E... 507 345-1040
Mankato *(G-3132)*

H&R Block Inc ....D... 507 280-8406
Rochester *(G-7130)*

Inter-Tax Inc ....E... 952 512-9000
Minnetonka *(G-6181)*

Larsonallen LLP ....E... 218 692-5750
Crosslake *(G-1151)*

RSM McGladrey Inc ....D... 507 288-5363
Rochester *(G-7242)*

Stevens Foster' Financial ....E... 952 843-4200
Minneapolis *(G-5755)*

TAXI CABS

Care Transportation Inc ....E... 320 253-7729
Saint Cloud *(G-7470)*

Fast Cab Services LLC ....D... 952 393-8542
Minneapolis *(G-4416)*

TELECOMMUNICATION EQPT REPAIR SVCS, EXC TELEPHONES

Matrix Communications Inc ....E... 763 475-5500
Minneapolis *(G-4966)*

Nextel Communications Inc ....D... 952 703-7600
Minneapolis *(G-5197)*

Norstan Communications Inc ....C... 952 352-4300
Minnetonka *(G-6202)*

Phoenix Distributing Inc ....E... 952 882-9949
Burnsville *(G-781)*

Spectrum Solutions Inc ....E... 651 634-1800
Saint Paul *(G-8976)*

TELECOMMUNICATIONS CARRIERS & SVCS: Wired

A T & T Corp ....B... 612 376-5401
Minneapolis *(G-3649)*

Ace Communications Group ....D... 507 896-3111
Houston *(G-2661)*

Arvig Enterprises Inc ....C... 218 346-5500
Perham *(G-6793)*

Bevcomm Inc ....E... 507 526-3252
Blue Earth *(G-529)*

Bhi Advanced Internet Inc ....E... 952 361-5557
Eden Prairie *(G-1605)*

Blue Earth Valley Telephone Co ....E... 507 787-2222
Wells *(G-9961)*

Broadband America, Corp ....E... 952 941-7900
Victoria *(G-9725)*

Citizens Telecommunications Co ....E... 952 491-5576
Mound *(G-6385)*

Convergeone Holdings Corp ....C... 651 796-6411
Eagan *(G-1522)*

Dell-Comm Inc ....D... 763 783-0035
Saint Paul *(G-8283)*

Embarq Minnesota Inc ....D... 952 556-5679
Chaska *(G-964)*

Focalpoint Inc ....D... 952 944-0932
Eden Prairie *(G-1666)*

Frontier Communications of MN ....C... 952 898-6422
Burnsville *(G-725)*

Hanson Communications Inc ....E... 320 235-2260
Willmar *(G-10005)*

Hickory Tech Information Soln ....D... 507 625-1691
Mankato *(G-3139)*

Hickory Tech Information Soln ....D... 507 625-1691
Mankato *(G-3140)*

Integra Telecom Holdings Inc ....E... 952 226-7000
Prior Lake *(G-6934)*

K N R Communication Services ....E... 763 478-2058
Brooklyn Park *(G-612)*

Larson Utilities Inc ....E... 507 557-2275
Franklin *(G-2181)*

Link Lakedale Inc ....E... 320 274-7777
Annandale *(G-141)*

McLeodusa Inc ....E... 800 593-1177
Saint Paul *(G-8626)*

Mid-State Telephone Co ....A... 320 354-7805
New London *(G-6417)*

North American Communications ....D... 651 994-6800
Eagan *(G-1542)*

Northstar Access ....E... 763 691-0885
Cambridge *(G-844)*

Onvoy Inc ....E... 952 230-4100
Minneapolis *(G-5282)*

Onvoy Inc ....E... 320 324-7530
Chokio *(G-1001)*

Otter Tail Telcom LLC ....E... 218 998-2000
Fergus Falls *(G-2111)*

Qwest Corp ....C... 612 663-2073
Minneapolis *(G-5452)*

Redwood Long Distance Co ....E... 507 644-3844
Wabasso *(G-9777)*

Skycom Inc ....E... 952 361-4248
Minneapolis *(G-5688)*

Tailwind Voice & Data Inc ....E... 763 577-4000
Minneapolis *(G-5785)*

TW Telecom Inc ....E... 952 351-2300
Hopkins *(G-2650)*

Verizon Business Network Svcs ....E... 612 607-1116
Cologne *(G-1093)*

SERVICES

Vibes Technologies Inc ....C... 763 971-6260
Minneapolis (G-5968)

TELECOMMUNICATIONS CARRIERS & SVCS:
Wireless

Abraham Technical Services Inc ....E... 763 428-3170
Rogers (G-7315)

Choice Communications Inc 651 230-7127
Minneapolis (G-4068)

Cumulus Media Inc ....E... 507 288-1025
Rochester (G-7090)

Embarq Minnesota Inc ....D... 952 556-5679
Chaska (G-964)

Heartland Services LLC ....E... 763 477-3000
Rockford (G-7301)

Hickory Tech Information Soln ....D... 507 625-1691
Mankato (G-3139)

Hickory Tech Information Soln ....D... 507 625-1691
Mankato (G-3140)

Nextel Communications Inc ....D... 952 703-7600
Minneapolis (G-5197)

PeopleNet Communications Corp ....C... 952 908-6200
Minnetonka (G-6209)

USA Mobility Wireless Inc ....E... 952 996-0400
Eden Prairie (G-1801)

Verizon Business Network Svcs ....E... 612 607-1116
Cologne (G-1093)

TELECONFERENCING SVCS

BT Americas Holdings Ltd ....E... 651 746-8739
Saint Paul (G-9191)

Norstan Inc ....C... 952 352-4000
Hopkins (G-2590)

TELEMARKETING BUREAUS

Aria Communications Corp ....C... 320 259-5206
Saint Cloud (G-7453)

Arrowhead Promotion ....B... 218 327-1165
Grand Rapids (G-2269)

Customer Traac Inc ....E... 763 553-2989
Minneapolis (G-4206)

Customer Traac Inc ....E... 218 435-2600
Fosston (G-2175)

Customerlink LLC ....C... 218 722-2800
Duluth (G-1289)

Data Listing Services LLC ....D... 952 948-5488
Burnsville (G-709)

Drs Acquisitions Inc ....D... 320 351-8100
Sauk Centre (G-9343)

Feather, Larson & Synhorst ....D... 651 480-0123
Hastings (G-2415)

G&S Staffing Services Inc ....A... 320 235-3949
Willmar (G-10002)

Gage Group LLC ....C... 763 595-3920
Minneapolis (G-4495)

Inteleserve Inc ....C... 800 390-4851
Saint Peter (G-9307)

Medical Messaging Center ....E... 320 255-5640
Saint Cloud (G-7549)

Meyer Associates Inc ....C... 320 259-4000
Saint Cloud (G-7552)

Sunshine Readers Inc ....E... 763 433-2534
Champlin (G-902)

Synergy Advantage Group Inc ....D... 320 695-2000
Browns Valley (G-628)

Tele Resources Inc ....D... 218 724-2026
Duluth (G-1482)

Tele Resources Inc ....C... 218 724-2026
Duluth (G-1483)

Teleconcepts Inc ....E... 763 566-5360
Minneapolis (G-5808)

Telemarketing Results Inc ....E... 763 519-0874
Minneapolis (G-5809)

Universal Marketing ....E... 218 722-1698
Duluth (G-1493)

Universal Power Marketing LLC ....C... 320 202-0243
Saint Cloud (G-7625)

TELEPHONE ANSWERING SVCS

Answer America LLC ....E... 651 644-7332
Saint Paul (G-8053)

Bell Telephone Inc ....D... 651 298-1332
Saint Paul (G-8099)

Norstan Inc ....C... 952 352-4000
Hopkins (G-2590)

7 West Secretarial Answering...............E... 952 936-4000
Eden Prairie (G-1775)

TELEPHONE EQPT INSTALLATION

Avtex Solutions LLC ....E... 952 831-0888
Minneapolis (G-3848)

Comm-Works Holdings LLC ....D... 763 258-5800
Minneapolis (G-4130)

Comm-Works LLC ....D... 763 258-5800
Minneapolis (G-4131)

Convergeone Holdings Corp ....C... 651 796-6411
Eagan (G-1522)

Dell-Comm Inc ....D... 763 783-0035
Saint Paul (G-8283)

Ideacom Mid-America Inc ....D... 651 292-0102
Saint Paul (G-8504)

Master Electric Co Inc ....D... 952 890-3555
Savage (G-9398)

Moorhead Electric Inc ....E... 218 284-1963
Moorhead (G-6330)

Norstan Communications Inc ....C... 952 352-4300
Minnetonka (G-6202)

North American Communications ....D... 651 994-6800
Eagan (G-1542)

Spectrum Solutions Inc ....E... 651 634-1800
Saint Paul (G-8976)

Techpower Inc ....E... 952 831-7444
Minneapolis (G-5806)

TELEPHONE SET REPAIR SVCS

Sel-Mor Distributing Co ....E... 952 929-0888
Minneapolis (G-5629)

TELEPHONE SOLICITATION SVCS

Dnk Management Inc ....D... 651 773-8077
Saint Paul (G-8305)

TELEPHONE SVCS

Advanced Cellular LLC...........................D... 952 469-4200
Lakeville (G-2889)

Capitol Co's Inc ....D... 651 454-4511
Saint Paul (G-7726)

CareCall Inc ....D... 320 253-0800
Sartell (G-9334)

Cooperative Response Center...............D... 507 437-2400
Austin (G-267)

Enventis Telecom Inc ....E... 218 720-2686
Duluth (G-1313)

Norstan Inc ....C... 952 352-4000
Hopkins (G-2590)

TELEVISION BROADCASTING STATIONS

Channel 12 ....E... 763 533-8196
Minneapolis (G-4055)

Duluth Superior Area ....E... 218 724-8567
Duluth (G-1304)

Fox Television Stations Inc ....C... 952 946-1234
Eden Prairie (G-1669)

Granite Broadcasting Corp ....D... 218 720-9666
Duluth (G-1341)

Granite Broadcasting Corp ....D... 218 720-9642
Duluth (G-1342)

Hubbard Broadcasting Inc ....A... 651 646-5555
Saint Paul (G-8499)

Kbjr Inc ....D... 218 727-8484
Duluth (G-1366)

KDLH News Channel ....D... 218 733-0303
Duluth (G-1368)

Kttc Television Inc ....D... 507 288-4444
Rochester (G-7159)

Midwest Kaal Corp ....E... 507 437-6666
Austin (G-283)

Multimedia Holdings ....C... 763 546-1111
Minneapolis (G-5148)

Northern Minnesota Public ....E... 218 751-3407
Bemidji (G-413)

Northwest Suburbs Community ....D... 763 533-8196
Minneapolis (G-5244)

Quincy Newspapers Inc ....D... 507 895-9969
La Crescent (G-2842)

Sinclair Broadcasting Group ....E... 651 646-2300
Saint Paul (G-8960)

Twin Cities Public Television................C... 651 222-1717
Saint Paul (G-9088)

United Communications Corp ....E... 507 625-7905
North Mankato (G-6515)

United Communications Corp ....E... 507 625-7905
Mankato (G-3232)

TELEVISION FILM PRODUCTION SVCS

In Fisherman Inc ....E... 218 829-1648
Baxter (G-330)

Metropolitan Productions Inc ....D... 612 333-1025
Minneapolis (G-5007)

New Paradigm Productions Inc ....E... 612 321-9091
Minneapolis (G-5192)

Ten Dollar Trophy LLC ....E... 952 912-9972
Hopkins (G-2644)

TEMPORARY HELP SVCS

Agri Temps Inc ....D... 320 235-1707
Willmar (G-9982)

Allied Professionals Inc ....B... 952 832-5101
Minneapolis (G-3716)

Care Network Inc ....E... 651 647-5400
Saint Paul (G-8161)

CDI Corp ....D... 507 282-8773
Rochester (G-7072)

Cynthia Cook Inc ....E... 952 854-4975
Minneapolis (G-4210)

Delta Co's LLC ....E... 952 929-5005
Minneapolis (G-4245)

Dfg Inc ....D... 612 343-8936
Minneapolis (G-4250)

Dobbs Temporary Services Inc ....E... 612 373-2600
Minneapolis (G-4268)

Doherty Employment Group Inc ....E... 952 832-8383
Minneapolis (G-4270)

Doherty Staffing Solutions ....D... 952 832-8300
Edina (G-1829)

Entegee Inc ....E... 763 383-4343
Minneapolis (G-4359)

Entegee Inc ....E... 651 739-7366
Saint Paul (G-9215)

Gary Halgran ....B... 651 917-3634
Saint Paul (G-8402)

George Konik Associates Inc ....D... 952 835-5550
Minneapolis (G-4524)

Gradstaff Inc ....E... 612 339-5332
Minneapolis (G-4545)

IG Inc ....D... 612 338-7581
Minneapolis (G-4687)

Industrial Help Inc ....E... 612 871-5650
Minneapolis (G-4698)

Interim Healthcare Of Lake ....B... 218 722-0053
Duluth (G-1359)

J-I-T Services Inc ....E... 763 545-6991
Hopkins (G-2560)

Jpg & Associates Inc ....E... 651 779-1072
Lake Elmo (G-2875)

Klick & Associate Inc ....E... 763 420-3296
Osseo (G-6627)

M S I Services ....E... 763 572-0500
Minneapolis (G-4924)

National Engineering Resources ....D... 763 561-7610
Minneapolis (G-5163)

Northern Counties Secretarial.............D... 763 427-0166
Anoka (G-210)

Primestaff Inc ....E... 651 697-2120
Saint Paul (G-8848)

Professional Radiology Svcs ....E... 763 560-0010
Minneapolis (G-5422)

Sapphire Technologies, LP ....D... 612 332-8700
Minneapolis (G-5602)

Sfn Group Inc ....C... 952 543-3300
Minneapolis (G-5646)

Sfn Group Inc ....C... 952 469-7583
Lakeville (G-2933)

Sfn Group Inc ....D... 651 501-5037
Saint Paul (G-5780)

Synico Staffing Inc ....A... 612 926-6000
Minneapolis (G-5780)

Teaching Temps Inc ....E... 763 797-9000
Minneapolis (G-5802)

TEMPORARY RELIEF SVCS

Community Action Partnership.............C... 651 645-6445
Saint Paul (G-8237)

TEN PIN CENTERS

AMF Bowling Centers Inc ....E... 763 566-6250
Minneapolis (G-3771)

Balyle Inc ....E... 320 253-2910
Sartell (G-9332)

Blainbrook Entertainment Ctr ....D... 763 755-8686
Minneapolis (G-3419)

Colonial Lanes Co ....E... 507 289-2341
Rochester (G-7086)

Degidio Inc ....E... 651 291-7105
Saint Paul (G-8282)

Lane Memory ....E... 612 721-6211
Minneapolis (G-4839)

Liberty Lanes Inc ....E... 218 773-3477
East Grand Forks (G-1570)

Maplewood Bowl Inc ....D... 651 774-8787
Saint Paul (G-8612)

Mermaid Inc ....C... 763 784-7350
Saint Paul (G-8637)

MPS Group Properties Inc ....E... 507 533-8330
Stewartville (G-9593)

Owatonna Fairlanes Corp ....E... 507 451-2524
Owatonna (G-6728)

PC Productions Inc ....E... 651 451-6222
Saint Paul *(G-7870)*
Philip's Investment Co ....D... 952 929-6810
Minneapolis *(G-5375)*
Rich Mgt Inc...............................D... 952 432-1515
Saint Paul *(G-7895)*
Rothgarn Enterprise Inc ....E... 651 345-2324
Lake City *(G-2854)*
Twin Town Bowl Inc.......................E... 507 387-3439
Mankato *(G-3210)*

TEXTILE BAGS WHOLESALERS

East Asian Trading Co Inc ....B... 763 473-3520
Minneapolis *(G-4307)*

THEATER COMPANIES

History Theatre Inc ....C... 651 292-4323
Saint Paul *(G-8486)*

THEATRICAL PRODUCERS & SVCS

Climb Theater Inc..........................D... 651 453-9275
Inver Grove Heights *(G-2743)*
Climb Theatre Inc..........................D... 651 453-9275
Inver Grove Heights *(G-2744)*
Commonweal Theatre Co ....E... 507 467-2905
Lanesboro *(G-2946)*
Guthrie Theater Foundation................C... 612 225-6000
Minneapolis *(G-4579)*
Ten Thousand Things Theatre.............E... 612 724-4494
Minneapolis *(G-5810)*

THEATRICAL PRODUCTION SVCS

Comedysportz Twin Cities ....E... 612 870-1230
Minneapolis *(G-4127)*
Great River Shakespeare ....E... 507 474-7900
Winona *(G-10099)*
Mini Kix Inc ....C... 218 829-7107
Baxter *(G-336)*
Ordway Center For The 651 282-3000
Saint Paul *(G-8790)*

TIMBER TRACT OPERATIONS

Carlson Timber Products Inc...............D... 320 245-2920
Sandstone *(G-9319)*

TIRE & TUBE REPAIR MATERIALS, WHOLESALE

Hanco Corp.................................E... 651 456-5600
Saint Paul *(G-7794)*

TIRE RECAPPING & RETREADING

Dickson Enterprises Inc ....E... 218 759-2000
Bemidji *(G-388)*
Marco Investments LLC ....E... 763 795-8145
Circle Pines *(G-1016)*
Morgan Tire & Auto Inc ....E... 651 452-4091
Saint Paul *(G-7846)*
Morgan Tire & Auto Inc ....E... 507 388-6461
Mankato *(G-3173)*
Morgan Tire & Auto Inc ....E... 612 861-2278
Minneapolis *(G-5130)*
Morgan Tire & Auto Inc ....E... 218 828-8552
Baxter *(G-338)*
Morgan Tire & Auto LLC ....E... 952 944-0458
Eden Prairie *(G-1730)*
Morgan Tire & Auto LLC ....E... 763 682-4979
Buffalo *(G-653)*
Morgan Tire & Auto LLC ....E... 763 571-4392
Minneapolis *(G-3545)*
Morgan Tire & Auto LLC ....E... 651 458-1812
Cottage Grove *(G-1105)*
Morgan Tire & Auto LLC ....E... 651 690-5007
Saint Paul *(G-8721)*
Morgan Tire & Auto LLC ....E... 651 388-3266
Red Wing *(G-6991)*
Morgan Tire & Auto LLC ....E... 507 354-4972
New Ulm *(G-6463)*
Morgan Tire & Auto LLC ....E... 763 525-1583
Minneapolis *(G-5131)*
Morgan Tire & Auto LLC ....E... 507 532-9686
Marshall *(G-3316)*
Morgan Tire & Auto LLC ....E... 320 235-1073
Willmar *(G-10028)*
Morgan Tire & Auto LLC ....E... 651 789-4361
Minneapolis *(G-6130)*
Wingfoot Commercial Tire Systs.........E... 507 454-5181
Winona *(G-10142)*

TIRES & TUBES WHOLESALERS

A & J Tba Inc 507 233-3000
New Ulm *(G-6437)*

American Tire Distributors Inc ....E... 952 345-0000
Minneapolis *(G-3761)*
Countrywide Tire & Rubber Inc ....E... 763 546-1636
Minneapolis *(G-4171)*
Samaritan Wholesale Tire Co ....E... 612 729-8000
Minneapolis *(G-5599)*
Triton Tire & Battery LLC ....E... 651 239-1200
Saint Paul *(G-7929)*
Universal Cooperatives Inc ....D... 651 239-1000
Saint Paul *(G-7938)*

TIRES & TUBES, WHOLESALE: Automotive

Bauer Built Inc.............................E... 651 646-1239
Saint Paul *(G-8092)*
Midstates Retreading & Whsle ....E... 507 288-7752
Rochester *(G-7183)*
Royal Tire Inc ....D... 320 258-7070
Saint Cloud *(G-7590)*
Tire Associates Warehouse Inc............E... 507 625-2975
Mankato *(G-3207)*
Universal Cooperatives Inc ....D... 651 239-1000
Saint Paul *(G-7938)*
Westside Wholesale Tire Inc...............E... 763 420-2100
Hamel *(G-2361)*
Wingfoot Commercial Tire Systs.........E... 507 454-5181
Winona *(G-10142)*

TIRES & TUBES, WHOLESALE: Truck

Automotive Restyling Concepts...........D... 763 535-2181
Minneapolis *(G-3840)*
Bauer Built Inc.............................E... 651 646-1239
Saint Paul *(G-8092)*
Midstates Retreading & Whsle ....E... 507 288-7752
Rochester *(G-7183)*
Royal Tire Inc ....D... 320 258-7070
Saint Cloud *(G-7590)*
Tire Associates Warehouse Inc............E... 507 625-2975
Mankato *(G-3207)*
Universal Cooperatives Inc ....D... 651 239-1000
Saint Paul *(G-7938)*

TITLE & TRUST COMPANIES

Access Information Systems Inc..........C... 952 888-8503
Minneapolis *(G-3666)*
Burnet Title LLC ....D... 952 844-6200
Edina *(G-1827)*
Collopy & Saunders Real Estate 952 829-2900
Eden Prairie *(G-1631)*
DCA Title Co ....E... 952 432-5600
Saint Paul *(G-7749)*
Lutheran Trust.............................E... 218 998-4058
Fergus Falls *(G-2090)*

TITLE ABSTRACT & SETTLEMENT OFFICES

Capitol Lien Records & Res.................E... 651 488-0100
Saint Paul *(G-8154)*
Consolidated Title & Abstract...............E... 218 722-1495
Duluth *(G-1281)*
Dakota County Abstract & Title ....E... 651 437-5600
Hastings *(G-2381)*
Edina Realty Home Services................D... 952 928-5900
Minneapolis *(G-4325)*
Edina Realty Title ....D... 952 928-5181
Minneapolis *(G-4326)*
North Star Title Inc ....D... 952 512-7400
Minneapolis *(G-5222)*
Northwest Title & Escrow Inc ....E... 651 490-9056
Saint Paul *(G-8769)*
Registered Abstractors Inc ....E... 763 427-3012
Anoka *(G-219)*
Rels Title Services LLC ....E... 651 647-4855
Saint Paul *(G-8887)*
Tri-County Abstract & Title ....E... 320 253-2096
Saint Cloud *(G-7619)*

TITLE INSURANCE AGENTS

RELS Title Services LLC ....D... 952 933-8804
Hopkins *(G-2614)*
Signature Title Co ....E... 952 942-5155
Eden Prairie *(G-1778)*

TITLE INSURANCE: Guarantee Of Titles

Universal Title & Financial ....E... 952 829-0899
Minneapolis *(G-5922)*

TITLE INSURANCE: Real Estate

Burnet Title LLC ....D... 952 844-6200
Edina *(G-1827)*
Commonwealth Land Title Insce ....E... 651 227-8571
Minneapolis *(G-4135)*
Consolidated Title & Abstract...............E... 218 722-1495
Duluth *(G-1281)*

Homeservices of America Inc ....E... 888 485-0018
Minneapolis *(G-4672)*
Old Republic National Title.................C... 612 371-1111
Minneapolis *(G-5268)*

TITLE SEARCH COMPANIES

First American Title Insurance ....E... 612 337-5900
Minneapolis *(G-4440)*
Isgn Fulfillment Services Inc ....D... 952 512-7400
Minneapolis *(G-4736)*
RELS Title Services LLC ....D... 952 933-8804
Hopkins *(G-2614)*

TOBACCO & PRDTS, WHOLESALE: Cigarettes

Bernick's Full-Line Vending ....E... 320 656-2131
Waite Park *(G-9817)*
Minter-Weisman Co ....B... 763 545-3706
Minneapolis *(G-5105)*

TOBACCO & TOBACCO PRDTS WHOLESALERS

A H Hermel Candy & Tobacco Co ....D... 507 387-5634
Mankato *(G-3098)*
Fritz Co Inc ....D... 651 459-9751
Newport *(G-6486)*
Granite City Jobbing Co Inc ....E... 320 252-1782
Saint Cloud *(G-7521)*
Henry's Foods Inc ....C... 320 763-3194
Alexandria *(G-104)*
Hermel Coffee Service ....E... 507 387-5634
Mankato *(G-3138)*
Sandstrom's Inc ....E... 218 326-0567
Grand Rapids *(G-2307)*
Watson Co Inc.............................E... 763 689-3722
Cambridge *(G-846)*

TOILETRIES, WHOLESALE: Cosmetics, Perfumes & Hair Prdts

Custom Hbc Corp ....D... 952 442-8241
Waconia *(G-9784)*
Minter-Weisman Co ....B... 763 545-3706
Minneapolis *(G-5105)*
Wise Essentials Inc ....E... 651 699-4468
Saint Paul *(G-9162)*

TOILETRIES, WHOLESALE: Hair Preparations

Barbers Hairstyling For Men ....D... 952 947-7777
Minneapolis *(G-3867)*

TOILETRIES, WHOLESALE: Toilet Preparations

Contract Hardware Co Inc ....E... 651 780-0010
Circle Pines *(G-1007)*

TOILETRIES, WHOLESALE: Toilet Soap

Master's Miracle Inc ....D... 763 493-3200
Osseo *(G-6635)*

TOILETRIES, WHOLESALE: Toiletries

Master's Miracle Inc ....D... 763 493-3200
Osseo *(G-6635)*

TOLL BRIDGE OPERATIONS

Minnesota Dakota & Western ....E... 218 285-5690
International Falls *(G-2727)*

TOOL REPAIR SVCS

Precision Repair & Calibration.............E... 763 784-1704
Minneapolis *(G-3572)*
Total Tool Supply Inc ....D... 651 646-4055
Saint Paul *(G-9073)*

TOUR OPERATORS

Iyanka Dakota Coaches Inc ....E... 507 644-3380
Morton *(G-6381)*
Tourco's Firstline Tours Inc 763 780-2985
Minneapolis *(G-3619)*
Travel Leaders Group LLC ....A... 952 914-6500
Eden Prairie *(G-1797)*

TOURIST AGENCY: Transportation, Lodging & Car Rental

American Express Travel....................E... 651 731-9396
Saint Paul *(G-9183)*
Blue Green Vacation Corp ....E... 888 456-0412
Bloomington *(G-490)*

SERVICES

Capital City Travel Inc ....E... 651 287-4906
Saint Paul *(G-8150)*

Emerald Travel Management Co 507 345-8797
Mankato *(G-3126)*

Ljk Co's Inc..............C... 952 944-5462
Minnetonka *(G-6188)*

Northeast Securities Corp..............612 379-8811
Minneapolis *(G-5225)*

TOURIST INFORMATION BUREAU

Duluth Entertainment Conv ....A... 218 722-5573
Duluth *(G-1298)*

Historical Society of MN ....E... 651 297-2555
Saint Paul *(G-8485)*

TOURIST LODGINGS

Briggs Hennum Inc ....E... 218 634-2168
Baudette *(G-314)*

Ruttger's Birchmont Lodge Inc ....E... 218 751-4131
Bemidji *(G-425)*

TOYS & HOBBY GOODS & SPLYS, WHOLESALE: Arts/Crafts Eqpt/Sply

Midwest Craft Distributors Inc..............E... 952 252-7043
Excelsior *(G-1947)*

TOYS & HOBBY GOODS & SPLYS, WHOLESALE: Bingo Games & Splys

Triple Crown Gaming Inc ....E... 320 251-5373
Saint Cloud *(G-7622)*

TOYS & HOBBY GOODS & SPLYS, WHOLESALE: Toys & Games

Mid-States Distributing Co Inc..............E... 651 698-8831
Saint Paul *(G-8652)*

Splatball Inc ....E... 612 378-0385
Minneapolis *(G-5721)*

TOYS & HOBBY GOODS & SPLYS, WHOLESALE: Toys, NEC

Gopher News Co ....D... 763 546-5300
Minneapolis *(G-4542)*

H Enterprises International ....E... 320 453-2626
Eden Valley *(G-1821)*

Manhattan Group LLC ....D... 612 337-9600
Minneapolis *(G-4942)*

TOYS & HOBBY GOODS & SPLYS, WHOLESALE: Video Games

Destineer Inc ....E... 763 231-8000
Minneapolis *(G-4249)*

TOYS, HOBBY GOODS & SPLYS WHOLESALERS

Food Market Merchandising Inc..............E... 952 894-0110
Minneapolis *(G-4462)*

TRACTOR REPAIR SVCS

Winter Truck Line Inc ....E... 218 935-2236
Mahnomen *(G-3092)*

TRADE SHOW ARRANGEMENT SVCS

Advanstar Holdings Corp..............218 740-7200
Duluth *(G-1232)*

Cenaiko Expo Inc ....E... 763 755-8111
Minneapolis *(G-3430)*

Cygnus Expositions ....D... 952 894-8007
Burnsville *(G-705)*

TRANSLATION & INTERPRETATION SVCS

Interpretation & Trans ....E... 651 292-9701
Saint Paul *(G-8521)*

Kj International Resources Ltd ....E... 612 288-9494
Minneapolis *(G-4814)*

Prisma International Inc ....E... 612 338-1500
Minneapolis *(G-5412)*

Tembua Inc ....E... 952 435-8178
Lakeville *(G-2937)*

University Language Center Inc ....E... 612 379-3823
Minneapolis *(G-5926)*

TRANSPORTATION AGENTS & BROKERS

Island Freight Brokerage LLC..............E... 507 288-5758
Rochester *(G-7143)*

Online Freight Services Inc..............E... 651 468-6868
Saint Paul *(G-7857)*

Telin Transportation Group LLC ....E... 763 262-3328
Becker *(G-359)*

TRANSPORTATION ARRANGEMENT SVCS, PASSENGER: Airline Ticket

Continental Airlines Inc..............D... 612 726-5679
Saint Paul *(G-7959)*

TRANSPORTATION ARRANGEMENT SVCS, PASSENGER: Carpool/Vanpool

First Student Inc..............C... 612 378-7833
Minneapolis *(G-4446)*

Outsource Administrators Inc ....E... 952 944-5462
Minnetonka *(G-6208)*

TRANSPORTATION ARRANGEMENT SVCS, PASSENGER: Tours, Conducted

Brennaville Inc ....E... 507 467-2512
Preston *(G-6895)*

TRANSPORTATION ARRANGEMNT SVCS, PASS: Travel Tour Pkgs, Whol

M L T Inc ....C... 952 474-2540
Minneapolis *(G-4921)*

TRANSPORTATION BROKERS: Truck

Alltemp Distribution Co ....E... 763 571-0215
Minneapolis *(G-3396)*

Berger Transfer & Storage Inc..............D... 651 639-2260
Saint Paul *(G-8104)*

Brenny Specialized Inc ....E... 320 363-6996
Saint Joseph *(G-7652)*

Hicks Trucking Co of ....E... 320 693-3292
Litchfield *(G-2985)*

Interlog USA Inc ....E... 612 789-3456
Minneapolis *(G-4718)*

Minn-Tex Express Inc ....E... 320 277-3562
Pierz *(G-6805)*

Promises + Inc..............763 497-3727
Albertville *(G-76)*

SAV Enterprises Inc..............E... 763 278-3340
Minneapolis *(G-3596)*

Schak Trucking Inc ....E... 507 247-5204
Tyler *(G-9713)*

Transway Express Inc ....E... 651 686-7000
Northfield *(G-6544)*

Waymore Transportation Inc ....E... 763 786-9076
Minneapolis *(G-3640)*

TRANSPORTATION EPQT & SPLYS, WHOL: Aircraft Engs/Eng Parts

Canard Aerospace Corp..............E... 952 944-7990
Shakopee *(G-9426)*

TRANSPORTATION EPQT & SPLYS, WHOLESALE: Acft/Space Vehicle

Wipaire Inc..............D... 651 451-1205
South Saint Paul *(G-9553)*

TRANSPORTATION EPQT & SPLYS, WHOLESALE: Marine Crafts/Splys

Code Welding & Mfg Inc ....E... 763 792-6632
Minneapolis *(G-3435)*

TRANSPORTATION EQPT & SPLYS WHOLESALERS, NEC

Bemidji Aviation Services Inc..............E... 218 751-1880
Bemidji *(G-377)*

TRANSPORTATION SVCS, AIR, SCHEDULED: Helicopter Carriers

Mesaba Airlines..............E... 651 367-5000
Eagan *(G-1537)*

Mesaba Aviation Inc ....A... 651 367-5000
Eagan *(G-1538)*

TRANSPORTATION SVCS, NEC

Aging Services For Communities ....E... 507 364-5663
Montgomery *(G-6263)*

Chamber Trill Public Transit ....E... 320 983-5064
Milaca *(G-3375)*

Mort's Transportation Inc..............E... 320 269-7340
Montevideo *(G-6255)*

Sav Logistics Inc..............E... 763 489-4213
Minneapolis *(G-3597)*

TRANSPORTATION SVCS, WATER: Bays & Sounds-Ocean, Freight

North Star International Inc ....E... 651 379-5030
Saint Paul *(G-7851)*

TRANSPORTATION SVCS: Airport

Safari Airport Taxi Service..............D... 763 424-9070
Minneapolis *(G-5587)*

Taylor Limousines Inc..............C... 612 722-4467
Minneapolis *(G-5795)*

TRANSPORTATION SVCS: Bus Line Operations

Metropolitan Transit Commn..............C... 612 341-4287
Minneapolis *(G-5010)*

Rochester City Line Co ....E... 507 288-4353
Rochester *(G-7230)*

TRANSPORTATION SVCS: Bus Line, Intercity

Red River Trails Inc ....E... 218 236-0300
Moorhead *(G-6337)*

TRANSPORTATION SVCS: Bus Line, Interstate

Jefferson Partners LP ....C... 612 359-3400
Minneapolis *(G-4757)*

TRANSPORTATION SVCS: Commuter Bus Operation

E Z Air Park Inc ....E... 651 454-1302
Saint Paul *(G-7754)*

TRANSPORTATION SVCS: Highway, Intercity, Special Svcs

Miller Medi Van Inc ....E... 612 332-2888
Minneapolis *(G-5044)*

TRANSPORTATION SVCS: Maintenance Facilities, Buses

Minnesota Department of Trans..........C... 218 828-2678
Baxter *(G-337)*

TRANSPORTATION SVCS: Railroad Switching

Bnsf Railway Co .,..............E... 218 727-8194
Duluth *(G-1255)*

Minnesota Commercial Railway..........D... 651 646-2010
Saint Paul *(G-8678)*

TRANSPORTATION SVCS: Railroad Terminals

Bnsf Railway Co ....C... 320 259-3208
Saint Cloud *(G-7462)*

Minnesota Commercial Railway..........D... 651 646-2010
Saint Paul *(G-8678)*

TRANSPORTATION SVCS: Rental, Hearse With Driver

Dunn Enterprises Inc ....C... 612 627-5661
Minneapolis *(G-4297)*

TRANSPORTATION SVCS: Rental, Local

Metropolitan Transportation..............D... 763 571-1541
Minneapolis *(G-3541)*

TRANSPORTATION SVCS: Vanpool Operation

Transit Team Inc..............E... 612 332-3323
Minneapolis *(G-5847)*

TRANSPORTATION: Air, Nonscheduled Passenger

3M Co..............D... 651 778-5302
Saint Paul *(G-9045)*

Wright Aero Inc..............E... 320 963-5094
Maple Lake *(G-3268)*

TRANSPORTATION: Air, Nonscheduled, NEC

Federal Express Corp ....B... 612 713-8500
Minneapolis *(G-4420)*

Northwest Airlines Inc..............A... 612 726-2111
Minneapolis *(G-5238)*

Employment codes: A=Over 500 employees, B=251-500,
C=101-250, D=51-100, E=25-50

2011 Harris Minnesota
Services Directory

© Harris InfoSource 1-866-281-6415
771

SERVICES

TRANSPORTATION: Air, Scheduled Freight

MN Airlines LLC ....A... 651 681-3900
Mendota Heights *(G-3367)*
Northwest Airlines Corp ....A... 612 726-2111
Eagan *(G-1543)*
Northwest Airlines Inc ....A... 612 726-2111
Minneapolis *(G-5238)*

TRANSPORTATION: Air, Scheduled Passenger

Chisholm-Hibbing Airport ....E... 218 262-3451
Hibbing *(G-2440)*
Compass Airlines Inc ....E... 612 713-6800
Minneapolis *(G-4146)*
Northwest Airlines Inc ....A... 612 726-3896
Saint Paul *(G-7855)*

TRANSPORTATION: Bus Transit Systems

Anoka County Traveler ....E... 763 323-5222
Minneapolis *(G-3405)*
Bauck Busing Ltd ....E... 218 346-4599
Perham *(G-6794)*
First Student Inc ....C... 651 628-0046
Saint Paul *(G-8381)*
Robert Lemieur & Sons Inc ....E... 320 632-9141
Little Falls *(G-3018)*
Rochester City Line Co ....E... 507 288-4353
Rochester *(G-7230)*
St Louis Park Transportation ....E... 952 591-1538
Minneapolis *(G-5727)*

TRANSPORTATION: Deep Sea Domestic Freight

SBS Transportation Inc ....E... 651 256-1555
Saint Paul *(G-8932)*

TRANSPORTATION: Local Passenger, NEC

AC Transportation Inc ....E... 763 235-2222
Osseo *(G-6591)*
Care Transportation Inc ....E... 320 253-7729
Saint Cloud *(G-7470)*
Crosby Ironton Transportation ....E... 218 546-6156
Crosby *(G-1146)*
Eclipse Transportation Inc ....E... 651 293-1111
Saint Paul *(G-7757)*
Grove Cottage Emergency Med ....D... 651 458-2865
Cottage Grove *(G-1103)*
Lakes Medi-Van Inc ....C... 218 847-1729
Detroit Lakes *(G-1204)*
Mahnomen County Heartland ....E... 218 935-2560
Mahnomen *(G-3088)*
Northland Transportation Inc ....E... 952 922-6876
Burnsville *(G-766)*
On Movin Inc ....E... 763 784-7111
Minneapolis *(G-3560)*
Palmer Bus Service of Bold MN ....E... 507 386-0210
Olivia *(G-6562)*
Peace Transportation Inc ....D... 952 595-9030
Minneapolis *(G-5358)*
Ready Bus Line Co Inc ....D... 507 895-2349
La Crescent *(G-2843)*

TRANSPORTATION: Sightseeing Buses

Shubat Transportation Co ....E... 218 262-1042
Hibbing *(G-2475)*

TRANSPORTATION: Sightseeing, Boat

Afton St Croix Co ....E... 651 436-8883
Afton *(G-6)*

TRANSPORTATION: Transit Systems, NEC

Darts ....C... 651 455-1560
Saint Paul *(G-7748)*
Duluth Transit Authority ....D... 218 722-7283
Duluth *(G-1306)*
Dunn Enterprises Inc ....C... 612 627-5661
Minneapolis *(G-4297)*
First Student Inc ....C... 651 628-0046
Saint Paul *(G-8381)*
Minnesota Department of Trans ....A... 612 349-7332
Minneapolis *(G-5074)*
Osseo Brooklyn School Bus Co ....C... 763 425-2542
Osseo *(G-6647)*
R&S Transport Inc ....D... 507 289-5080
Rochester *(G-7215)*
Supershuttle Minnesota Inc ....E... 612 827-7777
Saint Paul *(G-7965)*

TRAVEL AGENCIES

A A A Minneapolis ....D... 952 944-9585
Minneapolis *(G-3645)*
Carlson Holdings Inc ....A... 763 212-5000
Minnetonka *(G-6152)*
Carlson Travel Group Inc ....E... 651 406-6000
Saint Paul *(G-7728)*
Graves Hospitality Corp ....D... 612 677-1100
Minneapolis *(G-4547)*
Navigant International Rocky ....E... 612 375-2884
Minneapolis *(G-5175)*
Northfield Lines Inc ....E... 507 645-5267
Northfield *(G-6518)*
Ottertail Coaches Inc ....D... 218 739-3393
Fergus Falls *(G-2112)*
Outdoor Adventure Travel Inc ....E... 612 866-2503
Minneapolis *(G-5300)*
Outsource Administrators Inc ....E... 952 944-5462
Minnetonka *(G-6208)*
Rica Costa Ventures Inc ....E... 651 426-9262
Hugo *(G-2682)*
Travel Leaders 952 941-8900
Eden Prairie *(G-1796)*
Travel Leaders Group LLC ....A... 952 914-6500
Eden Prairie *(G-1797)*
Travel One Inc ....E... 952 854-2551
Minneapolis *(G-5849)*
Travelnet Solutions Inc ....E... 651 757-4905
Cottage Grove *(G-1108)*
Umi Co Inc ....D... 612 331-2566
Minneapolis *(G-5899)*

TRAVEL ARRANGEMENT SVCS: Passenger

Scs Dialaride ....E... 952 474-7441
Spring Park *(G-9566)*

TRAVEL CLUBS

A A A Minneapolis ....D... 952 944-9585
Minneapolis *(G-3645)*

TRAVELER ACCOMMODATIONS, NEC

Americ Inn of Ham Lake ....E... 763 755-2100
Anoka *(G-151)*
American Hospitality Mgt ....E... 507 446-8900
Owatonna *(G-6691)*
AmericInn Motel & Suites ....E... 952 758-7300
New Prague *(G-6421)*
AmericInn Shakopee ....D... 952 445-6775
Shakopee *(G-9418)*
Appletree Motel Partnership ....C... 952 854-9000
Minneapolis *(G-3790)*
Best Western Chaska River Inn ....E... 952 448-7877
Chaska *(G-955)*
Best Western Dakota Ridge ....E... 651 452-0100
Saint Paul *(G-7718)*
Best Western of Thief River ....D... 218 681-7555
Thief River Falls *(G-9663)*
Best Western Riverport Inn ....E... 507 452-0606
Winona *(G-10081)*
Bloomington Hospitality LLC ....B... 763 367-9200
Minneapolis *(G-3914)*
Bois Forte Enterprises ....B... 218 753-6400
Tower *(G-9686)*
BR Motels Inc ....E... 320 253-5530
Saint Cloud *(G-7464)*
Brutger Equities Inc ....E... 218 727-3110
Duluth *(G-1257)*
Bryanston Group Inc ....E... 651 636-6730
Saint Paul *(G-8137)*
Burnsville Development Ltd ....D... 952 435-2100
Burnsville *(G-689)*
C H Suites of Chanhassen MN ....E... 952 937-2424
Chanhassen *(G-912)*
Canal Park Lodge ....D... 218 279-6000
Duluth *(G-1260)*
Canal Properties Inc ....E... 218 720-3000
Duluth *(G-1261)*
Carlson Holdings Inc ....A... 763 212-5000
Minnetonka *(G-6152)*
Carlson Hotels Management Corp ....C... 612 339-4900
Minneapolis *(G-4015)*
Carpenter & Torgerson II LLC ....E... 507 536-0040
Rochester *(G-7071)*
Chin Yuen Silver Fox Inn Inc ....E... 763 295-4000
Monticello *(G-6267)*
Corporate Commission of The ....A... 320 532-8800
Onamia *(G-6568)*
Corporate Commission of The ....A... 320 384-7101
Hinckley *(G-2483)*
Country Inn & Suites By ....E... 651 982-9799
Forest Lake *(G-2159)*
Country Inn & Suites By ....E... 763 241-6990
Elk River *(G-1869)*

Country Inn & Suites Duluth ....D... 218 740-4500
Duluth *(G-1282)*
Country Inns & Suites By ....E... 952 854-5555
Minneapolis *(G-4169)*
Country Inns & Suites By ....E... 763 473-3008
Minneapolis *(G-4168)*
Country Inns & Suites By ....E... 763 212-2525
Minneapolis *(G-4170)*
Courtyard By Marriott ....D... 952 942-9100
Eden Prairie *(G-1636)*
Courtyard By Marriott ....D... 952 452-2000
Saint Paul *(G-7738)*
CP Saddle Brook LLC ....C... 952 854-7441
Bloomington *(G-492)*
Crestline Hotels & Resorts Inc ....D... 651 291-8800
Saint Paul *(G-8268)*
CSM Corp of Minnesota ....E... 651 746-8000
Saint Paul *(G-8273)*
CSM Corp of Minnesota ....E... 952 738-7300
Minneapolis *(G-4192)*
CSM Corp of Minnesota ....E... 952 829-0033
Eden Prairie *(G-1638)*
CSM Corp of Minnesota ....E... 612 340-1300
Minneapolis *(G-4193)*
CSM Corp of Minnesota ....E... 612 375-1700
Minneapolis *(G-4194)*
CSM Corp of Minnesota ....D... 952 593-1918
Minneapolis *(G-4195)*
Cynw LLC ....E... 763 425-5355
Maple Grove *(G-3238)*
D D D Motel Corp ....D... 507 625-9333
Mankato *(G-3224)*
D D D Motel Corp ....C... 507 345-1234
Mankato *(G-3121)*
Davidson Hotel Co ....E... 763 566-8000
Minneapolis *(G-4227)*
Dehn's Country Manor Inc ....E... 763 420-6460
Osseo *(G-6609)*
Dhm Minneapolis Hotel, LP ....C... 763 489-2570
Minneapolis *(G-4251)*
Diversified Motel Properties ....C... 218 728-3601
Duluth *(G-1294)*
Djont Operations LLC ....C... 952 854-1000
Minneapolis *(G-4265)*
Doubletree Corp ....E... 952 542-8600
Minneapolis *(G-4282)*
Drover's Inn & Restaurant Inc ....E... 320 252-6034
South Saint Paul *(G-9526)*
Duluth Lodging Inc ....E... 218 628-1464
Duluth *(G-1300)*
Duluth Lodging Inc ....E... 218 628-1464
Duluth *(G-1301)*
E T C Enterprises Inc ....E... 320 240-0567
Saint Cloud *(G-7500)*
Eagan Lodging Group LLC ....E... 651 450-1100
Inver Grove Heights *(G-2748)*
Eden Fch Prairie LLC ....E... 952 952-9000
Eden Prairie *(G-1649)*
Edgewater Management LLC ....E... 218 751-3603
Bemidji *(G-389)*
Em - Ty Corp ....D... 651 645-0311
Saint Paul *(G-8334)*
Enn Leasing Co II LLC ....E... 651 688-0363
Saint Paul *(G-7765)*
Enn Leasing Co II LLC ....E... 651 688-0363
Saint Paul *(G-7764)*
Fairfield Inn ....D... 218 723-8607
Duluth *(G-1317)*
Fch Minnetonka ....E... 952 912-9999
Minnetonka *(G-6168)*
First Class Hospitality Group ....E... 320 251-1500
Saint Cloud *(G-7510)*
Forstrom & Torgerson Hnw LLC ....E... 763 494-4498
Maple Grove *(G-3241)*
Forstrom & Torgerson Hs LLC ....E... 651 415-1956
Saint Paul *(G-8389)*
Forstrom & Torgerson LLP ....C... 651 482-0402
Saint Paul *(G-8390)*
Forstrom & Torgerson Ssnw LLC ....E... 763 494-8856
Maple Grove *(G-3242)*
Frolander Island Resort ....D... 218 386-3019
Warroad *(G-9870)*
G G Tucson Inc ....D... 218 723-8433
Duluth *(G-1330)*
Grand Marais Hotel Co Inc ....E... 218 387-2448
Grand Marais *(G-2260)*
Graves Hospitality Corp ....D... 612 677-1100
Minneapolis *(G-4547)*
Hgib LLC ....E... 952 831-1012
Bloomington *(G-501)*
Hie LLC ....E... 651 681-9266
Eagan *(G-1528)*
Hilton Garden Inn ....E... 651 686-4605
Eagan *(G-1529)*

SERVICES

Hilton Garden Inn - St Paul ....D... 651 735-4100
Saint Paul *(G-9230)*
Hilton Hotels Corp ....A... 612 376-1000
Minneapolis *(G-4650)*
Hinw LLC ....C... 763 425-3800
Willmar *(G-10009)*
Hinw LLC ....C... 763 425-3800
Maple Grove *(G-3245)*
Holiday Inn Express & Suites ....E... 651 275-1401
Stillwater *(G-9621)*
Holiday Inn Sunspree Resort ....E... 218 365-6565
Ely *(G-1914)*
Hsnb LLC ....E... 651 631-8002
New Brighton *(G-6410)*
Hsslp LLC ....E... 952 544-0495
Saint Louis Park *(G-7662)*
Hyatt Corp ....B... 612 370-1234
Minneapolis *(G-4683)*
I D D D Inc ....D... 320 352-5241
Sauk Centre *(G-9347)*
Improvement LP ....D... 218 262-3481
Hibbing *(G-2456)*
Infinity Motel Holdings LLC ....E... 320 763-9900
Alexandria *(G-106)*
International Management Co ....D... 218 283-4451
International Falls *(G-2724)*
Interstate Hotels & Resorts ....E... 952 854-5558
Minneapolis *(G-4727)*
Isle West Associates, LLP ....D... 612 331-1800
Minneapolis *(G-4737)*
Kelly Midwest Ventures LP ....D... 651 227-8711
Saint Paul *(G-8544)*
Kelly Midwest Ventures LP ....C... 320 253-0606
Saint Cloud *(G-7539)*
Kinseth Hotel Corp ....C... 952 884-8211
Minneapolis *(G-4811)*
Laird LLC ....E... 507 444-0818
Owatonna *(G-6721)*
Lakeland Lodging LP ....D... 218 829-8730
Alexandria *(G-110)*
Lakeside Hospitality LLP ....D... 218 847-2121
Brainerd *(G-572)*
Land & Cabins LLC ....D... 320 384-6488
Hinckley *(G-2485)*
Larken Inc ....D... 952 830-1300
Minneapolis *(G-4844)*
Layline Corp ....E... 651 385-9060
Red Wing *(G-6988)*
Libor Management LLC ....E... 763 561-0900
Minneapolis *(G-4871)*
Lino Lake Lodging LLC ....E... 763 746-9500
Lino Lakes *(G-2973)*
Lyon Lodging LLC ....E... 507 532-3070
Marshall *(G-3308)*
Lyric Block Development Corp ....C... 218 722-1202
Duluth *(G-1386)*
M & C Hotel Interests Inc ....C... 612 332-6000
Minneapolis *(G-4913)*
Madison Properties Inc ....D... 218 847-2121
Detroit Lakes *(G-1208)*
Mankato Fairfield Inn ....E... 507 386-1220
Mankato *(G-3161)*
Marcus Hotels Inc ....C... 612 338-2288
Minneapolis *(G-4946)*
Marriott ....E... 952 893-9300
Minneapolis *(G-4955)*
Marriott ....E... 763 577-1600
Plymouth *(G-6872)*
MB St Paul Inc ....D... 651 731-2220
Saint Paul *(G-8620)*
Midwest Heritage Inn of ....C... 952 858-8475
Bloomington *(G-505)*
Midwest of Rochester Inc ....D... 507 289-8866
Rochester *(G-7184)*
Midwest of Rochester Inc ....E... 507 289-8866
Rochester *(G-7185)*
Minnesota Liquor Retailers Inc ....E... 651 772-0910
Saint Paul *(G-8697)*
Minnetonka Minnesota Hotel L P ....D... 952 593-0000
Minnetonka *(G-6198)*
Mirumi Inc ....E... 952 445-9779
Shakopee *(G-9458)*
Moorhead Hospitality LP ....D... 218 284-1000
Moorhead *(G-6331)*
Mpls Hotel Management Ltd ....E... 507 281-8000
Rochester *(G-7188)*
Mplsp Hotel Corp ....D... 952 854-3400
Minneapolis *(G-5142)*
Murray Williamson ....E... 218 751-8481
Bemidji *(G-404)*
Nath Midwest Lodging LLC ....C... 952 853-1400
Minneapolis *(G-5158)*
National Lodging Co's Inc ....E... 507 825-5871
Pipestone *(G-6832)*
Nb Saint Paul Inc ....D... 651 731-2220
Saint Paul *(G-8742)*
Normandy Inn Inc ....E... 612 370-1400
Minneapolis *(G-5210)*
North Central Management Inc ....E... 763 509-9500
Osseo *(G-6642)*
Northcott Hospitality Intl ....D... 952 294-5000
Chanhassen *(G-934)*
Northcott Hospitality Intl ....E... 952 934-3888
Chanhassen *(G-933)*
Oak Hotels Inc ....E... 651 636-6730
Saint Paul *(G-8777)*
175 Fort LLC ....E... 651 225-1515
Saint Paul *(G-8787)*
Owatonna Hospitality Partners ....E... 507 455-1142
Owatonna *(G-6729)*
P R K Inc ....E... 612 341-3300
Minneapolis *(G-5307)*
Pah-Dt Minneapolis Suites ....D... 612 332-6800
Minneapolis *(G-5313)*
Park Gooseberry Motel Cabins ....E... 218 834-3751
Two Harbors *(G-9711)*
Pattern Stations Inc ....D... 763 441-6833
Monticello *(G-6282)*
Professional Hospitality LLC ....E... 320 259-8999
Saint Cloud *(G-7575)*
Professional Hospitality LLC ....E... 507 287-6758
Rochester *(G-7212)*
Radison Hotel ....C... 651 636-4567
Saint Paul *(G-8868)*
Radisson Hotels International ....C... 763 212-5000
Minnetonka *(G-6218)*
Radisson Hotels International ....C... 651 291-8800
Saint Paul *(G-8869)*
Raymond Management Co Inc ....E... 507 287-9050
Rochester *(G-7217)*
Red Roof Inns Inc ....E... 651 738-7160
Saint Paul *(G-9266)*
Red Roof Inns Inc ....E... 952 890-1420
Burnsville *(G-787)*
Regency Midwest Ventures LP ....C... 320 762-1124
Alexandria *(G-119)*
Regency Plymouth Hotel ....C... 763 559-6600
Minneapolis *(G-5485)*
Residence Inn ....E... 612 677-1000
Minneapolis *(G-5523)*
River Valley Hospitality LLC ....E... 952 854-1771
Minneapolis *(G-5544)*
Rivers Hotel Co Inc ....D... 507 457-0977
Winona *(G-10121)*
Riverside Lodging ....E... 651 388-0491
Red Wing *(G-7003)*
Rlj Bloomington Hotel LLC ....E... 952 854-0900
Minneapolis *(G-5549)*
Rogers Hospitality LLC ....E... 763 428-3000
Rogers *(G-7341)*
Sand Co Inc ....E... 507 388-8555
Mankato *(G-3191)*
Sandman Motel LLC ....E... 763 559-1222
Minneapolis *(G-5600)*
Sandman Motels LLC ....E... 952 932-9987
Hopkins *(G-2626)*
Seven Corners Hotel Partners ....C... 612 333-4646
Minneapolis *(G-5641)*
Seven Corners Hotel Partners ....C... 612 333-4646
Minneapolis *(G-5642)*
Shady Oak Hospitality LP ....E... 952 995-9000
Eden Prairie *(G-1776)*
Shaner Hotel Group LP ....D... 952 893-9300
Minneapolis *(G-5648)*
Shingle Creek Hospitality LLP ....E... 763 566-7500
Minneapolis *(G-5655)*
Six Continents Hotels Inc ....D... 952 831-8000
Minneapolis *(G-5683)*
Somerset Hospitality LLC ....E... 952 894-6124
Savage *(G-9407)*
Sonor Hotel Corp ....C... 507 288-1844
Rochester *(G-7257)*
Southern Hospitality Inc ....E... 952 831-9595
Minneapolis *(G-5709)*
St Cloud Suite Hotel Inc ....D... 320 654-1661
Saint Cloud *(G-7606)*
Starwood Hotels & Resorts ....C... 612 331-1900
Minneapolis *(G-5744)*
Starwood Hotels & Resorts ....C... 612 215-3720
Minneapolis *(G-5745)*
Sunstone Hotel Management Inc ....D... 507 289-8646
Rochester *(G-7268)*
Sunstone Hotel Properties Inc ....E... 507 282-2581
Rochester *(G-7269)*
Tb Duluth LLC ....C... 218 727-8981
Duluth *(G-1479)*
Tcbh Inc ....D... 651 454-3434
Saint Paul *(G-7918)*
Thm Master Te LLC ....D... 612 340-2000
Minneapolis *(G-5816)*
Tofte Management Co LLC ....C... 218 663-7296
Tofte *(G-9684)*
Torgerson Hospitality LLC ....D... 507 359-2941
New Ulm *(G-6477)*
Torgerson Properties LP ....D... 507 238-4771
Fairmont *(G-1983)*
Torgerson Properties LP ....D... 507 433-6720
Austin *(G-290)*
Tpi Core Inc ....D... 320 231-2301
Willmar *(G-10048)*
Tpi Core Inc ....D... 507 433-1000
Austin *(G-291)*
Travel Suites of Coon Rapids ....E... 763 780-3797
Minneapolis *(G-3621)*
Travelodge & Suite ....E... 218 233-5333
Moorhead *(G-6344)*
Travelodge Tower ....C... 651 735-2333
Saint Paul *(G-9078)*
Turnery Properties LP ....E... 763 546-6277
Minneapolis *(G-5866)*
University Inn Associates, A ....C... 612 379-8888
Minneapolis *(G-5924)*
USP Hotel Services LLC ....E... 651 578-2563
Saint Paul *(G-9287)*
Victoria Inn ....D... 320 587-6030
Hutchinson *(G-2716)*
W B M Holding Co ....E... 952 831-9595
Minneapolis *(G-5986)*
W2005 Fargo Hotels Realty, LP ....E... 952 854-1687
Bloomington *(G-525)*
W2005 New Century Hotel ....E... 952 835-6643
Minneapolis *(G-5990)*
W2005 New Century Hotel ....E... 763 541-1094
Hopkins *(G-2656)*
W2007 Equity Inns Realty LLC ....E... 952 854-0700
Minneapolis *(G-5991)*
Waterfront Plaza Hotel Co LLC ....E... 218 727-4663
Duluth *(G-1499)*
White Earth Band of Chippewa ....A... 218 935-2711
Mahnomen *(G-3091)*
Winona Inn LP ....E... 507 454-4390
Winona *(G-10150)*
Wks Vadnais Heights LLC ....E... 651 484-2400
Vadnais Heights *(G-9721)*
Wsi - Rwp LLC ....D... 901 821-4117
Bloomington *(G-527)*
Wyndham International Inc ....C... 952 831-3131
Minneapolis *(G-6090)*
Zenith Rogers LLC ....E... 763 425-0044
Rogers *(G-7348)*

TRAVERTINE: Dimension

Biesanz Stone Co ....E... 507 454-4336
Winona *(G-10082)*

TREE FARM

Wolcyn Tree Farms ....E... 763 689-3346
Cambridge *(G-847)*

TROPICAL FISH WHOLESALERS

A World of Fish Inc ....E... 612 866-2026
Minneapolis *(G-3651)*

TRUCK & FREIGHT TERMINALS & SUPPORT ACTIVITIES

Malark Logistics Inc ....D... 763 428-3564
Brooklyn Park *(G-616)*
Midwest Motor Express Inc ....E... 763 784-0650
Saint Paul *(G-8660)*
Mississippi Transport Inc ....D... 651 439-5773
Stillwater *(G-9630)*
United Parcel Service Inc ....E... 651 367-8200
Saint Paul *(G-7936)*
Vitran Express Inc ....E... 320 485-2333
Winsted *(G-10166)*
Vitran Express Inc ....C... 763 913-3450
Mounds View *(G-6391)*

TRUCK BODY SHOP

Truck Utilities Inc ....D... 651 484-3305
Saint Paul *(G-9084)*

TRUCK DRIVER SVCS

Ampro Services Inc ....E... 651 631-5924
Saint Paul *(G-8046)*
Hicks Trucking Inc ....E... 320 693-3292
Litchfield *(G-2986)*
Midwest Driver Corp ....B... 952 884-0765
Minneapolis *(G-5027)*

Employment codes: A=Over 500 employees, B=251-500, C=101-250, D=51-100, E=25-50
2011 Harris Minnesota Services Directory
© Harris InfoSource 1-866-281-6415
773

Physical Distribution Services ....E... 952 884-0765
Minneapolis *(G-5376)*

Severson Transport Inc ....E... 507 454-5090
Winona *(G-10127)*

Transport Leasing Contract Inc ....E... 763 585-7000
Minneapolis *(G-5848)*

TRUCK FINANCE LEASING

Wells Fargo Equipment Finance ....C... 612 667-9876
Minneapolis *(G-6044)*

TRUCK GENERAL REPAIR SVC

Anderson Diesel Truck Service ....E... 952 890-1580
Burnsville *(G-678)*

Anderson Diesel Truck Service ....E... 651 480-7991
Rosemount *(G-7361)*

Caledonia Haulers LLC ....C... 507 725-9000
Caledonia *(G-826)*

Carefree Services Inc ....E... 763 479-2600
Maple Plain *(G-3271)*

Dahl Trucking Inc ....D... 507 773-4226
Granada *(G-2256)*

Dave Syverson Truck Center Inc ....E... 507 289-3357
Rochester *(G-7093)*

Nelson Leasing Inc ....E... 320 235-2770
Willmar *(G-10029)*

Rihm Motor Co ....D... 651 646-7833
Saint Paul *(G-8902)*

St Cloud Truck Sales Inc ....D... 320 251-0931
Saint Cloud *(G-7442)*

TRUCK PARTS & ACCESSORIES:
Wholesalers

ABM Equipment & Supply Inc 952 938-5451
Hopkins *(G-2498)*

ABM Equipment & Supply LLC ....E... 952 938-5451
Hopkins *(G-2499)*

Astleford Equipment Co Inc ....E... 952 894-9200
Burnsville *(G-681)*

Bert's Truck Equipment of ....E... 218 233-8681
Moorhead *(G-6298)*

Clutch & Transmission Service ....E... 651 636-4311
Saint Paul *(G-8217)*

Clutch & Transmission Service ....D... 651 631-0959
Saint Paul *(G-8218)*

Crysteel Truck Equipment Inc ....E... 952 469-5678
Lakeville *(G-2899)*

Dave Syverson Truck Center Inc ....E... 507 289-3357
Rochester *(G-7093)*

Gerald N Evenson Inc ....E... 218 863-7101
Pelican Rapids *(G-6779)*

Istate Truck Inc 952 854-2044
Minneapolis *(G-4739)*

Jomar Investments Inc ....E... 651 686-6100
Saint Paul *(G-7811)*

Napco International LLC ....E... 952 931-2400
Hopkins *(G-2587)*

Olson & Johnson International ....E... 507 532-5718
Marshall *(G-3318)*

Rihm Motor Co ....D... 651 646-7833
Saint Paul *(G-8902)*

River Valley Truck Centers Inc ....D... 507 345-1129
Mankato *(G-3187)*

Smith's Winter Products ....E... 763 493-3332
Osseo *(G-6665)*

St Cloud Truck Sales Inc ....D... 320 251-0931
Saint Cloud *(G-7442)*

Valley Truck Parts & Service ....E... 218 773-3486
East Grand Forks *(G-1578)*

Westman Freightliner Inc ....E... 507 625-4118
Mankato *(G-3217)*

TRUCKING & HAULING SVCS: Animal & Farm Prdt

Keith Carlson Trucking Inc ....E... 651 923-4822
Goodhue *(G-2249)*

TRUCKING & HAULING SVCS: Building Materials

Anderson Trucking Service Inc ....C... 320 255-7400
Saint Cloud *(G-7449)*

Ats Inc ....C... 320 255-7400
Saint Cloud *(G-7455)*

Plaisted Co's Inc ....E... 763 441-1100
Elk River *(G-1890)*

TRUCKING & HAULING SVCS: Contract Basis

Action Moving Services Inc ....D... 952 894-8888
Burnsville *(G-672)*

Admiral-Merchants Motor ....E... 612 332-4819
Minneapolis *(G-3681)*

B J Transport Inc ....E... 651 436-4300
Afton *(G-7)*

Beskau Trucking Inc ....E... 651 437-9737
Hastings *(G-2377)*

Dart Transit Co ....B... 651 688-2000
Saint Paul *(G-7747)*

Dayton Freight Lines Inc ....E... 763 493-5841
Osseo *(G-6608)*

Fedex Ground Package System ....B... 651 748-8636
Mahtomedi *(G-3094)*

Going Going Gong Inc ....E... 651 482-1000
Saint Paul *(G-8418)*

Hicks Trucking Co of ....E... 320 693-3292
Litchfield *(G-2985)*

J & R Schugel Trucking Inc ....C... 507 359-2037
New Ulm *(G-6456)*

J C Trux Inc 218 927-4450
Aitkin *(G-20)*

Justman Freight Lines Inc ....E... 651 423-1024
Saint Paul *(G-7812)*

K-Way Express Inc ....D... 320 485-2325
Winsted *(G-10161)*

Manning Transfer Inc ....E... 763 784-4022
Minneapolis *(G-3527)*

Midwest Motor Express Inc ....D... 763 784-0650
Mounds View *(G-6390)*

Norsemen Inc ....E... 507 835-5060
Waseca *(G-9883)*

Piepho Moving & Storage Inc ....E... 507 289-4515
Rochester *(G-7204)*

Pioneer Press Inc ....D... 651 222-8298
Saint Paul *(G-8829)*

R & E Enterprises of Mankato ....E... 507 388-3364
Mankato *(G-3184)*

Supervalu Transportation Inc ....A... 952 828-4000
Eden Prairie *(G-1789)*

Tim Flanigan Trucking ....E... 218 385-3034
New York Mills *(G-6480)*

Transport Corp Of America Inc ....B... 651 686-2500
Eagan *(G-1557)*

Yrc Inc ....C... 651 452-0338
Saint Paul *(G-7954)*

TRUCKING & HAULING SVCS: Farm To Market, Local

D W Jones Trucking Inc ....E... 651 227-4854
Saint Paul *(G-8276)*

TRUCKING & HAULING SVCS: Furniture Moving & Storage, Local

Action Moving Services Inc ....D... 952 894-8888
Burnsville *(G-672)*

All Furniture Installation Inc ....E... 763 571-2203
Minneapolis *(G-3710)*

Bester Bros Transfer & Storage ....E... 651 451-1018
South Saint Paul *(G-9512)*

Dakt Enterprises Inc ....C... 952 474-6683
Eden Prairie *(G-1640)*

TRUCKING & HAULING SVCS: Furniture, Local W/out Storage

A A Metcalf Moving & Storage ....C... 651 484-0211
Saint Paul *(G-7967)*

Archbold Enterprises LLC ....E... 651 484-0211
Saint Paul *(G-8060)*

Omni Workspace Co ....C... 612 627-1600
Minneapolis *(G-5277)*

Rochester City Delivery Inc ....E... 507 289-2774
Rochester *(G-7229)*

TRUCKING & HAULING SVCS: Garbage, Collect/Transport Only

Ace Solid Waste Inc ....D... 763 427-3110
Anoka *(G-146)*

Phillips Recycling Systems LLC ....D... 320 251-5980
Saint Cloud *(G-7422)*

Tennis Sanitation LLC ....E... 651 459-1887
Saint Paul Park *(G-9298)*

Waste Management of Wisconsin ....C... 952 890-1100
Savage *(G-9412)*

Waste Management of Wisconsin ....E... 507 665-3096
Le Sueur *(G-2961)*

TRUCKING & HAULING SVCS: Haulage & Cartage, Light, Local

Manning Transfer Inc ....E... 763 784-4022
Minneapolis *(G-3527)*

T C B X Inc ....E... 651 644-5547
Minneapolis *(G-5783)*

TRUCKING & HAULING SVCS: Heavy, NEC

Anderson Trucking Service Inc ....C... 320 255-7400
Saint Cloud *(G-7449)*

Ats Inc ....C... 320 255-7400
Saint Cloud *(G-7455)*

Cenex Inc ....A... 800 232-3639
South Saint Paul *(G-9516)*

Hader Farms Inc ....E... 507 824-2543
Zumbrota *(G-10219)*

HI-Tech Express Inc ....E... 763 537-1690
Saint Paul *(G-8479)*

Manning Transfer Inc ....E... 763 784-4022
Minneapolis *(G-3527)*

Perkins Motor Transport Inc ....E... 651 463-4600
Northfield *(G-6539)*

Plaisted Co's Inc ....E... 763 441-1100
Elk River *(G-1890)*

Raveill Trucking Inc ....E... 218 768-2701
McGregor *(G-3340)*

Scherer & Sons Trucking Inc ....E... 320 363-8846
Saint Joseph *(G-7655)*

Vic's Heavy Haul Trucking ....D... 651 423-7401
Rosemount *(G-7377)*

TRUCKING & HAULING SVCS: Liquid Petroleum, Exc Local

Kane Transport Inc ....E... 320 352-2762
Sauk Centre *(G-9349)*

Wayne Transports Inc ....E... 651 437-6422
Rosemount *(G-7381)*

Western Co-Op Transport Assn ....D... 320 269-5531
Montevideo *(G-6261)*

TRUCKING & HAULING SVCS: Liquid, Local

Beskau Trucking Inc ....E... 651 437-9737
Hastings *(G-2377)*

Kane Transport Inc ....E... 320 352-2762
Sauk Centre *(G-9349)*

TRUCKING & HAULING SVCS: Lumber & Log, Local

Baumgartner Trucking Inc ....E... 507 895-8490
La Crescent *(G-2840)*

TRUCKING & HAULING SVCS: Machinery, Heavy

Midwest Specialized Trans ....E... 507 288-5649
Rochester *(G-7186)*

TRUCKING & HAULING SVCS: Mail Carriers, Contract

Baumgartner Trucking Inc ....E... 507 895-8490
La Crescent *(G-2840)*

Paradis Mail Service Inc ....E... 218 698-4613
Brooks *(G-623)*

Walbon Transport Inc ....C... 651 437-2011
Rosemount *(G-7380)*

TRUCKING & HAULING SVCS: Petroleum, Local

Kane Transport Inc ....E... 320 352-2762
Sauk Centre *(G-9349)*

Mississippi Transport Inc ....D... 651 439-5773
Stillwater *(G-9630)*

TRUCKING & HAULING SVCS: Star Routes, Local

P H Selly & Co Inc ....E... 507 334-3251
Faribault *(G-2025)*

TRUCKING, AUTOMOBILE CARRIER

Advanced Auto Transport Inc ....C... 651 777-7780
Saint Paul *(G-7990)*

Allied Systems Ltd ....C... 651 458-3005
Cottage Grove *(G-1096)*

TRUCKING, DUMP

D & G Excavating Inc ....E... 507 532-2334
Marshall *(G-3292)*

F M Trucking Inc ....E... 651 639-0446
Saint Paul *(G-8358)*

JME Of Monticello Inc ....E... 763 295-3122
Monticello *(G-6275)*

L & S Construction ....E... 507 648-3382
Sanborn *(G-9318)*

Max Johnson Trucking Inc ....E... 507 357-6313
Le Center *(G-2952)*

Metropolitan Gravel Co Inc ....D... 651 458-0170
  Newport *(G-6487)*

TRUCKING, REFRIGERATED: Long-Distance

D W Jones Trucking Inc ....E... 651 227-4854
  Saint Paul *(G-8276)*

Daggett Truck Line Inc ....D... 218 334-3711
  Frazee *(G-2184)*

Eickhoff Enterprises Inc ....D... 507 537-0919
  Marshall *(G-3294)*

Elliott Transport Systems Inc ....E... 218 236-9220
  Moorhead *(G-6313)*

Kottke Trucking Inc ....E... 320 833-5385
  Buffalo Lake *(G-666)*

Lawrence Transportation ....D... 507 454-3911
  Winona *(G-10111)*

Ltx Inc ....C... 507 282-6715
  Rochester *(G-7163)*

Ltx Inc ....E... 507 452-4738
  Winona *(G-10112)*

Mc Kimm Milk Transit Inc ....E... 320 587-3167
  Hutchinson *(G-2706)*

Minnesota Valley Transport Inc ....E... 507 354-3276
  New Ulm *(G-6462)*

Northwest Dairy Forwarding Co ....D... 763 434-6654
  Anoka *(G-211)*

Paradis Mail Service Inc ....E... 218 698-4613
  Brooks *(G-623)*

Schak Trucking Inc ....E... 507 247-5204
  Tyler *(G-9713)*

Transport Corp Of America Inc ....B... 651 686-2500
  Eagan *(G-1557)*

Walbon & Co Inc ....D... 651 437-2011
  Rosemount *(G-7378)*

Waymore Transportation Inc ....E... 763 786-9076
  Minneapolis *(G-3640)*

TRUCKING: Except Local

'Q' Carriers Inc ....E... 952 445-8718
  Shakopee *(G-9416)*

A T S Specialized Inc ....C... 320 255-7400
  Saint Cloud *(G-7445)*

AAA Cooper Transportation ....E... 651 638-9288
  Saint Paul *(G-7970)*

ABF Freight System Inc ....E... 320 259-5025
  Saint Cloud *(G-7432)*

Al Johnson Trucking Inc ....E... 612 253-1000
  Minneapolis *(G-3702)*

Am & S Trucking Inc ....E... 507 629-3224
  Tracy *(G-9689)*

Anderson Trucking Service Inc ....C... 320 255-7400
  Saint Cloud *(G-7449)*

Baarts Trucking Inc ....E... 507 436-5536
  Northrop *(G-6548)*

Barole Trucking Inc ....E... 651 209-1104
  Hugo *(G-2670)*

Battmann Holdings Inc ....D... 651 639-2800
  Saint Paul *(G-8091)*

Bay & Bay Transfer Co Inc ....C... 651 480-7991
  Rosemount *(G-7362)*

Becker HI-Way Frate ....E... 507 373-8513
  Albert Lea *(G-41)*

Beltmann Group Inc ....D... 651 639-2800
  Saint Paul *(G-8100)*

Bob Brink Inc ....D... 507 452-1568
  Winona *(G-10084)*

Bob Fischer Trucking ....E... 507 263-0384
  Hampton *(G-2364)*

C D Haugen Inc ....E... 218 751-2738
  Bemidji *(G-383)*

Caledonia Haulers LLC ....C... 507 725-9000
  Caledonia *(G-826)*

Chalich Trucking Inc ....E... 763 421-1095
  Anoka *(G-165)*

Cliff Viessman Inc ....E... 507 625-1435
  Mankato *(G-3223)*

Con-Way Freight Inc ....E... 507 451-2865
  Owatonna *(G-6705)*

Con-Way Freight Inc ....C... 763 783-7123
  Fridley *(G-2192)*

Con-Way Freight Inc ....E... 320 259-0245
  Waite Park *(G-9820)*

Conzemius Family LP ....E... 651 437-2107
  Hastings *(G-2379)*

Crysteel Truck Equipment Inc ....E... 507 726-6041
  Lake Crystal *(G-2857)*

Custom Transfer Inc ....E... 320 732-3013
  Long Prairie *(G-3041)*

D & A Truck Line Inc ....E... 651 769-1045
  Saint Paul Park *(G-9294)*

D & E Transport Inc ....D... 763 878-2880
  Clearwater *(G-1043)*

Daran Inc ....E... 763 856-4000
  Zimmerman *(G-10212)*

Dart Transit Co ....B... 651 688-2000
  Saint Paul *(G-7747)*

Dedicated Logistics Inc ....B... 651 631-5918
  Oakdale *(G-6550)*

Doug Bradley Trucking Inc ....E... 507 532-9681
  Marshall *(G-3293)*

Eagan Transport Inc ....E... 651 452-6268
  Saint Paul *(G-7755)*

Eagle Transport Services Inc ....E... 507 281-9787
  Rochester *(G-7101)*

Federal Express Corp ....C... 651 747-4122
  Saint Paul *(G-8368)*

Figgins Transport Ltd ....D... 218 326-9477
  Grand Rapids *(G-2277)*

Filmor Express Inc ....C... 507 263-2608
  Cannon Falls *(G-856)*

Floyd Wild Inc ....D... 507 537-0531
  Marshall *(G-3297)*

Foodliner Inc ....D... 651 345-2860
  Lake City *(G-2852)*

Fortune Transportation Co ....D... 507 831-2335
  Windom *(G-10073)*

Freerksen Trucking Inc ....E... 507 374-6708
  Dodge Center *(G-1228)*

Freightmasters Inc ....C... 651 688-6800
  Saint Paul *(G-7777)*

Gary J Aschenbrenner Trucking ....E... 507 233-2539
  New Ulm *(G-6451)*

Gerald N Evenson Inc ....E... 218 863-7101
  Pelican Rapids *(G-6779)*

Grounded Air Inc ....D... 763 780-1443
  Minneapolis *(G-3480)*

Hartz Truck Line Inc ....E... 218 681-3295
  Thief River Falls *(G-9669)*

J & R Schugel Trucking Inc ....C... 507 359-2037
  New Ulm *(G-6456)*

J B Hunt Transport Inc ....E... 612 362-9419
  Minneapolis *(G-4743)*

Justman Trucking Inc ....E... 651 423-1020
  Saint Paul *(G-7813)*

Kane Transport Inc ....E... 507 532-2788
  Marshall *(G-3302)*

Kerry Logistics Inc ....E... 763 717-1400
  Minneapolis *(G-3508)*

King Shipping Inc ....E... 763 428-5464
  Maple Grove *(G-3247)*

King Solutions Inc ....D... 763 428-5464
  Osseo *(G-6626)*

Kingsway Transportation System ....D... 507 288-9375
  Rochester *(G-7154)*

Kwik Kargo Inc Trucking ....E... 320 743-2021
  Clear Lake *(G-1035)*

Lake Center Industries Trans ....E... 507 457-3750
  Winona *(G-10109)*

Lakehead Trucking Inc ....E... 218 721-3521
  Duluth *(G-1379)*

Larson Transfer & Storage Co ....E... 952 884-0765
  Saint Paul *(G-4847)*

Le Febvre & Sons Inc ....D... 952 432-8228
  Saint Paul *(G-7822)*

Lessors Inc ....D... 651 789-9270
  Saint Paul *(G-7824)*

Long Haul Trucking Inc ....D... 763 497-3727
  Albertville *(G-75)*

Maiers Transport & Warehousing ....E... 320 251-6882
  Saint Cloud *(G-7548)*

Malark Motor ....E... 763 428-4880
  Osseo *(G-6632)*

Mathy Trucking Inc ....D... 507 777-4395
  Edgerton *(G-1824)*

McCollister's Transportation ....E... 763 502-2120
  Minneapolis *(G-3531)*

Midwest Specialized Trans ....E... 507 288-5649
  Rochester *(G-7186)*

Mohawk Moving & Storage Inc ....D... 763 717-3705
  Minneapolis *(G-6128)*

Northwest Dairy Forwarding Co ....D... 763 434-6654
  Anoka *(G-211)*

Patriot Holding Corp 612 338-5912
  Minneapolis *(G-5347)*

Physical Distribution Services ....E... 952 884-0765
  Minneapolis *(G-5376)*

Pioneer Industries Inc ....D... 612 374-2280
  Minneapolis *(G-5383)*

Polman Transfer Inc ....D... 218 631-1753
  Wadena *(G-9809)*

R & R Transportation Inc ....D... 218 439-6144
  Audubon *(G-255)*

Ramler Trucking Inc ....E... 320 845-4500
  Albany *(G-28)*

Robert Chapin ....D... 320 351-8901
  Sauk Centre *(G-9352)*

Root River Valley Transfer Inc ....D... 507 388-7670
  Mankato *(G-3231)*

Shaw Trucking Inc ....E... 763 434-3300
  Anoka *(G-225)*

Shorty's Heavy Duty Wrecker ....E... 763 784-1411
  Minneapolis *(G-3601)*

Smith Trucking Inc ....D... 507 376-5080
  Worthington *(G-10194)*

Stagecoach Express Inc ....E... 651 437-8138
  Hastings *(G-2407)*

Stan Koch & Sons Trucking Inc ....A... 763 302-5400
  Minneapolis *(G-5736)*

Stan Koch & Sons Trucking Inc ....E... 651 999-8500
  Saint Paul *(G-9003)*

Stemm Transfer & Storage Inc ....E... 320 251-4080
  Saint Cloud *(G-7613)*

Steve Yaggy Specialized Truck ....E... 507 282-1715
  Rochester *(G-7266)*

Styer Transportation Co ....E... 952 469-4491
  Lakeville *(G-2936)*

Summit Holdings Corp ....E... 952 445-8718
  Shakopee *(G-9479)*

Swift Transportation Corp ....E... 651 480-7850
  Inver Grove Heights *(G-2771)*

Taylor Truck Line Inc ....C... 507 645-4531
  Northfield *(G-6520)*

Terminal Transport Inc ....D... 651 407-6200
  Saint Paul *(G-9039)*

Thygeson Construction Co ....E... 218 681-1924
  Thief River Falls *(G-9679)*

Transport Designs Inc ....E... 952 894-8242
  Burnsville *(G-851)*

Transystems LLC ....E... 218 281-7514
  Crookston *(G-1138)*

Trout Enterprises Inc of Nthn ....E... 218 246-8165
  Deer River *(G-1174)*

Twin Express Inc ....E... 763 428-4969
  Rogers *(G-7346)*

Two Men & Truck ....E... 651 645-1279
  Saint Paul *(G-9285)*

Two Rivers Inc ....B... 715 262-5292
  Rosemount *(G-7376)*

UPS Ground Freight Inc ....D... 763 780-9800
  Circle Pines *(G-1023)*

Valley Transportation ....D... 507 754-5558
  Grand Meadow *(G-2265)*

Wagner Trucking Inc 320 524-2250
  Brandon *(G-592)*

Walbon & Co Inc ....D... 651 437-2011
  Rosemount *(G-7378)*

Walters Trucking Inc ....E... 320 352-2207
  Sauk Centre *(G-9354)*

Wayne Transports Inc ....E... 218 749-6050
  Virginia *(G-9764)*

Wayne Transports Inc ....E... 651 437-6422
  Rosemount *(G-7381)*

Wille Transport Inc ....D... 218 999-0900
  Cohasset *(G-1073)*

Wilson Lines of Minnesota Inc ....E... 651 459-8193
  Newport *(G-6490)*

TRUCKING: Local, With Storage

American Logistics Services ....D... 651 451-1349
  Cottage Grove *(G-1099)*

Battmann Holdings Inc ....D... 651 639-2800
  Saint Paul *(G-8091)*

Beltmann Group Inc ....D... 651 639-2800
  Saint Paul *(G-8100)*

Berger Transfer & Storage Inc ....D... 651 639-2260
  Saint Paul *(G-8104)*

C D Haugen Inc ....E... 218 751-2738
  Bemidji *(G-383)*

C W Logistics LLC 651 209-6814
  Eagan *(G-1518)*

Dakt Enterprises Inc ....C... 952 474-6683
  Eden Prairie *(G-1640)*

Freightmasters Inc ....C... 651 688-6800
  Saint Paul *(G-7777)*

Grounded Air Inc ....D... 763 780-1443
  Minneapolis *(G-3480)*

Harco Moving & Storage Inc ....E... 763 571-6227
  Minneapolis *(G-3482)*

K-Way Express Inc ....D... 320 485-2325
  Winsted *(G-10161)*

Keebler Co ....E... 651 484-0833
  Saint Paul *(G-8542)*

Kj & E Properties ....E... 218 727-8811
  Duluth *(G-1372)*

Larry Schefus Trucking Inc ....E... 507 644-5588
  Redwood Falls *(G-7023)*

Ltx Inc ....E... 507 452-4738
  Winona *(G-10112)*

Magnum Ltl Inc ....E... 763 795-9534
  Circle Pines *(G-1015)*

Maiers Transport & Warehousing ....E... 320 251-6882
  Saint Cloud *(G-7548)*

McCallum Transfer Inc ....E... 651 633-1612
  Minneapolis *(G-4970)*

SERVICES

McCollister's Transportation ....E... 763 502-2120
Minneapolis *(G-3531)*

P H Selly & Co Inc ....E... 507 334-3251
Faribault *(G-2025)*

Piepho Moving & Storage Inc ....E... 507 289-4515
Rochester *(G-7204)*

Piepho Moving & Storage Inc ....E... 507 289-4515
Rochester *(G-7205)*

Sonny Peterson Trucking Inc ....E... 320 547-2489
Swanville *(G-9659)*

Stockman Transfer Inc ....E... 320 864-2381
Glencoe *(G-2215)*

Transystems LLC ....C... 218 773-8813
East Grand Forks *(G-1576)*

Triangle Warehouse Inc ....D... 651 633-8912
Minneapolis *(G-5854)*

TRUCKING: Local, Without Storage

A & H Cartage Inc...................................E... 651 454-9550
Saint Paul *(G-7684)*

Al Johnson Trucking Inc ....E... 612 253-1000
Minneapolis *(G-3702)*

Aspen Waste Systems Inc ....E... 612 884-8000
Minneapolis *(G-3819)*

Baarts Trucking Inc ....E... 507 436-5536
Northrop *(G-6548)*

Bay & Bay Transfer Co Inc ....C... 651 480-7991
Rosemount *(G-7362)*

Bayer Trucking LLC...........................E... 320 254-3651
Belgrade *(G-361)*

Billington Contracting Inc ....E... 218 722-1213
Duluth *(G-1252)*

Bob Fischer Trucking ....E... 507 263-0384
Hampton *(G-2364)*

C D Haugen Inc ....E... 218 751-2738
Bemidji *(G-383)*

Con-Way Freight Inc ....E... 507 451-2865
Owatonna *(G-6705)*

Con-Way Freight Inc ....E... 651 686-2868
Eagan *(G-1521)*

Contact Cartage Inc ....E... 612 331-4780
Minneapolis *(G-4160)*

Cottonwood Truck Service Inc ....E... 651 451-7320
South Saint Paul *(G-9525)*

Daran Inc...E... 763 856-4000
Zimmerman *(G-10212)*

Dedicated Logistics Inc ....B... 651 631-5918
Oakdale *(G-6550)*

Delwin Transfer Inc ....E... 651 731-0510
Saint Paul *(G-9204)*

Dmz Trucking Inc ....E... 320 252-0313
Sauk Rapids *(G-9362)*

Elliott Transport Systems Inc ....E... 218 236-9220
Moorhead *(G-6313)*

F M Trucking Inc ....E... 651 639-0446
Saint Paul *(G-8359)*

Floyd Wild Inc..................................D... 507 537-0531
Marshall *(G-3297)*

Foodliner Inc ....D... 651 345-2860
Lake City *(G-2852)*

Gerald N Evenson Inc ....E... 218 863-7101
Pelican Rapids *(G-6779)*

Grounded Air Inc...............................D... 763 780-1443
Minneapolis *(G-3480)*

Istate Truck Center ....D... 651 455-9775
Inver Grove Heights *(G-2755)*

Kane Transport Inc ....D... 320 352-5800
Newfolden *(G-6482)*

Keebler Co ....E... 651 484-0833
Saint Paul *(G-8542)*

Kerry Logistics Inc............................E... 763 717-1400
Minneapolis *(G-3508)*

Lakehead Trucking Inc ....E... 218 721-3521
Duluth *(G-1379)*

Lakeville Motor Express Inc................B... 651 636-8900
Saint Paul *(G-8558)*

Larson Transfer & Storage Co ....E... 952 884-0765
Minneapolis *(G-4847)*

Lawrence Transportation ....D... 507 454-3911
Winona *(G-10111)*

Le Febvre & Sons Inc ....D... 952 432-8228
Saint Paul *(G-7822)*

Malark Motor....................................E... 763 428-4880
Osseo *(G-6632)*

Marson Contractors Inc......................E... 320 255-5506
Sauk Rapids *(G-9369)*

Mats Inc...E... 651 406-8300
Eagan *(G-1535)*

Mc Donough Truck Line Inc.................D... 507 334-9374
Faribault *(G-2020)*

McCallum Transfer Inc ....E... 651 633-1612
Minneapolis *(G-4970)*

Medstat Systems Inc ....E... 763 586-8146
Minneapolis *(G-3533)*

Norsemen Inc ....E... 507 835-5060
Waseca *(G-9883)*

Northland Transportation....................E... 952 885-0580
Prior Lake *(G-6946)*

Paradis Mail Service Inc ....E... 218 698-4613
Brooks *(G-622)*

Physical Distribution Services ....E... 952 884-0765
Minneapolis *(G-5376)*

Pioneer Press Inc..............................D... 651 222-8298
Saint Paul *(G-8829)*

R & E Enterprises of Mankato.............E... 507 388-3364
Mankato *(G-3184)*

Shorty's Heavy Duty Wrecker ....E... 763 784-1411
Minneapolis *(G-3601)*

Taylor Truck Line Inc ....C... 507 645-4531
Northfield *(G-6520)*

Transystems LLC..............................C... 218 773-8813
East Grand Forks *(G-1576)*

Transystems LLC..............................E... 218 233-8121
Moorhead *(G-6343)*

Trout Enterprises Inc of Nthn ....E... 218 246-8165
Deer River *(G-1174)*

Volk Transfer Inc..............................E... 507 388-1683
Mankato *(G-3213)*

Wagner Trucking Inc 320 524-2250
Brandon *(G-592)*

Walbon Co Trucking Svcs...................D... 651 437-2011
Rosemount *(G-7379)*

Walters Trucking Inc.........................E... 320 352-2207
Sauk Centre *(G-9354)*

Waste Management of Wisconsin ....C... 952 890-1100
Minneapolis *(G-3639)*

Waymore Transportation Inc ....E... 763 786-9076
Minneapolis *(G-3640)*

Wilson Oil Co Inc 651 388-5783
Red Wing *(G-7013)*

Wren Corp.......................................B... 651 636-8900
Saint Paul *(G-9169)*

TRUCKING: Long-Distance, Less Than Truckload

Fedex Freight Inc ....E... 507 444-0633
Owatonna *(G-6713)*

Fedex Freight Inc ....D... 651 697-9342
Saint Paul *(G-8369)*

Fedex Freight Inc ....E... 218 751-9122
Bemidji *(G-393)*

Mats Inc...E... 651 406-8300
Eagan *(G-1535)*

Morrell Transfer Inc ....E... 763 441-2011
Elk River *(G-1885)*

Scherer & Sons Trucking Inc ....E... 320 363-8846
Saint Joseph *(G-7655)*

USF Holland Inc ....E... 507 847-2625
Jackson *(G-2800)*

Vitran Express Inc ....E... 320 485-2101
Winsted *(G-10154)*

TRUCKING: Long-Distance, Truckload

Larry Schefus Trucking Inc.................E... 507 644-5588
Redwood Falls *(G-7023)*

TRUCKS, INDL: Wholesalers

Interstate Power Systems Inc ....D... 952 854-2044
Minneapolis *(G-4730)*

TRUST COMPANIES: National With Deposits, Commercial

Anchor Bank......................................E... 952 473-4606
Wayzata *(G-9905)*

Anchor Bank......................................E... 651 770-2341
Saint Paul *(G-8047)*

Anchor Bank......................................E... 651 457-1111
Saint Paul *(G-7699)*

First National Bank of Cold ....E... 320 685-8611
Cold Spring *(G-1085)*

Kleinbank ....E... 763 682-1142
Buffalo *(G-647)*

Kleinbank ....E... 952 442-4471
Waconia *(G-9787)*

University National Bank.....................E... 651 265-5600
Saint Paul *(G-9113)*

TRUST COMPANIES: State Accepting Deposits, Commercial

Bank of Elk River ....E... 763 441-1000
Elk River *(G-1863)*

Bremer Bank, National Assn...............E... 507 537-0222
Marshall *(G-3291)*

Bremer Trust National Assn ....E... 320 252-3918
Saint Cloud *(G-7466)*

First National Bank of St....................E... 507 931-4000
Saint Peter *(G-9303)*

First Rushmore Bancshares Inc ....D... 507 376-9747
Worthington *(G-10183)*

Plaza Park State Bank Inc ....E... 320 252-4200
Waite Park *(G-9834)*

TRUST MANAGEMENT SVCS: Charitable

Minneapolis Foundation ....E... 612 672-3878
Minneapolis *(G-5054)*

Spring Lake Park Lions Club...............E... 763 784-9179
Minneapolis *(G-3606)*

TRUST MANAGEMENT SVCS: Educational

Mc Knight Foundation.........................E... 612 333-4220
Minneapolis *(G-4969)*

TRUSTS, ESTATES & AGENCY ACCOUNTS

Lloyd Truss Systems ....E... 507 387-4250
North Mankato *(G-6508)*

Wilson - McShane Corp ....C... 952 854-0795
Minneapolis *(G-6074)*

TRUSTS, FIDUCIARY & CUSTODY INSTITUTIONS

U S Bancorp......................................B... 651 466-3000
Minneapolis *(G-5885)*

US Bank Trust National Assn..............A... 800 934-6802
Saint Paul *(G-9119)*

TURNKEY VENDORS: Computer Systems

Healthland Inc...................................C... 320 634-5331
Glenwood *(G-2226)*

UNIFORM SPLY SVCS: Indl

G&K Services Inc...............................C... 952 912-5500
Minnetonka *(G-6173)*

G&K Services Inc...............................C... 651 855-7000
Saint Paul *(G-8398)*

G&K Services Inc...............................C... 612 521-4771
Minneapolis *(G-4492)*

G&K Services Inc...............................E... 507 451-5710
Owatonna *(G-6716)*

UNISEX HAIR SALONS

AJK Cutters Inc.................................E... 952 933-7525
Minneapolis *(G-3701)*

Barbers Hairstyling For Men ....D... 952 947-7777
Minneapolis *(G-3867)*

Bixby Inc... 952 448-6520
Chaska *(G-956)*

C & R Ross Inc..................................E... 763 545-7347
Minneapolis *(G-3980)*

Cole's Salon.....................................E... 651 454-1390
Saint Paul *(G-7734)*

Cole's Salon Management Inc.............E... 952 226-5310
Savage *(G-9386)*

Cost Cutters Family Hair Care............E... 612 861-0040
Minneapolis *(G-4166)*

Denny Kemp Inc ....E... 612 676-0300
Minneapolis *(G-4248)*

Details Salon & Spa ....E... 651 696-8700
Saint Paul *(G-8289)*

Elizabeth Charles Corp ....C... 952 915-2900
Minneapolis *(G-4340)*

Elizabeth Charles Corp ....E... 952 915-2900
Saint Paul *(G-9212)*

Elizabeth Charles Corp ....D... 952 915-2900
Chanhassen *(G-922)*

Great Clips Inc ....D... 952 893-9088
Minneapolis *(G-4551)*

Image Shoppe Inc ....E... 952 949-1313
Eden Prairie *(G-1690)*

Regis Corp ....A... 952 947-7777
Minneapolis *(G-5504)*

Salon 4862 Inc..................................E... 612 298-8310
Minneapolis *(G-5595)*

Seaco Inc...C... 952 470-7400
Excelsior *(G-1953)*

Snips of Eden Prairie Inc ....E... 952 941-1495
Minneapolis *(G-5692)*

Supercuts Inc....................................A... 952 947-7777
Minneapolis *(G-5770)*

Top Secret Hair Salon ....E... 651 500-9233
Minneapolis *(G-3617)*

UNITED FUND COUNCILS

United Way Info & Referral ....E... 651 291-6795
Saint Paul *(G-9110)*

UPHOLSTERY CLEANING SVCS

Fibercare Inc..................E... 612 721-5048
Minneapolis *(G-4426)*

Rusciano-Hyland Inc ....E... 612 871-4434
Minneapolis *(G-5576)*

URANIUM ORE MINING, NEC

Mosaic Co ....C... 763 577-2700
Minneapolis *(G-5133)*

UTILITY LINE TREE TRIMMING SVCS

Arrowhead Tree Service Inc..................E... 218 729-9203
Duluth *(G-1245)*

Carrs Tree Service Inc ....E... 218 367-3355
Ottertail *(G-6686)*

Lake States Tree Service Inc ....D... 218 326-5872
Grand Rapids *(G-2290)*

S & S Tree Specialists Inc ....E... 612 872-3901
South Saint Paul *(G-9540)*

VACATION LODGES

Block E Lodging LLC ....D... 320 258-2580
Saint Cloud *(G-7461)*

Central Lakes Lodging LLC ....E... 218 828-0629
Baxter *(G-323)*

Holland Lodging Inc ....D... 218 847-6997
Detroit Lakes *(G-1196)*

Lodge At Brainerd Lake ....D... 218 822-5634
Brainerd *(G-573)*

Lutsen Resort Co ....E... 218 663-7212
Lutsen *(G-3056)*

Mankato Lodging LLC ....D... 507 388-8555
Mankato *(G-3163)*

Nath Management Inc ....E... 651 739-2377
Saint Paul *(G-8736)*

VACUUM CLEANER REPAIR SVCS

Sears, Roebuck & Co ....B... 651 291-4397
Saint Paul *(G-8939)*

Sears, Roebuck & Co ....B... 952 435-2380
Burnsville *(G-795)*

VALET PARKING SVCS

Class A Valet Inc ....E... 612 677-0071
Minneapolis *(G-4104)*

VALUE-ADDED RESELLERS: Computer Systems

Digital Datavoice Corp ....E... 651 452-0300
Saint Paul *(G-7752)*

Digital Images Inc 651 688-0888
Saint Paul *(G-7753)*

Highjump Software Inc ....D... 952 947-4088
Eden Prairie *(G-1686)*

Nuvo Network Management ....D... 952 933-4600
Hopkins *(G-2592)*

Parallel Technologies Inc ....C... 952 920-7185
Minneapolis *(G-5322)*

Spanlink Communications Inc ....D... 763 971-2000
Minneapolis *(G-5715)*

Spc Communications Inc ....E... 952 912-2800
Minneapolis *(G-5716)*

VAN CONVERSIONS

Associated Partnership Ltd ....C... 952 890-7851
Savage *(G-9383)*

Infiniti Marketing Inc ....E... 612 789-2025
Mound *(G-6388)*

VARIETY STORE MERCHANDISE, WHOLESALE

Fritz Co Inc ....D... 651 459-9751
Newport *(G-6486)*

J L Buchanan Inc 612 334-1710
Minneapolis *(G-4747)*

VEGETABLE CROPS MARKET PREPARATION SVCS

J & J Packing Inc ....E... 763 263-2296
Big Lake *(G-448)*

VEGETABLE PACKING SVCS

Dehn's Gardens Inc ....E... 763 753-2806
Anoka *(G-173)*

Hull Co ....E... 763 262-4855
Big Lake *(G-447)*

Metro Packaging Corp ....E... 763 586-0808
Minneapolis *(G-3538)*

VEHICLES FINANCE LEASING, EXC AUTOMOBILES & TRUCKS

ABC Bus Co's Inc ....D... 507 334-1871
Faribault *(G-1985)*

Wells Fargo Equipment Finance ....C... 612 667-9876
Minneapolis *(G-6044)*

VENDING MACHINE REPAIR SVCS

Lieberman Co's Inc ....D... 952 887-5299
Minneapolis *(G-4873)*

VENTURE CAPITAL COMPANIES

Norwest Equity Capital LLC ....E... 612 215-1600
Minneapolis *(G-5248)*

Norwest Venture Capital Mgt ....E... 612 215-1600
Minneapolis *(G-5249)*

VETERINARIAN, LIVESTOCK

East Central Veterinary ....E... 320 679-4197
Mora *(G-6357)*

Pipestone Veterinary Clinic ....E... 507 825-4211
Pipestone *(G-6837)*

Veterinary Medical Center Prof ....E... 507 372-2957
Worthington *(G-10197)*

Zumbrota Veterinary Clinic, PA ....E... 507 732-7301
Zumbrota *(G-10224)*

VETERINARIANS' OFFICES

Anoka Equine Veterinary Svcs ....E... 763 441-3797
Elk River *(G-1898)*

East Central Veterinary ....E... 320 679-4197
Mora *(G-6357)*

Feist Animal Hospital ....E... 651 646-7257
Saint Paul *(G-8371)*

Pipestone Veterinary Clinic ....E... 507 825-4211
Pipestone *(G-6837)*

Plymouth Heights Pet Hospital ....E... 763 544-4141
Minneapolis *(G-5392)*

Randall J Herman ....E... 763 559-3111
Minneapolis *(G-5466)*

Zumbrota Veterinary Clinic, PA ....E... 507 732-7301
Zumbrota *(G-10224)*

VETERINARY SVCS: Exc Livestock

Carver Lake Veterinary Center ....E... 651 578-3290
Saint Paul *(G-9193)*

Midwest Veterinary Specialty ....E... 763 754-5000
Minneapolis *(G-3543)*

VCA Animal Hospitals Inc ....E... 952 884-3228
Bloomington *(G-524)*

Vet Mart Inc ....E... 763 546-4452
Minneapolis *(G-5966)*

Veterinary Medical Center Prof ....E... 507 372-2957
Worthington *(G-10197)*

VETERINARY SVCS: Livestock

Veterinary Medical Center Prof ....E... 507 372-2957
Worthington *(G-10197)*

VIDEO & AUDIO EQPT, WHOLESALE

E P A Audio Visual Inc ....E... 763 477-6931
Rockford *(G-7310)*

J J Vanderson & Co ....E... 651 641-1376
Minneapolis *(G-3503)*

Navarre Corp ....C... 763 535-8333
Minneapolis *(G-5174)*

VIDEO CASSETTES, ACCESS & SPLYS, WHOLESALE

Dima Corp ....E... 507 373-6969
Albert Lea *(G-47)*

VIDEO PRODUCTION SVCS

Greer & Associates Inc ....E... 612 338-6171
Minneapolis *(G-4564)*

VIDEO REPAIR SVCS

Alpha Video & Audio Inc ....D... 952 896-9898
Minneapolis *(G-3733)*

National Camera Exchange Inc ....E... 952 898-4888
Burnsville *(G-762)*

VIDEO TAPE PRODUCTION SVCS

Hometime Video Publishing Inc ....E... 952 448-3812
Chaska *(G-968)*

In Fisherman Inc ....E... 218 829-1648
Baxter *(G-330)*

Metropolitan Productions Inc ....D... 612 333-1025
Minneapolis *(G-5007)*

VINEYARD MANAGEMENT & MAINTENANCE SVCS

Domaine Srene Vineyards Winery 763 473-4412
Osseo *(G-6610)*

VISITING NURSE

Barnabas Health Care Services ....C... 218 829-0901
Brainerd *(G-551)*

Minnesota Visiting Nurse Agcy ....C... 612 617-4600
Minneapolis *(G-5101)*

Seniors Caring Companions Inc ....E... 651 770-2288
Maplewood *(G-3288)*

VOCATIONAL REHABILITATION AGENCY

Ability Building Center ....C... 507 281-6262
Rochester *(G-7043)*

Cedar Valley Services Inc ....C... 507 433-2303
Austin *(G-265)*

Cedar Valley Services Inc ....E... 507 373-6064
Albert Lea *(G-42)*

Community Involvement Programs ....D... 612 362-4400
Minneapolis *(G-4143)*

Goodwill Industries Vocational ....D... 218 722-6351
Duluth *(G-1338)*

Kandi-Works Developmental ....E... 320 382-6156
Kandiyohi *(G-2814)*

Lifetrack Resources Inc ....D... 651 227-8471
Saint Paul *(G-8586)*

Merrick Inc 612 789-6200
Saint Paul *(G-8639)*

Midway Training Services Inc ....D... 651 641-0709
Saint Paul *(G-8656)*

Midwest Special Services Inc ....E... 651 778-1000
Saint Paul *(G-8664)*

Midwest Special Services Inc ....D... 763 557-1231
Minneapolis *(G-5037)*

Mille Lacs Cty Area ....E... 320 983-2162
Milaca *(G-3380)*

Northern Cass Dac Inc ....E... 218 547-1121
Walker *(G-9857)*

Occupational Development Ctr ....E... 218 751-6001
Bemidji *(G-417)*

Occupational Development Ctr ....C... 218 326-8574
Grand Rapids *(G-2305)*

Occupational Development Ctr ....E... 218 463-1123
Roseau *(G-7356)*

Occupational Development Ctr ....D... 218 681-4949
Thief River Falls *(G-9677)*

Occupational Development Ctr ....D... 218 258-8926
Buhl *(G-668)*

Options Inc ....D... 763 263-3684
Big Lake *(G-452)*

Productive Alternatives Inc ....D... 218 998-5630
Fergus Falls *(G-2117)*

Resource Inc ....D... 612 752-8000
Minneapolis *(G-5526)*

Rise Inc ....D... 763 786-8334
Minneapolis *(G-3585)*

Rise Inc ....D... 763 784-0900
Minneapolis *(G-3586)*

Winona ORC Industries Inc ....B... 507 452-1855
Winona *(G-10153)*

VOCATIONAL TRAINING AGENCY

Cedar Valley Services Inc ....C... 507 433-2303
Austin *(G-265)*

Cedar Valley Services Inc ....E... 507 373-6064
Albert Lea *(G-42)*

Mille Lacs Cty Area ....E... 320 983-2162
Milaca *(G-3380)*

Opportunity Partners Inc ....C... 952 938-5511
Hopkins *(G-2595)*

Options Inc ....D... 763 263-3684
Big Lake *(G-452)*

Summit Academy OIC ....D... 612 377-0150
Minneapolis *(G-5763)*

WALL COVERINGS WHOLESALERS

Hirshfield's Inc ....D... 612 377-3910
Minneapolis *(G-4655)*

WAREHOUSING & STORAGE FACILITIES, NEC

Dee Spee Delivery Service Inc ....E... 507 288-0695
Rochester *(G-7094)*

Eddie Bauer Inc ....E... 651 738-8653
Saint Paul *(G-9207)*

Goodwill Industries Inc ....C... 651 379-5800
Saint Paul *(G-8421)*

Employment codes: A=Over 500 employees, B=251-500,
C=101-250, D=51-100, E=25-50

2011 Harris Minnesota
Services Directory

© Harris InfoSource 1-866-281-6415

777

SERVICES

Goodwill Industries Inc ....E... 952 953-4410
Saint Paul *(G-7787)*

Goodwill Industries Inc ....E... 651 439-4207
Stillwater *(G-9620)*

Goodwill Industries Inc ....D... 651 603-1544
Saint Paul *(G-8422)*

Iron Mountain Inc ....E... 651 452-0169
Saint Paul *(G-7807)*

Target Corp ....C... 320 253-4740
Saint Cloud *(G-7616)*

Target Corp ....C... 612 304-6073
Minneapolis *(G-5791)*

WAREHOUSING & STORAGE, REFRIGERATED: Cold Storage Or Refrig

Alltemp Distribution Co ....E... 763 571-0215
Minneapolis *(G-3396)*

Atlas Cold Storage Midwest ....E... 507 732-4224
Zumbrota *(G-10216)*

Cloverleaf Cold Storage Co ....E... 952 469-1221
Lakeville *(G-2896)*

Cloverleaf Cold Storage Co ....E... 507 238-4211
Fairmont *(G-1961)*

Fairmont Refrigerated Service............E... 507 238-4211
Fairmont *(G-1966)*

WAREHOUSING & STORAGE, REFRIGERATED: Frozen Or Refrig Goods

Paul Newport-St Cold Storage ....E... 651 459-5555
Newport *(G-6488)*

WAREHOUSING & STORAGE: Automobile, Dead Storage

Auto Warehousing Co Inc ....E... 651 769-8383
Cottage Grove *(G-1100)*

WAREHOUSING & STORAGE: Farm Prdts

Western Consolidated Co-op................E... 320 394-2171
Holloway *(G-2493)*

WAREHOUSING & STORAGE: Furniture, Without Local Trucking

Omni Workspace Co ....C... 612 627-1600
Minneapolis *(G-5277)*

WAREHOUSING & STORAGE: General

Alltemp Distribution Co ....E... 763 571-0215
Minneapolis *(G-3396)*

CF Industries Inc ....E... 651 437-6191
Rosemount *(G-7365)*

CHS Inc ....D... 651 306-8088
South Saint Paul *(G-9521)*

Dedicated Logistics Inc......................B... 651 631-5918
Oakdale *(G-6550)*

Dedicated Logistics Inc......................E... 763 504-9229
Minneapolis *(G-4240)*

Duke Co's ....D... 612 331-4880
Minneapolis *(G-4289)*

Falls Distribution Inc ....E... 320 632-3999
Little Falls *(G-3004)*

Freightmasters Inc ....C... 651 688-6800
Saint Paul *(G-7777)*

Fulfillment Distribution Ctr ....A... 320 656-8880
Saint Cloud *(G-7513)*

Gamer Packaging Inc ....E... 612 788-4444
Minneapolis *(G-4498)*

Interline Brands Inc ....E... 651 644-7075
Saint Paul *(G-8515)*

J K F Warehouse ....E... 507 354-5528
New Ulm *(G-6457)*

Keebler Co ....E... 651 484-0833
Saint Paul *(G-8542)*

Kmart Corp ....B... 952 445-2936
Shakopee *(G-9449)*

Macy's Retail Holdings Inc.................E... 507 280-5400
Rochester *(G-7165)*

Meritex Enterprises Inc ....E... 651 855-9700
Minneapolis *(G-4992)*

Murphy Warehouse Co ....C... 612 623-1200
Minneapolis *(G-5151)*

Murphy Warehouse Co ....E... 612 623-1226
Minneapolis *(G-3549)*

Pan-O-Gold Baking Co ....E... 763 559-1515
Minneapolis *(G-5316)*

Paul A Schmitt Music Co.....................E... 763 566-4560
Minneapolis *(G-5349)*

Smiths Medical Asd Inc......................E... 651 628-7030
Saint Paul *(G-9274)*

Star Tribune Media Co LLC.................B... 612 673-7100
Minneapolis *(G-5740)*

Supervalu Inc ....A... 952 238-3400
Eden Prairie *(G-1786)*

Triangle Warehouse Inc ....D... 651 633-8912
Minneapolis *(G-5854)*

U-Haul Co of Minnesota ....D... 763 780-9746
Minneapolis *(G-3628)*

Uponor Inc ....E... 952 891-2000
Lakeville *(G-2939)*

Warehouse Depot LLC ....E... 612 728-5238
Minneapolis *(G-6021)*

Watkins Inc ....E... 507 457-6136
Winona *(G-10139)*

Young America Holdings Inc ....E... 320 864-6125
Glencoe *(G-2217)*

WAREHOUSING & STORAGE: Refrigerated

Artic Cold Storage Inc ....E... 320 253-9979
Saint Cloud *(G-7454)*

WAREHOUSING & STORAGE: Self Storage

Kurt Manufacturing Co Inc.................E... 763 572-4592
Minneapolis *(G-3512)*

WARM AIR HEATING & AC EQPT & SPLYS, WHOLESALE Air Filters

Midwest Mechanical Solutions ....E... 952 525-2003
Minneapolis *(G-5032)*

WARM AIR HEATING & AC EQPT & SPLYS, WHOLESALE Furnaces

Goodin Co...C... 612 588-7811
Minneapolis *(G-4540)*

Harbor City Oil Co ....E... 218 624-3633
Duluth *(G-1348)*

WARM AIR HEATING/AC EQPT/SPLYS, WHOL Dehumidifiers, Exc Port

Munters Corp......................................B... 952 831-9418
Burnsville *(G-761)*

WARM AIR HEATING/AC EQPT/SPLYS, WHOL Warm Air Htg Eqpt/Splys

Dependable Indoor Air Quality ....E... 763 757-5040
Minneapolis *(G-3454)*

Don Stevens Inc ....E... 651 452-0872
Eagan *(G-1525)*

Goodin Co...E... 320 259-6086
Saint Cloud *(G-7520)*

Hajoca Corp ....E... 763 315-0100
Minneapolis *(G-4589)*

Mammoth-Webco Inc ....B... 952 361-2711
Eden Prairie *(G-1717)*

S P S Co's Inc.....................................C... 952 929-1377
Minneapolis *(G-5582)*

Schwab-Vollhaber-Lubratt Inc ....D... 651 481-8000
Saint Paul *(G-8935)*

Triple J Enterprises Inc ....E... 952 853-9898
Minneapolis *(G-5858)*

Triple J Enterprises Inc ....E... 952 853-9898
Minneapolis *(G-5859)*

Uhl Co Inc ....D... 763 425-7226
Osseo *(G-6680)*

WARM AIR HEATING/AC EQPT/SPLYS, WHOL: Ventilating Eqpt/Sply

Crystal Distribution Inc ....D... 763 391-7790
Elk River *(G-1870)*

D C Sales Co Inc ....E... 612 728-8700
Minneapolis *(G-4213)*

First Supply LLC ....D... 507 287-0202
Rochester *(G-7115)*

WATCH REPAIR SVCS

Estate Jewelry & Coin Inc ....E... 952 881-8862
Minneapolis *(G-4373)*

WATER SOFTENER SVCS

Atlantis Pools Inc...............................E... 763 560-0103
Minneapolis *(G-3831)*

Culligan International Co ....E... 507 354-2311
New Ulm *(G-6447)*

Culligan Soft Water Service Co ....D... 952 933-7200
Minnetonka *(G-6157)*

WATER SOFTENING WHOLESALERS

Ecowater Systems LLC ....B... 651 739-5330
Saint Paul *(G-9206)*

WATER SPLY: Irrigation

West Central Irrigation Inc ....E... 320 239-2230
Starbuck *(G-9588)*

WATER SUPPLY

Allete Inc..C... 218 279-5000
Duluth *(G-1235)*

City of Duluth......................................A... 218 730-5230
Duluth *(G-1276)*

City of Owatonna ....D... 507 451-2480
Owatonna *(G-6701)*

City of Rochester ....C... 507 280-1540
Rochester *(G-7079)*

District Energy St Paul Inc ....E... 651 297-8955
Saint Paul *(G-8300)*

Red River Basin Commission ....E... 218 291-0422
Moorhead *(G-6335)*

Saint Paul Regional Water Svcs..........E... 651 776-6960
Saint Paul *(G-8928)*

Saint Paul Regional Water Svcs..........E... 651 266-1635
Saint Paul *(G-8929)*

Virginia, City of Inc ....D... 218 748-7540
Virginia *(G-9761)*

Willmar, City of Inc ....D... 320 235-4422
Willmar *(G-10056)*

WELDING EQPT & SPLYS WHOLESALERS

Airgas - North Central Inc ....E... 763 712-5100
Anoka *(G-148)*

American Welding & Gas ....E... 320 235-4774
Willmar *(G-9983)*

Minneapolis Oxygen Co ....E... 612 588-8855
Minneapolis *(G-5058)*

Mississippi Welders Supply Co ....E... 507 454-5231
Winona *(G-10118)*

Oxygen Service Co Inc ....D... 651 644-7273
Saint Paul *(G-8797)*

Prima Laserdyne Inc ....E... 763 433-3700
Champlin *(G-898)*

Toll Co ....E... 763 551-5355
Minneapolis *(G-5829)*

Welders Supply Co Inc ....E... 320 235-3430
Willmar *(G-10052)*

WELDING EQPT REPAIR SVCS

Electric Motor Repair Inc ....E... 612 588-4693
Minneapolis *(G-4337)*

WELDING REPAIR SVC

Aitkin Iron Works Inc..........................D... 218 927-2400
Aitkin *(G-24)*

Alexandria Pro-Fab Co Inc ....D... 320 852-7918
Alexandria *(G-82)*

American Manufacturing Inc ....E... 763 444-9225
Isanti *(G-2777)*

Bizal Mfg Inc......................................E... 763 571-4030
Minneapolis *(G-3418)*

Checker Machine Inc ....E... 763 544-5000
Minneapolis *(G-4057)*

Code Welding & Mfg Inc ....E... 763 792-6632
Minneapolis *(G-3435)*

Diesel Cast Welding Inc ....E... 763 780-5940
Minneapolis *(G-3455)*

Eagle Tool & Design Inc ....E... 763 784-7400
Minneapolis *(G-3460)*

Falls Fabricating ....C... 320 632-2322
Little Falls *(G-3005)*

Furin & Shea Welding & Fabctg ....E... 218 262-5271
Hibbing *(G-2446)*

Gauthier Industries Inc ....D... 507 289-0731
Rochester *(G-7125)*

Griffiths Holding Corp ....C... 763 559-2288
Minneapolis *(G-4572)*

Herman Manufacturing Co..................E... 507 553-5256
Wells *(G-9962)*

Industrial Welders ....E... 218 628-1011
Duluth *(G-1357)*

Lowry Manufacturing Co ....C... 320 283-5450
Lowry *(G-3055)*

M & L Industries Inc ....E... 763 428-4220
Rogers *(G-7329)*

Machinewell Inc ....D... 218 294-6101
Grygla *(G-2330)*

Mid-Continent Engineering Inc ....D... 612 781-0260
Minneapolis *(G-5023)*

Nedmac Inc ....E... 763 537-8435
Minneapolis *(G-5179)*

Nobel Welding & Manufacturing ....E... 651 426-1511
Hugo *(G-2671)*

Par Piping & Fabrication LLC ....E... 320 564-2173
Granite Falls *(G-2317)*

Remmele Engineering Inc...................D... 763 263-3650
Big Lake *(G-454)*

Sasker Manufacturing Inc ....E... 320 532-4268
Onamia *(G-6576)*

Tavis Metal & Fabrication Corp...........E... 763 428-8483
Rogers *(G-7342)*

Whirl-Air-Flow Corp ....E... 763 262-1200
Big Lake *(G-459)*

WELDING SPLYS, EXC GASES: Wholesalers

Minneapolis Oxygen Co ....E... 612 588-8855
Minneapolis *(G-5058)*

Oxygen Service Co Inc ....D... 651 644-7273
Saint Paul *(G-8797)*

Welders Supply Co Inc ....E... 320 235-3430
Willmar *(G-10052)*

WILDLIFE MANAGEMENT SVCS

Fergus Falls Fish & Game Club ....D... 320 630-0607
Dalton *(G-1155)*

WINDOW CLEANING SVCS

City Heights Inc ....E... 763 421-3345
Anoka *(G-166)*

Citywide Window Services Inc ....E... 763 421-3345
Anoka *(G-168)*

Marsden Holding LLC ....A... 651 641-1717
Saint Paul *(G-8615)*

WINDOW FURNISHINGS WHOLESALERS

Shade Warren Co ....D... 612 331-5939
Minneapolis *(G-5647)*

WINE & DISTILLED ALCOHOLIC BEVERAGES WHOLESALERS

Johnson Brothers Liquor Co ....B... 651 649-5800
Saint Paul *(G-8536)*

Wheaton Liquor ....E... 320 563-4155
Wheaton *(G-9972)*

WOMEN'S & CHILDREN'S CLOTHING WHOLESALERS, NEC

River's End Holdings LLC 952 912-2543
Hopkins *(G-2618)*

Rivers End Trading Co ....D... 952 912-2500
Hopkins *(G-2619)*

Winmark Corp ....C... 763 520-8500
Minneapolis *(G-6077)*

WOMEN'S & GIRLS' SPORTSWEAR WHOLESALERS

River's End Holdings LLC 952 912-2543
Hopkins *(G-2618)*

Rivers End Trading Co ....D... 952 912-2500
Hopkins *(G-2619)*

WOOD & WOOD BY-PRDTS, WHOLESALE

Central Wood Products ....E... 763 753-7374
Cedar *(G-876)*

WOOD CHIPS, WHOLESALE

Potlatch Corp ....D... 218 751-6144
Bemidji *(G-435)*

WORK EXPERIENCE CENTER

Functional Industries Inc ....D... 763 682-4336
Buffalo *(G-645)*

Midwest Special Services Inc ....C... 651 778-1000
Saint Paul *(G-8664)*

Midwest Special Services Inc ....D... 763 557-1231
Minneapolis *(G-5037)*

Rebuild Resources Inc ....E... 651 645-7055
Saint Paul *(G-8880)*

West Central Industries Inc..................D... 320 235-5310
Willmar *(G-10054)*

YOUTH CAMPS

Albert Lea Family YMCA ....E... 507 373-8228
Albert Lea *(G-31)*

Camp Widji Wagan...............................E... 218 365-2117
Ely *(G-1912)*

Duluth Area Family YMCA....................E... 218 722-4745
Duluth *(G-1297)*

Hastings YMCA ....E... 651 480-8887
Hastings *(G-2390)*

Itasca County Family Young.................D... 218 327-1161
Grand Rapids *(G-2287)*

Y M C A Infant Center ....E... 651 646-4557
Saint Paul *(G-9171)*

YMCA ....D... 320 222-9622
Willmar *(G-10059)*

YMCA Children's Center ....E... 651 777-8103
Saint Paul *(G-9173)*

YMCA of Greater Saint Paul ....E... 651 645-6605
Saint Paul *(G-9175)*

YMCA of Greater St Paul......................D... 218 365-2117
Ely *(G-1919)*

YMCA of Greater St Paul......................D... 651 292-4143
Saint Paul *(G-9178)*

YMCA of Greater St Paul......................D... 651 646-4557
Saint Paul *(G-9177)*

YMCA of Greater St Paul......................C... 651 483-2671
Saint Paul *(G-9176)*

YMCA of Greater St Paul......................C... 651 457-0048
Saint Paul *(G-7953)*

YMCA of Worthington, Minnesota ....E... 507 376-6197
Worthington *(G-10199)*

Young Men's Chrtn Assoc of ....C... 763 535-4800
Minneapolis *(G-6101)*

Young Men's Chrtn Assoc of ....D... 612 827-5401
Minneapolis *(G-6102)*

Young Men's Chrtn Assoc of ....E... 612 588-9484
Minneapolis *(G-6103)*

Young Men's Chrtn Assoc of ....C... 952 835-2567
Minneapolis *(G-6104)*

Young Women's Christian Assn ....D... 218 722-7425
Duluth *(G-1505)*

YWCA of Minneapolis ....A... 612 332-0501
Minneapolis *(G-6111)*

YOUTH SELF-HELP AGENCY

Storefront Group ....E... 612 861-1675
Richfield *(G-7038)*

ZOOLOGICAL GARDEN, NONCOMMERCIAL

City of Saint Paul ....E... 651 487-8200
Saint Paul *(G-8205)*

ZOOS & BOTANICAL GARDENS

Zoological Gardens, Minnesota ....C... 952 431-9299
Saint Paul *(G-7955)*

Employment codes: A=Over 500 employees, B=251-500,
C=101-250, D=51-100, E=25-50

2011 Harris Minnesota
Services Directory

© Harris InfoSource 1-866-281-6415
779

SERVICES